MW00342772

The Naval Institute Guide to

COMBAT FLEETS OF THE WORLD 2002-2003

Their Ships, Aircraft, and Systems

Compiled by
A. D. BAKER III

NAVAL INSTITUTE PRESS
Annapolis, Maryland

To Bernard Prézelin and Werner Globke—
two fine gentlemen, and true friends

Naval Institute Press
291 Wood Road
Annapolis, MD 21402

ISBN 1-55750-242-0

Printed in the United States of America on acid-free paper ♾
09 08 07 06 05 04 03 02 9 8 7 6 5 4 3 2
First printing

CONTENTS

PREFACE

For a world seemingly facing an era devoid of armed conflict on a global scale, there has been no significant slowing in the acquisition and modernization of new naval ships and systems since the last edition of this work. The ever-increasing complexity and cost of major naval systems, however, has continued to cause stretch-outs of existing programs and delays or cancellations in proposed programs. In the democracies, there has yet to be any effective outcry at the rising cost of defense in the face of perceived diminution of threat, and in the United States, the Department of Defense has apparently succeeded in convincing a receptive Congress that the country's already overwhelming military capabilities must be expanded still further. The potential troublemaker countries, on the other hand, for the most part have domestic problems that require the main thrust of their governments' attentions and expenditures.

The last quarter-century has seen a revolution in the composition and capabilities of the world's navies. While the current generations of combatant ships are of vastly greater capabilities than the ships they have replaced, there are also far fewer of them, making it necessary to stretch the endurance of their human operators when they must be deployed for long periods. Further, the crews must be of a far higher caliber in terms of training and character than those who could operate the simpler ships of the past. And over the same time frame, the trust and responsibility placed in the leadership of navies at sea has diminished as the revolution in communications and data-handling has centralized command functions. At a time when the Afghan War is being successfully run from Tampa, Florida, for instance, it does not seem justifiable for the U.S. Navy to invest in new seagoing command ships that in themselves will likely never be risked near the scene of combat. Indeed, a building is a lot cheaper to build than a ship, and a lot easier to maintain and modify. A more worrisome aspect of the trend toward centralization of control, however, is that the habits of leadership and decisiveness that characterized military leadership in the past will be lost; such a centralization of responsibility was a major cause of the collapse of Soviet military effectiveness, and with warships today becoming more and more like chess pieces in a global game, the habits of true leadership and acceptance of responsibility will be far more difficult to inculcate into the naval officer corps of the future.

Another major trend in the composition of navies has been toward a lower "tooth-to-tail" ratio of the numbers of truly combatant ships and the auxiliaries that support them or perform other missions for their respective navies, independent of their combat components. Nowhere is this trend more evident than in the United States Navy, which has the lowest percentage of armed warships within its overall fleet than any navy in the world. On the one hand, via the Military Sealift Command's vast fleet of prepositioning ships and fast cargo ships and with the equally huge (if shrinking) U.S. Maritime Administration Ready Reserve Force fleet of cargo vessels on call, the U.S. Department of Defense controls probably well over 90 percent of the world's militarily useful sealift assets; on the other, those floating assets are without any significant means of protecting themselves, and the navy lacks the assets to escort them. The same trend is evident in Britain's Royal Navy, where the destroyer/frigate force is to shrink to only 31 ships while the navy's amphibious warfare and sealift component is being expanded to more than a dozen ships. It can be argued that the threat on the open sea is diminishing, but the threat within littoral waters from coastal surveillance systems, land-based aircraft, coastal defense missiles and guns, and mines is not shrinking at all. For the U.S. Navy, the mine threat is of particular consequence, since its leadership has always neglected that vital area of naval warfare and shows no sign of changing its ways.

As ships grow individually more complex, it becomes more difficult to describe them adequately in a publication like *Combat Fleets*. True, the lists of ships are still useful, but the ability to describe concisely the relative merits of various command-and-control and weapons systems has become almost too complex to be reduced to simple listings of equipment fits. Even as recently as fifty years ago, it was enough to measure how many ships a navy had and how many guns and torpedo tubes they carried. Today, one must have an intimate knowledge of the workings of surveillance systems, communications, and the capabilities of a whole host of high-technology weaponry and sensors before being able to comprehend the true capabilities of one navy versus those of another. And it is also impossible in a book of this nature to provide more than a hint of the states of training and maintenance practices that distinguish a well-run navy from an inept one. Nonetheless, in the following thousand or so pages, *Combat Fleets* will again attempt to list everything from aircraft carriers to yard tugs in each of the world's fleets. It's a start. But the "remarks" sections are now at least as important as the tables of data, and users are urged to read them along with the listings of weapons and equipment.

How to Use the Book

For each ship class entry in the text, the first number between the diamond symbol and the class or ship name indicates the number of units in inventory as of 1 January 2002. Numbers following in parentheses indicate additional ships under construction and may be followed, after a plus sign, by additional numbers indicating further units planned or on option. When units within a class are retained in decommissioned reserve, a total is given on the class entry line, and the names of the ships or craft, where appropriate, are given in italics. Ships that are already completed but that were in overhaul or reconstruction as of 1 January 2002 are counted as part of the total inventory.

The ship type designation system used in *Combat Fleets* is defined in detail in the Terms and Abbreviations section; the ship-type letter designations are found in brackets after combatant header type sections within each fleet (as in "Destroyers [DD]") and after each class or single-ship entry in the Auxiliaries and Service Craft sections (as in "*Jones*-class large harbor tugs [YTB]"). For this edition, changes have been made in the data formats of the entries for weapons and sensors in order to make them easier to read.

Users are urged to consult the remarks sections for the various entries for additional information on construction programs, individual differences between units of a class, and further details of systems and capabilities. The remarks sections have been followed, where appropriate, by sections about deletions within the class, hull systems, aviation systems, combat systems, and other categories as appropriate. Unless otherwise specified, figures given in dollars ($) are in U.S. dollars.

A brief study of the Terms and Abbreviations section on the succeeding pages will help the user understand the condensed data format used in the book. Conversion tables between the English measurements system and the metric system are also given. One deviation, however, has been made from the use of the metric system because so many of the users are U.S. citizens lamentably unfamiliar with the metric system: *displacements for U.S.-owned ships have been retained in terms of long tons of 2,240 lbs.* For those seeking to make "exact" comparisons between a U.S. ship and a similar foreign vessel, convert the U.S. displacement figure to metric tons (1,000 kg) by multiplying it by 1.01605 or convert the metric displacement to English long tons by multiplying it by 0.98421.

Major naval weapons systems, sensors, and naval aircraft are described at the beginning of each country-of-origin entry, after any entries on numbers of personnel, base locations, fleet organization, naval aviation forces, marine or naval infantry organizations and strengths, and coastal defense resources. For more comprehensive data on naval weapons systems and sensors, see the Naval Institute's companion volume, the *Naval Institute Guide to World Naval Weapons Systems, 1997–1998,* edited by Dr. Norman Friedman. A comprehensive index of all ship names (and also NATO class nicknames for ship designs of Soviet or People's Republic of China origin) is included, and there are also addenda for late-arriving information and photography received through February 2002.

For those requiring a rapidly searchable, computer-resident database for maritime force information, *Combat Fleets 2002–2003* is also available in CD-ROM format from the Naval Institute Press, with all illustrations and textual material from the printed version preserved. Networkable versions of the CD-ROM are also available.

Sources and Acknowledgments

All information in *Combat Fleets* has been derived from unclassified, open-source publications and from correspondence received from around the world. The official publications of many navies have been consulted, where made available, but for some fleets, particularly that of North Korea, some of the data must be estimated.

Special mention needs to be made of the truly generous cooperation received from the editors of France's *Flottes de Combat,* Bernard Prézelin, and Germany's *Weyers Flottentaschenbuch,* Werner Globke; these two distinguished experts have unselfishly shared information and illustrations used in this edition, and it could not have been prepared without their unstinting aid at a time when both were hard at work on new editions of their own invaluable works.

Other published sources of particular value as sources for (and checks on) information for this edition have been the following periodicals: *Air International; The Almanac of Seapower; Deckplate; Defense News; Defense Technology Monthly; Flight; Gangut; Jane's Defence Weekly; Jane's International Defence Review; Marine News; Maritime Reporter and Engineering News; Military Technology Monthly; El Monitor; Morskoy sbornik; Nachrichten aus der U.S. Navy; Naval Aviation News; NAVINT; The Navy; Navy International; Navy News; Navy News and Undersea Technology; Navy Times; Navy Today; Okrety Wojenne; Panorama Difesa; Preview: The Journal of the Defence Procurement Agency; Revista Italiana Difesa; Revista Maritima; Sea Breezes; Sealift; Sea Power; Sea Technology; Seawaves Magazine* (on-line); *Ships Monthly; Ships of the World; Soldat und Technik; Sudostroeniye; Surface Warfare; Taifun; Tecnologia & Defesa; Undersea Technology; Undersea Warfare; Under Svensk Flagg;* U.S. Naval Institute *Proceedings; Warship International; Warship International Naval Review; Warship World; WorkBoat;* and *Work Boat International.* The latest editions of our sister references, *Almanacco Navale, Flottes de Combat, Jane's Fighting Ships,* and *Weyers Flottentaschenbuch,* edited by Giorgio Giorgerini, Bernard Prézelin, Commo. Stephen Saunders, and Werner Globke, respectively, were frequently consulted as well, as was the standard reference for registered merchant ships, the three-volume annual *Lloyd's Register of Ships* and its monthly updates. With the evolution of the Internet as a source of data (by far not all of it reliable, to be sure), this edition has continued to make considerable use of on-line databases and websites maintained by such fleets as those of the United States, Great Britain, Argentina, Belgium, Brazil, Chile, and Mexico, to name but a few. Many websites maintained by private individuals have also been consulted on a regular basis.

As usual, many friends, manufacturers, and officials have assisted with this edition, some with only a single photograph or item of information and others with a large volume of material. While not all photography received can be incorporated, even incomplete or indistinct views can provide important information about changes in configuration or capabilities.

Persons who have contributed specifically to the current edition include: Dan Arant; Victor M. Baca, editor of *Model Ship Journal* and proprietor of Photomarine Archives; Reginaldo J. da Silva Bacchi, technical consultant, *Tecnologia & Defesa;* Marilyn Barrett, public relations director, Bollinger Shipyards; Lt. (jg) Chuck Bell, public affairs officer, Mine Warfare Command; J. H. Bih, editor, *Defense Technology Monthly;* Larry Bond, author of fascinating technothrillers, consummate wargamer, and knowledgeable navalist; Curt Borgenstam, Jr., for numerous fine photos and information about Swedish Navy programs; Richard J. Boyle; Dr. Maurizio Brescia, historian of the ships of the Italian Navy; Siegfried Breyer, premier scholar of ship design and of the Russian and former Warsaw Pact navies, for photography and information; R. J. "Jo" Bunce, former editor of the RNZN's award-winning magazine *Navy Today,* for photos and data; Richard R. "Rick" Burgess, managing editor of *Sea Power* and contributing editor of *Naval Aviation News,* for many favors, not least of which was a thorough and knowledgeable review and revision of the U.S. Navy aviation section; Camil Busquets i Vilanova, for timely information about Spanish Navy programs and for superbly composed color photography; Rob Cabo, for excellent ship photos, very useful news, and cheerful support from the Netherlands; Chris Carlson, for open-source data on Russian programs; Christopher P. Cavas, news editor of *Navy Times,* for many excellent photos and much useful information; Philip Chang; Marion P. "Blade" Chapman, for engineering acumen and his encyclopedic knowledge of naval equipment fits; Raymond Cheung; Jaroslaw Cislak, for sharing his vast knowledge of the Polish Navy and for providing many fine photos; William H. Clarke, for photos from the Hampton Roads area; Paul C. Clifts; Douglas A. Crombie, for excellent photography; Paul Cropper, whose Internet service, Russian Military News (www.users.bigpond.com/pcropper/html/body_home.html), was an absolutely vital source of naval events in Russia and elsewhere; Michael J. Curry, manager, navy ships and services, Bath Iron Works; Gary Davies of Maritime Photographic, England's premier naval photography source, and now naval correspondent to *Ships Monthly;* Ralph Dunn, editor of DERA's *Preview,* for generously providing official M.O.D. artwork showing naval projects; Ralph Edwards, for superb photography and knowledgeable commentary from the Indian naval review of February 2001 and for much other useful information and photography; Dipl.-Ing. Hartmut Ehlers, prolific photographer and diligent researcher on the navies of the former Warsaw Pact and elsewhere; Ron Elias, Northrop Grumman Ship Systems, for photos of Ingalls-built warships; Alex Engel, for invaluable translations and some excellent photography; Ingrid Evans, Communications Department, Hollandse Signaalapparaten B.V. (now a part of the Thales empire); Frank Findler, of Winter & Findler/Findler & Winter, for much excellent photography; Capt. Johann R. Forster, USN (Ret.), for information on smallcraft programs; Dr. Zvonimir Freivogel, for photos and detailed information about the Croatian and Federal Yugoslav navies; Dr. Norman Friedman, authoritative author on naval and strategic subjects and always a generous and faithful friend; Lisa Gates, editor of the U.S. Military Sealift Command's excellent and colorful monthly *Sealift* newsletter; Ross Gillett, Australia's most prolific author on naval subjects; Paul Ginnane, for photos of naval auxiliaries; Werner Globke, editor of *Weyers Flottentaschenbuch,* for generous sharing of data and illustrations; Richard L. Goodlake, business development manager, Raytheon Systems; John Gourley, for some finely detailed digital views of naval equipment and naval ships; Luciano Grazioli, for sending not only his own excellent photos but also those of his colleagues, as well as providing information on naval events in Italy; Kurt Greiner of Seaphoto, an excellent source of first-rate naval photos; John Gresham, for enthusiastic support; Cdr. Alvin H. Grobmeier, USN (Ret.), who provided numerous detailed and authoritative lists of smallcraft in U.S. service as well as frequent naval news from around the world; Carlos Hernández González, for invaluable help with the Colombian and Venezuelan navies and for forwarding a large number of photos, both his own and those of the members of the FAV Club; Cathy Inglis, Tenix Shipbuilding W.A.; Sgt. Sarah Jardine, head, HMNZS *Philomel* photo section, for quickly providing RNZN photos; Vic Jeffery, command public relations officer, RAN, Rockingham, for supplying useful information on the RAN and the superb photography taken by the RAN's staff photographers in Western Australia; Mitsuhiro Kadota, for excellent photographs of ships and craft from Japan; Cdr. Hans Karr, German Navy, for interesting details of export submarine designs and a photo from Indonesia; Tohru Kizu, editor of the world's leading illustrated magazine on ships of all kinds, *Ships of the World;* Yohei Kondo, dean of Japanese naval affairs writers, for personal delivery of back issues of *Ships of the World;* Gerhard Koop, faithful chronicler of the Bundesmarine and its many developments; A. A. de Kruijf, for crucial photos and data; Col. Jürg Kürsener for excellent photos from his interesting travels; Richard Laporte, webmaster, Canadian Coast Guard, for rapid response to a few specific questions not covered on the Canadian Coast Guard's superbly detailed and formatted website (www.ccg-gcc.gc.ca); Donna Larocque, marketing department, Marinette Marine, for informative press releases and excellent photos; Boris Lemachko, whose numerous photos of the Russian and Ukrainian navies are absolutely unique; Lionel Leventhal, for constant encouragement; Claes Lindskog, Kockums ILS Dept.; Charles Loke, senior manager, naval marketing, Singapore Technologies Marine; Robin A. McClendon, marketing director, SeaArk Marine, for data about that company's exports; Jaroslaw Malinowski, editor of the fine Polish naval periodical *Okrety Wojenne,* for information about Eastern European navies; Mike Markowitz, for forwarding many useful articles; Paolo Marsan, for his own fine photos and those of Guy Schaeffer; Richard S. Martinson, president, Guardian Marine International, for information about his company's new fast patrol boat design; Carlo Martinelli, for a large number of excellent photos from the Mediterranean area; Mritunjoy Mazumdar, co-proprietor of the highly informative Indian Navy website (www.bharat-rakshak.com/NAVY/), for detailed information about the Indian Navy and numerous fine photos from the great Indian Naval Review of February 2001; Fu S. Mei, editor of the excellent Internet *Taiwan Defense Review* (www.TDReview.com), for news of the ROCN; Ted Minter, faithful correspondent on the U.S. Navy; the unfailingly helpful Dorothy Mitchell, Coast Guard Public Affairs, Curtis Bay, Md.; Martin Mokrus, a new contributor of excellent-quality photos; Julio Montes, for extensive data and many fine photos of Central American ships and craft; Samuel L. Morison, for generously sharing his intensive research on the state of the fleet of the U.S. Navy and for his exhaustive annual list of USN developments in the Naval Institute *Proceedings;* Brian Morrison, Warships & Marine Corps Museum, International, Australia, for hundreds of absolutely superb warship photos; John Mortimer, who has sent many fine warship photos; Harry Murdoch of Orange Shipbuilding, for information on the U.S. Army's tug program; Judy A. Oetelmans, Marketing Department, TWSA; Takatoshi Okano, for an excellent selection of photos of Japanese Maritime Self-Defense Force and Coast Guard ships and craft; Steve Pegge, for a number of useful suggestions for changes and additions to the text; Susan Pierter, director, communications, Bath Iron Works; IJsbrand Plokker, for excellent photography from Europe; Norman Polmar, editor of *Ships and Aircraft of the U.S. Fleet,* who gave much useful guidance; Antony Preston, editor (with the able assistance of George Paloczi-Horvath) of the absolutely indispensable naval newsletter, *NAVINT;* Jeanne and Don Preul of J&D Productions, for data and photos related to the *Kilo Moana* (AGOR 26); Bernard Prézelin, the generous and energetic editor of our sister publication, *Flottes de Combat,* for news of naval developments worldwide and a vast number of his excellent photos; Sara Price, Avondale Shipyard, for photos of the T-AKRs; Anil Raj of Friede Goldman Halter; Frank Randall, Public Affairs Office, Military Sealift Command; Patricia Raymond of Lockheed Martin, Naval Electronics and Surveillance Systems, Baltimore, for data and artwork depicting the *Kilo Moana* (AGOR 26); John C. Reilly, former head, Ships Histories Branch, Naval Historical Center; Bram Risseeuw, correspondent on the Netherlands, Irish, and South American navies—and others; Eivind Rodlie, for numerous photos of Norwegian units; Capitán de Corbeta John Rodriguez Asti, Peruvian Navy, for providing officially sanctioned photography and data about his navy; Brooks A. Rowlett, for forwarding numerous useful items of naval interest from the Internet; Jens Salzmann, for photography of German and Danish naval vessels; Selim San, for photos from Turkey; Jim Sanderson, for fine photos from the United Kingdom and California; Marcin Schiele, for information about Polish- and Russian-designed warships; George R. Schneider, for a vast number of excellent photos of U.S., South American, and other naval ships and craft, as well as Herculean labors at making sense of the U.S. Navy and U.S. Coast Guard smallcraft fleet lists; Alexandre Sheldon-Duplaix, for ideas as well as photos and facts; Dave Shirlaw, editor of Canada's excellent and indispensable on-line naval daily Internet report, *Seawaves Magazine* (www.seawaves.com); Capt. Piet Sinke, not only for photos but also for useful information pulled from the Internet and from his own travels; Adam Smigielski, for interesting and informative correspondence; Claire Stannard, public relations officer, Austal Ships, Fremantle, for photos of the fast transport *Westpac Express;* Ben Stans; Chris Stattler, of Australia's Warships & Marine Corps Museum, International, for many fine photos; Joe Straczek, RAN historian, for photos of U.S. MSC units; James B. Stricker, NOAA engineer, for information on NOAA's T-AGOS conversion programs; Ben Sullivan, for photos and useful information; Lori Sumner of NOAA, for information about their aircraft fleet; Rev. Albert T. Tappman, for spiritual guidance and financial advice; Raymond Taylor, for a photo of the catamaran *Joint Venture;* Dipl.-Ing. Stefan Terzibaschitsch, former editor of the comprehensive periodical *Nachrichten aus der U.S. Navy,* Germany's leading expert on the U.S. Navy, and longtime correspondent on all manner of things, including the music of the Baroque; Andrew C. Toppan, for information and photos (and whose Haze Gray and Underway warship database on the Internet at www.hazegray.org is a useful reference tool); Sarah J. Turgeon, Bath Iron Works; Captain Stefano Vignani, Port Captain Corps, Italian Navy, for data and illustrations on "CP" craft; Leo Van Ginderen, for many fine photos; Jasper Van Raemdonck, for current data about the Belgian Navy; Cdr. John Vonli, R.Nor.N., commanding officer of the important new missile craft *Skjold,* for photography and information about his fine ship; Neil Wallace, general manager, Defense Maritime Services Pty, Australia, for a listing of the ships and craft of his busy organization, as well as some fine photographs; Mike Welsford, for photos of the highest quality; Lt. Rick Wester, USCG Public Affairs, for generous, enthusiastic, and rapid responses to various requests; Michael Winter, of Winter & Findler (a.k.a. Findler & Winter) and editor of *Nachrichten aus der U.S. Navy,* for excellent photography and his highly informative periodical; Dieter Wolf, for a great many of his truly superb photographs; Christopher C. Wright III, editor of *Warship International;* Marian Wright, for excellent photos taken at Portsmouth, U.K.; Cem D. Yaylali, for photography from the Bosporus and news of the Turkish Navy; W. Michael Young, for fine photography from the San Diego area; and Steven J. Zaloga for some very useful photos and brochures. To all those others who helped as well but could not for various reasons be named here, my deepest thanks.

The director of the Naval Institute Press, Ron Chambers, provided the enthusiasm and support to both the book and CD-ROM versions of *Combat Fleets.* Naval Institute Press managing editor Rebecca E. Hinds provided production management and skillfully handled the difficult task of keeping track of where various sections of text and the numerous illustrations were at any given moment. Copy and production editor Jack Brostrom was simply fantastic at making the editor toe the line on consistency of nomenclature and format and did a superb job in organizing the 1.3-million word manuscript into a coherent whole; anyone lucky enough to have Jack as an editor will benefit enormously from his steady and imperturbable hand at the tiller. Deborah Patton compiled the extensive index with speed and precision, and Louise Martin performed magnificently the painstaking work of proofreading. Composition services for *Combat Fleets* were expertly provided by Charles Andrews, Cherie Snyder, Patt Rosendale, Gordon Becker, Jenel Fultz, William Adams, Kathy Becker, Joy Thompson, Sherry Fleming, Susan Reese, Ellen Betcke, and Sylvia Rebert of Atlis Graphics and Design, while project leader Leon Miller, with Anthony Cowden, Joe Jackson, and Debra Marmaud of Sonalysts, Inc., ably transposed the book into the versatile and easy-to-use CD-ROM version; the work of the professionals from these two fine companies is unsurpassed in their fields. Tom Harnish, director of marketing at the Naval Institute, with Susan Artigiani, Maureen Peterson, and jacket designer Brian Barth, made sure that potential purchasers were aware of our existence, in the United States and abroad. Fred H. Rainbow, editor-in-chief of the USNI *Proceedings,* and managing editor Julie Olver continued their enthusiastic support of the monthly "Combat Fleets" update in the *Proceedings.* Special thanks also go to Tom Marfiak, the executive director of the Naval Institute, for continuing to advocate *Combat Fleets.* My sincerest thanks to all of the above and to the numerous other Naval Institute friends who participated.

To my wife, Anne-marie, goes the greatest gratitude of all for her patience, good humor, practical advice, and—not least—technical abilities at convincing office equipment to function. To everyone else who has been of help over the past quarter-century, my heartfelt gratitude is once again expressed.

This will be the last edition of *Combat Fleets of the World* to be compiled by the present editor, who has been associated with the project since 1977 and, frankly, is in need of a rest and a change of intellectual scene.

A. D. Baker III
30 April 2002

TERMS AND ABBREVIATIONS

Most surface ship characteristics are presented as in the following sample (♦ indicates the beginning of a class or individual ship entry):

FRIGATES [FF]

♦ 0 (+ 4) F-100 design Bldr: Izar, Ferrol

	Laid down	L	In serv.
F 101 Álvaro de Bazán	14-6-99	27-10-00	10-02
F 102 Almirante Don Juan de Bourbón (ex-*Roger de Lauria*)	27-10-00	28-2-02	11-03
F 103 Blas de Lezo	3-02	7-03	1-05
F 104 Méndez Nuñez	7-03	9-04	2-06

D: 4,555 tons (5,802 fl) **S:** 28.5 kts (27 sust.)
Dim: 146.72 (133.20 pp) × 18.60 (17.50 wl) × 4.75 (4.84 at full load)
A: 8 RGM-84F Harpoon Block ID SSM; 48-cell Mk 41 VLS syst. (32 Standard SM-2 Block IIIA and 64 RIM-162 Evolved Sea Sparrow SAM); 1 127-mm 54-cal. Mk 45 Mod. 2 DP; 1 12-barrel 20-mm Meroka-2B CIWS; 2 single 20-mm 90-cal. AA; 4 fixed 324-mm Mk 32 Mod. 9 ASW TT; 1 SH-60B Seahawk LAMPS-III Block II ASW helicopter
Electronics:
Radar: 1 Thales Scout nav./surf. search; 1 Raytheon SPS-67(V)4 surf. search; 1 Lockheed Martin SPY-1D 3-D tracking, target-desig., and weapons control; 2 Raytheon SPG-62 target illuminators; 1 AESN RAN-30L/X Meroka f.c.; 1 FABA DORNA gun f.c.
Sonar: ENOSA-Raytheon DE 1160LF (I) hull-mounted; EDO UQN-4 deepwater echo sounder; EDO Model 5400 underwater telephone; provision for active/passive towed linear hydrophone array
EW: Indra SLQ-380 Aldebarán intercept/jammer suite; CESELSA Elnath Mk 9000 comms intercept; . . . laser detection and countermeasure syst.; Mk 36 Mod. 2 SRBOC decoy RL syst. (4 6-round Mk 137 RL); SLQ-25A Nixie acoustic torpedo decoy syst.
E/O: Thales Sirius optronic surveillance
M: CODOG: 2 G.E. LM-2500 gas turbines (23,324 shp each), 2 Bazán-Caterpillar 3600-series low-rpm diesels (6,000 shp each); 2 LIPS 4.65-m-dia., 5-bladed CP props; 46,648 shp max.
Electric: 4,400 kw tot. (4 × 1,100-kw Bazán-MTU 12C396 diesel sets)
Range: 5,000/18 **Endurance:** 21 days
Crew: 35 officers, 215 enlisted (incl. 11 air unit) (accomm. for 250, incl. 16 flag group)

Number of units: The number of units in inventory as of 1 January 2002. Additional ships or craft under construction or on order are given in parentheses, with a second number in parentheses indicating additional units planned. Any alternative designations for the class are given in parentheses in bold, and the number of units in reserve may be indicated in a *non*-bolded parentheses after the class name entry. The standardized type designation for each class is given in brackets, either on the class line or at the end of the bolded type designation header when there are more than one class of combatants of the same type in service, as in "Destroyers [DD]."

Bldr: The name and location of the building yard(s), often in abbreviated form (see abbreviations list below).

Dates: Dates are given in the sequence day-month-year or month-year. "In serv." is the commissioning date for warships or delivery date for noncommissioned units. Delivery dates for warships are frequently *not* the same as date of commissioning, which often comes considerably later, after training and certification. Where applicable, other dates may appear with the ship name and number entries, such as year of authorization for construction or dates for major modernizations, conversions, or decommissionings to reserve, as indicated. For some entries, a column may also be devoted to fleet or home port assignments.

D: Displacement. In most cases, standard displacement, as defined by the Treaty of Washington (1922), is given. Where possible, this information is followed by the full-load displacement in parentheses; there are occasional instances of other displacements, such as trials or normal or light ship (empty of all disposables). For submarines, two displacements are normally given: surfaced full load and submerged full load; when available, the standard surfaced displacement precedes the surfaced and submerged displacements.

S: Speed. Given in knots and taken as maximum unless specifically defined otherwise. In some cases, sustained or trials speeds are given. For submarines, surfaced speed precedes submerged speed.

Dim: Dimensions. Given as length overall × beam × draft (taken as maximum navigational unless otherwise defined); other significant dimensions are given in parentheses, where warranted. Length between perpendiculars (vertical reference points normally coinciding with bow waterline and rudderpost in single-rudder ships or stern waterline in multiple-rudder ships) is given as "pp," and length at waterline (if different) as "wl."

A: Armament. Generally given in the following order: antiship missiles, surface-to-air missiles, major guns, antisurface torpedo systems, point-defense surface-to-air missiles, antiaircraft guns, antisubmarine rocket or missile systems, antisubmarine torpedo systems, depth charges, mines and minelaying systems, and aircraft. For ships with a significant aircraft-carrying mission, a separate header, "Air group," is used. For guns, the caliber of the barrel is given after the bore; caliber times bore equals the length of the barrel.

Electronics: Electronic equipment. Presented in the following order: radars, sonar systems, TACAN (aircraft navigation beacon/control systems), electronic warfare (EW) systems and countermeasures, and electro-optical (E/O), where applicable. Within radars, "nav." indicates a navigational set and "f.c." indicates fire control. For sonars, nominal operating frequencies are given in kilohertz in parentheses or indicated by general category, e.g., "HF" for high-frequency (above 20 kHz), "MF" for medium frequency, "LF" for low frequency (7 kHz and below).

M: Machinery. The manufacturer's name and propulsion machinery model nomenclature, where known, are given, with multiple-drive systems headed by the accepted abbreviation, as in CODAG for COmbined Diesel And Gas turbine, CODOG for COmbined Diesel Or Gas turbine, and so forth. The number and type of propellers or other propulsive devices follows the first semicolon, with "CP" indicating a controllable-pitch propeller. The maximum horsepower of the system is given after the second semicolon, often followed for diesel plants by the sustained rating of the plant in parentheses. Auxiliary propulsion systems such as bow and stern side-thrusters or low-speed auxiliary propulsors are listed after a dash. To obtain kilowatt power from brake horsepower (bhp), multiply by 0.7457.

Boilers: For steam turbine–powered ships only. Make and model are followed by operating pressure and temperature.

Electric: Electrical generating plant. Total output is given in kilowatts (kw) or in kilovolt-amperes (kVA). Where known, details of the components of the plant are given in parentheses.

Range: Given in nautical miles, with the speed at which the range is achievable following a slash. Multiple entries may be included, particularly for submarines.

Fuel: Given in metric tons or, for smaller units, liters or U.S. gallons as specified; additional fuels may also be listed, such as aviation fuel or diesel fuel for auxiliary machinery or gasoline for embarked vehicles.

Endurance: The number of days for which the ship can operate unsupported, determined by the most critical disposable carried (food, fuel, water, etc.).

Crew: Either given as the normal total complement or broken down into officers, petty officers, and other enlisted personnel, as applicable. Additional personnel who can be carried follow a "+" sign, and total accommodations (if more than the standard complement) are given in parentheses.

Remarks: Programmatic, general design information, and significant operational information are given in the initial paragraph. For more important classes, the Remarks section may be subdivided into Hull systems (and also Propulsion systems, if warranted), Aviation systems, and Combat systems. For classes where a large number of units have either recently been discarded or placed in reserve, there will also be a Status section. When a significant number of ships within a class have been stricken or transferred elsewhere, a Disposals section will be included; when an entire class has been deleted since the last edition, a separate Disposal Note will be placed in sequence where the class appeared in the previous edition. Separate Note paragraphs include data not appropriate for the class entries, such as preliminary information about new programs, and may appear anywhere in the text.

SHIP TYPE DESIGNATION SYSTEM

A unified ship type designator system is applied to all ship classes, regardless of the local system employed by the navy being described; local designations, where employed, are provided in the ship class header line, followed in brackets by the letter system detailed below, *or* the brackets appear at the end of the ship type designation header for combatant classes. The system, which is not without its incongruities, is nonetheless the best available and is closely aligned with that employed by the U.S. Department of Defense and widely understood elsewhere. Note that the categorizations are both functional and by size of ship.

Ship descriptions are grouped together under classes when there is more than one (or prospects for more than one) unit of the design. The class of a ship does not change when it is transferred to or built for a country other than that which originated the design. Thus, a Russian-built Kilo-class submarine is a Kilo regardless of what the Chinese, Indian, Polish, Algerian, or other navies might locally call the class.

As modifications to the basic ship-type designators listed below, several suffixes and one prefix may be employed:

Prefix:

W For all ship types not subordinated to a navy, such as coast guards, customs services, border guards, or government-owned scientific ships.

Suffixes:

A For all ships or craft intended to operate with aerodynamic lift (wing-in-ground-effect craft) or pressurized air lift (surface-effect units, air-cushion vehicles). Two *exceptions* are SSA, for auxiliary submarine, and ATA, for auxiliary ocean tug.

G *For major surface combatants,* a "G" suffix means that the class is equipped with an area air-defense missile system with a maximum effective range of greater than 10 n.m. (which implies that the missiles provide an air-defense escort capability rather than merely self-defense). *For submarines and minor surface combatants,* the "G" suffix is used only when aerodynamic cruise missiles are the principal weapon system carried.

H Applied either for specialized aircraft-carrying ships capable of operating only vertical or short takeoff and landing fixed-wing aircraft or to other types of major combatants carrying three or more helicopters. An "H" suffix is *also* used to signify minor surface combatants that are equipped with hydrofoils.

N Used either to indicate that major ships have nuclear propulsion systems *or*, for service craft, that they are non-self-propelled.

T Employed to indicate that a specific type of ship has been equipped to perform additional duties as a training vessel (in AXT, for training ship, the "T" is a part of the basic designator). *Exceptions* are the designations AOT and AWT, where the "T" means "transport."

BASIC SHIP-TYPE DESIGNATORS

The designations for combatants (including mine warfare units and amphibious warfare units) are presented in the order in which ship types are presented in this book.

Aircraft Carriers:

CV Aircraft Carrier: warships intended primarily to carry and operate combat aircraft (as distinguished from "L"-series amphibious warfare ships that carry aircraft primarily in support of amphibious warfare operations).

CVV Aircraft Carrier, V/STOL: as for CV, but not capable of operating fixed-wing, conventional takeoff and landing (CTOL) aircraft, i.e., not equipped with arrestor gear and therefore capable only of operating vertical- or short takeoff or landing aircraft (V/STOL or VTOL).

Submarines:

SSB Ballistic-Missile Submarine: submarines equipped primarily to launch strategic ballistic missiles from vertically mounted tubes.

SSG Cruise-Missile Attack Submarine: Submarines designed to launch aerodynamic cruise missiles from launchers other than the normal torpedo tubes. By U.S. Navy custom, the "G" has not been applied to submarines that are equipped with vertical cruise-missile launch tubes, although the *Ohio*-class cruise-missile submarines will be officially termed SSGN.

SS Attack Submarine: submarines with a principal armament employing horizontal tubes to launch weapons such as torpedoes, mines, and cruise missiles; some SS or SSN may also have vertical tubes for cruise (but not, by definition, ballistic) missiles or mines.

SSC Coastal Submarine: submarines of less than 500 tons submerged displacement intended primarily for limited endurance and/or coastal defense missions.

SSA Auxiliary Submarine: submarines designed or adapted for noncombatant roles such as training, trials, or target duties.

SSM Midget Submarine: combatant submarines of less than 150 tons submerged displacement.

Major Surface Combatants:

C Cruiser: large surface combatants equipped with a major command, control, and communications capability in addition to major weapons systems. Cruisers having guns of greater than 130-mm and less than 180-mm bore are still referred to as CL, for Light Cruiser (only Peru now has such a ship in service). Cruisers now in service displace between 5,000 and 27,000 tons.

DD Destroyer: major surface combatants not possessing the scope of command, control, and communications capabilities of a cruiser and generally intended to perform supporting roles in a group of combatants centered on cruiser or carrier forces. Some older destroyers of less than 4,000 tons displacement are still in service, while some of the largest units now exceed 10,000 tons displacement.

FF Frigate: formerly applied to surface combatants with weapons systems tailored toward one specific role, such as antisubmarine warfare, but now generally applied to ships with lesser capabilities and of generally smaller size than a destroyer. The two categories are, indeed, beginning to blend, and there are frigates in service or planned ranging from 1,500 tons to over 6,000 tons full load displacement. For internal political reasons, some navies refer to ships as "frigates" when they are in fact destroyers, and a few navies refer to ships as "destroyers" that would more properly be termed frigates.

FFL Corvette: surface combatants of less than 1,500 tons but more than 1,000 tons full load displacement. Essentially, fourth-rate surface combatants. Note that the designation "corvette" as used here essentially refers to smaller frigates and does not correspond to the European concept of corvettes as any warship larger than a patrol craft but smaller than a frigate.

Minor Surface Combatants:

PS Large Patrol Ship: ships intended for offshore patrol duties and generally characterized by slower speeds and lesser armament than major surface combatants, trading speed for seaworthiness and endurance. In size, they are normally greater than 1,000 tons full load displacement.

PG Patrol Combatant: units of between 500 and 1,000 tons full load displacement intended for offshore operations and generally possessing speeds in excess of 25 knots. Most modern PGs are equipped with antiship missiles and are hence typed "PGG," a type often referred to as a "missile corvette."

PTG Guided-Missile Patrol Craft: craft of less than 500 tons full load displacement equipped to launch antiship missiles. The designation is traditional and derives from the late 1950s when the first such craft were essentially torpedo boat designs with missiles instead of torpedoes.

PT Torpedo Boat: any craft of up to 500 tons equipped primarily to launch antiship (vice antisubmarine) torpedoes—an almost extinct type.

PC Coastal Patrol Craft: gun and antisubmarine warfare weapon–equipped craft between 100 and 500 tons, not equipped to carry antiship missiles.

PB Patrol Boat: any craft of less than 100 tons equipped primarily to carry out patrol duties in relatively sheltered waters, harbors, or rivers.

PM River Monitor: armored, low-freeboard craft of less than 500 tons full load displacement intended for riverine duties. There is no separate category for smaller, unarmored riverine patrol craft, which are grouped with other PB (Patrol Boat) classes.

Mine Warfare Ships and Craft:

MM Minelayer: ships intended primarily to lay mines. They may also carry out tasks such as acting as flagships, mine countermeasures support ships, or training vessels.

MCS Mine Countermeasures Support Ship: vessels intended to provide command, control, and communications and logistics support specifically tailored to mine warfare operations. Such ships are frequently essentially auxiliaries, and some are also capable of operating mine countermeasures helicopters and/or of minelaying.

MHS Minehunting Ship: mine warfare vessels of 500 tons or greater full load displacement equipped to locate mines by means of specialized sensors and then to destroy them. Minehunters also capable of towing sweep arrays remain typed as minehunters. Some are also equipped to lay mines.

MSF Fleet Minesweeper: mine countermeasures units of greater than 500 tons full load displacement equipped primarily to tow sweep arrays of all kinds and *not* equipped with specialized bottomed-mine location systems (but normally having some sort of moored-mine avoidance sonar sensor). They may also be equipped to perform patrol and antisubmarine duties and are frequently equipped to lay mines. In general, this is an obsolescent type, and the numbers of such ships are declining.

MHC Coastal Minehunter: as for MHS, but intended for operation in more sheltered waters and displacing less than 500 tons full load.

MSC Coastal Minesweeper: as for MSF, but intended for operations in more sheltered waters; the designation is normally applied to minesweepers of between 250 and 500 tons full load displacement.

MSI Inshore Minesweeper: as for MSC, but intended for sheltered water operations or for harbor or roadstead work; the designation is applied to minesweepers of between 100 and 250 tons full load displacement.

MSB Minesweeping Boat: shallow water or riverine mine countermeasures craft displacing less than 100 tons full load.

MSD Minesweeping Drone: any mine countermeasures craft primarily intended for remote-controlled operation.

MSS Specialized Minesweeper: catch-all category for ships and craft equipped to perform either one specialized mine countermeasures role (such as line-charge laying or magnetic pulse generation) or for craft intended primarily to support mine disposal divers.

Amphibious Warfare Ships and Craft:

LPH Amphibious Warfare Helicopter Carrier: major ships intended primarily to operate helicopters to transport embarked troops; corresponds to U.S. Navy LPH, LHD, and LHA types. They may also carry vertical takeoff and landing fixed-wing aircraft embarked primarily for troop-support ground-attack duties.

LPD Amphibious Transport Dock: major ships designed to carry and launch craft from a wet well deck at the stern. Distinguished from LSDs by carrying larger numbers of troops at the expense of vehicles and cargo.

LSD Dock Landing Ship: another wet well–configured ship but with the cargo being predominantly vehicles.

LST Tank Landing Ship: ships designed to beach and discharge cargo via a bow ramp system. Applied to ships of this configuration of greater than 2,000 tons full load displacement and capable of landing 400 or more metric tons of cargo.

LSM Medium Landing Ship: a smaller version of the LST, generally between 500 and 2,000 tons full load displacement and capable of delivering a cargo of less than 400 metric tons to a beach.

LPA Amphibious Transport: ships primarily configured to carry assault troops, who are delivered to the beach via embarked landing craft launched via davits or cranes.

LCFS Fire Support Landing Craft: craft equipped with guns and/or rocket launchers for shore bombardment in support of amphibious assault troops.

LCU Utility Landing Craft: larger, generally open-topped, bow ramp–equipped landing craft capable of transporting at least 100 metric tons of vehicles and personnel to a beach. LCUs are not generally large enough to make extended ocean voyages in a loaded condition, and most can be transported in the wet wells of larger landing ships.

LCM Medium Landing Craft: beachable landing craft capable of transporting up to 100 tons of vehicle cargo and/or personnel and that can be transported to the scene of the amphibious assault aboard larger ships.

LCVP Vehicle/Personnel Landing Craft: bow ramp–equipped, ship-transportable craft capable of carrying troops and small vehicles to a beach; cargo capacity limited to around 15 tons maximum.

LCP Personnel Landing Craft: craft suitable only for transporting assault troops to a beach; if ramp-equipped, the ramp is suitable only for personnel, not vehicles.

LCW Special Warfare Support Craft: small, high-speed, low-observable craft used to transport special warfare forces.

LSDV Swimmer Delivery Vehicle: self-propelled submersibles intended to transport combat swimmers.

Auxiliaries:

ADG Deperming/Degaussing Ship: seagoing ships intended to provide mobile deperming services and/or to transport and support degaussing ranges.

AE Ammunition Ship: vessels intended to transport replenishment combat munitions for transfer at sea to combatant ships. U.S. Navy ammunition ships in service also carry cargo fuels.

AEM Missile Tender: auxiliaries configured to transport ballistic missiles or large cruise missiles.

AF Stores Ship: vessels intended primarily to transport refrigerated and dry provisions to combatants and to transfer their cargoes while under way. May also have smaller quantities of munitions, spares, and even replenishment fuels.

AFT Transport Stores Ship: as for AF, but without underway replenishment capability.

AG Miscellaneous Auxiliary: any auxiliaries whose functions are not defined by one of the other auxiliary definitions.

AGE Experimental Auxiliary: vessels configured to test weapons, sensors, communications systems, and so forth.

AGF Auxiliary Command Ship: vessels employed as flagships but clearly not configured as combatants.

AGI Intelligence Collection Ship: vessels configured for the collection of foreign intelligence, primarily electronic, but also including acoustic and electro-optical.

AGL Buoy Tender: vessels intended to transport, lay, retrieve, and, often, repair navigational and mooring buoys. They usually also have a significant salvage capability.

AGM Missile Range Instrumentation Ship: auxiliaries intended to collect data about domestic ballistic missile and cruise missile flight-paths and performance and, in some cases, also to act as communications relay vessels for space vehicles.

AGOR Oceanographic Research Ship: auxiliaries intended to collect information on the physical and biological properties of the sea.

AGP Patrol Craft Tender: ships specifically configured to provide logistic support, repairs, and often command facilities and munitions for minor combatant vessels.

AGS Hydrographic Survey Ship: auxiliaries intended primarily to perform bottom surveys and to process data intended for the creation of navigational charts. They frequently also have a significant oceanographic research capability.

AH Hospital Ship: auxiliaries intended for the care and transportation of wounded or otherwise incapacitated military or civilian personnel—and clearly identified as such. By international agreement, they must be painted white and carry prominent red crosses or red crescents viewable from above and each side and must not be armed (but Russian hospital ships double as transports, and Chinese hospital ships are armed).

AK Cargo Ship: auxiliaries intended primarily to transport dry cargo in support of naval forces. They may carry a minor proportion of their cargo in the form of refrigerated provisions and/or ammunition. AKs are not normally configured for underway transfer of cargo.

AO Oiler: auxiliaries intended to transport and transfer fuels to warships while under way, although they may have small quantities of ammunition, water, lube oil, provisions, etc., for transfer as well.

AOR Replenishment Oiler: auxiliaries configured to transport liquid and dry cargoes to warships while under way. While the principal cargo is fuels and water, the ships have a significant fraction of their transferable cargo in the form of ammunition, dry and refrigerated provisions, and spare parts—essentially, one-stop underway replenishment platforms.

AOS Special Liquids Tanker: auxiliaries intended to transport liquid cargoes other than ship propulsion fuels, lubricants, or water; generally applied to Russian Navy liquid nuclear waste transports and missile fuel transports.

AOT Transport Oiler: tankers intended primarily for point-to-point transportation of liquid cargoes and not generally capable of being employed for underway replenishment.

AP Transport: vessels intended for the point-to-point transport of personnel, distinguished from LPAs in that they are not intended to transport amphibious assault troops. They may also have a significant dry cargo and/or provisions transport capacity.

AR Repair Ship: ships intended to provide repair and spare parts services to surface combatants. This subsumes the U.S. Navy categories of AR (Repair Ship) and AD (Destroyer Tender).

ARC Cable Ship: auxiliaries intended to transport, lay, retrieve, and service undersea cables.

ARR Nuclear Propulsion Repair Ship: auxiliaries having specialized facilities for the servicing of shipboard nuclear propulsion plants, including facilities to transport nuclear fuel rods. This designator applies only to several Russian Navy classes and does not include ships configured to carry liquid radiological wastes (see AOS).

ARS Salvage and Rescue Ship: auxiliaries, usually of tug configuration, intended to support salvage, rescue, and firefighting operations.

AS Submarine Tender: auxiliaries intended to provide logistic support and repair services to submarines.

ASR Submarine Rescue Ship: auxiliaries intended for the rescue of personnel from sunken submarines. Most ASRs are also capable of performing general salvage and ocean towing duties.

ATA Ocean Tug: auxiliaries configured primarily for oceangoing towing, but usually also capable of secondary rescue, salvage, and firefighting missions.

AW Water Tanker: auxiliaries intended for the transport and underway transfer of water to other ships.

AWT Water Transport: as for AW, but without underway transfer capability.

AXT Training Ship: auxiliaries equipped primarily for the training of cadets and/or enlisted personnel. Also applies to large sail training vessels in naval service.

Service Craft:

YAG Miscellaneous Service Craft: service craft whose function is not covered by other definitions or that has several equally significant functions.

YAGE Experimental Service Craft: small trials craft for trials-associated duties with weapons systems, sensors, and other naval systems.

YC Open Barge: any open-topped, non-self-propelled dry cargo barges.

YD Floating Crane: most are non-self-propelled, but by convention (and because self-propulsion systems for floating cranes are only for very local movements and positionings), craft without propulsion systems do not receive an "N" suffix.

YDG Deperming/Degaussing Platform: nonseagoing craft intended to support deperming services or to support a degaussing range.

YDT Diving Tender: service craft primarily equipped to support noncombatant divers. (Large, seagoing diving tenders are generally typed ARS, while ships and craft configured primarily to support mine disposal divers are typed MSS.)

YE Ammunition Lighter: self-propelled, nonseagoing craft for local transport of munitions.

YF Covered Lighter: self-propelled craft for local transport of dry cargo. (A YFN is a covered or deckhouse-equipped non-self-propelled barge.)

YFB Ferry: self-propelled craft for local transport of vehicles as well as personnel (as distinguished from a YFL, which cannot transport vehicles).

YFDB Large Floating Dry Dock: open-ended floating dry docks with a lift capacity of 20,000 metric tons or more.

YFDM Medium Floating Dry Dock: open-ended floating dry docks with a lift capacity between 5,000 and 20,000 metric tons.

YFDL Small Floating Dry Dock: open-ended floating dry docks with a lift capacity of less than 5,000 metric tons.

YFL Launch: small, self-propelled craft for local transportation of personnel.

YFNB Large Covered Barge: large, towable, non-self-propelled barges for the ocean transport of dry cargo.

YFND Dry Dock Companion Barge: non-self-propelled barges equipped with machinery intended to support floating dry docks.

YFP Floating Power Barge: non-self-propelled craft equipped with generators or alternators to supply electricity (a few YFPs do have self-propulsion for local movement). The designation is also applied to craft employed to charge submarine batteries.

YFR Refrigerated Lighter: self-propelled craft for local transport of refrigerated (and, often, dry) provisions.

YFU Harbor Utility Lighter: beachable, ramp-equipped, self-propelled craft for local logistic support duties.

YG Garbage Lighter: self-propelled craft for the transport of garbage or for the treatment and disposal of human waste. Not good duty.

YGL Small Navigational Aids Tender: self-propelled service craft intended to service navigational aids buoys and other navigational markers; they may or may not be equipped to lay, recover, and service navigational aids buoys.

YGS Survey Craft: small self-propelled craft intended for the collection of bottom configuration data for the purpose of preparing navigational charts. They may either be independently operable or intended to be transported to the scene of operations aboard a larger vessel (usually an AGS).

YGT Target Service Craft: surface ships or craft of any size intended to act as targets or as specialized drone target control craft. (Stationary floating or towed targets are typed YGTN.)

YH Ambulance Craft: self-propelled local service craft intended for the transport of ill or injured personnel and, in some cases, to provide emergency medical services in remote, sheltered areas.

YM Dredge: self-propelled or, by convention, non-self-propelled craft equipped to deepen channels, harbors, or inland waterways.

YNG Net Tender: service ships or craft of any size intended to transport and/or service antisubmarine harbor defense nets and warning devices. They may also have a significant salvage capability due to heavy-lift facilities.

YO Fuel Lighter: self-propelled craft for local transport of fuels. They are generally for harbor use, but may have a limited seagoing capability.

YPB Floating Barracks: ships or craft intended primarily to provide stationary accommodations and support for personnel. If self-propelled, the capability is primarily for local movement.

YPT Torpedo Retriever: self-propelled craft intended to recover expended exercise torpedoes and missiles (and, in some cases, exercise mines).

YR Floating Workshop: non-self-propelled harbor craft equipped to perform repair and maintenance on other ships and craft.

YRC Cable tender: self-propelled local service craft for laying, retrieving, and, often, servicing underwater cables.

YRD Auxiliary Repair Dock: floating dry docks with one end enclosed in a ship-like bow intended to permit rapid towing (corresponds to U.S. Navy ARD).

YRG Tank Cleaning Craft: service craft intended to clean shipboard fuel tanks and sewage tanks.

YRRN Nuclear Propulsion Repair Barge: non-self-propelled harbor craft intended to support nuclear-powered ships and submarines.

YRS Salvage Craft: service craft of a variety of configurations intended to support salvage operations; included are salvage pontoons and small self-propelled harbor salvage craft (but not diving tenders, which are YDT).

YSS Service Submersible: small submersible craft employed for research, salvage, and/or personnel rescue.

YTB Large Harbor Tug: tugs intended for harbor and coastal service and having a total horsepower of 1,200 bhp or more.

YTM Medium Harbor Tug: tugs intended primarily for harbor service but capable of limited coastal operations and having a total horsepower between 400 and 1,200 bhp.

YTL Small Harbor Tug: tugs intended primarily for harbor and dockyard service and having a total horsepower of up to 400 bhp.

YTR Fireboat: self-propelled craft intended primarily for firefighting duties and not generally intended for towing.

YTS Sail Training Craft: craft powered primarily by sails and intended to provide seamanship training.

YXT Training Craft: smaller, self-propelled craft intended to provide seamanship, navigational, and maneuvering training and generally not intended for sustained seagoing operations.

ACRONYMS AND ABBREVIATIONS

A	Armament
AA	Antiaircraft
A&C	Shipbuilding Yard (*Atelier & Chantier*)
AAW	Anti-air Warfare
a.c.	Alternating current
accomm.	Accommodations
ADAWS	Action Data Automation Weapon System (U.K.)
ADI	Australian Defence Industries
AEW	Airborne Early Warning
AIP	Air-independent propulsion
ARM	Antiradiation Missile
ARPA	Automatic Radar Plotting Aid
ASM	Antiship Missile
ASROC	Antisubmarine Rocket (U.S.)
Ast. Nav.	Shipyard (*Astilleros Navales*)
ASW	Antisubmarine warfare
Auth.	Authorized
avg.	Average, normal
BAE	British Aerospace
bbl	barrels
bhp	Brake horsepower (diesel and gasoline engines)
Bldr	Builder
Bros.	Brothers
BW	Boat Works
BY	Boat Yard
CAAIS	Computer-Assisted Action Information System (U.K.)
cal.	caliber (length of gun barrel divided by bore diameter)
Cant.	Shipyard (*Cantieri*)
Ch.	Shipyard (*Chantier*)
CIC	Combat Information Center
CIWS	Close-In Weapon System (U.S., but now widely used)
C.N.	Naval shipyard (*Cantiere Navale, Chantier Naval*)
COD	Carrier Onboard Delivery (U.S.)

COGAG/CODAD/ COSAG/COGOG/ CODOG — Combined propulsion systems: CO = combined; D = diesel, G = gas turbine, S = steam; A = and, O = or—e.g., CODOG = combined diesel or gas turbine
Const. — Constructed or construction
cont. — Continuous
COOP — Craft of Opportunity
COTS — Commercial off-the-shelf
CP — Controllable-pitch (propeller)
cyl. — Cylinder
D — Displacement
dc — Direct current
d.c. — Depth charge
DD — Dry dock
del. — Delivered
desig. — Designation, designator
Det. — Detachment
D/F — Direction finding, direction finder
dia. — Diameter
DICASS — Directional command-activated sonobuoy system
DIFAR — Directional low-frequency analysis and ranging
Dim — Dimensions
DoD — Department of Defense (U.S.)
DP — Dual-purpose (gun, meaning for surface and antiaircraft firing)
DSRV — Deep Submergence Rescue Vessel (U.S.)
dwt — Deadweight tonnage
DY — Dockyard
EADS — European Aeronautic, Defence, and Space Co.: a joint venture (formed in 2000) of DaimlerChrysler and Thomson-CSF with BAE Systems, Matra BAe Dynamics, Aérospatiale-Matra, Alenia Marconi Systems, LFK (Lenkflugkörpersystem GmbH), DaimlerBenz Aerospace; other joint ventures include an agreement with Nortel, Ontario
ECCM — Electronic counter-countermeasures
ECM — Electronic countermeasures
EEZ — Economic Exclusion Zone
ELINT — Electronic intelligence
E.N. — Shipyard (*Empresa Nacional*)
Eng. — Engineering
E/O — Electro-optical
ESM — Electronic support measures (i.e., passive EW)
est. — Estimated
Est. — *Estalleiros*
EW — Electronic Warfare
f.c. — Fire-control
f.c.s. — Fire-control system
fl — Full load (displacement)
FLIR — Forward-looking infrared
FM — Frequency modulation
FRAM — Fleet Rehabilitation and Modernization (U.S.)
freq. — Frequency
ft. — Foot, feet
fwd — Forward
FY — Fiscal Year
g. — Gravity
G.E. — General Electric Co. (U.S.)
gen. — Generator
GFCS — Gun fire-control system
GHz — Gigahertz
G.M. — General Motors Corp. (U.S.)
GPS — Global Positioning System
GRP — Glass-reinforced plastic (fiberglass)
grt — Gross registered tons (a measurement of volume, not weight)
GWS — Guided Weapon System (U.K.)
HF — High frequency
HFD/F — High-frequency direction-finder
H.M. — Her Majesty's (U.K.)
HMAS — Her Majesty's Australian Ship
HMDY — Her Majesty's Dockyard
HMS — Her Majesty's Ship (U.K.)
hp — Horsepower
hr — Hours
IADT — Integrated automatic detection and tracking
IFF — Identification, friend or foe
IHI — Ishikawajima-Harima Heavy Industries: formed in 1960 with the merger of Ishikawajima Heavy Industries, Ltd., and Harima Heavy Industries, Ltd.; naval shipbuilding efforts combined with Sumatomo Heavy Industries in 2000 to form Marine United, Inc.
ihp — Indicated horsepower (for reciprocating steam engines)
IOC — Initial operational capability
IR — Infrared
IRST — Infrared search-and-track
ISAR — Inverse synthetic aperture radar
kg — Kilograms
kHz — Kilohertz
Kon. Mij. — Royal Company (Netherlands)
kph — Kilometers per hour
kT — Kilotons
kts — Knots
kVA — Kilovolt-Amperes
kw — Kilowatts
L — Launched
LAMPS — Light Airborne Multipurpose System (U.S. helicopter)
LF — Low frequency
LOFAR — Low-frequency analysis and ranging
m — Meters
M — Machinery
MAD — Magnetic anomaly detection
MARAD — Maritime Administration (U.S.)
max. — Maximum
MCM — Mine countermeasures
MEKO — *Mehrzweck Kombination* (German Blohm + Voss containerized modular shipboard systems installation system)
MF — Medium frequency
MFD/F — Medium-frequency direction-finder
Mfr. — Manufacturer
mg — Machinegun
min — Minutes
min. — Minimum
MIRV — Multiple independent reentry vehicle
mm — Millimeters
Mod. — Modified, modification
M.O.D. — Ministry of Defence (Germany, U.K.)
MPA — Maritime patrol aircraft
ms — Milliseconds
MSC — Military Sealift Command (U.S.)
MTU — Motoren und Turbinen Union
Mw — Megawatts
NATO — North Atlantic Treaty Organization
nav. — Navigation, navigational
Nav. — Naval
navaid — Navigational aid
NBC — Nuclear, biological, and chemical
NDY — Naval Dockyard
n.m. — Nautical miles
nrt — Net registered tonnage
NSY — Naval Shipyard
NTDS — Naval Tactical Data System
NY — Navy Yard
o.a. — Overall
PDMS — Point-Defense Missile System (U.S.)
pdr. — Pounder (referring to nominal weight of shell)
pp — Between perpendiculars
Pty. — Proprietary
R&D — Research and development
RBOC — Rapid-Blooming Overboard Chaff (U.S.)
rds — Rounds
RDY — Royal Dockyard
Recce — reconnaissance
RIB — Rigid inflatable boat
RL — Rocket launcher
RM — Relative motion (radar plot)
Ro/Ro — Roll-on/roll-off
ROV — Remotely operated vehicle
rpm — Revolutions per minute
S — Speed
SAM — Surface-to-air missile
SAR — Search-and-rescue
SATCOM — Satellite communications
SB — Shipbuilding
sec — Seconds
serv. — Service
SFCN — Société Française de Constructions Navale
SHF — Super-high frequency
shp — Shaft horsepower (steam and gas-turbine engines)
SINS — Ships' Inertial Navigation System (U.S.)
SLAR — Side-looking airborne radar
SLBM — Submarine-Launched Ballistic Missile
SLEP — Service Life Extension Program
Sqn. — Squadron
SRBOC — Super Rapid-Blooming Offboard Chaff (U.S.)
SSB — Single-sideband
SSM — Surface-to-surface missile
SSTD — Surface Ship Torpedo Defense
std. — Standard
STIR — Separate Track and Illumination Radar (U.S. and Dutch)
sub. — Submerged
surf. — Surface, surfaced
SURTASS — Surface Towed Array Surveillance System (U.S.)
sust. — Sustained
SWATH — Small waterplane area, twin-hull
SY — Shipyard
syst. — System
TACAN — Tactical Air Navigation System
TACTASS — Tactical Towed Acoustic Sensor System (U.S.)
TAS — Target Acquisition System (U.S.)
TASS — Towed Acoustic Array System (U.S.)
3-D — Three-dimensional (i.e., height, distance, and bearing)
TM — True motion (radar plot)
tot. — Total
TT — Torpedo tubes/launchers
t.v. — Television
2-D — Two-dimensional (i.e., distance and bearing)
UAV — Unmanned aerial vehicle
UHF — Ultra-high frequency
UNREP — Underway replenishment
V — Volts
VDS — Variable-depth sonar
VHF — Very high frequency
VLS — Vertical-launch system
V/STOL — Vertical/short takeoff and landing
VTOL — Vertical takeoff and landing
WASS — Whitehead Alenia Sistemi Subacquei (formerly Whitehead Motofides)
WIG — Wing-in-ground-effect
Wks. — Works
wl — Waterline

CONVERSION TABLES

◆ METERS (m.) to FEET (ft.)
based on 1 inch = 25.4 millimeters

m	0	1	2	3	4	5	6	7	8
	ft.	ft.	ft.	ft.	ft.	ft.	ft.	ft.	ft.
—	—	3.28084	6.5617	9.8425	13.1234	16.4042	19.6850	22.9659	26.2467
10	32.8084	36.0892	39.3701	42.6509	45.9317	49.2126	52.493	55.774	59.005
20	65.617	68.898	72.178	75.459	78.740	82.021	85.302	88.583	91.863
30	98.425	101.706	104.987	108.268	111.549	114.829	118.110	121.391	124.672
40	131.234	134.514	137.795	141.076	144.357	147.638	150.919	154.199	157.480
50	164.042	167.323	170.604	173.884	177.165	180.446	183.727	187.008	190.289
60	196.850	200.131	203.412	206.693	209.974	213.255	216.535	219.816	223.097
70	229.659	232.940	236.220	239.501	242.782	246.063	249.344	252.625	255.905
80	262.467	265.748	269.029	272.310	275.590	278.871	282.152	285.433	288.714
90	295.276	298.556	301.837	305.118	308.399	311.680	314.961	318.241	321.522
100	328.084	331.365	334.646	337.926	341.207	344.488	347.769	351.050	354.331
10	360.892	364.173	367.454	370.735	374.016	377.296	380.577	383.858	387.139
20	393.701	396.982	400.262	403.543	406.824	410.105	413.386	416.667	419.947
30	426.509	429.790	433.071	436.352	439.632	442.913	446.194	449.475	452.756
40	459.317	462.598	465.879	469.160	472.441	475.722	479.002	482.283	485.564
50	492.126	495.407	498.688	501.97	505.25	508.53	511.81	515.09	518.37
60	524.93	528.22	531.50	534.78	538.06	541.34	544.62	547.90	551.18
70	557.74	561.02	564.30	567.59	570.87	574.15	577.43	580.71	583.99
80	590.55	593.83	597.11	600.39	603.67	606.96	610.24	613.52	616.80
90	623.36	626.64	629.92	633.20	636.48	639.76	643.04	646.33	649.61
200	656.17	659.45	662.73	666.01	669.29	672.57	675.85	679.13	682.41
10	688.98	692.26	695.54	698.82	702.10	705.38	708.66	711.94	715.22
20	721.78	725.07	728.35	731.63	734.91	738.19	741.47	744.75	748.03
30	754.59	757.87	761.15	764.44	767.72	771.00	774.28	777.56	780.84
40	747.40	790.68	793.96	797.24	800.52	803.81	807.09	810.37	813.65
50	820.21	823.49	826.77	830.05	833.33	836.61	839.89	843.18	846.46
60	853.02	856.30	859.58	862.86	866.14	869.42	872.70	875.98	879.26
70	885.83	889.11	892.39	895.67	898.95	902.23	905.51	908.79	912.07
80	918.63	921.92	925.20	928.48	931.76	935.04	938.32	941.60	944.88
90	951.44	954.72	958.00	961.29	964.57	967.85	971.13	974.41	977.69
300	984.25	987.53	990.81	994.09	997.38	1000.66	1003.94	1007.22	1010.50
10	1017.06	1020.34	1023.62	1026.90	1030.18	1033.46	1036.75	1040.03	1043.31
20	1049.87	1053.15	1056.43	1059.71	1062.99	1066.27	1069.55	1072.83	1076.12
30	1082.68	1085.96	1089.24	1092.52	1095.80	1099.08	1102.36	1105.64	1108.92
40	1115.49	1118.77	1122.05	1125.33	1128.61	1131.89	1135.17	1138.45	1141.73
50	1118.29	1151.57	1154.86	1158.14	1161.42	1164.70	1167.98	1171.26	1174.54

◆ MILLIMETERS (mm.) to INCHES (in.)
based on 1 inch = 25.4 millimeters

mm	0	1	2	3	4	5	6	7	8
	in.	in.	in.	in.	in.	in.	in.	in.	in.
—	—	0.03937	0.07874	0.11811	0.15748	0.19685	0.23622	0.27559	0.31496
10	0.39370	0.43307	0.47244	0.51181	0.55118	0.59055	0.62992	0.66929	0.70866
20	0.78740	0.82677	0.86614	0.90551	0.94488	0.98425	1.02362	1.06299	1.10236
30	1.18110	1.22047	1.25984	1.29921	1.33858	1.37795	1.41732	1.45669	1.49606
40	1.57480	1.61417	1.65354	1.69291	1.73228	1.77165	1.81102	1.85039	1.88976

◆ MILLIMETERS (mm.) to INCHES (in.)
based on 1 inch = 25.4 millimeters (*continued*)

mm	0	1	2	3	4	5	6	7	8
	in.	in.	in.	in.	in.	in.	in.	in.	in.
50	1.96850	2.00787	2.04724	2.08661	2.12598	2.16535	2.20472	2.24409	2.28346
60	2.36220	2.40157	2.44094	2.48031	2.51969	2.55906	2.59843	2.63780	2.67717
70	2.75591	2.79528	2.83465	2.87402	2.91339	2.95276	2.99213	3.03150	3.07087
80	3.14961	3.18898	3.22835	3.26772	3.30709	3.34646	3.38583	3.42520	3.46457
90	3.54331	3.58268	3.62205	3.66142	3.70079	3.74016	3.77953	3.81890	3.85827
100	3.93701								

CONVERSION FACTORS

Meter	Yard	Foot	Inch	Centimeter	Millimeter
1	1.093 61	3.280 84	39.370 1	100	1 000
0.914 4	1	3	36	91.44	914.4
0.304 8	0.333 333	1	12	30.48	304.8
0.254	0.027 777 8	0.083 333	1	2.54	25.4 j
0.01	0.010 936 1	0.032 808 4	0.393 701	1	10
0.001	0.001 093 61	0.003 280 84	0.039 370 4	0.1	1

Nautical mile		Statute mile		Meters
1	=	1.151 52	=	1 853.18

◆ Boiler working pressure

Kilogram per square centimeter (atmosphere)		*Pounds per square inch*
1	equivalent →	14.223 3
0.070 307	← equivalent	1

◆ Conversion for Fahrenheit and centigrade scales

1 degree centigrade = 1.8 degrees Fahrenheit
1 degree Fahrenheit = 5/9 degree centigrade
t°F = 5/9(t − 32)°C.
t°C = (1.8t + 32)°F.

◆ Weights

1 kilogram = 2.204 62 *pounds* (av)
1 *pound* = 0.453 592 *kilograms*
1 ton (metric) = 0.984 21 *ton*
1 *ton* = 1.016 05 *metric ton*

◆ Power

1 CV = 0.986 32 *horsepower* (HP) 0.735 88 kilowatt (Greenwich) (75 kgm s)
1 *horsepower* (HP) = 1.013 87 (CV) 0.746 08 kilowatt (Greenwich)

ALBANIA

Republic of Albania

ALBANIAN NAVAL DEFENSE FORCES

Personnel (2001): About 2,500 total (500 officers), including about 350 Coast Guard troops

Bases: Naval headquarters is at Tirana. 1st Naval District Headquarters is at Durres and 2nd Naval District headquarters at Pasalimani, Vlore, with the 1st Naval Base at Shengjin and the 2nd at Sarande. Repair facilities at the Pasalimani base, destroyed during 1997, are being upgraded with assistance from Turkey, which is also assisting in reestablishing the Albanian Naval Academy. Italy's Customs Service *(Guardia di Finanza)* maintains four patrol boats at Durres.

Note: Renamed from the Coastal Defense Command of the Albanian Army in 1996. All former Soviet equipment was transferred prior to 1961. The last operational Whiskey-class (Project 613) submarine, *Qemel* (022), was retired at the end of 1995, although the hulks of all four units remained more or less afloat at Pasalimani through 2000.

TORPEDO BOATS [PT]

♦ 1 Chinese Shanghai-II class (Project 062)

P-123

Shanghai-II-class P-123—with Italian Guardia Finanza escort EPA/PA News, 2-97

D: 122.5 tons (134.8 fl) **S:** 28 kts **Dim:** 38.78 × 5.41 × 1.55 (props)
A: 2 twin 37-mm 63-cal. Type 74 AA; two twin 25-mm 80-cal. Type 81 AA; 2 single 533-mm TT
Electronics: Radar: 1 Type 351 (Pot Head) nav.
M: 2 Type L12-180 (1,200 bhp each) and 2 Type L12-180Z (910 bhp each) diesels; 4 props; 4,220 bhp
Electric: 39 kw **Range:** 750/16.5 **Endurance:** 7 days **Crew:** 36 tot.

Remarks: Transferred from China in 1974–75. Torpedo tubes removed from Huchuan-class torpedo boats have been mounted at the stern, firing aft. P-123 defected to Italy during 3-97 but was returned at the end of the year. Sisters P-121, P-122, P-421 (ex-P-931), P-422 (ex-P-932), and P-423 (ex-P-933) are beyond repair.

♦ 10 Chinese Huchuan-class semi-hydrofoils (5 non-operational)

S-101	S-201	S-210	S-305	S-307
S-102	S-209	S-214	S-306	S-406

Huchuan-class S-209 French Navy, 12-93

D: 39 tons (45.8 fl) **S:** 50 kts **Dim:** 22.30 × 3.80 (6.26 over fenders) × 1.15
A: 2 single 533-mm TT; 2 twin 14.5-mm 93-cal. Type 81 mg
Electronics: Radar: 1 Zarnitsa (Skin Head) nav.
M: 3 L12-180 diesels; 3 props; 3,600 bhp **Electric:** 5.6 kw tot.
Range: 500/30 **Crew:** 11 tot.

Remarks: Transferred 1974–75. The units listed here went to Italy in 1997, along with S-406, which was considered beyond repair by 1998; S-101 and S-305 were returned on 5-11-97, the others during 1998–99 after repairs in Italy. One other, pennant 902, defected 5-91 to Italy, where the crew requested asylum; the craft was returned in 10-91. At least six others had been cannibalized, and another dozen are beyond repair. Bow foils only; stern planes on surface. The foils have been removed from several of the boats.

Note: Twelve Soviet-supplied P-4-class (Project 123K) torpedo boats, built in the early 1950s, are in land storage and are unlikely to see further service.

PATROL CRAFT [PC]

♦ 1 Soviet Kronstadt class (Project 122B)
Bldr: Zelenodol'sk Zavod (In serv. ca. 1955)

F-322

D: 210 tons (320 fl) **S:** 18.7 kts (when new) **Dim:** 52.24 × 6.20 × 2.20
A: 1 85-mm Type 90K DP; 2 single 37-mm 63-cal. Type 70K AA; 3 twin 12.7-mm 79-cal. Type 2M-1 mg; 2 5-round RBU-1200 ASW RL; 2 d.c. racks (16 MGB-20 d.c. tot.)
Electronics: Radar: 1 Neptun surf. search—Sonar: Tamir-11M searchlight HF
M: 3 Type 9-D diesels; 3 props; 3,300 bhp **Electric:** 36 kw tot. (2 × 18 kw)
Range: 399/18.5; 3,000/8.5 **Endurance:** 10 days **Crew:** 49 tot.

Remarks: Four were transferred in 1958, of which two had been discarded by the early 1990s. F-324 ran aground off Brindisi, Italy, on 16-3-97 with 858 refugees aboard and was beyond repair. F-322 defected to Italy in 1995 and was returned to Albania during 1998. The sonar is probably no longer operational, and the obsolete radar listed may have been replaced with a commercial set.

PATROL BOATS [PB]

♦ 2 U.S. 45-foot Patrol Craft, Coastal (PCC) class
Bldr: Peterson Bldrs, Sturgeon Bay, Wis. (In serv. 27-2-99)

. . . .

D: 16.2 tons (17.7 fl) **S:** 35 kts (30 sust.) **Dim:** 13.86 × 3.96 × 0.86
A: small arms **Electronics:** Radar: 1 Raytheon 40X nav.
M: 2 MTU 8V183 TE92 diesels; 2 Hamilton 362 waterjets; 1,314 bhp
Range: 200/30 **Fuel:** 490 gal. **Crew:** 4 tot.

Remarks: Built mid-1990s as stock for now-canceled U.S. Special Defense Acquisition Fund; originally to have been donated to Albania in 2-97. Aluminum construction. Trailerable. Intended for riverine and harbor patrol. Ten sisters serve in the Egyptian Coast Guard, where they are armed with one 12.7-mm and two 7.62-mm mg.

♦ 3 ex-U.S. Sea Spectre PB Mk III class
Bldr: Peterson Bldrs, Sturgeon Bay, Wis. (In serv. 1976)

. . . . . . (ex-65PB753)   . . . . . . (ex-65PB758)
. . . . . . (ex-65PB757)

D: 28 tons (36.7 fl) **S:** 30 kts (now less) **Dim:** 19.78 × 5.50 × 1.80 (props)
A: . . . **Electronics:** Radar: 1 or 2 Furuno . . . nav.
M: 3 G.M. 8V71 TI diesels; 3 props; 1,800 bhp
Range: 450/26; 2,000/. . . **Endurance:** 3 days **Crew:** 1 officer, 8 enlisted

Remarks: Originally planned for transfer in 2-97, but delayed until 27-2-99. Have trouble making maximum speed. Aluminum hull construction. Can accept a variety of weapons up to 40-mm bore on forward mounting position and have four other weapons locations, including one atop the pilothouse for a twin 12.7-mm mg.

MINE WARFARE SHIPS

♦ 1 Soviet T-43-class ocean minesweeper [MSF]

M-222 (ex-741)

D: 535 tons (569 fl) **S:** 14 kts **Dim:** 58.0 × 8.75 × 2.5 (3.5 sonar)
A: 2 twin 37-mm 63-cal. V-11-M AA; 4 twin 12.7-mm 79-cal. mg; 2 BMB-1 d.c. mortars; 2 mine rails
Electronics:
Radar: 1 Decca . . . nav.; 1 Lin' (Ball End) surf. search
Sonar: Tamir-11 HF searchlight
M: 2 Type 9-D diesels; 2 CP props; 2,200 bhp **Electric:** 175 kw tot.
Range: 3,200/10; 4,400/8.3 **Fuel:** 68 tons **Crew:** 53 tot.

Remarks: Two units remained afloat into the 1990s, with one no longer in service by 1995 and the other, numbered AS-342, defecting to Brindisi, Italy, on 17-3-97 and interned; the ship was returned to Albania at the end of 1997.

♦ 2 Soviet T-301-class (Project 255) coastal minesweepers [MSC]

M-225   M-227

T-301-class M-225 French Navy, 7-99

D: 147.8 tons (164 fl) **S:** 12.5 kts **Dim:** 38.00 × 5.70 × 1.58
A: 1 45-mm Type 21-KM AA; 2 twin 12.7-mm 79-cal. mg; up to 18 mines
Electronics: Radar: 1 Decca . . . nav.—Sonar: Tamir-10 HF searchlight-type
M: 3 Type 3D-12 diesels; 3 props; 900 bhp (690 sust.)

MINE WARFARE SHIPS *(continued)*

Electric: 60 kw tot. (2 × 30-kw diesel-driven sets)
Range: 2,400/7.1 **Fuel:** 10.1 tons **Endurance:** 5 days **Crew:** 35 tot.

Remarks: Two others have been discarded, and two more have been cannibalized for spares. The hull shell plating has no compound curves. The two survivors may no longer be operable. Mine countermeasures gear includes OPT bottom contact sweep, MT-3 contact sweep, PEMT-4 coil sweep, and two BAT-2 acoustic sweeps. The sonars are probably no longer operable. Neither were operational at the end of 2001.

SERVICE CRAFT

♦ 1 Soviet Nyryat'-1-class (Project 522) diving tender [YDT]
(In serv. ca. 1960)

A-534

D: 105.4 tons (115 fl) **S:** 10 kts **Dim:** 28.50 × 5.50 × 1.70
A: none **Electronics:** Radar: 1 Mius (Spin Trough) nav.
M: 1 Type 6CSP 28/3C diesel; 1 prop; 450 bhp
Range: 900/9 **Endurance:** 10 days **Crew:** 22 tot.

Remarks: Can support hard-hat divers to 20-m depths.

Disposal note: Soviet-supplied Khobi-class coastal oiler *Semani* was out of service by 2000, as was the Tugur-class coastal tug A-252.

♦ 3 Soviet PO-2 (Yaroslavets)-class (Project 376) workboats [YFL]
Bldr: Yaroslavl Zavod (In serv. late 1950s)

A-151 A-252 A-253

D: 32.2 tons (38.2 fl) **S:** 9–10 kts **Dim:** 21.00 × 3.90 × 1.40 (max.; 1.26 mean)
Electronics: Radar: 1 Mius (Spin Trough) nav. or none
M: 1 Type 3D-6S1 diesel; 1 prop; 150 bhp
Electric: 10 kw tot. (1 × 10 kw, DGPN-8/1500 diesel driving)
Range: 1,600/8 **Fuel:** 1.5 tons **Endurance:** 5 days **Crew:** 4–6 tot.

Remarks: Can be operated safely in Force 8 winds and 2-m seas. Can break light ice and serve as a harbor tug.

♦ 1 ex-Italian LCT(3)-class repair tender [YR] (In serv. 1943–44)

A-223 (ex-M.O.C. 1203, A 5333)

D: 579 tons (fl) **Dim:** 58.25 × 9.22 × 2.0
Electronics: Radar: 1 BX-732 nav.
M: 2 diesels; 2 props; 1,000 bhp **Crew:** 1–2 officers, 20–26 enlisted

Remarks: Decommissioned from Italian Navy on 1-3-98 and reportedly transferred to Albania in 2001; had been transferred to Italy from the U.K. in 1956. M.O.C. = *Moto Officina Costiera* (Coastal Repair Ship). Equipped for minor repairs to smallcraft. Bow door/vehicle ramp welded closed.

Note: The customs service operates four Arcor 24–class inspection craft (2.1 tons, 35 kts, 7.7 m o.a.) delivered from France in 11-90. There are as many as 40 smaller craft in use on various lakes.

ALGERIA

Democratic and Popular Republic of Algeria

MARINE DE LA RÉPUBLIQUE ALGERIENNE

Personnel (2001): About 6,000 total, with about 470 officers (includes 500 total Coast Guard and 600 Naval Infantry)

Naval Aviation: The Algerian Air Force uses 3 Fokker F-27 (Maritime) Mk 400 and 2 Beech Super King Air 200T patrol aircraft for maritime surveillance and 3 Kamov Ka-28 Helix helicopters for search and rescue duties.

Bases: 1st Naval Region: Algiers. 2nd Naval Region: Mers el-Kébir. 3rd Naval Region: Jijel. Coast Guard: Annaba (with detachments in major ports).

Coastal Defense: There are four batteries of SS-C-3 Styx missiles, using twin-tube truck-mounted launchers; their operational status is uncertain.

ATTACK SUBMARINES [SS]

♦ 2 Soviet Kilo class (Project 677EM)
Bldr: United Admiralty SY, St. Petersburg (In serv. 1987, 1988)

012 Raïs Hadj M'barek 013 El Hadj Slimane

D: 2,325 tons surf./3,076 tons sub. **S:** 10 kts surf./17 kts sub.
Dim: 72.60 (70.0 wl) × 9.90 × 6.6
A: 6 bow 533-mm TT (18 torpedoes or 24 mines); 1 SA-N-5/8 SAM syst. (8 missiles)
Electronics:
Radar: 1 MRK-50E (Snoop Tray-2) search
Sonar: MGK-400 (Shark Gill) LF active/passive suite; passive hull array; MG-519 (Mouse Roar) HF active classification/mine avoidance
EW: Brick Pulp or Squid Head intercept; Quad Loop (6701E) D/F
M: 2 Type 2D-42 diesel generator sets (1,825 bhp/1,500 kw each), electric drive: 1 motor; 1 6-bladed prop; 5,900 shp—1 130-shp low-speed motor—2 low-speed maneuvering motors; 2 ducted props; 204 shp

Raïs Hadj M'barek (012) U.S. Navy, 5-95

Range: 6,000/7 surf.; 400/3 sub. **Fuel:** 172 tons **Endurance:** 45 days
Crew: 12 officers, 41 enlisted

Remarks: First unit left the Baltic on 15-9-87 for delivery, the second during 1-88; both returned to Russia for overhaul during 1993, with work on 012 completed 5-95 and on 013 early in 3-96.
Hull systems: Propulsion plant suspended for silencing. Hull has 32% reserve buoyancy at 2,350 m^3 surfaced displacement. At rest on the surface, the submarine trims down 0.4 m by the bow. Maximum diving depth is 300 m, normal depth 240 m, and periscope depth 17.5 m. Have anechoic hull coating. Two batteries, each with 120 cells, providing 9,700 kw/hr. Hull has six watertight compartments.
Combat systems: Combat system, designated Murena or MVU-110EM, can conduct two simultaneous attacks while tracking three other targets manually. Sonar suite supplemented by MG-519 active mine-avoidance set, MG-553 sound velocity meter, and MG-512 own-ship's cavitation detector. The manual SAM launch position is located in after portion of the sail. Weapons carried can include E53-777 wire-guided, E53-60 and E53-85 wake-homing, and E53-67 acoustic homing torpedoes and KMD-500, KMD-1000, KMD-II-500, KMD-II-1000, and UMD mines.

Note: Two Romeo-class submarines transferred from the USSR had become nonoperational by 1988 but remain in Algeria and are probably used as battery charging and pierside training hulks.

FRIGATES [FF]

Note: One Russian source has reported that the second Gepard-class (Project 1166.1) frigate, the *Burevestnik* (ex-*Al'batros*) was to be delivered to Algeria as the *Sidi Fradj* in 2000, but that unit remained at the builder's, far from completion, through 2001.

♦ 3 Soviet Koni class (Project 1159)
Bldr: Krasniy Metallist Zavod, Zelenodol'sk

	Laid down	L	In serv.
901 Mourad Raïs (ex-SKR-482)	10-6-78	22-1-79	20-12-80
902 Raïs Kellich (ex-SKR-35)	11-6-80	30-4-81	24-3-82
903 Raïs Korfo	19-1-83	11-11-83	8-1-85

Raïs Korfo (903)—returning from modernization L. V. Pappens, 11-00

Raïs Kellich (902)—as yet unmodified French Navy, 5-95

D: 1,593 tons normal (1,670 fl) **S:** 27 kts (29.67 trials; 22 on diesels)
Dim: 95.51 × 12.55 × 4.12 (5.72 over sonar)
A: 1 Osa-M (SA-N-4) SAM syst. (20 9M-33/Gecko missiles); 2 twin 76.2-mm 59-cal. AK-276 DP; 2 twin 30-mm 65-cal. AK-230 AA; 2 12-round RBU-6000 ASW RL (120 RGB-60 rockets); 2 mine rails (up to 14 mines)—903 only: 2 twin 533-mm TT—901 and 902 only: 2 d.c. racks (12 BB-1 d.c. tot.)
Electronics:
Radar: 1 Don-2 nav.; 1 MR-302 Rubka (Strut Curve) (903: Pozitiv-ME1.2) air/surf. search; 1 MPZ-301(Pop Group) missile f.c.—901, 902 only: 1 MR-105 Turel' (Hawk Screech) 76.2-mm gun f.c.; 1 (903: 2) MR-104 Rys' (Drum Tilt) gun f.c.
Sonar: Titan/Vychegda suite (hull-mounted MF and HF f.c.)
EW: 901, 902: 2 Bizan-4B (Watch Dog-B) intercept (2–18 GHz); 1 Cross Loop-A D/F; 2 16-round RK-16 decoy RL—903: . . . intercept/jamming array; 4 6-round . . . decoy RL

FRIGATES [FF] *(continued)*

M: CODAG: 1 M-813 gas turbine (18,000 shp), 2 Type 68-B, 8,000-bhp diesels, 3 props; 35,000 hp
Range: 4,456/14.98 **Crew:** 130 tot.

Remarks: In-service dates reflect delivery dates. Were the 5th, 7th, and 10th units of the class built. All were overhauled in 1992–94 and given new generators. 903 was sent to Kronshtadt, Russia, for overhaul in 5-97 for a modernization that was to have been concluded in 8-98 but was not completed until 11-00.
Combat systems: Depth charge racks bolt to mine rails. During the ongoing modernizations, a Pozitiv-ME1.2 single-face, rotating planar array air-search radar is replacing the MR-302, a second MR-104 gun fire-control radar is replacing the MR-105 atop the bridge, and a new EW system (possibly of Chinese origin) is being installed. The modified ships are receiving longer-range Splav 90R ASW rockets for the RBU-6000 launchers.

GUIDED-MISSILE PATROL COMBATANTS [PGG]

♦ 3 Soviet Nanuchka-II class (Project 1234E)
Bldr: Sudostroitel'noye Obyedineniye "Almaz," Petrovskiy SY, St. Petersburg

801 Raïs Hamidou (ex-*Zyb*)
802 Salah Raïs (ex-*Liven*)
803 Raïs Ali (ex-*Burun*)

Salah Raïs (802)—returning from modernization L. V. Pappens, 11-00

D: 560 tons (675 fl) **S:** 30 kts **Dim:** 59.3 × 12.6 × 2.4
A: 2 twin P-20 (SS-N-2C Styx) SSM (802: 4 quadruple launchers for Kh-35 Uran/SS-N-25 Switchblade SSM); 1 twin Osa-M (SA-N-4) SAM syst. (20 9M-33/Gecko missiles); 1 twin 57-mm 70-cal. AK-725 DP—802 only: 1 30-mm 54-cal. AK-306 gatling AA
Electronics:
Radar: 801, 803: 1 Mius nav.; 1 Rangout (Square Tie) surf. search/missile target desig., 1 MPZ-301 (Pop Group) SA-N-4 f.c.; 1 MR-103 (Muff Cob) gun f.c.—802: 1 . . . nav.; 1 Pozitiv-ME1.2 surf./air search; 1 Garpun-E (Plank Shave) surf. search/missile target desig.; 1 MR-104 Rys' (Drum Tilt) gun f.c.
EW: 801, 803: 1 Bell Tap intercept; 1 Cross Loop MFD/F; 2 16-round RK-16 decoy RL—802: . . . intercept/jamming; 4 6-round decoy RL
M: 3 M-517 diesels; 3 props; 30,000 bhp
Electric: 750 kw tot. (2 × 300-kw, 2 × 75-kw diesel sets)
Range: 900/30; 2,500/12 **Crew:** 10 officers, 50 enlisted

Remarks: 801 arrived in Algeria 4-7-80, 802 in 2-81, 803 in 5-82. They bore the listed ex-Russian names during construction phase. 802 was delivered to Kronshtadt in 5-97 for a modernization that was to have been concluded in 8-98 but was not completed until 11-00.
Combat systems: On 801 and 803, the Rangout surface target tracking radar antenna is mounted within the Band Stand radome atop the bridge. The SA-N-4 SAM system employs a ZIF-122 retractable launcher for the Gecko missiles. The AK-725 mount uses a ZIF-72 automatic, unmanned mounting. During the current modernizations, Kh-35 Uran antiship missiles are replacing P-20 missiles, the EW suite is being replaced by a suite possibly of Chinese origin, the MR-104 f.c. radar is replacing the original MR-103, and an AK-306 lightweight gatling AA gunmount is being added aft.

GUIDED-MISSILE PATROL CRAFT [PTG]

♦ 9 Soviet Osa-II class

644 645 646 647 648 649 650 651 652

Osa-II 650 French Navy, 1988

D: 184 tons (226 fl; 245 with emergency fuel) **S:** 40 kts **Dim:** 38.6 × 7.6 × 1.9
A: 4 single SS-N-2B Styx SSM launchers; 2 twin 30-mm 65-cal. AK-230 AA
Electronics: Radar: 1 Rangout (Square Tie) surf. search/missile target desig.; 1 MR-104 Rys' (Drum Tilt) gun f.c.
M: 3 M-504B diesels; 3 props; 15,000 bhp **Electric:** 200 kw
Range: 500/34; 750/25 **Fuel:** 40 tons (normal) **Endurance:** 5 days
Crew: 28 tot.

Remarks: Transferred 1976–78, except for one in 12-80. A shortage of parts for the M-504 diesels, which require frequent overhauls, has kept them from being fully effective.

♦ 2 Soviet Osa-I class (Project 205E)

641 642

D: 172 tons (209 fl) **S:** 38.5 kts **Dim:** 37.5 × 7.6 × 1.8
A: 4 single SS-N-2A Styx SSM launchers; 2 twin 30-mm 65-cal. AK-230 AA
Electronics: Radar: 1 Rangout (Square Tie) surf. search/missile target desig.; 1 MR-104 Rys' (Drum Tilt) gun f.c.
M: 3 M-503A diesels; 3 props; 12,000 bhp **Electric:** 200 kw tot.
Range: 500/34; 750/25 **Endurance:** 5 days **Crew:** 30 tot.

Remarks: Transferred 1967. Sister 643 lost in explosion 1981. May be inactive.

PATROL COMBATANTS [PG]

♦ 2 C-58 design Bldr: ONCN/CNE, Mers el-Kébir

	L	In serv.
351 Djebel Chenoua	3-2-85	11-88
352 El Chihab	2-90	6-95

Djebel Chenoua (351) French Navy, 1988

D: 496 tons (540 fl) **S:** 35 kts (31 sust.) **Dim:** 58.40 (54.00 pp) × 8.40 × . . .
A: 2 twin 14.5-mm 93-cal. 2M-7 AA
Electronics: Radar: 1 Decca 1226 nav.
M: 3 MTU 20V538 TB92 diesels; 3 props; 14,990 bhp
Range: . . ./. . . **Crew:** 6 officers, 46 enlisted

Remarks: Ordered 7-83. Reportedly of Bulgarian design. Difficulties in fitting out the prototype forced suspension of work on the other pair prior to launch. A planned third was not built.
Combat systems: Were originally to have mounted an OTOBreda 76-mm Compact forward and a twin OTOBreda 40-mm AA mount aft, with an optronic director for the 76-mm gun and an optical director for the twin 40-mm. A twin 30-mm Russian AK-230 gunmount has been removed from the forward position. It is still planned to outfit the pair with more modern and effective weapons.

PATROL CRAFT [PC]

Note: There are plans to acquire six 40-m patrol craft powered by MTU diesels; two would be built abroad and the others in Algeria with foreign assistance. A reported contract for license construction of up to 25 Russian Mirazh-class (Project 1431.2) high-speed patrol craft may have been under discussion in 1998, but as of end-2001, the project appeared dormant.

♦ 9 Brooke Marine 37.5-meter patrol boats
Bldrs: 341–343: Brooke Marine, Lowestoft; others: ONCN/CNE, Mers el-Kébir

	In serv.		In serv.
341 El Yadekh	12-82	347 El Saher	1993
342 El Morakeb	12-6-83	348 El Moukadem	1993
343 El Kechef	5-84	349 El . . .	1993
344 El Moutarid	1985	361	. . .
345 El Rassed	10-11-85	362	. . .
346 El Djari	10-11-86	363	. . .

El Morakeb (342) Skyfotos, 1983

PATROL CRAFT [PC] *(continued)*

D: 166 tons (250 fl) **S:** 27 kts **Dim:** 37.50 (34.74 pp) × 6.86 × 1.78
A: 341, 342: 1 76-mm 62-cal. OTOBreda DP; 2 twin 14.5-mm 93-cal. 2M-7 mg—343–349: 2 twin 14.5-mm 93-cal. Type 81 AA
Electronics: Radar: 1 Decca 1226 nav.
M: 2 MTU 12V538 TB92 diesels; 2 props; 6,000 bhp
Range: 2,500/15 **Crew:** 3 officers, 24 enlisted

Remarks: Also known as the "Kebir" class. 347–349 ordered 1984; three more were ordered in 1986 but have not been built, and plans to produce another four have been shelved. Based at Algiers, Annaba, Oran, Ghazaouet, and Djidjeli. These craft have been reported as under Coast Guard subordination from time to time but appear to be naval manned. 341 and 342 were refitted by Vosper Thornycroft in the U.K. during 1990–91.
Combat systems: The 76-mm gun on the first two is controlled by a lead-computing optical director.

AMPHIBIOUS WARFARE SHIPS

♦ 2 tank landing ships [LST]

	Bldr	L	In serv.
472 Kalaat beni Hammed	Brooke Marine, Lowestoft	18-4-84	4-84
473 Kalaat beni Rached	Vosper Thornycroft, Woolston	15-5-84	10-84

Kalaat beni Rached (473) French Navy, 1-96

Kalaat beni Hammed (472) Carlo Martinelli, 8-94

D: 2,130 tons (fl) **S:** 16 kts **Dim:** 93.0 (80.00 pp) × 15.0 × 2.5
A: 1 twin 40-mm 70-cal. OTOBreda AA; 2 twin 25-mm 80-cal. 2M-3M AA
Electronics:
Radar: 1 Decca TM 1226 nav.; 1 Marconi S800 gun f.c.
EW: Racal Cutlass intercept; Racal Cygnus jammer; 2 Wallop Barricade decoy RL
M: 2 MTU 12V1163 TB92 diesels; 2 props; 6,000 bhp
Range: 3,000/12 **Endurance:** 28 days (10 with troops)
Crew: 81 tot. + 240 troops

Remarks: 472 ordered in 10-81. 473 was subcontracted to Vosper Thornycroft on 18-10-82 and laid down on 20-12-82.
Hull systems: The vehicle deck is 75 m long by 7.4 m wide and is served by a 30-m by 7-m hatch. The bow ramp extends to 18 m and is 4–5 m wide, while the stern ramp measures 5 m by 4 m. The traveling crane has a 16-ton capacity. Minimum beaching gradient is 1:40. Can carry 650 tons of cargo, but beaching limit is 450. Helicopter deck aft. Pontoon sections can be stowed on deck forward.
Combat systems: A Matra Défense Naja optronic director was fitted for the twin 40-mm mount.

♦ 1 Soviet Polnocny-B-class (Project 771) medium landing ship [LSM] Bldr: Stocznia Polnocna, Gdansk, Poland (Transferred 9-76)

471

Polnocny-B-class 471 1982

D: 558 tons light, 640 tons std. (884 fl) **S:** 18 kts
Dim: 75.00 (70.00 wl) × 9.00 (8.60 wl) × 1.20 fwd/2.40 aft (2.07 mean)
A: 1 or 2 twin 30-mm 65-cal. AK-230 AA; 2 18-round 140-mm WM-18 barrage RL (180 rockets)
Electronics: Radar: 1 Mius (Spin Trough) nav., 1 MR-104 Rys' (Drum Tilt) f.c.
M: 2 Type 40DM diesels; 2 props; 4,400 bhp **Range:** 700/18; 2,000/16
Crew: 5 officers, 32 enlisted + 60–180 troops

Remarks: Transferred newly built in 9-76.
Hull systems: Has a bow door only. Hull has a "beak" projecting forward below the waterline at the bow to aid in beaching. Cargo: 237 tons max., including six tanks or 180 troops and their equipment; 30 vehicle crew are carried with tank loadout. Vehicle deck is 44.3 m long by 5.3 m wide and 3.6 m high; hatches to upper deck are for loading and ventilation only, as the upper deck cannot support much weight.

AUXILIARIES

Note: There are plans to acquire a 3,000- to 4,000-ton training ship for naval and merchant marine use; in addition to a crew of 85, it would carry up to 120 cadets.

♦ 1 250-grt survey ship [AGS]
Bldr: Matsukara Zosen, Hirao, Japan (L: 17-4-80)

A 673 El Idrissi

Remarks: Reportedly of 540 tons (fl), with a crew of six officers and 22 enlisted. Resembles a smaller edition of salvage ship 261, even to including an A-frame gantry at the stern (for oceanographic sampling gear), and carries two small survey launches in davits aft.

♦ 1 Chinese-built salvage ship [ARS]

261 El Mourafik

D: approx. 600 tons (fl) **S:** . . . kts **Dim:** 59.0 × 8.4 × 2.1
A: 2 single 12.7-mm mg **Electronics:** Radar: 1 . . . nav.
M: 2 Type 9D-8 diesels; 2 props; 2,200 bhp **Crew:** 60 tot.

Remarks: Was in Algeria by 9-90. May be subordinated to the Coast Guard. Has a firefighting monitor on the mast platform. An A-frame gantry at stern may also be used to handle small mooring and navigational buoys.

SERVICE CRAFT

♦ 1 ex-Soviet Poluchat-1-class (Project 368T) torpedo retriever [YDT] Bldr: Sosnovka Zavod

A 641

D: 84.7 tons (92.8 fl) **S:** 21.6 kts **Dim:** 29.60 × 6.10 (5.80 wl) × 1.56 (1.90 props)
Electronics: Radar: 1 Don-2 or Mius (Spin Trough) nav.
M: 2 M-50F-4 diesels; 2 props; 2,400 bhp **Range:** 250/21.6; 550/14
Crew: 1 officer, 2 warrant officers, 12 enlisted

Remarks: Transferred during early 1970s. Has Gira-KM gyrocompass and NEL-3 echo sounder. The hull has seven watertight bulkheads. There is a stern torpedo recovery ramp.

♦ 1 Soviet Nyryat-1-class diving tender [YDT]

VP 650 Yaudezan

D: 105.4 tons (115 fl) **S:** 10 kts **Dim:** 28.50 × 5.50 × 1.70
Electronics: Radar: 1 Mius (Spin Trough) nav.
M: 1 Type 6CSP 28/3C diesel; 1 prop; 450 bhp
Range: 900/9 **Endurance:** 10 days **Crew:** 22 tot. (incl. 6 divers)

Remarks: Transferred 1965. Can support hard-hat divers to 20-m depths.

♦ 1 floating dry dock [YFD] Bldr: M.A.N., Germany (In serv. 1991)

Bejaia

COAST GUARD

PATROL CRAFT [WPC]

♦ 7 Chui-E class

GC 251 El Mouderrib-I through GC 257 El Mouderrib-VII

El Mouderrib-I (GC 251) H&L Van Ginderen, 9-90

D: 363 tons (388 fl) **S:** 30.5 kts **Dim:** 58.77 × 7.20 × 2.20 (hull)
A: 1 twin 14.5-mm 93-cal. Type 81 AA **Electronics:** Radar: 1 Type 756 nav.
M: 3 Type 12VE 23015/2 diesels; 3 props: 6,600 bhp
Range: 2,000/14 **Crew:** 11 officers, 21 enlisted, 25 midshipmen

COAST GUARD PATROL CRAFT [WPC] *(continued)*

Remarks: Also known as the Huludao class. First three arrived in 3-90, two in 1-91, and final two in 7-91. Simplified version of Chinese Hainan-class antisubmarine patrol craft with enlarged superstructure and boats stowed on fantail. Have also been employed as midshipman training craft for the navy. An additional twin 14.5-mm mg mount can be mounted on a ring on the fantail, and during midshipman cruises they have carried a single 14.5-mm mg atop the after portion of the deckhouse.

PATROL BOATS [WPB]

♦ **7 Chinese-built GC 231–class search-and-rescue craft** (In serv. 1990–91)

GC 231 . . . . . .
GC 232 . . . . . .
GC 233 El Mounkid
GC 234 . . . . . .
GC 235 . . . . . .
GC 236 . . . . . .
GC 237 . . . . . .

Remarks: First three transferred 4-90, others the following year. Given names in 1995. Resemble small tugs but do not have towing equipment. Are about 25 m overall and probably can make about 12 kts maximum.

♦ **4 Type 20-GC class** Bldr: Baglietto, Italy (In serv. 8-76 to 12-76)

GC 325 El Hamil
GC 326 El Assad
GC 327 Markhad
GC 328 Etair

D: 44 tons (fl) **S:** 36 kts **Dim:** 20.4 × 5.2 × 1.7
A: 1 20-mm 90-cal. Oerlikon AA
M: 2 CRM 18DS diesels; 2 props; 2,700 bhp **Range:** 445/20 **Crew:** 11 tot.

Remarks: Given names in 1995. Six sisters have been discarded, and the status of the four possible survivors is unknown.

Note: The Algerian Customs Service possesses three 38.5-ton, P 1200–class patrol craft (*Bouzagza, Djurdjura,* and *Hodna*) and two 8-m, British-built P 802–class launches (*Aures* and *Hoggar*) delivered from the U.K. in 11-85; and up to a dozen 18-ton, 10-m *Djebel Antar*–class launches completed at Mers el-Kébir during 1982–83. The operational status of all these craft is unknown.

ANGOLA

People's Republic of Angola

MARINHA DI GUERRA

Personnel (2001): About 700 total

Bases: Headquarters at Luanda, with smaller bases at Cabinda, Lobito, Namibe, and Soro

Naval Aviation: One Fokker F-27-200 Maritime and two EMB 111 Bandeirante maritime patrol aircraft

Note: Portugal agreed in 11-00 to provide assistance with new patrol boats and spare engines and parts for existing craft; no details of the planned craft have been announced.

PATROL CRAFT [PC]

♦ **4 Mandume class** Bldr: E.N. Bazán, San Fernando, Spain

	L	In serv.		L	In serv.
P 100 Mandume	11-9-92	28-1-93	P 104 Atlantico	2-93	4-93
P 102 Polar	11-9-92	28-1-93	P 106 Golfinho	2-93	4-93

Polar (P 102) Izar (E.N. Bazán), 1-93

D: 104.5 tons (fl) **S:** 27.5 kts (25 sust.) **Dim:** 29.13 (26.50 pp) × 5.93 × 1.44
A: 1 20-mm 90-cal. Oerlikon GAM-B01 AA; 2 single 12.7-mm mg
Electronics: Radar: 1 Decca . . . nav.
M: 2 Paxman Vega 12-SETCWN diesels; 2 props; 3,560 bhp
Electric: 140 kw tot. **Range:** 800/15 **Crew:** 1 officer, 10 enlisted

Remarks: Ordered 12-90 for fisheries patrol duties. First unit laid down 18-12-91. Steel hull, aluminum superstructure. Seven watertight compartments. Have hydraulic drive to permit low-speed operations. Have Loran-C, Omega, Transit, and GPS receivers.

PATROL BOATS [PB]

♦ **3 Patrulheiro class** Bldr: C.N. Couach, Arcachon, France (In serv. 1993)

Patrulheiro Preservador Temerario

Patrulheiro C.N. Couach, 1993

D: . . . tons (fl) **S:** 25 kts **Dim:** 19.30 × 5.55 × . . .
A: small arms **Electronics:** Radar: 1 Furuno 1830-24MN nav.
M: 2 Baudouin V12BTI diesels; 2 props; 1,680 bhp
Range: 1,000/18 **Crew:** . . . tot.

Remarks: Intended for fisheries protection duties; operated for the Ministry of Fisheries. Composite GRP hull construction. Do not have pennant numbers.

ANGUILLA

MARINE POLICE

Personnel (2000): About 32 total

PATROL BOATS [WPB]

♦ **1 M160 class** Bldr: Halmatic, U.K. (In serv. 30-12-89)

Dolphin

D: 17.3 tons (fl) **S:** 27+ kts **Dim:** 15.40 (12.20 pp) × 3.86 × 1.15
A: 1 7.62-mm mg **Electronics:** Radar: 1 Decca 370BT nav.
M: 2 G.M. 6V92 TA diesels; 2 props; 1,100 bhp (770 sust.)
Range: 300/20 **Fuel:** 2,700 liters **Crew:** 6 tot.

Remarks: Provided by the U.K. government; sisters are in Turks and Caicos Islands and Virgin Islands police fleets (which see for appearance). Has davits aft for inflatable inspection boat.

♦ **1 U.S. Boston Whaler 27-foot class**
Bldr: Boston Whaler, Rockland, Mass. (In serv. 1990)

Lapwing

D: 2.2 tons (fl) **S:** 32 kts **Dim:** 8.5 × 3.0 × 0.5
M: 2 Evinrude gasoline outboards; 450 bhp **Crew:** 2 tot.

Remarks: Employed for fisheries protection, police, and search-and-rescue duties. GRP construction. Has a pilothouse and can tow small boats. Has no radar.

ANTIGUA-BARBUDA

COAST GUARD
ANTIGUA-BARBUDA DEFENCE FORCE

Personnel (2000): 6 officers, 48 enlisted

Base: Deepwater Harbor, St. John's

PATROL BOATS [WPB]

♦ **1 U.S. Dauntless class** Bldr: SeaArk, Monticello, Ark. (In serv. 1995)

P-02 Palmetto

D: 12 tons (15 fl) **S:** 28 kts **Dim:** 12.19 (11.13 wl) × 3.86 × 0.69 (hull)
A: 2 single 12.7-mm mg; 2 single 7.62-mm mg
Electronics: Radar: 1 Raytheon R40X nav.
M: 2 Caterpillar 3208TA diesels; 2 props; 850 bhp (720 sust.)
Range: 200/30; 400/22 **Fuel:** 250 gal. **Crew:** 5 tot.

Remarks: Ordered 4-94. Aluminum construction. C. Raymond Hunt, "Deep-Vee" hull design.

♦ **1 U.S. 65-foot Commercial Cruiser class**
Bldr: Swiftships, Inc., Morgan City, La. (In serv. 30-4-84)

P-01 Liberta

Liberta (P-01) PH2 Pixier, USN, 1987

D: 31.7 tons (36 fl) **S:** 22 kts **Dim:** 19.96 × 5.59 × 1.52
A: 1 12.7-mm M2 mg; 2 single 7.62-mm mg
Electronics: Radar: 1 Raytheon 1210 nav.
M: 2 G.M. Detroit Diesel 12V71 TI diesels; 2 props; 1,350 bhp (840 sust.)
Electric: 20 kw **Range:** 500/18 **Crew:** 9 tot.

Remarks: Aluminum construction. U.S. Grant-Aid donation; crews U.S. Coast Guard–trained.

♦ **1 ex-U.S. Coast Guard 82-foot Point class**
Bldr: J. Martinac SB, Tacoma, Wash. (In serv. 26-4-67)

P-03 Hermitage (ex-*Point Steele,* WPB 82359)

D: 66 tons (fl) **S:** 23 kts **Dim:** 25.3 × 5.23 × 1.95
A: 2 single 12.7-mm M2 mg
Electronics: Radar: 1 Raytheon SPS-64(V)1 nav.
M: 2 Caterpillar 3412 diesels; 2 props; 1,480 bhp
Range: 490/23.7; 1,500/8 **Fuel:** 5.7 tons **Crew:** 1 officer, 7 enlisted

Remarks: Deactivated by U.S. Coast Guard on 9-7-98 and transferred 17-7-98 as a grant; recommissioned 4-9-98.
Hull systems: Hull built of mild steel. High-speed diesels controlled from the bridge. Well-equipped for salvage and towing. Re-engined during the early 1990s.

SERVICE CRAFT

♦ **2 Boston Whaler 27-foot-class launches [WYFL]**
Bldr: Boston Whaler, Rockland, Mass. (In serv. 1988)

071 072

D: 2.2 tons (fl) **S:** 30 kts **Dim:** 8.2 × 3.0 × 0.5
A: small arms **M:** 2 Evinrude gasoline outboards; 400 bhp **Crew:** 2 tot.

Remarks: U.S. Grant-Aid. Foam-core, GRP hull construction.

Note: Also in service is an 8.23-m Hurricane RIB acquired in 1998 as replacement for an earlier unit.

ARGENTINA

Argentine Republic

ARMADA REPÚBLICA

Personnel (2000): Approximately 17,200 (2,150 officers), plus 7,000 civilians. Of the uniformed personnel total, around 2,500 are in the Marine Corps and 2,400 serve in naval aviation billets.

Organization: The administrative head of the Armada is the Jefatura del Estado Mayor de la Armada, under whom are the Subjefatura del Estado Mayor de la Armada and the Secretaria General Naval. To the former is subordinated the Dirección de Inteligencia Naval, Dirección de Bienestar Naval, Dirección de Instrucción Naval, Dirección de Material Naval, Servicio de Hidrografia Naval, Servicio de Communicaciones, Comando de Transito Maritimo, Servicio de Salvamento y Medio Ambiente, Servicio de Transportes Navals, and Comando de Operaciones Navales. Under the Comando de Operaciones Navales are the Comando de la Flota de Mar (with the 2° Division de Destructores, 1ª Division de Corbetas, 2ª Division de Corbetas, Comando Naval Anfibio, and Base Naval Puerto Belgrano), the Comando de la Aviación Naval (for subordinate organizations, see the Naval Aviation section below), and Comando de la Infantería de Marina (for subordinate organizations, see the Marines section below). Also subordinate to the Comando de Operaciones Navales are the Area Naval Atlantica (with the Division de Submarinos and Base Naval Mar del Plata), Area Naval Fluvial (with Base Naval Zarate), Fuerza Antartica Naval, Agrupación Lanchas Rapidas, and Base Naval Ushuaia.

Bases: Located at Zárate (Area Naval Fluvial), Mar del Plata, Puerto Belgrano, Caleta Paula, Ushuaia *(Almirante Berisso),* and Orcades. Naval shipyard and training facilities are located at Río Santiago, La Plata; the submarine base at Mar del Plata; the main naval base and dockyard facilities at Puerto Belgrano; and the Riverine Flotilla base at Zárate. A small patrol boat base was established in 1997 at Caleta Paula, Santa Cruz province. The Argentine Navy Engineering School was moved to Puerto Belgrano in 1998. Aviation bases are at Ezeiza (Buenos Aires), Puerto Belgrano *(Comandante Espora),* Trelew *(Almirante Zar),* Río Grande *(Almirante Hermes Quijada),* Punta Indio, and Ushuaia.

Naval Aviation: Fixed-wing aircraft include 2 Super Étendard fighter-bombers (with 8 more in storage), 5 S-2UP Turbo Tracker ASW aircraft (with 3 S-2G in storage), 8 MB-326GB attack/trainers, 1 Fokker F-28-3000M and 2 Fokker F-28-3132C transports, 6 P-3B Orion maritime patrol aircraft, 7 Beech Super King Air B200T reconnaissance/training/light transports, 1 Pilatus PC-6B/H2 Turbo Porter light transport, 10 Beech T-34C-1 trainers, and 1 Stearman PT-17 glider tug. Helicopters include 2 Agusta-Sikorsky ASH-3D (S-61) Sea King and 4 SH-3D (S-61D-4) Sea King ASW (with at least one equipped during 2000 to launch AM 39 Exocet missiles), 8 Bell UH-1H transports, and 4 AS.355MN Fennec reconnaissance and missile targeting.

Argentine Navy ASH-3D Sea King—with AM 39 Exocet Ignacio Amendolara, 7-00

The S-2UP Tracker configuration from S-2G aircraft has Garrett TPE-331-15 AW turbines in place of the original reciprocating engines and other improvements to give the aircraft 20 years' additional service.

The first two of six P-3B Orion maritime patrol aircraft were delivered 7-12-97 and 17-12-97 to *Almirante Zar* air base in Trelew; four more followed in 1998 to replace the L.188E Electras of Escuadrilla Aeronaval 6 de Exploración, and another two were transferred during 1999. Argentina also hopes later to acquire 6–8 ex-USN SH-3-series Sea King helicopters. Eight Lockheed Martin Argentina AT-63 Pampas land-based attack aircraft were ordered during 7-01.

Naval aviation assets are organized under the Comando de la Aviación Naval into Fuerza Aeronaval 6 (with the Escuadrilla de Transporte, Escuadrilla de Exploración, and Base Aeronaval *Almirante Zar*), Fuerza Aeronaval 2 (with the 2ª Escuadrilla de Caza y Ataque, 1ª and 2ª Escuadrilla de Helicopteros, Escuadrilla Antisubmarina, and Base Aeronaval *Comandante Espora* subordinated), and the Escuadra de Instrucción Aeronaval (with the Escuela de Aviación Naval, 1ª Escuadrilla de Caza y Ataque, and Base Aeronaval Punta Indio subordinated). There are also small airfields at Río Grande and Ushuaia and a Central Maintenance Unit at Bahía Blanca.

Marines: The Fuerza de Apoyo de Infantería is composed of Batallón 1, Batallón 2, the Batallón Vehículos Anfibios, the Compañía de Communicaciones, the Batallón de Artillería, and the Fuerza N° 1 (with Batallón 4 [reserve] and Batallón 5). Major bases are located at Río Gallegos and Baterias. The amphibious warfare support group is located at Puerto Belgrano. Small security detachments are maintained at Buenos Aires, Río Santiago, Punta Indio, Azul, Mar del Plata, *Comandante Espora* naval base, Zárate, Ezeiza, Trelew, Ushuaia, and Río Grande.

Note: Ship names are prefaced by A.R.A. *(Armada República Argentina).*

ATTACK SUBMARINES [SS]

♦ **2 TR-1700 class**
Bldr: Thyssen Nordseewerke, Emden

	Laid down	L	In serv.
S 41 Santa Cruz	6-12-80	28-9-82	14-12-84
S 42 San Juan	18-3-82	20-6-83	18-11-85

D: 1,770 tons std., 2,150 tons surf./2,356 tons sub.
S: 15 kts surf./13 kts snorkel/25 kts max. sub. **Dim:** 65.50 × 7.30 × 6.50
A: 6 bow 533-mm TT (22 SST-4 Mod. 1 wire-guided torpedoes and/or mines)

ATTACK SUBMARINES [SS] *(continued)*

Santa Cruz (S 41) H&L Van Ginderen, 4-88

Electronics:
Radar: 1 SMA MM/BPS-704 surf. search/nav.
Sonar: STN Atlas Elektronik CSU-83 suite with Thales DUUX-5 passive array
EW: Sea Sentry III intercept/radar warning
M: diesel-electric: 4 MTU 16V652 MB80 (1,680 bhp each), 4 alternator sets (1.1 Mw each); 1 6,600-kw motor; 1 prop; 8,970 shp (8,000 sust.)
Range: 14,000/8, 17,000/5 surf.; 20/25, 50/20, 110/15, 460/6 sub.
Fuel: 319 tons **Endurance:** 70 days
Crew: 8 officers, 21 enlisted + 12 spare or 30 commandos

Remarks: Ordered 30-11-77. Originally only the first unit was to have been built in Germany. Two smaller Type TR-1400 submarines were replaced in the program by two TR-1700 in a 2-82 change to the original order. The largest submarines built in Germany since World War I. Three sisters (of a planned four) were laid down at Argentina's Astilleros Domecq Garcia, but all work had ceased by the late 1980s: *Santa Fe* (S 43) was laid down 4-10-83 and *Santiago del Estero* (S 44) on 5-8-85, and some work was accomplished on the third unit. The remaining components were cannibalized for spares. Both have recently completed refits, S 42 at Puerto Belgrano and S 41 at Rio de Janeiro from 1-10-99 to 20-2-01.
Hull systems: Displacements also given as 2,116 tons surf./2,264 tons sub. Pressure hull 48.0 m long and 7.0 m in diameter. The Varta-made battery set has eight groups of 120 cells, 5,858-amp/10-hr, and weighs 500 tons. Range also given as 15,000/5 snorkel; 300/10, 70/20 sub. Have the ability to accept a U.S. Deep Sea Rescue Vehicle submersible and have a divers' lockout capability. Engineering equipment is mounted in double resilient mountings. Hull has 10% reserve buoyancy in surfaced condition. Maximum operating depth is 300 m.
Combat systems: Have Thales SINBADS (Submarine Integrated Battle and Data System) weapons control system and SAGEM plotting table. Torpedoes can be auto-reloaded in 50 seconds; swim-out launching is employed. Are equipped with an inertial navigation system and have Kollmorgen Model 76 search and attack periscopes.

♦ 1 German Type 209/1200 class

	Bldr	Laid down	L	In serv.
S 31 Salta	Howaldtswerke, Kiel	3-4-70	9-11-72	7-3-74

Salta (S 31) R. L. Scheina

D: 1,000 tons std., 1,140 tons surf./1,248 tons sub.
S: 11.5 kts surf./12 kts snorkel/22 kts max. sub. **Dim:** 55.9 × 6.30 × 5.50
A: 8 bow 533-mm TT (14 SST-4 Mod. 1 wire-guided torpedoes)
Electronics:
Radar: 1 Thales Calypso nav.
Sonar: STN Atlas Elektronik CSU-3 suite (including AN 526 active, AN 5039 passive, and AN 5041 active attack); Thales DUUX-2CN passive ranging array; Thales DUUG-1D acoustic intercept
EW: Thales DR-2000U intercept
M: 4 MTU 12V493 TY60, 600-bhp diesels, 4 425-kw generators, Siemens electric motor; 1 prop; 4,500 shp
Range: 6,000/8 snorkel; 230/8, 400/4 sub. **Fuel:** 63 tons **Endurance:** 40 days
Crew: 5 officers, 26 enlisted

Remarks: Built in four sections at Kiel and assembled at the Tandanor Shipyard, Buenos Aires. *Salta* was reported to be for sale in 1986 but entered Domecq Garcia SY 1988 for new engines and a new electronics suite; work ceased in 5-90 but had begun again by 10-91 and the submarine was relaunched during 10-94 and recommissioned in 3-95. Sister *San Luís* (S 32) began refit 1990 and was to have recommissioned in 1997–98, but the remaining work was halted in 12-96, and the submarine was stricken in 4-97.
Hull systems: Has four 120-cell, 11,500 amp-hr, Varta batteries totaling 257 tons.
Combat systems: The Thales M8 fire-control system is fitted.

DESTROYERS [DD]

♦ 2 British Sheffield class (1 *inactive*)

	Bldr	Laid down	L	In serv.
D 1 Hercules	Vickers, Barrow	16-6-71	24-10-72	12-7-76
D 2 *Santísima Trinidad*	Ast. Nav., Río Santiago	11-10-71	9-11-74	30-11-78

Hercules (D 1)—with helicopter hangar added aft Hector Terradas, 2000

Santísima Trinidad (D 2)—when active Argentine Navy

D: 3,150 tons (4,100 fl) **S:** 28 kts **Dim:** 125.0 (119.5 pp) × 14.34 × 4.2 (hull)
A: 4 single Exocet MM 38 SSM launchers; 1 114-mm 55-cal. Mk 8 DP; 2 single 20-mm 70-cal. Oerlikon AA; 2 triple 324-mm ILAS-3 ASW TT (WASS A-224S torpedoes)—D 1: 1 SH-3 Sea King helicopter; D 2: 1 AS.355MN Fennec helicopter
Electronics:
Radar: D 1 only: 1 Decca 1126 nav—both: 1 Kelvin-Hughes Type 1006 nav.; 1 Marconi Type 965M early warning; 1 Marconi Type 992Q surf./air search; 1 (D 2: 2) Marconi Type 909 missile and gun f.c.
Sonar: Graseby Type 184M LF hull-mounted, Kelvin-Hughes Type 162M bottomed-target classification
EW: Decca RDL-2 intercept, Decca RCM-2 jammer, 2 Corvus 8-round decoy RL
M: COGOG: 2 Rolls-Royce Olympus TM-3B gas turbines (27,200 shp each); 2 Rolls-Royce Tyne RM-1A cruise gas turbines (4,100 shp each); 2 5-bladed CP props
Electric: 4,000 kw tot. **Range:** 4,000/18 **Crew:** 270 tot.

Remarks: Ordered 18-5-70. D 2 was sabotaged on 22-8-75, delaying completion; initial trials were held on 7-3-80. Both reported to be for sale in 9-84, due to inability to obtain spares from Britain; D 2 was placed in reserve and used for cannibalization stores for D 1 until 1999, when she was reported being considered for reactivation for use as a fast transport for Marines (no progress has been made on this plan, which was first proposed in 1991). During 11-00, D 1 completed a refit in Chile, when an enlarged helicopter hangar replaced the original and the after missile director was removed.
Combat systems: Have ADAWS-4 data system and NATO Link 10 datalink. D 1, refitted in 1980, had MM 38 Exocet missiles added atop the hangar; in 1982, the mis-

DESTROYERS [DD] *(continued)*

siles were relocated in place of the boats abreast the stack and EW gear was fitted. The Sea Dart SAM system is still in place in both ships, but it is no longer operational.

FRIGATES [FF]

♦ 4 MEKO 360 H2 class   Bldr: Blohm + Voss, Hamburg

	Laid down	L	In serv.
D 10 Almirante Brown	8-9-80	28-3-81	2-2-83
D 11 La Argentina	31-3-81	25-9-81	19-7-83
D 12 Heroína	24-8-81	17-2-82	7-11-83
D 13 Sarandi	9-3-82	31-8-82	27-4-84

Sarandi (D 13) U.S. Navy, 10-95

Heroína (D 12) U.S. Navy, 10-95

D: 2,900 tons (3,360 fl) **S:** 30.5 kts
Dim: 125.90 (119.00 pp) × 15.00 × 4.32 (5.80 sonar)
A: 8 MM 40 Exocet SSM; 1 8-cell Albatros SAM syst. (24 Aspide missiles); 1 127-mm 54-cal. OTOBreda DP; 4 twin 40-mm 70-cal. OTOBreda AA; 2 triple 324-mm ILAS-3 ASW TT (18 WASS A-244S torpedoes); 1 d.c. rack (9 d.c.); 1 AS.355MN Fennec or SH-3D Sea King helicopter
Electronics:
Radar: 1 Decca 1226 nav.; 1 Thales ZW-06 surf. search; 1 Thales DA-08A air/surf. search; 1 Thales WM-25 track-while-scan f.c.; 1 Thales STIR f.c.; 2 Thales LIROD f.c.
Sonar: STN Atlas Elektronik KAE 80, hull-mounted MF
EW: Racal Rapids intercept, Racal Scimitar jammer, 2 20-round OTOBreda SCLAR decoy RL; G1738 towed torpedo decoy
M: COGOG: 2 Rolls-Royce Olympus TM-3B gas turbines (25,800 shp each); 2 Rolls-Royce Tyne RM-1C gas turbines (5,100 shp each) for cruise; 2 Escher-Wyss CP props; 51,600 shp max.
Electric: 2,600 kw (2 × 940-kw and 2 × 360-kw diesel sets)
Range: 4,500/18 **Crew:** 26 officers, 84 petty officers, 90 other enlisted

Remarks: Considered to be destroyers by the Argentine Navy. Ordered 11-12-78 as a class of six, four of which were to be built in Argentina, but altered to four total when the MEKO 140–series frigate program was introduced. Nigeria's *Aradu* is very similar. D 13 is the fleet flagship.

Combat systems: Have Thales SEWACO weapons data/control system. The Albatros SAM system has a 16-missile Aspide SAM rapid-reload magazine nearby. The two LIROD radar/optronic directors each control two 40-mm mounts, and a total of 10,752 rounds of ammunition can be carried. The sonar is a commercial version of the DSQS-21BZ. Can carry up to 10 ASW torpedoes for the helicopter, which is equipped to provide over-the-horizon targeting for the Exocet missiles.

♦ 6 MEKO 140 A16 class   Bldr: AFNE, Río Santiago, Ensenada

	Laid down	L	In serv.
F 41 Espora	10-3-80	23-1-82	5-7-85
F 42 Rosales	7-1-81	4-3-83	14-11-86
F 43 Spiro	1-4-82	24-6-83	24-11-87
F 44 Parker	9-2-82	31-3-84	17-4-90
F 45 Robinson	6-6-83	15-2-85	28-8-00
F 46 Gomez Roca (ex-*Seaver)*	1-12-83	14-11-86	10-01

Espora (F 41) German Navy, 5-99

Parker (F 44) H&L Van Ginderen, 4-97

Gomez Roca (F 46)—fitting out Hartmut Ehlers, 12-97

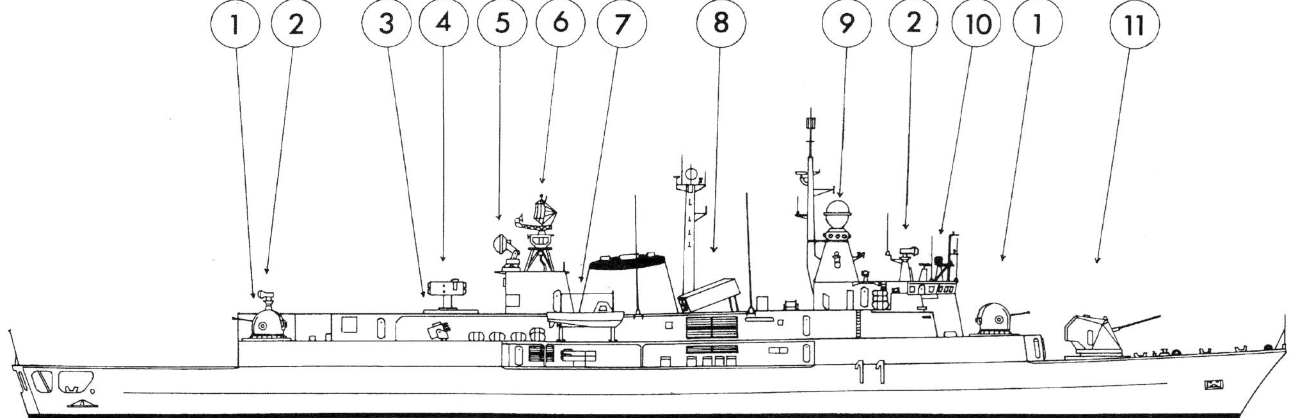

La Argentina (D 11) 1. Twin OTOBreda 40-mm AA 2. LIROD radar/optronic 40-mm gun director 3. SCLAR decoy launcher 4. octuple launcher for Albatros SAM system 5. STIR radar missile director 6. DA-08A early-warning radar antenna 7. ASW torpedo tubes 8. MM 40 Exocet antiship missiles 9. WM-25 track-while-scan radar director 10. ZW-06 surface-search radar 11. 127-mm 54-cal. OTOBreda gun Drawing by Robert Dumas

FRIGATES [FF] *(continued)*

D: 1,560 tons (1,790 fl) **S:** 27 kts **Dim:** 91.2 (86.4 pp) × 11.0 × 3.33 (hull)
A: 4 MM 38 Exocet SSM; 1 76-mm 62-cal. OTOBreda DP; 2 twin 40-mm 70-cal. OTOBreda AA; 2 single 12.7-mm mg; 2 triple 324-mm ILAS-3 ASW TT (WASS A-244S torpedoes); 1 AS.355MN Fennec helicopter
Electronics:
Radar: 1 Decca TM 1226 nav.; 1 Thales DA-05/2 surf./air search; 1 Thales WM-28 track-while-scan f.c., 1 Thales LIROD f.c.
Sonar: 1 STN Atlas Elektronik AQS-1 hull-mounted MF
EW: Decca RDC-2ABC intercept; Decca RCM-2 jammer; 2 Dagaie decoy RL
M: 2 SEMT-Pielstick 16 PC2-5V400 diesels; 2 5-bladed props; 22,600 bhp
Electric: 1,410 kVA tot. (3 × 470-kVA diesel sets) **Range:** 4,000/18
Fuel: 230 tons **Crew:** 11 officers, 46 petty officers, 36 other enlisted

Remarks: Ordered 8-79. Blohm + Voss design. F 44 flooded out 2-10-86, delaying completion. New hull numbers were assigned 1988 (originally were F 10–F 15). Fitting out of F 45 and F 46 was suspended in 1992, briefly restarted in 7-94, and resumed on 18-7-97. Not yet certain that F 46 was completed in 2001. F 41 and F 42 are now based at Mar del Plata, the others at Puerto Belgrano.
Hull systems: Have fin stabilizers. Carry 5 tons aviation fuel, 70 tons fresh water. A telescoping helicopter hangar is fitted on F 44 through F 46 only.
Combat systems: Have Thales DAISY combat data system. The LIROD radar/electro-optical system controls 40-mm mounts; a planned second set was not installed.

CORVETTES [FFL]

♦ 3 French Type A 69 class Bldr: DCN Lorient

	Laid down	L	In serv.
F 31 Drummond (ex-*Transvaal,* F 102; ex-*Commandant l'Herminier,* F 791)	12-3-76	5-3-77	10-78
F 32 Guerrico (ex-*Good Hope,* F 432; ex-*Lieutenant de Vaisseau le Henaff,* F 784)	11-10-76	13-9-77	10-78
F 33 Granville	1-12-78	28-6-80	22-6-81

Granville (F 33) Maritime Photographic, 11-93

Guerrico (F 32) Ignacio Amendolara, 2000

D: 1,170 tons (1,320 fl) **S:** 23.3 kts
Dim: 80.5 (76.0 pp) × 10.3 × 3.55 (5.25 sonar)
A: 4 MM 38 Exocet; 1 100-mm 55-cal. Model 1968 DP; 1 twin 40-mm 70-cal. OTOBreda AA; 2 single 20-mm 70-cal. Oerlikon AA; 2 single 12.7-mm Colt M2 mg; 2 triple 324-mm ILAS-3 ASW TT (WASS A-244S torpedoes)
Electronics:
Radar: 1 Decca RM 1226 nav.; 1 Thales DRBV-51A air/surf. search; 1 Thales DRBC-32E f.c.
Sonar: Thales Diodon hull-mounted MF
EW: Thales DR-2000 S3 intercept, Thales Alligator 51 jammer, 2 18-round Corvus (F 33: Matra Défense Dagaie) decoy RL
M: 2 SEMT-Pielstick 12 PC 2.2 V400 diesels; 2 CP props; 12,000 bhp
Electric: 840 kw tot. **Range:** 3,000/18; 4,500/16 **Endurance:** 15 days
Crew: 5 officers, 79 enlisted (accomm. for 95 tot.)

Remarks: The first two were originally ordered by South Africa, but delivery was embargoed and they were purchased by Argentina on 25-9-78. Have fin stabilizers.
Combat systems: Armament and some electronic gear differ from French Navy version. There is a Matra Défense Panda Mk 2 optronic director for the 100-mm gun. All now have OTOBreda twin 40-mm AA controlled by a Naja Mk 2 optronic director; the first two originally had older Bofors L60 40-mm gun mountings. The DRBV 51A radar incorporates IFF interrogation.

PATROL SHIPS [PS]

♦ 1 former U.S. oilfield tug/supply vessel
Bldr: Quality SY, Houma, La. (In serv. 1981; acquired 15-11-87)

A 2 Teniente Olivieri (ex-*Marsea 10*)

Teniente Olivieri (A 2) Argentine Navy, 1995

D: 1,640 tons (fl) **S:** 14 kts **Dim:** 56.29 × 12.20 × 3.66
A: 2 single 12.7-mm mg **Electronics:** Radar: . . .
M: 2 G.M. EMD 16-645-E6 diesels; 2 props; 3,700 bhp (3,230 sust.)—300-shp bow-thruster
Electric: 198 kw tot. **Range:** 2,800/10 **Crew:** 4 officers, 11 enlisted

Remarks: 293 grt/992 dwt. Purchased from the U.S. Maritime Administration 15-11-87 and delivered 5-88 as a "dispatch boat," i.e., a patrol vessel. Cargo capacity on 35.06 × 9.33-m open deck aft: 610 tons. As a commercial vessel, could carry 315 tons cargo fuel, 514 tons drilling water, 44 tons potable water, and 113 tons drilling mud; in Argentine service, carries 600 tons fuel or 800 tons water. Based at Puerto Belgrano and is used primarily as a supply vessel, carrying deck cargo and liquids to remote facilities.

Note: The planned 1-94 acquisition of the oilfield supply vessel *Erebus* listed in previous editions did not take place.

♦ 3 U.S. Abnaki and Achomawi class
Bldr: A 1, A 3: Charleston SB & DD Co., Charleston, S.C.; A 6: United Engineering, Alameda, Calif.

	Laid down	L	In serv.
A 1 Comandante General Irigoyen (ex-*Cahuilla,* ATF 152)	16-6-44	2-11-44	10-3-45
A 3 Francisco de Gurruchaga (ex-*Luiseno,* ATF 156)	7-11-44	17-3-45	16-6-45
A 6 Suboficial Castillo (ex-*Takelma,* ATF 113)	7-4-43	18-9-43	3-8-44

Suboficial Castillo (A 6) Ignacio Amendolara, 2-96

D: 1,291 tons (1,731 fl) **S:** 16 kts **Dim:** 62.48 (59.44 wl) × 11.73 × 5.20
A: 3 (A 3: 2) single 40-mm 60-cal. Bofors AA; 2 single 20-mm 70-cal. Oerlikon AA
Electronics: Radar: 1 Sperry Marine VT-3400C nav./surf. search
M: 4 G.M. 12-278A (A 6: Caterpillar D-399) diesels, electric drive; 1 prop; 3,000 shp
Electric: 400 kw tot. **Range:** 6,500/15; 15,000/8 **Fuel:** 363 tons **Crew:** 85 tot.

Remarks: Former fleet tugs. A 1 transferred 9-7-61 as an ocean tug and rerated a patrol ship in 1966. A 3 was purchased on 1-7-75. A 6 was transferred as a gift on 30-9-93; the ship had been decommissioned to reserve 30-9-83 from the USN and was unarmed at time of transfer. Retain tug and salvage facilities. All three received a new radar suite, gyro, and digital chart plotter in 1995.

PATROL SHIPS [PS] *(continued)*

♦ **1 U.S. Sotoyomo class**
Bldr: Levingston SB, Orange, Texas

	Laid down	L	In serv.
A 9 Alferez Sobral (ex-*Salish,* ATA 187, ex-ATR 114)	29-8-44	29-9-44	7-12-44

Alferez Sobral (A 9)—with the stricken *Comodoro Somellera* Yvan Gomel, via Paolo Marsan, 12-98

D: 534 tons (835 fl) **S:** 13 kts **Dim:** 43.59 (41.00 pp) × 10.31 × 4.01
A: 1 40-mm 60-cal. Bofors AA; 2 single 20-mm 70-cal. Oerlikon AA
Electronics: Radar: 1 Raytheon . . . nav.
M: 2 G.M. 12-278A diesels, electric drive; 2 props; 1,500 shp
Electric: 120 kw **Range:** 16,500/18 **Fuel:** 171 tons **Crew:** 49 tot.

Remarks: Former auxiliary ocean tug transferred 10-2-72. Had been retired by the late 1980s, but was restored to service due to her economy of operation and the lack of other assets. The ship has the larger bridge superstructure common to the rescue tug (ATR) version of the *Sotoyomo* class. The ship survived two Sea Skua missile hits amidships in 1982 during the Falklands War.
Disposals: *Yamona* (A 6, ex-ATA 146) was stricken in 1984 and *Saniviron* (A 8, ex-ATA 228) during 4-97. *Comodoro Somellera* (A 10, ex-*Catawba,* ATA 210, ex-ATR 137) was rammed and sunk by *Suboficial Castillo* (A 6) at Ushuaia during 8-98; salved, she was not repaired.

♦ **2 Murature class** Bldr: Arsenal Naval de Río Santiago

	Laid down	L	In serv.
P 20 Murature	30-3-40	28-7-43	12-4-45
P 21 King	15-6-38	3-11-43	18-11-46

King (P 21) Hartmut Ehlers, 4-00

D: 913 tons (1,032 fl) **S:** 18 kts **Dim:** 77.0 × 8.8 × 2.3
A: 3 single 105-mm 45-cal. Bofors DP; 1 twin and 2 single 40-mm 60-cal. Bofors AA; 5 single 12.7-mm mg
Electronics: Radar: 1 Decca 1226 nav.
M: 2 Werkspoor 4-cycle diesels; 2 props; 2,500 bhp
Range: 9,000/12 **Fuel:** 90 tons **Crew:** 130 tot.

Remarks: Riveted construction patrol gunboats. Since 1969, have been assigned to the Riverine Fleet and based at Zárate on the Paraná de las Palmas branch of the Río Paraná delta for training and patrol duties. Main guns are single-fire weapons manufactured prior to World War II.

GUIDED-MISSILE BOATS [PTG]

♦ **2 TNC 45 class** Bldr: Friedrich Lürssen Werft, Vegesack, Germany

	L	In serv.		L	In serv.
P 85 Intrépida	2-12-73	3-8-74	P 86 Indómita	8-4-74	10-4-75

Intrépida (P 85) Argentine Navy, 1994

D: 240 tons (265 fl) **S:** 37.8 kts **Dim:** 44.9 (42.3 pp) × 7.4 × 2.28 (props)
A: P 85 only: 2 single MM 38 Exocet SSM launchers—both: 1 76-mm 62-cal. OTOBreda Compact DP; 2 (P 85: 1) single 40-mm 70-cal. Bofors L70 AA; 2 single 533-mm TT (SST-4 wire-guided torpedoes)
Electronics:
Radar: 1 Decca 1226 nav.; 1 Thales WM-22 track-while-scan f.c.
EW: Decca Cutlass intercept
M: 4 MTU MD872 diesels; 4 props; 14,400 bhp **Electric:** 330 kw
Range: 640/36; 1,700/16 **Crew:** 5 officers, 37 enlisted

Remarks: Both were refitted 1995–96 and P 85 was equipped with Exocet missiles in place of the amidships single 40-mm AA. As of 5-01, P 86 remained in the original configuration. Both craft are normally based at Ushuaia. Have anti-rolling fin stabilizers.

PATROL BOATS [PB]

Note: Six new riverine patrol craft are sought for service on the Río Paraguay.

♦ **4 Israeli Dabur class**
Bldr: Israeli Aircraft Industries, Israel

	In serv.		In serv.
P 61 Baradero	2-8-79	P 63 Clorinda	23-4-79
P 62 Barranqueras	3-12-78	P 64 Concepción del Uruguay	13-4-79

Clorinda (P 63) Ignacio Amendolara, 1996

D: 31 tons (39 fl) **S:** 19 kts **Dim:** 19.80 × 5.50 × 1.80
A: 2 single 20-mm 70-cal. Oerlikon AA; 2 twin 12.7-mm Colt M2 mg
Electronics: Radar: 1 Decca 101 nav.
M: 2 G.M. 12V71 TA diesels; 2 props; 1,200 bhp (840 sust.)
Range: 450/13 **Crew:** 8 tot.

Remarks: Were deployed to the Gulf of Fonseca on the west coast of Central America during 1990–92 for UN peacekeeping duties. Now operate from Ushuaia. Were originally capable of 23 kts. Aluminum construction.

♦ **2 ex-U.S. Coast Guard 82-foot Point class**
Bldr: U.S. Coast Guard Yard, Curtis Bay, Md.

	In serv.
P 65 Punta Mogotes (ex-*Point Hobart,* WPB 82377)	13-7-70
P 66 Río Santiago (ex-*Point Carrew,* WPB 82374)	18-5-70

D: 64 tons (69 fl) **S:** 22.6 kts **Dim:** 25.3 × 5.23 × 1.95
A: 2 single 12.7-mm M2 mg
Electronics: Radar: 1 Raytheon SPS-64(V)1 nav.; 1 Furuno . . . nav.
M: 2 Caterpillar 3412 diesels; 2 props; 1,480 bhp
Range: 320/22.6; 1,200/8 **Fuel:** 5.7 tons **Crew:** 1 officer, 7 enlisted

Remarks: Stricken from U.S. Coast Guard 12-7-99 and donated to Argentina; recommissioned on 12-8-00. Based at the Naval Academy, Río Santiago, Buenos Aires. Hull built of mild steel. High-speed diesels controlled from the bridge. A small Furuno navigational radar was added after transfer.

PATROL BOATS [PB] *(continued)*

Punta Mogotes (P 65) Ignacio Amendolara, 8-99

♦ 1 historic relic patrol boat
Bldr: Arsenal Naval de Río Santiago (In serv. 1939)

P 55 Zurubi

Remarks: Based at Ushuaia until 1978, when retired. Restored during the 1990s as a historic craft (in the 1940s, she was the first Argentine naval vessel used to patrol the Beagle Channel) and employed primarily for public relations and official ceremonies. Wooden construction. Not armed. Currently based at Ushuaia.

MINE WARFARE SHIPS

♦ 2 British Ton-class minehunters [MHC]

	Bldr	L
M 5 Chaco (ex-*Rennington*)	J. S. Richards	27-11-58
M 6 Formosa (ex-*Ilmington*)	Camper & Nicholson	8-3-54

D: 385 tons (440 fl) **S:** 15 kts **Dim:** 46.33 (42.68 pp) × 8.76 × 2.50
A: 1 40-mm 60-cal. Bofors Mk 7 AA
Electronics:
Radar: M 5: 1 Raytheon R-40XX—M 6: 1 Furuno 1831 nav.
Sonar: Plessey Type 193 HF hull mounted
M: 2 Paxman Deltic 18A-7A diesels; 2 props; 3,000 hp
Electric: 1,500 kw tot. (2 × 750-kw diesel sets)
Range: 2,800/12 **Fuel:** 45 tons **Crew:** 37 tot.

Remarks: Refitted with a sonar as minehunters in 1968. Wooden construction. Both are based at Puerto Belgrano.
Disposals: *Chubut* (M 3, ex-*Santon*) and *Tierra del Fuego* (M 4, ex-*Bevington*) were stricken during 1996, while *Neuquen* (M 1, ex-*Hickleton*) and *Río Negro* (M 2, ex-*Tarlton*) followed in 4-97.
Combat systems: Minesweeping equipment carried includes Mk 3 and Mk 4 acoustic and W Mk 3 Oropesa mechanical sweeps.

AMPHIBIOUS WARFARE SHIPS AND CRAFT

Note: Plans to acquire a replacement (probably of the U.S. *Newport* class) for the *Cabo San Antonio* (Q 42) were canceled in 12-96, leaving the Argentine Marines with no organic lift resource; the icebreaker *Almirante Irizar* (Q 5) has been used to transport marines for exercises. The U.S.A. offered the *Newport* (LST 1179) as a grant in 1998, but it was not accepted.

♦ 1 Costa Sur–class amphibious transport [LPA]
Bldr: Principe & Menghe SY, Maciel I.

	Laid down	L	In serv.
B 4 Bahía San Blas	11-4-77	29-4-78	27-11-78

Bahía San Blas (B 4) Ignacio Amendolara, 7-00

D: 7,640 tons (10,894 fl) **S:** 16.3 kts **Dim:** 119.9 × 17.5 × 7.49
A: none **Electronics:** Radar: . . . nav.
M: 2 AFNE-Sulzer 6ZL 40/48 diesels; 2 props; 6,400 bhp **Crew:** . . . tot.

Remarks: 4,600 grt/5,800 dwt. Was to have been retired in 1998 but was instead adapted to support naval infantry forces and to act as a fleet supply ship. Repainted gray and based at Puerto Belgrano.
Hull systems: The forward crane was removed after 1998, and there are plans to put a helicopter flight deck over the forward hold. Remaining are one 5-ton, one 12.5-ton, and one 20-ton crane. Has a maximum cargo capacity of 9,856 m^3 (about 6,300 tons), including 210 m^3 refrigerated.

♦ 4 U.S. LCM(6)-class landing craft [LCM]
(In serv. 6-71)

EDM 1 EDM 2 EDM 3 EDM 4

D: 24 tons (56 fl) **S:** 10 kts **Dim:** 17.07 × 4.37 × 1.17 (aft)
A: 2 single 12.7-mm mg
M: 2 G.M. Gray Marine 64 HN9 diesels; 2 props; 330–450 bhp
Range: 130/10 **Crew:** 2 tot.

Remarks: Transferred in 6-71. Can carry up to 30 tons cargo.

♦ 8 U.S. LCVP-class landing craft [LCVP]

EDVP 30 through EDVP 37

D: 13 tons (fl) **S:** 9 kts **Dim:** 10.90 × 3.21 × 1.04 (aft)
M: 1 G.M. Gray Marine 64 HN9 diesel; 225 bhp **Range:** 110/9

Remarks: Cargo: 36 troops or 3.5 tons. Five others were discarded post-1982.

Note: The Argentine Marine Corps operates 18 LVTP-7 amphibious armored troop carriers, one LVTC-7 amphibious command vehicle, and one LVTR-7 amphibious vehicle recovery vehicle, as well as one or more U.S. LARC-5 amphibious cargo lighters.

AUXILIARIES

♦ 3 ex-U.S. Coast Guard Red-class general-use ships [AG]
Bldr: U.S. Coast Guard Yard, Curtis Bay, Md.

	Laid down	L	In serv.
Q 61 Ciudad de Zárate (ex-*Red Cedar,* WLM 688)	1-7-69	1-8-70	18-12-70
Q 62 Ciudad de Rosario (ex-*Red Wood,* WLM 685)	1-7-63	4-4-64	4-8-64
Q 63 Punta Alta (ex-Q 12, ex-*Red Birch,* WLM 687)	6-7-64	19-2-65	7-6-65

Ciudad de Zárate (Q 61) Ignacio Amendolara, 7-00

Ciudad de Rosario (Q 62) Ignacio Amendolara, 7-00

D: 371 tons light (556 fl) **S:** 14 kts (12.8 sust.)
Dim: 47.85 (45.72 pp) × 10.05 (9.60 wl) × 1.99
A: none
Electronics: Radar: 1 Raytheon SPS-65(V)9 nav.; 1 Furuno 1831 nav.
M: 2 Caterpillar D398A diesels; 2 CP props; 1,800 bhp—150-shp bow-thruster
Range: 2,248/12.8; 3,055/11.6 **Crew:** 4 officers, 27 enlisted (in U.S. service)

AUXILIARIES *(continued)*

Remarks: Former U.S. Coast Guard medium navigational aids tenders. Officially rated as "multipurpose ships" in 12-00, when Q 63 was renumbered. Q 63 was declared excess from the U.S. Coast Guard on 9-6-98 and transferred by donation on 10-6-98. Q 61 and Q 62 were transferred by donation on 30-7-99, with the former recommissioning on 28-3-00 and the latter on 14-10-99 at Curtis Bay, Md. Can break light ice: 1-ft. ice at 3 kts continuously or 2-ft. ice by ramming. Have a 10-ton buoy-handling derrick. Q 63 is based at Bahía Blanca and the other two are based at Zárate on the Río Paraná as transports, training craft, and humanitarian assistance vessels.

♦ 1 Antarctic support ship/icebreaker [AGB]
Bldr: Wärtsilä, Helsinki

	Laid down	L	In serv.
Q 5 Almirante Irizar	4-7-77	3-2-78	15-12-78

Almirante Irizar (Q 5)—red-orange hull, buff superstructure, red-orange stack, cranes, and topmast — Paolo Marsan, 8-99

D: 11,811 tons (14,899 fl) **S:** 17.2 kts **Dim:** 121.3 × 25.2 × 9.5
A: 2 single 12.7-mm mg
Electronics:
Radar: 2 Kelvin Hughes Nucleus 6000A (3-cm and 10-cm) nav.; 1 Raytheon RM-70 nav.; 1 Plessey AWS-2 air search
M: diesel-electric: 4 SEMT-Pielstick 8 PC 2.5 L/400 diesels; 4 4,000-kVA alternator sets, 2 Stromberg twin motors; 2 props; 16,200 shp
Electric: 2,640 kw tot. **Crew:** 123 ship's company + 100 scientists

Remarks: Ordered 17-12-75. Now used as an amphibious warfare transport for exercises. Was used as a hospital ship during the Falklands War. Red hull, cream upperworks.
Hull systems: Has Canadian RASair bubbler system fitted to keep ice from hull bottom. Has a 60-ton towing winch and two 16-ton cranes. Has 1,800 m^3 cargo capacity. Carries two hydrographic survey launches and two LCVP-type landing craft.
Combat systems: The two 40-mm AA guns have been replaced by 12.7-mm mg.

♦ 1 Puerto Deseado–class hydrographic survey ship [AGS]
Bldr: ASTARSA (Astilleros Argentinos Río de la Plata), San Fernando

	Laid down	L	In serv.
Q 8 Puerto Deseado (ex-Q 20)	17-3-76	4-12-77	26-2-79 (trials)

Puerto Deseado (Q 8)—with former pennant number — Argentine Navy

D: 2,133 tons (2,400 fl) **S:** 14 kts **Dim:** 76.81 (67.0 pp) × 15.8 × 3.5
Electronics: Radar: 1 Decca 1629 nav.—Sonar: . . . HF mapping
M: 2 M.A.N. 9L20/27 diesels (1,206 bhp each), 2 ABB alternators, 2 electric motors; 1,600 shp—Berg electric auxiliary propulsor; 1 CP prop; 160 shp
Electric: 1,280 kVA tot. **Range:** 12,000/12
Crew: 81 tot. (accomm. for 12 officers, 53 enlisted, 20 scientists)

Remarks: Assigned to CONICET (Consejo Nacional de Investigaciones Científicas y Técnicas) and used for hydrometeorological reporting and general oceanographic research work. Was readied for use as an auxiliary hospital ship during the Falklands War in 1982 and has been used in Antarctic survey and research work since 1996, with the hull painted orange.
Mission systems: Has four Hewlett-Packard 2108-A computers for data analysis/storage and seismic, gravimetric, and magnetometer equipment. Omega- and NAVSAT-equipped. Has geology laboratory.
Hull systems: Ice-reinforced hull. Re-engined in 1995, with electric slow-speed auxiliary propulsion added.

♦ 1 Comodoro Rivadavia–class hydrographic survey ship [AGS]
Bldr: Mestrina, Tigre

	L	In serv.
Q 11 Comodoro Rivadavia	29-11-73	6-12-74

Comodoro Rivadavia (Q 11) — H&L Van Ginderen, 8-88

D: 655 tons (827 fl) **S:** 12 kts **Dim:** 52.2 × 8.8 × 2.6
Electronics: Radar: 2 Decca 1226 (3-cm and 10-cm) nav.
M: 2 Werkspoor Stork RHO-218K diesels; 1,160 bhp
Range: 6,000/12 **Crew:** 36 tot.

Remarks: Has a small helicopter platform. Is equipped with Kelvin Hughes MS 32 echo sounder, Magnavox NAVSAT receiver, Trimble differential GPS receiver. Carries a 5.6-ton Callegari semi-rigid inflatable launch with a Johnson 70-bhp outboard motor, GPS receiver, and Hidronav survey system. Also fitted with two 8-m survey launches.

Disposal note: Of the two former merchant bulk carriers taken over from Astramar Compañía Argentina de Navegación S.A.C. and operated in revenue service, *Astra Federico* (B 8, ex-*Ciudad de San Fernando*) lost certification in 1999 and was stricken, and *Astra Valentina* (B 9, ex-*Ciudad de Tigre*) followed in 5-00. Collier *Río Gallegos* (B 6, ex-*Santa Cruz*) was sold during 1999.

♦ 1 ex-French Durance-class replenishment oiler [AOR]
Bldr: DCN Brest

	Laid down	L	In serv.
B 1 Patagonia (ex-*Durance*, A 629)	10-12-73	6-9-75	1-12-76

Patagonia (B 1)—arriving in Argentina — Ignacio Amendolara, 8-00

D: 7,600 tons (17,800 fl) **S:** 20 kts (19 sust.)
Dim: 157.20 (149.00 pp) × 21.20 × 8.65 (10.8 fl)
A: 2 single 40-mm 60-cal. Bofors AA
Electronics:
Radar: 2 Decca 1226 nav.
EW: Thales DR-2000 intercept, EADS Telegon HFD/F
M: 2 SEMT-Pielstick 16 PC 2.5 V400 diesels; 2 CP props; 20,760 bhp
Electric: 5,400 kw tot. **Range:** 9,000/15 **Fuel:** 750 tons
Crew: 8 officers, 62 petty officers, 89 other enlisted (in French service)

Remarks: Purchased spring 1999, transferred 12-7-99, and began a tow to Argentina late 7-99 for reactivation refit; renamed 31-8-99 and recommissioned 12-7-00. Had been placed in reserve during 7-97. Four sisters remain in French Navy service, and a near-sister is operated by Australia. Took part in the UNITAS 2000 international naval exercise.
Hull systems: Has two dual solids/liquids underway-replenishment stations per side. Can supply two ships alongside and refuel one astern. Has hangar for one small helicopter and a flight deck for larger helicopters. Tankage altered after delivery; no longer carries fuel oil or separate diesel fuel cargo. Cargo: 9,500 tons gas turbine fuel, 130 tons distilled water, 170 tons fresh provisions, 150 tons munitions, 50 tons spare parts.

AUXILIARIES *(continued)*

♦ 1 former merchant tanker [AOT]
Bldr: ASTARSA (Astilleros Argentinos Río de la Plata), Tigre

	Laid down	L	In serv.
B 13 Ingeniero Julio Krause	28-10-78	2-2-80	1981

D: 8,346 tons (fl) **S:** 14.5 kts (14 sust.) **Dim:** 111.51 (103.99 pp) × 17.21 × 6.70
M: 1 AFNE-Sulzer 8ZL40/48, 8-cyl. diesel; 1 CP prop; 5,800 bhp
Electric: 1,134 kw tot. (3 × 378-kw diesel sets) **Crew:** 32 tot.

Remarks: 4,814 grt/6,000 dwt. Taken over 5-3-93 from Argentine state petroleum agency, Yacimientos Petrolíferos Fiscales, and operated in revenue service. Cargo: 7,500 m^3 in 15 tanks.

♦ 2 Costa Sur–class transports [AP]
Bldr: Principe & Menghe SY, Maciel I.

	Laid down	L	In serv.
B 3 Canal Beagle	10-1-77	14-10-77	28-4-78
B 5 Cabo de Hornos (ex-*Bahía Camarones*)	29-4-78	4-11-78	18-7-79

Canal Beagle (B 3) Paolo Marsan, 8-99

D: 7,640 tons (10,894 fl) **S:** 16.3 kts **Dim:** 119.9 × 17.5 × 7.49
A: none **Electronics:** Radar: 2 . . . nav.
M: 2 AFNE-Sulzer 6ZL 40/48 diesels; 2 props; 6,400 bhp **Crew:** . . . tot.

Remarks: 4,600 grt/5,800 dwt. Used to supply remote stations and also carry passengers and cargo in commercial service. Sister *Bahía San Blas* (B 4) is now used as an amphibious warfare transport.
Hull systems: Have a maximum cargo capacity of 9,856 m^3 (about 6,300 tons), including 210 m^3 refrigerated. B 5 has two 1.5-ton, one 5-ton, one 20-ton, and one 40-ton cranes, while B 3 has one crane of 5-ton, one of 12.5-ton, and one of 25-ton capacity.

♦ 2 auxiliary ocean tugs [ATA]
Bldr: Ast. Vicente Forte, Buenos Aires

R 2 Querandi (In serv. 22-8-78) R 3 Tehuelche (In serv. 2-11-78)

Querandi (R 2) and Tehuelche (R 3) H&L Van Ginderen, 4-84

D: 370 tons (fl) **S:** 12 kts **Dim:** 33.6 × 8.4 × 3.0
M: 2 M.A.N. 6V 23.5/33 diesels; 1,200 bhp
Range: 1,200/12 **Crew:** 30 tot.

♦ 1 sail-training vessel [AXT]

	Bldr	L	In serv.
Q 2 Libertad	AFNE, Río Santiago	30-5-56	1962

Libertad (Q 2) H&L Van Ginderen, 7-99

D: 3,165 tons (3,765 fl) **S:** 12.5 kts
Dim: 103.7 (94.25 hull; 79.9 pp) × 14.31 × 6.75
A: 1 76.2-mm 50-cal. DP; 4 single 40-mm 60-cal. Bofors Mk 3 AA; 4 single 47-mm saluting cannon
M: 2 Sulzer diesels; 2 props; 2,400 bhp—sail area: 2,683.5 m^2 max.
Range: 12,000/. . . **Crew:** 26 officers, 192 enlisted, 54 cadets

Remarks: Foremast is 48.66 m high, mainmast 50 m, and mizzen 43.17 m. Has extensive medical and dental facilities.

Note: The former sail-training ship *Presidente Sarmiento* (1898) and the sail corvette *Uruguay* (1874) are maintained by the navy as museums at Buenos Aires.

SERVICE CRAFT

♦ 1 floating crane [YD]

♦ 2 miscellaneous floating dry docks [YFD]

Y 1 (ex-U.S. ARD 23) (In serv. 1944): 3,500-ton capacity; 149.0 × 24.7 × 7.3 (light)
Y 3: 750-ton capacity; 65.8 × 14

Floating dry dock Y 1 Ignacio Amendolara, 1997

Disposal note: Floating dry dock Y 4 is no longer in service, while dry docks A and B are not naval-owned.

♦ 1 flag officer launch [YFL]
Bldr: Cadenazzi SY, Tigre (In serv. 1979)

Q 73 Itati II

Itati II (Q 73) Alejandro Amendolara, 7-98

SERVICE CRAFT *(continued)*

D: 80 tons (fl) **S:** 15 kts **Dim:** . . . × . . . × . . .
M: 2 . . . diesels; 2 props; . . . bhp

Remarks: Large cabin cruiser stationed at the Apostadero Naval San Fernando, Buenos Aires, for ceremonial duties.

Disposal note: The presidential yacht *Tequera* (Q 72), listed in previous editions, was in fact sold during the late 1980s.

♦ **1 coastal and riverine survey craft [YGS]**
Bldr: AFNE, Río Santiago (In serv. 20-2-64)

Q 15 Cormorán

Cormorán (Q 15)—with survey launch *Monte Blanco* alongside
Ignacio Amendolara, 2000

D: 82 tons (102 fl) **S:** 11 kts **Dim:** 25.3 × 5.0 × 1.8
Electronics: Radar: 1 Decca 101 (3-cm) nav.; 1 Raytheon R-21 (3-cm) nav.
M: 2 G.M. Detroit Diesel 6-71 diesels; 2 props; 440 bhp **Crew:** 21 tot.

Note: Also used for riverine survey duties is the small launch *Monte Blanco,* transferred from the Secretaría de Agricultura Ganadería in 1996 and based at Buenos Aires; no data available. Does not carry a naval pennant number.
Disposal note: Coastal and riverine survey craft *Petrel* (Q 16) was stricken in 12-00.

♦ **3 Huarpe-class medium harbor tugs [YTM]** Bldr: . . . , Argentina

R 4 Mataco R 7 Ona R 8 Toba

Mataco (R 4) H&L Van Ginderen, 3-97

D: 208 tons (fl) **S:** 12 kts **Dim:** 30.3 × 8.4 × 3.2
M: 2 M.A.N. diesels; 1 prop; 830 bhp **Crew:** 2 officers, 8 enlisted

Remarks: Acquired in 1988 from another government agency. Sister *Huarpe* (R 1) was stricken during 1997.

♦ **6 U.S. YTL 422–class small harbor tugs [YTL]**
Bldrs: R 5, 16, 18: Robt. Jacobs, City I., N.Y.; R 6, 19: H. C. Grebe Co.; R 10: Everett Pacific BY, Everett, Wash. (In serv. 1944–45)

R 5 Mocovi (ex-YTL 441)
R 6 Calchaqu (ex-YTL 445)
R 10 Chulupi (ex-YTL 426)
R 16 Capayan (ex-YTL 443)
R 18 Chiquillan (ex-YTL 444)
R 19 Morcoyan (ex-YTL 448)

Mocovi (R 5) H&L Van Ginderen, 4-81

D: 70 tons (80 fl) **S:** 10 kts **Dim:** 20.16 × 5.18 × 2.44
M: 1 Hoover-Owens-Rentschler diesel; 300 hp **Electric:** 40 kw tot.
Fuel: 7 tons **Crew:** 5 tot.

Remarks: R 16, R 18, and R 19 leased 3-65, others 3-69; all purchased outright 16-6-77. All six were in service as of 2-01, R 5 and R 6 at Puerto Belgrano Naval Base, R 10 and R 18 at Mar del Plata Naval Base, and R 16 and R 19 at the Naval Academy, Río Santiago, Buenos Aires, the latter for cadet training.

♦ **2 small sail-training yachts [YTS]** Bldr: Tandanor, Buenos Aires

Q 26 Fortuna II: 31.5 tons
Q 74 Fortuna I: 17 tons

♦ **1 fisheries training craft [YXT]**
Bldr: Nishinippon-F.R. Shipbuilding, Japan (In serv. 15-1-85)

Q 51 Luisito

Luisito (Q 51) Ignacio Amendolara, 1-96

D: 22 tons light **S:** 9 kts (3 with net deployed) **Dim:** 19.0 × 4.1 × 2.0
M: . . .

Remarks: Assigned to the navy but employed in training fisheries students. A small stern-haul trawler.

PREFECTURA NAVAL ARGENTINA

Personnel (2001): Approx. 12,000 total (1,650 officers), plus 500 civilians

Note: The Prefectura Naval, which traces its origins to 1756, was transferred from naval control to the Ministry of Defense in 10-84; the navy would like to obtain control over the organization, but this does not seem likely to happen in the near future. Most personnel serve ashore in port security and control-of-shipping duties, and the organization is responsible for riverine and inshore security patrol out to the 12-mile limit, search and rescue, pilot services, firefighting and antipollution duties, and operation of the National Diving School. Ships and craft are painted white and have two unequal-width blue diagonal stripes on the hull sides with anchors superimposed on the larger stripe; "Prefectura Naval" appears on the sides. Smaller service craft have black hulls.

Organization: Ten districts: Río Paraná, Upper Río Paraná and Río Paraguay, Lower Río Paraná, Upper Río Uruguay, Lower Río Uruguay, Delta, Río Plate, Argentine Sea, Southern Argentine Sea, and Lakes.

Maritime Aviation: Five CASA C-212-200 Aviocar light transports (3 with Bendix RDS 32 radars for use as maritime patrol aircraft) and 2 AS.330 Super Puma, 2 Dauphin, and 6 float-equipped Schweizer 300C helicopters.

Prefectura Schweizer 300C helicopter Ignacio Amendolara, 2000

PREFECTURA NAVAL ARGENTINA PATROL SHIPS [WPS]

♦ **5 Halcón class** Bldr: E.N. Bazán, El Ferrol, Spain

	Laid down	L	In serv.
GC 24 Doctor Manuel Mantilla	16-2-81	29-6-81	20-12-82
GC 25 Azopardo	1-4-81	14-10-81	28-4-83
GC 26 Thompson	2-81	7-12-81	20-6-83
GC 27 Prefecto Pique	9-81	24-2-82	29-7-83
GC 28 Prefecto Derbes	11-81	16-6-82	20-11-83

Doctor Manuel Mantilla (GC 24) Alejandro Amendolara, 2000

D: 767 tons normal (900 fl) **S:** 21.5 kts **Dim:** 67.0 (63.0 pp) × 10.0 × 3.06
A: 1 40-mm 70-cal. AA OTOBreda-Bofors AA; 2 single 12.7-mm mg; 1 HB.350B Esquilo helicopter
Electronics: Radar: 1 Decca AC 1226 nav.; 1 Decca . . . nav.
M: 2 Bazán-MTU 16V956 TB91 diesels; 2 props; 9,000 hp (7,500 sust.)
Electric: 710 kw **Range:** 5,000/18 **Endurance:** 20 days
Crew: 10 officers, 24 enlisted, 4 cadets

Remarks: Ordered 3-79 to patrol 200-n.m. economic zone. Same class also built for Mexico. All are based at Buenos Aires, except GC 26 at Mar del Plata.
Hull systems: For rescue duties, are fitted to carry one 6.1-m rigid rescue craft with an Evinrude outboard and a capacity of 12 personnel; there is a four-person sick bay. Equipped with Magnavox MS 1102 SATNAV receivers.
Combat systems: The 40-mm gun is locally controlled, and the ships can carry 144 rounds of 40-mm ammunition.

♦ **1 former whale-catcher**
Bldr: NV IJsselwerf, Rotterdam, the Netherlands (In serv. 4-57)

GC 13 Delfín (ex-R 1)

Delfín (GC 13) Hartmut Ehlers, 1-98

D: 900 tons (1,280 fl) **S:** 15 kts **Dim:** 56.88 (50.98 pp) × 9.35 × 4.34
A: 1 20-mm 70-cal. Oerlikon AA; 2 single 12.7-mm mg
Electronics: Radar: 2 . . . nav.
M: 2 M.A.N.-Deutz 10-cyl. diesels; 1 prop; 2,965 bhp (2,300 sust.)—bow-thruster
Electric: 360 kw tot. (2 × 120-kw, 2 × 60-kw diesel sets)
Range: 6,720/10 **Crew:** 27 tot.

Remarks: Purchased 1969 from Calpe Shipping Co., Gibraltar, and converted for patrol duties, commissioning 23-1-70. Three sisters formerly served in the Norwegian Coast Guard.

PATROL CRAFT [WPC]

♦ **2 Lynch class** Bldr: AFNE, Río Santiago (In serv. 1964–67)

GC 21 Lynch GC 22 Toll

D: 100 tons (117 fl) **S:** 22 kts **Dim:** 27.44 × 5.80 × 1.85
A: provision for 1 20-mm 70-cal. Oerlikon AA
M: 2 Maybach diesels; 2 props; 2,700 hp
Range: 2,000/. . . **Crew:** 16 tot.

Remarks: Sister *Erezcano* (GC 23) stricken 1986. Designed after the U.S. Coast Guard Cape class.

PATROL BOATS [WPB]

♦ **1 Bazán 39–class fast launch**
Bldr: E.N. Bazán, San Fernando (In serv. 1997)

GC 142

D: 14.5 tons (fl) **S:** 38 kts **Dim:** 11.90 × 3.00 × 0.70
A: 1 12.7-mm mg **Electronics:** Radar: 1 . . . nav.
M: 2 M.A.N. D2848 diesels; 2 Hamilton 362 waterjets; 1,360 bhp
Range: 300/25 **Crew:** 5 tot.

Remarks: Plans to acquire more of this class did not reach fruition. GRP construction.

♦ **10 Alucat 1050–class riverine patrol launches**
Bldr: Damen, Gorinchem, the Netherlands (First 3: in serv. 8-94, others in 2-00)

GC 137 through GC 146

Alucat 1050–class GC 146 Hartmut Ehlers, 4-00

D: 10.5 tons (15 fl) **S:** 18 kts **Dim:** 11.45 × 3.80 × 0.60
Electronics: Radar: 1 Furuno 12/24 nav.
M: 2 Volvo Penta 61 ALD diesels; 2 Hamilton 273 waterjets; 600 bhp
Range: 290/. . . **Crew:** 4 tot.

Remarks: An enlarged version of the Alucat 850 class; used for antismuggling patrol along the river border with Paraguay. Seven more were ordered in 1999 for delivery in 2-00.

♦ **27 Alucat 850–class lake patrol launches**
Bldr: Damen, Gorinchem, the Netherlands (In serv. 1995 to 12-97)

LS 9201 through LS 9227

D: 9 tons (fl) **S:** 18 kts **Dim:** 9.20 × 3.25 × 0.60
Electronics: Radar: 1 Furuno 12/24 nav.
M: 2 Volvo Penta TAMD 41B diesels; 2 Hamilton 273 waterjets; 394 bhp
Range: 300/. . . **Crew:** 4 tot.

Remarks: LS 9213 through LS 9217 were delivered in 12-96 and LS 9218 through LS 9222 in 12-97. The other five were ordered in 1999. Aluminum construction.

♦ **18 Z-28 class** Bldr: Blohm + Voss, Hamburg (In serv. 9-79 to 1-80)

GC 64 Mar del Plata
GC 65 Martin Garcia
GC 66 Río Lujan
GC 67 Río Uruguay
GC 68 Río Paraguay
GC 69 Río Paraná
GC 70 Río Plata
GC 71 La Plata
GC 72 Buenos Aires
GC 73 Cabo Corrientes
GC 74 Quequen
GC 75 Bahía Blanca
GC 76 Ingeniero White
GC 77 Golfo San Matias
GC 78 Madryn
GC 79 Río Deseado
GC 80 Ushuaia
GC 81 Canal de Beagle

Río Deseado (GC 79) Hartmut Ehlers, 4-00

D: 81 tons (fl) **S:** 22 kts **Dim:** 27.65 (26.0 pp) × 5.30 × 1.65
A: 1 20-mm 90-cal. Oerlikon GAM-B01 AA; 2 single 12.7-mm mg
Electronics: Radar: 1 Decca 1226 nav.
M: 2 MTU 8V331 TC92 diesels; 2 props; 2,100 bhp (1,770 sust.)
Electric: 90 kVA **Range:** 780/18; 1,200/12 **Crew:** 3 officers, 11 enlisted

Remarks: Ordered 24-11-78. Fin stabilizers fitted. During the Falklands War, *Río Iguazú* (GC 83) was lost, and *Islas Malvinas* (GC 82) was captured and renamed *Tiger Bay* by British forces. Not all units carry the 20-mm gun.

♦ **34 GC 48 class**
Bldr: Cadenazzi SY, Tigre (except GC 88–114: Ast. Belen de Escobar)

GC 48–GC 61 (In serv. 1978–79)
GC 88–GC 95, GC 102–GC 114 (In serv. 1984–86)

PREFECTURA NAVAL ARGENTINA PATROL BOATS [WPB] *(continued)*

GC 48–class GC 92 Hartmut Ehlers, 4-00

D: 13 tons (15 fl) **S:** 25 kts **Dim:** 12.54 × 3.57 × 1.10
A: 1 12.7-mm mg
M: 2 G.M. Detroit Diesel 6V71N diesels; 2 props; 514 bhp
Range: 400/20 **Crew:** 3 tot.

Remarks: Some, including *Perco* (GC 48), have names.

♦ 1 patrol boat Bldr: Río Santiago Naval Base (In serv. 17-12-39)

GC 101 Dorado

D: 43 tons (fl) **S:** 12 kts **Dim:** 21.2 × 4.3 × 1.5
A: small arms **M:** 2 G.M. Gray Marine 6071-6A diesels; 2 props; 360 hp
Range: 1550/12 **Crew:** 1 officer, 6 enlisted

♦ 16 miscellaneous former pilot boats

GC 118 Lago Alumine (ex-SP 14)
GC 119 Lago Traful (ex-SP 15)
GC 120 Lago Lacar (ex-SP 24)
GC 121 Lago Fontana (ex-SP 32)
GC 123 Lago Viedma (ex-SP 20)
GC 124 Lago San Martín (ex-SP 21)
GC 125 Lago Buenos Aires (ex-SP 22)
GC 126 Lago Musters (ex-SP 26)
GC 129 Lago Colhue (ex-SP 16)
GC 130 Maria L. Pendo (ex-SP 18, ex-*Lago Argentino*)
GC 131 Lago Roca (ex-SP 28)
GC 132 Lago Puelo (ex-SP 29)
GC 133 Lago Futalaufquen (ex-SP 30)
GC 134 Lago Falkner (ex-SP 31)
GC 135 Lago Huechulafquen (ex-SP 34)
GC 136 Lago Colhe Huapi (ex-SP 33)

Lago Puelo (GC 132)—outboard push-tug SB 9 Alejandro Amendolara, 2000

Lago Alumine (GC 118) Hartmut Ehlers, 1-98

Remarks: Former pilot boats transferred to patrol duties in 1993 and 1995. GC 118 and GC 119 are 33.7 tons full load and were completed 1981. GC 123 and GC 124 are of 51 tons. GC 129 and GC 130 are of 47 tons. GC 131–133 are 16.5 m overall and were delivered in 1983. GC 121, 134, and 136 are of 7 tons and were built 1986–91.

AUXILIARIES

♦ 1 pilot station ship [WAG]
Bldr: ASTARSA (Astilleros Argentinos Río de la Plata), San Fernando

DF 15 Recalada (ex-*Río Limay*)

D: 10,070 tons (fl) **S:** 18 kts **Dim:** 147.61 (138.00 pp) × 20.20 × 8.25
M: 1 AFNE-GMT B750-7L reversing diesel; 1 prop; 10,500 bhp
Range: 14,000/18 **Fuel:** 1,197 tons **Crew:** 3 officers, 25 enlisted

Remarks: 9,059 grt. Acquired 9-91 to act as Río Plata pilot station ship in place of the *Recalada* (ex-*Lago Lacar*) and commissioned 24-12-91. Former general cargo ship, with forward cargo-handling gear removed and forward hatch reinforced as a helicopter platform. Has been given a 20-bed hospital facility. "Recalada" painted on hull sides.

♦ 1 salvage tug [WARS] Bldr: Sanym S.A., San Fernando (In serv. 21-10-77)

GC 47 Tonina

Tonina (GC 47)—inboard Damen "PushyCat" tug *Canal Emilio Mitre* (SB 8) Hartmut Ehlers, 1-98

D: 103 tons (153 fl) **S:** 11 kts **Dim:** 25.5 × 5.3 × 2.1
A: 1 20-mm 70-cal. Oerlikon AA; 2 single 12.7-mm mg
Electronics: Radar: 1 Decca 1226 nav.
M: 2 G.M. Detroit Diesel 16V71N 162-2000 diesels; 2 props; 1,500 hp
Range: 2,800/10 **Crew:** 3 officers, 8 enlisted

Remarks: Used as training ship until 1986. Has divers' facilities, including a decompression chamber.

SERVICE CRAFT

♦ 5 miscellaneous pilot launches [WYFL]

SP 19 Lago Nahuel Huapi
SP 23 Lago Faviano
SP 25 Lago Cardial
SP 27 Lago Quillen
SP 30 Lago Yehuin (ex-SP 35)

Remarks: SP 19 and SP 23 displace 51 tons. SP 25 and SP 27 displace 20 tons and were delivered 1981. SP 30 is of 7 tons and was completed in 1991. In 1993, six SP-series pilot boats were renumbered in the GC-series and transferred to patrol duties; another 10 followed in 1995. A craft numbered SPA 1, resembling a yacht but with a long poop deck, is also in service, name and function unknown.

♦ 6 miscellaneous small tugboats [WYTL]

SB 3
SB 4
SB 5
SB 8 Canal Emilio Mitre
SB 9
SB 10

Remarks: SB 8: 53 tons (fl); 10 kts; Damen "PushyCat 1500" design, built 1982.

♦ 1 fireboat [WYTR] (In serv. 1960)

SI 1 Rodolfo d'Agostini

♦ 1 sail-training yacht [WYTS] (L: 12–68)

Esperanza

D: 32 tons **S:** 15 kts (6 under power) **Dim:** 19.0 × 4.3 × 2.7
M: 1 G.M. diesel; 90 bhp **Crew:** 6 crew + 6 cadets

Remarks: Also in use are sailing yacht *Adhara II* (ex-*Gloria;* ex-*Cormorán,* GC 36), of 30 tons, with 1 G.M. auxiliary diesel, capable of 10–15 kts; *Dr. Bernardo Houssay* (ex-*El Austral*), a 46-ton ketch built in 1930 in Denmark and acquired in 1996; and cabin cruiser *Talita II.*

♦ 1 Dorado-class training craft [WYXT]
Bldr: Río Santiago Naval Base (In serv. 1940)

GC 43 Mandubi

D: 208 tons (270 fl) **S:** 11 kts **Dim:** 33.2 × 4.0 × 1.9
A: 2 single 12.7-mm mg
M: 2 M.A.N. G6V 23.5/33 diesels; 2 props; 880 bhp
Range: 800/14; 3,400/10 **Crew:** 12 crew + 20 trainees

Remarks: Sister *Dorado* (GC 34) and the similar *Robalo* (GC 45) were stricken 1985–86. Used as a training craft for cadets. Tug-type vessel.

Note: Also in use are over 400 smaller launches, RIBs, and service craft such as floating cranes.

AUSTRALIA

Commonwealth of Australia

Personnel (1-01): 11,090 total (2,168 officers, 8,922 enlisted), including 312 female officers and 1,197 female enlisted; 6,500 reserves (about 1,500 total active); approximately 5,000 civilians. The private firm Defence Maritime Services employs civilian personnel to operate various service craft.

Note: The operation and maintenance of support craft such as torpedo retrievers, tugs, and range support services was contracted for 10 years in mid-1997 to Defence Maritime Services Pty, Ltd. (DMS), a joint venture company established by P&O Maritime Australia and Serco Defence Services. DMS also provides submarine trials and support services and maintenance and training on all motor- and sail-training craft.

Bases: Maritime Headquarters is at Sydney, along with Fleet Base East, HMAS *Waterhen* (mine countermeasures), HMAS *Watson* (training), and HMAS *Kuttabul* (administration). Fleet Base West is at HMAS *Stirling,* Cockburn Sound, Fremantle, Western Australia, with administration, submarine base, HMAS *Albatross* air station at Nowra, HMAS *Creswell* Naval College, Jervis Bay firing range, and maintenance facilities. Other facilities include HMAS *Coonawarra* communications facility and patrol boat base at Darwin, Northern Terr.; Headquarters Patrol Force at HMAS *Cairns,* Cairns, Queensland; HMAS *Cerberus* (training and small warship facilities) at Westernport, Victoria; *Harold E. Holt* communications station at North West Cape, Western Australia; HMAS *Harman* area administration and communications station, Canberra; and Naval Headquarters, Port Kembla, Tasmania. Noncommissioned establishments include the Jervis Bay range facility; the Naval Supply Center, Sydney; Naval Armaments Depots at Kingswood, New South Wales, and Somerton, Victoria; and Naval Armament and Equipment Depots at Garden Island, Western Australia, and Maribyrnong, Victoria. An ammunition storage facility is to open in 2002 at Twofold Bay, New South Wales.

Naval Aviation: Commander, Australian Naval Aviation Forces, was reestablished 1-3-96 at HMAS *Albatross,* Nowra, New South Wales. About 900 personnel serve in aviation billets.

Aircraft in service include 11 Kaman SH-2G(A) Super SeaSprite shipboard ASW/attack helicopters in HS-805 Sqn., 16 Sikorsky S-70B-2 Seahawk shipboard ASW helicopters (U.S. Navy LAMPS-III equivalent, with MEL Super Searcher radar in place of LN-66, GE T700-401C turboshaft engines, 1 7.62-mm machinegun, 2 Mk 46 ASW torpedoes) in HS-816 Sqn., 8 Mk 50A Sea King helicopters in HS-817 Sqn., and 11 AS.350B Écureuil light utility helicopters in HC-723 Sqn.

Six of the Sea King helicopters have been modified for utility service (ASW equipment deleted) and rehabilitated to serve through 2008. RAN Sea Kings are powered by two Rolls-Royce Gnome H1400-1 turbines of 1,650 shp each and can carry either 23 troops or 2,750 kg of stores; range is about 500 n.m. at 100 kts, and maximum speed 138 kts.

The 16 S-70B-2 Seahawk helicopters were modernized with new ESM and forward-looking infrared sensors with 1993–94 budget funds; at a later date it is hoped to add a lightweight dipping sonar and an antiship missile-launching capability. The Seahawk helicopters began receiving Boeing AAR-54(V) missile-warning systems and Raytheon AAQ-27 FLIR in 2-00; the same equipment will later be fitted to the SH-2G(A) helicopters.

SH-2G(A) SeaSprite—with flotation bags deployed — Kaman, 2001

S-70B-2 Seahawk — LSPH Darren Yates, RAN, 1-01

Mk 50 Sea King — RAN, 1999

AS.350B Écureuil — RAN, 1999

On 17-1-97, the Kaman SH-2G(A) Super SeaSprite was selected as the helicopter for employment with the *Anzac*-class frigates; the first was delivered during 2-01 and the last was to be received in 2-02. They have a Litton LN-100G integrated tactical avionics system, Rockwell Collins GEM III GPS, Telephonics APS-143B(V)3 radar (with inverse synthetic aperture capability for target identification), Raytheon AAQ-47 (3FOV) FLIR, Elisra LWS-20 laser warning and AES-210 ESM, Litton Link 11, Northrop Grumman AAR-54(V) passive missile approach warning system, and Tracor ALE-47 decoy dispensers, but no sonar equipment. Other characteristics for the new SH-2G(A) Super SeaSprite helicopter include:

Rotor diameter: 13.51 m **Length:** 12.93 m folded/16.00 m over rotors
Weight: 6,441 kg (max. takeoff) **Speed:** 150 kts max.
Engines: 2 G.E. T700-GE-401 turboshafts (1,723 shp each)
Ceiling: 20,400 ft. (14,600 ft. hovering) **Range:** 546 n.m. **Endurance:** 5.3 hrs
Crew: 2 + up to 6 troops **Payload:** 2,296 kg
Weapons: 2 AGM-119B Penguin Mk 2 Mod. 7 ASM or 2 Mk 46 torpedoes or 2 Mk 11 d.c.

The remaining Bell 206B Kiowa utility helicopters were transferred to the Australian Army in 8-00, in return for additional AS.350B Écureuil helicopters. The two HS-748 fixed-wing EW training aircraft were retired on 22-6-00. The six Royal New Zealand Air Force A-4K Skyhawk fighter-bombers stationed since 1991 at HMAS *Albatross* in part to provide target training to the RAN were returned to New Zealand during 7-01.

The RAAF operates 19 P-3C Orion maritime patrol aircraft equipped with AQS-901 receiver/processors for the Australian-developed Barra SSQ-801 sonobuoy and capable of carrying two AGM-84A or -84C Harpoon antiship missiles. Under a 1994 contract with E-Systems, Greenville, Texas, 18 P-3Cs received Elta EL/M-2022A(V)3 radars, new EW intercept equipment, a new MAD sensor, GPS and SATCOM receivers, a new acoustic processor, anticorrosion treatment, and weight-saving measures during modernizations were scheduled to start 12-96 and complete by 8-01; the modernization is expected to permit the newly styled AP-3C Sea Sentinel aircraft to be operated until 2015. By 2-01, however, only four aircraft had been completed when responsibility for the program was transferred to Raytheon Australia at Avalon, Victoria; the others were expected to be completed by 1-04. Three ex-USN P-3B Orions perform training duties.

Aerial surveillance of Australia's immensely long northern coastline is conducted by the Customs Service Coastwatch, using contractor-operated aircraft with the assistance of RAAF Orions. National Jet Systems operates five de Havilland Canada Dash 8-202 MPA, five Reims F406 Caravan II, six Pilatus-Britten-Norman BN2B-20 Islanders, and one Rockwell Shrike Commander for the Coastwatch, while Reef Helicopters operates a Bell LongRanger IV helicopter in the Torres Strait region. The National Jet Systems contract is to run until 2004. One each Dash 8-202 MPA and Reims F406 operate from Broome, Darwin, and Cairns, while the Islanders are based at Broome, Darwin, Horn Island, and Cairns (the latter with the Shrike Commander). The Dash 8-202 MPAs and F406s carry the Texas Instruments APS-134 digital radar, and the Dash 8-202 MPAs have an integrated tactical data system, a Westcam 16T optronics surveillance turret with Mitsubishi IRST, and low-light television sensors.

Coast Defense: A network of surveillance radars, termed the Jindalee Operational Radar Network (JORN) over-the-horizon system, supports air defense along the northern coast. Operational trials of the Surface-wave Extended Coastal Area Radar (SECAR, also known as Project Iluka) began in 2000; it will provide a surface- and low-altitude search adjunct to the JORN.

Future Programs: Under the 12-00 Defence Capabilities Plan, the navy was to receive through 2015: three DDGs (the first to enter service in 2013); replacements for the ex-U.S. LSTs beginning in 2015; a replacement for *Tobruk* in 2010; replacement utility landing craft and two replacement underway replenishment oilers by 2009; upgrades to antiship missile defenses and improved antiship weaponry for the *Anzac*-class frigates; replacement patrol craft to enter service starting 2004–05; full updates to all six *Collins*-class submarines; a new submarine torpedo beginning in 2006; and a mid-life update to the Seahawk helicopter fleet.

WEAPONS AND SYSTEMS

The Royal Australian Navy primarily uses U.S. equipment and systems. U.S. Mk 48 torpedoes and Sub-Harpoon missiles have been purchased for use by submarines, and Harpoons are also carried by *Perry*-class frigates and RAAF P-3C, F/A-18, and F-111 aircraft. The 37 ships with Magnavox MX1100 SATNAV systems have been updated to use the Global Positioning System.

Kongsberg Defence & Aerospace, Norway, received a 5-year, $50.7 million contract in 1998 for Penguin air-to-surface antiship missiles; an additional $40 million was added during 1-99, with deliveries commencing during 7-01 and ending by end-2003.

The Australian-manufactured Mulloka sonar is a high-frequency set tailored to local coastal water/sound propagation conditions. The Karrawarra towed passive sonar array entered service in 1985 for submarines. The Albatross sonar system (formerly ASSTASS—Australian Surface Ship Towed Array Surveillance System) is being developed by Thales for use on the modernized *Perry*-class FFGs. To be incorporated in the update to the *Perry*-class frigates is the indigenously developed Petrel navigational and mine-avoidance sonar, with a vertical linear, stabilized active hydrophone array and a horizontal linear receiving array.

The Nulka (formerly Winnin) countermeasures system with hovering chaff/IR decoy rockets uses the same Mk 137 6-round launcher as the U.S. Mk 36 SRBOC system, with the Nulka tubes added; the production order was placed in 8-96.

The first Mini-Dyad reconfigurable permanent magnet influence sweep arrays were ordered during 1996; they employ a 6.4 × 0.53-m, hollow, two-section mild steel pipe with two reconfigurable strontium-ferrite inserts. The programmable Australian Acoustic Generator (AAG) was ordered on 5-6-01 for tow by the *Huon* class.

The BAe Systems Stonefish Mk III was selected in 5-00 to fulfill the Project Bayawirri (Defence Project SEA 2045) requirement to provide the RAN with an offensive sea mining capability that will employ air- or submarine-launched standoff mines, with a later submarine-launched variant to include a mobile-mine payload.

Major ships are equipped with one of 47 TESS (Tactical Environmental Support System) sets acquired in the early 1990s to assist the commanding officer with decisions about which sensors to employ under given environmental conditions. TESS 2, configured to overcome "Y2K" hardware and software problems, entered service prior to the end of 1999, and an improved TESS 3 is in development.

The Thales MU 90 Impact was selected early in 1-00 as winner in the Project SEA 2070 competition for a new lightweight ASW torpedo; some 200–300 are planned to be ordered in 2002. Australia is to cooperate with the U.S. Navy in the development of a new heavyweight submarine torpedo.

ATTACK SUBMARINES [SS]

Note: In order to preserve the recently established submarine-building capability in Australia, a new design may be ordered after 2002, with the first unit to be launched between 2010 and 2012.

♦ 5 (+ 1) Collins class (Kockums Type 471)

Bldr: Australian Submarine Corp., Port Adelaide, South Australia

	Laid down	L	In serv.
SSG 73 Collins	14-2-90	28-8-93	27-7-96
SSG 74 Farncomb	1-3-91	15-12-95	31-1-98
SSG 75 Waller	19-3-92	14-3-97	10-7-99
SSG 76 Dechaineux	4-3-93	12-3-98	23-2-01
SSG 77 Sheean	17-2-94	1-5-99	23-2-01
SSG 78 Rankin	12-5-95	26-11-01	...

Sheean (SSG 77) ABPH Tony Barclay-Jeffs, RAN, 1-01

Waller (SSG 75)—note tube protruding aft from casing for dispensing the towed sonar array Brian Morrison, 11-00

Collins (SSG 73)—with hull and sail modifications to reduce radiated noise RAN, 11-00

Dechaineux (SSG 76) LSPH Darren Yates, RAN, 2-01

D: 2,450 tons light, 3,051 surf./3,353 tons sub.
S: 10.5 kts surf./10.5 kts snorkel/21 kts sub. **Dim:** 77.42 × 7.80 × 7.00
A: 6 bow 533-mm TT (23 UGM-84C Harpoon SSM and Mk 48 Mod. 4 wire-guided torpedoes)
Electronics:
Radar: GEC-Marconi Type 1007
Sonar: Thales Scylla bow and flank arrays—first two: Thales Karrawarra TASS—others: Karrawarra or Thales Narama TASS
EW: ArgoSystems Phoenix AR-740-US intercept (SSG 76, 77: . . .)
M: diesel-electric: 3 Garden Island-Hedemora HV V18B/15Ub (VB 210) 18-cyl. diesel generator sets (6,000 bhp/4,425 kw tot.), 1 Jeumont-Schneider motor; 1 7-bladed (4.22-m-dia.) prop; 7,200 shp—100-hp retractable hydraulic emergency propulsor
Range: 11,500/10 surf. (see remarks); 9,000/10 snorkel; 32.6/21, 480/4 sub.
Endurance: 70 days **Crew:** 6 officers, 36 enlisted

Remarks: Contract announced 18-5-87 for six, with option for two more (later dropped). Cost about $550 million (U.S.) each. The Australian Submarine Corp. was originally a consortium of Kockums, Hardie Ltd., and the government-owned Australian Industrial Development Co. The bow and stern sections of first two were built at Malmö, Sweden, by Kockums. Initial surface trials for *Collins* began 31-10-94; first dive was made 11-6-95. All are being based at Fleet Base West, HMAS *Stirling,* south of Fremantle. Full operational capability for the class has been delayed until at least 2007.

In 7-96, it was announced that plans for possible backfitting of units of the class with air-independent propulsion had been dropped because of the excellent submerged endurance and low indescretion rates experienced with the *Collins.* Proposals to build two additional units (primarily to maintain the shipyard labor force) have been raised periodically; however, the RAN would prefer that construction funds be spent on surface ships.

None of the class was fully ready for operational deployments before 2000 because of software integration problems; the first two were able, however, to perform limited combat functions by 1998. The final software suite was not delivered until mid-1999 and required a one-year trials period in the *Collins.* The first two suffered a number of setbacks, including hydrodynamic flow problems that mask the passive sonar systems, cracked propellers, periscope vibration, engine and gearbox seal problems, and severe combat system software deficiencies. SSG 75 and SSG 76 began upgrading prior to delivery, with improvements to the sonar and the combat data and fire-control systems, while noise signature was reduced and vibration problems with the periscopes and propellers were effectively eliminated. The launch of SSG 78 was delayed from 3-00 so as to incorporate improvements during the construction process, and funds to update SSG 74 and SSG 78 were released on 14-9-00.

Hull systems: Said to be the quietest, most shock-resistant diesel-electric submarines in the world. Modular construction. Intended to meet a mission requirement of a 3,500-n.m. radius at 10 kts submerged, plus 47 days on station at 4 kts. Battery capacity gives 120 hrs at 4 kts. Diving depth is stated as "in excess of 180 meters."

All after *Collins* were to be completed with an anechoic tile hull coating; *Collins* was backfitted after comparative trials. Marconi SDG-1802 degaussing gear is fitted. The outer hull casing form has been altered to reduce flow noise; the prototype form was tested at sea in *Collins* in mid-1999, and *Dechaineux* and *Sheean* were similarly altered starting during 2000; all three have improved engine mountings to reduce vibration.

ATTACK SUBMARINES [SS] *(continued)*

Newcastle (FFG 06) Brian Morrison, 5-00

Combat systems: Have the Raytheon (originally Singer Librascope, then Rockwell Collins, and then Boeing) SCCS Mk 2 f.c.s., for which Version 2.0 software was delivered 12-99; the unsatisfactory system is to be replaced by the Raytheon CCS Mk 2 system. The EW suite is also to be replaced. They have a receive-only interface with the Link 11 combat information system datalink. Periscopes from Pilkington Optronics include a CK 43 search and a CH 93 attack.

The sonar suite is derived from the Thales (Thomson-Sintra) Eledone and includes a bow-mounted cylindrical passive array, a 5-kHz active array at the forward edge of the sail, bow-mounted mine avoidance active and passive intercept arrays, flank arrays, two aft-mounted intercept arrays, and towed array (developmental models of the Australian Karrawarra, with a 1,000-m array, 45 mm in diameter, in the first two; the installation in the later four to be decided by a competition between Karrawarra, Thomson-Sintra's Narama, and the U.S. TB-23 thin-line array system. There is also an 8–11 kHz underwater telephone, 16 self-noise measurement hydrophones, and 16 accelerometers. The British Strachan & Henshaw submerged signal and decoy ejector system is installed.

U.S. Tomahawk strategic cruise missiles may be added later. The Mk 48 Mod. 4 torpedoes were to be replaced shortly after 2000, as they had reached the end of their normal service lives, but new torpedoes will not begin delivery until 2006 or later.

Disposal note: The final *Oberon*-class submarine in service, *Otama* (SS 62), was decommissioned for disposal on 17-12-99.

Note: The remotely operated submarine personnel rescue vehicle *Remora* was delivered 1996 on a 5-year lease from the Australian Submarine Corp. Built in Canada by Can-Dive Marine Services, Vancouver, the 16.5-ton craft can operate in up to 550 m of water. In 1998, the general-purpose ship *Seahorse Spirit* was assigned as tender. As part of the complex, two 36-seat recompression chamber modules are carried on the tender.

GUIDED-MISSILE DESTROYERS [DDG]

Note: A replacement destroyer project, SEA 1400, is in the earliest stages of definition. The ships would be armed with U.S. Standard SM-2 and Evolved Sea Sparrow vertically launched SAMs. The use of an existing foreign ship design adapted to Australian requirements and built in Australia is preferred. On 25-5-00, the Australian Ministry of Defence declined the offer of ships of the U.S. *Kidd* (DDG 993) class to fulfill the role. The U.S. naval architectural firm Gibbs & Cox has offered a 5,900-ton, scaled-down, lesser-capability version of the *Arleigh Burke* class; the ships would carry SPY-1D Aegis, SM-2, Evolved Sea Sparrow, and RAM SAMs and RGM-84 Harpoon antiship missiles. Spain's Izar (formerly E.N. Bazán) has proposed the F-100 design, Germany's Blohm + Voss the Type 124 (*Sachsen* class), and BAe Systems a variant of the British Type 45 DDG.

Disposal note: The final U.S. *Charles F. Adams*–class guided-missile destroyer in RAN service, *Brisbane* (DDG 41, ex-U.S. DDG 27), was retired on 19-10-01. *Perth* (DDG 38, ex-U.S. DDG 25) was retired on 15-10-99 and *Hobart* (DDG 39, ex-U.S. DDG 26) on 12-5-00.

Darwin (FFG 04) Ralph Edwards, 3-01

GUIDED-MISSILE FRIGATES [FFG]

♦ 6 U.S. Oliver Hazard Perry class

Bldrs: First four: Todd, Seattle; FFG 05, 06: AMECON, Melbourne

	Laid down	L	In serv.
FFG 01 ADELAIDE (ex-FFG 17)	29-7-77	21-6-78	6-11-80
FFG 02 CANBERRA (ex-FFG 18)	1-3-78	1-12-78	21-3-81
FFG 03 SYDNEY (ex-FFG 35)	16-1-80	26-9-80	29-1-83
FFG 04 DARWIN (ex-FFG 44)	2-7-81	26-3-82	21-7-84
FFG 05 MELBOURNE	12-7-85	5-5-89	15-2-92
FFG 06 NEWCASTLE	11-88	21-2-92	11-12-93

D: 3,073 tons (3,962 fl) **S:** 29 kts
Dim: 138.80 (126.0 wl) × 13.72 × 4.52 (7.47 max.)
A: 1 Mk 13 Mod. 4 launcher (40 Standard SM-1A SAM and RGM-84C Harpoon missiles); 1 76-mm 62-cal.U.S. Mk 75 DP; 1 20-mm Mk 15 Phalanx CIWS; 2 single 12.7-mm M2 mg; 2 triple 324-mm Mk 32 ASW TT (Mk 46 Mod 5 torpedoes); 2 helicopters (see remarks)

Adelaide (FFG 01) Brian Morrison, 5-00

Darwin (FFG 04) Brian Morrison, 2-00

GUIDED-MISSILE FRIGATES [FFG] *(continued)*

Electronics:
Radar: 1 Cardion SPS-55 surf. search; 1 Raytheon SPS-49(V)2 air search; 1 Raytheon Mk 92 Mod. 2 track-while-scan gun/missile f.c.; 1 Raytheon SPG-60 STIR missile f.c.
Sonar: Raytheon SQS-56 (FFG 05, 06: Mulloka)—TACAN: URN-25
EW: Raytheon SLQ-32(V)2 intercept; Elbit EA 2118 intercept (2–40 GHz); modified Mk 36 SRBOC decoy syst. (4 10-round modified Mk 137 RL with Nulka capability); SLQ-25 Nixie towed torpedo decoy
E/O: Rademac 2500 surveillance and tracking; 2 Mk 24 target desig.
M: 2 G.E. LM-2500 gas turbines; 1 CP prop; 41,000 shp—2 350-shp drop-down electric propulsors
Electric: 3,000 kw tot. **Range:** 4,200/20; 5,000/18
Fuel: 587 tons (+ 64 tons helo fuel) **Crew:** 15 officers, 172 enlisted (+ air group)

Remarks: First two ordered 27-2-76, third on 23-1-79, fourth on 28-4-80; the two Australian-built ships were ordered 12-10-83. FFG 01 home port transferred to Fleet Base West, HMAS *Stirling,* near Fremantle, in 10-92; FFG 04 followed on 18-12-94 and FFG 02 on 9-1-96. The others are based at Fleet Base East, Sydney. The first two were originally due for retirement in 2008 and the next pair in 2012, but planned modernizations will delay the retirements to 2015 or later.
Hull systems: Two drop-down, diesel-electric-driven propellers are located forward beneath the hull for emergency propulsion and maneuvering. The selection of the Sikorsky S-70B2 helicopter for these ships required that the first three be lengthened 9 feet and have fin stabilization systems added at Garden Island Dockyard; the RAST helicopter downhaul and traversing system was also added. FFG 03 completed lengthening 1-89, FFG 01 in 8-89, and FFG 02 by end-1991. Have fin stabilizers and are equipped with the Prairie/Masker air bubbler system to reduce radiated machinery noise below the waterline.
Combat systems: The Australian-built units have Mulloka sonars in place of SQS-56. FFG 01 and FFG 02 had the two Mk 24 optical target designators atop the pilothouse and EW systems added after delivery. All carry WSC-3 UHF SATCOM sets. Israeli Elbit intercept equipment added 1989–90. The ships normally carry one S-70B-2 and one Écureuil helicopter, with the S-70B-2 Seahawk able to carry two Penguin Mk 2 Mod. 7 antiship missiles or two ASW torpedoes. Rademac 2500 electro-optical surveillance and tracking systems were ordered for all six in 9-95; delivered in mid-1998, they incorporate HK202 daylight television, Ranger-600 laser rangefinder, and LRTS thermal imager in one stabilized mounting. The 12.7-mm mg are located atop the pilothouse. In 1998, FFG 04 received four decoy rocket launchers, each with four tubes for Nulka decoys as well as six tubes for regular chaff rockets; the others have been similarly upgraded.
Modernization: Australian Defence Industries (ADI) was selected on 13-11-98 to perform an extensive $636 million modernization on all six ships under a contract finalized in 5-99. The work is being performed during 2001–05 at Garden Island Dockyard, Sydney, with completions to come between 2003 and 2006; the ships are to be upgraded in order of construction. The first update is to take about 50 weeks, and the others between 38 and 40 weeks. Lockheed Martin and Gibbs & Cox of the U.S.A. are assisting. The Mk 92 f.c.s. will be upgraded to Mod. 12, and one 8-cell Mk 41 verticle missile launch group (32 Evolved Sea Sparrow SAMs in quad packs) will be added forward of the Mk 13 missile launcher in place of the current helicopter replenishment spot. The Rafael-Elisra C-PEARL EW suite will replace the present SLQ-32 system, and UYQ-70 displays and a Link 16 capability will be added. The SPS-49(V)2 radar is also to be upgraded to SPS-49A(V)1, and the sonar is to be replaced by the Thales (Thomson-Marconi) TMS 4131 with Petrel 5424 mine-avoidance sonar; also added will be an improved torpedo detection capability using the Sea Defender suite with an Albatros detection sonar and the current SLQ-25A decoy system.

FRIGATES [FF]

♦ 3 (+ 5) Anzac (MEKO 200 ANZ) class

Bldr: Tenix Defence Systems (Transfield Shipbuilding), Williamstown, Victoria

	Laid down	L	In serv.
FF 150 Anzac	5-11-93	16-9-94	28-5-96
FF 151 Arunta (ex-*Arrerente*)	22-7-95	28-6-96	12-12-98
FF 152 Warramunga (ex-*Warumungu*)	26-7-97	23-5-98	31-3-01
FF 153 Stuart	25-7-98	17-4-99	7-02
FF 154 Parramatta	24-4-99	17-6-00	1-03
FF 155 Ballarat	4-8-00	2-3-01	5-04
FF 156 Toowoomba	8-4-02	8-03	5-05
FF 157 Perth	25-1-03	15-5-04	5-06

Anzac (FF 150) Vic Jeffery, 10-00

Arunta (FF 151) Brian Morrison, 5-00

Warramunga (FF 152) Brian Morrison, 4-01

D: 3,300 tons (3,600 fl) **S:** 27+ kts (20 on diesel)
Dim: 117.50 (109.50 pp) × 14.80 (13.80 wl) × 5.99 (4.37 hull)
A: 1 8-celled Mk 41 Mod. 5 VLS syst. (8 RIM-7P Sea Sparrow SAM); 1 127-mm 54-cal. United Defense Mk 45 Mod. 2 DP; provision for 1 20-mm Mk 15 Phalanx CIWS; 4 single 12.7-mm mg; 2 triple 324-mm Mk 32 ASW TT (Mk 46 Mod. 5 torpedoes); 1 SH-2G(A) Super SeaSprite helicopter
Electronics:
Radar: 1 STN Atlas Elektronik 9600-M ARPA nav.; 1 Ericsson 150HC Sea Giraffe target desig.; 1 Raytheon SPS-49(V)8 early warning; 1 CelsiusTech Ceros 200 f.c.
Sonar: Thales Spherion-B hull-mounted (7 kHz)
EW: Racal-Thorn Sceptre-A intercept (2–18 GHz); EADS PST 1720 comms intercept; Thales Telegon 10 Maigret HFD/F; Mk 36 Mod. 1 SRBOC decoy syst. (2 8-round Mk 137 RL with Sea Gnat Mk 214 and Nulka decoys); SLQ-25 Nixie towed torpedo decoy

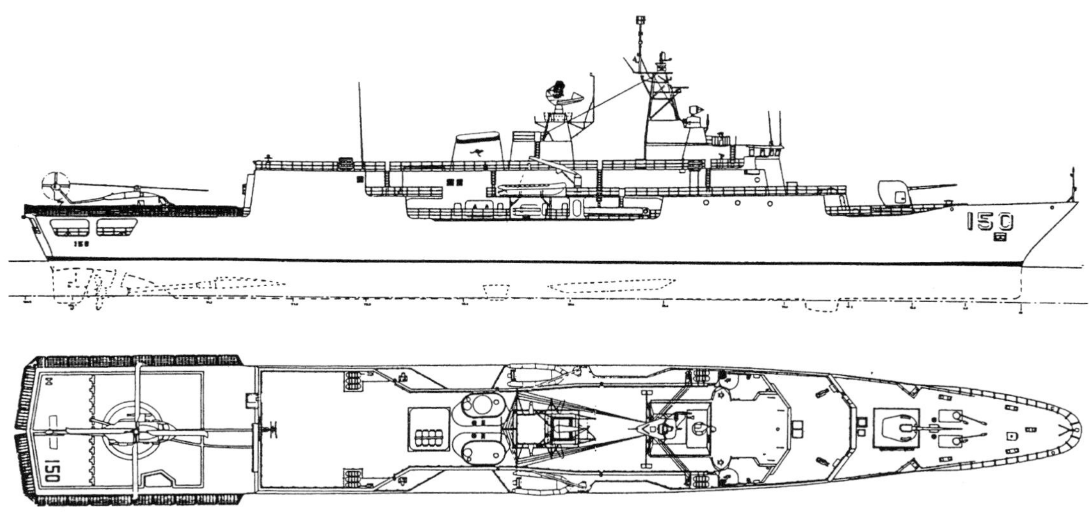

Anzac (FF 150) RAN

FRIGATES [FF] *(continued)*

Arunta (FF 151) Brian Morrison, 2-00

M: CODOG: 2 MTU 12V1163 TB83 diesels (4,420 bhp each), 1 G.E. LM-2500-30 gas turbine (30,172 shp); 2 CP props
Electric: 2,480 kw (4 × 620-kw MTU 8V396 TE54 diesel sets)
Range: 900/27; 6,000/18 (1 diesel); 7,000+/. . . **Fuel:** 423 tons
Crew: 22 officers, 41 petty officers, 100 other enlisted

Remarks: Contract awarded 14-8-89 to AMECON (Australian Marine Engineering Consolidated, Ltd.), with options for two or four more for New Zealand, which decided in 9-89 to order only two. AMECON was bought out in 1999 by the Transfield conglomerate, now known as Tenix. The design is based on the version of the MEKO 200 built in Germany for Portugal. The spelling for the name of the third unit was initially changed to *Warumungu* at the request of contemporary Aborigine tribal leaders but was restored in 1995 to commemorate earlier ships of the same name; an earlier decision to make a similar change for the second unit to *Arrerente* was rescinded 17-8-93. F 151 has been based at HMAS *Stirling,* Western Australia, since 10-3-00; the other two operate from Sydney.

Hull systems: Were originally to have had two G.E. LM-2500 gas turbines and a maximum speed of 31.75 kts; the starboard turbine was eliminated to save money. Either diesel can drive either or both shafts. Electrical current is at 400 V/60 Hz from the four Siemens generators; there are two switchboards. Fin stabilizers are fitted. Endurance is considerably greater than in other countries' units of this class, due to enhanced fuel supply. Carry 29 m^3 dry provisions, 26 m^3 refrigerated provisions, and 54 tons fresh water.

Combat systems: Have the CelsiusTech 9LV 453 Mk 3 combat data/fire-control system, with only one Ceros 200 director (although space for a second is present); the director has television and infrared tracking, as well as a J-band radar, a laser rangefinder, and t.v. and IR tracking. There are seven dual-screen Type IIA combat system displays, and the 9LV 453 system employs 55 Motorola 6820 and 68040 processors using Ada software. Also carried is an N-FOCSS command decision support system. The ships have NATO Link 11 data-sharing. The G-band Sea Giraffe radar employs a CelsiusTech 9GA XYZ antenna. The SPS-49(V)8 radar's antenna carries the antenna for the Cossor IFF interrogator.

The surface-to-air missiles are controlled by a Raytheon Mk 73 Mod. 1 system; FF 152 and later are equipped to employ the Evolved Sea Sparrow missile in "quad packs," which will quadruple the potential missile load. Weight and space for a Mk 15 Phalanx CIWS are retained.

The Spherion-B sonar has triple-rotation direct transmission to increase radiated sound level by 6 dB and incorporates a torpedo-warning feature. A lightweight version of the Indal RAST helicopter deck-handling system is incorporated. Have decoy rocket launchers, each with four tubes for Nulka decoys as well as six tubes for regular chaff rockets. Navigation equipment includes GPS receivers and two Sperry Mk 49 inertial navigational systems. Albatross (formerly ASSTASS—Australian Surface Ship Towed Array Surveillance System) is planned to be added post-2001.

FF 152 has the new faceted gunhouse for the 127-mm gun but retains the original 54-cal. barrel. The ship is equipped to launch the ESSM Sea Sparrow SAM, when available.

Modernization: A Warfighting Improvement Programme (WIP) that was to have updated the entire class was canceled late in 1999, although a number of lesser improvements are still likely to be carried out. United Defense Mk 25 Mod. 0 quad pack containers for the Mk 41 launchers are to be delivered between 8-02 and 8-03, although the ESSM Sea Sparrow missiles will probably not be available until after 2005 due to prolonged development delays in the U.S.A. FF 152 is to be the first ship in any navy to launch the new ESSM Sea Sparrow missile at sea. Two quadruple launch container groups for Harpoon missiles are planned to be added, and a towed sonar array is to be installed.

PATROL CRAFT [PC]

Note: A replacement program for the *Fremantle* class (Project SEA 1444) was instituted in 1998 after the collapse of hopes of building an Offshore Patrol Combatant based on the design prepared for Malaysia. The options range from craft of 50–60 m overall by 10 m beam and 3 m draft. The new design will have a remotely operated 30-mm gun system but no helicopter operations capability. The craft will be armed with a single 30-mm MSI-Defence Systems DS30B gun. A request for bids was issued during 9-01. The craft will be based at Darwin and Cairns, and the first is planned to enter service in 2004.

♦ 15 Fremantle class

Bldr: North Queensland Engineers & Agents, Cairns (P 203: Brooke Marine, Lowestoft, U.K.)

	L	In serv.	Based
FCPB 203 Fremantle	15-2-79	8-10-79	Cairns
FCPB 204 Warrnambool	25-10-80	14-3-81	Darwin
FCPB 205 Townsville	16-5-81	18-7-81	Cairns
FCPB 206 Wollongong	17-10-81	28-11-81	Darwin
FCPB 207 Launceston	23-1-82	1-3-82	Darwin
FCPB 208 Whyalla	22-5-82	3-7-82	Cairns
FCPB 209 Ipswich	25-9-82	13-11-82	Cairns
FCPB 210 Cessnock	15-1-83	5-3-83	Darwin
FCPB 211 Bendigo	9-4-83	28-5-83	Cairns
FCPB 212 Gawler	9-7-83	30-8-83	Darwin
FCPB 213 Geraldton	22-10-83	10-12-83	Darwin
FCPB 214 Dubbo	21-1-84	10-3-84	Darwin
FCPB 215 Geelong	14-4-84	2-6-84	Darwin
FCPB 216 Gladstone	28-7-84	8-9-84	Cairns
FCPB 217 Bunbury	3-11-84	15-12-84	Darwin

Dubbo (FCPB 214) John Mortimer, 8-97

D: 200 tons (230 fl) **S:** 30 kts **Dim:** 42.0 × 7.15 × 1.8
A: 1 40-mm 60-cal. Bofors AN-4 AA; 2 single 12.7-mm mg; 1 81-mm mortar
Electronics:
Radar: 1 Decca BridgeMaster-E ARPA surf. search
EW: AWA Type 133 PRISM intercept and D/F (2–18 GHz; not in FCPB 203, 204)
M: 2 MTU 16V538 TB91 diesels; 2 CP props; 7,200 bhp
Range: 1,450/28; 2,360/12; 4,800/8 **Crew:** 4 officers, 20 enlisted

Remarks: Ordered 9-77. Brooke Marine PCF-420 design. Five more (*Ballarat, Mildura, Armidale, Bundaberg,* and *Pirie*) were authorized in 1980 but canceled in 1982. Were to have been retired in 2000–03, but are now to be refurbished to delay start of retirements to 2008.

PATROL CRAFT [PC] *(continued)*

Fremantle (FCPB 203) Chris Sattler/H&L Van Ginderen, 1-98

Hull systems: FCPB 203 and 208 were given visual signature-reduction paint schemes in 1997, with the former in pale blue and the latter employing toned-down pennant numbers. The centerline Dorman 12JTM cruising diesel has now been removed from all.
Combat systems: The 40-mm guns were modernized during the late 1980s by the Government Ordnance Factory to improve firing rate and elevation and train speeds. Carry a 4.7-m Zodiac RIB for inspection missions. The surface-search radars can track 40 targets simultaneously.

PATROL BOATS [PB]

♦ 1 Southerly 65 class
Bldr: Geraldton Boat Bldrs, Geraldton, Western Australia (In serv. 21-5-96)

2003 Malu Baizam

Malu Baizam (2003) *The Navy,* 5-96

D: 85 tons (fl) **S:** 25 kts **Dim:** 19.95 (18.07 wl) × 5.64 × 1.46 (aft)
A: small arms **Electronics::** Radar: 1 JRC JMA-3610 nav.
M: 2 MTU 8V183 TE diesels; 2 props; 1,300 bhp **Electric:** 17 kw
Range: 650/21 **Fuel:** 5,000 liters **Crew:** 1 officer, 1 enlisted + 18 troops

Remarks: Assigned to Thursday Island at the Torres Strait sea border with Indonesia. Name means "Ocean Shark" in two local languages. Commanding officer is a lieutenant commander, with a senior enlisted assistant, and the craft can transport three 6-man 51st Far North Queensland Regiment Army patrols and three 4.2-m inflatable dinghies. Sister *Coral Snake* (AM 1353) is operated by the Australian Army, and near-sisters *Seal* (2001), *Shark* (2004), and *Dugong* are configured as diving tenders.
Hull systems: Equipped with Furuno FCV-581 echo sounder, GP-80 GPS receiver, and FAP-330 autopilot. Has sleeping accommodations for seven.

MINE COUNTERMEASURES SHIPS

♦ 4 (+ 2) Huon-class minehunters [MHC]
Bldr: Intermarine/Australian Defence Industries (ADI), Throsby Basin, Newcastle, New South Wales

	Laid down	L	In serv.
M 82 Huon	9-94	25-7-97	15-5-99
M 83 Hawkesbury	12-9-95	24-4-98	12-2-00
M 84 Norman	16-9-96	3-5-99	26-8-00
M 85 Gascoyne	13-9-97	11-3-00	2-6-01
M 86 Diamantina	4-8-98	2-12-00	(del.) 12-01
M 87 Yarra	5-99	19-01-02	(del.) 10-02

Gascoyne (M 85) John Mortimer, 11-00

Norman (M 84) Brian Morrison, 2-00

Hawkesbury (M 83) Chris Sattler/H&L Van Ginderen, 8-99

D: 720 tons (fl) **S:** 14+ kts (sust.; 6 on thrusters) **Dim:** 52.50 × 9.90 × 3.00
A: 1 30-mm 75-cal. MSI DS30B AA
Electronics:
Radar: 1 Kelvin-Hughes Type 1007 nav.
Sonar: Thomson-Marconi Type 2093M variable-depth minehunting
EW: AWA Type 133 PRISM radar warning; 2 12-round Wallop Super Barricade decoy RL
E/O: Radamec 1500 surveillance
M: 1 GMT BL230-BN diesel; 1 CP prop; 1,985 bhp—3 retractable 120-hp Riva Calzoni azimuthal thrusters
Electric: 1,200 kw tot. (3 × 350-kw Isotta-Fraschini ID 36SS diesel sets, 1 × 150-kw ID 36N emergency diesel set)
Range: 1,500/12 (with 30% fuel reserve) **Fuel:** 50+ tons
Endurance: 19 days **Crew:** 6 officers, 32 enlisted + up to 13 trainees

Remarks: Ordered 12-8-94. Design based on Italian Intermarine *Gaeta* class. All named for former RAN ships bearing the names of Australian rivers. The bare hull (with superstructure shell and masting) of M 82 was handed over in Italy on 16-7-95 and shipped via heavy-lift vessel, arriving in Australia 1-9-95 for fitting out; hulls of the second and later laid up in Australia.
Hull systems: Single-skin, monocoque foam-core GRP hull without ribs, frames, or stiffeners. Machinery on cradles suspended from bulkheads and overheads and non-integral fuel tanks to reduce acoustic transmissions. Two rudders are fitted. The shrouded azimuthal thrusters are mounted two aft and one centerline forward just abaft the variable-depth sonar housing. All but one main engine for the ships will be erected at ADI's Bendigo factory, while the generator sets are built in Italy.
Combat systems: Have the Thomson-Marconi Mullauna (modified Nautis-II M) combat data system with NATO Link 11 display capability; there are five display consoles. Carry two Bofors Underwater Systems Sutec Double Eagle remote-controlled minehunting submersibles, each with a searchlight, low-light television, and high-frequency sonar. Lightweight double Oropesa wire sweep gear is also carried, as is the Australian-developed Mini-Dyad reconfigurable permanent magnet influence sweep array. Have portable decompression chamber for divers. A Kelvin-Hughes GPS set is fitted. The 30-mm gun can fire at up to 600 rds/min.

MINE COUNTERMEASURES SHIPS *(continued)*

♦ **2 Bay-class catamaran inshore minehunters [MHI]** (stricken)
Bldr: Carrington Slipways, Tomago

	Laid down	L	In serv.
M 80 *Rushcutter*	31-5-84	8-5-86	1-11-86
M 81 *Shoalwater*	17-9-85	26-6-87	10-10-87

Rushcutter (M 80) Brian Morrison/H&L Van Ginderen, 7-99

D: 100 tons (170 fl) **S:** 10 kts **Dim:** 31.00 (28.00 wl) × 9.0 × 1.90
A: 2 single 12.7-mm mg
Electronics:
Radar: 1 Kelvin-Hughes Type 1006(4) nav.
Sonar: STN Atlas Elektronik MWS-80-5 syst. (DSQS-11M sonar)
M: 2 SACM-Poyaud 520-V8-S2 325-hp diesels, hydraulic drive; 2 Schottel azimuthal props; 340 shp
Range: 1,200/10 **Crew:** 2 officers, 11 enlisted

Remarks: Ordered late 1981; plans for six more were canceled. Due to difficulties with the original sonar system, the craft did not enter fully operational service until 1993; they were used for training and mine countermeasures duties in confined waters. Both based at HMAS *Waterhen,* Sydney. Placed in 60-day recall reserve on 28-7-00 and 11-8-00, respectively, and both retired on 14-8-01.
Hull systems: Glass-reinforced plastic construction; each of the two hulls is of 3.00-m beam. Main engines drive propulsion generators and ship's service generators. Reconfigured with two side-by-side exhaust funnels in 1992–93 to reduce noise. They pitch excessively in open waters.
Combat systems: The sonar transducer is mounted beneath the port hull. The sonar/mine-countermeasures control room is fitted in a dismountable deckhouse. Carry two PAP-104 remote-controlled, tethered minehunting submersibles. Can tow the Mini-Dyad reconfigurable permanent magnet influence sweep array.

Note: In addition to the Bay class, the RAN has a COOP (Craft-of-Opportunity) program for employing fishing craft as auxiliary mine-countermeasures craft. To equip the craft, a number of 100–500 kHz U.S. Klein Type 590 side-scan sonars have been purchased, each equipped with a Klein 595 transceiver/graphic recorder. Four Meridian Ocean Systems QUILS-II (Q-route Underwater Identification and Location System) were ordered during 1990 for use on COOP vessels. Also employed are the Mini-Dyad, a 6.4 × 0.53-m, hollow, two-section mild steel pipe with two strontium-ferrite inserts for countering magnetic mines. The HMAS *Creswell* navigational training ship *Seahorse Horizon,* operated by Defence Maritime Services, can also be used as an auxiliary minesweeper.

♦ **2 Large Auxiliary Minesweepers, MS(L) [MSA]**
Bldr: . . . , Singapore (In serv. 1982)

Y 298 Bandicoot (ex-*Greenville VII*)
Y 299 Wallaroo (ex-*Greenville V*)

Bandicoot (Y 298) H&L Van Ginderen, 2-99

D: 520 tons (fl) **S:** 11 kts **Dim:** 29.34 (26.83 pp) × 8.54 × 3.43
Electronics: Radar: 1 Furuno 7040D nav.
M: 2 Stork-Werkspoor diesels; 2 Kort-nozzle props; 2,160 bhp
Electric: 150 kw (2 × 75 kw; 2 G.M. 4-71 diesels)
Range: 6,300/11 **Endurance:** 24 days **Crew:** 12 tot.

Remarks: 242.37 grt. Acquired 3-8-90 and 8-8-90, respectively, from Maritime Pvt., Singapore, for use as COOP minehunters and as tugs to handle visiting foreign warships at Sydney. Arrived in Australia in 9-90 and completed conversion mid-1991. Originally had 30-ton bollard pull, but the towing capability was removed as part of the COOP conversion. Can tow the Mini-Dyad reconfigurable permanent magnet influence sweep array.

♦ **1 Small Auxiliary Minesweeper, MS(S) [MSA]**
1121 Bermagui (ex-*Nadgee 2*)

Bermagui (1121) John Mortimer, 12-97

D: 110 tons **S:** 10.5 kts **Dim:** 19.9 × . . . × . . .
Electronics:
Radar: 1 Furuno 7040D nav.
Sonar: Klein 590 towed side-scan HF
M: G.M. Detroit Diesel 12V71 diesel; 1 prop; 359 bhp **Crew:** 8 tot.

Remarks: Former tuna fishing boat purchased 1994 to replace the leased *Carol S.* Can tow the Mini-Dyad reconfigurable permanent magnet influence sweep array.

♦ **1 Small Auxiliary Minesweeper, MS(S) [MSA]**
Bldr: Kall Boatyard, . . . , Australia (In serv. 1974)

1185 Koraaga (ex-*Grozdana A.*)

Koraaga (1185) H&L Van Ginderen, 1-00

D: 119 tons (fl) **S:** 10.5 kts **Dim:** 21.9 × 6.4 × 3.0
Electronics:
Radar: 1 Furuno 7040D nav.
Sonar: Klein 590 towed side-scan HF
M: 1 Caterpillar D346 diesel; 1 prop; 470 bhp **Crew:** 9 tot.

Remarks: A former tuna boat purchased from Australian Fishing Enterprises and delivered to RAN 16-2-89. 119–120-grt wooden-hulled craft operated from HMAS *Waterhen,* Sydney, to develop tactics and doctrine for mine countermeasures equipment. Equipped with GPS receiver and HFD/F. Can tow the Mini-Dyad reconfigurable permanent magnet influence sweep array.

♦ **1 Small Auxiliary Minesweeper, MS(S) [MSA]**
Bldr: Australian SB Industries, Fremantle (In serv. 12-78)

1102 Brolga (ex-*Lumen*)

MINE COUNTERMEASURES SHIPS *(continued)*

Brolga (1102) H&L Van Ginderen, 1-97

D: 268 tons (fl) **S:** 11 kts **Dim:** 28.35 (26.37 pp) × 8.62 × 3.10
Electronics:
Radar: 2 . . . nav.
Sonar: Klein 590 towed side-scan HF
M: 2 Mirrlees-Blackstone ESL 8 Mk.2 diesels; 2 props; 1,080 bhp
Crew: 1 officer, 7 enlisted

Remarks: 264 grt. Former steel-hulled government lighthouse maintenance vessel at Brisbane, laid up 4-87 and transferred to RAN 2-2-88 for use in mine countermeasures trials. As of 1992, was considered to be a mine countermeasures asset and is to be retained until the new seagoing minehunters are available. Carries a Klein side-looking mapping sonar for route survey work. Can tow the Mini-Dyad reconfigurable permanent magnet influence sweep array.

♦ 3 mine countermeasures drones [MSD]
Bldr: Hamil Haven Yacht (In serv. 1991–92)

MSD 02 MSD 03 MSD 04

Minesweeping drone MSD 04 RAN, 1992

D: . . . tons **S:** 45 kts (8 sweeping) **Dim:** 7.3 × 2.8 × 0.6
M: 2 Yamaha gasoline outboards; 300 bhp

Remarks: For use with COOP craft. Can each tow a Mini-Dyad magnetized pipe at 8 kts for magnetic mine clearance. Are fitted with differential GPS receivers and the Sydelis Vega automated navigation system.

AMPHIBIOUS WARFARE SHIPS

♦ 0 (+ 3) "Multi-Role Auxiliaries" [LPH]
Bldr: . . .

"Multi-Role Auxiliary"—computer rendering RAN, 6-00

D: 13,594 tons light (22,095 fl) **S:** 22+ kts (18 on one engine)
Dim: 224.00 (200.8 pp/wl) × 40.00 (flight deck; 27.60 wl) × 7.2 (max.; 6.0 light)
A: none
Electronics:
Radar: 2 . . . nav., 1 . . . early warning, 1 3-D air search
EW: . . .
M: 2 low-speed diesels; 2 props; . . . bhp
Electric: 4,500 kw (6 × 750-kw diesel sets)
Range: 3,885/7.3; 6,460/18 (5,290/18 with troops aboard)
Fuel: 1,147 tons **Endurance:** 14 days
Crew: 25 officers, 150 enlisted + air group: 15 officers, 35 enlisted + troops: 300 in cabins, 800 additional in cabin modules + 76 staff

Remarks: An unofficial proposal was released in 6-00 for replacements for the two *Newport*-class transports, the *Tobruk* LST, and the oilers *Success* and *Westralia.* Each would carry six troop helicopters and an Army battalion, and they would also be able to conduct underway replenishment. An alternative would be a 29,000-ton, 247-m, gas turbine–powered "Littoral Support Ship" that could operate RAAF F/A-18 Hornet fighters. Part of either program would be construction of four 2,100-ton high-speed landing craft. Under present fiscal constraints, the program is unlikely to proceed as proposed.
Hull systems: Payload of 8,501 tons. Normal accommodations for 232 crew and 400 troops/passengers would include 158 3 × 3-m cabins immediately below the flight deck, each capable of berthing up to four personnel, plus three flag cabins in the bridge area; some 800 additional troops could be carried in portable berthing modules placed in the forward hangar. A 300-m^2 hospital would be fitted. Cargo in replenishment mode would be 5,353 tons diesel fuel, 871 tons aviation fuel, 250 tons ammunition, 400 tons fresh water, and 60 tons troop provisions. In amphibious lift mode, they would each carry 5,000 tons amphibious stores and vehicles, 250 tons ammunition, 400 tons fresh water, 100 tons troop provisions, and 800 tons of troop accommodations containers. As aircraft platforms, would carry 3,818 tons diesel fuel, 871 tons aviation fuel, 250 tons provisions, 400 tons fresh water, a 20-ton helicopter workshop module, 800 tons of troop containers, and 60 tons of troop provisions.
Two primary replenishment stations would be fitted to starboard, each with a 70-ton crane to support hoses; two secondary replenishment stations to port would use posts. Four 680-m^3/hr diesel cargo fuel pumps would be fitted; each of the four aviation fuel pumps would be able to handle 180 m^3/hr.
Aviation systems: Would have a flight deck 224 m long by 40 m wide, with two elevators and six UH-60 or four CH-47D landing spots and an area of 6,100 m^2; hangar deck area would be 2,050 m^2. With the flight deck used for vehicle stowage, 2,100 lane-meters would be available, plus the hangar deck's 841 lane-meters. The elevators would be large enough to accommodate MV-22 Osprey tilt-rotor transports.
Combat systems: No armament has been proposed as yet.

♦ 2 U.S. Newport-class Auxiliary Transports [LPA]
Bldr: National Steel SB, San Diego, Calif.

	Laid down	L	In serv.
L 51 Kanimbla (ex-*Saginaw,* LST 1188)	24-12-69	7-2-70	23-1-71
L 52 Manoora (ex-*Fairfax County,* LST 1193)	28-3-70	19-12-70	16-10-71

D: 4,975 tons light (8,450 fl) **S:** 22 kts (20 sust.)
Dim: 159.20 × 21.18 × 5.3 (aft; 1.80 fwd)
A: 6 single 12.7-mm mg; 4 UH-60 Blackhawk helicopters
Electronics: Radar: 1 Kelvin-Hughes Type 1007 nav.
M: 6 Alco 16-251 diesels; 2 CP props; 16,500 bhp—bow-thruster
Range: 14,250/14 **Fuel:** 1,750 tons + 250 tons aviation fuel
Crew: 12 officers, 168 enlisted + troops: 25 officers, 425 enlisted

Remarks: Decision to purchase made 15-12-93. Original official type designation was to have been THSS (Training and Helicopter Support Vessel), then LPH (Amphibious Warfare Helicopter Carrier), and finally as above in mid-1998. *Kanimbla* was to have been transferred on decommissioning 28-6-94, but transfer was held up until 24-8-94 by U.S. Senate; the ship was recommissioned on 29-8-94 and arrived in Sydney on 18-11-94. *Manoora* sailed to Sydney 15-8-94, arriving 19-9-94 with a mixed RAN and USN crew for decommissioning and transfer 27-9-94; formally commissioned 25-11-94. Two of a total class of 20 built for the U.S. Navy. Conversion contract for both let to Forgacs Dockyard, Newcastle, New South Wales, in 12-95; work commenced on L 52 on 23-5-96 for completion in 9-97 and on L 51 on 28-6-96 for completion in 8-98, but various problems delayed completion until mid-2000 for L 52 and 2-01 for L 51.

AMPHIBIOUS WARFARE SHIPS *(continued)*

Kanimbla (L 51)

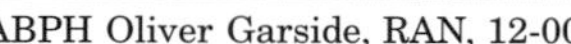

ABPH Oliver Garside, RAN, 12-00

Manoora (L52) RAN, 1-00

Manoora (L 52) Brian Morrison, 2-00

Hull systems: Can transport 2,000 tons of cargo on 1,765 m^2 of deck space. Aft is a stern door for loading and unloading vehicles. The tank deck has a 75-ton-capacity turntable at both ends. Modifications include deletion of the bow ramp and beaching capability; installation of bilge keels; erection of a hangar capable of accommodating four Australian Army S-70 Blackhawk or three RAN Sea King helicopters between the funnels (which required deleting the starboard landing craft davit); installation of a 70-ton crane forward to handle two LCM(8) landing craft and two Army LARC-5 wheeled amphibious vehicles; and reconverting two (of three originally installed) vehicle fuel tanks to provide tankage for 250 tons of aviation fuel for the helicopters, for which there are three landing spots (one forward, for use after the landing craft have been offloaded). Provision to carry four pontoon causeway sections was deleted. In L 51 only, medical facilities were enlarged to accommodate 90 patients. A classroom/briefing room was added to both, and accommodations for troops were improved. Evaporator capacity was increased to 300,000 liters/day. Future plans call for further conversion with command facilities, an elevator to permit stowing helicopters on the vehicle deck, and side vehicle-loading doors. Twelve Australian Army LARC-V amphibious resupply vehicles were being refurbished for use with these ships during 1998–99.
Combat systems: The single U.S. Mk 15 CIWS systems aboard each ship were removed in Australia and added to the RAN's pool of the weapons, but provision remains for their reinstallation. Installation of a Joint Task Force Headquarters (JTFHQ) on L 52 and L 51 was completed during 5-01 and later in 2001, respectively; occupying four compartments, the system provides the navy's most comprehensive afloat command, control, and communications facilities.

♦ 1 modified British Sir Bedivere–class Landing Ship Heavy (LSH) [LST]

	Bldr	Laid down	L	In serv.
L 50 Tobruk	Carrington Slipways, Tomago	7-2-79	1-3-80	23-4-81

Tobruk (L 50) A. A. de Kruijf, 11-00

D: 3,600 tons (6,000 fl) **S:** 17 kts **Dim:** 129.50 × 19.60 × 4.30
A: 4 single 12.7-mm mg
Electronics:
Radar: 1 Decca RM 916 nav.; 1 Kelvin-Hughes Type 1006 nav.
EW: Racal Matilda radar intercept, Mk 36 SRBOC decoy syst. (2 6-round Mk 137 RL)
M: 2 Mirrlees-Blackstone KDMR8 diesels; 2 props; 9,600 bhp
Electric: 1,990 kw tot. (4 × 460-kw diesel alternator sets, 1 × 150-kw diesel emergency set; 450-V, 60-Hz, 3-phase a.c.)
Range: 8,000/15 **Crew:** 13 officers, 131 enlisted

Remarks: A former light carrier used as a troopship, announced as a replacement for the *Sydney* 8-76. Homeported at Fleet Base East, Sydney. She is now expected to serve the RAN until 2010 and was refitted beginning early in 2000.
Hull systems: Can carry up to two Sea King troop helicopters operating from platform amidships and aft, and can carry up to 520 troops, 11 Leopard tanks, and other military vehicles, to a total of 1,300 tons cargo. Two LCVPs are carried in davits aft. Can carry two LCM(8) landing craft on deck. Two 4.5-ton cranes are mounted forward, and a 60-ton heavy-lift derrick is fitted before the bridge. The bow ramp is 14.6 m long and 3.93 m wide, while the stern ramp is 14.2 m long by 4.73 m wide. Can accommodate Australian Army NLE pontoon lighters *Caspor* (201) and *Pollux* (202) on the hull sides.
Combat systems: Two locally controlled single 40-mm 60-cal. AA guns were removed during 2000, but their platforms on the forecastle remain in place.

♦ 0 (+ 6) Landing Craft Heavy (LCH) replacement program [LCU]

Remarks: Under the Joint Project 2048 Amphibious Watercraft program, several designs are being studied as a replacement class for the *Balikpapan* class. A monohull design of some 1,291 tons (full load) and 70 m in length would be powered by a single 4,000-bhp diesel engine and would carry a cargo of over 200 tons at a speed of over 17 kts. An alternative catamaran design would displace 1,241 tons full load, be 61.5 m long, and be powered by two 4,000-bhp diesels driving waterjets. Both versions would accommodate 200 or more troops in modular 12-berth containers on the vehicle deck, would be beachable on a 1:50 slope, and would have a covered, drive-through vehicle cargo deck with bow and stern ramps and side access doors. A helicopter deck would be incorporated, and one 30-mm gun would be fitted.

♦ 6 Balikpapan-class Landing Craft Heavy (LCH) [LCU]

Bldr: Walkers Ltd., Maryborough, Queensland

	Laid down	L	In serv.
L 126 Balikpapan	5-71	15-8-71	1971
L 127 Brunei	7-71	15-10-71	5-1-73
L 128 Labuan	10-71	29-12-71	9-3-73
L 129 Tarakan	12-71	16-3-71	15-6-73
L 130 Wewak	3-72	18-5-72	10-8-74
L 133 Betano	9-72	5-12-72	8-2-74

D: 316 tons (503 fl) **S:** 10 kts (9 sust.) **Dim:** 44.5 × 10.1 × 1.9
A: 2 single 7.62-mm mg **Electronics:** Radar: 1 Decca RM 916 nav.
M: 2 G.M. Detroit Diesel 6-71 diesels; 2 props; 675 bhp

AMPHIBIOUS WARFARE SHIPS *(continued)*

Tarakan (L 129)—off East Timor ABPH Damian Pawlenko, 2000

Range: 3,000/10 (light); 1,300/9 (with 175 tons cargo); 2,280/9 (with 150 tons)
Crew: 2 officers, 12 enlisted

Remarks: Originally were to be army-subordinated, and L 126 did serve in the Australian Army until transferred to the RAN on 27-9-74. L 127 and L 133, used for many years as inshore survey craft, became diving training vessels at the Mine Warfare and Patrol Boat Base, HMAS *Waterhen,* Sydney, on 27-10-88 and 16-12-88, respectively. L 126 and L 129 were placed in storage ashore at Cairns in 1985; L 129 was reactivated 1988 as naval reserve research and training vessel at Cairns, and L 126 was reactivated for same purpose at Darwin in 2-90. L 130, placed in land storage in 1985, began reactivation in 6-99 for service at Darwin and recommissioned on 2-4-00. L 128 transferred to Cairns on 10-9-93. A Life-of-Type Extension (LOTE) overhaul for five of the class was begun in 2000 at Tropical Reef SY, Queensland, with work on the sixth to be contracted later for completion by late 2002; all are now to operate through 2008.
Disposals: *Salamaua* (L 131) and *Buna* (L 132) were transferred to Papua New Guinea in 1974.
Hull systems: Can carry three Leopard tanks; maximum cargo capacity is 180 tons. More-powerful diesel alternator sets were substituted during the LOTE refits, and a reverse-osmosis desalinization plant was added, along with new air-conditioning and sewage treatment equipment.

♦ 4 Landing Craft Vehicle and Personnel (LCVP) [LCVP]
Bldr: Geraldton Boat Builders, Geraldton, Western Australia (In serv. 1993)

(160) T 4 (1099) T 5 (1102) T 6 (1015) T 7

T 5 (1099)—being lowered from davits aboard *Tobruk* (L 50) RAN, 8-99

D: 5.5 tons light (11 fl) **S:** 21 kts (11 loaded)
Dim: 13.20 (11.37 wl) × 3.36 (3.20 wl) × 0.50 (loaded)
M: 2 Volvo Penta 42B Sterndrive diesels; 335 bhp
Range: 110/11 (loaded) **Fuel:** 0.75 tons **Crew:** 3 tot. + 36 troops

Remarks: T 5 and T 6 are carried by *Tobruk* and T 7 by *Success,* while T4 is kept as an operational spare at HMAS *Cairns.* Aluminum construction. Capable of transporting 36 fully armed troops or one Land Rover with half-ton trailer or 4.5 tons cargo in the 8-m-long cargo hold. Are maintained by Defence Maritime Services (DMS).

AUXILIARIES

Note: Since 12-97, port service auxiliaries and all service craft have been operated under contract to Defence Maritime Services Pty, Ltd. (see separate Defence Maritime Services section).

♦ 2 Pacific-class hydrographic survey ships [AGS]
Bldr: North Queensland Engineers & Agents (NQEA), Cairns

	Laid down	L	In serv.
HS 01 Leeuwin	30-8-96	19-7-97	27-5-00 (del. 4-12-99)
HS 02 Melville	9-5-97	6-98	27-5-00

Leeuwin (HS 01) Brian Morrison, 11-00

Leeuwin (HS 01)—note that the helicopter hangar is offset to port and the stack to starboard Brian Morrison, 11-00

D: 2,550 tons (fl) **S:** 14 kts **Dim:** 71.20 (63.60 pp) × 15.20 × 4.37
Electronics:
Radar: 1 . . . ARPA nav.
Sonar: C-Tech CMAS 36/39 hull-mounted HF mapping, STN Atlas Elektronik . . . mapping, Simrad . . . precision echo sounder
M: diesel-electric drive: 4 GEC-Ruston 6RK215 diesels, 4 GEC-Alsthom generator sets (800 kw each), 2 electric motors (1,000 kw each); 2 5-bladed props; 2,700 shp—azimuthal waterjet thruster (6 kts)
Range: 8,000/12 **Crew:** 10 officers, 36 enlisted

Remarks: Ordered 12-95. Based at Cairns, with three crews to rotate in operating each of the units some 300 days per year. Both were painted gray late in 2001.
Hull systems: Can each carry three *Fantôme*-class survey launches (see data under [YGS]) and accommodate a Bell 206 or AS.350B Écureuil helicopter (no hangar). Capable of surveying in waters 0 to 6,000 m deep and also able to perform oceanographic research. Ships' service power comes from 660-V transformers delivering power at 415 V/50 Hz. Have a dual-tank passive stabilization system. Navigational suite includes a GPS receiver, collision-avoidance sonar, electromagnetic and doppler logs, two gyrocompasses, and an autopilot.

Note: The above ships and the smaller *Paluma* class operate in support of the Australian Hydrographic Office, Wollongong, New South Wales. The agency operates a Fokker F-27 turboprop aircraft to support the Laser Airborne Depth Sounder; the system can measure depths to 50 m while the aircraft is flying at 500 m altitude and 145 kts and can survey about 50 km^2/hr. For the *Paluma*-class inshore survey craft, see under [YGS].

♦ 1 British Appleleaf-class underway replenishment oiler [AO]
Bldr: Cammell Laird, Birkenhead, Scotland

	L	In serv.
AO 195 Westralia (ex-*Appleleaf,* ex-*Hudson Cavalier*)	24-7-75	11-79

Westralia (AO 195) Brian Morrison, 12-00

D: 40,870 tons (fl) **S:** 16.4 kts **Dim:** 170.69 (163.51 pp) × 25.94 × 11.56
A: 4 single 12.7-mm mg; provision for 2 20-mm Mk 15 Phalanx CIWS
Electronics:
Radar: 2 Kelvin-Hughes Type 1007 nav.
EW: Racal Matilda radar warning
M: 2 Crossley-Pielstick 14 PC2V-400 diesels; 1 CP prop; 14,000 hp
Range: 7,260/15 **Fuel:** 2,498 tons **Crew:** 8 officers, 53 enlisted

Remarks: 20,440 grt/33,750 dwt. Leased 9-10-89 for five years, then purchased during 1994. Based at Fremantle. Refitted 12-78 to 11-79 for British Royal Fleet Auxiliary service: stack raised 3.5 m, dry cargo hold added forward, replenishment-at-sea working deck added amidships, and superstructure enlarged aft. Refitted 18-1-93 to 4-93 at Forgacs Engineering, Newcastle, and again in 1-96 to 3-96, when she was equipped to carry two Mk 15 Phalanx CIWS. Suffered an engine room fire and explosion 5-5-98; 4 killed, 5 injured. Repaired 4-99 to 11-99 by ADI Marine.
Hull systems: Cargo: 22,000 tons diesel fuel, 3,800 tons JP-5. Has one fueling station per side, plus an astern refueling position. Helicopter vertical replenishment (but not landing) platform and superstructure mounting for refrigerated provisions containers were added in 1991. During 1996 refit, another replenishment-at-sea winch was added and internal cargo piping system was revised.

♦ 0 (+ 2) replacement underway replenishment ships [AOR]
Bldr: . . .

D: 18,000–20,000 tons (fl) **S:** 20 kts **Dim:** . . .
M: . . .

Remarks: A decision is expected to be reached in 2002 on whether to build direct replacements for the *Success* (AOR 304) and *Westralia* (AO 195), with the first ship to replace the *Westralia* around 2007. The ships are to be able to carry 10,000 tons of

AUXILIARIES *(continued)*

ship fuel and 1,300 to 1,500 tons of aviation fuel, in addition to ammunition and provisions; they would have hangar and flight deck facilities for two helicopters. A low-noise propulsion system is sought. Designs being examined are the Spanish/Dutch *Amsterdam* class and the German Type 702 *(Berlin)* class.

♦ 1 modified French Durance-class underway replenishment ship [AOR]

	Bldr	Laid down	L	In serv.
AOR 304 SUCCESS	Vickers, Cockatoo DY	9-8-80	3-3-84	23-4-86

Success (AOR 304) Mitsuhiro Kadota, 10-00

D: 17,933 tons (fl) **S:** 18 kts **Dim:** 157.3 (149.0 pp) × 21.2 × 10.8
A: 2 single 40-mm 60-cal. Bofors AA; 2 20-mm Mk 15 Phalanx CIWS; 4 single 12.7-mm mg
Electronics:
Radar: 2 Kelvin-Hughes Type 1006 nav.; 1 Decca . . . nav.
EW: Racal Matilda radar intercept; Mk 36 SRBOC decoy syst. (2 6-round Mk 137 RL)
M: 2 SEMT-Pielstick 16 PC 2.5 diesels; 1 CP prop; 20,000 bhp
Electric: 5,440 kw tot. **Range:** 9,000/15 **Fuel:** 750 tons
Crew: 25 officers, 187 enlisted

Remarks: Ordered 9-79 from a design prepared by DCN, France. A proposed second ship was not built. Homeported at Fleet Base East, Sydney.
Hull systems: Carries 8,220 tons distillate fuel, 1,131 tons aviation fuel, 170 tons munitions, 183 tons provisions, 259 tons water, and 45 tons spare parts. Carries two stores-handling landing craft in davits. Able to refuel three ships simultaneously.
Combat systems: Fitted with two Mk 15 Phalanx CIWS atop the hangar in 1997, at the expense of one 40-mm AA. Hangar modified in 1991–92 to accept the Sea King helicopter, but normally carries an Écureuil. Fitted summer 1996 with prototype Pilgrim C-band Asynchronous Transfer Mode satellite communications system under Project Takari; also has a smaller commercial SATCOM system.

Disposal note: Catamaran-hulled personnel transport *Jervis Bay* (AKR 45) was returned to her owner on 11-5-01 at the expiration of her two-year charter.

SERVICE CRAFT

Note: Most service craft are now operated by contractor Defence Maritime Services Pty, Ltd.; see separate Defence Maritime Services section. In addition to the RAN-operated craft below, floating dry dock FD 1002 remains in service at Garden Island.

Floating dry dock FD 1002 Brian Morrison/H&L Van Ginderen, 3-99

♦ 4 Paluma-class Survey Motor Launches (SML) [YGS]

Bldr: EGLO Eng., Port Adelaide, South Australia

	Laid down	L	In serv.
AGSC 01 PALUMA	21-3-88	6-2-89	27-2-89
AGSC 02 MERMAID	19-7-88	24-11-89	4-12-89
AGSC 03 SHEPPARTON	21-9-88	5-12-89	24-1-90
AGSC 04 BENALLA	25-11-88	6-3-90	20-3-90

D: 320 tons (fl) **S:** 12 kts (10 sust.) **Dim:** 36.7 (33.0 pp) × 13.7 × 1.90
Electronics:
Radar: 1 JRC JMA-3710-6 nav.
Sonar: ELAC LAZ 72 side-scan mapping HF, Skipper S113 hull-mounted scanning HF

Benalla (AGSC 04) Navpic/James W. Goss, 11-92

M: 2 G.M. Detroit Diesel 12V92A TA diesels; 2 props; 1,290 bhp
Range: 1,800/10 **Fuel:** 41,000 liters **Endurance:** 14 days
Crew: 2 officers, 10 enlisted (accomm. for 18 tot.)

Remarks: Catamaran hulls. Based at HMAS *Cairns* on northeast Queensland coast to conduct Great Barrier Reef surveys. Work in pairs. Have Racal HYDLAPS (Hydrographic Data Logging and Processing System). AGSC 02 was used for trials with the Thomson-Marconi Sonar Pty Petrel 5424 obstacle/mine-avoidance sonar system.

♦ 8 Fantôme-class Survey Motor Boats [YGS]

Bldr: Pro Marine, Seaford, Victoria (In serv. 10-92 to 7-93)

(624) SMB 1005 FANTÔME
(1112) SMB 1006 MEDA
(1113) SMB 1007 INVESTIGATOR
(1499) SMB 1008 DUYFKEN
(320) SMB 1009 TOM THUMB
(321) SMB 1010 JOHN GOWLAND
(1114) SMB 1011 . . . . . .
(1115) SMB 1012 . . . . . .

Fantôme (SMB 1005/DMS 624)—in starboard davits aboard *Leeuwin* (HS 01); note the bow sonar dome for the mapping echo sounder Brian Morrison, 11-00

D: 7.48 tons (fl) **S:** 28 kts **Dim:** 10.70 (10.20 wl) × 2.90 × 0.60
Electronics: Radar: 1 JRC JMA-2141 nav.
M: 2 Volvo Penta AQAD 41D/SP290 diesels; 2 outdrives; 400 bhp
Range: 720/20 **Fuel:** 1,320 l **Endurance:** 36 hrs at 20 kts
Crew: 1 officer, 3 enlisted

Remarks: Naval operated, except for SMB 1009 and SMB 1010, which are stationed at the Hydrographic School, HMAS *Penguin,* and are managed and operated by Defence Maritime Services, which maintains all of them. The others are carried aboard the *Leeuwin* (HS 01) and *Melville* (HS 02).
Hull systems: Aluminum construction. Painted white, with orange top to pilothouse. Carry STN Atlas Elektronik Deso 22 echo sounder, Sercel NR 103 differential GPS, and magnetic compass and are equipped to carry portable side-scan mapping sonars.

♦ 1 Antarctic survey launch [YGS]

Bldr: Pro Marine, Seaford, Victoria (In serv. 1993)

(329) ASV 01 WYATT EARP

Wyatt Earp (ASV 01/DMS 329)—with overall red paint scheme Brian Morrison, 12-00

SERVICE CRAFT *(continued)*

D: 5.77 tons (fl) **S:** 22.5 kts **Dim:** 9.20 (8.15 wl) × . . . × 0.525
Electronics: Radar: 1 JRC JMA-2141 nav.
M: 2 Volvo Penta AQAD 41D/SP290 diesels; 2 outdrives; 400 bhp
Range: 306/18 **Fuel:** 880 liters **Crew:** 4 tot.

Remarks: Similar to the *Fantôme* class but configured especially for Antarctic service. Based at Port Kembla, Tasmania. Aluminum construction. Has STN Atlas Elektronik Deso 22 echo sounder and differential GPS receiver.

♦ 1 Sail Training Ship [YTS]
Bldr: Brooke Marine, Lowestoft, U.K. (In serv. 3-8-87)

Young Endeavour

Young Endeavour—at Sydney Brian Morrison/H&L Van Ginderen, 1-98

D: 200 tons (239 fl) **S:** 14 kts (sail)/10 kts (diesel)
Dim: 44.00 (31.00 hull, 28.30 wl) × 7.80 × 4.00
Electronics: Radar: 1 . . . nav.
M: 2 Perkins diesels; 1 prop; 334 bhp—845.6 m^2 sail area
Range: 1,500/7 (under power) **Crew:** 9 RAN officers, 24 trainees

Remarks: Gift of the U.K. government on Australia's 200th anniversary. Left U.K. 3-8-87 and arrived Sydney 25-1-88. RAN supplies officer/instructors for youth trainees. Based at Fleet Base East, Sydney.

♦ 1 Reserve Training Craft [YXT]
Bldr: Stebercraft, Taree, New South Wales (In serv. 1984)

P 225 Argus

D: 8.8 tons **S:** 25 kts **Dim:** 10.4 × 3.4 × 1.0
A: none **Electronics::** Radar: 1 FCR 1411 nav.
M: 2 Volvo Penta TAMD 60C diesels; 2 props; 304 bhp
Range: 400/24 **Crew:** 3 tot.

Remarks: Acquired 8-6-90 from Federal Police for use as Cairns Port Division RANR Torres Strait Reserve Unit training and liaison craft at Thursday Island.

DEFENCE MARITIME SERVICES PTY, LTD.

Note: Since 12-97, port service auxiliaries and all service craft have been operated under a 10-year contract to Defence Maritime Services (DMS); all such ships and craft are being repainted with dark blue or black hulls and buff or gray-colored superstructures. The official start of the contract was on 1-7-98. DMS is contracted to provide tugs, target services, practice weapon recovery, range support, submarine trials and calibration support, and a wide range of training services. DMS is also responsible for acquisition and maintenance of all boats and outboard motors carried aboard RAN ships and in addition is reponsible for over 120 mooring buoys, 18 floating fenders, and numerous buildings, vehicles, boat trailers, and other equipment. DMS has its own hull numbering system for smaller units, given here in parentheses, while the original RAN numbers are also still effective. Large units have neither RAN nor DMS numbers, and many craft have not yet received DMS numbers. The use of DMS numbers remains inconsistent, with some craft having an extra "0" before the actual number. Craft operating in the vicinity of Sydney seem also to have an *additional* small 5-digit number on the sides of their pilothouses.

AUXILIARIES

♦ 2 general-purpose tenders [WAG]
Bldr: Marystown SY, Marystown, Newfoundland, Canada

	In serv.
Seahorse Spirit (ex-*British Viking,* ex-*Balder Hudson*)	1980
Seahorse Standard (ex-*British Magnus,* ex-*Balder Cabot*)	1981

Seahorse Standard—with *Geraldton* (FCPB 213) in background DMS, 2000

D: 3,967 tons (fl) **S:** 12 kts (7 on one engine)
Dim: 72.07 (66.60 pp) × 16.41 (16.01 wl) × 5.25
Electronics:
Radar: *Seahorse Spirit:* 1 Decca RM 916C nav.; 1 Furuno FP-2010 ARPA nav.—*Seahorse Standard:* 1 Kelvin-Hughes Nucleus 6000A nav.; 1 Kelvin-Hughes Nucleus 5000R nav.
M: 2 Montreal Locomotive Works–Alco 12V251F V-12 diesels; 2 Liannen-Hjelset CP props; 5,480 bhp—CP thrusters: 2 fwd and 2 aft
Electric: 3,855 kVA tot. (2 × 1,200-kVA shaft alternators, 3 × 485-kVA diesel-driven sets)
Range: 14,400/10 **Fuel:** 850 tons **Endurance:** 60 days
Crew: 8–11 tot. (accomm. for 64)

Remarks: 2,090 grt. Purchased 1998 by Defence Maritime Services from Dramgate Ltd., London, U.K. *Seahorse Spirit* replaced *Protector* (now *Seahorse Horizon)* as submarine trials support ship at Adelaide in 4-98, and *Seahorse Standard* was assigned to HMAS *Stirling,* Western Australia, on 2-12-98. They are capable of being used for submarine rescue, Naval Reserve training, refueling at sea (via stern hoses), exercise torpedo retrieval, target towing, and deck transport of small mine countermeasures craft.
Hull systems: Former oilfield tug/supply vessels, with ice-strengthened hulls, dynamic positioning systems, pollution control equipment, a capability to support hard-hat divers to 54-m depths, and centerline moonpools. Both can support the *Remora* submarine rescue suite. Have Furuno SATCOM and F-851-S echo sounder and are GPS receiver-equipped. Have no helicopter deck, but do have a 41 × 11.5-m clear deck area capable of vertical replenishment operations. Retain oilfield cargo tankage, including 1,180 m^3 drill water, 600 m^3 potable water, and 12,000 ft.^{3} cement tanks; can transfer fuel and water to other ships at 150 tons/hr.

♦ 1 navigational training ship [WAXT]
Bldr: Elder-Prince Marine Services, Fremantle (In serv. 1984)

Seahorse Horizon (ex-*Protector,* ASR 241; ex-*Blue Nabilla;* ex-*Osprey*)

Seahorse Horizon Brian Morrison, 2-00

D: 390 tons light (670 fl) **S:** 11.5 kts (10.5 sust.)
Dim: 42.70 (40.75 wl; 38.99 pp) × 9.50 × 3.00 (max.)
Electronics:
Radar: 1 Kelvin-Hughes 1007 nav.; 1 Koden MD 3010 nav.
Sonar: Klein side-scan; Simrad Skipper obstacle-avoidance
M: 2 G.M. 12V-92A diesels; 2 CP props; 1,360 bhp—twin bow- and stern-thrusters
Electric: 700 kVA tot. (2 × 350-kVA diesel sets)
Range: 4,560/9.5 **Fuel:** 175 tons **Endurance:** 14 days
Crew: 1 officer, 5 unlicensed civilians or 9 RAN (accomm. for 31)

Remarks: 282 grt. Referred to as a "Sea Familiarization Vessel." Acquired 18-10-90 by the RAN from the Victorian Division of the National Safety Council, which had used her as a pollution control ship. Commissioned 20-3-91 and based at Adelaide from 1-96 to support *Collins*-class submarine trials. Decommissioned 17-4-98 and transferred to Defence Maritime Services to serve as interim seagoing training ship for the HMAS *Creswell* Naval College, Jervis Bay. Renamed 1-7-98. When trainees

DEFENCE MARITIME SERVICES AUXILIARIES *(continued)*

are embarked, the ship is manned by a commander and eight other RAN personnel; the civilian crew operates the ship when she is used as a diving tender or auxiliary mine clearance craft.
Hull systems: Had been lengthened 8 m and a helicopter platform added in 1988; the helicopter platform was removed during 1992. Has Magnavox and Trimble GPS receivers, Koden D/F, two echo sounders, and Inmarsat SATCOM. A six-man divers' recompression chamber is carried, and the ship can carry three 20-ft. standard freight containers on deck.

YARD AND SERVICE CRAFT

♦ 20 60-ton Flat-Top Lighters [WYC]
Bldr: Cockatoo Island DY, New South Wales (In serv. . . .)

(5) FTL 60101	(12) FTL 60109	(473) FTL 60120
(6) FTL 60102	(14) FTL 60110	(474) FTL 60121
(7) FTL 60103	(15) FTL 60115	(475) FTL 60111
(8) FTL 60104	(16) FTL 60116	FTL 60112
(9) FTL 60105	(470) FTL 60117	FTL 60113
(10) FTL 60107	(471) FTL 60118	FTL 60114
(11) FTL 60108	(472) FTL 60119	

D: 35.6 tons light (96.5 fl) **Dim:** 18.56 × 7.94 × . . .

Remarks: 61-ton-capacity steel barges used to transport general stores and ammunition on deck and sullage in hull tanks. Are based at Sydney, Fremantle, and HMAS *Creswell.* 11, 12, and 471 are used as paint stages, 14 as an "amenities lighter," 16 as a ferry wharf, and 470 as a fleet landing. FTL 60112–60114, at Fleet Base West, do not have DMS hull numbers.

♦ 3 Southerly 65-class diving tenders [WYDT]
Bldr: Geraldton Boat Builders, Geraldton, Western Australia

(462) 2001 Seal (In serv. 6-93) Dugong (In serv. 3-99)
2004 Shark (In serv. 8-93)

Dugong Phil Barling, RAN, 1-01

D: 85 tons (fl) **S:** 26 kts **Dim:** 19.95 (18.07 wl) × 5.35 × 1.64 (aft)
Electronics: Radar: 1 JRC JMA-2144 (*Dugong:* Furuno Mk 2) nav.
M: 2 G.M. Detroit Diesel 12V92 TA diesels; 2 props; 1,314 bhp
Electric: 7.5 kw tot. (1 × 7.5 kw, Kubota D1402 diesel driving)
Range: 450/20 (*Dugong:* 550/20) **Fuel:** 5,000 liters (*Dugong:* 6,780 liters)
Crew: 2 tot. + up to 18 divers

Remarks: First two ordered in 1992 as diving support tenders, with 2001 based at HMAS *Waterhen* and 2002 at Fleet Base West, Fremantle. *Dugong,* based at Sydney, was initially employed as a general-purpose launch but is now used for diver training and has no DMS or RAN hull number. Sister *Porpoise* (2002) went aground in Sydney Harbor during a storm on 25-9-95 and was subsequently sold for commercial service. Sister *Coral Snake* (AM 1353) is operated by the Australian Army, and near-sister *Malu Baizam* (2003) is configured as a patrol boat.
Hull systems: Are intended to support divers in waters up to 54 m deep. Also capable of employment as harbor patrol craft. Equipped with JRC JLU-121 GPS receiver, echo sounder, and Saura CP80 autopilot. Can maintain 3 kts minimum speed and 20 kts fully loaded in Sea State 2.

Note: Naval-manned landing craft *Brunei* (L 127) and *Betano* (L 133) are also employed as diving tenders, based at HMAS *Waterhen,* Sydney. Also available are an unknown number of aluminum Diving Demolition Boats built by Stessi Pty, Queensland. These can carry 10 or more personnel or 1,200 tons of cargo at 8 kts and are used to transport personnel and explosives; they displace 304 kg and are 5.26 m overall by 2.25 m beam.

♦ 6 miscellaneous concrete ammunition lighters [WYE]

(429) CAL 10011	(431) CAL 10013	(440) CAL 209
(430) CAL 10012	(432) CAL 10014	(443) CAL 5012

Remarks: 429–432 are of 100-ton capacity; 440 is 200-ton, and 443 is 50-ton. All are constructed of concrete, steel, and wood, and all are based at Spectacle Island ammunition magazine, Fleet Base East.

♦ 3 Wattle-class Crane Stores Lighters [WYF]
Bldr: Cockatoo DY, Sydney

	In serv.		In serv.
CSL 01 Wattle	15-8-72	(458) CSL 03 Telopea	31-10-72
(457) CSL 02 Boronia	25-9-72		

D: 147 tons (fl) **S:** 8 kts **Dim:** 24.22 × 10.00 (9.75 wl) × 1.66
M: 2 Caterpillar D333C diesels; 2 props; 600 bhp
Range: 320/8 **Endurance:** 24 hrs **Crew:** 4 tot.

Telopea (CSL 03/DMS 458) Phil Barling, RAN, 1-01

Remarks: Catamarans employed to transport ammunition and general stores and also for oil-spill containment duties. They can also tow lighters of up to 1,220 tons displacement. Have one 3-ton electric crane. Based on AWL 304 design, but with pilothouse aft. All three were due for disposal in 1997 but have been retained in service, CSL 02 and 03 at Sydney and CSL 01 (which has no DMS hull number) at Darwin.

♦ 10 Steber 43 Naval General-Purpose Workboats [WYFL]
Bldr: Steber Craft, . . . (In serv. 1998)

NGPWB 01 Patonga	NGPWB 05	NGPWB 09 Sea Witch
NGPWB 02	NGPWB 06	NGPWB 10
NGPWB 03	NGPWB 07	
NGPWB 04 Sea Dragon	NGPWB 08	

Patonga (NGPWB 01) Phil Barling, RAN, 1-01

D: 13.7 tons (fl) **S:** 25 kts (see remarks) **Dim:** 13.20 × 4.70 × 1.34
M: 2 (NGPWB 07–10: 1) . . . diesels; 1 or 2 props; . . . bhp
Range: 150/15 **Crew:** 3 tot. + 22 passengers (as tenders: 3 crew + 15 divers)

Remarks: GRP-hulled general-purpose launches usable as diving tenders and for light towing and stores transport (cargo: 2.05 tons). NGPWB 01–06 have two engines and can achieve 25 kts; the others have one engine and can reach 20 kts. All but NGPWB 01, 02, 07, and 08 are to receive navigational radars and GPS receivers; all have an echo sounder. NGPWB 01, 02, 07, and 08 are based at Sydney, NGPWB 03 at HMAS *Creswell,* NGPWB 04 and 09 at Fleet Base West, and NGPWB 06 at HMAS *Cerberus.* Only NGPWB 01 is assigned a DMS hull number, 1160.

♦ 4 Noosacat 930 harbor personnel boats [WYFL]
Bldr: Noosacat Australia, Noosaville, Queensland

0901 (In serv. 15-12-93) (452) 0903 (In serv. 4-94)
0902 (In serv. 2-94) (453) 0904 (In serv. 4-94)

Noosacat 930–class launch 0904 (DMS 453)
Brian Morrison/H&L Van Ginderen, 11-97

D: . . . tons **S:** 30 kts **Dim:** 9.30 (hull; 8.37 wl) × 3.495 (3.105 wl) × 0.70
Electronics: Radar: 0902 only: JRC JMA-2141 nav.
M: 2 Volvo Penta ADQ41DP diesels; 2 props; 400 bhp
Range: 240/20 **Crew:** 1 tot. + 20 passengers

DEFENCE MARITIME SERVICES YARD AND SERVICE CRAFT *(continued)*

Remarks: GRP-construction catamaran hull with 18 watertight compartments. Length given does not include protruding inboard/outboard propeller shafts. Can carry up to 1,900 kg payload, or 21 persons and 500 kg. 0903 and 0904 are based at Sydney, 0902 (RAN-operated) at HMAS *Creswell,* Jervis Bay, and 0901 at HMAS *Cerberus.* 0901 and 0902 do not have DMS hull numbers assigned.

♦ 1 Riviera-class VIP launch [WYFL]
Bldr: . . . (In serv. 1993)

(148) 38103 Tresco II

D: . . . tons **S:** 17.5 kts **Dim:** 11.58 × 4.11 × 1.05
M: 2 inboard/outboard-drive diesels; . . . bhp **Fuel:** 455 liters
Crew: 3 + 20 passengers

Remarks: GRP-hulled admiral's barge, based at HMAS *Waterhen,* Sydney. RAN hull number is 38103.

♦ 1 admiral's barge [WYFL]
Bldr: . . . (In serv. 2-93)

(1) AB 1201 Green Parrot

D: . . . tons **S:** 21 kts **Dim:** 12.70 (10.69 wl) × 3.90 × 0.93
M: 2 Perkins M 240 diesels; 2 props; 480 bhp—1 Perkins 102-4 auxiliary propulsion diesel; . . . bhp
Fuel: 600 liters **Crew:** 3 + 10 passengers

Remarks: Wooden-hulled craft with dark green hull and varnished wood topside. Based at HMAS *Waterhen,* Sydney, for ceremonial and VIP transportation duties.

♦ 4 Shark Cat 800 harbor personnel boats [WYFL]
Bldr: Shark Cat, Noosaville, Queensland (In serv. 1980s)

(649) 0801 (652) 0802 (655) 0803 0805

Shark Cat 800–class launch 0803 (DMS 655)
Brian Morrison/H&L Van Ginderen, 11-98

D: . . . tons **S:** 30 kts **Dim:** 8.35 (7.50 wl) × 2.80 × 1.0 (motors down)
Electronics: Radar: 1 portable Furuno . . . nav.
M: 2 Mercury gasoline outboards; 500 bhp
Range: 290/24 **Crew:** 1 tot. + 11 passengers (23 in emergency)

Remarks: GRP construction catamarans used for general-purpose, target towing, and naval police duties; with portable radar fitted, are also used in range clearance work. Based at Sydney, except for 0805 (with no DMS hull number) at HMAS *Creswell.*

♦ 12 Naval Work Boats [WYFL]
Bldr: North Queensland Engineers, Cairns (In serv. 1979–81)

(901) NWB 1230
(902) NWB 1260
(219) NWB 1281 Otter
(699) NWB 1282 Walrus
(220) NWB 1285 Grampus
(221) NWB 1286 Dolphin
(541) NWB 1287
(214) NWB 1288
(215) NWB 1289
(617) NWB 1290
(1140) NWB 1291
(222) NWB 1292 Turtle

Otter (NWB 1281/DMS 219) H&L Van Ginderen, 6-96

D: 12.56 tons (fl) **S:** 12 kts **Dim:** 12.42 × 3.82 (3.66 wl) × 1.08
M: 2 G.M. Detroit Diesel 6V53 diesels; 2 Kort-nozzle props; 274 bhp
Range: 240/12 **Fuel:** 1,380 liters **Endurance:** 20 hrs
Crew: 2 tot. + 10 passengers

Remarks: Some (including NWB 1288) are configured as diving tenders. Aluminum construction, poor maneuverability. Cargo capacity 2.5 tons in lieu of passengers. Have 3-ton bollard pull towing capacity. Seven Australian Army sisters sold 1993. Sister *Dugong* (NWB 1287) was stricken by 3-99, and several others have been discarded since. NWB 1230 and 1260 are based at Fleet Base West, NWB 1289 at Cairns, NWB 1287 and 1291 at Darwin, and the rest at Sydney. Have magnetic compass but no radar.

♦ 1 Halvorsen-design workboat [WYFL]
Bldr: Lars Halvorsens Pty (In serv. 1945–46)

(379) AWB 4011

AWB 4011 (DMS 379) Brian Morrison/H&L Van Ginderen, 2-99

D: 9.25 tons (13 fl) **S:** 11 kts **Dim:** 12.20 × 4.00 × 1.48
M: 1 G.M. Gray Marine 64HN9 diesel; 1 prop; 165 bhp
Range: 150/11 **Fuel:** 470 liters **Crew:** 1 tot. + 30 passengers

Remarks: Wooden-hulled craft based at Sydney to transport cargo and passengers. Open cockpit aft, low pilothouse. No radar fitted.

♦ 9 40-foot Mk 1 and 1963-design* workboats [WYFL]
Bldr: Phoenix Shipbuilding, Tasmania (In serv. ca. 1963)

(776) AWB 404
AWB 421
AWB 423
(422) AWB 424
(390) AWB 436
(224) AWB 440
AWB 1658
AWB 4006*
(428) AWB 4007*

AWB 436 (DMS 390) Phil Barling, RAN, 1-01

D: Mk 1: 9.11 tons (13.7 fl)—1963-design: 8.8 tons (13 fl)
S: 9.6 (1963-design: 9.9) kts **Dim:** 12.20 × 3.86 × 1.48
M: 1 G.M. Gray Marine 64HN9 diesel; 1 prop; 175 bhp
Range: 450/9.6 (1963-design: 145/9.9)
Fuel: 1,410 (1963-design: 477) liters **Crew:** 1 + up to 44 passengers

Remarks: Wooden-hulled craft employed for local passenger service and stores transport. No radars fitted. AWB stands for "Australian Workboat."

♦ 1 AWB Mod. II workboat [WYFL]
Bldr: Williamstown DY, Victoria (In serv. 1944–46)

(368) 4010

AWB 4010 (DMS 368) H&L Van Ginderen, 7-94

DEFENCE MARITIME SERVICES YARD AND SERVICE CRAFT
(continued)

D: 9.11 tons (13.7 fl) **S:** 9.9 kts **Dim:** 12.20 × 3.86 × 1.48
M: 1 G.M. . . . diesel; 1 prop; 170 bhp
Range: 450/9.9 **Fuel:** 1,410 liters **Crew:** 1 + up to 44 passengers

Remarks: Based at Sydney. Can carry up to 3 tons of cargo in lieu of passengers. Can be employed for light towing. Wooden construction.

♦ 1 AWB Short & Long Group Cabin workboat [WYFL]
Bldr: Phoenix SB Co., Tasmania (In serv. 1944–46)

4002

D: 9 tons (13 fl) **S:** 9.9 kts **Dim:** 12.50 × 3.86 × 1.48
M: 1 G.M. 64HN9 diesel; 1 prop; 165 bhp
Range: 145/9.9 **Fuel:** 477 liters **Crew:** 1 + up to 44 passengers

Remarks: Wooden hull modernized with GRP pilothouse and passenger cabin. Can carry up to 3 tons cargo in lieu of passengers. Based at Sydney. AWB in RAN class designation stands for "Australian Workboat." Does not have a DMS number. Sisters *Onyx* (AWB 416) and *Amethyst* (AWB 420) had ceased to be listed by 1-01.

♦ 27 7.2-meter Rigid Inflatable Boats [WYFL]
Bldr: Zodiac (Aust) Pty

0701 through 0727

D: 1,958 kg (fl) **S:** 31+ kts **Dim:** 7.20 × 2.74 × 0.53
M: 1 inboard/outboard gasoline sterndrive; . . . bhp
Range: 75/15 **Fuel:** 200 liters **Crew:** 18 passengers (25 emergency)

Remarks: GRP hull, Hypalon inflatable collar. Based at various shore facilities and also carried by ships for transportation and training duties.

Note: Also widely used are Mks I–III 4.7-m Zodiac RIBs, powered by 30- to 40-bhp gasoline outboard motors and capable of carrying 10–12 personnel or 1,100–1,300 kg of cargo. Open aluminum launches of the 5-m Lightweight Utility Boat (LUB) Types C and D are also widely used for training, diver support, inshore survey, and general utility work. Type C is 6.50 × 2.50 × 0.40 m and is powered by a 175-bhp Johnson gasoline outboard, while Type D is 5.125 × 1.90 × 0.40 m and is powered by a 40-bhp Johnson outboard; both types can achieve about 8 kts and can carry 6 or 7 people. Other light aluminum launches are the 4.3-m and 12-ft. aluminum dinghy classes: 4.3/4.3 × 1.85/1.54 m and weighing 150 kg (4.3-m) or 66 kg (12-ft.) without their outboard motors.

Note: Hydrographic survey launches *Tom Thumb* (320, ex-SMB 1009) and *John Gowland* (321, ex-SMB 1010) are managed and operated by Defence Maritime Services but remain RAN property (see under [YGS]). They are employed at the Hydrographic School.

♦ 6 Radio-Controlled Surface Targets [WYGT]
Bldr: Hydrofield, Queensland (In serv. . . .)

RCST 06 through RCST 11

D: . . . tons **S:** 25 kts **Dim:** 6.40 × 2.46 × 1.10
M: 1 Evinrude Ocean Runner gasoline outboard; 150 bhp **Range:** 200/25

Remarks: Orange-colored radio-controlled GRP-construction trimaran launches used to tow surface and air targets. Can be operated from cockpit. Two are based at Fleet Base West, Fremantle, and the others at HMAS *Creswell.* They do not have DMS hull numbers assigned.

Note: Used as towed targets are an unknown number of 6.4 × 4.4-m, 600-kg Mk 1 towed target sleds completed during 1980 at Garden Island Dockyard. Two are based at HMAS *Creswell* and a third is towed by the torpedo retriever *Trevally.*

♦ 4 Water and Fuel Lighters [WYO] Bldr: Williamstown DY, Victoria

	In serv.
(333) Warrigal (ex-WFL 8001)	10-84
(331) Wallaby (ex-WFL 8002)	3-2-83
(332) Wombat (ex-WFL 8003)	10-2-83
(334) Wyulda (ex-WFL 8004)	10-84

Wyulda (DMS 334)—with old number and paint scheme Vic Jeffery, 7-97

D: 265 tons light (1,210 fl) **S:** 7 kts light (6.3 loaded)
Dim: 39.25 (38.00 wl) × 11.00 (9.80 wl) × 4.80 (max.)
M: 2 G.E.C. diesels; 1 Harbormaster outdrive prop fwd, 1 aft; 564 bhp
Electric: 45 kVA tot. (1 G.M. diesel driving)
Range: 144/6 **Fuel:** 9.68 tons **Crew:** 4 tot.

Remarks: Used to transport and deliver diesel fuel and desalinized water and to remove and transport sullage and ballast liquids. Also employed for oil-spill containment. Cargo: 56 tons diesel fuel, 100 tons feedwater, 100 tons distilled water, 110 tons waste, and 80 tons ballast. Have one 400-ton/hr and three 40-ton/hr cargo pumps and a 1,000-kg capacity deck crane. *Warrigal* is based at Darwin, *Wallaby* and *Wombat* at Sydney, and *Wyulda* at Fremantle. Are expected to remain in service until 2013.

♦ 3 torpedo-recovery craft [WYPT]
Bldr: Williamstown DY, Victoria (In serv. 1970–71)

(417) TRV 801 Tuna
(415) TRV 802 Trevally
(1159) TRV 803 Tailor

Trevally (TRV 802/DMS 447) Brian Morrison, 11-98

D: 93 tons (fl) **S:** 13 (TRV 803: 12) kts
Dim: 26.96 (26.82 wl) × 6.38 (6.10 wl) × 2.11
Electronics:
Radar: TRV 801: 1 Kodan MD-3220 Mk 2 nav.—TRV 802: 1 Tokimec nav.—TRV 803: 1 JRC JMA-2144 nav.
M: 3 (TRV 803: 2) G.M. Detroit Diesel 6-71 diesels; 3 props; 684 (TRV 803: 456) bhp
Electric: 50 kVA tot. (2 × 25 kVA sets, G.M. 3-53 diesels driving)
Range: 420/12–13; 500/8 **Fuel:** 5.75 tons
Crew: 3 licensed officers, 3 nonrated (accomm. for 9–10)

Remarks: Named in 1982. TRV 801 is based at HMAS *Creswell,* Jervis Bay, and is also used for target towing; TRV 802 is at HMAS *Waterhen,* Sydney, and TRV 803 at HMAS *Stirling,* Western Australia. All were due to be stricken during the late 1990s, but no replacements have been procured. TRV 803 lacks the centerline diesel propulsion engine. TRV 802 is assigned a Mk 1 tow-target.

♦ 1 coastal tug [WYTB]
Bldr: Australian SB Industries, South Coogee, Western Australia

	Laid down	L	In serv.
2601 Tammar	20-4-83	10-3-84	15-3-84

Tammar (2601) ABPH Stuart Farrow, RAN, 7-98

D: 267 tons (302.4 fl) **S:** 11.5 kts **Dim:** 27.00 (24.38 wl; 23.63 pp) × 8.86 × 3.58
Electronics: Radar: 1 JRC JMA-2144 nav.
M: 2 G.M. 16V149 TI diesels; 2 Kort-nozzle props; 2,560 bhp
Electric: 50 kVA tot. **Range:** 900/12; 1,400/10 **Fuel:** 48 tons
Endurance: 2 days **Crew:** 4–6 tot. (accomm. for 10)

Remarks: 160 grt. Ordered 30-3-83 for use at HMAS *Stirling,* Fleet Base West, Western Australia, for towing, torpedo recovery, oil-spill containment, and target towing. Bollard pull 35 tons permits towing ships of up to 20,000 tons displacement. Has JRC JFV-60 echo sounder and GPS receiver. Has 68 tons ballast-water capacity. Does not have a DMS hull number assigned and may no longer wear RAN number 2601.

♦ 1 medium harbor tug [WYTM]
Bldr: Shoreline Eng., Portland, Victoria (L: 10-83)

1801 Quokka

D: 110 tons (fl) **S:** 11.3 kts
Dim: 18.17 (17.15 wl; 16.84 pp) × 6.20 (5.91 wl) × 2.40
Electronics: Radar: 1 JRC JMA-2144 nav.
M: 2 G.M. 8V53 diesels; 2 Kort-nozzle props; 633 bhp
Electric: 52 kw tot. (2 × 26-kw Stamford generator sets) **Range:** 750/10.5
Fuel: 12.6 tons **Endurance:** 2 days **Crew:** 6 tot. (civilian)

DEFENCE MARITIME SERVICES YARD AND SERVICE CRAFT
(continued)

Quokka (1801) ABPH Stuart Farrow, RAN, 7-98

Remarks: Reassigned to Darwin in 1998 for towing and target towing. Bollard pull: 11.3 tons. Has 13 m^3 ballast-water capacity. Is fitted with GPS and JRC JFV-60 echo sounder. Formerly carried naval number 1801 and has not been assigned a DMS hull number.

♦ 3 Bronzewing-class harbor tugs [WYTL]
Bldr: Stannard Bros., Sydney (HTS 504: Perrin Eng., Brisbane)

	In serv.
(152) (HTS 501) Bronzewing	12-68
(153) (HTS 502) Currawong	1969
(154) (HTS 504) Mollymawk	1966

Bronzewing (DMS 152) Phil Barling, RAN, 1-01

D: 34 tons (48.15 fl; HTS 504: 48.26 fl) **S:** 9.13 (HTS 504: 8) kts
Dim: 15.50 (14.12 wl) × 4.88 (4.57 pp) × 2.06
M: 2 G.M. diesels; 2 props; 340 bhp **Range:** 710/9.13 **Crew:** 3 tot. (civilian)

Remarks: Sister HTS 503 was given to Papua New Guinea in 1974. Named in 1983. Were due for disposal during 1996 but remain in service. Have 5.08-ton bollard pull and can tow barges of up to 1,220 tons displacement. HTS 504 is 15.55 m overall (14.39 wl), draws 2.07 m, and has larger stacks, not raked forward as in the other two. Do not have radar or gyrocompass.

♦ 1 sail-training craft [WYTS]
Bldr: . . . , Brisbane (In serv. 1982)

850576 Salthorse

D: 32.3 tons (fl) **S:** 8 kts (under power) **Dim:** 19.74 (15.24 wl) × 5.13 × 2.28
Electronics: Radar: 1 JRC JMA-2253 nav.
M: 1 Ford Lehman diesel; 1 prop; 120 bhp
Electric: 15 kVA tot. (1 × 8 kVA, Yanmar diesel-driven; 1 × 7 kVA emergency, Volvo Penta P7 1500 diesel driven)
Range: 1,400/6 (under power) **Fuel:** 600 gal. **Crew:** . . . tot.

Remarks: Ketch acquired in 1999 for officer training and recreation at HMAS *Creswell.* Steel hull with aluminum masts (17.5-m foremasthead). Has Furuno GP-30 GPS receiver. Designed by John Pugh.

♦ 5 Swarbrick III–class small training yachts [WYTS]
Bldr: Swarbrick Bros., Osbourne Park, Western Australia (In serv. 1984)

STY 3807 Alexander of Cresswell
STY 3808 Friendship of Leeuwin
STY 3809 Lady Peryhyn of Nirimba
STY 3810 Charlotte of Cerberus
STY 3811 Scarborough of Cerberus

D: 4.35 tons (fl) **S:** . . . kts **Dim:** 11.10 (9.60 wl) × 3.20 × 1.975
M 1 Yanmar 3 GMO diesel; 22 bhp **Crew:** 8 tot.

Remarks: GRP training yachts based at Sydney, Fremantle, HMAS *Cerberus,* and HMAS *Creswell.* STY stands for "Swarbrick Sail Training Yacht." Are planned to be replaced by new craft of about 14.0 m overall.

♦ 63 Tasar sail dinghies [WYTS] (In serv. 1970)

1925–2546 series

D: 93 kg (rigged) **S:** . . . kts **Dim:** 4.57 × 1.75 × 0.62 **Crew:** 2 tot.

Remarks: GRP sloops used at Fremantle, HMAS *Creswell,* HMAS *Cerberus,* NSO Tasmania, etc., for training and recreation. Survivors of 70 built for the RAN. Do not have DMS hull numbers. Mainsail is 8.36 m^2, jib 3.07 m^2.

♦ 1 ASI 315–class navigation and seamanship training craft [WYXT]
Bldr: Tenix SB WA, South Coogie, Western Australia

Seahorse Mercator (L: 15-10-98; in serv. 26-11-98)

Seahorse Mercator AB Helena Charter, RAN, 1-99

D: 165 tons (fl) **S:** 16 kts **Dim:** 31.50 (28.60 wl) × 8.21 × 2.60
Electronics: Radar: 1 Furuno FE 606 nav.; 1 Decca Bridgemaster ARPA nav.
M: 2 Caterpillar 3304 diesels; 2 props; 2,820 bhp (2,400 sust.)
Electric: 116 kw (2 × 50 kw; Caterpillar 3304 diesels; 1 × 16 kw)
Range: 2,880/8 **Fuel:** 27.9 tons **Endurance:** 15 days (7 days with 20 aboard)
Crew: 5 tot. + 3 instructors, 18 trainees

Remarks: Ordered early 1998 as a replacement for the *Ardent* (A 243, an exhibit at Darwin since 23-11-98). Twenty near-sisters operate as patrol boats in a number of Southwest Pacific–area island nation forces. Extensive navigational suite, including Furuno NAVSAT receiver, echo sounder, and doppler log. Operated in the Sydney area since 12-98 by a Defence Maritime Services civilian contract crew, assigned to HMAS *Waterhen.* Has a secondary capability to act as a mine countermeasures craft and is equipped with GPS and autopilot.

ROYAL AUSTRALIAN ARMY CORPS OF ENGINEERS

Personnel: Approx. 300

♦ 0 (+ 6–8) Amphibious Watercraft System (AWC) program [LCM]
Bldr: . . . (In serv. 2003–04)

D: 60 tons light **S:** . . . kts **Dim:** . . . × . . . × . . .
M: . . . **Crew:** up to 5 tot.

Remarks: Are to be liftable by 70-ton cranes, have a combat load of 35–50 tons, and be beachable on gradients up to 1:50. Are intended to replace Army LCM(8) craft for use with *Kanimbla* (L 51) and *Manoora* (L 52). All will be assigned to 10 Force Support Battalion, Townsville, Queensland. Responses to the request for bids were due by 30-5-01. Textron Marine & Land Systems has offered the LACV-30 air-cushion vehicle design with a payload of 27 tons on a 155.5-m^2 deck that can also accommodate a 90-person passenger module; the craft can travel at 36 kts loaded in calm seas (reduced to 17–19 kts in Sea States 1–2).

♦ 14 U.S. LCM(8)-class landing craft [WLCM]
Bldrs: AB 1050–1061: North Queensland Engineers, Cairns (In serv. 1967); others: Dillingham SY, Fremantle (In serv. 1972)

AB 1050 AB 1051 AB 1053 AB 1056 AB 1058–AB 1067

AB 1051—moored at the stern ramp of *Manoora* (L 52) RAN, 2000

ROYAL AUSTRALIAN ARMY CORPS OF ENGINEERS *(continued)*

D: 34 tons light (116 fl) **S:** 11 kts (9 loaded)
Dim: 22.70 × 6.41 × 1.37 (mean; 1.30 fwd/1.68 aft loaded)
M: 4 G.M. 6V71 diesels; 2 props; 600 bhp **Range:** 290/10 **Crew:** 3 tot.

Remarks: AB 1050 is named *Coconut Queen* and AB 1053 *Sea Widow.* Most based at Cairns and Fremantle, some in land storage.
Disposals: AB 1057 was transferred to Tonga in 1982; AB 1055 was stricken in 1984; and AB 1052 and AB 1054 were sold for civilian use in 1992.
Hull systems: Steel construction. AB 1050–1061 originally had range of 230 n.m. at 10 kts. Both variants have a 55-ton cargo capacity.

♦ 1 Special Action Forces Craft Offshore Large [WLCP]
Bldr: Geraldton Boat Builders, Geraldton, Western Australia (In serv. 1994)

AM 1353 Coral Snake

D: 85 tons (fl) **S:** 28 kts **Dim:** 19.95 (18.07 wl) × 5.64 × 1.46 (aft)
Electronics: Radar: 1 JRC JMA-2144 nav.
M: 2 G.M. Detroit Diesel 12V92 TA diesels; 2 props; 1,800 bhp
Range: 350+/25 **Fuel:** 8,000 liters **Crew:** 3 tot.

Remarks: Sister to RAN's *Seal* class, but with an Effer hydraulic crane at the stern and a smaller cabin topped by a flying bridge. Used to support divers and for transport of stores and personnel. Based in Western Australia.

♦ 12 ex-U.S. Army LARC-V (Design 8005) amphibious wheeled lighters [WLCP]
Bldr: . . ., U.S.A. (In serv. 1960s)

Four Australian Army LARC-V amphibious wheeled lighters in formation RAN, 2000

D: 8.9 tons light (13.4 fl) **S:** 8 kts loaded (55 kph on land)
Dim: 10.67 × 3.05 × 3.10 **M:** 1 . . . diesel; 1 prop; 300 bhp
Range: 70/8 (sea); 400 km/. . . (land) **Crew:** 1–2 tot.

Remarks: Acquired 1964–65 and deactivated early 1990s. Reactivated for service with landing ships *Manoora* and *Kanimbla,* with first completing 6-98 and six more by the end of 2-99; the original Cummins diesels were replaced. Based at Townsville. Some 52 additional are maintained in reserve. Cargo: 4,536 kg.

♦ 159 Assault Boats [WLCP]
Bldr: Australian Boat Mfrs., Ltd., Perth (In serv. 1990–91)

D: 210 kg light (1,500 kg fl) **S:** 10 kts **Dim:** 5.0 × 2.0 × . . .
M: 1 outboard; 40 bhp **Cargo:** 1,200 kg or 12 troops

Remarks: Intended to replace earlier craft of this type. Aluminum construction. Will float while loaded if flooded out.

♦ 2 NLE-class self-propelled pontoons [WYFL]

201 Caspor 202 Pollux

D: 32.6 tons light (127 loaded) **S:** 4–6 kts **Dim:** 25.60 × 7.46 × 1.25
M: 2 G.M. Detroit Diesel 4-71 diesels in Harbormaster portable outdrives; 224 bhp

Remarks: Composed of steel pontoon cubes 1.52 m square by 2.13 m high, which can be arranged either in 12 × 3 or 14 × 3.5 configuration; in the former, can carry 75 tons cargo or 50 personnel, and in the latter (used for stowage on sides of RAN landing ship *Tobruk*), 80 tons cargo or 50 personnel. NLE stands for "Naval Lighterage Equipment."

♦ 9 Shark Cat 880 Express–class launches [WYFL]
Bldr: Noosacat, Noosaville, Queensland (In serv. 1990–95)

AM 237 through AM 244 AM 428

D: . . . tons **S:** 40 kts (27 cruise) **Dim:** 9.40 (8.15 hull) × 2.82 × 0.63 (hull)
Electronics: Radar: 1 Furuno FR 1941 nav.
M: 2 Johnson gasoline outboards; 450 bhp
Fuel: 1,000 liters **Crew:** 2 tot. + 10 passengers

Remarks: GRP construction. Cargo capacity of 1.5 tons. Used for water safety patrol and local transport of personnel and stores. Each has an associated road trailer. These replace the 7-m Shark Cat–series launches acquired in 1980. Have Furuno FC 581 echo sounders, a Trimble GPS receiver, and three radio sets. Carry 110 liters of potable water.

♦ 5 9-meter rigid inflatable offshore safety launches [WYFL]

AM 227 AM 228 AM 229 AM 230 AM 231

Remarks: No data available.

AUSTRALIAN CUSTOMS NATIONAL MARINE UNIT

Note: Australian Customs craft are charged with Federal Police, quarantine, fisheries and wildlife protection, and other ancilliary duties.

♦ 8 Roebuck Bay–class customs patrol boats [WPB]
Bldr: Austal Ships, Henderson, Western Australia

	In serv.		In serv.
ACV 01 Roebuck Bay	2-99	ACV 05 Corio Bay	2-00
ACV 02 Holdfast Bay	10-99	ACV 06 Storm Bay	8-00
ACV 03 Botany Bay	16-9-99	ACV 07 Dame Roma Mitchell	8-00
ACV 04 Hervey Bay	2-00	ACV 08 Arnhem Bay	8-00

Holdfast Bay (ACV 02) Brian Morrison/H&L Van Ginderen, 1-00

D: 28 tons (trials) **S:** 21 kts **Dim:** 38.20 (32.10 wl) × 7.20 × 2.35
Electronics: Radar: 2 Kelvin-Hughes Nucleus 2 5000 ARPA nav.
M: 2 MTU 16V 2000 M70 diesels; 2 props; 2,800 bhp—bow-thruster
Range: 1,000/20 **Endurance:** 28 days **Crew:** 8 tot. + 8 passengers

Remarks: 30.2 dwt. Ordered 5-98 for $38 million (U.S.). Aluminum construction. One radar operates in X band, the other in S, and up to 50 contacts can be tracked simultaneously; an electronic chart system displays charts on the radar operating screens. Capable of towing craft of up to 150 tons displacement. Carry two 6-m inspection/landing launches equipped with SATCOM, each with two 90-bhp Yamaha outboard motors and a range of 150 n.m. at 25 kts. Are capable of supporting scuba divers and can transport 1 ton of cargo and eight law enforcement officers in addition to the crew, landing and recovering them. Have Austal Ocean Leveller ride-control system and fin stabilizers. The design is offered for export in an armed version.

Note: Other craft operated by the Australian Customs Service as of early 2001 included three Collector-class 6.99-m aluminum launches powered by Volvo Penta AQD40A stern drives (two based at Sydney, one at Brisbane); the Minister-class patrol craft *Charles Kingston,* 19.99 m long and powered by two MTY 396 V-8 diesels; the 22-m, aluminum-hulled *Delphinus,* powered by two MTY 183-series diesels; and the 24-m *Cheetah,* an aluminum-hulled catamaran powered by two MWM V-12 diesels.

AUSTRIA

Republic of Austria

AUSTRIAN ARMY DANUBE FLOTILLA

Personnel (2001): 2 officers, 30 enlisted

Base: *Marinekaserne Teggethof* at Vienna/Kuchelau. All craft operate on the Danube River and its tributaries.

PATROL BOATS [WPB]

♦ 1 Niederösterreich class
Bldr: Korneuberg Werft AG

	Laid down	L	In serv.
A 604 Niederösterreich	31-3-69	26-7-69	16-4-70

Niederösterreich (A 604) Erwin Sieche, 4-85

PATROL BOATS [WPB] *(continued)*

D: 73 tons (fl) **S:** 22 kts **Dim:** 29.67 × 5.41 × 1.10
A: 1 20-mm Oerlikon SPz Mk 66 AA; 1 12.7-mm M2 mg; 2 single 7.62-mm mg; 1 84-mm Carl Gustav PAR 66 mortar
M: 2 MWM V-16 diesels; 1,620 bhp
Range: 900/. . . **Fuel:** 9.3 tons **Crew:** 1 officer, 8 enlisted

Remarks: Re-engined 1985. Original plans called for building 11 more.

♦ **1 Oberst Brecht class** Bldr: Korneuberg Werft AG

A 601 OBERST BRECHT (In serv. 14-1-58)

D: 10 tons **S:** 14 kts **Dim:** 12.30 × 2.51 × 0.75
A: 1 12.7-mm M2 mg; 1 84-mm Carl Gustav PAR 66 mortar
M: 2 Graf & Stift 6-cyl. diesels; 290 bhp
Range: 160/10 **Crew:** 5 tot.

Remarks: A replacement was to be ordered in 2000.

SERVICE CRAFT

♦ **several motorized pontoons [WYAG]**

D: 8.5–40 tons (fl) **Dim:** 19.0 × 1.70 (some 3.00) × 0.7

Note: For police duty, four aluminum patrol craft were ordered in 1989 from Dieter Schulte Österreichse Schiffswerften AG, Autriche: 15.46 × 3.74 × 1.10 m, with 2 Volvo Penta TMD.70c diesels and Schottel rudder props, capable of 17.25 kts. The small 9.5-m patrol boat *Greif* (B 704), completed in 3-87, is also police subordinated.

♦ **10 M-boot 80–class launches [WYFL]**
Bldr: Schottel Werft, Spay, Germany (In serv. 1984)

D: 4.7 tons (fl) **S:** 14 kts **Dim:** 7.5 × 2.5 × 0.6
M: 1 Klöckner-Humboldt-Deutz V-12 diesel; . . . bhp

Remarks: Push-boat/personnel launches.

AZERBAIJAN

Republic of Azerbaijan

Personnel (2001): Approx. 1,000 total

Bases: All ships and craft are based at Baku.

Organization: The navy was formed on 27-7-92. There are patrol, gunboat, amphibious landing, and mine countermeasures divisions. Russia provided guidance, operational control of craft, and maintenance from 1995 to 1999.

PATROL CRAFT [PC]

♦ **1 ex-Turkish AB 25 class**
Bldr: Istinye SY

. . . (ex-AB 34, P 134)

D: 150 tons (170 fl) **S:** 22 kts **Dim:** 40.24 × 6.40 × 1.65
A: 1 40-mm 60-cal. Mk 3 Bofors AA; 1 20-mm 70-cal. Oerlikon AA; 2 single 12.7-mm mg; 2 4-railed Mk 20 Mousetrap ASW RL; 4 single d.c. release racks
Electronics:
Radar: 1 Decca TM 1226 nav.—Sonar: Plessey PMS-26 hull-mounted HF
M: 2 SACM-AGO V16CSHR diesels; 2 props; 4,800 bhp; 2 cruise diesels; 300 bhp
Crew: 3 officers, 28 enlisted

Remarks: Transferred during 7-00. Sisters remain in Turkish Navy service, and one is in the Georgian Navy. Fourteen others are assigned to the Marine Police. Built with French technical assistance. The cruise diesels are geared to the main shafts.

PATROL BOATS [PB]

♦ **1 ex-Russian Zhuk (Gryf) class (Project 1400 or 1400M)**
Bldr: . . . . . . (In serv. 1971–86)

137 (ex-AK-55)

D: 35.9 tons (39.7 fl) **S:** 30 kts
Dim: 23.80 (21.70 wl) × 5.00 (3.80 wl) × 1.00 (hull; 1.90 max.)
A: 1 twin 14.5-mm 93-cal. 2M-7 AA *or* 1 twin 12.7-mm 60-cal. Utës-Ma mg
Electronics: Radar: 1 Lotsiya nav.
M: Project 1400M: 2 M-401 diesels; 2 props; 2,200 bhp—Project 1400: 2 M-50F4 diesels; 2 props; 2,400 bhp
Electric: 48 kw total (2 × 21-kw, 1 × 6-kw diesel sets)
Range: 500/13.5 **Endurance:** 5 days **Crew:** 1 officer, 9 enlisted

Remarks: Former Caspian Flotilla unit transferred ca. 7-92. Was active as of 6-00.
Hull systems: Aluminum alloy hull. Range also reported as 700 n.m. at 28 kts, 1,100 n.m. at 15 kts.

MINE COUNTERMEASURES SHIPS AND CRAFT

♦ **2 ex-Russian Yevgenya-class (Project 1258) inshore minesweepers [MSI]** Bldr: Sudostroitel'noye Obyedineniye "Almaz" (Sredniy Neva), Kolpino (In serv. 1970–76)

237 (ex-RT-136) . . . (ex-RT-473)

D: 88.5 tons light, 94.5 tons normal (97.9 fl) **S:** 11 kts **Dim:** 26.13 × 5.90 × 1.40
A: 1 twin 14.5-mm 93-cal. 2M-7 or 25-mm 80-cal. 2M-3M AA; 1 7-round MRG-1 grenade launcher; 4 single d.c. racks (+ 8 d.c. emergency stowage)
Electronics: Radar: 1 Mius (Spin Trough) nav.—Sonar: MG-7 HF dipping
M: 2 Type 3D12 diesels; 2 props; 600 bhp—hydraulic slow-speed drive
Electric: 100 kw tot. (2 × 50-kw DG-50 diesel sets)
Range: 400/10 **Fuel:** 2.7 tons **Endurance:** 3 days
Crew: 1 officer, 9 enlisted (+ 2–3 clearance divers)

Remarks: Transferred 3-7-92. Referred to as "roadstead minesweepers" in Russian service.
Hull systems: Glass-reinforced plastic hull. Navigational equipment includes Girya-MA gyrocompass and NEL-7 echo sounder.
Combat systems: Employ a television minehunting system useful to 30-m depths that dispenses marker buoys to permit later disposal of mines by divers or explosive charges. The sonar is lowered via one of the stern davits. Carry GKT-1 mechanical, AT-2 acoustic, and SEMT-1 solenoid coil sweep gear. Have Khrom-KMN IFF system.

Disposal note: Sonya-class (Project 1258) coastal minesweepers BT-16, BT-103, and BT-155, stricken from the Russian Caspian Flotilla on 3-7-92 and transferred to Azerbaijan, were no longer in service as of 6-00.

AMPHIBIOUS WARFARE SHIPS AND CRAFT

♦ **1 ex-Russian Polnocny-B-class (Project 771A) medium landing ship [LSM]** Bldr: Stocznia Polnocna, Gdansk, Poland (In serv. 1967–70)

309 (ex-MDK-107)

D: 558 tons light, 640 tons std. (884 fl) **S:** 18 kts
Dim: 75.00 (70.00 wl) × 9.00 (8.60 wl) × 2.07 (mean; 1.20 fwd/2.40 aft)
A: 1 or 2 twin 30-mm 65-cal. AK-230 AA; 2 18-round 140-mm WM-18 barrage RL; 2 or 4 4-railed SA-N-8 SAM syst. (16 Strela-3M/Grail missiles)
Electronics: Radar: 1 Mius (Spin Trough), 1 MR-104 Rys' (Drum Tilt) f.c.
M: 2 Type 40DM diesels; 2 props; 4,400 bhp **Range:** 700/18; 2,000/16
Crew: 5 officers, 32 enlisted + 60–180 troops

Remarks: Stricken from the Russian Caspian Flotilla in 7-92 and transferred to Azerbaijan in 8-92. Was active as of 6-00.
Hull systems: Has a bow door only. Hull has a "beak" projecting forward below the waterline at the bow to aid in beaching. Hatches to upper deck are for loading and ventilation only. Cargo: 237 tons max., including six tanks or 180 troops and their equipment; 30 vehicle crew are carried with tank loadout. Vehicle deck is 44.3 m long by 5.3 m wide and 3.6 m high.

♦ **2 ex-Russian Polnocny-A-class (Project 770) medium landing ships [LSM]** Bldr: Stocznia Polnocna, Gdansk, Poland (In serv. 1962–67)

291 (ex-MDK-36) 380 (ex-MDK-37)

D: 600 tons light (820 fl) **S:** 19 kts
Dim: 73.00 (70.00 wl) × 9.00 (8.60 wl) × 1.98 (mean; 1.13 fwd/2.33 aft)
A: 2 twin 30-mm 65-cal. AK-230 AA; 2 18-round 140-mm WM-18 barrage RL (180 rockets); 4 4-railed SA-N-5/8 SAM systems (32 Strela-3M/Grail or Gremlin missiles)
Electronics: Radar: 1 Mius (Spin Trough) nav., 1 MR-104 Rys' (Drum Tilt) f.c.
M: 2 Type 40DM diesels; 2 props; 4,400 bhp **Range:** 700/18; 1,800/16
Crew: 4 officers, 38 enlisted + 35 vehicle crew

Remarks: Stricken 3-7-92 from the Russian Caspian Flotilla and transferred to Azerbaijan.
Hull systems: Cargo capacity includes up to five heavy tanks for a total of about 180 tons. Vehicle deck is 42.3 m long by 5.3 m wide and 3.6 m high.

♦ **1 ex-Russian T-4-class (Project 1785) landing craft [LCM]**

. . . (ex-D-603)

D: 35 tons light (93 fl) **S:** 10 kts (light) **Dim:** 19.9 × 5.6 × 1.4 (max. aft)
M: 2 Type 3D6 diesels; 2 props; 300 bhp **Range:** 1,500/10 **Crew:** 2 tot.

Remarks: Transferred at Baku 3-7-92. Can accommodate up to 50 tons cargo. Now nearly 40 years old and may have been discarded.

AUXILIARIES

♦ **1 ex-Russian Emba-class (Project 1172) cable layer [ARC]**
Bldr: Wärtsilä SY, Turku, Finland (In serv. 5-80)

EMBA

D: 1,443 tons (2,145 fl) **S:** 11.8 kts **Dim:** 75.90 (68.50 pp) × 12.60 × 3.10
Electronics: Radar: 2 Mius (Spin Trough) nav.
M: diesel-electric: 2 Wärtsilä Vasa 6R22 diesels; 2 shrouded Schottel props; 1,360 shp—bow tunnel thruster
Range: 7,000/7 **Endurance:** 25 days **Crew:** 38 tot. (civilian)

Remarks: 1,910 grt. Cargo: 300 tons cable. Transferred to Azerbaijan after 1992; may be subordinate to an agency other than the navy. Intended for use in shallow coastal areas, rivers, and harbors. Has one 5-ton crane.

♦ **1 ex-Russian Luga-class (Project 888) cadet training ship [AXT]**
Bldr: Stocznia Polnocna, Gdansk, Poland (In serv. 1977)

OKA

D: 1,474 tons (1,848 fl) **S:** 17 kts **Dim:** 71.40 × 11.60 × 4.17 (max.)
Electronics: Radar: 3 Don-2 nav.
M: 2 Cegielski-Sulzer 6TD48 diesels; 2 CP props; 3,600 bhp
Electric: 594 kw tot. **Range:** 7,500/11 **Endurance:** 30 days
Crew: 56 tot. + 8 instructors and 85 cadets

Remarks: *Oka* was based at the now-Azerbaijani port of Baku in the Caspian Sea to support the Kirov Naval Academy and was transferred to Azeri control in 1992 or 1993. Equipped for navigational training. Similar to Polish and East German units of the *Wodnik* class, but has a slightly larger superstructure, has its pilothouse one deck higher, and is not armed.

SERVICE CRAFT

♦ 1 ex-Russian Shelon' (TL-1127)-class (Project 1388) torpedo retriever [YPT] Bldr: Sosnovka Zavod (In serv. 1978–84)

930 (ex-TL . . .)

D: 270 tons (fl) **S:** 30 kts **Dim:** 46.0 × 6.0 × 2.0
Electronics: Radar: 1 Kuban nav.—Sonar: Oka-1 helicopter dipping-type (HF)
M: 2 M-504 diesels; 2 props; 10,000 bhp
Range: 1,500/10 **Endurance:** 10 days **Crew:** 20 tot.

Remarks: Apparently transferred to Azerbaijan during 1992; was active as of 6-00. High-speed hull with a covered torpedo-recovery ramp aft. Can be armed with a twin 25-mm 80-cal. AA mount forward.

♦ 1 ex-Russian Petrushka-class (Project TS-39 or UK-3) training cutter [YXT] Bldr: Stocznia Wisla, Gdansk, Poland (In serv. 1982–. . .)

385 (ex-. . .)

D: 212 tons light (236 fl) **S:** 10.5 kts **Dim:** 39.10 (36.00 pp) × 8.40 × 2.20
Electronics: Radar: 2 Mius (Spin Trough) nav.
M: 2 Wola H12, 1,000-rpm diesels; 2 props; 610 bhp
Electric: 180 kw tot. (2 × 90 kw; 2 Wola H6 diesels driving)
Range: 1,200/10.5 **Crew:** 13 tot. + 30 instructors and students

Remarks: Probably transferred summer 1992; was active as of 6-00. Has two classrooms and a navigational training facility on the bridge and an MFD/F loop on a short mast aft. Is equipped with NBC warfare defense measures. Very similar to the SK-620-class ambulance craft from the same builder. Has an echo sounder, gyrocompass, MFD/F, and electromagnetic log. Two 23-person-capacity workboats are carried.

BORDER GUARD

PATROL CRAFT [WPC]

♦ 2 ex-Russian Stenka (Tarantul) class (Project 205P)
Bldrs: Sudostroitel'noye Obyedineniye "Almaz," Petrovskiy SY, St. Petersburg; Yaroslavl Zavod; etc. (In serv. 1967–90)

. . . (ex-AK-234) . . . (ex-AK-374)

D: 170 tons light; 211 tons std. (245 fl) **S:** 35 kts
Dim: 39.80 (37.50 wl) × 7.60 (5.90 wl) × 1.96
A: 2 twin 30-mm 65-cal. AK-230 AA; 4 fixed 402-mm OTA-40 TT (4 SET-40 ASW torpedoes); 2 d.c. racks (12 d.c.)
Electronics:
Radar: 1 Baklan (Pot Drum) or Peel Cone nav./surf. search; 1 MR-104 Rys' (Drum Tilt) gun f.c.
Sonar: Bronza hull-mounted HF (helicopter dipping-type)
EW: SPO-3 intercept
M: 3 M-504B or M-520 diesels; 3 props; 15,000 bhp
Range: 500/35; 800/20; 1,500/11.5 **Endurance:** 10 days
Crew: 4–5 officers, 26–27 enlisted

Remarks: Transferred 7-92. The dipping sonar is recessed into the port side of the transom stern, although with no submarines in the Caspian Sea, it is unlikely that the sonar equipment or the torpedo tubes are maintained operational.

Note: Several small launches are also in service.

BAHAMAS

Commonwealth of the Bahamas

ROYAL BAHAMAS DEFENCE FORCES

Personnel (2001): Approx. 890 total

Base: HMBS *Coral Harbour,* New Providence I.

Note: Craft names are preceded by HMBS (Her Majesty's Bahamian Ship).

PATROL CRAFT [PC]

Note: Plans to purchase four 43-m "Nassau"-class patrol craft from Friede Goldman Halter were canceled in 2000.

♦ 2 Bahamas class
Bldr: Halter Marine Group–Moss Point Marine, Escatawpa, Miss. (In serv. 2000)

P 60 BAHAMAS (L: 14-7-99) P 61 NASSAU (L: . . .)

Nassau (P 61)—fitting out Leo Dirkx, 11-99

Bahamas (P 60)—fitting out Leo Dirkx, 8-99

D: 375 tons (fl) **S:** 24 kts **Dim:** 60.62 × 8.90 × 2.60
A: 1 25-mm Mk 88 Bushmaster low-angle; 3 single 7.62-mm mg
Electronics: Radar: . . .
M: 3 Caterpillar 3508 DITA diesels; 3 props; 3,900 bhp
Range: 3,000+/14 **Endurance:** 21 days **Crew:** 62 tot. accomm.

Remarks: Ordered 14-3-97 for $13 million each. Steel hulls, with aluminum superstructures fabricated at Halter's Gulfport, Miss., facility. Design is a licensed, expanded version of the Vosper "Europatrol 250." Are employed on counterdrug, search-and-rescue, EEZ patrol, and disaster relief missions. Keel laid for first unit on 19-12-97. Were originally to have been completed during 1-99 and 3-99. The 25-mm gun is in a Kollmorgen Mk 98 stabilized mounting.

♦ 3 Protector class
Bldr: Fairey Marine, Cowes, U.K. (In serv. 20-11-86)

P 03 YELLOW ELDER P 04 PORT NELSON P 05 SAMANA

Samana (P 05) RN, 1996

D: 100 tons (fl) **S:** 30 kts (26 sust.) **Dim:** 33.00 (28.96 wl) × 6.73 × 1.95 (props)
A: 1 20-mm 70-cal. Oerlikon Mk 7A AA; 2 single 7.62-mm mg
Electronics: Radar: 1 Furuno FR-701 nav.
M: 3 G.M. Detroit Diesel 16V149 TIB diesels; 3 props; 5,400 bhp
Range: 300/24; 1,400/14 **Fuel:** 16 tons **Crew:** 2 officers, 18 enlisted

Remarks: Ordered 12-84. Steel construction. Have Racal MNS 2000 navigation system.

PATROL BOATS [PB]

♦ 2 40-foot Dauntless class Bldr: SeaArk, Monticello, Ark. (In serv. 1-96)

P 42 P 43

P 42 and P 43 Royal Bahamas Defence Forces, 1996

D: 11 tons (15 fl) **S:** 28 kts **Dim:** 12.19 (11.13 wl) × 3.86 × 0.69 (hull)
A: 2 single 12.7-mm mg; 2 single 7.62-mm mg

PATROL BOATS [PB] *(continued)*

Electronics: Radar: 1 Raytheon R40X nav.
M: 2 Caterpillar 3208TA diesels; 2 props; 850 bhp (720 sust.)
Range: 200/30; 400/22 **Fuel:** 250 gal. **Crew:** 5 tot.

Remarks: U.S. Grant-Aid craft ordered 1995. Aluminum construction. C. Raymond Hunt, "Deep-Vee" hull design.

♦ **2 Wahoo-class launches**
Bldr: Boston Whaler, Edgewater, Fla. (In serv. 23-10-95)

P 112 P 113

D: 1.5 tons (fl) **S:** 35 kts **Dim:** 6.81 × 2.26 × 0.36
M: 2 Mariner gasoline outboards; 180 bhp
Range: 167/40; 750/. . . **Fuel:** 243 liters **Crew:** 3 tot.

Remarks: Standard "Whaler" hullform with open cockpit amidships.

♦ **2 Impact-class launches**
Bldr: Boston Whaler, Edgewater, Fla. (In serv. 25-9-95)

P 110 P 111

Impact-class patrol launch Royal Bahamas Defence Forces, 1996

D: 1.5 tons (2.25 fl) **S:** 40 kts **Dim:** 6.81 × 2.26 × 0.36
M: 2 Mariner gasoline outboards; 180 bhp
Range: 167/40; 750/. . . **Fuel:** 243 liters **Crew:** 3 tot.

Remarks: GRP hulls with semi-rigid inflatable gunwale, fitted for rescue and towing.

♦ **1 Challenger-class launch**
Bldr: Boston Whaler, Edgewater, Fla. (In serv. 9-95)

P 41

D: 8 tons (fl) **S:** 25 kts **Dim:** 8.23 × 1.7 × 0.3
A: 1 7.62-mm mg **Electronics:** Radar: none
M: 2 Evinrude gasoline outboards; 450 bhp **Crew:** 4 tot.

Remarks: GRP hull, fitted for rescue and towing.

♦ **1 Acklins class**
Bldr: Vosper Thornycroft (In serv. 10-12-77)

P 27 Inagua

D: 30 tons (37 fl) **S:** 19.5 kts **Dim:** 18.29 (17.07 pp) × 5.03 × 1.53
A: 2 single 7.62-mm mg **Electronics:** Radar: 1 Furuno . . . nav.
M: 2 Caterpillar 3408 TA diesels; 2 props; 950 bhp **Electric:** 29 kVA tot.
Range: 650/16 **Fuel:** 4 tons **Crew:** 11 tot.

Remarks: GRP construction, air-conditioned. First unit, *Acklins* (P 21), destroyed by fire in 1980. *San Salvador* (P 24) stricken 1982. *Eleuthera* (P 22), *Andros* (P 23), *Abaco* (P 25), and *Exuma* (P 26) were stricken during 1995, with P 23 preserved as a museum exhibit.

SERVICE CRAFT

♦ **1 support craft [YF]**

AO 1 Fort Montague (ex-. . .)

D: 90 tons (fl) **S:** 10 kts **Dim:** 28.6 × 7.0 × 1.8
A: 2 single 7.62-mm mg **Electronics:** Radar: 1 Decca . . . nav.
M: 2 G.M. Detroit Diesel 12-71 diesels; 2 props; 680 hp
Range: 3,000/10 **Crew:** 16 tot.

Remarks: Purchased 6-8-80. Fishing boat hull with long deckhouse.

Disposal note: Former U.S. Navy harbor utility craft *Fort Charlotte* (A 02, ex-YFU 97, ex-LCU 1611) was reportedly stricken during 1999.

BAHRAIN

State of Bahrain

DEFENSE FORCES

Personnel (2001): Approx. 1,300 total

Base: Mina Sulman

Naval Aviation: Two AS.365F Dauphin helicopters and two Eurocopter Bo-105 helicopters, the latter with RDR 1500B radars

GUIDED-MISSILE FRIGATES [FFG]

♦ **1 ex-U.S. Oliver Hazard Perry class**
Bldr: Bath Iron Works, Bath, Maine

	Laid down	L	In serv.
90 Sabha (ex-*Jack Williams,* FFG 24)	25-2-80	30-8-80	19-9-81

Sabha (90) Maritime Photographic, 2-99

D: 2,769 tons light (3,658 fl) **S:** 29 kts (30.6 trials)
Dim: 135.64 (125.9 wl) × 13.72 × 5.8 (6.7 max.)
A: 1 Mk 13 Mod. 4 launcher (4 Harpoon and 36 Standard SM-1 MR missiles); 1 76-mm 62-cal. Mk 75 DP; 1 20-mm Mk 15 Phalanx gatling CIWS; 4 single 12.7-mm mg; 2 triple 324-mm Mk 32 Mod. 7 ASW TT; 1–2 AS.365F Dauphin helicopters
Electronics:
Radar: 1 Cardion SPS-55 surf. search; 1 Raytheon SPS-49(V)4 air search; 1 Raytheon Mk 92 Mod. 2 missile/gun f.c.; 1 Lockheed Martin STIR (SPG-60 Mod.) missile/gun f.c.
Sonar: Raytheon SQS-56 hull-mounted LF
TACAN: URN-25
EW: Raytheon SLQ-32(V)2 passive; Mk 36 SRBOC decoy RL syst. (2 6-round Raytheon Mk 137 launchers); SLQ-25 Nixie towed acoustic torpedo decoy
E/O: 2 Mk 24 target desig.
M: 2 G.E. LM-2500 gas turbines; 1 5.5-m-dia. CP, 5-bladed prop; 41,000 shp (40,000 sust.)—2 350-shp drop-down electric propulsors
Electric: 3,000 kw tot.
Range: 4,200/20; 5,000/18 **Fuel:** 587 tons + 64 tons helicopter fuel
Crew: 21 officers, 195 enlisted (incl. aviation group)

Remarks: Decommissioned from U.S. Navy and transferred under Grant-Aid program 15-9-96.
Hull systems: Particularly well protected against splinter and fragmentation damage, with 19-mm aluminum-alloy armor over magazine spaces, 16-mm steel over the main engine-control room, and 19-mm Kevlar plastic armor over vital electronics and command spaces. Speed on one turbine alone is 25 kts; the auxiliary power system uses two retractable pods located well forward and can drive the ship at up to 6 kts. The two fin stabilizers extend 2.36 m and have a mean chord of 2.36 m; they are located 57.9 m abaft the bow perpendicular. Equipped with the Prairie/Masker air bubbler system to reduce radiated machinery noise below the waterline.
Combat systems: The Mk 92 Mod. 4 fire-control system controls missile and 76-mm gunfire; it uses a STIR antenna amidships and a U.S.-built version of the Thales WM-28 radar forward and can track four separate targets. A Mk 13 weapons-direction system is fitted. The only ship-launched ASW weapons are the Mk 46 Mod. 5 torpedoes in the two triple torpedo tubes; a total of 24 torpedoes can be carried. Harpoon missiles are launched via the SWG-1 launch control system. WSC-3 SATCOM equipment was removed prior to transfer. Did not have a towed passive sonar array.

GUIDED-MISSILE PATROL COMBATANTS [PGG]

♦ **2 Type FPB 62-001**
Bldr: Friedrich Lürssen Werft, Vegesack, Germany

50 Al Manama (In serv. 3-2-88) 51 Al Muharraq (In serv. 3-2-88)

Al Manama (50) C. E. Castle, 2-99

D: 632 tons (fl) **S:** 34.7 kts (32.25 sust.) **Dim:** 62.95 (59.90 pp) × 9.30 × 2.90
A: 4 MM 40 Exocet SSM; 1 76-mm 62-cal. OTOBreda Compact C Mod. 6 DP; 1 twin 40-mm OTOBreda 70-cal. L70B AA; 2 single 12.7-mm mg; 1 AS.365F Dauphin or Bo-105 helo
Electronics:
Radar: 1 Decca 1226 nav.; 1 Ericsson Sea Giraffe 50HC surf./air search; 1 CelsiusTech 9LV 200 f.c.
EW: Racal Cutlass B-1 intercept; Racal Cygnus jammer; Thales Telegon-8 HFD/F; 2 Matra Défense Dagaie decoy RL
E/O: 2 Matra Défense Panda Mk 2 optronic f.c.

GUIDED-MISSILE PATROL COMBATANTS [PGG] *(continued)*

M: 4 MTU 20V538 TB93 diesels; 4 props; 19,600 bhp
Electric: 408 kw (3 × 136 kw) **Range:** 4,000/16 **Fuel:** 120 tons
Crew: 7 officers, 18 petty officers, 18 ratings

Remarks: Ordered 2-84. Are well overdue for refit.
Combat systems: Have CelsiusTech 9LV 331 weapons-control system. Carry 900 rounds 76-mm, 4,400 rounds 40-mm ammunition. Two 20-mm AA have been replaced by machineguns. EW *system* is Racal 242, with SADIE processor. The raised helicopter platform incorporates an elevator to lower the helicopter to the hangar below.

GUIDED-MISSILE PATROL CRAFT [PTG]

♦ 4 TNC 45 class
Bldr: Friedrich Lürssen Werft, Vegesack, Germany

	In serv.		In serv.
20 Ahmed al Fateh	5-2-84	22 Abdul Rahman al-Fadel	10-9-86
21 Al Jaberi	3-5-84	23 Al Taweelah	25-3-89

Al Taweelah (23) C. E. Castle, 2-99

Al Jaberi (21) C. E. Castle, 2-99

D: 203 tons light (259 fl) **S:** 40.5 kts
Dim: 44.9 (42.3 fl) × 7.3 × 2.05 (2.31 props)
A: 4 MM 40 Exocet SSM; 1 76-mm 62-cal. OTOBreda DP; 1 twin 40-mm 70-cal. OTOBreda AA; 2 single 12.7-mm M2 mg
Electronics:
Radar: 1 Decca 1226 nav.; 1 Ericsson Sea Giraffe 50 surf./air search; 1 CelsiusTech 9LV 223 f.c.
EW: Racal RDL-2 ABC (22, 23: Cutlass B-1) intercept; 1 Matra Défense Dagaie decoy RL—22, 23 only: Racal Cygnus jammers
E/O: Matra Défense Panda optical backup f.c.
M: 4 MTU 16V538 TB92 diesels; 4 props; 15,600 bhp (13,460 sust.)
Electric: 405 kVA **Range:** 500/38.5; 1,500/16 **Fuel:** 45 tons
Crew: 6 officers, 30 enlisted

Remarks: First pair ordered 1979, second pair 5-85. Very similar to TNC 45–class units built for the United Arab Emirates. One of the class was refitted by the builder in Germany during 2000, and bids to refit another locally were requested during 2-99.
Combat systems: Carry 250 rounds 76-mm, 1,800 rounds 40-mm, and 6,000 rounds 12.7-mm ammunition. Also carry a Bofors 57-mm rocket flare launcher.

PATROL CRAFT [PC]

♦ 2 FPB 38 class
Bldr: Friedrich Lürssen Werft, Vegesack, Germany

	L	In serv.		L	In serv.
10 Al Riffa	4-81	3-3-82	11 Hawar	7-81	3-3-82

Hawar (11) Joe Straczek, 11-01

D: 188 tons normal (205 fl) **S:** 34 kts **Dim:** 38.5 (36.0 pp) × 7.0 × 2.2 (props)
A: 1 twin 40-mm 70-cal. OTOBreda AA; 2 mine rails
Electronics:
Radar: 1 Decca 1226 nav.; 1 CelsiusTech 9GR 600 f.c.
EW: Racal RDL-2 intercept; 1 Wallop Barricade decoy RL
E/O: 1 Matra Défense Lynx optical gun f.c.
M: 2 MTU 16V538 TB92 diesels; 2 props; 9,000 bhp (6,810 sust.)
Electric: 130 kVA **Range:** 550/31.5; 1,100/16 **Crew:** 3 officers, 24 enlisted

Remarks: Ordered 1979. Carry two 3-pdr. saluting cannon. A Bofors 57-mm flare rocket/chaff launcher is fitted abaft the mast.

PATROL BOATS [PB]

♦ 2 U.S. 65-foot Commercial Cruiser class
Bldr: Swiftships, Morgan City, La.

30 Al Jarim (In serv. 9-2-82) 31 Al Jasrah (In serv. 26-2-82)

Al Jarim (30) Navpic-Holland, 4-96

D: 33 tons (fl) **S:** 30 kts **Dim:** 19.17 × 5.56 × 1.98
A: 1 20-mm 90-cal. Oerlikon GAM-B01 AA
Electronics: Radar: 1 Decca 110 nav.
M: 2 G.M. 12V71 TI diesels; 2 props; 1,200 bhp **Range:** 1,200/18
Remarks: Aluminum construction. Overdue for retirement.

MINISTRY OF THE INTERIOR COAST GUARD

Personnel (2001): Approx. 260 total in seagoing component

Base: Al Hadd

PATROL BOATS [WPB]

♦ 4 M200 class
Bldr: Halmatic, Havant, U.K. (In serv. 1991–92)

Dera'a 2 Dera'a 6 Dera'a 7 Dera'a 8

Bahraini M200- *(background)* and M140-class patrol boats on trials Halmatic, 1992

D: 31.5 tons (fl) **S:** 25 kts **Dim:** 20.10 × 5.28 × 1.54
A: 2 single 7.62-mm mg **Electronics:** Radar: 1 Decca . . . nav.
M: 2 G.M. Detroit Diesel 12V71 TA diesels; 2 props; 820 bhp
Range: 500/20 **Fuel:** 6,800 liters **Crew:** 7 tot.
Remarks: Glass-reinforced plastic construction.

♦ 6 M140 class
Bldr: Halmatic, Havant, U.K. (In serv. 1991–92)

Saif 5 Saif 6 Saif 7 Saif 8 Saif 9 Saif 10

Bahraini M140 class Halmatic, 1992

COAST GUARD PATROL BOATS [WPB] *(continued)*

D: 17 tons (fl) **S:** 35 kts **Dim:** 14.40 × 3.86 × 1.15
A: 2 single 7.62-mm mg **Electronics:** Radar: 1 Decca . . . nav.
M: 2 G.M. Detroit Diesel 12V71 TA diesels; 2 props; 820 bhp
Electric: 17.6 kVA (1 G.M. diesel set)
Range: 440/20 **Fuel:** 3,400 liters **Crew:** 4 tot.

Remarks: Glass-reinforced plastic construction.

♦ 1 30-meter Wasp class
Bldr: Souter, Cowes, U.K. (In serv. 12-8-85)

Al Yusrah

D: 90 tons (103 fl) **S:** 23.6 kts **Dim:** 30.0 (26.75 wl) × 6.40 × 1.60
A: 1 20-mm 90-cal. Oerlikon GAM-B01 AA; 2 single 7.62-mm mg
Electronics: Radar: 1 . . . nav.
M: 2 G.M. Detroit Diesel 16V149 TI diesels; 2 props; 3,100 bhp
Electric: 47 kVA **Range:** 500/22; 1,000/12 **Fuel:** 17 tons **Crew:** 16 tot.

Remarks: Enlarged version of standard 20-m Wasp, ordered 3-8-84 and laid down 15-11-84. GRP construction. Outfitted as a yacht; a VIP lounge is built over the stern. Name also reported as *Al Muharraq.*

♦ 2 20-meter Wasp-class fiberglass-hulled
Bldr: Souter, Cowes, U.K. (In serv. 1983)

Dera'a 4 Dera'a 5

D: 34 tons (36.3 fl) **S:** 21 kts **Dim:** 20.0 (16.0 wl) × 5.0 × 1.5
A: 2 single 7.62-mm mg **Electronics:** Radar: 1 Decca . . . nav.
M: 2 G.M. Detroit Diesel 12V71 TI diesels; 2 props; 1,200 bhp **Crew:** 8 tot.

♦ 4 Sword class
Bldr: Fairey Marine, Cowes, U.K. (In serv. 1980)

Saif 1 Saif 2 Saif 3 Saif 4

D: 15.2 tons **S:** 28 kts **Dim:** 13.7 × 4.1 × 1.32
M: 2 G.M. Detroit Diesel 8V71 TI diesels; 2 props; 850 bhp
Range: 500/. . . **Crew:** 6 tot.

Remarks: GRP construction. Are due for disposal. Carry small arms only.

Disposal note: Tracker-class patrol boats *Dera'a 1* and *Dera'a 3* had been retired by 1999.

SERVICE CRAFT

♦ 1 miscellaneous support/supply boat [WYF]
Bldr: Halmatic, Havant, U.K. (In serv. 1992)

Safra 3

Safra 3 Halmatic, 1992

D: 165 tons (fl) **S:** 13 kts **Dim:** 25.91 × 5.87 × 1.57
A: none **Electronics:** Radar: 1 Decca . . . nav.
M: 2 G.M. Detroit Diesel 16V92 TA diesels; 2 props; 2,480 bhp
Electric: 74 kVA tot. (2 × 37-kVA diesel alternators)
Range: 700/13 **Crew:** 6 tot.

Remarks: GRP-construction hull with aluminum superstructure. Can carry up to 15 tons of deck cargo and personnel.

♦ 1 logistic support landing craft [WYF]
Bldr: Swiftships, Morgan City, La. (In serv. 21-10-82)

41 Ajirah

Ajirah (41) Navpic-Holland, 4-96

D: 428 tons (fl) **S:** 12 kts **Dim:** 39.62 × 10.97 × 1.30
A: none **Electronics:** Radar: 1 Decca . . . nav.
M: 2 G.M. Detroit Diesel 16V71N diesels; 2 props; 1,800 bhp
Fuel: 20 tons **Range:** 1,500/10 **Crew:** 2 officers, 6 enlisted

Remarks: Aluminum construction. Cargo: vehicles, supplies, up to 100 tons cargo fuel and 88 tons water. Has a bow ramp and 15-ton crane. Turning radius 77 m. Two sisters are in Venezuelan service.

♦ 1 Loadmaster II–class landing craft [WYF]
Bldr: Fairey Marine, Cowes, U.K. (In serv. 1981)

40 Sabha

Sabha (40) Navpic-Holland, 4-96

D: 150 tons (fl) **S:** 8 kts **Dim:** 22.5 × 7.5 × 1.2
M: 2 G.M. 8V92N diesels; 2 props; 776 bhp **Range:** 500/. . . **Crew:** 6 tot.

♦ 4 ex-U.S. Army LCU 1466–class utility landing craft [WYF]
Bldr: General Ship & Eng. Wks. (In serv. 1976–78)

42 Mashtan (ex-LCU . . . .) 44 Suwad (ex-LCU . . . .)
43 Rubodh (ex-LCU . . . .) 45 Jaradah (ex-LCU . . . .)

Jaradah (45) Joe Straczek, 11-01

D: 180 tons light (347 fl) **S:** 8 kts **Dim:** 35.08 × 10.36 × 1.60 (max.)
A: 2 single 12.7-mm mg **Electronics:** Radar: 1 . . . nav.
M: 3 G.M. Gray Marine 64 YTL diesels; 3 props; 1,200 bhp
Range: 1,200/6 (700/7 loaded) **Fuel:** 11 tons **Crew:** 11 tot.

Remarks: Transferred during 1991 from surplus U.S. Army stocks. Cargo: 150 tons in 15.8 × 9.0-m open deck with ramps at both ends.

♦ about 10 wooden motor dhows for logistics and patrol duties [WYFL]

♦ 1 Tiger-class utility hovercraft [WYFLA]
Bldr: AVL, Cowes, U.K. (In serv. 1995)

Nijood

D: 4.5 tons (fl) **S:** 35 kts **Dim:** 8.0 × 3.8 × 2.3 (high)
M: 1 AMC gasoline engine; 180 bhp

BANGLADESH

People's Republic of Bangladesh

Personnel (2000): 11,282 total (1,007 officers). The navy hopes to establish a battalion of marines.

Bases: BNS *Issah Khan* naval base and repair facilities at Chittagong; BNS *Patenga* naval academy; BNS *Haji Mohsin* naval base at Dhaka; BNS *Titumir* and *Mongla* facilities at Khulna; and BNS *Shaheed Moassam* facility at Kaptai. The government-owned Khulna Shipbuilding & Engineering Works, Ltd., was taken over by the navy in 2-99.

Naval Aviation: Two or more helicopters are to be purchased for use with the new frigate, and long-range plans call for procurement of land-based maritime reconnaissance aircraft.

Note: Naval ship names are preceded by BNS (Bangladesh Naval Ship).

FRIGATES [FF]

Note: In addition to the units listed below, the navy was said by Ukrainian sources to be negotiating with the Ukrainian Research-Design Shipbuilding Center for an export version of the "Sapsan-2100"-class multipurpose frigate as of 1-99; no contract has yet been reported, however. The 1,920-ton light displacement design (2,300 fl) would be 105 m overall, 12.8 m beam, and 3.5 m draft and would have a CODOG propulsion plant delivering speeds of up to 32 kts. Range would be 5,000 n.m. at 18 kts, and the ship would be equipped with eight antiship missiles, one 76-mm or 100-mm gun, and a helicopter. The unit would be built at Mikolayiv.

♦ 1 DW2000H design
Bldr: Daewoo Heavy Industries, South Korea

	Laid down	L	In serv.
F 25 Bangabandhu	. . .	. . .	30-5-01

Bangabandhu (F 25) Daewoo, 2001

D: 2,300 tons (fl) **S:** . . . kts **Dim:** 103.50 (98.00 pp) × 12.00 × 3.60
A: 4 Alenia Otomat Mk 2 Block IV SSM; 1 76-mm 62-cal. OTOBreda DP; 2 twin 40-mm 70-cal. OTOBreda Fast Forty AA; 2 single 12.7-mm mg; 2 triple 324-mm B515 ASW TT; 2 mine rails; 1 helicopter
Electronics:
Radar: Thales Variant surf. search; Thales DA-08 air search; Thales Lirod Mk 2 f.c.
Sonar: . . .
EW: Thales Cutlass 242 intercept and Scorpion jammer
E/O: Thales Mirador-FD surveillance/tracking/f.c.
M: 4 SEMT-Pielstick . . . diesels; 2 props; . . . bhp
Range: . . ./. . . **Crew:** . . .

Remarks: Request for bids issued 21-11-95 for a unit to replace one of the British-built frigates. Ordered 11-9-97. Paid for with funds from a $100 million Saudi Arabian grant. Departed for Bangladesh on 5-6-01.
Combat systems: Has Thales TACTICOS combat command/data system. A helicopter deck and hangar are fitted, although the navy has no aircraft. Provision was made for later installation of a short-range SAM system such as Sea Sparrow.

♦ 1 Chinese Jianghu-II class (Project 053H1)
Bldr: Hudong SY, Shanghai

	L	In serv.
F 18 Osman (ex-*Xiangtan,* 556)	1986	8-11-89

Osman (F 18) Brian Morrison, 10-01

D: 1,568 tons (1,702 fl) **S:** 25.5 kts **Dim:** 103.2 × 10.2 × 3.05 (hull)
A: 4 Fei Long-1 SSM; 2 twin 100-mm 56-cal. DP; 4 twin 37-mm 62-cal. Type 74 AA; 2 5-round Type 81 ASW RL; 4 d.c. mortars; 2 d.c. racks
Electronics:
Radar: 1 Type 756 nav.; 1 MX-902 (Eye Shield) air search; 1 Type 256 (Square Tie) missile target desig.
Sonar: Echo Type 5 MF hull-mounted
EW: RW-23-1 (Jug Pair) intercept
M: 2 SEMT-Pielstick 12 PA6 280 BTC diesels; 2 props; 16,000 bhp
Electric: 1,320 kw (3 × 400-kw, 1 × 120-kw diesel sets)
Range: 1,750/25; 4,000/15 **Endurance:** 15 days
Crew: 27 officers, 273 enlisted

Remarks: Taken from Chinese Navy inventory and not built new for Bangladesh; transferred 26-9-89 and arrived Chittagong 8-10-89. Badly damaged forward in 8-91 collision with merchant vessel; repaired 1992–93. Planned transfer of a second unit in 1990 was canceled.
Combat systems: Has a Wok Won nonstabilized optical director for the 100-mm guns but no fire-control radar; the other weapons are improvements on Soviet-era systems. The antiship missiles are an improved copy of the original Soviet Styx (Termit) system. The depth charge racks are mounted belowdecks and discharge through doors in the transom. The antiaircraft guns are on-mount controlled via ringsights.

♦ 1 ex-British Salisbury class (Type 61)
Bldr: Hawthorne Leslie, Hebburn-on-Tyne

	Laid down	L	In serv.
F 16 Umar Farooq (ex-*Llandaff,* F 61)	27-8-53	30-11-55	11-4-58

Umar Farooq (F 16) H&L Van Ginderen, 1999

D: 2,170 tons (2,408 fl) **S:** 24 kts **Dim:** 103.60 (100.58 pp) × 12.19 × 4.80
A: 1 twin 114-mm 45-cal. Mk 6 DP; 1 twin 40-mm 60-cal. Bofors Mk 5 AA; 1 3-round Mk 4 Squid ASW mortar
Electronics:
Radar: 2 . . . nav.; 1 Type 965 early warning; 1 Type 993 air/surf. search; 1 Type 277 height-finder; 1 Type 275 f.c.
Sonar: Type 174 HF search; Type 170B searchlight HF targeting
EW: UA-3 intercept, FH-4 HFD/F
M: 8 Admiralty 16VVS ASR 1 diesels; 2 props; 12,400 bhp
Range: 2,300/24; 7,500/16 **Crew:** 14 officers, 223 enlisted

Remarks: Transferred from U.K. 10-12-76. As of 10-98, retained all topside equipment aboard at transfer, making her a veritable museum of 1950s British naval technology. Had a major engineering plant failure in 1985; repaired. Has four additional 16VVS ASR 1 diesels driving generator sets. The 114-mm mount is controlled by a Mk 6 f.c.s., while the 40-mm mount is locally controlled. The Squid triple ASW mortar may have been removed.

♦ 2 ex-British Leopard class (Type 41)

	Bldr	Laid down	L	In serv.
F 15 Abu Bakr (ex-*Lynx,* F 27)	John Brown, Clydebank	13-8-53	12-1-55	14-3-57
F 17 Ali Haider (ex-*Jaguar,* F 37)	Wm. Denny, Dumbarton	2-11-53	30-7-57	12-12-59

Ali Haider (F 17) Brian Morrison, 2-01

D: 2,300 tons (2,520 fl) **S:** 23 kts **Dim:** 103.63 (100.58 pp) × 12.19 × 4.8 (fl)
A: 2 twin 114-mm 45-cal. Mk 6 DP; 1 40-mm 60-cal. Mk 9 AA; 2 single 20-mm 70-cal. Oerlikon AA
Electronics:
Radar: 3 . . . nav./surf. search; 1 Type 965 early warning; 1 Type 993 air/surf. search; 1 Type 275 f.c.
EW: UA-4 intercept, FH-5 HFD/F
M: 8 Admiralty 16VVS ASR 1 diesels; 2 CP props; 12,400 bhp
Range: 2,300/23; 7,500/16 **Crew:** 15 officers, 220 enlisted

Remarks: F 17 purchased 6-7-78; arrived Bangladesh 11-78 after overhaul. F 15 purchased 12-3-82, commissioned 19-3-82. F 15 is to continue in service as training ship, while F 17 was to be hulked on delivery of the new Korean-built frigate. Have fin stabilizers.
Combat systems: Squid ASW mortar and sonars removed while in Royal Navy service. 1 Mk 6 GFCS with Type 275 radar for the 114-mm guns. Local control only for the 40-mm; in F 17, the 40-mm mount may be a 70-cal. Bofors mounting. The Type 993 radar is probably no longer operational. A fourth small navigational or surface-search radar set antenna appears to be mounted atop the foremast on F 17.

GUIDED-MISSILE PATROL CRAFT [PTG]

♦ 5 Chinese Huangfeng class (Project 021)
Bldr: Jiangnan SY, Shanghai

P 8125 Durdharsha P 8127 Durnibar P 8131 Anirban
P 8126 Durdanta P 8128 Durdanda

D: 175 tons light, 186.5 tons normal (205 fl) **S:** 35 kts
Dim: 38.75 × 7.60 × 1.70 (mean)

GUIDED-MISSILE PATROL CRAFT [PTG] *(continued)*

Durdharsha (P 8125) French Navy, 1996

A: 4 HY-1 SSM; 2 twin 30-mm 65-cal. Type 69 AA
Electronics: Radar: 1 Type 256 (Square Tie) surf. search/target desig.
M: 3 M-503A diesels; 3 props; 12,000 bhp **Electric:** 65 kw tot.
Range: 800/30 **Crew:** 5 officers, 60 enlisted

Remarks: Chinese copy of the Soviet Osa-I (Project 205) design. First four commissioned in Bangladesh fleet on 10-11-88. Two sank during the 4-91 cyclone but have been salvaged; two others were damaged but have been repaired. P 8131 was delivered 6-92 as a replacement but ended up as a force enhancement. Lack fire-control radar director for the 30-mm guns (copies of the Russian AK-230 system), which are instead controlled by two remote ringsight directors. Reported crew size seems excessive.

♦ 5 Chinese Houku class (Project 024)

P 8111 Durbar　P 8113 Durvedya　P 8141 Uttal
P 8112 Duranta　P 8114 Durdam

D: 68 tons (79 fl) **S:** 37 kts **Dim:** 27.00 × 6.50 × 1.80 (1.30 hull)
A: 2 HY-1 SSM; 1 twin 25-mm 80-cal. Type 61 AA
Electronics: Radar: 1 Type 256 (Square Tie) surf. search/target desig.
M: 4 M-50F-4 (Type L-12V-180) diesels; 4 props; 4,800 bhp **Electric:** 65 kw tot.
Range: 400/30; 500/24 **Endurance:** 5 days **Crew:** 4 officers, 13 enlisted

Remarks: First two delivered 6-4-83, two others 10-11-83. P 8141 was delivered 8-92 as a replacement for one of the two badly damaged during the 4-91 cyclone, but both were ultimately repaired. Steel construction. The gunmount is a copy of the Russian 2M-3M mounting.

TORPEDO BOATS [PT]

♦ 8 Chinese Huchuan-class

P 8221 TB 1　P 8223 TB 3　P 8235 TB 35　P 8237 TB 37
P 8222 TB 2　P 8224 TB 4　P 8236 TB 36　P 8238 TB 38

TB 35 (P 8235)—with old letter prefix French Navy, 4-89

D: 39 tons (45.8 fl) **S:** 50 kts
Dim: 22.50 × 3.80 (6.26 over foils) × 1.15 (1.12 foilborne)
A: 2 twin 14.5-mm 79-cal. Type 81 AA; 2 fixed 533-mm TT
Electronics: Radar: 1 Type 753 nav.
M: 3 M-50F-4 (Type L12V-180) diesels; 3 props; 3,600 bhp **Electric:** 5.6 kw
Range: 500/30 **Crew:** 3 officers, 20 enlisted

Remarks: TB 1–4 are former Chinese Navy units commissioned in Bangladesh service 1-3-88. TB 35–38 were donated during 1992 by Pakistan to replace units sunk during the 1991 cyclone, but those have now been repaired. Cruising speed is 32 kts. Foils mounted forward only, with a small auxiliary foil beneath the bow to aid in getting foilborne; the stern has no hydrofoils and planes on the surface.

PATROL CRAFT [PC]

♦ 1 Chinese Haizhui class
Bldr: Guijian SY (In serv. 9-4-96)

P 711 Barkat

D: 150 tons (170 fl) **S:** 29 kts **Dim:** 41.0 × 5.41 × 1.80
A: 2 twin 37-mm 63-cal. Type 76 AA; 2 twin 25-mm 80-cal. Type 81 AA
Electronics: Radar: 1 Anritsu 726 UA nav./surf. search
M: 4 Type L12-180Z diesels; 4 props; 4,800 bhp (4,400 sust.)
Range: 750/16 **Crew:** 4 officers, 24 enlisted

Remarks: Donated as a replacement for discarded Shanghai-II-class units, of which this is an updated variant. Has fin stabilizers. Sisters operate in the Sri Lankan Navy.

♦ 2 Meghna class
Bldr: Vosper Pty, Tanjong Rhu, Singapore

P 211 Meghna (L: 19-1-84)　P 212 Jamuna (L: 19-3-84)

Jamuna (P 212)—outboard *Meghna* (P 211) Gilbert Gyssels, 1987

D: 410 tons (fl) **S:** 22 kts **Dim:** 46.50 (42.50 pp) × 7.50 × 2.00 (hull)
A: 1 57-mm 70-cal. Bofors SAK 57 Mk 1 AA; 1 40-mm 70-cal. Bofors AA; 2 single 7.62-mm mg
Electronics: Radar: 1 Decca TM 1229C nav.
M: 2 Paxman Valenta 12 CM diesels; 2 props; 6,000 bhp (5,460 sust.)
Electric: 218 kw tot. (2 × 109-kw diesel sets)
Range: 2,000/16 **Fuel:** 42 tons **Crew:** 3 officers, 45 enlisted

Remarks: Operated for the Ministry of Agriculture by the navy for 200-n.m. economic zone patrol and fisheries protection duties. Both were damaged during the 4-91 typhoon but have been repaired. P 212 may have been rearmed with two twin 40-mm AA in place of the 57-mm gun. Both have an Alenia NA 18B optronic gun director.

♦ 1 Chinese Hainan-class submarine chaser

P 812 Nirbhoy (In serv. 1-12-85)

Nirbhoy (P 812) French Navy, 1996

D: 375 tons normal (400 fl) **S:** 30.5 kts **Dim:** 58.77 × 7.20 × 2.20 (hull)
A: 2 twin 57-mm 70-cal. Type 66 AA; 2 twin 25-mm 80-cal. Type 61 AA; 4 5-round Type 81 ASW RL; 2 d.c. mortars; 2 d.c. racks; 2 mine rails
Electronics:
Radar: 1 Type 753 surf. search—Sonar: 1 Tamir-11 searchlight HF
M: 4 diesels; 4 props; 8,800 bhp **Range:** 2,000/14 **Crew:** 70 tot.

Remarks: Sister *Durjoy* (P 811) damaged beyond repair in 1995 and stricken. Both had been damaged during the 4-91 typhoon. All gunmounts are locally controlled.

♦ 3 Chinese Shanghai-II class

P 612 Tawfiq　P 613 Tamjeed　P 614 Tanveer

D: 122 tons (135 fl) **S:** 28.5 kts **Dim:** 38.78 × 5.41 × 1.55 (max.)
A: 2 twin 37-mm 63-cal. Type 74 AA; 2 twin 25-mm 80-cal. Type 61 AA
Electronics: Radar: 1 Type 351 (Pot Head) nav.
M: 2 Type L12-180 diesels (1,200 bhp each), 2 Type L12-180Z diesels (910 bhp each); 4 props; 4,220 bhp
Electric: 39 kw tot. **Range:** 750/16.5 **Crew:** 36 tot.

Remarks: Delivered 5-82. Two earlier units, delivered in 1974, were stricken by the late 1980s. *Shahed Daulut* (P 411), *Shaheed Farid* (P 412), *Shaheed Mohibullah* (P 413), and *Shaheed Akhtaruddin* (P 414) were stricken in 1995. *Tawheed* (P 611) of this class was assigned to the Coast Guard during 1995. The radar is a copy of the 1950s Soviet Reya set.

♦ 1 salvaged Pakistani patrol boat
Bldr: Brooke Marine, Lowestoft, U.K. (In serv. 20-5-65)

P 311 Bishkali (ex-*Jessore*)

D: 115 tons (143 fl) **S:** 24 kts **Dim:** 32.62 (30.48 pp) × 6.10 × 1.55
A: 2 single 40-mm 70-cal. OTOBreda AA
Electronics: Radar: 1 Decca . . . nav.
M: 2 MTU 12V538 diesels; 2 props; 3,400 bhp **Crew:** 30 tot.

PATROL CRAFT [PC] *(continued)*

Remarks: Sunk in 1971 war of independence; salvaged and repaired at Khulna SY and recommissioned 23-11-78.

♦ 2 ex-Indian Ajay class
Bldr: Hooghly D & E, Calcutta (In serv. 1-62)

P 312 Padma (ex-*Akshay,* P 3136)　P 313 Surma (ex-*Ajay,* P 3135)

D: 120 tons (151 fl) **S:** 18 kts **Dim:** 35.75 (33.52 pp) × 6.1 × 1.9
A: P 312: 2 quadruple 20-mm 90-cal. M-75 AA—P 313: 1 40-mm 60-cal. Bofors Mk 3 AA; 1 quadruple 20-mm 90-cal. M-75 AA
Electronics: Radar: 1 Decca . . . nav.
M: 2 Paxman YHAXM diesels; 2 props; 1,000 bhp
Range: 500/12; 1,000/8 **Crew:** 3 officers, 32 enlisted

Remarks: Indian version of British Ford class, donated by India and commissioned 12-4-73 and 26-7-74, respectively. Rearmed in late 1980s with Yugoslav-made weapons; P 313 has a 40-mm gun aft in place of one quadruple 20-mm mount.

♦ 2 ex-Yugoslav Kraljevica class (In serv. 1956)

P 314 Karniphuli (ex-PBR 502)　P 315 Tistna (ex-PBR 505)

Karniphuli (P 314)　French Navy, 1996

D: 190 tons (202 fl) **S:** 18 kts **Dim:** 41.0 × 6.3 × 2.2
A: 2 single 40-mm 60-cal. Bofors Mk 3 AA; 4 single 20-mm Hispano AA; 2 U.S. Mk 6 d.c. mortars; 2 d.c. racks; 2 5-round 128-mm artillery RL
Electronics:
Radar: 1 Decca 1229 nav.—Sonar: QCU-2 hull-mounted searchlight HF
M: 2 M.A.N. W8V 30/38 diesels; 2 props; 3,300 bhp
Range: 1,000/12 **Crew:** 4 officers, 40 enlisted

Remarks: Transferred 6-6-75. P 314 was reduced to reserve in 1988 but was re-engined in 1995 and reactivated; P 315 was re-engined in 1997–98. The sonar may no longer function.

PATROL BOATS [PB]

Note: Negotiations were ongoing in spring 1999 with Severnoye Design Bureau, St. Petersburg, Russia, for the design of high-speed patrol boats to be constructed in Bangladesh. During 6-00, two 9.50-m and six 5.40-m rigid inflatable patrol launches were ordered from Delta Power, Stockport, U.K.

♦ 4 Pabna-class riverine　Bldr: DEW Narayengonj, Dhaka

P 112 Noakhali (In serv. 7-72)　P 114 Bogra (In serv. 6-77)
P 113 Patuakhali (In serv. 11-74)　P 115 Rangamati (In serv. 6-77)

D: 69.5 tons (fl) **S:** 10 kts **Dim:** 22.9 × 6.1 × 1.9
A: 1 40-mm 60-cal. Bofors Mk 3 AA
M: 2 Cummins diesels; 2 props
Range: 700/8 **Crew:** 3 officers, 30 enlisted

Remarks: Last two differ in configuration, gun forward. Form River Patrol Squadron 11, based at Mongla. No radar fitted. Sister *Pabna* (P 111) of this class was assigned to the Coast Guard during 1995.

MINE WARFARE SHIPS

♦ 1 Chinese T-43-class (Project 010) fleet minesweepers [MSF]
Bldr: Wuzhang SY or Guangzhou SY, China (In serv. 27-4-95)

M 91 Sagar

Sagar (M 91)　French Navy, 1996

D: 500 tons (590 fl) **S:** 14 kts **Dim:** 60.0 × 8.60 × 2.16
A: 2 twin 37-mm 63-cal. Type 74 AA; 2 twin 25-mm 80-cal. Type 61 AA; 2 twin 12.7-mm 93-cal. mg; 2 d.c. mortars; 2 mine rails (12–16 mines)
Electronics:
Radar: 1 Type 756 nav.—Sonar: C-Tech CMAS-36/39 HF mine avoidance
M: 2 Type 9D diesels; 2 props; 2,200 bhp **Electric:** 550 kw tot.
Range: 3,200/10 **Fuel:** 70 tons **Crew:** 12 officers, 58 enlisted

Remarks: Design originated in Russia in the late 1940s and has been built in China since the late 1950s. M 91, ordered 1993 and newly built especially for Bangladesh, has acoustic and magnetic sweep gear in addition to MPT-1 and MPT-3 wire sweeps and paravanes. M 92–94 were to have been delivered one per year from 1996–98, but the order was apparently never consummated. The Canadian C-Tech mine avoidance sonar was delivered fall 1997 as a replacement for the obsolete Tamir-11 set.

♦ 4 ex-U.K. River-class fleet minesweepers [MSF]
Bldr: Richards (Shipbuilders) Ltd., Great Yarmouth (M 95: Lowestoft)

	Laid down	L	In serv.
M 95 Shapla (ex-*Waveney,* M 2003)	21-2-83	8-9-83	29-9-84
M 96 Shaikat (ex-*Carron,* M 2004)	21-2-83	23-9-83	29-9-84
M 97 Shurobi (ex-*Dovey,* M 2005)	3-3-83	1-12-83	30-3-84
M 98 Shaibal (ex-*Helford,* M 2006)	12-10-83	17-5-84	7-6-85

Shaibal (M 98)　Ben Sullivan, 10-94

D: 630 tons (770 fl) **S:** 14 kts (15 on trials; 12 sust.)
Dim: 47.60 (42.00 pp) × 10.50 × 3.10 (3.75 max.)
A: 1 40-mm 60-cal. Bofors Mk 3 AA; 2 single 7.62-mm mg
Electronics:
Radar: 2 Decca TM 1226 nav.
Sonar: C-Tech CMAS-36/39 HF mine-avoidance (not in M 98)
M: 2 Ruston 6 RKCM diesels; 2 4-bladed CP props; 3,040 bhp
Electric: 460 kw tot. **Range:** 4,500/10 **Fuel:** 88 tons
Crew: 9 officers, 23 enlisted

Remarks: 638 grt. Purchased 9-94 and delivered late 10-94. Had been decommissioned from Royal Navy 23-10-93. All four officially commissioned in Bangladesh service at Chittagong on 27-4-95. In 3-97, M 98 completed fitting out to serve as a survey vessel in support of the Franco-Bangladeshi Hydro Bangla Project, although a mine countermeasures capability was retained; a second ship may be similarly reequipped. The others are primarily employed as offshore patrol vessels.
Hull systems: Steel hulls with a single-compartment damage standard. Navigation gear includes two Kelvin-Hughes MS 48 echo sounders, Decca QM 14(1) and Decca HiFix Mk 6 radio navaids, and a satellite navigation receiver.
Combat systems: Have mechanical minesweeping capability only, having been transferred with a full suite of paravanes, cutters, and depressors. Have the Racal System 880 Integrated Minehunting System (QX3/1). The 40-mm gun is hand operated.

AMPHIBIOUS WARFARE CRAFT

♦ 1 Danish-built former commercial landing craft [LCU]
Bldr: Danyard, Frederikshavn (In serv. 1988)

L 900 Shahamanat

D: 366 tons (fl) **S:** 9.5 kts **Dim:** 47.0 × 10.4 × 2.4
A: . . . **Electronics:** Radar: . . .
M: 2 Caterpillar D343 diesels; 2 props; 720 bhp
Crew: 3 officers, 28 enlisted

Remarks: Acquired for naval service during 1990. A sister remains in commercial service. Resembles U.S. LCU 1466–class utility landing craft but has shorter vehicle cargo deck and longer poop deck with more extensive superstructure.

♦ 2 ex-U.S. Army LCU 1466 class [LCU]

L 901 Shah Poran (ex-*Cerro Gordo,* LCU 1512)
L 902 Shah Makhdum (ex-*Cadgel,* LCU 1566)

D: 180 tons light (347 fl) **S:** 8 kts **Dim:** 35.08 × 10.36 × 1.60 (max.)
A: 2 single 12.7-mm M2 mg
Electronics: Radar: 1 Canadian Marconi LN-66 nav.
M: 3 G.M. Gray Marine 64 YTL diesels; 3 props; 1,200 bhp
Range: 1,200/6 (700/7 loaded) **Fuel:** 11 tons **Crew:** 11 tot.

Remarks: Transferred during 1991 from surplus U.S. Army stocks and commissioned 16-5-92 after refits. Cargo: 150 tons in 15.8 × 9.0-m open deck with ramps at both ends.

♦ 4 Chinese Yuchai-class (Project 068) landing craft [LCM]

A 584 LCT 101　A 585 LCT 102　A 586 LCT 103　A 587 LCT 104

D: 85 tons (fl) **S:** 11.5 kts **Dim:** 24.8 × 5.2 × 1.3
A: 2 twin 14.5-mm 93-cal. Type 81 AA **Electronics:** Radar: none
M: 2 Type 12V-150 diesels; 2 props; 600 bhp
Range: 450/11.5 **Crew:** 23 tot. (incl. vehicle crew)

Remarks: Two transferred 4-5-86, two 1-7-86. Two badly damaged during the 4-91 cyclone but later repaired.

AMPHIBIOUS WARFARE CRAFT *(continued)*

Bangladeshi Navy Yuchai-class landing craft French Navy, 1996

♦ 3 Bangladeshi-design landing craft [LCM]
Bldr: Khulna SY (LCVP 013: DEW Narayangong)

LCVP 011 LCVP 012 LCVP 013

D: 83 tons (fl) **S:** 12 kts (light) **Dim:** 21.3 × 5.2 × 1.5 **A:** none
M: 2 Cummins diesels; 2 props; 730 bhp **Crew:** 1 officer, 9 enlisted

♦ 4 ex-U.S. LCM(8)-class landing craft [LCM]

D: 34 tons light (121 fl) **S:** 12 kts (light) **Dim:** 22.43 × 6.40 × 1.40 (aft)
M: 4 G.M. Detroit Diesel 6-71 diesels; 2 props; 560 bhp **Range:** 150/12

Remarks: Transferred 4-91 during U.S. Navy disaster relief efforts. Can carry 56 tons cargo or 150 troops. Aluminum construction.

AUXILIARIES

♦ 1 small underway-replenishment oiler [AO]
Bldr: . . . SY, Japan (In serv. 1983)

A 515 Khan Jahan Ali

Khan Jahan Ali (A 515) Gilbert Gyssels, 6-87

D: 2,900 tons (fl) **S:** 12 kts **Dim:** 76.1 × 11.4 × 5.3
A: 2 single 20-mm 70-cal. Oerlikon AA **Electronics:** Radar: 1 . . . nav.
M: 1 6-cyl. diesel; 1 prop; 1,350 bhp **Crew:** 3 officers, 23 enlisted

Remarks: 1,342 grt. Transferred 1983 from state-owned shipping line and equipped for underway refueling. Cargo: 1,500 tons.

♦ 1 Chinese Dinghai-class seagoing tug [ATA]
Bldr: Wuhu SY

A 721 Khadem

Khadem (A 721) Gilbert Gyssels, 6-87

D: 1,472 tons (fl) **S:** 14 kts **Dim:** 60.22 × 11.60 × 4.44
A: 2 single 12.7-mm mg **Electronics:** Radar: 2 . . . nav.
M: 2 diesels; 2 props; 2,640 bhp
Range: 7,200/14 **Crew:** 7 officers, 49 enlisted

Remarks: 980.28 grt. Transferred new 6-5-84.

♦ 1 ex-U.K. Island-class training ship [AXT]
Bldr: Hall Russell, Aberdeen

	L	In serv.
A 511 Shaheed Ruhul Amin (ex-*Jersey,* P 295)	18-3-76	15-10-76

Shaheed Ruhul Amin (A 511) *Flottes de Combat,* 1-94

D: 998 tons (1,280 fl) **S:** 16.5 kts **Dim:** 61.10 (51.97 pp) × 11.00 × 4.27
A: 1 40-mm 60-cal. Bofors Mk 3 AA; 2 single 7.62-mm FN mg
Electronics: Radar: 1 Type 1006 nav.—Sonar: Simrad SU side-scan
M: 2 Ruston 12 RK 3 CM diesels (750 rpm); 1 CP prop; 4,380 bhp
Electric: 536 kw **Range:** 11,000/12 **Fuel:** 310 tons
Crew: 5 officers, 29 enlisted (in Royal Navy service)

Remarks: Former offshore patrol vessel decommissioned from Royal Navy 16-12-93 and purchased as a replacement for the former ship of the same name and number in the Bangladeshi Navy (the former Canadian coastal passenger/cargo vessel *Anticosti*); recommissioned 29-1-94. Had been ordered 11-2-75. Sister *Orkney* (P 299) was offered in 5-99 but was not acquired.
Hull systems: Has fin stabilizers. Can maintain 12–15 kts in a Force 8 gale. Has Decca CANES-2 navaid. Avon Sea Raider semi-rigid dinghies replaced the original Geminis for inspection purposes. Can carry 28.6 tons detergent (a 6-hr supply) for oil-spill cleanup.

SERVICE CRAFT

♦ 1 self-propelled floating crane [YD]
Bldr: Khulna SY (In serv. 18-5-88)

A 731 Balaban

D: . . . tons **S:** 9 kts **Dim:** . . . × . . . × . . . **M:** . . .
Crew: 2 officers, 27 enlisted

Remarks: Lift capacity: 70 tons.

♦ 1 floating dry dock [YFDL]
Bldr: Tito SY, Trogir, Yugoslavia (In serv. 15-8-80)

A 701 Sundarban

Lift capacity: 3,500 tons **Dim:** 117.0 × 27.6 × 0.3 (loaded)

Remarks: Self-docking type with 7 sectional pontoons. Measures 17.6 m between dock walls, which are 101.4 m long. A second, commercial floating dry dock (16,500 tons capacity, 182.9 m overall, delivered 1981) is also available.

♦ 5 5-meter aluminum workboats [YFL]
Bldr: . . . , U.S.A. (In serv. 1993)

♦ 3 7-meter aluminum workboats [YFL]
Bldr: . . . , U.S.A. (In serv. 1993)

Remarks: Both workboat classes provided as Grant-Aid for riverine search-and-rescue work.

♦ 1 general-purpose harbor tender [YFU]
Bldr: . . . (Acquired 1989)

A . . . Sanket

D: 80 tons (fl) **S:** 16 kts **Dim:** 29.4 × 6.1 × 1.8
A: 1 20-mm 70-cal. Oerlikon AA **Electronics:** Radar: 2 . . . nav.
M: 2 Deutz Sea 16M diesels; 2 props; 2,430 bhp
Range: 1,000/16 **Crew:** 1 officer, 23 enlisted

Remarks: Taken over from civilian service in 1989; sister *Shamikha* remains in civilian service. Has the appearance of a small patrol boat and does not wear a pennant number.

♦ 1 coastal survey craft [YGS]

A 583 Agradoot (ex-. . .)

Remarks: Acquired 1996 from commercial service and refitted for commissioning in 1998. 45 m overall; no other data available.

♦ 1 coastal survey craft [YGS]
Bldr: . . . , Japan

A 513 Shahjalal (ex-*Gold 4*)

D: 600 tons (fl) **S:** 12 kts **Dim:** 40.2 × 9.1 × 2.5
A: 2 single 20-mm Oerlikon AA **M:** 1 16-cyl. diesel; . . . bhp
Range: 7,000/12 **Crew:** 3 officers, 52 enlisted

Remarks: Former Thai fishing boat confiscated and commissioned 15-1-87 for fisheries patrol duties, the "A"-series pendant number notwithstanding. Converted 1995–96 for use as a survey craft.

SERVICE CRAFT *(continued)*

♦ 2 Chinese Yuchin-class (Project 069) inshore survey craft [YGS]
(In serv. 1983)

A 581 Darshak A 582 Talleshi

Talleshi (A 582) French Navy, 1996

D: 83 tons (fl) **S:** 11.5 kts **Dim:** 24.1 × 5.2 × 1.1
M: 2 Type 12V150 diesels; 2 props; 600 bhp
Range: 700/11.5 **Crew:** 1 officer, 25 enlisted

Remarks: Former medium landing craft (LCM).

♦ 1 harbor fueling lighter [YO]

A 516 Imam Gazzali

Remarks: Acquired 1996 from commercial service. 45 m overall; no other data available.

♦ 1 small repair ship [YR]

A 512 Shahayak

D: 477 tons (fl) **S:** 11.5 kts **Dim:** 44.7 × 8.0 × 2.0
A: 1 20-mm 70-cal. Oerlikon AA **Electronics:** Radar: 1 . . . nav.
M: 1 Cummins 12 VTS diesel; 1 prop; . . . bhp
Range: 3,800/11.5 **Crew:** 1 officer, 44 enlisted

Remarks: Former riverine passenger ship. Purchased, re-engined and refitted at Khulna Shipyard, and commissioned as a tender in 1978.

Note: Two new tugs were ordered from Khulna Shipyard late in 1999; they were to incorporate equipment and materials of South Korean origin.

♦ 1 large harbor tug [YTB]
Bldr: . . . SY, Dhaka (In serv. 1995)

A 722 Sebak

Remarks: No data available. Appears to be about 400 tons full load and is probably capable of seagoing towing. Has a firefighting water monitor.

COAST GUARD

Personnel (2000): 20 officers, 250 enlisted

Bases: Headquarters and Eastern Section base at Chittagong; Western Section base at Khulna

Note: Force structure planning called for ordering two 35-m, two 25-m, and two harbor patrol boats in 1996 and a 60-m patrol craft, two more 35-m patrol boats, and two more harbor patrol boats in 1997; very little of this plan has been accomplished, however. An aircraft is sought for maritime patrol duties. Ships and craft are painted white and bear a broad red diagonal stripe, followed by narrow white and blue stripes, on the hull sides.

PATROL COMBATANTS [WPG]

♦ 1 HDP 600 class
Bldr: Hyundai SY, South Korea (In serv. 1997)

P 911 Madhumati

Madhumati (P 911) French Navy, 10-98

D: 635 tons (650 fl) **S:** 23.5 kts **Dim:** 60.80 × 8.00 × 2.70
A: 1 57-mm 70-cal. Bofors Mk 1 DP; 140-mm 70-cal. Bofors AA; 2 single 20-mm 70-cal. Oerlikon AA; 2 single 7.62-mm mg
Electronics:
Radar: 1 GEM SPN-753B nav.; Kelvin-Hughes Type 1007 nav./surf. search
E/O: NA 18L optronic f.c. director
M: 2 SEMT-Pielstick 16 PA 4V200 diesels; 2 props; 9,600 bhp
Range: 6,000/15 **Crew:** 7 officers, 36 enlisted

Remarks: Ordered 7-95 as the first unit to be built for the new coast guard. Has Vosper Series 300 fin stabilizers.

PATROL CRAFT [WPC]

♦ 1 PZ class
Bldr: Hong Leong–Lürssen SY, Butterworth, Malaysia (In serv. 10-99)

P 201 Ruposhi Bangla

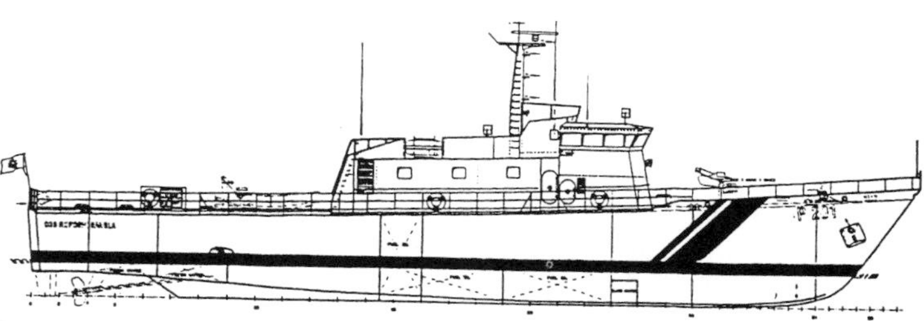

Ruposhi Bangla (P 201) Hong Leong–Lürssen, 1999

D: 195 tons (fl) **S:** 30 kts **Dim:** 38.50 (36.00 wl) × 7.00 × 1.75
A: 1 25-mm OTOBreda KBA AA; 2 single 7.62-mm Manroy mg
Electronics: Radar: 1 Furuno . . . nav.
M: 2 Paxman 12VP185 diesels; 2 props; 6,636 bhp
Electric: . . . kw tot. (3 Stamford generators, Perkins diesels driving)
Range: . . ./. . . **Fuel:** 41,000 liters **Crew:** 5 officers, 22 enlisted

Remarks: Updated version of the PZ design built for the Malaysian Marine Police from 1980 to 1984. Steel hull, aluminum superstructure. Carries two RIB rescue launches.

♦ 1 Chinese Shanghai-II class

P 61 Tawheed (ex-P 611)

Tawheed (P 61) Bangladeshi Coast Guard, 12-95

D: 122 tons (135 fl) **S:** 28.5 kts **Dim:** 38.78 × 5.41 × 1.55 (max.)
A: 2 twin 37-mm 62-cal. Type 74 AA; 2 twin 25-mm 80-cal. Type 61 AA
Electronics: Radar: 1 Type 751 (Pot Head) surf. search
M: 2 M-50F-4 1,200-bhp and 2 910-bhp diesels; 4 props; 4,220 bhp
Electric: 39 kw **Range:** 750/16.5 **Crew:** 36 tot.

Remarks: Transferred from the navy in 1996. Originally delivered 5-82.

♦ 2 ex-South Korean Sea Dolphin PKM 201 class
Bldr: Korea Tacoma SY, Chinhae, or Korea SB & Eng., Masan
(In serv. 1970s–80s)

P . . . (ex-PKM 2 . .) P . . . (ex-PKM 2 . .)

D: 113 tons (144 fl) **S:** 32 kts **Dim:** 33.10 (31.25 wl) × 6.92 × 1.75 (2.45 props)
A: 1 40-mm 60-cal. Bofors Mk 3 AA; 1 twin 30-mm 75-cal. Emerlec EX-30 AA; 2 single 20-mm 70-cal. Oerlikon AA
Electronics: Radar: 1 Raytheon 1645 nav./surf. search
M: 2 MTU 16V538 TB90 diesels; 2 props; 10,800 bhp (9,000 sust.)
Electric: 100 kw tot. (2 × 50-kw diesel sets)
Range: 500/32; 1,000/20 **Fuel:** 15 tons **Crew:** 5 officers, 26 enlisted

Remarks: Donated 4-00 and departed Chinhae 17-4-00 on a heavy-lift ship for delivery.

PATROL BOATS [WPB]

♦ 1 Pabna-class riverine
Bldr: DEW Narayengonj, Dhaka (In serv. 6-72)

P . . . Pabna (ex-P 111)

D: 69.5 tons (fl) **S:** 10 kts **Dim:** 22.9 × 6.1 × 1.9
A: 1 20-mm 70-cal. Oerlikon AA **M:** 2 Cummins diesels; 2 props
Range: 700/8 **Crew:** 3 officers, 30 enlisted

Remarks: Assigned to the Coast Guard during 1995.

BARBADOS

BARBADOS DEFENCE FORCE COAST GUARD

Personnel (2000): 11 officers, 85 enlisted

Base: HMBS *Willoughby Fort,* Bridgetown

Note: Ship names are prefixed HMBS (Her Majesty's Barbadian Ship).

PATROL CRAFT [WPC]

♦ **1 37.5-meter class**
Bldr: Brooke Marine, Lowestoft, U.K.

	L	In serv.
P 01 Trident	14-4-81	11-81

Trident (P 01) Maritime Photographic, 11-93

D: 155.5 tons (190 fl) **S:** 29 kts **Dim:** 37.50 × 6.86 × 1.70
A: 2 single 12.7-mm mg
Electronics: Radar: 1 Decca TM 1226C nav.
M: 2 Paxman Valenta 12RP 200 diesels; 2 props; 5,000 bhp
Range: 3,000/12 **Crew:** 28 tot.

Remarks: Refitted Bender SB & Repair, Mobile, Ala., 6-6-90 to 14-9-90; armament reduced from original one 40-mm 60-cal. Bofors AA and one 20-mm Rheinmetall AA. Refitted again in 1997–98 by Cable Marine. Near-sisters are in Algerian service.

PATROL BOATS [WPB]

♦ **2 U.S. 40-foot Dauntless class**
Bldr: SeaArk, Monticello, Ark.

P 04 (In serv. 4-97) P 05 (In serv. 4-99)

D: 15 tons (fl) **S:** 28 kts **Dim:** 12.19 (11.13 wl) × 3.86 × 0.69 (hull)
A: 2 single 12.7-mm mg; 2 single 7.62-mm mg
Electronics: Radar: 1 Raytheon R40X nav.
M: 2 Caterpillar 3208TA diesels; 2 props; 850 bhp (720 sust.)
Range: 200/30; 400/22 **Fuel:** 250 gallons **Crew:** 5 tot.

Remarks: P 04 ordered 10-96 for $396,000. Aluminum construction. C. Raymond Hunt, "Deep-Vee" hull design. Sisters operate in several Caribbean nation forces. One more is sought.

♦ **3 U.S. 22-foot Whaler class**
Bldr: Boston Whaler, Rockland, Mass./Edgewater, Fla.

P 08 (In serv. 1989) P 09 (In serv. 1989) P 10 (In serv. 1996)

D: 1.5 tons light (2.25 fl) **S:** 40 kts **Dim:** 6.81 × 2.26 × 0.36
A: 1 7.62-mm mg **Electronics:** Radar: 1 Raytheon R40X nav.
M: 2 Johnson OMC gasoline outboard engines; 360 bhp
Range: 167/40; 750/. . . **Fuel:** 243 liters **Crew:** 3 tot.

Remarks: GRP-hulled open launches. P 10, built in Florida, may differ in configuration.

Note: A 7.3-m Zodiac Hurricane RIB capable of 25 kts was delivered 7-95 for search-and-rescue duties.

BELARUS

BORDER GUARD

PATROL BOATS [WPB]

♦ **3 ex-Soviet Shmel' class (Project 1204)**
Bldr: Kamysh Burun Zavod, Kerch', or 61 Kommunara Zavod, Nikolayev (In serv. 1967–74)

D: 77.4 tons (fl) **S:** 24 kts **Dim:** 27.70 × 4.32 × 0.90 (2.00 molded depth)
A: 1 76.2-mm 48 cal. D-56TM low-angle gun (in a PT-76 tank turret); 1 twin 25-mm 80-cal. 2M-3M AA; 2 mine rails (up to 8 mines)
Electronics: Radar: 1 Donets-2 nav.—Sonar: NEL-7 echo sounder
M: 2 M-50F-4 diesels; 2 props; 2,400 bhp
Electric: 50 kw tot. (2 × 25-kw diesel sets)
Range: 240/20; 600/10 **Fuel:** 4.75 tons **Endurance:** 7 days
Crew: 1 officer, 2 warrant officers, 11 enlisted

Remarks: Transferred from Russia post-1991 and employed on the Dnieper River. One is former Russian Federal Border Guard unit PSKR-389.
Hull systems: The screws are mounted in tunnels to reduce draft. Armor includes 10 mm over the pilothouse and gun barbettes, 8 mm over the hull and internal bulkheads, and 5 mm over the deck and pilothouse. Have a Gradus-2 gyrocompass and NEL-7 echo sounder.
Combat systems: Some have also carried up to four 30-mm Plamya grenade launchers and four pintle-mounted 7.62-mm machineguns. One 7.62-mm machinegun is mounted coaxially with the 76-mm gun (for which 40 rounds are carried on-mount). Mine loads vary from 4 UDM-500 or 2 UDM-1000 to 6 KPM or 8 YaM mines.

SERVICE CRAFT

♦ **5 Gepard-class hovercraft launches [WYFLH]**
Bldr: Svir SY, Nikelskoye, Russia

D: . . . **S:** 35 kts **Dim:** 7.20 × 3.80 × . . .
M: 1 ZMZ-53 gasoline engine; 1 airscrew prop; 120 bhp
Range: 108/35 **Crew:** 4 tot.

Remarks: Carry an operator and three inspection personnel for use on the Dnieper River. The third was delivered on 17-4-01.

BELGIUM

Kingdom of Belgium

KONINKLIJE MARINE VAN BELGÏE

Personnel (2001): 2,550 tot. (290 officers, 1,200 petty officers, and 1,060 enlisted), including 62 in the Marine Infantry Division

Bases: Zeebrugge, with some small units based at Ostend. There is a naval training facility at Sint-Kruis, Bruges. Mine warfare training is conducted at Ostend. The shore staff is housed at Evere, and the operational staff is collocated with that of the Royal Netherlands Navy at Den Helder.

Naval Aviation: Three Aérospatiale AS.316B Alouette-IIIB helicopters, based at Koksijde. The air force uses five Westland Sea King Mk 48 helicopters in search-and-rescue duties; they are also based at Koksijde. The Alouette-IIIB helicopters are to be given new communications and navigation systems. The Navy hopes ultimately to obtain 11 NH-90 helicopters, 6 equipped for ASW and 5 for transport duties.

Belgian Navy Alouette-IIIB Rob Cabo, 1-01

Marine Infantry: The 100 personnel of "DIVMAR" are assigned to guard duty at naval bases, security details, and ceremonial honor guard duty. One of the three Belgian Army Paracommando battalions has maritime-oriented duties.

Note: The Belgian naval staff was formally integrated with that of the Netherlands at Den Helder on 28-3-96, and some training was integrated as of 25-9-96.

FRIGATES [FF]

♦ **0 (+ 2) "Multi-Purpose Escort Vessel" replacement frigates**
Bldr: . . .

D: 4,000–6,000 tons (fl) **S:** 28+ kts **Dim:** . . . × . . . × . . .
A: . . . vertical missile launch groups (. . . Aster-15 SAM); 1 100-mm DP; 1 NH-90 helicopter
M: . . .

Remarks: Proposed replacements for the *Wielingen* class, with the first to enter service after 2010. Will have antiship, ASW, and AAW capabilities. Designs being considered include the French Frégate d'Action Navale, a Dutch design, and the German

FRIGATES [FF] *(continued)*

Blohm + Voss MEKO A100 and A200 series. Weapons are to include surface-to-air missiles, a medium-caliber gun, and a CIWS, but no antiship missiles are to be carried, except for use by the helicopter.

♦ **3 Wielingen class (Type E 71)**

	Bldr	Laid down	L	In serv.
F 910 WIELINGEN	Boelwerf, Temse	5-3-74	30-3-76	20-1-78
F 911 WESTDIEP	Cockerill, Hoboken	2-9-74	8-12-75	20-1-78
F 912 WANDELAAR	Boelwerf, Temse	5-3-75	21-6-77	27-10-78

Wielingen (F 910) Findler & Winter, 6-00

Wandelaar (F 912) Chris Delgoffe/H&L Van Ginderen, 3-00

Westdiep (F 911) Bernard Prézelin, 5-01

D: 1,940 tons (2,430 fl) **S:** 26 kts on gas turbine/18 kts on diesels
Dim: 106.38 (103.00 pp) × 12.30 × 3.90 (5.40 over sonar)
A: 4 MM 38 Exocet SSM; 1 8-round Mk 29 SAM launcher (AIM-7P NATO Sea Sparrow missiles); 1 100-mm 55-cal. Model 1968 DP; 6 single 12.7-mm mg; 1 6-round 375-mm Bofors ASW RL; 2 fixed, internal launching racks for L 5 Mod. 4 ASW torpedoes
Electronics:
Radar: 1 Kelvin-Hughes KH 1007 nav.; 1 Thales Scout surf. search; 1 Thales DA-05 air search; 1 Thales WM-25 f.c.
Sonar: Computing Devices Canada SQS-510 hull-mounted (7.0 kHz)
EW: ArgoSystems AR 900B intercept; Elcos-1 HFD/F; Mk 36 SRBOC decoy syst. (2 6-round Mk 137 RL); SLQ-25 Nixie torpedo decoy syst.
E/O: 2 SAGEM VIGY EOMS optronic f.c. and surveillance
M: CODOG: 2 Cockerill CO-240V-12 diesels (3,000 bhp each); 1 Rolls-Royce Olympus TM-3B gas turbine (28,000 shp); 2 CP props
Electric: 2,000 kw (4 × 500-kw diesel sets) **Range:** 4,500/18; 6,000/16
Fuel: 280 tons **Crew:** 14 officers, 143 enlisted

Remarks: F 910 was reactivated in 1995 and refitted in 1997–98. F 912 was modernized at Antwerp during 2000–01. They are to remain in service to 2010–12.
Disposals: Sister *Westhinder* (F 913), newest of the class, decommissioned 1-7-93 and was towed to Ghent for scrapping 7-11-00.
Hull systems: Have lost 2 kts from original 28-kt trial speeds after modifications. Have Vosper fin stabilizers. Can make 15 kts on one diesel. Ring-laser gyros and new internal and external communications systems are being fitted, and the ships are to be given new diesel engines.
Combat systems: Have Thales SEWACO IV automatic tactical data system and Link 11 and Link 14 datalinks. Two SAGEM VIGY E/O sensors are provided, and optronic directors on platforms abreast the foremast can control the 100-mm gun, which has been upgraded to fire at 80 rds/min. Under a 6-95 contract, the Raytheon TM 1645/9X navigational radars were replaced with the Thales Scout, and the other radar systems were refurbished. The sonar has been upgraded from SQS-505A to SQS-510 standard with the addition of the UYS-501 programmable signal processor and display system. Are to receive new data plotting tables.

MINE WARFARE SHIPS

Note: A single 12,000-ton "Command and Supply Ship" is planned to replace both *Godetia* and *Zinnia.*

♦ **1 mine countermeasures support ship [MCS]** (In reserve)

	Bldr	Laid down	L	In serv.
A 961 *ZINNIA*	Cockerill, Hoboken	8-11-66	6-5-67	5-9-67

Zinnia (A 961)—in reserve alongside the stricken frigate *Westhinder* (F 913) H&L Van Ginderen, 4-00

D: 1,705 tons (2,685 fl) **S:** 18 kts (20 on trials)
Dim: 99.5 (94.2 wl) × 14.0 × 3.6 **A:** none
Electronics: Radar: 2 Decca 1229 nav.—EW: Telegon-6 HFD/F
M: 2 Cockerill-Ougree V12 TR 240 CO diesels; 1 CP prop; 5,000 bhp
Range: 14,000/12.5 **Fuel:** 150 m^3
Crew: 13 officers, 46 petty officers, 64 nonrated

Remarks: Fin stabilizers, telescoping helicopter hangar. Carries 500 tons cargo fuel for attached mine countermeasures units. Has been in reserve, stripped of armament and equipment, since 1993 and is to remain out of service until her retirement, scheduled for 2005. Underwater hull maintenance performed at NV SKB, Antwerp, in 10-98.

♦ **1 mine countermeasures support ship [MCS]**

	Bldr	Laid down	L	In serv.
A 960 GODETIA	Boelwerf, Temse	15-2-65	7-12-65	23-5-66

Godetia (A 960) Bernard Prézelin, 7-01

D: 1,700 tons (2,500 fl) **S:** 18 kts **Dim:** 91.83 (87.85 pp) × 14.0 × 3.5
A: 4 single 12.7-mm mg
Electronics: Radar: 2 Decca 1229 nav.—EW: Telegon-6 HFD/F
M: 4 ACEC-M.A.N. diesels; 2 CP props; 5,400 bhp
Range: 2,250/15; 8,700/12 **Fuel:** 294 tons
Crew: 10 officers, 37 petty officers, 48 nonrated

Remarks: Formerly could also serve as royal yacht. Received major midlife overhaul 1981–82. Recently also used for cadet training, with accommodations for 40 cadets. Scheduled for retirement in 2010 but may be extended to 2015 or even later if the hoped-for replacement is not built.
Hull systems: Can make 15 kts on one diesel. Has passive tank stabilization and protected closed-circuit ventilation. Can accommodate oceanographic research personnel and has space for a laboratory. Minesweeping cables are stowed on reels on the helicopter deck, which was extended aft to continue to permit one Alouette-III to land (but the forward end of the helicopter deck has been used for replacement sweep cable drum stowage for many years).

♦ **7 Tripartite-class minehunters [MHC]**
Bldr: Béliard Polyship, Ostend and Rupelmonde

	Laid down	L	In serv.
M 915 ASTER	26-4-83	29-6-84	18-12-85
M 916 BELLIS	9-2-83	22-2-85	18-9-86
M 917 CROCUS	9-10-84	2-10-85	5-2-87
M 921 LOBELIA	4-12-86	3-2-88	10-5-89
M 922 MYOSOTIS	6-7-87	4-10-88	14-12-89
M 923 NARCIS	25-2-88	20-6-89	27-9-90
M 924 PRIMULA	10-11-88	8-7-90	18-5-91

MINE WARFARE SHIPS *(continued)*

Crocus (M 917) Bernard Prézelin, 5-01

Myosotis (M 922) Findler & Winter, 6-01

D: 511 tons (595 fl) **S:** 15 kts **Dim:** 51.6 (47.1 pp) × 8.96 × 2.49 (hull)
A: 1 20-mm 90-cal. GIAT F-2 AA (except M 922); 2 single 12.7-mm M2 mg
Electronics:
Radar: Decca 1229 nav.
Sonar: Thales DUBM-21B variable-depth minehunting (100 kHz)
EW: Thales DR-2000S intercept; Telegon-4 HFD/F
M: 1 Brons/Werkspoor A-RUB 215X 12 diesel; 1 CP prop; 1,900 bhp (1,200 rpm)—2 120-hp maneuvering props (active rudder)—bow-thruster
Electric: 880 kw **Range:** 3,000/12
Crew: 6 officers, 39 enlisted (accomm. for 49)

Remarks: Ordered 12-2-81. Hulls were launched at Ostend and fitted out by Béliard Mercantile at Rupelmonde, Antwerp. M 915 was to have been converted to serve as a munitions transport but ran aground in Norwegian waters and was replaced by M 922 in 3-95. Six of the ships (not including M 922) are to undergo a Capability Upkeep Program (CUP) to keep them in service until 2015–20; they may be fitted with additional equipment to permit their use as minesweepers.
Disposals: Sisters *Dianthus* (M 918), *Fuchsia* (M 919), and *Iris* (M 920) were decommissioned during 1993 (all by 1-7-93) and placed up for sale; they were reconditioned and sold to France, with M 920 and M 919 delivered 28-3-97 and 29-5-97, respectively, and M 918 departing Belgium for France 15-9-97.
Hull systems: Glass-reinforced plastic construction. Three Astazou-IV, 320-kw gas-turbine generators and one 140-kw diesel set. Have active-tank stabilization.
Combat systems: Have two PAP-104 remote-controlled mine locators, automatic pilot, automatic track-plotter, Toran and Sydelis radio navigation systems, and conventional wire sweep. Carry portable divers' decompression van aft on 01 deck just above forecastle break. The portable sweep gear and 20-mm gun have been landed from M 922, and ammunition storage racks have been mounted in place of the portable divers' decompression chamber. During CUP modernization, the sonar system is to be improved, the tactical data system improved or replaced, the PAP-104 submersibles upgraded or replaced, a drifting mine detection capability added, and onboard systems integrated to permit reducing crew size.

Note: The KMV seagoing minesweeper program was canceled by the Belgian government on 12-5-00 before construction work had begun.

Disposal note: During 2001, the remaining, inactive four units of the U.S. *Dash*-class minehunter/minesweepers—*A. F. Dufour* (M 903, ex-Norwegian *Lagen,* ex-MSO 498), *De Brouwer* (M 904, ex-Norwegian *Nansen,* ex-MSO 499), *Georges Truffaut* (M 908, ex-AM 515), and *Françoise Bovesse* (M 909, ex-AMS 516)—were sold for scrap.

AMPHIBIOUS WARFARE SHIPS

♦ 0 (+ 1) Command/Logistic Support/Transport (CLST-H) [LPD]
Bldr: . . . (In serv. 2008)

D: 19,200 tons (fl) **S:** 18 kts **Dim:** 200.0 × . . . × . . .
A: . . .
Electronics: . . .
M: . . .
Range: 9,000/15 **Crew:** 60 tot. naval + . . . troops

Remarks: Ship would be a Ro/Ro vehicle carrier to transport Belgian and Luxembourgian army equipment. Estimated cost as of 6-01 was $169 million, of which Luxembourg is to pay 25%. Would also be capable of underway replenishment to escorts, operational command and control, hospital services, and providing training to naval and merchant marine cadets. The project was approved by the Belgian government 1-6-01. The design will be a variant of either the Dutch *Rotterdam* class or the French *Mistral* class.
Hull systems: Would be able to operate two medium-sized (Chinook) and five NH-90-size helicopters and would have a stern well to accommodate one LCAC or two LCMs.

AUXILIARIES

♦ 1 oceanographic research ship [AGOR]

	Bldr	Laid down	L	In serv.
A 962 Belgica	Boelwerf, Temse	17-10-83	6-1-84	5-7-84

Belgica (A 962) H&L Van Ginderen, 10-00

D: 835 tons (1,160 fl) **S:** 12 kts **Dim:** 50.90 (44.95 pp) × 10.00 × 4.40
Electronics: Radar: 1 Decca . . . nav.
M: 1 ABC 6M DZC-1000-150 diesel; 1 Kort-nozzle prop; 1,570 bhp
Electric: 640 kw **Range:** 20,000/12 **Fuel:** 158 tons
Crew: 15 naval + 11 scientists

Remarks: For use in North and Irish Seas for fisheries and hydrographic research and for fisheries patrol. Can carry two laboratory containers on deck. Has 150-hp thrusters fore and aft. Very bluff hull lines, bulbous bow. Painted white. Given major refit in 1999.

SERVICE CRAFT

♦ 1 ex-Swedish Kbv 171–class general-purpose craft [YAG]
Bldr: Karlskronavarvet, Karlskrona

	L	In serv.
A 963 Stern (ex-Kbv 171)	11-79	3-9-80

Stern (A 963) H&L Van Ginderen, 6-00

D: 375 tons (fl) **S:** 18.5 kts **Dim:** 49.90 (46.00 pp) × 8.52 × 2.40
Electronics: Radar: 2 Kelvin-Hughes 6000A nav.
M: 2 Hedemora V16A/15 diesels; 2 KaMeWa CP props; 4,480 bhp
Electric: 340 kVA tot. **Range:** 500/20; 3,000/12 **Crew:** 12 tot.

Remarks: Former Swedish Coast Guard Class "A" cutter purchased 28-9-98 for use as a general-purpose tender, training craft, and fisheries patrol craft; transferred 9-10-98 and commissioned in Belgian Navy 13-10-98. Will also be used in mine countermeasures system trials. Sister Kbv 172 is used by the Swedish Navy as a mine countermeasures support ship.
Hull systems: The glass-reinforced plastic sandwich hull had been lengthened by 6 m in 1981. Has helicopter platform, bow-thruster, a firefighting monitor, and Roll-Nix rudder roll-control system. The Simrad Subsea sonar was removed prior to transfer.

♦ 1 public affairs launch, former river patrol craft [YFL]
Bldr: Theodor Hitzler, Regensburg, Germany

	Laid down	L	In serv.
P 902 Libération	12-3-54	29-7-54	4-8-54

D: 27.5 tons (30 fl) **S:** 19 kts **Dim:** 26.00 (24.10 pp) × 4.13 (3.90 wl) × 0.93
A: 2 single 12.7-mm M2 mg **Electronics:** Radar: 1 Decca 1214 nav.
M: 2 MWM diesels; 2 props; 440 bhp **Range:** 870/14.6
Crew: 1 officer, 6 enlisted

SERVICE CRAFT *(continued)*

Libération (P 902) H&L Van Ginderen, 7-00

Remarks: Stricken 12-6-87 but returned to service 15-9-89. Based at Zeebrugge and employed primarily for public affairs purposes. Sister *Meuse* (P 903) is on display at the Royal Military Museum at Brussels, *Sambre* (P 904) is operated by the Sea Cadets youth group at Liège, *Schelde* (P 905) is on display at the Nationaal Scheepvaartmuseum at Antwerp, and *Leie* (P 901) is operated by a private owner. A sister is operated by the Federal Yugoslav Navy on the Danube.

♦ 1 personnel launch/tug [YFL]
Bldr: Scheeps en Yachtwerf Akerboom, Lisse, the Netherlands (In serv. 1958)

A 997 SPIN

Spin (A 997) H&L Van Ginderen, 7-00

D: 22.75 tons (32 fl) **S:** 8 kts **Dim:** 14.60 × 4.25 × 1.00
M: 1 diesel; 1 Voith-Schneider vertical cycloidal prop; 250 bhp
Crew: 1 chief petty officer, 3 nonrated

Remarks: Based at Ostend and used primarily as a personnel launch.

♦ 1 small royal yacht [YFL]

A 982 ALPA (ex-*Trifoglio*)

Remarks: A 23-ton, GRP-hulled cabin cruiser employed by King Albert II. Built at Poole, Dorset, U.K., in 1995 and based at Zeebrugge.

♦ 1 Valcke-class coastal tug [YTB] (In reserve)
Bldr: H. Bodewes, Millengen a/d Ryn

	Laid down	L	In serv.
A 950 *VALCKE* (ex-*Astroloog*, ex-*Steenbank*)	2-6-60	16-11-60	16-12-60

Valcke (A 950)—when active H&L Van Ginderen, 3-00

D: 420 tons (fl) **S:** 13 kts **Dim:** 30.08 × 7.55 × 3.10
Electronics: Radar: 1 Decca 1229 nav.
M: 2 Deutz BA8M 528, 4-cycle, single-acting 8-cyl. diesels, electric drive; 1 prop; 1,250 shp—1 30-shp bow-thruster
Fuel: 76 m^3 **Crew:** 3 chief petty officers, 6 enlisted

Remarks: 183 grt. Purchased 1980 from A. Smit. Based at Zeebrugge. Overhauled during 1995. Carries 18.1 m^3 fresh water. Was reported to have engineering problems as of late 1997; was back in operation in 1998, but by mid-2000 was again inactive. Sister *Ekster* (A 998, ex-*Astronoom*, ex-*Schouwenbank*) was scrapped beginning in 11-00.

♦ 1 medium coastal tug [YTM]
Bldr: C.N. & Atelier Const. de Hemiksem (In serv. 1971)

A 954 ZEEMEEUW

Zeemeeuw (A 954) H&L Van Ginderen, 7-99

D: 400 tons (fl) **S:** 9 kts **Dim:** 27.94 (26.60 pp) × 7.29 × 3.37
Electronics: Radar: 1 Decca 1229 nav.
M: 2 ABC 6-cyl. diesels; 2 props; 1,040 bhp
Electric: 96 kw tot. **Crew:** 2 chief petty officers, 4 enlisted

Remarks: 146 grt/24 nrt. Acquired from another Belgian government agency 17-8-81. Based at Zeebrugge and used on pollution-control duties.

♦ 1 ex-Dutch Westgat-class medium tug [YTM]
Bldr: Rijkswerf Willemsoord, Den Helder

	Laid down	L	In serv.
A 996 ALBATROS (ex-*Westgat*, A 872)	3-4-67	22-8-67	10-1-68

Albatros (A 996) H&L Van Ginderen, 4-00

D: 206 tons (fl) **S:** 12 kts **Dim:** 27.18 × 6.97 × 2.34
Electronics: Radar: 1 Kelvin-Hughes 14/9 nav.
M: 1 Bolnes diesel; 1 prop; 720 bhp **Crew:** 9 tot.

Remarks: Retired from Royal Netherlands Navy 12-3-96 and sold to Belgium 26-5-97 to replace the *Ekster* (A 998), transferring 23-7-97 after a refit.

♦ 2 Wesp-class medium harbor tugs [YTM]

	Bldr	In serv.
A 952 WESP (ex-*Stadssleepboot 63*, ex-*Stadssleepboot 43*)	C.N. de Liège-Monsin	1959
A 955 MIER (ex-*Stadssleepboot 66*, ex-*Stadssleepboot 46*)	St. Pieter SY, Hemiksem	23-3-62

D: 195 tons **S:** 11.3 kts **Dim:** 26.23 × 7.50 × 3.25
Electronics: Radar: 1 . . . nav.
M: 2 ABC Type 6MDUS diesels; 2 Voith-Schneider 20E/125 vertical cycloidal props; 1,000 bhp
Range: . . ./. . . **Crew:** 4 tot.

SERVICE CRAFT *(continued)*

Wesp (A 952) H&L Van Ginderen, 10-00

Remarks: Purchased from the Port of Antwerp 7-12-98 for $800,000. Delivered 4-99 after refit by SKB, Antwerp, and Antwerp city personnel. Names mean "Wasp" and "Ant," respectively. Have a 14-ton bollard pull and are capable of limited icebreaking.

Disposal note: *Bij*-class small tugs *Bij* (A 953) and *Krekel* (A 956) were laid up in 1999 and sold for scrap during 11-00.

♦ 1 sail-training craft [YTS]

	Bldr	Laid down	L	In serv.
A 958 ZENOBE GRAMME	Boelwerf, Temse	7-10-60	23-10-61	1962

Zenobe Gramme (A 958) Maritime Photographic, 9-00

D: 149 tons **S:** 9 kts under sail (8 under power)
Dim: 28.15 (23.10 wl; 31.50 over bowsprit) × 6.85 × 2.64
Electronics: Radar: 1 . . . nav.
M: 1 MWM 518A diesel; 232 bhp—240 m^2 max. sail area
Range: . . ./. . . **Fuel:** 9 tons **Crew:** 2 officers, 13 enlisted

Remarks: Fitted out as Bermudian ketch. Formerly also used for oceanographic research. Carries 22 tons lead and 4 tons bronze ballast. Mainmast is 31.5 m high.

Note: Also in service at the *Zeilschool van de Marine* (Sailing School of the Navy) are a number of small sailing craft and rowboats.

BELGIAN ARMY

♦ 1 Type 2000 TDX(M) assault hovercraft [LCPA]
Bldr: Griffon Hovercraft, Ltd., Salisbury Green, U.K. (In serv. 7-95)

A 999 BARBARA

Barbara (A 999) H&L Van Ginderen, 7-00

D: 3.7 tons light (5.6 fl) **S:** 35 kts (28 kph over land)
Dim: 11.00 (11.68 over skirt) × 4.56 (5.68 over skirt) × 2.75 (high; 4.30 over skirt)
A: 1 7.62-mm mg **Electronics:** Radar: 1 Raytheon . . . nav.
M: 1 Deutz BF8L-513 diesel driving 0.91-m-dia. lift fan and 1.8-m-dia. CP airscrew; 355 bhp (320 sust.)
Range: 200/35 **Fuel:** 385 liters **Crew:** 2 tot. + 16 troops

Remarks: Ordered 1995. Based at Lombardzijde as range safety craft, as a unit of the 14th Antiaircraft Regiment. Aluminum hull structure. Payload is 16 troops or 2 tons of equipment. Maximum speed can be attained in Sea State 1, while 25 kts is maintainable in Sea State 3. Able to travel over land and ice as well as water. Has a GPS receiver and HF and VHF radios. Can be accommodated in a C-130 Hercules transport. Cab top can be removed to permit carrying two 1-ton NATO standard cargo pallets.

♦ 10 Zodiac Mk 6HD personnel landing craft [LCP]
Bldr: Zodiac Boats, U.K. (In serv. 1997–99)

Belgian Army Zodiac Mk 6HD RIB H&L Van Ginderen, 7-00

D: 320 kg (without engines) **S:** 22–32 kts (depending on load)
Dim: 7.00 × 2.88 × . . . **M:** 2 Evinrude gasoline outboards; 140 bhp
Crew: 1–3 tot. + 15 fully equipped soldiers or 20 passengers

Remarks: RIBs. Seven received in 1997 for use by the paracommando brigade, with another three on order as of 4-98 and plans for one more.

Note: The Belgian Army also operates Zodiac AC 0348 and Zodiac AC 0338 RIBs. The AC 0348 is 4.25 × 1.75 m, can carry 5–6 persons, and weighs 100 kg empty and 990 kg max. load; it is powered by a single 25-bhp outboard or 10 paddles. The AC 0338 is 4.70 × 2.10 m, weighs 120 kg light and 1,910 kg max. load, and is also powered by a 25-bhp outboard; it can carry up to 10 persons.

BELIZE

DEFENCE FORCE MARITIME WING

Personnel (2001): Approx. 6 officers, 45 enlisted

Base: Headquarters and principal base at Placencia, Belize City; small detachment at Hunting Cay

Aviation: 2 Pilatus-Britten-Norman BN-2B Defender light maritime patrol aircraft and 1 Slingsby T67M Firefly trainer are operated by the Defence Force Air Wing.

PATROL BOATS [PB]

♦ 2 20-meter Wasp class
Bldr: Souter, Cowes, U.K.

PB 01 DANGRIGA (In serv. 4-8-83) PB 02 TOLEDO (In serv. 19-9-84)

D: 36.25 tons (fl) **S:** 18 kts **Dim:** 20.00 (16.00 pp) × 5.00 × 1.50
A: 1 12.7-mm mg; 4 single 7.62-mm mg
Electronics: Radar: 1 Decca 150 nav.

PATROL BOATS [PB] *(continued)*

Dangriga (PB 01) Belize Defence Force, via Julio Montes, 4-95

M: 2 G.M. 16V71 TI diesels; 2 props; 2,400 bhp **Electric:** 37 kw (2 × 18.5 kw)
Range: 430/18 **Fuel:** 5 tons **Crew:** 2 officers, 6 enlisted

Remarks: GRP construction. Can carry up to 30 troops. Completed 8-84, but not commissioned in-country until 19-9-84. Could make 23 kts when new. PB 01 was out of service in 1993 but was refitted and again operational in 1995.

SERVICE CRAFT

♦ **2 launches [YFL]**
Bldr: Bradley's BY, Belize (In serv. 1996)

OCEAN SENTINEL REEF SNIPER

Remarks: GRP construction. 10.67 m long and powered by two 200-bhp Yamaha gasoline outboards for 35-kt max. speeds.

♦ **2 Halmatic 22-foot rigid inflatable launches [YFL]**
Bldr: Halmatic, Hamble, U.K. (In serv. 1996)

BLUE MARLIN RANGER STINGRAY COMMANDO

Remarks: Powered by two 115-bhp Yamaha gasoline outboards for 35-kt max. speeds.

♦ **5 miscellaneous launches [YFL]**

Remarks: Mexican and Colombian craft confiscated 1995–97. Powered by two Yamaha 200-bhp gasoline outboard motors each for 35-kt max. speeds.

Note: The Police Maritime Wing operates up to 10 Boston Whaler Guardian-class foam-core, GRP-hulled launches in the P-1 series. Deliveries began in 1993. The craft are 3.86 tons (fl); can achieve 35 kts on 2 OMC gasoline outboards (200 bhp each); are 8.10 × 3.05 × 0.51 m; have a range of 250 n.m. at 30 kts; and carry a crew of three.

BENIN

People's Republic of Benin

Personnel (2001): Approx. 30 officers, 180 enlisted

Base: Cotonou

Naval Aviation: 1 Dornier Do-128 and 1 DHC-6 Twin Otter light twin-engine transports

PATROL BOATS [PB]

♦ **2 Chinese 25-meter class** (In serv. 1999)

P 798 MATELOT BRICE KPOMASSE P 799 LA SOTA

D: 82 tons **S:** 14 kts **Dim:** 25.0 × 4.1 × 1.4
A: 2 twin 14.5-mm 93-cal. AA **Electronics:** Radar: 1 JRC . . . nav.
M: 2 MWM V-8 diesels; 2 props; 1,000 bhp **Range:** 900/11 **Crew:** 12

Remarks: Donated by China. They are equipped with JRC (Japan Radio Corporation) Navigator GPS receivers.

La Sota (P 799) Navpic-Holland, 1-01

♦ **5 Boston Whaler patrol launches**
Bldr: Boston Whaler, Edgewater, Fla. (In serv. 1994)

P 14 P 15 P 201 P 204 P . . .

D: 1.5 tons (2 fl) **S:** 30 kts **Dim:** 6.81 × 2.26 × . . .
M: 2 gasoline outboards; 230 bhp **Crew:** 2 tot.

Remarks: "Unsinkable" GRP foam-core construction. P 201 (with a 75-bhp outboard motor) and P 204 (with a 110-bhp outboard) were acquired prior to 1994 and appear to be somewhat larger; they have an enclosed pilothouse near the stern. Two of the other three are painted white and are powered by a single outboard motor. Not all may be operable.

Disposal note: Patrol boat *Patriote* (P 17) was derelict and irreparable as of 1-01. The four Soviet-supplied Zhuk-class (Project 1400M) patrol boats—P 763, P 764, P 769, and P 779—have been sold for scrap.

BERMUDA

Crown Colony of Bermuda

BERMUDIAN POLICE

Base: Hamilton

SERVICE CRAFT

♦ **1 search-and-rescue launch [WYFL]**

BLUE HERON

Remarks: A cabin cruiser donated by the U.S. Drug Enforcement Agency in 5-96. About 14 m overall, the craft carries a crew and is assigned to the Joint Marine Interdiction Team.

♦ **3 Boston Whaler patrol and rescue launches [WYFL]**
Bldr: Boston Whaler, Rockland, Mass./Edgewater, Fla.

HERON I (In serv. 8-91) HERON II (In serv. 8-96) HERON III (In serv. 10-87)

D: 1.5 tons (2 fl) **S:** 30 kts **Dim:** 6.81 × 2.26 × . . .
M: 2 Yamaha gasoline outboards; 230 bhp **Crew:** 2 tot.

Remarks: "Unsinkable" GRP foam-core construction. *Heron II,* built at Edgewater, Fla., replaced an earlier craft with the same name and is 2.2 tons (fl) and 8.23 m overall.

♦ **2 Arctic-class rigid inflatable boats [WYFL]**
Bldr: Osbourne (*Rescue I:* Vosper-Halmatic, Havant), U.K.

RESCUE I (In serv. 9-98) RESCUE II (In serv. 5-88)

D: 1.45 tons (fl) **S:** 50 kts **Dim:** 7.32 × . . . × . . .
M: 2 Yamaha gasoline outboards; 230 bhp **Crew:** 3 tot.

Remarks: The original *Rescue I,* completed 9-86, was replaced by the present unit.

Note: The Bermuda Customs Service also operates patrol craft, including at least one Fairey Protector patrol boat.

BOLIVIA

Republic of Bolivia

Personnel (2002): 5,000. The 2,000-strong Almirante Grau naval infantry battalion has been disestablished and replaced by the antidrug Fuerza de Tarea "Diablos Azules" battalion.

Organization and Bases:

- 1st Naval District Beni on the Río Beni and Río Mamoré, with bases at Loma Suarez and Puerto Villarroel
- 2nd Naval District Mamoré, with bases Loma Suarez and Puerto Villarroel
- 3rd Naval District Madera on the Río Madre de Dios, with bases at Puerto Guayaramerin, Cachuela Esperanza, La Horquilla, and Ramón Dario Gutierrez
- 4th Naval District Titicaca, with a base at San Pedro de Tequina on Lake Titicaca
- 5th Naval District Santa Cruz de la Sierra, with a base at Puerto Quijarro on the Río Paraguay
- 6th Naval District Cobija on the Río Acre, with bases at Cobija, Madre de Dios, and Santa Rosa del Abuna
- Area Naval No. 1 Cochabamba, with the Astilleros Naval Puerto Villarroel and the task of transporting petroleum products from Puerto Villarroel to Trinidad and Guayaramerin
- Area Naval No. 2 Santa Cruz, with logistic support duties
- Area Naval No. 3 Bermejo, with Base Brigadier Gen. Nestor Paz Galarza at Bermejo
- The Fuerza de Tarea "Diablos Azules" has five task groups to provide combat and logistical support in antidrug operations. Its bases are located at Trinidad, Puerto Villarroel, Riberalta, Guayaramerin, and Copacabana.

Naval Aviation: 1 Cessna 402C light transport. Six air force Helibras AS.315B Gavião helicopters are provided for assistance to the navy as needed.

Marines: Almirante Grau Battalion, based at Tiquina.

Note: Prefix to ship names is ARB *(Armada de República Bolivia).* The navy also operates a commercial riverine cargo company, Transnaval, with six cargo barges and six tow-barges.

PATROL BOATS [PB]

Note: 27 launches of 8-, 11-, and 17-m length were ordered from Rodman Polyships, Vigo, Spain, during 1998 and delivered together during 2-99; no data available. One 11-m unit is numbered BTL-601, and one 17-m launch is numbered M-343.

♦ 32 Pirana Mk II patrol launches
Bldr: Boston Whaler, Rockland, Mass./Edgewater, Fla. (In serv. 1992–99)

LP-01 through LP-32

Remarks: Foam-core GRP-hulled open launches provided by the U.S.A. for drug enforcement duties. Characteristics similar to the other Bolivian Boston Whaler craft. Of the total, four were delivered in 1998 and six in 1999. All are assigned to the Diablos Azules special forces.

♦ 11 U.S. Whaler GRP-hulled
Bldr: Boston Whaler, Rockland, Mass.

LP-401 Comando
LP-404 Inti
LP-405 Mallcu
LP-408 Auxiliar
LP-409 Mariscal de Zapita
LP-601 Cobija
LP-602 Rapirran
LP-603 Puerto Rico
LP-604 Santa Rosa
LP-605 Porvenir
LP-606 Acre

D: 1.5 tons (2 fl) **S:** 40 kts **Dim:** 6.81 × 2.26 × . . .
A: 1 12.7-mm mg; small arms
M: 2 gasoline outboard motors; 360 bhp **Range:** 167/40; 750/. . . **Crew:** 3 tot.

Remarks: U.S. Grant-Aid for use in drug interdiction. Four delivered late 1989, two in 12-90, and nine in 1991, from which only 11 remained in service as of 1997. Foam-core GRP hull construction. An additional $397,000 worth of units of this class were ordered during 1994, along with several Zodiac-type rigid inflatable boats.

♦ 4 13-meter class
Bldr: Guayaramerin BY (L: 9-90)

PR-11 Presidente Paz Zamora
PR-21 Capitán Palomeque
PR-31 General Banzer
PR-32 Antofagasta

D: 8 tons **S:** 27 kts **Dim:** 13.0 × 3.2 × 0.5
A: 1 7.62-mm mg **M:** 2 diesels; 2 props; . . . bhp **Crew:** 4 tot.

Remarks: Wooden construction. Data apply to PR-21; the others are similar. Used for river service in the 1st, 2nd, and 3rd Naval Districts.

♦ 6 Capitán Bretel class
Bldr: . . . . . ., Bolivia (In serv. 1990s)

LP-410 Capitán Bretel
LP-411 Teniente Soliz
LP-412 Bacarreza
LP-413 Copacabana
LA-414 Guaqui
LP-415 Chaguaya

D: 5 tons **S:** 15 kts **Dim:** 12.9 × 3.9 × 1.0
A: 1 12.7-mm mg **Electronics:** Radar: 1 Raytheon 1900 nav.
M: 2 diesels; 2 props; . . . bhp **Crew:** 5 tot.

Remarks: Aluminum construction. Operate in the 4th Naval District. LA-414 is assigned to logistics support duties.

♦ 1 U.S.-built
Bldr: Hope/Progressive Shipbuilders, Houma, La. (In serv. 1985)

PR-501 Santa Cruz de la Sierra (ex-PR-51)

D: 46 tons (fl) **S:** 20 kts **Dim:** 20.4 × 5.8 × 1.2
A: 2 single 12.7-mm mg **Electronics:** Radar: 1 Furuno . . . nav.
M: 2 G.M. Detroit Diesel diesels; 2 props; . . . bhp
Range: 800/16 **Crew:** 10 tot.

Remarks: Aluminum-hulled unit used for patrol and logistics service on the Río Paraguay in the 5th Naval District.

SERVICE CRAFT

♦ 1 vehicle and personnel ferry [YFB]
Bldr: Astilleros Naval Puerto Villarroel (In serv. 22-7-98)

TB-01 Guayaramerin

Remarks: No data available.

♦ 2 Chinese-built personnel launches [YFL]
Bldr: . . . (In serv. 1996)

D: 7.4 tons **S:** 30 kts **Dim:** 11.50 × 2.38 × 0.45
M: 1 Type 12V150 diesel; 1 waterjet; 450 bhp **Crew:** 2 tot. + 7 passengers

♦ 10 miscellaneous river transports [YFL]
Bldr: Bolivia, various bldrs (In serv. . . .)

LT-02 Boliviamar
M-101 Almirante Grau
M-103 Comandante Arandia
M-105 Manuripi
M-223 Libertador
M-224 Trinidad
M-225 J. Chavez Suarez
M-315 Ingeniero Palacios
M-341 Ingeniero Gumucho
M-510 Suarez Arana

Remarks: No data available. Wooden or iron construction. M-341 displaces 70 tons (fl), is 24 × 6.5 m, has a range of 500 n.m. at 12 kts, and carries a crew of 11.

♦ 1 30-ton hydrographic survey launches [YGS]

LH-01 Pionera

♦ 2 hospital launches [YH]

AH-01 Julian Apaza BH-01 Xavier Pinto Telleria

Remarks: AH-01, paid for by the U.S.A., was assembled on Lake Titicaca in summer 1972; displacing 150 tons, the craft is 27.4 m long by 8.53 m beam and is powered by two outboard motors. BH-01, which operates on the Río Mamoré, was commissioned on 23-10-97 as AH-02 and was built by Astilleros Naval Puerto Villarroel; no data available.

♦ 6 fuel lighters [YO]

BTL-01 General Pando
BTL-02 Nicolas Suarez
BTL-03 Mariscal Cruz
BTL-04 Max Paredes
BTL-05 Capitán Olmos
BTL-06 V. A. H. Ugartche

Remarks: All of 40–45 tons with a capacity of 250,000 liters. BTL-01 through BTL-04 were prefabricated in the U.S.A. and assembled at Astilleros Naval Puerto Villarroel during 1976–77. BTL-05 was launched 29-11-91 by Astilleros Naval Puerto Villarroel, and the final unit was laid down by the same yard during 10-98.

♦ 6 small push-tugs [YTL]

TNR-01 through TNR-06

Remarks: First four were acquired 1976–77. TRN-05 was converted from a Brazilian-built barge in 1987 and is named *CN Julio Olmos Cardozo.* TNR-06 was laid down in 10-98 by Astilleros Naval Puerto Villarroel. They operate with the six fuel barges (see [YO]).

Note: A 160-ton catamaran-hulled training craft was launched 9-5-01 for service on Lake Titicaca.

BOTSWANA

PATROL BOATS [WPB]

♦ 2 U.S. Raider class
Bldr: Napco, Hopkins, Minn. (In serv. 1988)

D: 2.95 tons (fl) **S:** 40 kts **Dim:** 6.80 (6.40 wl) × 2.26 × 0.86
A: 2 single 12.7-mm mg **Electronics:** Radar: 1 Raytheon 1900 nav.
M: 2 gasoline outboard motors; 2 props; 310 bhp
Range: 167/40; 220/30; 750/. . . **Crew:** 3 tot.

Remarks: Provided under FY 88 Military Aid Program funds. Additional units have been requested. Use Boston Whaler GRP hulls molded in Rockland, Mass. Current status unknown.

Note: Several 18-ft. (5.49-m) airboats (airscrew propeller–driven, shallow-draft small craft) were purchased from the United States in 1991; the U.S. provided maintenance assistance in 1998–99.

BRAZIL

Federative Republic of Brazil

MARINHA DO BRASIL

Personnel (2000): 31,400 tot. (5,900 officers), plus 15,100 marines (680 officers)

Organization: Under the commander in chief *(comandante de marinha)* are the Base Naval do Rio, Centre de Apoio e Suporte Administrativo (CASOP), Força de Sub

MARINHA DO BRASIL *(continued)*

marinos, Força de Superficie (Surface Force), and two operating forces. Subordinated to the Força de Superficie are the Centro de Adestramento da Esquadra; the destroyer, frigate, corvette, amphibious ship, and support squadrons; and naval auxiliary vessels U 27 *(Brasil)* and A 11. Other than the main fleet organization, the Brazilian Navy is organized into six subsidiary Naval Districts, numbered and headquartered as follows:

- 1st Naval District, comprising the states of Espírito Santo and Rio de Janeiro, with the Grupamento Naval do Sudeste (GrupNSE) patrol force: P 44, P 45, R 22, R 23, and R 25
- 2nd Naval District, comprising the state of Bahia, with the Minesweeping Force (ForMinVar): minesweepers M 15–M 20 and patrol ships V 19 and V 23
- 3rd Naval District, comprising the states of Pernambuco, Ceará, Paraíba, Alagoas, and Rio Grande do Norte, with the Grupamento Naval do Nordeste (GrupNNE): P 40, P 41, P 42, V 18, and R 24
- 4th Naval District, comprising the states of Amazonas, Acre, Rondônia, Roraima, Pará, Maranhão, and Amapá, with the Amazon Flotilla (FlotAM): P 20, P 21, P 30–P 32, U 18, and U 19; and the Grupamento Naval do Norte (GrupNN) with V 20, V 22, V 24, P 10, and P 12–P 14
- 5th Naval District, based at Estação Naval do Rio Grande and comprising the states of Paraná, Santa Catarina, and Rio Grande do Sul, with Grupamento Naval do Sul (GrupNS): P 46, V 15, V 21, and R 21
- 6th Naval District, comprising the states of Mato Grosso and Mato Grosso do Sul, with the Mato Grosso Flotilla (FlotMT): U 17, P 11, P 15, G 15, G 17, and G 19
- 7th Naval District, Comando Naval de Brasília: no units assigned
- 8th Naval District, São Paulo: established 1997, units assigned not available

Bases: Rio de Janeiro (Base Naval Almirante Castro e Silva submarine base, Base Naval do Rio de Janeiro main naval base, and Arsenal de Marinha do Rio de Janeiro naval shipyard); Bahia (Base Naval de Aratu naval base and repair facility); Natal (Base Naval de Natal); Pará (Base Naval de Val-de-Cães riverine base and repair facility); Rio Grande do Norte (Base Naval Almirante Ary Parreiras naval base and repair facility); Mato Grosso do Sul (Base Fluvial de Ladário naval base and repair facility); Amazonas (Estação Naval do Rio Negro naval riverine base and repair facility); and Rio Grande (Estação Naval do Rio Grande). See also the marine and naval air sections.

There are port captaincies at Espírito Santo and Rio de Janeiro (1st Naval District); Bahia (2nd Naval District); Pernambuco, Ceará, Paraíba, Alagoas, and Rio Grande do Norte (3rd Naval District); Pará/Amapá (4th Naval District); Santa Catarina, Rio Grande do Sul, and Paraná (5th Naval District); Mato Grosso do Sul/Mato Grosso (6th Naval District); and São Paulo (8th Naval District).

Naval Aviation: Fixed wing aircraft: 16 AF-1 (A-4KU) and 2 AF-1A (TA-4KU) Skyhawk shipboard attack aircraft. Helicopters: 7 AS.332F (UH-14) Super Puma/Cougar (with AM 39 Exocet missiles), 6 SH-3H (SH-3B) and 7 SH-3D (SH-3A) Sea King (SH-3A are AM 39 Exocet capable), 19 Bell 206B JetRanger (IH-6B), 8 Helibras AS.315B Gavião (Aérospatiale Lama), 9 Westland Super Lynx, 5 Westland Mk 21 (SAH-11) Lynx, 20 AS.350B Esquilo-I (UH-12), and 23 Helibras AS.355F Esquilo-II (UH-13).

The six ex-USN Sea Kings delivered in 5-96 are equipped with AQS-18(V) dipping sonars. All Lynx-series helicopters are equipped to launch Sea Skua antiship missiles.

Brazil purchased 23 A-4KU and TA-4KU Skyhawk light attack fighters from Kuwait on 30-4-98; 16 AF-1 (A-4KU) and 2 2-seat AF-1A (TA-4KU) trainers are to be maintained operational for use aboard the carrier *Minas Gerais;* as of 10-00, only five had been returned to flyable service. The aircraft are based at Base Aérea Naval de São Pedro da Aldeia as VF-1 (1st Esquadrão de Aviõs de Interceptação e Ataque), and the squadron was to enter service by 7-99 with an initial 14 pilots out of a planned total of 30.

Naval aircraft are organized as follows:

Base Aérea Naval de São Pedro da Aldeia (BAeNSPA), Rio de Janeiro, except HU-5:

- VF-1: 1st Esquadrão de Aviõs de Interceptação e Ataque, with 16 AF-1 and 2 AF-1A Skyhawk light attack aircraft
- HU-1: 1st Esquadrão de Helicópteros de Emprego Geral, with 9 AS.355F2 Esquilo-II and 4 AS.350BA Esquilo-I helicopters
- HU-2: 2nd Esquadrão de Helicópteros de Emprego Geral, with 7 AS.332F1 Super Puma/Cougar helicopters
- HU-5: detachment based at Rio Grande, Rio Grande do Sul, with 3 AS.350 (UH-12) Esquilo-I
- HA-1: 1st Esquadrão de Helicópteros de Esclarecimento e Ataque Anti-Submarino, with 5 Mk 21 Lynx
- HS-1: 1st Esquadrão de Helicópteros Anti-Submarinos, with 4 SH-3A Sea King
- HI-1: 1st Esquadrão de Helicópteros de Instrução: 19 Bell 206B JetRanger III

Base Aérea de Manaus, Amazon region:

- HU-3: 3rd Esquadrão de Helicópteros de Emprego Geral: 5 AS.350A Esquilo-I

Base Aérea de Ladário, Mato Grosso do Sul:

- HU-4: 4th Esquadrão de Helicópteros de Emprego Geral: 2 AS.350A Esquilo-I

The Brazilian Air Force makes available to the navy 3 Gates Learjet (R-35A) and 20 EMB 111 (P-95A/B) Bandeirante in a sea-surveillance version. The air force also operates 2 Piper/Embraer Seneca IIs, 15 Neiva T-25 Universal aircraft, and 6 AS.332F (UH-14) Super Puma helicopters for search-and-rescue purposes and has ordered five EMB 120 Brasilia transports equipped with Ericsson Erieye phased array air early-warning radars. Also used occasionally in support of maritime surveillance is an R-35A Learjet with EW equipment. The Brazilian Air Force is to receive 16 surplus P-3A Orion maritime patrol aircraft from the United States and plans to update and activate two squadrons of the aircraft by 2008.

Marines: Headquartered at Fort São José, Rio de Janeiro. The Fleet Marine Force, supported by a command and services company and the Special Operations Battalion, has the Amphibious Division at Base de Fuzileiros Navais da Ilha do Governador, with a command company, tank company, communications company, 3 infantry battalions, an artillery battalion, and an antiaircraft battery; also subordinated are the Comando de Reforço at Base de Fuzileiros Navais da Ilha das Flores, with a combat engineering battalion, logistic battalion, amphibious assault vehicles battalion, police company, and electronic warfare company. In addition to a Center of Repairs and Special Supplies, the Marines are supported by the Admiral Sylvio de Camargo, Admiral Milciades Portela Alves, and Marambaia Island Instruction Centers. Security groups are stationed at each of the naval district headquarters.

A total of 26 U.S. AAV-7A1 amphibious armored, tracked personnel carriers are in service with the marines, 12 of them delivered new in 1-97 along with one AAVC-7A1 command vehicle and one AAVR-7A1 recovery vehicle. Air defense is provided by wheeled Bofors 40-mm 70-cal. AA mounts and Mistral heat-seeking missiles. The Marine Corps also operates the Bofors RBS-56 Bill antitank missile and in 1998 ordered 18 Royal Ordnance Factory 105-mm light artillery weapons, 14 CLANF amphibious vehicles, and 17 Steyr-Daimler-Puch SK-105 tank destroyers.

Coastal Defense: Coastal defense is the responsibility of the Brazilian Army, which took delivery of its first ASTROS II multiple-barreled rocket launcher in 5-98 for coast-defense use by the 8th Motorized Coastal Artillery Group, based at Rio de Janeiro.

Weapons and Sensors: Existing U.S. Mk 46 Mod. 2 ASW torpedoes are to be upgraded to Mod. 5, and additional Mk 46 Mod. 5 torpedoes are to be acquired. Bofors Tp 62 wire-guided torpedoes for submarines were ordered in 1998 for delivery after 2001.

Brazil's Consub manufactures the acoustic/magnetic MFC 01/100 modular mine, a 770-kg moored contact weapon with a 160-kg trotyl explosive charge that can be laid in depths from 10 to 100 m and is also available in a bottom-mine version with magnetic or acoustic-influence fuzing.

A number of Danish Terma navigational radars were ordered 1991 to equip patrol and service craft.

IPqM developed the SICONTA *(Sistema de Controle Tático)* modular combat data system for employment on various new and refitted warships; using the TTI-2700 display terminal and Link YB, it can share data with other similarly equipped ships. The prototype went to sea in the now-retired destroyer *Mariz e Barros,* and the system is being further developed by the navy.

AIRCRAFT CARRIERS [CV]

♦ 1 ex-French Clemenceau class

Bldr: Ch. de l'Atlantique, St. Nazaire

	Laid down	L	In serv.
A 12 São Paulo (ex-*Foch,* R 99)	2-57	28-7-60	15-7-63

D: 27,307 tons (32,780 fl) **S:** 32 kts
Dim: 265.0 (238.0 pp) × 31.72 (beam; 51.20 flight deck) × 7.50 (light draft; 8.60 fl)
Air group: 16 AF-1 and 2 AF-1A fighter-bombers; 4 SH-3A Sea King, 2 UH-13 Esquilo-II, and 2 UH-14 Super Puma helicopters
A: . . .
Electronics:
Radar: 1 Decca 1226 nav.; 1 DRBV-23B air search; 1 DRBV-15 3-D air-search; 2 DRBI-10 height-finder; 2 DRBC-32C f.c.; 1 NRBA-51 air-control (all by Thales)
TACAN: U.S. SRN-6
EW: ARBR-16 intercept; ARBR-17 intercept; ARBB-33 jamming; 2 AMBL-2A Sagaie decoy RL
M: 2 sets Parsons geared turbines; 2 props; 126,000 shp
Boilers: 6 watertube; 45 kg/cm^2, 450° C
Electric: 14,000 kw tot. (2 × 2,000-kw turboalternators, 6 × 2,000-kw diesel sets)
Range: 4,800/24; 7,500/18 **Fuel:** 3,720 tons **Endurance:** 60 days
Crew: 1,338 tot. (64 officers, 476 petty officers, 798 other enlisted) + 582 air group (in French service)

São Paulo (A 12) Bernard Prézelin, 1-00

São Paulo (A 12) Bernard Prézelin, 1-00

AIRCRAFT CARRIERS [CV] *(continued)*

São Paulo (A 12)—on post-overhaul trials Bernard Prézelin, 1-00

São Paulo (A 12)—note that all armament was removed prior to transfer Bernard Prézelin, 1-00

Remarks: Purchased 8-00 for $41 million (including cost of overhaul); transferred 15-11-00 and departed 1-2-01 for arrival in Brazil 20-2-01. Was built in a graving dock at St. Nazaire and towed to Brest for fitting out. Sister *Clemenceau,* retired on 1-10-97, was employed as a source of spares for the *São Paulo's* predelivery overhaul at Brest, which included removal of asbestos insulation and deletion of all armament.

As *Foch,* began a 14-month refit on 2-9-92, receiving new propulsion turbine rotors, refitted catapults certified for 6,000 further shots, a nose-gear catapult launch capability, and numerous habitability improvements. Further improvements were made during a 1995–97 refit, including increasing the size of the jet-blast deflectors and adding enlarged retractable "ski-jumps" to the forward ends of both catapults.

Hull systems: Armor protection includes the reinforced flight deck, armored bulkheads in engine room and magazines, and reinforced-steel bridge superstructure. The machinery spaces and boilers are enclosed in what amounts to an armored redoubt. Living spaces are air-conditioned. The island has three bridges: flag, navigation, and aviation.

Aviation systems: The flight deck is 257 m in length overall with an 8°, 165.5 × 29.5-m angled portion; the deck forward of the angled deck measures 93 × 28 m and the deck abreast the island is 35 m wide. Hangar is 180 m long, 22–24 m wide, and 7 m clear height. The two 16 × 11-m elevators, one forward on the main flight deck, one slightly abaft the island, are able to raise a 15-ton aircraft 8.5 m in 9 seconds. Two 50-m Mitchell-Brown Type BS5 steam catapults are able to launch 15- to 20-ton aircraft at 110 kts; one is located forward, the other on the angled deck. Has French-made mirror landing equipment. Carries 1,800 m^3 of jet fuel and about 3,000 m^3 of aviation munitions. A small, retractable 1.5° ski-jump structure at the forward end of each catapult was added around 1994.

The air group listed is an estimate, based on the use of all flyable Skyhawk light fighter-bombers and the helicopter complement of the *Minas Gerais.* Additional aircraft, should they become available, could be accommodated.

Combat systems: All but the navigational radars are unique to this ship, which should complicate maintenance. Has the SENIT 2 combat data system, updated to SENIT 8.01 (OP3A) status with three display stations. Defensive armament will presumably be added in Brazil.

Disposal note: The British *Colossus*-class aircraft carrier *Minas Gerais* (A 11) was withdrawn from service on 9-10-01.

NUCLEAR-POWERED ATTACK SUBMARINES [SSN]

Note: The Brazilian Navy has had a program under way since 1979 to develop a nuclear-powered attack submarine and has already devoted well over $1 billion to the development of a nuclear propulsion reactor, without significant results; most of the funding was withdrawn in 1994. A 2,700-ton nuclear-powered variant of the NAC-1 diesel submarine concept with an 11-Mw reactor was initially planned; two turbo-alternators would have driven one motor for 30-kt submerged speeds. A prototype electric propulsion motor for the nuclear submarine was completed during 1994 by the University of São Paulo's Electrotechnical Institute.

If built, the first SSN is to be named *Riachuelo.* As of 6-00, the Brazilian Navy was requesting a renewed effort to develop the submarine's planned 50-Mw reactor, still in the design stage; a prototype reactor would be completed in 2010 if funding is renewed. As many as four SSNs are ultimately foreseen. The Navy is said to be willing to sacrifice other more urgent programs in favor of continued work on the SSN.

ATTACK SUBMARINES [SS]

Note: As of 2001, work was under way on the design of a new diesel-electric submarine, designated the S-MB-10; the submarine would be of 2,150 tons surfaced displacement and be 69 m overall by 6.9 m beam. There is as yet no indication as to when construction of the design might be authorized.

♦ 4 (+ 1) German Type 209/1400 Mod. 3 class

Bldrs: S 30: Howaldtswerke Deutsche Werft (HDW), Kiel; others: Arsenal de Marinha do Rio de Janeiro (AMRJ)

	Laid down	L	In serv.
S 30 Tupi	8-3-85	25-4-87	6-5-89
S 31 Tamoio	15-7-86	18-11-93	17-7-95
S 32 Timbira	15-9-87	5-1-96	15-12-96
S 33 Tapajó (ex-*Tapajós*)	8-92	11-6-98	12-99
S 34 Tikuná (ex-*Tamandare*)	12-98	2003–04	3-05

Tupi (S 30) H&L Van Ginderen, 8-97

D: 1,150 tons light, 1,453 tons surf./1,590 tons sub. **S:** 11 kts surf./21.5 kts sub.
Dim: 61.20 × 6.20 (7.60 over stern planes) × 5.50
A: 8 bow 533-mm TT (16 Mk 24 Mod. 1 Tigerfish wire-guided torpedoes)

ATTACK SUBMARINES [SS] *(continued)*

Electronics:
Radar: 1 Thales Calypso-III search/nav.
Sonar: STN Atlas Elektronik CSU-83/1 suite (DBSQS-21 active; passive flank arrays)
EW: Thales DR-3000U intercept
M: 4 MTU 12V493 TY60, 600-bhp (S 34: MTU 12V396, 940-bhp) diesels, 4 A.E.G. 420-kw (S 34: 4 A.E.G. . . .-kw) generators, electric drive; 1 prop; 5,000 shp
Range: 10,000/8 snorkel; 25/21.5, 50/16, 230/8, 400/4 sub.
Fuel: 116 tons **Endurance:** 50 days **Crew:** 33 tot.

Remarks: S 30 was ordered 8-82 and handed over by the builders 20-8-88; after training in European waters, the submarine arrived at Rio de Janeiro 27-6-89. Plans to construct two more were canceled in 1992, but a fourth Brazilian-built unit was restored to the program in 10-94. The names of S 33 and S 34 were changed in 1995 to standardize names to indicate an Indian who is a member of a particular tribe. Construction of S 34 has been delayed by funding problems.

S 34 will be 0.85 m longer in order to use a different electric motor and more powerful diesels; also different will be the sensor and communications suites. The submarine will carry new torpedoes and is to have reduced radiated noise, a lower indiscretion rate, a freshwater distilling system, the ISUS 83-13 weapons-control system, ONA self-noise measurement hydrophones, a nonpenetrating periscope-mounted electronic intercept system, interfacing between the inertial navigational system and a GPS receiver, higher-precision gyros, the ability to launch mines and guided missiles from the torpedo tubes, improved endurance, fittings to accept a submarine rescue submersible and the ability to put two persons at a time in the rescue lock-out chamber, a distress-warning system, increased air-conditioning plant output, and automatic depth control.
Hull systems: Can make 25 kts submerged for a brief period. Diving depth: 250 m. Has a 480-cell battery. The bow pressure hull cap, with its integral torpedo tube foundations, is made in Germany, with the remainder of the structure being of Brazilian manufacture.
Combat systems: S 30 through S 33 have Ferranti KAFS A10 action data system, Kollmorgen Model 76 search and attack periscopes, and Sperry Mk 29 Mod. 2 Ship's Inertial Navigation System (SINS).

Disposal note: *Oberon*-class submarine *Tonelero* (S 21), used for several years for underway training, sank alongside while at Rio de Janeiro on 25-12-00 during the latter stages of a minor overhaul; the submarine was raised on 4-1-01 but was stricken 21-6-01. Sister *Humaitá* (S 20) was retired on 8-4-96, and *Riachuelo* (S 22) was decommissioned and relegated to museum service on 12-11-97 but is still carried on the naval list and has a nucleus crew.

The since-stricken Tonelero (S 21)—with *Tupi* (S 30) and *Tamoio* (S 31) beyond
Hartmut Ehlers, 4-00

FRIGATES [FF]

♦ 0 (+ 1) Barroso class
Bldr: Arsenal de Marinha do Rio de Janeiro (AMRJ)

	Laid down	L	In serv.
V 34 Barroso	21-12-94	. . .	6-06

Barroso (V 34) 1. 1 Lynx helicopter 2. 40-mm AA 3. EOS-400 optronic director 4. RAN-20S surface/air-search radar 5. MM 40 Exocet antiship missiles 6. Decca navigational radar 7. Orion RTN-30X gun fire-control radar 8. OFD optical gun director 9. 114-mm Vickers Mk 8 gun
Drawing by A. D. Baker III

D: 1,785 tons (2,350 fl) **S:** 27 kts
Dim: 100.66 (93.90 pp) × 11.40 × 3.96 (mean hull; 5.50 over sonar)
A: 4 MM 40 Exocet SSM; 1 114-mm 55-cal. Vickers Mk 8 DP; 1 40-mm 70-cal. Bofors Mk 3 AA; 2 triple 324-mm ASW TT (U.S. Mk 46 Mod. 2 torpedoes); 1 Super Lynx helicopter
Electronics:
Radar: 1 Decca TM 1226 nav.; 1 AESN RAN-20S air/surf. search; 2 Alenia-Elsag RTN-30X f.c.
Sonar: STN Atlas Elektronik ASO-94-2 (DSQS-21C) hull-mounted LF
EW: Elebra SLQ-2-IPQM active/passive syst.; 4 Elebra 12-round decoy RL
E/O: MSI Defense OFD (114-mm gun f.c.); Saab Dynamics EOS-400 (40-mm gun f.c.)
M: CODOG: 1 G.E. LM 2500 gas turbine (27,490 shp); 2 MTU 1163-series diesels (. . . bhp each); 2 CP props
Electric: 2,000 kw (4 Siemens 500-kw alternators)
Range: 4,000/15 **Crew:** 14 officers, 33 petty officers, 79 other enlisted

Remarks: Plans to construct a fifth, improved unit of the *Inhaúma* class were announced during 1992, but funding to order the V 34 was not made available until late in 1994. Three additional units were at one time planned, but work on V 34 itself has been progressing very slowly due to funding problems.
Hull systems: The hull is 4.2 m longer than that of the *Inhaúma* class to accommodate more-powerful diesel engines (for 20.5 kts on diesels alone) and provide more useful internal volume. The extra length allows installation of improved crew accommodations, additional rake and freeboard to the bow, and a longer helicopter deck. Vosper Thornycroft Series 500 fin stabilizers will be fitted.
Combat systems: The ship will use, insofar as possible, the same systems that are being employed in the modernization of the *Niterói* class, including the Siconta-2 combat data and direction system. The sonar fit may differ from that listed. The 40-mm gun mounting is the same as that employed by the Bofors Trinity CIWS but lacks the integral radar.

♦ 4 Inhaúma class
Bldr: First two: Arsenal de Marinha do Rio de Janeiro (AMRJ); others: EMAQ-Verolme Estaleiros, S.A., Angra dos Reis (now IVI-Indústria Verolme-Sihibras, S.A.)

	Laid down	L	In serv.
V 30 Inhaúma	23-9-83	3-12-86	12-12-89
V 31 Jaceguai	15-10-84	8-6-87	2-4-91
V 32 Julio de Noronha	15-11-87	12-91	27-10-92
V 33 Frontin	15-12-87	6-2-92	11-3-94

Julio de Noronha (V 32)—outboard a sister
Ricardo Bonalume, 4-01

Julio de Noronha (V 32)
U.S. Navy, 11-95

Jaceguai (V 31)
Hartmut Ehlers, 4-00

D: 1,670 tons light, 2,092 tons normal (2,350 fl) **S:** 26 kts
Dim: 95.77 (90.00 pp) × 11.40 × 3.70 (mean hull; 5.30 over sonar dome)
A: 4 MM 40 Exocet SSM; 1 114-mm 55-cal. Vickers Mk 8 DP; 2 single 40-mm 70-cal. Bofors L70 AA; 2 triple 324-mm ASW TT (U.S. Mk 46 Mod. 2 torpedoes); 1 SAH-11 Lynx helicopter

FRIGATES [FF] *(continued)*

Electronics:
Radar: 1 Decca TM 1226 nav.; 1 Siemens-Plessey AWS-4 air search; 1 Alenia Orion RTN-10X f.c.
Sonar: STN Atlas Elektronik DSQS-21C
EW: Racal Cutlass B-1 intercept; Racal Cygnus (V 30, 32: IpqM ET/SLQ-1/L) jammer; Telegon HFD/F; 2 6-round Plessey Shield decoy RL
E/O: Saab OES-400 optronic gun director
M: CODOG: 1 G.E. LM 2500 gas turbine, 27,490 shp; 2 MTU 16V956 TB91 diesels, 7,880 bhp; 2 CP props
Electric: 2,000 kw tot. (4 Siemens 500-kw diesel-driven alternators)
Range: 4,000/15 **Crew:** 20 officers, 115 enlisted (162 tot. accomm.)

Remarks: Originally were to have been a program of 12 smaller "corvettes." Four were authorized 11-81, with the first two ordered 15-2-82 and the others 9-6-86; were originally to be delivered in 1989, but were greatly delayed by shipyard labor problems and bankruptcy. Form the 1st Corvette Squadron, based at Rio de Janeiro.
Hull systems: Reported to suffer from topweight problems, which helped to delay the entry into full active service of the first two.
Combat systems: Have Ferranti CAAIS 450 with Ferranti WSA-421 weapons-control system. The U.S. Mk 15 Phalanx CIWS was selected 1988 for installation on the stern but has not yet been ordered. V 30 has a unique IPqM ET/SDR-2 EW suite with a directional ET/SLQ-1 jammer (8–16 GHz) antenna in a radome atop the after mast.

♦ 4 ex-U.K. Broadsword (Type 22) class
Bldr: Yarrow (Shipbuilders) Ltd., Scotstoun, Glasgow

	Ordered	Laid down	L	In serv.
F 46 Greenhalgh (ex-*Broadsword,* F 88)	8-2-74	7-2-75	12-5-76	3-5-79
F 47 Dodsworth (ex-*Battleaxe,* F 89)	4-9-75	4-2-76	18-5-77	28-3-80
F 48 Bosisio (ex-*Brilliant,* F 90)	7-9-76	24-3-77	15-12-78	10-4-81
F 49 Rademaker (ex-*Brazen,* F 91; ex-*Boxer*)	21-10-77	19-8-78	4-3-80	2-7-82

Greenhalgh (F 46) Francisco Ferro/*Tecnologia & Defesa,* 12-96

Dodsworth (F 47)—note that only the two outboard MM 38 Exocet antiship missile launch positions are occupied German Navy, 6-99

Bosisio (F 48) Hartmut Ehlers, 4-00

D: 3,900 tons (4,400 fl) **S:** 29 kts (18 cruise)
Dim: 131.20 (125.00 wl) × 14.80 × 4.30 (6.00 sonar)
A: 4 MM 40 Exocet SSM; 2 sextuple Sea Wolf GWS.25 SAM syst.; 2 single 40-mm 70-cal. Bofors L70 AA; 2 single 20-mm 90-cal. BMARC-Oerlikon GAM-B01 AA; 2 triple 324-mm STWS.2 ASW TT (Stingray torpedoes); 1 or 2 SAH-11 Lynx helicopters
Electronics:
Radar: 1 Kelvin-Hughes Type 1006 nav.; 1 Marconi Type 967-968 surf./air-search; 2 Marconi Type 910 f.c.

Greenhalgh (F 46)—note dual hangar aft, beneath Sea Wolf SAM launcher Hartmut Ehlers, 4-00

Sonar: Ferranti-Thomson Type 2050 hull-mounted, Type 2008 underwater telephone
EW: UAA-1 intercept, 2 Type 670 jammers, 4 6-round DLB decoy RL; Type 182 towed torpedo decoy
M: COGOG; 2 Olympus TM-3B gas turbines, 27,300 shp each for high speed; 2 Tyne RM-1A, 4,100 shp each for cruising; 2 CP props; 54,600 shp max.
Electric: 4,000 kw (4 Paxman Ventura 12PA 200CZ diesel sets)
Range: 1,200/29 (on Olympus); 4,500/18 (on Tyne)
Crew: 17 officers, 222 enlisted + 65 additional accomm.

Remarks: Agreement to purchase signed 18-11-94, with transfers ensuing as the ships retired from the Royal Navy. Purchase price was $170 million for the four. They provide Brazil with its first modern shipboard air-defense system. F 46 transferred and recommissioned 30-6-95, arriving in Brazil 24-10-95; F 47 and F 48 transferred and recommissioned 30-8-96, arriving at Rio de Janeiro 9-12-96; and F 49 transferred 30-4-97. The ships are assigned to the 1st Naval Division's 2nd Frigate Squadron, based at Rio de Janeiro.
Hull systems: Berthing and training facilities for 65 officer trainees per ship were added to all four by the end of 1992. Fin stabilizers and Prairie/Masker air bubbling radiated noise suppression systems are fitted.
Combat systems: F 46 was transferred with MM 38 Exocet missiles; plans to substitute MM 40 in the others prior to turnover did not reach fruition. Have the CAAIS combat data system. The 967-968 radar is a back-to-back array with track-while-scan features. F 49 has four 6-round Mk 137 chaff RL (Outfit DLD) in addition to standard Outfit DLC. Two Lynx helicopters can be carried, but only one would normally be aboard. Two single Bofors 40-mm mounts removed from the *Niterói* class during modernization have been fitted to all four on the upper deck forward of the hangar; the 20-mm guns have been resited on the upper deck abreast the gas turbine intakes.

♦ 6 Niterói (Vosper Thornycroft Mk 10) class
Bldrs: F 40–F 43: Vosper Thornycroft, Woolston; others: Arsenal de Marinha do Rio de Janeiro (AMRJ)

	Laid down	L	In serv.
F 40 Niterói	8-6-72	8-2-74	20-11-76
F 41 Defensora	14-12-72	27-3-75	5-3-77
F 42 Constituição	13-3-74	15-4-76	31-3-78
F 43 Liberal	2-5-75	7-2-77	18-11-78
F 44 Independência	11-6-72	2-9-74	3-9-79
F 45 União	11-6-72	14-3-75	12-9-80

União (F 45)—operational, unmodified Hartmut Ehlers, 4-00

Liberal (F 43)—with new weapons and sensors aboard Ricardo Bonalume, 4-99

Niterói (F 40)—undergoing modernization overhaul Ricardo Bonalume, 4-01

FRIGATES [FF] *(continued)*

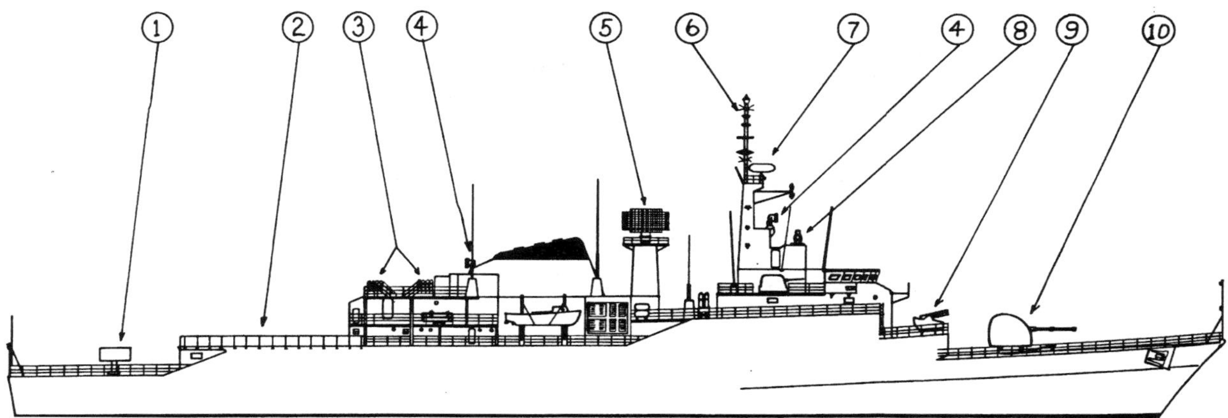

Liberal (F 43)—as modernized: 1. Albatros SAM launcher 2. helicopter flight deck 3. decoy rocket launchers 4. Orion RTN-30X weapon control radars 5. RAN-20S surface/air-search radar 6. MAGE EW array 7. surface-search radar 8. EOS-400 optronic gun director 9. twin 375-mm ASW rocket launcher 10. 114-mm Mk 8 gun
Drawing by A. D. Baker III

Liberal (F 43)—note the "stealth" gunhouse of the Bofors Mk 3 gunmount just abaft the pilothouse and the new suite of radar antennas Ricardo Bonalume, 4-99

Constitução (F 42) H&L Van Ginderen, 4-97

D: 3,200 tons (3,800 fl) **S:** 30.5 kts (28 cruising on gas turbines, 22 on diesels)
Dim: 129.24 (121.92 pp) × 13.52 × 4.20 (5.94 sonar)
A: F 41, F 43: 4 MM 40 Exocet SSM (paired); 1 octuple launcher for Albatros SAM syst. (8 Aspide missiles; no reloads); 1 114-mm 55-cal. Vickers DP; 2 single 40-mm 70-cal. Bofors Trinity AA; 1 2-round 375-mm Bofors SR-375A ASW RL; 2 triple 324-mm ASW TT (Stingray torpedoes); 1 d.c. rack (5 charges); 1 SAH-11 Lynx helicopter
others: 4 MM 40 Exocet (paired); 1 (F 42: 2 single) 114-mm 55-cal. Mk 8 Vickers DP; 2 single 40-mm 70-cal. Bofors AA; 2 3-round Sea Cat SAM syst.; 1 2-round 375-mm Bofors SR-375 ASW RL; 2 triple 324-mm ASW TT (Stingray torpedoes); 1 d.c. rack (5 charges); 1 SAH-11 Lynx helicopter

Electronics:
Radar: F 41, F 43: 1 Furuno . . . nav.; 1 Terma Scanter . . . surf. search; 1 AESN RAN-20S air/surf. search; 2 AESN RTN-30X f.c.—others: 1 Thales ZW-06 surf. search; 1 Plessey AWS-2 air search; 2 AESN Orion RTN-10X f.c.
Sonar: EDO 610E (F 41, F 43: Mod. 1) hull-mounted MF—F 40, F 41 also: EDO 700 VDS
EW: F 41, F 43: Elebra MAGE active/passive suite; Racal Cutlass B-1BW intercept; 4 12-round decoy RL—others: Racal RDL-3 (F 42: Racal Cutlass B-1BW) intercept; FH-5 HFD/F; 2 6-round Plessey Shield decoy RL
E/O: F 41, F 43: Saab-Combitech EOS-450 surveillance/f.c.

M: CODOG: 2 Rolls-Royce Olympus TM-3B gas turbines, 28,000 shp each; 4 MTU 16V956 TB91 diesels, 3,940 bhp each (F 41, F 43: MTU 16V1163 TB . . . diesels, . . . bhp each); 2 Escher-Wyss CP props; 56,000 shp max.

Electric: 4,002.5 kw tot. (4 × 1,000-kw diesel sets, 1 × 2.5-kw emergency set)
Range: 1,300/29; 4,200/19 (4 diesels); 5,300/17.5 (2 diesels)
Fuel: 480 tons + 26 tons aviation fuel **Crew:** 22 officers, 187 enlisted

Remarks: Ordered 20-9-70. The Brazilian-built units experienced considerable delays during fitting out. All are being extensively modernized, with F 43 to have been completed 6-98 and the final unit in 2001. Work on F 43 began at Rio de Janeiro during 12-96. As of 4-01, F 43 was still conducting sea trials to verify the new software; the second ship to be upgraded, F 41, was nearing the end of the modification effort; modification work on F 40 was under way; and the projected completion of the entire program had been slipped to 2005. The class constitutes the 1st Frigate Squadron, based at Rio de Janeiro.

Hull systems: Fitted with retractable fin stabilizers. An automated engineering plant monitoring system developed by the São Paulo Navy Technology Center (CTMSP), the Navy Research Institute (IPqM), and the Ship Design Center (CPN) was to have been installed during the modernizations but will now be fitted independently, starting late in 2001. MTU 1163–series diesels are replacing the original 16V956 TB91 engines during the modernizations. Have tankage for 50 tons of fresh water, and the two desalination plants can each produce 32 tons per day.

Combat systems: Under a 3-95, $385 million contract with Alenia of Italy, the AWS-2 radars are being replaced with RAN-20S surveillance radars, the RTN-10X weapons control radars with two RTN-30X, and the obsolete Sea Cat SAM systems by an Albatros SAM system with an octuple launcher for Aspide missiles on the fantail in all six ships. On 20-9-96 a contract was let to a consortium led by Elebra of Brazil with DCN France and three other Brazilian companies (Consub, Dolfin, and Holosys) to integrate Siconta-2, a variant of the French Navy SENIT 8 system, with the other combat systems; it replaces the original British CAAIS combat data system. Two Bofors 40-mm Mk 3 Trinity radar-directed guns are replacing the manually directed 40-mm mounts. In F 42 and F 43, the Albatros SAM launcher replaces the after 114-mm gunmount. A Saab Dynamics EOS-400 optronic fire-control system is being added atop the pilothouse. Racal Cutlass B-1B ESM is replacing RDL on F 40 and F 41, while an Elebra- and Brazilian Navy–developed ESM suite will be substituted on the others; all six will get an Elebra- and Brazilian Navy–developed MAGE active jammer system and four 12-round decoy rocket launchers. The ASW rocket launcher system is being upgraded to SR-375A and now uses Brazilian-made projectiles. The ASW torpedo tubes and sonar systems will be retained (including the VDS sets in F 41 and F 42), with the 610E hull-mounted sets upgraded to Mod. 1.

F 40, 41, 44, and 45 received four MM 40 Exocet SSM ordered in 1986; the other two initially retained the original MM 38 Exocets. The Branik ASW missile system (not installed in F 41 and F 42), a version of the Australian Ikara, has been deactivated and is being removed during modernizations, and the Sea Cat SAM systems are unlikely to be operational on those ships that still carry them.

♦ 4 U.S. Garcia class

Bldrs: D 27, D 29: Lockheed SB, Seattle; D 28: Avondale SY, New Orleans; D 30: Bethlehem SB, San Francisco

	Laid down	L	In serv.
D 27 Pará (ex-*Albert David,* FF 1050)	29-4-64	19-12-64	19-10-68
D 28 Paraíba (ex-*Davidson,* FF 1045)	20-9-63	3-10-64	7-12-65
D 29 Paraná (ex-*Sample,* FF 1048)	19-7-63	28-4-64	23-3-68
D 30 Pernambuco (ex-*Bradley,* FF 1041)	17-1-63	26-3-64	15-5-65

Pernambuco (D 30)—large hangar variant; outboard sister *Paraná* (D 29)
Ricardo Bonalume, 4-01

FRIGATES [FF] *(continued)*

Paraná (D 29)—small hangar variant, outboard sisters *Paraíba* (D 28) and *Pará* (D 27) Hartmut Ehlers, 4-00

Paraíba (D 28) U.S. Navy, 11-89

D: 2,624 tons (3,560 fl) **S:** 27 kts
Dim: 126.33 (121.90 wl) × 13.47 × 7.90 (over sonar)
A: 2 single 127-mm 38-cal. DP; 1 octuple Mk 112 ASROC ASW RL ; 2 triple 324-mm Mk 32 ASW TT; 1 SAH-11 Lynx helicopter
Electronics:
Radar: 1 LN-66 nav.; 1 SPS-10 surf. search; 1 Lockheed Martin SPS-40 air search, 1 Westinghouse Mk 35 f.c. (on Mk 56 director)
Sonar: D 27, D 28: SQS-26 BX bow-mounted LF—others: SQS-26 AXR
TACAN: SRN-15
EW: WLR-1 and WLR-3 intercept; ULQ-6 jammer; Mk 33 RBOC decoy syst. (2 6-round launchers); SLQ-25 Nixie towed torpedo decoy syst.
M: 1 set G.E. geared steam turbines; 1 prop; 35,000 shp
Boilers: 2 Foster-Wheeler turbopressurized; 83.4 kg/cm, 510° C
Electric: 2,000 kw tot. **Range:** 4,000/20 **Fuel:** 600 tons
Crew: 18 officers, 268 enlisted

Remarks: Considered to be destroyers by the Brazilian Navy. Recommissioned into Brazilian service on 18-9-89, 25-7-89, 24-8-89, and 25-9-89, respectively, having been decommissioned from U.S. Navy on 18-9-89, 8-12-88, 23-9-88, and 30-9-88. They form the 1st Destroyer Squadron, based at Rio de Janeiro.
Hull systems: Fin stabilizers and Prairie/Masker air bubbling radiated noise suppression systems are fitted. The boilers are vertical, have turbopressurized combustion, and are very difficult to maintain.
Combat systems: All have the Mk 56 gun fire-control system for the 127-mm guns and the Mk 114 ASW fire-control system. D 27 and D 29 carried SQR-15 TASS towed sonar arrays prior to transfer and retain the original small DASH drone helicopter hangars, which cannot accommodate Lynx helicopters. The other two had the hangar enlarged to 14.6 × 5.4 m to accommodate the SH-2F LAMPS-I helicopter. D 27 and D 29 have a reload magazine with 8 missiles for the ASROC system; the other two do not. The ASROC missiles, assuming any were transferred with the ships, are unlikely still to be viable. U.S. canister-launched RGM-84C Harpoon missiles were requested for these ships in 8-99, with each ship to receive four missiles; as of 4-01, however, the missiles had not been acquired.

Note: U.S. *Bostwick*-class frigate *Bauru* (ex-*McAnn,* DE 179) is maintained as a museum exhibit at Rio de Janeiro; the ship remains on the naval list and has a small naval caretaker crew.

PATROL SHIPS [PS]

♦ 4 ex-U.K. River class
Bldr: Richards (Shipbuilders), Ltd., Lowestoft (P 61: Great Yarmouth)

	Laid down	L	In serv.
P 60 Bracuí (ex-*Jorge Leite,* H 45; ex-*Itchen,* M 2009)	26-3-84	16-11-84	12-10-85
P 61 Benevente (ex-*Melo Baptista;* ex-*Blackwater,* M 2008)	16-1-84	29-8-84	20-6-85
P 62 Bocaina (ex-*Andromeda;* (ex-*Spey,* M 2013)	12-11-84	22-5-85	19-7-86
P 63 Babitonga (ex-*Arun,* M 2104)	4-2-85	20-8-85	29-8-86

Bocaina (P 62) Maritime Photographic, 8-98

Benevente (P 61) H&L Van Ginderen, 8-98

D: 630 tons (770 fl) **S:** 14 kts (15 on trials; 12 sust.)
Dim: 47.60 (42.00 pp) × 10.50 × 3.10 (3.75 max.)
A: 1 40-mm 60-cal. Bofors Mk 3 AA; 2 single 12.7-mm mg
Electronics: Radar: 2 Decca TM 1226 nav.
M: 2 Ruston 6 RKCM diesels; 2 4-bladed CP props; 3,040 bhp
Electric: 460 kw tot. **Range:** 4,500/10 **Fuel:** 88 tons
Crew: 7 officers, 7 petty officers, 16 other enlisted

Remarks: 638 grt. Former minesweepers ordered 23-8-96 for transfer on retirement from Royal Navy, 4-98 to 9-98. Two were originally to be employed as navigational buoy tenders and training ships and the other two converted to serve as survey ships. P 60 was transferred 8-4-98 and departed the U.K. 5-5-98; P 61 and P 62 transferred 10-7-98, and P 63 18-9-98. Two Brazilian Navy sisters serve as navigational buoy tenders and another unit was reconfigured as a hydrographic survey ship; another sister is operated by Trinidad and Tobago, while four others were bought by Bangladesh.
Hull systems: Have steel hulls built to commercial single-compartment damage standard. There have been upper-deck corrosion problems. Navigation gear includes two Kelvin-Hughes MS 48 echo sounders, Decca QM 14(1) and Decca HiFix Mk 6 radio navaids, and a NAVSAT receiver. Modifications in Brazil include installation of air-conditioning equipment.
Combat systems: Sweep gear removed prior to transfer. The 40-mm gun is locally controlled and is hand trained and elevated.

♦ 6 Imperial Marinheiro class
Bldr: L. Smit, Kinderdijk, the Netherlands

	L	In serv.
V 15 Imperial Marinheiro	24-11-54	8-6-55
V 19 Caboclo	28-8-54	4-55
V 20 Angostura	1955	1955
V 21 Bahiana	11-54	26-6-55
V 23 Purus	6-11-54	4-55
V 24 Solimões	24-11-54	1955

Bahiana (V 21) H&L Van Ginderen, 2-00

D: 911 tons (960 fl) **S:** 15 kts **Dim:** 55.72 × 9.55 × 3.6
A: 1 76.2-mm 50-cal. U.S. Mk 26 DP; 4 single 20-mm 70-cal. Oerlikon Mk 10 AA
Electronics: Radar: 1 Decca . . . nav.
M: 2 Sulzer diesels; 2 props; 2,160 bhp
Range: . . ./. . . **Fuel:** 135 tons **Crew:** 5 officers, 65 enlisted

Remarks: Oceangoing tug design with 15-ton bollard pull towing capacity. Were intended to be convertible for minesweeping or minelaying. Are officially designated "vedettes" and used on the Amazon River system in district patrols and in support of the 200-mile economic exclusion zone.

Disposals: *Iparanga* (V 17) was stricken during 1983; *Iguatemi* (V 16) on 9-8-96; and *Mearim* (V 22) on 4-12-98. *Forte de Coimbra* (V 18) was stranded on Baixinha Reefs, off Natal, on 12-11-96 and subsequently stricken.

PATROL COMBATANTS [PG]

♦ 2 Pedro Teixeira class
Bldr: Arsenal de Marinha do Rio de Janeiro (AMRJ)

	L	In serv.
P 20 Pedro Teixeira	11-6-72	17-12-73
P 21 Raposo Tavares	11-6-72	17-12-73

PATROL COMBATANTS [PG] *(continued)*

Pedro Teixeira (P 20) Brazilian Navy

Raposo Tavares (P 21) Brazilian Navy, 1995

D: 690 tons (fl) **S:** 14 kts **Dim:** 63.56 × 9.71 × 1.70
A: 1 40-mm 70-cal. Bofors L70 AA; 4 single 12.7-mm mg; 2 single 81-mm mortar/12.7-mm mg combinations; 2 single 7.62-mm mg; 1 UH-12 Esquilo-I helicopter
Electronics: Radar: 2 Decca . . . nav.
M: 2 MEP-M.A.N. V6V16/18 TLS diesels; 2 props; 3,840 bhp
Range: 6,800/10 **Crew:** 6 officers, 52 enlisted + up to 80 troops

Remarks: Assigned to the Amazon Flotilla. Carry two armed LCVPs on fantail. Hull has a small bow bulb. Have accommodations for 20 troops belowdecks; 60 others can be accommodated for brief periods on the upper deck. Maximum speed going upstream is about 8 kts.

♦ 1 old river monitor
Bldr: Arsenal de Marinha do Rio de Janeiro (AMRJ)

	Laid down	L	In serv.
U 17 Parnaíba	11-6-36	2-9-37	9-3-38

Parnaíba (U 17) Hartmut Ehlers, 5-00

D: 620 tons (720 fl) **S:** 12 kts **Dim:** 55.0 × 10.1 × 1.6
A: 1 76.2-mm 50-cal. U.S. Mk 22 DP; 2 single 40-mm 70-cal. Bofors AA; 4 single 20-mm 70-cal. Oerlikon Mk 10 AA
Electronics: Radar: 1 Furuno 3600 nav.; 1 Decca . . . nav.
M: 2 . . . diesels; 2 props; . . . bhp
Range: 3,800/10 **Fuel:** 90 tons **Endurance:** 16 days **Crew:** 90 tot.

Remarks: Assigned to the Mato Grosso Flotilla and wears an auxiliary pennant number. Has some side and deck armor protection. The original reciprocating steam propulsion plant was replaced in a 1-98 to 6-5-99 refit at the *Ladário* Riverine Naval Base, and she is expected to continue operating for the foreseeable future; a helicopter platform is to be erected over the stern. The 40-mm 70-cal. guns mounted aft were taken from *Niterói*-class frigates in refit; they replaced two 20-mm mounts.

PATROL CRAFT [PC]

♦ 12 Graúna Class

	Bldr	L	In serv.
P 40 Grajau	Arsenal de Marinha do Rio de Janeiro (AMRJ)	21-5-93	1-12-93
P 41 Guaiba	Arsenal de Marinha do Rio de Janeiro (AMRJ)	10-12-93	12-9-94
P 42 Graúna	Estaleiros Mauá, Niterói	10-11-93	14-8-94
P 43 Goiana	Estaleiros Mauá, Niterói	26-1-94	26-2-97
P 44 Guajará	Peenewerft, Wolgast, Germany	24-10-94	28-4-95
P 45 Guaporé	Peenewerft, Wolgast, Germany	25-1-95	29-8-95
P 46 Gurupá	Peenewerft, Wolgast, Germany	11-5-95	8-12-95
P 47 Gurupi	Peenewerft, Wolgast, Germany	6-9-95	23-4-96
P 48 Guanabara	INACE, Fortaleza, Ceará	5-11-97	9-7-99
P 49 Guarujá	INACE, Fortaleza, Ceará	5-98	30-11-99
P 50 Guaratuba	Peenewerft, Wolgast, Germany	16-6-99	1-12-99
P 51 Gravataí	Peenewerft, Wolgast, Germany	26-8-99	17-2-00

Guaporé (P 45) H&L Van Ginderen, 1-00

D: 213 tons light, 242 tons normal (263 fl)
S: 24.3 kts (22 sust., 26.5 on trials) **Dim:** 46.50 (42.50 pp) × 7.50 × 2.30
A: 1 40-mm 70-cal. Bofors 40L/70350 AA; 2 single 20-mm 90-cal. Oerlikon GAM-B01 AA
Electronics: Radar: 1 Decca 1290A nav. (I-band)
M: 2 MTU 16V396 TB94 diesels; 2 props; 6,688 bhp (5,560 sust.)
Electric: 300 kw tot. (2 × 100-kw diesel sets, 1 × 100-kw shaft generator)
Range: 2,200/12 **Fuel:** 23.25 tons **Endurance:** 18 days
Crew: 4 officers, 25 enlisted

Remarks: The first two were ordered in late 1987 to a design by Vosper QAF, Singapore, with actual work beginning late in 1988. The second pair was ordered in 9-90 and the third pair in 11-93. The fourth pair was ordered during mid-1994 and paid for from profits from the state Petrobras oil company. P 48 and P 49 were laid down at INACE (Industria Naval do Ceará, S.A.) 22-4-96. P 50 and P 51 were built with a construction loan from the German government for $30 million each.

The original contract with Estaleiros Mauá for P 42 and P 43 was canceled during 8-92 due to slow progress, and the craft ordered there were fitted out at AMRJ. The craft have been renumbered to reflect the delivery sequence; P 42 and P 43 were originally to have been P 40 and P 41.

Hull systems: The displacement has also been reported as 242 tons full load and as being 197 tons light and 217 tons full load.

Combat systems: Have a 10-person-capacity rigid inflatable inspection boat on the stern, handled by a telescoping electrohydraulic crane. The 40-mm gunmounts on the German-built units employ Mauser mountings.

♦ 3 Roraima class
Bldr: MacLaren Estaleiros e Serviços Marítimos, S.A., Niterói

	L	In serv.
P 30 Roraima	9-11-72	21-2-75
P 31 Rondônia	10-1-73	3-12-75
P 32 Amapá	9-3-73	1-76

Roraima (P 30) Brazilian Navy

D: 340 tons (365 fl) **S:** 14.5 kts **Dim:** 46.30 × 8.45 × 1.37
A: 1 40-mm 70-cal. Bofors AA; 4 single 12.7-mm mg; 2 single 81-mm/12.7-mm mortar/mg combination mountings; 2 single 7.62-mm mg
Electronics: Radar: 2 . . . nav.
M: 2 MEP-M.A.N. V6V16/18 TL diesels; 2 props; 1,824 bhp
Range: 6,000/11 **Crew:** 9 officers, 31 enlisted

PATROL CRAFT [PC] *(continued)*

Remarks: River gunboats operating in the Amazon Flotilla. Carry one armed LCVP on fantail, handled by crane. The 40-mm mount has a bulletproof gunhouse. The U.S.-design mortar/machinegun mounts are carried at the aft ends of the 02-level deckhouse, with the single machineguns being atop the pilothouse and at the aft end of the 01-level deckhouse.

♦ **6 Piratini class** Bldr: Arsenal de Marinha do Rio de Janeiro (AMRJ)

	In serv.
P 10 Piratini (ex-PGM 109)	30-11-70
P 11 Pirajá (ex-PGM 110)	3-71
P 12 Pampeiro (ex-PGM 118)	6-71
P 13 Parati (ex-PGM 119)	7-71
P 14 Penedo (ex-PGM 120)	9-71
P 15 Poti (ex-PGM 121)	10-71

Pirajá (P 11) Hartmut Ehlers, 5-00

D: 102 tons (fl) **S:** 18.0 kts (15.5 sust.) **Dim:** 28.95 × 6.10 × 1.55
A: 1 20-mm 70-cal. Oerlikon Mk 10 AA; 2 single 12.7-mm mg; 1 81-mm mortar
Electronics: Radar: 1 Decca RM 1070A nav.
M: 4 Cummins VT-12M diesels; 2 props; 1,100 bhp **Electric:** 40 kw
Range: 1,000/15; 1,700/12 **Crew:** 2 officers, 15 enlisted

Remarks: Design is based on that of the U.S. Coast Guard 95-ft. Cape class; the craft were funded by the United States. Formerly used for coastal patrol, but in 1996, P 11 and P 15 were attached to the Mato Grosso Flotilla, followed in 1997 by the others; they are all based at Ledário. A 20-mm mount has replaced the 81-mm mortar formerly carried forward, and the mortar was moved to the stern. Have GPS receivers.

PATROL BOATS [PB]

♦ **up to 16 AVINPA-21 class**
Bldr: ETN (Empresa Técnica Nacional, S.A.), Belém (In serv. . . .)

D: 40 tons light, 44.50 std. (48 fl) **S:** 41.8 kts (38 sust.)
Dim: 22.80 (20.00 wl) × 5.50 × 1.17 (0.90 hull)
A: . . .
Electronics: Radar: 1 . . . nav.
M: 2 MTU 12V396 TB93 diesels; 2 props; 3,560 bhp (2,960 sust.)
Electric: 64 kVA tot.
Range: 700/20 **Fuel:** 7,500 liters **Endurance:** 4 days **Crew:** 9 tot.

Remarks: Ordered 3-98 for riverine and coastal patrol; total program cost: $14.7 million. GRP construction. Design, based on that of the C.N. Baglietto (Varazze, Italy) *Meattini* class, was selected 1-98. Craft of similar design were built for the Italian Customs Service between 1972 and 1985 as the *Meattini* class and also for Algeria and the United Arab Emirates. Four of this class were to be assigned to the new Núcleos Especiais de Polícia Marítima (NEPOMS). The status of this program is uncertain, but at least some of the 16 ordered have been delivered.

♦ **144 LAEP-series riverine Training and Patrol Launches**
Bldr: Estaleiro Itajaí, S.A., and Estaleiro Wilson Sons, Guarujá (In serv. 1995–98)

D: . . . tons **S:** . . . kts **Dim:** 7.0, 8.0, 10.0, or 11.0 × . . . × . . .
A: small arms **M:** 1 Volvo Penta outdrive diesel; 1 prop; 230 bhp

Remarks: LAEP stands for *Lancha de Apoio ao Ensino e Patrulha* (Instruction Support and Patrol Launch). The original series of 5 LAEP-10 and 15 LAEP-7 launches were ordered from Estaleiro Wilson Sons 16-10-96. Are outboard-powered launches in either 7-m (LAEP-7), 8-m (LAEP-8), 10-m (LAEP-10), or 11-m (LAEP-11) length for riverine patrol and public assistance training. For example, 4 LAEP-11, the LAEP-10 launch *Calafate,* and 18 LAEP-8 patrol launches were acquired during 1997 for service in the 5th Naval District, based at Estação Naval do Rio Grande on the Rio Paraná. Five of the LAEP-10 variant are assigned to the new Núcleos Especiais de Polícia Marítima (NEPOMS).

♦ **6 Tracker-20-class patrol craft**
Bldr: Estaleiro do Sul, Porto Alegre (In serv.: LP 01–04: 5-91; others: 5-95)

LP 01 through LP 06

D: 39 tons (45 fl) **S:** 25 kts **Dim:** 20.90 (19.3 pp) × 5.18 × 1.55
A: 2 single 12.7-mm M2 mg **Electronics:** Radar: 1 Decca RM 1070A nav.
M: 2 MTU 8V396 TB83 diesels; 2 props; 2,000 bhp
Electric: 40 kw (2 × 20 kw) **Range:** 450/15
Fuel: 4.66 tons **Endurance:** 5 days **Crew:** 2 officers, 6 enlisted

Remarks: Construction was licensed from Fairey Marine, Cowes, U.K., in 4-87. The builder is also known as "Ebin So." First unit delivered 22-2-90, but the class was not formally commissioned until all were completed. Have molded GRP hulls. All are assigned to the Port Captain service, and they now wear the numbers 01 through 06 on their sides, rather than the formerly assigned pennant numbers P 8002 through P 8007.

LP 05—with Polish Navy training ship *Wodnik* in background Hartmut Ehlers, 4-00

♦ **10 U.S. Swift Mk II patrol craft**
Bldr: R 61–64: Swiftships, Morgan City, La.; others: DM-Comercio, Importação, e Manutenção de Productos Nauticos

R 61 through R 76

D: 22.5 tons (fl) **S:** 22 kts **Dim:** 15.66 × 4.55 × 1.1
A: 1 12.7-mm mg **Electronics:** Radar: 1 . . . nav.
M: 2 G.M. Detroit 12V71 TI diesels; 2 props; 850 bhp **Electric:** 6 kw
Range: 400/22 **Crew:** 6 tot.

Remarks: Employed by naval police and Port Captain service. Six were ordered 16-1-81 in Brazil. Four earlier units were built in the U.S.A. and transferred in 1972–73. Port Captain–subordinated units bear names and have hull numbers in the 5000 series.

MINE WARFARE SHIPS

♦ **6 German Schütze-class patrol minesweepers [MSC]**
Bldr: Abeking and Rasmussen, Lemwerder

	L	In serv.		L	In serv.
M 15 Aratú	27-5-70	5-5-71	M 18 Araçatuba	1971	13-12-72
M 16 Anhatomirim	4-11-70	30-11-71	M 19 Abrolhos	7-5-74	16-4-75
M 17 Atalaia	14-4-71	13-12-72	M 20 Albardão	9-74	21-7-75

Aratú (M 15) Brazilian Navy, 1996

D: 253 tons (280 fl) **S:** 24 kts **Dim:** 47.44 × 7.16 × 2.4
A: 1 40-mm 70-cal. Bofors AA **Electronics:** Radar: 1 . . . nav.
M: 4 Maybach diesels; 2 Escher-Wyss vertical cycloidal props; 4,500 bhp
Electric: 120 kw tot. + 340-kw sweep generator
Range: 710/20 **Fuel:** 22 tons **Crew:** 4 officers, 32 enlisted

Remarks: Four ordered 4-69, two 11-73. Fitted for magnetic, mechanical, and acoustic minesweeping. Wooden hulls. Overdue for replacement.

AMPHIBIOUS WARFARE SHIPS

♦ **2 U.S. Thomaston-class dock landing ships [LSD]**
Bldr: Ingalls Shipbuilders, Pascagoula, Miss.

	Laid down	L	In serv.
G 30 Ceará (ex-*Hermitage,* LSD 34)	11-4-55	12-6-56	14-12-58
G 31 Rio de Janeiro (ex-*Alamo,* LSD 33)	11-10-54	20-1-56	24-8-56

D: 6,880 tons (12,150 fl) **S:** 22.5 kts **Dim:** 155.45 × 25.60 × 5.40 (5.80 max.)
A: 3 twin 76.2-mm 50-cal. Mk 33 DP
Electronics: Radar: 1 CRP-3100 nav.; 1 SPS-10 surf. search
M: 2 sets G.E. geared steam turbines; 2 props; 24,000 shp
Boilers: 2 Babcock & Wilcox, 40.8 kg/cm^2 pressure
Range: 5,300/22.5; 10,000/20; 13,000/10 **Fuel:** 1,390 tons
Crew: 20 officers, 325 enlisted + troops: 29 officers, 312 enlisted

Remarks: G 30 was acquired upon decommissioning from the U.S. Navy 2-10-89. G 31 was decommissioned from the USN 30-9-90 and recommissioned 18-1-91 in Brazilian service.

AMPHIBIOUS WARFARE SHIPS *(continued)*

Rio de Janeiro (G 31) Hartmut Ehlers, 4-00

Hull systems: Can carry 2 LCU or 18 LCM(6) or 6 LCM(8) in the 119.2 × 14.6-m well deck, with 975 m^2 of vehicle parking space forward of the docking well. Carry 2 LCVPs and 2 LCPLs in davits. Maximum cargo capacity: 7,400 tons. Have two 50-ton cranes and a helicopter deck.
Combat systems: Two Mk 56 and two Mk 63 radar gun-director systems were removed in 1977, leaving the gunmounts with local control only. The obsolete SPS-6 air-search radar was deleted after transfer.

♦ 1 ex-U.S. Newport-class tank landing ship [LST]
Bldr: National Steel Shipbuilding, San Diego, Calif.

	Laid down	L	In serv.
G 28 Mattoso Maia (ex-*Cayuga,* LST 1186)	28-9-68	12-7-69	8-8-70

Mattoso Maia (G 28) Hartmut Ehlers, 4-00

D: 4,975 tons light (8,576 fl) **S:** 22 kts (20 sust.)
Dim: 159.2 (171.3 over horns) × 21.18 × 5.3 (aft; 1.80 fwd)
A: 1 20-mm Mk 15 Phalanx gatling CIWS; 4 single 12.7-mm mg
Electronics:
Radar: 1 Raytheon SPS-64(V)9 nav.; 1 Raytheon SPS-10F surf. search
M: 6 Alco 16-251 diesels; 2 CP props; 16,500 bhp
Range: 14,250/14 **Fuel:** 1,750 tons
Crew: 13 officers, 174 enlisted + troops: 20 officers, 294 enlisted (+ 72 emergency accomm.)

Remarks: Transferred 26-8-94 on 5-year lease with option to purchase, arriving 10-94 at Rio de Janeiro. Under the U.S. Defense Authorization Act for FY 99, she was offered for sale along with her sister *Peoria* (LST 1183), but Brazil did not buy the second ship and did not buy G 28 until 19-9-00. The U.S. Navy has nonetheless made a further attempt to sell the LST 1183 to Brazil, which sent an inspection team to study the ship in 5-01.
Hull systems: Can transport 2,000 tons cargo or, for beaching, 500 tons of cargo on 1,765 m^2 of deck space. A side-thruster propeller forward helps when marrying to a causeway. There is a 34-m-long, 75-ton-capacity mobile aluminum ramp forward, which is linked to the tank deck by a second from the upper deck. Aft are a 242-m^2 helicopter platform and a stern door for loading and unloading vehicles. Four pontoon causeway sections can be carried on the hull sides. The tank deck, which has a 75-ton-capacity turntable at both ends, can carry 23 AAV-7A1 armored personnel carriers or 29 M 48 tanks or 41 2.5-ton trucks, while the upper deck can accept 29 2.5-ton trucks. Normally carries 3 LCVPs and one LCP in Welin davits. Has two 10-ton cranes. Carries 141,600 gallons vehicle fuel.
Combat systems: Two Mk 63 radar gun-control systems were removed during 1977–78, the two twin 76.2-mm gunmounts in 1993–94. May still carry Canadian Marconi LN-66 navigational radar in lieu of SPS-64(V)9.

Disposal note: U.S. *De Soto County*–class landing ship *Duque de Caxias* (G 26, ex-*Grant County,* LST 1174) was retired on 17-2-00.

Note: The three U.S. LCU 1610–class utility craft *Guarapari* (L 10), *Tambaú* (L 11), and *Camboriú* (L 12) were decommissioned during 1991 and reassigned to local naval districts as logistics support craft; see data under [YFU] in the Service Craft section.

♦ 5 GED 801–class landing craft [LCM]
Bldr: GED 801: Arsenal de Marinha do Rio de Janeiro (AMRJ); others: INACE, Fortaleza, Ceará (In serv. 9-12-94)

GED 801 GED 802 GED 803 GED 804 GED 805

D: 61 tons (130 fl) **S:** 12 kts (light) **Dim:** 21.65 × 6.58 × 1.10 (aft, light)
M: 2 G.M. Detroit Diesel 12V71-series diesels; 2 props; 800 bhp (590 sust.)
Range: 190/12 (light) **Crew:** 5 tot.

Remarks: Design based on that of the U.S. LCM(8) class, for which plans were acquired in 1991. Brazilian type designation is EDVM. Completion date for first unit unknown; others all delivered on date above. Are assigned to the Grupamento de Embarcações de Desembarque. Cargo: 72 tons or 150 fully equipped troops in open tank deck, 56 m^2.

♦ 3 LCM(6)-class landing craft [LCM]
Bldr: . . . , Brazil

EDVM 301 EDVM 302 EDVM 303

D: 24 tons (56 fl) **S:** 10 kts **Dim:** 17.07 × 4.37 × 1.17 (aft)
M: 2 G.M. Detroit Diesel 6-71 diesels; 2 props; 330 bhp
Range: 130/10 **Crew:** 3 tot. + 80 troops for short distances

Remarks: Can carry 29 tons cargo.

♦ 30 EDVP-class landing craft [LCVP]
Bldrs: . . . , Japan (In serv. 1959–60), and . . . , Brazil (In serv. 1971)

EDVP 501 through EDVP 530

D: 13 tons (fl) **S:** 9 kts **Dim:** 10.90 × 3.21 × 1.04 (aft)
M: 1 Yanmar diesel; 1 prop; 180 bhp **Range:** 110/9 **Crew:** 3 tot. + 36 troops

Remarks: EDVP 501–521 are a wooden construction version of the standard U.S. Navy LCVP design; the others, built in 1971 in Brazil, have GRP hulls and are powered by a 153-bhp Saab Scania diesel. Can carry 36 troops or 3.5 tons cargo in the 5.24 × 2.29-m cargo space with 2.0-m-wide access through the bow ramp. Eight of them (armed with two single 12.7-mm mg each) are carried by Amazon Flotilla gunboats, and eight, supported by the tug/transport *Leverger,* are assigned to the Mato Grosso Flotilla.

♦ 28 U.S. AAV-7-series amphibious armored personnel carriers
Bldr: United Defense LP, San Jose, Calif. (new units)

D: 18.25 tons light (23.64 loaded) **S:** 30 mph land/7 kts water
Dim: . . . × . . . × . . . (1.83 draft, loaded)
A: 1 12.7-mm M85 mg
M: 1 G.M. Detroit Diesel 8V53T diesel; 2 tracks/waterjets; 400 bhp
Range: 300 miles/25 mph (land) **Crew:** 2 + 25 troops

Remarks: Employed by the Brazilian Marine Corps. Originally typed the LVTP-7. First prototype for U.S. Marine Corps was completed in 1967, and the vehicle entered production in 1971. Weights apply to troop version; command and recovery variants weigh slightly less. Two updated AAVP-7-A1 troop carrier versions were purchased from the U.S.A. in 8-92, and 14 new units (12 AAV-7A1 troop carriers, one AAVC-7A1 command vehicle, and one AAVR-7A1 recovery vehicle) were ordered 1996 and delivered 1-97. Have aluminum armor to hulls: up to 44 mm on sides, 30 mm on top and bottom, and 35 mm across stern. The cargo compartment is 4.26 m long by 1.82 m wide and 1.68 m high.

AUXILIARIES

♦ 1 target service vessel, former oilfield supply tug [AG]
Bldr: J. G. Hitzler, Lauemburg, Germany (L: 1968)

R 26 Trinidade (ex-*Nobistor*)

Trinidade (R 26)—with former pennant number Don S. Montgomery, USN, 10-90

D: approx. tons 1,400 (fl) **S:** 12.5 kts **Dim:** 53.67 × 11.00 × 3.55
A: 2 single 12.7-mm mg **Electronics:** Radar: 1 Furuno 1830 nav.
M: 2 MWM diesels; 2 props; 2,740 bhp
Range: 8,700/12.5 **Endurance:** 37 days **Crew:** 2 officers, 20 enlisted

Remarks: 1,308 grt/499 dwt. Former Panamanian-registry oilfield supply tug seized during 1987 for smuggling and converted for naval use at Arsenal de Marinha do Rio de Janeiro (AMRJ), beginning 11-1-89 and commissioning 31-1-90. Equipped with NAVSAT receiver. Used for target towing and recovering aerial targets. Originally wore pennant number R 26, then U 16; changed again spring 2001.

♦ 1 ex-U.K. River-class navigational aids tender [AGL]
Bldr: Richards, Great Yarmouth

	Laid down	L	In serv.
H 37 Garnier Sampaio (ex-*Helmsdale,* M 2010)	21-5-84	11-1-85	6-6-85

D: 630 tons (770 fl) **S:** 14 kts (15 on trials; 12 sust.)
Dim: 47.60 (42.00 pp) × 10.50 × 3.10 (3.75 max.) **A:** removed
Electronics: Radar: 2 Decca TM 1226C nav.
M: 2 Ruston 6 RKCM diesels; 2 4-bladed CP props; 3,040 bhp
Electric: 460 kw tot. **Range:** 4,500/10 **Fuel:** 88 tons
Crew: 7 officers, 7 petty officers, 16 other enlisted

Remarks: 638 grt. Former minesweeper, purchased 11-94 and transferred 2-95. Had been in reserve since late 1991. Began conversion as a navigational buoy tender and training ship at the Arsenal de Marinha do Rio de Janeiro (AMRJ), with the work then completed at Estaleiro de Ilha, S.A. (EISA), Itajaí, early in 1997. Is painted white, with orange stacks and mast.
Hull systems: Steel hull built to commercial standards, following the design of a North Sea oilfield supply vessel. Single-compartment damage standard. Navigation gear includes two Kelvin-Hughes MS 48 echo sounders, Decca QM 14(1) and Decca HiFix Mk 6 radio navaids, and a NAVSAT receiver. Modifications in Brazil include installation of an A-frame gallows crane at the stern, a 10-ton buoy crane amidships, and air-conditioning equipment.

AUXILIARIES *(continued)*

♦ **1 lighthouse and buoy tender [AGL]**
Bldr: Ebin S.A. Indústria Naval, Niterói

	Laid down	L	In serv.
H 34 Almirante Graça Aranha	end-1970	23-6-74	9-9-76

Almirante Graça Aranha (H 34) Hartmut Ehlers, 4-00

D: 1,343 tons (2,390 fl) **S:** 13 kts **Dim:** 75.57 × 13.0 × 3.71
A: none **Electronics:** Radar: 2 Decca . . . nav.
M: diesel; 1 CP prop; 2,000 bhp—1 bow-thruster
Crew: 13 officers, 82 enlisted (accomm.)

Remarks: Has a telescoping hangar for one Bell 206 JetRanger (UH-11) helicopter. Two LCVPs are carried as supply lighters. Has one electrohydraulic buoy-handling crane. Painted white, with red-orange stack and mast.

♦ **1 lighthouse and navigational buoy tender [AGL]**
Bldr: Ålborg Værft, Denmark (In serv. 10-57)

H 42 Barão de Teffé (ex-*Thala Dan*)

Barão de Teffé (H 42) Hartmut Ehlers, 12-97

D: approx. 5,500 tons (fl) **S:** 12 kts
Dim: 82.00 (75.14 hull, 65.54 pp) × 13.77 × 6.30
Electronics: Radar: 2 . . . nav.
M: 1 Burmeister & Wain 7-35VBF-62 diesel; 1 CP prop; 1,970 bhp
Electric: 680 kw (2 × 340-kw diesel sets) **Fuel:** 457 tons
Crew: 18 officers, 52 enlisted + scientific party

Remarks: 2,183 grt/2,164 dwt. Ice-reinforced former cargo ship purchased 5-82 from J. Lauritzen. Completed conversion as Antarctic support ship 28-9-82, including a helicopter deck over stern; can carry 2 UH-13 Esquilo-II helicopters. Reassigned to navigational aids tending duties in 1995.

♦ **1 icebreaker/research ship [AGOR]**
Bldr: G. Eides Sonner A/S, Hoylandsbygd, Norway (In serv. 1981)

H 44 Ary Rongel (ex-*Polar Queen*)

Ary Rongel (H 44)—with two Esquilo helicopters on deck aft Brazilian Navy, 1995

D: 3,670 tons (fl) **S:** 14.5 kts (12 sust.) **Dim:** 75.32 × 13.06 × 6.20 (max.)
A: none **Electronics:** Radar: 1 . . . nav.; 1 . . . nav.
M: 2 Krupp-MaK 6M453Ak diesels, 1 CP prop; 4,500 bhp—bow- and stern-thrusters
Electric: 1,720 kw tot (1 × 1,320-kw, 2 × 200-kw diesel sets)
Range: 17,000/12 **Fuel:** 790 tons **Endurance:** 60 days
Crew: 12 officers, 39 enlisted + 22 scientific party (90 max. accomm.)

Remarks: 1,982 grt. Former research and seal-survey ship purchased from Rieber Shipping A/S, Bergen, for $15.9 million in 3-94. Operated for the Brazilian Antarctic Program (PROANTAR) to support Brazil's *Comandante Ferraz* Antarctic station on King George Island in the South Shetland Archipelago. Hull painted red, superstructure white, masts and stack cream.
Hull systems: Has side loading doors, one 6-ton crane, one 25-ton derrick, and an A-frame gallows crane at the stern. Has 1,097 m^3 of refrigerated cargo space, two holds (each with an 18.7-m-long by 5.0-m-wide hatch). Has a helicopter flight deck and open deck stowage for two AS.350BA Esquilo-I helicopters. Has Inmarsat SATCOM terminal.

♦ **1 U.S. Robert D. Conrad–class oceanographic ship [AGOR]**
Bldr: Marietta Co., Pt. Pleasant, W.Va. (In serv. 8-2-65)

H 41 Almirante Câmara (ex-*Sands,* T-AGOR 6)

Almirante Câmara (H 41) Hartmut Ehlers, 12-97

D: 1,020 tons light (1,370 fl) **S:** 13.5 kts
Dim: 63.7 (58.32 pp) × 11.89 × 4.9 (mean)
Electronics: Radar: 1 RCA CRM-N1A-75 nav.; 1 . . . nav.
M: 2 Caterpillar D-378 diesels, electric drive; 1 prop; 1,000 shp
Electric: 1,470 kw **Range:** 10,000/12 **Fuel:** 211 tons
Crew: 8 officers, 18 enlisted + 15 oceanographers

Remarks: 1,110 grt/359 nrt. Loaned 1-7-74; purchased outright 21-9-90. Painted white, with red-orange stack and mast.
Hull systems: An auxiliary 620-hp gas turbine mounted in the stack casing powers a small electric maneuvering propeller for low-noise operations at an extremely low rpm; also has a bow-thruster. Equipped for gravimetric, magnetic, and geological research. Has echo sounders capable of measuring 11,000-m depths.

♦ **2 ex-U.K. River-class survey ships [AGS]**
Bldr: Richards (Shipbuilders), Ltd., Lowestoft

	Laid down	L	In serv.
H 35 Amorim do Valle (ex-*Humber,* M 2007)	21-10-83	17-5-84	7-6-85
H 36 Taurus (ex-*Jorge Leite;* ex-*Ribble,* M 2012)	17-9-84	7-5-86	28-6-86

Amorim do Valle (H 35) Brazilian Navy, 1996

D: 630 tons (770 fl) **S:** 14 kts (15 on trials; 12 sust.)
Dim: 47.60 (42.00 pp) × 10.50 × 3.10 (3.75 max.) **A:** removed
Electronics: Radar: 2 Decca TM 1226 nav.
M: 2 Ruston 6 RKCM diesels; 2 4-bladed CP props; 3,040 bhp
Electric: 460 kw tot. **Range:** 4,500/10 **Fuel:** 88 tons
Crew: 7 officers, 7 petty officers, 16 other enlisted

Remarks: 638 grt. Former minesweepers, purchased 11-94 and transferred 2-95. Had been in reserve since late 1991. H 36 was originally converted as a navigational aids tender and was modified again in 2000 and renamed. Are painted white, with orange stacks and masts. Steel hull, built to commercial single-compartment damage standards.

♦ **1 seismic survey ship [AGS]**
Bldr: Mjellem & Karlsen A/S, Bergen (In serv. 1984)

H 40 Antares (ex-*Lady Hamilton*)

D: 855 tons light (1,400 fl) **S:** 13.5 kts **Dim:** 55.0 × 10.3 × 4.3
Electronics: Radar: 2 Decca . . . nav.
M: 1 Burmeister & Wain Alpha diesel; 1 CP prop; 1,860 bhp—bow-thruster
Range: 10,000/12 **Crew:** 10 officers, 35 enlisted

AUXILIARIES *(continued)*

Antares (H 40) Hartmut Ehlers, 4-00

Remarks: 1,076 grt. Acquired from Racal Energy Resources and commissioned 6-6-88. Painted white with red-orange upperworks. Has small helicopter platform at stern.

♦ **1 Sirius class [AGS]** Bldr: Ishikawajima-Harima Heavy Industries, Tokyo

	Laid down	L	In serv.
H 21 SIRIUS	12-56	30-7-57	1-1-58

Sirius (H 21) H&L Van Ginderen, 5-95

D: 1,463 tons (1,900 fl) **S:** 15 kts **Dim:** 77.90 × 12.03 × 3.70
Electronics: Radar: 2 . . . nav.
M: 2 Sulzer 7T6-36 diesels; 2 CP props; 2,700 bhp
Range: 12,000/11 **Fuel:** 343 tons **Crew:** 102 tot. + 14 scientific party

Remarks: Carries 1 SAH-11 helicopter, 1 LCVP, and 3 small survey craft. Sister *Canopus* (H 22) was stricken 7-1-97.

♦ **1 Argus-class coastal survey ship [AGS]**
Bldr: Arsenal de Marinha do Rio de Janeiro (AMRJ)

	L	In serv.
H 31 ARGUS	6-12-57	29-1-59

D: 250 tons (350 fl) **S:** 15 kts **Dim:** 44.67 (41.14 pp) × 6.50 × 2.80
Electronics: Radar: 1 Decca 1226C nav.
M: 2 Caterpillar DT 379 diesels; 2 props; 1,200 bhp
Range: 3,000/15 **Fuel:** 35 tons **Endurance:** 20 days **Crew:** 34 tot.

Remarks: Based on the design of the Portuguese *Azevia*-class gunboat. Has a hangar and flight deck for one Esquilo-I helicopter.
Disposals: Sister *Taurus* (H 33) was stricken on 26-2-96 and *Orion* (H 32) on 1-2-01.

♦ **1 logistic support cargo ship [AK]**
Bldr: Ishikawajima do Brasil, Rio de Janeiro (In serv. 1986)

G . . . ATLANTICO SUL (ex-*Lloyd Atlantico*)

D: approx. 39,000 tons (fl) **S:** 19 kts **Dim:** 188.02 (178.01 pp) × 30.71 × 11.02
A: none **Electronics:** Radar: . . .
M: 1 Ishikawajima do Brasil–Sulzer 6RTA76 diesel; 1 prop; 16,560 bhp
Electric: 4,700 kw tot. (1 × 1,400-kw, 3 × 1,100-kw diesel sets)
Range: . . ./. . . **Crew:** . . .

Remarks: 22,201 grt/28,977 dwt. Former container ship purchased 2001 from Companhia de Navegação Lloyd Brasileiro (Lloydbras) for use as a logistics support vessel. Has four holds, equipped with fixed cell guides, and is of 1,210-TEU container capacity. Is equipped with two 35-ton and one 22-ton cranes and can provide power to up to 308 20-ft.-equivalent refrigerated cargo containers.

♦ **1 replenishment oiler [AO]**
Bldr: Ishikawajima do Brasil, Rio de Janeiro

	Laid down	L	In serv.
G 27 MARAJÓ	13-12-66	31-1-68	22-10-68

Marajó (G 27) Hartmut Ehlers, 4-00

D: 16,000 tons (fl) **S:** 13.6 kts **Dim:** 137.10 (127.69 pp) × 19.22 × 7.35
A: none **Electronics:** Radar: 2 . . . nav.
M: 1 Sulzer GRD 68 diesel; 1 prop; 8,000 bhp
Electric: 1,200 kw tot. **Range:** 9,200/. . . **Fuel:** 700 tons
Crew: 80 tot.

Remarks: 6,600 grt/11,119 dwt. Was to have been retired on completion of *Almirante Gastão Motta* but was refitted for further service; as of 2000 was planned for imminent retirement. Cargo capacity: 7,200 tons liquid. Has two liquid replenishment stations per side. Handicapped by low speed and an unreliable engine.

♦ **1 replenishment oiler [AOR]**
Bldr: Ishikawajima do Brasil, Rio de Janeiro

	Laid down	L	In serv.
G 23 ALMIRANTE GASTÃO MOTTA	11-12-89	1-6-90	26-11-91

Almirante Gastão Motta (G 23) French Navy, 4-97

D: 10,300 tons (fl) **S:** 20.5 kts **Dim:** 135.00 (128.00 pp) × 19.00 × 7.50
A: 2 single 12.7-mm mg **Electronics:** Radar: 2 Decca . . . nav.
M: 2 Wärtsilä Vasa 12V32 diesels; 1 CP prop; 11,700 bhp
Electric: 3,600 kw (2 × 900-kw shaft generators; 3 × 600-kw alternators, 3 Ishibras-Wärtsilä 4-R22 diesels driving)
Range: 10,000/15 **Fuel:** 600 tons
Crew: 13 officers, 108 enlisted + 12 spare berths

Remarks: 6,000 dwt. Ordered 15-12-87. Replaced the uncompleted conversion of the former Lloyd Brasileiro Steamship Co. tanker *Itatinga* (also to have been named *Almirante Gastão Motta,* G 29; sold 1987) as a replacement for *Marajó* (G 27), which was to have been stricken at the end of 1991 but remains in service.
Hull systems: Cargo fuel capacity: 4,400 tons; also carries 200 tons dry stores. Has a single replenishment station each side amidships and no astern refueling capability. No helicopter facilities.

♦ **2 Custódio de Mello–class transports [AP]**
Bldr: Ishikawajima Jukogyo, Tokyo

	Laid down	L	In serv.
G 20 CUSTÓDIO DE MELLO (ex-U 26)	12-53	10-6-54	1-12-54
G 21 ARY PARREIRAS	12-55	24-8-56	29-12-56

Soares Dutra (G 22)—stricken in 2001 Hartmut Ehlers, 4-00

D: 4,800 tons (8,600 fl) **S:** 15 kts **Dim:** 119.44 (110.34 pp) × 16.06 × 6.25
A: 2 single 76.2-mm 50-cal. U.S. Mk 26 DP; 2 single 20-mm 70-cal. Mk 10 Oerlikon AA
Electronics: Radar: 2 . . . nav.
M: 2 sets double-reduction geared steam turbines; 2 props; 4,800 shp
Boilers: 2 Foster-Wheeler 2-drum water-tube; 350° C **Fuel:** 861 tons
Crew: 127 tot. + up to 1,972 troops (497 normal)

Remarks: G 21: 4,874 grt/4,125 dwt; G 22: 5,026 grt/4,125 dwt. Are occasionally used in commercial service under the management of TRANSPOMAR (Comando da Força de Transporte da Marinha). Formerly used as training ship until replaced in that role by *Brasil* (U 27). Sister *Barroso Pereira* (G 16) was stricken 3-4-95 and *Soares Dutra* on 26-6-01.
Hull systems: All three have 425 m^3 of refrigerated cargo space and can carry about 4,000 tons general cargo in their three holds. Living spaces are mechanically ventilated and partially air-conditioned. G 21 and G 22 have a helicopter platform aft.

♦ **1 submarine rescue and general salvage ship [ASR]**
Bldr: Stord Vaerft A/S, Stord, Norway (In serv. 1979)

K 11 FELINTO PERRY (ex-*Holger Dane,* ex-*Wildrake*)

AUXILIARIES *(continued)*

Felinto Perry (K 11) Hartmut Ehlers, 12-97

D: 1,380 tons light (approx. 3,900 fl) **S:** 14.5 kts **Dim:** 77.78 × 17.48 × 4.66
A: none **Electronics:** Radar: 2 Raytheon . . . nav.
M: 2 Bergen Mek. Verksteder KVGB 12 diesels (4,880 bhp tot.); 2 Bergen Mek. Verksteder KVGB 16 diesels (6,520 bhp tot.); 2 Daimler-Benz OM414 diesels (910 hp); 2 1,712-kw generators, electric drive; 2 CP props; 7,000 shp—4 550-shp side-thrusters
Electric: 6,160 kw (2 × 2,280 kw, 2 × 300 kw) **Crew:** 9 officers, 56 enlisted

Remarks: 1,769 grt/496 dwt. Former North Sea oilfield rescue ship purchased 11-88 from Rederiet H. H. Faddersbjll A/S for use as a submarine rescue and general salvage ship as replacement for the U.S. *Penguin*-class submarine rescue ship *Gastão Moutinho* (K 10).
Hull systems: Very lavishly equipped for salvage and firefighting duties. Has a 19.0-m octagonal helicopter deck mounted above the pilothouse. Equipped with centerline moonpool and capable of conducting saturation diving to 300 m. Has an 8-man pressurized divers' lifeboat. Working deck is 238 m^2. Has one 30-ton, one 7-ton, and two 3-ton electrohydraulic cranes. Equipped with Kongsberg AOP 503 Mk II dynamic positioning system and has 4-point mooring system. Three water and two foam fire monitors, with 200-m water, 60-m foam range. Submarine rescue and salvage equipment is transported in a portable module.

♦ 3 Tritão-class oceangoing tugs [ATA]
Bldr: ESTANAVE, Manaus

	In serv.
R 21 Tritão (ex-*Sarandi*)	23-7-86
R 22 Tridente (ex-*Sambaiba*)	19-2-87
R 23 Triunfo (ex-*Sorocaba*)	8-10-87

Tritão (R 21) H&L Van Ginderen, 1-00

D: 819 tons (1,680 fl) **S:** 15 kts **Dim:** 53.52 (50.02 pp) × 11.61 × 3.35
A: 2 single 20-mm 70-cal. Mk 10 Oerlikon AA
Electronics: Radar: 2 . . . nav.
M: 2 Burmeister & Wain Alpha diesels; 2 props; 2,480 bhp—bow-thruster
Endurance: 45 days **Crew:** 49 tot.

Remarks: Begun as oilfield supply tugs for Petrobras but purchased 5-86 while still under construction. Intended for 200-n.m. economic zone patrol and SAR duties. Have bow-thrusters and are capable of 23.5-ton bollard pull for ocean towing.

♦ 2 Almirante Guilhem–class oceangoing tugs [ATA]
Bldr: Sumitomo Heavy Industries, Japan (L: 1976)

R 24 Almirante Guilhem (ex-*Superpesa 4*)
R 25 Almirante Guillobel (ex-*Superpesa 5*)

D: 2,400 tons (fl) **S:** 14 kts **Dim:** 63.15 × 13.40 × 4.50
A: 2 single 20-mm 70-cal. Mk 10 Oerlikon AA
Electronics: Radar: 2 Decca . . . nav.
M: 2 G.M. 20-645 ET diesels; 2 CP props; 7,200 bhp—525-shp bow-thruster
Electric: 550 kw **Fuel:** 670 tons **Crew:** 40 tot.

Remarks: Former oilfield supply tugs purchased 1980 from Superpesa Maritime Transport, Ltd., and commissioned 22-1-81. Have 84-ton bollard pull.

Almirante Guillobel (R 25) Hartmut Ehlers, 4-00

♦ 1 Stad Amsterdam–class sail training ship [AXT]
Bldr: Damen SY, Gorinchem, and Nista BV, Amsterdam, the Netherlands

	L	In serv.
Cisne Branco	4-8-99	12-99

Cisne Branco A. D. Baker III, 6-00

D: 1,038 tons (fl) **S:** 17 kts (under sail; 11 on engine)
Dim: 78.00 (60.50 hull) × 10.50 × 4.80 (max.)
M: 1 Caterpillar 3508 DITA SCAC diesel; 1 prop; 1,060 bhp—2,195 m^2 max. sail area—300-kw bow-thruster
Electric: 506 kVA tot. (2 × 200-kVA, 1 × 106-kVA diesel sets)
Crew: 8 officers, 14 enlisted, 55 cadets

Remarks: Ordered 9-98 for completion by 1-1-00 to permit participating in a race from Lisbon to Rio de Janeiro to commemorate the 500th anniversary of the discovery of Brazil. Three-masted, full-rigged ship with design based on the late-19th-century Dutch ship *Amsterdam.* Hull has 6.45-m molded depth.

♦ 1 cadet training ship, modified Mk 10 frigate design [AXT]
Bldr: Arsenal de Marinha do Rio de Janeiro (AMRJ)

	Laid down	L	In serv.
U 27 Brasil	18-9-81	23-9-83	21-8-86

Brasil (U 27) Alexander George, 7-00

D: 2,380 tons (3,400 fl) **S:** 18 kts (15 sust.)
Dim: 131.25 × 13.52 × 4.21 (mean, fl)
A: 2 single 40-mm 70-cal. Bofors L70 AA; 4 single 3-pdr. saluting cannon
Electronics: Radar: 2 Decca . . . nav.
M: 2 Ishikawajima do Brasil–Pielstick 6 PC. 2 L400 diesels; 2 props; 7,800 bhp
Range: 7,000/15 **Endurance:** 30 days
Crew: 28 officers, 190 enlisted + 204 cadets

Remarks: Uses hull of the Mk 10 frigate design, but has a less-powerful propulsion plant and far simpler weapons and electronics. Replaced transport *Custódio de Mello* (G 20, then U 26) for training cadets from the naval and merchant marine academies.
Hull systems: Has a command center with three remote training command spaces, a navigational training compartment for 40 trainees, and two other classrooms.

AUXILIARIES *(continued)*

Combat systems: A planned 76-mm OTOBreda Compact mount forward was not installed, nor was the planned helicopter hangar, although the helicopter platform can accommodate one light helicopter. There is a single remote optical director for the two 40-mm gunmounts. Has two commercial SATCOM systems.

YARD AND SERVICE CRAFT

Note: Small units without pennant numbers are assigned local dockyard numbers; craft attached to Rio de Janeiro have BNRJ-series numbers.

♦ 1 fisheries research oceanographic craft [YAG]
Bldr: INACE, Fortaleza, Ceará (In serv. 22-5-81)

U 15 Suboficial Oliveira

D: 108 tons (120 fl) **S:** 10 kts **Dim:** 35.5 × 6.7 × . . .
M: 2 diesels; 2 props; 740 bhp **Range:** 1400/8 **Crew:** 10 tot.

Remarks: For use by the Naval Research Institute on the "Capo Frio Project" for shrimp cultivation.

♦ 1 lightship [YAG]
Bldr: Ebin S.A. Indústria Naval, Niterói (In serv. 31-4-91)

Risca do Zumbi

D: 150 tons (fl) **Dim:** 20.0 × 8.0 × 1.5

Remarks: Anchored 12 n.m. off Rio Grande do Norte. Powered by solar panels.

♦ 6 munitions lighters [YE]

	In serv.		In serv.
São Francisco dos Santos	1964	Miguel dos Santos	1968
Ubirajara dos Santos	1968	Aprendiz Lédio Conceição	1968
Operario Luis Leal	1968	U 30 Almirante Hess	27-10-83

D: 88.2 tons (fl) **S:** 13.5 kts **Dim:** 23.6 × 6.0 × 2.0 **M:** . . .

Remarks: Last three transport torpedoes, the others projectiles only. Only U 30 has a pennant number.

♦ 1 personnel and stores transport [YF]
Bldr: Empresa Brasileira de Construção Naval (Ebrasa), Itajaí, Santa Catarina (L: 29-8-74)

Sargento Borges (ex-R 47)

D: 108.5 tons (fl) **S:** 10 kts **Dim:** 28.0 × 6.5 × 1.5
M: 2 diesels; 2 props; 480 bhp
Range: 400/10 **Crew:** 10 tot. + 106 passengers

Note: Also in service, with the Mato Grosso Flotilla, is the tug/transport *Leverger;* no data available.

♦ 4 Rio Pardo–class harbor passenger ferries [YFB]
Bldr: Inconav Niterói Shipbuilders (In serv. 1975–76)

Rio Chui (ex-R 42) Rio Oiapoque (ex-R 43)
Rio Negro (ex-R 41) Rio Pardo (ex-U 40)

Rio Negro — Brazilian Navy, 1993

D: 150 tons **S:** 14 kts **Dim:** 35.38 × 6.5 × 1.9
M: 2 diesels; 2 props; 1,096 bhp **Crew:** . . . tot. + 400 passengers

♦ 6 Rio Doce–class harbor ferries [YFB]
Bldr: G. deVries Leutsch, Amsterdam

	In serv.		In serv.
Rio Doce (ex-U 20)	12-5-54	Rio Real (ex-U 23)	1955
Rio das Contas (ex-U 21)	15-9-54	Rio Turvo (ex-U 24)	16-12-54
Rio Formoso (ex-U 22)	10-54	Rio Verde (ex-U 25)	12-8-54

D: 150 tons (200 fl) **S:** 14 kts **Dim:** 36.6 × 6.5 × 2.1
M: 2 Sulzer diesels; 2 props; 450 bhp
Range: 700/14 **Crew:** 10 tot. + 600 passengers

♦ 1 river transport [YFB]
Bldr: Estaleiro SNBP, Mato Grosso (In serv. 1982)

U 29 Piraim

D: 73.3 tons (91.5 fl) **S:** 7 kts **Dim:** 25.0 × 5.5 × 0.91
A: 4 single 7.62-mm mg **Electronics:** Radar: 1 Furuno 3600 nav.
M: 2 MWM diesels; 2 props; 400 bhp **Electric:** 60 kVA tot.
Range: 700/7 **Crew:** 2 officers, 13 enlisted, 2 civilian pilots

Remarks: Assigned to the Mato Grosso Flotilla. Can transport two marine platoons.

Piraim (U 29) — Hartmut Ehlers, 5-00

♦ 1 river transport [YFB]
Bldr: Amsterdam Droogdok, the Netherlands (In serv. 1951)

G 15 Paraguassu

Paraguassu (G 15) — Hartmut Ehlers, 5-00

D: 200 tons (285 fl) **S:** 12 kts **Dim:** 40.00 × 7.00 × 1.55
A: 6 single 7.62-mm mg **Electronics:** Radar: 1 Furuno 3600 nav.
M: 3 diesels; 1 prop; 1,500 bhp
Range: 2,000/10 **Crew:** 4 officers, 31 enlisted + 178 marines

Remarks: Former commercial river passenger vessel converted for troop use and commissioned 20-6-72. Operates in the Mato Grosso Flotilla, based at Ladário.

♦ 1 U.S. AFDL 34–class floating dry dock [YFDL]
Bldr: V. P. Loftis (In serv. 10-44)

G 27 Cidade de Natal (ex-U.S. AFDL 39, ex-ARDC 6)

Lift capacity: 2,800 tons **Dim:** 118.6 × 25.6 × 2.84 (light)

Remarks: Loaned 10-11-66; purchased 28-12-77. Concrete construction. 17.7-m clear width inside, 105.2-m length on blocks.

♦ 1 U.S. AFDL 1–class small floating dry dock [YFDL]
Bldr: Chicago Bridge & Iron (In serv. 12-43)

G 26 Almirante Jeronimo Gonçalves (ex-*Goiaz,* ex-AFDL 4, ex-AFD 4)

Lift capacity: 1,000 tons **Dim:** 60.96 × 19.51 × 1.04 (light)

Remarks: Loaned 10-11-66; purchased 28-7-77. Steel construction. 13.7-m clear width inside, 56.4-m length on blocks.

♦ 1 U.S. ARD 12–class floating dry dock [YFDL]
Bldr: Pacific Bridge, Alameda, Calif. (In serv. 11-43)

G 25 Afonso Peña (ex-*Ceará,* ex-ARD 14)

Afonso Peña (G 25) — Hartmut Ehlers, 4-00

Lift capacity: 3,500 tons **Dim:** 149.86 × 24.69 × 1.73 (light)

Remarks: Loaned 1963; purchased outright 28-12-77. Steel construction. Has a pointed bow to improve towing characteristics. Dock area is 118.6 m on blocks by 18.0 m clear width. Reported stricken in 1997, but appears still to be in service.

Note: Also in use for submarines at the Arsenal de Marinha do Rio de Janeiro (AMRJ) is the floating dry dock *Almirante Schiek,* completed in 1995; no data available.

YARD AND SERVICE CRAFT *(continued)*

♦ 2 personnel launches [YFL]

Tenente Fabio   Tenente Raul

D: 55 tons **S:** 10 kts **Dim:** 20.28 × 5.1 × 1.2 **M:** 1 diesel; 135 bhp
Cargo capacity: 22 tons **Range:** 350/10

Note: For service with the Mato Grosso Flotilla, the Capitania Fluvial do Pantanal, Mato Grosso, has several small launches for which no data are available: one floating classroom *(Agencia Escola Flutante),* one NAJA-19 launch, one LPPN-1 launch, three craft of the LAE-7 type, and eight of the LPF-6 type. The Capitania Fluvial do Teite-Paraná operates the school launch (ex-passenger ferry) *Ahanguera* (18.30 × 6.50 × 1.50 m; 525 n.m./7 kts).

♦ 1 historic personnel ferry [YFL]
Bldr: Vickers, Barrow-in-Furness, U.K. (In serv. 1910)

Laurindo Pitta

D: 514 tons (fl) **S:** . . . **Dim:** 39.04 × 7.77 × 4.60
Electronics: Radar: 1 . . . nav.
M: 2 . . . diesels; 2 props; . . . bhp

Remarks: Former large harbor tug, now used as a ferry from the Naval Cultural Center at Rio de Janeiro to the museum ship exhibits at Ilha Fiscal. Although stricken some years ago, she was restored to service in 2000, with the original reciprocating steam engines and boilers replaced by diesel engines.

♦ 3 U.S. LCU 1610–class harbor logistics transports [YFU]
Bldr: Arsenal de Marinha do Rio de Janeiro (AMRJ)

	L	In serv.
GED 10 Guarapari (ex-L 10)	16-6-77	27-3-78
GED 11 Tambaú (ex-L 11)	14-9-77	27-3-78
GED 12 Camboriú (ex-L 12)	. . .	1989

Tambaú (GED 11) Hartmut Ehlers, 4-00

D: 200 tons (396 fl) **S:** 11 kts **Dim:** 41.0 × 8.42 × 2.0
A: 3 single 12.7-mm mg **Electronics:** Radar: 1 . . . nav.
M: 2 G.M. Detroit Diesel 12V71 diesels; 2 props; 1,000 bhp
Range: 1,200/8 **Crew:** 6 tot. + 120 troops for short distances

Remarks: Former landing craft officially decommissioned in 1991 and reassigned to local naval establishments as logistics support craft. Typed EDCG *(Embarcações de Desembarque de Carga Generales).* Uncompleted sister *Tramandai* (L 13) was scrapped in 1983. Can carry 143 tons cargo; cargo space: 30.5 × 5.5 m. Have bow and stern vehicle ramps.

♦ 10 Achernar-class navigational aids tenders [YGL]
Bldr: Wilson Sons S.A. and Comércio, Indústria, e Agência de Navegação, Guarujá

	In serv.		In serv.
CPSP 02 Achernar	20-12-95	CPPR 05 Fomalhaut	2-12-96
SSN 224 Aldebaran	23-3-96	SSN 4204 Regulus	3-2-97
CPSF 03 Betelgeuse	5-6-96	SSN 506 Rigel	30-4-97
CPES 03 Capella	1-8-96	. . . . . .	1998
SSN 4103 Denebola	30-9-96	. . . . . .	1998

Rigel (SSN 506) IJ Plokker, 4-98

D: 102.4 tons (130 fl) **S:** 10.2 kts **Dim:** 19.76 (18.00 pp) × 6.04 × 1.98 (max.)
M: 2 Cummins NT855M diesels; 2 props; 648 bhp
Electric: 90 kVA tot. (2 × 45 kVA, Lister-Blackstone diesels driving)
Range: . . ./. . . **Fuel:** 13.2 m^3 **Crew:** 6 tot.

Remarks: Are described as "buoy tender launches." Prefixes to the pennant numbers apparently refer to operating bases. Designed in the Netherlands. Have an Effer Model 14500-1S electrohydraulic buoy crane with 7.2-ton capacity at 1.9-m radius or 2.2 tons at 6.5 m.

♦ 4 Comandante Varella–class navigational aids tenders [YGL]
Bldr: São João de Nilo SY (H 18: Arsenal de Marinha do Rio de Janeiro/AMRJ)

	Laid down	L	In serv.
H 18 Comandante Varella	1-8-78	18-9-81	30-9-82
H 19 Comandante Manhães	. . .	. . .	. . .
H 20 Tenente Castelho	. . .	. . .	15-12-83
H 25 Tenente Boanerges	. . .	. . .	1985

Comandante Varella (H 18) IJ Plokker, 4-98

D: 300 tons light (440 fl) **S:** 12 kts **Dim:** 37.51 (34.5 pp) × 8.60 × 2.56
M: 2 8-cyl. diesels; 2 props; 1,300 bhp **Range:** 2,880/12 **Crew:** 22 tot.

Remarks: Can be reconfigured as minelayers.

Disposal note: *Mestre João dos Santos*–class navigational aids tenders *Mestre João dos Santos* (H 13) and *Castelhanos* (H 24) were stricken during 2000.

♦ 1 "130-ton" navigational aid tender [YGL]
Bldr: . . . . . . (In serv. 21-1-84)

H 26 Faroleiro Mario Seixas

Remarks: 242-ton (fl) modified fishing trawler; no other data available. The similar-sized *Faroleiro Areas* (H 27) and *Faroleiro Nascimento* (H 30) were stricken during 2000.

Note: Also in service, with the Mato Grosso Flotilla, are the river buoy tenders *Lufada* and *Piracema;* no data available.

♦ 6 Paraíbano-class survey craft [YGS]
Bldr: Bormann, Rio de Janeiro

	In serv.		In serv.
H 11 Paraíbano	10-68	H 15 Itacurussa	3-71
H 12 Rio Branco	10-68	H 16 Camocim	1971
H 14 Nogueira da Gama (ex-*Jaceguai*)	3-71	H 17 Caravelas	1971

D: 32 tons (50 fl) **S:** 11 kts **Dim:** 16.0 × 4.6 × 1.3
M: 2 G.M. 6-71 diesels; 2 props; 330 bhp
Range: 600/11 **Crew:** 2 officers, 9 enlisted

Remarks: Wooden construction. Operate primarily with the Amazon Flotilla, with H 17 assigned to the Mato Grosso Flotilla. All were officially decommissioned in 1991 but have been retained as district survey support craft.

♦ 1 Doutor Montenegro–class river hospital ship [YH]
Bldr: Estaleiro Conave, Manaus (In serv. 1997)

U 16 Doutor Montenegro

D: 400 tons (fl) **S:** 6 kts **Dim:** 42.00 × 11.00 × . . .
Electronics: Radar: 1 . . . nav.
M: 2 . . . diesels; 2 props; 600 bhp
Range: . . ./. . . **Crew:** 8 officers, 41 enlisted, 11 medical personnel

Remarks: Officially typed NASH *(Navio de Asstencia Hospitalar).* Completed for the state of Acre in 1997 and handed over to the navy on 19-5-01. The ship has a rectangular barge-like hull and a flight deck for one UH-12 Esquilo-I helicopter. Serves in the Amazon Flotilla.

♦ 2 Oswaldo Cruz–class river hospital ships [YH]
Bldr: Arsenal de Marinha do Rio de Janeiro (AMRJ)

	Laid down	L	In serv.
U 18 Oswaldo Cruz	1981	11-7-83	31-5-84
U 19 Carlos Chagas	1982	16-4-84	12-84

Carlos Chagas (U 19) Brazilian Navy, 1996

YARD AND SERVICE CRAFT *(continued)*

D: 500 tons (fl) **S:** 9 kts **Dim:** 47.18 (45.00 pp) × 8.45 × 1.75
Electronics: Radar: 1 Decca . . . nav.
M: 2 diesels; 2 props; 714 bhp
Electric: 420 kVA (2 × 180-kVA, 1 × 60-kVA diesel sets)
Range: 4,000/9 **Fuel:** 77,450 liters
Crew: 5 officers, 22 enlisted + 5 doctor/dentists, 15 other health personnel

Remarks: Officially typed NASH *(Navio de Asstencia Hospitalar)*. Have two sick bays (6 total beds), an operating theater, two clinics, a dental laboratory, and X-ray facilities. Tankage for 34,200 liters fresh water. Have a flight deck for one UH-12 Esquilo-I helicopter. Serve in Amazon Flotilla.

♦ 1 river oiler [YO] Bldr: Papendrecht, the Netherlands (L: 16-3-38)

G 17 Potengi

Potengi (G 17) Hartmut Ehlers, 5-00

D: 594 tons **S:** 10 kts **Dim:** 54.5 × 7.5 × 1.8
A: 2 single 7.62-mm mg **Electronics:** Radar: 1 Furuno 3600 nav.
M: 2 diesels; 2 props; 550 bhp **Range:** 600/8 **Crew:** 19 tot.

Remarks: Assigned to the Mato Grosso Flotilla. In 1996, began conversion into a general-purpose riverine force support vessel at Ladário, completing 6-5-99 with tankage altered to carry diesel and aviation fuel and water and a deckhouse built over the cargo tank area. Cargo capacity: 450 tons.

♦ 1 torpedo recovery craft [YPT]
Bldr: INACE, Fortaleza (In serv. 2-12-83)

BACS 01 Almirante Hess (ex-U 30)

D: 91 tons (fl) **S:** 13 kts **Dim:** 23.6 × 6.0 × 2.0
Electronics: Radar: 1 Decca 110 nav.
M: 2 . . . diesels; 2 props; . . . bhp **Crew:** 14 tot.

Remarks: Decommissioned in 1991, then transferred to service craft category. Has an electrohydraulic crane and a stern ramp for recovery and stowage of up to four torpedoes.

♦ 4 StanTug 2207 design large harbor tugs [YTB]
Bldr: Scheepswerf Damen B.V., Gorinchem, the Netherlands

BNRJ 16 Intrepido BNRJ 18 Valente
BNRJ 17 Arrojado BNRJ 19 Impavido

Valente (BNRJ 18) George R. Schneider, 11-95

D: 200 tons (fl) **S:** 12.75 kts **Dim:** 22.65 (20.36 pp) × 7.25 × 2.81 (max. aft)
M: 2 Caterpillar 3508TA diesels; 2 Kort-nozzle props; 1,580 bhp

Remarks: 134 grt. 22.5 tons bollard pull. First two delivered 6-92, the others 9-92. "BNRJ" in the pennant number indicates assignment to the Rio de Janeiro naval base.

♦ 4 Comandante Marriog–class yard tugs [YTB]
Bldr: Turn-Ship, Ltd., U.S.A. (In serv. 1981)

BNRJ 03 Comandante Marriog (ex-R 15)
BNRJ 04 Comandante Didier (ex-R 14)
BNRJ 05 Tenente Magalhaes (ex-R 17)
BNRJ 06 Cabo Schram (ex-R 18)

Commandante Marriog (BNRJ 03) Hartmut Ehlers, 4-00

D: 115 tons (fl) **S:** 10 kts **Dim:** 19.8 × 7.0 × 2.0
M: 2 G.M. diesels; 2 props; 900 bhp **Crew:** 6 tot.

Remarks: "BNRJ" in the pennant number indicates assignment to the Rio de Janeiro naval base. Sisters *Audaz* (R 31) and *Guarani* (R 33) were stricken in 1986.

♦ 2 Isaias de Noronha–class tugs [YTM] (In serv. 1972–74)

BNRJ 01 Tenente Lahmeyer . . . D.N.O.G.

Tenente Lahmeyer (BNRJ 01) Brazilian Navy, 1996

D: 100 tons (fl) **Dim:** 32.0 × . . . × . . . **M:** . . .

Remarks: Name "D.N.O.G." refers to the Brazilian naval contingent in Europe during World War I. "BNRJ" in the pennant number indicates assignment to the Rio de Janeiro naval base.

♦ 2 Itapura-class water tankers [YW]
Bldr: . . . . . . (L: 1957)

Itapura (ex-R 42) Paulo Afonso (ex-R 43)

D: 485.3 tons **Dim:** 42.8 × 7.0 × 2.5 **M:** 1 diesel **Cargo:** 389 tons

♦ 3 miscellaneous small water tankers [YW]

Doutor Gondim (ex-R 38) Guairia (ex-R 40) Iguaçu (ex-R 41)

Remarks: *Doutor Gondim* is 485 tons (fl) and 42.8 × 7.0 × 2.5 m; capacity: 380 tons. No data available for the other two.

♦ 3 Voga Picada–class training craft [YXT]
Bldr: CARBRASMAR, Rio de Janeiro (In serv. 17-1-84)

U 31 Rosca Fina U 32 Voga Picada U 33 Leva Arriba

D: 50 tons (fl) **S:** 11 kts **Dim:** 18.60 × 4.70 × 1.20
Electronics: Radar: 1 . . . nav.
M: 1 MWM diesel; 1 prop; 650 bhp
Range: 200/11 **Crew:** 5 tot. + 11 trainees

Remarks: Used for maneuvering training at the Centro de Instruçao Almirante Braz de Aguiar, along with the captured ex-U.S.-registry fishing vessel *Night Hawk.*

♦ 3 Aspirante Nascimento–class training craft [YXT]
Bldr: Empresa Brasileira de Construção Naval (Ebrasa), Itajaí, Santa Catarina (In serv. 1980–81)

U 10 Aspirante Nascimento U 12 Guarda-Marinha Brito
U 11 Guarda-Marinha Jansen

D: 136 tons (fl) **S:** 10 kts **Dim:** 28.00 (25.00 pp) × 6.50 × 1.80
A: 1 12.7-mm mg **Electronics:** Radar: 1 Decca . . . nav.
M: 2 MWM D232V12 diesels; 2 props; 650 bhp
Range: 700/10 **Crew:** 2 officers, 10 enlisted + 24 midshipmen

Remarks: Used for navigation and seamanship training at the naval academy.

YARD AND SERVICE CRAFT *(continued)*

Guarda-Marinha Jansen (U 11) Brazilian Navy

♦ **6 Ajuri-class training craft [YXT]**
Bldr: Estaleiros Rio Negro (ERIN), Manaus (In serv.: first two: 14-6-96, others in 1997)

U . . . Ajuri U . . . Mutirum . . . .

D: 28 tons (fl) **S:** 15 kts **Dim:** 17.40 × 7.20 × 0.92
M: 2 . . . diesels; 2 props; . . . bhp

Remarks: Intended to provide training to local populations along the Amazon River network. Have a 15-student classroom deckhouse. First two ordered 1995 and four more 7-8-96. Also in use for the same purpose is the *Gaiva* (ex-SSN 6 of the Serviçio de Sinalização Náutica); no data available.

Note: Also used for training at the naval academy are two sailboats of 23.2-m and 16.5-m overall length and two other racing yachts. Five small riverine training support launches were ordered from Estaleiros Rio Negro (ERIN), Manaus, on 7-8-96 to operate with the *Ajuri* class above. The 144 riverine patrol launches in the LAEP *(Lancha de Apoio ao Ensino e Patrulha)* series described under Patrol Boats are also used for training.

BRUNEI

State of Brunei Darussalem

ANGKATAN TENTERA LAUT DIRAJA BRUNEI

Personnel (2000): 747 (including 58 officers and a Special Combat Squadron of 6 officers and 114 men for river duties)

Base: Muara

Naval Aviation: Three IPTN Indonesian-built CN-235 MPA light maritime patrol aircraft were ordered 3-95, along with a single CN-235 transport for use as a trainer; the patrol aircraft, equipped with Litton APS-504 surveillance radars, were to be delivered in 1999.

Note: Ship names are prefixed KDB (*Kapal Diraja Brunei*/Ship of the Rajah of Brunei).

FRIGATES [FF]

♦ **0 (+ 3) new construction**
Bldr: BAE Systems, Scotstoun, Scotland

	Start	L	In serv.
F . . . . Nakhoda Ragam	16-3-99	13-1-01	. . .
F . . . . Bendahara Sakam	15-11-99	23-6-01	. . .
F . . . . Jerambak	5-4-01	. . .	. . .

New Brunei frigate—builder's model BAE Systems, 1995

D: 1,500 tons (1,940 fl) **S:** 30+ kts **Dim:** 95.0 (89.9 wl) × 12.8 × 4.5 (max.; 3.6 hull)
A: 8 MM 40 Exocet Block 2 SSM; 1 Sea Wolf vertical missile launch SAM syst. (16 missiles); 1 76-mm 62-cal. OTOBreda SuperRapid DP; 2 single 30-mm 75-cal. DS-30 AA; 2 single 7.62-mm mg
Electronics:
Radar: 1 Thales Scout nav.; 1 BAE Systems AWS-9(3D) air search; 1 AMS 1802SW gun/missile f.c.
Sonar: Thomson-Marconi TMW 4130C1 hull-mounted (4–13 kHz)
EW: D- through J-band intercept (2–18 GHz); comms intercept; decoy RL
E/O: Rademac 2500 surveillance and tracking
M: 4 M.A.N.-Burmeister & Wain Paxman 20RK270 . . . diesels; 2 CP props; 40,504 bhp
Electric: . . . kw tot. (4 . . . diesel sets)
Range: 5,800/12 **Endurance:** 14 days
Crew: 8 officers, 54 enlisted + 24 passengers

Remarks: Bids requested 28-4-95 with contract originally to have been let by 3-95; the decision was announced in 12-95, but the actual contract was not signed until 14-1-98, due to delays in selecting the weapons system and weapons-control package. Design is a reduced version of the *Lekiu* class built for Malaysia. To cost about $323 million each.
Hull systems: Have fin stabilizers. Are able to meet normal loads on one generator. Carry two Osborne Pacific 24 RIBs.
Combat systems: Have GEC-Marconi Nautis command and weapons-control system with separate radar/E/O directors for the 76-mm gun and two thermal imagers. There will be eight tactical data display consoles. Will have helicopter platform but no support equipment. EW suite to include either GEC-Marconi Mentor 2002 integrated ESM/ECM or Racal Cutlass 242 intercept and Scorpion jammer; will have either Wallop SuperBarricade or GEC-Marconi Shield III decoy launchers. The sonar incorporates a torpedo warning capability. The 3-D air search radar is the same as the Type 996 used in Royal Navy ships.

GUIDED-MISSILE PATROL CRAFT [PTG]

♦ **3 Waspada class**
Bldr: Vosper Pty, Singapore

	L	In serv.		L	In serv.
P 02 Waspada	3-8-77	7-78	P 04 Seteria	22-6-78	1979
P 03 Pejuang	3-78	1979			

Seteria (P 04) Brian Morrison, 5-98

D: 150 tons (206 fl) **S:** 30 kts **Dim:** 36.88 (33.53 pp) × 7.16 × 1.8
A: 2 MM 38 Exocet SSM; 1 twin 30-mm BMARC-Oerlikon GCM-B01 AA; 2 twin 7.62-mm mg
Electronics:
Radar: 1 Kelvin-Hughes Type 1007 nav.
EW: Decca RDL-2 intercept
E/O: Rademac 2500 tracking and f.c.
M: 2 MTU 20V538 TB91 diesels; 2 props; 9,000 bhp (7,500 sust.)
Range: 1,200/14 **Fuel:** 16 tons **Crew:** 4 officers, 30 enlisted

Remarks: P 02 has enclosed upper bridge (open on other two) and facilities for training. Modernized in early 1990s with new EW suite and twin mg, but a planned 2-m hull stretch was canceled. Can accommodate 7 officers and 37 enlisted. New radars and electro-optical equipment were added 1998, with four Kelvin-Hughes color tactical displays added to P 02 and three to the others. They are planned to be retained in service into 2012.

PATROL BOATS [PB]

♦ **3 Periwa class**
Bldr: Vosper Pty, Singapore

	L	In serv.		L	In serv.
P 14 Periwa	5-74	9-9-74	P 16 Penyerang	20-3-75	24-6-75
P 15 Pemburu	30-1-75	17-6-75			

Penyerang (P 16) Navpic-Holland, 7-94

PATROL BOATS [PB] *(continued)*

D: 30 tons (38.5 fl) **S:** 32 kts **Dim:** 21.7 × 6.1 × 1.2
A: 2 single 20-mm 85-cal. BMARC-Oerlikon GAM B01 AA; 2 single 7.62-mm mg
Electronics: Radar: 1 Decca RM 1290 nav.
M: 2 MTU 12V331 TC81 diesels; 2,700 bhp
Range: 600/20; 1,000/16 **Crew:** 2 officers, 12 enlisted

Remarks: Wooden construction. One was reported inoperable as of 1996.

AMPHIBIOUS WARFARE CRAFT

♦ **2 Serasa-class landing craft [LCM]**
Bldr: Transfield Shipbuilding, Western Australia (L: 8-11-96)

L 33 Serasa L 34 Teraban

Serasa (L 33) Brian Morrison/H&L Van Ginderen, 5-98

D: 336 tons (fl) **S:** 12 kts **Dim:** 36.50 (32.95 hull; 30.00 wl) × 8.00 × 1.50
A: 2 20-mm 90-cal. Oerlikon GAM-B01 AA; 2 single 7.62-mm mg
Electronics: Radar: 1 Decca . . . nav.
M: 2 Caterpillar 3508 diesels; 2 props; 1,930 bhp
Range: 1,000/8 **Crew:** 3 officers, 9 enlisted

Remarks: Ordered 30-11-95 for delivery 8-96. Intended to carry deck cargo, vehicles, and liquid cargo (fuel and water in four tanks). There are two Caterpillar diesel-driven generator sets. Can transfer fuel, water, and stores to other craft at sea. In addition to a bow ramp, there are short loading ramps on both sides of the vehicle deck.

♦ **2 Loadmaster-class landing craft [LCM]**
Bldr: Cheverton, Cowes, U.K.

L 31 Damuan (In serv. 5-76) L 32 Puni (In serv. 2-77)

Puni (L 32) French Navy, 6-98

D: 64.3 tons (light) **S:** 8.5 kts **Dim:** 22.86 × 6.10 × 1.07
Electronics: Radar: 1 Decca RM 1216 nav.
M: 2 G.M. Detroit Diesel 6-71 diesels; 2 props; 348 bhp
Range: 300/8.5; 1,000/6 **Crew:** 8 tot.

Remarks: L 31 is 19.8 m overall and 60 tons light. Both can carry 30 tons cargo.

♦ **17 small armed river craft for the Special Combat Squadron [LCP]**

D: 3–5 tons (fl) **S:** 24–30 kts **Dim:** 5.0 to 6.0 × . . . × . . .
A: 1 7.62-mm mg **M:** 1 gasoline outboard; 140 bhp

Remarks: Used by the Special Combat Squadron infantry. Four have been retired.

SERVICE CRAFT

♦ **1 support launch [YFL]**
Bldr: Cheverton, Cowes, U.K. (In serv. 1982)

Burong Nuri

D: 23 tons (fl) **S:** 12 kts **Dim:** 17.8 × 4.3 × 1.5
Electronics: Radar: 1 Decca 060 nav.
M: 2 G.M. Detroit Diesel 6-71 diesels; 2 props; 400 bhp **Crew:** 5 tot.

Remarks: Used as tug, target tug, diving tender, or for antipollution duties. GRP construction.

MARINE POLICE

PATROL BOATS [WPB]

♦ **3 Bendeharu class**
Bldr: P.T. Pal, Surabaya, Indonesia (In serv. 1991)

P 21 Bendeharu P 22 Maharajalela P 23 Kemaindera

D: 68 tons (fl) **S:** . . . kts **Dim:** 28.5 × 5.4 × 1.7
A: 1 12.7-mm mg **M:** 2 MTU diesels; 2 props; 2,260 bhp **Crew:** 16 tot.

♦ **7 14.5-meter class**
Bldr: Singapore SB & Eng. (In serv. 5-10-87 to 12-87)

PDB 11 PDB 12 PDB 13 PDB 14
PDB 15 PDB 63 PDB 68

D: 20 tons (fl) **S:** 30 kts **Dim:** 14.54 × 4.23 × 1.20 (props)
A: 1 7.62-mm mg **Electronics:** Radar: 1 . . . nav.
M: 2 M.A.N. D2840 diesels; 2 props; 1,270 bhp
Range: 310/22 **Fuel:** 2,600 liters **Crew:** 7 tot.

Remarks: Aluminum construction craft similar to Singapore Marine Police Force's PT 1 class. Ordered 28-10-86.

♦ **11 PDB 01 class**
Bldr: Singapore SB & Eng. (In serv. . . .)

PDB 01 through PDB 11

Remarks: No data available. Are about half the size of the 14.5-m class and have the same navigational radar set.

♦ **2 FPB 512 class**
Bldr: Rotork Marine, U.K.

07 Behagia 10 Selamat

D: 8.8 tons (fl) **S:** 27 kts **Dim:** 12.7 × 3.2 × . . .
A: 3 single 7.62-mm mg **Electronics:** Radar: 1 Decca 060
M: 2 Ford Mermaid diesels; 2 Castoldi Type 06 waterjets; 430 bhp
Range: 100/12 **Crew:** 3 tot.

Remarks: GRP hulls, bow ramps. For patrol and transport duties.

Note: Also in service for riverine use are personnel launches *Aman* (01), *Damai* (02), *Sentosa* (04), and *Sejahtera* (06); no data available.

BULGARIA

Republic of Bulgaria

VOENNOMORSKI SILI

Personnel (2001): About 3,000 total (including 1,000 Marine Corps coast defense troops)

Bases: Headquarters, main naval base, training facilities, and air station at Varna; smaller naval bases at Atiya, Balchik, Burgas, and Sozopol and at Vidin on the Danube River. Repair facilities at Flotski Arsenal, Varna. Higher Naval School Nikola Yonkov Vaptsarov at Varna (to be closed).

Naval Aviation: Ten Mi-14PL Haze-A land-based ASW helicopters are in inventory, but as of 1995 only two were flyable.

Coastal Defense: Six twin-tubed SS-C-3 Styx self-propelled launch vehicles in a missile battalion. Some 130-mm and 100-mm fixed coastal artillery positions may still be in use.

Weapons and Sensors: Bulgarian naval units employ weapons and sensors largely of Soviet/Russian origin, although a locally made navigational radar is used. Bulgaria offers for export the PDM-1B shallow-water, tilt-rod-fused mine, which has a 17-kg explosive charge and is intended for anti-invasion use in waters 1–2 m deep.

Note: Defense Minister Georgi Ananiev reportedly decided during 2-99 to eliminate the Bulgarian Navy entirely, with coastal patrol and mine clearance work to be assigned to private firms; this plan was amended as of 7-99 to halving the size of the fleet and making it into entirely a coastal navy. As of 1999, the navy was receiving only 6.95% of the $270 million total defense budget. Under a 10-99 decision, the number of personnel in the Bulgarian armed forces was to be halved from the then-total of about 98,000, and service officer training academies were to be combined into one.

ATTACK SUBMARINES [SS]

Note: The remaining Soviet-era Romeo-class (Project 633) attack submarine, *Slava* (84), was originally to have been retired in 1994 or 1995 and by 2000 had become inoperable.

FRIGATES [FF]

♦ 1 Soviet Koni class (Project 1159T)
Bldr: Krasniy Metalist Zavod, Zelenodol'sk

	Laid down	L	In serv.
11 Smeli (ex-Soviet *Del'fin*)	25-5-71	21-4-73	19-7-75

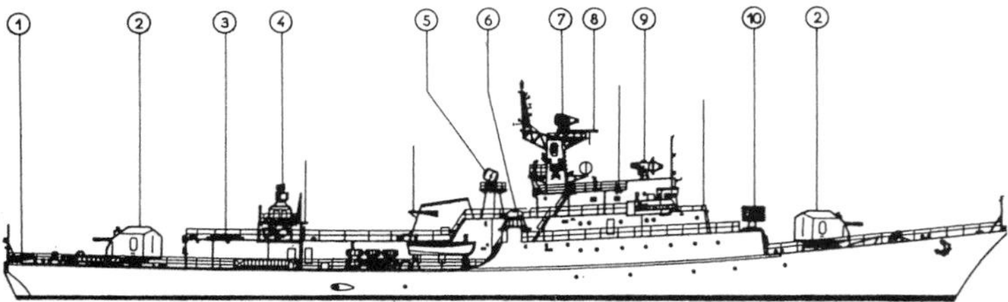

Smeli (11) 1. depth charge racks (atop mine rails) 2. twin 76.2-mm AK-726 DP gunmounts 3. twin-rail, retractable Osa-M (SA-N-4) SAM system 4. MPZ-301 (Pop Group) radar director for Osa-M system 5. MR-104 Rys' (Drum Tilt) radar director for 30-mm guns 6. twin 30-mm AK-230 AA gunmounts port and starboard 7. MR-302 Rubka (Strut Curve) surface/air-search radar 8. Don-2 navigational radar 9. MR-105 Fut-B (Hawk Screech) radar director for 76.2-mm guns 10. two 12-round RBU-6000 ASW rocket launchers Drawing by L. Gassier

Smeli (11) Siegfried Breyer Collection

Smeli (11) H&L Van Ginderen, 7-00

D: 1,515 tons normal (1,670 fl) **S:** 27 kts (29.67 on trials; 22 on diesels alone)
Dim: 95.51 × 12.55 × 4.12 (5.72 sonar)
A: 1 twin-rail Osa-M (SA-N-4) SAM syst. (20 9M-33/Gecko missiles); 2 twin 76.2-mm 59-cal. AK-726 DP; 2 twin 30-mm 65-cal. AK-230 AA2 12-round RBU-6000 ASW RL (120 RGB-60 rockets); 2 d.c. racks (6 BB-1 d.c. each); up to 14 mines (in lieu of d.c.)
Electronics:
Radar: 1 Don-2 nav.; MR-302 Rubka (Strut Curve) air/surf. search; 1 MPZ-301 (Pop Group) missile f.c.; 1 Fut-B (Hawk Screech) 76.2-mm gun f.c.; 1 MR-104 Rys' (Drum Tilt) 30-mm gun f.c.
Sonar: MG-322T Vychegda MF hull-mounted
EW: 2 Bizan'-4B (Watch Dog) intercept (2–18 GHz); 1 MFD/F; 2 16-round PK-16 decoy RL
M: CODAG: 1 M-813 18,000-shp gas turbine, 2 Type 68B, 8,000-bhp diesels; 3 props
Range: 1,800/14 **Crew:** 96 tot.

Remarks: Transferred 11-2-91 and recommissioned 1-6-91 after having been used by the Soviet Navy in the Black Sea for training foreign crews for export units of the class. Has had one refit in Russia since 1991.

GUIDED-MISSILE PATROL COMBATANTS [PGG]

♦ 1 Soviet Tarantul-II class (Project 1141.1M)
Bldr: Sudostroitel'noye Obyedineniye "Almaz," Petrovskiy SY, St. Petersburg

101 Mulnaya (ex-*Poltavskiy Komsomolets*)

D: 385 tons light (455 fl) **S:** 43 kts
Dim: 56.10 (49.50 pp) × 10.20 (9.40 wl) × 2.14 hull (4.0 props)

Mulnaya (101) H&L Van Ginderen, 7-00

A: 4 P-20/P-21 Termit (SS-N-2C Styx) SSM; 1 76.2-mm 59-cal. AK-176 DP; 1 4-round SA-N-8 SAM syst. (12 Igla-1 missiles); 2 single 30-mm 54-cal. AK-630 gatling AA
Electronics:
Radar: 1 Kivach-3 nav.; 1 Monolit (Band Stand) target detection and tracking; 1 MR-123 Vympel' (Bass Tilt) gun f.c.
EW: no intercept; 2 16-round PK-16 decoy RL
M: M-15E COGAG plant: 2 DMR-76 cruise gas turbines (4,000 shp each), 2 PR-77 boost gas turbines (12,000 shp each); 2 props; 32,000 shp
Electric: 500 kw tot. (2 × 200-kw, 1 × 100-kw diesel sets)
Range: 760/43; 1,400/13 **Fuel:** 50 tons **Endurance:** 10 days
Crew: 7 officers, 32 enlisted

Remarks: Transferred from Soviet Black Sea Fleet 6-90 to begin replacement of the obsolete Osa-I and Osa-II missile boats. Planned transfer of two more was canceled.
Hull systems: The cruise gas turbines exhaust through a stack, while the high-speed turbines exhaust through the transom stern, adding their residual thrust to the propulsive power; all four are employed simultaneously via planetary gearing for maximum power.
Combat systems: A Light Bulb missile datalink antenna is installed at the masthead, while the Band Stand radome conceals a missile target acquisition and guidance radar that can also operate in the passive mode. Some 252 rounds of 76.2-mm and 6,000 rounds of 30-mm ammunition are carried. Has racks for three smoke floats or small depth charges mounted at the stern.

GUIDED-MISSILE PATROL CRAFT [PTG]

♦ 3 Soviet Osa-I* and Osa-II-class (Project 205*/205M)

102 Uragon 111 Svetkavitsa* 113 Smerch*

Uragon (102)—Osa-II H&L Van Ginderen, 8-99

Smerch (113)—Osa-I H&L Van Ginderen, 8-99

D: 184 tons (226 fl) **S:** 40 kts **Dim:** 37.5 × 7.6 × 1.9 (mean)
A: 4 P-15M Termit (SS-N-2B Styx) SSM; 2 twin 30-mm 65-cal. AK-230 AA
Electronics:
Radar: 1 Rangout (Square Tie) surf. search/missile target desig.; 1 MR-104 Rys' (Drum Tilt) gun f.c.
M: 3 M-504B diesels; 3 props; 15,000 bhp **Electric:** 200 kw tot.
Range: 500/34; 750/25 **Endurance:** 5 days **Crew:** 28 tot.

Remarks: Transferred in 1978, 1982, and 1984. Based at Sozopol and rarely go to sea. 111 and 113 are Osa-I (Project 205) versions with hooded missile launchers; they displace 171 tons light (209.5 fl) and could achieve 38.5 kts on 12,000 bhp from their M-503A2 diesels when new. Inactive sisters *Burya* (103), an Osa-II, and *Typfun* (112), an Osa-I, were located at Sozopol as of 8-00. *Grum* (104) was stricken during 2001.

PATROL CRAFT [PC]

♦ 2 ex-Soviet Pauk-I class (Project 1241.2)
Bldr: Yaroslavl Zavod

13 Reshitelni (ex-MPK-146) 14 Bodri (ex-MPK-124)

PATROL CRAFT [PC] *(continued)*

Bodri (14) Siegfried Breyer Collection

Reshitelni (13) NATO, 1995

D: 425 tons (495 fl) **S:** 32 kts (28 sust.)
Dim: 58.5 (49.5 pp) × 10.2 (9.4 wl) × 2.14 (hull; 4.0 props)
A: 1 76.2-mm 59-cal. AK-176 DP; 1 4-round SA-N-8 SAM syst. (16 Igla-1 missiles); 1 30-mm 54-cal. AK-630 gatling AA; 2 5-tubed RBU-1200 ASW RL (30 RGB-12 rockets); 4 406-mm ASW TT; 2 d.c. racks (12 d.c.)
Electronics:
Radar: 1 Pechora nav.; 1 . . . (Peel Cone) nav./surf. search; 1 MR-123 Vympel' (Bass Tilt) f.c.
Sonar: MGK-345 Bronza MF hull-mounted and dipping
EW: 2 . . . (Half Hat-B) intercept; 2 16-round PK-16 decoy RL
M: 2 M-517 diesels; 2 props; 20,800 bhp (16,180 sust.)
Range: 2,000/20; 3,000/12 **Fuel:** 50 tons normal **Endurance:** 10 days
Crew: 7 officers, 32 enlisted

Remarks: Also known as the Molniya-2 class. Transferred 9-89 and 12-90 from the then-Soviet Black Sea Fleet. Based at Varna.
Hull systems: This class uses the same hull as the Tarantul-class missile corvette but has ASW armament vice antiship missiles and an all-diesel propulsion plant vice the Tarantul's COGAG/CODAG system. The large housing for a dipping sonar system projects 2 m out from the stern. The large hull-mounted sonar dome is located approximately beneath the gun fire-control radar. The hull is constructed of mild steel, while the middle part of the deck plating, some internal bulkheads, and much of the superstructure are made of aluminum-magnesium alloy. Range on normal fuel load is only 1,600 n.m. at 12 kts.
Combat systems: The combat data system is designated SU-580. There is a Kolonka-2 backup ringsight director for the single gatling AA gun. The MR-123 radar director can control both the 76.2-mm and 30-mm guns. Normal ammunition load is 152 rounds 76-mm (all ready-service, on-mount) and 2,000 rounds 30-mm. MGK-345 applies to both the hull-mounted and dipping sonars; the dipping sonar transducer can be lowered to 200 m.

♦ 4 Soviet Poti class (Project 204A)
Bldr: Zelnodol'sk Zavod, Tatarstan, Russia

41 Letyashi (ex-K-. . .) 44 Khabri (ex-K-159)
42 Bditelni (ex-K-. . .) 46 Bezstrashni (ex-K-. . .)

D: 428.5 tons (536.5 fl) **S:** 38 kts (32–34 sust.; 17.5 on diesels)
Dim: 58.62 (55.63 wl) × 8.14 × 2.38 (mean hull; 3.11 over sonar)
A: 1 twin 57-mm 75-cal. AK-275 DP; 2 12-tubed RBU-6000 ASW RL (96 RGB-60 rockets); 4 406-mm OTA-40-204 fixed ASW TT
Electronics:
Radar: 1 Don-2 nav.; 1 MR-302 Rubka (Strut Curve) surf./air search; 1 MR-103 Bars (Muff Cob) f.c.
Sonar: MG-312 Titan-2 hull-mounted MF search and HF attack
EW: 2 Bizan'-4B (Watch Dog) intercept (2–18 GHz); 2 16-round PK-16 decoy RL
M: CODAG: 2 M-520T diesels (4,800 bhp each), 2 GTK-D2 gas turbines (15,000 shp each); 2 props mounted in venturi tunnels

Khabri (44) H&L Van Ginderen, 7-00

Electric: 400 kw tot. (2 × 200-kw DG-200 diesel sets)
Range: 500/37; 1,500/17.5; 2,650/13.75 **Fuel:** 108 tons **Endurance:** 7 days
Crew: 4–5 officers, 52–55 enlisted

Remarks: *Khabri* transferred 28-6-75, *Letyashi* in 1986, and the other two in 1990. Sisters *Strogiy* (42, ex-K-160) and *Naporisti* (43) were stricken at the end of 1993. The others are unlikely to remain in service much longer; virtually all of their weapon and sensor systems are obsolete and unsupportable.
Hull systems: Gas turbines force air into tubes abaft the propellers in a kind of waterjet system. Hull has eight watertight bulkheads. The diesel engines have also been reported to be Type M-504A. With emergency fuel, range could be extended to 3,500 n.m. at 13.75 kts.
Combat systems: The MR-103 radar gun director is equipped with a television backup system. Have been updated with decoy rocket launchers and may still carry a WGS-2 Oka-M helicopter dipping sonar in addition to the hull-mounted sets. Navigation suite includes Kurs-4 gyrocompass, LG-4 log, ARP-50 HFD/F, NEL-5 echo sounder, AP-3 autoplot, and Al'batros automatic pilot. The ZIF-31B 57-mm gunmount has 1,100 rounds of ready-service ammunition.

MINE WARFARE SHIPS

Note: Offered for export is a 200-ton, 36-m-long by 10-m-beam catamaran mine countermeasures ship design to be armed with a 30-mm gun and a point-defense SAM system. The craft would be built of GRP, carry remote-controlled mine disposal submersibles, and be equipped with a computerized navigation and minehunting control system.

♦ 4 Soviet Sonya (Yakhont)-class (Project 1265) coastal minesweepers [MSC]
Bldr: Avangard Zavod, Petrozavodsk

61 Briz 62 Shkval 63 Priboy 64 Shtorm

Briz (61) Siegfried Breyer Collection

D: 401–427 tons (430–460 fl) **S:** 14 kts
Dim: 48.80 (46.00 wl) × 10.20 (9.20 wl) × 2.40–2.50 (mean hull; 2.75–2.85 max.)
A: 1 twin 30-mm 65-cal. AK-230M AA; 1 twin 25-mm 80-cal. 2M-3M AA; 5 mines
Electronics:
Radar: 1 Mius (Spin Trough) nav.
Sonar: MG-89 Serna HF hull-mounted, MG-35 underwater telephone, NEL-MZB echo sounder
M: 2 DRA-210-A or DRA-210-B diesels; 2 3-bladed CP props; 2,200 or 2,000 bhp—2 low-speed thrusters
Electric: 350 kw tot. (3 × 100-kw, 1 × 50-kw diesel sets; 380 V, 50 Hz a.c.)
Range: 1,700/10 **Fuel:** 27.1 tons **Endurance:** 15 days
Crew: 5–6 officers, 26–40 enlisted (45 tot. accomm.)

Remarks: Two transferred 1982, the others in 1985. Designed under Valeriy Ivanovich Nemudrov. Wooden construction with glass-reinforced plastic hull sheathing. Carry acoustic, loop and towed solenoidal magnetic, and net-sweep and mechanical sweep equipment and can lay linear mine disposal charges. The 25-mm mount is aimed by the on-mount operator, while the 30-mm mount is controlled by a Kolonka-1 ringsight director. Bollard pull: 10 tons at 9 kts.

♦ 4 Soviet Vanya-class (Project 257DME) coastal minesweepers [MSC]
Bldr: Avangard Zavod, Petrozavodsk

31 Iskar 32 Tsib'r 33 Dobrotich 34 Evstati Vinarov

D: 220 tons light, 254 tons std. (270 fl) **S:** 14 kts
Dim: 39.9 (38.0 wl) × 7.5 × 1.8 hull (2.08 max.)
A: 1 twin 30-mm 65-cal. AK-230 AA; 8–12 mines
Electronics: Radar: 1 Donets-2 nav.—Sonar: MG-69 Lan' HF hull-mounted
M: 2 M-870 FTK diesels; 2 CP props; 2,400 bhp
Electric: 250 kw tot. (2 × 100-kw DG-100 diesel sets, 1 × 50-kw DGR-50 set)
Range: 1,500/10; 2,400/9 **Endurance:** 5 days **Crew:** 37 tot.

MINE WARFARE SHIPS *(continued)*

Tsib'r (32)—with three sisters inboard H&L Van Ginderen, 7-00

Remarks: Two transferred in 1970, two in 1971, and two in 1985; sisters . . . (35) and *Kapitan 1 Rang Dimitri Paskadev* (36) deleted 1992. Wooden construction. The gunmount is controlled by a remote Kolonka-1 ringsight director. Updated version of standard Soviet Navy design with improved accommodations.

♦ **4 Soviet Yevgenya-class (Project 1258) inshore minesweepers [MSI]** Bldr: Sudostroitel'noye Obyedineniye "Almaz" (Sredniy Neva), Kolpino

65 66 67 68

D: 88.5 tons (91.5 fl) **S:** 11 kts **Dim:** 26.13 × 6.10 (5.90 wl) × 1.38
A: 1 twin 25-mm 80-cal. 2M-3M AA
Electronics: Radar: 1 Mius (Spin Trough) nav.—Sonar: MG-8 hull-mounted HF
M: 2 Type 3D12 diesels; 2 props; 600 bhp **Electric:** 100 kw tot.
Range: 300/10 **Fuel:** 2.7 tons **Endurance:** 3 days
Crew: 1 officer, 9 enlisted (+ 2–3 clearance divers)

Remarks: All transferred 1977. GRP construction. Employ a television minehunting system useful to 30-m depths that dispenses marker buoys to permit later disposal of mines.

♦ **6 Soviet Olya-class (Project 1259) harbor minesweepers [MSI]** Bldr: . . . . . ., Bulgaria (In serv. 1988–96)

51 52 53 54 55 56

Bulgarian Olya 52 H&L Van Ginderen, 7-00

D: 62 tons (66 fl) **S:** 12 kts (10 sust.) **Dim:** 22.77 × 4.50 × 1.40
A: 1 twin 12.7-mm Utës-M mg; . . . mines
Electronics: Radar: 1 Chernomore MR 2512 nav.
M: 2 Type 3D-6N diesels; 2 props; 470 bhp
Electric: 100 kw tot. (2 × 50-kw DG-50 diesel sets) **Range:** 400/8
Crew: 15 tot.

Remarks: Although not considered a successful design in Soviet service, the design was licensed to Bulgaria, which also offers it for export. GRP hull. Sweep gear includes AT-6 acoustic, SEMT-1 solenoid coil, and GKT-2 mechanical arrays. Not all are active.

AMPHIBIOUS WARFARE SHIPS

♦ **2 ex-Soviet Polnocny-A-class (Project 770) medium landing ships [LSM]** Bldr: Stocznia Polnocna, Gdansk, Poland

701 Sirius (ex-*Ivan Zagubanski*) 702 Antares (ex-*Anton Ivanov*)

Antares (702)—with much rust inside and out but still in commission; the bow doors are open H&L Van Ginderen, 7-00

D: 770 tons (fl) **S:** 19 kts **Dim:** 73.0 × 8.6 × 1.9 (aft)
A: 1 twin 30-mm 65-cal. AK-230 AA; 2 18-round 140-mm barrage RL
Electronics: Radar: 1 Mius (Spin Trough) nav.
M: 2 Type 40DM diesels; 2 props; 4,400 bhp
Range: 900/18; 1,500/14 **Crew:** 35 tot.

Remarks: Transferred 1986–87. Based at Atiya. Cargo: about 180 tons of vehicles. Normally used as logistics support transports but have been mostly inactive in recent years. Plans to convert them to serve as minelayers have been canceled.

♦ **17 Soviet Vydra-class (Project 106K) utility landing craft [LCU]** (14 in reserve) Bldr: Kherson SY (In serv. 1966–70)

from among: *601–613* 703 *704–706* 707 712

Vydra-class 705—although reportedly in reserve, appears to be in operating condition H&L Van Ginderen, 7-00

D: 308 tons (442 fl) **S:** 10.5 kts **Dim:** 54.5 × 7.7 × 2.4
A: 2 single . . . AA; . . . mines
Electronics: Radar: 1 Chernomore MR 2512 nav.
M: 2 Type 3D12 diesels; 2 props; 600 bhp
Range: 2,700/10 **Crew:** 1 officer, 4 enlisted

Remarks: Ten transferred from the USSR in 1970, and 14 others were built under license in Bulgaria between 1974 and 1978. Active are 703, 707, and 712; 601–613 were placed in reserve in 1993 and 704–706 in 1995, while 708–711 were stricken in 1993. From time to time have been used in moving civilian cargo. Cargo: 260 tons maximum or 3 heavy tanks or 10 GAZ-66 trucks or 200 troops. Active units have been altered to serve as minelayers if needed. Two were donated to Georgia on 6-7-01.

AUXILIARIES

♦ **1 Soviet Bereza-class (Type 130) deperming tender [ADG]** Bldr: Stocznia Polnocna, Gdansk, Poland (In serv. 7-89)

206 Kapitan 1 Rang Dimitri Dobrev

Kapitan 1 Rang Dimitri Dobrev (206) Siegfried Breyer Collection, 7-89

D: 1,850 tons light (2,051 fl) **S:** 13.8 kts **Dim:** 69.50 × 13.80 × 3.99
Electronics: Radar: 1 Kivach nav. **A:** none
M: 2 Zgoda-Sulzer 8AL25/30, 750-rpm diesels; 2 CP Kort-nozzle props; 2,940 bhp—bow-thruster
Electric: 1,185 kVA (2 × 480 kVA, 1 × 225 kVA) + 1,550 kw tot. (2 × 645 kw, 1 × 260 kw)
Range: 1,000/13.8 **Crew:** 48 tot.

Remarks: Intended for "degaussing surface ships and submarines, conducting magnetic field measurements of ships and vessels, [and] regulating ground fault neutralizers." Also used as naval cadet training ship. Eighteen others serve in the Russian Navy.
Hull systems: Can service two ships simultaneously. Have three laboratories, a machine shop, and a cable hold. Molded depth of hull is 5.60 m. A large crane is fitted aft to handle deperming cables.

♦ **1 Soviet Moma-class (Project 861) survey ship/buoy tender [AGS]** Bldr: Stocznia Polnocna, Gdansk, Poland (In serv. 1977)

401 Admiral Branimir Ormanov

D: 1,260 tons (1,540 fl) **S:** 17 kts **Dim:** 73.3 × 10.8 × 3.8
A: none **Electronics:** Radar: 2 Don-2 nav.
M: 2 Zgoda-Sulzer 6TD48 diesels; 2 CP props; 3,600 bhp
Endurance: 35 days **Range:** 8,700/11 **Crew:** 5 officers, 32 enlisted

AUXILIARIES *(continued)*

Admiral Branimir Ormanov (401) H&L Van Ginderen, 7-00

♦ 1 Mesar-class (Project 102) replenishment oiler [AOR]
Bldr: Russe, Bulgaria (In serv. 1987)

302 Atiya

Atiya (302) H&L Van Ginderen, 7-00

D: 3,240 (fl) **S:** 20 kts **Dim:** 97.5 × 13.2 × 5.2
A: 2 twin 30-mm 65-cal. AK-230 AA **Electronics:** Radar: 2 Don-2 nav.
M: 2 diesels; 2 props; 12,000 bhp **Range:** 12,000/15 **Crew:** 32 tot.

Remarks: Sister *Dimitri A. Dimitrov* (202), completed in 1979, was stricken and offered for sale on 12-12-96. Cargo capacity: 1,593 tons liquid. Conducts over-the-stern underway refueling; also has dry stores cargo. Unusually fine hull lines for an oiler design. "Mesar" is NATO nickname. The guns are controlled by two Kolonka-1 ringsight directors.

♦ 1 East German Type 700 salvage tug/icebreaker [ATA]
Bldr: V.E.B. Peenewerft, Wolgast (In serv. 20-3-64)

221 Jupiter

Jupiter (221) H&L Van Ginderen, 7-00

D: 700 tons (791 fl) **S:** 12.75 kts **Dim:** 44.71 (38.99 pp) × 10.72 × 3.91
A: none **Electronics:** Radar: . . .
M: 4 Johannisthal Type 12 KVD 21 diesels (550 bhp each), 4 generators, 2 electric motors; 2 props; 1,680 shp
Electric: 264 kw tot. (2 × 120-kw, 1 × 24-kw d.c. diesel sets)
Range: 3,000/12 **Crew:** 39 tot.

Remarks: 505 grt. Operated for the Varna Port Authority since the early 1990s, but remains under naval ownership and employs naval crew.

♦ 1 Dimitar Blagoev–class training ship [AXT]
Bldr: Georgi Dimitrov SY, Varna (In serv. 1969)

421 Dimitar Blagoev

Dimitar Blagoev (421) Cem D. Yaylali, 9-98

D: approx. 2,100 tons (fl) **S:** 14 kts **Dim:** 68.00 × 10.11 × 5.46
A: none **Electronics:** Radar: 2 . . . nav.
M: 2 Russkiy Dizel . . . diesels; 2 props; 1,200 bhp
Electric: 588 kw tot. (3 × 188-kw, 1 × 24-kw diesel sets) **Crew:** . . . tot.

Remarks: 1,129 grt. Former Nav. Mar. Bulgare passenger/cargo vessel acquired as a cadet training ship around 1997. The 191 m^3 cargo hold forward has two 2.2 × 2.8-m hatches, but the crane has been removed. Has accommodations for 94 passengers. Sister *Georgi Kirkov* may still be in commercial service.

SERVICE CRAFT

♦ 2 Project 245 diving tenders [YDT]

223 323

Project 245 diving tender 223 Siegfried Breyer Collection, 1994

D: 112 tons light (165 fl) **S:** 10 kts **Dim:** 27.9 × 5.2 × 2.2
M: 2 MCK 83-4 diesel generator sets, electric drive; 1 prop; 300 shp
Range: 400/10 **Crew:** 6 tot. + 7 divers

Remarks: Can support divers to 60 m. Stern A-frame gantry supports divers' stage. Can mount a twin 12.7-mm machinegun.

♦ 2 miscellaneous flag officer yachts [YFL]

Remarks: Names, pennant numbers, and characteristics data not available; the larger of the pair may serve as the presidential yacht.

Bulgarian Navy flag officer yacht H&L Van Ginderen, 7-00

A smaller Bulgarian Navy flag officer yacht H&L Van Ginderen, 7-00

SERVICE CRAFT *(continued)*

♦ **2 inshore survey craft [YGS]** (In serv. 1986–88)

231 331

D: 114 tons (fl) **S:** 12 kts **Dim:** 26.7 × 5.8 × 1.5
Electronics: Radar: 1 Chernomore MR 2512 nav.
M: 2 Type 3D12 diesels; 2 props; 600 bhp **Range:** 600/10 **Crew:** 9 tot.

♦ **1 support tanker [YO]** Bldr: Burgas SY, Burgas (In serv. 1994)

303

Support tanker 303 H&L Van Ginderen, 7-00

D: 1,250 tons (fl) **S:** 12 kts **Dim:** 55.4 × 11.0 × 3.5
A: 1 twin 23-mm AA **Electronics:** Radar: 2 Chernomore MR 2512 nav.
M: 2 Sulzer 6AL-20/24 diesels; 2 props; 1,500 bhp
Range: 1,000/8 **Crew:** 23 tot.

Remarks: Laid down in 1989, launched in 1993. Cargo: 650 tons. Has small crane to facilitate hose handling. Capable of coastal voyages. Replaced Type 024 fuel lighters 203 and 204.

♦ **2 fireboats [YTR]**

224 321

Fireboat 224—wrapped in deperming cables H&L Van Ginderen, 7-00

D: 531 tons (fl) **S:** 13 kts **Dim:** 38.50 × 10.00 × 3.03
A: 1 4-round Fasta-M SAM launcher (Strela-2M missiles)
Electronics: Radar: 1 Chernomore MR 2512 nav.
M: 2 diesels; 2 props; 2,060 bhp **Range:** 600/10
Endurance: 4–5 days **Crew:** 14 (+ 4 spare berths)

Remarks: Not, as stated in earlier editions, a variant of the YGS survey craft design. Have three 500-m^3/hr water monitors, with a range of 70–80 m. Completed 1996.

♦ **1 Polish Type B79/II sail-training craft [YTS]**
Bldr: Stocznia Komuny Paryskiej, Gdynia (In serv. 1984)

KALIAKRA

D: 381 tons (498 fl) **S:** 10.2 (under power)
Dim: 49.00 (42.70 hull; 36.00 pp) × 8.01 × 3.16
M: 1 Wola 68H12 diesel; 1 CP, 356 rpm, 1.5-m-dia. prop; 310 bhp—ketch-rigged (1,038 m^2 max./960 m^2 normal sail area)
Crew: 5 officers, 12 petty officers, 45 cadets

Remarks: 300 grt/100 dwt. A 3-masted barkentine used for naval and merchant marine officer cadet training. Has 63 total berths. Can also be used for oceanographic research and is advertised for private vacation cruising.

Note: Also in service are small torpedo retriever 205, small tug 222, and about five small barracks barges; no data available.

Kaliakra Maritime Photographic, 8-98

FRONTIER POLICE

Note: The Frontier Police is subordinated to the Ministry of the Interior.

PATROL CRAFT [WPC]

♦ **1 Soviet Shershen class (Project 206)**
Bldr: Zelenodol'sk or Yaroslavl SY

515 (ex-116)

D: 145 tons (170 fl) **S:** 45 kts **Dim:** 34.60 × 6.75 × . . .
A: 2 twin 30-mm 65-cal. AK-230 AA
Electronics:
Radar: 1 Baklan (Pot Drum) surf. search; 1 MR-104 Rys' (Drum Tilt) f.c.
M: 3 M-503A radial diesels; 3 props; 12,000 bhp
Electric: 56 kw tot (2 × 28-kw DG-28 diesel sets)
Range: 460/42; 600/35; 800/30 **Crew:** 20 tot.

Remarks: Survivor of 6 transferred new from the USSR in 1970; transferred to the Frontier Police without torpedo tubes. Sister 114 was still afloat at Sozopol in 8-00, but is in derelict condition and disarmed.

PATROL BOATS [WPB]

♦ **9 Soviet Zhuk class (Project 1400M)**

511 512 513 521 522 523 531 532 533

D: 35.9 tons (39.7 fl) **S:** 30 kts **Dim:** 23.80 (21.70 wl) × 5.00 (3.80 wl) × 1.00 (hull)
A: 2 twin 12.7-mm Utës-M mg **Electronics:** Radar: 1 Lotsiya nav.
M: 2 M-401B diesels; 2 props; 2,200 bhp
Electric: 48 kw total (2 × 21-kw, 1 × 6-kw diesel sets)
Range: 500/13.5 **Endurance:** 5 days **Crew:** 3 officers, 8 enlisted

Remarks: Transferred new in 1980–81.

♦ **2 U.S. 27-foot Vigilant-class**
Bldr: Boston Whaler, Rockland, Mass. (In serv. 4-93)

D: 1.5 tons light (2 tons fl) **S:** 40 kts **Dim:** 8.23 × 2.26 × . . .
A: 1 7.62-mm mg **M:** 2 Johnson outboard motors; 360 bhp
Range: 167/40; 750/. . . **Crew:** 3 tot.

Remarks: GRP hulls. Transferred for use in enforcing the UN embargo against Serbia on the Danube. Have an enclosed pilothouse, navigational radar, and a pedestal mount for a 7.62-mm mg aft. A third unit was badly damaged in a collision in 6-93 and discarded.

Note: There are also two British-built 25-kt RIBs with a range of 350 n.m., supplied for patrol duties on the Danube, and two locally built small patrol launches are illustrated.

FRONTIER POLICE PATROL BOATS [WPB] *(continued)*

Frontier Police launch 121—one small machinegun is mounted in a turret atop the pilothouse roof H&L Van Ginderen, 7-00

Frontier Police launch 122 H&L Van Ginderen, 7-00

BURUNDI

NAVAL SECTION OF THE BURUNDIAN GENDARMARIE

Personnel (2001): Approx. 100 total

Base: Bujumbura, Lake Tanganyika

Note: The current state of all the craft listed below is unknown after several years of turmoil.

PATROL BOATS [WPB]

♦ **1 Nicole class** Bldr: C.N. de Tanganyika, Bujumbura

P 106 . . . (L: 6-91)

D: 7 tons (fl) **S:** 18 kts **Dim:** 11.6 × 2.6 × . . .
A: 1 12.7-mm mg; 1 7.62-mm mg
M: 2 Cummins 4 BT3-9M diesels; 2 props; 260 bhp
Electric: 16 kVA (2 shaft generators) **Crew:** 6 tot. + 12 passengers

Remarks: Has also been reported as having Caterpillar diesels totaling 750 bhp for a 25-kt maximum speed. Sister *Nicole* (P 105) was inoperative as of 11-96.

♦ **1 Chinese Yulin class** Bldr: . . ., China (In serv. 1964–68)

D: 9.8 tons (fl) **S:** 20 kts **Dim:** 13.0 × 2.9 × 1.1
A: 1 twin and 1 single 14.5-mm mg **Electronics:** Radar: 1 Furuno . . . nav.
M: 1 3D6 diesel; 1 prop; 150 bhp **Crew:** 4–6 tot.

Remarks: Survivor of four transferred in the 1960s. Have larger superstructures than standard units of the class and have been equipped with navigational radars. Name is either *Ruvubu* or *Cohoha*.

CAMBODIA

Democratic Kampuchea

MARINE ROYAL KHMER

Personnel (2000): Up to 780 officers and 2,200 enlisted, including naval infantry. The total had been planned to rise to 825 officers and 4,275 enlisted, including the naval infantry, but has actually been declining.

Bases: Headquarters at Phnom Penh. Operating facilities at Ream (near Sihanoukville) for seagoing craft and at Chroy Chang for riverine craft.

Organization: Nine Coastal Division naval infantry battalions and seven River Division battalions.

PATROL CRAFT [PC]

♦ **2 Soviet Stenka class (Project 205P)**
Bldr: Sudostroitel'noye Obyedineniye "Almaz," Petrovskiy SY, St. Petersburg

1133 MONDOLKIRI 1134 RATANAKIRI

D: 170 tons (210 fl) **S:** 24 kts **Dim:** 39.5 × 7.6 × 1.8
A: 2 single 40-mm 60-cal. Bofors AA; 1 twin 23-mm ZSU-23 AA; 1 4-round SAM syst. (14 Igla-1/SA-14 missiles)
Electronics: Radar: 1 . . . nav.
M: 3 Caterpillar . . . . . . diesels; 3 props; . . . bhp
Range: . . ./. . . **Crew:** 5 officers, 20 enlisted

Remarks: Two delivered 10-85 and two 10-87, all without standard fit of four 400-mm ASW torpedo tubes and helicopter-type dipping sonar. Use Osa-I (Project 205) hull and propulsion. All four had a manned missile launcher atop the pilothouse and were rehabilitated for further service by UN forces during 1992. 1133 and 1134 were refitted and re-engined at Hong Leong–Lürssen Shipyard, Malaysia, starting in 1994 and returning on 10-2-96; they are no longer capable of speeds beyond about 24 kts but have been rearmed. Sisters 1101 and 1102 have been cannibalized.

Note: The two remaining Turya-class (Project 206) semi-hydrofoil gunboats are no longer in service, although their hulks remain afloat at Ream as floating barracks.

PATROL BOATS [PB]

♦ **2 Kaoh Chlam class**
Bldr: Hong Leong–Lürssen, Butterworth, Malaysia (In serv. 20-1-97)

1105 KAOH CHLAM 1106 KAOH RUNG

D: 41 tons (44 fl) **S:** 35 kts **Dim:** 21.0 × 5.00 × . . .
A: 1 14.5-mm 93-cal. AA; 2 single 12.7-mm 79-cal. mg
M: 2 Deutz-MWM TBD 616 V 16 diesels; 2 props; 2,948 bhp
Electric: 40 kw tot. (2 × 20-kw Onan MDKAE diesel-driven sets)
Range: 560/35 **Fuel:** 5,600 liters **Crew:** 13 tot.

Remarks: Laid down 12-3-96. Funded by the Malaysian government and designed by Fassmerwerft, Fassmer, Germany. Aluminum construction.

Disposal note: Soviet-supplied Zhuk-class (Project 199) patrol boats 41 and 42 had ceased to be operational by 2000. Also discarded have been the four Soviet Shmel'-class (Project 1204) river monitors 31 through 34.

♦ **2 U.S. PBR (Patrol Boat, Riverine) Mk II**
Bldr: Uniflite, Bellingham, Wash. (In serv. 1974)

D: 8.9 tons (fl) **S:** 24 kts **Dim:** 9.73 × 3.53 × 0.81
A: 1 14.5-mm mg; 1 6-round 120-mm rocket launcher
Electronics: Radar: 1 Raytheon 1900 (SPS-66) nav.
M: 2 G.M. Detroit Diesel 6V53N diesels; 2 Jacuzzi waterjets; 430 bhp
Range: 150/23 **Crew:** 4 tot.

Remarks: Survivors of a group donated in 1974. Glass-reinforced plastic hull, plastic armor. Have been considerably modified from the original design as delivered.

AMPHIBIOUS WARFARE CRAFT

♦ **1 ex-U.S. LCM(8)-class medium landing craft**

60

D: 34 tons light (121 fl) **S:** 12 kts **Dim:** 22.43 × 6.43 × 1.35 (fwd; 1.47 aft)
M: 4 G.M. Detroit Diesel 6-71 diesels; 2 props; 590 bhp
Range: 190/12 **Crew:** 4–5 tot. enlisted

Remarks: Probable Mk 4 aluminum version that began building in 1967. Cargo: 60 tons or 150 troops for short distances in a 12.8 × 4.3-m open well with 54.6 m^2 space. May have been donated during early 1990s UN intervention.

♦ **5 ex-U.S. LCM(6)-class medium landing craft [LCM]**

63 64 65 68 69

D: 24 tons (64 fl) **S:** 10.2 kts **Dim:** 17.07 × 4.37 × 1.22 (fwd; 1.52 aft)
M: 2 Gray Marine 64HN9 (G.M. 6V71 on Mk 3) diesels; 2 props; 330 bhp
Range: 140/10 **Crew:** 4–5 tot.

Remarks: Designed during World War II and built during the 1950s; all converted for various riverine service duties. Another six survive as hulks and may be returned to service.

Disposal note: By 2000, the two Soviet-supplied T-4-class and four Kano-class (Project 1598) landing craft were no longer in service.

Note: Also available may be two small tugs, up to 20 Zodiac RIBs brought by UN peacekeeping forces, and about 170 wooden canoes, around 10 of which have outboard motors. The 350-ton-capacity floating dry dock at Ream is no longer operational, but a marine railway capable of handling 500-ton craft was to have been completed in 1997.

CAMEROON

Republic of Cameroon

MARINE NATIONALE RÉPUBLIQUE

Personnel (2001): About 1,100 total, including 500 paracommandos

Bases: Douala (headquarters), Limbe, and Kribi

Naval Aviation: Three Dornier Do-128-6 maritime patrol aircraft with MEL Marec radar

PATROL CRAFT [PC]

♦ 1 French P 48S class
Bldr: Société Française de Constructions Navales (SFCN), Villeneuve-la-Garenne

	Laid down	L	In serv.
P 104 Bakassi	12-81	22-10-82	8-10-83

Bakassi (P 104) Bernard Prézelin, 8-99

D: 270 tons (308 fl) **S:** 26 kts **Dim:** 50.20 (47.00 pp) × 7.15 × 2.35
A: 2 single 40-mm 70-cal. Bofors AA **Electronics:** Radar: 2 Furuno . . . nav.
M: 2 SACM 195V16 CZSHR diesels; 2 props; 6,400 bhp **Electric:** 280 kw tot.
Range: 2,000/16 **Crew:** 6 officers, 21 petty officers, 12 nonrated

Remarks: Enlarged version of P 48 class, ordered 14-12-80. Was refitted at Lorient, France, from 1-99 to 8-99, when provision for launching 8 MM 40 Exocet SSM was deleted, a prominent exhaust stack was added amidships, the radars were replaced, and the EW system was deleted.
Combat systems: The Racal CANE 100 (Command and Navigation Equipment) is fitted. Two Matra Défense Naja optronic directors for the 40-mm AA are carried; they employ the RADOP ranging system, using data from the navigation radars.

♦ 1 French PR 48 class
Bldr: SFCN, Villeneuve-la-Garenne

	Laid down	L	In serv.
P 103 L'Audacieux	23-4-75	30-10-75	11-6-76

D: 250 tons (fl) **S:** 18 kts **Dim:** 47.50 (45.50 pp) × 7.10 × 2.25
A: 2 single 40-mm 60-cal. Bofors AA **Electronics:** Radar: 1 Decca 1226 nav.
M: 2 SACM V12CZSHR diesels; 2 props; 4,200 bhp **Electric:** 100 kw tot.
Range: 2,000/15 **Fuel:** 90 tons **Crew:** 4 officers, 21 enlisted

Remarks: Ordered 9-74. Had been reported inoperable and hulked, but was put back into service after a refit in 1995; may again be inoperable, however.

PATROL BOATS [PB]

♦ . . . Rodman 55 class
Bldr: Rodman-Polyships, Vigo, Spain (In serv. . . .)

D: 15.7 tons (fl) **S:** 25 kts **Dim:** 16.50 × 3.80 × 0.70
A: 1 7.62-mm mg **Electronics:** Radar: 1 Decca. . . nav.
M: 2 Bazán-M.A.N. D2848 LXE diesels; 2 Hamilton waterjets; 1,360 bhp (1,216 sust.)
Range: 500/25 **Crew:** 7 tot.

Remarks: Several reported ordered during 2000. GRP construction.

♦ 6 38-foot class
Bldr: Swiftships, Morgan City, La. (In serv. 1986–87)

PR 01 through PR 20 series

PR 02 on trials Swiftships, 1986

D: 11.7 tons (fl) **S:** 33 kts **Dim:** 11.58 × 3.81 × 1.00
A: 2 single 12.7-mm M2 mg; 2 single 7.62-mm mg
Electronics: Radar: 1 . . . nav.
M: 2 Stewart & Stevenson–G.M. 6V 92 MTA diesels; 2 props; 1,100 bhp
Range: 216/20 **Crew:** 4 tot.

Remarks: A contract for 30 of these craft (10 for the Gendarmerie) was signed 29-8-86, with all deliveries to be made by end-1987. For use on the Chad River, based at Douala. Aluminum construction. Hull of 1.90-m molded depth. The first 10 arrived in Cameroon in 3-87, the second 10 in 9-87. By early 1997, most were no longer operational.

Disposal note: The three NAPCO Raider-class launches are no longer in service.

♦ 1 Motto class
Bldr: A.C.R.E., Libreville, Gabon (In serv. 12-11-73)

Quartier-Maître Alfred Motto

Quartier-Maître Alfred Motto French Navy, 11-97

D: 96 tons (fl) **S:** 15.5 kts **Dim:** 29.10 × 6.20 × 1.85 (props)
A: 2 single 12.7-mm M2 mg **Electronics:** Radar: 1 . . . nav.
M: 2 Baudouin diesels; 2 props; 1,290 bhp **Crew:** 2 officers, 15 enlisted

Remarks: Out of service by 1991, but reactivated early in 1996 and in use for local patrol duties and troop transportation.

AMPHIBIOUS WARFARE CRAFT

♦ 2 small landing craft [LCM] (In serv. 1973)

Betika (ex-*Bakassi*) Bibundi

Betika—note pilothouse raised above vehicle deck French Navy, 11-97

D: 57 tons (fl) **S:** 9 kts **Dim:** 17.5 × 4.28 × 1.3
M: 2 Baudouin diesels; 490 bhp

Remarks: First unit built by Tanguy Marine, France; the second by Carena, Abidjan, Ivory Coast, with French assistance. Refitted in 1987.

SERVICE CRAFT

♦ 1 floating dry dock [YFDL]
Bldr: Flenderwerft, Lübeck, Germany (In serv. 23-7-87)

Bamusso

Remarks: Government-owned, for repair of commercial and government vessels. Capacity: 10,000 tons.

♦ 2 10-ton harbor launches [YFL]

Bimbia Sanaga

♦ 1 buoy tender [YGL]
Bldr: Cossens, Emden, Germany (In serv. 12-90)

Nyong

Nyong A. A. de Kruijf and Piet Sinke, 2-91

SERVICE CRAFT *(continued)*

D: 218 grt **S:** 11.5 kts **Dim:** . . . (41.40 pp) × 11.50 × 3.00
M: 2 MWM TBD-440-6K diesels; 2 props; 2,200 bhp **Crew:** 15 tot.

GENDARMERIE

PATROL BOATS [WPB]

♦ **4 SM.360 class**
Bldr: Simonneau Marine, Fontenay-le-Comte, France (In serv. 3-91)

D: 7.5 tons (fl) **S:** 27 kts **Dim:** 11.10 (10.10 hull) × 3.50 × 0.80
A: 1 7.62-mm mg **Electronics:** Radar: 1 Furuno . . . nav.
M: 2 Volvo TAMD61 diesels; 2 props; 900 bhp (504 sust.)
Range: 230/18 **Crew:** 1 officer, 5 enlisted

Remarks: Transferred from the navy 10-91. Aluminum construction.

♦ **up to 10 38-foot class**
Bldr: Swiftships, Morgan City, La. (In serv. 3-88)

Remarks: For characteristics, see naval entry of this class.

Note: Gendarmerie forces also operate up to six 9.1-m launches built by Société Africaine d'Étude de la Réalisation Industrielle (SAERI), Douala, in 1986–87 and several survivors from among the 12 Type 650 and Type 800 launches of 3.5 tons (Dim: 8.50 × 3.00 × 0.72) delivered 1977–82 by Chantiers Plascoa, Cannes, France.

CANADA

MARITIME COMMAND

Personnel (2001): 8,900 total active, plus 3,900 in the Naval Reserve (in 24 divisions) and 5,500 civil employees

Bases: Fleet headquarters at Ottawa, with bases at Esquimalt on the Pacific coast and Halifax on the Atlantic. At Nanoose Bay, Vancouver Island, is the Canadian Forces Maritime Experimental and Test Range, operated jointly with the U.S. Navy.

Organization: The unified military organization of Canada comprises four operational commands and two support groups under the Canadian Armed Forces. Operational commands include the Mobile Force (army), Air Command, Maritime Command, and Communications Command. These are supported by the Personnel Group and the Material Group. Canadian maritime aircraft are subordinated to the Air Command but are under the operational control of the Maritime Command.

The Fleet is organized into Maritime Command Atlantic (MARLANT) and Maritime Command Pacific (MARPAC). Subordinate to MARLANT are Maritime Operations Groups (MAROPGRU) 1 and 3, while subordinate to MARPAC are MAROPGRU 2 and 4.

Under a 12-99 decision, naval readiness is to be reduced, with only one Contingency Task Group (consisting of 1 DD, 2 FFs, 1 AOR, 1 SS, and 6 maritime patrol aircraft) available for deployment with a 30-day warning, one National Task Group (with similar composition) available within 60 days, and five additional *Halifax*-class frigates capable of deployment within 90 days. Ships of the first two groups will receive 120 days of sea-time annually, while the others will have only 80 days; additional ships will be retained on 180-day deployment readiness and may have as little as 20 days at sea per year.

CP-140 Aurora maritime patrol aircraft — David D. Broecker, 5-99

CH-124-series Sea King ASW helicopter — Winter & Findler, 4-99

CH-149 Cormorant search-and-rescue helicopter — AgustaWestland, 2000

Maritime Aviation: 18 CH-124A, 6 CH-124B, and 8 CH-124C Sea King ASW helicopters; 5 CH-149 Cormorant and 7 CH-113A Labrador SAR helicopters; 18 CP-140 Aurora maritime patrol aircraft; 3 CP-140A Arcturus for Arctic patrol and training; 3 CC-130E Hercules SAR aircraft/transports; and 2 CU-144 Challenger medical evacuation transports. The Sea King helicopters are long past due for replacement.

The government gave permission in 8-00 to solicit bids for 28 replacement shipboard ASW helicopters; the Sikorsky S-70 Maplehawk, Eurocopter Cougar, and AgustaWestland EH.101 have been offered. The decision on a winning bidder has been delayed to 8-02, with combat system selection delayed to 4-03.

The Westland AW-320 (a variant of the EH.101 Merlin design) was selected as the CH-149 Cormorant on 23-4-98 to replace the CH-113 Labradors, but the actual order for 15 was not placed until 10-00; the first four were delivered during 3-01. The first five Cormorants equip 442 Sqn., 19 Wing, Comox, B.C., while the others will serve in 103 Sqn., 9 Wing, Gander, Nfld.; 413 Sqn., 14 Wing, Greenwood, N.S.; and 424 Sqn., 8 Wing, Trenton, Ont. by the end of 2002. The aircraft are powered by G.E. Canada T700/T6A1 turboshaft engines.

The Aurora (a variant of the U.S. P-3 Orion airframe) has the Orion's A-NEW system, based on the miniaturized Univac ASQ-114 computer, which can store 65,000 words of 30 bits and has a retrieval time of 4 microseconds. There are 36 launching chutes for dropping active and passive sonobuoys and racks for 120 reserve sonobuoys. Other principal systems are 2 ASN-84 inertial navigation computers; doppler radar; tactical recorder; flight-control director; tactical datalink system: FLIR (Forward-Looking Infrared); SLAR (Side-Looking Airborne Radar) antennas; detectors for lasers; and a low-light television pod. The Aurora fleet began a modernization program in 7-97 incorporating upgrading the APS-116 radar to include a "spotlight" synthetic aperture capability, substitution of a 99-channel sonobuoy receiver, an acoustic processor and EW upgrade (including installation of ALR-76), installation of GPS, and updated communication gear; the first four are to complete in 2000 and the last in 2004, extending the fleet's life span through 2010, but two of the 18 are to be retired without modification.

The CP-140A Arcturus has the APS-134 radar, APN RAWS, ASW-502 autopilot, APN-510 doppler navigation radar, LN-33 inertial navigation system, and ASH-502 flight recorder—but no ASW equipment. A GPS receiver, ESM gear, and a 99-channel sonobuoy receiver/processor are to be added later. The aircraft are to be retired in 2003–04.

All of the CE-133 Silver Star and all but two EC-144C Challenger electronic support and training aircraft were retired in 1999–2000.

Maritime Aviation Squadron Organization:

14 Wing, CFB Greenwood, N.S.:	CP-140 Aurora: MP 404, MP 405, MP 415
	CP-140A Arcturus: MP 404
	CC-130 Hercules: 413 Sqn.
	CH-113A Labrador: 413 Sqn. (2 aircraft)
	Challenger 600/601: 434 Sqn.
12 Wing, CFB Halifax, N.S.:	CH-124A/B Sea King: HS 423, HT 406
19 Wing, CFB Comox, B.C.:	CP-140 Aurora: MP 407
	CH-113A Labrador (1 aircraft)
Victoria Municipal Airport, Esquimalt, B.C.:	CH-124A/B Sea King: HS 443

WEAPONS AND SYSTEMS

A. MISSILES

Surface-to-air missiles: NATO Sea Sparrow RIM-7P is used from Mk 48 vertical launchers in the *Halifax* class. It is to be replaced by Evolved Sea Sparrow starting late in 2004, with the missiles having been ordered spring 2001 for delivery starting in 2003.

Vertically launched Standard SM-2 MR Block II replaced Sea Sparrow in the *Iroquois* (Tribal) class. Ten new SM-2 Block IIIA missiles were ordered in 3-98.

Surface-to-surface missiles: Canada has purchased the U.S. AGM-84C Harpoon missile for use by CP-140 Aurora aircraft and the RGM-84C Harpoon for use by surface ships. In 1984, 34 RGM-84D shipboard versions were ordered; another 12 were ordered in 1998. As of 5-00, consideration was being given to procuring a limited number of AGM-84E Sea SLAM missiles for land-attack missions.

B. GUNS

76-mm 62-cal. OTOBreda SuperRapid: Single mount on the *Iroquois* class. See Italy section for data.

57-mm Bofors SAK Mk 2: Single mount on the *Halifax* class. See Sweden section for data.

WEAPONS AND SYSTEMS *(continued)*

40-mm Mk N1/1 Bofors AA on Mk 5c "Boffin" mounting: Standard 60-cal. gun on powered mount originally designed for twin 20-mm Oerlikon AA during World War II. Mounts formerly used for airfield defense in Europe. One mount each on *Kingston*-class reserve training ships.

20-mm U.S. Mk 15 Block I Phalanx CIWS: On *Iroquois*-class destroyers, *Halifax*-class frigates, and *Protecteur*-class replenishment ships. See characteristics in U.S. section.

C. TORPEDOES

U.S. Mk 46 Mod. 5: ASW torpedoes aboard ships, Sea King helicopters, and maritime patrol aircraft. A total of 524 are available (374 new, delivered 1988–91, and 150 updated former Mod. 1). A few Mk 44 ASW torpedoes may remain in inventory also.

U.S. Mk 48 Mod. 4: On submarines. 48 were ordered in 1985, 13 in 1988, and 26 on 23-6-89 to deliver by 6-91. *Upholder*-class submarines are being altered to employ it.

D. ELECTRONICS

♦ Radars

DA-08: Thales surface/air search in *Iroquois* class
LIROD-8: Thales X-band fire-control radar in *Iroquois* class
LW-08: Thales long-range air search in *Iroquois* class
Sea Giraffe 150HC: Swedish Ericsson surface search on the *Halifax* class
SPG-501: Raytheon-made STIR 1.8 tracker/illuminator in *Iroquois* class
SPG-503: Thales-made STIR 1.8 tracker/illuminator in *Halifax* class
SPS-49(V)5: Raytheon 2-D air-search radar on *Halifax* class
Type 1006: Kelvin-Hughes submarine general-purpose search radar

Note: Raytheon Systems Canada early in 2000 demonstrated the SWR-503, a shore-based HF surface-wave ocean surveillance sonar, intended for monitoring or detecting illegal drug and smuggling activities, piracy, illegal fishing, etc., to ranges greater than 200 n.m. from shore.

♦ Sonars

SQR-501 CANTASS: Towed passive linear hydrophone array for the *Halifax* class. Uses the "wet" end of the U.S. SQR-19A system with Canadian UYS-501 receiver/processor and UYQ-501 displays.

SQS-505: Hull-mounted and towed LF installed in the *Iroquois* class (SQA-502 hoist). SQS-505 TASP with digital acoustic processing and SHINPADS display was tested in an *Iroquois*-class ship 1985–88. Latest version, SQS-505(V)6, is carried by *Halifax* class vice planned SQS-510; it operates at 7 kHz. *Protecteur* class has SQS-505(V)3.

SQS-510: Hull-mounted MF set operating between 4.3 and 8.0 kHz, intended as successor to SQS-505

♦ Sonobuoys

SSQ-522 active, SSQ-527 passive LOFAR, and SSQ-530 passive DIFAR sonobuoys are used by helicopters and fixed-wing aircraft.

♦ Countermeasures

SLQ-25: U.S. Aerojet Nixie towed acoustic homing torpedo decoy
SLQ-501: MEL CANEWS (Canadian Electronic Warfare System) intercept for frigates and destroyers
SLQ-502: GEC-Marconi Shield rocket decoy launcher on *Iroquois* and *Halifax* classes and AORs; being updated with Australian Nulka rocket decoy launch capability
SLQ-503: Lockheed RAMSES (Reprogrammable Advanced Multimode Shipboard ECM System) jammer for the *Halifax* class
SLQ-504: Racal Kestrel 242 intercept
SRD-501: HFD/F system on *Iroquois*-class destroyers
SRD-502: Southwest-made Telegon-4 HFD/F on *Halifax*-class frigates
SRN-504: Combat direction-finding system for missile targeting; similar to the U.S. SSQ-108 system

♦ Communications

Canadian Maritime Forces employs two civilian communications satellites, Anik-E1 and Anik-E2.

ATTACK SUBMARINES [SS]

♦ 4 ex-U.K. Upholder class

Bldr: Cammell Laird, Birkenhead (SS 879: VSEL, Barrow-in-Furness)

	Laid down	L	In serv.
SS 876 VICTORIA (ex-*Unseen,* S 41)	12-8-87	14-11-89	20-7-91
SS 877 WINDSOR (ex-*Unicorn,* S 43)	13-3-90	16-4-92	25-6-93
SS 878 CORNER BROOK (ex-*Ursula,* S 42)	10-1-89	28-2-91	8-5-92
SS 879 CHICOUTIMI (ex-*Upholder,* S 40)	2-86	2-12-86	7-12-90

Corner Brook (SS 878)—as HMS *Ursula* (S 42) Paul C. Clift, 6-94

D: 1,870 tons std., 2,185 tons surf./2,400 tons sub.
S: 12 kts surf./20 kts sub. **Dim:** 70.26 (47.5 pressure hull) × 7.60 × 5.50
A: 6 bow 533-mm TT (18 tot. Alliant Mk 48 Mod. 4 torpedoes)
Electronics:
Radar: 1 Kelvin-Hughes Type 1007 nav./surf. search
Sonar: Type 2040 Argonaut bow active/passive; Type 2041 MicroPUFFS passive flank array; SUBTASS towed array; Type 2019 (PARIS) intercept
EW: Sperry Guardian Star intercept (2–18 GHz); 2 SSE Mk 8 decoy tubes (Type 2066 Bandfish and Type 2071 decoys)
M: 2 Paxman Valenta 16 RPA 200SZ 16-cyl. diesel generators (2,035 bhp each), 2 2,500-kw G.E.C.-Alsthom alternators, 1 double-armature electric motor; 1 7-bladed prop; 5,400 shp
Range: 8,000/8 snorkel; 54/20, 270/3 sub. **Fuel:** 200 tons
Endurance: 50 days **Crew:** 7 officers, 37 enlisted

Remarks: Leased for eight years for $427 million on 2-7-98, with another $98 million to be spent on improvements; at the end of the eight years, the quartet are to be purchased for a nominal £1. Delivery of SS 876 was to have come during 5-00, with the others to follow at six-month intervals, but piping weld problems delayed the work by about three months per boat. The reactivations were performed for prime contractor BAE Systems by Cammell Laird at Birkenhead, with the work on SS 876 started on 4-7-00.

SS 876 was handed over to Canada on 6-10-00 and recommissioned at Halifax on 2-12-00; after installation of Canadian equipment at Halifax, she became fully operational during 10-01 and was to transfer to the Pacific in 2-02. SS 877 was handed over on 6-7-01 and arrived in Canada during 10-01. SS 878 was to arrive during 1-02, and SS 879 in 5-02. Part of the lease cost is being offset by not charging the U.K. for troop training facilities in Canada. Included in the acquisition were four shore-based trainer sets, initial crew training, and spare parts for two to three years of operations.

The four had been decommissioned from U.K. service on 6-4-94, 16-10-94, 6-94, and 29-4-94, respectively. They are expected to operate for about 30 years. SS 876 will be based on the west coast at Esquimalt and the others on the east coast at Halifax. Are superior in virtually every respect to the contemporary Russian Kilo series.

Hull systems: Able to snorkel at 19 kts and can remain submerged 90 hours at 3 kts. Operating depth: more than 250 m. Single-hull design. Have rubber anechoic hull coating. Are intended to operate 15,000 hours (7 years) between overhauls. Need only 40–60 min./day battery charging at normal patrol speeds. Have 11% reserve buoyancy when surfaced. Use two 240-cell lead-acid batteries, providing 6,080 amp-hr at the 1-hour rate and 8,800 amp-hr at the 5-hour rate. There is a five-person divers' lockout chamber in the sail. The sail has a glass-reinforced plastic skin. A 200-kw air-independent auxiliary propulsion system may be added during midlife refits around 2013. Have extremely small acoustic and magnetic signatures.

Combat systems: During reactivation, are being fitted to launch U.S. Alliant Mk 48 torpedoes; the original DCC weapons-control system is being replaced with a Singer Librascope Mk 1 Mod. 0 (BYG-501) fire-control system using a UYK-20 computer; these are being recycled from the *Oberon* class and a shore trainer. Originally had two Ferranti FM 1600E computers, the Thorn E.M.I. 1553B data system, and an inertial navigation system. Have a Pilkington Optronics CK 35 search periscope with EW array and a CH 85 attack scope with infrared capability. Type 2040 sonar is a version of the Thales Argonaut system; the cylindrical transducer array is at the bow, with intercept hydrophones arranged along the sides. The Guardian Star electronic intercept equipment is also being recycled from the *Oberons*, and Canadian communications (including WSC-3 SATCOM gear) and cryptologic equipment is being substituted. The sonar system was to be updated during reactivation, including substitution of a Canadian-made SUBTASS towed array. Have two 102-mm SSE Mk 8 decoy and signal launch tubes. They will not be equipped to launch UGM-84 Harpoon missiles. Signals intelligence collection equipment is to be added.

Disposal note: The final *Oberon*-class submarine in Canadian service, *Onandaga* (SS 73), was paid off on 28-7-00 and will become an exhibit at the National War Museum, Ottawa.

GUIDED-MISSILE DESTROYERS [DDG]

Note: A replacement program for the *Iroquois* class, dubbed CADRE (Command and Control and Air-Defence Replacement), was to begin in 2000. Although new ships are preferred, upgrading four existing *Halifax*-class frigates with improved command, control, and communications facilities and area-defense SAM systems remains a possibility, as does installation of the necessary capabilities aboard the planned Afloat Logistics Support Ships (see under [AOR]).

♦ 4 Iroquois class (1 in *reserve*)

Bldrs: DDH 280, 281: Marine Industries, Sorel, Que.; DDH 282, 283: Davie SB, Lauzon, Que.

	Laid down	L	In serv.
DDH 280 IROQUOIS	15-1-69	28-11-70	29-7-72
DDH 281 *HURON*	15-1-69	3-4-71	16-12-72
DDH 282 ATHABASKAN	1-6-69	27-11-70	30-11-72
DDH 283 ALGONQUIN	1-9-69	23-4-71	30-9-73

Algonquin (DDH 283)—note lack of SATCOM radomes abreast the stack
Brian Morrison, 5-01

GUIDED-MISSILE DESTROYERS [DDG] *(continued)*

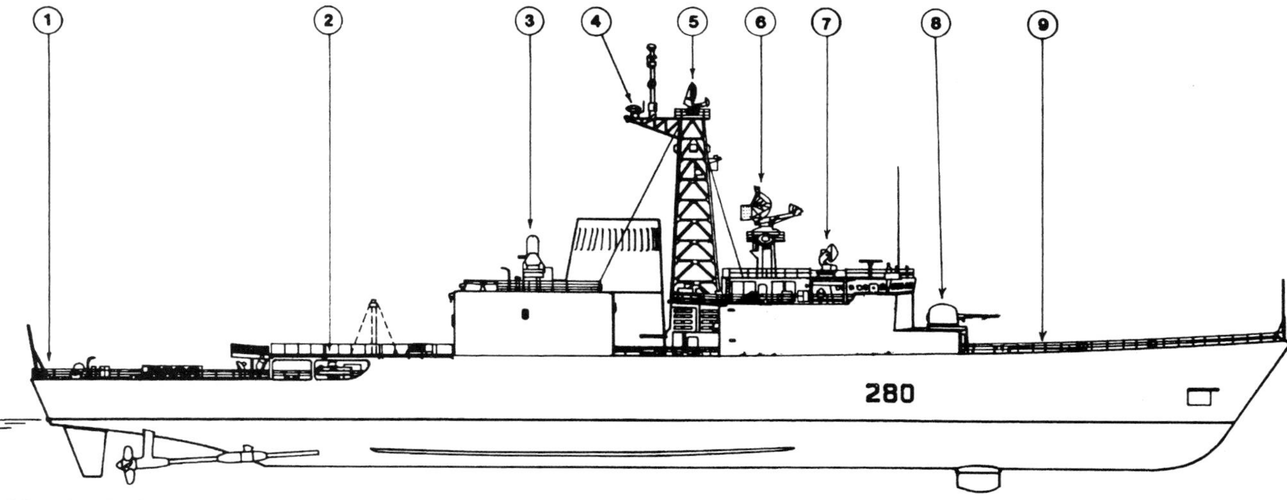

Iroquois (DDH 280) 1. VDS housing 2. triple Mk 32 ASW TT 3. 20-mm Mk 15 Phalanx CIWS 4. URN-25 TACAN antenna 5. SPQ-501 air/surface-search radar 6. SPQ-502 early-warning radar 7. SPG-501 tracker/illuminators (side-by-side) 8. 76-mm 62-cal. OTOBreda SuperRapid DP gun 9. Mk 41 vertical launch cells for Standard SM-2 missiles
Drawing by A. D. Baker III

Iroquois (DDH 280) Mike Welsford, 10-99

Athabaskan (DDH 282)—note SATCOM antenna radomes flanking the funnel and Sea King helicopter on the flight deck Jaroslaw Cislak, 6-99

D: 4,450 tons (5,100 fl) **S:** 29 kts (27 sust.)
Dim: 128.84 (121.31 pp) × 15.24 × 4.69 (7.86 max.)
A: 1 Mk 41 VLS group (29 Standard SM-2 Block IIIA missiles); 1 76-mm 62-cal. OTOBreda SuperRapid DP; 1 20-mm U.S. Mk 15 Block I Phalanx gatling CIWS (not on DDH 281); 2 triple 324-mm Mk 32 Mod. 5 ASW TT; 2 CH-124A Sea King helicopters
Electronics:
Radar: 2 Raytheon 1900 Pathfinder nav.; 1 Thales SPQ-501 (DA-08/2LS) surf./air search; 1 Thales SPQ-502 (LW-08) early warning; 2 Raytheon SPG-501 (STIR 1.8/OT-134) tracker/illuminators; 1 General Dynamics Mk 90 Phalanx f.c.; 1 Thales LIROD-8 gun f.c.
Sonar: SQS-505(V)4 hull-mounted; SQS-505(V)5 VDS; C-Tech Spectra 3000 mine-avoidance
TACAN: URN-25
EW: Racal SLQ-503 (CANEWS) intercept; SRD-503 HFD/F; U.S. ULQ-6B jammer; 4 6-round Plessey Shield decoy RL (with Nulka decoy-launch capability); SLQ-25 Nixie towed acoustic torpedo decoy
M: COGOG: 2 Pratt & Whitney FT4A-2 boost gas turbines (23,747 shp each), 2 G.M. Allison 570KF cruise gas turbines (6,445 shp each); 2 5-bladed CP props; 47,494 shp max.
Electric: 3,750 kw tot. **Range:** 3,500/20; 4,500/15
Crew: 26 officers, 266 enlisted + air group: 9 officers, 21 enlisted (DDH 281: 75 tot. caretaker crew)

Remarks: These ships have been updated under a design prepared by Litton Systems Canada. DDH 283 began a TRUMP ("Tribal" Update and Modernization Program) conversion period 26-10-87 at MIL-Davie, Lauzon, Que., but the conversion was delayed by two fires and other problems, and the ship was not accepted until 1-10-91, with first missile firings not until 18-1-92; the ship returned to the West Coast 12-93. DDH 280 began conversion 25-10-88 at the same facility and was accepted 15-5-92. Work on DDH 282 began 10-91 and completed 3-8-94, with the ship reentering full service in 5-95. DDH 281 began conversion 25-5-92 for completion 7-95.

DD 280 and DD 282 are based at Halifax, DD 283 at Esquimalt. DD 281 decommissioned at Esquimalt in 12-00 due to crew shortages but is to be maintained in 60- to 90-day activation reserve with a caretaker crew. The others are planned to begin retiring around 2004.

Hull systems: Modernization has increased the seaworthiness of the ships considerably, reducing the roll and limiting heel to 17° during turns. Limiting displacement is 5,220 tons. Have fin stabilizers. During modernization, a G.M. 1,000-kw diesel generator was fitted and accommodations and climate control were considerably improved. Water ballast compensation has been fitted for the fuel tanks.

Combat systems: The UYC-501 SHINPADS command-and-control system incorporates UYQ-504 and UYQ-507 computers and employs NATO Link 11 and 14 (Link 16 was to be added in 2000 and Link 22 is to be added around 2005–06). The U.S. Mk 41 VLS (Vertical Launch System) for 32 Standard SM-2 MR Block III SAMs replaced the OTOBreda 127-mm gun forward, while an OTOBreda 76-mm DP gun was installed in the former Sea Sparrow magazine area. The Mk 15 CIWS was placed atop the hangar, and ASW torpedo stowage and handling was improved. The Standard missiles are controlled by two illuminator/trackers and the 76-mm gun by the LIROD-8 radar/electro-optical director atop the pilothouse. The planned SLQ-503 jammer was not installed and the obsolescent U.S. ULQ-6 was instead retained. The U.S. SLQ-25 Nixie torpedo decoy was added, and the U.S. WSN-5 inertial navigation system and SRR-1 SATCOM are installed. All have the Bear Trap positive-control helicopter landing system. Have an onboard UYS-503(V) processor to analyze signals from helicopter-dropped sonobuoys. ASW systems in the modernized ships are basically unchanged, except for removal of the Limbo mortar and its depth-finding sonar.

Nulka decoy launchers were installed during 1999 by modifying the existing decoy launchers. Late in 1998, DDH 282 completed installation of an enhanced communications suite including a Matra Marconi SHF SATCOM system, an 8-transmitter Harris SRC-503 HF, 3 Harris narrowband transceivers, 10 UHF transceivers, 2 Have Quick II UHF SATCOM transceivers, Marconi VLF receivers, and a digital Inmarsat commercial SATCOM set for her role as STANAVFORLANT flagship starting in 4-99. Similar equipment had been added to DDH 282 by 1-99, while plans to upgrade the West Coast pair were canceled (although DD 283 has received a Have Quick UHF SATCOM). UHF transceivers and VLF communications receivers were also added, while the commercial SATCOM system was upgraded to Inmarsat-B in all but DD 281. All have WSC-4 and SSR-1 SATCOM. DDH 280 may retain a Koden MD 373 radar atop the hangar; in the others, the after Raytheon navigational set is located there for helicopter control.

FRIGATES [FF]

♦ 12 Halifax class

Bldrs: A: St. John SB, N.B.; B: MIL Group Davie SY, Lauzon, Que. (sterns by MIL, Tracy)

	Bldr	Laid down	L	In serv.
FFH 330 Halifax	A	19-3-87	30-5-88	29-6-92
FFH 331 Vancouver	A	19-5-88	8-7-89	23-8-93
FFH 332 Ville de Québec	B	16-12-88	16-5-91	14-7-94
FFH 333 Toronto	A	22-4-89	15-6-91	29-7-93
FFH 334 Regina	B	6-10-89	25-11-91	30-9-94
FFH 335 Calgary	B	15-6-91	28-8-92	12-5-95
FFH 336 Montreal	A	9-2-91	28-2-92	21-7-94
FFH 337 Fredericton	A	25-4-92	26-6-93	10-9-94
FFH 338 Winnipeg	A	19-3-93	25-6-94	23-6-95
FFH 339 Charlottetown	A	17-12-93	1-10-94	9-9-95
FFH 340 St. John's	A	24-8-94	12-2-95	24-6-96
FFH 341 Ottawa	A	29-4-95	22-11-95	28-9-96

FRIGATES [FF] *(continued)*

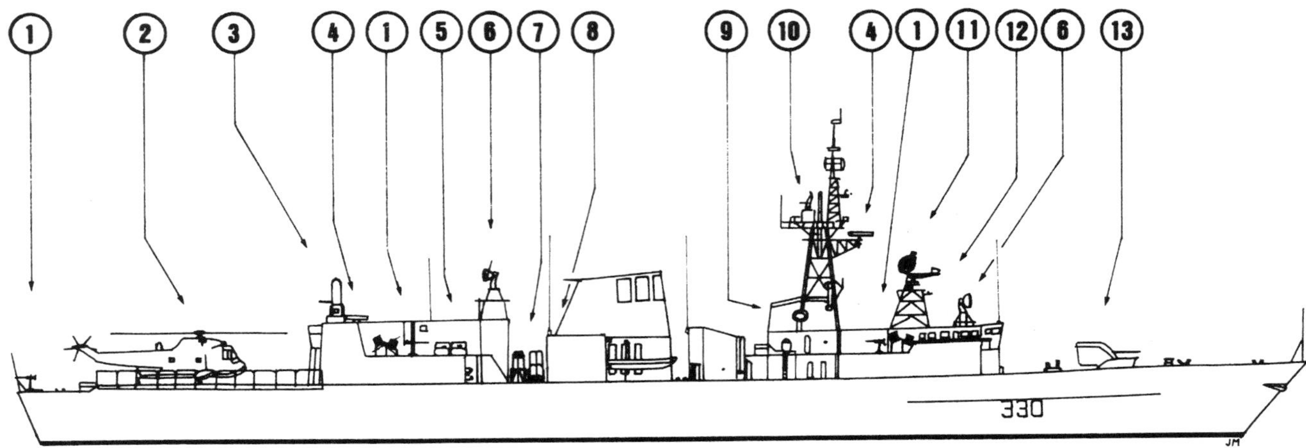

Halifax (FFH 330) 1. 12.7-mm machineguns 2. CH-124 Sea King helicopter 3. 20-mm Mk 15 Phalanx CIWS 4. navigational and helicopter-control radars 5. twin, fixed Mk 32 ASW TT in deckhouse at main deck level 6. SPG-503 tracker/illuminator radars 7. RGM-84 Harpoon SSM in quadruple launch canister groups 8. Mk 48 vertical launch cells for Sea Sparrow SAMs 9. OE-82 antennas for the U.S. WSC-3 UHF SATCOM system 10. Sea Giraffe 150HC search radar 11. SPS-49(V)5 air-search radar 12. decoy RL on bridge wings 13. 57-mm SAK 57 DP gun
Drawing by Jean Moulin

Winnipeg (FFH 338) Brian Morrison, 4-01

Fredericton (FFH 337)—note twin ports for deploying torpedo decoys to port, towed sonar array port to starboard on transom stern Dieter Wolf, 6-00

Calgary (FFH 335) Brian Morrison, 10-00

Halifax (FFH 330) Curt Borgenstam, 10-00

FRIGATES [FF] *(continued)*

Vancouver (FFH 331)—note vertical SAM launchers abreast stack, Phalanx CIWS on starboard side of the hangar roof, VERTREP position painted on bow, and helicopter haul-down and traversing system on flight deck Canadian Forces, 2000

D: 3,922 tons light, 4,305 tons std. (4,761 fl)
S: 29.2 kts (27 sust.; 18 max. on diesel)
Dim: 135.5 (124.50 pp) × 16.40 (14.80 wl) × 4.94 (mean hull; 6.15 max.)
A: 8 RGM-84C/D Harpoon SSM; 2 Mk 48 Mod. 0 Sea Sparrow VLS SAM launch groups (16 RIM-7M missiles); 1 57-mm 70-cal. Bofors SAK-57 Mk 2 DP; 1 20-mm Mk 15 Mod. 1 Block 1 Phalanx gatling CIWS; 4 single 12.7-mm mg; 2 paired, fixed 324-mm Mk 32 Mod. 9 ASW TT (Mk 46 Mod. 1 or 5 torpedoes); 1 CH-124A Sea King helicopter
Electronics:
Radar: 2 Sperry Mk 340X (FFH 335, 337–341: Kelvin-Hughes Type 1007) nav.; 1 Ericsson Sea Giraffe 150HC air/surf. search; 1 Raytheon SPS-49(V)5 long-range air search; 2 Thales SPG-503 (VM-25 STIR 1.8) f.c.
Sonar: SQS-505(V)6 hull-mounted; SQR-501 CANTASS towed array; WQC-501(V) underwater telephone; UYS-503 sonobuoy processor
TACAN: URN-25
EW: Racal SLQ-504 (CANEWS) intercept; Lockheed SLQ-503 (RAMSES) jammer; Southwest SRD-502 (Telegon-4) HFD/F; 4 six-round SLQ-502 (Marconi-GEC Shield-II) decoy RL; Aerojet SLQ-25 Nixie towed acoustic torpedo decoy—FFH 338 also: SRD-504 combat D/F

M: CODOG: 2 G.E. LM-2500-30 gas turbines (23,747 shp each at 3,600 rpm), 1 SEMT-Pielstick 20PA6-V280-BTC diesel (11,780 bhp max./8,675 bhp sust.); 2 Escher-Wyss CP props; 47,494 shp
Electric: 3,400 kw tot. (4 MWM TBO-602 V-16K diesel generator sets)
Range: 4,500/20 on one gas turbine; 6,000/15 diesel **Fuel:** 550 tons
Crew: 22 officers, 202 enlisted (peacetime complement: 180 tot.)

Remarks: First six ordered 29-7-83 from consortium of St. John Shipbuilding, Ltd., Paramax Electronics (later Unisys GSG Canada), and Sperry, with three subcontracted to Marine Industries (later MIL Group). Second flight of six ordered 18-12-87, all from St. John. FFH 330, 332, 333, 336, 337, 339, and 340 are assigned to MARLANT, the others to MARPAC. As many as three may be decommissioned to reserve as part of the navy's share of the 1999 defense cuts.
Hull systems: Full-load displacement has grown by 496 tons since construction began; limiting displacement is 5,100 tons. Do not have fin stabilizers. Measures have been taken to minimize the infrared signature, and the ships have NBC warfare–proof citadels. Have a bubbler noise-reduction system. The engines are raft-mounted to reduce radiated noise, but they have been found to be noisier than expected; FFH 336 has 12,500 synthetic rubber anechoic tiles on the hull on the exterior of the underwater hull in the vicinity of the machinery spaces to reduce radiated noise. The Indal Bear Trap helicopter haul-down and deck transit system is installed. Fuel capacity has been increased from the original 479 tons. FFH 330, 332, and 333 experienced propulsion diesel cracking problems; until repairs were made by the manufacturer during 1995–96, the unrepaired ships were restricted to 13–15 kts on diesel power.
Combat systems: The Thales UYQ-501(V) SHINPADS (Shipboard Integrated Processing and Display System) data system with UYC-501(V) databus is fitted. Were originally to have had the newer SQS-510 hull-mounted sonar. The transducer for the SQS-505(V)6 set is mounted in a C5 retractable dome. The SQR-501 CANTASS towed tactical passive hydrophone array system uses the "wet end" of the U.S. SQR-19A TACTASS. Have the UYS-503(V) sonobuoy data processing system.

A planned additional 12 VLS Sea Sparrow reload SAMs will not now be carried; as a further money-saving move, the ships do not have the latest version of the Harpoon missile weapons-control system, being fitted instead with SWG-1(V) vice SWG-1A. Have the SHINCOM (Shipboard Integrated Communications) system and are fitted with two U.S. OE-82 antennas for the WSC-3 UHF SATCOM system. One of the two navigational radar antennas is mounted atop the helicopter hangar, to port, to assist in helicopter takeoffs and landings; they may later be reequipped with a Thales Scout covert continuous-wave radar set forward. All are planned to receive the SRD-504 Combat Direction-Finding system, and the unpopular jamming system may be replaced.

Navigational equipment includes Sperry SQN-502/SRD-331 doppler speed log, two Sperry SSN-502 (Mk 49) inertial navigation systems, Tracor SRN/501 Omega-II receiver, and Internav SRN-501 Loran-C receiver. Hazeltine Mk 12 IFF equipment is installed.
Modernization: Four were planned to be backfitted with H.S.A. APAR 3-D search radar during post-2005 refits, funds permitting; installing the system would increase displacement by 105 tons, due to the need for ballasting. Are planned to receive Link 16 Cooperative Engagement Capability, and the EW suite is to be updated. The TIAPS (Towed Integrated Active-Passive Sonar) may be substituted for the CANTASS passive-only towed array after 2002. May be fitted to launch AGM-94E Sea SLAM land-attack missiles during updates to take place 2006–10. U.S. Evolved Sea Sparrow missiles will begin replacing the current RIM-7P version during refits starting late 2004, but the Mk 48 launchers will not be modified to accept quad packs to permit quadrupling the missile load.

PATROL SHIPS [PS]

◆ **12 Kingston-class Maritime Coastal Defense Vessels**
Bldr: Halifax Shipyard Division, St. John SB, Ltd., Group, Halifax, N.S.

	Laid down	L	In serv.
MCDV 700 Kingston	15-12-94	12-8-95	21-9-96
MCDV 701 Glace Bay	28-4-95	22-1-96	26-10-96
MCDV 702 Nanaimo	10-8-95	17-5-96	10-5-97
MCDV 703 Edmonton	7-12-95	16-8-96	21-6-97
MCDV 704 Shawinigan	28-3-96	15-11-96	14-6-97
MCDV 705 Whitehorse	25-7-96	24-2-97	17-4-98
MCDV 706 Yellowknife	4-11-96	5-6-97	18-4-98
MCDV 707 Goose Bay	22-2-97	4-9-97	26-7-98
MCDV 708 Moncton	31-5-97	5-12-97	12-7-98 (del.)
MCDV 709 Saskatoon	5-9-97	30-3-98	5-12-98
MCDV 710 Brandon	5-12-97	10-7-98	5-6-99
MCDV 711 Summerside	28-3-98	26-9-98	7-99

Goose Bay (MCDV 707) Derek Fox, 4-01

D: 772 tons light (979 fl) **S:** 14 kts **Dim:** 55.31 (49.00 pp) × 11.30 × 3.42
A: 1 40-mm 60-cal. Mk 1N/1 AA in Mk 5c Boffin mounting; 2 single 12.7-mm Browning M2 mg
Electronics:
Radar: 1 Kelvin-Hughes Nucleus 6000 X-band nav.; 1 Kelvin-Hughes Nucleus 6000 S-band surf. search
Sonar: Towfish towed passive array
EW: Shiploc intercept, VHFD/F

PATROL SHIPS [PS] *(continued)*

Moncton (MCDV 708) Jim Sanderson, 4-01

Saskatoon (MCDV 709) H&L Van Ginderen, 2-00

M: electric drive: 4 Wärtsilä-SACM UD232V12, 1,800-kw diesels driving 4 Jeumont ANR 53-50-4 alternator sets (715 kw each), 2 Jeumont DC CI 560L electric motors (1,150 kw each); 2 Lips FS-1000 Z-drive Kort-nozzle azimuthal props; 3,084 shp
Electric: 405 kw tot. (1 × 300-kw ship's service, 1 × 105-kw emergency)
Range: 5,000/8 **Endurance:** 18 days
Crew: 30 tot. as patrol ships, 36 tot. as route survey ships

Remarks: Were originally to have been steel-hulled mine countermeasures ships to replace the Bay-class former minesweepers and *Porte*-class ships used as training ships for naval reservists. Now primarily intended for offshore patrol duties and based at Halifax and Esquimalt, with four of the East Coast units to operate on the Great Lakes or in the Gulf of St. Lawrence from May to November each year; MCDV 700, 701, 707, 708, and 711 are assigned to the Atlantic Coast, the others to the Pacific. The ships are to have a 25-year service life and have a 93-ton lifetime displacement growth margin. These vessels have little or no wartime utility. MCDV 701 collided with a U.S. fishing boat off Boston on 27-1-98. Two of the class are to be transferred to the Department of Fisheries and Oceans.
Hull systems: Built to commercial standards, but naval standards were applied to stability, maneuverability, and the magazines. Were to be able to maintain 15 kts in State 2 sea, but can only achieve 14 kts under optimum conditions; they are not considered to be good seaboats. Accommodation arrangements permit adding female crewmembers. Trials with the first unit showed the ships to be top-heavy, and 9 tons of permanent ballast were added and some equipment was relocated. All have degaussing coil arrays fitted, but only in the first three is there a control system. Planned bow-thrusters omitted. Have a large radar signature.
Combat systems: Thomson-CSF provided the combat system integration management. The 40-mm AA guns are refurbished World War II mountings returned from Europe where they were used by the Canadian Army for airfield defense. Using modular systems, are capable of route survey work in support of mine countermeasures and of carrying a remote-controlled drone submersible for examining undersea objects. To permit a modicum of mine countermeasures capability for the class, two MacDonald Dettwiler modular minesweeping systems, four modular route survey systems, and one remotely controlled inspection submersible module were procured, with the latter using the Trailblazer 25 ROV; the ROV module is based at Esquimalt, while two route survey modules are on each coast. Two mechanical minesweeping arrays are kept at Halifax for towing by units of this class. Leica Navigation MX300 GPS receivers are installed in all.

MINE WARFARE SHIPS

Note: Mine countermeasures trials and support ships *Anticosti* (MSA 110, ex-*Jean Tide,* ex-*Lady Jean*) and *Moresby* (MSA 112, ex-*Joyce Tide,* ex-*Lady Joyce*) were paid off on 8-3-00. The 12 *Kingston*-class patrol ships have a potential mine warfare capability, but the necessary equipment has not been acquired in quantity.

AUXILIARIES

♦ 1 Quest-class oceanographic research ship [AGOR]

	Bldr	Laid down	L	In serv.
AGOR 172 Quest	Burrard DD, Vancouver	2-10-67	9-7-68	21-8-69

Quest (AGOR 172) H&L Van Ginderen, 8-94

D: 2,203 tons (fl) **S:** 16 kts **Dim:** 77.20 (71.62 pp) × 12.80 × 4.60
Electronics: Radar: 1 Decca 838 nav.; 1 Decca 939 nav.
M: 2 Fairbanks-Morse 38D8⅛-9 diesels, G.E. electric drive; 2 props; 2,950 shp—bow-thruster
Electric: 1,500 kw tot. (1 × 500 kw, 2 × 300 kw, 1 × 100 kw)
Range: 10,000/12 **Fuel:** 300 tons
Crew: civilian: 12 licensed officers, 27 unlicensed, 15 scientists

Remarks: In recent years, has performed sonobuoy research for the Defence Research Establishment, Atlantic (DREA), Special Projects Unit, operating from Halifax under the control of the Canadian Forces Auxiliary Vessel organization. Given a midlife refit commencing fall 1996 at Maystown SY with Lockheed Martin Canada as prime contractor, during which the acoustic signature was reduced. In 2-99, was to begin tests with the Towed Integrated Active-Passive Sonar (TIAPS) array.
Hull systems: Ice-reinforced hull. Has two electrohydraulic 5- and 9-ton cranes and a passive tank stabilization system. The small helicopter deck is now used for equipment stowage. Employs a Concurrent Model 6650 onboard data reduction and storage computer.

♦ 0 (+ 3) new replenishment ship/transports [AOR]

SMART (Strategic Multirole Aid and Replenishment Transport) MIL Eng.

D: 35,000 tons (fl) **S:** 21 kts **Dim:** 210.00 (195.00 pp) × 32.00 × 8.50
A: 2 20-mm Mk 15 Phalanx CIWS
Electronics:
Radar: . . .
Sonar: hull-mounted mine avoidance set
EW: CANEWS intercept system, provision for towed homing torpedo decoy
M: 2 medium-speed diesels; 1 prop; 27,200 bhp—bow- and stern-thrusters
Range: 10,800/15 **Crew:** 111 tot. + 75 joint force staff and up to 300 troops

Remarks: Intended as replacements for the *Protecteur* class and the already-stricken *Provider,* with the additional capability to transport and support peacekeeping forces and their equipment. Start of construction of the first was moved forward in 6-00 from 2006 to 2004, but the number to be built was reduced from four. The budgeted cost is $971 million (U.S.) for the three. May be new-construction Canadian-built ships (the SMART—Strategic Multirole Aid and Replenishment Transport—design by MIL Systems Engineering), converted merchant ships, or used foreign naval units. As of 5-01, there were no indications of an imminent contract announcement, and the project may be on hold.
Hull systems: Cargo to be 8,000–10,000 tons fuel, 500 tons aviation fuel, 300 tons ammunition, and 230 tons potable water, plus up to 300 standard 20-ft. cargo containers. Would have one liquid replenishment and one heavy jackstay solid replenishment station each side. Sealift cargo would be carried above the liquid cargo tankage and would include 2,500 lane-meters of vehicle cargo space for roll-on/roll-off vehicle cargo on two decks, accessed via ramps at the stern and on either side forward. There would be a 25-ton-capacity elevator from the helicopter hangar to both vehicle cargo decks; four helicopters could be carried. Self-propelled pontoon barges would be stowed on the ships' sides. Would have two helicopter landing positions for aircraft up to CH-47 Chinook size. Would be able to carry a 60-bed modular field hospital facility and 200 troops, or 300 troops and their equipment. Latest configuration (1998) resembles HMS *Argus,* with superstructure forward, stack structure aft to starboard, and a large open deck for helicopters or container cargo; the vehicle ramp would be on the starboard quarter and there would be a vehicle access door forward to starboard. Are to be able to navigate through 0.7-m ice.

♦ 2 Protecteur-class replenishment ships [AOR]

Bldr: St. John SB & DD, St. John, N.B.

	Laid down	L	In serv
AOR 509 Protecteur	17-10-67	18-7-68	30-8-69
AOR 510 Preserver	17-10-67	29-5-69	30-7-70

AUXILIARIES *(continued)*

Protecteur (AOR 509) Brian Morrison, 10-00

Protecteur (AOR 509) Brian Morrison, 10-00

D: 9,000 tons light (24,700 fl) **S:** 21 kts **Dim:** 172.0 (166.42 pp) × 23.16 × 9.15
A: 2 20-mm Mk 15 Mod. 0 Block I Phalanx CIWS; 6 single 12.7-mm mg; 3 CH-124A Sea King helicopters
Electronics:
Radar: 1 Decca TM 1629 nav.; 1 Decca TM 969 nav.
TACAN: URN-22A
EW: SLQ-504 (Racal Kestrel Type 242) intercept; Southwest SRD-502 (Telegon-4) HFD/F; 2 6-round Plessey Shield decoy RL; SLQ-25 Nixie towed torpedo decoy
M: 1 set Canadian G.E. geared turbines; 1 prop; 21,000 shp
Boilers: 2 Babcock & Wilcox watertube **Electric:** 3,500 kw
Range: 4,100/20; 7,500/11.5 **Crew:** 15 officers, 212 enlisted + up to 57 passengers

Remarks: AOR 510 based at Halifax, AOR 509 at Esquimalt. AOR 509 was refitted at Victoria SY from 5-4-01 to 9-01.
Hull systems: Cargo capacity: 13,250 tons total, with 12,000 tons distillate fuel, 600 tons diesel oil, 400 tons jet fuel, frozen and dry foods, spare parts, munitions, etc. Have four replenishment-at-sea stations, one elevator abaft the navigation bridge, and two 11-ton cranes on the afterdeck. Daily fresh-water distillation capacity is 80 tons. Can carry 28 officers, 264 enlisted, and 42 passengers. Can be used to carry military vehicles and troops for commando purposes. Carry four LCVPs.
Combat systems: Twin 76.2-mm gunmount, formerly carried at the extreme bow, was removed in both in 1983; locally controlled, it was of little use and had several times been washed overboard. Two single 40-mm AA have been removed from AOR 509. Were fitted to receive SQS-505 sonars, with the transducers in the bow bulb, but they were never installed.

SERVICE CRAFT

Note: Most service craft are operated by the Canadian Forces Auxiliary Vessels (CFAV) organization, which is headed by the Queen's Harbor Master, a naval officer, at the bases at Esquimalt and Halifax; nearly all personnel are civilian employees. CFAV is also responsible for providing pilots and for pollution control.

♦ 22 miscellaneous barges [YC]

Based at Esquimalt: YC 50, YC 53, YC 54, YC 404, YC 406, YC 408, YC 414, YC 416, YC 418
Based at Halifax: YC 415, YC 417, YC 419, YC 451, YC 453, YC 455, YC 457, YC 459, YC 461, YC 467, YC 494, YC 600, YC 601

Remarks: YC 50–54 are steel-hulled open lighters; the other Esquimalt units are wooden-hulled open lighters, with YC 418 used for storage. YC 415 is the flag-officer landing stage at Halifax; YC 417–461 and YC 467 are landing stages; YC 600 and 601 are cargo barges; YC 463 is described as a "spacer barge"; and YC 494 is operated for the Defence Research Establishment, Atlantic (DREA), in support of the *Quest* (AGOR 172).

♦ 2 floating cranes [YD]

YD 250 YD 253

Floating crane YD 250 at Esquimalt Canadian Forces, 1996

Remarks: YD 250 based at Esquimalt, YD 253 at Halifax. Crews of 5 each. Non-self-propelled; no other data available.

Disposal note: Ammunition lighters [YE] YE 216 and YE 217 were stricken during 5-01.

♦ 2 small deperming barges [YDGN]

YDG 2 YDG 3

Remarks: YDG 2 based at Halifax, YDG 3 at Esquimalt. Are also used as fuel barges and have messing facilities for 35 personnel each.

♦ 4 small diving tenders [YDT]
Bldr: Celtic SY, . . . (In serv. 1997)

D: 22 tons (fl) **S:** 36 kts **Dim:** 11.90 × 3.80 × 0.70
Electronics: Radar: 1 . . . nav.
M: 2 Caterpillar 3126 TA diesels; 2 WMC 357 waterjets; 740 bhp
Range: 600/29 **Crew:** 3 + up to 14 divers

Remarks: Aluminum construction, based two on each coast. Have blunt, planing bows. Bollard pull of 2.9 tons for towing service.

♦ 2 Gemini-class personnel launches [YFL] (In serv. 15-11-85)

YAG 650 Gemini YAG 651 Pegasus

Gemini (YAG 650) and Pegasus (YAG 651) Pradignac & Léo, 1991

D: . . . tons **S:** . . . kts **Dim:** 17.00 × 4.20 × 1.14
Remarks: Based at Halifax.

♦ 2 YAG-12-class personnel launches [YFL]
Bldr: Charlottetown SY, P.E.I. (In serv. . . .)

YFB 316 YFB 318

Personnel launch YFB 318 Hartmut Ehlers, 5-99

SERVICE CRAFT *(continued)*

D: 80.9 tons (85 fl) **S:** 9.5 kts (sust.) **Dim:** 22.86 × 5.08 × 1.73
Electronics: Radar: 1 Furuno . . . nav.
M: 2 Cummins . . . diesels; 2 props; 264 bhp **Range:** 420/9.5 **Crew:** 4 tot.

Remarks: Known locally as the "Blue Boats" for their hull color. Both based at Esquimalt. Are nearing the ends of their useful lives and may be replaced by contract craft. Sisters YAG 312, 315, 319, and 320 are employed as training craft at Esquimalt.

♦ 5 YFU 121–class Sea Trucks [YFL]

YFU 121 Sea Truck 1 — YFU 123 Sea Truck 3 — YFU 125
YFU 122 Sea Truck 2 — YFU 124

Remarks: Aluminum-construction, beachable landing craft with an enclosed pilothouse at the stern. YFU 121–123 are used to transport pilots, other personnel, and equipment at Esquimalt; the other two are based at Halifax. About 10 m overall.

♦ 5 target craft [YGTN]

YGT 8 — YGT 12 — YGT 13 — YGT 14 — YGT 15

Remarks: Based at Esquimalt; non-self-propelled, yellow-painted punts about 5 m in length.

♦ 2 special liquids barges [YON]

YOM 252 — YOM 402

Remarks: Based at Esquimalt. YOM 252 is a sullage lighter and also has maintenance facilities to repair local smallcraft. YOM 402 is used for pollution collection, treatment, and storage.

♦ 4 Experimental and Test Range Support Vessels [YPT]
Bldr: West Coast Manly SY, Vancouver (L: 10-11-90)

TSRV 610 Sechelt — TSRV 612 Sooke
TSRV 611 Sikanni — TSRV 613 Stikine

Sooke (TSRV 612)—alongside *Nanaimo* (MCDV 702) — W. Michael Young, 3-01

D: 254.7 tons (290 fl) **S:** 12.5 kts **Dim:** 33.00 (30.25 pp) × 7.70 × 2.46
Electronics: Radar: 1 . . . nav.—Sonar: . . .
M: 2 Caterpillar 3412 diesels; 2 props; 1,342 bhp (1,080 sust.)
Range: 1,000/12 **Crew:** 4–6 tot.

Remarks: Ordered 9-88 and delivered between 6-90 and 8-91 to serve the Maritime Experimental and Test Range, Nanoose Bay, Vancouver, as torpedo retrievers, range safety craft, etc. TSRV 610 and 612 were converted to act as diving tenders in 11-97, supporting divers to 80 m. TSRV 610 now operates from Halifax, the others from Esquimalt.

♦ 3 YRG 60–class sludge removal barges [YRGN]

YRG 60 — YRG 61 — YRG 62

Remarks: YRG 61 is at Esquimalt, the others at Halifax. Equipped with the Wheeler System steam-cleaning method for cleaning fuel tanks and bilges; the tanks are then cleaned with detergents and vacuum-collected for storage in the craft's storage tanks. Each has a crew of six and can hold 50,000 gallons of recycled oil.

♦ 5 Glen-class large harbor tugs [YTB]
Bldrs: YTB 640, 641: Yarrow, Esquimalt; others: Georgetown SY, P.E.I.

	In serv.		In serv.
YTB 640 Glendyne	8-8-75	YTB 643 Glenbrook	16-12-76
YTB 641 Glendale	16-9-75	YTB 644 Glenside	20-5-77
YTB 642 Glenevis	9-8-76		

D: 255 tons (350 fl) **S:** 11.5 kts **Dim:** 28.2 × 8.5 × 3.8
Electronics: Radar: 1 Decca 127B nav.

Glenside (YTB 644) — H&L Van Ginderen, 5-93

M: 2 Ruston AP-3 diesels; 2 Voith-Schneider vertical cycloidal props; 1,750 bhp
Fuel: 54 tons **Crew:** see Remarks

Remarks: Carry civilian crew of 3 officers, 4 unlicensed in harbor service; 6 officers, 4 unlicensed on coastal service. Carry 20 tons fresh water and are equipped for fire fighting. Rated at 18.3 tons bollard pull ahead, 15 tons astern, and 12 tons sideways.

♦ 1 medium harbor tug [YTM]

YTM 555 Island Defender

Remarks: Based at Esquimalt; no data available.

♦ 5 new Ville-class harbor tugs [YTL]
Bldrs: YTL 590, 594: Vito Steel & Barge Co.; others: Georgetown SY, P.E.I. (In serv. 1974)

YTL 590 Lawrenceville — YTL 593 Merrickville
YTL 591 Parksville — YTL 594 Marysville
YTL 592 Listerville

Merrickville (YTL 593) — H&L Van Ginderen, 1-98

D: 70 tons (fl) **S:** 9.8 kts (8.5 cruise) **Dim:** 14.20 (13.60 pp) × 4.50 × 1.93
M: 1 Caterpillar (YTL 593: G.M.) diesel; 365 (YTL 593: 165) bhp **Crew:** 3 tot.

Remarks: YTL 590 and 591 are based at Esquimalt, the others at Halifax. Are locally known as the Pup class. Bollard pull is 5.9 tons.

♦ 2 48-ton fireboats [YTR]
Bldr: . . . SY, North Vancouver, B.C. (In serv. 1992–93)

YFB 556 Fire Tug 1 — YFB 557 Fire Tug 2

Remarks: Three sisters were built for other government agencies.

♦ 2 130-ton fireboats [YTR]
Bldr: Vancouver SY, B.C. (In serv. 1978)

YTR 561 Firebird — YTR 562 Firebrand

Firebird (YTR 561)—black hull, red superstructure — Chris Cavas, 9-90

SERVICE CRAFT *(continued)*

D: 48 tons light (100 fl) **S:** 7.5 kts **Dim:** 23.20 × 6.25 × . . .
M: 1 Vivian diesel; Voith-Schneider vertical cycloidal prop; 240 bhp
Crew: 8 licensed officers, 4 unlicensed

Remarks: Based at Halifax and Esquimalt, respectively. Have two 5,700-liter/min, 250-p.s.i. firepumps and three water monitors and carry fire-suppressant foam.

♦ **1 sailing ketch for cadet training [YTS]**
Bldr: George Lawley, Neponset, Mass. (In serv. 1921)

QW 3 Oriole (ex-*Oriole IV*)

Oriole (QW 3) Canadian Forces, 2000

D: 78.2 tons (92 fl) **S:** 14 kts (sail; 8 under power)
Dim: 31.09 (27.58 hull) × 5.69 × 3.04
Electronics: Radar: 1 Furuno . . . nav.
M: 1 G.M. Detroit Diesel 6V71 diesel; 1 prop; 230 hp—1,300 m^2 max. sail area
Endurance: 60 days **Crew:** 1 officer, 5 enlisted, 18 trainees

Remarks: Built for George H. Gooderham of Toronto and acquired in 1949 by the Navy League of Canada. Transferred to navy in 1952. Is Canada's smallest and oldest commissioned ship. Based at Esquimalt and used to train students from the Naval Officers' Training Center and the Canadian Forces Fleet School. Has marconi rig, no power winches. Working sails total 570 m^2, plus a 650-m^2 spinnaker. The mainmast is 31.7 m high. Navigation equipment includes Raystar 920 GPS receiver with Gimbel transponder, Loran-C receiver, and Weatherfax receiver. Sailed with crew of 22 on 13-10-97 on a 17,000-n.m. voyage to Australia, New Zealand, and other South Pacific ports, returning 13-5-98.

Note: Also in use for sail training are the 11.13-m Class CS 36S GRP sloops *Tuna,* at the Fleet Training School, Halifax, and *Goldcrest,* at Esquimalt, both bought 5-85.

♦ **5 YAG 312–class training launches [YXT]**
Bldr: Charlottetown SY, P.E.I. (In serv. . . .)

YAG 312 YAG 314 YAG 315 YAG 319 YAG 320

D: 80.9 tons (85 fl) **S:** 9.5 kts (sust.) **Dim:** 22.86 × 5.08 × 1.73
Electronics: Radar: 1 Furuno . . . nav.
M: 2 Cummins . . . diesels; 2 props; 264 bhp **Range:** 427/9.5 **Crew:** 4 tot.

Remarks: Employed as training craft at Esquimalt. Sisters YFB 316 and 318 are used as personnel launches at Esquimalt. Similar in appearance to the *Nicholson* (PB 196) but have less-powerful propulsion plants.

♦ **1 ex-Mounted Police 70-foot Detachment-class patrol boat [YXT]** Bldr: Charlottetown SY, P.E.I. (In serv. 1968)

PB 196 Nicholson

D: 85 tons (fl) **S:** 16 kts **Dim:** 22.86 × 5.08 × 1.73
Electronics: Radar: 1 Sperry Mk 74 nav.
M: 2 Cummins VT-12 diesels; 2 props; 1,400 bhp
Range: 900/13 **Crew:** 18 tot.

Remarks: Sister *Standoff* (PB 199) was stricken in 1996. Used as a training craft by the naval reserve.

♦ **6 Ville-class former tugs [YXT]**
Bldr: Russel Bros., Owen Sound, Ont.

	In serv.
YTL 578 Cavalier (ex-*Listerville*)	12-10-44
YTL 582 Burrard (ex-*Lawrenceville*)	8-1-44
YTL 586 Queensville	5-12-44
YTL 587 Plainsville	23-11-44
YTL 588 Youville	5-12-44
YTL 589 Loganville	13-12-44

D: 25 tons **S:** 10 kts **Dim:** 12.0 × 3.15 × 1.35
M: 1 Cummins diesel; 150 bhp

Remarks: Used as training craft by the naval reserve. Sister *Beamsville* (YTL 583) was stricken in 1992.

COAST GUARD

Note: The resources of the Department of Fisheries and Oceans and the Canadian Coast Guard were combined into one agency under the Ministry of Fisheries and Oceans on 1-4-95. Ships, craft, and aircraft were gradually repainted in coast guard colors, with red hull (with white diagonal stripe), white superstructure, and funnel with red maple leaf. Other than small arms, the ships are not armed, but those assigned to patrol duties assist the Royal Canadian Mounted Police in drug interdiction and other police functions when needed.

Personnel (12-00): 713 Ships' Officers, 1,070 Ships' Crew. The Canadian Coast Guard Auxiliary has some 5,000 volunteer members and 1,600 privately owned craft.

Organization: Headquarters at Ottawa. Field offices for operating regions at Vancouver, B.C. (Pacific Region); Winnipeg, Man. (Central and Arctic Region); Québec City, Que. (Laurentian Region); Dartmouth, N.S. (Maritimes Region); and St. John's, Nfld. (Newfoundland Region).

Aviation: The Canadian Coast Guard operates 1 DeHavilland Dash-8 and 1 DeHavilland DHC-6 twin-engine fixed-wing transports and 28 helicopters (1 Sikorsky S-61N, 4 CH-146 Griffon/Bell 212, 4 Bell 206L and 2 Bell 206L-1 LongRanger, and 16 MBB BO-105CBS).

Note: Ships and craft are listed below in the order of the categories now assigned by the Canadian Coast Guard. Standard ship-type designations are given in brackets for each class. Ships and craft listed in the previous edition that are not listed here have been either retired or transferred to other Canadian Government agencies. Those seeking more information about the ships and craft, including plans and additional photography, should consult the excellent Canadian Coast Guard website at <www.ccg.gcc.gc.ca>.

OFFSHORE MULTI-TASK PATROL VESSELS [WPS]

♦ **1 Sir Wilfred Grenfell class [WPS]**
Bldr: Marystown SY, Marystown, Nfld.

	Region	In serv.
Sir Wilfred Grenfell	Newfoundland	1987

Sir Wilfred Grenfell Canadian Coast Guard

D: 3,753 tons (fl) **S:** 16 kts **Dim:** 68.48 (59.59 pp) × 15.30 × 5.42
Electronics:
Radar: 1 Decca Bridgemaster II C252 (X-band) nav.; 1 Decca Bridgemaster II C253 (S-band) nav.
M: 2 Deutz 268-2SBV16M and 2 Deutz SBV9M diesels, geared drive; 2 CP props; 12,864 bhp—bow- and stern-thrusters
Electric: 3,120 kw tot. (2 × 1,120-kw shaft generators; 2 × 440-kw, G.M. 12V-92T diesels driving
Range: 11,000/11.5 **Fuel:** 879 m^3 **Endurance:** 35 days
Crew: 9 officers, 11 non-officers

Remarks: 2,404 grt/1,265 dwt. Converted firefighting and anchor-handling tug/supply ship. Ice-strengthened hull. Based at St. John's, Nfld.
Hull systems: Has six fire monitors, two Hurricane 740 fast rescue RIBs, one Zodiac RIB, and a lifeboat. Is equipped with a 70-ton electrohydraulic crane, two 2.6-ton cranes, and two 12-ton winches. Navigational equipment includes Trimble Navtrac and Northstar GPS sets, Taiyo TD-C338-HS MFD/F, OAR 320E VHFD/F, and Elac LAZ-72 echo sounder.

♦ **1 Leonard J. Cowley class [WPS]**
Bldr: West Coast Manly SY, Vancouver

	Region	Laid down	L	In serv.
Leonard J. Cowley	Newfoundland	15-1-84	24-10-84	6-85

D: 1,470 tons light (2,080 fl) **S:** 15 kts
Dim: 72.01 (61.45 pp) × 14.20 × 4.51 (4.90 max.)
Electronics: Radar: 2 Sperry 3400 (S- and X-band) nav.
M: 2 Nohab Polar F312A diesels; 1 Kort-nozzle CP prop; 4,242 bhp—bow-thruster
Electric: 1,350 kw tot. (3 × 450-kw diesel sets)

OFFSHORE MULTI-TASK PATROL VESSELS [WPS] *(continued)*

Leonard J. Cowley Thomas E. W. Goyne, 11-96

Range: 12,000/12 **Fuel:** 400 m^3 **Endurance:** 28 days
Crew: 7 officers, 12 non-officers

Remarks: 2,243 grt/592 dwt. Ordered 8-11-83. Built for Pacific Region but now operates from St. John's, Nfld. Variants of this design are in Irish Navy and Mauritius Coast Guard service. Two single 12.7-mm mg can be mounted.
Hull systems: Has a helicopter deck and telescoping hangar. Both radars have CAS II ARPA capability and are linked to a Sperry/TRAC IVB Qubit integrated navigational computer/recorder. Carries two Zodiac RIBs and two workboats. Navigational equipment includes Trimble Navtrac XL and Northstar GPS, Taiyo TD-C338-HS MFD/F, Taiyo TD-L1620 HFD/F, and Elac LAZ-2300 and LAZ-72 echo sounders.

♦ 2 Cape Roger class [WPS]

	Region	Bldr	In serv.
Cape Roger	Newfoundland	Ferguson, Pictou, N.S.	8-77
Cygnus	Maritimes	Marystown SY, Nfld.	5-82

Cape Roger—in former gray paint scheme Susan Lindberg, 7-92

D: 1,461 tons (fl) **S:** 17 kts **Dim:** 62.50 (57.00 pp) × 12.22 × 5.30
Electronics:
Radar: *Cape Roger:* 1 Decca Bridgemaster II C252/6 (X-band) nav.; 1 Sperry Rascar 3400M (S-band) nav.—*Cygnus:* 1 Decca BT502 (X-band) nav.; 1 Decca Bridgemaster II (X-band) nav.; 1 Decca 2690 ARPA (S-band) nav.
M: 2 Wärtsilä-Nohab Polar F30.12V diesels; 2 CP props; 4,410 bhp—bow-thruster
Electric: 575 kw (2 × 250 kw, 1 × 75 kw)
Range: *Cape Roger:* 10,000/12—*Cygnus:* 10,800/13
Fuel: *Cape Roger:* 200 m^3—*Cygnus:* 401 m^3
Endurance: *Cape Roger:* 31 days—*Cygnus:* 21 days
Crew: 7 officers, 12 (*Cygnus:* 10) non-officers

Remarks: *Cape Roger:* 1,255 grt; *Cygnus:* 1,210 grt/1,442 dwt. Have two complete crews who alternate on 14-day patrols. Can be equipped with two 12.7-mm mg. *Cape Roger* (refitted in 1996) is based at St. John's, Nfld., *Cygnus* at Dartmouth, N.S.
Hull systems: *Cape Roger* has a telescoping helicopter hangar; both have 132-m^2 helicopter flight decks. Both completed refits in 1997 and are to serve for another 20 or more years. *Cape Roger* carries two Zodiac RIBs and two workboats, while *Cygnus* has one Hurricane RIB, one Avon Searider RIB, and one workboat. Navigational equipment on *Cape Roger* includes Trimble GPS, Furuno FD-177 MFD/F, Taiyo TD-1620 HFD/F, and JMC F-830 and JMC V-122 echo sounders; *Cygnus* has Northstar 8000 GPS, Taiyo TD L1620 VHFD/F, and Elac-Honeywell 1200, LAZ-5000, LAZ-51, and LAZ-72 echo sounders.

INTERMEDIATE MULTI-TASK (PATROL) CUTTERS [WPC/WPS]

♦ 1 Arrow Post class [WPC]
Bldr: Hike Metal Products, Wheatley, Ont.

	Region	In serv.
Arrow Post	Pacific	1994

D: approx. 300 tons **S:** 12 kts **Dim:** 28.97 × 8.80 × 3.35
Electronics:
Radar: 1 Raytheon Rasterscan R81-6 (X-band) nav.; 1 Raytheon Rasterscan R82-9 (X-band) nav.
M: 1 Caterpillar 12-cyl. 3512 TA diesel; 1 CP prop: 1,280 bhp—bow-thruster
Electric: 184 kw tot. (3 × 92-kw diesel sets)

Arrow Post Hike Metal Products, 199

Range: 2,800/11 **Fuel:** 52.6 m^3 **Endurance:** 28 days
Crew: 3 officers, 3 non-officers

Remarks: 228 grt. Based at Prince Rupert, B.C.
Hull systems: Carries two 4-m Zodiac RIBs. Navigation equipment include Northstar 941X and Taystar 9206 GPS, Raytheon 789 Loran, Taiyo TD-L1530 MFD/F JMC DF-550 VHFD/F, Wesmar SS265 side-scan sonar, and JRC JFF-10 and MV-10 echo sounders.

♦ 2 Gordon Reid class [WPS]
Bldr: Versatile Pacific SY, Vancouver

	Region	In serv.
Gordon Reid	Pacific	7-91
John Jacobson	Pacific	7-91

Gordon Reid Canadian Coast Guar

D: approx. 1,100 tons (fl) **S:** 17 kts **Dim:** 49.95 (46.00 wl) × 11.00 × 4.00
Electronics: Radar: 2 Decca Bridgemaster (X-band) nav.
M: 4 Deutz-MWM SBV-6M-628 diesels; 2 CP props; 4,800 bhp—bow-thruster
Electric: 830 kw tot. (3 × 250-kw, Mitsubishi 56B-PTR diesels driving; 1 × 80-kw emergency, Mitsubishi 6D144T diesel driving
Range: 2,500/12 **Fuel:** 148.2 m^3 **Endurance:** 28 days
Crew: 6 officers, 8 non-officers (24 tot. accomm.)

Remarks: 879.61 grt. Formerly listed as Type 500 Intermediate Search-and-Rescu Cutters. They are based at Victoria, B.C.
Hull systems: Have two 650-ton/hr-capacity fire and salvage pumps and roll stabilization tanks. A 7-m, 50-kt Hurricane 733 RIB rescue craft is launched from a stern ramp, and a Zodiac Mk III RIB and Dunlop inflatable boats are also carried Navigational equipment includes CSI MBX-1 GPS, Simrad-Taiyo C338HS MFD/F OAR 320E VHFD/F, and Datarmarine 3000 echo sounder.

♦ 1 Louisbourg class [WPC]
Bldr: Breton Industrial & Machinery, Port Hawkesbury, N.S.

	Region	In serv.
Louisbourg	Laurentian	1977

D: approx. 370 tons (fl) **S:** 13.5 kts **Dim:** 37.80 × 8.20 × 2.60
Electronics: Radar: 2 Decca Bridgemaster 180 (X-band) nav.
M: 2 Caterpillar 16-cyl. diesels; 2 props; 2,400 bhp
Electric: 280 kw tot. (2 × 140-kw diesel-driven sets)
Range: 3,840/10 **Fuel:** 56 m^3 **Endurance:** 16 days
Crew: 4 officers, 4 non-officers

Remarks: 295 grt. Based at Gaspé, Que.
Hull systems: Carries one 6.4-m Zodiac 640 Mk 2 rescue RIB, launched and recovered from a stern ramp. Navigational equipment includes Trimble NT 200D an

INTERMEDIATE MULTI-TASK (PATROL) CUTTERS [WPC/WPS] *(continued)*

Furuno 500 GPS, Tiayo 70-L1550 VHFD/F, and one Elac LAZ-12 and two Raytheon V860 echo sounders.

♦ 1 Tanu class [WPS]
Bldr: Yarrow Ltd., Esquimalt, B.C.

	Region	In serv.
TANU	Pacific	7-9-68

Tanu—in former gray paint scheme H&L Van Ginderen, 11-94

D: 880 tons (925 fl) **S:** 13.5 kts **Dim:** 54.69 (50.17 pp) × 9.96 × 4.75
Electronics:
Radar: 1 Raytheon M34 ARPA (X-band) nav.; 1 JRC JMA825-9 (S-band) nav.
Sonar: Wesmar HD600E fish-finding (60 kHz); JRC-JFF-11 echo sounder; Furuno FCV-1000 echo sounder
M: 2 Fairbanks-Morse 38D8⅛-8 diesels; 1 CP prop; 2,624 bhp—125-shp Pleuger active-rudder stern-thruster
Electric: 500 kw tot. (3 × 150-kw, 1 × 50-kw diesel sets)
Range: 5,000/11 **Fuel:** 236 m^3 **Endurance:** 22 days
Crew: 6 officers, 10 non-officers

Remarks: 753.7 grt. Refitted and modernized during 1987 at Allied Shipyard, North Vancouver, B.C. Can mount two 12.7-mm mg. Based at Patricia Bay, B.C.
Hull systems: Aluminum superstructure. Navigation equipment includes Sperry Mk 37 gyro and SRP-690 autopilot, Raystar 920 and Northstar 941X GPS sets, JRC-JNA 761 Loran-C receiver, Taiyo TD-C338HS MFD/F, and Taiyo TD-11520 VHFD/F. Has VHF and HF communications but no SATCOM. Hurricane 530 and 440 RIBs are carried, tended by a 2.2-ton crane.

♦ 1 E. P. le Québecois class [WPC]
Bldr: Les Chantier Maritime, Paspebiac, Que.

	Region	In serv.
E. P. LE QUÉBECOIS	Laurentian	1968

D: approx. 300 tons (fl) **S:** 11 kts **Dim:** 28.30 × 7.10 × 3.10
Electronics: Radar: 2 Furuno FR-2110 (X-band) nav.
M: 1 Caterpillar 3509-DITA diesel; 1 CP prop; 510 bhp—bow-thruster
Electric: 205 kw tot. (2 × 75-kw, 1 × 55-kw emergency sets)
Range: 2,800/10 **Fuel:** 35.6 m^3 **Endurance:** 9.5 days
Crew: 4 officers, 4 non-officers

Remarks: 186.38 grt. Refitted 1994. Based at Sept Îles, Que.
Hull systems: Carries one 7-m Hurricane RIB, launched and recovered via a stern ramp. Navigational equipment includes Northstar 941X GPS, Furuno LC-90 Loran, Taiyo VHFD/F, and Furuno FCV-582 echo sounder.

SMALL MULTI-TASK ICE-STRENGTHENED CUTTERS [WPC]

♦ 2 Harp class [WPC]
Bldr: Georgetown SY, Georgetown, P.E.I.

	Region	Laid down	L	In serv.
HARP	Newfoundland	15-12-85	20-9-86	12-12-86
HOOD	Newfoundland	15-12-85	5-11-86	12-12-86

D: 225 tons (fl) **S:** 11 kts **Dim:** 24.5 (21.50 pp) × 7.60 × 2.50
Electronics: Radar: 2 Decca Bridgemaster II C181/4 (X- and S-band) nav.
M: 2 Caterpillar 3408-BDITA diesels; 2 CP, Kort-nozzle props; 750 bhp
Electric: 80 kw (2 × 40-kw sets, Perkins 635A diesels driving)
Range: 500/9.5 **Fuel:** 34.6 m^3 **Crew:** 2 officers, 5 non-officers

Remarks: 179.2 grt. Ordered 26-4-85. Steel rescue ships to operate up to 100 n.m. from land. Have towing, firefighting, and medical evacuation capabilities. *Harp* is based at St. Anthony, Nfld., *Hood* at Twillingate, Nfld.
Hull systems: The hulls are reinforced to operate in light ice. Carry a Zodiac rescue RIB. Navigational equipment includes Magnavox MS-200 and Trimble NT-200D GPS, Furuno LC-90 Loran, Furuno FD-177 MFD/F, OAR 320E VHFD/F, and Elac LAZ-50 echo sounder.

Harp Canadian Coast Guard, 1988

SMALL MULTI-TASK CUTTERS [WPB/WPC]

♦ 3 Lewis Reef class [WPB]
Bldrs: *Lewis Reef:* Rivtow Straits, Ltd., Vancouver; others: Canoe Cove Mfr., Ltd., Sidney, B.C. (In serv. 1988–90)

ESTEVAN REEF LEWIS REEF ROBSON REEF

Lewis Reef—in former gray paint scheme

D: . . . tons **S:** 11.0–11.5 kts **Dim:** 17.50 × 5.20 × 2.40
Electronics: Radar: 1 Furuno FR-1510 nav.
M: 1 Deutz BA6M816 diesel; 1 CP prop; 444 bhp **Electric:** 25 kw tot.
Range: 1,100/10 **Fuel:** 5.3 m^3 **Endurance:** 5 days
Crew: 2 officers, 1 non-officer

Remarks: 52 grt. Based at Patricia Bay, B.C.; Prince Rupert, B.C.; and Sidney, B.C., respectively. Navigational equipment includes Northstar 941 GPS, Simrad-Taiyo L1520 MFD/F, and Furuno RU-1000 echo sounder. Carry a Zodiac RIB.

♦ 1 Cumella class [WPC]
Bldr: A. F. Theriault & Son, Ltd., Meteghan River, N.S. (In serv. 1983)

CUMELLA

D: approx. 110 tons (fl) **S:** 15 kts **Dim:** 23.20 × 4.80 × 2.00
Electronics: Radar: 1 Furuno FR-8050D nav.; 1 Furuno FR-8100D nav.
M: 2 G.M. Detroit Diesel V-6 diesels; 2 props; 1,680 bhp **Electric:** 10 kw tot.
Range: 600/12 **Fuel:** 7.3 m^3 **Crew:** 2 officers, 2 non-officers

Remarks: 79.95 grt. Assigned to Maritimes Region and based at Grand Manaan, N.B. Carries a Hurricane rescue RIB. Navigational equipment includes Northstar 941X GPS, Simrad-Taiyo TD-L1620 VHFD/F, and Elac LAZ-2120 echo sounder.

♦ 4 Point Henry class [WPB]
Bldr: Breton Industry & Machinery, Point Hawkesbury, N.S.

	Region	In serv.		Region	In serv.
POINT HENRY	Pacific	1980	POINT RACE	Pacific	4-82
ÎLE ROUGE	Laurentian	1980	CAPE HURD	Central & Arctic	4-82

D: 77 tons light (97 fl) **S:** 21–24 kts **Dim:** 21.30 × 5.50 × 1.70
Electronics: Radar: 2 . . . nav.
M: 2 MTU 8V396 TC82 (*Point Henry:* Caterpillar 3412) diesels; 2 props; 1,740 (*Point Henry:* 2,146) bhp
Range: 500/18; 1,400/16 **Fuel:** 7 tons **Crew:** 2 officers, 3 non-officers

SMALL MULTI-TASK CUTTERS [WPB/WPC] *(continued)*

Point Henry H&L Van Ginderen, 7-94

Remarks: 56.7 grt. Formerly typed as Small Search-and-Rescue Cutters (Type 400). *Point Henry* is based at Prince Rupert, B.C., *Île Rouge* at Tadoussas, Que., *Point Race* at Campbell River, B.C., and *Cape Hurd* at Goodrich, Ont. Aluminum alloy construction. Radar installations vary.

♦ 5 Sooke Post class [WPB]

Bldr: Philbrooks Shipyard, Ltd., Sidney, B.C.

	In serv.		In serv.
Sooke Post	1973	Chilcoe Post	1975
Kitimat II	1974	Comox Post	1975
Atlin Post	1975		

D: approx. 70 tons (fl) **S:** 15 kts **Dim:** 19.80 × 5.20 × 1.50
Electronics: Radar: 1 Furuno FP-150D nav.; 1 Furuno FR-1011 nav.
M: 2 G.M. Detroit Diesel V-12 diesels; 2 props; 1,100 bhp
Electric: 30 kw tot. (2 × 15-kw sets) **Range:** 400/12 **Fuel:** 5.4 m^3
Endurance: 10 days **Crew:** 3 officers, 1 non-officer

Remarks: 57 grt. All five are assigned to the Pacific Region, with *Sooke Post* and *Chilcoe Post* based at Port Hardy, B.C.; *Atlin Post* at Patricia Bay, B.C.; *Comox Post* at Tahsis, B.C.; and *Kitimat II* at Prince Rupert, B.C. Carry a 4.4-m Hurricane RIB.

♦ 1 Advent class [WPC]

Bldr: Alloy Manufacturing, Ltd., Lachine, Que. (In serv. 1972)

Advent

D: approx. 105 tons (fl) **S:** 16 kts **Dim:** 23.50 × 5.60 × 1.60
Electronics: Radar: 1 Sitex T-100 nav.; 1 Decca Bridgemaster C180/4 nav.
M: 2 G.M. Detroit Diesel 12V71 TI diesels; 2 props; 1,020 bhp
Electric: 60 kw tot. **Range:** 640/16 **Endurance:** 2 days
Crew: 2 officers, 2 non-officers

Remarks: 72 grt. Oilfield crewboat design. Assigned to Central and Arctic Region and based at Cobourg, Ont. Carries a Zodiac Mk 3 RIB and is equipped with an 8-m^2 hydrology laboratory. Navigational equipment includes an OAR 320E VHFD/F and Raytheon DC-2002 echo sounder.

INSHORE MULTI-TASK PATROL VESSELS [WPB]

♦ 10 miscellaneous inshore patrol launches [WPB]

	In serv.	GRT	Based
6C-4828	1986	18	Neguac, N.B.
A. H. Chevarie	1978	10.8	Summerside, P.E.I.
Aquariel	1985	31	Havre Boucher, N.S.
Arcadie	1990	18.3	Caraquet, N.B.
Howe Point	1989	11	Souris, P.E.I.
North Bar	1985	31	Sydney, N.S.
Otter Bay	1992	21.3	Victoria, B.C.
Tucho Mariner	1991	34.7	Hay River, N.W.T.
Tuebor	1985	34.7	St. John, N.B.
Vigilance	1989	28.3	Digby, N.S.
W. Ferguson	1990	18	Val Comeau, N.B.

Remarks: All are assigned to the Maritimes Region, except *Otter Bay* to the Pacific Region and *Tucho Mariner* to the Central and Arctic. Most are of modified lobster boat design, with a generally similar appearance. Overall lengths run from 12.8 m to 14.6 m, with the *Tucho Mariner* being the longest. They are used for general transportation and local patrol and rescue duties. All are powered by a single Caterpillar 3116 (275 bhp) or 3208 (340 bhp) diesel, and speeds range between 10 and 12.5 kts, except *A. H. Chevarie* at 20 kts. One or two small navigational radars are fitted, and the crews are generally one officer and two non-officers.

HEAVY GULF ICEBREAKERS [WAGB]

♦ 1 former commercial icebreaking tug/supply ship [WAGB]

Bldr: Burrard Yarrows Corp., Vancouver Div., North Vancouver, B.C. (In serv. 1983)

	Region	L	In serv.
Terry Fox	Maritimes	1982	1983

D: approx. 7,100 tons (fl) **S:** 16 kts
Dim: 88.02 (75.39 pp) × 17.94 (17.51 wl) × 8.30
Electronics:
Radar: 1 Decca ARPA (X-band); 1 Decca Bridgemaster Conrad nav; 1 Furuno FCR-1411 Mk 2 nav.
M: 4 Stork Werkspoor 8TM410 diesels; 2 CP props; 23,202 bhp—stern CP propeller thruster and bow jet-thruster
Electric: 3,500 kw tot. (2 × 1,000-kw shaft generators, 2 × 750-kw Caterpillar V-12 diesel-driven sets)
Range: 19,200/15 **Fuel:** 1,919 m^3 **Endurance:** 58 days
Crew: 10 officers, 14 non-officers

Remarks: 4,234-grt/2,113-dwt combination Arctic oilfield tug/supply and anchor-handling vessel with icebreaking hull, firefighting capability, and deck cargo capacity. Had been on charter since 8-91 from Gulf Canada Resources, Vancouver; was purchased 1-11-93 and formally commissioned 1-6-94. Named for a gallant Canadian athlete and cancer victim. Formerly classified as Type 1300. Based at Dartmouth, N.S.
Hull systems: Has a 231-m^2 helicopter deck and a 40-ton crane. The towing winch produces 220 tons bollard pull. Navigation equipment includes Magnavox MX-200 and Trimble Navtrac GPS, JMC 22215 MFD/F, Simrad-Taiyo VHFD/F, and 2 Elac LAZ-72 echo sounders. Carries two Zodiac RIBs and an aluminum workboat.

♦ 1 Louis S. St. Laurent class [WAGB]

Bldr: Canadian Vickers, Montreal

	Region	L	In serv.
Louis S. St. Laurent	Maritimes	3-6-66	8-69

Louis S. St. Laurent H&L Van Ginderen, 9-99

D: 13,800 tons (fl) **S:** 20 kts **Dim:** 119.63 × 24.46 × 9.91
Electronics:
Radar: 2 Sperry Rascar (X- and S-band); 1 Decca Bridgemaster (X-band)
M: 5 Krupp MaK 16M453C diesels (8,000 bhp each), 3 2,400-kw generator sets, 3 G.E. electric motors; 3 props; 27,000 shp
Electric: . . . kw (main generators + 2 Krupp MaK 6M282 diesel sets, 1,100 kw each)
Range: 23,000/16 **Fuel:** 4,800 m^3 **Endurance:** 205 days
Crew: 13 officers, 33 non-officers

Remarks: 11,441 grt. Had serious fires in 3-82 and on 30-12-85. During 1987 to 9-92 modernization, had new bow installed, original geared turbine steam plant with four Babcock & Wilcox boilers replaced, a Wärtsilä bubbler underhull deicing system added, and the original hangar below the flight deck replaced by telescoping hangar on deck. Based at Dartmouth, N.S.
Hull systems: Has Flume passive stabilization tanks, a 25-ton-capacity pedestal crane and two 5-ton cranes, and accommodations for 216 persons total. Carries an LCM-type landing craft. Scientific laboratories include three 45-m^2 wet labs, five 25-m^2 utility labs, and one 4-m^2 photo lab. Navigational equipment includes Magnavox MX-200 GPS, Taiyo 121 ATS MFD/F, OAR 320E VHFD/F, and LAZ-72 echo sounder.

MEDIUM GULF/RIVER ICEBREAKERS [WAGB]

♦ 1 Improved Radisson class [WAGB]

Bldr: Versatile Pacific, North Vancouver, B.C.

	Region	Laid down	L	In serv.
Henry Larsen	Newfoundland	15-8-85	3-1-87	1-7-88

Henry Larsen H&L Van Ginderen, 1992

D: 5,798 tons light, 6,172 tons normal (6,600 Great Lakes load, 8,290 fl)
S: 16.5 kts (13.5 cruise) **Dim:** 100.03 (87.95 pp) × 19.82 × 7.24

MEDIUM GULF/RIVER ICEBREAKERS [WAGB] *(continued)*

Electronics:
Radar: 2 Decca Bridgemaster II (X- and S-band); 1 Decca Bridgemaster Conrad (aft)
M: 3 Wärtsilä Vasa 16V32 diesels (8,160 bhp each), 3 G.E. 5,000-kw generators, 2 electric motors; 2 props; 16,328 shp
Electric: 2,078 kw tot. (1 × 924-kw Wärtsilä 6L22, 1 × 804-kw Caterpillar 3512, and 1 × 350-kw Caterpillar 3508 diesel-driven sets)
Fuel: 1,900 tons + 20 tons for helicopter **Range:** 15,000/13.5
Crew: 11 officers, 20 non-officers

Remarks: 6,166 grt/2,478 dwt (1,860 dwt Great Lakes, 2,490 dwt Arctic). Ordered 25-5-84. Design based on *Pierre Radisson* class, but with improved bow form. Based at Dartmouth, N.S. Refitted 1998 to 3-99 by St. John's Dry Dock.
Hull systems: Has Wärtsilä bubbler underwater deicing system, with two 600-kw generators associated. Has a 100-ton cargo hold, 20 tons of refrigerated cargo stowage, and an 8.5-ton crane. A 34-m^2 "special chart room" is fitted. Navigational equipment includes Magnavox MX 200 and Trimble Navtrac GPS, Sperry ADG autopilot, Taiyo 8121 ATS MFD/F, OAR 320E VHFD/F, an LAZ-72 (30-Hz) echo sounder, and a 50-Hz LAZ echo sounder.

♦ 2 Pierre Radisson class [WAGB]
Bldrs: *Pierre Radisson:* Burrard DD Co., Ltd., Vancouver; *Des Groseilliers:* Port Weller DD Co., Ltd., Ont.

	Region	L	In serv.
Pierre Radisson	Laurentian	3-6-77	6-78
Des Groseilliers	Laurentian	20-2-82	7-8-82

Des Groseilliers H&L Van Ginderen, 1-96

D: 6,400 tons (7,721 fl) **S:** 16.2 kts **Dim:** 98.25 (88.04 pp) × 19.84 × 7.43
Electronics:
Radar: 1 Sperry 3400 Rascar (X-band); 1 Decca Bridgemaster Conrad
M: diesel-electric: 6 Bombardier-Alco 16V251F diesels (17,580 bhp total); 6 G.E.C. alternators (11,100 kw); 2 G.E.C. motors; 2 props; 13,600 shp
Electric: 2,250 kw (main generators + 3 × 250-kw diesel sets)
Range: 15,000/13.5 **Fuel:** 2,215 m^3 **Endurance:** 120 days
Crew: 12 officers, 26 non-officers

Remarks: *Radisson:* 5,910 grt/2,820 dwt, with 440 m^3 cargo capacity. *Des Groseilliers:* 5,910 grt. Used on the St. Lawrence River and Great Lakes in winter, in Arctic during summer. Both are based at Québec City, Que.
Disposals: *Sir John Franklin* was badly damaged 20-6-96 but later returned to service; she was stricken in 2000, however.
Hull systems: *Radisson* carries an Orpheus scientific minisub. Both have a 500-m^3 cargo hold, two 8-ton cranes, a 22.4-ton bollard-pull towing winch, and a telescoping hangar and flight deck for one Bell 212 helicopter. Have passive-tank stabilization. Navigational equipment includes Magnavox MX-200 GPS, Taiyo 7DV330 Mk 2 MFD/F, OAR 320E VHFD/F, and two LAZ-72 echo sounders.

LIGHT ICEBREAKER/MAJOR NAVAIDS TENDERS [WAGB]

♦ 6 Martha L. Black class [WAGB]

	Bldr	Laid down	L	In serv.
Martha L. Black	Versatile Pacific, Vancouver	3-84	6-9-85	3-4-86
George R. Pearkes	Versatile Pacific Victoria, B.C.	3-84	30-11-85	17-4-86
Ann Harvey	Halifax Ind., N.S.	1984	12-12-85	29-6-87
Sir William Alexander	Marine Industries, Tracy, Que.	24-2-86	23-10-86	13-2-87
Edward Cornwallis	Marine Industries, Tracy, Que.	5-7-84	22-2-86	14-8-86
Sir Wilfrid Laurier	Canadian SB, Collingwood, Ont.	14-5-85	6-12-85	15-11-86

D: typical: 3,287 tons light (4,861 fl) **S:** 16.5 kts
Dim: 83.01 (75.01 pp) × 16.26 × 5.75–6.20
Electronics:
Radar: 2 Decca Bridgemaster II (X- and S-band) nav.; 1 Decca Bridgemaster Conrad nav. (not in *Pearkes* or *Laurier*)
M: diesel-electric: 3 Bombardier-Alco 16V-251F diesels (2,991 bhp each), 3 Canadian G.E. generators (2,100 kw each), 2 Canadian G.E. motors; 2 props; 7,100 shp—bow-thruster
Electric: 600 kw tot. (1 × 500-kw Caterpillar 3508TA, 1 × 100-kw Caterpillar 3306T diesel sets + power from main generator sets)
Range: 6,500/11 **Fuel:** 783.7 m^3 **Endurance:** 120 days
Crew: 10 or 12 officers, 15–16 non-officers

George R. Pearkes H&L Van Ginderen, 4-94

Remarks: *Black:* 3,818 grt/1,688 dwt; *Pearkes:* 3,809 grt/1,689 dwt; *Harvey:* 3,853 grt/1,815 dwt; *Alexander:* 3,728 grt/1,660 dwt; *Cornwallis:* 3,728 grt/1,660 dwt; *Laurier:* 3,812 grt/1,647 dwt. Construction of the pair assigned to Marine Industries was delayed by a strike; both have lower superstructures and derricks on kingposts, while on the others the derricks are stepped on the bridge face. *Cornwallis* was equipped to serve as a hydrographic survey ship during a 1997–98 refit. Are assigned and based as follows:

	Region	Based
Martha L. Black	Laurentian	Québec City, Que.
George R. Pearkes	Laurentian	Québec City, Que.
Ann Harvey	Newfoundland	St. John's, Nfld.
Sir William Alexander	Maritimes	Dartmouth, N.S.
Edward Cornwallis	Maritimes	Dartmouth, N.S.
Sir Wilfrid Laurier	Pacific	Victoria, B.C.

Hull systems: Dimensional and displacement data above refer to *Martha L. Black;* the others vary slightly. Carry 17.3 m^3 fuel for their one Bell 212 helicopter. Cargo capacity is 400 tons in forward hold, 50 tons aft. Carry 670 tons water ballast. Navigational equipment includes Magnavox MX-200 and Trimble Navtrack GPS, Taiyo 121 ATS MFD/F, PAR 320E VHFD/F, and two LAZ-72 echo sounders. One Zodiac Hurricane and one Zodiac RH 1 RIBs are carried.

♦ 1 Griffon class [WAGB]
Bldr: Davie SB, Lauzon, Que.

	Region	In serv.
Griffon	Central & Arctic	12-70

Griffon H&L Van Ginderen, 7-98

D: 3,096 tons (fl) **S:** 13.0 kts **Dim:** 71.32 (65.23 pp) × 15.09 × 4.73
Electronics: Radar: 2 Decca Bridgemaster II (X- and S-band) nav.
M: 4 Fairbanks-Morse 38D8⅛-8 diesels (1,334 bhp each), 4 820-kw generators, 2 electric motors; 2 props; 4,000 shp
Electric: 826 kw tot. (3 × 212-kw Caterpillar D353TA; 1 × 190-kw Paxman diesel sets)
Range: 5,500/11 **Fuel:** 368 m^3 **Endurance:** 90 days
Crew: 9 officers, 16 non-officers

Remarks: 2,212 grt/786 dwt. Major refit 1994–95 at Pascol Engineering, Thunder Bay, Ont., was intended to extend life to 2005. Based at Prescott, Ont.
Hull systems: Has a 970-m^3 cargo hold and one 15-ton buoy derrick. A 24-m^2 scientific laboratory is fitted. Has Flume passive tank stabilization. There is a 118-m^2 helicopter flight deck but no hangar. Navigational equipment includes Trimble Navtrack GPS, Taiyo 121 ATS MFD/F, OAR 320F VHFD/F, and LAZ-4401, Atlas 480, and Lowerance echo sounders.

♦ 1 J. E. Bernier class [WAGB]
Bldr: Davie SB, Lauzon, Que.

	Region	In serv.
J. E. Bernier	Newfoundland	8-67

D: 3,150 tons (fl) **S:** 13 kts **Dim:** 70.70 (64.80 pp) × 15.09 × 5.20
Electronics: Radar: 1 Sperry Rascar 3400M nav.; 1 Sperry 127 nav.
M: 4 Fairbanks-Morse 38D8⅛-8 diesels, 4 865-kw generators, 2 electric motors; 2 props; 4,218 shp
Electric: 848 kw tot. (4 × 212-kw Paxman 12RPHZ diesel-driven sets)
Range: 4,000/11 **Fuel:** 512 m^3 **Crew:** 9 officers, 12 non-officers

LIGHT ICEBREAKER/MAJOR NAVAIDS TENDERS [WAGB] *(continued)*

J. E. Bernier—with telescoping hangar extended H&L Van Ginderen, 7-96

Remarks: 2,457 grt/1,082 dwt. Refitted 5-89 to 7-90 and again 1992–93. Based at St. John's, Nfld.
Hull systems: Has telescoping helicopter hangar, a 320-m^2 helicopter deck, and Flume passive stabilization tanks. There is a 10-ton buoy derrick and a 214-m^3 cargo hold. Two Zodiac RIBs and two workboats are carried. Navigational equipment includes Taiyo 121 ATS MFD/F, OAR 320E VHFD/F, and two LSZ 440 echo sounders.

♦ 1 Sir Humphrey Gilbert class [WAGB]
Bldr: Davie SB, Lauzon, Que.

	Region	In serv.
Sir Humphrey Gilbert	Newfoundland	6-59

D: 3,056 tons (fl) **S:** 14.1 kts **Dim:** 72.50 (61.57 pp) × 14.70 × 5.00
Electronics: Radar: 1 Sperry 4016X-59CP nav.; 1 Sperry Rascar 29CP nav.
M: 4 Fairbanks-Morse 38D8⅛-8 diesels (1,280 bhp each), 4 865-kw generator sets, 2 electric motors; 2 props; 4,250 shp
Electric: 954 kw tot. (3 × 318-kw Deutz BA6M816R diesel-driven)
Range: 10,000/11 **Fuel:** 467 m^3 **Endurance:** 28 days
Crew: 10 officers, 15 non-officers

Remarks: 2,153 grt/960 dwt. Refitted 1983 to 1-86 at Halifax SY with a new bow and Wärtsilä bubbler system. Homeported at St. John's, Nfld.
Hull systems: Has a telescoping helicopter hangar, a 500-m^3 buoy hold, and a 20-ton derrick.

LIGHT ICEBREAKER/MEDIUM NAVAIDS TENDERS [WAGB]

♦ 2 Samuel Risley class [WAGB]

	Bldr	Region	In serv.
Samuel Risley	Vito Steel Boat & Barge, Vancouver	Central & Arctic	6-85
Earl Grey	Pictou SY, Pictou, N.S.	Maritimes	30-5-86

Earl Grey Canadian Coast Guard

D: 2,260 tons light (2,935 fl) **S:** 12 kts **Dim:** 69.73 (59.01 pp) × 14.36 × 5.84
Electronics:
Radar: 2 Decca Bridgemaster II (X- and S-band) nav.; 1 Decca Bridgemaster Conrad nav.
M: *Risley:* 4 Bombardier/Wärtsilä 12V22HE diesels; 2 Kort-nozzle CP props; 8,846 bhp—750-bhp bow-thruster—400-bhp stern-thruster
Grey: 4 Deutz SBV 9M628 diesels; 2 Kort-nozzle props; 8,718 bhp
Electric: *Risley:* 2,790 kw tot. (2 × 1,000-kw shaft generators; 2 × 395-kw, G.M. 16V71 diesels driving)—*Grey:* 2,232 kw tot. (2 × 800-kw shaft generators; 2 × 316-kw Caterpillar 3412DITA diesel-driven sets)
Range: *Risley:* 16,700/12; *Grey:* 18,000/11 **Fuel:** *Risley:* 692 m^3; *Grey:* 634 m^3
Endurance: 58 days **Crew:** 9 officers, 22 non-officers

Remarks: *Risley:* 1,967 grt/1,186 dwt; *Grey:* 1,988 grt/1,159 dwt. Design based on offshore supply vessel technology. Are able to break 0.6-m ice. *Risley* is based at Parry Sound, Ont.; *Grey* at Charlottetown, P.E.I.

Hull systems: Buoy crane capacity is 15 tons at 8-m radius, 8.5 tons at 20-m. Two fire monitors produce 600 m^2/hr to 75 m range. Have a towing winch with 90 tons bollard pull. *Risley* has a 29.8-m^2 oceanographic laboratory.

ICE-STRENGTHENED MEDIUM NAVAIDS TENDERS [WAGL]

♦ 2 Provo Wallis class [WAGL]
Bldr: Marine Industries, Sorel, Que.

	Region	In serv.
Provo Wallis	Maritimes	10-69
Bartlett	Pacific	12-69

Bartlett Hartmut Ehlers, 5-99

D: *Wallis:* . . . tons (fl); *Bartlett:* 1,722 tons (fl) **S:** 12.5 kts
Dim: *Wallis:* 63.78 × 13.09 × 3.66; *Bartlett:* 57.68 × 13.09 × 4.10
Electronics:
Radar: *Wallis:* Sperry Rascar 2500M (X-band) nav.; Sperry 3400M (S-band) nav.—*Bartlett:* 2 Decca Bridgemaster II (X- and S-band) nav.
M: 2 National Gas–Mirrlees-Blackstone KLSDM6 direct-drive diesels; 2 CP props; 2,100 bhp (1,760 sust.)—bow-thruster
Electric: *Wallis:* 995 kw tot. (3 × 270 kw, Iveco 8 281 SRM44 diesels driving; 1 × 185-kw, Paxman 8RPHZ emergency diesel set)—*Bartlett:* 1,056 kw tot. (3 × 352-kw, Paxman 8RPH diesels driving)
Range: 3,300/11 **Fuel:** *Wallis:* 240 m^3; *Bartlett:* 213 m^3
Endurance: 21 days **Crew:** 9 officers, 14 (*Wallis:* 15) non-officers

Remarks: *Wallis:* 1,313 grt/515 dwt (prior to lengthening); *Bartlett:* 1,317 grt. *Bartlett* was refitted in 1987 with a bow-thruster, flush 'tween decks hatches to the cargo hold, new winches, modifications to the navigation bridge, a new sewage system, and other improvements. She was refitted again 6-91 to 4-92 and in 1995 transferred to the Pacific, where she is based at Victoria, B.C.
Wallis, lengthened during a 5-89 to 5-90 refit at Marystown Shipyards, is 6 m longer and is fitted with bow- and stern-thrusters, new generators, a modified Liebherr boom crane, and a Miranda davit to handle an RI 22–class fast rescue RIB. She is based at St. John, N.B., operating with alternating crews.
Hull systems: Both have a 15-ton derrick tending the 507-m^3 cargo hold and carry one 9.1-m landing craft. Both have Magnavox MX-200 GPS, Taiyo 121 ATS MFD/F, and OAR 320E VHFD/F. *Wallis* has one and *Bartlett* two Elac LAZ-72 echo sounders.

♦ 1 Tracy class [WAGL]
Bldr: Port Weller DD, Ltd., Port Weller, Ont.

	Region	In serv.
Tracy	Laurentian	17-4-68

Tracy H&L Van Ginderen, 7-9(

D: 1,320 tons (fl) **S:** 13.5 kts **Dim:** 55.32 (50.30 pp) × 11.64 × 3.66
Electronics: Radar: 1 Sperry 340 (X-band) nav.; 1 Sperry 340CA (S-band) nav.
M: 2 Fairbanks-Morse 38D8⅛-8 diesels, 4 405-kw generators, 2 electric motors; 2 props; 2,500 shp—bow-thruster

ICE-STRENGTHENED MEDIUM NAVAIDS TENDERS [WAGL] *(continued)*

Electric: 422 kw tot. (3 × 110-kw Paxman 6RPHZ diesel-driven sets; 1 × 92-kw Paxman 4RPHZ emergency diesel-driven set)
Range: 5,000/12 **Fuel:** 155.1 m^3 **Endurance:** 17 days
Crew: 8 officers, 13 non-officers

Remarks: 963 grt/419 dwt. Based at Sorel, Que.
Hull systems: Has a 10-ton buoy derrick and a 5-ton bollard-pull towing winch. Carries an 8-m self-propelled work barge and a smaller workboat. Navigational equipment includes a Magnavox MX-200 GPS, Taiyo TD-C338 Mk II MFD/F, OAR 320E VHFD/F, and Elac 30-kHz and 50-kHz echo sounders.

♦ 1 Simcoe class [WAGL]
Bldr: Canadian Vickers, Montreal

	Region	In serv.
Simcoe	Central & Arctic	1962

Simcoe H&L Van Ginderen, 10-89

D: 1,392 tons (fl) **S:** 14 kts **Dim:** 54.62 (50.35 pp) × 11.64 × 3.83
Electronics: Radar: Decca Bridgemaster II (X- and S-band) nav.
M: 2 Paxman YLCZ 12-cyl. diesels (1,500 bhp each), 4 410-kw generators, 2 electric motors; 2 props; 2,000 shp
Electric: 650 kw tot. (2 × 270-kw Caterpillar 3406 diesel-driven; 1 × 110-kw Caterpillar 3304 diesel-driven emergency set)
Range: 5,000/10 **Fuel:** 156 m^3 **Endurance:** 21 days
Crew: 10 officers, 17 non-officers

Remarks: 961 grt/457 dwt. Based on Lake Ontario at Prescott, Ont.
Hull systems: The 532-m^3 buoy hold is tended by a 10-ton crane. Carries a Boston Whaler, a workboat, and a self-propelled work barge. Navigational equipment includes Magnavox MX-200 GPS, Marconi 2464A MFD/F, OAR 320E VHFD/F, and Elac LAZ-72 and STN Atlas Elektronik 480 echo sounders.

♦ 1 Simon Fraser class [WAGL]
Bldr: Burrard DD, Vancouver

	Region	In serv.
Simon Fraser	Maritimes	2-60

Simon Fraser Canadian Coast Guard, 1988

D: 1,375 tons (fl) **S:** 13.8 kts **Dim:** 62.26 (56.16 pp) × 12.86 × 4.27
Electronics: Radar: 2 Decca Bridgemaster II (X- and S-band) nav.
M: 4 Alco 251B-12V diesels (1,666 bhp each), 2 1,150-kw generators, 2 G.E. electric motors; 2 props; 2,900 shp
Electric: 580 kw tot. (2 × 240-kw, Baudoin 6P152SR 6P15.2 SRC diesel-driven sets; 1 × 100-kw Dorman 6 LETZ diesel emergency set)
Range: 5,000/10 **Fuel:** 200 m^3 **Endurance:** 20 days
Crew: 10 officers, 14 non-officers

Remarks: 1,353 grt/484 dwt. Refitted at Versatile Vickers SY, Montreal, from 1985 to 4-86; hangar removed, extra lifeboats added for search-and-rescue duties. Based at Québec City, Que.
Hull systems: Has a 123.5-m^2 helicopter deck. The 300-m^3 buoy hold is tended by a 12-ton crane. Navigational equipment includes Magnavox MX-200 GPS, Taiyo 121 ATS MFD/F, OAR 320E VHFD/F, Elac LAZ-72 echo sounder, and Skipper CSD101 echo sounder.

OFFSHORE RESEARCH AND SURVEY [WAGOR/WAGS]

♦ 1 John P. Tully–class survey ship [WAGS]
Bldr: Bel-Aire SY, Vancouver

	Region	Laid down	L	In serv.
John P. Tully	Pacific	30-1-84	27-10-84	5-85

John P. Tully—in former paint scheme Fisheries & Oceans, 1988

D: 2,200 tons (fl) **S:** 14 kts **Dim:** 68.92 (61.68 pp) × 14.18 × 4.50
Electronics: Radar: 1 Sperry 2500M nav.; 1 Sperry 3400M nav.
M: 2 Deutz SBV-628 8-cyl. diesels; 1 CP prop; 3,126 bhp—bow and stern jetpump thrusters
Electric: 1,880 kw tot. (4 × 470-kw diesel-driven sets)
Range: 12,000/10 **Fuel:** 483 m^3 **Endurance:** 50 days
Crew: 17 officers, 3 non-officers + up to 20 scientists/hydrographers

Remarks: 2,021 grt. Based at Patricia Bay, B.C.
Hull systems: A 190-m^2 helicopter deck is located forward. Four hydrographic sounding boats can be carried. There is a 5-ton crane. A 50-m^2 dry lab and a 6-m^2 wet oceanographic lab are fitted. Navigational equipment includes Trimble XL6PS GPS, Taiyo C338-RS MFD/F, Taiyo TD616 VHFD/F, and JEC JEV-216, Furuno FE-881, and Simrad EA-500 echo sounders.

♦ 1 Parizeau class [WAGOR]
Bldr: Burrard DD, Ltd., North Vancouver, B.C. (In serv. 1967)

Parizeau

Parizeau—in former paint scheme Michael Lindberg, 7-92

D: approx. 2,000 tons (fl) **S:** 14 kts **Dim:** 64.50 × 12.20 × 4.60
Electronics: Radar: 2 Decca Bridgemaster nav.
M: 2 Deutz 8-cyl. diesels; 2 CP props; 2,638 bhp—bow-thruster
Electric: 936 kw tot. (3 × 312-kw, Caterpillar 3400 diesels driving)
Range: 17,250/10 **Fuel:** 416.5 m^3 **Endurance:** 60 days
Crew: 6 officers, 14 non-officers + 23 scientists and technicians

Remarks: 1,314 grt. Homeported at Dartmouth, N.S.; assigned to Maritimes Region.
Hull systems: Has one 104-m^3 hold. Navigational equipment includes a Magnavox MX-300 GPS set, Northstar 800 Loran receiver, Taiyo ADDFTD-L1520 VHFD/F, Elac LAZ-440 echo sounder, Sperry Mk 37 gyro, and two Comnav 2000 autopilots. Carries a Zodiac Hurricane RIB. Laboratories include 70-m^2 upper and 40-m^2 lower hydrographic labs and a 15-m^2 dry lab. Can stow one 20-ft. container on deck.

♦ 1 Hudson class [WAGOR]
Bldr: Saint John SB & DD, Saint John, N.B. (In serv. 1963)

Hudson

D: approx. 5,400 tons (fl) **S:** 17 kts **Dim:** 90.4 × 15.4 × 6.8
Electronics: Radar: 2 Decca Bridgemaster II (X- and S-band) nav.
M: 4 Alco 16-cyl. diesels, 4 generators, 2 electric motors; 2 props; 8,636 shp

OFFSHORE RESEARCH AND SURVEY [WAGOR/WAGS]
(continued)

Hudson *Ships of the World,* 1998

Electric: 1,222 kw tot. (2 × 611-kw, Caterpillar D358D diesel-driven sets)
Range: 23,100/10.5 **Fuel:** 1,268 m^3 **Endurance:** 105 days
Crew: 11 officers, 26 non-officers

Remarks: 3,740 grt. Modernized 1990 by builder. Assigned to the Maritimes Region and based at Dartmouth, N.S.
Hull systems: Laboratories include 112-m^2 hydrographic, 20-m^2 oceanographic, 40-m^2 geological/chemical, and 18-m^2 general-purpose labs. Has a 1,380-m^2 helicopter flight deck and a 280-m^2 hangar. Also has a 4.3-ton crane and a 200-m^3 cargo hold. Navigational equipment includes a Magnavox MX-300 GPS terminal, TD-338H5 MFD/F, Taiyo VHFD/F, and Elac LAZ-440 echo sounder.

COASTAL/INSHORE RESEARCH AND SURVEY [WAGS/WYGS]

♦ 1 Matthew-class hydrographic survey ship [WAGS]
Bldr: Versatile Marine, Montreal (In serv. 1990)

Matthew

Matthew—in former all-white paint scheme H&L Van Ginderen, 9-94

D: approx. 1,150 tons (fl) **S:** 12 kts **Dim:** 50.3 × 10.5 × 4.3
Electronics: Radar: 1 Decca Bridgemaster nav.; 1 Decca BT 502 nav.
M: 2 Caterpillar 3508 8-cyl. diesels; 2 CP props; 1,810 bhp
Electric: 750 kw tot. (3 × 250-kw, Caterpillar 3406 diesels driving)
Range: 4,000/12 **Fuel:** 119 m^3 **Endurance:** 20 days
Crew: 5 officers, 8 non-officers + 6 scientists/technicians

Remarks: 856.8 grt. Assigned to Maritimes Region and based at Dartmouth, N.S.
Hull systems: Has a 90-m^2 helicopter deck. Carries two hydrographic survey launches, one Zodiac 520 RIB, and two smaller inflatable boats. Has a 107-m^2 cartographic lab and a 13.5-m^2 hydrology lab. Navigational equipment includes a Magnavox MX-300 GPS terminal, Taiyo TD-338HS MFD/F, Taiyo ADDFTD-L1620 VHFD/F, and Elac LAZ-series echo sounder.

♦ 1 R. B. Young–class hydrographic survey ship [WYGS]
Bldr: Allied Shipbuilding, North Vancouver, B.C.

R. B. Young

D: approx. 350 tons (fl) **S:** 11.6 kts **Dim:** 32.30 × 8.00 × 2.30
Electronics: Radar: 2 Raytheon R81 nav.
M: 2 Caterpillar 6-cyl. diesels; 2 CP props; 1,052 bhp—bow-thruster
Electric: 190 kw tot. (2 × 95-kw, Caterpillar diesels driving)
Range: 5,000/10 **Fuel:** 51 m^3 **Crew:** 4 officers, 3 non-officers + 3 scientists

Remarks: 299.96 grt. Assigned to Pacific Region and based at Patricia Bay, B.C.
Hull systems: Has a 17-m^2 wet laboratory. Navigational systems include a Simrad EM 1002 multibeam mapping sonar, Furuno FE-880 echo sounder, and Taiyo TA-L1520 MFD/F.

♦ 1 Louis M. Lauzier–class hydrographic survey ship [WYGS]
Bldr: Breton Industries, Ltd., Port Hawkesbury, N.S. (In serv. 1976)

Louis M. Lauzier

D: approx. 350 tons (fl) **S:** 12.5 kts **Dim:** 37.10 × 8.20 × 2.13
Electronics:
Radar: 1 JRC JMA-627-6 (X-band) nav.; 1 Decca 6520/CAD (X-band) nav.
M: 2 Cummins K2300 diesels; 2 props; 1,600 bhp—bow-thruster
Electric: 280 kw tot. (2 × 140-kw diesel-driven sets)
Range: 1,800/12.5 **Fuel:** 53 m^3 **Crew:** 3 officers, 7 non-officers

Remarks: 322.25 grt. Re-engined in 1986. Former fisheries protection ship. As of 2001 was on charter to the Memorial University of Newfoundland.
Hull systems: Navigational equipment includes Trimble Navtrac XL GPS, Taiyo TD-4550 VHFD/F, Elac LAZ-72 echo sounder, and Lowerance X-16 echo sounder.

♦ 1 Limnos-class hydrographic survey ship [WYGS]
Bldr: Port Weller DD, St. Catherines, Ont. (In serv. 1968)

Limnos

D: approx. 650 tons (fl) **S:** 10 kts **Dim:** 44.81 × 9.75 × 2.60
Electronics:
Radar: 1 Decca Bridgemaster ARPA (X-band) nav.; 1 Decca Bridgemaster (S-band) nav.
M: 2 Caterpillar 3412 diesels; 2 Harbormaster 360 azimuthal props; 1,006 bhp
Electric: 400 kw tot. (2 × 150 kw, 1 × 100 kw diesel-driven)
Range: 3,500/10 **Fuel:** 80 m^3 **Crew:** 6 officers, 8 non-officers + 14 scientists

Remarks: 460 grt. Modernized in 1981. Assigned to Central and Arctic Region and based at Burlington, Ont.
Hull systems: Has 10-m^2 dry and 6-m^2 wet laboratories. A 15-ton crane is fitted. One Boston Whaler 5-m launch and an Ambar 550 workboat are carried. Navigational equipment includes an STN Atlas Elektronik DESO-10 mapping sonar, Lowerance and Elac echo sounders, and Taiyo VHFD/F.

♦ 1 Vector-class hydrographic survey ship [WYGS]
Bldr: Yarrows, Ltd., Esquimalt, B.C. (In serv. 1967)

Vector

D: approx. 680 tons (fl) **S:** 12 kts **Dim:** 39.74 × 9.46 × 3.50
Electronics: Radar: 1 Decca 2090B nav.; 1 Raytheon M25 nav.
M: 1 Caterpillar 3208 diesel; 1 CP prop; 800 bhp
Electric: 740 kw tot. (2 × 370 kw, Caterpillar 3306 and 3406 diesels driving)
Range: 3,500/10 **Fuel:** 74 m^3 **Endurance:** 20 days
Crew: 5 officers, 7 non-officers + 8 scientists

Remarks: 515 grt. Performs general oceanographic research as well as survey work. Was re-engined in 1995. Assigned to Pacific Region and based at Patricia Bay, B.C.
Hull systems: Has a 65-m^2 laboratory. Equipped with Simrad EA500 mapping sonar, Firimp FCV-251 and JRC RD-5000 echo sounders, Northstar 941X GPS, and Taiyo TL-Lq520 VHFD/F.

SMALL NAVAIDS TENDERS [WYGL]

♦ 1 Traverse class [WYGL]
Bldr: Metalcraft Marine, Kingston, Ont. (In serv. 1998)

Traverse

D: . . . tons **S:** 9 kts **Dim:** 19.81 × 7.30 × 0.60
Electronics: Radar: 1 Furuno M1832 nav.
M: 2 Volvo Penta diesels; 2 props; 180 bhp
Electric: 30 kw tot. (1 × 30-kw diesel-driven set) **Range:** 800/8
Fuel: 2 m^3 **Endurance:** 10 days **Crew:** 1 officer, 3 non-officers

Remarks: 70.66 grt. Aluminum-construction, unpainted catamaran. Assigned to the Central and Arctic Region and based at Kenora, Ont.
Hull systems: Has a 1.5-ton buoy crane and carried a 5.5-m aluminum workboat. Navigational equipment includes a GPS set and two FCV 561 echo sounders.

♦ 4 Partridge Island class [WYGL]
Bldr: Breton Industrial & Marine, Hawkesbury, N.S.

	Region	Laid down	L	In serv.
Partridge Island	Maritime	1-11-84	2-7-85	31-10-85
Île des Barques	Laurentian	1-11-84	3-7-85	26-11-85
Ile Saint-Ours	Laurentian	7-5-85	25-4-86	15-5-86
Caribou Isle	Central & Arctic	7-5-85	7-5-86	16-6-86

Île Saint-Ours H&L Van Ginderen, 9-94

D: 133 tons (fl) **S:** 10 kts **Dim:** 23.00 (22.50 wl) × 6.00 × 1.35
Electronics: Radar: 1 Sperry Mk 1270 nav.
M: 2 G.M. 8V92 diesels; 2 props; 640 bhp **Electric:** 70 kw (2 generators)
Range: 1,800/8 **Fuel:** 26,000 liters **Endurance:** 7–10 days **Crew:** 5 tot.

SMALL NAVAIDS TENDERS [WYGL] *(continued)*

Remarks: First two ordered 23-7-84 and others 23-11-84. *Partridge Island* is based at St. John, N.B.; *Île des Barques* and *Île Saint Ours* at Sorel, Que.; and *Caribou Isle* at Sault Ste. Marie, Ont. Cargo capacity is 20 tons. Have a fire monitor with 2,500-liter/min capacity to 60 m range.

♦ 1 Tsekoa II class [WYGL]
Bldr: Allied Shipbuilders, Vancouver (In serv. 1984)

TSEKOA II

Tsekoa II R. Brytan, 3-97

D: . . . tons **S:** 12 kts **Dim:** 26.70 × 7.25 × 2.00
Electronics: Radar: 1 Raytheon R 80 nav.; 1 Raytheon R 81 nav.
M: 2 G.M. Detroit Diesel 8V92 diesels; 2 props; 640 bhp
Range: . . ./11 **Fuel:** 13 m^3 **Crew:** 3 officers, 4 non-officers

Remarks: 160.75 grt. Assigned to the Pacific Region and based at Victoria, B.C.
Hull systems: Has a 10-ton buoy crane and carries a Mk 5 Zodiac RIB.

♦ 2 Cove Isle class [WYGL]
Bldr: Canadian Dredge & Dock, Kingston, Ont. (In serv. 1980)

COVE ISLE GULL ISLE

D: 116 tons (fl) **S:** 12 kts **Dim:** 20.00 × 6.00 × 1.70
Electronics: Radar: 1 Decca Bridgemaster IIC 181/4 nav.
M: 2 Cummins diesels; 2 props; 500 bhp
Electric: 80 kw tot. (2 × 40-kw diesel-driven sets)
Range: 2,500/11 **Fuel:** 20.5 tons **Endurance:** 14 days
Crew: 1 officer, 4 non-officers

Remarks: 92.05 grt. Both are assigned to the Central and Arctic Region, with *Cove Isle* based at Parry Sound, Ont., and *Gull Isle* at Amherstburg, Ont.
Hull systems: Have a 20-ton buoy crane and a 4-ton-bollard-pull winch. Navigational equipment includes a Datamarine echo sounder and two Elac LAZ-series echo sounders.

♦ 1 Namao class [WYGL]
Bldr: Riverton Boatworks, Manitoba (In serv. 1975)

	Region	In serv.
NAMAO	Central & Arctic	1975

Namao Canadian Coast Guard, 1988

D: 386 tons (fl) **S:** 12 kts **Dim:** 33.62 × 8.53 × 2.13
Electronics: Radar: 1 Decca Bridgemaster IIC 181/4 nav.
M: 2 G.M. Detroit Diesel–Allison 12V149 diesels; 2 props; 1,350 bhp
Range: 3,000/11 **Fuel:** 34.5 m^3 **Crew:** 4 officers, 7 non-officers

Remarks: 327.91 grt. Assigned to the Central and Arctic Region and based at Selkirk, Man., employed as buoy tender on Lake Winnipeg.
Hull systems: Has a 220-m^3 cargo hold. Navigational equipment includes a Furuno GP-70 Mk 2 GPS, OAR 320E VHFD/F, and Raytheon DE 719C echo sounder.

SPECIAL RIVER NAVAIDS TENDERS [WYGL]

♦ 1 Eckaloo class [WYGL]
Bldr: Vancouver SY, Ltd., North Vancouver, B.C.

	L	In serv.
ECKALOO	31-5-88	31-8-88

Eckaloo H&L Van Ginderen, 1994

D: 534 tons (fl) **S:** 13 kts (11 sust.) **Dim:** 49.03 (48.01 pp) × 13.37 × 1.37
Electronics: Radar: 2 Decca Bridgemaster (X-band) nav.
M: 2 Caterpillar 3512TA diesels; 2 Kort-nozzle props; 2,116 bhp
Electric: 300 kw (3 × 100-kw, Caterpillar 3306T diesels driving)
Range: 2,000/11 **Fuel:** 100 m^3 **Endurance:** 15 days
Crew: 4 officers, 6 non-officers + 12 passengers

Remarks: 661.13 grt. Refitted in 1996 at NTCL Shipyard, Hay River, N.W.T. Assigned to the Central and Arctic Region, based at Hay River.
Hull systems: Flat hull bottom; tunnel-mounted propellers. Has a 6-ton-capacity (at 7.6-m radius) buoy crane. Can carry a portable Simrad Mesotech color-imaging Model 971 mapping sonar for survey duties. A 200-m^2 helicopter platform is fitted. Carries one 5.2-m Boston Whaler and one 4.3-m Zodiac RIB. Navigational equipment includes a Furuno GP-70 GPS, OAR 320E VHFD/F, four Furuno FCV-667 echo sounders, and one Elac LAZ-72 echo sounder.

♦ 1 Dumit class [WYGL]
Bldr: Allied SB, North Vancouver, B.C. (In serv. 7-79)

DUMIT

D: 628 tons (fl) **S:** 12 kts **Dim:** 50.91 (48.82 pp) × 12.58 × 1.64
M: 2 Caterpillar 12-cyl. diesels; 2 props; 2,250 bhp
Range: 9,000/10 **Fuel:** 175 tons **Crew:** 10 tot.

Remarks: 569 grt/85 dwt. Based at Hay River, N.W.T., assigned to the Central and Arctic Region. Can carry a portable Simrad Mesotech color-imaging Model 971 mapping sonar for survey duties.

♦ 1 Nahidik class [WAGL]
Bldr: Allied SB, North Vancouver, B.C. (In serv. 1974)

NAHIDIK

Nahidik Capt. Ali, Can. C.G., 1992

D: 1,122 tons (fl) **S:** 13 kts **Dim:** 53.35 (52.89 pp) × 15.24 × 1.98
Electronics: Radar: 1 Decca Bridgemaster II nav.; 1 Sperry Mk 127 nav.
M: 2 G.M. Detroit Diesel–Allison 12-645-ES diesels; 2 props; 1,600 bhp
Electric: 200 kw tot. (2 × 100-kw Kato sets, G.M. diesels driving)
Range: 5,000/12 **Fuel:** 231 m^3 **Crew:** 6 officers, 6 non-officers + 11 passengers

Remarks: 856 grt/562 dwt. Based at Hay River, N.W.T., assigned to the Central and Arctic Region.
Hull systems: Has a helicopter platform aft, twin side-by-side stacks, and a 328-m^3 cargo hold tended by a 10-ton crane. Navigational equipment includes a Magnavox MX-200 GPS, Taiyo TD-A121 MFD/F, OAR 320E VHFD/F, and Elac LAZ-72 and Furuno ED-222 echo sounders. Is also equipped with three Furuno FCV-667 video sounders linked to the display for the ED-222 set for survey purposes. Can carry a portable Simrad Mesotech color-imaging Model 971 mapping sonar.

♦ 1 Tembah class [WYGL]
Bldr: Allied SB, North Vancouver, B.C. (In serv. 10-63)

TEMBAH

D: 181 tons (fl) **S:** 13 kts **Dim:** 39.37 (36.58 pp) × 8.06 × 0.91
M: 2 Cummins 12-cyl. diesels; 2 props; 680 bhp **Electric:** 85.5 kw tot.
Range: 1,000/11 **Fuel:** 21 tons **Crew:** 9 tot.

Remarks: 189 grt. Has one 5-ton crane, serving a 1.2 × 2.2-m hatch. Based at Hay River, N.W.T., assigned to the Central and Arctic Region. Can carry a portable Simrad Mesotech color-imaging Model 971 mapping sonar for survey duties.

SPECIAL RIVER NAVAIDS TENDERS [WYGL] *(continued)*

Tembah Canadian Coast Guard

OFFSHORE/INSHORE FISHERIES RESEARCH [WAGOR]

♦ 2 Alfred Needler–class fisheries research ships [WAGOR]

Bldr: Ferguson, Pictou, N.S. (In serv. 1982)

ALFRED NEEDLER   WILFRED TEMPLEMAN

Alfred Needler—in former all-white paint scheme   H&L Van Ginderen, 8-94

D: approx. 1,300 tons (fl) **S:** 15 kts **Dim:** 50.3 × 11.0 × 4.3
M: 1 Bombardier-Alco 16V-251F diesel; 1 prop; 3,138 bhp
Electric: 875 kw tot. (1 × 350-kw, 2 × 200-kw, 1 × 125-kw diesel sets)
Range: 9,300/15 **Fuel:** 209.5 tons **Crew:** . . .

Remarks: 925 grt stern-haul trawlers used for fisheries research. *Needler* is based at Halifax, *Templeman* at St. John's, Nfld.

Note: Also in use for fisheries research are the *Calanus II* (1991, Laurentian Region, 160 grt); *Caligus; J. L. Hart* (1974, Maritimes, 93 grt); *Navicula* (1968, Maritimes, 106 grt); *Opilio* (1989, Maritimes, 74 grt); *Pandalus III* (1986, Maritimes, 13 grt); *Shamook* (1975, Newfoundland, 187 grt; 6 crew, 3 scientists); *Shark* (1971, Central and Arctic, 19 grt); *Teleost* (1996, Newfoundland); and *W. E. Ricker* (ex-*Callistratus,* 1,040 grt, completed 12-78 and operating on the Pacific coast with a crew of 24 plus 12 scientists).

MULTI-TASK LIFEBOATS [WYH]

♦ 8 U.S. Coast Guard 44-foot Motor Lifeboat class [WYH]

	Region	In serv.
BAMFIELD	Pacific	1964
PORT HARDY (ex-*Bull Harbor*)	Pacific	1969
TOFINO	Pacific	1970
TOBERMORY (ex-CG 108)	Central	1974
WESTFORT (ex-*Thunder Bay,* ex-CG 109)	Central	1974
SHIPPEGAN (ex-CG 115)	Maritimes	1975
CG 141 (ex-*Cap-aux-Meules*)	Maritimes	1982
SOURIS	Maritimes	1985

D: 17.9 tons (fl) **S:** 11.5 kts **Dim:** 13.45 × 3.86 × 1.20
Electronics: Radar: 1 Furuno FR-1510D or Raytheon 060 nav.
M: 2 Caterpillar 3208 diesels; 2 props; 360 bhp
Range: 150/10 **Fuel:** 1.2 tons **Crew:** 3–4 non-officers

Remarks: 11 grt. Are of self-righting, U.S. Coast Guard design. First unit was built at the U.S. Coast Guard Yard, Curtis Bay, Md.; the others in Canada. Are based at the ports whose names they bear, except for CG 141, which is maintained in standby at Mulgrave, N.S. Three others, *Cap Goélands, CG 117,* and *CG 118* serve as training craft.
Disposals: *Burgeo* (CG 114), CG 116 (ex-*Clark's Harbour*), CG 117 (ex-*Sambro*), CG 118 (ex-*Louisbourg*), and CG 140 (ex-*Port Mouton*) had been retired by 5-01.

A 44-ft. lifeboat in Canadian Coast Guard service Canadian Coast Guard

MULTI-TASK HIGH ENDURANCE LIFEBOATS [WYH]

♦ 10 Halmatic Arun 300B class [WYH]

Bldrs: A: Halmatic, Havant, U.K.; B: Georgetown SY, P.E.I.; C: Industries Raymond, Sept Îles, Que.; D: Hike Metal Products, Wheatley, Ont.

	Bldr	In serv.		Bldr	In serv.
BICKERTON	A	8-89	W. G. GEORGE	C	9-95
SPINDRIFT	B	10-93	CAP-AUX-MEULES	D	10-96
SPRAY	C	7-9-94	CLARK'S HARBOUR	D	9-96
W. JACKMAN	C	10-95	SAMBRO	D	1-97
SPUME	C	7-10-94	WESTPORT	D	5-97

Cap-aux-Meules H&L Van Ginderen, 8-96

D: 34 tons (fl) **S:** 20 kts **Dim:** 16.25 × 5.18 × 1.25
Electronics: Radar: 1 Furuno 1510 rasterscan or Decca Bridgemaster II nav.
M: 2 Caterpillar 3408BTA diesels; 2 props; 1,000 bhp
Range: 100/18; 150/16 **Endurance:** 1.5 days **Crew:** 2 officers, 2 non-officers

Remarks: 42 grt. Formerly typed as Large Search-and-Rescue Lifeboats (Type 310).
Hull systems: *Bickerton* has a Kevlar hull; the rest were built of aluminum. Low freeboard aids in picking up survivors. Navigation equipment includes a GP-70 GPS, Furuno FD-177 MFD/F, OAR 320E VHFD/F, and Furuno FCV-561 echo sounder.

MULTI-TASK MEDIUM-ENDURANCE LIFEBOATS [WYH]

♦ 5 (+ 22) U.S. Coast Guard 47-foot Motor Life Boat class [WYH]

Bldr: MIL Systems Engineering, Ottawa/Metalcraft Marine Group, Kingston, Ont., and Victoria Shipyards, Victoria B.C.

	In serv.		In serv.
CAPE SUTIL	12-98	CAPE MERCY	12-01
CAPE CALVERT	8-99	. . . . . .	5-02
CAPE ST. JAMES	11-99	. . . . . .	12-02
THUNDER CAPE	6-01		

D: 18.15 tons (fl) **S:** 25 kts **Dim:** 14.61 (13.11 wl) × 4.27 × 1.37
Electronics: Radar: 1 Furuno 1942 nav.
M: 2 Caterpillar 3196 diesels; 2 props; 675 bhp **Electric:** 10 kw tot.
Range: 200/22 **Fuel:** 1,560 liters **Crew:** 1 officer, 3 non-officers

Remarks: Eleven were ordered 1-4-97 to a U.S. Textron Marine design. The first three were assigned to the Pacific Region, with *Cape Sutil* based at Port Hardy, B.C. *Thunder Cape* is assigned to the Central and Arctic Region and is based at Meafort, Ont. Twenty more were ordered on 11-10-01 from Victoria Shipyards.
Hull systems: Aluminum construction, with deep-vee hullform. Can berth five survivors. Able to maintain 20 kts in 2-ft. seas and can tow craft displacing up to 150 tons. Can survive an end-for-end pitch-pole and are capable of operating in 80-kt gales with 9-m swells and 6-m breaking seas. Navigation equipment includes Magnavox MX-400BR GPS, FMC 5500 VHFD/F, and Sitex CV 106 echo sounder.

MULTI-TASK MEDIUM-ENDURANCE LIFEBOATS [WYH] *(continued)*

♦ 1 CGR-100-class rigid inflatable rescue boat [WYH]
Bldr: Hurricane Rescue Craft, Vancouver (In serv. 1986)

CGR-100

D: 10.5 tons (fl) **S:** 34 kts **Dim:** 14.00 × 4.80 × 0.69
Electronics: Radar: 1 Furuno FR-1510D nav.
M: 2 Caterpillar 3176B diesels; 2 Hamilton 302 waterjets; 670 bhp
Range: 250/26 **Fuel:** 1.3 m^3 **Crew:** 1 officer, 2 non-officers

Remarks: 21.44 grt. World's largest rigid-hull inflatable craft when delivered. Modernized in 1997 by Hike Metal Products, Wheatley, Ont. Is assigned to the Central and Arctic Region, based at Port Weller, Ont.
Hull systems: Has a deep-vee hullform with rigid inflatable collar. Navigational equipment includes a GP-70 Mk 2 GPS, OAR 320E VHFD/F, and Furuno FW-55 echo sounder.

MULTI-HULLED SURVEY AND SOUNDING [WYGS]

♦ 1 Frederick G. Creed class [WYGS]
Bldr: Swath Ocean Systems, San Diego, Calif. (In serv. 1988)

Frederick G. Creed

D: . . . tons **S:** 21 kts **Dim:** 20.40 × 9.75 × 2.60
Electronics: Radar: 1 Furuno 2110+ ARPA 23 nav.; 1 Furuno FR-8050D nav.
M: 2 G.M. Detroit Diesel 12V71 TA diesels; 2 props; 2,158 bhp
Electric: 66 kw tot. (2 × 33-kw, John Deere diesels driving)
Range: 1,500/16 **Fuel:** 15.8 m^3 **Endurance:** 3 days
Crew: 3 officers, 1 non-officer + 5 scientists

Remarks: 151.4 grt. SWATH (Small Waterplane Twin Hull) craft. Assigned to the Laurentian Region and based at Romouskie, Que. Has a Simrad EM-1000 multibeam mapping sonar and a 13.5-m^2 dry laboratory.

♦ 1 F. C. G. Smith class [WYGS]
Bldr: Georgetown SY, Georgetown, P.E.I. (In serv. 1985)

F. C. G. Smith

F. C. G. Smith H&L Van Ginderen, 7-96

D: . . . tons **S:** 10 kts **Dim:** 34.80 × 14.00 × 2.10
Electronics: Radar: 2 Decca Bridgemaster II C252 ARPA nav.
M: 2 Baudouin diesels; 2 props; 800 bhp **Electric:** 270 kw tot.
Range: 15,000/10 **Fuel:** 38 m^3 **Endurance:** 7 days
Crew: 4 officers, 3 non-officers + 3 scientists

Remarks: 438.5-grt catamaran. Assigned to the Laurentian Region and based at Québec City. Has a sweep boom sounding system with the Navtronics multichannel echo sounder system.

♦ 1 GC 03 class [WYGS]
Bldr: St. Catherine d'Alexandrie SY, Québec City, Que. (In serv. 1973)

GC 03

GC 03 H&L Van Ginderen, 4-93

D: . . . tons **S:** 10.5 kts **Dim:** 18.50 × 6.40 × 1.80
Electronics: Radar: 1 Sperry MIL 1040 nav.
M: 2 Caterpillar 3306 BTA diesels; 2 props; 584 bhp
Range: 400/9 **Fuel:** 1.4 m^3 **Crew:** 1 officer, 3 non-officers

Remarks: 56.64-grt catamaran. Assigned to Laurentian Region and based at Sorel, Que. Has a 12-m^2 hydrography lab and is equipped with a sweep boom sounding system, along with Seatec and Navitrac echo sounders.

SMALL MULTI-TASK UTILITY CRAFT [WYFL]

♦ 4 U.S. Coast Guard 41-foot Utility Boat class [WYFL]
Bldr: Matsumoto, Vancouver (*Sterne:* Shore Boatbuilders, Richmond, B.C.)

	In serv.		In serv.
Mallard	28-2-86	Skua	14-3-86
Osprey	3-5-86	Sterne	1987

D: 12.8 tons (15 fl) **S:** 26 kts **Dim:** 12.40 × 4.11 × 1.24
Electronics: Radar: Raytheon Rasterscan R-81 nav.
M: 2 Mitsubishi S6B MPTD diesels; 2 props; 640 bhp
Range: 312/26 **Crew:** 3 non-officers

Remarks: First three are assigned to the Pacific Region: *Mallard* at Powell River, B.C.; *Osprey* at Kitsilano, B.C.; and *Skua* at Ganges, B.C. *Sterne* is assigned to the Laurentian Region and is based at Québec City. Some 207 sisters were built in the U.S.A. for the U.S. Coast Guard.

♦ 5 miscellaneous utility launches [WYFL]

	In serv.	grt	Based at
CG 119 (ex-*Grebe*)	1973	20	Prescott, Ont.
Bittern	1982	21	Amherstburg, Ont.
Manyberries	1969	. . .	Canoe Cove, B.C.
Sora	1982	21	Amherstburg, Ont.
Waubino	1972	. . .	Gimli, Man.

Remarks: All are assigned to the Central and Arctic Region, except *Manyberries,* to the Pacific Region. *Sora* and *Bittern* are sisters, measuring 12.5 × 4.3 × 1.24 m and powered by two Cummins M903VT diesels producing 1,036 bhp for 26 kts. CG 119 is an unsinkable lifeboat, resembling a smaller version of the U.S. Coast Guard 44-ft. class and able to reach 18 kts on one 420-bhp diesel.

AIR-CUSHION VEHICLES [WYFLA]

♦ 2 AP.1-88/400 class air-cushion vehicles [WYFLA]
Bldr: GKN Westland/Hike Metal Products, Wheatley, Ont.

Sipu Muin (In serv. 4-98) Siyay (In serv. 9-98)

Siyay Hike Metal Products, 9-98

D: 70 tons (fl) **S:** 48 kts (calm water; 45 loaded) **Dim:** 28.50 × 11.00 × . . .
Electronics: Radar: 1 Sperry 1040 nav.
M: 4 Caterpillar 3412TTA diesels (990 bhp each; 2 for lift, 2 for propulsion); 2 Hoffman 4-bladed ducted airscrews; 1,960 bhp
Range: 540/45 **Fuel:** 11,000 liters **Crew:** 3 officers, 3 non-officers

Remarks: Ordered 5-96. GKN Westland is the prime contractor, with structural work by Hike Metal Products. *Sipu Muin* ("Sea Bear") is assigned to the Laurentian Region and based at Trois Riviéres Ouest, Montreal; *Siyay* is assigned to the Pacific Region and based at Richmond, B.C.
Hull systems: Longer version of AP.1-88/200 design with a 20-ton payload on a 13.1 × 4.6-m open deck for use in servicing and recovery of navigation buoys, search and rescue, light icebreaking, and oilspill recovery operations. Have a 3.8-m-wide bow ramp and can transport over 20 tons of cargo; a 0.5-ton-capacity Palfinger crane is fitted. Lift engines are operated at 900 bhp each, propulsion engines at 1,020 bhp. A small hospital is to be fitted into the cabin on *Siyay,* and the deck can support a fire-fighting truck.

♦ 1 AP.1-99-class rigid sidewall air-cushion vehicle [WYFLA]
Bldr: Westland/British Hovercraft, Cowes, U.K. (In serv. 15-7-87)

Waban-Aki

D: 47.6 tons light **S:** 50 kts (35 cruise) **Dim:** 24.5 × 11.2 × . . .
Electronics: Radar: 1 Decca RM 914C nav.
M: 4 Deutz BF 12L 513CP diesels; 2 Hoffman airscrews/6 lift fans; 2,400 bhp
Range: 600/35 **Crew:** 3 officer, 1 non-officer

Remarks: Ordered 26-2-86, laid down 23-7-86, and launched 1-5-87. Name means "People of the Dawn," a reference to the Indians living in the region of Québec. Assigned to the Laurentian Region and based at Trois Riviéres, Que. Cargo capacity: 12 tons.

AIR-CUSHION VEHICLES [WYFLA] *(continued)*

Waban-Aki H&L Van Ginderen, 5-93

♦ 1 British Hovercraft SRN-6 class [WYFLA]

CG 045

D: 10 tons (fl) **S:** 58 kts **Dim:** 14.8 × 7.7 × 4.8 (high)
M: 1 Rolls-Royce Gnome gas turbine; 1 airscrew/2 lift fans; 900 shp **Crew:** 3 tot.

Remarks: Sisters CG 039 and CG 083 have been stricken. Operates from Vancouver.

Disposal note: The AP.1-88/200-class air-cushion vehicle acquired in 1993 is no longer in service.

COLLEGE TRAINING VESSELS [WYXT]

♦ 3 U.S. Coast Guard 44-foot lifeboat–class training craft [WYXT]
Bldrs: *Cap Goélands:* Hike Metal, Wheatley, Ont. (In serv. 1985); others: Eastern Equipment, Ltd., Montreal (In serv. 1975)

Cap Goélands CG 117 CG 118

Remarks: Data essentially as for the lifeboat-assigned units of the class. CG 117 and CG 118 are assigned to the Coast Guard College at Sydney, N.S., while *Cap Goélands* is assigned to the Laurentian Region and based at Riviére-au-Renard, Que.

ROYAL CANADIAN MOUNTED POLICE

The Transport Management Branch, Services and Supply Directorate, of the Royal Canadian Mounted Police (RCMP) operates five craft greater than 17 m in length. The RCMP's Inland Water Transport Force has 377 boats less than 9.2 m long, ranging from car-top boats and canoes to rigid inflatables and larger inboard- and outboard-powered launches. The five large craft are:

Inkster: In serv. 27-6-96. A 19.75-m aluminum catamaran based at Prince Rupert, B.C. Has two M.A.N. D2840 LE401 V-10 diesels, totaling 1,640 bhp, for a speed of about 35 kts. A crew of four is carried.

Nadon, Higgitt, Lindsay, and *Simmonds:* 17.7-m catamarans with the same plant as *Inkster* and capable of 36 kts. *Simmonds* is based on the south coast of Newfoundland, the rest on the Pacific coast.

CAPE VERDE

Republic of Cape Verde

COAST GUARD

Personnel (2001): Approx. 40 total (14 officers)

Bases: Headquarters at Praia; repair facilities at Porto Grande on Isla de São Vicente

Maritime Aviation: One EMB 110P1 Bandeirante and one Dornier Do-228-212 maritime surveillance aircraft. The latter was acquired in 2000, replacing a similar aircraft lost on 7-8-99.

PATROL CRAFT [WPC]

♦ 1 ex-German Kondor-I class (Project 89.1)
Bldr: VEB Peenewerft, Wolgast

	Laid down	L	In serv.
P 521 Vigilante (ex-*Kühlungsborn*, BG 32, ex-GS-07, ex-G 445)	9-9-69	14-1-70	3-6-70

D: 327 tons (339 fl) **S:** 20 kts **Dim:** 52.00 × 7.12 × 2.40
A: none (as transferred)
Electronics: Radar: 1 Decca 360 nav.; 1 . . . surf. search
M: 2 Type 40DM diesels; 2 CP Kort-nozzle props; 4,400 bhp (4,000 sust.)
Range: 1,900/15; 2,200/11 **Crew:** 12 tot.

Remarks: Former East German "High Seas Minesweeper" taken over by Germany in 1991 and assigned to the German Border Guard *(Bundesgrenzschutz-See).* Donated to the Cape Verde Islands after a 5-98 to 9-98 conversion at A&R Neptun Boat Service GmbH, Rostock, to serve as a fisheries protection patrol craft; handed over 25-9-98. A helicopter platform atop a deckhouse replaced the original mine countermeasures winch and cable drum area aft; new communications gear radars were fitted. Two sisters have been transferred to Malta and five to Tunisia.

PATROL BOATS [WPB]

♦ 1 U.S. 51-foot Mk 4 class
Bldr: Peterson Bldrs, Sturgeon Bay, Wis. (In serv. 19-8-93)

P 151 Espadarte

Espadarte (P 151)—on builder's trials Peterson Builders, 4-93

D: 24 tons (fl) **S:** 24 kts **Dim:** 15.54 × 4.47 × 1.30
A: 1 twin 12.7-mm M2 mg; 2 single 7.62-mm mg
Electronics: Radar: 1 Furuno . . . nav.
M: 2 G.M. Detroit Diesel 6V92 TA diesels; 2 props; 900 bhp (520 sust.)
Electric: 15 kw tot. **Range:** 500/20 kts **Fuel:** 800 gallons **Crew:** 6 tot.

Remarks: Ordered 25-9-92, launched 8-4-93, and delivered in Cape Verde 11-93. Aluminum construction. Carries a 4.27-m rigid inflatable inspection craft (with a 50-bhp outboard motor) on the stern. Sisters operate in the Senegalese Navy.

♦ 1 Soviet Zhuk class (Project 1400M)

D: 35.9 tons (39.7 fl) **S:** 30 kts **Dim:** 23.80 (21.70 wl) × 5.00 (3.80 wl) × 1.00 (hull)
A: 2 twin 12.7-mm Utës-M mg **Electronics:** Radar: 1 Lotsiya nav.
M: 2 M-401B diesels; 2 props; 2,200 bhp
Electric: 48 kw total (2 × 21-kw, 1 × 6-kw diesel sets)
Range: 500/13.5 **Endurance:** 5 days **Crew:** 3 officers, 8 enlisted

Remarks: Survivor of three transferred in 1980; the other pair is providing spares.

CAYMAN ISLANDS

ROYAL CAYMAN ISLANDS POLICE

PATROL BOATS [WPB]

♦ 1 48-foot Dauntless class
Bldr: SeaArk, Monticello, Ark. (In serv. 7-94)

Cayman Protector

Cayman Protector SeaArk, 1994

PATROL BOATS [WPB] *(continued)*

D: 14 tons (fl) **S:** 26 kts **Dim:** 14.63 × 4.88 × 1.37 (props)
A: small arms **Electronics:** Radar: 1 Raytheon R40X nav.
M: 2 Caterpillar 3208TA diesels; 2 props; 850 bhp (720 sust.)
Range: 400/22 **Fuel:** 250 gallons **Crew:** 5 tot.

Remarks: Aluminum construction. C. Raymond Hunt, "Deep-Vee" hull design.

Note: Also in use is a small outboard-powered launch. The Customs Service also has one or more launches.

CHILE

Republic of Chile

ARMADA DE CHILE

Personnel (2001): Approx. 22,000, including 3,380 naval infantry, 1,600 coast guard, and 500 naval aviation. About 6,500 civilians are employed at various shore installations and dockyards.

Bases: Fleet Headquarters and Headquarters 1st Naval Zone at Valparaiso, which also has repair yard, naval air base, and principal training facilities; Headquarters 2nd Naval Zone is at Talcahuano, which also has major repair facilities and the submarine base; Headquarters 3rd Naval Zone at Punta Arenas, which has repair facilities and an air base; and Headquarters 4th Naval Zone at Iquique. Smaller facilities are located at Puerto Montt and at Puerto Williams, which has an air station.

Naval Aviation: Fixed-wing aircraft include 4 UP-3B Orion, 6 Embraer P-111 Bandeirante, and 3 EMB C-95 Bandeirante maritime surveillance aircraft; 2 UP-3A, 3 EMB C-95 Bandeirante, and 4 CASA 212M-100 Aviocar transports; 10 Pilatus PC-7 Turbo-Trainer light attack/trainers; and 10 Cessna O-2A Skymaster trainers. Helicopters include 6 Aérospatiale AS.532SC Cougars, 1 Aérospatiale AS.332B Super Puma, 6 MBB BO-105s, and 8 Bell 206A JetRangers. All Cougar and Super Puma helicopters are referred to as Cougars and are locally designated SH-32; the AS.532SCs are equipped with Thales HS-312 dipping sonars and AM 39 Exocet missiles.

Aircraft are based at the Torquemada Naval Air Station, Viña del Mar, with other airfields at Iquique, Punta Arenas, and Puerto Williams. The squadrons are organized as follows:

- HA-1 Shipboard Attack: 7 AS.532SC Cougar /AS.332 Super Puma (SH-32)
- HU-1 Utility Helicopter: 6 MBB BO-105, 8 Bell 206B
- VP-1 Maritime Reconnaissance: 4 UP-3B Orion, 6 P-111 Bandeirante
- VC-1 Transport and General-Purpose: 4 CASA 212M-100, 2 UP-3A Orion, and 3 EMB C-95 Bandeirante
- VT-1 Training: 10 PC-7 (also light attack), 10 O-2A Skymaster

Chilean UP-3B Orion Chilean Navy, 1998

Chilean Navy AS.532SC Cougar helicopter Maritime Photographic, 7-01

Chilean Navy BO-105 helicopter Julio Montes, 4-00

Naval Infantry: 1st Marine Infantry Detachment *Patricio Lynch* at Iquique; 2nd Marine Infantry Detachment *Miller* at Viña del Mar; 3rd Marine Infantry Detachment *Sargento Aldea* at Talcahuano; and 4th Marine Infantry Detachment *Cochrane* at Punta Arenas. There are also the 51st Commando Group at Valparaiso, a logistics battalion, and several engineering units. Artillery in use includes 18 155-mm Puteaux cannon made during World War I and a number of Korean-made 105-mm howitzers. Chile is seeking 30 LVTP-7 amphibious armored personnel carriers from the U.S.A.

Weapons and Systems: Most equipment is of Israeli, U.S., German, or British origin, but Chile has a growing military electronics industry and produces its own naval combat information systems. ASW torpedoes ordered from France in 1989 have not yet been delivered, due to lengthy delays in the MU-90 torpedo program. The Whitehead-Alenia Sistem Subacquei (WASS) Black Shark 533-mm torpedo was selected during 5-00 for use in new submarines.

DIESEL ATTACK SUBMARINES [SS]

♦ 0 (+ 2) Scorpène class
Bldrs: DCN, Cherbourg, France, and Izar, Cartagena, Spain

	Final assembly	Laid down	L	In serv.
S . . . O'Higgins	Izar, Cartagena	11-99	. . .	2005
S . . . Carrera	DCN, Cherbourg	. . .	. . .	2007

Scorpène class—official model DCN, 1997

D: 1,668 tons surf./1,908 tons sub. **S:** . . . kts surf./20+ kts sub.
Dim: 66.40 × 6.20 × 5.8 (surf.)
A: 6 bow 533-mm TT (18 DCN-WASS Black Shark wire-guided torpedoes and Aérospatiale SM 39 Exocet missiles)
Electronics:
Radar: 1 Kelvin-Hughes Type 1007 nav./surf. search
Sonar: Thales . . . suite, with passive flank and towed arrays
EW: ArgoSystems AR-900 intercept
M: diesel electric: 4 MTU . . . . diesels (840 bhp each), Jeumont axial-flux permanent magnet electric motor; 1 prop; . . . shp
Range: 6,500/8 surf.; 550/4 sub. **Endurance:** 50 days
Crew: 6 officers, 26 enlisted

Remarks: Ordered 17-12-97 for $420 million total. DCN is performing about 60% of the construction work, including manufacturing the pressure hulls and outfitting the bow and amidships sections; Izar is fitting out the stern sections, and each company will do final outfitting on one unit. Stern sections for *O'Higgins* left Cherbourg for Spain on 3-7-00 for outfitting.
Hull systems: Employ HLES 80 steel in the pressure hull, permitting diving depths in excess of 320 m. No air-independent propulsion system was ordered. A 360-cell battery is employed. All machinery is "rafted" for sound isolation. Only nine personnel will be on watch under normal conditions.
Combat systems: The UDS International SUBTICS (Submarine Tactical Information and Command System) weapons-control system will be similar to French Navy's SET *(Système d'Exploitation Tactique)* and will have 6 two-screen display consoles. The sonar suite will include a cylindrical bow transducer array, an active array, a passive ranging array, an acoustic intercept system, and passive flank arrays. A SAGEM SMS optronic search periscope and a SAGEM APS attack periscope will be fitted. A Litef integrated navigation system will be employed.

♦ 2 IKL Type 209/1400 Bldr: Howaldtswerke, Kiel, Germany

	Laid down	L	In serv.
20 Thomson	1-11-80	28-2-82	31-8-84
21 Simpson	15-2-81	29-7-83	18-9-84

D: 1,158 tons light; 1,285 tons surf./1,395 tons sub.
S: 11 kts surf./12 kts snorkel/21.5 kts sub.

DIESEL ATTACK SUBMARINES [SS] *(continued)*

Thomson (20) Maritime Photographic, 7-01

Simpson (21) George R. Schneider, 8-96

Dim: 61.00 × 6.20 (7.60 over stern planes) × 5.50 (surf.)
A: 8 bow 533-mm TT (16 SUT Mod. 1 wire-guided torpedoes)
Electronics:
Radar: 1 Thales Calypso-II nav./surf. search
Sonar: STN Atlas Elektronik CSU-3 suite
EW: Thales DR-2000U intercept
M: 4 MTU 12V493 AZ-80 diesels, 4 A.E.G. 450-kw generators, 1 Siemens electric motor; 1 7-bladed prop; 5,000 shp
Range: 10,000/8 snorkel; 16/21.5, 400/4 sub. **Fuel:** 116 tons
Endurance: 50 days **Crew:** 5 officers, 26 enlisted

Remarks: Ordered 12-80. Used components from a canceled Iranian order. 21, damaged in a collision 29-3-84 on trials, was completed 18-9-84. 20 was completed on 7-5-84.
Hull systems: Have higher casing than earlier IKL-designed submarines. Sail and masting are .5 m higher than on other ships of this class, to cope with heavy seas in Chilean operating areas.
Combat systems: The later sonar suite from the two *Oberons* may be transferred to this pair. Have Carl Zeiss SERO 40 Stab (stabilized) optical periscope system, with AS 40 attack and BS 40 search scopes.

♦ 1 British Oberon class
Bldr: Scott-Lithgow SB & Eng., Greenock, Scotland

	Laid down	L	In serv.
22 O'Brien	17-1-71	21-12-72	4-76

O'Brien (22) Maritime Photographic, 7-01

D: 1,650 tons light, 2,070 tons surf. (fl)/2,450 tons sub.
S: 15 kts surf./17.5 kts sub. **Dim:** 89.92 (87.45 pp) × 8.07 × 5.48
A: 6 bow 533-mm TT (22 SUT wire-guided and U.K. Mk 8 straight-running torpedoes)
Electronics:
Radar: 1 Kelvin-Hughes Type 1006 nav./surf. search
Sonar: STN Atlas Elektronik CSU-90 suite (see Remarks)
EW: Porpoise intercept
M: 2 1,840-hp Admiralty Standard Range 16 VVS-AS21 diesels, diesel-electric drive; 2 props; 6,000 shp
Range: 9,000/12 surf.; 11,000/8 snorkel **Fuel:** 298 m^3 (446 emergency)
Endurance: 56 days **Crew:** 6 officers, 62 enlisted

Remarks: Sister *Hyatt* (23) was stricken 10-4-00 to serve as a source of spares to keep the *O'Brien* operating until about 2004–05.
Combat systems: The two "short" torpedo tubes aft were for Mk 23 countermeasures homing torpedoes and are no longer in use. Has Pilkington Optronics CK 24 search and CH 74 attack periscopes. U.K. Mk.2 submerged signal and decoy ejector forward and Mk.4 Mod. 1B aft; both launch 102-mm devices. During 1993–94 was refitted by the Chilean firm SISDEF with STN Atlas Elektronik ISUS-90 combat system and CSU-90 sonar suite, plus a modified torpedo launching system.

DESTROYERS [DD]

♦ 3 ex-U.K. County class
Bldr: Fairfield SB & Eng., Govan (11: Swan Hunter, Wallsend-on-Tyne)

	Laid down	L	In serv.
11 Capitán Prat (ex-*Norfolk*)	15-3-66	16-11-67	7-3-70
12 Almirante Cochrane (ex-*Antrim*)	20-1-66	19-10-67	14-7-70
15 Almirante Blanco Encalada (ex-*Fife*)	1-6-62	9-7-64	21-6-66

Capitán Prat (11)—with short flight deck Maritime Photographic, 7-01

Almirante Cochrane (12) Maritime Photographic, 7-01

Almirante Blanco Encalada (15) Maritime Photographic, 7-01

Almirante Blanco Encalada (15) Maritime Photographic, 7-01

Capitán Prat (12) Maritime Photographic, 7-01

D: 5,510 tons (6,270 fl) **S:** 30.5 kts (28 sust.)
Dim: 158.55 (153.9 pp) × 16.46 × 6.3–6.5 (max.)
A: 4 MM 38 Exocet SSM; 2 8-cell Barak VLS SAM launch groups; 1 twin 114-mm 45-cal. Mk 6 DP; 2 single 20-mm 70-cal. Mk 4 Oerlikon AA; 2 triple 324-mm Mk 32 ASW TT (U.S. Mk 46 Mod. 5 torpedoes); 2 (11: 1) AS.332B Cougar helicopters (with SM 39 Exocet missiles)
Electronics:
Radar: 1 . . . nav.; 1 Type 965M early warning; 1 Marconi Type 992Q air search; 2 Elta EL/M-2228S AMDR Barak target desig.; 1 Plessey Type 903 gun f.c.
Sonar: Type 184 MF hull-mounted (7–9 kHz); Type 162 bottomed-target classification (15 kHz)
EW: UA-8/9 intercept; Type 667 jammers; FH-5 HFD/F; 4 18-round Wallop Barricade decoy RL

DESTROYERS [DD] *(continued)*

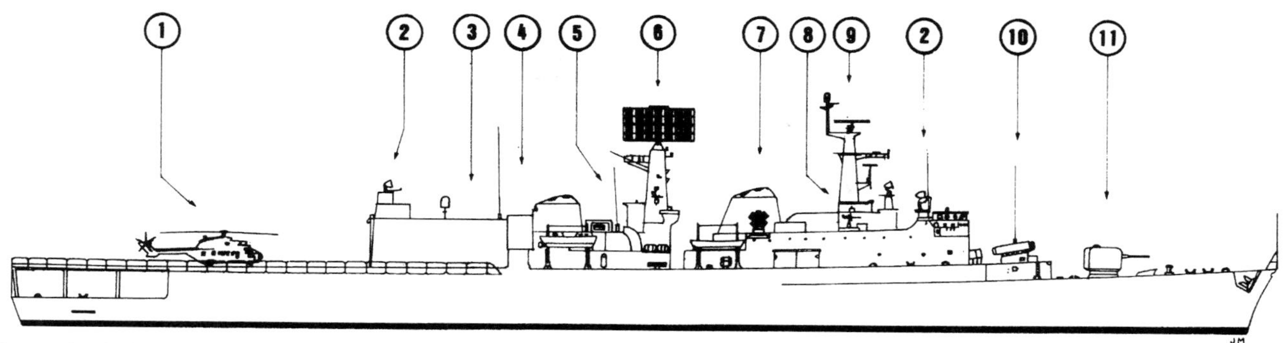

Almirante Blanco Encalada (15) 1. AS.532SC Cougar helicopter 2. EL/M-2228S AMDR target-acquisition radars 3. helicopter hangar 4. vertical launch group containers for Barak missiles 5. triple Mk 32 ASW TT 6. Type 965M early-warning radar 7. Barricade decoy rocket launchers 8. 20-mm Oerlikon AA 9. Type 992Q air/surface-search radar 10. MM 38 Exocet antiship missile containers 11. twin 114-mm Mk 6 dual-purpose gunmount Drawing by Jean Moulin

M: COSAG: 2 sets A.E.I. geared steam turbines (15,000 shp each) and 4 English Electric G6 gas turbines (7,500 shp each); 2 props; 60,000 shp
Boilers: 2 Babcock & Wilcox; 49.2 kg/cm², 510° C
Electric: 4,750 kw tot. (2 × 750-kw diesel sets, 2 turboalternators)
Range: 3,500/28 **Fuel:** 600 tons **Crew:** 36 officers, 434 enlisted

Remarks: *Cochrane* was purchased 22-6-84 and recommissioned 25-6-84. *Blanco Encalada* was purchased and transferred 12-8-87. *Prat* was transferred 6-4-82 in Chile. All have been converted to carry combat helicopters; *Blanco Encalada* had the Sea Slug missile facilities deleted and replaced with a larger helicopter hangar and flight deck to handle two helicopters at ASMAR, Talcahuano, completing 10-88, while a similar conversion of *Cochrane* was completed during 5-93 and work on the *Prat* had been concluded by early 2001.
Disposals: The unconverted *Almirante Latorre* (14, ex-*Glamorgan*) was placed in reserve on 30-12-98 and serves as a spares source.
Hull systems: Four pairs of fin stabilizers and twin rudders. Each propeller is driven by one steam turbine for cruise, adding one or two gas turbines for boost. There are three steam turboalternators and three gas-turbine generators.
Aviation systems: In 12 and 15, the original hangar (which opened to port) has been replaced by a twin hangar capable of holding two Cougar helicopters; the helicopter decks have been increased to 617 m² from the original 325 m²; two 55-m Indal Assist deck-traversing systems have been installed; and the new flight deck extends to the stern. In 11, there is only a single-place new hangar and the flight deck does not extend to the stern. The Cougar helicopters are equipped with Thales HS-312 dipping sonars and can launch either U.S. Mk 46 Mod. 2 torpedoes or AM 39 Exocet missiles.
Combat systems: The original ADAWS-1 combat data system has been replaced by the Chilean-developed SISDEF SP-100 system; employing the Ada computer language, it has several fully autonomous multifunction tactical consoles linked by a local area network, can track 512 radar targets and 100 ESM bearings simultaneously, and was first installed in *Blanco Encalada* in 1993. SP-100 employs three vertical display consoles and two horizontal plot displays. Normally, only two Exocet missiles are carried. *Blanco Encalada* had the Israeli Barak SAM system installed by 3-94; it was installed in *Cochrane* during a refit completed in 5-94. The Israeli Elta AMDR (Automatic Missile Detection Radar) antenna is located on the foremast, and the system is said to have a 90% chance of detecting a 0.1-m³, Mach 3 target at up to 15 km range; the Barak radar directors are mounted atop the pilothouse and abaft the after stack.

Note: *Almirante Williams*–class destroyers *Almirante Williams* (D 19, retired 10-1-96) and *Almirante Riveros* (D 18, stricken 11-94) are employed as floating barracks hulks.

FRIGATES [FF]

♦ 0 (+ 4 + 2) MEKO A200 class (Project Tridente)

Bldrs: First unit: Blohm + Voss, Hamburg, Germany; others: ASMAR, Talcahuano

	Laid down	L	In serv.
PF	2002	2004	2006
PF	2003	. . .	2007
PF	2004	. . .	2008
PF	2005	. . .	2009

D: 3,800–4,000 tons (fl) **S:** 27 kts **Dim:** 125.0 × . . . × . . .
A: 8 RGM-84 Harpoon or RBS-15 Mk 3 SSM; 1 127-mm 54-cal. OTOBreda DP; 2 8-cell Barak VLS SAM launch groups
Electronics:
Radar: . . .
Sonar: . . .
EW: . . .
M: 4 . . . diesels; 2 CP props; . . . bhp
Range: . . ./. . . **Crew:** . . .

Remarks: An initial agreement was made on 29-7-00 with Blohm + Voss, Germany, for licensed production of this class in Chile, and a letter of intent was signed on 21-5-01, with the intention to sign a final contract late in 2001 or early in 2002. The first four ships are to be general-purpose ships with air-defense capabilities, while the other two will emphasize ASW. CelsiusTech, Thales, Lockheed Martin Canada, and Chile's SISDEF were said to be short-listed as providers of the combat system integration. Lockheed Martin is offering the Standard SM-2 ER Block II long-range SAM, Evolved Sea Sparrow short-range SAM, the RAM Block I point-defense SAM, the Phalanx CIWS, the SPS-49 search radar, the SPY-1F Aegis radar system, and the United Defense 127-mm 62-cal. Mk 45 gun—all of which, if fitted, would require a far larger ship than is envisioned by the Chilean Navy. The Barak SAM systems would be taken from County-class destroyers when they are retired.

♦ 3 British Leander class

Bldr: Yarrow & Co., Scotstoun, Glasgow

	Laid down	L	In serv.
PF 06 Almirante Condell	5-6-71	12-6-72	21-12-73
PF 07 Almirante Lynch	6-12-72	6-12-73	25-5-74
PF 08 Ministro Zenteno (ex-*Achilles*)	1-12-67	21-11-68	9-7-70

Almirante Condell (PF 06) Maritime Photographic, 7-01

Almirante Condell (PF 06) Maritime Photographic, 7-01

Almirante Lynch (PF 07) H&L Van Ginderen, 10-99

D: 2,998 tons (3,190 fl), except PF 08: 2,660 tons (3,120 fl) **S:** 29 kts
Dim: 113.38 (109.73 pp) × 13.12 × 4.50 (5.49 props)
A: 4 MM 40 (PF 08: 2 MM 38) Exocet SSM; 1 twin 114-mm 45-cal. Mk VI DP; 1 4-round Sea Cat GWS.22 SAM syst.; 2 twin 20-mm 70-cal. Mk 24 Oerlikon AA; 2 triple 324-mm ASW TT; 1 AS.332B Super Puma ASW (PF 08: BO-105CBS or Bell 206A JetRanger) helicopter

FRIGATES [FF] *(continued)*

Electronics:
Radar: 1 Kelvin-Hughes Type 1006 nav.; 1 Marconi Type 966 early warning; 1 Marconi Type 992Q air/surf. search; 1 Plessey Type 903 gun f.c., 1 Plessey Type 904 Sea Cat f.c.
Sonar: Type 177 (PF 08: Type 184M) hull-mounted MF; Type 170B HF attack; Type 162 bottomed-target classification
EW: Elta NS-9003A intercept; Elta NS-9005 jammer; 4 twin-rail Wallop Barricade decoy RL
M: 2 sets White or English Electric geared steam turbines; 2 props; 30,000 shp
Boilers: 2 Babcock & Wilcox; 38.7 kg/cm^2, 450° C **Electric:** 2,500 kw tot.
Range: 4,500/12 **Fuel:** 500 tons
Crew: 22 officers, 11 chief petty officers, 214 other enlisted

Remarks: PF 06 and PF 07 were ordered 14-1-70. PF 08 paid off from the Royal Navy at the end of 3-90 and was sold to Chile later in the year, leaving as deck cargo aboard the heavy-lift ship *Super Servant 4* on 27-11-90. PF 06 rammed the U.S. *Pecos* (T-AO 197) during a refueling exercise on 26-6-98 and was repaired at San Diego.
Disposals: *General Baquedano* (PF 09, ex-*Ariadne*), purchased and transferred 3-6-92, was not modernized and was placed in reserve on 30-12-98 for use as a spares source.
Hull systems: PF 06 and PF 07 may be re-engined with diesels or gas turbines under a life-extension program to keep them in service through the next decade. Both have had the helicopter deck extended over the sides of the ship, while that on PF 08 remains in the original configuration.
Combat systems: The combat data system has been replaced by the Chilean-developed SISDEF Imagen SP-100(06) system; employing Ada computer language, it has several fully autonomous multifunction tactical consoles linked by a local area network and was first installed in PF 06 in 1993. A British MRS.3 gun fire-control system is fitted for the 114-mm mount. PF 06 and PF 07 originally had MM 38 Exocet missiles at the stern in lieu of the Limbo ASW mortar fitted in British ships; the missiles were exchanged for the later MM 40 and were relocated flanking the hangar in refits at the end of the 1980s, at which time the EW suites were updated with Israeli-supplied equipment. In addition, the hangars were raised and the helicopter pad was lengthened, permitting them to operate AS.332B Super Puma helicopters. Plans to fit the Israeli Barak SAM system have been canceled. PF 08 completed a less extensive modernization refit in 12-96; two launcher/containers for MM 38 Exocet missiles were added abreast the stack on the 01 level, but the hangar was not modified.

GUIDED-MISSILE PATROL CRAFT [PTG]

♦ 3 Israeli Reshev (Sa'ar IV) class Bldr: Israeli SY, Haifa

	L	In serv.	Transferred
LM 30 Casma (ex-*Romach*)	1-74	3-74	8-11-79
LM 31 Chipana (ex-*Keshet*)	23-8-73	10-73	30-12-79
LM 34 Angamos (ex-*Reshev*)	19-2-73	4-73	11-96

Casma (LM 30) Chilean Navy, 1997

D: 415 tons (450 fl) **S:** 32 kts **Dim:** 58.10 × 7.60 × 2.40
A: 4 Gabriel-II SSM; 2 single 76-mm 62-cal. OTOBreda DP; 2 single 20-mm 70-cal. Oerlikon AA; 1 12.7-mm M2 mg
Electronics:
Radar: 1 Thales THD 1040 Neptune search; 1 Elta M-2221 (Orion RTN-10X) f.c.
EW: Elta MN-53 intercept; Elta Rattler jammer; Elta EA-2118 comms intercept; 4 ACDS decoy RL; 72 LCRL decoy RL
M: 4 MTU 16V538 TB82 diesels; 4 props; 14,000 bhp (11,880 sust.)—see Remarks
Electric: 352 kw tot. (4 × 88 kw) **Range:** 1,500/30; 3,000/20; 5,000/15
Endurance: 10 days **Crew:** 8 officers, 44 enlisted

Remarks: LM 30 and LM 31 were acquired 8-11-79 and 30-12-79, respectively. The planned transfer of four additional units was canceled in 1984, but LM 33 and *Papudo* (LM 34) were purchased on 1-6-97, commissioned on 29-7-97, and arrived in Chile at Iquique on 29-7-97; LM 34 was later stricken for cannibalization. LM 30 was re-engined during 2000 at Talcahuano with MTU 16V396-series diesels producing a total of 13,000 bhp and a 31-kt maximum speed; work on a second ship began late in 2000. Harpoon SSMs were removed prior to transfer.

♦ 4 ex-German Type 148
Bldr: CMN, Cherbourg, France (LM 37, 38: Friedrich Lürssen Werft, Vegesack)

	Laid down	L	In serv.
LM 36 Guardiamarina Riquelme (ex-*Wolf,* P 6149)	23-1-73	11-1-74	26-2-74
LM 37 Teniente Orella (ex-*Elster,* P 6154)	29-6-73	8-7-74	14-11-74
LM 38 Almirante Uribe (ex-*Kranich,* P 6160)	9-5-74	26-5-75	6-8-75
LM 39 Teniente Serrano (ex-*Tiger,* P 6141)	11-10-71	27-9-72	30-10-72

Almirante Uribe (LM 38) Maritime Photographic, 7-01

Teniente Serrano (LM 39)—outboard a sister Findler & Winter, 10-98

D: 234 tons (264 fl) **S:** 35.8 kts **Dim:** 47.0 (45.9 pp) × 7.1 × 2.66 (fl)
A: 4 MM 38 Exocet SSM; 1 76-mm 62-cal. OTOBreda DP; 1 40-mm 70-cal. OTOBreda-Bofors AA or 8 mines in place of the 40-mm AA
Electronics:
Radar: 1 SMA 3RM 20 nav.; 1 Thales Triton-G air/surf. search; 1 Thales Castor-II f.c.
M: 4 MTU MD 872 16-cyl. diesels; 4 props; 14,000 bhp (at 1,515 rpm; 12,000 sust.)
Electric: 270 kw tot. **Range:** 570/30; 1,600/15 **Fuel:** 39 tons
Crew: 4 officers, 17 petty officers, 9 other enlisted

Remarks: LM 36 and LM 37 were transferred on decommissioning from German Navy on 27-8-97 to form a squadron to cover the 4th Naval Zone south of the Peruvian border. They arrived at Talcahuano 11-10-97. The other two were transferred in 10-98, along with sisters *Luchs* (P 6143) and *Pelikan* (P 6153), which were to be used for cannibalization spares. These four departed Germany 22-9-98 aboard the dock-ship *Clipper Cheyenne,* but LM 38 and LM 39 were badly damaged during a storm in the Bay of Biscay; all four arrived at Talcahuano on 27-11-98.

The craft were ordered for the German Navy 18-12-70 as CMN's type Combattante II A4L. Design by Friedrich Lürssen Werft, Vegesack. All hulls fitted out at Cherbourg by CMN.
Hull systems: Steel construction. Three of the class are being re-engined with MTU 16V396-series diesels producing 13,000 bhp total.
Combat systems: Have the Thales Vega fire-control system with Castor-II radar; Triton is used for target designation. All have the PALIS (Passive-Active Link) system for data sharing and can use NATO Link 11. OTOBreda-made Bofors 40-mm mountings with Mauser GRP-enclosed gunhouses have been fitted in place of the original open Bofors 40-mm L70 mountings aft. The German EW suite was removed prior to transfer.

♦ 2 Israeli Sa'ar II class (Non-operational)
Bldr: CMN, Cherbourg, France

LM 32 *Iquique* (ex-*Hanit*) (L: 1969)
LM 33 *Covadonga* (ex-*Hetz*) (L: 14-12-69)

Iquique (LM 32) Chilean Navy, 1992

D: 220 tons (250 fl) **S:** 40 kts **Dim:** 45.00 × 7.00 × 1.80 (2.50 props)
A: 6 Gabriel-I SSM in triple, trainable mountings; 1 76-mm 62-cal. OTOBreda DP; 2 single 12.7-mm M2 mg

GUIDED-MISSILE PATROL CRAFT [PTG] *(continued)*

Electronics:
Radar: 1 Thales THD 1040 Neptune search; 1 Elta M 2221 (Orion RTN-10X) f.c.
EW: Elta MN-53 intercept; Elta EA-2118 comms intercept; Elta Rattler jammer; 4 ACDS decoy RL; 72 LCRL decoy RL
M: 4 MTU MD871 diesels; 4 props; 14,000 bhp (10,000 sust.)
Range: 1,000/30; 1,600/20; 2,500/15 **Fuel:** 30 tons
Crew: 5 officers, 30–35 enlisted

Remarks: Purchased 12-88, transferred 1-89, and commissioned 3-5-89. U.S. Harpoon missiles were removed prior to transfer, and a second triple, trainable Gabriel launcher was installed on the aft mounting ring, which can alternatively accommodate a single 40-mm AA gun. Both were reported decommissioned during 2-00, probably for disposal.

PATROL COMBATANTS [PG]

♦ 6 Contramestre Micalvi–class (Project Taitão) multirole
Bldr: ASMAR, Talcahuano

	Laid down	L	In serv.
PSG 71 Contramestre Micalvi	2-1-92	27-9-92	27-1-93
PSG 72 Contramestre Ortiz	28-6-92	23-7-93	13-12-93
PSG 73 Aspirante Isaza	28-9-92	7-1-94	27-5-94
PSG 74 Aspirante Morel	28-12-92	21-4-94	5-7-94
PSG 77 Corneta Cabrales	. . .	4-4-96	29-6-96
PSG 78 Piloto Sibbald	. . .	5-6-96	29-8-96

Contramestre Ortiz (PSG 72) Maritime Photographic, 7-01

Corneta Cabrales (PSG 77) H&L Van Ginderen, 1-99

D: 483 tons (535 fl) **S:** 15 kts **Dim:** 42.50 (36.30 pp) × 8.50 × 3.90 (loaded)
A: 1 40-mm 60-cal. Bofors Mk. 3 AA; 2 single 20-mm 70-cal. Oerlikon AA
Electronics: Radar: 2 Decca . . . nav.
M: 2 Caterpillar 3512TA diesels; 2 props; 2,560 bhp (PSG 77, 78: 2 diesels; 2 props; 3,600 bhp)
Electric: 210 kw tot. **Range:** 1,650/12 normal; 3,400/12 max.
Fuel: 43 m^3 + 70 m^3 in cargo hold **Endurance:** 30 days
Crew: 5 officers, 18 enlisted + 30 passengers

Remarks: Designed with the assistance of NEVASABU, the Netherlands. Intended for offshore patrol duties, cargo and troop transportation, lighthouse and navigational buoy support, torpedo retrieval, and fisheries protection. May later be upgraded with the provision of a sonar, bow-thruster, fin stabilizers, and mine rails, but plans to add a mine countermeasures capability have been canceled. PSG 75 and PSG 76 were built for potential foreign sales but were instead purchased in 1996 for the Dirección General del Territorio Marítimo y de la Marine Mercante and are operated by Navy crews. PSG 77 was fitted in 4-99 for hydrographic survey duties for use by the Servicio Hidrográfico y Oceanográfico de la Armada de Chile (SHOA).
Hull systems: Have two generator sets, an electrohydraulic crane on the fantail, and provision for stowing two 9-ton cargo containers on deck aft. Have 70 m^3 stores or liquid fuel capacity (35 tons). Can carry 35 m^3 fresh water. Hull has a bulbous bow and eight watertight compartments. PSG 77 and PSG 78 have more-powerful propulsion plants and displace 522 tons (fl). PSG 77 has an STN Atlas Elektronik dual-frequency multibeam sounding sonar operating at 50 kHz to 1,500-m depths and at 200 kHz for depths to 300 m; also fitted is an STN Atlas Elektronik DESO-25 single-beam echo sounder, a Dynabase motion sensor, a forward-looking sonar, and an STN Atlas Elektronik Hydromap data acquisition, storage, and navigation workstation, while a survey launch carried by the ship has two DESO-17 echo sounders, Hydromap, and digital GPS.

Note: The four *Guacolda*-class former torpedo boats were not stricken in 1999–2000 as reported in the last edition but are now in service with the Chilean Coast Guard.

AMPHIBIOUS WARFARE SHIPS

♦ 1 ex-U.S. Newport-class tank landing ship [LST]
Bldr: National Steel & Shipbuilding, San Diego

	Laid down	L	In serv.
R 93 Valdivia (ex-*San Bernardino*, LST 1189)	12-7-69	28-3-70	27-3-71

Valdivia (R 93) Chilean Navy, 12-98

D: 4,975 tons light (8,576 fl) **S:** 22 kts (20 sust.)
Dim: 159.2 (171.3 over horns) × 21.18 × 5.3 (aft; 1.80 fwd)
A: 1 20-mm Mk 15 Phalanx gatling CIWS; 4 single 12.7-mm mg
Electronics:
Radar: 1 Raytheon SPS-64(V)9 nav.; 1 Raytheon SPS-10F surf. search
M: 6 Alco 16-251 diesels; 2 CP props; 16,500 bhp
Range: 14,250/14 **Fuel:** 1,750 tons
Crew: 13 officers, 244 enlisted + troops: 20 officers, 294 enlisted + 72 emergency accomm.

Remarks: Decommissioned from U.S. Navy 30-9-95 and transferred to Chile 8-12-95 on lease; offered for sale to Chile under the U.S. Defense Authorization Act for FY 99. Plans to acquire a second unit have been shelved. Ran aground mid-1997 but has been repaired. U.S. Navy sister *La Moure County* (LST 1194), which went hard aground on 12-9-00 in southern Chile, was stricken on 17-11-00 at Valparaiso and is being used as a spares source.
Hull systems: Can transport 2,000 tons of cargo or, for beaching, 500 tons on 1,765 m^2 of deck space. A side-thruster propeller forward helps when marrying to a causeway. There is a 34-m-long, 75-ton-capacity mobile aluminum ramp forward, which is linked to the tank deck by a second from the upper deck. Aft is a 242-m^2 helicopter platform and a stern door for loading and unloading vehicles. The tank deck, which has a 75-ton-capacity turntable at both ends, can carry 23 armored personnel carriers or 29 M 48 tanks or 41 2.5-ton trucks, while the upper deck can accept 29 2.5-ton trucks. Formerly carried 3 LCVP and 1 LCP in Welin davits. Has two 10-ton cranes. Carries 141,600 gallons vehicle fuel.

♦ 2 French BATRAL-class landing ship/transports [LSM]
Bldr: ASMAR, Talcahuano

	L	In serv.
R 92 Rancagua	26-3-82	1-7-83
R 95 Chacabuco (ex-R 93)	16-7-85	1-4-86

Rancagua (R 92) Maritime Photographic, 7-01

D: 770 tons (1,330 fl) **S:** 13 kts **Dim:** 79.40 (68.00 pp) × 13.16 × 3.50
A: 2 single 40-mm 60-cal. Bofors AA; 1 20-mm 70-cal. Oerlikon AA; 2 single 81-mm mortars
Electronics: Radar: 1 Decca 1229 nav.
M: 2 SEMT-Pielstick 12PA4 V185VG diesels; 2 props; 4,000 bhp
Electric: 360 kw **Range:** 4,500/13 **Crew:** 49 ship's company + 180 troops

Remarks: Constructed with French technical assistance. Sister *Maipo* (R 91) was placed in reserve in 1998 and stricken in 1999.
Hull systems: Cargo: 350 tons vehicles and/or dry cargo, 208 tons potable water or ballast. Bow ramp has 40-ton capacity. The helicopter platform can accommodate a Super Puma. Hull has eight watertight compartments and a double bottom.

♦ 2 Elicura-class logistics landing ships [LSM]

	Bldr	In serv.
R 90 Elicura (ex-AP 95)	ASMAR, Talcahuano	10-12-63
R 94 Orompello (ex-AP 94)	Dade DD Co., Miami, Fla.	15-9-64

D: 290 tons (750 fl) **S:** 11 kts **Dim:** 49.20 (46.00 pp) × 10.40 × 2.30
A: 2 single 20-mm 70-cal. Mk 10 Oerlikon AA
Electronics: Radar: 1 Raytheon 1500B Pathfinder nav.
M: 2 Cummins VT-17-700M diesels; 2 props; 1,006 bhp (900 sust.)
Electric: 120 kw tot. **Range:** 2,900/10.5 **Fuel:** 71 tons
Endurance: 15 days **Crew:** 19 tot. + 180 troops or 18 passengers

AMPHIBIOUS WARFARE SHIPS *(continued)*

Orompello (R 94) Chilean Navy, 1997

Remarks: Two near-sisters are operated by a Chilean commercial firm. The guns are not always aboard.
Hull systems: Have a bow ramp and one 10-ton-capacity cargo boom, with a smaller one forward. Cargo capacity: 380 tons. Can transport an infantry company of 180 troops if necessary and can carry tanks weighing up to 40 tons.

AUXILIARIES

♦ 1 ex-Canadian icebreaker/supply vessel [AGB]

Bldr: Vickers, Montreal (In serv. 10-69)

AP 46 Contre-Almirante Oscar Viel Toro (ex-*Norman McLeod Rogers*)

Contre-Almirante Oscar Viel Toro (AP 46) Chilean Navy, 1995

D: 6,320 tons (6,506 fl) **S:** 15.0 kts **Dim:** 90.10 (81.16 pp) × 19.13 × 6.10
A: none **Electronics:** Radar: 2 Kelvin-Hughes 14/12 nav.
M: 4 Fairbanks Morse 38D-8⅛-12 diesels, 8 1,380-kw generator sets, 2 electric motors; 2 props; 12,000 shp—2 Westinghouse gas turbines, geared drive; 16,000 shp
Electric: 1,455 kw (3 × 420-kw diesel sets)
Range: 12,000/12 **Fuel:** 1,095 tons **Crew:** 33 tot. (78 accomm.)

Remarks: 4,299 grt/2,357 dwt. Purchased 14-1-95 and refitted at ASMAR, Talcahuano, to support the *Teniente Marsh* and *Teniente Carvajal* scientific bases in the Antarctic. Had been used by the Canadian Coast Guard as a river icebreaker, supply ship, and navigational aids tender. Cargo: 900 tons. Can carry one helicopter and has a telescoping hangar. Re-engined during a 7-11-83 to 14-9-84 refit with both a diesel-electric and an alternate gas turbine propulsion system. Retains Canadian paint scheme with red hull and cream upperworks.

♦ 1 buoy tender and salvage ship [AGL]

Bldr: B. V. J. Pattje Scheepswerf, Waterhuizen, the Netherlands (In serv. 7-78)

63 Ingeniero George Slight Marshall (ex-*Vigilant*)

Ingeniero George Slight Marshall (63)—with since-sold tug *Colo Colo* (ATF 69) H&L Van Ginderen, 1-99

D: 816 tons (fl) **S:** 12.5 kts **Dim:** 52.96 (47.86 pp) × 11.16 × 3.52
A: 2 single 20-mm 70-cal. Oerlikon AA **Electronics:** Radar: 1 . . . nav.
M: 2 Ruston 6AP230 diesels; 2 props; 1,360 bhp—bow-thruster
Electric: 504 kw tot. (3 × 168-kw diesel sets)

Remarks: 817 grt/445 dwt. Purchased 1996 from the Mersey Docks and Harbour Co., which had employed her as a navigational buoy and salvage vessel in the River Mersey and Liverpool Bay area. Commissioned in Chilean service 5-2-97. Named for the late-19th-century English founder of the Chilean lighthouse system. Has one 15-ton buoy-handling derrick. The ship is also equipped for fire fighting and can lay and recover light communications cable over the bow.

♦ 1 ex-U.S. Robert D. Conrad–class research ship [AGOR]

Bldr: Marinette SB, Marinette, Wis.

	L	In serv.
Agor 60 Vidal Gormaz (ex-*Thomas Washington,* AGOR 10)	1-8-64	17-9-65

Vidal Gormaz (AGOR 60) Maritime Photographic, 7-01

D: 1,096 tons light (1, 370 fl) **S:** 13.5 kts (10 sust.)
Dim: 63.51 (58.37 pp) × 11.89 × 4.66 (hull)
A: 2 single 20-mm 70-cal. Oerlikon AA **Electronics:** Radar: 2 . . . nav.
M: 2 Fairbanks-Morse 38D8⅛-5 diesels (697 bhp each), electric drive; 1 prop; 1,000 shp—175-shp bow azimuth-thruster
Electric: 1,015 kw tot. (2 × 300-kw diesel-driven, 1 × 200-kw gas turbine–driven, 1 × 150-kw shaft-generator, 1 × 65-kw emergency)
Range: 8,200/11 **Fuel:** 211 tons **Endurance:** 32 days
Crew: 23 navy + 22 scientific party

Remarks: 1,151 grt/1,017 dwt. Transferred 28-9-92. Formerly assigned to the Scripps Institute of Oceanography, La Jolla, Calif., by the U.S. Office of Naval Research. Electric bow-thruster/propulsor provides up to 4.5 kts. Carries the Sea Beam bottom contour–mapping sonar system and was modernized 1981–84 with new oceanographic winches and cables to work to 4,000- to 5,000-m depths. Has a 21.5-m^2 wet lab and 137-m^2 dry laboratory.

♦ 1 replenishment oiler [AOR]

Bldr: Burmeister & Wain, Copenhagen

	L	In serv.
AO 53 Araucano	21-6-66	5-1-67

Araucano (AO 53)—refueling Peruvian frigate *Meliton Carvajal* (FM 51) Peruvian Navy, 2001

Araucano (AO 53)—in light condition, showing new bow bulb and enlarged hawsepipes; the forward 40-mm AA mounts were removed to reduce weight Leo Dirkx, 4-98

D: 17,300 tons (23,000 fl) **S:** 17 kts **Dim:** 160.93 × 21.95 × 8.80
A: 2 twin 40-mm 60-cal. U.S. Mk 1 Mod. 2 AA
Electronics: Radar: 2 . . . nav.
M: 1 Burmeister & Wain 62 VT 2 BF 140, 9-cyl. diesel; 1 prop; 10,800 bhp
Range: 12,000/14.5 **Crew:** 13 officers, 117 enlisted

Remarks: Ordered 19-2-65. Can replenish two ships alongside under way simultaneously. Carries 21,126 m^3 liquid and 1,444 m^3 dry cargo. Has two U.S. Mk 51 lead-

AUXILIARIES *(continued)*

computing directors for the 40-mm AA mounts; the original U.K. Mk 5 twin mounts have been replaced with U.S. mountings and the forward two pairs have been removed. A large bow bulb and greatly enlarged anchor hawse fittings were added prior to 1998.

♦ **1 transport and disaster relief ship [AP]** Bldr: ASMAR, Talcahuano

	Laid down	L	In serv.
AP 41 AQUILES	27-5-86	4-12-87	15-7-88

Aquiles (AP 41) Paolo Marsan, 4-01

D: 2,767 tons light (4,550 fl) **S:** 18 kts (15 sust.)
Dim: 103.00 (97.00 pp) × 17.00 × 5.50 **A:** none
Electronics: Radar: 2 . . . nav.
M: 2 MaK 8M453B diesels; 1 CP prop; 7,200 bhp—bow-thruster
Electric: 1,375 kw (1 × 500 kw, 2 × 400 kw, 1 × 75 kw) **Fuel:** 460 tons
Crew: 15 officers, 68 enlisted + 250 passengers

Remarks: 1,800 dwt. Has two cargo holds totaling 2,900 m^3 and one 20-ton electric crane. Can carry up to 890 tons ballast water and 470 tons potable water. The helicopter deck is large enough to accept a Super Puma. Has double-chine hullform with a bulbous bow.

♦ **1 ex-Swedish Älvsborg-class submarine tender [AS]**
Bldr: Karlskronavarvet, Karlskrona

	Laid down	L	In serv.
42 ALMIRANTE JOSÉ TORIBIO MERINO CASTRO (ex-*Älvsborg,* A 234, ex-M 02)	16-11-68	11-11-69	10-4-71

Almirante José Toribio Merino Castro (42)—still in Swedish Navy camouflage scheme Leo Dirkx, 3-98

D: 2,660 tons (fl) **S:** 16 kts **Dim:** 92.4 (83.3 pp) × 14.7 × 4.0
A: 3 single 40-mm 70-cal. Bofors SAK 40/48 AA
Electronics:
Radar: 1 Terma Scanter 009 nav.; 1 Raytheon . . . nav.; 1 Ericsson Sea Giraffe 50HC surf./air search; 1 CelsiusTech 9LV 200 f.c.
M: 2 Nohab-Polar 112VS, 12-cyl. diesels; 1 CP prop; 4,200 bhp—350-shp bow-thruster
Electric: 1,200 kw tot. **Crew:** 20 officers, 70 enlisted

Remarks: Purchased 10-96 for use as a submarine tender; transferred 7-2-97. Built as a minelayer for the Swedish Navy, but had been used as a submarine tender in peacetime and with accommodations for 205 submarine crew members; was laid up in Sweden at the end of 1993 and redesignated a "general support ship." Has a helicopter deck. Sister *Visborg* (M 03) remains a minelayer in the Swedish Navy.

♦ **2 Norwegian-built tug/supply vessels [ATA]**
Bldr: Aukra Bruk A/S, Aukra (In serv. 1973–74)

ATF 66 GALVARINO (ex-*Maersk Traveller*)
ATF 67 LAUTARO (ex-*Navimer I,* ex-*Maersk Tender*)

Galvarino (ATF 66) Maritime Photographic, 7-01

Lautaro (ATF 67) Chilean Navy, 1997

D: 941 tons light (2,380 fl) **S:** 15 kts (14 sust.)
Dim: 58.32 (52.20 pp) × 12.63 × 3.97
A: ATF 66: 2 single 20-mm 70-cal. Oerlikon AA—ATF 67: 1 40-mm 60-cal. Bofors AA
Electronics: Radar: 1 Furuno FR-240 nav.; 1 Terma Pilot 7T-48 nav.
M: 2 Atlas-MAK 8M 553AK diesels; 2 CP props; 6,400 bhp (5,300 sust.)—bow-thruster
Electric: 533 kw tot. (1 × 240 kw, 1 × 160 kw, 1 × 133 kw)
Range: . . ./. . . **Fuel:** 132 tons **Crew:** 5 officers, 15 enlisted

Remarks: 499 grt/832 dwt. Former anchor-handling tug/supply vessels. ATF 66 was purchased in 1987, left Europe 14-12-87, and was commissioned in Chile 26-1-88 for use as a patrol and search-and-rescue ship and logistics transport in Chile's southern regions. ATF 67 was acquired 21-12-90 from Athene Transport Corp. Cargo capacity: 1,400 tons. Ice-strengthened hulls. 65-ton bollard pull, 100-ton towing winch.
Disposals: *Janequero* (ATF 65, ex-*Maersk Transporter*) was placed in reserve at the end of 1998 and stricken in 1999.

♦ **1 Dutch-built Smit Lloyd 40–class tug/supply vessel [ATA]**
Bldr: Scheepswerf De Waal, Zaltbommel (In serv. 1972)

ATF 68 LEUCOTÓN (ex-*Lilen,* ex-*Smit Lloyd 44*)

Leucotón (ATF 68)—with 40-mm guns between stacks and pilothouse
Chilean Navy, 1997

D: 1,750 tons (fl) **S:** 13 kts **Dim:** 53.14 (49.31 pp) × 12.30 × 4.45
A: 2 single 40-mm 60-cal. Bofors AA
Electronics: Radar: 2 . . . nav. (X- and S-band)
M: 2 Burmeister & Wain Alpha 8430, 8-cyl. diesels; 2 CP props; 2,800 bhp—bow-thruster
Electric: 270 kw tot. (2 × 135-kw diesel sets)
Range: . . ./. . . **Fuel:** 259 tons **Crew:** 13 tot.

Remarks: 743 grt. Former anchor-handling tug/supply vessel acquired 6-8-90, modified for naval service at Punta Arenas, and commissioned on 29-1-91.
Disposals: *Colo Colo* (ATF 69, ex-*Lenga,* ex-*Smit Lloyd 46*) was sold to Omega Shipping, Ltd., Panama, and renamed *Sea Guardian* in 1999. *Yelcho* (ex-*Smit Kaylen J,* ex-*Smit Lloyd Matsas 5,* ex-*Smit Lloyd 43*) was placed in reserve 30-12-98 and later sold to Omega Shipping as the *Independent.*

♦ **1 sail-training ship [ATS]** Bldr: Izar, Cadiz, Spain

	L	In serv.
BE 43 ESMERALDA (ex-*Don Juan de Austria*)	12-5-53	9-54

Esmeralda (BE 43) A. D. Baker III, 6-00

AUXILIARIES *(continued)*

D: 3,420 tons (3,754 fl) **S:** 11 kts (under power)
Dim: 109.8 (94.1 pp) × 13.1 × 8.7
A: 2 single 47-mm saluting cannon **Electronics:** Radar: 1 . . . nav.
M: 1 Fiat diesel; 1,400 bhp—2,500 m^2 max. sail area
Range: 8,000/8 under power **Crew:** 271 ship's company + 80 midshipmen

Remarks: Four-masted schooner, ordered by Spain and sold to Chile in 1953. Similar to the Spanish *Juan Sebastian de Elcano.* Refitted in South Africa in 1977.

SERVICE CRAFT

♦ **1 historic relic, former monitor [YAG]**
Bldr: Laird, Scotland (L: 6-10-1865)

Huascar

Huascar H&L Van Ginderen, 2-99

D: 2,030 tons (fl) **S:** 12.3 kts **Dim:** 57.91 × 10.67 × 5.56
A: 1 twin 254-mm low-angle in turret; 2 single 40-pdr. cannon
M: 1 set reciprocating steam: 1 prop; 1,650 ihp **Boilers:** 4 fire-tube
Fuel: 300 tons (max.) **Crew:** 170 tot.

Remarks: Data above refer to ship as built. Although in exceptionally fine condition, she is not operational. Captured in damaged condition from Peru on 8-10-1879. Employed for many years as a gunnery training ship, then converted as a museum and stationary harbor flagship at Talcahuano. Built of iron. Has 114-mm armor belt with 52-mm ends. Turret armor varies from 135 to 203 mm. Conning tower has 76-mm armor. Peru continues to claim ownership.

♦ **2 miscellaneous floating cranes [YD]**

Remarks: One is of 30 tons capacity, one of 180 tons capacity.

♦ **1 Pisagua-class support logistics landing craft [YF]**
Bldr: SIMAR, Santiago (In serv. 11-7-95)

YFP 116 Pisagua

D: 32 tons light (95 fl) **S:** 8 kts **Dim:** 22.23 × 6.00 × 1.60
M: 2 diesels; 2 props; 300 bhp **Range:** 500/8 **Crew:** 6 tot.

Remarks: Design modeled after the U.S. LCM(8) class. Intended to provide logistics support to the Seamen's School at Isla Quiriquina. Cargo: 50 tons. Has a bow ramp and a small crane to starboard amidships.

♦ **1 1,300-ton-capacity covered floating dry dock [YFDL]**
Bldr: ASMAR, Talcahuano (In serv. 2-4-98)

Contralmirante Arturo Young Ward

Remarks: Displaces 1,105 tons light. Has sliding roof panels to provide a controlled environment.

♦ **1 1,200-ton-capacity floating dry dock [YFDL]**
Bldr: ASMAR, Talcahuano

	Laid down	L	In serv.
Ingeniero 3RO José Gutiérrez	5-9-90	27-9-91	27-9-91

Remarks: Length 80 m overall. Displaces 1,050 tons empty.

♦ **1 800-ton-capacity floating dry dock [YFDL]**
Bldr: Mohlen & Seebeck, Göstmunde, Germany (In serv. 6-08)

Manterola

Remarks: Employed at ASMAR, Talcahuano, since 2-4-60. Displaces 658 tons empty.

♦ **1 10,000-ton-capacity medium floating dry dock [YFDM]**
Bldr: ASMAR, Talcahuano (L: 8-10-83)

Valparaiso III

D: 4,150 tons (light)
Dim: 167.0 (151.2 on blocks) × 32.1 (26.1 interior width) × 3.95

Remarks: Built for shipyard, rather than naval service, but available to the navy.

♦ **2 ex-U.S. ARD 24–class medium floating dry docks [YFDM]**
(In serv. 1944)

131 Ingeniero Mery (ex-ARD 25) 132 Mutilla (ex-ARD 32)

Capacity: 3,500 tons **Dim:** 149.86 × 24.69 × 1.73 (light)

Remarks: 131 leased in 1973 and transferred to ASMAR in 10-88; 132 transferred to Chile 15-12-60 and transferred to ASMAR 28-2-63. Both at Talcahuano. Dock inside dimensions: 118.6 m on blocks, 18.0 m clear width, 6.3 m draft over blocks. Bow end closed and pointed. Displace 10,000 tons at full load condition.

♦ **1 ex-U.S. ARD 4–class medium floating dry dock [YFDM]**
Bldr: Pacific Bridge, Alameda, Calif. (In serv. 6-42)

133 Talcahuano (ex-*Waterford,* ARD 5)

Dim: 148.1 × 21.6 (14.9 clear width) × 1.6 (9.9 flooded max.)

Remarks: Capacity: 3,500 tons. Purchased 10-3-99; left for Chile under tow 12-5-99 and recommissioned at Talcahuano 30-8-99. Crew totaled 131 in U.S. service.

♦ **1 admiral's barge [YFL]** Bldr: ASMAR, Talcahuano (In serv. 1997)

Remarks: Laid down early 1996 as commander-in-chief's barge. No data available.

♦ **2 Meteoro-class personnel transports [YFL]**
Bldr: ASMAR, Talcahuano

	L	In serv.
YFP 110 Meteoro	29-1-68	3-6-68
YFP 112 Grumete Pérez Huemel	. . .	12-12-75

Meteoro (YFP 110) Chilean Navy, 1992

D: 165 tons (205 fl) **S:** 8 kts **Dim:** 24.4 × 6.7 × 2.6
A: 1 20-mm 70-cal. Oerlikon AA
M: 1 Cummins diesel; 365 bhp **Range:** 2,600/9 **Crew:** . . . tot.

Remarks: Both attached to the Seaman's School, Isla Quiriquina, as harbor transports. Modified fishing trawler design, with the main-deck superstructure extended. Can carry 15 tons of cargo in addition to 210 (YFP 112: 290) passengers. YFP 112 has a 370-bhp diesel and can achieve 10 kts. Sister *Sobenes* has been stricken.

Disposal note: Coastal tanker *Guardian Brito* (AO 55) was placed in disposal reserve in 1999.

♦ **1 large harbor tug [YTB]**
Bldr: Southern Shipbuilders, Faversham, U.K. (In serv. 6-8-75)

YT 115 Gálvez

D: 216 tons (fl) **S:** 11.5 kts **Dim:** 25.5 × 7.3 × 2.8
M: 2 diesels; 1 prop; 1,000 bhp

Remarks: 112 grt. Painted white. Subordinated to ASMAR, Talcahuano.

♦ **2 Cortés-class medium harbor tugs [YTM]**
Bldr: Ruhrorterschiffswerft & Maschinenfabrik, Duisburg, Germany
(In serv. 11-61)

Cortés Reyes

D: 100 tons (fl) **S:** 6.5 kts **Dim:** . . . × . . . × . . .
M: 1 diesel; 1 prop; 585 bhp

Remarks: Both employed at ASMAR, Talcahuano.

♦ **1 sail-training craft [YTS]**
Bldr: Naturoy Oy, Wilhelm Shauman AB, Pietarsaari, Finland (In serv. 25-1-78)

Blanca Estela

Remarks: 32-ton ocean-racing ketch, purchased new 3-9-77.

CHILEAN COAST GUARD

GENERAL DIRECTORATE OF THE MARITIME TERRITORY

(Dirección General del Territorio Marítimo y de la Marine Mercante)

Founded in 1848 and now responsible for regulating the Chilean merchant marine and water sports, coastal and port patrol, and navigational aids maintenance. Also intended to organize the merchant marine as a potential naval reserve. In addition to the units listed below, there are also a large number of very small launches, rigid inflatable boats, and so forth. The coast guard operates several navy-manned MBB BO-105 helicopters acquired in 1991. All personnel are seconded from the Chilean Navy.

Personnel (2001): About 1,600 tot.

COAST GUARD PATROL CRAFT [WPC]

♦ 8 Danubio 1 class
Bldr: ASMAR, Valparaiso (In serv. 2000–2001)

LEP 1605 Aysen	LEP 1609 San Antonio
LEP 1606 Corral	LEP 1610 Antofagasta
LEP 1607 Concepción	LEP 1611 Arica
LEP 1608 Caldera	LEP 1612 Puerto Natales

D: 107 tons (fl) **S:** 27 kts **Dim:** 33.10 (29.00 pp) × 6.00 × 1.90
A: 1 20-mm 70-cal. Oerlikon AA; 1 12.7-mm mg
Electronics: Radar: 1 Decca . . . nav.
M: 2 MTU 16V2000 M90 diesels; 2 props; 3,200 bhp
Electric: 104 kVA tot. (2 × 52-kVA diesel sets)
Range: . . ./. . . **Fuel:** . . . tons **Crew:** 2 officers, 12 enlisted

Remarks: Design locally derived from that of the 32-m Protector class. Ordered 4-99, with the first launched 12-11-99.

♦ 2 32-meter Protector class
Bldr: Fairey Marintechnik, Cowes, U.K. (In serv. 24-6-89)

LSG 1603 Alacalufe LSG 1604 Hallef

Alacalufe (LSG 1603) Chilean Navy, 1997

D: 107 tons (fl) **S:** 20 kts (18 sust.) **Dim:** 32.70 (28.96 wl) × 6.70 × 2.10
A: 1 20-mm 70-cal. Oerlikon AA; 1 12.7-mm mg
Electronics: Radar: 1 Decca . . . nav. **M:** 2 MTU diesels; 2 props; 2,600 bhp
Range: 1,100/16 **Fuel:** 20 tons **Crew:** 2 officers, 12 enlisted

Remarks: Although initially announced as being intended for the Customs Service when ordered in 1987 and labeled as "pilot boats" (LEP), they are now assigned to patrol and search-and-rescue duties in the Strait of Magellan area and are typed *Lanchas de Servicio General.*

♦ 4 Guacolda class
Bldr: Izar, San Fernando, Spain

	In serv.
LSG 1605 Guacolda (ex-80)	30-7-65
LSG 1606 Fresia (ex-81)	9-12-65
LSG 1607 Quidora (ex-83)	28-3-66
LPM 1608 Tegualda (ex-84)	1-7-66

Tegualda (LPM 1608) Maritime Photographic, 7-01

D: 134 tons (fl) **S:** 32 kts **Dim:** 36.20 (34.00 wl) × 5.60 × 1.68
A: 1 40-mm 70-cal. Bofors AA; 2 single 12.7-mm mg
Electronics: Radar: 1 Decca . . . nav.
M: 2 Mercedes-Benz MB839Bb diesels; 2 props; 4,800 bhp
Electric: 90 kVA tot. **Range:** 1,500/15 **Crew:** 18 tot.

Remarks: Designed by Friedrich Lürssen Werft, Germany, and built under license. Were equipped as torpedo boats, with two 40-mm AA and four fixed British Mk IV torpedo tubes using old straight-running British Mk 8 Mod. 3 torpedoes until redesignated as *Lanchas de Servicio General* on 26-12-97 and transferred to the Chilean Coast Guard; the torpedo equipment and after 40-mm gun were removed and a RIB launch and crane were added on the stern. Were to have been retired 1999–2000 but remained in service into 2001.

PATROL BOATS [WPB]

♦ 10 Israeli Dabur class
Bldr: Israeli Aircraft Industries, Be'er Sheva (In serv. 1973–77)

LPC 1814 Grumete Venanzio Díaz
LPC 1815 Grumete Luciano Bolados
LPC 1816 Grumete Santiago Salinas
LPC 1817 Grumete Blas Segundo Tellez
LPC 1818 Grumete Juan Bravo
LPC 1819 Grumete David Campos
LPC 1820 Grumete Samuel Machado
LPC 1821 Grumete Rudicindo Troncoso
LPC 1822 Grumete Domingo Johnson
LPC 1823 Grumete Manuel Hudson

Grumete Manuel Hudson (LPC 1823) Maritime Photographic, 7-01

D: 29 tons (39 fl) **S:** 19 kts **Dim:** 19.8 × 5.8 × 0.8
A: 2 single 20-mm 70-cal. Oerlikon AA; 2 single 12.7-mm mg
Electronics: Radar: 1 Decca 916 nav.
M: 2 G.M. 12V71 TI diesels; 2 props; 960 bhp (840 sust.)
Electric: 20 kw **Range:** 1,200/17 **Crew:** 2 officers, 8 enlisted

Remarks: LPC 1814–1819 were purchased used in 9-90 and commissioned in Chile 3-1-91, all for service in the 4th Naval Zone. LPC 1820–1823 were purchased in 1995 and commissioned on 16-3-95, based at Iquique. Quarters are air-conditioned and spacious. Aluminum construction. Carry a semi-rigid inflatable inspection boat aft. When new, could make 25 kts but are now operating at about 5 tons over designed displacement. In LPC 1823 and others, the aft 20-mm gun has been replaced by a 12.7-mm mg.

♦ 2 Anchova class
Bldr: MacLaren, Niterói, Brazil

	In serv.		In serv.
LPC 1808 Osorno	16-4-82	LPC 1810 Copahue	16-11-82

Copahue (LPC 1810) Leo Dirkx, 5-98

D: 31 tons (43 fl) **S:** 30 kts (20 sust.) **Dim:** 18.60 × 5.25 × 1.62
A: 1 20-mm Oerlikon AA; 1 12.7-mm mg
Electronics: Radar: 1 Decca 110 nav.
M: 2 MTU 8V331 TC81 diesels; 2 props; 1,740 bhp **Electric:** 10 kw
Range: 700/15 **Crew:** 1 officer, 5 enlisted

Remarks: Ordered 1977. Wooden construction. Named for volcanoes. ("Anchova" is the builder's class name.) Were originally intended to carry two 20-mm mounts.
Disposals: Sisters *Pillan* (LPC 1801) and *Troncador* (LPC 1802) were retired in 1998. *Rano-Kau* (LPC 1803), *Villarrica* (LPC 1804), *Corcovado* (LPC 1805), *Llaina* (LPC 1806), *Antuco* (LPC 1807), and *Choshuenco* (LPC 1809) were stricken during 1999–2000.

SERVICE CRAFT

♦ 15 Rodman 800–class harbor launches [WYFL]
Bldr: Rodman Polyship, S.A., Vigo, Spain (In serv. 1996)

PM 2031 through PM 2045

D: 9 tons (fl) **S:** 30 kts **Dim:** 8.9 × 3.0 × 0.8
A: 1 12.7-mm mg **Electronics:** Radar: 1 Raytheon . . . nav.
M: 2 Volvo Penta outdrive diesels; 300 bhp **Range:** 150/25 **Crew:** 3 tot.

SERVICE CRAFT *(continued)*

Rodman 800–class PM 2034 Maritime Photographic, 7-01

Remarks: GRP construction. Eighteen more may be ordered. Used for harbor patrol and search-and-rescue duties.

Note: Several earlier harbor patrol launches in the PM number series are also in service, including PM 2023.

♦ **1 service launch [WYFL]** (In serv. 1986)

LPM 1916 Petrohue

D: . . . tons **S:** 10 kts **Dim:** 9.7 × 3.1 × 0.9 **M:** 1 Perkins diesel; 85 bhp

♦ **1 ASMAR 1160 rigid inflatable search-and-rescue craft [WYH]**
Bldr: ASMAR, Talcahuano

LSR 1700 Tokerau (In serv. 14-2-92)

Tokerau (LSR 1700) ASMAR, 8-91

D: 7.8 tons light (10 fl) **S:** 25 kts (22 sust.)
Dim: 12.66 (11.73 hull, 10.78 wl) × 3.90 (3.30 hull) × 0.75
A: 1 7.62-mm mg **Electronics:** Radar: 1 Decca RD-80 nav.
M: 2 Volvo Penta TAMD-61A diesels; 2 Hamilton 291 waterjets; 612 bhp
Range: 310/20; 500/16 **Fuel:** 1,800 liters **Crew:** 4 tot. + up to 32 survivors

Remarks: LSR 1701, completed in 1993, operates from Hanga-Piko Harbor on Easter Island, in part as a contingency rescue launch for U.S. space shuttle astronauts. The GRP hull has 60-cm-diameter inflatable surrounding bulwark. Designed to self-right in case of capsizing in heavy seas. Extensive navigational suite, including Magellan NAV 1000 GPS receiver, Koden KS-5538 HFD/F, anemometer, echo sounder, and gyrocompass. Have diving, first-aid, and firefighting systems and carry a 6-man life raft. A plan to procure eight more has not been carried out. Sister Kimitahi (LSR 1701) was stricken on 29-12-00.

♦ **10 Maule-class search-and-rescue craft [WYH]**
Bldr: ASENAV, Valdivia (In serv. 1982–83)

LPM 1901 Maule	LPM 1905 Isluga	LPM 1909 Cau-Cau
LPM 1902 Lauca	LPM 1906 Loa	LPM 1910 Pudeto
LPM 1903 Aconcagua	LPM 1907 Maullín	
LPM 1904 Rapel	LPM 1908 Copiapó	

D: 14 tons (fl) **S:** 18 kts **Dim:** 13.3 × 3.5 × 1.0
A: 1 12.7-mm mg **Electronics:** Radar: 1 Raytheon . . . nav.
M: 2 MTU 6V331 TC82 diesels; 2 props; 1,320 bhp (1,012 sust.)

Note: There is another Chilean agency also charged with search-and-rescue duties. It operates a number of red- or red-and-white-painted craft, including at least one U.K.-built Arun-class seagoing rescue launch.

Aconcagua (LPM 1903) Leo Dirkx, 4-98

CHILEAN ARMY

The Chilean Army operates a number of ASMAR-built, British FBM Marine-designed combat support boats:

D: . . . tons **S:** 24 kts **Dim:** 8.38 (6.98 wl) × 2.49 × 0.66 (loaded)
M: 2 diesels; 2 waterjets; 424 bhp **Fuel:** 170 liters

Remarks: Aluminum construction. Capable of operating in Force 5 gales. Used for river crossing and local support duties. Equipped to act as push-tugs.

CHINA

People's Republic of China

PEOPLE'S LIBERATION ARMY NAVY

Personnel (2002): About 145,000, including about 7,000 naval infantry, 24,000 coast-defense artillery and missile troops, and 20,000 in naval aviation. Chinese People's Liberation Army (PLA) troops are being cross-trained in amphibious operations. During 2000, the U.S. Department of Defense provided Congress with a figure of 260,000 total People's Liberation Army Navy (PLAN) uniformed personnel, which seems excessive, given the size of the fleet; personnel strength is in any case planned to be reduced over the next several years. Most transport auxiliaries and service craft are civilian-manned.

Bases: Organized into three fleets. North Sea Fleet headquarters at Qingdao, with other major bases at Lüshun and Xiaopingdao and smaller facilities at Weihaiwei, Qingshan, Dalian, Huludao (including nuclear submarine construction and support), Lianyungang, Lingshan, Dahushan, Changshandao, Liushuang, Yushan, and Dayuanjiadun. East Sea Fleet headquarters at Ningbo, with other major bases at Zhoushan, Shanghai, and Fujan and lesser facilities at Chenjiagang, Dinghai, Wusong, Xinxiang, Wenzhou, Sanduao, Xiamen, Quandou, Wuhan (inland, submarine construction), and Xiangshan (submarines). South Sea Fleet headquarters at Zhanjiang, with other major bases at Yulin, Guangzhou, and Hong Kong and lesser facilities at Haikou, Huangfu, Shantou, Humen, Kuanchuang, Tsun, Mawai, Beihai, Pingtan, Sanzhou, Tang Chian Huan, Longmen, Bailong, Dongoun, Baimajing, and Xiachuandao. The two naval infantry brigades are stationed at Heieu.

Paranaval Forces: In addition to the PLAN, several other agencies operate armed ships, including the Customs Service *(Hai Guan),* the Maritime Section of the Public Security Bureau *(Hai Gong),* and the Maritime Command of the Border Security Force *(Gong Bian).* There is also a fisheries protection service.

Hong Kong: Although the former Royal Hong Kong Police Force and its Marine Region craft became Chinese government property as of 1-7-97, it continues to be subordinated to the Hong Kong government, as does the Hong Kong Government Flying Service (see separate listing for Hong Kong).

Naval Aviation: Under the operational control of the PLAN, the Naval Air Arm consists of a force of 20,000 personnel and more than 500 aircraft, including about 470 fixed-wing aircraft:

- about 235 Shenyang F-6 interceptors (MiG-19 Farmer copy)
- about 65 Xian F-7 Fishbed interceptors (a modified copy of the MiG-21F)
- about 7 Xian F-8D Finback all-weather fighters (earlier reports of 26 referred to *total* air force and naval production through 1999; one naval F-8D rammed a U.S. Navy EP-3E Aries-II surveillance aircraft on 31-3-01 and crashed at sea)
- about 7 Xian JH-7 Flying Leopard strike aircraft (more in production: as of 8-00, some 50–70 additional were to be delivered during 2005–06, using imported Spey Mk 202 engines built either by SNECMA or Rolls-Royce; the Chinese version of the Spey, the WS-9, has been unsuccessful)
- about 40 Nanchang A-5 Fantan strike aircraft
- about 50 B-5 bombers (Soviet Il-28 Beagle copy)
- about 30 B-6 (H-6D) bombers (Tu-16 Badger copy), some equipped to carry two HY-4 antiship missiles (version B-6D) and two converted in 1999–2000 for aerial refueling
- about 8 Soviet Be-6 Madge amphibians
- 3 Shaanxi Y-8 maritime patrol aircraft (a modified copy of the An-12 Cub)
- 8 or more Harbin Y-12 maritime surveillance aircraft, with Terma SLAR (aircraft are assigned to the China Maritime Services, ostensibly for environmental and oil-spill surveillance)

PEOPLE'S LIBERATION ARMY NAVY *(continued)*

- 7 Harbin SH-5 amphibians, powered by four 3,150-hp turboprops for a cruising speed of 300 kts and a 2,850-n.m. range (1,200-n.m. patrol radius at 45 tons max. takeoff weight); 10-ton payload (including 6 tons of depth bombs). Equipped with MAD boom, guns, and radar. First flight 3-4-76. Can operate 12 hours on four engines or 15 hours on two at 6,000-ft. altitude.

and about 30 helicopters:

- 12 Z-8 Super Frelon heavy shipboard helicopters (2 or 3 equipped with Thales HS-3125 dipping sonars)
- about 10 Z-9 (AS.365 Dauphin copy) light shipboard helicopters out of 50 licensed for production
- 4 Kamov Ka-28PL ASW and 4 Ka-28PS search-and-rescue helicopters delivered in 1999–2000 (2 other Ka-28PL were reported delivered in 1993 for evaluation)

Z-8 Super Frelon—note ASW torpedo on pylon *Ships of the World,* 1999

Z-9A Dauphin—note lack of stores pylons PLAN, 1998

The new Chinese Changhe Aircraft Industries Z-11 helicopter, a virtual copy of the Eurocopter AS.350B Écureuil, may be acquired in small numbers as a liaison helicopter. To date, none of the Sukhoi Su-27 fighters delivered from Russia during 1992–96 have entered PLAN service, but some of the 100 J-11 variants of the aircraft to be built at Shenyang may after 2001. Twelve Kamov Ka-28 Helix-A shipboard ASW helicopters were ordered during 1-98, but the number seems to later have been cut to four. As of 7-99, negotiations were ongoing with Russia for 50 Su-30MKK strike aircraft, some or all of which would go to the PLAN; the aircraft are to be equipped with AS-20 Kayak antiship missiles, a variant of the Kh-35 shipboard weapon, as well as R-27-series (AA-10 Alamo) air-to-air missiles purchased from Ukraine. FH-7 fighter-bombers may be equipped with Zvezda-Strela Kh-31 (AS-17 Krypton) antiship missiles.

The Xian **FH-7 Flying Leopard** fighter-bomber began to enter naval service late in 1998. Its export version is known as the FBC-1. The design appears to be patterned after the Anglo-French Jaguar and is about 30 years behind the U.S. and European state of the art. About 72 aircraft are to be operated in three regiments:

Wingspan: 12.7 m **Length:** 22.325 m **Height:** 6.575 m
Weight: 28,475 kg max. takeoff **Speed:** Mach 1.7 max. (625 kts at sea level)
Propulsion: 2 Rolls-Royce Spey 202 (WS-9) turbojets
Range: 1,969 n.m. ferry **Combat radius:** 889 n.m. **Fuel:** 10,050 kg max.
Combat load: 6.5 tons on 6 hard-points plus 2 wingtip AAM positions; weapons include C-802 antiship missiles

Naval Infantry: The current organization was established in 1980 as the 1st Brigade of Naval Infantry and is attached to the South Sea Fleet. It incorporates three naval infantry battalions, a tank battalion, an artillery battalion, several batteries of anti-tank and antiaircraft artillery, a reconnaissance (combat swimmer) company, an engineer/sapper company, an NBC warfare defense company, and a logistic support unit. The naval infantry employs T-59 tanks (Chinese version of the Russian T-54A), T-63 amphibious tanks (Russian PT-76 with 85-mm gun), Types 77 and 531 amphibious armored personnel carriers, 76-mm artillery, 82-mm and 120-mm mortars, the Hunjian-8 antitank missile, 82-mm and 107-mm recoilless rifles, and 37-mm AA guns. Amphibious forces for the other fleets appear to be drawn from Chinese Army (PLA) units.

WEAPONS AND SENSORS

The ballistic missiles on the Xia-class SSBNs and nearly all other weapons on Chinese ships are of Chinese manufacture, with many being copies or derivations of Soviet or European systems. Increasingly, however, Chinese weapons and sensors are of indigenous design and manufacture, although the technology employed remains three decades or more behind that found in equivalent Western naval systems.

A. MISSILES

♦ Strategic ballistic missiles

Ju Lang-1 (JL-1/CSS-N-3): Became "operational" 7-88 after proof launch from the one Xia-class submarine, but does not seem to have entered service. Single stage, solid fuel. *Ju Lang* means "Giant Voice."

Length: 10.0 m **Diameter:** 1.5 m
Weight: 14,000 kg **Range:** 2,700–3,600 km

Ju Lang-2 (JL-2/CSS-NX-4): Successor to the Ju Lang-1 (CSS-N-3), in development. Essentially a navalized version of the land-based DF-31A, JL-2 is to have a maximum range of 8,000 km and carry either a single 250–650 kT warhead or three 90-kT warheads. Three stages, solid propellant. First sea-based launch took place mid-1-01 from the modified Golf-class trials submarine. *Ju Lang* means "Giant Voice."

♦ Strategic cruise missiles

Hong Niao-3 (HN-3): A turbofan-powered weapon in development for launch from 533-mm submarine torpedo tubes. Range to be 2,500 km. An evolved version of the HN-1, which was only produced in small numbers for land launch; HN-2, which reportedly flew in 1996 and had a range of 1,500 km, did not enter production. All three may have been intended to carry a warhead weighing about 300–400 kg, possibly with a nuclear yield of 90 kT. Data for HN-1:

Length: 6.4 m **Diameter:** 520 mm **Wingspan:** 3.0 m
Weight: approx. 1,400 kg **Speed:** subsonic **Range:** 600 km

♦ Antiship cruise missiles

C-101 Hai Ying-3 (HY-3/CSS-C-5 Sabbot): Coast-defense and air-launched weapon with a 400-kg high-explosive, armor-piercing warhead. Has two ramjet sustainers.

Length: 7.20 m **Diameter:** 0.76 m **Wingspan:** 1.20 m
Weight: 2,000 kg **Speed:** Mach 2.0 **Range:** 50 km **Altitude:** 300 m

C-201 Hai Ying-2 (HY-2/CSS-N-1): Improved version of the Russian P-15 Termit (NATO SS-N-2 Styx). Uses a jettisonable solid-rocket booster and a solid-fuel sustainer, vice the liquid fuel used with the HY-1. Guidance is by gyro autopilot, with radar terminal homing. Have a 513-kg high explosive warhead.

Length: 7.36 m **Wingspan:** 2.41 m **Weight:** 2,998 kg
Speed: Mach 0.9 **Range:** 70 km **Altitude:** 30–100 m

Other versions include the Hai Ying-2A with infrared, vice radar, terminal homing, and the radar altimeter–equipped Hai Ying-2G with a 20-m cruise altitude, descending to 8 m during radar terminal homing. Also reported is a coast-defense variant (C-201W) with a range of 45 km.

C-202 Hai Ying-4 (HY-4/CSS-C-2 Silkworm): Air launched, carried two per B-6D (Badger) bomber. Turbojet engine, radar homing.

Length: 7.36 m **Wingspan:** 2.41 m **Weight:** 2,000 kg
Speed: Mach 0.85 **Range:** 135 km **Altitude:** 70–200 m

C-301 (CSS-C-6 Sawhorse): Coast-defense and land-attack weapon with two ramjet sustainer engines, in development since 1996. To have a 512-kg high-explosive, armor-piercing warhead. Employing inertial guidance with GPS course correction, the weapon will be powered by two ramjet sustainer engines and four solid-fuel boosters.

Length: 9.85 m **Diameter:** 0.76 m **Wingspan:** 1.20 m
Weight: 3,400 kg **Speed:** Mach 2.0 **Range:** 180 km
Altitude: 100–300 m cruise (7–50 m terminal)

C-601 (CSA-1 Kraken): Air-launched, rocket-powered weapon with a 510-kg warhead. Derived from the Russian P-15 Termit.

Length: 7.38 m **Diameter:** 0.76 m **Weight:** 2,440 kg
Speed: Mach 0.9 **Range:** 25–100 km **Altitude:** 30–100 m

C-611: Air-launched, turbojet variant of C-601 with the same warhead and speed and a 220-km range.

C-701: Television-guided antiship missile for aircraft, helicopter, or surface-ship launch. Still in development as of 2000. For shipboard launch, employs four-unit, square-section canister launchers. Rocket propelled. Offered for export by China National Precision Machinery Import and Export Corporation (CPMIEC).

Length: 2.507 m **Diameter:** 0.18 m **Wingspan:** . . . m **Weight:** 100 kg
Warhead: approx. 30 kg **Speed:** Mach 0.8 **Range:** 15 km (air-launched)

C-801 Ying Ji-1 (YJ-1 "Hawk Attack"/CSS-N-4 Sardine): Wholly Chinese weapon, using a box launcher similar to that of Exocet MM 40. The land-based version is Fei Long-7; the air- and submerged-launch versions are Ying Ji-6 and Ying Ji-8 Mod. 3, respectively (qq.v.). Propelled by solid rocket with two solid boosters. Has a 165-kg high-explosive, armor-piercing warhead. Offered for export by CPMIEC. The C-801A version has folding wings and can fit in the same tube as that used by the C-802 turbojet-powered version.

Length: 5.814 m **Diameter:** 0.36 m **Wingspan:** 1.18 m **Weight:** 815 kg
Speed: Mach 0.9 **Range:** 42 km **Altitude:** 255 m

C-802 Ying Ji-2 (YJ-2/CSS-N-8 Saccade): French Microturbo turbojet-powered version of YJ-1/C-801. Has high-explosive, armor-piercing warhead. Employs active radar and incorporates ECCM features. Said to be based very closely on the French Exocet missile system. Has been exported to Iran. Also available in land-based coast-defense version.

Length: 6.392 m over booster (5.160 m without) **Diameter:** 0.36 m
Wingspan: 1.18 m **Weight:** 715 kg (530 kg without booster)
Warhead: 165 kg **Speed:** Mach 0.85 **Range:** 15–120 km
Altitude: 20–30 m cruise (5–7 m terminal)

Fei Long-1 (FL-1/CSS-N-2 Safflower): Said to have entered service in 1980 aboard Luda-class destroyers and various frigate classes, but there is considerable confusion as to whether it even exists. Rocket powered. Has a 513-kg high-explosive, shaped-charge warhead. Radar- and infrared-homing versions said to be available.

Length: 6.42 m **Diameter:** 0.54 m **Wingspan:** 2.40 m
Weight: 2,000 kg **Speed:** Mach 0.9 **Altitude:** 30–100 m (8–15 m terminal)

WEAPONS AND SENSORS *(continued)*

Fei Long-2 (FL-2): Said to have entered service in 1993 as a shipboard weapon. Liquid fueled, rocket powered, with a 365-kg armor-piercing, high-explosive warhead. Radar homing. Some confusion exists regarding this missile, which has also been reported as the "Fei Long-7," weighing 1,800 kg and having a speed of Mach 1.4 and a cruise altitude of 50–100 m.

Length: 6.00 m **Diameter:** 0.54 m **Wingspan:** 1.705 m
Weight: 1,550 kg **Speed:** Mach 0.9 **Altitude:** 30–100 m (8–15 m terminal)

Shui Ying-1 ("Sea Eagle-1"/CSS-N-1): A direct copy of the Soviet P-15 Termit (SS-N-2A Styx). Radar homing, with a 400-kg high-explosive warhead. Rocket propelled.

Length: 5.80 m **Weight:** 2,300 kg **Range:** 40 km
Wingspan: 2.41 m **Speed:** Mach 0.85 **Altitude:** 100–300 m

Ying Ji-6 (YJ-6): Air-launched version of Ying Ji-1 (C-801). Identical in most respects to Ying Ji-1 except for range of 50 km when launched at altitude.

Ying Ji-8 (YJ-8) Mod. 3: Said to be a version of Ying Ji-1 (C-801) adapted for submerged launch from the torpedo tubes of Song-class submarines. It may instead be a variant of the Ying Ji-2 (C-802) turbojet-powered version of the Ying Ji-1.

Note: Forty-eight Russian 3M-80 Moskit (NATO SS-N-22 Sunburn) supersonic, sea-skimming missiles were ordered in 7-98 for use with Russian-built *Sovremennyy*-class guided-missile destroyers. Deliveries began in 5-00.

♦ Surface-to-air missiles

Hong Qian-2J (HQ-2J): Two-stage coast-defense SAM with 34-km range.

Hong Qian-7 (HQ-7): Chinese name for an unauthorized copy of the French Crotale Modulaire short-range shipboard SAM system. HQ-7 is aboard Luhai-class destroyer 167, Luhu-class destroyer 113, and the Jiangwei-II-class frigates. Imported Crotale Modulaire systems are aboard Luda-class destroyer 109 and Luhu-class destroyer 112.

Hong Qian-9 (HQ-9): Said to be in development during 2001 as a naval variant of the land-based Chinese version of the Russian SA-10 (also known as S-300) missile system. Whether China will use the Russian Navy SA-N-6 system's rotating launchers or fixed vertical launch cells is not yet known. Offered for export as the FT-2000. Has an approximate horizontal range of 100 km and altitude of 20 km.

Hong Qian-61 (HQ-61/CSA-N-1): Short-range SAM system that began development in the 1960s but was used only on the four frigates of the Jiangwei-I class. Cumbersome launcher with six cells for missiles with nonfolding fins; there are no reloads. Data below are from a Chinese source:

Length: 3.99 m **Diameter:** 0.286 m **Wingspan:** 1.66 m
Propulsion: single-stage, solid-fuel rocket **Speed:** Mach 3.0
Range: 10 km max./3 km min. **Altitude:** 8 km
Guidance: command, using radar tracker/illuminator, semiactive homing

FN-6: Shoulder-launched weapon introduced by CPMIEC in summer 2000. Can attack targets traveling up to 360 m/sec and is claimed to have a 70% kill probability.

Length: 1.495 m **Diameter:** 72 mm **Weight:** 16 kg with launcher
Range: 5 km max./0.5 km min. **Altitude:** 3,500 m max./15 m min.

Hong Nu-5 (HN-5): Land-based derivative of the Soviet SA-7. Weight: 16 kg; range: 4 km.

Hong Nu-5A (HN-5A): Heat-seeking weapons offered with the Type 90 close-in defense system. Navy version of the land-use PL-9.

Length: 2.90 m **Diameter:** 157 mm **Wingspan:** 856 mm
Weight: 115 kg **Warhead:** 35 kg **Speed:** Mach 2.1
Range: 10 km max./1 km min. **Altitude:** 4,500 m max./50 m min.

KS-1: Medium-range coast-defense SAM with guidance similar to that of HQ-61/HQ-7.

Length: 5.6 m **Diameter:** 0.4 m **Speed:** 1,200 m/sec
Range: 42 km max./7 km min. **Altitude:** 25 km max./0.5 km min.

LY-60N: Point-defense system revealed in 1995 with a missile based closely on the Alenia Aspide. Range is 10 km against targets 30–12,000 m in altitude. Sold to Pakistan for use on three Type 21 frigates but not used by the PLAN.

QW-1 Vanguard: Shoulder-launched, two-stage weapon entering service in 1994 as successor to the HN-5 series (which was a copy of the Russian SA-7 Grail), but with improved performance and a supercooled infrared seeker. Resembles the Russian SA-18. Manned twin-round and eight-round naval launchers are offered, as is a variant of the Type 76 twin 37-mm AA mount with two missiles. Made by CPMIEC.

Length: 1.532 m **Diameter:** . . . **Weight:** 16.5 kg **Warhead:** . . . kg
Range: 0.5–5.0 km **Altitude:** 30–4,000 m

Note: The Russian 9M-38M1 Smerch (NATO SA-N-7 Gadfly) surface-to-air missile is installed aboard the Russian-built *Sovremennyy*-class guided-missile destroyers.

♦ Air-to-air missiles

PL-2: Weight: 11 kg; range: 8 km; infrared homing.

PL-5: Speed: Mach 4.5; range: 16 km; infrared homing.

PL-7: Weight: 12 kg; range: 14 km; infrared homing.

PL-9: Weight: 120 kg; range: 5 km.

Note: Israeli-manufactured Python heat-seeking missiles arm PLAN F-8 interceptors.

B. SHIPBOARD CONVENTIONAL WEAPONS

♦ Guns

Note: The Russian twin AK-130 130-mm dual-purpose gun and AK-630 30-mm gatling guns are carried by *Sovremennyy*-class guided-missile destroyers.

130-mm 58-cal. DP: Chinese version of the twin mounting used on the now-discarded Kotlin-class destroyers of the Soviet Navy, but without cross-level stabilization.

Muzzle velocity: 900 m/sec **Rate of fire:** 65 rds/min/mount
Arc of elevation: –15° to +85° **Range:** 28,000 m surface

100-mm 56-cal. DP single and twin: The standard single and twin 100-mm mounts used on Chinese ships employ the gun developed in the 1930s for the Soviet Navy. The single mounts are a direct copy of the Soviet BU-34. The twin ENG-2 mountings are manned and have loading from below decks. Both versions can be locally controlled.

Shell weight: 13.5 kg **Muzzle velocity:** 850 m/sec
Rate of fire: 15 rds/min/barrel **Arc of elevation:** −5° to +40°
Range: 16,000 m (10,000 m effective)

100-mm 55-cal. DP twin: For the Luhai- and Luhu-class destroyers and Jiangwei-II-class frigates, a new twin 100-mm automatic gunmount has been designed, probably employing operating concepts copied from one of the two French Creusot-Loire 100-mm Compact mounts purchased in the late 1980s. Estimated performance characteristics are:

Muzzle velocity: 870 m/sec **Rate of fire:** 20, 45, or 90 rds/min/barrel
Arc of elevation: −15° to +80°
Range: 17,200 m (12,000 m max. effective; 6,000 m AA)

57-mm twin DP: Two types of twin, open, manned 57-mm 62-cal. mount are used: Type 66 and Type 76, the latter with fan-type ready-service feed. Neither is apparently considered very satisfactory.

37-mm Type 76A: Enclosed, automatic mount closely resembling the Italian OTO-Breda Dardo mounting, from which it is said to have been copied. Has 1,600 rounds ready-service on mount. Carried by Luda-III- and Luhu-class destroyers, Jiangwei- and Jianghu-V-class frigates, and some recent missile boats. Offered for export as the Type H/PJ-76A system. When sighted in 2-01, Yuting-class LST 909 displayed a variant of the mount adapted to accept an on-mount operator. Data for the gun include:

Muzzle velocity: 1,000 m/sec **Rate of fire:** 760 rds/min/barrel
Range: 3,500 m effective/9,400 m max.

37-mm Type 74 and Type 76: The Type 74 twin 37-mm 63-cal. mounting is a copy of the Soviet V-11M manned mount with manual cross-level stabilization. Type 76 uses the same guns but substitutes auto-loading from trays and retains personnel on-mount for elevation and training. On at least one Jianghu, two point-defense SAM launchers are fitted to each mount. Type 76, in conjunction with two PL-8H point-defense SAMs, has been offered for export as the Type 715-I system. The basic Type 76 is mounted on most Jianghu-series frigates and on Yuting-class landing ships. Type 76 characteristics include:

Rate of fire: 360–380 rds/min/barrel
Range: 9,400 m max. **Altitude:** 7,200 m

30-mm Type . . .: A copy of the Russian six-barreled 30-mm AK-630MI gatling gun mounting that completed development in 1995 in cooperation with Russia's Tulamach Zavod. Said to use a Chinese-developed fire-control system 100% more accurate that the MR-123 Vympel (Bass Tilt) radar system used on Russian ships. The associated search radar set is designated SR-47B and the tracking radar TR-47, and there is an OFD-630 optronic backup director. Normally, the gunmounts are to be installed in pairs. Has not yet been installed on an operational warship.

30-mm Type 69 twin: A copy of the Russian 30-mm 65-cal. AK-230.

25-mm Type 61: A copy of the standard Russian twin 25-mm 80-cal. 2M-3M mounting. No longer being manufactured, but many are still in use and others have been recycled for further use aboard auxiliaries.

14.5-mm Type 81: A twin, side-by-side 14.5-mm 79-cal. mounting developed in China and exported aboard small combatants as well as being employed domestically.

♦ Torpedoes

In addition to imported Italian WASS A-244 lightweight antisubmarine torpedoes and 15 TEST-71EM-NK wake-homing Russian torpedoes that were delivered with the Kilo-class submarines, China has developed and put into production the following domestic designs.

Yu-1: 533-mm straight-running air-steam weapon that entered production in 1971.

Yu-2: A copy of the Russian 1950s-era RAT-52 rocket-propelled antisubmarine torpedo. Entered service in 1971 after 14 years of development.

Yu-3: 533-mm electric-powered acoustic homing torpedo for submarines. Development began in 1964, and the weapon was accepted in 1984.

Yu-4A/4B: 533-mm submarine-launched antiship weapons. Yu-4A employs passive acoustic homing and was developed by the Dong Fen Factory; Yu-4B, developed by Xi Bei University, is passive/active. Both versions are said to be in production.

Current-production torpedoes also offered for export include the following.

ET-32: Heavyweight acoustic homing torpedo. Available in active and passive-only versions and also in an active/passive variant. Has both impact and proximity fuzes. Employs silver-zinc batteries. Exercise variant weighs 1,203 kg.

Diameter: 533 mm **Length:** 6.60 m **Weight:** 1,340 kg
Warhead: 190 kg HE **Speed:** 35 kts **Range:** 13 km
Depth: 6–250 m operating (up to 150-m launch depth)

ET-34: Wire-guided, electrically powered torpedo. Employs a combination of wire guidance and active or passive acoustic homing, with a 5-m range proximity fuze. Powered by a zinc-silver battery driving two coaxial propellers. Exercise version has a range of 9–10 km at high speed.

Diameter: 533 mm **Length:** 6.60 m **Weight:** . . . kg
Warhead: . . . kg **Speed:** 25 or 36 kts
Range: 25 km at 25 kts, 15–16 km at 36 kts **Depth:** 5–250 m

ET-36: Wire-guided, electrically powered torpedo. Employs a combination of wire guidance and active or passive homing, with a 5-m range proximity fuze. Exercise version has a range of 8 km at 40–42 kts.

WEAPONS AND SENSORS *(continued)*

Diameter: 533 mm **Length:** 6.60 m **Weight:** . . . kg
Warhead: . . . kg **Speed:** 28 or 40–42 kts
Range: 30 km at 28 kts, 18–20 km at 40–42 kts **Depth:** 5–300 m

ET-52: Lightweight ASW torpedo for aircraft and surface launch. A probable copy of either the U.S. Mk 46 or Italian A-244.

Diameter: 324 mm **Length:** 2.60 m **Weight:** 235 kg
Warhead: 45 kg **Speed:** 42 kts **Range:** 10 km **Depth:** 6–400 m

VA-111 Shkval: High-speed torpedoes were ordered from Kazakhstan in mid-1998, but they were reportedly delivered without a fire-control system and were not put to use.

♦ ASW rockets

The five-tubed ASW rocket launcher used on most Chinese ASW-capable ships is referred to as the EDS-32 or Type 81; although the launcher outwardly resembles that of the Russian RBU-1200, the weapon has over twice the range (3,200 m max./55 m min.) using the Type 62 rocket. The larger EDS-25A (Type 75), 12-tubed ASW rocket launcher on Luda-class destroyers fires the Type 81 rocket to 2,500-m maximum ranges. The Type 87 rocket launcher is an improved version of the Type 81 using a two-stage rocket to reach ranges of up to 5,000 m. Copies of the Soviet BMB-1 and BMB-2 depth charge mortars are also used.

Note: The "CY-1" antisubmarine missile purported to be launched from the Luda-class destroyers is almost certainly a journalistic creation. Russian RBU-1000 rocket launchers, primarily for defense against homing torpedoes but also employable against submarines, will be carried on Russian-built *Sovremennyy*-class guided-missile destroyers.

♦ Artillery rockets

A new 122-mm, 40-tubed artillery rocket launcher has been tested. The rockets weigh 66.6 kg, and the warhead weight is 18.4 kg. Three of the launchers, on specially configured trucks, were carried aboard a merchant cargo ship to provide shore bombardment during a March 1996 naval demonstration opposite Taiwan, but the weapon has not since been publicized and appears on no PLAN ships.

♦ Mines

Older Chinese-designed mines reported in service include the L-1, L-2, and L-3 large, medium, and antenna-equipped moored mines; L-4 moored acoustic mine; L-4A and L-4B with solid-state circuitry, which entered service in 1980 and 1985, respectively; C-1 acoustic bottom mine; C-2 solid-state-electronics acoustic bottom mine; C-3 counter–mine-countermeasures mine for use in waters 6 to 100 m deep; C-4 lightweight, man-portable mine; C-5 man- or mule-portable pressure mine for riverine use; T-1 (or PRAM) rocket-propelled rising mine, which entered service in 1987; and T-2-1 remote-controlled mine. Current-production mines offered for export include the following.

EM-11: Multipurpose bottom mine, which comes in Type 500 and Type 1000 variants, both layable by aircraft or submarine. The Type 500 can be laid at 80-m minimum spacing and the Type 1000 at 50-m. The fuze type is not specified, but probably includes combinations of acoustic, magnetic, and pressure. Target counter up to 20 targets. Some versions may be layable in water up to 100 m deep. Data for Type 500 (Type 1000):

Length: 2.79 m (3.35 m) aircraft/1.98 m (2.90 m) submarine
Diameter: 450 m (533 m) **Weight:** 500 kg (1,000 kg)
Warhead: 300 kg (700 kg) **Depth:** 5–30 m (5–50 m)
Service life in water: 1 year

EM-12: Bottom mine, layable by aircraft, surface ships, and submarines. Can be fitted with any combination of acoustic, magnetic, and pressure fuzes. An exercise version, which can be laid at depths up to 50 m, is also available; it weighs either 570 kg or 950 kg, depending on which length (1.86 m or 2.96 m) is employed.

Length: 1.5 or 2.6 m **Diameter:** 533 mm **Weight:** 570 or 950 kg
Warhead: 320 or 700 kg **Depth:** 5–200 m
Service life in water: 2 years

EM-52: Rocket-propelled mine. When laid at its maximum depth, can deliver its warhead to an area of 3,400 m^3. Equipped with a 1- to 99-target counter.

Length: 3.70 m **Diameter:** 450 mm **Weight:** 620 kg
Warhead: 140 kg RS 211 **Range:** . . . km
Depth: 110 m max. **Service life in water:** 1 year

EM-55: Rocket-propelled rising anchored mine. Produced in a 533-mm version for laying by submarines and a 450-mm version for laying by surface ships. Fuzing is magnetic, active or passive acoustic, or combinations thereof. Can be set to activate up to 480 hours after laying and to self-destruct up to 8,640 hours later.

Length: 3.54 or 3.35 m **Weight:** 840 or 620 kg
Warhead: 130 kg **Depth:** 50–200 m **Service life in water:** 1 year

EM-56: Self-propelled mine, laid by submarines. Has a combination LF acoustic and pressure fuze.

Length: 7.738 m **Diameter:** 533.4 mm **Weight:** 1,840 kg
Warhead: 380 kg TNT **Range:** 13+ km
Depth: 45 m max. **Service life in water:** 9 months

EM-57: Remote-controlled mine, for control by submarines, in two variants, Type 500 and Type 1000. Usable against surface ships and submarines, it employs either an acoustic/magnetic or magnetic induction fuze and can be activated by the controlling submarine at ranges of up to 30 km. Data for Type 500 (Type 1000):

Length: 2.14 m (3.14 m) **Diameter:** 450 mm (533 mm)
Weight: 510 kg (1,010 kg) **Warhead:** 300 kg (700 kg) TNT
Depth: 6–100 m **Service life in water:** 6 months

EM-71: Multipurpose exercise ground mine. Comes in three variants (Type 1000U, Type 500A, and Type 500S) and can be laid by aircraft, surface ships, or submarines. Can be equipped with LF acoustic/magnetic, magnetic alone, or magnetic/pressure fuze.

Length: 3.0, 2.865, or 1.52 m **Weight:** 700, 500, or . . . kg

C. ELECTRONIC SYSTEMS

Chinese radars, formerly either made in the USSR or copied from Russian models, are increasingly of Chinese design and manufacture. French Thales (formerly Thomson-CSF) radars are used on the largest surface combatants, while British-made Litton-Decca RM 1290A/D ARPA navigational radars are widely employed on major combatants as navigational and surface-search sets. Japanese electronics systems, including Oki and Anritsu navigational radars, are also widely used. The major radar sets currently in use include the following.

Name	*Origin*	*Band*	*Function*
Ball End	USSR	E/F	Surface search (obsolescent)
Bean Sticks	China	S	Long-range air early warning, with 16 yagi antenna arrays
ESR-1	China	X?	Low-flier detection
Fin Curve	U.K.	I	Nav. (Decca 707 copy)
Fog Lamp	China	I	100-mm gun f.c. on Luda, Luhai classes; Chinese EFR-1
Hai Ying	France?	S	Long-range air search (God Eye)
Pea Sticks	China	S	Long-range air early warning; 16 yagi transmitter arrays
Rice Field	China	G	3-D phased-array air search (Chinese "Sea Eagle")—in two versions
Skin Head	USSR	I	Surface search; few, if any, left
Type 341	China	I	Gun control (Rice Lamp)
Type 343	USSR	I	Gun f.c. (Sun Visor-B)
Type 347G	China	I	Gun f.c.
Type 351	USSR	X	Copy of Russian Reya (Pot Head)
Type 352/352C	USSR	. . .	Target detection and tracking (Square Tie)
Type 354	China	E/F	Surface search (Eye Shield)
Type 360	China	E/F	Successor to Type 354 (Eye Shield); also target desig. Made by Nanjing Marine Radar Institute, which calls it the Type 2405. Has a mechanically stabilized antenna.
Type 363	China	S	Early warning, yagi array
Type 702	China	X	Gun f.c.
Type 726	Japan	X	Imported Anritsu sets, used on patrol craft
Type 756	China	S	Nav. (copy of Decca 1226 or 1229 set)
Type 765	China	E/F	Missile targeting on Houjian class; may be a variant of the Type 360

IFF systems have only come into general use since the early 1980s. Chinese sonars are of Soviet design derivation, with an active program under way to acquire modern Western systems. The BM/HZ-8610 intercept system is employed on some larger warships; covering 2–18 GHz, it has 5-MHz frequency accuracy and 2.5° bearing accuracy. Also employed is the GT-1 chaff dispensing system, while U.S.-designed Mk 137 decoy rocket launchers (as used with the Mk 36 SRBOC system) are offered for use on export warships. Two Great Wall communications satellites were launched during 1984–85, but there is no indication that they are used by the PLAN, other than possibly by the new Luhu- and Luhai-class destroyers, which appear to have satellite communications antenna radomes, although the radomes may instead cover steerable jammer arrays.

CLASS NAMES AND PENNANTS

The class names used below are generally those assigned by Western intelligence services; the Chinese Navy uses a project number system for which few of the designations are known, and there is also an export project number system employed in foreign sales efforts. The Western nicknames are a mix of geographic, dynastic, and animal names, while a few others are mere nonsense words.

For combatants, three-digit hull numbers are assigned. Small combatants have a four-digit pennant number, the first digit of which signifies area subordination. Until recently, auxiliaries had three-digit numbers preceded by a letter signifying their function, but that system has now been superseded by one employing two or more Chinese ideographs describing the ship's fleet (first character: *Bei* for North Sea Fleet, *Dong* for East Sea Fleet, and *Nan* for South Sea Fleet) and function. In addition, the numerous ships subordinated to the various districts of the Maritime Border Defense Force have four-digit pennants preceded by a letter signifying the district; known prefixes include "S" for Shenyang, "N" for Nanjing (commonly seen in the Shanghai area), and "G" for Guangzhou.

Note: The Hudong and Zhonghua Shipyards at Shanghai were merged early in 2001 and now trade as the Hudong Zhonghua Shipbuilding Group.

AIRCRAFT CARRIERS [CV]

Note: Although rumors were rampant during mid-1992 that China was arranging to purchase the incomplete Russian Navy carrier *Varyag,* both China and Russia officially denied that the sale was to take place. The ship was finally purchased by a Chinese entrepreneur as an exhibit, but attempts to tow it to China in 2000 were thwarted by Turkish refusal to permit the vessel to pass through the Bosporus.

In 11-92, the Chinese press carried a story that "Paramount Leader" Deng Xiaoping had decided to go forward with a plan to design and build a carrier in China, with the effort to begin during 1993. Later reports said that there were to be two 48,000-ton carriers in service by 2005, indicating that construction might commence on the first in 1997–98. In 1996, the Russian Nevelskoye Design Bureau received a contract to provide conceptual designs for the proposed Chinese carriers, which would appear to indicate that actual construction was still several years away. In 5-98, however, it was announced that carrier construction had been delayed into the 2001–05 five-year construction plan, with initial operating capability not expected until about 2020. By 1-99, Chinese officials were saying that all planning for carrier construction had been postponed for at least 10 years, making the 2020 operational date unlikely. During 1-01, the *Far Eastern Economic Review* reported that all plans to acquire a carrier had been cancelled.

NUCLEAR-POWERED BALLISTIC-MISSILE SUBMARINES [SSBN]

♦ **0 (+ 4) . . . class (Project 094)**
Bldr: Huludao SY

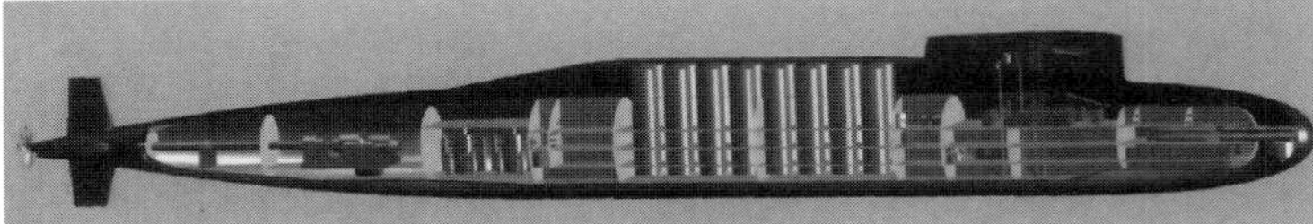

Project 094 SSBN—artist's speculation U.S. Navy, 1997

Remarks: Construction of four nuclear-powered ballistic-missile submarines of the Project 094 design was expected to commence early in this decade, with the first to become operational by 2009–10, but the program was reported in 1-10 to have been delayed in favor of the Project 093 SSN program. The SSBNs are intended to carry 16 Ju Lang-2 (JL-2) missiles, each with a range of 8,000 km and carrying 400-kT warheads. Will reportedly receive Russian passive towed-array sonar equipment and a new Russian torpedo fire-control system. The accompanying drawing, released by the U.S. Navy, must be taken as highly speculative.

♦ **1 Xia class (Project 092)** (Nonoperational)
Bldr: Huludao SY

	Laid down	L	In serv.
406	1971	30-4-81	10-88

Xia-class 406 *Ships of the World,* ca. 1988–89

D: 7,000 tons sub. **S:** 22 kts sub. **Dim:** 120.0 × 10.0 × 8.0
A: 12 Ju Lang-1 (CSS-N-3) strategic missiles; 6 bow 533-mm TT
M: 1 58-MW pressurized-water nuclear reactor, two steam turbines; 1 prop; 14,400 shp
Endurance: 90 days **Crew:** 100 tot.

Remarks: The Xia-class submarine was launched from the same facility that builds the Han-class nuclear-powered attack submarine, 200 km northeast of Beijing in Liaoning province. The design is essentially that of the Han, lengthened to accommodate the missile tubes. At least two additional units were expected, but construction of further units was canceled around 1985 in favor of developing an all-new, larger design with longer-range missiles. The single Xia was based near Qingdao at a base equipped with a 12-story-high underground maintenance cavern. Began a refit in 1995, reportedly for completion in 1998, but reports in 1-01 indicated that the submarine may instead have been scrapped.
Hull systems: Pressure hull plating thickness is 40 mm. Maximum operating depth is 300 m. Onboard machinery noise is said to be uncomfortably high.
Combat systems: The first Ju Lang-1 submerged launch took place from the Golf-class trials submarine on 12-10-82 to a range of 1,600 km. The missile is believed to have two solid-propulsion stages and to have a range of 1,700 km. The first Xia missile launch took place between 14-7-78 and 27-7-88, and no further launches have been announced. The EW suite may incorporate the Thales DR-2000U intercept set. Navigational aids include an inertial navigation system, stellar sight, receiver for U.S. Navstar navigational satellite data, and Omega receiver.

NUCLEAR-POWERED ATTACK SUBMARINES [SSN]

♦ **0 (+ 1 + . . .) . . . class (Project 093)**
Bldr: Huludao SY (In serv. 2006–07)

Project 093 SSN—artist's speculation U.S. Navy, 1997

D: 6,000 tons sub. **S:** 30 kts sub. **Dim:** 107.0 × 11.0 × 7.5
A: 6 533-mm TT fwd (. . . torpedoes, mines, antiship missiles)
M: 2 pressurized water reactors, geared electric drive; 1 prop; 20,000 shp
Crew: 100 tot.

Remarks: The U.S. Director of Naval Intelligence stated in 1997 that a new Chinese SSN class, Project 093, was under construction at "Bohai" (probably meaning Huludao) Shipyard, with the first unit to launch after the turn of the century. An 8-99 report indicated that the first was to be laid down late that year, but, as of 1-01, there were reports that the first unit would not be completed until after 2005. The Project 093 design was said to be intended to launch antiship missiles as well as torpedoes from its torpedo tubes, with the cruise missile probably being a follow-on to the current C-801 and capable of being submerged-launched. All data above are speculative.

♦ **5 Han class (Project 091)** Bldr: Huludao SY

	Laid down	L	In serv.
401	1965–68	26-12-70	1-8-74
402	. . .	1977	1980
403	. . .	1983	21-9-84
404	. . .	. . .	1988
405	. . .	6-90	1991

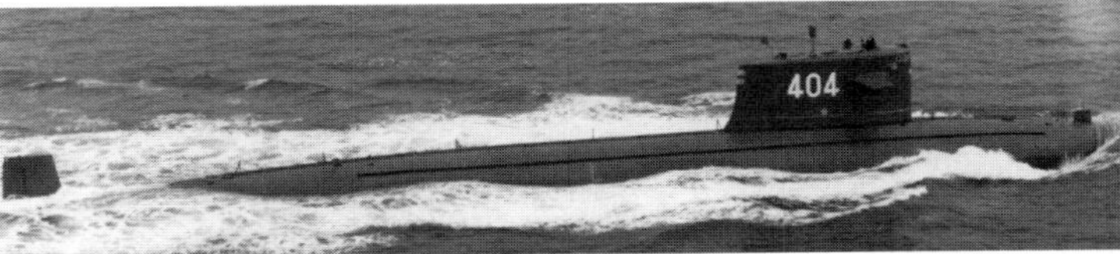

Han-class 404—long-hulled variant U.S. Navy, 2-96

Han-class 402—short-hulled variant *Ships of the World,* 1990

D: 4,500 (403–405: 5,550) tons sub. **S:** 25 kts sub.
Dim: 90.0 (403–405: 98.0) × 9.0 × 7.4
A: 6 bow 533-mm TT (Ying Ji-8 Mod. 3 antiship missiles, Yu-3 ASW and Yu-4 antiship torpedoes, and mines)
Electronics:
Radar: . . . nav.
Sonar: . . . active; Thales DUUX-5 passive hull array
EW: CEIEC Model 921-A intercept
M: 1 48-MW pressurized-water nuclear reactor, two steam turbines; 1 prop; 12,000 shp
Endurance: 60 days **Crew:** 75 tot.

Remarks: The trials series for the first unit was very protracted, and the two earliest units proved unreliable, being referred to by the Chinese Navy—at least initially—as "sharks without teeth." One Western visitor referred to the Han as a "Whiskey with a reactor" in terms of the level of technology employed. Overall, are not considered a successful design. Name of first unit is *Long March 1.* A submarine named *Hai Long,* possibly of this class, set a Chinese record for submerged operations, 31 days, in March–April 1995. All assigned to the North Sea Fleet and based near Qingdao, but only 404 was fully active as of 1999.
Hull systems: Pressure hull plating thickness is 40 mm. Maximum operating depth is 300 m.
Combat systems: Reported to carry both straight-running and wire-guided torpedoes. Contrary to some reports, the longer units do not carry cruise missiles in tubes abaft the sail. The Model 921-A EW system is said to be a copy of the Israeli Timnex 4CH(V)2 intercept system. The EW suite may incorporate the Thales DR-2000U intercept set. 403–405 received inertial guidance systems during construction; these have been backfitted to the earlier pair. All five will reportedly receive Russian passive towed-array sonar equipment and a new torpedo fire-control system.

Disposal note: The single Wuhan-class (Project 033G) cruise-missile trials submarine, 351, is believed to have been discarded by the mid-1990s. The submarine was intended to launch missiles from elevated tubes while surfaced, while subsequent PLAN cruise-missile developments have been directed at employing submerged-launch weapons from standard torpedo tubes.

ATTACK SUBMARINES [SS]

♦ **2 (+ 3) Song class (Project 039)** Bldr: Wuhan SY

320 (In serv. . . .) 321 (L: 9-99) 322 (In serv. 2000) 323 (L: 2001)

Song-class 320 *Ships of the World,* 1998

D: 1,700 tons surf./2,250 tons sub. **S:** 15 kts surf./22 kts sub.
Dim: 74.9 × 8.4 × 5.3
A: 6 bow 533-mm TT (Ying Ji-8 Mod. 3 antiship missiles, Yu-3 ASW and Yu-4 antiship torpedoes, and mines)
Electronics:
Radar: 1 . . . nav./surf. search
Sonar: Thales TSM 2233 Eledone passive bow array; Thales TSM 2255 Fenelon or Chinese SQB-2 flank array
EW: CEIEC Model 921-A intercept

ATTACK SUBMARINES [SS] *(continued)*

Song-class 320 *Ships of the World,* 2000

M: diesel-electric: 4 MTU 16V396 SE 83/84 diesels, 2 generator sets; 1 7-bladed prop; 6,092 shp
Range: 22/22, 72/3 sub. **Crew:** 60 tot.

Remarks: All data above are estimates. Initially referred to by Western agencies as the "Wuhan-C." Some elements of the French *Agosta* class may have been incorporated in the design. 320 was launched 5-94, and acceptance trials began 8-95 but were protracted due to high noise levels. The design overall is distinctly not modern-appearing, and series production may be curtailed in favor of additional imports of superior Russian Kilo-series submarines. As of 2-02, the 320 was still not operational, a fourth had been launched, and a fifth was building.
Hull systems: The sail on 320 is unusual in form, in that it is stepped, with the bow planes mounted on the lower, forward portion, which also houses a forward-looking hydrophone array. 321 has a normal, high sail. Said to be a very noisy design with significant equipment problems.
Combat systems: A number of small hydrophones are mounted atop the bow. The submarine is capable of submerged-launching the "No. 8 Mod. 3" antiship missile (probably meaning the Ying Ji-8 Mod. 3), believed to be a submerged-launch variant of the C-801 antiship missile.

♦ 3 Improved Kilo class (Russian Project 636)
Bldr: United Admiralty Shipyard, St. Petersburg (368: Krasnoye Sormovo Zavod 199, Nizhniy Novgorod)

	L	In serv.
366 Lin San Liu (ex-B-871)	24-4-97	1-98
367 . . . . . . (ex-B-466)	17-6-98	2-12-98
368 . . . . . . (ex-B-. . .)	2001	4-4-01

D: 2,350 tons surf./3,126 tons sub. **S:** 11 kts surf./19 kts sub.
Dim: 73.80 × 9.90 × 6.60 (max.; 6.20 mean hull amidships, surf.)
A: 6 bow 533-mm TT (18 torpedoes or 24 mines); 1 Fasta-4 SAM syst. (6 Igla-M missiles)

Project 636 Kilo-class 366—in repair at Shanghai, alongside a former U.S. Army repair barge H&L Van Ginderen, 5-00

Project 636 Kilo-class 367—en route China aboard lift-ship *Super Servant 3* RAAF, 1-99

Electronics:
Radar: 1 MPK-50E nav./surf. search
Sonar: MGK-400 (Shark Gill) LF active/passive suite; passive hull array; MG-519 (Mouse Roar) active object avoidance; MT-553 sound velocity measurement; MG-512 self-cavitation measurement
EW: MPM-25EM intercept
M: 2 Type 4-2AA-42M turbocharged diesel generator sets (1,500 kw each at 700 rpm), 1 electric motor; 1 7-bladed prop; 5,500 shp—1 MT-140 electric low-speed motor (183 shp)—2 MT-168 internal electric creep/maneuvering motors; 2 ducted props; 204 shp (for 3 kts)
Range: 7,500/7 snorkel; 400/3 sub. **Endurance:** 45 days
Crew: 13 officers, 12 warrant officers, 12 petty officers, 15 nonrated

ATTACK SUBMARINES [SS] *(continued)*

Remarks: An across-the-board improvement over the standard Project 877–series Kilo that has been offered for foreign sale since 1993. The first two were ordered in 7-94 and the third during 5-00 for around $100 million; begun in 1992 for the Soviet Navy, the third boat was said to be 98% complete as of 5-00. Reports that a further 17 are to be built under license in China cannot be verified and are probably incorrect. The first unit departed the Baltic as deck cargo late 11-97 to arrive in China during 1-98; by 5-00, that submarine was under repair at Shanghai. The second departed the Baltic 11-12-98 as deck cargo on *Super Servant 3.* Both are based at Ningbo.
Hull systems: Offers improved sound quieting over the Project 877 series and a greater degree of automation. The electric propulsion motor is mounted on a flexible raft, and the maximum shaft rpm has been halved to 250 rpm. Maximum snorkeling speed is 8–10 kts. The bow has been reshaped to improve flow, and some auxiliary machinery has been moved aft from the bow compartment to reduce noise interference with the passive bow sonar array. More-efficient models of the diesel generator sets have been added. The 7.2-m-diameter pressure hull has been lengthened to 53.0 m to accommodate the rafted main engines, allowing more tankage for additional diesel fuel. Pressure-hull thickness is 24–27 mm, except in some reinforced areas, where it is 30–35 mm thick. There are three 614-mm-diameter access hatches. The outer hull is coated with .8-m square rubber anechoic tiles, attached with glue over special studs. Stern planes, rudder, and the bow planes mounted just forward of the sail are controlled by a Pirit-23 hydraulic system. The two maneuvering propellers are mounted in internal ducts just forward of the stern planes, with the shafts to the motors protruding directly aft through the after pressure bulkhead. Normal operating depth: 240 m; maximum operating depth: 300 m. Periscope depth is 17.5 m; there are two attack periscopes with 1.5× and 6× magnification. There are two 120-cell Type 446 lead-acid batteries. Height from keel to the top of the 5-m-high sail is 14.7 m.
Combat systems: Only the two outer torpedo tubes in the lower row can accommodate TEST-71EM-NK wire-guided torpedoes (of which China has purchased 15), while all tubes can launch Types 53-65KE, 53-56B, 53BA, and SET-53ME torpedoes; an automatic reload system permits reloading within 2 minutes. Torpedoes can be launched down to 240-m depths. Using 12 in the tubes and 12 in the racks, 24 Type AM-1 mines can be carried in lieu of some torpedoes; mines can be laid only to a depth of 50 m. The third unit is reportedly equipped to launch 3M-54E Klub-S supersonic antiship missiles.

The combat system is the digital MVU-110EM, with three computer/processors; five targets can be tracked simultaneously (two automatically). Radio communication gear fitted includes two P-654-MP transmitters, three P-680-1 HF/VHF receivers, 1 P-683-1 LF receiver, 1 P-625 UHF transceiver, and 1 P-608H portable set. The MPM-25EM intercept array incorporates the transponder for the Khrom-K IFF system.

♦ 2 Russian Kilo class (Russian Project 877E)
Bldr: Krasnoye Sormovo Zavod 199, Nizhniy Novgorod (In serv. 1995–96)

364 (ex-B-171) 365 (ex-B-177)

Project 877E Kilo-class 364 *Ships of the World,* 2000

D: 2,325 tons surf./3,076 tons sub. **S:** 10 kts surf./17 kts sub.
Dim: 74.30 (70.00 wl) × 10.00 × 6.60
A: 6 bow 533-mm TT (18 torpedoes or up to 24 mines); 1 shoulder-launched SAM position (8 9K-32M Strela missiles)
Electronics:
Radar: 1 MRK-50E (Snoop Tray-2) nav./surf. search
Sonar: MGK-400 (Shark Gill) LF active/passive suite; passive hull array; MG-519 (Mouse Roar) HF active classification/mine avoidance
EW: MRP-25ZM (Brick Pulp) intercept; 6701E (Quad Loop) D/F
M: 2 Type 2D-42, 1,825-bhp diesel generator sets (1,825 bhp/1,500 kw each), electric drive: 1 motor; 1 6-bladed prop; 5,900 shp—130-shp low-speed motor—2 102-shp emergency propulsion motors
Range: 6,000/7 surf.; 400/3 sub. **Endurance:** 45 days
Crew: 12 officers, 41 enlisted

Remarks: First unit departed the Baltic as deck cargo on heavy-lift ship *Sea Tern* in mid-12-94. The second unit was launched 31-3-95 and delivered 5-9-95 at St. Petersburg, then transported to China aboard a heavy-lift ship. Although it was announced during spring 1997 that they were to be refitted at Bol'shoy Kamen Shipyard on the Russian Primoriy Peninsula, the contract was not signed until 2-99; one was inoperable at Shanghai as of 8-98, in need of a new diesel generator set. Based at Ningbo.
Hull systems: Propulsion plant is suspended raft–mounted for silencing. Hull has 32% reserve buoyancy at 2,350 m^3 surfaced displacement. At rest on the surface, trims down 0.4 m by the bow. Maximum diving depth is 300 m, normal depth 240 m, and periscope depth 17.5 m. Has an anechoic hull coating. There are two batteries, each with 120 cells, providing 9,700 kw/hr. Hull has six watertight compartments.
Combat systems: Combat system, designated Murena or MVU-110EM, can conduct two simultaneous attacks while tracking three other targets manually. Sonar suite is supplemented by MG-519 active mine-avoidance set, MG-553 sound velocity meter, and MG-512 own-ship's cavitation detector. The SAM launch position is located in after portion of the sail. Weapons carried on standard export version can include TEST-71ME wire-guided, E53-60 and E53-85 wake-homing, and E53-67 acoustic homing torpedoes and KMD-500, KMD-1000, KMD-II-500, KMD-II-1000, and UMD mines.

♦ 19 Ming class (Project 035)
Bldr: Wuhan SY (In serv. 1975–2001)

233 305 306 342 352 353 354 356 357 358
359 360 361 362 363 . . . .

Ming-class 359 *Ships of the World,* 1999

Ming-class 358 China Shipbuilding Trading Co., 1999

Ming-class 357 U.S. Navy, 9-94

D: 1,584 tons surf./2,113 tons sub. **S:** 15 kts surf./10 kts snorkel/18 kts sub.
Dim: 76.00 × 7.60 × 5.10
A: 8 533-mm TT (6 fwd, 2 aft; 16 torpedoes or 28 mines)
Electronics:
Radar: 1 Snoop Plate nav./surf. search
Sonar: Herkules active/passive; Feniks passive
EW: CEIEC Model 921-A or Thales DR-2000U intercept
M: diesel-electric: 2 Type 6E390ZC diesels (2,600 bhp each); 2 props; 3,500 shp—2 75-shp creep motors
Range: 8,000/8 snorkel; 330/4 sub. **Endurance:** 60 days
Crew: 9 officers, 46 enlisted

Remarks: First two launched in 1975, third in 1982; series construction then commenced again around 1988, with units 15 and 16 launched during 1997, when four more were said to be on order, of which two were launched that year. One of the first three built was lost after a fire. Based on the Romeo design, but with a different propulsion plant and fuller hullform. All are assigned to the East Sea Fleet. Design offered for export as Project ES5E.
Hull systems: Diving depth: 300 m. The 20th unit, launched late in 2000, is said to be 2 m longer than the earlier units.
Combat systems: There are no reload torpedoes for the two aft tubes. Later units have passive sonar arrays patterned after the French DUUX-5 (Thales TSM 2255 Fenelon) system, with three flank transducers per side mounted in the casing.

♦ up to 32 Soviet Romeo class (Project 033)
Bldrs: Wuhan SY, Guangzhou SY, Jiangnan SY, Huludao SY (In serv. 1960–84)

From among: 213–218, 227, 228, 237–239, 249–260, 268–272, 275–280, 286, 287, 291–304, 343–350, 355

Romeo-class 272 H&L Van Ginderen, 3-95

D: 1,319 tons surf./1,712 tons sub. **S:** 15.2 kts surf./13 kts sub.
Dim: 76.60 × 6.70 × 4.95
A: 8 533-mm TT (6 fwd, 2 aft; 14 torpedoes or 28 mines)
Electronics:
Radar: 1 Snoop Plate nav./surf. search
Sonar: Tamir-5L active; Feniks passive (see Remarks)
EW: CEIEC Model 92-A intercept
M: diesel-electric: 2 Type 1Z38 diesels, 2,400 bhp each; 2 props; 2,700 shp—2 electric creep motors; 100 shp tot.
Range: 14,000/9 surf.; 350/9 sub. **Endurance:** 60 days
Crew: 8 officers, 43 enlisted

Remarks: Generally similar to the Soviet version built in the late 1950s, but with numerous changes in equipment and detail. The first to be built entirely with Chinese-produced materials and equipment, named *New China No. 42,* was not completed until 22-6-69. Some 84 were built for the PLAN, plus four each for export to

ATTACK SUBMARINES [SS] *(continued)*

Egypt (1982–83) and North Korea (1973–75). One reserve unit was reported in the Chinese press to have been successfully reactivated during 1994, and one was lost in an accident in 1993–94.
Hull systems: Maximum operating depth: 300 m. Has a 224-cell battery providing 6,600 amp-hr.
Combat systems: One unit (probably 250) has one of the two Thales DUUX-5 passive sonar suites delivered in 1983, and the export version is offered with that gear plus an enlarged chin sonar dome. Hull 250 is also reported to have the Thales DR-2000U intercept suite.

AUXILIARY SUBMARINES [SSA]

♦ **1 Soviet Golf-class (Project 031) ballistic-missile trials submarine** Bldr: Dalian SY

	Laid down	L	In serv.
200	1961	1964	1966

D: 2,500 tons surf./2,900 tons sub. **S:** 14 kts sub. **Dim:** 99.00 × 8.50 × 6.50
A: 1 Ju Lang-2 ballistic missile; 10 533-mm TT (6 fwd, 4 aft)
Electronics:
Radar: 1 Snoop Tray nav./surf. search
Sonar: Russian Herkules active/passive array
EW: . . . intercept
M: 3 Type 37D diesels, electric drive; 3 5-bladed props; 6,000 shp
Range: 9,000/5 **Crew:** 87 tot.

Remarks: Plans and components were furnished by the Soviet Union at a time when relations between the two countries were good. Originally equipped to launch three Russian R-11FM (Chinese designation Type 1060) missiles while surfaced only, but the missiles were never supplied. Altered from 1968 to 1972 with only two tubes for Ju Lang-1 missile submerged-launch trials, but did not launch first successful Chinese SLBM until 12-10-82. After many years with little use, was reconfigured to launch the second-generation Ju Lang-2 SLBM, with the first (and, to date, only) reported at-sea launch taking place in mid 1-01.

GUIDED-MISSILE DESTROYERS [DDG]

Note: A model of a modified version of the Luhai-class destroyer design with a single stack and what appeared to be vertical-launch cells (possibly for the HQ-9 SAM system) was on display during 2000. Numbered 168, the design was said to be either Project 52B or 54.

♦ **2 (+ 2) ex-Russian Sovremennyy (Sarych) class (Project 956A)**
Bldr: 136, 137: Severnaya Verf 190, St. Petersburg; 138, 139: Baltiyskiy Zavod

	Laid down	L	In serv.
136 HANG ZHOU (ex-*Yekaterinburg*, ex-*Vazhnyy*)	4-11-88	23-5-94	25-12-99
137 FU ZHOU (ex-*Aleksandr Nevskiy*, ex-*Vdumchivyy*)	22-2-89	16-4-99	25-12-00
138	. . .	. . .	2005
139	. . .	. . .	2005

Fu Zhou (137) Jim Sanderson, 12-00

Fu Zhou (137)—while on trials, with Russian pennant number
Flottenkommando, Germany, 7-00

Hang Zhou (136)—amidships detail, showing the distinct clutter of this elderly design
Curt Borgenstam, 1-00

Fu Zhou (137) Leo Van Ginderen, 12-00

Fu Zhou (137)—calling at Portsmouth, England, en route to China
Maritime Photographic. 12-00

GUIDED-MISSILE DESTROYERS [DDG] *(continued)*

Hang Zhou (136) Curt Borgenstam, 1-00

D: 6,500 tons light, 7,940 normal (8,480 fl) **S:** 33.4 kts (32.7 sust.)
Dim: 156.37 (145.00 wl) × 17.19 (16.30 wl) × 5.99 (mean hull; 7.85 max.)
A: 8 P-270 Moskit or P-100 Moskit-M (SS-N-22 Sunburn) SSM (3M-80 or 3M-82 missiles); 2 single-rail 9R-90 Uragan (SA-N-7 Gadfly) SAM syst. (MS-196 launchers, 48 9M-38 Buk-M1 or 9M-38M1 Smerch missiles); 2 twin 130-mm 54-cal. AK-130 DP (2,000 rds); 2 twin 30-mm 54-cal. AK-630M gatling AA (16,000 rds); 2 single 45-mm Type 21-KM saluting cannon; 2 twin 533-mm DTA-53 TT (no reloads); 2 6-tubed RBU-1000 ASW RL (48 RGB-10 rockets); up to 40 mines; 1 Ka-28 Helix-A ASW helicopter
Electronics:
Radar: 3 MR-212/201 Vaygach-U (Palm Frond) nav./surf. search; 1 MR-760MA Fregat-MA (Top Plate-B) 3-D air search; 6 OP-3 (Front Dome) SAM f.c.; 1 MR-184M Lev (Kite Screech-C) 130-mm gun f.c., 2 MR-123 Vympel (Bass Tilt) 30-mm gun f.c.; 1 Mineral surf. target tracking and desig.
Sonar: 1 MG-335MS Platina-S (Bull Horn) MF bow-mounted; MG-7 (Whale Tongue) HF f.c.
EW: 2 MP-405M Start-2 or MR-401 intercept syst. (MRP-11M/12M) (Bell Shroud); 2 Bell Squat intercept; 4 Foot Ball-B intercept; MR-407 jamming syst; 2 2-tubed PK-2M trainable decoy RL (ZIF-121 launchers; 200 rockets); 8 fixed 10-round PK-10 decoy RL
E/O: 1 Squeeze Box multisensor; 1 Tall View periscope; 2 Watch Box bridge periscopes; 2 or 4 Spektr-F (Half Cup) laser warning
M: 2 sets TV-12 geared steam turbines; 2 4-bladed props; 110,000 shp (99,500 sust.)—2 drop-down azimuthal stern-thrusters—1 drop-down bow-thruster
Boilers: 4 turbopressurized Type KVN-98/64, 640 kg/cm^2, 500° C
Electric: 4,900 kw tot. (2 × 1,250-kw turboalternators; 4 × 600-kw diesel sets)
Range: 1,345/32.7; 3,920/18 (5,340/18.4 with overload fuel)
Fuel: 1,740 tons + 5 tons aviation fuel **Endurance:** 30 days
Crew: accomm. for 38 officers, 330 enlisted

Remarks: A letter of intent to order the first pair was signed on 20-11-97; the final contract for $667 million for the pair was signed during 1-98. *Hang Zhou* was handed over to Chinese control 24-2-99; sea trials began 8-7-99 and she arrived in China on 15-2-00. *Fu Zhou* conducted sea trials from 27-6-00 to 15-8-00 in the Baltic and was handed over on 25-11-00. These are the incomplete 18th and 19th units of the class initially ordered for the Russian Navy. Although one had been launched, work on both had been suspended; the first was 65% complete when purchased and the other 35%. The ships are primarily intended for surface warfare tasks, including antiship, shore-bombardment, and antiair defense; the minimal ASW capability is primarily for self-defense. Although this is by no means a state-of-the-art design (the ships were designed in the mid-1960s), they are vastly superior to anything else in Chinese service. Both are based at Dinghai, near the East Sea Fleet main base at Ningbo.

Two more were ordered on 4-1-02, although China was reported unhappy that the work was assigned to Baltiyskiy Zavod rather than to Severnaya Verf. The ships are to have enhanced helicopter facilities, two Kashtan CIWS in place of the 30-mm gatling AA guns, and vertically-launched 3M54E antiship missiles in place of the Moskit system. One may use materials assembled for the *Buynyy,* laid down in 1991 but later scrapped, while the second may use materials for the *Vechnyy,* which was not begun.

Hull systems: The propulsion plant is essentially the same as that of the preceding Russian Kresta-I and Kresta-II classes and employs turbopressurized boilers. Fin stabilizers are fitted.

Combat systems: The first pair were begun as Project 956A ships to carry longer cruise-missile tubes to accept a probable extended-range Moskit missile and a naval version of the SA-17 Grizzly SAM, vice the SA-N-7 system's original 9K-37 Smerch missiles. The SAM launchers are apparently limited to launch angles within 30° of the centerline, a significant handicap; there may be only 16 ready-service missiles per launcher, with the other four requiring assembly and loading onto the ready-service rings.

Forty-eight Moskit antiship missiles were ordered for these ships in 7-98, with the first 24 not delivered until 5-00. The ships have the large Band Stand (Monolit or Mineral) radome associated with surface-to-surface missile targeting systems. There are also two small spherical Light Bulb radomes on the sides of the stack that are missile datalink-associated.

The 130-mm guns are of a fully automatic, water-cooled model, capable of AA or surface fire; they are restricted to firing arcs of 40° each side of the centerline. The AK-630 guns are restricted to firing arcs of −5° across the centerline through 160° for the forward mounts, and 15° off centerline forward through 170° for the after mounts. Squeeze Box is an optronic gunfire-control director combining a laser rangefinder, low-light-level television, and infrared devices.

Shenzhen (167)—note the sliding missile reload hatch above the numerals 6 and 7, just abaft the HQ-7 SAM launcher and the heavy (and vulnerable) battery of cruise missile launchers amidships *Ships of the World,* 1999

Shenzhen (167)—launching an antiship missile *Ships of the World,* 2000

DESTROYERS [DD]

♦ 1 Luhai-class (Project 52)
Bldr: Dalian SY

	Laid down	L	Trials	In serv.
167 Shenzhen	5-96	16-10-97	16-10-98	1-99

Shenzhen (167) *Ships of the World,* 2000

DESTROYERS [DD] *(continued)*

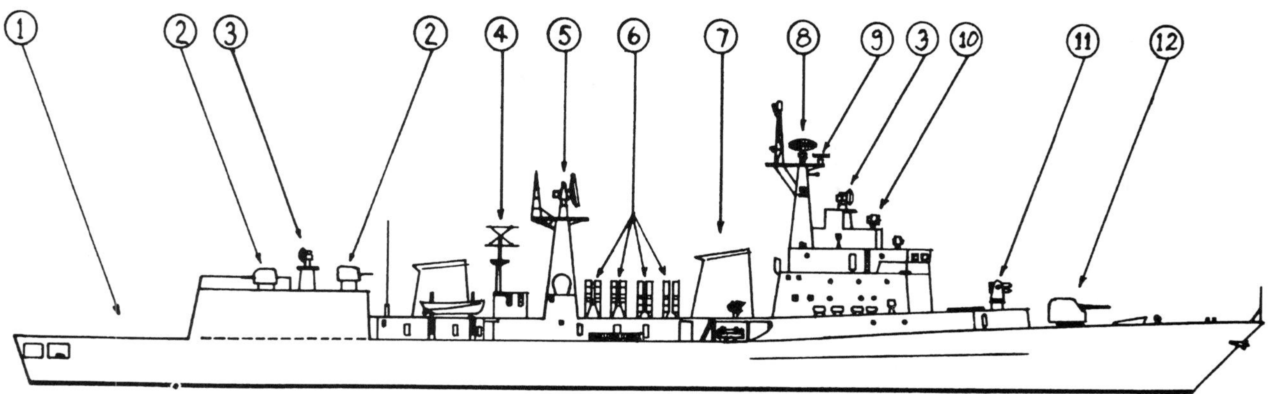

Shenzhen (167) 1. helicopter deck 2. twin 37-mm Type 76A AA 3. Type 347G radar director for 37-mm AA 4. Type 363 early-warning radar 5. Sea Eagle 3-D air-search radar 6. 16 C-802 or C-801A SSM launch containers in four groups of four 7. decoy launchers on platforms above the triple ASW torpedo tubes 8. Sea Tiger air-search radar 9. navigational radar 10. radar director for the 100-mm gunmount 11. octuple launcher for the HQ-7 SAM system 12. twin 100-mm 55-cal. DP gunmount

Drawing by A. D. Baker III

D: 6,600 tons (fl) **S:** 29 kts **Dim:** 153.0 × 16.5 × 6.0
A: 16 C-802 Ying Ji-2 (CSS-N-8 Saccade) or C-801A Ying Ji-1 (CSS-N-4 Sardine) SSM; 1 8-round HQ-7 SAM syst. (16 missiles); 1 twin 100-mm 55-cal. DP; 4 twin 37-mm 63-cal. Type 76A AA; 2 triple 324-mm ILAS-3 ASW TT; 2 Z-9A (later: Ka-28 Helix-A) helicopters
Electronics:
Radar: 2 Decca RM 1290A/D ARPA nav., 1 . . . surf./air search, 1 Thales Sea Tiger (TSR-3004) air search; 1 Sea Eagle (Rice Field) 3-D air search; 1 Type 363 early warning; 2 Type 347G 37-mm f.c.; 1 EFR-1 (Fog Lamp) 100-mm f.c.; 1 . . . missile illuminator
Sonar: . . . bow-mounted LF
EW: 2 . . . . . . intercept, ... jammers; BM 8610 intercept/jammer array, 2 15-round decoy RL
E/O: 2 GDG-775 radar/t.v./laser/IR directors
M: CODOG: 2 Mashproekt-Zorya DN-80 reversible gas turbines (36,300 shp each), 2 MTU 12V1163 TB83 diesels (4,420 bhp each); 2 CP props; 72,600 shp max.

Remarks: An enlarged version of the Luhu class. The name was originally reported as *Yantai* and may have been changed late in the construction process. Sea trials commenced in 9-98, after what would have been a remarkably short fitting-out period by Chinese standards. As completed, shows few advances over the preceding Luhu class other than a doubling of the number of antiship missiles. 167 is assigned to the South Sea Fleet and is based at Zhanjiang. A reported sister ship may have been scrapped while under construction.
Hull systems: The gas turbines in this ship were manufactured in Ukraine, but China signed a technology transfer contract with Zorya in 5-01 that is intended to result in production of the DA-80 (or DN-80) engine in China for future warships.
Combat systems: ASW capabilities have been reduced from those of the Luhu class, as there is no VDS or towed array and the ASW rocket launchers have been omitted. The space between the SAM launcher and the bridge superstructure is occupied by a belowdecks reload magazine; there is no provision for vertical launchers. A twin hangar and a French-designed Samahe harpoon-type recovery and dual deck traversing system are fitted for the helicopters.

Harbin (112) JMSDF, 7-99

♦ 2 Luhu class (Project 053HT or 053H2)

	Bldr	Laid down	L	In serv.
112 Harbin	Qiuxin SY, Shanghai	24-5-90	6-91	2-2-93
113 Qingdao	Jiangnan SY, Shanghai	1991	10-93	3-96

Qingdao (113) RAAF, 1997

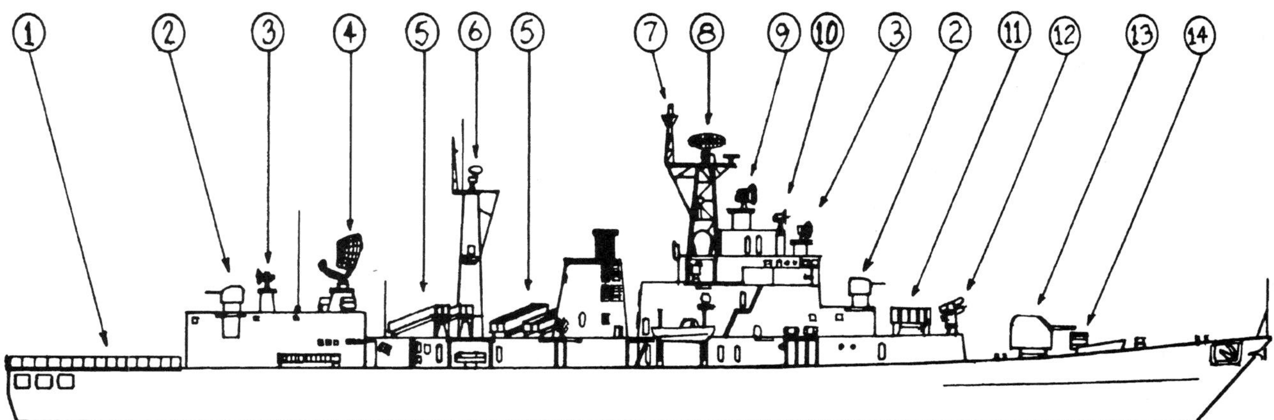

Qingdao (113) 1. helicopter platform with French Samahe landing system 2. twin 37-mm Type 76A AA 3. Type 347G radar f.c. directors for 37-mm AA 4. Hai Ying early-warning radar 5. 8 C-802 or C-801A SSM launch containers in four groups of two 6. ESR-1 sea-skimmer detection radar 7. EW intercept antenna array 8. Sea Tiger air-search radar 9. EFR-1 radar director for the 100-mm gunmount 10. radar director for the HQ-7 SAM system 11. on-deck reload magazine for the HQ-7 SAM system 12. octuple launcher for the HQ-7 SAM system 13. twin 100-mm 55-cal. DP gunmount 14. 12-round Type 75 ASW rocket launchers

Drawing by A. D. Baker III

DESTROYERS [DD] *(continued)*

Qingdao (113) H&L Van Ginderen, 5-98

D: 4,800 tons (5,700 fl) **S:** 31.5 kts (20 on diesel)
Dim: 148.0 (142.6 wl) × 16.0 (15.6 wl) × 7.5 (5.0 hull)
A: 8 C-801A Ying Ji-1 (CSS-N-4 Sardine) or C-802 Ying Ji-2 (CSS-N-8 Saccade) SSM; 1 8-round HQ-7 (112: Crotale Modulaire) SAM syst. (16 missiles); 1 twin 100-mm 55-cal. DP; 4 twin 37-mm 63-cal. Type 76A AA; 2 triple 324-mm ILAS-3 ASW TT; 2 12-round Type 75 ASW RL; 2 Z-9A helicopters
Electronics:
Radar: 2 Decca RM 1290A/D ARPA nav.; 1 . . . surf./air search; 1 Thales Sea Tiger (TSR-3004) air search; 1 Hai Ying (God Eye) early warning; 1 ESR-1 sea-skimmer detection; 2 Type 347G 37-mm f.c.; 1 EFR-1 (Fog Lamp) 100-mm f.c.—112 only: 1 Thales DRBC-32F (Castor-C) Crotale SAM target illuminator
Sonar: . . . . . . LF bow-mounted; HF fire-control; ESS-1 MF VDS
EW: 2 . . . . . . intercept; . . . . . . jammers; BM 8610 intercept/jammer array, 2 15-round decoy RL
E/O: 2 GDG-775 radar/t.v./laser/IR directors
M: CODOG: 2 G.E. LM-2500 gas turbines (26,800 shp each), 2 MTU 12V1163 TB83 diesels (4,420 bhp each); 2 CP props; 53,600 shp max.
Range: 4,000/16 **Endurance:** 15 days **Crew:** 230 tot.

Remarks: China's first modern surface combatant design, equipped with weapon and sensor systems that are only a couple of decades behind those aboard contemporary Western units. First unit initially was incorrectly reported to have been named *Zhanjiang.*
Hull systems: Have an unusually high freeboard. Are air-conditioned and have a full NBC warfare protection system. Hull has two sets of nonretractable fin stabilizers. A twin hangar and a French-designed Samahe harpoon-type recovery and dual deck traversing system are fitted for the helicopters.
Combat systems: Have a combat information center (CIC) equipped with the Alenia IPN-10 combat data system and the Link-W datalink. The EW suite may employ a derivative of the Thales RAPIDS (Radar Passive Identification System) intercept and RAMSES (Reprogrammable Multimode Shipborne ECM System) jammers; the two radomes on the sides of the forward superstructure appear to conceal steerable jammers. Located at bridge level are two GDG-775 multifunction optronic directors; equipped with a ranging radar, a laser rangefinder, low-light t.v., and IR sensors, they are normally operated from the CIC. The twin 100-mm gunmount is of a new, fully enclosed, automatic design based on that of the single French mount on the Jianghu-IV-class frigate *Siping.* Surface-to-air missile reloads are contained in a box magazine immediately abaft the launcher.

♦ **1 Luda-II class** Bldr: Dalian SY

	Laid down	L	In serv.
166 Zhuhai	8-88	10-90	10-91

Zhuhai (166)—with temporary pennant number
Brian Morrison/H&L Van Ginderen, 8-95

Zhuhai (166) U.S. Navy, 5-94

D: 3,250 tons light, 3,670 tons std. (3,960 fl) **S:** 35 kts (32 sust.)
Dim: 132.00 (127.50 pp) × 12.80 × 4.39 (5.30 sonar)
A: 8 C-801 Ying Ji-1 (CSS-N-4 Sardine) SSM; 2 twin 130-mm 58-cal. DP; 4 twin 37-mm 63-cal. Type 76A AA; 2 12-round Type 75 ASW RL; 2 triple 324-mm ASW TT (WASS A-244 torpedoes); 2 mine rails (38 max. mines)
Electronics:
Radar: 1 Decca RM 1290A/D ARPA nav.; 1 ESR-1 sea-skimmer detection; 1 Sea Eagle (Rice Field) 3-D air search; 1 Type 363 long-range air early warning; 1 Type 343 (Sun Visor-B) 130-mm f.c.; 2 Type 347G AA gun f.c.
Sonar: . . . . . . MF bow-mounted; ESS-1 MF VDS
EW: 2 . . . intercept, 2 RW-23-1 (Jug Pair-2) intercept; 2 . . . jammers; 2 15-round decoy RL
M: 2 sets geared steam turbines; 2 props; 72,000 shp (60,000 sust.)
Boilers: 4 **Range:** 1,100/32; 2,970/18; 5,000/14 **Endurance:** 10 days
Crew: 27 officers, 275 enlisted

Remarks: Hull number temporarily changed to 168 during 8-95 naval review in Indonesia. Improved version of Luda design incorporating a bow-mounted sonar, VDS, C-801 antiship missiles, and the Italian Alenia IPN-10 combat data system.
Combat systems: The EW suite may be a modified copy of the Thales DR-2000S intercept and the Alligator jammer systems, but the decoy rocket launchers are of Chinese design. The VDS appears to be a copy of the U.S. Raytheon DE 1160 or 1164 system. The long-range air early-warning radar, mounted on a pedestal atop the after conning station between the mainmast and the after stack, employs four yagi arrays and differs from the earlier Bean Sticks and Pea Sticks. The antenna for the ESR-1 sea-skimmer detection radar is mounted atop the foremast, while the antenna for the Sea Eagle three-dimensional air-search radar is atop the mainmast. All of the search radar antennas are mechanically stabilized, indicating a lack of computer capability in Chinese radar design. The box launchers for the C-801 antiship missiles are fixed in bearing and elevation; all eight launchers are identical.

♦ **15 Luda class (Project 051)**
Bldrs: Hongqi SY; Lüda (Dalian) SY; Donglang SY, Guangzhou; Zhonghua SY, Shanghai (In serv. 1972–91)

105 Jinan	110 Dalian	161 Changsha
106 Xian	131 Nanjing	162 Nanning
107 Yinchuan	132 Hefei	163 Nanchang
108 Xining	133 Chongqing	164 Guilian
109 Kaifeng	134 Zunyi	165 Zhanjiang

Kaifeng (109)—modernized with 16 antiship missiles, a Crotale Modulaire point defense SAM system aft, and three twin 37-mm Type 76A automatic 37-mm AA; two twin 25-mm AA are retained abreast the forward stack, while the radar suite has been updated to include a Thales Sea Tiger air-search radar (antenna atop the main mast amidships) and the EW suite has been replaced and augmented by decoy rocket launchers on the fantail *Ships of the World,* 4-00

Yinchuan (107)—with Bean Sticks early-warning radar antenna on a pole mast amidships and no AA fire-control radar aft JMSDF, 7-99

DESTROYERS [DD] *(continued)*

Luda-class Hefei (132) 1. 4 BMB-2 depth-charge mortars 2. twin 130-mm 58-cal. DP gunmounts 3. twin 37-mm 63-cal. Type 74 AA mounts 4. Type 341 Rice Lamp AA radar directors 5. triple trainable launchers for C-201 SSMs 6. Bean Sticks early-warning radar 7. Type 352C Square Tie surface target detection and tracking radar 8. Type 354 Eye Shield air/surface-search radar 9. Wok Won optical director for 130-mm guns 10. twin 25-mm 80-cal. Type 61 AA mounts 11. 12-round Type 75 ASW rocket launchers
Drawing by A. D. Baker III

Chongqing (133) JMSDF, 6-00

Jinan (105)—the only Luda with helicopter facilities, added at the expense of the after twin 130-mm and 37-mm gunmounts *Ships of the World*

D: 3,250 tons light, 3,670 tons std. (3,960 fl) **S:** 35 kts (32 sust.)
Dim: 132.00 (127.50 pp) × 12.80 × 4.39 (hull; 5.30 sonar)
A: 109 only: 1 8-round Crotale Modulaire SAM syst. (8 reloads); 16 C-801 Ying Ji-1 (CSS-N-4 Sardine) SSM—all others: 6 C-201 Hai Ying-2 (CSS-N-1) SSM—all: 2 twin 130-mm 58-cal. DP; 4 (109: 3) twin 37-mm 63-cal. Type 76A AA; 2 twin 25-mm 80-cal. Type 61 AA; 2 12-round Type 75 ASW RL; 4 single BMB-2 d.c. mortars; 2 d.c. racks; 2 mine rails (38 mines max.)
Electronics:
Radar: 1 Fin Curve or Decca RM 1290A/D ARPA nav.; 1 Type 354 (Eye Shield) short-range air search; 1 Bean Sticks or Pea Sticks (antenna variant) early warning; 1 Type 352C (Square Tie) antiship missile targeting; 1 Type 343 (Sun Visor-B) 130-mm gun f.c. (not on all); 2 Type 341 (Rice Lamp) AA gun f.c. (not on all)—108, 110, 165, and 166 also: Sea Eagle (Rice Field) long-range 3-D air search—109 also: 1 Thales Sea Tiger air search; Thales DRBC-32E Castor-IIJ SAM f.c.; 1 Type 347G 37-mm gun f.c.
Sonar: . . . . . . MF hull-mounted
EW: 2 Jug Pair (RW-23-1) intercept—109 only: 2 15-round decoy RL
M: 2 sets geared steam turbines; 2 props; 72,000 shp (60,000 sust.) **Boilers:** 4
Range: 1,100/32; 2,970/18; 5,000/14 **Endurance:** 10 days
Crew: 27 officers, 275 enlisted (normal complement: 220 tot.)

Remarks: Also known as Project EF4. First unit, 105, completed 12-72 at Dalian. Design based on the unsuccessful Russian Project 41 *(Tallin)* class. Completed in the following order: 105, 160 (lost), 106, 161, 107, 162, 131, 108, 132, 109, 163, 110, 133, 134, 164, and 165. Ships in the 10X series were built at Lüda (Dalian) and are based in the North Sea Fleet; 13X-series ships were built at Shanghai and are based in the East Sea Fleet; and 16X-series were built at Guangzhou and are based in the South Sea Fleet. One South Sea Fleet ship of this class (probably 160) was lost after an explosion during 8-78 near Zhanjiang. Plans to modernize the entire class with British equipment fell through in 1983.
Combat systems: Equipment varies greatly from ship to ship, with only five (105, 108, 131, 161, and 162) having fire-control radar systems, even on the Soviet Wasp Head (Wok Won) 130-mm stabilized optical director for the 130-mm guns. All are now equipped for underway fueling. The ships are said to lack sufficient electrical generating capacity to operate all weapons and sensor systems simultaneously.
The 57-mm mounts originally carried on a few units have been replaced with 37-mm guns during overhauls. Pea Sticks long-range air-search radar is carried by 107, 131, 132, and 162; the remainder have Bean Sticks. 108, 110, and 132 had a larger variant of the Rice Screen (Sea Eagle) 3-D phased-array air-search radar atop the after mast and were intended to act as leaders; in 132, the Rice Screen was replaced by a commercial SATCOM antenna in 1999, possibly only temporarily, but 164 and 165 had had Sea Eagle added by that year. The Bean Sticks air early-warning radar's antenna has 32 yagi radiators, while that of the Pea Sticks has only 16. 131 and 164 may have bow-mounted sonars. The triple missile launcher mounts rotate; on 209, the 4-round launch groups are fixed.
Modifications: The class prototype, 105, completed a refit in 5-87 with a helicopter flight deck and hangar in place of the after twin 130-mm DP mount, after twin 37-mm AA, and the 4 d.c. mortars; she also has a new sonar, improved EW equipment, satellite navigation gear, and an Alenia IPN-10 combat data system. She had previously been employed as a trials ship for equipment to be used in this and later classes. The other ships do not have air-conditioning, NBC warfare protection systems, or a central combat command space (CIC). In 9-97, 132 had been fitted with the antenna for a commercial SATCOM system atop the mainmast and a Type 341 Rice Lamp AA fire-control radar on a platform aft.
109 was backfitted with a Crotale NG octuple SAM launcher in place of the after 37-mm gunmount; a reload magazine is installed just forward of the launcher. To control the SAM system, a Thales DRBC-32F (Castor-IIJ) radar was added. By 1999, 109 had been further modified with four sets of quadruple, fixed launch containers for antiship missiles, and enclosed, automatic Type 76A AA mounts had replaced the manned mounts. 110 carries two copies of the Italian ILAS-3 (B-515) ASW torpedo tube mounting and probably has WASS A-244 torpedoes. 165 and one or two others may have EW suite consisting of Thales DR-2000S intercept, Thales Alligator jammer, and two Chinese-designed 15-round decoy rocket launchers.

FRIGATES [FF]

♦ 7 (+ 3) Jiangwei-II class (Project F22)

	Bldr	Laid down	L	In serv.
521	Hudong SY, Shanghai	11-96	5-6-97	11-98
522	Hudong SY, Shanghai	1-97	8-8-97	2-99
523	Hudong SY, Shanghai	11-97	6-98	10-99
524	Hudong SY, Shanghai	1-98	8-98	5-00
525	Hudong SY, Shanghai	1998	1999	2000
526	Hudong SY, Shanghai	1998	. . .	3-00
564 Yichang	Hudong SY, Shanghai	1998		2001
565	Hudong SY, Shanghai		2002	2002
566	Hudong SY, Shanghai		2002	2002
567	Hudong SY, Shanghai			1-03

Jiangwei-II-class Yichang (564) John Mortimer, 10-01

Jiangwei-II-class 521 *Ships of the World*, 2001

FRIGATES [FF] *(continued)*

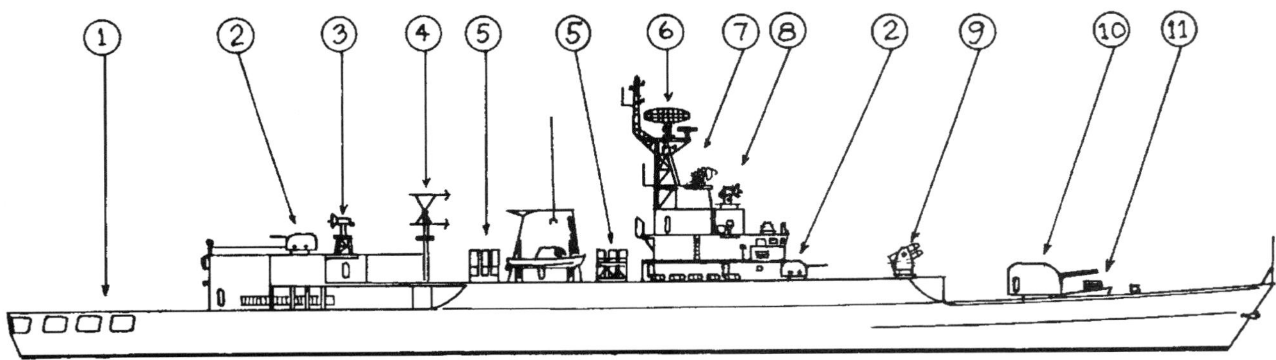

Jiangwei-II class 1. helicopter flight deck 2. twin 37-mm 63-cal. Type 76A automatic AA 3. Type 341 Rice Lamp gun fire-control radar 4. Type 363 early-warning radar 5. six C-802 Ying Ji-2 SSM in triple, fixed sets 6. Type 360 air/surface-search radar 7. Type 343 radar director for 100-mm gunmount 8. radar illuminator/tracker for HQ-7 SAM system 9. octuple launcher for HQ-7 SAM system 10. twin 100-mm 55-cal. ENG-2 DP gunmount 11. 6-round Type 87 ASW rocket launchers Drawing by A. D. Baker III

Jiangwei-II-class 522 JMSDF, via *Ships of the World,* 4-00

D: 1,700 tons (2,180 fl) **S:** 27.2 kts **Dim:** 112.0 × 12.4 × 3.5 (hull)
A: 8 C-802 Ying Ji-2 (CSS-N-8 Saccade) SSM; 1 8-round HQ-7 SAM syst. (16 missiles); 1 twin 100-mm 55-cal. ENG-2 DP; 4 twin 37-mm 63-cal. Type 76A AA; 2 6-round Type 87 ASW RL; 1 Z-9A helicopter
Electronics:
Radar: 1 Decca RM 1290A/D ARPA nav.; 1 Type 360 (SR-60) air/surf. search; 1 Type 363 early warning; 1 . . . SAM tracker/illuminator; 1 Type 343 (Sun Visor-B) 100-mm surface gun f.c.; 1 Type 341 (Rice Lamp) 37-mm AA f.c.
Sonar: S-07H bow-mounted MF
EW: NRJ-5 syst.: RWD-8 intercept; NJ81-3 jammer; 2 6-round PJ46 decoy RL
M: 4 Type 18E390VA diesels; 2 CP props; 23,674 bhp
Electric: 1,720 kw (4 × 400 kw, 1 × 120 kw) **Range:** 4,000/18 **Crew:** 170 tot.

Remarks: First two may originally have been ordered for Pakistan. First unit ran trials late 1998. 521 and 522 are assigned to the East Sea Fleet.
Combat systems: Differ from the Jiangwei-I class primarily in having a less cumbersome and far more effective SAM system, the after pair of 37-mm AA mounts a deck higher, and the Type 343 (Sun Visor-B) gun f.c. radar antenna mounted on a stabilized pedestal rather than a manned director. There may be an E/O surveillance and/or f.c. device atop the pilothouse, possibly a single GDG-775 multisensor director. ASW ordnance is limited to short-range rocket launchers. The manufacturer's designation for the Type 360 radar is Type 2405.

♦ 4 Jiangwei-I class (Project 055) Bldr: Hudong SY, Shanghai

	Laid down	L	In serv.
539 Anqing	1988	7-91	12-91
540 Huainan	1989	12-91	12-92
541 Huaibei	1990	3-93	8-93
542 Tonqing	1991	9-93	10-94

Tonqing (542) *Ships of the World,* 2000

Anqing (539) *Ships of the World,* 2000

Huainan (540) *Ships of the World,* 200

'RIGATES [FF] *(continued)*

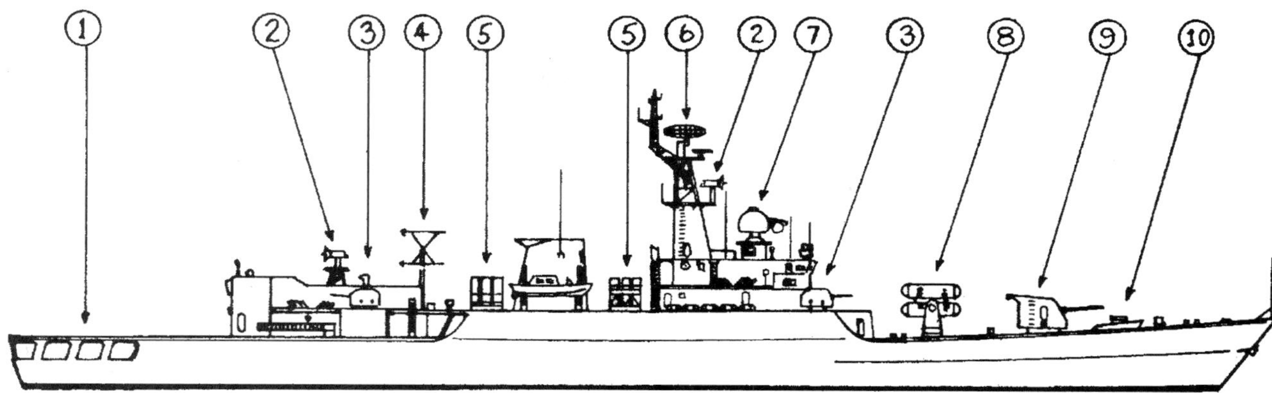

iangwei-I class 1. helicopter flight deck 2. Type 341 Rice Shield AA fire-control radars 3. twin 37-mm 63-cal. Type 76A automatic AA 4. Type 363 early-warning radar 5. six -802 Ying Ji-2 SSM in triple, fixed sets 6. Type 360 air/surface-search radar 7. Wok Won gun director with Type 343 f.c. radar 8. sextuple, nonreloading launcher for HQ-61 AM system 9. twin 100-mm 56-cal. ENG-2 DP gunmount 10. 6-round Type 87 ASW rocket launchers — Drawing by A. D. Baker III

'uaibei (541) — JMSDF, via *Ships of the World,* 6-00

: 1,700 tons (2,180 fl) **S:** 27.2 kts **Dim:** 112.0 × 12.4 × 3.5 (hull)
: 6 C-802 Ying Ji-2 (CSS-N-8 Saccade) SSM; 1 6-round HQ-61 SAM syst. (no reloads); 1 twin 100-mm 56-cal. ENG-2 DP; 8 37-mm 63-cal. Type 76A AA; 2 6-round Type 87 ASW RL; 1 Z-9A helicopter
lectronics:
Radar: 1 Decca RM 1290A/D ARPA nav.; 1 Type 360 (SR-60) air search; 1 Type 363 early warning; 1 Type 343 (Sun Visor-B) surface gun f.c.; 2 Type 341 (Rice Shield) AA f.c.
Sonar: S-07H bow-mounted MF
EW: NRJ-5 syst.: RWD-8 intercept; NJ81-3 jammer; 2 6-round PJ46 decoy RL
I: 4 Type 18E390VA diesels; 2 CP props; 23,674 bhp
lectric: 1,720 kw (4 × 400 kw, 1 × 120 kw) **Range:** 4,000/18 **Crew:** 170 tot.

emarks: *Huaibei* was temporarily renumbered 548 during an 8-95 visit to Indone-a. 539 has also been reported to be named *Tianshan.*
ombat systems: Have China's first computerized weapons data and control sys-m, CCS-3, which incorporates a combat datalink. The surface-to-surface missile unchers are oriented athwartships, fore and aft of the stack, with the forward set med to starboard. The unusual sextuple SAM launcher forward is not served by a load magazine; the large diameter of the tubes is necessitated by the missiles' hav-g nonfolding fins, and the missile has a range of only 5.4 n.m. No provision seems have been made for ASW torpedoes, depth charges, or mines; there is also no tor-do decoy system. The Type 76A 37-mm AA mounts are of the new, enclosed version. he helicopter is intended for over-the-horizon targeting for the missiles, liaison, and arch and rescue; it can carry ASW torpedoes but has no ASW sensors. There is a rench-style harpoon-type helicopter haul-down system but no deck traversing rrangements. The complete EW suite is referred to as the NRJ-5 system and incor-rates a 2–18 GHz intercept capability, 8–16 GHz noise jammer, and 7–16 GHz de-ption jammer.

6 Jianghu-V class Bldr: Jiangnan SY, Shanghai (In serv. 1993–96)

58 Zigong	561 Shantou
59 Kangding	562 . . . . . .
60 Dongguan	563 . . . . . .

igong (558)—note enclosed "mack"-type stack, surmounted by the early-warning dar antenna — 92 Wing Det., RAAF, 2-95

Kangding (559) — 92 Wing Det., RAAF, 1-99

Zigong (558) — U.S. Navy, 10-95

Shantou (561) — PLAN, 1996

D: 1,425 tons (1,702 fl) **S:** 25.5 kts **Dim:** 103.2 × 10.2 × 3.05 (hull)
A: 4 C-201 Hai Ying-2 (CSS-N-1) SSM; 2 twin 100-mm 56-cal. DP; 4 twin 37-mm 63-cal. Type 76A AA; 2 5-round Type 75 ASW RL
Electronics:
Radar: 1 Decca RM 1290A/D ARPA nav.; 1 Type 360 surf./air search; 1 Type 363 early warning; 1 Type 343 (Sun Visor-B) 100-mm gun f.c.; 1 Type 341 (Rice Lamp) 37-mm gun f.c.
Sonar: EH-5A MF hull-mounted
EW: Elettronica Newton-Beta suite: 2 Type 211 (Jug Pair) intercept; Type 318 noise jammer; Type 521 deception jammer; 2 15-round decoy RL
M: 2 SEMT-Pielstick 12 PA6 280 BTC diesels; 2 props; 16,000 bhp (14,400 sust.)
Electric: 1,320 kw (3 × 400 kw, 1 × 120 kw)
Range: 1,750/25; 3,000/18 **Endurance:** 10 days **Crew:** 195 tot.

Remarks: A simplified version of the Jianghu-II put back into production after the first four Jiangwei-class frigates, probably as an inexpensive way to maintain order of battle. They are visually distinguishable by the "mack"-type stack, which has the long-range air-search radar antenna mounted on its forward edge. The final unit was completed during 2-96.
Combat systems: The ASW suite, including the rocket launchers, sonar, and 2KJ-5 display console, is designated SJD-5. The EW suite employs Type 923 omnidirectional

FRIGATES [FF] *(continued)*

antennas for the Type 521 deception jammer, and Type 981 omnidirectional and Type 929 directional antennas, all mounted on the mast and superstructure sides; the equipment is of Italian design, license-built in China. The 100-mm guns are controlled by the Wok Won director atop the pilothouse (with integral Type 343 Sun Visor radar), while the Rice Lamp radar aft provides range inputs to the 37-mm guns, which are arranged to cover one quadrant for each mount. The 100-mm guns have a rate of fire of 25 rds/min and a range of 16 km and employ a French-designed autoloader. The 37-mm mounts are automatic. There is a Matra Défense Naja manned optronic backup director for the 37-mm mounts, located between the after pair of 37-mm mounts. The surface/air-search radar evidently also performs target detection and designation for the antiship missiles, as there is no Type 352C (Square Tie) radar fitted; it probably can also function (like Type 352C) in the passive mode. The missile launcher mounts rotate. Depth charge equipment is not carried.

♦ 1 Jianghu-IV class (Project 053HT(H)) Bldr: Hudong SY, Shanghai

	L	In serv.
544 Siping	9-85	11-86

Siping (544)—note triple ASW torpedo tube mount swung out beneath the helicopter flight deck, above which a Z-9A Dauphin is hovering
Naval and Merchant Ships, 1996

D: 1,600 tons (1,820 fl) **S:** 25.5 kts **Dim:** 103.2 × 10.2 × 3.05 (hull)
A: 2 C-201 Hai Ying-2 (CSS-N-1) SSM; 1 100-mm 55-cal. Creusot-Loire Compact DP; 4 twin 37-mm 63-cal. Type 76 AA; 2 triple 324-mm ILAS-3 ASW TT (WASS A-244S torpedoes); 2 5-round Type 81 ASW RL; 1 Z-9A helicopter
Electronics:
Radar: 1 Decca RM 1290A/D ARPA nav.; 1 Type 354 (Eye Shield) air search; 1 ESR-1 sea-skimmer detection; 1 Type 347G (Rice Lamp) gun f.c.
Sonar: Type EH-5 HF hull-mounted
EW: 2 RW-23-1 (Jug Pair) intercept; U.S. Mk 33 RBOC decoy syst. (2 6-round RL)
M: 2 SEMT-Pielstick 12 PA6 280 BTC diesels; 2 props; 16,000 bhp (14,400 sust.)
Electric: 1,320 kw (3 × 400 kw, 1 × 120 kw) **Range:** 1,750/25; 4,000/15
Endurance: 15 days **Crew:** 25 officers, 160 enlisted

Remarks: The first Chinese combatant to incorporate a helicopter facility and Western ASW torpedoes. Adding the helicopter to the Jianghu design cost the after medium caliber gunmount and twin SSM positions.
Combat systems: The 100-mm gun, which can fire at 90 rds/min, is controlled by a Matra Défense Naja laser/electro-optical director for AA firing and by an optical director of Chinese origin for surface firing. The AA gun fire-control radar antenna atop the hangar may also be used for helicopter control. ESR-1 replaced the original Type 352C (Square Tie) antiship missile targeting radar on the foremast in the mid-1990s and may also be able to provide surface target range and bearing data.

♦ 3 Jianghu-III class (Project 053HT) Bldr: Hudong SY, Shanghai

535 Huangshi (In serv. 14-12-86) 537 Zhoushan (In serv. 1993)
536 Wuhu (In serv. 1987)

D: 1,655 tons std., 1,800 tons normal (1,960 fl)
S: 28 kts **Dim:** 103.20 × 10.83 × 3.10 (hull)
A: 8 C-801 Ying Ji-1 (CSS-N-4 Sardine) SSM; 2 twin 100-mm 56-cal. ENG-2 DP; 4 twin 37-mm 63-cal. Type 76 AA; 2 5-round Type 81 ASW RL; 2 BMB-2 d.c. mortars
Electronics:
Radar: 1 Decca RM 1290A/D ARPA nav.; 1 Type 354 (Eye Shield) air search; 1 Type 352C (Square Tie) missile targeting; 1 Type 341 (Rice Lamp) f.c.; 1 Type 343 (Sun Visor) f.c.—537 also: 1 Type 363 long-range air search
Sonar: Type EH-5 bow-mounted MF
EW: Elettronica Newton-Beta suite; Type 211 intercept; Type 318 noise jammer; Type 521 deception jammer; 2 . . .-round decoy RL
M: 2 SEMT-Pielstick 12 PA6 280 BTC diesels; 2 props; 16,000 bhp (14,400 sust.)

Huangshi (535)—with Haiqing-class patrol craft 634 in foreground
Ships of the World, 200

Zhoushan (537)—with paired C-801 missile launchers and Type 363 early-warnin radar
Ships of the World, 199

Electric: 1,720 kw (4 × 400 kw, 1 × 120 kw)
Range: 1,750/25; 3,000/18 **Endurance:** 10 days **Crew:** 168 tot.
Remarks: An improved version of the Jianghu-I/II series, on the same hull an propulsion plant but with a full shelter deck amidships supporting four pairs of SS launchers. Four similar ships were delivered to Thailand in 1991–92, two with heli copter facilities in place of the after 100-mm gunmount. All PLAN units are based i the East Sea Fleet at Dinghai.
Hull systems: Equipped with fin stabilizers. The export versions had a more pow erful propulsion plant.
Combat systems: Have a Wok Won (copy of the Russian Wasp Head) optical direc tor forward (with Type 343 radar) for surface gunfire and a Type 341 (Rice Lamp radar director aft for AA. The 100-mm mounts are auto-loading. The EW intercep system is reportedly based on the Italian Elettronica Newton system. In 537, th antiship missile tubes are paired symmetrically, whereas in the other two they ar staggered; this may indicate that 537 can carry a later missile, possibly the C-80 Ying Ji-2 (CSS-N-8 Saccade)

♦ 21 Jianghu-I and -II* class (Projects 053, 053H)

Bldrs: Jianghu-I: Jiangnan SY, Shanghai; Jianghu-II: Hudong SY, Shanghai (In serv. 1975–86)

509 Changde	516 Jiujiang*	545 Linfen*
510 Shaoxing	517 Nanping	551 Maoming
511 Nantong	518 Ji'an	552 Yibin
512 Wuxi	519 Changzhi	553 Shaoguan*
513 Huayin	533 Ningbo*	554 Anshun
514 Zhenjiang	534 Jinhua*	555 Zhaotong
515 Xiamen	543 Dandong*	557 Jishou*

Jiujiang (516)—with twin 100-mm gunmounts
JMSDF, via *Ships of the World,* 5-9

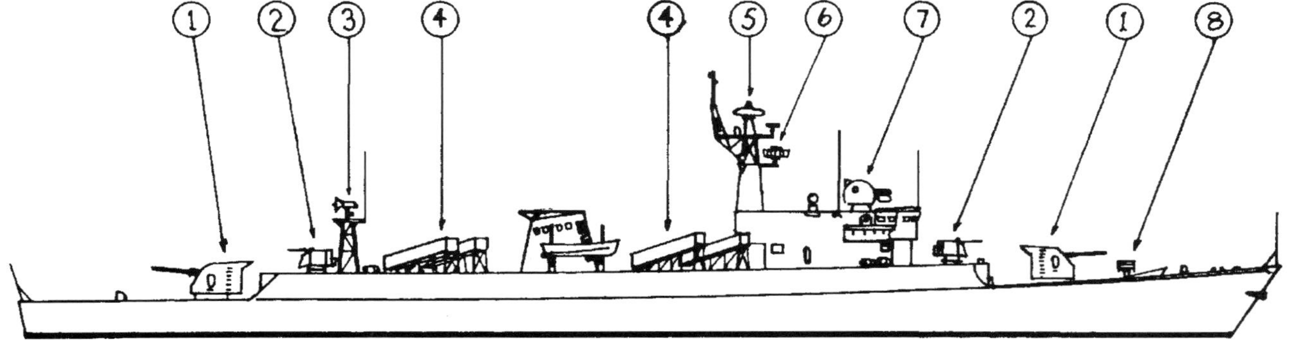

Jianghu-III class 1. twin 100-mm 56-cal. ENG-2 DP gunmounts 2. twin 37-mm 63-cal. Type 76 AA 3. Type 341 Rice Lamp AA f.c. radar 4. eight C-801 Ying Ji-1 SSM in eigh fixed canister launchers 5. Type 354 Eye Shield air/surface-search radar 6. Type 352C Square Tie surface target detection and tracking radar 7. Wok Won director with Type 34 f.c. radar 8. 5-round Type 81 ASW rocket launchers
Drawing by A. D. Baker II

FRIGATES [FF] *(continued)*

Jianghu-I-class Wuxi (512) 1. BMB-2 depth-charge mortars 2. single 100-mm 56-cal. DP gunmounts 3. twin 37-mm 63-cal. Type 74 AA 4. twin trainable launcher for SSM 5. Type 354 Eye Shield air/surface-search radar 6. navigational radar 7. Type 352C Square Tie surface target detection and tracking 8. optical rangefinder for 100-mm guns 9. 5-round Type 81 ASW rocket launchers
Drawing by A. D. Baker III

Changde (509)—with flat-paneled stack Maritime Photographic, 5-97

Nantong (511) JMSDF, via *Ships of the World,* 4-00

D: 1,425 tons (1,702 fl) **S:** 25.5 kts **Dim:** 103.2 × 10.2 × 3.05 (hull)
A: Jianghu-I: 4 C-201 Hai Ying-2 (CSS-N-1) SSM; 2 single 100-mm 56-cal. DP; 6 twin 37-mm 63-cal. Type 74 or 76 AA; 2 or 4 5-round Type 81 ASW RL; 4 BMB-2 d.c. mortars; 2 d.c. racks; 2 mine rails—Jianghu-II: 4 C-201 Hai Ying-2 (CSS-N-1) SSM; 2 twin 100-mm 56-cal. ENG-2 DP; 4 twin 37-mm 63-cal. Type 74 or 76 AA; 2 5-round Type 81 ASW RL; 4 BMB-2 d.c. mortars; 2 d.c. racks; 2 mine rails
Electronics:
Radar: 1 Type 756 nav.; Decca RM 1290A/D ARPA nav.; 1 Type 354 (Eye Shield) surf./air search; 1 Type 352C (Square Tie) antiship missile targeting—Jianghu-II also: 1 Type 343 (Sun Visor-B) 100-mm surface f.c.; 1 Type 341 (Rice Lamp) AA f.c.—543 and possibly others: 1 Type 363 long-range air search
Sonar: EH- 5 MF hull-mounted
EW: none or 2 RW-23-1 (Jug Pair) intercept—some: U.S. Mk 36 SRBOC decoy syst. (2 6-round Mk 137 RL)
M: 2 SEMT-Pielstick 12 PA6 280 BTC diesels; 2 props; 16,000 bhp (14,400 sust.)
Electric: 1,320 kw (3 × 400 kw, 1 × 120 kw)
Range: 1,750/25; 3,000/18 **Endurance:** 10 days **Crew:** 195 tot.

Remarks: Have also been referred to as Project EF3H or the *Changsha* class. The first unit, 515, was launched 28-6-75 and commissioned 28-12-75; construction of the class continued into 1993, with 557 being the last completed. Units with square stacks were built by Jiangnan SY; the Hudong units have rounded stacks. Two sisters with twin 57-mm vice 100-mm guns were built for Egypt and delivered in 1984–85, and sister *Xiangtan* (556) was transferred to Bangladesh in 1990. *Kaifeng* (520) was reported stricken during 1993.
Combat systems: Ships with twin 100-mm ENG-2 mounts (533, 534, 543, 545, 553, 557) are referred to as Jianghu-II; they omitted two twin 37-mm AA as partial weight compensation and are the only units with a Wok Won director for the 100-mm guns. The twin 100-mm ENG-2 mounts are auto-loading. In the Jianghu-I group, 100-mm gunfire control is by a simple stereoscopic rangefinder. 509 through 519 have the manually fed Type 74 37-mm AA mount; later units have Type 76 with auto-feed. On at least one unit of the class, the 37-mm mounts each have two co-mounted launchers for QW-1 or HN-5 point-defense SAMs. Only Jianghu-I units 515 and 516 have four ASW rocket launchers. The antiship missiles are carried in two twin, fixed-elevation, trainable launchers.

GUIDED-MISSILE PATROL CRAFT [PTG]

♦ 7 (+ . . .) Houjian class (Project 520T)
Bldr: Huangpu SY, Shanghai

	L	In serv.		L	In serv.		L	In serv.
770	1-91	7-91	773	5-95	7-95	776	. . .	2000
771	7-94	2-95	774	. . .	1998			
772	2-95	4-95	775	. . .	1998			

Houjian-class 770 China Shipbuilding Trading Co., 1999

GUIDED-MISSILE PATROL CRAFT [PTG] *(continued)*

Houjian-class 771 China Shipbuilding Trading Co., 1996

D: 542 tons (normal) **S:** 33.6 kts (32 sust.) **Dim:** 65.39 × 8.40 × 2.38
A: 770–775: 6 C-801 Ying Ji-1 (CSS-N-4 Sardine) SSM; 1 twin 37-mm 63-cal. Type 76A AA; 2 twin 30-mm 65-cal. Type 69 AA—776 only: 6 C-801 Ying Ji-1 (CSS-N-4 Sardine) SSM; 1 76.2-mm 59-cal. AK-176 DP; 1 30-mm 54-cal. AK-630 gatling AA
Electronics:
Radar: 1 Decca RM 1290A/D ARPA nav.; 1 Type 765 missile targeting; 1 Type 347G (776: MR-123-02 Vympel) gun f.c.
EW: Type 900-series intercept/jammer
M: 3 SEMT-Pielstick 12PA6V 280MPC diesels; 3 props; 17,280 bhp (15,840 sust.)
Range: 1,800/18; 2,200/. . . **Crew:** 47 tot.

Remarks: 770–773 were based at Hong Kong as of 7-97. Design offered for export, as Project EM3D(H), with OTOBreda 76-mm Compact in place of the twin 37-mm mount, optronic gun directors, and decoy rocket launchers. Production for PLAN had been thought to have ended in 1998, but 776 was photographed during 2000, modified with Russian guns and gun fire-control equipment.
Combat systems: First six have Type 88C weapons-control system. There is an unmanned electro-optical director for the 30-mm AA, and a radar director with separate optronic director for the enclosed-model 37-mm AA. The missiles are mounted one-over-two. The seventh unit, 776, has an imported Russian 76.2-mm gunmount and radar fire-control system, either for trials or as the start of a new construction series with more-formidable defensive armament. Although at first the lower, inboard antiship missile canisters were sometimes not carried, recent photographs show all six positions occupied.

♦ 14 (+ . . .) Houxin class (Project 343M or 037-II)
Bldr: Qiuxin SY, Shanghai (In serv. 6-91–. . .)

751–760 764–767

Houxin-class 756 Maritime Photographic, 5-97

Houxin-class 759 JMSDF, via *Ships of the World,* 5-99

D: 478 tons (fl) **S:** 32 kts **Dim:** 62.00 × 7.20 × 2.24 (mean hull)
A: 4 C-801 Ying Ji-1 (CSS-N-4 Sardine) SSM; 2 twin 37-mm 63-cal. Type 76A AA; 2 twin 14.5-mm 93-cal. Type 61 AA
Electronics:
Radar: 1 Anritsu Type 723 nav.; 1 Type 352C (Square Tie) missile targeting; 1 Type 341 (Rice Lamp) gun f.c.
EW: . . .
M: 4 diesels; 4 props; 13,200 bhp **Range:** 750/18; 2,000/14 **Crew:** . . . tot.

Remarks: Design based on that of the Haizhui-class subchaser/patrol boat. First unit was ordered 23-12-87 and laid down in 1989. Pennant numbers have been changed in some. Six others have been delivered to Myanmar. Design is a simpler, less-expensive variant of the Houjian class.

♦ up to 30 Huangfeng class (Project 021)
Bldr: Jiangnan SY, Shanghai (In serv. 1960–75)

3103, 3113–3115, 3128–3131, 5100, 6119, 7100, and others

Huangfeng-class 6119—with 25-mm guns and no f.c. radar
JMSDF, via *Ships of the World,* 5-99

Huangfeng-class 3114—with 30-mm gunmounts and spherical radome covering a presumed gun fire-control radar *Ships of the World*

D: 167 tons light, 186.5 normal (205 fl) **S:** 35 kts
Dim: 38.75 × 7.60 × 1.70 (mean hull; 2.99 over props)
A: 4 C-201 Hai Ying-2 (CSS-N-1) SSM; 2 twin 25-mm 80-cal. Type 81 or 30-mm 65-cal. Type 69 (Russian AK-230) AA
Electronics:
Radar: 1 Type 352 (Square Tie) surf. search/target desig.—some: 1 Type . . . (Round Ball) gun f.c.
M: 3 M-503A (42-160) diesels; 3 props; 12,000 bhp **Electric:** 65 kw tot.
Range: 800/30 **Crew:** 28 tot.

Remarks: Around 104 units were built for the PLAN, but many have been discarded or transferred to foreign clients, including four to Pakistan and five to Bangladesh, the most recent in 1992. The design is a copy of the Russian Project 205E Osa but with simplified systems; at least four Project 205E units were transferred from the USSR circa 1960 and had two twin 30-mm AA but no radar gun fire-control systems. Three newly built, modified versions known as the Hounan class (Chinese Project 021) were built for Yemen in 5-95.
Hull systems: Soviet-design M-503A multirow radial diesels are difficult to maintain and offer only about 600 hours between overhauls; it is unlikely that the Chinese-made version is more reliable. Have hull portholes, not found on the Russian-built versions.
Combat systems: Most Chinese-built units had two twin 25-mm AA until early 1980s, when increasing numbers began to appear with a Chinese-built version of the 30-mm Soviet AK-230 AA. More recently, several have had a "Round Ball" radome installed aft for a probable fire-control radar for the 30-mm AA. The 1980s also saw the introduction of IFF equipment.

Note: The 10 Houdong-class missile boats ordered by Iran in the early 1990s (five delivered in 9-94, five in 3-96) are of an entirely new design of about 135 tons full load displacement; to date, none have been noted in PLAN service.

♦ up to 15 Houku class (Project EM1A or 24) (In serv. circa 1968–. . .)

Houku-class 1103—and two sisters Poly Technologies, 1986

D: 68 tons std., 74 tons normal (79.19 fl) **S:** 37 kts
Dim: 27.0 × 6.50 (6.30 wl) × 1.8 (1.295 mean hull)
A: 2 C-201 Hai Ying-2 (CSS-N-1) SSM; 1 twin 25-mm 80-cal. Type 61 AA
Electronics: Radar: 1 Type 352 (Square Tie) surf. search/missile target desig.
M: 4 M-50 diesels; 4 props; 4,800 bhp **Electric:** 65 kw tot.
Range: 500/24 **Endurance:** 5 days **Crew:** 2 officers, 15 enlisted

Remarks: Also referred to as Hegu class. Another 25 or so may remain in reserve; an additional 50 or so have been discarded, and one has been retained on land as a museum exhibit. Steel-hulled improvement on the Soviet-supplied Komar class, which

GUIDED-MISSILE PATROL CRAFT [PTG] *(continued)*

is no longer operational in the PLAN. Most are now fitted with an IFF transponder. Offered for export with 4 C-801 missiles, which may also have been backfitted into some Chinese Navy units. Units of this class were exported to Pakistan (4), Bangladesh (4), and Egypt (6).

TORPEDO BOATS [PT]

♦ up to 20 Huchuan-class (Project 025 and 026) semi-hydrofoils

Bldr: Hudong SY, Shanghai (In serv. 1966–80)

Huchuan-class 1247—Project 026 variant, with gunmount forward *Ships of the World*

D: 39 tons (45.8 fl) **S:** 50 kts **Dim:** 22.50 × 3.80 (6.26 over foils) × 1.146
A: 2 fixed 533-mm TT; 2 twin 14.5-mm 93-cal. Type 81 mg
Electronics: Radar: 1 Type 756 nav.
M: 3 M-50F-4 diesels; 3 props; 3,600 bhp **Electric:** 5.6 kw
Range: 500/30 **Crew:** 11 tot.

Remarks: Survivors of 120 built; all remaining units are in the North Sea Fleet. The class was exported to Albania, Bangladesh, Pakistan, and Tanzania and also built in Romania. Not all units have the foils fitted forward. No foils were fitted aft, as the stern planes on the sea surface, but there are auxiliary foils forward to assist in getting the boat "on foil." In the Project 025 units, both gunmounts are aft; in later-construction Project 026 units, one mount is forward. Project 025 units had Skin Head radar, while Project 026 ships have a Type 756 slotted-waveguide radar antenna.

PATROL CRAFT [PC]

♦ 26 or more Haiqing class (Project 037I)

Bldr: Qiuxin SY, Shanghai (In serv. 1992–. . .)

634, 710–717, 743, 744, 761–763, 786–792, and others

Haiqing-class 634 *Ships of the World,* 2001

Haiqing-class patrol craft 713 and 712—outboard Houxin-class missile craft 767 and 766 ANBw/FAFIO, 9-97

D: 478 tons (fl) **S:** 28 kts **Dim:** 62.80 × 7.20 × 2.40
A: 2 twin 37-mm 63-cal. Type 76 AA; 2 twin 14.5-mm 93-cal. Type 81 AA; 2 6-round Type 87 ASW RL
Electronics: Radar: 1 Anritsu Type 723 nav.—Sonar: HF hull-mounted
M: 4 Type PR 230ZC diesels; 4 props; 4,000 bhp
Range: 1,300/15 **Crew:** 71 tot.

Remarks: Appears to be a replacement for the Hainan class and is said to be building at the rate of about three per year; two other yards are said to have entered the program. One has been exported to Sri Lanka. Units are now operating in all three fleets.

♦ 2 Haijiu class

Bldr: . . . . . . (In serv. 1987–. . .)

688 697

Haijiu-class 688—with VDS at stern and exhaust stack amidships Navpic-Holland, 5-98

D: 450 tons (fl) **S:** 28 kts **Dim:** 62.0 × 7.20 × 2.24 (hull)
A: 1 twin 57-mm 62-cal. Type 66 AA; 2 twin 30-mm 65-cal. Type 69 (AK-230) AA; 4 6-round Type 87 ASW RL; 2 BMB-2 d.c. mortars; 2 d.c. racks; 2 mine rails
Electronics:
Radar: 1 Type 351 (Pot Head) surf. search; 1 Round Ball gun f.c.
Sonar: HF hull-mounted; Thales SS 12 VDS
M: 4 diesels; 4 props; 8,800 bhp **Range:** 750/18 **Crew:** 70 tot.

Remarks: A lengthened version of the Hainan class, with somewhat newer AA weapons. Have an optical f.c. director. Have the French Thales SS 12 variable-depth sonar in lieu of aft twin 57-mm mount of two earlier units. 688 has a funnel; 697 does not. Range can be extended to 1,800 n.m. by using void tankage. Sister 694 reported scrapped in 1995 and 693 by 1998.

♦ 94 Hainan class (Project 037) (In serv. 1964–. . .)

From among: 275–285, 290, 302, 305, 609, 610, 618–622, 626–629, 636–687, 689–692, 695–699, 701, 707, 723–733, 740–742

Hainan-class 649 Chris Delgoffe/H&L Van Ginderen, 5-00

Hainan-class 680 JMSDF, via *Ships of the World,* 5-99

D: 395 tons (430 fl) **S:** 30.5 kts (28 sust.) **Dim:** 58.77 × 7.20 × 2.24 (hull)
A: 2 twin 57-mm 62-cal. Type 66 AA; 2 twin 25-mm Type 61M AA; 4 5-round Type 81 ASW RL; 2 BMB-2 d.c. mortars; 2 d.c. racks; 2 mine rails
Electronics:
Radar: 1 Type 351 (Pot Head) surf. search
Sonar: Tamir-11 hull-mounted searchlight HF
M: 4 diesels; 4 props; 8,800 bhp **Range:** 750/18; 1,800/14 **Crew:** 78 tot.

Remarks: The first unit was laid down in 8-62, launched in 12-63, and ran trials in 3-64. Early units (which are beginning to be retired) had two single 76.2-mm DP U.S. Mk 26 vice the 57-mm AA and had Skin Head radars. Two were transferred to Pakistan in 1976 and two more in 1980. Eight were delivered to Egypt in 1983–85; eight to Bangladesh in 1982–85; six to North Korea in 1975–78; and 12 to Myanmar in 1991–94.

♦ 13 (+ . . .) Haizhui class

Bldr: Guijian SY (In serv. 1992–. . .)

2327 2329 4339 4340 and others

Haizhui-class 4340 Chris Delgoffe/H&L Van Ginderen, 5-00

D: 150 tons (170 fl) **S:** 29 kts **Dim:** 41.0 × 5.41 × 1.80
A: 1 twin 37-mm 63-cal. Type 76 AA; 1 twin 25-mm 80-cal. Type 81 AA; 2 twin 14.5-mm 93-cal. AA

PATROL CRAFT [PC] *(continued)*

Haizhui-class 4339 Chris Delgoffe/H&L Van Ginderen, 5-00

Electronics:
Radar: 1 Anritsu 726 UA or Decca RM 2090 ARPA nav./surf. search
M: 4 Type L12-180Z diesels; 4 props; 4,800 bhp (4,400 sust.)
Range: 750/16 **Crew:** 4 officers, 24 enlisted

Remarks: Successor to the Shanghai-II design. Being built in small numbers for domestic use and also for export, with seven delivered to Sri Lanka through 1998 and two more ordered in 1999. Differ from the Shanghai-II in having four more-powerful diesel engines and power-operated 37-mm AA mounts. Some or all probably have fin stabilizers.

♦ **up to 80 Shanghai-II class (Project 062)** (In serv. 1962–88)

Shanghai-II 3314—with two Type 81 ASW rocket launchers forward 1988

Shanghai-II-class 6338 *Ships of the World,* 1984

D: 122.5 tons (134.8 fl) **S:** 28.5 kts
Dim: 38.78 × 5.41 × 1.49 (hull; 1.554 full load)
A: 2 twin 37-mm 63-cal. Type 74 AA; 2 twin 25-mm 80-cal. Type 61M AA; 4 d.c. in tilt racks—some: 2 5-round Type 81 ASW RL
Electronics:
Radar: 1 Type 756 nav. or Type 351 (Pot Head) or Skin Head surf. search
Sonar: HF searchlight-type (not on all)
M: 2 M-50F-4, 1,200-bhp, and 2 Type 12D6, 910-bhp diesels; 4 props; 4,200 bhp
Electric: 39 kw tot. **Range:** 750/16.5 **Endurance:** 7 days **Crew:** 36 tot.

Remarks: No longer being constructed, and numbers are declining through transfers abroad and attrition; well over 300 were built. At least 72 others have been transferred to foreign navies, and Romania also built the design. Very unsophisticated and sparsely equipped. The Type 12D6 diesels are used during cruising, with the high-speed M-50F-4 diesels being cut in for maximum speeds. Type 756 navigational radars have replaced the earlier Pot Head (or Skin Head on the earliest units), and a number were noted during the mid-1980s with two EDS-32 (Type 81) ASW rocket launchers added forward; presumably a sonar had been installed as well.

PATROL BOATS [PB]

Note: The number of PLAN patrol boats is unknown but is far exceeded by craft assigned to the various paranaval organizations such as the Customs Service, Marine Police, Border Security groups, and Border Defense organization. One naval class for which some data are available is described below.

♦ **. . . 25-meter class** (In serv. 1960s–90s)
D: 82 tons **S:** 14 kts **Dim:** 25.0 × 4.1 × 1.4
A: 2 twin 14.5-mm 93-cal. Type 81 AA
Electronics: Radar: 1 Type 756 or Fin Curve (or none)
M: 2 3D6 diesels; 2 props; 900 bhp **Range:** 900/11 **Crew:** 12

Remarks: Also employed by other agencies. Have also been exported, to Albania and Benin, the latter with MWM diesels and a Japanese radar.

Note: Large numbers of black-painted, unarmed, high-speed craft of several classes resembling naval patrol craft have appeared in South China Sea waters in recent years; these craft are apparently involved in sanctioned (or at least officially ignored) smuggling and are not officially subordinated to any Chinese governmental agency.

25-meter patrol boat J 1301 H&L Van Ginderen, 3-95

MINE WARFARE SHIPS

Note: In the late 1980s, China was reported to be planning to construct 20–40 GRP-hulled minehunters, possibly of the Italian *Lerici* class, with the first one or two to build in Italy. Financial constraints and international outrage at internal events in China have apparently delayed the program, and China's mine countermeasures capabilities are severely limited and growing increasingly obsolete.

♦ **1 Bulieijian-class minelayer [MM]** (In serv. 1988)

814 Wolei

D: 3,100 tons (fl) **S:** 18 kts **Dim:** 93.8 × 14.4 × 4.0
A: 4 twin 37-mm 63-cal. Model 76 AA; approx. 300 mines
Electronics: Radar: . . . **M:** 4 . . . diesels; 2 props; 6,400 bhp
Range: 6,000/14 **Crew:** approx. 200 tot.

Remarks: Also known as Wolei class. The existence of this class is in doubt.

♦ **41 Soviet T-43-class (Project 010) fleet minesweepers [MSF]** (13 in reserve) Bldrs: Wuchang SY, Guangzhou SY (In serv. 1956–70s, mid-1980s–. . .)

364–366, 377–379, 386–389, 396–399, 801–803, 807–809, 821–823, 829–832, 853, 854, 863, 994–996, and others

T-43-class minesweeper 831 Chris Delgoffe/H&L Van Ginderen, 5-00

D: 500 tons (590 fl) **S:** 14 kts **Dim:** 60.0 × 8.6 × 2.16
A: 2 twin 37-mm 63-cal. Type 74 AA; 2 twin 25-mm Type 61 AA; 2 twin 12.7-mm mg; 2 BMB-2 d.c. mortars; 2 mine rails (12–16 mines)
Electronics:
Radar: 1 Ball End surf. search or Type 756 nav.
Sonar: Tamir-11 hull-mounted searchlight HF
M: 2 Type 9D diesels; 2 props; 2,200 bhp **Electric:** 550 kw tot.
Range: 3,200/10 **Fuel:** 70 tons **Crew:** 10 officers, 60 enlisted

Remarks: Around four 58-m, 570-ton units were transferred from the USSR in the 1950s; the majority, however, are long-hulled ships and were built in China. Production began again in the mid-1980s at Guangzhou, and one new unit was delivered to Bangladesh during 1995. Several others were built or converted as surveying ships, civilian research ships, and submarine rescue ships.
Combat systems: At least three minesweepers had an 85-mm DP gun forward, probably now replaced with a twin 37-mm mount. Have acoustic and magnetic sweep gear in addition to MPT-1 and MPT-3 wire sweeps and paravanes. Lightweight side-by-side 12.7-mm mounts are replacing the original over-and-under mountings. A few still retain the obsolescent Russian Ball End navigational radar.

♦ **2 (+ . . .) Wosao-class coastal minesweepers [MSC]**
Bldr: Wusung SY, Shanghai (In serv. 1988–. . .)

4422 4423

Wosao-class minesweeper 4422 Chris Delgoffe/H&L Van Ginderen, 5-00

MINE WARFARE SHIPS *(continued)*

Wosao-class 4423—outboard 4422; note the differences in the bridge configuration from the earlier 4422 Chris Delgoffe/H&L Van Ginderen, 5-00

D: 310 tons (fl) **S:** 15.5 kts **Dim:** 44.79 × 6.20 × 2.27
A: 2 twin 25-mm 80-cal. Type 61 AA; 2 mine rails
Electronics: Radar: 1 Type 756 nav.—Sonar: probably none
M: 2 Type 12-180 diesels; 2 props; 2,000 bhp
Range: 500/. . . **Crew:** 3 officers, 14 enlisted

Remarks: 4422 is equipped only to sweep moored mechanical mines. 4423, with a modified bridge incorporating bridge wings, was first sighted during 1997, and there is some indication that more may be under construction. Both are based at Shanghai. Steel hulled. The design is offered for export with explosive sweep, magnetic, and acoustic sweep gear. Employs boom-mounted side-looking sonar equipment for mine location and safe route mapping.

♦ **20 Fushun-class coastal minesweepers [MSC]**
Bldr: . . . . . . (In serv. 1976–. . .)

D: 275 tons (fl) **S:** 25 kts **Dim:** 40.0 (37.00 pp) × 5.5 × 3.0
A: 1 twin 37-mm 63-cal. Type 74 AA
M: 2 M-50F-4 diesels, 2 12D6 diesels; 4 props; 4,220 bhp

Remarks: Modified version of Shanghai-II class with twin davits aft and cable reel in place of after armament. This design has also been listed as the Yenkuan and Wochang classes, but all are apparently of the same design. Some or all may have been discarded. Has steel hull and is probably usable only against moored, mechanical mines.

♦ **46 Futi-class (Project 312) drone minesweepers [MSD]**
(42 in reserve) (In serv. 1984–. . .)

D: 46.95 tons (fl) **S:** 11.5 kts **Dim:** 20.94 × 4.20 (3.90 wl) × 1.30
M: 1 Type 12-150C diesel; 1 CP prop; 300 hp (see Remarks)
Range: 150/11.5 **Crew:** 3 tot. (for ferrying)

Remarks: Normally operated by radio control to a range of 3 n.m., but can be manned. All but four were reportedly in land storage by 1993; officially stated not to be good seaboats. Electric propulsion for sweeping at 1–5 kts. Diesel generator amidships powers integral electromagnet for magnetic sweeping and a noisemaker for actuating acoustic mines. All equipment is shock mounted. Laser precision navigation system. Class has been exported to Thailand and Pakistan.

AMPHIBIOUS WARFARE SHIPS

Note: Although much has been made of the possibility of China conducting an invasion of Taiwan, the navy itself lacks the capability to provide even a small portion of the necessary amphibious lift, and very few of China's merchant marine and fishing assets would be suitable to conduct an opposed landing.

♦ **10 Yuting-class landing ships [LST]**
Bldr: Zhonghua SY, Shanghai (In serv. 1991 to 1-97, 2000–01)

908 910 934 935 936 937 938 991 . . . . . .

Yuting-class 908—this unit has Type 76A enclosed, automatic 37-mm AA mounts, but they are modified to accept an on-mount operator
JMSDF, via *Ships of the World,* 2-01

Yuting-class 910—also with Type 76A gunmounts
Chris Delgoffe/H&L Van Ginderen, 5-00

D: 3,430 tons (normal) **S:** 18 kts **Dim:** 119.50 × 16.40 × 2.80
A: 3 twin 37-mm 63-cal. Type 76 or Type 76A AA
Electronics: Radar: 2 Type 756 nav.
M: 2 SEMT-Pielstick 12 PA6 280MPC diesels; 2 props; 9,490 bhp
Range: 3,000/14 **Crew:** 104 tot.

Remarks: Updated version of the Yukan class, distinguishable principally by the helicopter platform aft and lighter defensive armament. The stack is also higher and the tripod mainmast more massive than on the Yukan class. Cargo capacity is 500 tons maximum, with a cargo deck area of 810 m^2. 938 is the first of four of a new series and was completed during 1-00.

♦ **7 Yukan-class (Project 072) landing ships [LST]**
Bldr: Zhonghua SY, Shanghai (In serv. 1978–80)

927 928 929 930 931 932 933

Yukan-class 930 *Ships of the World,* 1999

Yukan-class 928 JMSDF, via *Ships of the World,* 2-01

D: 3,110 tons (fl) **S:** 18 kts **Dim:** 119.50 × 15.60 × 2.82
A: 4 twin 57-mm 62-cal. Type 66 AA; 4 twin 25-mm 80-cal. Type 61 AA
Electronics: Radar: 2 Type 756 nav.
M: 2 SEMT-Pielstick 12 PA6 V280 diesels; 2 props; 9,600 bhp
Range: 3,000/14 **Crew:** 109 tot.

Remarks: Built to replace aging World War II–era U.S. LSTs, these ships are larger and considerably faster than their predecessors. Carry two U.S.-design LCVPs. At least one has a twin 57-mm DP gunmount forward and only two twin 37-mm AA. The bow ramp is 17.2 m long by 4.8 m wide and can support a 50-ton vehicle; the stern ramp can support a 20-ton vehicle. Beaching load is 500 tons. Two modified units of this design were built as Yantai-class fleet supply ships; see under [AF].

♦ **1 Yudeng-class medium landing ship [LSM]**
Bldr: Zhonghua SY, Shanghai (In serv. 8-94)

990

Yudeng-class 990 China Shipbuilding Trading Co.

D: 1,460 tons normal (1,850 fl) **S:** 17 kts **Dim:** 87.00 × 12.60 × 2.25
A: 2 twin 37-mm 63-cal. Model 74 AA **Electronics:** Radar: 1 Type 756 nav.
M: 2 SEMT-Pielstick 6PA6L-280 diesels; 2 props; 4,740 bhp
Range: 1,500/14 **Crew:** 74 tot.

Remarks: Launched 3-91. Only one unit built. More of a vehicle cargo vessel than a combatant in appearance; resembles a reduced version of the Yukan-class LST. Has an electrohydraulic, telescoping cargo crane amidships. Cargo capacity is 250 tons, with cargo decks totaling 440 m^2. A bow door and ramp are fitted.

♦ **8 Yudao-class (Project 073) medium landing ships [LSM]**
(6 in reserve) (In serv. 1980–. . .)

965 969 970 972 977 981 984 985

D: 1,460 tons (fl) **S:** . . . **Dim:** 82.07 (78.00 pp) × 12.60 × 3.10 (max.)
A: 4 twin 25-mm 80-cal. Type 61 AA **Electronics:** Radar: 1 Type 756 nav.
M: . . . diesels; 2 props; . . . bhp **Crew:** 5 officers, 60 enlisted

Remarks: Probably intended as replacements for the World War II–era U.S. LSM 1 class. Resemble a smaller version of the LST 1 design but have a blunt bow to accommodate the tank-deck ramp. Sister 975 has been relegated to museum service at Qingdao, and at least six others have been placed in reserve or discarded. A variation of this design was offered to the Philippines in 1992. Design does not appear particularly seaworthy and would not be suitable for extended voyages. All known units are in the East Sea Fleet.

AMPHIBIOUS WARFARE SHIPS *(continued)*

Yudao-class 984 Boris Lemachko Collection

♦ 12 (+ . . .) Yuhai-class utility landing craft [LCU]
Bldrs: Wuhu SY and . . . SY (In serv. 1995–. . .)

6562 7593 N 1122 and others

Yuhai-class N 1122—of the Nanjing Maritime Border Defense Force
Chris Delgoffe/H&L Van Ginderen, 5-00.

D: 799 tons (fl) **S:** 14 kts **Dim:** 58.4 × 10.4 × 2.7
A: 1 twin 25-mm 80-cal. Type 61 AA **Electronics:** Radar: 1 Type 756 nav.
M: 2 M.A.N. 8L 20/27 diesels; 2 props; 4,900 bhp
Range: 1,000/12 **Crew:** 56 tot.

Remarks: Most may be other than naval subordinated. Essentially an enlarged LCU. Appears to have been designed with commercial or logistic support duties rather than military service in mind. Bow ramp only. Cargo capacity is two tanks and 250 troops, or up to 150 tons of miscellaneous cargo. Two have been built for Sri Lanka, and construction may be continuing.

♦ 23 Yuling-class (Project 079) utility landing craft [LCU]
(In serv. 1971–75)

D: 600 tons (fl) **S:** 15 kts **Dim:** 56.55 × 10.40 × 2.25
A: 4 twin 14.5-mm 93-cal. 2M-7 mg **Electronics:** Radar: 1 Type 756 nav.
M: 2 diesels; 2 props; . . . bhp
Range: 1,000/15 **Endurance:** 15 days **Crew:** 25 tot.

Remarks: Cargo capacity: 150 tons beaching load. Molded depth of the hull is 5.56 m. Have a blunt bow incorporating a beaching ramp.

♦ 235 Yunnan-class (Project 067) landing craft [LCM]
(200 in reserve) Bldr: Huangzhou SY (In serv. 1968–. . .)

Yunnan-class S 2309—of the Shenyang Maritime Border Defense Force
Ships of the World, 1998

D: 133.2 tons (fl) **S:** 10.5 kts **Dim:** 27.50 (24.07 pp) × 5.40 × 1.40
A: 1 or 2 twin 14.5-mm 93-cal. Type 82 mg
M: 2 diesels; 2 props; 600 bhp **Range:** 500/10 **Crew:** 6 tot.

Remarks: Production was thought to have ceased in 1992, but a 1995 Chinese article noted that a new series built since 1989 had improved engine controls, better navigational systems, improved seaworthiness to operate in Wind Force 6–7, and endurance extended to 10 days. Cargo: 46 tons (1 tank). Cargo deck: 15.0 × 4.0 m.

♦ 50 Yuqin-class (Project 069) landing craft [LCM] (40 in reserve)
(In serv. 1962–72)

Yuqin-class N 2332—of the Nanjing Maritime Border Defense Force
H&L Van Ginderen, 3-95

Yuqin-class 4507—naval unit with enclosed pilothouse, outboard a small tug
Chris Delgoffe/H&L Van Ginderen, 5-00

D: 58 tons light (110 fl) **S:** 11.5 kts (9 loaded) **Dim:** 24.1 × 5.2 × 1.1
A: 1 twin 14.5-mm 93-cal. AA **M:** 2 diesels; 2 Type 12V50 props; 600 bhp

Remarks: Two transferred to Bangladesh in 1984 as survey craft. Can carry up to 110 troops over short distances.

♦ 30+ Yuchai-class (Project 068) landing craft [LCM]
Bldr: Kailing SY, Zhoushan

Yuchai-class Y 761 Ross Gillett, 9-84

D: 85 tons (fl) **S:** 11.5 kts **Dim:** 24.8 × 5.2 × 1.3
A: 2 twin 14.5-mm 93-cal. mg **M:** 2 Type 12V-150 diesels; 2 props; 600 bhp
Range: 450/11.5 **Crew:** 23 tot. (incl. vehicle crews)

Remarks: Number in Chinese service unknown. Two each were built for Bangladesh (in the early 1980s) and Tanzania (in 1995). First observed in the late 1960s.

♦ 0 (+ 1) wing-in-ground-effect personnel landing craft [LCMA]
Bldr: Quixin Shipyard, Shanghai (In serv. 2000)

Remarks: Reported under construction in 9-99 and intended to carry 100 troops. No further information had emerged as of 6-01.

♦ 8 or more Payi-class air-cushion personnel landing craft [LCPA]

8531 through 8538 or higher

D: approx. 12 tons (fl) **S:** 40 kts **Dim:** 15.0 × . . . × . . .
A: none **Electronics:** Radar: none
M: 2 diesel-engines; 2 ducted airscrew props; . . . bhp **Crew:** 2 + 8–10 troops

Remarks: Several were used during the 3-96 amphibious landing demonstration opposite Taiwan. Swiveling puff ports forward and a rudder abaft the propellers are used for control.

AMPHIBIOUS WARFARE SHIPS *(continued)*

Payi-class air-cushion personnel landing craft 8538—with a Yuting-class LST in background *Ships of the World,* 2000

♦ **1 or more Jingsah-II-class air-cushion landing craft [LCPA]**
452

Jingsah-II-class air-cushion personnel landing craft 452 *Ships of the World,* 1994

D: 61 tons (70 fl) **S:** 55 kts **Dim:** 27.2 × 13.8 × 9.6 (high)
A: 2 twin 14.5-mm 93-cal. AA **Electronics:** Radar: 1 . . . nav.
M: 2 turboprop propulsion engines, 1 gas-turbine lift engine; 2 ducted airscrew propellers; . . . bhp

Remarks: A further development of the Dagu-A prototype, which was completed in 1979 and is now probably out of service. Class nickname has also been rendered as "Jingoah." Cargo: 16.8 tons. Designed by Shanghai SB Research and Development Institute, but a considerable portion of the design concept is based on British Hovercraft work. There are six centrifugal lift-fans.

GRP-hulled, outboard motor–propelled personnel landing craft—manually deployed down the bow ramp of a Yukan-class LST *Ships of the World,* 1999

AUXILIARIES

There is no authoritative, comprehensive information on the PLAN's logistic support fleet, but China has designated and built large numbers of auxiliary vessels, running the spectrum of logistics support, repair, hydrographic survey, and research types, including a great many tugs and small oilers. Known types and classes are listed below.

♦ **4 or more Yanbai-class degaussing/deperming tenders [ADG]**
(In serv. . . .)

Shuguang 203 Haizu 746
Haizu 745 Dongqin 863

D: 746 tons (fl) **S:** 16.5 kts **Dim:** 65.00 × 9.00 × 2.60
A: 1 twin 37-mm 63-cal. AA Type 74 AA
Electronics: Radar: 1 Type 756 or Fin Curve nav.
M: diesel-electric: 2 Type 12VE 230ZC diesels, 2 Type ZDH-99/57 motors; 2 props; 2,200 bhp
Range: 800/16.5 **Crew:** approx. 60 tot.

Yanbai-class degaussing tender Shuguang 203 French Navy, 11-97

Remarks: Resemble enlarged T-43-class minesweepers. Main engine generator sets are used to provide current for deperming ships and submarines of up to 7,000 tons displacement. Two twin 25-mm gunmounts have been removed.

♦ **2 Dayun-class fleet supply vessels [AF]**
Bldr: Hudong SY, Shanghai (In serv. 1992)

Nanyun 951 Nanyun 952

Dayun-class Nanyun 952 *Ships of the World,* 1992

Dayun-class Nanyun 952 92 Wing Det., RAAF, 2-95

D: 10,975 tons **S:** 20 kts **Dim:** 156.2 × 20.6 × 6.8
A: 2 twin 37-mm 63-cal. Type 76A AA; 2 twin 25-mm 80-cal. Type 61 AA
Electronics: Radar: 2 Type 756 nav.
M: 2 Xin Zhong–M.A.N. K9Z60/105E diesels; 2 props; 9,000 bhp **Crew:** . . .

Remarks: Appear to be an adaptation of the Dajiang-class submarine tender to serve as fleet supply vessels and personnel transports, but have lower freeboard. Carry four small landing craft. Two small electric cranes forward serve probable refrigerated holds. Have a helicopter platform but no hangar.

♦ **2 Yantai-class fleet supply ships [AF]**
Bldr: Zhongua SY, Shanghai (In serv. 1992)

. . . 800 . . . 801

D: 3,330 tons (fl) **S:** 18 kts **Dim:** 115.00 × 15.60 × 3.00
A: 1 twin 37-mm 63-cal. AA **Electronics:** Radar: 1 Type 756 nav.
M: 2 SEMT-Pielstick 12 PA6 V280 diesels; 2 props; 9,600 bhp
Range: 3,000/14 **Crew:** 100 tot.

Remarks: Appears to be a modification of the Yukan tank landing ship design with a shorter forecastle, blunter bow-form, no bow door, and cargo-handling cranes fore and aft, tending two holds forward of the bridge superstructure and one aft. Both are assigned to the South Sea Fleet.

♦ **1 Yanbing-class icebreaker [AGB]** Bldr: . . . (In serv. late 1970s)

Haidiao 723 (ex-*Haidiao* 525, ex-*Haibing* 723)

D: approx. 5,000 tons (fl) **S:** 16 kts **Dim:** 94.5 × 17.1 × 5.9
A: 4 twin 37-mm 63-cal. Type 74 AA
Electronics: 1 Fin Curve nav.; 1 Type 756 nav.
M: 2 or 4 diesels; 2 props; . . . bhp **Crew:** approx. 100 tot.

Remarks: An enlarged variant of the Yanha class. Since the mid-1990s, has been equipped for intelligence collection duties, with two radomes on the centerline forward of the bridge. Can also be used for ocean towing.

AUXILIARIES *(continued)*

Yanbing-class icebreaker Haidiao 723—traversing the Tsugaru Strait on an intelligence-collection mission JMSDF, via *Ships of the World,* 5-00

♦ **3 Yanha-class icebreakers [AGB]** Bldr: Qiuxin SY, Shanghai

Haibing 519 (In serv. 1989?) Haibing 722 (L: 1972)
Haibing 721 (L: 26-12-69)

Two Yanha-class icebreakers—at Quinhuandao H&L Van Ginderen, 3-95

D: 3,200 tons **S:** 16 kts **Dim:** 84.0 × 15.0 × 5.0
A: 4 twin 37-mm 62-cal. Type 74 AA; 4 twin 25-mm 80-cal. Type 61 AA
Electronics: Radar: 2 Fin Curve nav.
M: 2 diesels, electric drive; 2 props; 5,200 bhp **Crew:** 90 tot.

Remarks: Differ in details of superstructure. Can break 1.2-m ice, can also be used as ocean tugs, and have been employed as intelligence collectors on occasion. Resemble a slightly smaller version of the Yanbing class, with one less level of superstructure above the bridge and no after mast. *Haibing 519* has a small tripod mast aft not found on the others.

♦ **1 Wuhu-B-class trials ship [AGE]**
Bldr: Wuhu SY (L: 3-9-97)

Shiyan 970 (ex-909)

Wuhu-B-class weapons trials support ship Shiyan 970—fitting out at Shanghai French Navy, 11-97

Shiyan 970 *Ships of the World,* 1999

D: 6,000 tons (fl) **S:** 20 kts **Dim:** 130.0 × 17.5 × 7.00 **A:** none
Electronics:
Radar: 1 or 2 . . . nav., 1 Type 354 (Eye Shield) air search
Sonar: . . .
EW: . . .
M: 2 diesels; 2 props; . . . bhp
Range: . . ./. . . **Crew:** . . . tot.

Remarks: 4,630 grt. Has a large helicopter deck but no hangar. Thus far, most of the antenna positions have remained empty. Dimensional data, displacement, and speed were reported in a Chinese publication. Operational compartments are enlarged to permit seating trainees. Has also been referred to as an intelligence collection ship, and the prefix to the hull number means "experimental."

♦ **1 Yanxi-class weapons trials support ship [AGE]**
Bldr: . . . SY, Shanghai (In serv. 1970)

Hsun 701

D: 1,200 tons (fl) **S:** 16 kts **Dim:** 60.0 × 11.0 × 3.5
A: 1 twin 37-mm 63-cal. Type 74 AA; 2 twin 14.5-mm 93-cal. AA
Electronics: Radar: 1 Fin Curve nav.
M: 2 Type 8300Z diesels; 2 props; 2,200 bhp **Range:** 4,500/11

Remarks: Apparently intended to support antiship cruise-missile trials or, possibly, to act as a drone target launch and recovery ship.

♦ **1 Dadie-class intelligence collection ship [AGI]**
Bldr: Wuhan SY, Wuchang (In serv. 1987)

Beidiao 841

Dadie-class Beidiao 841 *Ships of the World*

D: 2,550 tons (fl) **S:** 17 kts **Dim:** 94.0 × 11.3 × 4.0
A: 2 twin 14.5-mm 93-cal. Type 81 AA
Electronics:
Radar: 2 Type 756 or Decca RM 1290A/D ARPA nav.
EW: see Remarks
M: 2 diesels; 2 props; . . . bhp **Crew:** 15 officers, 145 enlisted

Remarks: Subordinated to North Sea Fleet. Has been deployed as far as the Japanese coast. Has a bow centerline anchor and a sharply raked bow, and therefore may be equipped with a bow-mounted sonar array. Intercept arrays are mounted on the lattice masts and atop the pilothouse. Has one machinegun mount on the forecastle and two side by side on the stern.

Note: The Yanbing and Yanha classes of icebreakers and several civilian-subordinated oceanographic research vessels have also performed intelligence collection missions.

♦ **3 or more Yannan-class navigational buoy tenders [AGL]**
Bldr: Zhonghua SY, Shanghai (In serv. late 1970s)

Dongce 263 Beibiao 982 Beibiao 983

Yannan-class Beibiao 982 U.S. Navy, 7-94

D: 1,550 tons (fl) **S:** 14 kts (sust.) **Dim:** 71.40 (63.00 pp) × 10.50 × 3.60
A: 2 twin 37-mm 62-cal. Type 74 AA; 2 twin 14.5-mm 93-cal. Type 81 AA
Electronics: Radar: 1 Fin Curve nav.
M: 2 Type 8300Z diesels; 2 props; 2,200 bhp

Remarks: Design built for both military and civil use. Buoy tender version of the Youdian-class small cable ship.

Note: Also in naval service is a newer navigational aids tender numbered 802; no data available, but the ship is probably of about the same size as the Yannan-class units.

AUXILIARIES *(continued)*

Navigational aids tender 802—at Shanghai; note heavy side fendering grid, cleared fantail with articulated hydraulic crane, and rectangular stack
Chris Delgoffe/H&L Van Ginderen, 5-00

♦ 1 . . . . . .-class missile-range instrumentation ship [AGM]
Bldr: Qiuxin SY, Shanghai (L: 9-3-97)

DONGDIAO 232 (ex-970, ex-909)

Missile-range instrumentation ship Dongdiao 232
JMSDF, via *Ships of the World,* 7-00

D: approx. 4,600 tons (fl) **S:** 17 kts **Dim:** 121.0 × 15.8 × 4.8
A: 1 twin 37-mm 63-cal. Type 74 AA; 2 twin 25-mm 80-cal. Type 61 AA
Electronics:
Radar: 3 . . . nav., 2 . . . missile-tracking/telemetry
EW: . . . intercept
M: 2 SEMT-Pielstick 6PC2-5L diesels; 2 props; 7,200 bhp (14,400 sust.)
Range: 5,000/15 **Crew:** . . . tot.

Remarks: Has tracking radars atop pilothouse, after lattice mast and a large telemetry dish on a pedestal amidships, and a theodolite tracking camera in a dome forward of the bridge. Helicopter deck and hangar fitted. Electrohydraulic weapons-recovery cranes fitted at forward end of helicopter deck. Has a commercial Marisat SATCOM antenna. Characteristics data above are based on the Daxin-class cadet training ship *Zhenghe* (81), to which this ship is similar. Equipment aboard would also make the ship suitable for intelligence collection duties.

♦ 3 Yuanwang-class space event support ships [AGM]
Bldr: Hudong SY, Shanghai (In serv.: first two 1980, third 4-95)

YUANWANG 1 YUANWANG 2 YUANWANG 3

Yuanwang 3 H&L Van Ginderen, 4-00

Yuanwang 1 U.S. Navy, 1-95

D: 17,100 tons (21,000 fl) **S:** 20 kts **Dim:** 190.0 × 22.6 × 7.5
A: none **Electronics:** see Remarks
M: 1 Dalian-Sulzer 8LRB66 diesel; 1 prop; 17,400 bhp
Range: 18,000/20 **Endurance:** 100 days **Crew:** 470 (incl. technicians)

Remarks: *Yuanwang* means "Long Look." The first two, initially observed during the 5-80 Chinese ICBM tests in the central Pacific, were refitted 1986–87 and again in 1991–92.
Hull systems: Among the 54 research-associated antennas are one large parabolic tracking antenna, two log-periodic HF ("fish-spine") antennas, several precision theodolite optical tracking stations, and two smaller missile-tracking radars, as well as positions for later installation of equipment. Have a large helicopter deck but no hangar. Also have a bow-thruster and retractable fin stabilizers. Navigational equipment includes a SINS (Ship's Inertial Navigation System) and NAVSAT receiver. Equipped with satellite communications gear; the first two were refitted in 1990 with improved communications and data-handling gear.
Yuanwang 3 differs from the earlier pair in having a larger superstructure block just forward of the helicopter deck and the funnel mounted further forward. The ship also has a single mast aft, supporting a large, trainable HF yagi antenna. At least three small SATCOM antennas are fitted, along with three large, trainable SATCOM dish antennas.

♦ 1 Xiangyanghong 10–class space event support ship [AGM]
Bldr: Hudong SY, Shanghai (In serv. 1980)

YUANWANG 4 (ex-*Xiangyanghong 10*)

Yuanwang 4—as *Xiangyanghong 10,* prior to conversion U.S. Navy, 1-94

D: 10,975 tons **S:** 20 kts **Dim:** 156.2 × 20.6 × 6.8
M: 2 Xin Zhong–M.A.N. K9Z60/105E diesels; 2 props; . . . bhp

Remarks: Converted during a 4-month refit from a high-seas oceanographic research and survey ship to a "seaborne monitor and control section of China's monitor and control system for satellite launches" at Chengxi Shipyard, China Shipbuilding Industrial Group, Nanjing; reentered service 18-7-99. As an oceanographic research ship, conducted a 150-day Antarctic expedition 20-11-84 to 10-4-85 with submarine tender J 121 and a landing ship named *Great Wall 2.*
Hull systems: Uses same hull and propulsion as the Dajiang-class submarine tenders, but has twin, side-by-side funnels; the crane forward is smaller, and the kingposts abaft the stacks and the heavy foremast support large log-periodic HF antennas. Has hangar space for two Z-8 Super Frelon helicopters. Retractable fin stabilizers are fitted.

♦ 2 Kan Yang–class hydrographic survey ships [AGS]
Bldr: . . . . . . (In serv. circa 1980)

NANCE 426 NANCE 428

Kan Yang–class Nance 428 OS2 John Bouvia, USN, 11-90

D: approx. 600 tons (fl) **S:** approx. 14 kts **Dim:** approx. 50.0 × 8.0 × . . .
A: 1 twin 25-mm 80-cal. Type 61 AA **Electronics:** Radar: 1 . . . nav.
M: 2 . . . diesels; 2 props; . . . bhp

Remarks: Small survey craft operating in South Sea Fleet. *Nance* means "survey, fathom, or measure."

AUXILIARIES *(continued)*

♦ **1 Ganzhu-class hydrographic survey ship [AGS]**
Bldr: Zhujiang SY (In serv. 1975)

Nance 420 (ex-K 420)

Ganzhu-class Nance 420 1975

D: 1,000 tons (fl) **S:** 20 kts **Dim:** 65.0 × 9.0 × 3.0
A: 2 twin 37-mm 63-cal. Type 74 AA; 2 twin 25-mm 80-cal. Type 61 AA; 2 twin 14.5-mm 93-cal. Type 82 AA
M: 4 diesels; 2 props; 4,400 bhp **Crew:** 120 tot.

Remarks: Operates in South Sea Fleet. Has also been referred to as the Yen Hsi or Yanxi class.

♦ **4 Yanlai-class hydrographic survey ships [AGS]**
(In serv. early 1970s)

Dong Biao 200 Dong Biao 226 Nance 427 Dong Biao 943

Yanlai-class Dong Biao 226 U.S. Navy, 5-94

D: 1,100 tons (fl) **S:** 16 kts **Dim:** 72.0 × 9.8 × 3.0
A: 2 twin 37-mm 63-cal. Type 74 AA; 2 twin 25-mm 80-cal. Type 61 AA
Electronics: Radar: 1 Fin Curve nav.
M: 2 Kolomna Type 9D-8 diesels; 2 props; 2,200 bhp
Range: 4,000/14 **Crew:** approx. 100 tot.

Remarks: Funnel amidships; large crane aft. May now all carry the *Nance* prefix to the hull number.

♦ **3 Modified T-43-class hydrographic survey ships [AGS]**
Bldr: . . . . . . (In serv. late 1960s)

993 994 995

Modified T-43-class survey ship 994 Boris Lemachko Collection

D: 500 tons (590 fl) **S:** 14 kts **Dim:** 60.0 × 8.6 × 2.16
A: 1 twin 37-mm 63-cal. Type 74 AA; 2 twin 14.5-mm 93-cal. AA
Electronics: Radar: 1 Fin Curve nav.
M: 2 Type 9D-8 diesels; 2 props; 2,200 bhp
Range: 3,200/10 **Fuel:** 70 tons **Crew:** approx. 70 tot.

Remarks: Have an extended after deckhouse and four-point mooring capability, but no minesweeping equipment. Resemble the Russian Navy radiated-noise measurement version of the T-43 class. Have also been referred to as the Shuguang class.

♦ **2 Qiongsha-class hospital ships [AH]**
Bldr: Guangzhou SY (In serv. 1980–. . .)

833 Nankang . . . .

D: 2,150 tons (fl) **S:** 16.2 kts **Dim:** 86.0 (76.0 pp) × 13.4 × 3.9
A: 4 twin 14.5-mm 93-cal. Type 82 AA

Qiongsha-class hospital ship Nankang (833) *Ships of the World,* 1993

Electronics: Radar: 2 Fin Curve nav.
M: 3 8NVD48A-2U diesels; 3 props; 3,960 bhp **Electric:** 575 kw tot.
Fuel: 195 tons **Crew:** 59 tot.

Remarks: Built for South Sea Fleet service. Similar to the troop transport version but are configured as hospital ships; white-painted and bearing International Red Cross markings, they nonetheless retain the standard armament suite. Pennant numbers are now plain, without a letter or character prefix.

♦ **7 or more Hongqi 081–class cargo ships [AK]**
Bldr: . . . . . . (In serv. 1970s)

433 443 528 755 756 771 836

Hongqi 081–class cargo ship 755 French Navy, 11-97

D: 1,950 tons (fl) **S:** 14 kts **Dim:** 62.0 (58.0 wl) × 12.0 × 4.5
A: 2 twin 25-mm 80-cal. Type 61 AA **Electronics:** Radar: 1 Type 756 nav.
M: 1 diesel; 1 prop; 1,200 bhp **Range:** 2,500/11 **Crew:** 30 tot.

Remarks: 875 grt/1,100 dwt. Used to support offshore island garrisons; appear to be able to carry some passengers. Sisters in commercial service.

♦ **2 Romanian Galati-class cargo ships [AK]**
Bldr: Santierul SY, Galati (In serv. early 1970s)

Haiyun 318 Haijiu 600

D: 5,200 tons (fl) **S:** 12.5 kts **Dim:** 100.60 (93.70 pp) × 13.92 × 6.60
A: . . . **Electronics:** Radar: 2 . . . nav.
M: 1 Sulzer 5TAD56 diesel; 1 prop; . . . bhp **Electric:** 345 kw
Range: 5,000/12.5 **Fuel:** 250 tons **Crew:** 50 tot.

Remarks: One sister serves as a repair ship (see under [AR]), and six others were in merchant service under the Chinese flag. One may now operate in the South Sea Fleet under changed number 809. Cargo capacity: 3,750 dwt.

♦ **7 or more Danlin-class cargo ships [AK]** (In serv. 1960–62)

Haileng 531 Haileng 592 Haiyun 794 Haiyun 975
Haileng 591 Haileng 594 Haiyun 972

Danlin-class cargo ship Haiyun 794 7-89

D: 1,290 tons (fl) **S:** 14 kts **Dim:** 60.5 × 9.0 × 4.0
A: 1 twin 37-mm 63-cal. Type 74 AA; 2 twin 14.5-mm 93-cal. AA
Electronics: Radar: 1 Fin Curve or Type 756 nav.
M: 1 Type 6DRN 30/50 diesel; 1 prop; 750 bhp **Crew:** 35 tot.

Remarks: Haiyun series in East Sea Fleet; Haileng series in South Sea Fleet. Other units are in civilian service. Three holds, served by two electrohydraulic cranes. About 750 dwt of cargo, including refrigerated stores.

AUXILIARIES *(continued)*

♦ . . . trawler-type coastal cargo ships [AK]

Trawler-type coastal cargo ship N 1121—of the Nanjing Maritime Border Defense Force — Ross Gillett, 9-84

Remarks: There were a number of units of this design (including N 1121 and N 3215), most of which seem to have been subordinated to the Maritime Border Defense Force districts. Of about 450 tons (fl) displacement, they have a single cargo hold amidships, are equipped with a Type 756 navigational radar, and are armed with two twin side-by-side 14.5-mm mg mounts. Maximum speed is about 9 kts on a single 300-bhp Type 12-150C diesel.

♦ 2 Fuqing-class replenishment oilers [AO]
Bldr: Dalian SY (In serv. 1980–82)

Beiyun 575 Taikang — Dongyun 615 Fencang

Fuqing-class oiler Fencang (Dongyun 615) — H&L Van Ginderen, 11-97

Fencang (Dongyun 615)—with SATCOM radome added atop after superstructure — JMSDF, via *Ships of the World,* 6-00

D: 14,600 tons (21,740 fl) **S:** 18.6 kts **Dim:** 168.2 (157.0 pp) × 21.8 × 9.4
A: Beiyun 575: 4 twin 37-mm 63-cal. Type 74 or 76A AA—Dongyun 615: 2 twin 14.5-mm 93-cal. mg
Electronics: Radar: 2 Fin Curve nav.
M: 1 Dalian-Sulzer 8RLB 66 diesel; 1 prop; 17,400 bhp (15,000 sust.)
Electric: 2,480 kw **Range:** 18,000/14.6 **Crew:** 26 officers, 120 enlisted

Remarks: A sister, *Nasr* (A 47), was delivered to Pakistan in 1988. The third PLAN ship of the class, *Hongcang* (X 950), was placed in merchant service in 1989 and renamed *Hailang. Taikang* was armed during 1994, but *Fencang* remained unarmed until 2000.
Hull systems: Have two liquid replenishment stations per side, with constant-tension solid transfer stations each side just forward of the stack. Have a helicopter deck but no hangar. Have four small electric cranes for stores handling. Carry 11,000 tons fuel oil, 1,000 tons diesel fuel, 200 tons feedwater, 200 tons potable water, and 50 tons lube oil.

♦ 1 Russian Komandarm Fedko–class replenishment ship [AOR]
Bldr: Kherson SY, Kherson (In serv. 2-6-96)

Nanyun 953 Nancang (ex-*Vladimir Peregudov*)

Nancang (Nanyun 953) — PO Eric Murata, USN, 3-97

Nancang (Nanyun 953) — Brian Morrison/H&L Van Ginderen, 5-98

D: approx. 37,000 tons (fl) **S:** 16.4 kts (15.48 sust.)
Dim: 188.90 (165.00 pp) × 25.33 × 10.41 (12.0 max.)
A: provision for: 3 twin 30-mm 65-cal. AA **Electronics:** Radar: . . .
M: 1 Bryansk–Burmeister & Wain 6DKRN74/160-3 diesel; 1 prop; 10,600 bhp
Electric: 2,000 kw tot. (3 × 500-kw, 5 × 100-kw diesel sets)
Range: 12,000/15.48 **Fuel:** 1,606 tons heavy oil, 305+ tons diesel
Endurance: 45 days **Crew:** . . .

Remarks: Laid down 1-89 for the Soviet Navy as a replenishment oiler, with design modified from that of a standard 27,400-dwt product oiler class. Purchased by China in 1992 for a reported $10 million and delivered nearly complete in spring 1993 to Dalian SY for fitting out. Handed over to the PLAN on 8-5-96. A near-sister was built in Russia for the Indian Navy.
Hull systems: Is equipped to carry two liquid and one sliding-stay solid transfer stations per side and can also refuel over the stern. A sponson has been added across the transom stern to support a helicopter deck, and there is a small hangar. Superstructure was enlarged, with a deckhouse added forward of bridge area and working deck built over the cargo tank area. Additional generators were also added. Cargo: 23,000 tons fuel, water, and solid stores. Merchant version had 10 cargo tanks totaling 31,398 m^3, but several tanks have been converted to dry cargo stowage or engineering and berthing spaces in this ship.
Combat systems: Has provision for three AA mounts, controlled from cupola-mounted lead-computing optical directors.

♦ 3 Jinyou-class transport oilers [AOT]
Bldr: Kanashashi SY, Japan (In serv. 1989–90)

Dongyun 622 — Dongyun 625 — Dongyun 675

Jinyou-class Dongyun 625 — James W. Goss/NAVPIC, 6-95

D: 2,500 tons light (4,800 fl) **S:** 15 kts **Dim:** 99.0 × 31.8 × 5.7
A: none **Electronics:** Radar: 2 Type 756 nav.
M: 1 SEMT-Pielstick 8PC2.2L diesel; 1 prop; 3,000 bhp
Range: 4,000/9 **Cargo:** 25,000 bbl liquid **Crew:** 40 tot.

♦ 3 or more Shengli-class transport oilers [AOT]
Bldr: Hudong SY, Shanghai (In serv. 1981–. . .)

Dongyun 620 — Dongyun 621 — Dongyun 632

Shengli-class Dongyun 621—with *Hongqi 081*–class cargo ship 755 astern — 11-00

D: 4,940 tons (fl) **S:** 14 kts **Dim:** 101.0 (92.0 pp) × 13.8 × 5.5
A: 1 twin 37-mm 63-cal. Type 74 AA; 2 twin 25-mm 80-cal. Type 61 AA
Electronics: Radar: 2 Type 756 nav.
M: 1 Type 6 ESDZ 43 diesel; 1 prop; 2,600 bhp **Range:** 2,400/14

Remarks: 3,318.5 dwt. Cargo: 3,002 tons fuel oil (4,240 m^3). A number of sisters serve in commercial service.

♦ 20 or more Fulin-class transport oilers [AOT]
Bldr: Hudong SY, Shanghai (In serv. 1972–. . .)

Dongyun 560	Dongyun 606	Dongyun 628	Nanyun 922
Dongyun 563	Dongyun 607	Dongyun 629	Nanyun 923
Dongyun 582	Dongyun 609	Dongyun 630	Nanyun 924
Dongyun 583	Dongyun 620	Dongyun 632	Nanyun 941
Dongyun 589	Dongyun 623	Dongyun 633	

AUXILIARIES *(continued)*

Fulin-class Dongyun 632 Chris Delgoffe/H&L Van Ginderen, 5-00

D: 2,200 tons (fl) **S:** 10 kts **Dim:** 66.0 × 10.0 × 4.0
A: 2 twin 25-mm 80-cal. Type 61 AA
Electronics: Radar: 1 Fin Curve nav.
M: 1 diesel; 1 prop; 600 bhp **Range:** 1,500/8 **Crew:** 30 tot.

Remarks: Part of a series of more than 20, the others of which went into merchant service. Several reported to have a single underway replenishment rig. Resemble an enlarged Fuzhou.

♦ **24 or more Fuzhou-class transport oilers [AOT]**
Bldr: Hudong SY, Shanghai (In serv. 1964–70)

Dongyun 570	Dongyun 629	Nanyun 910	Nanyun 935
Dongyun 573	Nanyun 903	Nanyun 912	Nanyun 938
Dongyun 580	Nanyun 904	Nanyun 920	Nanyun 940
Dongyun 581	Nanyun 906	Nanyun 926	Nanyun 945
Dongyun 582	Nanyun 907	Nanyun 927	N 1101
Dongyun 606	Nanyun 909	Nanyun 930	N 1104

Fuzhou-class N 1104—of the Nanjing Maritime Border Defense Force
Chris Delgoffe/H&L Van Ginderen, 5-00

D: 1,200 tons (fl) **S:** 10–12 kts **Dim:** 60.0 (55.0 pp) × 9.0 × 3.5
A: 2 twin 25-mm 80-cal. Type 61 AA; 2 twin 14.5-mm 93-cal. Type 82 AA
Electronics: Radar: 1 Fin Curve or Type 756 nav.
M: 1 diesel; 1 prop; 600 bhp **Crew:** 30 tot.

Remarks: Cargo: 600 tons. Five also built in a water-tanker version. Some of the oilers (including N 1101) are subordinated to Maritime Border Defense Force. Some are not armed. Dongyun units are in the East Sea Fleet, Nanyun units in the South Sea Fleet; others may serve the North Sea Fleet.

♦ **5 Leizhou-class transport oilers [AOT]**
Bldr: . . . . . . (In serv. early 1960s)

D: 900 tons **S:** 10–12 kts **Dim:** 53.0 (48.0 pp) × 9.8 × 3.0
A: 2 twin 37-mm 62-cal. Type 74 AA; 2 single 14.5-mm 93-cal. AA
M: 1 diesel; 1 prop; 600 bhp **Crew:** 30 tot.

Remarks: Four others built in a water-tanker version; another was built as a cargo ship (Y 737) with a single kingpost and two cargo holds amidships. Others are in civilian service.

♦ **4 Qiongsha-class troop transports [AP]**
Bldr: Guangzhou SY (In serv. 1980–. . .)

830 831 832 835

Qiongsha-class transport 832 U.S. Navy, 5-83

D: 2,150 tons (fl) **S:** 16.2 kts **Dim:** 86.0 (76.0 pp) × 13.4 × 3.9
A: 4 twin 14.5-mm 93-cal. Type 82 AA
Electronics: Radar: 2 Fin Curve nav.
M: 3 8NVD48A-2U diesels; 3 props; 3,960 bhp
Electric: 575 kw tot. **Fuel:** 195 tons **Crew:** 59 tot. + 400 troops

Remarks: Built for South Sea Fleet service. Carry about 400 troops. Cargo holds fore and aft, each tended by two 1-ton derricks, can accommodate 350 tons. Carry four merchant marine–type lifeboats in Welin davits vice landing craft. Near-sisters *Nankang* (833) and one other are configured as hospital ships. Pennant numbers are now plain, without a letter or character prefix.

Small, unarmed catamaran-hulled transport assigned to the Shenyang Maritime Border Defense Force—seen off Dalian; no data available
Ships of the World, 1998

♦ **1 Romanian Galati-class repair ship [AR]**
Bldr: Santieral SY, Galati (In serv. early 1970s)

D: 5,200 tons (fl) **S:** 12.5 kts **Dim:** 100.60 (93.70 pp) × 13.92 × 6.60
A: . . . **M:** 1 Sulzer 5TAD56 diesel; 1 prop; . . . bhp **Electric:** 345 kw tot.
Range: 5,000/12.5 **Fuel:** 250 tons

Remarks: Converted from a cargo ship with minimal external alterations. Of nine sisters purchased by China, two others serve the navy as cargo ships.

♦ **3 or more Youzhong-class cable ships [ARC]**
Bldr: Zhonghua SY, Shanghai (In serv. 1982–. . .)

G 2693 N 2304 N 2404

D: 750 tons (fl) **S:** 14.5 kts **Dim:** 59.0 × 10.50 × 2.8
A: 2 twin 14.5-mm 93-cal. Type 82 AA **Electronics:** Radar: 1 Fin Curve nav.
M: 2 Type 8300Z diesels; 2 props; 2,200 hp

Remarks: Smaller version of Youdian class, with shallower draft and only 50 m^3 of cable stowage. All three are assigned to Maritime Border Defense Forces.

♦ **6 or more Youdian-class cable ships [ARC]**
Bldr: Zhonghua SY, Shanghai (In serv. late 1970s)

Nanlan 233	Beilan 764	Donglan 873
Nanlan 234	Beilan 765	Donglan 874

Youdian-class Donglan 874 Navpic-Holland, 5-98

D: 1,550 tons (fl) **S:** 14 kts (sust.) **Dim:** 71.40 (63.00 pp) × 10.50 × 3.60
A: 2 twin 37-mm 62-cal. Type 74 AA; 2 or 4 twin 14.5-mm 93-cal. Type 82 AA
Electronics: Radar: 1 Fin Curve nav.
M: 2 Type 8300Z diesels; 2 props; 2,200 bhp

Remarks: Design built for both military and civil use. Cable tank has 187-m^3 capacity. Can lay up to 100-mm-thick cable. The buoy-tender version of the design is referred to as the Yannan class.

♦ **1 Daozha-class salvage ship [ARS]**
Bldr: Zhonghua SY, Shanghai (In serv. 1993)

Daozha . . .

D: 4,000 tons (fl) **S:** 18 kts **Dim:** 84.0 × 12.6 × 5.4
A: . . . **Electronics:** Radar: . . .
M: 2 diesels; 2 props; 8,600 bhp **Range:** . . ./. . . **Crew:** 125 tot.

Remarks: Large tug-type vessel with twin, side-by-side funnels amidships and an extended forecastle with a crane at the aft end. Fitted for ocean towing.

♦ **1 ex-Russian Ingul (Pamir)-class (Project 1452) salvage tug [ARS]** Bldr: United Admiralty SY, St. Petersburg (In serv. 1977)

. . . Hua Ru (ex-*Bars*)

D: 3,320 tons (4,040 fl) **S:** 20 kts (18.75 cruise)
Dim: 92.79 (80.40 pp) × 15.63 × 5.85 **Electronics:** Radar: 2 . . . nav.
M: 2 Type 58D-4R, 16-cyl. diesels; 2 CP props; 9,000 bhp
Electric: 1,060 kw (4 × 240-kw, 1 × 100-kw diesel sets)
Range: 9,000/18.7; 15,000/12 **Fuel:** 675 tons heavy oil, 155 tons diesel
Endurance: 60 days **Crew:** 35 tot. (civilian) + 18 salvage party + 50 passengers

AUXILIARIES *(continued)*

Remarks: 2,781 grt/1,140 dwt. Commercial version of Russian Navy salvage tug class, purchased in 1997 from Far Eastern Shipping Co. (FESCO), Vladivostok, and refitted at Shanghai, apparently for the PLAN.

Hull systems: Very powerful tug with constant-tension highline personnel rescue system, salvage pumps, firefighting equipment, and complete diving gear, capable of supporting divers to 60-m depths from two stations. Has 94-ton bollard pull and is equipped with one 60-ton and one 30-ton towing winch. An NK-300 submersible television camera system is installed. Has four 500-m^3/hr firefighting pumps. Carries one each of the Project 1393A, 1394A, and 338PKV motorboats. Has three cargo holds (400 m^3 aft, 300 m^3 forward, and 120 m^3 rescue equipment stowage). Can carry 182 tons of potable water.

♦ **1 Kansha-class salvage ship [ARS]**
Bldr: Zhonghua SY, Shanghai (In serv. 7-81)

HAILAO . . .

D: 1,400 tons (fl) **S:** 13.5 kts **Dim:** 69.9 × 10.5 × 3.6
A: . . . **Electronics:** Radar: . . .
M: 2 Type 8300ZC diesels; 2 props; 2,200 bhp **Range:** 2,400/13.5

Remarks: Carries a French-supplied SM-358-S salvage submersible: 7 m overall, with 300-m working depth. Has one 5-ton crane forward and a 2-ton crane aft. Operates in East Sea Fleet.

♦ **4 Tuzhong-class salvage tugs [ARS]**
Bldr: Zhonghua SY, Shanghai (In serv. late 1970s)

T 154 T 710 T 830 T 890

Tuzhong-class T 710 *Ships of the World*

D: 3,600 tons (fl) **S:** 18.5 kts **Dim:** 84.90 (77.00 pp) × 14.00 × 5.50
A: none **Electronics:** Radar: 1 Fin Curve nav. (see Remarks)
M: 2 Type 9 ESDZ 43/82B diesels; 2 CP props; 9,000 bhp
Range: 18,000/. . . **Crew:** approx. 60 tot.

Remarks: Powerful salvage tugs equipped for fire fighting and emergency repairs. Have high-capacity pumps and a 35-ton-capacity towing winch. T 710 has a Type 352 (Square Tie) cruise-missile fire-control radar on the foremast, possibly for weapons trials purposes. There is provision to install at least two twin 37-mm AA mounts.

♦ **3 Yanting-class salvage ships [ARS]** (In serv. 1972–74)

HAILAO 456 HAILAO 520 HAILAO 523

D: 320 tons (fl) **S:** 10 kts **Dim:** 31.5 × 7.0 × 2.5
A: 2 twin 14.5-mm 93-cal. Type 82 AA **Electronics:** Radar: . . .
M: 1 Type 3D12 diesel; 1 prop; 300 bhp **Crew:** 18 tot.

Remarks: Trawler hulls adapted for salvage duties.

♦ **3 Dinghai-class salvage ships [ARS]**
Bldr: . . . (In serv. 1964–65)

HAILAO 446 HAILAO 447 HAILAO 511

D: 400 tons (fl) **S:** 11 kts **Dim:** 37.5 × 7.0 × 3.5
A: 2 twin 14.5-mm 93-cal. Type 82 AA **Electronics:** Radar: 1 Fin Curve nav.
M: 1 Type 3D12 diesel; 1 prop; 300 bhp **Crew:** 30 tot.

Remarks: Design adapted from a small cargo ship class. One hatch tended by a 2-ton boom aft. Probably equipped as diving tenders.

♦ **3 Dajiang-class submarine tenders [AS]**
Bldr: Hudong SY, Shanghai (In serv. 1976–80)

121 CHANGXINGDAO 302 CHONGMINGDAO 506 YONGXINGDAO

Chongmingdao (302) JMSDF, via *Ships of the World,* 2-01

Changxingdao (121) 92 Wing Det., RAAF, 1994

D: 10,087 tons (fl) **S:** 20 kts **Dim:** 156.2 × 20.6 × 6.8 **A:** none
Electronics: Radar: 2 Fin Curve; 1 Type 354 (Eye Shield) air/surf. search
M: 2 Xin Zhong–M.A.N. K9Z60/105E diesels; 2 props; . . . bhp

Remarks: Also capable of employment as general salvage vessels. Carry two Z-8 Super Frelon helicopters in a double hangar. 121 differs in not having the deep anchor recesses at the stern (evidently intended to permit a four-point moor). The huge crane forward tends two trainable cradles just forward of the bridge; the cradles are semicircular in section and support salvage-and-rescue submersibles.

The 35-ton submersibles first appeared in 1986, are 14.88 m overall and 2.60 m in diameter, and can reportedly dive to 600 m. Carrying a crew of 3–4, they can rescue up to 22 personnel from waters up to 200 m deep or can be used for underwater salvage work, being equipped with a sonar, t.v., and manipulator arm. Capable of speeds up to 4 kts, the submersibles have an endurance of 20 hours at 2 kts. They can also be used to carry up to six swimmers and have a lockout capability.

The ships share the hull and propulsion of the space support ship *Yuanwang 4* (formerly the research ship *Xiangyanghong 10*) and probably also have fin stabilizers. 506 was transferred to the Academy of Sciences in 1983 and renumbered R 327; a large log-periodic HF communications antenna was added, and the ship was evidently employed for an Antarctic research expedition. By 1989, the ship had been returned to naval service and is based at Yulin in the South Sea Fleet.

♦ **2 Dalang-II-class submarine support ships [AS]**
Bldr: Wuhu SY

428 (L: 6-96) 911 (In serv. 1986)

Dalang-II-class 911 French Navy, 11-97

D: 3,700 tons (4,200 fl) **S:** 16 kts **Dim:** 115.0 × 14.6 × 4.3
A: 2 twin 37-mm 63-cal. Type 74 AA; 2 twin 25-mm 80-cal. Type 61 AA
Electronics: Radar: 1 Type 756 nav. **M:** 2 diesels; 2 props; 4,000 bhp
Range: 8,000/14 **Crew:** approx. 200 tot.

Remarks: Primarily intended for general salvage and towing duties in support of submarines. Other than an electrohydraulic crane aft, they have few outward attributes of a repair or resupply tender and are probably intended to provide in-port berthing and command facilities.

♦ **1 Dazhi-class submarine tender [AS]**
Bldr: Hudong SY, Shanghai (In serv. 1965)

920

Dazhi-class 920

D: 5,800 tons (fl) **S:** 14 kts **Dim:** 106.7 × 15.3 × 6.1
A: 2 twin 37-mm 63-cal. Type 74 AA; 4 twin 25-mm 80-cal. Type 61 AA
Electronics: Radar: 1 Type 756 nav. **M:** 1 diesel; 1 prop; . . . bhp

AUXILIARIES *(continued)*

Remarks: The only PLAN submarine tender equipped on the Soviet scheme with spare torpedoes, a battery-charging station, and command and control facilities and for light repair duties; the others are primarily intended for submarine rescue and salvage. Assigned to the East Sea Fleet. Has not been photographed since the mid-1960s and may no longer be in service.

♦ **2 Dalang-I-class submarine rescue ships [ASR]**
Bldr: Guangzhou SY

332 (ex-122) (In serv. 1986) 503 (In serv. 11-75)

Dalang-I-class 332 Chris Delgoffe/H&L Van Ginderen, 5-00

D: 3,500 tons (4,000 fl) **S:** 16 kts **Dim:** 111.9 × 14.6 × 4.3
A: 4 twin 37-mm 63-cal. Type 74 AA; 2 twin 14.5-mm 93-cal. Type 82 AA
Electronics: Radar: 1 Fin Curve nav. **M:** 2 diesels; 2 props; 4,000 bhp
Range: 8,000/14 **Crew:** approx. 180 tot.

Remarks: Primarily intended for general salvage and towing duties in support of submarines. Have nothing in common with the Dalang-II class. 332 differs from 503 in having a larger, more elaborate superstructure and a rectangular stack; she also carries a submersible decompression chamber in an A-frame gantry to port.

♦ **1 Hudong-class submarine rescue ship [ASR]**
Bldr: Hudong SY, Shanghai (In serv. 1969)

Haijiu 512 (ex-J 301)

Hudong-class Haijiu 512 Ross Gillett, 9-84

D: 5,000 tons (fl) **S:** 15 kts **Dim:** 95.0 × 17.0 × 4.5
A: 3 twin 37-mm 63-cal. Type 74 AA; 2 twin 14.5-mm 93-cal. Type 82 AA
Electronics: Radar: 1 Fin Curve nav.
M: 1 diesel; 1 prop; 3,600 bhp **Range:** 5,000/12

Remarks: Has a large gantry over the stern for lowering a submarine rescue chamber and is equipped with stern-quarter anchors to permit a four-point moor.

♦ **2 Dazhou-class submarine rescue ships [ASR]**
Bldr: . . . . . . (In serv. 1976–77)

Haijou 502 Haijou 504

D: 1,100 tons (fl) **S:** 18 kts **Dim:** 79.0 × 9.5 × 2.6
A: 1 twin 37-mm 63-cal. Type 74 AA; 2 twin 14.5-mm 93-cal. Type 82 AA
Electronics: Radar: 1 Fin Curve nav.
M: 2 diesels; 2 props; . . . bhp **Crew:** approx. 120 tot.

Remarks: Both assigned to South Sea Fleet, where they have also been employed in intelligence gathering. Flush-decked, low-freeboard ships resembling hydrographic survey ships and having no obvious submarine rescue equipment visible.

♦ **8 Hujiu-class seagoing tugs [ATA]** Bldr: . . . (In serv. 1980s)

147 155 622 711 717 837 842 843

D: 750 tons (fl) **S:** 13.5 kts **Dim:** 49.0 (44.5 pp) × 9.5 × 3.7
A: none **Electronics:** Radar: 1 Type 756 nav.; 1 Fin Curve nav.
M: 2 LVP 24 diesels; 2 CP props; 1,800 bhp **Electric:** 336 kVA
Range: 2,200/13.5; 1,100/9 (towing) **Fuel:** 135 tons

♦ **2 Dinghai-class seagoing tugs [ATA]**
Bldr: Wuhu SY (In serv. late 1970s)

717 837

D: 1,472 tons (fl) **S:** 14 kts **Dim:** 60.22 × 11.60 × 4.44
A: none **Electronics:** Radar: 1 Type 756 nav.
M: 2 diesels; 2 props; 2,460 hp **Range:** 7,200/14
Crew: 7 officers, 49 enlisted

Dinghai-class 837 French Navy, 11-97

Remarks: 980.28 grt. Class also built for civil use. Have a 25-ton-capacity towing winch and are equipped for fire fighting. One sister transferred to Bangladesh Navy in 5-84. 837 is assigned to the East Sea Fleet.

♦ **17 Soviet Gromovoy-class seagoing tugs [ATA]**
Bldr: China (In serv. early 1960s)

149 166 680 684 802 811 814 822 827
156 167 683 716 809 813 817 824

Gromovoy-class 802—in refit 7-89

D: 795 tons (890 fl) **S:** 11 kts **Dim:** 45.7 (41.5 pp) × 9.45 × 4.6
A: 2 twin 12.7-mm or 14.5-mm mg/AA
Electronics: Radar: 1 Fin Curve, Type 756, or Oki X-NE-12 nav.
M: 2 diesels; 2 props; 1,200 bhp
Range: 7,000/7 **Fuel:** 175 tons **Crew:** 30 tot.

Remarks: Soviet commercial tug design, built under license. 149–167 operate in North Sea Fleet, 680–716 in the South Sea Fleet, and the others in the East Sea Fleet.

♦ **4 Soviet Roslavl-class seagoing tugs [ATA]** (In serv. 1958–65)

J 120 Haituo 302 Haituo 403 854

Roslavl-class 854 Chris Delgoffe/H&L Van Ginderen, 5-00

D: 750 tons (fl) **S:** 11 kts **Dim:** 44.5 × 9.5 × 3.5
A: 2 twin 14.5-mm 93-cal. Type 82 AA **Electronics:** Radar: 1 . . . nav.
M: 2 diesels, electric drive; 2 props; 1,200 bhp
Range: 6,000/11 **Fuel:** 90 tons **Crew:** 28 tot.

Remarks: One was transferred from the USSR; the others were built in China circa 1964–65. Some sources indicate that as many as 19 may be in naval service.

♦ **9 or more Fuzhou-class water tankers [AWT]**
Bldr: Hudong SY, Shanghai (In serv. 1964–70)

Haishui 629 Nanshui 913 Nanshui 938
Haishui 637 Nanshui 933 Nanshui 939
Haishui 644 Nanshui 937 Nanshui 940

D: 1,200 tons (fl) **S:** 10–12 kts **Dim:** 60.0 (55.0 pp) × 9.0 × 3.5
A: 2 twin 25-mm 80-cal. Type 61 AA; 2 twin 14.5-mm 93-cal. Type 82 AA
Electronics: Radar: 1 Fin Curve or Type 756 nav.
M: 1 diesel; 1 prop; 600 bhp **Crew:** 30 tot.

AUXILIARIES *(continued)*

Fuzhou-class water tanker Nanshui 938 Giorgio Arra, 1996

Remarks: Also used by the PLAN in a transport oiler version. Lack raised cargo expansion tank top amidships. Cargo: approx. 600 tons. Some East Sea Fleet (Haishui) units are not armed.

♦ **4 Leizhou-class water tankers [AWT]**
Bldr: . . . . . . (In serv. early 1960s)

HAISHUI 412 HAISHUI 555 HAISHUI 558 HAISHUI 645

Leizhou-class water tanker Haishui 645—without armament
Chris Delgoffe/H&L Van Ginderen, 5-00

D: 900 tons **S:** 10–12 kts **Dim:** 53.0 (48.0 pp) × 9.8 × 3.0
A: 2 twin 37-mm 62-cal. Type 74 AA; 2 single 14.5-mm 93-cal. AA
M: 1 diesel; 1 prop; 600 bhp **Crew:** 30 tot.

Remarks: Five sisters serve as fuel tankers and can be distinguished by their raised cargo expansion trunks down the centerline of the welldeck. East Sea Fleet unit *Haishui 645* had been disarmed by 1997, and the others may have been also.

♦ **1 Shichang-class aviation training ship [AXT]**
Bldr: Qiuxin SY, Shanghai (In serv. 28-12-96)

82 SHICHANG

Sichang (82)—with flight deck configured for personnel berthing modules
RAN, 5-98

Sichang (82) Brian Morrison/H&L Van Ginderen, 5-98

D: 9,500 tons (fl) **S:** 17.5 kts **Dim:** 125.0 × 19.0 × 10.6
A: none **Electronics:** Radar: 2 Decca . . . nav.
M: 2 diesels; 2 props; . . . bhp
Range: 8,000/. . . **Crew:** 200 tot. as navigational training ship

Remarks: Officially described as a training ship and as a "national defense mobilization ship," *Shichang* was originally to have been converted from the roll-on/roll-off vehicle cargo ship *Hua Yuan Kou.* The ship is equipped with a helicopter flight deck running most of her length. A modular helicopter hangar and control space can be erected on the forward portion of the flight deck, which can also be used for the transport of up to 300 standard 20-ft. cargo containers. Space is provided for the transport of a large number of personnel, and provision was made for a 30-person staff hospital with full surgical and X-ray facilities; up to 100 medical trainees can be accommodated. There are two navigational plotting spaces, capable of holding up to 60 trainees.

♦ **1 Daxin-class naval cadet training ship [AXT]**

	Bldr	L	In serv.
81 ZHENGHE	Qiuxin SY, Shanghai	12-7-86	27-4-87

Zhenghe (81) U.S. Navy, 1994

D: 4,500 tons (5,448 fl) **S:** 20 kts (17 sust.) **Dim:** 132.07 × 16.40 × 5.30
A: 2 twin 57-mm 62-cal. Type 66 AA; 2 twin 30-mm Type 69 (AK-230) AA; 2 5-round Type 81 ASW RL
Electronics:
Radar: 2 Type 756 nav.; 1 Type 354 (Eye Shield) air search; 1 Round Ball f.c.
Sonar: EH-5 hull-mounted HF searchlight-type
M: 2 SEMT-Pielstick 6PC2-5L diesels; 2 props; 7,800 bhp
Range: 5,000/15; 10,000/. . .
Crew: 190 ship's company + 30 instructors, 180 cadets

Remarks: As completed, bore pennant V 856. Resembles a coastal passenger ship. Has a helicopter deck aft. Officially stated to employ British navigation and radar systems. Subordinated to the naval academy; has made voyages to Hawaii (1989) and the Indian Ocean. Named for Emperor Yongli's eunuch admiral, who led seven great exploratory voyages in the Indian Ocean between 1405 and 1453, traveling as far as Africa; his first voyage carried 27,000 men in 317 ships.

YARD AND SERVICE CRAFT

The number of PLAN service craft is not even approximately known. In service are a vast number of service types, such as yard oilers, tugs, barges, floating dry docks, dredges, personnel launches, and the like. No details are available.

NON-NAVAL PATROL BOATS AND CRAFT

Most patrol craft and boats in Chinese waters are not assigned to the PLAN but are rather subordinated to local Maritime Border Defense Forces, the Customs Service, the Chinese Coast Guard (about which little is known), the Ministry of Fisheries, and various police forces. They number in the thousands, and very little information has become available about any of them. A few classes for which data have been published are described and/or illustrated here.

PUBLIC SECURITY BUREAU OFFSHORE PATROL SHIPS [WPS]

♦ **2 . . . class**
Bldr: Wuzhou SY, China (In serv. 1999)

D: . . . tons **S:** . . . kts **Dim:** . . . × . . . × . . .
M: 4 Deutz 620-series, 16-cyl. diesels; 2 props; 12,000 bhp

Remarks: An order was announced in 1-99 for what are apparently two seagoing patrol ships for an agency not previously connected with ships or craft. Have Zahnradfabrik BW 755 gearboxes and Centa hydraulic engine couplings.

PATROL CRAFT [WPC]

♦ **. . . Wuting class (Project 206 and 611)**
Bldrs: Wuxi SY and Huangpu SY (In serv. 1987–. . .)

Wuting-class Project 611 patrol craft H 3101 French Navy, 11-97

D: 162 tons normal (180 fl) **S:** 17 (Project 611: 28.5) kts
Dim: 43.80 × 6.50 × 1.65 (mean)
A: 1 or 2 twin 14.5-mm 93-cal. Type 82 AA (see Remarks)
Electronics: Radar: . . .
M: 2 Deutz-MWM TBD-234 (Project 611: MTU 12V396 TB94) diesels; 2 props; 2,448 (Type 611: 4,400) bhp
Range: 1,000/15 (Project 611: 600/16) **Endurance:** 5 days **Crew:** 24 tot.

NON-NAVAL PATROL CRAFT [WPC] *(continued)*

Remarks: First Project 611 units were ordered in 12-89. Built in large numbers. Also referred to as the Huludao class. Design offered for export also. Some have a twin 25-mm mount forward and two twin 14.5-mm mounts aft; others are unarmed.

♦ **3 search-and-rescue/patrol craft**
Bldr: Guan Bee SY, Singapore (In serv. 1990–91)

Hu Jiu Sheng 1 Sui Jiu Sheng 1 Yan Jiu Sheng 1

D: 365 tons (fl) **S:** 28 kts **Dim:** 49.97 × 8.00 × 1.80
A: probably 1 twin 14.5-mm 93-cal. Type 82 AA
Electronics: Radar: 1 or 2 . . . nav.
M: 3 MTU 12V396 TB93 diesels; 3 props; 6,600 bhp **Crew:** 8 tot.

Remarks: 290 grt. Intended for search-and-rescue work, oilspill patrol, etc. All three launched 30-6-90. Probably subordinated to regional governments rather than to the PLAN.

♦ **2 Project P-58A** Bldr: Huangpu SY, Guangzhou (In serv. 1989)

Hai Guan 901 Hai Guan 902

Type P-58A customs patrol craft Hai Guan 901

D: 400 tons (fl) **S:** 28 kts **Dim:** 58.00 × 7.60 × 2.20
A: 1 twin 37-mm 63-cal. Type 74 AA; 2 twin 14.5-mm 93-cal. AA
Electronics: Radar: 1 or 2 . . . nav.
M: 4 MTU 16V396 TB93 diesels; 4 props; . . . bhp
Range: 1,000/16; 1,500/12 **Endurance:** 7 days **Crew:** . . . tot.

Remarks: Serve as Customs Force flagships in South China area. Variations of this design have been delivered to Pakistan and Algeria. The hullform is the same as that of the Hainan-class ASW patrol craft.

♦ **12 or more Huxin class**
Bldr: . . . . . . (In serv. 1980s)

Hai Guan 62 Hai Guan 233 and others

D: 165 tons (fl) **S:** 13 kts **Dim:** 28.0 × 4.2 × 1.6
A: 2 twin 14.5-mm 93-cal. Type 82 AA **Electronics:** Radar: 1 . . . nav.
M: 2 diesels; 2 props; 2,200 bhp **Range:** 400/10 **Crew:** 26 tot.

PATROL BOATS [WPB]

♦ **2 Swedish SRC 90E class**
Bldr: Storebro Bruks AB, Storebro (In serv. 1998)

D: 6.5 tons (8.5 fl) **S:** 40 kts (37 loaded) **Dim:** 111.88 (10.80 wl) × 2.90 × 0.79
A: . . . **Electronics:** Radar: 1 . . . nav.
M: 2 Saab Scania DSI-14 diesel; 1 FF-Jet FF-410 waterjet; 560 bhp (at 3,800 rpm; 340 sust.)
Range: . . ./. . . **Fuel:** 600 liters **Crew:** 2 tot.

Remarks: Purchased in 1998 for the "Chinese Coast Guard." Patrol boat version of Swedish ambulance craft; capable of carrying 1 ton of cargo in addition to 10 troops or 4–5 stretcher cases. Hulls constructed of carbon-fiber reinforced vinyl ester sandwich.

♦ **1 (+ . . .) Cougar catamarans** Bldr: . . .

D: 5 tons **S:** 35 kts **Dim:** 14.0 (13.50 wl) × 5.15 × 1.30 **A:** . . .
M: 2 MWM diesels; 2 props; 1,230 bhp **Range:** 500/35 **Crew:** 3–5 tot.

Remarks: Prototype and molds for this GRP design were delivered by Cougar Holdings, Hamble, U.K., in 2-87 for license production in China. Program status is uncertain, although at least one has been completed and assigned to the Gong Bian customs organization.

Unarmed patrol craft 03 of the Chinese Coast Guard—white hull with broad diagonal red stripe and narrow alternating blue and white stripes
French Navy, 11-97

Unarmed fisheries inspection patrol craft 603—off Shanghai
Navpic-Holland, 5-98

COLOMBIA

Republic of Colombia

ARMADA DE REPÚBLICA

Personnel (2001): Approx. 18,750 total, including 11,050 marines, 100 naval aviation, and 200 coast guard. In 8-99, a 4,000-strong Marine Riverine Brigade was formed.

Bases: Headquarters at Bogotá. Principal bases are located at Cartagena (ARC *Bolivar*) on the Atlantic coast, Bahía Málaga (ARC *Bahía Málaga*) on the Pacific coast, and Leticia on the Río Meta; smaller riverine bases are located at Puerto Leguízamo on the Río Putumayo and at Puerto Orocué and Puerto Carreño. There is a coast guard base for the San Andrés Archipelago Command at San Andrés Island and a small station at Providencia. Enlisted training is conducted at Barranquilla (ARC *Barranquilla*); warrant officer training at Barranquilla; and officer training at the naval academy at Cartagena de Indias. A new naval base may be built at El Portete near the Venezuelan border.

Organization: The chain of command runs from the Commander General of the Navy, to the Second Commander of the Navy, under whom are the Chief of Naval Operations, Chief of Logistic Operations, Chief of Material, Chief of Human Development, and Commandant of Marines. Under the Chief of Naval Operations are the Atlantic Naval Force, Pacific Naval Force, Southern Naval Force (at Leguízamo Naval Base on the Río Putumayo), Riverine Naval Force (at Barrancabermeja on the Río Magdalena), and Coast Guard Corps. The actual bases and stations are subordinated to the Chief of Logistic Operations. Under the Chief, Atlantic Naval Force (headquartered at ARC *Bolívar,* Cartagena), are subordinated the Surface and Submarine Flotillas, 1st Marine Brigade, Atlantic Air Naval Group, and Atlantic Coast Guard Group. Under the Chief, Pacific Naval Force (headquartered at ARC *Bahía Málaga*) are the 2nd Marine Brigade, Pacific Air Naval Group, and Pacific Coast Guard Group.

Naval Aviation: Fixed-wing aircraft include 2 Aero Commander, 2 Piper PA-28 Cherokee, 2 Piper PA-31 Turbo Navajo, 1 Shorts 330, and 3 Cessna Stationair liaison transports. Helicopters include at least 1 Eurocopter AS.550S-2, 2 MBB BO-105CB, and 1 Bell 206.

Marine Corps: Headquartered at Bogotá. Organized into three brigades:

- 1st Marine Brigade under command of the Atlantic Naval Force, with the 1st, 3rd, and 5th Marine Battalions, Special Forces Battalion, 31st and 33rd Counterinsurgency Battalions, 1st Naval Military Police Battalion, 1st Training Battalion, 1st Combat Service Support Battalion, and 1st Marine Training Center
- 2nd Marine Brigade (headquartered at Buenaventura) under command of the Pacific Naval Force, with the 2nd and 6th Battalions, 30th Counterinsurgency Battalion, 2nd Naval Military Police Battalion, and 2nd Marine Training Center
- River Brigade (organized 8-99, with 4,000 personnel; headquartered at Puerto Leguízamo on the Río Putumayo but under the command of the Marine Headquarters, Bogotá) with the 50th, 60th, 70th, 80th, and 90th Marine River Battalions

The 8th Independent Battalion provides security services at the Navy and Marine Corps Headquarters, Bogotá.

Note: Ship names are preceded by ARC *(Armada República de Colombia)*.

ATTACK SUBMARINES [SS]

♦ **2 German Type 209/1200 class** Bldr: Howaldtswerke, Kiel

	L	In serv.		L	In serv.
SS 28 Pijao	10-4-74	17-4-75	SS 29 Tayrona	16-7-74	18-7-75

Pijao (SS 28)—with *Tayrona* (SS 29) on the opposite side of the pier
Hartmut Ehlers, 6-95

ATTACK SUBMARINES [SS] *(continued)*

D: 1,000 tons std., 1,180 tons surf./1,285 tons sub.
S: 11.5 kts surf./22 kts sub. (1 hr) **Dim:** 56.10 × 6.20 × 5.50 (surf.)
A: 8 bow 533-mm TT (14 tot. SST Mod. 0 wire-guided torpedoes)
Electronics:
Radar: 1 Thales Calypso-II nav./surf. search
Sonar: STN Atlas Elektronik CSU-3-2 suite with PRS-3-4 passive-ranging; Thales AUUD-1C acoustic intercept
EW: Thales DR-2000U intercept
M: 4 MTU 12V493 TY60, 600-bhp diesels, 4 A.E.G. 405-kw generators, 1 Siemens motor; 1 prop; 5,000 shp (3,670 kw)
Range: 8,000/8, 11,300/4 snorkel; 460/4 sub. **Fuel:** 85 tons
Endurance: 30 days **Crew:** 7 officers, 24 enlisted

Remarks: Ordered 1971. Both refitted beginning 11-90 in Germany at Howaldtswerke (HDW) facility at Gaarden, with SS 28 completing 30-5-91 and SS 29 in 8-91.
Hull systems: The four 120-cell batteries weigh a total of 257 tons and produce 11,500 amp-hr. Maximum operating depth: 250 m.
Combat systems: The Thales M8 Mod. 24 combat data system is carried, with the Mk 8 Mod. 24 torpedo f.c.s. Have Type AS C18 attack periscope and Type BS 19 search periscope.

MIDGET SUBMARINES [SSM]

♦ **2 Italian S.X. 506 midgets** Bldr: COS.M.O.S, Livorno (In serv. 1972–74)

SS 20 Intrépido SS 21 Indomable

Indomable (SS 21) Hartmut Ehlers, 10-90

D: 58 tons surf./70 tons sub. **S:** 8.5 kts surf./7 kts sub. **Dim:** 23.0 × 2.0 × 4.0
M: 1 diesel generator set, electric drive; 1 prop; 300 shp
Range: 1,200/7 surf.; 60/7 sub. **Crew:** 5 tot. + 8 frogmen

Remarks: Sisters *Roncador* (SS 23) and *Quitasueño* (SS 24) were out of service by the mid-1980s. Cargo capacity: 2,050 kg of explosives, 8 fully equipped combat swimmers, and 2 submarine vehicles (for the swimmers) supported by a fixed system on lower part of the hull, one on each side. Of little practical use except for training, due to short range and meager performance. They are served by the special floating dry dock/tender *Mayor Jaime Arias* (DF 170).

FRIGATES [FF]

♦ **4 FS 1500 class** Bldr: Howaldtswerke, Kiel, Germany

	Laid down	L	In serv.
FM 51 Almirante Padilla	3-81	8-1-82	31-10-83
FM 52 Caldas	6-81	14-6-82	14-2-84
FM 53 Antioquia	22-6-81	28-8-82	30-4-84
FM 54 Independiente	22-6-81	21-1-83	27-7-84

Almirante Padilla (FM 51) Peruvian Navy, 2000

D: 1,600 tons (1,850 fl) **S:** 27 kts **Dim:** 95.3 (90.0 pp) × 11.3 × 3.5 (hull)
A: 8 MM 40 Exocet SSM; 1 76-mm 62-cal. OTOBreda DP; 1 twin 40-mm 70-cal. OTOBreda AA; 2 triple 324-mm Mk 32 ASW TT; 1 MBB BO-105CB or AS.550S-2 liaison helicopter
Electronics:
Radar: 1 . . . nav.; 1 Thales Sea Tiger air search; 1 Thales Castor-IIB f.c.
Sonar: STN Atlas Elektronik ASO 4-5 hull-mounted
EW: Argo Phoenix AC-672 intercept; Thales SUSIE analyzer; Phillips/EMI Scimitar deception jammer; Telegon HFD/F; 2 Matra Défense Dagaie decoy RL
M: 4 MTU 20V1163 TB82 diesels; 2 CP props; 23,000 bhp (21,000 sust.)
Electric: 2,120 kw **Range:** 5,000/14 **Fuel:** 200 tons **Crew:** 92 tot.

Remarks: Ordered 1980. Formerly typed CM as *Corbetas Misileras* (missile corvettes) but were retyped FM as *Fragatas Misileras Ligeras* (light missile frigates) in 1999. FM 51 and FM 52 were refitted at Kiel during 1992–97; the other two were refitted at Cartagena Navy Yard, with work on FM 53 having begun during 7-98.
Hull systems: Have fin stabilizers. Engines were a new model not previously installed in a ship. Were to be re-engined beginning in 1994, but funds were not available. All four have had the helicopter deck extended to permit operating Bell 212 and Bell 412P helicopters.
Combat systems: Have the Thales TAVITAC combat direction system, with Thales Vega II f.c.s. for the 76-mm gun and two Matra Défense Canopus optronic directors. The Israeli Barak SAM system has long been planned for installation forward of the bridge and abreast the hangar but has not yet been purchased. Normally carry only four MM 40 Exocet missiles.

PATROL SHIPS [PS]

♦ **1 U.S. Cherokee-class former fleet tug**
Bldr: Charleston SB & DD, Charleston, S.C.

	Laid down	L	In serv.
RM 73 Sebastian de Belalcazar (ex-*Carib,* ATF 82)	7-9-42	7-2-43	24-7-43

D: 1,235 tons (1,675 fl) **S:** 15 kts **Dim:** 62.48 (59.44 wl) × 11.73 × 4.67
A: 1 76.2-mm 50-cal. Mk 26 DP **Electronics:** Radar: 1 . . . nav.
M: diesel-electric: 4 G.M. 12-278 (RM 74: Busch-Sulzer BS-539) diesels; 1 prop; 3,000 shp
Electric: 300 kw **Range:** 7,000/15; 15,000/8 **Fuel:** 363 tons **Crew:** 75 tot.

Remarks: Although reported stricken in 1987, were back in service during 1990. RM 72 was originally transferred on loan in 1961 and purchased 31-3-78; RM 73 was reactivated from the U.S. Maritime Administration National Defense Reserve Fleet

Independiente (FM 54) Peruvian Navy, 2000

PATROL SHIPS [PS] *(continued)*

Pedro de Heredia (RM 72)—since stricken Colombian Navy, 1999

and transferred 15-3-79. Used as patrol and rescue ships. The Mk 26 gun mounting uses a Mk 22 gun; it is locally controlled by ringsights.
Disposals: Near-sister, *Abnaki*-class *Rodrigo de Bastedas* (RM 74; ex-*Hidatsa,* ATF 102) was stricken during 1999, and *Bahía Solano* (RM 76; ex-*Jacarilla,* ATF 104) was retired in 1987. *Pedro de Heredia* (RM 72; ex-Choctaw, ATF 70) had been stricken by 6-01.

PATROL CRAFT [PC]

Note: The Colombian Navy hopes eventually to operate eight Riverine Combat Elements from seven Advanced Riverine Bases. The groups will be comprised of a total of eight 10.7- to 12.4-m command craft, 24 22-ft. Boston Whaler Piranha patrol craft, and eight ex-U.S. Army utility landing craft acting as logistic support craft and mother ships.

Additional patrol craft and patrol boats are assigned to the Coast Guard (q.v.).

♦ 1 Sargento 2° Julio Correa Hernández–class river patrol craft
Bldr: . . . (In serv. . . .)

Sargento 2° Julio Correa Hernández (ex-. . .)

D: 120 tons (fl) **S:** . . . kts **Dim:** 32.0 × 8.0 × . . .
A: 7 single 12.7-mm mg **Electronics:** Radar: 1 . . . nav.
M: 2 . . . diesels; 2 props; . . . bhp
Range: . . ./. . . **Endurance:** 45 days **Crew:** 15 tot. + 45 passengers

Remarks: Completed an 11-month conversion in 8-97 to serve as command ship for Piranha-class patrol launches of the Flotilla Fluvial de Oriente on the Meta and Orinoco Rivers. Hull and superstructure are covered over 80% of their area with bulletproof plate. Former commercial riverine tug.

♦ 2 Río Hacha–class large river patrol craft
Bldr: Union Industrial de Barranquilla, Barranquilla (In serv. 1956)

CF 135 Río Hacha CF 137 Arauca

Arauca (CF 137)—with old number

D: 170 tons (184 fl) **S:** 13 kts **Dim:** 47.25 × 8.23 × 1.0
A: 2 single 76.2-mm 50-cal. Mk 26 DP; 4 single 20-mm AA
M: 2 Caterpillar diesels; 2 props; 800 bhp **Range:** 1,000/12 **Crew:** 27–43 tot.

Remarks: Do not have radars. The Mk 26 gun mountings use Mk 22 guns; they are locally controlled by ringsights. Operate on the Río Putumayo. Sister *Leticia* was disarmed and equipped as a hospital boat.

PATROL BOATS [PB]

♦ 9 U.S. 40-foot river patrol boats
Bldr: Bender SB & Repair, Mobile, Ala. (In serv. 10-93)

LR 181 Tenerife LR 184 Orocué LR 187 Monclart
LR 182 Tarapacá LR 185 Calamar LR 188 Caucaya
LR 183 Mompox LR 186 Magangué LR 189 Mitú

D: 21 tons (fl) **S:** 29 kts **Dim:** 12.40 × 2.89 × 0.61
A: 1 twin and 1 single 12.7-mm M2 mg; 2 single 7.62-mm mg; 1 40-mm Mk 19 grenade launcher

40-ft. river patrol boat Bender, 10-9

Electronics: Radar: 1 Raytheon 1900 nav.
M: 2 Caterpillar 3208TA diesels; 2 Rolla surface-piercing props; 850 bhp
Range: 500/15 **Fuel:** 1.9 tons (2217 liters) **Crew:** 5 tot. + 12 troops

Remarks: Intended to conduct antidrug trade patrol on Colombian rivers. Aluminum construction. Can be transported in a C-130 transport. Have a GPS receiver, VHF AM and FM radios, and an HF radio. The propellers are mounted within tunnels.

♦ 14 U.S. PBR Mk II–class patrol craft
Bldr: Uniflite, Bellingham, Wash. (In serv. 1968–71)

LR I Río Magdalena LR III Río Sinu LR V Río San Jorge
LR II Río Cauca LR IV Río Atrato 9 others

Río San Jorge (LR V) Hartmut Ehlers, 11-9

D: 8.9 tons (fl) **S:** 30 kts (24 sust.) **Dim:** 9.73 × 3.53 × 0.81
A: 1 twin 12.7-mm mg; 1 7.62-mm mg; 1 60-mm mortar
Electronics: Radar: 1 Raytheon 1900 nav.
M: 2 G.M. 6V53T diesels; 2 Jacuzzi waterjets; 550 bhp (296 sust.)
Range: 150/22 **Crew:** 6 tot.

Remarks: Glass-reinforced plastic construction, plastic armor. First five transferred in 11-89, nine more in 10-93. The first five, LR I–LR V, are ex-U.S. Navy hull 31RP6886, 31RP7121, 31RP7128, 31RP7129, and 31RP7130, while the others were new. Another 10 of an 11-m variant may be acquired; they would carry thre 12.7-mm mg, one 60-mm mortar, and a 40-mm grenade launcher.

♦ 137 U.S. 22-foot Piranha class
Bldr: Boston Whaler, Rockland, Mass., and Edgewater, Fla. (In serv. 1990–2000)

Dim: 1.5 tons light (2 fl) **S:** 35 kts **Dim:** 6.81 × 2.26 × . . .
A: 2 single 12.7-mm mg **Electronics:** Radar: 1 SPS-66 nav.
M: 2 outboard motors; 250 bhp **Range:** 167/40 **Crew:** 3–4 tot.

Remarks: Glass-reinforced plastic construction, for riverine patrol use. The first five were transferred in 1990, and three additional units were ordered in 12-91; another 51 ordered in 3-93 were delivered in 10-93. An additional 78 units ordered in 199 may be somewhat larger, as they are intended to transport 12 troops each.

♦ 10 Diligente-series river patrol launches
Bldr: Ast. Naval, Cartagena (In serv. 1952–54)

LR 121 Diligente LR 126 Humberto Cortés
LR 122 Juan Lucio LR 127 Calibio
LR 123 Alfonso Vargas LR 128 Carlos Galindo
LR 124 Fritz Hagale LR 129 Valerosa
LR 125 Vengadora LR 130 Luchadora

D: 33 tons (fl) **S:** 13 kts **Dim:** 23.2 × 3.7 × 0.8
A: 1 or 2 single 20-mm 70-cal. Oerlikon AA; 0 or 4 single 81-mm mortars
M: 2 G.M. Detroit Diesel 4-71 diesels; 2 props; 280 bhp **Crew:** 10 tot.

Remarks: Reactivated from storage during mid-1990s to combat drug trade. Units with two 20-mm guns have no mortars. Not all are identical. Do not have radars.

AMPHIBIOUS WARFARE CRAFT

♦ 8 ex-U.S. Army LCU 1466–class utility landing craft [LCU]
(In serv. 1954)

TM 246 Morrosquillo (ex-LCU . . .)
TM 247 Uruba (ex-*Carolina,* LCU 1543)
TM 248 Bahía Honda (ex-. . . . . .)
TM 249 Bahía Potrete (ex-*Chattanooga,* LCU 1583)
TM 251 Bahía Solano (ex-LCU . . .)
TM 252 Bahía Cupica (ex-LCU . . .)
TM 253 Bahía Utria (ex-LCU . . .)
TM 254 Bahía Málaga (ex-LCU . . .)

AMPHIBIOUS WARFARE CRAFT *(continued)*

Morrosquillo (TM 246) Colombian Navy, 1999

D: 180 tons light (347 fl) **S:** 8 kts **Dim:** 35.08 × 10.36 × 1.60 (aft)
A: 2 single 12.7-mm mg **Electronics:** Radar: 1 Raytheon . . . nav.
M: 3 Gray Marine 64 YTL diesels; 3 props; 675 bhp **Electric:** 40 kw
Range: 1,200/6 (700/7 loaded) **Fuel:** 11 tons **Crew:** 11 tot.

Remarks: First four transferred from U.S. Army reserve stocks in 10-90 and became operational in 1-92; the others were transferred during 1992. Cargo: 150 tons or 300 troops on the 15.8 × 9.0-m deck with a 4.3 m-wide bow ramp. Used as troop transports and tenders to patrol craft on the river system.

♦ 2 Ocho de Octubre–class ramped personnel landing craft [LCP]
Bldr: Swiftships, Inc., Morgan City, La. (In serv. 1992)

. . . Ocho de Octubre . . . Veintisiete de Octubre

D: 6 tons **S:** . . . kts **Dim:** 13.6 × . . . × . . .
A: 1 12.7-mm mg; 2 single 7.62-mm mg
M: 2 . . . . . . diesels; 2 props **Crew:** 4 tot. + 8 marines

Remarks: GRP construction. Are reportedly similar to the Colombian Sea Truck–type landing craft.

Note: Former U.S. LCM(8) landing craft *B. Sapzurro* (240) is assigned to the coast guard.

♦ 2 Sea Truck–type landing craft [LCVP]
Bldr: Rotork, U.K. (In serv. 1989–90)

PM 107 Jamie Rook PM 108 Manuela Saenz

D: 9 tons (fl) **S:** 25 kts **Dim:** 12.7 × 3.2 × 0.7
A: 1 12.7-mm mg; 2 single 7.62-mm mg
Electronics: Radar: 1 . . . nav.
M: 2 Caterpillar diesels; 2 props; 240 bhp

Remarks: Based at Cartagena and used for local patrol and logistics support duties. GRP construction. Have a small bow ramp and can carry light vehicles. Cargo capacity: 4 tons.

♦ 4 ex-U.S. LCVP landing craft [LCVP]

3602 Altair 3603 Castor 3604 Pollux 3605 Vega

D: 13 tons (fl) **S:** 9 kts **Dim:** 10.90 × 3.21 × 1.04 (aft)
M: 1 Gray Marine 64HN9 diesel; 225 bhp **Range:** 110/9

Remarks: Transferred late in 1993. Built in late 1960s. Glass-reinforced plastic hulls. Can carry 36 troops or 3.5 tons cargo. Cargo deck is 5.24 × 2.29 m, with 2.00-m-wide access through the bow ramp.

AUXILIARIES

♦ 2 Malpelo-class oceanographic research ships [AGOR]
Bldr: Martin Jansen Werft, Leer, Germany (In serv. 24-7-81)

BO 155 Providencia BO 156 Malpelo

Providencia (BO 155) Colombian Navy, 1999

D: 1,090 tons (fl) **S:** 13 kts **Dim:** 50.3 (44.0 pp) × 10.0 × 4.0
M: 2 M.A.N. 6-cyl. diesels; 1 Kort-nozzle prop; 1,570 bhp
Range: 16,000/11.5 **Crew:** 5 officers, 16 enlisted + 6 scientists

Remarks: 830 grt. Operated for DIMAR (Dirección General Maritima Portuario), BO 155 for geophysical research and BO 156 for fisheries. White painted, naval manned. Have a bow-thruster and flapped Becker rudder. Prime contractor was Ferrostaal, Kiel.

♦ 2 ex-German Type 701A patrol boat tenders [AGP]
Bldr: Flensburger Werft, Flensburg

	Laid down	L	In serv.
BL 161 Cartagena de Indias (ex-*Lüneburg,* A 1411)	8-7-64	3-5-65	31-1-66
BL 162 Buenaventura (ex-*Nienburg,* A 1416)	16-11-65	28-7-66	1-8-68

Cartagena de Indias (BL 161) Findler & Winter, 10-97

Buenaventura (BL 162) Findler & Winter, 5-98

D: 1,896 tons (3,483 fl) **S:** 17 kts **Dim:** 104.15 (98.00 pp) × 13.22 × 4.29
A: 2 twin 40-mm 70-cal. Bofors AA
Electronics: Radar: 1 Kelvin-Hughes 14/9 nav.
M: 2 Maybach MD 874 diesels; 2 CP props; 5,600 bhp
Electric: 1,935 kw tot. **Range:** 3,000/17; 3,200/14 **Crew:** 71–82 tot.

Remarks: BL 161, decommissioned from the German Navy 2-6-94, was initially offered to Colombia in 1995 and declined and then was offered to Kazakhstan, Spain, and Peru; the second offer was accepted late in 1996, and the ship was purchased 27-6-97 for recommissioning 2-11-97 after a refit at HDW, Kiel. BL 162 was decommissioned from the German Navy 26-3-98, transferred the same date, and departed Germany for Colombia 29-5-98. They are used as offshore command and logistics support ships for patrol craft.
Hull systems: Configured to carry more than 1,100 tons of cargo, including 640 tons fuel, 205 tons ammunition, 100 tons spare parts (10,000 separate items), and 131 tons fresh water, plus 267 m^3 of refrigerated stores. Equipped with fin stabilizers, one 3-ton and two 2-ton cranes, and a small helicopter deck.
Combat systems: Lead-computing optical directors are furnished for the 40-mm mounts.

♦ 1 hydrographic survey ship [AGS]
Bldr: Lindigoverken, Lindigo, Sweden (L: 28-5-54)

BO 154 Gorgona

D: 560 tons (574 fl) **S:** 13 kts **Dim:** 41.15 × 9.00 × 2.83
A: 2 single 12.7-mm mg **Electronics:** Radar: 1 . . . nav.
M: 2 Nohab diesels; 2 props; 900 bhp **Crew:** 45 tot.

Remarks: Former lighthouse tender, laid up in the early 1980s; began reactivation in late 1990 for further service as a survey ship, completing during 1992. May have been re-engined.

♦ 1 ex-U.S. hydrographic survey ship [AGS]
Bldr: Niagara SB, Buffalo, N.Y. (In serv. 11-11-43)

BO 153 Quindio (ex-U.S. YFR 433)

D: 380 tons (600 fl) **Dim:** 40.4 × 9.10 × 2.5
M: 2 Union diesels; 2 props; 600 bhp **Crew:** 2 officers, 15 enlisted

Remarks: Former refrigerated stores lighter, leased 7-64 and purchased 31-3-78. Used on coastal survey duties.

♦ 1 sail training ship [AXT]
Bldr: Celaya, Bilbao, Spain (In serv. 7-9-68)

Gloria

D: 1,150 tons (1,300 fl) **S:** 10.5 kts (under power)
Dim: 76.00 (64.7 wl) × 10.6 × 6.6
M: 1 diesel; 530 bhp—1,400 m^2 max. sail area (bark-rigged)
Endurance: 60 days **Crew:** 10 officers, 41 enlisted + 88 cadets

AUXILIARIES *(continued)*

Gloria A. D. Baker III, 6-00

SERVICE CRAFT

♦ 2 (+ 10) Nodriza-class riverine cargo lighters [YF]
Bldr: Cartagena Naval SY (In serv. 12-98 to . . .-00)

146 147

D: 260 tons **S:** 9 kts **Dim:** . . . × . . . × . . .
A: 8 single 12.7-mm mg **Electronics:** Radar: 1 . . . nav.
M: 2 diesels; 2 props; 880 bhp **Crew:** 18 + 82 troops

Remarks: First two launched 9-98 and completed 12-98. Intended to provide afloat logistic support to riverine forces. As many as 40 total may be built.

♦ 1 cargo lighter [YF]
Bldr: J. J. Pattje & Zonen, Waterhuizen, the Netherlands (In serv. 1954)

TM 45 Serranilla (ex-*Tropic Ace,* ex-*Rita IV,* ex-*Gimen,* ex-*Rita,* ex-*Beth,* ex-*Silesia,* ex-*Hanna,* ex-*Else II*)

D: approx. 400 tons (fl) **S:** . . . kts **Dim:** 39.27 × 6.67 × 2.49
M: 1 Burmeister & Wain Alpha diesel; 1 prop; . . . bhp

Remarks: 225 grt/265 dwt. Former drug-runner, captured by the Colombian Navy and used as a local stores transport.

♦ 1 floating dry dock/midget submarine tender [YFDL]

DF 170 Mayor Jaime Arias

Mayor Jaime Arias (DF 170) Hartmut Ehlers, 6-95

D: 700 tons (fl) **Capacity:** 165 tons **Dim:** 42.7 × . . . × . . .

Remarks: Employed primarily as the mother ship for Colombia's two midget submarines.

Note: On loan to the Compañía Colombiana de Astilleros Limitada (CONASTIL) are the former Colombian Navy service craft *Capitán Rodriguez Zamora* (ex-U.S. Navy floating dry dock ARD 28), *Victor Cabillos* (ex-U.S. dry dock service craft YFND 16), and *Mantilla* (ex-U.S. floating repair shop YR 66).

♦ 1 ex-U.S. LCPL Mk 11–class personnel launch [YFL]
Bldr: Miami Beach Yacht Co., Miami Beach, Fla. (In serv. 1966)

. . . . . . (ex-36PL6465)

D: 9.75 tons light (13 fl) **S:** 19 kts **Dim:** 10.98 (9.26 pp) × 3.97 × 1.13
Electronics: Radar: 1 SPS-59 (Canadian Marconi LN-66) nav.
M: 1 G.M. 8V71 TI diesel; 350–425 bhp
Range: 150/19 **Fuel:** 630 liters **Crew:** 3 tot. + 17 passengers

Remarks: Donated to Colombia in 1993, having been stricken from the USN in 1990 at San Diego. Glass-reinforced plastic construction.

♦ 1 admiral's yacht [YFL]

Contralmirante Bell Salter

Remarks: Based at Cartagena. No characteristics data available.

♦ 1 Cienaga de Mallorquin–class buoy tender [YGL]
Bldr: UNIAL, Barranquilla (In serv. 9-5-97)

. . . Cienaga de Mallorquin

D: 162 tons (fl) **S:** . . . kts **Dim:** 21.00 × 7.0 × 1.20
M: 2 G.M. Detroit Diesel 6-71N diesels; 348 bhp

Remarks: Has a 6.5-ton-capacity navigational aids buoy crane. Based at Barranquilla.

♦ 2 riverine hospital craft [YH]
Bldr: Cartagena Naval DY (In serv. 1956)

BD 33 Socorro (ex-*Alberto Gomez,* TF 53)
BD 35 Teniente Hernando Gutierrez (ex-TF 52)

Socorro (BD 33) Colombian Navy, 1999

D: 70 tons **S:** 9 kts **Dim:** 25.00 × 5.50 × 0.75
A: 2 single 12.7-mm mg **M:** 2 G.M. diesels; 2 props; 270 bhp
Range: 650/9 **Crew:** 12 tot. + medical staff

Remarks: Originally built as riverine transports for 56 troops; now used as mobile surgeries.

♦ 1 Río Hacha–class riverine hospital ship [YH]
Bldr: Union Industrial de Barranquilla, Barranquilla (In serv. 1956)

BD 36 Leticia

D: 170 tons (184 fl) **S:** 13 kts **Dim:** 47.25 × 8.23 × 1.00
A: 2 single 12.7-mm mg **M:** 2 Caterpillar diesels; 2 props; 800 bhp
Range: 1,000/12 **Crew:** 39 tot. + 6 medical staff

Remarks: Former river gunboat. Sister to the two *Río Hacha*–class river gunboats. Has a six-bed ward, surgery facilities, etc.

♦ 1 ex-U.S. small harbor tug [YTL] Bldr: Henry C. Grebe (In serv. 2-9-43)

RM 73 Teniente Ricardo Sorzano (ex-YTL 231)

D: 70 tons (80 fl) **S:** 9 kts **Dim:** 20.2 × 5.2 × 1.5
M: 1 Cooper-Bessemer diesel; 240 bhp **Electric:** 15 kw
Fuel: 7 tons **Crew:** 10 tot.

Remarks: Loaned in 1963, purchased 31-3-78. On more or less permanent loan to the Compañía Columbiana de Astilleros Limitada (CONASTIL) dockyard, Cartagena, but also available to support naval operations.

♦ 2 river tug/transports [YTL]
Bldr: Servicio Naviero Armada República de Colombia, Puerto Leguízamo

RR 92 Igaraparaña (In serv. 6-85) RR 95 Mana Casias (In serv. 6-86)

D: 104 grt **S:** 7 kts **Dim:** 31.2 × 7.2 × 0.9
M: 2 G.M. 4-71 diesels; 2 props; 230 bhp
Range: 1,600/7 **Crew:** 1 officer, 6 enlisted

♦ 5 Capitán Castro–class riverine tugs [YTL]

RR 81 Capitán Castro
RR 84 Capitán Alvaro Ruis
RR 86 Capitán Rigoberto Giraldo
RR 87 Teniente Vladimir Valeck
RR 88 Teniente Luis Bernal

D: 50 tons **S:** 9 kts **Dim:** 19.20 × 4.25 × 0.75
M: 2 G.M. 4-71 diesels; 260 bhp

Remarks: Sister *Cándido Leguízamo* (RR 82) was stricken in 1987.

♦ 10 miscellaneous service craft

NF 141 Filogonio Hichamón, RM 76 Josué Avarez, RM 93 Segiri, RM . . . Calima, RR 96 Inrida, RR . . . Mitu, TM 44 Tolú, Teniente Luis Guillermo Alcala (ex-*Joanna*), TM . . . Teniente de Navio Alejandro Bal Domero Salgado, TM . . . Teniente Primo Alcala

Remarks: Characteristics unknown; placed in service in 1981 to help combat drug traffic in the Caribbean. Many are captured former drug runners. Craft with RR- and RM-series pennants are small tugs; TM 44 is used as a diving tender and others in similar support roles.

COAST GUARD

Note: The Colombian Coast Guard is subordinated to—and operated by—the Colombian Navy.

PATROL CRAFT [WPC]

♦ 2 Juan Nepomuceno Eslava class
Bldr: Bender SB & Repair Co., Mobile, Ala.

	In serv.
GC 113 José Maria Garcia de Toledo	15-6-94
GC 114 Juan Nepomuceno Eslava	25-5-94

Juan Nepomucena Eslava (GC 114) Maritime Photographic, 6-01

D: 131 tons (fl) **S:** 28 kts **Dim:** 35.36 × 7.62 × 2.10
A: 1 25-mm 87-cal. Mk 38 Bushmaster low-angle; 2 single 12.7-mm M2 mg
Electronics: Radar: 1 Raytheon . . . nav.
M: 2 MTU . . . diesels; 2 props; . . . bhp
Range: 2,000/. . . **Crew:** 5 officers, 20 enlisted

Remarks: Used for drug detection and enforcement, search and rescue, and fisheries patrol. Have modern command and control, data processing, and equipment monitoring capabilities. Have reached 32 kts in light condition.

♦ 1 ex-Spanish Cormorán class
Bldr: Izar (formerly E.N. Bazán), Ferrol (In serv. 28-12-89)

PO 41 Espartana (ex-GC 41; ex-*Cormorán,* P 41)

Espartana (PO 41) Colombian Navy, 8-96

D: 300 tons (374 fl) **S:** 33 kts **Dim:** 55.60 × 7.59 × 1.97 (hull)
A: 1 40-mm 70-cal. Bofors AA; 1 20-mm 70-cal. Oerlikon AA
Electronics: 1 Raytheon 1620/6 nav.
M: 3 Bazán-MTU MA 16V956 TB91 diesels; 3 props; 13,500 bhp
Range: 2,000/15 **Crew:** 5 officers, 27 enlisted

Remarks: Purchased 5-3-95. Refitted at Cadiz prior to delivery. Based at San Andrés Island. Has an Alcor-C optronic director for the 40-mm gun. Launched 10-85 on speculation but was not purchased by any foreign fleet, and the ship was accepted for Spanish Navy service in 1989. Was decommissioned from the Spanish Navy in early 1994 and returned to the builder after only four years' service. A second hull was built but not completed.

♦ 2 U.S. 110-foot Commercial Cruiser class
Bldr: Swiftships, Morgan City, La.

GC 103 José Maria Palas (In serv. 10-89)
GC 104 Medardo Monzon (In serv. 4-90)

José Maria Palas (GC 103) H&L Van Ginderen, 1-96

D: 100 tons (fl) **S:** 25 kts (22 cruise) **Dim:** 33.53 × 7.62 × 2.13
A: 1 40-mm 60-cal. Mk. 3 AA; 2 single 12.7-mm mg
Electronics: Radar: 1 . . . nav.
M: 4 G.M. 12V71 TI diesels; 4 props; 2,400 bhp
Range: 1,800/15 **Fuel:** 31,608 liters **Crew:** 3 officers, 16 enlisted

Remarks: Procured via the U.S. Foreign Military Sales program. Aluminum construction. The 40-mm gun is mounted on the fantail.

♦ 1 U.S. 105-foot Commercial Cruiser class
Bldr: Swiftships, Berwick, La. (In serv. 2-83)

GC 102 C. N. Rafael del Castillo y Rada

D: 103 tons (fl) **S:** 25 kts **Dim:** 31.5 × 6.6 × 2.1
A: 1 40-mm 60-cal. U.S. Mk 3 AA; 2 single 12.7-mm mg
M: 2 MTU 12V331 TC92 diesels; 2 props; 7,000 bhp **Electric:** 113 kw
Range: 1,600/25; 2,400/15 **Crew:** 3 officers, 16 enlisted

Remarks: Sister *Carlos Alban* (AN 22) serves in the Customs Service. Aluminum construction. Had been out of service between 1986 and 1992. The 40-mm gun is mounted on the fantail.

♦ 2 ex-Spanish Lazaga class
Bldr: Izar (formerly E.N. Bazán), La Carraca, Cadiz

	L	In serv.
PO 42 Capitán Pablo José de Porto (ex-PM 116; ex-*Recalde,* P 06)	16-10-75	15-12-77
PO 43 C. T. C. I. M. Jorge Enrique Marquez Duran (ex-PM 117; ex-*Cadarso,* P 03)	8-1-75	10-7-76

C.T.C.I.M. Jorge Enrique Marquez Duran (PO 43) Maritime Photographic, 6-01

D: 275 tons (397 fl) **S:** 29.7 kts **Dim:** 57.40 (54.40 pp) × 7.60 × 2.70
A: 1 40-mm 70 cal. Bofors AA; 1 20-mm 90-cal. Oerlikon GAM-B01 AA; 2 single 12.7-mm M2 mg
Electronics: Radar: 1 Raytheon 1620/6 nav.; 1 . . . surf. search
M: 2 MTU MA-16V956 TB91 diesels; 2 props; 7,780 bhp **Electric:** 405 kVA tot.
Range: 2,260/27; 4,200/17 **Fuel:** 112 tons **Crew:** 4 officers, 35 enlisted

Remarks: Purchased 6-97; refitted at E.N. Bazán, San Fernando, Spain, and handed over on 9-9-98. Both had been decommissioned 30-6-93 from Spanish naval service and placed in reserve. During refits prior to transfer, they were rearmed, new radars were provided, and accommodations for a small number of marines were added; a 76-mm gun and its associated H.S.A. WM-22 track-while-scan radar set were removed.

♦ 2 U.S. Asheville class
Bldrs: GC 111: Peterson SB, Sturgeon Bay, Wis.; GC 112: Tacoma Boat, Tacoma, Wash.

	Laid down	L	In serv.
GC 111 Albuquerque (ex-*Welch,* PG 93)	8-8-67	25-7-68	8-9-69
GC 112 Quitasueño (ex-*Tacoma,* PG 92)	24-7-67	13-4-68	14-7-69

Quitasueño (GC 112) Hartmut Ehlers, 6-95

D: 225 tons (245 fl) **S:** 40 kts (16 cruising) **Dim:** 50.14 (46.94 wl) × 7.28 × 2.9
A: 1 76.2-mm 50-cal. Mk 34 DP—GC 112 only: 1 40-mm 70-cal. Bofors L70 AA—both: provision for 2 twin 12.7-mm mg
Electronics: Radar: 1 Canadian Marconi LN-66 nav.; 1 Raytheon 1900 nav.
M: CODOG: 1 G.E. 7LM-1500-PE 102 gas turbine; 13,300 shp (12,500 sust.); 2 Cummins VT 12-875M diesels, 1,650 bhp (1,450 sust.); 2 CP props
Electric: 100 kw **Range:** 325/35; 1,700/16 **Fuel:** 50 tons **Crew:** 25 tot.

Remarks: Leased 16-5-83. Towed to Jonathan Corp., Norfolk, Va., for reactivation for use on antidrug patrol. GC 112 is based at San Andrés Island. Offer of two more not taken up due to difficulty of maintaining engineering plants on this pair, which are generally inoperative. The Mk 63 gun f.c.s., with SPG-50 f.c. radar, has been removed, leaving the 76.2-mm gun with local control capability only. The U.S. Mk 3 40-mm gun formerly mounted on the fantail of GC 111 has been removed to allow for the space to be configured as a small helicopter deck; the gun on the fantail of GC 112 is now of a later Bofors model. Transferred to the coast guard in 1992.

COAST GUARD *(continued)*

PATROL BOATS [WPB]

♦ 2 261-B class Bldr: Mako Marine, Miami, Fla. (In serv. 12-92)

GC 26 Escorpión GC 27 Libra

D: . . . tons **S:** 24 kts **Dim:** 7.92 × 2.59 × 0.61
A: 1 12.7-mm M2 mg; 2 single 7.62-mm M-60 mg
Electronics: Radar: 1 Raytheon R40X nav.
M: 2 Evinrude gasoline outboards; 350 bhp **Range:** . . ./. . . **Crew:** 3 tot.

Remarks: GRP hulled. Can be carried aboard a C-130 Hercules.

♦ 2 U.S. Sea Spectre PB Mk III class
Bldr: Peterson Bldrs, Sturgeon Bay, Wis. (In serv. 1975–79)

GC 105 Jaime Gomez GC 106 Juan Peña

Jaime Gomez (GC 105) Hartmut Ehlers, 11-90

D: 28 tons (36.7 fl) **S:** 30 kts (now less) **Dim:** 19.78 × 5.50 × 1.80 (props)
A: 2 single 12.7-mm mg; 2 single 7.62-mm mg; 1 40-mm Mk 19 grenade launcher
Electronics: Radar: 1 . . . nav.
M: 3 G.M. 8V71 TI diesels; 3 props; 1,800 bhp **Electric:** 30 kw tot.
Range: 450/26; 2,000/. . . **Endurance:** 3 days **Crew:** 1 officer, 8 men

Remarks: Transferred to Colombia in 1990. Aluminum construction. The 40-mm weapon is in a special stabilized Mk 3 Mod. 9 mounting with a removable reload magazine. Not as heavily armed as when in U.S. Navy service.

♦ 4 ex-U.S. Coast Guard 82-foot Point class
Bldr: Coast Guard Yard, Curtis Bay, Md. (GC 144: J. Martinac SB, Tacoma, Wash.)

	In serv.
GC 141 Cabo Corrientes (ex-*Point Warde,* WPB 82368)	. . .
GC 142 Cabo Manglares (ex-*Point Wells,* WPB 82343)	20-11-63
GC 143 Cabo Tiburón (ex-*Point Estero,* WPB 82344)	11-12-66
GC 144 Cabo de la Vela (ex-*Point Sal,* WPB 82352)	5-12-66

D: 64 tons (66–69 fl) **S:** 23.7 kts (see Remarks) **Dim:** 25.3 × 5.23 × 1.95
A: 2 single 12.7-mm M2 mg
Electronics: Radar: 1 Raytheon SPS-64(V)1 nav.
M: 2 Caterpillar 3412 diesels; 2 props; 1,480 bhp
Range: 490/23.7; 1,500/8 **Fuel:** 5.7 tons **Crew:** 1 officer, 7 enlisted

Remarks: Transferred by donation 29-6-00, 13-10-00, 8-2-01, and 29-5-01, respectively, on retirement from U.S. Coast Guard. Hull built of mild steel. High-speed diesels controlled from the bridge. Well-equipped for salvage and towing and in excellent condition, despite their age. Considered to be heavy rollers.

Note: In addition to the craft above, a 10-m, GRP-hulled launch numbered GC 61 is assigned to patrol duties at Barranquilla; built by Industrias Profibra, Barranquilla, no other information available.

SERVICE CRAFT

♦ 1 ex-U.S. LCM(8)-class landing craft [LCM]

GC 240 B. Sapzurro

D: 34 tons light (121 fl) **S:** 9 kts **Dim:** 22.43 × 6.43 × 1.35 (fwd; 1.47 aft)
M: 4 G.M. Detroit Diesel 6-71 or 2 12V-71 diesels; 2 props; 590 bhp
Range: 190/9 (loaded) **Crew:** 4–5 enlisted

Remarks: Transferred late in 1993. Cargo: 60 tons or 150 troops for short distances in the 12.8 × 4.3-m open well with 54.6 m^2 space.

♦ 1 miscellaneous small launch [WYFL]

GC 101 David Salas

Remarks: No data available. Small launch of local construction.

Note: The Colombian Customs Service, the DIAN (Dirección de Impuestos y Aduanas Nacionales), has an antidrug role but is hampered by a lack of suitable craft to perform the function. Its craft no longer carry weapons larger than small arms. Craft in service include the patrol craft *Olaya Herrera* (AN 21) and *Carlos Alban* (AN 22) and the launch *Felix J. Lievano.*

COMOROS

Federal Islamic Republic of the Comoros

Base: Moroni

FISHERIES PATROL BOATS [WPB]

♦ 2 Japanese Yamayuri class Bldr: Ishihara DY, Takasago (In serv. 10-81)

Kasthala Ntringhui

D: 27 tons (40.3 fl) **S:** 20.7 kts **Dim:** 18.0 × 4.3 × 0.82 (1.1 prop)
A: 2 single 12.7-mm mg **Electronics:** Radar: 1 . . . nav.
M: 2 Nissan Type RD 10TA 06 diesels; 2 props; 900 bhp **Crew:** 6 tot.

Remarks: Identical to craft built for the Japanese Maritime Safety Agency. Employed in fisheries protection.

Note: Also in service with the civil police is a small launch named *Barracuda.*

CONGO

Democratic Republic of the Congo

Personnel (2001): Approx. 200 total, plus up to 600 marines

Bases: Banana, Boma, Kalemie (Lake Tanganyika), and Matadi

Note: The name of the country was changed from Zaire on 17-5-97 by the winning forces in the civil war that deposed the dictator Mobutu.

PATROL CRAFT [PC]

♦ 1 Chinese Shanghai-II class

106 . . . . . .

D: 122.5 tons (134.8 fl) **S:** 28.5 kts **Dim:** 38.78 × 5.41 × 1.49 (1.554 max.)
A: 2 twin 37-mm 63-cal. Type 74 AA; 2 twin 25-mm 60-cal. Type 81 AA
Electronics: Radar: 1 Type 351 Pot Head nav.
M: 2 Type L12-180, 1,200-bhp diesels; 2 Type L12-180Z, 910-bhp diesels; 4 props; 4,200 bhp
Electric: 39 kw tot. **Range:** 750/16.5 **Endurance:** 7 days **Crew:** 36 tot.

Remarks: Two operable units were delivered 2-87, but the *Ubangi* (103) sank 23-11-00 at Boma. Four earlier units delivered in 1976–78 are beyond repair. Intended for coastal patrol duties at the mouth of the Congo River, operating from Boma.

Note: All craft formerly operated on Lake Tanganyika had ceased operations by mid-1997. There may be a number of additional small riverine patrol and logistics support craft.

CONGO

Republic of the Congo

Personnel (2001): Not available; probably less than 100

Base: Pointe-Noire, Brazzaville, and Mossaka

Note: The naval forces are divided into a Coastal Navy and a River Navy. Most of all of the craft listed below were in poor condition by the mid-1990s, and none at all may be operable.

COASTAL NAVY

PATROL CRAFT [PC]

♦ 3 Spanish Piraña class Bldr: E.N. Bazán, Cadiz

	In serv.
P 601 Marien Ngouabi (ex-*L'Intrépide*)	10-11-82
P 602 Les Trois Glorieuses (ex-*Le Vaillant*)	1-83
P 603 Les Maloango (ex-*Le Terrible*)	3-83

D: 125 tons (138 fl) **S:** 34 kts (29 sust.) **Dim:** 32.70 (30.60 pp) × 6.15 × 1.55
A: 1 40-mm 70-cal. OTOBreda AA; 1 20-mm Oerlikon GAM B01 AA; 2 single 12.7-mm Browning M2 mg
Electronics: Radar: 1 Raytheon RM 1220/6X8 nav.
M: 2 MTU 12V538 TB92 diesels; 2 props; 6,120 bhp (5,110 sust.)
Electric: 210 kw **Range:** 1,000/17 **Crew:** 3 officers, 16 enlisted

Remarks: Ordered in 1980. Arrived in Congo 1-6-83; renamed on delivery. By 8-85 they were badly in need of an overhaul, which began at builders in 1985. Were again quickly brought to near-inoperability, and their current status is uncertain. Had Matra Défense Panda optronic director for the 40-mm gun.

OASTAL NAVY PATROL CRAFT [PC] *(continued)*

es Maloango (P 603) French Navy, 12-90

RIVER NAVY

ATROL BOATS [PB]

ote: Two or more Mangust-class (Project 12150) patrol launches were said to be on der from Russia for "Congo" as of 9-99, but whether the Republic of the Congo or e Democratic Republic of the Congo (ex-Zaire) was meant is not known.

2 Arcor-43-class GRP-hulled
Bldr: Arcor, . . ., France (In serv. 1982)

NDRE MATSOUA MAÎTRE CHRISTIAN MALONGGA MOKOKO

: 12 tons (fl) **S:** 25 kts **Dim:** 13.00 (11.60 pp) × 4.0 × 1.5
: 1 7.62-mm mg **M:** 2 diesels; 2 props; 450 bhp

2 Arcor-38-class GRP-hulled
Bldr: Arcor, . . ., France (In serv. 1982)

NSEIGNE DE VAISSEAU YAMBA LAMASS . . . . . .

: 7.5 tons (fl) **S:** 28 kts **Dim:** 11.40 (9.90 pp) × 3.60 × 1.10
: 1 7.62-mm mg **M:** 2 diesels; 2 props; 250 bhp

Up to 10 locally built outboard-powered craft

emarks: No characteristics data available.

OOK ISLANDS

ote: The Cook Islands is an independent republic but is under the protection of New aland. Craft name is preceded by CIPPB (Cook Islands Pacific Patrol Boat).

ATROL BOAT [PB]

1 Australian ASI 315 class Bldr: Australian SB Ind. (WA), South Coogie

	Laid down	L	In serv.
E KUKUPA	5-6-88	27-1-89	1-9-89

: 165 tons (fl) **S:** 20 kt (sust.) **Dim:** 31.50 (28.60 wl) × 8.10 × 2.12
small arms
ectronics:
Radar: 1 Furuno 1011 nav.
EW: Furuno 120 MF–HFD/F; Furuno 525 VHFD/F
: 2 Caterpillar 3516 diesels; 2 props; 2,820 bhp (2,400 sust.)
ectric: 116 kw (2 × 50 kw, 1 × 16 kw) **Range:** 2,500/12 **Fuel:** 27.9 tons
ndurance: 8–10 days **Crew:** 3 officers, 14 enlisted

emarks: A unit of the Australian "Pacific Patrol Boat" foreign aid program. Ex-emely well equipped with navaids: SATNAV receiver, doppler log, etc. Carries a m Stressl aluminum boarding boat with a 40-hp outboard.

Te Kukupa H&L Van Ginderen, 6-95

COSTA RICA

Republic of Costa Rica

COAST GUARD
(Servicio Nacional Guardacostas)

Personnel (2001): 250 total

Bases: Golfito, Puntarenas, and Puerto Limón

Maritime Aviation: The Air Section of the Civil Guard has four Cessna 206 and three Cessna O-2A fixed-wing aircraft and two Hughes 500E helicopters.

Note: A supply of U.S. 20-mm 70-cal. single gunmounts has been acquired, should the larger units need heavier armaments. Most of the larger craft listed are in poor condition and will have to be discarded shortly. The name of the organization has been changed from the *Guardia Civil Sección Marítimo,* and a new pennant numbering system now indicates the length in feet of the class, followed after a dash by the number of the individual craft.

PATROL CRAFT [WPC]

♦ **1 U.S. 105-foot Commercial Cruiser class**
Bldr: Swiftships, Morgan City, La. (In serv. 2-78)

SNGC 105-1 ISLA DEL COCO (ex-SP 1055)

Isla del Coco (SNGC 105-1) Swiftships, 4-85

D: 118 tons (fl) **S:** 33 kts (30 sust.) **Dim:** 31.73 × 7.1 × 2.16
A: 1 12.7-mm M2HB mg; 2 twin 7.62-mm mg; 1 60-mm mortar
Electronics: Radar: 1 Furuno . . . nav.
M: 3 MTU 12V331 TC92 diesels; 3 props; 10,500 bhp
Electric: 80 kw (2 × 40 kw)
Range: 1,200/18 **Fuel:** 21 tons **Crew:** 3 officers, 11 enlisted

Remarks: Refitted 1984 to 3-85 by builders; overhauled in 2001. Aluminum construction.

PATROL BOATS [WPB]

♦ **3 ex-U.S. Coast Guard Point class**
Bldr: U.S. Coast Guard Yard, Curtis Bay, Md.

	In serv.
SNGC 82-2 SANTAMARIA (ex-SP 822; ex-*Point Camden,* WPB 82373)	4-5-70
SNGC 82-3 JUAN RAFALE MORA (ex-SP 823; ex-*Point Chico,* WPB 82339)	29-10-62
SNGC 82-4 PANCHA CARRASCO (ex-*Point Bridge,* WPB 82338)	10-10-62

D: 64 tons (69 fl) **S:** 23.7 kts **Dim:** 25.3 × 5.23 × 1.95
A: 2 12.7-mm M2HB mg **Electronics:** Radar: 1 SPS-64(V)1 nav.

PATROL BOATS [WPB] *(continued)*

Santamaria (SNGC 82-2) Costa Rican C.G., 2-00

M: 2 Caterpillar 3412 diesels; 2 props; 1,480 bhp
Range: 490/23.7; 1,500/8 **Fuel:** 5.7 tons **Crew:** 1 officer, 7 enlisted
Remarks: SNGC 82-2 was transferred 15-12-99, SNGC 82-3 on 22-6-01, and SNGC 82-4 on 28-9-01. Sister *Colonel Alfonso Monje* (SNGC 82-1, ex-SP 821; ex-*Point Hope,* WPB 82302), transferred in 5-91, had been stricken by 5-01.

♦ **1 ex-U.S. Coast Guard Cape class**
Bldr: Coast Guard Yard, Curtis Bay, Md.

	In serv.	Transferred
SNGC 95-1 Astronauta Franklin Chang (ex-SP 951; ex-*Cape Henlopen,* WPB 95328)	5-12-58	28-9-89

D: 90 tons (fl) **S:** 20 kts **Dim:** 28.96 × 6.10 × 1.55
A: 2 single 12.7-mm M2HB mg
Electronics: Radar: 1 Raytheon SPS-64(V)1 nav.
M: 2 G.M. 16V149 TI diesels; 2 props; 2,470 bhp **Electric:** 60 kw
Range: 550/20; 1,900/11.5 **Endurance:** 5 days **Crew:** 1 officer, 13 enlisted

♦ **1 U.S. 36-foot aluminum patrol launch**
Bldr: Swiftships, Morgan City, La. (In serv. 3-86)

SNGC 36-1 Puerto Quepos (ex-*Telamanca,* SP 361)

Puerto Quepos (SNGC 36-1) Costa Rican C.G., 2-00

D: 9 tons (10.7 fl) **S:** 24 kts **Dim:** 10.97 × 3.05 × 0.80
A: 1 12.7-mm M2HB mg; 1 60-mm mortar
Electronics: Radar: 1 Raytheon 1900 nav.
M: 2 G.M. DD8240 MT diesels; 2 props; 500 bhp
Range: 248/18 **Crew:** 1 officer, 3 enlisted

Remarks: *Sister Cariara* (SP 362) had been discarded by 5-01.

♦ **2 U.S. 65-foot Commercial Cruiser class**
Bldr: Swiftships, Morgan City, La. (In serv. 1978)

SNGC 65-3 Cabo Blanco (ex-SP 658)
SNGC 65-4 Isla Burica (ex-SP 654)

Isla Burica (SNGC 65-4) Costa Rican C.G., 2-00

D: 24.9 tons (35 fl) **S:** 23 kts (19 sust.) **Dim:** 19.77 (17.90 wl) × 5.56 × 1.98
A: 1 12.7-mm M2HB mg; 2 twin 7.62-mm mg; 1 60-mm mortar
Electronics: Radar: 1 Furuno . . . nav.
M: 2 MTU 8V331 diesels; 2 props; 1,400 bhp **Electric:** 20 kw
Range: 1,300/18 **Fuel:** 4.8 tons **Crew:** 2 officers, 7 enlisted

Remarks: Aluminum construction. Refitted by builder in 1985–86 but are no again in poor condition. Sister *Cabo Velas* (SP 656) was derelict by mid-1995 an *Punta Uvita* (SP 654) was out of service by 1998.

♦ **4 miscellaneous Whaler patrol launches**
Bldr: Boston Whaler, Rockland, Mass. (In serv. 1983)

SNGC 20-1 Tauro
SNGC 20-2 Villa Mar
SNGC 22-1 Cocori
SNGC 24-1 Escorpión

Costa Rican Boston Whaler Costa Rican C.G., 2-(

D: 1.2–2.0 tons (fl) **S:** 22–24 kts **Dim:** see Remarks
A: 1 12.7-mm M2HB mg; 1 7.62-mm mg **Electronics:** Radar: 1 . . . nav.
M: 1 gasoline outboard; 70 bhp **Crew:** 5 tot.

Remarks: Survivors of 13 delivered 1983. Foam-core GRP construction. Lengths d fer, with pennant numbers indicating the length in feet.

SERVICE CRAFT

♦ **1 U.S. 42-foot aluminum hospital launch [YH]**
Bldr: Swiftships, Morgan City, La. (In serv. 9-86)

SNGC 42-1 Primera Dama (ex-*Donna Margarita,* SP 421; ex-*Puntarenas*

D: 11 tons (16.2 fl) **S:** 34 kts **Dim:** 12.80 × 4.26 × 0.90
M: 2 G.M. 8V92 TI diesels; 2 props; 700 bhp
Range: 300/30; 450/18 **Crew:** 1 officer, 3 enlisted

Remarks: Former patrol craft employed as a hospital launch.

Note: Also in use are six U.S.-funded, locally manufactured Apex RIB launches, ea powered by two Honda outboard motors, and one locally built 12.2-m GRP launch.

CROATIA

HRVATSKA RATNA MORNARIČA

Personnel (2001): Approx. 2,900 total, plus nine companies of naval infantry

Bases: Headquarters at Lora-Split, with facilities at Šibenik, Split, Pula, and Plo and minor facilities at Lastovo and Vis. The River Patrol flotillas are based at Sis on the Sava and Osijek on the Drava.

Naval Infantry: Nine companies, deployed to Brač, Dubrovnik, Jelsa, Korčul Lošinj, Pelješac, Pula, Šibenik, and Zadar

Coastal Defense: At least two batteries of coastal defense missiles, each with t Tatra 815 trucks and each truck equipped with four RBS-15 antiship missiles, a in service with the Croatian Navy. There are also 16 radar-directed coastal artille batteries.

Organization: The Croatian Navy was created 12-9-91. All ships are incorporat in the Fleet, which has the 1st Brigade (missile patrol combatants, fast minelaye Patrol Ship Division, Landing Ship Section, Submarine Section, Minesweeper S tion, Training Ship Section, and Auxiliary Section.

Maritime Aviation: Three CASA/Tusas Aerospace Industries (Turkey) CN-235 ma itime patrol aircraft are operated by the Croatian Air Force, whose Mi-24 attack h licopters have been used to drop antisubmarine torpedoes in coordination with nav surface craft.

Note: Ship names are prefaced by HRM (*Hrvatska Ratna Mornariča*). All photograp in this section attributed to the Croatian magazine *HVG* are courtesy of Dr. Zvonin Freivogel.

MIDGET SUBMARINES [SSM]

Note: A 120-ton midget submarine with four 533-mm torpedo tubes and the abili to transport four swimmer delivery vehicles is said to be in the planning stages. F swimmer delivery vehicles, see under [LSDV] in the Amphibious Warfare Ships a Craft section.

MIDGET SUBMARINES [SSM] *(continued)*

♦ 1 Modified Una (M-100D) class (Type C-11)
Bldr: RH-ALAN-Brodosplit, Split (In serv. 5-85/17-9-96)

P 01 Velebit (ex-*Soca,* P 914)

Velebit (P 01) Dario Vuljanič, *HVG,* 1997

D: 88 tons surf./99 tons sub. **S:** 8.0 kts surf./11.0 kts sub.
Dim: 20.92 × 2.70 × 4.42 (molded depth)
A: 6 500-kg mines or 4 R1 swimmer delivery vehicles, externally carried
Electronics:
Radar: . . .
Sonar: STN Atlas Elektronik PP-10 active and PSU-1-2 passive
M: 1 diesel-driven (140-bhp) generator, two 20-kw Koncar electric motors; 1 5-bladed prop; 54 shp
Range: 500/8 snorkel; 135/3 sub. **Endurance:** 7 days
Crew: 4 crew + 6 swimmers

Remarks: Captured in 1991 during the breakup of Yugoslavia. The building yard at Split added a section to the Type M-100D hull, incorporating a diesel generator set. The modified submarine was relaunched in 9-93. No second unit is foreseen for the immediate future.
Hull systems: The original displacement was 76 tons surfaced/88 submerged, and the original length was 18.8 m overall. Working depth is 105 m, with test depth at 120 m and an estimated collapse depth of 182 m. Theoretically capable of remaining submerged for 96 hours. Originally had no radar, but a small portable navigational set may have been added. There is a GPS receiver aboard. Has two 128-cell, 1,450 amp-hr (5-hour rate) batteries.

GUIDED-MISSILE PATROL CRAFT [PTG]

♦ 2 (+ 2) Kralj Petar Krešimir IV class (Type R-03)
Bldr: Kraljevica SY

	L	In serv.
RTOP 11 Kralj Petar Krešimir IV (ex-*Sergei Masera,* RTOP 501)	21-3-92	7-92
RTOP 12 Kralj Dmitar Zvonimir (ex-*Milan Spasič*)	30-3-01	11-01

Kralj Petar Krešimir IV (RTOP 11)—submarine support ship *Faust Vrančič* (PT 73) is in the background, at left Dario Vuljanič, *HVG,* 1997

D: 350 tons (385 fl) **S:** 36 kts (32.5 sust.)
Dim: 53.63 (RTOP 12: 55.10) × 8.54 × 2.00
A: 8 RBS-15 SSM; 1 57-mm 70-cal. Bofors SAK 57 Mk 1 DP; 1 30-mm 54-cal. AK-630 gatling AA; 2 single 12.7-mm mg; 4 AIM-70 or 6 SAG-1 mines
Electronics:
Radar: 1 Decca RM 1290A nav.; 1 CelsiusTech 9LV 249 Mk 2 search/f.c. suite
EW: 2 18-round Wallop Barricade decoy RL
M: 3 Soviet M-504B-2 diesels; 3 props; 14,550 bhp
Electric: 420 kw (3 × 140-kw diesel sets)
Range: 1,700/20 (RTOP 12: 1,700/18) **Endurance:** 10 days
Crew: 5 officers, 12 noncommissioned officers, 16 enlisted

Remarks: The first unit was captured incomplete and finished by Croatia. Construction of the second employs some components left behind in 1991 but is largely of new material; funding problems have slowed construction, and the craft was launched without armament and without some superstructure elements. Two additional units are tentatively planned, with the names *Kralj Tomislav, Nikola Subic Zrinski,* or *Ban Josip Jelacic* to be used.
Hull systems: Hull has 11 watertight compartments, a round bilge-form, and no fin stabilizers. Have a CBR protection system, Collins and Harris communications gear, a Furuno Loran-C receiver, a DB-14B echo sounder, and a Thales doppler log.

Combat systems: The missiles were originally delivered for coast defense use and were adapted for shipboard launching. The missile containers can be stacked two high to double the loadout. There is a Russian Kolonka-2 ringsight director for the 30-mm gatling gun. RTOP 12 lacks the f.c. radars and the 30-mm gun.

♦ 1 Rade Končar class (Type 240 or R-02)
Bldr: Tito SY, Kraljevica

	L	In serv.
RTOP 21 Šibenik (ex-*Vlado Četovič,* RT 402)	28-8-77	3-78

Šibenik (RTOP 21)—with only two missiles aboard Dario Vuljanič, *HVG,* 2000

D: 242 tons (271 fl) **S:** 39 kts (37 sust.) **Dim:** 45.00 × 8.00 × 1.80 (2.50 props)
A: 4 RBS-15 SSM; 1 57-mm 70-cal. Bofors SAK 57 Mk 1 DP; 1 30-mm 54-cal. AK-630 gatling AA
Electronics:
Radar: 1 Decca 1226 nav.; 1 CelsiusTech 9LV 202 Mk 2 target detection/f.c. suite
EW: 2 18-round Wallop Barricade decoy RL
M: CODAG: 2 Rolls-Royce Proteus gas turbines (4,500 shp each), 2 MTU 20V538 TB92 diesels (3,600 bhp each); 4 CP props; 16,200 hp max.
Electric: 300 kVA tot. **Range:** 880/23; 1,650/15 **Endurance:** 7 days
Crew: 5 officers, 10 petty officers, 15 other enlisted

Remarks: Of Yugoslav design, using Swedish fire control and guns and Soviet missiles. Steel hull, aluminum superstructure. Has CBR warfare protection. The after 57-mm mount was removed and replaced with a Soviet-supplied 30-mm gatling gun on a cylindrical magazine pedestal to improve antimissile defenses; the gatling gun, however, is controlled only by a Kolonka-2 ringsight director mounted in a cupola just abaft the mast.

PATROL CRAFT [PC]

♦ 4 Mirna class (Type 140)
Bldr: Kraljevica SY (In serv. 1982–84)

PB 61 "Novi Grad" (ex-*Koprivnik* or *Biokovo,* PČ 171)
PB 62 Šolta (ex-*Mukos,* PČ 176)
PB 63 "Vrlika" (ex-*Cer,* PČ 180)
PB 64 Hrvatska Kostajnica (ex-*Durmitor,* PČ 181)

Šolta (PB 62) Dario Vuljanič, *HVG,* 2000

D: 125.3 tons (142.3 fl) **S:** 29 kts **Dim:** 32.00 (29.25 pp) × 6.68 × 1.76 (2.41 max.)
A: 1 40-mm 70-cal. Bofors L70 AA; 1 quadruple 20-mm 90-cal. M75 AA; 1 4-round Fasta-4M SAM syst. (12 Igla missiles); 8 Type MDB-MT3 d.c.
Electronics:
Radar: 1 Decca 1216C nav.—Sonar: Simrad SQS-5Q3D/SF hull-mounted HF
M: 2 SEMT-Pielstick 12 PA4 200GDS diesels; 2 props; 6,000 bhp—electric motors for low speeds (6 kts)
Range: 400/20 **Fuel:** 16.2 tons **Crew:** 2 officers, 19 enlisted

Remarks: Ordered in 1979. PB 61 and 62 were captured badly damaged but have been repaired. All four may be transferred to the new coast guard. The names *Novi Grad* and *Vrlika,* attributed to PB 61 and PB 63, are unofficial.
Hull systems: Endurance at 20 kts can be increased to 530 n.m. in emergencies. Peacetime endurance is 4 days; wartime: 8 days.

PATROL CRAFT [PC] *(continued)*

"Vrlika" (PB 63) Dario Vuljanič, *HVG,* 1998

Combat systems: A quadruple-rack launcher for SA-7 Grail/Igla infrared point-defense missiles has been added abaft the mast. Two quadruple illumination/chaff launchers are now mounted aft. The Croatian units of the class have a quadruple 20-mm gunmount aft, while Federal Yugoslav units have a single mount.

PATROL BOATS [PB]

♦ **1 M 301–class riverine** Bldr: Macvanska, Mitroviča (In serv. 1952)

PB 91 (ex-*Slavonač,* RLM 307)

PB 91 Siegfried Breyer Collection, 1993

D: 38 tons (fl) **S:** 12 kts **Dim:** 19.4 × 4.4 × 1.4
A: 1 40-mm 60-cal. Bofors AA; 2 single 12.7-mm mg
Electronics: Radar: 1 . . . nav.
M: 2 . . . diesels; 2 props; 300 bhp **Crew:** 9 tot.

Remarks: Based at Sisak on the Sava River with PB 92 (q.v.) and PB 93, for which no data is available.

♦ **1 PB 92 class** Bldr: Breki, Domagoj (In serv. 1950s)

PB 92

PB 92 Siegfried Breyer Collection, 1993

D: 46 tons (fl) **S:** 12 kts **Dim:** 20.5 × 4.5 × 1.4
A: 1 40-mm 60-cal. Bofors AA; 1 quadruple and 1 single 12.7-mm mg
M: 2 diesels; 2 props; 300 bhp **Range:** 400/12 **Crew:** 10 tot.

Remarks: Based at Sisak on the Sava River.

Note: Based at Osijek on the Danube River are patrol launches *Breki, Vukovar '91, Domagoj, Tomislav, Okic, Tina,* and an unnamed small launch; no data available, except that *Tina* is armed with a triple 20-mm AA mount forward, while the smaller *Vukovar '91* has a 40-mm Bofors mount.

Vukovar '91—small river patrol boat with large 40-mm Bofors gun Dario Vuljanič, *HVG*

MINE WARFARE SHIPS AND CRAFT

♦ **1 ex-Soviet Osa-I-class (Project 205) fast minelayer [MM]**

PBM 41 DUBROVNIK (ex-RB 41; ex-*Mitar Acev,* RC 301)

Dubrovnik (PBM 41) Dario Vuljanič, *HVG,* 1999

D: 172 tons (209.5 fl) **S:** 38.5 kts **Dim:** 37.5 × 7.6 × 1.8
A: 2 twin 30-mm 65-cal. AK-230 AA; 2 mine rails
Electronics: Radar: 1 Rangout (Square Tie) surf. search
M: 3 M-503A diesels; 3 props; 12,000 bhp **Electric:** 200 kw
Range: 500/34; 750/25 **Endurance:** 5 days **Crew:** 4 officers, 26 enlisted

Remarks: Transferred to Yugoslavia from the USSR 1965–69. Captured badly damaged but repaired at Šibenik. Sister *Velimir Skorpik* (RT 42; ex-*Zihaca Jovanovic-Spanac,* RC 310) was stricken during 1994. Can be operated at 220 tons full load, with 11 tons extra fuel. Because Styx missiles were not available, the four hooded launch rails were removed in 1995 and mine rails were installed, flanking the superstructure. The Rys' (Drum Tilt) gun fire-control radar has been removed.

♦ **0 (+ 1 +. . .) MPMB-class coastal minesweeper [MSC]**
Bldr: RH-ALAN d.o.o., Vela Luka SY, Korčula (L: . . .)

. . . . . .

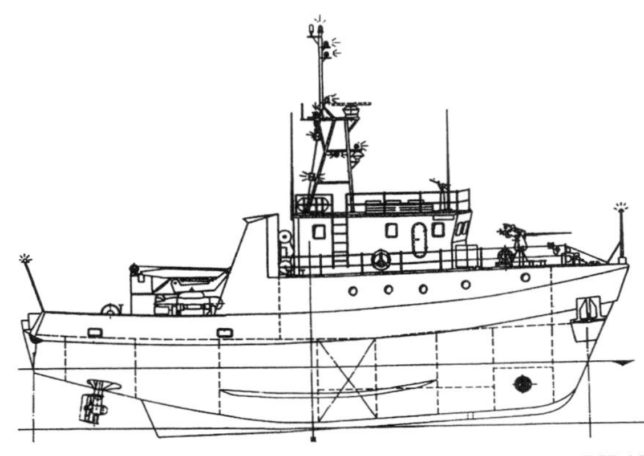

MPMB coastal minesweeper RH-ALAN, 1996

D: 173 tons (fl) **S:** 11 kts **Dim:** 25.70 × 6.80 × 2.64
A: 1 20-mm 90-cal. M71 AA; mines
Electronics:
Radar: 1 Kelvin-Hughes 5000 ARPA nav.
Sonar: Reson mine avoidance, Klein 2000 side-scan route survey

MINE WARFARE SHIPS AND CRAFT *(continued)*

M: 2 MTU 8V183 TE62 diesels; 2 Holland Roerpropeler azimuthal props; 990 bhp—1 bow-thruster; 190 shp
Endurance: . . ./. . . **Crew:** 14 tot.

Remarks: The prototype began construction during 1996, but the program has been much delayed by the lack of funding; the craft was supposed to have been in service by 31-7-97 but remains in land storage at the building yard. Has a glass-reinforced plastic hull, with form derived from that of a fishing craft. Would carry one-each ECA PAP 105 remote-controlled mine countermeasures and Super Sea Rover submersibles and would be equipped with an MDL-3 wire mechanical sweep array.

AMPHIBIOUS WARFARE SHIPS AND CRAFT

♦ 2 Silba-class tank landing craft/minelayers [LSM]

	Bldr	L	In serv.
DBM 81 Cetina (ex-*Rab,* DBM 242)	Brodosplit, Split	18-7-92	19-2-93
DBV 82 Krka	Brodosplit, Split	17-9-94	9-3-95

Krka (DBV 82)—note 40-mm gun forward Dario Vuljanič, *HVG,* 2000

Cetina (DBM 81) Dario Vuljanič, *HVG,* 1997

D: 750 tons normal (880 fl) **S:** 13 kts (12 sust.)
Dim: 49.70 (43.90 pp) × 10.20 × 2.60 (max.)
A: DBM 82 only: 1 40-mm 70-cal. Bofors L70 AA—DBM 81 only: 2 twin 30-mm 65-cal. AK-230 AA; 1 quadruple 20-mm 90-cal. M-75 AA—both: 1 4-round MTU-4 SAM launcher (. . . Strela-2M missiles); 2 mine rails (94 SAG-1 mines)
Electronics: Radar: 1 Decca 1290A nav.
M: 2 Burmeister & Wain Alpha 10V23L-VO diesels; 2 CP props; 3,100 bhp
Range: 1,200/12
Crew: 3 officers, 6 senior petty officers, 24 other enlisted + up to 300 troops

Remarks: DBM stands for "landing ship, minelayer," while DBV indicates use as a water tanker. The first ship of the class was completed in 1990 and is in Federal Yugoslav Navy hands. A planned third unit for Croatia, reportedly intended to be named *Zrmanja,* had not been laid down as of 6-01; other names reported under consideration for the ship are *Kupa* and *Neretva.*
Hull systems: Have bow and stern ramps, with continuous covered vehicle deck also used for portable mine rails. Cargo capacity: 460 tons, or 6 tanks totaling 264 tons, or up to 7 armored personnel carriers; in DBV 82, ballast tankage is presumably employed to transport fresh water to offshore island garrisons.
Combat systems: Have two 128-mm illumination rocket launchers. On DBM 81, the 30-mm gunmounts are mounted port and starboard, just abaft the bridge, while the 20-mm mount is located near the stern. On DBV 82, the single gunmount is located forward.

♦ 1 DTM 211–class landing craft/minelayer [LCU]
Bldr: Yugoslavia (In serv. 1950s)

DTM 219 "Jastreb" (ex-DTM 217)

D: 240 tons (410 fl) **S:** 10.3 kts **Dim:** 49.80 × 8.60 (6.55 wl) × 1.66 (2.10 max.)
A: 1 triple 20-mm M-75 AA; 2 mine rails (98 SAG-1 mines)
M: 3 Torpedo B.539RM/22 diesels; 3 props; 768 bhp
Range: 500/9.3 **Crew:** 27 tot.

"Jastreb" (DTM 219) Dario Vuljanič, *HVG,* 2000

Remarks: DTM= *Desantni Tenkonosac/Minopolagac.* Near-duplicate of the World War II German MFP-D class. Equipped with 1-m-wide hull sponsons, extending beam to 8.6 m and providing space for two mine rails with a total capacity of up to 100 small mines. Has a bow ramp. Can carry 140 tons of vehicles or 200 troops. Was re-engined in 1973. The similar *Slavyy* (DSM 110), initially put into service for the Croatian Navy, had been retired by 5-97. The name *Jastreb* is unofficial and may no longer be carried.

♦ 1 ex-German Siebel Ferry–class utility landing craft [LCU]
Bldr: . . . (In serv. 1943–44)

DSM 110 (ex-DST 105)

DSM 110 Dario Vuljanič, *HVG,* 1998

D: 129 tons (167 fl) **S:** 9 kts **Dim:** 25.84 × 14.05 × 1.09
A: 2 single 20-mm 90-cal. M-71 AA; 2 mine rails **Electronics:** Radar: 1 . . . nav.
M: 2 Mercedes-Benz truck diesels; 2 props; 400 bhp
Range: . . ./. . . **Crew:** 2 officers, 18 enlisted

Remarks: Catamaran with twin pontoon-type hulls. Refitted and re-engined at Pula in 1956. Sister PDS 713 is configured as a dredge (see under [YM]).

♦ 1 DJČ 621–class (Type 22) landing craft [LCVP]
Bldr: Gleben SY, Vela Luka, Korčula (In serv. 1976–77)

DJČ 106 (ex-DJČ 624)

DJČ 106—with DJČ 613– and DJČ 601–class units Dario Vuljanič, *HVG,* 2000

D: 48 tons (. . . fl) **S:** 30 kts **Dim:** 22.30 × 4.84 × 1.07 (1.58 props)
A: 1 20-mm 90-cal. M-71 AA; 1 30-mm BP-30 grenade launcher
Electronics: Radar: 1 Decca 101 nav.
M: 2 MTU . . . . . . diesels; 2 waterjets; 1,740 bhp
Range: 320/22 **Crew:** 8 tot. + 40 troops

Remarks: DJČ = *Desantni Jurisni Čamac.* Of the units of the DJČ 621 class captured, three were assigned as civilian fireboats and one (ex-DJČ 622) is used by a police agency; of the two employed by the navy, DJČ 105 (ex-DJČ 623) was discarded in 1996 and DJČ 106 (ex-DJČ 624) was stricken in 1997 but restored to service in 1998. GRP construction hull with bow ramp. Can carry 15 tons of vehicles in the 32-m^2 cargo area.

AMPHIBIOUS WARFARE SHIPS AND CRAFT *(continued)*

♦ 2 DJČ 613–class (Type 21) landing craft [LCVP]
Bldr: Gleben SY, Vela Luka, Korčula (In serv. 1976–77)

DJČ 104 (ex-DJČ 615) DJČ 107 (ex-DJČ 613)

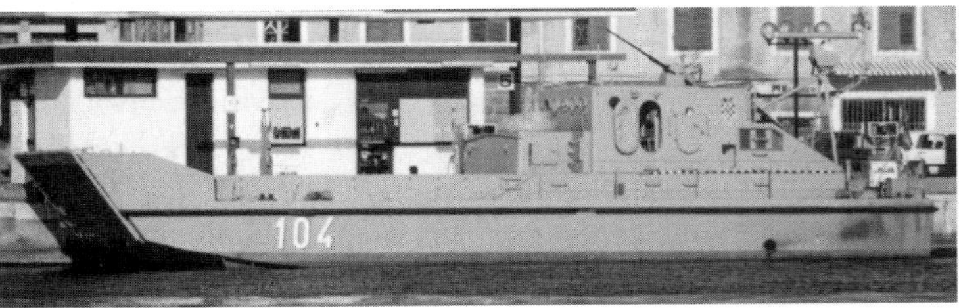

DJČ 104 Dario Vuljanič, *HVG,* 1997

D: 32 tons (38 fl) **S:** 23.5 kts **Dim:** 21.30 × 4.84 × 1.07 (1.58 props)
A: 1 20-mm M-71 AA—2 30-mm BP-30 grenade launchers
Electronics: Radar: 1 Decca 101 nav.
M: 1 MTU 12V331 TC81 diesel; 1 prop; 1,450 bhp
Range: 320/22 **Crew:** 6 tot. + 40 troops

Remarks: DJČ = *Desantni Jurisni Čamac.* Glass-reinforced plastic construction with bow ramp. Can carry vehicles totaling 6 tons in the 32-m^2 cargo area. Two others of the four captured were badly damaged and were not repaired.

♦ 3 DJČ 601–class (Type 11) personnel landing craft [LCVP]
Bldr: Gleben SY, Vela Luka, Korčula (In serv. 1987)

DJČ 101 (ex-DJČ 602) DJČ 103 (ex-DJČ 612)
DJČ 102 (ex-DJČ 603)

DJČ 102 Dario Vuljanič, *HVG,* 1996

D: 32 tons (38 fl) **S:** 23 kts **Dim:** 21.30 × 4.84 × 1.07 (1.58 props)
A: 1 20-mm M-71 AA—1 30-mm BP-30 grenade launcher
Electronics: Radar: 1 Decca 101 nav.
M: 1 MTU 12V331 diesel; 1 prop; 1,250 bhp
Range: 320/22 **Crew:** 6 tot. + 40 troops

Remarks: GRP construction with bow ramp. Can carry vehicles totaling 6 tons in the 32-m^2 cargo area.

Note: Also in service is fast personnel landing craft BDČ . . . (ex-BDČ 82), said to be of British origin; no data available.

♦ 2 Mala-class (Type R2) swimmer delivery vehicles [LSDV]
Bldr: Brodosplit, Split

D: 1.4 tons **S:** 4.4 kts **Dim:** 4.90 × 1.22 × 1.32 (1.70 fins) **A:** 2 50-kg mines
M: 1 electric motor; 1 prop; 6 hp **Range:** 18/4.4; 23/3.7 **Crew:** 2 tot.

Remarks: Diving depth: 60 m. Free-flooding personnel space enclosed within clear plastic dome. Sweden has acquired one, and six were sold to Libya; the USSR may also have received examples. Croatia is said to have captured two of the four Yugoslav units of this class; one of the pair is described as being of Type R2M, indicating some modification.

Note: Also available are two R1 "chariot"-type swimmer delivery vehicles with a length of 3.72 m, a beam of 1.05 m, and a surfaced draft of 0.80 m. The craft have a range of 6 n.m. at 3 kts on their 1-kw electric motors and can dive to 60 m. Three personnel can be carried astride the craft.

AUXILIARIES

♦ 1 submarine rescue and salvage ship [ASR] (In reserve)
Bldr: Tito SY, Belgrade (In serv. 10-9-76)

PT 73 *Faust Vrančič* (ex-*Spasilac,* PS 12)

D: 1,590 tons (fl) **S:** 13.4 kts **Dim:** 55.50 × 12.00 × 3.84 (4.34 max.)
A: provision for 2 quadruple M-75 and 2 single M-71 20-mm AA
Electronics: Radar: 1 . . . nav. **M:** 2 diesels; 2 Kort-nozzle props; 4,340 bhp
Electric: 540 kVA **Range:** 4,000/13.4 **Crew:** 53 tot. (72 accomm.)

Remarks: Resembles an oilfield supply vessel, with low freeboard aft. Sister *Aka* was in the Iraqi Navy, and one Yugoslav Navy unit (ex-*Zlatica*) was sold to Libya. Equipped for underwater cutting and welding, towing, salvage lifting, fire fighting, and other salvage tasks. Can carry up to 250 tons deck cargo and transfer 490 tons cargo fuel, 48 tons cargo water, and 5 tons lube oil. Can support divers to 300 m with a three-section decompression chamber. Also has the capability to support a small rescue submersible. Has a bow-thruster and can lay a four-point moor. Has been inactive since early 1997.

Faust Vrančič (PT 73) H&L Van Ginderen, 2-97

♦ 1 Soviet Moma-class cadet training ship [AXT]
Bldr: Stocznia Polnocna, Gdansk, Poland (In serv. 1971)

PT 72 Andrija Mohorovičič (ex-PS 72, ex-PH 72, ex-PH 33)

Andrija Mohorovičič (PT 72) Dario Vuljanič, *HVG,* 1999

D: 1,260 tons (1,540 fl) **S:** 17 kts **Dim:** 73.3 × 10.8 × 3.8
Electronics: Radar: 1 Don-2 nav.
M: 2 Zgoda-Sulzer 6TD48 diesels; 2 CP props; 3,600 bhp
Range: 8,700/11 **Crew:** 4 officers, 33 enlisted

Remarks: Transferred from the USSR in 1972. Carries one survey launch. Has a 5-ton crane for navigational buoy handling and four laboratories totaling 35 m^2 deck space. Formerly used for oceanographic research, hydrographic surveys, and buoy tending, but now employed mostly for training for the Croatian Naval Academy.

SERVICE CRAFT

♦ 1 diving tender [YDT]
Bldr: Macvanska Mitroviča (In serv. 1952)

BRM 83 Zirje

Zirje (BRM 83) Laušič, *HVG*

D: 38 tons (46 fl) **S:** 12 kts **Dim:** 20.50 (19.4 pp) × 4.50 × 1.42
A: 1 40-mm 60-cal. Bofors AA; 1 quadruple 12.7-mm mg
Electronics: Radar: 1 Decca 101 nav.
M: 2 diesels; 2 props; 304 bhp **Range:** 400/12 **Crew:** 9 tot.

Remarks: Same basic design as Federal Yugoslav Navy BRM 82–series transports. Sister BRM 82 became the 1st Croatian Guards Corps patrol craft *Zečevo.*

Note: Also in service are the former Federal Yugoslav Navy diving tenders BRM 53 and BRM 51; no data available.

♦ 1 PT 71–class cargo lighter [YF] Bldr: Split SY, Croatia (In serv. 1956)

PT 71 Medusa

D: 310 tons (428 fl) **S:** 7 kts **Dim:** 43.1 × 7.2 × 4.85
M: 1 Burmeister & Wain diesel; 1 prop; 300 bhp

Remarks: PT = *Pomocni Transporter.*

SERVICE CRAFT *(continued)*

Medusa (PT 71) Dario Vuljanič, *HVG,* 2000

◆ **1 yacht [YFL]**

UČKA (ex-*Podgorika)*

Učka H&L Van Ginderen, 2-97

Remarks: Former Yugoslav presidential yacht. Resembles a large cabin cruiser and may have been built by C.N. de l'Esterel, Cannes, France. No data available.

◆ **1 yacht [YFL]**

JADRANKA (ex-*Smile)*

Jadranka Dario Vuljanič, *HVG,* 2000

Remarks: No data available.

◆ **5 BMT 1–class personnel and cargo launches [YFL]**

BMT 1 KAKANJ (ex-BM 64) BMT 4 . . . . . .
BMT 2 KRASNIČA BMT 5 . . . . . .
BMT 3 . . . . . .

D: 38 tons (46 fl) **S:** 12 kts **Dim:** 20.50 (19.4 pp) × 4.50 × 1.42
A: 1 20-mm 90-cal. M-71 AA **Electronics:** Radar: 1 . . . nav.
M: 2 diesels; 2 props; 304 bhp **Range:** 400/12 **Crew:** 10 tot.

Remarks: Same basic design as the diving tender BRM 83 (see under [YDT]). *Kakanj* is ex-Yugoslav, while *Krasniča* was launched 1-2-96, when a third was under construction at Punat/Krk. Five were said to be in service as of 11-98. Wooden hulls.

◆ **1 ex-German Siebel Ferry–class dredge [YM]**
Bldr: . . . (In serv. 1943–44)

PDS 713 (ex-DSM 105, ex-DST 105, ex-. . .)

D: 129 tons (167 fl) **S:** 9 kts **Dim:** 25.84 × 14.05 × 1.09
Electronics: Radar: 1 . . . nav.
M: 2 Mercedes-Benz truck diesels; 2 props; 400 bhp
Range: . . ./. . . **Crew:** . . . tot.

Remarks: Catamaran with twin pontoon-type hulls, built as a landing craft. One of two Croatian survivors of 10 originally in Yugoslav service. Refitted and re-engined at Pula in 1956. Sister DSM 110 remains configured as a landing craft (see under [LCU]).

◆ **2 LR 67–class harbor tugs [YTM]**
Bldr: Split SY, Croatia (In serv. 1960s)

LR 71 LR 73

LR 71 H&L Van Ginderen, 2-97

D: 550 tons (fl) **S:** 11 kts **Dim:** 32.0 × 8.0 × . . .
M: 2 diesels; 1 prop; . . . bhp

Remarks: LR = *Lučki Remorker* (harbor tug). Sisters LR 72 and LR 77 remain in Federal Yugoslav Navy hands.

◆ **2 small riverine tugs [YTL]**

R 301 BIZON R 303

Remarks: Based at Sisak on the Save River; no data available.

◆ **1 sail-training craft [YTS]**

KRALJIČA JELENA (ex-*ACI No. 1)*

Remarks: No data available.

Disposal note: M 117–class training craft and former minesweeper *Lastovo* (LM 117) was sold for commercial use.

1ST CROATIAN GUARDS CORPS

Note: The 1st Croatian Guards is a triservice presidential guard and operates a small number of craft based at Pula and in the Brioni Islands.

◆ **3 Galeb-class (Type 15) riverine and lake patrol craft [WPB]**

CISTA VELIKA DUBRAVIČE KRASNIČA

D: 19.5 tons (fl) **S:** 16 kts **Dim:** 16.87 × 3.90 × 0.65 (0.70 props)
A: 1 20-mm M-71 AA; 1 quadruple 14.5-mm 93-cal. mg
Electronics: Radar: 1 Decca 110 nav.
M: 2 diesels; 2 props; 330 bhp **Range:** 160/12 **Crew:** 6 tot.

Remarks: Steel hull; glass-reinforced plastic superstructures. Four sisters were delivered to the Sudan in 5-89, and a number of others remain in Federal Yugoslav service. These three came under Croatian control and were commissioned during 8-92; they have since been transferred to the 1st Croatian Guards Corps.

◆ **1 BMT 1–class patrol boat [WPB]**

ZEČEVO (ex-BRM 82)

Zečevo Dario Vuljanič, *HVG,* 2000

D: 38 tons (46 fl) **S:** 12 kts **Dim:** 20.50 (19.4 pp) × 4.50 × 1.42
A: 1 20-mm 90-cal. M-71 AA **Electronics:** Radar: 1 . . . nav.
M: 2 diesels; 2 props; 304 bhp **Range:** 400/12 **Crew:** 10 tot.

Remarks: Same basic design as the naval diving tender BRM 83 and the BMT 1–class personnel launches. Wooden hull.

Note: A number of other small patrol craft are in 1st Croatian Guards Corps service, including *Zalac* (M2), armed with one 20-mm AA.

COAST GUARD

Note: A separate coast guard was established during 1998 by incorporating the Maritime Police patrol and Harbor Master pilot craft. The planned transfer of the navy's Mirna-class patrol craft did not occur, however. Coast guard craft are painted white and have a broad blue and narrow red diagonal stripe on the hull sides forward, with

COAST GUARD *(continued)*

crossed anchors on the blue stripe. Home port is indicated by a small pennant number on the bow, with "PU" indicating Pula, and so forth. Coast guard units carry the inscription "Kapetanija" on the hull sides.

Craft known to be in service at Pula include the GRP-hulled launches 1-PU and 2-PU, and GRP-hulled fast launch *Blitvenića* (2 SB). One small landing craft is also in Marine Police service.

Coast Guard patrol launch Blitvenića (2 SB) Dario Vuljanić, *HVG,* 1999

CUBA

Republic of Cuba

MARINA DE GUERRA REVOLUCIONARIA

Personnel (2001): Approx. 2,000 total, including 1,000 naval infantry. There are also about 8,000 reserves. Active personnel numbers are being reduced as the number of operable ships and craft declines.

Naval Aviation: The four Kamov Ka-28 Helix-A and four Mil Mi-14PL Haze-A ASW helicopters are probably no longer operational.

Bases: The navy is organized into three districts, headquartered at Cabañas, Cienfuegos, and Holguín. Principal bases are at Cabañas, Canasi, Cienfuegos, Havana (where most repair work is accomplished), Mariel, Punta Ballenatos, and Varadero. The Naval Infantry Regiment is housed at Granma.

Coastal Defense: In addition to Russian P-20/21 Termit (SS-C-3 Styx-C) truck-mounted antiship missiles delivered in the 1980s, the Cuban Navy has adapted shipboard Styx missiles for land launch, using the indigenously developed Bandera-VI mobile launcher.

Disposal Note: Of the three Soviet-provided Koni-class (Project 1159) frigates, the *Mariel* (350, ex-SKR 28; in serv. 24-9-81) remained intact into 1999 when it was announced that she would be restored to service, but instead the ship remains derelict; the second unit (356, name not known; delivered 8-2-84) was sold to the Cayman Islands in 8-96 and renamed *Captain Keith Tibbetts* for use as a sunken attraction for scuba divers at Cayman Brac; and the *Monkada* (353, ex-SKR-451; in service 10-4-88) was sunk for the same purpose off the Cuban coast on 16-7-98.

PATROL COMBATANTS [PG]

♦ 1 Soviet Modified Pauk class (Project 1241PE)
Bldr: Volodarskiy SY, Rybinsk (In serv. 22-5-90)

321

D: 425 tons (495 fl; 554 max.) **S:** 32 kts (28 sust.)
Dim: 58.5 (49.5 pp) × 10.40 (9.40 wl) × 2.14 (hull; 4.0 props)
A: 1 76.2-mm 59-cal. AK-176 DP; 1 Fasta-4M SAM syst. (16 9M-313 Igla-1 missiles); 130-mm 54-cal. AK-630 gatling AA; 2 twin 25-mm 80-cal. 2M-3M AA; 2 5-round RBU-1200 ASW RL (30 RGB-12 rockets); 4 fixed 533-mm TT (2 SET-65E and 2 53-65KE torpedoes); 2 d.c. racks (12 d.c.)
Electronics:
Radar: 1 Mius (Spin Trough) nav.; 1 Positiv-E (Cross Dome) air/surf. search, 1 MR-123E Vympel AME (Bass Tilt) f.c.
Sonar: MGK-345 MF hull-mounted and MF dipping
EW: 2 16-round PK-16 decoy RL

Modified Pauk 321—with 25-mm gunmounts added abreast the sonar housing at the stern French Navy, 12-98

M: 2 M-521-TM5 diesels; 2 props; 17,330 bhp
Range: 2,000/20; 2,600/14; 3,000/12 **Fuel:** 50 tons **Endurance:** 10 days
Crew: 7 officers, 32 enlisted

Remarks: Delivered under tow. Three additional units were to have been transferred, but the collapse of the USSR and the crumbling Cuban economy forced cancellation. Differs from standard Russian Navy version in having a larger pilothouse, incorporating a Positiv radar, and using 533-mm torpedo tubes (which are able to carry antiship as well as ASW torpedoes) vice 400-mm ASW TT. Four virtually identical units were built for India, one was retained by the Russian Navy, and two others were never delivered by the builder. The Cuban unit was nonoperational by 1997 but was refitted and reactivated during 1999.
Hull systems: The large housing for a dipping sonar system projects 1.5 m out from the stern. The large hull-mounted sonar dome is located approximately beneath the gun fire-control radar. The hull is constructed of mild steel, while the middle part of the deck plating, some internal bulkheads, and much of the superstructure are made of aluminum-magnesium alloy. Range with normal fuel allowance is only 1,600 n.m. at 12 kts.
Combat systems: The combat data system is designated SU-580E. There is a Kolonka-2 backup ringsight director for the single gatling AA gun; the MR-123 radar director can control both the 76.2-mm and 30-mm guns. Normal ammunition load is 152 rounds 76-mm (all ready-service, on-mount) and 2,000 rounds 30-mm. In 1999, twin 25-mm AA mounts were added flanking the VDS housing at the stern. MGK-345 applies to both the hull-mounted and dipping sonars; the dipping sonar transducer can be lowered to 200 m.

PATROL CRAFT [PC]

♦ 6 Soviet Osa-II class (Project 205EM)

261 262 267 268 271 274

Cuban Navy Osa-II U.S. Navy, 8-84

D: 184 tons (226 normal fl; 245 overload) **S:** 40 kts (35 sust.)
Dim: 38.6 (37.5 wl) × 7.6 (6.3 wl) × 2.0 (hull; 3.1 props)
A: 2 twin 30-mm 65-cal. AK-230 AA; 1 shoulder-launcher for Strela or Igla-1 heat-seeking missiles
Electronics:
Radar: 1 Rangout (Square Tie) surf. search; 1 MR-104 Rys' (Drum Tilt) gun f.c.
M: 3 M-504 or M-504B diesels; 3 props; 15,000 bhp **Electric:** 400 kw tot.
Range: 500/34; 750/25 **Endurance:** 5 days **Crew:** 4 officers, 24 enlisted

Remarks: Two transferred in 1977, three in 1978, two in 1979, two in 11-81, two in 1-82, and two in 2-82. Seven have been discarded. As of 1997, the missiles had been removed from all and transferred to shore-based launchers; the shipboard launchers have been retained aboard, however. The remaining craft are rarely operated.

MINE WARFARE CRAFT

♦ 4 Soviet Yevgenya-class (Project 1258) inshore minesweepers
Bldr: Sredniy Neva SY, Kolpino

D: 88.5 tons light, 94.5 tons normal (97.9 fl) **S:** 11 kts
Dim: 26.13 (24.20 wl) × 5.90 (5.10 wl) × 1.38
A: 1 twin 25-mm 80-cal. 2M-3M AA; 1 7-round MRG-1 grenade launcher; 4 d.c. in individual tilt racks (+ 8 emergency stowage)
Electronics:
Radar: 1 Mius (Spin Trough) or Kivach nav.
Sonar: MG-7 HF dipping
M: 2 Type 3D12 diesels; 2 props; 600 bhp—hydraulic slow-speed drive

MINE WARFARE CRAFT *(continued)*

Electric: 100 kw tot. (2 × 50-kw diesel sets) **Range:** 400/10 **Fuel:** 2.7 tons
Endurance: 3 days **Crew:** 1 officer, 9 enlisted (+ 2–3 clearance divers)

Remarks: Two transferred in 11-77, one in 9-78, two in 11-79, two in 12-80, two in 12-81, one in 10-82, and two in 11-84; two others, delivered 9-84, were further transferred to Nicaragua. At least eight have been stricken. Equipped to search for mines in depths of up to 30 m using towed television camera, marker buoys, and standard wire cable gear. Glass-reinforced plastic construction.

AUXILIARIES

♦ 1 Spanish-built navigational buoy tender [AGL]
Bldr: Maritime del Musel, Gijón (In serv. 1979)

H 102 Taino

D: 1,100 tons **S:** 12 kts **Dim:** 53.0 (42.0 pp) × 10.4 × 3.5
M: 2 diesels; 2 props; 1,550 bhp **Electric:** 360 kw **Crew:** . . . tot.

Remarks: 669 grt/572 dwt. Primarily a buoy tender, but can also be used for hydrographic surveys.

♦ 1 Soviet Biya-class hydrographic survey ship [AGS]
Bldr: Stocznia Polnocna, Gdansk, Poland (In serv. 1972–76)

H 103 Guama (ex-GS 186)

D: 750 tons (fl) **S:** 13 kts **Dim:** 55.0 × 9.2 × 2.6
Electronics: Radar: 1 Don-2 nav. **M:** 2 diesels; 2 CP props; 1,200 bhp
Range: 4,700/11 **Fuel:** 90 tons **Endurance:** 15 days **Crew:** 25 tot.

Remarks: Transferred 11-80. Carries one survey launch and has one 5-ton crane. Also useful as a navigational buoy tender. Operated for the Institute of Hydrography.

♦ 1 hydrographic survey vessel, converted trawler [AGS]
Bldr: Ast. Talleres de Celaya, Bilbao, Spain (In serv. 1968)

H 101 Siboney

D: 600 tons (fl) **S:** 11.4 kts **Dim:** 40.2 × 8.3 × 2.6
M: 2 Stork-Werkspoor RHD-216K diesels; 1 prop; 910 bhp
Electric: 160 kw **Crew:** . . . tot.

♦ 1 cargo ship [AK] Bldr: . . . . . . (In serv. 1965)

Arenal

Remarks: 763 grt. Acquired 12-82. No other data available. May no longer be in service.

♦ 1 Soviet Pelym-class (Project 1799) training ship [AXT]

40 (ex-SR-77)

Cuban Pelym-class 40 2-82

D: 1,050 tons (1,200 fl) **S:** 13.5 kts **Dim:** 64.06 × 11.71 × 3.51
Electronics: Radar: 1 Don-2 nav.
M: 1 diesel; 1 prop; 1,536 bhp **Range:** 1,000/13.5 **Crew:** 40 tot.

Remarks: Arrived in Cuba 2-82 under tow. As delivered, was equipped to deploy, operate, and recover a deperming cable array. By 1999 was being employed as fleet training ship, with the portable deperming gear deleted.

SERVICE CRAFT

♦ 2 Soviet Yelva-class (Project 1893) diving tenders [YDT]

D: 295 tons (fl) **S:** 12.4 kts **Dim:** 40.90 (37.00 pp) × 8.00 × 2.07
Electronics: Radar: 1 Mius (Spin Trough) nav.
M: 2 Type 3D12A diesels; 2 props; 600 bhp **Electric:** 200 kw
Range: 1,870/12 **Endurance:** 10 days **Crew:** 30 tot.

Remarks: Transferred in 1978. Can support seven divers at once to 60 m. Have a built-in decompression chamber. May no longer be in service.

♦ 1 yacht [YFL]

A 11 Granma

Remarks: Small cabin cruiser in which Fidel Castro returned to Cuba in 1956. Maintained by the navy as a museum.

♦ 3 Lamda-class survey craft [YGS] (In serv. 1960s)

H 76 H 77 H 78

D: 150 tons (fl) **S:** 10 kts **Dim:** 29.0 × 6.0 × 2.1 **M:** 1 diesel; 1 prop; 250 bhp

Remarks: Converted, wooden-hulled fishing boats.

♦ 3 Soviet Prometey-class large harbor tugs [YTB]

D: 319 tons (fl) **S:** 12 kts **Dim:** 29.8 (28.2 pp) × 8.30 × 3.20
A: 3 single 12.7-mm 79-cal. mg
Electronics: Radar: 1 Mius (Spin Trough) nav.
M: 2 Type 6D30/50.4 diesels; 2 CP props; 1,200 bhp
Electric: 50 kw (2 × 25 kw) **Crew:** 8 tot.

Remarks: Two transferred in 1967, one in 1972. Bollard pull: 14 tons.

MINISTRY OF THE INTERIOR BORDER GUARD
(Tropas de Guardia Frontera)

PATROL CRAFT [WPC]

♦ 3 Soviet Stenka class (Project 205P)

D: 170 tons (210 fl) **S:** 36 kts **Dim:** 39.50 × 7.0 × 1.80
A: 2 twin 30-mm 65-cal. AK-230 AA
Electronics:
Radar: 1 Baklan (Pot Drum) surf. search, 1 MR-104 Rys' (Drum Tilt) gun f.c.
EW: 2 16-round PK-16 decoy RL
M: 3 M-504 diesels; 3 props; 15,000 bhp
Range: 500/35; 800/20 **Crew:** 5 officers, 27 enlisted

Remarks: Two transferred in 2-85, two in 9-85; one had ceased to operate by 2000. Do not have the four fixed 400-mm ASW TT and stern-mounted dipping sonar found on the standard version and have no antisubmarine capability.

PATROL BOATS [WPB]

♦ 18 Soviet Zhuk-class (Project 1400) patrol craft

Cuban Border Guard Zhuk 532 U.S. Coast Guard, 1992

D: 35.9 tons (39.7 fl) **S:** 30 kts
Dim: 23.80 (21.70 wl) × 5.00 (3.80 wl) × 1.00 (hull)
A: 1 twin 12.7-mm 60-cal. Utës-M mg **Electronics:** Radar: 1 Lotsiya nav.
M: 2 M-401B diesels; 2 props; 2,400 bhp
Electric: 48 kw total (2 × 21-kw, 1 × 6-kw diesel sets)
Range: 500/13.5 **Endurance:** 5 days **Crew:** 3 officers, 14 enlisted

Remarks: One transferred in 12-71, one in 7-74, four in 10-75, two in 12-76, four in 1977–79, six in 1980 (including three in 12-80), three in 1984, four in 9-85, and two in 9-89. At least 17 others have been passed onward to Nicaragua or stricken. Have enclosed, side-by-side machinegun mountings.

♦ 1 22-knot patrol launch

Guanabacoa Bldr: . . . . . ., Cadiz, Spain (L: . . .)

♦ 6 fast launches Bldr: . . . SY, Spain (In serv. 1971–72)

Camilo Cienfuegos, Cuartel Moncada, Escambray, Finlay, Maceo, Marti

Remarks: No other information available. Some or all may no longer be in service.

CYPRUS

Republic of Cyprus

Personnel (2001): Approx. 350 total, including maritime police personnel

Base: Limassol. A new base at Paphos began construction in fall 1998, allegedly for use by visiting Greek warships.

Maritime Aviation: Three Agusta-Bell 47G helicopters are assigned coastal patrol duties, as is one Pilatus-Britten-Norman BN-2A Maritime Defender coastal reconnaissance aircraft.

Coastal Defense: At least 24 truck-mounted MM 40 Exocet Block 2 antiship missiles were acquired from France during 1994 for the National Guard; each truck carries two missiles.

NAVAL COMMAND OF THE NATIONAL GUARD

PATROL BOATS [PB]

♦ **1 Type 32L**
Bldr: C.N. de l'Esterel, Cannes, France (In serv. 24-5-83)

P 01 Salamis

Salamis (P 01)—as rearmed H&L Van Ginderen, 5-00

D: 98 tons (fl) **S:** 32 kts (30 sust.) **Dim:** 32.1 × 6.45 × 1.9
A: 2 2-round Simbad SAM syst. (Mistral missiles); 1 40-mm 70-cal. OTOBreda-Bofors AA; 1 20-mm 90-cal. Rheinmetall AA
Electronics: Radar: 1 Decca 1226 nav.
M: 2 SACM 195 CZSHRY 12 diesels; 2 props; 4,680 bhp
Range: 1,500/15 **Crew:** 22 tot.

Remarks: Wooden construction. Manned launchers for the point-defense SAM system were aboard by 5-00, mounted atop the superstructure abaft the mast. Sister *Aphrodite* was operated by the Maritime Police.

♦ **1 ex-Greek Dilos class** Bldr: Hellenic SY, Skaramanga (In serv. 1979)

P 02 Kyrinia (ex-*Knossos,* P 269)

D: 75 tons (86 fl) **S:** 27 kts **Dim:** 29.00 (27.00 wl) × 5.00 × 1.62
A: 2 single 20-mm 70-cal. Oerlikon Mk 10 AA
Electronics: Radar: 1 Decca 1226C nav.
M: 2 MTU 12V331 TC81 diesels; 2 props; 2,720 bhp
Range: 1,600/25 **Crew:** 15 tot.

Remarks: Donated 3-00. Designed by Abeking & Rasmussen, Germany. Round-bilge, steel-construction hull. Sisters operate in the Georgian Coast Guard and in the Greek Coast Guard and Customs services.

MARITIME POLICE

PATROL BOATS [WPB]

♦ **1 Israeli Shaldag class**
Bldr: Israel Shipyards, Haifa (In serv. 2-98)

PV 22 . . . . . .

Cypriot Maritime Police Shaldag-class PV 22 H&L Van Ginderen, 5-00

D: 40 tons (56 fl) **S:** 46 kts **Dim:** 24.80 × 6.00 × 1.15
A: 1 20-mm 90-cal. Oerlikon AA; 2 single 12.7-mm mg
Electronics: Radar: 1 Furuno FR 8250 nav.
M: 2 MTU 12V396 TE 94 diesels; 2 waterjets; 3,260 bhp
Electric: 50 kw tot. (2 × 25-kw, 440-V a.c. diesel sets)
Range: 890/45; 990/33 **Endurance:** 2–3 days **Crew:** 15 tot.

Remarks: Acquired late in 1997. Deep-vee, aluminum-construction hull with five watertight compartments. Air-conditioned.

♦ **2 Yugoslav FAC-23 class**
Bldr: Brodotehnika, Belgrade (In serv. 21-11-91)

PV 20 Poseidon PV 21 Evagoras

Evagoras (PV 21) Dieter Wolf, 5-00

D: 57 tons (fl) **S:** 42 kts **Dim:** 24.60 (20.60 pp) × 5.70 × 1.05
A: 1 20-mm 90-cal. Rheinmetall AA; 2 single 7.62-mm mg; 1 ISBRS unguided rocket launcher
Electronics: Radar: 1 Decca 1226 nav.
M: 2 diesels; 2 KaMeWa waterjets; 4,270 bhp
Range: 400/40; 600/20 **Endurance:** 5 days **Crew:** 9 tot.

Remarks: Aluminum construction. One seems to have borne the temporary name *Sergey Krtanovic.*

♦ **1 Plascoa 18-meter class**
Bldr: C.N. de l'Esterel, Cannes, France (In serv. 1982)

PL 2 Kimon

D: 28 tons (fl) **S:** 26 kts **Dim:** 17.2 × 5.2 × 1.3
A: 1 12.7-mm mg **Electronics:** Radar: 1 Decca 1226 nav.
M: 2 MTU diesels; 2 props; . . . bhp **Crew:** 8 tot.

Remarks: GRP construction. Another unit of this class was discarded in 1991.

♦ **5 ex-East German SAB 12 launches**

PL 11 Karpasta (ex-GS 10, ex-G 50)
PL 12 Ilarion (ex-GS 25, ex-G 52)
PL 13 Kourion (ex-GS 27, ex-G 55)
PL 14 Dionysos (ex-GS 12, ex-G 55)
PL 15 Akamas (ex-GS 28, ex-G 57)

Akamas (PL 15) Dieter Wolf, 5-00

D: 14 tons (fl) **S:** 16 kts **Dim:** 12.6 × 4.0 × 1.1
A: small arms **Electronics:** Radar: 1 Decca . . . nav.
M: 2 Volvo Penta TAMD-series diesels; 2 props; 540 bhp **Crew:** 5 tot.

Remarks: Transferred 12-92 from the German *Bundesgrenzschutz See* (Maritime Border Guard).

NORTH CYPRUS

Turkish Federated State of Cyprus

Note: The independence of North Cyprus is not recognized by the United Nations. Defense forces are Turkish controlled and largely Turkish manned.

PATROL BOATS [PB]

♦ **1 Turkish-built**
Bldr: Profilo Holding Proteksan SY, Tuzla, Istanbul (L: 23-9-88)

74 Ras Denktas

D: 10 tons (fl) **S:** 28 kts **Dim:** 11.9 × 3.5 × . . .
A: 1 12.7-mm mg **Electronics:** Radar: 1 Raytheon . . . nav.
M: 2 Volvo Aquamatic diesels; 2 props; 400 bhp **Range:** 250/. . . **Crew:** 6 tot.

Note: Also in service is *Caner Gönyeli* (P 145), a 14.6-m, 700-bhp patrol craft built at Taskizak Shipyard, Turkey.

DENMARK

Kingdom of Denmark

DET KONGELIGE DANSKE SØVÆRN

Personnel (2000): 4,209 total (913 officers, 2,800 enlisted, 496 conscripts), plus 5,500 naval reservists and 4,400 in the Naval Home Guard. The wartime mobilization strength was cut from 9,800 to 7,300 in 6-99.

Bases: Frederikshavn and Korsør in Denmark, Grønnedal in Greenland

Naval Aviation: Eight Mk 80A/90 Lynx helicopters. All eight are being refurbished to Mk 90B configuration under a 1-98 contract to GKN Westland, U.K.; the original Gem 42 engines and equipment are being transferred to new airframes and Sea Spray 3000 radars, a FLIR, and a capability to launch Sea Spray antiship missiles are being added. The first refurbished aircraft was delivered on 11-7-00.

The Danish Air Force has 2 Gulfstream G-III and 1 Bombardier Challenger CL-604 maritime patrol aircraft and 8 Sikorsky S-61A-1 Sea King helicopters in 772 Squadron, all based at Værløse, for search-and-rescue duties. The air force helicopters are to be replaced with the Sikorsky S-92IU Helibus. The Challenger CL-604 was delivered in 7-98, and two more were ordered late in 2000, to be equipped with Telephonics Corp APS-143B(V)3 OceanEye radar.

Danish Mk80A/90 Lynx—painted a deep royal blue Jaroslaw Cislak, 6-95

Coastal Defense: Two mobile Harpoon coast defense batteries each consist of two trucks, with four missiles each, and a third command center vehicle. The batteries employ RGM-84A missiles removed from the stricken frigates of the *Peder Skram* class. The fortress of Stevns at the Baltic approaches to the Great Belt is equipped with 150-mm artillery and 40-mm AA guns, and there are also six coastal radar stations.

Weapons and Sensors: Most equipment is of European origin, except for the U.S. Sea Sparrow and Harpoon missile systems. The Harpoon inventory was upgraded from Block IC to Block II under a 3-99 contract with Boeing. Some 3,000 SM.2G sea mines were delivered 1990–93. NATO Link 11 datalink is employed by major surface units, and Denmark is participating in the Link 22 development program. Eurotorp MU-90 ASW torpedoes were ordered in 1-99 for use on the *Flyvefisken* class. The Danish firm Terma A/S provides navigational and surface-search radars. Chemring Chimera dual-mode seduction rounds were ordered early in 2000 for use with Terma's 130-mm Soft-Kill Weapon System decoy launchers.

Rapidly interchangeable modules ordered for use on combatants under the Stanflex program included the following as of 1-00:

- 19 76-mm 62-cal. OTOBreda dual-purpose guns
- 10 sets of twin quadruple launch cells for Harpoon antiship missiles
- 20 sets of two triple Mk 48 vertical launch cells for RIM-7P Sea Sparrow SAMs (each to be able to carry four ESSM Sea Sparrows per cell when the missile becomes available, post-2005)
- 5 mine countermeasures containers
- 4 ASW sets, each with Thales Salmon active VDS (18.5 and 19.45 kHz)
- 22 crane modules
- 2 oceanographic/hydrographic survey modules
- . . . sets of mine rails (60 mines per set)
- 4 sets of twin tubes for MU-90 ASW torpedoes
- . . . tubes for Bofors Tp 613 wire-guided antiship torpedoes

In addition, plans call for procuring containerized hospital, command-and-control, and sealift modules for use on larger ships.

Note: Ship names are prefaced by HDMS (His Danish Majesty's Ship).

ATTACK SUBMARINES [SS]

Note: Denmark is a partner in the Viking (formerly Submarine 2000) program with Sweden and Norway. The joint Viking Submarine Corp. was founded in 3-00 by Kockums, Kongsberg, and Odense Staalskipværft to design, and eventually construct, the submarines. Denmark hopes to acquire four, Sweden two, and Norway four.

♦ **1 ex-Swedish Näcken class (Type A-14)**
Bldr: Kockums, Malmö

	Laid down	L	In serv.
S 325 Kronborg (ex-*Näcken*)	11-72	17-4-78	25-4-80

Kronborg (S 325)—in Swedish Navy service Jaroslaw Cislak, 9-99

D: 1,218 tons surf./1,313 tons sub.
S: 10 kts surf./20 kts sub. **Dim:** 57.9 × 5.7 × 4.1
A: 6 bow 533-mm TT (8 Tp 61B or Tp 613 torpedoes or mines); 2 bow 400-mm TT (4 Tp 422 or 431 torpedoes)
Electronics:
Radar: 1 Terma . . . nav./surf. search
Sonar: STN Atlas Elektronik CSU-83 suite (DBQS-21) with FAS-3-1 passive flank arrays
EW: ArgoSystems AR-700-S5 intercept
M: 1 MTU 16V652 MB diesel (1,800 bhp), 1 Jeumont-Schneider generator, 1 ASEA motor; 1 5-bladed prop; 1,500 shp—2 United Stirling V4-275R Mk I air-independent 75-kw generators
Electric: 150 kw (1 Scania diesel set) **Crew:** 5 officers, 14 enlisted

Remarks: Leased for $35.4 million on 13-2-01 and transferred 17-8-01 after a refit at Kockums; training with a Danish crew was to begin in 8-01. In 2005, Denmark has the option to purchase the submarine outright or return it. Began conversion at Kockums 11-87 to install two United Stirling V4-275R Mk I Stirling-cycle engines; relaunched 6-9-88, the submarine began trials 23-11-88 and recommissioned in the Swedish Navy 11-4-89.
Hull systems: Has an anechoic hull coating. The 168-cell Tudor electric battery installation is mounted on shock absorbers. Stern planes are x-configuration; bow planes are on the sail. Diving depth: 300 m; collapse depth: 500 m. During AIP conversion, an 8-m section containing the Stirling engines, liquid oxygen tanks, and auxiliary machinery was added. Using the closed-cycle plant, the submarine can remain submerged for over two weeks.
Combat systems: An Ericsson IDPS central data system (Swedish Navy designation SESUB 900C) furnishes, in addition to tactical information, data on the main engines; it uses two Censor 932 computers. Has U.S. Kollmorgen Model 76 search-and-attack periscope.

Disposal note: Type 205 submarines *Narhvalen* (S 320) and *Nordkaperen* (S 321) were retired during 2001.

♦ **3 ex-Norwegian Kobben class (Type 207)**
Bldr: Rheinstahl Nordseewerke, Emden, Germany

	Laid down	L	In serv.
S 322 Tumleren (ex-*Utvaer,* S 303)	24-3-65	30-7-65	1-12-65
S 323 Sælen (ex-*Uthaug,* S 304)	31-5-65	3-10-65	16-2-66
S 324 Springeren (ex-*Kya,* S 317)	26-5-63	20-2-64	15-1-64

Tumleren (S 322) Winter & Findler, 11-00

D: 412 tons light; 459 tons surf./524 tons sub.
S: 13.5 kts surf./17 kts sub. **Dim:** 46.61 × 4.60 × 4.58
A: 8 bow 533-mm TT (8 Tp 61-3 wire-guided torpedoes)
Electronics:
Radar: 1 Terma . . . nav./surf. search
EW: Racal Sealion intercept
Sonar: STN Atlas Elektronik PSU-83 suite
M: 2 MTU 12V493 AZ80 diesels (600 bhp each), 2 405-kw generators, 1 1,100-kw motor; 1 2.3-m-dia. prop; 1,700 shp max.
Range: 5,000/8 snorkel; 14/17, 141/6 sub. **Crew:** 7 officers, 17 enlisted

ATTACK SUBMARINES [SS] *(continued)*

Soelen (S 323) Derek Fox, 6-01

Remarks: Purchased from Norway in 1986. German IKL Type 207 design, based on Type 205 but deeper diving. Refitted at Urivale SY, Bergen; S 322 completed in 10-89, S 323 on 9-7-90, and S 324 in 5-91 (delivered in 7-91). S 323 sank 3-12-90 while under tow without crew; raised on 17-12-90, she was repaired by 9-93, as the damage, despite flooding of the pressure hull, was found to have been minimal. S 323 was refitted in 2000 with air-conditioning and improved battery cooling to permit her to deploy to the Mediterranean. All are to be stricken during 2002–03.
Hull systems: During modernization, were re-engined and lengthened by 1.60 m. Maximum diving depth is 190 m.
Combat systems: Have Thorn-EMI D3 fire-control system and Pilkington Optronics CK 34 search periscope.

FRIGATES [FF]

♦ . . . (+ 2) SF 3000 Project Command and Support Vessels
Bldr: Odense Staalskibsværjt A/S, Odense

	Laid down	L	In serv.
F	2003	. . .	6-06
F	. . .	. . .	2007

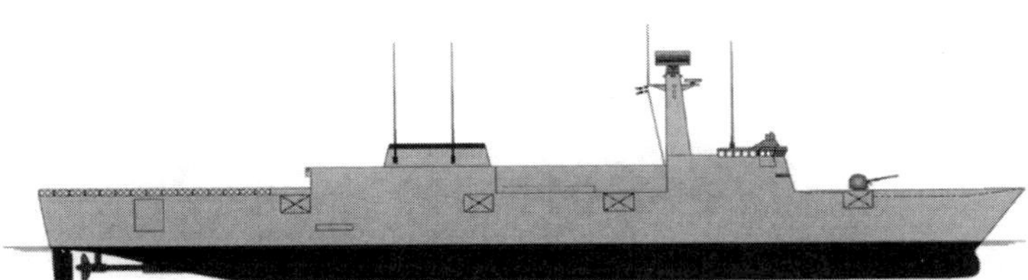

SF 3000 Project Danish Navy, 1998

D: 4,600 tons (6,000 fl) **S:** 24–26 kts **Dim:** 140.00 × 19.0 × 6.3
A: 8 AGM-84C Block II Harpoon SSM; . . . Mk 48 VLS cells (. . . Sea Sparrow ESSM SAM); 1 76-mm 62-cal. DP; 1 . . . CIWS; . . . MU-90 ASW torpedoes; 1 or 2 . . . helicopters
Electronics:
Radar: . . .
Sonar: . . .
M: . . . diesels; 2 CP props; 21,460 bhp
Range: 9,000/15 **Endurance:** 28 days
Crew: 100 tot. + 75 command staff + 25 aviation crew

Remarks: Approved 6-99 for ordering under the 2000–03 Procurement Plan. Ordered 1-02. Intended as multipurpose units for peacetime expeditionary support operations, using six to eight portable functional modules installed amidships, to carry either a 20-strong task group commander and staff, a 50-strong maritime component commander and staff, or a 70-strong combined joint task force commander and staff. A 22 ISO-standard module hospital facility is also to be fittable. Missions foreseen include ASW (with VDS module and torpedo tubes), mine countermeasures, and humanitarian aid.
Hull systems: Will have side and stern ramps to handle up to 46 vehicles and will have 280 lane-meters of parking. To carry one 10- to 12-ton or two 5-ton helicopters. An 84-m-long by 10.5-m-wide by 4.5-m-high section aft is to be equipped to take various operational modules and/or vehicles up to tank weight.
Combat systems: The 127-mm gun will be either a new OTOBreda or United Defense Mk 45 Mod. 4 62-cal. mounting or a surplus U.S. Navy Mk 45 Mod. 2 mounting, with the mount being placed in two Stanflex canisters mounted one atop the other; seven other Stanflex containers would carry Mk 48 VLS or 76-mm guns. Will carry antitorpedo and antimissile decoys.

Note: In addition to the above units, approval was given 6-99 for the construction of two to four 3,500- to 4,000-ton, helicopter-equipped Stanflex 1000 fisheries patrol vessels; the first is to be ordered during the 2000–03 procurement plan and to enter service in 2007 or 2008, the second to be ordered during the 2008–12 plan, and two more to be ordered post-2012. The ships would be about 115 m overall and are to have a speed of 27 kts.

CORVETTES [FFL]

♦ 3 Niels Juel class (Type KV 72)
Bldr: Ålborg Værft, Ålborg

	Laid down	L	In serv.
F 354 NIELS JUEL	20-10-76	17-2-78	26-8-80
F 355 OLFERT FISCHER	6-12-78	10-5-79	16-10-81
F 356 PETER TORDENSKIOLD	3-12-79	30-4-80	2-4-82

Peter Tordenskiold (F 356) Jürg Kürsener, 5-00

Niels Juel (F 354) H&L Van Ginderen, 10-00

Peter Tordenskiold (F 356) Jaroslaw Cislak, 6-00

D: 1,100 tons (1,320 fl) **S:** 30 kts (20 on diesel)
Dim: 84.00 (80.00 pp) × 10.30 × 3.10
A: 8 RGM-84C Block II Harpoon SSM; 6 Mk 48 Mod. 3 or 6 VLS SAM modules (6 or 12 Sea Sparrow RIM-7P missiles); 1 76-mm 62-cal. OTOBreda Compact DP; 1 d.c. rack
Electronics:
Radar: 2 Terma Scanter Mil 009 nav.; 1 EADS TRS-3D air search; 1 CelsiusTech 9GR 600 surf. search; 1 CelsiusTech 9LV 200 gun f.c. (with Type 771 low-light t.v. tracker); 1 General Dynamics Mk 95 missile f.c. syst. (2 directors)
Sonar: Plessey PMS-26 hull-mounted MF (10 kHz)
EW: Racal Cutlass B-1 intercept; Telegon HFD/F; 2 12-round Thorn-EMI DL-12T decoy RL (Chemring Chimera decoys)
M: CODOG: 1 G.E. LM-2500 gas turbine (26,600 shp), 1 MTU 20V956 TB82 diesel (4,800 bhp); 2 CP props
Electric: 1,500 kw (3 × 500-kw diesel sets) **Range:** 800/28; 2,500/18
Fuel: 130 tons **Crew:** 18 officers, 9 chief petty officers, 63 other enlisted

Remarks: Ordered 5-12-75. F 356 underwent a midlife overhaul from 15-5-96 to 10-98; F 354 began hers in late 1998 and F 355 in late 1999.
Combat systems: During the midlife refits, the DataSAAB CEPLO data system was replaced by the Terma-CelsiusTech SF-300 system, a variant of the 9LV Mk 3 system with NATO Link 11 datalink; the octuple Mk 29 Sea Sparrow launcher on the fantail was replaced by up to four sets of triple Mk 48 Mod. 3 modular vertical Sea Sparrow SAM launchers with the later RIM-7P missile (two modules are normally carried); and the EADS (ex-DaimlerChrysler, ex-DASA, ex-Telefunken) TRS-3D surveillance and weapons-control radar replaced the original Plessey AWS-5. Two cranes have been mounted at the after corners of the forecastle to handle reload missiles and boats. The ships are expected to serve until 2010 or later and are to be given a NATO Maritime Command-and-Control Information System (MCCIS) and UHF/SHF SATCOM capabilities. Four single 20-mm Oerlikon AA guns are no longer carried.

PATROL SHIPS [PS]

Note: There are a total of seven crews for the five fisheries patrol vessels described below; the crews are rotated to the ships while on station off Greenland and the Faeroe Islands.

PATROL SHIPS [PS] *(continued)*

♦ 4 Thetis class (Stanflex 2000) Bldr: Svendborg Skibsværft, Svendborg

	Laid down	L	In serv.
F 357 Thetis	10-10-88	14-7-89	1-7-91
F 358 Triton	27-6-89	16-3-90	2-12-91
F 359 Vædderen	19-3-90	21-12-90	9-6-92
F 360 Hvidbjørnen	2-1-91	11-10-91	30-11-92

Hvidbjørnen (F 360) Findler & Winter, 6-01

Thetis (F 357)—note door in transom stern for towed seismic array
Maritime Photographic, 6-99

D: 2,600 tons (3,500 fl) **S:** 21.5 kts **Dim:** 112.50 (99.75 pp) × 14.40 × 6.00
A: 1 76-mm 62-cal. OTOBreda SuperRapid DP; 1 or 2 single 20-mm 70-cal. Oerlikon AA; 2 d.c. racks; 1 Lynx Mk 80A/90 helicopter
Electronics:
Radar: 1 Terma Scanter Mil 009 nav.; 1 Furuno FR-1505 DA surf. search; 1 Plessey AWS-6 air search; 1 CelsiusTech 9LV 200 Mk 3 f.c.
Sonar: C-Tech CTS-36 hull-mounted; Thales Salmon HF VDS (not in F 357—see Remarks)
EW: Racal Sabre intercept; Racal Scorpion jammer; Telegon HFD/F; 2 12-round DL-12T decoy RL (Sea Gnat decoys)
M: 3 M.A.N.–Burmeister & Wain 12V 28/32 diesels; 1 KaMeWa CP prop; 12,000 bhp (6,366 sust.)—800-shp bow-thruster—1,090-shp retractable azimuthal thruster (for 8 kts)
Electric: 1,440 kw tot. (3 × 480-kw, G.M. 16-cyl. diesel sets—see Remarks)
Range: 8,500/15.5 **Endurance:** 21+ days
Crew: 12 officers, 48 enlisted + 12 passengers

Remarks: Ordered 10-87. Intended primarily for fisheries patrol. *Thetis* was equipped during spring 1991 at Århus Shipyard with a towed array with six pneumatic seismic survey "guns" for use in oil exploration along the eastern coast of Greenland under charter to the Nunaoil consortium; her first oil survey voyage began 12-7-91, and the ship is still employed on similar duties July through October. All four are based at Frederikshavn and are assigned to the 1st Squadron, with F 357 in Division 11 and the others in Division 12.
Hull systems: Engines are on resilient mountings to reduce radiated noise. Have ice-reinforced hulls. The single rudder is of the Becker flapped type. Retractable fin stabilizers and liquid anti-roll tanks are fitted. The 28 × 14-m helicopter deck can accommodate heavy helicopters such as the Sea King; the hangar can accommodate a Lynx. All deck gear is mounted below the forecastle on the first platform and one deck below the helicopter platform.
Combat systems: Have the CelsiusTech 9LV 200 Mk 3 weapons-direction system for the 76-mm gun, with t.v. tracker/director and four multifunction operator consoles. The 20-mm guns are not normally mounted. There are provisional plans to equip the ships with eight 3-cell Mk 48 Mod. 3 vertical-launch Sea Sparrow SAM modules (with three target illuminators), two triple ASW TT, eight Harpoon missiles, two point-defense SAM launchers, and two decoy rocket launchers; in addition, the combat system would be improved by adding two radar directors, a towed passive linear hydrophone array, and the U.S. SLQ-25 Nixie towed torpedo decoy system. The program is unfunded, and its completion is less and less likely.

Disposal note: The patrol ship *Beskyterren* (F 340) was donated to Estonia during 6-00, without replacement.

GUIDED-MISSILE PATROL CRAFT [PTG]

♦ 14 Flyvefisken-class (Stanflex 300) multifunctional
Bldr: Ålborg Værft, Ålborg

	Laid down	L	In serv.
P 550 Flyvefisken	15-8-85	26-4-86	19-12-89
P 551 Hajen	16-6-88	6-12-88	19-7-90
P 552 Havkatten	16-12-88	30-5-89	1-11-90
P 553 Laxen	18-5-89	17-10-89	22-3-91
P 554 Makrelen	13-10-89	7-3-90	1-10-91
P 555 Støren	5-2-90	14-12-90	24-4-92
P 556 Sværdfisken	. . .	1-91	1-2-93
P 557 Glenten	1-91	8-92	29-4-93
P 558 Gribben	. . .	10-92	1-7-93
P 559 Lommen	. . .	. . .	21-1-94
P 560 Ravnen	. . .	. . .	17-10-94
P 561 Skaden	. . .	. . .	10-4-95
P 562 Viben	. . .	. . .	15-1-96
P 563 Søløven	. . .	6-6-95	28-5-96

Glenten (P 557)—as missile boat, with Harpoon and Sea Sparrow but without torpedoes
A. A. de Kruijf, 5-00

Skaden (P 561)—as missile boat, with torpedo tubes flanking missile installation aft
Findler & Winter, 5-99

Støren (P 555)—in mine countermeasures configuration
H&L Van Ginderen, 6-00

D: 320 tons (450 fl) **S:** 35 kts (30 sust.; 19 diesel; 6 hydraulic)
Dim: 54.00 (50.00 pp) × 9.00 × 2.50 (max. hull)
A: Gunboat/mine countermeasures: 1 76-mm 62-cal. OTOBreda SuperRapid DP; 2 single 12.7-mm mg—guided-missile boat: 4 RGM-84C Harpoon SSM; 2 triple Mk 48 Mod. 3 VLS SAM group (Sea Sparrow RIM-7P missiles); 1 76-mm OTOBreda 62-cal. SuperRapid DP; 2 533-mm TT (wire-guided Tp 613 torpedoes) or . . . 324-mm ASW TT (MU-90 ASW torpedoes)—minelayer: Sea Sparrow modules, 76-mm gun, and 60 mines—survey ship: none

GUIDED-MISSILE PATROL CRAFT [PTG] *(continued)*

Makrelen (P 554)—in mine countermeasures configuration
Findler & Winter, 5-00

Flyvefisken (P 550)—unarmed, with hydrographic survey module aft and additional navigational radar in place of the surface/air-search set
Guy Schaeffer, via Paolo Marsan, 6-00

Electronics:
Radar: 1 Terma Scanter Mil 009 nav. or 1 Furuno FR-1505 DA surf. search, 1 Plessey AWS-6 (P 557 and later: EADS TRS-3D/16; P 560: none) air search; Terma-CelsiusTech 9LV 200 f.c. (see Remarks)
Sonar: C-Tech CTS-36 hull-mounted HF (36 kHz); Thales Salmon (TSM 2640) MF towed array (19 kHz)
EW: Racal Mermaid intercept (0.6–40 GHz); 2 6-round Terma DL-6T decoy RL (Chemring Chimera decoys)
M: CODAG: 1 G.E.-Fiat LM-500 gas turbine (5,680 shp) centerline, 2 MTU 16V396 TB94 diesels (3,480 bhp each), 1 G.M. Detroit Diesel 12V71 diesel (500 bhp) to windmill centerline prop and to power slow-speed hydraulic drive system; 3 props (CP outboard)—bow-thruster
Electric: 600 kw (3 × 200 kw; G.M. 6-71 diesels driving) **Range:** 2,400/18
Crew: 4 officers, 13 enlisted as patrol boat; 4 officers, 15 enlisted as missile boat (29 tot. accomm.)

Remarks: P 550 through P 556, all originally completed in the gunboat configuration, were ordered 27-7-85 to a Karlskrona design. A second group of six was ordered during 6-90, originally without the gas turbines, guns, and other equipment. The final units were ordered under the 1993–94 budget. P 550 began trials 27-10-87.

The boats are intended to be convertible to perform antiship, ASW, and patrol duties, as well as being configurable as minesweepers, fast minelayers, survey ships, oceanographic research ships, buoy tenders, fishery protection ships, and other semicombatant and auxiliary missions. P 558 was outfitted as a hydrographic survey ship during 1995, with all armament deleted and a modular charthouse/deckhouse added aft; she was replaced by P 560 (which also had the air-search radar replaced by an additional navigational set) as of 2000. All are to have their electronics updated between 2002 and 2006.

Hull systems: The hull for P 550 was fabricated in Sweden by Karlskrona. Foam-core, glass-reinforced plastic hull construction; due to weight-saving measures, the eighth and later boats displace about 15 tons less. The boats employ passive tank stabilization at low speeds, when they are powered by hydraulic drive for noise suppression; at high speeds, rudder roll control is employed, and there are trim tabs fitted at the stern. The outboard, diesel-driven props are controllable pitch; the centerline screw is windmilled by the auxiliary diesels when the gas turbine is not operating, in order to reduce drag. All machinery is controlled from the bridge. Kevlar armor panels are incorporated. Navigation systems include Decca precision radio navaid receiver and GPS receiver, and Sperry/Anschütz gyros.

Combat systems: Employ a Terma-CelsiusTech Flexfire 9LV Mk 3 weapons control system; the associated 9LV 200 fire-control radar is mounted on the port side, atop the pilothouse, but was removed from the temporarily disarmed P 560. Most have the U.S. WSC-3 UHF communications system (not SATCOM), and NATO Link 11 is being added to all.

To outfit the class, the following portable modules were procured: 16 76-mm guns, 16 cranes, 16 minelaying sets, 16 air-defense sets, 12 antiship missile and fire-control sets, 12 torpedo tube sets, 5 mine clearance sets, and 16 electronic warfare sets; later it is hoped to add 6 ASW modules. Seven sonar sets and three towed linear hydrophone arrays were ordered for use on the ships. In mid-1992, the Bofors Underwater Systems Double Eagle remotely operated vehicle was selected as the minehunting disposal vehicle for the class, and six ship-sets (12 ROVs) were acquired.

The modular mine countermeasures sets each consist of two Danyard-built, remote-controlled minehunting drones (each towing a Thales TSM 2054 side-scan sonar), with the IBIS 43 minehunting system and Thales 2061 tactical mine countermeasures data system. The second minehunting suite ship-set was delivered in 12-91, six more were delivered in 1994–95, and approval for another three was given on 29-5-96. The first drone, MRF 1, was completed 3-91; MRF 1 and MRF 2 operate with P 552 (see the Mine Warfare Ships section for description). P 562 and P 563 are more or less permanently outfitted for mine countermeasures duties.

Four modular Sea Sparrow SAM systems were ordered from Raytheon in 11-93 for installation in these boats, with an option for 10 more sets. Three are three Mk 48 Mod. 3 launchers per module, and each ship-set includes an autonomous fire-control radar system. Eurotorp MU-90 ASW acoustic homing torpedoes were ordered in 1-99 for use on this class. When wire-guided torpedoes are carried, a section of the bulwark on the fantail is removed to permit the single tubes to train out for launching.

Disposal note: The final two *Willemoes*-class missile/torpedo boats in service, the *Rodsteen* (P 546) and *Sehested* (P 547) were to have been retired during 2001. Sisters *Bille* (P 540), *Bredal* (P 541), *Hammer* (P 542), *Huitfeldt* (P 543), and *Krieger* (P 544) were placed in reserve in 1999, while *Suenson* (P 548) and *Willemoes* (P 549) were laid up in 2000, with none planned to be reactivatible.

PATROL CRAFT [PC]

Note: The following units are used on fisheries protection duties and carry pennant numbers in the service craft series. Approval was given in 6-99 under the 2000–04 Defense Plan to construct 10 125-ton "Minor Standard Craft Mk 1" (with a design based on that of the four MRD-STOR-class drone minesweepers; see under [MSD]) and six 175-ton "Minor Standard Craft Mk 2" to replace existing patrol craft; the Mk 1 will have space for one Standard Flex container and the Mk 2 for two. The craft would be used in midshipman training and hydrographic survey duties in peacetime, in addition to their fisheries protection duties; in wartime, combat system modules would be added. As of 6-01, however, no contract announcements had been made.

♦ 3 Agdlek class
Bldr: Svendborg Værft, Svendborg

Y 386 Agdlek (In serv. 12-3-74)
Y 387 Agpa (In serv. 14-5-74)
Y 388 Tulugaq (In serv. 26-6-79)

Agdlek (Y 386) Danish Navy, 1994

PATROL CRAFT [PC] *(continued)*

D: 300 tons (fl) **S:** 12 kts **Dim:** 31.4 × 7.7 × 3.3
A: provision for 2 single 20-mm 70-cal. Oerlikon AA
Electronics:
Radar: 1 Terma 20T48 nav.; 1 Skanter Mil 009 nav.; 1 Furuno FR-1505 DA surf. search
M: 1 Burmeister & Wain Alpha AO8-26 VO diesel; 800 bhp **Crew:** 15 tot.

Remarks: Assigned to Division 19, 1st Squadron, and based at Frederikshavn for fisheries patrol service in Greenland waters. Can carry two survey launches. Y 388 has only one navigational radar (but is equipped with Inmarsat), is .3 m longer, displaces 330 tons (fl), and can make 14 kts. All have a Telegon HFD/F set. No longer carry 20-mm AA but probably have one or more 7.62-mm mg aboard.

♦ 9 Barsø class
Bldr: Svendborg Værft, Svendborg

	In serv.		In serv.
Y 300 Barsø	13-6-69	Y 305 Vejrø	17-10-69
Y 301 Drejø	1-7-69	Y 306 Farø	17-5-73
Y 302 Romsø	21-7-69	Y 307 Læsø	23-7-73
Y 303 Samsø	15-8-69	Y 308 Romø	3-9-73
Y 304 Thurø	12-9-69		

Romso (Y 302) Hartmut Ehlers, 7-01

Læsø (Y 307)—converted as a diving tender Danish Navy, 1998

D: 155 tons (fl) **S:** 11 kts **Dim:** 25.5 × 6.0 × 2.8
A: 1 12.7-mm mg (not in Y 307)
Electronics: Radar: 1 Furuno FR-1505 DA nav.
M: 1 Burmeister & Wain Alpha diesel; 1 prop; 385 bhp
Crew: 4 officers, 16 enlisted

Remarks: Y 307, with a decompression chamber forward, is disarmed and is used as a diving tender; her forecastle extends directly aft to the bridge area, and there is a large constant-tension towed acoustic array–handing rig on the fantail. Y 306–308 have broader pilothouses. All have a Telegon HFD/F set. Have not carried the former two single 20-mm Oerlikon AA mounts on the bridge deck abreast the stack since the mid-1990s.

PATROL BOATS [PB]

♦ 3 VTS 3–class Guardships
Bldr: Mulder & Rijke, the Netherlands (In serv. 1997–98)

VTS 3 VTS 4 VTS 5

D: 34 tons (fl) **S:** 33 kts **Dim:** 17.0 × 4.9 × . . .
A: provision for 1 7.62-mm FN mg
Electronics:
Radar: 1 Furuno M-1831 nav.; 1 Furuno FR-1505 Mk 2 nav./surf. search
M: 2 MWM TBD 616 V12 diesels; 2 waterjets; 979 bhp
Range: 300/30 **Crew:** 3 tot.

Remarks: Used as patrol and chase boats in the Danish Belt and Straits areas. Are typical Dutch police boats, equipped with reinforced hull sides to permit coming alongside. Also equipped for rescue duties.

Disposal note: The wooden-hulled former trawler *Lunden* (Y 343) was retired during 2000.

Note: The Home Guard *(Marine Hjemmeværnets)* is responsible for coastal waters surveillance, harbor traffic control, naval installations guard duties, and search-and-rescue operations. The paramilitary organization had about 4,400 personnel in 2001 and operated the following craft in the MHV series:

♦ 18 Aldebaran (MHV 800) class
Bldr: Søby Motorfabrik & Staalskibsværft, Æro

	In serv.		In serv.
MHV 801 Aldebaran	9-7-92	MHV 810 Luna	30-5-96
MHV 802 Carina	1-11-92	MHV 811 Apollo	30-11-96
MHV 803 Aries	30-3-93	MHV 812 Hercules	30-5-97
MHV 804 Andromeda	30-9-93	MHV 813 Baunen	17-12-97
MHV 805 Gemini	28-2-94	MHV 814 Budstikken	8-98
MHV 806 Dubhe	1-7-94	MHV 815 Kureren	30-5-99
MHV 807 Jupiter	30-11-94	MHV 816 Patrioten	25-2-00
MHV 808 Lyra	30-5-95	MHV 817 Partisan	11-00
MHV 809 Antares	30-11-95	MHV 818 Sabotøren	8-01

Antares (MHV 809) Findler & Winter, 7-00

Baunen (MHV 813) Findler & Winter, 8-00

D: 80 tons (83 fl) **S:** 13 kts **Dim:** 23.70 (20.26 pp) × 5.60 × 2.00
A: 2 single 7.62-mm mg; provision for 1 20-mm 70-cal. Oerlikon AA
Electronics: Radar: 1 Furuno FR-1505 DA nav./surf. search
M: 2 Saab Scania DSI-14 diesels; 2 props; 900 bhp
Range: 990/11 **Fuel:** 7,800 liters **Endurance:** 3 days
Crew: 4 officers, 4 enlisted

Remarks: Intended as the long-overdue replacements for the numerous Home Guard patrol craft, some of which dated to the 1920s. The first three were ordered in 5-91, a second increment in 7-92, and a third in 9-93, with the intent being to order six per year thereafter through the planned total of 25 needed; however, under the 1993–94 budget, only an additional four were funded, and the program is proceeding at a more leisurely pace than was first envisioned. Six more were ordered in 2-97, with an option for another seven that has not yet been exercised. Steel construction.

Disposal note: Of the units of the MHV 20 class, *Budstikken* (MHV 21) was retired during 1999, *Kureren* (MHV 22) and *Patrioten* (MHV 24) in 2000, and *Partisan* (MHV 23) and *Sabatøren* (MHV 25) in 2001, with MHV 20 due to follow shortly thereafter.

♦ 6 MHV 90–class, steel-hulled
Bldr: Svendborg Værft, Svendborg (MHV 91–93: Sakskjbing)

	In serv.		In serv.
MHV 90 Bopa	1975	MHV 93 Hvidsten	1975
MHV 91 Brigaden	1974	MHV 94 Ringen	1974
MHV 92 Holger Danske	1975	MHV 95 Speditøren	1975

D: 85 tons (130 fl) **S:** 10.7 kts **Dim:** 19.8 × 5.7 × 1.6
A: 2 single 7.62-mm mg **Electronics:** Radar: 1 Furuno FR-1505 DA nav.
M: 1 Burmeister & Wain diesel; 400 bhp **Crew:** 6 tot.

PATROL BOATS [PB] *(continued)*

Holger Danske (MHV 92) Findler & Winter, 7-00

♦ 3 MHV 70–class, wooden-hulled
Bldr: Royal Dockyard, Copenhagen (In serv. 1958)

MHV 70 SATURN MHV 71 SCORPIUS MHV 72 SIRIUS

Sirius (MHV 72) H&L Van Ginderen, 7-98

D: 78 tons (130 fl) **S:** 10 kts **Dim:** 20.1 × 5.1 × 2.5
A: 2 single 7.62-mm mg **Electronics:** Radar: 1 Raytheon 1290S nav.
M: 1 diesel; 200 bhp **Crew:** 6 tot.

♦ 4 MHV 80 class

	Bldr	In serv.
MHV 80 FÆNØ (ex-MHV 69, ex-MS 6)	Svendborg	7-41
MHV 81 ASKØ (ex-Y 386, ex-M 560, ex-MS 2)	Holbæk	1-8-41
MHV 84 BAAGØ (ex-Y 387, ex-M 561, ex-MS 3)	Korsør	9-8-41
MHV 85 HJORTØ (ex-Y 389, ex-M 564, ex-MS 7)	Korsør	24-9-41

Baagø (MHV 84) Guy Schaeffer, via Paolo Marsan, 6-00

D: 74 tons (80 fl) **S:** 11 kts **Dim:** 24.4 × 4.9 × 1.6
A: 2 single 7.62-mm mg **Electronics:** Radar: 1 Raytheon RM 1290S nav.
M: 1 diesel; 350 bhp **Crew:** 9 tot.

Remarks: Transferred from the navy to home guard service in 1958. Former inshore minesweepers. Wooden hulls.

Disposals: *Manø* (MHV 83) was retired in 1999 and *Enø* (MHV 82) and *Lyø* (MHV 86) in 2000.

MINE WARFARE SHIPS

♦ 2 Falster-class minelayers [MM] Bldr: Frederikshavn Værft

	Laid down	L	In serv.
N 81 FYEN	4-62	3-10-62	18-9-63
N 82 MØEN	10-62	6-6-63	20-4-64

Møen (N 82) Findler & Winter, 5-00

Møen (N 82) Winter & Findler, 6-95

D: 1,880 tons (fl) **S:** 16.5 kts **Dim:** 77.0 (72.5 pp) × 12.8 × 3.4
A: 1 twin 76.2-mm 50-cal. U.S. Mk 33 DP; 4 mine rails (400 mines)
Electronics:
Radar: 1 Terma Pilot nav.; 1 CWS-2 air/surf. search; 1 NWS-2 surf. search; 1 M-46 f.c.
EW: Racal Cutlass B-1 intercept; Telegon HFD/F; 2 multi-rail 57-mm rocket flare/decoy RL
M: 2 G.M. Electromotive Div. 16-567D3 diesels; 2 CP props; 4,800 bhp
Range: . . ./. . . **Fuel:** 130 tons
Crew: N 81: 10 officers, 108 enlisted; N 82: 20 officers, 69 enlisted + 66 cadets

Remarks: N 82 was built with U.S. "offshore" funds as MMC 15. The Turkish ship *Nusret* is essentially identical. N 82 is used strictly for cadet training (with temporary accommodations for cadets on the mine deck), while N 81 acts as "school ship."

Disposals: *Sjælland* (N 83) and *Falster* (N 80) were stricken in 2000.
Combat systems: The after twin 76.2-mm gunmount and two twin 20-mm AA have been removed. Plans to add Mistral point-defense SAM launchers and an updated Terma TDS combat data system have been canceled for the two remaining ships.

♦ 2 Lindormen-class coastal minelayers [MM]
Bldr: Svendborg Værft, Svendborg

	Laid down	L	In serv.
N 43 LINDORMEN	2-2-77	7-6-77	16-2-78
N 44 LOSSEN	9-7-77	11-10-77	14-6-78

Lindormen (N 43) Bernard Prézelin, 9-99

MINE WARFARE SHIPS *(continued)*

D: 575 tons (fl) **S:** 14 kts **Dim:** 43.30 (40.00 pp) × 9.00 × 2.65
A: 3 single 20-mm 70-cal. Oerlikon AA; 50–60 mines
Electronics: Radar: 1 NWS-3 nav.
M: 2 Frichs-Wichmann 7AX diesels; 2 props; 4,200 bhp
Electric: 192 kw tot. **Crew:** 27 tot.

Remarks: Controlled minefield planters. Have a single door at the stern.

♦ 4MRD-STOR-class drone minesweepers [MSD]
Bldr: Danyard, Ålborg (In serv. 1998–99)

	In serv.		In serv.
MSF 1	8-98	MSF 3	1-99
MSF 2	. . .	MSF 4	1-99

MSF 1 Findler & Winter, 5-00

MSF 1—note side-scan sonar "fish" beneath A-frame crane at stern
Dieter Wolf, 5-00

D: 102 tons (125 fl) **S:** 12 kts (11 sust.)
Dim: 26.50 (24.15 wl; 23.90 pp) × 7.00 × 2.20
Electronics:
Radar: 1 Raytheon 40 nav.—Sonar: Thales STS 2054 towed side-scan HF
M: 2 Saab Scania DSI 14.74.M diesels; 2 Schottel SPJ.82T azimuthal waterjets; 960 bhp—bow-thruster
Range: 420/10 **Crew:** 3–4 tot. (for transits; accomm. for 11 tot.)

Remarks: The prototype Surface Auxiliary Vessel (SAV), SF 100, was delivered in 1-96 to a somewhat smaller design, and the four production versions were ordered during 1-97. GRP construction. Can be operated by crews as inshore minehunter/minesweepers or by remote control in pairs by *Flyvefisken*-class multipurpose craft. Ten more, configured as patrol craft, are to be procured to replace the aged *Barsø* class.
Combat systems: Employ the IN-SNEC sonar and television datalink and INFOCOM low-rate craft command datalink. Use containerized mine countermeasures equipment. Can be used to deploy Sutec Double Eagle mine location and disposal ROVs or to stream sweep gear, including the Australian Dyad magnetic sweep. Have a 7-kN bollard pull at 8.5 kts.

♦ 6 MRF 1–class drone minesweepers [MSD]
Bldr: Danyard, Ålborg (In serv. 1991–96)

MRD 1 (In serv. 3-91)	MRD 3	MRD 5
MRD 2 (In serv. 12-91)	MRD 4	MRD 6

MRD 2 A. A. de Kruijf, 8-99

D: 32 tons (38 fl) **S:** 12 kts **Dim:** 18.20 (16.90 wl) × 4.75 × 1.20
Electronics: Radar: 1 Furuno . . . nav.—Sonar: Thales TSM 2054 towed side-scan
M: 2 G.M. Detroit Diesel . . . diesels; 2 Schottel Type 80 waterjets; 350 bhp
Crew: 4 tot. (debarked during operations)

Remarks: MRD 3–6 ordered 7-94. Intended to operate two per Stanflex 300 multipurpose combatant; the first two operate with *Havkatten* (P 552). In 2-01, a sister was ordered for test in Sweden.
Hull systems: Glass-reinforced foam-core plastic hull construction. MRD 2 and later have smaller stacks.
Combat systems: Australian ADI Mini-Dyad reconfigurable permanent magnet influence sweep arrays were ordered during 1996 for use with these craft; they employ a 6.4 × 0.53-m, hollow, two-section, mild steel pipe with two reconfigurable strontium-ferrite inserts.

AUXILIARIES

♦ 2 Gunnar Thorson–class pollution control ships [AG]
Bldr: Ørskov Staalskibværft, Frederikshavn

Gunnar Thorson (In serv. 8-5-81) Gunnar Seidenfaden (In serv. 2-7-81)

Gunnar Seidenfaden H&L Van Ginderen, 6-00

D: 672 tons (750 fl) **S:** 14.5 kts **Dim:** 55.61 (49.10 pp) × 12.40 × 3.87
M: 2 Burmeister & Wain Alpha 8V23L-VO diesels; 2 CP props; 2,320 bhp—bow-thruster
Electric: 564 kw tot. (2 × 208-kw, 1 × 148-kw diesel sets)

Remarks: 869 grt/684 dwt. Transferred from the Ministry of the Environment in early 1996. Modified anchor-handling offshore supply tug design. Have firefighting equipment. One 7-ton crane was added in 1988 to allow them to act as navigational buoy tenders. *Thorson,* based at Copenhagen, is also equipped to act as a salvage vessel. *Seidenfaden* is based at Korsør. Both have civilian crews. Have red-orange-painted hulls, cream superstructure with broad and narrow red-orange diagonal stripe on sides.

♦ 1 royal yacht [AG] Bldr: Royal Dockyard, Copenhagen

	Laid down	L	In serv.
A 540 Dannebrog	2-1-31	10-10-31	20-5-32

D: 1,130 tons (fl) **S:** 14 kts **Dim:** 74.9 × 10.4 × 3.7
A: 2 single 37-mm saluting cannon
Electronics: Radar: 1 Skanter Mil 009 nav.
M: 2 Burmeister & Wain Alpha 6 T23L-KVO diesels; 2 CP props; 1,600 bhp
Electric: 676 kw tot. **Crew:** 55 tot. (incl. passengers)

Remarks: Was re-engined and had a new electrical generating plant installed in winter 1980/81. Does not wear the assigned pennant number. Equipped with SATCOM transceiver in 1992.

AUXILIARIES *(continued)*

Dannebrog (A 540) H&L Van Ginderen, 7-94

Note: Danish icebreakers were transferred from the Ministry of Industry to the Ministry of Defense in early 1996. During summer months they are maintained by the Danish Navy at Frederikshavn. All remain civilian manned. They have black-painted hulls and cream superstructures.

♦ 1 Thorbjørn-class icebreaker [AGB]
Bldr: Svendborg Skibsværft, Svendborg (L: 6-80)

A 553 THORBJØRN

Thorbjørn (A 553)—outboard *Isbjørn* (A 552) Werner Schiefer, 10-96

D: 2,250 tons (fl) **S:** 16.5 kts **Dim:** 65.11 (57.92 pp) × 15.35 × 4.92
M: 4 Burmeister & Wain Alpha 16U28L-VO diesels; 2 props; 6,360 bhp
Electric: 840 kw tot. (3 × 280-kw diesel sets)
Range: 21,800/16 **Fuel:** 855 tons **Crew:** . . . tot.

Remarks: 1,547 grt/2,345 dwt. Can be used for hydrographic surveys when not needed for icebreaking and can also act as a tug. Geared drive vice electric. Assigned to Division 15, 1st Naval Squadron, and based at Frederikshavn.

♦ 2 Danbjørn-class icebreakers [AGB]
Bldr: Lindø Værft, Odense

A 551 DANBJØRN (In serv. 1965) A 552 ISBJØRN (In serv. 1966)

Danbjørn (A 551) Werner Schiefer, 10-96

D: 3,685 tons (fl) **S:** 14 kts **Dim:** 77.15 (67.98 pp) × 17.33 × 6.50
M: 6 Holeby–Burmeister & Wain 12-26MTBH-40V diesels (1,750 bhp each), 6 1,370-kw generators, 8 electric motors (870 shp each fwd, 1,750 shp each aft); 4 props (2 fwd); 5,240 shp
Electric: 1,312 kw tot (4 × 328 kw)
Range: 11,480/16.5 **Fuel:** 580 tons **Crew:** 34 tot.

Remarks: 3,023 grt. Assigned to Division 15, 1st Naval Squadron, and based at Frederikshavn.

♦ 1 Elbjørn-class icebreaker [AGB]
Bldr: Frederikshavn Værft & Flydedok A/S (In serv. 1954)

A 550 ELBJØRN

Elbjørn (A 550) H&L Van Ginderen, 2-99

D: 1,400 tons (fl) **S:** 12 kts **Dim:** 47.71 × 12.02 × 4.40
M: 3 Kosan Frichs 8-cyl. diesels (1,200 bhp each), 3 800-kw generators, 2 motors; 3 props (1 fwd); 3,600 shp
Electric: 400 kw tot. **Crew:** . . . tot.

Remarks: 893 grt. Used for hydrographic survey work in the summer. Assigned to Division 15, 1st Naval Squadron, and based at Frederikshavn.

SERVICE CRAFT

♦ 2 Sea Truck–design pollution control craft [YAG]

	Bldr	In serv.
METTE MILJØ	Carl B. Hoffman SY, Esbjerg	22-2-80
MARIE MILJØ	Søren Larsen SY, Nykøbing Mors	22-2-80

Mette Miljø Guy Schaeffer, via Paolo Marsan, 6-00

D: 157 tons **S:** 10 kts **Dim:** 29.8 × 8.0 × 1.6
M: 2 Grena GF 24 diesels; 2 props; 660 bhp **Crew:** 8 tot. (civilian)

Remarks: Transferred from the Ministry of the Environment early in 1996. Have orange hulls and cream superstructures.

♦ 2 Miljø 101–class pollution control boats [YAG]
Bldr: Eljvinds, Svendborg

MILJØ 101 (In serv. 1-11-77) MILJØ 102 (In serv. 1-12-77)

Miljø 102 Guy Schaeffer, via Paolo Marsan, 6-00

SERVICE CRAFT *(continued)*

D: 16 tons **S:** 15 kts **Dim:** 16.2 × 4.2 × 2.2
M: 1 MWM TBD232 V12 diesel; 1 prop; 454 bhp
Range: 350/8 **Crew:** 3 tot. (naval)

Remarks: Transferred from the Ministry of the Environment early in 1996. Glass-reinforced plastic construction. Carry spill containment gear.

♦ **1 mine transport [YE]** Bldr: Holbæk Bådeværft (In serv. 1949)

MSA 4 (ex-MK 5, ex-Y 383)

D: 34 tons (fl) **S:** 8 kts **Dim:** 19.0 × 4.2 × 1.5 **M:** 1 diesel; 1 prop; 150 bhp

Remarks: Wooden-hulled fishing boat hull with pilothouse aft. Also employed as a controlled-minefield cable tender.

♦ **1 Y 378–class fast launch [YFL]**

Y 378

Y 378 A. A. de Kruijf, 8-99

Remarks: Small, GRP-hulled cabin cruiser, based at Korsør; no data available.

♦ **6 921-class harbor personnel launches [YFL]**

921 through 926

921-class launch 925 Guy Schaeffer, via Paolo Marsan, 6-00

Remarks: GRP personnel launches employed for local transportation at Danish naval bases; no data available.

♦ **1 ex-Swedish Kbv 236 class [YFL]** (In serv. 1961–72)

Told (ex-Kbv . . .)

Told A. A. de Kruijf, 8-99

D: 17 tons **S:** 22 kts **Dim:** 16.2 × 3.7 × . . .
M: 2 Volvo Penta TAMD 120A diesels; 2 props; 700 bhp

Remarks: Former Swedish Coast Guard launch acquired in 1999 and based at Korsør. Aluminum hull construction. Sister *Viben* serves the Ministry of Fisheries as an inspection launch.

♦ **6 SKA 11–class inshore survey launches [YGS]**
Bldr: Jeros Marine A/S, Rantsausminde

	In serv.		In serv.		In serv.
SKA 11	1980	SKA 13	1982	SKA 15	1984
SKA 12	1981	SKA 14	1982	SKA 16	1985

SKA 13 Hartmut Ehlers, 6-94

D: 52 tons (fl) **S:** 13 kts **Dim:** 19.96 (19.20 pp) × 5.20 × 2.10
Electronics: Radar: 1 Skanter Mil 009 nav.
M: 1 G.M. 16V-71N diesel; 1 prop; 540 bhp **Electric:** 15 kw tot.
Fuel: 10,000 liters **Crew:** 1 officer, 5 enlisted

Remarks: GRP construction. Have an EMRI ACU autopilot and a Navitronic Seadig 201 survey system with HDH-1 data-handler and a Hewlett-Packard 9825 computer. Designed to operate in Greenland waters.

Disposal note: U.S. YO 65–class fuel lighters *Rimfaxe* (A 568, ex-YO 226) and *Skinfaxe* (A 569, ex-YO 229) were sold to a Nigerian commercial operator on 31-1-01 and operate under the names *Chinky Star* and *Betty Nelo,* respectively.

Skinfaxe (A 569)—since stricken Winter & Findler, 5-00

♦ **1 torpedo transport/retriever [YPT]**
Bldr: Åbenrå Skibsværft, Åbenrå (In serv. 18-7-86)

A 559 Sleipner

Sleipner (A 559) H&L Van Ginderen, 10-94

D: 450 tons (fl) **S:** 11 kts **Dim:** 36.50 (34.00 pp) × 7.60 × 2.70
Electronics: Radar: 1 Terma Skanter Mil 009 nav.
M: 1 Callesen 427 EOT diesel; 1 prop; 575 bhp **Crew:** 6 tot.

Remarks: Replaced earlier former coastal freighter of the same name. Cargo capacity: 150 tons. Black hull, yellow superstructure.

♦ **3 small torpedo retrievers [YPT]**
Bldr: Eivinds Plasticjolle & Bødeverft, Svendborg (In serv. . . .)

TO 8 Hugin TO 9 Munin TO 10 Mimer

D: 23 tons (fl) **S:** 15 kts **Dim:** 16.15 × 4.15 × 1.25
Electronics: Radar: 1 Terma Scanter Mil 009 nav.
M: 1 MWM diesel; 1 prop; 450 bhp **Crew:** 4 tot.

Remarks: Are similar in appearance to pollution control craft *Miljø 101* and *Miljø 102* and employ the same GRP-construction hull.

♦ **2 20-grt dockyard tugs [YTL]**
Bldr: Assens Skibsværft (In serv. 1983)

Balder Hermod

D: . . . tons **S:** 8.7 kts **Dim:** 11.85 × 4.00 × 1.65
M: 1 G.M. 6-71 series diesel; 1 prop; 300 bhp

SERVICE CRAFT *(continued)*

♦ **2 small sail-training yawls [YTS]**
Bldr: Molich, Hundested (In serv. 1960)

Y 101 Svanen Y 102 Thyra

Svanen (Y 101) H&L Van Ginderen, 6-99

D: 32 tons (fl) **S:** 7.5 kts (power) **Dim:** 19.2 × 4.8 × 2.4
M: 1 Volvo Penta diesel; 1 prop; 72 bhp—sail area: 500 m² max.

♦ **1 Y 375–class training boat [YXT]**
Bldr: Botved (In serv. 1974)

Y 376

Y 376 A. A. de Kruijf, 8-99

D: 12 tons (fl) **S:** 26 kts **Dim:** 13.3 × 4.5 × 1.1 **A:** 1 7.62-mm mg
Electronics: Radar: 1 NWS-3 nav. **M:** 2 diesels; 2 props; 680 hp

Remarks: Officially typed as a "*Bevogtningsbåd.*" Has facilities for combat swimmers. Near-sister Y 375 burned and sank 27-5-95 off the island of Lessoe.

Note: The ships and craft of the Ministry of Fisheries *(Den Danske Stat-Fiskerministeriet)* are described and illustrated in the 1998–99 and earlier editions. In service in 2001 were fisheries patrol craft *Havørnen;* fisheries research ship *Dana;* fisheries research craft *Jens Væver* and *Leda;* salvage, rescue, and fire-fighting tug *Veskysten; Nordjylland*-class search-and-rescue ships *Nordjylland* and *Nordsøen;* and inspection launch *Viben* (a former Swedish Coast Guard Kbv 236–class launch).

DJIBOUTI

Republic of Djibouti

Personnel (2001): About 120 total

Base: Djibouti (also used as a base by the French Navy's Indian Ocean Squadron)

PATROL BOATS [PB]

♦ **2 Moussa Ali class**
Bldr: Plascoa, Cannes, France

P 10 Moussa Ali (In serv. 8-6-85) P 11 Mont Arreh (In serv. 16-2-86)

Moussa Ali (P 10) Plascoa, 1995

D: 30 tons (35 fl) **S:** 24.5 kts **Dim:** 23.30 × 5.50 × 1.50
A: 1 20-mm 90-cal. GIAT AA; 1 12.7-mm Browning mg
Electronics: Radar: 1 Decca 36 MN nav.
M: 2 UNI Diesel V12-520 M25 diesels; 2 props; 1,700 bhp
Range: 460/15; 750/12 **Crew:** 15 tot.

Remarks: GRP construction. Ordered 10-84 as a gift from France.

♦ **1 Boghammar hydroplane launch**
Bldr: Boghammar Marin, Stockholm, Sweden (In serv. 1989)

D: 6.4 tons (fl) **S:** 45 kts **Dim:** 12.80 × 2.66 × 0.90
A: small arms **Electronics:** Radar: 1 Decca 170 nav. or none
M: 2 Volvo Penta TAMD-71A diesels; 2 props; 716 bhp
Range: 500/38 **Crew:** 5–6 tot.

Remarks: Donated in 11-96 by the Ethiopian government from among its units gathered at Djibouti in 1993. Aluminum construction. Has a stepped hydroplane hullform.

♦ **2 Iraqi . . . class**

P 12 P 13

P 13 French Navy, 11-95

D: approx. 20 tons (fl) **S:** 27 kts **Dim:** 21.0 × . . . × . . .
A: 1 triple 14.5-mm 93-cal. mg **M:** 2 diesels; 2 props; . . . bhp

Remarks: Transferred 1989–90. No other data available. Appear to have GRP hulls.

♦ **3 Iraqi Sawari class**

P 5 P 6 P 7

D: 7 tons (fl) **S:** 25 kts **Dim:** 11.0 × 2.5 × 0.6
A: . . . **M:** 2 diesels; 2 props; . . . bhp

Remarks: Transferred 1989–90 as a gift of the Iraqi government. GRP construction open launches.

Disposal note: The former Ethiopian Navy Zhuk-class (Russian Project 1400) patrol boat donated in 11-96 is no longer in use.

AMPHIBIOUS WARFARE CRAFT

♦ **1 ex-French LCM(8)-class landing craft [LCM]**
Bldr: CMN, Cherbourg, France

. . . . . . (ex-CTM 14)

D: 56 tons light (150 fl) **S:** 9.5 kts **Dim:** 23.80 × 6.35 × 1.25
A: 2 single 12.7-mm mg **Electronics:** Radar: 1 . . . nav.
M: 2 Poyaud 520 V8 diesels; 2 props; 480 bhp
Range: 380/8 **Fuel:** 3.4 tons **Crew:** 6 tot.

AMPHIBIOUS WARFARE CRAFT *(continued)*

Remarks: Transferred in 1999 from the French Navy. Cargo capacity: 90 tons. The machineguns are usually not mounted.

Note: Several small RIB launches may still be operable.

DOMINICA

COAST GUARD

Personnel (2001): About 30 total

Base: Roseau

PATROL BOATS [WPB]

♦ **1 U.S. 40-foot Dauntless class**
Bldr: SeaArk, Monticello, Ark. (In serv. 1995)

D 05 Ukale

Ukale (D 05) SeaArk, 11-95

D: 11 tons (15 fl) **S:** 28 kts **Dim:** 12.19 (11.13 wl) × 3.86 × 0.69 (hull)
A: 1 7.62-mm mg **Electronics:** Radar: 1 Raytheon R40X nav.
M: 2 Caterpillar 3208TA diesels; 2 props; 850 bhp (720 sust.)
Range: 200/30; 400/22 **Fuel:** 250 gallons **Crew:** 5 tot.

Remarks: Ordered 4-94. Aluminum construction. C. Raymond Hunt, "Deep-Vee" hull design.

♦ **1 U.S. 65-foot Commercial Cruiser class**
Bldr: Swiftships, Morgan City, La. (In serv. 2-5-84)

D-4 Melville

Melville (D-4) Maritime Photographic, 11-93

D: 34 tons (fl) **S:** 23 kts **Dim:** 19.96 × 5.58 × 1.52
A: small arms **Electronics:** Radar: 1 Raytheon 1210 nav.
M: 2 G.M. 12V71 TI diesels; 2 props; 1,350 bhp **Electric:** 20 kw
Range: 500/18 **Crew:** 6 tot.

Remarks: One of three sisters presented to Caribbean island republics by the U.S. government, the others going to Antigua-Barbuda (see photo) and St. Lucia. Aluminum construction. Blue hull, white upperworks.

SERVICE CRAFT

♦ **2 U.S. Boston Whaler utility launches [WYFL]**
Bldr: Boston Whaler, Rockland, Mass. (In serv. 1988)

Observer Vigilance

Observer Maritime Photographic, 11-93

D: 2.4 tons (fl) **S:** 28 kts **Dim:** 8.2 × 2.6 × 0.3
M: 1 Evinrude V6 gasoline outboard; 225 bhp **Crew:** 3 tot.

Remarks: Glass-reinforced, foam-core construction. Employed for patrol and SAR duties. Is capable of towing smallcraft.

Note: Also in use is the similar-sized, U.S.-supplied *Rescuer,* a RIB acquired in 1994 and powered by two Johnson gasoline outboards; the craft is equipped with a Raytheon navigational radar and has a crew of two.

DOMINICAN REPUBLIC

MARINA DE GUERRA

Personnel (2001): Approx. 3,800 officers and enlisted (including marines)

Note: Bases are located at Santo Domingo (the headquarters, *27 de Febrero*), Las Calderas, Haina, and Puerto Plata. Many of the older ships and craft described below are in only marginal operating condition.

Maritime Aviation: The Dominican Republic Air Force operates four Cessna T-41D light training aircraft and two Aérospatiale AS.316B Alouette-III helicopters on coastal patrol and search-and-rescue duties.

PATROL SHIPS [PS]

♦ **2 ex-U.S. Cohoes-class former net tenders**

	Bldr	L	In serv.
P 208 Separación (ex-*Passaconaway,* AN 86)	Marine Iron & Railway, Duluth, Minn.	30-6-44	27-4-45
P 209 Calderas (ex-*Passaic,* AN 87)	Leatham D. Smith, Sturgeon Bay, Wis.	29-6-44	6-3-45

Calderas (P 209)—alongside *Prestol Botello* (C 454); note bow "horns" Alexandre Sheldon-Duplaix, 5-99

PATROL SHIPS [PS] *(continued)*

Separación (P 208)—note lack of lift-rig horns at bow
Alexandre Sheldon-Duplaix, 9-99

D: 650 tons (785 fl) **S:** 12.3 kts **Dim:** 51.36 (44.5 pp) × 10.31 × 3.3
A: P 208 only: 2 single 76.2-mm 50-cal. U.S. Mk 26 DP—both: 3 single 20-mm 70-cal. Mk 10 Oerlikon Mk 10 AA
Electronics: Radar: 1 Raytheon SPS-64(V)6 nav./surf. search
M: diesel-electric: 2 Busch-Sulzer BS-539 diesels, 1 motor; 1 prop; 1,200 shp
Electric: 120 kw tot. **Fuel:** 88 tons **Crew:** 5 officers, 59 enlisted

Remarks: Reactivated from the U.S. Maritime Commission's reserve fleet, where they had been laid up since 1963, and transferred 9-76. Despite low speed and general unsuitability, they are employed as patrol ships, tugs, general support ships, navigational aids tenders, and hydrographic survey ships. P 208 had the net tender "horns" at the bow removed and a new, curved stem added; she also received a second 76.2-mm gun on the forecastle and new radars. P 209 is used primarily as a survey ship and has a deckhouse in place of the 76.2-mm gun. Sister *Cambiaso* (P 207; ex-*Etlah,* AN 79) had been hulked by 12-94.

♦ 1 ex-U.S. Admirable class
Bldr: Associated SB, Seattle

	Laid down	L	In serv.
C 454 Prestol Botello (ex-*Separación;* ex-*Skirmish,* MSF 303)	8-4-43	16-8-43	30-6-44

D: 600 tons (903 fl) **S:** 15 kts **Dim:** 54.24 × 10.06 × 4.4
A: 1 76.2-mm Mk 26 DP; 2 single 40-mm 60-cal. Mk 3 Bofors AA; 4 single 20-mm 70-cal. Mk 10 Oerlikon AA
Electronics: Radar: 1 Raytheon SPS-64(V)9 nav.
M: 2 Cooper-Bessemer GSB-8 diesels; 2 props; 1,710 bhp **Electric:** 240 kw
Range: 5,600/9 **Fuel:** 260 tons **Crew:** 8 officers, 82 enlisted

Remarks: Former minesweeper transferred 13-1-65. Renamed in 1976; pennant number changed from BM to C (*Cañonero*—gunboat) in 1995 during a refit. All weapons are locally controlled. Sister *Tortuguero* (C 455; ex-*Signet,* MSF 302) was stricken and hulked in 1997.

♦ 2 ex-U.S. Coast Guard Balsam class
Bldr: Marine Iron & SB, Duluth, Minn.

	Laid down	L	In serv.
C 456 Almirante Juan Alejandro Acosta (ex-*Citrus,* WMEC 300, ex-WLB 300, ex-WAGL 300)	29-4-42	15-8-42	30-5-43
C 457 Almirante Didiez Burgos (ex-*Buttonwood,* WLB 306)	5-10-42	30-11-42	24-9-43

D: C 456: 694 tons light; 935 tons std. (1,025 fl)—C 457: 697 tons light (1,038 fl)
S: 13 kts **Dim:** 54.86 (51.81 pp) × 11.28 × 4.24
A: 3 single 12.7-mm M2 mg; 4 single 7.62-mm M-60 mg
Electronics: Radar: 2 Raytheon SPS-64(V)1 nav.
M: C 456: 2 Cooper-Bessemer 8-cyl. diesel generator sets, 2 electric motors; 1 prop; 1,000 shp—C 457: 2 G.E. EMD 8-645E6A diesel generator sets, 2 electric motors; 1 prop; 1,200 bhp—bow-thruster

Almirante Juan Alejandro Acosta (C 456) Alexandre Sheldon-Duplaix, 2000

Electric: 400 kw tot. (C 457: 3 G.M. 6-71 and 1 8V71 diesels driving)
Range: C 456: 7,600/12.9—C 457: 5,500/10 **Crew:** 8 officers, 42 enlisted

Remarks: C 456 was transferred 29-9-95 from U.S. Coast Guard (from which she had been decommissioned on 1-9-94) as Grant-Aid. C 457, which was transferred 28-6-01 on retirement, had remained configured as a buoy tender; the ship had been given a major modernization and re-engined during 3-91 to 3-93. They were built as icebreaking navigational buoy tenders and have 20-mm waterline ice-protection plating. During 1943, C 456 sank a German submarine off Miami. Carry a RIB inspection dinghy.

PATROL CRAFT [PC]

♦ 1 ex-U.S. PGM 71 class Bldr: Peterson SB, Sturgeon Bay, Wis.

GC 102 Betelgeuse (ex-PGM 77)

Betelgeuse (GC 102)—alongside *Enriquillo* (RM 22)
Alexandre Sheldon-Duplaix, 2000

D: 130 tons (145.5 fl) **S:** 16 kts **Dim:** 30.8 (30.2 pp) × 6.4 × 1.85
A: 1 20-mm 70-cal. Oerlikon AA; 2 single 12.7-mm mg
Electronics: Radar: 1 . . . nav.
M: 2 Caterpillar D-348TA diesels; 2 props; 1,450 bhp
Range: 1,000/12 **Crew:** 3 officers, 17 enlisted

Remarks: Transferred 14-1-66. One of many gunboats of this class transferred to smaller navies by the United States. Re-engined and armament reduced in 1980.

PATROL BOATS [PB]

♦ 2 110-foot Commercial Cruiser class
Bldr: Swiftships, Morgan City, La.

GC 107 Colón (ex-*Canopus*) (In serv. 6-84) GC 109 Orion (In serv. 8-84)

Colón (GC 107) Alexandre Sheldon-Duplaix, 9-99

D: 93.5 tons (fl) **S:** 23 kts (20 sust.) **Dim:** 33.53 × 7.32 × 1.83
A: 1 40-mm 60-cal. Bofors Mk 3 AA; 2 single 12.7-mm mg
Electronics: Radar: 1 . . . nav.

PATROL BOATS [PB] *(continued)*

M: 3 G.M. 12V92 TI diesels; 3 props; 2,700 bhp
Range: 1,500/12 **Crew:** 3 officers, 16 enlisted

Remarks: Aluminum construction. The 40-mm gun is mounted aft. GC 107 was renamed in 1992.

♦ 3 ex-U.S. Coast Guard 82-foot Point class
Bldr: Coast Guard Yard, Curtis Bay, Md. (GC 103: J. Martinac SB, Tacoma, Wash.)

	In serv.
GC 101 Aries (ex-*Point Martin,* WPB 82379)	20-8-70
GC 102 Antares (ex-*Point Batan,* WPB 82340)	21-11-62
GC 103 Sirius (ex-*Point Spencer,* WPB 82349)	25-10-66

Aries (GC 101) Alexandre Sheldon-Duplaix, 9-99

D: 64 tons (66–69 fl) **S:** 23.7 kts (see Remarks) **Dim:** 25.3 × 5.23 × 1.95
A: 2 single 12.7-mm M2 mg
Electronics: Radar: 1 Raytheon SPS-64(V)1 nav.
M: 2 Caterpillar 3412 diesels; 2 props; 1,480 bhp
Range: 490/23.7; 1,500/8 **Fuel:** 5.7 tons **Crew:** 1 officer, 7 enlisted

Remarks: GC 101 and 102 were transferred 22-9-99 and GC 103 12-12-00, all by donation. Hull built of mild steel. High-speed diesels are controlled from the bridge. Are well-equipped for salvage and towing, but are considered to be heavy rollers.

♦ 4 U.S. 85-foot Commercial Cruiser class
Bldr: Sewart Seacraft, Berwick, La.

	In serv.
GC 103 Procion (ex-U.S. 85NS671)	1967
GC 104 Aldebarán (ex-U.S. 85NS721	1972
GC 106 Bellatrix (ex-U.S. 85NS673)	1967
GC 108 Capella (ex-U.S. 85NS683)	1968

Procion (GC 103)—outboard *Bellatrix* (GC 106) and *Orion* (GC 109) Alexandre Sheldon-Duplaix, 5-99

D: 60 tons (fl) **S:** 21.7 kts **Dim:** 25.9 × 5.7 × 2.1
A: 3 single 12.7-mm mg **Electronics:** Radar: 1 . . . nav.
M: 2 G.M. 16V71N diesels; 2 props; 1,400 bhp
Range: 800/20 **Crew:** 5 officers, 14 enlisted

♦ 2 miscellaneous small patrol launches
GC 110 Luperon (In serv. 1988) GC 111 Alto Velo

Remarks: GC 110 is reported to be a cabin cruiser about 18 m overall. No further data available.

AUXILIARIES

♦ 1 U.S. Sotoyomo-class auxiliary ocean tug [ATA]
Bldr: Levingston SB, Orange, Tex.

	Laid down	L	In serv.
RM 22 Enriquillo (ex-*Stallion,* ATA 193)	26-10-44	24-11-44	1-2-45

Enriquillo (RM 22) Alexandre Sheldon-Duplaix, 9-99

D: 534 tons (860 fl) **S:** 13 kts **Dim:** 43.59 × 10.31 × 3.96
A: 1 76.2-mm 50-cal. U.S. Mk 26 DP; 2 single 20-mm 70-cal. Mk 10 Oerlikon AA
Electronics: Radar: 1 Raytheon 1500B nav.; 1 . . . nav.
M: 2 G.M. 12-278A diesels, electric drive; 1 prop; 1,500 shp **Electric:** 120 kw
Range: 8,000/8 **Fuel:** 160 tons **Crew:** 45 tot.

Remarks: Leased from the U.S.A. 30-10-80 and donated outright 10-6-97. Sister *Caonabo* (RM 18; ex-*Sagamore,* ATA 208), was returned to U.S. control in 1993 for scrapping.

SERVICE CRAFT

♦ 1 ex-U.S. floating crane [YD]
Grua Flotante (ex-YD 86)

Grua Flotante Alexandre Sheldon-Duplaix, 1-94

D: 1,407 tons (1,560 fl) **Dim:** 42.67 × 21.3 × . . .

Remarks: Leased from the U.S.A. during 1-71 and donated outright 10-6-97. Has 90-ton lift capacity.

♦ 1 ex-U.S. Navy floating dry dock [YFDL]
Bldr: Chicago Bridge & Iron (In serv. 1943)

DF-1 (ex-*Endeavor,* AFDL 1)

Lift capacity: 1,000 tons **Dim:** 60.96 × 19.51 × 1.07 (light)

Remarks: Leased from U.S.A. 8-3-86 and donated outright 10-6-97. Length on blocks: 56.39 m; clear width: 13.75 m; draft over blocks: 4.42 m; max. draft: 8.23 m.

♦ 2 miscellaneous harbor launches [YFL]
BA 1 Cojinoa BA 14 Beata

Remarks: No data available.

SERVICE CRAFT *(continued)*

♦ 1 ex-U.S. Coast Guard White-class (133-foot) navaids tender [YGL]
Bldr: Erie Concrete & Steel Supply, Erie, Pa.

	Laid down	L	In serv.
1 TORTUGUERO (ex-*White Pine,* WLM 547, ex-YC 548)	12-6-43	28-8-43	11-7-44

Tortuguero (1) Alexandre Sheldon-Duplaix, 9-99

D: 435 tons (600 fl) **S:** 9.8 kts **Dim:** 40.49 × 9.14 × 2.67
A: none **Electronics:** Radar: 1 Raytheon SPS-64(V) nav.
M: 2 diesels; 2 props; 600 bhp **Electric:** 90 kw tot.
Range: 2,100/9.8; 4,500/5.1 **Fuel:** 40 tons **Crew:** 24 tot.

Remarks: Donated on decommissioning from the U.S. Coast Guard on 29-6-99. Had been transferred to the U.S. Coast Guard from the U.S. Navy on 3-8-48. Has one 10-ton buoy-handling derrick.

Disposal note: Coastal survey craft *Neptuno* (BA 10, ex-*Toro*) was stricken during 1999.

♦ 4 miscellaneous dredges [YM]

Two Dominican Republic Navy dredges Alexandre Sheldon-Duplaix, 9-99

Remarks: Acquired 1995–96, primarily from Spain, when the navy was given the responsibility to keep Dominican harbors clear. All are non-self-propelled.

♦ 1 U.S. YO 153–class small oiler [YO]
Bldr: Ira S. Bushey, Brooklyn, N.Y.

	Laid down	L	In serv.
BT 5 CAPITÁN BEOTEGUI (ex-U.S. YO 215)	23-4-45	30-8-45	17-12-45

Capitán Beotegui (BT 5) Alexandre Sheldon-Duplaix, 6-97

D: 370 tons (1,076 fl) **S:** 8 kts **Dim:** 47.63 × 9.32 × 3.66
A: 2 single 20-mm 70-cal. Mk 10 Oerlikon AA **Electronics:** Radar: none
M: 1 Union diesel; 1 prop; 525 bhp **Electric:** 39 kw tot. **Crew:** 23 tot.

Remarks: Loaned by U.S.A. during 4-64 and donated outright 10-6-97. Cargo: 6,071 barrels fuel (660 tons). Sister *Capitán W. Arvelo* (BT 4) sank at sea during 2-89.

♦ 2 Hercules-class harbor tugs [YTM]
Bldr: Ast. Navales Dominicanos (In serv. 1960)

RP 12 HERCULES RP 13 GUACANAGARIX

D: 200 tons (fl) **S:** . . . kts **Dim:** 21.4 × 4.8 × 2.7
M: 1 Caterpillar diesel; 1 prop; 500 bhp **Crew:** 8 tot.

♦ 1 ex-U.S. Navy medium harbor tug [YTM]
Bldr: . . . . (In serv. 1944)

RM 17 MAGUA (ex-. . .)

Magua (RM 17) Alexandre Sheldon-Duplaix, 9-99

Remarks: Transferred during late 1990s. Rebuilt with new pilothouse above original structure and fitted with a broader stack.

♦ 1 harbor tug, former LCM(6)-class landing craft [YTM]

RDM 303 OCOA

D: 50 tons (fl) **S:** 9 kts **Dim:** 17.1 × 4.3 × 1.2
M: 2 G.M. Detroit Diesel 6-71 diesels; 2 props; 450 bhp
Range: 130/9 **Crew:** 5 tot.

Remarks: Modified for use as a tug about 1976. Retains bow ramp.

♦ 1 U.S. YTL 422–class small tug [YTL]
Bldr: Robert Jacob, City Island, NY (In serv. 25-7-45)

RP 16 BOHECHIO (ex-*Mercedes,* ex-YTL 600)

D: 70 tons (80 fl) **S:** 10 kts **Dim:** 20.1 × 5.5 × 2.4
M: 1 Hoover-Owens-Rentschler diesel; 1 prop; 375 bhp
Crew: 6 tot. **Fuel:** 7 tons

Remarks: Leased from U.S.A. during 1-71 and donated outright 10-6-97.

Note: Also in service is the small harbor tug *Puerto Hermoso* (RP 14); no data available.

♦ 1 sail-training craft for naval academy [YTS] (In serv. 1979)

BA 7 NUBE DEL MAR (ex-*Catuan*)

D: 40 tons (fl) **S:** 12 kts **Dim:** 12.8 × 3.6 × . . .
M: 1 Volvo Penta 21A diesel; 1 prop; 75 bhp

♦ 1 navigational training craft [YXT]
Bldr: Ast. Navales Dominicanos, Santo Domingo (In serv. 1975)

BA 15 RAMBO (ex-*Jurel*)

D: 24 tons (fl) **S:** 9 kts **Dim:** 13.7 × 3.6 × 1.3
A: 1 7.62-mm mg **Electronics:** Radar: . . .
M: 1 G.M. Detroit Diesel 4-71 diesel; 101 bhp—70 m^2 tot. auxiliary sail
Crew: 4 tot.

Remarks: Used for training, light cargo hauling (7 tons max.), and patrol. Sisters *Carite* (BA 3), *Atún* (BA 6), and *Picúa* (BA 9) had been discarded by 1995.

ECUADOR

Republic of Ecuador

ARMADA DE GUERRA

Personnel (2002): About 4,000 total, including about 1,200 marines and 250 naval aviation personnel. During 1999, the naval personnel force was being drawn down significantly due to severe economic conditions.

Bases: Principal naval bases are located at Guayaquil, Jaramijó, Salinas, and San Lorenzo. Naval infantry are based at Guayaquil, Oriente, and in the Galapagos Islands, where there is also a small naval facility. The naval academy is located at Salinas and the Naval War College at Guayaquil, the principal naval facility and fleet headquarters. The facilities at Jaramijó were expanded in 1998–99.

Naval Aviation: Two Bell-Heli-Dyne 412EP Sentinel, 2 Bell 230T, and 4 Bell 206B JetRanger helicopters; 1 CASA CN-235, 1 Beech Super King Air 200T, 4 Cessna 337, 1 Cessna 320E, and 1 Cessna Citation light transports; and 3 Beech T-34C-1 trainers. The two navalized Bell 412EP Sentinel ASW/ASUW helicopters were delivered in 10-98 and 1-99; they are equipped with AlliedSignal RDR-1500B radar, WESCAM 16DS(W) t.v./IR sensor, AQS-18A dipping sonar, one Mk 46 ASW torpedo (or two ASM), and a datalink.

Note: Pennant numbers on Ecuadorian ships are changed every few years. Ship names are prefaced with BAE *(Buque de Armada de Ecuador)*.

ATTACK SUBMARINES [SS]

Note: Discussions with Israel for the purchase of that country's three IKL 500 *(Gal)*–class small submarines were revealed during 1-99, but the negotiations ended with the conclusion of peace negotiations with Peru, which was followed by a declaration by the Ecuadorian president that new arms purchases were being abandoned.

♦ 2 German Type 209/1300 Bldr: Howaldtswerke, Kiel

	Laid down	L	In serv.
S 101 SHYRI	5-8-74	6-10-76	6-11-77
S 102 HUANCAVILCA	20-1-75	15-3-77	16-3-78

Shyri (S 101)—with Coast Guard patrol boat *Río Puyango* (LG-41) in background *Ships of the World,* 2000

D: 1,100 tons light; 1,265 tons surf./1,395 tons sub.
S: 11 kts surf./21.4 kts sub. (1 hr) **Dim:** 59.50 × 6.30 × 5.50
A: 8 bow 533-mm TT (14 SST Mod. 0 wire-guided torpedoes)
Electronics:
Radar: 1 Thales Calypso nav./surf. search
Sonar: STN Atlas Elektronik CSU-3 suite: A526 passive, CSU AN407 A9 active, Thales DUUX-2 passive-ranging hull array
EW: Thales DR-2000U intercept
M: 4 MTU 12V493 TY60 diesels, 4 Siemens 405-kw generators, electric drive: 1 Siemens motor; 1 prop; 5,000 shp (4,600 sust.)
Range: 8,400/8, 11,200/4 snorkel; 25/20, 445/4 sub.
Fuel: 87 tons normal/106 tons max. **Endurance:** 45 days
Crew: 5 officers, 28 enlisted

Remarks: Ordered 3-74. S 101 was refitted at her builders in 1983, S 102 in 1984; both underwent local refits in 1993–94 but were in need of further work by 1999, when S 101 began a refit at ASMAR, Valparaiso, Chile. The 257-ton battery installation includes four sets of 120 cells and is rated at 11,500 amp-hr. Have Thales M8 Mod. 24 torpedo f.c.s. Both are based at Guayaquil.

FRIGATES [FF]

♦ 2 British "Exocet Leander" Batch 2B conversions

	Bldr	Laid down	L	In serv.
FM-01 PRESIDENTE ELOY ALFARO (ex-*Penelope,* F 127; ex-*Coventry*)	Vickers-Armstrong, Barrow-in-Furness	14-3-61	17-8-62	31-10-63
FM-02 MORAN VALVERDE (ex-*Danae,* F 47)	HM Dockyard, Devonport	16-12-64	31-10-65	7-9-67

D: 2,650 tons (3,200 fl) **S:** 28 kts
Dim: 113.38 (109.73 pp) × 12.50 × 4.80 (6.20 props)
A: 4 MM 38 Exocet SSM; 3 2-round Simbad SAM syst. (36 Mistral missiles); 2 single 40-mm 60-cal. Mk 9 AA; 2 triple 324-mm ILAS-3 ASW TT (WASS A-244S torpedoes); 1 Bell 412EP Sentinel helicopter
Electronics:
Radar: 1 Type 1006 nav.; 1 Type 994 air/surf. search; 1 Type 965 early warning; 2 Type 904 f.c.
Sonar: Type 184P (7.5 kHz) hull-mounted; Type 162M (50 Hz) HF classification; Type 185 underwater telephone
EW: UA-8/9 passive; Type 668 or 669 jammer; FH-12 HFD/F; 2 6-round DLD decoy RL (Raytheon Mk 137 launchers)

Moran Valverde (FM-02) Ecuadorian Navy, 1996

Presidente Eloy Alfaro (FM-01) Maritime Photographic, 6-01

M: 2 sets White–English Electric geared steam turbines; 2 props; 30,000 shp
Boilers: 2 Babcock & Wilcox 3-drum; 38.7 kg/cm^2, 450° C
Electric: 1,900 kw tot. **Range:** approx. 4,000/12 **Fuel:** 460 tons
Crew: 20 officers, 228 enlisted (in U.K. service)

Remarks: FM-01 paid off from Royal Navy service 31-3-91, was sold with FM-02 to Ecuador 25-4-91, and recommissioned 25-5-91. FM-02 transferred at the end of 7-91 on completion of Royal Navy service. Both ships have been badly in need of overhauls and rearming, and a contract for refits appears to have been signed with ASMAR of Chile early in 2001.
Hull systems: Have twin rudders and one pair of fin stabilizers, set well aft of amidships.
Combat systems: When transferred, had the CAAIS combat data system, but the Chilean SISDEF 100 system is to be substituted during forthcoming refits. French Simbad point-defense SAM system launchers have been added, one atop the pilothouse and two abreast atop the hangar. The former two Sea Cat SAM system launchers and their associated Type 904 radar directors have been removed. Were transferred without MM 38 antiship missiles, which were procured later. The torpedo tubes, mounted on the main deck just abaft the helicopter hangar, were taken from units of the *Wadi M'ragh* class. The 40-mm guns are power operated and entirely locally controlled. The Bell 412EP helicopters were to be equipped with antiship missiles. A commercial SATCOM system has been added. In FM-01, the EW intercept gear has been replaced by Israeli-made equipment and a SATCOM system has been added.

GUIDED-MISSILE PATROL COMBATANTS [PGG]

♦ 6 Italian modified Wadi M'ragh class (2 in *reserve*)

	Bldr	Laid down	L	In serv.
CM-11 ESMERALDAS	CNR, Muggiano	27-9-79	5-10-80	7-8-82
CM-12 MANABÍ	CNR, Ancona	1-2-80	5-2-81	21-6-83
CM-13 LOS RÍOS	CNR, Muggiano	1-9-79	28-2-81	1-10-83
CM-14 EL ORO	CNR, Ancona	1-3-80	5-2-81	10-12-83
CM-15 *GALAPAGOS*	CNR, Muggiano	20-10-80	5-7-81	26-5-84
CM-16 *LOJA*	CNR, Ancona	6-2-81	27-2-82	26-5-84

Manabí (CM-12)—with Bell 206B JetRanger on deck Peruvian Navy, 2000

D: 620 tons (700 fl) **S:** 37 kts **Dim:** 62.3 (57.8 pp) × 9.3 × 2.8
A: 6 MM 40 Exocet SSM; 1 4-round Albatros SAM system (Aspide missiles, no reloads); 1 76-mm 62-cal. OTOBreda DP; 1 twin 40-mm 70-cal. OTOBreda AA—4 units only: 2 triple 324-mm ILAS-3 ASW TT (WASS A-244S torpedoes); 1 Bell 206B helicopter
Electronics:
Radar: 1 Decca TM 1226 nav.; 1 AESN RAN-10S air/surf. search; 1 AESN Orion 10X f.c.; 1 AESN Orion 20X f.c.
Sonar: Thales Diodon hull-mounted (11–13 kHz)
EW: Elettronica ELT-318 Newton Gamma intercept; Telegon HFD/F; 1 20-round 105-mm OTOBreda SCLAR decoy RL
M: 4 MTU 20V956 TB92 diesels; 4 props; 24,400 bhp (20,400 sust.)
Electric: 750 kw **Range:** 1,200/31; 4,000/18 **Fuel:** 126 tons **Crew:** 51 tot.

GUIDED-MISSILE PATROL COMBATANTS [PGG] *(continued)*

Esmeraldas (CM-11)—with only three Exocet canisters aboard *Ships of the World,* 2000

Remarks: Ordered in 1978 from CNR del Tirreno. Have more-powerful engines than earlier Libyan units of class. Were to be modernized with updated electronics and a combat information datalink capability, but funds are not available and all are in need of refits.
Combat systems: Have the Selenia IPN-10 data system, with NA 21 Mod. 0 radar f.c.s. and two CO3 directors for guns and SAM system. Also have a helicopter platform, but no hangar.

GUIDED-MISSILE PATROL CRAFT [PTG]

♦ **3 FPB 45 class** (1 *in reserve*)
Bldr: Friedrich Lürssen Werft, Vegesack, Germany

	L	In serv.		L	In serv.
LM-21 *Quito*	20-11-75	13-7-76	LM-24 Cuenca	12-76	17-7-77
LM-22 Guayaquil	5-4-76	22-12-77			

Quito (LM-21) Ecuadorian Navy, 1996

D: 250 tons (265 fl) **S:** 35 kts **Dim:** 45.0 × 7.0 × 2.4
A: 4 MM 38 Exocet SSM; 1 76-mm 62-cal. OTOBreda DP; 1 twin 35-mm 90-cal. Oerlikon AA
Electronics:
Radar: 1 Decca TM 1226 nav.; 1 Thales Triton air/surf. search; 1 Thales Pollux f.c.
EW: Thales DR-2000S intercept
M: 4 MTU 16V396 diesels; 4 props; 13,600 bhp **Electric:** 330 kw tot.
Range: 600/30 **Fuel:** 39 tons **Crew:** 34 tot.

Remarks: Were re-engined in 1994–95, but LM-21 was in reserve by 2000. Carry 250 rounds of 76-mm and 1,100 rounds of 35-mm ammunition. Have the Thales Vega gunfire-control system.

♦ **2 Manta class** Bldr: Friedrich Lürssen Werft, Vegesack, Germany

LM-25 Manta (In serv. 11-6-71)
LM-27 Nueva Rocafuerte (ex-*Tena*) (In serv. 23-6-71)

Manta (LM-25) Ecuadorian Navy, 1996

D: 119 tons (134 fl) **S:** 35 kts **Dim:** 36.2 × 5.8 × 1.7
A: 4 IAI Gabriel-II SSM; 1 twin 30-mm 75-cal. Emerlec AA
Electronics:
Radar: 1 . . . nav.; 1 Thales Pollux f.c.
EW: Thales DR-2000S intercept
M: 3 Mercedes-Benz diesels; 3 props; 9,000 bhp
Range: 700/30; 1,500/15 **Fuel:** 21 tons **Crew:** 19 tot.

Remarks: Similar to the Chilean *Guacolda* class, but faster. New guns were added in 1979. Gabriel missiles (in four single, fixed launch canisters) and Thales Vega fire-control system (without Triton search radar) replaced two single 533-mm TT in 1980–81; the missiles are no longer regularly carried and may have passed their shelf-life expiration dates. Replacements for the craft were being sought as long ago as 1987. Sister *Tulcan* (LM-26) was lost in a collision with a commercial tug during 9-98.

AMPHIBIOUS WARFARE SHIPS AND CRAFT

♦ **1 ex-U.S. LST 542–class tank landing ship [LST]**
Bldr: Chicago Bridge & Iron

	Laid down	L	In serv.
TR-61 Hualcopo (ex-*Summit County,* LST 1146)	15-2-45	23-5-45	1-6-45

D: 1,650 tons (4,080 fl) **S:** 11.6 kts **Dim:** 100.04 × 15.24 × 4.3
A: 2 twin 40-mm 60-cal. Bofors Mk 1 Mod. 2 AA; 4 single 40-mm 60-cal. Bofors Mk 3 AA; 2 single 20-mm 70-cal. Oerlikon AA
Electronics: Radar: 1 . . . nav.
M: 2 G.M. 12-567A diesels; 2 props; 1,700 bhp **Electric:** 300 kw tot.
Range: 7,200/10 **Crew:** 119 ship's company + 147 troops

Remarks: Bought 14-2-77. Used as a transport. Has an ice-reinforced waterline, an asset of limited value in tropical waters. In poor condition after a serious fire in 7-98 and may not be operational. Cargo capacity is about 600 tons.

♦ **10 river personnel launches [LCP]**
Bldr: ASTINAVE, Guayaquil

D: . . . tons **S:** 20 kts **Dim:** 6.70 × . . . × . . .
A: 1 7.62-mm mg **M:** 2 gasoline outboards; 200 bhp **Crew:** 2 + 21 troops

Remarks: Ordered in 1991. Kevlar plastic construction. Same class is operated by the coast guard and army.

AUXILIARIES

♦ **1 oceanographic research ship [AGOR]**
Bldr: Ishikawajima Harima, Tokyo (In serv. 21-10-81)

BI-91 Orion (ex-*Dometer*)

Orion (BI-91)—red hull, white superstructure Maritime Photographic, 6-01

D: approx. 1,500 tons (fl) **S:** 12.5 kts **Dim:** 70.19 (64.22 pp) × 10.72 × 3.60
Electronics: Radar: 2 Decca 1226 nav.
M: 3 G.M. Detroit Diesel–Allison 16V92 TA diesels (960 bhp each), 3 600-kw generator sets, 2 electric motors, reverse-reduction gearing; 2 props; 900 shp
Electric: 700 kw tot. **Range:** 6,000/12
Crew: 6 officers, 25 enlisted + 19 scientists

Remarks: 1,105 grt/461 dwt. Delivery name, *Dometer,* was changed to *Orion* on arrival for commissioning. Equipped to conduct physical and biological oceanography, geophysical research, and hydrographic surveys for the Instituto Oceanográfico de la Armada del Ecuador; also does weather reporting. Earlier bore pennants HI-91 and HI-92.

♦ **ex-British Kinterbury-class supply ship [AK]**
Bldr: Cleland SB, Wallsend-on-Tyne (In serv. 20-9-77)

TR-62 Calicuchima (ex-*Throsk,* A 379)

Calicuchima (TR-62)—as *Throsk* (A 379) James W. Goss/Navpic, 6-91

D: 2,193 tons (fl) **S:** 14 kts **Dim:** 70.57 (64.31 pp) × 11.90 × 4.57
A: none **Electronics:** Radar: 1 Type 1006 nav.
M: 2 Mirrlees-Blackstone diesels; 1 prop; 3,000 bhp
Range: 1,500/14; 5,000/10 **Crew:** 8 officers, 16 enlisted

AUXILIARIES *(continued)*

Remarks: 1,150 dwt. Former Royal Corps of Transport ammunition transport. Purchased 11-91, departed for Ecuador 2-92, and commissioned 24-3-92. Can carry 760 tons cargo in the two holds, which total 750 m^3, plus 25 tons on deck. Has two cranes.

♦ **1 coastal transport tanker [AOT]**
Bldr: ASTINAVE, Guayaquil (In serv. 1985)

TR-65 Taurus (ex-T-66)

D: approx 1,800 tons (fl) **S:** 11 kts **Dim:** 53.1 × 11.0 × 4.4 **A:** . . .
M: 2 G.M. Detroit Diesel 6-71 diesels; 1 prop; 750 bhp **Crew:** 20 tot.

Remarks: 1,110 grt/1,175 dwt. Transferred to naval service in 1987.

♦ **1 ex-U.S. Achomawi-class fleet tug [ATA]**
Bldr: Charleston SB & DD, Charleston, S.C.

	Laid down	L	In serv.
RA-70 Chimborazo (ex-*Chowanoc,* ATF 100)	24-4-43	20-8-43	21-2-44

Chimborazo (RA-70) Maritime Photographic, 6-01

D: 1,235 tons (1,675 fl) **S:** 16.5 kts **Dim:** 62.48 (59.44 wl) × 11.73 × 4.67
A: 2 single 12.7-mm mg **Electronics:** Radar: 1 Decca 916 nav.
M: 4 Busch-Sulzer BS-539 diesels, electric drive; 1 prop; 3,000 shp
Electric: 400 kw tot. **Range:** 7,000/15; 16,000/8 **Fuel:** 376 tons **Crew:** 85 tot.

Remarks: Purchased 1-10-77 from U.S.A. Has earlier borne pennants R-710, R-71, and R-106. Near-sister *Cayambe* (RA-71) was in the coast guard.

♦ **1 sail-training ship [AXT]**
Bldr: Ast. Celaya, Bilbao, Spain

	L	In serv.
BE-51 Guayas	23-9-76	23-7-77

Guayas (BE-51)—pennant number is not displayed A. D. Baker III, 6-00

D: 934 grt **S:** 10.5 kts **Dim:** 76.2 × 10.6 × 4.2
M: 1 G.M. 12V149T diesel; 1 prop; 700 bhp
Crew: 50 tot. + 80 cadets (accomm. for 180)

Remarks: 934 grt/234 dwt. Steel-hulled barque.

SERVICE CRAFT

♦ **1 inshore oceanographic research craft [YAG]**
Bldr: Halter Marine, New Orleans (In serv. 1975)

LH-94 Rigel (ex-LH-92)

D: 50 tons **S:** 10 kts **Dim:** 19.7 × 5.2 × 1.1
M: 2 diesels; . . . bhp **Crew:** 2 officers, 8 enlisted

♦ **3 ex-U.S. ARD 12–class auxiliary repair docks [YFDL]**
Bldr: Pacific Bridge, Alameda, Calif. (In serv. 1944–45)

DF-81 Amazonas (ex-ARD 17)
DF-82 Napo (ex-ARD 24)
DF-83 . . . (ex-*Alamagordo,* ARDM 2; ex-ARD 26)

Capacity: 3,500 tons **Dim:** 149.9 × 24.7 × 1.7 (light)

Remarks: DF-81 transferred 7-1-61, DF-82 in 1988, and DF-83 (which had been converted to service nuclear-powered attack submarines) on 26-2-01. Pointed bow. Length over blocks: 118.6 m; 18.0 m clear width. *Amazonas* earlier bore pennant DF-121. In 7-99, the U.S. Congress approved the offer for sale of the *Endurance* (ARDM 3, ex-ARD 18), but the ship was not accepted by Ecuador.

Disposal note: U.S. YR 24–class repair barge *Putamayo* (BT-84, ex-YR 34) was stricken during 1999.

♦ **5 Tungurahua-class medium harbor tugs [YTM]**
Bldr: . . . . . . (In serv. 1950s–60s)

RB-74 Antizana (ex-R-723)
RB-75 Sirius (ex-R-724)
RB-76 Altar (ex-R-725)
RB-77 Tungurahua (ex-R-722)
RB-78 Quilotoa (ex-R-726)

D: 490 grt **S:** 8 kts **Dim:** 30.6 × . . . × 2.5
M: . . . diesels; 1 prop; . . . bhp

♦ **1 medium harbor tug [YTM]** (In serv. 1952)

RB-72 Sangay (ex-*Losa*)

D: 295 tons (390 fl) **S:** 12 kts **Dim:** 32.6 × 7.9 × 4.25
M: 1 Fairbanks-Morse diesel; 1 prop; . . . bhp

Remarks: Bought in 1964 and renamed in 1966. Earlier bore pennants R-720, R-102, and R-53.

♦ **1 former U.S. Army medium harbor tug [YTM]**
Bldr: Equitable Bldg., New Orleans (In serv. 1945)

RB-73 Cotopaxi (ex-*R. T. Ellis*)

D: 150 tons **S:** 9 kts **Dim:** 25.0 × 6.62 × 2.9 **M:** 1 diesel; 1 prop; 650 bhp

Remarks: Bought in 1947. Earlier bore pennants R-721, R-103, and R-52.

♦ **1 ex-British Water-class water lighter [YW]**
Bldr: Drypool, Hull (In serv. 1968)

TR-64 Quisquis (ex-*Waterside,* Y 20)

D: 344 tons (fl) **S:** 11 kts **Dim:** 40.02 (37.50 pp) × 7.50 × 2.44
Electronics: Radar: 1 Decca . . . nav.
M: 1 Lister-Blackstone ERS-8MGR diesel; 1 prop; 600 bhp
Electric: 155 kw tot. **Range:** 1,500/11 **Crew:** 8 tot.

Remarks: 285 grt. Purchased 11-91 and delivered 2-92. Cargo: 150 tons. Sister *Watercourse* may be purchased later.

♦ **1 ex-U.S. water lighter [YW]**
Bldr: Leatham D. Smith, Sturgeon Bay, Wis. (In serv. 17-9-45)

TR-63 Atalhuapa (ex-YW 131)

D: 440 tons (1,390 fl) **S:** 7 kts **Dim:** 53.1 × 9.8 × 4.6
M: 1 G.M. 8-278 diesel; 1 prop; 640 bhp **Fuel:** 25 tons **Crew:** 20 tot.

Remarks: Transferred 2-5-63; purchased 1-12-77. Stricken in 1988 but restored to service in 1990. Despite small size and minimal freeboard, has been used to deliver water to the Galapagos Islands. Cargo: 930 tons water. Has earlier borne pennants T-63, T-62, T-33, T-41, and A-01.

COAST GUARD

Personnel (2002): Approx. 50 officers, 350 enlisted

Note: "LG" in pennant number system stands for *Lancha de Guarda (de Costa).*

Disposal note: U.S. *Abnaki*-class patrol ship and former seagoing tug *Cayambe* (RA-71; ex-*Los Rios;* ex-*Cusabo,* ATF 155) was stricken during 1999.

PATROL CRAFT [WPC]

♦ **2 Espada class** Bldr: Trinity–Moss Point Marine, Escatawpa, Miss.

LG-33 5 de Agosto (In serv. 5-91)
LG-34 27 de Febrero (In serv. 11-91)

D: 120 tons (fl) **S:** 27 kts **Dim:** 34.14 (31.62 pp) × 6.86 × 2.14 (max.)
A: 1 40-mm 60-cal. Bofors Mk 3 AA; 2 single 12.7-mm M2 mg
Electronics: Radar: 1 Decca TM 1226 nav.
M: 2 G.M Detroit Diesel 16V149 MTI diesels outboard (1,280 bhp each), 1 G.M. Detroit Diesel 16V92 TAB cruise diesel centerline (860 bhp); 3 props; 3,420 bhp
Range: 1,500/13 **Crew:** 5 officers, 14 enlisted

Remarks: Built under U.S. Foreign Military Sales program for Galapagos Islands service. Carry a 10-person rigid inflatable inspection boat.

COAST GUARD PATROL CRAFT [WPC] *(continued)*

5 de Agosto (LG-33)—on trials Halter Marine, 5-91

♦ 1 U.S. PGM 71 class
Bldr: Peterson Bldrs, Sturgeon Bay, Wis. (In serv. 30-11-65)

LG-31 25 de Julio (ex-*Quito*)

D: 130 tons (147 fl) **S:** 17 kts **Dim:** 30.81 (30.20 pp) × 6.45 × 2.3
A: 1 40-mm 60-cal. Bofors Mk 3 AA; 2 twin 20-mm 70-cal. Oerlikon Mk 24 AA; 2 single 12.7-mm mg
Electronics: Radar: 1 Raytheon 1500B Pathfinder nav.
M: 4 MTU diesels; 2 props; 3,520 bhp **Electric:** 30 kw tot.
Range: 1,000/12 **Fuel:** 16 tons **Crew:** 15 tot.

Remarks: Built as U.S. PGM 75 as foreign aid. Transferred from the Ecuadorian Navy to Coast Guard in 1980 and discarded in 1983; refitted and re-engined in 1988–89 for further service. Earlier bore pennants LGC-31 and LC-71. Sister *24 de Mayo* (LG-32; ex-*Guayaquil;* ex-LC-71; ex-LGC-32; ex-LC-72; ex-U.S. PGM 76) was lost in a collision with merchant ship *Dole Ecuador* on 29-8-95.

PATROL BOATS [WPB]

♦ 2 U.S. 45-foot PCR class
Bldr: Swiftships, Morgan City, La. (In serv. 9-92)

LG-37 8 de Octubre LG-38 27 de Octubre

8 de Octubre (LG-37) Skeets Photo/Swiftships, 7-92

D: 17 tons (fl) **S:** 28 kts **Dim:** 13.72 × 3.58 × 0.51 (at rest)
A: 2 single 12.7-mm M-2HB mg; 2 single 7.62-mm M-60D mg
Electronics: Radar: 1 Raytheon 40X nav.
M: 2 G.M. Detroit Diesel 6V92TA diesels; 2 Hamilton 362 waterjets; 900 bhp
Range: 650/22 **Fuel:** 1,045 gallons **Endurance:** 5 days **Crew:** 4 tot. + 8 troops

Remarks: PCR = Patrol Craft, Riverine. Act as command and control craft for groups of smaller riverine patrol craft. Left New Orleans as deck cargo 14-9-92.

Hull systems: Aluminum construction, with Kevlar armor over crew positions. Made 32 kts on trials; can make 28 kts at 105% combat load at 100° F and can operate in Sea State 2 conditions. Can be transported on trailers.
Combat systems: The 12.7-mm mg are mounted in tubs that can also accommodate twin 12.7-mm mg or 40-mm Mk 19 grenade launchers. Communications equipment includes a VHF transceiver with direction finder, HF/SSB transceiver, and two UHF handheld radios. Navigation equipment includes magnetic compass, depth sounder and handheld GPS receiver.

♦ 6 Río Puyango class
Bldrs: First two: Halter Marine, New Orleans; others: ASTINAVE, Guayaquil

	In serv.		In serv.
LG-41 Río Puyango	6-86	LG-44 Río Chone	11-3-88
LG-42 Río Mateje	6-86	LG-45 Río Daule	17-6-88
LG-43 Río Zarumilla	11-3-88	LG-46 Río Babhoyo	17-6-88

D: 17 tons (fl) **S:** 26 kts **Dim:** 13.41 (12.39 pp) × 4.12 × 0.76
A: 1 12.7-mm M-2HB mg; 1 7.62-mm M-60D mg
Electronics: Radar: 1 Furuno 2400 nav.
M: 2 G.M. 8V71 TI diesels; 2 props; 850 bhp **Electric:** 12 kw
Range: 500/18 **Fuel:** 1.6 tons **Crew:** 1 officer, 4 enlisted

Remarks: First two were purchased for service in the Galapagos Islands. The other four were built in Ecuador from U.S.-supplied kits. Have a 250-gal./min fire monitor to starboard and two firepumps to port. Aluminum construction. Used for drug interdiction.

♦ 6 river patrol craft Bldr: ASTINAVE, Guayaquil (In serv. 1991)

D: . . . tons **S:** 20 kts **Dim:** 6.70 × . . . × . . .
A: 1 7.62-mm mg **M:** 2 gasoline outboards; 200 bhp **Crew:** 2 tot. + 21 troops

Remarks: Ordered in 1991. Kevlar plastic construction. Additional units may be ordered later. Same class is operated by the naval infantry and army.

♦ 1 ex-U.S. Coast Guard 82-foot Point class
Bldr: J. Martinac SB, Tacoma, Wash. (In serv. 25-8-67)

LG-32 24 de Mayo (ex-*Point Richmond,* WPB 82370)

D: 64 tons (69 fl) **S:** 23.7 kts (see Remarks) **Dim:** 25.3 × 5.23 × 1.95
A: 2 single 12.7-mm mg **Electronics:** Radar: 1 Raytheon SPS-64(V)1 nav.
M: 2 Caterpillar 3412 diesels; 2 props; 1,480 bhp
Range: 490/23.7; 1,500/8 **Fuel:** 5.7 tons **Crew:** 1 officer, 7 enlisted

Remarks: Purchased 22-8-97 to replace another unit of the same name. Hull of mild steel. High-speed diesels, controlled from the bridge.

ECUADORIAN ARMY

PATROL BOATS [WPB]

♦ 10 riverine craft Bldr: ASTINAVE, Guayaquil

D: . . . tons **S:** 20 kts **Dim:** 6.70 × . . . × . . .
A: 1 7.62-mm mg **M:** 2 gasoline outboards; 200 bhp **Crew:** 2 + 21 troops

Remarks: Ordered in 1991. Kevlar plastic construction. Same class is operated by the coast guard and naval infantry.

EGYPT

Arab Republic of Egypt

Personnel (2001): Approx. 19,000 total, including 2,000 in coast guard, plus 14,000 reserves

Bases: Naval facilities are located at Aboukir, Alexandria, Hurghada, Mers Matruh, Safaqa, and Suez.

Maritime Aviation: The navy has 10 SH-2G(E) shipboard ASW helicopters. The air force operates 9 Westland Sea King Mk 47 helicopters and 9 AS.12 wire-guided missile–equipped Aérospatiale AS.342L Gazelle helicopters in support of the navy. The air force also has two Beech 1900C light coastal surveillance aircraft with Litton radar and Singer S-3075 ESM. The 10 SH-2G(E) helicopters were delivered 1997–98 after conversion by Kaman Helicopters from SH-2F configuration at a cost of $380 million; they received G.E. T700-401 engines and Allied Signal/Bendix AQS-18(V) dipping sonars. Ten more ex-USN SH-2G SeaSprites may be purchased later. Egyptian Air Force E-2C Hawkeye aerial surveillance and tracking aircraft had their APS-138 radars changed to APS-145 during 2000, permitting overland surveillance. Two Schiebel Camcopter 5.1 UAV helicopters were ordered in 5-01 for use from Egyptian Navy frigates; the aircraft have an endurance of 6 hours, carry a color video camera, and are to be delivered early in 2002.

Coastal Defense: The navy is responsible for coastal defenses. Fifty coast-defense truck-mounted versions of the Otomat missile were purchased in 1983 for use by three trucks, each able to carry two missiles. There are two naval-controlled artillery brigades, equipped with Soviet-made 100-mm, 130-mm, and 152-mm guns. Five U.S. TPS-59(V)2 coastal surveillance radars were upgraded in 2000 to -(V)3E and given a capability to detect and track theater ballistic missiles. Six SPS-48E 3-D early warning radars were ordered from the U.S.A. on 29-6-01 for land-based use.

Weapons and Sensors: Egypt bought 32 U.S. Harpoon missiles and 46 Mk 46 ASW torpedoes during 1994 in support of its acquisition of *Knox*-class frigates. Another 42 Harpoons were purchased during 1998. In 9-97, 84 Mk 46 Mod. 5 ASW torpedoes were purchased from Alliant Techsystems in the U.S.A.

H-2G(E) Super SeaSprite Robert F. Dorr, 1998

Otomat missiles are being updated to the Otomat Mk 2 configuration (Teseo) em-oyed by the Italian Navy under a 12-00 contract to Alenia Marconi Systems; the ork is to be completed by 5-05. Four Raytheon 20-mm Phalanx CIWS (three Block 0, e Block IB) were ordered during 6-01 for installation on unspecified ships.

ote: Ship names are preceded by ENS (Egyptian Navy Ship).

TTACK SUBMARINES [SS]

0 (+ 2) Moray 1400 class

Bldr: Ingalls SB, Pascagoula, Miss.

	Laid down	L	In serv.
. . . . .	. . .	. . .	2005
. . . . .	. . .	. . .	2007

: 1,600 tons sub. **S:** 25 kts sub.
: 6 533-mm TT (18 weapons)
lectronics:
Radar: . . .
Sonar: . . .
EW: . . .
: . . .
ange: 9,000/4 surf.; 304/4 sub. **Endurance:** 50 days **Crew:** 50 tot.

emarks: Designed by RDM, Rotterdam. After several years of delays, a letter of in-nt to purchase the ships was signed 15-9-00, but U.S. government concurrence had ot been obtained as of 10-01; they would be funded by the U.S. foreign military aid ogram. Lockheed Martin Naval Electronics and Surveillance Systems would sup-y the SUBICS 900 combat system and systems integration.

4 Chinese-built Romeo class (Project 033)

Bldr: . . . (In serv. 1983–84)

49 852 855 858

odernized Romeo-class 855 H&L Van Ginderen, 10-96

odernized Romeo-class 855—outboard sister 858 Chris Delgoffe/H&L Van Ginderen, 3-00

: 1,320 tons surf./1,712 tons sub. **S:** 15.2 kts surf./13 kts sub.
im: 77.60 × 6.70 × 4.95
: 6 bow and 2 stern 533-mm TT (14 UGM-84C Harpoon SSM and NT-37F torpedoes, or up to 28 mines)
lectronics:
Radar: 1 Snoop Plate nav./surf. search
Sonar: STN Atlas Elektronik CSU-3-4 active/passive suite, with PSU-2-83 passive array and STU-3 sonar training set
EW: ArgoSystems Phoenix AR-700-S5 intercept
: 2 Type 37D diesels (2,000 bhp each), 2 generators, 2 motors; 2 props; 2,700 shp—2 50-shp creep motors
ange: 14,000/9 surf.; 7,000/5 snorkel; 350/4 sub.
ndurance: 60 days **Crew:** 8 officers, 43 enlisted

emarks: Two units, launched in 1980, were delivered from China on 28-3-83; the econd Chinese-built pair was delivered 3-1-84 and commissioned 21-5-84. Six Soviet-uilt units were transferred earlier, five in 1966 and one in 1969; of these, two were discarded by the mid-1980s, two were laid up in 1989, and two remained nominally operational into 1994, when they were abandoned, although 831, 840, and 843 remained at the Alexandria Naval Base into 2001.

Hull systems: Have 224 battery cells, producing 6,000 amp-hr. Normal maximum operating depth is 270 m (300 m max.). Displacements and dimensions above reflect pre-modernization figures; the submarines may be a bit longer due to the enlarged chin sonar dome, and the displacement figures have probably risen considerably, reducing reserve buoyancy.

Modernization: Loral Sonar Systems began modernizing the quartet in 4-92. They received new 54-ton-capacity air-conditioning systems; new power distribution systems with two new 7-kVA, 60-Hz, 120-V a.c. motor generator sets; U.S. Alliant NT-37F wire-guided torpedoes and Sub-Harpoon missile launch capability (while retaining the ability to launch existing stocks of Chinese-supplied straight-running torpedoes); a Loral Librascope ENFCS (Egyptian Navy Fire Control System) with two multifunction displays; a Librascope-assembled STN Atlas Elektronik sonar suite (with a greatly enlarged chin sonar dome and topside sonar dome); Kollmorgen Model 76 periscopes and Model 86 optronic telescoping masts; Boeing ArgoSystems AR-700-S5 EW equipment (with the array mast also accommodating GPS, D/F, and UHF communications antennas); an inertial navigation system; and a towed buoyant radio communications cable system (with the cable drum housed in the extended lower forward portion of the sail). Also installed were a Link Y datalink system to permit over-the-horizon targeting and encrypted communications equipment. The first unit completed modernization early in 1994 and the last during 1-96. Kollmorgen optronic surveillance systems were ordered for the boats in 1-00, with deliveries to be completed by 1-02.

DESTROYERS [DD]

Note: Ex-British Z-class destroyer *El Fateh* (921, ex-*Zenith,* ex-*Wessex*) had been relegated to alongside training duties by 2000; see under Training Ships [AXT].

GUIDED-MISSILE FRIGATES [FFG]

♦ 4 ex-U.S. Oliver Hazard Perry class

	Bldr	Laid down	L	In serv.
901 Sharm el-Sheikh (ex-*Fahrion,* FFG 22)	Todd, Seattle	1-12-78	24-8-79	16-1-82
906 Toushka (ex-*Lewis B. Puller,* FFG 23)	Todd, San Pedro	23-5-79	15-3-80	17-4-82
911 Mubarak (ex-*Copeland,* FFG 25)	Todd, San Pedro	24-10-79	26-7-80	7-8-82
916 Taba (ex-*Gallery,* FFG 26)	Bath Iron Works	17-5-80	20-12-80	5-12-81

Toushka (906) William C. Clarke, 1-99

Mubarak (911) Cem D. Yaylali, 5-99

Sharm el-Sheikh (901) Chris Delgoffe/H&L Van Ginderen, 3-00

GUIDED-MISSILE FRIGATES [FFG] *(continued)*

D: 2,948 tons light (3,881 fl) **S:** 29 kts (30.6 on trials)
Dim: 135.64 (125.9 wl) × 13.72 × 5.8 (7.62 max.)
A: 1 single-rail Mk 13 Mod. 4 launcher (4 RGM-84C Harpoon and 36 Standard SM-1 MR missiles); 1 76-mm 62-cal. Mk 75 DP; 1 20-mm Mk 15 Phalanx gatling CIWS; 4 single 12.7-mm mg; 2 triple 324-mm Mk 32 Mod. 7 ASW TT; 1 or 2 SH-2G(E) Super SeaSprite ASW helicopters
Electronics:
Radar: 1 . . . nav.; 1 Cardion SPS-55 surf. search.; 1 Raytheon SPS-49(V)4 air search; 1 UNISYS Mk 92 Mod. 4 missile/gun f.c.; 1 Lockheed STIR (SPG-60 Mod.) missile/gun f.c.; 1 General Dynamics Mk 90 Phalanx f.c. (on mount); 1 JRC . . . helicopter control
Sonar: Raytheon SQS-56 hull-mounted LF
TACAN: URN-25
EW: Raytheon SLQ-32(V)2 passive; Mk 36 SRBOC decoy RL syst. (2 6-round Mk 137 launchers); SLQ-25 Nixie towed acoustic torpedo decoy
M: 2 G.E. LM-2500 gas turbines; 1 5.5-m-dia., CP, 5-bladed prop; 41,000 shp (40,000 sust.)—2 350-shp drop-down electric propulsors
Electric: 3,000 kw tot.
Range: 4,200/20; 5,000/18 **Fuel:** 587 tons + 64 tons helicopter fuel
Crew: 17 officers, 195 enlisted (217 max. accomm.)

Remarks: 911, transferred 18-9-96 under the U.S. Grant-Aid program, was originally to have been renamed *Sharm el-Sheikh.* 916 was transferred by sale ($106 million, including 35 Standard missiles, 12 Mk 46 Mod. 5 torpedoes, and gun ammunition) on 25-9-96 and was given a 3-month refit in the U.S. prior to departure. 911 and 916 were formally dedicated in Egypt 13-7-97. 901 was decommissioned from the USN 3-3-98 and transferred 31-3-98 as Grant-Aid; 906 followed on 18-9-98, also as Grant-Aid, but underwent refit on the U.S. East Coast prior to departing for Egypt, arriving 12-98. All except 901 are former U.S. Naval Reserve Force training ships.
Hull systems: Particularly well protected against splinter and fragmentation damage, with 19-mm aluminum-alloy armor over magazine spaces, 16-mm steel over the main engine-control room, and 19-mm Kevlar plastic armor over vital electronics and command spaces. Speed on one turbine alone is 25 kts; the auxiliary power system uses two retractable pods located well forward and can drive the ships at up to 6 kts. Two nonretractable fin stabilizers are fitted. Are equipped with the Prairie/Masker air bubbler system to reduce radiated machinery noise below the waterline.
Combat systems: The Mk 92 Mod. 4 fire-control system controls missile and 76-mm gun fire; it uses a STIR (modified SPG-60) antenna amidships and a U.S.-built version of the Thales WM-28 radar forward and can track four separate targets. The Mk 75 gun is a license-built version of the OTOBreda Compact. A Mk 13 weapons-direction system is fitted. There are two Mk 24 optical missile and gun target designators mounted in tubs atop the pilothouse. Up to 24 Mk 46 Mod. 5 torpedoes can be carried. Harpoon missiles are launched from the Mk 13 launcher via the SWG-1 launch control system. Were not transferred with towed sonar arrays. All received a navigational radar prior to transfer, and a JRC navigational radar has been added atop the hangar for helicopter control.

FRIGATES [FF]

♦ 2 Chinese Jianghu-I class Bldr: Hudong SY, Shanghai

951 Najim al-Zafir (In serv. 27-10-84) 956 El Nasser (In serv. 16-4-85)

Najim al-Zafir (951) French Navy, 11-95

El Nasser (956) Chris Delgoffe/H&L Van Ginderen, 3-00

D: 1,586 tons (1,702 fl) **S:** 25.5 kts **Dim:** 103.20 × 10.20 × 3.05 (hull)
A: 2 twin, trainable launchers for C-201 SSM; 2 twin 57-mm 70-cal. Type 76 DP; 6 twin 37-mm 63-cal. Type 74 AA; 4 5-round Type 81 ASW RL; 4 BMB-2 d.c. mortars; 2 internal d.c. racks; 2 mine rails
Electronics:
Radar: 1 Decca RM 1290A nav.; 1 Type 756 nav.; 1 Type 354 (MX-902 Eye Shield) air/surf. search; 1 Type 352C (Square Head) missile target desig.
Sonar: E-5 hull-mounted HF searchlight
EW: Elettronica Newton-Beta suite (Type 211 intercept; Type 318 noise jammer; Type 521 deception jammer); Litton Triton intercept
M: 2 SEMT-Pielstick 12 PA 6 280BTC diesels; 2 props; 14,400 bhp
Electric: 1,320 kw tot.
Range: 1,750/25; 4,000/15 **Endurance:** 15 days **Crew:** 195 tot.

Remarks: Ordered in 1982. There are reported plans to remove the after armamen and superstructure and install a helicopter hangar and flight deck.
Combat systems: Differ from Chinese Navy units in having twin 57-mm guns vic single or twin 100-mm mounts fore and aft, and in having an enclosed housing fo the optical rangefinder atop the bridge. There is no radar fire-control equipment fo the eight gun mounts, all of which are locally controlled via on-mount sights. Elet tronica EW equipment was added after delivery, along with a second navigationa radar. U.S. Litton Triton radar threat warning receivers were added during 1994.

♦ 2 Spanish Descubierta class Bldr: E.N. Bazán, Cartagena

	Laid down	L	In serv
F 941 Abuqir (ex-*Centinela*)	31-10-78	6-10-79	21-5-84
F 946 El Suez (ex-*Serviola*)	28-2-79	20-12-79	27-10-84

Abuqir (F 941) Chris Delgoffe/H&L Van Ginderen, 3-00

D: 1,363 tons (1,575 fl) **S:** 26 kts **Dim:** 88.88 (85.80 pp) × 10.40 × 3.70
A: 8 RGM-84C Harpoon SSM; 1 8-round Mk 29 SAM launcher (24 RIM-7M NATO Sea Sparrow missiles); 1 76-mm 62-cal. OTOBreda Compact DP; 2 single 40-mm 70-cal. Bofors AA; 1 2-round 375-mm Bofors ASW RL; 2 triple 324-mm Mk 32 ASW TT (Stingray torpedoes)
Electronics:
Radar: 1 Thales ZW-06/Z nav./surf. search; 1 Thales DA-05/2 air/surf. search; 1 Thales WM-25 f.c.
Sonar: Raytheon DE 1167LF and hull-mounted VDS (7.5 kHz)
EW: Elettronica Beta intercept/jammer suite; Telegon HFD/F
M: 4 Bazán-MTU16V956 TB91 diesels; 2 CP props; 18,000 bhp
Electric: 1,810 kw tot. **Range:** 6,000/18 **Fuel:** 250 tons
Crew: 10 officers, 106 enlisted (accomm. for 146)

Remarks: Originally ordered 25-5-76 for the Spanish Navy, but sold to Egypt in 1982 while building. F 946 completed 28-2-84 and F 941 on 6-9-84.
Hull systems: Have fin stabilizers, plus the U.S. Prairie/Masker bubbler system to reduce sound radiation below the waterline.
Combat systems: Have the Thales Nederland SEWACO weapons-control system Carry 600 rounds of 76-mm ammunition. The U.S.A. supplied the Harpoon missiles in 1984; the ships normally carry fewer than the maximum loadout. Have separate IFF interrogation antenna on the after mast below and to starboard of the DA-05/2 antenna.

♦ 2 ex-U.S. Knox class Bldr: Avondale SY, Avondale, La.

	Laid down	L	In serv
961 Damiyat (ex-*Jesse L. Brown,* FFT 1089)	8-4-71	18-3-72	17-2-73
966 Rasheed (ex-*Moinester,* FFT 1097)	25-8-72	12-7-73	2-11-74

Damiyat (961) Chris Delgoffe/H&L Van Ginderen, 3-00

D: 3,130 tons light (4,260 fl) **S:** 27+ kts
Dim: 134.00 (126.49 wl) × 14.33 × 4.77 (7.83 over sonar)

'RIGATES [FF] *(continued)*

:asheed (966) Chris Delgoffe/H&L Van Ginderen, 3-00

.: 8 RGM-84C Harpoon SSM (see Remarks); 1 127-mm 54-cal. Mk 42 DP; 1 20-mm Mk 15 CIWS; 1 8-cell Mk 112 ASROC ASW RL; 2 pair 324-mm Mk 32 Mod. 9 fixed ASW TT; 1 SH-2G(E) Super SeaSprite LAMPS-I ASW helicopter

lectronics:

Radar: 1 Raytheon SPS-64(V)9 nav.; 1 Norden SPS-67 surf. search; 1 Lockheed SPS-40D air search; 1 Western Electric SPG-53F gun f.c.; 1 General Dynamics Mk 90 Phalanx f.c.

Sonar: EDO-G.E. SQS-26CX bow-mounted LF

TACAN: SRN-15A

EW: Raytheon SLQ-32(V)2 intercept; Mk 36 SRBOC decoy syst. (2 6-round Mk 137 RL); T-Mk 6 Fanfare towed acoustic torpedo decoy

I: 1 set Westinghouse geared steam turbines; 1 prop; 35,000 shp

oilers: 2 Combustion Engineering V2m, M-Type; 84 kg/cm^2, 510° C

lectric: 3,000 kw tot. (3 × 750-kw turbogenerators, 1 × 750-kw diesel set)

:ange: 4,300/20 **Fuel:** 750 tons max. **Crew:** 17–20 officers, 255–267 enlisted

:emarks: Transferred on lease, 961 on 27-7-94 and 966 on 28-6-94; purchased outght 25-3-98. Both had been used in recent years as U.S. Naval Reserve Force trainig ships. Sisters *Francis Hammond* (FF 1067) and *Hepburn* (FF 1055), decommisoned from USN service 2-7-92 and 20-12-91, respectively, were transferred 1-3-96 r use as cannibalization spares under Grant-Aid.

Iull systems: Bow bulwarks and a spray strake have been added forward to reduce eck wetness, a problem in this class; the addition added 9.1 tons and extended the verall length from the original 133.59 m. Have a TEAM (SM-5) computer system for ie continual monitoring of the ship's electronic equipment. Antirolling fin stabilizrs are fitted. The Prairie/Masker bubbler system is fitted to hulls and propellers to educe radiated noise. By 2000, were said to be having boiler problems.

'ombat systems: Never received a Mk 25 BPDMS (Basic Point Defense Missile Sysm) launcher for Sea Sparrow; a 20-mm Mk 15 Phalanx CIWS gatling AA system as added after 1982. The ASW torpedo tubes are fixed, in the forward end of the angar superstructure, aimed outboard at an angle of 45°. Have the Mk 114 ASW re-control system. The ASROC system has an automatic reloading magazine beneath ie bridge; no ASW missiles were transferred and the launcher may be removed and eplaced with two quadruple canister launcher sets for Harpoon missiles. Some 4,000 ounds of 127-mm and 40,000 rounds of 20-mm ammunition were transferred for use ith these ships.

Neither ship ever had a variable-depth sonar; both received SQR-18A(V)2 ACTASS during the 1980s, but the system was not transferred with the ships. Carry Mk 68 gunfire-control system with SPG-53D or -53F radar. The ASW TDS (Tactial Data System) is installed, and they also have a form of "mini-NTDS" called FISTS (Frigate Integrated Shipboard Tactical System) that employs off-the-shelf esktop computers. Also have SQR-17 sonar datalink processors. May receive an lettronica EW suite in place of SLQ-32.

'ATROL SHIPS [PS]

'ote: The ex-British *Black Swan*–class sloop *Tariq* (931, ex-*Malek Farouk,* ex-*'himbrel*) is now a stationary training platform but remains in commission; see uner Training Ships [AXT].

;UIDED-MISSILE PATROL CRAFT [PTG]

0 (+ 4) Ambassador Mk III class

Bldr: Friede Goldman Halter, . . . Miss.

	Laid down	L	In serv.
. . . . .	2001	. . .	7-04
. . . . .	. . .	. . .	. . .
. . . . .	. . .	. . .	. . .
. . . . .	. . .	. . .	5-05

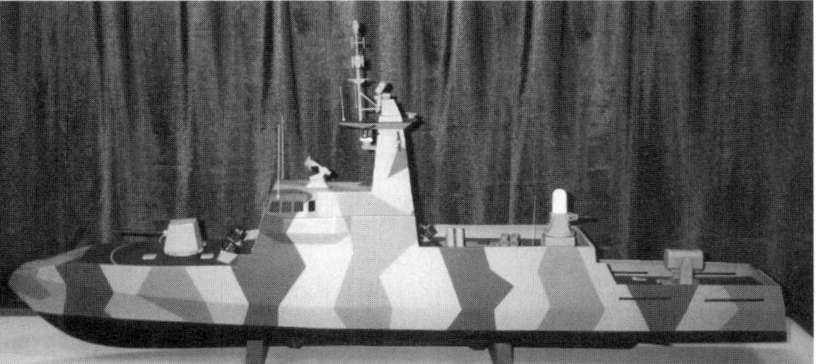

.mbassador Mk III class—builder's model Friede Goldman Halter, 4-01

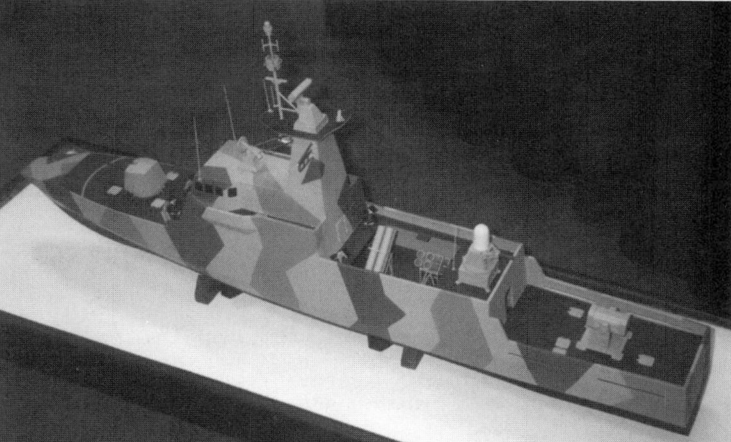

Ambassador Mk III class—builder's model Friede Goldman Halter, 4-01

D: 550 tons (fl) **S:** 41 kts **Dim:** 60.62 × 8.90 × 2.80

A: 8 RGM-84 Harpoon SSM; 1 21-round Mk 31 SAM syst. (RIM-116A RAM missiles); 1 76-mm 62-cal. OTOBreda–United Defense SuperRapid DP; 1 20-mm Phalanx Block I gatling CIWS

Electronics:

Radar: 1 . . . nav.; 1 EADS-Raytheon TRS-3D/16 3-D search; 1 . . . f.c.

EW: . . . intercept; . . . decoy syst. (4 6-round RL)

M: 6 MTU (DCX)–Detroit Diesel 4000 diesels, 3 props; 30,418 bhp

Range: . . ./. . . **Endurance:** 21 days **Crew:** 41 tot.

Remarks: Using mostly U.S. Foreign Military Assistance funding, a class of guided-missile patrol craft is to be built in a U.S. yard for a total cost of around $1.3 billion ($400 million for the bare craft). Design and builder were selected 2-1-01, contingent on U.S. government approval, which was expected in 4-01 but had not been given as of 1-02. The basic design is a variation of the Vosper Thornycroft Europatrol 250, but with signature reduction measures incorporated. There will be two sets of nonretracting fin stabilizers. Lockheed Martin is to provide combat system integration and technical services.

♦ 6 Chinese Houku class (1 in *reserve*)

Bldr: . . . (In serv. 27-10-84)

609 611 613 615 617 *619*

Houku-class 613 French Navy, 1999

D: 68 tons light, 73.88 tons normal (79.19 fl) **S:** 37 kts

Dim: 27.0 × 6.50 × 1.80 (1.295 hull)

A: 2 HY-2 SSM; 1 twin 23-mm 60-cal. AA

Electronics:

Radar: 1 Type 352C (Square Tie) search/target desig.

EW: Litton Triton radar intercept

M: 4 M-50F-4 (Type L-12V-180) diesels; 4 props; 4,800 bhp **Electric:** 65 kw tot.

Range: 500/24 **Endurance:** 5 days **Crew:** 2 officers, 15 enlisted

Remarks: Delivered 9-84 and commissioned together the following month. Steel construction. Former hull numbers were 401–406. The Type 352C radar can also be employed as a passive radar intercept and direction-finding device. The gunmount is a standard Soviet 2M-3M mounting with Egyptian-made guns substituted for the original 25-mm weapons. Equipped with U.S. Litton Triton radar threat warning receivers during 1994.

♦ 6 Ramadan class (1 in *reserve*)

Bldr: Vosper Thornycroft, Portchester, U.K.

	Laid down	L	In serv.
670 Ramadan	22-9-78	6-9-79	20-7-81
672 Khyber	23-2-79	31-1-80	15-9-81
674 *El Kadesseya*	23-4-79	19-2-80	6-4-82
676 El Yarmouk	15-5-79	12-6-80	18-5-82
678 Badr	29-9-79	17-6-81	17-6-82
680 Hettein	29-2-80	25-11-80	28-10-82

D: 262 tons (312 fl) **S:** 35 kts **Dim:** 52.0 (48.0 pp) × 7.6 × 2.0 (hull)

A: 4 Otomat Mk 1 SSM; 1 76-mm 62-cal. OTOBreda Compact DP; 1 twin 40-mm 70-cal. OTOBreda AA

Electronics:

Radar: all Marconi: 1 S 810 nav.; 1 S 820 air/surf. search; 2 ST 802 f.c.

EW: Racal Cutlass-E intercept; Racal Cygnus jammer; Telegon HFD/F; Protean decoy syst. (4 36-round RL)

GUIDED-MISSILE PATROL CRAFT [PTG] *(continued)*

El Kadesseya (674)—laid up at Alexandria
Chris Delgoffe/H&L Van Ginderen, 3-00

M: 4 MTU 20V538 TB91 diesels; 4 props; 16,000 bhp **Electric:** 420 kw tot.
Range: 2,000/15 **Fuel:** 43 tons **Crew:** 4 officers, 27 enlisted

Remarks: Ordered 4-9-77. First pair arrived in Egypt 13-11-81, second pair 23-7-82, and third pair in 12-82. 674 was reported to be nonoperational in 2000.
Combat systems: Have the Marconi Sapphire fire-control system, with two ST 802 radar/t.v. directors and two Lawrence Scott optical directors, and the Ferranti CAAIS automated data system. Soviet shoulder-launched SA-7 Grail surface-to-air missiles are reportedly carried. Two had their radars upgraded under a 1998 contract with Alenia-Marconi Systems, and a contract for the other four was let in 3-01, with the work to be completed in 53 months. All six are to have their communications systems upgraded by Alenia-Marconi under a 3-00 contract. Alenia-Marconi also won a contract in 4-00 to update command and control systems on this class, with the work to be completed by mid-2003; the Nautis-3 system will replace the CAAIS equipment, but much of the same software will be retained.

♦ 6 October class Bldr: Alexandria Naval DY (In serv. 1980–81)

781 783 785 787 789 791

October class H&L Van Ginderen, 7-80

D: 71 tons (82 fl) **S:** 40 kts **Dim:** 25.3 × 6.0 × 1.8
A: 2 Otomat Mk 1 SSM; 2 twin 30-mm 75-cal. Oerlikon A32 AA
Electronics:
Radar: 1 Alenia-Marconi S 810 nav./surf. search; 1 Alenia-Marconi ST 802 f.c.
EW: Litton Triton radar intercept; 2 6-round MEL Protean Decoy RL
M: 4 CRM 18V-12D/55 YE diesels; 4 props; 5,400 bhp
Range: 400/30 **Crew:** 20 tot.

Remarks: Wooden hulls, built at Alexandria Naval Dockyard, Egypt, 1969–75. Fitted out by Vosper Thornycroft at Portchester, Portsmouth, England, 1979–81, with Italian-French missiles and British guns; the diesels are Italian. Basic design is that of the former Soviet Komar class. 791 was lost overboard during delivery 16-12-80, salvaged and returned to the U.K. 30-6-81, and completed repairs 13-8-82. Use Marconi Sapphire radar/t.v. fire-control system. Were equipped with U.S. Litton Triton radar threat warning receivers during 1994.

♦ 6 ex-Soviet Osa-I class (Project 205E) (2 in *reserve*)

631 633 *637* *639* 641 643

Osa-I-class 641 H&L Van Ginderen, 6-97

D: 171 tons (209.5 fl) **S:** 38.5 kts
Dim: 38.6 (37.5 wl) × 7.6 (6.3 wl) × 1.8 (hull; 2.9 props)
A: 4 P-20/21 Termit (SS-N-2C Styx) SSM; 1 SA-7 Grail SAM launch position; 2 twin 30-mm 65-cal. AK-230 AA; 2 single 12.7-mm mg
Electronics:
Radar: 1 Rangout (Square Tie) surf. search/target desig.; 1 MR-104 Rys' (Drum Tilt) gun f.c.
EW: Litton Triton radar intercept
M: 3 M-503A2 diesels; 3 props; 12,000 bhp **Electric:** 200 kw tot.
Range: 500/34; 750/25 **Endurance:** 5 days **Crew:** 4 officers, 24 enlisted

Remarks: Survivors of 13 transferred 1966–68. All carry shoulder-launched SA- Grail (SA-N-5) SAMs, launched from a tub amidships. Four, 631, 635, 637, and 63 were inoperable by end-1989, but 637 was restored to service in 1991 and 633 an 639 were again operational by 1993; by 1998, 639 was again out of service. Equippe with Litton Triton radar intercept systems in 1994.

PATROL CRAFT [PC]

Note: Negotiations were under way as of early 1999 for the purchase of one or mo ex-U.S. Navy *Cyclone*-class patrol craft, although other designs were also bein studied.

♦ 8 Chinese Hainan class

	In serv.		In ser
430 Al Nour	23-10-83	442 Al Qatar	21-5-8
433 Al Hadi	23-10-83	445 Al Saddam	6-8
436 Al Hakim	21-5-84	448 Al Salam	6-8
439 Al Wakil	21-5-84	451 Al Rafia	6-8

Four Egyptian Navy Hainan-class patrol craft
Chris Delgoffe/H&L Van Ginderen, 3-(

D: 375 tons normal (392 fl) **S:** 30.5 kts **Dim:** 58.77 × 7.20 × 2.20 (hull)
A: 2 twin 57-mm 70-cal. Type 76 DP; 2 twin 23-mm 60-cal. AA; 4 5-round Type 81 ASW RL; 2 BMB-2 d.c. mortars; 2 d.c. racks; 2 mine rails
Electronics:
Radar: 1 Type 351 (Pot Head) surf. search
Sonar: Tamir-11 (MG-11) hull-mounted searchlight-type (25–31 kHz)
EW: none
M: 4 Type 9D-8 diesels; 4 props; 8,800 bhp **Range:** 2,000/14 **Crew:** 70 tot.

Remarks: First pair arrived 10-83, next three 2-84, and final trio 6-84. Four were receive two triple 324-mm ASW TT and Stingray torpedoes, along with a U.S. L brascope fire-control system and a new sonar, but the work was not accomplishe The original 25-mm AA guns were reportedly replaced with Egyptian-made 23-m weapons on the same 2M-3M mountings. May now carry a commercial navigation radar in addition to the not-very-effective Pot Head.

♦ 4 Chinese Shanghai-II class

793 795 797 799

D: 122.5 tons normal (134.8 fl) **S:** 28.5 kts **Dim:** 38.78 × 5.41 × 1.55
A: 2 twin 37-mm 63-cal. Type 74 AA; 2 twin 23-mm 60-cal. AA
Electronics: Radar: 1 Type 351 (Pot Head) surf. search
M: 2 Type L-12V-180 diesels (1,200 bhp each), 2 Type L12-180SZ diesels (910 bhp each); 4 props; 4,220 bhp
Electric: 39 kw **Range:** 750/16.5 **Endurance:** 7 days **Crew:** 36 tot.

Remarks: Transferred in 1984 with transfer numbers E 601–604. Do not have dept charges, as do Chinese Navy examples. The original 25-mm guns have reportedly bee exchanged for Egyptian-made 23-mm weapons on the same 2M-3M mountings.

♦ 5 Soviet Shershen class

753 755 757 759 761

D: 145 tons (170 fl) **S:** 45 kts **Dim:** 34.60 × 6.75 × 1.5
A: 2 twin 30-mm 65-cal. AK-230 AA; 1 SA-7 Grail shoulder-launched SAM positio
Electronics:
Radar: 1 Baklan (Pot Drum) surf. search; 1 MR-104 Rys' (Drum Tilt) f.c.
M: 3 M-503A diesels; 3 props; 12,000 bhp (8,025 sust.)
Electric: 84 kw tot. (3 × 28-kw diesel sets)
Range: 460/42; 800/30 **Fuel:** 30 tons **Crew:** 22 tot.

Remarks: Survivors of seven transferred 1967–68. Four were armed with two 2 round 122-mm artillery rocket launchers instead of torpedoes; the launchers hav subsequently been removed, as have the torpedo tubes.

'ATROL CRAFT [PC] *(continued)*

tricken Egyptian Shershen-class 751—derelict at Alexandria; masts of training ιips *El Fateh* (921) and *Tariq* (931) are seen in the background
Chris Delgoffe/H&L Van Ginderen, 3-00

ATROL BOATS [PB]

5 modified Soviet P-6 class (Project 183)

)1 Thar 713 Nisr . . . Al Bahr
)3 Nur 719 Nimr

: 56 tons (66.5 fl) **S:** 45 kts **Dim:** 25.90 × 6.24 × 1.24 (hull; 1.70 props)
: 2 twin 23-mm 60-cal. AA **Electronics:** Radar: 1 Decca 1226 nav.
: 4 M-50F-4 diesels; 4 props; 4,800 bhp **Electric:** 100 kw tot.
ange: 600/33; 1,000/14 **Fuel:** 7.2 tons **Crew:** 16 tot.

emarks: Survivors of some 20 torpedo boats transferred during the early 1960s. 'ooden construction. All had been laid up by 1985, but these five were reported back service as of 1991. They may, in fact, have new hulls built at the Alexandria Naval ockyard, and the engines may be Italian CRM 12D/SS diesels vice the original ιuipment listed here. The former twin 25-mm 2M-3M gunmounts have been adapted r Egyptian-made guns. No longer carry a BM-21 122-mm artillery rocket launcher t.

IINE WARFARE SHIPS

4 Soviet Yurka-class (Project 266E) fleet minesweepers [MSF]

30 Aswan 533 Giza 536 Qena 539 Sohag

ohag (539)—alongside a sister Chris Delgoffe/H&L Van Ginderen, 3-00

: 520 tons normal (560 fl, 619 max.) **S:** 16 kts **Dim:** 52.10 × 9.60 × 2.65
: 2 twin 30-mm 65-cal. AK-230 AA; 2 mine rails (10 tot. mines)
lectronics:
Radar: 1 Don-2 nav.
Sonar: Tamir-11 (MG-11) hull-mounted searchlight (25–30 kHz)
: 2 M-503B-3E diesels; 2 CP props; 5,000 bhp
lectric: 500 kw tot. (2 × 200-kw, 1 × 100-kw diesel sets)
ange: 600/16; 1,500/12 **Endurance:** 7 days **Crew:** 50 tot.

emarks: Delivered new in 1969. Modernization plans for new MTU diesels, towed de-scan sonar, and remotely-operated minehunting vehicles have been set aside. By)98, 536 was in reserve, but the ship was in refit during 2000.
ull systems: Low magnetic signature, aluminum-steel alloy hull, with low mag- ɜtic signature machinery. Degaussing equipment is automatically controlled, with cal coils around massive equipment. Use special measures to reduce acoustic sig- ɜture. Maximum sweep speed with arrays deployed is 14 kts.
ombat systems: Are intended to sweep mines in 25- to 150-m depths. Did not have ιe standard MR-104 Rys' (Drum Tilt) radar fire-control system. The sonar trans- ιcer is mounted in a large dome that can be hoisted within the hull.

6 Soviet T-43-class (Project 254K) fleet minesweepers [MSF]
(1 in *reserve*)

)1 Gharbiya 507 Daqahliya 513 Sinai
)4 *Sharkiya* 510 Bahariya 516 Assiout

Assiout (516) M. Ottini, 3-98

D: 535 tons (569 fl) **S:** 14 kts **Dim:** 59.10 × 8.75 × 2.50
A: 2 twin 37-mm 63-cal. V-47M AA; 4 twin 12.7-mm mg; 2 BMB-1 d.c. mortars; 2 mine rails (20 tot. mines)
Electronics:
Radar: 1 Decca . . . nav.
Sonar: Tamir-11 (MG-11) hull-mounted searchlight (25–30 kHz)
EW: 2 Watch Dog-A intercept (2–18 GHz)
M: 2 Type 9D diesels; 2 CP props; 2,200 bhp **Electric:** 550 kw tot.
Range: 1,500/14; 4,400/8.3 **Fuel:** 68 tons **Endurance:** 7 days
Crew: 5 officers, 48 enlisted

Remarks: Survivors of a group delivered in the early 1970s; all were of the early 1950s–built "short hull" version. Plans to modernize them with new engines, Gayrobot Pluto remote-controlled submersibles, and towed side-scan sonars have been abandoned. These ships are not equipped to deal with modern bottom mines. 507 and 510 were in refit as of 2000.

♦ 3 U.S. coastal minehunters [MHC]
Bldr: Swiftships, Morgan City, La.

	L	Del.	In serv.
542 Dat Assawari (ex-CMH 1)	4-10-93	25-4-94	13-7-97
545 Navarin (ex-CMH 2)	13-11-93	20-6-94	13-7-97
548 Burullus (ex-CMH 3)	4-12-93	30-7-94	13-7-97

Burullus (548) Chris Delgoffe/H&L Van Ginderen, 3-00

D: 175 tons (203 fl) **S:** 12.4 kts **Dim:** 33.53 (31.91 wl) × 8.23 (7.62 wl) × 2.24
A: 2 single 12.7-mm Browning M2 mg
Electronics:
Radar: 1 Sperry Rastar nav.
Sonar: Thales-Thoray TSM 2022 hull-mounted HF
M: 2 MTU 12V183 TE61 DB51L diesels; 2 Schottel SRP.300E Z-drives; 1,034 bhp—1 White Gill 300-shp thruster (4 kts)
Electric: 170 kw tot. (2 × 85-kw, 380/220-V a.c., 50-Hz sets)
Range: 2,000/10 **Fuel:** 26,500 liters **Crew:** 5 officers, 20 enlisted

Remarks: Ordered 12-90; originally to have been a class of six. Two delivered to Egyptian waters in 11-95 and one in 2-96. GRP construction hull. Design based on a successful fishing boat class by the same builder. Also for use as route survey craft in peacetime.
Hull systems: Completed at considerably over the designed displacement, 188 tons. Electrical power at 380 and 220 V ac, 50 Hz, and 24 V dc.
Combat systems: Capable of mine neutralization in waters up to 100 m deep. Have Paramax integrated mine-countermeasures control system, a simplified version of the U.S. Navy's SYS-12 system. Navigational aids include GPS, Loran-C receiver, HF radio navaid, dynamic positioning system, doppler speed log, bathythermograph, and gyrocompass. Sonars by Thoray, Lexington, Mass., a joint venture of the U.S. Raytheon and French Thomson-Sintra (now Thales) companies. Carry two Westinghouse-made Gayrobot Marine Pluto mine neutralization vehicles. Have a portable decompression chamber for mine clearance divers.

♦ 2 U.S. mine route survey craft [MSA]
Bldr: Swiftships, Morgan City, La. (In serv. 1-10-94)

RSV 1 Safaga RSV 2 Abu el-Ghoson

D: 155.2 tons (165 fl) **S:** 12.4 kts **Dim:** 27.43 × 7.54 × 2.27
A: 1 12.7-mm Browning M2 mg
Electronics:
Radar: 1 Furuno FR-2020 nav.—Sonar: EG&G side-scan VHF
M: 2 MTU 12V183 TE61 diesels; 2 props; 900 bhp—60-shp bow-thruster
Electric: 100 kw tot. (2 × 50-kw, 380/220-V a.c., 50-Hz sets)
Range: 1,500/10 **Fuel:** 22,710 liters **Crew:** 2 officers, 14 enlisted

MINE WARFARE SHIPS *(continued)*

Safaga (RSV 1) Chris Delgoffe/H&L Van Ginderen, 3-00

Remarks: Ordered 11-90. GRP construction. Intended to survey harbor and coastal navigational channels during peacetime to chart bottom obstructions. Also equipped to stream Edo-Western 606A-602 shallow and 606A-604 deep tow-body side-scan sonars.

Note: Former U.S. Naval Reserve COOP-conversion route-survey craft ex-YP 663 and ex-YP 665 were transferred to Egypt in 1988, departing the U.S. as deck cargo on 20-12-88 for use as interim route-survey craft; they have probably been retired.

AMPHIBIOUS WARFARE SHIPS

♦ **3 Soviet Polnocny-A-class (Project 770) medium landing ships [LSM]** Bldr: Stocznia Polnocna, Gdansk, Poland

301 303 305

Polnocny-A-class 305—with sterns of two Vydra-class landing craft obscuring the stern at the right Chris Delgoffe/H&L Van Ginderen, 3-00

D: 704 tons std., 751 tons normal (770 fl) **S:** 18.5 kts
Dim: 73.00 (70.00 pp) × 8.62 × 0.90 (fwd; 1.85 aft)
A: 1 twin 30-mm 65-cal. AK-230 AA; 2 18-round 140-mm artillery RL (180 rockets)
Electronics: Radar: 1 Decca . . . nav.; 1 MR-104 Rys' (Drum Tilt) gun f.c.
M: 2 Kolomna Type 40DM diesels; 2 props; 4,000 bhp
Range: 900/18; 1,500/14 **Endurance:** 5 days **Crew:** 4 officers, 38 enlisted

Remarks: Transferred in 1974. Cargo: five T-54A tanks or 180 tons.

♦ **9 ex-Soviet Vydra-class (Project 106K) utility landing craft [LCU]** Bldr: Kherson SY, Russia (In serv. 1967–69)

330 332 334 336 338 340 342 344 346

Vydra-class 344—with single 40-mm AA guns Chris Delgoffe/H&L Van Ginderen, 6-00

D: 308 tons (442 fl) **S:** 10.5 kts **Dim:** 54.5 × 7.7 × 2.4
A: 2 single 40-mm 60-cal. Bofors Mk 3 AA or 2 twin 37-mm 63-cal. AA
Electronics: Radar: 1 Decca . . . nav.
M: 2 Type 3D12 diesels; 2 props; 600 bhp
Range: 2,500/10 **Crew:** 20 tot. + 100 troops

Remarks: Built new for Egypt. Some (including 332 and 338) have twin 37-mm 63-cal. Soviet VM-47 AA vice 40-mm; guns have been removed altogether in others, as have been the BM-21 122-mm artillery rocket launchers mounted in several units of the class during the 1970s. Cargo: 260 tons.

♦ **5 U.S. Seafox-class swimmer delivery craft** Bldr: Uniflite, Bellingham, Wash. (In serv. 1982–83)

21 23 27 28 30

D: 11.3 tons (fl) **S:** 30+ kts **Dim:** 11.0 × 3.0 × 0.84
A: 2 single 12.7-mm Browning M2 mg; 2 single 7.62-mm M-60 mg
Electronics: Radar: 1 Canadian Marconi LN-66 nav.
M: 2 G.M. Detroit Diesel 6V92 TA diesels; 2 props; 900 bhp **Crew:** 3 tot.

Remarks: Survivors of 10 originally acquired, ordered in 1982. Glass-reinforced plastic construction. Based at Aboukir.

AUXILIARIES

♦ **1 presidential yacht [AG]** Bldr: Samuda, Poplar, U.K. (In serv. 1865)

El Horria (ex-*Mahroussa*)

El Horria Chris Delgoffe/H&L Van Ginderen, 3-0[illegible]

D: 4,561 tons (fl) **S:** 16 kts **Dim:** 145.64 (128.02 wl, 121.92 pp) × 13.03 × 5.26
M: 3 sets geared steam turbines; 3 props; 5,500 bhp
Boilers: 5 Inglis watertube **Fuel:** 346 tons **Crew:** 160 tot.

Remarks: World's oldest active naval ship. Had been retired by the mid-1980s, but was reactivated in 1992. Available for training, presidential yacht, and barracks duties. Iron hull construction. Had been converted to steam turbine propulsion at Glasgow in 1905.

♦ **6 Soviet Okhtenskiy-class oceangoing tugs [ATA]** Bldr: Petrozavod SY, St. Petersburg

103 Al Meks	107 Antar	111 Al Iskandarani
105 Al Agami	109 Al Dikhila	113 Kalir

Al Agami (105) Chris Delgoffe/H&L Van Ginderen, 6-0[illegible]

D: 663 tons light (926 fl) **S:** 13.3 kts **Dim:** 47.3 (43.0 pp) × 10.3 × 5.5
Electronics: Radar: 1 or 2 Don-2 or Mius (Spin Trough) nav.
M: diesel-electric: 2 Type D5D50 diesels; 1 prop; 1,500 shp **Electric:** 340 kw
Range: 6,000/13; 7,800/7 **Fuel:** 197 tons **Crew:** 38 tot.

Remarks: Two transferred complete in 1966; two assembled in Egypt at Alexandri[a] Naval Dockyard from components built at St. Petersburg. Bollard pull: 27 tons initial, 17 sustained.

♦ **1 U.K. Z-class training ship [AXT]** Bldr: William Denny & Bros., Dumbarton, Scotland

	Laid down	L	In serv.
921 El Fateh (ex-*Zenith*, ex-*Wessex*)	19-5-42	5-6-44	22-12-4[illegible]

D: 1,730 tons (2,575 fl) **S:** 31 kts **Dim:** 110.57 × 10.87 × 4.92 (5.2 props)
A: 4 single 114-mm 45-cal. Mk 6 DP; 2 SA-7 Grail point-defense SAM launch positions; 1 twin 40-mm 60-cal. Mk 5 AA; 2 twin 37-mm 63-cal. AA; 2 quadruple 533-mm TT
Electronics:
Radar: 1 Decca 916 nav.; 1 Marconi SNW-1 air/surf. search, 1 Type 275 f.c.
Sonar: none—EW: none

AUXILIARIES (continued)

El Fateh (921)—when operational H&L Van Ginderen, 4-94

M: 2 sets Parsons geared steam turbines; 2 props; 40,000 shp (36,000 sust.)
Boilers: 2 Admiralty 3-drum
Range: 2,800/20; 5,300/15 **Fuel:** 588 tons **Crew:** 186 crew + . . . cadets

Remarks: Employed on midshipman training duties, but no longer goes to sea. Purchased from the U.K. in 1955 and refitted there, completing 7-56. Modernized with a new air-search radar in 1964. Reboilered in 1993 and was expected to remain in service until 2000.
Combat systems: Uses a single Fly 4 director with a World War II–era Type 275 radar to control the 114-mm guns. Sonar and ASW ordnance have been removed. Armament was modified in late 1980s, with Chinese-made twin 37-mm AA replacing old British 40-mm mounts, AA mounts placed on a platform between torpedo tube mounts and abreast the foremast, and one set of torpedo tubes removed. As of 1995, the 40-mm twin mount had been restored, along with the torpedo tubes, while 37-mm mounts were located abreast the forward superstructure and port and starboard on the platform abaft the stack—the heaviest armament ever borne by a unit of this class.

♦ 1 ex-British Black Swan–class training hulk, ex-sloop [AXT]
Bldr: Yarrow & Sons, Scotstoun, Glasgow

	Laid down	L	In serv.
931 Tariq (ex-*Malek Farouk,* ex-*Whimbrel*)	31-10-41	25-8-42	13-1-43

Tariq (931)—moored outboard the *El Fateh* (921)
Chris Delgoffe/H&L Van Ginderen, 3-00

D: 1,470 tons (1,925 fl) **S:** 19 kts (17 sust.) **Dim:** 91.29 × 11.79 × 3.48
A: 3 twin 102-mm 45-cal. Vickers Mk 19 DP; 2 twin 40-mm 60-cal. Bofors AA; 4 d.c. mortars; 2 d.c. racks
Electronics: Radar: 2 Decca . . . nav.—Sonar: Type 147 searchlight HF
M: 2 sets Parsons geared steam turbines; 2 props; 4,300 shp (3,870 sust.)
Boilers: 2 Admiralty 3-drum
Range: 3,700/17; 9,200/10 **Fuel:** 403 tons **Crew:** 180 tot.

Remarks: Transferred in 1949. By the mid-1980s, had been relegated to accommodations service. Subsequently has been refitted and made once again seagoing as a training ship, although she has not been to sea since the mid-1990s. Is very little changed from her World War II appearance and eminently worthy of preservation when finally retired.
Combat systems: At one time, had stowage for as many as 110 depth charges. The sonar is probably inoperative. Type 282 ranging radar has been removed from the lead-computing director for the 102-mm guns. The 40-mm weapons are locally controlled and are probably of Spanish manufacture.

SERVICE CRAFT

♦ 1 Soviet Nyryat'-I-class diving tender [YDT]

D: 92 tons (116.1 fl) **S:** 11 kts **Dim:** 28.58 × 5.20 × 1.70
Electronics: Radar: 1 SNN-7 nav.
M: 1 Type 6CSP 28/3C diesel; 1 prop; 450 bhp **Range:** 1,500/10 **Crew:** 15 tot.

Remarks: Transferred in 1964. One sister was stricken in 1991. The charthouse/laboratory is 6 m^2, and there are two 1.5-ton derricks.

♦ 7 Soviet Toplivo-2-class coastal-transport tankers [YO]
Bldr: Alexandria SY, Egypt (In serv. 1972–77)

210 Ayeda 4	213 Al Nil	216 Ayeda 3
211 Maryut	214 Akdu	
212 Al Furat	215 Maryut Atbarah	

Ayeda 4 (210) Chris Delgoffe/H&L Van Ginderen, 3-00

D: 466 tons (1,180 fl) **S:** 10 kts **Dim:** 54.26 (49.40 pp) × 9.40 × 3.40 (max.)
Electronics: Radar: 1 Mius (Spin Trough) nav.
M: 1 Russkiy Dizel 6 DR 30/50-5-2 diesel; 1 prop; 600 bhp **Electric:** 250 kw
Range: 1,500/10 **Fuel:** 19 tons **Crew:** 16 tot.

Remarks: 308 grt/508 dwt. Part of a series of 26 ordered in Egypt for the USSR prior to that country's expulsion. Cargo: 606 m^3 (500 tons diesel oil); some are used as water tankers. Other names reported (not correlated to hull numbers) are *Dina, El Porat,* and *Karun.* Sister *Al Mazilla* (217) was reported stricken in 1997.

♦ 2 Soviet Poluchat-I-class torpedo retrievers [YPT]

001 002

D: 84.7 tons (92.8 fl) **S:** 21.6 kts **Dim:** 29.60 × 5.98 × 1.56 (hull)
A: 2 twin 14.5-mm 93-cal. 2M-7 AA
Electronics: Radar: 1 Mius (Spin Trough) nav.
M: 2 M-50F-4 diesels; 2 props; 1,700 bhp **Electric:** 14 kw tot.
Range: 250/21.6; 550/14; 900/10 **Crew:** 3 officers, 12 enlisted

Note: Also reported in service is the former trawler *Amira Rama,* used on lighthouse supply duties since 1987.

♦ 1 naval academy navigational training ship [YXT]

El Kousser (ex-*El Emir Fawzia*)

Remarks: No data available other than that she is said to be of 1,000 tons displacement.

♦ 1 Soviet Sekstan-class training tender [YXT]
Bldr: Laivateolissus SY, Turku, Finland (In serv. 1953–57)

160

D: 280 tons (400 fl) **S:** 9 kts **Dim:** 40.6 × 9.3 × 4.3
Electronics: Radar: 1 Don-2 or Mius (Spin Trough) nav.
M: 1 diesel; 1 prop; 400 bhp
Range: 8,000/9 **Endurance:** 37 days **Crew:** 24 tot.

Remarks: Wooden-construction former degaussing tender, built in the mid-1950s. Now used as a training craft at the naval academy.

♦ 1 500-ton naval academy training yacht [YXT]

Intisar (ex-*Fakr el Bihar*)

Intisar Chris Delgoffe/H&L Van Ginderen, 3-00

Remarks: Former yacht, attached to the naval academy.

Note: Several naval tugs operate at the Alexandria base, and a 60-m large tug [YTB] for towing, salvage, logistic support, and search-and-rescue duties was building for the navy at Zhenjiang Shipyard, Jiangshu, China, during 2001.

COAST GUARD

Note: The coast guard is a branch of the naval service in Egypt. Its personnel are included in the total of 16,000 listed above.

PATROL CRAFT [WPC]

♦ **10 Type 83 class** Bldr: . . . (In serv. 1997–. . .)

346 through 355

D: 85 tons (fl) **S:** 24 kts **Dim:** 25.5 × 6.5 × 1.7
A: 1 twin 23-mm 60-cal. AA; 1 20-mm 90-cal. GAM-B01 Oerlikon AA
Electronics: Radar: 1 Furuno . . . nav.
M: 2 diesels; 2 props; . . . bhp **Crew:** 12 tot.

Remarks: First two reported in service 13-7-97. May be a locally built version of the Commercial Cruiser design.

♦ **9 U.S. Commercial Cruiser design**
Bldrs: 35–37: Swiftships, Morgan City, La.; others: Osman Ahmed Osman & Co., Ismailia, Egypt (In serv.: 35–37: 15-1-85; 38: 9-9-85; 39: 24-10-85; 40: 24-11-85; others: 1986)

35 36 37 38 39 40 41 42 43

Commercial Cruiser 37 French Navy, 4-99

D: 102 tons (fl) **S:** 27 kts **Dim:** 28.30 × 5.66 × 1.60
A: 1 twin 23-mm 60-cal. AA; 1 14.5-mm 90-cal. 2M-8 AA
Electronics: Radar: 1 Furuno . . . nav.
M: 2 MTU 12V331 TC92 diesels; 2 props; 2,660 bhp
Range: 1,000/12 **Fuel:** 11.7 tons **Crew:** 2 officers, 12 enlisted

Remarks: Ordered 11-83. First three built in U.S.; remainder assembled in Egypt from U.S.-supplied components. Steel construction. Original armament of one 20-mm and one 12.7-mm guns has been replaced by surplus Soviet-made weapons, with 23-mm guns replacing the original 25-mm 80-cal. guns.

♦ **6 Timsah-II class**
Bldr: Timsah SY, Ismailia (In serv. 1988–89)

07 Timsah 7 through 012 Timsah 12

Timsah-II class Siegfried Breyer Collection

D: 99 tons (106 fl) **S:** 27 kts (24 sust.) **Dim:** 28.35 × 5.66 × 1.50
A: 2 single 20-mm 90-cal. Oerlikon GAM-B01 AA
Electronics: Radar: . . .
M: 2 MTU 12V331 TC92 diesels; 2 props; 2,660 bhp
Range: 600/. . . **Fuel:** 10 tons **Crew:** 13 tot.

Remarks: Revised version of original Timsah class, with different engines and waterline exhausts vice stack. Ordered 1-85.

♦ **5 Timsah class**
Bldr: Timsah SY, Alexandria (In serv. 1981–84)

01 02 04 05 06

D: 100 tons (fl) **S:** 25 kts **Dim:** 29.0 × 5.2 × 1.48
A: 1 single 20-mm 90-cal. Oerlikon GAM-B01 AA
Electronics: Radar: 1 . . . nav.
M: 2 MTU 8V331 diesels; 2 props; 2,960 bhp
Range: 600/. . . **Fuel:** 10 tons **Crew:** 13 tot.

Timsah-class 02 at left—with Timsah 05 across the pier Fouad Sadek, 7-92

Remarks: First unit laid down 1-1-80, launched 11-81, and delivered 12-81. Sister *Timsah 3* (03) lost 1993.

PATROL BOATS [WPB]

♦ **2 48-foot Patrol Craft Coastal (PCC) class**
Bldr: Peterson Bldrs, Sturgeon Bay, Wis. (In serv. 10-95, . . .)

81 82

D: 20 tons (fl) **S:** 32 kts **Dim:** 14.77 × 3.96 × 0.86
A: 1 12.7-mm M2 mg; 2 single 7.62-mm mg
Electronics: Radar: 1 Raytheon . . . nav.
M: 2 MTU 8V183 TE92 diesels; 2 Hamilton 362 waterjets; 1,314 bhp
Range: 300/30 **Crew:** 4 tot.

Remarks: Aluminum construction. Ordered as a larger version of the 10-unit, 45-ft PCC class delivered to Egypt in 6-95.

♦ **10 45-foot Patrol Craft Coastal (PCC) class**
Bldr: Peterson Bldrs, Sturgeon Bay, Wis. (In serv. 6-95)

71 through 80

Peterson 45-ft. patrol boats Peterson Builders, 1995

D: 16.2 tons (17.7 fl) **S:** 34 kts **Dim:** 13.86 × 3.96 × 0.86
A: 1 12.7-mm M2 mg; 2 single 7.62-mm mg
Electronics: Radar: 1 Raytheon 40X nav.
M: 2 MTU 8V183 TE92 diesels; 2 Hamilton 362 waterjets; 1,314 bhp
Range: 200/30 **Fuel:** 490 gallons **Crew:** 4 tot.

Remarks: Aluminum construction. Standard U.S. Navy export design. Can be transported on trailers. Two sisters serve the Albanian Navy.

♦ **4 small patrol craft**
Bldr: Canal Naval Const., Port Fuad

D: 10 tons **S:** . . . **Dim:** 10.49 × . . . × . . . **M:** 1 Thornycroft diesel

Remarks: Ordered 12-12-83; last two delivered in 1986. No further data available.

♦ **6 MV70 class, GRP-hulled**
Bldr: Crestitalia, Ameglia (La Spezia), Italy (In serv. 1981–82)

D: 33 tons (41.5 fl) **S:** 35 kts **Dim:** 21.0 × 5.2 × 0.9
A: 1 twin 30-mm 75-cal. Oerlikon A32; 1 20-mm Oerlikon AA; 2 single 12.7-mm mg
M: 2 MTU 12V331 TC92 diesels; 2 props; 2,800 bhp **Range:** 500/32

♦ **29 DC-35 class** Bldr: Dawncraft, Wroxham, U.K. (In serv. 1977)

D: 4 tons (fl) **S:** 25 kts **Dim:** 10.7 × 3.5 × 0.8
M: 2 Perkins T6-354 diesels; 2 props; 390 bhp **Crew:** 4 tot.

COAST GUARD PATROL BOATS [WPB] *(continued)*

DC-35 class — Maritime Photographic, 2-97

Remarks: GRP construction. For harbor police duties. One lost 9-94.

Note: Also reported to be in service are four small harbor tugs delivered in 1982 by Damen, Gorinchem, the Netherlands: *Khafra, Khoufou, Krier,* and *Ramses.*

CUSTOMS SERVICE

PATROL BOATS [WPB]

♦ **12 U.S. Sea Spectre PB Mk III class**
Bldr: Peterson Bldrs, Sturgeon Bay, Wis. (In serv. 1980–81)

D: 28 tons (36.7 fl) **S:** 30 kts **Dim:** 19.78 × 5.50 × 1.80 (props)
A: 2 single 12.7-mm mg **Electronics:** Radar: 1. . . nav.
M: 3 G.M. Detroit Diesel 8V71 TI diesels; 3 props; 1,800 bhp
Range: 450/26; 2,000/. . . **Endurance:** 3 days
Crew: 1 officer, 8 noncommissioned

EL SALVADOR

Republic of El Salvador

FUERZA NAVAL DE EL SALVADOR

Personnel (2002): About 700 total. The 400-strong *Doce de Octubre* naval infantry company has been disbanded and the special combat team placed under army control.

Bases: Acajutla, La Libertad, La Unión, and El Triunfo

Maritime Aviation: The Salvadoran Air Force uses Cessna O-21 and Douglas C-47 (and the turboprop version, T-67) fixed-wing aircraft for coastal surveillance and also has a flight of UH-1H helicopters that support the Fuerza Naval. The maritime support aircraft are operated from El Tamarindo near La Unión and at the Comalapa Air Force Base.

Note: The contract to acquire two 32-m Protector-class patrol craft from Chile's ASMAR, Valparaiso, was cancelled during 2001. U.S. Coast Guard *Balsam*-class buoy tender Madrona (WLB 302) was to be transferred on 30-5-02 for use as a patrol ship. Pennant number prefixes were changed fleet-wide during 2001.

PATROL CRAFT [PC]

♦ **3 aluminum-hulled** Bldr: Camcraft, Crown Point, La.

PM-6 (In serv. 24-10-75) PM-7 (In serv. 3-12-75) PM-8 (In serv. 11-75)

D: 100 tons (fl) **S:** 25 kts **Dim:** 30.5 × 6.4 × 1.5
A: GC-6 only: 1 20-mm 70-cal. Mk 68 AA—GC-7, GC-8: 2 single 12.7-mm M2HB mg—all: 1 81-mm mortar
Electronics: Radar: 1 Furuno . . .
M: 3 G.M. 12V71 TI diesels; 3 props; 1,200 bhp
Range: 780/24 **Crew:** 15 tot.

PM-7—on land for maintenance — Julio Montes, 9-00

Remarks: Rebuilt 1985–86 by Lantana Boatyard, Lantana, Fla., with the deckhouse extended 6 m and new radar and radios installed. When purchased, had operated for several years as commercial oilfield crewboats in the Gulf of Mexico.

PATROL BOATS [PB]

Note: Two 12.19-m (40-ft.) patrol boats were acquired during 2001; no other information available.

♦ **1 U.S. 77-foot Commercial Cruiser class**
Bldr: Swiftships, Morgan City, La. (In serv. 6-5-85)

PM-11

PM-11 — COPREFA. via Julio Montes, 12-94

D: 48 tons (fl) **S:** 26 kts **Dim:** 23.47 × 6.10 × 1.52
A: 1 20-mm 70-cal. Mk 68 AA; 2 single 12.7-mm mg; 1 81-mm mortar
Electronics: Radar: 1 Furuno . . . nav.
M: 3 G.M. 12V71 TI diesels; 3 props; 1,800 bhp
Range: 600/18 **Fuel:** 7,600 liters **Crew:** 10 tot.
Remarks: Aluminum construction.

♦ **1 U.S. 65-foot Commercial Cruiser class**
Bldr: Swiftships, Morgan City, La. (In serv. 14-6-84)

PM-10

PM-10 — Julio Montes, 10-93

PATROL BOATS [PB] *(continued)*

D: 36 tons (fl) **S:** 23 kts **Dim:** 19.96 × 5.59 × 1.52
A: 2 single 12.7-mm M2HB mg; 1 81-mm mortar
Electronics: Radar: 1 Furuno . . . nav.
M: 2 G.M. 12V71 TI diesels; 2 props; 1,350 bhp (1,200 sust.)
Electric: 20 kw tot. **Range:** 500/18 **Crew:** 6 tot.

Remarks: Aluminum construction. Out of service by 1989, but has been repaired and reactivated.

♦ 1 ex-U.S. Coast Guard 82-foot Point class
Bldr: J. Martinac SB, Tacoma, Wash. (In serv. 17-3-67)

PM-12 (ex-*Point Stuart,* WPB 82358)

D: 64 tons (66 fl) **S:** 23.7 kts **Dim:** 25.3 × 5.23 × 1.95
A: 2 single 12.7-mm M2 mg
Electronics: Radar: 1 Raytheon SPS-64(V)1 nav.
M: 2 Caterpillar 3412 diesels; 2 props; 1,480 bhp
Range: 490/23.7; 1,500/8 **Fuel:** 5.7 tons **Crew:** 1 officer, 7 enlisted

Remarks: Transferred by grant 26-4-01. Hull built of mild steel. High-speed diesels controlled from the bridge. Has a 4.27-m Avon Searider rigid inflatable boat powered by a 40-bhp outboard engine.

♦ 2 coastal interceptors
Bldr: Mercougar, North Miami, Fla. (In serv. 1988)

LR-02 LR-. . .

Coastal Interceptor LR-02—with two Johnson 110-bhp gasoline outboards
Julio Montes, 9-00

D: . . . tons (fl) **S:** 26 kts **Dim:** 12.19 × 3.86 × . . .
A: 2 single 12.7-mm mg; 2 single 7.62-mm mg
Electronics: Radar: 1 Furuno 2400 nav.
M: 2 Ford Merlin 6-cyl. diesels; 2 Arneson outdrives; 600 bhp
Range: 350/20 **Fuel:** 1,892 liters **Crew:** 6 tot.

Remarks: Built under U.S. FY 87 Military Aid Program; ordered 18-12-87. Plans to acquire 20 more did not reach fruition. Can be transported by road on trailers, of which one per boat was acquired. GRP hulls. Three of the five acquired had been retired by 1998, and the two others were reported stricken in 5-01.

♦ 9 Protector class
Bldr: SeaArk, Monticello, Ark. (In serv. 1988–89)

PC-0301 through PC-0310 series

Protector-class unit—on land for maintenance Julio Montes, 9-00

D: 8.9 tons (fl) **S:** 28 kts **Dim:** 12.40 (11.13 wl) × 3.04 × 0.53 (hull)
A: 2 single 12.7-mm mg; 2 single 7.62-mm mg; 6 M-16 rifles
Electronics: Radar: 1 Furuno 2400 nav.
M: 2 Caterpillar 3208TA diesels; 2 props; 690 bhp
Range: 575/20 **Fuel:** 1,993 liters **Crew:** 6 tot.

Remarks: Formerly operated by the naval infantry. Aluminum construction. Two ha[ve] been discarded by 1998.

♦ 5 Piranha-class riverine
Bldr: Lantana Boatyard, Lantana, Fla. (In serv. 2-87)

From among: PF-01 through PF-06

Three Piranha-class patrol boats Julio Montes, 2-9[.]

D: 9 tons (fl) **S:** 26 kts (22 sust.) **Dim:** 12.19 × 3.05 × 0.53
A: 2 single 12.7-mm mg; 2 single 7.62-mm mg; 1 60-mm mortar
Electronics: Radar: 1 Furuno 3600 nav.
M: 2 Caterpillar 3208 TA diesels; 2 props; 630 bhp
Endurance: 5 days **Crew:** 5 tot.

Remarks: Aluminum construction with Kevlar plastic armor. Lengthened version o[f] an eight-unit class built for Honduras in 1986. Operated by the marines. "LOF" stand[s] for *Lanchas de Operaciones Fluviales.*

Note: During 1998, two prototype riverine patrol boats were completed using modi[-]fied drop tanks from C-123K Provider transport aircraft; armed with one 7.62-mm M-60D and two single 5.56-mm M-249 light machineguns, the camouflage-painted trailer-transportable craft are powered by a single Mercury outboard engine and hav[e] a crew of three. One craft uses only the drop tanks for flotation, while the other ha[s] a central, wooden hull in addition.

Trimaran patrol boat prototype Julio Montes, 9-0[0]

AMPHIBIOUS WARFARE CRAFT

♦ 3 U.S. LCM(8)-class landing craft [LCM]

BD-02 BD-04 BD-05

El Salvador's LCM(8) landing craft Julio Montes, 9-0[0]

D: 34 tons light (121 fl) **S:** 12 kts **Dim:** 22.43 × 6.40 × 1.40 (aft)
A: 2 single 12.7-mm mg **Electronics:** Radar: 1 Furuno 2400 nav.
M: 4 G.M. 6-71 diesels; 2 props; 590 bhp
Range: 150/12 **Cargo:** 58 tons or 120 troops **Crew:** 6 tot.

AMPHIBIOUS WARFARE CRAFT *(continued)*

Remarks: Two transferred in 1987 (of which LD-03 was lost) and two in 1996 (recommissioned 7-6-96). Two others, the original LD-04 and LD-05, have been discarded, as has the LCM(6)-class landing craft LD-01.

Note: For use by army special forces personnel, four small outboard-powered Zodiac RIBs have been acquired. Four ex-U.S. Coast Guard 44 ft motor lifeboats [YH] were transferred during 2001 and have been renumbered PRM-01 through PRM-04.

MINISTRY OF PUBLIC SECURITY
POLICE MARITIME UNIT

Note: Established 28-3-99, with training for personnel commenced 11-98 by the navy. Craft are tasked with customs and security patrols along the Jaltepeque and Costa del Sol, La Paz Province, and will later be extended.

♦ **10 Rodman 800–class harbor launches [WPB]**
Bldr: Rodman Polyship S.A., Vigo, Spain (In serv. 1999)

L-01-01 through L-01-10

Rodman patrol launch L-01-10 Julio Montes, 2000

D: 9 tons (fl) **S:** 30 kts **Dim:** 8.9 × 3.0 × 0.80
A: small arms **Electronics:** Radar: 1 Raytheon . . . nav.
M: 2 Volvo Penta outdrive diesels; 300 bhp **Range:** 150/25 **Crew:** 3 tot.

Remarks: Cost $100,000 each. Armament consists only of crew's Galil semiautomatic rifles. GRP construction. Class also used by the Chilean Coast Guard.

EQUATORIAL GUINEA

Republic of Equatorial Guinea

Personnel (2001): Approx. 100 total

Note: Craft are based at Malabo on the island of Bioko and at Bata on the mainland at Río Muni. Neither of the craft listed below was operable as of 2000, but both were repairable.

PATROL BOATS [PB]

♦ **1 68-foot U.S.-built (Nonoperational)**
Bldr: Lantana Boatyard, Lantana, Fla.

	Laid down	L	In serv.
037 *Isla de Bioko*	3-87	3-88	5-88

D: 33 tons (fl) **S:** 24 kts (28 on trials) **Dim:** 20.73 × 5.50 × 1.50
A: 1 12.7-mm M2 mg; 2 single 7.62-mm mg
Electronics: Radar: 1 Furuno 3600 nav.
M: 2 G.M. Detroit Diesel 8V92 TI diesels; 2 props; 1,170 bhp
Range: 800/15 **Crew:** 2 officers, 10 enlisted

Remarks: Aluminum construction; delivered unpainted. Paid for by U.S. Grant-Aid program. A planned, larger ship from the same builder was not funded.

Isla de Bioko (037) Lantana Boatyard, 1988

♦ **1 ex-Nigerian P/20 class** (Nonoperational)
Bldr: Van Mill Marine Service, Hardinxveld-Giessendam, the Netherlands (In serv. 17-1-86)

Riowele (ex-P 220)

D: 45 tons (fl) **S:** 32.5 kts **Dim:** 20.26 (18.00 wl) × 5.30 × 1.75
A: 1 20-mm 90-cal. Rheinmetall AA; 2 single 7.62-mm mg
Electronics: Radar: 1 Decca . . . nav.
M: 2 MTU 6V331 TC82 diesels; 2 props; 2,250 bhp
Range: 950/25; 1,200/11 **Crew:** 2 officers, 10 enlisted

Remarks: Transferred as a gift from Nigeria 27-6-86. GRP construction.

ERITREA

Republic of Eritrea

Personnel (2001): Approx. 500 total

Bases: Massawa on the mainland and Dahlak Islands, with access to Djibouti for repairs

PATROL CRAFT [PC]

♦ **3 U.S. 104-foot Commercial Cruiser class**
Bldr: Swiftships, Morgan City, La. (In serv. 4-77)

P-201 P-203 P-204

D: 118 tons (fl) **S:** 32 kts **Dim:** 31.73 × 7.10 × 2.16
A: 2 twin 23-mm ZSU-23 AA; 2 single 12.7-mm mg
Electronics: Radar: 1 Decca RM 916 nav.
M: 2 MTU MB 16V538 TB90 diesels; 2 props; 7,000 bhp
Range: 1,000/18 **Crew:** 21 tot.

Remarks: Purchased after successful bid in 11-96 from among former Ethiopian Navy units at Djibouti. Retained original pennant numbers. P-201 is armed with two twin 30-mm Emerlec EX-30 AA. Aluminum construction.

PATROL BOATS [PB]

♦ **6 Israeli Super Dvora class**
Bldr: RAMTA–Israeli Aircraft Industries, Be'er Sheva (In serv. 1994)

P-111 P-112 P-113 P-114 P-115 P-116

D: 48 tons (54 fl) **S:** 36–46 kts **Dim:** 22.40 × 5.49 × 1.00
A: 2 single 20-mm 70-cal. Oerlikon AA; 2 single 12.7-mm mg
Electronics: Radar: 1 Raytheon . . . nav.
M: 3 G.M. Detroit Diesel 16V92 TA diesels; 3 Arneson surface-piercing props; 2,070 bhp
Electric: 30 kw **Range:** 700/14 **Crew:** 1 officer, 8 enlisted

Remarks: Transferred in pairs in 12-93, 3-94, and 6-94. Aluminum construction. All based at Massawa.

PATROL BOATS [PB] *(continued)*

♦ **15–20 small launches**

Remarks: Small, 4.5- to 6.0-m, GRP-hulled craft with twin 75-bhp outboard motor propulsion and 12.7- or 14.5-mm machineguns and small artillery rocket launchers for armament. No further data available.

AMPHIBIOUS WARFARE CRAFT

♦ **1 Chamo-class utility landing craft [LCU]**
Bldr: Schichau Seebeckwerft A.G., Bremerhaven, Germany (In serv. 12-88)

Denden (ex-*Chamo*)

D: approx. 750 tons (fl) **S:** 10 kts **Dim:** 60.20 (55.40 pp) × 12.02 × 1.44
A: . . . **Electronics:** Radar: 1 . . . nav.
M: 2 MTU 6V396 TC62 diesels; 2 props; 1,332 bhp
Electric: 304 kw tot. (2 × 152-kw sets, MTU diesels driving)
Range: . . ./. . . **Crew:** . . . tot.

Remarks: 995 grt/352 dwt. Former Ethiopian Shipping Lines commercial landing ship taken over for Eritrean commercial service and in 1998 taken over for the navy. A sister was destroyed during the early 1990s revolution. Has a bow door and a 4.5-m-long by 4.3-m-wide vehicle ramp. Can transport up to 24 standard 20-ft. cargo containers on deck.

♦ **2 Soviet T-4-class (Project 1785) landing craft [LCM]**

LST-63 LST-64

D: 35 tons light (93 fl) **S:** 10 kts (light) **Dim:** 20.4 × 5.4 × 1.2 (max. aft)
M: 2 Type 3D6 diesels; 2 props; 300 bhp
Range: 300/8 **Endurance:** 2 days **Crew:** 2–3 tot.

Remarks: Survivors of four transferred to Ethiopia. Can accommodate up to 50 tons cargo on the 9.5 × 3.9-m vehicle deck. Based at Massawa.

ESTONIA

ESTONIAN NAVY
(Eesti Merevägi)

Personnel (2001): 30 officers, 270 enlisted; planned to rise eventually to 600 total

Bases: Principal base at Tallinn, with a small base at Paldiski

Note: A joint Baltic Squadron ("Baltron") was formed with Latvia and Lithuania during 1997.

PATROL SHIPS [PS]

♦ **1 ex-Danish Modified Hvidbjørnen class**
Bldr: Ålborg Værft, Ålborg

	Laid down	L	In serv.
A 230 Admiral Pitka (ex-*Beskyterren,* F 340)	15-12-74	27-5-75	27-2-76

Admiral Pitka (A 230) Winter & Findler, 1-01

D: 1,640 tons (1,970 fl) **S:** 18 kts **Dim:** 74.70 (69.00 pp) × 12.16 × 4.50
A: 1 76.2-mm 50-cal. U.S. Mk 22 DP; 1 . . . helicopter
Electronics:
Radar: 1 Skanter Mil 009 nav.; 1 . . . nav.; 1 Plessey AWS-6 air search
Sonar: 1 Plessey PMS-26 hull-mounted (10 kHz)
EW: Racal Cutlass B-1 intercept; Telegon HFD/F; 2 6-round decoy RL
M: 4 Burmeister & Wain Alpha V23-LU diesels; 1 CP prop; 7,440 bhp
Electric: 1,140 kw tot. (1 × 452-kw shaft alternator, 2 × 344-kw diesel alternator sets)
Range: 6,000/13 (one engine) **Crew:** 10 officers, 46 enlisted

Remarks: Donated by Denmark in 6-00 and recommissioned 21-11-00 after a refit. Ice-reinforced hull with Flume-type passive roll stabilization. Has helicopter hangar and deck, but no helicopter was transferred with the ship. The obsolete 76.2-mm gun is largely of ceremonial value.

PATROL CRAFT [PC]

♦ **2 ex-Finnish Rihtniemi class**
Bldr: Rauma-Repola, Rauma (In serv. 21-2-57)

P 423 Suurpo (ex-*Rymattyla,* 52) P 422 Ristna (ex-*Rihtniemi,* 51)

D: 115 tons (135 fl) **S:** 18 kts **Dim:** 34.0 × 5.7 × 1.8
A: 2 twin 23-mm 60-cal. Sako AA **Electronics:** Radar: 1 Decca 1226 nav.
M: 2 Mercedes-Benz diesels; 2 CP props; 2,500 bhp **Crew:** 20 tot.

Remarks: Transferred at the end of 1999 after retirement. Former convertible minesweeper/gunboats, modernized and lengthened 1977–81. The sonar and two RBU-1200 ASW rocket launchers were removed after transfer.

Disposal note: Former East German modified Kondor-I-class patrol craft *Sulev* (M 412, ex-*Komet,* D 42) had been discarded by 9-00.

PATROL BOATS [PB]

♦ **1 Russian Zhuk class (Project 1400)**
Bldr: . . . (In serv. 1976)

P 401 Grif

Grif (P 401)—out of the water for the winter Stefan Marx, 1997

D: 35.9 tons (39.7 fl) **S:** 30 kts
Dim: 23.80 (21.70 wl) × 5.00 (3.80 wl) × 1.00 (hull)
A: 1 twin 12.7-mm 79-cal. Utës-M mg **Electronics:** Radar: 1 Lotsiya nav.
M: 2 M-401 diesels; 2 props; 2,200 bhp
Electric: 48 kw total (2 × 21-kw, 1 × 6-kw diesel sets)
Range: 500/13.5 **Endurance:** 5 days **Crew:** 1 officer, 9 enlisted

Remarks: Ex-Russian numbers 631 and 635 were sold in 1992 by the Russian Border Guard to a private Estonian scrap firm but were confiscated by the Estonian Home Defense League on 8-6-92. *Leopard* (P 402) was not put into service and is stored on land as a source of spares. Aluminum alloy hull. Capable of operating in up to Sea State 4 or 5. Normally maintained ashore during winter months due to light hull plating.

MINE COUNTERMEASURES SHIPS AND CRAFT

♦ **2 ex-German Type 331B minehunters [MHC]**
Bldr: Burmester, Bremen

	L	In serv.
M 311 Wambola (ex-*Cuxhaven,* M 1078)	11-3-58	11-3-59
M 312 Sulev (ex-*Lindau,* M 1072)	16-2-57	24-4-58

Wambola (M 311) Curt Borganstam, 5-01

MINE COUNTERMEASURES SHIPS AND CRAFT *(continued)*

…ulev (M 312) Findler & Winter, 5-01

D: 388 tons (402 fl) **S:** 16.5 kts **Dim:** 47.45 × 8.5 × 2.8 (3.68 with sonar extended)
A: 1 40-mm 70-cal. Bofors AA
Electronics:
Radar: 1 Raytheon SPS-64(V) nav.
Sonar: EFS DSQS-11A
EW: 2 6-round Hot Dog decoy RL
M: 2 MTU 16V538 TB90 diesels; 2 CP props; 5,000 bhp
Electric: 220 kw tot. **Range:** 1,400/16; 3,950/9
Crew: 5 officers, 29 enlisted + 6 divers

Remarks: M 311 was donated after planned retirement from the German Navy on …-2-00 and recommissioned at Tallinn 29-9-00. M 312, which was transferred at Tallinn after striking from the German Navy on 27-9-00, recommissioned on 9-10-00. Had been converted to minehunters in 1975–79 from Klasse 320, *Lindau*-class, wooden-hulled minesweepers. Sister *Göttingen* (M 1070), donated 1-01 for use as cannibalization spares, was lost on . . .-01 en route Tallinn under tow.
Hull systems: Wooden construction, with nonmagnetic engines. Minehunting speed is 6 kts, on two 50-kw electric motors.
Combat systems: Six divers and two French PAP-104 remote-controlled minehunting devices are carried. Have no mechanical sweep gear. The 40-mm gun is controlled by a Bofors lead-computing optical director on the bridge.

♦ 2 ex-German Type 394 inshore minesweepers [MSI]
Bldr: Krögerwerft, Rendsburg

	L	In serv.
M 414 Kalev (ex-*Minerva,* M 2663)	25-8-66	16-6-67
M 415 Olev (ex-*Diana,* M 2664)	13-12-66	21-9-67

Olev (M 415) A. A. de Kruijf, 6-00

D: 238 tons (246 fl) **S:** 14.3 kts **Dim:** 38.01 × 8.03 × 2.10
A: 1 40-mm 70-cal. Bofors AA
Electronics: Radar: 1 STN Atlas Elektronik TRS-N
M: 2 Mercedes-Benz MB 820 Db diesels; 2 props; 2,000 bhp
Electric: 554 kw tot. **Range:** 648/14; 1,770/7 **Fuel:** 30 tons
Crew: 2 officers, 23 enlisted (in German service)

Remarks: Transferred 19-6-97 and 8-8-97, respectively, after reactivation refits and training period at Olpenitz, Germany. Had been stricken from German service 6-2-95. Both had engine overhauls at Wilhelmshaven prior to transfer. Sister *Atlantis* was on offer to Lithuania at end-1996. Wooden construction. Have a 260-kw sweep current generator. Atop the pilothouse is a Bofors lead-computing director for the 40-mm gun. The former German Navy research service craft *Holnis* was towed to Estonia during 2-01 for use as spares support for these craft.

SERVICE CRAFT

♦ 1 ex-Danish Mågen-class [YAG]
Bldr: Helsinger Værft (In serv. 5-60)

A 532 Ahti (ex-A 431, ex-*Mallemukken,* Y 385)

Ahti (A 532) Stefan Marx, 1997

D: 175 tons (190 fl) **S:** 10 kts **Dim:** 27.00 × 7.20 × 2.75
A: 1 twin 25-mm 80-cal. Russian 2M-3M AA
Electronics: Radar: 1 Terma 20T48 nav.; 1 Terma Scanter Mil 009 nav.
M: 1 Burmeister & Wain Alpha diesel; 1 prop; 350 bhp **Crew:** 14 tot.

Remarks: Transferred as a gift 19-3-94; had been stricken from the Danish Navy in 1992 after 33 years' service in Greenland and Faeroes area service. Arrived in Estonia 29-3-94 and recommissioned same day. The 25-mm gunmount is on the forecastle, and the two single 20-mm mounts carried in Danish service were removed prior to transfer. Served as fleet flagship and operational headquarters until 1997. Pennant number changed 1-1-00.

♦ 1 ex-Russian general-purpose craft [YAG]
Bldr: Yantar Zavod, Kaliningrad (In serv. 1986)

A 432 Laine (ex-*Revalia*)

D: 87 tons (fl) **S:** 9 kts **Dim:** 18.4 × 5.4 × 1.6
Electronics: Radar: 1 Mius (Spin Trough) nav.
M: 1 diesel; 235 bhp **Crew:** 3 officers, 14 enlisted

Remarks: Acquired in 1994 and commissioned 1-2-94. Former harbor personnel ferry, now used as a general-purpose tender and for navigational training.

♦ 1 Kalev-class minelaying submarine relic [YAG]
Bldr: Vickers-Armstrong, Barrow-in-Furness (L: 7-7-36)

Lembit

D: 600 tons surf./820 tons sub. **S:** 13.5 kts surf./8.5 kts sub.
Dim: 58.00 × 7.30 × 3.30
A: 4 bow 533-mm TT (8 torpedoes); 10 minelaying tubes (20 total mines)
Electronics: Radar: . . .
M: 2 Vickers diesels (600 bhp each), 2 generator sets, 2 electric motors (450 shp each); 2 props; 1,200 bhp surf./900 shp sub.
Range: 2,000/10 surf. **Crew:** 38 tot.

Remarks: Returned to Estonia at Tallinn in 1979 for use as a memorial; the ship had been taken over 13-8-40 when Estonia was overrun by Russia and had apparently been used in trials through the 1970s. Although officially commissioned as a unit of the new Estonian Fleet in 8-92, she is not operable and is in fact a memorial at Tallinn. The mines were carried two per tube in inclined tubes in the saddle tanks flanking the pressure hull. Was originally equipped with one 45-mm AA and one 20-mm AA. Sister *Kalev* was lost in 11-41.

SERVICE CRAFT *(continued)*

Disposal note: Ex-Danish launch *Mardus* (A 433, ex-*Rylen*) was stricken during 2000.

MARITIME BORDER GUARD

(Eesti Piirivalve)

A small coastal patrol force was established under the Ministry of Internal Affairs on 22-4-92 when the first of four Kbv 236–class 16.2-m patrol craft donated by Sweden was delivered to the Estonian Maritime Border Guard. In wartime, it would come under the Commander-in-Chief of Defense Forces.

Personnel (2001): 300 tot.

Maritime Aviation: The *Piirivalve Lennusalk* (Border Guard Aviation Group) operates 2 ex-Luftwaffe Let 410UVP light transports and 2 ex-Luftwaffe Mi-8S/TB Hip SAR helicopters, all based at Tallinn International Airport. One Mi-8S/TB and a former East German commercial Mi-8T are in storage at Pärnu awaiting funding to equip them for SAR duties.

Note: In addition to the ships and craft listed below, a unit named *Oisko* was added early in 1999; no data available. A unit named *Vapper* (PVL 111) was noted during 2000.

PATROL COMBATANTS [WPG]

♦ **1 Finnish Silmä class** Bldr: Laivateollisuus Oy, Turku

	Laid down	L	In serv.
PVL 107 Kõu (ex-*Silmä*)	30-8-62	23-3-63	19-8-63

Kõu (PVL 107) H&L Van Ginderen, 6-00

D: 530 tons **S:** 15 kts **Dim:** 48.3 × 8.3 × 4.3
A: 1 twin 25-mm 80-cal. 2M-3M AA
Electronics: Radar: 3 . . . nav.—Sonar: Simrad SS 105 (14 kHz)
M: 1 Werkspoor diesel; 1 prop; 1,800 bhp **Crew:** 22 tot.

Remarks: Transfer announced 1-12-94; the ship was transferred 1-95 and recommissioned during 4-95. Equipped for fire fighting, towing, and salvage. A firefighting monitor is located at the extreme bow. Two RIB inspection launches are handled by an electrohydraulic crane.

PATROL CRAFT [WPC]

♦ **1 ex-Norwegian Storm class**
Bldr: Bergens Mekaniske Verksted, Bergen (L: 24-5-66)

PVL 105 Torm (ex-*Arg,* P 968)

D: 105 tons (125 fl) **S:** 37 kts **Dim:** 36.53 × 6.3 × 1.55
A: 1 twin 25-mm 80-cal. 2M-3M AA; 1 twin 14.5-mm 93-cal. mg
Electronics: Radar: 1 Decca TM 1226 nav.
M: 2 Maybach MB 872A (MTU 16V538 TB90) diesels; 2 props; 7,200 bhp
Range: 550/36 **Crew:** . . . tot.

Remarks: Stricken from the Norwegian Navy during 1993. PVL 105 was rehabilitated during 1994 and transferred 16-12-94 with armament systems deleted. Sisters were donated to Latvia and Lithuania.

♦ **1 ex-Finnish Viima class** Bldr: Laivateollisuus Oy, Turku

	L	In serv.
PVL 106 Maru (ex-*Viima*)	20-7-64	12-10-64

Maru (PVL 106) Findler & Winter, 6-96

D: 135 tons **S:** 23 kts **Dim:** 35.7 × 6.6 × 2.0
A: 1 twin 14.5-mm 93-cal. AA; 1 7.62-mm mg
Electronics: Radar: 1 . . . nav.
M: 3 Maybach diesels; 3 CP props; 4,050 bhp **Crew:** 12 tot.

Remarks: A variant of the Finnish Navy's *Ruissalo* class. Transfer announced 1-12-94, with the craft arriving in Estonia during 1-95 and recommissioning in 4-95. Radar has unusual double slotted waveguide configuration.

AIR-CUSHION PATROL BOATS [WPBH]

♦ **1 2000-TDX(M) class**
Bldr: Griffon Hovercraft, Salisbury Green, Southampton, U.K. (10-99)

PVL . . .

D: 6.75 tons (fl) **S:** 50 kts (33 loaded) **Dim:** 11.04 × 4.60 × 0.52
A: provision for 1 7.62-mm mg **Electronics:** Radar: 1 Furuno . . . nav.
M: 1 Deutz BF8L-513 diesel; 1 lift fan, 1 shrouded CP airscrew; 320 bhp
Range: 300/25 (loaded) **Fuel:** 284 liters **Crew:** 2 tot. + 16 troops

Remarks: Can carry 2,200 kg of cargo in lieu of troops. GRP construction hull.

PATROL BOATS [WPB]

♦ **1 Pikker class** Bldr: . . . SY, Tallinn (L: 22-12-95; in serv. 4-96)

PVL 103 Pikker

Pikker (PVL 103) Estonian Border Guard, 4-98

D: 88 tons (fl) **S:** 24 kts **Dim:** 30.0 × 5.8 × 1.5
A: 1 twin 14.5-mm 93-cal. AA; 2 single 7.62-mm mg
Electronics: Radar: 1 . . . nav.
M: 2 Type 12YH 18/20 diesels; 2 props; 2,700 bhp **Crew:** 6 tot.

Remarks: Was to have been the first of a class of 10, but the others were canceled due to financial constraints. Capable of search and rescue, fire fighting, towing, pollution control, and light icebreaking duties in ice up to 30 cm thick. Carries one rigid inflatable rescue and inspection dinghy.

♦ **3 ex-Finnish Koskelo class** Bldr: Valmet, Helsinki (In serv. 1955–60)

PVL 100 (ex-*Telkkä*) PVL 101 (ex-*Kuikka*) PVL 102 (ex-*Kaakuri*)

D: 75 tons (97 fl) **S:** 23 kts **Dim:** 29.42 × 5.02 × 1.5
A: 1 12.7-mm mg **Electronics:** Radar: 2 . . . nav.
M: Mercedes-Benz diesels; 2 props; 2,700 bhp **Crew:** 11 tot.

Remarks: Transferred to Estonia 16-11-92. Modernized and re-engined 1970–74 by Laivateollisuus, Turku. Sisters *Koskelo, Kuovi,* and *Kiisla* were stricken from the Finnish Coast Guard in 1986–87, *Kurki* in 1990.

AMPHIBIOUS WARFARE CRAFT

♦ **1 Russian Serna-class fast medium landing craft [WLCM]**
Bldr: Volga Zavod, Nizhniy Novgorod (In serv. 10-94)

PVL 104 Tiir

Tiir (PVL 104) Stefan Marx, 1997

D: 53 tons light (105 fl) **S:** 30 kts **Dim:** 25.65 × 5.85 × 1.52 (1.30 at speed)
A: . . . **Electronics:** Radar: 1 Liman nav.
M: 2 Zvezda M-503A-3 diesels; 2 shrouded props; 3,300 bhp
Electric: 32 kw tot. (2 × 16-kw DGR-16/1,500 diesel sets)
Range: 100/30 (loaded); 600/30 (half-load) **Crew:** 4 tot.

BORDER GUARD AMPHIBIOUS WARFARE CRAFT *(continued)*

Remarks: Private venture design by the R. Alekseyev Central Hydrofoil Design Bureau. Four prototypes were built, two of which were sold to a commercial operator in the United Arab Emirates in 1994 and the other delivered to the Russian Baltic Fleet. The design is on offer for export for naval and civilian customers. "Serna" is the builder's project name.
Hull systems: Said to have a useful load of 45–50 tons on a 13 × 4 × 2.5-m cargo deck that extends about 2 m beneath the pilothouse. A portable canopy and seats for 100 personnel can be installed. The semi-planing hull incorporates an air cavity to provide underhull lubrication. Aluminum-magnesium alloy construction with an articulating bow ramp. Range of 600 n.m. with half load can be achieved by using reserve void tanks to carry fuel.

AUXILIARIES

♦ 1 ex-U.S. Coast Guard Balsam-class navigational buoy tender [WAGL] Bldr: Duluth Iron & SB Co., Duluth, Minn.

	Laid down	L	In serv.
PVL 109 Valvas (ex-*Bittersweet,* WLB 389)	16-9-43	11-11-43	11-5-44

Valvas (PVL 109) Stefan Marx, 1998

D: 697 tons light (1,038 fl) **S:** 13 kts **Dim:** 54.9 (51.8 pp) × 11.3 × 4.0
A: 2 single 12.7-mm M2 mg
Electronics: Radar: 1 Raytheon SPS-64(V)1 nav.
M: 2 diesels, electric drive; 1 prop; 1,200 shp
Electric: 400 kw tot. **Range:** 4,600/12; 14,000/7.4
Fuel: varies **Crew:** 6 officers, 47 enlisted (in USCG service)

Remarks: PVL 109 was retired from the U.S. Coast Guard 18-8-97 and donated to Estonia, transferring 5-9-97. Acts as the flagship for the coast guard. Sister *Pawpaw* (WLB 308) was under consideration for transfer as well but she has not been. Very robustly constructed vessel that still has many years' service remaining despite advanced age.
Hull systems: Hull is of icebreaker form and can break light ice. Has a 20-ton buoy derrick.

SERVICE CRAFT

♦ 1 Russian Nyryat-2-class diving tender [WYDT]
Bldr: Yaroslavl Zavod (In serv. 1970)

PVK 019 (ex-EVA-206, ex-. . .)

PVK 019 Stefan Marx, 1997

D: 50 tons (fl) **S:** 9 kts **Dim:** 21.0 × 3.90 × 1.40
Electronics: Radar: 1 Mius (Spin Trough) nav.
M: 1 Type 3D-6 diesel; 1 prop; 150 bhp
Range: 1,600/8 **Endurance:** 5 days **Crew:** 6 tot.

Remarks: Acquired in 1992. Standard Soviet Project 376 utility launch class, configured as a diving tender to support up to four divers. Steel hull.

♦ 2 FF Jet Combi Patrol 10–class launches [WYFL]
Bldr: FF Marine, Finland (In serv. 1994)

PVK 012 PVK 016

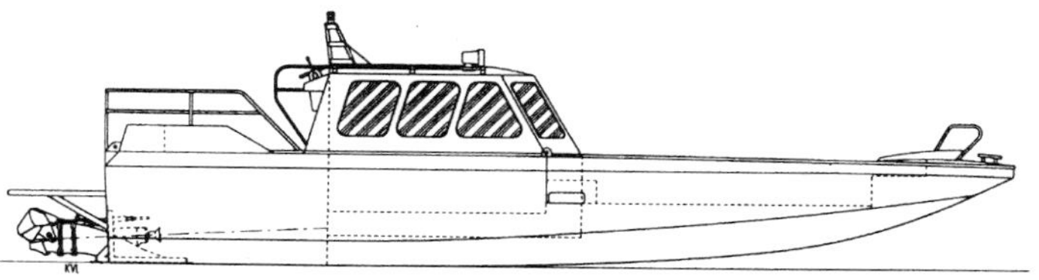

FF Jet Combi Patrol 10–class launch NAVINT, 1996

D: . . . tons **S:** . . . kts **Dim:** 10.00 × 2.75 × 0.60
M: 1 Cummins 6CTA8.3-M2 diesel; 1 KaMeWa FF 310 waterjet; 400 bhp
Crew: 6 tot.

Remarks: Gifts from Finland for use on Lake Peipus in smuggling prevention and fisheries patrol. Transferred 8-94 and 11-94. The foredeck can accept 1,000 kg of cargo.

♦ 3 ex-Swedish Kbv 236–class launches [WYFL] (In serv. 1961–72)

PVK 001 (ex-Kbv 257) PVK 002 (ex-Kbv 259) PVK 003 (ex-Kbv 246)

PVK 003 Hartmut Ehlers, 9-96

D: 17 tons **S:** 22 kts **Dim:** 16.2 × 3.7 × 1.4
A: small arms **Electronics:** Radar: 1 . . . nav.
M: 2 Volvo Penta TAMD 120A diesels; 2 props; 700 bhp **Crew:** 5 tot.

Remarks: PVK 001 transferred from the Swedish Coast Guard 4-4-92, the others 20-10-93; recommissioned 10-4-92, 1-94, and 6-12-93, respectively. Aluminum construction.

♦ 1 ex-Finnish training craft [WYXT]
Bldr: Valmet, Turku

PVL 108 Linda (ex-*Kemiö,* 93; ex-*Valvoja II*)

Linda (PVL 108)—as the Finnish *Kemiö* H&L Van Ginderen, 1992

D: 340 tons (fl) **S:** 11 kts **Dim:** 36.70 × 9.40 × 3.20
A: 1 twin 25-mm 80-cal. 2M-3M AA **Electronics:** Radar: 1 . . . nav.
M: 1 Burmeister & Wain Alpha diesel; 1 prop; 480 bhp **Electric:** 5 kw
Fuel: 38.5 tons **Crew:** 10 tot.

Remarks: 406 grt. Transferred 12-92. Former buoy tender, acquired by the Finnish Navy from the Board of Navigation in 1983 and refitted for naval service as a command ship by Hollming, Rauma. Based at Riga and also used as training ship by the Marine Education Seamanship School, Tallinn.

Note: Other PVK-series harbor patrol craft of more than 12-m length include PVK 006–008 and 013–015, all ex-Finnish 13.7-ton icebreaking launches; PVK 017 (ex-EVA 203), a small passenger-carrying tender; and PVK 018 (ex-EVA 204), a 22-kt launch donated by Finland in 1993. PVK 019 is a diving tender (q.v.). Also in use are the following launches of less than 12-m length: PVK 004, built in 1987, donated by

BORDER GUARD SERVICE CRAFT *(continued)*

the U.S.A., and commissioned 1-12-93; PVK 005, of Finnish origin and commissioned 9-93; PVK 009, of Danish origin and commissioned 9-93; PVK 010, completed 4-94; PVK 011, completed 1980 in Sweden and commissioned in Estonia 15-6-94; PVK 020, completed 1982 in Sweden and transferred 5-95; and PVK 021, completed 1988 in Finland and transferred 9-94.

Note: Ships and craft operated by Estonia's Shipping and Navigation Authority *(Eesti Veeteede Amet)* include the ex-Finnish icebreaker *Tarmo;* ex-Russian Samara-class survey and navaids tender EVA 307 (ex-*Zenit*); ex-Russian Kamenka-class survey and navaids tender EVA 308 (ex-*Vern'er,* GS-108); ex-Russian BGK-380-class inshore survey craft EVA 309 (ex-BGK-117) and EVA 310 (ex-BGK-630); ex-Russian PO-2 (Yaroslavets)-class survey launch EVA 311 (ex-BGK-931); ex-Russian T-4-class landing craft EVA 314; and ex-Finnish *Seili*-class navaids tender EVA 316 (ex-*Lonna*). Characteristics data and illustrations for these units can be found in the 1998–99 and earlier editions.

Ex-Finnish *Karhu*-class icebreaker *Karu* (ex-*Kapten Tchubakov,* ex-*Kapitan Chubakov,* ex-*Karhu*), acquired by Russia in 1987, was transferred to Estonia in 1990 and restored to her original name in 1-93; she is operated by the Tallinn Port Authority. Russian Navy Baltic Fleet *Emba*-class cable tender *Nepryada* was purchased from Russia in 1997 and may be operated by either the Shipping and Navigation Board or another government agency.

FÆROE ISLANDS

Note: The Faeroe Islands are a semi-autonomous territory of Denmark.

COAST GUARD AND FISHERY PROTECTION SERVICE

(Færøar Landsstyri)

Personnel (2002): Approx. 65 total

Base: Tórshavn, Strømø Island

PATROL SHIPS [WPS]

♦ **1 Brimil-class fisheries patrol ship**
Bldr: Myklebust Mek Verksted A/S, Gursken, Norway (In serv. 2000)

BRIMIL

D: approx. 1,900 tons (fl) **S:** . . . kts **Dim:** 63.60 (55.75 pp) × 12.60 × 4.30
M: 1 Ulstein-Normo KVMB12 diesel (. . . bhp), 1 Ulstein-Normo KRMB6 cruise diesel (. . . bhp); 1 CP prop; . . . bhp
Range: . . ./. . . **Crew:** . . .

Remarks: 1,500 grt. Hull fabricated by Kleven Verft A/S, Ulsteinvik, and then fitted out by Myklebust. The main engine is installed to port, the "daughter" engine to starboard; only one can be geared to the propeller at a time.

♦ **1 fisheries protection ship and rescue tug**
Bldr: Solvær Værft, Norway (In serv. 1976)

TJALDRID

D: 650 tons (fl) **S:** 15 kts **Dim:** 44.51 (38.49 pp) × 10.11 × 4.02
A: provision for 1 20-mm 70-cal. Oerlikon Mk 10 AA
Electronics: Radar: 4 . . . nav.
M: 2 MWM 6-cyl. diesels; 1 prop; 2,400 bhp—bow-thruster
Electric: 236 kw tot. (3 × 78-kw diesel sets)
Range: 5,300/14.5 **Fuel:** 122 tons **Crew:** 18 tot. + 4 divers

Remarks: 437 grt/125 nrt. Acquired in 1987. Equipped for fire fighting, salvage, and ocean towing. The 57-mm single-fire gun formerly carried has been replaced by provision for a single 20-mm 70-cal. Oerlikon gun. Of the four radars carried, one is a large Raytheon S-band set suitable for surface-search work; an HFD/F set is also installed. To support salvage divers, a portable decompression chamber can be carried.

FALKLAND ISLANDS

Note: The Falkland Islands are a colony of the United Kingdom. The Royal Navy is responsible for physical security in the waters around the Falklands and the other British territories in the South Atlantic; the *Leeds Castle* (P 258) relieved her sister *Dumbarton Castle* (P 265) during 4-01 as South Atlantic station ship. The two ships listed below provide fisheries surveillance within the declared exclusion zone surrounding the Falkland Islands.

Maritime Aviation: In addition to RAF assets stationed in the Falklands, the local government has acquired a Dornier Do-228-200 maritime surveillance aircraft with Sperry Primus radar and two Pilatus-Britten-Norman Defender twin-engine surveillance aircraft.

FISHERIES PATROL SHIPS [WPS]

♦ **1 Polish Project B675**
Bldr: Stocznia imeni Komuny Paryskiej, Gdynia (In serv. 12-7-94)

DORADA

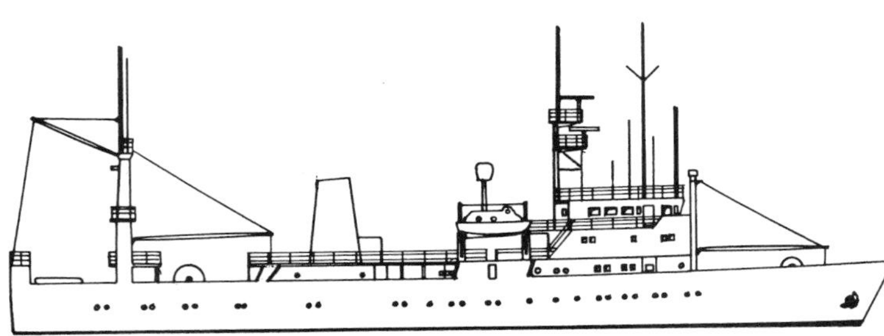

Dorada Drawing by A. D. Baker III

D: approx. 3,300 tons (fl) **S:** 16 kts (14.8 sust.)
Dim: 76.60 (69.00 pp) × 14.60 × 5.25 **A:** small arms
Electronics: Radar: 2 Furuno 2120 nav.
M: 1 Cegielski-Sulzer 12ATV25H diesel; 1 CP prop; 2,366 bhp—1 Cegielski-Sulzer 6ATV25H cruise diesel; 1,183 bhp—bow-thruster
Electric: 2,100 kw tot. (2 × 640-kw diesel sets, 1 × 50-kw diesel set; 400 V, 50 Hz)
Range: 14,000/12 **Fuel:** 440 m^3 heavy oil; 50 m^3 diesel **Endurance:** 45 days
Crew: 26 tot. (incl. 11 scientific staff and cadets)

Remarks: 2,360 grt/1,185 dwt. Laid down in 1991 as a stern-haul trawler and fish-processing ship for a British owner who defaulted. Operated briefly for a New Zealand company but placed under arrest for debts on 13-2-96. Conversion to fisheries patrol ship begun 20-8-97 at Lyttelton, New Zealand, for Byron Marine, Ltd. Medical and berthing facilities were upgraded, new deck machinery installed, and oceanographic gear-handling equipment added. Conversion was completed 12-12-97, and the ship departed for the Falklands the next day. Carries two rigid inflatable inspection launches aft. Has two auxiliary boilers.

♦ **1 former stern-haul fish processing trawler**
Bldr: Charles D. Holmes & Co., Ltd., Beverley, Hull, U.K. (In serv. 1-73)

CRISCILLA (ex-*Lady Hammond,* ex-*Hammond Innes*)

Criscilla H&L Van Ginderen, 1998

D: approx. 1,400 tons (fl) **S:** 15 kts **Dim:** 53.62 (50.91 pp) × 11.31 × . . .
Electronics: Radar: 1 Koden MD 3120 nav.; 1 Furuno 2110 ARPA nav.
M: 1 Stork-Werkspoor 6TM410 6-cyl., 4-stroke diesel; 1 prop; 2,500 bhp
Electric: 488 kw tot. (2 × 244-kw diesel sets; 440 V, 50 Hz a.c.)
Range: . . ./. . . **Crew:** 15 tot.

Remarks: 924 grt/437 dwt. Originally chartered from Marbella, Ltd., 1998 through 5-00; charter has been extended. Has red hull and white superstructure, with "Fisheries Patrol" painted prominently amidships on the hull sides. Carries one Avon Searaider rigid inflatable inspection boat. Has an MFD/F, echo sounder, SATCOM terminal, and GPS.

FIJI

Republic of Fiji

Personnel (2002): Approx. 330 total

Note: The navy is subordinate to the Minister of Home Affairs. All units are based at Walu Bay, Suva. Training is conducted at RFNS *Captain Stanley Brown,* Togalevu. Ship names are preceded by RFNS (Republic of Fiji Naval Ship). Regular economic exclusion zone patrols were ended 1-98 due to financial constraints.

Naval Aviation: The Fiji Air Wing was dissolved in 5-95. The French Navy provides occasional maritime surveillance flights by Falcon 200 aircraft stationed at New Caledonia.

PATROL CRAFT [PC]

♦ 3 ASI 315 class
Bldr: Transfield ASI Pty, Ltd., South Coogie, W.A., Australia

201 Kula (In serv. 28-5-94)　203 Kiro (In serv. 14-10-95)
202 Kikau (In serv. 27-5-95)

Kiro (203)—note 20-mm gun forward　Brian Morrison, 9-98

D: 148 tons (162 fl) **S:** 26+ kts
Dim: 32.60 (31.50 hull; 28.60 wl) × 8.20 × 1.60 (hull)
A: 1 20-mm 70-cal. Oerlikon Mk 10 AA; 2 single 7.62-mm mg
Electronics: Radar: 1 Furuno . . . nav.
M: 2 Caterpillar 3516 Phase II diesels; 2 props; 2,820 bhp (2,400 sust.)—1 Caterpillar 3412 TA cruise diesel; 1 Hamilton 521 waterjet; 775 bhp
Electric: 186 kVA (2 Caterpillar 3306T diesel sets)
Range: 600/18; 2,500/12 **Fuel:** 28 tons **Endurance:** 8–10 days
Crew: 4 officers, 15 enlisted

Remarks: With the change in Fiji's government, the order placed on 3-10-85 for four Australian "Pacific Forum" ASI 315–class patrol boats was canceled, and the boats were earmarked for Tonga and other Pacific island nations. The program was reinstated during 7-92, but for only three boats, at least initially; the order was placed in 12-92. Name for 203 was originally to have been *Ruve*. Are of the improved, lighter-weight version built for Hong Kong and Kuwait and are the only units of the class to carry weapons heavier than a 12.7-mm mg. Carry a 5-m aluminum boarding boat. Have an extensive navigational suite.

PATROL BOATS [PB]

♦ 2 former oilfield support craft
Bldr: Beaux's Baycraft, La. (In serv. 1979–80)

101 Levuka (ex-*Maranatha*)　102 Lautoka (ex-*Rapture*)

D: 97 tons (fl) **S:** 27 kts **Dim:** 33.80 × 7.40 × 1.50
A: 1 12.7-mm mg **Electronics:** Radar: 2 Decca . . . nav.
M: 4 G.M. Detroit Diesel 12V71 TI diesels; 4 props; 2,156 bhp **Crew:** . . .

Remarks: Aluminum craft purchased 9-87 and commissioned 22-10-87 and 28-10-87, respectively. Correlation of former names to Fijian names uncertain.

♦ 4 ex-Israeli Dabur class
Bldr: Israeli Aircraft Industries, Be'er Sheva (In serv. 1973–77)

301 Vai　302 Ogo　303 Saku　304 Saqa

Ogo (302)　H&L Van Ginderen, 1-96

D: 25 tons (35 fl) **S:** 19 kts **Dim:** 19.8 × 5.8 × 0.8
A: 2 single 20-mm 70-cal. Oerlikon AA; 2 single 7.62-mm mg
Electronics: Radar: 1 Decca Super 101 Mk 3 nav.
M: 2 G.M. Detroit Diesel 12V71 TI diesels; 2 props; 960 bhp
Electric: 20 kw tot. **Range:** 1,200/17 **Crew:** 2 officers, 7 enlisted

Remarks: Former Israeli Navy units acquired and commissioned 22-11-91. Were considered surplus as of 2000 and may be offered to other Fiji government agencies as launches. Aluminum construction. Could make 25 kts when new; range may have been reduced to 450 n.m. at 13 kts. 301 has only one 20-mm AA.

Note: The small yacht [YFL] *Cagi Donu* is operated by the navy for the prime minister.

FINLAND

Republic of Finland

SUOMEN MERIVOIMAT

Personnel (2000): 7,450 total, including the Coastal Artillery and Coastal Infantry Force; the total includes some 5,100 conscripts serving 11-month national service tours. There are also large numbers of reservists.

Organization and Bases: In 8-98, the fleet was combined into a single rapid-reaction force, with the Finnish Army Coastal Artillery and Coastal Infantry forces integrated within the navy. The major organizational commands are now the Gulf of Finland Naval Command, at Uppinniemi; the Archipelago Sea Naval Command, at Pansio; the Kotka Coastal Command; and the Uusimaa Jaeger Brigade, at Tammisaari.

Maritime Aviation: The navy has no aircraft of its own. The separate Frontier Guard (q.v.) operates a number of helicopters and fixed-wing aircraft. The air force operates one Fokker 27 Mk 400 M twin-engine maritime surveillance aircraft and six Mil Mi-8 Hip helicopters for SAR duties.

Coastal Defense: The two Coastal Artillery regiments operate Swedish RBS-15 antiship missiles mounted four per vehicle on Sisu trucks, 155-mm and 130-mm fixed artillery, and 100-mm fixed and mobile artillery.

WEAPONS AND SYSTEMS

The minelayer *Pohjanmaa* has a single-barrel automatic Bofors 120-mm gun with the following characteristics:

Length: 46 calibers **Weight without munitions:** 28.5 tons
Projectile weight: 35 kg **Muzzle velocity:** 800 m/sec
Max. rate of fire: 80 rds/min **Arc of elevation:** −10° to +80°
Training speed: 40°/sec **Elevation speed:** 30°/sec
Max. effective range for surface fire: 12,000 m

The other major weapons employed are Swedish RBS-15 antiship missiles, Bofors 40-mm L70 AA guns, and 23-mm 60-cal. Finnish-made Sako AA twin mountings.

The Finnyards SONAC PTA towed sonar, a 78-m passive array with 24 hydrophones designed to be towed at 3–12 kts on a 600-m cable, can be installed on *Rauma*-class missile boats.

Combatant ships are being treated with an application of HPA-1 (High-Performance Absorber) radar signature reduction coating, a sandwich of GRP and various doped resins that significantly reduces radar signal returns in the 5–18 GHz range.

Note: Of the two *Turunmaa*-class patrol combatants, the *Turunmaa* (03) was retired in 1999 and the *Karjala* (04) was to retire during 2001.

GUIDED-MISSILE PATROL CRAFT [PTG]

♦ 1 (+ 1) Rauma 2000 class
Bldr: Aker Finnyards, Rauma

	Laid down	L	In serv.
74 Hamina	8-97	5-98	24-8-98 (del.)
75	2001	. . .	4-03

Hamina (74)　Finnish Navy, 1998

Hamina (74)　Finnish Navy, 1998

D: 235 tons (268 fl) **S:** 32 kts **Dim:** 50.80 (44.30 pp) × 8.30 × 2.00
A: 4 RBS-15SF SSM; 1 40-mm 70-cal. Bofors AA; 1 6-round Sako SAM syst. (. . . Mistral missiles) *or* 1 twin 23-mm Sako AA; 2 single 12.7-mm mg; provision for 4 9-round Saab Elma LLS.920 ASW RL

GUIDED-MISSILE PATROL CRAFT [PTG] *(continued)*

Electronics:
Radar: 1 Thales Scout nav./surf. search
Sonar: provision for Finnyards SONAC-PTA towed array
EW: . . . intercept; 2 32-round Wallop Barricade decoy RL
M: 2 MTU 16V538 TB93 diesels; 2 KaMeWa 90SII waterjets; 8,000 bhp
Electric: 386 kw tot. (2 × 193-kw Saab Scania 11DGSJGM diesel-driven sets; 220 V a.c.)
Range: 500/30 **Fuel:** . . . tons **Crew:** 5 officers, 14 enlisted

Remarks: 74 was ordered 26-1-97 for $21.6 million. Originally, plans called for three more to be ordered in 2000 and another four later, but only the second has been ordered, on 20-2-01, and no more are now planned. These are hoped to be employed as leaders for the new class of multipurpose surface-effect combatants.
Hull systems: Aluminum hull structure with six watertight compartments; superstructure is constructed of composite materials rather than aluminum. Have extensive signature reduction measures; the engineering plant is on resilient mountings to reduce the acoustic signature, and the engine exhaust is ducted through seawater spray to reduce the infrared signature. The craft have a full NBC warfare protective system.
Combat systems: 74 has the Danish INFOCOM ICS-2000 integrated communications suite, but no combat data system was aboard as of 26-6-01, when EADS received the combat system development contract. A Saab Dynamics EOS-400 optronic gun director controls the 40-mm mount, which is in a special low-radar-reflectivity gunhouse. The twin 23-mm AA mount is interchangeable with a twin launcher for Mistral point-defense SAMs; neither was aboard at completion. As completed, had no ASW equipment. A Thales-Nederland Tacticos combat management system was leased for trials in 74 from 1-00 to 8-00 and then removed. The Lacroix ATOS (Anti-Threat Optronic System) rocket-powered decoy system is to be installed in 2002; it uses two 16-round launchers firing 80-mm rockets.

♦ 4 Rauma (Helsinki-II) class   Bldr: Finnyards, Rauma

	In serv.		In serv.
70 Rauma	18-10-90	72 Porvoo	27-4-92
71 Raahe	20-8-91	73 Naantali	23-6-92

Rauma (70)—with VDS aft and only two missile canisters installed
Jaroslaw Cislak, 6-99

Porvoo (72) Winter & Findler, 6-01

D: 215 tons (248 fl) **S:** 30+ kts **Dim:** 48.00 (41.00 pp) × 8.00 × 0.87
A: up to 6 RBS-15SF SSM; 1 40-mm 70-cal. Bofors L70-600E AA; 1 6-round Sako SAM launcher (. . .Mistral missiles); 2 single 12.7-mm mg; 2 9-round Saab Elma LLS.920 ASW RL; mines
Electronics:
Radar: 1 Raytheon . . . ARPA nav.; 1 9GA 208 surf. search; 1 9LV 225 f.c.
Sonar: Simrad SS 304 hull-mounted HF; provision for Finnyards SONAC-PTA towed array (see Remarks)
EW: MEL Matilda-E (9EW 300) intercept, 1 32-round Wallop Barricade decoy RL; EADS COLDS laser countermeasure
M: 2 MTU 16V538 TB93 diesels; 2 Riva Calzone IRC 115 waterjets; 8,000 bhp
Electric: 386 kw (2 × 193 kw; 2 Saab Scania DS11 diesel driving)
Crew: 5 officers, 14 enlisted

Remarks: Construction approved 2-87, with the first laid down fall 1987. Shorter and shallower in draft than the *Helsinki* class. First unit was originally to have been named *Luokka*.
Combat systems: Have CelsiusTech 9LV Mk 3 weapons-control system with two multifunction operator consoles and two navigational radar consoles, the 9LV200 Mk 3 optronic fire-control system, and the 9EW 300 EW system. The surface-to-air missile launcher is a Finnish-designed converted 23-mm 60-cal. AA gunmount equipped with infrared and t.v. cameras for fire control; two 23-mm guns are interchangeable with the missile mountings. Two portable ship-sets of the Finnyards SONAC-PTA (Passive Towed Array) sonar have been acquired for this class; it can be installed in about 24 hrs at the expense of the after two RBS-15 missile canisters. The COLDS (Common Opto-electronic Laser Detection System) detects laser missile seekers and directs an equivalent pulse-repetition-frequency laser beam of its own against a safe spot on the ocean to spoof the missile.

♦ 4 Helsinki (PB 80) class   Bldr: Wärtsilä, Helsinki

	Laid down	L	In serv.
60 Helsinki	3-9-80	5-11-80	1-9-81
61 Turku	1-1-84	1985	1-6-85
62 Oulu	. . .	. . .	1-10-85
63 Kotka	. . .	. . .	16-6-86

Turku (61) A. A. de Kruijf, 6-00

Turku (61)—note VDS equipment and three missile canisters aboard
Findler & Winter, 6-00

D: 250 tons (280 fl) **S:** 30 kts **Dim:** 45.00 × 8.90 × 3.00 (props)
A: 3 or 4 RBS-15SF SSM; 1 57-mm 70-cal. Bofors SAK 1 DP; 2 twin 23-mm 60-cal. Sako AA; 2 d.c. racks (3 d.c. each); mines
Electronics:
Radar: 1 Raytheon . . . ARPA nav., 1 9GA 208 surf. search, 1 9LV 225 f.c.
Sonar: Simrad SS 304 hull-mounted HF; Finnyards SONAC-PTA towed array
EW: Thales DR-2000U intercept; 2 32-round Wallop Barricade decoy RL
M: 3 MTU 16V538 TB92 diesels; 3 props; 12,000 bhp
Range: . . ./. . . **Crew:** 30 tot.

Remarks: Prototype ordered 5-10-78; three others ordered 13-1-83. Further construction was deferred in favor of the Rauma class above. Aluminum hull.
Combat systems: The DataSaab EOS-400 optronic f.c.s. is mounted atop the pilothouse to control the 57-mm gun on 61–63, which had a revised pilothouse shape; 60 was later brought up to same standard. The 23-mm mounts are controlled by Galileo lead-computing directors mounted on the after corners of the bridge deck. Minelaying missions require dismounting the depth charge racks and RBS-15SF missiles, of which up to eight can be carried if required (paired atop one another). The towed-array sonar hoist and reel system replaces the after starboard missile rack position and the craft are now normally seen with three missiles and the sonar.

PATROL AIR-CUSHION CRAFT [PBA]

♦ 0 (+ 1 + 3) NB 432–class (T2000) patrol surface-effect craft
Bldr: Aker Finnyards, Rauma (In serv. 9-01)

D: 84 tons **S:** 50 kts **Dim:** 27.40 × 15.40 × . . .
A: . . . SSM—. . . AA—. . . torpedoes
M: 2 Honeywell/Vericor TF40 gas turbines (4,600 shp each); 2 shrouded airscrew props
Range: . . ./. . . **Crew:** 9 tot.

Remarks: Ordered 9-7-99 for $12.1 million as prototype for a possible additional surface-effect patrol craft class; three more are planned if the first is successful. Aluminum and composite structure, with "stealth" signature-reduction features. Planned for launch in spring 2001. Thales has offered a combat data system and its Surf low-probability-of-intercept radar for use on these craft. EADS received a contract for the combat data and control system on 26-6-01.

PATROL CRAFT [PC]

♦ 2 Rihtniemi class

	Bldr	L	In serv.
54 Raisio	Laivateollisuus, Turku	2-7-59	12-9-59
55 Röytta	Laivateollisuus, Turku	2-6-59	14-10-59

PATROL CRAFT [PC] *(continued)*

Raisio (54) H&L Van Ginderen, 1994

D: 115 tons (135 fl) **S:** 18 kts **Dim:** 34.0 × 6.0 × 1.8
A: 2 twin 23-mm 60-cal. Sako AA; 2 5-round RBU-1200 ASW RL; mines
Electronics:
Radar: 1 Decca 1226 nav.
Sonar: Simrad SS 304 hull mounted HF; Finnyards SONAC-PTA towed passive array
M: 2 Mercedes-Benz diesels; 2 CP props; 2,500 bhp **Crew:** 20 tot.

Remarks: Former convertible minesweeper/gunboats, modernized 1977–81. Now used primarily for navigational training. Were fitted with a Finnish-developed towed sonar array in 1991–93. Near-sisters *Rihtniemi* (51) and *Rymattyla* (52) were transferred to Estonia on retirement late in 1999, and *Ruissalo* (53) was stricken during 1994. 54 and 55 are to be retired shortly.

MINE WARFARE SHIPS AND CRAFT

Note: In addition to the ships and craft listed in this section as having minelaying capabilities, most other classes of Finnish combatants, auxiliaries, and service craft are also equipped for minelaying.

♦ 2 Hämeenmaa-class minelayers [MM] Bldr: Finnyards, Rauma

	Laid down	L	In serv.
02 Hämeenmaa	2-4-91	11-11-91	15-4-92
05 Uusimaa	12-11-91	6-92	2-12-92

Uusimaa (05) Maritime Photographic, 6-99

D: 1,000 tons (1,330 fl) **S:** 20 kts **Dim:** 77.00 (69.60 pp) × 11.60 × 3.00
A: 2 single 40-mm 70-cal. Bofors AA; 1 6-round Sako SAM launcher (. . . Mistral missiles); 2 twin 23-mm 60-cal. Sako AA; 2 5-round RBU-1200 ASW RL (60 RGB-12 rockets); 2 d.c. racks (6 d.c. each); 4 mine rails (100–150 mines; 200 m rail-length total)
Electronics:
Radar: 3 Selesmar . . . ARPA nav.
Sonar: Simrad SS 304 hull-mounted HF
EW: MEL Matilda intercept; 2 12-round Wallop Super Barricade decoy RL
M: 2 Wärtsilä-Vasa 16V22MD diesels; 2 CP props; 6,400 bhp—250-shp bow-thruster
Crew: 45 tot. (accomm. for 100)

Remarks: Authorized 9-88 and originally ordered 7-89 from Wärtsilä Shipyard, Helsinki, for delivery 1991; reordered 29-12-89 after Wärtsilä's bankruptcy. Have bow and stern ramps to permit use as logistics transports as well as minelayers and also have side loading ports. Have four mine rails exiting stern. Built to Ice Class IA standards and able to break 40-cm ice continuously; the bow is cut away sharply above the waterline to facilitate ice navigation. Have a Rademac System 2400 optronic director atop the pilothouse for the 40-mm guns. Two Galileo lead-computing directors are mounted fore and aft for the 23-mm weapons.

♦ 1 minelayer/training ship [MM] Bldr: Wärtsilä, Helsinki

	Laid down	L	In serv.
01 Pohjanmaa	4-5-78	28-8-78	8-6-79

Pohjanmaa (01) Bernard Prézelin, 8-00

Pohjanmaa (01) Bernard Prézelin, 8-00

D: 1,100 tons (1,476 fl) **S:** 19 kts **Dim:** 78.30 × 11.60 × 3.20
A: 1 57-mm 70-cal. Bofors SAK 1 DP; 2 single 40-mm 70-cal. Bofors L70 AA; 2 twin 23-mm 60-cal. AA; 2 single 12.7-mm mg; 2 5-round RBU-1200 ASW RL; 2 d.c. racks (6 d.c. each); 120 mines
Electronics:
Radar: 2 Raytheon . . . ARPA nav.; 1 Thales Scout surf. search; 1 Thales DA-05 air search; 1 CelsiusTech 9GA 208 search; 1 CelsiusTech 9LV 100 f.c.
Sonar: 2 hull-mounted HF sets (one for bottomed-target classification)
EW: ArgoSystems . . . intercept, 2 18-round Wallop Barricade decoy RL
M: 2 Wärtsilä-Vasa 16V22 diesels; 2 CP props; 5,800 bhp—bow-thruster
Electric: 1,070 kw tot. **Range:** 3,500/17 **Crew:** 80 ship's company + 70 cadets

Remarks: Modernized in 1997–98.

Uusimaa (05) Maritime Photographic, 6-99

MINE WARFARE SHIPS AND CRAFT *(continued)*

Combat systems: Has CelsiusTech 9LV 200 gun fire-control system. Two twin 23-mm AA forward were replaced by two single 12.7-mm mg during 1992. The original Bofors 120-mm DP gunmount was replaced in 1998. The training facilities are fitted in portable containers mounted on the two internal mine rails and are easily removable if the ship is required for combat.

♦ 3 Pansio-class coastal minelayer/antipollution ships [MM]
Bldr: Olkiluoto SY, Telakka

475 Pyhäranta (In serv. 26-4-92)
576 Pansio (In serv. 25-9-91)
777 Porkkala (In serv. 29-10-92)

Pansio (576) H&L Van Ginderen, 5-99

Porkkala (777) H&L Van Ginderen, 5-99

D: 450 tons (fl) **S:** 10 kts **Dim:** 44.00 (39.20 wl) × 10.00 × 2.00
A: 1 twin 23-mm 60-cal. Sako AA; 12.7-mm mg; 50 mines (100 m rail-length total)
Electronics: Radar: 1 Raytheon . . . ARPA nav.
M: 2 MTU 12V 183 TE62 diesels; 2 props; 1,500 bhp—bow-thruster **Crew:** 12 tot.

Remarks: Ordered 5-90 for delivery 1991–92 as combination coastal minelayers, antipollution ships, landing craft, and vehicle/cargo carriers to supply Coastal Artillery facilities. Have bow and stern ramps as well as side-loading ports. Mine rails total 100 m on vehicle deck, which can also accommodate four 40-ft. standard cargo containers or two large cargo trucks. Have a 15-ton electrohydraulic knuckle crane to port forward and a 1.2-ton crane aft. Capable of light icebreaking. Employ the Polaris ProMare minefield planning system.

♦ 4 Soviet Osa-II-class (Project 205ME) fast minelayers [MM]

11 Tuima 12 Tuisku 14 Tuuli 15 Tyrsky

Tuima (11) H&L Van Ginderen, 4-94

D: 184 tons (226 normal fl, 245 overload) **S:** 40 kts (35 sust.)
Dim: 38.6 (37.5 wl) × 7.6 (6.3 wl) × 2.0 (hull; 3.1 props)
A: 2 twin 30-mm 65-cal. AK-230 AA; 2 mine rails (. . . mines)
Electronics: Radar: 1 Raytheon . . . ARPA nav.
M: 3 M-504B diesels; 3 props; 15,000 bhp **Electric:** 400 kw tot.
Range: 500/34; 750/25 **Endurance:** 5 days **Crew:** 4 officers, 24 enlisted

Remarks: Transferred 1974. 11 was converted to fast minelayer in 1992–93 by deleting the missile installation and adding rails on deck for mines; 14 followed in 1994. 12 and 15 had the missile systems removed at the end of 1995 and were converted for minelaying during 1996. The craft were also re-engined, and the missile targeting and gun fire-control radars were removed. A rigid inflatable rubber inspection dinghy is now carried atop the superstructure aft, handled by a telescoping electrohydraulic crane on the fantail. The mine rails extend from the gunmount on the forecastle to the stern.

♦ 2 minelaying barges [MM]
Bldr: Lehtinen, Rauma (In serv. 1987)

721 821

D: 130 tons (fl) **Dim:** 15.0 × 7.0 × 1.5 **A:** . . . mines

Remarks: Non-self-propelled craft intended primarily to transport mines but also capable of being used to lay mines.

♦ 6 Kuha-class inshore minesweepers [MSI]
Bldr: Laivateollisuus, Turku

	In serv.		In serv.
21 Kuha 21	28-6-74	24 Kuha 24	7-3-75
22 Kuha 22	10-1-74	25 Kuha 25	17-6-75
23 Kuha 23	7-3-75	26 Kuha 26	13-11-75

Kuha 21 (21)—as modified Finnish Navy, 1998

D: 125 tons (fl) **S:** 12 kts **Dim:** 31.60 × 6.90 × 2.00
A: 1 twin 23-mm 60-cal. Sako AA; 1 12.7-mm mg
Electronics:
Radar: 1 Decca . . . nav.—Sonar: Patria Finavitec SONAC HF minehunting
M: 2 Cummins NT-380M diesels; 2 outboard-drive props; 660 bhp
Crew: 2 officers, 12 enlisted

Remarks: Glass-reinforced plastic hulls. Plans for eight additional units were canceled. Modernized and lengthened by Tyovenne Shipyard, Uusikaupunki, completing 22-12-97, 26-6-98, 30-9-98, 13-11-98, 12-12-99, and 30-5-00, respectively.
Hull systems: Flexibly mounted engines drive rudder/propellers through hydrostatic transmissions. Were originally 90 tons (fl) and 26.6 m overall.
Combat systems: Can tow the Type F-82 electrode sweep, and also have provisions for mechanical and acoustic mine sweeping. One unit has been equipped for trials with the Finnish Elesco FIMS (Family of Integrated Minesweeping Systems) sweep array with MRK-960 three-electrode magnetic sweep and MKR-400 pipe-type noncontrollable noisemaker; the data processing system is Elesco's SSCP, with differential GPS.

♦ 7 Kiiski-class inshore minesweepers [MSI]
Bldr: Fiskar's Turun, Turku

	Laid down	L	In serv.
521 Kiiski 1	. . .	. . .	1983
522 Kiiski 2	20-1-83	21-10-83	4-11-83
523 Kiiski 3	14-2-83	10-11-83	28-11-83
524 Kiiski 4	5-4-83	28-11-83	12-12-83
525 Kiiski 5	16-5-83	2-5-84	24-5-83
526 Kiiski 6	29-8-83	9-5-84	24-5-83
527 Kiiski 7	12-9-83	10-5-84	24-5-83

Kiiski 5 (525) H&L Van Ginderen, 5-93

D: 17.7 tons (20 fl) **S:** 10.7 kts **Dim:** 15.18 (13.00 pp) × 4.10 × 1.20
A: none **Electronics:** Radar: 1. . . nav.
M: 2 Valmet 611 CSMP diesels; 2 Hamilton Model 1341 waterjets; 340 bhp
Range: 250/10 **Crew:** 4 tot.

Remarks: Were to have been operated either by crews or under remote control by *Kuha*-class inshore minesweepers, but are now operated in manned mode only. Glass-reinforced plastic construction. Tow a Type F-82 electrode sweep to counter magnetic mines and can also counter acoustic mines.

AMPHIBIOUS WARFARE CRAFT

♦ 3 Kampela-class utility landing craft [LCU]

Bldr: Enso-Gutzeit, Savonlinna (557: Finnmekano, Teija)

371 Kampela 1 (In serv. 29-7-76) 557 Kampela 3 (In serv. 23-10-79)
376 Kampela 2 (In serv. 21-10-76)

Kampela 2 (376) 7-96

D: 90 tons (260 fl) **S:** 9 kts **Dim:** 32.5 × 8.0 × 1.5
A: 2 single 12.7-mm mg; 20 mines
Electronics: Radar: 1 Decca 1226 nav.; 1 Decca . . . nav.
M: 2 Saab Scania diesels; 2 props; 460 bhp **Crew:** 10 tot.

Remarks: 371 is operated for Coastal Artillery logistics support. The twin 23-mm mounts formerly fitted on the bridge wings have been replaced by single 12.7-mm machineguns.

♦ 3 Kala-class utility landing craft [LCU]

Bldr: Rauma-Repola, Rauma (In serv. 1956–59)

Kala 1 Kala 4 Kala 6

Kala 6 Alexandre Sheldon-Duplaix, 7-88

D: 60 tons (200 fl) **S:** 9 kts **Dim:** 27.0 × 8.0 × 1.8
A: 2 single 12.7-mm mg; 34 mines
Electronics: Radar: 1 Decca 1226 nav.
M: 2 Valmet diesels; 2 props; 360 bhp **Crew:** 10 tot.

Remarks: Sisters *Kala 2* and *Kala 5* were stricken in 1992, *Kala 3* in 1993.

♦ 2 Lohi-class personnel transports [LCP]

Bldr: Savonlinna SY (In serv. 7-9-84)

251 Lohi 452 Lohm

Lohi (251) Hartmut Ehlers, 9-96

D: 28 tons (38 fl) **S:** 24 kts **Dim:** 20.50 × 5.90 × 1.00
A: 1 twin 23-mm 60-cal. Sako AA; 1 12.7-mm mg
Electronics: Radar: 1 Decca 1226 nav.
M: 2 Wizeman–Mercedes-Benz diesels; 2 KaMeWa waterjets; 1,100 bhp
Range: 240/24 **Crew:** 4 tot.

Remarks: Have a near-vertical bow door and ramp for landing embarked personnel. Ordered 17-1-83 and laid down 8-83 and 9-83. Aluminum construction. Used as VIP transports, patrol craft, hospital launches, etc. Guns not always mounted. Operated for the Coastal Artillery.

♦ 36 Meriusko-class assault boats [LCP]

Bldr: Alumina Varvet, Kokkola

U 200 series U 300 series U 400 series

Meriusko-class U 206—with modified pilothouse H&L Van Ginderen, 7-00

D: 8.5 tons (10.2 fl) **S:** 36 kts (30 loaded) **Dim:** 11.3 × 3.5 × 0.6
M: 2 Volvo TAMD70E diesels; 2 Hamilton 291 waterjets; 600 bhp—*or* 1 MTU V8 diesel; 1 waterjet
Crew: 3 tot. + 25 troops

Remarks: Small bow ramp. U 203 and one other have cable-handling equipment to enable them to act as boom defense boats. Design by Wico-Boat Oy (now Finnspeed) and known commercially as the "Sea-Wico" class. The first 11, completed 1983–86, originally had a low pilothouse and no radar but now have a full-height structure and radar; later units have a larger pilothouse.

♦ 2 Vietivisko-class assault boats [LCP]

Bldr: Alumina Varvet, Kokkola (In serv. 1983)

U 201 U 202

D: 10.72 tons (fl) **S:** 25 kts **Dim:** 11.3 × 3.5 × 0.6
M: 2 Volvo TAMD70E diesels; 2 props; 600 bhp

Remarks: Similar to Meriusko class.

AUXILIARIES

♦ 1 Halli-class pollution cleanup ship and vehicle transport [AG]

	Bldr	Laid down	L	In serv.
899 Halli	Hollming, Rauma	18-3-86	25-6-86	1-87

Halli (899) H&L Van Ginderen, 9-93

D: 1,600 tons (fl) **S:** 11.3 kts **Dim:** 60.50 × 12.40 × 3.0
Electronics: Radar: 3 different nav.
M: 2 Wärtsilä-Vasa 6R22 diesels; 2 Aquamaster azimuthal props; 2,650 bhp
Range: 3,000/11.3 **Crew:** 13 tot.

Remarks: 1,400 grt/1,200 dwt. Operated for the Ministry of the Environment by the Ministry of Navigation under navy control with a civilian crew. Enlarged version of *Hylje.* Employs the MacGregor-Navire MacLORI pollution collection system, sweeping a 30-m path at 1.5 kts. Has 360-m^3 waste-collection tank. Can also be used as a landing ship and logistic support vessel; has an 11-m bow ramp for 48-ton vehicles.

♦ 1 Hylje-class pollution cleanup and vehicle transport ship [AG]

Bldr: Laivateollisuus, Turku (In serv. 3-6-81)

799 Hylje

AUXILIARIES *(continued)*

D: 1,436 (fl) **S:** 7 kts **Dim:** 49.90 × 12.50 × 3.00
Electronics: Radar: 2 Raytheon . . . nav.
M: 2 Saab-Scania DSI-14 diesels; 2 Jastram RP03 retractable, steerable props; 590 bhp
Electric: 690 kVA tot. (2 × 300-kVA Stamford, 1 × 90-kw Stamford diesel sets)
Range: . . ./. . . **Fuel:** 55 m^3 **Crew:** 7 tot. (accomm. for 14)

Remarks: Operated for the Ministry of the Environment by the Ministry of Transportation under navy control with a civilian crew. Can carry 100 tons of deck cargo on the flush open deck forward, and there is a bow ramp with 42 tons capacity. A 6-ton crane is fitted. Storage tanks can hold 550 m^3 of recovered seawater/oil slurry and 860 m^3 recovered of cargo oil. One 10-m boat and one 13-m oil-skimming boat carried, and there is a 120-m^3/hr foam monitor. Can be operated in light ice.

♦ 1 intelligence collector [AGI] Bldr: Valmet, Turku (In serv. 1963)

99 Kustaanmiekka (ex-*Valvoja III*)

Kustaanmiekka (99) H&L Van Ginderen, 4-94

D: 340 tons (fl) **S:** 11 kts **Dim:** 36.70 × 9.40 × 3.20
A: provision for 2 single 12.7-mm mg **Electronics:** Radar: 1. . . nav.
M: 1 Burmeister & Wain Alpha diesel; 1 prop; 480 bhp
Fuel: 38.5 tons **Crew:** 10 tot.

Remarks: 406 grt. Former buoy tender, acquired from Board of Navigation in 1989 and refitted for naval service by Hollming, Rauma. As of late 1993, had been converted into an intelligence collector, with a large dielectric radome aft and intercept antennas on foremast. Sister *Kemiö* (93) was transferred to Estonia in 12-92.

♦ 1 salvage ship [ARS] Bldr: Laivateollisuus, Turku (In serv. 1960)

420 Parainen (ex-*Pellinki,* ex-*Meteor*)

Parainen (420)—with gunmount installed forward K. Brzoza, 6-95

D: 700 tons (fl) **S:** 12 kts **Dim:** 38.50 × 9.25 × 4.10
A: 1 twin 23-mm 60-cal. Sako AA **Electronics:** Radar: 1. . . nav.
M: 2 Crossley diesels; 1 prop; 1,200 bhp **Crew:** 17 tot.

Remarks: 404 grt. Former tug, acquired 1978 from Oy Neptun AB, then refitted and equipped for salvage duties by Teijon Telakka. Gunmount not always aboard. Operated for the Coastal Artillery. Late note: The ship was sold for commercial use during 2001.

SERVICE CRAFT

♦ 1 trials craft [YAGE] Bldr: Reposaaron Konepaja, Pori

	Laid down	L	In serv.
826 Isku	11-68	4-12-69	1970

D: 180 tons (fl) **S:** 18 kts **Dim:** 33.35 × 8.70 × 1.80
A: . . . mines **Electronics:** Radar: 1 Raytheon . . . ARPA nav.
M: 4 Soviet M-50-F4 diesels; 4 props; 4,800 bhp **Crew:** 25 tot.

Isku (826) Finnish Navy, 1990

Remarks: "Seasled" planing hull with rectangular planform. Built as a guided-missile patrol boat and armed with four Soviet P-15 Termit (SS-N-2A Styx) missiles and a twin 30-mm AK-230 AA mount. Never made designed speed and was relegated to trials duties. In 1989–90, was lengthened 7 m by Uusikaupunki Shipyard, with the deckhouse lengthened, mine rails added, and an articulated crane added near the bow.

♦ 1 modified Valas-class diving tender [YDT]
Bldr: Hollming Oy, Rauma (In serv. 10-80)

98 Mersu

D: 300 tons (fl) **S:** 12 kts **Dim:** 30.65 × 8.1 × 3.4
A: 1 twin 23-mm 60-cal. Sako AA; 1 12.7-mm mg; 28 small mines
Electronics: Radar: 1 Decca . . . nav.
M: 1 Wärtsilä-Vasa 22 diesel; 1 prop; 1,450 bhp
Crew: 1 officer, 6 enlisted + 20 divers

Remarks: Can also be used to transport 300 personnel. Appearance generally as the *Valas* class.

♦ 4 Valas-class general-service tenders [YF]
Bldr: Hollming Oy, Rauma (In serv. 1979–81)

97 Valas 121 Vahakari 222 Vaarlehti 323 Vänö

Vaarlehti (222)—note the gunmount on the centerline amidships, next to the stack, which is offset to starboard H&L Van Ginderen, 5-97

D: 100 tons (275 fl) **S:** 12 kts **Dim:** 30.65 × 7.85 × 3.40
A: 1 twin 23-mm 60-cal. Sako AA; 1 12.7-mm mg; 28 small mines
Electronics: Radar: 1 Decca . . . nav.
M: 1 Wärtsilä Vasa 22 diesel; 1 prop; 1,300 bhp **Crew:** 11 tot.

Remarks: Ordered in 1978. Can break .4-m ice. Carry 35 tons of cargo or 150 passengers. Stern ramp for vehicle loading or minelaying. 121, 222, and 323 are operated by the Coastal Artillery.

♦ 1 presidential yacht [YFL] Bldr: Uusikaupunki SY (In serv. 5-84)

Kultaranta VII

Kultaranta VII H&L Van Ginderen, 3-93

SERVICE CRAFT *(continued)*

D: 15 tons (fl) **S:** 25 kts **Dim:** 12.5 × 4.0 × 1.4
M: 2 diesels; 2 props; 700 bhp

Remarks: Described as a "communications ship" and used as a presidential yacht in summer and for search and rescue and medical transport in winter.

♦ **4 Hila-class personnel and stores transports [YFL]**
Bldr: Kotkan Telakka (In serv. 1991–94)

237 Hila 238 Harun 339 Hästö 430 Högsåra

Hästö (339) Hartmut Ehlers, 9-96

D: 50 tons (fl) **S:** 12 kts **Dim:** 15.00 × 4.00 × 1.80
Electronics: Radar: 1 . . . nav.
M: 2 Volvo Penta TAMD-61E diesels; 2 props; 416 bhp **Crew:** 4 tot.

Remarks: Ordered 8-90. Used by the Coastal Artillery as personnel and stores carriers. Have ice-strengthened steel hulls, with 339 having greater sheer to the bow area.

♦ **7 Vihuri-class personnel transport and command launches [YFL]** Bldr: Waterman, Turku (In serv. 1991–93)

511 Jymy 531 Syöksy 992 Träskö 994 Alskär
521 Raju 541 Vinha 993 Torsö

Torsö (993) Hartmut Ehlers, 9-96

D: 13 tons (14.5 fl) **S:** 35 kts (30 sust.) **Dim:** 13.65 × 4.00 × 0.60
M: 2 MTU diesels; 2 FF waterjets; 772 bhp **Crew:** 6 tot.

Remarks: 521, 531, and 541 are configured as command launches used by the navy, while the others are configured as ambulance/personnel launches under Coastal Artillery control. GRP construction. Class prototype *Vihuri* was lost to fire in late 1991 and *Jymy* was built as a replacement.

♦ **2 Askeri-class personnel transport and command launches [YFL]** Bldr: Kotkan Telakka (In serv. 1991–92)

91 Viiri 241 Askeri

D: 20 tons (25 fl) **S:** 22 kts **Dim:** 16.0 × 4.4 × 1.4
Electronics: Radar: 1 Raytheon 1900 Pathfinder nav.; 1 . . . nav.
M: 2 Volvo Penta TAMD-series diesels; 2 props; 1,100 bhp **Crew:** 6 tot.

Remarks: 241 is used by the Coastal Artillery. GRP construction.

Viiri (91) Hartmut Ehlers, 9-96

♦ **10 L 100–class personnel transports [YFL]**
Bldr: Finnspeed Boats Oy (In serv. 1991–92)

L 100 through L 109

L 108 H&L Van Ginderen, 7-00

D: 13 tons (fl) **S:** 13 kts **Dim:** 13.0 × 4.0 × 0.6
Electronics: Radar: 1 Raytheon 1900 Pathfinder nav.
M: 1 Volvo TAMD 71 diesel; 380 bhp

Remarks: Glass-reinforced plastic construction craft intended for interisland transport and conscript boat-handling training duties. Seven were delivered in 1991, the others in 1992. Finnspeed is the successor to Wico-Boat Oy and is owned by Hollming Shipyard.

♦ **6 Hauki-class personnel transports [YFL]**
Bldr: First three: Linnan Telakka, Turku; others: Valmet Oy, Kolka (In serv. 1978–80)

133 Havouri 235 Hirsala 431 Hakuni
232 Hauki 334 Hankoniemi 436 Houtskär

Houtskär (436) Hartmut Ehlers, 9-96

D: 46 tons (fl) **S:** 10 kts **Dim:** 14.4 × 4.6 × 2.2
Electronics: Radar: 1 Raytheon 1900 Pathfinder nav.
M: 2 Valmet 611 CSM diesels; 1 prop; 586 bhp **Crew:** 2 tot.

Remarks: Cargo: 40 personnel or 6 tons of supplies. Can break .2-m ice. Operated for the Coastal Artillery.

SERVICE CRAFT *(continued)*

♦ 1 Pikkala-class personnel transport [YFL]
Bldr: Crichton-Vulkan SY, Turku (In serv. 1946)

96 Pikkala (ex-*Delta,* ex-*Fenno*)

Pikkala (96) Hartmut Ehlers, 9-96

D: 66 tons (fl) **S:** 10 kts **Dim:** 23.0 × 4.4 × 2.0
Electronics: Radar: 1 Raytheon 1900 Pathfinder nav.
M: 1 Valmet diesel; 1 prop; 180 bhp **Crew:** 5 tot.

Remarks: Built as a commercial interisland personnel ferry. Acquired for the navy 28-10-67 and given her current name. Refitted in 1977 and again in 1988. Initially used for training but now employed as a personnel transport and public affairs craft for both the Ministry of Defense and the navy. Oldest unit in the Finnish Navy.

♦ 1 fuel and water lighter [YO]
PA 3 (In serv. 1979)

D: 540 tons (fl) **S:** 2 kts (normally towed) **Dim:** . . . × . . . × . . .

♦ 1 cable tender [YRC]
Bldr: Rauma-Repola, Rauma (L: 15-12-65)

92 Putsaari

D: 430 tons (fl) **S:** 10 kts **Dim:** 45.5 × 8.9 × 2.3
M: 1 Wärtsilä diesel; 1 prop; 450 bhp—bow-thruster **Crew:** 20 tot.

Remarks: Refitted in 1987 by Wärtsilä. Has two 10-ton cable winches and bow cable-laying sheaves. Capable of operating in light ice.

♦ 2 harbor tugs [YTM] Bldr: Teijon Telakka (In serv. 12-85)
731 Haukipää 831 Kallanpää

Kallanpää (831) H&L Van Ginderen, 9-93

D: 38 grt **S:** 9 kts **Dim:** 14.0 × 5.0 × 2.3
M: 2 diesels; 2 vertical cycloidal props; 360 bhp **Crew:** 2 tot.

♦ 1 Tiira-class training launch [YXT]
Bldr: Valmet-Laivateollisuus, Turku

	Laid down	L	In serv.
56 Kajava	25-11-85	25-3-86	28-8-86

Kihu—while still in Finnish service H&L Van Ginderen, 1990

D: 65 tons (fl) **S:** 25+ kts **Dim:** 26.80 (24.20 pp) × 5.50 × 1.40 (1.85 props)
A: provision for 1 or 2 twin 23-mm 60-cal. Sako AA
Electronics: Radar: 1 . . . nav.—Sonar: Simrad SS 242 hull-mounted
M: 2 MTU 8V396 TB82 diesels; 2 props; 2,286 bhp
Electric: 62 kVA tot. **Fuel:** 8 tons **Crew:** 2 officers, 6 enlisted

Remarks: Transferred in 1999 from the Frontier Guard. Development of the *Lokki* design, with hard-chine vice round-bilged hullform. Aluminum construction. Sister *Kihu* was donated to Lithuania late in 1997, and *Tiira* had been discarded by 2000.

♦ 1 Lokki-class training launch [YXT]
Bldr: Valmet-Laivateollisuus, Turku (In serv. 27-11-81)

57 Lokki

D: 53 tons (60 fl) **S:** 25 kts **Dim:** 26.80 × 5.20 × 1.40 (1.85 props)
A: provision for 1 twin 23-mm 60-cal. Sako AA
Electronics: Radar: 1 . . . nav.
M: MTU 8V396 TB83 diesels; 2 props; 2,040 bhp
Electric: 62 kVA tot. **Crew:** 2 officers, 6 enlisted

Remarks: Transferred in 1999 from the Frontier Guard. Aluminum construction. Ordered 17-5-80.

♦ 1 training craft, former patrol craft prototype [YXT]
Bldr: Fiskar's Turan, Veneveistamo SY/Laivateollisuus

30 Hurja

D: 54 tons (60 fl) **S:** 42 kts **Dim:** 21.7 × 5.0 × 2.0
A: removed **Electronics:** Radar: 1 . . . nav.
M: 3 diesels; waterjets; 3,800 bhp **Crew:** 10 tot.

Remarks: Glass-reinforced plastic prototype hull delivered 1-7-80 to Laivateollisuus for fitting out. The gunmount was aft. This class was intended to replace at least seven of the *Nuoli* class during the 1980s, but no further orders materialized and *Hurja* is now employed in naval reserve training.

Note: Used at the naval academy for basic training are launches 681, 683, and 685; no data available.

MINISTRY OF THE INTERIOR FRONTIER GUARD

Personnel (2002): Approx. 650 total

Note: All ships now have dark green hulls with a red-white-red diagonal stripe. Upperworks are gray.

Aviation: Fixed-wing aircraft include 2 Dornier Do-228-212 maritime patrol aircraft with GEC-Marconi Seaspray 2000 maritime surveillance radars. Helicopters include 4 Agusta-Bell AB-412EP Griffin maritime surveillance helicopters, 3 Aérospatiale AS.332L1 Super Pumas with French dipping sonars for ASW work, and 4 Agusta-Bell AB-206B JetRanger utility helicopters.

PATROL SHIPS [WPS]

♦ 1 Merikarhu class
Bldr: Finnyards, Rauma (In serv. 28-10-94)

Merikarhu

Merikarhu H&L Van Ginderen, 8-00

D: 1,100 tons (fl) **S:** 15+ kts **Dim:** 57.80 (52.12 pp) × 11.00 × 4.60
A: provision for 1 twin 23-mm 60-cal. Sako AA
Electronics: Radar: 1 Decca . . . nav.; 1 Selesmar . . . surf. search
M: 2 Wärtsilä 8R22/26 diesels; 1 CP prop; 3,640 bhp
Electric: 1,050 kVA (shaft generator, plus 2 × 270-kw diesel sets) **Crew:** 30 tot.

Remarks: Ordered late spring 1993 as an offshore patrol and environmental cleanup vessel. An improved version of the *Tursas* class. Has 30-ton bollard-pull towing capacity.

PATROL COMBATANTS [WPG]

♦ 2 Tursas class
Bldr: Rauma-Repola Oy, Uusikaupunki

	Laid down	L	In serv.
Tursas	4-9-85	31-1-86	6-6-86
Uisko	4-4-86	19-6-86	27-1-87

D: 750 tons (fl) **S:** 15.5 kts **Dim:** 49.00 (43.80 pp) × 10.40 × 4.00
A: 1 twin 23-mm 60-cal. Sako AA
Electronics: Radar: 2 . . . nav.—Sonar: Simrad SS 105 (14 kHz)
M: 2 Wärtsilä-Vasa 8-R22 diesels; 2 props; 3,200 bhp
Electric: 1,070 kw (1 × 750 kw, 2 × 160 kw) **Fuel:** 73 tons **Crew:** 32 tot.

FRONTIER GUARD PATROL COMBATANTS [WPG] *(continued)*

Tursas 5-94

Remarks: First unit ordered 12-12-84, second 20-3-86. Ice-strengthened hulls; equipped for towing and salvage duties. A sister was ordered for Sweden in 1989.

♦ 1 improved Valpas class

Bldr: Laivateollisuus Oy, Turku (In serv. 15-12-77)

TURVA

Turva H&L Van Ginderen, 1993

D: 550 tons (fl) **S:** 16 kts **Dim:** 48.5 × 8.6 × 3.9
A: provision for 1 twin 23-mm 60-cal. Sako AA
Electronics: Radar: 2 . . . nav.—Sonar: Simrad SS 105 (14 kHz)
M: 2 Wärtsilä diesels; 1 prop; 2,000 bhp **Crew:** 22 tot.

Remarks: Ordered 24-6-75. An improved *Valpas,* similar in appearance.

♦ 1 Valpas class

Bldr: Laivateollisuus Oy, Turku

	Laid down	L	In serv.
VALPAS	20-5-70	22-12-70	21-7-71

D: 545 tons **S:** 15 kts **Dim:** 48.3 × 8.7 × 4.0
A: provision for 1 twin 23-mm 60-cal. Sako AA
Electronics: Radar: 2 . . . nav.—Sonar: Simrad SS 105 (14 kHz)
M: 1 Werkspoor TMABS-398 diesel; 1 CP prop; 2,000 bhp **Crew:** 22 tot.

Remarks: Ice-strengthened and equipped for towing, firefighting, and salvage duties.

PATROL CRAFT [WPC]

♦ 1 (+ 2) Telkkä class

Bldr: Workboat Työvene, Uusikaupunki

	In serv.		In serv.
TELKKÄ	7-99	. . . . . .	2004
. . . . . .	2002		

D: 400 tons (fl) **S:** 22 (*Telkkä:* 20.5) kts **Dim:** 49.20 × 7.50 × 3.70 (max.)
A: 1 twin 23-mm 60-cal. Sako AA **Electronics:** Radar: . . .
M: *Telkkä:* 2 Cummins-Wärtsilä 16V170 diesels; 2 CP props; 5,580 bhp (sust.)—others: 2 12V200 diesels; 2 CP props; 6,700 bhp
Electric: 375 kVA tot. (2 × 170-kVA, 1 × 35-kVA Valmet diesel sets)
Fuel: 55,000 liters **Crew:** 8 tot. + 12 passengers

Remarks: Second and third units ordered 8-12-00.
Hull systems: Steel hull with aluminum superstructure. Has an integrated navigation and environmental monitoring system, digital chart system, autopilot, dynamic positioning system, two gyrocompasses, echo sounder, radio D/F, GPS receiver, and infrared surveillance camera. Oilspill recovery equipment includes deployable spill-containment booms and a 50-m^3-capacity rubber storage barge. A firefighting monitor with a range of 100 m is fitted, and a rigid inflatable rescue boat is stowed on a launch-and-recover ramp at the stern.

♦ 2 Kiisla class

Bldr: Hollming Oy, Rauma

	Laid down	L	In serv.
KIISLA	12-2-86	18-9-86	25-5-87
KURKI	3-8-89	. . .	11-90

Kiisla French Navy, 6-97

D: 250 tons (270 fl) **S:** 25 kts **Dim:** 48.30 (41.80 pp) × 8.80 × 2.20
A: 1 twin 23-mm 60-cal. Sako AA
Electronics:
Radar: 2 . . . nav. —Sonar: Simrad SS 304 hull-mounted and VDS
M: 2 MTU 16V538 TB93 diesels; 2 KaMeWa 90S62 waterjets; 4,500 bhp
Electric: 264 kw tot. **Fuel:** 53 tons **Crew:** 22 tot.

Remarks: *Kiisla* ordered 21-11-84; three more ordered 22-11-88, of which two were later canceled. Aluminum construction. Can also act as minesweepers, minelayers, or ASW escorts; in the ASW mode, can carry two 5-round Soviet RBU-1200 RL. Equipped for fire fighting and carry a 5.7-m rigid inflatable inspection boat. Have Rademac 2100 E/C electro-optical surveillance device atop pilothouse.

PATROL BOATS [WPB]

♦ 2 (+ . . .) 10.5-meter rigid inflatable rescue boats

Bldr: Delta Power Services, . . . , U.K. (In serv. 12-00)

D: 4.6 tons (fl) **S:** 50+ kts **Dim:** 10.5 × . . . × . . .
Electronics: 1 . . . nav.
M: 2 Yamaha gasoline outboards; 500 bhp **Crew:** 3 tot.

Remarks: Ordered 6-00. Have GRP foam-sandwich hulls with 600-mm-dia. rigid inflatable collar. Have color radar and electronic charts. Intended for patrol, rescue, and smuggler interception. Delta is said to have earlier delivered other, smaller search-and-rescue RIBs.

♦ 2 (+ . . .) RIB C-3500 class rigid inflatable rescue boats

Bldr: Boomeranger Boats Oy, Loviisa

D: 4.5 tons (fl) **S:** 50 kts (47 sust.) **Dim:** 10.2 × 3.5 × . . .
Electronics: Radar: 1 . . . nav.
M: 2 Mariner gasoline outboards; 500 bhp **Crew:** 3 tot. + 2 passengers

Remarks: First unit delivered 5-96, second early in 1998. Aluminum structure with inflatable rubber buoyancy collar. Have an enclosed pilothouse.

♦ 10 (+ 15–20) RV-90 class

Bldr: Uudenkaupungin Telakka, Uusikaupunki (In serv. 3-92 to 1996)

RV-150 RAJU	RV-154 . . .	RV-157 . . .	RV-160 . . .
RV-151 . . .	RV-155 . . .	RV-158 . . .	
RV-152 . . .	RV-156 . . .	RV-159 . . .	

D: 23.7 tons (25 fl) **S:** 12 kts **Dim:** 15.00 (12.83 pp) × 4.00 × 1.80
Electronics: Radar: 1 . . . nav. **M:** 1 Caterpillar 3408 diesel; 1 prop; 476 bhp

Remarks: Second two on option for delivery fall 1993, and 10 were hoped to be in service by 1996. Icebreaking tug-type hulls. As many as 25–30 may ultimately be built to replace the older RV-series patrol launches.

♦ 7 RV-37 class

Bldr: Hollming Oy, Rauma (In serv. 1978–85)

RV-37 RV-38 RV-39 RV-40 RV-41 RV-142 RV-243

D: 20 tons (fl) **S:** 12 kts **Dim:** 14.3 × 3.6 × 1.6
Electronics: Radar: 1 . . . nav. **M:** 1 Mercedes-Benz diesel; 300 bhp

♦ 14 PV-11-class patrol launches

Bldr: Fiskar's Turun, Turku (In serv. 9-84)

PV-11, -12, -104, -108, -205, -209, -210, -212, -306, -307 + 4 others

D: 10 tons **S:** 29 kts **Dim:** 10.0 × . . . × . . .
M: 2 Volvo Penta diesels; 2 waterjets; . . . bhp **Crew:** 2 tot.

Note: Also in use for patrol and search-and-rescue duties by the Frontier Guard are 27 older patrol craft: 9 RV-9 series (built 1959–60) of 12 tons, 11 RV-10 series (1961–63) of 18 tons, and 7 RV-30 series (1973–74) of 19 tons. All can make 10 kts.

♦ 5 rigid inflatable boats

Bldr: Avon Boats, U.K. (In serv. 1993)

D: . . . **S:** 50 kts **Dim:** 8.4 × . . . × . . .
M: 2 outboard engines; 450 bhp **Crew:** 4 tot.

Remarks: Ordered 3-93 for use in search-and-rescue duties and as antismuggling inspection boats.

FRONTIER GUARD *(continued)*

AIR-CUSHION PATROL CRAFT [WPBA]

♦ 6 2000-TDX(M)-class air-cushion vehicles

Bldr: Griffon Hovercraft, Salisbury Green, Southampton, U.K. (In serv. 1-12-94 to 1999)

D: 6.8 tons (fl) **S:** 50 kts (33 loaded) **Dim:** 11.0 × 4.60 × . . .
A: provision for 1 7.62-mm mg **Electronics:** Radar: 1 . . . nav.
M: 1 Deutz BF8L513 diesel; 1 shrouded CP airscrew; 320 bhp
Range: 300/25 (loaded) **Crew:** 2 tot. + 16 troops

Remarks: Can carry 2,200 kg of cargo in lieu of troops. First two delivered 1-12-94, third on 27-5-95. Three more were ordered in early 1998. GRP construction hull.

♦ 1 SAH-2200-class air-cushion vehicle

Bldr: Slingsby Amphibious Hovercraft Co., U.K. (In serv. 9-92)

D: 5.5 tons (fl) **S:** 50 kts **Dim:** 10.60 × 4.20 × . . .
A: provision for 1 7.62-mm mg **Electronics:** Radar: 1 Raytheon R41 nav.
M: 1 Cummins 6CTA-8.3M1 diesel; 1 shrouded CP airscrew; 300 bhp
Range: 500/50 **Fuel:** 510 liters **Crew:** 2 tot. + 12 troops

Remarks: Can carry 1,200 kg of cargo in lieu of troops.

Note: The icebreakers and other ships and craft operated by the Board of Navigation *(Merenkulkuhallitus),* the cable ship operated by the Central Board of Post and Telegraphy *(Suomen Posti-ja Lennatinhallitus & Post-och Telegrafstyrelsen),* and the survey ships operated by the Ministry of Trade and Industry are described and illustrated in the 1998–99 and earlier editions.

FRANCE

French Republic

Personnel (1-1-02): 44,743 total, including 4,948 officers, 30,111 career petty officers, 7,909 enlisted ratings, and 1,775 volunteers; 10,569 civilians were also employed. The government-owned DCN *(Direction de la Construction Navale)* employs around 12,500 civil servants and was given permission to begin privatization 6-7-01.

Organization and Bases: Fleet command is concentrated at the Interforces Operations Center in Paris. The First Maritime Region is headquartered at Brest and the Second at Toulon. The Naval Action Force *(Force d'Action Navale),* based at Toulon, includes the aircraft carrier, four amphibious warfare ships, three logistics support ships, and nine destroyers and frigates, including *Cassard* and *Jean Bart.* Based at Brest are the Force Oceanique Stratégique, with the ballistic missile and attack submarines, and the Anti-Submarine Action Group, with destroyers, A-69-class corvettes, and two logistics support ships. Also based at Brest is the Mine Warfare Force, although five minehunters are normally based at Toulon. Small naval bases are located overseas at Fort-de-France, Martinique; Degrad des Cannes, French Guiana; St.-Denis, La Réunion; Nouméa, New Caledonia; and Papeete, Tahiti. Major naval shipyards are located at Brest (major warships), Toulon (major warships), and Cherbourg (submarines and patrol craft). Aviation facilities are listed in the Naval Aviation section.

Naval Aviation: Details may be found in the aviation section following the aircraft carrier entries. Principal aircraft totals as of 1-02 were to include (frontline units in parentheses): 50 (29) Super Étendard and 10 (10) Rafale-M fighters; 2 (2) E-2C Hawkeye surveillance aircraft; 25 (18) Atlantique Mk 2, 5 (4) Gardian, and 4 (4) Falcon 50 maritime patrol aircraft; and 8 (7) Super Frelon, 32 (16) WG-13 Lynx, and 15 (15) Panther helicopters. Of 86 training and logistic support fixed-wing aircraft and helicopters, 70 were to be in active service.

Gendarmarie: The French Navy provides patrol boats to the maritime forces of the Gendarmarie Maritime, with about 1,200 total personnel. The Gendarmarie Maritime is subordinate directly to the Ministry of Defense and is headquartered at Paris. Its personnel wear standard French Navy uniforms. Within France, its craft and personnel are organized into four groups, based at Toulon, Rochefort, Lorient, Brest, and Cherbourg. Overseas afloat forces are assigned at Pointe-à-Pitre, Guadaloupe; Dakar, Senegal; Cayenne, French Guiana; Papeete, Tahiti; Djibouti; Port des Galets, La Réunion; and Nouméa, New Caledonia. The assigned craft and their port subordination are listed in the naval section.

The Gendarmarie Nationale is a separate organization with about 2,700 officers and 77,000 noncommissioned officers, as well as some 1,300 civilian employees. The organization has several hundred river and seagoing craft, plus 29 Écureuil and 11 Alouette-III helicopters.

Special Forces: Maritime troop assets comprise the French Army's Grupement des Fusiliers-Marins Commandos, with 3,500 personnel, and an amphibious combat swimmer company from the French Foreign Legion.

WEAPONS AND SYSTEMS

Note: France's major military electronics firm, Thomson-CSF, changed its corporate name to Thales on 18-12-00. The missile design, development, and manufacturing efforts of France's Aérospatiale Matra and the U.K.'s BAE Systems (including its subsidiary Alenia Marconi Systems) were combined early in 3-01 as MBDA, which stands for Matra BAE Dynamics, Alenia Marconi Systems, and Aérospatiale Matra.

A. MISSILES

♦ Strategic ballistic missiles

M 4: Employed on the two remaining *Le Redoutable*–class SSBNs. Entered service in 1985 aboard *L'Inflexible.* Made by Aérospatiale Matra. Characteristics include:

Total height: 11.05 m **Diameter:** 1.93m
Launch weight: 36 tons (first stage: 20 tons; second stage: 8 tons; third stage: 1.5 tons)
Payload: 6 × 150-kt warheads **Launch:** powder charge
Thrust: First stage: 70 tons; second stage: 30 tons; third stage: 7 tons
Duration of thrust: first stage: 65 sec; second stage: 75 sec; third stage: 45 sec
Max. range: 4,000 (M 4B: 5,000) km

The six TN-70 warheads spread over a 150 × 350-km area at a range of 4,000 km.

M 45: Made by Aérospatiale Matra. Weights and dimensions essentially the same as the M 4. Uses the TN-75 reentry vehicle to a range of 5,000 km, although one was officially reported to have traveled 6,000 km on 4-3-86. Operational in late 1996 aboard *Le Triomphant.*

M 51: A new weapon being developed by the EADS Launch Vehicles and G2P (Groupement pour la Propulsion a Pudre [SNECMA and SNPE]) consortium for the "second generation" ballistic-missile submarines and expected to enter service in 2008 aboard *Le Terrible* (S 619). Weighing 55 tons at launch, the M 51 is to have a range of 7,000 km (3,240 n.m.). Originally to have carried 10–12 TN-75 independently targeted warheads (MIRVs), the missile will now carry four, and it will employ the third stage of the M 45 missile. M 51 will be backfitted into earlier units of the *Le Triomphant* class.

♦ Surface-to-air missiles

SAAM *(Système d'Autodéfense Anti-Missile):* The Aérospatiale SAAM was intended to become operational in 2001 aboard the carrier *Charles de Gaulle,* although it will now be delayed. It will be vertically launched from eight-missile Sylver modular cell groups. Guidance will be supported by the Thales Arabel I/J-band missile detection radar, which has a range of 100 km. The SAMP/T version is intended for land-based use. The two-stage Aster-15 missile, which will be highly maneuverable, will have the following characteristics:

Length: 4.20 m **Diameter:** 0.18 m **Wingspan:** 0.36 m
Weight: 298 kg **Warhead:** 15 kg **Maneuverability:** 15 g
Speed: 1,000 m/sec (Mach 2.5) **Range:** 2–20 km

The first 12 operational Aster-15 missiles were ordered during 1995 and 20 more in 1996; under the 1997 budget, 40 were ordered.

A 30-km range version, Aster-30, is also in development in a system known as SAMP/N *(Sol-Air Moyenne Portée/Naval)* to replace the SM-1 MR missile as part of the NATO project FSAF *(Famille de Systèmes Surface-Air Futurs),* which is also known as the LAMS (Local Area Missile System). It was be installed on the *Forbin*-class frigates to enter service around 2006. The development is being shared by France's Aérospatiale (25%) and Thales (25%), and MBDA (50%), with the United Kingdom, Germany, and Spain also involved. The system will incorporate the French Arabel and Astral radars in French service. The following characteristics have been announced:

Length: 4.80 m **Diameter:** 0.18 m **Weight:** 450 kg
Warhead: 15 kg **Speed:** Mach 3.5
Range: 3–70 km **Altitude:** 60–20,000 m

Note: The Masurca area-defense SAM system ceased to be supported in 2000, and only a single launcher remains aboard an active ship, the destroyer *Duquesne* (D 603).

Standard SM-1 MR: A one-stage U.S.-designed and -manufactured solid-fuel missile.

Length: 4.60 m **Diameter:** .41 m **Weight:** 590 kg
Max. range: 50,000 m **Interception altitude:** 60–80,000 ft.
Guidance: semiactive homing, proximity fuze

The complete system, in addition to the missile, consists of a Mk 13 launcher with a vertical stowage-loader containing 40 missiles, various computers, a DRBJ-11B height-finding radar, and two SPG 51C tracking radars. SM-1 MR is carried only by the two C 70 AAW-type destroyers.

Crotale/Crotale EDIR: A French Air Force missile adapted for naval use. Electronics are by Thales and the missile by Matra. Characteristics for the R440N missile are:

Length: 2.930 m **Diameter:** 0.156 m **Wingspan:** 0.54 m with fins extended
Weight: 85.1 kg **Warhead:** 14 kg **Launcher:** octuple
Speed: Mach 2.4 **Range:** 13,000 m **Interception altitude:** 150–12,000 ft.
Guidance: beam-riding; detonation by infrared fuze incorporated in the missile

Installed on the F 67 and C 70 destroyer classes, four Saudi Arabian frigates, and two Chinese combatants (China has copied the system, with the pirated version known as HQ-61). In French ships, it is used with DRBV-51C radar and has a Thales Ku-band tracking radar.

Crotale has been updated to enable it to handle Mach 2.0 targets at altitudes down to 4 m. The missiles, named Crotale EDIR *(Écartometrie Différentielle Infra-Rouge),* were equipped with a new proximity fuze, and an infrared tracker was added to the launcher/director; their range was increased from 8,000 m to 13,000 m.

Crotale Modulaire: A lightweight system, Crotale Modulaire employs an octuple launcher and any of a number of control systems. It has been purchased by Oman and the United Arab Emirates.

Crotale NG: A further improvement of the basic Crotale missile, Crotale NG ("New Generation") uses a VT-1 hypervelocity (Mach 3.5) missile and is carried by *La Fayette*–class frigates. The VT-1 missile has a 14-kg warhead and employs computer-controlled command guidance, using simultaneous inputs from the shipboard system's J-band radar, t.v., and infrared trackers. Under the 1997 budget, 33 were ordered, and the last of 55 ordered in the late 1980s were delivered during 1997. One source indicates that only about 200 have been manufactured, using U.S. Vought-made components dating from around 1990–92.

Thales teamed with the Russian Fakel design bureau to develop a vertical-launch version of the VT-1 missile, using a cold-launch gas generator ejection system; it was to be available for production by 2001–02, but the program seems to have halted.

VL Mica: System announced 2-00 for introduction around 2003, if funded (which has not yet happened). A modification of the current air-to-air Mica, to have an altitude of 10 km and range of 10–12 km, with 8-cell launch vertical launch groups firing at as little as 2-second intervals. Guidance would be by infrared and active radar seek-

WEAPONS AND SYSTEMS *(continued)*

ers, using thrust-vector control. Also offered for land use. Manufacturer: Matra-BAE Dynamics.

SADRAL *(Système d'Autodéfense Rapprochée Anti-aérienne Léger):* A point-defense, 6-round, short-range system employing the Mistral IR-homing missile with laser-backup proximity and impact fuzing. Manufacturer: Matra. Characteristics for the missile itself are:

Length: 1.80 m **Diameter:** 0.90 m **Weight:** 24 kg
Warhead: 3 kg (1,500 tungsten balls) **Speed:** Mach 2.5
Range: less than 500 to around 6,000 m **Min. altitude:** 3 m

SIMBAD *(Système Intégré de Mistral Bimunition pour l'Autodéfense):* A lightweight, twin launcher system for Mistral. In the French Navy, it is aboard the destroyers *Primauguet, La Motte-Picquet,* and *Latouche-Tréville;* the *Floréal*-class patrol ships; dock landing ships; and the *Durance*-class replenishment vessels.

♦ Surface-to-surface missiles

Note: The ANF *(Anti-Navir Futur)* antiship missile program was terminated 23-12-99 when it was realized that the projected unit cost would preclude significant foreign orders.

SCALP Naval: A surface ship– and submarine-launched variant of SCALP-EG proposed for use as a strategic weapon on the Barracuda-class SSN and the new *Frégates d'Action Navale* class (from which it would be vertically launched from the Sylver VLS system). The missile is propelled by a MicroturboTR160-30 turbojet and employs a combination of inertial guidance, GPS, and terrain reference for navigation, with an autonomous target recognition system using a BAE Systems/Detexis infrared sensor.

Length: . . . **Diameter:** . . . **Wingspan:** . . .
Weight: 1,300 kg **Warhead weight:** . . .
Speed: Mach 0.9 **Range:** more than 600 km

SCALP-EG *(Système de Crioisière Conventionnel Autonome à Longue Protée Précis–Emploi Général Purpose):* Manufacturer: Matra-BAE Dynamics. Some 500 of these 300-km-range missiles were ordered 1-98 for the French Air Force and Navy for $745 million, with delivery to begin in 2003. The weapon is a variant of the Storm Shadow ASM produced by the same company for the U.K. and uses a video datalink to assist in targeting.

MM 15: A surface-launched variant of the AS 15 air-launched missile, which see for details. Not used by the French Navy. Manufacturer: Aérospatiale.

MM 40 Exocet: An improved version of the MM 38 and the AM 39, the Aérospatiale MM 40 is an over-the-horizon missile whose range is adapted to radar performance and which is able to use fire-control data relayed by an outside source. It employs a cylindrical GRP launcher, which, because it is lighter and has fewer fittings than the rectangular metal launcher used by the MM 38, potentially increases firepower by allowing more missiles to be carried. To employ the range of the missile fully, over-the-horizon targeting must be provided by helicopters or aircraft. The missile is initially under inertial guidance, switching to radar terminal homing at a preset distance from the target (usually 12–15 km), and the seeker incorporates a number of electronic counter-countermeasures features. It can cruise at preset altitudes between 3 and 15 m. The current Exocet Block 2 features evasive maneuvering, an improved seeker, electronic counter-countermeasures (ECCM), and improved sea-skimming capability.
MM 40 is employed by a number of countries worldwide. Qatar purchased one battery of a land-launched version, as has Saudi Arabia. France plans to acquire only 30 new missiles between 2001 and 2011.

Length: 5.80 m **Diameter:** 0.35 m **Wingspan:** 1.135 m
Weight: 850 (Block 2: 855) kg **Warhead weight:** 165 kg
Speed: Mach 1.0 **Range:** 65 km

SM 39 Exocet: A submarine torpedo-tube-launched version of the Exocet concept, SM 39 began in 1981 aboard the *Narval*-class submarine *Requin.* With its solid-fueled launch/ejection capsule, the missile fits within a 533-mm torpedo tube. After broaching the surface, the missile rises to 50 m and then descends to cruising altitude. The system became operational in 1985. The only export order has come from Pakistan. Manufacturer: Aérospatiale.

Length: 4.69 m (5.80 in capsule) **Diameter:** 0.35 m **Wingspan:** 1.135 m
Weight: 652 kg (1,350 with capsule) **Warhead weight:** 165 kg
Speed: Mach 1.0 **Range:** 50 km

MM 38 Exocet: A fire-and-forget homing missile with solid-fuel propulsion. Manufacturer: Aérospatiale. The fire-control solution requires a fix on the target provided by the surface radar of the firing ship and uses the necessary equipment for launching the missile and determining the correct range and height bearing of the target. A total of 1,260 was built for 19 navies, some of which have retired the system. Remaining stocks are reaching the end of their shelf lives, and only nine nations (Greece, Indonesia, Malaysia, Morocco, Nigeria, Thailand, Argentina, Ecuador, and Peru) have ordered replacement propellant sections, which should keep the missile in use until 2011–21. The French Navy plans to refuel and upgrade about 50 MM 38s.
The missile is launched at a slight elevation (about 15°). After the boost phase, it reaches its flight altitude of between 3 and 15 m, maintained by a radar altimeter. During the first part of the flight, the missile is automatically guided by an inertial system that has received the azimuth of the target. When within about 12–15 km of the target, an automatic homing radar begins to seek the target and, when it picks it up, directs the missile. Great effort has been made to protect the missile from countermeasures during this phase. A "Super ADAC" seeker, with improved antijamming features, is offered for backfit to earlier missiles. Detonation takes place upon impact or by pseudo-proximity (time-to-target estimation) fuze, based on interception conditions, size of the target ship, and the condition of the sea.

Length: 5.20 m **Diameter:** 0.35 m **Wingspan:** 1.00 m
Weight: 735 kg **Warhead weight:** 165 kg
Speed: Mach 1.0 **Range:** 42 km

Note: The development of the Polyphem fiber-optically guided missile is now under the aegis of EADS-LFK, and that missile is now described in the German section.

♦ Air-to-ground missiles

ASMP-A *(Air-Surface à Moyenne Portée-Ameliore):* A development contract was issued to EADS-Aérospatiale-Matra in 10-00, with deployment to take place in 2007 to replace the current ASMP; a production engineering contract was issued on 4-1-01. The ASMP-A will have a range of up to 500 km.

ASMP *(Air-Surface à Moyenne Portée):* ASMP has a 300-kT nuclear warhead, uses inertial guidance, has a radar altimeter, and is very resistant to countermeasures. Range is dependent on the altitude and speed of the launch aircraft. ASMP can achieve Mach 3.0 at launch at high altitudes. It became operational 1-5-86 on the French Air Force Mirage IV and during 7-88 on the Mirage 2000N and entered service in 1990–91 on Super Étendard fighter-bombers. Manufacturer: Aérospatiale.

Length: 5.38 m **Diameter:** 0.35 m **Wingspan:** 0.956 m
Weight: 840 kg **Speed:** Mach 2.4 **Range:** 100–300 km

AM 39 Exocet: The air-to-sea version of the MM 38, operational since 1978 and currently employed by Atlantique Mk 2 and Super Étendard aircraft. After being launched, it has the same flight characteristics as the MM 38. Range is dependent on the altitude and speed of the launch aircraft. Manufacturer: Aérospatiale.

Length: 4.633 m **Diameter:** 0.348 m **Wingspan:** 1.004 m
Weight: 670 kg **Warhead weight:** 165 kg
Speed: Mach 1.0 **Range:** 50–70 km

AS 30: Radio command or laser-designated weapon for firing from a maneuvering aircraft at medium, low, or very low altitude. Used by the Super Étendard. Range is dependent on the speed and altitude of the launch aircraft. The laser-guided version (AS 30L) entered service in 1996 for use on modernized Super Étendard aircraft; it is 3.65 m long and weighs 540 kg. The most recent order was for 20 under the 1997 budget. Manufacturer: Aérospatiale.

Length: 3.785 m **Diameter:** 0.342 m **Wingspan:** 1.000 m
Weight: 528 kg **Range:** 1,500 m min.; 9,000–12,000 m max.

AS 20: Training missile for the AS 30. Radio command guidance. Range is dependent on the launch aircraft's speed and altitude. Manufacturer: Aérospatiale.

Length: 2.60 m **Diameter:** 0.25 m **Wingspan:** 0.80 m
Weight: 140 kg **Range:** 4,000–8,000 m

AS 15TT: For use by light helicopters; developed under the Saudi Arabian Sawari program. Uses the Thales Agrion radar for target determination and tracking. Export weapon only; not employed by the French Navy. Manufacturer: Aérospatiale. First production deliveries in 3-85. Trials were held during 1992 with a small combatant–launched version, the MM 15T, but no sales resulted.

Length: 2.16 m **Weight:** 96 kg **Warhead weight:** 30 kg
Speed: 280 m/sec **Range:** 15+ km

AS 12: A wire-guided system with optical aim. Used by WG-13 Lynx helicopters and exported to several countries. Manufacturer: Aérospatiale.

Length: 1.870 m **Diameter:** 0.210 m **Wingspan:** 0.650 m
Weight: 75 kg **Range:** 1,500 m min.; 7,500–8,000 m max.

♦ Air-to-air missiles

R 550 Magic: Manufacturer: Matra. The Magic 2 version is now in service for Super Étendard fighters:

Length: 2.75 m **Diameter:** 0.157 m **Wingspan:** 0.660 m
Weight: 89 kg **Warhead weight:** 11.5 kg
Range: 300–8,000 m **Guidance:** infrared-homing

Mica: An active-radar or infrared-homing missile being developed as the successor to Magic for use on the Rafale-M fighter. Manufacturer: Matra. MICA = *Missile d'Interception, de Combat, et d'Autodéfense.* The program is a fusion of Matra's in-house effort and the Italian Selenia Aspide Mk 2. Uses command-inertial guidance with active terminal homing.

Length: 3.10 m **Diameter:** 0.16 m **Weight:** 100 kg
Warhead weight: 12 kg **Speed:** Mach 4 **Range:** 50–60 km

Sidewinder: Manufacturer: Ford Instrument, later Raytheon (see U.S.A. section).

B. GUNS

100-mm Compact: Single-barrel automatic, for export only. Manufacturer: USINOR/Creusot-Loire. Weighing 13.5 tons, it carries 12 rounds ready to fire on the mount and 12 in an auxiliary ready magazine. Standard installations have a 42-round magazine, while those for Malaysia had 90-round magazines. Firing rates of 20, 45, or 90 rds/min can be selected. Maximum surface range is 15 km, while practical range against air targets is 6 km. Proximity-fuzed, prefragmented; high explosive; and illuminant rounds are available. Also used by Saudi Arabia and China.

Length of barrel: 55 calibers **Mount weight:** 17.3 tons
Muzzle velocity: 870 m/sec **Rate of fire:** 20, 45, or 90 rds/min, or single fire
Arc of elevation: −15° to +80°
Max. training speed: 50°/sec **Max. elevation speed:** 33°/sec
Range: 17,200 m **Max. effective range for surface fire:** 12,000 m
Max. effective range for antiaircraft fire: 6,000 m

100-mm Models 1953, 1964, and 1968: Single-barrel automatic guns for use against aircraft, surface vessels, or land targets. Model 1968 is a lighter version of Model 1953; Model 1964 is virtually identical to Model 1953. The ammunition is the same for all three. Models 1953 and 1964 require two operators on-mount, while Model 1968 can operate in full automatic.
Model 1953 and Model 1964 use an analog fire-control system with electromechanical and electronic equipment for the fire-control solution. The director can be operated in optical and radar modes. Used in *Jeanne d'Arc* and the *Suffren* class.
Model 1968 used a digital fire-control system, with central units and memory disks or magnetic tape for data storage. Light radar gun director; optical direction equipment can be added. Used in the *Tourville* class. The first four units of the *Georges Leygues* class and the A 69–class frigates employ a hybrid system of digital and analog computers. In *Primauguet* and later *Georges Leygues*–class frigates, the *Cassard*

WEAPONS AND SYSTEMS *(continued)*

class, and the *Suffren* class, control is effected by multiple sensors. Characteristics of Model 1968:

Length of barrel: 55 calibers **Mount weight:** 22 tons
Max. rate of fire: 78 rds/min **Arc of elevation:** −15° to +80°
Max. training speed: 40°/sec **Max. elevation speed:** 25°/sec
Range: 17,000 m at 40° elevation
Max. effective range for surface fire: 15,000 m
Max. effective range for antiaircraft fire: 8,000 m

Under the CADAM *(CADence de tir AMéliorée)* program, the rate of fire of all three versions was increased from the original 60 rds/min to 78 rds/min. A variant with a new 42-round ready-service stowage rack will permit firing 62 rounds before reloading is required from the magazine below.

40-mm L/60: French-made, Bofors-designed general-purpose weapon used aboard the patrol ship *Albatros,* P 400–class gunboats, and a few amphibious warfare and auxiliary classes in single mountings.

Length of barrel: 60 calibers **Weight:** 2 tons **Muzzle velocity:** 853 m/sec
Rate of fire: 130 rds/min **Range:** 3,600 m max. practical

30-mm OTOBreda-Mauser Model F "Single 30": Selected in 1994 as the light weapon for future surface combatants—the *Artillerie Nouvelle de Petit Calibre.* Uses the U.S. Bushmaster-II gun with GAU-8-type ammunition including TP, HEI, HEI-SD, API, and APDS projectiles. The muzzle velocity is 1,000 m/sec, and the firing rate 800 rds/min. Are controlled either by the VIGY optronic system, manned remote directors located nearby, or, in an emergency, by a single operator on-mount.

20-mm CN MIT-20F2: A general-purpose weapon on a DCN-designed mounting, used aboard P 400–class gunboats, mine countermeasures ships, and a number of amphibious warfare classes. Generally known as the "F2." Manufacturer: GIAT. Has two 300-round ready-service magazines attached.

Length: 2.60 m overall **Weight:** 322 kg empty **Muzzle velocity:** . . .
Rate of fire: 650–720 rds/min **Arc of elevation:** −15° to +65°

20-mm 70-cal. Oerlikon: Employs 60-round ammunition canisters. Being phased out.

Length: 2.20 m overall **Weight:** 480 kg empty **Muzzle velocity:** . . .
Rate of fire: 450 rds/min **Arc of elevation:** −15° to +90°

C. TORPEDOES

	Use*	Length (m)	Weight (kg)	Diameter (mm)	Range (km)	Speed (kts)	Depth (m)
F 17 Mod. 1	B	—	1,300	533	—	35	—
F 17 Mod. 2	B	5.38	1,300	533	18	40	600
F 21	B	. . .	533	50	50	. . .	. . .
L 4	C	3.03	525	533	6	300	
L 5 Mod. 1	B	—	1,000	533	—	35	—
L 5 Mod. 3	B	—	1,300	533	7.7	35	—
L 5 Mod. 4	A	4.40	935	533	7.0	35	500
Mk 46	C	2.59	232	323.7	11	—	—
MU-90	B, C	2.96	285	323.7	10	29–50	1,000

*A = for surface-ship use, B = for submarine use, C = for aircraft use

Note: The French Thomson-Marconi Murène and Italian Whitehead Alenia Systemi Subacquei (WASS) A-290 torpedo programs were combined into one effort in 1991 as the MU-90 Impact under a consortium called Eurotorp. Some 300 are expected to be produced for the French Navy and another 300 for Italy, and the weapon was to have entered service around 2000. The first 50 operational weapons were ordered under the FY 97 budget. MU-90 is usable in waters as little as 25 m deep. MU-90 uses a 50-kg warhead, travels at either 29 or 50 kts, and can operate between 25-m and 1,000-m depths. It employs a silver oxide–aluminum battery and has a pumpjet propulsor. A hard-kill, antitorpedo version, MU-90HK, is being developed.

The E 15 Mod. 2 export torpedo employs L 3, E 14, and Z 16 torpedoes updated with AH 8 homing heads and silver-zinc batteries and offers 2,000-m detection range, 300-m depth capability, 31-kt speed, and a range of 12 km with a 300-kg warhead. DCN St.-Tropez and STN Atlas Elektronik are offering to develop for export a wake-homing version of the F 17 torpedo.

The F 21 is being developed jointly by DCN and WASS as the BlackShark/IF21 and is being offered for export. The French Navy plans to use it to replace the F 17 heavyweight series. Sea trials are expected in 2003.

D. MINES

FG 18 and FG 29: For use by submarines. Weight: 1,000 kg, with 600 kg explosives.

FG 26: For use by surface ships.

E. RADARS

♦ Navigational radars

DRBN-32: French Navy designator for the Decca 1226 navigational radar.
DRBN-34A: French Navy designator for the Decca 1229-series navigational radars.
Decca 20V90: An ARPA-equipped successor to DRBN-32, with 48 ordered from Decca in 4-99. Used earlier in the *La Fayette* class. DRBN number not yet known. Also known as the BridgeMaster E.

♦ Air-search radars

DRBV-21A: On *Floréal*-class frigates and the *Foudre.* Frequency-agile surveillance radar using the solid-state transmitter of the DRBV-26C and the antenna of the DRBV-22A. Range: more than 100 km. L-band. Thales Mars TRS 3015 is the commercial version.
DRBV-22A: Mounted in A 69–class escorts. L-band.
DRBV-22D: *Jeanne d'Arc* only. L-band.
DRBV-26A: S-band. Mounted in the *Tourville* class and first four of the *Georges Leygues* class. Range: 280 km. Commercial name: Thales Jupiter.
DRBV-26C: An upgraded DRBV-26A with solid-state transmitter. Range: 360 km. Carried by the *Cassard* class.
DRBV-26D: A further development of the DRBV-26 for the *Charles de Gaulle* and future antiaircraft combatants. Thales commercial Jupiter-I using Thales Nederland LW-08 antenna.

♦ Height-finding/three-dimensional radars

DRBI-23: Monopulse radar mounted in the *Duquesne.*
DRBJ-11B: S-band, pulse-coded radar for the *Cassard*-class guided-missile destroyers and the carrier *Charles de Gaulle* (in the D variant). Range: 300 km.
DRBV-27: ASTRAL (Air Surveillance and Targeting Radar, L-band) in development for use with the FAMS missile program. Range: 400 km. Commercial name: Thales TRS 3505.
Herakles: 3-D, E/F (S)-band multifunction set in development by Thales as a primary air and surface surveillance and fire-control system. A navalized version of the Master-A land system. Rotates 360°/sec while performing electronic scanning in elevation and azimuth. Range to 200 km. Capable of tracking 200 targets.

♦ Surface and low-altitude air-search radars

DRBV-15: S-band, pulse-doppler design, with pulse-compression and frequency agility, intended to replace the DRBV-51. In *Primauguet, La Motte-Picquet,* and *Latouche-Tréville.* Range: 110 km.
DRBV-15C: Improved DRBV-15 with stabilized antenna. Range: 100 km against aircraft and 50 km against missiles. Aboard the missile range instrumentation ship *Monge, La Fayette*–class frigates, and the carrier *Charles de Gaulle.* Commercial name: Sea Tiger Mk 2.
DRBV-50: Mounted on *Jeanne d'Arc.*
DRBV-51A: Mounted on A 69–class corvettes.
DRBV-51B: Mounted on the *Tourville* class.
DRBV-51C: Mounted on the initial four of the *Georges Leygues* class.

♦ Fire-control radars

ARABEL *(Antenne Radar à Balayage Électronique):* SDC X-band multifunction radar associated with SAAM. Used on the carrier *Charles de Gaulle* and will be aboard *Forbin*-class destroyers.
DRBC-32A: For the 100-mm guns on the *Jeanne d'Arc.* X-band.
DRBC-32D: Mounted on the *Tourville* class. X-band.
DRBC-32E: Mounted on the first four *Georges Leygues*–class destroyers and the A 69–class corvettes. X-band.
DRBC-33A: Monopulse and frequency agile. On the *Cassard* and *Suffren* classes and the final three *Georges Leygues*–class destroyers.
DRBR-51: Tracking radar for the Masurca on *Duquesne.* C-band (5-cm) tracker, with 7-cm command signal.
SPG-51C: U.S. tracker/illuminator for the Standard system on the *Cassard* class.

F. ELECTRO-OPTICS

DIBC-2A: Optronic director for small-caliber guns. Commercial name is VIGY 105.
DIBV-1A: Vampir infrared detection and surveillance system by Thales used aboard the destroyer *Cassard* and the *Charles de Gaulle.*
DIBV-2A: Lightweight version of DIBV-1A for destroyers.

G. SONARS

♦ Surface ship sonars

	Type	Frequency	Comments
DSBV-61B	Towed	VLF	Passive linear array system
DSBV-62C	Towed	VLF	Passive linear array system
DSBX-1	Towed	LF	SLASM variable-depth set
DUBA-25	Hull	8/9/10 kHz	TSM 2400; see Remarks
DUBM-21B	Hull	100/420 kHz	TSM 2021; on Tripartite minehunters
DUBM-21D	Hull	100/420 kHz	Digital DUBM-21B; on *Sagittaire*
DUBM-40A	Towed	745 kHz	For smallcraft
DUBM-41	Towed	500 kHz	Side-scan minehunting; on *Glycine* class
DUBM-42	Towed	500 kHz	Multibeam DUBM-41 with DUBM-60 forward-looking sonar
DUBM-43A	Handheld	VHF	U.S. Klein side-scan for mine clearance divers
DUBV-23	Bow	4.9–5.4 kHz	See Remarks
DUBV-24	Hull	5 kHz center	Average range: 6,000 m; on *Jeanne d'Arc*
DUBV-24C	Hull	5 kHz center	See Remarks
DUBV-43C	Towed	5 kHz center	See Remarks
DUPM-1	Handheld	50–90 kHz	For divers

Remarks: DUBV-23 and DUBV-43 are used simultaneously and, under normal sound-propagation conditions, achieve ranges of 10,000 m (20,000 under ideal conditions); they are carried on *Tourville* and the three early units of the *Georges Leygues* class. The four later units of the *Georges Leygues* class carry DUBV-43C VDS, which operates at depths of up to 700 m; *Primauguet, La Motte-Picquet,* and *Latouche-Tréville* have a sonar suite comprising the DUBV-43C VDS, the DUBV-24C hull-mounted sonar (in place of DUBV-23) and the DSBV-61 towed array (with a range of over 150 km).

The DUBA-25 is installed on the A 69 escorts and the destroyer *Cassard* (her sister *Jean Bart* has the DUBV-24C). The DSBV-62C towed array, intended for the *Tourville* class and the frigate *Dupleix,* has a 3-km-long towing cable.

The DSBX-1 SLASM *(Système de Lutte Anti-Sous-Marine),* a variable-depth towed active array is aboard the destroyers *Tourville* and *De Grasse;* it employs two 1-kHz transmitters and a receiver array in a 10-ton towed body and can be operated down to 600-m depths. Thales (formerly Thomson-Marconi) is now embarked with BAE Systems in developing a new very-low-frequency active sonar (the ATBF, *Actif Très Basse Fréquence*) and ATAS (Active Towed Array Sonar).

WEAPONS AND SYSTEMS *(continued)*

The DUBM-41B can be towed at 10 kts and covers a 400-m swath, compared to the -kt/50-m capability of the DUBM-41. Thales is offering the Versatile Underwater System (VERSUS) as an upgrade to current DUBM-21 and TSM 2022 minehunting sonar arrays. VERSUS would include a propelled variable-depth sonar with the TSM 2022 transducer and a towed TSM 2054 side-scan sonar, along with new signal-processing capabilities to allow identification of mines to 200-m depths.

♦ Submarine sonars

French listening devices, active-passive sonars, and underwater telephone equipment include:

DMUX-20: Sonar suite designation for the *Améthyste* class.
DSUV-22: Hydrophone array on the *Améthyste* class. Part of the commercial Eledone array from Thales. Also known as Scylla or TSM 2040.
DSUV-23: Passive hydrophone array on ballistic-missile submarines.
DSUV-61B: Towed passive array for ballistic-missile submarines.
DSUV-62C: Towed passive array for the *Améthyste* class.
DSUX-21: Multifunction system for *L'Inflexible* and *L'Indomptable.*
DUUA-2B: Active set on the modernized *Améthyste* class, with a 10° beam searchlight set operating at 8 kHz. Has a 2.5–15 Hz passive narrowband and broadband adjunct.
DUUG-2: Sonar intercept in the *Améthyste* class.
DUUG-6: Velox M5; stand-alone sonar intercept system.
DUUV-23: Panoramic passive array on ballistic-missile submarines.
DUUX-5: Fenelon passive hull array. Can track three targets simultaneously, covers 2–15 kHz, and has three hydrophone arrays on each side of the submarine.

♦ Helicopter sonars

	Frequency	Remarks
DUAV-4	21/22.5/24 kHz	On WG-13 Lynx; 150 m max depth

♦ Sonobuoys

	Frequency	Remarks
DSTA-3E	9/10/11 kHz	16-channel active; 20 or 100 m deep
DSTV-4L/M (TSM 8010)	10 Hz–20 kHz	31-channel passive; 20 or 100 m deep (300 m option in DSTV-4M)
DSTV-7 (TSM 8030)	5 Hz–20 kHz	99-channel passive LOFAR
TSM 8040	6.5/7.5/9.5 kHz	Commercial DICASS active
TSM 8050A/B	6.0/6.71/7.5/8.4/ 9.4/10.5 kHz	Commercial 12-channel active; A: 20 or 150 m deep; B: 20 or 450 m

H. COMBAT INFORMATION SYSTEMS

SENIT *(Système d'Exploitation Naval des Informations Tactique):* This system serves the following principal purposes:

- It establishes the combat situation from the manual collection of information derived from detection equipment on board and from the automatic or manual collection of information from external sources.
- It disseminates the above data to the ship and to other vessels by automatic means (Links 11 and 14).
- It assists in decision making and transmits to the target-designation console all the information it requires.

The several versions of the SENIT are similar in general concept but differ in construction and programming in order to ensure fulfillment of the various missions assigned to each type of ship:

SENIT 3: Two Type 1230 computers. In the *Tourville* class.
SENIT 4: One Iris N 55 computer, seven display consoles. In the *Georges Leygues* class.
SENIT 5: The original TAVITAC commercial system from Thales.
SENIT 6: Seven Type 15M 125X computers and 13 consoles. In *Cassard* class.
SENIT 7: Thales TAVITAC 2000, with two Type MLX 32 computers and five color video display consoles. In the *La Fayette* class. Also known as SACEIT *(Système Automatisé de Commandement et d'Exploitation des Informations Tactiques).*
SENIT 8: Derived from SENIT 6 for the *Charles de Gaulle.* Also known as SISC *(Système d'Intégration du Système de Combat).* Has 25 consoles and eight 32-bit computers. Able to maintain 2,000 contacts.
SENIT 8.01: A reduced version of SENIT 8 being installed in *Georges Leygues*–class destroyers. Also referred to as the OP3A enhanced self-defense combat system, it interfaces with the *existing* SENIT systems. Employs six operators. May later be fitted to *La Fayette*–class frigates, major amphibious ships, and replenishment ships. Intended to detect "leakers" at up to 10 km range and respond in less than 3 seconds.

AIDCOMER *(Aide de Commandement à la Mer):* A decision-making system intended to provide artificial-intelligence assistance in situation assessment, decision making, and resource management of ships and aircraft within a task force, as well as to act with the land-based SYCOM NG command-and-control system. Interfaces with the SENIT data systems and with the Syracuse SATCOM system and contains an extensive threat database.

OPSMER or SEAO *(Système Embarqué d'Aide aux Opérations):* A simplified version of AIDCOMER intended for destroyers and the *Forbin*-class frigates. A version will also be carried aboard ballistic-missile and nuclear-powered attack submarines. The *Foudre*-class landing ships and the command ship/oiler *Var* have specialized versions as well.

ALTESSE *(Alerte et Ténue de Situation de Surface):* A decision aid system by Thales to be carried by *La Fayette*–class frigates to improve ESM system performance and to provide an overview of the local surface situation. Installed in *Tourville* in 1995.

DLT D3: All submarines use the DLT *(Direction de Lancement Torpilles)* D3. There are three identical data displays for current and historical target data, and the system can be used to launch torpedoes and missiles.

I. COUNTERMEASURES

♦ Intercept systems

For surface ships: ARBR/ARBA-10C/D, ARBR-16 (Thales DR-2000 Mk 1), ARBR-17 (Thales DR-4000S; C–G band), and ARBR-21 (Thales DR-3000). Also ARBG-1A SAIGON *(Système Automatisé d'Interception et de Goniométrie)* for interception of VHF through UHF communications. The ARBG-2 Énigme is aboard *Charles de Gaulle.*

For submarines: ARUR-10B/C, ARUR-11 (with DALIA analyzer), ARUR-12 (with DALIA analyzer), and ARUX-1.

For aircraft: ARAR-12 (with DALIA analyzer) and ARAR-13 with DALIA for Atlantique Mk 2 aircraft.

♦ Jammers

ARBB-32: For surface ships; work against reception antennas and jammers. Manufacturer: Électronique Serge Dassault.

ARBB-33: Dassault's Salamandre integrated EW suite.

♦ Countermeasures launchers

Dagaie (AMBL-1B): DAGAIE = *Dispositif d'Autodéfense pour la Guerre Antimissiles Infra-rouge et Électro-magnétique.* Manufacturer: Matra Défense. Launches both IR and chaff-type decoys, relying on input from SENIT systems. The launcher holds 10 "suitcases," each with 33 projectiles of four charges in the antiradar version or 34 projectiles in the infrared version. An improved version is known as Dagaie Mk 2 (AMBL-1C). In development is a version to launch up to six Spartacus antitorpedo decoys. Weight: 500 kg. Range: 750 m.

Sagaie (AMBL-2A): SAGAIE = *Système d'Autodéfense pour la Guerre Anti-missiles Infra-rouge et Électro-magnétique.* Manufacturer: Matra Défense. Launches decoy rockets for confusion, seduction, or distraction. The launcher is trainable and holds 10 containers launching infrared or radar-jamming rockets 170 mm in diameter and weighing 45 kg. An antitorpedo round is being developed, either the Euroslat SLAT or the Whitehead Alenia (WASS) A-200 LCAW, of which 10–12 would be carried on the launcher. Range: 3,000 m. Launcher weight: 1,600 kg.

Note: In development is the 12-round New Generation Decoy System (NGDS).

♦ Torpedo countermeasures

SLAT *(Système de Lutte Anti-Torpilles):* A directional towed array detector to be used in conjunction with the Spartacus active decoy, which is to be launched by Sagaie; in development. Also known as Salto, the system will employ the Alto 42-element towed, linear acoustic intercept array to detect torpedoes and the Contralto countermeasure system. A prototype system went to sea at the end of 1994. A joint development contract with French government and Euroslat (a consortium of DCN, Thales, and Whitehead Alenia Sistemi Subacquei/WASS) was signed in 1-01.

SLQ-25 Nixie: U.S.-made towed acoustic torpedo decoy in surface combatants.

SPDT-1A: Torpedo detector in development by Crozet-Safare.

J. COMMUNICATIONS

The French Navy uses a number of systems to ensure communications with the fleet. Land-based transmissions over the range of VLF through SHF are available. Satellite communications systems for which there are shipboard transceivers are:

Syracuse I and II *(System de Radio-Communications Utilizant un Satellite):* New-construction or modified major ships are receiving radome-mounted antennas for the Syracuse-series satellite communications transmission system. The system became fully operational in 1987. Syracuse operates at 7–8 GHz and transmission rate is 2400-bit voice/75-baud telemetry per second. Syracuse II, which relieved Syracuse I in 1994, employs a constellation of Télécom 2A, 2B, and 2C satellites (launched 16-12-91, 16-4-92, and 1995, respectively). The reception antennas are 0.90 m in diameter on surface ships and 0.40 m in diameter on Atlantique Mk 2 aircraft. Syracuse II is to be superseded between 2005 and 2010 by Syracuse III, the Anglo-French BIMILSATCOMM, European EUMILSATCOMM, or Franco-Anglo-American NMILSAT.

Astarte *(Avion Station Relais de Transmissions Exceptionnelles):* To ensure communications with submerged ballistic-missile submarines, the ELF Astarte system entered service in 1988, with a transmitter at Rosnay. Also being used is an airborne system using U.S. VLF equipment mounted in four C-160 Transall aircraft.

Inmarsat (International Maritime Satellite Organization): Temporary installations of the commercial Inmarsat transceiver are frequently found aboard French warships for telephone, telegraphic, and telecopying uses. The navy leases 35 sets.

K. SPACE SURVEILLANCE

The first French, Italian, and Spanish Hélios surveillance satellite was launched 7-7-95, using technology derived from the civilian Spot program. The Hélios constellation employs four satellites with an altitude of 685 km and was expected to have an operational life of three years for each satellite. In 2002, the Hélios II version with infrared imaging is scheduled to be launched in cooperation with Germany, Spain, and Italy. The first Zénon electronic listening satellite was to be launched in 1999.

NUCLEAR-POWERED AIRCRAFT CARRIERS [CVN]

Note: The French Senate recommended during 9-00 that a second new carrier, with conventional propulsion, be funded during the 2002–08 defense spending plan. The ship would have a longer flight deck than that of the cramped *Charles de Gaulle* and would have a less capable self-defense system.

♦ 1 Charles de Gaulle class   Bldr: DCN, Brest

	Laid down	L	Del.	In serv.
R 91 Charles de Gaulle (ex-*Richelieu*)	14-4-89	14-5-94	28-9-00	18-5-01

NUCLEAR-POWERED AIRCRAFT CARRIERS [CVN] *(continued)*

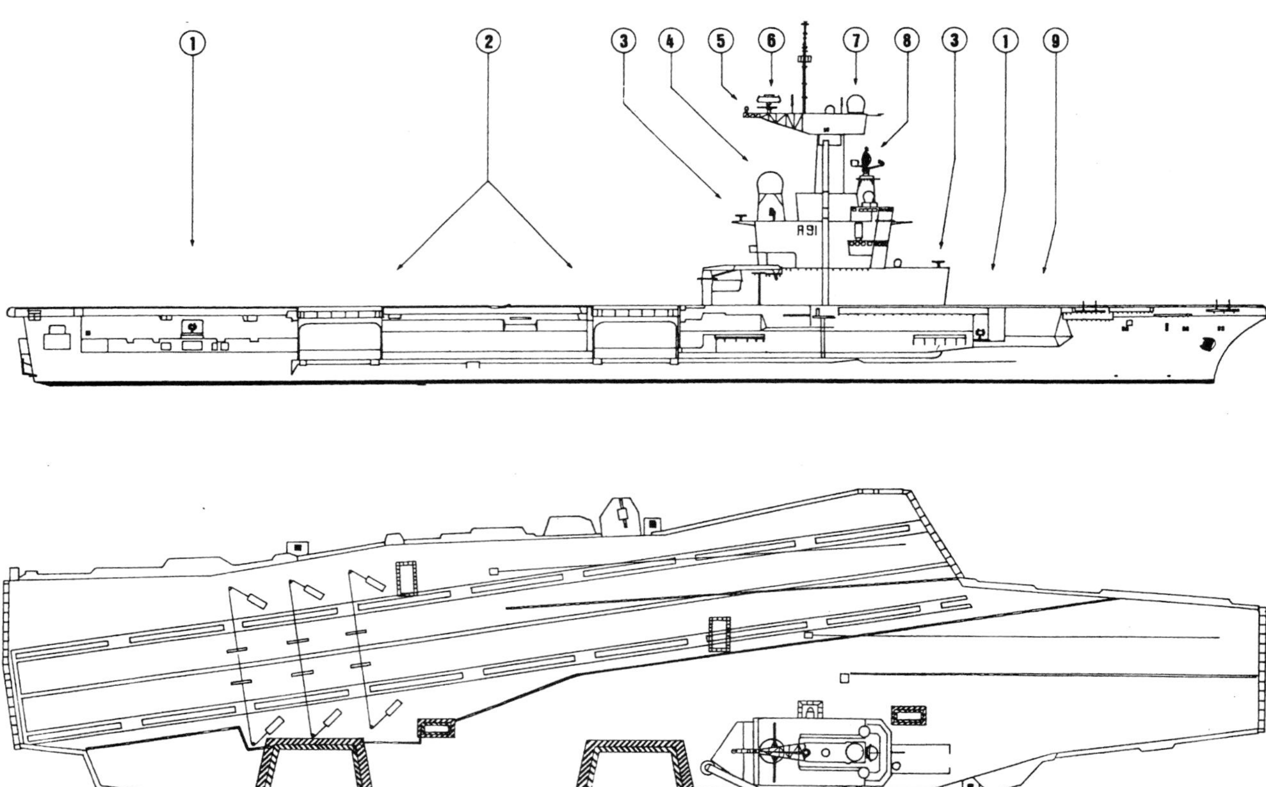

Charles de Gaulle (R 91) 1. Sagaie decoy launcher 2. aircraft elevators 3. DRBN-34 navigational and air-control radars 4. DRBJ-11B height-finding radar 5. DIBV-1 infrared sensor 6. DRBV-15C air- and surface-search radar 7. Arabel missile target-designation and -illumination radar 8. DRBV-26D early-warning radar 9. SAAM missile launch group
Drawing by Jean Moulin from *Flottes de Combat*

Charles de Gaulle (R 91)—after modifications to angled deck; the large rectangular structure beneath the angled deck amidships will house the Sylver A 50 vertical launchers for the SAAM missile system
Bernard Prézelin, 9-00

D: 37,085 tons (40,600 fl) **S:** 27 kts (23.5 sust.; see remarks)
Dim: 261.50 (238.00 pp) × 64.36 (31.50 wl) × 8.70 (9.50 max.)
Air group: 12 Rafale-M interceptors; 20 Super Étendard strike fighters; 2 E-2C Hawkeye surveillance and air-control aircraft; 2 Super Frelon heavy transport helicopters; 3 Dauphin SAR helicopters
A: 2 16-round Sylver A50 vertical-launch SAAM syst. (32 Aster-15 missiles); 2 6-round Sadral point-defense SAM syst. (Mistral missiles); 8 single 20-mm 90-cal. GIAT F2 AA
Electronics:
Radar: 2 DRBN-34 (Decca 1229) nav.; 1 DRBJ-11B height-finder; 1 DRBV-15C air/surf. search; 1 DRBV-26D early warning; 1 Arabel SAAM target desig.
TACAN: VRBP-20A
EW: ARBR-21 radar intercept; ARBG-2 Enigme comms intercept; 2 ARBB-33 jammers, 4 6-round AMBL-2A Sagaie decoy RL; SLAT torpedo decoy syst.
E/O: DIBV-1 surveillance; 2 DIBC-2A panoramic electro-optical f.c.
M: 2 150-Mw K15 pressurized-water reactor plants; double-reduction geared steam turbines; 2 5-bladed props; 83,000 shp
Electric: 21,400 kw tot. (4 × 4,000-kw turboalternators; 4 × 1,100-kw diesel sets; 4 × 250-kw turboalternators)
Endurance: 45 days
Crew: 1,950 tot. (177 officers, 890 petty officers, 883 nonrated, including 550 tot. in the air group); can also carry up to 800 troops

Remarks: Ordered 4-2-86. Work began 24-11-87 and the ship was to have been launched 1-5-92, but in 6-89 it was announced that the original 1996 date of operation would be delayed two years, and significant further delays have since transpired. The hull was briefly afloat on 20-12-92 to reposition it within the graving dock for the addition of the angled deck. Was christened 7-5-94 but not floated out until 14-5-94. Dockside propulsion trials commenced 26-5-98. Sea trials were to commence 1-7-98 but were delayed to 27-1-99 by problems with the propulsion system and had to be halted due to an electrical generation capacity problem; sea trials recommenced 18-3-99. Ownership of the ship was passed to the French Navy 1-2-97. As of 12-00, the ship's construction had cost $2.67 billion, 20% over budget.

An $80 million post-shakedown yard period starting in fall 1999 was provided for extending the angled deck, improving reactor safety, replacing corroded piping, curing rudder vibration, and improving power supply to the reactor water cooling circulation pumps; the work was extended, however, delaying commissioning. Post-repair trials began 19-5-00. Other changes made were the removal of the yardarms and the provision of a crew gangway position low at the stern. During a precommissioning cruise to the West Indies in 11-00, lost a propeller blade and had to return to Toulon for repairs, which were not fully completed until 10-01.

On 9-7-01, consideration of whether to construct a second unit was postponed to the 2009–14 program.

Hull systems: The SATRAP *(Système Automatique de Tranquillisation et de Pilotage)* system controls seakeeping behavior to permit air operations in sea states up to 5 or 6; it incorporates two groups of 12 lead stabilization weights totaling 500 tons that are moved athwartships on rails to reduce roll to 0.5°. Four pairs of fin stabilizers and a rudder roll stabilization system are also installed. The low-mounted hull sponsons are designed to provide additional righting moment when they are immersed at approximately 7° roll. Pressurized and filtered air is employed by the NBC-protection citadel. Special attention has been paid toward reducing the ship's signa-

NUCLEAR-POWERED AIRCRAFT CARRIERS [CVN] *(continued)*

Charles de Gaulle (R 91)—after commissioning Dr. Guido Alfano, 5-01

Charles de Gaulle (R 91)—with gangway structure added low at the stern centerline; the large oval exhaust serves the aircraft engine test stand
Bernard Prézelin, 9-01

Charles de Gaulle (R 91)—showing the modifications to extend the angled deck
Bernard Prézelin, 9-00

Charles de Gaulle (R 91)—details of the island structure, port side
Bernard Prézelin, 9-00

Charles de Gaulle (R 91)—detail of the starboard side of the island
Bernard Prézelin, 7-00

ture by shaping the hull and island to reduce the radar return, sound-isolating engineering systems, and installing a comprehensive degaussing system. In addition to being able to embark up to 800 troops, the ship can accept a modular hospital installation with 50 beds and two operating rooms.

Propulsion systems: The plant is located in five compartments. The reactors, which are identical to those in the ballistic-missile submarines of the *Le Triomphant* class, also supply steam for the turboalternators and the catapults and are contained within protective structures. Each main turboalternator propulsion set incorporates a high-pressure and a low-pressure turbine driving a single shaft through double-reduction gearing. Electrical power is available in 3-phase, 440 V, 60 Hz; 1- and 3-phase, 440 V, 400 Hz; 115 V, 60 Hz for lighting; and 28 V emergency lighting. The ship, however, lacks adequate propulsion power for aviation activities and was restricted to 25 kts after 1-01 due to temporary use of mismatched spare propellers from *Clemenceau* and *Foch* until six new, tailored units can be fabricated; the temporary port propeller has caused vibration problems and the temporary screws limit maximum speed to only 25.2 kts. The new propellers were to be ready early in 2002.

Aviation systems: As initially operational in 2001, the ship was to carry 4 Rafale-M and 29 Super Étendard fighters, 2 E-2C Hawkeye surveillance aircraft, and 2 Super Frelon and 2 Dauphin helicopters. Ultimately, the ship is intended to carry 32 Rafale fighters, 3 E-2C Hawkeye surveillance aircraft, and 4 helicopters. The flight deck is 261.5 m long, with a 195-m, 8.3° angled-deck portion. The angled deck was belatedly found to be 4.4 m too short for safe operation of the E-2C aircraft in all weather and was extended during 2001. Maximum flight deck width is 64.36 m, for an area of more than 12,300 m^2. There are two 75-m U.S. Type C13 F steam catapults, each capable of launching aircraft of up to 25 metric tons weight, with one on the angled deck and the other on the port side of the bow—an arrangement that emphasizes deck parking arrangements over an ability to launch and land simultaneously. Three arrestor wires are fitted. There are two 21 × 12-m, 36-ton deck-edge elevators, both to starboard amidships, and two ammunition elevators. The nuclear propulsion arrangement requires the island to be mounted much farther forward than is standard practice, ahead of both elevators. The 138-m-long by 29-m-broad (4,600 m^2) by 6.1-m-high hangar is lower than that on the *Clemenceau* class, but considerably larger in area and better protected; it can accommodate 23 fixed-wing aircraft and 2 helicopters at a time. Aviation fuel capacity is normally 3,600 m^3, with provision for up to 5,000 m^3 if necessary. The munitions magazines can accommodate 2,100 tons. The ship has the Matra Défense DALAS *(Dispositif d'Aide à l'Appontage au Laser)* deck approach and landing laser system.

Combat systems: The SENIT 8 combat data and control system uses eight Hewlett-Packard PA-VME RISC processors and 24 HP 9000 Series 700 UNIX workstations, of which 15 are dual-screen system operator consoles; it is able to track 100 targets and attack 10 simultaneously through the Arabel radar. SENIT 8 incorporates the SYTEX *(Système de Transmissions Extérieures)* communications control with Thales SDG *(Système de Grand Diffusion)* integrated-services digital communications system with high-speed fiber-optic voice and data transmission network; SCEB *(Système de Contrôle des Emissions du Bâtiment);* the AIDCOMER command decision support system; and the GESVOL aviation coordination system, which tracks pilot and aircraft assignments, launch data such as aircraft weight and speed, and weather and monitors airborne aircraft and flight plans. GESVOL employs Hewlett-Packard Vectra computers, Sun Microsystems displays, and an Ethernet data movement system. The ship has NATO Link 11, Link 14, and Link 16 datalinks. An inertial navigation system is carried. The Aster-15 missile system will not be available for installation until 2005. Sylver is an acronym for *Système de Launcement Vertical.* The 20-mm guns are normally not mounted but are carried aboard.

Note: The carrier *Foch* (R 99) was stricken 15-11-00 and sold to Brazil for further service. Sister *Clemenceau* (R 98) was retired 1-10-97 and used as a source of spares for the *Foch.*

CRUISER-HELICOPTER CARRIERS [CH]

♦ 1 helicopter-carrier and cadet training ship

Bldr: Brest Arsenal

	Laid down	L	In serv.
R 97 JEANNE D'ARC (ex-*La Résolue*)	7-7-60	30-9-61	30-6-64

D: 10,575 tons (13,270 fl) **S:** 26.5 kts (cruising)
Dim: 182.00 (172.00 wl) × 24.00 (22.00 wl) × 7.30 (aft max.)
Air group: up to 8 helicopters (Super Frelon, Dauphin, Lynx, etc.)

CRUISER-HELICOPTER CARRIERS [CH] *(continued)*

Jeanne d'Arc (R 97) SeaPhoto, 2-99

Jeanne d'Arc (R 97)—the 100-mm guns at the stern were removed during 10-00
Bernard Prézelin, 5-00

A: 6 MM 38 Exocet SSM; 2 single 100-mm 55-cal. Model 1953 DP; 4 single 12.7-mm mg

Electronics:

Radar: 2 DRBN-34 nav.; 1 DRBV-22D air search; 1 DRBV-50 surf./air search; 3 DRBC-32A f.c.

Sonar: DUBV-24C hull-mounted (5 kHz)

TACAN: U.S. SRN-6

EW: ARBR-16 intercept; ARBX-10 radar intercept; 2 8-round AMBL-2A Syllex decoy RL

Jeanne d'Arc (R 97) John Mortimer, 2-0

M: 2 sets Rateau-Bretagne geared steam turbines; 2 props; 40,000 shp
Boilers: 4 asymmetric, multitube; 45 kg/cm², 450° C **Electric:** 4,400 kw tot.
Range: 3,000/26.5; 3,750/25; 5,500/20; 6,800/16 **Fuel:** 1,360 tons
Crew: 31 officers, 182 petty officers, 414 other enlisted, 150 cadets

Remarks: Replaced the former cruiser *Jeanne d'Arc* as a training ship for officer cadets. In wartime, she was intended to be used for ASW missions, for amphibious assault, or as a troop transport. The number of Super Frelon heavy helicopters can be quickly augmented by simple structural changes. The ship was expected to serve until 2003 and then be replaced by a modified unit of the *Foudre* class, but in 1998 her expected service was extended to 2006.
Hull systems: In addition to the navigation bridge, the forward superstructure contains a helicopter-control bridge, a modular-type information-and-operations center, and a combined control center for amphibious operations. The engineering spaces are divided into two compartments, each with two boilers and a turbine, separated by a bulkhead.
Aviation systems: The 62 × 21-m flight deck aft of the island structure permits the simultaneous takeoff of two helicopters, while two others can be stationed forward of the takeoff area and another two astern, one on each side of the 12-ton-capacity elevator at the after end of the flight deck. The hangar deck can, if some of the living quarters used by midshipmen are removed, accommodate eight helicopters. At the after end of the hangar deck, there are machine shops for maintenance and repair, including helicopter electronic equipment, and an area for inspection; the compartments for handling weapons and ammunition (torpedoes, missiles, etc.) are also there. During her 1998–99 world cruise, *Jeanne d'Arc* carried three Dauphin, one Alouette-III and two French Army Cougar helicopters.
Combat systems: Two additional 100-mm guns mounted aft were removed during 10-00 to reduce personnel requirements. The DRBI-10 height-finding radar was removed in 1983–84.

NAVAL AVIATION

Organization: Authority over naval aviation has been assigned since 19-6-98 to a single rear admiral: ALAVIA. Combatant squadrons have two-digit numbers followed by *F* (for *Flotille*), while support squadron numbers are followed by *S*.

Bases: Landivisiau (shipboard fighters); Lann-Bihoué and Nîmes-Garons (maritime patrol); Lanvéoc-Poulmic and Hyères (helicopters); and Cuers-Pierrefeu (repair/rework). The base at St.-Mandrier was to be closed during 2002.

Operational Flotillas:

Formation	Base	No. and Type	Mission
4F	Lann-Bihoué	2 E-2C Hawkeye	aerial surveillance
11F	Landivisiau	15 Super-Étendard	attack
12F	Landivisiau	10 Rafale-M F1	interception
17F	Landivisiau	14 Super-Étendard	attack
21F	Nîmes-Garons	9 Atlantique	maritime patrol
23F	Lann-Bihoué	9 Atlantique	maritime patrol
24F	Lann-Bihoué	4 Falcon 50M	maritime surveillance
		3 Nord 262E	maritime surveillance
		4 Xingu	training and liaison
25F	Faaa, Tahiti, & Tontouta, New Caledonia	4 Gardian	maritime surveillance
28F	Nîmes-Garons	3 Nord 262E	maritime surveillance
		4 Xingu	training and liaison
31F	Hyères	8 Lynx WG-13	shipboard ASW and attack
32F	Lanvéoc-Poulmic	7 Super Frelon	transport and rescue
34F	Lanvéoc-Poulmic	8 Lynx WG-13	shipboard ASW and attack
35F	Hyères	9 Dauphin	rescue and liaison
		6 Alouette-III	rescue and liaison
36F	Hyères	15 Panther	patrol and attack
10S	Hyères	. . . Nord 262	training
		. . . Xingu	training
		. . . Alouette-III	training
22S	Lanvéoc-Poulmic	. . . Alouette-III	training
50S	Lanvéoc-Poulmic	. . . MS 880 Rallye	training
		. . . Cap 10	training
56S	Nîmes-Garons	4 Nord 262	training
57S	Landivisiau	. . . Falcon 10 Mer	training and transportation

NAVAL AVIATION *(continued)*

Notes: Formation 4F was established 10-3-00. 6F was disestablished 15-9-00. 11F is to transfer to the Rafale-M in 2007. 12F, dissolved 31-12-99, is being reconstituted in 2002 with the first operational Rafale-Ms. 16F was dissolved 28-7-00, and the shipboard photoreconnaissance mission was transferred to six modified Super Étendard fighters. 17F will transfer to the Rafale-M in 2010. 24F, inactive since 1998, was reactivated 10-3-00 and will receive four Falcon 50M surveillance aircraft in 12-02. 25F was established 1-9-00 to replace 9S and 12S. 33F was dissolved 1-10-99 and its missions transferred to the reconstituted 35F, which also operates with an interservice French Army Puma rescue helicopter group from Cazaux. The six Dauphin helicopters of 32F are deployed to facilities at Touquet, Cherbourg, Lanvéoc, La Rochelle, and Hyères (and also, on occasion, to Ajaccio). Support squadrons 2S, 3S, 9S, and 12S were disestablished in 2000.

PRINCIPAL COMBAT AIRCRAFT

A. SHIPBOARD FIXED-WING AIRCRAFT

♦ **Rafale-Marine interceptor/attack** Manufacturer: Dassault

Rafale-M—single-seat interceptor, operational unit Bernard Prézelin, 1-01

Wingspan: 10.86 m **Length:** 15.27 m **Height:** 5.00 m
Weight: 14,000 kg (19,000 max.) **Speed:** Mach 2.0
Propulsion: 2 SNECMA M88-2 turbojets (7,500 kg thrust each)
Max. ceiling: 50,000 ft. **Range:** 1,000 n.m.
Weapons: 4 missiles, 1 30-mm cannon; MM 40, ASMP, or AS 30 missiles, bombs and/or rockets in attack mode
Avionics: RBE-2 radar, Spectre EW suite, Link 16

Remarks: Planned acquisition of 86 aircraft was cut to 60 in 2-96. The first naval prototype flew 11-91, and the first production prototype aircraft was delivered 9-96. Have jump-strut nose gear to assist takeoff. The empty weight of the naval interceptor version is 760 kg more than that of the land version. Considerable use was made of composite material.

The first 10 operational aircraft were ordered in 5-97. Seven more were ordered 14-1-99 with an option for another seven (now to be of the two-seat Rafale-BM variant; see below) planned to be taken up in 2001; the first of these is to deliver in 2006. The first two operational aircraft were delivered 4-12-00, and 10 were to be in service by 2-02 with 12F, formed at Landivisiau in 6-01. Five to 10 two-seaters will begin delivery to 11F in 2004, and 17F will convert to the F3 standard aircraft by 2010, with the last Rafale-M F3 to deliver in 2012.

The first 12 are of the F1 version, equipped only as interceptors, with Mica radar-guided and Magic-2 IR-seeking missiles (but without the capability to carry the ASMP standoff weapon, automatic terrain-following capability, the Spectre defensive subsystem, a helmet-mounted sight, or voice-commanded controls); all were to be updated to F1.1 configuration with Link 16 capability and IR-seeking Mica missiles by the end of 2002. The F2 ground-attack variant will have the ability to carry SCALP and AASM missiles and bombs, while the F3 will be capable of launching the ASMP missile for nuclear strikes.

In 9-00, a decision was made to acquire only 20 single-seat aircraft, with the remainder to be of a new, two-seat Rafale-BM variant that will marry the M-series airframe to the two-seat cockpit of the French Air Force B variant, at the loss of the internal cannon. The 15th naval Rafale is to be the prototype and is planned to fly in 2005; the first production version (the 21st Rafale Navale airframe) would enter service in 2006. The entire fleet is planned to be upgraded eventually to the F4 multi-role configuration.

SNECMA is developing the M88-3 engine with 9,000-kg thrust for introduction into French aircraft, including the Rafale, around 2010 and is doing research on an M88-3D version with thrust vectoring.

♦ **Super Étendard fighter-bomber** Manufacturer: Dassault

Super Étendard Bernard Prézelin, 12-00

Wingspan: 9.60 m **Length:** 14.50 m **Height:** 3.85 m
Weight: 11,900 kg **Speed:** Mach 1.0 at 11,000 m; Mach 0.97 at low altitude
Propulsion: 1 SNECMA 8 K 50 turbojet, 5,000 kg thrust
Max. ceiling: 35,000 ft.
Range: 750 n.m. (1 hr 45 min or, with external fuel, 2 hr 15 min)
Weapons: 2 30-mm cannon, bombs, rockets, or 1 AM 39 Exocet or ASMP or 2 AS 30L laser-guided missiles

Remarks: Have been modified to carry the ANT 52 nuclear bomb. During 1990–97, 50 Super Étendards received the Anémone radar, Thales Sherloc radar warning receiver and Barracuda jammer EW equipment, podded Alkan Type 5081 chaff and flare dispensers, head-up display, and a SAGEM UAT 90 computer in place of the UAT 10 and other improvements. The aircraft are to be phased out of service between 2004 and 2010. Aircraft destined for service aboard *Charles de Gaulle* are equipped to carry AS 30L laser-guided ground attack missiles. Six aircraft have been modified to perform photoreconnaissance duties.

Note: Two Grumman E-2C Hawkeye radar surveillance aircraft were ordered 5-95 for $561.8 million, and a third was ordered on 28-3-01 for delivery by 9-03. The E-2Cs have APS-145 radar, four-color displays, JTIDS (Link 16) datalink, Loral high-speed processors, and Allison T56A-147 turboshaft engines. The first was delivered 28-4-98 and the second during 6-98, with the first arriving in France 18-12-98 and the second during 3-99. An option exists for a fourth E-2C. Data for the E-2C can be found in the U.S.A. section.

French Navy E-2C Hawkeye French Navy, 1999

B. LAND-BASED MARITIME RECONNAISSANCE

♦ **Atlantique Mk 2** Manufacturer: Dassault-Bréguet

Atlantique Mk 2 Bernard Prézelin, 12-00

Wingspan: 37.30 m **Length:** 32.62 m **Height:** 10.80 m
Weight: 46,200 kg (25,000 light) **Speed:** 320 kts
Propulsion: 2 Rolls-Royce Tyne 21 turboprops (6,000 shp each)
Max. ceiling: 30,000 ft. **Range:** 4,300 n.m. (18 hr)
Weapons: 2 AM 39 Exocet missiles or 8 ASW torpedoes, depth charges, sonobuoys, etc. (3,000 kg total)
Avionics: Iguane radar, MAD Mk 3, FLIR system, Tango FLIR camera, DSAX-1 sonobuoy processor, ARAR-13 EW gear

Remarks: The original plan was to acquire 42 at the rate of three per year, but in 1992, the force goal was reduced to 28 and in 1996 it was reduced to 22. The first operational aircraft entered service 7-89. The final unit of 28 ordered was delivered 21-11-97, and six are being rotated through storage and overhaul to maintain 22 operational. To be backfitted with Thales SADANG sonobuoy processing system.

A single Mk 3 prototype has been converted by the manufacturer in hopes of garnering export sales. The aircraft features 6-bladed Dowty carbon-composite propellers, is powered by two Allison–Rolls-Royce AE2100H gas turbines, has a new combat control system with eight operator positions, and is equipped with a modern "glass" cockpit.

♦ **Gardian SAR and surveillance** Manufacturer: Aérospatiale

Gardian French Navy

PRINCIPAL COMBAT AIRCRAFT *(continued)*

Wingspan: 16.30 m **Length:** 17.15 m **Height:** 5.32 m
Weight: 15,200 kg **Speed:** Mach 0.86
Propulsion: 2 Garrett ATF 3-6 turbojets **Max. ceiling:** 42,000 ft.
Range: 2,200 n.m. (5 hr 30 min) **Weapons:** none

Remarks: A version of the Falcon 20 transport, with Varan radar. A ventral trap door permits launching rescue equipment.

Note: Four Falcon 50 SURMAR (Surveillance Maritime) jet transports were ordered in 1995 (with an option for a fifth, which may be ordered post-2002). Configured for search-and-rescue duties with Thales/EADS OM 100 Ocean Master search radar and Chlio FLIR and carrying eight 25-person liferafts, the first was delivered 11-98, the third in 3-01, and the fourth in 3-02.

French Navy Falcon 50 Bernard Prézelin, 11-00

C. HELICOPTERS

♦ NH-90 antisubmarine
Manufacturer: Aérospatiale-MBB-AgustaWestland

NH-90 prototype NHIndustries, 1997

Rotor diameter: 16.00 m **Length:** 19.50 m (13.14 folded)
Height: 5.20 m **Weight:** 10,600 kg max. **Speed:** 157 kts (132 cruise)
Propulsion: 2 Rolls-Royce or Turbomeca 322-01/02 turboshafts; 2,120 shp
Max. ceiling: 20,000 ft. **Endurance:** 4 hr 45 min
Weapons: MU-90 torpedoes, AM 39 missiles (total: 2,000 kg max.)

Remarks: Cooperative European venture. Prototype rolled out 29-9-95. Intended to replace the Super Frelon and the WG-13 Lynx in the French Navy beginning in 2005. Planned acquisition of 60 was reduced to 27 in 5-96, with 14 equipped for ASW and 13 for the transport and SAR role. Composite materials employed in construction. In the ASW configuration, would carry pilot, copilot, and two equipment operators. Will have Thales FLASH dipping sonar and a MAD sensor. Italian versions will have G.E.-FiatAvio T700/T6E1 turboshaft engines.

♦ Super Frelon heavy transport
Manufacturer: Aérospatiale

Super Frelon Bernard Prézelin, 7-99

Rotor diameter: 18.90 m **Length:** 23.00 m **Height:** 6.70 m
Weight: 13,000 kg **Speed:** 145 kts
Propulsion: 3 Turbomeca III C3 turboshafts (1,500 shp each)
Max. ceiling: 10,000 ft. **Range:** 420 n.m. (3 hr 30 min) **Weapons:** None

Remarks: No longer equipped for the ASW or ship-attack role. Despite their age, are to be kept in service until 2005. Have ORB-42 radar. Can carry 27 passengers or 3 tons of cargo.

♦ Lynx (WG-13) antisubmarine/antiship
Manufacturer: AgustaWestland-Aérospatiale

Lynx Bernard Prézelin, 11-00

Rotor diameter: 12.80 m **Length:** 15.2 m **Height:** 3.60 m
Weight: 4,150 kg **Speed:** 150 kts
Propulsion: 2 Rolls-Royce BS 360 turboshafts (900 shp each)
Max. ceiling: 12,000 ft. **Endurance:** 2 hr 30 min, part in transit, part hovering
Weapons: Mk 46 torpedoes, AS 12 wire-guided missiles

Remarks: Have ORB 31 radar and DUAV-4 dipping sonar. Capable of localization, classification, and attack of submarine and surface targets.

♦ Panther (AS.365MF) SAR and transport
Manufacturer: Aérospatiale

Panther Bernard Prézelin, 2-01

Dauphin Bernard Prézelin, 4-01

Rotor diameter: 13.29 m **Length:** 11.41 m **Height:** 4.00 m
Weight: 4,250 kg max. **Speed:** 175 kts max. (155 max. cruise; 135 cruise)
Propulsion: 2 Turbomeca Arreil 1 MN turboshafts **Max. ceiling:** . . . ft.
Radius: 225 n.m. (4 hr) **Fuel:** 1,100 liters **Weapons:** none

Remarks: Fifteen Aérospatiale-Matra AS.565MB Panther helicopters (a derivative of the AS.365N2 Dauphin 2) were delivered 1993–98 and assigned to 35F at Lanvéoc-Poulmic to replace Alouette-IIIs. Each can carry up to 12 passengers. Have an ORB-32 radar, doppler radar altimeter, and Nadir Mk II navigational computer. The Panthers supplement the six similar AS.365N2 Dauphin ordered 1988–89. Flight duration is 4 hours.

Radar-equipped Alouette-III Bernard Prézelin, 1-01

PRINCIPAL COMBAT AIRCRAFT *(continued)*

Nord 262 Bernard Prézelin, 11-00

Xingu Bernard Prézelin, 3-01

NUCLEAR-POWERED BALLISTIC-MISSILE SUBMARINES [SSBN]

Note: To augment security, names and pennant numbers ceased to be displayed on 1-1-83.

♦ 2 (+ 2) Le Triomphant class
Bldr: DCN, Cherbourg

	Laid down	L	In serv.
S 616 Le Triomphant	9-6-89	26-3-94	21-3-97
S 617 Le Téméraire	18-12-93	21-1-98	23-12-99
S 618 Le Vigilant	1997	3-02	2004 (del.)
S 619 Le Terrible	2003	. . .	2010 (del.)

Le Triomphant (S 616) Bernard Prézelin, 1-01

Le Téméraire (S 617) Bernard Prézelin, 9-99

D: 12,640 tons surf./14,335 tons sub. **S:** 25+ kts sub.
Dim: 138.00 × 12.50 × 10.60
A: 16 M 45 SLBM; 4 bow 533-mm TT (18 SM 39 antiship missiles and F 17 Mod. 2 torpedoes)
Electronics:
Radar: 1 DRUA-33 nav./search
Sonar: DMUX-80 suite: DUUV-23 panoramic passive array; DSUV-61B towed linear array; DUUX-5 acoustic intercept
EW: ARUR-13 (Thales DR-4000U and DR-3000U) intercept suite
M: 1 Type K15, 150-Mw pressurized-water reactor; 1 pumpjet prop; 41,500 shp—diesel-electric emergency propulsion: 2 SEMT-Pielstick 8 PA4 V200 diesel generator sets (1,225 bhp/900 kw each); 5,000 n.m. range
Crew: 2 crews in rotation, each of 15 officers, 96 enlisted

Remarks: A "new generation," first announced in 1981. During 9-92 it was announced that the class would be curtailed at four vice the planned five. Work on S 616 was ordered slowed late in 9-91 for financial reasons; she was rolled out of the production hall on 13-7-93. Problems with pressure hull welds delayed sea trials for S 616 until 15-4-94; her first operational patrol began in 3-97. S 618 was ordered 27-5-93; production of S 618 was slowed under the FY 95 budget. It had been hoped to order the fourth in FY 97, but the planned order was delayed to 28-7-00. Are expected to last 25 years each, with refits and recorings at 7-year intervals.
Hull systems: Use NLES 100, high-elasticity steel for the pressure hull, giving a potential 500-m diving depth. Careful attention was paid to radiated noise reduction, including an elaborate "rafted" (isolated) propulsion plant and a pumpjet propulsor. Have sail-mounted bow planes and vertical surfaces at ends of stern planes. More highly automated than their predecessors, hence the smaller crews.
Combat systems: The first three have (or will have) the M 45 missile with TN-75 warheads. The canceled fifth unit was to have had the now-canceled M 5 missile; the replacement M 51 missile, which was not to be available until 2015, was advanced to 2008 in 1998 (but again delayed, to 2010, in 2001) and will be carried by S 619. Have Syracuse II SATCOM capability, the SEAO/OPSMER combat decision-making system, and a precision navigation system. A SAGEM OMS optronic mast is fitted; gyro-stabilized, it carries t.v., infrared, and X-band radar sensors, an SFIM L-series search periscope, and an MRA-2 star-tracking navigational periscope.

♦ 2 Le Redoutable class
Bldr: DCN, Cherbourg

	Laid down	L	In serv.
S 613 L'Indomptable	4-12-71	17-9-74	23-12-76
S 615 L'Inflexible	27-3-80	23-6-82	1-4-85

L'Inflexible (S 615) Bernard Prézelin, 4-01

L'Indomptable (S 613) Bernard Prézelin, 6-98

D: 8,087 tons surf./8,913 (S 615: 8,094) tons sub.
S: 20+ kts sub. **Dim:** 128.70 × 10.60 × 10.00
A: 16 M 4 SLBM; 4 bow 550-mm TT (18 SM 39 Exocet antiship missiles and/or L 5 Mod. 3 and F 17 Mod. 2 torpedoes)
Electronics:
Radar: 1 DRUA-33 nav./search
Sonar: DMUX-21 suite: DUUV-23 panoramic passive array; DUUX-5 acoustic intercept; DSUV-61B towed passive array
EW: ARUR-12 (Thales DR-4000U and DR-2000U) intercept suite
M: 1 pressurized-water reactor, 2 steam turbines with 1 set of turbo-reduction gears; 1 prop; 16,000 shp—2 SEMT-Pielstick 8 PA4 V185 alternator sets (450 kw each) for battery charging; 5,000 n.m. range
Crew: 2 crews in rotation, each of 15 officers and 120 enlisted

Remarks: S 613 was modernized from 12-87 to 6-89 to carry M 4 missiles; S 615 was equipped from the outset with the M 4. S 615, ordered 9-78, had most characteristics in common with the five preceding SSBNs of the *Le Redoutable* class but took advantage of many technological advances in propulsion, sonar systems, navigation systems, etc.; her first patrol began 25-5-85. Both are based at Île Longue, Brest. S 613 is to strike in 2003 and S 615 in 2007, but the latter may be extended in service if S 619 is delayed in completion.
Disposals: *Le Redoutable* (S 611), unmodified, completed her last patrol early in 1991 and, after trials employment, was stricken 12-91 for eventual use as a museum exhibit; work began 23-3-93 to remove her reactor compartment. *Le Terrible* (S 612) was stricken 1-7-96, *Le Foudroyant* (S 610) 30-4-98, and *Le Tonnant* (S 614) during 9-99.
Hull systems: Maximum operating depth: 200 m for S 613, 300 m for S 615. During S 613's modernization, the "turtle-deck" casing at the bow was reconfigured as in *L'Inflexible,* and the sail was reconfigured, with the diving planes being raised.
Combat systems: Have the SEAO/OPSMER combat decision-aid system and Pivair SPS-S optronic periscopes.

NUCLEAR-POWERED ATTACK SUBMARINES [SSN]

♦ 0 (+ 6) Barracuda class Bldr: DCN, Cherbourg

	Laid down	L	Trials	In serv.
S	2003	. . .	2008	2010
S	2005	. . .	2010	2012
S	2007	. . .	2012	2014
S	2009	. . .	2014	2016
S	2011	. . .	2016	2018
S	2013	. . .	2018	2020

D: 4,000 tons sub. **S:** . . . kts **Dim:** . . . × . . . × . . .
A: . . . vertical-launch land-attack cruise missiles; . . . bow 533-mm TT (wire-guided torpedoes and mines)
Electronics:
Radar: . . .
Sonar: . . .
EW: . . .
M: 1 Type K15, 150-Mw pressurized-water reactor; 1 pumpjet prop; 41,500 shp—diesel-electric emergency propulsion: 2 SEMT-Pielstick 8 PA4 V200 diesel generator sets (1,225 bhp/900 kw each); 5,000 n.m. range
Endurance: 70 days **Crew:** 60 tot.

Remarks: Successor to the SMAF *(Sous-Marins d'Attaque Futurs)* program. Feasibility studies began 5-10-98, with the first submarine to have been ordered in 2001, although that will probably be delayed. They will be deeper-diving than the *Améthyste* class and will be equipped with improved combat systems and improved sound quieting. Will be entirely a French design and will be faster than current French SSNs. The six are to be in service to 2050. Were originally to have cost about $950 million each, but the Finance Ministry demanded a reduction to about $675 million each in 1-00—an unattainable goal if performance is not to suffer severely.

♦ 6 Améthyste class (Type SNA 72) Bldr: DCN, Cherbourg

	Laid down	L	In serv.
S 601 Rubis (ex-*Provence*)	11-12-76	7-7-79	23-2-83
S 602 Saphir (ex-*Bretagne*)	1-9-79	1-9-81	6-7-84
S 603 Casabianca (ex-*Bourgogne*)	9-81	22-12-84	21-4-87
S 604 Émeraude	10-82	12-4-86	15-9-88
S 605 Améthyste	31-10-83	14-5-88	3-3-92
S 606 Perle	22-3-87	22-9-90	7-7-93

Améthyste (S 605) Ben Sullivan, 8-00

Perle (S 606) Brian Morrison, 2-01

D: 2,280 tons std., 2,410 tons surf./2,680 tons sub.
S: 26.5 kts (23.5 sust.) sub. **Dim:** 73.60 × 7.60 × 6.45
A: 4 bow 533-mm TT (14 F 17 Mod. 2 torpedoes and SM 39 missiles, or up to 32 FG 29 mines)
Electronics:
Radar: 1 DRUA-33 nav./search
Sonar: DMUX-20 suite; DSUV-22 multifunction passive array; DUUA-2B active (8 kHz); DUUX-5 acoustic intercept, TUUM underwater telephone; DSUV-62C towed passive array; DUUG-2 sonar intercept
EW: ARUR-13 (Thales DR-4000U and DR-2000U) intercept suite
M: 1 CAS-48 48-Mw pressurized-water reactor, two 3,950-kw turboalternator sets, 1 electric motor; 1 prop; 9,500 shp—1 electric motor driven by batteries powered by 1 SEMT-Pielstick 8 PA4 V185 diesel generator set (480 kw)
Electric: 1,700 kw (2 × 850-kw alternators) **Endurance:** 60 days
Crew: two crews, each of 10 officers, 52 petty officers, 8 other enlisted

Remarks: *Améthyste* is both the name of the fifth unit and an acronym for *Amélioration Tactique Transmission Écoute* (reduced radiated noise transmission). S 602 was brought up to *Améthyste* standard from 10-89 to 5-91; S 601 from 9-92 to 7-93; S 603 during 1993–94; and S 604 from 5-94 to 12-95.

Names for the first three were changed in 11-80. *Rubis*'s reactor became operational early in 2-81 and trials started 6-81. S 605 and S 606 were ordered 17-10-84 and *Turquoise* (S 607) 24-4-90. Late in 9-91, it was announced that the eighth unit, *Diamant* (S 608), would not be built and that work on S 607 would not start until 1993. In 6-92, S 607 was canceled outright, but by 9-92, it had been decided to offer the incomplete submarine as a diesel-powered unit for export; no customer was found, however.

S 604 experienced a leak in the secondary steam loop on 30-3-94, resulting in the death of the commanding officer and nine other personnel. S 602 experienced excessive radioactivity in the primary reactor loop in 9-00 and was withdrawn from service for six months to undergo an unscheduled recoring. All six are based at Toulon. S 601 is planned to strike in 2010.
Hull systems: The pressure hull is constructed of HLES 80, 100,000-psi steel; the superstructure and external bow form are built of GRP. Diving depth is more than 300 m. The ships have two SAGEM Minicin inertial navigation systems and two databuses. Endurance on battery power is about 15 hours. The bow was reconfigured to a more streamlined shape and lengthened by 1.5 m in the four modernized units. The reactor uses natural water circulation cooling at speeds below 6 kts; the entire engineering plant is considerably noisier than on U.S. and British-built nuclear submarines.
Combat systems: All have the TITAC automated combat data system and NATO Link 14. Are receiving the SEAO/OPSMER combat decision-aid system. The number of reload weapons has been reduced to provide additional berthing. Have Pivair SPS-S optical search periscopes and the SFIM K-series search periscope.

Disposal note: Of the Agosta-class diesel-electric attack submarines, *Agosta* (S 620) was decommissioned 28-2-97 and placed in special reserve to await striking or foreign sale, and *Bévéziers* (S 621) followed on 6-2-98; *La Praya* (S 622) was retired 30-6-00; and *Ouessant* (S 623), which was to have been retained active as a trials platform for new submarine equipment, was decommissioned 1-7-01.

GUIDED-MISSILE DESTROYERS [DDG]

♦ 0 (+ 2 + 2) Forbin class (Project Horizon)
Bldr: DCN, Lorient

	Laid down	L	In serv.
D 616 Forbin	. . .	. . .	12-06
D 617 Chevalier Paul	. . .	. . .	4-08

Forbin (D 616)—artist's rendering French Navy, 2000

Forbin class—official model Norman Friedman, 10-01

D: 5,600 tons (6,700 fl) **S:** 29 kts
Dim: 150.60 (142.00 wl) × 20.40 (17.60 wl) × 5.40 (mean hull)
A: 8 MM 40 Mod. 2 Exocet SSM; 6 8-cell Sylver A50 SAM launch groups (32 tot. Aster-30 and 16 Aster-15 missiles); 2 6-round Sadral SAM syst. (Mistral missiles); 2 single 76-mm 62-cal. OTOBreda SuperRapid DP; 2 single 20-mm 90-cal. GIAT F2 AA; 4 fixed ASW torpedo launchers (MU-90 Impact torpedoes); 1 NH-90 helicopter (AM 39 Exocet missiles and/or MU-90 Impact torpedoes)
Electronics:
Radar: 2 DRBN-34 nav.; 1 EMPAR target desig./tracking; 1 DRBV-27 Astral missile target desig./f.c.; 1 MSTIS gun f.c.
Sonar: Thales-Marconi TMS 4110CL hull-mounted LF
EW: . . . intercept; 2 12-round Matra Défense NGDS decoy syst.; SLAT torpedo countermeasures syst.
E/O: DIBV-1A Vampir IR detection and tracking
M: CODAG: 2 Fiat-G.E. LM 2500 gas turbines, 2 SEMT-Pielstick . . . diesels, geared drive; 2 props; 62,560 shp max.—bow-thruster
Range: 3,500/25; 7,000/18 **Endurance:** 45 days
Crew: 190 tot. (accomm. for 222)

Note: Agreement was reached with the U.K. and Italy to design a ship acceptable to all three navies in a venture initially announced 12-3-91. An international joint-venture corporation, Horizon Ltd., was established 21-2-95 to build at least the initial units of the class for the three partner countries by the three then-prime contractors, GEC-Marconi, DCN International, and Orissonte SpA. The U.K. pulled out of the platform portion of the program on 21-4-99 but remains committed to the SAM

GUIDED-MISSILE DESTROYERS [DDG] *(continued)*

Forbin class—official model Norman Friedman, 10-01

program. On 16-9-99, it was decided that France and Italy would go ahead with a joint program, and an order for two ships was finally placed on 26-10-00. Plans for two more were canceled during 5-96 but are now to be reinstated, with the ships to be completed in 2010 and 2012 to replace *Cassard* and *Jean Bart*.

Hull systems: Will have fin stabilizers. Numerous radar, heat, and acoustic signature reduction measures are to be incorporated.

Combat systems: The combat data system will probably be a variant of SENIT 8. The ships will have an integrated communications system and will be NATO Improved Link 11–, Link 14–, and Link 16–compatible; they are to have Syracuse SHF and, possibly, EHF SATCOM systems, as well as Inmarsat UHF SATCOM. The helicopter will be used for ASW and for attacking surface ships with missiles and will be launchable and recoverable in up to Sea State 6. The torpedoes will be ejected through shutters in the hull sides beneath the helicopter pad.

Jean Bart (D 615) Bernard Prézelin, 7-00

Jean Bart (D 615) Bernard Prézelin, 7-00

Cassard (D 614) Bernard Prézelin, 7-00

♦ 2 Cassard class (Type C 70)

	Bldr	Laid down	L	In serv.
D 614 CASSARD	DCN, Lorient	3-9-82	6-2-85	29-7-88
D 615 JEAN BART	DCN, Lorient	12-3-86	19-3-88	1-9-91

D: 4,230 tons (4,730 fl) **S:** 29.6 kts

Dim: 139.00 (129.00 pp) × 14.00 × 6.50 (4.20 hull)

A: 8 MM 40 SSM; 1 Mk 13 SAM launcher (40 Standard SM-1 MR missiles); 2 6-round Sadral SAM syst. (39 tot. Mistral missiles); 1 100-mm 55-cal. Model 1968 DP; 2 single 20-mm 70-cal. Oerlikon AA; 4 single 12.7-mm mg; 2 fixed KD-59E torpedo catapults (10 L 5 Mod. 4 ASW torpedoes); 1 AS.365MF Panther liaison helicopter

Electronics:

Radar: 2 DRBN-34A (Decca RM 1229) nav./helicopter control; 1 DRBJ-11B 3-D air search; 1 DRBV-26C early warning; 2 Raytheon SPG-51C missile illumination; 1 DRBC-33A gun f.c.

Sonar: DUBA-25A (D 615: DUBA-24C) hull-mounted; TUUM-2D underwater telephone; NUBS-8A echo sounder—D 615 also: U/RDT-1A torpedo detection syst.

EW: ARBR-17 intercept; ARBB-33 Salamandre jammer; ARBG-1A Saigon comms VHFD/F; Telegon-10 HFD/F; 2 330- to 340-round AMBL-1C (Dagaie 2) decoy RL; 2 6-round AMBL-2A Sagaie countermeasures RL; SLQ-25 Nixie towed acoustic torpedo decoy syst.

E/O: DIBV-1A Vampir surveillance, DIBC-1A (Piranha III) IR/t.v./laser weapons director

M: 4 SEMT-Pielstick 18 PA6 V280 BTC diesels; 2 5-bladed props; 42,300 bhp

Electric: 3,400 kw (4 × 850-kw Jeumont-Schneider alternators, 4 AGO 195-V12-CSHR diesels driving)

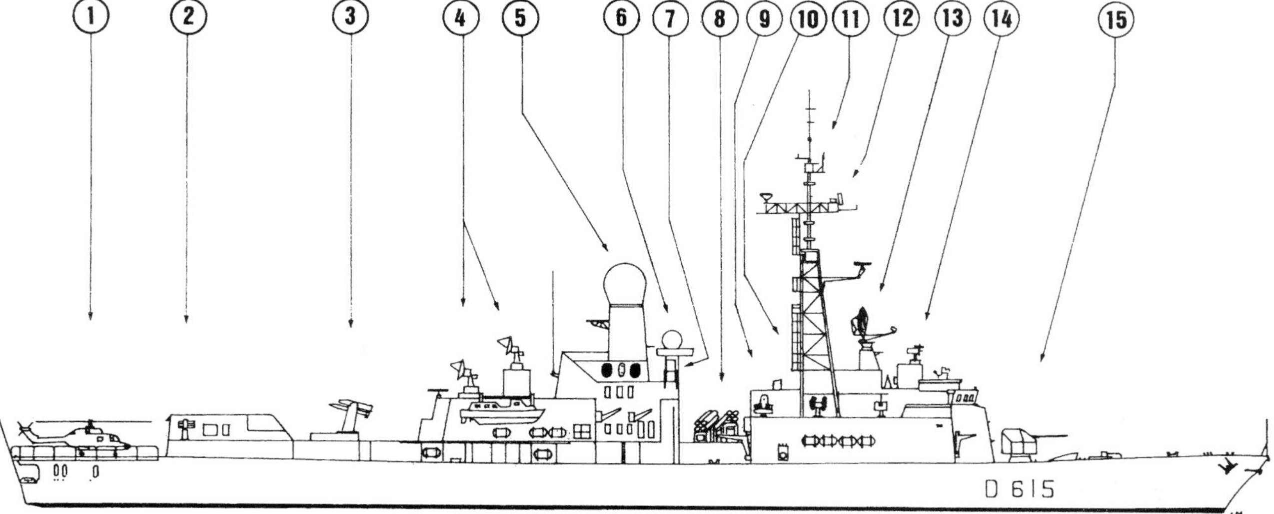

Jean Bart (D 615) 1. helicopter platform 2. Sadral SAM system (port and starboard) 3. Mk 13 launcher for Standard SM-1 SAM system 4. SPG-51C tracker-illuminator radars for the Standard SAM system 5. DRBJ-11B 3-D air-search radar 6. Syracuse SATCOM antenna radomes (port and starboard) 7. ARBB-33 ECM antennas 8. MM 40 Exocet antiship missiles (four missiles per set) 9. Dagaie decoy launcher 10. Sagaie decoy launcher 11. ARBR-17 ESM antennas 12. DIBV-1A Vampir IR surveillance syst. 13. DRBV-26C early-warning radar 14. DRBC-33 100-mm gun f.c. radar 15. 100-mm Model 1968 DP gun Drawing by Jean Moulin from *Flottes de Combat*

GUIDED-MISSILE DESTROYERS [DDG] *(continued)*

Cassard (D 614) Bernard Prézelin, 8-00

Georges Leygues (D 640)—as training ship John Mortimer, 2-0[illegible]

Range: 4,800/24; 8,000/17 **Fuel:** 600 tons **Endurance:** 30 days
Crew: 25 officers, 154 petty officers, 71 nonrated

Remarks: Typed as *Frégates Lance-Missiles* (FLM). Part of the 1977–82 program; D 614 was authorized under the 1978 budget and D 615 under 1979. A third and fourth were authorized in 1983 but were canceled 27-2-84; they were to have been named *Chevalier Paul* (D 616) and *Courbet* (D 617). Both are based at Toulon.
Hull systems: There are 16 watertight bulkheads to the hull. Aluminum superstructure. Fin stabilizers are fitted. Have an NBC warfare protection citadel system. The main engines are rated at 10,800 bhp at 1,050 rpm. A SAMAHE 210 *(Système d'Aide à la Manutention des Hélicoptères Embarqués)* deck traversing system is fitted for the helicopter. Have two "Mini SINS" inertial navigation aids.
Combat systems: Have the SENIT 6 digital data system, with Link 11 and 14 datalink capability. The DRBC-33 radar fire-control director has a Piranha III optronic attachment and is backed up by a Najir III DMaB optronic t.v./laser director. Also installed are two Matra Défense Type 88-DD00-ZA optronic target designators. The Mk 13 SAM launchers and missile fire-control systems were taken from the retired destroyers *Kersaint* and *Bouvet*. Both were at one time planned to receive the SAMP/N SAM system with Aster-30 missiles in place of Standard SM-1 MR. The Model 1968 CADEM gun has a 78-rd/min firing capability. The helicopter can be used to provide over-the-horizon targeting for the antiship missiles.

The intended DRBJ-11B radar in D 614 was initially replaced by DRBV-15 because of developmental problems; she was brought up to the same standard as D 615 in 1992. The EW sensor arrays are integrated by the NEWSY system, with a dedicated computer. Thales SPIN jam-resistant HF radios are fitted, as is the Syracuse SATCOM. The space beneath the helicopter deck was intended to accommodate a DSBV-61 towed linear passive hydrophone array system.

Note: Of the two *Suffren*-class guided-missile destroyers, the *Suffren* (D 602) was placed in disposal reserve 2-4-01, and the Masurca SAM system on the *Duquesne* (D 603) is no longer operational; the class is now listed as a [DD] after the *Tourville* class.

Montcalm (D 642)—modernized unit; note dual helicopter hangar, massive VDS installation, and new antenna for the DRBV-51C radar atop the foremast
Bernard Prézelin, 6-0[illegible]

DESTROYERS [DD]

♦ 7 Georges Leygues class (Type F 70) Bldr: DCN, Brest

	Laid down	L	In serv.
D 640 Georges Leygues	16-9-74	17-12-76	10-12-79
D 641 Dupleix	17-10-75	2-12-78	16-6-81
D 642 Montcalm	5-12-75	31-5-80	28-5-82
D 643 Jean de Vienne	26-10-79	17-11-81	25-5-84
D 644 Primauguet	19-11-81	17-3-84	5-11-86
D 645 La Motte-Picquet	9-2-82	6-2-85	18-2-88
D 646 Latouche-Tréville	31-5-85	19-3-88	16-7-90

Primauguet (D 644)—unmodernized unit; note the higher bridge superstructure typical of D 644–646 Bernard Prézelin, 3-0[illegible]

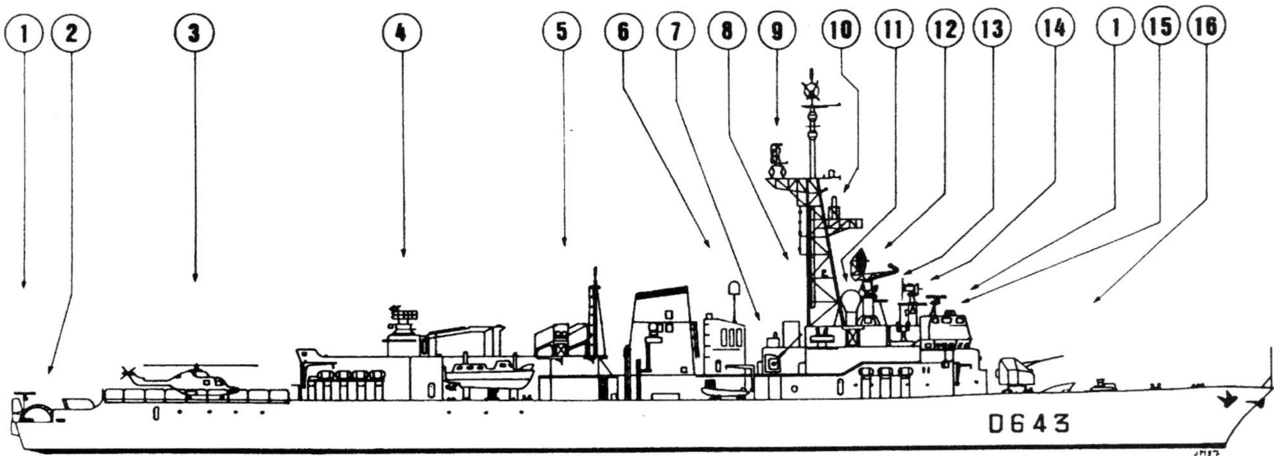

Jean de Vienne (D 643) 1. DRBN-32 radar for helicopter landing control 2. DUBV-43C VDS 3. Lynx helicopter 4. Crotale SAM launcher (abaft reload magazine) 5. MM 40 Exocet antiship missile launchers (now two twin sets per side on D 643 only) 6. Inmarsat SATCOM antenna radome 7. 30-mm AA 8. Dagaie decoy launcher 9. DRBC-51C air-search and targeting radar 10. DIBC-2A IR surveillance sensor and f.c. director 11. Syracuse SATCOM antenna radomes 12. DRBV-26 early-warning radar 13. ARBB-36 ECM antennas 14. DRBC-32E gun f.c. radar 15. Sadral SAM syst. 16. 100-mm Model 1968 DP gun. This drawing in general applies to D 641–643.
Drawing by Jean Moulin from *Flottes de Comba[illegible]*

DESTROYERS [DD] *(continued)*

Dupleix (D 641)—modernized, with improved self-defense features ABPH Tony Barclay-Jeffs, RAN, 3-01

La Motte-Piquet (D 645)—unmodernized unit Bernard Prézelin, 4-01

Latouche-Tréville (D 646)—with four MM 40 Exocet missiles aboard Hartmut Ehlers, 3-00

D: D 640: 3,550 tons (4,350 fl)—D 641–643: 3,831 tons (4,500 fl)—D 644–646: 3,680 tons (4,580 fl)
S: 30 kts (gas turbines); 21 kts (diesels)
Dim: 139.00 (129.00 pp) × 14.00 × 5.50 (hull; 5.80–5.86 props)
A: D 640 only: 4 MM 38 Exocet; 1 8-round Crotale EDIR SAM syst. (26 missiles); 2 2-round Simbad SAM syst.; 1 100-mm 55-cal. Model 1968 CADAM DP; 2 single 20-mm 70-cal. Oerlikon Mk 10 Mod. 23 AA; 2 single 12.7-mm mg; 2 fixed KD-59E torpedo catapults (10 L 5 Mod. 4 ASW torpedoes); 2 WG-13 Lynx helicopters
D 641–646: 4–8 MM 40 (D 641: 4 MM 38) Exocet SSM; 1 8-round Crotale EDIR SAM syst. (26 missiles)—D 641–643 only: 2 6-round Sadral SAM syst. (39 Mistral missiles)—D 645 only: 2 2-round Simbad SAM syst. (. . . Mistral missiles)—all: 1 100-mm 55-cal. Model 1968 CADAM DP—D 641–643: 2 single 30-mm 70-cal. OTOBreda-Mauser AA; others: 2 single 20-mm 70-cal. Oerlikon Mk 10 Mod. 23 AA—all: 2 single 12.7-mm mg; 2 fixed KD-59E torpedo catapults (10 L 5 Mod. 4 ASW torpedoes); 1–2 WG-13 Lynx helicopters

Electronics:
Radar: D 640, 641, 643: 2 DRBN-32 nav.; 1 DRBV-26 early warning; 1 DRBV-51C surf./air search; 1 DRBC-32E gun f.c.—D 642, 644–646: 2 DRBN-32 nav.; 1 DRBV-15A surf./air search; 1 DRBC-33A gun f.c.
Sonar: D 640–643: DUBV-23 hull-mounted; DUBV-43B (D 643: DUBV-43C) VDS—D 641 also: DSBV-62C towed array—D 644–646: DUBV-24C hull-mounted; DUBV-43C VDS; DSBV-61A towed array
EW: D 640, 641, 643: ARBR-16 (DR-2000S) intercept; ARBB-36A jammer; ARBR-11B D/F; ARBX-10 radar intercept; Telegon-4 HFD/F; 2 33- or 34-round AMBL-1C Dagaie Mk 2 decoy RL; 2 twin Replica floating radar decoys; SLQ-25A Nixie towed acoustic torpedo decoy syst.—D 642, 644–646: ARBR-17 (DR-4000) intercept; ARBB-32B jammer; 2 33- or 34-round AMBL-1C Dagaie Mk 2 decoy RL; 2 twin Replica floating radar decoys; SLQ-25 Nixie towed acoustic torpedo decoy syst.—D 644, 645 also: ARBG-1A Saigon HF/VHF comms monitoring syst.
E/O: D 640, 641, 643, 645: DIBV-2A Vampir IR surveillance—D 640–643: 2 DIBC-2A f.c.—D 645, 646: Piranha III t.v./IR f.c. for 100-mm gun

M: CODOG: 2 Rolls-Royce Olympus TM-3B gas turbines (26,000 shp each), 2 SEMT-Pielstick 16 PA6C V280 diesels (5,360 bhp each); 2 4-bladed CP props; 52,000 shp max. (gas turbine; 46,000 shp sust.; 10,720 bhp on diesels)
Electric: 3,400 kw (4 × 850-kw diesel alternator sets)
Range: 1,000/30; 10,000/15 (diesels) **Fuel:** 600 tons distillate
Crew: D 640: 15 officers, 90 petty officers, 111 nonrated—D 643 and other OP3A modernization ships: 22 officers, 145 petty officers, 77 nonrated—D 645: 20 officers, 120 petty officers, 95 nonrated

Remarks: D 645 and D 646 were built at Brest and fitted out at Lorient Dockyard. The final three had a modified sensor suite and the pilothouse placed one deck higher. D 646 is based at Brest; D 641–644 are based at Toulon as part of the Force d'Action Navale (FAN). D 640 is based at Toulon, became companion ship to the cadet training ship *Jeanne d'Arc* in 7-99, and was to be retired during 2000 but will now operate until 2008. The others were scheduled to retire between 2004 and 2014 but are now planned to be retained until they have been in service for 30 years—without further significant modernization.

Hull systems: Denny Brown 21.5-m^2 automatic fin stabilizers are fitted, and the propellers have air venting to reduce cavitation noise. The propeller shafts are not cross-connectable. Have an NBC warfare protective citadel, and the navigation bridge is equipped with two optical periscopes. Accommodations for female crewmembers are incorporated in all. An Arcor 670 launch is carried to port, a 9-m, 250-bhp VD 9 launch to starboard, and two Zodiac RIBs stowed on deck. The helicopter deck has a SPHEX

DESTROYERS [DD] *(continued)*

(Système Pousseur pour Hélicoptère Embarqué Expérimental) Compact-II landing system with harpoon-type landing grid and two deck-traversing rails to move the helicopters in and out of the spacious hangar, which is 13.5 m long, 11.4 m wide, and 4.3 m high.

Propulsion systems: Main propulsion and auxiliary equipment is divided among four compartments: from forward to aft, forward auxiliary room, turbine room, diesel room with the reduction gears, and after auxiliary room. Full speed on the gas turbines can be reached in 3 minutes from a standing start. On diesel power and with the DUBV-43 sonar in the water, maximum speed is 19 kts. The propulsion control system transfers power automatically from the diesels to the gas turbines. Centralized control of the propulsion machinery from the bridge greatly reduces the engineering staff required (3 officers, 23 petty officers, 24 ratings).

Combat systems: Have the SENIT 4 data system with eight multifunction display stations, are equipped for NATO Link 11 and Link 14, and have Syracuse II SHF and commercial Inmarsat SATCOM equipment. All have the "Minicin" inertial navigation system. The helicopters can be used for ASW with Mk 46 Mod. 5 torpedoes or Mk 54 depth bombs or for antiship duties with AS 12 missiles. In D 643, there are four twin racks for MM 40 missiles, while in the other MM 40 ships there are two quadruple racks. Normally, only four missiles are carried in the MM 40 ships.

Under the OP3A *(Opération d'Amélioration de l'Autodéfense Anti-missiles)* program, all but D 640 were to be equipped with Mistral infrared-homing missiles with either sextuple Sadral or twin Simbad launchers, two 30-mm OTOBreda-Mauser mounts in place of the 20-mm mounts, two DIBC-2A (SAGEM VIGY 105) optronic directors, a DIBV-2A Vampir infrared surveillance and tracking system, and the ARBB-36A jamming system. The control position for the new weapons systems, installed first in D 643 in 1996, is located in a new deckhouse atop the bridge superstructure and is used to provide own-ship defense within a 10-km radius. OP3A provides very rapid reaction time as well as continuous monitoring of the ship's vicinity by a variety of optical, infrared, and radar sensors; a total of 16 video displays are provided for the various operators, with the unified system being known as SENIT 8.01 (or SARA) and interfaces with the principal SENIT 4 system. The deckhouse is surmounted by a faceted conical cockpit structure for the close-defense systems control petty officer, who has windows to see outside and is surrounded by the control displays. D 641 completed similar modifications in 4-99, and D 642 received the equipment during 1999–2000. The 30-mm guns can be controlled either from the OP3A station by means of the VIGY 105 E/O system; from small manned directors placed one deck above the guns; or, in an emergency, by an on-mount operator. Six ready-service reload Mistral missiles can be stowed near each Sadral launcher. D 644–646 are to be equipped to carry two Simbad modular twin, manned launchers for the Mistral missile rather than the more expensive Sadral. The 12.7-mm mg are mounted near the Crotale SAM launcher. D 641–643 have the SEAO/OPSMER combat decision-aid system.

The VDS employs a 10-ton "fish" and has been modified to operate at depths down to 700 m; it is normally operated concurrently with the bow-mounted sonar. D 644 and D 645 have the SAIGON *(Système Automatisé d'Interception et de Goniométries de Émissions)* VHF/UHF communications intercept system. During refits, the ARBB-32 jammer is being replaced by ARBB-36 (Dassault Salamandre). D 642, D 644, and D 646 have a new antenna for the DRBV-15 radar.

♦ 2 Tourville class (Type F 67, ex-C 67A) Bldr: DCN, Lorient

	Laid down	L	In serv.
D 610 Tourville	3-70	13-5-72	21-6-74
D 612 De Grasse	1972	30-11-74	1-10-77

Tourville (D 610) Bernard Prézelin, 4-01

Tourville (D 610) Bernard Prézelin, 4-01

De Grasse (D 612) Bernard Prézelin, 3-01

De Grasse (D 612) Bernard Prézelin, 3-01

D: 4,650 tons (5,885 fl) **S:** 32 kts
Dim: 152.75 (142.0 pp) × 15.80 (15.30 wl) × 5.70 (hull; 6.60 props)
A: 6 MM 38 Exocet SSM; 1 8-round Crotale EDIR SAM syst. (24 tot. missiles); 2 single 100-mm 55-cal. Model 1968 DP; 2 single 20-mm 70-cal. Mk 10 Mod. 23 Oerlikon AA; 4 single 12.7-mm mg; 2 fixed KD-59E torpedo catapults (10 L 5 Mod. 4 ASW torpedoes); 1–2 WG-13 Lynx ASW helicopters
Electronics:
Radar: 2 DRBN-32 nav.; 1 DRBV-26A early warning; 1 DRBV-51B air/surf. search; 1 DRBC-32D f.c.; 1 DRBC-32 f.c.
Sonar: DUBV-23 hull-mounted; DSBX-1 SLASM bistatic active VDS with SYVA torpedo-warning adjunct
EW: ARBR-16 intercept; ARBB-32 jammer; 2 8-round Syllex decoy RL; SLQ-25 Nixie towed acoustic torpedo decoy syst.
E/O: DIBV-1A Vampir IR surveillance
M: 2 sets Rateau double-reduction geared steam turbines; 2 props; 54,400 shp
Boilers: 4 asymmetric, multitube, automatic-control; 45 kg/cm², 450° C
Electric: 4,440 kw (2 × 1,500-kw turbogenerators, 3 × 480-kw diesel alternators)
Range: 1,900/30; 4,500/18 **Crew:** 24 officers, 178 petty officers, 96 ratings

Remarks: Sister *Duguay-Trouin* (D 611), refitted 2-93 to 1-94 and equipped as a flagship, was retired 13-7-99 without modernization. D 610 is to be retired in 2008 and D 612 not until 2011. Both are based at Brest.

Hull systems: Had a heavy stiffening strake added after completion at the upper deck level amidships to prevent hull cracking. Fin stabilizers and an NBC warfare protective citadel are fitted. During her Crotale installation refit, D 610 had her boilers converted to burn distillate fuel, which had been burned by the others from the outset. During 1990s modernizations, provisions storage areas were improved and the former Malafon ASW missile magazine was converted to accommodations and office spaces.

Combat systems: The SENIT 3 data system is fitted. D 610 was equipped with the Crotale antiaircraft missile system in 1980, and D 612 in 1981. In preparation for Crotale, the third 100-mm gunmount atop the helicopter hangar on D 610 was removed; it was never carried by D 612. The Crotale EDIR missile system was substituted in 1990. Carry AS 12 wire-guided missiles, as well as Mk 46 Mod. 5 torpedoes and depth charges for the helicopters.

During refit from 2-94 to 9-95, D 610 was refitted and received the prototype DSBX-1 SLASM *(Système de Lutte ASM)* towed low-frequency active sonar array installation and provision for the Milas antisubmarine missile system in place of Malafon (France has since left the Milas program). In addition, ARBB-33 jammers were added, the Thales Altesse decision aid was added, and Syracuse II replaced the Syracuse I SATCOM system. Planned replacement of the obsolescent Syllex countermeasures launchers by two Sagaie launchers has not occurred. D 612 received the same modifications during 9-95 to 8-96 refit. Both have the SEAO/OPSMER combat decision-aid system.

♦ 1 Suffren class

	Bldr	Laid down	L	In serv.
D 603 Duquesne	DCN, Brest	1-2-65	11-2-66	1-4-70

Duquesne (D 603) H&L Van Ginderen, 10-99

D: 5,335 tons (6,910 fl) **S:** 34 kts
Dim: 157.60 (148.00 pp) × 15.54 × 7.25 (max.)
A: 4 MM 38 Exocet SSM; 2 single 100-mm 55-cal. Model 1964 DP; 4 single 20-mm 70-cal. Oerlikon AA; 4 single 12.7-mm mg; 2 fixed KD-59E torpedo catapults (10 L 5 Mod. 4 ASW torpedoes)

DESTROYERS [DD] *(continued)*

Duquesne (D 603) Bernard Prézelin, 4-01

Electronics:
Radar: 1 DRBN-32 nav.; 1 DRBV-15 air/surf. search; 1 DRBI-23 3-D air search; 1 DRBC-33A gun f.c.
Sonar: DUBV-23 hull-mounted; DUBV-43 VDS
TACAN: NRBP-2A (U.S. URN-20)
EW: ARBR-17 intercept; ARBB-33 Salamandre jammer; Telegon-4 HFD/F; 2 6-round AMBL-2A Sagaie decoy RL; SLQ-25 Nixie towed acoustic torpedo decoy syst.
E/O: DIBC-1A (Piranha III) optronic weapons director
M: 2 sets Rateau double-reduction geared steam turbines; 2 props; 72,500 shp
Boilers: 4 multitube, automatic-control; 45 kg/cm^2, 450° C
Electric: 3,440 kw (2 × 1,000-kw turbogenerators, 3 × 480-kw diesel alternators)
Range: 2,000/30; 2,400/29; 5,100/18
Crew: 24 officers, 209 petty officers, 113 ratings

Remarks: Typed as *Frégates Lance-Missiles* (FLM). Built under the 1960–65 plan. Sister *Suffren* (D 602) was placed in disposal reserve on 2-4-01, several years ahead of schedule. The Masurca SAM system was reportedly deactivated during 2000. Based at Toulon.
Hull systems: Three pairs of nonretractable fin stabilizers provide excellent seaworthiness. Living and operating spaces are air-conditioned. Has an NBC warfare protection citadel.
Combat systems: In a refit ending during 1991, the DRBC-33 fire-control radar with Piranha III optronic (t.v., laser, infrared) attachment was substituted for DRBC-32, the ARBR-17 and ARBB-33 EW equipment was substituted for earlier equipment, the *Amélie* microcomputer-assisted data system was added, the Masurca SAM system was updated, the SENIT 1 combat data system was updated to SENIT 2, the DRBI-23 radar received a transistorized transmitter and receiver, and the DUBV-43 variable-depth sonar was modernized. The 100-mm guns fire at up to 78 rds/min. Has two SAGEM DMA optronic target designation sights. The Malafon ASW missile system was removed in 1998, and the Masurca SAM system was no longer being operated as of 2000, although the launcher and two DRBR-51 radar tracker/illuminators are still aboard; 48 missiles were carried for the single twin-rail launcher. Syracuse SATCOM equipment is fitted.

FRIGATES [FF]

◆ **0 (+ 17) Frégates d'Action Navale program**
Bldr: DCN, Lorient (In serv. 2008–15)

D: 4,500 tons (. . . fl) **S:** . . . kts **Dim:** . . . × . . . × . . .
A: . . . SCALP-EG SSM; 1 100-mm or 155-mm gun; 1–2 NH-90 helicopters
Electronics: . . .
M: . . .
Range: . . ./. . . **Crew:** fewer than 100 tot.

Remarks: Intended to replace the *Tourville-* and *Georges Leygues*–class destroyers. Two versions are planned to be built on the same hull, propulsion system, and combat data system: eight in the ASW-oriented FASM *(Frégate d'Action Anti-Sous-Marin)* configuration and nine in the land-attack cruise missile–configured FAVT *(Frégate d'Action Vers la Terre)* version. The cruise missile envisioned for the latter version is apparently to be a vertically launched variant of the SCALP-EG, with a new airframe married to the current guidance system. Both versions will be able to launch the land-attack missiles, but only the FAVT will have independent targeting facilities; the FASM will have a more elaborate sonar suite. Both will also have vertically launched Aster-15 SAMs for self-defense, and a 127-mm DP gun is planned. The basic design may be based on an enlarged variant of the *La Fayette* class. That all 17 will actually be built is unlikely.

◆ **5 La Fayette class**
Bldr: DCN, Lorient

	Laid down	L	In serv.
F 710 La Fayette	15-12-90	13-6-92	22-3-96
F 711 Surcouf	6-7-92	3-7-93	7-2-97
F 712 Courbet	15-9-93	12-3-94	1-4-97
F 713 Aconit (ex-*Jauréguiberry*)	5-8-96	8-7-97	3-6-99
F 714 Guépratte	1-10-98	3-3-99	29-10-01

Guépratte (F 714) Bernard Prézelin, 4-01

La Fayette (F 710) Bernard Prézelin, 7-00

Courbet (F 712) Flottenkommando, 10-00

Aconit (F 713) Bernard Prézelin, 5-01

D: 3,200 tons (3,600 fl) **S:** 25 kts
Dim: 124.20 (115.00 pp) × 15.40 (13.60 wl) × 4.10 (hull; 4.80 max.)
A: 8 MM 40 Exocet Block 2 SSM; 1 8-round Crotale CN2 SAM syst.; (24 VT-1 missiles); 1 100-mm 55-cal. Model 1968 CADAM DP; 2 single 20-mm 90-cal. GIAT F2 AA; 2 single 12.7-mm mg; 1 AS.565MA Panther helicopter

FRIGATES [FF] *(continued)*

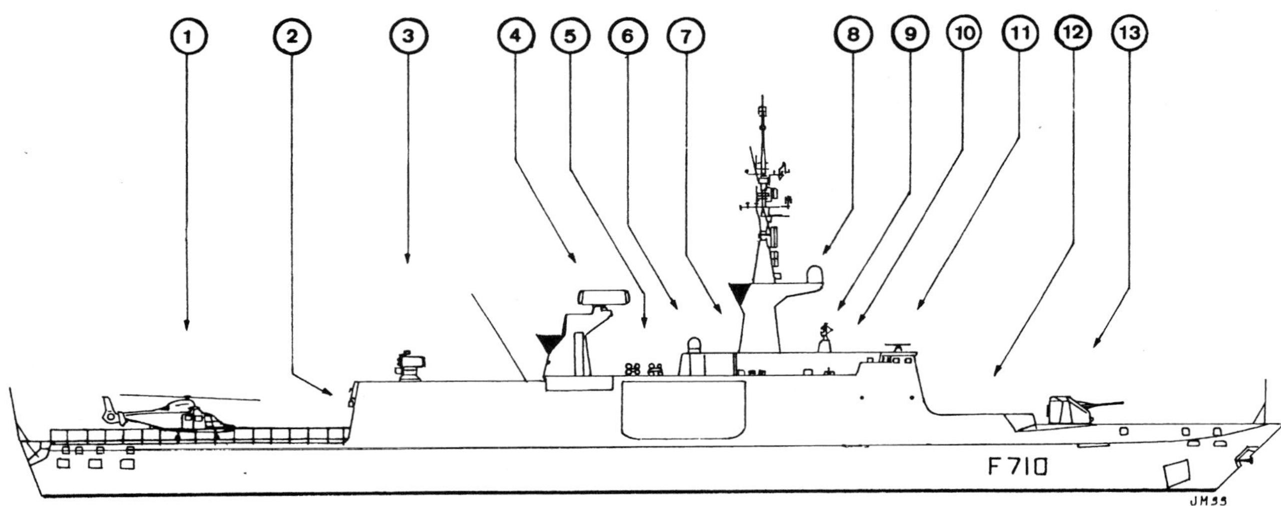

La Fayette (F 710) 1. Panther helicopter 2. helicopter hangar 3. Crotale SAM launcher 4. DRBV-15C search and targeting radar 5. MM 40 Exocet missiles 6. Inmarsat SATCOM antenna radome 7. Dagaie decoy launcher 8. Syracuse II SHF SATCOM antenna radome 9. Castor-IIJ gun f.c. radar 10. 20-mm F2 AA on bridge wings 11. Decca 20V90 navigational radar 12. Space and volume reserved for later backfitting of the SAAM missile system 13. 100-mm Model 1968 DP gun

Drawing by Jean Moulin from *Flottes de Combat*

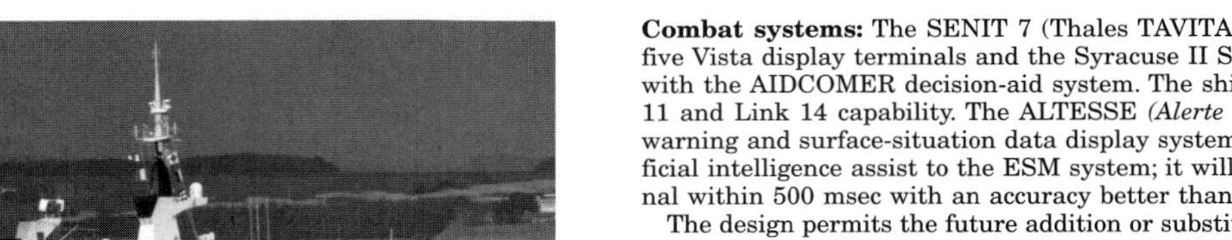

Courbet (F 712) Mike Welsford, 10-00

Electronics:

Radar: 2 Decca 20V90 nav.; 1 DRBV-15C 3-D surf./air search; 1 Castor-IIJ f.c.; 1 Crotale f.c.

Sonar: none

EW: ARBR-21 intercept; ARBB-33 Salamandre jammer—F 710–712: ARBG-1A Saigon VLF–UHF/DF—F 713, 714: ARBG-2 Maigret; 2 33- or 34-round AMBL-1C Dagaie Mk 2 decoy RL; SLQ-25 Nixie towed acoustic torpedo decoy syst.

E/O: SAGEM TDS 90 target desig. sight

M: 4 SEMT-Pielstick 12 PA6 V280 STC, 1,050-rpm, sequentially turbocharged diesels; 2 5-bladed CP props; 21,000 bhp (23,200 overload)—bow-thruster

Electric: 2,150 kw (3 × 750-kw diesel sets: 440 and 115 V, 60 and 400 Hz)

Range: 7,000/15; 9,000/12 **Fuel:** 350 tons usable + 80 m^3 aviation fuel

Endurance: 50 days

Crew: 15 officers, 85 petty officers, 53 ratings + 25 commandos

Remarks: Although typed as frigates, they are intended for patrol of overseas possessions and a role in the protection of Europe in a crisis and have no ASW sensors or weapons; their effectiveness is further hindered by their low maximum speed. The first three were ordered 14-3-88 and the second three 23-9-92; construction of the sixth unit, *Ronarc'h* (F 715), was canceled during 5-96. Six similar ships with heavier armament were built for Taiwan, and three are under construction for Saudi Arabia. F 710 was brought up to the same equipment standard as the second and third units during a 2-98 to 6-98 refit. The first three are based at Toulon as part of the Naval Action Force (FAN).

Hull systems: A particular effort has been made to reduce the ships' signatures; the diesel propulsion engines are mounted in pairs on isolation platforms, and the superstructure, masts, and forecastle are covered with a radar-reflecting GRP-resin compound. Much of the superstructure is built of a sandwich of GRP and balsa wood layers. Vertical hull and superstructure surfaces are slanted at ±10° to control radar reflectivity. The ships are also fitted with degaussing equipment, extensive NBC warfare protection, and, on all but F 714, the Prairie/Masker hull and propeller air bubbling system to reduce acoustic radiation. Special armor is provided for the magazines and operations spaces. All chocks and bollards are covered to reduce radar reflectivity. Boats are stowed in superstructure recesses that are covered with retractable screens to reduce radar reflection; near the waterline on both beams is a door providing access to the boats once launched.

The ships employ a modified deep-vee hullform, fin stabilizers, and rudder-controlled roll reduction to improve seaworthiness. There are two rudders, and the hullform incorporates twin skegs aft. Hull has 11 watertight compartments. A stern compartment holds 5-m semi-rigid boats for use by embarked commando forces; the boats are placed in the sea and recovered via a traveling crane on the inside of the stern door. The SAMAHE *(Système d'Aide à la Manutention des Hélicoptères Embarqués)* deck transit system is installed for helicopter movement on the 30 × 15-m flight deck, and there is a 1.8-m-diameter grid for the Harpoon positive landing system; the ships are able to launch and recover 10-ton helicopters in sea states up to 5 to 6. Can carry up to 60 tons fresh water (and evaporators can produce up to 36 tons per day) and 80 m^3 of aviation fuel (sufficient for 150 flying hours).

Combat systems: The SENIT 7 (Thales TAVITAC 2000) combat data system with five Vista display terminals and the Syracuse II SATCOM system are carried, along with the AIDCOMER decision-aid system. The ships are equipped with NATO Link 11 and Link 14 capability. The ALTESSE *(Alerte et Ténue de Situation de Surface)* warning and surface-situation data display system is being installed to provide artificial intelligence assist to the ESM system; it will provide direction finding of a signal within 500 msec with an accuracy better than 0.5°.

The design permits the future addition or substitution of later weapon systems, including two 8-cell Sylver vertical launch installations for Aster-15 missiles between the 100-mm gun and the bridge area, the associated Arabel radar, and the SLAT antitorpedo system. Some 600 rounds of 100-mm ammunition can be carried. One of the two Decca radars is mounted aft for helicopter control; both have ARPA consoles on the bridge and in CIC. The 20-mm AA mounts were still not carried as of early 1999. The Castor-IIJ gunfire-control radar can provide a second missile guidance channel. A digital internal communications system is fitted. F 710 has been used for trials with sextuple launchers for the Contralto rocket-propelled torpedo decoy system. Are planned to be backfitted with the OP3A/SENIT 8.01 self-defense combat control system, including improved EW arrays. F 713 and F 714 have a later-model communications intercept system, the German ARBG-2 Maigret system.

CORVETTES [FFL]

♦ 10 D'Estienne d'Orves class (Type A 69) Bldr: Lorient Arsenal

	Laid down	L	In serv.
F 788 Second-Maître Le Bihan	1-11-76	13-8-77	7-7-79
F 789 Lieutenant de Vaisseau Le Hénaff	11-13-77	16-9-78	13-2-80
F 790 Lieutenant de Vaisseau Lavallée	11-11-77	29-5-79	16-8-80
F 791 Commandant l'Herminier	7-5-79	7-3-81	19-1-86
F 792 Premier-Maître l'Her	15-12-78	28-6-80	15-12-81
F 793 Commandant Blaison	15-11-79	7-3-81	28-4-82
F 794 Enseigne de Vaisseau Jacoubet	11-4-79	26-9-81	23-10-82
F 795 Commandant Ducuing	1-10-80	26-9-81	17-3-83
F 796 Commandant Birot	23-3-81	22-5-82	14-3-84
F 797 Commandant Bouan (ex-*Commandant Levasseur*)	12-10-81	23-4-83	11-5-84

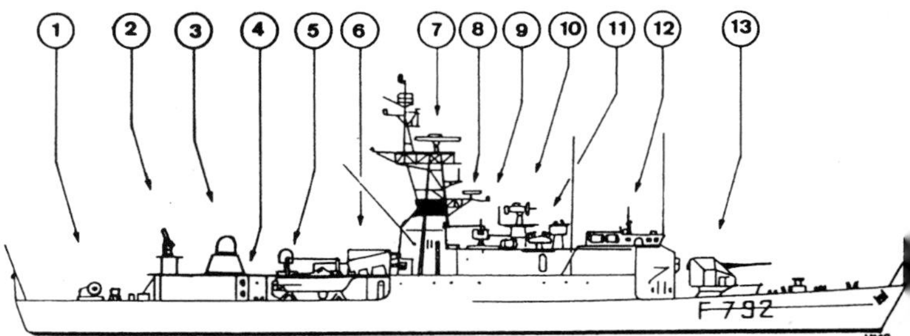

Premier-Maître l'Her (F 792) 1. SLQ-25 Nixie towed acoustic torpedo decoy and handling gear 2. Simbad SAM launcher 3. Syracuse II SHF SATCOM antenna radome 4. fixed ASW torpedo tubes in deckhouse 5. Inmarsat commercial SATCOM antenna radome 6. MM 40 Exocet antiship missile launchers 7. DRBV-51A air/surface-search radar 8. DRBN-32 navigational radar 9. 20-mm AA 10. DRBC-32E gun f.c. radar 11. Dagaie decoy launcher 12. 12.7-mm mg 13. 100-mm Model 1968 DP

Drawing by Jean Moulin from *Flottes de Combat*

D: F 788–791: 1,100 tons (1,250 fl)—F 792, 793: 1,140 tons (1,290 fl)—F 794–797: 1,175 tons (1,330 fl)

S: 23.3 kts **Dim:** 80.00 (76.00 pp) × 10.30 × 3.00–3.20 (5.30–5.50 sonar)

CORVETTES [FFL] *(continued)*

Commandant Bouan (F 797)—with Simbad SAM launcher aft, Syracuse II SATCOM, MM 40 Exocet antiship missiles, and four 12.7-mm mg
Bernard Prézelin, 6-00

Second-Maître le Bihan (F 788)—one of two still retaining a 375-mm ASW rocket launcher aft; note the lack of any antiship missiles Findler & Winter, 2-01

Commandant Blaison (F 793)—with Syracuse II SATCOM but with Simbad SAM platform empty Bernard Prézelin, 3-01

Enseigne de Vaisseau Jacoubet (F 794)—with Simbad missile launcher aboard
Cem D. Yaylali, 7-00

A: F 792–797: 4 MM 40 Exocet SSM—F 790 only: 2 MM 38 Exocet SSM—all: 1 100-mm 55-cal. Model 1968 CADAM DP—F 792–797 only: 1 2-round Simbad SAM syst. (. . .Mistral missiles)—all: 2 single 20-mm 70-cal. Mk 10 Mod. 23 Oerlikon AA; 2 or 4 single 12.7-mm mg—F 788 and 791 only: 1 6-round 375-mm Model 1972 F1 ASW rocket launcher—all: 4 fixed ASW TT (L 5 torpedoes; no reloads)

Electronics:
Radar: 1 DRBN-32 nav.; 1 DRBV-51A surf./air search; 1 DRBC-32E f.c.
Sonar: DUBA-25 hull-mounted MF
EW: ARBR-16 intercept; 2 33- or 34-round AMBL-1A Dagaie Mk 1 decoy RL; SLQ-25 Nixie towed acoustic torpedo decoy syst.

M: 2 SEMT-Pielstick 12 PC2 V400 diesels; 2 CP props; 12,000 bhp
Electric: 840 kw (2 × 320-kw, 1 × 200-kw diesel-driven sets)
Range: 4,500/15 **Endurance:** 15–20 days
Crew: 7 officers, 63 petty officers, 20 ratings—F 791–797 also: 9 commandos

Remarks: Very economical and seaworthy ships designed for coastal antisubmarine warfare, but available for scouting missions, training, and showing the flag. Although originally intended to accommodate a commando of 1 officer and 17 troops, they were not carried in practice until F 793 was modified to accommodate 9 special forces personnel during 1993 (F 791–797 now all have this feature). F 794–797 are based at Toulon and the others at Brest. F 792 and F 793 were transferred from Toulon to Brest during 2000.

Disposals: The original *Lieutenant de Vaisseau Le Hénaff* and *Commandant l'Herminier* were completed to a slightly modified design for South Africa and then sold to Argentina, which also ordered an additional unit. *Détroyat* (F 784) was retired 25-7-97, *Jean Moulin* (F 785) 14-5-99, *D'Estienne d'Orves* (F 781) 30-6-99, *Amyot d'Inville* (F 782) 30-7-99, *Drogou* (F 783) 27-7-00, *Quartier-Maître Anquetil* (F 786) 30-6-00, and *Commandant de Pimodan* (F 787) . . .-7-00. The sale to Turkey of the F 781–783 and F 786–788 was announced during 11-00. F 788 will retire in 2002, and the other surviving units are now to be retired between 2009 and 2014.

Hull systems: Only F 794–796 have fin stabilizers; F 797 has a "dynamic" stabilization system. Stacks and masts were modified from F 785 onward; the heightened stack was backfitted in earlier units. F 791 has 2 SEMT-Pielstick 12 PA6 BTC diesels totaling 14,400 bhp, with infrared signature suppression features; protracted trials delayed her commissioning.

Combat systems: The control system for the 100-mm gun consists of a DRBC-32E monopulse, X-band radar, and a semi-analog, semi-digital computer; there is also a Matra Défense Naja optical director. F 782 completed a refit in 11-86 with a new 100-mm gun, the U.S. SLQ-25 Nixie torpedo decoy, an upgraded sonar, Dagaie launchers, L 5 ASW torpedo capability, and a waste processing system; the others have been similarly upgraded during subsequent refits. Twin-launcher Simbad point-defense missile system trials were conducted with F 792 in 1989; another ship tested the Crotale Modulaire launcher in place of the 100-mm gun in 1987–88. In F 793, the ASW rocket launcher was replaced by an antenna for the Syracuse II SATCOM system in a refit completed 19-5-93; F 792 and F 794–796 have been similarly fitted, and ASW rocket launchers had been removed from all but F 788 and F 791 by 11-97. Toulon-based units have had a platform added aft atop the torpedo room deckhouse to accommodate the Simbad launcher, which had been installed in F 786, F 792, and F 797 by mid-1997. Most carry an Inmarsat terminal, with the antenna radome mounted amidships.

PATROL SHIPS [PS]

♦ 6 Floréal-class surveillance ships
Bldr: Chantiers de l'Atlantique, St.-Nazaire

	Laid down	L	In serv.	Based at
F 730 Floréal	2-4-90	6-10-90	27-5-92	La Réunion
F 731 Prairial	11-9-90	16-3-91	20-5-92	Papeete
F 732 Nivôse	16-1-91	11-8-91	15-10-92	Nouméa
F 733 Ventôse	28-6-91	14-3-92	20-4-93	Fort-de-France
F 734 Vendémiaire	17-1-92	23-8-92	20-10-93	Papeete
F 735 Germinal	17-8-92	14-3-93	17-5-94	Brest

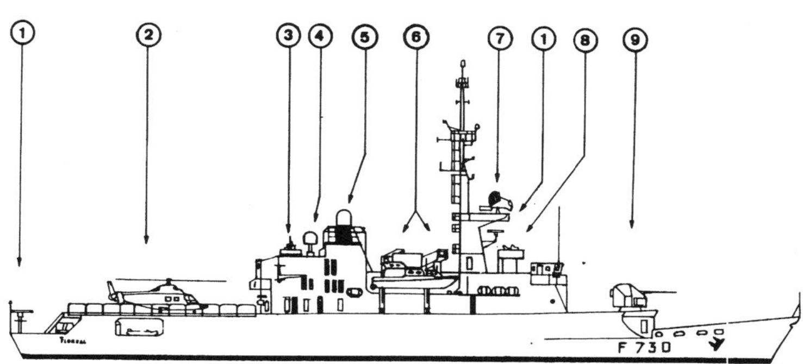

Floréal (F 730) 1. DRBN-34A navigational and helicopter approach control radars 2. Panther helicopter 3. 20-mm F2 AA 4. Inmarsat SATCOM antenna radome 5. Syracuse II SHF SATCOM antenna radome 6. MM 38 Exocet missile launchers 7. DRBV-21A air-search radar 8. Najir optronic gun f.c. radar 9. 100-mm Model 1968 DP gun Drawing by Jean Moulin from *Flottes de Combat*

Germinal (F 735) Bernard Prézelin, 3-00

D: 2,600 tons (2,950 fl) **S:** 20 kts **Dim:** 93.50 (85.20 pp) × 14.00 × 4.40
A: 2 MM 38 Exocet SSM; 1 100-mm 55-cal. Model 1968 CADAM DP; 2 single 20-mm 90-cal. GIAT F2 AA; 1 AS.565MA Panther or AS.319 Alouette-III helicopter (see Remarks)—F 735 also: 1 2-round Simbad SAM syst. (. . . Mistral missiles)

Electronics:
Radar: 2 DRBN-34A (Decca RM 1229) nav.; 1 DRBV-21A surf./air search
Sonar: none
EW: F 730, 733 only: ARBG-1A Saigon VHF–UHFD/F

M: 4 SEMT-Pielstick 6 PA6 L280 BTC diesels; 2 CP props; 8,800 bhp—250-kw bow-thruster

PATROL SHIPS [PS] *(continued)*

Prairial (F 731) Mitsuhiro Kadota, 11-00

Vendémiaire (F 734) Mitsuhiro Kadota, 11-00

Germinal (F 735) Bernard Prézelin, 3-00

Electric: 1,770 kw (3 × 590-kw sets, 3 Baudouin 12 P15 2SR diesels driving)
Range: 10,000/15 **Fuel:** 390 tons **Endurance:** 50 days
Crew: 13 officers, 45 petty officers, 42 ratings + 13 aviation party

Remarks: Intended for operations in low-risk areas for ocean surveillance, economic exclusion zone patrol, fisheries protection, and maritime policing duties. The first two were ordered 20-1-89, the next two 9-1-90, and the final pair during 2-91. Military equipment was added at the Lorient Arsenal after delivery by the builder. Home port for F 735 was changed from Brest in 1999 when she was relieved by *Georges Leygues* (D 640) as companion ship for the training vessel *Jeanne d'Arc.* Two sisters were ordered for Morocco in 10-98.
Hull systems: Constructed to Veritas commercial standards. Design emphasis was on seaworthiness, with helicopter operations possible in up to Sea State 5. Equipped with fin stabilizers. The helicopter hangar can accept the AS.332F Super Puma and will be able to accommodate the NH-90; they were initially assigned Alouette-III helicopters. Helicopter deck is 23 × 14 m. Have accommodations for 24 commandos, if required.
Combat systems: There is no SENIT combat data system. The 100-mm gun is controlled by a Matra Défense Najir optronic director. Provision is made for later installation of ARBR-17 (Thales DR-2000) intercept equipment and two Dagaie decoy rocket launchers. Two Simbad twin launchers for Mistral point-defense SAMs can be installed on the 20-mm gun foundations normally carried. One of the DRBN-34A radars has the antenna mounted on a post on the fantail to assist in helicopter landing control. Antennas for the Syracuse II SATCOM system have been installed in F 730 and F 733, while the others are fitted with an Inmarsat terminal.

♦ 1 fisheries patrol ship

Bldr: C.N. Le Trait, Le Havre (In serv. 1967)

P 681 ALBATROS (ex-*Névé*)

Albatros (P 681) Bernard Prézelin, 3-97

D: 1,940 tons (2,800 fl) **S:** 15 kts **Dim:** 85.00 (75.00 pp) × 13.50 × 6.00
A: 1 40-mm 60-cal. Bofors AA; 2 single 12.7-mm mg
Electronics: Radar: 2 Decca 1226 nav.—EW: ARUR-10B intercept
M: 2 SACM-AGO UD33V12 diesel generator sets (1,120 kw each), 2 electric motors; 1 prop; 2,310 shp—2 250-shp electric cruise motors
Electric: 750 kw (2 × 375-kw diesel sets) **Range:** 14,700/14; 25,000/9
Crew: 6 officers, 23 petty officers, 19 ratings + 15 passengers

Remarks: Former stern-haul trawler purchased 4-83 from Société Navale Caenaise for use in Antarctic-area fisheries patrol duties off Kerguelen, Crozet, St. Paul, and Amsterdam Islands. Commissioned in French naval service 23-3-84. Re-engined at Lorient during a 7-90 to 3-91 refit. Scheduled to remain in service until 2015. Based at La Réunion.
Hull systems: Has extensive hospital facilities, a 200-ton cargo capacity, and a helicopter vertical replenishment area aft, but no landing platform. Carries one launch and one small landing craft. Has an Inmarsat SATCOM terminal.

PATROL CRAFT [PC]

♦ 3 Flamant (OPV 54) class

	Bldr	Laid down	L	In serv.
P 676 FLAMANT	CMN, Cherbourg	3-94	24-4-95	18-12-97
P 677 CORMORAN	Leroux & Lotz, Lorient	25-5-94	15-5-95	29-10-97
P 678 PLUVIER	CMN, Cherbourg	1995	2-12-96	18-12-97

Flamant (P 676) Mike Welsford, 8-99

Pluvier (P 678) Bernard Prézelin, 4-00

D: 314 tons (390 fl) **S:** 23 kts (22 sust.)
Dim: 54.00 (48.50 pp) × 9.80 × 2.60 (2.90 props) **A:** 2 single 12.7-mm mg
Electronics: Radar: 1 Decca 250 nav.; 1 Decca 20V90 ARPA nav.
M: 2 Deutz-MWM TBD 620 V16 diesels (3,000 bhp each), 2 Deutz-MWM TBD 234 V12 diesels (980 bhp each); 2 CP props; 7,960 bhp tot.
Electric: 370 kw tot. (2 × 150-kw sets, Deutz-MWM TBD 234 diesels driving; 1 × 70-kw diesel set)
Range: 1,400/23; 4,500/12; 14,000/7.5 **Fuel:** 55 tons **Endurance:** 21 days
Crew: 4 officers, 10 petty officers, 6 ratings

Remarks: Typed PSP *(Patrouilleurs de Service Public).* Three units were ordered during 1992, but construction was delayed by the closing of the original contract yar

PATROL CRAFT [PC] *(continued)*

and the transfer of part of the contract to CMN, which also acquired the design rights; another hull was completed by Leroux & Lotz (LNI), Lorient, for Mauritania, and four larger versions were built for Morocco. Two more, to have been ordered spring 1995 for the French Navy, were canceled. P 676 is based at Cherbourg, the others at Brest.
Hull systems: Commercial design employing a deep-vee hullform capable of operating at speed in a State 4 sea. Have a stern embarkation ramp for a 7-m Hurricane rigid inflatable, waterjet-propelled inspection boat capable of 30 kts. Can also carry up to 22 passengers. A 400-m^3/hr firefighting monitor is installed, and there are two 7-m^3-capacity spill recovery holding tanks. Any combination of engines can be used to drive the shafts.
Combat systems: During 1998, P 677 was fitted with two additional navigational radars, the antennas mounted on the pilothouse roof. An Inmarsat-M SATCOM terminal is fitted.

♦ 1 Grèbe class

	Bldr	L	In serv.
P 679 Grèbe	SFCN, Villeneuve La Garenne	16-11-89	8-90

Grèbe (P 679) H&L Van Ginderen, 9-99

D: 300 tons (410 fl) **S:** 24 kts (23 sust.)
Dim: 52.00 (44.50 pp) × 9.80 × 2.30 (2.75 props)
A: 2 single 12.7-mm mg **Electronics:** Radar: 1 Decca 2690 ARPA nav.
M: 2 SACM-RVR UD33V12 RVR diesels; 2 CP props; 4,800 bhp—2 90-kw electric auxiliary propulsion motors; 250 shp (7.5 kts)
Electric: 370 kw tot. (2 × 150 kw, 1 × 70 kw)
Range: 1,400/23; 4,500/12; 14,000/7.5 (electric power) **Fuel:** 55 tons
Endurance: 21 days **Crew:** 4 officers, 9 petty officers, 6 ratings

Remarks: Ordered 13-7-88 and began trials 13-9-89. Based at Brest and used primarily as a fisheries protection craft. Commercial Espadon 50 design employing a deep-vee hullform capable of operating at speed in a State 4 sea. Has a stern embarkation ramp for an EDL 700, 7-m, waterjet-propelled RIB inspection boat capable of 30 kts. A 400-m^3/hr firefighting monitor is installed, and there are two 7-m^3-capacity spill-recovery holding tanks. An Inmarsat-M SATCOM terminal is fitted.

♦ 1 Jonathan-class fisheries protection craft
Bldr: SOCARENAM, Boulogne (In serv. 1990)

P 740 Fulmar (ex-*Jonathan*)

Fulmar (P 740) Bernard Prézelin, 4-99

D: 550 tons (680 fl) **S:** 12 kts **Dim:** 40.00 × 8.50 × 4.70
A: 1 12.7-mm mg **Electronics:** Radar: 2 Furuno . . . nav.
M: 1 Stork-Wärtsilä diesel; 1 prop; 1,200 bhp—bow-thruster
Range: 3,500/12 **Endurance:** 30 days **Crew:** 1 officer, 8 enlisted

Remarks: Former 200-grt side-haul fishing cutter purchased 10-96 from Meas Christian, Dunkerque, for use as a local patrol craft by the Gendarmarie Maritime at St.-Pierre and Miquelon. Was converted for naval service from 10-96 to 6-97 by LNI SY and DCN Lorient and commissioned during 2-99. Has an Inmarsat-M SATCOM terminal.

♦ 10 P 400 (Super PATRA) class Bldr: CMN, Cherbourg

	Laid down	L	In serv.	Op. Area/Base
P 682 L'Audacieuse	11-4-83	21-3-84	10-9-86	Cherbourg
P 683 La Boudeuse	15-6-83	21-5-84	25-7-86	Indian Ocean
P 684 La Capricieuse	12-9-83	31-10-84	26-9-86	Fr. Guiana
P 685 La Fougeuse	25-11-83	17-12-84	19-2-87	Fr. Guiana
P 686 La Glorieuse	21-2-84	25-1-85	25-3-87	Nouméa
P 687 La Gracieuse	26-4-84	26-3-85	17-7-87	Tahiti
P 688 La Moqueuse	4-10-84	8-4-86	25-3-87	Nouméa
P 689 La Railleuse	27-12-84	2-9-86	16-5-87	Tahiti
P 690 La Rieuse	14-3-85	17-10-86	13-6-87	Indian Ocean
P 691 La Tapageuse	13-8-85	16-2-87	24-2-88	Tahiti

La Boudeuse (P 683) H&L Van Ginderen, 3-00

L'Audacieuse (P 682) Mike Welsford, 6-00

D: 373 tons (480 fl) **S:** 23 kts **Dim:** 54.50 (50.00 pp) × 8.00 (7.70 wl) × 2.54
A: 1 40-mm 60-cal. AA; 1 20-mm 90-cal. GIAT F2 AA; 2 single 7.62-mm mg
Electronics: Radar: 1 DRBN-32 nav.
M: 2 SEMT-Pielstick 16 PA4 V200 VGDS diesels; 2 props; 8,000 bhp
Electric: 360 kw tot. (3 × 120-kw diesel sets)
Range: 4,200/15 **Fuel:** 73 tons **Endurance:** 15 days
Crew: 4 officers, 14 petty officers, 11 nonrated + 20 passengers

Remarks: First six ordered 5-82, the remainder 6-3-84.
Hull systems: Propulsion problems with P 682 greatly delayed the entire program, and the ships are well beyond their 422-ton designed displacement. P 682, P 683, and P 685 were fitted with two exhaust stacks abaft the bridge during 1990 to replace an unsuccessful underwater exhaust system; the others completed the modification by end-1995. Have two 35-m^3 cargo holds.
Combat systems: Carry 840 rounds of 40-mm and 2,100 rounds of 20-mm ammunition. Deck reinforced for possible addition of two Exocet missiles and a fire-control radar.

♦ 1 Sterne class
Bldr: A&C de la Perriere, Lorient

	Laid down	L	In serv.
P 680 Sterne (ex-PM 41)	18-5-79	31-10-79	18-7-80

Sterne (P 680) Bernard Prézelin, 10-00

D: 250 tons (340 fl) **S:** 19 kts **Dim:** 49.00 (43.60 pp) × 7.50 × 2.80
A: 2 single 12.7-mm mg
Electronics: Radar: 1 Furuno . . . nav.; 1 Decca 2690 ARPA nav.
M: 2 SACM V12 CZSHR diesels; 2 props; 4,200 bhp
Electric: 240 kw tot. (2 × 120 kw)
Range: 1,500/19; 4,900/12 **Endurance:** 15 days
Crew: 3 officers, 10 petty officers, 6 nonrated

PATROL CRAFT [PC] *(continued)*

Remarks: Constructed to merchant marine specifications for fisheries patrol duties within the 200-n.m. economic zone, including rescue services. Equipped with an infirmary. Based at Brest. Has a passive tank stabilization system. Can patrol at speeds up to 6.5 kts on an electrohydraulic drive system connected to the starboard propeller. Two RIB inspection dinghies are carried. An Inmarsat-M SATCOM terminal has been added.

♦ 2 Trident ("PATRA") class

	Bldr	L	In serv.	Based at
P 671 GLAIVE	Auroux, Arcachon	25-8-76	2-4-77	Cherbourg
P 672 ÉPÉE	CNM, Cherbourg	31-3-76	9-10-76	Lorient

Epée (P 672) Bernard Prézelin, 7-01

D: 120 tons (150 fl) **S:** 26 kts **Dim:** 40.70 (38.5 wl) × 5.90 × 1.60
A: 1 40-mm 60-cal. AA; 2 single 7.62-mm mg
Electronics: Radar: 1 DRBN-32 nav.
M: 2 AGO 195V12 CZSHR diesels; 2 CP props; 5,000 bhp (4,400 sust.)
Electric: 120 kw **Range:** 750/20; 1,500/15; 1,750/10
Crew: 2 officers, 15 enlisted

Remarks: Transferred to Gendarmerie Maritime control in 1986–87. Thirty were planned, then 14, but only four were finally built. Two sisters were also built for the Ivory Coast, and another, initially commissioned as *Rapiere* (P 674) in the French Navy, was sold to Mauritania in 1982. Were to have been retired during 2001–02 but have been extended to 2005–06 until they can be replaced by two new *Géranium*-class patrol boats.
Disposals: *Trident* (P 670) was stricken summer 1996, *Pertuisane* (P 673) early in 1997.
Combat systems: Carry 500 rounds of 40-mm and 2,000 rounds of 12.7-mm ammunition. Six SS 12 wire-guided missile launchers atop the superstructure have been replaced by the two 7.62-mm mg.

PATROL BOATS [PB]

Note: The Gendarmarie Maritime hopes to order some 22 20-m-long patrol boats between 2002 and 2010 to replace the large number of boats requiring replacement. The first 11 were ordered on 5-12-01 from Bénéteau Marine, L'Herbaudière, with the other 11 to be ordered in 2002 or 2003; no data available.

♦ 2 Jonquille-class vedettes
Bldr: Guy Couach–Plascoa, Bordeaux

	Laid down	L	In serv.	Based at
P 721 JONQUILLE	21-11-95	4-7-96	19-11-96	Papeete
P 723 JASMIN	1996	13-1-97	10-97	Port-des-Galets

Jonquille (P 721) Bernard Prézelin, 7-97

D: 82 tons (98 fl) **S:** 30 kts (28 sust.) **Dim:** 32.00 (29.00 wl) × 6.50 × 1.10
A: 1 12.7-mm mg; 1 7.62-mm mg
Electronics: Radar: 1 Decca BridgeMaster II CH180/6 nav.
M: 2 MWM-Deutz TRD 616 V16 diesels; 2 props outboard; 2,882 bhp—1 MWM-Deutz TRD 616 V12 diesel; 1 Hamilton 422 waterjet centerline; 1,082 bhp
Electric: 90 kw tot. (2 × 45-kw Onan diesel sets; 380 V a.c.)
Range: 1,200/15 **Endurance:** 10 days **Crew:** 12 tot.

Remarks: Builder's Plascoa-32 design. Have GRP hulls and GRP sandwich superstructures capable of withstanding 9-mm bullets. Are fitted with Sercel NR 58 GPS receivers and a JMC V-108A echo sounder. Differ from the *Géranium* class in having a different hullform and superstructure configuration; the hull is not pierced with portholes. Carry one RIB inspection boat. Are expected to serve for 25 years.

♦ 2 Géranium-class vedettes
Bldr: DCN, Lorient

	L	In serv.	Based at
P 720 GÉRANIUM	27-6-96	31-10-96	Cherbourg (Gendarmerie Maritime)
P 722 VIOLETTE	1996	2-97	Pointe-à-Pitre, Guadaloupe

Géranium (P 720) H&L Van Ginderen, 5-97

D: 73 tons light, 80 tons std. (100 fl) **S:** 30 kts (28 sust.)
Dim: 32.15 (30.50 pp) × 6.10 × 1.80
A: 1 12.7-mm mg; 1 7.62-mm mg
Electronics: Radar: 1 Decca Bridgemaster II CH180/6 nav.
M: 2 MWM-Deutz TRD 616 V16 diesels; 2 props outboard; 2,882 bhp—1 MWM-Deutz TRD 616 V12 diesel; 1 Hamilton 422 waterjet centerline; 1,082 bhp
Electric: 90 kw tot. (2 × 45-kw Onan diesel sets; 380 V a.c.)
Range: 1,200/15 **Endurance:** 10 days **Crew:** 14 tot.

Remarks: An expanded version of the 24-m P 60 class. P 720 made 30.5 kts on trials. Have GRP hulls and GRP sandwich superstructures capable of withstanding 9-mm bullets. Are fitted with Sercel NR 58 GPS receivers and a JMC V-108A echo sounder. Two sisters are in Affaires Maritime police service. Two more were to have been ordered in 2000 to replace the *Gliave* and *Épée* in Gendarmerie Maritime service, but no contract has been announced.

♦ 2 P 60 class
Bldr: DCN, Lorient

	L	In serv.	Based at
P 775 STELLIS	30-3-92	5-9-92	Cayenne, Fr. Guiana
P 776 STÉNIA	2-93	1-3-93	Pariacabo, Fr. Guiana

Stellis (P 775) H&L Van Ginderen, 7-00

D: 52 tons (60 fl) **S:** 28 kts **Dim:** 24.90 × 6.10 × 1.70 (max.)
A: 1 12.7-mm mg **Electronics:** Radar: 1 DRBN-32 nav.
M: 3 . . . diesels; 2 props, 1 waterjet; 2,520 bhp
Range: 700/22 **Crew:** 2 crews of 4 tot. each

Remarks: Operated for the Gendarmerie Maritime. Carry a rigid inflatable inspection craft handled by hydraulic crane to port. Hull forefoot is raked sharply forward.

♦ 6 Type V 14
Bldrs: Stento, Balaruc-les-Bains; DCN, Lorient (P 791: Sibiril, Grantec)

	In serv.	Based at
P 760 PÉTULANTE	30-3-85	Nouméa, New Caledonia
P 761 MIMOSA	20-3-87	Ajaccio
P 764 . . . (ex-Y 764)	10-4-88	Toulon
P 778 RÉSÉDA	1-10-87	Adour
P 789 MÉLIA	27-3-87	Toulon
P 791 HORTENSIA	1-8-90	Brest

PATROL BOATS [PB] *(continued)*

Hortensia (P 791) Bernard Prézelin, 4-00

D: 16 tons (20 fl) **S:** 20 kts **Dim:** 14.60 (13.20 wl) × 4.60 × 1.90 (1.20 hull)
A: 1 12.7-mm mg; 1 7.62-mm mg **Electronics:** Radar: 1 Decca 060 nav.
M: 2 Baudouin 12 F 11S diesels; 2 props; 800 bhp
Range: 360/18 **Crew:** 7 tot.

Remarks: GRP hulls. Designed by DCN Cherbourg. P 760 was begun as Y 760 by Corrocoat-Sodipia, Veyssière. Carry a rigid inflatable inspection dinghy on davits at the stern. The names became official in 1993, but P 764 has not been named. Twelve sisters serve as service launches (see under [YFL]) and three others as fireboats (see under [YTR]). Sister *Vétiver* (P 790) was transferred to the local government at Mayotte, La Réunion, in 1997. P 760 is due for disposal in 2004.

♦ 2 Volte 43 class
Bldr: Tecimar, St.-Nazaire (In serv. 23-6-75)

P 772 Oeillet P 774 Camélia

Camélia (P 774) Bernard Prézelin, 7-00

D: 14 tons **S:** 21 kts **Dim:** 13.30 × 4.10 (3.90 wl) × 1.10
A: 1 12.7-mm mg **Electronics:** Radar: 1 Decca 1220 nav.
M: 2 G.M. Detroit Diesel 8V71 diesels; 2 props; 670 bhp
Range: 400/20 **Crew:** 4 tot.

Remarks: Hull molded of layered polyester. Carry a RIB inspection boat at the stern. P 772, crewed by the Gendarmerie Maritime at Toulon and used primarily for training, is planned for retirement in 2002. P 774 was to have retired in 1999 but will now also operate at least into 2002. The unnamed P 771 was transferred to Djibouti, and P 770 was stricken 20-11-91.

♦ 15 Arcor 34 police launches
Bldr: Arcor (In serv. 1985–96)

	Based at		Based at
P 703 Lilas	Dunkerque	P 711 Gentiane	. . .
P 704 Bégonia	Rochefort	P 712 Fuchsia	. . .
P 705 Pivoine	St.-Raphaël	P 713 Capitaine Moulié	. . .
P 706 Nymphéa	Boulogne	P 714 Lieutenant Jamet	. . .
P 707 MDLC Robert	St.-Malo	P 715 Bellis	. . .
P 708 Gendarme Perez	Sete	P 716 MDLC Jacques	. . .
P 709 MDLC Richard	. . .	P 717 Lavande	Gruissan
P 710 Général Delfosse	. . .		

D: 7 tons (fl) **S:** 25 kts **Dim:** 10.32 × 3.74 × 1.03
A: 1 7.62-mm mg **Electronics:** Radar: 1 Furuno . . . nav.
M: 2 Volvo Penta TAMD-61 diesels; 2 props; 500 bhp **Crew:** 4 tot.

Remarks: Originally intended for the Gendarmerie Nationale but were transferred to the Gendarmerie Maritime during 1993–96. GRP construction, painted white. There are some differences in superstructure configuration, with later units having a higher pilothouse.

Capitaine Moulié (P 713) Bernard Prézelin, 6-99

MINE WARFARE SHIPS

Note: The tender *Loire* (A 615) is, in effect, a mine countermeasures support ship [MCS]. However, because she has an auxiliary "A" pennant—and for convenience—she is listed with her *Rhin*-class sister under [AR].

♦ 13 Tripartite-class coastal minehunters [MHC]
Bldr: DCN, Lorient (M 651–653: Béliard, Ostend and Antwerp, Belgium)

	Laid down	L	In serv.
M 641 Éridan	20-12-77	2-2-79	16-4-84
M 642 Cassiopée	26-3-79	28-9-81	5-5-84
M 643 Andromède	6-3-80	22-5-82	19-10-84
M 644 Pégase	22-10-80	24-4-83	30-5-85
M 645 Orion	17-8-81	6-2-85	14-1-86
M 646 Croix du Sud	22-4-82	6-2-85	14-11-86
M 647 Aigle	2-12-82	8-3-86	1-7-87
M 648 Lyre	14-10-83	15-11-86	16-12-87
M 649 Persée	20-10-84	9-3-88	4-11-88
M 650 Sagittaire	1-2-93	14-1-95	2-4-96
M 651 Verseau (ex-*Iris,* M 920)	23-5-86	19-6-87	3-10-88
M 652 Céphée (ex-*Fuchsia,* M 919)	31-10-85	27-11-86	20-3-88
M 653 Capricorne (ex-*Dianthus,* M 918)	4-4-85	16-4-86	18-8-87

Capricorne (M 653) Findler & Winter, 3-01

Pégase (M 644) Findler & Winter, 3-01

D: 535 tons (605 fl) **S:** 15 kts (on main engine); 7 kts (hunting)
Dim: 51.50 (47.10 pp) × 8.90 × 2.49 (hull; 3.50 max.)
A: 1 20-mm 90-cal. GIAT F2 AA; 2 single 12.7-mm mg—M 647, 649 also: 2 single 7.5-mm mg
Electronics:
Radar: 1 DRBN-34A nav.
Sonar: DUBM-21B (M 650: DUBM-21D) hull-mounted HF minehunting
M: 1 Brons-Werkspoor A RUB 215V12 diesel; 1 CP prop; 1,900 bhp—2 ACEC electric maneuvering props, 120 shp each—bow-thruster
Electric: 910 kw tot. (3 × 250-kw gas turbine–driven, 1 × 160-kw diesel-driven)
Range: 3,000/12 **Crew:** 5 officers, 32 petty officers, 12 ratings

MINE WARFARE SHIPS *(continued)*

Céphée (M 652) Rob Cabo, 4-00

Orion (M 645) H&L Van Ginderen, 3-00

Remarks: France, Belgium, and the Netherlands cooperated in building these ships for the requirements of the three countries, and others were built for Indonesia. The original *Sagittaire* (M 650) was transferred to Pakistan 24-9-92 and was replaced with a new-construction unit; two other hulls were also built for Pakistan. M 651–653 were purchased from Belgium during 1996; they transferred 28-3-97, 29-5-97, and 28-8-97, respectively. M 647–649 are based at Toulon, the others at Brest.
Hull systems: Hull is built of glass-reinforced polyester plastic. Have an NBC warfare protective citadel.
Combat systems: Have the EVEC-20 automatic plotting table, Decca HiFix and Sydelis and Toran radio precision navigation equipment, and two PAP-104 remote-controlled minehunting submersibles. No longer carry a six-person portable decompression chamber module at the aft end of the forecastle deck, having replaced it with a lightweight, helicopter-transportable chamber. Have one OD-3 mechanical drag sweep and in 1985 began to receive the AP-4 acoustic sweep capability. M 650 has the digital DUBM-21D sonar, with hybrid circuitry, Mustang computer, higher-definition displays, built-in test equipment, and integration into the tactical system.
Modernization: Under a 2-99 contract, all are being updated with the Thales TSM 2022 Mk 3 sonar and a Propelled Variable-Depth Sonar (PVDS) based on the Bofors Double Eagle remotely operated submersible vehicle (10 units to be shared among the 13 ships). A new mine warfare command-and-control system will also be substituted, while the PAP-104 submersibles will be updated, differential GPS receivers added, and a new autopilot fitted. The first ship to receive the modernization will be M 643, beginning in 5-01, with the others to be worked on at the rate of four per year and the program to be completed in 2005 with M 650.

♦ 4 Vulcain-class mine countermeasures divers' tenders [MSA]

	Bldr	Laid down	L	In serv.
M 611 VULCAIN	La Perriere, Lorient	15-5-85	17-1-86	11-10-86
A 613 ACHÉRON	CMN, Cherbourg	5-2-86	19-11-86	17-6-87
M 614 STYX	CMN, Cherbourg	20-5-86	3-3-87	22-7-87
M 622 PLUTON	La Perriere, Lorient	11-10-85	13-5-86	12-12-86

D: 409 tons (490 fl) **S:** 13.7 kts **Dim:** 41.60 (36.96 pp) × 7.50 × 3.20
A: 1 (M 622: 2 single) 12.7-mm mg **Electronics:** Radar: 1 DRBN-32 nav.
M: 2 SACM-MGO V16 ASHR diesels; 2 Kort-nozzle CP props; 2,200 bhp—75-shp bow-thruster
Electric: 176 kw tot. **Range:** 2,850/13.5; 7,400/9 **Fuel:** 92 m^3
Crew: 1 officer, 8 petty officers, 6 ratings + 12 divers

Achéron (A 613)—training unit H&L Van Ginderen, 7-97

Pluton (M 622) Guy Schaeffer, via Paolo Marsan, 2-00

Styx (M 614) Derek Fox, 10-00

Remarks: Typed BBPD *(Bâtiment de Plongeurs Démineurs)*. Derived from the *Chamois*-class local support-tender design and used as mine-clearance diver-support tenders, except A 613, which is training ship for the diving school. M 611 and M 622 were ordered 11-10-84, the other pair in 7-85 under subcontract. Can support 12 divers. Hydraulic crane on fantail can lift 5 tons at 6-m radius, 3.5 tons at 10 m. The Sydelis automatic route recording system is fitted. There is a two-person decompression chamber.

♦ 3 modified Glycine-class mine route survey craft [MSA]
Bldr: SOCARENAM, Boulogne

	Laid down	L	In serv.
M 770 ANTARÈS	10-92	30-8-93	15-12-93
M 771 ALTAÏR	1993	11-93	30-7-94
M 772 ALDÉBARAN	15-11-93	2-94	15-3-95

Aldébaran (M 772) Bernard Prézelin, 7-00

D: 295 tons (340 fl) **S:** 10 kts **Dim:** 28.30 (24.50 pp) × 7.70 × 3.80
A: 1 12.7-mm mg
Electronics: Radar: 1 DRBN-34A nav.—Sonar: DUBM-41B towed side-scan
M: 1 Baudouin 12B 152 S5 diesel; 1 CP prop; 800 bhp—bow-thruster
Electric: 175 kVA tot. (115 kVA from shaft generator, 660 kVA from 1 Deutz D 226 B6 diesel set)

MINE WARFARE SHIPS *(continued)*

Aldébaran (M 772)—note machinegun atop pilothouse Bernard Prézelin, 7-00

Range: 3,600/10 **Fuel:** 50 m^3
Crew: 13 petty officers, 12 nonrated (accomm. for 24)

Remarks: Typed BINRS *(Bâtiment d'Instruction à la Navigation et de Remorquage de Sonar)* in the dual role of training craft and tow vessel for a DUBM-41B minehunting side-scan sonar. Can search waters up to 80 m deep. Can also tow a mechanical minesweeping array and are intended for wreck reconnaissance, search and rescue, and economic exclusion zone patrol, if needed. Carry an Oropesa float aft to support the towed sonar. Equipped with Sydelis route-recording system, autopilot, and GPS receiver and has two 4.5-ton cranes at the stern to handle minehunting systems. Two half-sisters are typed BIN *(Bâtiment d'Instruction à la Navigation)* [YXT] and are used for maneuvering training.

Note: The mine countermeasures systems trials ship [AGE] *Thétis* (A 785) and nine diving tenders [YDT] of the *Coralline* class can serve as mine route clearance charting units (qq.v.).

AMPHIBIOUS WARFARE SHIPS AND CRAFT

♦ 0 (+ 2) Mistral-class helicopter-carrying landing ships [LH]
Bldrs: DCN, Brest, and Alstom, St.-Nazaire

	Laid down	L	In serv.
L 9013 Mistral	2002	. . .	2005
L 9014 Tonnerre	2003	. . .	7-06

Mistral (L 9013)—computer image DCN, 2001

D: 19,500 tons (21,000 fl) **S:** 20 kts
Dim: 210.0 (199.00 wl) × 32.00 (28.00 wl) × 6.20
Air group: 20 French Army Cougar or French Navy NH-90 helicopters
A: 2 6-round Simbad SAM syst. (. . .Mistral missiles); 2 20-mm 90-cal. GIAT F2 AA; 4 single 12.7-mm mg
Electronics:
Radar: 2 . . . nav.; 1 . . . surf./air search
EW: . . .
M: 4 . . . diesel generator sets (4,850 kw each), electric drive; 2 azimuthal thruster props; 20,400 shp—bow-thruster
Range: 6,000/18; 11,000/15 **Endurance:** 45 days
Crew: 160 tot. + 450 troops (900 for short voyages)

Remarks: Ordered 6-12-00 to replace *Ouragan* and *Orage*. Originally typed *Transports de Chalands de Débarquement* and to have been near-sisters to the *Foudre* class, they will now be known as *Porte-Hélicoptères d'Assaut*. Are to cost about $236 million each. Bow sections and accommodations modules will be built by Alstom at St.-Nazaire, with the remainder of the hulls and fitting out to be accomplished at DCN Brest. L 9013 is to replace the training ship *Jeanne d'Arc;* based at Brest, she will be specially configured to carry cadets and displays of French military equipment and will not normally be available for amphibious warfare duties. A similar ship may be built for Belgium.

Mistral (L 9013)—official model Norman Friedman, 10-00

Aviation systems: Are to have a 2,300-m^2 helicopter hangar with a capacity of 16 NH-90 helicopters, two elevators to starboard aft, a 1,000-m^3 operations direction space, and an 800-m^3 hospital with two operating rooms and 55 beds. They will have a bow-to-stern flight deck totaling 5,000 m^2 and equipped with six deck landing spots for aircraft up to CH-53E Super Stallion and MV-22B Osprey size. There will be 1,600 lane-meters of vehicle parking space, enabling the carriage of 54.5-ton Leclerc heavy tanks, and there will be side-loading vehicle ramps. An 850-m^2 (57.5 m long × 15.4 m broad × 8.2 m high) stern docking well will accommodate one CDIC or four LCM(8)-size landing craft or two U.S. Navy LCAC air-cushion landing craft.
Combat systems: Will have Syracuse SHF, U.S. Fleetsatcom, RITA, and Inmarsat-M SATCOM systems.

♦ 2 Foudre-class (TCD 90) dock landing ships [LSD]
Bldr: DCN, Brest

	Laid down	L	In serv.
L 9011 Foudre	26-3-86	19-11-88	7-12-90
L 9012 Sciroco	9-5-95	14-12-96	21-12-98

Sciroco (L 9012)—note that the antenna for the DRBV-21A search radar is on a platform *before* the mast on this ship Bernard Prézelin, 8-00

Foudre (L 9011)—the antenna for the DRBV-21A search radar is on a platform *abaft* the mast on this ship Bernard Prézelin, 6-99

D: L 9011: 8,190 tons light, 9,300 tons std. (11,880 fl; 17,200 flooded)—L 9012: 8,230 tons light (12,013 fl; 17,205 flooded)
S: 21 kts **Dim:** 168.00 (160.00 pp) × 23.50 (22.00 wl) × 5.60 (9.10 flooded)
A: 2 2-round Simbad SAM syst (. . . Mistral missiles); 3 single 30-mm OTOBreda-Mauser AA; 4 single 12.7-mm mg; 4 Army AS.332 Super Puma helicopters
Electronics:
Radar: 1 Decca 2459 nav./surf. search; 2 DRBN-34A (Decca RM 1229) nav.; 1 DRBV-21A surf./air search
EW: ARBB-36 jammer, SLQ-25 Nixie towed acoustic torpedo decoy syst.
E/O: 2 DIBC-2A weapons control

AMPHIBIOUS WARFARE SHIPS AND CRAFT *(continued)*

Sciroco (L 9012)—showing stern door to well deck Bernard Prézelin, 5-01

Sciroco (L 9012) Bernard Prézelin, 5-01

M: 2 SEMT-Pielstick 16 PC2.5 V400 diesels; 2 CP props; 20,760 bhp—940-shp bow-thruster
Electric: 4,250 kw (5 × 850-kw diesel sets)
Range: 11,000/15 **Fuel:** . . . **Endurance:** 30 days
Crew: 18 officers, 101 petty officers, 99 nonrated + troops: 35 officers, 435 enlisted

Remarks: TCD = *Transport de Chalands de Débarquement.* L 9011 was ordered 5-11-84 and conducted trials 19-11-89. Two others were to be ordered in 1986 and 1988 but were deferred and have since been recast as the *Mistral* class. L 9012 was ordered 11-4-94. They are intended to carry one mechanized regiment, plus 1,080 tons of combat vehicles and cargo for the Rapid Action Force, and are also able to act as logistics support ships. L 9011 has been brought up to the same standard of weapons and sensor equipage as L 9012 and has been given a variant of the OP3A (SENIT 8.01) enhanced self-defense control system, with OTOBreda-Mauser 30-mm guns, 2 DIBC-21 (SAGEM VIGY 105) optronic directors, and EW intercept gear.
Hull systems: Have an NBC warfare protective citadel. Docking well is 122.0 × 14.30 (1,740 m^2) × 7.70 m (high) for two CDIC (EDIC replacement), one large tug, 10 CTM landing craft, or one patrol boat. The vehicle cargo area of 1,360 m^2 can be extended by using the forward third of the dock floor, which can be separated by a cofferdam and kept dry for vehicle stowage; a 56-ton, 13.5 × 8-m elevator connects the dock floor and cargo decks. Have 7,000-m^3 ballast capacity to flood down for loading and unloading embarked craft, with up to 3 m of water over the sill; can ballast down fully in 30 minutes and de-ballast in 45. Have side-loading doors. Carry two LCVP-type landing craft. A passive roll stabilization system was installed in L 9011 during 1993–94. Can carry a total of 150 metric tons of cargo fuel. Medical spaces total 600 m^2. Typical combat load would include 10 LCK, 6 AMX-30 tanks, 15 AMX-10 combat vehicles, 8 infantry fighting vehicles, 22 jeeps, 29 5.5-ton trucks, 29 half-ton trucks, a tow truck, and a grid-laying vehicle. L 9012 can accommodate 54.5-ton Leclerc heavy tanks. There are two rudders.
Aviation systems: Helicopter deck is 47.0 × 23.0 m (1,080 m^2) with two spots equipped with SAMAHE hold-down systems. Hangar can accommodate up to 4 Super Puma helicopters. The 30.0 × 15.0-m, portable, single-spot helicopter and vehicle stowage platform at the stern breaks down into five 25-ton floatable sections that can be lifted off by the 37-ton-capacity vehicle and boat crane. Can carry 184,000 liters JP-5 fuel for the helicopters.
Combat systems: Both now have the SENIT 8.01 (OP3A) combat system, with Link 11 reception. They have extensive command/communications facilities, including Syracuse and Inmarsat SATCOM systems. L 9011 will later receive the French Army Rodéo air-control radar, with its antenna on a platform on the after side of the lattice mast; she received the DRBV-21A (Thales Mars) air-search radar during her 1997 refit, which also saw the single 40-mm and two single 20-mm AA replaced with the new enclosed 30-mm gunmounts. One DRBN-34A radar is mounted aft to assist in helicopter flight control.

♦ 2 Ouragan-class dock landing ships [LSD] Bldr: DCN, Brest

	Laid down	L	In serv.
L 9021 Ouragan	6-62	9-11-63	1-6-65
L 9022 Orage	6-66	22-4-67	1-4-68

D: 5,965 tons (8,500 fl; 15,000 flooded) **S:** 17.3 (L 9021: 15) kts
Dim: 149.00 (144.50 pp) × 21.50 × 5.40 (8.70 flooded)
A: 2 2-round Simbad SAM syst. (. . . Mistral missiles); 2 single 40-mm 60-cal. Bofors (L 9022: 2 single 30-mm OTOBreda-Mauser) AA; 4 single 12.7-mm mg
Electronics:
Radar: 2 DRBN-34 nav.
E/O: 2 DIBC-2A optronic weapons directors
M: L 9021: 2 SEMT-Pielstick 12 PC2 V2 diesels; 2 CP props; 8,640 bhp—L 9022: 2 SEMT-Pielstick 12 PC2.1 V400 diesels; 2 CP props; 9,400 bhp

Ouragon (L 9021) Bernard Prézelin, 5-01

Orage (L 9022)—note 30-mm gun to starboard, Simbad missile launcher to port at the forward end of the helicopter deck Bernard Prézelin, 6-00

Orage (L 9022)—the bridge superstructure is to starboard of the helicopter deck on this class Bernard Prézelin, 8-00

Electric: 2,650 kw tot. **Range:** 9,000/15
Crew: 12 officers, 78 petty officers, 115 ratings + up to 470 troops

Remarks: TCD = *Transport de Chalands de Débarquement.* Were originally to have been replaced in 1992, then to be retired in 2000 and 2003, but have now been extended to 2004 and 2006, respectively.
Hull systems: The bridge is mounted to starboard of the permanent helicopter deck. Both have repair facilities. Can carry 349 troops, including 14 officers, or 470 troops for a short distance. The 120-m-long docking well, which has a 14 × 5.5-m stern gate, can be submerged by 3 m. Movement of the sluices and valves is automatic, using pumps (3,000 m^3/hr) controlled from a central position. A removable deck in six sections covers 36 m of the after part of the well and allows the landing and takeoff of heavy helicopters. A 90-m-long temporary deck in 15 sections can be used to stow cargo or vehicles, but its use reduces the number of landing craft that can be carried. They can embark either two EDIC landing craft for infantry and tanks, carrying 11 light tanks or trucks, or eight LCM(8) with tanks or vehicles and, in addition, heavy helicopters on the landing platform. If used as cargo carriers, they can embark 1,500 tons of material. Lifting equipment includes two 35-ton cranes.
Combat systems: A combined command center permits the simultaneous direction of helicopter and amphibious operations. The SQS-17 sonar on L 9021 has been removed, as have the ship's former two 120-mm mortars. Both had two Simbad light SAM launchers added in 1992 in place of two 40-mm mounts. Now have Syracuse II SATCOM facilities, as well as an Inmarsat transceiver. Plans to replace the remaining two 40-mm guns with 30-mm OTOBreda-Mauser gunmounts have been canceled, but both have two SAGEM DIBC-2A (VIGY 105) panoramic electro-optical weapons-control systems as part of a reduced version of the OP3A/SENIT 8.01 self-defense combat control system.

AMPHIBIOUS WARFARE SHIPS AND CRAFT *(continued)*

♦ 5 Champlain-class medium landing ships [LSM]

Bldrs: L 9030, 9031: DCN, Brest; others: At. Français de l'Ouest, Grand-Quevilly

	Laid down	L	In serv.	Based at
L 9030 Champlain	1973	17-11-73	5-10-74	Toulon
L 9031 Francis Garnier	1973	17-11-73	21-6-74	Fr. Guiana
L 9032 Dumont d'Urville	4-81	27-11-81	5-2-83	Papeete
L 9033 Jacques Cartier	10-81	28-4-82	23-9-83	New Caledonia
L 9034 La Grandière	27-8-84	11-12-85	20-1-87	Toulon

Francis Garnier (L 9031) Bernard Prézelin, 2-01

Champlain (L 9030) J. G. Stemmelen, 6-99

La Grandière (L 9034)—high superstructure version French Navy, 1994

D: L 9030, 9031: 770 tons (1,330 fl)—others: 820 tons (1,385 fl)
S: 16 kts (13 cruising) **Dim:** 80.00 (68.00 pp) × 13.00 × 3.00 (2.50 hull)
A: L 9030, 9031: 2 single 40-mm 60-cal. AA; 2 single 81-mm mortars; 2 single 12.7-mm mg—others: 2 single 20-mm 90-cal. GIAT F2 AA; 2 single 81-mm mortars; 2 single 12.7-mm mg
Electronics: Radar: 1 DRBN-32 nav.
M: 2 SACM 195 V12 CSHR diesels; 2 CP props; 3,600 bhp **Electric:** 360 kw tot.
Range: 3,500/13 **Crew:** 3 officers, 15 petty officers, 26 ratings

Remarks: A sister ship was built for Gabon, Morocco has three, Ivory Coast has one, and Chile has built three. L 9034, built on speculation, was acquired for the French Navy. The first two are planned for retirement in 2005 and the other three between 2008 and 2010.
Hull systems: Cargo (first two): 350 tons. Have living quarters for a landing team (5 officers, 15 noncommissioned officers, and 118 troops) and space for its 12 vehicles, including Guépard armored personnel carriers. L 9032–9034 are able to transport 180 troops; they have a 40-ton-capacity bow ramp, improved accommodations, and carry one LCVP and one LCP landing craft. Their superstructure is one deck higher, and they can carry a 330-ton vehicle cargo for beaching and 208 tons of potable water. All five have a helicopter deck aft; the one on L 9034 is longer than that on the others.

♦ 2 CDIC utility landing craft [LCU]

Bldr: SFCN, Villeneuve-la-Garenne

	L	In serv.
L 9061 Rapière	25-2-88	28-7-88
L 9062 Hallebarde	3-11-88	17-2-89

D: 369 tons light (384 fl; 751 fl with cargo) **S:** 10.96 kts
Dim: 59.40 (55.45 pp) × 11.90 × 1.10 (1.76 aft)
A: fitted for 2 single 20-mm 90-cal. GIAT F2 AA
Electronics: Radar: 1 Furuno . . . nav.
M: 2 SACM UD30V12 M1 diesels; 2 props; 1,080 bhp

Hallebarde (L 9062) Bernard Prézelin, 4-98

Rapière (L 9061)—outboard *Hallebarde* (L 9062) Bernard Prézelin, 10-00

Electric: 156 kw tot. **Range:** 2,880/8 **Fuel:** 20 tons
Endurance: 15 days **Crew:** 6 petty officers, 12 nonrated

Remarks: CDIC = *Chaland de Débarquement d'Infanterie et de Chars* (landing ship for infantry and tanks). Based at Toulon. Named in 1997. Although intended for service with ships of the *Foudre* class, these ships have sufficient navigational equipment and accommodations to permit a coastal voyage of several days' duration. Plans to construct three more were canceled. Are to be retired in 2008 and 2009. Cargo capacity: 336 tons in the 40.0 × 10.4-m cargo deck, which has a 4.5-m-wide ramp at the bow. The mast folds to permit entry into the landing ship's docking well. The armament is not usually carried.

♦ 2 EDIC 700 utility landing craft [LCU]

Bldr: SFCN, Villeneuve-la-Garenne

	L	In serv.
L 9051 Sabre	3-3-87	13-6-87
L 9052 Dague	10-9-87	19-12-87

Sabre (L 9051) Guy Schaeffer, via Paolo Marsan, 6-99

D: 282 tons light (726 fl) **S:** 12 kts
Dim: 59.40 (55.85 pp) × 11.90 × 1.40 (hull; 1.70 max.)
A: fitted for: 1 20-mm 90-cal. GIAT F2 AA; 2 single 12.7-mm mg
Electronics: Radar: 1 DRBN-32 nav.
M: 2 SACM-Wärtsilä UD30V12 MB diesels; 2 props; 1,400 bhp
Electric: 156 kw tot. **Range:** 1,000/10 **Fuel:** 20 tons
Crew: 1 officer, 7 petty officers, 9 ratings

Remarks: Financed by the French nuclear testing center (DIRCEN). L 9051 is based at Papeete, L 9052 at Djibouti. Cargo capacity: 340 tons on the 28.5 × 8-m cargo deck, with bow ramp. An identical sister was built for Senegal and two others for Lebanon. The armament is not usually installed. Are to be retired in 2007.

♦ 1 utility transport/ferry [LCU]

Bldr: Ch. Serra, La Seyne (In serv. 2-10-87)

L 9090 Gapeau

Gapeau (L 9090) ANBw/FAFIO, 4-99

AMPHIBIOUS WARFARE SHIPS AND CRAFT *(continued)*

D: 509 tons light (1,058 fl) **S:** 10 kts **Dim:** 66.00 × 12.20 × 3.30 (max.)
A: none **Electronics:** Radar: 1 DRBN-34A nav.
M: 2 . . . . . . diesels; 2 props; . . . bhp
Crew: 3 petty officers, 3 nonrated + 30 passengers

Remarks: Designed to serve as support craft for the Centre d'Essais de la Méditerranée missile range, Île de Levant. Cargo capacity: 460 tons on the drive-through deck, with bow and stern ramps. Due to more-extensive superstructure (which spans the vehicle deck to increase its useful length), the ship cannot be transported aboard the large landing ships.

♦ 16 U.S.-design LCM(8)-class landing craft [LCM]
Bldr: CMN, Cherbourg (three by C.N. Auroux, Arcachon)

CTM 3	CTM 22 KIEN AN	CTM 28 TONKIN
CTM 17	CTM 23 SONG CAN	CTM 29 NUI DHO
CTM 18	CTM 24	CTM 30 KHOAN BO
CTM 19 DO HA	CTM 25	CTM 31 PHU DOAN
CTM 20 NÉKÉ GRAV	CTM 26	
CTM 21 GUÉRÉO	CTM 27 INDOCHINE	

Kien An (CTM 22) Bernard Prézelin, 6-00

D: 56 tons light (150 fl) **S:** 9.5 kts **Dim:** 23.80 × 6.35 × 1.25
A: 2 single 12.7-mm mg **Electronics:** Radar: 1 portable . . . nav.
M: 2 Poyaud-Wärtsilä 18 V8 M1 diesels; 2 props; 450 bhp **Range:** 380/8
Fuel: 3.4 tons **Endurance:** 48 hours at half power **Crew:** 6 tot.

Remarks: CTM = *Chaland de Transport de Matériel.* CTM 3 is the survivor of an earlier series and was completed in 1964; the others were completed in 1982–92. Cargo capacity: 90 tons. The machineguns are usually not mounted. The French Army Transport Corps has six other units of the class, based at La Pallice. CTM 17 and 18 are based at Lorient, CTM 19–23 and 27–31 at Toulon, CTM 24 and 25 at Djibouti, and CTM 26 at Dakar. Navy sisters CTM 2, 5, 9, 10, and 12–16 were stricken in 1999; CTM 15 and 16 were transferred to the Ivory Coast in 3-99, CTM 14 to Djibouti in 1999, CTM 5 to Senegal in 5-99, and one other to Morocco in 5-99. CTM 3 is due for disposal in 2004.

Disposal note: The U.S. LCM(3)-design landing craft LCM 1057 and LCM 1058 were retired during 2000–01.

♦ 20+ LCVP Bldr: . . . . (In serv. . . .)

D: 13 tons (fl) **S:** 8 kts **Dim:** 10.90 × 3.21 × 1.09 (aft)
M: 1 diesel; 225 bhp **Range:** 110/8

Remarks: GRP construction, based on standard U.S. design. Can carry 36 troops or 3.5 tons cargo in the 5.2 × 2.3-m cargo well. At least 20 are in service, aboard various landing ships and auxiliaries.

AUXILIARIES

♦ 1 Type RR 2000 multipurpose support ship [AG]

	Bldr	Laid down	L	In serv.
A 633 TAAPE	Ch. de la Perriere, Lorient	22-10-82	14-4-83	30-6-83

Taape (A 633) Bernard Prézelin, 5-01

D: 383 tons (505 fl) **S:** 14.2 kts **Dim:** 41.02 (38.50 pp) × 7.5 × 3.18
A: none **Electronics:** Radar: 1 DRBN-32 nav.
M: 2 SACM-Wärtsilä UD30V16 M3 (MGO V16 ASHR) diesels; 2 CP Kort-nozzle props; 2,800 bhp
Range: 6,000/12 **Crew:** 2 officers, 7 petty officers, 2 nonrated + 6 passengers

Remarks: Ordered 11-10-82. Construction financed by the nuclear test center (DIRCEN). A variation of the FISH (Feronia International Shipping)-class oilfield tug/supply vessel design, which was also used in the *Chamois*-class tenders. Transported in the landing ship *Orage* in 4-84 to Muraroa for duty in the Pacific; she was based at Papeete until spring 1998, when she returned to Toulon. Due for disposal in 2005.
Hull systems: Bollard pull: 24.8 tons. Can carry 100 tons of cargo on the long, open afterdeck.

♦ 4 Chamois-class multipurpose support ships [AG]
Bldr: Ch. de la Perriere, Lorient

	Laid down	L	In serv.
A 768 ÉLAN	16-3-77	28-7-77	7-4-78
A 774 CHEVREUIL	15-9-76	8-5-77	7-10-77
A 775 GAZELLE	30-12-76	7-6-77	13-1-78
A 776 ISARD	2-11-77	2-5-78	15-12-78

Isard (A 776)—painted white; note the helicopter deck above the deckhouse aft
Bernard Prézelin, 7-00

Gazelle (A 775)—with gallows crane at stern Bernard Prézelin, 2-01

Chevreuil (A 774)—no crane aft, portable deckhouse abaft bridge
Guy Schaeffer, via Paolo Marsan, 6-00

D: 305 tons light (505 fl) **S:** 14.5 kts **Dim:** 41.50 (36.96 pp) × 7.50 × 3.18
A: none **Electronics:** Radar: 1 DRBN-32 nav.
M: 2 SACM-Wärtsilä UD30V16 M3 (MGO V16 AFHR) diesels; 2 CP Kort-nozzle props; 2,800 bhp
Range: 7,200/12 **Fuel:** 92 m^3 **Crew:** 2 officers, 16 petty officers, 2 nonrated

Remarks: A 776 is equipped as a combat swimmers' support ship and tender for the ERIC wire-guided submersible (2 tons, 4 m overall, 600-m diving depth); the ship often performs intelligence collection duties for the DGSE (Directorate General for External Security). A 774 is employed mostly to carry cargo, while A 768 is used primarily as a water tanker. All but A 776 can also be used for coastal towing, for cleaning up oil spills, as transports for 28 passengers, as minelayers, or as torpedo retrievers. A 776 is to be retired in 2003 and the others between 2004 and 2008 (A 775 was not stricken in 1999 as reported in the previous edition).

AUXILIARIES *(continued)*

Disposals: *Chamois* (A 767) was stricken 1-9-95 and transferred to Madagascar in 5-96.
Hull systems: Have two rudders and an 80-hp bow-thruster. The stern winch has a 28-ton bollard pull. A portable 50-ton gallows crane for mooring buoy handling can be shipped at the stern. All but A 776 can carry 100 tons dry cargo on deck, or 125 tons fuel and 40 tons water, or 65 tons fuel and 125 tons water. A 776 has a ULISM decompression chamber capable of simulating pressures to a water depth of 150 m; she also has a longer after superstructure, supporting divers' rubber dinghies and a small helicopter deck.

♦ 1 chartered submersible support ship [AG]
Bldr: Aukra Bruk A/S, Aukra, Norway (In serv. 1975)

Aquitaine Explorer (ex-*Abeille Supporter,* ex-*Seaway Hawk,* ex-*Seaway Devon)*

Aquitaine Explorer—in yellow and white paint scheme, with blue bulwarks at the bow Bernard Prézelin, 4-01

D: 2,500 tons (fl) **S:** 14 kts **Dim:** 63.58 (55.00 pp) × 13.42 × 5.75
Electronics: Radar: 2 . . . nav.
M: 2 Atlas-MaK 12M453AK diesels; 2 CP props; 8,000 bhp—bow-thruster
Electric: 500 kw tot. (1 × 300 kw, 2 × 100 kw)
Range: 7,900/14 **Fuel:** 530 tons
Crew: 11 ship's company + 27 passengers (incl. 6 divers)

Remarks: 1,189 grt/1,330 dwt. Oilfield tug/supply vessel chartered from the Société Abeille International by the Délégation Général pour l'Armement (Direction des Missiles et de l'Espace) for support of the Landes missile range until 7-00, when management was switched to ABC Maritime and the name was changed; the ship is owned by Société Boulonnaise de Remorquage, Lorient. Based at Bayonne. Carries the undersea work submersible *Licorne* and the deep-submergence work vehicle *Abyssub* 5000.
Hull systems: Hull reinforced for operation in light ice. Has a 30-ton A-frame gantry at the stern, one 10-ton electrohydraulic crane, and one 4-ton crane. Divers' facilities include two decompression chambers and a diving bell. Has a dynamic positioning system, Sydelis radio navigation system, and passive hull stabilization. Equipped with a 100-ton bollard pull winch aft. Painted yellow and white.

♦ 1 mine countermeasures experimental ship [AGE]
Bldr: DCN, Lorient

	Laid down	L	In serv.
A 785 Thétis (ex-*Néreide*)	8-3-86	15-11-86	9-11-88

Thétis (A 785) Bernard Prézelin, 6-00

D: 900 tons (1,050 fl) **S:** 15 kts **Dim:** 59.00 (53.00 pp) × 10.90 × 3.80
A: 2 single 12.7-mm mg; mines
Electronics:
Radar: 1 DRBN-32 nav.
Sonar: DUBM-42 Lagadmor towed array; TSM 2022 Mk 3 (PVDS) towed array
M: 2 SACM-Wärtsilä UD30V12 M6 diesels; 2 CP props; 2,500 bhp—2 electric motors for low speeds; 120 shp—200-hp bow-thruster
Electric: 875 kw tot. (4 diesel-driven alternators) **Range:** 6,000/12
Crew: 2 officers, 36 enlisted + 10 technicians

Remarks: Typed BEGM *(Bâtiment d'Expérimentation de la Guerre des Mines).* Operates for the Groupe d'Études Sous-Marines de l'Atlantique (GESMA) under the direction of the Direction Générale des Armements (DGA), primarily as a mine countermeasures trials ship. Ordered 11-10-84. A second unit was in the 1984–88 Building Plan but was canceled. Uses the same hull and machinery as the *La Pérouse*–class hydrographic survey ships. Performs trials with the DUBM-42 Lagadmor towed minehunting sonar (for which a winch with 700 m of cable is provided), a new remotely operated mine-disposal vehicle, and the AD-4 acoustic sweep. In late 1994, conducted trials with the Thales PVDS (Propelled Variable-Depth Sonar) using a Bofors-Sutec Double Eagle ROV equipped with Thales's TSM 2022 Mk 3 high-frequency (165 kHz and 400 kHz) sonar and low-light-level television; the device can operate at 5 kts up to 600 m ahead of the control ship and at depths to 200 m, and it weighs 400 kg. Normally carries three Double Eagle ROVs and is also conducting trials with the Redermor variable-depth minehunting sonar (with a 300-m depth capability, a range of 1,000 m, a length of 5 m, and a weight of 3 tons, powered by four 7.5-kw electric motors).

♦ 1 chartered oilfield tug/supply ship for sonar research [AGE]
Bldr: Halter Marine, New Orleans, La. (In serv. 1980)

Langevin (ex-*Martin Fish,* ex-*Percy Navigator)*

Langevin—blue lower hull, white above Bernard Prézelin, 9-99

D: approx. 2,700 tons (fl) **S:** 12 kts **Dim:** 67.67 (65.84 pp) × 13.42 × 4.88
Electronics: Radar: 2 . . . nav.
M: 3 G.M. EMD 16V149 TI diesel generator sets, 2 electric motors; 2 props; 3,600 shp
Range: . . . **Crew:** . . .

Remarks: 1,600 grt. Former oilfied tug/supply vessel chartered 5-90 from Compagnie Nationale de Navigation for use by the Direction des Constructions Navales (DCN), Sous-Direction Études de la DCN de Toulon, for a variety of purposes connected with the new-generation nuclear-powered ballistic-missile submarine program. In 9-95, began trials with the ATBF-2 low-frequency active, towed, surface-ship sonar array system. Has an Inmarsat-M SATCOM terminal.

Disposal note: The shipboard weapons trials ship *Île d'Oléron* (A 610) was retired on 1-2-01.

♦ 1 intelligence collection ship [AGI]
Bldr: Dubigeon, Nantes

	Laid down	L	In serv.
L 9077 Bougainville	28-1-86	3-10-86	25-2-88

Bougainville (L 9077) Bernard Prézelin, 10-99

D: 3,600 tons light (5,200 fl) **S:** 15 kts (14.6 sust.)
Dim: 112.78 (105.00 pp) × 17.00 × 4.34 **A:** 2 single 12.7-mm mg
Electronics: Radar: 2 DRBN-32 nav.—EW: ARBG-2 comms intercept suite
M: SACM-Wärtsilä 195 V12 RVR (UD33V12 M5) diesels; 2 CP props; 4,800 bhp—1 400-hp side-thruster
Electric: 1,600 kw tot. (2 × 480-kw, 2 × 320-kw diesel-driven sets)
Range: 6,000/12 **Fuel:** . . . tons **Endurance:** 45 days
Crew: 6 officers, 17 petty officers, 29 ratings + 30 technicians

Remarks: A former BTMS *(Bâtiment de Transport Moyen et de Soutien),* built for the Directorate of Nuclear Experimentation for use between Papeete and the Muraroa Test Center. Ordered 22-11-84; completed after launch by Ch. de l'Atlantique, St.-Nazaire, when the building yard closed. Converted 12-98 to 7-99 to serve as an electronic intelligence collection vessel in place of the *Berry* (A 644).

AUXILIARIES *(continued)*

Bougainville (L 9077) Bernard Prézelin, 7-00

Hull systems: Miniature LSD design with still-functional 78.00 × 11.48 (10.2 clear)-m docking well for landing craft or 40 20-ft. containers. Maximum cargo weight in the docking well: 1,200 tons. Draft aft is 9.20 m when flooded, providing 3.15 m clear over deck. A 37-ton crane with 12-m reach is mounted to starboard, aft. A 6-m ramp to starboard can accommodate 53 tons. Has 70 m^3 of helicopter fuel, and the helicopter deck can accommodate two medium helicopters. Can also act as a repair and stores ship. Ship's boats include an LCVP and a launch.
Mission systems: Has Inmarsat-M commercial SATCOM and a Syracuse I SATCOM system with only one antenna, mounted on the starboard aft corner of the helicopter deck. Communications D/F and intercept antennas have been mounted on the main-mast in support of the MINREM *(Moyens Interarmées de Renseignements Électromagnétiques)* data collection system.

♦ 2 Alcyon-class chartered moorings tenders [AGL]
Bldr: A&C de la Manche, Dieppe

Alcyon (ex-*Bahram*) (In serv. 1981) Ailette (ex-*Cyrus*) (In serv. 1982)

Alcyon—sea-green hull, white upperworks Bernard Prézelin, 8-00

Ailette Bernard Prézelin, 8-99

D: approx. 1,900 tons (fl) **S:** 13.5 kts **Dim:** 53.01 (51.01 pp) × 13.01 × 4.50
Electronics: Radar: 2 . . . nav.
M: 2 Bergens-Normo KVMB-12 diesels; 2 CP props; 5,200 bhp—bow-thruster
Crew: 7 tot.

Remarks: 487 grt/1,000 dwt. Typed BSHM *(Bâtiment de Soutien de Haute Mer)*. Oil-field tug/supply vessels chartered in 1988 from the Compagnie des Moyens de Surface Adaptes a l'Exploitation des Oceans (SURF) for service at Brest as moorings tenders and pollution control ships.

Hull systems: The 30-ton portal crane at the stern has been replaced by a buoy-handling crane on the afterdeck. Have two firefighting water monitors. Are also equipped for antipollution duties and have a 500-m^3-capacity holding tank. Hulls painted green, superstructures white. Bollard pull: 60 tons initial.

♦ 1 missile-range tracking ship [AGM]

	Bldr	Laid down	L	In serv.
A 601 Monge	Ch. de l'Atlantique, St.-Nazaire	26-3-90	6-10-90	4-11-92

Monge (A 601)—white-painted Leo Van Ginderen, 2-01

Monge (A 601) Bernard Prézelin, 4-00

D: 17,760 tons (21,040 fl) **S:** 15.8 kts **Dim:** 225.60 (203.40 pp) × 24.84 × 7.66
A: 2 single 20-mm 90-cal. GIAT F2 AA; 2 single 12.7-mm mg; 2 Super Frelon helicopters
Electronics:
Radar: 2 DRBN-34A nav.; 1 DRBV-15C air search; 1 Gascogne tracking; 2 Armor tracking; 1 Savoie tracking; 1 Stratus (L-band) tracking (1 transmission antenna, 1 tracking)
TACAN: NRPB-3A
M: 2 SEMT-Pielstick 8 PC2.5 L400 diesels; 1 CP prop; 9,000 bhp—1,340-shp bow-thruster
Electric: 7,560 kw (6 × 1,200-kw, 1 × 360-kw diesel sets) **Range:** 15,000/15
Endurance: 60 days **Crew:** 10 officers, 98 enlisted + 184 scientific staff

Remarks: Accepted from builder for trials 6-3-91. Tracking equipment began installation 3-6-91, with operational trials beginning 5-92. Painted white. Intended to remain in service for 30 years. Employed as tracking and telemetry support ship for strategic ballistic-missile trials.
Hull systems: Computer-controlled passive tank stabilization system to reduce roll to 9° maximum in Sea State 6. The hangar can accommodate two Super Frelon helicopters. Carries 160 tons aviation fuel.
Mission systems: The Thales TAVITAC 2000 command system is installed. Syracuse I, Syracuse II, and Marisat SATCOM systems are fitted, along with Navstar NAVSAT receivers. Extensive tracking equipment is installed, as on her predecessor, including lidar green-laser upper atmospheric analysis equipment. There are also 14 telemetry antennas.

♦ 1 oceanographic and hydrographic research ship [AGOR]
Bldr: DCN, Brest

	Laid down	L	In serv.
A 757 D'Entrecasteaux	7-69	30-5-70	10-10-70

D'Entrecasteaux (A 757)—white-painted Bernard Prézelin, 3-00

D: 1,630 tons light; 2,058 tons std. (2,450 fl) **S:** 15 kts
Dim: 95.65 (89.00 pp) × 13.00 × 4.20 (5.50 props)
A: none **Electronics:** Radar: 2 DRBN-32 nav.
M: 2 diesel engines, electric drive; 2 CP props; 2,720 shp—2 retractable Schottel propellers (1 fwd, 1 aft)
Range: 12,000/12
Crew: 8 officers, 28 petty officers, 41 ratings + 38 scientists/technicians

AUXILIARIES *(continued)*

D'Entrecasteaux (A 757)—note that the freeboard is one deck higher to port over most of the length of the ship Bernard Prézelin, 2-01

Remarks: For oceanographic research and hydrographic duties. Planned for disposal in 2006. Based at Brest.
Hull systems: Has a dynamic mooring/maneuvering system permitting station keeping in 5,000-m depths. Can take soundings and surveys to a depth of 5,000 m. Has a helicopter platform and hangar for an Alouette-III, electrohydraulic oceanographic equipment cranes, one landing craft, three hydrographic launches, a hull-mounted scanning sonar, and three echo sounders (one stabilized). Has Trident, Sydelis, Toran, Transit, Omega, and GPS navigation equipment, plus Hydrac and Hydrai automatic data systems.

♦ 0 (+ 2) Beautemps-Beaupré–class hydrographic survey ships [AGS]
Bldr: Alstom, St.-Nazaire

	Laid down	L	In serv.
A . . . Beautemps-Beaupré	3-01	. . .	12-02
A . . . Porquoi Pas?	2002	. . .	2004

D: 2,300 tons (3,292 fl) **S:** 14 kts **Dim:** 80.64 × 14.90 × 6.20
Electronics: Radar: 2 Decca . . . nav.
M: diesel-electric: 4 diesel alternator sets, 1 motor; 1 prop; 12,000 shp—590-shp tunnel bow-thruster—2 295-shp azimuthal stern-thrusters
Range: . . ./. . . **Endurance:** 45 days **Crew:** 25 tot. + 25 survey party

Remarks: First ship ordered 7-3-01. Capable of both ocean survey and oceanographic research duties and are replacing the stricken survey ship *L'Espérance* and the AGOR *D'Entrecasteaux.* Were originally to have been ordered in 1996. Designed to merchant marine standards after the civilian research ship *Thalassa.* Will have multipath, deep-ocean echo sounders and are equipped with a 10-ton crane. The second ship will be slightly larger and will be jointly funded by the Navy and IFREMER *(Institute Français de Recherches pour l'Exploitation de la Mer).* Both will carry 9-m survey launches built by KL Industrie, Auray.

♦ 4 La Pérouse–class hydrographic survey ships [AGS]
Bldr: DCN, Lorient

	Laid down	L	In serv.
A 791 La Pérouse	11-6-85	15-11-86	20-4-88
A 792 Borda	2-9-85	15-11-86	16-6-88
A 793 La Place	1-9-87	9-11-88	5-10-89
A 795 Arago	26-6-89	6-9-90	9-7-91

Borda (A 792)—white-painted A. A. de Kruijf, 3-01

Borda (A 792) A. A. de Kruijf, 3-01

D: 850 tons light; 970 tons std. (1,100 fl) **S:** 15 kts
Dim: 59.00 (53.00 pp) × 10.90 × 3.63 **A:** 2 single 7.5-mm mg
Electronics: Radar: 1 DRBN-32 nav.—Sonar: see Remarks
M: 2 SACM-Wärtsilä UD30V12 M6 diesels; 2 CP props; 2,500 bhp—160-shp bow-thruster
Electric: 620 kw tot. **Range:** 6,000/12
Crew: 3 officers, 10 petty officers, 18 nonrated + 11 survey party

Remarks: First two ordered 24-7-84; the second two, ordered 22-1-86, were originally to have been built by Ch. Normandie, Grand Quevilly, which closed. Painted white and operated for the Service Hydrographique et Océanographique de la Marine (SHOM). A 795 is based at Papeete, A 793 at New Caledonia, and the others at Brest.

Mission systems: All but A 791 can carry two 8-m hydrographic survey launches and are equipped with the Hydrac and Hydrai survey data systems. A 791 is equipped with a DUBM-21C minehunting sonar for trials, wreck identification, and channel certification; the other three have the Thales-Marconi CSFTSM 5425 Lennermor multifunction wreck identification/echo sounder. Other navigation/hydrographic equipment includes Trident, Sydelis, Toran, RANA, and Navstar receivers, Atlas DESO-20 100-kHz and 66/210-kHz echo sounders (also on the two survey launches), a Raytheon 12-kHz echo sounder, Sippican bathythermograph, Barringer magnetometer, and Edgerton side-looking sonar. All carry one scientific and two data-reduction computers. As of 6-01, new 9-m hydrographic survey launches were being constructed for this class by KL Industrie, Auray.

Disposal note: *L'Espérance*-class survey ship *L'Espérance* (A 756) was retired 27-9-00; sister *L'Estafette* (A 766) was retired during 12-91.

♦ 4 Durance-class replenishment oilers [AOR]
Bldr: DCN, Brest (A 631: CNIM, La Seyne)

	Laid down	L	In serv.
A 607 Meuse	2-6-77	2-12-78	2-8-80
A 608 Var	12-78	9-5-81	29-1-83
A 630 Marne	4-8-82	6-2-85	16-1-87
A 631 Somme	3-5-85	3-10-87	7-3-90

Marne (A 630) Bernard Prézelin, 3-01

Somme (A 631) Camil Busquets i Vilanova, 7-01

Meuse (A 607) Bernard Prézelin, 6-00

D: A 607: 7,600 tons (17,800 fl)—others: 7,800 tons (17,900 fl)
S: 20 kts (19 sust.) **Dim:** 157.20 (149.00 pp) × 21.20 × 8.65 (10.80 max.)
A: 1 40-mm 60-cal. AA; 2 single 20-mm 70-cal. Mk 10 Mod. 23 Oerlikon AA; 4 single 12.7-mm mg; 2 (A 630, 631: 3) 2-round Simbad SAM syst. (. . . Mistral missiles); 1 Alouette-III or WG-13 Lynx helicopter
Electronics:
Radar: 2 DRBN-32 or DRBN-34A nav.
EW: Thales DR-2000 intercept; Telegon HFD/F; SLQ-25 Nixie towed acoustic torpedo decoy syst.
M: 2 SEMT-Pielstick 16 PC2.5 V400 diesels; 2 CP props; 20,760 bhp
Electric: 5,400 kw tot. **Range:** 9,000/15 **Fuel:** 750 tons
Crew: 10 officers, 62 petty officers, 91 ratings (all but A 607: 45 command staff also)

Remarks: A 631 was ordered 3-84 from CNM, La Seyne, on speculation and purchased 10-87 for the French Navy; the ship is identical to A 608 and A 630. A near-sister was built in Australia for the RAN, and two smaller variants were built for Saudi Arabia. Sister *Durance* (A 629) was placed in reserve 7-97 and transferred to Argentina 12-7-99.
Hull systems: Have one SYTAR *(Système de Tensionnement Automatique pour Ravitaillement à la Mer)* dual solid and two liquid underway replenishment stations per side and are also equipped to refuel over the stern under way. Cargo: A 607: 5,090

AUXILIARIES *(continued)*

tons fuel oil, 4,014 tons diesel, 1,140 tons JP-5, 250 tons distilled water, 180 tons provisions, 122 tons munitions, and 45 tons spare parts; A 608 and A 630: 5,090 tons fuel oil, 3,310 tons diesel, 1,090 tons JP-5, 260 tons distilled water, 170 tons ammunition, 180 tons provisions, and 15 tons spares; A 631: 9,250 tons fuel oil, 250 tons water, 190 tons provisions, and 45 tons spares. The helicopter deck is large enough to accept Super Frelon helicopters.
Combat systems: In A 607, the 40-mm AA is aft; in the others, it is forward. May receive two Dagaie Mk 2 countermeasures rocket launchers, and are planned to receive a reduced version of the OP3A self-defense combat control system. Simbad manned-launch systems for Mistral point-defense SAMs are mounted on the after corners of the forward superstructure block at the bridge deck level and, on A 630 and A 631, atop the pilothouse. All except A 607 are equipped as flagships for a major area commander and can accommodate 257 persons, including 45 commandos; their forward superstructure blocks are extended aft by 8 m to provide increased accommodations, and the two beam-mounted stores cranes immediately abaft the bridge are replaced by a single, centerline crane; the Syracuse I SATCOM system and the SEAO/OPSMER computerized combat decision aid system are fitted. Most are equipped with Inmarsat terminals. All except A 607 carry two LCVP landing craft.

♦ 1 Jules Verne–class multipurpose repair ship [AR]
Bldr: DCN, Brest

	Laid down	L	In serv.
A 620 Jules Verne (ex-*Achéron*)	1969	30-5-70	1-6-76

Jules Verne (A 620) H&L Van Ginderen, 10-99

Jules Verne (A 620) H&L Van Ginderen, 10-99

D: 7,815 tons (10,250 fl) **S:** 18 kts **Dim:** 147.00 × 21.56 × 6.50
A: 2 single 40-mm 60-cal. AA; 4 single 12.7-mm mg
Electronics: Radar: 1 DRBN-32 nav.; 1 Decca BridgeMaster II nav.
M: 2 SEMT-Pielstick 12 PC V400 diesels; 1 prop; 12,000 bhp
Electric: 3,800 kw tot. **Range:** 9,500/18
Crew: 16 officers, 150 petty officers, 116 ratings + 130 passengers

Remarks: Six years after being launched as an ammunition ship, the uncompleted *Jules Verne* was converted to a floating workshop to provide support to a force of 3–6 surface warships. Completed a 6-month overhaul in France on 29-6-95 and another in 12-97. Collided with the oiler *Var* (A 608) during 5-98. Based at Toulon. Was to be retired in 2007 but may be retained until 2012.
Hull systems: Has significant capabilities for both regular maintenance and battle-damage repair. The 13 workshops include mechanical, engine, electrical, sheet-metal, and electronics. Also carries torpedoes and ammunition. Has four 12-ton cranes and a 16-bed medical facility with a decompression chamber. Has a 300-m^2 hangar for two helicopters and a 500-m^2 flight deck.

♦ 1 Garonne-class general-purpose repair ship [AR]
Bldr: DCN, Lorient

	Laid down	L	In serv.
A 617 Garonne	23-12-63	8-8-64	1-9-65

Garonne (A 617) South African Navy, 1997

D: 2,320 tons (fl) **S:** 15 kts **Dim:** 101.50 (92.05 pp) × 13.80 × 3.70
A: 1 40-mm 60-cal. AA; 2 single 20-mm 70-cal. Mk 10 Mod. 23 Oerlikon AA; 3 single 12.7-mm mg
Electronics: Radar: 1 DRBN-32 nav.
M: 2 SEMT-Pielstick 12 PA4 185VG diesels; 1 prop; 3,600 bhp
Electric: 920 kw tot. **Range:** 13,000/13
Crew: 6 officers, 39 petty officers, 69 ratings

Remarks: Designed for overseas service and operates primarily in the Pacific and Indian Oceans. The forecastle was extended aft over that in the *Rhin* class in order to provide more room for eight workshops, including electronics, hull, engine, and armament repair; metalworking; and carpentry. The 30-ton crane formerly carried on the fantail has been removed. There is a 5-ton crane with 12-m reach amidships. Now planned to be retired in 2006.

Note: The French Navy hopes to build two sister repair ships to replace the *Garonne* in 2005 and the *Jules Verne* in 2007.

♦ 2 Rhin-class repair tenders [AR] Bldr: Lorient Arsenal

	Purpose	Laid down	L	In serv.
A 615 Loire	Minesweepers	9-7-65	1-10-66	10-10-67
A 621 Rhin	Electronics	24-4-61	17-3-62	1-3-64

Loire (A 615) Selim San, 11-00

Loire (A 615) Rob Cabo, 4-00

D: A 615: 2,050 tons (2,445 fl)—A 621: 2,035 tons (2,445 fl)
S: 16.5 kts **Dim:** 101.05 (92.05 pp) × 13.10 × 4.25
A: 3 single 40-mm 60-cal. AA—A 615 also: 3 single 12.7-mm mg
Electronics: Radar: 1 (A 615: 3) DRBN-32 nav.
M: A 615: 2 SEMT-Pielstick 12 PA4 V185 diesels; 1 prop; 3,600 bhp—A 621: 2 SEMT-Pielstick 16 PA2V diesels; 1 prop; 3,200 bhp
Electric: 920 kw tot. **Range:** 13,000/13
Crew: 11 officers, 67 petty officers, 78 ratings

Remarks: A 615 is specifically equipped to support mine countermeasures ships, while A 621 is equipped for electronics systems repair. Sister *Rhône* (A 622) was stricken 17-3-97 and is used as a breakwater at Lorient; A 621 is to follow in 2002 (delayed from 1999 in 1998), but A 615 is to remain in service until 2008.
Hull systems: A 615 has a divers' decompression chamber. Both have a helicopter platform, but only A 615 has a hangar (for one Alouette-III). There is about 700 m^2 of workshop space and 1,700 m^3 of storeroom space. Both have one 5-ton (at 12-m) crane and Inmarsat SATCOM terminals.

♦ 1 Mérou-class chartered salvage and rescue tug [ARS]
Bldr: Scheepswerf Waterhuizen B.V. J. Pattje, Groningen (In serv. 1982)

Mérou (ex-*King Fish*)

AUXILIARIES *(continued)*

Mérou—painted gray, with white pilothouse Bernard Prézelin, 10-00

D: approx. 2,500 tons (fl) **S:** 14.2 kts **Dim:** 59.52 (51.82 pp) × 15.02 × 5.00
Electronics: Radar: 2 . . . nav.
M: 4 Wichmann AXAG diesels; 2 CP props; 7,992 bhp—500-shp bow- and stern-thrusters
Range: 6,300/12 **Fuel:** 244 tons **Endurance:** 50 days
Crew: 4 officers, 5 unlicensed + up to 29 passengers

Remarks: 1,471 grt/1,477 dwt. Leased from FISH (Feronia International Shipping) in 1987 and based at Toulon; purchased in 1998 by Compagnie Chambon and charter extended to 7-00.
Hull systems: Bollard pull: 100 tons initial, up to 250 tons under way. Has one 1,200-m^3/hr firepump and two water cannon with 120-m range. Equipped for antipollution duties with extensive pollution cleanup equipment. Ice-strengthened hull.

♦ 1 Carangue-class chartered salvage and rescue tug [ARS]
Bldr: Samsung SB, Koje, South Korea (In serv. 1980)

Carangue (ex-*Pilot Fish,* ex-*Maersk Handler,* ex-*Smit Lloyd* 119, ex-*Atlas Tasman*)

Carangue—painted gray, with white pilothouse Bernard Prézelin, 10-00

D: approx. 2,500 tons (fl) **S:** 16 kts **Dim:** 64.42 (56.42 pp) × 13.81 × 5.09
Electronics: Radar: 2 . . . nav.
M: 2 Bofors-Nohab Polar F2116V-D diesels: 2 CP props; 7,040 bhp—725-shp bow-thruster
Electric: 725 kw tot. (3 × 200-kw, 1 × 125-kw diesel sets)
Range: 21,000/10 **Crew:** 4 officers, 4 unlicensed

Remarks: 1,179 grt/2,100 dwt. Oilfield deck-cargo and anchor-handling tug chartered in 1995 from FISH (Feronia International Shipping) for towing and antipollution duties in the Mediterranean, based at Toulon. Purchased in 1998 by Compagnie Chambon and charter extended to 1-7-00. Bollard pull: 90 tons initial, 150 sustained. Has two 600-m^3/hr firepumps serving two water cannon with 90-m range. Has extensive pollution cleanup equipment.

♦ 2 chartered Abeille Flandre–class salvage tugs [ARS]
Bldr: Ulstein Hatlo A/S, Ulsteinvik, Norway (In serv. 1978–79)

Abeille Flandre (ex-*Neptun Suecia*)
Abeille Languedoc (ex-*Neptun Gothia*)

Abeille Flandre—black hull, white upperworks Bernard Prézelin, 8-99

D: approx. 3,800 tons (fl) **S:** 17 kts **Dim:** 63.40 (58.60 pp) × 14.74 × 6.90
Electronics: Radar: 2 . . . nav.
M: 4 MaK 8M453AK diesels; 2 CP props; 12,796 bhp—2 350-shp bow-thrusters
Electric: 1,536 kw tot. (2 × 352-kw, 3 × 256-kw, 1 × 64-kw diesel sets)
Range: . . ./. . . **Fuel:** 1,450 tons **Crew:** 2 officers, 10 unlicensed

Remarks: 1,576 grt/1,550 dwt. Chartered from Societé Provençale de Gestion Maritime (PROGEMAR) as a result of the *Amoco Cadiz* disaster. Both purchased in 1998 by Compagnie Chambon. *Abeille Flandre* is based at Brest, *Abeille Languedoc* at Cherbourg. Ice-strengthened hulls. Among world's most powerful tugs. Bollard pull: 160 tons. Hull painted black, superstructure white.

Note: Under an agreement signed 19-3-90 by the French Navy, the Ministry of Maritime Affairs, and the Dunkerque Society of Towing and Salvage, the commercial salvage tugs *Robuste, Puissant,* and *Hardi* (all 2,600 bhp, 40-ton bollard pull), based at Dunkerque, are maintained at the call of the Préfet Maritime de Cherbourg to ensure the safety of navigation in the Calais area. They have green hulls and white superstructures. The salvage tug *Far Turbot* (competed 4-80; 1,621 grt, 18 kts, 10,000 bhp) was chartered from 1-4-00 to 1-4-01 for salvage and spill cleanup duties and based at Dover, U.K.; she was replaced by the 58-m British salvage tug *Anglian Monarch* (160-ton bollard pull) in 4-01.

♦ 2 Type RR 4000–class seagoing tugs [ATA]
Bldr: Breheret, Couëron, Nantes

	L	In serv.		L	In serv.
A 634 Rari	16-4-84	5-2-85	A 635 Revi	15-5-84	6-2-85

Rari (A 634) Bernard Prézelin, 7-00

D: 1,057 tons light (1,557 fl) **S:** 14.5 kts **Dim:** 51.00 (49.50 wl) × 12.60 × 4.10
A: none **Electronics:** Radar: 1 DRBN-32 nav.
M: 2 SACM-Wärtsilä UD33V12 M6 (AGO 195 V12 RVR) diesels; 2 CP props; 4,000 bhp—2 2.5-ton side-thrusters
Electric: 600 kw (2 × 300 kw) **Range:** 6,000/12 **Fuel:** 300 tons
Crew: 2 officers, 9 petty officers, 10 ratings + 18 passengers

Remarks: Built for DIRCEN, the French Pacific nuclear testing center, and formerly based at Muraroa. A 634 was transferred to Brest in 1998; A 635 remains based at Papeete.
Hull systems: Bollard pull: 47 tons. Have a 14-ton quadrantial gantry at the extreme stern and two water cannon for fire fighting. Can carry fuel cargo in ballast tanks or 400 tons of cargo on the open deck aft.

♦ 2 Tenace-class seagoing tugs [ATA]

	Bldr	L	In serv.
A 664 Malabar	Oelkers, Hamburg	16-4-75	3-2-76
A 669 Tenace	Oelkers, Hamburg	12-71	15-11-73

Malabar (A 664) A. A. de Kruijf, 5-00

D: 970 tons (1,440 fl) **S:** 13.5 kts **Dim:** 51.0 × 11.5 × 5.7
Electronics: 1 DRBN-32 (Decca 1226) nav.; 1 Decca 060 nav.
M: 2 MaK 9-cyl. diesels; 1 Kort-nozzle CP prop; 4,600 bhp
Electric: 502 kw (2 × 227-kw, 1 × 48-kw diesel-driven sets)
Range: 9,500/13 **Fuel:** 500 tons **Crew:** 2 officers, 15 petty officers, 13 ratings

Remarks: Based at Brest. Sister *Centaure* (A 674) was stricken in 12-98 and sold to Turkey, transferring 16-3-99. A 669 is to be retired between 2005 and 2007 and A 664 between 2006 and 2011.
Hull systems: Pumps include one of 350 m^3/hr (serving two fire monitors with a range of 60 m) and one of 120 m^3/hr, plus numerous smaller salvage and firefighting pumps. Carry two RIBs each. Have Inmarsat SATCOM terminals. Living quarters are air-conditioned. Bollard pull: 60 tons.

AUXILIARIES *(continued)*

Tenace (A 669) Rob Cabo, 1-00

SERVICE CRAFT

Note: In addition to the craft described below, there are large numbers of miscellaneous non-self-propelled service craft in service at Brest and Toulon. Noted at Brest during 9-99 were BUG 3, 7, 22, 25, 28, 30, and 32; CEM 4 and 5; CIC 8; CICGH 24; CICI 6; CIE 27; CIEM 31; and CIGH 21 and 23, most of which are either small launches or non-self-propelled barges of one sort or another.

♦ 2 Phaéton-class submarine towed-array tenders [YAG]

Bldr: Chaudronnerie Industrielle de Bretagne (CIB), Brest

Y 656 PHAÉTON (L: 7-94)   Y 657 MACHAON (L: 18-5-94)

Machaon (Y 657) Bernard Prézelin, 3-01

D: 69 tons (fl) **S:** 8.5 kts **Dim:** 19.20 (16.50 wl) × 6.82 (6.50 hull) × 1.20
Electronics: Radar: 1 Decca 181-4 nav.
M: 2 SACM UD18V8 M1 diesel; 1 Schottel SPJ 57 waterjets; 326 bhp—1 Hydro Armor Type 800 bow-thruster (660 kg thrust)
Range: . . ./. . . **Crew:** 4 tot.

Remarks: Intended to tow, install, and recover submarine towed linear passive hydrophone arrays. Y 656 is based at Toulon, Y 657 at Brest. Hull has a pronounced bow bulb, with upswept bottom aft between sidewalls creating a combined monohull/catamaran hullform. Aluminum construction. Have a large cable reel amidships and carry a Zodiac RIB.

♦ 1 modified Glycine-class ASW trials tender [YAGE]

Bldr: J. Chauvet, Paimbœuf (L: 7-86)

L'AVENTURIÈRE II

L'Aventurière II Bernard Prézelin, 4-01

D: 250 tons (295 fl) **S:** 10 kts **Dim:** 28.30 (24.50 pp) × 7.86 × 3.75
Electronics: Radar: 1 Furuno . . . nav.—Sonar: . . .
M: 1 Poyaund diesel; 1 CP prop; 650 bhp—150-shp bow-thruster
Range: 3,600/10 **Fuel:** 49 m^3 **Crew:** . . . tot.

Remarks: 270 grt. No hull number. Used by GESMA *(Group d'Etudes Sous-Marines de l'Atlantique)* at Brest in mine warfare research. Civilian crewed and technically owned by DCN rather than the French Navy, hence the lack of a pennant number.

♦ 1 sonar trials support tender [YAGE]

Bldr: IMC, Tonnay-Charente (In serv. 1983)

BR 69478301 DORA

Dora (BR 69478301) Bernard Prézelin, 9-98

D: . . . tons **S:** . . . kts **Dim:** 41.10 (38.00 pp) × 10.72 × 2.93
Electronics: Radar: 2 . . . nav.—Sonar: . . .
M: 2 MWM TBD 234V8 diesels; 2 props; 740 bhp—bow-thruster

Remarks: Used at Brest by DCN *(Direction des Constructions Navales)* for acoustic trials. Has a large crane forward to handle arrays and a cable reel and winch aft for towed systems. Has a blunt bow-form. Civilian operated and technically not part of the navy. DCN craft have serial numbers, often preceded by two letters indicating the name of their base or the letters DCN.

Note: The similar but smaller, 120-ton, 30-m *Mérou* is used by DCN and DGA *(Direction Générale des Armements)* at Toulon for underwater systems trials. DCN operates a large number of miscellaneous launches at Brest and other naval bases.

Mérou Guy Schaeffer, via Paolo Marsan, 8-00

♦ 1 catamaran weapons trials tender [YAGE]

Bldr: SFCN, Villeneuve-la-Garenne (In serv. 1975)

DCN 72 49453 PÉGASE

Pégase (DCN 72 49453) H&L Van Ginderen, 6-99

D: 120 tons (fl) **S:** . . . kts **Dim:** 25.00 × 8.00 × 2.20
A: 1 550-mm TT **Electronics:** Radar: . . .
M: 2 diesels; 2 props; 880 bhp **Crew:** 4 tot.

Remarks: Civilian operated and based at the ECAN St.-Tropez torpedo trials center. Is assisted by the small GRP-hulled launch *Heraclea* (DCN 72 49443).

Disposal note: DCN torpedo trials retriever [YPT] *Sambracite* was stricken during 2000. The French Navy weapons trials tender [YAGE] *Denti* (A 743) was retired during 2001.

♦ 6 (+ 1) miscellaneous self-propelled floating cranes [YD]

GFA 1   GFA 3   GFA . . . ALPAGA
GFA 2   GFA 4 LAMA   GFA . . . GIRAFE

SERVICE CRAFT *(continued)*

Crane GFA 3—with tug *Sicié* (A 680) H&L Van Ginderen, 10-99

Remarks: Are quite similar but have differing lift capacities of 7.5 to 15 tons maximum. GFA = *Grue Flottante Automotrice. Alpaga* (completed 1984) and *Girafe* are based at Brest, the others at Toulon. Construction of a new floating crane by DCN Lorient is planned.

♦ 1 degaussing (deperming) tender [YDG]

Y 732 Station de Démagnétisation No. 3

Station de Démagnétisation No. 3 (Y 732) Bernard Prézelin, 6-96

D: 260 tons **S:** 10 kts **Dim:** 38.2 × 4.3 × 2.4
M: 1 diesel; 1 prop; 375 bhp **Crew:** 5 tot.

Remarks: A sister was built in Pakistan for the Pakistani Navy. Wooden hull construction.

♦ 10 Coralline-class diving tenders [YDT]

Bldr: DCN, Lorient (In serv. 1990–92)

A 790 Coralline	Y 793 Liseron	Y 797 Giroflée
Y 790 Dionée	Y 794 Magnolia	Y 798 Acanthe
Y 791 Myosotis	Y 795 Ajonc	
Y 792 Gardénia	Y 796 Genet	

Dionée (Y 790) Bernard Prézelin, 2-01

D: 44 tons (fl) **S:** 13 kts **Dim:** 21.00 × 4.50 × 1.10
Electronics: Radar: 1 Furuno . . . nav.—Sonar: Klein . . . towed side-scan
M: 2 diesels; 2 props; 264 bhp **Crew:** 4 tot. (A 790: 7 tot.)

Remarks: A 790 was completed 2-90 to replace *Palangrin* (Y 743) as radiological monitoring craft at Cherbourg. Y 790 and Y 791 are assigned as training craft at the École de Plongée, while Y 792 and Y 798 serve as training craft for mine-disposal frogmen at Toulon. The others are employed as diving support craft and general-purpose diving tenders at Toulon, Cherbourg, and Brest. All but A 790 carry a two-person decompression chamber and have received Klein towed side-scan sonars for object location and identification (and can therefore act as minefield route clearance craft); they can carry a RIB atop the after superstructure.

Genet (Y 796)—diving tender Bernard Prézelin, 5-00

Myosotis (Y 791)—diver rescue craft Carlo Martinelli, 5-97

Gardénia (Y 792)—diver training craft Guy Schaeffer, via Paolo Marsan, 8-00

♦ 1 combat swimmer diving tender [YDT]

	Bldr	L	In serv.
A 722 Poséidon	SICCNAV, St.-Malo	5-12-74	14-1-77

Poséidon (A 722) Bernard Prézelin, 4-01

D: 200 tons (239 fl) **S:** 13 kts **Dim:** 40.5 (38.5 pp) × 7.2 × 2.2
Electronics: Radar: 1 DRBN-32 nav.
M: 1 SACM-Wärtsilä UD30V12 M3 diesel; 1 prop; 600 bhp
Endurance: 8 days **Crew:** 1 officer, 5 petty officers, 9 nonrated + 27 trainees

SERVICE CRAFT *(continued)*

Remarks: Used for training combat frogmen. Refitted in 1994 and equipped with a large hydraulic crane on the fantail. Based at Toulon. Is scheduled to be retired between 2002 and 2005.

Note: Small harbor motor launches *Pastenauge* and *Stenella* are used as diving tenders at Brest.

♦ 14 Thomery-class motor lighters [YF]
Bldr: CIB, Brest (In serv. 1988–99)

CHA 23 Telgruc
CHA 24 Tévennec
CHA 25 Lambézellec
CHA 27 through CHA 31
CHA 33 through CHA 38

CHA 34 H&L Van Ginderen, 7-00

D: 20 tons (50 fl) **S:** 7 kts **Dim:** 15.2 × 4.4 × 1.6
M: 1 Poyaud-Wärtsilä UD18L6 M4 diesel; 300 bhp

Remarks: Carry stores and personnel in harbor and roadstead service. Early units (CHA 1–26) were converted LCM(3) landing craft; later units were purpose-built but use bow ramps recycled from stricken landing craft. CHA 27–34 were completed in 1988, 35–38 in 1989. CHA 8, 14, 17, and 19 were retired during 1994–95.

♦ 7 Ariel-class coastal personnel transports [YFB]
Bldrs: Y 613–696, 741: SFCN, Villeneuve-la-Garenne; Y 700–702: DCN, Brest

	L		L
Y 613 Faune	8-9-71	Y 701 Ondine	4-10-79
Y 662 Dryade	10-12-72	Y 702 Naiade	4-10-79
Y 696 Alphée	10-6-69	Y 741 Elfe	14-4-70
Y 700 Néréide	17-2-77		

Alphée (Y 696) Bernard Prézelin, 4-00

D: 195 tons (225 fl) **S:** 15 kts **Dim:** 40.5 × 7.45 × 3.3
Electronics: Radar: 1 DRBN-32 nav.
M: 2 MGO (1,640 bhp tot.) or Poyaud (1,730 bhp tot.) diesels; 2 props
Crew: 9 tot. + 400 passengers (250 seated)

Remarks: All based at Brest, except Y 702 at Toulon. Y 662 is to retire during 2002 and the others between 2005 and 2010; no replacements have been ordered.

Disposals: *Ariel* (Y 604) was stricken during 1999 and *Korrigan* (Y 661) during 2001.

♦ 1 Merlin-class coastal personnel transport [YFB]
Bldr: C.N. Franco-Belges (L: 14-6-73)

Y 671 Morgane

Mélusine (Y 736)—since stricken Bernard Prézelin, 7-96

D: 170 tons **S:** 11 kts **Dim:** 31.5 × 7.06 × 2.4
M: 2 MGO diesels; 2 props; 960 bhp **Crew:** . . . tot.

Remarks: Based at Toulon. No radar. Carries up to 400 passengers. Sisters *Merlin* (Y 735) and *Mélusine* (Y 736) were stricken in 1998. Y 671 is scheduled for retirement in 2003.

♦ 1 floating dry dock [YFDL] (In serv. 1975)

Remarks: Capacity: 3,500 tons. Based at Papeete.

♦ 2 Gouandour-class personnel launches [YFL]
Bldr: DCN, Lorient

Y 766 Rostellec (L 3-01) Y 767 Gouandour (L: 7-00)

Rostellec (Y 766) Bernard Prézelin, 3-01

D: 25 tons **S:** . . . kts **Dim:** 16.50 × 4.65 × . . .
M: 2 . . . diesels; 2 props; . . . bhp

Remarks: GRP hull. Can carry 45 passengers. Y 766 is based at Lorient.

♦ 1 Surf-class service launch [YFL] Bldr: . . . (In serv. 1990)

Y 789 Haari

D: 9 tons (fl) **S:** 25 kts **Dim:** 13.00 × 4.00 × 0.70
M: 2 diesels; 2 waterjets; . . . bhp **Crew:** 3 tot.

Remarks: GRP-hulled craft with rigid inflatable fenders on hull sides, built for the Muraroa nuclear test range. Sisters *Mamanu* (Y 752) and *Burao* (Y 788) were transferred to Morocco during 10-99.

♦ 12 Type V 14 service launches [YFL]
Bldrs: A: Sibiril, Grantec; B: Stento, Balaruc-les-Bains

	Bldr	In serv.		Bldr	In serv.
Y 754 Taina	A	22-2-91	Y 777 Palingrin	B	1-4-88
Y 755 Miri	A	12-92	Y 779	B	17-3-88
Y 762	A	29-8-91	Y 780	A	6-93
Y 763	A	17-12-90	Y 781	B	25-6-88
Y 765 Avel Mor	A	15-2-92	Y 786 Aute	A	18-6-91
Y 776	B	8-1-88	Y 787	B	20-3-87

Palingrin (Y 777)—radiological monitoring craft Bernard Prézelin, 9-99

Y 781—pilot boat variant H&L Van Ginderen, 10-99

SERVICE CRAFT *(continued)*

Avel Mor (Y 765)—VIP transportation craft; gray-painted near-sister *Miri* (Y 755) is moored across the pier — Guy Schaeffer, via Paolo Marsan, 9-98

D: 16 tons (20 fl) **S:** 20 kts **Dim:** 14.60 (13.20 pp) × 4.60 × 1.90
A: Y 763 only: 1 12.7-mm mg **Electronics:** Radar: 1 Decca 060 nav.
M: 2 Baudouin 12 F 11S diesels; 2 props; 800 bhp **Range:** 360/18 **Crew:** 4 tot.

Remarks: GRP hulls. Carry a RIB inspection dinghy on davits at the stern. Y 763 is classed as a *vedette de servitude côtière* (VSC); Y 755 and Y 779–781 as *vedettes de pilotage* (VP); Y 754, Y 786, and Y 787 as *vedettes de servitude et de transport d'autorités* (VSTA); and Y 776 and Y 777 as *vedettes de surveillance radiologique* (VSR). The last two have modified superstructures with the pilothouse further forward. Y 786 and Y 787 are based at Mururoa and Papeete and have extended passenger cabins. Y 780 has two 500-bhp diesels and can make 23 kts.

♦ 2 weapons range safety patrol boats [YFL]
Bldrs: C.N. de l'Esterel, Cannes

	L	In serv.		L	In serv.
A 712 Athos	20-11-79	22-11-79	A 713 Aramis	9-9-80	22-9-80

Aramis (A 713) — M. Ottini, 3-99

D: 80 tons (99.5 fl) **S:** 28 kts **Dim:** 32.1 × 6.5 × 1.9
A: 1 20-mm 70-cal. Oerlikon AA **Electronics:** Radar: 1 DRBN-32 nav.
M: 2 SACM-Wärtsilä Type 195 V12 diesels; 2 props; 4,640 bhp **Range:** 1,500/15
Crew: 1 officer, 11 enlisted (incl. 6 divers)

Remarks: Typed VSS *(Vedettes de Surveillance des Sites).* Based at Bayonne for use at the Landes Test Center, both as range safety craft and for weapons recovery duties. Wooden hulls. Are planned to be retired in 2004 and 2005, respectively.

Disposal note: Large personnel launch *Tréberon* (Y 703) was retired during 2001.

Note: Numerous other small launches [YFL] are used for harbor service to transport stores and personnel and to support divers. DP 23 through DP 25 are based at Brest, along with EN 1 and EN 2, which are assigned to the Poulmic Naval School.

♦ 1 small mooring-buoy tender [YGL]
Bldr: IMC, Rochefort-sur-Mer

	L	In serv.
Y 692 Telenn Mor	4-4-85	16-1-86

D: 518 tons (fl) **S:** 8 kts **Dim:** 41.40 (37.00 pp) × 9.10 × 1.88
M: 2 diesels; 2 Saver thrusters; 900 bhp **Electric:** 350 kw tot. **Crew:** 10 tot.

Remarks: Based at Brest. Has fixed lift-horns at the bow and a heavy electro-hydraulic crane amidships. Can also be used for salvage work.

Telenn Mor (Y 692) — Bernard Prézelin, 9-00

♦ 1 Calmar-class small mooring-buoy tender [YNG]
Bldr: . . . . . . (In serv. 12-8-70)

Y 698 Calmar

Calmar (Y 698) — Bernard Prézelin, 2-01

D: 270 tons light **S:** 9.5 kts **Dim:** . . . × . . . × . . .
M: 1 Baudouin diesel; 1 prop; 180 bhp

Remarks: Based at Toulon since early 2001 and now planned for disposal in 2003.

Disposal note: *La Prudente*–class mooring-buoy tenders *La Prudente* (Y 749) and *La Persévérante* (Y 750) were retired during 2001; their sister *La Fidèle* (Y 751) sank 30-4-97 after an explosion. Single-unit mooring-buoy tender *Tupa* (Y 667) was stricken during 2000.

♦ 25 liquid cargo barges [YON/YSR/YW]

Sludge barge CIEM 36—moored at Brest — Chris Delgoffe/H&L Van Ginderen, 7-00

Water barge CIE 28 — H&L Van Ginderen, 10-99

D: . . . **S:** 9 kts **Dim:** . . . × . . . × . . . **M:** 1 diesel; 430 bhp

SERVICE CRAFT *(continued)*

Remarks: Nos. 1 and 11 are at Toulon, No. 2 at Brest, Nos. 5 and 6 in Tahiti, No. 12 at Lorient, others at the CEP *(Centre d'Expérimentation Pacifique).* Eleven are configured as fuel lighters (CIC), six as sludge barges (CIEM), three as pollution storage barges (CIEP), and five as water lighters (CIE). Some are not self-propelled.

♦ 0 (+ 2) Esterel-class coastal tugs [YTB]
Bldr: SOCARENAM, Boulogne

	Laid down	L	In serv.
Y 601 Esterel	2001	. . .	2-02
Y 602 Luberon	2001	. . .	6-02

Esterel (Y 601)—computer rendering SOCARENAM, 2001

D: 480 tons (640 fl) **S:** 10 kts **Dim:** 36.30 (33.00 wl) × 11.45 × 5.00
Electronics: Radar: . . .
M: 2 ABC 8DZ1000.179 diesels, electric drive; 2 Voith-Schneider vertical cycloidal props; 5,120 shp
Range: 1,500/10 **Crew:** 8 tot.

Remarks: Ordered 15-12-00. Intended to support the carrier *Charles de Gaulle* at Toulon. To have 50-ton initial bollard pull and be 12 m high. Hull has five watertight compartments.

♦ 15 (+ 8) Type RPC 12 large harbor tugs [YTB]
Bldrs: A: LNI (Ch. de la Perriere/Leroux & Lotz), Lorient; B: SOCARENAM, Boulogne

	Bldr	In serv.	Based at
Coastal service:			
A 675 Fréhel	A	23-5-89	Cherbourg
A 676 Saire	A	6-10-89	Cherbourg
A 677 Armen	A	6-12-91	Brest
A 678 La Houssaye	A	30-10-92	Lorient
A 679 Kéréon (ex-*Sicié*)	A	5-12-92	Brest
A 680 Sicié	A	6-10-94	Toulon
A 681 Taunoa	B	9-3-96	Toulon
A 682 Oave	B	2002	. . .
Harbor service:			
Y 638 Lardier	B	12-4-95	. . .
Y 639 Giens	B	2-12-94	. . .
Y 640 Mengam	B	6-10-94	Toulon
Y 641 Balaguier	B	8-7-95	Toulon
Y 642 Taillat	B	18-10-95	Toulon
Y 643 Nividic	B	13-12-96	Brest
Y 646 Eckmühl	B	2002	. . .
Y 647 Le Four	B	13-3-98	Brest
Y 649 Port-Cros	B	21-6-97	. . .
Y 662 Lavezzi	B	. . .	. . .
Y . . . Saranier	B	. . .	. . .
Y . . . Men-Hir	B	. . .	. . .
Y . . . Tévennec	B	. . .	. . .
Y . . . Rozel	B	. . .	. . .
Y . . . Larmor	B	. . .	. . .

D: 220 tons (259 fl) **S:** 11 kts (10 sust.) **Dim:** 25.00 (23.50 pp) × 8.40 × 2.20
Electronics: Radar: 1 Decca . . . nav.
M: 2 SACM-Wärtsilä UD30V12 M3 diesels; 2 Voith-Schneider 18 GII/115 vertical cycloidal props; 1,360 bhp
Electric: 195 kw (3 × 65-kw diesel alternator sets)
Range: 800/10 **Fuel:** 32 m^3 **Crew:** A-pennants: 8 tot.—Y-pennants: 5 tot.

Remarks: General type is RPC *(Remorqueur Portuaire et Côtier).* Units with "A"-pennants are classed as coastal tugs *(remorqueurs côtiers)* and units with "Y"-pennants as dockyard tugs *(remorqueuer de rade ci-après).* The program has been behind schedule and underfunded; as of 5-01, only Y 662 of the remaining seven had been ordered.
Hull systems: Equipped with firefighting water cannon that can spray 3,400 liters/min and a 4,000-liter emulsion tank. Have a 12-ton bollard pull hydraulic towing winch with 140 m of cable.

Port-Cros (Y 649)—harbor tug variant Camil Busquets i Vilanova, 10-00

La Houssaye (A 678)—coastal version Bernard Prézelin, 10-99

♦ 3 Maito-class large harbor tugs [YTB]
Bldr: SFCN, Villeneuve-la-Garenne

	Laid down	L	In serv.
A 636 Maito	24-6-83	6-1-84	27-2-84
A 637 Maroa	30-8-83	20-1-84	30-3-84
A 638 Manini	15-11-84	19-4-85	12-9-85

Maito (A 636) Bernard Prézelin, 8-00

D: 228 tons light (280 fl) **S:** 11 kts **Dim:** 27.60 (24.50 wl) × 8.90 × 3.50
Electronics: Radar: 1 DRBN-32 nav.
M: 2 SACM-Wärtsilä UD30L6 M6 diesels; 2 Voith-Schneider vertical cycloidal props; 1,280 bhp
Range: 1,200/11 **Crew:** 6 tot. + 4 passengers

Remarks: Built for service at Muraroa for DIRCEN. A 636 has been based at Brest since 1998, and the other two remain at Papeete. Bollard pull: 12 tons. Have a firefighting water cannon and are fully seagoing.

♦ 3 Bélier-class large harbor tugs [YTB]
Bldr: DCN, Cherbourg

	L	In serv.
A 695 Bélier	4-12-79	25-7-80
A 696 Buffle	18-1-80	19-7-80
A 697 Bison	20-11-80	16-4-81

D: 356 tons light (500 fl) **S:** 11 kts **Dim:** 31.78 (29.00 pp) × 9.24 × 4.30
Electronics: Radar: 1 DRBN-32 nav.

SERVICE CRAFT *(continued)*

Bélier (A 695) Bernard Prézelin, 8-00

M: 2 SACM-Wärtsilä UD33V12 M4 diesels, electric drive; 2 Voith-Schneider vertical cycloidal props; 2,600 bhp
Electric: 160 kw tot. **Crew:** 1 officer, 7 petty officers, 4 nonrated

Remarks: Bollard pull: 25 tons. Have one firefighting monitor atop pilothouse. All based at Toulon. Were intended to last 30 years in service.

♦ 3 Actif-group large harbor tugs [YTB]

	Bldr	In serv.
A 671 Le Fort	Forges et Chantiers de la Gironde, Bordeaux	12-7-71
A 692 Travailleur	FCM, Le Havre	11-7-63
A 693 Acharné	C.N. de la Perriere, Lorient	5-7-74

Acharné (A 693) Mike Welsford, 10-00

D: 226 tons light (288 fl) **S:** 11.8 kts **Dim:** 28.3 (25.3 pp) × 7.9 × 4.3
Electronics: Radar: 1 Decca 914C nav.
M: 1 MGO ASHR diesel; 1,100–1,450 bhp **Range:** 4,100/11 **Crew:** 12 tot.

Remarks: Similar, but not identical, ships. Bollard pull: 17 tons.

Disposals: *Courageux* was stricken in 1980; *Hercule* (A 667), *Robuste* (A 685), and *Valeureux* (A 688) in 1993; *Actif* (A 686) in 7-95; *Laborieux* (A 687) in 1998; and *L'Utile* (A 672), *Lutteur* (A 673), and *Efficace* (A 694) in 1999. A 671 and A 692 are to be retired in 2002 and A 693 in 2003.

♦ 4 101-class push-tugs for ballistic-missile submarines [YTM]

Bldr: Lorient-Naval Industries, Lorient (In serv. 1993)

101 102 103 104

Push-tug 104 Bernard Prézelin, 9-00

D: 44 tons light **S:** 6 kts **Dim:** 17.00 (15.9 pp) × 6.4 × 2.4
M: 2 Poyaud-Wärtsilä UD25L6 M4 diesels; 2 cycloidal props; 456 bhp (440 sust.)
Crew: 2 tot.

Remarks: Were to have been completed in 1989 by La Perriere, Lorient; the contract was taken over by the new operators of the building facility. Have a hydraulically powered quadrantial push-fender at the bow.

♦ 4 No. 1–class push-tugs for ballistic-missile submarines [YTM]

1 2 3 4

Remarks: Same characteristics as the 101 class, which was to have replaced them; they remain in service, however.

♦ 30 P.1-class push-tugs [YTM]

Bldr: La Perriere, Lorient, and DCN, Lorient (In serv. 1976–97)

2 3 4 6 12 through 38

P.1-class push-tug 22 Bernard Prézelin, 8-00

D: 24 tons (fl) **S:** 9.2 kts **Dim:** 11.50 (11.25 wl) × 4.30 × 1.45
M: 2 Poyaud-Wärtsilä UD18V8 M1 (2–6: UD6PZ M1) diesels; 2 props; 456 bhp (440 sust.)
Range: 191/9.1, 560/8 **Fuel:** 1.7 tons **Crew:** 2 tot.

Remarks: For dockyard use. Primarily for pushing, but have 4.1-ton bollard pull. No names or NATO pennant numbers assigned, and the "P." prefix to the side number has been dropped. 2 through 18 were completed 1976–83, the others in 1989–97. Sister 11 was transferred to the Ivory Coast in 9-99.

♦ 2 Acajou-class medium harbor tug [YTM]

Y 620 Chataignier Y 740 Papayer

D: 105 tons **S:** 11 kts **Dim:** 21.0 (18.4 pp) × 6.9 × 3.2
M: 1 diesel; 1 prop; 700 bhp

Remarks: Built during the 1960s. Have two-letter contraction of names on bows instead of official pennant numbers. Bollard-pull capacity: 10 tons. Y 740 is to strike between 2002 and 2005 and Y 620 in 2005.

Disposals: *Bouleau* (Y 612) was stricken in 1980; *Equeurdreville* (Y 635) in 1986; *Okoumé* (Y 682) in 1991; *Balsa* (Y 607) and *Hêtre* (Y 654) in 1992; *Acajou* (Y 601), *Charme* (Y 623), *Chêne* (Y 624), and *Pin* (Y 689) in 1994; *Cormier* (Y 629), *Érable* (Y 618), *Hevea* (Y 655), *Palétuvier* (Y 686; correction from last edition), *Platane* (Y 695), *Merisier* (Y 669), *Saule* (Y 708), and *Sycomore* (Y 704) in 1996–97; *Ébène* (Y 717), *Frêne* (Y 644), and *Olivier* (Y 719) in 1998; *Marronier* (Y 738), *Latanier* (Y 663), *Mélèze* (Y 668), *Manguier* (Y 666), *Peuplier* (Y 688), and *Noyer* (Y 739) in 1999; and *Santal* (Y 720) in 2000. Y 719 was donated to Senegal during 12-98 and Y 738 and Y 669 to the Ivory Coast in 1999.

♦ 2 Bonite-class small harbor tugs [YTL]

Bldr: SFCN, Châlon-sur-Seine

Y 630 Bonite (In serv. 1975) Y 634 Rouget (In serv. 1974)

Bonite (Y 630) Bernard Prézelin, 6-00

D: 83 tons (93 fl) **S:** 10 kts **Dim:** 20.80 × 6.16 × 2.60
M: Poyaud-Wärtsilä UD12150 M1 diesel; 1 prop; 380 bhp

Remarks: Have two-letter contractions of names on bows instead of official pennant numbers. Bollard pull: 7 tons. Are planned to be retired in 2005.

♦ 4 Aigrette-class small harbor tugs [YTL]

Y 617 Mouette Y 621 Mésange Y 636 Martinet Y 729 Eider

D: 65 tons **S:** 9 kts **Dim:** 18.4 × 5.7 × 2.5
M: 1 Poyaud-Wärtsilä UD8150 M1 diesel; 1 prop; 250 bhp **Range:** 1,700/9

SERVICE CRAFT *(continued)*

Remarks: Built during the early 1960s. Have two-letter contractions of names on bows instead of official pennant numbers. Resemble the larger *Acajou*-class tugs. Bollard pull capacity: 3.5 tons. Y 617 and Y 636 are planned to be retired during 2002 and the other two in 2003.
Disposals: *Ibis* (Y 658) is on loan to Senegal. *Cigogne* (Y 625), *Cygne* (Y 632), *Alouette* (Y 720), *Sarcelle* (Y 724), and *Vanneau* (Y 722) were stricken in 1993; *Moineau* (Y 673), *Pinson* (Y 691), *Passereau* (Y 687), and *Toucan* (Y 726) in 1994; *Bengali* (Y 611), *Engoulevent* (Y 723), *Fauvette* (Y 687), *Goéland* (Y 648), *Macreuse* (Y 727), *Marabout* (Y 725), *Martin-Pecheur* (Y 675), and *Pivert* (Y 694) in 1996–97; *Ara* (Y 730) in 1998; and *Colibri* (Y 628), *Gélinotte* (Y 748), *Grand-duc* (Y 728), *Loriot* (Y 747), and *Merle* (Y 670) in 1999.

♦ **3 Type V 14 small fireboats [YTR]** Bldr: Alain Sibiril, Carentec

Y 783 (In serv. 12-4-94)
Y 784 La Loude (In serv. 25-2-94)
Y 785 (In serv. 24-11-93)

Y 783—painted red Bernard Prézelin, 11-00

D: 14 tons light (23.5 fl) **S:** 17 kts **Dim:** 14.60 (13.20 pp) × 4.60 × 1.90
Electronics: Radar: 1 Decca 060 nav.
M: 2 Baudouin V6T diesels; 2 props; 750 bhp

Remarks: Have two fire monitors, each with a 150-m^3/hr pump and a range of 120 m. Same GRP hull and basic superstructure as Type V 14 patrol boats and service launches. Are painted all red. Three more are planned to be built to replace the *Cascade* class.

♦ **1 Cascade-class fireboat [YTR]**
Bldr: SFCN, Villeneuve-la-Garenne (In serv. 1968)

Y 746 Embrun

Embrun (Y 746) H&L Van Ginderen, 2-99

D: 81 tons (fl) **S:** 11 kts **Dim:** 23.8 × 5.3 × 1.7
M: 1 Poyaud-Wärtsilä UD6PZ M1 diesel; 1 prop; 400 bhp

Remarks: Has two fire monitors atop the pilothouse, one atop the foremast, and one on a folding mast aft. Painted red with white superstructure. Planned to strike in 2002.
Disposals: *Geyser* (Y 646) was stricken in 1993, *Gave* (Y 645) and *Oued* (Y 684) in 1994, *Cascade* (Y 618) in 1996, and *Aiguière* (Y 745) in 2001.

♦ **2 auxiliary sail training barkentines [YTS]**
Bldr: Chantiers de Normandie, Fécamp

A 649 Étoile (L: 7-7-32) A 650 Belle Poule (L: 8-2-32)

D: 225 tons (275 fl) **S:** 9 kts (under power)
Dim: 40.45 (37.50 hull; 32.25 pp) × 7.40 × 3.65
M: 1 Baudouin diesel; 300 bhp—425 m^2 max. sail area
Crew: 1 officer, 5 petty officers, 12 ratings + 20 cadets

Remarks: Assigned to the naval academy. Oregon pine hull construction. The tallest mast is 32.50 m high. A 650 was given a major refit 11-93 to 16-5-94, receiving a new 300-bhp diesel and increasing powered speed to 9 kts.

Belle Poule (A 650) Bernard Prézelin, 5-00

♦ **1 sail-training yawl [YTS]** Bldr: Fidèle, Marseille (L: 1932)

A 653 La Grande Hermine (ex-*La Route Est Belle,* ex-*Ménestrel*)

La Grande Hermine (A 653) Bernard Prézelin, 10-98

Remarks: A 14-m yawl purchased in 1964 for the reserve officers' school. D: 7 tons (13 fl).

♦ **1 sail-training ketch [YTS]**
Bldr: Florimond-Guignardeau, Sables-d'Olonne (L: 18-3-27)

A 652 Mutin

Mutin (A 652) H&L Van Ginderen, 8-9[illegible]

SERVICE CRAFT *(continued)*

D: 42 tons (57 fl) **S:** 11 kts **Dim:** 33.0 (21.0 wl) × 6.5 × 3.4 (1.6 fwd)
M: 1 Baudouin 6-cyl. diesel; 1 prop; 112 bhp—312 m^2 max. sail area
Electric: 10 kw tot. **Crew:** 12 tot. + 13 trainees

Remarks: Assigned to the annex of the seamanship school. Mainmast is 18 m tall.

♦ 2 Glycine-class navigational training craft [YXT]
Bldr: SOCARENAM, Boulogne-sur-Mer

	Laid down	L	In serv.
A 770 Glycine	8-91	1992	11-4-92
A 771 Eglantine	11-91	1992	9-9-92

Glycine (A 770) Bernard Prézelin, 2-01

D: 250 tons (295 fl) **S:** 10 kts **Dim:** 28.30 (24.50 pp) × 7.70 × 3.75
A: none **Electronics:** Radar: 1 Furuno . . . nav.
M: 1 Baudouin 12B152 S5 diesel; 1 CP prop; 800 bhp—150-shp bow-thruster
Electric: 175 kVA tot (115-kVA shaft generator, 1 × 60-kVA Deutz D 226 B6 diesel set)
Range: 3,600/10 **Fuel:** 49 m^3 **Crew:** 10 ship's company + 16 cadets

Remarks: 270 grt. Trawler-hulled craft built to replace the basic navigational and ship-handling training ships *Engageante* (A 772) and *Vigilante* (A 773), which were stricken during 1992. Typed BIN *(Bâtiment d'Instruction à la Navigation).* Carry a single Zodiac RIB. Three near-sisters listed under mine warfare ships are styled BINRS *(Bâtiment d'Instruction à la Navigation et de Remorquage de Sonar)* in the dual role of training craft and tow vessel for a DUBM-41B minehunting side-scan sonar; another serves as the DCN ASW systems trials craft *L'Aventurière II.*

♦ 8 Léopard-class navigational training craft [YXT]

	Bldr	Laid down	L	In serv.
A 748 Léopard	SICNAV, St.-Malo	6-4-81	4-6-81	4-12-82
A 749 Panthère	SICNAV, St.-Malo	9-6-81	3-9-81	4-12-82
A 750 Jaguar	SICNAV, St.-Malo	27-9-81	29-10-81	18-12-82
A 751 Lynx	La Perriere, Lorient	23-7-81	27-2-82	18-12-82
A 752 Guépard	SICNAV, St.-Malo	11-10-82	1-12-82	1-7-83
A 753 Chacal	SFCN, Villeneuve-la-Garenne	11-10-82	11-2-83	10-9-83
A 754 Tigre	La Perriere, Lorient	16-4-82	8-10-82	1-7-83
A 755 Lion	La Perriere, Lorient	21-2-82	13-12-82	10-9-83

Guépard (A 752) Bernard Prézelin, 5-00

Tigre (A 754) Bram Risseeuw, 5-00

D: 335 tons (460 fl) **S:** 15 kts **Dim:** 43.00 (40.15 pp) × 8.30 × 3.21
A: 2 single 20-mm 70-cal. Mk 10 Mod. 23 Oerlikon AA
Electronics: Radar: 1 DRBN-32 nav.
M: 2 SACM 75 V16 ASHR diesels; 2 props; 2,200 bhp
Electric: 160 kw tot. **Range:** 4,100/12
Crew: 1 officer, 7 petty officers, 6 ratings + 2 officer instructors, 2 petty officer instructors, 18 trainees

Remarks: First four authorized in 1980, second group in 1981. Also for use as anti-pollution patrol vessels if required. Were intended to serve for 25 years each.

♦ 2 training tenders [YXT] Bldr: Ch. Bayonne (In serv. 1971)
Y 706 Chimère Y 711 Farfadet

Farfadet (Y 711) Bernard Prézelin, 6-00

D: 100 tons **S:** 11 kts **Dim:** 30.50 × 5.25 × 1.75
Electronics: Radar: 1 DRBN-34A nav. **M:** 1 diesel; 200 bhp

Remarks: Used by the training facility at Poulmic for training in basic seamanship. Were due for disposal in 2000, but have been extended to 2010.

FRENCH ARMY

The Armée de Terre 519th Régiment du Train operates several small units and landing craft at La Pellice.

PATROL BOATS [WPB]

♦ 1 Cassiopée class Bldr: Arcor (In serv. . . .)
D 300098 Cassiopée

Cassiopée (D 300098) Bernard Prézelin, 6-99

D: . . . tons **S:** 24 kts **Dim:** 14.0 × 3.90 × . . .
A: small arms **Electronics:** Radar: 1 Raytheon . . . nav.
M: 2 . . . diesels; 2 props; 560 bhp

♦ 1 Type E 400052 Bldr: PechAlu, Hennebont (In serv. 8-94)
E 400052 Andromède

Andromède (E 400052) Bernard Prézelin, 10-00

FRENCH ARMY PATROL BOATS [WPB] *(continued)*

D: . . . tons **S:** 23 kts **Dim:** 14.50 (13.00 pp) × 5.10 × 1.35
M: 2 diesels; 2 CP props; 710 bhp **Crew:** 12 tot.

Remarks: Used to train army divers. Based at La Pallice.

AMPHIBIOUS WARFARE CRAFT

♦ 6 U.S. LCM(8)-class landing craft [WLCM]
Bldr: CMN, Cherbourg (In serv. . . .)

CTM 12 CTM 13 CTM 14 CTM 15 CTM 16 CTM 17

CTM 14—note conning station atop pilothouse Bernard Prézelin, 7-00

D: 56 tons (150 fl) **S:** 9.5 kts **Dim:** 23.80 × 6.35 × 1.17
M: 2 Poyaud 520 V8 diesels; 2 props; 450 bhp **Range:** 380/8 **Crew:** 4 tot.

Remarks: Essentially identical to the French Navy version, but have an enclosed conning station atop the pilothouse. Operated by the French Army Transport Corps and based at La Pallice.

Disposal note: Rhine River landing craft *Mayenne* (L 924) and *Meurthe* (L 925) had been retired by 2001.

♦ 14 U.S. Army LARC XV–class amphibious landing craft [WLCP]

LARC XV-57 through LARC XV-68 LARC XV-70 LARC XV-71

French Army LARC XV-58—afloat Bernard Prézelin, 3-98

D: 20.8 tons light (35.7 fl) **S:** 8.25 kts water/29.5 mph land
Dim: 13.72 × 4.42 × 4.75 (high, on land) **M:** 2 diesels; 1 prop; 600 bhp
Range: 45/8.25 water, 300/29.5 mph land **Crew:** 2 tot.

Remarks: U.S. Army Design 8004 craft transferred during the late 1950s. Four-tired vehicles, each with a 15-ton payload and an unloading ramp. LARC XV-58 is named *Aflou* and -64 *Fort Boyard*.

AFFAIRES MARITIMES
MARITIME POLICE

Administered by the Ministry of Equipment and Transport for the enforcement of maritime laws and regulations. Except for the officers (members of the Affaires Maritimes who serve on land and are commissioned), the personnel are civilians. Hull numbers begin with PM *(Police Maritime)*.

Note: Craft are now painted with blue hull sides aft and diagonal blue-white-red stripes separating the gray hull sides forward.

PATROL BOATS [WPB]

Regional Surveillance Craft *(Vedettes Régionales de Surveillance)*:

♦ 1 DCN 32-meter class
Bldr: DCN, Lorient (In serv. 25-8-95)

PM 32 Armoise (Based at St.-Nazaire)

D: 73 tons (91 fl) **S:** 23 kts **Dim:** 31.15 (30.50 wl) × 6.100 × 1.80
A: 1 7.5-mm mg
Electronics: Radar: 1 Decca C180/6 nav.; 1 Raytheon R20XX nav.
M: 2 MWM-Deutz TBD234V15 diesels; 2 props; 3,000 bhp—1 MWM-Deutz TBD234V16 diesel; 1 waterjet; 680 bhp
Electric: 70 kw tot. **Range:** 1,200/16 **Crew:** 9 tot.

Remarks: GRP hull. A sister to the Gendarmerie Maritime patrol boats *Géranium* (P 720) and *Violette* (P 722).

Armoise (PM 32) Bernard Prézelin, 1-0

♦ 1 Origan class
Bldr: DCN, Lorient (In serv. 5-7-93)

PM 31 Origan (Based at Boulogne)

Origan (PM 31) Paolo Marsan, 4-9

D: 70 tons (84 fl) **S:** 22 kts **Dim:** 28.00 × 5.50 × 1.60 (1.20 hull)
A: 1 7.5-mm mg
Electronics: Radar: 1 Decca . . . nav.; 1 Furuno . . . nav.
M: 2 MWM-Deutz . . . . . . diesels; 2 props; 2,100 bhp—1 MWM-Deutz TBD234V16 diesel; 1 waterjet; 680 bhp
Range: 1,200/16 **Endurance:** 80 hours **Crew:** 9 tot.

♦ 1 Iris class
Bldr: C.N. de l'Esterel, Cannes (L: 21-12-88)

PM 40 Iris (ex-P 696) (Based at Lorient)

Iris (PM 40)—SATCOM antenna radome added Bernard Prézelin, 4-0

D: 210 tons (230 fl) **S:** 23 kts **Dim:** 45.80 × 8.50 × 2.25
A: 1 12.7-mm mg **Electronics:** Radar: 2 Furuno . . . nav.
M: 2 MTU 16V396 TB83 diesels; 2 props; 4,000 bhp
Electric: 300 kw tot. **Range:** 3,000/13 **Crew:** 15 tot.

Remarks: Built for Thales as a sales demonstrator for weapons systems. Taken ove for the French Navy, which operated her from 1990 to 1993, when she was placed i reserve until acquired by the Affaires Maritimes in 1996. Medical facilities and tw RIB inspection launches have been added. Has Vosper fin stabilizers. Propulsion plan is highly automated.

♦ 1 Gabian class
Bldr: C.N. de l'Esterel, Cannes (In serv. 1986)

PM 30 Gabian (Based at La Rochelle)

Gabian (PM 30) Bernard Prézelin, 10-0

D: 76 tons (fl) **S:** 23 kts **Dim:** 32.10 × 6.46 × 3.03 (molded depth)
A: 1 12.7-mm mg **Electronics:** Radar: 1 . . . nav.
M: 2 Baudouin diesels; 2 props; 900 bhp
Range: 1,280/15 **Endurance:** 100 hours **Crew:** 8 tot.

MARITIME POLICE PATROL BOATS [WPB] *(continued)*

♦ **1 A.E.C. Ancelle class** Bldr: C.N. de l'Esterel, Cannes (In serv. 1963)

PM 26 Patron Louis Renet (Based at Marseille)

Patron Louis Renet (PM 26) Guy Schaeffer, 7-99

D: 74 tons (fl) **S:** 24 kts **Dim:** 31.45 × 5.75 × 3.08 (molded depth)
A: 1 7.5-mm mg **Electronics:** Radar: 1 . . . nav.
M: 2 Baudouin diesels; 2 props; 900 bhp
Range: 1,380/15 **Endurance:** 72 hours **Crew:** 9 tot.

Remarks: Sister *Administrateur-en-Chef Ancelle* (PM 25) was retired during 2-00.

♦ **1 Mauve class** Bldr: C.N. de l'Esterel, Cannes (In serv. 1984)

PM 29 Mauve (Based at Bayonne)

Mauve (PM 29) Bernard Prézelin, 6-99

D: 65 tons (fl) **S:** 26 kts **Dim:** 30.50 × 5.70 × 2.78 (molded depth)
A: 1 12.7 mm mg; 1 7.5-mm mg **Electronics:** Radar: 1 . . . nav.
M: 2 MWM-Deutz diesels; 2 props; 2,120 bhp
Range: 900/15.5 **Endurance:** 61 hours **Crew:** 9 tot.

Remarks: Re-engined in 1990. Sister to the Customs Service's *Avel Gwalarn* (DF 41) and *Suroit* (DF 42).

♦ **1 Tourne-Pierre class**
Bldr: CMN, Cherbourg (In serv. 1984)

PM 28 Tourne-Pierre (Based at Lorient)

Tourne-Pierre (PM 28)—in old paint scheme
Guy Schaeffer, via Paolo Marsan, 9-98

D: 71 tons (fl) **S:** 22 kts **Dim:** 28.95 × . . . × . . .
A: 1 12.7-mm mg **Electronics:** Radar: 1 . . . nav.
M: 2 MWM-Deutz diesels; 2 props; 2,120 bhp
Range: 1,150/15 **Endurance:** 100 hours **Crew:** 8 tot.

Remarks: Re-engined in 1990 and received a new exhaust stack in 7-91.

Inshore Surveillance Craft *(Vedettes de Surveillance Rapprochée)*:

♦ **0 (+ 1) FPB 40 class**
Bldr: Océa, Les Sables d'Olonne (In serv. 2002)

PM . . . . . .

D: 15 tons light **S:** 25 kts **Dim:** 12.7 × . . . × . . .
A: small arms **Electronics:** Radar: 1 Furuno M1832 nav.
M: 2 . . . diesels; 2 props; . . . bhp
Range: . . ./. . . **Crew:** 3 tot.

Remarks: GRP construction. Ordered in 6-99, but work had not commenced as of 5-01.

♦ **4 FPB 50 Mk 2 class**
Bldr: Océa, Les Sables d'Olonne

	In serv.	Based at
PM 100 Calisto	27-4-01	Ajaccio
PM 101 Deimos	27-4-01	Sète
PM 102 Telesto	18-5-01	Nice
PM 103 Phobos	18-5-01	Martigues (near Marseille)

D: 22 tons (fl) **S:** 25 kts **Dim:** 16.15 × 4.81 × 1.20
A: small arms **Electronics:** Radar: 1 Furuno M1832 nav.
M: 2 M.A.N. 2866LE403 diesels; 2 props; 500 bhp
Range: 300/23 **Crew:** 4 tot.

Remarks: Ordered 6-99; were originally to have been six.

♦ **1 Arcor 56 class**
Bldr: CNA, la Teste (In serv. 1991)

PM 64 Cap d'Ailly (Based at Dieppe)

Cap d'Ailly (PM 64) M. Ottini, 7-00

D: 25 tons (fl) **S:** . . . kts **Dim:** 17.00 × 4.85 × . . .
A: small arms **Electronics:** Radar: 1 Furuno. . . nav.
M: 2 Baudouin diesels; 2 props; 1,400 bhp **Crew:** 4 tot.

♦ **1 Eider class** Bldr: Polymer, Tregunc (In serv. 1988)

PM 63 Eider (Based at Morlais)

Eider (PM 63) Bernard Prézelin, 7-01

D: 28 tons **S:** 20 kts **Dim:** 16.80 × 4.50 × 2.10 (molded depth)
A: none **Electronics:** Radar: 1 Furuno . . . nav.
M: 2 M.A.N. diesels; 2 props; 1,250 bhp **Crew:** . . .

♦ **1 Pétrel class** Bldr: C.N. de l'Esterel, Cannes (In serv. 1985)

PM 61 Pétrel (Based at Brest)

D: 26 tons (fl) **S:** 25 kts **Dim:** 17.10 × 4.58 × 2.24 (molded depth)
A: small arms **Electronics:** Radar: 2 Furuno . . . nav.
M: 2 Poyaud diesels; 2 props; 450 bhp **Endurance:** 30 hours **Crew:** . . .

Disposal note: Arcor 43-class *Valériane* (PM 54) was retired during 2001.

MARITIME POLICE PATROL BOATS [WPB] *(continued)*

Pétrel (PM 61)—in old paint scheme Bernard Prézelin, 5-96

Inshore Surveillance Craft *(Vedettes de Surveillance Littoral):*

♦ 5 Pointe du Hoc class (In serv. 1994)

PM 290 Pointe du Hoc	PM 292 An Alre	PM 295 La Varde
PM 291 L'Arundel	PM 294 Île Dumet	

Île Dumet (PM 294)—in old paint scheme Bernard Prézelin, 8-96

D: 10 tons (fl) **S:** 27 kts **Dim:** 11.80 × . . . × . . .
M: 2 diesels; 2 props; 460 bhp

♦ 18 miscellaneous units

PM 269 Mor Braz (ex-*La Cauchoise*), PM 270 Korrigan, PM 271 Auzance, PM 273 Lou Labech (1981–82): 8.0 m o.a.; 140 bhp
PM 279 Sarriette (1988): 26 kts; 10.90 m o.a.; 500 bhp
PM 281 Pertuisane (1988): 8 tons; 25 kts; 10.60 m o.a.; 460 bhp
PM 283 Girondine (1988): 17 kts; 9.15 m o.a.; 440 bhp
PM 284 Cap de Nice (1990): 26 kts; 10.30 m o.a.; 500 bhp
PM 285 Syndic Victor Salez (1990): 18 kts; 8.15 m o.a.; 250 bhp
PM 286 An Oriant (1991): 20 kts; 8.00 m o.a.; 140 bhp
PM 287 Men Goe (1991): 18 kts; 7.00 m o.a.; 85 bhp
PM 288 Catalane (1992): 26 kts; 11.40 m o.a.; 500 bhp
PM 290 Pointe du Hoc, PM 291 L'Arundel, PM 292 An Alre, PM 294 Île Dumet, PM 295 La Varde (all 1994): 10 tons; 27 kts; 11.80 m; 460 bhp
PM 293 Colibri (1994): 12 tons; 27 kts; 11.98 m o.a.; 750 bhp

Cap de Nice (PM 284) Guy Schaeffer, via Paolo Marsan, 5-00

Remarks: In addition to the above launches, there are a number of units between 5.0 and 7.0 m overall.

Note: The French Customs Service *(Douanes)*, under the Ministry of the Budget, also operates patrol craft with hull numbers beginning with "DF" *(Douanes Française)*. The following aircraft were in use in 2001: 2 Cessna 404 twin-engine light transports, 13 Riems Aviation 406 light aircraft (3 equipped for oilspill detection), and 6 AS.335 F2 Écureuil helicopters. As of 2000, some 650 personnel were assigned. Principal patrol craft and boats as of 2002 include:

- 1 *Arafenua* class: *Arafenua* (DF 48): 105 tons, 25 kts; based at Papeete.
- 8 *Haize Hegoa* class: *Alizé* (DF 31), *Vent d'Aval* (DF 37), *Haize Hegoa* (DF 43), *Mervent* (DF 44), *Vent d'Autan* (DF 45), *Avel Sterenn* (DF 46), *Lissero* (DF 47), and one other: 75 tons, 28 kts
- 2 *Avel Gwalarn* class: *Avel Gwalarn* (DF 41) and *Suroît* (DF 42): 67 tons, 28 kts
- 1 *Vent d'Amont* class: *Vent d'Amont* (DF 40): 71 tons, 25 kts
- 2 *Mistral* class: *Mistral* (DF 38) and *Aquilon* (DF 39): 45 tons, 30 kts
- 3 *Cers* class: *Tramontana* (DF 17), *Umarinu* (DF 18), and *Cers* (DF 19): 34 ton 27.5 kts
- 3 *Rafale* class: *Sua Louiga* (DF 24), *Marinda* (DF 30), and *Rafale* (DF 49): 41 ton 34 kts
- 1 *Gregau* class: *Gregau* (DF 16): 41 tons, 28 kts
- 8 *Noirot* class: *Noirot* (DF 12), *Nordet* (DF 14), *Norues* (DF 15), *Karina* (DF 20 *Macari* (DF 21), *Lagarde* (DF 25), *Orsuro* (DF 28), and *Muntese* (DF 29): 35 ton 28 kts
- 2 *Libecciu* class: *Libecciu* (DF 26) and *Levant* (DF 27): 30 tons, 28 kts
  4 *Aigly* class: *Liane* (DF 50), *Yser* (DF 51), *Aigly* (DF 56), and *Touloubre* (DF 57 13.5 tons, 27 kts
- 1 *Aunis* class: *Aunis* (DF 1): 143-ton motor yacht employed for training
- 1 *Louisiane* class: *Louisiane* (DF 2): 24 tons; used for training
- 1 training launch: *Pingouin:* 6.8 m

In addition, there were 27 *vedettes de surveillance rapprochée* (VSR) between 8. and 13.5 m in overall length and nine *vedettes portuaire* (VSP) of less than 8 m lengt overall.

The Gendarmerie Nationale, although it had transferred the majority of its ma itime assets to the Gendarmerie Maritime, as of 2001 still operated the patrol launche G 9501 (17 m, 22 kts) and G 7501 (13.3 m, 20 kts) on the Rhine River and th 15.8-m diver-training launch *Antibes* (G 9602) at Antibes.

GABON

Gabonese Republic

MARINE GABONAISE

Personnel (2002): Approx. 60 officers, 440 enlisted

Bases: Port-Gentil and Mayumba

Maritime Aviation: One Embraer EMB 111 Bandeirante maritime patrol aircra is operated by the air force.

PATROL CRAFT [PC]

♦ 2 French Super PATRA class
Bldr: CMN, Cherbourg

	Laid down	L	In ser
P 07 Général d'Armée Ba Oumar	2-7-86	18-12-87	6-8-8
P 08 Colonel Djoué Dabany	5-89	29-3-90	24-10-9

Général d'Armée Ba Oumar (P 07)—note twin stacks and 57-mm gun forward French Navy, 7-9

Colonel Djoué Dabany (P 08)—note lack of stacks and lighter armament Bernard Prézelin, 11-9

D: 371.5 tons (446 fl) **S:** 24.5 kts
Dim: 54.60 (50.0 pp) × 8.00 (7.70 wl) × 2.54 (2.08 hull)

PATROL CRAFT [PC] *(continued)*

: P 07: 1 57-mm 70-cal. Bofors SAK 57 Mk 2 DP; 1 20-mm GIAT F2 AA—P 08: 2 single 20-mm 90-cal. GIAT F2 AA
lectronics: 1 Decca 1226C nav.
: 2 SACM-Wärtsilä UD33V16 M7 diesels; 2 CP props; 8,000 bhp
lectric: 360 kw **Range:** 4,400/14.5 **Fuel:** 73 tons **Endurance:** 15 days
rew: 4 officers, 28 enlisted + 23 passengers or 20 troops

emarks: P 07 ordered 11-84, P 08 during 2-89.
ombat systems: For search-and-rescue use, carry an inflatable launch and can acommodate 23 rescued personnel. Have two contraband storerooms. P 07 has a Ma-a Défense Naja optronic gun director for the 57-mm gun. Armament was reduced n P 08 to save money, and delivery of the unit was delayed by re-engining. P 07 had vin stacks installed during a 1991–92 refit in France, as in the French Navy versions of the class.
isposal note: The wooden-hulled patrol craft *Général Nazaire Boulingui* (P 10) was eported stricken in 1999.

MPHIBIOUS WARFARE SHIPS AND CRAFT

1 Champlain-class troop transport [LPA]
Bldr: Atelier Français de l'Ouest, Grand Quevilly, Rouen, France

	Laid down	L	In serv.
05 Président el Hadj Omar Bongo	7-3-83	16-4-84	3-11-84

résident el Hadj Omar Bongo (L 05) French Navy, 1999

: 820 tons (1,386 fl) **S:** 16 kts **Dim:** 80.00 (68.0 pp) × 13.00 × 2.50
: 1 40-mm 70-cal. Bofors AA; 2 single 20-mm 90-cal. GIAT F2 AA; 1 7.62-mm mg
lectronics: Radar: 1 Decca 1226 nav.
: 2 SACM 195V12 diesels; 2 CP props; 3,600 bhp
lectric: 360 kw tot. **Range:** 4,500/13 **Crew:** 47 tot. + 138 troops

emarks: Purchase announced 28-2-84. By tradition, the largest ship of the Gabonese avy bears the name of the nation's "president for life." Refitted in 1996–97 at Cape own, South Africa, by Denel, during which time the bow doors were welded closed, iminating the beaching capability.
ull systems: Cargo capacity: 340 tons of stores and 208 tons of potable water. Cargo handled by a large electrohydraulic crane just forward of the bridge. Has a helipter platform aft, although the navy has no aircraft. Carries one Tanguy Marine)-m Sea Truck–type landing craft and one 12-m Tanguy Marine personnel launch.

1 utility landing craft [LCU] Bldr: DCAN, Dakar (In serv. 11-5-76)

Ianga

: 152 tons (fl) **S:** 9 kts **Dim:** 24.0 × 6.4 × 1.3
: 2 single 12.7-mm mg **Electronics:** Radar: Decca 101 nav.
: 2 Poyaud V8-520 diesels; 2 props; 480 bhp **Range:** 600/5 **Crew:** 10 tot.

emarks: Equipped with a bow door and ramp. Refitted in 1997–98 at LNI, Lorient, rance.

ote: In 1989, the gendarmerie received a 10-unit afloat patrol launch flotilla built y Simonneau, Fontenay, France. Included were one 11.8-m and two 8.10-m patrol aft, each powered by a Volvo Penta TAMD-608 inboard/outboard diesel of 235 bhp, ong with seven 6.8-m personnel landing craft powered by one 110-bhp Volvo Penta QAD-30/DP diesel each. Some are likely to have ceased to function.

THE GAMBIA

epublic of the Gambia

ersonnel (2002): Approx. 40 total

ase: Banjul

ote: The "unification" of the Gambia and Senegal, agreed to on 1-2-82 but never onsummated, was canceled on 30-9-89. The naval organization's name was officially anged from the Marine Unit of the Gambian National Army to the Gambian Navy uring 8-96.

ATROL BOATS [PB]

1 U.S. 51-foot class
Bldr: Peterson Bldrs, Sturgeon Bay, Wis. (In serv. 1-94)

14 Bolongkantaa

D: 24 tons (fl) **S:** 24 kts **Dim:** 15.54 × 4.47 × 1.30
A: fitted for: 1 twin 12.7-mm mg; 2 single 7.62-mm mg
Electronics: Radar: 1 Raytheon R41X nav.
M: 2 G.M. Detroit Diesel 6V92A diesels; 2 props; 900 bhp
Electric: 15 kw tot. **Range:** 500/20 **Fuel:** 800 gallons **Crew:** 6 tot.

Remarks: Ordered late in 1993 and paid for by the U.S.A. Aluminum construction. Carries a 4.27-m RIB inspection craft (with a 50-bhp outboard motor) on the stern. The contract included training in operation and maintenance. Sisters were given to Cape Verde, Senegal, and Guinea-Bissau. Has not been seen with armament aboard.

GEORGIA

Republic of Georgia

GEORGIAN NAVY

Personnel (2002): Approx. 350 total

Bases: Main facility at Poti, with naval academy and minor patrol boat base at Batumi

Note: The Romanian government transferred one "corvette" to Georgia in 2000 and also provided naval uniforms; the actual type and class of ship or craft transferred, however, is not available.

HYDROFOIL GUIDED-MISSILE PATROL BOATS [PTGH]

♦ **1 ex-Ukrainian Matka (Vikhr')-class (Project 206MR) semi-hydrofoil**
Bldr: Sudostroitel'noye Obyedineniye "Almaz" (Sredniy Neva), Kolpino, Russia

P 302 Tbilisi (ex-*Konotop,* U 150; ex-R-15) (In serv. 1979–81)

D: 233 tons (258 fl; 268 max.) **S:** 42 kts
Dim: 38.60 (37.50 wl) × 12.5 (7.6 hull; 5.9 wl) × 2.10 (hull; 3.26 foils)
A: 2 P-15M Termit (SS-N-2C Styx) SSM; 1 76.2-mm 59-cal. AK-176M DP; 1 30-mm 54-cal. AK-630 gatling AA; . . . SA-14/16 shoulder-launched SAM
Electronics:
Radar: 1 Cheese Cake nav.; 1 Garpun (Plank Shave) target detection/tracking; 1 MR-123 Vympel-AM (Bass Tilt) gun f.c.
EW: no intercept equipment; 2 16-round PK-16 decoy RL
M: 3 M-520TM5 diesels; 3 props; 14,400 bhp
Electric: 300 kw tot. (1 × 100-kw DGF2A-100/1500 and 1 × 200-kw DRGA-2A-200/1500 diesel sets; 380 V, 50 Hz a.c.)
Range: 600/35; 1,200/22–24; 1,800/11–12
Fuel: 38 tons (max. overload) **Endurance:** 8 days **Crew:** 25–28 tot.

Remarks: Transferred from the Russian Black Sea Fleet to Ukraine in poor condition 12-8-97; donated to Georgia late in 1999 (at which time it was said that her new name would be *Eduard Shevardnadze*).
Hull systems: Steel hull with aluminum/magnesium alloy superstructure. The stern planes on the surface while the bow is supported by the hydrofoils at high speeds. Both the foils and the transom stern flap are remotely controlled via a Baza 02065 gyro system to improve the ride.
Combat systems: Positions for EW intercept antennas remain empty. Can employ weapons in Sea State 6. Carries 152 rounds of 76.2-mm and 2,000 rounds of 30-mm ammunition. Has SPO-3 radiation-warning equipment and the R-784 automated radio system. Missiles may not have been transferred with the craft.

PATROL CRAFT [PC]

♦ **1 ex-Russian Stenka (Tarantul) class (Project 205P)**
Bldr: Sudostroitel'noye Obyedineniye "Almaz," Petrovskiy SY, St. Petersburg

P 301 Batumi (ex-PSKR-638) (In serv. 1967–90)

D: 170 tons light; 211 tons std. (245 fl) **S:** 35 kts
Dim: 39.80 (37.50 wl) × 7.60 (5.90 wl) × 1.96
A: 2 single 37-mm 63-cal. Type 70K (Model 1939) AA
Electronics:
Radar: 1 Baklan (Pot Drum) or Reyd (Peel Cone) nav./surf. search; 1 MR-104 Rys' (Drum Tilt) gun f.c.
EW: SPO-3 intercept
M: 3 M-504 or M-520 diesels; 3 props; 15,000 bhp
Range: 500/35; 800/20; 1,500/12 **Endurance:** 10 days
Crew: 4–5 officers, 26–27 enlisted

Remarks: Transferred from Russia in 1999, along with ex-PSKR-692, which was intended for the coast guard but has not yet been activated. The original twin 30-mm AK-230 gunmounts have been replaced with old 37-mm manually operated guns, and the ASW torpedo tubes were removed, along with the sonar system.

PATROL BOATS [PB]

♦ **2 Zhuk (Gryf) class (Project 1400M)**
Bldr: P 103: Batumi Ship Repair Yard (In serv. 1995)

P 103 Anastasiya P 104 . . . . . .

D: 35.9 tons (39.7 fl) **S:** 30 kts
Dim: 23.80 (21.70 wl) × 5.00 (3.80 wl) × 1.00 (hull; 1.90 max.)

PATROL BOATS [PB] *(continued)*

A: 1 twin 12.7-mm 60-cal. Utës-Ma mg **Electronics:** Radar: 1 Lotsiya nav.
M: 2 M-401 diesels; 2 props; 2,200 bhp
Electric: 48 kw total (2 × 21-kw, 1 × 6-kw diesel sets)
Range: 500/13.5 **Endurance:** 5 days **Crew:** 1 officer, 9 enlisted

Remarks: P 104 was donated by Ukraine in 3-97 to the Georgian Border Department but has apparently been handed over to the navy. Aluminum alloy hull.

♦ 4 Aist-class (Project 1398) launches
Bldr: Sretenskiy Zavod, Kokuy (In serv. 1975–86)

D: 3.55 tons (5.8 fl) **S:** 20 kts **Dim:** 9.50 × 2.60 × 0.50
A: 1 7.62-mm mg **Electronics:** Radar: none
M: 1 3D-20 diesel; 1 waterjet; 235 bhp **Fuel:** 0.37 tons **Crew:** . . . tot.

Remarks: Rail-transportable launches originally designed for employment on the Amur-Ussuri River system in the Soviet Far East.

♦ 1 ex-Russian Project 360
Bldr: Sudostroitel'noye Obyedineniye "Almaz," Petrovskiy SY, St. Petersburg

101 Tolya (ex-*Merkuriy*) (In serv. 1961–64)

D: 58 tons (70 fl) **S:** 38 kts **Dim:** 27.0 × 6.5 × 1.4
A: 1 37-mm 63-cal. Type 70-K (Model 1939) AA
Electronics: Radar: 1 . . . nav. **M:** 4 M-50F-3 diesels; 4 props; 4,800 bhp
Endurance: 5 days **Crew:** . . . tot.

Remarks: Former Black Sea Fleet flag officer yacht transferred to Georgia during 1997 for use as a patrol boat. The manually operated gun is on the stern.

♦ 1 ex-Russian Poluchat-I (TL-1) class (Project 368T)
Bldr: Sosnovka Zavod (In serv. 1960–77)

P 102 (ex-TL-. . .)

Poluchat-I-class patrol boat P 102—with a Stenka-class patrol craft in background; note the altered armament on the Stenka and the 37-mm AA on the stern of patrol craft *Tolya* (101) at left Hartmut Ehlers, 8-00

D: 84.7 tons (92.8 fl) **S:** 21.6 kts **Dim:** 29.60 × 6.10 (5.80 wl) × 1.56 (1.90 props)
A: 2 single 37-mm 63-cal. Type 70-K (Model 1939) AA; 1 17-round 140-mm BM-14-17 PU artillery RL
Electronics: Radar: 1 Don-2 or Mius (Spin Trough) nav.
M: 2 M-50F-4 diesels; 2 props; 2,400 bhp
Range: 250/21.6; 550/14 **Crew:** 1 officer, 2 warrant officers, 12 enlisted

Remarks: Former torpedo retriever. Date of transfer and source uncertain; may have been left behind at Poti by departing Russian forces. Has a Gira-KM gyrocompass and NEL-3 echo sounder. The hull has seven watertight bulkheads.

Note: Four Russian Black Sea Fleet Yevgenya-class (Project 1258) inshore minesweepers (probably ex-RT-439, RT-588, RT-823, and RT-1202) were transferred to Georgia in 1998 but have not been put into service.

SERVICE CRAFT

♦ 1 ex-Russian Kulik-class (Project 1415PV) workboat [YFL]
Bldrs (class): Sosnovka Zavod, Rybinsk; Yaroslavl Zavod; etc. (In serv. 1976–90s)

82 (ex-RK-. . .)

D: 42 tons (54 fl) **S:** 11 kts **Dim:** 21.20 × 3.93 × 1.40
A: 1 12.7-mm mg **Electronics:** Radar: 1 Lotsiya nav. (not always fitted)
M: 1 Type 3D12A or 3D12L diesel; 1 prop; 300 bhp
Electric: 12 kw tot. (DGR 1A-16/1500 generator)
Range: 200/11 **Endurance:** 5 days **Crew:** 4 tot. + 27 passengers

Remarks: Date of transfer unknown. Acts as a tug and patrol boat at Poti. Designed by Redan Central Design Bureau.

Note: Two former Bulgarian Navy Vydra-class utility landing craft were transferred 16-7-01 for logistics support duties.

GEORGIAN BORDER DEPARTMENT COAST GUARD

Base: Poti

PATROL CRAFT [WPC]

♦ 1 ex-Turkish AB 25 class
Bldr: Taskizak SY (In serv. 21-2-69)

Kutaisi (ex-AB 30; P 130, ex-P 1230)

D: 150 tons (170 fl) **S:** 22 kts **Dim:** 40.24 × 6.4 × 1.65
A: 1 40-mm 60-cal. Mk 3 Bofors AA; 1 20-mm 70-cal. Oerlikon AA; 2 single 12.7-mm mg
Electronics: Radar: 1 Decca . . . nav.—Sonar: Plessey PMS-26 hull-mounted MF
M: 2 SACM-AGO V16CSHR diesels; 2 props; 4,800 bhp—2 cruise diesels; 300 bhp
Crew: 3 officers, 28 enlisted

Remarks: Transferred as a gift from Turkey 5-12-98. Cruise diesels are geared to the main shafts. May be assigned to the coast guard rather than the navy. ASW equipment has been removed.

♦ 1 ex-German Type 331B former minehunter
Bldr: Burmester, Bremen

	L	In serv.
P 22 Ayety (ex-*Minden,* M 1085)	9-6-59	22-1-60

Ayety (P 22) German Navy, 19..

D: 388 tons (402 fl) **S:** 16.5 kts **Dim:** 47.45 × 8.5 × 2.8
A: 1 40-mm 70-cal. Bofors AA **Electronics:** Radar: 1 Raytheon SPS-64(V)5 nav.
M: 2 MTU 16V538 TB90 diesels; 2 CP props; 5,000 bhp—2 50-shp electric cruise motors (6 kts)
Electric: 220 kw tot. **Range:** 1,400/16; 3,950/9 **Crew:** 5 officers, 29 enlisted

Remarks: Donated by Germany and transferred disarmed on 22-10-98; delivered to Georgia aboard heavy-lift ship *Condock V,* arriving 16-11-98 at Poti. Had been decommissioned 4-12-97. Was converted in 1975–79 to a minehunter from a Klasse 32.. *Lindau*-class, wooden-hulled minesweeper. Painted white prior to transfer and has diagonal "coast guard" striping on the hull sides forward. Planned transfer of two more did not take place.
Hull systems: Wooden construction, with nonmagnetic engines.
Combat systems: The 40-mm gun is controlled by a lead-computing optical director on the bridge. The DSQS-11A minehunting sonar was removed prior to transfer and no towed sweep gear was retained, although the sweep winch remains in place.

PATROL BOATS [WPB]

♦ 2 U.S. 40-foot Dauntless class
Bldr: SeaArk, Monticello, Ark.

P 208 (In serv. 2-98) P 209 (In serv. 3-99)

D: 15 tons (fl) **S:** 28 kts **Dim:** 12.19 (11.13 wl) × 3.86 × 0.69 (hull)
A: 2 single 12.7-mm mg; 2 single 7.62-mm mg
Electronics: Radar: 1 Raytheon R40X nav.
M: 2 Caterpillar 3208TA diesels; 2 props; 850 bhp (720 sust.)
Range: 200/30; 400/22 **Fuel:** 250 gallons **Crew:** 5 tot.

Remarks: Paid for by the U.S. Defense Special Weapons Threat Reduction Program. C. Raymond Hunt, "Deep-Vee" hull design. Sisters operate in several Caribbean navies and other nation forces.

♦ 2 ex-Greek Dilos class Bldr: Hellenic SY, Skaramanga (In serv. 1977–88)

P 201 Iveriya (ex-*Lindos,* P 269) P 205 Gryf (ex-*Dilos,* P 267)

D: 75 tons (86 fl) **S:** 27 kts **Dim:** 29.00 (27.00 wl) × 5.00 × 1.62
A: 2 single 20-mm 70-cal. Oerlikon AA **Electronics:** Radar: 1 . . . nav.
M: 2 MTU 12V331 TC81 diesels; 2 props; 2,720 bhp
Range: 1,600/25 **Crew:** 15 tot.

Remarks: Transferred by donation, P 201 during 1-98 and P 205 during 9-99. Designed by Abeking & Rasmussen, West Germany, for air/sea rescue. Round-bilge steel construction hull.

♦ 2 ex-Turkish SG 40 class
Bldr: . . ., Turkey (In serv. . . .)

P 206 (ex-SG 48) P 207 (ex-SG 40)

D: 45 tons (fl) **S:** 12 kts **Dim:** 16.8 × 4.20 × 1.10
A: 1 12.7-mm mg **Electronics:** Radar: 1 Decca . . . nav.
M: 2 G.M. Gray Marine 64HN9 diesels; 2 props; 450 bhp
Range: 200/12 **Crew:** 7 tot.

Remarks: Transferred as a gift 27-2-98. Wooden hulled.

♦ 1 (+ 1) ex-U.S. Coast Guard 82-foot Point class
Bldr: Coast Guard Yard, Curtis Bay, Md. (In serv. 8-8-62)

	In serv.
P 210 Tsotne Dadiani (ex-*Point Countess,* WPB 82335)	8-8-62
P 211 . . . . . . (ex-*Point Baker,* WPB 82342)	30-10-63

COAST GUARD PATROL BOATS [WPB] *(continued)*

Tsotne Dadiani (P 210)—outboard Turkmenistan's *Merjen* (129)
Hartmut Ehlers, 11-00

D: 64 tons (66 fl) **S:** 23.7 kts **Dim:** 25.3 × 5.23 × 1.95
A: 2 single 12.7-mm Colt M2 mg
Electronics: Radar: 1 Hughes-Furuno SPS-73 nav.
M: 2 Caterpillar 3412 diesels; 2 props; 1,480 bhp
Range: 490/23.7; 1,500/8 **Fuel:** 5.7 tons **Crew:** 1 officer, 7 enlisted

Remarks: P 210 was transferred by donation during 6-00 and P 211 was to be transferred 5-2-02. Hull built of mild steel. High-speed diesels, controlled from the bridge. Well-equipped for salvage and towing.

AMPHIBIOUS WARFARE CRAFT

♦ **1 ex-Russian Ondatra (Akula)-class (Project 1176) landing craft [WLCM]** (In serv. 1971–79)

D: 90 tons normal (107.3 fl) **S:** 11.5 kts **Dim:** 24.50 × 6.00 × 1.55
A: none **Electronics:** Radar: 1 Mius (Spin Trough) nav. (portable)
M: 2 Type 3D12 diesels; 2 props; 600 bhp
Range: 330/10; 500/5 **Endurance:** 2 days **Crew:** 6 tot. (enlisted)

Remarks: Origin uncertain; may have been transferred by Ukraine rather than Russia. Cargo well is 13.7 × 3.9 m and can accommodate one 40-ton tank or up to 50 tons of general cargo; some 20 troops or vehicle crew can be carried.

Disposal note: Two T-4-class (Project 1785) landing craft taken over at Poti in 1992 are no longer in service.

♦ **2 ex-U.K. Rigid Raider assault boats Mk 3 [WLCP]**
Bldr: RTK Marine, Poole, Dorset (In serv. 1996–98)

D: 2.2 tons light **S:** 40 kts (36 loaded) **Dim:** 7.58 × 2.75 × . . .
M: 1 Yamaha gasoline outboard; 220 bhp **Crew:** 2 tot. + 8 commandos

Remarks: Transferred at Poti 11-1-99.

GERMANY

Federal Republic of Germany

DEUTSCHE MARINE

Personnel (2000): 21,600 total (including 5,017 officers and 5,600 conscripts). In addition, there were 9,800 naval reservists.

Bases: Fleet headquarters is at Glücksburg, with Flag Officer, Naval Command, at Rostock. North Sea bases are located at Borkum, Emden, and Wilhelmshaven. Baltic bases are at Kiel, Eckernförde, Olpenitz, and Warnemünde. Naval training is conducted at Brake, Bremerhaven, Glückstadt, List/Sylt, and Plön. Naval repair facilities (arsenals) are located at Kiel and Wilhelmshaven. All submarines are now based at Kiel, while the frigates are based at Wilhelmshaven, missile boats at Warnemünde, and all mine countermeasures units at Olpenitz. The bases at Neustadt and Grossenbrode were closed during 2000.

Naval Aviation: Name changed to Marineflieger *Flotilla* on 1-4-94. About 4,000 personnel serve in the Marineflieger. Aircraft include 14 Bréguet Atlantic Mk 1 maritime patrol aircraft (4 modified for EW duties), 53 MRCA PA 200 Tornado fighter-bombers, 22 Sea King Mk 43 SAR helicopters, 16 Westland/Bréguet Lynx Mk 88 and 7 Super Lynx Mk 88A shipboard ASW helicopters, 4 Dornier Do-228-212 light transports (2 for VIP transport, 2 for pollution control surveillance), and 4 AIA Westwind target tugs (contractor operated).
Organization:

- Naval Air Group MFG 2 *(Marine Flieger Geschwader)* at Eggebek: 2 attack and 1 reconnaissance squadrons of Tornados (18 aircraft each)
- Naval Air Group MFG 3 at Nordholz: 2 squadrons of Atlantics and 1 of Lynx helicopters, plus 2 Dornier Do-228-212 for pollution-control duties
- Naval Air Group MFG 5 at Kiel-Holtenau: 1 squadron of Sea Kings and 2 Dornier Do-228-212 transports; Sea King detachments for SAR duties are maintained at Borkkum, Sylt, and Helgoland

The Atlantic Mk 1 maritime patrol aircraft have been rehabilitated to remain in service until 2010, at which time they will be over four decades old; new avionics and communications suites are being fitted, and a forward-looking infrared is being added. Ten to 12 replacement maritime patrol aircraft are to be procured, with the first to deliver in 2010.

Twenty Sea Kings have been upgraded to permit carrying four Sea Skua antiship missiles, a Sea Spray Mk 3 search radar, electronic intercept gear, chaff, Link 11 computer data system, an ALR-68 radar warning system, and the Bendix AQS-18 dipping sonar.

The Lynx Mk 88 ASW helicopters employ the DAQS-18 dipping sonar. The seven Super Lynx Series 100 (RN HAS.8 equivalent) were ordered in 10-96, with the first completed 15-7-99, and the earlier Lynx units are being upgraded to Mk 88A status to extend service to 2012; all are being equipped to launch Sea Skua antiship missiles and will have Marconi Seaspray 3000 radars and a FLIR system.

Procurement of 38 NH-90 helicopters to replace the SH-3D and Lynx is anticipated; at least six will be in search-and-rescue configuration, and the aircraft are now expected to enter service with the German Navy in 2007.

German Navy Tornado Findler & Winter, 7-00

German Navy Atlantic Mk 1 Findler & Winter, 7-00

German Navy Super Lynx Mk 88A—note chin-mounted radar and nose EW antennas Findler & Winter, 7-00

German Navy Lynx Mk 88 Findler & Winter, 7-00

German Navy Dornier Do-228-212 Findler & Winter, 7-00

German Navy Sea King Mk 43—in SAR configuration Findler & Winter, 6-00

WEAPONS AND SYSTEMS

A. MISSILES

♦ Surface-to-air missiles

Standard SM-2 Block III: On board the Type 124 guided-missile destroyers (see U.S. section for characteristics)

Standard SM-1 MR: On board the *Charles F. Adams*–class destroyers (see U.S. section for characteristics)

RIM-116A RAM (Rolling Airframe Missile): Developed as a close-in defense weapon in cooperation with General Dynamics in the United States. The system will carry 21 missiles per launcher. By 1995 some 2,000 missiles had been ordered from RAMSYS GmbH, along with 52 Mk 49 launchers.

♦ Surface-to-surface missiles

MM 38 Exocet: On board Type 123 frigates and Type 143A, 143, and 148 guided-missile patrol boats (see French section for characteristics)

Harpoon (RGM-84A/C): Carried by the Type 122 frigates and by the *Charles F. Adams*–class destroyers (see U.S. section for characteristics)

Polyphem: Manufacturer: EADS-LFK *(Lenkflugkörpersysteme)*. Development was begun by TRIFOM: Aérospatiale Matra (France), EADS (formerly DaimlerChrysler Aerospace) (Germany), and Consorzio Italmissile (Italy), with Northrop Grumman affiliation in the U.S.A. Intended for submerged launch from submarines against surface targets, low-flying aircraft, or helicopters; launched horizontally from torpedo tubes, using discarding container. Guidance is by fiber-optic cable, with GPS and/or inertial guidance to the vicinity of target. It is also to be available as a land or surface ship–launched weapon useful against tanks, surface ships, and helicopters. Powered by a small turbojet engine. Smaller versions for land use to ranges of 30 km and a vertically launched submarine version are also foreseen. Four of the 60-km-range strike version or six of the 14.4-km antihelicopter version could be accommodated in one 533-mm torpedo tube and launched individually. The submarine-launched strike version may employ a self-powered launch capsule that can travel 7 km before disgorging the missile, in order to disguise the position of the launch platform. Data for the Polyphem include:

Length: 2.74 m **Diameter:** 254 mm **Weight:** 108.8 kg
Warhead: 20 kg **Speed:** Mach 0.45 **Range:** 60 km

Triton: A variant of Polyphem under development by the LFK division of EADS. Triton will not use a launch capsule (instead, "windable" wings are to be wrapped around the fuselage) and will have a variable-thrust solid rocket motor instead of a turbojet; range is to be 15 km and speed up to 720 km/hr. It will have a combined blast-fragmentation/penetration/shaped-charge warhead with impact fuze. Submerged launch trials were conducted in 3-01 and test launches from a Type 206 submarine are to take place in 2002. Triton may enter production in 6-04, possibly for use in the Type 212 submarines, as well as being offered for export.

Note: The Swedish Saab Bofors RBS-15 Mk 3 has been selected as the eventual replacement for the MM 38 Exocet antiship missile and is to be installed first on the new Type 130 corvettes; see data in the Swedish section.

♦ Air-to-surface missiles

Kormoran and U.S. HARM: Carried by Tornado aircraft. Some 262 Kormoran-I missiles were remanufactured to Kormoran-II configuration between 1992 and 1998 by Messerschmidt-Bölkow-Blohm (MBB). The original 165-kg warhead was enlarged to 220 kg and has 21 fragments vice 16, a phased-array radar seeker has been substituted, post-boost coast-glide cruise is employed to increase range, and logistic support and reliability were to be improved.

B. GUNS

127-mm U.S. Mk 42 Mod. 10: On two *Charles F. Adams*–class destroyers

76-mm OTOBreda Compact: On frigates and Type 143, 143A, and 148 guided-missile patrol boats. All mounts have been upgraded by OTOBreda to have a 120-rd/min firing rate.

40-mm 70-cal. Bofors: In single or twin mounts on many types of ships. Replaced by open OTOBreda mountings in combatants. Bofors Trinity elevating masses and 100-round ready-service magazines were ordered in 1986 to update existing 40-mm mounts.

27-mm Mauser MLG 27 (MN 27 GS): Up to 90 remotely controlled mounts are to be procured to replace existing 40-mm and 20-mm mounts. Developed from the 45-cal. BK 27 aircraft gun, it fires a frangible subcaliber round with a 1.75-kg projectile; 90 rounds are carried on-mount. The associated E/O fire-control system, developed by STN Atlas Elektronik, includes day and night vision sensors and provides automatic target tracking.

Mount weight: 850 kg **Projectile weight:** 225 g
Muzzle velocity: 1,150 m/sec **Rate of fire:** 1,700 rds/min
Arc of elevation: −15° to +60° **Range:** 4,000 m surf./2,500 m air

20-mm 90-cal. RH 202 AA: Rheinmetall guns in single mountings

C. ASW WEAPONS

♦ Rocket launchers

U.S. ASROC Mk 16 system: With a Mk 112 octuple launcher for missiles having a Mk 46 ASW torpedo payload. In the *Charles F. Adams* class, where it is probably no longer operational, although the launchers are retained on board.

♦ Torpedoes

U.S. Mk 46 Mod. 5 ASW: On *Charles F. Adams*–class destroyers, frigates, Atlantic Mk 1 ASW patrol aircraft, and Lynx helicopters

DM-1 Seeschlange: Wire-guided on submarines. The anti–surface ship version for Type 143 missile boats is SST-4 and the export ASW version is the SUT (see descriptions below). Data for DM-1:

Diameter: 533 mm **Weight:** 1,370 kg **Warhead:** 275 kg
Speed: 18 or 34 kts **Range:** 20,000 m

DM-2A1 Seeal: Wire-guided for Type 206 submarines.

Diameter: 533 mm **Warhead:** 100 kg **Speed:** 33 kts **Range:** 10,000 m

DM-2A3 Seehecht: Wire-guided; used on submarines. Export version is known as Seehake. In early 1996, STN Atlas Elektronik received an order for 20 new DM-2A3 torpedoes, plus kits to upgrade 20 DM-2A1 to DM-2A3. The DM-2A4 version for the Type 212 submarines will be deeper diving and will have a new 275-kw stepless permanent-magnet DC motor propulsion system driving counter-rotating propellers; the first production examples are to begin delivery in 2003. DM-2A3 data include:

Diameter: 533 mm **Length:** 6.60 m **Weight:** 1,370 kg
Warhead: 260 kg **Speed:** 35 kts **Range:** 20,000 m

The following torpedoes have been sold for export:

SST-4: A wire-guided, antisurface weapon in either Mod. 0 version with impact fuzing or Mod. 1 with proximity fuze.

Diameter: 533 mm **Length:** 6.08 m **Weight:** 1,414 kg **Warhead:** 260 kg
Speed: 34 kts max. **Range:** 11,000 m/34 kts; 20,000 m/28 kts; 36,000 m/23 kts

SUT (Surface/Underwater Target): Dual-purpose wire-guided weapon derived from the German Navy's Seeschlange and Seeal. Some 439 have been exported. SUT Mod. 2 has a computerized acoustic data processor to transmit target data to the launching ship.

Diameter: 533 mm **Length:** 6.39 m **Weight:** 1,414 kg **Warhead:** 260 kg
Speed: 34 kts max. **Range:** 12,000 m/34 kts; 28,000 m/23 kts

MU-90 Impact: An initial contract for $281 million was placed with Eurotorp (a consortium of Whitehead Alenia Sistemi Subacquie/WASS, DCN, and Thales) and STN Atlas Elektronik early in 1998 for 285 antisubmarine homing torpedoes. See French section for system details.

D. MINES

DM-11: Spherical moored contact or remote detonated. Entered service in 1968.

Diameter: 830 mm **Weight:** 550 kg **Mooring depth:** 300 m max.

DM-41: Seabed mine with mechanical, acoustic, magnetic, or pressure fuzing or remote-controlled detonation. Deployed from surface ships, aircraft, or portable mine belts on Type 206A submarines.

Length: 2.40 m **Diameter:** 534 mm **Weight:** 771 kg (535 kg explosives)

DM-51: Seabed anti-invasion mine. Entered service in the late 1980s. Has an active acoustic sensor or can be remote-control detonated.

Diameter: 710 mm **Height:** 300 mm **Weight:** 110 kg

DM-61: Joint German-Danish weapons also known as "Seabed Mine 80." Bottom mine with acoustic, magnetic, and pressure fuzing (or a combination of the three), using an onboard microprocessor. Built by STN Atlas Elektronik. 3,000 were delivered 1990–93.

Length: 2.00 m **Diameter:** 600 mm **Weight:** 730 kg

Note: Also in service is a small anti-invasion, beach protection mine. The "Seemine G3" is under development.

E. ELECTRONICS

Thales Nederland and the multinational corporation EADS established ET Marinesysteme GmbH on 19-4-01 to maintain existing Thales Nederland (formerly H.S.A or Signaal) combat systems on German and Dutch naval units, develop the combat system for the German Type 130 corvette program, continue development of the APAR radar, and cooperate on development of a joint Maritime Tactical Ballistic Missile Defence system.

In addition to the U.S. radars mounted in the *Charles F. Adams*–class destroyers the German Navy uses Thales Nederland radars and radars developed by EADS (originally Daimler Aerospace SA/DASA; later DaimlerChrysler Aerospace).

WEAPONS AND SYSTEMS *(continued)*

Aside from the SQS-23 sets on the *Adams* class, sonars are of German origin, built by STN Atlas Elektronik (formerly Krupp Atlas). These include the DSQS-21BZ (ASO-80), DSQS-23BZ (ASO-90), and ELAC 1BV on surface ships, and the DBQS-21D (CSU-83), WSN AN 410A, GHG AN 5039A1, and SRS-M1H for submarines. The DSQS-21-series sonars were updated in 1996–97 to provide a capability to detect mines. In development for surface ships are the EFS/Thales (Thomson-Marconi) LFTASS (Low-Frequency Active Towed Array Sonar System) and a new hull-mounted set. The STN Atlas Elektronik COTASS (Compact Towed Array Sonar System) began trials in 11-00 on the research ship *Planet* for use in a torpedo detection system; COTASS employs an active towed array about 200 m abaft the ship and a passive receiving array 500 m abaft the active array.

STN Atlas Elektronik is developing the MTW (Mini-Torpedo Welcome), an antitorpedo homing device launched from surface ships by rocket and employing an underwater rocket motor while homing on the target torpedo.

The STN Atlas Elektronik Modular Sensor Platform (MSR) was ordered in 1998, with 66 to be delivered by 2003 for use on ships. The two-axis stabilized mount carries a thermal imager, a daylight t.v. camera, and a laser rangefinder, and the system is to be used for passive surveillance, tracking, and weapons control.

EADS's LFK division manufactures the COLDS (Common Opto-electronic Laser Detection System), which detects a laser missile seeker and directs a laser beam of equivalent pulse repetition frequency against a safe spot on the ocean surface to spoof the missile.

The Buck Neue Technologien DM39 Bullfighter IR/radar decoy was selected early in 2000 to replace earlier 130-mm decoy rounds launched by the Mk 36 SRBOC system in the Type 122 and Type 124 frigates.

The STN Atlas Elektronik Seefuchs mine countermeasures system uses the Seefuchs I mine identification vehicle (which rides a sonar beam to the vicinity of a contact and then uses its own sonar and t.v. camera to inspect the object) and the Seefuchs-C expendable mine disposal vehicle. The disposal drone is 1.3 m long and weighs 40 kg; it costs about $50,000—well in excess of the cost of many bottom mines.

Note: Friedrich Lürssen Werft took over the naval shipbuilding assets of the bankrupt Bremer Vulkan Marine Schiffbau GmbH in 9-97 and Schweers, Berne, during 6-01; Lürssen also owns Krögerwerft, Rendsburg. Blohm + Voss (owned by Thyssen-Krupp), Thyssen Nordseewerke, and Howaldtswerke Deutsche Werft (HDW) were considering a corporate merger as of 1-01; HDW took over the Swedish submarine builder Kockums in 1999. HDW and Fincantieri of Italy announced a joint venture to design, produce, and market naval and merchant ships on 8-5-01.

ATTACK SUBMARINES [SS]

♦ 0 (+ 4) Type 212A

Bldr: ARGE U 212 Consortium (HDW, Kiel, and Thyssen Nordseewerke, Emden)

	Bldr	Start	L	In serv.
S 181 U 31	HDW, Kiel	1-7-98	10-01	30-3-04
S 182 U 32	Thyssen, Emden	11-7-00	11-03	31-5-05
S 183 U 33	HDW, Kiel	30-4-01	8-04	30-1-06
S 184 U 34	Thyssen, Emden	12-01	5-05	29-9-06

Type 212A—artist's rendering — Jochen Sachse/HDW, 2000

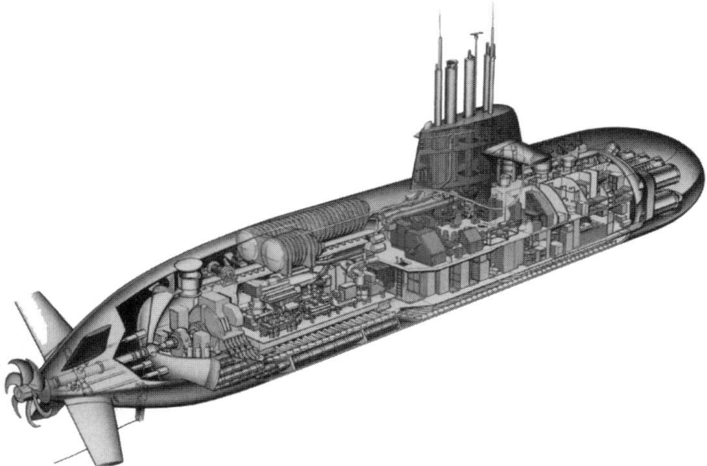

Type 212A — HDW

D: 1,370 tons light; 1,460 tons surf./1,840 tons sub.
S: 12 kts surf./20 kts sub.; 8 kts on fuel cells **Dim:** 57.15 × 7.00 × 6.80 × 7.00
A: 6 bow 533-mm TT (DM-2A3 Seehecht or DM-2A4 wire-guided torpedoes or Triton fiber-optic wire-guided missiles)—provision for minelaying belt (24 tot. mines)

Electronics:
Radar: Kelvin-Hughes Type 1007 nav./search
Sonar: CSU-90 suite with EFS DBQS-40FTC MF active/passive, FAS 3-1 flank array, PRS-3-15 passive ranging, AN 5039A1 intercept, EFS/AlliedSignal FMS-52 (MOA 3070) active mine-avoidance (30 and 70 kHz), EFS DSQS-21DG bow MF active, and TAS-3 towed LF linear passive hydrophone array
EW: EADS FL-1800U intercept; HDW-WASS C303/S Circe torpedo decoy syst. (40 tubes)

M: diesel-electric, with 9 Siemens Polymer Electrolytic Membrane fuel cells (34 kw each) for air-independent cruising, 1 MTU 8V183 SE83 diesel generator set (1,040 kw), 1 Siemens Permasyn motor; 1 7-bladed prop; 2,400 shp
Range: 8,000/8 surf.; 420/8 sub. **Crew:** 5 officers, 22 enlisted

Remarks: Program development began in 1988. Units are to cost around $406 million each and the entire program eventually to cost around $2.7 billion if two planned additional groups of four are funded. The contract for detailed design and construction was signed with German Submarine Consortium (Howaldtswerke, Thyssen Nordseewerke, Ferrostaal AG, and Thyssen Rheinstahl Technik GmbH) on 6-4-94 but did not take effect until the German FY 95 budget was approved. Italy is building two sisters, with an option to build two more. All four initial German units are to be assigned to Submarine Squadron 1.

Hull systems: Use a nonmagnetic Type 1.3964 austenitic steel pressure hull, 6.80 m in diameter forward, tapering via a conical section to 5.75 m abaft the control room; i.e., the boats are single-hulled forward and double-hulled aft. There are two accommodations decks forward. The engineering plant is suspended in a raft for sound reduction, with individual equipment also using soundproof mountings. The air-independent propulsion (AIP) system will employ a solid-polymer, metal-hydride fuel-cell system. The ship control system is by DataSAAB. Will use Hawker sodium sulfide batteries. Hydrazine gas generators will be used to blow ballast tanks for emergency surfacing. There are no separate watertight compartments within the pressure hull.

Combat systems: The MSI-90U Mk 2 combat system is an improved version of the Norsk Forsvarsteknolgi A/S (Norway) MSI-90U, used previously in Norway's *Ula* class. It can track 25 targets and control eight torpedoes and four missiles simultaneously.

The sonar suite incorporates six passive ranging transducers, flank arrays, a 0.3- to 12-kHz bow array, a mine-avoidance set, an echo sounder, two self-noise sensors, and a towed passive linear array (10–1,200 Hz), the first of its type in a German submarine. The mine avoidance sonar will operate at 30 kHz for detection and 70 kHz for classification.

The torpedo tubes will use the water-ram ejection method, using two water rams. The torpedo tube arrangement is asymmetrical, with two rows of three tubes, four of which are to port of the centerline. Fiber-optic, wire-guided missiles are being considered for use against smaller seaborne or even inland targets; the system is also to be usable against ASW helicopters and low-flying aircraft.

Communications equipment includes HF, VHF, UHF, and VLF radios and Inmarsat-C and UHF SATCOM sets. Navigation equipment includes a Litef PL-41 Mk 4 inertial navigation system, electromagnetic log, and echo sounder. The EW system antenna will be mounted on the Carl Zeiss SERO 40 periscope system; an optical rangefinder and GPS antenna will be collocated on the BS 40 search periscope and optical and laser rangefinders on the AS 40 attack periscope. The FL-1800U EW system will cover 2–18 GHz and will employ a pressurized USK800/4 antenna with a second integrated GPS antenna.

♦ 12 Type 206A

Bldrs: A: Howaldtswerke Deutsche Werft, Kiel; B: Rheinstahl Nordseewerke, Emden—Modernized by: C: Howaldtswerke; D: Thyssen Nordseewerke

	Bldr/Mod.	Laid down	L	In serv.
S 194 U 15	A/D	1-6-70	15-6-72	17-7-74
S 195 U 16	B/C	1-11-70	29-8-72	9-11-73
S 196 U 17	A/C	1-10-70	10-10-72	28-11-73
S 197 U 18	B/C	1-4-71	31-10-72	19-12-73
S 171 U 22	B/D	18-11-71	27-3-73	26-7-74
S 172 U 23	B/D	5-3-72	5-5-73	2-5-75
S 173 U 24	B/D	20-3-72	26-6-73	16-10-74
S 174 U 25	A/C	1-7-71	23-5-73	14-5-74
S 175 U 26	B/D	14-7-72	20-11-73	13-3-75
S 177 U 28	B/C	4-10-72	22-1-74	18-12-74
S 178 U 29	A/C	10-1-72	5-11-73	27-11-74
S 179 U 30	B/D	5-12-72	4-4-74	13-3-75

U 23 (S 172) — Findler & Winter, 10-00

D: 450 tons surf./520 tons sub. **S:** 10 kts surf./5 kts snorkel/17 kts sub.
Dim: 48.60 × 4.70 × 4.30 (surf.)
A: 8 bow 533-mm TT (8 DM-2A3 Seehecht torpedoes or 16 mines); 24 mines in external mine belt container

ATTACK SUBMARINES [SS] *(continued)*

U 15 (S 194) A. A. de Kruijf, 6-00

U 26 (S 175) Michael Setzer, 2000

Electronics:
Radar: 1 Kelvin-Hughes 1625x 6/U nav./search
Sonar: STN Atlas Elektronik DBQS-21D integrated suite, with passive and active bow arrays, flank array, DUUX-2 intercept array, etc.
EW: Thales DR-2000U intercept; Thorn-EMI SARIE-2 analyzer
M: 2 MTU 12V493 AZ80 GA diesels (600 bhp each), 2 405-kw generators, 1 electric motor; 1 prop; 2,300 shp (1,800 sust.)
Range: 4,500/5 snorkel; 200/5 sub. **Fuel:** 23.5 tons
Crew: 4 officers, 18 enlisted

Remarks: *U 13* through *U 24* were authorized in 1969, *U 25* through *U 30* in 2-70. Modernization from Type 206 to Type 206A began with *U 29* at HDW 9-6-87 and *U 23* at Thyssen 18-7-87; the final unit, *U 26,* was completed in 2-92. As of 12-2-98, all Type 206A units were transferred from Kiel to Eckernförde as 1. UBootgeschwader; 3. UBootgeschwader is also based at Eckernförde. *U 28* is to be retired 31-12-02, two more in 2005, and two in 2006, with the remaining seven to remain active for several more years beyond 2005. The first two to be retired have been offered to the United Arab Emirates, Poland, and Malaysia.
Disposals: Of the unmodernized Type 206 units, *U 27* (S 176) was stricken 13-6-96 for scrapping (sold for scrap 5-00) and *U 20* (S 199) was retired 26-9-96. *U 13* and *U 14* were retired 18-9-97 and 25-9-97, respectively, intended for later sale to Indonesia. *U 19* was stricken 30-4-98 and *U 21* 11-6-98; both had been planned for transfer to Indonesia, along with *U 20.* On 1-9-98, Indonesia deferred acquisition of *U 19–U 21,* and ex-*U 13* and ex-*U 14* remained in Germany under the Indonesian flag until handed back in 11-98 to the German Navy for scrapping during 1999. *U 20* and *U 13* were scrapped at Emden and Kiel, respectively, during 2000.
Hull systems: Pressure hulls are constructed of high tensile strength, austenitic (nonmagnetic) steel. Use three Hawker (ex-Varta) batteries of 92 cells each, weighing 98 tons total. Have Anschütz Nautoplot automatic plot, Rockwell WRN-6(V) SATNAV receiver, Aeronautical & General Instruments AGILOG electromagnetic log, and Anschütz Std 6S and Litef PL 41 Mk 3 compasses.
Combat systems: Have the STN Atlas Elektronik SLW-83 (CSU-83) weapons-control system with four ISUS display terminals, DBQS-21D active/passive sonars, provision for a towed passive hydrophone array, new periscopes, extensively overhauled propulsion plants, GPS receivers, and accommodations improvements. SARIE-2 (Selective Automatic Radar Identification Equipment) is fitted as stand-alone equipment with manual input to the combat system. One unit has conducted trials with an STN Atlas Elektronik acoustic passive target classification system. Carl Zeiss ASC 17 optical attack and NavS search periscopes are fitted.

AUXILIARY SUBMARINES [SSA]

♦ **2 Type 205A/B** Bldr: Howaldtswerke, Kiel

	Laid down	L	In serv.
S 190 U 11	1-4-66	9-2-68	21-6-68
S 191 U 12	1-9-66	10-9-68	14-1-69

U 11 (S 190) Mike Welsford, 6-00

U 12 (S 191) Mike Welsford, 11-00

D: U 11: 419 tons surf./455 tons sub. **S:** 10 kts surf./17 kts sub.
Dim: 45.80 × 4.60 (U 11: . . .) × 3.80 **A:** see Remarks
Electronics:
Radar: Thales Calypso-II search
Sonar: U 11: STN Atlas Elektronik SRS-M1H, GHG AN 5039A1—U 12: STN Atlas Elektronik DBSQS-90FTC suite, with FAS 3-1 flank array, PRS-3-15 passive ranging, AN 5039A1 passive, Ferranti FMS 52 HF mine-avoidance active, DSQS-21DG bow active, and TAS-3 towed array
EW: Thales DR-2000U intercept
M: 2 MTU 12V493 AZ80 GA diesels (600 bhp each), 2 405-kw generators, 1 electric motor; 1 prop; 2,300 shp (1,800 sust.)
Range: 3,950/4 snorkel; 228/4 sub. **Crew:** 4 officers, 17 enlisted

Remarks: Neither is considered to be a combatant. *U 11* has been used since 1988 as a "padded" torpedo target with a bulged outer hull added amidships; she is designated Type 205A. *U 12* has been used in trials with the sonar suite intended for the Type 212 since 1992 and is designated Type 205B; the hump on the casing forward of the sail houses the towed array reel and winch. Both were reassigned to Eckernförde from Kiel in 2-98. *U 11* is to be retired 31-12-03 and *U 12* not before 2006. *U 12,* with crew, was leased 1-11-00 to provide ASW target services at Portsmouth, U.K. The Dutch frigate *Philips Van Almonde* collided with *U 12* 5-11-00 at Portsmouth, damaging the submarine's sonar system.
Disposals: *U 2* was stricken 19-3-92; *U 3* in 1968; *U 4* and *U 8* in 1974; *U 5* in 1975; *U 6* and *U 7* in 1974; *U 9* on 16-2-93; and *U 10* on 3-6-93. *U 9* became a museum exhibit at Speyer and *U 10* an exhibit at Wilhelmshaven.
Hull systems: Pressure hulls were built with an improved antimagnetic steel. Normal operating diving depth: 150 m.
Combat systems: Neither has operational weapons systems; as built, they had eight 533-mm bow-mounted torpedo tubes and an H.S.A. Mk 8 f.c.s. *U 11* was used for trials in 2000 with the HDW-WASS Circe torpedo countermeasures system, which employs six tubes to eject stationary sonar jamming devices, mobile target emulators, and stationary target emulators that employ doppler shift to simulate target movement.

MIDGET SUBMARINES [SSM]

♦ **1 Orca class** Bldr: EFS (In serv. . . .)

D: 28 tons sub. **S:** 5+ kts sub. **Dim:** 12.0 × 2.0 × . . .
M: battery, 1 electric motor; 1 prop; . . . shp **Range:** 150/5 **Crew:** . . . tot.

Remarks: Dry diver delivery submersible for special operations, with single operator. Built some years ago, but existence not disclosed until 10-96. Equipped with forward-looking sonar, t.v. cameras, downward-looking doppler sonar, an underwater telephone, and echo sounders. Navigational equipment includes a GPS receiver, and there is a telescopic mast-mounted t.v. camera for surface observation. No diesel generator set, but the battery provides an endurance of up to 96 hours. Can be deployed from shore, surface ships, or a submarine.

MIDGET SUBMARINES [SSM] *(continued)*

Orca-class midget submarine — STN Atlas Elektronik

GUIDED-MISSILE DESTROYERS [DDG]

♦ 2 U.S. Charles F. Adams class (Type 103B)

Bldr: Bath Iron Works, Bath, Maine

	Laid down	L	In serv.
D 185 LÜTJENS (ex-DDG 28)	1-3-66	11-8-67	22-3-69
D 186 MÖLDERS (ex-DDG 29)	12-4-66	13-4-68	20-9-69

Lütjens (D 185) — Camil Busquets i Vilanova, 6-00

D: 3,550 tons (4,720 fl) **S:** 35 kts **Dim:** 134.4 (128.1 pp) × 14.38 × 6.40 (max)
A: 1 Mk 13 missile launcher (4 RGM-84A/C Harpoon and 36 Standard SM-1 MR missiles); 2 21-round Mk 49 RAM point-defense SAM launchers (RIM-116A missiles); 2 single 127-mm 54-cal. Mk 42 Mod. 10 DP; 2 single 20-mm 90-cal Rheinmetall Rh-202 AA; 1 Mk 16 ASROC ASW syst. (8-round Mk 112 launcher); 2 triple 324-mm Mk 32 Mod. 5 ASW TT (Mk 46 Mod. 5 torpedoes)
Electronics:
Radar: 1 Kelvin-Hughes 14/9 nav.; 1 Raytheon SPS-10 surf. search, 1 Lockheed SPS-40 air search; Hughes SPS-52 3-D air search; 2 Raytheon SPG-51C missile f.c.; 1 Lockheed SPQ-9 gun f.c.; 1 Lockheed SPG-60 missile/gun f.c.
Sonar: STN Atlas Elektronik DSQS-21B(2) bow-mounted LF
TACAN: URN-20
EW: EADS FL-1800S Stage I intercept Mk 36 SRBOC decoy syst. (2 6-round Mk 137 RL); SLQ-25 Nixie towed acoustic torpedo decoy syst.

Mölders (D 186) — Mike Welsford, 7-00

M: 2 sets Westinghouse geared steam turbines; 2 props; 70,000 shp
Boilers: 4 Combustion Engineering; 84 kg/cm^2 pressure, 510° C
Electric: 3,200 kw tot. **Range:** 1,600/30; 4,030/18; 6,000/14
Fuel: 950 tons **Crew:** 19 officers, 318 enlisted

Remarks: Authorized in 1964. Sister *Rommel* (D 187, ex-DDG 30) was deactivated 1-10-98 and stricken 30-6-99. D 186 is scheduled to be retired 31-12-03 and D 185 in 2004, but both dates may be advanced due to financial restrictions. The two survivors form the 1st Destroyer Squadron, based at Wilhelmshaven.
Hull systems: Problems with the boilers in 1995 caused the class to be temporarily laid up for repairs.
Combat systems: Were modernized in the 1980s with most of the improvements originally planned for the U.S. Navy units of the class: the Mk 13 missile system was revised to permit carrying Harpoon antiship missiles; the Mk 68 gunfire-control system was replaced by the Mk 86 GFCS with SPQ-9 and SPG-60 radars (the latter permitting a third SAM fire-control channel as well); the U.S. Norden Systems SYS-2(V)1 sensor data fusion system and the Mk 36 Super RBOC chaff system were added; the German FL-1800S EW system was substituted for WLR-6; and Raytheon solid-state transmitters were incorporated into the SQS-23 sonar systems. Subsequently, DSQS-21B(2) sonar replaced the SQS-23. Have Satir-1 NTDS datalink.

GUIDED-MISSILE FRIGATES [FFG]

Note: Preliminary requirements are being developed for the Type 125, a general-purpose, eight-unit frigate class intended to begin entering service around 2010 to replace the Type 122 (*Bremen*-class) frigates. No design details are yet available, and the class will probably not be ordered before 2004–06, if at all. The ships are planned to have "autonomous internal zones" divided by flexible watertight blast- and fragmentation-resistant bulkheads.

♦ 0 (+ 3) Sachsen class (Type 124)

	Bldr	Start	L	Del.	In serv.
F 219 SACHSEN	Blohm + Voss, Hamburg	1-2-99	20-1-01	29-11-02	31-12-03
F 220 HAMBURG	HDW, Kiel	1-9-00	6-03	15-12-04	15-12-04
F 221 HESSEN	Thyssen, Emden	14-9-01	5-04	15-12-05	15-12-05

Mölders (D 186) — Findler & Winter, 8-00

GUIDED-MISSILE FRIGATES [FFG] *(continued)*

Sachsen (F 219)—on trials Peter Voss, 8-01

Sachsen (F 219) Michael Nitz, 8-01

Sachsen (F 219)—after outdocking Michael Nitz, 1-01

D: 5,690 tons (fl) **S:** 29 kts (18 on diesels alone)
Dim: 143.00 (132.15 wl) × 17.44 (16.68 wl) × 5.00 (hull; 7.00 over sonar)
A: 8 RGM-84F Harpoon SSM; 32-cell Mk 41 Mod. 10 VLS syst. (24 Standard SM-2 Block IIIA and 32 Evolved Sea Sparrow SAM); 2 21-round Mk 49 RAM point-defense SAM launchers (RIM-116A missiles); 1 76-mm 62-cal. OTOBreda SuperRapid DP; 2 single 27-mm Rheinmetall-Mauser MLG 27 (MN 27 GS) AA; 2 triple 324-mm ASW TT (MU-90 torpedoes); 2 Super Lynx helicopters (NH-90 later)
Electronics:
Radar: 2 STN Atlas Elektronik 9600M ARPA nav./surf. search; 1 Thales Triton-G surf. search; 1 ET Marinesysteme APAR 3-D phased-array target desig. and tracking; 1 Thales SMART-L early warning
Sonar: DSQS-24BZ (STN Atlas Elektronik ASO-90) hull-mounted (6–9 kHz); provision for STN Atlas Elektronik TASS 6-3 (LFTASS) active towed array
TACAN: URN-25
EW: EADS FL-1800 Stage II ELOKA intercept; . . . active; EADS Maigret comms intercept; Mk 36 SRBOC decoy syst. (6 6-round Mk 137 launchers, DM39 Bullfighter 130-mm decoys); . . . torpedo decoy
E/O: SMP 500 surveillance; provision for Thales Sirius IRSCAN
M: CODAG: 1 G.E. 7 LM-2500 PF/MLG gas turbine (31,500 shp), 2 MTU 20V1163 TB93 diesels (10,050 bhp each at 1,350 rpm); 2 5-bladed Escher-Wyss CP props; 51,600 hp max.
Electric: 4,000 kw tot. (4 × 1,000-kw diesel generator sets; 400 V and 115 V, 60 Hz a.c.)
Range: 4,000+/18 **Endurance:** 21 days
Crew: 38 officers, 64 senior petty officers, 140 ratings + staff: 3 officers, 4 senior petty officers, 6 ratings

Remarks: Approval was given 13-6-96 for construction for three, with an option for a fourth (to have been named *Thüringen* and very unlikely to be built). The building yards formed the ARGE-124 consortium under the leadership of Blohm + Voss. The ships will be equipped to serve as task force command units. F 219 will serve as combat systems trials ship for the class. First steel was cut for assembly of F 219 on 27-2-98; bow and stern sections were delivered afloat by Lürssen Werft to Blohm + Voss in 1999.
Hull systems: Designed to have as much commonality as possible with the Type 123 but have enhanced signature-reduction features. Are of all-steel construction and employ the MEKO modular equipment installation concept. Some 270 tons of growth margin is built into the design. Accommodations for a task group commander and staff are fitted, and provision is made for female crewmembers. Will have rudder roll-rate stabilization system, using the single rudder. Turning radius will be about 570 m, and the ships will be able to operate helicopters of up to 15 tons weight in Sea State 6.

The unusual propulsion plant employs a cross-connected gearbox, and the entire engineering plant has an integrated monitoring system. The gas turbine engine is installed within a special MTU-designed sound-quieting module. Will have the same three box-girder hull strength feature as Type 123 and will have seven main watertight compartments. There will be a library, physical fitness room, and four mess compartments; the sickbay will have five berths. The helicopter deck will be equipped with an MBB–Forder & Hebesysteme HHS deck-traversing and handling system.
Combat systems: The combat data system is based on the Thales SEWACO-FD architecture; there will be 17 display consoles, one databus with 11 interface units, a mass memory system, two large-screen displays, two data recording modules, a closed t.v. system, 11 bus interface units, a Cosmos console, and two OP-SW-CDS workstations. There will be two optical target-designation sights on the bridge wings. Will have NATO Link 11 and Link 16 combat data–sharing links, with provision for later installation of Link 22. Mk XII Mod. 4 IFF will be provided.
Were originally to have carried a U.S. Mk 45 127-mm 54-cal. dual-purpose gun. May later carry LCAW lightweight antisubmarine weapons. The Standard SM-2 Block IVA missile may be substituted in part later to provide defense against theater ballistic missile attack.
The SMART-L radar will be able to maintain up to 1,000 tracks, while APAR can maintain 200 tracks and provide guidance illumination for more than 30 tracks (the combat system allows for 16 air targets to be attacked at once, along with two surface and two subsurface contacts). The orientation of the four phased-array faces of the APAR radar was changed late in 1997 to fore and aft, port and starboard, rather than at 45° off the centerline as originally intended. Initial sea trials with the APAR radar will be carried out aboard the F 219. The Rhode & Schwarz integrated communications suite includes UHF/SHF SATCOM, an integrated message-handling and control system (IMUS), and cryptographic equipment. Navigational equipment includes two NAVSAT terminals, two inertial navigational system (MINS), and a weather satellite receiver.

FRIGATES [FF]

♦ 4 Brandenburg class (Type 123)

	Bldr	Laid down	L	In serv
F 215 Brandenburg	Blohm +Voss, Hamburg	11-2-92	28-8-92	14-10-94
F 216 Schleswig-Holstein	Howaldtswerke, Kiel	1-7-93	3-6-94	24-11-95
F 217 Bayern	Thyssen, Emden	16-12-93	30-6-94	15-6-96
F 218 Mecklenburg-Vorpommern	Bremer Vulkan, Bremen	23-11-93	8-7-95	6-12-96

Bayern (F 217) Mike Welsford, 9-00

Brandenburg (F 215) Findler & Winter, 8-00

Schleswig-Holstein (F 216) Findler & Winter, 9-00

FRIGATES [FF] *(continued)*

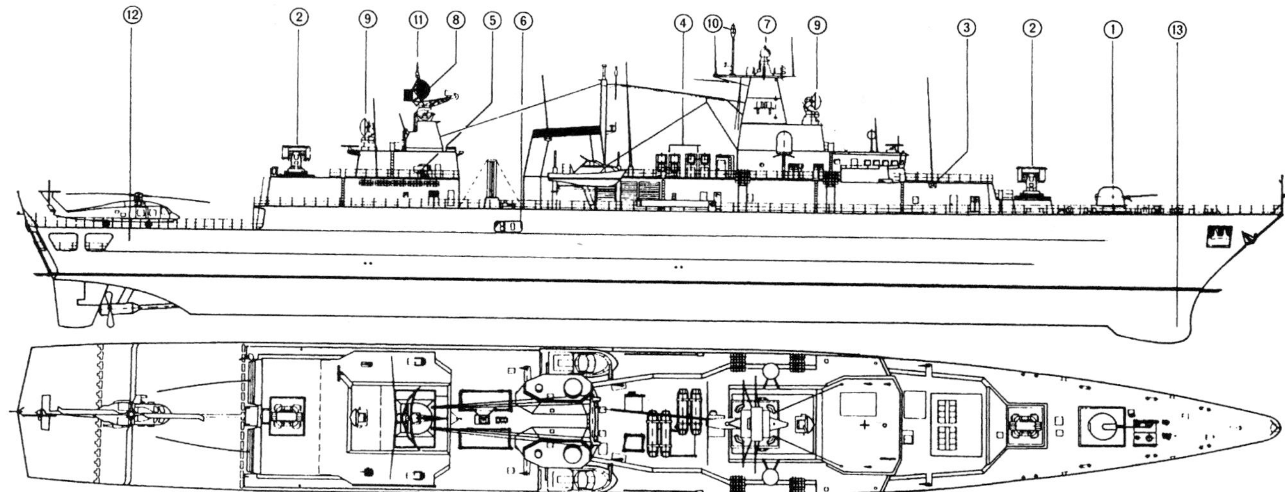

Brandenburg (F 215) 1. 76-mm OTOBreda DP gun 2. RAM missile launchers 3. Mk 41 Mod. 4 vertical-launch system for Sea Sparrow missiles 4. MM 38 Exocet antiship missile launch canisters 5. SCLAR decoy launcher 6. Mk 32 Mod. 9 fixed ASW TT 7. SMART-S search radar 8. LW-08 early-warning radar 9. STIR radar missile tracker/illuminators 10. FL-1800S Stage II EW antenna suite 11. Type 1990 IFF interrogator antenna atop LW-08 antenna 12. provision for future towed sonar array 13. DSQS-23BZ bow sonar
Drawing by Blohm + Voss

Mecklenburg-Vorpommern (F 218) Findler & Winter, 8-00

D: 3,600 tons (4,490 fl) **S:** 29+ kts (gas turbines; 18 on diesels)
Dim: 138.85 (126.90 pp) × 16.70 (15.74 wl) × 4.35 (6.30 over sonar)
A: 8 MM 38 Exocet SSM; 1 Mk 41 Mod. 4 vertical-launch SAM syst. (16 RIM-7M Sea Sparrow missiles); 2 21-round Mk 49 RAM point-defense SAM syst. (RIM-116A missiles); 1 76-mm 62-cal. OTOBreda SuperRapid DP; 2 single 20-mm 90-cal. Rheinmetall Rh-202 AA; 2 paired, fixed 324-mm Mk 32 ASW TT; 1–2 Super Lynx helicopters
Electronics:
Radar: 2 Raytheon Raypath nav.; 1 Thales LW-08 early warning; 1 Thales SMART-S air/surf. search and targeting; 2 Thales STIR-18 f.c.
Sonar: STN Atlas Elektronik DSQS-23BZ (ASO-90) hull-mounted (6–9 kHz); provision for TASS 6-3 (LFTASS) towed array
EW: EADS FL-1800S Stage II intercept; 2 18-round OTOBreda SCLAR decoy RL—F 216, 217 also: EADS Maigret comms intercept system (1–1,000 MHz)
M: CODOG: 2 G.E. 7 LM-2500 9A-ML gas turbines (25,840 shp each), 2 MTU 20V956 TB92 diesels (5,535 bhp each); 2 5-bladed Escher-Wyss CP props; 51,680 shp max.
Electric: 3,000 kw tot. (4 × 750-kw van Kaick sets, MWM TBD-602-V16K diesels driving; 400 V and 115 V, 60 Hz a.c.)
Range: 4,000+/18 **Endurance:** 21 days
Crew: 26 officers, 193 enlisted (incl. 22 air department) + 11 command staff

Remarks: Ordered 28-6-89 from a consortium led by Blohm + Voss, with Thyssen Nordseewerke and Howaldtswerke. Comprise the 6th Frigate Squadron, based at Wilhelmshaven.

Hull systems: Employ Blohm + Voss MEKO modular outfitting concepts, with extremely strong hull structure having six double-walled bulkheads, two internal 1.2-m-square box girders at the outer edge of the upper deck over 80% of the hull length, and a centerline 1.5 × 0.6-m box girder for strength. There are 12 major watertight compartments and four damage control zones, each with its own zone control station. Two diesel-driven and 10 electric firepumps are fitted. Steel superstructure. Fin stabilizers are fitted. Have extensive signature-reduction measures, with a radar cross section only 10% as large as that of the preceding Type 122. Have 230-ton displacement growth margin.

Combat systems: Have the STN Atlas Elektronik SATIR-III F-123 combat data system, using U.S. UYK-43 computers, 14 STN Atlas Elektronik BM 802-52 multifunction consoles, Ada programming language, and distributed data concepts. Are NATO Link 11 datalink-compatible. Have the Norden TMS (Track Management System) radar track data fusion system. The SMART (Signal Multibeam Acquisition Radar for Targeting) radar surmounts the foremast. SCOT-3 SHF SATCOM terminals were ordered for these ships during 6-97. The ASW system is the EFS ASO-90, using Mk 264 torpedo control panels cannibalized from *Hamburg*-class destroyers; the torpedo tubes are fixed and launch through the hull sides at a 45° angle from the centerline from positions on the main deck abreast the funnels. Are receiving the STN Atlas Elektronik–Zeiss Eltro WBA *(Wärmebildanlage)* MSP 500 stabilized thermal-imaging sensor. Ophelios thermal imagers, a t.v. camera, and a laser rangefinder for the 20-mm mounts were installed beginning in 1999.

The vertical-launch SAM module forward is arranged so that the number of launch cells can be doubled at a later date. The 76-mm gun can also be controlled by the target-designation sights mounted on the bridge wings. A Thales Vespa transponder system is used for helicopter control. The hull-mounted sonar had a mine-detection capability added during 1996–97. The STN Atlas Elektronik TASS 6-3 towed passive linear hydrophone array (15 Hz–1.2 kHz, with 2,400-kHz broadband) was to be backfitted around 1997 but has not yet been procured. A joint French-German Low Frequency Active Sonar System operating at 2–3 kHz is planned to be backfitted. Have the Honeywell-ELAC UT 2000 underwater telephone.

♦ 8 Bremen class (Type 122A)

	Bldr	Laid down	L	In serv.
F 207 Bremen	Bremer-Vulkan	9-7-79	27-9-79	7-5-82
F 208 Niedersachsen	AG Weser, Bremen	9-11-79	9-6-80	15-10-82
F 209 Rheinland-Pfalz	Blohm + Voss, Hamburg	25-9-79	3-9-80	9-5-83
F 210 Emden	Nordseewerke, Emden	23-6-80	17-12-80	7-10-83
F 211 Köln	Blohm + Voss, Hamburg	16-6-80	29-5-81	19-10-84
F 212 Karlsruhe	Howaldtswerke, Kiel	10-3-81	8-1-82	19-4-84
F 213 Augsburg	Bremer-Vulkan	4-4-87	17-9-87	3-10-89
F 214 Lübeck	Thyssen, Emden	1-6-87	15-10-87	19-3-90

Bremen (F 207) Bernard Prézelin, 3-01

Rheinland-Pfalz (F 209) Findler & Winter, 1-01

FRIGATES [FF] *(continued)*

Emden (F 210)—with new air-search radar — Findler & Winter, 6-00

Lübeck (F 214) — Bernard Prézelin, 3-01

Augsburg (F 213) — Findler & Winter, 5-01

D: 2,950 tons (3,800 fl) **S:** 30 kts
Dim: 130.00 (121.80 wl) × 14.40 × 4.26 (6.00 sonar)
A: 8 RGM-84C Harpoon SSM; 1 8-round Mk 29 launcher for NATO Sea Sparrow SAM syst. (24 RIM-7M missiles); 2 21-round Mk 49 RAM SAM launchers (RIM-116A missiles); 1 76-mm 62-cal. OTOBreda DP; 2 single 20-mm 90-cal. Rheinmetall Rh-202 AA; 2 twin fixed 324-mm Mk 32 Mod. 9 ASW TT (Mk 46 Mod. 5 torpedoes); 2 Lynx Mk 88 helicopters
Electronics:
Radar: 1 S.M.A. 3RM 20 nav.; 1 Thales DA-08 (F 210–212: EADS TRS-3D/32 3-D) air search; 1 Thales WM-25 track-while-scan f.c.; 1 Thales STIR-18 missile f.c.
Sonar: STN Atlas Elektronik DSQS-21BX (BO) bow-mounted LF
EW: EADS FL-1800S Stage II intercept array (7.5–17 GHz); Mk 36 SRBOC decoy syst. (4 6-round Mk 137 launchers, DM39 Bullfighter 130-mm decoys); SLQ-25 Nixie acoustic torpedo decoy syst.
E/O: F 207, 210: STN Atlas Elektronik–Zeiss Eltro WBA tracker
M: CODOG: 2 G.E.-Fiat LM-2500 GT (51,000 shp), 2 MTU 20V956 TB92 diesels (11,070 bhp); 2 5-bladed Escher-Wyss CP props
Electric: 3,000 kw (4 × 750-kw diesel sets) **Range:** 5,700/17 **Fuel:** 610 tons
Crew: 21 officers, 160 enlisted + air complement: 6 officers, 12 enlisted

Remarks: First six ordered 7-77, the last two 6-12-85. Bremer-Vulkan performed the weapons and electronics outfitting and integration. Comprise the 2nd and 4th Frigate Squadrons, based at Wilhelmshaven. Are to be retired beginning in 2010, as they are not considered suitable for service life-extension modernizations.
Hull systems: Fin stabilizers are fitted. Have the U.S. Prairie/Masker bubbler system to reduce radiated noise. Have a citadel NBC protection system. F 212 has a revised engine air intake system. During refits from 1992 to 1997, enhanced signature-reduction measures were incorporated.
Combat systems: Have the SATIR tactical data system (with Unisys UYK-7 computers). Are Link 11 compatible. The Norden TMS (Track Management System) radar track data fusion system was fitted during late-1990s refits. The helicopters are equipped with DAQS-13D dipping sonar and Mk 46 Mod. 5 torpedoes. A Thales Vesta helicopter transponder and the Beartrap haul-down and deck control system are installed. Carry 16 torpedoes for the helicopters and eight for the tubes. Three sets of U.K. SCOT 1A SHF SATCOM gear were acquired for use aboard deployed units of this class.
The ships were designated Type 122A on completion of refits from 1992 to 1999, during which two Mk 49 RAM launchers were installed atop the hangars, the WM-25 fire-control systems were updated, the UYK-7 computers were replaced by UYK-43s, and the EW suite was upgraded to FL-1800S Stage II status with Racal SADIE processors and EADS high-resolution color displays. A concurrent effort was to have been made to replace the DA-08 search radar with the EADS TRS-3D/32 (C-band), but as of early 2001 only three ships had been modified. The hull-mounted sonar had a mine-detection capability added during 1996–97. F 210 is equipped with the prototype STN Atlas Elektronik–Zeiss Eltro WBA *(Wärmebildanlage)* MSP 500 stabilized thermal-imaging sensor, which is to be backfitted in all; the system can control the 76-mm gun. Ophelios thermal imagers, a t.v. camera, and a laser rangefinder were added for the 20-mm mounts beginning in 1999.

CORVETTES [FFL]

♦ 0 (+ 5) Type 130 new-construction
Bldr: ARGE K 130 Consortium (Blohm + Voss, Thyssen Nordseewerke, and Lürssen Werft)

	Bldr	Laid down	L	In serv.
P	Blohm + Voss	. . .	. . .	5-07
P	Blohm + Voss	. . .	. . .	. . .
P	Lürssen	. . .	. . .	. . .
P	Lürssen	. . .	. . .	. . .
P	Thyssen	. . .	. . .	11-08

Type 130—computer rendering — Blohm + Voss, 2000

D: 1,650 tons (fl) **S:** 26 kts **Dim:** 88.30 (82.80 pp) × 12.23 × . . .
A: 8 RBS-15 Mk 3 SSM; 8 Polyphem short-range, vertical-launch SSM; 2 21-round Mk 49 RAM SAM launcher (RIM-116 Block IA missiles); 176-mm 62-cal. OTOBreda DP; 2 single 27-mm Mauser MLG 27 AA; 4 portable mine rails (. . . mines); 2 . . . drone helicopters
Electronics:
Radar: 2 . . . nav.; EADS TRS-3D/16 surf./air search; 2 Thales Mirador radar-E/O directors
Sonar: . . . hull-mounted; STN Atlas Elektronik COTASS active/passive towed array
EW: EADS SPN/KJS-500 intercept; 4 . . . decoy RL; EADS COLDS laser countermeasure
E/O: STN Atlas Elektronik MSP 500 stabilized E/O gun director
M: . . .; 2 CP props; 19,850 b/shp
Range: 2,500/15 **Endurance:** 7 days **Crew:** 50 tot. (accomm. for 76)

Remarks: A new class of up to 15 guided missile–carrying corvettes, to be named for German cities, was planned to replace the Type 143, 143A, and 148 missile boats; the last of the first group of five was to complete in 2004 and the last of a third group of five in 2012, but there were numerous program delays, and by 2000, the 15th unit would have been completed in 2015. The program was cut to five in 11-00. The team of Blohm + Voss, Friedrich Lürssen Werft, and Thyssen Nordseewerke (with EADS Deutschland and H.S.A. as systems integrators) was selected 20-7-00, but the order was not placed until 14-12-01. The ships are to cost about $186 million each. The design is based closely on Blohm + Voss's MEKO A100 design, but the MEKO modular weapons and sensor installation system will not be employed. All are planned to be based at Warnemünde.
Hull systems: The propulsion system will probably employ two diesel engines with an underwater exhaust system to reduce IR signature; waterjets may be used in place of propellers. Accommodations will be provided for a flag officer and 25 staff in addition to the normal crew. The hull and superstructure are configured to reduce the radar cross section to less than that of a Type 143 PTG.
Combat systems: The combat system will be based on the Thales SEWACO-FD and will incorporate Links 11 and 16 and seven multifunction display consoles. Two different antiship missile systems are planned; the larger will at least initially be the U.S. Harpoon system, while the shorter-ranged Polyphem missiles will be vertically launched, using four cells on either side of the helicopter flight deck. The flight deck aft is to be able to accommodate a Lynx or NH-90 helicopter, but there will be no hangar other than a small one for the two drone surveillance helicopters, which are planned to enter service in 2006 and will in theory serve as the ship's principal sensors, operating at a radius of up to 100 km from the ship. The 76-mm guns are to be recycled from stricken PTGs. A torpedo defense system is to be added starting in 2008; it will employ adjuncts to the sonar array and a launcher mounted in place of the after RAM launcher, which will be moved to a higher location.

GUIDED-MISSILE PATROL CRAFT [PTG]

♦ **10 Type 143A** Bldrs: A: Lürssen Werft, Vegesack; B: Kröger, Rendsburg

	Bldr	Laid down	L	In serv.
P 6121 Gepard (S 71)	A	11-7-79	25-9-81	15-12-82
P 6122 Puma (S 72)	A	17-12-79	8-2-82	15-2-83
P 6123 Hermelin (S 73)	B	1-2-80	8-12-81	28-4-83
P 6124 Nerz (S 74)	A	24-7-80	18-8-82	14-7-83
P 6125 Zobel (S 75)	B	3-7-80	30-6-82	29-9-83
P 6126 Frettchen (S 76)	A	22-12-80	26-1-83	16-12-83
P 6127 Dachs (S 77)	B	9-3-80	14-12-82	22-3-84
P 6128 Ozelot (S 78)	A	25-6-81	7-6-83	25-5-84
P 6129 Wiesel (S 79)	A	5-10-80	8-8-83	12-7-84
P 6130 Hyäne (S 80)	A	7-12-81	5-10-83	13-11-84

Hyäne (P 6130) Findler & Winter, 5-01

D: 300 tons (390.6 fl) **S:** 36 kts (32 fl)
Dim: 57.6 (54.4 pp) × 7.76 × 2.99 (2.56 hull)
A: 4 MM 38 Exocet SSM; 1 21-round Mk 49 RAM point-defense SAM syst. (RIM-116A missiles); 1 76-mm 62-cal. OTOBreda DP; 2 single 12.7-mm mg; 2 mine rails
Electronics:
Radar: 1 SMA 3RM 20 nav.; 1 Thales WM-27 track-while-scan f.c.
EW: EADS FL-1800S Stage II intercept; 2 6-round Buck-Wegmann Hot Dog/Silver Dog decoy RL; Wolke chaff dispenser
M: 4 MTU 16V956 TB91 diesels; 4 props; 16,000 bhp (at 1,515 rpm)
Electric: 540 kw tot. **Range:** 600/30; 2,600/16 **Fuel:** 116 tons
Crew: 4 officers, 18 petty officers, 12 ratings

Remarks: Ordered in 1978 from AEG-Telefunken, with shipbuilders listed above as subcontractors. Design is a repeat of the Type 143, with the RAM point-defense SAM system in place of the Type 143's after 76-mm gun and mine rails in place of the wire-guided torpedoes. Were originally to have been retired by 2007, but in 1999 they began refits to extend their lives by 10 years. Constitute the 7th Fast Patrol Boat Squadron, based at Warnemünde.

Frettchen (P 6126) Findler & Winter, 5-01

Hull systems: Wood-planked hull on steel frame. Round-bilge hullform.
Combat systems: Type 143A missile patrol boats carry the AGIS fire-control system combined with Thales WM-27M radar. AGIS has two computers, one for fire control and the other for real-time threat processing. WM-27 has two antennas within its dome, one for search and one for tracking. An automatic datalink permits AGIS to share information with other Type 143/143A units and with major surface combatants. The combat data systems were to be updated starting in 1999 by a consortium led by Thales.

The craft lack the after optical gun director found on the Type 143. Chaff is dispensed from a vertical pipe attached to the after side of the tripod mast. Mk 49 RAM launchers were added on the sterns on all during 1993–97 refits. Early in 2000, P 6123 was the first to complete an EW suite update with Racal SADIE processors and high-resolution color displays by EADS. P 6128 conducted highly successful trials with the STN Atlas Elektronik MSP 500 stabilized E/O director for the 76-mm gun during 9-00; the director will be mounted on the 76-mm gunhouses of the rest of the class.

♦ **10 Type 143** Bldrs: A: Lürssen Werft, Vegesack; B: Krögerwerft, Rendsburg

	Bldr	Laid down	L	In serv.
P 6111 Albatros (S 61)	A	4-5-72	22-10-73	1-11-76
P 6112 Falke (S 62)	A	25-10-72	21-3-74	13-4-76
P 6113 Geier (S 63)	A	14-2-73	18-9-74	2-6-76
P 6114 Bussard (S 64)	A	4-7-73	14-4-75	14-8-76
P 6115 Sperber (S 65)	B	18-1-73	15-1-74	27-9-76
P 6116 Greif (S 66)	A	12-12-73	4-9-75	25-11-76
P 6117 Kondor (S 67)	B	19-6-73	6-3-75	17-12-76
P 6118 Seeadler (S 68)	A	12-6-74	17-11-75	28-3-77
P 6119 Habicht (S 69)	B	25-1-74	5-6-75	23-12-77
P 6120 Kormoran (S 70)	A	26-11-74	14-4-76	29-7-77

Ozelot (P 6128) Maritime Photographic, 6-00

GUIDED-MISSILE PATROL CRAFT [PTG] *(continued)*

Geier (P 6113) Maritime Photographic, 6-00

Greif (P 6116) Mike Welsford, 5-00

Kondor (P 6117) Bernard Prézelin, 5-00

D: 300 tons (393 fl) **S:** 36 kts (32 fl)
Dim: 57.6 (54.4 pp) × 7.76 × 2.82 (2.56 hull)
A: 4 MM 38 Exocet SSM; 2 single 76-mm 62-cal. OTOBreda DP; 2 Stinger point-defense SAM launch positions; 2 fixed, aft-launching 533-mm TT (Seeal wire-guided torpedoes; no reloads)
Electronics:
Radar: 1 SMA 3RM 20 nav.; 1 Thales WM-27 track-while-scan f.c.
EW: Racal Octopus suite: Cutlass intercept and Scorpion jammer; 2 6-round Buck-Wegmann Hot Dog/Silver Dog decoy RL; Wolke chaff dispenser
M: 4 MTU 16V956 TB91 diesels; 4 props; 16,000 bhp (at 1,515 rpm)
Electric: 540 kw **Range:** 600/30; 2,600/16 **Fuel:** 116 tons
Crew: 4 officers, 19 petty officers, 17 ratings

Remarks: Ordered in 1972. Were to be refitted to Type 143A standard, becoming Type 143B, but the program was canceled. They are planned to serve until about 2010. Constitute the 2nd Squadron, based at Warnemünde.
Hull systems: Wood-planked, round-bilge hull with steel frames.
Combat systems: See remarks on the AGIS combat data system under the Type 143A entry. During 1988–92, the WM-27 radar fire-control systems were updated and various ECCM measures were added. There is a secondary OGR-7/3 optical f.c.s. for the aft 76-mm gun. Combat systems are being updated by a Thales-led consortium.

♦ **5 Type 148** Bldrs: A: Lürssen Werft,Vegesack; B: CMN, Cherbourg

	Bldr	Laid down	L	In serv.
P 6146 FUCHS (S 46)	A	10-3-72	21-5-73	17-10-73
P 6148 LÖWE (S 48)	A	10-7-72	10-9-73	9-1-74
P 6155 ALK (S 55)	B	9-4-74	15-11-74	7-1-75
P 6156 DOMMEL (S 56)	A	13-12-73	30-10-74	12-2-75
P 6157 WEIHE (S 57)	B	2-7-74	13-2-75	3-4-75

Dommel (P 6156) Bernard Prézelin, 4-00

Alk (P 6155) Findler & Winter, 6-01

D: 234 tons (264 fl) **S:** 35.8 kts **Dim:** 47.0 (45.90 pp) × 7.10 × 2.66 (fl)
A: 4 MM 38 Exocet; 1 76-mm 62-cal. OTOBreda DP; 1 40-mm 70-cal. OTOBreda-Bofors AA; . . . Sidewinder shoulder-launched SAMs
Electronics:
Radar: 1 SMA 3RM 20 nav.; 1 Thales Triton-G air/surf. search; 1 Thales Castor-II f.c.
EW: Racal Octopus suite (Cutlass intercept, Scorpion jammer); 2 6-round Buck-Wegmann Hot Dog/Silver Dog decoy RL, Wolke chaff dispenser
M: 4 MTU 16V538 TB90 (MD 872) diesels; 4 props; 14,000 bhp (at 1,515 rpm; 12,000 sust.)
Electric: 270 kw tot. (3 × 90-kw diesel sets) **Range:** 570/30; 1,600/15
Fuel: 39 tons **Crew:** 4 officers, 17 petty officers, 9 ratings

Remarks: Ordered 18-12-70. Design by Friedrich Lürssen Werft, Vegesack. All hulls were fitted out at Cherbourg. P 6148 hit a rock in Norwegian waters 9-98, damaging her bow severely, but was repaired with a new bow section at Kiel. Now constitute the 5th Squadron at Olpenitz. Current plans call for retiring P 6146 in 9-02, P 6148 in 9-03, P 6155 in 4-02, P 6156 in 6-02, and P 6157 in 4-03; they have been offered for sale to Egypt.

GUIDED-MISSILE PATROL CRAFT [PTG] *(continued)*

Disposals: *Iltis* (P 6142) and *Storch* (P 6152) were stricken 15-10-92 and 12-11-92, respectively, and transferred to Greece, departing 1-2-94. *Marder* (P 6144) was stricken 25-4-94 and *Häher* (P 6151) 24-6-94; both departed for Greece 16-3-95. *Wolf* (S 49, P 6149) and *Elster* (S 54, P 6154) were stricken 27-8-97 and transferred to Chile. *Pelikan* (S 53, P 6153) was stricken 4-6-98, *Luchs* (S 43, P 6143) 27-8-98, and *Tiger* (S 41, P 6141) and *Kranich* (S 60, P 6160) 24-9-98; all four were transferred to Chile in 10-98, with P 6143 and P 6153 for use as cannibalization spares sources. *Leopard* (S 45, P 6145) and *Jaguar* (S 47, P 6147) were stricken 15-9-00 and departed for Greece 9-10-00. *Pinguin* (S 58, P 6158) was retired 27-6-01, *Reiher* (S 59, P 6159) in 6-01, and *Panther* (S 50, P 6150) 27-9-01, all three for later sale to Egypt, along with the five remaining active units.
Hull systems: Steel construction.
Combat systems: Have the Thales Vega fire-control system with Pollux radar; Triton is used for target designation. All have the PALIS (Passive-Active-Link) system for data sharing and can use NATO Link 11. OTOBreda-made Bofors 40-mm mountings with Mauser GRP enclosed gunhouses have been fitted in place of the original open Bofors 40-mm L70 mountings aft.

MINE WARFARE SHIPS

♦ 12 Type 332 coastal minehunters [MHC]

Bldrs: A: Abeking & Rasmussen, Lemwerder; B: Lürssen Werft, Vegesack; C: Krögerwerft, Rendsburg

	Bldr	Laid down	L	In serv.
M 1058 Fulda	A	12-95	29-9-97	16-6-98
M 1059 Weilheim	B	12-95	26-2-98	3-12-98
M 1060 Weiden	A	1-3-90	14-5-92	30-3-93
M 1061 Rottweil	C	17-4-90	12-3-92	7-7-93
M 1062 Sulzbach-Rosenberg	B	1-9-92	27-4-95	23-1-96
M 1063 Bad Bevensen	B	19-11-90	21-1-93	9-12-93
M 1064 Grömitz	C	2-4-91	22-4-93	23-8-94
M 1065 Dillingen	A	15-1-92	26-5-94	25-4-95
M 1066 Frankenthal	B	5-12-89	6-2-92	16-12-92
M 1067 Bad Rappenau	A	20-2-91	3-6-93	19-4-94
M 1068 Datteln	C	11-11-91	27-1-94	8-12-94
M 1069 Homburg	B	17-2-92	21-4-94	15-8-95

Frankenthal (M 1066) Camil Busquets i Vilanova, 5-01

Homburg (M 1069) Jürg Kürsener, 7-00

D: 590 tons (650 fl) **S:** 18 kts **Dim:** 54.40 (51.00 pp) × 9.20 × 2.60 (3.3 props)
A: 1 40-mm 70-cal. Bofors AA; 2 Stinger/Fliegerfaust point-defense SAM positions; up to 60 mines
Electronics:
Radar: 1 Raytheon SPS-64(V) nav.
Sonar: STN Atlas Elektronik DSQS-11M minehunting
EW: Thales DR-2000 intercept; 2 6-round Buck-Wegmann Hot Dog/Silver Dog decoy RL
M: 2 MTU 16V396 TB84 diesels; 2 Voith-Schneider vertical cycloidal props; 6,140 bhp—low-speed drive
Electric: 690 kw tot. (3 × 230 kw; 3 MWM 6-cyl. diesels driving)
Range: . . ./. . .
Crew: 5 officers, 6 chief petty officers, 13 petty officers, 6 ratings

Sulzbach-Rosenberg (M 1062) Findler & Winter, 10-00

Bad Rappenau (M 1067) Selim Sam, 7-00

Remarks: First 10 were ordered 26-2-88 from prime contractor Messerschmidt-Bölkow-Blohm. Two more were added to the 1996 budget and ordered 8-95; the hulls for both were fitted out by Krögerwerft. The design is a minehunter version of Type 343 with a slightly different hullform, minehunting sonar, and low-speed drive. Constitute the 1st Mine Countermeasures Squadron, based at Olpenitz.
Hull systems: Shock mountings are provided for virtually every piece of equipment and for all crew seats. Navigation systems are, surprisingly, not extensive.
Combat systems: Have the STN Atlas Elektronik MWS 80-4 minehunting system with SATAM command system. Carry two Pinguin B3 remote-controlled mine location/destruction submersibles and four mine-clearance divers. The Pinguin weighs 1.35 tons, is 3.5 m long, travels at up to 8 kts, and has an STN Atlas Elektronik AIS 11 high-frequency sonar. Haux Spacestar three-man decompression chambers for mine disposal divers are carried. The 40-mm gun is in a standard Bofors mounting but has the Trinity autoloading feature. The Stinger SAM-launching positions are in armored tubs on the upper deck amidships.

Five of the class are to receive a new minehunting system: MA 2000 (*Minenabwehr Ausrüstung* 2000) uses two 99-ton Seepferd drones, each towing an underwater sensor vehicle with side-scan, mine-avoidance, and buried-mine detector sonars; the ships will also carry an EFS Expendable Mine Disposal System. M 1060 conducted trials with the STN Atlas Elektronik–Zeiss Eltro WBA *(Wärmebildanlage)* stabilized thermal sensor system, which can be used to control the gun.

♦ 5 Type 333 coastal minehunter conversions [MHC]

Bldrs: A: Abeking & Rasmussen, Lemwerder; B: Krögerwerft, Rendsburg

	Bldr	Laid down	L	In serv.
M 1091 Kulmbach	A	14-9-87	15-6-89	24-4-90
M 1095 Überherrn	A	15-12-86	30-8-88	19-9-89
M 1096 Passau	A	1-7-88	1-3-90	18-12-90
M 1097 Laboe	B	2-3-87	13-9-88	7-12-89
M 1099 Herten	B	16-6-88	22-12-89	26-2-91

Kulmbach (M 1091)—as modified Findler & Winter, 9-00

MINE WARFARE SHIPS *(continued)*

Kulmbach (M 1091)—as modified Findler & Winter, 9-00

Herten (M 1099)—as yet unmodified Findler & Winter, 10-00

D: 620 tons (fl) **S:** 18 kts **Dim:** 54.40 (51.00 pp) × 9.20 × 2.50 (3.20 props)
A: 2 single 40-mm 70-cal. OTOBreda-Bofors AA; 2 Stinger/Fliegerfaust point-defense SAM positions; up to 60 mines
Electronics:
Radar: 1 Raytheon SPS-64 nav.; 1 WM-20/2 track-while-scan f.c.
Sonar: STN Atlas Elektronik DSQS-11M hull-mounted retractable HF
EW: Thales DR-2000 intercept; 2 6-round Buck-Wegmann Hot Dog/Silver Dog decoy RL
M: 2 MTU 16V396 TB84-DB51L diesels; 2 Escher-Wyss CP props; 6,080 bhp
Electric: 1,050 kw (3 MWM TBD 601 65 diesels driving, 639 bhp each)
Range: . . ./. . . **Crew:** 4 officers, 20 petty officers, 13 ratings

Remarks: Ordered from prime contractor Messerschmidt-Bölkow-Blohm (MBB) 10-1-85 as Type 343 minesweepers. Under a 1-98 contract with STN Atlas Elektronik, these five have been modified as Type 333 minehunters by Peenewerft, Wolgast. M 1091 was the first completed, on 24-9-99, with M 1097 following in 3-00. Are based at Olpenitz.
Hull systems: Constructed using antimagnetic steel left over from the Type 206 submarine program.
Combat systems: The SM 343 conversions have the DSQS-11M hull-mounted variable-depth minehunting sonar, remotely operated minehunting submersibles (either PAP 104 Mk 5 or Pinguin B3, eventually to be supplanted by the Seefuchs I identification and Seefuchs-C expendable mine disposal drones), support systems for mine disposal divers (including a three-man decompression chamber), and modifications to the propulsion plant and rudders to permit low-speed operations.
Have PALIS and Link 11 datalink, a SARIE signal analyzer for the EW system, and a NAVSTAR SATNAV receiver. The WM-20 radar systems come from stricken *Zobel*-class torpedo boats. The 40-mm Bofors guns are in OTOBreda mountings and have enclosed GRP gunhouses made by Mauser.

♦ 5 Type 352 drone mine countermeasures craft control ships [MSA]

Bldrs: A: Lürssen Werft,Vegesack; B: Krögerwerft, Rendsburg

	Bldr	Laid down	L	In serv.
M 1090 Pegnitz	A	6-7-87	13-3-89	9-3-90
M 1092 Hameln	A	18-6-86	15-3-88	29-6-89
M 1093 Auerbach/Opf	A	3-1-89	18-6-90	7-5-91
M 1094 Ensdorf	A	15-3-88	8-12-89	25-9-90
M 1098 Siegburg	B	13-10-87	14-4-89	17-7-90

D: 620 tons (fl) **S:** 18 kts **Dim:** 54.40 (51.00 pp) × 9.20 × 2.50 (3.20 props)
A: 2 40-mm 70-cal. OTOBreda-Bofors AA; 2 Stinger/Fliegerfaust point-defense SAM positions; up to 60 mines
Electronics:
Radar: 1 Raytheon SPS-64 nav.; 1 H.S.A. WM-20/2 track-while-scan f.c.
Sonar: STN Atlas Elektronik DSQS-11M hull-mounted retractable HF
EW: Thales DR-2000 intercept, 2 6-round Buck-Wegmann Hot Dog/Silver Dog decoy RL
M: 2 MTU 16V396 TB84-DB51L diesels; 2 Escher-Wyss CP props; 6,080 bhp
Electric: 1,050 kw (3 MWM TBD 601 65 diesels, 639 bhp each, driving)
Range: . . ./. . . **Crew:** 4 officers, 20 petty officers, 13 ratings

Siegburg (M 1098)—as modified to drone controller Piet Sinke, 6-99

Ensdorf (M 1094)—as modified Findler & Winter, 1-01

Remarks: Ordered from prime contractor Messerschmidt-Bölkow-Blohm (MBB) 10-1-85 as Type 343 minesweepers. Under a 12-97 contract with STN Atlas Elektronik, have been converted to HL 352 *(Hohlstab Lenkboot)* drone control vessels; M 1093 was the first to complete, in 11-99, and all were finished by end-2001. M 1092 and M 1094 were converted by Friedrich Lürssen Werft, the others by Abeking & Rasmussen. All are based at Olpenitz.
Hull systems: Constructed using antimagnetic steel left over from the Type 206 submarine program.
Combat systems: As converted, they now can control three of the existing Seehund drones each, but with a new control system developed jointly with the Netherlands; also carried are a mine-avoidance sonar and remotely controlled submersibles for use in clearing moored mines. In the latter part of the 2000 decade, the MA 2000 program will result in another modernization that will employ the planned Seepferd drone, which will deploy a towed mine location sonar and sophisticated hull-mounted sonars, with all sensors integrated via computer. Seepferd is expected to displace 99 tons and to be 26 m overall. Also under development are Seewolf expendable bottomed-mine disposal drone and the smaller Seefuchs expendable disposal drone.
Have PALIS and Link 11 datalink, a SARIE signal analyzer for the EW system, and a NAVSTAR SATNAV receiver. The WM-20 radar systems come from stricken *Zobel*-class torpedo boats. The 40-mm Bofors guns are in OTOBreda mountings and have enclosed GRP gunhouses made by Mauser.

Disposal note: Of the *Lindau*-class minehunters, Type 331A variants *Flensburg* (M 1084) and *Fulda* (M 1086) were stricken 6-91 and 26-3-92, respectively; M 1084 was transferred to the city of Duisburg as *Jugendschiff Ruhrort* on 7-4-95. Of the Type 331B variants, *Weilheim* (M 1077) was stricken 15-6-95, *Wetzlar* (M 1075) on 30-6-95 (sold for scrap 1-7-96), *Tübingen* (M 1074) on 26-6-97 (sold for private use in Italy), *Göttingen* (M 1070) on 11-9-97 (transferred to Estonia for cannibalization spares 2-01 but lost en route), *Minden* (M 1085) on 4-12-97 (transferred to Georgia 22-10-98), *Völklingen* (M 1087) on 23-3-99 (transferred to Latvia 24-3-99), *Koblenz* (M 1071) on 4-12-99 (transferred to Lithuania the same day), *Cuxhaven* (M 1078) on 15-1-00 (transferred to Estonia 9-00), *Lindau* (M 1072) on 27-9-00 (transferred to Estonia 9-10-00), and *Marburg* (M 1080) on 25-5-00 (transferred to Lithuania 16-11-00).
Of the six Type 351 drone control ships, *Ulm* (M 1083) was retired 21-9-99, *Paderborn* (M 1076) on 30-6-00, and *Schleswig* (M 1073), *Düren* (M 1079), *Konstanz* (M 1081), and *Wolfsburg* (M 1082) on 29-9-00; all six were transferred to South Africa on 15-1-01 and departed on 25-1-01 as deck cargo.

♦ 18 Type HL 351 Troika drones [MSD]

Bldr: MAK, Kiel

	In serv.		In serv.
Seehund 1	1-8-80	Seehund 10	11-11-81
Seehund 2	1-8-80	Seehund 11	11-11-81
Seehund 3	1-8-80	Seehund 12	11-11-81
Seehund 4	17-7-81	Seehund 13	1-9-82
Seehund 5	17-7-81	Seehund 14	1-9-82
Seehund 6	17-7-81	Seehund 15	1-9-82
Seehund 7	17-9-81	Seehund 16	13-5-82
Seehund 8	17-9-81	Seehund 17	13-5-82
Seehund 9	17-9-81	Seehund 18	13-5-82

D: 91 tons (96.5 fl) **S:** 9.4 kts **Dim:** 24.92 × 4.46 × 1.8
M: 1 MWM TRHS 518A diesel; Schottel prop; 445 hp
Electric: 208 kw **Range:** 520/8.8 **Crew:** 3 tot. (for transit)

Remarks: Ordered 1977 to operate three-apiece with the Type 351 control ships. Beginning in 1999, were converted to work with the Type 352–conversion control ships.

MINE WARFARE SHIPS *(continued)*

Seehund 17 Findler & Winter, 3-01

Seehund 3 Dieter Wolf, 10-00

Combat systems: Essentially remote-controlled, self-propelled magnetic minesweeping solenoids with all machinery highly shock-protected. Also able to stream two sets Type SDG-21 Oropesa mechanical minesweeping gear.

♦ 3 Type 394A inshore minesweepers [MSI]
Bldr: Krögerwerft, Rendsburg

	L	In serv.
M 2658 Frauenlob	26-2-65	27-9-66
M 2660 Gefion	19-6-65	17-2-67
M 2665 Loreley	14-3-67	29-3-68

Frauenlob (M 2658) Findler & Winter, 6-00

D: 238 tons (246 fl) **S:** 14.3 kts **Dim:** 38.01 × 8.03 × 2.10
A: 1 40-mm 70-cal. Bofors AA
Electronics: Radar: 1 STN Atlas Elektronik TRS-N nav.
M: 2 MTU 12V493 TY70 diesels; 2 props; 2,200 bhp **Electric:** 554 kw tot.
Range: 648/14; 1,770/7 **Fuel:** 30 tons **Crew:** 4 officers, 20 enlisted

Remarks: Formerly had "Y," and earlier "W," series pennants. The five remaining units were to have been stricken in 1996. Instead, the 7th Minesweeping Squadron, Neustadt, to which they belonged, was decommissioned on 1-4-96 and the craft were reconstituted as the 3rd Minesweeping Squadron and moved to Olpenitz, where they have been used along with Type 520 landing craft for basic training duties. Were to be stricken on 31-3-02.
Disposals: *Nixe* (M 2655) was sold to the city of Hamburg 8-4-94. *Nautilus* (M 2659) was stricken 28-4-94 after incurring damage and was sold for scrap 1-7-96. *Minerva* (M 2663) and *Diana* (M 2664) were stricken 16-2-95 and transferred to Estonia in 1997. *Atlantis* (M 2666) and *Acheron* (M 2667) were stricken 20-3-95 (the former was donated as a museum ship at Dresden 23-4-00 and the latter sold for scrap 1-7-96). *Medusa* (M 2661) was stricken 14-6-01 and *Undine* (M 2662) on 28-6-01.
Hull systems: Wooden construction. Differed from earlier Type 393 in having a 260-kw diesel sweep-current generator.
Combat systems: There is a lead-computing optical director on the bridge for the 40-mm gun. Equipped to sweep mechanical, magnetic, and acoustic mines.

Note: The hulk of Type 394 minesweeper *Gazelle* is stationed at the Naval Technical School, Parow, with the last remaining *Schütze*-class minesweeper, the *Widder,* for use in familiarization, seamanship, and damage control training; both remain armed and fully equipped but do not carry pennant numbers and do not get under way.

♦ 1 Type 340 mine countermeasures diver support ship [MSA]
Bldr: Burmester, Bremen

	L	In serv.
M 1052 Mühlhausen (ex-*Walther von Ledebur,* A 1410; ex-Y 841)	30-6-66	21-12-67

Mühlhausen (M 1052) Walter Angermeier, 6-99

D: 775 tons (825 fl) **S:** 19 kts **Dim:** 63.20 × 10.60 × 3.00
A: none **Electronics:** Radar: 1 Kelvin-Hughes 14/9 nav.
M: 2 Maybach 16-cyl. diesels; 2 props; 5,200 bhp
Electric: 1,620 kw tot. **Crew:** . . . tot.

Remarks: Employed in mine warfare research until decommissioning on 24-3-94. Reactivated 3-3-95 and converted to serve as replacement for *Stier* (M 1050), recommissioning under her new name 6-4-95. As a research ship, was equipped with mechanical, acoustic, and magnetic mine countermeasures gear. Has two 600-kw sweep current generators. Refitted and updated at Peenewerft, completing fall 1997 with new diver support equipment. Wooden construction. Based at Eckernförde.

AMPHIBIOUS WARFARE SHIPS AND CRAFT

Note: Plans to construct two amphibious warfare dock landing ships [LPD] similar to the Netherlands' *Rotterdam* (L 800) were announced 11-00.

♦ 3 Type 520 utility landing craft [LCU]
Bldr: Howaldtswerke, Hamburg

	In serv.		In serv.
L 762 Lachs	17-2-66	L 769 Zander	13-7-66
L 765 Schlei	17-5-66		

Lachs (L 762) H&L Van Ginderen, 6-00

D: 166 tons (403 fl) **S:** 11 kts **Dim:** 40.04 (36.7 pp) × 8.8 × 1.6 (2.1 max.)
A: provision for 2 single 20-mm Rheinmetall Rh 202 AA; mines
Electronics: Radar: 1 Kelvin-Hughes 14/9 nav.
M: 2 MWM 12-cyl. diesels; 2 props; 1,200 bhp **Electric:** 130 kVA
Range: 1,200/11 **Crew:** 17 tot.

Remarks: Design based on the American LCU 1646 class. Cargo: 237 tons max.; 141.6 normal. The survivors are now attached to the Mine Warfare Command and are maintained at Olpenitz as part of the 3rd Minesweeping Squadron. Their armament has been removed. L 769 is to be stricken during 3-02.
Disposals: Sisters *Renke* (L 798) and *Salm* (L 799) transferred to Greece 16-11-89; *Barbe* (L 790), *Delphin* (L 791), and *Dorsch* (L 792) were stricken 26-9-91 and transferred to Greece. *Forelle* (L 794) was stricken 1-11-91 (transferred to Greece), *Makrele* (L 796) on 8-11-91, *Karpfen* (L 761) on 30-1-92, *Rochen* (L 764) and *Muräne* (L 797) on 14-2-92 (both transferred to Greece 20-10-92), *Brasse* (L 789) on 16-4-92, *Stör* (L 766) and *Tümmler* (L 767) on 16-9-92, *Felchen* (L 793) and *Inger* (L 795) on 30-9-92, *Butt* (L 786) on 4-12-92, *Wels* (L 768) on 11-12-92, *Flunder* (L 760) on 16-5-01, and *Plötze* (L 763) on 7-9-01. Sold for scrap were L 761, 766, 767, and 789 on 17-7-96 and L 768, 786, and 795 on 19-7-95.

AMPHIBIOUS WARFARE SHIPS AND CRAFT *(continued)*

♦ 4 Type 521 landing craft [LCM]
Bldr: Rheinwerft, Walsum (In serv. 1966–67)

LCM 14 Sardelle
LCM 23 Krabbe (ex-L 782)
LCM 25 Muschel (ex-L 784)
LCM 26 Koralle (ex-L 785)

Krabbe (LCM 23) Wolfgang Kramer, 6-01

D: 116 tons (168 fl) **S:** 10.6 kts **Dim:** 23.56 × 6.40 × 1.46
Electronics: Radar: 1 . . . nav.
M: 2 MWM 8-cyl. diesels; 2 props; 684 bhp
Electric: 28 kw tot. **Range:** 690/10; 1,430/7 **Crew:** 7 tot.

Remarks: Design based on U.S. LCM(8). Cargo: 60 tons or 50 troops. LCM 23 was reactivated 14-6-95 and converted for use as an oilspill skimmer craft at Warnemünde. Two are now assigned to Kiel, one to Wilhelmshaven, and one to Parow. Reverted to original LCM-series numbers in mid-1990s.
Disposals: Sisters LCM 1–11 were transferred to Greece and shipped on 25-4-91. Most of the other units of the class have been converted to serve as pollution clearance craft and transferred to various local governments: *Sprotte* (LCM 12) to Kiel on 7-9-93; *Sardine* (LCM 13), stricken 18-3-93, to Brunsbütte; *Orfe* (LCM 16), stricken 18-10-93, to Mecklenburg-Vorpommern (and sold 11-2-94 to a commercial operator); *Maräne* (LCM 17), stricken 30-4-93, to the Bremerhaven Fire Brigade 6-7-95; *Saibling* (LCM 18), stricken 27-4-93, to the city of Husum, Schleswig-Holstein; *Stint* (LCM 19), stricken 1-4-93, to Lübeck; and *Äsche* (LCM 20), stricken 22-4-93, to Warnemünde. *Hering* (LCM 15) was stricken 20-7-94 (later sold for scrap), *Krille* (LCM 22, L 781) on 20-6-96, *Hummer* (LCM 21) on 10-3-00, *Garnele* (LCM 27) on 17-3-00, *Auster* (LCM 24) on 24-3-00, and *Languste* (LCM 28) on 31-3-00.

AUXILIARIES

♦ 1 Type 760 ammunition ships [AE]
Bldr: Orenstein & Koppel, Lübeck

	Laid down	L	In serv.
A 1435 Westerwald	3-11-65	25-2-66	11-2-67

Westerwald (A 1435) Findler & Winter, 5-01

D: 3,460 tons (4,014 fl) **S:** 17 kts **Dim:** 105.27 × 14.02 × 3.70 (4.50 max.)
A: removed **Electronics:** Radar: 1 Kelvin-Hughes 14/9 nav.
M: 2 Maybach MD 874 diesels; 2 CP props; 5,600 bhp—bow-thruster
Electric: 1,285 kw tot. **Range:** 3,500/17 **Crew:** 31 tot. (civilian)

Remarks: Similar to the Type 701 replenishment tenders, but carries only ammunition. Cargo: 1,080 tons. Two 3-ton electric cranes are fitted, as well as three lighter-capacity cargo booms. Originally had two twin 40-mm and two lead-computing directors. Homeported at Wilhelmshaven. Sister *Odenwald* (A 1436) was stricken 19-12-01.

♦ 3 Type 143 intelligence collection ships [AGI]
Bldr: Flensburger Schiffbaugesellschaft, Flensburg

	Laid down	L	In serv.
A 50 Alster	14-3-88	3-11-88	5-10-89
A 52 Oste	21-11-86	15-5-87	30-6-88
A 53 Oker	15-12-86	24-9-87	24-11-88

D: 2,375 tons (3,200 fl) **S:** 20 kts **Dim:** 83.50 (75.70 pp) × 14.60 × 4.18
A: provision for 2 single 27-mm Mauser MLG 27 AA
Electronics:
Radar: 1 . . . nav.; 1 . . . surf. search; 1 . . . ranging and tracking
Sonar: STN Atlas Elektronik AISYS passive array
EW: 300 MHz–40 GHz intercept suite; EADS COLDS laser countermeasure
M: 2 Deutz-MWM SBV 16M 628 diesels; 2 fixed-pitch, 6-bladed props; 8,800 bhp—2 380-shp electric motors for low speed, quiet operations (2 MWM-KHD 604 V12 diesel generator sets)
Electric: . . . kw tot. (3 Deutz MWM 6-cyl., 280-bhp diesels driving)
Range: . . ./. . . **Crew:** 42 ship's company + 38 technicians

Oker (A 53) Aldo Petrina, 1-01

Alster (A 50) A. A. de Kruijf, 6-00

Remarks: A 52 and A 53 were ordered 3-7-85 as replacements for ships of the same names; A 50 was ordered 15-12-86. Built to commercial standards. All three are based at Kiel. A 50 deployed to the Adriatic early 4-99. The COLDS (Common Opto-electronic Laser Detection System) detects laser missile seekers and projects an equivalent pulse-repetition-frequency beam at a safe spot on the ocean surface to spoof the missile. Also carry electro-optical surveillance equipment. During refits beginning in 1999, were to have been given gun armament, replenishment-at-sea facilities, and improved accommodations, but the guns have not yet been installed.

♦ 0 (+ 1) Type 751 oceanographic research ship [AGOR]
Bldr: Thyssen Nordseewerke, Emden

	Laid down	L	Del.	In serv.
A . . .	29-04-02	. . .	31-10-03	. . .

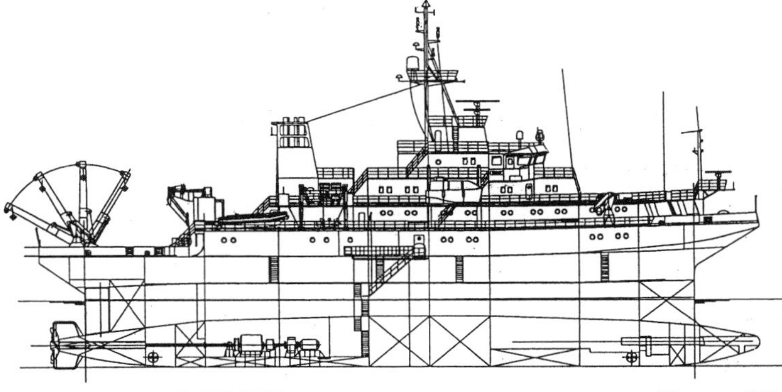
Type 751 research SWATH Thyssen, 1999

D: 3,500 tons (fl) **S:** 15 kts (sust.) **Dim:** 73.00 × 27.20 (25.00 deck) × 6.80
A: 1 fixed, submerged 533-mm TT
Electronics: Radar: 2 . . . nav.—Sonar: trials installations
M: diesel-electric drive: 2 . . . . . . diesels, 5,400 kw tot. generator capacity, 2 Jeumont-Framatome axial-flux permanent magnet motors; 2 shrouded props; 6,000 shp—2 bow- and 2 stern-thrusters
Range: 5,000/15 **Endurance:** 30 days
Crew: 25 tot. + 20 trials personnel or scientists

Remarks: The *Wehrforschungs und Erpropungsschiff* (WFES) trials vessel was ordered 7-12-00. Will initially conduct trials of the DM-2A4 torpedo and then will support trials of the Type 212 submarines during 2004–06. May be named *Planet*.

AUXILIARIES *(continued)*

Hull systems: Employs a SWATH (Small Waterplane Area, Twin-Hull) catamaran configuration. A containerized fuel cell will supply emergency and in-port electrical requirements. A stern radial gallows equipment crane will be installed, and there will be a twin-drum towing winch. Up to five portable laboratory/equipment vans will be accommodated. The trials torpedo tube will be installed in the lower, starboard hull pontoon. A full suite of oceanographic equipment, including precision cranes, will be carried, and the ship will be equipped for trials with new sonar systems.

♦ 1 Type 750 oceanographic research ship [AGOR]
Bldr: J. R. Köser Norderwerft, Hamburg

	Laid down	L	In serv.
A 1452 Planet (ex-Y 843)	30-4-64	23-9-65	15-4-67

Planet (A 1452)—white hull and yellow stack, mast, and cranes   Piet Sinke, 6-00

D: 1,513 tons (1,917 fl) **S:** 13.9 kts **Dim:** 80.43 (74.00 pp) × 12.60 × 3.97
Electronics: Radar: 2 . . . nav.—Sonar: mapping sonars (see remarks)
M: 4 MWM TB RS 18/22-21 AE 1, 12-cyl., 850-hp diesels, electric drive; 1 prop; 1,390 bhp
Electric: 650 kw tot. **Range:** 9,300/13.4 **Crew:** 39 tot. + 13 scientists

Remarks: Operated for the Ministry of Communications by a civilian crew. Hangar for one helicopter. Capable of conducting geophysical, meteorological, biological, chemical, and hydrographic research. Was scheduled to be retired 12-96 but now will not be retired until 31-12-03.
Hull systems: Denny-Brown stabilizers, 125-bhp Pleuger active rudder, and bow-thruster fitted. Main engines provide 560 kw of the total ship's service electrical power. Stern broadened to starboard in 1988 for cable handling; also has cable sheaves at the bow.
Mission systems: The antenna atop the foremast is for a balloon-tracking radar. Began trials 11-00 with a new torpedo-detection sonar employing a hull-mounted sonar and the STN Atlas Elektronik Compact Towed-Array Sonar System (COTASS).

♦ 2 Type 704 replenishment oilers [AO]
Bldr: Krögerwerft, Rendsburg

	L	In serv.
A 1442 Spessart (ex-*Okapi*)	13-2-75	23-9-77
A 1443 Rhön (ex-*Okene*)	23-8-74	5-9-77

Spessart (A 1442)   Bernard Prézelin, 4-00

Rhön (A 1443)   Bernard Prézelin, 3-01

D: 14,260 tons (fl) **S:** 16.3 kts **Dim:** 130.15 × 19.33 × 8.20
A: 2 Stinger/Fliegerfaust point-defense SAM positions
Electronics: Radar: 1 . . . nav.
M: 1 MAK 12-cyl. diesel; CP prop; 8,000 bhp **Electric:** 2,000 kw tot.
Range: 7,400/16 **Crew:** 42 tot. (civilian)

Remarks: 6,103 grt/10,800 dwt. Purchased from Bulk Acid Carriers, Monrovia, Liberia, in 1976 and converted as replenishment oilers, A 1442 by Bremerhaven Naval Arsenal and A 1443 by Krögerwerft. Fitted with one underway-replenishment station per side. Cargo: 9,500 m^3 distillate fuel, 1,650 m^3 fuel oil, 400 m^3 water. Hull has a pronounced bulbous bow. Protected shoulder-launched SAM positions were added during the mid-1990s.

♦ 3 Type 703 small replenishment oilers [AO]
Bldr: Lindenauwerft, Kiel

	Laid down	L	In serv.
A 1425 Ammersee	28-3-66	9-7-66	2-3-67
A 1426 Tegernsee	21-4-66	22-10-66	23-3-67
A 1427 Westensee	28-10-66	8-4-67	6-10-67

Ammersee (A 1425)   Mike Welsford, 5-00

Westensee (A 1427)   Bernard Prézelin, 5-01

D: 2,191 tons (fl) **S:** 12.5 kts **Dim:** 71.94 × 11.22 × 4.40
Electronics: Radar: 2 . . . nav.
M: 2 MWM 12-cyl. diesels; 1 KaMeWa CP prop; 1,200 bhp
Electric: 635 kw tot. **Range:** 3,250/12 **Crew:** 21 tot. (civilian)

Remarks: Cargo capacity: 1,130 m^3 fuel, 60 m^3 water. The one alongside-refueling station can work to either beam. Sister *Walchensee* (A 1424) was refitted at Elsflether Werft from 13-1-99 to 11-3-99, but was stricken 19-12-01 and offered to Egypt. The ships are frequently used to accompany deploying Type 143/143A missile boats.

♦ 1 (+ 1) Type 702 (KSV 90) replenishment ships [AOR]
Bldrs: Flensburger Schiffbau-Gessellschaft (FSG) and Lürssen-Krögerwerft

	Laid down	L	In serv.
A 1411 Berlin	4-1-99	30-4-99	11-4-01
A 1412 Frankfurt/Main	28-8-00	5-1-01	2-02

D: 10,115 tons light (20,243 fl) **S:** 20 kts
Dim: 173.70 (162.00 pp) × 24.00 × 7.40
A: 4 single 20-mm 90-cal. Rheinmetall Rh 202 AA; provision for 2 Stinger/Fliegerfaust point-defense SAM positions
Electronics: Radar: 3 . . . nav.—Sonar: . . . mine-avoidance
M: 2 M.A.N.-B&W 12V32/40 diesels; 2 5-bladed props; 14,154 bhp—bow-thruster
Electric: . . . kw tot. (4 × . . . kw, Deutz-MWM . . . diesels driving)
Range: . . ./. . . **Endurance:** 45 days
Crew: 60 ship's crew + 50 medical staff + 30 helicopter group + 140 troops (233 tot. accomm.)

Remarks: 18,640 grt. Typed *Einsatzgruppe Versorgungsschiffen* (deployment group support ships). In early 1994, the program was cut from four ships (to have been completed in 1998, 1999, 2005, and 2006) to one, and approval to build the ship was granted 10-96. A 1412 was restored in the 1996 budget, with construction authorized 6-98. Plans to request the third and fourth again after 2010 had been dropped by 1-01. A 1411 was originally to have been named *Schwarzwald* and A 1412 *Sauerland.* FSG built the hulls, with Lürssen providing electrical system outfitting and Krögerwerft the superstructures, final outfitting, and trials services. Work on A 1411 began

AUXILIARIES *(continued)*

Berlin (A 1411) Findler & Winter, 10-00

24-9-98, and the ship was handed over to the Military Procurement Office 14-11-99; commissioning was delayed by software problems. A 1411 is based at Wilhelmshaven, and A 1412 is to be based at Kiel.

Hull systems: Carry 9,000 m^3 (7,600 tons) of diesel fuel, 600 m^3 (490 tons) of aviation fuel, 1,100 m^3 of potable water, 50 m^3 of boiler feed water, 60 m^3 of lube oil, 100 tons of spare parts, 230 tons of provisions, and 195 tons of ammunition. One sliding-stay replenishment station per side and two electrohydraulic container and cargo cranes are fitted; they are also able to refuel over the stern. Have a helicopter deck and hangar to accommodate two Sea Kings or NH-90s. Employ double-hull construction, and there is a pronounced bow bulb.

The ships can embark a modular Operations Rescue Center (*Marine-Einsatzettungssystem*/MERZ), supplied by Dornier GmbH; it consists of 26 20-ft. cargo containers equipped to provide emergency surgery, intensive care, internal medicine, and dental capabilities for up to 50 patients. Maximum container stowage is 84 20-ft. container-equivalents.

Combat systems: Will be able to carry antennas for a portable SCOT-1A SHF SATCOM set, on either side of the funnel, and will normally have a commercial Marisat system aboard. The guns are mounted on the four corners of the first level of the aft superstructure block. Two planned Stinger/Fliegerfaust point-defense SAM positions were omitted. One X-band radar is mounted aft for helicopter landing/takeoff operations.

♦ 1 Type 701C missile boat and submarine supply ship [AOR]

	Bldr	Laid down	L	In serv.
A 1418 Meersburg	Flensburger Werft	5-8-65	22-3-66	25-6-68

Meersburg (A 1418) H&L Van Ginderen, 7-00

D: 1,900 tons (3,679 fl) **S:** 17 kts **Dim:** 114.19 (108.04 pp) × 13.22 × 4.29
A: 1 twin 40-mm 70-cal. Bofors AA
Electronics: Radar: 1 Kelvin-Hughes 14/9 nav.
M: 2 Maybach MD 874 diesels; 2 CP props; 5,600 bhp
Electric: 1,935 kw tot. **Range:** 3,000/17; 3,200/14 **Crew:** 71–82 tot.

Remarks: Employed in support of Type 206A submarines. Based at Eckernförde. Not planned to be retired until 2006, when a replacement may be available.

Disposals: The similarly converted *Glücksburg* (A 1414) was stricken 1-11-01. *Coburg* (A 1412) was transferred to Greece 30-9-91, and *Saarburg* (A 1415) was stricken 14-4-94 and recommissioned 29-9-94 for transit to Greece for transfer on 19-10-94.

Hull systems: Lengthened 11.5 m in 1975–77 to carry spare Exocet missiles and other supplies for Type 143 and Type 148 missile boats. Stowage for spare parts was increased to 30,000 items, with inventory management by the Nixdorf computer system. Is equipped with fin stabilizers and one 3-ton and two 2-ton cranes.

♦ 1 Type 701E frigate supply ship [AOR]

	Bldr	Laid down	L	In serv.
A 1413 Freiburg	Blohm + Voss, Hamburg	1965	15-4-66	27-5-68

D: 3,900 tons (fl) **S:** 17 kts **Dim:** 118.30 × 13.22 × 4.29
A: 1 twin 40-mm 70-cal. Bofors AA

Freiburg (A 1413) Findler & Winter, 5-00

Electronics:
Radar: 1 Kelvin-Hughes 14/9 nav.—EW: Thales DR-2000S intercept
M: 2 Maybach MD 874 diesels; 2 CP props; 5,600 bhp
Electric: 1,935 kw tot. **Range:** 3,000/17; 3,200/14 **Crew:** 71–82 tot.

Remarks: Converted 1981–84 to support Type 122 frigates. Is equipped with helicopter facilities to permit vertical replenishment, space for nine spare Harpoon missiles, repair facilities for Lynx Mk 88 helicopters, and new articulated cranes. Equipped with fin stabilizers. The original twin Bofors L70 mount aft was fully operational in 1996 and had a Bofors lead-computing director aboard in a state of preservation. The forward mount was removed between 1993 and 1995. To be retired on 31-12-02 and transferred to Egypt.

♦ 6 Type 404 multipurpose tenders [AR]

Bldrs: A 511, 512: Bremer Vulkan, Bremen; A 513, 514: Neue Flensburger Schiffsbau, Flensburg; A 515, 516: Flenderwerke/Krögerwerft, Vegesack

	Laid down	L	In serv.	Current function
A 511 Elbe	11-5-92	24-6-92	28-1-93	PTG tender
A 512 Mosel	29-12-93	22-4-93	22-7-93	minecraft tender
A 513 Rhein	7-10-92	11-3-93	22-9-93	minecraft tender
A 514 Werra	11-11-92	17-6-93	9-12-93	minecraft tender
A 515 Main	3-8-92	15-6-93	23-6-94	PTG tender
A 516 Donau	25-6-93	24-3-94	22-11-94	PTG tender

Donau (A 516) Findler & Winter, 5-00

Mosel (A 512) Findler & Winter, 3-01

AUXILIARIES *(continued)*

Rhein (A 513) Hartmut Ehlers, 2-00

D: 3,590 tons (fl) **S:** 15 kts (11 cruise) **Dim:** 100.58 (87.00 pp) × 15.40 × 4.10
A: 2 single 20-mm 90-cal. Rheinmetall Rh 202 AA; 2 Stinger-Fliegerfaust shoulder-launched SAM positions
Electronics: Radar: 1 . . . nav.
M: 1 Deutz-MWM SBV 12M 628 diesel; 1 prop; 3,360 bhp—47-kN bow-thruster
Electric: 1,200 kw tot. **Range:** 2,000/11 **Endurance:** 30 days
Crew: 4 officers, 36 enlisted + 12 squadron staff, 38 technicians

Remarks: Ordered 10-90. Built to commercial standards. The planned conversion of A 515 as a trials ship for equipment for the new Type 124 guided-missile frigates has been canceled. A 516 began lengthening by 24 m 1-6-01 to increase storage capacity to serve the 2nd *Schnellbootgeschwader,* while one of the others may be converted to serve as a submarine tender. As of 2001, A 511 served missile boats of the 7th Squadron, A 512 mine countermeasures ships of the 5th Squadron, A 513 mine countermeasures ships of the 6th Squadron, A 514 mine countermeasures ships of the 1st Squadron, and A 515 missile boats of the 5th Squadron.
Hull systems: Can carry up to 24 standard-sized 20-ft., 7.5-ton containers for supplies and repair shops, 450 tons of cargo fuel, 11 m^3 of lube oil, 150 m^3 of fresh water, 27 tons of provisions, and 129 tons of ammunition. There are alongside underway refueling stations on either beam and two more for over-the-stern refueling. Have a helicopter platform aft with refueling facilities but no hangar. Have one 12.5-ton (at 15 m; 3-ton at 21-m reach) electrohydraulic crane; a second, to have been emplaced on the forecastle, was omitted. The hull has 13 watertight compartments, with watertight cargo passage doors between the five cargo holds, which are equipped with 1,250-kg- and 800-kg-capacity bridge cranes. The engines have also been listed as being of model 510BL6. A Becker flapped rudder of 7.24 m^2 area is fitted to improve harbor maneuvering. The distilling plant can produce 10 m^3 of potable water per day.
Combat systems: As an interim defensive armament, two 20-mm AA mounts have been added on the forecastle at its after end. The SAM positions are located atop the pilothouse.

♦ 6 Baltrum-class (Type 722 and 754*) seagoing tugs [ATA]
Bldr: Schichau, Bremerhaven

	Laid down	L	In serv.
A 1439 Baltrum (ex-Y 1661, ex-A 1454)*	29-6-66	2-6-67	8-10-68
A 1440 Juist (ex-Y 1644, ex-A 1456)*	23-9-67	15-8-68	1-10-71
A 1441 Langeoog (ex-Y 1665, ex-A 1453)*	12-7-66	2-5-67	14-8-68
A 1451 Wangerooge	1-10-65	4-7-66	9-4-68
A 1452 Spiekeroog	20-11-65	26-9-66	14-8-68
A 1455 Norderney	29-5-67	28-2-68	15-10-70

Wangerooge (A 1451)—Type 722 salvage tug Findler & Winter, 8-00

D: 854 tons (1,025 fl) **S:** 13.6 kts **Dim:** 51.78 × 12.11 × 4.20
A: removed **Electronics:** Radar: 1 Kelvin-Hughes 14/9 nav.
M: 4 MWM TRHS 518 V16-31 AE 16-cyl. diesel generator sets (700 kw each), electric drive; 2 Kort-nozzle shrouded props; 2,400 shp
Electric: 540 kw **Range:** 5,000/10 **Crew:** 31 tot. (civilian in A 1439, A 1440)

Remarks: A 1439–1441 were converted as Type 754 training support tugs in 1977–78, with accommodations for up to 33 additional personnel; A 1439 and A 1440 are employed as diving training ships based at Neustadt and carrying recompression chambers. The other three are configured as Type 722 salvage and rescue tugs; A 1451 is used at Cuxhaven in support of aircrew survival training, and the other two act as submarine safety vessels. Bollard pull: 33 tons. Until early 1993, a single 40-mm gun was retained aboard each ship in a state of preservation. All are fitted for fire fighting.

Juist (A 1440)—Type 754 training support tug Werner Schiefer, 5-97

♦ 1 Helgoland-class (Type 720) salvage tug [ATA]
Bldr: Schichau, Bremerhaven

	Laid down	L	In serv.
A 1458 Fehmarn	23-4-65	25-11-65	1-2-67

Fehmarn (A 1458) Findler & Winter, 4-99

D: 1,304 tons (1,558 fl) **S:** 16.6 kts **Dim:** 67.91 × 12.74 × 4.20
A: removed
Electronics: Radar: 1 Kelvin-Hughes 14/9 nav.; 1 Decca . . . nav.
M: 4 MWM 12 RS 18/22-21 AE 1 diesel generator sets (700 kw each), electric drive; 2 props; 3,300 shp
Electric: 1,065 kw tot. **Range:** 6,400/16 **Crew:** 34 tot.

Remarks: Serves as a safety tender to the submarine training establishment. Sister *Helgoland* (A 1457) was stricken 19-12-97 and transferred to Uruguay 21-9-98. A 1458 is equipped to serve as a mine planter, if required. Has a high-frequency sonar for salvage work and is equipped for fire fighting. The ice-strengthened hull permits use as a harbor icebreaker. A twin Bofors-OTOBreda 40-mm 70-cal. AA mount can be mounted on the forecastle. Bollard pull: 35 tons.

♦ 1 Eisvogel-class (Type 721) icebreaking tug [ATA]
Bldr: Hitzler, Lauenburg

	Laid down	L	In serv.
A 1401 Eisvogel	10-3-59	28-4-60	11-3-61

Eisvogel (A 1401) Dieter Wolf, 10-00

AUXILIARIES *(continued)*

D: 496 tons (641 fl) **S:** 13 kts **Dim:** 37.80 × 9.73 × 4.60
Electronics: Radar: 2 . . . nav.
M: 2 Maybach 12-cyl. diesels; 2 KaMeWa CP props; 2,400 bhp
Electric: 180 kw **Range:** 2,000/12 **Crew:** 16 tot. (civilian)

Remarks: Completed refit 10-91 at Warnowwerft, Warnemünde. Sister *Eisbär* (A 1402) was stricken 30-10-97 and operates as the commercial *Cardinal D.* Has a 20-ton bollard pull capability. Based at Kiel. Is expected to operate until 2012. Provision is made to install a 40-mm Bofors AA aft.

♦ 1 Type 441 sail training ship [AXT]

	Bldr	Laid down	L	In serv.
A 60 Gorch Fock	Blohm + Voss, Hamburg	24-2-58	23-8-58	17-12-58

Gorch Fock (A 60) A. D. Baker III, 6-00

D: 1,819 tons (2,005 fl) **S:** 12 kts (15 under sail)
Dim: 89.32 (81.44 hull; 70.20 pp) × 12.02 × 5.25
Electronics: Radar: 2 . . . nav.
M: 1 Deutz-MWM SBV 6 M 628 diesel; 1 KaMeWa CP prop; 1,660 bhp—1,904 m^2 max. sail area
Electric: 450 kw tot. (3 × 150 kw; 3 Deutz-MWM 6-234 250-bhp diesels driving)
Range: 1,100/10 **Crew:** 10 officers, 56 enlisted, 140 cadets

Remarks: Has made 296 n.m. progress in one day. Underwent a major refit in 1985, and was re-engined by Motorenwerke Bremerhaven during a refit 21-1-91 to 24-5-91. While the ship was in overhaul during spring 2000, the Norwegian bark *Statsraad Lehmkuhl* was chartered in her stead. Has Marisat commercial SATCOM and an extensive navigation aids suite. Carries 350 tons of permanent ballast.

YARD AND SERVICE CRAFT

♦ 2 Type 738 pollution-control ships [YAG] Bldr: C. Lühring, Brake

	Laid down	L	In serv.
Y 1643 Bottsand	14-11-83	22-9-84	26-10-84
Y 1644 Eversand	. . .	. . .	11-6-88

Bottsand (Y 1643) Jürg Kürsener, 9-01

D: approx. 1,100 tons (fl) **S:** 10 kts **Dim:** 46.30 × 12.00 × 3.10
Electronics: Radar: 1 . . . nav.
M: 2 Deutz BA 12M 816 diesels; 2 rudder-props; 1,600 bhp—2 omnidirectional bow-thrusters; 400 bhp
Crew: 3 officers, 3 unlicensed (civilian)

Remarks: 500 grt/650 dwt. Y 1643 was built for the Niedersachsen Ministry for the Environment, but was turned over to the German Navy on loan 24-1-85. Y 1643 is based at Warnemünde and Y 1644 at Wilhelmshaven.

Hull systems: Twin hulls, hinged near the stern to open scissors-fashion to 65°, leaving a 42-m-wide V-shaped opening to collect oil spills at the rate of approximately 140 m^3/hr, at a speed of 1 kt. When folded, can also be used as coastal tankers and bunkerage craft. Six cargo/spill tanks total 790 m^3.

♦ 3 Type 748 multipurpose trials craft [YAGE]

	Bldr	Laid down	L	In serv.
Y 860 Schwedeneck	Nobiskrug, Rendsburg	20-5-86	14-10-86	20-10-87
Y 861 Kronsort	Elsflether Werft, Elsfleth	6-10-86	9-5-87	2-12-87
Y 862 Helmsand	Krögerwerft, Rendsburg	18-3-87	31-7-87	11-2-88

Kronsort (Y 861) Jim Sanderson, 6-99

Helmsand (Y 862) H&L Van Ginderen, 6-00

D: 1,018 tons (fl) **S:** 14.5 kts **Dim:** 56.50 (50.00 pp) × 10.80 × 3.65
Electronics: Radar: 2 Raytheon . . . nav.
M: 3 MTU 6V396 TB93 (700 bhp each) diesels, electric drive, 2 750-kw AEG alternators; 1 prop; 1,490 shp—side-thrusters fore and aft
Range: 2,400/12 **Crew:** 13 civilians + 10 technicians

Remarks: 850 grt. Ordered 14-12-85 with Lürssen Werft as prime contractor, subcontracted to yards above. Y 862 was used for trials with the Mauser 27-mm guns and associated fire-control system.
Hull systems: Have space for four modular trials equipment containers—two on the fantail, two amidships—and a quadrantial scientific equipment gallows crane at the stern. Y 860 is fitted with a Siemens three-phase Permasyn propulsion motor as prototype for its installation in the Type 212 submarines. All three have NAVSTAR GPS.

♦ 5 Type 745 small multipurpose trials tenders [YAGE]

	Bldr	Laid down	L	In serv.
Y 863 Stollergrund	Krögerwerft, Rendsburg	26-5-88	1-9-88	31-5-89
Y 864 Mittelgrund	Elsflether Werft	26-5-88	26-4-89	21-9-89
Y 865 Kalkgrund	Krögerwerft, Rendsburg	7-9-88	2-2-89	8-11-89
Y 866 Breitgrund	Elsflether Werft	10-1-89	2-10-89	14-2-89
Y 867 Bant	Krögerwerft, Rendsburg	. . .	13-7-89	16-5-90

D: 400 tons (456 fl) **S:** 12.5 kts **Dim:** 38.55 (34.60 wl; 32.12 pp) × 9.20 × 3.10
Electronics: Radar: 2 . . . nav.
M: 1 KHD-SBV 6M 628 diesel; 1 prop; 1,210 bhp
Electric: 372 kw (2 MWM D234V8 diesels driving) **Range:** 900/12
Fuel: 18 tons **Endurance:** 5 days **Crew:** 6 civilian + 6 technicians

Remarks: Built under subcontract from Lürssen Werft. Nine were originally programmed. Two more were planned for delivery post-1995, but budget constraints forced their cancellation. All are based at the Eckernförde Armed Forces Technical Center, except Y 867 at Wilhelmshaven.
Hull systems: A torpedo recovery ramp is located to starboard through the transom stern, with a divers' stage to port. Have space for two trials equipment vans on stern and a Becker flap rudder to improve low-speed maneuvering.

YARD AND SERVICE CRAFT *(continued)*

Bant (Y 867) Findler & Winter, 8-00

Mittelgrund (Y 864) Bernard Prézelin, 9-99

♦ **1 Type 741 trials tender [YAGE]** Bldr: Schürenstedt, Bardenfleth

	Laid down	L	In serv.
A 1409 Wilhelm Pullwer (ex-Y 838, ex-SP 2)	4-10-65	16-8-66	22-12-67

Wilhelm Pullwer (A 1409) Findler & Winter, 3-99

D: 132 tons (160 fl) **S:** 12.5 kts **Dim:** 31.54 × 7.50 × 2.20
Electronics: Radar: 1 . . . nav.
M: 2 Mercedes-Benz 8 cyl. diesels; 2 Voith-Schneider cycloidal props; 792 hp
Electric: 120 kw **Crew:** 17 civilian + trials personnel

Remarks: Used in experimental trials. Wooden hull. Built as a net tender. Sister SP 1 (A 1408, ex-Y 837) was stricken 31-10-94 after having been damaged in a grounding.

♦ **2 Type 711 self-propelled floating cranes [YD]**
Bldr: Rheinwerft, Walsum

Y 875 Hiev (In serv. 2-10-62) Y 876 Griep (In serv. 15-5-63)

Griep (Y 876) Findler & Winter, 2-01

D: 1,830 tons (1,875 fl) **S:** 6 kts **Dim:** 52.9 × 22.0 × 2.1
M: 3 MWM 600-bhp diesels, electric drive; 3 vertical cycloidal props; 1,425 bhp
Electric: 358 kVA tot. **Crew:** 12 tot. (civilian)

Remarks: Electric crane capacity: 100 tons.

♦ **2 Wolkan-class (Type 945) diving tenders [YDT]**
Bldr: . . . (In serv. 1960)

Bums Düker (ex-Y 1685)

Bums—with a Type 745 trials ship on other side of the pier Hartmut Ehlers, 8-94

D: . . . tons **S:** 9 kts **Dim:** 26.4 × 6.8 × 1.5
M: 1 . . . diesel; 1 prop; . . . bhp

Remarks: *Bums* is based at Eckernförde; *Düker* operates from Wilhelmshaven. Are employed as diving tenders and general trials support craft. Have a 3-ton derrick aft. Sister *Poseidon* was scrapped in the U.K. in 9-98.

♦ **1 East German Warnow-class (Project 1344) diving tender [YDT]** Bldr: Yachtswerft, Berlin (In serv. 1974)

A 41

A 41 H&L Van Ginderen, 11-98

YARD AND SERVICE CRAFT *(continued)*

D: 25.5 tons (fl) **S:** 8 kts **Dim:** 15.25 × 3.97 × 0.92
M: 1 Type 6VD 14.5/12-1 diesel; 1 prop; 140 bhp (100 sust.) **Crew:** 3 tot.

Remarks: Former small harbor tug used as a diving tender at Warnemünde.
Disposals: A 17, originally activated for further service in 1991, had been stricken by end-1992. Six others were not taken over; all 11 in the class had been discarded by the *Volksmarine* during 7-90. Two others taken over by the German Navy for service at Peenemünde, A 15 and A 16, were discarded early in 1995.

♦ 2 Type 712 small floating dry docks [YFDL]
Bldr: Krupp, Rheinhausen

Hebewerk A (In serv. 13-1-61) Hebewerk 2 (In serv. 15-3-61)

D: 1,000 tons **Dim:** 66.01 × 21.10 × . . .

Remarks: Serviced by four Type 713 *Hebeponton* (lifting pontoons): 500 tons, 56 m by 14.8 m.

Disposal note: *Schwimmdock B* (Y 879) was stricken on 31-12-00.

♦ 1 Type 715 small floating dry dock [YFDL]
Bldr: Flenderwerke, Lübeck (In serv. 8-9-67)

Y . . . Druckdock *("Dock C")*

"Dock C" (Druckdock)—semi-submerged, with pressure-test cylinder immersed Dieter Wolf, 8-97

D: . . . tons **Dim:** 93.0 × 26.5 × 3.6

Remarks: Contains a large pressure vessel used to test submarine pressure hulls.

♦ 1 Type 715 medium floating dry dock [YFDM]
Bldr: Howaldtswerke, Hamburg (In serv. 1961)

Y 842 Schwimmdock 3

Schwimmdock 3 (Y 842) Piet Sinke, 6-90

D: 8,000 tons **Dim:** 164.0 × 30.0 × 3.5

Remarks: Seven-pontoon sectional dock.

♦ 5 Type 905 range safety and rescue craft [YFL]
Bldr: Lürssen Werft, Bremen-Vegesack

	Laid down	L	In serv.
Y 835 Todendorf	11-92	5-10-93	25-11-93
Y 836 Putlos	3-93	25-1-94	24-2-94
Y 837 Baumholder	7-93	24-2-94	30-3-94
Y 838 Bergen	9-93	14-4-94	22-6-94
Y 839 Munster	10-93	13-6-94	10-8-94

D: 100 tons (fl) **S:** 18 kts **Dim:** 28.7 × 6.5 × 1.4
M: 2 Klöckner-Humboldt-Deutz TBD 234 diesels; 2 props; 2,054 bhp
Range: . . ./. . . **Crew:** 6 tot. (accomm. for 15)

Remarks: Operated as gunnery range safety craft on behalf of the German Army. A plastic fabric-covered temporary structure can be erected over the stern.

Todendorf (Y 835)—with temporary shelter erected aft A. A. de Kruijf, 6-00

♦ 2 Type 945 personnel launches [YFL]
Bldr: Hans Boost, Trier (In serv. 30-8-92)

Y 1678 MA 1 Y 1685 Aschau

MA 1 (Y 1678) Findler & Winter, 6-00

D: . . . tons (fl) **S:** . . . kts **Dim:** 16.2 × 4.5 × . . . (2.0 molded depth)
Electronics: Radar: 1 Hagenuk MD 505 Rasterscan nav.
M: 1 M.A.N. D 2866 TE diesel; 1 4-bladed prop; 300 bhp (at 2,100 rpm)
Crew: 2 tot. + up to 50 passengers

Remarks: Ordered 27-8-90. Y 1678 is assigned to Wilhelmshaven, Y 1685 to Eckernförde. Capable of operating in light ice conditions and up to 5 n.m. offshore.

♦ 1 support launch [YFL] Bldr: Motorenwerk, Bremerhaven (In serv. . . .)

Y 1686 AK 2

AK 2 (Y 1686) Piet Sinke, 6-00

D: 46 tons **S:** 10 kts **Dim:** 19.80 × 4.40 × 1.20
Electronics: Radar: 1 . . . nav. **M:** 1 M.A.N. diesel; 280 bhp

♦ 5 Type 946 utility trials launches [YFL] Bldr: Hans Boost, Trier

	In serv.
Y 1671 AK 1	3-85
Y 1672 AK 3	3-85
Y 1676 MA 2	5-85
Y 1677 MA 3	7-85
Y 1687 Borby	9-85

YARD AND SERVICE CRAFT *(continued)*

MA 3 (Y 1677) Findler & Winter, 5-98

D: 25 tons (fl) **S:** . . . **Dim:** 12.00 × 3.90 × 1.90 (molded depth)
M: 1 M.A.N. D2540 MTE diesel; 1 prop; 366 bhp **Crew:** . . .

Remarks: "MA" in alphanumeric name means the craft is assigned to the Wilhelmshaven Arsenal, and "AK" craft are assigned to the Kiel Arsenal. Are equipped with a bow fender for use as push-tugs.

♦ 4 Type 740 utility launches [YFL] Bldr: . . . (In serv. . . .)

Y 1674 AM 6 Y 1675 AM 8 Y 1683 AK 6 MT-Boot

AK 6 (Y 1683) A. A. de Kruijf, 6-00

D: 18.5 tons (fl) **S:** 18.5 kts **Dim:** 15.50 (14.40 wl) × 3.14 × 1.37
Electronics: Radar: 1 . . . nav.
M: 2 Klöckner-Humboldt-Deutz 6-cyl. diesels; 2 Schottel vertical cycloidal props; 500 bhp

Remarks: Used as general-purpose launches. "AM" craft are assigned to Eckernförde, AK 6 to the Kiel Arsenal. *MT-Boot,* with a flush fantail area and a small crane aft, is also attached to Eckernförde but does not bear an official pennant number.
Disposals: AK 5 (Y 1673) and *Peter Bachmann* (Y 1684) were stricken 26-1-93 and 4-3-94, respectively. AM 1, ST 1, and ST 2 served as navigational training craft and were transferred to the Border Guard on 3-5-78.

♦ 1 Type 743 support launch [YFL]
Bldr: Fritz Staack, Lübeck (In serv. 1980)

Y 1679 AM 7

D: 27 tons (fl) **S:** 10 kts **Dim:** 16.30 × 4.38 × 1.06
Electronics: Radar: 1 . . . nav. **M:** 1 MWM diesel; 1 prop; 180 bhp

Remarks: Glass-reinforced plastic construction. Assigned to Eckernförde. Similar in appearance to the Type 740 launches but has a higher pilothouse.

♦ 19 Type 934 personnel launches [YFL]

V 3 through V 21

V 13—with canvas cover unrigged aft Piet Sinke, 6-00

D: . . . tons (fl) **S:** 11 kts **Dim:** 14.5 × . . . × . . .
M: 2 6-cyl. M.A.N. diesels; 2 props; . . . bhp

♦ 3 ex-East German MB-14-class (Project 407) launches [YFL]
Bldr: Yachtswerft, Berlin (In serv. 1976–81)

B 33 B 34 B 83

B 83—white-painted Hartmut Ehlers, 8-01

D: 18 tons (24 fl) **S:** . . . kts **Dim:** 14.55 (13.13 wl) × 3.97 × 1.05
M: 1 Type 6VD15.4/12-1 diesel; 1 prop; 140 bhp **Crew:** 2 tot.

Remarks: B 33 and B 34 are at the Technical Training Establishment, Parow; B 83 is at Warnemünde.

P 16—one of a class of at least 20 small GRP-construction personnel launches employed at naval bases and schools; the canvas hood over the after portion of the cockpit is removable A. A. de Kruijf, 6-00

♦ 3 Type 718 battery-charging craft [YFP]
Bldr: Jadewerft, Wilhelmshaven (LP 2: Oelkers, Hamburg)

LP 1 (In serv. 18-2-64) LP 2 (In serv. 17-4-64) LP 3 (In serv. 16-9-74)

LP 3 H&L Van Ginderen, 6-00

D: 192 tons (234 fl) **S:** 8 kts **Dim:** 27.6 × 7.0 × 1.6
M: 1 MTU diesel; 250 bhp **Electric:** 960 (LP 3: 1,110) kw **Crew:** 6 tot.

Remarks: Each has two 405-kw generators and one (LP 3: two) 150-kw generator for charging submarine batteries. LP 3 is 7.5 m in beam, has a 1.8-m draft, displaces 267 tons (fl), and differs in appearance in having the pilothouse flush with the forward edge of the superstructure, while on the others it is set back about 1 m.

♦ 12 Type 737 fuel barges [YON] (In serv. 1986–87)

Ölschute 1 through Ölschute 12

D: . . . **Dim:** 20.00 × . . . × . . . **Cargo:** 150 tons

YARD AND SERVICE CRAFT *(continued)*

Ölschute 11—red below the main deck, black above — Winter & Findler, 6-97

♦ 2 miscellaneous ex-East German fuel barges [YON]

ex-C 41 (Capacity: 550 tons) ex-C 65 (Capacity: 250 tons)

♦ 1 Type 730D accommodations barge [YPB]

Bldr: J. I. Sietas, Hamburg (In serv. 12-89)

Y 811 Knurrhahn

Knurrhahn (Y 811) — Findler & Winter, 7-01

D: 1,424 tons (fl) **Dim:** 48.0 × 14.0 × 1.8 **Crew:** 230 berths

Remarks: Refitted 1998 at Elsflether Werft.

♦ 4 Vogtland-class (Type 650) barracks barges [YPB]

Bldr: Peenewerft, Wolgast (In serv. 1984)

Y 890 Vogtland (ex-H 71) Y 893 Uckermark (ex-H 91)
Y 891 Altmark (ex-H 11) Y 895 Wische (ex-*Harz,* H 31)

Altmark (Y 891)—outboard *Wische* (Y 895) — Guy Schaeffer, via Paolo Marsan, 6-00

D: 2,393 tons (fl) **Dim:** 89.41 × 13.22 × 2.36
Electric: 4,800 kw tot. (4 × 1,200-kw diesel sets) **Fuel:** 500 tons
Crew: accomm. for 230 in 2-, 4-, and 6-person staterooms

Remarks: NATO Ohre class. Built as Project 162 to replace East Germany's non-self-propelled *Jugend*-class barracks/base ships and officially described as *Wohn-und-Kampfschiff.* Stationed at Wilhelmshaven. Sister *Havilland* (Y 892, ex-H 51) was sold 22-5-93 and *Börde* (Y 894, ex-H 72) by 1995. *Vogtland* (Y 890, ex-H 71) and *Uckermark* (Y 893, ex-H 91) were not stricken during 1998 as previously reported but may be in 2002. Y 895 was refitted in early 1999 at Elsflether Werft.
Hull systems: Equipped with one 8-ton Type 2Hy SWK8 electrohydraulic crane. Have a cinema, gymnasium, sauna, "club," and bakery. Mess can seat 84 at one sitting. The original propulsion engines and bow-thruster have been removed and the armament deleted.

♦ 2 Type 430 torpedo recovery craft [YPT]

Bldrs: Burmester, Bremen, and Schweers, Bardenfleth

Y 855 TF 5 (L: 28-2-66) Y 856 TF 6 (L: 4-5-66)

TF 5 (Y 855) — Hartmut Ehlers, 7-01

D: 56 tons (63.5 fl) **S:** 17 kts **Dim:** 25.22 × 5.40 × 1.60
Electronics: Radar: 1 . . . nav.
M: 1 MWM 12-cyl. diesel; 1 prop; 1,000 bhp **Crew:** 6 tot.

Remarks: Wooden construction. Have a recovery ramp at the stern.
Disposals: TF 101 was stricken 16-6-89, TF 107 (Y 873) on 31-8-89 (transferred to Greece), TF 108 (Y 874) on 16-11-89 (transferred to Greece), TF 106 (Y 872) on 12-4-90 (transferred to Greece), TF 4 (Y 854) on 28-9-90 (transferred to Greece), TF 2 on 15-10-92, TF 3 (Y 853) on 28-2-94, and TF 1 (Y 851) on 24-5-95 (sold to the Netherlands in 1998).

♦ 2 ex-East German Project 414 (Type 660) harbor tugs [YTB]

Bldr: Yachtwerft/Volkswerft, Stralsund

	In serv.
Y 1656 Wustrow (ex-*Zander,* A 45)	25-5-89
Y 1658 Dranske (ex-*Kormoran,* A 68)	12-12-89

Wustrow (Y 1656) — Findler & Winter, 8-00

D: 286 tons (320 fl) **S:** 10.5 kts **Dim:** 30.87 (29.30 pp) × 8.77 × 2.50
Electronics: Radar: 1 . . . nav.
M: 1 SKL 6VD26/20 AL-1 diesel; 1 Kort-nozzle prop; 1,200 bhp (720 sust.)
Electric: 150 kw tot. **Range:** 1,800/10 **Crew:** 13 tot.

Remarks: 140 grt. Three units were completed of a planned six to replace earlier Volksmarine tugs. Designed to carry 23-mm gunmounts abreast the stack amidships. Fitted with one water monitor for fire fighting. Sister *Koos* (Y 1651) was stricken 28-9-95 and sold to Turkey 7-10-96. The other two were scheduled to strike by 31-12-98 but have remained in service.

♦ 6 Type 725 large harbor tugs [YTB]

Bldrs: Y 812–815: Husemer Schiffswerft; others: Orenstein & Koppel, Lübeck

	Laid down	L	In serv.
Y 812 Lütje Horn	30-8-89	. . .	9-90
Y 814 Knechtsand	22-9-89	. . .	10-90
Y 815 Schärhorn	13-10-89	. . .	16-11-90
Y 816 Vogelsand	1-4-86	30-1-87	14-4-87
Y 817 Nordstrand	1-4-86	24-10-86	20-1-87
Y 819 Langeness	1-4-86	28-11-86	15-5-87

D: 445 tons (fl) **S:** 12 kts **Dim:** 30.25 (28.00 pp) × 9.10 × 2.55
Electronics: Radar: 1 . . . nav.
M: 2 Deutz SBV 6M 628 diesels; 2 Voith-Schneider Model 24 G-11/165 vertical cycloidal props; 2,230 hp
Range: . . . **Crew:** 10 tot. (civilian)

Remarks: 212 grt. Bollard pull: 23 tons. Class originally was intended to replace *all* older harbor tugs, with an eventual total of 15 planned. Launched via crane. Second trio ordered 5-89. Plan to build six more during the mid-1990s was canceled due to the availability of the new, East German–built Type 660 tugs and the decline in the size of the navy.

Disposal note: *Heppens*-class (Type 724) tug *Neuende* (Y 1680) was sold to Greece during 1999, along with sister *Heppens* (Y 1681), which had been stricken 18-12-98.

YARD AND SERVICE CRAFT *(continued)*

Vogelsand (Y 816) Findler & Winter, 5-01

♦ **1 Type 368 training ketch [YTS]** (In serv. 1942–44)

Y 834 NORDWIND (ex-W 43)

Nordwind (Y 834)—white-painted, with brown bulwarks and masting
H&L Van Ginderen, 6-00

D: 100 tons (110 fl) **S:** 11 kts **Dim:** 27.00 (24.00 hull; 21.48 pp) × 6.39 × 2.94
Electronics: Radar: 1 Kelvin-Hughes 14/9 nav.
M: 1 Demag 5-cyl. diesel; 1 prop; 137 bhp—195 m^2 max. sail area
Range: 1,200/7 **Crew:** 10 tot.

Remarks: Wooden-hulled former patrol fishing cutter taken over by the U.S. Navy in 1945 and acquired 1-7-56 by the German Navy. Operated for the Mürwik Naval School.

Note: There are also 70 smaller sail-training craft, all bearing names, including 26 Type 914 (5 m long), 10 Type 913 (7.64 m long); 25 Type 910 (most 10.46 m o.a.); 6 Type 911; and 1 Type 912.

Disposal note: The last Type 705 water lighter, FW 5 (A 1405), was stricken 14-12-00. Sister FW 2 was transferred to Turkey in 1975 and FW 3 to Greece in 1976. FW 4 (A 1404) was stricken 12-4-91 and transferred to Turkey the same day; FW 6 (A 1406) was stricken 7-90 and transferred to Greece 5-3-91. FW 1 (A 1403), stricken 21-1-94, was to have gone to Turkey, but the transfer was canceled.

ARMY RIVER ENGINEERS

Organized into four companies located on the Rhine at Krefeld, Koblenz, Neuwied, and Wiesbaden. Each company has nine landing craft, three patrol craft, and a tug. The craft based at Krefeld are numbered 80101–80131, those at Koblenz 30111–30131, those at Neuwied 85011–85031, and those at Wiesbaden 85111–85131. All craft are painted forest green.

PATROL BOATS [WPB]

♦ **12 25-meter class** Bldr: Hitzler, Regensburg (In serv. 1953–54)

Army 25-meter patrol boat H&L Van Ginderen, 1985

D: 27 tons (fl) **S:** 20.5 kts **Dim:** 25.0 × 3.8 × 1.0
A: 2 single 12.7-mm mg **Electronics:** Radar: 1 . . . nav.
M: 2 MWM RHS 418A diesels; 2 props; 440 bhp **Crew:** 7 tot.

Remarks: Sister craft are operated by Belgium and Yugoslavia. The guns are normally not mounted.

AMPHIBIOUS WARFARE CRAFT

♦ **14 Mannheim 59–class landing craft [WLCM]**
Bldr: Schiffs und Motorenwerke AG, Mannheim (In serv. 1959–60)

Mannheim 59–class landing craft F-85032 H&L Van Ginderen, 9-97

D: 89 tons (200 fl) **S:** 9 kts **Dim:** 27.4 × 7.2 × 1.2
A: 4 single 7.62-mm mg **Electronics:** Radar: 1 . . . nav.
M: 2 MWM RHS 518A diesels; 2 props; 432 bhp **Crew:** 9 tot.

Remarks: Cargo: 70 tons normal, 90 tons max. Five served in the German Navy until 4-65. Have a bow ramp and shallow tank deck. One was transferred to Tonga during 1989, and eight were put up for sale in 8-91.

♦ **12 Bodan-class landing craft [WLCM]** Bldr: . . .

Bodan-class landing craft F-85031 H&L Van Ginderen, 9-97

ARMY RIVER ENGINEERS AMPHIBIOUS WARFARE CRAFT *(continued)*

D: 150 tons (fl) **S:** 6 kts **Dim:** 30.0 × 5.8 × . . .
A: 1 20-mm 70-cal. Oerlikon AA **Electronics:** Radar: 1 . . . nav.
M: 4 MWM diesels; 4 Schottel vertical cycloidal props; 596 bhp

Remarks: Each consists of 12 pontoon sections, with a folding ramp at either end and a small raised pilothouse module to starboard. Cargo capacity: 90 tons.

♦ **16 MB 3–class river-crossing craft [WLCP]**
Bldr: Schottel (In serv. 1988–91)

MB 3–class river-crossing craft H&L Van Ginderen, 6-00

D: 0.39 tons light (4.7 fl) **S:** 8.5 kts (loaded; 16 light)
Dim: 7.00 (6.45 pp) × 3.24 × 0.45 (loaded)
M: 2 diesels; 2 Schottel pumpjets; 356 bhp **Crew:** 2 tot. + 10 passengers

Note: The German Army also operates 144 sisters, including some in the MB 3.2 bridge erection boat configuration.

SERVICE CRAFT

♦ **4 river tugs [WYTM]** Bldr: . . .

River tug T-821 H&L Van Ginderen, 4-95

D: . . . **S:** 11 kts **Dim:** 28.0 × 5.9 × 1.2
A: 2 single 7.62-mm mg **Electronics:** Radar: 1 . . . nav.
M: 2 KHD SBF 12M716 diesels; 2 props; 760 bhp **Crew:** 7 tot.

Remarks: Have a small tub forward for one 12.7-mm mg. Had previously been numbered T-80001, T-80101, T-85001, and T-85101.

COAST GUARD

A loosely organized German Coast Guard was formed on 1-7-94 and employs the ships and craft of the Border Guard, Customs Service, various police organizations, the Ministry of Fisheries, and the Shipping Administration. These organizations retain responsibility for the operation and maintenance of their own vessels and craft.

MINISTRY OF THE INTERIOR SEA BORDER PATROL *(Bundesgrenzschutz-See)*

Personnel (2002): Approx. 600 total

Bases: Headquarters at Neustadt. Operating bases at Cuxhaven, Frankfurt/Oder, Karnin, Sassnitz, Stralsund, and Warnemünde. Organized into three flotillas, headquartered at Neustadt, Cuxhaven, and Warnemünde.

Maritime Aviation: In service as of 1-00 were 13 Eurocopter EC 155 (AS.365N4 Dauphin), 9 EC 135, 13 Bell UH-1D, 8 Bell 212, and 17 BO-105CBS-5EL "Super Five" helicopters; several AS.330 Puma helicopters and a few AS.318C Alouettes are also used. Helicopters are based at Bonn/Hangelar.

Note: Craft have blue hulls with white superstructures. Seagoing units now carry the word *Küstenwache* (Coast Guard) on their hull sides and have the Küstenwache black, red, and yellow diagonal strip on each side of the hull. All 40-mm guns were removed during 1996–97.

PATROL SHIPS [WPS]

♦ **0 (+ 3) new-construction seagoing**
Bldrs: Yantar Verf, Kaliningrad, Russia, and Abeking & Rasmussen, Lemwerder

	Laid down	L	In serv.
BG 24 Bad Bramsted	. . .	10-01	2002
BG 25	. . .	. . .	2002
BG 26	. . .	. . .	2003

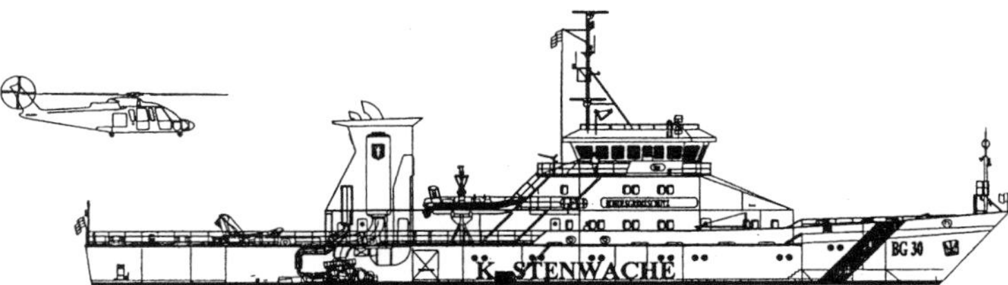

New-construction patrol ship Abeking & Rasmussen, 2001

D: 800 tons (fl) **S:** 21.5 kts **Dim:** 65.90 × 10.60 × 3.20
A: 2 single 7.62-mm mg **Electronics:** Radar: 2 . . . nav.
M: 1 MTU 16V1163 diesel, electric drive; 1 prop; 6,974 bhp—bow-thruster
Crew: 14 tot.

Remarks: Ordered 21-7-00. Will have a helicopter deck capable of accepting an NH-90 helicopter. Aluminum-alloy superstructure. All three will be dual-assigned to the Coast Guard *(Küstenwache)*. The hulls are being built in Russia. BG 24 was delivered to Abeking & Rasmussen on 6-11-01 for fitting out.

♦ **1 seagoing** Bldr: Elsflether Werft, Elsfleth

	Laid down	L	In serv.
BG 21 Bredstedt	3-3-88	18-12-88	24-5-89

Bredstedt (BG 21) H&L Van Ginderen, 7-96

D: 673 tons (770 fl) **S:** 25 kts (12 cruise) **Dim:** 65.40 (57.25 pp) × 9.20 × 2.92
A: 2 single 7.62-mm mg
Electronics: Radar: 1 Decca AC 2960BT nav.; 1 Decca . . . nav.
M: 1 MTU 20V 1163 TB 93 diesel; 1 prop; 10,880 bhp (8,323 sust.)—A.E.G. diesel-electric cruise set; 500 shp (12 kts)—bow-thruster
Electric: 788 kw (2 × 344 kw, MTU 12V 183 diesels driving; 1 × 100 kw)
Range: 2,450/20; 7,000/10 **Crew:** 18 tot. + 4 spare berths

Remarks: 673 grt. Ordered 21-11-87; trials began 20-5-89. Has a helicopter platform aft and a stern ramp–launched Avon Searaider inspection/rescue launch; a second RIB is carried to port amidships. Two firefighting water monitors are fitted. A single 40-mm AA was removed in 1996.

PATROL CRAFT [WPC]

♦ **2 ex-East German Sassnitz class (Type 620)**
Bldr: VEB Peenewerft, Wolgast

	Laid down	L	In serv.
BG 22 Neustrelitz (ex-*Sassnitz,* P 6165, ex-591)	. . .	1988	31-7-90
BG 23 Bad Düben (ex-*Binz,* 593)	3-5-89	26-2-90	15-5-96

Bad Düben (BG 23) Findler & Winter, 12-00

D: 331 tons (369 fl) **S:** 25 kts **Dim:** 48.90 (45.00 pp) × 8.65 × 2.15
A: 2 single 7.62-mm mg
Electronics: Radar: 1 Decca AC 2690 BT nav.; 1 Decca . . . nav.
M: 2 MTU 12V595 TE90 diesels; 2 props; 8,812 bhp
Electric: 366 kw (1 × 183-kw, 2 × 128-kw diesel sets)
Range: 2,400/20 **Endurance:** 5 days **Crew:** 7 officers, 26 enlisted

Remarks: The first of nine laid down out of a planned dozen for the Volksmarine and up to 38 others for the USSR and Poland; as prototype was given project number 151.0. When first seen by NATO, the class was given the temporary code "Bal-Com-10." *Sassnitz* was equipped with eight tubes for the Soviet SS-N-25 antiship missile for trials purposes, but they had been removed by the summer of 1990; the craft was decommissioned on 12-7-91 and transferred to the Border Guard by 10-91, along with sisters *Sellin* (BG 24, ex-592) and *Binz* (ex-593), which had never been operated by the German Navy. Three others were acquired by Poland on 3-10-90 and completed there. The unconverted *Sellin* was placed up for sale early in 1999.

SEA BORDER PATROL PATROL CRAFT [WPC] *(continued)*

Under an order placed 12-5-92, BG 22 was re-engined by her builder; the original plant incorporated three Type M 520 multirow radial diesels of 5,400 bhp each, driving three shafts for a top speed of 37 kts. The original armament of one 76.2-mm AK-176 DP gun, one 30-mm AK-630 gatling gun, and one SA-N-5 SAM system was removed, and the TSR-333 and Drum Tilt radars were replaced by modern surface surveillance radars. The superstructure was extended aft and the pilothouse deckhouse enlarged. A lead-computing director served a 40-mm gun, which was removed in 1997. BG 23 was given a similar reconstruction 1995–96.

Disposal note: Former East German Kondor-I-class patrol minesweeper *Boltenhagen* (BG 31, ex-GS 09, ex-G 443) was donated to Malta on 24-7-97. Sister *Ahrenskoop* (BG 33, ex-GS 08, ex-G 415) was transferred to Tunisia on 5-8-97. Earlier, two sisters had been transferred to Malta and four to Tunisia.

♦ **6 Neustadt class** Bldr: Lürssen Werft, Vegesack

	Laid down	L	In serv.
BG 11 Neustadt	25-11-68	27-2-69	25-11-69
BG 12 Bad Bramstedt	10-1-69	2-4-69	1969
BG 14 Duderstadt	21-2-69	3-6-69	1970
BG 15 Eschwege	27-3-69	16-9-69	19-3-70
BG 16 Alsfeld	31-5-69	11-11-69	1970
BG 17 Bayreuth	15-9-69	9-1-70	1970

Eschwege (BG 15) A. A. de Kruijf, 6-98

D: 191 tons (218 fl) **S:** 30 kts **Dim:** 38.50 (36.00 pp) × 7.00 × 2.15
A: 2 single 7.62-mm mg
Electronics: Radar: 1 AESN ARP 1645 nav.; 1 . . . nav.
M: 2 Maybach 16-cyl. diesels; 2 props; 7,200 bhp—cruise engine: 1 MWM cruise diesel; 1 prop; 685 bhp
Electric: 156 kw tot. **Range:** 450/27 **Fuel:** 15 tons **Crew:** 24 tot.

Remarks: Two planned additional units were canceled. Two 40-mm AA were originally carried; the remaining mount was removed in 1997.
Disposals: *Uelzen* (BG 13) was transferred to Mauritania in 2-90. *Rosenheim* (BG 18) was stricken in 1999. BG 12 is to be retired during 2002.

PATROL BOATS [WPB]

♦ **3 Europa 1 class**
Bldr: Schless-Werft, Wessel (In serv. 1975)

Europa 1 Europa 2 Koblenz

Europa 2 Dieter Wolf, 4-98

D: 10 tons **S:** 22.7 kts **Dim:** 14.50 × 3.80 × 0.95
Electronics: Radar: 1 Kelvin-Hughes 18/12R nav.
M: 1 M.A.N. D 2556/MXE diesel; 1 prop; 240 bhp

Remarks: These launches replaced the former East German MB-12-class patrol launches *Vogtland* (BG 51, ex-GS 17), *Rhön* (BG 52, ex-BS 26, ex-G 52), and *Spreewald* (BG 53, ex-GS 16, ex-G 51).

♦ **4 BG 41–class riverine (In serv. 1994)**

BG 41 Schwedt BG 43 Frankfurt/Oder
BG 42 Küstrin/Kiez BG 44 Aurith

Remarks: For service in the Oder River system. No data available.

♦ **3 former East German Bremse (GB 23) class**
Bldr: VEB Yachtswerft, Berlin (In serv. 1971–72)

BG 62 Uckermark (ex-GS 23, ex-G 34)
BG 63 Altmark (ex-GS 21, ex-G 21)
BG 64 Börde (ex-GS 50, ex-G 35)

Börde (BG 64) Dieter Wolf, 8-97

D: 25 tons light (48 fl) **S:** 17 kts **Dim:** 22.59 (20.97 wl) × 4.70 × 1.60
A: 2 7.62-mm mg **Electronics:** Radar: 1 Furuno FR 80310 nav.
M: 1 Motorenwerke Rosslau Type 6VD 18/15 AL 1 diesel; 1 prop; 510 bhp
Range: 300/12 **Fuel:** 485 liters **Crew:** 6 tot.

Remarks: Formerly used by the East German Border Guard for patrol on rivers and inland waterways. Five sisters were transferred to Tunisia, two to Jordan, and two to Malta in 1992. *Prignitz* (BG 61, ex-GS 31, ex-G 20) was retired 16-11-00. BG 62 and BG 64 are based at Warnemünde, BG 63 at Sassnitz.

Note: The former East German GSE 12–class launch *Oderbruch* (BG 54) is based at Frankfurt/Oder; no data or photo available. Under charter as a patrol boat in 2001 was the yacht *Nobody.* The 99.9-grt tug *Rettin* (BG 5) remains in service, based at Neustadt; launched 29-1-76, the 22.5-m, 590-bhp tug can achieve 9 kts and has a crew of four.

MINISTRY OF FOOD AND AGRICULTURE FISHERIES PROTECTION SHIPS

Note: The fisheries protection ships are part of the new German Coast Guard formed in 1994 and have black hulls with "Küstenwache" on the sides in place of the original "Fischereischutz" (Fisheries Protection). Superstructures are gray, masts are yellow, and shipboard boats are orange, while the Coast Guard *(Küstenwache)* black, red, and yellow diagonal strip is painted on each side of the hull.

PATROL SHIPS [WPS]

♦ **1 (+ 1) Seeadler class** Bldr: Peenewerft, Wolgast

Seeadler (In serv. 6-00) Frithjof (In serv. . . .)

Seeadler Wolfgang Kramer, 6-00

D: . . . tons **S:** 19 kts (20 on trials) **Dim:** 72.40 (67.20 pp) × 12.50 × 5.00
Electronics: Radar: 2 . . . ARPA X-band; 1 . . . ARPA S-band
M: 2 MTU 16V 595 TE 70L diesel generator sets; 2 CP props; 10,200 bhp—2 electric low-speed motors; 2,000 shp—5.2-ton thrust bow-thruster
Electric: 2,381 kw tot. (2 × 1,030-kw sets, 2 MTU 12V396 TE diesels driving; 1 × 321-kw emergency set, MTU 12V183-series diesel driving)
Range: . . ./. . . **Fuel:** 400 m^3 **Crew:** 19 tot. (accomm. for 27)

FISHERIES PROTECTION PATROL SHIPS [WPS] *(continued)*

Remarks: 1,774 grt/515 dwt. First unit ordered 3-98 to replace the old *Warnemünde;* the second ship is planned. *Seeadler* is based at Rostock, and *Frithjof* will be based at Cuxhaven.
Hull systems: Both the main diesel engines and the electric cruise engines drive the same two propellers through gearboxes, and both systems can be used simultaneously. Has two Becker flapped rudders to aid maneuverability and is fitted with fin stabilizers. Two RIB inspection boats are carried. There is a helicopter deck, but no hangar. Carries 125 m³ of ballast water, 40 m³ of fresh water, and 5 m³ of lube oil. Has an automated data collection system and meteorological equipment.

♦ **1 Seefalke class** Bldr: Orenstein & Koppel, Lübeck (In serv. 4-8-81)
SEEFALKE

Seefalke H&L Van Ginderen, 5-99

D: 2,386 tons (fl) **S:** 20.5 kts **Dim:** 82.91 (76.21 pp) × 13.11 × 4.72
M: 2 MWM TBD 510-8 diesels; 2 CP props; 8,000 bhp
Electric: 1,000 kw tot. (2 × 500-kw diesel sets)
Range: 9,700/17 **Fuel:** 345.5 tons **Crew:** 29 tot.

Remarks: 1,786 grt/468 dwt. Equipped to operate in the East Greenland Sea, with fin stabilizers, elaborate navigation equipment, a helicopter platform, a bow-thruster, and a seven-bed infirmary.

♦ **1 Meerkatze class** Bldr: Lürssen Werft, Vegesack (In serv. 1976)
MEERKATZE

Meerkatze H&L Van Ginderen, 5-96

D: 2,386 tons (fl) **S:** 15.5 kts **Dim:** 77.02 (66.71 pp) × 11.79 × 5.14
M: 4 MWM TBD602 V16K diesels (934 bhp each), electric drive; 2 props; 1,564 shp
Crew: 30 ship's company + 15 passengers/scientists

Remarks: 1,751 grt.

♦ **1 Frithjof class** Bldr: Schlichting, Travemünde (In serv. 1967)
EMSSTROM (ex-*Frithjof*)

Emsstrom—as *Frithjof* Werner Schiefer, 9-96

D: 2,140 tons (fl) **S:** 15 kts **Dim:** 76.76 (66.71 pp) × 11.79 × 5.14
M: 3 MWM 16-cyl. diesels (1,281 bhp each), 4 × 740-kw generators, 2 motors; 2 props; 2,800 shp—1 active propeller aft—bow-thruster fwd
Electric: 668 kw tot. (1 × 420-kw, 1 × 195-kw, 1 × 53-kw diesel sets)
Range: 13,000/15 **Fuel:** 550 tons **Crew:** 35 tot.

Remarks: 1,716 grt. Homeported at Cuxhaven. Ice-strengthened hull. Renamed in 1998.

Note: The Ministry of Food and Agriculture also operates fisheries patrol launches *Narwhal* (1998: 60 tons, 21 kts) and *Goldbutt* (1997: 59 tons, 23 kts) for service in home waters, research ships *Walther Herwig III* and *Solea,* and the research launch *Greif.* German government-owned research and survey ships and the various vessels of the Water and Navigation Board Maritime Police *(Schiffahrtspolizei)* are described in the 1998–99 and earlier editions; most of these ships are also assigned to the coast guard. The green and white-painted Customs Service *(Zoll)* craft and large numbers of boats and launches operated by local marine police organizations are illustrated in the 1998–99 and earlier editions of this book; many customs service units are also part of the coast guard.

GHANA

Republic of Ghana

Personnel (2000): 132 officers, 1,080 enlisted, 85 civilian employees

Bases: Headquarters at Burma Camp, Accra. The Western Naval Command is located at Sekondi and the Eastern Naval Command at Tema.

Naval Aviation: As of 2000, only one Pilatus-Britten-Norman Defender was in use for maritime patrol, with three more in storage.

PATROL SHIPS [PS]

♦ **2 ex-U.S. Coast Guard Balsam class**
Bldr: Marine Iron SB Co. (P 30: Duluth Iron & SB Co.)

	Laid down	L	In serv.
P 30 ANZONE (ex-*Woodrush,* WLB 407)	4-2-44	28-4-44	22-9-44
P 31 BONSU (ex-*Sweetbrier,* WLB 401)	3-11-43	30-12-43	26-7-44

Anzone (P 30) Lt. Cdr. R. Coguiel, 6-01

D: 697 tons light (1,038 fl) **S:** 12.8–13 kts **Dim:** 54.9 (51.8 pp) × 11.3 × 4.0
A: 2 single 12.7-mm mg **Electronics:** Radar: 1 Hughes-Furuno SPS-73 nav.
M: 2 diesels, electric drive; 1 prop; 1,200 shp **Electric:** 400 kw tot.
Range: P 30: 10,500/13; 31,000/7.5—P 31: 8,000/12; 23,500/7.5
Crew: 6 officers, 47 enlisted (in USCG service)

Remarks: Very robustly constructed vessels that still have a number of years' service remaining despite their advanced age. WLB 407 was decommissioned from the U.S. Coast Guard 28-4-01 and transferred 4-5-01, while WLB 401 was transferred on 26-10-01. Both are to be used as patrol ships and as transport and supply ships for peacekeeping forces.
Hull systems: Have a 20-ton derrick and icebreaking hulls. Both have exceptionally long endurance.

PATROL CRAFT [PC]

♦ **2 Modified FBP 57 class**
Bldr: Friedrich Lürssen Werft, Vegesack, Germany

	Laid down	L	In serv.
P 28 ACHIMOTA	1978	14-3-79	27-3-81
P 29 YOGAGA	1978	14-3-79	27-3-81

Achimota (P 28) French Navy, 4-97

PATROL CRAFT [PC] *(continued)*

D: 380 tons (410 fl) **S:** 30 kts **Dim:** 58.10 × 7.62 × 2.83
A: 1 76-mm 62-cal. OTOBreda DP; 1 40-mm 70-cal. OTOBreda-Bofors AA
Electronics:
Radar: 1 Decca TM 1226C nav.; 1 Thales Canopus-B surf. search
E/O: Thales Nederland LIOD optronic gun director
M: 3 MTU 16V538 TB91 diesels; 3 props; 10,800 bhp (9,210 sust.)
Crew: 5 officers, 50 enlisted

Remarks: Used for fisheries patrol and search-and-rescue duties. Carry a rubber dinghy for air/sea rescue and inspection purposes. A planned refit for P 29 in 1998–99 was canceled for lack of funds. Ammunition supply includes 250 rounds of 76-mm and 750 rounds of 40-mm.

♦ 2 Modified FPB 45 class
Bldr: Friedrich Lürssen Werft, Vegesack, Germany

	Laid down	L	In serv.
P 26 Dzata	16-1-78	19-9-79	4-12-79
P 27 Sebo	1-78	19-9-79	2-5-80

Sebo (P 27) French Navy, 1996

D: 212 tons (252 fl) **S:** 30 kts **Dim:** 44.90 (42.25 wl) × 7.00 × 2.50 (props)
A: 2 single 40-mm 70-cal. OTOBreda-Bofors AA
Electronics: Radar: 1 Decca TM 1226 nav.
M: 2 MTU 16V538 TB91 diesels; 2 props; 7,200 bhp (6,140 sust.)
Electric: 408 kVA tot. **Range:** 1,100/25; 2,000/15 **Crew:** 5 officers, 40 enlisted

Remarks: Used for fisheries patrol and search-and-rescue duties. A planned refit for P 26 in 1998–99 was canceled for lack of funds. Have 57-mm illumination flare RL on sides of both 40-mm mounts.

GREECE

Hellenic Republic

Personnel (2000): 3,692 officers, 16,258 enlisted (including 7,408 conscripts)

Bases and Organization: Salamis and Suda Bay for ships, Marathon for aircraft. The fleet is divided into three naval districts: Aegean, Ionian, and Northern Greece.

Naval Aviation: Eight Sikorsky S-70B-6 Aegean Hawk helicopters are in service for use on the MEKO 200 frigates; equipment includes the AQS-18(V)3 dipping sonar, APS-143 radar, and ALR-66(V)2 EW suite, and they are to be equipped with the Norwegian Penguin Mk 2 Mod. 7 antiship missile. Two more S-70B-6 were ordered in 5-00, and all 10 are to be fitted with FLIR. Also in use are 10 Agusta-Bell AB-212 shipboard helicopters (two configured for EW work) and 2 AS.319 Alouette-III helicopters for training. All helicopters are based at Marathon.

Hellenic Air Force 353 Squadron, at Elefsis, operates six Greek Navy–owned, ex-U.S.Navy P-3B Orion maritime patrol aircraft acquired in 1995 on a three-year, cost-free lease after $63 million in refurbishment; the aircraft are being further updated by Hellenic Aerospace Industry, with the first completed early in 2001. Four Hellenic Air Force Embraer 145SA AEW and maritime patrol aircraft are to be equipped with Ericsson Erieye AEW and surveillance radars; a Saab 340 with the same equipment was loaned during 1999 for familiarization. Mirage 2000EG fighters of 331 Geraki and 332 Aegeas Squadrons at Tanagra are equipped to launch two AM 39 Exocet antiship missiles each, and four Super Puma helicopters were delivered in 2000 for SAR work.

Weapons and Sensors: Nearly all equipment is of Western European or U.S. manufacture. Additional Penguin Mk 2 Mod. 7 antiship missiles were ordered in 9-96 for use with the S-70B-06 helicopters, and 20 RGM-84C Harpoon missiles were ordered late in 1997. Two Crotale NG SAM systems were ordered from Thales in 10-98; the intended platform was not announced, but they were probably intended for naval base defense.

Coastal Defense: Three land-based MM 40 Exocet missile batteries were delivered during 1993 for use on various Aegean islands as coast-defense weapons.

Note: Ship names are prefixed by HS (Hellenic Ship).

ATTACK SUBMARINES [SS]

♦ 0 (+ 3 + 1) Type 214

	Bldr	Start	L	Del.
S . . . Katsonis	Howaldtswerke, Kiel	30-3-01	1-12-03	30-3-05
S	Hellenic SY, Skaramanga	30-3-02	1-10-05	30-3-07
S	Hellenic SY, Skaramanga	30-3-03	1-9-06	28-2-08

Greek Navy Type 214 HDW, 1998

Greek Navy Type 214—artist's rendering HDW, 2000

D: 1,700 tons surf./1,860 tons sub.
S: . . . kts surf./. . . kts sub. (2–6 kts sub. on fuel cells) **Dim:** 65.00 × 6.30 × . . .
A: 8 bow 533-mm TT (16 tot. wire-guided torpedoes and UGM-84C Harpoon missiles)
Electronics:
Radar: . . .
Sonar: cylindrical MF bow passive array; LF through MF passive flank array; towed LF linear passive array; passive ranging array; active range and bearing array
EW: Elbit Timnex 2 intercept; Sonartech Atlas torpedo-detection and tracking syst.
M: 2 MTU 16V 396–series diesel generator sets (1,000+ kw each), 1 Siemens Permasyn motor; 1 prop; . . . shp—2 120-kw Siemens PEM fuel-cell auxiliary propulsion units
Range: 12,000/. . . surf.; 1,248/4 sub. on fuel cells **Endurance:** 50 days
Crew: 27 tot. (accomm. for 35)

Remarks: An agreement to order was announced 9-10-98, the program was approved by the Greek government in 7-99, and the contract for three for $1.26 billion was signed 31-3-00, with an option for a fourth; as part of the contract, two German Navy missile craft are being given to Greece. The design is an expanded version of the German-Italian Type 212 design. Sea trials for the German-built unit are planned to start 1-6-04, and the submarine is to be commissioned in 2006. Work on the first of the Greek-assembled units is to start 31-3-02, and sea trials for the pair are scheduled for 6-06 and 5-07, respectively.
Hull systems: Inner and outer hull of austenitic steel. Battery set to develop 600–900 V. To have 10% reserve buoyancy.
Combat systems: May employ the Unisys Kanaris combat system rather than an STN Atlas Elektronik ISUS 90 system. Sonar array to include cylindrical MF passive array forward, MF/LF passive flank system (with three arrays per side), towed LF passive array, an active ranging set, and a bow-mounted active mine-avoidance set. An optronic, non–hull-penetrating periscope and a standard, penetrating optical attack periscope will be fitted. Four of the eight weapons tubes will have expulsion systems to enable launching Harpoon missiles; the other tubes are of the swim-out launch variety.

♦ 4 Type 209/1200 Bldr: Howaldtswerke, Kiel

	Laid down	L	In serv.
S 116 Poseidon	15-4-76	21-3-78	22-3-79
S 117 Amfrititi	16-9-76	14-6-78	14-8-79
S 118 Okeanos	1-10-76	16-11-78	15-11-79
S 119 Pontos	15-1-77	22-3-79	29-4-80

Amfrititi (S 117) H&L Van Ginderen, 6-97

ATTACK SUBMARINES [SS] *(continued)*

D: 1,185 tons surf./1,285 tons sub. **S:** 11.5 kts surf./22 kts sub.
Dim: 56.10 × 6.20 × 5.90
A: 8 bow 533-mm TT (14 AEG SUT Mod. 0 wire-guided torpedoes)
Electronics:
Radar: Thales Calypso-II nav./search
Sonar: STN Atlas Elektronik CSU-3-4 suite: AN 526 passive, AN 406 A9 active, Thales DUUX-2 passive ranging
EW: Thales DR-2000U intercept
M: diesel-electric: 4 MTU 12V493 TY60 diesels (550 bhp each), each linked to an AEG generator of 420 kw; 1 Siemens motor; 1 prop; 5,000 shp
Range: 11,300/4 snorkel; 28/20, 466/4 sub. **Fuel:** 85 tons
Endurance: 50 days **Crew:** 6 officers, 25 enlisted

Remarks: Essentially a lengthened variant of the Type 209/1100 with added fuel. These submarines are planned for modernization on completion of the Type 209/1100 modernization program.
Hull systems: Diving depth: 250 m. May later be lengthened to accommodate two 120-kw Siemens PEM fuel-cell auxiliary propulsion units.
Combat systems: Have Thales SINBADS M8/42 weapons control with Mk 8 torpedo f.c.s. The EW system may have been replaced by the Boeing ArgoSystems AR-740.

♦ 4 Type 209/1100 Bldr: Howaldtswerke, Kiel

	Laid down	L	In serv.
S 110 Glavkos	1-9-68	15-9-70	5-11-71
S 111 Nereus	15-1-69	7-6-71	10-2-72
S 112 Triton	1-6-69	19-10-71	23-11-72
S 113 Proteus	1-10-69	1-2-72	23-11-72

Nereus (S 111) Guy Schaeffer, via Paolo Marsan, 6-00

Nereus (S 111)—sail detail H&L Van Ginderen, 6-00

D: 990 tons (light); 1,100 tons surf./1,207 tons sub.
S: 11.5 kts surf./22 kts sub. **Dim:** 54.10 × 6.20 × 5.90
A: 8 bow 533-mm TT (10 AEG SUT Mod. 0 wire-guided torpedoes and 4 UGM-84C Harpoon missiles)
Electronics:
Radar: Thales Calypso-II nav./search
Sonar: STN Atlas Elektronik CSU-83-90 suite with DBSQS-21 active set, flank arrays and DUUX-2 passive ranging
EW: ArgoSystems AR-700-S5 intercept
M: diesel-electric: 4 MTU 12V493 TY60 diesels (550 bhp each), each linked to an AEG generator of 420 kw; 1 Siemens motor; 1 prop; 5,000 shp
Range: 8,600/4 snorkel; 25/20, 230/8, 400/4 sub. **Fuel:** 49 tons
Endurance: 50 days **Crew:** 7 officers, 29 enlisted

Remarks: Have been updated to the same standard as the German Type 206A class under a contract placed 5-5-89 in Germany. S 112 completed in 7-93 at HDW, Kiel; S 110 in 12-95 at Salamis; and S 111 in 11-97 at Salamis. Work began on S 113 in 12-99 at Salamis for completion in 1999.
Hull systems: Single-hull design with two ballast tanks. Diving depth: 250 m. All have a battery arrangement with four groups of 120 cells producing 11,500 amp-hr. Have two periscopes.
Combat systems: During their updates, received Sub-Harpoon launch capability with the new HDW torpedo-tube launch system, new electronics, STN Atlas Elektronik CSU-83-90-series sonar suite, Unisys Kanaris fire-control system, Magnavox GPS receiver, and Omega SATNAV receiver; crews grew by five. The combat system integrates a Unisys UYK-44 with the original torpedo fire-control system and can control the launch of Harpoon missiles as well as four SUT Mod. 0 wire-guided torpedoes simultaneously. One source reports that the new EW system is the Racal Sealion system rather than the listed ArgoSystems AR-700-S5.

GUIDED-MISSILE DESTROYERS [DDG]

♦ 4 ex-U.S. Navy Charles F. Adams class

	Bldr	Laid down	L	In serv.
D 218 Kimon (ex-*Semmes,* DDG 18)	Avondale SY	18-8-60	20-5-61	10-12-62
D 219 Nearchos (ex-*Waddell,* DDG 24)	Todd, Seattle	6-2-62	26-2-63	28-8-64
D 220 Formion (ex-*Joseph Strauss,* DDG 16)	New York SB, Camden, N.J.	27-12-60	9-12-61	20-4-63
D 221 Themistoklis (ex-*Berkeley,* DDG 15)	New York SB, Camden, N.J.	29-8-60	29-7-61	15-12-62

Nearchos (D 219) Luciano Grazioli, 3-00

Themistoklis (D 221) ANBw/FAFIO, 8-00

D: 3,570 tons light (4,825 fl) **S:** 31.5 kts
Dim: 133.19 (128.0 wl) × 14.32 × 6.1 (8.3 over sonar)
A: 1 Mk 13 single missile launcher (6 RGM-84A/C Harpoon and 34 Standard SM-1 MR missiles); 2 single 127-mm Mk 42 DP; 1 8-round Mk 112 ASROC ASW RL (8 or 12 tot. missiles); 2 triple 324-mm Mk 32 ASW TT
Electronics:
Radar: 1 Raytheon SPS-64(V) nav.; 1 Raytheon SPS-10F surf. search; 1 Lockheed Martin SPS-40D air search; 1 Hughes SPS-52B 3-D air search; 2 Raytheon SPG-51C missile f.c.; 1 Western Electric SPG-53A gun f.c.
Sonar: Raytheon DE 1191 hull-mounted LF (5–7 kHz)
TACAN: URN-25
EW: SLQ-32(V)2 intercept; SLQ-20 intercept; WLR-1 intercept (not on D 219); Mk 36 SRBOC decoy syst. (4 6-round Mk 137 RL), T Mk 6 Fanfare towed torpedo decoy syst.

GUIDED-MISSILE DESTROYERS [DDG] *(continued)*

Kimon (D 218) Bernard Prézelin, 5-01

M: 2 sets Westinghouse (D 218, 220: General Electric) geared steam turbines; 2 props; 70,000 shp
Boilers: 4 Combustion Engineering; 84 kg/cm^2, 520° C **Electric:** 2,200 kw tot.
Range: 1,600/30; 6,000/14 **Fuel:** 900 tons **Crew:** 22 officers, 318 enlisted

Remarks: D 218 was transferred on lease to Greece 13-9-91, arriving in-country and recommissioning 12-9-92; the other three were transferred 1-10-92 at San Diego and formally commissioned 30-4-93. The leases were extended for 5 years in 1997. Permanent transfer of DD 218–220 as Grant-Aid was authorized by the U.S. Congress in 10-98. Sister *Richard E. Byrd* (DDG 23) was transferred 1-10-92 for use as a cannibalization spares and pierside training vessel. D 221 was to be retired on 31-1-02 and D 220 later in 2002; the other two are to be retained until 2010.
Combat systems: The Greek Navy has modernized all four with the DE 1191 hull-mounted sonar in place of SQS-23 and with the Thales STACOS combat system added. Have U.S. Mk 68 gun fire-control system, Mk 70 SAM fire-control system, and Mk 114 ASW fire-control system. They employ the Mk 16 Mod. 1 ASROC ASW missile system, with a magazine for four spare missiles in D 218 and D 219 only.

GUIDED-MISSILE FRIGATES [FFG]

♦ 0 (+ 2) new construction

Remarks: One guided-missile frigate, with an option for a second, was intended to be ordered during 2001, although funding problems will probably delay the order into 2002 or later. The finalist designs include the Dutch *De Zeven Provinciën* and the Blohm + Voss Type 124 *(Sachsen)* classes. Construction had been planned to start in 2004. The ships are to have U.S. Mk 41 vertical missile launch systems.

FRIGATES [FF]

♦ 4 MEKO 200 Mk 3 class

	Bldr	Laid down	L	In serv.
F 452 Hydra	Blohm + Voss, Hamburg	17-12-90	25-6-91	12-11-92
F 453 Spetsai	Hellenic SY, Skaramanga	11-8-92	9-12-93	24-10-96
F 454 Psara	Hellenic SY, Skaramanga	12-12-93	20-12-94	30-4-98
F 455 Salamis	Hellenic SY, Skaramanga	20-12-94	15-3-96	16-12-98

Salamis (F 455) Mike Welsford, 11-99

D: 2,710 tons (3,200 fl) **S:** 31.75 kts (21 on diesel)
Dim: 117.50 (109.50 pp) × 14.80 (13.80 wl) × 6.00 (4.12 hull)
A: 8 RGM-84C Harpoon SSM; Mk 48 Mod. 2 VLS (16 RIM-7M NATO Sea Sparrow SAM); 1 127-mm 54-cal. Mk 45 DP; 2 20-mm Mk 15 gatling CIWS; 2 triple 324-mm Mk 32 ASW TT (Mk 46 Mod. 5 torpedoes); 1 Sikorsky S-70B-6 Seahawk helicopter (with Penguin Mk 2 Mod. 7 missiles and Mk 46 Mod. 2 torpedoes)
Electronics:
Radar: 1 Decca 2690BT ARPA nav.; 1 Thales MW-08 3-D air search; 1 Thales DA-08 early warning; 2 Thales STIR-18 f.c.

Spetsai (F 453) Luciano Grazioli, 12-00

Sonar: Raytheon DE 1160 (SQS-56) hull-mounted (7.5 kHz) and VDS (12 kHz); WQC-2A underwater telephone; UQN-4A echo sounder
EW: ArgoSystems AR-700 intercept; ArgoSystems APECS-II jammer; EADS Telegon-10 HFD/F; Mk 36 Mod. 2 SRBOC decoy syst. (4 6-round Mk 137 RL); SLQ-25 Nixie towed torpedo decoy syst.
E/O: SAR-8 infrared surveillance
M: CODOG: 2 MTU 20V956 TB82 diesels (5,200 bhp each), 2 G.E. LM-2500-30 gas turbines (30,328 shp each); 2 CP props
Electric: 2,480 kw (4 × 620-kw diesel sets)
Range: 900/31.75; 4,100/18 (diesel) **Fuel:** 300 tons
Crew: 22 officers, 151 enlisted + 16 staff

Remarks: Basic order to Blohm + Voss 10-2-89, with subcontract for Greek-built trio placed 16-5-89. The Greek-assembled trio was far behind schedule due to financial difficulties at the builder's; to speed the program, portions of F 453 were prefabricated in Germany. Armament and electronics were in large part financed by U.S. arms credits, although most equipment is European.
Hull systems: The design is basically similar to the version of the MEKO 200 built for Portugal, and Turkey has similar ships. Have fin stabilizers.
Combat systems: The Thales STACOS Mod. 2 combat data system is installed. Have NATO Link 11 and 14 datalinks, Thales Vesta helicopter transponder, Mk 73 Mod. 1 SAM control system, and SWG-1A(V) Harpoon missile launch system. The sonar system employs a single processor for both the hull sonar and VDS, which uses the towed array from Raytheon's DE 1167 system.

♦ 7 (+ 1) ex-Dutch Kortenaer class
Bldr: Royal Schelde, Vlissingen

	Laid down	L	In serv.
F 450 Elli (ex-*Pieter Florisz,* F 812)	2-7-77	15-12-79	10-10-81
F 451 Limnos (ex-*Witte de With,* F 813)	13-6-78	27-10-79	18-9-82
F 459 Adrias (ex-*Callenburgh,* F 808)	30-6-75	12-3-77	26-7-79
F 460 Aegeon (ex-*Banckert,* F 810)	25-2-76	13-7-78	29-10-80
F 461 Navarinon (ex-*Van Kinsbergen,* F 809)	2-9-76	16-4-77	24-4-80
F 462 Kontouriotis (ex-*Kortenaer,* F 807)	8-4-75	18-12-76	26-10-78
F 463 Bouboulina (ex-*Pieter Florisz,* F 826; ex-*Willem Van Der Zaan)*	15-1-80	8-5-82	1-10-83
F . . . . . . (ex-*Jan Van Brakel,* F 825)	16-11-79	16-5-81	14-4-83

Navarinon (F 461) NAVPIC-Holland, 10-00

Aegeon (F 460) H&L Van Ginderen, 6-00

D: 3,000 tons (3,786 fl) **S:** 30 kts **Dim:** 130.2 (121.8 pp) × 14.4 × 4.4 (6.0 props)
A: F 450, 451: 8 RGM-84A/C Harpoon SSM; 1 8-round Mk 29 SAM syst. (24 RIM-7M Sea Sparrow missiles); 2 single 76-mm 62-cal. OTOBreda DP; 2 Mk 15 Phalanx gatling CIWS; 4 fixed 324-mm Mk 32 ASW TT; 2 AB-212 ASW helicopters—
F 459–464: 8 RGM-84A/C Harpoon SSM; 1 8-round Mk 29 SAM syst. (24 RIM-7M Sea Sparrow missiles); 1 76-mm 62-cal. OTOBreda DP; 1 20-mm Mk 15 Phalanx gatling CIWS; 2 single 20-mm 70-cal. Oerlikon Mk 10 AA; 4 fixed 324-mm Mk 32 ASW TT; 2 AB-212 ASW helicopters

FRIGATES [FF] *(continued)*

Limnos (F 451)—with two 76-mm guns and two Mk 15 CIWS
H&L Van Ginderen, 2-96

Bouboulina (F 463) A.A. de Kruijf, 9-01

Electronics:
Radar: 1 Thales ZW-06 surf. search; 1 Thales LW-08 early warning; 1 Thales WM-25 track-while-scan f.c.; 1 Thales STIR-18 f.c.
Sonar: Canadian Westinghouse SQS-505 hull-mounted (7 kHz)
EW: F 450, 451: Elettronica Sphinx intercept syst.; Elettronica Ramses jammer—others: Elettronica ELT/715 intercept—all: Mk 36 SRBOC decoy syst. (4 6-round Mk 137 launchers); SLQ-25 Nixie towed torpedo decoy syst.
M: COGOG: 2 Rolls-Royce Tyne RM-1C cruise gas turbines (4,900 shp each), 2 Rolls-Royce Olympus TM-3B gas turbines (25,800 shp each); 2 LIPS CP props; 51,600 shp max.
Electric: 3,000 kw (4 × 750-kw SEMT-Pielstick PA4 diesel generator sets)
Range: 4,700/16 (on one Tyne turbine) **Crew:** 17 officers, 159 enlisted

Remarks: F 450, ordered in 7-81, was transferred to Greece 26-6-81, along with F 451. Both were taken from production originally intended for the Dutch navy in order to speed delivery. Plans to build a third ship in Greece were canceled. F 459, F 460, and F 461 were bought from the Netherlands Navy and transferred on 14-5-93, 30-3-94, and 1-3-95, respectively; all were formally recommissioned in Greek service 30-6-95. F 462 was purchased 3-6-97, reactivated, and delivered 15-12-97. Ex-*Pieter Florisz* was decommissioned from the Netherlands Navy 24-1-01 and purchased by Greece 7-6-01 for transfer 1-12-01. The ex-*Jan Van Brakel* was retired from the Dutch navy 1-7-01 and was to be purchased later in the year.
Hull systems: Have Denny-Brown fin stabilizers. The helicopter hangar was lengthened 2.2 m on the first two to accept Italian-built helicopters vice the Lynx used by the Dutch; it has not been lengthened on the former Netherlands Navy ships.
Combat systems: Have the Thales SEWACO II combat data system and NATO Link 10 and Link 11 datalink capability. One U.S. Mk 15 CIWS 20-mm gatling AA was to have been added in place of the after 76-mm gun for close-in defense in the original pair, but instead in 1991 the 76-mm weapon was retained, *two* Mk 15 CIWS were added port and starboard forward of the hangar (in place of the Corvus decoy rocket launchers), the number of Harpoon missiles was doubled over the original installation, and U.S. Hycor Mk 137 decoy rocket launchers were added on the forward superstructure—all of which must have had a detrimental effect on stability. The ex-Netherlands Navy ships had their Harpoon missiles and Goalkeeper CIWS removed prior to transfer and were to be brought up to the same armament standard as the first two ships by using 76-mm guns removed from decommissioned destroyers; instead, a single Phalanx CIWS was added atop the hangar, while additional Harpoon missiles were procured from the United States. The pair purchased in 2001 had no CIWS when transferred. Normally, only one helicopter is carried.
Modernization: Under an initial agreement signed early in 1998 with Royal Schelde Group in the Netherlands, the ships are to be reequipped with more-modern gas turbine engines and to have their sensors, weapons systems, and command systems updated under a program intended to extend their service lives by 15 years. A 32-missile-capacity vertical missile launching system for the ESSM version of Sea Sparrow may be installed at the cost of one helicopter space, while the flight decks would be strengthened to support S-70B-6 helicopters. The first ship would be refitted in the Netherlands and the others in Greece with Dutch supervision; the work was to be completed between 2003 and 2005 and would also have included updating the sonars to SQS-510, adding the Thales Scout low-intercept radar and the Thales Mirador E/O surveillance and tracking system, and upgrading the EW system (with Thales DR-3000 or ArgoSystems equipment). The work, however, has yet to commence.

♦ 2 U.S. Knox class Bldr: Avondale SY, New Orleans

	Laid down	L	In serv.
F 456 Epirous (ex-*Connole,* FF 1056)	23-3-67	20-7-68	30-8-69
F 457 Thraki (ex-*Trippe,* FF 1075)	29-7-68	1-11-69	19-9-70

D: 3,132 tons light (4,190 fl) **S:** 27+ kts
Dim: 134.00 (126.49 wl) × 14.33 × 4.77 (7.83 over sonar)
A: 4 RGM-84A/C Harpoon SSM (using ASROC launcher syst.); 1 127-mm 54-cal. Mk 42 DP; 4 Stinger shoulder-launched SAM positions; 1 20-mm Phalanx Mk 15 CIWS; 2 single 12.7-mm mg; 1 8-round Mk 112 ASROC ASW RL (12 missiles); 4 fixed 324-mm Mk 32 Mod. 9 ASW TT; 1 Mk 9 d.c. rack (6 Mk 9 d.c.); 1 AB-212 ASW helicopter

Epirous (F 456) Findler & Winter, 2-01

Thraki (F 457) Camil Busquets i Vilanova, 10-99

Electronics:
Radar: 1 Raytheon SPS-64(V) nav.; 1 Raytheon SPS-10F surf. search; 1 Lockheed SPS-40D air search; 1 Western Electric SPG-53 gun f.c.
Sonar: Edo-G.E. SQS-26CX hull-mounted LF
TACAN: SRN-15A
EW: Raytheon SLQ-32(V)2 intercept; Mk 36 SRBOC decoy syst. (4 6-round Mk 137 RL); T Mk 6 Fanfare towed acoustic torpedo decoy syst.
M: 1 set Westinghouse geared turbines; 1 prop; 35,000 shp
Boilers: 2 Babcock & Wilcox D-Type; 84 kg/cm², 510° C
Electric: 3,000 kw (3 × 750-kw Westinghouse turbo, 1 × 750-kw G.M. 16V 71 diesel-driven)
Range: 4,300/20 **Fuel:** 750 tons **Crew:** 17 officers, 271 enlisted

Remarks: F 457 transferred on lease 30-7-92, F 456 on 30-8-92; formally recommissioned 30-4-93. Not considered satisfactory ships by the Greek Navy.
Disposals: *Makedonia* (F 458; ex-*Vreeland,* FF 1068) was stricken during 12-98 but remains afloat as a spares source. F 457 was to be discarded with the delivery of the former Dutch Navy *Pieter Florisz.* F 456 should be retired soon.
Hull systems: Anti-rolling fin stabilizers are fitted in all. Prairie/Masker bubbler systems are fitted to hulls and propellers to reduce radiated noise. All three have had spray strakes added to the hull sides and bulwarks added at the bow to reduce deck wetness.
Combat systems: The combat control system includes the SWG-1A Harpoon launch control system, Mk 1 gun target designation system, and Mk 114 underwater firecontol system (for the Mk 16 Mod. 3 ASROC system and ship-launched torpedoes). All received the ASWTDS (ASW Tactical Data System) during the 1980s. The ASROC system has an automatic reloading magazine beneath the bridge; it is also used to stow Harpoon missiles, which are launched from the starboard pair of launcher cells. The ASW torpedo tubes are fixed, in the forward end of the hangar superstructure, aimed outboard at an angle of 45°. The SQS-35 variable-depth sonar system had been deactivated in U.S. Navy service, with the sonar fish being used only as the towpoint for the SQR-18A towed passive linear hydrophone array, which was not transferred with the ships. The SATCOM system was removed prior to transfer. A depth-charge rack has been added on the starboard quarter, and four launch positions for Stinger IR-homing, shoulder-launched SAMs have been fitted.

CORVETTES [FFL]

Note: As of late 2000, an order for three corvettes was planned to be placed by the end of 2001, with the ships to be equipped with MM 40 Exocet antiship missiles and the RAM surface-to-air missile system; the ships would be about 90 m long, and the first would complete at a Greek yard around 2005. Blohm + Voss, Vosper Thornycroft, and the naval architectural firm of Gibbs & Cox are contending for the contract. The Vosper design is for an 86-m ship powered by MTU 16V956 TE 90 diesels.

The Vosper Thornycroft offering for the Greek corvette program
Vosper Thornycroft, 2000

PATROL COMBATANTS [PG]

♦ 2 (+ 2 + 2) P 100 class   Bldr: Hellenic SY, Skaramanga

	Laid down	L	In serv.
P 57 Pyrpolitis	1-91	16-9-92	4-5-93
P 61 Polemistis	16-9-92	21-6-93	16-4-94
P	. . .	. . .	. . .
P	. . .	. . .	. . .
P	. . .	. . .	. . .
P	. . .	. . .	. . .

Pyrpolitis (P 57) Luciano Grazioli, 9-01

Polemistis (P 61) H&L Van Ginderen, 8-00

D: 555 tons (fl) **S:** 24.7 kts (at 450 tons; 23.8 sust.)
Dim: 56.50 (51.53 wl) × 10.00 (9.50 wl) × 2.50 (max.)
A: 1 76-mm 62-cal. OTOBreda Compact DP; 1 40-mm 70-cal. Bofors AA; 2 single 20-mm 90-cal. Rheinmetall AA; portable mine rails (36 U.S. Mk 6 or 18 German Mk 18 mines)
Electronics:
Radar: 1 Decca 1690 nav.; 1 Thales Triton air/surf.search; 1 Alenia RTN-10X f.c.
M: 2 Wärtsilä-Nohab 16V25 diesels; 2 props; 10,000 bhp
Electric: 690 kVA tot. (3 × 230-kVA diesel sets)
Range: 900/23.8; 2,200/15 **Fuel:** 104 tons **Endurance:** 10 days
Crew: 36 tot. + 25 troops

Remarks: Revised version of the modified Osprey design; the design is also known as the "Hellenic 56" class. Two units (with an unexercised option for a third) were ordered 19-2-89, and the first unit was reportedly laid down in 1-91. P 61 began trials during 2-93. Were not formally commissioned until 30-6-95. Four more were tentatively ordered 9-2-98, but the final contract for two additional units (with an option for two more to be exercised by 7-01) was not signed until 28-5-01.
Hull systems: Other sources indicate only 50 tons of fuel is carried. Can carry 40 tons of fresh water. There are two RIB inspection boats aboard, handled by a 1.3-ton-capacity crane. The ships have a steel hull with aluminum alloy superstructure.
Combat systems: The 76-mm gun is to be controlled by an Alenia NA 21 weapons-control system (RTN-10X radar). Two pairs of Harpoon SSM launchers can also be accommodated but have not been installed. The single 40-mm gun aft is to be replaced by a twin Breda 40-mm mount when funds permit. The two ordered in 2001 are to have the Thales TACTICOS combat data system, Variant search radar, LIROD Mk 2 radar/E/O fire-control system, and Mirador E/O directors and will have a twin 30-mm EVO-OTOBreda 30-mm AA mount aft in place of the twin 40-mm mount of the earlier pair; the ships will also have the Decca BridgeMaster-E navigational radar, a NATO Link 11 capability, and the Thales DR-3000 SLW EW system.

♦ 2 modified Osprey 55 series
Bldr: Hellenic SY, Skaramanga

	Laid down	L	In serv.
P 18 Armatolos	8-5-89	19-12-89	9-3-90
P 19 Navhamos	9-11-89	16-5-90	15-7-90

D: 515 tons (fl) **S:** 24.7 kts (at 415 tons)
Dim: 54.75 (50.83 pp) × 10.50 (8.08 wl) × 2.55 (hull)
A: 1 76-mm 62-cal. OTOBreda Compact DP; 2 single 20-mm 90-cal. Rheinmetall AA; 2 portable mine rails
Electronics:
Radar: 1 Decca 1226 nav.; 1 Thales Triton air/surf. search; 1 Alenia RTN-10X f.c.
EW: Thales DR-2000S intercept; 2 . . . decoy RL

Armatolos (P 18) Dieter Wolf, 10-97

M: 2 MTU 1163 TB 93 diesels; 2 props; 9,870 bhp
Electric: 480 kw (2 × 240 kw, 2 MTU 12V183 AA51 diesels driving)
Range: 500/22 **Crew:** 36 ship's company + 25 troops

Remarks: Design licensed from Frederikshavn Værft, Denmark. The first two (with an option for two more) were ordered in 3-88, with plans to construct up to 10, but further units were canceled in favor of the P 100 class, a very similar design of indigenous origin. Were not formally commissioned until 30-6-95. Similar ships are operated by Morocco and Senegal, and the original shorter-hulled version is operated by Mauritania and Myanmar. Have a stern ramp and internal stowage for a rigid-inflatable inspection/SAR launch at the stern.
Combat systems: Were originally planned to carry four Harpoon missiles amidships, an OTOBreda twin 40-mm AA mount aft, the Plessey AWS-6 air/surface-search radar, and a Thales WM-25 track-while-scan weapons fire-control system, with an associated LIROD director. The 76-mm guns and associated Alenia NA 20 weapons-control system (with RTN-10X) radar were recycled from decommissioned *Gearing*-class destroyers and new search radars were added in 1995.

♦ 5 ex-German Thetis class (Type 420)   Bldr: Roland Werft, Bremen

	Laid down	L	In serv.
P 62 Niki (ex-*Thetis,* P 6052)	19-6-59	22-3-60	1-7-61
P 63 Doxa (ex-*Najade,* P 6054)	22-3-60	6-12-60	12-5-62
P 64 Elevtheria (ex-*Triton,* P 6055)	15-8-60	5-8-61	10-11-62
P 65 Karteria (ex-*Hermes,* P 6053)	8-10-59	9-8-60	16-12-61
P 66 Agon (ex-*Andreia;* ex-*Theseus,* P 6056)	1-7-61	20-3-62	15-8-63

Niki (P 62)—outboard a sister; note the newly added enclosed bridge on P 62 and the open bridge on the other ship Flottenkommando, 6-98

D: 575 tons light (732 fl) **S:** 19.5 kts **Dim:** 69.78 (65.5 pp) × 8.20 × 2.65 (hull)
A: 1 twin 40-mm 70-cal. OTOBreda-Bofors AA; 2 single 12.7-mm mg; 2 triple 324-mm Mk 32 ASW TT (Mk 46 Mod. 5 torpedoes); 2 Mk 9 d.c. racks (6 Mk 9 d.c. each)
Electronics:
Radar: 2 Decca . . . nav.
Sonar: STN Atlas Elektronik ELAC 1BV hull-mounted HF
EW: Thales DR-2000S intercept with Thorn-EMI SARIE analyzer; 4 6-round Buck-Wegmann Hot Dog decoy RL; T Mk 6 Fanfare towed torpedo decoy syst.
M: 2 M.A.N. V8V 24/30 diesels; 2 props; 6,800 bhp **Electric:** 540 kw tot.
Range: 2,760/15 **Fuel:** 78 tons **Crew:** 5 officers, 43 enlisted

Remarks: Former torpedo-recovery boats, designed for operations in the Baltic. The first two were transferred to Greece and recommissioned 6-9-91; the second pair was transferred 7-9-92 and formally commissioned into Greek service 30-4-93. Delivery of P 66 was delayed until 20-10-93 due to the need to replace an engine; she was formally commissioned in Greek service 30-6-95. The class underwent renovation in Greece, with new air-conditioning, refurbished accommodations, addition of two more generator sets, and improved firefighting capability. All are attached to the destroyer command.
Hull systems: P 63 had the forward superstructure extended toward the bow to accommodate a small medical facility. Original speeds have dropped considerably; when new, they could make 23.5 kts.
Combat systems: Have the Thales Mk 9 torpedo f.c.s. and a Bofors optical lead-computing gun director. The original German armament of one quadruple Bofors 375-mm ASW rocket launcher forward and a twin Bofors 40-mm AA aft was replaced after delivery in Greece, and triple, trainable ASW TT have replaced the original four fixed 533-mm TT.

GUIDED-MISSILE PATROL CRAFT [PTG]

♦ 0 (+ 3 + 4) Super Vita class
Bldr: Elefsis Shipyard and Industrial Enterprises

	Laid down	L	In serv.
P	9-00	. . .	9-03
P	. . .	. . .	. . .
P	. . .	. . .	9-04

Vosper Super Vita design for Greece Vosper Thornycroft, 1999

D: 570 tons (fl) **S:** 34.2 kts **Dim:** 61.90 × 9.50 × . . .
A: 4 MM 40 Exocet Mk 2 SSM; 1 21-round Mk 31 Mod. 1 RAM SAM syst. (RIM-116A Block I missiles); 1 76-mm 62-cal. OTOBreda SuperRapid DP; 1 twin 30-mm EVO-OTOBreda AA; 2 fixed, aft-firing 533-mm TT (. . . wire-guided torpedoes)
Electronics:
Radar: 1 Decca BridgeMaster-E ARPA nav.; 1 Thales Scout Mk 2 surf. search; 1 Thales MW-08 air search, 1 Thales Sting f.c.
EW: ArgoSystems AR-900 active/passive suite; Mk 36 SRBOC decoy syst. (2 6-round Mk 137 RL)
E/O: Thales Mirador-FD surveillance, tracking, and gun f.c.
M: 4 MTU 16V595-series diesels; 4 props; . . . bhp
Electric: 750 kw tot. (3 × 250 kw, MTU GR183 TE52 diesels driving)
Range: . . ./. . . **Endurance:** 7 days **Crew:** 45 tot.

Remarks: The 21-9-99 contract included an order for three and an option to build four more in Greece. The initial trio is to cost about $324 million, with the contract including the transfer of two U.K. Hunt-class minehunters.
Hull systems: Steel hull with aluminum superstructure. One pair Vosper nonretractable fin stabilizers. Will carry a RIB, handled by an electrohydraulic crane.
Combat systems: Are to employ the Thales TACTICOS combat data system. There will be two displays for the BridgeMaster-E navigational radar. The Sperry Mk 39 Mod. 3A ring-laser gyro will be fitted. The antiship missile system was ordered on 31-8-00 and included 27 missiles with an option for 24 more.

♦ 9 Combattante IIIN class
Bldr: P 20–23: CMN, Cherbourg; others: Hellenic SY, Skaramanga

	L	In serv.
P 20 Antipliarchos Lascos	6-7-76	2-4-77
P 21 Antipliarchos Blessas	10-11-76	19-7-77
P 22 Antipliarchos Troupakis	6-1-77	8-11-77
P 23 Antipliarchos Mykonios	5-5-77	10-2-78
P 24 Simaiforos Kavalouthis	10-11-79	14-7-80
P 26 Ipopliarchos Deyiannis	14-7-80	12-80
P 27 Simaiforos Xenos	8-9-80	31-3-81
P 28 Simaiforos Simitzopoulos	12-10-80	6-82
P 29 Simaiforos Starakis	1981	12-10-81

Antipliarchos Troupakis (P 22)—with Exocet missiles H&L Van Ginderen, 9-98

D: P 20–23: 385 tons (447 fl)—P 24–29: 396 tons (fl) **S:** 36.5 (P 24–29: 32.6) kts
Dim: 56.65 (53.00 pp) × 8.00 × 2.70 (props; 2.04 hull)
A: P 20–23: 4 MM 38 Exocet SSM; 2 single 76-mm 62-cal. OTOBreda DP; 2 twin 30-mm 75-cal. Emerlec AA; 2 fixed, aft-launching 533-mm TT (2 SST-4 wire-guided torpedoes)—P 24–29: 6 Penguin Mk 2 SSM; 2 single 76-mm 62-cal. OTOBreda Compact DP; 2 twin 30-mm 75-cal. Emerlec AA; 2 fixed, aft-launching 533-mm TT (2 SST-4 wire-guided torpedoes)
Electronics:
Radar: 1 Decca 1226 nav.; 1 Thales Triton surf./air search; 1 Thales Castor f.c.
EW: Thales DR-2000S intercept
E/O: 2 Matra Défense Panda optronic director for the 30-mm guns

Simaiforos Xenos (P 27)—with Penguin missiles H&L Van Ginderen, 7-00

M: P 20–23: 4 MTU 20V538 TB92 diesels; 4 props; 20,800 bhp (18,000 sust.)—P 24–29: 4 MTU 20V538 TB91 diesels; 4 props; 15,000 bhp (13,400 sust.)
Electric: 450 kw (3 × 150-kw diesel-driven sets; 440 V, 60 Hz)
Range: 800/32.5; 2,000/15 **Crew:** 7 officers, 36 enlisted

Remarks: First four ordered 22-5-75. Second group, built in Greece, and with less expensive weapon, sensor, and propulsion systems, ordered 22-12-76. Sister *Antipliarchos Kostakos* (P 25) was rammed and sunk by the Greek ferry *Samena* on 4-11-96, with a loss of four lives.
Hull systems: Have excellent habitability; accommodations and operations spaces are air-conditioned.
Combat systems: Each 76-mm gun has 350 rounds, with 80 in ready service; the mounts have been updated to fire at 100 rds/min. The Emerlec 30-mm mounts are furnished with 3,200 rounds and fire at 700 rds/barrel/min. P 20–23 have a Thales Vega weapon-control system; the later ships have Vega II. The Penguin missiles in P 24–29 were to be refurbished to remain in service until 2015 under a 2-98 contract with Kongsberg.

♦ 6 ex-German Type 148
Bldr: CMN, Cherbourg (P 51: Lürssen, Vegesack)

	Laid down	L	In serv.
P 30 Antipliarchos Pezopoulos (ex-*Iltis,* P 6142)	2-2-72	12-12-72	8-1-73
P 51 Simaiforos Votsis (ex-*Storch,* P 6152)	12-3-73	25-3-74	17-7-74
P 74 Plotarhis Vlakavas (ex-*Marder,* P 6144)	15-4-72	5-5-73	14-7-73
P 75 Plotarhis Maridhakis (ex-*Häher,* P 6151)	5-4-73	26-4-74	12-6-74
P 76 Plotarhis Sakipis (ex-*Jaguar,* P 6147)	29-11-72	20-9-73	13-11-73
P 77 Plotarhis Tournas (ex-*Leopard,* P 6145)	13-9-72	3-7-73	21-8-73

Plotarhis Maridhakis (P 75)—awaiting transfer, with *Plotarhis Vlakavas* (P 74), both still in German colors and with German pennant numbers
Hartmut Ehlers, 7-94

D: 234 tons (264 fl) **S:** 35.8 kts **Dim:** 47.0 (45.9 pp) × 7.1 × 2.66 (fl)
A: 4 MM 38 Exocet SSM; 1 76-mm 62-cal. OTOBreda DP; 1 40-mm 70-cal. Bofors AA; 8 mines in place of the 40-mm AA
Electronics:
Radar: 1 SMA 3RM 20 nav.; 1 Thales Triton-G air/surf. search; 1 Thales Castor-II f.c.
EW: Thales DR-2000 intercept; 2 6-round Buck-Wegmann Hot Dog decoy RL; Wolke chaff dispenser
M: 4 MTU MD 872 16-cyl. diesels; 4 props; 14,000 bhp (at 1,515 rpm; 12,000 sust.)
Electric: 270 kw tot. **Range:** 570/30; 1,600/15 **Fuel:** 39 tons
Crew: 5 officers, 37 enlisted

Remarks: Ordered 18-12-70, as CMN's Combattante II A4L type. Design by Friedrich Lürssen Werft, Vegesack. Fitted out at Cherbourg. The first two were transferred from Germany late in the summer of 1992 after having been stricken 15-10-92 and 16-11-92, respectively; after refits, the pair left Germany for Greece 1-2-94. The second pair left Germany 16-3-95 as deck cargo after having been stricken 25-4-94 and 24-6-94, respectively. All four were formally recommissioned 30-5-95. P 76 and P 77 arrived in Greece 23-10-00, having been stricken from German service 15-9-00. Steel construction

GUIDED-MISSILE PATROL CRAFT [PTG] *(continued)*

♦ 4 Combattante II class — Bldr: CMN, Cherbourg

	L	In serv.
P 14 Ipopliarchos Arliotis (ex-*Evniki*)	26-4-71	4-72
P 15 Ipopliarchos Anninos (ex-*Navsithoi*)	8-9-71	6-72
P 16 Ipopliarchos Konidis (ex-*Kimothoi*)	20-12-71	7-72
P 17 Ipopliarchos Batsis (ex-*Kalypso*)	26-1-71	12-71

Ipopliarchos Arliotis (P 14) Peter Voss, 10-86

D: 234 tons (255 fl) **S:** 36.5 kts **Dim:** 47.0 (44.0 pp) × 7.1 × 2.5 (fl)
A: 4 MM 38 Exocet SSM; 2 twin 35-mm 90-cal. Oerlikon GDM-A AA; 2 fixed, aft-launching 533-mm TT (SST-4 wire-guided torpedoes)
Electronics:
Radar: 1 Decca 1226 nav.; 1 Thales Triton air/surf. search; 1 Thales Castor f.c.
EW: Thales DR-2000S intercept
M: 4 MTU MD 872 diesels; 4 props; 12,000 bhp
Range: 850/25; 2,000/15 **Fuel:** 39 tons **Crew:** 4 officers, 36 enlisted

Remarks: Ordered in 1969. Steel hull, light steel alloy superstructure. The Thales Vega weapon-control system is planned to be updated.

♦ 2 Kelefstis Stamou class — Bldr: C.N. de l'Esterel, Cannes

P 286 Diopos Antoniou (In serv. 28-7-75)
P 287 Kelefstis Stamou (In serv. 4-12-75)

Diopos Antoniou (P 286) Carlo Martinelli, 8-98

D: 80 tons (115 fl) **S:** 30 kts **Dim:** 32.0 × 5.8 × 1.5
A: 4 Aérospatiale SS 12 wire-guided SSM; 1 20-mm 90-cal. Rheinmetall AA; 2 single 12.7-mm mg
Electronics: Radar: 1 Decca 1226 nav.
M: 2 MTU 12V331 TC81 diesels; 2 props; 2,700 bhp
Range: 1,500/15 **Crew:** 17 tot.

Remarks: Wooden-hulled craft ordered by Cyprus but acquired by Greece. Pennant numbers were P 28 and P 29 until 1980. The wire-guided missiles are difficult to keep on-target with the optical joystick-control system and are of dubious utility.

TORPEDO BOATS [PT]

♦ 4 ex-German Jaguar (Type 141) class
Bldr: Friedrich Lürssen Werft, Vegesack

	Laid down	L	In serv.
P 50 Esperos (ex-*Seeadler*)	23-9-57	1-2-58	29-8-58
P 53 Kyklon (ex-*Greif*)	5-2-58	28-6-58	3-3-59
P 54 Lalaps (ex-*Kondor*)	2-1-58	17-5-58	24-2-59
P 56 Tyfon (ex-*Geier*)	27-5-58	1-10-58	3-6-59

Lalaps (P 54) H&L Van Ginderen/F. Heine, 10-99

D: 195 tons (221 fl) **S:** 42.5 kts **Dim:** 42.62 × 7.10 × 2.39
A: 2 single 40-mm 70-cal. Bofors AA; 4 fixed 533-mm TT (SST-4 wire-guided torpedoes); mines in lieu of after torpedo tubes
Electronics: Radar: 1 Decca 1226 nav.
M: 4 Maybach 16-cyl. diesels; 4 props; 14,400 bhp **Electric:** 192 kw
Range: 500/39; 1,000/32 **Crew:** 39 tot.

Remarks: Transferred 1976–77. Wooden-planked hull skin on metal frame. The 40-mm guns have been given new autoloading systems. Long overdue for retirement.
Disposals: *Kataigis* (P 51, ex-P 197, ex-*Falke*) was stricken late in 1981, *Kentauros* (P 52; ex-*Habicht,* P 6075) in 1985, and *Skorpios* (P 55, ex-*Kormoran*) during 1995. Three others—ex-*Albatros,* ex-*Bussard,* and ex-*Sperber*—were transferred to be cannibalized for spares.

♦ 4 Norwegian Nasty class — Bldr: Båtservice, Mandal

	In serv.		In serv.
P 196 Andromeda	11-66	P 199 Pigassos	4-67
P 198 Kykonos	2-67	P 228 Toxotis	5-67

Kykonos (P 198) A. A. de Kruijf, 2001

D: 69 tons (76 fl) **S:** 40 kts **Dim:** 24.50 (22.86 pp) × 7.50 × 1.95
A: 1 40-mm 70-cal. Bofors AA; 1 20-mm 70-cal. Mk 10 Oerlikon AA; 4 fixed 533-mm TT
Electronics: Radar: 1 Decca 1226 nav.
M: 2 MTU 12V331 TC83 diesels; 2 props; 3,060 bhp
Range: 676/17 **Fuel:** 10 tons **Crew:** 20 tot.

Remarks: Wooden construction. Had been discarded in 1983 but were refurbished and re-engined for further service in 1988. Originally had two Napier Deltic T1827 K diesels of 3,140 bhp each. Carry straight-running torpedoes. Long past due for retirement.

PATROL CRAFT [PC]

Note: Six new coastal patrol craft are planned.

♦ 2 U.S. Asheville class — Bldr: Peterson Bldrs, Sturgeon Bay, Wis.

	In serv.
P 229 Tolm (ex-*Green Bay,* PG 101)	5-12-69
P 230 Ormi (ex-*Beacon,* PG 99)	21-11-69

Ormi (P 230)—with new 40-mm mount aft H&L Van Ginderen, 8-99

D: 225 tons (240 fl) **S:** 16 kts **Dim:** 50.14 (46.94 pp) × 7.28 × 2.90
A: 1 76.2-mm 50-cal. Mk 34 DP; 1 40-mm 70-cal. Bofors L70 AA; 2 single 12.7-mm mg
Electronics:
Radar: 1 Decca . . . nav.; 1 Sperry SPS-53 nav.; 1 Western Electric SPG-50 gun f.c.
M: 2 Cummins 875V12 diesels; 2 props; 1,450 bhp
Range: 325/35; 1,700/16 **Fuel:** 50 tons **Crew:** 3 officers, 21 enlisted

PATROL CRAFT [PC] *(continued)*

Remarks: Transferred 22-11-89, having been in reserve since 4-77, and commissioned 6-90 after overhauls in Greece. Have Mk 63 f.c.s. for the 76.2-mm gun, with the associated SPG-50 radar mounted on the gunhouse and the director atop the pilothouse. The original manually operated U.S. 40-mm 60-cal. Mk 3 AA aft has been replaced by a more modern Bofors mount in both. The original G.E. LM-1500 gas turbine, which could propel the craft to 40-kt speeds, was removed prior to transfer.

PATROL BOATS [PB]

Disposal note: The final remaining naval unit of the *Dilos* class, the *Knossos* (P 269), was donated to Cyprus during 3-00. Sisters *Lindos* (P 268) and *Dilos* (P 267) were transferred to Georgia in 1998 and fall 1999, respectively. The two remaining *E. Panagopoulos I*–class patrol boats are now used as explosive ordnance disposal diver launches; see under [LCP].

MINE WARFARE SHIPS AND CRAFT

Note: Two new minelayers are planned.

♦ 1 modified U.S. LSM 1–class minelayer [MM]
Bldr: Charleston Naval SY, Charleston, S.C.

	Laid down	L	In serv.
N 05 AMVRAKIA (ex-MMC 7, ex-LSM 303)	8-10-44	14-11-44	6-1-45

D: 720 tons (1,100 fl) **S:** 13 kts **Dim:** 62.0 × 10.5 × 2.4
A: 4 twin 40-mm 60-cal. Mk 1 Mod. 2 Bofors AA; 6 single 20-mm 70-cal. Mk 10 Oerlikon AA; 100–300 mines, depending upon type
Electronics: Radar: 1 Decca 1226C nav.
M: 2 G.M. 16-278A diesels; 2 props; 2,800 bhp **Range:** 3,500/12 **Crew:** 65 tot.

Remarks: Former U.S. LSM 1–class landing ship, converted prior to transfer in 1953.
Disposals: *Aktion* (N 04, ex-MMC 6, ex-LSM 301) was stricken 23-10-00.
Combat systems: Have four derricks, two forward and two aft, for handling mines and two minelaying rails. They have four 30-cm and one 60-cm searchlights. Four Mk 51 Mod. 2 optical f.c.s. are fitted for the 40-mm AA.

♦ 2 ex-U.K. Hunt-class minehunters
Bldr: Vosper Thornycroft, Woolston

	Laid down	L	In serv.
M 62 EVROPI (ex-*Bicester,* M 36)	2-1-85	4-6-85	14-2-86
M 63 KALLISTO (ex-*Berkeley,* M 40)	9-9-85	3-12-86	14-1-88

Kallisto (M 63) Jim Sanderson, 3-01

Evropi (M 62) Maritime Photographic, 8-00

D: 625 tons (725 fl) **S:** 17 kts (15 sust.; 8 on hydraulic drive)
Dim: 60.00 (56.60 pp) × 9.85 × 2.20 (hull; 3.40 max.)
A: 1 30-mm 75-cal. DES-30B AA; 2 single 7.62-mm mg
Electronics:
Radar: 1 Kelvin-Hughes Type 1007 nav.
Sonar: Thales Type 193M Mod. 1 variable-depth minehunting (100/300 kHz), with Mills Cross Type 2059 submersible-tracking set incorporated
M: 2 Ruston-Paxman Deltic 9-59K diesels (1,600 rpm); 2 props; 1,900 bhp (1,770 sust.)—slow-speed hydraulic drive for hunting (8 kts)—bow-thruster
Electric: 1,140 kw (3 200-kw Foden FD 12 Mk 7 diesel alternators for ship's service, plus 1 525-kw Deltic 9-55B diesel alternator for magnetic minesweeping and 1 60-kw emergency set)
Range: 1,500/12 **Crew:** 5 officers, 40 enlisted (in U.K. service)

Remarks: Equipped for both hunting and sweeping mines. M 62 was stricken from the Royal Navy on 1-7-00 and M 63 on 28-2-01; they were transferred to Greece on 31-7-00 and 28-2-01 as part of the arrangement to produce British-designed missile craft in Greece.

Hull systems: Glass-reinforced plastic hull. One Deltic 9-59B diesel (645 bhp) drives the 525-kw sweep current alternator *or* four Dowty hydraulic pumps can be used to power the props during minehunting; the Deltic 9-59B engine also provides power for the bow-thruster and the sweep winch. Have the Ferranti-Thomson VIMOS (Vibration Monitoring System), which reduces radiated noise by 3–10 dB.
Combat systems: Are equipped with the CAAIS DBA-4 (64 contact-tracking) data system and Decca Mk 21 HiFix navigation system. Carry 6 or 7 divers and two French PAP 104 Mk 3 remote-controlled mine location submersibles. Have Sperry Osborn TA 6 acoustic, M. Mk 11 magnetic loop and M. Mk 8 Orepesa wire sweeping gear as well. EW equipment was not transferred with the ships.

♦ 2 ex-Italian U.S. Adjutant-class minehunters [MHC]
Bldr: Henry C. V. Grebe & Co., Kingston, N.Y.

	In serv.
M 60 ERATO (ex-*Castagno,* M 5504, ex-MSC 74)	7-8-55
M 61 EVIKI (ex-*Gelso,* M 5509, ex-MSC 75)	8-3-54

Erato (M 60) Luciano Grazioli, 6-99

D: 354.5 tons (405 fl) **S:** 11.4 kts **Dim:** 43.92 (42.1 pp) × 8.23 × 2.68
A: 1 twin 20-mm 70-cal. Mk 24 Oerlikon AA
Electronics: Radar: 1 SMA SPN-703 nav.—Sonar: FIAR SQQ-14(IT) HF VDS
M: 2 G.M. 8-268A diesels; 2 props; 880 bhp—1 Voith-Schneider vertical cycloidal propulsor for minehunting; 310 shp
Range: 2,500/10 **Fuel:** 40 tons **Crew:** 3 officers, 38 enlisted

Remarks: Built for Italy under the U.S. Military Aid Program and transferred to Greece on 10-10-95 after retirement from Italian service. Converted from minesweepers in 1983–84 by substituting the SQQ-14 sonar for the original UQS-1 and providing facilities for mine clearance divers and remote-controlled minehunting submersibles. Have wooden hulls and nonmagnetic fittings.
Combat systems: Sonar upgraded to SQQ-14(IT) with solid-state electronics. Employ the Pluto remote-controlled submersible, capable of 4.5-kt speeds. Divers aboard use CAM-T destruction charges.

♦ 8 U.S. MSC 294–class coastal minesweepers [MSC]
Bldr: Peterson Bldrs, Sturgeon Bay, Wis.

	In serv.
M 211 ALKYON (ex-MSC 314)	3-12-68
M 213 KLIO (ex-*Argo,* ex-MSC 317)	7-8-68
M 214 AVRA (ex-MSC 318)	3-10-68
M 240 PLEIAS (ex-MSC 319)	22-6-67
M 241 KICHLI (ex-MSC 308)	14-7-64
M 242 KISSA (ex-MSC 309)	1-9-64
M 247 DAFNI (ex-MSC 307)	23-9-64
M 248 AEDON (ex-MSC 310)	13-10-64

Aedon (M 248) Camil Busquets i Vilanova, 2-00

D: 300 tons (394 fl) **S:** 13 kts **Dim:** 44.32 × 8.29 × 2.55
A: 1 twin 20-mm 70-cal. Mk 24 Oerlikon AA
Electronics: Radar: 1 Decca. . . nav.—Sonar: UQS-1D HF
M: 2 Waukesha L-1616 diesels; 2 props; 1,200 bhp
Range: 2,500/10 **Fuel:** 40 tons **Crew:** 4 officers, 27 enlisted

Remarks: Built for Greece under the Military Aid Program; transferred on completion. Are planned to be re-engined, and a new sonar may be procured.
Disposals: *Aigli* (M 246, ex-MSC 299) was stricken during 1996. *Doris* (A 475, ex-M 245, ex-MSC 298) was employed as a hydrographic survey ship until stricken in 1995.

MINE WARFARE SHIPS AND CRAFT *(continued)*

♦ 1 ex-Belgian U.S. Adjutant-class coastal minesweeper [MSC]
Bldr: Consolidated SB, Morris Heights, N.Y.

	In serv.
M 210 Thalia (ex-*Blankenberge,* ex-MSC 170)	5-54

D: 330 tons (402 fl) **S:** 13 kts (8 sweeping) **Dim:** 43.0 (41.50 pp) × 7.95 × 2.55
A: 1 twin 20-mm 70-cal. Mk 24 Oerlikon AA
Electronics: Radar: 1 Decca . . . nav.—Sonar: UQS-1D HF
M: 2 G.M. 8-268A diesels; 2 props; 880–1,000 bhp
Range: 2,500/10 **Fuel:** 40 tons **Crew:** 4 officers, 27 enlisted

Remarks: Transferred to Belgium on completion and then transferred to Greece on 29-7-69. Used primarily as a training ship. Wooden construction.
Disposals: *Antiopi* (M 205; ex-*Herve,* ex-MSC 153) was stricken during 1995; *Atalanti* (M 202; ex-*St. Truiden,* ex-MSC 169) and *Phedra* (M 206; ex-*Malmedy,* ex-MSC 154) on 1-6-00; and *Niovi* (M 254; ex-*Laroche,* ex-MSC 171) on 23-10-00.

♦ 4 ex-U.S. 50-foot-class minesweeping boats [MSB]

D: 21 tons (fl) **S:** 8 kts **Dim:** 15.20 × 4.01 × 1.31
M: 1 Navy DB diesel; 60 bhp **Range:** 150/8 **Crew:** 6 tot.

Remarks: Wooden-hulled former personnel launches loaned in 1972 and purchased during 1981. Intended for harbor use. Are around 50 years old.

AMPHIBIOUS WARFARE SHIPS

Disposal note: Ex-U.S. *Cabildo*-class dock landing ship *Nafkratoussa* (L 153; ex-*Fort Mandan,* LSD 21) was stricken 29-2-00.

♦ 5 (+ 1) Jason-class tank landing ships [LST] Bldr: Elefsis SY

	Laid down	L	In serv.
L 173 Chios	18-4-87	16-12-88	30-5-96
L 174 Samos	9-87	6-4-89	20-5-94
L 175 Ikaria	9-5-88	11-98	6-10-99
L 176 Lesbos	6-4-89	5-7-90	2-99
L 177 Rodos	20-11-89	6-10-99	5-00
L 178	. . .	. . .	. . .

Samos (L 174) Greek Navy, 1995

Chios (L 173) H&L Van Ginderen, 6-97

D: 4,400 tons std. (4,916 fl) **S:** 16 kts
Dim: 115.90 (106.00 pp) × 15.30 × 3.44 (mean)
A: 1 76-mm 62-cal. OTOBreda DP; 2 single 40-mm 70-cal. Bofors AA; 2 single 20-mm 90-cal. Rheinmetall Rh 202 AA
Electronics:
Radar: 1 Furuno . . . nav.; 1 Kelvin-Hughes Type 1007 nav.; 1 Thales TRS 3030 Triton V air/surf. search; 1 Thales Castor gun f.c.
EW: . . . . . . radar warning; Mk 36 Mod. 1 SRBOC decoy syst. (2 6-round Mk 137 RL)
M: 2 Wärtsilä Nohab 16V25 diesels; 2 props; 10,600 bhp (9,200 sust.)
Range: . . ./. . .
Crew: 108 ship's company + 245–310 troops (1,200 in emergency)

Remarks: Ordered 15-5-86 as replacements for the U.S. LST 1/511 class. The program was considerably delayed by the builder's financial troubles, with the last ship originally scheduled to complete 9-90. A sixth ship was added to the program in 2000, with the order expected in 2001.
Hull systems: Have a raised helicopter deck aft capable of supporting one Agusta-Bell AB-212B helicopter. Two LCVP landing craft and two lifeboats are carried. The bow ramp is capable of supporting 55-ton vehicles; there is also a stern loading ramp and a ramp from the upper deck amidships to the tank deck. Cargo: 250 tons (up to 20 heavy tanks, or 17 amphibious armored personnel carriers, or 15 trucks and 50 tons of ammunition).
Combat systems: Have two Matra Défense Panda Mk 2 optical gun directors. The 20-mm AA listed do not appear to have been mounted on L 174.

♦ 2 ex-U.S. Terrebonne Parish–class tank landing ships [LST]
Bldrs: L 104: Bath Iron Works; L 116: Christy Corp.

	Laid down	L	In serv.
L 104 Oinoussai (ex-*Terrell County,* LST 1157)	3-3-52	6-12-52	19-3-53
L 116 Kos (ex-*Whitfield County,* LST 1169)	. . .	22-8-53	14-9-54

Kos (L 116) H&L Van Ginderen, 9-97

D: 2,590 tons (6,225 fl) **S:** 12 kts **Dim:** 112.35 × 16.7 × 3.7
A: 3 twin 76.2-mm 50-cal. AA; 3 single 20-mm 90-cal. Rheinmetall AA
Electronics: Radar: 1 . . . nav.; 1 SPS-10 surf. search; 2 Mk 34 f.c.
M: 4 G.M. 16-278A diesels; 2 CP props; 6,000 bhp
Crew: 115 ship's company + 395 troops

Remarks: Purchased 17-3-77. Have Mk 63 GFCS for the 76.2-mm guns. Carry four LCVPs in davits.

Disposal note: U.S. LST 1–class tank landing ship *Lesbos* (L 172; ex-*Boone County,* LST 389) and LST 511–class *Ikaria* (L 154; ex-*Potter County,* LST 1086) were stricken during 1999; *Rodos* (L 157; ex-*Bowman County,* LST 391) in 1997; and *Kriti* (L 171; ex-*Page County,* LST 1076) on 31-12-99. *Syros* (L 144, ex-LST 325), stricken 1-11-99, was donated to a U.S. museum organization and returned to U.S. waters during 12-00.

♦ 1 ex-U.S. LSM 1–class medium landing ship [LSM]
Bldr: Charleston Naval SY, Charleston, S.C.

	Laid down	L	In serv.
L 164 Ipopliarchos Rousen (ex-LSM 399)	29-12-44	18-1-45	13-8-45

Ipopliarchos Krystallidis (L 165)—since stricken
H&L Van Ginderen/F. Heine, 10-99

D: 743 tons beaching (1,095 fl) **S:** 12.5 kts **Dim:** 62.03 × 10.52 × 2.54
A: 1 twin 40-mm 60-cal. Mk 1 Mod. 2 Bofors AA; 4 single 20-mm 70-cal. Mk 10 Oerlikon AA
Electronics: Radar: 1 Decca . . . nav.
M: 2 G.M. 16-278A (L 165: Fairbanks-Morse 38D8⅛-10) diesels; 2 props; 2,800 bhp
Electric: 240 kw tot. **Range:** 4,900/12 **Fuel:** 161 tons **Crew:** 60 tot.

Remarks: Transferred 3-11-58.
Disposals: *Ipopliarchos Tornas* (L 162, ex-LSM 102) was stricken during 1990; *Ipopliarchos Grigoropoulis* (L 161, ex-LSM 45) and *Ipopliarchos Daniolos* (L 163, ex-LSM 227) during 1993, with one going to the U.S.A. as a museum ship; and *Ipopliarchos Krystallidis* (L 165, ex-LSM 541) on 15-5-00.

♦ 4 (+ 4) Russian Pomornik (Zubr)-class (Project 1232.2) air-cushion vehicle landing craft [LCUA]
Bldrs: L 180, 182: Sudostroitel'noye Obyedineniye "Almaz," Dekabristov SY, St. Petersburg, Russia; L 181, 183: Morye Zavod, Feodosiya, Ukraine

	In Greek serv.
L 180 Kefallinia (ex-MDK-50)	22-1-01
L 181 Ithaki (ex-*Ivan Bohun,* U 421)	3-01
L 182 Zakynthos (ex-MDK-. . .)	9-01
L 183 Kerkyra (ex-*Horlivka,* U 423)	. . .-01

Kefallinia (L 180)—prior to transfer Boris Lemachko, 2000

AMPHIBIOUS WARFARE SHIPS *(continued)*

Ithaki (L 181)—as Ukraine Navy *Horlivka* (U 423), with sister *Kramator'sk* (U 422) at the left Boris Lemachko, 2000

D: 340 tons light, 415 normal (550 fl) **S:** 63 kts (55 sust.)
Dim: 57.3 (56.2 hull) × 25.6 (22.0 hull) × 21.9 (high)
A: 2 or 4 4-round Igla-1M (SA-N-8) SAM syst. (32 9M-36 Strela-3/Gremlin missiles); 2 single 30-mm 54-cal. AK-630M gatling AA; 2 22-round 140-mm MS-227 Ogon' retractable artillery RL (132 rockets); up to 80 mines in lieu of vehicle cargo, using portable rails
Electronics:
Radar: 1 SRN-207 Ekran nav.; 1 MR-123-2 Vympel gun f.c.
E/O: 1 . . . surveillance/f.c.; 1 periscope
M: 5 NK-12MV (M-70) gas turbines (12,100 shp each/10,000 shp sust.; 2 to power lift fans); 3 ducted CP airscrew propellers, 4 NO-10 lift fans; 36,300 shp for propulsion
Electric: 200 kw tot. (2 × 100-kw GTG-110 gas turbine sets)
Range: 300/55 with 130-ton payload; 1,000/55 light **Fuel:** 56 tons
Endurance: 5 days (1 day with full troop complement)
Crew: 4 officers, 27 enlisted + 140–360 troops

Remarks: Officially typed "Fast Transport Vessels." Two were tentatively ordered from Russia in 6-99 and two more from Ukraine on 8-9-99. The final contracts were signed 24-1-00 to provide one refurbished, 1993-vintage Russian Baltic Fleet unit; one "new" unit (one of the two incomplete units available as of 1994) delivered from the Almaz yard (for $101 million combined); and two "new" craft (actually refurbished former Russian Black Sea Fleet units transferred to Ukraine in 1996) from Ukraine's Ukrspetsexport for $100 million. The first Russian-provided unit, L 180, was originally completed in 1993 and was relaunched 27-10-00, arriving in Salamis 18-1-01. The second Russian unit, L 182, was relaunched 28-5-01 for delivery during 7-01. The Ukrainian-furnished units were refurbished at Feodosiya during 2000–01. An option for four more from Russia for $51 million each was to be signed by 24-1-01 but was still pending as of 6-01. Maintenance of the craft is under contract to Hellenic Aerospace Industry (HAI). In Russian service, there have been significant reliability problems with the class. Are the "fast transport ships" for a new Greek "rapid reaction force."
Hull systems: The dimensions above include the flexible skirt. The hull, intended to have a 16-year service life, is a complex structure constructed in part with flammable light alloys. The vehicle deck can hold up to eight M 113 armored personnel transport vehicles or three Leopard 1A5 heavy tanks, plus a detachment of infantry—or up to 140 troops and 130 tons of combat cargo. Have small bow and stern ramps.
Propulsion systems: Three of the gas-turbine engines are mounted on pylons and drive airscrew propellers; they are equipped with exhaust thrust diverters to enhance mobility. The lift-fan gas turbines drive four blowers to maintain skirt pressure; they are mounted near the stern in the wing compartments and exhaust through the stern. The engines for all four craft were made in Ukraine.
Combat systems: The navigational radar is mounted within a lozenge-shaped radome. The retractable artillery rocket launchers are located near the bow in the hull wing-walls and are reloaded belowdecks; the rockets have a range of 4.5–10 km and are launched via a DVU-3 control system. The Greek ships have two navigational radars, SATNAV receivers, a receiver for the Decca coastal radio navaid system, MFD/F, and a night-vision system.

♦ 6 German Type 520 utility landing craft [LCU]
Bldr: Howaldtswerke, Hamburg

	In serv.
L 167 Ios (ex-*Barbe,* L 790)	26-11-65
L 168 Sikinos (ex-*Dorsch,* L 792)	17-3-66
L 169 Irakleia (ex-*Forelle,* L 794)	20-4-66
L 170 Folegandros (ex-*Delfin,* L 791)	25-11-65
L 178 Naxos (ex-*Renke,* L 798)	2-9-66
L 179 Paros (ex-*Salm,* L 799)	23-9-66

Ios (L 167) H&L Van Ginderen, 9-97

D: 166 tons (403 fl) **S:** 11 kts **Dim:** 40.04 (36.70 pp) × 8.80 × 1.60 (2.10 max.)
A: 2 single 20-mm 90-cal. Rheinmetall AA
Electronics: Radar: 1 Kelvin-Hughes 14/9 nav.
M: 2 MWM 2-cyl. diesels; 2 props; 1,200 bhp **Electric:** 130 kVA tot.
Range: 1,200/11 **Crew:** 17 tot.

Remarks: Design based on the U.S. LCU 1626 class. L 178 and 179 were transferred on 16-11-89, L 167–170 on 31-1-92. Two others, ex-*Rochen* (L 764) and ex-*Mürane* (L 797) were transferred 20-10-92 as cannibalization spares. Cargo: 237 tons max.; 141.6 tons normal. Have ramps fore and aft.

♦ 2 ex-British LCT(4)-class utility landing craft [LCU]
Bldr: . . ., U.K. (In serv. 1945)

L 185 Kythera (ex-LCT 1198) L 189 Milos (ex-LCT 1300)

D: 280 tons light (640 fl) **S:** 9.5 kts **Dim:** 57.07 × 11.79 × 1.30 (aft)
A: 2 20-mm 70-cal. Oerlikon AA **M:** 2 Paxman diesels; 2 props; 1,000 bhp
Range: 500/9.5; 3,100/7 **Crew:** 12 tot.

Remarks: Transferred in 1946. Survivors of a group of 12. Cargo: 350 tons.

♦ 11 ex-German Type 521 landing craft [LCM]
Bldr: Rheinwerft, Walsum (In serv. 1965–67)

ABM 20 (ex-*Seetaucher,* LCM 1)
ABM 21 (ex-*Seenadel,* LCM 2)
ABM 22 (ex-*Seedrache,* LCM 3)
ABM 23 (ex-*Seespinne,* LCM 4)
ABM 24 (ex-*Seeotter,* LCM 5)
ABM 25 (ex-*Seezunge,* LCM 6)
ABM 26 (ex-*Seelilie,* LCM 7)
ABM 27 (ex-*Seefeder,* LCM 8)
ABM 28 (ex-*Seerose,* LCM 9)
ABM 29 (ex-*Seenelke,* LCM 10)
ABM 30 (ex-*Huchen,* LCM 11)

ABM 21 H&L Van Ginderen, 9-94

D: 116 tons (168 fl) **S:** 10.6 kts max. **Dim:** 23.56 × 6.40 × 1.46
A: none **Electronics:** Radar: 1 . . . nav.
M: 2 MWM 8-cyl. diesels; 2 props; 684 bhp
Range: 690/10; 1,430/7 **Crew:** 7 tot. + 50–60 troops

Remarks: ABM 29 was transferred 5-3-91, the others on 25-4-91. Design based on the U.S. LCM(8) class. ABM 29 has a 2-ton cargo boom and a 20-kw generator and can act as an armament stores tender (carrying up to 18 torpedoes); the others can carry up to 60 tons of cargo. As of late 1994, were showing OA 21–series pennant numbers. By 1998, some or all may have been given names and L-series pennants, with the name *Serifos* (L 195) reported.

♦ 12 LCVP 36–class landing craft [LCVP]
Bldr: Motomarine SA, Athens (In serv.. . .)

D: 13 tons (fl) **S:** 8 kts **Dim:** 10.90 × 3.21 × 1.04 (aft)
M: 1 . . . diesel; 200 bhp

Remarks: Ordered in late 1999 as part of the contract for the three Type 214 submarines. Were to be of GRP construction.

♦ 7 LCVP-type landing craft [LCVP]
Bldr: Viking Marine, Piraeus (In serv. 1-80)

D: 13 tons (fl) **S:** 8 kts **Dim:** 10.90 × 3.21 × 1.04 (aft)
M: 1 G.M. 6-71 diesel; 200 bhp

♦ up to 32 ex-U.S. LCVP-type landing craft [LCVP]

D: 13 tons (fl) **S:** 9 kts **Dim:** 10.90 × 3.21 × 1.04 (aft)
M: 1 Gray Marine 64HN9 diesel; 225 bhp **Range:** 110/9

Remarks: Carried by LSTs. Cargo: 36 troops or 3.5 tons. Ten were transferred in 11-56, 4 in 7-58, 10 in 1-62, 4 in 6-64, 3 in 10-69, and the remainder in 3-71; two were returned to the U.S. with the LST *Syros* during 12-00. Are being replaced by new-construction units in the *Jason*-class tank landing ships.

♦ 3 M-10C-class air-cushion landing craft [LCPA]
Bldr: ABS Hovercraft, U.K. (In serv.: 1 on 26-6-98, others in 2000)

D: 26 tons (fl) **S:** 50 kts (light; 35 loaded) **Dim:** 20.6 × 8.80 × 0.35 (at rest)
A: 1 12.7-mm mg **Electronics:** Radar: 1 . . . nav.
M: 2 Deutz BF12L513C diesels; 2 lift fans, 2 airscrew props; 1,050 bhp
Range: 600/30 **Fuel:** 4,600 liters **Crew:** 1 officer, 2 enlisted

Remarks: Several were said to be planned for acquisition as of 2-00.
Hull systems: Capable of carrying one tracked vehicle or 50 seated troops or one 20-ft. cargo container or 20 stretcher cases. The hull is constructed of GRP carbon fiber and vinyl laminate, with a GRP/foam-sandwich deck and Kevlar-reinforced superstructure. Can clear 1-m obstacles and can operate in 2.5-m seas.

♦ 1 UWC-7-class special forces craft [LCP]
Bldr: Fabio Buzz Design sri, Brianza, Italy (In serv. 20-4-01)

UWC-7

D: . . . tons **S:** 60+ kts **Dim:** 12.80 × . . . × . . .
A: 1 12.7-mm mg; 1 40-mm Mk 19 grenade launcher
Electronics: Radar: 1 . . . nav.

AMPHIBIOUS WARFARE SHIPS *(continued)*

M: 2 . . . diesels; 2 props; 1,500 bhp
Range: 350–400/. . . **Crew:** 4 tot. + 12 commandos

Remarks: A high-speed, GRP-hulled, racing RIB design, donated by private citizen Theodore Angelopoulos to the Greek Navy's Underwater Demolition Unit *(Monas Yporvryhion Katastrofon),* based at Skaramanga. Said to be worth $917,000. The Underwater Demolition Unit also operates at least one planing-hulled swimmer delivery craft of about the same size.

♦ 2 E. Panagopoulos I–class ordnance disposal launches [LCP]
Bldr: Hellenic SY, Skaramanga (In serv. 1980–81)

P 70 E. Panagopoulos II P 96 E. Panagopoulos III

D: 35 tons (fl) **S:** 38 kts **Dim:** 23.00 (21.00 wl) × 5.00 × 0.97
A: 1 12.7-mm mg **Electronics:** Radar: 1 Decca . . . nav.
M: 2 MTU 12V331 TC92 diesels; 2 props; 3,060 bhp **Crew:** 6 tot.

Remarks: Aluminum alloy hull with hard-chine form. Sister *E. Panagopoulos I* (P 61) was stricken in 1991. Both were stricken during 1993 but brought back into service around 1996 as explosive ordnance divers' launches.

AUXILIARIES

♦ 1 ex-German ammunition ship [AE] Bldr: Dubigeon, Nantes, France

	Laid down	L	In serv.
A 415 Evros (ex-German *Schwarzwald,* A 1400; ex-French *Amalthée*)	30-6-55	31-1-56	7-6-56

D: 2,395 tons (fl) **S:** 15 kts **Dim:** 80.18 × 11.99 × 4.65
A: 2 twin 40-mm 70-cal. Bofors AA
M: 1 Sulzer 6-SD-60 diesel; 3,000 bhp **Electric:** 500 kw
Range: 4,500/15 **Crew:** 32 tot.

Remarks: 1,667 grt. Former cargo ship, purchased 2-60 by the German Navy and converted for naval use, commissioning 11-10-61. Transferred to Greece 2-6-76.

♦ 1 ex-German intelligence collection ship [AGI]
Bldr: Unterweser, Bremerhaven

	L	In serv.	Converted
A 373 Hermis (ex-*Oker,* ex-*Hoheweg*)	29-8-60	19-10-60	11-2-72

Hermis (A 373) NAVPIC-Holland, 9-00

D: 1,187 tons (1,497 fl) **S:** 15 kts **Dim:** 72.83 (68.35 pp) × 10.50 × 5.60
A: none **Electronics:** Radar: 2 . . . nav.—EW: intercept suite
M: 1 Klöckner-Humboldt-Deutz 8-cyl. diesel, electric drive; 1 prop; 1,800 bhp—1 KHD 8-cyl. auxiliary propulsion diesel, electric drive; 400 shp (8 kts)
Range: . . ./. . . **Crew:** 10 officers, 50 enlisted

Remarks: Former fishing trawler converted for intelligence collection duties for the West German Navy. Stricken 4-12-87 and transferred to Greece 12-2-88. Sister ex-*Alster* (A 50) was transferred to Turkey 2-89 and has since been stricken. The intercept suite includes the U.S. Southwest Research Institute AS-505 communications D/F system.

♦ 1 netlayer and mooring-buoy tender [AGL]
Bldr: Krögerwerft, Rendsburg (In serv. 4-60)

A 307 Thetis (ex-U.S. AN 103)

Thetis (A 307) D. Dervissis, 7-79

D: 560 tons (975 fl) **S:** 12.8 kts **Dim:** 48.50 (51.70 over horns) × 10.60 × 3.70
A: 1 40-mm 60-cal. Mk 3 Bofors AA; 3 single 20-mm 70-cal. Mk 10 Oerlikon AA
Electronics: Radar: 1 Decca 707 nav.
M: 1 M.A.N. G7V 40/60 diesel; 1 prop; 1,470 bhp
Range: 6,500/10.2 **Fuel:** 134 tons **Crew:** 5 officers, 45 enlisted

Remarks: Launched in 1959, transferred in 4-60. Can carry 1,600 rounds of 40-mm and 25,200 rounds of 20-mm ammunition. Fitted with bow lift horns and a large winch forward and aft.

♦ 2 Ikaravoyiannos Theophilopoulos–class lighthouse tenders [AGL] Bldr: Anastassiadis Tsortanidis, Perama

A 479 Ikaravoyiannos Theophilopoulos (In serv. 2-1-76)
A 481 St. Lykoudis (In serv. 17-3-76)

Ikaravoyiannos Theophilopoulos (A 479) H&L Van Ginderen, 10-93

D: 1,350 tons (1,450 fl) **S:** 15 kts **Dim:** 63.24 (56.50 pp) × 11.6 × 4.0
A: none **Electronics:** Radar: 2 Decca . . . nav.
M: 1 MWM TBD-500-8UD diesel; 2,400 bhp **Crew:** 40 tot.

Remarks: Near-sisters to hydrographic survey ship *Naftilos* (A 478). Have a helicopter platform aft.

♦ 1 Pytheas-class hydrographic survey ship [AGS]
Bldr: Anastassiadis Tsortanidis, Perama

	L	In serv.
A 474 Pytheas	19-9-83	12-83

D: 670 tons (840 fl) **S:** 15 kts **Dim:** 50.00 (44.91 pp) × 9.60 × 4.22
M: 2 G.M. Detroit Diesel 12V92 TA diesels; 2 props; 1,800 bhp (1,020 sust.)
Crew: 8 officers, 50 enlisted

Remarks: Programmed in 1979, ordered in 5-82. Carries two survey launches. A near-sister, *Aegeon,* was completed in 1985 for the civilian National Maritime Research Center.

♦ 1 Naftilos-class hydrographic survey ship [AGS]
Bldr: Anastassiadis Tsortanidis, Perama

	L	In serv.
A 478 Naftilos	19-11-75	3-4-76

Naftilos (A 478) H&L Van Ginderen, 9-99

D: 1,380 tons (1,480 fl) **S:** 15 kts **Dim:** 63.1 (56.5 pp) × 11.6 × 4.0
M: 2 Burmeister & Wain SS28LH diesels; 2 props; 2,640 bhp
Crew: 8 officers, 66 enlisted

AUXILIARIES *(continued)*

Remarks: Near-sisters *Ikaravoyiannos Theophilopoulos* (A 479) and *St. Lykoudis* (A 481) are configured as lighthouse tenders. Can carry two survey launches. The helicopter deck has been replaced by two oceanographic equipment-handling gallows cranes.

♦ 2 ex-German Type 701C replenishment oilers [AO]
Bldrs: A 464: Flensburger Schiffswerft, Flensburg; A 470: Blohm + Voss, Hamburg

	Laid down	L	In serv.
A 464 Axios (ex-*Coburg,* A 1412)	9-4-65	15-12-65	9-7-68
A 470 Aliakmon (ex-*Saarburg,* A 1415)	1-3-66	15-7-66	30-7-68

Aliakmon (A 470) Selim San, 2-00

D: 3,709 tons (fl) **S:** 17 kts **Dim:** 114.90 (108.00 pp) × 13.20 × 4.20
A: 2 twin 40-mm 70-cal. Bofors AA **Electronics:** Radar: 1 . . . nav.
M: 2 Maybach MD 872 diesels; 2 CP props; 5,600 bhp—bow-thruster
Electric: 1,935 kw **Range:** 3,000/17; 3,200/14 **Crew:** 82 tot.

Remarks: A 464 transferred and recommissioned 30-9-91; A 470 transferred 19-10-94 and was formally recommissioned in Greek service 30-6-95. A 464 completed conversion to increase cargo fuel stowage from 640 tons to 1,400 tons at Skaramanga Shipyard in 9-00, and A 470 was under conversion during 2001. Spaces formerly devoted to carrying spare parts and 205 tons of ammunition were converted to fuel tanks, but 131 tons of fresh water and 267 m^2 of refrigerated stores can still be accommodated. Have a fin stabilization system and one 3-ton and two 2-ton electric cranes. There are two lead-computing optical directors for the 40-mm guns.

♦ 2 ex-U.S. Patapsco-class oilers [AO]
Bldr: Cargill, Inc., Savage, Minn.

	Laid down	L	In serv.
A 377 Arethousa (ex-*Natchaug,* AOG 54)	15-8-44	6-12-44	11-6-45
A 414 Ariadni (ex-*Tombigbee,* AOG 11)	23-10-42	18-11-43	13-7-44

Arethousa (A 377) H&L Van Ginderen, 1-96

D: 1,850 tons (4,335 fl) **S:** 13 kts **Dim:** 94.72 (89.00 pp) × 14.78 × 4.78
A: 2 single 76.2-mm 50-cal. U.S. Mk 26 DP; 2 single 20-mm 90-cal. Rheinmetall AA
Electronics: Radar: 1 . . . nav.; 1 SPS-5 surf. search; 1 Mk 26 f.c.
M: 2 G.M. 16-278A diesels; 2 props; 3,300 bhp **Electric:** 460 kw
Fuel: 295 tons **Crew:** 6 officers, 40 enlisted

Remarks: 2,575 dwt. Former gasoline tankers, transferred 7-59 and 7-7-72, respectively; A 414 was purchased outright 11-7-78. Cargo: 2,040 tons. Have one Mk 52 radar g.f.c.s. and one Mk 51 lead-computing g.f.c.s., but they may no longer be operational. Can rig one liquid refueling station per side, forward.

♦ 0 (+ 1) Italian Etna-class replenishment oiler [AOR]
Bldr: Elefsis SY

	Laid down	L	In serv.
A . . . Promthefs	. . .	2-02	. . .

D: 6,700 tons (13,400 fl) **S:** 21 kts **Dim:** 146.50 (137.00 pp) × 21.00 × 7.25
A: 2 single 40-m 70-cal. Bofors AA; 1 20-mm Mk 15 Phalanx CIWS; 2 single 20-mm AA
Electronics: Radar: . . .
M: 2 G.M.T.-Sulzer 12 ZAV 40S diesels; 2 props; 22,400 bhp—1,000-kw bow-thruster
Range: 7,600/18 **Crew:** 160 tot. (accomm. for 243)

Remarks: Construction approved 7-99. To be built with assistance from Italy's Fincantieri at a cost of $128 million. No construction progress reported as of 7-01.
Hull systems: Can carry 5,400 tons of gas turbine/diesel fuel, 1,200 tons aviation fuel, 160 tons of fresh water, 2,100 m^3 (about 280 tons) of ammunition, 30,000 fresh rations, 30,000 dry-food rations, 20 tons of spare parts, and 20 tons of lubricant and has space on deck for 12 cargo containers. Two replenishment stations on each beam.

♦ 2 Zeus-class coastal tankers [AOT] Bldr: Hellenic SY, Skaramanga

A 375 Zeus (In serv. 21-2-89) A 376 Orion (In serv. 5-5-89)

Zeus (A 375)—with *Arethousa* (A 377) in dry dock in background
Werner Schiefer, 11-98

D: approx. 2,100 tons (fl) **S:** 10.9 kts **Dim:** 67.02 (60.35 pp) × 10.00 × 4.20
A: none **Electronics:** Radar: 1 . . . nav.
M: 1 MWM–Burmeister & Wain 12V 20/27 diesel; 1 prop; 1,600 bhp
Crew: 28 (accomm.)

Remarks: 866 grt/1,240 dwt. Ordered 9-86. Cargo: 960 m^3 diesel or fuel oil, 102 m^3 JP-5, 115 m^3 fresh water, 146 m^3 potable water. Freeboard when loaded is only 0.45 m. Improved version of the *Ouranos* class, with a hose-handling crane on the platform forward. Sister *Stymfalia* (A 469) is configured as a water tanker [AWT].

♦ 2 Ouranos-class coastal tankers [AOT] Bldr: Kynossoura SY, Piraeus

	In serv.		In serv.
A 416 Ouranos	29-1-77	A 417 Hyperion	27-2-77

D: 2,100 tons (fl) **S:** 12 kts **Dim:** 67.70 (60.40 pp) × 10.00 × 4.70
A: 2 single 20-mm 70-cal. Mk 10 Oerlikon AA
Electronics: Radar: 1 . . . nav.
M: 1 M.A.N.–Burmeister & Wain 12V20 diesel; 1 prop; 1,750 bhp **Crew:** 28 tot.

Remarks: Cargo: 1,323 m^3.

♦ 1 ex-U.K. Bustler-class salvage tug [ARS]
Bldr: Henry Robb, Leith, Scotland

	Laid down	L	In serv.
A 428 Atlas (ex-*Nisos Zakynthos,* ex-HMS *Mediator*)	18-10-43	21-6-44	8-11-44

D: 1,118 tons (1,630 fl) **S:** 16 kts **Dim:** 62.48 (59.4 pp) × 12.32 × 5.18
M: 2 Atlas diesels; 2 props; 3,200 bhp
Range: 3,400/11 **Fuel:** 340 tons **Crew:** 42 tot.

Remarks: Purchased from the Royal Navy in 1965 by a private owner. Acquired 1-8-79 by the Greek Navy and commissioned during 12-79.

♦ 1 Zeus-class water tanker [AWT]
Bldr: Hellenic SY, Skaramanga (In serv. 1990?)

A 469 Stymfalia

Stymfalia (A 469)—outboard fuel tanker sister *Orion* (A 376)
H&L Van Ginderen, 7-93

D: approx. 2,100 tons (fl) **S:** 10.9 kts **Dim:** 67.02 (60.35 pp) × 10.00 × 4.20
A: none **Electronics:** Radar: 1 . . . nav.
M: 1 MWM–Burmeister & Wain 12V 20/27 diesel; 1 prop; 1,600 bhp
Crew: 28 (accomm.)

Remarks: 866 grt/1,240 dwt. Ordered in 9-86; begun and launched by Khalkis SY but completed by Hellenic SY. Cargo: approx. 1,300 m^3 liquid. Two sisters, *Zeus* (A 375) and *Orion* (A 376), are configured as fuel transports [AOT].

♦ 1 training ship [AXT] Bldr: Anastassiadis Tsortanidis, Perama

	Laid down	L	In serv.
A 74 Aris	10-76	4-10-78	1-8

AUXILIARIES *(continued)*

Aris (A 74) Guy Schaeffer, via Paolo Marsan, 5-99

D: 2,400 tons (2,630 fl) **S:** 17.8 kts **Dim:** 100.00 (95.00 pp) × 11.00 × 4.50
A: 1 76.2-mm 50-cal. U.S. Mk 26 DP; 2 single 40-mm 70-cal. Bofors AA; 4 single 20-mm 90-cal. Rheinmetall AA; 1 light helicopter
Electronics: Radar: 2 Decca TM 1226C nav.
M: 2 MAK diesels; 2 props; 10,000 bhp
Crew: 21 officers, 94 enlisted + 359 cadets

Remarks: Can serve as a hospital ship or transport in wartime. Completion delayed by payment dispute. During a 1986 refit, the ship received a new command center and the helicopter facility was reactivated. Marisat SATCOM equipment was added in 1988. There are two lead-computing optical directors for the 40-mm guns. The 76.2-mm gun is probably now intended more as a saluting battery than a practical weapon.

SERVICE CRAFT

♦ 1 Italian Pisa-class armored cruiser historic relic [YAG]
Bldr: Orlando & Co., Livorno

	L	In serv.
Averoff (ex-*Georges Averoff*)	12-3-1910	5-1911

Averoff H&L Van Ginderen, 9-97

D: 9,958 tons (normal) **S:** 22.5 kts (as designed) **Dim:** 140.8 (129.8 pp) × 21.0 × 7.5
A: nonfunctional: 2 twin 234-mm 45-cal. low-angle; 4 twin 190-mm 45-cal. low-angle; 8 single 76.2-mm low-angle; 4 76.2-mm AA; 6 single 37-mm AA
M: 2 sets vertical triple expansion steam; 2 props; 19,000 ihp
Boilers: 22 Belleville water-tube, low-pressure **Range:** 7,125/10
Fuel: 600 tons coal, 1,500 tons oil **Crew:** 670 tot. (when operational)

Remarks: Stricken in 1946. Maintained afloat in excellent condition by the Greek Navy as a memorial at Piraeus. All data above refer to the ship when operational. Armor included 203-mm belt, tapering to 83-mm at the ends; 50-mm deck; 203-mm on the turrets; and 178-mm on the conning tower.

♦ 5 miscellaneous floating cranes [YD]

♦ 2 Pandora-class personnel ferries [YFB]
Bldr: Perama SY

A 419 Pandora (In serv. 26-10-73) A 420 Pandrosos (In serv. 1-12-73)

D: 350 tons (390 fl) **S:** 11 kts **Dim:** 46.80 × 8.30 × 1.90
Electronics: Radar: 1 Decca 1226 nav. **M:** 2 diesels; 2 props; . . . bhp

Remarks: Can carry up to 500 personnel for short periods. No passenger berthing is fitted.

Pandora (A 419) H&L Van Ginderen, 9-94

♦ 1 floating dry dock [YFDM]
Bldr: Elefsis SY (L: 2-5-88; In serv. 9-5-88)

Naval Drydock No. 7

Remarks: 6,000 tons capacity, 145.0 m o.a. Technical assistance in construction came from Götaverken, Arendal, Sweden.

♦ 1 floating dry dock [YFDM]
Bldr: M.A.N., Blexen, Germany (In serv. 1968)

Naval Drydock No. . . .

Remarks: 5,000-ton lift capacity. 140.0 m o.a. by 24.0 m between fenders by 7.40 clear draft over blocks. Based at Salamis.

Note: Floating dry docks 1, 3, and 6 were based at Suda Bay, but one was stricken in 1996; no information available on current status.

♦ 1 wooden trireme rowing galley [YFL]
Bldr: . . . . . . (In serv. 1987)

Olympias

D: approx. 120 tons (fl) **S:** 9–12 kts **Dim:** 37.0 × 5.2 × 1.5
M: 170 oars in three rows; auxiliary square sail
Crew: 10 officers, 170 galley "slaves"

Remarks: Built for historical research and to commemorate the Greek naval tradition. As rowers are volunteers, whips are unnecessary. Oregon pine construction. Refitted in 1992. Was on display ashore at Port Faliron as of 2000.

Note: Small harbor launches BB 32 and BB 35 are employed at the Salamis Naval Base, and there may be others of the class.

♦ 1 Strabon-class inshore survey craft [YGS]
Bldr: Emanuil-Maliris SY, Perama

	L	In serv.
A 476 Strabon	9-88	27-2-89

Strabon (A 476) H&L Van Ginderen, 10-94

D: 252 tons (fl) **S:** 12.5 kts **Dim:** 32.70 × 6.10 × 2.50
M: 1 M.A.N. D2842LE diesel; 1 prop; 1,200 bhp **Crew:** 2 officers, 18 enlisted

♦ 5 liquid-cargo barges [YON/YWN] Bldr: Elefsis SY (In serv. 1988)

D: approx. 400 tons (fl) **Dim:** 27.1 × 7.2 × 1.5

Remarks: Cargo: 300 tons. Four for fuel oil, the other for water.

♦ 4 ex-German Type 430 torpedo retrievers [YPT]
Bldr: Schweers, Bardenfleth

	L
A 460 Evrotas (ex-*TF 106,* Y 872)	10-6-66
A 461 Arachthos (ex-*TF 108,* Y 874)	22-9-65
A 462 Strymon (ex-*TF 107,* Y 873)	13-9-65
A 463 Nestos (ex-*TF 4,* Y 854)	21-10-65

D: 56 tons (63.5 fl) **S:** 17 kts **Dim:** 25.22 × 5.40 × 1.60
Electronics: Radar: 1 . . . nav.
M: 1 MWM 12-cyl. diesel; 1 prop; 1,000 bhp **Crew:** 6 tot.

Remarks: A 460 transferred 5-3-91, A 461 on 12-4-90, A 462 on 16-11-89, and A 463 on 28-9-90. All have wooden hulls and a stern torpedo recovery ramp.

♦ 2 Kiklops-class coastal tugs [YTB]
Bldr: Hellenic SY, Skaramanga (In serv. 1989)

A 422 Kadmos A 435 Kekrops

D: . . . tons **S:** . . . kts **Dim:** . . . × . . . × . . . **M:** . . .

Remarks: Ordered 1-86. No data available.

SERVICE CRAFT *(continued)*

♦ **3 Heraklis-class coastal tugs [YTB]**
Bldr: Anastassiadis Tsortanidis, Perama

A 423 Heraklis (In serv. 6-4-78)
A 424 Jason (In serv. 6-3-78)
A 425 Odisseus (In serv. 28-6-78)

Jason (A 424) Werner Schiefer, 11-98

D: 345 tons **S:** 12 kts **Dim:** 30.0 × 7.9 × 3.4 **M:** 1 MWM diesel; 1,200 bhp

♦ **2 Atromitos-class harbor tugs [YTB]** (In serv. 20-6-68)

A 410 Atromitos A 411 Adamastos

D: 310 tons **S:** 10 kts **Dim:** 30.0 × 7.9 × 3.0 **M:** 1 diesel; 1 prop; 1,260 bhp

♦ **1 ex-U.S. Army Design 3006–class large harbor tug [YTB]**

A 432 Gigas (ex-LT 1941) (In serv. 1954–55)

D: 295 tons (390 fl) **S:** 12.75 kts **Dim:** 32.61 × 8.08 × 3.71
M: 1 Fairbanks-Morse 38D8⅛ diesel; 1 prop; 1,200 bhp **Electric:** 80 kw
Range: 3,300/12 **Fuel:** 54 tons **Crew:** 16 tot.

Remarks: Transferred 26-11-61. Bollard pull: 12 tons.

♦ **3 ex-U.S. YTM 764–class large harbor tug [YTB]**
Bldr: Luders Marine Construction, Stamford, Conn. (A 412 in serv. 11-5-45)

A 409 Achilleus (ex-. . .)
A 412 Aias (ex-U.S. *Ankachak,* YTM 767, ex-YTB 501)
A 429 Perseus (ex-. . .)

Perseus (A 429) Werner Schiefer, 11-98

D: 260 tons (350 fl) **S:** 11 kts **Dim:** 30.48 × 7.62 × 2.92
M: 2 Enterprise diesels; 1 prop; 1,270 bhp **Crew:** 8 tot.

Remarks: A 409 transferred 7-47; previous identity unknown (former name *Confident* attributed to the craft is incorrect). A 412 transferred 1972. Date of transfer and former name/hull number for A 429 not available.

♦ **3 ex-German Heppens-class medium harbor tugs [YTM]**
Bldr: Schichau, Bremerhaven

	Laid down	L	In serv.
A 439 Atrefs (ex-*Ellerbek,* Y 1682)	29-12-70	2-6-71	26-11-71
A 440 Diomedes (ex-*Heppens,* Y 1681)	19-3-71	15-9-71	17-12-71
A 441 Theseus (ex-*Neuende,* Y 1680)	29-12-70	2-6-71	27-10-71

D: 232 tons (319 fl) **S:** 12 kts **Dim:** 26.51 × 7.42 × 2.81
Electronics: Radar: 1 . . . nav.
M: 1 MWM 8-cyl. diesel; 800 bhp **Electric:** 120 kw tot. **Crew:** 6 tot.

Remarks: A 439 transferred to Greece in 3-95. A 440 was stricken from German Navy 18-12-98 and sold to Greece in 3-99 along with A 441.

♦ **1 ex-U.S. YTM 518–class medium harbor tug [YTM]**
Bldr: Gibbs Gas Engine Co., Jacksonville, Fla. (In serv. 2-1-45)

A 428 Nestor (ex-U.S. *Wahpeton,* YTM 527)

Nestor (A 428) Werner Schiefer, 11-98

D: 260 tons (310 fl) **S:** 11 kts **Dim:** 30.8 × 8.5 × 3.3
M: 2 G.M. diesels; 1 prop; 820 bhp **Crew:** 8 tot.

Remarks: Transferred 22-11-89.

♦ **1 ex-U.S. YTM 174–class medium harbor tug [YTM]**
Bldr: Gulfport Boiler Works, Port Arthur, Texas (In serv. 12-3-42)

A 427 Danaos (ex-U.S. *Dekanisora,* YTM 252, ex-YT 252, ex-BYT 4)

D: 210 tons (320 fl) **S:** 12 kts **Dim:** 31.1 × 7.6 × 3.0
M: 2 G.M. diesels; 1 prop; 820 bhp **Crew:** 8 tot.

Remarks: Transferred 22-11-89.

♦ **4 ex-German Lütje Horn–class small harbor tugs [YTL]**

	L
A 413 Pilefs (ex-*Lütje Horn,* Y 812)	9-5-58
A 436 Minos (ex-*Mellum,* Y 813)	23-10-58
A 437 Pelias (ex-*Knechtsand,* Y 814)	3-12-58
A 438 Ægeus (ex-*Schärhorn,* Y 815)	9-5-58

Pelias (A 413) Werner Schiefer, 9-05

D: 52.2 tons (57.5 fl) **S:** 10 kts **Dim:** 15.2 × 5.06 × 2.2
M: 2 Deutz 8-cyl. diesels; 2 Voith-Schneider cycloidal props; 340 bhp
Range: 550/9 **Crew:** 4 tot.

Remarks: A 413 was stricken from the German Navy 18-12-89 and transferred 5-3-91, A 436 stricken 20-12-90 and transferred 25-4-91, A 437 stricken 18-10-90 and transferred 5-3-91, and A 438 stricken 2-8-90 and transferred 5-3-91. Sister *Trischen* (Y 818) was stricken 20-12-90 and transferred 25-4-91, but was used for cannibalization spares.

♦ **3 miscellaneous sail training craft [YTS]**

A 233 Maistros A 234 Sorokos A 359 Ostria

Remarks: A 233 and A 234 are 14.8 m long and displace 12 tons; A 359 is smaller.

♦ **3 Doirani-class water lighters [YW]**

A 434 Prespa (ex-*Doirani*) (In serv. 10-10-72)
A 467 Doirani (In serv. 1972)
A 468 Kalliroe (In serv. 26-10-72)

SERVICE CRAFT *(continued)*

Kalliroe (A 468) H&L Van Ginderen, 4-96

D: 850 tons (fl) **S:** 13 kts **Dim:** 54.77 × 7.95 × 3.87
Electronics: Radar: 1 Decca . . . nav. **M:** 1 MWM 6-cyl. diesel; 1,300 bhp

Remarks: A 434 is 600 dwt. A 467 is 58.88 m o.a., 4.02 m draft, and 765 dwt. A 468 is 671 dwt and has a 1,005-bhp MWM diesel. A 434 was taken over from another government agency during 1979. Have a very low freeboard when fully loaded.

♦ **2 ex-German FW 1–class water lighters [YW]**
Bldrs: A 433: Jadewerft, Wilhelmshaven; A 466: Renke, Hamburg

	Laid down	L	In serv.
A 433 Kerkini (ex-FW 3)	14-6-63	15-10-63	11-5-64
A 466 Trichonis (ex-FW 6)	4-11-63	25-2-64	19-6-64

Kerkini (A 433) H&L Van Ginderen, 12-84

D: 598 tons (624 fl) **S:** 9.5 kts **Dim:** 44.03 (41.10 pp) × 7.80 × 2.63
Electronics: Radar: 1 Kelvin-Hughes 14/9 nav.
M: 1 MWM 12-cyl. diesel; 1 prop; 230 bhp **Electric:** 83 kw
Range: 2,150/9 **Crew:** 12 tot.

Remarks: A 433 was transferred 22-4-76, A 466 on 5-3-91. Cargo: 350 m^3.

GREEK ARMY

AMPHIBIOUS WARFARE CRAFT

♦ **4 (+ 26) Ultra-Fast Strike Catamarans (UFASC) [LCP]**
Bldr: EBO Hellenic Arms Industry (In serv.: first four: 1994)

D: . . . tons **S:** 45+ kts **Dim:** 7.0 × . . . × . . .
A: 1 12.7-mm mg; 2 7-round 70-mm RL
M: 1 gasoline outboard; 150 or 200 bhp
Range: 250/36 **Endurance:** 7.5 hr **Crew:** 3 tot.

Remarks: Intended to replace 30 L-19-class fast launches used by Greek special forces in the Aegean Sea islands. GRP hull construction. The production version was to be 9.0 m o.a. and have a small commercial navigational radar, but there has been no report of a contract.

MINISTRY OF THE MERCHANT MARINE
HELLENIC COAST GUARD
(Limenikon Soma)

Personnel (2002): 1,098 officers, 2,015 subofficials, 2,277 Port Guard personnel, and 489 cadets

Bases: Headquarters at Piraeus, with facilities at Corfu, Chalcis, Elefsis, Heraklion, Igoumenitsa, Kavala, Mytilene, Patra, Rafina, Rhodes, Thessalonica, and Volos. Small patrol boats are also based at a great many Greek mainland and island ports.

Maritime Aviation: Three Reims Aviation F 406 Surpolmar AC-21, 2 Cessna 172RG Cutlass, and 2 SOCATA TB20 Trinidad light aircraft operate from the Greek Air Force base at Dekelia for coastal patrol. Four Eurocopter AS.332C1 Super Puma helicopters are used for SAR duties, equipped with Bendix 1500B search radars, Thales Clio FLIR, a Spectrolab searchlight, and various rescue and medical gear; the first two were delivered 21-12-99 and the second pair during 3-00. The F 406 aircraft are fitted with FLIR, an underside 360° surveillance radar, and a side-looking radar mounted within the tail cone.

Note: Ships are painted dark gray and bear a blue-white-blue diagonal hull stripe with crossed-anchor icon and "Coast Guard" or "Hellenic Coast Guard" in Greek and English on the hull sides.

PATROL BOATS [WPB]

♦ **3 CB-90NEX class** Bldr: Dockstavarvet, Docksta, Sweden (In serv. 6-7-98)
LS-134 LS-135 LS-136

LS-135 H&L Van Ginderen, 9-98

D: 13.2 tons light (18 fl) **S:** 46 kts **Dim:** 16.10 (13.00 wl) × 3.80 × 0.80
A: . . . **Electronics:** Radar: 1 Furuno FAR-2815 ARPA nav.
M: 2 Volvo TAMD 163P diesels; 2 KaMeWa PF 450 waterjets; 1,540 bhp
Range: 160/20 **Fuel:** 1.5 tons **Crew:** 4 tot. + 10 passengers

Remarks: Ordered 12-97 and delivered 6-98. GRP construction. Design based on builder's *Enforcer* patrol boat demonstrator variant of an assault landing craft design. Capable of being beached. Cockpit has armor protection.

♦ **4 Dilos class** Bldr: Hellenic SY, Skaramanga (In serv. 1977–88)
LS-010 LS-020 LS-030 LS-040

LS-030 H&L Van Ginderen, 1-99

D: 75 tons (86 fl) **S:** 27 kts **Dim:** 29.00 (27.00 wl) × 5.00 × 1.62
A: 2 single 20-mm Oerlikon AA **Electronics:** Radar: 1 . . . nav.
M: 2 MTU 12V331 TC81 diesels; 2 props; 2,720 bhp
Range: 1,600/25 **Crew:** 15 tot.

Remarks: Design by Abeking & Rasmussen, Germany. Used for air/sea rescue. Three each also built for the navy and customs service. Round-bilge steel-construction hull.

♦ **43 Sunquestor 53–class inshore patrol boats**
Bldr: Motomarine, Glifadha, Athens (In serv. 1994–96)
LS-115 through LS-123 LS-125 through LS-147

LS-116—first series, with low superstructure A. A. de Kruijf, 8-00

D: 23.5 tons (fl) **S:** 34 kts (trials)
Dim: 16.26 (13.41 pp) × 4.68 × 0.76 (1.38 max.)
A: 1 12.7-mm mg; 1 7.62-mm mg **Electronics:** Radar: 1 . . . nav.
M: 2 M.A.N. D2840-LXE diesels; 2 props; 1,640 bhp
Range: 500/25 **Fuel:** 3,650 liters **Crew:** 5 tot.

COAST GUARD PATROL BOATS [WPB] *(continued)*

LS-137—second series, with high pilothouse further forward
H&L Van Ginderen, 5-00

Remarks: Ordered in 1993. Employ GRP hulls molded by Colvic Craft, Colchester, U.K., using standard Sunquestor 53 yacht hulls. Can carry one spare crewmember if required. The first two were delivered in early 1994 and the last four of the initial batch in 5-94. LS 124 was lost through fire in 2-96. The second-series craft have a revised superstructure with a higher pilothouse.

♦ 16 LS-51-class inshore patrol boats Bldr: Olympic Marine, Lavrio

LS-51, LS-52, LS-101, LS-155, LS-156, LS-157, LS-252, and others

LS-156—of the LS-51 class H&L Van Ginderen, 7-93

LS-252—of the LS-51 class H&L Van Ginderen, 8-93

D: 13 tons (fl) **S:** 23 kts **Dim:** 13.2 × 3.5 × 1.0
A: 1 7.62-mm mg **Electronics:** Radar: 1 Decca . . . nav.
M: 2 diesels; 2 props; 600 bhp **Range:** 400/18 **Crew:** 4 tot.

Remarks: U.K. Keith Nelson GRP hull design. Very similar to the OL 44 class.

♦ 13 OL 44 class Bldr: Olympic Marine, Lavrio

LS-55, LS-65, LS-84, LS-88, LS-97, LS-106, LS-107, LS-110, LS-112, LS-114, and others

D: 13.8 tons (fl) **S:** 23 kts **Dim:** 13.50 (12.10 wl) × 4.35 × 0.61
A: 1 7.62-mm mg **Electronics:** Radar: 1 Decca . . . nav.
M: 2 diesels; 2 props; 600 bhp **Crew:** 4–6 tot.

Remarks: Keith Nelson–design hulls. GRP construction.

Note: There are an additional 86 small patrol boats, including 20 of 8.2-m, 17 of 7.9-m, and 26 of 5.8-m length, for which characteristics are unavailable.

LS-106—of the OL 44 class NAVPIC-Holland, 5-01

SERVICE CRAFT

♦ 4 LS-413-class pollution control vessels [WYAG]

Bldr: Astilleros Gondan, Castropol, Spain (In serv. 1993–94)

LS-413 LS-414 LS-415 LS-423

Pollution control craft LS-415 and a sister Dieter Wolf, 7-94

D: 198 tons (230 fl) **S:** 15 kts **Dim:** 29.00 × 6.20 × 2.50
Electronics: Radar: 1 Furuno . . . nav.
M: 2 Caterpillar 3512 DITA diesels; 2 props; 2,560 bhp (sust.)
Range: 500/13 **Crew:** 12 tot.

Remarks: 198 grt. Have a rounded-down stern with roller to aid in setting pollution-control booms. LS-423 is referred to by the name *Alpha*.

♦ 11 miscellaneous antipollution craft [WYAG]

LS-66, LS-69, LS-70, LS-101, LS-401, LS-410, and others

Pollution control craft LS-410—note bow ramp and hull sponsons
Stefan Marx, 1998

Remarks: No data available.

♦ 38 8.23-meter class [WYFL] Bldr: . . . . . .

Remarks: Outdrive-powered GRP craft. Also in service for patrol/SAR duties are 26 5.7-m U.S. Chris Craft launches [WYFL] and 18 semi-rigid inflatable boats [WYFL] (the latter used by the 48-man Underwater Mission Squad). The Greek Coast Guard also has about 24 outboard-powered RIB launches [WYFL] in service.

COAST GUARD SERVICE CRAFT *(continued)*

B. LS-347—a modern, high-speed GRP-hulled craft with a rigid inflatable collar around the sides of the hull and a Raytheon radar; no data available NAVPIC-Holland, 5-01

♦ **10 18-meter Arun-class lifeboats [WYH]**
Bldr: Motomarine, Athens (In serv. 1997–98)

LS-511 LS-515 and others

Arun-class lifeboat LS-515—black hull, red superstructure Dieter Wolf, 6-99

D: 34 tons (fl) **S:** 18 kts **Dim:** 18.00 × 5.34 × 1.50
Electronics: Radar: 1 . . . nav.
M: 2 Caterpillar 3408BTA diesels; 2 props; 1,000 bhp **Crew:** 5 tot.

Remarks: 34 grt. GRP hull molded by Halmatic, Northam, U.K. An enlarged version of a standard lifeboat used by the U.K., Canada, and Iran, among others. Have Furuno Loran C90 radio navaid, Anschutz gyrocompass, and integrated communication system on bridge. Their low freeboard aids in picking up survivors. Hulls painted black, with orange superstructure.

Note: The Greek Coast Guard is also responsible for maintaining fireboats [WYTR] at major ports, including PS-6, PS-11, and two others at Piraeus.

Fireboat PS-6—painted all red H&L Van Ginderen, 9-99

Note: The Greek Customs Service also operates about 20 boats in its Anti-Smuggling Flotilla, including one 240-ton Vosper Europatrol 250 Mk 1 patrol craft (A./L. 50) with provision for a 40-mm gun, three *Dilos*-class patrol boats (A./L. 16–18, sisters to units in the navy and coast guard), and 10 50-ton OL 76-class patrol boats.

GREENLAND

Note: Greenland has an independent domestic policy but is under the protectorship of Denmark for foreign affairs and defense matters.

GREENLAND POLICE

♦ **3 (+ 1) Sisak-class patrol craft [WPC]**
Bldr: Torshavnar Skipasmidja, Skala (In serv. 1999–2001)

Sisak I Sisak II Sisak III Sisak IV

D: . . . tons **S:** 13 kts **Dim:** 24.15 (21.50 pp) × 6.30 × 2.30
A: small arms **Electronics:** Radar: . . .
M: 2 Caterpillar 3508TA diesels; 2 props; 800 bhp
Range: . . ./. . . **Crew:** . . . tot.

Remarks: 139 grt. First three ordered 5-97, fourth in 1999. Modified fishing boats for police and fisheries protection duties.

GRENADA

COAST GUARD

Personnel (2002): About 60 total, under the Commissioner of Police

Bases: Headquarters is at Prickly Bay, with small facilities at Grenville, Hillsborough, and the capital, St. George's.

PATROL BOATS [WPB]

♦ **1 U.S. Dauntless class**
Bldr: SeaArk, Monticello, Ark. (In serv. 8-9-95)

PB 02 Levera

Levera (PB 02) SeaArk, 9-95

D: 11 tons (fl) **S:** 28 kts **Dim:** 12.19 (11.13 wl) × 3.86 × 0.69 (hull)
A: 2 single 12.7-mm mg; 2 single 7.62-mm mg
Electronics: Radar: 1 Raytheon R40X nav.
M: 2 Caterpillar 3208TA diesels; 2 props; 850 bhp (720 sust.)
Range: 200/30; 400/22 **Fuel:** 250 gallons **Crew:** 5 tot.

Remarks: Ordered 4-94 by the U.S. Government; donated as foreign aid. Aluminum construction. C. Raymond Hunt, "Deep-Vee" hull design.

♦ **1 U.S. 106-foot Guardian class**
Bldr: Lantana Boatyard, Lantana, Fla. (In serv. 21-11-84)

PB 01 Tyrrel Bay

D: 94 tons (fl) **S:** 24 kts **Dim:** 32.31 × 6.25 × 2.13 (props)
A: 2 single 12.7-mm mg; 2 single 7.62-mm mg
Electronics: Radar: 1 Furuno 1411 Mk II nav.
M: 3 G.M. Detroit Diesel 12V71 TI diesels; 3 props; 2,250 bhp
Electric: 100 kw **Fuel:** 21 tons **Crew:** 4 officers, 12 enlisted

Remarks: Laid down 1-84 to U.S. Government order. Aluminum construction. Has a Magnavox MX4102 NAVSAT receiver. Was overhauled in fall 1995 at St. Croix.

PATROL BOATS [WPB] *(continued)*

Tyrrel Bay (PB 01) Lantana, 11-84

♦ 2 U.S. Boston Whaler series
Bldr: Boston Whaler, Rockland, Mass. (In serv. 1988–89)

D: 1.3 tons (fl) **S:** 40 kts **Dim:** 6.81 × 2.26 × 0.40
A: 1 12.7-mm mg **M:** 2 gasoline outboards; 240 bhp
Range: 167/40 **Crew:** 4 tot.

Remarks: Foam-core, "unsinkable" construction.

Note: Also in use are a RIB donated by the United States during 1994 and a locally built, outboard-powered wooden launch.

GUATEMALA

Republic of Guatemala

Personnel (2002): About 1,250 total (including 130 officers and 650 Marines)

Bases: Santo Tomás de Castilla on the Atlantic coast and Puerto Quetzal on the Pacific coast

Organization: Two fleets: Base Naval del Atlántico (BANATLAN) at Santo Tomás de Castilla, and Base Naval del Pacifico (BANAPAC) at Puerto Quetzal; subordinate to BANAPAC is the Sipacate Naval Detachment with the Centro de Adiestramento de Infantería de Marina (Marine Training Center). Craft over 20 m long carry GC-series pennants, while smaller units carry P-series pennants. The two marine infantry battalions are based at Puerto Barrios on the Atlantic coast and at Puerto Quetzal; each consists of two rifle companies and one police company.

Note: Acquisition plans call for procuring three additional 32-m patrol boats and one 19.8-m patrol boat, funds permitting. All of the patrol craft and patrol boats of 65-ft. length and larger listed below were cycled through refit at Network Shipyard, Inc., Pierre Part, La., between 4-93 and 11-96; all units received new engines, had their accommodations renovated, and had new galley equipment, new pumps and generator sets, Furuno radars and communications suites (including single sideband radios), Raytheon GPS receivers, Data Marine echo sounders, and Danforth compasses installed. New engine controls and firefighting systems were fitted, and the repair yard provided training in all the new systems.

PATROL CRAFT [PC]

♦ 1 U.S. Broadsword class
Bldr: Halter Marine, Chalmette, La. (In serv. 4-8-76)

GC-1051 Kukulkan

Kukulkan (GC-1051) Stuart A. Carpenter, 1-96

D: 90.5 tons light (110 fl) **S:** 25+ kts **Dim:** 32.0 (29.4 wl) × 6.3 × 1.9 (props)
A: 2 single 20-mm 90-cal. Oerlikon GAM-B01 AA; 2 single 12.7-mm M2HB mg
Electronics: Radar: 1 Furuno . . . nav.
M: 4 G.M. Detroit Diesel 8V92TA diesels; 2,600 bhp
Electric: 70 kw tot. (2 × 35-kw Perkins diesel sets)
Range: 1,150/20 **Fuel:** 16 tons **Crew:** 5 officers, 15 enlisted

Remarks: Aluminum construction. The original two G.M. 16V149-series engines were replaced, reducing speed from 32 kts. Based at Puerto Quetzal. Named for the Mayan wind god.

PATROL BOATS [PB]

Note: The United States was to supply one boat and three helicopters for drug trade interdiction during 4-00 under Operation Maya-Jaguar; no information is available as to whether the equipment has been delivered.

♦ 1 U.S. Dauntless class
Bldr: SeaArk, Monticello, Ark. (In serv. 3-97)

P . . . Iximche

D: 11 tons (fl) **S:** 28 kts **Dim:** 12.19 (11.13 wl) × 3.86 × 0.69 (hull)
A: 1 7.62-mm mg **Electronics:** Radar: 1 Raytheon R40X nav.
M: 2 Caterpillar 3208TA diesels; 2 props; 850 bhp (720 sust.)
Range: 200/30; 400/22 **Fuel:** 250 gallons **Crew:** 5 tot.

Remarks: Donated by the U.S. Government as foreign aid. Aluminum construction. C. Raymond Hunt, "Deep-Vee" hull design.

♦ 2 U.S. 85-foot Commercial Cruiser class
Bldr: Sewart Seacraft, Berwick, La.

	In serv.
GC-851 Utatlan (ex-U.S. 85NS672)	5-67
GC-852 Subteniente Osorio Saravia (ex-U.S. 85NS722)	11-72

Subteniente Osorio Saravia (GC-852) José Turcios, via Julio Montes, 3-01

D: 43.5 tons (54 fl) **S:** 22 kts **Dim:** 25.9 × 5.8 × 2.2 (props)
A: 2 single 20-mm 90-cal. Oerlikon GAM-B01 AA; 2 single 12.7-mm M2HB mg
Electronics: Radar: 1 Furuno . . . nav.
M: 3 G.M. Detroit Diesel 8V92TA diesels; 3 props; 1,950 bhp
Electric: 70 kw tot. (2 × 35-kw Perkins diesel sets)
Range: 780/15 **Fuel:** 8 tons **Crew:** 7 officers, 10 enlisted

Remarks: Aluminum construction. Both refitted 1995–96 (see description in note at beginning of section) and rearmed after return to Guatemala. GC-851 is based Santo Tomás de Castilla, GC-852 at Puerto Quetzal.

♦ 6 U.S. Cutlass class
Bldr: Halter Marine, New Orleans

	In serv.		In serv.
GC-651 Tecunuman	26-11-71	GC-654 Tzacol	8-76
GC-652 Kaibil Balan	8-2-72	GC-655 Bitol	8-76
GC-653 Azumanche	8-2-72	BH-656 Gucumatz (ex-GC-H-656, ex-GC-656)	8-81

Kaibil Balan (GC-652) José Turcios, via Julio Montes, 3-01

D: 34 tons (45 fl) **S:** 25 kts **Dim:** 19.7 × 5.2 × 0.9
A: all but BH-656: 2 single 20-mm 90-cal. Oerlikon GAM-B01 AA; 2 single 12.7-mm M2HB mg—BH-656: 3 single 12.7-mm M2HB mg

PATROL BOATS [PB] *(continued)*

Gucumatz (BH-656) José Turcios, via Julio Montes, 3-01

Electronics: Radar: 1 Furuno . . . nav.
M: 2 G.M. Detroit Diesel 8V92TA diesels; 2 props; 1,300 bhp
Electric: 70 kw tot. (2 × 35-kw Perkins diesel sets)
Range: 400/15 **Crew:** 2 officers, 8 enlisted

Remarks: Aluminum construction. GC-651, GC-654, and GC-655 are based at Santo Tomás de Castilla, the others at Puerto Quetzal. BH-656 is used as a survey craft; painted white and with a blue-bordered diagonal red stripe on the hull side; she is based in the Pacific and was rearmed for patrol duties during 1995. All were refitted 1993–95 as per note at beginning of section, with their original two 12-cylinder G.M. Diesels replaced by three engines and more-powerful generators substituted to handle the increased electrical load. At the same time, the pilothouse was enlarged.

♦ 3 or more Inmensa-class launches
Bldr: . . . . . ., Guatemala (In serv. mid-1990s)

Kocapave . . . .

D: 1.7 tons (fl) **S:** . . . kts **Dim:** 7.60 × 1.9 × . . .
A: 1 7.62-mm mg **M:** 1 Evinrude gasoline outboard; 150 bhp

Remarks: Locally built, GRP-hulled craft distinguished by considerable sheer to the open hull and a proportionately thick sheer strake.

♦ 8 U.S. 27-foot Vigilant class
Bldr: Boston Whaler, Rockland, Mass. (In serv. 1993–96)

GC-271 Tohil — GC-275 . . . . . .
GC 272 . . . . . . — GC-276 . . . . . .
GC-273 Tepeu — GC-277 . . . . . .
GC-274 . . . . . . — GC-278 . . . . . .

Tepeu (GC-273) Julio Montes, 2-96

D: 2 tons (4.5 fl) **S:** 35 kts **Dim:** 8.23 × 3.00 × 0.50
A: 1 7.62-mm mg **Electronics:** Radar: 1 Furuno . . . nav.
M: 2 Evinrude gasoline outboards; 300 bhp **Crew:** 4 tot.

Remarks: Were on order as of 5-93 under U.S. aid. Have an enclosed pilothouse and GPS receiver. Four are based on each coast for use by the marines.

♦ 16 river patrol craft
Bldr: Trabejos Baros SY, Guatemala (In serv. 1979)

12 wooden-hulled:

Alioth	Kochab	Procyon	Spica
Deneb	Mirfa	Schedar	Stella Maris
Dubhe	Pollux	Sirius	Vega

4 aluminum-hulled:

Escuintla — Lago Atitlán — Mazatenango — Retalhuleu

D: . . . tons **S:** 19 or 28 kts **Dim:** 9.14 × 3.66 × 0.61
A: 2 single 7.62-mm mg
M: 1 diesel; 1 prop; 150 or 300 bhp **Range:** 400–500 nm

Remarks: Wooden-hulled group has 150-bhp diesels and can make 19 kts; the aluminum-hulled craft have 300-bhp engines and can reach 28 kts. Operated by the marines.

♦ 4 captured fishing craft

Mavro-I — Mero — Pampano — Sardina

Remarks: Captured while engaged in smuggling and used for local patrol. No data available. Two are based on the Pacific coast.

AMPHIBIOUS WARFARE CRAFT

♦ 2 U.S. Machete-class personnel landing craft [LCP]
Bldr: Halter Marine, New Orleans (In serv. 4-8-76)

D-361 Picuda — D-362 Barracuda

D: 6 tons **S:** 36 kts **Dim:** 11.0 × 4.0 × 0.76
M: 2 G.M. 6V53 PI diesels; 2 waterjets; 540 bhp **Crew:** 2 tot. + 20 troops

Remarks: Square bows, aluminum construction. Operated by the Marine Infantry Training Center on the Pacific coast.

SERVICE CRAFT

♦ 1 vehicle and passenger ferry [YFB]

T-691 15 de Enero

15 de Enero (T-691) H&L Van Ginderen, 1-96

Remarks: A 21-m craft based at Santo Tomás de Castilla.

♦ 2 miscellaneous sail training craft [YTS]

Margarita — Ostuncalco

Remarks: Based at Santo Tomás de Castilla with the training yacht *Mendieta.*

♦ 1 training craft [YXT]

Mendieta

Remarks: A former yacht, based at Santo Tomas de Castilla.

GUERNSEY

Note: Guernsey, in the Channel Islands, is a semiautonomous territory of the United Kingdom.

FISHERIES PATROL BOATS [WPB]

♦ 1 Stan Patrol 1850 patrol boat
Bldr: Damen SY, Gorinchem, the Netherlands (In serv. 1998)

Leopardess

Leopardess *Workboat,* 1998

D: . . . tons **S:** 23.5 kts **Dim:** 18.50 × . . . × . . .
Electronics: Radar: 1 . . . nav.
M: 2 Volvo Penta TAMD 122P turbocharged diesels; 2 props; 1,140 bhp
Range: . . ./. . . **Crew:** up to 6 tot.

Remarks: Aluminum construction. Carries an outboard-powered 5.4-m rigid inflatable rescue launch. Based at St. Peter Port. Painted gray.

GUINEA

Republic of Guinea

Personnel (2002): About 100 total

Bases: Conakry and Kakanda

PATROL BOATS [PB]

♦ 1 Stan Launch 43–class fisheries inspection launch
Bldr: Damen Shipyard, Gorinchem, the Netherlands (In serv. 2-99)

Matakang

D: . . . tons **S:** 8.1 kts **Dim:** 12.65 × 3.65 × 1.35
Electronics: Radar: 1 Furuno. . . nav.
M: 1 Caterpillar 3304 T/B diesel; 1 prop; 140 bhp

Remarks: Carries a rigid inflatable inspection dinghy and has a Furuno GPS terminal and echo sounder.
Disposal note: U.S.-built patrol boats *Intrépide* (P-328) and *Vigilante* (P-300) have been inoperable since before 2000 and are unlikely to see further service.

GUINEA-BISSAU

Republic of Guinea-Bissau

Personnel (2002): About 300 total

Base: Bissau

Naval Aviation: One Cessna 337 for coastal surveillance

PATROL BOATS [PB]

Note: One R 800–class, 8.7-m, 28-kt, GRP-construction patrol launch was purchased from Rodman Polyships, Vigo, Spain, in 1999; no further details are available.

♦ 2 Cacine class
Bldr: CONAFI, Vila Real de San António, Portugal (In serv. 9-3-94)

LF-01 Cacine   LF-02 Cacheu

Cacheu (LF-02) Ars. do Alfeite, 3-94

D: 55 tons (fl) **S:** 28 kts **Dim:** 20.40 (19.94 pp; 18.50 wl) × 5.80 × 1.00
A: small arms **Electronics:** Radar: 1 Furuno FR 2010 nav.
M: 3 MTU 12V183 TE92 diesels; 3 Hamilton MH 521 waterjets; 3,000 bhp
Crew: 1 officer, 8 enlisted

Remarks: LF = *Lanchas Rápidas de Fiscalização* (Fast Customs Launches). Ordered 14-1-91 for the Ministry of Fisheries; a planned third was canceled. Both were fitted out at the Alfeite Arsenal, Lisbon. Paid for by the Republic of China (Taiwan). Glass-reinforced plastic hull with aluminum deck and superstructure. Intended to perform fisheries protection and customs enforcement duties.

♦ 1 U.S. 51-foot Mk 4 class
Bldr: Peterson Bldrs, Sturgeon Bay, Wis. (In serv. 22-10-93)

LF-03 Ilha de Caio

D: 24 tons (fl) **S:** 24 kts **Dim:** 15.54 × 4.47 × 1.30
A: 1 twin 12.7-mm M2 mg; 2 single 7.62-mm mg
Electronics: Radar: 1 Furuno FR 2010 nav.
M: 2 G.M. Detroit Diesel 6V92 TA diesels; 2 props; 900 bhp (520 sust.)
Electric: 15 kw tot. **Range:** 500/20 **Fuel:** 800 gallons **Crew:** 6 tot.

Remarks: Ordered 25-9-92. Aluminum construction. Contract included training in operation and maintenance. Carries a 4.27-m RIB with a 50-bhp outboard motor. Identical to the unit of the class illustrated under Cape Verde.

Disposal note: Landing craft LDM-100 (ex-Portuguese LDM 119) was out of service by 2000.

SERVICE CRAFT

♦ 1 1,600-ton-capacity floating dry dock

Remarks: Delivered 10-90 from the United States.

Note: The customs service operates one Netherlands-built, 33-ton patrol boat, the *Naga,* completed in 1981.

GUYANA

Cooperative Republic of Guyana

DEFENSE FORCES SEA DIVISION

Personnel (2002): About 60 total, with 130 reserves

Bases: Georgetown and Benab

Maritime Aviation: China agreed early in 2001 to supply a Y-12 light transport for maritime surveillance duties.

PATROL SHIPS [PS]

♦ 1 ex-U.K. River class
Bldr: Richards (Shipbuilders), Ltd., Great Yarmouth

	Laid down	L	In serv.
1026 Essequibo (ex-*Orwell,* M 2011)	4-6-84	7-2-85	27-3-85

Essequibo (1026) Derek Fox, 7-01

D: 630 tons (770 fl) **S:** 14 kts (15 on trials; 12 sust.)
Dim: 47.60 (42.00 pp) × 10.50 × 3.10 (3.75 max.)
A: 1 20-mm 70-cal. Oerlikon AA; 2 single 7.62-mm mg
Electronics: Radar: 1 Decca TM 1226 nav.
M: 2 Ruston 6 RKCM diesels; 2 4-bladed CP props; 3,040 bhp
Electric: 460 kw tot. **Range:** 4,500/10 **Fuel:** 88 tons
Crew: 7 officers, 23 enlisted in RN service

Remarks: 638 grt. Retired from Royal Navy service 13-7-00, was sold to Guyana during 4-01, and recommissioned 22-6-01. Had been disarmed and used as a cadet training ship prior to retirement; the armament listed above was that aboard when the ship was active as a minesweeper. Sisters serve in the Bangladesh and Brazilian navies.
Hull systems: Steel hull built to commercial standards, following the design of a North Sea oilfield supply vessel. Single-compartment damage standard. Navigation gear includes two Kelvin-Hughes MS 48 echo sounders.
Combat systems: Was unarmed at time of purchase; when serving as a minesweeper, the ship was armed with one 40-mm 60-cal. Mk 7 Bofors AA and two 7.62-mm mg. All sweep gear has been removed.

Disposal note: Boston Whaler *Houri* (DFS 1018) and former fishing boat *Waitipu* (DFS 1008) had been discarded by 8-00.

HAITI

Republic of Haiti

COAST GUARD

Personnel (2002): About 40 total

Bases: Headquarters at Port au Prince, with secondary facilities at Les Cayes and Port de Paix

PATROL BOATS [WPB]

♦ 4 U.S. 25-foot Guardian class
Bldr: Boston Whaler, Edgewater, Fla. (In serv. 6-96)

D: 2.2 tons (fl) **S:** 28 kts **Dim:** 7.6 × 2.4 × 0.2
A: small arms **M:** 1 gasoline outboard; 225 bhp **Crew:** 2–3 tot.

Remarks: Delivered between 30-5-96 and mid-June 1996 as U.S. Grant-Aid. Refitted at Miami during 1999. Have foam-core, "unsinkable" GRP sandwich hulls.

HONDURAS

Republic of Honduras

FUERZA NAVAL REPÚBLICA

Personnel (2002): About 900 total, including 350 naval infantry

Bases: Amapala, La Ceiba, Puerto Castilla, Puerto Cortés, and Puerto Trujillo

Naval Aviation: Two Lake Seawolf amphibians were delivered in 1987.

PATROL CRAFT [PC]

♦ 3 U.S. 105-foot class Bldr: Swiftships, Morgan City, La.

FNH 101 Guaymuras (In serv. 4-77)
FNH 102 Honduras (In serv. 3-80)
FNH 103 Hibures (In serv. 3-80)

Honduras (FNH 102)—with old pennant number
Honduran Navy, via Julio Montes

D: 103 tons (111 fl) **S:** 24 kts **Dim:** 32.00 × 7.20 × 3.1 (props)
A: 1 twin 20-mm 90-cal. Hispano-Suiza HS-404 AA in IAI TCM-20 mount; 1 20-mm 70-cal. U.S. Mk 68 AA; 2 single 12.7-mm mg; 2 single 5.6-mm MAG-58 mg
Electronics: Radar: 1 . . . nav.
M: 2 MTU diesels; 2 props; 7,000 bhp **Electric:** 80 kw tot.
Range: 1,200/18 **Fuel:** 21 tons **Crew:** 3 officers, 14 enlisted

Remarks: Aluminum construction. Originally bore pennants FNH 1051–1053, changed in 1993.

PATROL BOATS [PB]

♦ 2 U.S. 106-foot Guardian class
Bldr: Lantana Boatyard, Lantana, Fla.

FNH 104 Tegucigalpa (ex-FNH 107) (In serv. 1983)
FNH 105 Copan (ex-FNH 106) (In serv. 6-86)

D: 94 tons (fl) **S:** 35 kts **Dim:** 32.31 × 6.25 × 2.13 (props)
A: 1 20-mm G.E. M 197 Sea Vulcan-20 gatling gun; 1 20-mm 70-cal. U.S. Mk 68 AA; 2 single 12.7-mm Browning M2HB mg
Electronics: Radar: 1 Furuno . . . nav.
M: 3 G.M. Detroit Diesel 16V92 TI diesels; 3 props; 3,900 bhp **Electric:** 100 kw
Range: 1,500/18 **Fuel:** 21 tons **Crew:** 4 officers, 12 enlisted

Remarks: Aluminum construction. Have Magnavox MX 4102 NAVSAT receiver and two echo sounders. A Kollmorgen HSV-20NCS optronic control system is fitted for the gatling gun. A third unit, to have been named *Comayguela,* was canceled and became Jamaica's *Paul Bogle.*

Copan (FNH 105)—with old pennant number; the gatling gun is shown in the inset
General Electric, via Julio Montes, 1993

♦ 5 U.S. 65-foot Commercial Cruiser class
Bldr: Swiftships, Morgan City, La.

	In serv.
FNH 651 Nacaome (ex-*Aguan,* ex-*Gral*)	12-73
FNH 652 Goascoran (ex-*Gral. J. T. Cabanas*)	1-74
FNH 653 Petula	1980
FNH 654 Ulua	1980
FNH 655 Chuluteca	1980

D: 33 tons (36 fl) **S:** 28 or 36 kts **Dim:** 19.9 (17.4 wl) × 5.6 × 1.6 (props)
A: 2 single 20-mm 70-cal. U.S. Mk 68 AA; 2 single 12.7-mm M2HB mg; 1 combination 81-mm mortar/12.7-mm M2HB mg
Electronics: Radar: 1 Decca . . . nav.
M: 2 G.M. 12V71 TI or MTU diesels; 2 props; 1,300 or 1,590 bhp **Electric:** 20 kw
Range: 2,000/22 **Fuel:** 5 tons **Crew:** 2 officers, 7 enlisted

Remarks: First pair was originally ordered for Haiti, delivered to Honduras for use as customs launches in 1977, and later transferred to the navy. The others, ordered 1979, have more-powerful diesels. Aluminum construction.

♦ 1 or more high-speed chase boats
Bldr: . . . (In serv. 1996–. . .)

FNH 3701

FNH 3701—on travel trailer
Julio Montes, 1996

D: approx 8 tons (fl) **S:** . . . kts **Dim:** 11.27 × . . . × . . .
A: 2 single 12.7-mm M2HB mg **Electronics:** Radar: 1 Furuno 3600 nav.
M: 2 . . . diesels; 2 props; . . . bhp **Crew:** 5 tot.

Remarks: Origins uncertain. GRP construction.

PATROL BOATS [PB] *(continued)*

♦ 3 Piranha-class river patrol craft
Bldr: Lantana Boatyard, Lantana, Fla. (In serv. 3-2-86)

D: 8.16 tons (fl) **S:** 26 kts (22 sust.) **Dim:** 11.00 (10.06 wl) × 3.05 × 0.53
A: 2 single 12.7-mm mg; 2 single 7.62-mm mg
Electronics: Radar: 1 Furuno 3600 nav.—EW: VHF D/F
M: 2 Caterpillar 3208 TA diesels; 2 props; 630 bhp
Endurance: 5 days **Crew:** 5 tot.

Remarks: Aluminum construction, with Kevlar armor. Five others have been discarded, and these last three may no longer be operational.

♦ 15 Taiwanese ARP-2001-class riverine patrol launches
Bldr: . . ., Taiwan (In serv. 29-5-96)

D: 2 tons (fl) **S:** . . . kts **Dim:** 4.60 × . . . × . . .
A: 1 7.62-mm mg **M:** 1 Mercury gasoline outboard; 115 bhp **Crew:** 4 tot.

Remarks: Open launches, delivered as a gift. Aluminum construction. Sisters are used by the Taiwanese Marine Corps. Three are based at Amapala, four at Puerto Castilla, two at Puerto Cortés, and the others at Tegucigalpa.

♦ 8 U.S. 25-foot Outrage-class inshore patrol launches
Bldr: Boston Whaler, Rockland, Mass. (In serv. 1982–90)

D: 2.2 tons **S:** 35 kts **Dim:** 7.62 × 2.40 × 0.40
A: 1 12.7-mm mg; 1 7.62-mm mg **Electronics:** Radar: 1 Furuno 3600 nav.
M: 2 Evinrude gasoline outboard engines; 2 props; 300 bhp
Range: 200/35 **Crew:** 4 tot.

Remarks: Foam-core GRP construction. The radar is not always fitted. Four others have been discarded.

AMPHIBIOUS WARFARE CRAFT

♦ 1 utility landing craft [LCU]
Bldr: Lantana Boatyard, Lantana, Fla.

	Laid down	L	In serv.
FNH 1491 Punta Caxinas	11-86	. . .	5-88

Punta Caxinas (FNH 1491) Lantana, 5-88

D: 419 tons light (625 fl) **S:** 14.5 kts **Dim:** 45.42 × . . . × . . . (loaded)
A: none **Electronics:** Radar: 1 Furuno 3600 nav.
M: 3 Caterpillar 3416 diesels; 3 props; 2,025 bhp
Range: 3,500/12 **Crew:** 3 officers, 15 enlisted

Remarks: Cargo can include 100 tons of vehicles or cargo on deck, or four standard 20-ft. cargo containers and 50,000 gallons of fuel. Has a Magnavox NAVSAT receiver.

♦ 3 U.S. LCM(8)-class landing craft [LCM]

FNH 7401 Warunta FNH 7402 Tansin FNH 7403 Caratasca

D: 56 tons (116 fl) **S:** 12 kts **Dim:** 22.43 × 6.40 × 1.40 (aft)
A: 2 single 12.7-mm mg **Electronics:** Radar: 1 . . . nav.
M: 4 G.M. 6-71 diesels; 2 props; 620 bhp
Range: 140/9 **Crew:** 3–4 tot. + 150 troops for brief periods

Remarks: Transferred in 1987. Cargo: 54 tons in the 13.4 × 4.4-m cargo well.

AUXILIARIES

♦ 1 ex-U.S. Coast Guard Hollyhock-class buoy tender [AGL]
Bldr: Moore Dry Dock Co., Oakland, Calif.

	Laid down	L	In serv.
FNH 252 Yojoa (ex-*Walnut,* WLM 252, ex-WAGL 252)	5-12-38	22-3-39	27-6-39

D: 825 tons (986 fl) **S:** 12 kts **Dim:** 53.4 × 10.4 × 3.7
M: 2 diesels; 2 props; 1,350 bhp
Range: 6,500/12; 10,000/7.5 **Crew:** 4 officers, 36 enlisted

Remarks: Transferred 1-7-82 for navaids support duties. Has one 20-ton buoy derrick. The original reciprocating steam propulsion plant was replaced in 1958. Refitted in 1989 at Tracor Marine, Ft. Lauderdale, Fla.

SERVICE CRAFT

♦ 6 miscellaneous ex-fishing boats for logistics support [YFU]

FN 7501 Juliana	FN 7503 Carmen	FN 7505 Yosuro
FN 7502 San Rafael	FN 7504 Mairy	FN 7506 Jose Gregori

HONG KONG

HONG KONG POLICE FORCE MARINE REGION

Personnel (2002): About 2,600 total

Bases: Headquarters at Tsim Sha Tsui, Kowloon, with “Sea Division” bases at Aberdeen, Ma Liu Shui, Sai Wan Ho, Tai Lam Chung, and Tui Min Hoi.

Maritime Aviation: The Government Flying Service (GFS; name changed from Royal Hong Kong Auxiliary Air Force on 1-4-93) operates maritime patrol–configured BAe Jetstream 41 aircraft for coastal patrol; 3 AS.332 L2 Super Puma, 2 Sikorsky S-70A-27, 5 Sikorsky S-76A+, and 3 Sikorsky S-76C helicopters for rescue work; and 2 Slingsby T-67M Firefly light aircraft for training. Five EC-155 B1 helicopters are replacing all Sikorsky helicopters in 2002. The GFS operates from Chek Lap Kok airport. The Chinese military has based 10 Z-9A Haitun (AS.365 Dauphin) helicopters at Sek Kong airfield since 1-7-97.

Note: Although Hong Kong came under Chinese control 1-7-97, the former Royal Hong Kong Police Force and its Marine Region craft continue to be subordinated to the Hong Kong government, which retains a considerable—if declining—degree of autonomy. Mounted machineguns are no longer carried.

PATROL CRAFT [WPC]

♦ 0 (+ 6) Keka class
Bldr: Australian Submarine Corp., Adelaide, and Cheoy Lee SY, Hong Kong (In serv. . . .)

D: 120 tons (fl) **S:** 25 kts (sust.) **Dim:** 31.00 (28.00 pp) × 6.50 × 1.80
A: small arms
Electronics: Radar: 1 Litton-Sperry SM5000 nav.
M: 2 MTU 16V2000 N90 SR diesels; 2 props; 3,600 bhp—1 waterjet loiter propulsion syst.; . . . shp
Electric: 160 kw (2 × 80-kw diesel sets)
Range: 1,300/15 **Fuel:** 20,000 liters **Endurance:** 7 days
Crew: 3 officers, 26 enlisted

Remarks: Similar to craft built for the Thai Navy. Delivered 5-10 through 5-02. Aluminum construction.

♦ 2 Sea Panther–class command boats Bldr: Hong Kong SY, Kowloon

	Laid down	L	Del.	In serv.
PL 3 Sea Panther	17-6-86	17-4-87	27-7-87	1-2-88
PL 4 Sea Horse	17-6-86	14-7-87	28-9-87	1-2-88

Sea Horse (PL 4) Giorgio Arra, 10-96

D: 420 tons (450 fl) **S:** 14 kts **Dim:** 40.0 × 8.5 × . . . (3.2 molded depth)
A: fitted for 2 single 12.7-mm mg
Electronics: Radar: 1 Decca C342 ARPA nav.; 1 Decca C348 ARPA nav.
M: 2 Caterpillar 3512 diesels; 2 props; 2,350 bhp **Range:** 1,300/14
Crew: 27–33 tot. + two platoons of police for short periods

Remarks: The original Racal CANE 100 data logging and navigational plot system was replaced by ARPA equipment when the Decca radio navaid system ceased functioning in the Hong Kong area.

PATROL CRAFT [WPC] *(continued)*

♦ 6 ASI-315 Pacific Forum class
Bldr: Transfield ASI Pty, Ltd., South Coogee, Western Australia

	In serv.		In serv.
PL 51 Protector	18-10-92	PL 54 Preserver	7-4-93
PL 52 Guardian	18-1-93	PL 55 Rescuer	17-5-93
PL 53 Defender	4-3-93	PL 56 Detector	23-6-93

Detector (PL 56) Giorgio Arra, 6-96

D: 148 tons (170 fl) **S:** 26+ kts (24 sust.)
Dim: 32.60 (31.50 hull; 28.60 wl) × 8.20 × 1.60 (hull)
A: equipped for: 1 12.7-mm Browning mg; 2 single 7.62-mm mg
Electronics: Radar: 1 Decca . . . nav.
M: 2 Caterpillar 3516 TA Phase II diesels; 2 props; 5,640 bhp (4,400 sust.)—1 Caterpillar 3412 TA cruise diesel; 1 Hamilton 521 waterjet; 775 bhp
Electric: 186 kVA (2 Caterpillar 3306T diesel sets)
Range: 600/18 **Fuel:** 21,000 liters **Endurance:** 8–10 days **Crew:** 19 tot.

Remarks: Ordered 8-91. Modified standard Australian foreign-aid patrol boat design, with less draft and fuel and a third engine added centerline for cruising. Carry a 5-m RIB boarding boat. Can carry a divisional commander and staff. Have a GEC V3901 stabilized optronic device for surveillance and data recording. Near-sisters serve the Kuwaiti Coast Guard.

PATROL BOATS [WPB]

Note: Early in 1999, two 30-m patrol boats and the first two of a planned 10 21-m patrol boats were ordered from Lung Teh SY, Kowloon; no data yet available.

♦ 6 PL 40 class
Bldr: Cheoy Lee SY, Kowloon (In serv. 2-00 to 7-00)

PL 40 PL 41 PL 42 PL 43 PL 44 PL 45

D: 15 tons (fl) **S:** 35 kts **Dim:** 13.07 × 3.96 × 0.70
A: small arms **Electronics:** Radar: 1 Decca BridgeMaster-E 180 nav.
M: 2 Deutz-M.A.N. D 2842 LE 403 diesels; 2 Hamilton waterjets; 720 bhp
Crew: 4 tot.

Remarks: Ordered spring 1999. U.S. Peterson Builders design.

♦ 5 Sea Stalker 1500 class
Bldr: Damen, Gorinchem, the Netherlands (In serv. 1999–2000)

PL 85 PL 86 PL 87 PL 88 PL 89

PL 88 A. A. de Kruijf, 6-99

D: . . . tons **S:** 60+ kts (42 sust.) **Dim:** 14.77 × 2.71 × 1.18 (aft)
A: fitted for 2 single 7.62-mm mg
Electronics: Radar: 1 . . . nav. (X-band)
M: 3 Mercruiser Bulldog HP500 V-8 outdrive gasoline engines; 3 surface-piercing Bravo-1 props; 1,500 bhp
Range: . . ./. . . **Fuel:** 1.1 m^3 **Crew:** 5 tot. + 3–4 "specialists"

Remarks: Ordered 6-98. Aluminum construction. Designed in the U.K by Cougartek. Crew and passengers ride in shock-mounted seats. Made 62 kts on trials. Last unit delivered 10-99.

PL 88 A. A. de Kruijf, 6-99

♦ 14 Damen Mk 3 design
Bldr: Chung Wah SB & Eng, Kowloon

	Laid down	L	In serv.
PL 70 King Lai	28-2-84	14-7-84	29-10-84
PL 71 King Yee	28-2-84	17-7-84	29-11-84
PL 72 King Lim	28-2-84	29-7-84	17-12-84
PL 73 King Hau	15-3-84	2-11-84	31-1-85
PL 74 King Dai	15-3-84	8-11-84	28-2-85
PL 75 King Chung	15-3-84	12-11-84	1-4-85
PL 76 King Shun	17-8-84	26-1-85	17-5-85
PL 77 King Tak	25-8-84	4-2-85	10-6-85
PL 78 King Chi	17-8-84	1-2-85	2-7-85
PL 79 King Tai	1-12-84	29-4-85	19-8-85
PL 80 King Kwan	1-12-84	4-5-85	18-9-85
PL 82 King Yan	8-3-85	19-8-85	4-11-85
PL 83 King Yung	8-3-85	30-8-85	25-11-85
PL 84 King Kan	8-3-85	2-9-85	18-12-85

King Hau (PL 73)—machinegun no longer mounted Douglas A. Cromby, 11-96

D: 85 tons (97 fl) **S:** 25 kts **Dim:** 26.50 (24.27 pp) × 5.80 × 1.80
A: fitted for 1 7.62-mm mg
Electronics: Radar: 1 Decca RM 1290 nav.
M: 2 MTU 12V396 TC83 diesels; 2 props; 2,966 bhp—1 M.A.N. MB OM-424A V-12 cruise diesel; 1 waterjet; 465 bhp
Range: 600/14; 1,400/8 **Crew:** 17 tot.

Remarks: PL 70–78 ordered 10-83; PL 79–84 ordered 1-12-84. Damen's Stan Patrol 2600/Chung Wah's Mk 3 design, a modified version of the Damen Mk 1 design. Can make up to 7 kts on the centerline waterjet. Carry an Avon Searaider semi-rigid inspection boat. Sister *King Mei* (PL 81) was stricken in 1985 after damage. Three near-sisters were built for the Hong Kong Customs Service.

♦ 8 Damen Mk 1 design
Bldr: Chung Wah SB & Eng., Kowloon

	In serv.		In serv.
PL 60	29-2-80	PL 65	2-9-80
PL 61	29-2-80	PL 66	8-9-80
PL 63	1980	PL 67	1980
PL 64	1980	PL 68	1-81

D: 86 tons (normal) **S:** 23 kts **Dim:** 26.2 × 5.9 × 1.80
A: removed **Electronics:** Radar: 1 Decca 150 nav.
M: 2 MTU 12V396 TC82 diesels (1,300 bhp each), 1 M.A.N. D2566 cruise diesel (195 bhp); 3 props (Schottel on centerline); 2,600 bhp
Range: 1,400/8 **Crew:** 1 officer, 13 constables

Remarks: PL 60 was laid down during 9-79 to a Dutch design. The cruise engine provides 7- to 8-kt max. speeds. The 12.7-mm mg has been removed.
Disposals: Damen Mk 2 variants PL 57, PL 58, and PL 59 were discarded in 1999. Mk 1 PL 62 was transferred to the customs service in 1995.

PATROL BOATS [WPB] *(continued)*

PL 66 H&L Van Ginderen, 8-94

♦ **7 Petrel-class harbor patrol craft**
Bldr: Chung Wah SB & Eng. Co. (In serv. 1986–87)

PL 11 Petrel PL 12 Auk PL 13 Gull PL 14 Tern PL 15 Skua PL 16 Puffin PL 17 Gannet

Auk (PL 12) Brian Morrison, 1-99

D: 36 tons **S:** 12 kts **Dim:** 16.0 × 4.6 × 1.5
A: small arms **Electronics:** Radar: 1 Decca . . . nav.
M: 2 Cummins NTA 855M diesels; 2 waterjets; 700 bhp **Crew:** 7 tot.

Remarks: Are equipped with one water monitor for firefighting.

♦ **3 40-foot patrol launches** Bldr: Cheoy Lee SY, Hong Kong

PL 6 Jetstream (In serv. 17-4-86) PL 7 Swiftstream (In serv. 25-5-86) PL 8 Tidestream (In serv. 12-6-86)

D: 24 tons (fl) **S:** 18 kts **Dim:** 16.4 × 4.5 × 0.85
A: small arms **Electronics:** Radar: 1 Decca . . . nav.
M: 2 MTU diesels; 2 Hamilton 421 waterjets; 455 bhp
Range: 300/15 **Crew:** 8 tot.

Remarks: GRP construction. Replaced a trio by the same builder with the same names. Employed for patrol of the Deep Bay area.

SERVICE CRAFT

♦ **7 Challenger-class launches [WYFL]**
Bldr: Boston Whaler, Edgewater, Fla. (In serv. 1996)

PL 51 through PL 57

D: 1.86 tons light **S:** 25 kts **Dim:** 7.62 × 1.80 × 0.38
M: 2 Evinrude gasoline outboards; 450 bhp **Crew:** 2 tot. + 10 passengers

Remarks: GRP foam-core hull, fitted for rescue and towing. Also suitable for harbor patrol.

♦ **4 PL 46–class catamaran personnel launches [WYFL]**
Bldr: Sea Spray Boats, Fremantle, Western Australia (In serv. 1992)

PL 46 PL 47 PL 48 PL 49

D: . . . tons (fl) **S:** 30 kts **Dim:** 11.4 × 4.2 × 1.3
M: 2 Caterpillar 3208TA diesels; 2 props; 550 bhp **Crew:** 4 tot.

Remarks: GRP construction. First unit delivered 6-92 to replace earlier personnel launches. Can carry 16 constables or 6 VIPs.

PL 46 H&L Van Ginderen, 8-94

♦ **11 PL 22–class catamaran personnel launches [WYFL]**
Bldr: Sea Spray Boats, Fremantle, Western Australia (In serv. 1992–93)

PL 22 through PL 32

D: 5 tons (fl) **S:** 35 kts **Dim:** 9.90 × 4.20 × 1.20
Electronics: Radar: 1 Koden MD 3400 nav.
M: 2 Caterpillar 3208TA diesels; 2 props; 710 bhp
Range: . . ./. . . **Fuel:** 2 tons **Crew:** 4 tot.

Remarks: Aluminum construction. Prototype was completed in 6-92, four others during 1992, and the remainder in 1993. Can maintain 25 kts in Sea State 4.

Note: All of the rigid inflatable boats listed below are organized into the Small Boat Unit and are referred to as "High Speed Interceptors." The 7-m Typhoon-class rigid inflatables PV 30 through PV 37 were discarded during 1999.

♦ **3 9.5-meter Typhoon RIB launches [WYFL]**
Bldr: Task Force Boats, U.K.

PV 10 PV 11 PV 12

Remarks: Capable of 50 kts. Powered by two V-8, 270-bhp outboard motors.

♦ **4 Tempest RIB launches [WYFL]**
Bldr: Task Force Boats, U.K.

PV 14 PV 15 PV 16 PV 17

♦ **9 Stillinger RIB launches [WYFL]**
Bldr: Stillinger, U.K.

PV 90 through PV 98

Note: The Hong Kong Customs Service operates four Damen 26-m patrol boats similar in appearance and characteristics to sisters in police service: *Sea Glory* (6), *Sea Guardian* (7), *Sea Leader* (8), and PL 62 (transferred from the police in 1995). Two 32.15-m patrol boats were ordered from Wang Tak SY, Kowloon, early in 1999; these have a speed of 25 kts derived from two MTU 16V1200 diesels, and both were delivered during 7-00.

The Environmental Protection Department operates several craft, including the pollution clean-up vessel *Dr. Catherine Lam,* and the Marine Department operates boats equipped to handle navigational buoys and markers.

Customs launch Sea Glory (6) Douglas A. Cromby, 11-96

HUNGARY

Republic of Hungary

HUNGARIAN ARMY MARITIME WING

Note: The Hungarian Army Maritime Wing was to be dissolved on 30-6-01, with the 6 *Nestin*-class riverine minesweepers, 45 AN-2-class mine countermeasures launches and 5 service craft to be disposed of before or after that date. They were to be transferred to police or border guard forces or sold for commercial use or scrap.

ICELAND

Republic of Iceland

COAST GUARD
(Landhelgisgæslan)

Personnel (2002): Approx. 130 total

Base: Reykjavik

Maritime Aviation: One Fokker F-27 Mk 200 Friendship patrol aircraft and 1 AS.365N Dauphin II, 1 AS.332L-1 Super Puma, and 1 AS.350B Écureuil helicopters.

Note: Icelandic Coast Guard vessels have red, white, and blue diagonal stripes on either side of their dark gray-painted hulls, and the word *Landhelgisgæslan* (Coast Guard) is painted on both sides amidships.

FISHERIES-PROTECTION SHIPS [WPS]

♦ 2 Ægir class

	Bldr	L	In serv.
ÆGIR	Ålborg SY, Denmark	1967	1968
TÝR	Dannebrog Vaerft, Århus, Denmark	10-10-74	15-3-78

Týr—outboard the *Ægir,* with *Baldur* alongside — Werner Globke, 7-99

D: 1,150 tons (1,500 fl) **S:** 20 kts **Dim:** 69.84 (62.18 pp) × 10.02 × 5.02
A: 1 40-mm 60-cal. Bofors Mk 3 AA
Electronics:
Radar: 1 Sperry Rasterscan nav.; 1 Plessey AWS-6 air search
Sonar: *Týr* only: Sirad hull-mounted HF
M: 2 M.A.N. R8V 40/54 diesels; 2 KaMeWa CP props; 8,600 bhp
Electric: 630 kVA **Range:** 10,000/19 **Crew:** 22 tot.

Remarks: Although built 10 years apart, these two ships are nearly identical. *Týr* is 70.90 m o.a. The original single-fire 6-pdr. (57-mm) guns, made in 1896, were replaced in 1989–90, and an articulating boat crane was placed at the starboard forward end of the helicopter platform to handle rigid inflatable launches. The radar fit was enhanced in 1994, and the flight deck was extended and the hull beneath it plated up in 1997. Have a 20-ton bollard-pull towing winch and passive antirolling tanks.

♦ 1 Odinn class

	Bldr	Laid down	L	In serv.
ODINN	Ålborg SY, Denmark	1-59	9-59	1-60

Odinn — Werner Globke, 7-99

D: 1,000 tons (fl) **S:** 18 kts **Dim:** 63.63 (56.61 pp) × 10.0 × 4.8
A: 1 40-mm 60-cal. Bofors Mk 3 AA
Electronics: Radar: 2 Sperry Rasterscan nav.
M: 2 Burmeister & Wain diesels; 2 props; 5,050 bhp
Range: 10,000/18 **Crew:** 22 tot.

Remarks: Rebuilt in 1975 by Århus Flydedock, Denmark, with a hangar, helicopter deck, and passive antirolling tanks. An articulated crane was added to starboard at the forward end of the helicopter deck in 1989 to handle RIB inspection and rescue craft. The original single-fire 6-pdr. (57-mm) gun was replaced in 1990.

SERVICE CRAFT

♦ 1 inshore survey craft [WYGS]
Bldr: Vélsmidja Seydhisfjördhur H/H, Seydhisfjörda (In serv. 8-5-91)

BALDUR

Baldur—alongside the *Týr* — Werner Globke, 7-99

D: 54 tons (fl) **S:** 12 kts **Dim:** 20.0 × 5.2 × 1.7
Electronics: Radar: 1 Furuno . . . nav.
M: 2 Caterpillar 3406TA diesels; 2 props; 640 bhp **Crew:** 5 tot.

Note: The 2,100-grt civilian agency oceanographic research ship *Arni Fridriksson* was delivered during 5-00 by ASMAR, Talcahuano, Chile, for the Icelandic Marine Research Institute. The ship is 70 m o.a. by 13.8 m in beam, and the single-screw diesel-electric propulsion plant produces about 4,000 shp for 16-kt speeds.

INDIA

Republic of India

INDIAN NAVY

Personnel (2002): About 53,000 total (7,500 officers), including 1,000 Marine Commando force and 5,000-strong Naval Air Arm, plus 45,000 civilians

Note: In 1996, a number of Indian cities were officially renamed to reflect local linguistic and cultural customs. The major locations of naval interest are Mumbai (formerly Bombay), Chennai (formerly Madras), Kochi (formerly Cochin), and Kanoor (formerly Cannanore). The new names are employed in the listings below.

Bases: Headquarters is at INS *India,* New Delhi. Western Command Headquarters is at Mumbai and includes submarine base INS *Varabahu* and missile boat base INS *Agnibahu;* there is also a small naval facility at Okha near the Pakistani border. Eastern Command Headquarters is at Vishakhapatnam ("Vizag") and includes the submarine base INS *Virbahu;* also subordinate to Eastern Command are small naval facilities at Chennai, Calcutta, Port Blair (INS *Jarawa*) in the Andaman Islands, and Camorta in the Nicobar Islands and the naval VLF submarine communications facility at Vijayaraghavapuram. Southern Command Headquarters is at Kochi and includes the research and development station, INS *Dronacharya.* The naval academy, now at Goa, is planned to move to INS *Jawarhalal Nehru* at Ezhimala. The College of Naval Warfare is at Karanja; the engineering school is at INS *Shivaji;* the supply school is at INS *Hamla,* Mumbai; and enlisted new-entry training is carried out at INS *Chilka,* Vishakhapatnam. The Marine Gas Turbine Overhaul Center, INS *Eksila,* near Vishakhapatnam, was commissioned on 27-8-00.

Approval was given 24-11-94 for a 7-year, $433 million program to build a new major fleet base, INS *Sea Bird,* at Karwar to be ready in 2002 to begin replacement of Mumbai; completion of the entire facility is expected to take 30 years.

Naval air stations are at INS *Garuda,* Wellington Island, Kochi; INS *Hansa,* Goa; INS *Sea Bird,* Karwar; INS *Utkrosh,* Port Blair; INS *Rajali,* Arakkonam; Chennai; Mumbai; Vishwanath; Uchipuli, Tamil Nadu; Ramanathuram; Ramnad; and Bangalore.

Naval Aviation: Shipboard aircraft include 13 Sea Harrier Mk 51 V/STOL fighters equipped with Magic air-to-air missiles; 29 Sea King helicopters (5 Mk 42/42A delivered 8-80; 6 Mk 42C transports delivered from 5-2-87; and 18 Mk 42B, equipped with Sea Eagle antiship missiles and Sintra-Alcatel MS-12 dipping sonars, delivered 1989–91); 18 Ka-27/28 Helix-A ASW helicopters (3 configured as trainers); 1 Ka-31 Helix AEW helicopter; 6 Ka-25 Hormone ASW helicopters; 2 ALH liaison helicopters; and 20 Chetak (Alouette-III) light ASW/liaison helicopters. Three Sea Harrier Mk 60 and 2 T.Mk 4 Harrier two-seat trainers are also in service. For land-based maritime surveillance, 5 Il-38 May, 8 Tu-142MKE Bear-F Mod. 3, 6 BN-42B/T Maritime Defender, and 26 Do-228 fixed-wing aircraft are in use. Training and logistics-support aircraft include 3 Mk 60 Harrier and 2 ex-Royal Navy T.Mk 4 Harrier V/STOL trainers; 8 HPT-32 propeller-driven Deepak and 12 HAL Kiran Mk I, IA, and II jet trainers; and 10 HAL HS.748M transports.

Plans to acquire six more Tu-142MKE aircraft by 2002 did not reach fruition, but four of the original Tu-142MKEs had been equipped to launch Kh-31A antiship missiles by 3-00; the Il-38 and Tu-142MKE aircraft are being upgraded in Russia with the Russian SeaDragon ASW operations suite in batches of five aircraft. Four Tu-22M3 Backfire bombers were to be transferred from Russia in 2001 under a 5-10-00 agreement, but a final contract had not been signed by 5-01. Five additional Ka-31 Helix-D aerial surveillance helicopters were ordered on 7-2-01, in addition to three ordered earlier; the first was to be delivered during 12-01. Five "Ka-27" Helix helicopters were refurbished at Sevastopol' from 10-00 to 2-01.

Of a planned total of 36 Dornier Do-228 coastal surveillance aircraft, 26 were in service by 2001, with six fitted with Elisra EW and Elta 2022 surveillance radars. The BN-42B/T Maritime Defender coastal patrol aircraft are being refurbished and re-engined with Allison 150 B17C turboprops (320 shp each).

Six single-seat and two-seat Sea Harriers have been lost since deliveries began, three of them in 1993–94; a single-seater was lost 7-2-96 and another single-seater 25-5-01. A Sea Harrier damaged in a 1997 landing accident was rebuilt in the U.K. during 1999–2000. One Ka-28 was lost 29-3-99.

Plans to order additional Sea Harriers were abandoned in favor of participation in the development of the Indian Light Combat Aircraft, which may enter Indian Navy service from shore bases around 2015 (delayed from 2003 in 2001). Some $125 million was allocated in 6-99 to update the existing Mk 51 Sea Harriers, which are increasingly obsolescent, but the update program was later canceled (although a new plan to update the aircraft with Elta 2032 radars was reported in 4-01). Plans to purchase up to 40 MiG-29K (marinized MiG-29SMT) fighters and 6 MiG-29 two-seat trainers were cut to a total of 22 aircraft early in 2001, and the planned order was then deferred.

A total of 40 naval variants of the HAL Advanced Light Helicopter (ALH) are planned to replace the Chetak for liaison, transport, search-and-rescue, and, later, ASW duties; the initial production order for 12, placed early in 1997, included two for the navy and two for the coast guard, but deliveries have been behind schedule, and the first two were delivered to the navy in liaison configuration at the end of 2001. A shipboard ASW variant is not planned to enter service until about 2015. Data for the ALH include:

Weight: 2,352 kg (5,000 max.) **Speed:** 156 kts
Engines: 2 Turbomeca TM 333-2B turbines (2,000 shp)
Range: 216 n.m. with 700-kg payload **Fuel:** 2,850 liters

Indian Air Force 6 Sqn. ("Dragons") operates 7 SEPECAT/HAL Jaguar-IM fighter-bombers dedicated to the maritime strike role and armed with two BAe Sea Eagle antiship missiles each.

Naval aircraft squadron home base assignments are:

Squadron	*Aircraft*	*Location*
300 Sqn.	Sea Harrier Mk 51, T.Mk 60	INS *Hansa,* Dabolim, Goa
310 Sqn.	Dornier Do-228-101	INS *Hansa,* Dabolim, Goa
312 Sqn.	Tu-142M Bear-F	INS *Rajali,* Arakkonam
315 Sqn.	Il-38 May	INS *Hansa,* Dabolim, Goa
318 Sqn.	BN-42B/T Maritime Defender	INS *Utkrosh,* Port Blair, Andaman Islands
321 Sqn.	Chetak	INS *Kunjali,* Colaba, Mumbai
330 Sqn.	Sea King Mk 42B	INS *Kunjali,* Colaba, Mumbai
331 Sqn.	Chetak	INS *Garuda,* Kochi, Kerala
333 Sqn.	Ka-28 Helix	INS *Hansa,* Dabolim, Goa
336 Sqn.	Sea King Mk 42, Mk 42A	INS *Garuda,* Kochi, Kerala
339 Sqn.	Sea King Mk 42C	INS *Kunjali,* Colaba, Mumbai
550 Sqn.	BN-2B/T Islander, HPT-32 Deepak	INS *Garuda,* Kochi, Kerala
551 Sqn.	HJT-16 Kiran	INS *Hansa,* Dabolim, Goa
561 Sqn.	Chetak	INS *Rajali,* Arakkonam
562 Sqn.	Chetak	INS *Garuda,* Kochi, Kerala

Indian Navy Sea Harrier FRS.51 formation British Aerospace

Indian Navy Sea King Mk 42B Brian Morrison, 2-01

Indian Navy Ka-25A Hormone at top, with two Ka-28 Helix Brian Morrison, 2-01

Indian Navy Chetak Brian Morrison, 2-01

Two Indian Navy Il-38 May ASW aircraft Brian Morrison, 2-01

Indian Navy Tu-142 Bear-F Brian Morrison, 2-01

Indian Navy Do-228 Mritunjoy Mazumdar, 2-01

Weapons and Sensors: A mixture of Western (primarily British and Dutch) and Soviet weapons and sensors are used, with Western designs built in India under license, principally by Bharat Electronics. Hindustan Aeronautics, Ltd. (HAL), is developing an air-to-ground missile for air force and navy use; it will have a range of 100 km at Mach 0.85 at a 30,000-foot altitude and will have a 35-kg payload. Also under development by HAL are the Koral surface-launched antiship missile and the 9-km-ranged Trishul SAM, the latter based on the Russian SA-8 but with a guidance system derived from the Indian Army's PIW-519 radar director, itself a modification of the Contraves Flycatcher system. Trishul was supposed to be in service by 10-98; but the first (and unsuccessful) firing did not take place until 11-98, and the first successful launch did not take place until 14-5-00. Recent reports indicate it will not be ready for service before 2004–05, initially employing a single-armed launcher, then a six-rail launcher, and ultimately a vertical-launch system. A serious explosion destroyed several prototype missiles during 4-01, further delaying the trials program, and a subsequent trial launch was again unsuccessful.

Sixteen Zvezda Kh-35 Uran antiship missiles were delivered from Russia in 1997 for use with the *Delhi,* and 50 additional missiles were ordered in 1998. British Sea Eagle antiship missiles, in use with Indian Air Force Jaguar fighter-bombers, may be replaced with an air-launched version of the Russian Kh-35 Uran (the AS-20 Kayak); integration problems caused cancellation of plans to integrate Sea Eagle with Il-38 and Tu-142MKE land-based patrol aircraft, but the planned Tu-22M Backfire-C force may be equipped with Kh-31A (AS-17 Krypton) antiship missiles. The Russian 3M-54E subsonic antiship/land-attack missile is being procured for use from submarines and surface combatants.

The supersonic Bramhos (alternate designation PJ-10), said to be a reworked version of the Russian 3M-55 Oniks (NATO's SS-NX-26 Yakhont) antiship missile, was being developed during 2000 for launch by surface ships and aircraft as an antiship and strategic land-attack weapon. The weapon is said to have a potential range of 300 km and to carry a 500-kg warhead; a nuclear-warhead version is being designed, and the missile may also be altered for submarine launch. A reportedly successful test was carried out on 12-6-01 at Chandipur Missile Test Range.

A submarine-launched missile named Sagarika ("Oceanic") has been under development since 1991. To be powered by a ramjet sustainer, it is intended to have a range of 300 (one source says 800) km. Sagarika is to employ terrain-following guidance, accept target information from satellites or RPVs, and cruise 15–100 m above the surface and was to have been operational by 2002 (although there have been no reported test firings). A conventional warhead will be used initially, but a nuclear warhead may be substituted later.

The Dhanush production variant of the Prithvi missile is being developed for launch by surface ships; the weapon will initially have a range of 250 km and a 500-kg payload, but a 500-km version is also planned. The initial firing at sea on 11-4-00 from the patrol ship *Subhadra* was a failure.

A decision was made in 1996 to procure the Israeli Barak vertical-launch, point-defense SAM system and a single set was ordered for the carrier *Viraat* in 1997 (with installation planned for completion late in 2001). Six more sets were ordered 6-2-01.

Bharat Electronics has developed a navalized mounting for the Russian 30-mm automatic 2A42 cannon used on Indian Army BMP-2 infantry fighting vehicles; the "Medak" mount also incorporates a coaxial 7.62-mm mg and can be locally or remotely controlled. The mounting is intended eventually to replace 40-mm single Bofors guns in coast guard ships and craft and possibly in the Indian Navy's *Sukanya*-class patrol ships; it is also aboard the replenishment ship *Aditya.*

Some eight Dvigitel TEST-71EM-NK wire-guided torpedoes were purchased for use with the 10th Project 877 Kilo-class submarine. The Naval Scientific Laboratory, Vishakhapatnam, is developing the Shyena "Advanced Experimental Torpedo."

Bharat Electronics develops and manufactures radar, sonar, and EW systems based on European-developed prototypes under license. Early in 1993, a license agreement was signed with Hollandse Signaal-Apparaaten (now Thales Nederland) to manufacture H.S.A.-developed radars and other electronic equipment to replace Soviet-made gear on Indian naval ships during the 1990s. Equipment that entered service during the 1990s includes:

Name	*Prototype*	*Function*
Aparna	Garpun-E	X(I)-band antiship missile targeting
Rashmi (PIN-524)	H.S.A. ZW-06	X(I)-band navigation/surf. search
RAWL-02 (PLN-517)	H.S.A. LW-02	L(D)-band air early warning
RAWS-03 (PFN-513)	H.S.A. DA-05	L(D)-band air/surf. search

Bharat's APSOH digital sonar can employ both hull-mounted and VDS transducer arrays and features automated detection classification, as well as tracking and adaptive signal processing. An Indian-developed submarine sonar suite designated Panchendriya began testing at sea in 1997 on the Foxtrot-class *Karanj* (S 21); it was allegedly to be incorporated fleetwide by 2000 (but was still in trials status as of 2001, with no production yet programmed). The Ahalya helicopter dipping sonar is also being tested.

AIRCRAFT CARRIERS [CV]

♦ 0 (+ 1) Air-Defense Ship (ADS) project

Bldr: Cochin Shipyard, Ltd., Kochi

	Laid down	L	In serv.
. . . . . .	2002?	. . .	2011–12

D: 33,000 tons (fl) **S:** 32 kts **Dim:** approx. 250.0 × 42.00 × . . .
Air group: 16 Light Combat Aircraft (LCA) and/or MiG-29K fighters; 10 Sea King, 8 Advanced Light Helicopter (ALH), 2 Ka-31 Helix AEW helicopters
A: . . .
Electronics: . . .
M: 4 HAL-G.E. LM-2500 gas turbines; 2 props; 108,000 shp
Range: . . ./. . . **Crew:** 1,350 tot.

Remarks: Approved by the finance and defense ministries by 3-99, the ADS was given Cabinet Committee on Security approval in 6-99 to allocate roughly $750 million for construction of a ship whose genesis began in the mid-1980s; the projected cost has more than doubled since 1993. Will have a small air group for its size and is to employ a ski-jump bow for takeoffs and arrestor wires for landing (i.e., STOBAR: Short Take-Off But Arrested Landing). The design is said to be based on one for a somewhat larger ship prepared by France's DCN under a 21-12-88 contract. No construction contract had been issued as of 6-01.

The Air-Defense Ship *Ships of the World,* 2000

Combat systems: Is to have an antimissile SAM system, an E/O backup weapons-control system, ASW torpedoes, and a sonar set.

♦ 0 (+ 1) ex-Russian Modified Kiev class (Project 11434)

Bldr: Chernomorskiy (Nosenko) SY 444, Nikolayev

	Laid down	L	In serv.
. . . . (ex-*Admiral Gorshkov,* ex-*Admiral Flota Sovetskogo Soyuza Gorshkov,* ex-*Baku*)	26-12-78	1-4-82	30-12-87

Proposed appearance of the Admiral Gorshkov after conversion to aircraft carrier Nevelskoye Design Bureau, 1999

D: 33,000 tons light, 40,000 tons std. (44,570 fl; 48,500 max.) **S:** 29 kts
Dim: 273.10 (243.00 wl) × 53.0 (32.7 wl) × 10.2 (mean hull; 11.5 over sonar)
Air group: 8 MiG-29K fighter-bombers, 8 Mk 51 Sea Harrier fighter-bombers, . . . Ka-28 ASW helicopters, . . . Ka-31 Helix aerial surveillance helicopters
A: 24 8-round Kinzhal (SA-N-9) SAM syst. silos (192 9M-330 Gauntlet missiles); 2 single 100-mm 70-cal. AK-100 DP (1,200 rounds); 8 single 30-mm 54-cal. AK-630 gatling AA (48,000 rounds); 1 10-round RPK-5 Liven' ASW RL (120 rockets)
Electronics:
Radar: 3 MR-212/201 Vaygach-U (Palm Frond) nav.; 2 MR-320M Topaz-M (Strut Pair) air/surf. search; 1 MR-760 Fregat-M2 (Plate Steer) 3-D air search; 4 MR-360 Podkat (Cross Sword) SAM f.c.; 1 MR-145 Lev (Kite Screech-B) 100-mm f.c.; 4 MR-123 Vympel (Bass Tilt) 30-mm f.c.; 2 . . . (Fly Trap) automatic aircraft landing aid
Sonar: Polinom suite: Orion (Horse Jaw) LF hull-mounted, Platina (Horse Tail) LF VDS
TACAN: . . . (Cake Stand)
EW: Kantata-M suite: 8 . . . (Foot Ball–series) intercept, 8 . . . (Wine Flask) jammers, 2 . . . (Cage Pot) intercept, 4 . . . (Bell Bash) jammers, 4 . . . (Bell Thump) jammers; 1 . . . (Cross Loop) MFD/F; 1 . . . (Park Plinth) VHFD/F; 1 . . . (High Ring) MHFD/F; 2 . . . (Prim Wheel) D/F; 2 twin PK-2 trainable decoy RL
E/O: 3 . . . (Tin Man) television; 4 . . . (Tilt Pot) fixed t.v.; 2 bridge periscopes
M: 4 sets geared steam turbines; 4 4-bladed props; 180,000 shp
Boilers: 8 turbopressurized, 64 kg/cm^2
Electric: 15,000 kw tot. (6 × 1,500-kw turboalternators, 4 × 1,500-kw diesel sets)
Range: 4,050/29; 7,000/18; 8,000/16.3; 13,500/10
Fuel: 7,000 tons + 1,500 tons aviation fuel **Endurance:** 30 days
Crew: 383 officers, 1,229 enlisted + 430 tot. air group + 50 flag staff

Remarks: Most data above (other than the removal of antiship missiles and the projected air group) refer to the ship when in Russian Navy service. Negotiations to sell the *Admiral Gorshkov* to India began in 1994, and India signed a "letter of interest" on 21-12-98 to acquire the ship for free and modernize her with Russian equipment at Severodvinsk, where she arrived under tow 13-7-99. A joint protocol signed 5-11-99 stated that a contract for the transfer of the ship to India was expected to be signed during the first quarter of 2000, but it was not signed until 4-10-00, and a formal contract is still awaited. As of 6-01, it was hoped to complete negotiations by 9-01 or 10-01, and the price had reportedly been lowered. The Indian defense budget for 3-01 through 3-02 did not include funds to acquire and modify the ship, but what were termed "final negotiations" to acquire the ship were begun during 2-02.

Has not been to sea under her own power since 1991; she suffered a major fire while laid up during 1993 and a steam line break and subsequent 18-hour fire at Rosta Shipyard, Murmansk, on 1-2-94. Modifications are said to be expected to cost $734 million, while some $616 million is to be expended on MiG-29K aircraft and $207 million on Ka-31 helicopters for the ship.

AIRCRAFT CARRIERS [CV] *(continued)*

Hull systems: Has a deeper draft than the preceding *Kiev* class and also trims down by the stern. The boilers produce up to 98 tons of steam per hour. Fin stabilizers are fitted.
Aviation systems: The bow would be altered to become a 14.3° takeoff ski jump for conventional fighter aircraft, and no catapults would be fitted. There would be two takeoff positions, each with a jet-blast deflector and aircraft detents. The ship was originally intended to carry 14 Yak-41M Freehand and 8 Yak-38 Forger VTOL fighters and 16 Ka-27-series helicopters (10 ASW, 2 AEW, and 2 SAR/utility). The angled portion of the flight deck is 195 × 20.7 m. Adding wire-type arrestor gear would probably reduce the already small capacity of the 130-m-long by 22.5-m-wide by 6.6-m-high hangar. Two inboard aircraft elevators (19 × 10 m and 19 × 5 m) and three weapons elevators to the flight deck were fitted but may have to be moved and enlarged under the new configuration.
Combat systems: Twelve P-500 Bazalt (SS-N-12 Sandbox) antiship missile tubes would be removed from the upper deck forward. No long-range air-defense SAM system is fitted; the 8-cell Kinzhal (SA-N-9) vertical-launch silos were disposed 12 forward of the SS-N-12 installation, six in a row on the port side of the angled deck aft, and two rows of three to starboard of the after elevator, while the four MR-360 radar detection/track/directors are mounted port and starboard above the bridge and abaft the island. Two RPK-5 Liven' ASW rocket launchers replace the RBU-6000 launchers on the forecastle; RPK-5 (also known as UDAV-1) is primarily used as a torpedo countermeasure launcher but can also launch ASW rockets. The ASW fire-control system is known as Sprut.
Admiral Gorshkov carried the Mars-Passat (Sky Watch) fixed planar phased-array radar mounted on the island sides to give 360° coverage; it was not satisfactory, however, and is nonoperational. A secondary 3-D radar, MR-760 Fregat-M2, is mounted above the 9-m-high cylindrical array for the Cake Stand TACAN-cum-air-control system antenna. In addition to the systems listed, there are numerous whip, wire, and cage/VHF communications antennas. The communications suite is called Buran. Low Ball SATCOM antenna radomes were mounted fore and aft of the Cake Stand tower, while two Punch Bowl radar satellite targeting system datalink radomes flanked the island; there were also two Pert Spring satellite communications antennas, but all SATCOM equipment is liable to be removed prior to transfer.

V/STOL AIRCRAFT CARRIERS [CVV]

♦ **1 U.K. Hermes class** Bldr: Vickers-Armstrong, Barrow-in-Furness

	Laid down	L	In serv.
R 22 VIRAAT (ex-*Hermes*)	21-6-44	16-2-53	18-11-59

Viraat (R 22) John Mortimer, 2-01

Viraat (R 22) Brian Morrison, 2-01

D: 23,900 tons (28,706 fl) **S:** 28 kts
Dim: 226.85 (198.12 pp) × 48.78 (27.43 wl) × 8.80
Air group: 10–12 Sea Harrier Mk 51 fighters; 6 Sea King Mk 42B ASW helicopters; 3 Sea King Mk 42C logistics helicopters; 4 Ka-28 Helix ASW helicopters; 2 Chetak liaison helicopters
A: 1 Barak SAM VLS group (8 missiles); 2 single 40-mm 60-cal. Bofors Mk 3 AA; 2 twin 30-mm 65-cal. AK-230M AA
Electronics:
Radar: 2 Decca Type 1006 nav.; 1 Bharat RAWL early warning; 1 Bharat RAWS-J air/surf. search; 1 Elta EL/M-2221 GM STGR missile f.c.
Sonar: Graseby Type 184M hull-mounted (8–9 kHz) (probably inactivated)
TACAN: FT13-S/M
EW: Elettronica-Bharat RAWS/PFN-513 Ajanta intercept; 2 8-tubed Corvus decoy RL
M: 2 sets Parsons geared steam turbines; 2 props; 76,000 shp
Boilers: 4 Admiralty 3-drum **Electric:** 9,000 kw tot.
Range: 6,500/14 **Fuel:** 4,200 tons + 320 tons aviation fuel
Crew: 143 officers, 1,207 enlisted (incl. air group) + 750 troops

Remarks: Purchased 19-4-86, having been paid off from the Royal Navy 12-4-84 and stricken 1-7-85; turned over to Indian control 14-11-86 during the reactivation and minor modernization overhaul and recommissioned 12-5-87 at Devonport. Formally commissioned in India 15-2-89. The name means "Mighty." Had been converted from a standard carrier to a helicopter commando carrier in 1971–73, then converted again in 1976–77 as an ASW helicopter carrier. Suffered severe engine-room flooding 10-9-93 when a main seawater induction valve failed in port during repairs. Was to have begun a final two-year major refit at Mumbai in 1997, but the start was delayed until 7-99, curtailed to 14–18 months, and limited to a $50 million expenditure; the work was completed during 2-01 (other than addition of the Barak missile system during 5-01), and the ship is now planned for retirement in 2010.
Hull systems: Has 25- to 50-mm armor over magazines and machinery spaces; flight deck is approx. 20 mm thick. During reactivation, NBC warfare protection was improved. Has limited steaming endurance.
Aviation systems: Modified during British service 5-80 to 9-5-81 to operate Sea Harrier V/STOL attack fighters, receiving a 230-ton, 45.7-m-long by 13.7-m-wide by 4.9-m-high 12° ski-jump takeoff ramp. Retained commando transport capability for 750 troops and continues to carry four LCVP landing craft aft. Has two aircraft elevators. The Sea King Mk 42B ASW helicopters are equipped to launch Sea Eagle antiship missiles. There are two aircraft elevators, one to port on the angled deck and one aft on the centerline.
Combat systems: Has the British CAAIS computerized combat data system. At time of transfer, had Deck Approach Projector System (DAPS), Horizon Approach Path Indicator (HAPI), the CTL all-weather approach system landing aids, new Decca Type 1006 navigational radars, and an Italian TACAN system (replacing the U.K. system removed in 4-82) added. New EW equipment was added in India. Carries up to 80 ASW torpedoes for the helicopters. Two 40-mm AA have been added, one at the forward end of the flight deck to starboard of the ski jump and the other just forward of the island. A Bharat-made radar has replaced the Type 994 surface/air-search set. The two Sea Cat GWS.22 point-defense missile launchers had been removed by 1995 and were replaced with Russian twin 30-mm gunmounts removed from stricken ships; these are controlled by simple ringsight directors.

Viraat (R 22)—prior to installation of the Barak SAM system Ralph Edwards, 2-01

V/STOL AIRCRAFT CARRIERS [CVV] *(continued)*

Modernization: The 1999–2000 refit incorporated a new long-range radar, an improved communications suite, a new shipboard damage-control alarm system, fire curtains in the hangar space, and faster aircraft elevator operation. One 8-cell, vertically launched Israeli Barak SAM system was ordered for the ship in 1997 but installation was not completed until 5-01. Two Russian Kashtan CIWS may be purchased later.

NUCLEAR-POWERED ATTACK SUBMARINES [SSN]

Note: Negotiations with Russia for the purchase of two Project 971 Bars-class (NATO Akula-I) nuclear-powered attack submarines, reported under way in 3-99, came to naught, but on 5-12-00, it was reported that India was hoping to lease a Russian Navy Akula-I SSN for training and familiarization purposes. The Russian offer became the lease of two Akulas to be leased for 5 years for $5 billion, with the submarines to be delivered in 2004; India rejected the offer on cost gounds during 2-02.

♦ 0 (+ 1 + 4?) Advanced Technology Vessel (ATV) class

Bldr: . . . . . . SY, Vishakhapatnam (In serv. 2009 or later)

D: 9,400 tons (sub.) **S:** 24 kts **Dim:** 124.0 × 12.0 × . . .
A: . . . Sagarika land-attack missiles; . . . TT
M: 1 or 2 pressurized water reactors; steam turbines; 1 or 2 props; . . . shp

Remarks: Data above are a preliminary estimate released by Western intelligence agencies and may have no basis in fact. The prototype was reportedly planned to be laid down in 2001 or 2002 for launch in 2006 or 2007, which would put commissioning in about 2009–10, but no start announcement had been made by the end of 2001; a total of five may be planned. Related research has been ongoing in India since 1974 toward the construction of an indigenously designed and constructed nuclear-powered submarine, with few concrete results to date. In 4-96, it was reported that the program was experiencing severe delays and cost overruns and that it might be canceled. In 6-96, it was reported that initial trials in 11-95 and 12-95 with a prototype reactor for the submarine at Kalpakkam atomic power plant had been entirely unsuccessful. The reactor, under design since 1985 at the Bhaba Atomic Research Center, Mumbai, was said to weigh 600 tons, and the submarine was intended to carry missiles: both a 1,000-km cruise missile and a 300-km ballistic missile have been said to be in development. Russia is said to have been providing design and engineering assistance for the program since 1989.

ATTACK SUBMARINES [SS]

Note: Long-range Indian Navy plans approved early in 2000 call for the construction of 24 submarines in India by 2030; 12 of these would be of Russian design and 12 of European design. The submarines would be assembled at Mazagon Dock, Mumbai.

♦ 0 (+ 6–12) Scorpène class

Bldr: DCN, Cherbourg, France, and Mazagon DY, Mumbai (In serv. 2008–. . .)

D: 1,668 tons surf./1,908 tons sub. **S:** . . . kts surf./20+ kts sub.
Dim: 66.40 × 6.20 × 5.8 (surf.)
A: 6 bow 533-mm TT (18 wire-guided torpedoes and Aérospatiale SM 39 Exocet antiship missiles)
Electronics:
Radar: 1 . . . nav./surf. search
Sonar: Thales . . . suite, with passive flank and towed arrays
EW: . . . intercept
M: diesel electric: 4 MTU . . . diesels (840 bhp each), Jeumont axial-flux permanent magnet electric motor; 1 prop; . . . shp
Range: 6,500/8 surf.; 550/4 sub. **Endurance:** 50 days
Crew: 6 officers, 26 enlisted

Remarks: An agreement for indigenous production of an initial six—with an eventual total of 12 planned—was signed with DCN, France, on 28-6-01. Chile has also ordered two and Spain hopes to build four. The submarines were said to be planned to be superior to the Agosta-90B submarines sold by France to Pakistan.
Hull systems: Employ HLES-80 steel in the pressure hull, permitting diving depths in excess of 320 m. No air-independent propulsion system was ordered. A 360-cell battery is employed. All machinery is "rafted" for sound isolation. Only nine personnel will be on watch under normal conditions. Some or all may have a MESMA air-independent auxiliary propulsion (AIP) system, which would lengthen the hull and increase displacements from the figures given above.
Combat sytems: The UDS International SUBTICS (Submarine Tactical Information and Command System) weapons-control system would be similar to the French Navy's SET *(Système d'Exploitation Tactique)* and would have six two-screen display consoles. The sonar suite would include a cylindrical bow transducer array, an active array, a passive ranging array, an acoustic intercept system, and passive flank arrays.

♦ 0 (+ 3 + 6) Russian Amur 1650 class (Project 677E)

Bldr: First three: Admiralteiskiye Verf 194, St. Petersburg; others: Mazagon Dock, Mumbai

	Laid down	L	In serv.
S	26-12-97	. . .	. . .
S	. . .	. . .	. . .
S	. . .	. . .	. . .

D: 1,650 tons normal surf./2,300 tons sub. **S:** 11 kts surf./21 kts sub.
Dim: 67.00 × 7.10 × 4.40
A: 6 bow 533-mm TT (18 tot. torpedoes or missiles, or . . . mines)
Electronics:
Radar: 1 . . . nav./surf. search
Sonar: bow active, bow and flank passive, towed linear passive
EW: . . . intercept
M: 2 2D-42-series diesel generator sets; 1 SED-1, 2,000-kw electric motor generator; 1 prop; 2,700 shp
Range: 6,000/. . . snorkel; 550/3 sub. **Endurance:** 45 days
Crew: 34 tot. (accomm. for 41)

Remarks: The first unit was laid down in anticipation of an Indian order. Lada (Project 677) is the domestic project name for the largest of the family of six different Amur-series export designs by the Rubin Central Design Bureau under a program initiated in 1989. Project Amur is available in versions from 550 to 2,000 tons surfaced displacement. A larger variant with fuel-cell air-independent auxiliary propulsion was laid down for the Russian Navy on the same date. As of 6-01, India was said to be nearing ordering three of the class to be built in Russia for $400 million each and six more to be built under license in India for a probably highly overoptimistic $250 million each.
Hull systems: Volumetric displacement is 1,765 m^3 submerged. A conservative design, with sail-mounted bow planes and cruciform stern control surfaces. Intended to operate 10 years between overhauls. Two battery groups. Generator sets are probably to be powered by tried-and-true 2D-42-series diesel engines. Said to be "8 to 10 times" quieter than the Project 877 Kilo. To use brushless generators to reduce noise. Will have an inertial navigational system. Crew figure given is with a two-section watch. Accommodations are in separate cabins. All waste products would be retained aboard until return to port. Normal operating depth limit is 250 m.
Combat systems: Attack periscope is to have night-vision features and a laser rangefinder. To have trailing-wire communications antenna. The radar and intercept antennas will be on the same mast, and the radar will have a low-power mode for concealed operations. Will use the Litiy combat system, with eight display consoles.

♦ 4 German Type 209/1500

	Bldr	Laid down	L	In serv.
S 44 SHISHUMAR	Howaldtswerke, Kiel	1-5-82	13-12-84	28-9-86
S 45 SHANKUSH	Howaldtswerke, Kiel	1-9-82	11-5-84	20-11-86
S 46 SHALKI	Mazagon DY, Mumbai	5-6-84	30-9-89	7-2-92
S 47 SHANKUL	Mazagon DY, Mumbai	3-9-89	21-3-92	28-5-94

Shankul (S 47) Brian Morrison, 2-01

Shishumar (S 44) John Mortimer, 2-01

Shankul (S 47)—note slight separation in the casing forward of the sail at the location of the Gäbler crew rescue sphere Brian Morrison, 2-01

D: 1,450 tons std.; 1,660 tons surf./1,850 tons sub. **S:** 13 kts surf./22.5 kts sub.
Dim: 64.40 × 6.50 × 6.20
A: 8 bow 533-mm TT (14 AEG SUT Mod. 1 wire-guided torpedoes); mines (see remarks)
Electronics:
Radar: Kelvin-Hughes Type 1007 nav./surf. search
Sonar: STN Atlas Elektronik CSU-83 search and attack suite, Thales DUUX-5 passive ranging and intercept
EW: Argo Phoenix-II AR-700 intercept, C 303 acoustic decoys
M: 4 MTU 16V493 TY 60 (or AZ 80) diesels (800 bhp each), 4 430-kw generators, 2 Siemens motors; 1 7-bladed prop; 6,100 shp (4,600 sust.)
Range: 13,000/10, 18,000/4.5 surf.; 8,200/8 snorkel; 30/20, 400/4.5, 524/4 sub.
Fuel: 157 tons **Endurance:** 50 days **Crew:** 8 officers, 28 enlisted

ATTACK SUBMARINES [SS] *(continued)*

Remarks: The order for these four, signed 11-12-81, included a later-dropped option to build two additional units in India. The Indian-built pair was delivered several years late and cost more than twice as much as the pair built in Germany. Although a renewed plan to build two more was announced during 5-93 and a preliminary contract may have been signed in 10-96 (and funding for the project was provided in 4-97), final Ministry of Defence approval to build two Type 75 boats of a modified design was not given until 6-99; DCN, France, was to supply technical assistance in adapting the original design for submerged launch of cruise missiles, but the program was on hold due to German sanctions imposed in 5-98. As of 2-00, India was negotiating with Howaldtswerke again, with a view toward modifying the two new units to launch the Russian Klub missile and possibly refitting the earlier four with the same missile; the rescue sphere system would have to be removed to provide sufficient magazine space in the torpedo room. By 1-01, however, further Type 209 production was stated to be no longer planned due to the alleged obsolescence of the design. S 44 began a refit at Mazagon Dockyard in 1999, and the other three were to complete midlife refits by 2005. All based at Mumbai, in the 10th Submarine Squadron.
Hull systems: Maximum operating depth: 250 m. A Gäbler spherical escape chamber is installed forward of the sail to provide emergency exit from within the two-compartment pressure hull. The four 132-cell Hawker (ex-Varta) batteries in the German-built pair weigh 280 tons; the Indian-built units have license-built British Chloride Industrial Batteries, Ltd., batteries and the later MTU 12V493 AZ 80 diesel variant.
Combat systems: Have the Singer-Librascope SFCS Mk 1 weapons-control system and Kollmorgen Model 76 search and attack periscopes. Strap-on minelaying pods were purchased for these ships; each can hold 24 mines. The first two Indian-built units received Thales ASM DUUX-5 Fenelon sonars, which were to be backfitted to the German-built pair during short refits commencing in 1995; also to be upgraded were the original CSU-3/4 sonar suites on the first pair. S 46 and S 47 have French Nereides towed buoyant VLF communications antenna cables. Six ship-sets of the Thales ASM TSM 2272 Eledone active/passive sonar suite were ordered for delivery in 1997–99 and were probably intended for installation on the proposed fifth and sixth ships and backfitting on the first four during the midlife refits now under way.

♦ 10 Soviet Kilo class (Project 877EKM)

Bldr: United Admiralty SY 199, St. Petersburg (S 63: Nizhniy Novgorod Zavod)

	Laid down	L	Del.	In serv.
S 55 Sindhugosh (ex-B-888)	29-5-83	29-6-85	25-11-85	30-4-86
S 56 Sindhuvaj (ex-B-898)	1-4-86	27-7-86	25-11-86	12-6-87
S 57 Sindhuraj (ex-B-. . .)	. . .	. . .	. . .	20-10-87
S 58 Sindhuvir (ex-B-860)	15-5-87	13-9-87	25-12-87	26-8-88
S 59 Sindhuratna (ex-B-. . .)	. . .	. . .	. . .	22-12-88
S 60 Sindhukesari (ex-B-804)	20-4-88	16-8-88	29-10-88	16-2-89
S 61 Sindhukirti (ex-B-468)	5-4-89	26-8-89	30-10-89	4-1-90
S 62 Sindhuvijay (ex-B-597)	6-4-90	27-7-90	27-10-90	8-3-91
S 63 Sindhurakshak (ex-B-. . .)	. . .	26-6-97	. . .	24-12-97
S 65 Sindhushastra (ex-B-. . .)	. . .	14-10-99	5-00	16-7-00

Sindhushastra (S 65)—the 10th Indian Navy Kilo — Brian Morrison, 2-01

Sindhurakshak (S 63) — Brian Morrison, 2-01

Sindhukirti (S 61) — John Mortimer, 2-01

D: 2,325 tons surf./3,076 tons sub. **S:** 10 kts surf./17 kts sub.
Dim: 74.3 (70.0 wl) × 10.0 × 6.6
A: 6 bow 533-mm TT (18 Type E53-777 wire-guided, E53-60 and E53-85 wake-homing, and E53-67 acoustic homing torpedoes or 24 mines—S 57–59, 60, 65 also: 3M-54E Klub-S antiship missiles); 1 Fasta-4 SAM syst. (8 9M-32M Strela-M missiles)
Electronics:
Radar: 1 MRK-50 Albatros (Snoop Tray-2) nav./search
Sonar: MGK-400 Rubikon (Shark Gill) LF active/passive suite with passive hull array; MG-519 Arfa (Mouse Roar) HF active classification/mine avoidance; MG-553 sound-velocity measuring; MG-512 cavitation detection; MG-53 sonar intercept
EW: Brick Pulp or Squid Head intercept; 6701E (Quad Loop) D/F
M: electric drive: 2 Type 4-2DL42M diesel generator sets (1,825 bhp; 1,500 kw at 700 rpm), 1 motor; 1 6-bladed prop; 5,900 shp—1 130-shp low-speed motor—2 low-speed maneuvering motors; 2 ducted props; 204 shp (3 kts)
Range: 6,000/7 snorkel; 400/3 sub. **Fuel:** 172 tons **Endurance:** 45 days
Crew: 12 officers, 41 enlisted

Remarks: Based at Vishakhapatnam and Mumbai. S 63 arrived in India 5-3-98; she and S 65 (pennant number S 64 was not used) were built from surplus components originally assembled for Russian Navy production. S 58 was overhauled at Zvezdochka Machine-Building Enterprise, Yagriy Island, Severodvinsk, Russia, for $80 million, beginning in 6-97 and completing 29-7-99; she recommissioned in India 31-10-99. S 57 and S 60 arrived at Admiralteyskiy Verf, St. Petersburg, in 4-99, with S 60 completed during 8-01 and S 57 in 10-01. S 59 was delivered to Severodvinsk for a $70 million overhaul during 5-00, but work did not commence until 3-6-01; it is scheduled for completion during 6-02. All four refitted units, plus the S 65, are equipped to launch the Novator 3M-54E Klub-S (NATO SS-NX-27 Alfa) antiship missile.

Units based at Vishakhapatnam are assigned to the 11th Submarine Squadron and those based at Mumbai to the 12th. The Indian Navy is said to consider these submarines not to be the equal of the navy's German-designed Type 209/1500 class.
Hull systems: Have two Indian-made battery sets, each with 120 cells, providing 9,700 kwh. Hull has six watertight compartments and 32% reserve buoyancy. When at rest on the surface, the submarine trims down 0.4 m by the bow. Maximum diving depth is 300 m, normal depth 240 m, and periscope depth 17.5 m. Have a rubber anechoic hull coating. The propulsion plant is suspended for silencing. Said to be improved in quieting over the basic Project 877 version, with improvements suggested by the Indian Navy. S 65 is said to have further improved noise-reduction features and an updated propulsion plant.
Combat systems: Have the MVU-110EM Murena combat data system, which can conduct two simultaneous attacks while tracking three other targets manually. Only two of the torpedo tubes can launch wire-guided weapons and missiles. The shoulder-launched SAM launch position is located in the after portion of the sail. Units overhauled in Russia are receiving the capability to launch Russian Novator 3M-54E Klub-S antiship and 91RE1 ASW cruise missiles from the torpedo tubes; the Indian Navy claims a land-attack capability for the Klub-S, of which four per ship will be carried. Units with missile capability receive the 3P-14PE fire-control system. All 10 are eventually to be missile-capable. S 65 is said to have later sonar systems than the others and is probably the unit equipped to launch the eight TEST-71EM-NK wire-guided torpedoes purchased from Russia.

♦ 3 Soviet Foxtrot class (Projects 641M and 641K)

Bldr: Admiraltesikiye Verfi 194, St. Petersburg

	Laid down	L	In serv.
S 21 Karanj	24-1-68	28-4-68	2-7-69
S 40 Vela	28-9-71	28-1-72	10-10-72
S 42 Vagli	1-2-73	19-4-73	16-12-73

Karanj (S 21)—with three sonar domes atop the casing for the Panchendriya passive-ranging sonar system — Brian Morrison, 2-01

D: 1,957 tons surf. (2,203 max.)/2,484 tons sub.
S: 15.5 kts surf./10 kts snorkel (max.)/18 kts sub. (max., electric)
Dim: 91.30 (89.70 wl) × 7.50 × 6.06 (surf.)
A: 6 bow and 4 stern 533-mm TT (22 Type 53-56WA and SET-53M torpedoes, or 32 Type AMD-1000 or MDT mines and 6 torpedoes)
Electronics:
Radar: 1 RKL-101 Flag nav./search
Sonar: MG-10M Gerkules HF active; MG-200 Arktika MF passive; MG-15 Tuloma underwater telephone; MG-13 Svyet-M sonar intercept
EW: 1 MRP-25 Nakat-M (Stop Light) intercept; Type 6701E Iva (Quad Loop) HFD/F
M: 3 Type 2D-42M diesels (1,825 bhp each), 3 electric motors (1 × 2,700-shp PG-102, 2 × 1,350-shp PG-101); 3 5- or 6-bladed props; 5,400 shp (sub.)—1 140-shp PG-104 electric low-speed motor on center shaft
Range: 20,000/8 surf.; 11,500/8 snorkel; 36/18, 380/2 sub.
Fuel: 360 tons **Endurance:** 70 days **Crew:** 8 officers, 67 enlisted

ATTACK SUBMARINES [SS] *(continued)*

Karanj (S 21) Mritunjoy Mazumdar, 2-01

Remarks: All were new on delivery. Most have had at least one refit in the USSR. S 40 collided with the destroyer *Rana* during 1990, with 17 killed. S 21 is retained primarily for sonar trials purposes. S 40 was to have completed an overhaul during 1999. The three constitute the 9th Submarine Squadron, based at Mumbai.
Disposals: *Kandheri* (S 22) was retired in 1990, *Kalvari* (S 23) during 1996, *Vagsheer* (S 43) in 1997, and *Kursura* (S 20) in 1998 (now a museum exhibit). *Vagir* (S 41) was placed in reserve in 1999 and is not expected to return to service.
Hull systems: Battery set has 448 cells. Can dive in as little as 45 seconds and have 527 tons reserve buoyancy in surfaced condition. The pressure hull has seven watertight compartments. Operating depth is 240 m normal, 280 maximum. Have an SPChM-FU-90 air-conditioning system.
Combat systems: S 21 has been employed since 1997 in trials with Bharat Electronics's Panchendriya passive sonar detection and targeting suite; three identical domes, one at the bow and two others before and abaft the sail, have been fitted. The after torpedo tubes in these submarines may no longer be used. Have the Leningrad-641 torpedo fire-control system. The MG-200 passive sonar has a range of about 18 km and the MG-10M active set a range of about 3.5 km.

Note: For operation by special forces personnel, the Indian Navy purchased 11 CE-2F/X100 two-man chariot submersibles from COS.M.O.S., Italy, in 1990. The craft displace 2,100 kg, are 7 m long, and have a range of 25 n.m.

GUIDED-MISSILE DESTROYERS [DDG]

♦ 0 (+ 3) ...... class (Project 15A)
Bldr: Mazagon Dock, Ltd., Mumbai

	Laid down	L	In serv.
D 63	...	...	2006
D 64	...	...	...
D 65	...	...	...

D: 5,500 tons (6,900 fl) **S:** 28 kts **Dim:** 163.00 × 17.60 × 6.40
A: ....
Electronics:
Radar: ...
Sonar: ...
EW: ...
M: CODOG: 2 Mashproekt-Zorya DA-80 reversible gas turbines (36,300 shp each), 2 Bergen Mek.Verk.–Garden Reach KVM-18 diesels (4,960 bhp each); 2 CP props; 72,600 shp
Electric: ... kw tot. (4 × ...-kw turbogenerators, 1 × ...-kw diesel set)
Range: 5,000/... **Crew:** 40 officers, 320 enlisted

Remarks: Funding for three was requested in 8-98 as Project 15A. They are to have improved electronics of Western design origin. Construction has been delayed pending a redesign to incorporate land-attack missiles, but a contract was expected to be signed during 6-01. The officially projected completion year for the first ship is probably overoptimistic. They may be equipped with Israeli Barak vertical-launch point-defense missile systems.

♦ 3 Delhi class (Project 15)
Bldr: Mazagon Dock, Ltd., Mumbai

	Laid down	L	In serv.
D 61 Delhi	14-11-87	1-2-91	15-11-97
D 60 Mysore	2-2-91	4-6-93	2-6-99
D 62 Mumbai (ex-*Bombay*)	14-12-92	20-3-95	22-1-01

Delhi (D 61) Brian Morrison, 2-01

Mysore (D 60) Brian Morrison, 2-01

Delhi (D 61)—note twin hangar and VDS "fish" in the centerline slot at the stern
Ralph Edwards, 2-01

D: 5,500 tons (6,900 fl) **S:** 28 kts **Dim:** 163.00 × 17.60 × 6.40
A: 16 Kh-35 Uran (SS-N-25 Switchblade) SSM (3M-24E missiles); 2 ZR-90 Shtil (SA-N-7) SAM syst. (2 single-rail MS-196 launchers; 48 Altair 9M-38M13 Buk-M3 missiles); 1 100-mm 59-cal. AK-100 DP; 2 twin 30-mm 54-cal. AK-630M gatling AA; 1 quintuple 533-mm PTA-53 TT (Gidropribor SET-65E ASW torpedoes); 2 12-round RBU-6000 ASW RL; 2 Sea King Mk 42B helicopters (Sea Eagle antiship missiles and/or WASS A-244S torpedoes)
Electronics:
Radar: 3 MR-212/201 Vaygach-U (Palm Frond) nav./surf. search; 1 Bharat RALW-02 early warning; 1 Salyut MR-755M2 Fregat-M2 (Half Plate) surf./air search; 1 Bharat Apurna (Garpun-Bal/Plank Shave) antiship missile target-desig.; 6 OP-3 (Front Dome) missile f.c.; 1 MR-145 Lev (Kite Screech) 100-mm gun f.c.; 2 MR-123 Vympel (Bass Tilt) 30-mm gun f.c.
Sonar: Bharat HUMVAD syst.: APSOH LF hull-mounted and VDS
EW: Elettronica-Bharat Ajanta intercept suite; Elettronica TQN-2 jammer; 2 2-round PK-2 decoy RL (200 rockets)
M: CODOG M-36N plant: 2 Mashproekt-Zorya DN-50 reversible gas turbines (27,000 shp max./23,100 shp sust. each), 2 Bergen Mek.Verk.–Garden Reach KVM-18 diesels (4,960 bhp each); 2 CP props; 54,000 shp (see remarks)
Electric: ... kw tot. (4 × ...-kw turbogenerators, 1 × ...-kw diesel set)
Range: 5,000/... **Crew:** 40 officers, 320 enlisted

Remarks: First unit was ordered 3-86 and cost $583.5 million. The third was renamed early in 2000.
Hull systems: The gas turbine installation has also been described as employing two M-36 "plants" that incorporate the listed DT-59 turbines. Hull lines are said to have been derived from the Kashin class. Have nonretracting fin stabilizers. D 61 reached 32 kts on 64,000 shp, and 13 kts astern, on trials. Harpoon-type helicopter landing aid and deck traversing equipment is installed. Have an NBC water washdown system, and the ships are divided internally into six independent citadels with independent power and communications systems. D 60 has enhanced air-conditioning capability to prevent overheating of electronic components.
Combat systems: Soviet and European weapons and European-designed/Indian-improved-and-manufactured electronics are being employed. The Bharat-built Shikari combat data system is said to be a variant of the AESN IPN-10 system and can track 12 targets and engage six simultaneously, while the Ajanta EW suite is based on the Elettronica INS-3 system. A Russian Purga ASW weapons-control system is fitted. The RALW-02 radar is a license-built Thales LW-02. Variable-depth sonars are handled by Indal-GRSE Model 15-750 deck-handling equipment; the designation indicates that the transducer may be derived from that of the Graseby Model 750 hull-mounted sonar. The hull-mounted component of the sonar system has also been reported to be Bharat Electronics's license-built Thales TSM 2633 Spherion. The 100-mm gun has 320 ready-service projectiles but no reloads; 12,000 rounds of 30-mm ammunition can be carried (8,000 ready service). D 60 is said to incorporate improved electronics and D 62 an improved sonar suite. The Russian SAM system is known as the Kashmir in Indian service.

GUIDED-MISSILE DESTROYERS [DDG] *(continued)*

Mumbai (D 62) Brian Morrison, 2-01

♦ **5 Soviet Kashin class (Project 61ME)**
Bldr: 61 Kommunara Zavod 445, Nikolayev

	L	In serv.
D 51 RAJPUT (ex-*Nadezhnyy*)	9-77	30-9-80
D 52 RANA (ex-*Gubitel'nyy*)	10-78	28-6-82
D 53 RANJIT (ex-*Lovkiy*)	6-79	24-11-83
D 54 RANVIR (ex-*Tolkovoy*)	3-83	28-8-86
D 55 RANVIJAY (ex-*Tverdyy*)	2-86	15-1-88

Rajput (D 51) Brian Morrison, 2-01

Rana (D 52) Ralph Edwards, 2-01

Ranvir (D 54)—with higher helicopter platform Brian Morrison, 2-01

Rajput (D 51)—note door over VDS housing beneath the helicopter platform
Ralph Edwards, 2-01

D: 4,050 tons (4,870 fl) **S:** 30 kts
Dim: 146.20 (134.50 wl) × 15.80 (14.00 wl) × 4.87 (hull)
A: D 51–54: 4 P-20/21 Termit (SS-N-2C Styx) SSM—D 55: 16 Kh-35 Uran SSM (4-round KT-184 launchers; 3M-24E missiles)—all: 2 2-rail SA-N-1 Volna-P SAM

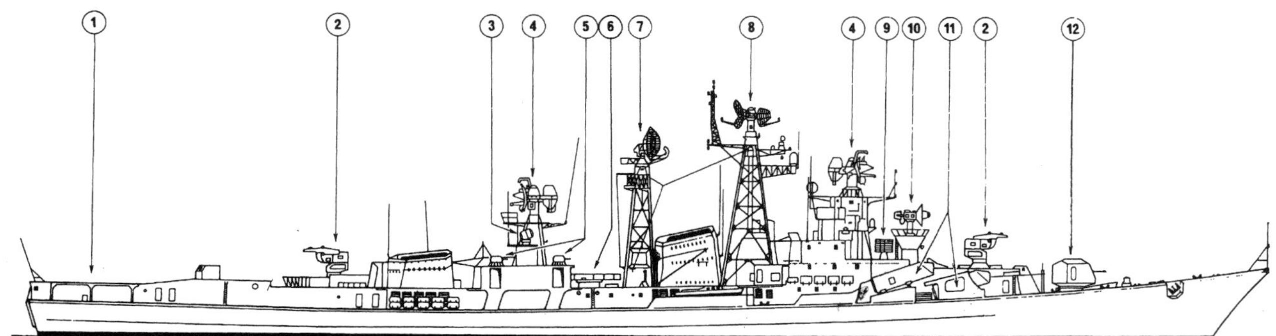

Rajput (D 51) 1. helicopter deck atop VDS housing 2. twin launcher for Volna-P (SA-N-1) SAM syst. 3. MR-104 Rys' (Drum Tilt) 30-mm radar gun directors 4. Yatagan (Peel Group) SAM control radars 5. twin 30-mm AK-230 AA 6. quintuple 533-mm TT mount 7. MR-500 Kliver (Big Net) early-warning radar 8. MP-310U Angara-M (Head Net-C) surf./air-search radar 9. RBU-6000 ASW RL (two abreast) 10. MR-105 Turel' (Owl Screech) fire-control radar for the 76.2-mm gunmount 11. P-20/21 Termit (SS-N-2C Styx) SSM launch tubes 12. twin 76.2-mm DP gunmount
Drawing by Robert Dumas, *Flottes de Combat*

GUIDED-MISSILE DESTROYERS [DDG] *(continued)*

syst. (32 B-601 Goa missiles); 1 twin 76.2-mm 59-cal. AK-726 DP; 4 twin 30-mm AK-230 65-cal. (D 54, 55: 4 single 30-mm 54-cal. AK-630 gatling) AA; 1 5-tube 533-mm PTA-53-61 TT; 2 12-round RBU-6000 ASW RL (192 RGB-60 rockets); 1 Ka-25 Hormone-A (D 54, 55: Ka-28 Helix-A) ASW helicopter

Electronics:

Radar: 2 Volga (Don Kay) nav.; 1 MP-310U Angara-M (Head Net-C) surf./air search; 1 MP-500 Kliver (Big Net) early warning; 2 Yatagan (Peel Group) SAM f.c.; 1 MR-105 Turel' (Owl Screech) 76.2-mm gun f.c.; 2 MR-104 Rys' (Drum Tilt) 30-mm AA f.c. (D 54, 55: MR-123 Vympel [Bass Tilt] f.c.)

Sonar: MG-335 Platina hull-mounted MF; hull-mounted HF attack; MF VDS

EW: D 51–54: 2 Nakhat-M (Watch Dog) intercept (2–18 GHz)—D 55: 2 Ajanta intercept—all: 2 Krab-11 (Top Hat-A) jammers; 2 Krab-12 (Top Hat-B) jammers; 4 16-round PK-16 decoy RL

M: COGAG M-3 plant: 4 Type M-8E gas turbines, 2 props (300 rpm max.); 96,000 shp (72,000 sust.)

Electric: 2,400 kw tot. (4 × 600-kw gas turbine sets)

Range: 900/32; 4,000/18 **Fuel:** 940 tons **Crew:** 37 officers, 350 enlisted

Remarks: New-construction Project 61E units, not conversions from former Soviet Navy units. Received Russian names for identification purposes during construction, meaning "Reliable," "Destructive," "Adroit," "Steadfast," and "Intelligent," respectively. D 51 and D 52 are based at Vishakhapatnam, the others at Mumbai. D 55 was in modernization refit at Mumbai Naval Dockyard as of 2-01.

Hull systems: Fin stabilizers are fitted. The main propulsion plant is derated from that of sisters in Russian service but is less effective in tropical conditions. D 54 and D 55 have the helicopter platforms at the stern about 1 m higher to accommodate the additional height of the Helix helicopter.

Combat systems: In contrast to Soviet Navy "Modified Kashins," the SS-N-2C missiles on Indian units were mounted forward and fire forward, while the after twin 76.2-mm gunmount was omitted in favor of a hangar below the main deck level in the location occupied by an aft 76.2-mm magazine in Soviet units; it is accessed via an inclined elevator. Carry 1,200 rounds for the 76.2-mm ZIF-67 gunmount. The MR-104 f.c. radars have been upgraded by DRDL in India and can detect targets operating at up to 900 kts. All are being refitted with the Ajanta EW system in place of Russian equipment; they may also receive Israeli Barak vertical-launch point-defense missile systems. D 55 received 16 Kh-35 Uran antiship missiles in place of the SS-N-2C launchers during 2001, and D 54 is to follow. There may also be plans to replace the SA-N-1 SAM system with Barak, although one report indicates that the Russian system is being upgraded with digital fire control and an optical backup control system.

FRIGATES [FF]

♦ 0 (+ 3) Nilgiri class (Project 17)

Bldr: Mazagon Dockyard, Mumbai

	Laid down	L	In serv.
F . . . Nilgiri	12-7-01	. . .	12-05 (del.)
F	. . .	. . .	. . .
F	. . .	. . .	2007

D: 4,600 tons (. . . fl) **S:** 30+ kts **Dim:** 143.0 × 17.0 × . . .

A: 8 3S-14NE vertical SSM launchers (8 3M-54E Klub-N missiles); 1 ZR-90 Shtil/Uragan (SA-N-7) SAM syst. (MS-196 launcher, 24 9M-38M13 Smerch missiles); 1 76-mm 62-cal. OTOBreda SuperRapid DP; 2 Kashtan CIWS (8 missiles on-mount; 64 9M-311/SA-N-11 Grison missiles; 2 30-mm gatling AA per mount also); 2 4-round Fasta-series SAM syst. (Igla-2M missiles); 2 pair fixed 533-mm DTA-53 TT (SET-65E ASW and 53-65KE antiship torpedoes); 1 12-round RBU-6000 ASW RL (60 Splav 90R rockets); 1 Ka-31 or Ka-28 Helix or ALH helicopter

Electronics:

Radar: 1 Decca BridgeMaster-E ARPA nav.; 2 MR-212/201-1 nav./surf. search; 1 MR-760MA Fregat-M2EM (Top Plate) 3-D air search; 1 Bharat RAWL-2 early warning; 1 MR-352 Pozitiv-E (Cross Dome) CIWS target desig.; 1 Oerlikon-Contraves-Bharat Shikari (TMX-Ka) 76-mm gun f.c.; 4 OP-3 (Front Dome) SAM f.c.; 2 3P-87 (Hot Flash) on-mount CIWS f.c.; 1 Bharat Apurna (Garpun-E/Plank Shave) missile surf. target desig.

Sonar: Bharat-Thales HUS 001 (TSM 2630 Spherion) bow-mounted MF

EW: . . .

M: CODOG: 2 G.E.-HAL LM-2500 gas turbines, 2 MTU . . . diesels; 2 CP props; 60,000 shp max.

Range: . . ./. . . **Crew:** 35 officers, 222 enlisted

Remarks: During 5-99, approval was given to begin constructing the first of three Project 17 "stealth" frigates of Indian design. Total cost is to be $562.5 million. The construction schedule is unduly optimistic, given past Indian naval shipbuilding performance. Work on fabricating modules for the first unit began 18-12-00. Severnoye Design Bureau, Russia, and DCN, France, reportedly are providing design and technical assistance, although it was revealed early in 5-01 that there was no final design for the ship, a month before the first was to be laid down.

♦ 0 (+ 3 + 3) Talwar class (Russian Project 11356)

Bldr: Severnyy Werf, St. Petersburg, Russia

	Laid down	L	In serv.
F . . . Talwar (ex-*Kashmir*)	10-3-99	12-5-00	5-02
F . . . Trishul (ex-*Arunchal Pradesh*)	23-9-99	24-11-00	12-02
F . . . Tabar (ex-*Toofan*, ex-*Sikkim*)	26-5-00	25-5-01	5-03

D: 3,300 tons normal (3,780 fl) **S:** 32 kts (30 sust.)

Dim: 125.3 (116.9 pp) × 15.2 (13.2 wl) × 4.9 (hull; 7.3 over sonar dome)

A: 8 3S-14NE vertical SSM launchers (8 3M-54E Klub-N missiles); 1 ZR-90 Shtil/Uragan (SA-N-7) SAM syst. (single-rail MS-196 launcher, 24 9M-38M13 Smerch missiles); 1 100-mm 59-cal. A-190 DP; 2 Kashtan CIWS (8 missiles on-mount; 64 9M-311/SA-N-11 Grison missiles; 2 30-mm gatling AA per mount also); 2 4-round Fasta-series SAM launchers (Igla-1E missiles); 2 pair fixed 533-mm DTA-53 TT (SET-65E ASW and 53-65KE antiship torpedoes); 1 12-round RBU-6000 ASW RL (60 Splav 90R rockets); 1 Ka-31 or Ka-28 Helix or ALH helicopter

Talwar (F . . .)—fitting out H&L Van Ginderen, 7-00

Talwar (F . . .)—fitting out; note lack of provision for a VDS installation at the stern H&L Van Ginderen, 7-00

Electronics:

Radar: 1 Decca BridgeMaster-E ARPA nav.; 2 MR-212/201-1 nav./surf. search; 1 MR-760MA Fregat-M2EM (Top Plate) 3-D air search; 1 MR-352 Pozitiv-E (Cross Dome) CIWS target desig.; 1 MR-221 100-mm f.c.; 4 OP-3 (Front Dome) SAM f.c.; 2 3P-87 (Hot Flash) on-mount CIWS f.c.; 1 Garpun-E (Plank Shave) missile surf. target desig.

Sonar: Zvezda M-1 suite: MGK-345 Bronza bow-mounted LF and SSN-137 (Steer Hide) LF VDS (see remarks)

EW: ASOR intercept/jammer suite; 8 10-round PK-10 Smelyy decoy syst. (KT-216 RL)

M: COGAG M-7 plant: 2 M-62 cruise gas turbines (6,000 shp each), 2 M-8K boost gas turbines (21,642 shp each); 2 5-bladed props; 55,284 shp max.

Electric: 3,200 kw tot. (4 × 800-kw diesel sets)

Range: 700/30; 3,900/20; 4,500/18 **Fuel:** 800 tons **Endurance:** 30 days

Crew: 200 tot.

Remarks: Government approval for construction for the first three was given in 5-98, and a contract was signed 17-11-97; the Russian yard was said already to have begun construction but was reported to be four months behind schedule as of 2-99 due to misappropriation of two-thirds of the $64 million advance payment by India. The keel-laying dates above refer to the placing of the first hull section on the construction ways; at that time, about a third of the hull modules for the first ship had been completed. Plans to build three more of the class in India were approved in 6-99. The Indian designation is Project 17A. Program cost reported at $931.5 million. The first was only about 30% complete at launch. The names mean "Shield," "Trident," and "Axe," respectively.

Hull systems: Hull and propulsion system are similar to the 1960s-vintage Krivak, with the forecastle extended further aft. The entirely new superstructure is shaped to reduce the radar return. Maximum propeller rpm is 300. Overall length also reported as 124.8 m and full load displacement as 3,620 tons.

Combat systems: The 3M-54E supersonic antiship missiles employ vertical launchers and are to have a range of up to 300 km; Indian officials have stated that the missiles will also have a land-attack role. The 100-mm gun has 350 ready-service rounds, while each Kashtan CIWS system has 32 missiles and 3,000 rounds of 30-mm ammunition. The bow-mounted sonar has a range of 2–6 km and the reported VDS a range of 8 km, although at least the *Talwar* apparently has no provision for a VDS installation. The hull-mounted sonar has also been referred to as the "Humsa," and the VDS as the "SSSN-113."

♦ 0 (+ 3) Improved Godavari class (Project 16A)

Bldr: Garden Reach SB & Eng., Calcutta

	Laid down	L	In serv.
F 31 Bramaputra	1989	29-1-94	14-4-00
F 32 Beas	1994	26-2-98	2002
F 33 Betwa	2001	2004	2005

Bramaputra (F 31) Mritunjoy Mazumdar, 2-01

FRIGATES [FF] *(continued)*

Bramaputra (F 31) John Mortimer, 2-01

Bramaputra (F 31)—note the large double helicopter hangar
Mritunjoy Mazumdar, 2-01

D: 3,850 tons (4,450 fl) **S:** 27 kts **Dim:** 126.4 (123.6 pp) × 14.5 × 4.6 (hull)
A: 16 Kh-35 Uran SSM (4 4-round KT-184 launchers; 3M-24E missiles); provision for 1 8-round Trishul SAM syst. (20 missiles); 1 8-round Barak vertical-launch point-defense SAM syst.; 1 76-mm 62-cal. OTOBreda SuperRapid DP; 4 single 30-mm 54-cal. AK-630 gatling AA; 2 triple 324-mm ILAS-3 ASW TT (WAAS *A-244S* or NST-58 torpedoes); 1 Sea King Mk 42B ASW helicopter; 1 Chetak or ALH liaison helicopter
Electronics:
Radar: 1 Decca BridgeMaster-E nav.; 1 Bharat Rashmi (ZW-06) surf. search; 1 Bharat RAWS-03 surf./air search; 1 Bharat RAWL-02 early warning; 1 Bharat Aparna surf. targeting; 3 Oerlikon-Contraves-Bharat Shikari (TMX-Ka) f.c.
Sonar: Bharat-Thales HUS 001 (TSM 2630 Spherion) bow-mounted MF; provision for Thales towed passive array
TACAN: Bharat FT13-S/M
EW: Bharat INDRA or Ajanta Mk IIC suite; 4 24-round Wallop/Grintek Ultrabarricade decoy RL; Graseby G 738 towed torpedo decoy
E/O: 1 OFC-3 gun f.c.
M: 2 sets Bhopal Eng. Y160 geared steam turbines; 2 5-bladed props; 31,000 shp
Boilers: 2 Babcock & Wilcox, 3-drum; 38.7 kg/cm², 450° C
Electric: . . . kw tot. (2 × 750-kw turbogenerators, 3 × . . .-kw diesel sets)
Range: 4,500/12; 3,500/18
Crew: 40 officers, 313 enlisted (incl. 13 aviation)

Remarks: Design is very similar to the previous *Godavari* class but with updated weapon and sensor suites. The difficulty in obtaining equipment ordered in Russia prior to the 1991 revolution delayed completion, and F 31 was commissioned without a SAM system. Named for rivers.
Hull systems: The propulsion system duplicates that of the *Godavari* class. The design is the antithesis of stealthy, with high, vertical hull sides, much topside clutter, and numerous corner reflectors. Have one pair of nonretractable fin stabilizers.
Combat systems: Employ a Bharat Electronics–developed variant of the Contraves IPN-10 (SADOC-1) combat direction system, with 10 Barco MPRD 9651 display/control consoles, linked by an FMC Unicom databus. Rashmi is an indigenously made version of the Thales ZW-06 radar, while RAWL-02 is an updated version of the Thales LW-02, and RAWS-03 is a version of the Thales DA-05. The Aparna target detection and tracking radar, a licensed-production version of the Russian Garpun-E (Plank Shave) operates in the X-band and is dedicated solely to the antiship missile fire-control system. The three Shikari f.c. radars control the 76-mm and 30-mm guns and will provide illumination for the Trishul SAM system when it is installed. The 8-round launcher for Trishul is intended to be fitted atop the deckhouse forward of the bridge. An infrared search-and-track sensor is to be fitted later. A JRC commercial Inmarsat SATCOM terminal is fitted.
The planned Trishul SAM system uses command-to-line-of-sight control and has a range of about 9 km; due to delays in development, two 8-cell Barak point-defense missile systems for each ship were ordered on 6-2-01. The OTOBreda 76-mm 62-cal. gun employs South African projectiles with Naschem and Fuchs anti–sea skimmer fuzes. The nomenclature for the sonar set has also been given as the HUMVAD. F 31 is said to carry shoulder-launched Igla-M infrared point-defense SAMs as an interim fit until Barak and/or Trishul are available.

♦ 3 Godavari class (Type 16) Bldr: Mazagon Docks, Mumbai

	Laid down	L	In serv.
F 20 Godavari	2-6-78	15-5-80	10-12-83
F 21 Gomati	1981	20-3-84	16-4-88
F 22 Ganga	1980	15-11-81	1-1-86

Godavari (F 20) John Mortimer, 2-01

Ganga (F 22)—the protruding sponsons supporting the antiship missile launchers readily distinguish this class from the later *Bramaputra* class
Mritunjoy Mazumdar, 2-01

Gomati (F 21)—note the MR-104 fire-control radars on platforms abreast the after pylon mast Brian Morrison, 2-01

D: 3,700 tons (4,300 fl) **S:** 29 kts **Dim:** 125.6 (123.6 pp) × 14.4 × 4.05 (hull)
A: 4 P-20/21 Termit (SS-N-2C Styx) SSM; 1 2-rail Osa-ME (SA-N-4) SAM syst. (20 9M-33M Gecko missiles); 1 twin 57-mm 70-cal. AK-257 DP; 4 twin 30-mm 65-cal. AK-230 AA; 2 triple 324-mm ILAS-3 ASW TT (WASS A-244S or NST-58 torpedoes); 1 Sea King Mk 42B ASW helicopter; 1 Chetak helicopter
Electronics:
Radar: 2 Thales-Bharat ZW-06A surf. search; 1 MR-310U Angara-M (Head Net-C) air/surf. search; 1 Bharat RALW-02 early warning; 1 MPZ-310 (Pop Group) SAM f.c.; 1 MR-103 Bars (Muff Cob) 57-mm gun f.c.; 2 MR-104 Rys' (Drum Tilt) 30-mm gun f.c.
Sonar: Bharat-Thales TSM 2630 Spherion hull-mounted MF (F 20: Canadian Westinghouse SQS-505)
TACAN: Bharat FT13-S/M
EW: Bharat Ajanta intercept; 4 24-round Wallop/Grintek Ultrabarricade decoy RL; Graseby G 738 towed torpedo decoy
M: 2 sets Bhopal Eng. geared steam turbines; 2 5-bladed props; 31,000 shp
Boilers: 2 Babcock & Wilcox, 3-drum; 38.7 kg/cm², 450° C
Electric: 3,000 kw tot. (2 × 750-kw turbogenerators, 3 × 500-kw diesel sets)
Range: 4,500/12 **Fuel:** 438 tons
Crew: 51 officers, 262 enlisted (accomm. for 362)

Remarks: Design derived from the *Leander* class, with the same propulsion plant but a considerably larger hull. The electronics and weapons systems are a very diverse selection of Western European–designed/Indian-built and Russian systems. Are named for rivers.
Hull systems: Steel superstructure. Have two pairs of Vosper nonretractable fin stabilizers. The hangar is sized for two Sea Kings, but only one (often with a Chetak light helo aboard also) is normally carried for stability reasons. A helicopter landing and traversing system is fitted. Carry 91 tons of fresh water.
Combat systems: The Selenia IPN-10 combat data system is employed. Bharat's RALW-02 radar uses the same antenna as the Thales DA-08. There are two backup manual directors for the twin AK-230 30-mm AA guns and two for the AK-57 57-mm mount. Probably also carry Igla-2M shoulder-launched heat-seeking point-defense SAMs.

FRIGATES [FF] *(continued)*

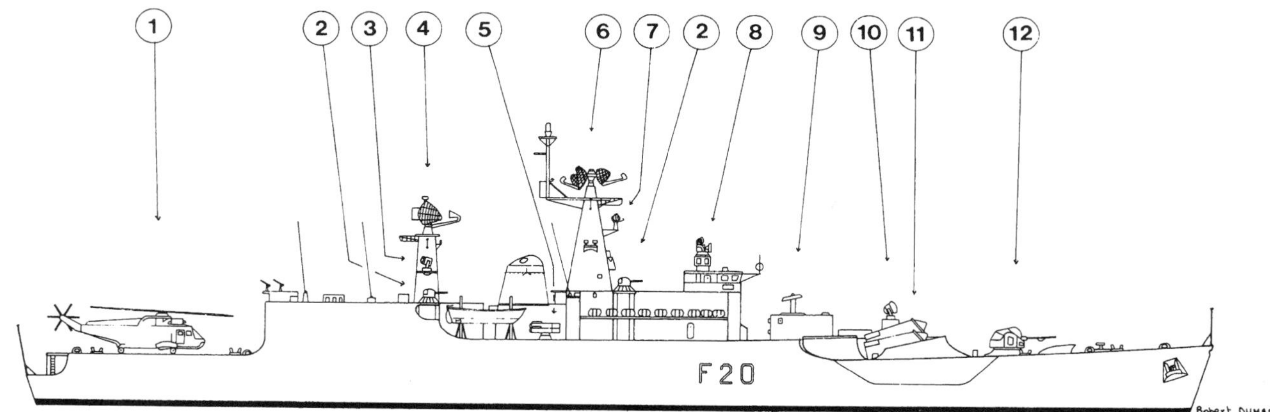

Godavari (F 20) 1. Sea King Mk 42 helicopter 2. twin 30-mm AK-230 AA 3. MR-104 Rys' (Drum Tilt) 30-mm gun radar directors 4. Bharat RALW-02 early-warning radar 5. triple ILAS-3 ASW TT 6. MR-310U Angara-M (Head Net-C) surf./air-search radar 7. ZW-06A nav./surf. search radar 8. MPZ-310 (Pop Group) SAM fire-control radar 9. ZIF-122 launcher for the Osa-ME (SA-N-4) SAM system 10. MR-103 Bars (Muff Cob) radar/electro-optical director for the 57-mm gunmount 11. P-20/21 Termit (SS-N-2C Styx) SSM 12. twin 57-mm AK-257 DP gunmount
Drawing by Robert Dumas, *Flottes de Combat*

♦ 5 U.K. Leander class

Bldr: Mazagon Docks, Mumbai

	Laid down	L	In serv.
F 34 Himgiri	1967	6-5-70	23-11-74
F 35 Udaygiri	14-9-70	24-10-72	18-2-76
F 36 Dunagiri	1-73	9-3-74	5-5-77
F 41 Taragiri	1974	25-10-76	16-5-80
F 42 Vindhyagiri	1976	12-11-77	8-7-81

Himgiri (F 34) Brian Morrison, 2-01

Dunagiri (F 36)—note the small telescoping helicopter hangar and the pit abaft the light deck for the Limbo mortar Ralph Edwards, 2-01

Taragiri (F 41)—with large helicopter hangar in extended position John Mortimer, 2-01

D: F 34–36: 2, 682 tons (2,962 fl)—F 41, 42: 2,970 tons (3,250 fl)
S: 30 kts **Dim:** 113.38 × 13.1 × 4.27 (F 41, 42: 5.50 max.)
A: 1 twin 114-mm 45-cal. Vickers Mk 6 DP; 2 twin 30-mm 65-cal. AK-230 AA—F 34–36: 1 3-round Limbo Mk 10 ASW mortar; 1 Chetak helicopter—F 41 and 42: 1 2-round 375-mm Bofors ASW RL; 2 triple 324-mm ILAS-3 ASW TT; 1 Sea King helicopter

Vindhyagiri (F 42)—the Bofors ASW rocket launcher is mounted at the forecastle break, just forward of the twin 114-mm gunmount John Mortimer, 2-01

Dunagiri (F 36) John Mortimer, 2-01

Electronics:
Radar: 1 Decca 1226 nav.; 1 Thales ZW-06 surf. search; 1 Bharat RALW-02 early warning; 1 Thales M 44 gun f.c.
Sonar: F 34, 35: APSOH hull mounted—F 36: Can. Westinghouse SQS-505 MF hull-mounted—F 34–36: Can. Westinghouse SQS-502 target depth-determining (for Limbo)—F 41, 42: Thales Diodon hull-mounted MF
TACAN: F 41 and 42 only: Bharat FT13-S/M
EW: Bharat Ajanta-P intercept; Racal Cutlass jammer; Telegon-4 HFD/F; Graseby G 738 towed torpedo decoy syst.

M: 2 sets Bhopal Eng. geared steam turbines; 2 5-bladed props; 30,000 shp
Boilers: 2 Babcock & Wilcox, 3-drum; 38.7 kg/cm², 450° C
Electric: 2,500 kw tot.
Range: approx. 4,500/12 **Fuel:** 382 tons **Crew:** 40 officers, 370 enlisted

Remarks: The first two built were very similar to British versions of the *Leander* class, but later units were progressively improved, using Thales-designed radars and an ever-greater proportion of Indian-built components. Are very crowded, due to unusually large crews. F 41 experienced severe fire damage in 1994 that took several years to repair. F 36 suffered a dockyard fire on 10-11-99. Although reported stricken in 1997, F 35 was officially stated to be in service in 12-00 and was undergoing a refit at Mumbai as of 2-01 to the same configuration as F 34 and F 36. The similar *Krishna* (F 46, ex-British *Andromeda*), purchased in 5-94, is used strictly for training and is decribed under [AXT].

Disposals: *Nilgiri* (F 33) was stricken on 31-5-96.

Combat systems: F 41 and F 42 have very large telescoping hangars and carry their twin Bofors ASW RLs on the forecastle; their hangars can accommodate a Sea King Mk 42 ASW helicopter, and their flight decks incorporate Canadian Bear Trap haul-down gear. F 41 and F 42 also have openings in the hull sides beneath the helicopter deck at the stern. F 34 and F 36 have been refitted with smaller telescoping helicopter hangars, and F 36 has had her variable-depth sonar removed. The former two Sea Cat SAM launchers have been replaced in the entire class by two twin AK-230 gunmounts salvaged from discarded Osa-series missile boats. The ships probably also carry Igla-2M shoulder-launched heat-seeking point-defense SAMs.

CORVETTES [FFL]

♦ 7 (+ 1) Khukri class (Project 25/25A)

	Bldr	Laid down	L	In serv.
P 49 Khukri	Mazagon DY, Mumbai	27-9-85	3-12-86	23-8-89
P 46 Khutar	Mazagon DY, Mumbai	13-9-86	15-4-89	7-6-90
P 44 Kirpan	Garden Reach SB, Calcutta	15-11-85	16-8-88	12-1-91
P 47 Khanjar	Garden Reach SB, Calcutta	15-11-85	16-8-88	22-10-91
P 61 Kora	Garden Reach SB, Calcutta	10-1-90	23-9-92	10-8-98
P 62 Kirch	Garden Reach SB, Calcutta*	1992	1996	22-1-01
P 63 Kulish	Garden Reach SB, Calcutta	31-1-92	18-8-97	20-8-01
P . . . Kharmuk	Garden Reach SB, Calcutta	27-8-97	6-4-00	2003

Kirch (P 62)—the latest Project 25A variant, with OTOBreda 76-mm gun and a Shikari gun-control radar Brian Morrison, 2-01

Kora (P 61)—the first Project 25A variant, with 16 antiship missiles but retaining the Russian 76.2-mm gun and f.c. radar Brian Morrison, 2-01

Kirpan (P 44)—Project 25 version, with four antiship missiles Ralph Edwards, 2-01

Khutar (P 46)—note the bulk of the P-20/21 Termit antiship missile launchers and the blast shielding worked into the face of the superstructure Ralph Edwards, 2-01

*Fitted out by Mazagon DY

D: 1,350 tons (fl; P 61 and later: 1,400 fl) **S:** 28 kts (25 sust.)
Dim: 91.11 × 10.45 × 2.50 (hull; 4.45 max.)
A: first four: 4 P-20/21 Termit (SS-N-2C) Styx SSM—P 61 and 62: 16 Kh-35 Uran-E (SS-N-25 Switchblade) SSM (4 4-round KT-184 launchers; 3M-24EM6 missiles)—all: 1 76.2-mm 59-cal. AK-176M (P 62 and later: 76-mm 62-cal. OTOBreda SuperRapid) DP; 2 single 30-mm 54-cal. AK-630 gatling AA; 2 SA-N-5 shoulder-launched SAM positions (Igla-2M missiles)
Electronics:
Radar: 1 Bharat 1245 (P 62: Bharat Rani) nav.; 1 MR-352 Pozitiv-E (Cross Dome) air search; 1 Bharat Aparna antiship missile target desig.; 1 MR-123 Vympel (Bass Tilt) (P 62 and later: 1 Oerlikon-Contraves-Bharat Shikari/TMX-Ka) gun f.c.
Sonar: none
EW: Bharat Ajanta-P Mk II intercept—first four: 2 or 4 16-round PK-16 decoy RL—P 61 and later: 4 10-round PK-10 decoy RL—all: NPOL towed torpedo decoy
E/O: 1 Oventus infrared surveillance and tracking
M: 2 Kirloskar-SEMT-Pielstick 18 PA6 V280 diesels; 2 CP props; 14,400 bhp (10,600 sust.)
Electric: 1,400 kw tot. (4 × 350-kw, 415-V, 50-Hz, diesel-driven sets)
Range: 4,000/16 **Fuel:** 140 m^3 **Crew:** 9 officers, 70 enlisted

Remarks: Intended to replace the Petya class. First two ordered 12-83, next pair in 1985; units 5 through 8 were ordered 4-90 as Project 25A and were originally to have incorporated gas turbines in the propulsion system and a Soviet-supplied Osa-M SAM system. Four more were at one time planned. Construction of these fairly simple ships has taken a great deal of time. P 61 carried a crew of 14 officers and 120 enlisted during a Persian Gulf cruise in 3-99. Based at Mumbai and Vishakhapatnam.
Hull systems: The diesels in the first four were made in France. Have nonretracting fin stabilizers and are fully air-conditioned. P 61 and later displace 50 tons additional and are 91.16 m overall.
Combat systems: Have no ASW capability. The Alenia IPN-10 combat data system (license-built as the Vympal system by Bharat in unit 2 onward) is fitted. All have a Magnavox MX 1102-NV NAVSAT receiver and an STN Atlas Elektronik echo sounder. The Pozitiv-E air-search radar, in a radome (NATO Cross Dome) at the masthead, is a Russian set with a 70- to 75-n.m. range and was derived from the target-designation component of the Cross Sword radar control system for the Soviet SA-N-9 SAM system. No helicopter hangars are fitted. P 61 and later have helicopter landing systems designed by SOFMA of France, carry four decoy rocket launchers, and have the Ajanta-P Mk II EW system. In P 62 and later, the Russian 76.2-mm gun has been replaced by an OTOBreda 76-mm 62-cal. SuperRapid DP mount with a European-designed f.c. radar and control system. In P 61 and later, the Kh-35 antiship missiles can be launched at 1-second intervals. *Kulish* and *Kharmuk* are to have only eight antiship missiles to save on topweight; reportedly, however, they may receive Trishul SAM systems in place of the 76-mm gunmount—although with the delay in the Trishul program, that seems doubtful.

♦ 2 Soviet Petya-III class

Bldr: Khabarovsk Zavod

P 73 Anjadip (In serv. 2-73) P 75 Amini (In serv. 3-74)

Anjadip (P 73) Brian Morrison, 2-01

D: 950 tons (1,150 fl) **S:** 29 kts
Dim: 81.80 (78.00 pp) × 9.20 × 2.72 (hull; 5.82 over sonar)
A: 2 twin 76.2-mm 59-cal. AK-276 DP; . . . Igla-2M shoulder-launched SAMs; 4 16-round RBU-2500 ASW RL; 1 3-tube 533-mm TT mount; 2 d.c. racks; 2 mine rails
Electronics:
Radar: 1 Don-2 nav.; 1 Fut-N (Slim Net) air/surf. search; 1 Fut-B (Hawk Screech) gun f.c.
Sonar: Titan hull-mounted MF
EW: Telegon HFD/F
M: CODOG: 1 Type 61-D3 diesel (6,000 bhp), 2 M-2 gas turbines (15,000 shp each); 3 props (centerline CP)—2 75-kw auxiliary electric motors (3 kts)
Range: 450/29; 4,800/10 **Fuel:** 130 tons **Crew:** 8 officers, 90 enlisted

Remarks: Survivors of 12 new-construction, export-version ships transferred in 1969 1972, and 1975. Are overcrowded, as the Indian Navy operates them with about 28 more personnel than did the Soviet Navy. Are being replaced by the much more capable *Khukri* class, which does not, however, have an ASW capability. Are assigned to the 32nd Patrol Vessel Squadron.
Disposals: *Kanjar* (P 82) and *Amindivi* (P 83) were stricken during 1986–88 *Kavaratti* (P 80) during 8-86, *Kiltan* (P 79) in 1987, *Katchal* (P 81) in 1990, *Kamorta* (P 77) in 1991, *Kadmath* (P 78) during 9-92, *Arnala* (P 68) during 1999, and *Androth* (P 69) in 2000. *Andaman* (P 74) foundered 21-8-90 in the Bay of Bengal.
Hull systems: Have fin stabilizers. The electric auxiliary propulsors are retractable and are mounted at the extreme stern for use in harbor maneuvering.

PATROL SHIPS [PS]

♦ 0 (+ . . .) proposed multipurpose ships

D: 2,000 tons (fl) **S:** 30 kts (20 on diesel) **Dim:** 103.00 (97.00 pp) × 12.5 × . . .
A: 1 76.2-mm 59-cal. AK-176 or 76-mm 62-cal. OTOBreda SuperRapid DP; 1 30-mm 54-cal. AK-630 gatling AA
Electronics: Radar: . . .
M: CODAG: 2 . . . gas turbines, 2 diesels; 2 CP props
Range: 7,500/. . . **Crew:** 14 officers, 110 enlisted

Remarks: Remains in concept design as a follow-on to the *Sukanya* class, intended to perform offshore patrol, 200-n.m. economic zone patrol, fisheries protection, and search-and-rescue duties and also to be employable as survey ships. Would have a helicopter facility and be capable of operating aircraft in up to Sea State 4 and remaining effective in up to Sea State 7. Would have four diesel generator sets.

PATROL SHIPS [PS] *(continued)*

♦ 6 Sukanya class

	Bldr	Laid down	L	In serv.
P 50 SUKANYA	Korea-Tacoma, Masan	. . .	1989	31-8-89
P 51 SUBHADRA	Korea-Tacoma, Masan	. . .	1989	25-1-90
P 52 SUVARNA	Korea-Tacoma, Masan	. . .	22-8-90	4-4-91
P 53 SAVITRI	Hindustan SY, Vishakhapatnam	6-88	23-5-89	27-11-90
P 54 SARYU	Hindustan SY, Vishakhapatnam	. . .	16-10-89	8-10-91
P 56 SUJATA	Hindustan SY, Vishakhapatnam	11-88	25-10-91	3-11-93

Subhadra (P 51)—adapted for ballistic-missile launch trials, with a stabilized launch platform in the center of the flight deck, enhanced EW equipment, and a TACAN set
Brian Morrison, 2-01

Sujata (P 56) Brian Morrison, 2-01

Sukanya (P 50)—with the Indian flag supplanting the D/F loop at the masthead while acting as a reviewing ship for the 2-01 naval review at Mumbai
Brian Morrison, 2-01

D: 1,650 tons (1,890 fl) **S:** 21.7 kts **Dim:** 101.95 (96.00 pp) × 11.50 × 3.40
A: 1 40-mm 60-cal. Bofors Mk 3 AA; . . . Igla-2M shoulder-launched SAMs; 4 single 12.7-mm mg; 1 Chetak helicopter
Electronics:
Radar: 1 Bharat 1245 nav.; 1 Decca 2459 surf. search
TACAN: P 51 only: Bharat FT13-S/M
EW: P 51 only: Bharat Ajanta-P Mk II intercept
M: 2 Kirloskar-SEMT-Pielstick 16 PA6 V280 diesels; 2 props; 12,800 bhp
Range: 7,000/15 **Fuel:** 300 tons + 40 tons aviation fuel **Endurance:** 60 days
Crew: 10 officers, 60 enlisted (accomm. for 16 officers, 141 enlisted)

Remarks: Construction funded by the Oil & Natural Gas Commission. First three were ordered from South Korea in 3-87, and the others, built with Korean assistance, in 8-87. Three more were ordered for the Indian Coast Guard in 1990. Intended for offshore patrol vessel duties for the protection of oil platforms and the Indian economic exclusion zone. P 51 acts as trials ship for the Dhanush ballistic-missile system. Sister *Sharada* (P 55) was sold to Sri Lanka and delivered on 9-12-00.
Hull systems: Have a helicopter beacon, fin stabilizers, a firefighting water monitor on the hangar roof, pollution control equipment, a towing capability, and Inmarsat SATCOM. Carry 60 tons of fresh water and 9 tons of lube oil and are fitted with freshwater generators.
Combat systems: The 40-mm gun is a simple Mk 3 powered mounting with local control only. A dual 30-mm 2A42 AA/12.7-mm Medak AA mount may be substituted. Carry a rigid inflatable inspection dinghy to starboard. P 51 was altered during 1999 at Mumbai to act as trials ship for a navalized version of the Dhanush ballistic missile. P 51 conducted the first launch at sea on 11-4-00 at the Balasore Test Range, Orissa. The missiles were stored in the helicopter hangar and moved to a stabilized platform set into the helicopter deck for erection and launching. P 51 is also equipped with EW gear, SATCOM, and new navigational radar.

GUIDED-MISSILE PATROL COMBATANTS [PGG]

♦ 2 Soviet Nanuchka-II class (Project 1234E)

Bldr: Sudostroitel'noye Obyedineniye "Almaz," Petrovskiy SY, St. Petersburg

	In serv.
K 71 VIJAYDURG (ex-*Priliv*)	12-76
K 72 SINDHURDURG (ex-*Priboy*)	5-77

Vijaydurg (K 71) John Mortimer, 2-01

D: 560 tons (660 fl) **S:** 32 kts **Dim:** 59.3 × 12.6 × 2.6 (3.1 max.)
A: 4 P-20/21 Termit (SS-N-2C Styx) SSM; 1 twin-rail Osa-M (SA-N-4) SAM syst. (20 9M-33M Gecko missiles); 1 twin 57-mm 70-cal. AK-257 DP
Electronics:
Radar: 1 Don-2 nav.; 1 Rangout (Square Tie) surf. target desig.; 1 MPZ-301 (Pop Group) SAM f.c.; 1 MR-103 Bars (Muff Cob) gun f.c.
EW: 2 16-round PK-16 decoy RL
M: 3 Type M-521-TM5 diesels; 3 props; 25,996 bhp
Range: 900/30; 2,500/12 (1 engine) **Endurance:** 10 days
Crew: 7 officers, 42 enlisted

Remarks: Arrived in India in 3-77 and 8-77, respectively. Bore the listed Russian names during construction. Sister *Hosdurg* (K 73, ex-*Uragan*) was stricken 6-99 due to hull corrosion. The other two are based at Mumbai as the 21st Missile Vessel Squadron and are operational. Three or more additional units were reportedly ordered 20-12-82, but no deliveries took place. Poor sea boats.
Hull systems: The diesels each are composed of two tropicalized, end-for-end coupled, 56-cylinder M-504 radial diesel engines, with the gearboxes between them. Kirloskar-Cummins heat exchangers and condensers were added during the 1980s to improve engine performance.
Combat systems: The Band Stand radome covers a Rangout antenna in these export units. Rangout can also be used in a purely passive mode to detect and track targets.

GUIDED-MISSILE PATROL CRAFT [PTG]

♦ 0 (+ 2 + . . .) Tarantul-IV class (Project 12418)

	Bldr	L	In serv.
K . . . PRABAL	Mazagon Dock, Mumbai	28-9-00	2-02
K . . . PRALAYA	Mazagon Goa SY, Goa	14-12-00	. . .

Prabal (K . . .)—fitting out at Mumbai Ralph Edwards, 2-01

GUIDED-MISSILE PATROL CRAFT [PTG] *(continued)*

D: 500 tons (fl) **S:** 40 kts (35 sust.)
Dim: 56.9 × 13.00 (max.; 8.75 wl) × 2.65 (hull; 4.51 props)
A: 8 Kh-35 Uran-E (SS-N-25 Switchblade) SSM (2 4-round KT-184 launchers; 3M-24EM6 missiles); 1 76-mm 62-cal. OTOBreda SuperRapid DP; 1 4-round Strela-3 (SA-N-8) SAM syst. (12 Igla-2M missiles); 2 single 30-mm 54-cal. AK-630M gatling AA; 2 single 7.62-mm mg
Electronics:
Radar: 1 Decca BridgeMaster-E ARPA nav.; 1 Pozitiv-E (Cross Dome) air search; 1 Bharat Aparna (Garpun-E) surf. target detection/desig.; 1 Bharat Lynx gun f.c.
EW: . . . . intercept, 2 . . . decoy RL
M: M-15E COGAG plant: 2 DMR-76 cruise gas turbines (4,000 shp each), 2 PR-77 boost gas turbines (12,000 shp each); 2 props; 32,000 shp
Electric: 500 kw tot. (2 × 200-kw, 1 × 100-kw diesel sets; 415 V, 50 Hz a.c.)
Range: 760/43; 1,650/12 **Fuel:** 122,634 liters **Endurance:** 10 days
Crew: 5 officers, 52 enlisted

Remarks: An improvement over an export version of the Tarantul design offered by Russia in 1993. *Prabal* was laid down 30-8-98 and was fitting out as of 2-01.
Hull systems: Maximum speed listed is achievable in 15° C air temperature; 35 kts is said to be achievable under tropical conditions.
Combat systems: The Aparna (a license-built version of the Russian Garpun radar) radar system can track 15 targets simultaneously, either in active or passive mode.

♦ 11 (+ 4) Tarantul-I class (Project 1241RE)

	Bldr	L	In serv.
K 40 Veer	Volodarskiy SY, Rybinsk	10-86	12-5-87
K 41 Nirbhik	Volodarskiy SY, Rybinsk	10-87	3-2-88
K 42 Nipat	Volodarskiy SY, Rybinsk	11-88	15-1-89
K 43 Nishank	Volodarskiy SY, Rybinsk	6-89	12-9-89
K 44 Nirghat	Volodarskiy SY, Rybinsk	3-90	4-6-90
K 45 Vibhuti	Mazagon Dock, Mumbai	26-4-90	3-6-91
K 46 Vipul	Mazagon Dock, Mumbai	3-1-91	16-3-92
K 47 Vinash	Mazagon Goa SY, Goa	24-1-92	20-11-93
K 48 Vidyut	Mazagon Goa SY, Goa	12-12-92	16-1-95
K 83 Nashak	Mazagon Dock, Mumbai	12-11-93	29-12-94
K 98 Prahar	Mazagon Goa SY, Goa	26-8-95	1-3-97
K	Garden Reach SB & Eng., Calcutta	2000	. . .
K	Garden Reach SB & Eng., Calcutta	2000	. . .
K	Garden Reach SB & Eng., Calcutta	. . .	. . .
K	Garden Reach SB & Eng., Calcutta	. . .	. . .

Nipat (K 42)—note the Ajanta EW array on the platform halfway up the mast
Mritunjoy Mazumdar, 2-01

Nirbhik (K 41)—with boost gas turbine exhaust doors open in the transom stern
Brian Morrison, 2-01

D: 385 tons light (455 normal, 477 full load) **S:** 43 kts
Dim: 56.92 (49.50 pp) × 10.55 (9.40 wl) × 2.14 (hull; 4.0 props)
A: 4 P-20/21 Termit (SS-N-2C Styx) SSM; 1 76.2-mm 59-cal. AK-176 DP; 1 4-round SA-N-8 SAM syst. (12 Igla-2M missiles); 2 single 30-mm 54-cal. AK-630 gatling AA; 4 single 7.62-mm mg

Prahar (K 98)—without Ajanta gear Brian Morrison, 2-01

Electronics:
Radar: 1 Kivach-3 or Decca BridgeMaster-E nav.; 1 Bharat Aparna or Garpun-E (Plank Shave) surface targeting; 1 MR-123 Vympel (Bass Tilt) gun f.c.
EW: K 40–44, 46: Ajanta Mk II intercept—all: 2 16-round PK-16 decoy RL
M: M-15E COGAG plant: 2 DMR-76 cruise gas turbines (4,000 shp each), 2 PR-77 boost gas turbines (12,000 shp each); 2 props; 32,000 shp
Electric: 500 kw tot. (2 × 200-kw, 1 × 100-kw diesel sets; 415 V, 50 Hz a.c.)
Range: 760/43; 1,400/13 **Fuel:** 122,634 liters **Endurance:** 10 days
Crew: 5 officers, 52 enlisted

Remarks: First five ordered from the USSR in 1984 for delivery 1986–89. Six to be built by Mazagon Dockyard at Mumbai were ordered 1-87, followed by orders for a reported nine to be built at Mazagon's Goa facility and three or more at Garden Reach Shipbuilding, Calcutta. Some sources indicate that as many as 35 are (or were) planned, but construction has slowed and funding has dwindled; Garden Reach has fallen far behind the planned construction schedule, and its first unit apparently did not make the announced 5-01 completion date. Active units are assigned to the 22nd Missile Vessel Squadron.
Hull systems: Stainless-steel-alloy, seven-watertight-compartment hull with aluminum alloy superstructure, decks, and internal bulkheads. Very strong and rugged construction. Have difficulty maneuvering below 10 kts. Beginning with the units to be delivered in 1993, it had been intended to power the craft with one HAL-G.E. LM-2500 gas turbine (28,000 shp) and two Kirloskar-MTU 12V538 TB92 diesels (3,000 bhp max., 2,555 bhp sust.), driving two shafts in a CODOG arrangement, but all craft to date have had the standard, Russian-supplied propulsion system.
Combat systems: The weapons system employs analog computers and has many backup features. Normally carry two infrared-homing and two radar-homing missiles. The Garpun-E (NATO Plank Shave) radar set (license-produced by Bharat as the Aparna for later units) can also serve as a passive radar intercept receiver. Carry 252 ready-service 76.2-mm rounds and another 150 in reserve. The 7.62-mm mg are mounted at the base of the mast, two per side.

Note: The remaining Project 205ME (Osa-II class) missile craft no longer carry missiles and are used as patrol craft; see under [PC].

PATROL CRAFT [PC]

♦ 4 Soviet Pauk-II class (Project 1241PE)
Bldr: Volodarskiy SY, Rybinsk

	In serv.		In serv.
P 33 Abhay	3-89	P 35 Aksay	1-91
P 34 Ajay	24-1-90	P 36 Agray	2-91

Ajay (P 34) Brian Morrison, 2-01

D: 425 tons (495 fl) **S:** 32 kts (28 sust.)
Dim: 58.5 (49.5 pp) × 10.2 (9.4 wl) × 2.14 (hull; 4.0 props)
A: 1 76.2-mm 59-cal. AK-176 DP; 1 4-round Fasta-M (SA-N-8) SAM syst. (16 Igla-2M missiles); 1 30-mm 54-cal. AK-630 gatling AA; 2 5-round RBU-1200 ASW RL (30 RGB-12 rockets); 4 single 533-mm TT (2 SET-65E ASW and 2 53-65KE antiship torpedoes); 2 d.c. racks (6 d.c. each)
Electronics:
Radar: 1 Pechora nav.; 1 MR-352 Pozitiv-E (Cross Dome) surf./air search; 1 MR-123E Vympel-AME (Bass Tilt) gun f.c.
Sonar: MGK-345 Bronza hull-mounted MF and MF dipping syst.
EW: 2 16-round PK-16 decoy RL

PATROL CRAFT [PC] *(continued)*

Abhay (P 33)—note the dipping sonar compartment extending over the stern
Brian Morrison, 2-01

M: 2 Type M-521-TM5 diesels; 3 props; 17,330 bhp
Range: 2,000/20; 3,000/12 **Fuel:** 50 tons **Endurance:** 10 days
Crew: 7 officers, 32 enlisted

Remarks: The Indian units of the class (and the unit built for Cuba) differ from the standard Russian version in having larger torpedo tubes, the pilothouse set further forward on the superstructure, and Cross Dome radar substituted for the MR-302 Rubka (Strut Curve).
Hull systems: The large housing for the dipping sonar system projects 1.5 m out from the stern. The large hull-mounted sonar dome is located approximately beneath the gunfire-control radar. The hull is constructed of mild steel, while the middle part of the deck plating, some internal bulkheads, and much of the superstructure are made of aluminum-magnesium alloy. Have specially tropicalized propulsion diesels.
Combat systems: The combat data system is designated SU-580E. There is a Kolonka-2 backup ringsight director for the single gatling AA gun; the MR-123E radar director can control both the 76.2-mm and 30-mm guns. Normal ammunition load is 152 rounds 76.2-mm (all ready-service, on-mount) and 2,000 rounds 30-mm. The torpedo tubes must be trained out several degrees to launch. MGK-345 applies to both the hull-mounted and dipping sonars, and the dipping sonar transducer can be lowered to 200 m.

♦ **1 (+ 3) Modified SDB Mk 3 class**
Bldr: Garden Reach SB & Eng., Calcutta (In serv. 1999–. . .)

	L	In serv.
T 62 Trinket	6-99	28-9-00
T 63 Tillichang	10-11-99	4-01
T 64 Tarasa	5-5-00	24-8-01
T 65 Tarmougli	. . .	12-01

D: 260 tons (fl) **S:** 25+ kts **Dim:** 46.0 × . . . × . . .
A: 2 single 30-mm Medak AA
Electronics: Radar: 1 Bharat 1245 nav.
M: 2 MTU 16V 538 TB92 diesels; 2 props; 6,820 bhp **Crew:** 32 tot.

Remarks: An enlarged version of the four built in the 1980s. Intended for coastal patrol, smuggling interdiction, fisheries protection, and policing duties.

♦ **4 SDB Mk 3 class** Bldr: Mazagon Dock, Goa (In serv. 1984–85)

T 58 T 59 T 60 T 61 Rajkamal

Rajkamal (T 61) 11-92

D: 167 tons (210 fl) **S:** 30 kts **Dim:** 37.80 (32.20 pp) × 7.50 × 1.85
A: 2 single 40-mm 60-cal. Bofors Mk 3 AA
Electronics: Radar: 1 Bharat 1245 nav.
M: 2 MTU 16V 538 TB92 diesels; 2 props; 6,820 bhp **Crew:** 32 tot.

Remarks: Intended as an improved version of the SDB Mk 2 with better hullform and less rake to propeller shafts. Probably also have a centerline cruise engine. Speed has also been reported as 28 kts for Goa-built units. May have depth charge racks stored ashore.
Disposals: *Ajay* (T 56) was transferred to Mauritius in 1993, and T 57 was stricken during 1998.

♦ **2 SDB Mk 2 class** Bldr: Garden Reach SB & Eng., Calcutta (In serv. 1980)

T 54 T 55

D: 160 tons light (203 fl) **S:** 29 kts **Dim:** 37.50 × 7.50 × 1.75
A: 1 40-mm 60-cal. Bofors AA
Electronics: Radar: 1 Decca 1226 nav.
M: 2 Deltic 18-42K diesels; 2 props; 6,240 bhp—1 165-bhp Kirloskar-Cummins NH-220 cruise diesel (centerline, for speeds to 6 kts)
Electric: 220 kVA tot. **Range:** 1,400/14 **Crew:** 4 officers, 26 enlisted

Remarks: Although reported stricken during 1995, were both in use at the 2-01 Indian Naval Review at Mumbai. Two d.c. racks have been removed and stored ashore.

♦ **2 Soviet Osa-II class (Project 205ME)** (In serv. 1976)

K 92 Pratap K 96 Chatak

D: 180 tons (222 fl; 245 overload) **S:** 40 kts (36 sust.)
Dim: 38.6 × 7.6 × 1.8 (hull; 2.9 props)
A: 2 twin 30-mm 65-cal. AK-230 AA; . . . Igla-2M shoulder-launched SAMs
Electronics:
Radar: 1 Rangout (Square Tie) surf. search/target detection; 1 MR-104 Rys' (Drum Tilt) gun f.c.
M: 3 M-504B diesels; 3 props; 15,000 bhp **Electric:** 400 kw tot.
Range: 500/34; 750/25 **Fuel:** 40 tons normal **Endurance:** 5 days
Crew: 4 officers, 24 enlisted

Remarks: New-construction units delivered during 1976 and now well past normal operating age. Are assigned to the 25th Missile Vessel Squadron. The MR-104 gun directors have been upgraded in India, and Kirloskar-Cummins heat exchangers and condensers were fitted to the diesels to improve performance in tropical conditions. The antiship missile launchers were to have been removed in all during 2000 but were still aboard K 92 in 2-01.
Disposals: *Charag* (K 97) was stricken during 5-96 and *Chamak* (K 95) by 1998, while *Pralaya* (K 91) and *Chapal* (K 94) were reported stricken during 2001. K 92, reportedly stricken during 5-96, remained afloat and possibly in operating condition as of 2-01. *Prabal* (K 93), stricken 29-12-99, is now on exhibit.

PATROL BOATS [PB]

♦ **4 (+ 16) Israeli Super Dvora Mk II class**
Bldr: T-80, T-81: Ramta, Israel; others: Vasco SY, Panaji, Goa

	L	In serv.		L	In serv.
T-80	24-6-98	. . .	T-82	. . .	2000
T-81	11-98	6-6-99	T-83	. . .	2001

Indian Navy Super Dvora—with a *Godavari*-class frigate in background
Brian Morrison, 2-01

Indian Navy Super Dvora—with French submarine *Perle*, a Thai frigate, and the skyline of Mumbai in the background Mritunjoy Mazumdar, 2-01

D: 48 tons (54 fl) **S:** 46 kts **Dim:** 22.40 × 5.49 × 1.00
A: 2 single 20-mm 90-cal. AA; . . . Igla-2M shoulder-launched SAMs
Electronics: Radar: 1 Koden . . . nav.
M: 2 MTU 12V396 TB93 diesels; 2 Arneson surface-piercing, articulating props; 4,570 bhp
Electric: 30 kw tot. **Range:** 700/14 **Crew:** 2 officers, 8 enlisted

Remarks: Referred to as XFAC (eXtra Fast Attack Craft) by the Indian Navy. Do not wear their pennant numbers. A license for indigenous construction was signed 24-9-96, with the first Indian-built unit to complete in 9-97 and additional units at 3-month intervals, although the program ran far behind schedule, with the Israeli prototype not commissioned until 7-98. Are to cost about $8.5 million each. As many as 20 may be built, with some going to the coast guard. Sisters are in the Israeli, Sri Lankan, and Slovenian navies. Are fitted with an Elop optronic low-light-level surveillance and weapons direction device.

MINE WARFARE SHIPS

♦ **0 (+ 10) new-construction coastal minehunters [MHC]**
Bldr: Goa SY

Remarks: Construction of a license-built version of a standard modern Western European GRP-construction, twin-screw minehunter is planned, if funding permits. The

MINE WARFARE SHIPS *(continued)*

Tripartite, Karlskrona *Landsort,* Vosper Thornycroft *Sandown,* and Intermarine *Lerici* designs have been considered. In 1990, it was reported that pennant numbers M 89 through M 94 would be assigned to six minehunters to be built at Goa. No contracts have been let to date, however, and the program does not have a high priority.

♦ 12 Soviet Natya-class (Project 266ME) fleet minesweepers [MSF] Bldr: Sudostroitel'noye Obyedineniye "Almaz" (Sredniy Neva), Kolpino

	In serv.		In serv.
M 61 Pondicherry	4-78	M 67 Karwar	9-86
M 62 Porbandar	4-78	M 68 Cannanore	11-87
M 63 Bedi	7-79	M 69 Cuddalore	11-87
M 64 Bhavnagar	7-79	M 70 Kakinada	5-87
M 65 Alleppy	8-80	M 71 Kozhikode	12-88
M 66 Ratnagiri	8-80	M 72 Konkan	12-88

Pondicherry (M 61) Brian Morrison, 2-01

Alleppy (M 65) Brian Morrison, 2-01

Porbandar (M 62) Brian Morrison, 2-01

D: 750 tons std., 804 tons normal (873 fl) **S:** 17.6 kts (16 sust.)
Dim: 61.00 (57.60 wl) × 10.20 × 2.98 (hull)
A: 2 twin 30-mm 65-cal. AK-230 AA; 2 twin 25-mm 80-cal. 2M-3 AA—M 67 and later: 2 4-round SA-N-8 SAM syst. (18 Igla-2M missiles)—all: 2 5-round RBU-1200 ASW RL (60 RGB-12 projectiles); 2 mine rails (8 mines max.)
Electronics:
Radar: 1 Don-2 nav.; 1 MR-104 Rys' (Drum Tilt) gun f.c.
Sonar: MG-89 HF hull-mounted (49 kHz)
M: 2 M-503B-3E diesels; 2 CP props; 5,000 bhp
Electric: 600 kw tot. (3 × 200-kw DGR-200/1500 diesel sets)
Range: 1,800/16; 3,000/12; 5,200/10 **Fuel:** 87 tons **Endurance:** 10–15 days
Crew: 10 officers, 89 enlisted

Remarks: The second group of six, ordered 20-17-82, were delivered out of pennant number sequence. Can be used as ASW escorts. One reportedly has been modified to act as an intelligence collector. Units assigned to the Western Fleet are in the 19th Mine Countermeasures Squadron; those assigned to the Eastern Fleet are in the 21st.
Hull systems: Differ from the units in the Russian Navy in that they do not have a ramp at the stern. The stem is cut back sharply below the waterline. Low-magnetic-signature, aluminum-steel-alloy hull construction. Have the DGR-450/1500P diesel-driven degaussing system. Their air-conditioning capacity is enhanced over their Russian Navy sisters and they also have about 100 kw more generator capacity. The main engines are a derated version of the diesels that power Russian high-speed small combatants and have a low operating time between overhauls. Carry 45 tons of water but do not have distilling equipment. Navigational equipment includes a GKU-2 gyrocompass, NEL-MZB echo sounder, Rumb MFD/F, Pirs-1M receiver for Decca radio navaid, and AP-4 automatic position plot. Khmel-1 infrared position-keeping and signalling equipment is carried.
Combat systems: The RBU-1200 ASW rocket launchers are primarily used for detonating mines. Sweep gear includes GKT-2 mechanical, AT-2 acoustic, and TEM-3 magnetic arrays, handled by two articulated KBG-5-TMI jib cranes fitted at the stern. The sonar incorporates a downward-looking, high-frequency, bottomed-mine-detection component with a range of 350–400 m. Some 2,149 rounds are carried for each 30-mm gunmount.

♦ 5 Soviet Yevgenya-class (Project 1258E) inshore minesweepers [MSI] Bldr: Sudostroitel'noye Obyedineniye "Almaz" (Sredniy Neva), Kolpino (In serv.: first three: 15-5-83; others: 3-2-84)

M 83 Mahe	M 85 Mangalore	M 87 Mulki
M 84 Malwan	M 86 Malpe	

D: 88.5 tons (91.5 fl) **S:** 12 kts **Dim:** 26.13 × 5.90 × 1.38
A: 1 twin 25-mm 80-cal. 2M-3M AA
Electronics:
Radar: 1 Mius (Spin Trough) nav.
Sonar: MG-7 HF hull-mounted HF mine location
M: 2 Type 3D12 diesels; 2 props; 600 bhp
Range: 300/10 **Fuel:** 2.7 tons **Endurance:** 3 days
Crew: 1 officer, 9 enlisted (+ 2–3 clearance divers)

Remarks: Glass-reinforced plastic construction. A plan to build additional units under license in India was dropped. Equipped for shallow-water minehunting to depths of 30 m with a towed television and marker-buoy dispenser. All are based at Kochi as the 18th Mine Countermeasures Squadron. Sister *Magdala* (M 88) was reportedly stricken during 2001.

AMPHIBIOUS WARFARE SHIPS

Note: A larger dock-landing ship is in the design/planning stage.

♦ 2 (+ 1 + 3) Magar-class tank landing ships [LST]

	Bldr	L	In serv.
L 20 Magar	Garden Reach SB & Eng., Calcutta	7-11-84	15-7-87
L 23 Gharial	Hindustan SY, Vishakhapatnam	2-4-91	14-2-97
L	Garden Reach SB & Eng., Calcutta	. . .	. . .

Magar (L 20)—with a Sea King helicopter on the flight deck aft
Brian Morrison, 2-01

Magar (L 20)—note the helicopter hangar within the superstructure and the twin, side-by-side stacks
Brian Morrison, 2-01

D: 3,200 tons (5,655 fl) **S:** 15 kts **Dim:** 124.80 (120.00 pp) × 17.50 × 3.50
A: 4 single 40-mm 60-cal. Bofors Mk 3 AA; . . . Igla-2M shoulder-launched SAMs; 2 18-round 122-mm barrage RL
Electronics: Radar: 1 . . . nav.—EW: Bharat Ajanta intercept
M: 2 SEMT-Pielstick 8 PC2 V400 Mk 3 diesels; 2 props; 8,560 bhp (7,900 sust.)
Electric: 1,660 kw tot. (2 × 500-kw, 2 × 250-kw, 2 × 50-kw, 1 × 60-kw diesel sets)
Range: 3,000/14 **Fuel:** 420 tons **Crew:** 16 officers, 120 enlisted

Remarks: The second unit was ordered in 1985 and only completed 12 years later; the third, ordered in 4-90, was nearing launch by 8-98 but as of 6-01 was still not in the water. Three more (down from originally five) were ordered on 12-12-01, with the first to deliver in 6-05. L 23, fitted out at Garden Reach SB, has a crew totaling 143 and is assigned to the Eastern Fleet; she ran aground 11-12-99 with minor damage. L 20 is assigned to the Western Fleet.
Hull systems: Carry four Sea Truck–type LCVPs in separate davits amidships. Have a helicopter deck and hangar aft for a Sea King Mk 42C transport. There is a vehicle ramp forward from the upper deck to the tank deck. Both are now able to carry 15 Indian Arjun heavy tanks. No stern door/ramp. Can beach on a 1:40 gradient.

Note: Negotiations for four modernized versions of the Polish Project 773–series landing ship design, begun in 1998, were not successful.

AMPHIBIOUS WARFARE SHIPS *(continued)*

♦ 6 Polnocny-C (Project 773I) and -D (Project 773IM*) -class medium landing ships [LSM]
Bldr: Stocznia Marynarki Wojennej, Gdynia, Poland

	L		L
L 16 Shardul	19-5-75	L 19 Mahish*	25-6-84
L 17 Sharabh	4-9-75	L 21 Guldar*	4-6-85
L 18 Cheetah*	19-10-83	L 22 Kumbhir*	3-5-86

Mahish (L 19)—Project 773IM unit with raised helicopter deck
Brian Morrison, 2-01

D: 1,192 tons normal (1,305 max. fl) **S:** 16.3 kts
Dim: 81.30 (76.00 pp) × 9.30 (8.61 wl) × 1.22 (fwd; 2.30 aft, loaded)
A: 2 twin 30-mm 65-cal. AK-230 AA; 2 18-round 140.4-mm WM-18 barrage RL (180 rds tot.)
Electronics:
Radar: 1 Don-2 (L 18–21: Kivach) nav.; 1 MR-104 Rys' (Drum Tilt) gun f.c.
M: 2 Type 40DM diesels; 2 props; 4,400 bhp
Electric: 360 kVA tot. (4 × 90-kVA diesel sets)
Range: 975/13 **Crew:** 11 officers, 107 enlisted + 84 troops

Remarks: All constructed for India. L 16 and L 17 were delivered in 1976, L 18 in 12-84, L 19 in 7-85, L 21 in 11-86, and L 22 in 2-86. First four (Polnocny-C/Project 773I) do not have a helicopter platform as on the Polnocny-D (Project 773IM) variant. Cargo: 350 tons and up to 140 troops. The upper deck is primarily a shelter for the tank deck and cannot support heavy vehicles; there is no ramp to the tank deck, the hatch forward being intended for ventilation and for access during loading vehicles aboard by crane.
Disposals: Project 773I units *Ghorpad* (L 14) and *Khesari* (L 15), in reserve since 1993, were reportedly stricken during 2001 and 1999, respectively.

♦ 10 Vasco da Gama–class (LCU Mk III) utility landing craft [LCU]
Bldrs: L 34, 35: Hoogly DY, Calcutta; L 36–40: Goa SY

	L	In serv.
L 31	. . .	. . .
L 32	. . .	. . .
L 33	. . .	. . .
L 34 Vasco Da Gama	29-11-77	28-1-80
L 35	16-3-80	17-12-83
L 36	13-1-79	1-12-80
L 37	22-7-85	1986
L 38 Midhur	2-86	1987
L 39 Mangala	2-86	25-3-87
L 40	. . .	25-3-87

L 35—with narrow after deckhouse and no bulwarks to hull sides
92 Wing Det. A, RAAF, 2-99

D: 500 tons (fl) **S:** 9 kts **Dim:** 57.50 (53.20 pp) × 8.20 × 1.57 (aft)
A: 2 single 40-mm 60-cal. Bofors Mk 3 AA
Electronics: Radar: 1 Decca TM-1229 nav.
M: 3 Kirloskar-M.A.N. W8V 17.5/22 AMAL diesels; 3 Kort-nozzle props; 1,686 bhp
Range: 1,000/8 **Crew:** . . . tot.

Remarks: Goa SY was a subsidiary of Mazagon Docks, Mumbai. L 31–33 are a new series; builder and dates unknown. The minelaying capability attributed to this class is not evident in photography.
Hull systems: Total complement, including embarked troops, is said to be 287, with a cargo capacity of 250 tons (space for two PT-76 amphibious light tanks or two BMP-1 armored personnel carriers). L 31–33 and L 35 have the pilothouse set further aft, the after deckhouse not flush with sides of hull, and a smaller stack; they also lack bulwarks amidships (there is an inboard bulwark along the sides of the vehicle deck). L 31 (and possibly L 32 and L 33) also has a much lower forecastle.

L 37—with after deckhouse to full width of the hull and hull bulwarks amidships
92 Wing Det. A, RAAF, 2-99

AUXILIARIES

♦ 1 Modified Sandhayak-class research ship [AGOR]
Bldr: Garden Reach SB & Eng., Calcutta

	L	In serv.
A 74 Sagardhwani	5-91	30-7-94

Sagardhwani (A 74) Brian Morrison, 2-01

D: 1,339 tons (2,050 fl) **S:** 16 kts **Dim:** 85.06 (78.80 pp) × 12.80 × 3.67
A: none
Electronics: Radar: 1 Decca TM-1629 nav.; 1 . . . meteorological
M: 2 GRSE-M.A.N. G8V 30/45 ATL diesels; 2 props; 3,920 bhp—1 Pleuger 200-bhp active rudder (5 kts)
Electric: 1,700 kw tot. (2 × 500-kw, 2 × 350-kw diesel sets)
Range: 6,000/16; 14,000/10 **Fuel:** 231 tons
Crew: 10 officers, 70 enlisted + 16 scientists

Remarks: 1,949 grt. Hull and propulsion plant are the same as the *Sandhayak*-class survey ships, but A 74 has been configured as a research ship for the Naval Physical and Oceanographic Laboratory, Kochi. Officially referred to as the Marine Acoustic Research Ship (MARS).
Hull systems: There are a total of eight laboratories to permit conducting acoustic, geological, meteorological, chemical, and physical oceanography; most of the laboratories are acoustically isolated from the ship's structure. The superstructure is set nearer the stern than that on her half-sisters, with the deck forward of the pilothouse cleared as a helicopter pad (for a Chetak) and a 10-ton quadrantial gallows-type equipment crane carried at the stern. First ship in the Indian Navy with accommodations for female personnel. Carries 116 tons of fresh water.

Note: The modern and elaborately equipped research ships operated by the National Oceanographic Institute are non-naval. They include *Sagar Kanya, Sagar Sampada, Samudra Manthan, Samudra Sarveshak, Samudra Nidhi,* and *Samudra Sandhari.* The small inshore research craft Gaveshani and a sister launched in 1976 are also civilian.

♦ 9 Sandhayak-class hydrographic survey ships [AGS]
Bldr: Garden Reach SB & Eng., Calcutta (*Darshak, Sarvekshak:* Goa SY, Goa)

	L	In serv.
J 18 Sandhayak	6-4-77	26-2-81
J 19 Nirdeshak	16-11-78	4-10-83
J 14 Nirupak	10-7-81	14-8-85
J 15 Investigator	8-8-87	11-1-90
J 16 Jumuna	4-9-89	31-8-91
J 17 Sutlej	1-12-91	19-2-93
J 21 Darshak	28-4-98	28-4-01
J . . . Sarvekshak	11-99	14-1-02

Sutlej (J 17) Brian Morrison, 2-01

AUXILIARIES *(continued)*

Nirdeshak (J 19) Brian Morrison, 2-01

D: 1,329 tons (1,929 fl) **S:** 16.75 kts **Dim:** 85.77 (78.80 pp) × 12.80 × 3.34
A: 1 40-mm 60-cal. Bofors Mk 3 AA; 1 Chetak helicopter
Electronics: Radar: 1 Decca TM-1629 nav.
M: 1 GRSE-M.A.N. G8V 30/45 ATL diesel; 1 prop; 3,860 bhp—1 Pleuger 200-bhp active rudder (5 kts)
Electric: 1,006 kw tot. (5 × 200-kw, 1 × 6-kw diesel sets)
Range: 14,000/14 **Fuel:** 248 tons
Crew: 14 officers, 134 enlisted + 30 survey party

Remarks: 2,050 grt/535 dwt. Carry traditional paint scheme: white hull and superstructure with "buff" stack and mast. The Goa-built units were laid down in 5-96 and 8-96, respectively, and may have a secondary mission as hospital ships. Another hull of this type, *Sagardhwani* (A 74), is configured for oceanographic research (see [AGOR]).
Hull systems: Have a telescoping helicopter hangar. Carry four inshore survey launches with Hydrodist position-fixing system. Equipment includes three precision depth-finders, Decca Navigator, Decca HiFix, taut-wire measuring gear, a gravimeter, and Telegon-4 HFD/F. Carry 163 tons of potable water and 5 tons of aviation fuel.

♦ 1 hospital ship [AH] Bldr: Hindustan SY, Calcutta (L: 28-8-81)

LAKSHADWEEP

D: 865 tons (fl) **S:** 12 kts **Dim:** 52.0 (46.8 pp) × 9.5 × 3.0
M: 2 diesels; 2 props; 900 bhp
Crew: 19 ship's company + 15 medical staff, 90 hospital berths

Remarks: Laid down 2-81.

♦ 1 Deepak-class replenishment oiler [AO]
Bldr: Bremer Vulkan Schiffbau, Bremen-Vegesack, Germany (In serv. 21-2-76)

A 57 SHAKTI

Shakti (A 57) NAVPIC-Holland, 1-98

D: 6,785 tons (22,000 fl) **S:** 20 kts **Dim:** 168.43 (157.50 pp) × 23.0 × 9.14
A: 4 single 40-mm 60-cal. Bofors Mk 3 AA; 24 Igla-2M shoulder-launched SAMs
Electronics:
Radar: 2 Decca 1226 nav.
EW: Bharat Ajanta intercept; EADS Telegon-4 HFD/F
M: 1 set Type BV/BBC geared steam turbines; 1 prop; 16,500 shp
Boilers: 2 Babcock & Wilcox **Range:** 5,500/18.5
Crew: 16 officers, 179 enlisted

Remarks: 12,690 grt/15,800 dwt. Sister *Deepak* (A 50) was stricken 30-4-96. The name means "Strength." Refitted during 2001 at the Mumbai Naval Dockyard.
Hull systems: Has two liquid-replenishment stations per side, with British-style jackstay rigs, plus over-the-stern fueling. Has a telescoping hangar and flight deck for one Chetak helicopter. Carries 12,624 tons of fuel oil, 1,280 tons of diesel fuel, 1,495 tons of aviation fuel, 812 tons of fresh water, and some dry cargo. Has a degaussing system.

♦ 1 Rajabagan Palan–class replenishment oiler [AOR]
Bldr: Garden Reach SB & Eng., Calcutta

	Laid down	L	In serv.
A 59 ADITYA (ex-*Rajabagan Palan*)	1986	15-11-93	3-4-00

Aditya (A 59) Brian Morrison, 2-01

Aditya (A 59) John Mortimer, 2-01

D: 24,612 tons (fl) **S:** 20 kts **Dim:** 172.00 × 23.00 × 9.14
A: 3 single 30-mm 2A42/7.62-mm Medak dual AA; 24 Igla-2M shoulder-launched SAMs; 1 Chetak or Sea King Mk 42B helicopter
Electronics: Radar: . . .
M: 2 ECR-M.A.N./Burmeister & Wain 16V 40/45 diesels; 1 prop; 23,936 bhp—bow-thruster
Electric: 4,500 kw tot. (2 × 1,500-kw shaft generators, 3 × 500-kw diesel sets)
Range: 10,000/16
Crew: 16 officers, 140 enlisted + 6 aircrew (197 tot. accomm.)

Remarks: 16,211 dwt. Ordered 7-87; was to have been in service by 1997. A second unit was planned, but no reports of progress have been received and the unit may have been canceled. Design is a modified version of the *Deepak* class, with a repair capability added and the navigating bridge superstructure block moved forward. Commissioning was delayed by propulsion problems. Attached to the Eastern Fleet and based at Vishakhapatnam. As of 17-2-01, had completed 189 underway replenishments.
Hull systems: Cargo: 14,200 m^3 (12,000 tons) diesel and aviation fuel, 2,250 m^3 fresh water, and 2,170 m^3 (5,000 tons) ammunition, provisions, and spares. Can carry six standard cargo containers on deck. Has Canadian Hepburn replenishment equipment, with one fueling station and one solid-stores transfer station per side. A 20-ton cargo crane is fitted. The hangar can accommodate a Sea King helicopter. Is fully air-conditioned and has a repair workshop to assist other ships.
Combat systems: The locally operated Medak gunmounts are adapted from a turret designed for use on armored personnel carriers, where the turret has both a 30-mm cannon and a 7.62-mm machinegun; the machinegun cannot be seen in available photos of naval installations, however.

♦ 1 Russian Komandarm Fedko–class replenishment ship [AOR]
Bldr: Admiralty Shipyard 194, St. Petersburg

	L	In serv.
A 58 JYOTI	8-12-95	19-7-96

Jyoti (A 58) Brian Morrison, 2-01

Jyoti (A 58) John Mortimer, 2-01

D: 39,900 tons (fl) **S:** 16.4 kts (15.25 sust., loaded)
Dim: 178.24 (165.00 pp) × 25.33 × 10.41 (loaded)
A: 24 Igla-2M shoulder-launched SAMs **Electronics:** Radar: . . .
M: 1 Bryansk–Burmeister & Wain 6DKRN60/195 diesel; 1 prop; 10,948 bhp
Range: 12,000/15 **Fuel:** 1,606 tons heavy oil, 305 tons diesel
Crew: 16 officers, 30 senior enlisted, 46 junior enlisted (as delivered)

AUXILIARIES *(continued)*

Remarks: 21,142 grt. Begun as a 21,053-grt/28,400-dwt commercial tanker and converted prior to delivery as an underway replenishment oiler. Basic Russian project number is 15966. The largest ship in the Indian Navy. The name means "Light." A near-sister was commissioned in China in 6-96, and two merchant sisters were completed for various owners, *Indra* (ex-*Pulkovo*) and *Belania* (ex-*Pavlovsk*). Collided with unknown vessel in the Malacca Strait 16-11-98, suffering significant hull damage.
Hull systems: Liquid cargo: 31,398 m^3 (25,040 tons) in 10 tanks. Has an ice-strengthened hull of double-hull construction, with external deck stiffeners. There are two refueling stations per side, and the ship can also refuel over the stern. Cargo pumps include four steam turbine–driven, 750-m^3/hr pumps. Carries 192 tons of potable water and 60 tons of feedwater for the auxiliary boiler.
Combat systems: Was delivered unarmed and was still without fixed defensive systems as of late 2000, when it was announced that she might be equipped with a point-defense SAM system.

♦ 2 Nicobar-class transports [AP]

	Bldr	In serv.
NICOBAR	Stocznia Szczecinska im. A. Warskiego, Szczecin, Poland	6-91
ANDAMANS	Hindustan SY, Vishakhapatnam	5-99

Nicobar 92 Wing Det. A, RAAF, 1999

D: approx. 20,000 tons (fl) **S:** 16 kts **Dim:** 157.00 (144.00 pp) × 21.00 × 6.71
A: none **Electronics:** Radar: 2 . . . nav.
M: 2 Cegielski–Burmeister & Wain 6L35MC 6-cyl. diesels; 2 props; 7,088 bhp—1 CP bow-thruster
Electric: 1,080 kw tot. (5 × 216-kw diesel sets; 400 V, 50 Hz a.c.)
Range: 8,450/15.5 **Fuel:** 751 tons heavy oil, 151 tons diesel
Crew: . . . tot.

Remarks: 14,195 grt/4,963 dwt. Requisitioned 3-99 from the Shipping Corporation of India, Mumbai (which operated the *Nicobar* for the Government of India Andaman & Nicobar Islands Administration), for military logistics support to the Andaman and Nicobar Islands. Data here apply specifically to *Nicobar; Andamans* may differ.
Hull systems: Passenger/cargo vessels with two holds forward and a large helicopter platform aft. As commercial vessels, had accommodations for 63 cabin, 300 berth, and 900 deck passengers. Can carry 39 standard 20-ft. cargo containers. Have NAVSAT and commercial SATCOM gear.

♦ 1 Soviet Ugra-class (Project 1886E) submarine tender [AS]
Bldr: Chernomorskiy Zavod, Nikolayev (In serv. 28-12-68)

A 54 AMBA

D: 6,780 tons (7,980 fl) **S:** 20 kts **Dim:** 144.8 × 18.1 × 5.8
A: 2 twin 76.2-mm 59-cal. AK-276 DP
Electronics:
Radar: 1 Don-2 nav.; 1 Fut-N (Slim Net) surf./air search; 2 Fut-B (Hawk Screech) f.c.
Sonar: MG-10 hull-mounted searchlight HF
M: 4 Type 2D-42 diesels (1,900 bhp each), electric drive; 2 props; 6,000 shp
Range: 6,500/17; 11,500/9 **Fuel:** 820 tons **Crew:** 18 officers, 202 enlisted

Remarks: Has a helicopter platform, quarters for 750, two 6-ton cranes, and one 10-ton crane. Based at Mumbai and rarely goes to sea.

♦ 1 submarine rescue, salvage, and diving support ship [ASR]
Bldr: Mazagon DY, Mumbai

	Laid down	L	In serv.
A 15 NIREEKSHAK	8-82	1-84	8-6-89 (Indian Navy)

D: 3,600 tons (fl) **S:** 12 kts **Dim:** 70.50 × 17.50 × 5.00
A: none **Electronics:** Radar: 2 . . . nav.
M: 2 Bergens Mek. Verk. KRM-8 diesels; 2 CP props; 5,015 bhp—2 bow-thrusters; 910 shp—2 stern-thrusters; 910 bhp
Electric: 2,340 kw tot. (1 × 1,140-kw shaft alternator, 4 × 300-kw diesel alternator sets; 415 V, 3-phase a.c.)
Range: . . . **Crew:** 15 officers, 48 enlisted

Remarks: 2,160 grt. Chartered 8-6-89 for three years, with an option for purchase, to replace the Russian T-58-class submarine rescue ship *Nistar* (A 55) until two since-canceled new units became available. Had been built as a commercial oilfield support ship and is capable of a variety of salvage and rescue missions.
Hull systems: Can support 12 divers at up to 300 m. Has two 6-man decompression chambers and one 3-man diving bell. Equipped with Kongsberg ADP 503 Mk II dynamic positioning system, a 4-point mooring system, one 10-ton crane, and a passive-tank stabilization system. Carries the submarine rescue chamber formerly aboard the *Nistar;* it can rescue personnel down to 200 m. Navigational suite includes an echo sounder, autopilot, gyrocompass, D/F, and Decca Navigator radio navaid.

♦ 2 Modified Gaj–class oceangoing tugs [ATA]
Bldr: Garden Reach SB & Eng., Calcutta

A 53 MATANGA (In serv. 1983) A 54 AMBIKA (In serv. 1994)

Matanga (A 53) John Mortimer, 2-01

D: 1,600 (fl) **S:** 15 kts **Dim:** 67.80 × 12.30 × 4.00
A: 1 40-mm 60-cal. Bofors Mk 3 AA
M: 2 GRSE-M.A.N. G7V diesels; 2 CP props; 3,920 bhp
Range: 8,000/12 **Fuel:** 242 tons **Crew:** 8 officers, 70 enlisted

Remarks: 1,313 grt/460.6 dwt. Fitted for diving and salvage work. Have 40-ton bollard pull. Half-sister *Gaj* (A 51) was stricken in 1996. A 53, launched 29-10-83, carries a diver's decompression chamber and other salvage equipment.

♦ 1 Tir-class cadet training ship [AXT] Bldr: Mazagon DY, Mumbai

	L	In serv.
A 86 TIR	15-4-83	21-2-86

Tir (A 86) Brian Morrison, 2-01

Tir (A 86) Brian Morrison, 2-01

D: 2,400 tons (3,200 fl) **S:** 18 kts **Dim:** 105.85 × 13.20 × 4.8
A: 1 twin 40-mm 60-cal. Mk 5 Bofors AA
Electronics:
Radar: 1 Bharat-Decca TM-1229 nav.; 1 Bharat-Decca 1245 nav.; 1 . . . nav.
EW: Racal Cutlass intercept
M: 2 Kirloskar-SEMT-Pielstick 18 PA6 V280 BTC diesels; 2 props; 6,970 bhp
Electric: 1,000 kw tot. (4 × 250-kw diesel alternator sets; 415 V, 50 Hz a.c.)
Range: 6,000/12 **Fuel:** 285 m^3
Crew: 25 officers, 204 enlisted + 10 instructors, 120 cadets

Remarks: Ordered in 1981; was to have been completed during 3-84, but was delayed by labor and management problems. A second ship was ordered 5-86 from the same builder but was subsequently cancelled. The name means "Arrow." Is assigned to the 1st Training Squadron and based at Kochi.
Hull systems: Has a helicopter deck but no hangar. Has Telegon-4 HFD/F, Decca collision-avoidance system, satellite navigation facilities, echo sounder, doppler log, plotting table, and four saluting cannon. Boats include two motorboats, four GRP dinghies, two RIBs, one motor whaleboat, and one sail-equipped whaleboat. Has 135-m^3 fresh water capacity and can generate 75 tons per day.

AUXILIARIES *(continued)*

♦ 1 ex-U.K. Leander-class training frigate [AXT]
Bldr: HM Dockyard, Portsmouth

	Laid down	L	In serv.
F 46 Krishna (ex-*Andromeda,* F 57)	25-5-66	24-5-67	2-12-68

Krishna (F 46) Arjun Sarup, 10-01

Krishna (F 46) Ben Sullivan, 8-95

D: 2,680 tons (3,140 fl) **S:** 25 kts
Dim: 113.38 (109.73 pp) × 13.12 × 4.60 (5.60 props)
A: 3 single 40-mm 60-cal. Bofors Mk 3 AA; 1 Chetak helicopter
Electronics:
Radar: 1 Kelvin-Hughes Type 1006 nav.; 1 Type 967-968 surf./air search
Sonar: removed
EW: UAA-1 intercept; 2 Type 670 jammers; Type 182 towed acoustic torpedo decoy
M: 2 sets White–English Electric geared steam turbines; 2 5-bladed props; 30,000 shp
Boilers: 2 Babcock & Wilcox 3-drum; 38.7 kg/cm², 450° C
Electric: 2,500 kw tot. **Range:** approx. 4,500/12 **Fuel:** 500 tons
Crew: 19 officers, 241 enlisted (in RN service)

Remarks: Purchased 5-94 for a nominal price, having been decommissioned 7-4-93 and placed in 180-day recall reserve 4-6-93. Underwent a 12-week reactivation overhaul at Devonport, running trials 31-7-95 and departing for India at the end of 8-95. Is employed purely as a training ship. While in British service, underwent conversion from a late-construction "Broad-beamed Leander" to incorporate Sea Wolf SAM system, antiship missiles, and improved ASW capability. Four sisters were discarded by the Royal Navy. Assigned to the Southern Naval Command, 1st Training Squadron, and based at Kochi.
Hull systems: Speed reduced about 2 kts from original due to weight growth. Has fin stabilizers.
Combat systems: During reactivation for Indian Navy service, the Sea Wolf system, two sets of triple ASW torpedo tubes, and four 20-mm single AA mounts were deleted, as were the Type 910 SAM control radar, the decoy rocket launchers, and the sonar suite. Hand-operated 40-mm AA mounts have been placed on the former Sea Wolf platform forward and on either beam amidships.

SERVICE CRAFT

Note: The majority of Indian Navy service craft do not carry pennant numbers, making it difficult to distinguish them from commercial craft in some instances. Hulls are normally painted black, with upperworks either white or yellow ("buff"). The following entries are not exhaustive but represent only those units for which either photography or some data are available.

♦ 3 diving tenders [YDT]
Bldr: Cleback SY (In serv. 1979, 2-84, 8-84)

D: 36 tons (fl) **S:** 12 kts **Dim:** 14.89 (13.37 pp) × 4.40 × 1.21
M: 2 Premier Auto–Meadows diesels; 2 props; 130 bhp **Fuel:** 2 tons

♦ 3 Madhur-class personnel ferries [YFB]
Bldr: Goa SY, Goa (In serv. . . .)

Madhur Manjula Modak

Madhur—black hull, white superstructure Brian Morrison, 2-01

D: approx. 175 tons (fl) **S:** 11 kts **Dim:** 28.10 (25.15 pp) × 7.62 × 1.47
M: 2 diesels; 2 props; 604 bhp **Crew:** 6 tot. + 156 seated passengers

Remarks: The three listed units are based at Mumbai; there may be additional units in service. Also in use at Mumbai is the slightly larger *Nancy;* no data available.

Nancy Brian Morrison, 2-01

♦ 1 medium floating dry dock [YFDM]
Bldr: . . . . . ., USSR (In serv. 1988)

FDN-1

Floating dry dock FDN-1 NAVPIC-Holland, 5-98

D: 7,345 tons light
Dim: 188.70 (176.40 over pontoon) × 41.03 (40.00 beam walls) × 3.80 (empty)

Remarks: Normally based at Port Blair in the Andaman Islands. Refitted in 1998 by Hindustan DY, Vishakhapatnam. Has 12 anchors.

♦ . . . personnel launches [YFL]
Bldr: Goa SY, Goa (In serv. . . .)

D: . . . tons **S:** 19 kts **Dim:** 17.80 (17.00 pp) × 5.00 × 1.40
M: 2 Kirloskar-Cummins diesels; 2 props; 1,000 bhp **Crew:** 4 tot.

Remarks: General-purpose utility launch design. No radar.

♦ . . . mooring buoy tenders [YGL]
Bldr: Goa SY, Goa (In serv. . . .)

D: . . . tons **S:** 10 kts **Dim:** 32.00 (30.00 pp) × 9.60 × 2.30
M: 2 diesels; 2 props; 992 bhp **Crew:** 20 tot.

Remarks: Single mooring buoy–handling crane on the forecastle. Have no hold, but there is a working deck forward of the bridge superstructure.

♦ 4 inshore survey craft [YGS] Bldr: Goa SY (In serv. 1984–85)

J 33 Makar J 34 Mithun J 35 Meen J 36 Mesh

D: 185 tons (210 fl) **S:** 12.5 kts **Dim:** 37.50 (35.20 pp) × 7.50 × 1.85
A: 1 40-mm 60-cal. Bofors Mk 3 AA (not normally aboard)
Electronics: Radar: 1 Decca TM-1629 nav. **M:** 2 diesels; 2 props; 1,124 bhp
Range: 1,500/12.5 **Crew:** 4 officers, 24 enlisted

Remarks: J 34 was launched 28-5-83 and J 35 on 10-8-83. Steel hulled. Have the same hulls as the SDB Mk 2 patrol-boat class, but with a less-powerful propulsion plant. Painted white except for a large black area amidships on the hull sides to mask exhaust staining. Carry a derrick-served inshore survey launch on the fantail, to port.

♦ 1 coastal tanker [YO] Bldr: Goa SY (In serv. 1990)

Pushkar

D: approx. 1,300 tons (fl) **S:** 12 kts **Dim:** 60.12 (56.10 pp) × 9.80 × 3.00
M: 2 Kirloskar-M.A.N. diesels; 2 props; 1,540 bhp (1,270 sust.) **Crew:** 22 tot.

Remarks: Has six cargo tanks.

SERVICE CRAFT *(continued)*

Pushkar—black hull, yellow upperworks   Brian Morrison, 2-01

♦ **1 coastal tanker [YO]**
Bldr: Central Inland Water Transport Corp., Rajabagan SY, Mumbai

PALAN (In serv. 5-86)

D: approx. 1,200 tons (fl) **S:** 12 kts **Dim:** 57.94 (54.39 pp) × 9.10 × 3.10
M: 2 Kirloskar-M.A.N. diesels; 1 prop; 1,440 bhp

Remarks: 624 grt/715 dwt.

♦ **2 Poshak-class fuel lighters [YO]** Bldr: Rajabagan SY, Mumbai

POSHAK (In serv. 4-82) PURAN (In serv. 1988)

D: 650 tons **S:** 8 kts **Dim:** 36.3 × 7.6 × 2.4
M: 1 M.A.N. diesel; 255 bhp **Cargo:** 200 tons

♦ **2 Purak-class fuel lighters [YO]** Bldr: Rajabagan SY, Mumbai

PURAK (In serv. 3-6-77) PRADHAYAK (In serv. 2-78)

D: 960 tons (fl) **S:** 9 kts **Dim:** 49.7 × 8.1 × 3.0
M: 1 diesel; 1 prop; 560 bhp **Cargo:** 376 tons

Note: Also in service, at Mumbai, is the small fuel lighter *Varida;* no data available.

Varida   Brian Morrison, 2-01

♦ **1 torpedo trials and retrieval craft [YPT]**
Bldr: P.S. & Co., Mumbai (In serv. 8-9-83)

A 71 ASTRAVAHINI

Remarks: No details available.

♦ **2 torpedo retrievers [YPT]** Bldr: Goa SY

A 72 . . . . . . (In serv. 16-9-82) A. . . . . (L: 5-11-80)

D: 110 tons (fl) **S:** 11 kts **Dim:** 28.50 (24.80 pp) × 6.10 × 1.40
M: 2 Kirloskar-M.A.N. 12-cyl. diesels; 2 props; 720 bhp **Crew:** 13 tot.

Remarks: Can stow two full-sized torpedoes on deck and two on the recovery ramp.

♦ **3 Madan Singh–class large harbor tugs [YTB]**
Bldr: Tebma SY, Chennai (In serv. 1999)

MADAN SINGH SHAMBHU SINGH TARAFDAR

Tarafdar—black hull, white superstructure   Brian Morrison, 2-01

D: . . . tons **S:** . . . kts **Dim:** . . . × . . . × . . .
M: 1 Wärtsilä 8L20 diesel; 1 prop; . . . bhp

♦ **4 Bajarang-class large harbor tugs [YTB]**
Bldr: Mazagon Goa SY (In serv. 1991)

BAJARANG BALRAM . . . .

Balram—black hull, yellow superstructure   Brian Morrison, 2-01

D: approx. 400 tons (fl) **S:** 12 kts **Dim:** 29.70 (29.00 pp) × 9.70 × 4.30
M: 2 Kirloskar-SEMT-Pielstick 8 PA4 V200 diesels; 2 Voith-Schneider vertical cycloidal props; 3,200 bhp
Crew: 12 tot.

Remarks: 216 grt. Have 30-ton bollard pull. Fitted with three monitors for fire fighting. *Bajarang* and *Balram* are based at Mumbai. *Anand,* formerly listed with this class, is a smaller tug of earlier design; no data available.

♦ **1 coastal tug [YTB]**
Bldr: Garden Reach SB & Eng., Calcutta (In serv. 7-82)

RAJAJI

D: 428 tons **S:** 12.5 kts **Dim:** 30.5 × 9.5 × 3.8
M: 2 Garden Reach–M.A.N. diesels; 2 Kort-nozzle props; 2,120 bhp

♦ **6 or more miscellaneous large harbor tugs [YTB]**
Bldr: Mazagon DY, Mumbai (In serv. 1973–74), and Goa SY (In serv. . . .)

AJARAL ANAND ARJUN ATHAK BALBIR BALSHIL

Anand   Ralph Edwards, 2-01

Balbir   Ralph Edwards, 2-01

SERVICE CRAFT *(continued)*

D: . . . tons **S:** 11 kts **Dim:** 29.25 (25.00 pp) × 8.50 × 2.60
M: 2 diesels; 2 Kort-nozzle props; 2,228 bhp **Crew:** 12 tot.

Remarks: Not a uniform class; there are at least three different appearance groups. Data above are believed to apply to the *Athak,* which has a lower superstructure, with the pilothouse only a half-deck above the main deck.

♦ 1 sail training craft [YTS] Bldr: Goa SY, Goa

	L	In serv.
TARANGINI	23-12-95	12-11-97

Tarangini Brian Morrison, 2-01

D: 420 tons (fl) **S:** . . . kts **Dim:** 54.0 (42.8 pp) × 8.5 × 4.0
M: 2 Kirloskar-Cummins diesels; 2 props; 640 bhp—1,035 m² max. sail area
Range: 2,000/. . . (on diesels) **Crew:** 15 tot. + 45 cadets

Remarks: Bark-rigged craft ordered in late 1993. Designed by Three Quays Marine Services; is similar to the British sail-training ship *Lord Nelson.* Has three masts, square rigged on the fore and main. Carries 85 tons of ballast. Assigned to the Southern Naval Command, 1st Training Squadron, and based at Kochi.

♦ 1 sail-training craft [YTS]
Bldr: Alcock-Ashdown, Bhavnagar (In serv. 20-4-81)

VARUNA

D: 130 tons (fl) **Dim:** 30.5 × . . . × . . .

Remarks: Two-masted brig for training 26 Sea Cadets. Assigned to the Southern Naval Command, 1st Training Squadron, and based at Kochi.

♦ 2 water lighters [YW]
Bldr: *Ambuda:* Rajabagan SY, Mumbai; *Kochi:* Mazagon DY, Mumbai

AMBUDA KOCHI

D: 200 tons **S:** 9 kts **Dim:** 32.0 × . . . × 2.4
M: 1 diesel; 1 prop; . . . bhp

Remarks: *Ambuda* was laid down 18-1-77. A planned third unit was not built.

COAST GUARD

The Indian Coast Guard was established 1-2-77 to ensure surveillance of India's 200-n.m. economic zone. Now commanded by an Indian Navy vice admiral, it consisted initially of ships and craft transferred from the navy. The Indian Customs Service was merged with the coast guard in April 1982. Although operationally subordinate to the Ministry of Defense, the coast guard is funded by the Department of Revenue. The name "Coast Guard" is written in large black letters on the sides of ship hulls, which are painted white and have diagonal coast guard–style stripes.

Personnel (2001): 667 officers, 3,834 enlisted, 750 civilians

Bases: Headquarters at New Delhi, with regional headquarters at Mumbai, Chennai, and Port Blair (Andaman Islands). District headquarters are at Mumbai, Campbell Bay, Kochi, Diglipur, Haldia, New Mangalore, Paradip, Porbandar, and Vishakhapatnam. Stations are maintained also at Mandapam, Okha, Tuticorin, and Vadinar.

Coast Guard Aviation: 17 Dornier Do-228 maritime surveillance aircraft and 17 Chetak helicopters were in service as of 4-01, with 7 more Do-228 on order. The first two HAL Advanced Light Helicopters for the coast guard were ordered early in 1997. As many as 48 additional Chetak helicopters are to be ordered during 2004–06. Coast guard squadrons in service include:

- No. 700 Sqn. at Calcutta: 6 Do-228
- No. 744 Sqn. at Chennai: 6 Do-228
- No. 745 Sqn. at Port Blair: 6 Do-228 (with 1 Chetak on detachment)
- No. 750 Sqn. at Daman: 6 Do-228, 2 Chetak (from 800 Sqn.)
- No. 800 Sqn. at Goa: 3 Chetak
- No. 841 Sqn. at Mumbai: 4 Chetak
- No. 848 Sqn. at Chennai: 5 Chetak

PATROL SHIPS [WPS]

♦ 3 Samar class
Bldr: Hindustan SY, Vishakhapatnam

	Laid down	L	In serv.
42 SAMAR	1990	26-8-92	14-2-96
43 SANGRAM	1992	18-3-95	29-3-97
44 SARANG	1993	8-3-97	5-99

Samar (42) Brian Morrison, 2-01

Sangram (43) Mitsuhiro Kadota, 5-01

Sarang (44) Brian Morrison, 5-01

D: 1,765 tons (2,005 fl) **S:** 22 kts **Dim:** 101.95 (96.00 pp) × 11.50 × 3.50
A: 1 76-mm 62-cal. OTOBreda SuperRapid DP; 2 single 7.62-mm mg; 1 Chetak helicopter
Electronics:
Radar: 1 Bharat 1245 nav.; 1 Decca 2459 surf. search
TACAN: Bharat FT13-S/M
E/O: 1 Bharat-Radamec System 2400 optronic f.c. and surveillance
M: 2 Kirloskar-SEMT-Pielstick 16 PA6 V280 diesels; 2 props; 12,800 bhp
Electric: . . . **Range:** 7,000/15 **Fuel:** . . .
Crew: 12 officers, 112 enlisted (accomm. for 145 tot.)

Remarks: Ordered 4-90. Are half-sisters to seven *Sukanya*-class units in the Indian Navy. A total of 12 was originally planned, then cut to six, and now terminated at three. Intended for offshore patrol vessel duties for the protection of oil platforms and the Indian economic exclusion zone. *Sangram* means "Struggle" in Hindi.
Hull systems: Differ from the Indian Navy *Sukanya* class in having heavier gun armament, having twin funnels flanking the helicopter hangar (which can accommodate a Sea King), lacking the deckhouse forward of the bridge, and having the helicopter deck terminate well short of the stern. Have fin stabilizers, a firefighting water monitor, towing capability, and Inmarsat satellite communications. Additional accommodations are provided for passengers.
Combat systems: The 76-mm guns in the first two proved too expensive to maintain and operate and more powerful than is needed in the ships' essentially policing role, but plans to replace the 76-mm gun in the third unit were not carried out. The ships have a Bharat-made Radamec 2400 optronic director for the 76-mm gun.

♦ 9 Vikram class Bldr: Mazagon DY, Mumbai (last two: Goa)

	L	In serv.		L	In serv.
33 VIKRAM	26-9-81	20-12-83	38 VIVEK	5-11-87	19-8-89
34 VIJAYA	. . .	12-4-85	39 VIGRAHA	12-88	12-4-90
35 VEERA	30-6-84	3-5-86	40 VARAD	2-9-89	19-7-90
36 VARUNA	1-2-86	27-2-88	41 VARAHA	. . .	11-3-92
37 VAJRA	31-1-87	22-12-88			

COAST GUARD PATROL SHIPS [WPS] *(continued)*

Vijaya (34)—with 40-mm gun forward — Ralph Edwards, 2-01

Varaha (41)—with 30-mm gun forward — Brian Morrison, 2-01

D: 1,064 tons (1,224 fl) **S:** 22 kts
Dim: 74.10 (69.00 pp) × 11.40 × 3.20 (3.68 props)
A: 1 40-mm 60-cal. Bofors Mk 3 or 30-mm 2A4Z/7.62-mm Medak AA (see remarks); 2 single 7.62-mm mg; 1 Chetak helicopter
Electronics: Radar: 1 Bharat-Decca 1226 nav.; 1 Bharat-Decca 1230 nav.
M: 2 SEMT-Pielstick 16 PA6 V80 diesels; 2 CP props; 12,800 bhp
Electric: 560 kw tot. (2 × 200-kw, 1 × 160-kw diesel alternators; 415 V, 3-phase a.c.)
Range: 4,000/16 **Fuel:** 180 tons **Crew:** 11 officers, 85 enlisted

Remarks: First three ordered in 1979, second three in 1983. 36 has training facilities on the fantail in lieu of the antipollution equipment. Design is not fully satisfactory; cannot operate helicopter in heavy weather due to rolling.
Hull systems: Have nonretractable fin stabilizers. Equipped with two 250-m^3/hr pumps and two firefighting monitors. Have a 4.5-ton crane, are air-conditioned, and carry diving and pollution-control equipment. There is a hangar for the Chetak helicopter. Carry two RIB inspection craft and a GRP launch.
Combat systems: Carry one Matra Défense Lynx optronic gun director for the 40-mm gun, which is being replaced during refits by a dual 30-mm 2A42/7.62-mm Medak AA mounting, derived from the turret fitted to BMP-2 armored personnel carriers.

PATROL CRAFT [WPC]

♦ 7 Jija Bai Mod. 1 class

Bldr: Garden Reach SB & Eng., Calcutta (224, 225: Goa SY, Vasco da Gama)

	In serv.		In serv.
221 Priyadarshini	25-5-92	226 Kanak Lata Barua	27-3-97
223 Annie Beseant	7-7-91	227 Bhikaji Cama	24-9-97
224 Kamla Devi	20-5-92	228 Sucheta Kripalani	16-3-98
225 Amrit Kaur	20-3-93		

Amrit Kaur (225)—with the new 30-mm Medak gunmount forward — John Mortimer, 2-01

D: 215 tons light (306 fl) **S:** 24 kts (23 sust.)
Dim: 46.00 × 7.50 × 1.85 (2.50 props)
A: 1 40-mm 60-cal. Bofors Mk 3 AA; 2 single 7.62-mm mg—224, 225: 1 30-mm 2A42 and 7.62-mm Medak AA; 2 single 7.62-mm mg
Electronics: Radar: 1 Bharat-Decca 1245/6X or Decca 1226 nav.
M: 2 MTU 12V538 TB82 diesels; 2 4-bladed props; 5,940 bhp (4,025 sust.)
Electric: 240 kw tot. (3 × 80-kw, 415-V, 50-Hz diesel sets)
Range: 2,400/12 **Crew:** 5 officers, 32 enlisted

Remarks: A further refinement of the *Tara Bai* design, with greater beam. Sister *Razya Sultana* (222) foundered in bad weather 9-11-95 off Paradeep. In early 1998, 225 acted as trials platform for the Medak dual 30-mm/12.7-mm naval mounting, which is being backfitted in the other units. A modified version of this design has been offered for export; equipped with waterjet engines and two Medak gunmounts, it would have a maximum speed of 35 kts.

♦ 6 Tara Bai class

Bldrs: 71, 72: Singapore SB & Eng., Ltd.; others: Garden Reach SB & Eng., Calcutta

	L	In serv.		L	In serv.
71 Tara Bai	4-87	20-5-87	74 Akka Devi	. . .	9-8-89
72 Ahalya Bai	5-87	9-9-87	75 Naiki Devi	. . .	19-3-90
73 Lakshmi Bai	. . .	20-3-89	76 Ganga Devi	. . .	19-11-90

Tara Bai (71) — French Navy, 1996

D: 173 tons normal (195 fl) **S:** 26 kts
Dim: 44.90 (42.30 wl) × 7.00 × 1.89 (2.59 props)
A: 1 40-mm 60-cal. Bofors Mk 3 AA; 2 single 7.62-mm mg
Electronics: Radar: 1 Decca 1226 nav.
M: 2 MTU 12V538 TB82 diesels; 2 props; 5,940 bhp
Electric: 260 kw (2 × 100 kw, 1 × 60 kw) **Range:** 2,400/12
Fuel: 30 tons **Endurance:** 7 days **Crew:** 5 officers, 27 enlisted + 2 spare

Remarks: First two were ordered 6-86, with license to build the other four in India. Are air-conditioned and have a 5-ton bollard-pull towing hook and a rigid inflatable boat. Carry 10 tons of fresh water, with a 3-ton/day distiller. Have HF/DF, an echo sounder, and an autopilot. Intended for SAR, fisheries patrol, sovereignty patrol, etc. Hull design is based on standard Lürssen 45-m hull; steel construction. The new dual 30-mm/7.62-mm Medak naval mounting is to be backfitted to this class.

♦ 7 Jija Bai class

Bldr: Garden Reach SB & Eng., Calcutta (64: Sumidagawa SY, Tokyo)

	In serv.		In serv.
64 Jija Bai	22-2-84	68 Habbahkhatun	27-4-85
65 Chand Bai	22-2-84	69 Ramadevi	3-8-85
66 Kittur Chinnama	21-5-83	70 Avvayar	19-10-85
67 Rani Jindan	21-10-83		

Jija Bai (64) — Sumidigawa, 1983

D: 181 tons light (273 fl) **S:** 25 kts (sust.)
Dim: 44.02 (41.10 pp) × 7.40 × 1.50 (hull)
A: 1 40-mm 60-cal. Bofors Mk 3 AA; 2 single 7.62-mm mg
Electronics: Radar: 1 Decca 1226 nav.
M: 2 MTU 12V538 TB82 diesels; 2 props; 5,940 bhp (4,030 sust.)
Range: 2,375/14 **Crew:** 7 officers, 27 enlisted

Remarks: Same basic design as the Philippine Coast Guard's *Bessang Pass* class; also known as Type 956. Plans to build eight more were dropped in favor of the *Tara Bai* class. The new dual 30-mm/12.7-mm Medak naval mounting is to be backfitted to this class.

AIR-CUSHION PATROL BOATS [WPBH]

♦ 6 8000TDX class

Bldrs: H 181, 182: Griffon Hovercraft, Woolston, U.K.; others: Garden Reach SB & Eng., Calcutta (In serv. 7-00 to 1-02)

H 181 H 182 H 183 H 184 H 185 H 186

D: 27 tons (fl) **S:** 42 kts **Dim:** 21.15 (19.85 hull) × 11.30 (8.70 hull) × . . .
A: 1 12.7-mm mg **Electronics:** Radar: 1 . . . nav.

COAST GUARD AIR-CUSHION PATROL BOATS [WPBH]
(continued)

M: 2 MTU 12V183 TB32 diesels; 2 ducted CP airscrew props; 1,600 bhp
Range: 365/42 **Fuel:** 2,000 liters **Crew:** 4 tot. + 80 troops

Remarks: Aluminum construction. The two British-built units were shipped 3-7-00. Maximum hover height: 1.25 m. Can make 50 kts in light condition and can carry an 8-ton payload.

PATROL BOATS [WPB]

♦ 2 (+ . . .) Offshore Patrol Boats
Bldr: . . ., Surat

D: . . . tons **S:** 32 kts **Dim:** . . . × . . . × . . .
M: 2 diesels; 2 waterjets; . . . bhp

Remarks: First unit launched 10-00 for delivery in 2001. Aluminum construction. No other data available. Appear to be a commercial fast yacht design. Have hatches for two gunners with handheld weapons.

♦ 9 (+ 6) P-2000 Interceptor Boats
Bldr: Anderson Marine Pty, Kadras/Goa SY (In serv. 1993–. . .)

	In serv.		In serv.		In serv.
C 131	16-11-93	C 134	20-5-95	C 137	4-9-96
C 132	16-11-93	C 135	25-3-95	C 138	4-9-96
C 133	20-5-95	C 136	25-3-95	C 140	1998

C 134 (C 34) Brian Morrison, 2-01

D: 49 tons (fl) **S:** 40 kts **Dim:** 20.80 (18.00 pp) × 5.80 × 1.00
A: 1 7.62-mm mg **Electronics:** Radar: 1 Furuno . . . I-band nav.
M: 2 Deutz-MWM TBD 234 V12 diesels outboard (823 bhp each), 1 Deutz-MWM TBD 234 V8 550-bhp loiter diesel centerline; 3 Hamilton 402–series waterjets; 2,200 bhp
Range: 600/15 **Crew:** 4 officers, 6 enlisted

Remarks: Ten were ordered in 9-90, with an option for six more. Built in cooperation with Seaking Industries, with design services from Amgram, Ltd., Sussex, U.K. GRP hulls laid up by Anderson Marine employ molds originally built by Watercraft, Shoreham, U.K. for the Royal Navy *Archer* class. Are based at Goa and Kochi. Although the official pennant numbers are as given above, they wear only the last two digits. Sister C 139 was leased to Mauritius during 2001. Were originally to have had a 20-mm Oerlikon AA forward, but a remotely controlled 7.62-mm machinegun has been substituted.

♦ 6 South Korean Swallow 65 design
Bldr: Swallow Craft, Pusan (In serv. 1980–82)

C 01 C 02 C 04 C 05 C 06 C 63

D: 32 tons (35 fl) **S:** 20 kts **Dim:** 20.0 × 4.8 × 1.3
A: 1 7.62-mm mg **Electronics:** Radar: 1 . . . nav.
M: 2 G.M. Detroit Diesel 12V71 TA diesels; 2 props; 840 bhp
Range: 400/20 **Crew:** 8 tot.

Remarks: C 01–C 06 were placed in service 24-7-80; C 62 and C 63 were taken over from India Oil Corp. 22-5-82. C 03 was stricken around 1996, C 62 in 2000.

♦ 5 12.5-meter class Bldr: Mandovani Marine, . . . (In serv. 1980s)

D: 10 tons (fl) **S:** 18 kts **Dim:** 12.5 × . . . × . . .
M: 2 Cummins diesels; 2 Hamilton waterjets; 550 bhp

Remarks: GRP construction, deep-vee hullform.

An Indian Coast Guard fast interceptor launch—propelled by two Yamaha gasoline outboards and equipped with a Furuno radar and hatches for two gunners with handheld weapons; no data available Brian Morrison, 2-01

Note: Fisheries Protection Craft *Kallyani, Kayerii, Karuna, Keishna,* and *Kalpaka,* delivered 10-96 by Cochin Shipyard, belong to another Indian government agency; no data are available other than that they are 16.20 × 4.50 × 2.50 and are powered by two MWM diesel engines. The border security force also operates a small number of 17-m patrol boats for riverine border patrol and harbor antismuggling duties. The customs service operates fast patrol launches and also station craft in each major port.

Indian Border Security Force 17-meter launch Amalya Bai—outboard sister *Ranilakshmi Bai* Leo Dirkx, 1-98

INDONESIA

INDONESIAN NAVY
(Tentara Nasional)

Personnel (2002): 47,500, including 15,000 marines and 1,000 naval aviatio[illegible] Plans were announced during 2-00 to expand the marine force to 22,800 and the [illegible] to 52,500 by 2005.

Bases and Organization: In 2000, the *Tentara Nasional* was reorganized into four regional naval commands: the Western, Central, Eastern, and Northern. The Eastern Command is headquartered at Surabaya, and the Western Command at Teluk Ratai on Sumatra. There are also the Training Command, the Military Sea Communications Command, and the Military Sealift Command. Principal naval bases are at Tanjung Priok near Jakarta; Ujung, near Surabaya (the principal dockyard); Sabang, We Island; Medan, Sumatra; Ujung Pandang, Celebes; Balikpapan, Borneo; Biak Island, north of New Guinea; Tanjung Pinang, Bintan Island, near Singapore; Manado, Celebes; Teluk Ratai, Sumatra; Banjarmasin, Borneo; and Manokwari, New Guinea.

Marine Commando Corps: Reorganized 27-3-01 into the 1st Marine Corps Group (Pasukan Korps Marinir 1), based at Surabaya with 6,500 personnel, and the Independent Marine Corps Brigade, based at Jakarta with about 3,500 personnel. Plans call for the creation of a second Marine Corps Group in 2004, to be based at Piabung, at Teluk Ratai, Sumatra. Ultimately, the Marine Commando Corps hopes to have 22,800 uniformed personnel.

Naval Aviation: Organized into the *Skwadron Udara* 200, with 4 DC-100 Lark Commander, 2 F-33A Bonanza, 1 TB-9 Tampico, and 1 PA-38 Tomahawk light transports; *Skwadron Udara* 400, with 1 or more Alouette-II, 3 NBO-105CB, 3 Wasp HAS.1, 3 NAS-332F Super Puma, and 4 or more NB-412S helicopters; *Skwadron Udara* 600, with 7 NC-212M-200 Aerocar and 2 DHC-5D Buffalo transports; and *Skwadron Udara* 800, with 20 GAF N-22B Nomad, 3 GAF N-22SL Searchmaster, and 6 GAF N-24A Nomad light transport/surveillance aircraft. All squadrons are based at Lanudal Juanda, Surabaya, with headquarters at Dinas Penerbangan Angkatan Laut, Dinerbal. One NC-212M-200 transport was lost on 7-1-01.

The three Indonesian Aerospace–built NAS-332F Super Puma helicopters are fitted with AS 39 Exocet antiship missiles, Omega ORB-22 radar, Thales HS-12 dipping sonar, and ASW torpedoes. Five Nuritanio-CASA CN-235 maritime patrol aircraft with Thales Ocean Master 100 radars were ordered 6-96 but have not been delivered. Two Mil Mi-17I and 8 Mi-2 helicopters were ordered 14-5-01. Three Eurocopter EC-120B Colibri helicopters were delivered during 7-01.

The Air Force has two Boeing 737-200 Surveiller long-range maritime patrol aircraft (the first delivered 6-83) with Slammer side-looking radar; also used for maritime patrol are three C-130H-MP and six Nuritanio-CASA CN-235. Fourteen Hawk 100 and 10 Hawk 200 light fighters are used for training and maritime strike duties.

Note: The names of Indonesian ships are preceded by the designation KRI (*Kapalperang Republik Indonesia,* or Ship of the Republic of Indonesia). As of 5-00, only about 20% of the seagoing ships were fully operational, due to the difficulty in obtaining spare parts and, in the case of the former East German units, problems with operating their machinery in tropical conditions. As of 8-00, strong consideration was reportedly being given to ordering new warships from South Korean yards.

ATTACK SUBMARINES [SS]

♦ 2 German Type 209/1300 Bldr: Howaldtswerke, Kiel

	Laid down	L	In serv.
401 Cakra	25-11-77	10-9-80	18-3-81
402 Nanggala (ex-*Candrasa*)	14-3-78	10-9-80	6-7-81

D: 1,100 tons std.; 1,265 tons surf./1,395 tons sub.
S: 11 kts surf./21.5 kts sub. **Dim:** 59.50 × 6.30 × 5.50
A: 8 bow 533-mm TT (14 AEG SUT Mod. 0 wire-guided torpedoes)
Electronics:
Radar: 1 Thales Calypso-II nav./search
Sonar: STN Atlas Elektronik CSU-3-2 suite: AN 526 passive, 407 A9 passive; Thales DUUX-2 intercept
EW: Thales DR-2000U intercept

ATTACK SUBMARINES [SS] *(continued)*

Cakra (401) NAVPIC-Holland, 6-93

Nanggala (402) Brian Morrison, 8-95

M: 4 MTU 12V493 AZ80 GA31L diesel generator sets (600 bhp each), 1 Siemens electric motor; 1 prop; 5,000 shp (4,600 sust.)
Range: 8,200/11, 1,200/4 snorkel; 16/21.5, 25/20, 230/8, 400/4 sub.
Fuel: 87 tons (108 emergency) **Endurance:** 50 days **Crew:** 6 officers, 28 enlisted

Remarks: Ordered 2-4-77 from a consortium headed by Ferrostaal, Essen. Both received thorough refits by the builder, *Cakra* completing in 1987 and *Nanggala* in 9-89. 401 was refitted again from 6-93 to 6-96 in Indonesia with new batteries and an improved combat data system, and 402 began a similar refit in 10-97.
Hull systems: Maximum operating depth: 250 m. Have four Hagen 120-cell batteries, producing 11,500 amp-hr and weighing 257 tons.
Combat systems: Have the Thales SINBADS weapons control. Equipped with Kollmorgen Model 76 attack periscope and a search periscope.

FRIGATES [FF]

♦ 6 ex-Dutch Van Speijk class

Bldrs: 351, 352, 356: Nederlandse Dok en Scheepsbouw Mij, Amsterdam; others: Koninklijke Maatschappij de Schelde, Vlissingen

	Laid down	L	In serv.
351 Ahmad Yani (ex-*Tjerk Hiddes,* F 804)	1-6-64	17-12-65	16-8-67
352 Slamet Riyadi (ex-*Van Speijk,* F 802)	1-10-63	5-3-65	14-2-67
353 Yos Sudarso (ex-*Van Galen,* F 803)	25-7-63	19-6-65	1-3-67
354 Oswald Sihaan (ex-*Van Nes,* F 805)	25-7-63	23-6-66	9-8-67
355 Abdul Halim Perdanakasuma (ex-*Evertsen,* F 815)	6-7-65	18-6-66	21-12-67
356 Karel Satsuitubun (ex-*Isaac Sweers,* F 814)	6-5-65	10-3-67	15-5-68

Oswald Sihaan (354) Brian Morrison, 8-95

Ahmad Yani (351) Brian Morrison, 8-95

Yos Sudarso (353) Brian Morrison, 8-95

D: 2,305 tons (2,940 fl) **S:** 28.5 kts **Dim:** 113.42 (109.75 pp) × 12.51 × 4.57
A: 4 RGM-84A Harpoon SSM (see remarks); 2 4-round Sea Cat SAM syst. or 2 2-round Simbad SAM syst. (Mistral missiles); 1 76-mm 62-cal. OTOBreda DP; 4 single 12.7-mm mg; 2 triple 324-mm Mk 32 ASW TT (U.S. Mk 46 Mod. 2 torpedoes); 1 Wasp HAS.1 helicopter
Electronics:
Radar: 1 Decca TM 1229C nav.; 1 Thales DA-05/2 surf./air search; 1 Thales LW-03 early warning; 0 or 2 Thales M-44 f.c. (for Sea Cat; removed from ships with Simbad systems); 1 Thales M-45 gun f.c.
Sonar: 1 Thales PHS-32 hull-mounted MF
EW: British UA-8 and UA-9 intercept; FH-12 HFD/F (355, 356: UA-13 VHFD/F instead); 2 8-round Corvus decoy RL
E/O: 353, 354, 356: 1 Thales LIOD Mk 2 f.c.
M: 2 sets Werkspoor–English Electric double-reduction geared steam turbines; 2 props; 30,000 shp
Boilers: 2 Babcock & Wilcox; 38.7 kg/cm^2, 450° C **Electric:** 1,900 kw
Range: 4,500/12 **Crew:** 180 tot.

Remarks: 351 was decommissioned from the Dutch Navy 6-1-86 and 352 on 13-9-86; they were transferred to Indonesia on 13-10-86 and 1-11-86, respectively. 353 and 354 decommissioned 2-87 for transfer 2-11-87 and 11-88, respectively. 355 transferred 1-11-89 and 356 on 1-11-90. Design is based on the British *Leander* class, but with a broader enclosed bridge and two Sea Cat SAM systems, each with a radar director.
Hull systems: New infrared suppression stack caps were added during the early 1980s. Have fin stabilizers.
Combat systems: Major modifications were begun in 1977 while still in Dutch service; the twin Mk 6 114-mm DP gunmount was replaced by the OTOBreda Compact 76-mm weapon, the Limbo ASW mortar was deleted and two triple ASW TT were added, the hangar was enlarged, and new sonars, radars, and the SEWACO-II data system were added. Modernizations took place: 351: 15-12-78 to 1-6-81; 352: 24-12-76 to 3-1-78; 353: 15-7-77 to 30-11-79; and 354: 31-3-78 to 1-8-80. Provision was made for carrying up to eight Harpoon SSM, but only four have been carried in practice; the U.S. SWG-1A launch control system is employed. The U.S. SQR-18A towed passive sonar array was removed from 355 and 356 before transfer, but they retain the associated small deckhouse at the extreme stern. During 1996–97, 353, 354, and 356 were equipped with LIOD Mk 2 optronic gun directors, and the SEWACO-II combat direction system was updated; all were supposed to have their obsolete Sea Cat SAM systems removed and replaced with two manned Simbad launchers for Mistral heat-seeking SAMs.

♦ 3 ex-U.K. Tribal class (In reserve)

Bldrs: 331: Alex Stephen & Sons, Govan; 332: John I. Thornycroft, Ltd., Woolston; 333: HM Dockyard, Devonport

	Laid down	L	In serv.
331 *Martha Khristina Tiyahahu* (ex-*Zulu,* F 124)	13-12-60	3-7-62	17-4-64
332 *Wilhelmus Zakarias Yohannes* (ex-*Gurkha,* F 122)	3-11-58	11-7-60	13-2-63
333 *Hasanuddin* (ex-*Tartar,* F 133)	22-10-59	19-9-60	26-2-62

Hasanuddin (333) Brian Morrison, 8-95

FRIGATES [FF] *(continued)*

D: 2,300 tons (2,700 fl) **S:** 24 kts
Dim: 109.73 (106.68 pp) × 12.95 × 3.80 (5.30 props)
A: 2 single 114-mm 45-cal. Mk 5 DP; 2 4-round Sea Cat GWS.21 SAM syst.; 2 single 20-mm 70-cal. Oerlikon Mk 10 AA; 2 single 12.7-mm mg; 1 3-round Limbo Mk 10 ASW mortar; 1 d.c. rack (3 d.c.); 1 Wasp HAS.1 helicopter (with Mk 44/46 ASW torpedoes)
Electronics:
Radar: 1 Decca Type 978 nav.; 1 Type 993 air/surf. search; 1 Marconi Type 965 early warning; 1 Plessey Type 903 gun f.c.; 2 Type 262 missile f.c.
Sonar: Graseby Type 177 hull-mounted search (7–9 kHz); Graseby Type 170B hull-mounted attack (15 kHz); Kelvin-Hughes Type 162 bottomed-target classification (50 kHz)
EW: . . . intercept; 2 8-round Corvus decoy RL
M: COSAG: 1 set Parsons-Metrovick geared steam turbines (15,000 shp) and 1 Yarrow-A.E.I. G6 gas turbine (7,500 shp); 1 5-bladed prop; 22,500 shp
Boilers: 1 Babcock & Wilcox 3-drum; 38.7 kg/cm², 450° C
Range: 5,400/12 **Crew:** 26 officers, 242 enlisted

Remarks: Survivors of a class of seven Royal Navy "General-Purpose" frigates, stricken 3-84 after having been recommissioned during the Falklands War. Purchased by Indonesia 16-4-84 and towed to Vosper Thornycroft, Woolston, for overhaul/modernization during 4-84/5-84. 331 began post-refit trials 22-3-85 and recommissioned 2-5-85; 332 recommissioned 21-10-85. 333 completed activation 22-1-86 and recommissioned 3-4-86. All were in reserve as of 2001. Virtually all their major weapons and all sensor systems are obsolete.
Hull systems: Have twin rudders and one pair of fin stabilizers. The steam turbine is mounted to port and the single gas turbine to starboard, sharing a common gearbox. Speed on the gas turbine alone is 17 kts. The helicopter flight deck has a small hangar beneath, into which the aircraft is lowered by elevator; the resultant hole is covered with segmented panels normally stowed beside the Limbo mortar position.
Combat systems: Have an MRS.3 director with Type 903 radar for the 114-mm guns and two modified MRS.8 directors with Type 262 radars for the Sea Cat systems. 332 had the Type 199 variable-depth sonar removed prior to transfer. The obsolete Sea Cat SAM systems were to have been replaced with two Simbad twin, manned launchers for Mistral heat-seeking missiles during the late 1990s.

♦ 4 ex-U.S. Claud Jones class

Bldrs: 341, 343: Avondale Marine, Westwego, La.; 342, 344: American SB, Toledo, Ohio

	L	In serv.
341 Samadikun (ex-*John R. Perry,* DE 1034)	29-7-58	5-5-59
342 Martadinata (ex-*Charles Berry,* DE 1035)	17-3-59	25-11-60
343 Mongisidi (ex-*Claud Jones,* DE 1033)	27-5-58	10-2-59
344 Ngurah Rai (ex-*McMorris,* DE 1036)	26-5-59	4-3-60

Samadikun (341) Chris Delgoffe/H&L Van Ginderen, 5-00

Mongisidi (343) Brian Morrison, 8-95

D: 1,720 tons (1,970 fl) **S:** 22 kts
Dim: 95.10 (91.75 wl) × 11.84 × 3.70 (hull; 5.54 sonar)
A: 341, 342: 1 76.2-mm 50-cal. Mk 34 DP; 1 twin 37-mm 63-cal. AA; 1 twin 25-mm 80-cal. 2M-3M AA; 2 single 12.7-mm mg; 2 triple 324-mm Mk 32 ASW TT (U.S. Mk 44 torpedoes); 2 Mk 6 d.c. mortars; 1 Mk 9 d.c. rack (18 total d.c.)—343, 344: 2 single 76.2-mm 50-cal. Mk 34 DP; 2 single 12.7-mm mg; 2 triple 324-mm Mk 32 ASW TT
Electronics:
Radar: 1 Decca 1226 nav.; 1 SPS-10 surf. search; 1 SPS-6E air search; 1 SPG-52 gun f.c.
Sonar: 341: EDO 786—342: SQS-45(V)—343: SQS-39(V)—344: SQS-42(V) hull-mounted MF
EW: WLR-1 intercept (not in 341)
M: 4 Fairbanks-Morse 38ND8⅛ diesels; 1 prop; 9,240 bhp (7,000 sust.)
Electric: 600 kw tot. **Range:** 3,590/22; 10,300/9 **Fuel:** 296 tons
Crew: 12 officers, 159 enlisted

Remarks: 341 was transferred 20-2-73, 342 on 31-1-74, and 343 and 344 on 16-12-74. All four were refitted 1979–82 at Subic Bay Naval Station, the Philippines. All remain in commission, as they are easy to maintain and inexpensive to operate, although their weapon systems and sensors are obsolete.
Combat systems: Have the Mk 70 Mod. 2 gunfire-control system for the 76.2-mm mounts and the Mk 105 ASW fire-control system. 341 and 342 have a twin Soviet 37-mm AA mount in place of one 76.2-mm on fantail and a twin 25-mm at the forecastle break, abaft the stack. Navigational radar was added 1980–81. 341 has no EW equipment but does have additional ASW ordnance. The Hedgehog ASW spiggot mortars have been removed.

TRAINING FRIGATES [FFT]

♦ 1 Hajar Dewantara class

Bldr: Uljanic SY, Split, Yugoslavia (Croatia)

	Laid down	L	In serv.
364 Hajar Dewantara	11-5-79	11-10-80	20-8-81

Hajar Dewantara (364) Vic Jeffery, 5-94

Hajar Dewantara (364) 92 Wing Det. A, RAAF, 1-94

D: 1,850 tons (fl) **S:** 27 kts **Dim:** 96.70 (92.00 wl) × 11.20 × 3.55
A: 4 MM 38 Exocet SSM; 1 57-mm 70-cal. Bofors SAK 57 Mk 1 DP; 2 single 20-mm 90-cal. Rheinmetall AA; 2 fixed ASW TT (2 AEG SUT wire-guided torpedoes); mines; 1 NBO-105 liaison helicopter
Electronics:
Radar: 1 Decca 1229 nav.; 1 Thales WM-28 track-while-scan f.c.
Sonar: Thales PHS-32 hull-mounted MF
EW: Thales SUSIE-I intercept
M: CODOG: 1 Rolls-Royce Olympus TM-3B gas turbine (27,250 shp); 2 MTU 16V956 TP91 diesels (7,000 bhp); 2 CP props
Range: 1,150/27 (gas turbine); 4,000/20 (diesels) **Fuel:** 338 tons
Crew: 11 officers, 80 enlisted + 14 instructors, 100 students

Remarks: Ordered 14-3-78 to the same basic design as the ship laid down in 1977 for Iraq. A second unit, reportedly ordered in 7-83, did not materialize. Can also be used as a troop transport.
Hull systems: Has fin stabilizers. Carries 114 tons of water ballast, 50 tons of potable water, 7 tons of helo fuel, and two LCVP-type landing craft. The gas turbine is rated at 22,300 hp max. in the tropics.
Combat systems: Has the Thales SEWACO GM 101-41 computerized data system. Carries 1,000 rounds of 57-mm and 3,120 rounds of 20-mm ammunition. The torpedo tubes are located at the stern, under the helicopter deck; they launch their wire-guided weapons directly aft. Two rails for launching 128-mm rocket flares are mounted on either side of the 57-mm gunmount.

CORVETTES [FFL]

Note: Plans announced 5-00 call for ordering as many as 14 new corvettes at a cost of $3 billion; the funds to pay for the program are, of course, unavailable.

CORVETTES [FFL] *(continued)*

♦ 3 Fatahilah class

Bldr: Wilton-Fijenoord, Schiedam, the Netherlands

	Laid down	L	In serv.
361 Fatahilah	31-1-77	22-12-77	16-7-79
362 Malahayati	28-7-77	19-6-78	21-3-80
363 Nala	27-1-78	11-1-79	11-8-80

Nala (363)—with helicopter hangar   Chris Delgoffe/H&L Van Ginderen, 5-00

Fatahilah (361)—no hangar   H&L Van Ginderen, 10-98

Malahayati (362)   Chris Delgoffe/H&L Van Ginderen, 1-00

D: 1,160 tons (1,450 fl) **S:** 30 kts (21 on diesels) **Dim:** 83.85 × 11.10 × 3.30
A: 361, 362: 4 MM 38 Exocet SSM; 2 2-round Simbad SAM launchers (Mistral missiles); 1 120-mm 46-cal. Bofors DP; 1 40-mm 70-cal. Bofors L70 AA; 2 single 20-mm 90-cal. Rheinmetall AA; 1 2-round 375-mm Bofors SR-375A ASW RL; 2 triple 324-mm Mk 32 ASW TT (U.S. Mk 44 torpedoes)—363: 4 MM 38 Exocet SSM; 2 2-round Simbad SAM launchers (Mistral missiles); 1 120-mm 46-cal. Bofors L46 DP; 2 single 40-mm 70-cal. Bofors L70 AA; 2 single 20-mm 90-cal. Rheinmetall AA; 1 NBO-105 liaison helicopter
Electronics:
Radar: 1 Decca . . . nav.; 1 Decca AC 1229 nav.; 1 Thales DA-05/2 surf./air search; 1 Thales WM-28 track-while-scan gun f.c.
Sonar: Thales PHS-32 hull-mounted MF
EW: Thales SUSIE-I intercept; 2 8-round Corvus decoy RL
E/O: 1 Thales LIROD t.v./laser/IR backup gun director
M: CODOG: 1 Rolls-Royce Olympus TM-3B gas turbine (22,360 shp, tropical); 2 MTU 16V956 TB81 diesels (8,000 bhp); 2 CP props
Electric: 1,350 kw **Range:** 4,250/16 (diesels) **Crew:** 11 officers, 71 enlisted

Remarks: Ordered 8-75. Are the most effective Indonesian major surface combatants.

Hull systems: Have an NBC warfare citadel. Living spaces are air-conditioned. Have nonretractable fin stabilizers.

Combat systems: 363 has a helicopter deck that folds around the helicopter to form a hangar, two single 40-mm AA instead of one, and *no* ASW torpedo tubes. All have the Thales DAISY computerized combat data system. Ammunition supply: 400 rounds 120-mm, 3,000 rounds 40-mm, 12 ASW torpedoes, 54 Nelli and Erica ASW rockets, 50 rounds chaff. The Simbad twin, manned SAM launchers were ordered for these ships in 1996 and installed during 1997.

PATROL COMBATANTS [PG]

♦ 16 Parchim-I class (Type 133.1) (Nonoperational)

Bldr: VEB Peenewerft, Wolgast, East Germany

	Laid down	L	In serv.
371 Kapitan Patimura (ex-*Prenzlau,* 231)	15-9-80	26-6-81	11-5-83
372 Untung Suropati (ex-*Ribnitz-Damgarten,* 233)	1-4-81	1982	29-10-83
373 Nuku (ex-*Waren,* 224)	9-6-80	27-3-81	23-11-82
374 Lambung Mangkurat (ex-*Angermünde,* 214)	. . .	. . .	26-7-85
375 Tjut Nya Dhien (ex-*Lübz,* P 6169, ex-221)	2-10-79	11-6-80	12-2-82
376 Sultan Thaha Syaifuddin (ex-*Bad Doberan,* 222)	15-12-79	30-9-80	30-6-82
377 Sutanto (ex-*Wismar,* P 6170, ex-241)	2-10-78	6-7-79	9-7-81
378 Sutedi Senoputra (ex-*Parchim,* 242)	9-1-79	9-10-79	9-4-81
379 Wiratno (ex-*Perleberg,* 243)	2-4-79	15-1-80	19-9-81
380 Memet Sastrawiria (ex-*Bützow,* 244)	2-7-79	12-3-80	30-12-81
381 Tjiptadi (ex-*Bergen,* 213)	. . .	. . .	1-2-85
382 Hasan Basry (ex-*Güstrow,* 223)	3-3-80	31-12-80	10-11-82
383 Iman Bonjol (ex-*Teterow,* P 6168, ex-234)	1-7-81	27-3-82	27-1-84
384 Pati Unus (ex-*Ludwigslust,* 232)	15-12-80	1-10-81	4-7-83
385 Teuku Umar (ex-*Grevesmühlen,* 212)	. . .	3-9-82	21-9-84
386 Silas Papare (ex-*Cut Meutia;* ex-*Gädebusch,* P 6167, ex-211)	1981	1982	31-8-84

Untung Suropati (372)   Chris Delgoffe/H&L Van Ginderen, 5-00

Sutanto (377)   92 Wing Det. A, RAAF, 5-95

D: 792 tons light; 873 tons normal (908 fl) **S:** 24.3 kts
Dim: 75.20 (69.00 pp) × 9.78 (8.95 wl) × 2.65 (hull; 4.40 sonar)
A: 1 twin 57-mm 70-cal. AK-257 DP; 1 twin 30-mm 65-cal. AK-230 AA; 2 4-round SA-N-5 Fasta-series SAM syst.; 4 fixed 406-mm ASW TT; 2 12-round RBU-6000 ASW RL; 2 d.c. racks (6 d.c. each)
Electronics:
Radar: 1 TSR-333 nav.; 1 MR-302 Rubka (Strut Curve) air/surf. search; 1 MR-123 Vympel (Muff Cob) f.c.
Sonar: MG-332T hull-mounted MF; HF dipping sonar
EW: 2 Baklan-B (Watch Dog) intercept (2–18 GHz); 2 16-round PK-16 decoy RL
M: 3 Type M-504A-3, 56-cyl. diesels; 3 props; 14,250 bhp
Electric: 900 kw tot. (1 × 500-kw, 2 × 200-kw diesel sets)
Range: 1,200/20; 2,200/14 **Endurance:** 10 days
Crew: 9 officers, 71 enlisted (normally operated with 59 tot.)

Remarks: Transfer was announced in 7-92 and approved by German Bundestag 2-9-92. 371 and 372 arrived in Indonesia 22-11-93, where they were subjected to further, more extensive modifications, including conversion of voids into additional fuel tankage. Four served briefly in the German Navy, hence the "P"-series former pennants. Twelve near-sisters operate in the Russian Navy. 371 and 372 were recommissioned 23-9-93, 373 on 15-12-93, 374 on 12-7-94, 375 and 376 on 25-2-94, 377 on 10-3-95, 378 and 379 on 19-9-94, 380 on 2-6-95, 381 and 382 on 10-5-96, 383 on 26-4-94, 384 on 21-7-95, and 385 and 386 on 12-7-96—all while still in Germany. Two of the class were to be activated during the 1-4-00 to 30-3-01 fiscal year. An unwise purchase, as their weapon and sensor systems are increasingly unsupportable and their engineering plants unsuitable for tropical climates. A mid-2001 report stated that *none* of this class was operational and that a contract had been signed with Germany's Deutz to re-engine six of them at P.T. PAL SY, Surabaya.

PATROL COMBATANTS [PG] *(continued)*

Sutedi Senoputra (378) Leo Dirkx, 10-98

Hull systems: The centerline shaft has a controllable-pitch propeller; the other two propellers are fixed pitch. Have fin stabilizers, but reportedly suffer from poor stability due to excessive topweight.
Combat systems: In an exception to German export policy toward former East German naval units, they retained their original armament and sensors on transfer to Indonesia. The helicopter-type dipping sonar deploys through a door on the starboard side of the main deck superstructure; next to it is another door with a second dipping device, possibly a bathythermograph. The d.c. racks exit through doors in stern.

GUIDED-MISSILE PATROL CRAFT [PTG]

♦ 4 PSK Mk 5 class Bldr: Korea-Tacoma SY, Masan, South Korea

	In serv.		In serv.
621 Mandau	20-7-79	623 Badek	2-80
622 Rencong	20-7-79	624 Keris	2-80

Badek (623) Brian Morrison, 8-95

Mandau (621)—with only two MM 38 Exocet missiles aboard Brian Morrison, 8-95

D: 250 tons (290 fl) **S:** 41 kts **Dim:** 53.58 × 8.00 × 1.63 (hull)
A: 4 MM 38 Exocet SSM; 1 57-mm 70-cal. Bofors SAK 57 Mk 1 DP; 1 40-mm 70-cal. Bofors AA; 2 single 20-mm 90-cal. Rheinmetall AA
Electronics:
Radar: 1 Decca AC 1229 nav.; 1 Thales WM-28 f.c.
EW: Thales DR-2000S Mk 1 intercept
M: CODOG: 1 G.E.-Fiat LM-2500 gas turbine (25,000 shp); 2 MTU 12V331 TC81 diesels (1,120 bhp each); 2 CP props
Electric: 400 kw tot. **Range:** 2,500/17 **Crew:** 7 officers, 36 enlisted

Remarks: First unit laid down 5-77. Modification of the U.S. *Asheville*-class design. A planned second group of four was not ordered. Have an Alenia NA-18 optronic backup gun director. 623 and 624 have electronic intercept gear. Indonesia has not contracted with Aérospatiale to have the Exocet missiles overhauled, and their future effectiveness is doubtful.

PATROL CRAFT [PC]

♦ 0 (+ 4) Lürssen PB 57 Variant V Bldr: P.T. PAL SY, Surabaya

803 Todak (In serv. 2001)
804 Hiu (In serv. 2002)
805 Layang (In serv. 2003)
806 Dorang (In serv. 2004)

Todak (803) Brian Morrison, 10-01

D: 447 tons (fl) **S:** 27 kts **Dim:** 58.10 (54.40 wl) × 7.62 × 2.85 (props)
A: 1 57-mm 70-cal. Bofors SAK 2 DP; 1 40-mm 70-cal. Bofors SAK 40 AA; 2 single 20-mm 90-cal. Rheinmetall AA
Electronics:
Radar: 1 Kelvin-Hughes Type 1007 nav.; 1 Thales Scout Variant surf. search; 1 Thales LIROD Mk 2 76-mm gun f.c.
EW: Thales DR-3000S1 intercept; EADS Telegon-8 HFD/F; 1 330- or 340-round Matra Défense Dagaie decoy RL
E/O: 1 Thales LIOD Mk 2 IR/t.v./laser 40-mm gun director

PATROL CRAFT [PC] *(continued)*

M: 2 MTU 16V956 TB92 diesels; 2 props; 8,850 bhp
Electric: 324 kw (3 × 108 kw) **Range:** 2,200/27; 6,100/15
Fuel: 110 tons **Endurance:** 15 days **Crew:** 9 officers, 44 enlisted

Remarks: Four were ordered 6-93 for delivery 1997–98, later changed to having sea trials for the first unit take place in 1998; there are no reports that any have been launched or completed, however, and the entire project appears to have been adversely affected by Indonesia's economic woes.
Combat systems: Were to have the Thales TACTICOS combat system with two multifunction operator consoles and one tactical plotting table. In addition to the two gun directors, there will be a manned target-designation sight at the forward end of the fantail.

♦ 2 Lürssen PB 57 Variant IV Bldr: P.T. PAL SY, Surabaya

801 Pandrong (In serv. 1990) 802 Sura (In serv. 1991)

Pandrong (801) Brian Morrison, 11-99

D: 428 tons (fl) **S:** 27.25 kts **Dim:** 58.10 (54.40 wl) × 7.62 × 2.75 (props)
A: 1 57-mm 70-cal. Bofors SAK 2 DP; 1 40-mm 70-cal. Bofors SAK 40 AA; 2 single 20-mm 90-cal. Rheinmetall AA
Electronics:
Radar: 1 Decca 2459 nav./surf. search
EW: Thales DR-2000S3 intercept; EADS Telegon-8 HFD/F; 1 330- or 340-round Matra Défense Dagaie decoy RL
E/O: 1 Thales LIOD Mk 2 IR/t.v./laser gun director
M: 2 MTU 16V956 TB92 diesels; 2 props; 8,260 bhp
Electric: 324 kw (3 × 108 kw) **Range:** 2,200/27; 6,100/15
Fuel: 110 tons **Endurance:** 15 days **Crew:** 9 officers, 44 enlisted

Remarks: Similar to the Variant II group but lack the sonar and torpedo tubes and having only one search radar. The LIOD optronic director was moved to the main-mast platform.

♦ 4 Lürssen PB 57 Variant II ASW craft
Bldrs: Lürssen, Vegesack, and P.T. PAL SY, Surabaya

	L	In serv.		L	In serv.
650 Andau	15-4-86	4-88	652 Tongkak	...	4-4-89
651 Singa	1-10-86	8-88	653 Ajak	...	4-4-89

Singa (651) Hans Karr, 5-99

D: 423 tons (fl) **S:** 27.25 kts **Dim:** 58.10 (54.40 wl) × 7.62 × 2.73 (prop)
A: 1 57-mm 70-cal. Bofors SAK 2 DP; 1 40-mm 70-cal. Bofors SAK 40 AA; 2 single 20-mm 90-cal. Rheinmetall AA; 2 fixed 533-mm TT (aft-launching, 2 reloads; AEG SUT wire-guided torpedoes)

Singa (651)—torpedo tubes at stern draped in canvas 92 Wing Det. A, RAAF, 8-95

Electronics:
Radar: 1 Decca 1226 nav.; 1 Thales WM-22 track-while-scan f.c.
Sonar: Thales PHS-32 hull-mounted MF
EW: Thales DR-2000S3 intercept; EADS Telegon-8 HFD/F; 1 330- or 340-round Matra Défense Dagaie Mk 2 decoy RL
E/O: Thales LIOD 73 IR/t.v./laser 57-mm gun f.c.
M: 2 MTU 16V956 TB92 diesels; 2 props; 8,260 bhp
Electric: 324 kw (3 × 108 kw) **Range:** 2,200/27; 6,100/15
Fuel: 110 tons **Endurance:** 15 days **Crew:** 9 officers, 44 enlisted

Remarks: Optimized for ASW. The midbody for 650 was shipped from Germany 1-84 for addition of the bow, stern, and armament in Indonesia. 651 was shipped 7-84. Have the Thales DALIA signal analyzer for the EW suite.

♦ 4 Lürssen PB 57 Variant I search-and-rescue craft
Bldrs: Friedrich Lürssen, Vegesack, and P.T. PAL SY, Surabaya

	In serv.		In serv.
811 Kakap	29-6-88	813 Tongkol	26-2-89
812 Kerapu	5-4-89	814 Barakuda (ex-*Bervang*)	5-4-89

Tongkol (813) Brian Morrison, 2-01

Barakuda (814)—note bulwarks around reviewing stand atop pilothouse and the rescue launches carried on the stern Brian Morrison, 8-95

D: 356 tons (half load; 425 fl) **S:** 30.5 kts (28.1 sust.)
Dim: 58.10 (54.40 wl) × 7.62 × 2.73 (prop)

PATROL CRAFT [PC] *(continued)*

A: 1 40-mm 70-cal. Bofors SAK 40 AA; single 7.62-mm mg—813 only: 2 single 14.5-mm 93-cal. mg
Electronics:
Radar: 1 Decca 2459 nav.—814 also: 1 Decca . . . nav.
EW: Thales DR-2000S intercept
M: 2 MTU 16V956 TB92 diesels; 2 props; 8,260 bhp
Electric: 270 kVA (2 × 135 kVA; 450 V, 60 Hz) **Range:** 2,200/28; 6,100/15
Endurance: 15 days **Crew:** 9 officers, 40 enlisted + 8 spare berths

Remarks: Ordered in 1982, with midbody sections for the first two shipped from Germany. Manned and operated by the Indonesian Navy for the customs service, which paid for them. Intended for search-and-rescue and inspection duties. 814 was converted in 1995 to act as the presidential yacht.
Combat systems: Have a 13 × 7.1-m flight deck to accommodate one NBO-105. Carry 1,000 rounds of 40-mm ammunition. Two water cannon with 294-m^3/hr capacity and 70-m range are fitted. Two rescue launches are stowed aft. 814 has a reviewing platform/open bridge atop the pilothouse; 812 is similarly equipped but lacks the extra navigational/surface-search radar added to 814. As of 2-01, two small rescue launches on 813 had been replaced by a single RIB, handled by a new boat crane, and two 14.5-mm mg had been added at the extreme stern.

♦ 1 Indonesian design Bldr: P.T. PAL, Surabaya (In serv. 1983)

861 WAIGEO

Waigeo (861) George R. Schneider, 9-87

D: approx. 150 tons (fl) **S:** 20 kts **Dim:** 32.0 × . . . × . . .
A: 1 40-mm 60-cal. Bofors Mk 3 AA; 2 single 12.7-mm mg
Electronics: Radar: 1 Decca . . . nav.
M: 2 . . . . . . diesels; 2 props; . . . bhp **Crew:** 22 tot.

Remarks: Design appears to be based on that of the *Attack* class, but they have lower freeboard, a more massive superstructure, and no bow bulwarks. A sister numbered 860 appears to have been discarded.

♦ 8 Australian Attack class

Bldrs: 847, 848, 859, 862: Walkers, Ltd.; others: Evans Deakin, Ltd.

	Laid down	L	In serv.
847 SIBARAU (ex-*Bandolier*)	7-68	2-10-68	14-12-68
848 SULIMAN (ex-*Archer*)	7-67	2-12-67	15-5-68
857 SIGALU (ex-*Barricade*)	12-67	29-6-68	26-10-68
858 SILEA (ex-*Acute*)	4-67	29-8-67	26-4-68
859 SIRIBUA (ex-*Bombard*)	4-68	6-7-68	5-11-68
862 SIADA (ex-*Barbette*)	11-67	10-4-68	16-8-68
863 SIKUDA (ex-*Attack*)	9-66	8-4-67	17-11-67
864 SIGUROT (ex-*Assail*)	. . .	18-11-67	12-7-68

Suliman (848) H&L Van Ginderen, 4-99

D: 146 tons (fl) **S:** 21 kts **Dim:** 32.76 (30.48 pp) × 6.2 × 1.9
A: 1 40-mm 60-cal. Bofors AA; 1 7.62-mm mg
Electronics: Radar: 1 Decca RM 916 nav.
M: 2 Davey-Paxman Ventura 16 YJCM diesels; 3,460 bhp
Range: 1,220/13 **Fuel:** 20 tons **Crew:** 3 officers, 19 enlisted

Remarks: Light-alloys superstructure. Air-conditioned. 847 was transferred 16-11-73, 848 in 1974, 857 on 22-4-82, 858 on 6-5-83, 859 later in 1983, 862 on 2-2-85, 863 on 24-5-85, and 864 on 30-1-86.

PATROL BOATS [PB]

♦ 0 (+ 5) Seaflyer class

Bldr: EGI-Droge SB, Rosario, Argentina (In serv. . . .)

D: . . . tons **S:** 65 kts **Dim:** 13.25 × . . . × . . .
A: . . . **Electronics:** Radar: . . .
M: 1 Seatek diesel; 1 prop; 600 bhp
Range: 500/. . . **Crew:** . . .

Remarks: Ordered late in 1997 but may not have been delivered. GRP construction. Intended to combat pirates and smugglers. Twenty sisters were ordered for the United Arab Emirates at the same time.

♦ 18 Kal Kangean class Bldr: P.T. Kabrick Kapal (In serv. 1987–90)

1101 through 1118

D: 44.7 tons (fl) **S:** 18 kts **Dim:** 24.5 × 4.3 × 1.0
A: 1 twin 25-mm 80-cal. 2M-3M AA; 1 twin 14.5-mm 93-cal. 2M-7 AA
Electronics: Radar: 1 . . . nav.
M: 2 diesels; 2 props; . . . bhp **Range:** . . ./. . . **Crew:** . . . tot.

Remarks: Ordered in 1984. Make use of surplus Soviet gunmounts removed from discarded Indonesian Navy ships and craft. Their very low freeboard limits their seaworthiness. Names include *Kal Kangean* (1101), *Kal Lau, Kal Sapudi,* and *Kal Lawu.*

MINE COUNTERMEASURES SHIPS

♦ 2 Tripartite-class coastal minehunters [MHC]

Bldr: Van der Giessen de Noord, Alblasserdam, the Netherlands

	Laid down	L	In serv.
711 PULAU RENGAT (ex-*Willemstad*)	29-3-85	23-7-87	26-3-88
712 PULAU RUPAT (ex-*Vlardingen*)	22-7-85	27-8-87	26-3-88

Pulau Rupat (712) Brian Morrison, 8-95

Pulau Rupat (712)—note the second 20-mm AA aft where European navy units normally carry a diver's decompression chamber John Mortimer, 6-01

D: 510 tons (568 fl) **S:** 15.5 kts
Dim: 51.50 (47.10 pp) × 8.90 × 2.47 (2.62 max.)
A: 2 single 20-mm 90-cal. Rheinmetall AA
Electronics:
Radar: 1 Decca AC 1229 nav.
Sonar: Thales TSM 2022 hull-mounted HF minehunting
M: 2 MTU 12V396 TCDb51 diesels; 2 CP props; 1,900 bhp—2 75-hp bow-thrusters; 2 120-hp Schottel active rudders (7 kts)
Electric: 910 kw tot. (3 × 250 kw, 1 × 160 kw)
Range: 3,500/10; 3,000/12 **Endurance:** 15 days **Crew:** 46 tot.

Remarks: Ordered 29-3-85 and 30-8-85; taken from Royal Netherlands Navy production. Both left for Indonesia 18-8-88. Planned construction of up to 10 more in Indonesia did not materialize.
Hull systems: Glass-reinforced plastic construction.
Combat systems: The minehunting system is the Thales IBIS V. Carry two PAP-104 Mk 5 remote-controlled minehunting/destruction submersibles. Have TSM 2060 plot and TMV 628 Trident III radio location system. Sweep equipment includes Fiskars F-82 magnetic sweep tail, SA Marine AS203 acoustic gear, and OD-3 mechanical sweep; there are two sweep-gear cranes. The guns are located on the forecastle and abaft the superstructure.

MINE COUNTERMEASURES SHIPS *(continued)*

♦ **9 ex-German Kondor-II-class patrol minesweepers [MSC]** (6 in *reserve*) Bldr: VEB Peenewerft, Wolgast

	L	In serv.
721 *Pulau Rote* (ex-*Grossenhain;* ex-*Wolgast,* V 811)	13-4-70	1-6-71
722 *Pulau Raas* (ex-*Hettstedt,* 353)	10-4-73	9-8-73
723 *Pulau Romang* (ex-*Pritzwalk,* 325)	30-7-71	22-12-71
724 *Pulau Rimau* (ex-*Bitterfeld,* M 2672, ex-332)	30-12-71	26-6-72
725 Pulau Rondo (ex-*Zerbst,* 335)	29-3-72	7-8-72
726 Pulau Rusa (ex-*Oranienburg,* 341)	7-6-72	30-9-72
727 Pulau Rangsang (ex-*Jüterbog,* 342)	30-6-72	1-11-72
728 *Pulau Raibu* (ex-*Sömmerda,* M 2670, ex-311)	30-11-72	7-4-73
729 *Pulau Rempang* (ex-*Grimma,* 336)	5-7-73	19-11-73

Pulau Rondo (725) John Mortimer, 6-01

D: 414 tons (479 fl) **S:** 18 kts **Dim:** 56.52 × 7.78 × 2.46
A: 2 twin 25-mm 80-cal. 2M-3M AA; 1 14.5-mm 93-cal. mg; 2 mine rails
Electronics: Radar: 1 TSR-333 nav.—Sonar: MG-11 Tamir-11 HF (24.5–30 kHz)
M: 2 Type 40DM diesels; 2 CP Kort-nozzle props; 4,400 bhp
Electric: 625 kw (5 × 125-kw diesel sets)
Range: 2,000/15 **Endurance:** 10 days **Crew:** 6 officers, 24 enlisted

Remarks: Transfer was announced in 7-92, and all were delivered together via heavy-lift ship to Surabaya for refit and reactivation 22-10-93. Former Volksmarine units, with two having later served briefly in the German Navy. 726 and 727 were formally recommissioned 2-2-95, and 725 is also active, but the others' condition may be too poor to reactivate them.
Combat systems: Original armament was retained. Most of the sweep gear was transferred with the ships, but they were to be employed primarily as patrol boats. Are being fitted with Australian Dyad towed magnetic mine countermeasures devices, with 725 as the trials ship. The forward twin 25-mm AA has been replaced by a single 14.5-mm mg in the active units.

♦ **1 Soviet T-43-class minesweeper [MSC]**

701 Pulau Rani

D: 535 tons (569 fl) **S:** 14 kts **Dim:** 59.10 × 8.75 × 2.50
A: 2 twin 37-mm 63-cal. V-47M AA; 4 twin 12.7-mm mg; 2 BMB-1 d.c. mortars; 2 mine rails (20 tot. mines)
Electronics:
Radar: 1 . . . nav.
Sonar: Tamir-11 (MG-11) hull-mounted searchlight (25–30 kHz)
EW: 2 Bizan-4 (Watch Dog-A) intercept (2–18 GHz)
M: 2 Type 9D diesels; 2 CP props; 2,200 bhp **Electric:** 550 kw tot.
Range: 1,500/14; 4,400/8.3 **Fuel:** 68 tons **Endurance:** 7 days
Crew: 5 officers, 48 enlisted

Remarks: Five were transferred from Russia during 1962–64; three were retired during the early 1980s. 701 was incorrectly reported to have been discarded in 1998. Sister *Pulao Ratawo* (702), in a collision with the merchant ship *Iris* on 17-5-00, was beached at Madura Island, Tanjung Priok, and will not be repaired. Used primarily for patrol duties.

AMPHIBIOUS WARFARE SHIPS

Note: Other Indonesian Navy–operated, amphibious warfare–capable ships and craft are listed later in the Military Sealift Command (KOLINLAMIL) section. Four new tank landing ships were planned prior to Indonesia's economic difficulties, and a request was made for one ex-U.S. Navy *Newport*-class LST.

♦ **6 Teluk Semangka–class tank landing ships [LST]**
Bldr: Korea-Tacoma SY, Masan, South Korea

	In serv.		In serv.
512 Teluk Semangka	20-1-81	515 Teluk Sampit	6-81
513 Teluk Penyu	20-1-81	516 Teluk Banten	5-82
514 Teluk Mandar	7-81	517 Teluk Ende	2-9-82

D: 1,800 tons (3,770 fl) **S:** 15 kts **Dim:** 100.0 × 15.4 × 4.2 (3.0 mean)
A: 3 (516, 517: 2) single 40-mm 70-cal. Bofors AA; 2 single 20-mm 90-cal. Rheinmetall AA; 2 single 12.7-mm M2 mg
Electronics: Radar: 1 JRC . . . nav.; 1 Raytheon . . . surf. search
M: 2 diesels; 2 props; 6,860 bhp (5,600 sust.) **Electric:** 750 kw tot.
Range: 7,500/13 **Crew:** 13 officers, 104 enlisted + 202 troops

Teluk Penyu (513)—standard unit, without helicopter hangar Brian Morrison, 8-95

Teluk Ende (517)—command unit, with large helicopter hangar and raised helicopter deck Brian Morrison, 8-95

Remarks: The first four were ordered in 6-79; 516 and 517, modified as command ships and fitted with helicopter hangars, were ordered in 6-81. 517 has been equipped to act as a hospital ship but remains armed.
Hull systems: Cargo: 690 tons (17 main battle tanks); max. beaching load: 1,800 tons. Carry four LCVP-type landing craft. There is a 50-ton-capacity turntable in the tank deck and an elevator to the upper deck. 516 and 517 have a large hangar incorporated into the superstructure, the helicopter deck raised one level, the forward helicopter positions deleted, the landing craft davits moved forward of the superstructure, and increased command facilities to act as flagships; they each can carry three NAS-332 Super Puma helicopters.
Combat systems: The 40-mm mounts in 516 and 517, both on the forecastle, are open topped to save weight; their associated Bofors lead-computing director was not installed, although a raised mounting position remains in place between the guns, but both gunmounts have 128-mm rocket flare launchers on either side of the shielding.

♦ **1 ex-U.S. LST 542–class tank landing ship [LST]**
Bldr: American Bridge, Ambridge, Pa.

	Laid down	L	In serv.
511 Teluk Bone (ex-*Iredell County,* LST 839)	25-9-44	12-11-44	6-12-44

Teluk Bone (511) Brian Morrison, 8-95

D: 1,650 tons light (4,080 fl) **S:** 11.6 kts **Dim:** 99.98 × 15.24 × 4.29
A: 4 single 40-mm 60-cal. Mk 3 Bofors AA; 2 twin 37-mm 63-cal. AA
Electronics: Radar: 2 . . . nav.
M: 2 G.M. 12-567A diesels; 2 props; 1,800 bhp
Electric: 300 kw tot. **Range:** 6,000/9 (loaded) **Fuel:** 590 tons
Crew: 119 ship's company + 264 troops

Remarks: Transferred in 7-70 under the U.S. Military Assistance Program. Can carry 2,100 tons of cargo. Sisters *Teluk Bajer* and *Teluk Tomani* are in the Military Sealift Command, as is the Japanese-built near-sister *Teluk Amboina.* Will probably soon be discarded.
Disposals: *Teluk Langsa* (501, ex-LST 1128), *Teluk Kau* (504, ex-LST 652), *Teluk Ratai* (509, ex-*Teluk Sindoro;* ex-M/V *Inagua Shipper;* ex-*Presque Isle,* APB 44, ex-LST(M) 678), and *Teluk Saleh* (510; ex-*Clarke County,* LST 601) were placed in reserve in 1995–96 and are used as storage hulks.

AMPHIBIOUS WARFARE SHIPS *(continued)*

♦ 12 ex-German Frosch-I-class (Type 108) medium landing ships [LSM]
Bldr: VEB Peenewerft, Wolgast

	Laid down	L	In serv.
531 Teluk Gelimanuk (ex-*Hoyerswerda,* 611)	25-11-74	1-7-75	12-11-76
532 Teluk Celukan Bawang (ex-*Hagenow,* 632, ex-612)	7-3-75	19-12-75	1-12-76
533 Teluk Cendrawasih (ex-*Frankfurt/Oder,* 613)	10-6-75	2-1-76	2-2-77
534 Teluk Berau (ex-*Eberswalde-Finow,* 634, ex-614)	10-9-75	15-7-76	28-5-77
535 Teluk Peleng (ex-*Lübben,* 632, ex-631)	11-12-75	2-10-76	15-3-78
536 Teluk Sibolga (ex-*Schwerin,* 612, ex-632)	17-3-76	18-1-77	19-10-77
537 Teluk Manado (ex-*Neubrandenburg,* 633)	21-8-76	6-4-77	28-12-77
538 Teluk Hading (ex-*Cottbus,* 614, ex-634)	22-11-76	16-6-77	26-5-78
539 Teluk Parigi (ex-*Anklam,* 635)	21-2-77	22-9-77	14-7-78
540 Teluk Lampung (ex-*Schwedt,* 636)	15-5-77	27-12-77	7-9-79
541 Teluk Jakarta (ex-*Eisenhüttenstadt,* 615)	18-8-77	8-3-78	4-1-79
542 Teluk Sangkulirang (ex-*Grimmen,* 616)	2-11-77	30-5-78	15-6-79

Teluk Cendrawasih (533) Leo Dirkx, 10-98

Teluk Sangkulirang (542)—note mine-rail round-downs flanking the stern Brian Morrison, 8-95

D: 1,744 tons normal (1,900 fl) **S:** 19 kts (18 sust.)
Dim: 90.70 × 11.12 × 2.80 (mean; 3.40 max.)
A: 1 twin and 1 single 37-mm 63-cal. AA—536 also: 2 twin 25-mm 80-cal. 2M-3M AA; 2 mine rails (40 mines max.)
Electronics:
Radar: 1 TSR-333 nav.; 1 MR-302 Rubka (Strut Curve) surf./air search
EW: 533, 534 only: 2 16-round PK-16 decoy RL
M: 2 Type 61B 16-cyl. diesels; 2 CP props; 12,000 bhp
Range: 2,450/14 **Crew:** 42 tot.

Remarks: Purchase announced 7-92. Used to supply outlying naval and military facilities. 535 was the first to arrive in Indonesia, 22-11-93. 540 was damaged by heavy seas in the Bay of Biscay during her delivery voyage. 531 was recommissioned for Indonesian service 12-7-94, 532 on 25-2-94, 533 on 9-12-94, 534 on 10-3-95, 535 on 23-9-93, 536 on 15-12-93, 537 on 2-6-95, 538 on 12-7-94, 539 on 21-7-95, 540 on 26-4-94, 541 on 19-9-94, and 542 on 9-12-94—all while still in Germany.
Hull systems: Cargo capacity: 400–600 tons, or 12 light tanks and a company of troops. Complex bow door/ramp mechanism; no stern ramp. The vehicle deck totals 425 m^2 and is 4.2 m high. During reactivation, the air-conditioning was improved and a sick bay was added.
Combat systems: The original gun armament of two twin 57-mm 70-cal. AK-257 DP, along with their associated radar director, and two twin 30-mm 65-cal. AK-230 AA was removed from all prior to delivery. Also removed were two 40-tube artillery rocket launchers, where fitted, and two PK-16 decoy rocket launchers. A twin V-11-M mount has replaced the forward 57-mm mount and a single 37-mm AA has replaced the after 57-mm gun, while 25-mm gunmounts have replaced the 30-mm mounts abreast the stack on 536 and possibly others; all gunmounts were recycled from stricken Soviet-built units formerly in Indonesian service.

♦ 2 Frosch-II-class (Type 109) amphibious support ships [LSM]
Bldr: VEB Peenewerft, Wolgast

	Laid down	L	In serv.
543 Teluk Sirebon (ex-*Nordperd,* E 171, ex-E 35)	26-1-78	30-8-78	3-10-79
544 Teluk Sabang (ex-*Südperd,* E 172, ex-E 36)	16-4-78	30-10-78	26-2-80

Teluk Sirebon (543) Chris Delgoffe/H&L Van Ginderen, 5-00

Teluk Sabang (544)—at start of delivery voyage to Indonesia, prior to installation of armament; note the large crane forward Hartmut Ehlers, 4-95

D: 1,530 tons normal **S:** 16 kts **Dim:** 90.70 × 11.12 × 3.40 (max.)
A: 1 twin and 1 single 37-mm 63-cal. AA; 2 mine rails (40 mines max.)
Electronics:
Radar: 1 TSR-333 nav.; 1 MR-302 Rubka (Strut Curve) surf./air search
EW: 2 16-round PK-16 decoy RL
M: 2 Type 61B 16-cyl. diesels; 2 CP props; 12,000 bhp **Crew:** 35 tot.

Remarks: Purchase announced 7-92. Both were recommissioned 25-4-95 after reactivation at Neustadt and arrived in Indonesia during 6-95. Are numbered as landing ships in Indonesian service.
Hull systems: Were typed as "High Seas Supply Ships" *(Hochseeversorger)* in Volksmarine service and have a 650-ton deadweight cargo capacity. Differed from the Frosch-I class in having an 8-ton Type 2Hy SWK8 crane amidships and two cargo hatches, and in having 25-mm (mounted starboard forward to cover the beach) in place of 30-mm AA. The bow ramp was retained to permit a beaching capability, and they presumably can be used as assault landing ships, if needed. During reactivation, the air-conditioning was improved and a sick bay was added.
Combat systems: Two 16-tube PK-16 chaff rocket launchers were added in 1986, just forward of bridge. The gun armament of two twin 57-mm 70-cal. AK-257 DP and two twin 30-mm 65-cal. AK-230 AA was removed prior to delivery. Old Soviet weapons from storage were added after arrival in Indonesia.

♦ 20 U.S. LCM(6)-class landing craft [LCM]
Bldr: . . . SY, Taiwan (In serv. 1988)

D: 24 tons (57.5 fl) **S:** 13 kts (light) **Dim:** 17.07 × 4.37 × 1.14
M: 2 G.M. Detroit Diesel 6V71 diesels; 2 props; 450 bhp
Range: 130/9 (loaded) **Crew:** 5 tot. + 80 troops

Remarks: GRP construction. Cargo: 30 tons. Cargo well is 11.9 × 3.7 m.

♦ approx. 24 LCVP Mk 7 class [LCVP]

Indonesian Navy LCVP—GRP-construction unit from LST *Teluk Penyu* (513) H&L Van Ginderen, 8-95

D: 13 tons (fl) **S:** 9 kts **Dim:** 10.90 × 3.21 × 1.04 (aft)
M: 1 Gray Marine 64HN9 diesel; 225 bhp **Range:** 110/9

AMPHIBIOUS WARFARE SHIPS *(continued)*

Remarks: Eighteen Korean-built units, delivered in 1981–82 with new LSTs, have GRP hulls. The others are survivors from among those delivered on World War II–era U.S.-built LSTs. Can carry 36 troops or 3.5 tons cargo. Cargo deck is 5.24 × 2.29 m, with 2.00-m-wide access through the bow ramp.

♦ 6 Sekoci-class personnel landing craft [LCP]
Bldr: Fasharkan Mentigi Naval DY (In serv. 5-94)

D: . . . tons (fl) **S:** 35 kts **Dim:** 28.0 × . . . × . . .
M: 2 . . . . . . diesels; 2 props; . . . bhp **Crew:** . . . tot. + 30 troops

Remarks: GRP construction. Have a bow ramp for disembarking troops and light vehicles.

AUXILIARIES

♦ 1 command ship [AGF]
Bldr: Ishikawajima Harima, Tokyo, Japan (L: 13-6-61)

561 Multatuli

Multatuli (561) Brian Morrison, 8-95

D: 3,220 tons (6,741 fl) **S:** 18.5 kts **Dim:** 111.35 (103.0 pp) × 16.0 × 6.98
A: 2 twin and 2 single 37-mm 63-cal. AA; 2 twin 14.5-mm 93-cal. 2M-7 AA
Electronics: Radar: 1 . . . nav.
M: 1 Burmeister & Wain diesel; 5,500 bhp
Range: 6,000/16 **Fuel:** 1,400 tons **Crew:** 134 tot.

Remarks: Built as a submarine-support ship; converted as a fleet command ship in the late 1960s. Acts as fleet flagship for the Eastern Command. Has a helicopter platform aft. Equipped with a British Marconi ICS-3 integrated communications suite. Can supply fuel and stores to ships in company. Construction of two similar ships of about 10,000 tons, to carry fuel, troops, and hospital facilities, is planned as a long-term goal.

♦ 1 Baruna Jaya VIII–class research ship [AGOR]
Bldr: CMN, Cherbourg, France (In serv. 1998)

KAL-IV-06 Baruna Jaya VIII

Baruna Jaya VIII (KAL-IV-06) A. A. de Kruijf, 9-98

D: 1,350 tons (fl) **S:** 13 kts **Dim:** 66.5 × 12.0 × 4.5
A: none **Electronics:** Radar: 1 Furuno . . . X-band nav.; 1 . . . S-band nav.
M: 2 Pielstick 5 PA5 L255 diesels; 1 CP prop; 2,990 bhp—200-shp bow-thruster—150-shp active rudder
Range: 7,500/12 **Crew:** 11 officers, 30 enlisted + 23 scientific staff

Remarks: Was to have been ordered 2-11-95, but the contract was delayed until early 1998. Will be employed for oil exploration work in eastern Indonesian waters. Equipped with a Marisat commercial SATCOM terminal.

♦ 4 Baruna Jaya I–class research ships [AGOR]
Bldr: CMN, Cherbourg, France

	In serv.
KAL-IV-02 Baruna Jaya I	15-9-89
KAL-IV-03 Baruna Jaya II	12-89
KAL-IV-04 Baruna Jaya III	4-90
KAL-IV-05 Baruna Jaya IV	2-11-95

D: 1,180 tons (1,350 fl) **S:** 14 kts **Dim:** 60.03 (55.28 pp) × 11.61 × 5.31
A: none

Baruna Jaya II (KAL-IV-03)—with two survey launches aboard
Brian Morrison, 8-95

Baruna Jaya III (KAL-IV-04) Brian Morrison, 8-95

Baruna Jaya I (KAL-IV-02)—with lattice mast forward to support a SATCOM antenna
Chris Sattler/H&L Van Ginderen, 1-97

M: 2 Niigata-Pielstick 5 PA5 L255 diesels; 1 CP prop; 2,990 bhp—200-shp bow-thruster—150-shp active rudder
Electric: 1,000 kw tot. (2 × 500-kw diesel sets)
Range: 7,500/12 **Crew:** 8 officers, 29 enlisted + 26 scientific staff

Remarks: 300 grt/450 dwt. First three were originally ordered from C.N. la Manche, Dieppe, in 2-85. *Baruna Jaya IV,* ordered in 1993, is 1,425 tons (fl) and is specially equipped for fisheries research. Operated by the Indonesian Navy Hydrographic Office for the "owners," the Agency for the Assessment and Application of Technology. Carry a small landing craft and one or more inshore survey launches and have a large A-frame gantry crane across the stern. *Baruna Jaya I* has a Marisat SATCOM radome added forward of the pilothouse, atop a lattice mast.

Baruna Jaya III is on long-term charter to Racal Survey for cable-route survey operations. She completed a refit at Pan United, Singapore, in 9-00, receiving a dual Simrad EM12D double-swath deep-ocean survey echo sounder, Elac BottomChart Mk II high-resolution medium- and shallow-depth bathymetric system, and Simrad EA500 dual-frequency deepwater single-beam echo sounder; the ship is also fitted with Thales Posidonia 6000 hydroacoustic positioning system, deep-tow GeoChirp II side-scan sonar and bottom profiler, a 16-transducer hull-mounted sub-bottom profiler, a cesium magnetometer, a gravity piston-corer, a vibro-corer, and a computerized data recording system.

Note: Also in service is *Baruna Jaya VII,* a slightly smaller ship of unknown origin.

♦ 1 hydrometeorological and oceanographic ship [AGOR]
Bldr: Sasebo Heavy Industries, Japan (In serv. 12-1-63)

933 Jalanidhi

D: 740 tons (985 fl) **S:** 12.7 kts **Dim:** 53.9 (48.5 pp) × 9.5 × 4.3
Electronics: Radar: 1 Nikkon Denko . . . nav.; 1 Furuno . . . nav.
M: 1 M.A.N. G6V 30/42 diesel; 1 prop; 1,000 bhp **Electric:** 261 kw tot.
Range: 7,200/10.5 **Fuel:** 165 tons
Crew: 13 officers, 74 enlisted + 26 technician/scientists

AUXILIARIES *(continued)*

Jalanidhi (933) H&L Van Ginderen, 3-99

Remarks: Has a weather-balloon facility aft and a stern ramp for net hauls.

♦ **1 Burudjulasad-class hydrographic survey ship [AGS]**

	Bldr	L	In serv.
931 Burudjulasad	Schlichtingwerft, Travemünde	8-65	1967

Burudjulasad (931) H&L Van Ginderen, 4-99

D: 1,815 tons (2,165 fl) **S:** 19 kts **Dim:** 82.00 (78.00 pp) × 11.40 × 3.50
A: provision for: 1 twin 37-mm 63-cal. AA; 2 twin 12.7-mm mg
Electronics: Radar: 1 Decca TM 262 nav. (probably replaced)
M: 4 M.A.N. V6V 22/30 diesels; 2 CP props; 6,400 bhp **Electric:** 1,008 kw
Range: 14,500/15.7 **Fuel:** 600 tons
Crew: 15 officers, 93 enlisted + 28 technicians

Remarks: Can carry one light helicopter. Equipped to perform oceanographic and hydrometeorological research, as well as hydrographic surveys. Carries one LCVP landing craft and three hydrographic launches. Refitted in the U.K. 3-86 to 10-86. Armament of one twin 37-mm AA and two twin 12.7-mm mg was added circa 1991, with the twin 37-mm mount installed just forward of the bridge and the machineguns placed in the tubs abaft the boats, but these had been removed by 1999.

♦ **1 U.K. Hecla-class hydrographic survey ship [AGS]**
Bldr: Yarrow & Co., Blythswood, Scotland

	Laid down	L	In serv.
932 Dewa Kembar (ex-*Hydra,* A144)	14-5-64	14-7-65	5-5-66

D: 1,915 tons (2,733 fl) **S:** 14 kts **Dim:** 79.25 (71.63 pp) × 14.94 × 4.00
A: 2 single 12.7-mm mg
Electronics: Radar: 2 Decca 1226 nav.—Sonar: British Type 2034 side-scan
M: diesel-electric: 3 Paxman 12YJCZ Ventura diesels (1,190 bhp each), 3 G.E.C.-A.E.I. 610-kw generators, electric motor; 1 prop; 2,000 shp—bow-thruster
Electric: 820 kw tot. (2 × 300-kw diesel-driven sets; 1 × 200-kw and 1 × 20-kw diesel emergency sets)
Range: 12,000/11; 20,000/9 **Fuel:** 450 tons **Crew:** 14 officers, 109 enlisted

Remarks: Purchased 18-4-86 and refitted by Vosper Thornycroft, Southampton, 24-4-86 to 16-7-86; recommissioned 10-9-86 and left for Indonesia 1-10-86. Retains Marisat satellite communications gear. Carries two survey launches.
Hull systems: Has a passive-tank stabilization system. Main propulsion generators operate at 510 V. Has a hangar and platform for a light helicopter.

Dewa Kembar (932) Chris Sattler/H&L Van Ginderen, 11-97

♦ **1 ex-U.K. Rover-class replenishment oiler [AO]**
Bldr: Swan Hunter, Hebburn-on-Tyne

	L	In serv.
903 Arun (ex-*Green Rover,* A 268)	19-12-68	15-8-69

Arun (903) Chris Delgoffe/H&L Van Ginderen, 5-00

D: 4,700 tons light (11,522 fl) **S:** 19.25 kts (17 sust.) **Dim:** 140.5 × 19.2 × 7.3
A: 2 single 40-mm 60-cal. Bofors AA; 2 single 20-mm 70-cal. Oerlikon AA
Electronics: Radar: 1 Kelvin-Hughes Type 1006 nav.; 2 . . . nav.
M: 2 SEMT-Pielstick 16 PA4 diesels; 1 CP prop; 15,300 bhp **Electric:** 2,720 kw
Range: 14,000/15 **Fuel:** 965 tons **Crew:** 16 officers, 31 enlisted

Remarks: 7,510 grt/6,822 dwt. Purchased 1-92 and sailed to Indonesia 9-92 after refit at Swan Hunter, Wallsend. Has 13 cargo tanks totaling 8,155 m^3 and one 387-m^3 dry cargo/provisions hold. Cargo capacity includes 7,460 m^3 for fuel, 325 m^3 for water, and 70 m^3 for lube oil; 600 m^3 of aviation fuel or gasoline can be carried in lieu of ship fuel. The helicopter deck aft can handle up to a Sea King–sized aircraft, but there is no hangar. Re-engined 1973–74. Had been placed in reserve on 30 days' notice 27-5-88, with a six-man crew. Armament was added late in 1996.

♦ **1 Sorong-class replenishment oiler [AO]**
Bldr: Trogir SY, Yugoslavia (In serv. 4-65)

911 Sorong

Sorong (911) Brian Morrison, 8-95

D: approx. 8,700 tons (fl) **S:** 15 kts **Dim:** 112.17 × 15.4 × 6.6
A: 4 12.7-mm mg **Electronics:** Radar: 1 . . . nav.
M: 1 diesel; 1 prop; . . . bhp **Crew:** 110 tot.

AUXILIARIES *(continued)*

Remarks: 4,090 grt/5,100 dwt. Cargo: 3,000 tons fuel/300 tons water. Can conduct underway alongside replenishments using hoses from jackstay rigs at amidships king-post stations port and starboard; can also refuel over the stern.

♦ 1 small transport oiler [AOT]
Bldr: . . . . . (In serv. . . .)

906 Sungai Jerong

Remarks: Has been in service since at least 1996 and appears to have been built in Russia or another former Warsaw Pact country during the 1960s. Armed with one 37-mm 63-cal. AA gun. Further data wanted.

♦ 1 ex-U.S. Achelous-class repair ship [AR]
Bldr: Chicago Bridge & Iron, Seneca, Ill.

	Laid down	L	In serv.
921 Jaja Widjaja (ex-*Askari,* ARL 30, ex-LST 1131)	8-12-44	2-3-45	15-3-45

D: 2,130 (3,640 fl) **S:** 11 kts **Dim:** 99.98 × 15.24 × 4.25
A: 4 quadruple 40-mm 60-cal. Bofors Mk 2 AA (possibly removed)
Electronics: Radar: 2 . . . nav. **M:** 2 G.M. 12-267A diesels; 2 props; 1,800 bhp
Electric: 520 kw tot. **Fuel:** 590 tons **Crew:** 11 officers, 169 enlisted

Remarks: Leased 31-8-71; purchased 22-2-79. Cargo capacity: 300 tons. Former bow doors are now welded shut. Carries two LCVP landing craft and has two 10-ton derricks. There were two U.S. Mk 51 Mod. 2 directors for the AA guns.

Note: The hulk of the Russian Don-class (Project 310) submarine tender *Ratulangi* is still afloat and was displayed at the 8-95 naval review at Jakarta, but the ship is nonoperational.

♦ 1 Soputan-class salvage tug [ARS]
Bldr: Dae Sun SB & Eng., Pusan, South Korea (In serv. 27-9-96)

923 Soputan

Soputan (923) Brian Morrison, 8-95

Soputan (923) Brian Morrison, 8-95

D: approx. 2,100 tons (fl) **S:** 13.5 kts **Dim:** 66.20 × 11.93 × 4.51
A: . . . **Electronics:** Radar: 2 Decca . . . nav.
M: 4 Pielstick–Sang Yong . . . 8-cyl. diesels, electric drive; 1 prop; 12,240 shp—bow-thruster
Range: . . ./. . . **Crew:** 42 tot.

Remarks: 1,279 grt/1,470 dwt. Very large and capable firefighting and salvage tugs with an unusual two-deck forecastle design. 923 was delivered in 7-95 but not commissioned for more than a year thereafter. Has a 120-ton bollard pull capacity. A reported second unit was begun in 1999 with aid from Dae Sun SB and components from Daewoo SY, Okpo; it may be of a different design, as the ship has been described as having only 7,500 bhp and a 2001 report called the ship a former ferry.

♦ 1 ex-U.S. Cherokee-class fleet tug [ATA]
Bldr: United Eng., Alameda, Calif.

	Laid down	L	In serv.
922 Rakata (ex-*Menominee,* ATF 73)	27-9-41	14-2-42	25-9-42

Rakata (922) Brian Morrison, 8-95

D: 1,640 tons (fl) **S:** 15 kts **Dim:** 62.5 × 11.7 × 4.7
A: 1 76.2-mm 50-cal. U.S. Mk 26 DP; 2 single 40-mm 60-cal. U.S. Mk 3 AA; 2 twin 25-mm 80-cal. 2M-3M AA
Electronics: Radar: 1 . . . nav.
M: 4 G.M. 12-278A diesels, Allis-Chalmers electric drive; 1 prop; 3,000 shp
Electric: 260 kw tot.
Range: 6,500/16; 15,000/8 **Fuel:** 315 tons **Crew:** 67 tot.

Remarks: Transferred 3-61. Placed in reserve in 1990 but was operational again by 1995.

♦ 1 sail-training barkentine [AXT]
Bldr: H.C. Stülcken & Sohn, Hamburg (L: 21-1-52; in serv. 9-7-53)

Dewaruci

Dewaruci A. D. Baker III, 6-00

D: 847 tons (fl) **S:** 9 kts **Dim:** 58.30 (41.50 pp) × 9.5 × 4.23
M: 1 M.A.N. diesel; 575 bhp—max. sail area: 1,091 m^2
Crew: 110 ship's company + 78 cadets

Remarks: Steel construction. Has been very active in the past several years, calling at U.S. East Coast ports during 6-00.

Note: For the smaller sail training craft [YTS] *Arung Samudera* and *Phinbi Nusantara,* see under Service Craft.

SERVICE CRAFT

♦ 1 Lampo Batang–class medium harbor tug [YTM]
Bldr: Ishikawajima Harima, Tokyo (L: 4-61)

934 Lampo Batang

D: 250 tons **S:** 11 kts **Dim:** 28.1 × 7.6 × 2.6
M: 2 M.A.N. diesels; 2 props; 600 bhp
Range: 1,000/11 **Fuel:** 18 tons **Crew:** 13 tot.

♦ 2 Tambora-class medium harbor tugs [YTM]
Bldr: Ishikawajima Harima, Tokyo (both L: 6-61)

935 Tambora 936 Bromo

SERVICE CRAFT *(continued)*

D: 250 tons (fl) **S:** 10.5 kts **Dim:** 24.1 × 6.6 × 3.0
M: 2 M.A.N. diesels; 2 props; 600 bhp
Range: 690/10.5 **Fuel:** 9 tons **Crew:** 15 tot.

Remarks: 935 is on loan to the Indonesian Army.

♦ 1 sail-training schooner [YTS]
Bldr: Hendrik Oosterbroek, Tauranga, New Zealand (L: 7-91)

ARUNG SAMUDERA (ex-*Adventurer*)

Arung Samudera H&L Van Ginderen, 1-98

D: 280 tons (fl) **S:** 10 kts (under power) **Dim:** 39.00 (31.60 wl) × 6.50 × 2.60
Electronics: Radar: 1 Furuno . . . X-band nav.
M: 2 Ford 2725E diesels; 2 props; 292 bhp—max. sail area: 433.8 m^2
Crew: 20 tot.

Remarks: 96 grt. Taken over and commissioned 9-1-96.

Note: Also in use for training at the naval academy is the smaller, noncommissioned sailing craft *Phinbi Nusantara;* no data available. There are probably numerous other small tugs, launches, fuel lighters, and so forth, in service, but no information is available about their numbers or characteristics.

MILITARY SEALIFT COMMAND
(Kolinlamil)

The Military Sealift Command was formed in 1978 to coordinate the Indonesian Navy's logistic support for its far-flung bases and outposts in the Indonesian Archipelago. Some of the units have been taken over from the Indonesian Army and others from the navy.

AMPHIBIOUS LOGISTICS TRANSPORTS

♦ 1 Teluk Amboina–class tank landing ship [LST]
Bldr: Sasebo Heavy Industries, Japan (L: 17-3-61)

503 TELUK AMBOINA

Teluk Amboina (503) Brian Morrison, 8-95

D: 4,145 tons (fl) **S:** 13 kts **Dim:** 99.90 (95.41 pp) × 15.24 × 4.60
A: 6 single 37-mm 63-cal. Soviet V-47M AA
M: 2 M.A.N. V6V 22.30 diesels; 2 props; 3,200 bhp (2,850 sust.)
Electric: 135 kw **Range:** 4,000/13 **Fuel:** 1,200 tons
Crew: 88 ship's company + 212 passengers

Remarks: Built as war reparations. A near-duplicate of the U.S. LST 542 design. Cargo: 2,100 tons max.; can carry 654 tons of cargo water. Has a 30-ton crane and davits for four LCVPs.

Note: Two former U.S. Navy LST 542–class tank landing ships transferred to the Military Sealift Command for cattle and cargo transport service, the *Teluk Bajer* (502, ex-LST 616) and the *Teluk Tomini* (508, ex-M/V *Inagua Crest;* ex-M/V *Brunei;* ex-*Polk County,* LST 356), were placed in reserve in 1995–96 and are unlikely to see further service.

♦ 3 Kupang-class utility landing craft [LCU]
Bldr: Surabaya DY

582 KUPANG (In serv. 3-11-78) 584 NUSANTARA (In serv. 1980)
583 DILI (In serv. 27-2-79)

D: 400 tons (fl) **S:** 11 kts **Dim:** 42.9 (36.27 pp) × 9.14 × 1.80
M: 4 diesels; 2 props; 1,200 bhp **Range:** 700/11 **Crew:** 17 tot.

Remarks: Design based on the U.S. LCU 1610 class. Cargo: 200 tons.

♦ 1 Amurang-class landing craft [LCU]
Bldr: Korneuberg SY, Austria (In serv. 1968)

580 DORE

D: 182 tons (255 fl) **S:** 8 kts **Dim:** 38.30 (36.00 pp) × 10.00 × 1.30
M: 2 diesels; 2 props; 420 bhp **Range:** 600/8 **Crew:** 14 tot.

Remarks: 200 grt. Sister *Banten* and one other are in merchant service. Naval unit *Amurang* (581) was lost at sea during 9-92.

AUXILIARIES

♦ 2 Hungarian Tisza-class cargo ships [AK]
Bldr: Angyalfold SY, Budapest (In serv. 1963–64)

959 TELUK MENTAWI 960 KARAMAJA

Karamaja (960) Piet Sinke, 6-93

D: 2,000 tons (fl) **S:** 12 kts **Dim:** 74.5 (67.4 pp) × 11.3 × 4.6
A: 2 twin 14.5-mm 93-cal. 2M-7 AA **Electronics:** Radar: 1 . . . nav.
M: 1 Lang 8-cyl. diesel; 1,000 bhp **Electric:** 746 kw
Range: 4,200/10.7 **Fuel:** 98 tons **Crew:** 26 tot.

Remarks: 1,296 grt/1,280 dwt. Taken over from the army in 1978. Cargo: 1,100 tons. Sisters *Telaud* (951), *Nusatelu* (952), *Natuna* (953), and *Karamundsa* (957) had been stricken by 1991.

♦ 1 Biscaya-class cargo ship (AK)
Bldr: . . . (In serv. 1950s)

952 NUSU TELU

Nusu Telu (952) Brian Morrison, 8-95

Remarks: A small coastal cargo vessel dating from the late 1950s and armed with one twin 12.7-mm mg mount forward. Is about half the size of the *Tisza*-class AK. No other data available.

♦ 1 small transport tanker [AOT]
Bldr: . . . . . . , Japan (In serv. 1969)

902 SAMBU (ex-*Taiyo Maru No. 3*)

D: 2,800 tons (fl) **S:** 11 kts **Dim:** 70.4 × 11.4 × 5.8
A: 2 twin and 2 single 12.7-mm mg **Electronics:** Radar: 3 . . . nav.
M: 1 diesel; 1 prop; . . . bhp **Crew:** . . . tot.

Remarks: Purchased in 1978.

MILITARY SEALIFT COMMAND AUXILIARIES *(continued)*

Sambu (902) Brian Morrison, 8-95

♦ **1 small transport tanker [AOT]**
Bldr: . . . SY, Japan (In serv. 1965)

901 Balikpapan (ex-*Komado V*)

Balikpapan (901)—alongside survey ship *Dewa Kembar* (932)
Chris Delgoffe/H&L Van Ginderen, 5-00

D: . . . **S:** 11 kts **Dim:** 69.6 × 9.6 × 4.9
Electronics: Radar: 1 . . . nav.
M: 1 diesel; 1 prop; 1,300 bhp **Crew:** 26 tot.

Remarks: 1,780-dwt commercial tanker purchased in 1977.

Disposal note: Former passenger/cargo ship *Tanjung Oisina* (972, ex-*Tjut Njak Dhien,* ex-*Prinses Irene)* was aground and being scrapped near Jakarta as of 11-00.

SERVICE CRAFT

♦ **. . . coastal cargo lighter(s) [YF]**
Bldr: Fasharkan DY, Manokwari, Irian Jaya

D: . . . **S:** 8 kts **Dim:** 31.1 × 6.26 × 1.80 **M:** diesels

Remarks: 200 dwt. First unit delivered 7-3-82. Others may have been built.

INDONESIAN ARMY (ADRI)
(Jawatan Angkutan Darat Militer)

SERVICE CRAFT

♦ **3 ADRI XLI–class logistics landing craft [WYF]**
Bldr: P.T. Kodja i, Tanjung Priok (In serv. 1982)

ADRI XLI ADRI XLII ADRI XLIII

D: approx. 480 tons (fl) **S:** . . . kts **Dim:** 32.80 (28.50 pp) × 8.54 × 2.65
M: 2 G.M. Detroit Diesel 12V71-series diesels; 2 props; 680 bhp

Remarks: 171 grt.

♦ **5 ADRI XXXIII–class logistics landing craft [WYF]**
Bldrs: P.T. Kodja i and P.T. Adiguna Shipyards, Tanjung Priok (In serv. 1979–81)

ADRI XXXIII ADRI XXXV ADRI XXXVII
ADRI XXXIV ADRI XXXVI

D: approx. 300 tons (fl) **S:** . . . kts **Dim:** 32.01 (28.25 pp) × 8.50 × 1.35
M: 2 G.M. Detroit Diesel 8V71N diesels; 2 props; 460 bhp
Electric: 70 kw tot. **Crew:** . . . tot.

Remarks: 169 grt/150 dwt. Have a bow ramp and can be beached.

♦ **1 ADRI XXXII–class logistics landing craft [WYF]**
Bldr: P.T. Ippa Gaya Baru, Tanjung Priok (In serv. 1979)

ADRI XXXII

ADRI XXXII H&L Van Ginderen, 8-95

D: approx. 490 tons (fl) **S:** . . . kts **Dim:** 37.01 × 10.71 × 1.65
M: 2 G.M. Detroit Diesel 12V71TI diesels; 2 props; 1,050 bhp

Remarks: 390 grt/300 dwt. Deck cargo only.

♦ **1 ADRI XL–class general cargo lighter [WYF]**
Bldr: . . . . SY, Indonesia (In serv. 1981)

ADRI XL

D: approx. 520 tons (fl) **S:** 12 kts **Dim:** 44.73 (40.01 pp) × 7.60 × 2.65
M: 2 G.M. Detroit Diesel 16V71N diesels; 2 props; 910 bhp

Remarks: 320 grt/300 dwt.

♦ **2 ADRI XXXVIII–class general cargo lighters [WYF]**
Bldr: P.T. Adiguna SY, Tanjung Priok (In serv. 1981)

ADRI XXXVIII ADRI XXXIX

D: approx. 145 tons (fl) **S:** . . . kts **Dim:** 26.14 (23.09 pp) × 6.80 × 1.46
M: 2 Baudouin 12F11SR 12-cyl. diesels; 2 props; 468 bhp

Remarks: 125 grt/100 dwt.

♦ **4 ADRI XVI–class general cargo lighters [WYF]**
Bldr: Wroclawska Stocznia Rzeczna, Wroclaw, Poland (In serv. 1963–64)

ADRI XVI ADRI XVII ADRI XVIII ADRI XIX

D: approx. 700 tons (fl) **S:** 7 kts **Dim:** 53.52 (49.99 pp) × 8.26 × 2.59
M: 2 Karl Liebknecht S.K.L. 12-cyl. diesels; 2 props; 600 bhp
Electric: 25 kw tot.

Remarks: 443 grt/549 dwt. Two holds and two 3-ton derricks.

♦ **1 ADRI III–class general cargo lighter [WYF]**
Bldr: Vereenigde Prauwen Verer, Tanjung Priok (In serv. 1954)

D: . . . tons **S:** . . . kts **Dim:** 34.45 (32.01 pp) × 5.49 × . . .
M: 1 Werkspoor diesel; 234 bhp

Remarks: 157 grt/152 dwt.

Note: The Indonesian Air Force logistics fleet has been sold or stricken.

SEA COMMUNICATIONS AGENCY

The Sea Communications Agency was established in 1978 to patrol Indonesia's 200-n.m. economic zone and to maintain navigational aids. Its full name is the Indonesian Directorate General of Sea Communication/Department of Transport, Communications, and Tourism. Patrol boats are now painted with blue hull (with white and red diagonal stripes) and white superstructure.

PATROL CRAFT [WPC]

♦ **4 Golok class** Bldr: Schlichtingwerft, Harmsdorf, Germany

	In serv.		In serv.
PAT 206 Golok	12-3-82	PAT 208 Pedang	12-5-82
PAT 207 Panan	12-3-82	PAT 209 Kapak	12-5-82

Kapak (PAT 209) Chris Sattler/H&L Van Ginderen, 11-98

D: 200 tons (fl) **S:** 28 kts **Dim:** 37.50 × 7.00 × 2.00
A: 1 20-mm AA **M:** 2 MTU 16V652 TB61 diesels; 2 props; 4,200 bhp
Range: 1,500/18 **Crew:** 18 tot.

Remarks: Intended for search-and-rescue duties. Have a 120-m^3/hr firepump and water monitor, rescue launch, and eight-man sick bay. Hulls were built by Deutsche Industrie Werke, Berlin.

SEA COMMUNICATIONS AGENCY PATROL CRAFT [WPC]
(continued)

♦ **5 Kujang class** Bldr: SFCN, Villeneuve-la-Garenne, France

	Laid down	L	In serv.
PAT 201 Kujang	5-80	17-10-80	19-8-81
PAT 202 Parang	7-80	18-11-80	19-8-81
PAT 203 Celurit	9-80	20-3-81	1981
PAT 204 Cundrik	7-9-80	10-11-80	1981
PAT 205 Belati	2-81	21-5-81	10-81

Cundrik (PAT 204) Chris Sattler/H&L Van Ginderen, 11-98

D: 126 tons (162 fl) **S:** 28 kts **Dim:** 38.32 (35.46 pp) × 6.00 × 1.78 (2.60 props)
A: 1 12.7-mm mg **Electronics:** Radar: 1 . . . nav.
M: 2 S.A.C.M. AGO V12 195 CZ SHR T5; 2 props; 4,400 bhp
Range: 1,500/18 **Crew:** 18 tot.

Remarks: Equipped for search-and-rescue duties.

PATROL BOATS [WPB]

♦ **6 PAT 01 class** Bldr: Tanjung Priok SY (In serv. 1978–79)

PAT 01 PAT 02 PAT 03 PAT 04 PAT 05 PAT 06

D: 12 tons (fl) **S:** 14 kts **Dim:** 12.15 × 4.25 × 1.0
A: 1 7.62-mm mg **M:** 1 Renault diesel; 260 bhp

Note: In addition to patrol boats, the Sea Communications Agency operates a large number of commercial passenger vessels in interisland service and is also responsible for undersea communications cable laying and maintenance and for navigational aids and dredging. Complete descriptions of the ships and craft thus employed are included in previous editions. In service as of 6-01 were:

- 1 or more *Fudi*-class vehicle and passenger ships: *Fudi* (In serv. 2000)
- 7 14,610- to 14,800-grt *Dobensolo*-class passenger ships: *Dobensolo, Diremai, Bukit Siguntang, Lambelu, Sinabung, Kelud,* and *Doro Londa* (In serv. 1993–2001)
- 4 6,041-grt *Leuser*-class passenger ships: *Binaiya, Kukit Raya, Bukit Siguntang Mahameru,* and *Tilongkabila* (In serv. 1994–95)
- 5 5,685- to 6,041-grt *Lawit*-class passenger ships: *Lawit, Tatamailu, Awu, Telimutu,* and *Sirimau* (In serv. 1986–92)
- 5 13,861- to 13,954-grt *Kerinci*-class passenger ships: *Kerinci, Kambuna, Rinjani, Umsini,* and *Tidar* (In serv. 1983–88)
- 2 569-grt *Karakata*-class navigational aids tenders: *Karakata* and *Kumba* (In serv. 1976)
- 2 1,705-grt *Majang*-class navigational aids and lighthouse supply ships: *Majang* and *Mizan* (In serv. 1963)
- 1 1,250-dwt *Biduk*-class cable tender and navigational aids tender: *Biduk* (In serv. 1952)
- 4 miscellaneous dredges: *Batang Anai, Irian,* and two others

Fudi Chris Delgoffe/H&L Van Ginderen, 5-00

Kelud H&L Van Ginderen, 1-00

Kerinci Chris Delgoffe/H&L Van Ginderen, 5-00

Note: The Customs Agency operates more than 100 patrol boats, all armed with one or more 12.7-mm mg:

- 5 BC 10001 class (In serv. 1999–2000): BC 10001, 10002, 20001–20003
- 10 BC 1601 class (In serv. 11-98 to 6-99): BC 1601–1610
- 4 12.6-m class (In serv. 1995): . . .
- 41 FBP 28 class (In serv. 1981–96): BC 4001–4006, 5001–5006, 6001–6005, 7001–7005, 8001–8005, 9001–9005, and nine others
- 7 BC 2001 class (In serv. 1980–81): BC 2001–2007
- 7 BC 3001 class (In serv. 1979–81): BC 3001–3007
- 3 BC 1001 class (In serv. 1975): BC 1001–1003
- up to 40 BC 401 class (In serv. 1960–62): BC 501–504, 601–604, 701–704, 801–804, and 901–904

Remarks: The first two of the BC 10001 class were built by Friedrich Lürssen Werft, Germany, and delivered 11-5-99 and 11-99; the others were built by P.T. Pal, Surabaya, Indonesia, and delivered 9-99 to 11-99. Data include:

D: 85 tons (fl) **S:** 40 kts **Dim:** 28.2 × 6.6 × 1.4
A: 2 single 7.62-mm mg **Electronics:** Radar: 1 Furuno FR8731 nav.
M: 2 MTU 16V396 TE94 diesels; 2 props; 2,996 bhp
Range: 1,100/30 **Crew:** 3 officers, 8 enlisted

Customs patrol craft BC 10001 Dieter Wolf, 4-99

FPB 28-class BC 7001 Chris Delgoffe/H&L Van Ginderen, 5-00

The BC 1601 class craft were also built by Friedrich Lürssen. Capable of 50 kts and employing a wave-piercing hullform, the 11-ton craft are powered by two 300-bhp MTU diesels, have a crew of five, and are armed with a 7.62-mm machinegun. Dimensions: 16.0 × 2.8 × 1.0.

Note: The National Police organization operates 57 or more patrol craft and boats, many armed with up to three single 20-mm Oerlikon AA. These are described and illustrated in previous editions and include:

- 9 DKN 908 class (In serv. 1961–64): DKN 908–916
- 10 DKN 504 class (In serv. 1963–64)
- 6 *Carpenteria* class (In serv. 1976–77): KAL-II.201 through KAL-II.206
- 32 "Chase Boats" (In serv. 1982–86)

Seven Jasa-class "inspection/navigation craft"—the *Antares, Altair, Adhara, Arcturus, Aldebaran, Mokmer,* and *Marapa*—are stationed at the ports of Sabang, Sibolga, Belawan, Tanjung Pinang, Jayapura, Banjarmasin, and Samarinda. Built by Jasa Marina Indah SY, they were delivered two in 1999, three on 31-1-00, and two on 29-2-00. No data are available other than that they are of 550 grt.

IRAN

Islamic Republic of Iran

IRANIAN NAVY

Personnel (2002): Approx. 1,100 officers, 11,400 enlisted. This does not include the Pasdaran Revolutionary Guard Corps Navy, which is listed separately.

Bases: Fleet headquarters and principal dockyard at Bandar Abbas, with lesser facilities in the Persian Gulf at Kharg Island and Khorramshahr, on the Arabian Sea at Chah Bahar, and on the Caspian Coast at Bandar Anzali, where the Fourth Naval Zone (with headquarters at Noushehr) operates some 50 patrol boats. Russian shipyards are to assist Iran in developing a submarine repair facility.

Maritime Aviation: Believed available for service are 4 ex-Russian Mi-8AMT(Sh)/Mi-171 helicopters (delivered in 4-00, with up to 20 more planned to be acquired), 6 ASH-3D Sea King, 6 AB-212, and 2 RH-53D helicopters. Fixed-wing assets remaining include 3 P-3F Orion long-range maritime patrol aircraft, 4 Fokker F-27-400M Friendship transports, and 4 Falcon 20 transports. The Iranian Air Force employs several Lockheed C-130H-MP long-range maritime reconnaissance aircraft and 5 Dornier Do-228 light maritime reconnaissance aircraft.

Iranian Navy P-3F Orion U.S. Navy, 8-94

Iranian Navy ASH-3D Sea King French Navy, 1998

Weapons: Guns and torpedoes are of Russian, U.S., Italian, Swedish, and British origin. Only a dozen U.S. Harpoon missiles were supplied, and all had been expended by 1988. Chinese C-802 turbojet-powered antiship missiles (known in Iran as the Tondar) are being acquired for use on Houdong-class missile boats and are being backfitted onto the Combattante-IIB-class missile boats and the Vosper Mk 5 corvettes. A variety of Russian, locally designed, and Chinese-supplied mines are available, including the Chinese rocket-propelled MC-52 rising mine. U.S.-supplied Standard SM-1 and Italian Sea Killer antiship missiles are no longer operational on ships.

During 3-00, Iran announced that it had developed an improved version of the U.S. Standard SM-1 (RIM-66) missile with digitized electronics and a semiactive command guidance system. The missile was said to be installed on Combattante-class guided-missile craft. Also claimed to be in production was a locally made version of the Chinese C-802 (Tondar) antiship missile, which is said to have an improved guidance and datalink system. An air-launched version of the C-802, the Fajr-e Darya, was tested during 2000; it may incorporate French-provided technology.

Coastal Defense: Several hundred Chinese-supplied HY-4 (CSS-C-2 Silkworm) and C-801 (FL-7, known as the Karus in Iran and CSS-C-3 Seersucker to NATO) antiship missiles are employed at coastal positions, and there have been attempts to launch them from a naval auxiliary vessel as well. C-802 Tondar missiles have also been adapted for land launch. Reports of the acquisition of Russian 3M-80 Moskit (NATO SS-N-22 Sunburn) missiles for shore-based use appear to be without foundation.

ATTACK SUBMARINES [SS]

♦ 3 Russian Kilo class (Project 877EKM)

Bldr: United Admiralty Shipyard, St. Petersburg

	Laid down	L	Del.	In serv.
901 Taregh (ex-B-175)	5-4-91	24-9-91	25-12-91	21-11-92
902 Nuh (ex-B-224)	30-4-92	16-10-92	31-12-92	7-8-93
903 Yunes (ex-B-. . .)	. . .	1993	25-11-96	26-1-97

D: 2,325 tons surf./3,076 tons sub. **S:** 10 kts surf./17 kts sub.
Dim: 72.60 (70.0 wl) × 9.90 × 6.6
A: 6 bow 533-mm TT (18 Type 53-77 wire-guided, E53-60 and E53-85 wake-homing, and E53-67 acoustic homing torpedoes, or 24 mines)—1 Fasta-4 shoulder-launched SAM syst. (8 Strela missiles)

Yunes (903) French Navy, 12-96

Nuh (902) 5-93

Electronics:
Radar: 1 MRK-50E Tobol (Snoop Tray-2) search
Sonar: MGK-400 (Shark Gill) LF active/passive suite; passive hull array; MG-519 (Mouse Roar) HF active classification/mine avoidance; MG-519 active mine-avoidance; MG-553 sound velocity meter; MG-512 own-ship's cavitation detection
EW: Brick Pulp or Squid Head intercept; 6701E (Quad Loop) D/F
M: 2 Type 2D-42 diesel generator sets (1,825 bhp/1,500 kw each), electric drive: 1 motor; 1 6-bladed prop; 5,900 shp—1 130-shp low-speed motor—2 low-speed maneuvering motors; 2 ducted props; 204 shp
Range: 6,000/7 surf.; 400/3 sub. **Fuel:** 172 tons **Endurance:** 45 days
Crew: 12 officers, 41 enlisted

Remarks: Ordered under Russian B-series hull numbers. First unit (whose name means "Morning Star") left the Baltic under Russian flag 26-9-92 and arrived in Iranian waters around 10-11-92. Second unit (whose name is Farsi for "Noah") departed the Baltic in mid-6-93 and arrived at the end of 7-93. The option for the third, whose name means "Jonah," was taken up during 10-92, but delivery of the completed unit was delayed by well over a year due to payment problems; the ship began her delivery voyage 25-11-96 and arrived 19-1-97. All three are based at Bandar Abbas. Due to battery cooling problems, poor training, and inadequate maintenance, they are far less of a threat than their technical characteristics would imply; two were said to be nonoperational as of 4-01, in need of overhauls that may be performed in Russia, although all three were officially stated to have participated in an exercise during 6-01.

Hull systems: The two batteries, each with 120 cells, providing 9,700 kwh, have proven unsatisfactory, lacking adequate cooling and hence increasing discharge rate and reducing lifespan. Propulsion plant is suspended for silencing. Hull has six watertight compartments, with 32% reserve buoyancy at 2,350 m^3 surfaced displacement. At rest on the surface, they trim down 0.4 m by the bow. Maximum diving depth is 300 m, normal depth 240 m, and periscope depth 17.5 m. Have an anechoic hull coating.

Combat systems: Have the MVU-110EM Murena combat data system, which can conduct two simultaneous attacks while tracking three other targets manually. The shoulder-launched SAM position is located in the after portion of the sail. Iran is seeking 3M-53E Novator Alfa supersonic, submerged-launch antiship missiles for these submarines.

Note: The two or three North Korean and 1980s-vintage, indigenously designed midget submarines [SSM] formerly operated by Iran are believed to have been discarded. Other Iranian submersible projects are listed under the entry for the Swimmer Delivery Vehicle [LSDV].

FRIGATES [FF]

Note: As of 10-01, Iran was negotiating with Russia's Severnaya Verf for the purchase of one or more Project 20382 frigates for $150 million each; Project 20382 would be an export version of the Russian Navy's newly ordered Project 20380 (q.v.).

♦ 3 Saam (Vosper Mk 5) class

	Bldr	Laid down	L	In serv.
71 Alvand (ex-*Saam*)	Vosper Thornycroft	22-5-67	25-7-68	20-5-71
72 Alborz (ex-*Zaal*)	Vickers, Newcastle	3-3-68	25-7-68	1-3-71
73 Sabalan (ex-*Rastam*)	Vickers, Barrow	10-12-67	4-3-69	28-2-72

Alvand (71) John Mortimer, 2-01

FRIGATES [FF] *(continued)*

Alvand (71) Mritunjoy Mazumdar, 2-01

Alvand (71)—note two triple ASW TT and four antiship missile launchers on the fantail, along with the twin 35-mm AA gunmount (the director for which appears to be missing from its mounting just abaft the stack) Brian Morrison, 2-01

Alborz (72) French Navy, 1997

D: 1,250 tons (1,540 fl) **S:** 39 kts (17.5 on diesels)
Dim: 94.5 (88.4 pp) × 11.07 × 3.25
A: 4 C-802 SSM; 1 114-mm 55-cal. Vickers Mk 8 DP; 1 twin 35-mm 90-cal. Oerlikon AA; 3 single 20-mm 90-cal. Oerlikon GAM-B01 AA; 2 single 12.7-mm mg; 2 single 81-mm mortar; 1 3-round Limbo Mk 10 ASW mortar—71 and possibly others: 2 triple 324-mm ASW TT
Electronics:
Radar: 1 Decca 1226 nav.; 1 Plessey AWS-1 air search; 2 Oerlikon-Contraves Sea Hunter RTN-10X fire control; 1 Type 352C missile target-detection and tracking
Sonar: Graseby Type 174 hull-mounted search (7–9 kHz); Type 170 hull-mounted attack (15 kHz)
EW: Decca RDL-2AC intercept; FH-5 HFD/F
M: CODOG: 2 Rolls-Royce Olympus TM-3A gas turbines; 2 Paxman 16-cyl. Ventura diesels for cruising; 2 CP props; 46,000 shp (turbines), 3,800 bhp (diesels)
Range: 5,000/15 **Fuel:** 150 tons (250 with overload) **Crew:** 135 tot.

Remarks: Ordered 25-8-66. All were renamed in 1985. Sister *Sahand* (ex-*Faramarz*), hit by three Harpoon missiles and cluster bombs, was lost to U.S. forces 19-4-88. *Sabalan,* severely damaged on the same date, was declared repaired by the Iranian Navy during 1989; although operational, the ship appears to have severe speed restrictions. All three were active during a 6-01 exercise.
Hull systems: Air-conditioned. Have retractable fin stabilizers. Aluminum superstructure.
Combat systems: Vickers Mk 8 automatic guns replaced the originally fitted semiautomatic Mk 6 during refits in the 1970s. Twin 23-mm 87-cal. ZU-23-2 Soviet AA mounts replaced the original Sea Cat SAM launcher and were in turn replaced by single 20-mm mounts. The original quintuple-mount, trainable Sea Killer antiship missile system aft was replaced by fixed racks for Chinese-supplied C-802 missiles during 1996–98, and the associated target detection and tracking radar (which can also operate in the passive mode) has been stepped on a new lattice mast integrated into the forward edge of the original pylon mainmast. As of 2-01, 71 had two sets of triple ASW torpedo tubes added aft, abreast the Limbo mortar well; the origin of the tubes and whatever ASW torpedoes they may carry is unknown.

CORVETTES [FFL]

♦ 0 (+ 3) Zolfaqar class

	Laid down	L	In serv.
. . . Mouj	1997	2-3-01	. . .
. . .	. . .	. . .	. . .
. . .	. . .	. . .	2003

D: 1,000 tons **S:** 30 kts **Dim:** 88.0 × . . . × . . .
A: . . .
Electronics: . . .
M: . . .
Range: . . . **Crew:** . . .

Note: A "destroyer" class to be capable of 30-kt speeds was said to be under design for construction in Iran as of 9-96; in late 9-00, the first unit was said to be ready for launch. The ship is to accommodate a missile-armed helicopter and is to be capable of antisubmarine, antiship, and antiaircraft missions. The initial ship was planned to be completed in 2001 and the third in 2003. The "hull" is said to be of 70% Iranian manufacture and the "missile launcher" 90%, indicating a large foreign input.

PATROL SHIPS [PS]

♦ 2 U.S. PF 103 class Bldr: Levingston SB, Orange, Texas

	Laid down	L	In serv.
81 Bayandor (ex-PF 103)	20-8-62	7-7-63	18-5-64
82 Naghdi (ex-PF 104)	12-9-62	10-10-63	22-7-64

Bayandor (81) 1990

Naghdi (82) H&L Van Ginderen, 7-94

D: 900 tons (1,135 fl) **S:** 20 kts **Dim:** 83.82 × 10.06 × 3.05 (4.27 sonar)
A: 2 single 76.2-mm 50-cal. Mk 34 DP; 1 twin 40-mm 60-cal. Bofors Mk 1 Mod. 2 AA; 2 single 20-mm 90-cal. Oerlikon GAM-B01 AA; 2 single 12.7-mm M2 mg
Electronics:
Radar: 1 Decca 1226 nav.; 1 Raytheon 1650 nav.; 1 SPS-6C air search
Sonar: SQS-17A hull-mounted HF search (probably removed)
M: 2 Fairbanks-Morse 38D8⅛-10 diesels; 2 props; 5,600 bhp
Electric: 600 kw tot. (2 × 300 kw; 2 Fairbanks-Morse 38F5¼ × 6 diesels driving)
Range: 2,400/18; 3,000/15 **Fuel:** 110 tons **Crew:** 133 tot.

Remarks: Built and transferred under the Military Aid Program. Sisters *Milanian* (83, ex-PF 105) and *Kahnamuie* (84, ex-PF 106) were reported lost to Iraqi forces by 1982–83. 82 was refitted and re-engined during 1988. Due to removal of ASW systems and gunfire-control equipment, they are now of limited utility. 81 collided with the U.S. guided-missile cruiser *Gettysburg* (CG 64) on 13-10-96 with little damage incurred.
Combat systems: Twin Soviet 23-mm 87-cal. ZU-23-2 AA were added forward of the bridge in place of the single Hedgehog ASW spiggot mortar during the 1980s; the mount was in turn replaced with a single 20-mm AA. Had Mk 63 GFCS for the 76.2-mm guns (radar on the forward gunmount) and a Mk 51 Mod. 2 GFCS with lead-computing optical director for the 40-mm mount. By 1990, the depth charge equipment had been removed from both and replaced by a single 20-mm at the extreme stern, while the Mk 34 fire-control radar associated with the original Mk 63 control system had been removed from the forward 76.2-mm gunmount.

GUIDED-MISSILE PATROL CRAFT [PTG]

Note: As of 4-01, Iran was reported to be negotiating with Russia for the purchase of an unknown number of Project 12421 (Tarantul-III) guided-missile patrol craft, to be armed with 3M-80E Moskit (SS-N-22 Sunburn) antiship missiles.

♦ 10 Combattante-IIB class Bldr: CMN, Cherbourg

	L	In serv.		L	In serv.
P 221 Kaman	8-1-76	6-77	P 228 Gorz	28-12-77	15-9-78
P 222 Zoubin	14-4-76	6-77	P 229 Gardouneh	23-2-78	23-10-78
P 223 Khadang	15-7-76	15-3-78	P 230 Khanjar	27-4-78	1-8-81
P 226 Falakhon	2-6-77	31-3-78	P 231 Neyzeh	5-7-78	1-8-81
P 227 Shamshir	12-9-77	31-3-78	P 232 Tabarzin	15-9-78	1-8-81

D: 249 tons (275 fl) **S:** 36 kts **Dim:** 47.0 × 7.1 × 1.9
A: 4 C-802 SSM; 1 76-mm 62-cal. OTOBreda DP; 1 40-mm 70-cal. Bofors AA
Electronics:
Radar: 1 Decca 1226 nav.; 1 Thales WM-28 track-while-scan f.c.
EW: Thales TMV-433 suite (DR-2000 receiver, Alligator 5-A jammer, DALIA analyzer)

GUIDED-MISSILE PATROL CRAFT [PTG] *(continued)*

Shamshir (P 227)—with four C-802 antiship missiles U.S. Navy, 7-96

Shamshir (P 227)—detail of bridge area; note optical gun director at the center of the open bridge U.S. Navy, 7-96

M: 4 MTU 16V538 TB91 diesels; 4 props; 14,400 bhp **Electric:** 350 kw
Range: 700/33.7 **Fuel:** 41 tons **Crew:** 31 tot.

Remarks: Contracted 19-2-74 and 14-10-74. The last three were embargoed at Cherbourg in 4-79 and released 22-6-81. P 232 was captured off Spain 13-8-80 by anti-Khomeini forces but later abandoned at Toulon. *Peykan* (P 224) was lost to Iraqi forces in 11-80, and *Joshan* (P 225) was sunk by U.S. forces on 19-4-88.
Combat systems: P 231 and P 232 had no Harpoon tubes on delivery, and all Harpoon missiles delivered by the U.S. are believed to have been expended by 1988. Were given a C-802 missile launch capability during 1996–98. Iran claimed in 3-00 that these craft carry an updated version of the U.S. Standard SM-1 surface-to-air missile, which seems highly unlikely.

PATROL CRAFT [PC]

♦ 3 U.S. PGM 71 class
Bldr: Peterson Bldrs, Sturgeon Bay, Wis. (In serv. 1967–70)

211 Parvin (ex-PGM 103) 213 Nahid (ex-PGM 122)
212 Bahram (ex-PGM 112)

D: 102 tons light (142 fl) **S:** 17 kts **Dim:** 30.81 × 6.45 × 2.3
A: 1 40-mm 60-cal. Mk 3 AA; 1 20-mm 90-cal. Oerlikon GAM-B01 AA; 2 single 12.7-mm Colt M2 mg
Electronics: Radar: 1 . . . nav.
M: 8 General Motors 6-71 diesels; 2 props; 2,120 bhp **Electric:** 30 kw tot.
Range: 1,000/17 **Fuel:** 16 tons **Crew:** 30 tot.

Remarks: Thought to have been sunk during the Iran-Iraq War, but have been sighted still in service. The ASW equipment originally fitted (SQS-17 hull-mounted sonar, Mousetrap ASW rocket launchers, and depth charges) has been removed, and the original radar may have been replaced.

♦ 3 U.S. Coast Guard Cape class
Bldr: U.S. Coast Guard, Curtis Bay, Md. (In serv. 1956–59)

201 Keyvan 202 Azadi (ex-*Tiran*) 203 Mehran

Azadi (202) U.S. Navy

Iranian unit of the Cape class U.S. Navy

D: 85 tons (107 fl) **S:** 20 kts **Dim:** 29.0 × 6.2 × 2.0
A: 1 40-mm 60-cal. Bofors Mk 3 AA; 1 twin 23-mm 87-cal. ZU-23-2 AA; 2 single 12.7-mm Colt M2 mg
Electronics: Radar: 1 . . . nav.
M: 4 Cummins VT-12-M700 diesels; 2,200 bhp
Electric: 40 kw tot. **Range:** 1,500/15 **Crew:** 15 tot.

Remarks: Sister *Mahvan* (204) was lost between 1980 and 1983. 202 and 203 were damaged during the Iran-Iraq War but have been refitted for further service. The ASW ordnance (and probably the sonar as well) has been removed.

PATROL BOATS [PB]

♦ 9 U.S. Mk III class
Bldr: Marinette Marine, Marinette, Wis. (In serv. 1975–76)

D: 28 tons (36.7 fl) **S:** 24 kts **Dim:** 19.78 × 5.50 × 1.80 (props)
A: 1 20-mm 90-cal. Oerlikon GAM-B01 AA; 1 twin and 2 single 12.7-mm mg
Electronics: Radar: 1 LN-66 nav.
M: 3 G.M. 8V71 TI diesels; 3 props; 1,800 bhp
Range: 450/26; 2,000/. . . **Endurance:** 3 days **Crew:** 9 tot.

Remarks: Survivors of 20 originally delivered, the remainder lost in the Iran-Iraq War or worn out and scrapped. Aluminum construction, with the pilothouse offset to starboard. A 20-mm Oerlikon AA mounting has replaced the 12.7-mm machinegun formerly carried forward. Based at Bushehr and Bandar Abbas.

♦ 6 or more U.S. 50-foot class
Bldr: Peterson Bldrs, Sturgeon Bay, Wis. (In serv. 1975–78)

D: 20.1 tons (22.9 fl) **S:** 28 kts **Dim:** 15.24 × 4.80 × 1.9
A: 2 single 12.7-mm mg **Electronics:** Radar: 1 Raytheon SPS-66 nav.
M: 2 G.M. Detroit Diesel 8V71 TI diesels; 3 props; 850 bhp (460 sust.)
Range: 750/26 **Crew:** 6 tot.

Remarks: Sixty-one were ordered in 1976; 19 were delivered complete from the U.S., and the others were shipped as kits for assembly in Iran by Arvandan Maritime Corp., Abadan, where they were still being assembled into the 1980s. Placed under naval control in 1990. Many were lost during the Iran-Iraq War, and a number of the kits were apparently never completed. The survivors are all said to operate in the Caspian Sea. Aluminum construction. Some have been equipped with British Tiger Cat surface-to-air missiles to be employed in a surface-to-surface mode.

♦ up to 6 U.S. Enforcer class
Bldr: Bertram Yacht, Miami (In serv. 1972)

D: 4.7 tons (fl) **S:** 28 kts **Dim:** 9.5 × 3.4 × 0.9
A: 1 12.7-mm mg **Electronics:** Radar: 1 Apelco AD7-7 nav.
M: 2 G.M. 6V53 diesels; 2 props; 360 bhp **Range:** 146/16 **Crew:** 4 tot.

Remarks: Survivors of 36 delivered. GRP hull construction.

MINE WARFARE SHIPS

Note: Of the four U.S. *Falcon*-class coastal minesweepers transferred in the late 1950s, *Shahrokh* (301), long operational in the Caspian Sea as a training craft, had been discarded by 1995 but was refitted as a training craft and renamed *Hemzeh; Simorgh* (302) was lost to Iraqi action in 1980–81; *Karkas* (303) was lost in the Iran-Iraq War; and *Shabaz* (304) was lost in a fire in 1975.

♦ 1 U.S. Cape-class inshore minesweeper [MSI]

	Bldr	In serv.
312 Riazi (ex-MSI 14)	Tacoma Boat, Tacoma, Wash.	15-10-64

D: 203 tons (239 fl) **S:** 12.5 kts **Dim:** 34.06 × 7.14 × 2.40
A: 1 12.7-mm mg **Electronics:** Radar: 1 Decca 303 nav.
M: 4 G.M. Detroit Diesel 6-71 diesels; 2 props; 960 bhp **Electric:** 120 kw
Range: 1,000/9 **Fuel:** 20 tons **Crew:** 5 officers, 16 enlisted

Remarks: Wooden construction. Built for Iran under the Military Aid Program. Was thought lost with sister *Harachi* (311; ex-*Kahnamuie,* ex-MSI 13) during the Iran-Iraq War, but is apparently still in service—although probably not very effective in her intended role. Appearance as for sisters in the Turkish Navy.

AMPHIBIOUS WARFARE SHIPS AND CRAFT

♦ 2 (+ . . .) "dock landing ships" [LST]
Bldr: Construction Jihad, Nuh-e Nabi SY, Bandar Abbas

102 Chavoush (L: 30-9-95) 103 Chalak (L: 6-96)

D: approx. 1,400 tons (fl) **S:** . . . kts **Dim:** 62.0 × 20.0 × . . .
A: . . .
M: . . . diesels; 2 props; . . . bhp

AMPHIBIOUS WARFARE SHIPS AND CRAFT *(continued)*

Remarks: 1,151 grt. Said to have an 800-ton cargo capacity and a docking well. Proportions indicate a barge-like design unlikely to have much utility as assault ships. Despite official description as "dock landing ships," they are probably not equipped to ballast down to launch amphibious craft and vehicles. Molded depth of hull is 6.5 m.

♦ 4 Hengam-class tank landing ships [LST]
Bldr: Yarrow & Co., Scotstoun, U.K.

	L	In serv.		L	In serv.
511 Hengam	27-9-73	12-8-74	513 Lavan	12-6-78	16-1-85
512 Larak	7-5-74	12-11-74	514 Tonb	6-12-79	11-7-85

Tonb (514) 2-91

Tonb (514) 2-91

D: 2,940 tons (fl) **S:** 14.5 kts **Dim:** 92.96 (86.87 wl) × 14.94 × 3.00 (max.)
A: 4 twin 23-mm 87-cal. ZU-23-2 AA; 1 40-round 122-mm BM-21 RL; 2 single 12.7-mm mg; 2 4-round Fasta-M SAM syst. (Igla-1 missiles)
Electronics: Radar: 1 Decca TM 1229 nav.—TACAN: URN-25
M: 511, 512: 4 Paxman Ventura 12 YJCM diesels; 2 CP props; 5,600 bhp—513, 514: 4 MTU 12V562 TB61 diesels; 2 CP props; 5,800 bhp
Electric: 1,280 kw tot. **Range:** 3,500/12 **Fuel:** 295 tons
Crew: 75 ship's company + 168 troops

Remarks: Were used to transport small combatant craft during the Iran-Iraq War. 513 and 514, laid up since completion, were released by the British Government 5-10-84 on the excuse that they would be used in the unlikely role of hospital ships. Negotiations continued into 1985 for the construction of two more, originally ordered in 7-77, for which considerable material had been accumulated.
Hull systems: Have a flight deck for one Sea King–sized helicopter aft. Cargo capacity is 600 tons on 39.6 × 8.8 × 4.5-m (high) vehicle deck, with a 15-m-long bow ramp. Can also carry up to 300 tons of liquid cargo in lieu of some vehicle stowage. Can stow 12 Russian T-55 tanks. Upper deck forward has a 10-ton crane to handle two Uniflote cargo lighters (LCVP) and 12 Z-boat rubber personnel landing craft. Intended for logistics support (when 10 20-ton or 30 10-ton containers would be carried) or for amphibious assault.
Combat systems: 513 has an additional Decca 1216 nav. radar. First two had British SSR 1520 IFF gear.

♦ 2 Arya Sahand–class tank landing ships [LST]
Bldr: Teraoka SY, Japan (In serv. 1978)

Iran Asr (ex-*Arya Akian*) Iran Ghadr (ex-*Arya Dokht*)

D: 614 tons light (2,274 fl) **S:** 11 kts **Dim:** 53.65 (48.01 pp) × 10.81 × 3.00
A: 2 single 12.7-mm mg; mines **Electronics:** Radar: 1 . . . nav.
M: 2 diesels; 2 props; 2,200 bhp **Crew:** 30 tot.

Remarks: 984 grt/1,660 dwt. Blunt-bowed, commercial landing craft taken over by the Iranian Navy at the outset of the Iran-Iraq War. Have a bow ramp, single hatch with sliding cover, and one 10-ton cargo boom. Mines are deck-stowed atop the hatch cover and launched over the side. Sister *Iran Ajr* (ex-*Arya Rakhsh*) was captured 21-9-87 by U.S. forces while laying mines in international waters and scuttled 26-9-87. Sisters *Iran Bahr* (ex-*Arya Sahand*) and *Iran Badr* (ex-*Arya Boum*) were lost during 1980.

Iran Ajr—just prior to scuttling, with a U.S. Navy LCM(8) landing craft alongside U.S. Navy, 9-87

♦ 3 (+ . . .) MIG-S-3700-class utility landing craft [LCU]
Bldr: Construction Jihad, Nuh-e Nabi SY, Bandar Abbas

101 Foque (L: 17-6-88) 103 . . . . . . (L: 27-9-95)
102 . . . . . . (L: 27-9-95)

D: 276 tons (fl) **S:** 10 kts **Dim:** 36.60 × 8.00 × 1.50
A: . . . **Electronics:** Radar: . . .
M: 2 MWM TBD 234 V8 diesels; 2 props; 879 bhp
Range: 400/10 **Crew:** 8 tot.

Remarks: Shipyard also known as the Martyr Darvishi Marine Co. Cargo: 150 tons on deck, plus 57 tons of potable water and 79 tons of cargo fuel in tanks. Hull has extremely low freeboard at tank deck, with no sidewall protection, rendering these ships of little use outside harbors and sheltered waters.

Note: Said to be in service is a single 50-m landing craft with a beam of 10.4 m. The craft resembles the MIG-S-3700 class.

♦ 1 (+ . . .) Iranian-designed air-cushion personnel landing craft [LCPA] Bldr: . . . (In serv. 1-00)

D: . . . **S:** 43 kts (loaded) **Dim:** . . . × . . . × . . .
M: . . .
Range: 324/43 **Crew:** . . . tot. + 26 troops

Remarks: Prototype completed by 1-00 for the Ministry of Defense, with the intent to mass-produce the design.

♦ 4 BH.7 Wellington Mk 4– and Mk 5A–class air-cushion landing craft [LCPA] Bldr: British Hovercraft, Cowes, U.K. (In serv. 1970–75)

D: 50–55 tons (fl) **S:** 65 kts **Dim:** 23.9 × 13.8 × 10.36 (high)
A: 2 single 12.7-mm mg **Electronics:** Radar: 1 Decca 914 nav.
M: 1 Rolls-Royce Proteus 15M549 gas turbine; 1 6.4-m-dia. prop; 4,250 shp
Electric: 110 kVA **Range:** 400/56 **Fuel:** 9 tons

Remarks: Four of the original six were of the logistics-support version, with a 14-ton payload. Two were of the Mk 4 version with recesses for two SSM, which were never mounted. The Mk 4 uses the Gnome 15M541 engine of 4,750 hp and can carry 60 troops in side compartments, as well as assault vehicles on its 56-m cargo deck. Speed in both versions is reduced to 35 kts in a 1.4-m sea. Overhauled at the builders, with new engines, skirts, and so forth, two in 2-84 and two more in 1985. Two others, plus eight SR-N6 Winchester-class hovercraft, are inoperable or have been scrapped.

♦ 1 15-meter swimmer delivery vehicle [LSDV]
Bldr: Isfahan University-. . ., Bandar Abbas (In serv. 29-8-00)

Al Sabiha–15

D: . . . tons **S:** . . . kts **Dim:** 15.0 × . . . × . . .
A: demolition charges, small arms
M: 1 electric motor; 50 shp **Crew:** 2 tot. + 3 swimmers

Remarks: In 7-96, an Iranian newspaper claimed that Isfahan Technical University, under project "Underwater Oasis," had constructed the hull for the first of a new generation of midget submarines. The craft later underwent some 250 hours of sea trials and is said to be able to operate anywhere in the Persian Gulf.

AUXILIARIES

♦ 7 Delvar-class support ships [AE/AK/AW]
Bldr: Karachi SY & Eng. Wks., Pakistan (In serv. 1978–82)

Charak Chiroo Dayer Dilim Delvar Sirjan Souru

D: approx. 1,300 tons (fl) **S:** 9–11 kts **Dim:** 63.45 (58.48 pp) × 11.00 × 3.03
A: 1 twin 23-mm 87-cal. ZU-23-2 AA
Electronics: Radar: 1 Decca 1226 nav.
M: 2 M.A.N. G6V-23.5/33 ATL diesels; 2 props; 1,560 bhp **Crew:** 20 tot.

Remarks: 900 grt. *Delvar* and *Sirjan* are configured as ammunition lighters; *Dayer* and *Dilim* (with rounded sterns and one crane vice two) are water tankers, and the others are coastal cargo lighters. Designed and built with British assistance. All can be used to plant mines.

AUXILIARIES *(continued)*

Delvar-class support ship Piet Sinke, 2-87

♦ 13 Hendijan-class general-purpose tenders [AG]

Bldr: Damen, Hardinxveld, the Netherlands (last four: Martyr Darvishi Marine Industries, Bandar Abbas)

	In serv.		In serv.		In serv.
Bakhtaran	1985	Genavah	9-88	Nayband	(L: 8-12-92)
Koramshahr	1985	Sirik	4-89	Rostam	1995
Hendijan	1987	Gaveter	1990	Nayband	4-99
Kalat	1987	Bahregan	1991		
Konarak	11-88	Mogan	11-92		

Bahregan U.S. Navy, 2-96

D: 650 tons (fl) **S:** 25 (*Nayband:* 27) kts
Dim: 50.75 (48.75 pp) × 10.24 (8.55 wl) × 2.65
A: 1 20-mm 90-cal. Oerlikon GAM-B01 AA
Electronics: Radar: Decca 2070A nav.
M: 2 MWM TBD604V12 (*Nayband:* Mitsubishi S16U-MPTK) diesels; 2 props; 2,162 (*Nayband:* 6,560) bhp
Electric: 180 kw tot. (2 × 90-kw diesel sets)
Crew: 15 tot. + 90–100 troops

Remarks: 439–445 grt/337 dwt. Iranian class designation is MIG-S-4700-SC. Used to transport cargo and personnel over short distances and also as patrol craft. Were referred to as "destroyers" in reports of a 6-01 exercise. Cargo: 40 tons on deck, 12 tons below, plus 40 tons of potable water. *Bahregan* was originally named *Geno.* One unit of this class was reported launched 30-9-95, probably *Rostam.* Well into the 1990s, Damen Shipyard continued to provide prefabricated modules from which the units are assembled in Iran. *Nayband,* the first of a new series, has more-powerful engines and two 52-kw diesel generator sets

♦ 1 Bushehr-A-class navigational buoy tender [AGL]

D: approx. 3,000 tons (fl) **S:** . . . kts **Dim:** 67.0 × 14.0 × 6.0
A: none **M:** 1 diesel; 1 prop; . . . bhp

Remarks: Has a large crane at the break of the forecastle and a second, smaller crane before the bridge, both tending a large buoy hold. No other data available. May belong to a ports and harbor authority rather than the navy.

♦ 1 large replenishment oiler [AOR]

	Bldr	Laid down	L	In serv.
431 Kharg	Swan Hunter, Wallsend-on-Tyne	1-76	3-2-77	25-4-80

Kharg (431) French Navy, 1997

D: 33,014 tons (fl) **S:** 21.5 kts **Dim:** 207.15 (195.00 pp) × 25.50 × 9.14
A: 1 76-mm 62-cal. OTOBreda Compact DP; 6 twin 23-mm 87-cal. ZU-23-2 AA
Electronics: Radar: 2 Decca 1229 nav.—TACAN: URN-20
M: 1 set Westinghouse geared steam turbines; 1 prop; 26,870 shp
Boilers: 2 Babcock & Wilcox 2-drum **Electric:** 7,000 kw **Crew:** 248 tot.

Remarks: Ordered 10-74. 21,100 grt/20,000 dwt. Carries fuel and ammunition and acts as the flagship of the Iranian Navy. Design is a greatly modified version of the Royal Navy's *Olwen* class. Ran initial trials 11-78, but delays in fitting out made delivery before the revolution impossible; remained at the builders until released 5-10-84. Delivered without armament. Has Inmarsat SATCOM equipment. Can accommodate three Sea King–sized helicopters. Completed a refit 16-10-93.

♦ 2 Bandar Abbas–class small replenishment oilers [AOR]

Bldr: C. Lühring, Brake, Germany

421 Bandar Abbas (L: 14-8-73) 422 Booshehr (L: 22-3-74)

Booshehr (422)—with telescoping hangar extended LSPH K. Degener, RAN, 12-90

D: 4,673 tons (fl) **S:** 20 kts **Dim:** 108.0 × 16.6 × 4.5
A: 1 twin 23-mm 80-cal. AA; 2 single 20-mm Oerlikon GAM B01 AA; 2 SA-7 Grail shoulder-launched SAM positions
Electronics: Radar: 1 Decca 1226 nav.; 1 Decca 1229 nav.
M: 2 M.A.N. R6V 52/56 diesels; 2 props; 12,000 bhp
Range: 3,500/16 **Crew:** 60 tot.

Remarks: 3,186 grt/3,250 dwt. Have a telescoping helicopter hangar. Carry fuel, food, ammunition, and spare parts. Armed after delivery. Used for patrol duties from 1984 on, due to a shortage of operable combatants. 421 suffered an explosion at Bandar Abbas 26-12-98, with five killed and 10 injured. Both participated in a major 6-01 exercise.

♦ 1 ex-U.S. Amphion-class repair ship [AR] Bldr: Tampa SB, Fla.

	Laid down	L	In serv.
441 Chah Bahar (ex-*Amphion,* AR 13)	20-9-44	15-5-45	30-1-46

D: 8,670 tons light (14,450 fl) **S:** 16 kts **Dim:** 150.0 × 21.4 × 8.4
A: removed **M:** 1 set geared steam turbines; 1 prop; 8,500 shp
Boilers: 2 Foster-Wheeler "D"; 30.6 kg/cm^2, 382° C **Electric:** 3,600 kw
Range: 13,950/11.5 **Fuel:** 1,850 tons **Crew:** accomm. for 921

Remarks: Transferred on loan in 10-71 and purchased 1-3-77. Employed as a stationary repair facility at Bandar Abbas and no longer mobile.

♦ 2 water tankers [AW] Bldr: Mazagon Dock, Mumbai, India

411 Kangan (L: 4-78) 412 Taheri (L: 17-9-78)

Kangan (411) U.S. Navy

D: 12,000 tons (fl) **S:** 12 kts **Dim:** 147.95 (140.00 pp) × 21.50 × 5.00
A: 1 twin 23-mm 87-cal. ZU-23-2 AA; 2 single 12.7-mm mg
Electronics: Radar: 1 Decca 1229 nav.
M: 1 M.A.N. 7L52/55A diesel; 7,385 bhp **Crew:** 20 tot.

Remarks: 9,430 dwt. Intended to supply Persian Gulf islands. Liquid cargo: 9,000 m^3. Also used in patrol duties from 1984 on. Have a helicopter landing pad amidships and carry two hose-handling boats in davits forward.

Disposal note: The former imperial yacht *Hamzeh* (ex-*Chah Sevar*) was apparently out of service by 1998, as her name was transferred to the former minesweeper *Sharokh,* which was reactivated that year as cadet training ship in the Caspian Sea.

♦ 1 ex-U.S. Falcon-class training ship [AXT]

Bldr: Peterson Bldrs, Sturgeon Bay, Wis. (L: 1958)

155 Hamzeh (ex-*Sharokh,* ex-MSC 276)

D: 320 tons (378 fl) **S:** 12.5 kts **Dim:** 43.00 (41.50 wl) × 7.95 × 2.55
A: . . . **Electronics:** Radar: 1 . . . nav.
M: 2 G.M. Electromotive Div. 8-268A diesels; 2 props; 890 bhp
Range: 2,500/10 **Fuel:** 27 tons **Crew:** . . .

Remarks: Hull number has also been reported as 301, and the ship is also said to operate as a diving tender. Wooden, nonmagnetic construction.

SERVICE CRAFT

♦ 1 large floating dry dock [YFDB]

Bldr: M.A.N.-G.H.H., Nordenham/Blexen, Germany (L: 22-11-85)

Dolphin

D: 28,000 tons lift **Dim:** 240.00 × 52.50 × . . .

SERVICE CRAFT *(continued)*

Remarks: Docking well is 230.00 m over keel blocks, 41.00 m free width, 8.50 m floodable over blocks.

♦ **1 ex-U.S. floating dry dock [YFDL]**
Bldr: Pacific Bridge, Alameda, Calif. (In serv. 7-44)

400 (ex-*Arco,* ARD 29)

D: 3,500 tons lift **Dim:** 149.8 × 25.6 × 1.7 (light)

Remarks: Transferred 1-3-77.

♦ **1 garbage disposal lighter [YG]**
Bldr: Karachi SY & Eng. Wks. (In serv. ca. 1985)

1712

Remarks: Has a 120-m^3 hopper amidships, a trash compactor, and a conveyer bucket system to eject garbage over the stern. Has two diesel propulsion engines. No further data available.

♦ **1 inshore survey craft, former yacht [YGS]**
Bldr: Malahide SY, Dublin, Ireland

Abnegar (ex-*Glimmer*)

D: 85 tons (fl) **S:** . . . kts **Dim:** 20.7 × . . . × . . .
M: 1 Kelvin T8 diesel; 240 bhp

Remarks: Acquired in 1974.

♦ **3 coastal fuel lighters [YO]**
Bldr: Scheepswerf Ravestein, Deest, the Netherlands (In serv. 1983)

Iran Parak Iran Shalak Iran Youshat

D: approx. 800 (fl) **S:** 6 kts **Dim:** 40.01 (38.82 pp) × 10.01 × 2.6
M: 2 G.M. 6-71 diesels; 2 props; 730 bhp **Electric:** 12 kw **Fuel:** 5 tons

Remarks: 400 grt/540 dwt. Originally purchased for commercial purposes.

♦ **2 Ksew-class fuel lighters [YO]**
Bldr: Karachi SY & Eng. Wks. (In serv. 1981)

1703 1704

D: . . . **S:** 8 kts **Dim:** 30.51 × 9.30 × 1.83
M: 2 M.A.N. diesels; 2 props; 326 bhp

Remarks: 195 grt/200 dwt.

♦ **5 StanTug 2400/2600–class large harbor tugs [YTB]**

	Bldr	L	In serv.
Hamoon	Deltawerf, Sliedrecht, Neth.	. . .	4-84
Hirmand	Damen, Hardinxveld, Neth.	1-8-84	1984
Menab	Damen, Hardinxveld, Neth.	. . .	1985
Hari-Rud	Damen, Hardinxveld, Neth.	. . .	1985
Sefid-Rud	Damen, Hardinxveld, Neth.	. . .	1985

D: 300 tons (fl) **S:** 12 kts **Dim:** 25.63 (23.53 pp) × 6.81 × 3.19
M: 2 MTU GV396 TC62 diesels; 2 props; 1,200 bhp

Remarks: First two are 24.0 m long. Last three are of 122 grt and are 25.63 m long. May be employable as minelayers.

♦ **2 ex-German large harbor tugs [YTB]**
Bldr: Oelkers (In serv. 1962–63)

1 (ex-*Karl*) 2 (ex-*Ise*)

D: 320 tons **S:** 11.5 kts **Dim:** 26.6 × 7.2 × 3.6 **M:** . . .

Remarks: 134 grt. Acquired 17-6-74. Have a fire monitor on a platform abaft mast.

♦ **2 StanTug 2200–class small harbor tugs [YTL]**
Bldr: B.V. Scheepswerf K. Damen, Hardinxveld-Giessendam, Netherlands (In serv. 1985)

Aras Atrak

D: 91 grt **S:** 12 kts **Dim:** 22.00 × 7.12 × 2.65 **M:** 2 MTU diesels; . . . bhp

♦ **2 water barges [YWN]** Bldr: Karachi SY & Eng. Wks. (In serv. 1977–78)

1701 1702

D: approx. 2,100 tons (fl) **Dim:** 65.0 × 13.0 × 2.6

Remarks: 1,410 grt.

♦ **10 Qa'em-series training craft [YXT]**
Bldr: Iranian Defense Marine Industries

D: 65 tons (fl) **S:** . . . kts **Dim:** 18.75 × 5.75 × . . .
M: . . . diesels; . . . props; . . . bhp

Remarks: *Qa'em 3* and *Qa'em 5,* launched at a Caspian Sea port 30-9-96, were said to be the seventh and eighth of the class, and two more were completed around 5-00. Hull molded depth is 2.17 m. No further details available. Also referred to as the *Kilas-e-Qasem* class.

Disposal note: Persian Gulf training craft and former imperial yacht *Kish* was reported to have been stricken by 2000.

Note: Karachi Shipyard and Engineering Works, Pakistan, delivered seven other yard and service craft between 1977 and 7-81. All were designed in Great Britain. A variety of craft were built, all initially numbered 1701 through 1718. Types included a self-propelled dredge (1711) [YM], a pontoon barge (1710) [YFN], and a 31-m diving tender (1705) [YDT] very similar in appearance to the *Ksew*-class fuel lighters.

PASDARAN REVOLUTIONARY GUARD CORPS NAVY

Note: This organization, with about 20,000 personnel (most in non-seagoing billets), is administered separately from the Iranian Navy. In recent years, cooperation between the two forces is said to have been improved, but the Revolutionary Guard Corps Navy's goals remain ideologically oriented and its leadership erratic.

GUIDED-MISSILE PATROL CRAFT [WPTG]

♦ **10 Chinese Houdong class** (In serv. 1995–96)

P 313-1 Fath	P 313-5 Fajr	P 313-9 Hadid
P 313-2 Nasr	P 313-6 Shams	P 313-10 Qadr
P 313-3 Saf	P 313-7 Me'raj	
P 313-4 Ra'd	P 313-8 Falaq	

Houdong-class P 313-5—first series, with original pennant number
French Navy, 9-94

Houdong-class P 313-7 and a sister—second series, en route to Iran as deck cargo, with original pennant number U.S. Navy, 3-96

D: 118 tons (135 fl) **S:** 37 kts (34 sust.)
Dim: 34.10 × 6.70 × 1.8 (1.295 mean hull)
A: 4 C-802 SSM; 1 twin 30-mm 65-cal. Model 69 AA; 1 twin 23-mm 87-cal. ZSU-23-2 AA
Electronics:
Radar: 2 Type RM 1070A nav.; 1 Type 341 (Rice Lamp) gun f.c.
EW: last five: . . . intercept
M: 2 MTU 16V396 TB94 diesels; 2 props; 6,220 bhp **Electric:** 65 kw
Range: 500/24; 1,050/18 **Endurance:** 5 days **Crew:** 2 officers, 14 enlisted

Remarks: Referred to locally as the Thondor class. Were originally numbered 301 through 310. Reportedly were ordered in 1991 or 1992. First five were delivered in 9-94; the second five, with added EW gear, in 3-96. P 313-3 was noted in 10-97 with a twin 23-mm mount installed abaft the lattice mast, and the others have probably been similarly equipped.

PATROL BOATS [WPB]

♦ **6 MIG-S-2600-PB class**
Bldr: Joolaee Iran Marine Industries (In serv. . . .)

D: 80 tons (85 fl) **S:** 35 kts **Dim:** 26.20 × 6.20 × 1.40 (hull)
A: 1 12-round 107-mm artillery RL; 1 twin 14.5-mm 79-cal. AA
M: 4 MWM TBD-234-V16 diesels; 4 props; 4,000 bhp **Crew:** 10 tot.

Remarks: Also known as the Zafar class. Offered for export sale, and at least one prototype was built for Pasdaran Revolutionary Guard service. Design appears to be based on the North Korean Chaho class (of which three were transferred in 4-87 and since discarded).

♦ **10 (+ . . .) MIG-G-1900 class**
Bldr: Iran Marine Industries (In serv. 1992–. . .)

MIG-G-1900 series U.S. Navy

REVOLUTIONARY GUARD PATROL BOATS [WPB] *(continued)*

D: 28 tons (30 fl) **S:** 36 kts **Dim:** 19.45 × 4.20 × 0.90
A: 1 twin 23-mm 87-cal. ZSU-23-2 AA
Electronics: Radar: 1 . . . nav.
M: 2 MWM TBD 234-V12 diesels; 2 props; 1,646 bhp **Crew:** 8 tot.

Remarks: Hullform is based closely on the U.S. Mk III patrol boat, but built with German-supplied diesel engines and with the pilothouse on the centerline.

♦ 50 MIG-G-1800-TRB class Bldr: Iran Marine Industries (In serv. . . .)

MIG-G-1800-TRB class U.S. Navy

D: 28 tons (30 fl) **S:** 18 kts **Dim:** 18.67 × 5.76 × 1.05
A: 1 twin 23-mm 87-cal. ZSU-23-2 AA
Electronics: Radar: 1 . . . nav.
M: 2 MWM TBD 234-V12 diesels; 2 props; 1,646 bhp **Crew:** 10 tot.

Remarks: Intended primarily for customs service and police duties. Has a large deckhouse extending over nearly the entire length of the hull and appears unsuitable for open-water operations.

♦ . . . MIG-G-1200-SC class Bldr: Iran Marine Industries (In serv. . . .)

D: 8 tons (fl) **S:** 23 kts **Dim:** 12.40 × 3.00 × 0.56
A: 1 14.5-mm 93-cal. mg; small arms
M: 2 gasoline outboards; 400 bhp **Crew:** 15 tot.

♦ . . . MIG-G-0900-CPB class Bldr: Iran Marine Industries (In serv. . . .)

D: 5 tons (fl) **S:** 30 kts **Dim:** 9.20 × 2.82 × 0.40
A: small arms **M:** 2 gasoline outboards; 400 bhp **Crew:** 3 tot.

♦ . . . MIG-G-0790-PB class Bldr: Iran Marine Industries (In serv. . . .)

D: 2.55 tons (fl) **S:** 40 kts **Dim:** 7.95 × 2.41 × 0.55
A: small arms **M:** 2 gasoline outboards; 400 bhp **Crew:** 2 tot.

♦ . . . MIG-G-0700-PB class Bldr: Iran Marine Industries (In serv. . . .)

D: 1.7 tons (fl) **S:** 35 kts **Dim:** 7.00 × 2.50 × 0.35
A: small arms **M:** 1 gasoline outboard; 150 bhp **Crew:** 2 tot.

Remarks: Open launch with the forward area decked over.

♦ . . . MIG-G-0500-PL class Bldr: Iran Marine Industries (In serv. . . .)

D: 1.1 tons (fl) **S:** 40 kts **Dim:** 5.00 × 2.15 × 0.30
A: small arms **M:** 1 gasoline outboard; 115 bhp **Crew:** 2 tot.

Remarks: GRP construction, open hull.

Note: Other indigenous classes offered for export include the smaller MIG-G-0600-CN3, MIG-G-0610-GP, MIG-G-0500-PL (a 5-m Boston Whaler copy), MIG-G-0800-GP1 (an 8-m Whaler copy), MIG-G-0800-GP2 (same design, with a cabin, and powered by two outboards), and MIG-G-1200-PS (a personnel launch with a cabin over nearly the entire length).

♦ 32 "Boghammar Boat" special forces craft
Bldr: Boghammar Marin, Stockholm, Sweden (In serv. 1986–. . .)

"Boghammar Boat" P 120—with rocket launcher on bow and machinegun aft French Navy, 1998

D: 6.4 tons (fl) **S:** 45 kts **Dim:** 12.80 × 2.66 × 0.90
A: 2 single 12.7-mm mg or 23-mm 87-cal. ZU-23-2 AA; 1 106-mm recoilless rifle and/or RPG-7 antitank RL or 12-round 107-mm RL
Electronics: Radar: 1 Decca 170 nav. or none
M: 2 Volvo Penta TAMD-71A diesels; 2 props; 716 bhp
Range: 500/38 **Crew:** 5–6 tot.

Remarks: Known locally as the Toragh class. Ordered in 1984, ostensibly for customs service duties; 37 had been delivered by 7-87 for use by Revolutionary Guards in attacks on undefended merchant ships, and ultimately as many as 51 may have been received. U.S. forces destroyed five during 1987–88, of which one was salvaged and taken to the U.S.A. for use as a training target. Three Iranian units were returned to Sweden in 1992 for refit. Two versions were delivered: Model RL-118 and Model RL-130-4A.
Hull systems: Have aluminum-construction, stepped-hydroplane hullform. Were reportedly being re-engined with Seatek diesels in 1991.
Combat systems: A variety of armaments have been observed, with weapons fitted from whatever was available and according to missions foreseen.

♦ 35 or more GRP launches Bldr: Boston Whaler, Rockland, Mass.

Two small Pasdaran GRP launches Leo Dirkx, 1-99

D: 1.3 tons (fl) **S:** 40 kts **Dim:** 6.7 × 2.3 × 0.4 (prop)
A: 1 12.7-mm mg and/or 1 12-round 107-mm RL
M: 2 gasoline outboard motors; 240 shp

Remarks: Some imported, some built locally in Iran. Used for harassing attacks on unarmed merchant vessels during the Iran-Iraq War.

Note: Also in use by the Revolutionary Guards are 7.5-m Damen, Gorinchem-built assault boats; a few wooden dhows of around 23 m o.a. for mine laying; European-manufactured semi-rigid inflatable craft; and Iranian-built copies of the British Watercraft 800-series open workboat, the latter capable of 40-kt speeds.

AMPHIBIOUS LANDING CRAFT

Note: The Pasdaran Revolutionary Guards troops are also transported aboard naval *Hengam*-class landing ships, and there are several commercial landing craft that can also be pressed into service.

♦ 3 Iran Hormuz 24–class medium landing ships [WLSM]
Bldr: . . ., Inchon, South Korea (In serv. 1985–86)

24 Farsi 25 Sardasht 26 Sab Sahel

D: . . . tons **S:** 12 kts **Dim:** 73.1 × 14.2 × 2.5
A: . . . **Electronics:** Radar: . . .
M: 2 Daihatsu 6DLM-22 diesels; 2 props; 2,400 bhp
Crew: 30 tot. + 110 passengers or 140 troops

Remarks: 2,014 grt. Although operated ostensibly in commercial service, these craft are said to support Pasdaran operations. Are beachable and have a bow vehicle ramp. Can accommodate nine medium tanks.

♦ 3 Hejaz-class (MIG-S-5000) medium landing ships [WLSM]
Bldr: Ravenstein SY, the Netherlands (In serv. 1984–85)

21 Hejaz 22 Karabala 23 Amir

D: 1,280 tons (fl) **S:** 9 kts **Dim:** 65.0 × 12.0 × 1.5
A: . . . **Electronics:** Radar: . . .
M: 2 M.A.N. V12V-12.5/14 or MWM TBD 604 V12 diesels; 2 props; 1,460 bhp
Crew: 12 tot.

Remarks: 21 and 22 definitely work for the Pasdaran, while 23 probably does. Ramped landing craft with 600-ton cargo capacity. The design is also built at Bandar Abbas as the MIG-S-5000 class, for commercial use.

♦ 8 or more Type 412 Sea Truck landing craft [LCVP]
Bldr: Rotork, U.K.

D: 9 tons (fl) **S:** 28 kts **Dim:** 12.7 × 3.2 × 0.9
A: 2 or 4 single 7.62-mm mg
M: 2 Volvo Penta diesels; 2 props; 240 bhp

Remarks: GRP construction. Can carry up to 30 troops or a small vehicle. Also offered for export in a locally built version as the MIG-G-1200-SC class. Four have been stricken.

Note: Locally built, GRP-hulled smallcraft are also used to transport special forces personnel; a typical design is known as the Yavar class and is some 7.2 × 2.5 × 1.0 m in dimension and can achieve 25 kts.

♦ 2 (+ . . .) special forces landing craft [LCP]
Bldr: Boghammar Marin, Stockholm, Sweden (In serv. 1992, 1996)

Boghammar special forces landing craft—fitting out for Iran Maritime Photographic, 8-92

REVOLUTIONARY GUARD AMPHIBIOUS LANDING CRAFT
(continued)

D: 9 tons (fl) **S:** 54 kts **Dim:** 15.30 × 3.65 × 1.00
A: . . . **M:** 2 MWM 234V12 diesels; 2 props; . . . bhp
Range: . . ./. . . **Crew:** 3 tot. + 20 troops

Remarks: Enlarged version of the standard "Boghammar Boat" with stepped hydroplane hull and a small ramp for troops worked into the stem of the hull. Second unit ordered 8-95.

IRAQ

Republic of Iraq

Personnel (2002): About 600 total

Bases: The few remaining operational craft and a number of hulks are maintained on the Shatt-al-Arab at Basra (which is largely silted in) and at Khor-al-Zubayr.

Naval Aviation: Some of the surviving Iraqi Air Force Mirage F.1EQ fighter-bombers can carry one or two AM 39 Exocets. No naval aircraft survive.

Coastal Defense: As of 2000, some five batteries of CSS-C-3 coastal defense missiles had been restored to service.

Note: The training frigate *Ibn Maghid* (507, ex-*Ibn Khaldum*) was caught at Basra at the start of the 1991 war and was seriously damaged. The ship has not moved under its own power in over 10 years and, given the difficulty of Iraqi access to the open sea and the ship's deteriorated condition, is unlikely ever to be restored to service.

GUIDED-MISSILE PATROL CRAFT [PTG]

♦ 1 Soviet Osa-I (Project 205 Moskit)

R 15 Haziran

D: 165 tons light; 209.5 tons normal (220 fl)
S: 38.5 kts (36 sust.) **Dim:** 38.6 × 7.6 × 1.73
A: 4 P-15U Termit (SS-N-2A Styx) SSM; 2 twin 30-mm 65-cal. AK-230 AA
Electronics:
Radar: 1 Rangout (Square Tie) surf. search/target desig.; 1 MR-104 Rys' (Drum Tilt) gun f.c.
M: 3 M-503A2 diesels; 3 props; 12,000 bhp **Electric:** 200 kw tot.
Range: 500/34; 750/25 **Endurance:** 5 days **Crew:** 4 officers, 24 enlisted

Remarks: Survivor of six transferred 1971–74. Badly damaged during 1991 Desert Storm war but was reportedly repaired and at sea by 1999. Status of the missile system is uncertain, but it is possible that existing stocks of Chinese land-based anti-ship cruise missiles have been adapted for use on this craft. Can be operated at 220 tons full load with 11 extra tons of fuel in void tanks.

PATROL BOATS [PB]

♦ . . . 21-meter Sawari class

D: approx. 20 tons (fl) **S:** 27 kts **Dim:** 21.0 × . . . × . . .
A: 1 triple 14.5-mm mg **M:** 2 diesels; 2 props; . . . bhp

Remarks: No other data available. Appear to have GRP hulls. Two sisters were donated to Djibouti in 1989–90.

♦ 70 or more 11-meter Swary series

Bldr: . . . . . ., Iraq (In serv. 1989–91)

D: 7 tons (fl) **S:** 25–27 kts **Dim:** 11.0 × 2.5 × 0.6
A: 1 or 2 single 14.5-mm mg; 1 32-round 57-mm artillery RL
Electronics: Radar: 1 . . . nav.
M: 2 or 3 outboard motors; 2 or 3 props; . . . bhp **Crew:** 4–6 tot.

Remarks: GRP-hulled open boats first displayed in 1989 at the Baghdad Arms Show. Armament and propulsion configurations vary, and there are variants with different overall lengths of up to 12.5 m. This type of craft accounted for most of the small combatants reported sunk or damaged by UN Coalition forces in 1991. Several hundred were reportedly constructed. Three were donated to Djibouti in the late 1980s.

AUXILIARIES

Disposal note: Custody of the Italian *Stromboli*-class replenishment oiler *Agnadeen* (A 102) (completed in 1984 and sequestered at Alexandria, Egypt, since 1986) was awarded to the builder, Fincantieri, in 8-96, but the ship remains moored at Alexandria. The 7,359-grt seagoing presidential yacht *Al Mansur* has been inoperable since 1991, while the smaller seagoing yacht *Qadisiyat Saddam* was presented to the king of Saudi Arabia in 1987 when it became apparent that it could not safely be delivered to Iraqi waters. Riverine presidential yacht *Al Qadisiya* (1,070 grt) has been laid up since the mid-1980s. Characteristics for *Al Mansur* and *Al Qadisiya* can be found in earlier editions.

Agnadeen (A 102)—still stranded at Alexandria, Egypt, where she has lain since 1986 — Chris Delgoffe/H&L Van Ginderen, 3-00

IRELAND

Irish Republic

IRISH NAVAL SERVICE
(An Seirbhis Chabhlaigh)

Personnel (2001): 1,050 total, including 115 officers (the authorized force is 158 officers, 568 petty officers, 540 enlisted ratings), plus 445 reserves

Base: Administrative and operational headquarters at Haulbowline Island, Cork. Naval Reserve companies at Dublin (two), Cork, Limerick, and Waterford.

Naval Aviation: The Irish Air Force operates two AS.365 Dauphin II helicopters for the navy and three others for land service, but these aircraft are to be replaced, probably with Agusta A-109 helicopters. Two CASA CN-235-100MPA maritime patrol aircraft were delivered 12-94 for maritime surveillance duties. Two Sikorsky S-61N helicopters have been chartered since 1991 to provide search-and-rescue services from Shannon Airport.

Note: Ship names are preceded by L.É. (*Long Éirennach,* "Irish Ship"). As an economy measure, the Irish Naval Service and Air Corps may be combined into a single coast guard.

PATROL SHIPS [PS]

♦ 2 Roísín class Bldr: Appledore Shipbuilders, U.K.

	L	In serv.
P 51 Roísín	13-9-99	15-12-99
P 52 Niamh	10-2-01	18-9-01

Roísín (P 51) — Findler & Winter, 6-01

D: 1,400 tons (1,579 fl) **S:** 22 kts
Dim: 78.84 (73.00 pp) × 14.00 × 3.50 (mean; 3.90 max.)
A: 1 76-mm 62-cal. OTOBreda SuperRapid DP; 2 single 12.7-mm mg; 4 single 7.62-mm mg
Electronics:
Radar: 1 Kelvin-Hughes I-band search; 1 Kelvin-Hughes F-band search
E/O: 1 Radamec 1500/2400 tracking and surveillance (laser rangefinder, t.v., and IR imager)
M: 2 Wärtsilä 16V26 diesels; 2 Lips CP props; 13,600 bhp—460-shp Brunvol electric azimuthal bow-thruster
Electric: 1,400 kw tot. (3 × 400 kw, Caterpillar 3412T diesels driving; 1 × 200 kw, Caterpillar 3306 diesel driving; all 380 V, 50 Hz)
Range: 6,000/15 **Fuel:** 251 tons **Endurance:** 21 days
Crew: 22 tot. (accomm. for 51)

Remarks: P 51 was ordered 16-12-97, originally to replace *Deirdre* (P 20). The design is a variant of the *Vigilant* design built in Chile for the Mauritius Coast Guard. Designed by Polar Associates, Canada. Construction costs of $34 million (not including the 76-mm gun) were 65% funded by the European Union. P 52 was ordered 6-4-00 to replace the *Deirdre;* her commissioning date was delayed several months by gearbox problems found during trials.
Hull systems: Have a deep-vee hullform with twin rudders and a signature-reduction superstructure shape to reduce the radar signature when the ship is coming toward the radar. There are two fire monitors, with a single 600-m^3/hr firepump. Have Brown Brothers retractable fin stabilizers and a four-berth sick bay. Can carry several 20-ft. standard freight containers to support overseas-deployed Irish peacekeeping forces. Have a Kelvin-Hughes Integrated Bridge System (IBS) and a Litton-Decca ISIS-1500 engineering monitoring and control system. Two Delta 6.70-m rigid inflatable inspection launches, each powered by a 70-bhp outboard engine, are carried, as is one Avon 5.4-m RIB.

♦ 1 P 31 class Bldr: Verolme Dockyard, Co rk

	Laid down	L	In serv.
P 31 Eithne	15-12-82	19-12-83	7-12-84

D: 1,760 tons (1,915 fl) **S:** 19 kts **Dim:** 81.00 × 12.00 × 4.30
A: 1 57-mm 70-cal. Bofors SAK 57/70 Mk 1 DP; 2 single 20-mm 90-cal. Rheinmetall AA; 2 single 7.62-mm mg; 1 AS.365 Dauphin II helicopter

PATROL SHIPS [PS] *(continued)*

Eithne (P 31) William M. Rau, 7-00

Electronics:
Radar: 1 Decca TM 1229C nav.; 1 Decca AC 1629C nav.; 1 Thales DA-05/4 surf./air search
Sonar: Plessey PMS-26L hull-mounted (10 kHz)
TACAN: MEL RRB transponder
M: 2 Ruston Paxman 12RKCM diesels; 2 CP props; 7,200 bhp (6,640 sust.)
Electric: 1,625 kVA tot. (3 × 400 kw, 1 × 100 kw)
Range: 7,000/15 **Fuel:** 290 tons **Crew:** 9 officers, 76 enlisted

Remarks: Ordered 23-4-82. Construction of a second unit was deferred, in part because the yard closed in 1983. Refitted 1998–99.
Hull systems: Denny-Brown retractable fin stabilizers are installed. Has considerable firefighting capability, with three firefighting water monitors, and can be replenished under way at sea. Boats include a 7.3-m crew boat, 5.5-m inspection boat, and Avon Searaider semi-rigid inflatable boats with 90-hp outboard motors. Has a Harpoon landing system for the helicopter. The Kelvin-Hughes Integrated Bridge System (IBS) was installed in 1999.
Combat systems: Has Thales LIOD t.v./laser/IR fire-control system and two Thales t.v./optical target designators for the 57-mm gun. Carries two Wallop 57-mm flare RL.

♦ **3 Emer class** Bldr: Verolme Dockyard, Cork

	L	In serv.		L	In serv.
P 21 Emer	1977	16-1-78	P 23 Aisling	3-10-79	21-5-80
P 22 Aoife	12-4-79	29-11-79			

Emer (P 21) H&L Van Ginderen, 9-97

Aisling (P 23) Marion Wright, 8-01

D: 1,003 tons (fl) **S:** 18.5 kts **Dim:** 65.20 (58.50 pp) × 10.40 × 4.36
A: 1 40-mm 60-cal. Mk 7 Bofors AA; 2 single 20-mm 90-cal. Oerlikon GAM-B01 AA; 2 single 7.62-mm mg
Electronics:
Radar: 1 Kelvin-Hughes Mk IV nav.; 1 Kelvin Hughes Mk VI surf. search
Sonar: Simrad SU side-scan hull-mounted (34 kHz)
M: 2 SEMT-Pielstick 6 PA6 L280 diesels; 1 CP prop; 4,800 bhp
Range: 4,500/18; 6,750/12 **Fuel:** 170 tons **Crew:** 5 officers, 41 enlisted

Remarks: Developed version of the *Deirdre* with raised forecastle instead of bow bulwarks, to improve sea keeping. P 21 was extensively refitted during 1995.
Hull systems: Have advanced navigational aids and fin stabilizers. P 22 and P 23 have a 225-kw bow-thruster, a computerized plotting table, and a new-pattern LaMeWa controllable-pitch propeller. Only P 23 has evaporators. All have three Lamou-Markon alternators.
Combat systems: The 40-mm gun is locally controlled. New 20-mm AA and a Marisat SATCOM terminal were added in 1989, and all are now fitted with a SATNAV receiver and receivers for the Decca Mk 53 Navigator radio navaid system. All were given a new radar suite during mid-1990s refits.
Disposal note: Patrol ship *Deirdre* (P 20) was retired 14-6-01 and was sold commercial for conversion into a cruise ship.

PATROL COMBATANTS [PG]

♦ **2 ex-U.K. Peacock class** Bldr: Hall Russell, Aberdeen

	Laid down	L	In serv.
P 41 Orla (ex-*Swift*, P 243)	23-9-83	11-9-84	3-5-85
P 42 Ciara (ex-*Swallow*, P 242)	24-4-83	30-3-84	16-11-84

Orla (P 41) Bram Risseeuw, 5-01

Orla (P 41) H&L Van Ginderen, 7-00

D: 662 tons (712 fl) **S:** 28 kts (25 sust.) **Dim:** 62.60 (60.00 pp) × 10.00 × 2.72
A: 1 76-mm 62-cal. OTOBreda Compact DP; 2 single 12.7-mm mg; 2 single 7.62-mm mg
Electronics:
Radar: 1 Kelvin-Hughes 500A nav.; 1 Kelvin-Hughes Mk IV nav.
M: 2 APE-Crossley-SEMT-Pielstick 18 PA6 V280 diesels; 2 3-bladed props; 14,188 bhp—1 Schottel S103 drop-down, shrouded prop; 181 shp
Electric: 755 kw tot. **Range:** 2,500/17 **Fuel:** 44 tons
Crew: 6 officers, 33 enlisted (incl. boarding party)

Remarks: Former patrol boats at Hong Kong, purchased 8-10-88 and commissioned in Irish service 21-11-88. Three sisters were sold to the Philippines.
Hull systems: Have two rudders. Were bad rollers until deeper bilge keels were fitted. Carry two Avon Searaider 5.4-m-o.a., 30-kt, 10-man semi-rigid rubber inspection dinghies.
Combat systems: The 76-mm gun is controlled by a BAE Systems GSA.7 Sea Archer optronic director. Two 12.7-mm mg were added in 1989. Two 50-mm rocket flare launchers are fitted. A Marisat SATCOM terminal is carried. The present radar suite was fitted in 1993, along with a Nucleus 6000A command data system.

SERVICE CRAFT

♦ **4 naval service launches [YFL]**

Barbara Heck   Colleen II   Freya   . . . . .

Freya Chris Hockaday, 7-96

SERVICE CRAFT *(continued)*

Remarks: *Colleen II,* built in 1972, is the commanding officer's launch at Cork. The other three are miscellaneous, newer, 12-m craft operated by the naval reserve as "Port and Territorial Waters Patrol Vessels."

♦ **3 miscellaneous sail-training craft [YTS]** Bldr: Dufour, France

CREIDNE NANCY BET TAILTE

Remarks: First two are Bermuda ketches, 15.8 m and 14.6 m long, respectively, operated by the naval reserve *(An Slua Muiri). Tailte* is 10.7 m long and is operated by the regular navy.

Note: Also in use for training are five 5.5-m sail/oar boats.

DEPARTMENT OF DEFENCE

SERVICE CRAFT

♦ **1 passenger launch [WYFL]**
Bldr: Zwolle, the Netherlands (In serv. 1962)

DAVID F

David F Chris Hockaday, 7-96

D: approx. 100 tons (fl) **S:** 9.5 kts **Dim:** 23.0 × 6.4 × . . .
M: 1 Gardner diesel; 1 prop; 230 bhp

Remarks: 69 grt. On charter from 1970 to 1-89, then taken over outright.

♦ **1 small passenger launch [WYFL]**
Bldr: Arklow Eng. Co., Arklow (In serv. 1981)

FIACH DUBH (ex-*White Point*)

D: . . . tons (fl) **S:** 8 kts **Dim:** 13.31 × . . . × . . .
M: 1 Gardner diesel; 180 bhp

Remarks: Taken over in 11-85. Can carry up to 51 passengers.

♦ **1 small passenger launch [WYFL]**
Bldr: . . ., Den Oever, the Netherlands (In serv. 1971)

FAINLEOG (ex-*Greta*)

D: . . . tons **S:** 14.5 kts **Dim:** 14.21 × . . . × . . .
M: 1 Saab Scania V8 diesel; 410 bhp

Remarks: 15 grt. Taken over in 11-82. Carries up to 50 passengers.

♦ **1 small tug [WYTL]**
Bldr: Arklow Eng. Co., Arklow (In serv. 1979)

SEABHAC (ex-*Raffeen*)

D: . . . tons (fl) **S:** 8 kts **Dim:** 10.87 × . . . × . . .
M: 1 Gardner diesel; 180 bhp

Remarks: 9 grt. Taken over in 1982.

Note: The 120-ton sail-training craft *Asgard II* is the Irish National Youth Training Vessel; she is, on occasion, used by the Irish Defence Forces but does not belong to the Department of Defence. The 19.8-m Netherlands-registered sailing yacht *Brime* was taken over by the Irish government in 3-94 and is available to the navy for training.

The Commissioner of Irish Lights lighthouse tender *Granuaile* was replaced early in 2000 by a 2,625-grt ship of the same name built by Damen, Gorinchem, the Netherlands.

A 320-grt fisheries protection craft was ordered from Appledore Shipbuilders, U.K., in 2000 for delivery in 2001.

The Irish Marine Emergency Service was renamed the Irish Coast Guard early in 2000. It has responsibility for search and rescue, pollution-control efforts, and other emergency services and operates six smallcraft.

The establishment of a new Irish Sea Safety Agency at the end of 2001 was approved during 8-01. The organization will absorb the Marine Survey Office and may also incorporate the Coast Guard.

ISLE OF MAN

Note: The Isle of Man is a semiautonomous territory of the United Kingdom.

DEPARTMENT OF AGRICULTURE, FISHERIES, AND FORESTRY

FISHERIES PATROL CRAFT [WPB]

♦ **1 20-meter class**
Bldr: Souter Marine, Cowes, U.K. (In serv. 11-99)

BARRULE

Barrule Souter Marine, 11-99

D: . . . tons **S:** 12 kts (sust.) **Dim:** 20.0 × . . . × . . .
M: 2 Caterpillar 3408C; 2 props; 910 bhp
Range: 576/12 **Endurance:** 2 days **Crew:** 5 tot.

Remarks: Ordered 1-99; designed by TT Boat Design, Ltd. Steel construction. Intended for territorial patrol, fisheries monitoring, and law enforcement. Carries a 6-m Delta Rigid RIB inspection dinghy capable of 30 kts. Replaced the 11.75-m *Enbarr.*

ISRAEL

State of Israel

ISRAELI NAVY
(Heyl Yam)

Personnel (2002): Active: about 6,500 total (880 officers), of whom about 300 are specially trained as commandos and frogmen and 2,500 enlisted are conscripts. Reserves: 500 total.

Bases: Ashdod, Eilat, and Haifa. Major repairs are conducted at Haifa.

Maritime Aviation: One S.365G Dolpheen (the prototype U.S. Coast Guard HH-65A Dolphin) and six AS.565SA Atelef (Bat) helicopters are operated by Israeli Air Force squadron Tayeset 193 for shipboard service. Tayeset 195 operates three Navy-owned IAI Westwind 1124N Shahaf maritime reconnaissance aircraft (equipped with APS-504(V)2 search radars and able to launch two Gabriel antiship missiles) and has 2[illegible] Bell 212 helicopters for coastal surveillance and SAR; the Shahafs were being replaced by five Beech 200T King Air maritime patrol craft on order in 2001.

Note: Ship and craft names/numbers are preceded by INS-Israeli Naval Ship.

WEAPONS AND SYSTEMS

The Israeli Navy primarily uses foreign weapons, such as 76-mm OTOBreda Compact, OTOBreda 40-mm, and Oerlikon guns. Israeli industry has perfected the Gabriel antiship and Barak antimissile SAM missile systems:

Gabriel-I: A 560-kg, solid-propellant, surface-to-surface missile. After being fired, it climbs to about 100 m, then, at 7,500 m from the launcher, descends slowly to an altitude of 20 m. Optical or radar guidance is provided in azimuth, and a radio altimeter determines altitude. At a distance of 1,200 m from the target, the missile descends to 3 m, under either radio command or semiactive homing. The explosive charge is a 75-kg conventional warhead. Obsolescent, it may have been retired.

Gabriel-II: A development of the Gabriel-I that carries a television camera and transceiver for azimuth and altitude commands. The television is energized when the missile has attained a certain height and sends to the firing ship a picture of the areas that cannot be picked up by shipboard radar. The operator then can send any necessary corrections during the middle and final phases of the missile's flight and thus find a target that cannot be seen either by the naked eye or on radar. The range of the Gabriel-II is about 40 km.

WEAPONS AND SYSTEMS *(continued)*

Barak: A surface-to-air point-defense system, originally developed for use with an elevatable/trainable 8-cell box launcher, now using 8-cell vertical launch groups. It entered service in 1996 and is also used by Chile and Singapore. Characteristics include:

Length: 2.175 m **Diameter:** 170 mm **Wingspan:** 685 mm
Weight: 97.9 kg **Warhead:** 22 kg (tungsten pellets)
Speed: Mach 1.6 **Range:** 10 km engagement **Guidance:** Semiactive homing

Barak's system weight with 32 rounds requires 1.3 m of deck space, plus 2 m^3 of belowdecks volume. The intended fire-control system employs the AMDR (Advanced Missile Detection Radar), an S-band, pulse-doppler set capable of tracking 250 Mach 0.3–3.0 targets.

The U.S. RGM-84 Harpoon was first acquired in 1978 and is used on guided-missile patrol ships and craft, in the Block IB and IC versions; 16 additional missiles were purchased in 1998. Israel is alleged by the U.S. Department of Defense to have modified its Harpoons for improved range and performance and may intend to produce its own modified Harpoons for export. Also reported is the fitting of a datalink to the missiles, which permits the launching ship or a surveillance helicopter to designate targets using the missile's radar seeker data. Reports of a long-range, submerged-launch, nuclear warhead–equipped version, however, are very unlikely to be correct.

Fourteen U.S. Vulcan/Phalanx 20-mm close-in weapon systems were delivered for use in various units of the Sa'ar classes. Also in use are U.S.-supplied Redeye hand-held, IR-homing missiles.

Most radar, weapons control, combat data, communications, and electronics warfare systems are now made in Israel, based primarily on European and U.S. models. In development since 1991 have been the Rafael ATC-1 towed torpedo decoy and Scutter expendable torpedo decoy, the latter a 1-m-long by 10-cm-diameter device weighing 7.8 kg and having an endurance of 10 minutes to a depth of 300 m.

ATTACK SUBMARINES [SS]

♦ 3 Dolphin (IKL Type 800) class

Bldrs: HDW, Kiel, and Thyssen Nordseewerke, Emden (see remarks)

	Laid down	L	In serv.
Dolphin	1-4-92	15-4-96	27-7-99 (del. 29-3-99)
Leviathan	10-92	27-5-97	29-6-99 (del.)
Tekuma	7-94	9-7-98	22-10-00 (del. 25-7-00)

Dolphin H&L Van Ginderen, 6-99

Leviathan—en route to Israel Michael Nitz, 10-99

Tekuma Winter & Findler, 6-00

Tekuma Dieter Wolf, 7-99

D: 1,565 tons surf./1,720 tons sub. **S:** 11 kts snorkel/20 kts sub.
Dim: 57.30 × 7.40 × 6.20 (13.90 high, masts retracted)
A: 10 bow 533-mm swim-out TT (16 DM-2A3 Seehake wire-guided torpedoes; UGM-84C Harpoon antiship and Triton antihelicopter missiles)
Electronics:
Radar: 1 . . . search
EW: Timnex 4CH(V)2 intercept (2–18 GHz)
Sonar: STN Atlas Elektronik CSU-90-1 suite, with DBSQS-21D active, AN 5039A1 passive, PRS-3-15 passive ranging, and FAS-3-1 passive flank arrays
M: diesel-electric: 3 MTU 16V493 AZ80 diesels (800 bhp each), 3 diesel generator sets (313 kw each), 2 Siemens motors; 1 7-bladed prop; 5,000 shp (2,850 sust.)
Range: 8,000/8, 14,000/4 snorkel; 25/20, 420/8 sub.
Endurance: 60 days **Crew:** 6 officers, 24 enlisted

Remarks: Authorized in 3-88, initially to replace the relatively recent IKL 500 submarines. Permission to build two, vice the originally planned three, was finally given in 8-89, but the project was canceled in 11-90. Originally, the ships were to be assembled at Ingalls Shipyard, Pascagoula, Miss., using sections prefabricated by HDW in Germany. In 1-91, the project was revived when the German government offered to finance fully the construction of two in Germany, using a German combat system vice the originally planned U.S. systems. Germany informed Israel in 5-93 that a hoped-for third unit would not be forthcoming, but the submarine was reinstated in 2-95, with Israel and Germany sharing the $300 million cost equally; the name was originally reported as *Dakar.* Work on the first unit began at Kiel 15-2-92; fitting out work was performed by Thyssen at Emden. The submarines are painted a blue-green shade said to render them less visible in Mediterranean waters. Based at Haifa.
Hull systems: Operating depth is 350 m, collapse depth 700 m. Have 10% reserve buoyancy and two 216-cell batteries. Turning circle is 200 m in diameter at 15 kts submerged. The diesel engines have also been said to be of the 16V396 SE84 6BSL model, of 1,400 bhp each.
Combat systems: Have the STN Atlas Elektronik ISUS 90-1 combat data system and Kollmorgen Model 76 search and attack periscopes. Are equipped with swimmer lock-out facilities in the sail and boat stowage for eight special forces personnel. The torpedo tube arrangement is said to be very cramped, as additional tubes were fitted into the original design. The wire-guided torpedoes are an export version of the German Navy's DM-2A3, assembled by Lockheed Martin Tactical Systems Co. in cooperation with STN Atlas Elektronik. The EADS Triton fiber-optic-guided antihelicopter missile is being developed for these submarines; based on the technology of the Polyphem missile, it will have a 15-km range and can also be used against helicopters, surface craft, and coastal targets.

Disposal note: The three German-built IKL 500–class submarines *Gal* (72), *Tanin* (74), and *Rahav* (76) were retired during 1999. All three are offered for sale; a reported sale to Ecuador early in 1999 fell through when that country concluded peace with Peru, and Poland declined to purchase them in 3-01.

CORVETTES [FFL]

♦ 0 (+ 5) Sa'ar V+ class

Bldr: Northrop Grumman Litton Ship Systems, Pascagoula, Miss.

Remarks: Negotiations were under way during 2001 between Israel and Northrop Grumman for a class of up to five improved versions of the Sa'ar V class to replace the *Nirit* class by 2011. The ships would be armed with 16 Israeli Advanced Naval Attack Missiles (ASAM) and 16 Next-Generation Defense Missiles; the former is to have a 200-km range against land and seaborne targets, a loiter capability, a datalink to the launch platform and/or a targeting aircraft or helicopter, and a dual radar and infrared seeker. The program would be paid for with part of the annual U.S. $2.2 billion military aid fund.

♦ 3 Sa'ar V class

Bldr: Northrop Grumman Litton Ship Systems (formerly Ingalls SB), Pascagoula, Miss.

	Laid down	L	In serv.
501 Eilat	24-2-92	9-2-93	24-5-94
502 Lahav	25-9-92	20-8-93	23-9-94
503 Hanit	5-4-93	4-3-94	7-2-95

Eilat (501)—in service Maritime Photographic, 2-97

CORVETTES [FFL] *(continued)*

Eilat (501)—on builder's trials Ingalls SB, 1994

Lahav (502)—on builder's trials; note two groups of four 8-cell vertical launchers for Barak missiles, four forward of the bridge and four abaft the stack Ingalls SB, 1994

D: 1,075 tons (1,275 fl) **S:** 33+ kts (20 on diesels)
Dim: 85.64 (76.60 wl) × 11.88 (10.39 wl) × 3.17 (hull)
A: 8 RGM-84C Harpoon SSM; 8 8-round Barak vertical-launch SAM groups (64 missiles); 1 20-mm Mk 15 Phalanx CIWS; 2 single 20-mm 70-cal. Oerlikon AA; 4 single 7.62-mm mg; 2 triple 324-mm Mk 32 ASW TT (U.S. Mk 46 Mod. 5 torpedoes); 1 AS.565SA Atelef helicopter (with rockets, etc.) (see remarks)
Electronics:
Radar: 1 Cardion SPS-55 surf. search; 1 Elta EL/M-2228S 3-D variant air search; 2 Elta EL/M-2221 GM STGR f.c.; 1 Mk 90 Phalanx f.c.
Sonar: EDO Type 796 Mod. 1 hull-mounted (6–8 kHz); provision for Rafael Coris-TAS towed passive array (10–1,600 Hz)
EW: Elisra NS-9003A intercept (2–18 GHz); Tadiran NATACS MMI COMINT and D/F (20–500 MHz); 2 Rafael RAN-1010 jammers; Elbit DESEAVER decoy syst. (3 72-tube RL, 2 24-tube smoke RL); SLQ-25 Nixie towed acoustic torpedo decoy syst.
E/O: 2 El-Op MSIS multisensor, stabilized weapon directors
M: CODOG: 1 G.E. LM-2500 gas turbine (30,000 shp), 2 MTU 12V1163 TB82 diesels (3,000 bhp each); 2 KaMeWa CP props; 30,000 shp max.
Electric: 1,880 kw (4 × 470-kw Siemens-MTU diesel sets)
Range: 3,500/17 **Endurance:** 20 days
Crew: 16 officers, 7 CPOs, 41 ratings + air group: 4 officers, 6 CPOs

Remarks: Was originally to have been a class of eight, then four. Three (with the option for a fourth not taken up) were ordered 8-2-89. Formal christening for *Eilat* occurred 19-3-93, and the ship was delivered to Israel 12-93 for final fitting out, with an initial projected fully operational date of mid-1996 that slipped to late 1997/early 1998; the other two experienced similar delays. Cost around $260 million each.
Hull systems: Design emphasizes radar, noise, and heat signature suppression. Have 11 watertight compartments and Prairie/Masker bubbler underwater noise radiation suppression system.
Combat systems: The AIO III combat system by Elta has Elta EL/S-9000 computers (based on the Motorola 68020 microprocessor) and 17 display consoles. An OTO-Breda 76-mm dual-purpose gun can be substituted for the Phalanx mount but to date has not been. The EL/M-2228S radar functions as an automatic missile detection system. Were intended eventually to carry three Elta EL/M-2221-GM missile fire-control radars, two flanking the foremast and one aft. The Ku-band search radar in the Phalanx CIWS can be used to provide target designation services for the Barak missiles. Have the ICS-2 integrated communications suite. The planned eight single launcher containers for Gabriel-II antiship missiles were not installed due to top-weight problems, and the planned G.E. 25-mm gatling guns have yet to replace the old Oerlikon 20-mm interim mountings.

GUIDED-MISSILE PATROL CRAFT [PTG]

♦ **6 Nirit class** Bldr: Israel Shipyards, Ltd., Haifa

	Laid down	L	In serv.	Conversion completed
Hetz	1984	10-90	3-91	—
Kidon	. . .	7-74	9-74	7-2-94
Yafo	. . .	2-75	4-75	1-7-98
Nitzahon	. . .	10-7-78	9-78	1995
Romat	. . .	1981	10-81	2000?
Keshet	. . .	10-82	1982	2001?

Hetz Israeli Navy, via Norman Polmar, 1995

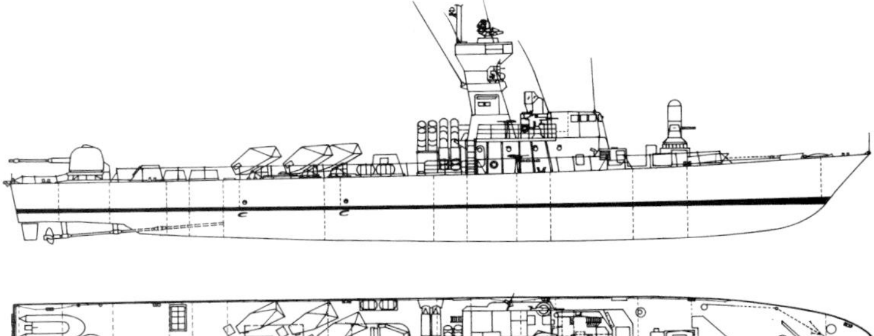

Nirit class Israeli SY

Nirit class (not Hetz or Kidon)—with quintuple missile launcher aft and only the starboard weapons director fitted C. E. Castle, 4-99

Kidon—with heavy davits aft and an extensive masthead D/F array C. E. Castle, 4-9

GUIDED-MISSILE PATROL CRAFT [PTG] *(continued)*

D: 488 tons (fl) **S:** 32 kts (30 sust.)
Dim: 61.70 (58.21 wl) × 7.62 (7.09 wl) × 2.76
A: 2 or 4 RGM-84C Harpoon SSM; 6 Gabriel-II SSM; 4 8-round Barak point-defense SAM vertical-launch groups; 1 76-mm OTOBreda Compact DP; 1 20-mm Mk 15 Phalanx CIWS; 2 single 20-mm 70-cal. Oerlikon AA; 4 single 12.7-mm mg
Electronics:
Radar: 1 Elta EL/M-2218-S AMDR K-band surf./air search; 1 or 2 Elta EL/M-2221 GM STGR f.c. (see remarks)
EW: Elta . . . intercept; 1 45-tube trainable decoy RL; 8 smoke RL; 2 24-tube decoy RL
E/O: 1 El-Op MSIS
M: 4 MTU 16V538 TB93 diesels; 4 props; 16,376 bhp (at 1,700 rpm)
Electric: . . . kw tot. (4 × 440-V, 60-Hz diesel sets)
Range: 3,000/17 **Fuel:** 116 tons **Crew:** 50 tot.

Remarks: *Hetz* was begun as a third unit of the *Romat* class but left incomplete as an economy measure; work began again in 1989 to complete her as the seagoing trials ship for the Barak antimissile missile system and advanced electronics intended for the *Eilat* class and for backfit into earlier missile combatants. The decision to update *Romat* and *Keshet* was made during 8-98.
Hull systems: Have a round-bilge, semi-displacement mild-steel construction hull with more-powerful diesel engines than earlier ships of the series. The five converted ships were lengthened during modernization, while *Hetz* was built with the longer hull.
Combat systems: The four Barak vertical-launch groups are recessed into the after deck. The radar directors (essentially Israeli-made versions of the Alenia Orion RTN-10X) are mounted on platforms abreast the tower mast. The starboard director antenna is of open-mesh configuration, while at least on *Hetz* the portside antenna has a solid reflector dish. There is an optronic director for the Gabriel-II antiship missiles and an integrated weapons fire-control system. *Kidon* (and probably the others) can be fitted with heavy, paired davits on either beam aft, purpose unknown; *Kidon* also has an extensive masthead D/F array.

♦ 2 Aliyah (Sa'ar 4.5) class
Bldr: Israel SY, Haifa

	L	In serv.
Aliyah	10-7-80	8-80
Geoula	10-80	31-12-80

Aliyah French Navy, 1983

Geoula or Aliyah—with Dolpheen helo Israeli Navy, 1989

D: 500 tons (fl) **S:** 31 kts (29 sust.)
Dim: 61.70 (58.21 wl) × 7.62 (7.09 wl) × 2.78
A: 4 RGM-84C Harpoon SSM; 4 Gabriel-II SSM; 1 20-mm Mk 15 Phalanx CIWS; 2 single 20-mm 70-cal. Oerlikon AA; 4 single 12.7-mm mg; 1 light helicopter
Electronics:
Radar: 1 Thales TH-D 1040 Neptune surf./air search; 1 Alenia Orion RTN-10X f.c.
EW: Elisra NS 9003/5 intercept/jammer syst.; NATACS comms intercept; Elisra NS 9010 D/F; 1 45-tube trainable decoy RL; 4 24-tube chaff RL; 4 single smoke RL
M: 4 MTU 16V956 TB91 diesels; 4 props; 14,000 bhp
Range: 1,500/30; 4,000/17 **Fuel:** 116 tons **Crew:** 53 tot.

Remarks: Each *Aliyah* was intended to lead a group of missile boats. *Aliyah* was reported to be for sale as of 8-98 but was still in service as of 2001. The helicopter was intended to provide an over-the-horizon targeting capability to utilize fully the range capabilities of the Harpoon missiles, which are mounted athwartships in the gap between the fixed hangar and the bridge superstructure. The Gabriel missile launch containers are mounted forward between the CIWS and the bridge superstructure. U.S. Mk 15 CIWS replaced original 40-mm mount forward. Have the Elbit Automatic Countermeasures Dispensing System (ACDS).

♦ 1 Reshev (Sa'ar IV) class
Bldr: Israel SY, Haifa

	L	In serv.
Atzmaut	3-12-78	2-79

Reshev class—rigged as a missile boat French Navy, 1983

Reshev class—rigged for ASW Israeli Navy, 1999

D: 415 tons (450 fl) **S:** 32 kts **Dim:** 58.10 × 7.62 × 2.40
A: 4 RGM-84C Harpoon SSM; 6 or 8 Gabriel-II SSM; 1 76-mm 62-cal. OTOBreda Compact DP; 1 20-mm Mk 15 Phalanx CIWS; 2 single 20-mm 70-cal. Oerlikon AA; 4 single 12.7-mm mg
Electronics:
Radar: 1 Thales TH-D 1040 Neptune surf./air search; 1 Alenia Orion RTN-10X f.c.
EW: Elisra NS 9003/5 intercept/jammer suite; NATACS comms intercept; Elisra NS 9010 D/F; 0 or 1 45-tube trainable decoy RL; 4 or 6 24-tube fixed decoy RL; 4 single smoke RL
M: 4 MTU 16V956 TB91 diesels; 4 props; 14,000 bhp (10,680 sust.)
Range: 1,650/30; 4,000/17.5 **Crew:** 45 tot.

Remarks: Three of this design were built in Israel for South Africa, and six others were built there under license at Durban. *Atzmaut* is the only Israeli Navy Sa'ar IV not to have been lengthened and modernized.
Disposals: Sisters *Keshet* and *Romach* were transferred to Chile 1979–80; the planned transfer of *Reshev* and one other in 1984 was canceled, then reinstated in late 1996, with *Reshev* and *Tarshish* transferred in 11-96 (departing Israel 1-6-97). *Komemiyut* and *Moledet* were transferred to Sri Lanka 9-12-00.
Hull systems: Quarters are air-conditioned.
Combat systems: Original missile armament was seven fixed Gabriel launchers. The 76-mm gun has been specially adapted for shore bombardment. The elaborate ECM/ESM system was designed by the Italian firm Elettronica and manufactured in Israel. Has the Elbit Automatic Countermeasures Dispensing System (ACDS). Can be rigged for ASW, with a portable dipping sonar at the stern in place of the 76-mm mount and one triple 324-mm Mk 32 ASW TT on the port side; in that circumstance, the missile complement is reduced to four Gabriel and two Harpoon missiles.

PATROL BOATS [PB]

♦ 1 Alligator-class semi-submersible
Bldr: K-10 Corp., U.S.A. (In serv. 6-98)

D: 23.4 tons (fl) **S:** 30 kts (8 semi-sub.) **Dim:** 19.81 × 3.96 × . . .
A: . . .
Electronics: Radar: 1 . . . nav.
M: 2 . . . diesels; 2 props; . . . bhp
Range: . . ./. . . **Crew:** . . .

Remarks: Intended to ballast down to barely awash for clandestine operations at low speeds; all topside masts and antennas can be retracted or folded. The hull and superstructure are configured to be low-observable. Has a 5-ton payload. Tested by the U.S. Navy prior to delivery.

♦ 3 T 2212 class
Bldr: T-Craft International, Cape Town, South Africa (In serv. 11-97)

D: 23 tons (45 fl) **S:** 41 kts (37 sust.) **Dim:** 22.00 × 7.00 × 0.90
A: 1 20-mm Oerlikon AA **Electronics:** Radar: 1 . . . nav.
M: 2 MTU 12V183 TE92 diesels; 2 waterjets; 2,000 bhp
Range: 525/30 **Crew:** 4 tot. + 15 passengers

Remarks: Purchased new in 11-98. This design had not proved successful in South African Navy service.
Hull systems: An unusual catamaran hullform with hydrofoils between the hulls. GRP construction. Have accommodations for 16 but can be operated with as few as four personnel. Carry a 3.4-m rigid inflatable rescue boat aft.

♦ 13 Super Dvora Mk I and Mk II classes
Bldr: RAMTA–Israeli Aircraft Industries (IAI), Be'er Sheva (In serv. 1-89 to 1994)

Mk I: 811 through 819 Mk II: 820 through 823

PATROL BOATS [PB] *(continued)*

Super Dvora Mk II–class 823 French Navy, 1996

Super Dvora—export boat, rigged for shipping H&L Van Ginderen, 10-96

D: 48 tons (54 fl) **S:** 36–38 kts **Dim:** 22.40 × 5.49 × 1.00
A: 2 single 20-mm 70-cal. Oerlikon AA; 2 single 12.7-mm mg; provision for Hellfire SSM and/or 1 84-mm Carl Gustav mortar
Electronics: Radar: 1 Raytheon . . . nav.
M: Mk I: 2 MTU 12V396 TB93 diesels; 2 Arneson outdrive semi-submerged props; 3,260 bhp—Mk II: 3 MTU 12V396 TE94 diesels; 3 Arneson ASD 16 outdrive semi-submerged props; 4,175 bhp
Electric: 30 kw **Range:** 700/14 **Crew:** 1 officer, 8 enlisted

Remarks: Improved version of basic Dvora design. Of six Mk I units ordered 3-87, the first was delivered 1-89 and the rest in 1989–90. The Mk II version was delivered during 1993–94. A planned Mk III version with three engines was not built. As of 4-01, IAI was negotiating to have the design built in the U.S.A. so that it could be purchased for foreign navies under the U.S. Foreign Military Sales program. A longer version of the basic design is in development for the Israeli Navy, and the builder is also working on a 17-m version to be known as "Wasp."
Exports: Six Mk I and 4 Mk II have been delivered to Sri Lanka, 4 Mk I to Eritrea, 2 Mk II to Slovenia, and 2 Mk II to India. A license was granted in 1996 for indigenous construction of this class at Goa, India.
Hull systems: Aluminum construction.
Combat systems: Can be armed with depth charges, ASW torpedoes, or 130-mm barrage rocket launchers and can also be fitted with an Elop optronic low-light-level surveillance and weapons direction device. Trials were conducted on 815 in 1997 with the General Dynamics Typhoon triple 12.7-mm mg mount forward. U.S.-supplied 25-mm Bushmaster guns may replace one or both 20-mm mountings.

♦ up to 12 Dabur class
Bldr: Israeli Aircraft Industries, Be'er Sheva (In serv. 1973–77)

Dabur-class 854 ANBw/FAFIO, 8-97

D: 25 tons (35 fl) **S:** 25 kts (22 cruise) **Dim:** 19.8 × 5.8 × 0.8
A: 2 single 20-mm 70-cal. Oerlikon AA; 2 single 12.7-mm mg
Electronics:
Radar: 1 Decca 926 nav.
E/O: El-Op low-light t.v. surveillance and weapons desig.
M: 2 G.M. Detroit Diesel 12V71 TI diesels; 2 props; 960 bhp
Electric: 20 kw tot. **Range:** 1,200/17 **Crew:** 1 officer, 5 enlisted

Remarks: First 10 (now retired) were built in the U.S.A. by Sewart Seacraft. Five were given to Christian forces in Lebanon in 1976 (later returned), six were sold to Chile in 1991 and four more in 1995, four were sold to Argentina, four were transferred to Fiji in 11-91, and four were sold to Nicaragua in 1978. A dozen of the remaining Israeli Navy units were reportedly for sale as of 8-98, but at least one was still in active service in 4-99; the exact number still in service (if any) is not available. Pennant numbers are in the 850s, when worn.
Hull systems: Aluminum construction. Air-conditioned quarters. Small enough for transport by truck.

AMPHIBIOUS WARFARE SHIPS AND CRAFT

Note: Construction of two new landing ships was planned, but funding has not materialized; they would be approx. 117.0 × 17.0 × 2.2 m and have a helicopter platform and facilities for several hundred troops. The Israeli Army also employs several 54-ton (light) river-crossing craft capable of transporting 130-ton loads.

AUXILIARIES

♦ 2 miscellaneous patrol craft tenders [AGP]

NAHARYA (ex-. . .) NIR (ex-*Ma'oz*)

Remarks: *Nir* is a 4,000-ton oilfield-supply vessel used as an alongside missile-boat tender at Haifa; the ship was built for oilfield supply work in 1976 by Todd Shipyards, Seattle, Wash. *Naharya* (origins unknown) is used for a similar purpose at Eilat. Both are essentially immobile.

♦ 1 training ship [AXT] Bldr: Kasado DY, Japan (In serv. 1979)

QESHET (ex-. . .)

D: . . . **S:** . . . **Dim:** 115.0 × . . . × . . .
M: . . . diesels; . . . props; . . . bhp

Remarks: Former 2,800-grt/4,634-dwt passenger/cargo vessel equipped as a training ship for the navy and merchant marine; replaced the *Nogah* in 1991. May also have been involved in Barak missile trials.

Note: The National Police also employ several 8.3-ton (fl) Snaparit-class patrol launches on the Sea of Galilee.

ITALY

Italian Republic

ITALIAN NAVY

(Marina Militare)

Personnel (1-01): 38,580 total (4,850 officers, 16,650 petty officers, 17,000 other enlisted), including the 3,500-man San Marco Regiment. There were also about 15,000 civilian employees.

Bases: The principal bases are at La Spezia (surface combatants of the First Division, submarines, and mine countermeasures ships) and Taranto (surface combatants of the Second Division), with regional bases at Ancona and Naples and facilities at Augusta, Sicily; Brindisi (Third Division, with amphibious ships); Cagliari, Sardinia; La Maddalena, Sardinia; Messina, Sicily; and Venice.

Marines: The San Marco Battalion *(Battaglione San Marco)* has been expanded with a second rifle company and grew to regiment size in 1998; a helicopter support group with 6 SH-3D Sea King troop carrier and 6 AB-212 fire support helicopters is attached. For use by seaborne assault troops, there are 24 LVTP-7 amphibious armored personnel carriers and 1 LVTC-7 amphibious armored command post.

Naval Aviation: About 1,600 personnel are involved in Italian naval aviation. The Marinavia operates 16 AV-8B+ and 2 two-seat TAV-8B Harrier shipboard fighters and 79 helicopters: 29 SH-3D Sea King and 50 AB-212. Of the latter, 23 SH-3D are employed for shore-based ASW and for use aboard *Giuseppe Garibaldi,* and 44 AB-212 light ASW helicopters are available for service aboard frigates and destroyers and for training; 6 SH-3D and 6 AB-212 have been stripped of ASW equipment and are dedicated to the support of the San Marco Battalion. The two SH-3D squadrons are based at Luni (1st Squadron) and Catania (3rd Squadron). The 2nd, 4th, and 5th (AB-212) Squadrons are based at Luni, Taranto, and Catania, respectively. All 18 Harriers are assigned to GRUPAER and are based ashore at Grottaglie, near Taranto.

Sixteen EH.101 heavy helicopters were ordered in 7-97 to replace the Sea Kings; see data below. The first flew on 6-12-99. To replace the AB-212s, which were built under license from Bell Helicopter by AgustaWestland in Italy, it is planned to acquire 56 NH-90 helicopters (see France entry for description) powered by G.E.-FiatAvio T700/T6E1 turbines.

Four more Harriers are sought as attrition replacements, and the Harrier is expected to serve in the Italian Navy until around 2020. In 10-94, 33 AIM-120 AMRAAM and 42 AGM-65 Maverick missiles were ordered for use with the Harriers, which are also equipped to drop Mk 81, 82, and 83 free-fall bombs, Mk 20 Rockeye bomblet-carriers, and unguided LAU rocket pods; another 233 AIM-120B versions of the missile were ordered early in 1997. All Italian Harriers, including the two-seat trainers, are powered by the 23,800-lb.-thrust Rolls-Royce Pegasus F 402 RR-408 engine, and the single-seaters have APG-65 radars and 25-mm guns.

The navy would like to acquire Grumman E-2C Hawkeye radar aircraft for land-based operations in support of the Harriers.

The air force conducts fixed-wing maritime ASW patrol, using 14 navy-crewed Bréguet Atlantic Mk 1 aircraft ordered in 1968 and delivered by 1973; 4 more are in reserve. The Atlantics are based at Catania (No. 86 Squadron) and Cagliari/Elmas (No. 88 Squadron). They have been modernized to Atlantique Mk 2 standard with Iguane radar, Litton inertial navigation systems, a new acoustic processor, and sonobuoy dispensers. Further modernizations were begun in 1998 to keep them in service past 2008, but plans as of 2000 called for ordering 14 new aircraft, with the first to deliver in 2007. The number of Atlantiques is to be reduced to 12 by 2005. Italian Air Force Tornado strike fighters carry the Kormoran I missile for antiship missions (see Germany entry for aircraft and missile data). Fifteen AgustaWestland-built variants of the U.S. Coast Guard Sikorsky HH-3F Pelican helicopter are used by the Protezione Civile for search-and-rescue service. The Italian Coast Guard *(Guardia Costiera)* and Customs Service *(Guardia di Finanza Servizio Navale)* have their own air forces, which are listed in the sections devoted to them.

Italian Navy AV-8B+ Harrier **Italian Navy, 1997**

♦ EH.101 Series 100

Italian Navy EH.101 prototype EH Industries

Rotor diameter: 18.59 m **Length:** 22.81 m (15.75 folded)
Weight: 14,600 kg max. **Speed:** 150 kts cruise (167 max.)
Engines: 3 G.E. T700/T6A turboshaft; 2,040 shp each
Endurance: 5 hr **Crew:** 4 tot.
Armament: 4 MU-90 ASW torpedoes or 2 Marte Mk 2 ASM; 1 12.7-mm mg
Sensors: APS-784 radar, Helras Mk 2 dipping sonar, ALR-735 EW, GaliFlir FLIR, ELT/156X(V2) radar warning, RALM/1 laser warning

Remarks: Built by AgustaWestland at Vergiate. Of the 16 initially ordered, eight will be equipped as above, four will be of the ASVW/E (Anti–Surface Vessel Warfare/Enhanced) variant with Eliradar HEW-784 surface-search and target-tracking radar, and the remaining four (with an option for a further eight) will be configured as assault transports with a cargo hook, a different EW suite with flare launchers, a GaliFlir FLIR turret, an MM/APS-705B radar, a 12.7-mm mg turret, and stub wings for rocket launchers. The SAR-configured units will have APS-784E radars optimized for surface search, and the utility transports will have an SMA-705 radar. All versions will have FLIR and countermeasures systems. An eventual total of 64 is foreseen.

♦ SH-3D Sea King

Italian Navy SH-3D Sea King Luciano Grazioli, 6-99

Rotor diameter: 18.90 m **Length:** 22.16 m **Weight:** 9,300 kg max.
Speed: 118 kts cruise (144 max.) **Engines:** 2 1,400-shp turboshaft
Endurance: 4 hr 50 min **Crew:** 3 tot.
Armament: 2 Mk 46 torpedoes, depth charges, or 2 Marte Mk 2 ASM

♦ AB-212

Italian Navy AB-212—aboard Alpino (A 5384) Bernard Prézelin, 10-00

Rotor diameter: 14.60 m **Length:** 17.40 m **Height:** 4.40 m
Weight: 5,086 kg max. **Speed:** 100 kts cruise (130 max.)
Engine: 1 1,290-shp turboshaft **Ceiling:** 5,000 ft.
Endurance: 4 hr 15 min **Crew:** 3 tot.
Armament: 2 Mk 46 torpedoes, depth charges, or 2 AS-12 missiles
Sensors: AQS-13B dipping sonar

Italian Air Force Atlantic Mk 1 Bernard Prézelin, 3-01

WEAPONS AND SYSTEMS

A. MISSILES

♦ Surface-to-air missiles

Note: Italy has joined with France in the development of the FSAF/FAMS surface-to-air missile program as a replacement for the systems currently employed; the missiles to be employed will be the French-made Aster-15 and Aster-30 (see France section).

Standard SM-2 Block IIIA: Italy requested 50 Raytheon Standard SM-2 Block IIIA missiles for $135 million in 7-00. These are to replace existing SM-1 missiles and will require modifications to Italian ships to permit their use. See U.S.A. section for characteristics.

Standard SM-1 ER and SM-1 MR: See U.S.A. section for characteristics.

Aspide: Manufacturer: Alenia–OTO Sistemi Missilistici SpA. Aspide is, in effect, the Italian version of the U.S. Sea Sparrow. The system employs an octuple, 7-ton Albatros launcher built by OTOBreda and is controlled by the NA-30 radar fire-control system. Elevation: +5° to +65°. A quadruple launcher has been produced for use on export corvettes. The Aspide 2000, now in development, is to have a 30–40% increase in dynamic performance, plus guidance and ECCM enhancements; it is intended either as an interim replacement until the joint Aster-15 is available or as a fallback should the French missile not be procured.

Length: 3.673 m **Diameter:** 0.204 m **Wingspan:** 0.644 m
Weight: 217 kg at launch **Range:** 10,000 m
Altitude: 15 m min.; 5,000 m max. **Guidance:** semiactive homing

♦ Surface-to-surface missiles

Ulysses: Manufacturer: Alenia–OTO Sistemi Missilistici SpA. Formerly known as Teseo Mk 3. The conceptual Otomat Mk 3 design is to form the basis for the new weapon, which will incorporate reduced-signature ("stealth") features, a dual-mode infrared and radar seeker system, in-flight retargeting, infrared target identification gear, advanced counter-countermeasures features, and an advanced overland and overwater navigation system. It will have a range of 180 km and a 210-kg warhead, as well as improved target detection and discrimination. An air-launched variant is planned as well, but no information is available as to when it might enter service, and its development was on hold as of 2000.

Otomat Mk 2 ("Teseo Mk 2"): Manufacturer: Alenia–OTO Sistemi Missilistici SpA. Differs from the original 60-km-range Otomat Mk 1 in having an Italian (SMA) single-axis active radar homing head (8–16 GHz) instead of a French seeker and in employing folding wings; the Italian Navy's Teseo variant employs a datalink from a targeting helicopter to determine initial course to target. The original fixed-wing Otomat Mk 1/Teseo Mk 1 is also still in use by the Italian Navy. Alenia has offered to provide a new radar seeker, a new mission computer, an inertial midcourse guidance system with GPS receiver, terminal maneuvering, and trajectory height and impact-point selection. Saudi Arabia was the sole purchaser of the ERATO (Extended-Range Automatic Targeting Otomat) version.

WEAPONS AND SYSTEMS *(continued)*

A Mk 4 variant is to be available in 2005 and will incorporate repackaged avionics to reduce volume and increased fuel capacity; there will also be a new radar signal processor and a GPS receiver to permit use against land targets, and the missile will have insensitive propellants and warhead munitions. Data for the Otomat Mk 2 include:

Length: 4.460 m **Diameter:** 0.460 m (1.060 with boosters)
Wingspan: 1.19 m **Weight:** 780 kg **Warhead weight:** 210 kg (65 kg Hertol)
Propulsion: Turbomeca TR 281 Arbizon-III turbojet (400 kg thrust)
Speed: 300 m/sec (Mach 0.9) **Range:** 5.5 km min.; 185 km max.
Guidance: autopilot, active radar homing

♦ Air-to-surface missiles

Marte Mk 2: Made by Alenia–OTO Sistemi Missilistici SpA for use by Sea King helicopters. Guidance is by gyro autopilot and radar altimeter over midcourse, with active pseudo-monopulse radar homing, using the same seeker as the Otomat. Fuzing is influence and impact. The airframe is basically that of the now-retired Sistel Sea Killer surface-launched antiship missile, itself based on the U.S. Sea Sparrow airframe.

Length: 4.84 m (with 1.09-m booster) **Diameter:** 31.6 cm
Wingspan: 98.7 cm (cruciform) **Weight:** 340 kg **Warhead weight:** 70 kg
Speed: Mach 0.8 **Range:** more than 20 km

Alenia began developing a Marte Mk 2/S variant in 1998 for use with the NH-90 helicopter. The weapon was to be ready to enter production in 2001, will be smaller and lighter than the Mk 2, and will employ a J-band active radar seeker:

Length: 3.80 m **Weight:** 320 kg **Warhead weight:** 70 kg
Speed: Mach 0.8 **Range:** 25+ km

Note: The French S.N.I.A.S. AS-12 wire-guided antiship missile has been adopted for use by AB-212 helicopters. The Harrier fighter-bombers use U.S. AGM-65 Maverick air-to-ground missiles, of which 42 were ordered 9-94.

♦ Air-to-air missiles

The U.S. AIM-120B AMRAAM is used by the Harrier fighter-bombers; 33 were ordered in 9-94 and another 233 early in 1997.

B. GUNS

Note: The well-known naval gun-manufacturing firms of OTO Melara and Breda merged late in 1994 and now trade under the name OTOBreda; OTOBreda, in turn, is a division of Alenia Difesa SpA.

127-mm OTOBreda Compact: The mount weighs 37.5 tons, employs a single-barrel automatic gun, and has a fiberglass shield. The gun has a muzzle brake; it can automatically fire 66 rounds, thanks to three loading drums, each with 22 rounds. Two hoists serve two loading trays with rounds coming from the magazine at the rate of 12 per minute, and a drum may be loaded even while the gun is firing. An automatic selection system allows a choice of ammunition (antiaircraft, surface target, pyrotechnics, or chaff for cluttering radar). The mount has been purchased by Argentina, Canada, Japan, the Netherlands (refurbished Canadian mounts), Nigeria, Peru, South Korea, and Venezuela.

Length: 54 calibers **Muzzle velocity:** 807 m/sec
Rate of fire: 43 rds/min (automatic setting) **Arc of elevation:** −15° to +83°
Max. effective range for surface fire: 15,000 m
Max. effective range for antiaircraft fire: 7,000 m

A lightweight, 22-ton 127/54LW version with reduced elevation (−15° through +70°) and a much smaller gunhouse began tests at sea on the *Bersagliere* in late 2000. An extended-range munition with a range of 70 km is to be developed. The 127/54LW has a 40-rpm firing rate and a faceted, radar reflection reduction gunhouse.

76-mm OTOBreda Compact: Single-barreled, light antiaircraft, automatic fire; entirely remote control with muzzle brake and cooling system. Used worldwide. Development is continuing on a course-corrected shell for this weapon, using a shipboard datalink to the projectile. Has 80 ready-service rounds in the drum. The current SuperRapid version of the weapon weighs 7.5 tons and fires at 1, 10, or 120 rds/min, with 85 rounds on-mount. The weapon is now offered with a faceted gunhouse to reduce radar signature.

Length: 62 calibers **Mount weight:** 7.35 tons
Muzzle velocity: 925 m/sec **Rate of fire:** 85 rds/min
Max. effective range for surface fire: 8,000 m
Max. effective range for antiaircraft fire: 4,000–5,000 m

76-mm OTOBreda: Single-barreled, automatic, for air, surface, and land targets; obsolescent and now found on only four Italian Navy corvettes and several auxiliaries.

Length: 62 calibers **Muzzle velocity:** 850 m/sec
Rate of fire: 60 rds/min
Max. effective range for surface fire: 8,000 m
Max. effective range for antiaircraft fire: 4,000–5,000 m

40-mm OTOBreda/Bofors Compact twin:

Length: 70 calibers **Projectile weight:** 0.96 kg
Muzzle velocity: 1,000 m/sec **Rate of fire:** 300 rds/min/barrel
Number of ready-service rounds: 444 or 736 (depending on installation)
Max. effective range for antiaircraft fire: 3,500–4,000 m
Fire control: Dardo system (Alenia RTN-20X radar)
Fuzing: impact or proximity

30-mm 80-cal. OTOBreda/Mauser: Employed by the Guardia di Finanza and available for export. Available in enclosed twin and single mountings. Gas operated. Can be fired at 800 rds/min in short bursts and 1–300 rds/min in rapid-fire mode.

Muzzle velocity: 1,040 m/sec **Rate of fire:** 800 rds/min
Arc of elevation: −13° to +85°
Max. effective range: 1,500 m surface/3,000 m air

25-mm 87-cal. Oerlikon-OTOBreda KBA: A new lightweight mount being procured to replace the venerable 20-mm Oerlikon mountings employed for close-defense, mine-disposal, and policing functions. Open, crew-served mounting.

C. TORPEDOES

U.S. Mk 46 Mod. 5 and Italian Whitehead Alenia Sistemi Subacquei (WASS, formerly Whitehead Motofides) A-244 small ASW torpedoes are used on ships (using the triple B-515 tube mount, similar to the U.S. Mk 32 Mod. 5 ASW torpedo tube set) and helicopters. They are to be replaced over the next decade by the Eurotorp MU-90 Impact light ASW torpedo.

The WASS A-290 lightweight ASW torpedo project, begun in 1981, was merged with the French Murène program in 1990 and is now known as MU-90 Impact. Its lithium battery produces 50-kt speeds. The 2.75-m-long weapon is expected to enter service in 2002 for use with aircraft, surface ships, and the Milas missile. Italy plans to order 300, with an option for 100 more. The Franco-Italian production consortium is known as Eurotorp.

The WASS A-184 wire-guided torpedo is a 533-mm weapon with a range of more than 15,000 m. Length: 6.0 m; weight: 1,245 kg. A variant with terminal wake-homing in lieu of active acoustic terminal homing is also in service. The Mod. 3 variant, which entered service in 1996, employs the new TOSO active/passive acoustic seeker.

Trials began in 1998 with an upgraded version of the A-184 known as BlackShark for use with the Type 212A submarines; it has a new ASTRA multibeam acoustic seeker, silver-zinc batteries, a fiber-optic guidance link, a new brushless motor, and quieter propellers; series production is to begin in 2005, and the weapon will be offered jointly for export by DCN, France, and WASS as the BlackShark/IF21. Maximum speed is 50 kts and maximum range 50 km, using a silver oxide–aluminum battery.

WASS is also developing the A-200-series mini-torpedo, a 123.8-mm-diameter, 914.4-mm-long weapon weighing only 12.5 kg. The A-200/A, for the Italian Navy, would be air-dropped from conventional 127-mm sonobuoy dispensers, while the A-200/N would add a booster rocket for surface launch to 8 km ranges (Germany and Norway are potential customers); a sextuple launcher would be used. The A-200 employs a dc electric motor, has 17-kt speed, and is intended to provide evidence that an actual submarine has been attacked; it employs a shaped-charge warhead. The A-202, also in development, would weigh some 16 kg, is to have an active/passive acoustic seeker, and would be used by combat swimmers, who would launch it from "Medusa" portable launchers; it is also to be launchable from tubes in midget submarines.

D. ANTISUBMARINE WEAPONS

Milas *(Missile de Lutte Anti-Sousmarine)*: Under development by OTOBreda and France's Matra Défense using the Otomat propulsion section. Initial trials were conducted during 1989. At-sea firings began in 1993, but initial operational service, once to have been reached in 1996, was most recently delayed to 2002. The French Navy abandoned the program in 1998.

Length: 6.0 m **Diameter:** 0.46 m **Wingspan:** 1.06 m
Weight: 800 kg (1,800 in launcher)
Speed: 1,080 kph **Range:** 5–55 km **Altitude:** 200 m (cruise)

Depth charges: WASS began developing the MS 500 depth charge in 1990; the weapon has a 100-kg CBX destructive charge and a lethal radius of 50 m.

E. MINES

The following Italian-made mines are available for domestic and export use:

- MR-80: Mod. A weighs 1,035 kg (with 856 kg explosive), Mod. B 790 kg (with 611 kg explosive), and Mod. C 630 kg (with 451 kg explosive). All versions can be used to 300-m depths.
- Manta: 240-kg (170 kg explosive) bottom influence mine; usable to 100-m depths
- Seppia: 870-kg (200 kg explosive) mine usable in waters up to 300 m in depth
- MAS/22: 22-kg (17 kg explosive), beach-defense, bottom contact mine
- MAL/17: 22-kg (17 kg explosive), beach-defense, moored contact mine
- TAR 6: 1,104-kg (175 kg explosive), submarine-laid, moored contact
- VS-SM-600: 780-kg (600 kg explosive) bottom influence mine

F. RADARS

The Italian Navy has used a number of American search and missile-control radars (SPS-12, SPS-52, SPG-51, SPG-55, etc.), but now primarily uses systems developed in Italy by Gem, Elettronica, SMA, and the Selenia-Elsag division of Alenia (now known by the initials "AESN"). The designation system employed by the Italian armed forces is like that used in the United States except that the prefix letters before the slash (omitted in the ship listings that follow) are "MM" *(Marina Militare)* vice "AN."

Type	*Band*	*Remarks*
MM/BPS-704	I/S (X)	SMA 3 RM 20 adapted for submarines
MM/BX-732	I	Gem nav. set widely employed on smaller ships
MM/SPG-70	I/J (X)	AESN gun and missile f.c. (RTN-10X Orion for Argo syst.)
MM/SPG-74	I/J (X)	AESN 40-mm gun f.c. (RTN-20X Dardo)
MM/SPG-75	I/J (X)	AESN missile f.c. (RTN-30X for Albatros syst.)
MM/SPN-703	I	SMA nav. radar; also known as 3 RM 28B
MM/SPN-704	I	SMA nav. radar, 3 RM 20 for surface ships
MM/SPN-720	I	Landing-aid radar; a variant of SPS-702
MM/SPN-728	X	SMA nav./helicopter-control; dual antenna
MM/SPN-748	X	Gem Elettronica nav.
MM/SPN-749(V)	I (X)	Gem Elettronica nav. set on *Garibaldi;* 2 antennas (9345–9405 MHz)
MM/SPN-751	I (X)	Commercial nav. set, used in auxiliaries
MM/SPN-753 (V)	I	Gem Elettronica nav. set; introduced in 1989
MM/SPQ-2A/D	I/J (X)	SMA nav./surf. search/air search set; obsolescent
MM/SPS-702	I	SMA frequency-agile, sea-skimmer detector; modern version of SPQ-2
MM/SPS-768	D (S)	AESN 3-D air search; also known as RAN-3L
MM/SPS-774	E/J (S/X)	AESN air/surf. surveillance; also known as RAN-10S; entered service in 1980
MM/SPY-790	G	AESN EMPAR 3-D frequency-agile phased array surf./air search

WEAPONS AND SYSTEMS *(continued)*

G. SONARS

Type	*Function*	*Frequency*	*Manufacturer*
DE 1160B	Hull	MF	AESN-Raytheon
DE 1164	Hull or VDS	MF	AESN-Raytheon
SQS-23G	Hull	MF	Sangamo-G.E. (U.S.)
SQQ-14	Minehunting	HF	Unisys (U.S.)
SQQ-14IT	Minehunting	HF	FIAR

Note: Submarines use a variety of sonar equipment produced by AESN; see individual ship classes for details.

H. TACTICAL INFORMATION SYSTEM

The Italian Navy has developed the SADOC system, which is compatible with British, American NTDS, and French SENIT combat data systems through NATO Link 11.

I. COUNTERMEASURES

A wide variety of intercept arrays, many with stabilized cylindrical radome antennas, are in use. The Lambda intercept system employs the SLQ-D and SLR-4 intercept arrays, combined with a superheterodyne receiver; the similar Newton has a simpler receiver. Elettronica's Nettuno integrated ECM/ESM system employs four stabilized radome-mounted antennas.

The OTOBreda SCLAR chaff rocket-launching system is used on frigates and larger ships; it has 20 tubes for 105-mm rockets in a trainable, elevatable launcher. The SCLAR-H rapid response system is capable of launching 102- to 150-mm-diameter projectiles. A number of British Wallop Barricade chaff rocket launchers were ordered 1984 (as the Type 207/E system), and the French Matra Défense Sagaie decoy launcher is used on the *Luigi Durand de la Penne*–class guided-missile destroyers.

The WASS C303 Effector decoy system for submarines employs two 21-tube launcher arrays mounted in the sail.

Note: Diesel engine manufacturer Grandi Motori Trieste (GMT) was purchased by Wärtsilä NSD Corp. in 3-99 and is now trading as Wärtsilä NSD Italia SpA, abbreviated to Wärtsilä NSD below. Fincantieri and Howaldtswerke Deutsche Werft (HDW) of Germany announced a joint venture to design, produce, and market naval and merchant ships on 8-5-01.

V/STOL AIRCRAFT CARRIERS [CVV]

♦ 0 (+ 1) Andrea Doria class

Bldr: Fincantieri, Muggiano, La Spezia

	Laid down	L	In serv.
C . . . ANDREA DORIA	17-7-01	2005	2007

D: 22,290 (26,660 fl) **S:** 29 kts (16 on one engine)
Dim: 234.40 (215.60 pp) × 39.00 (max.; 29.50 wl) × 7.40 (mean hull; 8.70 max.)
Air group: 8 AV-8B+ Harrier or 12 EH.101 helicopters or a mix
A: 4 8-cell Sylver vertical-launch missile groups (132 Aster-15 SAM); 2 single 76-mm 62-cal. OTOBreda SuperRapid DP; 3 single 25-mm 87-cal. Oerlikon-OTOBreda KBA AA; 4 fixed 324-mm ASW TT (MU-90 Impact torpedoes)
Electronics:
Radar: 2 SMA SPN-753 nav.; 1 AESN SPS-791 RASS surf. search; 1 AESN RAN-40S early warning; 1 AESN SPY-790 EMPAR target desig./tracking; 2 AESN SPG-76 (RTN-30X/I) gun f.c.; 1 SPN-41 CCA
Sonar: . . . bow-mounted MF and HF mine-avoidance
EW: passive intercept and active; 2 20-round SCLAR-H decoy launchers; 2 SLAT torpedo decoy launchers; towed acoustic torpedo decoy syst.

Andrea Doria—artist's rendering Italian Navy, 2000

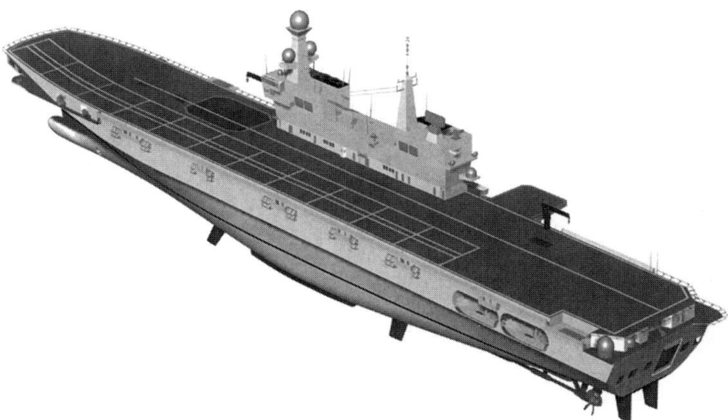

Andrea Doria—computer rendering Italian Navy, 2000

M: CODLOG: 4 G.E.-Fiat LM-2500 gas turbines; 2 5-bladed CP props; 118,000 shp—diesel-electric cruise from shaft generators (9 kts)—bow and stern tunnel thrusters
Electric: 17,600 kw tot. (6 × 2,200-kw Wärtsilä NSD diesel sets; 2 × 2,200-kw propeller-shaft generators; 660 V, 50 Hz)
Range: 7,000/16
Crew: 486 ship's company + 145 flag staff + 211 air group + 360 troops (450 in emergency)

Remarks: Initial design funding was provided in the 1996 budget; construction approved 2-98, with provisional order placed 22-11-00. Initially referred to as the UMPA *(Unità Maggiore Per Operazione Anfibe)* but officially conceded to be an aircraft carrier late in 1998 and is now called the NUM = *Nuova Unità Maggiore* (New Major Unit). Will be the largest warship built in Italy since World War II. Was initially to have been named *Luigi Einaudi.* Will be a multirole ship employable as an amphibious warfare asset, vehicle ferry, disaster relief ship, strike carrier, or sea-control ship. To cost about $854 million, exclusive of the missile system and air group.
Hull systems: A planned 25 × 14–m docking well at the stern for four LCM(6)-size landing craft or two LCM(8) or one U.S. LCAC had been deleted by 2000. Will be able to carry 12 60-ton Ariete tanks or 100 light trucks. There will be two 60-ton-capacity

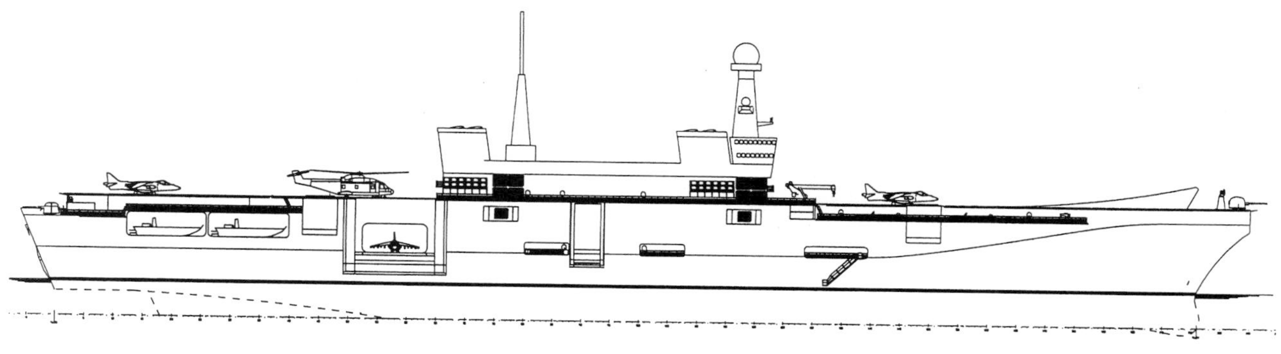

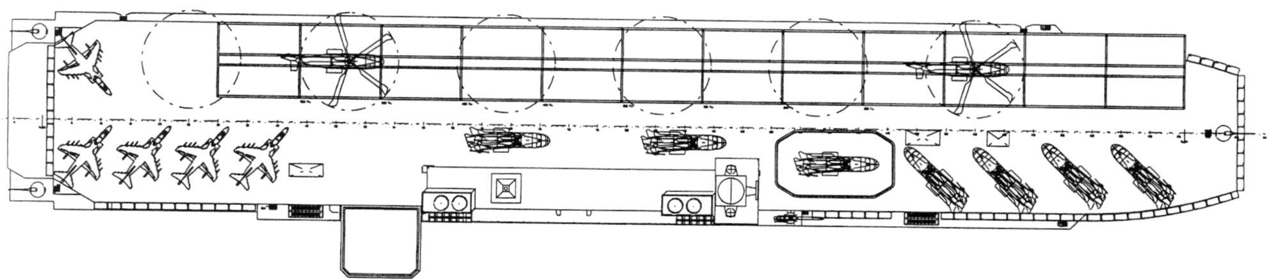

Andrea Doria—the Nuovo Unità Maggiore Italian Navy, 2000

V/STOL AIRCRAFT CARRIERS [CVV] *(continued)*

vehicle loading ramps, one aft and one to starboard. Two pairs of fin stabilizers will be fitted. The shaft generators can be used to power two electric motors to provide cruise and loitering speeds of up to 9 kts. Primary electrical current will be 660-V, 50-Hz a.c., stepped down to 440 V, 380 V, and 115 V by eight converters, as needed. Will have a hospital with three operating rooms and complete X-ray, CAT scan, dental, and laboratory services.
Aviation systems: The 5,900-m^2 flight deck is to be 232.6 m long by 34.50 m wide and will have a 12° ski-jump takeoff ramp to port. There will be six deck spots for EH.101 or NH-90 helicopters. The 2,500-m^2 garage/hangar is to be 134.2 m long, 21 m wide, and 6.0 m high (with an 11-m-high area for maintenance); it will hold 12 EH.101 helicopters or 8 AV-8B or U.S. Joint Strike Fighter (JSF) aircraft and will also be able to accommodate vehicles. The normal air group will be five Harriers and nine EH.101 helicopters, but the elevators and hangar are sized to accommodate the JSF. There will be two 30-ton elevators, one outboard aft to starboard and one just forward of the island, with the after elevator doubling as a vehicle ramp for operations alongside a pier.
Combat systems: An order is expected in 2002 to Alenia Marconi Systems to provide the combat systems integration. Will have SHF and UHF SATCOM terminals and will be NATO JTIDS datalink compatible. The two 76-mm guns and their radar directors may not be aboard initially, and the torpedo tubes may not be fitted, in which case only a navigational and mine-avoidance HF sonar may be fitted.

♦ 1 Giuseppe Garibaldi class — Bldr: Italcantieri, Monfalcone

	Laid down	L	In serv.
C 551 Giuseppe Garibaldi	26-3-81	4-6-83	30-9-85

Giuseppe Garibaldi (C 551)—with seven Harriers and three Sea Kings on deck
Italian Navy, 2000

Giuseppe Garibaldi (C 551) H&L Van Ginderen, 6-99

Giuseppe Garibaldi (C 551) Bernard Prézelin, 4-01

D: 10,100 tons (13,850 fl) **S:** 29.5 kts
Dim: 180.20 (173.80 wl; 162.80 pp) × 30.40 (23.80 wl) × 6.70 (8.20 over sonar)
Air group: 16 SH-3D Sea King helicopters, or 10 AV-8B+ Harrier and 1 Sea King
A: up to 8 Teseo Mk 1 and Mk 2 SSM; 2 8-round Albatros SAM syst. (48 Aspide missiles); 3 twin 40-mm 70-cal. OTOBreda Dardo AA; 2 triple 324-mm B-515 ASW TT (U.S. Mk 46 Mod. 5 torpedoes)
Electronics:
Radar: 1 SMA SPN-749(V)2 nav. (2 antennas); 1 SMA SPS-702 surf. search; 1 SPS-768 (RAN-3L) air early warning; 1 AESN SPS-774 (RAN-10S) air search; 1 Hughes SPS-52C 3-D air search; 3 AESN SPG-74 (RTN-20X) gun f.c.; 3 AESN SPG-75 (RTN-30X) missile f.c.; 1 AESN SPN-728(V)1 CCA
Sonar: Raytheon DE 1160 bow-mounted LF
TACAN: SRN-15A; Type 718 beacon
EW: Elettronica SLQ-732 Nettuno integrated receiver/jammer syst.; SwRI Seagle D/F with AS-505 antenna; 2 2-round SCLAR 105-mm decoy RL; SLQ-25 Nixie towed torpedo decoy syst.
M: 4 G.E.-Fiat LM-2500 gas turbines; 2 5-bladed props; 80,000 shp
Electric: 9,360 kw tot. (6 Wärtsilä NSD B230-12M diesel alternator sets)
Range: 7,000/20 **Crew:** 550 ship's company + 230 air group + 45 flag staff

Remarks: Ordered 20-2-78. Ship type: *Incrociatore Porta-Aeromobili.* Serves as fleet flagship. The addition of Harrier V/STOL fighters permits the ship to act in air-defense and strike roles, as well as her initial mission of ASW. Planned to be retired in 2016.
Hull systems: Steel superstructure. To permit helicopter operations in heavy weather, much attention was given to stability, and the ship has two pairs of fin stabilizers. The bow has a small "ski-jump" sheer, which is of assistance in Harrier launchings. There are five decks: the flight deck; the hangar deck, which is also the main deck; and two decks and a platform deck below the hangar deck. Thirteen watertight bulkheads divide the ship into 14 sections, and the interior can be sealed against NBC warfare. The propulsion train employs Tosi reverse/reduction gearing rather than controllable-pitch propellers. No longer carries personnel transport launches MEN 215 and MEN 216.
Aviation systems: The flight deck is 173.8 m long. There are two elevators, one forward of and one abaft the island. There are six flight-deck spaces for flight operations. The 110 × 15 × 6–m hangar can accommodate 12 Sea Kings, or 10 Sea Harriers and 1 Sea King. A Marconi Deck Approach Projector Sight (DAPS) landing aid was added during 1994.
Combat systems: Has the IPN-20 (SADOC-2) computerized data system with 13 consoles and is capable of handling 200 threat tracks simultaneously. Has Marisat HF SATCOM gear and can employ NATO Link 11, 14, and 16. The number of antiship missiles was doubled when Otomat Mk 2 launchers, stacked one atop the other, were substituted for the original Mk 1 version late in the 1980s; only four missiles, or a mix of Otomat Mk 2 and Teseo Mk 2 missiles, are normally carried, however. The AESN SPY-790 EMPAR is planned to replace the SPS-774 radar system.

ATTACK SUBMARINES [SS]

Note: Italian submarines ceased carrying their pennant numbers on the sides of their sails in 1995.

♦ 0 (+ 2 + 2) German Type 212A — Bldr: Fincantieri, Muggiano

	Laid down	L	In serv.
S	3-7-99	1-03	2-05
S	7-00	4-04	5-06

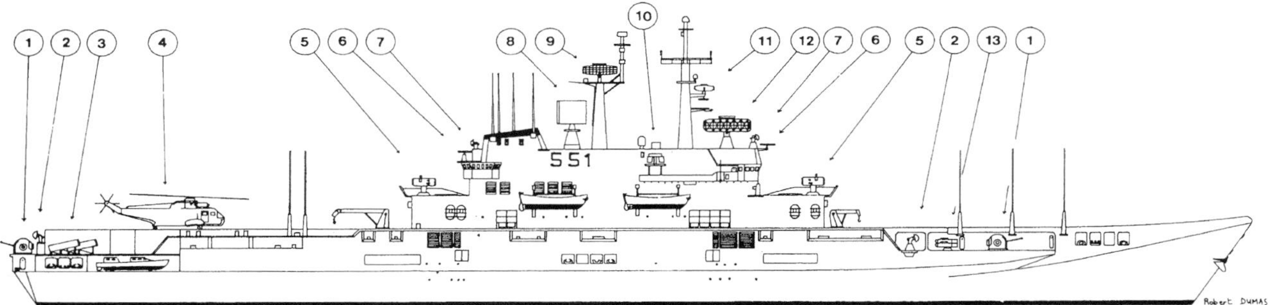

Giuseppe Garibaldi (C 551) 1. 40-mm twin Dardo AA 2. SPG-74 f.c. radar for Dardo system 3. Teseo Mk 2 SSM canisters 4. SH-3D Sea King helicopter 5. Albatros SAM system launcher 6. antennas for the SPN-749(V)2 navigational radar 7. SPG-75 illuminator for Albatros SAM system 8. SPS-52C 3-D search radar 9. SPS-774 surface/air-search radar 10. SLQ-732 Nettuno intercept array 11. SPN-703 surface-search radar 12. SPS-768 early-warning radar 13. triple 324-mm ASW TT
Drawing by Jean Moulin, from *Flottes de Combat*

ATTACK SUBMARINES [SS] *(continued)*

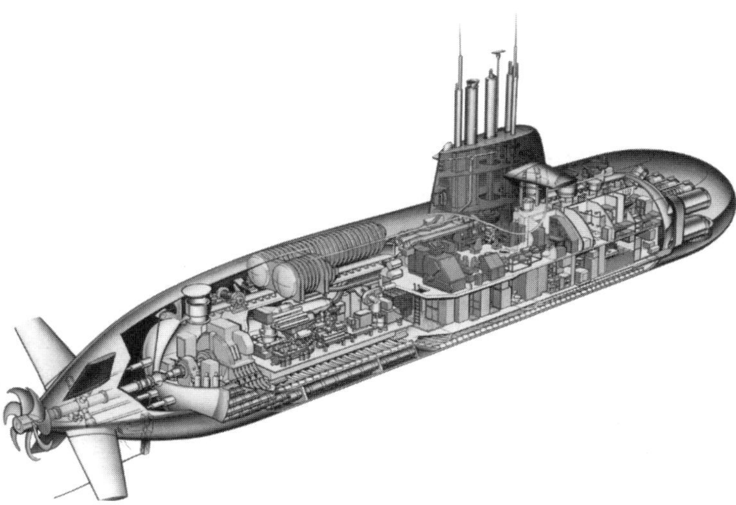

Type 212A HDW, 2000

D: 1,370 tons std., 1,460 tons surf./1,840 tons sub.
S: 12 kts surf./20 kts sub. (6–8 on fuel cells) **Dim:** 57.15 (55.90 pp) × 7.00 × 7.00
A: 6 bow 533-mm TT (14 WASS A-184 Mod. 3 wire-guided torpedoes); provision for a minelaying belt (24 tot. mines)
Electronics:
Radar: SMA BPS-704 search
Sonar: STN Atlas Elektronik DBQS-40FTC (CSU-90) suite: FAS 3-1 flank array; PRS 3-15 passive ranging; AN 5039A1 intercept; STN Atlas Elektronik/AlliedSignal FMS-52 (MOA 3070) mine-avoidance active (30 and 70 kHz); DSQS-21DG bow MF active; TAS-3 towed linear passive hydrophone array
EW: EADS FL-1800U intercept; HDW-WASS C303/S Circe torpedo decoy syst. (40 tubes)
M: diesel-electric, with 9 Siemens Polymer Electrolytic Membrane fuel cells (34 kw each) for air-independent cruising, 1 MTU 8V183 SE83 diesel generator set (1,040 kw), 1 Siemens Permasyn motor; 1 prop; 4,184 shp
Range: 8,000/8 surf.; 420/8 sub. **Crew:** 5 officers, 19 enlisted

Remarks: Being built under a late-1995 cooperative agreement between Italy and Germany; program development began in Germany in 1988. Formally ordered during 3-98 for $1.38 billion. Subassembly work on the first unit commenced during 5-99.
Hull systems: Will use a nonmagnetic Type 1.3964 austenitic steel pressure hull, 7.0 m in diameter forward, tapering via a conical section to 5.75 m abaft the control room; i.e., the boats are single-hulled forward and double-hulled aft. There will be two accommodations decks forward. The engineering plant is suspended in a raft for sound reduction, with individual engines also using soundproof mountings. The air-independent propulsion (AIP) system will employ an advanced Howaldtswerke solid-polymer, metal-hydride fuel cell system. Will have hydrazine gas generators to blow tanks for emergency surfacing. An Italian-developed ship control system will be employed. Normal maximum operating depth will be more than 200 m.
Combat systems: The combat system is to be an improved version of the Norsk Forsvarsteknolgi A/S MSI-90U, used previously in Norway's *Ula* class; it will employ the AESN-Elsag MAGICS display consoles and a dual-redundant databus. The EW system antenna will be mounted on the Carl Zeiss SERO 14 surveillance periscope with an optical rangefinder and GPS antennas. The SERO 15 attack periscope will be equipped with optical and laser rangefinders. The FL-1800U electronic intercept system will cover 2–18 GHz and will employ a pressurized USK800/4 antenna with an integrated GPS antenna. Will have a LITEF PL-41 Mk 4 inertial navigation system.

The sonar suite incorporates six passive ranging transducers, flank arrays, a 0.3- to 12-kHz bow array, a mine avoidance set, an echo sounder, two self-noise sensors, and a towed passive linear array (10–1,200 Hz). The mine avoidance sonar will operate at 30 kHz for detection and 70 kHz for classification.

The torpedo tubes will use the water-ram ejection method, using two water rams. The torpedo tube arrangement is asymmetrical, with two rows of three tubes, placing four tubes to port of the centerline.

♦ 2 Primo Longobardo class — Bldr: Italcantieri, Monfalcone

	Laid down	L	In serv.
S 524 Primo Longobardo	19-12-91	20-6-92	14-12-93
S 525 Gianfranco Gazzana Priaroggia	12-11-92	26-6-93	12-4-95

Gianfranco Gazzana Priaroggia (S 525) Carlo Martinelli, 2-99

D: 1,653 tons surf./1,862 tons sub. **S:** 11 kts surf./19 kts sub.
Dim: 66.35 (65.70 pp) × 6.83 × 6.00
A: 6 bow 533-mm TT (12 WASS A-184 Mod. 3 wire-guided torpedoes)
Electronics:
Radar: 1 SMA BPS-704 nav.
Sonar: S 524: AESN IPD-70/S active (200 Hz–7.5 kHz)/passive; AESN MD 100S passive ranging flank array; Velox M5 sonar intercept—S 525: STN Atlas Elektronik ISUS 90-20 integrated suite
EW: Elettronica BLD-727 Thetis intercept
M: diesel-electric: 3 Wärtsilä NSD A210-16NM diesel alternator sets (895 kw each), 1 ABB electric motor; 1 7-bladed prop; 4,270 shp (3,000 sust.)
Range: 11,000/11 surf.; 5,100/5 snorkel; 240/4.5 sub. **Fuel:** . . . tons
Endurance: 45 days **Crew:** 7 officers, 43 enlisted

Remarks: Ordered 28-7-88. The design is a further development of the two preceding classes, employing improved hydrodynamic form. S 525 commenced a modernization refit at Muggiano late in 10-99 for completion in 2001; the refit of S 524 is to follow that of *Salvatore Pelosi* (S 522).
Hull systems: The pressure hull has a single watertight bulkhead, and the boats carry more fuel than their predecessors. Maximum operating depth is 300 m, with 600-m crush depth. The casing above the pressure hull is higher than on the two preceding classes, and the sail is larger. Have SEPA 8518 autopilot ship controls. During modernizations, are receiving anechoic hull coatings and Litton Mk 39 Mod. 3C and Mk 39 Mod. 3A ring-laser gyros.
Combat systems: As completed, had the SMA SACTIS BSN-716 combat system with NATO Link 11 receiving capability; combat systems in both were being updated during modernization refits with a German STN Atlas Elektronik ISUS 90-20 integrated sonar and combat data system suite under a 1998 contract with Fincantieri. The new German sonar system has a bow-conformal passive hydrophone array, an active/passive cylindrical bow array, and a passive ranging array; the new weapons system permits the control of four wire-guided torpedoes simultaneously. Navigation systems include Litton PL-41 inertial, Ferranti autopilot, Transit satellite navigation receiver, and Omega radio navigation receiver. Have U.S. Kollmorgen periscopes: S76 Model 322 attack with laser rangefinder and ESM array, and S76 Model 323 search with radar rangefinder and ESM antennas. Underwater telephone operates at 15 kHz. Can employ U.S. UGM-84 Sub-Harpoon antiship missiles, but none have been procured.

♦ 2 Salvatore Pelosi class — Bldr: Fincantieri, Monfalcone

	Laid down	L	In serv.
S 522 Salvatore Pelosi	23-7-86	29-11-86	14-7-88
S 523 Giuliano Prini	30-7-87	12-12-87	11-11-89

Giuliano Prini (S 523) Mike Welsford, 9-99

Salvatore Pelosi (S 522) Paul C. Clift, 5-98

D: 1,476 tons surf./1,662 tons sub.
S: 11 kts surf./12 kts snorkel/19 kts sub. **Dim:** 64.36 × 6.83 × 5.66
A: 6 bow 533-mm TT (12 WASS A-184 wire-guided torpedoes)
Electronics:
Radar: 1 SMA BPS-704 nav.
Sonar: AESN IPD-70/S active (200 Hz–7.5 kHz)/passive; AESN MD 100S passive ranging flank array; Velox M5 sonar intercept
EW: Elettronica BLD-727 intercept
M: 3 Wärtsilä NSD A210-16NM diesel generator sets (895 kw each), 1 twin Marelli 3,140-kw motor (2,400 kw sust.); 1 7-bladed prop; 4,270 shp max. (at 233 rpm)
Range: 6,150/11 surf.; 2,500/12 snorkel; 250/4 sub. **Fuel:** 144 tons
Endurance: 45 days **Crew:** 7 officers, 43 enlisted

ATTACK SUBMARINES [SS] *(continued)*

Remarks: Ordered 7-3-83. An improved version of the *Nazario Sauro* class, with 0.5 m length added amidships and one watertight bulkhead added to the pressure hull. Are to be updated with a German STN Atlas Elektronik ISUS 90-20 integrated sonar and combat data system suite under a 1998 contract with Fincantieri; they are also to receive improved silencing features and improved ship control systems. S 522 was to begin a refit at Muggiano on completion of work on S 525 in 2001, while S 523 is to be refitted at the Taranto Naval Shipyard.
Hull systems: Do not have a "crash-dive" ballast tank as in the *Sauro* class. Pressure hull is fabricated of U.S. HY-80 steel. Maximum operating depth is 300 m, collapse depth 600 m. Have two 148-cell batteries with 6,500 amp-hr. During modernization, are having SEPA 8518 autopilots and Litton Mk 39 Mod. 3A and Mk 39 Mod. 3C gyros added, and the hulls are having a revised upper casing and anechoic coatings fitted.
Combat systems: Prior to modernization, had an SMA BSN-716(V)2 SACTIS combat data-weapons control system with NATO Link 11 receive-only capability. The new German sonar system will have a bow-conformal passive hydrophone array, an active/passive cylindrical bow array, and a passive ranging array; it will permit the control of four wire-guided torpedoes simultaneously. Have one each Kollmorgen S76 Model 322 and 323 periscopes (one with laser rangefinder, one with ranging radar, both with ESM antennas). Have 15-kHz active ranging/underwater telephone transducers at the bow. Navigation systems include Litton PL-41 inertial, Ferranti autopilot, Transit satellite navigation receiver, and Omega radio navigation receiver. Have the capability to launch U.S. Sub-Harpoon SSMs, but missiles have not been acquired.

♦ 3 Nazario Sauro class

Bldr: Italcantieri, Monfalcone (S 519: C.R.D.A., Monfalcone)

	Laid down	L	In serv.
S 519 Carlo Fecia di Cossato	15-7-76	16-11-77	1-3-80
S 520 Leonardo da Vinci	1-7-76	20-10-79	6-11-82
S 521 Guglielmo Marconi	23-10-79	20-9-80	16-10-82

Guglielmo Marconi (S 521) Luciano Grazioli, 5-01

Guglielmo Marconi (S 521) Luciano Grazioli, 5-01

D: 1,442 tons surf./1,637 tons sub. **S:** 11 kts surf./12 kts snorkel/19.3 kts sub.
Dim: 63.85 × 6.83 × 5.70 (12.38 keel to top of sail)
A: 6 bow 533-mm Type B.512 TT (12 WASS A-184 wire-guided torpedoes)
Electronics:
Radar: 1 SMA BPS-704 nav.
Sonar: AESN IPD-70/S active (200 Hz–7.5 kHz)/passive; AESN MD 100S passive ranging flank array; Velox M5 sonar intercept
EW: Elettronica BLD-727 intercept
M: diesel-electric: 3 Wärtsilä NSD A210-16NM generator sets (895 kw each), 1 twin 3,140-kw motor (2,400 kw sust.); 1 7-bladed prop; 4,270 shp (3,000 sust.)
Range: 6,150/11 surf.; 2,500/12 snorkel; 19.3/19.3, 250/4 sub.
Fuel: 144 tons **Endurance:** 35 days **Crew:** 7 officers, 42 enlisted

Remarks: Two authorized in 1972; a second pair ordered 12-2-76. S 519 began a midlife refit in 1990 to improve habitability and replace batteries; S 521 followed in 1992 and S 520 in 1993–95.
Disposals: *Nazario Sauro* (S 518), used in recent years for systems trials, was decommissioned during 6-01.
Hull systems: Normal diving depth is 250 m, 300 m maximum; crush depth is 600 m. Batteries: two 148-cell, 6,000-amp-hr (1-hr rate). S 521 has a smaller "crash-dive" ballast tank than the others.
Combat systems: The original SISU-1 fire-control system has been replaced by the SMA SACTIS BSN-716(V)1, and they are planned to be refitted with the STN Atlas Elektronik ISUS 90 combat data system. Have a Kollmorgen Model 76 attack periscope and a search periscope.

HELICOPTER-CARRYING GUIDED-MISSILE CRUISERS [CHG]

♦ 1 Vittorio Veneto class

	Bldr	Laid down	L	In serv.
C 550 Vittorio Veneto	CNR, Castellammare	10-6-65	5-2-67	12-7-69

Vittorio Veneto (C 550) Italian Navy, 2000

Vittorio Veneto (C 550) Cem D. Yaylali, 9-01

D: 8,130 tons (9,500 fl) **S:** 30.5 kts
Dim: 179.60 (170.61 pp) × 19.42 (hull) × 5.50 (7.90 max.)
Air group: 6 AB-212 ASW helicopters
A: 1 twin-rail Mk 20 Mod. 7 Aster launch syst. (20 ASROC ASW and 40 Standard SM-1 ER SAM); Teseo Mk 1 and Mk 2 SSM; 8 single 76-mm 62-cal. OTOBreda Compact DP; 3 twin 40-mm 70-cal. OTOBreda Dardo AA; 2 triple 324-mm ASW TT
Electronics:
Radar: 1 SMA SPN-748 nav.; 1 SMA SPS-702 surf. search; 1 AESN SPS-768 (RAN-3L) early warning; 1 Hughes SPS-52C 3-D air search; 2 Sperry-RCA SPG-55C missile f.c.; 4 AESN SPG-70 (RTN-10X) gun f.c.; 2 AESN SPG-74 (RTN-20X) gun f.c.
Sonar: SQS-23G hull-mounted (5–7 kHz)
TACAN: SRN-15A
EW: SLR-4 intercept; 3 SLQ-B jammers; 2 SLQ-C jammers; VHFD/F; MFD/F; 2 20-round OTOBreda SCLAR decoy RL; SLQ-25 Nixie towed torpedo decoy syst.
M: 2 sets Tosi geared steam turbines; 2 props; 73,000 shp
Boilers: 4 Foster-Wheeler; 43 kg/cm^2, 450° C **Electric:** 6,800 kw tot.
Range: 3,000/28; 6,000/20 **Fuel:** 1,200 tons **Crew:** 53 officers, 504 enlisted

Remarks: Has been replaced as fleet flagship by *Giuseppe Garibaldi.* Ran aground 21-4-97 at Vlore, Albania, but was pulled off two days later; repairs took about six months. Was to be retired during 2000, but service has been extended to around 2005. Based at Taranto.
Hull systems: The 40 × 18.5–m flight deck is served from a hangar immediately below by two 18 × 5.3–m elevators. The 27.5 × 15.3–m hangar is two decks in depth and would not accommodate the new NH-90 helicopter. Two sets of antirolling fin stabilizers are fitted. Listed beam does not include sponsons outboard of the SCLAR launchers forward, Teseo launchers amidships, or flight deck aft.
Combat systems: Has the SADOC-1 combat data system, a U.S. Mk 76 SAM control system, four Argo fire-control systems for the 76-mm guns, and two Dardo control systems for the 40-mm guns. The U.S. Norden Systems SYS-1(V)2 sensor data fusion system is installed. The Aster (ASROC/Terrier) missile launch system can launch either ASROC ASW missiles or Standard SM-1 ER SAMs and has a total capacity of 60 missiles on three horizontal magazine drums. Has very extensive, stabilized electronic intercept arrays. The 76-mm guns are not of the modern Compact model.

HELICOPTER-CARRYING GUIDED-MISSILE CRUISERS [CHG] *(continued)*

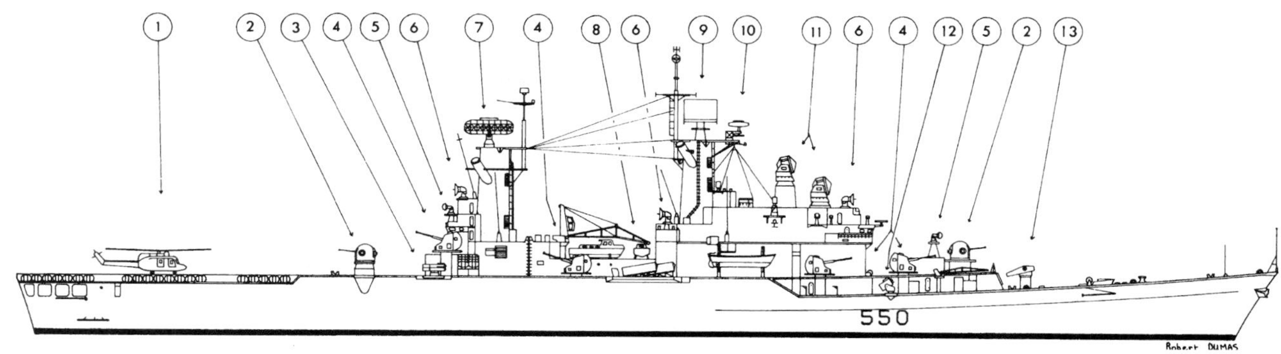

Vittorio Veneto (C 550) 1. AB-212 helicopter 2. twin 40-mm Dardo AA mount 3. triple 324-mm ASW TT 4. 76-mm OTOBreda Compact DP gun 5. SPG-74 f.c. radar for 40-mm Dardo system 6. SPG-70 f.c. radar for 76-mm guns 7. SPS-768 early-warning radar 8. Teseo Mk 2 antiship missile canisters 9. SPS-52C 3-D air-search radar 10. SPS-702 surface/air-search radar 11. SPG-55C radar-illuminators for Standard SM-1 SAM system 12. SCLAR decoy RL 13. Mk 20 Aster launcher for Standard SM-1 SAMs and ASROC ASW missiles
Drawing by Robert Dumas, from *Flottes de Combat*

GUIDED-MISSILE DESTROYERS [DDG]

♦ 0 (+ 2) Project Horizon program
Bldr: Fincantieri, Riva Trigoso

	Laid down	L	In serv.
D 570	...	...	2007
D 571	...	...	2009

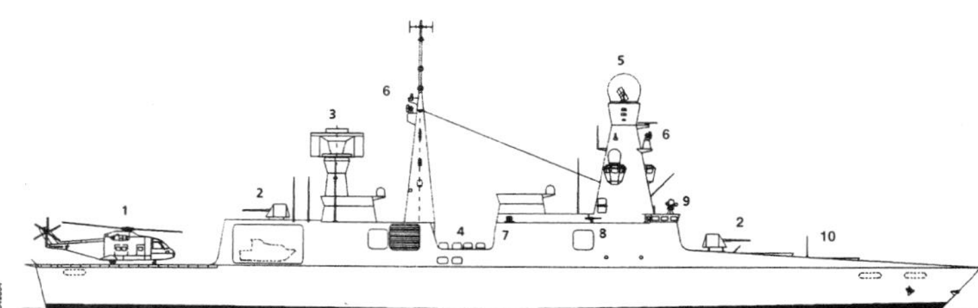

Horizon-class 1. EH.101 Merlin helicopter 2. 76-mm OTOBreda SuperRapid DP gun 3. RAN-40S early-warning radar 4. eight Teseo Mk 2 antiship missiles 5. SPY-790 EMPAR target designation/tracking/illumination radar 6. SPG-76 76-mm gun f.c. 7. decoy RL 8. 25-mm AA 9. SPS-791 RASS surface-search radar 10. Sylver A50 vertical-launch missile cell groups
Drawing by Maurizio Brescia

Italian Navy Project Horizon configuration—artist's rendering
Italian Navy, 2000

Italian Navy Project Horizon configuration study—computer rendering
Italian Navy, 2000

D: 5,800 tons (6,700 fl) **S:** 29 kts
Dim: 150.60 (141.80 wl) × 20.40 (18.10 wl) × 5.40 (mean hull)
A: 8 Teseo Mk 2 SSM; 6 8-cell Sylver A50 SAM launch groups (32 Aster-30 and 16 Aster-15 missiles); 3 single 76-mm 62-cal. OTOBreda SuperRapid DP; 2 single 25-mm 87-cal. Oerlikon-OTOBreda KBA AA; 4 ASW torpedo launchers (MU-90 Impact torpedoes); 1 EH.101 or NH-90 helicopter

Electronics:
Radar: 1 Gem . . . ARPA nav.; 1 AESN SPS-791 RASS surf. search; 1 . . . helicopter flight control; 1 AESN SPY-790 EMPAR target desig./tracking; 1 AESN RAN-40S (S1850M) early warning; 3 AESN SPG-76 (RTN-30X/I) gun f.c.
Sonar: Thales TMS 4110CL hull-mounted LF
EW: Elettronica JANEWS intercept; 2 OTOBreda SCLAR-H 20-round decoy RL; SLAT torpedo countermeasures syst.
E/O: SAGEM Vampir IR detection and tracking
M: CODAG: 2 G.E.-Fiat LM-2500 gas turbines, 2 SEMT-Pielstick or Wärtsilä . . . . . . diesels (5,800 bhp each), geared drive; 2 props; 62,560 shp max.—bow-thruster
Range: 7,000/18; 3,500/25 **Endurance:** 45 days
Crew: 190 tot. (accomm. for 222)

Remarks: Are the result of a 12-3-91 agreement made with France and the U.K. to design a ship acceptable to all three navies. An international joint-venture corporation, Horizon Ltd., was established 21-2-95 by the three prime contractors, GEC-Marconi, DCN International, and Orizzonte SpA, to build at least the initial units of the class for the three partner countries. Italy originally planned to buy six ships, then four, to replace the *Audace*-class destroyers and the two already-stricken *Andrea Doria*–class cruisers. The program was reduced to two during 12-93 because of the expense incurred in the purchase of the ex-Iraqi *Lupo*-class frigates. The British pullout from the program on 21-4-99 put the program in temporary limbo, but France and Italy agreed 7-9-99 to continue and the first two were ordered 14-11-01. The two deleted units may later be restored, with the first to complete in 2013 and the second in 2016, both equipped for ballistic-missile-defense duties. France is building two similar ships as the *Forbin* class.
Hull systems: Plans to incorporate a state-of-the-art, integrated propulsion/electrical generation plant have been dropped.
Combat systems: The combat data system is being developed by Alenia and Datamat. The ships are to have an integrated communications system and will be compatible with NATO Improved Link 11, Link 14, and Link 16. They were to have SHF and possibly EHF SATCOM systems. The helicopter is to be used for ASW and for attacking surface ships with missiles. The 76-mm mounts will be installed two abreast forward and one centerline atop the helicopter hangar to act as the point-defense system.

♦ 2 Luigi Durand de la Penne class
Bldr: Fincantieri, Riva Trigoso (fitted out at Muggiano)

	Laid down	L	Del.	In serv.
D 560 Luigi Durand de la Penne (ex-*Animoso*)	26-7-86	29-10-89	18-3-93	11-12-93
D 561 Francesco Mimbelli (ex-*Ardimentoso*)	3-12-89	13-4-91	19-10-93	11-12-93

Luigi Durand de la Penne (D 560) Findler & Winter, 2-01

D: 4,500 tons (5,400 fl) **S:** 31.5 kts (21 on diesels)
Dim: 147.70 (135.60 pp) × 16.10 (15.00 wl) × 5.10 (hull; 6.80 over sonar; 7.10 over props)
A: 8 Teseo Mk 1 and Mk 2 SSM; 1 U.S. Mk 13 Mod. 4 SAM launch syst. (40 Standard SM-1 MR missiles); 1 8-round Albatros point-defense SAM syst. (16 Aspide missiles); 1 127-mm 54-cal. OTOBreda DP; 3 single 76-mm 62-cal. OTOBreda SuperRapid DP; 2 triple 324-mm B-515 ASW TT; 2 AB-212 helicopters

GUIDED-MISSILE DESTROYERS [DDG] *(continued)*

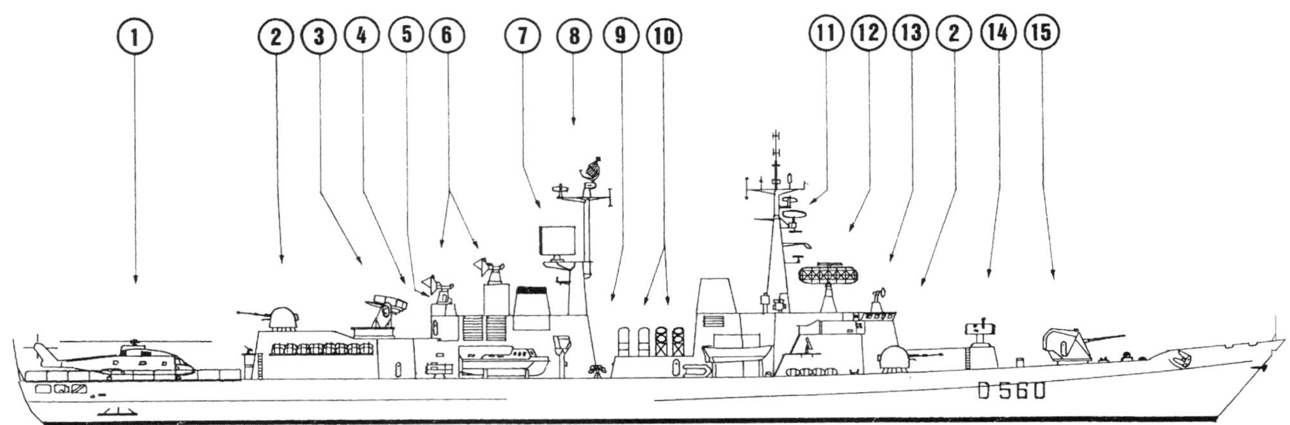

Luigi Durand de la Penne (D 560) 1. EH.101 helicopter 2. 76-mm OTOBreda SuperRapid DP gun 3. Mk 13 Mod. 4 SAM system launcher 4. triple 324-mm ASW TT 5. SPG-76 gun f.c. radars 6. SPG-51D SAM target illuminators 7. SPS-52C 3-D radar 8. SPS-774 surface/air-search radar 9. Sagaie decoy RL 10. Teseo Mk 2 antiship missiles 11. SPS-702 surface-search radar 12. SPS-768 early-warning radar 13. SPG-76 radar gun f.c. director 14. Albatros SAM system launcher 15. 127-mm OTOBreda DP gun
Drawing by Robert Dumas, from *Flottes de Combat*

Francesco Mimbelli (D 561) H&L Van Ginderen, 6-00

Luigi Durand de la Penne (D 560) Italian Navy, 2000

Francesco Mimbelli (D 561)—note slot in stern for VDS housing
H&L Van Ginderen, 9-99

Electronics:

Radar: 1 Gem SPN-748 nav.; 1 SMA SPN-703 nav.; 1 SMA SPS-702 surf. search; 1 AESN SPS-774 (RAN-10S) surf./air search; 1 AESN SPS-768 (RAN-3L) early warning; 1 Hughes SPS-52C 3-D air search; 2 Raytheon SPG-51D SAM f.c.; 4 AESN SPG-76 (RTN-30X) missile and gun f.c.

Sonar: AESN-Raytheon DE 1164LF hull-mounted (3.5 kHz); AESN-Raytheon DE 1167LF integrated VDS (7.5 kHz)

TACAN: SRN-15A

EW: Elettronica SLQ-732 Nettuno integrated intercept; Elettronica SLC 705 jammers; Rohde & Schwarz . . . COMINT intercept; 2 6-round Matra Défense Sagaie decoy RL; SLQ-25 Nixie towed acoustic torpedo decoy syst.

M: CODOG: 2 G.E.-Fiat LM-2500 gas turbines (27,500 shp each); 2 Wärtsilä NSD BL230-20DVM diesels (6,300 bhp each); 2 5-bladed CP props
Electric: . . . **Range:** 7,000/18 (diesel) **Fuel:** . . .
Crew: 32 officers, 345 enlisted (accomm. for 35 officers, 365 enlisted)

Remarks: Ordered 9-3-86. Names changed 10-6-92 to honor World War II heroes. A planned two additional units were abandoned in favor of Italian participation in the Anglo-French Horizon program.
Hull systems: Steel superstructure, with Mirex (Kevlar-derivative) armor. Two sets of fin stabilizers are fitted. Have a twin helicopter hangar, 18.5 m long. The flight deck is 24.0 × 13.0 m and is equipped with the Italian Navy's first haul-down and deck-transit system; it can accept Sea King and EH.101 helicopters. Have U.S. Prairie/Masker air-blowing, noise-masking system and flexibly mounted auxiliary engineering systems to reduce emitted noise below the waterline.
Combat systems: Have the SADOC-2 (IPN-20) combat data/weapons control system, with 10 operator consoles, two CDG-3032 mainframe computers, and NDC-160 processors. Four NA-30 weapons-control systems handle the Albatros SAM system and the four guns; the U.S. Mk 74 control system is fitted for the Standard missiles. Standard SM-2 Block IIIA missiles may be substituted for the aging SM-1 missiles. The U.S. Norden Systems SYS-1(V)2 sensor data fusion system is installed. The 127-mm guns come from the "B" positions of the modernized *Audace* and *Ardito*. The 76-mm SuperRapid guns are intended to perform as a close-in defense against sea-skimming missiles. Milas antisubmarine missiles will be substituted for some of the Teseo antiship missiles when Milas becomes operational after 2002 (but only 12 Milas are to be procured for the two ships). The Alenia Marconi SPY-790 EMPAR is planned to replace the SPS-774 radar system.

♦ 2 Audace class

	Bldr	Laid down	L	In serv.
D 550 Ardito	Nav. Mec. Castellammare	19-7-68	27-11-71	5-12-73
D 551 Audace	C.N. del Tirreno, Riva Trigoso	27-4-68	2-10-71	16-11-72

Audace (D 551)—note radomes for SHF SATCOM antennas added port and starboard atop the bridge superstructure, with Marisat SATCOM radome centerline
Bernard Prézelin, 5-01

D: 3,600 tons light; 3,950 tons std. (4,554 fl) **S:** 33 kts
Dim: 140.70 × 14.65 × 4.60 (hull; 6.10 max.)
A: 8 Teseo Mk 1 and Mk 2 SSM; 1 Mk 13 Mod. 4 SAM launch syst. (40 Standard SM-1 MR missiles); 1 8-round Albatros SAM syst. (. . . Aspide missiles); 1 127-mm 54-cal. OTOBreda Compact DP; 4 single 76-mm 62-cal. OTOBreda SuperRapid DP; 2 triple 324-mm Mk 32 Mod. 5 ASW TT; 2 AB-212 ASW helicopters

GUIDED-MISSILE DESTROYERS [DDG] *(continued)*

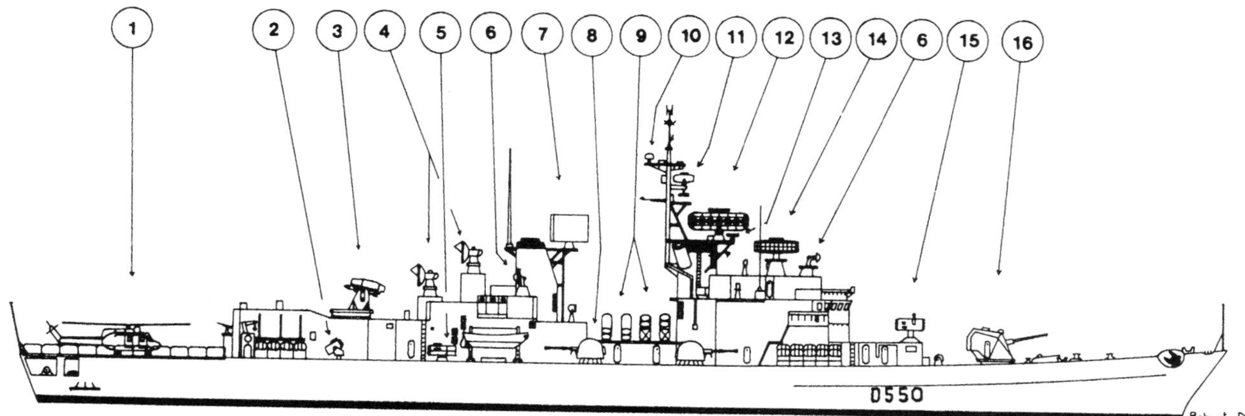

Ardito (D 550) 1. AB-212 helicopter 2. SCLAR decoy launcher 3. Mk 13 Mod. 4 launcher for Standard SM-1 SAMs 4. SPG-51C illuminators for Standard SM-1 SAMs 5. triple 324-mm ASW TT 6. SPG-76 f.c. radar for 76-mm guns 7. SPS-52C 3-D radar 8. 76-mm OTOBreda SuperRapid DP guns 9. Teseo Mk 2 antiship missile canisters 10. SRN-15A TACAN 11. SPQ-2D surface-search radar 12. SPS-768 early-warning radar 13. SPN-748 navigational radar 14. SPS-774 surface/air-search radar 15. Albatros launcher for Aspide SAMs 16. 127-mm OTOBreda DP gun

Drawing by Robert Dumas, from *Flottes de Combat*

Audace (D 551) Bernard Prézelin, 5-01

Ardito (D 550) Camil Busquets i Vilanova, 3-01

Electronics:
Radar: 1 SMA SPN-748 nav.; 1 SMA SPQ-2D surf./air search; 1 AESN SPS-774 (RAN-10S) surf./air search; 1 AESN SPS-768(V)3 (RAN-3L) early warning; 1 Hughes SPS-52C 3-D air search; 2 Raytheon SPG-51C missile f.c.; 3 AESN SPG-76 (RTN-30X Dardo-E) f.c.
Sonar: CWE-610A hull-mounted MF
TACAN: SRN-15A
EW: SLR-4 intercept; 3 SLQ-B jammers; 2 SLQ-C jammers; 2 20-round SCLAR decoy RL; SLQ-25 Nixie towed torpedo decoy syst.

M: 2 sets geared steam turbines; 2 props; 73,000 shp
Boilers: 4 Foster-Wheeler; 43 kg/cm^2, 450° C **Electric:** 5,200 kw tot.
Range: 4,000/25 **Crew:** 30 officers, 350 enlisted

Remarks: D 551 is to be retired in 2005, D 550 in 2007. Have two pairs of fin stabilizers.

Combat systems: The SPS-768 (RAN-20S) air-search radar replaced SPS-12 in D 550 and RAN-3 in D 551. D 550 completed a modernization refit during 3-88 with an Albatros SAM launcher in place of the "B" 127-mm gun, upgraded SuperRapid 76-mm guns, the Dardo-E f.c.s. replacing the original Argo system, and four aft-launching wire-guided 533-mm torpedo tubes deleted at the stern; in addition, an SPS-774 (RAN-10S) radar was added for target acquisition for the Albatros system's Aspide missiles, other radars and the EW system were upgraded, and Teseo SSM launch positions were added amidships between the funnels. The overall combat data system is now SADOC-2 (IPN-20). The U.S. Norden Systems SYS-1(V)2 sensor data fusion system was installed, as were the Mk 13 Mod. 5 weapons-direction system and Mk 74 Mod. 13 missile fire-control system. D 551 completed a similar modernization in 1991.

GUIDED-MISSILE FRIGATES [FFG]

Note: The Italian Navy hopes to construct up to eight FNG (Frigate, New Generation) general-purpose guided-missile frigates of about 4,000 tons full load displacement to replace the *Maestrale* and *Lupo* classes, possibly employing elements of the Horizon design but emphasizing an ASW capability. The ships would carry the Milas antisubmarine missile. The first unit would enter service around 2010.

FRIGATES [FF]

♦ **4 Artigliere class**
Bldr: Fincantieri, Ancona (F 585: Fincantieri, Riva Trigoso)

	Laid down	L	Completed	Del.	In serv.
F 582 Artigliere (ex-*Hitteen,* F 14)	31-3-82	27-7-83	3-85	28-10-94	5-7-96
F 583 Aviere (ex-*Thi Qar,* F 15)	9-82	19-12-84	1985	4-1-95	5-7-96
F 584 Bersagliere (ex-*Al Yarmouk,* F 17)	12-3-84	20-6-85	4-87	20-3-96	5-7-96
F 585 Granatiere (ex-*Al Qadissiya,* F 16)	15-4-83	31-3-84	1986	8-11-95	5-7-96

Bersagliere (F 584)—with 127-mm OTOBreda 127/54LW gunmount forward for trials Steve Zaloga, 3-01

Granatiere (F 585) Maurizio Brescia, 2001

D: 2,213 tons (2,525 fl) **S:** 35 kts (20.5 diesel)
Dim: 113.2 (106.0 pp) × 11.98 × 3.84
A: 8 Teseo Mk 1 and Mk 2 SSM; 1 8-round Albatros SAM syst. (Aspide missiles; no reloads); 1 127-mm 54-cal. OTOBreda DP; 2 twin 40-mm 70-cal. OTOBreda Dardo AA; 2 single 20-mm 70-cal. Mk 10 Oerlikon AA; 1 AB-212 helicopter
Electronics:
Radar: 1 SMA SPN-703 nav.; 1 AESN SPQ-712 (RAN-12L/X) surf. search; 1 AESN SPS-774 (RAN-10S) air search; 1 AESN SPG-73 (RTN-10X) f.c.; 2 AESN SPG-74 (RTN-20X) f.c.
Sonar: removed
EW: AESN SLQ-747 (INS-3M) integrated suite; 2 20-round SCLAR decoy RL; SLQ-25 Nixie towed acoustic torpedo decoy syst.

FRIGATES [FF] *(continued)*

Aviere (F 583) Carlo Martinelli, 4-99

Artigliere (F 582) ANBw/FAFIO, 1-99

M: CODOG: 2 G.E.-Fiat LM-2500 gas turbines (25,000 shp each); 2 Wärtsilä NSD A230-20M diesels (3,900 bhp each); 2 CP props
Electric: 3,120 kw tot. (4 × 780-kw Wärtsilä NSD diesel-driven sets)
Range: 900/35 on gas turbines; 3,450/20.5, 5,300/16 on diesels
Crew: 17 officers, 170 enlisted

Remarks: Ordered by Iraq during 2-81. The Italian Council of Ministers decided in 1-92 to incorporate them into the Italian Navy as "Fleet Patrol Ships" *(Pattugliatori),* with the ASW systems removed; funding of $375 million to purchase and refit the ships was finally provided by the Italian Senate 16-7-93. All were commissioned 8-7-96 at La Spezia, where they are assigned to the First Division; two are home-ported at Augusta and two at Brindisi.
Hull systems: Have enhanced air-conditioning systems and refrigeration equipment over the earlier *Lupos.* Fin stabilizers are fitted. The hangar, as completed for Italian service, is telescoping.
Combat systems: Have the AESN IPN-10 Mini-SADOC combat data system with NATO Link 11 capability; there are two weapons-designation plotting tables and four display consoles. The NA-21 control system is fitted for the Albatros SAM system. The 127-mm gun and SAM were originally controlled by two Elsag Mk 10 Mod. 0 systems with NA-10 radar directors, and the 40-mm fire control was provided by two Dardo systems. The original German Atlas ASO-4-2-V hull mounted sonar and two sets of ASW torpedo tubes were removed during conversion. The AB-212 helicopters lack a dipping sonar but are fitted with updated APS-707 radar, RQH-5 EW suites, and TG-2 over-the-horizon target designation capability for the ships' Teseo missiles. F 584 carries the low-observable OTOBreda 127-mm 54-cal. lightweight gunmount for trials.

♦ 8 Maestrale class Bldr: CNR, Riva Trigoso (F 571: CNR, Muggiano)

	Laid down	L	In serv.
F 570 Maestrale	8-3-78	2-2-81	7-3-82
F 571 Grecale	21-3-79	12-9-81	5-2-83
F 572 Libeccio	1-8-79	7-9-81	5-2-83
F 573 Scirocco	26-2-80	17-4-82	20-9-83
F 574 Aliseo	26-2-80	29-10-82	20-9-83
F 575 Euro	15-4-81	25-3-83	7-4-84
F 576 Espero	1-8-82	19-11-83	4-5-85
F 577 Zeffiro	15-3-83	19-5-84	4-5-85

Espero (F 576) Jim Sanderson, 2001

Aliseo (F 574) Bernard Prézelin, 5-01

Maestrale (F 570) Bernard Prézelin, 6-00

Libeccio (F 572) Maurizio Brescia, 6-00

Euro (F 575) Douglas A. Cromby, 4-00

FRIGATES [FF] *(continued)*

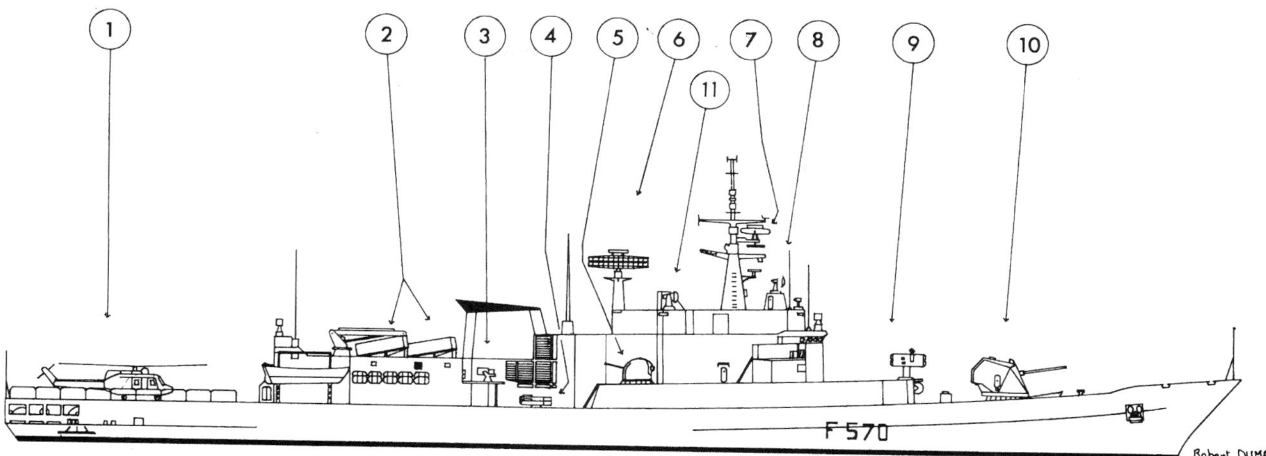

Maestrale (F 570) 1. AB-212 helicopter 2. Teseo Mk 2 antiship missile canisters 3. SCLAR decoy RL 4. triple 324-mm ASW TT 5. twin 40-mm Dardo AA 6. SPS-774 surface/air-search radar 7. SPS-702 surface-search radar 8. SPG-75 f.c. radar for 127-mm gun 9. Albatros launcher for Aspide SAMs 10. 127-mm OTOBreda DP gun 11. SPG-74 f.c. radars for 40-mm Dardo gunmounts
Drawing by Robert Dumas, from *Flottes de Combat*

D: 2,700 tons light (3,060 normal; 3,200 fl) **S:** 33 kts (21 max. on diesels)
Dim: 122.73 (116.40 pp) × 12.88 × 4.20 (hull; 5.95 max.)
A: 4 Teseo Mk 1 and Mk 2 SSM; 1 8-round Albatros SAM syst. (24 Aspide missiles); 1 127-mm 54-cal. OTOBreda DP; 2 twin 40-mm 70-cal. OTOBreda Dardo AA; 2 fixed 533-mm ASW TT (WASS A-184 wire-guided torpedoes); 2 triple 324-mm Mk 32 Mod. 9 ASW TT (U.S. Mk 46 Mod. 5 torpedoes); 2 AB-212 ASW helicopters
Electronics:
Radar: 1 SMA SPN-703 nav.; 1 SMA SPS-702 surf. search; 1 AESN SPS-774 (RAN-10S) surf./air search; 1 AESN SPG-75 (RTN-30X for NA-30A f.c.s.); 2 AESN SPG-74 (RTN-20X for Dardo f.c.s.)
Sonar: Raytheon DE 1164 hull-mounted MF; Raytheon DE 1164 VDS
EW: Elettronica SLR-4 Newton intercept with CO-NEWS comms intercept; 2 SLQ-D jammers; 2 20-round SCLAR (F 571: Matra Défense Dagaie) decoy RL; SLQ-25 Nixie towed torpedo decoy syst.
M: CODOG: 2 G.E.-Fiat LM-2500 gas turbines (25,000 shp each); 2 Wärtsilä NSD B230-20DVM diesels (5,073 bhp each); 2 CP props
Electric: 3,120 kw tot. (4 × 780-kw diesel-driven sets)
Range: 1,500/30; 3,800/22; 6,000/15 **Endurance:** 90 days
Crew: 24 officers, 208 enlisted

Remarks: F 570–F 575 were ordered during 12-76, and F 576 and F 577 during 10-80. The design is an enlarged version of the Lupo, with better seaworthiness and hangar space for two helicopters at the expense of four antiship missiles and about 2.5 kts maximum speed. They are not planned to receive a midlife modernization. F 570 is to be retired in 2011, F 571–574 in 2013, F 575 in 2014, and the others in 2015.
Hull systems: Helicopter deck is 12 × 27 m. Have fin stabilizers and the U.S. Prairie/Masker air-bubbler noise-suppression system.
Combat systems: Have the SADOC-2 (IPN-20) computerized data system. There is a Galileo OG-30 optronic backup director to the NA-30A gun f.c.s. and two MM 59 optical backup directors for the 40-mm guns. The DE 1164 sonar is a VDS version of DE 1160 and operates on the same frequencies; the two sonar systems employ identical transducers, and an HF adjunct sonar has been fitted in the hull dome to detect moored mines. Plans call for modifying all to carry the Milas antisubmarine missile—to replace some or all of the Teseo SSMs. Were to receive two French Matra Défense Dagaie decoy launching systems, beginning in 1991 with F 571, but no further installations have occurred.

♦ 4 Lupo class   Bldr: CNR, Riva Trigoso (F 567; CNR, Muggiano)

	Laid down	L	In serv.
F 564 Lupo	8-10-74	29-7-76	20-9-77
F 565 Sagittario	4-2-76	22-6-77	18-11-78
F 566 Perseo	28-2-77	8-7-78	1-3-80
F 567 Orsa	1-8-77	1-3-79	1-3-80

Sagittario (F 565) 8-00

Perseo (F 566)—the white radome for the SPS-702 CORA radar antenna atop the bridge easily distinguishes ships of the *Lupo* class from the larger *Maestrale*-class frigates
H&L Van Ginderen, 6-99

Orsa (F 567)—with telescoping hangar extended H&L Van Ginderen, 6-97

D: 2,208 tons (2,340 on trials; 2,525 fl)
S: 35.23 kts (*Lupo* on trials; 32 at 80% power; 20.3 on 2 diesels)
Dim: 113.55 (106.00 pp) × 12.00 × 4.00 (hull; 5.70 max.)
A: up to 8 Teseo Mk 1 and Mk 2 SSM; 1 8-cell Mk 29 SAM launcher (RIM-7H Sea Sparrow or Aspide missiles; no reloads); 1 127-mm 54-cal. OTOBreda DP; 2 twin 40-mm 70-cal. OTOBreda AA; 2 triple 324-mm Mk 32 Mod. 9 ASW TT (U.S. Mk 46 Mod. 5 torpedoes); 1 AB-212 ASW helicopter
Electronics:
Radar: 1 SMA SPN-748 nav.; 1 AESN SPQ-2F surf. search; 1 SMA CORA SPS-702 surf./air search and target desig.; 1 AESN SPS-774 (RAN-10S) surf./air search; 1 U.S. Mk 91 Mod. 1 SAM f.c.; 1 AESN SPG-70 (Orion RTN-10X for NA-10 Mod. 2 Argo f.c.s.); 2 AESN SPG-74 (Orion RTN-20X for Dardo f.c.s.)
Sonar: Raytheon 1160B hull-mounted MF
EW: Elettronica SLR-4 Newton intercept suite; 2 SLQ-D jammers; 2 20-round OTOBreda SCLAR decoy RL; SLQ-25 Nixie towed acoustic torpedo decoy syst.
M: CODOG: 2 G.E.-Fiat LM-2500 gas turbines (25,000 shp each); 2 Wärtsilä NSD A230-20M diesels (4,950 bhp each); 2 CP props

FRIGATES [FF] *(continued)*

Electric: 3,120 kw tot. (4 × 780-kw Fiat 236 SS diesel alternator sets)
Range: 900/35; 3,450/20; 4,350/16 (on diesels) **Crew:** 15 officers, 169 enlisted

Remarks: Six ships of the same class were ordered for Venezuela, four for Peru, and four for Iraq (which became the *Artigliere* class, q.v.). All four Italian ships are based at Taranto. F 564 is scheduled to be retired in 2005, F 565 in 2006, F 566 in 2007, and F 567 in 2010.
Hull systems: Have fin stabilizers. The highly automated machinery plant is mounted in four compartments: auxiliaries, gas turbines, reduction gearing, and diesel alternator sets. The helicopter hangar is telescoping.
Combat systems: Have the AESN SADOC-2 (IPN-20) combat data system with NATO Link 11 capability. The Otomat/Teseo Mk 2 launchers are mounted two per side abreast the hangar and two per side on the forward superstructure. The *Lupo* had her radar antennas redistributed in 1978–79 and a new mast added at the after end of the stack; the others were completed to the new configuration. The SAM system uses the U.S. Mk 29 launcher and a U.S. director rather than the later Albatros system; the system has been modified to accept the later RIM-7M version of Sea Sparrow and can also launch Aspide missiles. During refits beginning in 1991, the SMA CORA SPS-702 ducting radar was added to provide target data for the antiship missiles; the antenna is placed in a radome atop the pilothouse. Two single 20-mm 70-cal. Mk 10 Oerlikon AA can be added, if required.

CORVETTES [FFL]

♦ 8 Minerva class
Bldr: Fincantieri, Muggiano and Riva Trigoso

	Yard	Laid down	L	In serv.
F 551 Minerva	Riva Trigoso	11-3-85	25-3-86	10-6-87
F 552 Urania	Riva Trigoso	11-3-85	21-6-86	10-6-87
F 553 Danaide	Muggiano	26-5-85	18-10-86	13-2-88
F 554 Sfinge	Muggiano	26-5-85	16-5-87	13-2-88
F 555 Driade	Riva Trigoso	18-3-88	12-3-89	7-9-91
F 556 Chimera	Muggiano	21-12-88	4-7-90	15-1-91
F 557 Fenice	Riva Trigoso	6-9-88	4-12-90	11-9-90
F 558 Sibilla	Riva Trigoso	16-10-89	15-2-90	16-5-91

Danaide (F 553) Bernard Prézelin, 7-00

Urania (F 552) Luciano Grazioli, 9-00

Danaide (F 553) Bernard Prézelin, 7-00

D: 1,029 tons (1,285 fl) **S:** 25 kts (24 sust.)
Dim: 86.60 (80.00 pp) × 10.50 × 3.16 (hull; 4.80 max.)
A: 1 8-round Albatros SAM syst. (8 Aspide missiles); 1 76-mm 62-cal. OTOBreda SuperRapid DP; 2 triple 324-mm B-515 ASW TT (U.S. Mk 46 Mod. 5 torpedoes)
Electronics:
Radar: 1 SMA SPN-728(V)2 nav.; 1 AESN SPS-774 (RAN-10S) surf./air search; 1 AESN SPG-76 (RTN-30X) for SAM and Dardo-E f.c.s.
Sonar: 1 Raytheon-Elsag DE 1167 hull-mounted (7.5–12 kHz)
EW: AESN SLQ-747 (INS-3) intercept/jammer suite; 2 Type 207/E (Wallop Barricade) decoy RL; SLQ-25 Nixie towed torpedo decoy syst.
E/O: 1 Elsag NA-18L Pegaso gun director

Danaide (F 553) Mike Welsford, 6-00

M: 2 Wärtsilä NSD BM230-20DVM diesels; 2 CP props; 11,000 bhp
Electric: 2,080 kw tot. (4 Isotta-Fraschini ID36.55 S12V diesels driving)
Range: 3,500/18 **Crew:** 7 officers, 106 enlisted

Remarks: First four authorized in 11-82; second four ordered in 1-87. Intended for surveillance, coastal escort, fisheries protection, training, and search-and-rescue duties. F 556 was delivered 15-1-91, F 557 on 11-9-90, and F 558 in 4-91; a year of trials and work-up ensued before commissioning. The first four are based at Augusta, Sicily.
Hull systems: Have fin stabilizers. The stacks have been raised and deflectors added since completion to reduce turbulence.
Combat systems: Have the AESN SADOC-2 combat data system with NATO Link 11 capability; there are two computers and three display consoles. The Dardo-E radar f.c.s. controls the SAM system or the gun, which also can be controlled by the NA-18L optronic director. Spherical radomes for Elmer Omega Transit SP 1090 satellite navigation system antennas were added during 1988. All now have the solid-dish OA-7104 antenna for the SPS-774 radar. Have weight and space reserved for addition of an Aspide reload facility, four Teseo Mk 2 SSMs, and a variable-depth sonar.

PATROL SHIPS [PS]

♦ 0 (+ 2) Sirio class
Bldr: Fincantieri, Riva Trigoso

	Laid down	L	Del.	In serv.
P . . . Sirio	. . .	. . .	8-02	2-03
P . . . Orione	. . .	. . .	11-02	5-03

Sirio (P . . .)—computer rendering, showing configuration when 76-mm gun is installed Italian Navy, 2000

D: 1,280 tons light (1,580 fl) **S:** 22 kts (21.8 on 80% power)
Dim: 88.40 (80.00 pp) × 12.20 × 3.43 (hull)
A: provision for 1 76-mm 62-cal. OTOBreda SuperRapid DP; fitted with 2 single 25-mm 87-cal. Oerlikon-OTOBreda KBA AA; 1 AB-212 or NH-90 helicopter
Electronics:
Radar: 1 . . . ARPA nav.; 1 Alenia RASS surf. search; provision for 1 AESN SPG-76 (RTN-25X) f.c.
Sonar: none
EW: Elettronica . . . intercept
E/O: . . . optronic surveillance and f.c.
M: 2 Wärtsilä NSD W12 V26XN diesels; 2 CP props; 11,588 bhp—bow-thruster
Electric: 2,250 kVA tot. (3 × 750-kVA, 3 Isotta-Fraschini 1708 T2ME diesels [600 kw each] driving; 390 V, 50 Hz)
Range: 3,300/17; 6,000/12 **Endurance:** 15 days
Crew: 6 officers, 48 enlisted (accomm. for 10 officers, 60 enlisted)

Remarks: Program title: NUPA (*Nuove Unità per il Pattugliamento d'Altura,* or New High Seas Patrol Ship). A further, simplified version of the NUMC (*Comandante Cigala Fulgosi* class) design, intended for fisheries and antismuggling patrol. Ordered 30-8-00 for $70 million each. Plans for a third were canceled. The ships are being built with funds from the Transport and Navigation Ministry.
Hull systems: The hull and superstructure are shaped to reduce radar reflection. The boat pockets recessed into the superstructure amidships will be covered by Faraday-shield mesh to eliminate radar returns, and exhaust cooling will be fitted. Will have a composite materials superstructure. The helicopter hangar is telescoping. Both Flume-type passive-tank stabilization and fin stabilizers will be fitted, and there are two rudders. The hull lacks the bulbous bow form given to the NUMC ships. Limiting displacement will be 1,890 tons (3.84-m mean hull draft). Will be equipped with two 300-ton/hr firefighting water monitors and a 25-ton/hr oil-spill recovery pumping system.
Combat systems: Equipped only for patrol and policing duties, with no significant air defense and no ASW capabilities; IFF and NATO Link 11 equipment, however, will be fitted. There will be provision to mount a 76-mm gun forward, but it will not be fitted on completion.

PATROL SHIPS [PS] *(continued)*

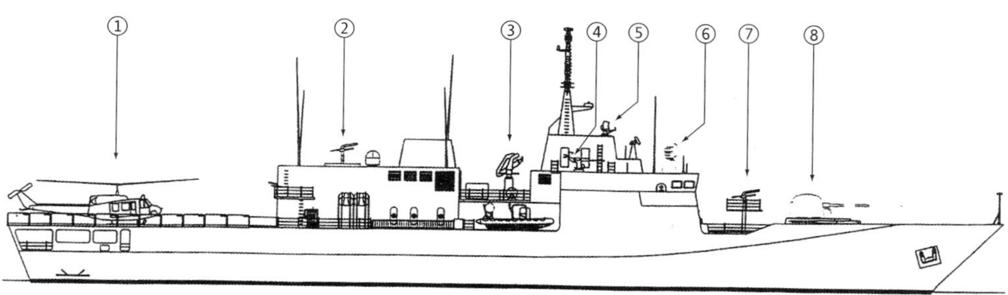

Sirio (P . . .) 1. AB-212 helicopter 2. firefighting monitor atop hangar 3. articulating boat crane 4. 25-mm OTOBreda AA 5. surface-search radar 6. location for SPG-76 f.c. radar 7. firefighting monitor 8. location for 76-mm OTOBreda DP gun
Italian Navy

♦ 0 (+ 4) Comandante Cigala Fulgosi class

Bldr: Fincantieri, Riva Trigoso (fitted out at Fincantieri, Muggiano)

	Laid down	L	Del.	In serv.
P 490 Comandante Cigala Fulgosi	25-6-99	7-10-00	2-02	. . .
P 491 Comandante Borsini	. . .	17-2-01	6-02	. . .
P 492 Comandante Bettica	9-3-00	25-6-01	2-03	. . .
P 493 Comandante Foscari	. . .	24-11-01	6-03	. . .

Comandante Cigala Fulgosi (P 490)—being moved onto barge for transit to fitting-out yard
G. Ghilione, via A. A. de Kruijf, 10-00

Comandante Cigala Fulgosi (P 490)—being moved onto barge for transit to fitting-out yard
Fincantieri, 10-00

D: 1,520 tons (fl) **S:** 25+ kts **Dim:** 88.40 (80.00 pp) × 12.20 × . . .
A: 1 76-mm 62-cal. OTOBreda SuperRapid DP; 2 single 25-mm 87-cal. Oerlikon-OTOBreda KBA AA; 1 AB-212 or NH-90 helicopter
Electronics:
Radar: 1 Alenia RASS surf. search; 1 AESN SPG-76 (RTN-30X/I) f.c.
Sonar: none
EW: Elettronica . . . intercept, 2 20-round OTOBreda SCLAR-H decoy RL
E/O: . . . optronic surveillance and f.c.
M: 2 Wärtsilä NSD 18V 26XN diesels; 2 CP props; 17,370 bhp—bow-thruster
Electric: 2,700 kw tot. (3 × 900 kw, Isotta-Fraschini 1712 T2M2 diesels driving; 380 V/50 Hz and 440 V/60 Hz)
Range: 3,500/14 **Endurance:** 10 days **Crew:** 59 tot. (accomm. for 70)

Remarks: Program title: NUMC (*Nuove Unitá Minori Combattenti,* or New Minor Combatant Unit). Provisionally ordered 12-98 for $104 million each, with delivery of the first to come 32 months after start of construction; contract confirmed 4-99. Will be used for economic exclusion zone patrol. The completed hulls are placed on a barge for tow to Fincantiere's Muggiano yard for fitting out.

Hull systems: The hull and superstructure are shaped to reduce radar reflection. The boat pockets recessed into the superstructure amidships will be covered by Faraday-shield mesh to eliminate radar returns, and exhaust cooling will be fitted. The helicopter hangar is telescoping. Fin stabilizers are fitted, and the underwater portion of the hull has a pronounced bulbous bow form. P 493 employs a GRP superstructure, lower mast, and helicopter hangar delivered 1-01 by Intermarine; incorporating layers of Kevlar and GRP ballistic protection around the bridge and carbon fiber to shield against electromagnetic interference, the new structure weighs 60% less than the steel structures in the earlier three. Two 10-ton/day reverse-osmosis water desalinization systems will be fitted.

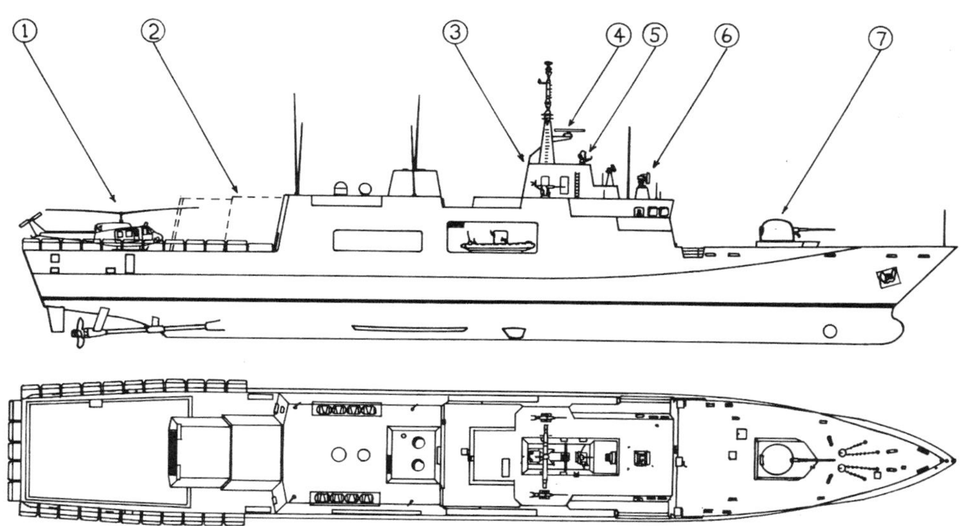

Comandante Cigala Fulgosi (P 490) 1. AB-212 helicopter 2. telescoping hangar 3. 25-mm OTOBreda AA 4. navigational radar 5. RASS surface-search radar 6. SPG-76 f.c. radar for 76-mm gun 7. 76-mm OTOBreda DP gun
Drawing by A. D. Baker III

PATROL SHIPS [PS] *(continued)*

Combat systems: Have an Alenia-Marconi command system with NA-25 gun control, and they have an Elmer integrated internal/external communications suite. There are no significant air defense and no ASW capabilities.

♦ **4 Cassiopea class** Bldr: Fincantieri, Muggiano

	Laid down	L	In serv.
P 401 Cassiopea	16-3-87	19-7-88	21-10-89
P 402 Libra	16-3-87	27-7-88	23-3-91
P 403 Spica	5-9-88	27-5-89	23-3-91
P 404 Vega	30-6-89	24-2-90	8-5-92

Cassiopea (P 401) Luciano Grazioli, 5-00

Vega (P 404) Luciano Grazioli, 9-00

Vega (P 404) H&L Van Ginderen, 6-99

D: 1,126 tons (1,491 fl) **S:** 21 kts (20 continuous)
Dim: 79.80 (71.50 pp) × 11.80 (11.40 wl) × 3.60 (hull)
A: 1 76-mm 62-cal. OTOBreda DP; 2 single 20-mm 70-cal. Mk 10 Oerlikon AA; 1 AB-412 helicopter
Electronics:
Radar: 1 SMA SPN-748(V)2 nav.; 1 AESN SPS-702(V)2 surf. search; 1 AESN SPG-70 (RTN-10X) f.c.
EW: . . . intercept and D/F gear
M: 2 Wärtsilä NSD BL230-16 diesels; 2 CP props; 8,800 bhp max. (7,490 sust.)
Electric: 1,620 kw (3 × 500-kw Isotta-Fraschini ID36.55 SS6V gen. sets; 1 × 120-kw emergency set)
Range: 3,300/17 **Fuel:** 165 tons **Endurance:** 35 days
Crew: 6 officers, 54 enlisted (accomm. for 10 officers, 70 enlisted)

Remarks: Operated on fisheries patrol, antipollution, and search-and-rescue duties. Construction authorized 31-12-82, funded by the Ministry of the Merchant Marine; ordered 12-86. There were originally to have been eight; the projected fifth unit, to have been named *Orione,* and a planned sixth were canceled in 1991.
Hull systems: Have pollution analysis, oil disposal, cargo transport, light repair, firefighting, and towing capabilities and can accommodate rescued personnel. Have passive tank stabilization, and fin stabilizers are fitted. A 500-m^3 tank is aboard to hold polluted water. Have a 22.0 × 8.0–m helicopter deck and a telescoping hangar. Hull has 8.50-m molded depth.
Combat systems: The old-model 76-mm guns and fire-control systems were taken from scrapped *Carlo Bergamini*–class frigates. The guns may later be replaced by the new Oerlikon-OTOBreda 25-mm mounting.

♦ **2 Albatros class**
Bldr: Nav. Mec. Castellammare di Stabia

	Laid down	L	In serv.
F 544 Alcione (ex-U.S. PC 1620)	1953	19-9-54	23-10-55
F 545 Airone (ex-U.S. PC 1621)	1953	21-11-54	29-12-55

Airone (F 545) Luciano Grazioli, 9-01

D: 800 tons (950 fl) **S:** 19 kts **Dim:** 76.30 (69.49 pp) × 9.65 × 2.72 (hull)
A: 1 twin and 1 single 40-mm 70-cal. OTOBreda-Bofors AA; 2 triple 324-mm ASW TT
Electronics: Radar: 1 . . . nav., 1 SPQ-2 surf. search—Sonar: QCU-2
M: 2 Fiat M409 diesels; 2 props; 5,200 bhp (3,500 sust.)
Electric: 1,200 kw tot. **Range:** 2,988/18 **Fuel:** 100 tons
Crew: 6 officers, 96 enlisted

Remarks: Survivors of four ASW corvettes built with U.S. funding; *Albatros* (F 541) was decommissioned 30-4-86 and stricken 30-4-89, while *Aquila* (ex-Dutch *Lynx*) was stricken early in the 1990s. Based at Brindisi, both are used for training and make only brief trips to sea. F 544 was at one time fitted for mine countermeasures, with mine clearance divers' dinghies, paravanes, and two equipment davits at the stern. Both were to be stricken on 1-2-02.

♦ **2 converted ex-U.S. Agile class**

	Bldr	L	In serv.
P 5431 Storione (ex-M 5431, MSO 506)	Martinolich SB, San Diego	13-11-54	23-2-56
P 5433 Squalo (ex-M 5433, MSO 518)	Tampa Marine, Tampa, Fla.	1955	20-6-57

Squalo (P 5433) Luciano Grazioli, 9-01

D: 665 tons (750 fl) **S:** 14 kts **Dim:** 52.27 × 10.71 × 4.00 (fl)
A: 1 40-mm 60-cal. Mk 3 Bofors AA
Electronics: Radar: 1 SMA SPN-703 nav.; 1 Gem BX-732 nav.
M: 2 G.M. 8-278ANW diesels; 2 CP props; 1,600 bhp
Range: 3,000/10 **Fuel:** 46 tons **Crew:** 4 officers, 58 enlisted

Remarks: Former fleet minesweepers. Wooden construction. Sister *Sgombro* (M 5432, ex-MSO 517) was placed in reserve 10-9-90 for eventual disposal; *Salmone* (M 5430, ex-MSO 507), which had been used for fisheries protection duties since 1989, was similarly retired during 1991 and stricken 31-3-96. The entire class had originally been scheduled for disposal in 1982–83, and the two remaining units were to have been retired during 1992; instead, their sweep gear was removed and they have been given a minor refit to permit them to perform fisheries protection duties. They will be replaced by units of the new NUMC design (*Comandante Cigala Fulgosi* class).

GUIDED-MISSILE PATROL COMBATANTS [PGG]

Note: Of the six Iraqi missile "corvettes" built in Italy and sequestered at La Spezia since the late 1980s, *Saad ibn abi Wakkad* (F 218) and *Kalid ibn al Walid* (F 216) were sold to Malaysia 27-10-95 and refitted for delivery in 4-97. *Abdullah ben abi Sarh* (F 214) and *Salahi ad Deen* (F 220) were sold to Malaysia in 3-97 for delivery in 1999 after refits. The helicopter-capable *Mussa ben Nussair* (F 210) and *Tariq ibn Ziad* (F 212) remain laid up at Muggiano.

HYDROFOIL GUIDED-MISSILE PATROL CRAFT [PTGH]

Disposal note: *Sparveiro*-class guided-missile hydrofoils *Falcone* (P 422), *Astore* (P 423), *Grifone* (P 424), *Gheppio* (P 425), and *Condor* (P 426) were placed in terminal reserve in 10-99 and were made available for foreign sale (with no interest shown to date). *Sparveiro* (P 420) was stricken 30-9-91 and *Nibbio* (P 421) on 10-10-96. Tentative plans for a replacement craft evolved into the much larger *Comandante Cigala Fulgosi*–class patrol ships.

PATROL CRAFT [PC]

♦ 1 (+ 3) Esploratore class Bldr: Co.I.Nav.Al., Cadimare, La Spezia

	L	Del.	In serv.
P 405 Esploratore	4-11-96	26-6-97	7-11-98
P 406 Sentinella	13-11-97	4-98	24-4-99
P 407 Vedetta	11-1-97	10-98	9-4-00
P 408 Staffetta	10-99	12-1-01	1-02

Vedetta (P 407) G. Ghilione, via A. A. de Kruijf, 9-00

Sentinella (P 406) Maurizio Brescia, 3-99

D: 164.5 tons light (230.5 fl) **S:** 22 kts (20 sust.)
Dim: 37.16 (34.70 pp) × 7.50 (7.06 wl) × 1.90 (hull; 2.30 max.)
A: 1 20-mm 70-cal. Mk 10 Oerlikon AA; 2 single 7.62-mm mg
Electronics:
Radar: 2 SMA SPS-753B/C nav./surf. search
E/O: AESN Medusa surveillance and tracking
M: 2 Isotta-Fraschini M1712 T2 diesels; 2 CP props; 3,810 bhp
Electric: 500 kw tot. (2 × 250-kw Marelli M7B-250 gen., VMDS9 diesels driving)
Range: 1,200/20 **Crew:** 2 officers, 13 enlisted

Remarks: First three (with an option for a fourth) were approved in 1996 budget to replace the converted U.S. *Adjutant*-class minesweepers used in U.N. patrol service in the Red Sea; P 408 was ordered during 2-98. Based at Brindisi. The names mean "Scout," "Sentry," "Dispatch Rider," and "Lookout," respectively. Originally ordered in 12-93 from C.N. Ortona, which went out of business; the new builder is a temporary consortium of small yacht-building companies. The 20-mm gun may later be replaced by a new Oerlikon-OTOBreda 25-mm 87-cal. mount.

Disposal note: The two remaining U.S. *Adjutant*-class patrol craft, former minesweepers *Bambú* (P 495, ex-M 5521; ex-U.S. MSC 214) was stricken during 2001, and *Palma* (P 498, ex-M 5525; ex-U.S. MSC 238) was to be stricken on 1-2-02.

MINE WARFARE SHIPS

Note: Three to four (reduced in 2000 from six) units of a new seagoing mine-countermeasures vessel class equipped for minehunting and deep sweeping are planned, with construction to start around 2008. A version of the U.K. Plessey 2095 (improved 2093) sonar would be employed, and the ships would be able to sweep in depths of up to 400 m. A gas turbine–powered air-cushion vehicle design is preferred, although the design might be patterned on the U.S. *Osprey* (MHC 51) class, itself a greatly enlarged version of the *Lerici / Gaeta* series.

♦ 8 Gaeta-class minehunter/minesweepers [MHC]
Bldr: Intermarine, Sarzana

	Laid down	L	In serv.
M 5554 Gaeta	5-8-88	28-7-90	9-10-93
M 5555 Termoli	5-12-88	15-12-90	28-5-93
M 5556 Alghero	5-4-89	4-5-91	28-5-93
M 5557 Numana	5-8-89	26-10-91	11-6-94
M 5558 Crotone	5-12-89	11-4-92	11-6-94
M 5559 Viareggio	...	3-10-92	26-10-96
M 5560 Chioggia	...	9-4-94	1997 (del. 5-5-96)
M 5561 Rimini	...	17-9-94	1998 (del. 19-10-96)

Numana (M 5557) Bernard Prézelin, 10-00

Alghero (M 5556) Camil Busquets i Vilanova, 2-00

Numana (M 5557) Bernard Prézelin, 10-00

D: 665 tons (697 fl) **S:** 14.3 kts **Dim:** 52.45 (46.50 pp) × 9.87 × 2.95
A: 1 20-mm 70-cal. Mk 10 Oerlikon AA
Electronics:
Radar: 1 SMA MM/SPN-728 nav.
Sonar: FIAR SQQ-14 (IT) minehunting HF, with U.K. Type 2048 (Plessey Speedscan) side-scan mapping
M: 1 Wärtsilä NSD BL230-BN diesel; 1 prop; 1,985 bhp (3 retractable 120-hp Riva Calzoni thrusters for 6-kt hunting speed)
Electric: 900 kw (3 × 250-kw ID 36SS diesel sets; 1 × 150-kw ID 36N diesel set)
Range: 1,500/14; 2,500/12 **Fuel:** 49 tons **Endurance:** 12 days
Crew: 4 officers, 43 enlisted (including 7 mine-disposal divers)

Remarks: Names were announced in 1980, but the first six ships were not ordered until 30-4-88. Two additional units were ordered in 1992 but canceled in 7-92 as an economy measure; M 5560 and M 5561 were then reordered during 1993 to assure continuity of work at the yard. Are essentially a lengthened version of the *Lerici* design. Six very similar sisters were ordered by the Royal Australian Navy, and the U.S. Navy's *Osprey* class is an enlarged variant.
Hull systems: As for the *Lerici* class, but have a new minehunting auxiliary thruster system and an additional main generator set. Carry a Galeazzi two-man decompression chamber and are fitted with passive tank stabilization (by using stabilization tanks to carry fuel, the range can be extended by 1,500 n.m. at 12 kts).
Combat systems: Have the SSN-714 MACTIS command and control system. Carry one MIN-77 and one Gaymarine Pluto remote-controlled mine disposal submersibles and Oropesa Mk 4 mechanical sweep gear. The minehunting sonar is an Italian-built version of the SQQ-14 (with digital processor) with the addition of the Plessey Speedscan (Type 2048) side-scan route-mapping sonar to the towed transducer array to provide a mine-route clearance capability. Have a Motorola MHS-1C NAVSAT receiver. The new Oerlikon-OTOBreda 25-mm gun may replace the World War II–vintage 20-mm mounting.

MINE WARFARE SHIPS *(continued)*

♦ 4 Lerici-class minehunter/minesweepers [MHC]
Bldr: Intermarine, Sarzana

	L	In serv.		L	In serv.
M 5550 Lerici	3-9-82	4-5-85	M 5552 Milazzo	4-1-85	14-12-85
M 5551 Sapri	5-4-84	14-12-85	M 5553 Vieste	18-4-85	14-12-85

Vieste (M 5553) Carlo Martinelli, 3-99

D: 488 tons (520 fl) **S:** 15 kts **Dim:** 49.98 (45.50 pp) × 9.56 × 2.70
A: 1 20-mm 70-cal. Mk 10 Oerlikon AA
Electronics:
Radar: 1 SMA SPN-703 nav.
Sonar: FIAR SQQ-14/IT minehunting HF, with U.K. Type 2048 (Plessey Speedscan) side-scan mapping
M: 1 Wärtsilä NSD B230-8M diesel; 1 prop; 1,840 bhp—2 retractable auxiliary thrusters; 470 hp for 7 kts
Electric: 650 kw (2 × 250-kw ID 36SS diesel sets; 1 × 150-kw diesel set)
Range: 1,500/14; 2,500/12 **Fuel:** 49 tons **Endurance:** 15 days
Crew: 4 officers, 43 enlisted (including 6–7 mine-clearance divers)

Remarks: Ordered 4-78. Delivery of the first two ships was delayed by the presence of a bridge blocking the seaward exit from the yard. Sisters were built for Nigeria and Malaysia. All four are to receive new navigational track maintenance and navigational systems.
Hull systems: Glass-reinforced, shock-resistant plastic construction throughout. Hull material is 140 mm thick. While minehunting, speed is 7 kts, using the two drop-down, shrouded thrusters. Range at 12 kts can be extended to 4,000 n.m. by using the passive roll stabilization tanks to carry fuel.
Combat systems: Have the SSN-714 command and control system and Motorola MHS-1A navigation system. The original U.S. SQQ-14 high-frequency minehunting sonar with a retractable transducer has been upgraded to the digital, Italian-made, repackaged SQQ-14/IT, which incorporates the Plessey Speedscan (Type 2048) side-scan sonar for route survey work at up to 12 kts. Carry 6–7 divers, who use CAM mine-destructor charges. One Pluto remote-controlled submersible disposal and one MIN-77 locating submersible are carried by each ship, along with Oropesa Mk 4 mechanical sweep gear.

♦ 1 Alpino-class mine countermeasures support ship [MCS]
Bldr: C.N. del Tirreno, Riva Trigoso

	Laid down	L	In serv.
A 5384 Alpino (ex-F 580, ex-*Circe*)	27-2-63	10-6-67	14-1-68

Alpino (A 5384) Camil Busquets i Vilanova, 2-00

Alpino (A 5384) Bernard Prézelin, 10-00

D: 2,000 tons (2,689 fl) **S:** 22 kts **Dim:** 113.3 (106.4 pp) × 13.3 × 3.80 (hull)
A: 3 single 76-mm 62-cal. OTOBreda DP; 2 single 20-mm 70-cal. Mk 10 Oerlikon AA; 1 AB-212 helicopter
Electronics:
Radar: 1 SMA SPN-748 nav.; 1 AESN SPS-702(V)3 surf. search; 1 R.C.A. SPS-12 air search; 2 AESN SPG-70 (RTN-10X Argo systems) f.c.
M: 4 Tosi OTV-320 diesels; 2 props; 16,800 bhp **Electric:** 2,400 kw tot.
Range: 4,200/17 **Fuel:** 275 tons **Crew:** 13 officers, 150 enlisted

Remarks: Former frigate, converted 14-4-96 to 31-1-97 to serve as a mine forces flagship, mine countermeasures support ship, combat divers' support ship, and signals intelligence collection ship. Officially redesignated a *Nave Comando e Supporto Forze di CMM* on 27-2-98 and renumbered A 5384. Based at La Spezia. The conversion replaced a new-construction vessel that had been programmed to be ordered in 1998. Sister *Carabiniere* (F 581) has been refitted to act as a trials ship (see under [AGE]).
Hull systems: Has fin stabilizers. Two Tosi-Metrovik G6 gas turbines (7,700 shp each) were removed during conversion; the original maximum speed was 28 kts on all six engines.
Combat systems: Sonars, ASW torpedo tubes, and EW systems were removed during the conversion. Originally mounted six single 76-mm old-pattern DP gunmounts. Retains the hangar and flight deck. An articulated crane to handle divers' rigid inflatable launches is mounted to port, forward of the bridge. A decompression chamber and diver-support crane have been added at the extreme stern.

AMPHIBIOUS WARFARE SHIPS AND CRAFT

Note: Initial planning is under way for a new LPD class to displace on the order of 14,000 tons full load. The design would be able to transport some 1,200 troops and their equipment and may be based on that of a commercial roll-on/roll-off cargo ship.

♦ 1 modified San Giorgio–class dock landing ship [LPD]
Bldr: Fincantieri, Riva Trigoso

	Laid down	L	Del.	In serv.
L 9894 San Giusto	7-4-92	2-12-93	14-4-94	11-6-94

San Giusto (L 9894) Vic Jeffery, RAN, 12-99

San Giusto (L 9894)—note three sets of davits for landing craft on sponson below the level of the flight deck Italian Navy

D: 5,600 tons (7,950 fl) **S:** 20 kts
Dim: 137.00 (118.00 pp) × 25.00 (20.50 hull) × 6.00
A: 1 76-mm 62-cal. OTOBreda Compact DP; 2 twin 20-mm 70-cal. Mk 24 Oerlikon AA; 3 CH-47 Chinook or 3 SH-3D Sea King or 5 AB-212 helicopters
Electronics:
Radar: 1 DMS SPN-753 nav.; 1 SMA SPS-702 surf. search; 1 AESN SPG-70 (RTN-10X) f.c.
EW: AESN SLR-730 intercept; AESN SLQ-747 jammer
M: 2 Fincantieri-DMD A.420.12 diesels; 2 CP props; 16,800 bhp—1,000-shp bow-thruster
Electric: 3,330 kw (4 × 770 kw, 1 × 250 kw) **Range:** 4,500/20; 7,500/16
Crew: 16 officers, 182 enlisted + 204 cadets and 62 instructors, or 349 troops (33 officers, 316 enlisted)

Remarks: Modified version of the *San Giorgio* class, intended to act as training ship for the naval academy at Livorno in peacetime. Authorized during 11-90 and ordered during 3-91. Based at Brindisi. To receive midlife modernization around 2007.
Hull systems: Has a broader island superstructure than the earlier *San Giorgio* class, and the boats are stowed on a sponson to port to restore flight deck area, providing a taxiway between the landing area at the stern and a smaller one to port at the bow. Up to six medium-sized helicopters can be accommodated on deck. There is no bow vehicle ramp, but the side doors and ramps are larger than on the earlier units. Is able to carry 34 combat vehicles totaling up to 1,200 tons below decks, and additional light vehicles can be carried on the flight deck. About 85 tons (80 m^3) of combat stores and 30 tons (80 m^3) of provisions can be accommodated. Landing craft include three 63-ton MTM-series medium landing craft in the 20.5 × 7.0–m stern docking well and three 14-ton MTP-series personnel landing craft in davits to port, plus one 9-ton motor launch.
Combat systems: Has the IPN-20/SADOC-2 combat control system with two multifunction and four single-function operator consoles. Is equipped to send and receive NATO Link 11. The 76-mm gun is not of the newest (SuperRapid) model, but it has been upgraded to fire at up to 85 rpm.

AMPHIBIOUS WARFARE SHIPS AND CRAFT *(continued)*

♦ 2 San Giorgio–class dock landing ships [LPD]
Bldr: Fincantieri, Riva Trigoso

	Laid down	L	In serv.
L 9892 San Giorgio	26-5-85	25-2-87	13-2-88
L 9893 San Marco	26-3-85	21-10-87	6-5-89

San Giorgio (L 9892)—undergoing conversion at Taranto; note the flight deck continued right to the bow and the deletion of the bow doors
Dr. Guido Alfano, via Luciano Grazioli, 5-01

San Marco (L 9893)—in original configuration, with 76.2-mm gun forward and bow doors for vehicle landing
Flotten Kommando, 2001

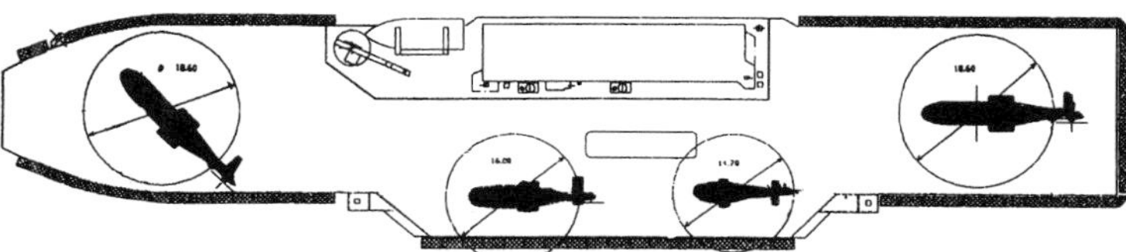

Revision to the flight deck of the San Giorgio class—the new extension of the flight deck to port amidships covers the relocated landing craft stowage
Italian Navy, 1999

D: 5,000 tons light, 6,687 tons std. (7,665 fl; 8,400 flooded down)
S: 21 kts (sust.) **Dim:** 133.30 (118.00 pp) × 20.50 × 5.25 (6.50 flooded down aft)
A: 2 single 20-mm 70-cal. Mk 10 Oerlikon AA; 2 single 12.7-mm mg; 3 CH-47 Chinook or 3 SH-3D Sea King or 5 AB-212 helicopters
Electronics: Radar: 1 SMA SPN-748 nav.; 1 SMA SPS-702 surf./air search
M: 2 Wärtsilä NSD A420-12, 12-cyl., 4-stroke diesels; 2 CP props; 16,800 bhp—1,000-bhp bow-thruster
Electric: 3,330 kw (4 × 770 kw, 1 × 250 kw) **Range:** 4,500/20; 7,500/16
Crew: 17 officers, 146 enlisted + 345 troops

Remarks: L 9892, initially requested in 1980, was approved in 1983 and ordered 5-3-84. L 9893, ordered 26-3-85 with funds from the Ministry of Civil Protection, is configured for disaster-relief service and has more extensive medical facilities. Both were fitted out at Muggiano and are based at Brindisi, and both are being modernized (see below).
Hull systems: In 1999–2000 with L 9892 and in 2001 with L 9893, the flight deck space has been enlarged during refits at Taranto through the deletion of the 76-mm gun, extension of the flight deck to the bow, and the adding of a 5-m-wide sponson to port, providing spots fore and aft for EH.101 helicopters and two spots on the sponson for smaller helicopters. The bow doors were sealed, the two 13.0-m LCVPs resited below the sponson, the flight deck fitted for night operations, and aircraft support facilities enhanced. They continue to carry three 18.5-m LCMs, launched via a 20.5 × 7.0–m stern docking well equipped with a 40-ton traveling bridge crane. The helicopters are stowed on deck, not in the 100 × 20.5–m vehicle hangar below, which can hold 30 or more armored personnel carriers. The flight deck is served by a 13.5 × 3.5–m, 30-ton elevator and a 16-ton crane. There is stowage for 99 m^3 of refrigerated and 300 m^3 of dry stores and 60 tons of aviation fuel. Evaporators producing 90 tons water per day are fitted. Have passive tank stabilization.
Combat systems: The old-model 76-mm gun and its associated AESN Argo NA-10 f.c.s. were removed during the modernizations. Either a U.S. RAM or Stinger point-defense missile system is to be added later.

♦ 9 MTM 217–class vehicle landing craft [LCM]
Bldrs: MEN 217–222: MEN Fincantieri, Muggiano, La Spezia (In serv. 9-10-87 to 8-3-88); others: C.N. Balsamo (In serv. 1993)

MEN 217 through MEN 222 MEN 227 MEN 228 MEN 551

MEN 227
Carlo Martinelli, 4-96

D: 62 tons (64.6 fl) **S:** 9 kts **Dim:** 18.50 × 5.10 × 0.90
M: 2 Fiat-AIFO 8280 diesels; 2 props; 560 bhp (400 sust.)
Range: 300/9 **Crew:** 3 crew + 80 troops

Remarks: GRP construction, with design based strongly on that of the U.S. LCM(6) class. First three were built for *San Giorgio*, next three for *San Marco*. Three more were ordered during 3-91 for *San Giusto*. Cargo capacity: 30 tons. The hull numbering designation has been changed from MTM *(Mototrasporti Medi)* to MEN, and the craft no longer carry the formerly assigned NATO "L"-series pennants.

♦ 5 U.S. LCM(6)-class vehicle landing craft [LCM] (In serv. 1943–44)

MTM 544 MTM 545 MTM 547 MTM 548 MTM 549

D: 23.6 tons (56 fl) **S:** 9.5 kts **Dim:** 17.07 × 4.37 × 1.22 (fwd; 1.52 aft)
A: 2 single 12.7-mm mg
M: 2 Gray Marine 64HN9 diesels; 2 props; 450 bhp (330 sust.)
Range: 130/9.5 (loaded) **Crew:** 4–5 tot.

Remarks: Transferred from the United States in 1953. Until 1986 were numbered as MTM 9908–9922. Have been overhauled for further service. Now mostly employed as local-service cargo lighters, and at least three have carried yardcraft pennant numbers: MEN 220, MEN 222, and MEN 223. Ten other units were discarded 1994–96. Cargo: 30 tons or up to 80 troops for short distances. Cargo deck is 11.43 × 2.82 m. Four others of this class are operated by the Italian Army.

♦ 17 MTP 96–class vehicle and personnel landing craft [LCVP]
Bldrs: MDN 94, 95: Tecnomatic, Ancona (In serv. 1985); MDN 96–101: Tecnomatic, Bari (In serv. 1987–88); others: Tecnoplast, Venice (In serv. 1991–94)

MDN 94 through MDN 101 MDN 108 MDN 109 MDN 114 through MDN 120

MDN 120
Carlo Martinelli, 6-98

D: 14.3 tons (fl) **S:** 26 kts **Dim:** 13.70 × 3.80 × 0.70
M: 2 Fiat-AIOF 836J-SRM diesels; 2 props or waterjets; 700 bhp
Range: 180/24 **Crew:** 3 tot. + 45 troops

Remarks: GRP personnel launches for use with the *San Giorgio* class. Assigned NATO "L"-series pennants are no longer carried, and the craft have been renumbered from the original MTP *(Mototrasporti Personale)* series to MDN. The last three built had waterjets, and the propellers are being replaced by waterjets in the earlier units. Have a small bow ramp and can transport light vehicles. Cargo: 45 troops or 4.5 tons.

Note: For use by the San Marco Battalion seaborne assault troops, there are 24 LVTP-7 armored personnel carriers and 1 LVTC-7 armored command post, all tracked amphibious craft transferred from the United States. Personnel transports MEN 215 and MEN 216, built to be carried by the carrier *Giuseppe Garibaldi* for amphibious assault missions, are now used as personnel ferries and are described in the Service Craft section under [YFL]. The *Mario Marino*–class combat swimmer support craft are listed as diving tenders [YDT] under Service Craft.

AUXILIARIES

♦ 1 Alpino-class weapons systems trials ship [AGE]
Bldr: C.N. del Tirreno, Riva Trigoso

	Laid down	L	In serv.
F 581 Carabiniere (ex-*Climene*)	9-1-65	30-9-67	28-4-68

D: 2,000 tons (2,689 fl) **S:** 23 kts **Dim:** 113.3 (106.4 pp) × 13.3 × 3.80 (hull)
A: 8 Sylver A43 VLS cells (8 Aster-15 missiles); 1 76-mm 62-cal. OTOBreda DP; 2 triple 324-mm ILAS-3 ASW TT

AUXILIARIES *(continued)*

Carabiniere (F 581) Bernard Prézelin, 2-01

Electronics:
Radar: 1 SMA SPN-748 nav.; 1 AESN SPS-702(V)3 surf. search; 1 R.C.A. SPS-12 air search; 2 AESN SPG-70 (RTN-10X Argo systems) gun f.c.; 1 AESN-Elsag SPY-790 EMPAR target desig./tracking
Sonar: Raytheon DE 1164 MF
EW: AESN SLQ-747 integrated intercept/jammer suite
M: 4 Tosi OTV-320 diesels; 2 props; 16,800 bhp
Electric: 2,400 kw tot. **Range:** 4,200/17 **Fuel:** 275 tons
Crew: 13 officers, 150 enlisted

Remarks: Former frigate, refitted to act as weapons trials ship in place of *Quarto* (A 5314); reclassified as an auxiliary 1-1-93. Completed a 15-month overhaul and modification in 10-00 to serve as system validation platform for Italian Navy use of the Aster-15 SAM system, with trials commencing 9-01. A further 10-month overhaul is to be completed by late 2003, when the ship will begin to test the complete French/Italian PAAMS (Principal Anti-Air Missile System) configuration. F 581 will also conduct trials with the French SLAT antitorpedo system during 2002. Sister *Alpino* (A 5384, ex-F 580) remains in service as a mine countermeasures support ship [MCM].
Hull systems: Has fin stabilizers. Two 7,700-shp Tosi-Metrovik G6 gas turbine engines have been removed.
Combat systems: Received a bow-mounted sonar, improved combat data system, and EW equipment during a refit that ended 7-85. The fish for the DE 1164 VDS is no longer carried, although the hoist gear, winch, and cable reel were overhauled during 2000 and remain installed at the stern. Conducted initial sea trials with the AESN-Elsag EMPAR (European Multifunction Phased-Array Radar) from 7-95 to 4-96; the associated AESN SADOC-3 combat system began installation during 12-94. Conducted the first Milas AS missile at-sea launch during 5-95; the canister launcher (now removed) was identical to that employed for the Teseo Mk 2 antiship missile and was mounted forward of the bridge superstructure, firing to starboard.

♦ 0 (+ 1) modified Alliance-class intelligence collector [AGI]
Bldr: Fincantieri, Muggiano

	Laid down	L	In serv.
A	20-1-01	11-01	2-02

The modified Alliance-class intelligence collector—computer rendering
Italian Navy, 2000

D: 2,466 tons (3,180 fl) **S:** 17 kts (16.5 sust.)
Dim: 93.50 (82.00 pp) × 15.20 × 5.10
A: 2 single 25-mm 87-cal. OTOBreda KBA AA; 2 single 12.7-mm mg
Electronics:
Radar: 2 Qubit–Kelvin-Hughes Nucleus 6000 nav. (X- and S-band)
Sonar: . . .
M: 2 Wärtsilä NSD B230-12M diesels, AEG CC 3127 generators; electric drive: 2 AEG 1,500-kw permanent magnet motors; 2 props; 4,000 shp—side-thrusters fore and aft
Electric: 1,850 kw tot. (including 1 × 1,605-kw Kongsberg gas-turbine set)
Range: 8,000/12 **Crew:** 12 officers, 76 enlisted (94 max. accomm.)

Remarks: Program title: NUPS (*Nuovo Unità di Supporto Polivalente,* or New Multipurpose Support Unit). Ordered 10-12-99 for $67.28 million. Based on the design of the NATO acoustic research ship *Alliance* and the Taiwanese research ship *Ta Kuan.* To carry some 27 different electronic and acoustic intelligence collection systems in order to collect communications, electronics, acoustic, and imagery intelligence. Will be operated in the Black Sea, Red Sea, Indian Ocean, Arabian Gulf, and Persian Gulf.
Hull systems: Will have Flume-type passive tank stabilization. A helicopter deck is fitted aft, but no hangar. The ship will carry a remotely operated reconnaissance submersible.

♦ 5 Ponza-class navigational aids tenders [AGL]
Bldr: C.N. Mario Morini, Ancona

	Laid down	L	In serv.
A 5364 Ponza (MTF 1304)	25-3-87	24-9-88	20-12-88
A 5366 Levanzo (MTF 1305)	25-3-87	22-6-89	6-9-89
A 5367 Tavolara (MTF 1306)	25-3-87	28-11-88	28-2-89
A 5368 Palmaria (MTF 1307)	25-3-87	25-2-89	19-5-89
A 5383 Procida (MTF 1308)	14-9-89	23-6-90	14-11-90

Tavolara (A 5367) Maurizio Brescia, 6-00

D: 402 tons light (608 fl) **S:** 14.8 kts **Dim:** 56.72 (50.00 pp) × 10.00 × 2.40
A: provision for 2 single 7.62-mm mg
Electronics: Radar: 1 SMA SPN-732 nav.
M: 2 Isotta-Fraschini ID36 SS8V diesels; 2 CP Kort-nozzle props; 1,800 bhp (1,690 sust.)—1 120-shp bow-thruster
Electric: 464 kw tot. (2 × 232 kw) **Range:** 1,500/14; 2,800/10
Crew: 2 officers, 32 enlisted

Remarks: MTF = *Mototrasporti Fari.* Employed as lighthouse supply and navigational buoy tenders. First four ordered 23-9-86. A variation of the design used for the MTC 1011–class coastal transports. Have one 15-ton-capacity electrohydraulic crane aft and one 1.5-ton crane forward. A 20-mm 70-cal. Mk 10 Oerlikon AA gun can be mounted atop the pilothouse.

♦ 0 (+ 2) Aretusa-class coastal survey ships [AGS]
Bldr: Intermarine, Sarzana

	Laid down	L	In serv.
A 5304 Aretusa	1998	8-5-00	. . .
A 5305 Galatea	. . .	7-6-00	. . .

Galatea (A 5305)—shortly after launch
Dr. Guido Alfano, via Luciano Grazioli, 6-00

D: 390 tons (fl) **S:** 13 kts **Dim:** 39.21 (36.0 pp) × 12.60 × 3.60
A: 1 20-mm 70-cal. Mk 10 Oerlikon AA
Electronics: Radar: 1 . . . nav.
M: 2 Isotta-Fraschini V1708 T2ME diesels, ABB/AMA 400 Ma6 electric motors; 2 double-prop azimuthal thrusters; . . . shp—bow-thrusters
Range: 1,700/13 **Crew:** 4 officers, 20 enlisted + 4 passengers (31 tot. accomm.)

Remarks: Were to be 300-ton units ordered 2-90 from Intermarine, Sarzana, as replacements for *Mirto* (A 5306) and *Pioppo* (A 5307), but were deferred for financial reasons and later redesigned. Finally ordered from Intermarine in 10-97; were to have been completed in 9-99 and 11-99.
Hull systems: Are of catamaran configuration, with GRP hulls having a bulbous bow configuration. Have two 5,000-m-depth echo sounders, one 5,000-m-depth multibeam mapping sonar, one 600-m-depth side-scan echo sounder, medium- and short-range radionavigation systems, a bottom-sampling device (1,500 m depth), a differential GPS receiver, a bottom profiler, and a data-recording system. The main deck between the hulls is 34.8 m long, and the hulls have a beam of 3.6 m each.

AUXILIARIES *(continued)*

Aretusa (A 5304) Dr. Guido Alfano, via Luciano Grazioli, 5-00

♦ **1 Ammiraglio Magnaghi–class hydrographic survey ship [AGS]**
Bldr: C.N. del Tirreno, Riva Trigoso

	Laid down	L	In serv.
A 5303 Ammiraglio Magnaghi	13-6-73	11-9-74	2-5-75

Ammiraglio Magnaghi (A 5303) Luciano Grazioli, 5-01

D: 1,550 tons (1,700 fl) **S:** 17 kts **Dim:** 82.70 (76.80 pp) × 13.70 × 3.60
A: provision for 1 40-mm 70-cal. OTOBreda-Bofors AA
Electronics: Radar: 1 SMA SPN-703 nav.
M: 2 Wärtsilä NSD B306-SS diesels; 1 CP prop; 3,000 bhp—1 electric auxiliary propulsion engine; 240 shp (4 kts)—bow-thruster
Range: 4,200/16; 5,500/12 **Crew:** 15 officers, 120 enlisted + 15 scientists

Remarks: Built under the 1972 construction program. Equipped for survey and oceanographic studies and for search-and-rescue duties. Based at Genoa and assigned to the Istituto Idrografico della Marina.
Hull systems: Has Flume-type passive tank stabilization. Chemistry, physical oceanography, photo, and hydrology labs, computerized data loggers, and an underwater TV capability are fitted. Has a helicopter pad aft. Received the Qubit TRAC V/CHART 100 integrated hydrographic data acquisition system during a major overhaul in 1990–91 that also saw modifications to the stack. Can accommodate four small hydrographic survey launches, but normally only two are aboard.

♦ **2 U.S. Adjutant-class hydrographic survey ships [AGS]**

	Bldr	L	In serv.
A 5306 Mirto (ex-M 5539)	C.N. OTOBreda, Marghera	2-11-54	4-8-56
A 5307 Pioppo (ex-M 5515, ex-MSC 135)	Bellingham SY, Wash.	8-53	30-7-54

Mirto (A 5306) Maurizio Brescia, 2001

D: 322 tons (405 fl) **S:** 12 kts **Dim:** 43.92 (42.10 pp) × 8.23 × 2.68
Electronics: Radar: 1 SPN-750 nav.
M: 2 G.M. 8-268A diesels; 2 props; 1,200 bhp
Range: 2,500/10 **Fuel:** 40 tons **Crew:** 4 officers, 35 enlisted

Remarks: Former minesweepers. Superstructure enlarged and stack raised when converted to coastal survey duties. To be retired on completion of the two new *Aretusa*-class survey ships. Based at Genoa and assigned to the Istituto Idrografico della Marina.

Mission systems: Survey equipment includes Elac Deneb Special scanning sonar, Atlas DESO 25 mapping sonar, Toran-F, Raydist, Mini Ranger III, and Loran-C.

♦ **0 (+ 1) vehicle cargo ship [AK]**
Bldr: . . . (In serv. . . .)

Remarks: Either a tailored new-construction or converted merchant vehicle transport ship is sought to support out-of-area deployments by the navy's amphibious forces.

♦ **6 Gorgona-class coastal cargo ships [AK]**
Bldr: C.N. Mario Morini, Ancona

	L	In serv.
A 5347 Gorgona (MTC 1011)	12-7-86	23-12-86
A 5348 Tremiti (MTC 1012)	13-9-86	2-3-87
A 5349 Caprera (MTC 1013)	8-11-86	10-4-87
A 5351 Pantelleria (MTC 1014)	31-1-87	26-5-87
A 5352 Lipari (MTC 1015)	7-5-87	10-7-87
A 5353 Capri (MTC 1016)	18-6-87	16-9-87

Capri (A 5353)—note the lack of a crane on the cargo deck aft and the vehicle ramp at the stern, features that distinguish the *Gorgona* class from the similar *Ponza*-class navigational aids tenders, which have a large articulating crane aft and no ramp; an RP 101–class tug is in the foreground Luciano Grazioli, 5-01

Lipari (A 5352) H&L Van Ginderen, 6-97

D: 631 (fl) **S:** 14+ kts **Dim:** 56.72 × 10.00 × 2.50
A: 2 single 7.62-mm mg; portable mine rails
Electronics: Radar: 1 SMA SPN-732 nav.
M: 2 CRM 12D/SS diesels; 2 props; 1,520 bhp
Electric: 484 kw (2 × 192 kw, 1 × 100 kw)
Range: 1,500/14 **Crew:** 4 officers, 28 enlisted

Remarks: MTC = *Mototrasporti Costieri.* Replaced World War II–era MTCs of the MZ class. A 5347 is based at La Spezia, A 5348 at Ancona, A 5349 and A 5350 at La Maddalena, and the last two at the naval academy in Livorno. A 20-mm 70-cal. Mk 10 Oerlikon AA gun can be mounted atop the pilothouse.
Hull systems: Have two electrohydraulic cranes. Are intended to carry palletized cargo on their open decks and fuel and water below decks. Have an articulating vehicle ramp at the stern to load and unload vehicle cargo while Med-moored.

♦ **1 Etna-class replenishment oiler [AOR]**
Bldr: Fincantieri, Riva Trigoso

	Laid down	L	In serv
A 5326 Etna	4-7-96	12-7-97	29-7-98 (del.)

D: 6,700 tons (13,400 fl) **S:** 21 kts **Dim:** 146.50 (137.00 pp) × 21.00 × 7.25
A: provision for: 1 76-mm 62-cal. OTOBreda Compact DP; 2 single 25-mm 87-cal. Oerlikon-OTOBreda KBA AA; 1 EH.101 or 1 SH-3D Sea King or 2 AB-212 helicopters

AUXILIARIES *(continued)*

Etna (A 5326) Maurizio Brescia, 1999

Etna (A 5326) Luciano Grazioli, 11-98

Electronics:
Radar: 2 SPN-748 nav.; 1 SPQ-702 surf. search; provision for 1 AESN SPG-75 (RTN-30X) f.c.
M: 2 Wärtsilä-Sulzer 12 ZAV 40S diesels; 2 props; 22,400 bhp—1,000-kw bow-thruster
Range: 7,600/18 **Crew:** 160 tot. (accomm. for 243)

Remarks: Intended to accompany *Giuseppe Garibaldi.* Program was frozen in 2-90 but revived and approved in 1993. Was to have been laid down 3-94, but construction was delayed more than a year for lack of adequate funding. Construction contract signed 3-1-95. Has not been very active since delivery. A sister was ordered for the Greek Navy in 7-99 for construction under license in Greece.
Hull systems: Can carry 5,400 tons of gas turbine/diesel fuel, 1,200 tons of aviation fuel, 160 tons of fresh water, 2,100 m^3 (about 280 tons) of ammunition, 30,000 fresh rations, 30,000 dry-food rations, 20 tons of spare parts, and 20 tons of lubricant and has space on deck for 12 cargo containers. Has two replenishment stations on each beam.
Combat systems: Planned gun armament is not yet aboard; the one quadruple 25-mm gatling CIWS originally planned is to be replaced with the 25-mm guns if and when she is armed. Has two different commercial SATCOM terminals.

♦ 2 Stromboli-class replenishment oilers [AOR]
Bldr: C.N. del Tirreno, Riva Trigoso

	Laid down	L	In serv.
A 5327 Stromboli	1-10-73	20-2-75	31-10-75
A 5329 Vesuvio	1-7-74	4-6-77	18-11-78

Stromboli (A 5327) Bernard Prézelin, 5-01

Stromboli (A 5327) Bernard Prézelin, 5-01

D: 4,200 tons (8,706 fl) **S:** 19.5 kts
Dim: 129.00 (118.5 pp) × 18.00 × 6.50 (3.17 light)
A: 1 76-mm 62-cal. OTOBreda DP; 2 single 20-mm 70-cal. Mk 10 Oerlikon AA
Electronics:
Radar: 1 SMA SPN-703 nav.; 1 SMA SPQ-2 surf. search; 1 AESN SPG-70 (RTN-10X) f.c.
M: 2 Wärtsilä NSD C428-SS diesels: 1 LIPS 4-bladed CP prop; 11,200 bhp (9,600 sust.)
Electric: 2,350 kw **Range:** 10,000/16 **Crew:** 10 officers, 114 enlisted

Remarks: Were to be retired 2005–08, but no replacement program has been announced. Sister *Agnadeen,* completed and handed over to Iraq, has been sequestered at Alexandria, Egypt, since 1986; in 8-96, custody of the vessel was awarded to the shipbuilder, Fincantieri, and the ship may be made sold for use or scrap.
Hull systems: Cargo: 1,370 tons fuel oil, 2,830 tons diesel, 480 tons aviation fuel, and 200 tons miscellaneous (torpedoes, missiles, projectiles, spare parts). Capable of serving one unit on each beam using constant-tension fueling rigs, each capable of delivering 650 m^3/hr of fuel oil and 480 m^3/hr of diesel fuel or aviation fuel. Can also refuel over the stern at the rate of 430 m^3/hr. There are also constant-tension cargo transfer rigs on either side, each capable of transferring 1.8-ton loads, as well as two stations for lighter loads. The ships can also replenish via helicopters, although they do not have hangars. Twenty repair-party personnel can also be accommodated, and the ships can carry up to 250 passengers.
Combat systems: Have an NA-10 Argo f.c.s. for the old-model 76-mm gun.

♦ 1 Anteo-class salvage ship/submersible tender [ARS]

	Bldr	Laid down	L	In serv.
A 5309 Anteo	C.N. OTOBreda, Mestre	1977	11-11-78	31-7-80

Anteo (A 5309) Luciano Grazioli, 9-96

D: 2,857 tons (3,120 fl) **S:** 18.3 kts **Dim:** 98.40 (93.00 pp) × 15.80 × 5.20
A: 1 twin 20-mm 70-cal. Mk 24 Oerlikon AA; provision for 1 AB-212 helicopter
Electronics: Radar: 1 SMA SPN-748 nav.; 1 SMA SPN-751 nav.
M: 3 Wärtsilä NSD A230-12V diesels (4,050 bhp each), electric drive (2 motors); 1 prop; 5,600 shp (5,360 sust.)—500-shp bow-thruster
Range: 4,000/14 **Fuel:** 270 tons **Crew:** 12 officers, 125 enlisted

Remarks: Ordered in 1977. Based at La Spezia.
Hull systems: Carries USN-style submarine rescue equipment, including a McCann rescue bell capable of operating at up to 150 m depth and two decompression chambers. A Type MSM-1/S, 22-ton salvage submersible named *Usel* is also carried; 9.0 × 2.5 × 2.7 m in size and displacing 24 tons, the *Usel* can submerge to 600 m and has a 120-hr autonomous endurance with a 4-kt max. speed. Also carried is a Gaymarine Pluto remote-controlled underwater vehicle. During 2000, the ship was equipped with the SRV300 rescue submersible. The ship supports saturation diving to 350 m and has a 27-ton bollard pull towing capacity at 10 kts. There is a telescoping helicopter hangar. A flume-type passive stabilization tank system is fitted.

♦ 1 Proteo-class salvage ship/submersible tender [ARS]
Bldr: CNR, Ancona (In serv. 24-8-51)

A 5310 Proteo (ex-*Perseo*)

Proteo (A 5310)—with dummy armament for movie role H&L Van Ginderen, 7-99

AUXILIARIES *(continued)*

D: 1,865 tons (2,147 fl) **S:** 16 kts **Dim:** 75.10 × 11.70 × 6.10
A: 2 single 20-mm 70-cal. Mk 10 Oerlikon AA
Electronics: Radar: 1 SMA SPN-748 nav.
M: 2 Fiat diesels; 1 prop; 4,800 bhp
Range: 7,500/13 **Crew:** 8 officers, 114 enlisted

Remarks: Seized by German forces after launch in 1944 and towed to Trieste; returned to Ancona and resumed fitting out in 1949. Relieved by *Anteo* (A 5309) as submarine rescue ship but is retained as an auxiliary services training vessel. Has a submersible decompression chamber, extensive divers' support equipment, and a four-point mooring capability. Refitted 1984–85 with a new stack and an electrohydraulic crane. Played a destroyer in the film *U-571,* complete with two twin dummy gunmounts.

♦ 6 Ciclope-class seagoing tugs [ATA] Bldr: C.N. Ferrari, La Spezia

	L	In serv.		L	In serv.
A 5319 Ciclope	20-2-85	11-9-85	A 5328 Gigante	. . .	18-7-86
A 5324 Titano	2-3-85	7-12-85	A 5330 Saturno	29-7-87	5-4-88
A 5325 Polifemo	15-6-85	21-4-86	A 5365 Tenace	31-8-87	9-7-88

Tenace (A 5365) Luciano Grazioli, 5-01

Polifemo (A 5325) Luciano Grazioli, 3-00

D: 600 tons (658 fl) **S:** 14.5 kts **Dim:** 38.95 (32.30 pp) × 9.85 × 3.32
A: none **Electronics:** Radar: 1 SMA SPN-748 nav.
M: 2 Wärtsilä NSD BL230-6L diesels; 1 CP prop; 3,264 bhp
Electric: 500 kw (2 × 200 kw, 1 × 100 kw) **Range:** 3,000/14.5 **Crew:** 12 tot.

Remarks: An enlarged and improved version of the *Atlante* class. Last two ordered 29-5-86. Bollard pull: 45 tons initial, 36 tons sustained at 8.3 kts. Have two 130-m^3/hr water cannon and a 23-ton-capacity foam tank.

♦ 2 Atlante-class seagoing tugs [ATA]
Bldr: C.N. Visitini, Donada (Both in serv. 14-8-75)

A 5317 Atlante A 5318 Prometeo

Prometeo (A 5318) Luciano Grazioli, 10-00

D: 478 tons light (750 fl) **S:** 13.5 kts **Dim:** 38.9 × 9.6 × 3.70
A: none **Electronics:** Radar: 1 SMA SPN-748 nav.
M: 1 Tosi QT 320/8SS diesel; 1 CP prop; 2,670 bhp (3,000 max.)
Range: 4,000/12 **Crew:** 25 tot.

♦ 2 modified Simeto-class water transport tankers [AWT]
Bldr: C.N. De Poli, Pellestrina

A 5376 Ticino (In serv. 12-3-94) A 5377 Tirso (In serv. 10-6-94)

Tirso (A 5377) H&L Van Ginderen, 2-00

D: 663 tons light (1,983 fl) **S:** 13 kts **Dim:** 69.82 (63.60 pp) × 10.06 × 3.90
A: 2 single 7.62-mm mg **Electronics:** Radar: 2 SMA SPN-753B(V) nav.
M: 2 Wärtsilä NSD B230-6 diesels; 1 prop; 2,400 bhp—125-shp bow-thruster
Electric: 420 kw tot. (3 × 140-kw diesel sets)
Range: 1,800/12 **Crew:** 3 officers, 33 enlisted

Remarks: Ordered 5-92. Very similar to the *Simeto.* Molded depth: 4.85 m. Cargo: 1,200 tons of fresh water. A 5376 operates from La Spezia and A 5377 serves the area around Sicily. Have a position abaft the stack for a 20-mm 70-cal. Mk 10 Oerlikon AA gun.

♦ 1 Simeto-class water transport tanker [AWT]
Bldr: CINET, Molfetta

	Laid down	L	In serv.
A 5375 Simeto	14-3-86	4-2-88	9-7-88

Simeto (A 5375) Luciano Grazioli, 9-01

D: 1,914 tons (fl) **S:** 13 kts **Dim:** 68.35 (63.60 pp) × 10.06 × 3.90
A: 2 single 7.62-mm mg **Electronics:** Radar: 1 SMA SPN-748 nav.
M: 2 Wärtsilä NSD B230-6 diesels; 1 prop; 2,400 bhp—125-shp bow-thruster
Electric: 420 kw (3 × 140-kw Isotta-Fraschini ID30 SS6L diesel sets)
Range: 1,650/12 **Crew:** 2 officers, 24 enlisted

Remarks: Replaced the canceled *Tevere* (A 5355)—the second unit of that name and number—which was scrapped incomplete in 1985 when her builder, Ferbex, went bankrupt. *Simeto*'s design is based on that of the *Basento* class. Cargo: 1,200 tons.

♦ 1 Piave-class water transport tanker [AWT]

	Bldr	L	In serv.
A 5354 Piave	C.N. Orlando, Livorno	18-12-71	23-5-73

Piave (A 5354) Luciano Grazioli, 7-00

D: 5,003 tons (fl) **S:** 13.6 kts **Dim:** 97.8 (86.7 pp) × 13.4 × 5.9
A: 2 single 7.62-mm mg **Electronics:** Radar: 1 SMA SPN-748 nav.
M: 2 diesels; 2,560 bhp **Range:** 1,500/12 **Crew:** 7 officers, 48 enlisted

AUXILIARIES *(continued)*

Remarks: Cargo: 3,500 tons. Sister *Tevere* (A 5355) was sold commercially in 1976. Formerly carried two twin 40-mm 60-cal. AA.

♦ 2 Basento-class water transport tankers [AWT]
Bldr: INMA, La Spezia

A 5356 Basento (In serv. 19-7-71) A 5358 Brenta (In serv. 18-4-72)

Brenta (A 5358) Luciano Grazioli, 9-00

D: 1,930 tons (fl) **S:** 12.5 kts **Dim:** 68.65 × 10.07 × 3.90
A: removed **Electronics:** Radar: 1 SMA SPN-703 nav.
M: 2 Fiat LA-230 diesels; 1 prop; 1,730 hp
Range: 1,650/12.5 **Crew:** 3 officers, 21 enlisted

Remarks: Cargo: 1,200 tons. Can carry two single 20-mm AA. Able to make 13.1 kts in light condition. Sister *Bradano* (A 3357) was stricken on 1-12-01, and A 5358 was to follow on 1-2-02.

♦ 1 full-rigged sail training ship [AXT]
Bldr: Nav. Mec. Castellammare

	Laid down	L	In serv.
A 5312 Amerigo Vespucci	12-5-30	22-2-31	15-5-31

Amerigo Vespucci (A 5312) A. D. Baker III, 6-00

D: 3,545 tons (4,146 fl) **S:** 10 kts (under power)
Dim: 101.00 (over bowsprit; 82.38 hull; 70.72 pp) × 15.56 × 6.7
A: removed **Electronics:** Radar: 2 SMA SPN-748 nav.
M: 2 Tosi E6 diesels, electric drive: 2 Marelli motors; 1 prop; 1,900 shp—2,100 m^2 max. sail area
Range: 5,450/6.5 **Crew:** 13 officers, 228 enlisted, 150 cadets

Remarks: Steel construction, including masts. Refitted in 1984. Employed for the annual naval academy training cruises. No longer carries armament of four single 40-mm 60-cal. Bofors and one 20-mm 70-cal. Oerlikon AA, but is equipped with four 76-mm saluting cannon.

♦ 1 sail-training barkentine [AXT]
Bldr: Chantiers Dubigeon, Nantes, France (In serv. 1934)

A 5311 Palinuro (ex-*Cdt. Louis Richard*)

D: 1,042 tons (1,341 fl) **S:** 10 kts (7.5 under sail)
Dim: 68.9 (59.0 pp) × 10.1 × 4.8 **Electronics:** Radar: 1 SPN-748 nav.
M: 1 M.A.N. G8V23.5/33 diesel; 450 bhp—1,152 m^2 max. sail area
Range: 5,385/7.5 under power **Crew:** 4 officers, 44 enlisted

Remarks: Former French cod-fishing craft bought in 1951, refitted and recommissioned 16-7-55. Steel hull. Carries two 76-mm saluting cannon.

Palinuro (A 5311) Findler & Winter, 6-01

SERVICE CRAFT

♦ 1 Meattini-class submarine rescue launch [YAG]
Bldr: Baglietto, Varazze (In serv. . . .)

MEN 209

MEN 209 Luciano Grazioli, 4-93

D: 42 tons (fl) **S:** 34 kts **Dim:** 20.10 × 5.20 × 0.93 (hull)
A: none **Electronics:** Radar: 1 Furuno . . . nav.
M: 2 CRM 18D-S2 diesels; 2 props; 2,500 bhp
Range: 560/21 **Fuel:** 5.8 tons **Crew:** . . . tot.

Remarks: A white, yacht-like craft officially classified as a *Motoscafo Soccorso Sommergibili* (Submarine Rescue Boat). Same hull and propulsion as the customs service's *Meattini* class, but with an enlarged superstructure. Has a commercial SATCOM terminal.

♦ 2 ex-British LCT(3)-class miscellaneous service craft [YAG]
(In serv. 1943–44)

A 5331 M.O.C. 1201
A 5334 M.O.C. 1204

D: A 5331: 579 tons; A 5334: 711 tons (fl) **Dim:** 58.25 × 9.22 × 2.0–2.2
Electronics: Radar: 1 BX-732 nav.
M: 2 diesels; 2 props; 1,000 bhp **Crew:** 1–2 officers, 20–26 enlisted

Remarks: Transferred from the U.K. in 1956. M.O.C. = *Moto Officina Costiera* (Coastal Repair Ship). A 5331 is based at Augusta and is used for torpedo recovery and as a diving tender. A5334 is based at La Spezia and is used as a coastal repair craft. Both have had the bow door/ramp welded closed and are no longer armed.
Disposals: M.O.C. 1203 (A 5333) was decommissioned 1-3-98 and transferred to Albania in 1999. M.O.C. 1205 (A 5335) was retired 30-9-98 and M.O.C. 1202 (A 5332) on 31-3-99.

SERVICE CRAFT *(continued)*

M.O.C. 1201 (A 5331) Luciano Grazioli, 6-98

♦ 1 underwater systems trials craft [YAGE]
Bldr: C.N. Picchiotti, Viareggio

	L	Del.	In serv.
A 5320 Vincenzo Martellotta	28-5-88	2-3-89	22-12-90

D: 340 tons (fl) **S:** 17.5 kts **Dim:** 44.50 × 7.90 × 2.30
A: 1 533-mm fixed TT; 1 triple 324-mm B-515 ASW TT
Electronics: Radar: 1 . . . nav.—Sonar: . . .
M: 2 Isotta-Fraschini ID36 N12V diesels; 2 CP props; 3,500 bhp—1 . . . drop-down outdrive aft for low-speed operations—bow-thruster
Range: 700/15 **Crew:** 1 officer, 8 enlisted + 8 technicians

Remarks: A revised version of the *Raffaele Rossetti* (A 5315), intended for ASW torpedo trials, the laying and recovery of acoustic buoys, and trials with remotely controlled underwater vehicles. Has a bulbous bow, unlike A 5315, and can lay a three-dimensional torpedo-tracking hydrophone array. Operated from La Spezia with A 5315 by the Commission for War Materials Experiments.

♦ 1 underwater systems trials craft [YAGE]
Bldr: C.N. Picchiotti, Viareggio

	L	In serv.
A 5315 Raffaele Rossetti	21-7-86	20-12-86

Raffaele Rossetti (A 5315) Carlo Martinelli, 3-99

Raffaele Rossetti (A 5315) Carlo Martinelli, 9-98

D: 282 tons (320 fl) **S:** 14.5 kts **Dim:** 44.60 (40.00 pp) × 7.90 × 2.10
A: 2 533-mm TT (1 submerged, *Sauro*-type; 1 surface, *Maestrale*-type, for A-184-series wire-guided torpedoes); 1 triple 324-mm B-515 ASW TT
Electronics: Radar: 1 . . . nav.—Sonar: . . .
M: 2 Isotta-Fraschini ID36 N12V diesels; 2 CP props; 3,500 bhp
Electric: . . . kw (2 gen.) **Range:** 12,000/12
Crew: 1 officer, 8 enlisted + 8 technicians

Remarks: Ordered 3-84 for torpedo, sonar, and electronic warfare equipment trials. Has a 96-cell battery for electric, low-speed, silent propulsion. Operated from La Spezia with A 5320 by the Commission for War Materials Experiments.

♦ 1 Aragosta-class weapons trials craft [YAGE]
Bldr: C.N. Apuana, Marina di Currara (In serv. 1957)

A 5305 Murena (ex-*Scampo,* M 5466)

Murena (A 5305) Carlo Martinelli, 2-94

D: 130 tons (188 fl) **S:** 13.5 kts **Dim:** 32.35 × 6.47 × 2.14
A: 1 triple 324-mm B-515 ASW TT **Electronics:** Radar: 1 BX-732 nav.
M: 2 Fiat-MTU MB 820D diesels; 2 props; 1,000 bhp **Electric:** 340 kw
Range: 2,000/9 **Fuel:** 15 tons **Crew:** 4 officers, 12 enlisted

Remarks: Former inshore minesweeper, with a new superstructure and enclosed bridge. Formerly carried a fixed 533-mm torpedo tube at the stern, which has been fitted with a recovery ramp. The triple ASW TT mount is carried to port, just abaft the superstructure, while to starboard is an articulating hydraulic recovery crane.

♦ . . . floating cranes [YD]

Floating crane GA 1013—GA 1012 and GA 1017 are identical
Luciano Grazioli, 4-96

Remarks: Sisters GA 1012, GA 1013, and GA 1017 are just three of a number of non-self-propelled floating cranes in service; no data available. GA 60 is a smaller floating crane employed at Taranto.

♦ 1 degaussing tender [YDG]
Bldr: Intermarine-Crestitalia, Ameglia, La Spezia (In serv. 1989)

JDG 10

D: 135 tons (fl) **S:** 2–4 kts **Dim:** 25.20 × 8.00 × 0.95
M: 2 outboard engines; 110 bhp **Crew:** . . .

Remarks: Barge-like hull with tapered ends. Outboard engines are mounted within vertical wells through the hull.

♦ 2 Mario Marino–class swimmer support craft [YDT]
Bldr: Intermarine-Crestitalia, Ameglia, La Spezia

	Laid down	L	In serv.
Y 498 Mario Marino (ex-MEN 213)	8-9-83	1984	23-10-84
Y 499 Alcide Pedretti (ex-MEN 214)	8-9-83	1984	21-12-84

SERVICE CRAFT *(continued)*

Alcide Pedretti (Y 499) Carlo Martinelli, 11-98

D: 69.5 tons light (96.6 fl) **S:** 28 kts **Dim:** 22.85 × 6.90 × 1.06 (1.50 max.)
Electronics: Radar: 2 . . . nav.
M: 2 Isotta-Fraschini ID36 SS12V diesels; 2 props; 3,040 bhp
Range: Y 498: 236/28; 264/23.2—Y 499: 450/23.5
Crew: 1 officer, 7 enlisted + . . . swimmers

Remarks: Typed MAS *(Motoscafi Appoggio Subacquei).* Built for Raggruppamento Incursori assault swimmers (COMSUBIN), based at La Spezia. GRP construction. Y 499 has a recessed stern for diver recovery and a divers' stage and decompression chamber fitted. One near-sister was built for the United Arab Emirates.

♦ **1 Cheradi-class personnel ferry [YFB]** (In serv. 1993)

CHERADI

Cheradi Luciano Grazioli, 5-01

Remarks: Replaced the ferry *Tarantola* at Taranto Naval Base. No characteristics data available.

♦ **7 GO 51–series medium floating dry docks [YFDM]**
Bldr: C.N. Ferrari, La Spezia

GO 51 through GO 57

GO 51–series floating dry dock GO 53 Carlo Martinelli, 5-91

Capacity: 6,000 tons **Dim:** 150.2 × 29.6 (21.6 internal) × 1.50 (light; 14.95 max.)

Remarks: GO 52, completed in 1979, may be to a somewhat different design; the others were completed between 10-2-90 and 1996. GO 53 was laid down 30-1-89 and launched 10-2-90 for use at Augusta, Sicily. A new floating dry dock of about 6,000 tons capacity was completed by Metalcast, La Spezia, in 1998.

♦ **13 miscellaneous small dry docks [YFDL/YFDM]**

	In serv.	Capacity (tons)		In serv.	Capacity (tons)
GO 1	1942	1,000	GO 18B	1920	600
GO 5	1893	100	GO 20	1935	1,600
GO 8	1904	3,800	GO 22	1935	1,000
GO 10	1900	2,000	GO 23	1935	1,000
GO 11	1911	2,700	GO 51	1971	2,000
GO 17	1917	500	GO 58	1995	2,000
GO 18A	1920	800			

Floating dry dock GO 20—at Augusta Luciano Grazioli, 6-99

♦ **6 or more Azteca-class personnel launches [YFL]**
Bldr: Crestitalia, Ameglia, La Spezia (In serv. . . .)

MCN 1574 MCN 1579 MCN 1594
MCN 1578 MCN 1583 MCN 1614

MCN 1594 Luciano Grazioli, 11-98

D: 5 tons **S:** 24 kts **Dim:** 9.00 × 3.16 × 0.80
M: 2 AIFO CP3M diesels; 2 props; 320 bhp
Range: 240/18 **Crew:** 4 tot.

Remarks: MCN 1574 and 1579 are of the same design as the Coast Guard CP 1001 class; MCN 1578, 1594, and 1614 are of a later model with a larger cabin and pilothouse.

♦ **2 MEN 215–class personnel launches [YFL]**
Bldr: Intermarine-Crestitalia, Ameglia, La Spezia (In serv. 1986)

MEN 215 MEN 216

MEN 216 Carlo Martinelli, 6-86

D: 82 tons (fl) **S:** 28 kts (23 sust.) **Dim:** 27.28 × 6.98 × 1.10
Electronics: Radar: 1 SMA SPN-732 nav.
M: 2 Isotta-Fraschini ID36 SS12V diesels; 2 props; 3,200 bhp
Electric: 50 kVA (2 × 25-kVA gen.) **Range:** 250/14
Crew: 4 tot. + 250 passengers

Remarks: Built to be carried by the carrier *Giuseppe Garibaldi* as commando transports and for search-and-rescue, disaster relief, and other transport duties. GRP construction. Now used as personnel ferries at the La Spezia and Taranto naval bases respectively.

♦ **32 or more miscellaneous personnel launches [YFL]**

MBN 1143, 1154, 1159
MCN 1594, 1602, 1605, 1611, 1617, 1618, 1619, 1623, 1631, 1633, 1643, 1644, 1647, 1649, 1651, 1661, 1662
MDN 90, 91, 102, 103, 107, 110, 111, 113, 119, 173
MEN 216, 1011

SERVICE CRAFT *(continued)*

MDN 107—MDN 103 and MDN 173 are sisters H&L Van Ginderen, 2-00

MCN 1647—MCN 1651, MCN 1661, and MCN 1643 are identical, while MCN 1602 has a lower passenger cabin aft with circular ports Luciano Grazioli, 6-98

GRP-hulled utility launch MBN 1154—MBN 1143 and MBN 1159 are sisters Luciano Grazioli, 6-99

Remarks: No data available. Miscellaneous personnel and utility launches.

Disposal note: The yacht-cum-ambulance craft *R. Paolucci* was retired in 1999.

♦ 4 seagoing fuel lighters [YO] Bldr: Cantieri Ferrari, La Spezia

	L	In serv.
A 5370 MCC 1101	26-10-85	26-8-86
A 5371 MCC 1102	16-11-85	6-12-86
A 5372 MCC 1103	3-2-86	18-5-87
A 5373 MCC 1104	14-11-87	20-5-88

MCC 1102 (A 5371) Luciano Grazioli, 8-99

D: 863 tons (fl) **S:** 13 kts **Dim:** 47.30 × 10.00 × 3.30
Electronics: Radar: 1 SMA SPN-732 nav.

MCC 1103 (A 5372)—with a small deckhouse projecting on the tank deck at the forward end of the poop Carlo Martinelli, 7-95

M: 2 Isotta-Fraschini ID36 SS6V diesels; 2 props; 1,320 bhp
Range: 1,500/12 **Crew:** 2 officers, 9 enlisted

Remarks: Cargo: 550 tons. MMC = *Motocisterne Combustibili* (fuel lighter).

♦ 4 GGS 1010–class harbor fuel lighters [YO]
Bldr: C.N. De Poli, Pellestrina, Venice

GRS/G 1010 GRS/G 1011 GRS/G 1012 GRS/J 1013

GRS/J 1013 Luciano Grazioli, 6-94

D: approx. 700 tons (fl) **S:** 11 kts
Dim: 39.10 (37.50 pp) × 8.50 × 3.10 (4.00 molded depth)
M: 2 AIFO 8281 SRM 08 diesels; 2 props; 544 bhp **Crew:** 12 tot.

Remarks: 508 dwt. Cargo: 500 m^3. GRS/G-designated units carry fuel, while GRS/J 1013 carries JP-5 aircraft fuel. Three sisters serve as water tankers (GGS 1012, 1013, and 1014).

Note: Also in use are an unknown number of non-self-propelled fuel barges [YON] in the GRS-series, of which GRS 1002, illustrated, is a typical example.

♦ 1 MEN 212–class torpedo retriever [YPT]
Bldr: Intermarine-Crestitalia, Ameglia, La Spezia (In serv. 10-83)

MEN 212

Torpedo retriever MEN 212—at top, with smaller retrievers MCN 1595 and MCN 1625 in foreground H&L Van Ginderen, 8-00

D: 32 tons (fl) **S:** 23 kts **Dim:** 17.65 × 5.10 × 1.00
M: 2 diesels; 2 props; 1,380 bhp **Range:** 250/20 **Crew:** 4 tot.

Remarks: Can stow three recovered torpedoes. Glass-reinforced plastic construction.

♦ 4 small torpedo retrievers [YPT]
Bldr: Intermarine-Crestitalia, La Spezia (In serv. 1980s)

MCN 1595 MCN 1603 MCN 1622 MCN 1625

SERVICE CRAFT *(continued)*

Remarks: No characteristics available. Have a stern ramp for weapon recovery. GRP construction. A sister, *Whitehead I,* is operated by the torpedo manufacturer Whitehead Alenia Sistemi Subacquei (WASS). There is also an even smaller weapons recovery launch, MCN 1590, which operates from La Spezia.

♦ 9 Porto-class large harbor tugs [YTB]

Bldr: first six: C.N. De Poli, Pellestrina; others: C.N. Giacalone, Mazzara del Vallo, Trapani

	L	In serv.
Y 421 Porto Empedocle	4-12-85	19-3-86
Y 422 Porto Pisano	22-10-85	20-8-85
Y 423 Porto Conte	21-11-85	28-9-85
Y 425 Porto Ferraio	21-7-85	3-4-85
Y 426 Porto Venere	13-5-85	12-2-85
Y 428 Porto Salvo	13-9-85	4-7-85
Y 413 Porto Fossone	...	24-9-90
Y 416 Porto Torres	3-9-90	16-1-91
Y 417 Porto Corsini	2-11-90	4-3-91

Porto Ferraio (Y 425)—with mast folded Luciano Grazioli, 5-01

D: 412 tons (fl) **S:** 11.5 kts **Dim:** 32.36 (28.00 pp) × 8.50 × 3.32
Electronics: Radar: 1 BX-732 nav.
M: 1 Wärtsilä NSD B230-8M diesel; 1 CP prop; 1,600 bhp
Electric: 200 kw (2 × 100 kw)
Range: 1,800/11.5 **Fuel:** 46 tons **Crew:** 13 tot.

Remarks: First six ordered 2-6-83. The other three were originally ordered 29-10-87 from Ferbex, Naples, then were reordered 18-5-88 from Giacalone after Ferbex closed; laid down 18-5-88. Bollard pull: 25 tons (15 tons at 5 kts). Have two water cannon and two 130-m^3/hr pumps. The final three have two 200-kw generator sets. All have an ELAC LAZ-50 echo sounder.

♦ 2 Porto d'Ischia–class medium harbor tugs [YTM]

Bldr: CNR, Riva Trigoso (In serv. 1969–70)

Y 436 Porto d'Ischia Y 443 Riva Trigoso

Porto d'Ischia (Y 436) Carlo Martinelli, 2-99

D: 250 tons (297 fl) **S:** 12 kts **Dim:** 25.5 × 7.1 × 3.3
M: 1 diesel; 1 CP prop; 850 bhp **Range:** 2,600/12

♦ 10 RP 125–class small harbor tugs [YTL]

Bldrs: A: C.N. Vittoria, Adria; B: C.N. Ferrari, La Spezia; C: CINET, Molfetta

	Bldr	In serv.		Bldr	In serv.
Y 478 RP 125	A	1983	Y 483 RP 130	B	10-8-84
Y 479 RP 126	A	24-9-83	Y 484 RP 131	B	28-8-84
Y 480 RP 127	B	29-3-84	Y 485 RP 132	C	7-7-84
Y 481 RP 128	B	4-84	Y 486 RP 133	C	3-11-84
Y 482 RP 129	B	5-6-84	Y 487 RP 134	B	1985

RP 132 (Y 485) Luciano Grazioli, 5-01

D: 78 tons (120 fl) **S:** 9.5 kts **Dim:** 19.85 (17.00 pp) × 5.20 × 2.10
M: 1 Fiat-AIFO 828-SM diesel; 1 prop; 368 bhp **Electric:** 28 kw
Range: 400/9.5 **Crew:** 3 tot.

Remarks: 76 grt. First six ordered 18-8-83. Have one 120-m^3/hr water cannon.

♦ 10 RP 113–class small harbor tugs [YTL]

Bldr: C.N. Visitini, Donada

	In serv.		In serv.
Y 463 RP 113	1978	Y 471 RP 120	1980
Y 464 RP 114	1980	Y 472 RP 121	1980
Y 465 RP 115	1980	Y 473 RP 122	1980
Y 466 RP 116	1980	Y 474 RP 123	1980
Y 470 RP 119	1980	Y 475 RP 124	1981

RP 115 (Y 465) Luciano Grazioli, 4-96

Remarks: Characteristics similar to the RP 101 class, but with a larger superstructure. Details differ. RP 117 (Y 467) and RP 118 (Y 468) deleted, date not available. All normally have a crew of three.

♦ 12 RP 101–class small harbor tugs [YTL]

Bldr: C.N. Visitini-Loreo, Donada (In serv. 1972–75)

Y 403 RP 101	Y 408 RP 105	Y 456 RP 109
Y 404 RP 102	Y 410 RP 106	Y 458 RP 110
Y 406 RP 103	Y 413 RP 107	Y 460 RP 111
Y 407 RP 104	Y 452 RP 108	Y 462 RP 112

RP 106 (Y 410) Luciano Grazioli, 5-01

D: 36 tons (75 fl) **S:** 12 kts **Dim:** 18.8 × 4.5 × 1.9 **M:** 1 diesel; 270 bhp

SERVICE CRAFT *(continued)*

♦ **3 VF 681–class fireboats [YTR]**
Bldr: C.N. De Poli, Pellestrina

VF 681 (In serv. 7-89) VF 683 Enrico Squarcina (In serv. . . .)
VF 682 (In serv. 18-11-89)

Enrico Squarcina (VF 683) H&L Van Ginderen, 10-96

Remarks: First two serve at Venice. Have red hulls with white superstructures. Two fire monitors are fitted atop the stack structure and a third on the bow. No data available.

♦ **4 VF 444–class fireboats [YTR]**
Bldr: . . . (In serv. . . .)

VF 441 Massimo Inzan VF 442 VF 443 VF 444

VF 444 H&L Van Ginderen, 10-96

Remarks: No data available.

♦ **4 or more MEN 223–class fireboats [YTR]**

MEN 223 MEN 224 MEN 233 MEN 234

MEN 233 Luciano Grazioli, 2-98

Remarks: A smaller version of the VF 681 class. Have an articulating boom-mounted fire monitor aft and another fire monitor on the foredeck. No data available.

Note: Other fireboats in service include the large VF 543 and the tiny VF 51.

VF 543—appears to be larger than any of the craft in the three listed classes of fireboats H&L Van Ginderen, 5-99

♦ **2 sail-training ketches [YTS]**
Bldr: . . . . . .

A . . . Aquarius (In serv. 6-94) A . . . Orsa Maggiore (In serv. 30-1-94)

Orsa Maggiore—returning from an around-the-world cruise Luciano Grazioli, 2-98

Remarks: Both of 70 tons; no other data available. *Orsa Maggiore* was assigned to the naval academy at Livorno 30-12-94 and has made two world cruises, the more recent during 2001.

♦ **1 RORC-class cruising yacht [YTS]**
Bldr: Sangermani, Chiavari (In serv. 7-10-65)

A 5313 Stella Polare

D: 41 tons (47 fl) **S:** . . . **Dim:** 20.9 × 4.7 × 2.9
M: 1 Mercedes-Benz diesel; 1 prop; 96 bhp—197 m^2 max. sail area
Crew: 2 officers, 14 cadets

Remarks: Based at the naval academy, Livorno.

♦ **1 sail-training yawl [YTS]**
Bldr: Sparkman & Stevens, U.S.A. (In serv. 1963)

A 5322 Capricia

D: 49.9 tons net **S:** . . . kts **Dim:** 22.54 × 5.05 × . . .
M: 1 G.M. Detroit Diesel diesel; 160 bhp—254 m^2 max. sail area

Remarks: Donated by Italian Senator Agnelli and commissioned 1-94 for use at the La Spezia sailing club when the yard building the *Cristoforo Colombo II* went bankrupt.

♦ **1 sail-training yawl [YTS]** Bldr: Costaguta, Genoa (In serv. 5-1-61)

A 5316 Corsaro II

D: 41 tons **S:** . . . kts **Dim:** 20.9 × 4.7
Electronics: Radar: 1 Decca 060
M: 1 auxiliary engine; 96 bhp—205 m^2 max. sail area
Crew: 2 officers, 14 cadets

Remarks: Based at the naval academy, Livorno. Very similar to *Stella Polare* (A 5313).

♦ **1 sail-training yawl [YTS]**
Bldr: C.N. Baglietto, Varazze (In serv. 16-10-48)

A 5302 Caroly

SERVICE CRAFT *(continued)*

Caroly (A 5302) Luciano Grazioli, 7-99

D: 50.9 tons (60 fl) **S:** 9 kts (6.5 power) **Dim:** 26.60 (23.75 pp) × 4.80 × 3.10
M: 1 G.M. Detroit Diesel diesel; 100 bhp—210 m^2 max. sail area
Fuel: 1,390 liters **Crew:** 13 officers, 3 enlisted

Remarks: Donated to the navy 25-4-83.

Note: There are also a number of smaller sail-training craft in use by the Sezioni Veliche, the local branch of Marivela, the Italian Navy's sporting organization, including the sloop *Scorpione* and boats named *Aquilante, Barracuda, Calypso, Gabbiano, Galatea, Gemini, Grifone Bianco, Murena, Pellicano, Penelope, Quadrante, Sestante, Ussaro,* and *Zeffiro.*

♦ 3 GGS 1010–class small water lighters [YW]
Bldr: C.N. De Poli, Pellestrina, Venice (In serv. 2-90 to 2-91)

GGS 1012 GGS 1013 GGS 1014

GGS 1013 Luciano Grazioli, 5-01

D: approx. 700 tons (fl) **S:** 11 kts **Dim:** 39.10 (37.50 pp) × 8.50 × 3.10
M: 2 AIFO 8281 SRM 08 diesels; 2 props; 544 bhp **Crew:** 12 tot.

Remarks: 508 dwt. Cargo: 500 m^3. Four sisters serve as fuel tankers. Have a lower superstructure than the fuel-carrier version and a 4.00-m molded depth.

♦ 1 small water lighter [YW] Bldr: . . . (In serv. . . .)

A 5359 Bormida (ex-GGS 1011)

D: 471 tons (fl) **S:** 7 kts **Dim:** 40.2 × 7.2 × 2.2
M: 2 . . . . . . diesels; 1 prop; 130 bhp **Crew:** 6 tot.

Remarks: Former yard fuel lighter, converted to water tanker in 1974. Cargo capacity: 260 tons. Used only in local service.

♦ 5 GGS 172–class water barges [YWN]

GGS 172 GGS 173 GGS 175 GGS 178 XI

Remarks: All of about 500 tons capacity. Also in use are five water barges in the GGS 502–507 series.

♦ 4 TIRMA Project navigational training craft [YXT] Bldr: . . .

D: 120–140 tons (fl) **S:** . . . kts **Dim:** 33.00 × . . . × . . .
Electronics: Radar: . . .
M: 2 diesels; 2 props; . . . bhp

Remarks: Were to be ordered in 2000 for delivery starting in 2001 to replace the *Aragosta* class at the naval academy; as of 6-01, however, no contract had been announced. Will have composite construction hulls and very extensive navigational aids and communications suites, but no armament.

♦ 5 Aragosta-class training craft [YXT]

	Bldr	L	In serv.
A 5378 Aragosta (ex-M 5450)	CRDA, Monfalcone	8-56	19-7-57
A 5379 Astice (ex-M 5452)	CRDA, Monfalcone	16-1-57	19-7-57
A 5380 Mitilo (ex-M 5459)	Picchiotti, Viareggio	1-6-57	11-7-57
A 5381 Polipo (ex-M 5463)	Costaguta, Voltri	15-6-57	10-7-57
A 5382 Porpora (ex-M 5464)	Costaguta, Voltri	1-6-57	10-7-57

Aragosta (A 5378)—with deckhouse aft for divers' decompression chamber
H&L Van Ginderen, 8-94

D: 120 tons (178 fl) **S:** 13.5 kts **Dim:** 32.35 × 6.47 × 2.14
A: none **Electronics:** Radar: 1 BX-732 nav.
M: 2 Fiat-MTU MB 820D diesels; 2 props; 1,000 bhp **Electric:** 340 kw
Range: 2,000/9 **Fuel:** 15 tons **Crew:** 2 officers, 13 enlisted

Remarks: Former inshore minesweepers of a design based on the British "Ham"-class design. Originally 20 in the class. Built with U.S. Military Assistance Program funds. Wooden construction. The single 20-mm AA forward has been removed. A 5381 and A 5382 were reclassified 1984–85 for use as administrative tenders and navigational training craft at the naval academy. A 5378 is equipped as a combat swimmer training craft and has a decompression chamber in a deckhouse aft. Two now-stricken sisters (GLS 501, GLS 502) served as ferries, and *Murena* (A 5305) still serves as a torpedo trials and retriever craft [YAGE].

Note: There are a large number of harbor service craft, launches, and so forth with hull numbers in the G, GAA, GAS, GD, GGS, GHIF, GT, GTM, MCN, MDN, MEN, and VS series. Open barges [YC] GD 325–328, 18.0 × 5.97 m, were laid down in 1989 by C.N. Vernaglione, Taranto (GD 328 by C.N. Balsamo, Brindisi). GHIF 261, 20.00 × 5.00 m, was laid down 10-8-89 by Vernaglione, Taranto. G 14, a sullage barge, was delivered 5-90 by C.N. Solimano, Savona.

COAST GUARD
(Guardia Costiera)

The Guardia Costiera was created as a branch of the Port Captain Corps *(Comando Generale delle Capitanerie di Porto)* of the Italian Navy on 8-6-89 and operates under the control of the Ministry of Transport and Navigation in peacetime and the navy in wartime; it has police, fisheries protection, oil-spill recovery, and SAR duties. The Guardia Costiera is the Italian agency responsible for rescue at sea under the Hamburg International Convention of 27-8-49.

Personnel (31-12-99): 9,445 tot. (1,190 officers, 8,255 enlisted). The personnel complement is scheduled to grow to 11,000 by 2001. Two teams of frogmen are based one at Naples and one at San Benedetto del Tronto.

Organization: Coast Guard headquarters are at Rome, and there are 13 Maritime Districts and 13 Maritime Area Operations Commands; additionally, there are 48 harbor offices, 44 maritime district offices, 140 local maritime offices, three fixed-wing air bases, one helicopter base, two Loran-C stations, one SARSAT station, and six antipollution operations centers.

Aviation: One ATR-42-420MP and 14 Piaggio P-166DL3/SEM fixed-wing aircraft for surveillance duties and 8 AB-412EP helicopters. The three Gruppi Aerei are based at Sarzana/Luni, Catania/Fontanarossa, and Pescara. A second ATR-42-420MP is to be delivered during 3-03.

Two Guardia Costiera Piaggio P-166DL3/SEM Luciano Grazioli, 5-99

Armament: Guardia Costiera ships and craft are normally unarmed, but a 25-mm OTOBreda KBA is mounted on the *Saettia,* a 20-mm cannon can be installed on the CP 409, CP 405, and CP 401 classes, and 7.62-mm machineguns can be installed on CP 200– and CP 300–series boats. Smaller boats can carry submachineguns and Franchi SPAS 15 riot guns.

Note: All units now have white hulls and lower superstructures. All have a broad red diagonal hull stripe, with narrow white and green trailing diagonals; within the red stripe is a black anchor in a white circle. The words *"Guardia Costiera"* have replaced *"Capitanerie"* on the hull sides. Hull numbers are in red. Decks are dark green or light gray.

COAST GUARD *(continued)*

Guardia Costiera AgustaWestland-Bell AB-412EP COGECAP, Rome

PATROL CRAFT [WPC]

♦ 0 (+ 4) Improved Saettia class

Bldr: Fincantieri, Muggiano

	In serv.		In serv.
CP 902 Ubaldo Diciotti	4-02	CP 904 Luigi Dattilo	12-02
CP 903 Michele Fiorillo	8-02	CP 905 Oreste Corso	4-03

Improved Saettia class—builder's model Norman Friedman, 10-00

D: 340 tons light (392 normal; 427 fl) **S:** 31 kts (29 sust.)
Dim: 52.85 (47.20 pp) × 8.10 × . . .
A: 1 25-mm OTOBreda KBA AA
Electronics: Radar: 2 Gem SPN-753XS(V)2 nav. (X- and S-band)
M: 4 Isotta-Fraschini V1716 T2MSD diesels; 4 CP props; 12,660 bhp (at 2,030 rpm)—bow-thruster
Electric: 624 kw tot. (3 × 208 kw, Isotta-Fraschini L1306 T2ME diesels driving)
Range: 1,800/16 **Crew:** 3 officers, 27 enlisted

Remarks: Three ordered 14-9-00, with an option for a fourth later taken up. CP 902 and CP 903 were laid down on 28-6-01. Revised version of the *Saettia,* as modified for Guardia Costiera work; will have a flush deck, cleared aft for helicopter hovering access. Nonretractable fin stabilizers will be fitted. Will carry an Achille M-4 remotely operated surveillance submersible with a 300-m operating depth, two RIBs with 90-bhp outboard motors, and four 100-person inflatable life rafts.

♦ 1 Saettia class

Bldr: Fincantieri, Muggiano

	Laid down	L	In serv.
CP 901 Saettia	6-84	12-84	12-85

Saettia (CP 901) H&L Van Ginderen, 1-00

D: 322 tons light (392 normal; 427 fl) **S:** 40 kts (37.5 sust.)
Dim: 51.70 (47.20 pp) × 8.10 × 2.15
A: 1 25-mm OTOBreda KBA AA
Electronics: Radar: 2 Gem SPN-753SX(V)2 nav.
M: 4 MTU 16V538 TB93 diesels; 4 props; 17,600 bhp (16,560 sust.)
Electric: 450 kw tot. (3 × 150-kw Isotta-Fraschini ID38 SS6V diesel sets)
Range: 1,800/18 **Endurance:** 12 days **Crew:** 29 tot.

Remarks: Built as a demonstrator for Fincantieri's DA-360T-design guided-missile patrol craft and never acquired by the Italian or any foreign navy despite attempts to sell her. Laid up since the early 1990s, she was acquired by the coast guard and modified by the builder, delivered on 20-7-99. The original armament of one 76-mm OTOBreda Compact gun, a twin 40-mm 70-cal. Dardo AA mount, and four Otomat SSMs has been removed, along with the associated fire-control radars. A modified mast was fitted in 2000 and the gun during 2001. Based at Messina.

♦ 1 CP 409–class high-endurance patrol and rescue craft

Bldr: CNR, Ancona (In serv. 1992)

CP 409 Giulio Ingianni

Giulio Ingianni (CP 409) Bernard Prézelin, 10-00

D: 196 tons normal (205 fl) **S:** 21 kts **Dim:** 34.60 × 7.15 × 2.20
A: provision for 1 20-mm 70-cal. Oerlikon AA
Electronics: Radar: 1 Decca 20V90 ARPA nav.; 1 Decca 2050/6 nav.
M: 2 Isotta-Fraschini ID36 SS16V.200 diesels; 2 KaMeWa CP props; 2,910 bhp
Range: 1,000/18 **Crew:** 13 tot.

Remarks: Ordered in 1991. Steel hull with light alloy superstructure. Carries a U.S.-made Boston Whaler Outrage-19 5.8-m launch powered by two 60-bhp Yamaha outboards. Has an electrohydraulic telescoping crane to assist in recovery, a firefighting water monitor on the mast platform, and a stern wedge to improve speed and fuel economy. Equipped with Vosper fin stabilizers. Has a Racal Decca GPS receiver, a Taiyo TL 900A Loran-C receiver, and MF, VHF, and UHF D/F receivers.

♦ 4 CP 405–class high-endurance patrol and rescue craft

Bldr: Bacino di Carenaggio SpA, Trapani (In serv. 1991–92)

CP 405 Francesco Mazzinghi
CP 406 Antonio Scialoia
CP 407 Michele Lolini
CP 408 Mario Grabar

Antonio Scialoia (CP 406)—as modified with pilothouse one deck higher Maurizio Brescia, 10-99

D: 136 tons (fl) **S:** 24 kts **Dim:** 29.50 × 6.70 × 1.83
Electronics: Radar: 1 Decca . . . ARPA nav.
M: 2 Isotta-Fraschini ID36 SS8V diesels; 2 props; 6,500 bhp
Range: 1,000/. . . **Crew:** 16 tot. + 50 rescuees

Remarks: Steel hull with light alloy superstructure. No "daughter boat" rescue craft. Have two water cannon for firefighting. CP 406 is named for Italy's greatest maritime law scholar, CP 405 for the first commanding general of the Port Captain Corps of the Italian Navy. CP 408 launched 31-3-90, CP 406 the following month. Have GPS and Loran-C receivers, plus HF, VHF, and UHF D/F equipment. CP 405 and CP 406 were modernized and re-engined during 1998–99, CP 407 during 1999–2000, and CP 408 during 2001, all with new superstructures and electronics and two new engines in place of the original four CRM 12D/SS diesels totaling 5,500 bhp.

♦ 4 CP 401–class high-endurance patrol and rescue craft

Bldr: CNR, Ancona (In serv. 1987–91)

CP 401 Oreste Cavallari
CP 402 Renato Pennetti
CP 403 Walter Fachin
CP 404 Gaetano Magliano

COAST GUARD PATROL CRAFT [WPC] *(continued)*

Gaetano Magliano (CP 404) Luciano Grazioli, 12-00

D: 100 tons (fl) **S:** 22 kts **Dim:** 28.60 × 6.20 × 2.00
Electronics: Radar: 1 Decca . . . ARPA nav.; 1 . . . nav.
M: 4 Isotta-Fraschini ID36 SS8V diesels; 2 props; 3,520 bhp
Range: 1,000/. . . **Crew:** 11 tot. + 50 rescuees

Remarks: Carry a 3.8-ton, 8.00 × 2.40 × 0.70–m "daughter boat" for rescue work on ramp aft. Can be equipped to carry one 20-mm AA and two single 7.62-mm mg. CP 403 was delivered 1-9-90. All are named for former members of the Port Captain Corps who died or were wounded during World War II or were lost at sea. Have fin stabilizers. Carry Loran-C and GPS receivers and HF and VHF D/F gear.

PATROL BOATS [WPB]

♦ 5 (+ 25) Class 200 patrol boats
Bldr: C.N. Rodriquez SpA, Messina

	In serv.		In serv.		In serv.
CP 265	21-2-01	CP 275	. . .	CP 285	. . .
CP 266	22-6-01	CP 276	. . .	CP 286	. . .
CP 267	22-6-01	CP 277	. . .	CP 287	. . .
CP 268	18-10-01	CP 278	. . .	CP 288	. . .
CP 269	8-01	CP 279	. . .	CP 289	. . .
CP 270	. . .	CP 280	. . .	CP 290	. . .
CP 271	. . .	CP 281	. . .	CP 291	. . .
CP 272	. . .	CP 282	. . .	CP 292	. . .
CP 273	. . .	CP 283	. . .	CP 294	. . .
CP 274	. . .	CP 284	. . .	CP 295	2003

CP 266 Luciano Grazioli, 3-01

D: 42.3 tons light (53.2 max. fl) **S:** 34 kts **Dim:** 25.00 (22.00 wl) × 5.76 × 0.92
Electronics: Radar: 1 Gem SPN-753X nav.
M: 3 Isotta-Fraschini V1312 T2 diesels; 2 props + centerline waterjet; 3,600 bhp (2,958 sust.)
Electric: 88 kw tot. (2 × 44-kw diesel sets)
Range: 630/31; 690/28; 730/25; 900/18 **Fuel:** 12.6 m^3 **Crew:** . . . tot.

Remarks: Twenty-five were ordered in late 1999 for delivery within 30 months, with an option for five additional included in the contract. Aluminum construction. Carry a 4.5-m rigid inflatable inspection launch with a 45-bhp gasoline outboard motor. Equipment includes SOLIS-SART satellite beacon system, D/F loop, and GPS.

♦ 4 CP 261–class GRP-construction patrol launches
Bldr: Intermarine, La Spezia (In serv. 1-00)

CP 261 CP 262 CP 263 CP 264

D: 30 tons **S:** 30 kts **Dim:** 16.4 × 4.5 × 1.0
M: 2 MAN D22482 LE 4012 diesels; 2 props; 2,000 bhp
Range: 300/. . . **Crew:** 5 tot.

♦ 3 CP 256–class inshore patrol launches
Bldr: Italcraft, Gaeta (In serv. 1985–89)

CP 256 CP 257 CP 258

CP 256 Carlo Martinelli, 2-99

D: 20.75 tons (23.7 fl) **S:** 33 kts **Dim:** 16.00 × 5.25 (4.98 wl) × 0.98
Electronics: Radar: 1 . . . nav.
M: 2 CRM 12D/S-2 diesels; 2 Riva-Calzoni IRC 43 DC waterjets; 1,700 bhp
Range: 350/24 **Fuel:** 3,500 liters **Crew:** 7 tot.

Remarks: GRP hull. Have Loran-C receivers and an echo sounder.

♦ 4 CP 254–class inshore patrol launches
Bldr: Tecnomarine, Viareggio (In serv. 1984–89)

CP 254 CP 255 CP 259 CP 260

CP 254 H&L Van Ginderen, 9-91

D: 21 tons (22.5 fl) **S:** 31 kts **Dim:** 15.10 × 5.25 × 0.98
Electronics: Radar: 1 . . . nav.
M: 2 Isotta-Fraschini ID36 SS6V diesels; 2 Riva-Calzoni IRC-43-DL waterjets; 1,520 hp
Range: 320/24 **Crew:** 7 tot.

Remarks: GRP hull. Have Loran-C receivers and an echo sounder.

♦ 8 CP 246/247–class Canav-design inshore patrol launches
Bldr: Canados Navale, Ostia Lido, Rome (CP 246: Navaltecnica, Anzio)

CP 246 (In serv. 1977) CP 247 through CP 253 (In serv. 1980–81)

CP 253 Luciano Grazioli, 12-99

D: 22 tons (fl) **S:** 27–30 kts **Dim:** 15.00 × 4.85 × 1.60
A: small arms **Electronics:** Radar: 1 . . . nav.
M: 2 Isotta-Fraschini ID36 SS6V diesels; 2 props; 1,380 bhp
Range: 350/. . . **Crew:** 7 tot.

COAST GUARD PATROL BOATS [WPB] *(continued)*

Remarks: CP 246 is considered to be a separate class, and the others are essentially of an improved version. Wooden hulls. All have VHF and HF/SSB D/F gear.

♦ 5 CP 239–class inshore patrol launches
Bldr: Rodriguez, Messina (CP 244, 245: Navaltecnica, Messina)

CP 239, CP 242, CP 243 (In serv. 1971)   CP 244, CP 245 (In serv. 1976)

CP 239 Luciano Grazioli, 3-96

D: 25 tons (fl) **S:** 25–28 kts **Dim:** 16.80 × 5.02 × 1.80
Electronics: Radar: 1 . . . nav.
M: 2 Isotta-Fraschini ID36 SS6V diesels; 2 props; 1,380 bhp
Range: 450/. . . **Crew:** 7 tot.

Remarks: Wooden hulls. Have Loran-C receivers and VHF (FM) and HF/SSB D/F gear. CP 240 sank during the summer of 1991. CP 241 was stricken 7-4-01. CP 242 is to be decommissioned 30-9-02 and stricken 31-12-02, and the rest are to be decommissioned 30-9-03 and stricken 31-12-03.

♦ 4 CP 231 (Super Speranza)–class inshore patrol launches
Bldr: Rodriguez, Messina (In serv. 1966–70)

CP 233   CP 234   CP 237   CP 238

CP 238 Luciano Grazioli, 8-00

D: 14 tons (16 fl) **S:** 26 kts **Dim:** 13.40 × 4.80 × 1.30
Electronics: Radar: 1 . . . nav.
M: 2 AIFO 8281 SRM diesels; 2 props; 900 bhp
Range: 400/. . . **Crew:** 7 tot.

Remarks: Wooden construction. All have been re-engined.
Disposals: CP 232 has been on exhibit on land at Livorno since 1998. CP 231 and CP 236 were decommissioned 30-9-01 and stricken 31-12-01; CP 235 was stricken 31-5-01. CP 234 is to be decommissioned 30-9-02 and stricken 31-12-02. CP 234, CP 235, and CP 236 were to be transferred to Albania after striking. CP 233 is to be decommissioned 30-9-03 and stricken 31-12-03.

♦ 1 CP 228–class inshore patrol launch
Bldr: Navaltecnica, Anzio (In serv. 1967)

CP 230

D: 15.1 tons (fl) **S:** 22–24 kts **Dim:** 13.40 × 4.75 × 1.26
M: 2 AIFO 8281 SRM diesels; 2 props; 900 bhp **Range:** 400/20 **Crew:** 7 tot.

Remarks: Wooden construction.
Disposals: Sister CP 228 is exhibited as a gate guard on land at Trieste. CP 229 was decommissioned 30-9-01 and stricken 31-12-01 and was to be transferred to Albania during 2002. CP 230 is to be decommissioned 30-9-02 and stricken 31-12-02.

CP 230 Luciano Grazioli, 10-99

AUXILIARIES

♦ 1 U.S. Cherokee-class oceanographic research ship [WAGOR]
Bldr: Charleston Shipbuilding and Dry Dock, Charleston, S.C.

	Laid down	L	In serv.
CP 451 Bannock (ex-ATF 81)	3-8-42	7-1-43	28-6-43

Bannock (CP 451) Luciano Grazioli, 8-00

D: 1,278 tons (1,675 fl) **S:** 16 kts
Dim: 62.57 (59.59 pp) × 11.73 (11.97 over fenders) × 4.10
Electronics: Radar: 1 AESN . . . nav.; 1 Koden . . . nav.
M: 4 G.M. Electromotive Div. 12-278 diesels, 2 × 1,800-kw M1B 315 MC alternators, 1 VM 1316 TI MH 14 electric motor; 1 prop; 3,000 shp—150-shp bow-thruster
Electric: 300 kw tot. (3 × 100-kw d.c. diesel sets)
Range: 12,000/10 **Fuel:** 300 tons **Endurance:** 60 days **Crew:** 25 tot.

Remarks: 1,277 grt/866 dwt. Former U.S. Navy fleet tug, transferred to Italy on loan in 10-62 for the CNR–Navi Armemento Oceanographiche by Fratelli Cosulich SpA, Genoa, and refitted 1963–64 by O.A.R.N., Genoa, to serve as a research ship in the Mediterranean. Acquired in 12-92 for the Guardia Costiera and now operated in support of the University of Tor Vergata. Retains her original U.S. Navy name, for an Indian tribe in southern Idaho.
Hull systems: Has one 2-ton derrick. Has Koden KS 5150 and Lodestar 2460 D/F receivers, JRC Inmarsat transceiver and Navstar 602S NAVSAT receiver, Koden LR 770 Loran-C receiver, and Decca 10350 automatic plot.

SERVICE CRAFT

♦ 1 ex-Italian Navy oceanographic research craft [WYAG]
Bldr: Navalmeccanico Senigallia (In serv. 1975)

CP 452 Barbara (ex-P 492)

Barbara (CP 452) H&L Van Ginderen, 2-00

D: 180 tons (190 fl) **S:** 9 kts **Dim:** 30.50 × 6.30 × 2.40
Electronics: 1 Gem BX-732 nav.
M: 2 Fiat-AIFO 828 SRM diesels; 2 props; 600 bhp
Range: 2,000/9 **Crew:** 8 tot.

Remarks: Purchased in 1975 by the Italian Navy for use in oceanographic research and in support of missile tests, but used from 1986 to 1996 as a range patrol craft at

COAST GUARD SERVICE CRAFT *(continued)*

Sardinia. Transferred to the Guardia Costiera early in 1998 and operated as a training, oceanographic research craft in cooperation with the University of Cagliari. Has a 7.5-ton electrohydraulic crane at the stern.

Disposal note: The 20-ton research craft CP 453, loaned to the coast guard for ecological research in 1999, was handed over to the receiver when the craft's sponsor, the Polo Tecnologico Mercantile Marittimo, went bankrupt.

♦ 2 miscellaneous pollution control craft [WYAG]

CP 9 CP 12

CP 12 Maurizio Brescia, 5-01

Remarks: No data available. CP 12 is a catamaran with debris collection gear between the hulls. CP 15 is preserved as an exhibit.
Disposals: CP 3 was retired in 1995 and CP 13 in 1998. CP 7, CP 8, CP 12, CP 16, and CP 19 were decommissioned 28-2-01 and stricken 31-5-01.

♦ 72 Keith Nelson–design harbor launches [WYFL]

	Bldr	In serv.
CP 2002	Vosper Thornycroft, Woolston	1971
CP 2007	Bianchi & Cecchi, Genoa	1974
CP 2011, 2012, 2014, 2017	Motomar, Lavagna, Genoa	1972–75
CP 2020, 2021, 2023	Bianchi & Cecchi, Genoa	1973–74
CP 2024	Navaltecnica, Messina	1973
CP 2025–2031	Keith Nelson, Viareggio	1975–76
CP 2032–2035	Motomar, Lavagna	1975–76
CP 2036–2045	Keith Nelson, Viareggio	1976–78
CP 2046–2048	Motomar, Palermo	1978
CP 2049–2065	Balsamo, Brindisi	1978–79
CP 2066–2068	C.N. La Spezia	1980
CP 2069–2077	Balsamo, Brindisi	1980–83
CP 2078–2083	Mericraft, Baia, Naples	1985
CP 2201–2205	Motomar, Palermo	1986

CP 2073—Keith Nelson launch, CP 2069 group Maurizio Brescia, 5-01

CP 2034—Keith Nelson launch, CP 2032 group Luciano Grazioli, 5-01

CP 2028—Keith Nelson launch, CP 2025 group Luciano Grazioli, 12-99

D: 11–15 tons **S:** 14–22 kts **Dim** (typical): 12.57 × 3.64 × 1.10
M: 2 AIFO V85, V85M, or 828M, Cummins V504M or VT8-370M, Isotta-Fraschini ID32 SS6L, ID32 SS6LM, or 6L diesels; 2 props; 420–800 bhp
Range: 400/. . . **Crew:** 4 tot.

Remarks: A relatively homogenous group of GRP-hulled craft based on a British pilot boat design, with numerous variations in superstructure and propulsion plants. CP 2024, equipped with two D/F loops for aircraft rescue duties, is larger: 15 tons; 13.70 × 3.76 × 1.30 m; 24 kts. CP 2006–2009, 2018–2048, and 2201–2205 carry Pirelli self-inflating Type CP 65 rescue rafts in stern recesses. All have VHF (FM) D/F, a Loran-C receiver, and an echo sounder. There was a proposal to order 20 replacements in 2000, but no contract has been announced.
Disposals: CP 2016 (now on exhibit at Taranto) was retired in 1997 and CP 2022 on 31-3-01. CP 2001, 2003–2006, 2008–2010, 2013, 2015, 2018, and 2019 were decommissioned 30-9-01 and stricken 31-12-01. CO 2007 is to be decommissioned 28-0-02 and stricken 31-8-02. CP 2011, 2020, 2023, and 2034 are to be decommissioned 30-9-02 and stricken 31-12-02. CP 2002, 2012, 2014, 2017, 2021, and 2026–2033 are to be decommissioned 30-9-03 and stricken 31-12-03.

♦ 13 CP 6001-class harbor launches [WYFL]

Bldr: Intermarine-Crestitalia, Ameglia, La Spezia (CP 6013–CP 6022: Benetti/Azimut, Viareggio)

CP 6007, CP 6010 (In serv. 25-3-86)
CP 6011 (In serv. 21-11-86)
CP 6013, CP 6014 (In serv. 14-11-88)
CP 6015–6022 (In serv. 1988)

CP 6003—since stricken Luciano Grazioli, 12-00

D: 3.72 tons **S:** 22–24 kts **Dim:** 8.00 × 2.50 × 0.50
Electronics: Radar: 1 . . . nav.
M: 2 VM 4R692-H9 diesels; 2 Castoldi 06 waterjets; 180 bhp
Range: 180/22 **Crew:** 3 crew + 4 passengers

Remarks: GRP, "unsinkable"-construction craft for use in shallow waters.
Disposals: CP 6003–6006, 6008, 6009, and 6012 were decommissioned 30-9-01 and stricken 31-12-01; CP 6007 and 6010 are to be decommissioned 30-9-02 and stricken 31-12-02; and CP 6011 is planned to be decommissioned 30-9-03 and stricken 31-12-03.

♦ 8 CP 524-class harbor launches [WYFL]

Bldr: C.N. Vittoria, Rovigo (In serv. 1999)

CP 524 through CP 531

D: 6.5 tons (7.5 fl) **S:** 34 kts **Dim:** 9.73 × 3.50 × 0.70
M: 2 Isotta-Fraschini L1306 T2 diesels; 2 Castoldi 06 waterjets; 870 bhp
Range: 250/34 **Crew:** 3 tot.

♦ 37 (+ 12) CP 512-class GRP-hulled harbor launches [WYFL]

	Bldr	In serv.
CP 512–CP 523	C.N. del Golfo, Gaeta	1999–2000
CP 540–CP 564	Cantiere Tencara, Porto Marghera	2001 through 4-02
CP 565–CP 576	C.N. Stanisci	. . .

COAST GUARD SERVICE CRAFT *(continued)*

CP 520—the CP 524 class is similar in appearance Luciano Grazioli, 4-01

D: 6.5 tons (7.5 fl) **S:** 34 kts **Dim:** 9.73 × 3.50 × 0.70
M: 2 Isotta-Fraschini ID32 SS62M diesels; 2 props; 600 bhp
Range: 250/34 **Crew:** 3 tot.

Remarks: Same design as the CP 506 class except for having propellers instead of waterjets; there are minor differences between the boats built by the different builders. The CP 565 group was to be ordered during 2001.

♦ 6 CP 506–class GRP-hulled harbor launches [WYFL]
Bldr: C.N. del Golfo, Gaeta (In serv. 1990)

CP 506 CP 507 CP 508 CP 509 CP 510 CP 511

CP 511 H&L Van Ginderen, 9-91

D: 6.5 tons (7.5 fl) **S:** 34 kts **Dim:** 9.73 × 3.50 × 0.70
M: 2 Isotta-Fraschini ID32 SS62M diesels; 2 Castoldi 06 waterjets; 600 bhp
Range: 250/34 **Crew:** 3 tot.

♦ 2 CP 504–class, GRP-hulled harbor launches [WYFL]
Bldr: Intermarine-Crestitalia, Ameglia, La Spezia (In serv. 1981)

CP 504 CP 505

CP 504 Carlo Martinelli, 3-93

D: 6.5 tons (fl) **S:** 28 kts **Dim:** 8.92 × 2.78 × 0.60
Electronics: Radar: 1 . . . nav.
M: 2 AIFO 8361 SRM diesels; 2 Castoldi 06 waterjets; 480 bhp
Range: 200/28 **Crew:** 3 tot.

Remarks: Both are to be decommissioned 30-9-02 and stricken 31-12-02.

Disposal note: CP 502–class harbor launches CP 502 and CP 503 were retired 30-9-01 and stricken 31-12-01. Harbor launch CP 501 was retired 31-3-01. All six harbor launches of the CP 1001 class (CP 1001 through CP 1006) were decommissioned 30-9-01 and stricken 31-12-01.

♦ 36 CP 5001–series fast launches [WYFL]

	Bldr	In serv.
CP 5002, 5008	Vasnautica, Milan	1969–71
C P 5013, 5014, 5016–5020, 5029, 5032, 5038–5041, 5043	Marine Union, Milan	1973–79
CP 5034, 5035, 5037, 5045, 5050	Motomar, Milan	1973–79
CP 5053, 5054	Marine Union, Milan	1971
CP 5056, 5057	Motomar, Milan	1973
CP 5059–5060	Various	1988, 1990
CP 5062–5064	Various	1988–90

	Speed	Dim	Horsepower
CP 5002, 5008	24 kts	5.30 × 2.13 × 0.30	80–100 bhp
CP 5013 group	28–30 kts	6.50 × 2.20 × 0.30	130–140 bhp
CP 5034 group	22 kts	5.20 × 2.18 × 0.30	75–85 bhp + 20 bhp aux.

CP 5018 Luciano Grazioli, 4-96

Remarks: All GRP construction. Powered by two Mercury or Yamaha gasoline outboard motors. Normal crew is two. All except CP 5038–5040 and CP 5054 carry two Pirelli CP 25 self-inflating rescue rafts. CP 5005, 5006, 5021, 5052, and 5058 are exhibited on land as gate guards at various stations.

♦ 7 shallow-draft launches [WYFL]

CP 115 (Vio, 1969): 9.00 × 2.20 × 0.70; 25 kts; 1 AIFO diesel, 145 bhp
CP 117–119 (1974): 7.17 × 2.28; 20 kts; 95 bhp
CP 121 (Oscar, 1985): 9.20 × 2.34 × 0.70; 21 kts; 1 AIFO diesel, 132 bhp
CP 122 (De Poli, 1991): 21.52 × 3.75 × 1.25; 25 kts; 1 AIFO diesel, 220 bhp; a sister to the naval service craft MEN 210
CP 123 (Cucchini, 1992): 9.15 × 2.29 × 0.30; 25 kts; 1 AIFO diesel, 180 bhp

CP 123—CP 121 and CP 115 are very similar Luciano Grazioli, 6-99

CP 122—a personnel transport MARICOGICAP Roma, 1994

Remarks: All of the above craft operate on the Venice lagoon. All are built of wood except CP 122, which is of steel construction.

♦ 8 CP 151–class shallow-draft launches [WYFL]

CP 151 through CP 158

Remarks: Waterjet propelled. Built by Motomar Palermo.

COAST GUARD SERVICE CRAFT *(continued)*

♦ 150 miscellaneous rigid inflatable boats [WYFL]

from among GC 002/B through GC 211/B

GC 091/B—a typical Guardia Costiera RIB, powered by a single Johnson outboard
Luciano Grazioli, 11-00

Remarks: Semi-rigid inflatable boats, including one for the Gruppo Subacqueo frogman group. Are powered by a single Johnson outboard and are road-transportable. Several different designs with very similar characteristics; most were made by Novus/Novmarine.

♦ 3 CP 455–class ambulance boats [WYH]
Bldr: C.N. del Golfo, Gaeta (In serv. 1999)

CP 454 CP 455 CP 456

D: 19.4 tons (fl) **S:** 26 kts **Dim:** 16.40 × 4.55 × 1.20
M: 2 Isotta-Fraschini 1306L T2 diesels; 2 props; . . . bhp
Range: 400/. . . **Crew:** . . .

Remarks: Equipped with a centerline stern gangway to facilitate moving patients from craft at sea and onto a pier.

♦ 4 CP 314–class medium-endurance rescue boats [WYH]
Bldr: C.N. Baglietto, Varezze (CP 318: Rodriquez, Messina)

CP 314 (L: 20-2-88) CP 317 (In serv. 1991)
CP 316 (In serv. . . .) CP 318 (In serv. 5-91)

CP 318 Luciano Grazioli, 3-97

D: 43.1 tons (45 fl) **S:** 20 kts **Dim:** 18.05 (17.96 wl) × 5.75 × 1.20
Electronics: Radar: 1 . . . nav.
M: 2 Deutz . . . diesels; 2 props; 1,700 bhp **Range:** 400/16
Crew: 7 tot. + 20 rescuees

Remarks: Sister CP 315 burned out and was scrapped. GRP construction with low amidships freeboard to facilitate rescues. Have fin stabilizers. Self-righting design. A total of 18 was planned at one time. Have a Loran-C receiver and HF and VHF D/F gear. All have been re-engined.

♦ 1 Vosper Thornycroft medium-endurance rescue boat [WYH]
Bldr: Keith Nelson Italia, Viareggio (In serv. 1977)

CP 313 DANTE NOVARRO

D: 57 tons (fl) **S:** 21 kts **Dim:** 22.85 × 6.10 × 1.75
Electronics: Radar: 1 . . . nav.
M: 2 Isotta-Fraschini ID36 SS diesels; 2 props; 2,760 bhp
Range: 1,000/18 **Crew:** 11 tot.

Remarks: GRP hull. Has a Loran-C receiver and HF and VHF D/F gear.

Dante Novarro (CP 313) Luciano Grazioli, 2-90

♦ 1 CP 312–class seagoing rescue lifeboat [WYH]
Bldr: Friedrich Scheers, Bardenfleth, Germany (In serv. 1972)

CP 312 BRUNO GREGORETTI

Bruno Gregoretti (CP 312)—note the "daughter boat" rescue launch stowed on the inclined launchway at the stern Carlo Martinelli, 10-98

D: 65 tons (fl) **S:** 19 kts **Dim:** 23.20 × 5.30 × 1.50
Electronics: Radar: 1 . . . nav.
M: 1 Mercedes-Benz 12V493 diesel (1,310 bhp), 2 Mercedes-Benz MB 836 diesels (480 bhp each); 3 CP props; 2,270 bhp
Range: 1,000/15 **Crew:** 11 tot.

Remarks: Typical West German lifeboat design, with a steel Maierform hull and stern ramp for 6.5-m rescue boat CVP 312/S (6.75 × 2.20 × 0.52; 1.8 tons; 54 bhp; range 200/8). CP 312 has a Loran-C receiver and VHF (AM and FM), HF/SSB, and UHF D/F receivers. CP 312 is scheduled to be decommissioned 30-9-03 and stricken 31-12-03.

Disposal note: The sole CP 307–class rescue lifeboat, *Michelle Fiorillo* (CP 307), was stricken 1-4-01. U.S. Coast Guard 44-ft. rescue lifeboat CP 304 was stricken 1-4-01, and her sister CP 303 was decommissioned 30-9-01 and stricken 31-12-01. The remaining CP 301–class, wooden-hulled lifeboats of the Ogni Tempo series have been stricken, except for CP 301, on exhibit at Citavecchia.

♦ 6 CP 829 (Giubileo)–class inshore rescue lifeboats [WYH]
Bldr: C.N. Vittoria, Rovigo (In serv. 2000–. . .)

CP 829 CP 830 CP 831 CP 836 CP 837 CP 838

CP 836—outboard CP 831 and CP 838, with CP 829 and a sister at left; this variant of the basic design carries eight encapsulated life rafts aft Antonio Scrimali, 4-01

D: 12 tons normal (13 fl) **S:** 30 kts **Dim:** 12.73 × 4.30 × 0.90
Electronics: Radar: 1 . . . nav.
M: 2 Isotta-Fraschini L1306 T2MS DHSCV diesels; 2 KaMeWa FF310 waterjets; 1,086 bhp
Range: 160/16 **Crew:** 3 tot.

COAST GUARD SERVICE CRAFT *(continued)*

Remarks: Ordered in 2000. Intended to rescue passengers from commercial aircraft crashes at sea. Aluminum construction. Have eight 65-person encapsulated life rafts in quick-release racks on either side aft and a low fantail to assist in bringing survivors aboard. Loran-C receiver, autopilot, doppler log, echo sounder, and VHF (AM and FM) and HF/SSB D/F gear are fitted.

♦ 42 CP 825–class inshore rescue lifeboats [WYH]
Bldr: C.N. Vittoria, Rovigo (In serv. 1999–. . .)

CP 825 through CP 828   CP 839 through CP 862
CP 832 through CP 835   CP 872 through CP 881

CP 840—note that the rescue area is over the stern — Luciano Grazioli, 5-01

D: 12 tons **S:** 30 kts **Dim:** 12.73 × 4.30 × 0.80
Electronics: Radar: 1 . . . nav.
M: 2 Isotta-Fraschini L130 T2MLL diesels; 2 KaMeWa FF 310 waterjets; 1,072 bhp
Range: 160/16 **Crew:** 3 tot.

Remarks: A faster version of the CP 814 class. CP 852 was commissioned 16-3-01, CP 856 and CP 857 on 4-5-01; the rest are to be completed during 2001–02. CP 839 and later differ in having a rescue platform at the stern and in not carrying encapsulated life rafts.

♦ 11 CP 814–class inshore rescue lifeboats [WYH]
Bldr: C.N. Vittoria, Rovigo (In serv. 1996–99)

CP 814 through CP 824

CP 818—with amidships rescue areas and rigid inflatable collar around the hull — Jasper Van Raemdonck, 6-99

D: 12.5 tons normal (13.5 fl) **S:** 32 kts (16 sust.) **Dim:** 11.85 × 4.10 × 0.80
Electronics: Radar: 1 . . . nav.
M: 2 Cummins 6 CTA 8.3 M2 Diamond diesels; 2 KaMeWa FF310 waterjets; 840 bhp
Range: 160/16 **Crew:** 3 tot.

Remarks: Builder's FRB 38 design. First two were delivered in 5-96, CP 819 in 9-96. Aluminum-hulled, self-righting design with rigid inflated rubber fender. Have Loran-C receiver, autopilot, doppler log, echo sounder, and VHF (AM and FM) and HF/SSB D/F gear.

♦ 9 CP 863–class rigid inflatable inshore rescue craft [WYH]
Bldr: Codecasa Due SpA, Viareggio (In serv. 4-5-01 to . . .)

CP 863   CP 865   CP 867   CP 869   CP 871
CP 864   CP 866   CP 868   CP 870

D: 9.3 tons (normal) **S:** 30.5 kts **Dim:** 10.60 × 4.10 × 0.76
Electronics: 1 Seatrack SC 1204 nav.
M: 2 Volvo Penta TAMD 71B diesels; 2 Hamilton 291 waterjets; 748 bhp
Range: 180/30 **Crew:** 3 tot.

Remarks: Improved version of the CP 807 class, with an aluminum, self-righting hull and rubber inflated outer fender section. Carry two inflatable rafts, each with 64-person capacity.

♦ 7 CP 807–class rigid inflatable inshore rescue craft [WYH]
Bldr: Codecasa Due SpA, Viareggio (In serv. 1996)

CP 807   CP 809   CP 811   CP 813
CP 808   CP 810   CP 812

CP 813 — Luciano Grazioli, 6-95

D: 9.3 tons (normal) **S:** 30.5 kts **Dim:** 10.60 × 4.10 × 0.76
Electronics: 1 Seatrack SC 1204 nav.
M: 2 Volvo Penta TAMD 71B diesels; 2 Hamilton 291 waterjets; 748 bhp
Range: 180/30 **Crew:** 3 tot.

Remarks: Improved version of the CP 801 class, with an aluminum, self-righting hull and rubber inflated outer fender section. Carry two inflatable rafts, each with 64-person capacity.

♦ 3 CP 804–class rigid inflatable inshore rescue craft [WYH]
Bldr: Codecase Due SpA, Viareggio (In serv. fall 1992–spring 1993)

CP 804   CP 805   CP 806

CP 804 — MARICOGECAP, Rome, 1995

D: 9.1 tons (normal) **S:** 30.6 kts **Dim:** 10.60 × 4.10 × 0.74
Electronics: 1 Seatrack SC 1204/RD nav.
M: 2 Volvo Penta TAMD 71B diesels; 2 Hamilton 291 waterjets; 748 bhp
Range: 180/30 **Crew:** 3 tot.

Remarks: Variant of the CP 801 design, with an enclosed pilothouse. Have an aluminum, self-righting hull and rubber outer section. Carry two inflatable rafts, each with 64-person capacity. Electronic equipment includes an Intermark intercoastal navigation system, Garmin 100 GPS receiver, and King DL 8008 log.

♦ 3 CP 801–class rigid inflatable inshore rescue craft [WYH]

CP 801   CP 802   CP 803

D: 9.1 tons (normal) **S:** 30.6 kts (29 sust.) **Dim:** 10.60 × 4.10 × 0.74
Electronics: 1 Seatrack SC 1204/RD nav.
M: 2 Volvo Penta TAMD 71B diesels; 2 Hamilton 291 waterjets; 748 bhp
Range: 180/29 **Fuel:** 970 liters **Crew:** 6 tot. + up to 40 rescued personnel

Remarks: The Dutch Damen Valentijn class, built under license. Have an aluminum, self-righting hull with an inflatable rubber outer section. Can be launched and recovered over a beach. Equipped with Garmin 100 GPS receivers, the Intermark coastal navigation system, an autopilot, a Loran-C receiver, a Furuno FE 4300 echo sounder, and a VHFD/F. Carry two inflatable rafts, each with 64-person capacity.

COAST GUARD SERVICE CRAFT *(continued)*

CP 801 MARICOGECAP, Rome, 1995

♦ 9 CP 701–class rigid inflatable inshore rescue craft [WYH]
Bldr: Novamarine Due, Olbia (In serv. 1992–93)

CP 701 through CP 709

CP 701 MARICOGECAP, Rome, 1995

D: 6 tons (fl) **S:** 30 kts **Dim:** 9.60 × 3.15 × 0.55
Electronics: Radar: 1 Seatrack SC 1004/RD nav.
M: 2 AIFO 8061 SRM diesels; 2 Castoldi TD 238 waterjets; 600 bhp
Range: 280/. . . **Crew:** 3 tot. + 40 rescued personnel

Remarks: GRP hull construction with inflated rubber skirt. Equipment includes a Furuno FD 527 D/F, Furuno FE 4300 echo sounder, Garmin GPS 100 GPS receiver, Loran receiver, and autopilot. Contract to construct sisters CP 710–712 was canceled.

♦ 2 CP 603–class (Seppietta-class) inshore rescue craft [WYH]
Bldr: Italcraft, Gaeta (L: 6-5-88)

CP 604 CP 605

D: 3.5 tons **S:** 16 kts **Dim:** 8.50 × 2.78 × 0.80
M: 2 VM HR 694 diesels; 1 prop; 248 bhp **Range:** 200/16 **Crew:** 2 tot.

Remarks: Sister CP 603 was decommissioned 30-9-01 and stricken 31-12-01 and was to be transferred to Albania during 2002.

Disposal note: Seppietta-class inshore rescue craft CP 601 and CP 602 were decommissioned 30-9-01 and stricken 31-12-01.

ITALIAN ARMY

The Italian Army's Amphibious Troop Command *(Comando Truppe Anfibie dell'Esercito Italiano)* operates a number of small craft on the Venice lagoon, under the Sile Amphibious Battalion *(Battaglione Anfibio "Sile")*. In addition to the craft listed below, the battalion also operates small reconnaissance launches EI G/3 and EI G/206, ambulance launch EI G/28, 14 U.S.-built LVTP-7 tracked amphibious troop assault vehicles, and 11 small personnel launches and rigid inflatable boats. Four waterjet-powered launches are to be acquired.

AMPHIBIOUS WARFARE CRAFT

♦ 4 U.S. LCM(6)-class landing craft [WLCM] (In serv. 1974)

EI G/28 EI G/29 EI G/30 EI G/31

D: 60 tons (fl) **S:** 11 kts (9.5 loaded) **Dim:** 17.02 × 4.32 × 1.1
M: 2 diesels; 2 props; 520 bhp **Range:** 360/11 (light)

♦ 2 U.S. LCVP-class landing craft [WLCVP] (In serv. 1974)

EI G/26 EI G/27

D: 13 tons (fl) **S:** 9 kts **Dim:** 11.0 × 3.3 × 0.9
M: 1 diesel; 1 prop; 250 bhp **Range:** 180/9

♦ 70 C 200–class GRP-hulled river crossing boats [WLCP]
Bldrs: Six by Posillipo, Sabaudia; 13 by S.A.I. Ambrosini, Passignano sul Trasimeno; others by Nautica Rio, Sarnico (In serv. 1990–91)

Italian Army C 200 class H&L Van Ginderen, 9-98

D: 2 tons (fl) **S:** 27 kts **Dim:** 6.28 (5.00 pp) × 2.48 × 0.80
M: 1 Volvo Penta AQAD-31A diesel; 1 prop; 130 bhp
Range: 240/18 **Crew:** 2 crew + 5 passengers

Remarks: Operated by the regular army and not part of the Venice lagoon force.

SERVICE CRAFT

♦ 2 command boats [WYAG] (In serv. 1987–88)

EI G/208 EI G/210

EI G/210 Aureliano Molinari, 5-95

D: 21.5 tons (fl) **S:** 25 kts **Dim:** 15.5 × 4.4 × 1.2
M: 2 diesels; 2 props; 880 bhp **Range:** 428/25

♦ 4 Azteca-class reconnaissance launches [WYFL]
Bldr: Crestitalia, Ameglia, La Spezia (In serv. 1981)

EI G/32 EI G/33 EI G/48 EI G/49

EI G/49 Piet Sinke, 7-98

D: 5.2 tons (fl) **S:** 23 kts **Dim:** 9.00 × 3.16 × 0.80
M: 2 AIFO CP3M diesels; 2 props; 320 bhp **Range:** 240/18 **Crew:** 4 tot.

Remarks: GRP monohedron hull. First two are based at Ravenna, the others at Venice.

♦ 1 personnel launch [WYFL]

EI G/142

D: 50 tons (fl) **S:** 25 kts **Dim:** 21.52 × 3.75 × 1.25
M: 1 AIFO diesel; 1 prop; 2,200 bhp

Remarks: Sister to coast guard CP 122 and naval MEN 210. Steel construction.

Note: EI G/135 is a smaller personnel launch based at Ravenna.

♦ 1 fuel lighter [WYO] (In serv. 1980)

EI G/44

D: 95 tons (fl) **S:** 8 kts **Dim:** 21.0 × 3.8 × 1.7 **M:** 2 diesels; 2 props; 290 bhp

ITALIAN ARMY SERVICE CRAFT *(continued)*

♦ **1 medium harbor tug [WYTM]** (In serv. 1988)

EI G/209

D: 45 tons (fl) **S:** 13.5 kts **Dim:** 20.7 × 5.0 × 1.1
M: 2 diesels; 1 prop; 880 bhp **Range:** 250/13.5

ITALIAN AIR FORCE

Note: The Italian Air Force operates a total of nine air-sea rescue boats: AMMA 901–903, AMMA 1021, AMMA 1050, AMMA 1053, AMMA 1054, AMMA 1056, and AMMA 1058. No characteristics data are available. Also in use is the launch AMMC 715.

Italian Air Force launch AMMC 715 H&L Van Ginderen, 8-00

CUSTOMS SERVICE
(Guardia di Finanza, Servizio Navale)

The Comando Generale of the Guardia di Finanza is organized into 16 administrative areas, 20 operational sectors, and 28 squadrons. In addition to craft in Italian ports, others operate on rivers and lakes.

Personnel (2000): 5,400 tot.

Aviation: Two ATR-42-400MP and 12 Piaggio P-166DL3/SEM maritime patrol aircraft; 1 AgustaWestland A-109C, 1 AgustaWestland A-109IFR, 19 AgustaWestland A-109AII, 14 AgustaWestland-Bell AB-412, 15 Nardi-Hughes NH-500MD, 38 Nardi-Hughes NH-500MC, and 8 Nardi-Hughes NH-500M helicopters.

The two ATR-42-400MP transports, configured as maritime patrol aircraft with a Texas Instruments SV-2022 search radar in a pod, an infrared/television turret, and GPS receivers, were ordered in 1996; the first was delivered late in 12-96 and the second 10-3-97, but they did not enter service until 1999. They are based at Pratica di Mare and operated by the Gruppo Esplorazione Marittima.

PATROL CRAFT [WPC]

♦ **1 (+ 3) Improved Antonio Zara class**
Bldr: Fincantieri, Muggiano

	Laid down	L	In serv.
P.03 Giovanni Denaro	14-11-96	4-11-97	1998

Giovanni Denaro (P.03) Fincantieri, 1996

D: 335 tons (fl) **S:** 34.5 kts **Dim:** 51.00 (47.25 pp) × 7.50 × 2.00
A: 1 30-mm 80-cal. OTOBreda-Mauser AA; 2 single 7.62-mm mg
Electronics:
Radar: 2 Gem GEMANT 2V3 nav.
E/O: AESN-Elsag Mk 3A Medusa gun director; 2 CSDA-10 desig. sights
M: 4 MTU 16V396 TB94 diesels; 2 props; 12,848 bhp
Electric: 369 kw tot. (2 × 170-kw, 1 × 29-kw diesel sets)
Range: 2,700/15 **Crew:** 3 officers, 10 petty officers, 20 finanzieri

Remarks: 380 grt. Ordered 10-95. Reportedly planned originally to be named *Medaglia d'Oro.* Design based on the *Antonio Zara,* but with a more powerful propulsion plant. Has fin stabilizers, improved accommodations, and the Alenia Gem CTI-10 navigational data recording system. Three more craft of this class are planned.

♦ **2 Antonio Zara class** Bldr: Fincantieri, Muggiano

	Laid down	L	In serv.
P.01 Antonio Zara	. . .	22-4-89	23-2-90
P.02 Vizzari	31-5-88	25-11-89	4-90

Antonio Zara (P.01) Luciano Grazioli, 6-01

D: 316.5 tons (fl) **S:** 27 kts **Dim:** 51.00 (47.25 pp) × 7.50 × 1.90
A: 1 twin 30-mm 80-cal. OTOBreda-Mauser AA; 2 single 7.62-mm mg
Electronics:
Radar: 1 SPN-748 nav.; 1 SPN-751 nav.
E/O: AESN-Elsag Pegaso-F gun f.c.s. with two CSDA-10 target desig.
M: 2 Wärtsilä NSD BL230-12 diesels; 2 props; 7,270 bhp (6,610 sust.)
Range: 2,700/15 **Crew:** 2 officers, 10 petty officers, 20 finanzieri

Remarks: Design based on builder's *Ratcharit* class for Thailand, but with a less powerful propulsion plant and lighter armament. Has the Alenia IPN-10 combat data system.

PATROL BOATS [WPB]

Classes typed as Vedette d'Altura (seagoing patrol boat):

♦ **26 Corrubia class**
Bldrs: G.90–G.100: C.N. del Golfo, Gaeta (In serv.: first two: 1990–91; others: 1996–97); G.101–G.103: Crestitalia, Ameglia, La Spezia (In serv. 1996–97); G.104–G.115: Intermarine, Sarzana, La Spezia (In serv. 1997–99)

G.90 Corrubia	G.99 Garzone	G.108 Conversano
G.91 Giudice	G.100 Lippi	G.109 Inzerilli
G.92 Alberti	G.101 Lombardi	G.110 Letizia
G.93 Angelini	G.102 Miccoli	G.111 Mazzarella
G.94 Cappelletti	G.103 Trezza	G.112 Nioi
G.95 Ciorlieri	G.104 Apruzzi	G.113 Partipilo
G.96 D'Amato	G.105 Ballali	G.114 Puleo
G.97 Fais	G.106 Bovienzo	G.115 Zannotti
G.98 Feliciani	G.107 Carreca	

Conversano (G.108)—Corrubia-III-series unit, with 20-mm gun
Werner Schiefer, 1-99

Angelini (G.93)—Corrubia-II series, with enclosed 30-mm gun
Luciano Grazioli, 12-99

D: G.90, G.91: 75 tons (83.3 fl)—others: 92 tons (fl) **S:** 43 kts
Dim: 26.80 × 7.60 × 1.20 (G.90, G.91: 26.17 × 7.40 × 1.06)
A: G.90–G.103: 1 30-mm 80-cal. OTOBreda-Mauser AA; 2 single 7.62-mm mg—G.104–G.115: 1 20-mm 90-cal. Astra AA; 2 single 7.62-mm MG 42/59 mg

CUSTOMS SERVICE PATROL BOATS [WPB] *(continued)*

Electronics:
Radar: G.90–G.91: 1 Gem GEMANT 2V1 nav.; 1 Gem SC-1410 nav.—others: 1 Gem GEMANT 2V3 ARPA nav.; 1 Gem SC-1210C/G/L nav.
E/O: Alenia-Elsag Medusa Mk 3 (G.90, G.91: Mk 2) gun f.c.
M: G.90, G.91: 2 Isotta-Fraschini ID36 SS16V diesels; 2 props; 6,400 bhp—others: 2 MTU 16V396 TB 94 diesels; 2 props; 7,684 bhp (6,964 sust.)
Range: 700/35 **Crew:** 1 officer, 4 petty officers, 8 finanzieri

Remarks: First two were essentially prototypes and are referred to as the Corrubia-I series; G.92 through G.103 (the Corrubia-II series) have longer, broader hulls, and the final units (the Corrubia-III series) have a different armament.
Hull systems: GRP construction. All have a Loran-C receiver, Magnavox MX 1402 NAVSAT receiver, and Furuno FE 881 echo sounder.

♦ 12 Bigliani (CNL 39) class
Bldrs: G.78, G.79, G.88, G.89: Intermarine, Sarzana, La Spezia (In serv. 1997–99); others: Crestitalia, Ameglia, La Spezia (In serv.: G.80, G.81: 10-10-87; G.82–G.87: 1991–92)

G.78 Ottonelli	G.82 Galiano	G.86 Buonocore
G.79 Barletta	G.83 Macchi	G.87 Squitieri
G.80 Bigliani	G.84 Smalto	G.88 La Malfa
G.81 Cavaglia	G.85 Fortuna	G.89 Rosati

Macchi (G.83) H&L Van Ginderen, 7-95

D: 73 tons (84.7 fl) **S:** 43 (G.80, G.81: 45) kts
Dim: 27.00 (G.80, G.81: 26.40) × 6.95 × 1.20 (G.80, G.81: 1.06)
A: 1 30-mm 80-cal. OTOBreda-Mauser AA; 2 single 7.62-mm mg
Electronics:
Radar: G.78, G.79, G.88, G.89: 1 Gem GEMANT 2V3 ARPA nav.; 1 Gem SC-1210/C/G/L nav.—G.80, G.81: 1 Gem SPN-749 ARPA nav.; 1 Gem BX-3072A nav.—G.82–G.87: 1 Gem GEMANT 2V1 ARPA nav., 1 Gem SC-1410 nav.
E/O: 1 Alenia Medusa Mk 3 (G.80, G.81: Mk 1) gun f.c.
M: 2 MTU 16V396 TB94 diesels; 2 props; 7,680 bhp (6,964 sust.)
Range: 700/25; 1,200/18.5 **Crew:** 1 officer, 3 petty officers, 8 finanzieri

Remarks: The prototype pair, G.80 and G.81, are referred to as the Bigliani-I series. G.82–G.87 (the Bigliani-II series) are longer and have a revised superstructure and mast configuration, while G.78, G.79, G.88, and G.89 (the Bigilani-III series) have later electronics. Other than G.80 and G.81, the craft were not completed in pennant number sequence. Two lengthened sisters with larger superstructures were built as training craft; see under [YXT]. The original *Bigliani* and *Cavaglia* were ordered from C.N. Liguri, Riva Trigoso, and were to displace 210 tons each; the completed craft were rejected for service and smaller replacements of a new design were ordered in 1984 from Intermarine.

♦ 50 Meattini class
Bldrs: Baglietto, Varazze; Picchiotti, Viareggio; Italcraft, Gaeta; Navaltecnica, Messina; Cantiere di Pisa; Cantiere di Lavagna; Cantiere di Chiavari (In serv. 1972–78)

G.11 Amici	G.30 Cicalese	G.50 D'Agostino
G.12 Di Bartolo	G.31 Di Sessa	G.51 Fiore
G.13 R.D. 26	G.32 Coppola	G.52 Nuziale
G.14 Gori	G.33 Rizzi	G.53 Tavano
G.15 Ramaci	G.35 Baccile	G.54 De Alexandris
G.16 Denaro	G.36 Cavatorto	G.55 Stefannini
G.18 Arcioni	G.37 Fusco	G.56 Tridenti
G.19 Steri	G.38 De Turris	G.57 Fazio
G.20 Cotugno	G.39 Chiaramida	G.58 Atzei
G.21 Manoni	G.40 Cav. D'Oro	G.59 Cicale
G.22 Giannotti	G.41 Bianca	G.60 Fidone
G.23 Carrubba	G.42 Nuvoletta	G.62 Tavormina
G.24 Uglielmi	G.43 Preite	G.63 Colombina
G.25 Salone	G.46 Silanos	G.64 Darida
G.27 Russo	G.47 Ignesti	G.65 Pizzighella
G.28 Zara	G.48 Barreca	G.66 Sciuto
G.29 Rando	G.49 Ciraulo	

D: 40 tons (fl) **S:** 35.4 kts **Dim:** 20.10 × 5.20 × 0.90 (hull)
A: 1 12.7-mm mg **Electronics:** Radar: 1 Gem SC-1210 nav.
M: 2 CRM 18D/S2 diesels; 2 props; 2,500 bhp
Electric: 48 kw (2 × 24 kw) **Range:** 560/21 **Fuel:** 5.8 tons
Crew: 4 petty officers, 7 finanzieri

Remarks: GRP construction. Were planned to have been retired by the end of 2000 but remain in service for lack of any replacements.

Sciuto (G.66) Luciano Grazioli, 12-99

Disposals: *Meattini* (G.10), *Bambace* (G.17), *Esposito* (G.26), *D'Aleo* (G.34), *Mazzeo* (G.44), and *Sguazzini* (G.61) were stricken during 1996–97.
Combat systems: The original armament of one 20-mm 70-cal. Mk 10 Oerlikon and two single 7.62-mm mg has been reduced.

♦ 2 Gabriele-class wooden-hulled
Bldr: Cantiere Picchiotti, Viareggio (In serv. 1966–67)

G.70 Gabriele G.71 Grasso

Gabriele (G.70) Marc Ottini, 6-99

D: 54 tons (fl) **S:** 34.2 kts **Dim:** 23.20 × 6.60 × 1.00
A: 1 12.7-mm mg **Electronics:** Radar: 1 Gem SC-1210 nav.
M: 3 CRM 18-DS/3 diesels; 3 props; 2,500 bhp
Range: 730/19.7 **Crew:** 4 petty officers, 7 finanzieri

Craft typed as Vedette Veloci (fast patrol boat):

Note: The "V" prefix in the hull number for all of the Guardia di Finanza patrol launches stands for *"Vedetta."*

♦ 2 V.6001-class interceptor craft
Bldr: Intermarine, Sarzana, La Spezia

V.6001 (In serv. 1998) V.6002 (In serv. 1999)

D: 12 tons (fl) **S:** 70 kts **Dim:** 16.40 × 2.90 × 0.70
A: . . . **Electronics:** Radar: 1 Pathfinder 24-NM nav.
M: 3 Seatek 6-4V-10D diesels; 3 Rolla surface-piercing props; 1,500 bhp (sust.)
Range: 374/45 **Crew:** 4 tot.

Remarks: Advanced composite Kevlar and GRP laminate hull construction. Have a single rudder. Navigational aids include a Trimble Navtrac GPS receiver.

♦ 1 V.6000-class interceptor craft
Bldr: F. Buzzi Design, . . . (In serv. 1994)

V.6000

D: 7.8 tons light (10 fl) **S:** 64 kts **Dim:** 14.20 × 2.74 × 0.80
A: . . . **Electronics:** Radar: 1 Gem SC-1005-RDN nav.
M: 3 Seatek 6-4V-9L diesels; 3 Rolla surface-piercing props; 1,740 bhp
Range: 360/45 **Crew:** 4 tot.

Remarks: Plans to build nine more were canceled in favor of the V.6001 class.

♦ 1 V.6100-class prototype interceptor craft
Bldr: Bruno Abbate, Naples (In serv. 1994)

V.6100

D: 7.6 tons light (8.8 fl) **S:** 60+ kts **Dim:** 13.41 × 2.74 × 0.55 (0.80 over props)
A: . . . **Electronics:** Radar: 1 Gem SC-1005-RDN nav.
M: 2 Seatek 6-4V-9L diesels; 2 Rolla surface-piercing props; 1,160 bhp
Range: 360/45 **Crew:** 4 tot.

Remarks: Advanced composite laminate hull construction. Has a single rudder set well abaft the hull. Navigational aids include a Trimble Navtrac GPS receiver.

♦ 20 V.5001-class patrol launches
Bldr: C.N. Moschini, Fano (In serv. 1995–2000)

V.5001 through V.5020

D: 20.04 tons (27.1 fl) **S:** 52 kts (45 sust.) **Dim:** 16.50 × 4.60 × 1.20
A: 1 7.62-mm mg **Electronics:** Radar: 1 Gem SC-1210C/G/L nav.
M: 2 MTU 8V396 TE94 diesels; 2 waterjets; 3,000 bhp **Electric:** 3.5 kw
Range: 150/35 **Crew:** 2 petty officers, 2 finanzieri

Remarks: GRP construction. Builder's Super-Drago design. First unit laid down 3-10-88, second on 2-3-89; were initially rejected after trials failed to produce the required 50 kts and the craft were overweight. The final four are of a modified design.

CUSTOMS SERVICE PATROL BOATS [WPB] *(continued)*

V.5001—with cruiser *Vittorio Veneto* (C 550) in background Carlo Martinelli, 10-98

♦ **2 prototype patrol launches**
Bldr: Intermarine, Sarzana, La Spezia

V.5000 (In serv. 1992) V.5100 (In serv. 1988)

D: 20.04 tons (27.3 fl) **S:** 52 kts (45 sust.) **Dim:** 16.50 × 4.60 × 1.20
A: 1 7.62-mm mg **Electronics:** Radar: 1 Gem BX-132 nav.
M: 2 Isotta-Fraschini ID36 SS8V diesels; 2 waterjets; 2,200 bhp (1,950 sust.)
Electric: 3.5 kw tot. **Range:** 420/35 **Crew:** 2 petty officers, 3 finanzieri

♦ **8 V.4000-class patrol launches**
Bldr: Italcraft, Venice; Cantieri della Spezia; and Technomarine (In serv. 1981–83)

V.4000 V.4002 V.4005 V.4010
V.4001 V.4004 V.4007 V.4011

V.4010 Guardia di Finanza, 1994

D: 6.9 tons (fl) **S:** 47.7 kts **Dim:** 13.1 × 3.0 × 0.7
A: small arms **Electronics:** Radar: 1 Gem BX-132 nav.
M: 2 Isotta-Fraschini ID32 SS61 diesels; 2 props; 720 bhp
Range: 275/35 **Fuel:** 0.7 tons **Crew:** 4 tot.

Remarks: Survivors of a class of 15. Wooden construction.

Craft typed as Vedette (patrol boat):

♦ **34 V.5800-class patrol launches**
Bldr: Mericraft, Motomar, Balsamo; and S. Prospero (In serv. 1979–85)

V. 5800 through V.5833

V.5828 Maurizio Brescia, 5-01

D: 15.6 tons (fl) **S:** 26 kts **Dim:** 12.6 × 3.6 × 1.2
A: 1 7.62-mm mg **Electronics:** Radar: 1 Gem BX-732 nav.
M: 2 Fiat-AIFO 828 SRM diesels; 2 props; 1,000 bhp (880 sust.)
Range: 645/19 **Fuel:** 0.4 tons **Crew:** 5 tot.

Remarks: GRP construction. Keith Nelson–designed hulls. Near-sisters are in the coast guard and the Carabinieri fleets. All are essentially identical, unlike the coast guard series.

♦ **80 V.5500-class patrol launches**
Bldr: Intermarine-Crestitalia, Ameglia, La Spezia (In serv. 1979–81)

from among V. 5500 through V.5581

V.5573 Aureliano Molinari, 6-95

D: 7.8 tons (fl) **S:** 33.8 kts **Dim:** 12.00 × 3.80 × 0.60
A: small arms **Electronics:** Radar: 1 Gem BX-732 nav.
M: 2 AIFO 8361 SRM diesels; 2 Castoldi 06 waterjets; 480 bhp
Range: 230/14.9 **Fuel:** 0.6 tons **Crew:** 5 tot.

Remarks: GRP construction. V.5512 was lost in an accident, and one other has been retired. Sisters operate in the Portuguese Navy.

♦ **5 V.5901-class patrol launches**
Bldr: Motomar, Lavagna (In serv.: V.5901–V.5904: 1977; V.5581: 1998)

V.5901 V.5902 V.5903 V.5904 V.5581

D: 10.5 tons (fl) **S:** 23 kts **Dim:** 12.3 × 3.3 × 1.0
M: 1 Fiat-AIFO CP3-SM diesel; 380 bhp
Range: 630/20 **Fuel:** 1.6 tons **Crew:** 3 tot.

♦ **2 V.5300-class patrol launches**
Bldr: Motomar, Lavagna (In serv. 1979–82)

V.5301 V.5302

D: 5.1 tons (fl) **S:** 36 kts **Dim:** 8.3 × 2.8 × 0.5
M: 1 AIFO 8361-SM diesel; 1 prop; 480 bhp
Range: 154/36 **Fuel:** 0.5 tons **Crew:** 3 tot.

Remarks: GRP construction. Sister V.5300 has been retired.

Craft typed Vedette Litiranee, Portuali, e per Acque Interne (V.A.I.):

♦ **5 V.A.I.500-class launches**

V.A.I.500 V.A.I.501 V.A.I.502 V.A.I.503 V.A.I.504

Remarks: No data available; completed 1985–93.

♦ **6 V.A.I.400-class launches**
Bldr: Cantieri Oscar and Cantieri Cucchini, Venice (In serv. 1985–93)

V.A.I.400 V.A.I.401 V.A.I.402 V.A.I.403 V.A.I.404 V.A.I.405

V.A.I.401 Luciano Grazioli, 6-99

D: . . . tons **S:** 21–25 kts **Dim:** 9.20 × 2.34 × 0.70
M: 1 AIFO diesel; 1 prop; 132 or 185 bhp

Remarks: Employed at Venice. Wooden construction. Coast guard sisters also serve at Venice.

♦ **85 V.A.I.200-class launches**
Bldrs: First unit: Mericraft, Baia, Naples; others: Cantieri Fiat de Napoli (In serv. 1986–89)

V.A.I.200 through V.A.I.270 V.A.I.272 through V.A.I.285

V.A.I.219 Luciano Grazioli, 7-99

CUSTOMS SERVICE PATROL BOATS [WPB] *(continued)*

D: 4 tons (fl) **S:** 35 kts **Dim:** 8.10 (6.58 pp) × 2.48 × 0.65
M: 2 G.M. 6-92HT-9 diesels; 2 Castoldi Model 06 waterjets; 296 bhp
Range: . . ./. . . **Crew:** 3 tot.

Remarks: GRP construction. For harbor, river, and lake service. Sister V.A.I.271 was rammed and sunk 17-8-98 by chemical tanker *Chemsea* at Ravenna.

AUXILIARIES

♦ 1 training ship [WAXT]
Bldr: C.N. Lucchese, Venice (In serv. 1971)

GIORGIO CINI

Giorgio Cini Luciano Grazioli, 3-94

D: 770 tons (fl) **S:** 14 kts **Dim:** 54.00 × 10.20 × 2.9
A: 1 12.7-mm mg
Electronics:
Radar: 1 Gem GEMANT 2V1-RS nav.; 1 Gem SC-1210C/G/L nav.; 1 . . . nav.
M: 1 Fiat B306-SS diesel; 1 prop; 1,500 bhp
Range: 800/14 **Fuel:** 65 tons **Crew:** 1 officer, 29 petty officers + 60 students

Remarks: Former merchant marine training ship, acquired in 1981; operational in 1984 after a refit. Carries a wide variety of navigation aids and communications equipment for training purposes.

SERVICE CRAFT

♦ 1 hydrofoil personnel launch [WYFLH]
Bldr: C.N. del Golfo, Gaeta (In serv. 1999)

V. . . . DI AMATO

D: . . . tons **S:** 30 kts **Dim:** 24.00 × 7.40 (hull) × 1.20 (foilborne)
M: 2 MTU 16V396 TB 94 diesels; 2 props; 5,760 bhp

Remarks: 130 grt. Former commercial hydrofoil ferry, purchased in 1999 for transportation, SAR, and patrol duties. GRP hull.

♦ 2 Brig. Francesco Mazzei–class training craft [WYXT]
Bldr: Intermarine, Sarzana, La Spezia

	Laid down	L	In serv.
MAZZEI	22-4-96	16-5-97	24-4-98
VACCARO	23-9-96	1-9-97	29-4-98

Mazzei Carlo Martinelli, 10-98

D: 114.6 tons (fl) **S:** 35+ kts **Dim:** 35.50 (31.39 pp) × 7.55 × 2.10 (max.)
A: 1 30-mm 80-cal. OTOBreda-Mauser AA; 2 single 7.62-mm MG 42/59 mg
Electronics:
Radar: 1 Gem GEMANT 2V3 ARPA nav.; 1 Gem SC-1210C/G/L nav.
E/O: 1 Alenia-Elsag Medusa Mk 3 gun f.c.
M: 2 MTU 16V396 TB94 diesels; 2 props; 6,964 bhp (5,920 sust.)
Electric: 192.5 kw tot. (2 × 90-kw, 1 × 12.5-kw diesel sets)
Range: 900/20 **Crew:** 14 tot. + 3 instructors, 18 trainees

Remarks: 230 grt. Enlarged versions of the Bigliani-III series of patrol boats with a longer superstructure. Can be used for patrol duties if required. GRP hull construction.

♦ 1 105-foot Commercial Cruiser–class training craft [WYXT]
Bldr: Sewart Swiftships, Berwick, La. (In serv. 1980)

GENNA (ex-G.72, ex-*Gandora*, ex-*Pandora*)

Genna Luciano Grazioli, 7-00

D: 120 tons (fl) **S:** 35 kts **Dim:** 32.20 × 7.20 × 3.10
A: 1 12.7-mm mg
Electronics: Radar: 1 Furuno 865-3424 nav.; Furuno 711 nav.
M: 3 MTU 12V331 TC92 diesels; 3 props; 2,940 bhp **Electric:** 30 kw tot.
Range: 1,380/30 **Crew:** 13 tot.

Remarks: Former Guardia Costiera patrol boat transferred to the Guardia di Finanza in 1984 and used in recent years for training.

Note: Also in service are nine small sailboats for recreation and training and about 100 RIB service launches.

CARABINIERI

(Commando Generale dell'Arma dei Carabinieri)

Note: The Carabinieri's seagoing force *(Comando Generale dell'Arma dei Carabinieri Servizio Navale)* was established in 1969 for patrol out to the 3-n.m. limit, along with search-and-rescue, research, and police duties. The Carabinieri was made Italy's fourth official armed service during 4-00 and reports directly to the Minister of Defense; including ground and aviation personnel, some 110,000 personnel were in uniform during 2000. Carabinieri aviation assets include 12 Vulcan Air (ex-Partenavia) P.68 Observer maritime surveillance aircraft. Boats currently in service include:

- 1 S 001 launch (In serv. 5-98): 18 tons; 13.50 × 4.40 × 1.10; 20 kts
- 6 700-series launches (Carabinieri 701–706): 22 tons; 15.07 × 4.91 × . . .; 21 kts
- 17 600-series Keith Nelson launches (Carabinieri 601–616, Carabinieri 623; in serv. 1984–85): 11–12 tons; 12.54 × 3.61 × . . .; 20–21 kts
- 30 N 500–series launches (N 501–528, N 621, N 622; in serv. 1985): 5.8 tons; 10.00 × 3.40; 22 kts
- 3 S 500–series launches for combat swimmer support (S 501–503; in serv. . . .): 7 tons; 10.0 × 3.40; 22 kts
- 23 500-series launches: 2.6 tons; 6.46 × 2.37; 20 kts
- 54 400-series launches: 1.4 tons; 5.50 × 2.10; 25 kts
- 17 or more 300-series launches in the Venice lagoon area: 4 tons; 9.20 × 2.30 × 0.7; 25 kts
- 15 or more 200-series launches
- 21 or more miscellaneous personnel and inspection launches in the 100 series

Carabinieri launch N 519—black hull with red trim strip and white superstructure
Luciano Grazioli, 6-00

Note: The National Police *(Polizia di Stato)* also operate a sizable force of patrol boats and launches, with 108 in operation as of 1996, when there were some 630 personnel in the organization. Craft include PS 212, PS 287, PS 288, PS 358, PS 361–363, PS 385, PS 399, PS 400, PS 401, PS 409–439, PS 441, PS 445–460, PS 466, PS 468, PS 499, PS 500–507, PS 544–554 (Squalo class), and PS 661 (Squalo class). The largest craft are about 12 m long and displace about 9 tons (fl). The Polizia also operates eight P-68 Observer aircraft, the first of which was delivered 11-11-99.

The Prison Police *(Polizia Penitenziaria)* operate at least nine small patrol boats numbered in the V-1 series.

CARABINIERI *(continued)*

Polizia launch PS 478—blue hull with white superstructure Piet Sinke, 7-98

Polizia Penitenziaria patrol boat V-9—outboard sister V-7; painted gray H&L Van Ginderen, 9-98

IVORY COAST

Republic of Côte d'Ivoire

MARINE IVOIRIENNE

Personnel (2001): 950 total (75 officers, 875 enlisted), including 80 naval infantry

Base: Principal base and repair facilities at Abidjan, with minor facilities at San Pédro, Sassandra, and Tabou

PATROL CRAFT [PC]

♦ 1 French Patra class
Bldr: Auroux, Arcachon

	Laid down	L	In serv.
L'Ardent	15-4-77	21-7-78	6-10-78

L'Ardent French Navy, 12-96

D: 125 tons (148 fl) **S:** 26.3 kts **Dim:** 40.70 (38.50 pp) × 5.90 × 1.55
A: 1 40-mm 70-cal. Bofors AA; 1 20-mm 70-cal. Oerlikon Mk 10 AA; 2 single 7.62-mm mg
Electronics: Radar: 1 Decca 1226 nav.
M: 2 AGO 195 V12CZ SHR diesels; 2 CP props; 5,000 bhp (4,400 sust.)
Electric: 120 kw **Range:** 750/20; 1,750/10 **Endurance:** 5 days
Crew: 2 officers, 17 enlisted

Remarks: Ordered 1-77. Sister *Le Intrépide* was nonoperational by 1999, and *Le Ardent* was in very poor condition but still capable of getting under way.

Disposal note: French-built P-48-class patrol craft *Le Valeureux,* in poor condition for many years, was stricken during 2000; sister *Le Vigilant* had been hulked by 1995.

AMPHIBIOUS WARFARE SHIPS AND CRAFT

Disposal note: BATRAL-E-class medium landing ship *Éléphant* as of 2000 was being operated by a private firm on commercial charter, although the ship is still owned by the navy.

♦ 2 ex-French LCM(8)-class landing craft [LCM]
Bldr: CMN, Cherbourg

. . . . . . (ex-CTM 15) . . . . . . (ex-CTM 16)

Ex-CTM 15—in French Navy service Guy Schaeffer, via Paolo Marsan, 8-96

D: 56 tons light (150 fl) **S:** 9.5 kts **Dim:** 23.80 × 6.35 × 1.25
A: 2 single 12.7-mm mg **Electronics:** Radar: 1 . . . nav.
M: 2 Poyaud 520 V8 diesels; 2 props; 480 bhp **Range:** 380/8
Fuel: 3.4 tons **Endurance:** 48 hr (at half power) **Crew:** 6 tot.

Remarks: Transferred 3-99. Cargo capacity: 90 tons.

♦ 3 Type 412 fast assault boats [LCP]
Bldr: Rotork, U.K. (In serv. 1979–80)

D: 5.2 tons (8.9 fl) **S:** 21 kts **Dim:** 12.65 × 3.20 × 0.90
M: 2 Volvo AQAD-40A outdrive diesels; 2 props; 240 bhp

Remarks: GRP construction. Can carry 30 troops. Have a small bow ramp. Two were originally assigned to civilian tasks but were later taken over for the navy.

SERVICE CRAFT

♦ 2 ex-French Surf-class launches [YFL]
Bldr: Allais, Dieppe (In serv. 1989)

. . . . . . (ex-*Burao,* Y 788) . . . . . . (ex-*Mamanu,* Y 752)

Ex-Burao (Y 788)—just prior to transfer Bernard Prézelin, 8-99

D: 9 tons (fl) **S:** 25 kts **Dim:** 13.0 × 4.0 × 0.7
Electronics: Radar: 1 . . . nav.
M: 2 diesels; 2 waterjets; . . . bhp **Crew:** 3 tot.

Remarks: Transferred 10-99. Originally built for use at the Muraroa nuclear test station. Have a GRP hull with an inflated rubber fender around the upper strake.

♦ 2 ex-French Acajou-class medium harbor tugs [YTM]

. . . . . . (ex-*Marronnier,* Y 738) . . . . . . (ex-*Merisier,* Y 669)

D: 105 tons **S:** 11 kts **Dim:** 21.0 (18.4 pp) × 6.9 × 3.2
M: 1 diesel; 1 prop; 700 bhp

Remarks: Transferred 10-99. Built during the 1960s. Bollard-pull capacity: 10 tons.

♦ 1 ex-French P.1-class push-tug [YTM] Bldr: La Perriere, Lorient

. . . . . . (ex-11, ex-P.11)

D: 24 tons (fl) **S:** 9.2 kts **Dim:** 11.50 (11.25 wl) × 4.30 × 1.45
M: 2 Poyaud-Wärtsilä UD 18 V8 M1 diesels; 2 props; 456 bhp (440 sust.)
Range: 191/9.1; 560/8 **Fuel:** 1.7 tons **Crew:** 2 tot.

Remarks: Transferred in 9-99 for dockyard use. Primarily for pushing, but has a 4.1-ton bollard pull.

Note: The Gendarmerie operates the 15-ton launch *Le Barracuda* (in serv. 1974; 18 kts), an Arcor-30 launch (in serv. 1985; 20 kts), and two Arcor-31 launches (in serv. 1982; 5 tons), condition unknown.

JAMAICA

DEFENCE FORCE COAST GUARD

Personnel (2001): 26 officers, 169 enlisted (plus reserves: 16 officers, 39 enlisted)

Bases: Port Royal (HMJS *Cagway*), Coast Guard Station *Discovery Bay,* and a small facility at Middle Cay in the Pedro Cays

Maritime Aviation: The Jamaica Defence Force has three Bell 412EP Griffon and four Eurocopter AS.355N Ecureuil 2 helicopters for SAR duties and employs one Cessna 21-M, one Pilatus-Britten-Norman BN-2A, and one Beech 100 King Air fixed-wing aircraft on coastal patrol and liaison duties. Aircraft operate from Kingston's Norman Manley International Airport, Kingston, and Up Park Camp.

PATROL BOATS [WPB]

♦ **1 Guardian class** Bldr: Lantana Boatyard, Lantana, Fla. (In serv. 26-9-85)

P 8 Paul Bogle (ex-*Comayguela*)

Paul Bogle (P 8) Lantana, 9-85

D: 93 tons (fl) **S:** 33 kts **Dim:** 32.31 × 6.25 × 1.24 (2.13 props)
A: 2 single 12.7-mm M2 mg **Electronics:** Radar: 1 Furuno 2400 nav.
M: 3 MTU 8V396 TB92 diesels; 3 props; 3,600 bhp
Electric: 100 kw (2 G.M. 4-71 diesels driving) **Endurance:** 7 days
Crew: 4 officers, 16 enlisted

Remarks: Begun and launched for Honduras, then purchased by Jamaica. Was originally to have been renamed *Cape George.* Aluminum construction. Sisters serve in Grenada and Honduras. The 20-mm AA added during the mid-1980s has been replaced by a 12.7-mm machinegun. Refitted in U.S.A. during 11-97.

♦ **1 Fort Charles class** Bldr: Teledyne Sewart, Berwick, La. (In serv. 1974)

P 7 Fort Charles

Fort Charles (P 7) H&L Van Ginderen, 11-95

D: 130 tons (fl) **S:** 32 kts **Dim:** 34.5 × 5.7 × 2.1
A: 2 single 12.7 mm M2 mg **Electronics:** Radar: 1 Sperry 4016 nav.
M: 2 MTU 16V538 TB90 diesels; 2 props; 6,000 bhp
Range: 1,200/18 **Crew:** 4 officers, 16 enlisted

Remarks: Can carry 24 soldiers or serve as an 18-bed floating infirmary. When refitted by Atlantic Marine at Jacksonville, Fla., in 1980–81, the craft's hull was lengthened by 3 m forward. Refitted again in 1998.

♦ **2 ex-U.S. Coast Guard 82-foot Point class**
Bldr: CG 251: J. Martinac SB, Tacoma, Wash.; CG 252: Coast Guard Yard, Curtis Bay, Md.

	In serv.
CG 251 Savannah Point (ex-*Point Nowell,* WPB 82363)	1-6-67
CG 252 Belmont Point (ex-*Point Barnes,* WPB 82371)	21-4-70

D: 64 tons (66 fl) **S:** 23.7 kts **Dim:** 25.3 × 5.23 × 1.95
A: 2 single 12.7-mm M2 mg
Electronics: Radar: 1 Hughes-Furuno SPS-73 nav.
M: 2 Caterpillar 3412 diesels; 2 props; 1,480 bhp
Range: 490/23.7; 1,500/8 **Fuel:** 5.7 tons **Crew:** 1 officer, 7 enlisted

Remarks: Transferred by donation, CG 251 on 19-10-99 and CG 252 on 12-1-00. Hull built of mild steel. Are well-equipped for salvage and towing.

♦ **3 Avanu class**
Bldr: Offshore Marine Performance, Miami, Fla. (In serv. 20-4-92)

CG 101 CG 102 CG 103

D: 3 tons (fl) **S:** 48 kts **Dim:** 9.96 × 2.49 × 0.51
A: 1 7.62-mm mg **Electronics:** Radar: 1 Raytheon R40X nav.
M: 2 Johnson OMC gasoline outboard motors; 450 bhp **Crew:** 3 tot.

Remarks: Cigarette boat–design, GRP-construction planing hulls. Used for counternarcotics patrol and interception.

♦ **4 Dauntless class** Bldr: SeaArk, Monticello, Ark.

CG 121 (In serv. 10-9-92) CG 123 (In serv. 12-92)
CG 122 (In serv. 10-11-92) CG 124 (In serv. 5-94)

CG 121 SeaArk, 9-92

D: 15 tons (fl) **S:** 28 kts **Dim:** 12.19 (11.13 wl) × 3.86 × 0.69 (hull)
A: 2 single 12.7-mm mg; 2 single 7.62-mm mg
Electronics: Radar: 1 Raytheon R40X nav.
M: 2 Caterpillar 3208TA diesels; 2 props; 850 bhp (720 sust.)
Range: 200/30; 400/22 **Fuel:** 250 gallons **Crew:** 5 tot.

Remarks: Aluminum construction. First unit ordered 6-91 under U.S. FY 89 Foreign Military Sales program; second unit authorized 10-91 under FY 90 program. Two more were subsequently ordered under U.S. aid programs. C. Raymond Hunt, "Deep-Vee" hull design.

♦ **2 U.S. Guardian-27 class**
Bldr: Boston Whaler, Rockland, Mass. (In serv. 7-92)

CG 091 CG 092

D: 2.25 tons (3.75 fl) **S:** 36 kts **Dim:** 8.10 × 3.05 × 0.50
A: 1 7.62-mm mg **Electronics:** Radar: 1 Raytheon R40X nav.
M: 2 Johnson OMC gasoline outboard engines; 400 bhp
Range: 167/40; 750/. . . **Fuel:** 243 liters **Crew:** 3 tot.

Remarks: "Unsinkable," rigid foam-core GRP construction. Unlike the Guardian-22 class, have a small enclosed pilothouse amidships.

♦ **6 U.S. Guardian-22 class**
Bldr: Boston Whaler, Rockland, Mass. (In serv. 1990)

CG 051 CG 052 CG 053 CG 054 CG 055 CG 056

D: 1.5 tons light (2.25 fl) **S:** 40 kts **Dim:** 6.81 × 2.26 × 0.36
A: 1 7.62-mm mg **Electronics:** Radar: 1 Raytheon R40X nav.
M: 2 Johnson OMC gasoline outboard engines; 360 bhp
Range: 167/40; 750/. . . **Fuel:** 243 liters **Crew:** 3 tot.

Note: Also used by the coast guard is a 12-m sail-training craft. The Kingston Constabulary operates a 12-m Bertram patrol craft acquired in 1984 and a 19.8-m search-and-rescue boat purchased from Swiftships, Morgan City, La., in 1986.

JAPAN

MARITIME SELF-DEFENSE FORCE

(Kaijo Jieitai)

Personnel (2001): 45,812 total active, plus 1,100 reservists and 3,703 civilian employees. A Special Guard Force with 60 commandos was formed in 2001.

Organization: Under a 1998 reorganization, the principal units of the Japan Maritime Self-Defense Force (JMSDF) are assigned to the Escort Fleet and Submarine Fleet (both headquartered at Yokosuka); two Minesweeping Flotillas (at Kure and Yokosuka); five District Fleets (at Yokosuka, Kure, Sasebo, Maizuru, and Ominato) composed of older destroyers, frigates, missile craft, amphibious warfare units, and mine countermeasures units; and the Training Fleet.

Bases: Principal ship bases are at Yokosuka, Sasebo, and Kure, with other bases at Maizuru, Hanshin, and Ominato. Naval aviation facilities are listed in the Naval Aviation section below.

Naval Aviation: About 8,000 personnel are assigned. As of 1-01, the JMSDF had 328 operational aircraft, including 189 fixed-wing aircraft and 139 helicopters. Fixed-wing aircraft included 86 P-3C Orion maritime patrol, 13 US-1A SAR seaplanes, 4 YS-11M/M-A and 5 YS-11T-A transports, 5 EP-3D EW aircraft, 4 U-36A EW training/target service aircraft, 1 UP-3C, 1 UP-3D, 1 UC-90 photo-mapping and 5 LC-90 EW/utility aircraft, 22 TC-90 light transports, and 4 KM-2 and 38 T-5 trainers. Helicopters included 21 HSS-2B Sea King and 79 SH-60J Seahawk ASW, 10 MH-53E mine countermeasures, 14 UH-60J and 4 S-61A SAR, and 4 OH-6J, 6 OH-6D, and 1 Bell 47G2A utility/trainers. Several Japanese Air Self-Defense Force (JASDF) C-130H transports are equipped to perform aerial sea minelaying.

Fixed-wing fleet naval air bases include: 1st Fleet Air Wing, Kameya; 2nd Fleet Air Wing, Hachinohe; 4th Fleet Air Wing, Atsugi; and 5th Fleet Air Wing, Naha, Okinawa. Helicopter fleet naval air bases include: 21st Fleet Air Wing, Tateyama; 22nd Fleet Air Wing, Omura; and 31st Fleet Air Wing, Iwakuni. A new fleet air wing helicopter base was opened at Maizuru on 22-3-01. The Air Training Command has bases at Shimofusa, Tokushima, Usuki, and Kanoya.

Under the FY 97 budget, one P-3C was converted into a UP-3E surveillance aircraft (with SLAR, GPS, SATCOM, and improved cameras). The last P-3C was delivered in 8-97; of 101 built, 98 were built under license by Kawasaki and the original three were built by Lockheed Martin. Other P-3Cs are being converted to EP-3D electronic warfare configuration, with the seventh unit (a conversion) approved in the FY 01 budget.

Ultimately, it is planned to procure 100 SH-60J helicopters to complete replacement of the SH-3 Sea Kings, while a total of 18 UH-60Js will replace the S-61As for search-and-rescue duties. The SH-60J fleet is to be upgraded to SH-60J-kai in a two-stage program; the one FY 97 SH-60J was delivered in 1999 as the upgrade prototype, with the FY 98 example similarly equipped. The modifications will improve performance and allow the aircraft to perform maritime surveillance and law enforcement missions. Upgrades include a composite main rotor hub and blades, and active sonar linked to a new onboard tactical data system, an inverse synthetic aperture radar (ISAR), FLIR, upgraded EW support gear, decoy launchers, a laser-based landing aid, and the capability to launch ASM-1 antiship missiles. The Lockheed Martin AGM-114M Hellfire-II antiship missile is to be procured at the rate of 6–10 rounds per year for use from SH-60J helicopters.

Shin-Meiwa is converting one US-1A SAR seaplane to US-1A-kai configuration, with Allison AE2500 turboprops, new avionics, and a pressurized hull, as a prototype for a proposed US-X successor; the US-X would weigh about 50 metric tons and would have a 5,180-km range (compared to 4,225 km for the current US-1A) and a 25,000-ft. ceiling (10,000 ft. for the US-1A).

The JASDF operates 14 Raytheon Corporate Jets U-125A search-and-rescue aircraft, with an eventual total of 27 planned through 2005. The U-125A is a variant of the Hawker HS-125-800 corporate jet transport. The aircraft are configured with observation windows, FLIR, dinghy launcher, and marker-buoy launchers.

P-3C Orion—note the increasingly common single black radome atop the fuselage, forward, and the black radome below the E/O sensor pod beneath the fuselage
Mitsuhiro Kadota, 5-01

EP-3 Orion electronic warfare aircraft—note the two radomes atop the fuselage and one beneath
Ships of the World, 1996

UP-3C surveillance aircraft Mitsuhiro Kadota, 5-01

US-1A search-and-rescue amphibian Takatoshi Okano, 10-00

U-36A target simulation and towing aircraft Mitsuhiro Kadota, 7-00

YS-11T-A transport Mitsuhiro Kadota, 5-00

UC-90 photo-mapping aircraft—TC-90 trainer and LC-90 EW/utility variants are very similar
Ships of the World

T-5 trainer *Ships of the World*

MH-53E mine countermeasures helicopter Takatoshi Okano, 7-99

SH-60J ASW helicopter Mitsuhiro Kadota, 7-99

UH-60J SAR helicopter—note the two external fuel pods on the stub wings above the cockpit area Mitsuhiro Kadota, 5-01

HSS-2B land-based ASW and utility helicopter Mitsuhiro Kadota, 8-99

Aircraft procurement:
- Fiscal Year 1998: 1 US-1A SAR amphibian, 1 EP-3D Orion electronic warfare, 6 SH-60J ASW helicopters, 1 UH-60J SAR helicopter, and 2 OH-6D training helicopters
- Fiscal Year 1999: 9 SH-60J, US-1A, 2 TC-90
- Fiscal Year 2000: 7 SH-60J, 3 TC-90, 1 OH-6DA
- Fiscal Year 2001: 3 SH-60J, 3 UH-60J, 1 EP-3 (conversion)

WEAPONS AND SYSTEMS

Until the 1970s, most Japanese weapons and detection gear were of American design, built under license in Japan. Subsequently, ships have been equipped with Japanese-designed, long-range, pulse-compression air-search radars and with the 76-mm and 127-mm OTOBreda guns. U.S. Vulcan/Phalanx 20-mm CIWS (Close-In Weapon System) and Harpoon antiship missiles were procured in quantity, with the latter now slowly being supplanted by the Mitsubishi SSM-1 family of antiship missiles (see below).

The U.S. Standard SM-1 MR and SM-2 and Sea Sparrow RIM-7F surface-to-air missiles are in use, with the latter supplemented by the RIM-7M for use in vertical launchers. In 1990, some 100 Harpoon and 145 Standard SM-1 and SM-2 missiles were ordered from the United States. In 1994, an additional 56 Standard and 16 Harpoon missiles were ordered; the final 138 Standard missiles were of the SM-2 Block III version, and five additional were ordered during 3-98. In 5-99, 16 SM-2 Block IIIB missiles were ordered from Raytheon. In 1994, 27 Vertical-Launch ASROC missiles for the newest destroyers and frigates were purchased from the United States, and procurement has continued, with Japan having bought over 400 to date.

Mitsubishi has a license to build the U.S. Mk 46 Mod. 5 NEARTIP ASW torpedo, while the indigenously designed Type 89 (formerly GRX-2, a U.S. Mk 48 ADCAP equivalent) high-speed homing torpedo for submarine service and the Type 73 (formerly GRX-4) short-range ASW torpedo for aircraft have been developed for use from P-3 aircraft, helicopters, and surface ships; the Type 73 is equivalent to the U.S. Mk 50 and was to enter service during the mid-1990s.

A Japanese-developed pintle mounting for the three-barreled G.E. (now Lockheed Martin) Sea Vulcan 20P 20-mm M197 gatling gun is used aboard JMSDF mine countermeasures craft and by a great many Japanese Coast Guard ships and craft as the JM-61-MB; it uses the same basic mount as did the twin 20-mm 70-cal. Mk 24 Oerlikon AA gun and has 300 rounds ready-service on mount. An enclosed, fully automatic version with a separate electro-optical director is used by PG 01–class guided-missile hydrofoils and by several new coast guard ships and craft. In both versions, the gun has a rate of fire of 750–1,500 rds/min, a maximum range of 6,000 yards, and a muzzle velocity of 1,287 m/sec.

Mitsubishi and Kawasaki are cooperating on a Sparrow AAM replacement that will also replace Sea Sparrow; antiship radiation-homing (ARM) and beach-defense missiles are also in development.

Japan employs the 1955-vintage, four-tubed Bofors Erika 375-mm ASW rocket launcher system, which is referred to as the Type 71 for the year of its introduction into the JMSDF; it can launch 250-kg rockets to a range of 1,635 m.

SSM-1 (Type 88): The original air-launched ASM-1 (Type 80) entered service in 1982 with the air force. The SSM-1 (Type 88) entered service beginning in the late 1980s as a coast-defense weapon, with 54 trucks equipped with the missiles, which employ two solid booster rockets at takeoff. The shipboard version, the SSM-1B (Type 90), entered service in 1992 (with 384 ultimately manufactured). All three versions are powered by a Mitsubishi TJM-2 turbojet and employ active radar homing. ASM-2 (Type 93) uses IR homing and entered service in 1994. A longer-range antiship missile designated SSM-2 began development in 1988 but does not yet appear to have entered production. Data for the SSM-1B include:

Length: 5.08 m **Diameter:** 35 cm **Wingspan:** 1.2 m
Weight: 661 kg **Warhead:** 225 kg **Speed:** Mach 0.9 **Range:** 150 km

♦ Naval radars

Name	*Band*	*Remarks*
FCS-1	X (I/J)	Mitsubishi Electric; also known as Type 72
FCS-2-12E	. . .	Mitsubishi Electric; radome-enclosed for guns and Sea Sparrow SAM; also known as Type 79 (Type 72 in earlier analog version)
FCS-2-21A	. . .	Mitsubishi Electric; open radar mount for gun control; 8–20 GHz
FCS-3	. . .	Phased-array, 360°-scanning "Mini-Aegis" weapons control system now in development
OPN-11	X (I)	Koden navigational set
OPS-9	X (I/J)	Furuno navigational set; slotted-waveguide antenna
OPS-11C	X (G/H)	Melco air/surface search; Japanese-design, bedspring antenna
OPS-12	D	NEC 3-D phased-array with planar antenna
OPS-14	L	Melco air search; OPS-14B has MTI (Moving-Target Indication); OPS-14C has further improvements; 1,250–1,350 MHz
OPS-15	D	Furuno surface search; based on U.S. SPS-10
OPS-16	X	JRC (Japan Radio Corporation) surface search
OPS-17	X	JRC surface search
OPS-18	C	JRC surface search/navigational
OPS-19	I	JRC navigational set; slotted-waveguide antenna
OPS-24	. . .	Furuno planar-array successor to OPS-14 series
OPS-28/28B	X (G/H)	JRC navigational set; slotted-waveguide antenna
OPS-29	X	Koden navigational set
SPG-51C	X	U.S. Raytheon radar for Standard SAM
SPG-62	X	U.S. Raytheon Mk 99 illuminator for Aegis system
SPS-52C	(E/F)	U.S. Hughes 3-D for SAM-equipped ships
SPY-1D	S	U.S. G.E. phased planar array 3-D radar for Aegis system
ZPS-4	X (I)	JRC navigational/surface search for submarines; antenna in radome
ZPS-6	X (I)	JRC navigational/surface search for submarines; slotted-waveguide antenna

♦ Sonars

Name	*Freq.*	*Remarks*
OQS-3, -3A	LF	NEC or Hitachi license-built version of U.S. SQS-23; bow- or hull-mounted
OQS-4	LF	NEC-developed improvement on SQS-23/OQS-3
OQS-8	MF	Raytheon-Hitachi equivalent to U.S. DE 1167/SQS-56
OQS-101	LF	NEC equivalent to U.S. SQS-53; bow-mounted dome
OQS-102	LF	NEC equivalent to U.S. SQS-53C
RQS-1	HF	Handheld mine detection sonar for divers
SQQ-32	HF	Raytheon variable-depth minehunting set on *Yaeyama* class
SQS-23B	LF	U.S. Sangamo-built equipment
SQS-35(J)	MF	U.S. EDO-built VDS in last five *Chikugo*-class frigates
SQS-36D/J	MF	NEC license-built version of U.S. system
ZQQ-4	. . .	Oki bow array for *Yuushio* class
ZQQ-5, -5B	. . .	Hughes-Oki bow array for *Harushio* class; system also incorporates clip-on ZQR-1 array
ZQR-1	LF	Clip-on towed linear passive array; equivalent to U.S. BGR-15
ZQS-2, -2B	HF	License-built version of Plessey Type 193M minehunting sonar; ZQS-2B is a version of the later Type 2093
ZQS-3	HF	Hitachi/NEC; updated version of ZQS-2B

Note: Ishikawajima-Harima Heavy Industries (IHI) and Sumitomo Heavy Industries consolidated their naval shipbuilding activities in 2000, forming Marine United, Inc., which laid down its first naval ship, a destroyer, at the former IHI yard in Yokohama early in 2001. In 5-01, IHI and Kawasaki Heavy Industries merged their shipbuilding efforts, and Mitsui is expected to join the group later. Hitachi Zosen and NKK agreed to consolidate their shipbuilding efforts into a single company during 2-00, with the new organization to be established around 10-02.

SUBMARINES [SS]

♦ 4 (+ 6) Oyashio class

	Budget	Bldr	Laid down	L	In serv.
SS 590 Oyashio	1993	Kawasaki, Kobe	26-1-94	15-10-96	16-3-98
SS 591 Michishio	1994	Mitsubishi, Kobe	16-2-95	18-9-97	10-3-99
SS 592 Uzushio	1995	Kawasaki, Kobe	6-3-96	26-11-98	9-3-00
SS 593 Makishio	1996	Mitsubishi, Kobe	26-3-97	22-9-99	29-3-01
SS 594 Isoshio	1997	Kawasaki, Kobe	9-3-98	27-11-00	3-02
SS 595 Narushio	1998	Mitsubishi, Kobe	2-4-99	4-10-01	3-03
SS 596	1999	Kawasaki, Kobe	27-3-00	11-02	3-04
SS 597	2000	Mitsubishi, Kobe	30-1-01	9-03	3-05
SS 598	2001	Kawasaki, Kobe	2002	2004	3-06
SS 599	2002	Mitsubishi, Kobe	2003	2005	3-07

Michishio (SS 591) Takatoshi Okano, 10-00

Uzushio (SS 592) *Ships of the World,* 1-01

Makishio (SS 593)—at commissioning *Ships of the World,* 3-01

Oyashio (SS 590) *Ships of the World,* 3-99

D: 2,750 tons std. surf./3,600 tons sub. **S:** 12 kts surf./20 kts sub.
Dim: 81.70 × 10.30 (8.90 wl) × 7.40
A: 6 bow 533-mm Type HU-603B TT (20 Type 89 torpedoes and UGM-84C Harpoon missiles)
Electronics:
Radar: 1 JRC ZPS-6 nav./surf. search
Sonar: Hughes-Oki ZQQ-6 suite; ZQR-1 towed passive array
EW: ZLA-7 intercept suite
M: 2 Kawasaki 12V-25/25S diesels (1,700 bhp each), 2 1,850-kw alternators, 2 tandem Fuji or Toshiba electric motors; 1 prop; 7,750 shp
Crew: 10 officers, 59 enlisted

Remarks: An entirely new design, with SS 590 approved under the 1993 budget. SS 592, budgeted to cost $534 million, has increased-strength hull steel. SS 593, to the same standard, was ordered 8-96. SS 590 and SS 592 constitute the 2nd Submarine Squadron, 2nd Submarine Flotilla, Yokosuka; SS 591 and SS 593 are in the 1st Submarine Squadron, 1st Submarine Flotilla, Kure.
Hull systems: The casing above the pressure hull is much higher than in previous Japanese designs and is tapered downward at the bow to accommodate the bow-mounted torpedo tubes and chin sonar array; the sail is of a new, tapered configuration. The outer hull has an anechoic coating.
Combat systems: Combat system designation is ZYQ-3. The towed hydrophone array is housed at the aft end of the casing. There are two conformal flank passive hydrophone arrays, the upper running nearly the full length of the submarine and the lower, shorter one running from just forward of the sail to roughly amidships.

♦ 6 Harushio class

	Budget	Bldr	Laid down	L	In serv.
SS 583 Harushio	1986	Mitsubishi, Kobe	21-4-87	26-7-89	30-1-90
SS 584 Natsushio	1987	Kawasaki, Kobe	8-4-88	20-3-90	20-3-91
SS 585 Hayashio	1988	Mitsubishi, Kobe	9-12-88	17-1-91	25-3-92
SS 586 Arashio	1989	Kawasaki, Kobe	8-1-90	17-3-92	17-3-93
SS 587 Wakashio	1990	Mitsubishi, Kobe	12-12-90	22-1-93	1-3-94
SS 588 Fuyushio	1991	Kawasaki, Kobe	12-12-91	16-2-94	7-3-95

Fuyushio (SS 588) Takatoshi Okano, 4-01

Arashio (SS 586) *Ships of the World*

Harushio (SS 583) *Ships of the World,* 2000

D: 2,450 tons std. surf./2,750 tons sub. **S:** 12 kts surf./20 kts sub.
Dim: 77.40 × 10.50 × 7.70
A: 6 amidships 533-mm Type HU-603B TT (20 Type 89 torpedoes and UGM-84C Harpoon missiles)
Electronics:
Radar: 1 JRC ZPS-6 nav./surf. search
Sonar: Hughes-Oki ZQQ-5B passive suite; . . . active; ZQR-1 (U.S. BQR-15) TASS towed passive array
EW: ZLA-7 intercept suite
M: 2 Mitsubishi-M.A.N. V8/V24-30 MATL diesels (1,700 bhp each), 2 1,850-kw alternators, 2 tandem Toshiba electric motors; 1 prop; 7,220 shp
Crew: 10 officers, 65 enlisted

SUBMARINES [SS] *(continued)*

Remarks: An improved *Yuushio* design, incorporating provision for Sub-Harpoon missiles, a towed passive sonar array and passive flank arrays, a new EW suite, additional dc power, additional noise-reduction features (including anechoic coating), and a VLF radio receiver with towed wire antenna. SS 583 and SS 584 are assigned to the 5th Submarine Squadron, 1st Submarine Flotilla, Kure; SS 585, SS 586, and SS 588 to the 3rd Submarine Squadron, 1st Submarine Flotilla, Kure; SS 587 to the 6th Submarine Squadron, 2nd Submarine Flotilla, Yokosuka. Sister *Asashio* (SS 589), reclassified as training ship TSS 3601 on 9-3-00, had seen only three years' frontline service, mostly on trials duties.
Hull systems: Pressure hull is built of NS 110 steel (110 kg/mm^2 yield). Employ two Yuasa 480-cell battery sets.

♦ 5 Yuushio (Type S 122) class

	Bldr	Laid down	L	In serv.
SS 578 Hamashio	Kawasaki, Kobe	8-4-82	1-2-84	5-3-85
SS 579 Akishio	Mitsubishi, Kobe	15-4-83	21-1-85	5-3-86
SS 580 Takeshio	Kawasaki, Kobe	3-4-84	19-2-86	3-3-87
SS 581 Yukishio	Mitsubishi, Kobe	11-4-85	23-1-87	11-3-88
SS 582 Sachishio	Kawasaki, Kobe	11-4-86	17-2-88	24-3-89

Takeshio (SS 580) Takatoshi Okano, 10-00

Yukishio (SS 581)—demonstrating a rapid surfacing Takatoshi Okano, 10-00

Sachishio (SS 582) Chris Delgoffe/H&L Van Ginderen, 5-00

D: 2,250 tons surf./2,500 tons sub.
S: 12 kts surf./13 kts snorkel (max.)/20 kts sub. **Dim:** 76.20 × 9.90 × 7.40
A: 6 amidships 533-mm Type HU-603 TT (20 Type 72, Type 80, and Type 89 torpedoes and UGM-84C Harpoon SSM)
Electronics:
Radar: 1 JRC ZPS-6 nav./surf. search
Sonar: Hughes-Oki ZQQ-5B passive suite; SQS-36J active; ZQR-1 (U.S. BQR-15) TASS towed passive array
EW: ZLA-6 intercept suite
M: 2 Mitsubishi-M.A.N. V8/V24-30 MATL diesels (1,700 bhp each), 2 Kawasaki alternator sets (2,840 kw tot.), 2 tandem Fuji electric motors; 1 prop; 7,220 shp
Crew: 10 officers, 65 enlisted

Remarks: SS 578 is assigned to the 2nd Submarine Squadron, 6th Submarine Flotilla, Yokosuka; SS 579 to the 5th Submarine Squadron, 1st Submarine Flotilla, Kure; SS 580, SS 581, and SS 582 to the 4th Submarine Squadron, 2nd Submarine Flotilla, Yokosuka.

Disposals: Sister *Yuushio* (SS 573) became training submarine ATSS 8006 on 1-8-96; *Mochishio* (SS 574) became ATSS 8007 on 1-8-97; *Setoshio* (SS 575) became ATSS 8008 on 10-3-99, was renumbered TSS 3602 during 3-00, and was retired 30-3-01; *Okishio* (SS 576) was redesignated training submarine TSS 3603 on 29-3-01; and *Nadashio* (SS 577) was stricken on 5-6-01. The others are to be retired at one per year, phasing into duty as training submarines before disposal.
Hull systems: Double-hull design. Use two 480-cell Nihon-Denchi batteries. All have the U.S. Masker bubbler acoustic noise reduction system. Have pressure hulls of NS 80 (80 kg/mm^2 yield) and a 450-m maximum depth. SS 579 and later incorporate greater automation.
Combat systems: Have the ZYQ-1 computer/sonar data display system. Have a towed VLF communications antenna.

AUXILIARY SUBMARINES [SSA]

Note: The designation ATSS for submarines relegated to training duties was changed to TSS during 3-00.

♦ 1 Harushio class Bldr: Mitsubishi, Kobe

	Program	Laid down	L	In serv.
TSS 3601 Asashio (ex-SS 589)	1992	24-12-92	12-7-95	12-3-97

Asashio (TSS 3601) Chris Delgoffe/H&L Van Ginderen, 5-00

D: 2,900 tons std. surf./3,200 tons sub. **S:** 12 kts surf./20 kts sub.
Dim: 87.00 × 10.50 × 7.70
A: 6 amidships 533-mm Type HU-603B TT (6 Type 89 torpedoes and UGM-84C Harpoon missiles)
Electronics:
Radar: 1 JRC ZPS-6 nav./surf. search
Sonar: Hughes-Oki ZQQ-5B passive suite; . . . active; ZQR-1 towed passive array
EW: ZLA-7 intercept suite
M: 2 Kawasaki 12V-25/25S diesels (1,700 bhp each), 2 2,840-kw generator sets, 2 1,850-kw alternator sets, 2 tandem Fuji electric motors; 1 prop; 7,220 shp
2 88-kw Sterling VA-275 Mk-II air-independent propulsion modules
Crew: 10 officers, 62 enlisted + . . . trainees

Remarks: Reclassified as a training ship 9-3-00 after only three years of front-line service. As compared to earlier units of the class, was fitted with new, more highly automated engineering control systems and an anechoic hull coating; the boat conducted an additional year of fitting out and trials time between launch and commissioning. Is assigned with TSS 3603 to the 1st Submarine Training Squadron, 2nd Submarine Flotilla, Yokosuka. Recommissioned 12-12-01 after AIP conversion.
Hull systems: Pressure hull built of NS 110 steel (110 kg/mm^2 yield). Employs two Yuasa 480-cell battery sets. Has a non-hull-penetrating optronic search periscope. Lengthened by 8.6 when Sterling engine module added.

♦ 1 Yuushio class
Bldr: Kawasaki, Kobe

	Laid down	L	In serv.
TSS 3603 Okishio (ex-SS 576)	17-4-80	5-3-82	1-3-83

Okishio (TSS 3603)—as SS 576 Takatoshi Okano, 7-99

D: 2,200 tons surf./2,450 tons sub.
S: 12 kts surf./13 kts snorkel (max.)/20 kts sub. **Dim:** 76.20 × 9.90 × 7.40
A: 6 amidships 533-mm Type HU-603 TT (6 Type 72, Type 80, and Type 89 torpedoes and UGM-84C Harpoon SSM)
Electronics:
Radar: 1 JRC ZPS-6 nav./surf. search
Sonar: Hughes-Oki ZQQ-5B passive; SQS-36J active; ZQR-1 (U.S. BQR-15) TASS towed passive array
EW: ZLA-6 intercept suite
M: 2 Mitsubishi-M.A.N. V8/V24-30 MATL diesels (1,700 bhp each), 2 Kawasaki alternator sets (2,840 kw tot.), 2 tandem Fuji electric motors; 1 prop; 7,220 shp
Crew: 10 officers, 65 enlisted + . . . trainees

AUXILIARY SUBMARINES [SSA] *(continued)*

Remarks: Redesignated a training submarine 29-3-01 and assigned to the 1st Submarine Training Squadron, 2nd Submarine Flotilla, Yokosuka.
Disposals: *Setoshio* (TSS 3602, ex-ATSS 8008, ex-SS 575) was retired 30-3-01.
Hull systems: Double-hull design. Uses two 480-cell Nihon-Denchi batteries. Has the U.S. Masker bubbler acoustic noise reduction system. The pressure hull was fabricated of NS 80 (80 kg/mm^2 yield) steel, and the boat has a 450-m maximum operating depth.
Combat systems: Has a ZYQ-1 computer/sonar data display system and a towed VLF communications antenna.

HELICOPTER-CARRYING DESTROYERS [DDH]

♦ 0 (+ 4) 13,500-ton class

	Bldr	Laid down	L	In serv.
DDH 145	. . .	. . .	. . .	2008
DDH 146	. . .	. . .	. . .	. . .
DDH 147	. . .	. . .	. . .	. . .
DDH 148	. . .	. . .	. . .	. . .

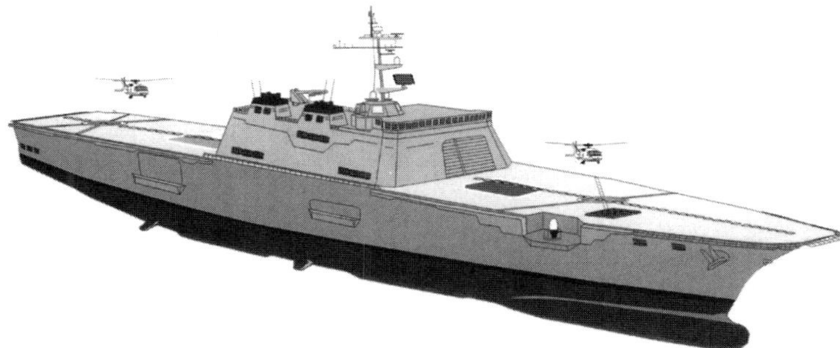

13,500-ton DDH concept—version with superstructure separating flight deck into forward and aft portions *Ships of the World,* 2001

D: 13,500 tons standard (18,000 fl) **S:** 30 kts **Dim:** . . . × . . . × . . .
Air group: 3 SH-60J ASW helicopters; 1 MH-53E mine countermeasures helicopter
A: Mk 41 VLS (64 cells; RIM-7M Sea Sparrow and Vertical-Launch ASROC missiles); 2 20-mm Mk 15 Mod. 12 Block I Phalanx CIWS; 2 triple 324-mm Type 68 ASW TT (Type 73 or Mk 46 Mod. 5 torpedoes)
Electronics:
Radar: 1 OPS-20 nav.; 1 JRC OPS-28D air/surf. search; 1 Melco OPS-24 air search; 1 FCS-3 missile and gun f.c.
Sonar: . . . bow-mounted; . . . TASS
EW: . . .
M: 4 IHI-G.E. LM-2500 gas turbines; 2 CP props; approx. 120,000 shp
Range: . . ./. . . **Crew:** . . . tot.

Remarks: Intended to replace the *Shirane* and *Haruna* classes, with the first to be requested under the FY 03 budget. The initial design had a flight deck space fore and aft, with superstructure amidships incorporating a hangar and with the stack uptakes offset to starboard, but the latest version resembles European small aircraft carriers, with the exception of not having a ski-jump bow. Two aircraft elevators and two sets of fin stabilizers will be fitted.

♦ 2 Shirane class

	Bldr	Laid down	L	In serv.
DDH 143 Shirane	IHI, Tokyo	25-2-77	18-9-78	17-3-80
DDH 144 Kurama	IHI, Tokyo	17-2-78	20-9-79	27-3-81

Kurama (DDH 144) Brian Morrison, 6-00

Shirane (DDH 143) Mitsuhiro Kadota, 4-00

D: 5,200 tons (6,800 fl) **S:** 32 kts **Dim:** 158.8 × 17.5 × 5.3 (hull)
A: 2 single 127-mm 54-cal. U.S. Mk 42 Mod. 7 DP; 1 8-round Mk 29 SAM launcher (24 RIM-7F Sea Sparrow missiles); 2 20-mm Mk 15 Phalanx CIWS; 1 8-round Mk 112 ASROC ASW RL (16 missiles); 2 triple 324-mm Type 68 ASW TT (Type 73 or Mk 46 Mod. 5 torpedoes); 3 SH-60J ASW helicopters
Electronics:
Radar: 1 Koden OPN-11 nav.; 1 NEC OPS-12 3-D air search; 1 JRC OPS-28 surf./air search; 1 Thales WM-25 Sea Sparrow f.c.; 2 FCS-1A gun f.c.; 1 . . . helo control; 2 Mk 90 Phalanx f.c.
Sonar: NEC OQS-101 bow-mounted LF; EDO-NEC SQS-35(J) MF VDS; EDO-NEC SQR-18A TACTASS towed passive array
TACAN: ORN-6 (U.S. URN-25)
EW: Melco NOLQ-1 intercept; Fujitsu OLR-9B jammer; Mk 36 SRBOC decoy syst. (4 6-round Raytheon Mk 137 RL); SLQ-25 acoustic torpedo decoy syst.

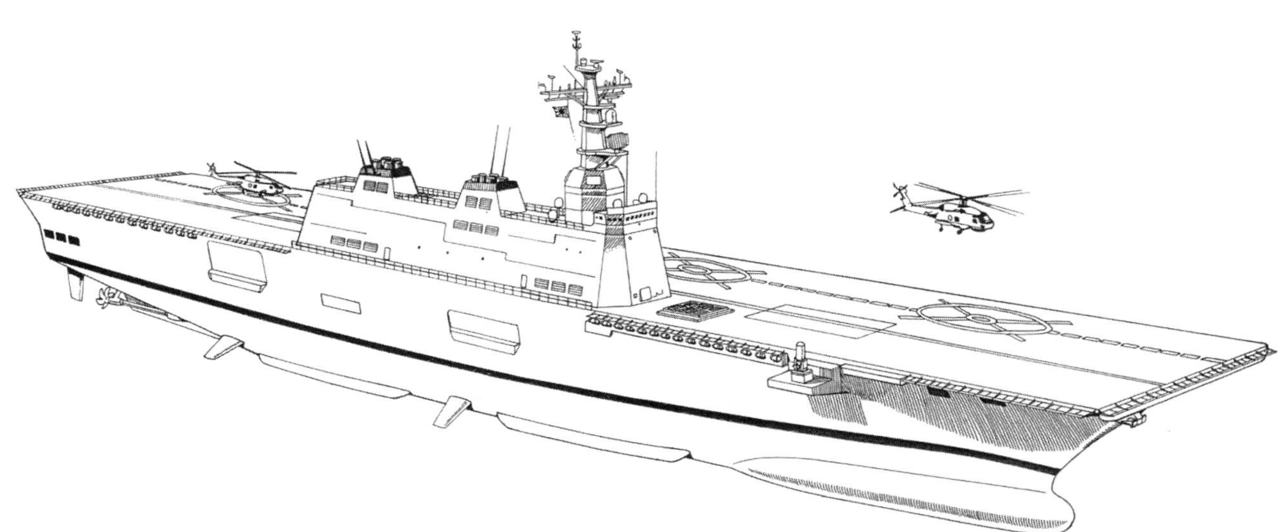

13,500-ton DDH concept—version with full flight deck and superstructure confined to the starboard side *Ships of the World,* 7-01

HELICOPTER-CARRYING DESTROYERS [DDH] *(continued)*

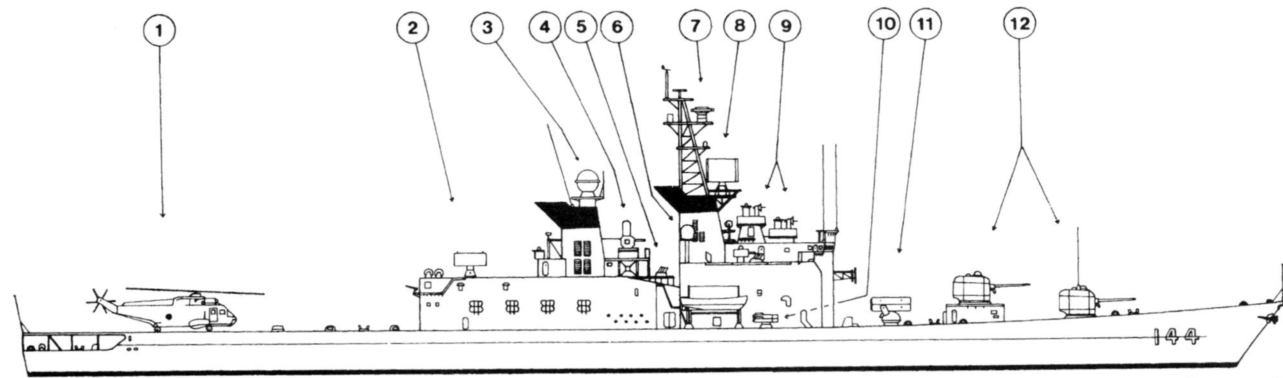

Kurama (DDH 144) 1. HSS-2B ASW helicopter (now carries SH-60J) 2. Mk 29 launcher for Sea Sparrow RIM-7 missiles 3. WM-25 track-while-scan fire-control radar 4. Mk 15 Phalanx CIWS 5. Mk 137 decoy launchers 6. Superbird SHF SATCOM antenna radomes 7. OPS-28 surface-search radar 8. OPS-12 3-D air-search radar 9. FCS-1A fire-control radars 10. Type 68 triple ASW TT 11. Mk 112 ASROC ASW missile launcher 12. 127-mm 54-cal. Mk 42 DP guns   Drawing by Robert Dumas, from *Flottes de Combat*

Kurama (DDH 144)—showing the large helicopter hangar and the VDS installation   Brian Morrison, 6-00

Haruna (DDH 141)   Mitsuhiro Kadota, 10-00

Hiei (DDH 142)   Takatoshi Okano, 11-00

M: 2 sets G.E.-Ishikawajima geared steam turbines; 2 props; 70,000 shp
Boilers: 2 (60 kg/cm^2, 480° C) **Crew:** 360 tot.

Remarks: Modified *Haruna* class. Each ship can carry a rear admiral and 20 staff; DDH 143 is flagship of the 1st Escort Flotilla, based at Yokosuka; DDH 144 is flagship of the 2nd Escort Flotilla, Sasebo. DDH 144 became the first Japanese warship to visit Russia in 71 years during a 7-96 call at Vladivostok.
Hull systems: Have two pair Vosper Thornycroft fin stabilizers fitted, and the Canadian Beartrap helicopter haul-down and deck traversing system is installed for the helicopters. Have U.S. Prairie and Masker bubble-generating systems to reduce radiated noise. There are two stacks, slightly staggered off centerline, compared to one on the *Haruna* class.
Combat systems: Both have a TDPS (Target Data Processing System) with a U.S. UYK-20 computer and OYQ-6 Tactical Data Processing System. Can employ NATO Link 11 and Link 14 data transmission systems. A U.S. Mk 114 fire-control system is employed for ASROC and torpedo launching. The helicopter landing-control radar is mounted to port of the after stack. The Japanese-developed Superbird SHF SATCOM system is fitted.

♦ 2 Haruna class

	Bldr	Laid down	L	In serv.
DDH 141 Haruna	Mitsubishi, Nagasaki	19-3-70	1-2-72	22-3-73
DDH 142 Hiei	IHI, Tokyo	8-3-72	13-8-73	27-12-74

D: 4,950 tons (6,550 fl) **S:** 31 kts **Dim:** 153.0 × 17.5 × 5.3 (hull)
A: 2 single 127-mm 54-cal. U.S. Mk 42 Mod. 7 DP; 1 8-round Mk 29 SAM launcher (16 RIM-7F Sea Sparrow missiles); 2 20-mm Mk 15 Phalanx CIWS; 1 8-round Mk 112 ASROC launcher (16 missiles); 2 triple 324-mm Type 68 ASW TT (Type 73 or Mk 46 Mod. 5 ASW torpedoes); 3 SH-60J ASW helicopters
Electronics:
Radar: 1 Koden OPN-11 nav.; 1 JRC OPS-28 surf./air search; 1 Melco OPS-11C air search; 1 FCS-2-12E Sea Sparrow missile f.c.; 2 FCS-1A gun f.c.; 2 Mk 90 Phalanx f.c.
Sonar: Sangamo-Mitsubishi OQS-3 bow-mounted LF
TACAN: U.S. URN-25 (ORN-6)
EW: Melco NOLQ-1-3 intercept; Fujitsu OLR-9 jammer; OPN-7B D/F; OPN-11B D/F; Mk 36 SRBOC decoy syst. (4 6-round Raytheon Mk 137 RL); SLQ-25 towed acoustic torpedo decoy syst.

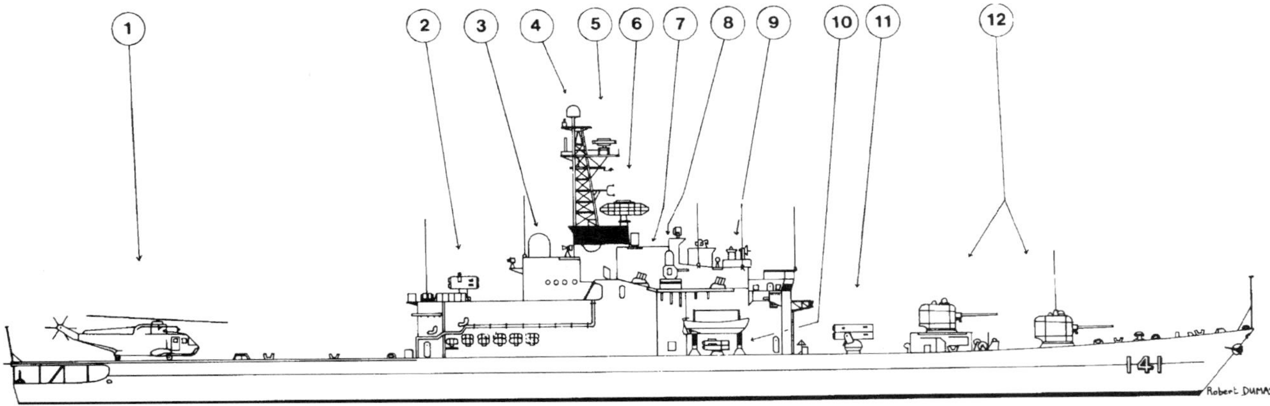

Haruna (DDH 141) 1. HSS-2B ASW helicopter (SH-60J now carried) 2. Mk 29 launcher for Sea Sparrow RIM-7 missiles 3. FCS-2-12E radar SAM director 4. ORN-6 TACAN 5. OPS-28 surface-search radar 6. OPS-11C surface/air-search radar 7. Mk 137 decoy launchers 8. Mk 15 Phalanx CIWS 9. FCS-1A radar director for 127-mm guns 10. Type 68 triple ASW TT 11. Mk 112 ASROC ASW missile launcher 12. 127-mm 54-cal. Mk 42 guns   Drawing by Robert Dumas, from *Flottes de Combat*

HELICOPTER-CARRYING DESTROYERS [DDH] *(continued)*

Hiei (DDH 142) Takatoshi Okano, 11-00

M: 2 sets G.E.-Ishikawajima geared steam turbines; 2 props; 70,000 shp
Boilers: 2 (60 kg/cm^2, 480° C) **Crew:** 36 officers, 304 enlisted

Remarks: DDH 141 was given a midlife modernization from 1986 to 1988; DDH 142 followed from 31-8-87 to 16-11-88. DDH 141 is flagship for 3rd Escort Flotilla, Maizuru, and DDH 142 is the 4th Escort Flotilla flagship at Kure. Are planned to be retired in 2008 and 2009.
Hull systems: The single combined mast/stack ("mack") is off centerline to port. Have two pair Vosper Thornycroft fin stabilizers. A Canadian Beartrap helicopter haul-down and traversal system is installed in the flight deck.
Combat systems: During modernizations, the superstructures were enlarged to accommodate additional electronics, a Sea Sparrow launcher was added atop the hangar and an FCS-2-12 director abaft the mack, two Mk 15 Phalanx CIWS were placed atop the superstructure, the aft FCS-1A was moved to atop the bridge, and new EW gear was added (including the Mk 36 decoy RL system). The OYQ-6 Combat Direction System (using the U.S. UYK-20A computer) was installed, replacing OYQ-3. Although provision was made for its mounting, a planned VDS was not installed, and antiship missile launchers were not added. The Japanese-developed Superbird SHF SATCOM system is carried.

GUIDED-MISSILE DESTROYERS [DDG]

♦ 0 (+ 2) 7,700-ton class

	Bldr	Laid down	L	In serv.
DDG 177	. . .	. . .	. . .	2006
DDG 178	. . .	. . .	. . .	. . .

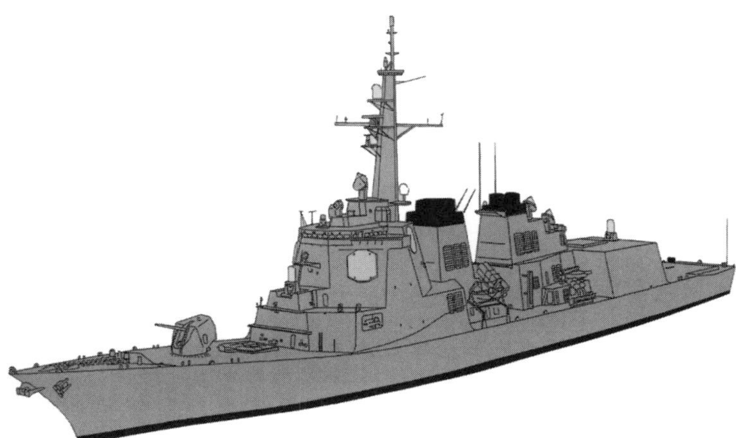

7,700-ton Aegis destroyer concept—note helicopter hangar aft *Ships of the World*/JMSDF, 2001

D: 7,700 tons light (10,000+ fl) **S:** 30 kts **Dim:** . . . × . . . × . . .
A: Mk 41 VLS syst. (96 tot. cells: 32 fwd, 64 atop hangar; SM-2 Block III and ESSM Sea Sparrow SAMs, Vertical-Launch ASROC ASW missiles); 8 SSM-1B SSM (2 quadruple sets); 1 127-mm 54-cal. OTOBreda DP; 2 20-mm Mk 15 Mod. 12 Block I Phalanx CIWS; 2 triple 324-mm Type 68 ASW TT (Type 73 or Mk 46 Mod. 5 torpedoes); 2 SH-60J helicopters
Electronics:
Radar: 1 . . . nav.; 1 Lockheed Martin SPY-1D(V) Aegis 3-D; 3 Raytheon SPG-62 missile target illumination; 1 FCS-2-23 gun f.c.; 2 General Dynamics Mk 90 Phalanx f.c.
Sonar: NEC OQS-102 bow-mounted LF; Oki OQR-2 (SQR-19A(V)) TASS
TACAN: ORN-. . .
EW: NOLQ-2 intercept; NOLQ-2 D/F; OLT-3 jammer; Mk 36 SRBOC decoy syst. (4 6-tubed Raytheon Mk 137 RL); SLQ-25A(V) Nixie acoustic torpedo decoy syst.
E/O: . . . surveillance and tracking
M: 4 IHI-G.E. LM-2500 gas turbines; 2 CP props; approx. 100,000 shp

Remarks: A fifth Aegis destroyer was added to the 2001–05 procurement plan in 2-98 and a sixth on 7-1-00 to improve strategic ballistic-missile defense capabilities; the ships are to cost $1.13 billion each. The design is essentially an enlargement of the *Kongo* so as to incorporate twin helicopter hangars on either side of the after missile launch group.
Combat systems: Are to have the U.S. CEC (Cooperative Engagement Capability) and be capable of employment as theater ballistic-missile defense ships, using the U.S. Standard SM-2 Block III missile. Will make considerable use of COTS (Commercial off-the-Shelf) computer and display equipment.

♦ 4 Kongo class

	Bldr	Laid down	L	In serv.
DDG 173 Kongo	Mitsubishi, Nagasaki	8-5-90	26-9-91	25-3-93
DDG 174 Kirishima	Mitsubishi, Nagasaki	7-4-92	19-8-93	16-3-95
DDG 175 Myoko	Mitsubishi, Nagasaki	8-4-93	5-10-94	14-3-96
DDG 176 Chokai	IHI, Tokyo	29-5-95	27-8-96	20-3-98

Chokai (DDG 176) W. Michael Young, 6-01

Kongo (DDG 173) *Ships of the World,* 5-00

Myoko (DDG 175) H&L Van Ginderen, 1999

Kirishima (DDG 174) Takatoshi Okano, 10-97

GUIDED-MISSILE DESTROYERS [DDG] *(continued)*

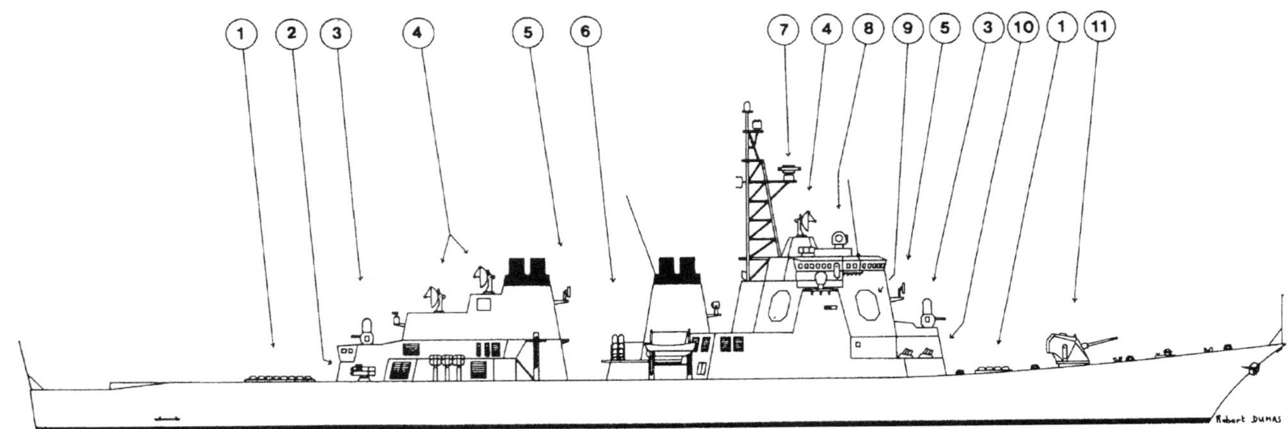

Kongo (DDG 173) 1. Mk 41 vertical launch system launcher-cell groups 2. Type 68 triple ASW TT 3. Mk 15 CIWS 4. SPG-62 radar target illuminators 5. OE-82 SATCOM antennas for the WSC-3 UHF SATCOM system 6. Harpoon antiship missiles (two groups of four) 7. OPS-28D surface/air-search radar 8. FCS-2-21 radar gun director 9. SPY-1D Aegis radar antenna array 10. Mk 137 decoy launchers 11. 127-mm 54-cal. OTOBreda DP gun Drawing by Robert Dumas, from *Flottes de Combat*

D: 7,250 tons light (9,485 fl) **S:** 30 kts
Dim: 161.00 (150.50 pp) × 21.00 (20.00 wl) × 6.20 (hull)
A: 8 RGM-84C Harpoon SSM; Mk 41 VLS (90 Standard SM-2 MR Block III SAM and Vertical-Launch ASROC ASW missiles); 1 127-mm 54-cal. OTOBreda DP; 2 20-mm Mk 15 Mod. 12 Block I Phalanx CIWS; 2 single 12.7-mm mg; 2 triple 324-mm Type 68 ASW TT (Type 73 or Mk 46 Mod. 5 torpedoes)
Electronics:
Radar: 1 JRC OPS-20 nav.; 1 JRC OPS-28D surf./air search; 1 Lockheed Martin SPY-1D Aegis 3-D; 3 Raytheon SPG-62 (Mk 99) illuminators; 1 FCS-2-21 gun f.c.; General Dynamics Mk 90 Phalanx f.c.
Sonar: NEC OQS-102 bow-mounted LF; Oki OQR-2 (SQR-19A(V)) TASS
TACAN: ORN-. . .
EW: NOLQ-2 intercept; NOLQ-2 D/F; OLT-3 jammer; Mk 36 SRBOC decoy syst. (4 6-round Raytheon Mk 137 RL); SLQ-25 Nixie acoustic torpedo decoy syst.
M: 4 IHI-G.E. LM-2500 gas turbines; 2 CP props; approx. 100,000 shp
Electric: 6,000 kw tot. **Range:** 4,500/20 **Fuel:** 1,000 tons **Crew:** 310 tot.

Remarks: The design is an enlarged version of the U.S. *Arleigh Burke* class, adding a backup surface/air-search radar, using a faster-firing 127-mm gun with a dedicated fire-control system, and incorporating a more elaborate EW system with active jamming. First unit ordered 24-6-88. The great expense caused a considerable resistance to program, delaying its start by two years; as of 1995, they cost about $1.48 billion each. The ships are intended to assist in the aerial defense of Japan, as well as acting as AAW escorts for task forces. DDG 173 is assigned to the 62nd Escort Squadron, 2nd Escort Flotilla, Sasebo; DDG 174 to the 61st Escort Squadron, 1st Escort Flotilla, Yokosuka; DDG 175 to the 63rd Escort Squadron, 3rd Escort Flotilla, Maizuru; and DDG 176 to the 64th Escort Squadron, 4th Escort Flotilla, Kure.
Hull systems: Are equipped with the U.S. Prairie and Masker bubbler noise-radiation suppression systems and have infrared exhaust signature provisions. Do not have fin stabilizers, relying on broad, fixed bilge keels and hullform for roll-reduction. The deck abaft after VLS missile installation is intended for use as a helicopter platform, but there is no hangar or deck-handling gear; twin stabilized horizon indicators are carried on the after superstructure to aid landings.
Combat systems: The combat data system is designated OYQ-8. Have U.S. NATO Link 11 and 14 capability; DDG 176 had Link 16 on completion, and it was backfitted in the others. The VLS cells hold 61 missiles aft, 29 forward. The SPG-62 radar illuminators support three Mk 99 Mod. 1 missile fire-control direction systems, and the underwater battery fire-control system is the U.S. Mk 116 Mod. 7. Have the U.S.-made WSN-5 inertial navigation system and U.S. WSC-3 UHF SATCOM with two OE-82C antennas; also installed is the Japanese-developed Superbird SHF SATCOM system, with antennas flanking the bridge. The IFF transponder is the U.S. UPX-29; interrogation is via the SPY-1D radar. The OQS-102 sonar is equivalent to the U.S. SQS-53C. The 12.7-mm mg and night-vision equipment were added to detect and deter infiltration craft.

♦ 2 Hatakaze class

		Bldr	Laid down	L	In serv.
DDG 171	Hatakaze	Mitsubishi, Nagasaki	20-5-83	9-11-84	27-3-86
DDG 172	Shimakaze	Mitsubishi, Nagasaki	30-1-85	30-1-87	23-3-88

Hatakaze (DDG 171) Mitsuhiro Kadota, 10-00

Shimakaze (DDG 172) Brian Morrison, 6-00

Shimakaze (DDG 172) Brian Morrison, 6-00

D: 4,650 tons (5,600 fl) **S:** 32 kts (30 sust.) **Dim:** 150.0 × 16.4 × 4.80 (hull)
A: 1 single-rail Mk 13 Mod. 4 missile launch syst. (40 Standard SM-1 MR missiles); 8 RGM-84C Harpoon SSM; 2 single 127-mm 54-cal. Mk 42 Mod. 7 DP; 2 20-mm Mk 15 Phalanx CIWS; 2 single 12.7-mm mg; 1 8-round Mk 112 ASROC ASW RL; 2 triple 324-mm Type 68 ASW TT (Type 73 or Mk 46 Mod. 5 ASW torpedoes)
Electronics:
Radar: 1 JRC OPS-28B surf./air search; 1 Melco OPS-11C air search; 1 Hughes SPS-52C 3-D air search; 2 Raytheon SPG-51C SAM f.c.; 2 FCS-2-21C gun f.c.; 2 Raytheon Mk 90 Phalanx f.c.
Sonar: NEC OQS-4 Mod. 1 bow-mounted MF
TACAN: NEC ORN-6
EW: Melco NOLQ-1-3 intercept/jammer syst.; OLR-9B intercept; Mk 36 Mod. 2 SRBOC decoy syst. (4 6-round Raytheon Mk 137 RL); SLQ-25 Nixie towed acoustic torpedo decoy syst.
M: COGAG: 2 Rolls-Royce Spey SM-1A cruise gas turbines (13,325 shp each) and 2 Olympus TM-3D boost gas turbines (24,700 shp each); 2 CP props; 74,100 shp
Range: . . ./. . . **Crew:** 260 tot.

GUIDED-MISSILE DESTROYERS [DDG] *(continued)*

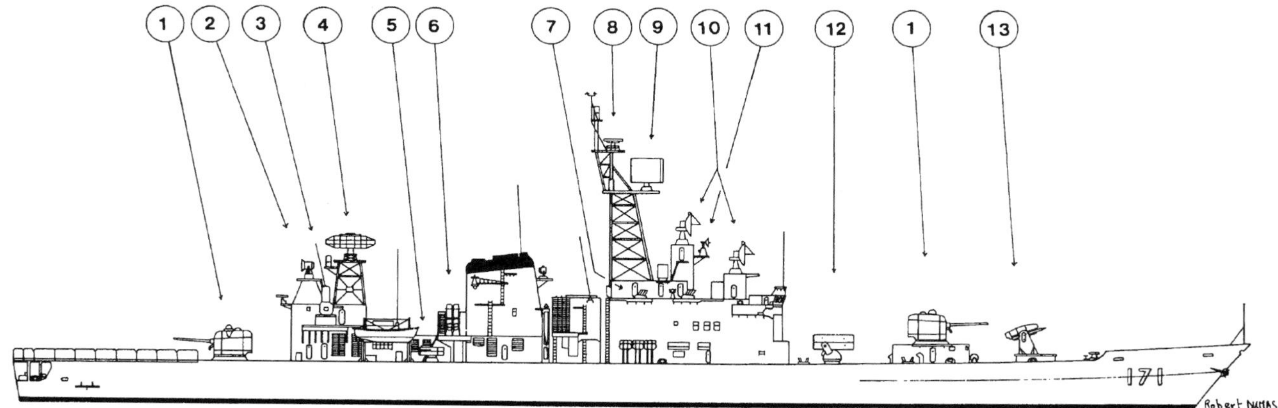

Hatakaze (DDG 171) 1. 127-mm 54-cal. Mk 42 DP guns 2. FCS-2-21C radar directors for the 127-mm guns 3. Mk 15 Phalanx CIWS 4. OPS-11C surface/air-search radar 5. Type 68 triple ASW TT 6. Harpoon SSM (two groups of four) 7. Mk 137 decoy launchers 8. OPS-28B surface/air-search radar 9. SPS-52C 3-D air-search radar 10. SPG-51C radar illuminators for Standard SM-1 MR SAMs 11. telemetry antenna (since removed) 12. Mk 112 ASROC ASW rocket launcher 13. Mk 13 Mod. 4 launcher for Standard SM-1 MR SAMs

Drawing by Robert Dumas, from *Flottes de Combat*

Remarks: DDG 171 is assigned to the 61st Destroyer Division, 1st Escort Flotilla, Yokosuka; DDG 172 to the 63rd Escort Squadron, 3rd Escort Flotilla, Maizuru.

Combat systems: Have the U.S. Mk 74 Mod. 13 missile fire-control system (with two SPG-51C radar tracker/illuminators) for the Standard missile system. Have Link 11 and 14 datalinks, the OYQ-4 Mod. 1 combat data system, the NYPX-2 IFF system, and the WSC-3 UHF SATCOM with two OE-82C antennas; also installed is the Japanese-developed Superbird SHF SATCOM system, with antennas flanking the bridge. There is a landing pad for a helicopter but no hangar. Have been equipped with 12.7-mm mg and night-vision equipment to detect and deter infiltration craft.

♦ 3 Tachikaze class

	Bldr	Laid down	L	In serv.
DDG 168 Tachikaze	Mitsubishi, Nagasaki	19-6-73	12-12-74	26-3-76
DDG 169 Asakaze	Mitsubishi, Nagasaki	27-5-76	15-10-77	27-3-79
DDG 170 Sawakaze	Mitsubishi, Nagasaki	14-9-79	4-6-81	30-3-83

Asakaze (DDG 169) Takatoshi Okano, 4-00

Sawakaze (DDG 170) Mitsuhiro Kadota, 10-00

Tachikaze (DDG 168) Takatoshi Okano, 4-00

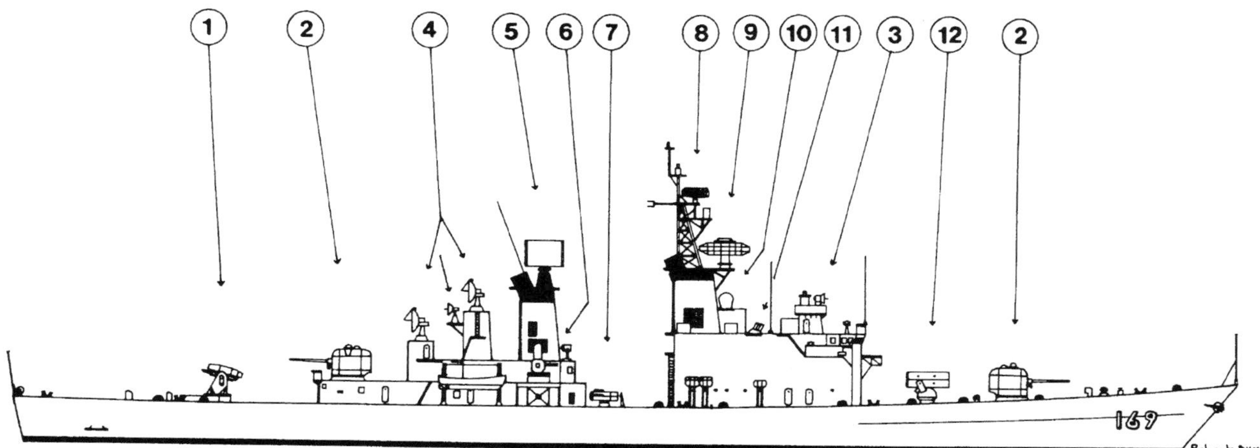

Asakaze (DDG 169) 1. Mk 13 Mod. 4 launcher for Standard SM-1 MR SAMs 2. 127-mm 54-cal. Mk 42 DP guns 3. FCS-1A radar director for 127-mm guns 4. SPG-51C radar illuminator for Standard SM-1 MR SAMs 5. SPS-52C 3-D air-search radar 6. Mk 15 Phalanx CIWS 7. Type 68 triple ASW TT 8. OPS-17 surface-search radar 9. OPS-11B surface/air-search radar 10. OLT-3 EW jammer antenna array 11. Mk 137 decoy launchers 12. Mk 112 ASROC ASW missile launcher

Drawing by Robert Dumas, from *Flottes de Combat*

GUIDED-MISSILE DESTROYERS [DDG] *(continued)*

Tachikaze (DDG 168)—note accommodations deckhouse aft in place of the after 127-mm gunmount Mitsuhiro Kadota, 4-00

D: 3,850 tons (4,800 fl) **S:** 32 kts **Dim:** 143.0 × 14.3 × 4.7 (hull)
A: 1 Mk 13 Mod. 4 missile launch syst. (40 Standard SM-1 MR SAM and RGM-84C Harpoon SSM); 2 (DDG 168: 1) single 127-mm 54-cal. Mk 42 Mod. 7 DP; 2 20-mm Mk 15 Phalanx CIWS; 2 single 12.7-mm mg; 1 8-round Mk 112 ASROC ASW RL; 2 triple 324-mm Type 68 ASW TT (Type 73 or Mk 46 Mod. 5 torpedoes)
Electronics:
Radar: 1 JRC OPS-17 (DDG 170: OPS-28) surf./air search; 1 Melco OPS-11B air search; 1 Hughes SPS-52C 3-D air search; 2 Raytheon SPG-51C SAM f.c.; 1 FCS-1A (DDG 170: FCS-2) gun f.c.; 2 General Dynamics Mk 90 Phalanx f.c.
Sonar: NEC OQS-3 (DDG 170: OQS-4) bow-mounted MF
EW: NEC NOLQ-1 (DDG 168: NOLR-6) intercept; Fujitsu OLT-3 jammer; Mk 36 Mod. 2 SRBOC decoy syst. (4 6-round Raytheon Mk 137 RL); SLQ-25 Nixie towed acoustic torpedo decoy syst.
M: 2 sets Mitsubishi geared steam turbines; 2 props; 70,000 shp
Boilers: 2 (60 kg/cm^2, 480° C) **Crew:** 250 (DDG 168: 277) tot.

Remarks: DDG 168 became flagship of the Fleet Escort Force in 1998 and is based at Yokosuka. DDG 169 assigned to the 64th Escort Squadron, 4th Escort Flotilla, Kure, and DDG 170 to the 62nd Escort Squadron, 2nd Escort Flotilla, Sasebo.
Hull systems: The propulsion plant is identical to that of the *Haruna* class.
Combat systems: Have the OYQ-4 Mod. 1 combat data system and are Link 14 compatible. The missile-control system is Mk 74 Mod. 13 and uses the two SPG-51C radar tracker/illuminators. Have the U.S. Mk 114 ASW weapons-control system. The ASROC launcher has a reload magazine below the bridge. The after 127-mm mount was replaced by a deckhouse in DDG 168 in 1998 to increase accommodations. The WSC-3 UHF SATCOM system, with two OE-82C antennas, is fitted; also installed is the Japanese-developed Superbird SHF SATCOM system, with antennas flanking the bridge. Have been equipped with two 12.7-mm mg and night-vision equipment to detect and deter infiltration craft.

DESTROYERS [DD]

♦ 0 (+ 3 + 5) Takanami (4,600-ton) class

	Bldr	Laid down	L	In serv.
DD 110 Takanami	Sumitomo, Yokosuka	25-4-00	26-7-01	3-03
DD 111 Onami	Mitsubishi, Nagasaki	17-5-00	20-9-01	3-03
DD 112	Marine United, Yokohama	7-01	8-02	3-04
DD 113	. . .	5-02	. . .-03	3-05
DD 114	. . .	5-02	. . .-03	3-05

Takanami (DD 110)—artist's rendering *Ships of the World,* 10-01

Takanami (DD 110)—immediately after launch Mitsuhiro Kadota, 7-01

D: 4,650 tons (approx. 5,350 fl) **S:** 32 kts (30 sust.)
Dim: 151.0 × 17.4 × 5.3 (mean hull)
A: 8 SSM-1B SSM; Mk 41 VLS launch syst. (32 Standard SM-2 MR SAM and Vertical-Launch ASROC ASW missiles); 1 127-mm 54-cal. OTOBreda DP; 2 20-mm Mk 15 Phalanx gatling CIWS; 2 triple 324-mm HOS-302 ASW TT (Type 73 or Mk 46 Mod. 5 torpedoes); 1 SH-60J ASW helicopter
Electronics:
Radar: 1 JRC OPS-20 nav.; 1 JRC OPS-28D surf./air search; 1 Melco OPS-24 air search; 2 FCS-2-21 gun/SAM f.c.; 2 General Dynamics Mk 90 Phalanx f.c.
Sonar: OQS-5 bow-mounted MF; OQR-2 TASS towed passive array
TACAN: ORN-6 (U.S. URN-25)
EW: NOLQ-3 intercept/active syst.; OPN-7B and OPN-11 comms intercept; OLT-3 and OLT-5 jammers; Mk 36 SRBOC decoy syst. (4 6-round Raytheon Mk 137 RL); SLQ-25 Nixie towed acoustic torpedo decoy syst.
M: COGAG: 2 Kawasaki–Rolls-Royce Spey SM-1C cruise gas turbines (13,500 shp each), 2 G.E.-IHI LM-2500 boost gas turbines (16,500 shp each); 2 CP props; 60,000 shp max.
Range: . . ./. . . **Crew:** 170 tot.

Remarks: Funding approved for first two under FY 98 and the third under FY 99; DD 113 and 114 requested under FY 01. Eight total are planned. Improved version of the *Murasame* class.
Hull systems: Propulsion plant duplicates that of the preceding *Murasame* class, with a consequent slight loss in maximum speed.
Combat systems: To have the OYQ-9 combat data system and be equipped with Link 11 datalink capability. Taking advantage of the larger hull, the ships mount a larger gun than the *Murasame* class, while they have a Mk 41 vertical missile launch group with twice as many cells but no Mk 48 launch system cells; this will permit greater versatility in loadouts in the future. Will have Superbird SHF SATCOM capability but not WSC-3 UHF SATCOM facilities. The U.S. SQQ-28 helicopter-deployed sonobuoy datalink is to be fitted. May have two 12.7- or 20-mm guns and night-vision equipment to detect and deter infiltration craft.

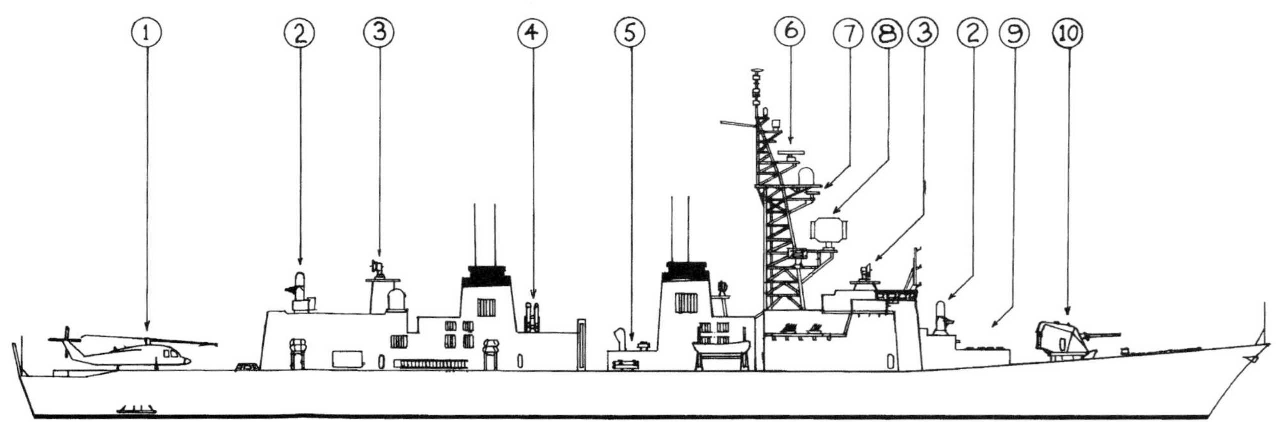

Takanami (DDG 110) 1. SH-60J ASW helicopter 2. Mk 15 Phalanx CIWS atop helicopter hangar 3. FCS-2-21 missile and gun radar directors 4. SSM-1B antiship missiles (two groups of four) 5. HOS-302 triple ASW TT 6. OPS-28D surface-search radar 7. OPS-20 navigational radar 8. OPS-24 3-D air-search radar 9. Mk 41 vertical-launch system (32 cells) 10. 127-mm 54-cal. OTOBreda DP gun Drawing by A.D. Baker III

DESTROYERS [DD] *(continued)*

♦ 7 (+ 2) Murasame class

	Bldr	Laid down	L	In serv.
DD 101 Murasame	IHI, Tokyo	18-8-93	23-8-94	12-3-96
DD 102 Harusame	Mitsui, Tamano	11-8-94	16-10-95	24-3-97
DD 103 Yudachi	Sumitomo, Uraga	18-3-96	19-8-97	4-3-99
DD 104 Kirisame	Mitsubishi, Nagasaki	3-4-96	21-8-97	18-3-99
DD 105 Inazuma	Mitsubishi, Nagasaki	8-5-97	9-9-98	15-3-00
DD 106 Samidare	IHI, Tokyo	11-9-97	24-9-98	21-3-00
DD 107 Ikazuchi	Hitachi, Maizuru	25-2-97	24-6-99	14-3-01
DD 108 Akebono	IHI, Tokyo	29-10-99	25-9-00	3-02
DD 109 Ariake	Mitsubishi, Nagasaki	18-5-99	16-10-00	3-02

Harusame (DD 102) Brian Morrison, 6-00

Kirisame (DD 104) Brian Morrison, 6-00

Samidare (DD 106) Takatoshi Okano, 10-00

Yudachi (DD 103) Brian Morrison, 6-00

Ikazuchi (DD 107)—on trials *Ships of the World,* 2000

D: 4,400 tons (approx. 5,100 fl) **S:** 33 kts (30 sust.)
Dim: 151.00 (145.00 wl) × 17.40 (15.70 wl) × 5.20
A: 8 SSM-1B SSM; Mk 48 VLS missile launch syst. (16 RIM-7M Sea Sparrow SAM); 1 Mk 41 VLS launch group (16 Vertical-Launch ASROC ASW missiles); 1 76-mm 62-cal. OTOBreda Compact DP; 2 20-mm Mk 15 Mod. 1 Block I Phalanx CIWS; 2 triple 324-mm HOS-302 ASW TT (Type 73 or Mk 46 Mod. 5 torpedoes); 1 SH-60J ASW helicopter
Electronics:
Radar: 1 JRC OPS-20 nav.; 1 JRC OPS-28D surf./air search; 1 Melco OPS-24 air search; 2 FCS-2-21 gun/SAM f.c.; 2 General Dynamics Mk 90 Phalanx f.c.
Sonar: Mitsubishi OQS-5 bow-mounted MF; OQR-2 TASS towed passive array
TACAN: ORN-6 (U.S. URN-25)
EW: NOLQ-3 intercept/active syst.; OPN-7B and OPN-11 comms intercept; OLT-3 and OLT-5 jammers; Mk 36 SRBOC decoy syst. (4 6-round Raytheon Mk 137 RL); SLQ-25 Nixie towed acoustic torpedo decoy syst.
M: COGAG: 2 Kawasaki–Rolls-Royce SM-1C Spey cruise gas turbines (13,500 shp each), 2 G.E.-IHI LM-2500 boost gas turbines (16,500 shp each); 2 CP props; 60,000 shp max.
Electric: . . . kw tot. **Range:** 4,500/18 **Crew:** 170 tot.

Remarks: First unit authorized under FY 91 budget and second under FY 92. Two were approved under FY 94, and another pair under FY 95. Only one was requested under FY 96 (DD 107, ordered 7-96). DD 108 and DD 109 were approved under the FY 97 budget. DD 101 and DD 102 are assigned to 1st Escort Squadron, 1st Escort Flotilla, Yokosuka; DD 103 and DD 104 to the 6th Escort Squadron, 2nd Escort Flotilla, Sasebo; and DD 105 and DD 106 to the 4th Escort Squadron, 4th Escort Flotilla, Kure.

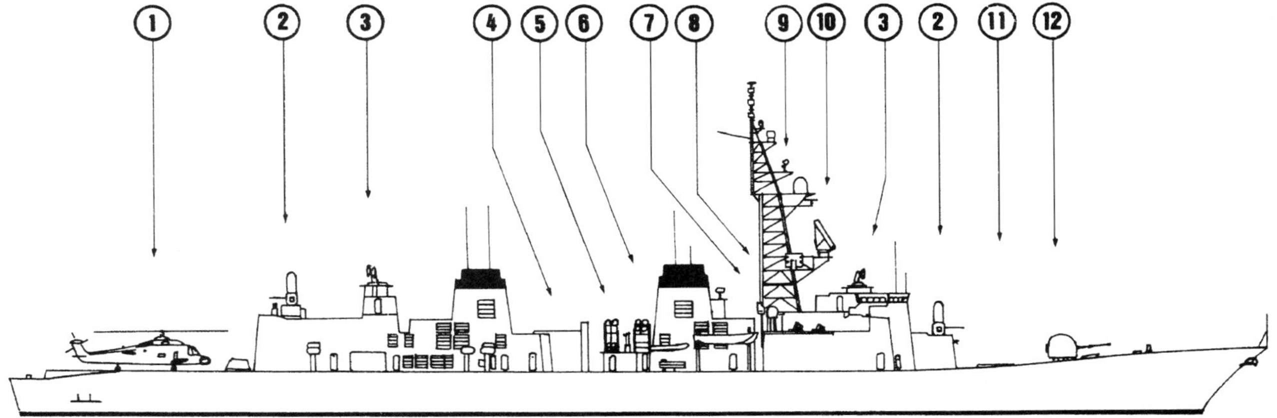

Murasame (DD 101) 1. SH-60J ASW helicopter 2. Mk 15 Phalanx CIWS atop helicopter hangar 3. FCS-2-21 gun and Sea Sparrow SAM radar directors 4. Mk 48 vertical-launch system for Sea Sparrow SAMs 5. SSM-1B antiship missiles (two groups of four) 6. HOS-302 triple ASW TT 7. Superbird SHF SATCOM antenna radomes 8. NOLQ-3 EW antenna array 9. OPS-28D surface/air-search radar 10. OPS-24 3-D air-search radar 11. Mk 41 vertical-launch system cell group for ASROC ASW missiles 12. 76-mm 62-cal. OTOBreda DP gun Drawing by Jean Moulin, from *Flottes de Combat*

DESTROYERS [DD] *(continued)*

Hull systems: Both the Rolls-Royce and G.E. gas turbines are considerably downrated from their normal maximum power. Although the plant could in theory generate a total of 106,500 shp, and any turbine or combination of turbines can be connected to either shaft, the maximum output is limited to 60,000 shp. Berthing for the crew is two high, and there is a small gymnasium.
Combat systems: Have the OYQ-7 Mod. 9 or, in later units, OYQ-9 combat data system and are equipped with Link 11. There are two VLS groups, a Mk 41 system group with 16 cells forward for Vertical-Launch ASROC missiles (and, later, Standard SM-2 SAMs), and a shorter Mk 48 group amidships with 16 cells for Sea Sparrow SAMs. SM-2 missiles will eventually be able to be launched from a *Murasame*-class unit and then controlled by an Aegis-equipped *Kongo,* as in the U.S. CEC cooperative engagement system. Planned adoption of the RIM-7P Evolved Sea Sparrow (ESSM) SAM will quadruple the total SAM capacity. Have Superbird SHF SATCOM capability but no WSC-3 UHF SATCOM facilities. The U.S. SQQ-28 helicopter-deployed sonobuoy datalink is fitted. Are being equipped with two 12.7- or 20-mm guns and night-vision equipment to detect and deter infiltration craft.

♦ 8 Asagiri class

	Bldr	Laid down	L	In serv.
DD 151 Asagiri	IHI, Tokyo	13-2-85	19-9-86	17-3-88
DD 152 Yamagiri	Mitsui, Tamano	5-2-86	8-10-87	25-1-89
DD 153 Yuugiri	Sumitomo, Uraga	25-2-86	21-9-87	28-2-89
DD 154 Amagiri	IHI, Tokyo	3-3-86	9-9-87	17-3-89
DD 155 Hamagiri	Hitachi, Maizuru	20-1-87	4-6-88	31-1-90
DD 156 Setogiri	Sumitomo, Uraga	9-3-87	12-9-88	14-2-90
DD 157 Sawagiri	Mitsubishi, Nagasaki	14-1-87	25-11-88	6-3-90
DD 158 Umigiri	IHI, Tokyo	31-10-88	9-11-89	12-3-91

Amagiri (DD 154) Brian Morrison, 2-01

Asagiri (DD 151) Brian Morrison, 6-00

Yuugiri (DD 153) Takatoshi Okano, 5-01

Hamagiri (DD 155)—with later OPS-24 air-search radar Takatoshi Okano, 7-00

D: 3,500 tons (4,300 fl) **S:** 30 kts **Dim:** 136.50 × 14.60 × 4.50 (mean hull)
A: 8 RGM-84C Harpoon SSM; 1 8-round Mk 29 missile launcher (18 RIM-7F Sea Sparrow missiles); 1 76-mm 62-cal. OTOBreda Compact DP; 2 20-mm Mk 15 Phalanx CIWS; 1 8-round Mk 112 ASROC ASW RL (. . . reloads); 2 triple 324-mm Type 68 ASW TT (Type 73 or Mk 46 Mod. 5 torpedoes); 1 SH-60J ASW helicopter
Electronics:
Radar: 1 JRC OPS-20 nav.; 1 JRC OPS-28C or -28D surf./air search; 1 Melco OPS-14C (DD 155–158: OPS-24) air search; 1 FCS-2-21A gun f.c.; 1 FCS-2-12E SAM f.c.; 2 General Dynamics Mk 90 Phalanx f.c.
Sonar: Mitsubishi OQS-4A bow-mounted MF; EDO-NEC OQR-1 (U.S. SQR-18A(V) TASS) towed passive array
TACAN: ORN-6 (U.S. URN-25)
EW: NEC NOLR-6C intercept; NOLR-9C D/F; Fujitsu OLT-3 D/F; Mk 36 SRBOC decoy syst. (2 6-round Raytheon Mk 137 RL); SLQ-25 Nixie acoustic torpedo decoy syst.
M: COGAG: 4 Kawasaki–Rolls-Royce Spey SM-1A gas turbines; 2 CP props; 53,900 shp
Electric: . . . **Range:** . . . **Fuel:** . . . **Crew:** 220 tot.

Remarks: An improved *Hatsuyuki* design. DD 151 was ordered 29-3-84, DD 152–154 on 23-3-85, DD 155–157 in 3-86, and DD 158 in 3-87; DD 158 was the only ship authorized of two requested under FY 86. DD 151, 152, and 157 are assigned to the 2nd Escort Squadron, 2nd Escort Flotilla, Sasebo; DD 153, 155, and 156 to the 7th Escort Squadron, 3rd Escort Flotilla, Maizuru; and DD 154 and 158 to the 5th Escort Squadron, 1st Escort Flotilla, Yokosuka.
Hull systems: Have fin stabilizers and a Beartrap/RAST-type helicopter landing and deck-traversing system. The after mast on DD 151 was moved to port and raised after initial trials to avoid stack heat damage; in the other ships, the mast is raised and retained on the centerline, while the after stacks are offset slightly to port. The U.S. Prairie/Masker bubble underwater noise suppression system is fitted.

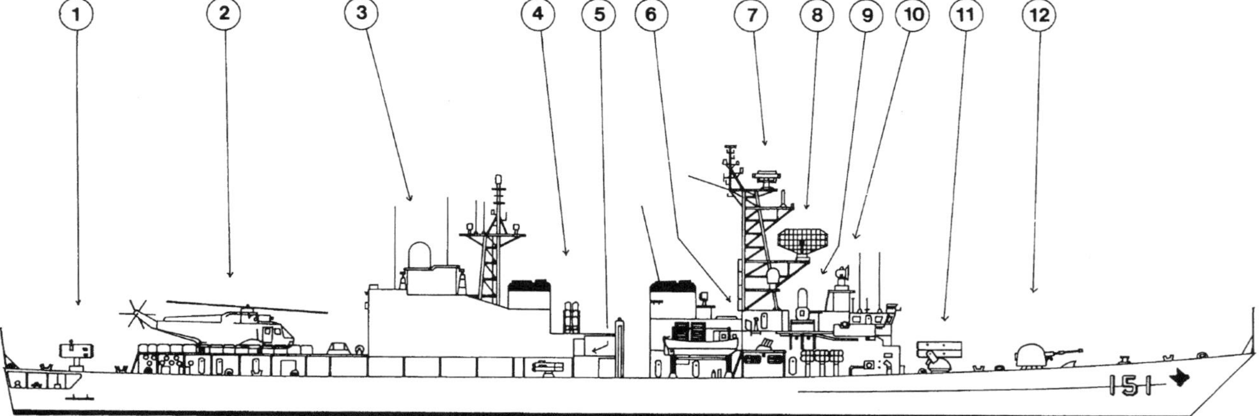

Asagiri (DD 151) 1. Mk 29 launcher for Sea Sparrow SAMs 2. HSS-2B ASW helicopter (now replaced by SH-60J) 3. FCS-2-12E radar director for Sea Sparrow SAMs 4. Harpoon antiship missiles (two groups of four) 5. Type 68 triple ASW TT 6. Mk 137 decoy launchers 7. OPS-28C surface/air-search radar 8. OPS-14C air-search radar (OPS-24 on later ships of the class) 9. Mk 15 Phalanx CIWS (port and starboard) 10. FCS-2-21A 76-mm radar director 11. Mk 112 ASROC ASW missile launcher 12. 76-mm 62-cal. OTOBreda DP gun
Drawing by Robert Dumas, from *Flottes de Combat*

DESTROYERS [DD] *(continued)*

Combat systems: Have the OYQ-6 combat data and command system, employing the U.S.-built UYK-20A computer and the Japanese OJ-194B digital display indicator. The OPS-24 D-band air-search radar mounted in the last four employs hundreds of miniature transmitters arrayed on its planar face. A radome on a foremast platform houses the antenna for the U.S. SQQ-28 datalink system for the SH-60J ASW helicopter. DD 158 was first to complete with a towed tactical passive sonar array, which was backfitted in the rest. Have the Superbird SHF SATCOM system. NOLR-8 intercept equipment may be fitted in later units. Are being equipped with two 12.7- or 20-mm guns and night-vision equipment to detect and deter infiltration craft.

◆ **11 Hatsuyuki class**

	Bldr	Laid down	L	In serv.
DD 122 Hatsuyuki	Sumitomo, Uraga	14-3-79	7-11-80	23-3-82
DD 123 Shirayuki	Hitachi, Maizuru	3-12-79	4-8-81	8-2-83
DD 124 Mineyuki	Mitsubishi, Nagasaki	7-5-81	17-10-82	26-1-84
DD 125 Sawayuki	IHI, Tokyo	22-4-81	21-6-82	15-2-84
DD 126 Hamayuki	Mitsui, Tamano	4-2-81	27-5-82	18-11-83
DD 127 Isoyuki	IHI, Tokyo	20-4-82	19-9-83	23-1-85
DD 128 Haruyuki	Sumitomo, Uraga	11-3-82	6-9-83	14-3-85
DD 129 Yamayuki	Hitachi, Maizuru	25-2-83	10-7-84	3-12-85
DD 130 Matsuyuki	IHI, Tokyo	7-4-83	25-10-84	19-3-86
DD 131 Setoyuki	Mitsui, Tamano	26-1-84	3-7-85	31-1-87
DD 132 Asayuki	Sumitomo, Uraga	22-12-83	16-10-85	20-2-87

Hatsuyuki (DD 122) Mitsuhiro Kadota, 6-00

Matsuyuki (DD 130) Takatoshi Okano, 10-00

Asayuki (DD 132) Takatoshi Okano, 3-00

Shirayuki (DD 123) Chris Delgoffe/H&L Van Ginderen, 5-00

D: DD 122–128: 2,950 tons (3,700 fl)—DD 129–132: 3,050 tons (3,800 fl)
S: 30 kts **Dim:** 131.70 (126.00 wl) × 13.70 × 4.10 (DD 129–132: 4.30 hull)
A: 4 or 8 RGM-84C Harpoon SSM; 1 8-round Mk 29 missile launcher (18 RIM-7F Sea Sparrow missiles); 1 76-mm 62-cal. OTOBreda Compact DP; 2 20-mm Mk 15 Phalanx gatling CIWS; 1 8-round Mk 112 ASROC ASW RL (16 missiles); 2 triple 324-mm Type 68 ASW TT (Mk 73 or Mk 46 Mod. 5 torpedoes); 1 SH-60J ASW helicopter
Electronics:
Radar: 1 JRC OPS-18-1 surf. search; 1 Melco OPS-14B air search; 1 FCS-2-21 gun f.c.; 1 FCS-2-12A SAM f.c.; 2 General Dynamics Mk 90 Phalanx f.c.
Sonar: NEC OQS-4A hull-mounted MF; EDO-NEC OQR-1 towed passive array
TACAN: U.S. URN-25 (ORN-6)
EW: NEC NOLQ-6C intercept—DD 131–132 only: OLR-9B D/F—all: Fujitsu OLT-3 jammer; Mk 36 SRBOC decoy syst. (2 6-round Raytheon Mk 137 RL)
M: COGOG: 2 Kawasaki–Rolls-Royce Olympus TM-3B gas turbines (25,000 shp each), 2 Tyne RM-1C gas turbines (5,000 shp each); 2 CP props; 50,000 shp (45,000 normal max.)
Range: . . ./. . . **Fuel:** . . . **Crew:** 17–19 officers, 144–153 enlisted

Remarks: DD 122, 123, and 125 are assigned to the 21st Escort Squadron, Yokosuka District Fleet; DD 124 and 126 to the 3rd Escort Squadron, 3rd Escort Flotilla, Maizuru; DD 129, 130, and 131 to the 8th Escort Squadron, 4th Escort Flotilla, Kure; and DD 127, 128, and 132 to the 23rd Escort Squadron, Sasebo District Fleet. Sister *Shimayuki* (DD 133) was redesignated TV 3513 on 18-3-99 and is employed as a training ship.
Hull systems: The Olympus engines are rated at 22,500 shp for cruise, 25,000 shp max., while the Tyne cruise engines are rated at 4,620 shp cruise/5,000 shp max. and can provide speeds up to 19.5 kts. Helicopter deck has the Canadian Beartrap traversing/landing system. Have fin stabilizers. Stack incorporates passive infrared cooling features and a water-spray system. DD 129 and later have steel vice aluminum superstructures. Most of the class easily made 32 kts on trials.
Combat systems: First seven have OYQ-5 TDPS (Tactical Data Processing System) with a U.S. UYK-20 computer; later units have OYQ-6. Have Link 14 data relay receiver only. Received OQR-1 (U.S. SQR-18) TACTASS towed passive linear arrays after completion, with DD 130 receiving hers under an FY 90 refit. DD 122 and

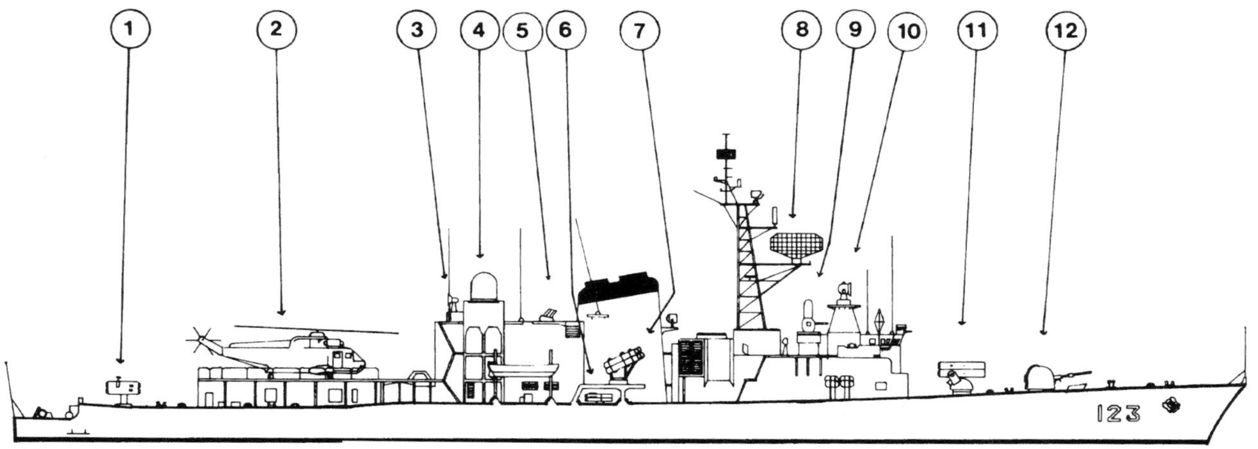

Shirayuki (DD 123) 1. Mk 29 launcher for Sea Sparrow SAMs 2. HSS-2B ASW helicopter (now replaced by SH-60J) 3. helicopter hangar 4. FCS-2-12A radar director for Sea Sparrow SAMs 5. Mk 137 decoy launchers 6. Type 68 triple ASW TT 7. Harpoon SSM (two groups of two or four) 8. OPS-14B air-search radar 9. Mk 15 Phalanx CIWS (port and starboard) 10. FCS-2-21 radar director for 76-mm gun 11. Mk 112 ASROC ASW missile launcher 12. 76-mm 62-cal. OTOBreda DP gun

Drawing by Robert Dumas, from *Flottes de Combat*

DESTROYERS [DD] *(continued)*

DD 123 initially lacked the Mk 15 Phalanx CIWS, which was added in the mid-1990s. DD 131 and DD 132 have later EW equipment. All have NYPX-2 IFF systems and Superbird SHF SATCOM equipment. Are being equipped with two 12.7- or 20-mm guns and night-vision equipment to detect and deter infiltration craft. Increasingly, only four Harpoon missiles are being carried, rather than the full complement of eight.

♦ 2 Takatsuki class

	Bldr	Laid down	L	In serv.
DD 164 Takatsuki	IHI, Tokyo	8-10-65	7-1-66	15-3-67
DD 165 Kikizuki	Mitsubishi, Nagasaki	15-3-66	25-3-67	27-3-68

Takatsuki (DD 164) Takatoshi Okano, 4-00

Kikizuki (DD 165) Takatoshi Okano, 4-01

D: 3,250 tons (4,550 fl) **S:** 32 kts **Dim:** 136.0 (131.0 pp) × 13.4 × 4.4 (mean)
A: 4 RGM-84C Harpoon SSM; 1 8-round Mk 29 SAM launcher (16 RIM-7F Sea Sparrow missiles); 1 127-mm 54-cal. Mk 42 Mod. 7 DP—DD 165 only: 1 20-mm Mk 15 Phalanx CIWS—both: 1 8-round Mk 112 ASROC ASW RL (no reloads); 1 4-round 375-mm Type 71 (Bofors Erika) ASW RL; 2 triple 324-mm Type 68 ASW TT (Type 73 or Mk 46 Mod. 5 torpedoes)
Electronics:
Radar: 1 JRC OPS-17 surf. search; 1 Melco OPS-11B-Y air search; 1 G.E. Mk 35 gun f.c.; 1 FCS-2-12B SAM f.c.; 1 General Dynamics Mk 90 Phalanx f.c.
Sonar: Sangamo OQS-3 hull-mounted MF; U.S. SQS-35(J) MF VDS; EDO-NEC OQR-1 (SQR-18A TACTASS) towed passive array
EW: NEC NOLR-6C intercept; Fujitsu OLT-3 jammer; Mk 36 SRBOC decoy syst. (2 6-round Raytheon Mk 137 RL); SLQ-25 towed acoustic torpedo decoy syst.
M: 2 sets Mitsubishi geared steam turbines; 2 props; 60,000 shp
Boilers: 2 Mitsubishi–Combustion Eng. (43 kg/cm^2, 454° C)
Range: 7,000/20 **Fuel:** 900 tons **Crew:** 260 tot.

Remarks: DD 164 was authorized under the 1981–82 budget to receive extensive modernization, completing in 10-85; DD 165 refitted under the 1983–84 budget, completing 26-12-87. Are assigned to the 24th Escort Squadron, Maizuru District Fleet. Both deployed in 3-99 as part of the Special Training Unit naval cadet training cruise.
Disposals: Of the two unmodernized units of the class, *Mochizuki* (DD 166) was reclassified as auxiliary ASU 7019 on 1-4-95 and later stricken, and *Nagatsuki* (DD 167) was stricken 1-4-96.
Hull systems: DD 165 has fin stabilizers, DD 164 does not.
Combat systems: Have OYQ-5 combat data systems. The DASH drone helicopter hangar and after 127-mm gun were removed during modernization; gained was a Mk 29 launcher aft for Sea Sparrow, 8 Harpoon missiles, a Mk 15 Phalanx CIWS gatling AA gun, upgrading of the OQS-3 sonar, provision for a U.S. SQR-18A TACTASS towed passive hydrophone array, replacement of the after Mk 56 gun f.c.s. with FCS-2-12, substitution of the NOLR-6C EW system, addition of Link 14 digital datalink equipment, and installation of the U.S. Mk 36 SRBOC decoy-launching system. The TASS array is streamed from the VDS fish. Probably to reduce topweight, only two paired sets of launch containers for Harpoon missiles are now carried, although they carried eight missiles until the late 1990s. DD 164 has not been given a Phalanx CIWS.

♦ 1 Yamagumo class Bldr: Sumitomo, Uraga

	Laid down	L	In serv.
DD 121 Yugumo (ex-DDK 121)	4-2-76	31-5-77	24-3-78

D: 2,150 tons (2,750 fl) **S:** 27 kts **Dim:** 114.9 × 11.8 × 4.0 (hull)
A: 2 twin 76.2-mm 50-cal. Mk 33 DP; 1 8-round Mk 112 ASROC ASW RL; 1 4-round 375-mm Type 71 (Bofors Erika) ASW RL; 2 triple 324-mm Type 68 ASW TT (Type 73 or Mk 46 Mod. 5 torpedoes)

Yugumo (DD 121) *Ships of the World,* 7-01

Electronics:
Radar: 1 JRC OPS-17 surf. search; 1 Melco OPS-11 air search; 2 FCS-1 gun f.c.
Sonar: NEC OQS-3A hull-mounted MF; EDO SQS-35(J) VDS
EW: NEC NOLR-5 intercept
M: 6 Mitsubishi 12UEV 30/40N diesels; 2 props; 26,500 bhp
Range: 7,000/20 **Crew:** 210–220 tot.

Remarks: A version of the earlier *Minegumo* class, completed with ASROC ASW missile launcher instead of DASH drone helicopter facilities. The former DDK designation ("K" for ASW "Killer") has been dropped. DD 121 is assigned to the 25th Escort Squadron, Ominato District Fleet, and will probably soon be stricken or downgraded to auxiliary service.
Disposals: Sisters *Yamagumo* (DDK 113) and *Makigumo* (DDK 114) were reclassified as training ships on 20-6-91 and later stricken; *Asagumo* (DD 115) became auxiliary ASU 7018 on 18-10-93 and was later stricken; *Aokumo* (DDK 119) became training ship TV 3512 on 18-3-99; and *Akigumo* (DD 120, ex-DDK 120) became TV 3514 on 13-6-00.

FRIGATES [FF]

♦ 6 Abukuma class

	Bldr	Laid down	L	In serv.
DE 229 Abukuma	Mitsui, Tamano	17-3-88	21-12-88	12-12-89
DE 230 Jintsu	Hitachi, Kanegawa	14-4-88	31-1-89	2-2-90
DE 231 Oyodo	Mitsui, Tamano	8-3-89	19-12-89	23-1-91
DE 232 Sendai	Sumitomo, Uraga	14-4-89	26-1-90	15-3-91
DE 233 Chikuma	Hitachi, Maizuro	14-2-91	22-1-92	24-2-93
DE 234 Tone	Sumitomo, Uraga	8-2-91	6-12-91	8-2-93

Jintsu (DE 230) Takatoshi Okano, 9-00

Abukuma (DE 229) Takatoshi Okano, 3-01

D: 2,050 tons (approx. 2,550 fl) **S:** 27 kts **Dim:** 109.0 × 13.4 × 3.8 (hull)
A: 4 RGM-84C Harpoon SSM; 1 76-mm 62-cal. OTOBreda Compact DP; 1 20-mm Mk 15 Phalanx CIWS; 1 8-round Mk 112 ASROC ASW RL; 2 triple 324-mm Type 68 ASW TT (Mk 73 or Mk 46 Mod. 5 torpedoes)
Electronics:
Radar: 1 JRC OPS-28 surf./air search; 1 Melco OPS-14C air search; 1 FCS-2-21A gun f.c.; 1 General Dynamics Mk 90 Phalanx f.c.
Sonar: OQS-8 bow-mounted MF
EW: NEC NOLQ-6C intercept; Fujitsu OLT-3 jammer; Mk 36 SRBOC decoy syst. (2 6-round Raytheon Mk 137 RL)
M: CODOG: 2 Kawasaki–Rolls-Royce Spey SM-1C gas turbines (13,500 shp each), 2 Mitsubishi S12U MTK S200 diesels (5,000 bhp each max.; 3,000 sust.); 2 CP props; 27,000 shp max.
Range: . . ./. . . **Crew:** 115 tot.

FRIGATES [FF] *(continued)*

Chikuma (DE 233) *Ships of the World,* 7-01

Remarks: First pair authorized under the FY 86 budget, second pair under FY 87, and third pair under FY 89. One more requested for FY 90 was rejected, and no more frigates are planned. First two were ordered 26-3-87, second two 26-2-88, and last two 24-1-89. The design has considerable improvements in sensors and firepower over the austere *Yubari* and *Ishikari* designs. DE 229 and 230 are assigned to the 31st Escort Squadron, Maizuru District Fleet; the others to the 26th Escort Squadron, Sasebo District Fleet, except for DE 233, transferred to the 25th Escort Squadron, Ominato District Fleet, 13-6-00.
Hull systems: Hull molded depth is 7.80 m. Have a helicopter VERTREP station aft, but no landing area.
Combat systems: Have the OYQ-1 automated combat data system. The RAM (RIM-116A) point-defense SAM is planned to be added, although Japan has yet to order the system from the U.S. or Germany. Also planned for later addition is the U.S. SQR-19A towed tactical sonar system (TASS). The hull-mounted sonar is essentially the same as the U.S. Raytheon DE 1167. Have been fitted with Skybird SHF SATCOM equipment. Carry only four Harpoon missiles, possibly to reduce topweight. No torpedo decoy system is fitted.

♦ 2 Yubari class

	Bldr	Laid down	L	In serv.
DE 227 Yubari	Sumitomo, Uraga	9-2-81	22-2-82	18-3-83
DE 228 Yubetsu	Hitachi, Maizuru	14-1-82	25-1-83	14-2-84

Yubari (DE 227)—with four Harpoon missiles aboard *Ships of the World,* 2000

Yubetsu (DE 228)—with six Harpoon missiles aboard *Ships of the World,* 2000

D: 1,470 tons (1,760 fl) **S:** 25 kts **Dim:** 91.0 × 10.8 × 3.6 (hull)
A: 6 or 8 RGM-84C Harpoon SSM; 1 76-mm 62-cal. OTOBreda DP; 1 4-round 375-mm Type 71 (Bofors Erika) ASW RL; 2 triple 324-mm Type 68 ASW TT (Type 73 or Mk 46 Mod. 5 torpedoes)
Electronics:
Radar: 1 Fujitsu OPS-19B nav.; 1 JRC OPS-28C surf./air search; 1 FCS-2-21 gun f.c.
Sonar: OQS-4 hull-mounted MF
EW: NEC NOLQ-6C intercept; Fujitsu OLT-3 jammer; Mk 36 SRBOC decoy syst. (2 6-round Raytheon Mk 137 decoy RL)
M: CODOG: 1 Kawasaki–Rolls-Royce Olympus TM-3B gas turbine (28,390 shp); 1 Mitsubishi 6DRV 35/44 diesel (5,000 bhp max.); 2 CP props
Range: . . ./. . . **Crew:** 98 tot.

Remarks: An enlarged version of the *Ishikari* class, presumably because the earlier ship was too cramped for the mission requirements. DE 227 was ordered under the FY 79 budget, DE 228 under FY 80. A third was requested for FY 82 but was not authorized. Both are assigned to the 27th Escort Squadron, Ominato District Fleet, with DE 226.
Combat systems: Have the OYQ-5 combat data system. Did not receive the planned Mk 15 Phalanx CIWS or a torpedo decoy system. The number of Harpoon missiles carried has been reduced to six in recent years.

♦ 1 Ishikari class

	Bldr	Laid down	L	In serv.
DE 226 Ishikari	Mitsui, Tamano	17-5-79	18-3-80	30-3-81

Ishikari (DE 226)—with four Harpoon missiles aboard *Ships of the World,* 2000

D: 1,200 tons (1,450 fl) **S:** 25 kts **Dim:** 84.5 × 10.0 × 3.5 (mean hull)
A: 4 RGM-84C Harpoon SSM; 1 76-mm 62-cal. OTOBreda DP; 1 4-round 375-mm Type 71 (Bofors Erika) ASW RL; 2 triple 324-mm Type 68 ASW TT (Type 73 and Mk 46 Mod. 5 torpedoes)
Electronics:
Radar: 1 Fujitsu OPS-19B nav.; 1 JRC OPS-28 surf./air search; 1 FCS-2-21 gun f.c.
Sonar: OQS-4 hull-mounted MF
EW: NEC NOLQ-6C intercept; Fujitsu OLT-3 jammer; Mk 36 SRBOC decoy syst. (2 6-round Raytheon Mk 137 RL)
M: CODOG: 1 Kawasaki–Rolls-Royce Olympus TM-3B gas turbine (28,390 shp), 1 Mitsubishi 6DRV 35/44 diesel (5,000 bhp max.); 2 CP props
Range: . . ./. . . **Crew:** 90 tot.

Remarks: Ordered under the FY 77 program. Smaller, more lightly armed, faster, and with fewer sensors than the preceding *Chikugo* class. Is assigned to the 27th Escort Squadron, Ominato District Fleet.
Hull systems: Aluminum superstructure. A highly automated ship with a very small crew for her size. Either the gas turbine or the single diesel will drive both propellers. Can make 19 kts max. on diesel.
Combat systems: The Combat Information Center (CIC) is below the waterline and is equipped with the OYQ-5 combat data system. Normally carries only four Harpoon SSM but four more could be fitted if required.

♦ 1 Chikugo class

	Bldr	Laid down	L	In serv.
DE 225 Noshiro	Mitsui, Tamano	27-1-76	23-12-76	31-8-77

Noshiro (DE 225) *Ships of the World,* 2000

D: 1,530 tons (1,800 fl) **S:** 25 kts **Dim:** 93.0 × 10.8 × 3.5 (hull)
A: 1 twin 76.2-mm 50-cal. U.S. Mk 33 DP; 1 twin 40-mm 60-cal. Mk 1 Mod. 2 AA; 1 8-cell Mk 112 ASROC ASW RL (no reloads); 2 triple 324-mm Type 68 ASW TT (Type 73 or Mk 46 Mod. 5 torpedoes)

FRIGATES [FF] *(continued)*

Electronics:
Radar: 1 JRC OPS-16 surf. search; 1 Melco OPS-14 air search; 1 FCS-1B gun f.c.
Sonar: Hitachi OQS-3A hull-mounted MF; EDO SQS-35(J) VDS
EW: NEC NOLR-5 intercept
M: 4 Mitsubishi 28VBC-38 diesels; 2 props; 16,000 bhp
Range: 10,700/12; 12,000/9 **Crew:** 12 officers, 152 enlisted

Remarks: DE 225 is assigned to the 22nd Escort Squadron, Kure District Fleet, and was to be retired during the spring of 2002.
Disposals: *Chikugo* (DE 215) was stricken 15-4-96, *Ayase* (DE 216) on 1-8-96, *Mikuma* (DE 217) on 8-7-97, *Iwase* (DE 219) on 16-10-98, *Tokachi* (DE 218) on 15-4-98, *Chitose* (DE 220) on 13-4-99, *Niyodo* (DE 221) on 24-6-99, *Teshio* (DE 222) on 27-6-00, *Yoshino* (DE 223) on 15-5-01, and *Kumano* (DE 224) on 18-5-01.
Combat system: The SQS-35(J) towed, variable-depth sonar was mounted only in the last five units of the class, stowed in an open well at the stern, offset to starboard. These were the smallest ships in any navy to carry ASROC. A Mk 51 Mod. 3 lead-computing director (no radar) controls the twin 40-mm mount.

HYDROFOIL GUIDED-MISSILE PATROL BOATS [PTGH]

♦ 3 modified Italian Sparviero class
Bldr: Sumitomo, Uraga

	Laid down	L	In serv.
PG 821 PG 01	25-3-91	17-7-92	22-3-93
PG 822 PG 02	25-3-91	17-7-92	22-3-93
PG 823 PG 03	8-3-93	15-6-94	13-3-95

PG 02 (PG 822) Takatoshi Okano, 10-00

PG 01 (PG 821) Takatoshi Okano, 10-00

D: 50 tons (63 fl) **S:** 50 kts (in calm sea; 46 sust.)
Dim: 22.95 (24.56 foils retracted) × 7.01 (12.06 max. over foils) × 1.87 (1.45 over foils at speed, 4.37 at rest)
A: 4 SSM-1B SSM; 1 20-mm JM-61-MB gatling AA
Electronics:
Radar: 1 JRC OPS-28-2 surf. search
EW: . . . intercept; Mk 36 SRBOC decoy syst. (2 6-round Raytheon Mk 137 RL)
M: 1 G.E. LM-500 gas turbine; 1 waterjet; 5,200 shp (4,000 sust.)
Range: 400/45 **Crew:** 11 tot.

Remarks: First two were approved under FY 90, but the third unit, approved under FY 91, was deferred to help pay the cost of Japanese participation in the aftermath of the Persian Gulf War and was requested again under the FY 92 budget. A fourth unit, requested under FY 95, was turned down. The license to construct this modified version of the Italian Navy's *Sparviero* class (itself a modified version of the U.S. Navy's *Tucumcari,* PGH 1) was not granted until 3-91. All three are assigned to the Ominato District Fleet as the 1st Missile Boat Squadron, based at Amarushi.
Hull systems: The titanium hydrofoils are retractable, the bow unit swinging forward through an arc and the after pair pivoting outboard through an arc.
Combat systems: The gatling gun employs a simple pintle mounting and is of the same type as is employed on JMSDF mine countermeasures ships and JCG patrol ships and craft. Have Link 11 datalink.

GUIDED-MISSILE PATROL BOATS [PTG]

♦ 0 (+ 6 + 4) Hayabusa class (200-ton PG)
Bldr: Mitsubishi, . . .

	Laid down	L	In serv.
PG 824 Hayabusa	9-11-00	13-6-01	3-02
PG 825 Wakataka	9-11-00	13-9-01	3-02
PG 826	10-01	5-02	3-03
PG 827	10-01	8-02	3-03
PG 828	10-02	. . .-03	3-04
PG 829	10-02	. . .-03	3-04
PG 830	10-03	. . .-04	3-05
PG 832	10-04	. . .-05	3-06
PG 833	10-05	. . .-06	3-07
PG 834	10-06	. . .-07	3-08
PG 835	10-06	. . .-07	3-08

Hayabusa (PG 824)—artist's rendering *Ships of the World,* 2001

D: 200 tons (. . . fl) **S:** 46 kts **Dim:** 50.1 × 8.4 × . . .
A: 4 SSM-1B SSM; 1 76-mm 62-cal. OTOBreda Super Compact DP; 2 single 12.7-mm mg
Electronics:
Radar: 1 JRC OPS-28-2 surf. search; 1 FCS-2-21 gun f.c.
EW: NOLQ-6-series intercept; Mk 36 SRBOC decoy syst. (2 6-round Raytheon Mk 137 RL)
E/O: . . . surveillance and tracking syst.
M: 3 G.E. LM-500-GO7 gas turbines; 3 waterjets; 16,200 shp
Range: . . ./. . . **Crew:** 40 tot.

Remarks: New design, substituted for further hydrofoil construction. More than three times the displacement of the PG 01 series. First two were approved under the FY 99 budget, second pair under FY 00, and third pair under FY 01, with a total of 10 planned. Engines ordered 5-00. Are to carry RIBs for boarding and inspection duties. Will have a SATCOM system with two antennas. The 76-mm gun will be fitted in a faceted gunhouse to reduce radar reflectivity.

MINE WARFARE SHIPS

♦ 2 Uraga-class mine countermeasures support ship/minelayers [MCS]

	Bldr	Laid down	L	In serv.
MST 463 Uraga	Hitachi Zosen, Maizuru	19-5-95	22-5-96	19-3-97
MST 464 Bungo	Mitsui, Tamano	31-8-95	24-4-97	23-3-98

Uraga (MST 463)—unarmed Mitsuhiro Kadota, 10-01

MINE WARFARE SHIPS *(continued)*

Bungo (MST 464)—with 76-mm gun and radar director; note the central door/ramp in the transom for deploying sweep gear to mine countermeasures craft and the four flush doors flanking it on two levels for the minelaying rails
Takatoshi Okano, 4-00

D: 5,650 tons (8,400 fl) **S:** 22 kts **Dim:** 141.0 (136.0 pp) × 22.0 × 5.4
A: MST 464 only: 1 76-mm 62-cal. OTOBreda DP—both: 230 large mines
Electronics:
Radar: 1 JRC OPS-18 nav.; 1 Melco OPS-14B air search—MST 464 only: 1 FCS-2-21A gun f.c.
M: 2 Mitsui 12V42M-A diesels; 2 props; 19,800 bhp—bow-thruster
Range: 4,600/20 **Crew:** 129 tot. + 32 mine warfare staff

Remarks: First unit approved under the FY 94 budget and second under FY 95. MST 463 is flagship for the Escort Fleet Minesweeper Flotilla, Yokosuka. MST 464 is based at Kure.
Hull systems: Hull has a bulbous forefoot. Have a hangar and flight deck for one CH-53E mine countermeasures helicopter. There is a stern door centerline, served by an articulating ramp to permit the service and resupply of craft being supported.
Combat systems: Flanking the stern door on either side on two deck levels are doors covering mine rails. MST 463 is fitted to receive a radar director and gun, but neither has been installed as yet.

Note: The former 1st and 2nd Fleet Minesweeper Flotillas have been combined into a single Fleet Minesweeper Flotilla.

♦ 3 Yaeyama-class deep-sea mine countermeasures ships [MHS]

	Bldr	Laid down	L	In serv.
MSO 301 Yaeyama	Hitachi, Kanagawa	30-8-90	29-8-91	16-3-93
MSO 302 Tsushima	Nippon Kokan, Tsurumi	20-7-90	11-9-91	23-3-93
MSO 303 Hachijo	Nippon Kokan, Tsurumi	17-5-91	15-12-92	24-3-94

Tsushima (MSO 302) Takatoshi Okano, 2-01

Hachijo (MSO 303) Takatoshi Okano, 2-00

D: 1,000 tons (1,150 fl) **S:** 14 kts **Dim:** 67.0 × 11.8 × 3.1
A: 1 20-mm JM-61-MB gatling AA
Electronics:
Radar: 1 Fujitsu OPS-19 nav.
Sonar: ZQS-3 (Raytheon SQQ-32) minehunting HF VDS; Klein AQS-14 towed side-scan
M: 2 Mitsubishi 6NMU-series diesels; 2 CP props; 2,400 bhp—bow-thruster
Crew: 60 tot.

Remarks: First two units were authorized by the FY 89 budget, with two per year thereafter planned to a total of six, but only one was authorized under FY 90. Three more were planned during FY 1992–95 period, but further procurement has been canceled. Constitute the Escort Fleet's 51st Minesweeping Division, Yokosuka.
Hull systems: Wooden-hulled construction, with glass-reinforced plastic sheathing.
Combat systems: Equipped to deploy the Type S-7 autonomous minehunting vehicle and Type S-8 deep-sea mine disposal system, the latter a version of the U.S. Honeywell SLQ-48 remote-controlled submersible vehicle. Also carry Type S-2 noisemakers. Equipped with the Marisat commercial satellite communications system as well as sophisticated navigational equipment.

♦ 4 (+ 8) Sugashima-class minehunter/minesweepers [MHC]

	Bldr	Laid down	L	In serv.
MSC 681 Sugashima	Nippon Kokan, Tsurumi	8-5-96	25-8-97	16-3-99
MSC 682 Notojima	Hitachi, Kanagawa	8-5-96	3-9-97	16-3-99
MSC 683 Tsunoshima	Hitachi, Kanagawa	7-8-97	22-10-98	13-3-00
MSC 684 Naoshima	Nippon Kokan, Tsurumi	17-4-98	7-10-99	16-3-01
MSC 685 Toyoshima	Hitachi, Kanagawa	25-4-99	13-9-00	3-02
MSC 686 Ukushima	Nippon Kokan, Tsurumi	17-5-00	17-9-01	3-03
MSC 687 Izushima	Hitachi, Kanagawa	27-4-00	31-10-01	3-03
MSC 688	Nippon Kokan, Tsurumi	17-4-01	9-02	3-04
MSC 689	. . .	4-02	. . .	3-05
MSC 690	. . .	4-02	. . .	3-05

Tsunoshima (MSC 683) Takatoshi Okano, 2-01

Notojima (MSC 682) Mitsuhiro Kadota, 10-00

D: 510 tons (620 fl) **S:** 15.5 kts (14 sust.)
Dim: 58.00 (54.00 pp) × 9.50 (9.40 wl) × 2.50 (3.00 max.)
A: 1 20-mm JM-61-MB gatling AA
Electronics:
Radar: 1 OPS-39B nav.
Sonar: Hitachi ZQS-4 minehunting HF VDS
M: 2 Mitsubishi 8NMU-TAI diesels; 2 CP props; 1,800 bhp—2 175-shp electric cruise motors (on main shafts)—bow-thruster
Electric: . . . **Range:** 2,500/10 **Crew:** 5 officers, 32 enlisted (accomm. for 45)

Remarks: First two units approved under the FY 95 budget, MSC 683 under FY 96, MSC 684 under FY 97, MSC 685 under FY 98, MSC 686 and 687 under FY 99, MSC 688 under FY 00, and MSC 689 and 690 under FY 01. A total of 12 is planned. These are the first Japanese mine countermeasures units with fully computerized combat systems. MSC 681, 682, and 683 are assigned to the 3rd Minesweeper Division, Yokosuka; MSC 684 is assigned to the Escort Fleet, 2nd Minesweeping Division, Sasebo.
Hull systems: Wooden construction. Forecastle is extended aft to provide shelter for remotely operated minehunting submersibles. Have twin funnels athwartships.

MINE WARFARE SHIPS *(continued)*

Combat systems: Use an NEC-built variant of the GEC-Marconi Nautis-IIM tactical data system. The sonar is a license-built Thales Type 2093M, and the hoist gear is within the forward part of the superstructure. Carry two French PAP 105 Mk 5 remote-controlled minehunting submersibles. Sweep equipment includes an Australian Dyad magnetic and acoustic array and Oropesa Type 6 wire sweep gear. Have WRN-7 GPS receiver and Decca Hyperfix precision radio navigation aids.

♦ 9 Uwajima-class minehunter/minesweepers [MHC]

	Bldr	Laid down	L	In serv.
MSC 672 Uwajima	Nippon Kokan, Tsurumi	18-5-89	23-5-90	19-12-90
MSC 673 Ieshima	Hitachi, Kanagawa	12-5-89	12-6-90	19-12-90
MSC 674 Tsukishima	Hitachi, Kanagawa	27-5-91	23-7-92	17-3-93
MSC 675 Maejima	Hitachi, Kanegawa	1-6-92	10-6-93	15-12-93
MSC 676 Kumejima	Nippon Kokan, Tsurumi	17-2-93	9-11-93	12-12-94
MSC 677 Makishima	Hitachi, Kanagawa	12-5-93	26-5-94	12-12-94
MSC 678 Tobishima	Nippon Kokan, Tsurumi	22-6-93	31-8-94	10-3-95
MSC 679 Yugeshima	Hitachi, Kanegawa	10-4-94	24-5-96	11-12-96
MSC 680 Nagashima	Nippon Kokan, Tsurumi	14-4-94	30-5-96	25-12-96

Ieshima (MSC 673) Takatoshi Okano, 2-01

Makishima (MSC 677) Takatoshi Okano, 8-99

D: 490 tons (590 fl) **S:** 14 kts **Dim:** 57.7 × 9.40 × 2.90
A: 1 20-mm JM-61-MB gatling AA
Electronics:
Radar: 1 OPS-18B nav.
Sonar: Hitachi ZQS-3 minehunting HF VDS
M: 2 Mitsubishi 6NMU-TAI diesels; 2 CP props; 1,440 bhp
Electric: 1 × 1,450-kw dc; 2 × 160-kw a.c. **Range:** 2,400/10 **Crew:** 45 tot.

Remarks: A revised version of the *Hatsushima* class, lengthened primarily to permit two-high vice three-high bunking for enlisted personnel. Were to have been of GRP construction but are built of wood. MSC 672 is assigned to the Maizuru District Fleet; MSC 673, 675, and 677 to the Sasebo District Fleet; MSC 674 and 676 to the 42nd Minesweeping Division, Kure District Fleet; and MSC 678, 679, and 680 to the Escort Fleet, 1st Minesweeping Division, Kure.
Combat systems: Carry S-2 towed noisemakers and S-4 (with ZQS-2B sonar) and S-7 Mod.1 (with ZQS-3 sonar) autonomous minehunting vehicles.

♦ 11 Hatsushima-class minehunter/minesweepers [MHC]

	Bldr	Laid down	L	In serv.
MSC 660 Hahajima	Nippon Kokan, Tsurumi	20-5-83	27-6-84	18-12-84
MSC 662 Newajima	Hitachi, Kanagawa	21-5-84	5-6-85	12-12-85
MSC 663 Etajima	Nippon Kokan, Tsurumi	22-5-84	17-6-85	12-12-85
MSC 664 Kamishima	Nippon Kokan, Tsurumi	10-5-85	20-6-86	16-12-86
MSC 665 Himeshima	Hitachi, Kanagawa	16-5-85	10-6-86	16-12-86
MSC 666 Ogishima	Hitachi, Kanagawa	16-5-86	10-6-87	19-12-87
MSC 667 Moroshima	Nippon Kokan, Tsurumi	22-5-86	11-6-87	19-12-87
MSC 668 Yurishima	Nippon Kokan, Tsurumi	14-5-87	13-5-88	15-12-88
MSC 669 Hikoshima	Hitachi, Kanagawa	12-5-87	2-6-88	15-12-88
MSC 670 Awashima	Hitachi, Kanagawa	12-5-88	6-6-89	13-12-89
MSC 671 Sakushima	Nippon Kokan, Tsurumi	17-5-88	6-6-89	13-12-89

Etajima (MSC 663) Takatoshi Okano, 2-01

Awashima (MSC 670) Mitsuhiro Kadota, 10-00

D: 440 tons (536 fl) **S:** 14 kts **Dim:** 55.00 (52.00 pp) × 9.40 × 2.40
A: 1 20-mm JM-61-MB gatling AA
Electronics:
Radar: 1 Fujitsu OPS-9 or OPS-18B nav.
Sonar: NEC-Hitachi ZQS-2B hull-mounted minehunting HF
M: 2 Mitsubishi YV12ZC-18/20 diesels; 2 CP props; 1,440 bhp
Electric: MSC 660–665: 1,690 kw tot. (2 × 725-kw diesel sweep gen., 3 × 80-kw ship's service diesel sets)—MSC 666–671: 1,770 kw tot. (1 × 1,450-kw gas turbine sweep gen., 2 × 160-kw ship's service diesel set)
Range: 2,400/10 **Crew:** 45 tot.

Remarks: An expansion of the preceding *Takami* design. MSC 660 and 664 are assigned to the Ominato District Fleet, 45th Minesweeper Division; MSC 661, 662, and 663 are assigned to the Maizuru District Fleet, 44th Minesweeping Division; MSC 665 and 666 are assigned to the Escort Fleet, 4th Minesweeping Division, based at Sasebo; MSC 667 and 669 are assigned to the Sasebo District Fleet, 46th Minesweeper Division; and MSC 668, 670, and 671 are assigned to the Yokosuka District Fleet, 41st Minesweeping Division.
Disposals: Sister *Hatsushima* (MSC 649) was redesignated YAS 98 on 10-3-95. *Ninoshima* (MSC 650) and *Miyajima* (MSC 651) were redesignated YAS on 1-3-96. Later units were to be retired at two per year through 3-01, with no further units planned to be redesignated YAS. *Enoshima* (MSC 652) was stricken 5-12-96, *Ukishima* (MSC 653) on 12-3-97, *Oshima* (MSC 654) on 23-3-98, *Narushima* (MSC 657) on 25-6-99, *Chichijima* (MSC 658) on 13-3-00, *Torishima* (MSC 659) on 1-12-00, and *Takashima* (MSC 661) on 4-6-01. *Niijima* (MSC 655) was reclassified as mine-countermeasures support ship MCL 722 on 23-3-98 and *Yakushima* (MSC 656) as MCL 723 on 13-5-99.
Hull systems: Wooden construction. MSC 664 and 665 have Mitsubishi 122C-15/22 diesels; MSC 666 and 667 have Mitsubishi 6NMU-TAI diesels.
Combat systems: The sweep tail generates 4,300 amps. Carry Type S-2 towed noise-makers and Type S-4 autonomous minehunting vehicles with ZQS-2B sonars; these carry and lay their own disposal charges.

♦ 2 Hatsushima-class mine countermeasures drone control ships [MSA] Bldr: Nippon Kokan, Tsurumi

	Laid down	L	In serv.
MCL 722 Niijima (ex-MSC 655)	4-8-80	2-6-81	26-11-81
MCL 723 Yakushima (ex-MSC 656)	15-6-81	22-6-82	17-12-82

Yakushima (MCL 723) Takatoshi Okano, 7-99

MINE WARFARE SHIPS *(continued)*

Niijima (MCL 722)—with SAM-class drone alongside under tow
Takatoshi Okano, 2-01

D: 440 tons (536 fl) **S:** 14 kts **Dim:** 55.00 (52.00 pp) × 9.40 × 2.40
A: 1 20-mm JM-61-MB gatling AA
Electronics:
Radar: 1 Fujitsu OPS-9 nav.
Sonar: NEC-Hitachi ZQS-2B hull-mounted minehunting HF
M: 2 Mitsubishi YV12ZC-18/20 diesels; 2 CP props; 1,440 bhp
Electric: 1,690 kw tot. (2 × 725-kw diesel sweep gen., 3 × 80-kw ship's service diesel sets)
Range: 2,400/10 **Crew:** 45 tot.

Remarks: Former coastal minehunter/minesweepers. MCL 722 was reclassified on 23-3-98 and MCL 723 on 13-5-99 to act as control ships for the Swedish-built SAM-series drone mine countermeasures craft. Have retained mechanical, acoustic, and magnetic sweep gear. Both are assigned to the 101st Minesweeper Division, Kure.

♦ 6 SAM-01 class radio-controlled mine countermeasures craft [MSD]

Bldr: Karlskronavarvet, Karlskrona, Sweden (In serv. 1998–99)

NAME 1 SAM-01	NAME 3 SAM-03	NAME 5 SAM-05
NAME 2 SAM-02	NAME 4 SAM-04	NAME 6 SAM-06

SAM-03 (NAME 3)—note row of eight danbuoy swept-lane markers across the stern
JMSDF, 2000

D: 15 tons (20 fl) **S:** 8 kts **Dim:** 18.0 × 6.10 × 0.70 (1.60 prop)
M: 1 Volvo-Penta TAMD 70D diesel; 1 Schottel shrouded prop; 210 bhp
Range: 330/7

Remarks: Two were delivered to Japan in 2-98, with two further ordered in 4-98 and delivered 10-2-99, and two more delivered late in 1999. Are controlled two-each by MCL 721 and MCL 722, based at Kure. The catamarans also automatically lay eight swept-channel danbuoy markers. SAM = Self-propelled Acoustic and Magnetic. Sisters operate in the Swedish Navy.

Note: Former mine countermeasures craft redesignated as YAS are used as diving tenders, including mine disposal diving; see under Service Craft section.

AMPHIBIOUS WARFARE SHIPS

♦ 1 (+ 2 + 1) Osumi-class dock landing ships [LSD]

	Bldr	Laid down	L	In serv.
LST 4001 Osumi	Mitsui, Tamano	7-12-95	18-11-96	11-3-98
LST 4002 Shimokita	Mitsui, Tamano	30-11-99	29-11-00	3-02
LST 4003 Kunisaki	Hitachi	7-9-00	13-12-01	2-03
LST 4004	. . .	. . .	. . .	. . .

Osumi (LST 4001) Takatoshi Okano, 10-00

Osumi (LST 4001)—at Istanbul, with relief supplies Cem D. Yaylali, 10-99

Shimokita (LST 4002)—at launch Takatoshi Okano, 11-00

Osumi (LST 4001)—note that the breadth of the island structure virtually prohibits use of the upper deck for fixed-wing flight operations Mitsuhiro Kadota, 9-00

D: 8,900 tons light (approx. 13,000 fl) **S:** 22 kts **Dim:** 178.0 (170.0 wl) × 25.8 × 6.00
A: 2 20-mm Mk 15 Phalanx CIWS
Electronics:
Radar: 1 JRC OPS-20 nav.; 1 JRC OPS-28 surf. search; 1 Melco OPS-14C air search; 2 General Dynamics Mk 90 Phalanx f.c.

AMPHIBIOUS WARFARE SHIPS *(continued)*

M: 2 Mitsui–SEMT-Pielstick 16V42M-A diesels; 2 props; 26,000 bhp
Electric: 17,000 kw tot. (4 × 4,000-kw, 1 × 1,000-kw diesel sets)
Range: . . ./. . . **Crew:** 135 tot. + 330 troops (1,000 for brief periods)

Remarks: LST 4001 was ordered during 9-93. LST 4002 was authorized under the FY 98 budget and LST 4003 under FY 99. LST 4001 is based at Kure.
Hull systems: The official "standard" displacement appears to be several thousand tons below the actual figure. Although given an LST type-designation, the design is in reality a dock landing ship configured to accept two U.S. LCAC 1–class air-cushion vehicle landing craft in a 60- to 70-m-long docking well; there is no bow door, and the ship is not intended to beach. Although the upper deck is a relatively unobstructed 130 m long, only the after portion is used as a helicopter landing position (for two CH-47 Chinook-size aircraft). The remainder of the deck is used for vehicle cargo stowage. There are two vehicle elevators rising to the flight deck, one forward on the centerline and one to starboard abaft the island superstructure, but neither is large enough to accommodate a helicopter. The elevators serve a 50 × 15–m vehicle cargo deck, which also has side ramps port and starboard; abreast the side ramps on the centerline is a vehicle turntable. Cargo capacity is 1,400 tons, including up to 14 Type 90 heavy tanks. In an emergency, up to 1,000 passengers can be accommodated. The superstructure is shaped to reduce radar reflection, and its width precludes using the flight deck for fixed-wing aircraft operations. Carries two nonbeachable personnel launches.
Combat systems: A previously-planned 76-mm gun will not be installed.

♦ 0 (+ 3) planned new vehicle landing ships [LST]
Bldr: . . . . . .

	Laid down	L	In serv.
LSU 1	. . .	. . .	. . .
LSU 2	. . .	. . .	. . .
LSU 3	. . .	. . .	. . .

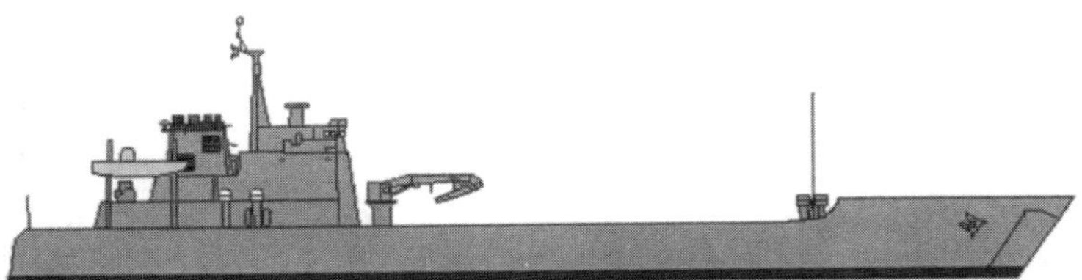
New 1,900-ton landing ship *Ships of the World,* 2001

D: approx. 1,900 tons std. **S:** . . . kts **Dim:** . . . × . . . × . . .
A: none **Electronics:** Radar: 1 . . . nav.
M: 2 . . . diesels; 2 CP props; . . . bhp
Range: . . ./. . . **Crew:** . . .

Remarks: Program was announced in 12-00 after it was discovered that the large *Osumi*-class "LSTs" cannot be used effectively in emergency assistance missions to offshore Japanese islands. The new ships will be beachable and will have a bow ramp. The first was requested under the FY 02 budget, and the three ships are to be attached to the Yokosuka and Ominato districts. Will not be armed, but provision will be made for installing a gunmount and a radar director, if required.

♦ 1 Miura-class landing ship [LST]
Bldr: IHI, Tokyo

	Laid down	L	In serv.
LST 4153 Satsuma	26-5-75	12-5-76	17-2-77

Satsuma (LST 4153) *Ships of the World,* 5-01

Satsuma (LST 4153)—note the LCM(6) landing craft stowed beneath the traveling gantry crane *Ships of the World,* 2000

D: 2,000 tons (3,200 fl) **S:** 14 kts **Dim:** 98.0 (94.0 pp) × 14.0 × 3.0
A: 1 twin 76.2-mm 50-cal. U.S. Mk 33 DP; 1 twin 40-mm 60-cal. Mk 1 Mod. 2 Bofors AA
Electronics:
Radar: 1 JRC OPS-18 nav.; 1 Melco OPS-14 surf./air search; 1 Western Electric Mk 34 f.c.
M: 2 Kawasaki-M.A.N. V8V 22/30 AMTL diesels; 2 props; 4,400 bhp
Range: . . ./. . . **Crew:** 118 tot. ship's company + 200 troops

Remarks: Based at Yokosuka, assigned to the Escort Fleet. Sister *Miura* (LST 4151) was stricken 7-4-00 and *Ojika* (LST 4152) on 10-8-01.
Hull systems: Flat-bottomed hull design based on that of the U.S. LST 1 class. Carries up to 1,800 tons of cargo. Vehicle deck can hold 10 Type 74 battle tanks. Carries two LCVPs in davits and two LCM(6) on deck, the latter served by a traveling gantry with folding rails that can be extended over the sides.
Combat systems: A U.S. Mk 51 Mod. 2 lead-computing gun f.c.s. aft controls 40-mm mount.

♦ 1 Atsumi-class tank landing ship [LST]
Bldr: Sasebo Heavy Industries

	Laid down	L	In serv.
LST 4103 Nemuro	18-11-76	16-6-77	27-10-77

Nemuro (LST 4103) Takatoshi Okano, 6-00

D: 1,550 tons (2,470 fl) **S:** 13 kts **Dim:** 89.0 × 13.0 × 2.8
A: 2 twin 40-mm 60-cal. Mk 1 Mod. 2 Bofors AA
Electronics: Radar: 1 Fujitsu OPS-9 nav.
M: 2 Kawasaki-M.A.N. V8V 22/30 AMTL diesels; 2 props; 4,400 bhp
Range: 4,300/12 **Crew:** 100 tot. ship's company + 130 troops

Remarks: Sister *Atsumi* (LST 4101) was retired 13-2-98 and *Motobu* (LST 4102) on 12-4-99. LST 4103 is assigned to the Ominato District Fleet.
Hull systems: Can carry 20 vehicles or 400 tons of cargo. Two LCVPs are carried in davits, and one LCVP or LCM can be transported on deck, amidships.
Combat systems: Has two U.S. Mk 51 Mod. 2 lead-computing gun f.c.s. to control the 40-mm guns.

♦ 2 Yura-class utility landing craft [LCU]
Bldr: Sasebo Heavy Industries

	Laid down	L	In serv.
LSU 4171 Yura	23-4-80	10-8-80	27-3-81
LSU 4172 Noto	23-4-80	1-11-80	27-3-81

Noto (LSU 4172) Takatoshi Okano, 11-00

D: 500 tons (590 fl) **S:** 12 kts **Dim:** 58.0 × 9.5 × 1.7 (aft)
A: 1 20-mm JM 61-MB gatling AA **Electronics:** Radar: 1 OPS-. . . nav.
M: 2 Fuji 6L 27.5X diesels; 2 CP props; 3,000 bhp
Range: . . ./. . . **Crew:** 32 tot. ship's company + 70 troops

Remarks: Both were in the 1979–80 budget; request for a third in the FY 81 budget was denied. Have bow doors and ramp and an open cargo deck. LSU 4171 is assigned to the Kure District Fleet and LSU 4172 to the Maizuru District Fleet.

♦ 2 LC 01–class utility landing craft [LCU]
Bldr: Sasebo Naval Dockyard

	Laid down	L	In serv.
LCU 2001 LC 01	11-5-87	1-10-87	17-3-88
LCU 2002 LC 02	15-5-91	1-10-91	11-3-92

AMPHIBIOUS WARFARE SHIPS *(continued)*

LC 02 (LCU 2002) *Ships of the World,* 6-00

D: 420 tons **S:** 12 kts **Dim:** 52.0 × 8.7 × 1.6
A: 1 20-mm JM-61-MB gatling AA **Electronics:** Radar: 1 OPS-. . . nav.
M: 2 Mitsubishi 6SU-MTK diesels; 2 props; 3,000 bhp **Crew:** 28 tot.

Remarks: First unit was approved under the FY 86 budget and ordered 24-3-87; the second was approved under FY 90. Have bluff bow/ramp and an open cargo deck. LCU 2001 is assigned to the Sasebo District Fleet and LCU 2002 to the Yokosuka District Fleet.

♦ 3 (+ 3 + 2) U.S. LCAC 1–class air-cushion landing craft
Bldr: Textron Marine and Land Systems, New Orleans

	In serv.		In serv.		In serv.
LA-01	11-97	L-03	11-01	L-05	2002
LA-02	2-98	L-04	2-02	L-06	2002

LA-02 Takatoshi Okano, 10-00

D: 93 tons light (166.6 fl; 181.6 overload) **S:** 54 kts (40 when loaded)
Dim: 26.80 (24.69 hull) × 14.33 (13.31 hull) × 0.87 (at rest)
A: none **Electronics:** Radar: 1 . . . nav.
M: 4 Avco TF40B gas turbines (2 for lift); 2 3.58-m-dia. shrouded airscrews, 4 centrifugal 1.60-m-dia. lift fans; 15,820 shp
Electric: 120 kw tot. (2 × 60-kw Turbomach T-62 APU)
Range: 223/48 (light); 200/40 (loaded) **Fuel:** 6.2 tons (7,132 gallons)
Crew: 5 tot. + 25 troops

Remarks: Decision to order in 11-93 for use on new *Osumi*-class LSTs. First unit funded under the FY 93 budget and the second under FY 95; the third and fourth were requested under FY 99, and two more were approved under FY 00 and ordered 22-5-01. Two more are planned for the fourth *Osumi.*
Hull systems: Cargo capacity: 60 tons normal/75 tons overload. Bow ramp is 8.8 m wide, stern ramp 4.6 m. The deck has 168 m^2 of parking area and is 204 m long by 8.3 m wide. Are difficult to tow if broken down and are vulnerable to defensive fire. Operator, engineer, navigator, and nine troops travel in starboard side compartments; deck hand, assistant engineer, load master, and 16 troops travel in port compartments. Cannot carry troops on deck, limiting their utility. Navigational equipment includes a GPS receiver. Are able to transport one Japanese Type 90 main battle tank or four Type 89 armored fighting vehicles.

♦ 4 U.S.-design LCM(6)-class landing craft

Japanese version of the LCM(6) Takatoshi Okano, 6-99

D: 24 tons (56 fl) **S:** 10 kts **Dim:** 17.07 × 4.37 × 1.17 (aft)
M: 2 Yanmar diesels; 2 props; 450 bhp **Range:** 130/9
Crew: 3 tot. + 80 troops for short distances

Remarks: Unnumbered units carried aboard the *Miura*-class LSTs. Built in Japan. Able to carry about 34 tons of vehicles or cargo. Others have been built as service craft with YF-series numbers (see under Service Craft section).

♦ 6 U.S.-design LCVP-class landing craft

D: 13 tons (fl) **S:** 8 kts **Dim:** 10.90 × 3.21 × 1.04 (aft)
M: 1 Yanmar diesel; 1 prop; 180 bhp **Crew:** 3 tot.

Remarks: Japanese-built, GRP hulls. Unnumbered units carried by the older LSTs. Also in service are seven employed as service craft and carrying YF-series hull numbers.

Japanese version of the LCVP Takatoshi Okano, 6-99

AUXILIARIES

♦ 1 Tenryu-class target service ship [AG]
Bldr: Sumitomo, Uraga

	Laid down	L	In serv.
ATS 4203 Tenryu	19-6-98	14-4-99	13-3-00

Tenryu (ATS 4203) Takatoshi Okano, 10-00

Tenryu (ATS 4203)—with Firebee target on launcher *Ships of the World,* 3-00

D: 2,400 tons (approx. 3,500 fl) **S:** 22 kts **Dim:** 106.0 × 16.5 × 4.0 (mean hull)
A: 1 76-mm 62-cal. OTOBreda DP
Electronics:
Radar: 1 JRC OPS-18 surf. search; 1 Melco OPS-14B air search; 1 TMCATS target control (see remarks); 1 FCS-2-21A f.c.
Sonar: . . .
TACAN: URN-25
M: 4 Fuji 8L 27.5SX diesels; 2 props; 12,800 bhp—bow-thruster **Crew:** 150 tot.

Remarks: Requested under the FY 97 budget as a replacement for *Azuma* (ATS 4201). Design was originally to have been a 4,700-ton, greatly enlarged *Kurobe* (ATS 4202) with a large hangar and flight deck for drones, helicopters, and VTOL aircraft (if acquired). The program was reduced to a much smaller, 2,400-ton, improved version of *Kurobe* for budgetary reasons, and the new ship is not capable of operating VTOL aircraft. Based at Kure.
Mission systems: Has the same Target Multi-Control and Tracking System (TMCATS) radar as does the *Kurobe.* Carries, launches, controls, recovers, and services U.S. Ryan BQM-34J Firebee high-speed and Northrop MQM-74C Chukar supersonic target drones. Also used for air-controlling U-36A manned target-tow aircraft.

♦ 1 Kurobe-class target service ship [AG]

	Bldr	Laid down	L	In serv.
ATS 4202 Kurobe	Nippon Kokan, Tsurumi	31-7-87	23-5-88	23-3-89

D: 2,270 tons (approx. 3,200 fl) **S:** 20 kts **Dim:** 101.0 × 16.5 × 4.0
A: 1 76-mm 62-cal. OTOBreda Compact DP
Electronics:
Radar: 1 JRC OPS-18 surf. search; 1 Melco OPS-14B air search; 1 TMCATS target control (see remarks); 1 FCS-2-21A f.c.
M: 4 Fuji 8L 27.5SX diesels; 2 props; 9,160 bhp
Range: . . ./. . . **Crew:** 17 officers, 126 enlisted

AUXILIARIES *(continued)*

Kurobe (ATS 4202) Takatoshi Okano, 10-00

Remarks: Approved under the FY 86 budget as a supplement to *Azuma* (ATS 4201). Based at Kure.
Mission systems: Carries, launches, controls, recovers, and services U.S. Ryan BQM-34J Firebee high-speed and Northrop MQM-74C Chukar supersonic target drones. Also used for air-controlling U-36A manned target-tow aircraft. Has the TMCATS (Target Multi-Control and Tracking System) phased-array radar, with four planar arrays mounted on the faces of the tower mast; the system tracks targets and weapons and records the track data for analysis, employing TELES (Telemetry Measuring System). The large open deck and hangar aft are primarily for target drone operations, but helicopters can be accommodated.

♦ 0 (+ 3) Hiuchi-class multimission ships [AG]
Bldr: Nippon Kokan, Turumi

	Laid down	L	In serv.
AMS 4301 Hiuchi	18-1-01	4-9-01	3-02
AMS . . .	. . .	. . .	. . .
AMS . . .	. . .	. . .	. . .

D: 980 tons **S:** 15 kts **Dim:** 65.0 × 12.5 × 3.5
Electronics: . . .
M: 2 . . . diesels; 2 props; 5,000 bhp **Crew:** 40 tot.

Remarks: Intended to replace the ASU 81 class. Will be used for training, target-drone launching, diver support, safety patrol, supply duties, ocean towing, and fire-fighting. For appearance, see photo in addenda.

♦ 2 ASU 81–class target-support craft [AG] Bldr: . . .

	Laid down	L	In serv.
ASU 84 (ex-YAS 104)	4-2-72	15-6-73	19-9-73
ASU 85 (ex-YAS 105)	20-2-73	16-7-73	19-9-73

ASU 85 Mitsuhiro Kadota, 7-01

D: 490 tons (543 fl) **S:** 14.5 kts **Dim:** 51.5 × 10.0 × 2.6
Electronics:
Radar: ASU 84: Koden OPS-29 nav.—ASU 85: Fujitsu OPS-19 nav.
M: 2 Akasaka UH527-42 diesels; 2 props; 1,600 bhp
Range: 2,500/12 **Crew:** 26 ship's company + 14 technicians

Remarks: Intended to carry, control, recover, and service up to six drone target aircraft. ASU 85: 500 tons std. Are assigned to district fleets, ASU 85 at Yokosuka and ASU 84 at Kure.
Disposals: ASU 81 (ex-YAS 101) was stricken 27-10-97, ASU 82 (ex-YAS 102) on 14-8-98, and ASU 83 (ex-YAS 103) on 15-6-01.

♦ 1 Hayase-class miscellaneous auxiliary [AG]
Bldr: Ishikawajima-Harima Heavy Industries, Tokyo

	Laid down	L	In serv.
ASU 7020 Hayase (ex-MST 462)	16-9-70	21-6-71	6-11-71

D: 2,000 tons (3,050 fl) **S:** 18 kts **Dim:** 99.0 × 13.0 × 3.8
A: 1 twin 76.2-mm 50-cal. Mk 34 DP; 2 single 20-mm JM-61-MB gatling AA; 2 triple 324-mm Type 68 ASW TT (Mk 73 or Mk 46 Mod. 5 torpedoes); 116 mines
Electronics:
Radar: 1 JRC OPS-16C nav./surf. search; 1 Melco OPS-14 air search; 1 Western Electric Mk 34 f.c.
Sonar: U.S. SQS-11A hull-mounted MF; 1 ZQS-1B hull-mounted HF
M: 4 Kawasaki-M.A.N. V6V 22/30 ATL diesels; 2 props; 6,400 bhp
Range: 7,500/14 **Crew:** 180 tot.

Hayase (ASU 7020) Takatoshi Okano, 7-99

Remarks: Former mine countermeasures support ship and minelayer, reclassified 20-3-98 and now assigned to the 1st Submarine Flotilla, Kure, as a general support vessel.
Combat systems: Fantail cleared as a platform for helicopters. Has five mine rails exiting through the transom stern. Equipped with the U.S. Mk 63 gun f.c.s. for the 76.2-mm mounting.

♦ 1 400-ton-class yacht [AG] Bldr: Hitachi, Kanagawa

	Laid down	L	In serv.
ASY 91 Hashidate	10-10-98	26-7-99	30-11-99

Hashidate (ASY 91) Mitsuhiro Kadota, 4-00

D: 400 tons (approx. 560 fl) **S:** 20 kts **Dim:** 62.0 × 9.4 × 2.0
Electronics: Radar: 1 . . . nav.
M: 2 . . . diesels; 2 props; 5,500 bhp
Range: . . ./. . . **Crew:** 29 tot. + 60 passengers

Remarks: Requested under the FY 97 budget as a replacement for *Hiyodori* (ASY 92, ex-PC 320) as the JMSDF C-in-C's ceremonial yacht. Has facilities to act in disaster relief service. Hull painted blue, superstructure white. Based at Yokosuka.

♦ 1 Shirase-class icebreaker [AGB]

	Bldr	Laid down	L	In serv.
AGB 5002 Shirase	Nippon Kokan, Tsurumi	5-3-81	11-12-81	12-12-83

Shirase (AGB 5002)—with red-orange hull and stack and cream-colored superstructure Mitsuhiro Kadota, 11-00

D: 11,660 tons (18,900 fl) **S:** 19 kts **Dim:** 134.0 × 28.0 × 9.2
Electronics:
Radar: 1 OPS-22 nav.; 1 Melco OPS-18 surf. search; 1 . . . weather
TACAN: ORN-6 (U.S. URN-25)
M: 6 M.A.N.-Mitsui 12V42M diesels, electric drive; 3 props; 30,000 bhp
Range: 25,000/15 **Crew:** 37 officers, 137 enlisted + 60 passengers

Remarks: Built under the 1979–80 budget to replace *Fuji* (AGB 5001). The only ship in the JMSDF named for a person: Lt. Nobu Shirase, who led the first Japanese

AUXILIARIES *(continued)*

Antarctic expedition in 1912. Plans at one time called for completing a 22,000-ton, *nuclear*-powered replacement for *Shirase* in 2002. AGB 5002 is assigned to the Yokosuka District Fleet.
Hull systems: Cargo capacity: 1,000 tons. Has a hangar and flight deck for two S-61A and one OH-6D helicopter. Has a large radome-covered weather radar atop the hangar. Is also equipped to conduct oceanographic research. Has been equipped with a Navi-Sailor 2400 ECDIS electronic chart display system.

♦ 1 experimental weapons systems trials ship [AGE]

	Bldr	Laid down	L	In serv.
ASE 6102 Asuka	Sumitomo, Uraga	21-4-93	21-6-94	22-3-95

Asuka (ASE 6102) *Ships of the World,* 2000

D: 4,200 tons (4,900 fl) **S:** 27 kts **Dim:** 151.0 × 18.0 × 5.0 (mean hull)
A: provision for: 1 8-cell U.S. Mk 41 vertical missile launch group syst.; 1 SH-60J ASW helicopter
Electronics:
Radar: 1 Fujitsu OPS-19 nav.; 1 Melco OPS-14B air search; 1 Mitsubishi FCS-3 SAM f.c.
Sonar: . . . bow-mounted LF; flank-mounted active/passive array; towed array
EW: . . . intercept
M: COGLAG: 1 IHI-G.E. LM-250 gas turbine, 2 Rolls-Royce SM1C Spey gas turbines; 2 CP props; 43,000 shp max. (electric drive below 21 kts)
Range: . . ./. . . **Crew:** 71 ship's company + 100 technicians

Remarks: Requested under the FY 92 budget as an ASW sensor and weapons systems trials ship. Assigned to the 5th Research Center, Kurihama.
Hull systems: Propulsion plant is bridge controlled and drives the propellers at low rpm to reduce radiated noise. The hull has special vibration-damping structures in the vicinity of the very large sonar array, which occupies a 40-m-long sonar dome extending beneath the ship's keel as far aft as the tower mainmast. An air-bubbler system is also installed. Has provision for female crewmembers. Fin stabilizers and a helicopter haul-down and traversing system are fitted. The hangar can accommodate an SH-60J ASW helicopter.
Combat systems: Conducts trials with surface warfare systems including the FCS-3 radar weapons-control system, which can track 10 targets simultaneously and employs four planar arrays to cover 360°; the XAAM-4 vertically launched SAM; the Canadian Davis "Dres Ball" infrared stack emission suppression system; the ASO self-propelled ASW target; the S-10 underwater navigation system; the K-RX2 ASW mine; composite armor; and radar-absorbent coatings. Has also conducted trials with infrared surveillance equipment and torpedo countermeasures systems. Provision was made for the installation of an 8-cell Mk 41 vertical missile launch system forward, but it has not yet been fitted.

♦ 1 Kurihama-class underwater weapons trials ship [AGE]

	Bldr	Laid down	L	In serv.
ASE 6101 Kurihama	Sasebo Heavy Industries	23-3-79	20-9-79	8-4-80

Kurihama (ASE 6101) *Ships of the World,* 2000

D: 959 tons (approx. 1,400 fl) **S:** 15 kts **Dim:** 68.0 × 11.6 × 3.3
A: various **Electronics:** Radar: 1 Fujitsu OPS-9B nav.
M: 2 Fuji 6S 30B diesels; 2 CP props; 2,600 bhp—2 200-shp electric auxiliary propulsors—retractable bow-thruster
Crew: 42 ship's company + 13 technicians

Remarks: In FY 79 budget. Operated for the Technical Research and Development Institute by the 5th Research Center, Kurihama.
Hull systems: Has Flume-type passive stabilization tanks and gas turbine–powered generators in the superstructure. Can be rigged for silent operation.
Combat systems: Has been used in trials with the S-8 deep minesweeping system, G-RX4 ASW torpedo, a torpedo countermeasures system, a mine countermeasures computer, noise simulators, an antisubmarine sonar, a data-recording buoy, sonobuoy arrays, mines, a low-frequency sonar, an expendable radio jammer decoy, a towed surface array radio receiver, and the K-RX2 ASW mine. Has gun test facilities on the fantail and a torpedo elevator to port. Is equipped with acoustic target tracking equipment.

♦ 2 ocean surveillance ships [AGI]

	Bldr	Laid down	L	In serv.
AOS 5201 Hibiki	Mitsui, Tamano	28-11-89	27-7-90	30-1-91
AOS 5202 Harima	Mitsui, Tamano	26-12-90	11-9-91	10-3-92

Harima (AOS 5202) Takatoshi Okano, 10-00

Harima (AOS 5202) Takatoshi Okano, 5-01

D: 3,715 tons **S:** 11 kts **Dim:** 71.50 (67.00 pp) × 29.90 × 7.50
Electronics:
Radar: 1 JRC OPS-18 nav.; 1 Fujitsu OPS-19 nav.
Sonar: NQQ-2 SURTASS
M: Diesel-electric: 4 Mitsubishi S6U MPTK 1,200-bhp diesels, 4 800-kw alternators, 2 motors; 2 props; 3,200 shp
Range: 3,800/10 **Fuel:** 640 tons **Crew:** 40 tot.

Remarks: First unit approved under the FY 89 budget, second under FY 90. A total of five was originally planned. AOS 5201 became fully operational around 3-92 at the completion of installation, trials, and check-out of the SURTASS (Surveillance Towed-Array Sonar System) towed linear passive acoustic array and the satellite data-relay gear in the U.S.A. Both are based at Kure.
Mission systems: Are a Japanese equivalent of the U.S. T-AGOS 19 class, employing U.S.-supplied towed linear surveillance passive hydrophone array and WSC-6 satellite data relay (with the analysis center located near Yokosuka). Have SWATH (Small Waterplane Area, Twin Hull) configuration. The SURTASS employs a 2,600-m-long array with an 1,800-m-long towing cable.

♦ 1 Nichinan-class hydrographic survey ship [AGS]

	Bldr	Laid down	L	In serv.
AGS 5105 Nichinan	Mitsubishi, Shimonoseki	7-8-97	11-6-98	24-3-99

Nichinan (AGS 5105)—note the large cable sheaves at the bow *Ships of the World,* 2000

D: 3,300 tons (4,100 fl) **S:** 20 kts (18 sust.) **Dim:** 111.0 × 17.0 × 4.5 (mean hull)
Electronics:
Radar: . . .
Sonar: SeaBeam 2112 multibeam mapping (HF)

AUXILIARIES *(continued)*

M: 3 diesel generator sets, electric drive: 2 motors; 2 CP props; 8,660 shp (5,800 sust.)—twin bow- and stern-thrusters
Range: 15,000/14 **Crew:** 90 tot.

Remarks: Requested under the FY 96 budget to replace *Akashi* (AGS 5101) as a combination cable repair and hydrographic survey ship. Based at Kurihama, operated by the JMSDF's Ocean Management Group.
Mission systems: Carries a 5-ton, 2.9-m-long cable repair remotely operated submersible; a deployable environmental measurement buoy; a WQM-1B acoustic measurement buoy; AICM-2F ocean current measurement equipment; a magnetic cable location system; bottom core samplers; and four cranes. Equipped with a large articulating crane aft, to port; a quadrantial oceanographic equipment gantry at the stern; and cable sheaves at the bow.

♦ 2 Futami-class hydrographic survey ships [AGS]

	Bldr	Laid down	L	In serv.
AGS 5102 Futami	Mitsubishi, Shimonoseki	20-1-78	9-8-78	27-2-79
AGS 5104 Wakasa	Hitachi, Maizuru	21-8-84	25-5-85	25-2-86

Futami (AGS 5102) Takatoshi Okano, 10-00

Wakasa (AGS 5104) *Ships of the World,* 2000

D: 2,050 tons (3,175 fl) **S:** 16 kts **Dim:** 96.80 (90.00 pp) × 15.00 × 4.50
A: none **Electronics:** Radar: 1 JRC OPS-18 nav.
M: AGS 5102: 2 Kawasaki-M.A.N. V8V 22/30 ATL diesels; 2 CP props; 4,400 bhp—AGS 5104: 2 Fuji 6LS 27-5XF diesels; 2 CP props; 4,580 bhp—both: bow-thruster
Electric: 1,800 kw tot. **Fuel:** 556 tons **Crew:** 105 tot.

Remarks: Configured for both hydrographic surveying and cable laying. Have three diesel and one gas-turbine generator sets. Carry one RCV-225 remote-controlled unmanned submersible. AGS 5104, ordered 29-3-84 under the FY 83 budget, has a taller stack and differs somewhat in equipage. Both are based at Kurihama, operated by the JMSDF's Ocean Management Group.

♦ 1 Suma-class hydrographic survey ship [AGS]

Bldr: Hitachi Heavy Industries, Maizuru

	Laid down	L	In serv.
AGS 5103 Suma	24-9-80	1-9-81	30-3-82

Suma (AGS 5103)—note the intercept antennas on the after mast Takatoshi Okano, 6-00

D: 1,180 tons **S:** 15 kts **Dim:** 72.0 × 12.8 × 3.4
A: none **Electronics:** Radar: 1 OPS-. . . nav.
M: 2 Fuji 6 LS 27.5X diesels; 2 CP props; 3,000 bhp—bow-thruster
Crew: 65 tot.

Remarks: Built under the 1979–80 budget. Carries one 7.9-m boat and one 11-m inshore survey launch. Flume-type passive tank stabilization is fitted. Operated by the JMSDF's Ocean Management Group and based at Kurihama.

♦ 0 (+ 2 + . . .) 13,500-ton replenishment oilers [AOR]

Bldr: Mitsui, Tamano

	Laid down	L	In serv.
AOE 425	1-02	2-03	3-04
AOE 426	1-03	2-04	3-05

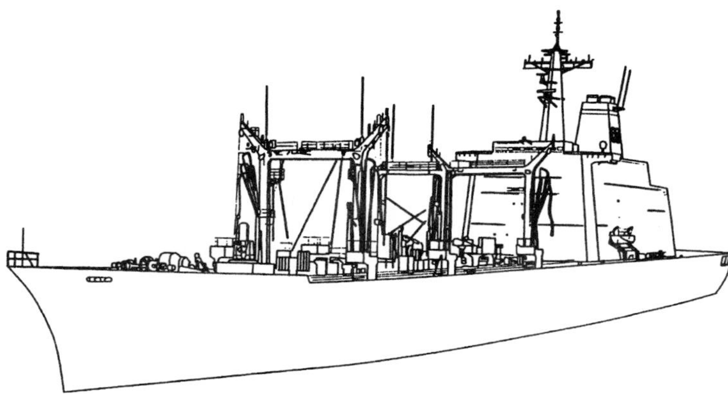
AOE 425—provisional sketch; note the helicopter hangar and flight deck aft *Ships of the World,* 11-99

D: 13,500 tons (25,000 fl) **S:** . . . kts **Dim:** . . . × . . . × . . .
A: none **Electronics:** Radar: . . .
M: 2 Mitsui . . . diesels; 2 props; . . . bhp

Remarks: The first was approved under the FY 00 budget to replace the *Sagami* (AOE 421). The second will enhance the current replenishment force. Are the largest naval ships built in Japan since World War II.

♦ 3 Towada-class replenishment oilers [AOR]

	Bldr	Laid down	L	In serv.
AOE 422 Towada	Hitachi, Maizuru	17-4-85	25-3-86	24-3-87
AOE 423 Tokiwa	IHI, Tokyo	12-5-88	23-3-89	12-3-90
AOE 424 Hamana	Mitsui, Tamano	8-7-88	18-5-89	29-3-90

Hamana (AOE 424) Brian Morrison, 6-00

Tokiwa (AOE 423) Mitsuhiro Kadota, 10-00

D: 8,300 tons (15,850 fl) **S:** 22 kts
Dim: 167.00 (160.00 pp) × 22.0 × 8.40 (15.90 molded depth) **A:** none
Electronics:
Radar: 1 JRC OPS-18-1 nav.
EW: . . . intercept; Mk 36 SRBOC decoy syst. (4 6-round Mk 137 RL)
M: 2 Mitsui 16V42M-A diesels; 2 props; 26,400 bhp
Electric: 3,200 kw (4 × 800-kw diesel sets)
Range: 10,500/20 **Fuel:** 1,659 tons **Crew:** 140 tot.

Remarks: All-purpose liquid, solid stores, and ammunition ships, with two liquid and one solid transfer stations per side. Cargo: 5,700 tons total. Helicopter deck aft for vertical replenishment. No provision for armament. All are assigned directly to the Escort Fleet, AOE 422 based at Kure, AOE 423 at Yokosuka, and AOE 424 at Maizuru.

AUXILIARIES *(continued)*

Towada (AOE 422) Mitsuhiro Kadota, 9-00

♦ **1 Sagami-class replenishment oiler [AOR]**

	Bldr	Laid down	L	In serv.
AOE 421 Sagami	Hitachi, Maizuru	28-9-77	4-9-78	30-3-79

Sagami (AOE 421) Mitsuhiro Kadota, 10-00

D: 5,000 tons (11,600 fl) **S:** 22 kts **Dim:** 146.0 (140.0 pp) × 19.0 × 7.3
A: none
Electronics:
Radar: 1 JRC OPS-16 nav.
EW: . . . intercept; Mk 36 SRBOC decoy syst. (4 6-round Mk 137 RL)
M: 2 Type 12 DRV diesels; 2 props; 18,600 bhp
Range: 9,500/20 **Crew:** 130 tot.

Remarks: Assigned directly to the Escort Fleet and based at Sasebo. Has three stations per side: two for liquid transfers, one for solid. Has a large helicopter deck but no hangar. In addition to fuel oil, diesel fuel, and JP-5 aviation fuel, carries food and ammunition. Equipped with four commercial SATCOM terminals. To be retired in 3-04.

♦ **1 Muroto-class cable layer [ARC]**

	Bldr	Laid down	L	In serv.
ARC 482 Muroto	Mitsubishi, Shimonoseki	28-11-78	25-7-79	27-3-80

Muroto (ARC 482) *Ships of the World,* 2000

D: 4,544 tons std. **S:** 17 kts **Dim:** 131.0 × 17.4 × 5.7
A: none **Electronics:** Radar: 1 Fujitsu OPS-9 nav.
M: 2 Mitsubishi MTU V8V 22/30 diesels; 2 CP props; 4,400 bhp—bow-thruster
Crew: 122 tot.

Remarks: Able to lay cable over bow or stern at 2–6 kts. Similar to the commercial *Kuroshio Maru.* Also has extensive facilities for oceanographic research. Has two commercial SATCOM terminals. Based at Kure.

♦ **1 Chihaya-class submarine rescue ship [ASR]**

	Bldr	Laid down	L	In serv.
ASR 403 Chihaya	Mitsui, Tamano	13-10-97	8-10-98	23-3-00

D: 5,400 tons (6,200 fl) **S:** 20 kts **Dim:** 127.5 × 20.0 × 5.1
Electronics: Radar: 2 . . . nav.
M: 2 Mitsui 12V42M-A diesels; 2 CP props; 19,700 bhp—2 bow- and 2 stern-thrusters
Range: 6,000/13 **Crew:** 125 tot.

Chihaya (ASR 403) Takatoshi Okano, 3-00

Remarks: Requested under the FY 96 budget. An enlarged version of *Chiyoda* (ASR 405) with a similar rescue submersible handling system amidships. Serves as flagship for the 1st Submarine Flotilla at Kure. Has Superbird SHF SATCOM terminal.
Hull systems: Carries a 40-ton, 12.4-m deep-submergence rescue vehicle (DSRV) and a small remotely operated work submersible. The DSRV mates directly to large decompression chambers and is lowered and recovered through a centerline moonpool. A computerized Rescue Information Center is fitted. Is able to support saturation divers to 415-m depths. Has a raised platform at the stern for helicopters up to MH-53E size.

♦ **1 Chiyoda-class submarine rescue ship [ASR]**

	Bldr	Laid down	L	In serv.
ASR 405 Chiyoda	Mitsui, Tamano	19-1-83	7-12-83	27-3-85

Chiyoda (ASR 405) *Ships of the World,* 2000

D: 3,690 tons (4,450 fl) **S:** 17 kts (16 sust.)
Dim: 112.5 (106.0 pp) × 17.6 (18.0 max.) × 4.8
A: none **Electronics:** Radar: 1 JRC OPS-16 surf. search.
M: 2 Mitsui 8LV42M diesels; 2 CP props; 11,500 bhp—bow- and stern-thrusters
Crew: 120 tot.

Remarks: Acts as flagship for the 2nd Submarine Flotilla, Yokosuka. A diver from ASR 405 reached 320 m on 11-8-87. Is equipped with commercial HF and Superbird SHF SATCOM equipment.
Hull systems: Carries a deep-submergence rescue vehicle (DSRV) launched 15-10-84 by Kawasaki, Kobe; its characteristics include:

D: 40 tons **S:** 4 kts **Dim:** 12.4 × 3.2 × 4.3 (high)
M: electric motors; 40 hp **Crew:** 12 passengers

The DSRV is deployed over the side, using hoist equipment similar to that of the U.S. Navy's *Pigeon* (ASR 21) class. There is also a deep-diving rescue bell. The helicopter platform can accommodate an HSS-2 Sea King.

Disposal note: Submarine rescue ship *Fushimi* (ASR 402) was retired 24-3-00.

♦ **1 Kashima-class cadet training ship [AXT]**

	Bldr	Laid down	L	In serv.
TV 3508 Kashima	Hitachi, Kanegawa	20-4-93	23-2-94	26-1-95

Kashima (TV 3508) Mitsuhiro Kadota, 10-00

D: 4,050 tons **S:** 25 kts **Dim:** 143.0 × 18.0 × 4.6
A: 1 76-mm 62-cal. OTOBreda Compact DP; 2 triple 324-mm Type 68 ASW TT (Type 73 and Mk 46 Mod. 5 torpedoes); 4 saluting cannon
Electronics:
Radar: 1 Fujitsu OPS-19 nav.; 1 Melco OPS-14C surf. search; 1 FCS-2-22 f.c.
Sonar: . . .
EW: probable NORL-6 intercept
M: CODOG: 2 . . . . . . diesels (. . . bhp each), 2 Kawasaki–Rolls-Royce Spey SM1C gas turbines (26,150 shp each); 2 CP props; 52,300 shp max.
Range: . . ./. . . **Crew:** 370 (incl. cadets)

AUXILIARIES *(continued)*

Remarks: Authorized under the FY 91 budget, but construction was deferred as part-payment for Japan's contribution to the Persian Gulf War; requested again under FY 92 and approved. Has a modest wartime potential as a command ship. Is flagship of the Training Fleet, based at Kure.
Hull systems: Has accommodations for both male and female cadets, all berthed in two-person staterooms. The large open deck aft acts as a ceremonial, assembly, and exercise area but is also able to accept helicopters.

♦ 1 Hatsuyuki-class training ship [AXT]
Bldr: Mitsubishi, Nagasaki

	Laid down	L	In serv.
TV 3513 Shimayuki (ex-DD 133)	8-5-84	29-1-86	31-3-87

Shimayuki (TV 3513) Takatoshi Okano, 6-99

D: 3,050 tons (3,800 fl) **S:** 30 kts
Dim: 131.70 (126.00 wl) × 13.70 × 4.30 (mean hull)
A: 8 RGM-84C Harpoon SSM; 1 8-round Mk 29 missile launcher (18 Sea Sparrow missiles); 1 76-mm 62-cal. OTOBreda Compact DP; 2 20-mm Mk 15 Phalanx CIWS; 1 8-round Mk 112 ASROC ASW RL (16 missiles); 2 triple 324-mm Type 68 ASW TT (Type 73 and Mk 46 Mod. 5 torpedoes); 1 SH-60J ASW helicopter
Electronics:
Radar: 1 JRC OPS-18-1 surf. search; 1 Melco OPS-14B air search; 1 FCS-2-21 gun f.c.; 1 GFCS-2-12 SAM f.c.; 2 General Dynamics Mk 90 Phalanx f.c.
Sonar: NEC OQS-4A hull-mounted MF; OQR-1 towed passive array
TACAN: U.S. URN-25 (ORN-6)
EW: NEC NOLQ-6C intercept; OLR-9B D/F; Fujitsu OLT-3 jammer; Mk 36 SRBOC decoy syst. (2 6-round Raytheon Mk 137 RL)
M: COGOG: 2 Kawasaki–Rolls-Royce Olympus TM-3B gas turbines (25,000 shp each), 2 Tyne RM-1C gas turbines (5,000 shp each); 2 CP props; 45,000 shp (50,000 max.)
Range: . . ./. . . **Fuel:** . . . **Crew:** 19 officers, 153 enlisted

Remarks: The newest unit of the *Hatsuyuki* class was redesignated TV 3513 on 18-3-99 and is employed as a cadet training ship, assigned to the 1st Training Squadron, Kure.
Hull systems: The Olympus engines are rated at 22,500 shp for cruise, 25,000 shp max., while the Tyne cruise engines are rated at 4,620 shp cruise/5,000 shp max. and provide speeds up to 19.5 kts. Helicopter deck has the Canadian Beartrap traversing/landing system. Has fin stabilizers and a steel superstructure. Stack incorporates passive infrared cooling features and a water-spray system.
Combat systems: Has OYQ-6 TDPS (Tactical Data Processing System) with Link 14 data relay receiver only. Received OQR-1 (U.S. SQR-18) TACTASS towed passive linear array after completion. Has NYPX-2 IFF systems and Superbird SHF SATCOM equipment.

♦ 2 Yamagumo-class training ships [AXT]
Bldr: Sumitomo, Uraga

	Laid down	L	In serv.
TV 3512 Aokumo (ex-DDK 119)	2-10-70	30-3-72	25-11-72
TV 3514 Akigumo (ex-DD 120, ex-DDK 120)	7-7-72	23-10-73	24-7-74

Aokumo (TV 3512) Mitsuhiro Kadota, 10-00

Akigumo (TV 3514) Takatoshi Okano, 1-01

D: 2,150 tons (2,750 fl) **S:** 27 kts **Dim:** 114.9 × 11.8 × 4.0 (hull)
A: 2 twin 76.2-mm 50-cal. Mk 33 DP; 1 8-cell Mk 112 ASROC ASW RL; 1 4-tubed 375-mm Type 71 (Bofors Erika) ASW RL; 2 triple 324-mm Type 68 ASW TT (Type 73 and Mk 46 Mod. 5 torpedoes)
Electronics:
Radar: 1 JRC OPS-17 surf. search; 1 Melco OPS-11 air search; 1 Westinghouse Mk 35 gun f.c.; 1 Western Electric Mk 34 gun f.c.
Sonar: NEC OQS-3A hull-mounted MF; EDO SQS-35(J) VDS
EW: NEC NOLR-5 intercept
M: 6 Mitsubishi 12UEV 30/40N diesels; 2 props; 26,500 bhp
Range: 7,000/20 **Crew:** 210–220 tot.

Remarks: A modified version of the earlier *Minegumo* class, completed with ASROC ASW missile launcher instead of DASH drone helicopter facilities. TV 3512 was reclassified as a cadet training ship 18-3-99, followed by TV 3514 on 13-6-00. Both are assigned to the 1st Training Squadron, Kure.
Disposals: Sisters *Yamagumo* (DDK 113) and *Makigumo* (DDK 114) were reclassified as training ships 20-6-91 and later stricken. Sister *Asagumo* (DDK 115) became auxiliary ASU 7018 on 18-10-93 and was later stricken.
Combat systems: Has a U.S. Mk 56 gun director forward (with Mk 35 radar) and Mk 63 gun f.c.s. aft (Mk 34 radar on the after gunmount).

Disposal note: *Minegumo*-class training ship and former escort destroyer *Murakomo* (TV 3511, ex-DDK 118) was stricken 13-6-00. Sisters *Minegumo* (TV 3509, ex-DDK 116) and *Natsugumo* (TV 3510, ex-DDK 117) were stricken 18-3-99.

SERVICE CRAFT

Note: Japanese navy service ships and craft employ a two- or three-letter designator system to define their functions. Self-propelled units have two-digit hull numbers following the letter designator (as in "YO 01"). Non-self-propelled craft with the same functions have three-digit numbers starting with "1" (as in "YO 102"); craft converted from another function had three-digit hull numbers starting with "2," but there are some anomalies.

♦ 1 catamaran "sweeper boat" [YAG]
Bldr: . . . (In serv. 30-3-79)

YS 01

D: 80 tons **S:** 9 kts **Dim:** 22.0 × 7.80 × 1.40
M: 2 diesels; 2 props; 460 bhp **Crew:** 6 tot.

Remarks: Debris clearance craft, stationed at Iwakuni Air Station seaplane base; used to clear floating debris in seaplane landing lanes and as a marker-buoy tender.

♦ 2 YV 01–class seaplane buoy tenders [YAG]

YV 02 (In serv. 28-3-69) YV 03 (In serv. 20-3-70)

YV 03 Takatoshi Okano, 4-94

D: 45 tons **S:** 10 kts **Dim:** 20.0 × 4.40 × 1.00 **M:** 2 diesels; 2 props; 240 bhp

Remarks: Maintain seaplane fairway marker buoys. Sister YV 01 was stricken 16-3-01, and the other two were to follow at one-year intervals.

Note: A 60-ton replacement YV was requested under the FY 99 budget but was not authorized.

♦ 1 YAL 01–class mine trials and service craft [YAGE]
Bldr: . . . (In serv. 22-3-76)

YAL 01

YAL 01 Takatoshi Okano, 7-97

SERVICE CRAFT *(continued)*

D: 240 tons (265 fl) **S:** 12 kts **Dim:** 37.00 × 8.00 × 1.90
A: mine rails **M:** 2 Type 64 H 19-E-4A diesels; 2 props; 800 bhp **Crew:** 16 tot.

♦ **1 YL 119–class barge (non-self-propelled) [YCN]**
Bldr: . . . (In serv. 20-3-71)

YL 119

D: 200 dwt **Dim:** 34.00 × 13.00 × 1.00

♦ **3 YL 116–class barges (non-self-propelled) [YCN]**

YL 116 (In serv. 21-12-63) YL 117 (In serv. 25-2-64) YL 118 (In serv. 31-3-66)

D: 100 dwt **Dim:** 21.50 × 8.40 × 1.00

♦ **1 YL 114–class barge (non-self-propelled) [YCN]**

YL 115 (In serv. 12-3-63)

D: 80 dwt **Dim:** 18.40 × 7.40 × 0.90

Remarks: Sister YL 114 was stricken 5-9-95.

♦ **1 YC 09–class self-propelled floating crane [YD]**

YC 09 (In serv. 25-2-74)

YC 09 *Ships of the World,* 1995

D: 260 tons **S:** 6 kts **Dim:** 26.0 × 14.0 × 0.9 **M:** 2 diesels; 2 props; 280 bhp

♦ **3 YC 06–class self-propelled floating cranes [YD]**

YC 06 (In serv. 31-3-69) YC 07 (In serv. 28-2-70) YC 08 (In serv. 29-3-72)

YC 06 *Ships of the World*

D: 150 tons **S:** 5 kts **Dim:** 24.0 × 10.0 × 0.8 **M:** 2 diesels; 2 props; 240 bhp

Disposal note: YC 05–class floating crane YC 05 was stricken 20-6-00.

♦ **4 (+ 2) YDT 01–class diving tenders [YDT]**
Bldr: First two: Yokohama Yacht; others: Maekata SY, Sasebo

	Laid down	L	In serv.
YDT 01	14-6-99	17-12-99	24-3-00
YDT 02	14-6-99	22-12-99	24-3-00
YDT 03	13-7-00	18-10-00	21-3-01
YDT 04	20-4-01	7-01	12-01
YDT 05	. . .	. . .	. . .
YDT 06	. . .	. . .	. . .

YDT 02 Takatoshi Okano, 4-00

YDT 03 *Ships of the World,* 3-01

D: 309 tons light; 380 tons normal (440 fl) **S:** 15 kts **Dim:** 46.0 × 8.6 × 2.2
A: none **Electronics:** Radar: 1 . . . nav.
M: 2 6NSDL diesels; 2 props; 1,500 bhp
Electric: 240 kw tot. (2 × 120-kw diesel sets)
Range: . . ./. . . **Crew:** 15 tot. + 15 explosive ordnance disposal divers

Remarks: First two requested under the FY 97 budget to begin replacement of YAS-redesignated former minesweepers as mine clearance diver and general-purpose diving tenders and as exercise torpedo and missile recovery ships. The initial request was disapproved, but two units were approved under FY 98, YDT 03 under FY 99, YDT 04 under FY 00; and YDT 05 and YDT 06 under FY 01.
Hull systems: Have diving team accommodations amidships. A large electrohydraulic crane for boat and weapons recovery is mounted aft at the forecastle break. Two 4.2-m RIBs are carried for swimmer support. Have a submersible divers' stage at the stern, to port.

♦ **2 Hatsushima-class mine clearance divers' support craft [YDT]**
Bldr: Nippon Kokan, Tsurumi (YAS 01: Hitachi, Kanagawa)

	Laid down	L	In serv.
YAS 01 Ninoshima (ex-MSC 650)	8-5-78	9-8-79	19-12-79
YAS 02 Miyajima (ex-MSC 651)	8-11-78	18-9-79	29-1-80

Miyajima (YAS 02) Takatoshi Okano, 6-00

D: 440 tons (536 fl) **S:** 14 kts **Dim:** 55.00 (52.00 pp) × 9.40 × 2.40
A: 1 20-mm JM-61-MB gatling AA **Electronics:** Radar: 1 Fujitsu OPS-9 nav.
M: 2 Mitsubishi YV12ZC-18/20 diesels; 2 CP props; 1,440 bhp
Electric: 240 kw tot. (3 × 80-kw diesel sets) **Range:** 2,400/10 **Crew:** 45 tot.

Remarks: Former minesweepers, now used as mine-disposal divers' tenders. MSC 650 and 651 were redesignated YAS on 1-3-96. Wooden construction. Have had a small deckhouse built over the former sweep winch position. They will shortly be replaced by further units of the YDT 01 class. Sister *Hatsushima* (YAS 98, ex-MSC 649) was stricken 13-7-01.

Disposal note: The last *Takami*-class mine clearance divers' support craft, the *Okitsu* (YAS 96, ex-MSC 646), was stricken 21-3-00.

SERVICE CRAFT *(continued)*

♦ 7 YL 09–class landing craft lighters [YF]
Bldr: Ishihara DY, Takasago

	Laid down	L	In serv.
YL 09	24-11-79	3-3-80	28-3-80
YL 10	. . .	17-12-82	28-2-83
YL 11	21-12-87	14-3-88	25-3-88
YL 12	8-12-92	29-1-93	15-3-93
YL 13	4-3-94	29-8-94	26-9-94
YL 14	10-3-95	7-95	28-7-95
YL 15	23-4-98	7-9-98	30-9-98

YL 10 Takatoshi Okano, 2-97

D: 50 tons light (120.5 fl) **S:** 9–10 kts **Dim:** 27.00 × 7.00 × 1.04
M: 2 Isuzu E 120 T-MF6 RE diesels; 2 props; 560 bhp **Crew:** 5 tot.

Remarks: Officially typed "Cargo Craft." 50 dwt. Resemble a U.S. LCM(8) landing craft and have a bow ramp and two 2-ton stores cranes. YL 13–15 have UM6 SD1 TCC diesels.

Disposal note: YL 08–class cargo lighter YL 08 was stricken 21-3-00.

♦ 11 YF 2121–class landing craft cargo lighters [YF]
Bldr: Ishihara Dockyard, Takasago

	In serv.
YF 2121	1989
YF 2124	26-2-90
YF 2125	20-3-90
YF 2127	27-3-92
YF 2128	31-3-92
YF 2129	21-3-92
YF 2132	31-3-93
YF 2135	30-3-95
YF 2138	13-3-96
YF 2151	2001
YF 2152	2001

YF 2135 Chris Delgoffe/H&L Van Ginderen, 5-00

D: 33 tons (56 fl) **S:** 10 kts **Dim:** 17.00 × 4.30 × 0.70
M: 2 Isuzu E120-MF6R diesels; 2 props; 480 bhp **Range:** 130/9 **Crew:** 4 tot.

Remarks: Officially designated as "Communications Boats." Design based on the U.S. LCM(6) landing craft. Employed as local transports for stores and personnel. Cargo: 30 tons or up to 80 personnel. YF 2138 has UM6 SD1 TCA diesels.

♦ 1 YF 2137–class 30-ton GRP personnel launch [YFL]
Bldr: . . . (In serv. 27-9-95)

YF 2137

YF 2137 Takatoshi Okano, 3-01

D: 38.2 tons **S:** 26.5 kts **Dim:** 22.5 × 5.1 × 0.9
Electronics: Radar: 1 . . . nav.
M: 2 MTU 12V183 TE92 diesels; 2 props; 1,820 bhp **Crew:** 2 tot.

Remarks: Approved under FY 94, laid down 9-5-95, and launched 13-9-95. Can carry 92 personnel. GRP construction.

♦ 4 YF 2131–class GRP personnel launches [YFL]
Bldr: Ishihara Dockyard, Takasago

YF 2131 (In serv. 31-3-92)
YF 2133 (In serv. 15-3-93)
YF 2136 (In serv. 30-3-95)
YF 2140 (In serv. 22-3-96)

YF 2136 *Ships of the World,* 3-95

D: 5.3–5.5 tons (fl) **S:** 15 kts **Dim:** 11.0 × 3.2 × 0.5–0.6
M: 1 UM6 BG1 TCB diesel; 1 prop; 210 bhp **Crew:** 2 tot.

Remarks: First two have less-powerful engines and can only achieve 15 kts; they also have a continuous upper deck line. GRP construction with heavy rubber fenders. Can carry 15 passengers

♦ 1 YF 2126–class GRP personnel launch [YFL]
Bldr: Shinju Zosen (In serv. 30-3-94)

YF 2134

YF 2134 *Ships of the World,* 3-94

D: 12 tons **S:** 18 kts **Dim:** 15.0 × 4.2 × 0.7
M: 2 Type UM6 BD1 diesels; 2 props; 520 bhp
Crew: 3 tot. + 40 passengers

Remarks: Requested under FY 93 budget. GRP construction officers' barge.

♦ 3 YF 2123–class personnel launches [YFL]
Bldr: Ishihara Dockyard, Takasago

YF 2123 (In serv. 30-1-87)
YF 2126 (In serv. 28-3-91)
YF 2130 (In serv. 31-3-92)

D: 14.3 tons **S:** 10 kts **Dim:** 15.0 × 4.2 × 1.6
M: 2 Type UM6 BD1 diesels; 2 props; 480 bhp

Remarks: YF 2130 was in FY 91 budget; laid down 5-12-91 and launched 3-3-92. An updated version of the single-unit YF 2020 class.

♦ 3 YF 1029–class GRP-hulled personnel launches [YFL]
Bldr: Ishihara Dockyard, Takasago

YF 1029 (In serv. 1982)
YF 1030 (In serv. 1982)
YF 1031 (In serv. 25-3-88)
YF 1032 (In serv. 27-3-98)
YF 1033 (In serv. 21-3-00)

YF 1033 *Ships of the World,* 3-00

SERVICE CRAFT *(continued)*

D: 11 tons (13.5 fl) **S:** 18 kts **Dim:** 13.50 (12.40 pp) × 3.80 × 0.70
M: 2 Isuzu 6BDITC-MRD diesels; 2 props; 360 bhp
Crew: 2 tot. + 20 passengers

Remarks: YF 1033 has Mitsubishi UM6 BG1 TCC diesels.

♦ 7 U.S. LCVP-class service launches [YFL]

YF 2072 YF 2073 YF 2080 YF 2084 YF 2085 YF 2086 YF 2087

D: 8 tons (13 fl) **S:** 9 kts **Dim:** 10.5 × 3.2 × 0.6
M: 1 Yanmar 6CH-DTE diesel; 1 prop; 180 bhp **Crew:** 3 tot.

Remarks: GRP-hulled versions of the standard U.S. Navy LCVP design, with bow ramp. Can carry up to 40 personnel.
Disposals: YF 2069 was stricken 16-2-94, YF 2074 on 30-3-94, YF 2078 on 29-9-95, YF 2079 on 2-11-95, YF 2081 on 30-10-95, and YF 2083 on 18-1-96.

♦ 11 YF 2088–class personnel launches [YFL]
Bldr: Ishihara Dockyard, Takasago

YF 2117 through YF 2119 YF 2139 YF 2143 through YF 2149

YF 2118 Takatoshi Okano, 5-01

D: 5.9 tons (5.9 fl) **S:** 10–11 kts **Dim:** 11.0 × 3.2 × 0.6
M: 1 UM6 BG1 TCA diesel; 1 prop; 135 bhp **Crew:** 2 tot.

Remarks: GRP construction. YF 2139, completed 8-3-96, and higher-numbered units are repeats of the earlier units, most of which were built in the late 1980s. YF 2143, YF 2144, and YF 2145 were delivered 25-3-98, while YF 2146 and YF 2147 were ordered during 1988 and completed 19-3-99. YF 2148 and YF 2149 were delivered 21-3-00 and are powered by UM6 BG1 TCX diesels.
Disposals: YF 2088 and YF 2090 were stricken 25-3-98, YF 2089 on 7-1-99, YF 2092 on 19-3-99, YF 2093 on 31-3-99, YF 2095 on 29-3-99, YF 2094 on 6-3-00, YF 2111 through YF 2113 on 28-1-00, YF 2114 on 17-3-00, YF 2115 on 21-3-00, and YF 2116 on 21-9-93.

♦ 2 YF 1022–class personnel launches [YFL]
Bldr: . . . (In serv. 1980)

YF 1027 YF 1028

D: 9 tons (11 fl) **S:** 14 kts **Dim:** 13.00 × 3.80 × 0.60
M: 2 Type E 120 T-MF6RE diesels; 2 props; 280 bhp
Crew: . . . + 73 passengers

Remarks: Sister YF 1022 was stricken 27-9-95, YF 1024 and YF 1025 on 31-3-98, and YF 1026 on 5-11-99.

♦ 4 miscellaneous service launches [YFL]

	Tons (light)	Dim	S (kts)	bhp
YF 2075	22	17.0 × 3.7 × 0.7	10	400
YF 2076, YF 2077	0.8	7.0 × 2.2 × 0.3	8	22
YF 2120	12.6	15.0 × 3.6 × 0.7	10	230

Remarks: YF 2075 is essentially a U.S. LCM(6) landing craft adapted as a utility craft. YF 2120 is a wooden-hulled craft resembling a tugboat, but with open personnel seating fore and aft.

♦ 3 miscellaneous dockyard service craft [YFL]

YD 03 (In serv. 1978): 1.7 tons; 7.60 × 1.90
YD 04 (In serv. 25-12-79): 0.5 tons
YD 05 (In serv. 21-3-00): 1.6 tons; 7.1 × 1.8

YD 05 *Ships of the World,* 3-00

Remarks: YD 05, a GRP-hulled open launch propelled by a 25-bhp Yamaha outboard, was approved under the FY 99 budget. The 0.8-ton YD 01 was stricken 3-12-99 and the identical YD 02 on 6-3-00.

♦ 9 YO 29–class fuel lighters [YO] Bldr: Maehata Iron Works, Sasebo

	Laid down	L	In serv.
YO 29	2-7-91	25-9-91	28-11-91
YO 30	9-91	25-11-91	24-1-92
YO 31	11-91	22-1-92	19-3-92
YO 33	26-4-93	8-93	21-9-93
YO 34	17-2-95	19-5-95	28-7-95
YO 35	17-2-95	28-7-95	20-9-95
YO 36	14-5-97	10-7-97	7-10-97
YO 37	6-10-97	18-12-97	6-3-98
YO 38	15-5-98	28-7-98	30-9-98

YO 38 *Ships of the World,* 9-98

D: 490 tons (750 fl) **S:** 10 kts **Dim:** 46.4 × 7.8 × 2.2
M: 2 Isuzu UM6 SD1 T diesels; 2 props; 460 bhp **Crew:** 10 tot.

Remarks: Cargo: 340 m^3 liquid, plus a small hold aft for dry cargo. YO 34 and YO 35 have 6MA-series diesels of 250 bhp each.

♦ 2 YO 28–class fuel lighters [YO] Bldr: Maehata Iron Works, Sasebo

YO 28 (In serv. 27-7-90) YO 32 (In serv. 16-10-92)

YO 28 Mitsuhiro Kadota, 4-99

D: 270 tons **S:** 9 kts **Dim:** 27.7 × 6.8 × 2.6
M: 2 Isuzu UM6 SD1 T diesels; 2 props; 360 bhp

♦ 7 YO 21–class fuel lighters [YO]

	Bldr	Laid down	L	In serv.
YO 21	Yoshiura SB	. . .	15-3-80	31-3-80
YO 22	Yoshiura SB	11-11-80	26-2-81	28-2-81
YO 23	Yoshiura SB	26-11-82	12-3-83	31-3-83
YO 24	Yoshiura SB	4-11-83	20-1-84	29-2-84
YO 25	Naikai, Innoshima	14-11-88	15-7-88	20-9-88
YO 26	Sagami, Yokosuka	18-4-88	28-7-88	26-9-88
YO 27	Sumidigawa, Tokyo	. . .	2-6-89	18-7-89

YO 23 *Ships of the World,* 1995

D: 490 tons (694 fl) **S:** 9–10 kts **Dim:** 45.5 × 7.8 × 2.9
M: 2 Yanmar 6 MA diesels; 2 props; 460 bhp **Crew:** 10 tot.

Remarks: YO 25 and 26, with 520-m^3 cargo capacity, were authorized under the FY 87 budget. YO 27, under FY 88, was ordered 6-12-88 and carries 630 m^3 of cargo.

♦ 1 YO 14–class fuel lighter [YO]
Bldr: . . . . . . (In serv. 31-3-76)

YO 14

D: 490 dwt **S:** 9 kts **Dim:** 45.0 × 7.8 × 2.9 **M:** 2 diesels; 2 props; 460 bhp

SERVICE CRAFT *(continued)*

♦ 2 YO 10–class fuel lighters [YO]
Bldr: . . .

YO 12 (In serv. 21-3-67) YO 13 (In serv. 31-3-67)

YO 13 Takatoshi Okano, 3-96

D: 290 dwt **S:** 9 kts **Dim:** 36.5 × 6.8 × 2.6 **M:** 2 diesels; 2 props; 360 bhp

Remarks: Sister YO 10 was stricken 6-3-98 and YO 11 during 1998.

♦ 5 YG 07–class jet engine fuel craft [YO]
Bldr: IHI, Tokyo; YG 205: Maehata Iron Works

	In serv.		In serv.
YG 201 (ex-YG 07)	30-3-73	YG 204	2-7-89
YG 202 (ex-YO 20, ex-YG 08)	29-3-77	YG 205	16-7-90
YG 203	20-9-88		

YG 204 *Ships of the World,* 1995

D: 270 dwt **S:** 9 kts **Dim:** 36.0 × 6.80 × 2.80
M: 1 Shinko-Zaki Ogaki S617-S1CM diesel; 1 prop; 360 bhp **Crew:** 5 tot.

Remarks: YG 08 was reclassified YO 20 in 1979, then again reclassified YG 202 in 1981. YG 203 and YG 204 are 37.7 m o.a. YG 205 was ordered 13-12-89 under the FY 90 budget and launched 21-5-90; she has UM6 SD1 T diesels and two shafts.

♦ 1 YB 01–class oil sludge removal lighter [YSR]

YB 01 (L: 31-3-75)

D: 176.7 tons **S:** 9 kts **Dim:** 27.5 × 5.2 × 1.9
M: 1 diesel; 230 bhp **Cargo:** 100 tons

♦ 4 YB 101–class oil sludge removal barges (non-self-propelled) [YSRN]
Bldr: . . . (In serv. 1975–76)

YB 101 YB 102 YB 103 YB 104

YB 102 *Ships of the World*

D: 100 dwt **Dim:** 17.0 × 5.2 × 2.0

♦ 18 (+ 2) YT 58–class large harbor tugs [YTB]
Bldr: Yokohama Yacht (YT 89, 90: Ishihara DY, Takasago)

	L	In serv.		L	In serv.
YT 58	. . .	31-10-78	YT 72	25-4-90	27-7-90
YT 63	. . .	27-9-82	YT 73	13-5-91	31-7-91
YT 64	. . .	30-9-83	YT 74	7-91	9-91
YT 65	. . .	20-9-84	YT 78	24-5-94	28-7-94
YT 66	. . .	20-9-85	YT 79	22-7-94	29-9-94
YT 67	7-6-86	4-9-86	YT 81	6-96	7-96
YT 68	9-6-87	9-9-87	YT 84	21-8-98	20-10-98
YT 69	15-6-87	16-9-87	YT 86	10-12-99	21-3-00
YT 70	14-6-88	2-9-88	YT 89	22-12-00	16-3-01
YT 71	19-5-89	28-7-89	YT 90	26-12-00	16-3-01

YT 79—with inflated fender alongside Mitsuhiro Kadota, 2-01

D: 262 tons **S:** 11 kts **Dim:** 28.40 × 8.60 × 2.50
Electronics: Radar: 1 . . . nav. **Crew:** 10 tot.
M: 2 Niigata 6L25BX diesels; 2 pivoting Kort-nozzle props; 1,800 bhp

Remarks: The design has evolved over its 24-year construction history, with improved equipment in the later units. Have one or two firefighting water cannon. YT 70 was rated at 1,600 bhp. YT 89 and YT 90 were laid down 11-5-00.

♦ 4 YT 53–class large harbor tugs [YTB]

YT 53 (In serv. 1974) YT 56 (In serv. 13-7-76)
YT 55 (In serv. 22-8-75) YT 57 (In serv. 22-8-77)

YT 56 Takatoshi Okano, 4-00

D: 195 tons (200 fl) **S:** 11 kts **Dim:** 25.70 × 7.00 × 2.30
M: 2 Kubota M6D20BUCS diesels; 1 prop; 1,500 bhp **Crew:** 10 tot.

Disposal note: Of the YT 35–class medium harbor tugs, YT 35 was stricken 26-6-91, YT 40 on 30-9-94, YT 41 on 5-8-94, YT 44 and YT 45 on 21-3-00, YT 46 on 25-8-00, and YT 48 during 2001.

♦ 9 (+ 1) YT 75–class harbor pusher tugs [YTM]
Bldr: Yokohama Yacht (YT 87, 88: Nagasaki Zosen)

	Laid down	L	In serv.
YT 75	13-5-92	27-8-92	29-9-92
YT 76	10-3-93	23-7-93	30-7-93
YT 77	10-3-93	8-93	16-9-93
YT 80	14-4-95	10-95	29-11-95
YT 82	9-96	12-96	3-97
YT 83	23-6-97	26-1-98	2-3-98
YT 85	28-8-98	2-12-98	5-3-99
YT 87	14-5-99	24-1-00	15-3-00
YT 88	14-5-99	30-8-99	5-10-99
YT 91	2001	. . .	. . .

SERVICE CRAFT *(continued)*

YT 87 Takatoshi Okano, 10-00

D: 50 tons (75 fl) **S:** 8 kts **Dim:** 17.0 × 4.8 × 1.20
M: 2 Type UM6 SD1 TCB diesels; 2 props; 500 bhp **Crew:** 4 tot.

Remarks: YT 91 was approved under the FY 01 budget.

♦ 3 YT 60–class harbor pusher tugs [YTL]
Bldr: Yokohama Yacht

YT 60 (In serv. 31-3-80) YT 61 (In serv. 26-3-80) YT 62 (In serv. 16-3-81)

YT 61 *Ships of the World,* 1995

D: 30 tons (37 fl) **S:** 8.6 kts **Dim:** 15.50 × 4.20 × 1.50 (0.97 hull)
M: 2 Isuzu E 120-MF64A diesels; 2 cycloidal props; 380 bhp

♦ 3 YT 34–class harbor pusher tugs [YTL]

YT 51 (In serv. 28-2-72) YT 54 (In serv. 24-3-75) YT 59 (In serv. 16-1-79)

YT 59 Takatoshi Okano, 10-00

D: 28 tons (30 fl) **S:** 9 kts **Dim:** 14.50 × 4.00 × 1.00
M: 2 diesels; 2 props; 320 bhp **Crew:** 3 tot.

Remarks: YT 59 displaces 30 tons std. Sisters YT 27 and 33 were stricken during 1979, YT 32 during 1981, YT 34 on 8-7-91, YT 39 on 26-3-93, YT 38 on 30-3-94, YT 36 on 29-11-95, YT 42 on 2-3-98, YT 43 on 2-10-98, YT 47 on 5-10-99, and YT 49 on 16-3-01.

♦ 1 (+ 1) YR 01–class fireboats [YTR]
Bldr: Ishikawajima-Harima Heavy Industries

	Laid down	L	In serv.
YR 01	28-8-00	18-1-01	16-3-01
YR 02	8-01	11-01	3-02

YR 01 *Ships of the World,* 3-01

D: 60 tons **S:** 19 kts **Dim:** 25.0 × 5.5 × 1.1
Electronics: Radar: 1 . . . nav.
M: 2 UM6 WG1 TCG diesels; 2 props; 1,500 bhp **Crew:** 10 tot.

Remarks: YR 01 was approved for construction under the FY 99 budget and YR 02 under FY 00. Have a UM6 RB1 TCG diesel to power the pump supporting the three water monitors forward and are fitted with a crane aft.

♦ 11 "Y"-group sailboats [YTS]

Y 7021 through Y 7031

Remarks: Y 7021 and Y 7022 were delivered 26-2-85, Y 7025 and Y 7026 on 30-10-92, and Y 7029–Y 7031 on 24-3-95. Y 7014 and Y 7015 were stricken 30-10-92, Y 7016 and Y 7017 on 25-3-94; and Y 7018–Y 7020 on 24-3-95. All are attached to the Etajima Naval Academy. Small GRP-hulled sloops; no other data available.

♦ 8 YW 17–class water lighters [YW]
Bldr: Maehata Iron Works, Sasebo (YW 17: Shikoku Dockyard)

	L	In serv.		L	In serv.
YW 17	19-7-88	27-9-88	YW 21	1-97	3-97
YW 18	9-5-89	28-7-89	YW 22	15-12-97	4-3-98
YW 19	30-9-92	29-12-92	YW 23	16-7-99	21-3-00
YW 20	30-5-94	20-9-94	YW 24	9-99	23-3-00

YW 23—in light condition *Ships of the World,* 3-01

D: approx. 450 tons (fl) **S:** 10 kts **Dim:** 37.7 × 6.8 × 2.8
M: 2 UM6 SD1 T diesels; 2 props; 360 bhp **Crew:** 5 tot.

Remarks: 310 dwt. Water lighters are required because many JMSDF warships lack the means to make potable water, relying on onboard tankage only.

Disposal note: YW 12–class water lighters YW 15 and YW 16 were stricken 21-3-00.

♦ 0 (+ 1) YTE 13–class training tender [YXT]
Bldr: . . . . . .

	Laid down	L	In serv.
YTE 13	8-01	1-02	3-02

Remarks: Approved under the FY 00 budget to replace YTE 11; no data available. Will be assigned to the Etajima Naval Academy to teach officer cadets ship handling and navigation. Will carry 25 cadets.

♦ 1 Tokiwa-class training tender [YXT]
Bldr: Hitachi, Kanegawa

	Laid down	L	In serv.
YTE 12 (ex-*Tokiwa*)	1980	12-1-82	12-1-83

D: 110 tons light, 142 std. (180 fl) **S:** 14 kts **Dim:** 35.0 × 7.5 × 1.5
M: 2 diesels; 2 props; 1,100 bhp **Crew:** 18 tot.

Remarks: Built to test glass-reinforced plastic (GRP) construction techniques for building future mine countermeasures ships and for testing shock resistance and sound transmission properties. Lines are based on the former inshore minesweeper *Atada;* flush deck and no minesweeping gear as completed. When the trials were completed, the craft was adapted for cadet navigational and ship-handling training duties at Etajima Naval Academy.

SERVICE CRAFT *(continued)*

YTE 12 *Ships of the World,* 1996

♦ 1 YTE 11–class navigational training tender [YXT]

Bldr: Ando Iron Works (In serv. 31-3-73)

YTE 11

D: 120 tons (170 fl) **S:** 13 kts **Dim:** 33.0 × 7.0 × 1.5
M: 2 Shinko-Zaki Ogaki SG175/CM diesels; 2 props; 1,400 bhp

Remarks: Based at Etajima Naval Academy to teach officer cadets ship handling and navigation. Can carry 25 cadets.

♦ 9 "B"-series miscellaneous training craft [YXT]

B 4006: 8 tons; 13.00 × 3.20 × 0.50; 14 kts (In serv. 16-3-76)
B 4007, 4011: 1 ton; 5.00 × 2.10 × 0.40; 22 kts (Both in serv. 26-1-76)
B 4014–4016: 8 tons; 13.00 × 3.20 × 0.50; 14 kts (In serv. 1978–80)
B 4017: 16 tons; 17.4 × 3.9 × 1.5; 10 kts; 180 bhp (In serv. 28-3-85)
B 4021, 4022: . . . (In serv. 22-3-96)

Remarks: GRP hulled. B 4016 is capable of 18 kts. B 4006 is basically the same as B 4014–B 4016. B 4017 has a GRP hull with pilothouse offset to port. B 4008 was stricken 22-3-96 and B 4012 and 4013 on 22-3-96.

♦ 72 "C"-class rowing boats [YXT]

C 5135–C 5218 series

C 5206—with willing crew Takatoshi Okano, 5-01

D: 1.5 tons **Dim:** 9.0 × 2.5 × . . .

Remarks: C 5204–C 5208 were delivered 20-3-98, C 5209–C 5212 in 3-99, and C 5213–C 5218 on 21-3-00. The total number is maintained through a regular retirement of four or more per year and replacement by new units, with all now being of a uniform design. Are stationed at the Etajima Naval Academy or at other training facilities.
Disposals: Recent retirements include C 5148–C 5152 on 22-3-00, C 5156 on 14-3-01, and C 5153 on 51-3-01.

♦ 40 "T"-class punts [YXT]

T 6077 T 6081 through T 6120

T 6115 Takatoshi Okano, 3-01

D: 0.5 tons **Dim:** 6.0 × 1.6 × . . .
M: 1 Tohhatsu or Yamaha outboard; . . . bhp

Remarks: Molded GRP construction. The wooden-hulled T 6077 may also still be in service. T 6110–T 6113 were delivered 22-3-96, T 6118–T 6120 on 20-3-98. T 6067–T 6069 were stricken 24-3-95; T 6070, T 6071, T 6074, and T 6076 on 22-3-96; and T 6078–T 6080 on 20-3-98. Are stationed at the Etajima Naval Academy or at other training facilities.

JAPAN COAST GUARD

The name of the organization was changed to the Japan Coast Guard on 1-4-00. The preceding Maritime Safety Agency (MSA), which was organized in 1948, underwent a massive expansion in the 1970s, which by 1982 made it one of the world's largest and best-equipped coast guards. It is directed by the Department of Transportation. Although most of its ships are armed, they are not considered part of the navy and fly only the national colors (a red disk on a white background), not the ensign flown by naval ships. Most ships and craft are now painted white, with the stylized Coast Guard "S" in blue on the hull sides; a few patrol craft and service craft are still painted gray. Most units have green-painted decks. The words "Japan Coast Guard" are being painted on the hull or superstructure sides.

Personnel (2000): approx. 12,000 total (2,600 officers)

Organization: The coast guard is organized into 11 districts, 65 offices, 25 detachments, 52 stations, 14 air stations, 11 district communications centers, and a traffic advisory service. There are also 4 hydrographic observatories and 132 aids-to-navigation offices.

Aviation: As of 1-01, the Japan Coast Guard operated 32 fixed-wing aircraft (including 2 Saab 340B and 2 Dassault-Breguet Falcon 900 long-range search-and-rescue aircraft; 7 Beech 350, 2 Beech B200T Super King Air, and 10 Beech 200T Super King Air search-and rescue aircraft; 5 YS-11A transports; and 1 Cessna U206G light transport/utility aircraft) and 46 helicopters (4 Aérospatiale AS.332L1 Super Puma, 4 Sikorsky S-76C, 8 Bell 412, 26 Kawasaki-Bell 212, and 4 Bell 206B). All fixed-wing aircraft bear names; as examples, the two Saab 340B aircraft (MA 951 and MA 952) are named *Hamataka No. 1* and *Hamataka No. 2,* the two Falcon 900 aircraft (LAJ 570 and LAJ 571) are named *Ootaka No. 1* and *Ootaka No. 2,* Super Puma MH 686 is named the *Umitaka,* and Beech 350 MA 867 is named *Toki.*

Air Stations are located as follows: 1st Region Headquarters at Otaru on Hokkaido, with subsidiary air stations at Chitose, Hakodate, and Kushiro; 2nd Region Headquarters at Shiogama, Miyaga Prefecture, with subsidiary air stations at Miyaga and Sendai; 3rd Region Headquarters at Yokohama, with a subsidiary air station at Haneda Airport near Tokyo; 4th Region Headquarters at Nagoya, Aichi Prefecture, with a subsidiary air station at Ise; 5th Region Headquarters at Kobe, with a subsidiary air station at Yao, Osaka Prefecture; 6th Region Headquarters at Ujina, Hiroshima Prefecture; 7th Region Headquarters at Moji-ka, Kita-Kyushu, Fukuoka Prefecture, with a subsidiary air station at Fukuoka; 8th Region Headquarters at Maizuru, Kyoto Prefecture, with a subsidiary air station at Miho, Shimane Prefecture; 10th Region Headquarters at Kagoshima; and 11th Region Headquarters at Naha on Okinawa, with subsidiary air stations at Ishigaki Island and Yaeyama.

Falcon 900 long-range SAR aircraft Ootaka No. 1 (LAJ 570)
Takatoshi Okano, 7-99

Saab 340B long-range SAR aircraft Hamataka No. 1 (MA 951)
Takatoshi Okano, 5-01

Beech 200T SAR aircraft MA 819 *Ships of the World*

JAPAN COAST GUARD *(continued)*

Beech 350 SAR aircraft MA 864A Takatoshi Okano, 7-99

YS-11A transport LA 782 Mitsuhiro Kadota, 4-00

AS.332L1 Super Puma MH 686 Takatoshi Okano, 5-01

Sikorsky S-76C MH 905 Takatoshi Okano, 5-01

Kawasaki-Bell 212 MH 563 Mitsuhiro Kadota, 4-00

Programs: Approved for construction during the FY 01 budget period (1-4-01 to 31-3-02) were two 350-ton and one 30-ton cutters, one 20-ton navaids tender, and two 17-ton service craft.

Note: The organization and designations of the ships and craft below is a compromise between the Japan Coast Guard system, which is based as much on mission as on size, and the system adopted for this book as a whole, which is based on size and capabilities. Thus, some of the classes below will not meet the strict requirements of the standard *Combat Fleets* designation system, but it was felt that keeping classes with the same Japanese type designator together should take precedence. The letter designations used by the Coast Guard include:

- PL—Patrol vessel, Large
- PM—Patrol vessel, Medium
- PS—Patrol vessel, Small
- PC—Patrol Craft
- CL—Craft, Large
- LS—Lighthouse service vessel, Small
- MA—Medium (fixed-wing) Aircraft
- MH—Medium Helicopter

PATROL SHIPS [WPS]

♦ 1 Shikishima-class high-endurance helicopter-carrying cutter

Bldr: IHI, Tokyo

	Laid down	L	In serv.
PLH 31 Shikishima	4-28-90	27-6-91	8-4-92

Shikishima (PLH 31) Mitsuhiro Kadota, 4-00

Shikishima (PLH 31) Mitsuhiro Kadota, 2-01

D: 6,500 tons light; 7,175 tons std. (9,350 fl) **S:** 25 kts **Dim:** 150.0 × 16.5 × 7.00
A: 2 twin 35-mm 90-cal. Oerlikon AA; 2 single 20-mm JM-61-MB gatling AA; 2 single 12.7-mm M2 mg; 2 Aérospatiale AS.332L1 Super Puma helicopters
Electronics:
Radar: 1 JMS 1596 nav.; 1 JMA 8303 surf. search; 1 JMA 3000 helo control; 1 Melco OPS-14C surf./air search
M: 2 IHI–SEMT-Pielstick 16 PC2.5 V400 diesels; 2 CP props; 20,800 bhp—bow-thruster
Range: 20,000/18 **Crew:** 110 tot. + 30 aircrew

Remarks: Intended to act as escort for a ship to carry plutonium from Europe to Japan for use in nuclear electric power generation stations, but, after a single such voyage in 8-93 escorting the chartered plutonium transport *Akatsuki Maru* (ex-*Pacific Crane*), has been used as a general patrol ship assigned to the Yokohama Maritime Safety Department.
Combat systems: The enclosed 20-mm gatling gunmounts are the same as those used on the JMSDF's PG 01–class missile hydrofoils. There are two optronic directors for the twin 35-mm mountings. The planned ORN-6 TACAN was not fitted. Is equipped with two water cannon for fire fighting and harassment control. Has SHF and commercial UHF SATCOM gear.

COAST GUARD PATROL SHIPS [WPS] *(continued)*

♦ 2 Mizuho-class high-endurance helicopter-carrying cutters

	Bldr	Laid down	L	In serv.
PLH 21 Mizuho	Mitsubishi, Shimonoseki	27-8-84	5-6-85	19-3-86
PLH 22 Yashima	Nippon Kokan, Tsurumi	3-8-87	20-1-88	1-12-88

Mizuho (PLH 21) Takatoshi Okano, 5-01

Yashima (PLH 22) Mitsuhiro Kadota, 5-01

D: 4,960 tons light; 5,317 tons std. (5,259 fl) **S:** 23.3 kts
Dim: 130.00 (123.00 wl) × 15.50 × 5.25
A: 1 35-mm 90-cal. Oerlikon AA; 1 20-mm JM-61-MB gatling AA; 2 Kawasaki-Bell 212 helicopters
Electronics: Radar: 2 JMA 3000 nav.; 1 JMA 8303 nav.
M: 2 IHI–SEMT-Pielstick 14 PC2.5 V400 (PLH 22: 12 PC2 V) diesels; 2 CP props; 18,200 bhp—bow-thruster
Electric: 1,875 kVA (3 diesel sets) **Range:** 8,500/22 **Crew:** 130 tot.

Remarks: Intended to operate 200 n.m. to sea or farther, if necessary. Are the first Japan Coast Guard class to carry two helicopters. Have a flight deck–traversing system and two pairs of fin stabilizers. An SHF SATCOM system was added to PLH 21 in 1989, and both have Marisat commercial SATCOM. PLH 21 is based at Nagoya.

♦ 2 Ryukyu-class high-endurance helicopter-carrying cutters

	Bldr	Laid down	L	In serv.
PLH 09 Ryukyu	Mitsui, Tamano	24-6-98	10-9-99	31-3-00
PLH 10 Daisen	Nippon Kokan, Tsurumi	8-3-99	27-4-01	3-10-01

Ryukyu (PLH 09) Takatoshi Okano, 5-01

Ryukyu (PLH 09) *Ships of the World,* 3-00

D: 3,100 tons (3,900 fl) **S:** 22 kts **Dim:** 105.00 (100.00 wl) × 15.00 × 4.85
A: 1 35-mm 90-cal.; 1 20-mm JM-61-MB gatling AA; 1 Kawasaki-Bell 212 helicopter
Electronics: Radar: 1 . . . nav.; 1 . . . surf. search; 1 . . . helo control
M: 2 diesels; 2 CP props; 16,000 bhp—bow-thruster
Range: 5,700/18 **Crew:** . . .

Remarks: Intended to operate 100 n.m. or more to sea. Design is a modernized version of the preceding *Tsugaru* class, with somewhat finer hull lines and a bulbous forefoot to the bow. Have a Marisat UHF SATCOM installation. The 20-mm gun is in a new, remotely operated, automatic mounting. PLH 09 is based at Naha, Okinawa, and patrols the Nansei Islands area.

♦ 7 Tsugaru-class high-endurance helicopter-carrying cutters

	Bldr	Laid down	L	In serv.
PLH 02 Tsugaru	IHI, Tokyo	18-4-78	6-12-78	17-4-79
PLH 03 Oosumi	Mitsui, Tamano	1-9-78	1-6-79	18-10-79
PLH 04 Hayato (ex-*Uraga*)	Hitachi, Maizuru	14-3-79	12-10-79	5-3-80
PLH 05 Zao	Mitsubishi, Nagasaki	23-10-80	29-10-81	19-3-82
PLH 06 Chikuzen	Kawasaki, Kobe	20-4-82	18-3-83	28-9-83
PLH 07 Settsu	Sumitomo, Uraga	5-4-83	21-4-84	27-9-84
PLH 08 Echigo	Mitsui, Tamano	29-3-88	4-7-89	28-2-90

Oosumi (PLH 03)—with 40-mm gun and no 20-mm gun Mitsuhiro Kadota, 4-00

D: 3,221 tons light; 3,730 tons std. (4,037 fl) **S:** 21.5 kts
Dim: 105.40 (100.00 wl) × 14.60 × 4.85
A: PLH 02, 03: 1 40-mm 60-cal. Bofors AA—others: 1 35-mm 90-cal. Oerlikon AA—PLH 02, 05–07: 1 20-mm 70-cal. Oerlikon AA—all: 1 Kawasaki-Bell 212 helicopter
Electronics:
Radar: 1 JMA 1596 nav.; 1 JMA 1576 surf. search; 1 . . . helo control
M: 2 SEMT-Pielstick 12 PC2.5 V400 diesels; 2 CP props; 15,600 bhp (13,260 bhp sust.)—bow-thruster
Electric: 1,160 kw tot. (2 × 520 kw, 1 × 120 kw) **Range:** 5,700/18
Fuel: 864 tons **Crew:** 21 officers, 7 warrant officers, 28 enlisted + 15 spare

Remarks: Intended to operate 100 n.m. or more to sea. Redesignated from PL in 1985–86. Have two pair of fin stabilizers and Flume-type passive stabilization tanks in the superstructure. The engines were manufactured by different builders. Have a Marisat UHF SATCOM installation.

COAST GUARD PATROL SHIPS [WPS] *(continued)*

Hayato (PLH 04)—with 35-mm gun Mitsuhiro Kadota, 5-01

♦ 1 Soya-class high-endurance helicopter-carrying cutter

	Bldr	Laid down	L	In serv.
PLH 01 Soya	Nippon Kokan, Tsurumi	12-9-77	3-7-78	22-11-78

Soya (PLH 01) *Ships of the World,* 1994

D: 3,139 tons light; 3,562 tons std. (4,089 fl) **S:** 21 kts **Dim:** 98.6 × 15.6 × 5.2
A: 1 40-mm 60-cal. Bofors AA; 1 20-mm 70-cal. Oerlikon AA; 1 Kawasaki-Bell 212 helicopter
Electronics: Radar: 4 . . . nav. (1 aft for helo control)
M: 2 Nippon Kokan–Pielstick 12 PC2.5 V400 diesels; 2 CP props; 16,000 bhp (13,260 hp sust.)
Electric: 1,160 kw tot. (2 × 520 kw, 1 × 120 kw)
Range: 5,700/18 **Fuel:** 650 tons **Crew:** 71 tot.

Remarks: Built under the 1977 program. Has an icebreaking bow and operates in the north. Passive tank stabilization only, no bow-thruster. Has a rounded stern, vice the squared one on the *Tsugaru* class. Redesignated PLH from PL on 13-12-85. The armament is not normally fitted.

♦ 1 Izu-class (3,500-ton) disaster-relief cutter

	Bldr	Laid down	L	In serv.
PL 31 Izu	Nippon Kokan, Tsurumi	22-3-96	7-2-97	25-9-97

Izu (PL 31) Mitsuhiro Kadota, 5-01

D: 3,680 tons (fl) **S:** 20 kts **Dim:** 110.40 × 15.00 × 3.60
A: 1 20-mm JM-61-MB gatling AA
Electronics: Radar: 1 JMA . . . nav.; 1 JMA . . . surf. search
M: 2 . . . . . . diesels; 2 CP props; 12,000 bhp—bow-thruster **Crew:** . . . tot.

Remarks: PL 31, approved under the FY 95 budget, replaced an earlier unit with the same name and number. Has a large helicopter platform aft but no hangar. Equipped with a bow-thruster and passive stabilization tanks. Has extensive medical facilities and is intended to serve in disaster relief roles. Based at Yokohama.

♦ 4 Hakata-class (1,000-ton) high-endurance cutters

	Bldr	Laid down	L	In serv.
PL 05 Hakata	IHI, Tokyo	22-10-97	7-6-98	26-11-98
PL 06 Dejima	Mitsui, Tamano	1-9-98	28-6-99	29-10-99
PL 07 Satsuma	Kawasaki, Kobe	4-9-98	3-6-99	29-10-99
PL 08 Motobu	Mitsui, Tamano	8-9-99	9-6-00	31-10-00

Dejima (PL 06) Mitsuhiro Kadota, 4-00

Motobu (PL 08) Mitsuhiro Kadota, 5-01

D: 1,365 tons light; 1,930 tons std. (2,055 fl) **S:** 20 kts **Dim:** 93.5 × 11.5 × 4.0
A: 1 35-mm 90-cal. Oerlikon AA; 1 20-mm JM-61-MB gatling AA; 1 12.7-mm mg
Electronics: Radar: 2 . . . nav.
M: 2 Fuji S540B diesels; 2 CP props; 7,000 bhp—2 bow-thrusters
Range: 4,400/19 **Crew:** . . . tot.

Remarks: Design evolved from the *Ojika* design. PL 08 is based at Naha, Okinawa, and operates in the waters off the Senkaku Islands, primarily as a fisheries patrol ship.

♦ 3 Ojika-class (1,000-ton) high-endurance cutters

	Bldr	Laid down	L	In serv.
PL 02 Erimo (ex-*Ojika*)	Mitsui, Tamano	28-9-90	23-4-91	3-10-91
PL 03 Kudaka	Hakodate DY	9-9-93	10-5-94	25-10-94
PL 04 Yahiko (ex-*Satsuma*)	Sumitomo, Uraga	21-9-94	29-5-95	26-10-95

Erimo (PL 02)—note stern door open to recover lifeboat Mitsuhiro Kadota, 4-00

D: 1,268 tons light, 1,883 tons std. (2,006 fl) **S:** 20 kts
Dim: 91.40 (87.00 pp) × 11.00 × 3.50
A: 1 20-mm JM-61-MB gatling AA

COAST GUARD PATROL SHIPS [WPS] *(continued)*

Erimo (PL 02) Mitsuhiro Kadota, 4-00

Electronics: Radar: 1 . . . nav.; 1 . . . surf. search
M: 2 Fuji S540B diesels; 2 CP props; 7,000 bhp—2 bow-thrusters
Range: 4,400/19 **Crew:** 38 tot.

Remarks: PL 02 ordered in 11-89. PL 04 was renamed in 1999 and PL 02 on 31-10-00. PL 03 was contracted to Hitachi, which subcontracted her to Hakodate Dockyard.
Hull systems: PL 03 and PL 04 are 1,250 tons standard/1,880 tons full load and incorporate a cargo hold beneath the helicopter pad that is tended by a telescoping crane. All four have a computerized rescue data system, special display room, helicopter platform, and fin stabilization. There is a stern dock for an "unsinkable" rescue craft. Have 30-ton bollard pull towing capacity. Equipped with SHF and commercial UHF SATCOM systems.

♦ 1 Nojima-class (1,000-ton) high-endurance cutter

	Bldr	Laid down	L	In serv.
PL 01 Oki (ex-*Nojima*)	IHI, Tokyo	16-8-88	30-5-89	21-9-89

Oki (PL 01) Mitsuhiro Kadota, 5-01

D: 820 tons light; 993 tons std. (1,500 fl) **S:** 20 kts (19 sust.)
Dim: 85.00 × 10.50 × 3.50 **A:** 1 20-mm JM-61-MB gatling AA
Electronics:
Radar: 1 . . . nav.; 1 . . . surf. search
Sonar: side-looking wreck-location HF
M: 2 Fuji S8540B diesels; 2 CP props; 7,000 bhp
Electric: 450 kVA tot. (3 × 150-kVA diesel-driven sets)
Range: 4,400/19 **Crew:** 39 tot.

Remarks: 850 grt. Authorized under the 1986 budget. Sharp sheer to bow to improve seakeeping while keeping amidships freeboard low. Unusual in having a raised helicopter deck over the fantail and a second bridge above and abaft the main pilothouse. Fin stabilizers are fitted. Has a Marisat commercial UHF SATCOM system. A rescue diving crew is assigned to the ship. Renamed during 1999. Based at Sakai and operates in the Sea of Japan.

♦ 27 Shiretoko-class high-endurance cutters

	Bldr	L	In serv.
PL 101 Shiretoko	Mitsui, Tamano	13-7-78	8-11-78
PL 102 Esan	Sumitomo, Oshima	8-78	16-11-78
PL 103 Wakasa	Kawasaki, Kobe	8-78	29-11-78
PL 104 Shimanto (ex-*Yahiko*)	Mitsubishi, Shimonoseki	8-78	16-11-78
PL 106 Rishiri	Shikoku DY	27-3-79	12-9-79
PL 107 Matsushima	Tohoku DY	11-4-79	14-9-79
PL 108 Iwaki	Naikai, Innoshima	28-3-79	10-8-79
PL 109 Shikine	Usuki SY, Usuki	27-4-79	20-9-79
PL 110 Suruga	Kurushima DY, Onishi	20-4-79	28-9-79
PL 111 Rebun	Narasaki SY, Muroran	6-79	21-11-79
PL 112 Chokai	Nipponkai Heavy Ind., Toyama	6-79	30-11-79
PL 113 Nojima (ex-*Ashizuri*)	Sanoyasu DY, Oshima	6-79	31-10-79
PL 114 Tosa (ex-*Oki*)	Tsuneishi SY, Numakuma	6-79	16-11-79
PL 115 Noto	Miho SY, Shimuzu	7-79	30-11-79
PL 116 Yonakuni	Hiyashigane SY, Nagasaki	6-79	31-10-79
PL 117 Kurikoma (ex-*Kudaka*, ex-*Daisetsu*)	Hakodate DY	22-8-79	31-1-80
PL 118 Shimokita	Ishikawajima, Tokyo	9-79	12-3-80
PL 119 Suzuka	Kanasashi SY, Toyohashi	4-10-79	7-3-80
PL 120 Kunisaki	Koyo DY, Mihara	8-10-79	29-2-80
PL 121 Genkai	Oshima SY, Oshima	9-79	31-1-80
PL 122 Goto	Onomichi SY, Onomichi	10-79	29-2-80
PL 123 Koshiki	Kasado DY, Kasado	9-79	25-1-80
PL 124 Hateruma	Osaka DY	11-79	12-3-80
PL 125 Katori	Tohoku DY, Shiogama	5-80	17-10-80
PL 126 Kunigami	Kanda SY, Kawashiri	28-3-80	21-10-80
PL 127 Etomo	Naikai, Innoshima	30-9-81	17-3-82
PL 128 Amagi (ex-*Mashu*)	Shikoku DY, Kochi, Takamatsu	14-10-81	12-3-82

Rishiri (PL 106)—with 40-mm gun Takatoshi Okano, 5-01

Katori (PL 125)—with 35-mm gun Mitsuhiro Kadota, 5-01

D: 965.3–974.0 tons std. (1,350–1,360 fl) **S:** 20 kts
Dim: 77.8 (73.6 pp) × 9.6 × 3.42
A: PL 101–104, 106–117, 119–121, 123: 1 40-mm 60-cal. Bofors AA—PL 118, 122, 124–128: 1 35-mm 90-cal. Oerlikon AA—PL 101–104: 1 20-mm 70-cal. Oerlikon AA
Electronics: Radar: 1 JMA 1596 nav.; 1 JMA 1576 surf. search
M: 2 Niigata 8MA 40 or Fuji 8 S40B diesels (see remarks); 2 CP props; 7,000 bhp
Electric: 625 kVA tot. **Range:** 4,406/17 **Fuel:** 191 tons **Crew:** 41 tot.

Remarks: Building program helped small shipyards to stay in business. Intended to patrol the 200-n.m. economic zone. PL 120 had a serious fire 15-2-82. Name of PL 117 changed 1-4-88 and again on 1-8-94.
Disposals: *Motobu* (PL 105), renamed *Ojika* on 1-10-00, received serious damage in a collision with fishing boat *Zentoku Maru No. 3* on 6-10-00 and was stricken 20-10-00.
Hull systems: PL 101, 103, 107, 108, 110–113, 117, 121, 122, 124, and 127 have Fuji 8S40B diesels. Carry 153 tons of water. Fuel capacities and endurances vary. Have Flume-type passive tank stabilization, with tanks in superstructure. Range greater for some; PL 127 has a range of 5,200 n.m. at 17 kts.

♦ 1 Daio-class high-endurance cutter

	Bldr	L	In serv.
PL 16 Muroto	Naikai, Taguma	5-8-74	30-11-74

COAST GUARD PATROL SHIPS [WPS] *(continued)*

Daio (PL 15)—since stricken Mitsuhiro Kadota, 4-00

D: 939.5 tons std. (1,206 fl) **S:** 20.4 kts **Dim:** 76.6 (73.0 pp) × 9.6 × 3.18
A: 1 40-mm 60-cal. Mk 3 Bofors AA; 1 20-mm 70-cal. Oerlikon AA
Electronics: Radar: 1 JMA 1596 nav.; 1 JMA 1576 surf. search
M: 2 Fuji 8S40B diesels; 2 props; 8,120 bhp **Electric:** 500 kVA tot.
Range: 4,400/18 **Crew:** 45 tot.

Remarks: Similar to the *Erimo* class but has slightly more beam and more-powerful engines. Based at Aburatsu, Sister *Daio* (PL 15) was retired on 26-8-01.

♦ 1 Miura-class (3,000-ton) high-endurance training cutter [WPST]

	Bldr	Laid down	L	In serv.
PL 22 Miura	IHI, Tokyo	12-3-97	11-3-98	28-10-98

Miura (PL 22) Takatoshi Okano, 10-00

D: 3,167 tons **S:** 18 kts **Dim:** 115.0 × 14.0 × . . .
A: 1 20-mm JM-61-MB gatling AA **Electronics:** Radar: 3 . . . nav.
M: 2 . . . diesels; 2 CP props; 8,000 bhp—bow-thruster
Range: 8,000/18 **Crew:** 40 officers, 110 enlisted

Remarks: PL 22 is employed primarily for Japan Coast Guard School enlisted training duties. Externally PL 22 is very similar to the *Kojima* (PL 21). Has a large helicopter deck but no hangar and is equipped with Flume-type water tank stabilization system. Hull has 7.3-m molded depth. Has both SHF and UHF SATCOM systems.

♦ 2 Kojima-class (3,000-ton) training cutters [WPST]

	Bldr	Laid down	L	In serv.
PL 21 Kojima	Hitachi, Maizuru	7-11-91	10-9-92	11-3-93

Kojima (PL 21) H&L Van Ginderen, 7-99

D: 2,650 tons light; 2,950 tons std. (3,136 fl) **S:** 18 kts
Dim: 115.00 × 14.00 × 3.53
A: 1 35-mm 90-cal. Oerlikon AA; 1 20-mm JM-61-MB gatling AA; 1 12.7-mm mg
Electronics: Radar: 2 JMA 1596 nav.
M: 2 . . . . . . diesels; 2 CP props; 7,886 bhp—bow-thruster
Range: 7,000/15 **Crew:** 118 tot.

Remarks: Authorized under FY 90 budget. Used as a coast guard officer cadet training ship at Kure Academy. Officially of the "3,000-ton" class. Has both SHF and UHF SATCOM systems. The after deck serves as a helicopter platform and ceremonial/exercise space; there is no hangar. Flume-type water-tank stabilization is fitted.

PATROL COMBATANTS [WPG]

♦ 1 Teshio-class (500-ton) medium-endurance icebreaking cutter

	Bldr	Laid down	L	In serv.
PM 15 Teshio	Nippon Kokan, Tsurumi	7-10-94	20-4-95	19-10-95

Teshio (PM 15) *Ships of the World,* 10-95

D: 563 tons (883 fl) **S:** 14.5 kts **Dim:** 54.90 × 10.60 (10.20 wl) × 3.30
A: 1 20-mm JM-61-MB gatling AA **Electronics:** Radar: 2 . . . nav.
M: 2 . . . . . . diesels; 2 Kort-nozzle props; 3,600 bhp—bow-thruster
Crew: 35 tot.

Remarks: Approved under the FY 93 budget. Icebreaking hull with 5.0-m molded depth, able to break 75-cm ice by ramming and 55-cm ice at 3 kts continuous. Hullform is unusual for an icebreaking hull in that it has a hard chine amidships and single-curvature hullform over most of the middle portion of the hull. A television surveillance camera is fitted atop the pilothouse.

♦ 4 Amami-class (350-ton) medium-endurance cutters

	Bldr	Laid down	L	In serv.
PM 95 Anami	Hitachi, Maizuru	22-10-91	22-6-92	28-9-92
PM 96 Kurakami (ex-*Matsuura*)	Mitsubishi, Shimonoseki	9-9-94	31-5-95	24-11-95
PM 97 Kunashiri	Mitsubishi, Nagasaki	30-9-97	26-5-98	26-8-98
PM 98 Minabe	Mitsubishi, Nagasaki	30-9-97	26-5-98	26-8-98

Kurakami (PM 96)—as *Matsuura* Mitsuhiro Kadota, 4-99

Minabe (PM 98) Takatoshi Okano, 9-00

D: 230 tons (249 fl) **S:** 25 kts (20 sust.) **Dim:** 56.00 × 7.50 × 1.50
A: 1 20-mm JM-61-MB gatling AA
Electronics: Radar: 2 . . . nav.
M: 2 Fuji 8S40B diesels; 2 props; 8,120 bhp (7,000 sust.) **Crew:** 33 tot.

Remarks: Carry a 5.5-m rigid inflatable rescue boat on an internal ramp at the stern. The gunmounts on PM 97 and PM 98 are on raised bandstands. PM 96 was renamed on 3-4-00. Two additional 350-ton-class cutters approved in the FY 01 budget will probably be of a new class.

COAST GUARD PATROL COMBATANTS [WPG] *(continued)*

♦ 14 Teshio-class (500-ton) medium-endurance cutters

	Bldr	L	In serv.
PM 01 Natsui (ex-*Teshio*)	Shikoku DY, Kochi	30-5-80	30-9-80
PM 02 Oirase	Naikai, Taguma, Innoshima	15-5-80	29-8-80
PM 03 Echizen	Usuki Iron Wks., Usuki	2-6-80	30-9-80
PM 04 Tokachi	Narazaki, Muroran	21-11-80	24-3-81
PM 05 Hitachi	Tohoku SY, Shiogoma	15-11-80	19-3-81
PM 06 Okitsu	Usuki Iron Wks., Usuki	5-12-80	17-3-81
PM 07 Isazu	Naikai, Taguma, Innoshima	29-10-81	18-2-82
PM 08 Chitose	Shikoku DY, Kochi	7-7-81	17-11-82
PM 09 Kumano	Naikai, Taguma, Innoshima	8-81	10-3-83
PM 10 Sorachi	Tohoku SY, Shiogama	27-4-84	27-9-84
PM 11 Yubari	Usuki Iron Wks., Usuki	20-8-85	28-11-85
PM 12 Motoura	Shikoku DY, Takamatsu	7-8-86	21-11-86
PM 13 Kano	Naikai, Taguma, Innoshima	7-8-86	13-11-86
PM 14 Sendai	Shikoku DY, Takamatsu	21-1-88	1-6-88

Kano (PM 13) Mitsuhiro Kadota, 5-01

D: 540–562 tons (670–692 fl) **S:** 18.0–18.6 kts
Dim: 67.80 (63.00 pp) × 7.90 × 2.65
A: 1 20-mm JM-61-MB gatling AA **Electronics:** Radar: 2 JMA 159B nav.
M: 2 Fuji 6S32F or Arataka 6 M31EX diesels; 2 CP props; 3,000 bhp
Electric: 240 kVA tot. **Range:** 3,500/16 **Endurance:** 15 days **Crew:** 33 tot.

Remarks: 540 grt. PM 07 is also used for training and has a lengthened after deckhouse. PM 12 has Niigata 6M31 diesels, a range of 3,900 n.m. at 16 kts, and a full load displacement of 692 tons. PM 01 was renamed during 11-95.

♦ 2 Takatori-class (350-ton) medium-endurance cutters

	Bldr	L	In serv.
PM 89 Takatori	Naikai, Taguma, Innoshima	8-12-77	24-3-78
PM 94 Kumano	Naikai, Taguma, Innoshima	2-11-78	23-2-79

Takatori (PM 89)—laying oil-spill containment boom Mitsuhiro Kadota, 5-01

D: 469 tons normal (634 fl) **S:** 15.7 kts **Dim:** 45.70 (44.25 pp) × 9.20 × 3.88
A: none **Electronics:** Radar: 1 JMA 1596 nav.; 1 JMA 1576 surf. search
M: 2 Niigata 6M31EX diesels; 1 CP prop; 3,000 bhp
Electric: 200 kVA **Range:** 750/15 **Crew:** 34 tot.

Remarks: 469 grt. Rescue-tug types, equipped for firefighting, salvage, and pollution control duties. Two firefighting water cannon (3,000 liters/min each) are fitted. Carry an 8-m rescue boat and a 4.6-m speedboat and can lay an oil-spill containment boom.

♦ 20 Bihoro-class (350-ton) medium-endurance cutters

	Bldr	In serv.
PM 73 Bihoro	Tohoku SY, Shiogama	28-2-74
PM 74 Kuma	Usuki Iron Wks., Usuki	28-2-74
PM 75 Fuji	Usuki Iron Wks., Usuki	7-2-75
PM 76 Kabashima	Usuki Iron Wks., Usuki	25-3-75
PM 77 Okishiri (ex-*Sado*)	Tohoku SY, Shiogama	1-2-75
PM 78 Ishikari	Tohoku SY, Shiogama	13-3-76
PM 79 Abakuma	Tohoku SY, Shiogama	30-1-76
PM 80 Isuzu	Naikai SY, Taguma	10-3-76
PM 81 Kikuchi	Usuki Iron Wks., Usuki	6-2-76
PM 82 Kuzuryu	Usuki Iron Wks., Usuki	18-3-76
PM 83 Horobetsu	Tohoku SY, Shiogama	21-1-77
PM 84 Shirakami	Tohoku SY, Shiogama	3-3-77
PM 85 Matsuura (ex-*Sagami*)	Naikai SY, Taguma	30-11-76
PM 86 Tone	Usuki Iron Wks., Usuki	30-11-76
PM 87 Misasa (ex-*Yoshino*)	Usuki Iron Wks., Usuki	28-1-77
PM 88 Kurobe	Shikoku DY, Kochi	15-2-77
PM 90 Chikugo	Naikai, Taguma	27-1-78
PM 91 Yamakuni	Usuki Iron Wks., Usuki	26-1-78
PM 92 Katsura	Shikoku DY, Kochi	15-2-77
PM 93 Shinano	Tohoku SY, Shiogama	23-2-78

Fuji (PM 75) Takatoshi Okano, 9-00

Kuzuryu (PM 82) Takatoshi Okano, 7-99

D: 495 tons light; 636 tons normal (657 fl) **S:** 18 kts **Dim:** 63.35 × 7.80 × 2.53
A: 1 12.7-mm mg
Electronics:
Radar: 1 JMA 1596 nav.; 2 JMA 159B or 1 JMA 1576 nav./surf. search
M: 2 Niigata 6M31EX diesels; 2 CP props; 3,000 bhp
Electric: 200 kVA tot. (2 × 100-kVA diesel sets)
Range: 3,260/16 **Crew:** 34 tot.

Remarks: PM 77 was renamed on 24-1-01, PM 85 on 3-4-00, and PM 87 on 18-5-00. The 20-mm JM-61-MB gatling guns have been replaced by a shielded 12.7-mm mg.

♦ 3 Kunashiri-class (350-ton) medium-endurance cutters

	Bldr	In serv.
PM 68 Kamishima	Usuki Iron Wks., Usuki	31-1-72
PM 70 Miyake	Tohoku SY, Shiogama	25-1-73
PM 72 Yaeyama	Usuki Iron Wks., Usuki	20-12-72

D: 498 tons (574 fl) **S:** 17.5 kts **Dim:** 58.04 × 7.38 × 2.40
A: 1 20-mm 70-cal. Oerlikon (U.S. Mk 10 mount) *or* 1 12.7-mm mg
Electronics: Radar: 1 JMA 1596 nav.; 1 JMA 1576 surf. search
M: 2 Niigata 6M31EX diesels; 2 props; 3,000 bhp **Electric:** 120 kVA
Range: 3,040/16 **Crew:** 40 tot.

Remarks: PM 68 has 6MF32H diesels, 2,600 bhp. PM 72 has controllable-pitch propellers. The 20-mm mounts are being replaced by 12.7-mm machineguns.
Disposals: *Kunashiri* (PM 65) and *Minabe* (PM 66) were stricken 31-7-98, *Sarobetsu* (PM 67) on 24-1-01, and *Awaji* (PM 71) on 22-2-01.

Disposal note: The last *Yahagi*-class (350-ton) medium-endurance cutter, the *Misasa* (PM 69, ex-*Okinawa*), was stricken 18-5-00.

PATROL CRAFT [WPC]

♦ 3 Tsurugi-class (180-ton) "High-Speed Special Patrol Ships"
Bldr: Hitachi Zosen, Kanegawa

	Bldr	Laid down	L	In serv.
PS 201 Tsurugi	Hitachi, Kanagawa	15-3-00	9-11-00	15-2-01
PS 202 Hotaka	Sumitomo, Shimonoseki	11-5-00	14-12-00	16-3-01
PS 203 Norikura	Mitsui, Tamano	23-5-00	14-12-00	16-3-01

COAST GUARD PATROL CRAFT [WPC] *(continued)*

Tsurugi (PS 201) *Ships of the World,* 3-01

Norikura (PS 203) *Ships of the World,* 3-01

D: 220 tons (fl) **S:** 40 kts **Dim:** 50.0 × 8.0 × . . .
A: 1 20-mm JM-61-MB gatling AA **Electronics:** Radar: . . .
M: 3 . . . . . . diesels; 3 waterjets; 15,000 bhp

Remarks: Acquired to permit pursuit of North Korean incursion craft on the Sea of Japan coast. Based at Niigata, Maizuru, and Kanazawa, respectively. Named for mountains. Have IR search and E/O surveillance systems and carry a large rigid inflatable inspection boat.

♦ **11 Mihashi-class (180-ton) short-endurance cutters**

	Bldr	Laid down	L	In serv.
PS 01 Shinzan (ex-*Akiyoshi*, ex-*Mihashi*)	Mitsubishi, Shimonoseki	16-12-87	18-6-88	9-9-88
PS 02 Saroma	Hitachi, Kanagawa	12-12-88	28-6-89	28-11-89
PS 03 Inasa	Mitsubishi, Shimonoseki	18-5-89	20-10-89	31-1-90
PS 04 Kirishima	Hitachi, Kanegawa	10-5-90	18-1-90	22-3-91
PS 05 Kamui	Mitsubishi, Shimonoseki	12-4-93	15-11-93	31-1-94
PS 06 Banna (ex-*Bizan*)	Hitachi, Kanagawa	6-4-93	15-11-93	31-1-94
PS 07 Ashitaki	Mitsui, Tamano	9-12-93	24-6-94	30-9-94
PS 08 Kurama	Mitsubishi, Shimonoseki	21-9-94	25-5-95	29-8-95
PS 09 Arase	Hitachi, Kanagawa	9-4-96	4-10-96	1-97
PS 10 Sanbe	Mitsubishi, Shimonoseki	9-4-96	22-10-96	29-1-97
PS 11 Mizuki	Mitsui, Tamano	16-3-99	28-4-00	9-6-00

Mizuki (PS 11)—with rubbing fenders on the hull sides and an optronic director–controlled 20-mm gatling gun Takatoshi Okano, 5-01

D: 182 tons normal (197 fl) **S:** 35 kts **Dim:** 46.0 × 7.5 × 1.7
A: 1 12.7-mm mg (PS 03, 11: 1 20-mm JM-61-MB gatling AA)
Electronics: Radar: 1 Furuno . . . nav.

Ashitaki (PS 07)—with 12.7-mm mg and normal hull sides Mitsuhiro Kadota, 5-01

M: 2 Mitsubishi S16U-MTK (SEMT-Pielstick 16 PA4 V200 VGA) diesels (3,200 bhp each), 1 Mitsubishi S8U-MTK (SEMT-Pielstick 12 PA4 V200 VGA) diesel (2,500 bhp); 2 props, 1 waterjet
Range: 650/34 **Crew:** 15 tot.

Remarks: An expansion of the preceding *Shizuki* class, incorporating a centerline waterjet propulsor. First four are 43.0 m o.a. and displace 180 tons light, 200 tons fl; the later units are referred to as the *Banna* class (formerly *Bizan* class) and carry a crew of 13. The name for PS 01 was changed on 28-1-97 and again on 24-1-01.
Mission systems: During 2000, PS 03 had the 12.7-mm mg replaced by an automatic 20-mm gatling gun with an optronic director atop the pilothouse; PS 11 was completed with the same armament and has thick rubbing fenders on the hull sides in the bow area.

♦ **2 Takatsuki-class (130-ton) short-endurance cutters**

	Bldr	Laid down	L	In serv.
PS 108 Takatsuki	Sumidigawa, Tokyo	. . .	. . .	23-3-92
PS 109 Nobaru	Hitachi, Kanagawa	8-9-92	27-1-93	22-3-93

Takatsuki (PS 108) Mitsuhiro Kadota, 5-01

D: 114 tons (180 fl) **S:** 35 kts **Dim:** 35.0 × 6.70 × 1.20
A: 1 12.7-mm mg **Electronics:** Radar: 1 . . . nav.
M: 2 MTU 16V396 TB 94 diesels; 2 KaMeWa 71 waterjets; 5,300 bhp
Crew: 10 tot.

Remarks: An improved version of the *Akagi* class, incorporating outdrive surface-piercing propulsors. Have infrared surveillance and low-light t.v. cameras atop the pilothouse. PS 108 is based at Uwajima and performs SAR and fisheries protection duties.

♦ **7 Akagi-class (130-ton) short-endurance cutters**

	Bldr	Laid down	L	In serv.
PS 101 Akagi	Sumidigawa, Tokyo	31-7-79	5-12-79	26-3-80
PS 102 Tsukuba	Sumidigawa, Tokyo	7-7-81	29-10-81	24-2-82
PS 103 Kongo	Ishihara DY, Takasago	1-8-86	17-12-86	16-3-87
PS 104 Katsuragai	Yokohama Yacht	14-10-87	21-1-88	24-3-88
PS 105 Hiromine	Ishihara DY, Takasago	. . .	8-1-88	24-3-88
PS 106 Shizuki	Sumidigawa, Tokyo	26-10-87	21-12-87	24-3-88
PS 107 Takashio	Sumidigawa, Tokyo	28-10-87	23-12-87	24-3-88

D: 105 tons light; 134 tons normal (189 fl) **S:** 26.5 kts
Dim: 35.0 (33.0 wl) × 6.3 × 1.3
A: 1 12.7-mm mg **Electronics:** Radar: 1 . . . nav.
M: 2 Fuji-Pielstick 16 PA4 V185 VG diesels; 2 props; 4,800 bhp
Electric: 40 kVA tot. **Range:** 570/20 **Crew:** 12 tot.

COAST GUARD PATROL CRAFT [WPC] *(continued)*

Kongo (PS 103) Takatoshi Okano, 9-00

Akagi (PS 101) Mitsuhiro Kadota, 5-01

Remarks: Carry a 25-man rubber rescue dinghy. The machinegun can be interchanged with a firefighting water cannon. PS 104 and PS 105 are optimized for service on Japan's Inland Sea and have longer superstructures and an enlarged pilothouse. First five have glass-reinforced plastic hulls and 4-day endurance; PS 106 and PS 107 have a 4.0-m-molded-depth, aluminum alloy hull of deep-vee form and are powered by two Ikegai-MTU 16V652 TB 81 diesels: 4,400 bhp for 27 kts; they have two 60-kVA generators.

♦ 1 Kagayuki-class (32-meter) coastal patrol craft
Bldr: Mitsubishi, Shimonoseki

	Laid down	L	In serv.
PC 105 Hamayuki (ex-*Kagayuki*)	16-3-99	28-9-99	24-12-99

Hamayuki (PC 105)—gray hull, white superstructure Takatoshi Okano, 4-00

D: 100 tons (. . . fl) **S:** 36 kts **Dim:** 32.0 × 6.50 × . . .
A: 1 12.7-mm mg **Electronics:** Radar: 1 . . . nav.
M: 2 . . . diesels; 2 waterjets; 5,200 bhp **Crew:** 30 tot.

Remarks: PC 105 was approved under the FY 99 budget. Completed with rubbing fenders on the hull sides forward, but they had been removed by 4-00. Name was changed on 22-2-01.

♦ 1 Matsunami-class (35-meter) coastal patrol craft
Bldr: Mitsubishi, Shimonoseki (In serv. 22-2-95)

PC 01 Matsunami

Matsunami (PC 01) Takatoshi Okano, 5-01

D: 165 tons (204 fl) **S:** 28.3 kts (25 sust.) **Dim:** 38.00 (35.50 wl) × 8.0 × . . .
A: none **Electronics:** Radar: 1 . . . nav.
M: 2 . . . . . . diesels; 2 waterjets; 5,300 bhp **Range:** 7,000/14 **Crew:** 30 tot.

Remarks: Yacht-like unit with three-level superstructure. Built under the FY 93 program, PC 01 is configured as an oceanographic research craft for the emperor. Internal fittings are luxurious, and the craft is, in effect, the imperial yacht.

♦ 4 Asogiri-class (30-meter) coastal patrol craft

	Bldr	Laid down	L	In serv.
PC 101 Asogiri	Yokohama Yacht	12-5-94	7-10-94	19-12-94
PC 102 Murozuki	Ishihara DY	21-9-94	6-6-95	27-7-95
PC 103 Wakagumo	Sumidigawa, Tokyo	12-3-96	. . .-96	17-7-96
PC 104 Naozuki	Sumidigawa, Tokyo	. . .	14-10-96	23-1-97

Murozuki (PC 102) *Ships of the World,* 1995

D: 101 tons normal **S:** 30 kts **Dim:** 33.00 × 6.30 × 2.00
A: 1 12.7-mm M2 mg **Electronics:** Radar: 1 . . . nav.
M: 2 diesels; 2 props; 5,200 bhp **Crew:** . . .

Remarks: Have an infrared/t.v. optronic surveillance system. The machinegun is not normally mounted. Are painted with gray hull sides and white superstructures.

♦ 15 Hayanami-class (35-meter) coastal patrol craft

	Bldr	Laid down	L	In serv.
PC 11 Hayanami	Sumidigawa, Tokyo	9-9-92	7-1-93	25-3-93
PC 12 Setogiri (ex-*Shikinami*)	Sumidigawa, Tokyo	21-7-93	13-10-93	24-3-94
PC 13 Mizunami	Ishihara DY, Takasago	30-7-93	27-12-93	24-3-94
PC 14 Ionami	Sumidigawa, Tokyo	9-12-93	11-4-94	30-6-94
PC 15 Kurinami	Sumidigawa, Tokyo	10-3-94	3-10-94	30-1-95
PC 16 Hamanami	Sumidigawa, Tokyo	29-8-95	. . .	28-3-96
PC 17 Shinonome	Sumidigawa, Tokyo	29-8-95	. . .	29-2-96
PC 18 Haruname	Ishihara DY, Takasago	4-9-95	. . .	28-3-96
PC 19 Kiyozuki	Ishihara DY, Takasago	4-9-95	. . .	23-2-96
PC 20 Ayanami	Yokohama Yacht	13-9-95	. . .	28-3-96
PC 21 Tokinami	Yokohama Yacht	13-9-95	. . .	28-3-96
PC 22 Hamagumo	Sumidigawa, Tokyo	2-12-98	16-4-99	27-8-99
PC 23 Awanami	Sumidigawa, Tokyo	2-12-98	14-5-99	27-8-99
PC 24 Uranami	Sumidigawa, Tokyo	10-3-99	3-10-99	24-1-00
PC 25 Shikinami	Sumidigawa, Tokyo	7-4-00	4-8-00	24-10-00

D: 113 tons normal **S:** 25 kts **Dim:** 35.00 × 6.30 × 1.20
A: none **Electronics:** Radar: 1 . . . nav.
M: 2 . . . . . . diesels; 2 props; 4,000 bhp
Range: . . ./. . . **Crew:** 13 tot.

COAST GUARD PATROL CRAFT [WPC] *(continued)*

Hamanami (PC 16)—early group, without firefighting mast
Takatoshi Okano, 10-00

Shikinami (PC 25)—later version, with firefighting mast
Mitsuhiro Kadota, 5-01

Remarks: Two firefighting water cannon are mounted abreast on the foredeck, and there is no fitting for a machinegun mount. All have infrared and low-light-level t.v. surveillance sensors atop the pilothouse. PC 22 and later have a tall telescoping mast supporting a firefighting water monitor, a second monitor atop the pilothouse, and a maximum speed of 24 kts. The name for PC 12 was changed on 10-10-00. Are painted white.

♦ 23 Murakomo-class (30-meter) coastal patrol craft

	Bldr	In serv.
PC 201 Murakomo	Mitsubishi, Shimonoseki	24-3-78
PC 202 Kitagumo	Hitachi, Kanagawa	17-3-78
PC 203 Yukigumo	Hitachi, Kanagawa	27-9-78
PC 204 Asagumo	Mitsubishi, Shimonoseki	21-9-78
PC 205 Hayagumo	Mitsubishi, Shimonoseki	30-1-79
PC 206 Akigumo	Hitachi, Kanagawa	28-2-79
PC 207 Yaegumo	Mitsubishi, Shimonoseki	16-3-79
PC 208 Natsugumo	Hitachi, Kanagawa	22-3-79
PC 209 Yamagiri	Hitachi, Kanagawa	29-6-79
PC 210 Kawagiri	Hitachi, Kanagawa	27-7-79
PC 211 Bizan (ex-*Teruzuki*)	Maizuru Heavy Ind.	26-6-79
PC 212 Natsuzuki	Maizuru Heavy Ind.	26-7-79
PC 213 Miyazuki	Hitachi, Kanagawa	13-3-80
PC 214 Nijigumo	Mitsubishi, Shimonoseki	29-1-81
PC 215 Tatsugumo	Mitsubishi, Shimonoseki	19-3-81
PC 216 Iseyuki (ex-*Hamayuki*)	Hitachi, Kanagawa	27-2-81
PC 217 Isonami	Mitsubishi, Shimonoseki	19-3-81
PC 218 Nagozuki	Hitachi, Kanagawa	29-1-81
PC 219 Yaezuki	Hitachi, Kanagawa	19-3-81
PC 220 Yamayuki	Hitachi, Kanagawa	16-2-82
PC 221 Komayuki	Mitsubishi, Shimonoseki	10-2-82
PC 222 Asagiri	Mitsubishi, Shimonoseki	17-2-82
PC 223 Umigiri	Hitachi, Kanagawa	23-2-83

D: 88 tons light; 125 tons normal (149 fl) **S:** 31 kts
Dim: 31.0 (28.5 pp) × 6.3 × 1.17
A: 1 12.7-mm M2 mg **Electronics:** Radar: 1 . . . nav.
M: 2 Ikegai MTU 16V652 TB81 diesels; 2 props; 4,800 bhp (4,400 sust.)
Electric: 40 kVA tot. **Range:** 350/28 **Crew:** 10 tot.

Remarks: The name for PC 216 was changed on 22-2-01 and that of PC 211 during 1999. Hull sides are painted gray and superstructures white. Have a firefighting monitor on the foredeck, to port.

Yamayuki (PC 220)
Mitsuhiro Kadota, 5-01

♦ 2 Natsugiri-class (23-meter) coastal patrol craft
Bldr: Ishihara Dockyard (In serv. 29-1-90)

PC 86 Natsugiri PC 87 Suganami

Natsugiri (PC 86)
Mitsuhiro Kadota, 5-01

D: 55 tons (68 fl) **S:** 27.5 kts **Dim:** 27.0 × 5.6 × 1.2
A: none **Electronics:** Radar: 1 . . . nav.
M: 2 . . . . . . diesels; 2 props; 3,000 bhp **Electric:** 40 kVA tot. (2 × 20 kVA)
Range: 200/. . . **Crew:** 9 tot.

Remarks: Put in the FY 1988 budget for service in the Yokosuka area as a result of the poor performance of earlier 23-m-series patrol craft during the rescue efforts after the collision of the submarine *Nadashio* (SS 577) with a fishing boat. Have longer hulls and greater propeller tip clearance to reduce pitching. Are painted white.

♦ 3 Shimagiri-class (23-meter) coastal patrol craft
Bldr: Mitsubishi, Shimonoseki

	In serv.		In serv.
PC 83 Shimagiri	7-2-84	PC 85 Hayagiri	22-2-85
PC 84 Okinami (ex-*Setogiri*)	22-3-85		

Hayagiri (PC 85)
Ships of the World, 12-00

D: 40 tons (50 fl) **S:** 30 kts **Dim:** 23.00 × 5.30 × 1.12
A: PC 85 only: 1 20-mm 70-cal. Oerlikon AA
Electronics: Radar: 1 FRA 10 Mk 2 nav.
M: 3 Mitsubishi 12V175RTC diesels; 3 props; 3,000 bhp **Electric:** 40 kVA
Range: 250/21.5 **Crew:** 10 tot.

♦ 9 Akizuki-class (23-meter) coastal patrol craft
Bldr: Mitsubishi, Shimonoseki

	In serv.		In serv.
PC 72 Urayuki	31-5-75	PC 79 Shimanami	23-12-77
PC 75 Hatagumo	21-2-76	PC 80 Yuzuki	22-3-79
PC 76 Makigumo	21-2-76	PC 81 Tamanami (ex-*Hanayuki*)	27-3-81
PC 77 Hamazuki	29-11-76		
PC 78 Isozuki	18-3-77	PC 82 Awagiri	27-12-82

COAST GUARD PATROL CRAFT [WPC] *(continued)*

Urayuki (PC 72) Mitsuhiro Kadota, 4-01

D: 77 tons light; 110 tons normal (123.7 fl) **S:** 22.1 kts
Dim: 26.00 × 6.30 × 1.12
A: none **Electronics:** Radar: 1 FRA 10 Mk 2 nav.
M: 3 Mitsubishi 12 DM 20 MTK diesels; 3 props; 3,000 bhp
Electric: 40 kVA **Range:** 290/21.5 **Crew:** 10 tot.

Remarks: All have a folding rescue platform at the waterline on the starboard side. Aluminum hull construction.
Disposals: *Shinonome* (PC 65) was stricken in 1996, *Akizuki* (PC 64) on 11-3-96, and *Iseyuki* (PC 73) on 22-2-01.

Disposal note: Of units of the *Shikinami* (23-meter) class, *Shikinami* (PC 54) was stricken 7-3-94; *Isenami* (PC 57) on 13-6-94; *Tomonami* (PC 55) on 2-12-94; *Takanami* (PC 58) on 13-1-95; *Wakanami* (PC 56) in 1-95; *Kiyozuki* (PC 62) on 8-2-96; *Mochizuki* (PC 60), *Haruzuki* (PC 61), and *Urazuki* (PC 63) on 11-3-96; *Wakagumo* (PC 71) on 28-6-96; *Mutsuki* (PC 59) early in 1997; *Tamanami* (PC 67) and *Minegumo* (PC 68) on 12-8-99; *Kiyonami* (PC 69) on 8-12-99; *Uranami* (PC 66) on 7-1-00; *Okinami* (PC 70) on 9-10-00; and *Asoyuki* (PC 74) during 2001.

PATROL BOATS [WPB]

♦ 109 Suzukaze-class (20-meter) inshore patrol boats

	Bldr	Laid down	L	In serv.
CL 11 Suzukaze	Sumidigawa, Tokyo	. . .	. . .	20-2-92
CL 12 Asakaze	Ishihara DY, Takasago	. . .	. . .	9-3-92
CL 13 Sugikaze	Yokohama Yacht	. . .	. . .	28-2-92
CL 14 Fujikaze	Shinki Zosen, Osaka	. . .	. . .	24-3-92
CL 15 Miyakaze	Wakamatsu Zosen	. . .	. . .	25-3-92
CL 16 Hibakaze	Kiso Zosen	. . .	. . .	19-3-92
CL 17 Satakaze	Nagasaki Zosen	. . .	. . .	25-3-92
CL 18 Tomakaze	Sumidigawa, Tokyo	6-8-92	26-11-92	22-1-93
CL 19 Yurikaze	Sumidigawa, Tokyo	6-8-92	25-12-92	8-2-93
CL 20 Fusakaze	Yokohama Yacht	18-8-92	7-1-93	24-2-93
CL 21 Umekaze	Shinki Zosen, Osaka	18-8-92	17-2-93	25-3-93
CL 22 Shigikaze	Ishihara DY, Takasago	19-8-92	30-11-92	22-1-93
CL 23 Uzukaze	Ishihara DY, Takasago	19-8-92	12-1-93	16-2-93
CL 24 Akikaze	Nagasaki Zosen	18-9-92	27-1-93	26-2-93
CL 25 Kurekaze	Kiso Zosen	3-9-92	27-1-93	26-2-93
CL 26 Mojikaze	Wakamatsu Zosen	30-9-92	4-2-93	22-3-93
CL 27 Sodekaze	Yokohama Yacht	7-1-93	26-2-93	31-3-93
CL 28 Kinukaze	Nagasaki Zosen	7-1-93	26-2-93	29-3-93
CL 29 Mayakaze	Ishihara DY, Takasago	7-1-93	2-3-93	29-3-93
CL 30 Setokaze	Nagasaki Zosen	7-1-93	26-2-93	29-3-93
CL 31 Makikaze	Sumidigawa, Tokyo	2-2-93	24-5-93	28-6-93
CL 32 Himekaze	Ishihara DY, Takasago	2-2-93	28-5-93	29-6-93
CL 33 Kugakaze	Kiso Zosen	19-1-93	3-6-93	28-6-93
CL 34 Kamikaze	Ishihara DY, Takasago	8-7-93	12-93	24-1-94
CL 35 Umikaze	Yokohama Yacht	8-7-93	12-93	27-1-94
CL 36 Kirikaze	Yokohama Yacht	8-7-93	12-93	4-2-94
CL 37 Hakaze	Shinki Zosen, Osaka	9-7-93	12-93	14-2-94
CL 38 Shachikaze	Shinki Zosen, Osaka	9-7-93	12-93	25-1-94
CL 39 Isekaze	Wakamatsu Zosen	14-7-93	12-93	24-3-94
CL 40 Nijikaze (ex-*Komakaze*)	Nagasaki Zosen	21-7-93	12-93	27-1-94
CL 41 Kishikaze	Nagasaki Zosen	21-7-93	12-93	4-2-94
CL 42 Kikukaze	Ishihara DY, Takasago	9-9-93	10-2-94	24-3-94
CL 43 Otokaze	Yokohama Yacht	9-9-93	23-2-94	29-3-94
CL 44 Hirokaze	Nagasaki Zosen	3-9-93	16-2-94	29-3-94
CL 45 Ashikaze	Kiso Zosen	28-9-93	28-2-94	29-3-94
CL 46 Toyokaze	Sumidigawa, Tokyo	27-7-93	13-1-94	24-3-94
CL 47 Satsukaze	Nagasaki Zosen	21-7-93	12-10-94	4-2-94
CL 48 Shiokaze	Yokohama Yacht	8-2-94	9-6-94	14-7-94
CL 49 Awakaze	Yokohama Yacht	8-2-94	9-6-94	14-7-94
CL 50 Hamakaze	Sumidigawa, Tokyo	10-2-94	9-6-94	28-7-94
CL 51 Miokaze	Shinki Zosen, Osaka	1-2-94	30-5-94	22-7-94
CL 52 Tomokaze	Kiso Zosen	2-2-94	24-6-94	26-7-94
CL 53 Kibikaze	Sumidigawa, Tokyo	10-2-94	21-6-94	28-7-94
CL 54 Nachikaze	Ishihara DY, Takasago	25-1-94	30-6-94	29-7-94
CL 55 Mitsukaze	Ishihara DY, Takasago	25-1-94	23-6-94	29-7-94
CL 56 Hatakaze	Wakamatsu Zosen	7-2-94	15-6-94	29-7-94
CL 57 Sekikaze	Nagasaki Zosen	8-2-94	15-6-94	29-7-94
CL 58 Terukaze	Kiso Zosen	2-6-94	1-12-94	27-1-95
CL 59 Shimakaze	Wakamatsu Zosen	30-5-94	12-12-94	31-1-95
CL 60 Sasakaze	Yokohama Yacht	30-5-94	1-12-94	31-1-95
CL 61 Kiikaze	Ishihara DY, Takasago	12-5-94	8-12-94	26-1-95
CL 62 Ikikaze	Shinki Zosen, Osaka	13-5-94	1-11-94	27-1-95
CL 63 Minekaze	Sumidigawa, Tokyo	10-5-94	28-11-94	27-1-95
CL 64 Torikaze	Sumidigawa, Tokyo	10-5-94	31-10-94	26-1-95
CL 65 Amakaze	Nagasaki Zosen	31-5-94	30-11-94	30-1-95
CL 66 Aokaze	Nagasaki Zosen	31-5-94	16-11-94	30-1-95
CL 67 Kunikaze (ex-*Ogikaze*)	Ishihara DY, Takasago	12-5-94	30-11-94	31-1-95
CL 68 Tachikaze	Yokohama Yacht	30-5-94	1-11-94	31-1-95
CL 69 Deigo	Ishihara DY, Takasago	28-2-95	19-9-95	28-9-95
CL 70 Yuna	Sumidigawa, Tokyo	28-2-95	22-9-95	1-11-95
CL 71 Adan	Nagasaki Zosen	1-3-95	9-95	13-11-95
CL 72 Kijikaze	Kiso Zosen	. . .	15-2-96	28-3-96
CL 73 Hatsukaze	Nagasaki Zosen	1-8-95	. . .	29-2-96
CL 74 Yurakaze	Nagasaki Zosen	1-8-95	10-1-96	19-3-96
CL 75 Hinokaze (ex-*Yanakaze*)	Shinki Zosen, Osaka	1-8-95	. . .	22-3-96
CL 76 Tosatsubaki (ex-*Washikaze*)	Kiso Zosen	29-8-95	. . .	22-3-96
CL 77 Mutsukaze	Sumidigawa, Tokyo	29-8-95	6-2-96	28-3-96
CL 78 Tonekaze	Nagasaki Zosen	22-12-95	27-2-96	29-3-96
CL 79 Shizukaze	Wakamatsu, Kitakyushu	18-12-95	31-1-96	28-3-96
CL 80 Komakaze	Shinki Zosen, Osaka	19-12-95	22-2-96	28-3-96
CL 81 Yukikaze	Yokohama Yacht	25-1-96	23-4-96	30-7-96
CL 82 Nakakaze	Yokohama Yacht	25-1-96	26-4-96	30-7-96
CL 83 Kawakaze	Kiso Zosen	21-12-95	19-3-96	19-6-96
CL 84 Kiyokaze	Ishihara DY, Takasago	11-1-96	26-4-96	30-7-96
CL 85 Hikokaze	Sumidigawa, Tokyo	21-1-96	19-3-96	28-6-96
CL 86 Osakaze	Wakamatsu, Kitakyushu	18-12-95	22-3-96	19-6-96
CL 87 Wakakaze	Shinki Zosen, Osaka	12-1-96	26-4-96	31-7-96
CL 88 Ikekaze	Yokohama Yacht	25-12-95	22-3-96	28-6-96
CL 89 Nomokaze	Nagasaki Zosen	22-12-95	25-3-96	28-6-96
CL 90 Yumikaze	Shinki Zosen, Osaka	19-12-95	29-3-96	28-6-96
CL 91 Kumakaze	Yokohama Yacht	25-12-95	19-3-96	28-6-96
CL 92 Harukaze	Ishihara DY, Takasago	. . .	2-8-96	1-11-96
CL 93 Hoshikaze	Ishihara DY, Takasago	. . .	. . .	18-11-96
CL 94 Oitsukaze	Kiso Zosen	12-3-97	2-9-97	25-11-97
CL 95 Kochikaze	Ishihara DY, Takasago	12-3-97	5-9-97	25-11-97
CL 96 Hamanasu	Sumidigawa, Tokyo	18-3-97	17-9-97	18-12-97
CL 97 Akashia	Sumidigawa, Tokyo	18-3-97	17-9-97	18-12-97
CL 98 Tosamizuki	Shinki Zosen, Osaka	13-3-97	17-9-97	18-12-97
CL 99 Okikaze	Yokohama Yacht	12-3-97	29-9-97	18-12-97
CL 100 Sachikaze	Wakamatsu, Kitakyushu	18-3-97	11-9-97	18-12-97
CL 101 Ogikaze	Yokohama Yacht	12-3-97	29-9-97	18-12-97
CL 102 Natsuzaze	Nagasaki Zosen	12-3-97	25-9-97	18-12-97
CL 103 Sawakaze	Sumidigawa, Tokyo	16-12-98	16-2-99	31-3-99
CL 104 Benibana	Sumidigawa, Tokyo	16-12-98	22-2-99	31-3-99
CL 105 Yamazakura	Yokohama Yacht	16-12-98	26-2-99	30-3-99
CL 106 Kaido	Yokohama Yacht	16-12-98	26-2-99	30-3-99
CL 107 Sazanka	Yokohama Yacht	16-12-98	26-2-99	30-3-99
CL 108 Aoi	. . .	16-12-98	10-2-99	31-1-99
CL 109 Suisen	Sumidigawa, Tokyo	16-12-98	24-2-99	31-3-99
CL 110 Yaezakura	Kiso Zosen	16-12-98	23-2-99	30-3-99
CL 111 Yanakaze	Ishihara DY, Takasago	16-12-98	25-2-99	30-3-99
CL 112 Yukitsubaki	Sumidigawa, Tokyo	16-12-98	8-2-99	31-3-99
CL 113 Washikaze	Ishihara DY, Takasago	16-12-98	4-3-99	30-3-99
CL 114 Nogekaze	Ishihara DY, Takasago	27-10-99	15-2-00	9-3-00
CL 115 Imakaze	Nagasaki Zosen	11-12-00	28-2-01	30-3-01
CL 116 Komakusa	. . .	18-12-00	3-3-01	30-3-01
CL 117 Shiragiku	Ishihara DY, Takasago	20-12-00	26-2-01	30-3-01
CL 118 Katsukaze	Yokohama Yacht	27-12-00	23-2-01	29-3-01
CL 119 Satsuke	. . .	20-12-00	2-3-01	30-3-01

Amakaze (CL 65)—first to be repainted all white Takatoshi Okano, 9-00

COAST GUARD PATROL BOATS [WPB] *(continued)*

Shizukaze (CL 79)—in original gray-hulled paint scheme
Mitsuhiro Kadota, 5-01

D: 19 tons (23 fl) **S:** 30 kts **Dim:** 20.00 × 4.30 × 1.00
A: 1 12.7-mm mg or none **Electronics:** Radar: 1 . . . nav.
M: 2 M.A.N. D-2842LYE diesels; 2 props; 1,820 bhp
Range: 160/30 **Crew:** 5 tot.

Remarks: Replacements for *Chiyokaze* class. Gun is interchangeable with a fire-fighting water cannon; usually they carry neither. Had white superstructures and gray hulls without the stylized blue "S" as completed, but CL 65 was repainted all white (with the "S") in 9-00, and CL 119 was completed that way. Some, including CL 53 and CL 59, have been fitted with fendering at the bows. Five more were requested under the FY 01 budget but not approved.

♦ 4 Isokaze-class (15-meter) inshore patrol boats
Bldr: Yokohama Yacht

CL 01 Isokaze (In serv. 23-3-89)
CL 02 Hayakaze (In serv. 23-3-89)
CL 03 Nadakaze (In serv. 15-3-91)
CL 04 Kotokaze (In serv. 15-3-91)

Nadakaze (CL 03)
Takatoshi Okano, 9-00

D: 18–19 tons (22.8–23.0 fl) **S:** 20 (CL 03, 04: 29) kts **Dim:** 18.00 × 4.30 × . . .
A: none **Electronics:** Radar: 1 . . . nav.
M: CL 01, 02: 2 Nissan RD10-TA06 diesels; 2 props; 900 bhp—CL 03, 04: 2 . . . . . . diesels; 2 props; 1,400 bhp
Range: 180/19 (CL 03, 04: 150/29) **Crew:** 5 (CL 03, 04: 6) tot.

Remarks: Revised *Yamayuri* design, with higher superstructure and finer hull lines. CL 01 and 02 were laid down 20-9-88 and launched 7-2-89; CL 03 and 04, laid down 17-9-90 and launched 8-2-91. Second pair is considered a separate class, displacing more and having more-powerful engines.

♦ 52 Yamayuri-class (15-meter) inshore patrol boats
Bldrs: A: Ishihara DY, Takasago; B: Sumidigawa, Tokyo; C: Yokohama Yacht; D: Shinki Zosen, Osaka; E: Nobutaka SY; F: Shigi SY, Sakai

	Bldr	In serv.		Bldr	In serv.
CL 205 Yaguruma	B	31-7-79	CL 215 Hamagiku	C	19-9-79
CL 206 Miyagiku (ex-*Hamanasu*)	B	29-9-79	CL 216 Fuyume	A	30-7-79
			CL 217 Tsubaki	A	10-8-79
CL 207 Suzuran	B	31-7-79	CL 222 Akebi	A	29-10-79
CL 208 Isogiku	B	12-9-79	CL 223 Shirahagi	B	25-1-80
CL 209 Isegiko	B	31-8-79	CL 226 Tsutsuji	B	22-2-80
CL 210 Ayame	C	29-10-79	CL 227 Ashibi	A	20-12-79
CL 211 Ajisai	C	26-9-79	CL 228 Satozakura	A	26-2-80
CL 212 Himawari	C	29-10-79	CL 231 Ezogiku	C	18-11-80
CL 213 Hazakura	C	29-8-79	CL 232 Hayagiku (ex-*Akashio*)	B	18-11-80
CL 214 Hinagiku	A	9-7-79			

	Bldr	In serv.		Bldr	In serv.
CL 233 Kozakura	C	18-11-80	CL 249 Mokuren	D	25-1-83
CL 234 Shirame	A	28-11-80	CL 250 Isofuji	A	7-3-83
CL 235 Sarubia	A	28-11-80	CL 251 Tamatsubaki	B	26-1-84
CL 236 Suiren	D	19-12-80	CL 252 Yodoki	D	22-11-83
CL 237 Hatsugiku	A	29-1-81	CL 253 Iozakura	A	25-11-83
CL 238 Hamayura	A	29-1-80	CL 254 Himetsubaki	A	18-1-84
CL 239 Airisu	C	18-2-82	CL 255 Tokikusa	B	24-2-84
CL 240 Yamabuki	B	17-12-81	CL 256 Mutsugiku	B	15-11-84
CL 241 Shirayuri	E	1-2-82	CL 257 Terugiko	F	19-12-84
CL 242 Karatachi	A	17-12-81	CL 258 Mayazakura	A	20-12-84
CL 243 Kobai	A	18-2-82	CL 259 Yamagiko	C	22-1-85
CL 244 Hamayuu	A	29-1-82	CL 260 Tobiume	A	24-1-85
CL 245 Sasayuri	B	25-1-83	CL 261 Kotozakura	B	28-2-85
CL 246 Kosumosu	A	17-2-83	CL 262 Minogiku	A	14-2-85
CL 247 Takagiku (ex-*Shiogiku*)	B	29-11-82	CL 263 Kuroyuri	C	15-11-84
			CL 264 Chiyogiku	F	8-3-88
CL 248 Yamahagi	C	29-11-82			

Minogiku (CL 262)—standard version
Takatoshi Okano, 9-00

Isofuji (CL 250)—waterjet-propelled version
Ships of the World, 1996

D: 27 tons light; 35.7 tons normal (40.3 fl) **S:** 20 kts
Dim: 18.00 (16.60 wl) × 4.30 × 0.82 (1.10 props)
A: small arms **Electronics:** Radar: 1 . . . nav.
M: 2 RD10T AO6 diesels; 2 props; 900 bhp
Range: 180/19 **Crew:** 6 tot.

Remarks: Have three water cannon for fire fighting. CL 250 and CL 252–CL 263 have waterjets vice propellers and can make 21.9 kts; their engines are type S6A-MTK (450 bhp each), and the craft are externally distinguishable by having their pilothouses set closer to amidships and by the protective frame over the waterjet effluxes at the stern. The final unit, CL 264, reverted to the original propulsion plant. CL 240 also has a modified pilothouse.
Disposals: *Sazanka* (CL 218) and *Yaezakura* (CL 221) were stricken 16-3-99; *Aoi* (CL 219), *Suisen* (CL 220), *Benibana* (CL 224), and *Yukisubaki* (CL 229) on 17-3-99; *Yamayuri* (CL 201) on 25-2-00; *Muratsubaki* (CL 225) on 15-3-01; and *Tachibana* (CL 202), *Komakusa* (CL 203), *Shiragiku* (CL 204), and *Satsuki* (CL 230) on 16-3-01.

♦ 2 Hayate-class (12-meter) guard boats
Bldr: Yokohama Yacht (In serv. 21-12-87)

GS 01 Hayate GS 02 Inazuma

D: 7.9 tons (8.2 fl) **S:** 30 kts **Dim:** 12.20 (11.90 pp) × 3.20 × 1.5
M: 2 . . . diesels; 2 props; 580 bhp **Range:** 195/28 **Crew:** 8 tot.

Remarks: Ordered 9-6-87. Hull molded depth: 1.5 m. Officially typed "Guard Boats, Small" and used at Kansai International Harbor until 1996, when they were transferred to the Osaka Special Security Base. Aluminum hulls.

Note: The coast guard ordered 30 6-m Avon Searider rigid inflatable launches during spring 2000 for use in patrolling waters off Okinawa during an economic summit; the craft are powered by two 90-bhp Yamaha gasoline outboard engines.

COAST GUARD PATROL BOATS [WPB] *(continued)*

Hayate (GS 01)—with fenders added at the bow *Ships of the World,* 7-94

AUXILIARIES

♦ 1 Tsushima-class navigational aids tender [WAG]

	Bldr	Laid down	L	In serv.
LL 01 Tsushima	Mitsui, Tamano	10-6-76	7-4-77	9-9-77

Tsushima (LL 01) Mitsuhiro Kadota, 5-01

D: 1,718 tons light (2,055 fl) **S:** 16 kts (17.6 trials)
Dim: 75.00 (70.00 wl) × 12.50 × 4.15 **Electronics:** Radar: 2 . . . nav.
M: 1 Fuji-Sulzer 8S 40C diesel; 1 CP prop; 4,200 bhp—bow-thruster
Electric: 900 kVA tot. **Range:** 12,000/15 **Fuel:** 477 tons **Crew:** 54 tot.

Remarks: Intended for use as a lighthouse supply ship and also has equipment to test the luminosity of lighthouses and other navigational lights and to test the accuracy of radio navaids; is not equipped to lay or recover navigational aid buoys. Has Flume-type passive stabilization tanks in the after part of the superstructure. Intelsat SATCOM was added in 1988 and SHF SATCOM capability by 1992. Based at Tsushima.

♦ 3 Hokuto-class navigational buoy tenders [WAGL]

	Bldr	Laid down	L	In serv.
LL 11 Hokuto	Sasebo DY	19-10-78	20-3-79	29-6-79
LL 12 Kaio	Sasebo DY	17-7-79	20-10-79	11-3-80
LL 13 Ginga	Kawasaki, Kobe	13-6-79	16-11-79	18-3-80

Hokuto (LL 11) Mitsuhiro Kadota, 5-01

D: 620 tons light (839 fl) **S:** 13.8 kts **Dim:** 55.00 (51.00 wl) × 10.60 × 2.65
M: 2 Asakasa MH23 (LL 11: Hanshin 6L 24SH) diesels; 2 props; 1,400 bhp
Electric: 300 kVA tot. **Range:** 3,460/13 **Fuel:** 62 tons
Crew: 9 officers, 20 enlisted + 2 technicians

Remarks: Intended to recover, service, and redeploy heavy navigational buoys.

Note: The Japan Coast Guard's other buoy tender, the smaller *Miyojo* (LM 11) is described in the Service Craft section.

♦ 1 Shoyo-class survey ship [WAGS]

	Bldr	Laid down	L	In serv.
HL 01 Shoyo	Mitsui, Tamano	4-10-96	23-6-97	20-3-98

Shoyo (HL 01) Mitsuhiro Kadota, 4-00

D: 3,128 tons (fl) **S:** 17 kts (16.5 sust.) **Dim:** 98.00 × 15.20 × 3.60
M: . . . . . diesels, electric drive; 2 CP props; 5,600 shp
Range: 12,000/16.5 **Crew:** 37 tot.

Remarks: Replaced the former *Shoyo* (HL 01). Name can also be rendered *Shouyou.* Carries a 10-m survey boat equipped with a Reson Seabat 9001S mapping sonar. Principal mapping sonar is the U.S.-made Sea Beam 2112, 12-kHz system. Carries 6-ton, 10-m Manbo-II-class inshore survey launches capable of maintaining 10 kts. Has Flume-type passive tank stabilization system. No helicopter facilities.

♦ 2 Meiyo-class survey ships [WAGS]

	Bldr	Laid down	L	In serv.
HL 03 Meiyo	Kawasaki, Kobe	24-7-89	29-6-90	24-10-90
HL 05 Kaiyo	Mitsubishi, Shimonoseki	7-7-92	26-4-93	7-10-93

Meiyo (HL 03) Mitsuhiro Kadota, 7-00

D: 550 tons light; 621 tons normal (1,035 fl) **S:** 15 kts **Dim:** 60.00 × 10.5 × 3.0
Electronics: Radar: 2 . . . nav.
M: 2 Daihatsu 6 DLM-24S(L) diesels; 2 CP props; 2,200 bhp—bow-thruster
Electric: 480 kw tot. (2 × 160-kw shaft gen., 2 × 80-kw diesel sets)
Range: 5,000/14.5 **Crew:** 38 tot.

Remarks: 1,096 grt. Carry the same survey equipment as the larger *Takuyo* (HL 02), plus the 11,000-m-depth, 12-kHz U.S.-made Sea Beam 2112 mapping sonar. Navigation equipment includes Loran-C, GPS, and doppler log. Carry a 16-m survey launch to port. Have Flume-type, superstructure-mounted passive roll-damping, and also pitch-damping tanks. The engines are on sound-damping mountings.

♦ 1 Tenyo-class survey ship [WAGS]

	Bldr	Laid down	L	In serv.
HL 04 Tenyo	Sumitomo, Uraga	11-4-86	5-8-86	27-11-86

D: 435 tons light (770 fl) **S:** 14.2 kts **Dim:** 56.0 × 9.8 × 2.9
Electronics: Radar: 2 JMA 1596 nav.
M: 2 Akasaka MH23 diesels; 2 CP props; 1,300 bhp
Electric: 320 kVA (2 × 160-kVA diesel sets) **Range:** 5,400/12
Crew: 38 tot. (18 officers, 25 enlisted accomm.)

COAST GUARD AUXILIARIES *(continued)*

Tenyo (HL 04) *Ships of the World,* 1995

Remarks: 430 grt. Carries one 10-m survey boat. Has superstructure-mounted passive tank stabilization. Survey equipment includes the 11,000-m-depth-capable, 12-kHz Sea Beam mapping sonar. Homeported at Tokyo.

♦ 1 Takuyo-class (2,600-ton) survey ship [WAGS]

	Bldr	Laid down	L	In serv.
HL 02 Takuyo	Nippon Kokan, Tsurumi	14-4-82	24-3-83	31-8-83

Takuyo (HL 02) Mitsuhiro Kadota, 5-01

D: 2,481 tons light; 2,979 tons normal (3,370 fl) **S:** 18.2 kts
Dim: 96.00 (90.00 wl) × 14.20 × 4.51 (mean; 4.91 max. over sonar)
Electronics: Radar: 2 . . . nav.
M: 2 Fuji 6S40B diesels; 2 CP props; 5,200 bhp—bow-thruster
Electric: 965 kVA tot. **Range:** 12,800/16.9 **Endurance:** 50 days
Crew: 24 officers, 36 enlisted + 22 survey party

Remarks: 2,481 grt. Has U.S.-made Sea Beam 210 12-kHz, side-looking, contour-mapping sonars, plus precision echo sounders, and so forth. Carries two survey launches. Has superstructure-mounted Flume-type passive tank stabilization. Navigational equipment includes Magnavox MX 702 SATNAV receiver and Loran-C. Homeported at Tokyo.

SERVICE CRAFT

♦ 1 Katsuran-class radiation monitoring craft [WYAG]
Bldr: Ishihara Dockyard, Takasago (In serv. 18-12-97)

MS 03 Katsuran

Katsuran (MS 03) *Ships of the World,* 12-97

D: 26 tons (fl) **S:** 25 kts **Dim:** 19.6 × 4.5 × 2.3 (molded depth)
M: 2 diesels; 2 props; 1,800 bhp **Range:** . . ./. . . **Crew:** . . . tot.

♦ 1 Saikai-class radiation monitoring craft [WYAG]
Bldr: Ishihara Dockyard, Takasago (In serv. 4-2-94)

MS 02 Saikai

D: 24 tons (fl) **S:** 15 kts **Dim:** 18.1 × 4.3 × 1.3
M: 2 diesels; 2 props; 1,000 bhp **Range:** 170/. . . **Crew:** 8 tot.

Saikai (MS 02) Takatoshi Okano, 9-97

♦ 1 Kinagusa-class catamaran radiation monitoring craft [WYAG]
Bldr: Ishihara Dockyard, Takasago (In serv. 31-1-92)

MS 01 Kinagusa

Kinagusa (MS 01) Chris Delgoffe/H&L Van Ginderen, 5-00

D: 39 tons (fl) **S:** 15 kts **Dim:** 18.0 × 9.0 × 1.3
M: 2 diesels; 2 props; 1,000 bhp **Range:** 170/. . . **Crew:** 8 tot.

♦ 11 Polar Star–class oil-spill surveillance craft [WYAG]
Bldr: Yanmar, Gamagori

	In serv.		In serv.
SS 36 Polar Star	28-3-96	SS 42 Pollux	12-3-96
SS 37 Subaru	28-3-96	SS 43 Aries	12-3-96
SS 38 Lyra	12-3-96	SS 44 Triton	22-3-96
SS 39 Aquarius	22-3-96	SS 45 Pulsar	12-3-96
SS 40 Scorpio	22-3-96	SS 46 Haimuru	12-3-96
SS 41 Libra	12-3-96		

Triton (SS 44)—note the fender along the hull sides and the diver's ladder at the stern Takatoshi Okano, 4-00

D: 4.7 tons **S:** 30 kts **Dim:** 8.0 × 3.0 × . . .
Electronics: Radar: 1 Furuno . . . nav.
M: 2 inboard/outboard diesels; . . . bhp **Crew:** 2–3 tot.

Remarks: Commercial cabin cruiser–type craft of about 6 m length. GRP construction. Have a Furuno navigational radar.

COAST GUARD SERVICE CRAFT *(continued)*

♦ **2 Lynx-class oil-spill surveillance craft [WYAG]**
Bldr: Yanmar, Gamagori (In serv. 25-3-99)

SS 65 Lynx SS 66 Taurus

Taurus (SS 66) *Ships of the World,* 3-99

D: 5 tons **S:** 50 kts **Dim:** 12.00 × 2.80 × . . .
Electronics: Radar: 1 Furuno . . . nav.
M: 2 inboard/outboard diesels; 2 props; 700 bhp

Remarks: GRP construction. Incorrectly listed as units of the New Orion class in the last edition.

♦ **16 New Orion–class oil-spill surveillance craft [WYAG]**
Bldr: Yanmar, Gamagori

	In serv.		In serv.
SS 51 Orion	25-3-93	SS 59 Capella	18-3-96
SS 52 Pegasus	25-3-93	SS 60 Serpens	12-3-96
SS 53 Neptune	23-3-94	SS 61 Sirius	21-3-97
SS 54 Jupiter	24-3-94	SS 62 Antares	21-3-97
SS 55 Venus	24-3-94	SS 63 Vega	20-3-98
SS 56 Cassiopeia	22-3-95	SS 64 Spica	26-3-99
SS 57 Phoenix	22-3-95	SS 67 Leo	24-3-99
SS 58 Carina	24-3-95	SS 68 Deneb	30-3-01

Cassiopeia (SS 56) Takatoshi Okano, 10-00

D: 4.9 tons (5 fl) **S:** 40 kts **Dim:** 10.0 × 2.6 × . . .
Electronics: Radar: 1 Furuno . . . nav.
M: 2 Volvo KD 42 diesels; 2 props; 460 bhp **Crew:** 2 tot.

Remarks: First two authorized in the FY 92 budget, laid down 25-11-92, and launched 11-3-93. SS 64 was ordered in 1998 to replace SS 12. GRP construction. The names are rendered in English above, as they appear most frequently in that form in Japan Coast Guard publications.

♦ **1 Southern Cross–class oil-spill surveillance craft [WYAG]**
Bldr: . . . . . . (In serv. 20-9-84)

SS 35 Southern Cross

D: 4.7 tons **S:** 25 kts **Dim:** 7.00 × 2.30 × . . .
M: 1 Yanmar AQ 260A inboard/outboard diesel; 1 prop; 130 bhp **Range:** 70/25

Remarks: GRP-construction, unsinkable lifeboat design, with turtleback forecastle and poop. Name is rendered *Sazankurosu* in Japanese, but the craft is carried by the name *Southern Cross* in Japanese references. No radar fitted.

♦ **9 Old Orion–class oil-spill surveillance craft [WYAG]**
Bldr: Yanmar, Arai (In serv. 1974–79)

SS 18 Polaris	SS 25 Andromeda	SS 32 Betelgeuse
SS 23 Perseus	SS 27 Hercules	SS 33 Aldebaran
SS 24 Centaurus	SS 30 Comet	SS 34 Pleiades

D: 4.8 tons (fl) **S:** 21 kts **Dim:** 6.00 × 2.40 × . . .
M: 1 Yanmar AQ 200 inboard/outboard diesel; 1 prop; 280 bhp
Range: 76/21 **Crew:** 6 tot.

Remarks: GRP construction. Survivors of a class of 32. Recent retirements include *Leo* (SS 21) on 24-3-00 and *Deneb* (SS 21) on 30-3-01. No radar fitted.

Andromeda (SS 25) Takatoshi Okano, 7-99

♦ **1 (+ . . .) 23-meter-class navigational aids tender [WYGL]**
Bldr: Sumidigawa, Uraga (In serv. 16-3-01)

LM 208 Koun (In serv. 16-3-01)

Koun (LM 208) *Ships of the World,* 3-01

D: 47 tons normal (50 fl) **S:** 17 kts **Dim:** . . . × . . . × . . .
Electronics: Radar: 1 . . . nav.
M: 2 . . . diesels; 2 props; 1,820 bhp **Crew:** 11 tot.

Remarks: First of a new series. White-painted on completion.

♦ **9 Hakuun-series (24-meter) navigational aids tenders [WYGL]**
Bldr: Sumidigawa, Tokyo (LM 107: Yokohama Yacht)

	In serv.		In serv.
LM 107 Toun	3-79	LM 204 Houn	22-2-91
LM 114 Tokuun	6-3-96	LM 205 Reiun	28-2-92
LM 201 Shoun	26-3-86	LM 206 Genun	19-3-96
LM 202 Seiun	6-9-88	LM 207 Ayabane	9-3-00
LM 203 Sekiun	12-3-91		

Ayabane (LM 207) *Ships of the World,* 3-00

D: 57.6 tons light; 62.7 tons normal (75 tons fl) **S:** 14.5 kts
Dim: 24.00 (23.00 pp) × 6.00 × 1.00
Electronics: Radar: 1 FRA-10 Mk III nav.
M: 2 G.M. 12V71 TI diesels; 2 props; 1,080 bhp (980 sust.)
Electric: 30 kVA **Range:** 420/13 **Fuel:** 2 tons **Crew:** 10 tot.

Remarks: LM 201 and LM 202 replaced 23-m craft of the same names. LM 202, built under the FY 88 budget, was laid down 6-9-88 and launched 7-12-88. LM 206 was laid down 12-9-95 to an improved design with enlarged pilothouse. LM 207 was laid down 2-9-99. Class name-ship *Hakuun* (LM 106) was stricken 30-3-01.

COAST GUARD SERVICE CRAFT *(continued)*

Disposal note: Single-unit navigational aids tender *Ayabane* (LM 112) was stricken 24-2-00.

♦ 1 Zuiun-class (270-ton) navigational aids tender [WYGL]

	Bldr	Laid down	L	In serv.
LM 101 Zuiun	Usuki Iron Wks., Usuki	19-1-83	27-4-83	27-7-83

Zuiun (LM 101) *Ships of the World,* 1996

D: 370 tons normal (398 fl) **S:** 15.1 kts **Dim:** 44.50 (41.40 pp) × 7.50 × 2.23
Electronics: Radar: 1 JMZ 1596 nav.; 1 JMA 159B surf. search
M: 2 Mitsubishi-Akasaka MH23-series diesels; 2 CP props; 1,300 bhp
Electric: 120 kw tot. **Range:** 1,440/14.5 **Fuel:** 34 m^3 **Crew:** 20 tot.

Remarks: Lighthouse service vessel, not equipped to lay or recover navigational aids. Cargo: 85 tons. One diesel is model MH23F, the other MH23. A second unit was requested under the FY 85 budget but not approved.

♦ 1 Miyojo-class navigational buoy tender [WYGL]
Bldr: Ishikawajima, Tokyo (In serv. 25-3-74)

LM 11 Miyojo

Miyojo (LM 11) *Ships of the World,* 1996

D: 248 tons light; 260 normal (303 fl) **S:** 11 kts **Dim:** 27.0 × 12.0 × 2.58
M: 2 Niigata 6MG 16HS diesels; 2 CP props; 600 bhp **Electric:** 135 kVA
Range: 1,360/10 **Fuel:** 15 tons **Crew:** 18 tot.

Remarks: Has a catamaran hull and can recover, service, and redeploy heavy navigational buoys.

♦ 2 (+ 1) Nahahikari-class inshore navigational aids tenders [WYGL] Bldr: Nagasaki Zosen

LS 233 Nahahikari (In serv. 13-3-00) LS 234 Michihikari (In serv. 22-3-01)

Michihikari (LS 234)—in the new all-white paint scheme *Ships of the World,* 3-01

D: 27 tons (29 fl) **S:** 25 kts **Dim:** 20.0 × 4.8 × 1.1
Electronics: Radar: 1 . . . nav.
M: 2 M.A.N. D-2842LYE diesels; 2 props; 1,800 bhp
Range: 160/25 **Crew:** 11 tot.

Remarks: Intended to replace the *Hatsuhikari* class and are an improved version of the *Himehikari* class. A third craft was approved in the FY 01 budget.

♦ 2 Himehikari-class inshore navigational aids tenders [WYGL]
Bldr: Nagasaki Zosen (In serv. 23-3-99)

LS 231 Himehikari LS 232 Matsuhikari

Himehikari (LS 231) Takatoshi Okano, 9-00

D: 23 tons (27 fl) **S:** 29 kts (25 sust.) **Dim:** 20.0 × 4.5 × 1.1
Electronics: Radar: 1 . . . nav.
M: 2 M.A.N. D-2842LYE diesels; 2 props; 1,820 bhp
Range: 160/29 **Crew:** . . . tot.

Remarks: Essentially the same design and appearance as the *Suzukaze*-class (CL) small patrol boats, with fenders added on the sides aft and a small boat carried to starboard aft on davits. Construction was approved under the FY 99 budget. Have a firefighting monitor (water cannon) on the bow.

♦ 13 Hatsuhikari-class inshore navigational aids tenders [WYGL]
Bldr: Yokohama Yacht (LS 216: Sumidigawa, Tokyo; LS 217–221: Ishihara DY, Takasago)

	In serv.		In serv.
LS 208 Nishihikari	14-7-79	LS 216 Fusahikari	18-2-88
LS 209 Kamihikari	17-12-79	LS 217 Haruhikari	6-1-89
LS 210 Shimahikari	17-12-79	LS 218 Setohikari	31-1-89
LS 211 Akihikari	27-2-81	LS 219 Tohikari	28-2-90
LS 212 Wakahikari	5-3-82	LS 220 Takahikari	31-1-90
LS 213 Miyohikari	18-3-83	LS 221 Sekihikari	31-1-90
LS 214 Urahikari	27-1-84		

Shimahikari (LS 210) Takatoshi Okano, 6-00

D: 20 tons light; 25 tons normal (35.2 fl) **S:** 16.3 kts (15 sust.)
Dim: 17.20 × 4.30 × 0.80
M: 2 Isuzu E-120T-MF6R diesels; 2 props; 560 bhp
Range: 230/14.5 **Endurance:** 2 days **Crew:** 8 tot.

Remarks: Are officially the "17-meter" class. Pilothouse configurations vary.
Disposals: *Hatsuhikari* (LS 204) was stricken 10-3-99, *Matsuhikari* (LS 206) on 5-3-99, *Nahahikari* (LS 205) on 25-2-00, and *Michihikari* (LS 207) on 8-3-01.

♦ 11 Shoko-class inshore navigational aids tenders [WYGL]
Bldr: Ishikawajima, Tokyo (LS 181: Nippon Hikoki, Yokosuka; LS 194, 195: Ishihara DY, Takasago)

	In serv.		In serv.
LS 181 Keiko	29-6-79	LS 191 Kyoko	21-1-86
LS 186 Toko	30-6-79	LS 192 Suiko	30-1-87
LS 187 Getsuko	30-6-79	LS 193 Saiko	2-2-87
LS 188 Taiko	24-1-85	LS 194 Aiko	24-11-87
LS 189 Choko	20-12-85	LS 195 Hakuko	24-11-87
LS 190 Miyoko	24-12-85		

COAST GUARD SERVICE CRAFT *(continued)*

Toko (LS 186) *Ships of the World*

D: 9.4 tons light (14 fl) **S:** 15 kts **Dim:** 12.00 × 3.20 × 0.60
M: 1 diesel; 1 prop; 210 bhp **Range:** 120/13.5 **Crew:** 6 tot.

Remarks: GRP construction. Are officially the "12-meter" class. *Shoko* (LS 185) was stricken 31-3-01.

♦ 3 Reiko No. 1–class navigational aids tenders [WYGL]
Bldr: . . .

	In serv.		In serv.
LS 168 Reiko No. 1	2-12-86	LS 170 Reiko No. 3	30-11-87
LS 169 Reiko No. 2	30-11-87		

Reiko No. 2 (LS 169) *Ships of the World,* 1996

D: 4.5 tons (4.9 fl) **S:** 15 kts **Dim:** 9.9 × 2.5 × 1.1
M: 1 diesel; 1 prop; 115 bhp **Range:** 130/13 **Crew:** 8 tot.

Remarks: GRP construction. Are officially of the "10-meter" class.

♦ 5 Zuiko No. 1–class navigational aids tenders [WYGL]
Bldr: . . .

	Laid down	L	In serv.
LS 161 Zuiko No. 1	20-9-85	20-11-85	5-12-85
LS 164 Zuiko No. 2	29-9-85	26-11-85	12-12-85
LS 165 Zuiko No. 3	8-10-85	2-12-85	18-12-85
LS 166 Zuiko No. 4	16-10-85	19-12-85	17-1-86
LS 167 Zuiko No. 5	24-10-85	9-1-86	24-1-86

Zuiko No. 2 (LS 164) *Ships of the World,* 1996

D: 4.5 tons (4.9 fl) **S:** 14 kts **Dim:** 9.9 × 2.8 × 1.6
M: 1 diesel; 1 prop; 115 bhp **Range:** 130/13 **Crew:** 8 tot.

Remarks: GRP construction. Are officially a "10-meter" class.

♦ 7 Kaiko No. 1–class navigational aids tenders [WYGL]
Bldr: Nippon Hikoki, Yokosuka

	In serv.		In serv.
LS 148 Kaiko No. 4	10-12-81	LS 157 Kaiko No. 8	17-1-84
LS 149 Kaiko No. 5	1982	LS 158 Kaiko No. 9	13-2-84
LS 154 Kaiko No. 6	1982	LS 160 Kaiko No. 10	21-2-84
LS 155 Kaiko No. 7	12-1-84		

Kaiko No. 9 (LS 158) *Ships of the World*

D: 5.0 tons (5.2 fl) **S:** 13 kts **Dim:** 9.00 × 2.25 × . . .
M: 2 Nissan FD606 diesels; 1 prop; 230 bhp **Range:** 130/12.5 **Crew:** 6 tot.

Remarks: GRP construction. Are officially a "10-meter" class. *Kaiko No. 1* (LS 144), *Kaiko No. 2* (LS 145), and *Kaiko No. 3* (LS 146) were stricken 31-3-01.

♦ 6 Hamashio-class (20-meter) inshore survey boats [WYGS]
Bldr: HS 21–23: Yokohama Yacht; HS 24–26: Ishihara DY, Takasago

	In serv.		In serv.
HS 21 Hamashio	25-3-91	HS 24 Okishio	4-3-99
HS 22 Isoshio	25-3-93	HS 25 Iseshio	10-3-99
HS 23 Uzushio	20-12-95	HS 26 Hayashio	10-3-99

Uzushio (HS 23) Takatoshi Okano, 9-00

D: 27 tons light (42 fl) **S:** 15 kts **Dim:** 20.30 × 4.50 × 1.00
M: 2 diesels; 2 props; 900 bhp—1 cruise diesel; 1 prop; 115 bhp
Range: 200/. . . **Crew:** 10 tot.

♦ 1 Akashi-class (15-meter) inshore survey boat [WYGS]
Bldr: . . . (In serv. 1977)

HS 35 Kurushima

D: 21 tons normal (26.8 fl) **S:** 10.2 kts **Dim:** 15.0 × 4.0 × 0.84
M: 1 Nissan-MTU UD626 diesel; 180 bhp **Range:** 630/9.7 **Crew:** 7 tot.

Remarks: GRP hull. Sister *Akashi* (HS 31) was stricken 4-12-95 and *Hayatomo* (HS 33) and *Kurihama* (HS 34) on 22-2-99.

♦ 5 Shirasagi-class oil-spill recovery craft [WYSR]
Bldrs: Various (In serv. 1977–79)

OR 01 Shirasagi	OR 03 Mizunagi	OR 05 Isoshigi
OR 02 Shiratori	OR 04 Chidori	

Chidori (OR 04) *Ships of the World*

COAST GUARD SERVICE CRAFT *(continued)*

D: 78.5 tons light; 100 tons normal (153 fl) **S:** 6.8 kts **Dim:** 22.0 × 6.4 × 0.9
M: 2 UD 626 diesels; waterjet drive; 390 bhp **Range:** 160/6 **Crew:** 7 tot.

♦ 3 Uraga-class oil-spill skimmer craft [WYSR]
Bldr: Lockheed, U.S.A.

	In serv.		In serv.
OS 01 Tsurumi (ex-*Uraga*)	31-3-75	OS 03 Naruto	25-2-76
OS 02 Bisan	31-3-75		

Bisan (OS 02) *Ships of the World*

D: 9 tons (11 fl) **S:** 6 kts **Dim:** 8.26 × 5.00 × 0.70
M: 1 HR-6 diesel; 2 props; 90 bhp **Range:** 90/4.5 **Crew:** 4 tot.

Remarks: Can be broken down into sections for truck transport. Catamaran hulls, with oil-spill and debris sweeping gear between. All OR/OS/OX-series cleanup craft are painted bright red-orange.

♦ 18 M 101–class oil-spill extender barges [WYSRN]
Bldrs: Various (In serv. 1974–76)

OX 01 M 101 through OX 06 M 106
OX 08 M 108 through OX 19 M 119

M 107 (OX 07)—since stricken Mitsuhiro Kadota, 5-01

D: 48 tons (93 fl) **Dim:** 22.00 × 7.20 × 0.45

♦ 1 New Hiryu–class large fireboat [WYTR]
Bldr: Nippon Kokan (NKK), Tsurumi

	Laid down	L	In serv.
FL 01 Hiryu	18-3-97	5-9-97	24-12-97

D: 280 tons normal (322 fl) **S:** 14.0 kts **Dim:** 35.10 × 12.20 × . . .
M: 2 diesels; 2 azimuthal CP props; 4,000 bhp **Crew:** 14 tot.

Remarks: Replacement design for the original *Hiryu* (FL 01) class, with the first authorized under the FY 96 budget. To date, no further units have been ordered.
Hull systems: Catamaran hulls. Has four 5,000-liter/min fire monitors atop the tower mast (two of them on telescoping masts), one 20,000-liter/min monitor atop the pilothouse, and a 1,000-liter/min monitor at the bow of each hull. FL 01 is stationed at Yokohama.

Hiryu (FL 01)—with telescoping fire monitor masts retracted
Mitsuhiro Kadota, 5-01

Note: Most JCG patrol ships, boats, and craft are also fitted for fire fighting.

♦ 4 Old Hiryu–class large fireboats [WYTR]
Bldr: Nippon Kokan, Yokohama (FL 05: Yokohama Yacht)

	In serv.		In serv.
FL 02 Shoryu	4-3-70	FL 04 Kairyu	18-3-77
FL 03 Nanryu	4-3-71	FL 05 Suiryu	24-3-78

Kairyu (FL 04)—with telescoping fire monitor mast fully raised and all monitors spraying Takatoshi Okano, 9-00

D: 200.3 tons normal (216 fl) **S:** 13.7 kts **Dim:** 27.50 × 10.40 × 2.1
M: 2 Ikegai-MTU MB820Db diesels; 2 props; 2,200 bhp
Electric: 70 kVA tot. **Range:** 300/13 **Crew:** 14 tot.

Remarks: Catamaran hulls. Intended for fighting supertanker fires. Have a 14.5-m^3 tank for firefighting chemicals, one 45-m-range chemical sprayer, and seven 60-m-range water cannon. One fire monitor is atop a telescoping mast. Class name-ship *Hiryu* (FL 01) was stricken during 12-97.

COAST GUARD SERVICE CRAFT *(continued)*

♦ **8 Ninobiki-class medium fireboats [WYTR]**
Bldrs: FM 02, 06, 08, 10: Sumidigawa, Tokyo; others: Yokohama Yacht

	In serv.		In serv.
FM 02 Yodo	30-3-75	FM 07 Kegon	29-1-77
FM 04 Shiraito	25-2-75	FM 08 Minoo	27-1-78
FM 05 Kotobiki	31-1-76	FM 09 Ryusei	24-3-80
FM 06 Nachi	14-2-76	FM 10 Kyotaki	25-3-81

Ryusei (FM 09) *Ships of the World*

D: 89 tons normal (99 fl) **S:** 13.4 kts **Dim:** 23.00 × 6.00 × 1.55
M: 1 Ikegai MTU MB820Db and 2 Nissan UDV 816 diesels; 3 props; 1,600 bhp
Electric: 40 kVA **Range:** 180/13.4 **Crew:** 12 tot.

Remarks: Have four firepumps: one of 6,000 liters/min, two of 3,000 liters/min, and one of 2,000 liters/min. Have two 750-liter and one 5,000-liter foam tanks. Sister *Otowa* (FM 03) was retired 12-8-99 and *Ninobiki* (FM 01) on 31-10-00.

♦ **2 C I–class training craft [WYXT]**
Bldr: Yanmar, Arai

C I (In serv. 26-3-99) C II (In serv. 24-3-00)

C II—red-orange hull, white upperworks *Ships of the World,* 3-00

D: 1.5 tons **S:** 27 kts **Dim:** 5.40 × 2.10 × . . .
M: 1 Yanmar inboard/outboard diesel; 1 prop; 96 bhp **Crew:** 4 tot.

Remarks: Open-cockpit, GRP-hulled runabouts; replaced craft with same name. Have a red-orange hull and white superstructure.

♦ **1 A-class training craft [WYXT]**
Bldr: . . . (In serv. 26-3-96)

Aoba

Aoba *Ships of the World,* 3-96

D: 15 tons (19 fl) **S:** 22 kts **Dim:** 16.0 × 4.1 × . . .
M: 1 diesel; 380 bhp **Crew:** 3 instructors, 12 students

Remarks: Replaced a similar craft of the same name. GRP-construction cabin cruiser.

JERSEY

Note: Jersey, in the Channel Islands, is a semiautonomous territory of the United Kingdom.

PATROL BOATS [WPB]

♦ **1 Norman le Brocq class**
Bldr: Souter, Cowes, U.K. (In serv. 1998)

Norman le Brocq

D: 17 tons (fl) **S:** 24 kts **Dim:** 15.00 × . . . × . . .
A: small arms **Electronics:** Radar: 1 . . . nav.
M: 2 Saab Scania DSI-11 diesels; 2 props; 1,000 bhp
Range: . . ./. . . **Crew:** 3 tot.

Remarks: Ordered 20-11-97. GRP construction. Has one Avon Searider rigid inflatable inspection dinghy mounted on a ramp at the stern. Used for local police and fisheries protection duties.

JORDAN

Hashemite Kingdom of Jordan

Personnel (2001): 665 total, including headquarters personnel and combat swimmers

Base: Aqaba

Note: The Coastal Guard was restyled the Royal Jordanian Naval Force in 1991. The United States delivered two 40-ft. and one 65-ft. patrol boats from surplus stocks on 14-12-96 and the U.S. Coast Guard three "cutters" in 1999.

PATROL CRAFT [PC]

♦ **3 Hawk-class patrol boats**
Bldr: Vosper Thornycroft, Portchester (In serv. 10-91)

101 Al Hussein 102 Al Hussan 103 Abdullah

Al Hussein (101) ANBw/FAFIO, 8-97

D: 95 tons light (124 fl) **S:** 32.5 kts **Dim:** 30.45 (26.55 pp) × 6.87 × 1.50 (hull)
A: 1 twin 30-mm 75-cal. Oerlikon–Royal Ordnance GCM-A03-2 AA; 1 20-mm 90-cal. Oerlikon GAM-B01 AA; 2 single 7.62-mm mg
Electronics:
Radar: 1 Kelvin-Hughes Type 1007 nav.
EW: 2 Wallop Stockade decoy RL
M: 2 MTU 16V396 TB94 diesels; 2 props; 5,800 bhp—2 Volvo TAMD 71A cruise diesels; . . . bhp
Range: 750/15 **Fuel:** 18 tons **Crew:** 3 officers, 13 enlisted

Remarks: Ordered 3-88. 101 was launched during 12-88 and ran trials 17-5-89; 102 completed in 12-89 and 103 during 6-90. All were commissioned after delivery together as deck cargo in 9-91. GRP construction. Have a Rademac 2000 optronic director for the 30-mm mount.

PATROL BOATS [PB]

♦ **1 ex-U.S. Navy 65-foot Air/Sea Rescue Boat**

. . . . . . (ex-65AR682)

D: 27.6 tons (31.5 fl) **S:** 24 kts **Dim:** 19.80 × 5.25 × 1.14
A: . . . **Electronics:** Radar: 1 SPS-. . . nav.
M: 2 G.M. Detroit Diesel 12V71T diesels; 2 props; 1,170 bhp
Electric: 10 kw tot. (1 × 10-kw Onan Model 10 MDZB-3R set)
Range: 250/24 **Fuel:** 3,028 liters **Crew:** 6 tot.

Remarks: Donated in late 1996. Aluminum construction craft similar to U.S. Navy 65-ft. torpedo retriever design. Can accommodate eight litter patients but is probably to be used as a patrol boat. Had previously been employed at Subic Bay, the Philippines, by the U.S. Navy.

♦ **4 U.S. Bertram 38-foot class** Bldr: Bertram Yacht, Miami (In serv. 1974)

FAYSAL HAN HASAYU MUHAMMED

U.S. Bertram 38-ft. patrol launch ANBw/FAFIO, 8-97

D: 8 tons **S:** 25 kts **Dim:** 11.6 × 4.0 × 0.5
A: 1 12.7-mm mg; 2 single 7.62-mm mg
Electronics: Radar: 1 Decca . . . nav.
M: 2 G.M. Detroit Diesel 8V71S diesels; 2 props; 600 bhp
Range: 240/20 **Crew:** 8 tot.

Remarks: GRP construction. Since delivery, have had a flying bridge built on above the original cockpit.

SERVICE CRAFT

♦ **2 ex-U.S. Navy 40-foot Personnel Boat Mk 4 launches [YFL]**
Bldr: . . . . . . (In serv. 1991)

. . . . (ex-40PE9002) . . . . (ex-40PE9003)

D: 7.9 tons light (11.6 fl) **S:** 15.9 kts **Dim:** 12.26 × 3.68 × 0.86
M: 1 G.M. Detroit Diesel 6-71 diesel; 1 prop; 280 bhp
Range: 120/12 **Crew:** 3 tot.

Remarks: Donated in late 1996. GRP-hulled craft formerly carried by aircraft carriers. Can carry 40 passengers but are probably to be employed primarily in patrol duties.

♦ **3 U.K. Sea Truck utility launches [YFL]**
Bldr: Rotork, U.K. (In serv. 9-91)

AL FAISAL AL HASHIM AL HAMZA

Al Hashim Royal Jordanian Navy, 1996

D: 9 tons (fl) **S:** 28 kts **Dim:** 12.7 × 3.2 × 0.9
A: 1 12.7-mm mg; 1 7.62-mm mg **Electronics:** Radar: 1 Decca . . . nav.
M: 2 Perkins diesels; 2 props; 240 bhp **Crew:** 2 tot. + 30 troops

Remarks: Delivered with the Hawk-class patrol boats. For use on the Dead Sea. Truck transportable. Have a bow ramp and are beachable.

Note: The 15-m pilot boat/patrol craft *Husni* at Aqaba, delivered in 1988 by Trinity Marine's Equitable Shipyard, New Orleans, is not under naval control.

KAZAKHSTAN

Personnel (2001): About 250 total; to expand to 3,000

Bases: Headquarters at Aktau (formerly Shevchenko) and minor facilities at Bautino on the Caspian Sea and at Atyrau on the Aral Sea

Naval Aviation: Three Mil Mi-8 and 6 Mi-2 helicopters

Note: The armed forces of Kazakhstan were founded during 5-92. The naval flotilla of the border guard was formally dedicated on 17-8-96 at Aktau. An "Advanced Naval School of the Defense Ministry of the Republic of Kazakhstan" was established at Aktau on 9-8-01 with 180 trainees and 44 instructors. Turkish Navy AB 25–class patrol craft AB 32 was transferred 3-7-99; see addenda for data.

PATROL BOATS [PB]

♦ **1 Russian Zhuk class (Project 1400M)**

	Bldr	Laid down	L	In serv.
BERKUT	Zenit Zavod, Ural'sk	1996	22-5-98	15-7-98

D: 35.9 tons (39.7 fl) **S:** 30 kts
Dim: 23.80 (21.70 wl) × 5.00 (3.80 wl) × 1.00 (hull)
A: 1 twin 14.5-mm 93-cal. 2M-7 AA **Electronics:** Radar: 1 Lotsiya nav.
M: 2 M-401B diesels; 2 props; 2,200 bhp
Electric: 48 kw total (2 × 21-kw, 1 × 6-kw diesel sets)
Range: 500/13.5 **Endurance:** 5 days **Crew:** 1 officer, 9 enlisted

Remarks: Two others were to be transferred in 2-96 from the Russian Caspian Flotilla but were apparently not put into service. *Berkut* means "Golden Eagle."

♦ **1 U.S. 42-foot Dauntless class**
Bldr: SeaArk, Monticello, Ark. (In serv. 17-8-96)

ABAY

Abay SeaArk, 11-95

D: 11 tons (12.7 fl) **S:** 35 kts **Dim:** 12.80 × 4.27 × 1.32 (max.)
A: 1 12.7-mm mg; 2 single 7.62-mm mg
Electronics: Radar: 1 Furuno . . . nav.
M: 2 G.M. Detroit Diesel 8V92 TA diesels; 2 props; 1,270 bhp
Electric: 12 kw tot. **Range:** 200/30; 400/22 **Fuel:** 250 gallons **Crew:** 4 tot.

Remarks: Transferred as aid by the U.S. Defense Nuclear Agency and delivered 11-95. Aluminum construction. C. Raymond Hunt, "Deep-Vee" hull design. Is equipped with GPS receiver, VHF radio, air conditioning, and a siren.

♦ **2 Saygak class (Project 1408M)**
Bldr: Zenit Zavod, Ural'sk (In serv. 1995)

D: 13 tons (fl) **S:** 38 kts (35 sust.) **Dim:** 14.05 × 3.50 × 0.65
A: 1 7.62-mm mg **Electronics:** Radar: 1 . . . nav.
M: 1 Type M-401B (12CHSN18/20) diesel; 1 waterjet; 1,000 bhp
Electric: 8 kw (1 Type DGK8/1500 diesel driving; 27 V)
Range: 135/35 **Fuel:** 1.15 tons **Crew:** 2 tot. + 4–8 police personnel

Remarks: Locally built version of a class designed for Russian use on the Amur-Ussuri River system in the Far East. Rail transportable, the craft are intended for use in coastal waters in seas up to Sea State 3. Aluminum alloy construction.

♦ **5 U.S. 27-foot Vigilant class**
Bldr: Boston Whaler, Edgewater, Fla. (In serv. 17-8-96)

Kazakhstani Vigilant Boston Whaler, 1995

PATROL BOATS [PB] *(continued)*

D: 2.27 tons light (4.0 fl) **S:** 34 kts **Dim:** 8.10 × 3.05 × 0.48
A: 1 12.7-mm mg; 2 single 7.62-mm mg
Electronics: Radar: 1 Furuno . . . nav.
M: 2 Johnson gasoline outboards; 350 bhp
Range: . . ./. . . **Fuel:** 648 liters **Crew:** 4 tot.

Remarks: Presented as aid under a U.S. Defense Nuclear Agency contract. Delivered 11-95. GRP foam-core construction.

Disposal note: The four ex-German KW 15–class patrol boats transferred in 1995 after refits were out of service as of 2000.

SERVICE CRAFT

♦ **1 former fishing trawler [YFU]**

Tyulen II

Remarks: Acquired in 1997. Measures 39 m o.a. and is powered by one 578-bhp diesel for 10 kts. Used for logistics support and fisheries inspection duties. No other information available.

Note: As of 8-01, some 20 "small hydrographic launches" were also said to be in service.

KENYA

Republic of Kenya

Personnel (2002): Approx. 1,200 total, plus 120 marines and 400 civilian employees

Bases: Mombasa and Magogoni. The navy also operates nine coastal radar stations.

GUIDED-MISSILE PATROL CRAFT [PTG]

♦ **2 Province class**
Bldr: Vosper Thornycroft, Portchester, U.K.

	Laid down	L	In serv.
P 3126 Nyayo	11-84	20-8-86	23-7-87
P 3127 Umoja	11-84	5-3-87	7-9-87

Nyayo (P 3126) Brian Morrison, 2-01

Nyayo (P 3126) Ralph Edwards, 2-01

D: 311 tons light (363 fl) **S:** 40 kts **Dim:** 56.7 (52.0 pp) × 8.2 × 2.1
A: 4 Otomat Mk 2 SSM; 1 76-mm 62-cal. OTOBreda Compact DP; 1 twin 30-mm 90-cal. BMARC-Oerlikon GCM-A02 AA; 2 single 20-mm 90-cal. BMARC-Oerlikon GAM-B01 AA
Electronics:
Radar: 1 Decca AC 1226 nav.; 1 Plessey AWS-4 surf./air search; 1 Thales LIROD-423 radar/optronic f.c.
EW: Racal Cutlass-E intercept; Racal Cygnus jammer; 2 18-round Wallop Barricade decoy RL
M: 4 Paxman Valenta 18 RP 200 CM diesels; 4 props; 17,900 bhp (15,000 sust.)—2 electric cruise outdrives; 160 bhp
Electric: 420 kw tot. **Range:** 2,000/15 **Fuel:** 45.5 tons **Crew:** 40 tot.

Remarks: Ordered 9-84. Generally similar to craft built for Oman and Egypt. Use the Ferranti WSA.423 combat data/fire-control system. Carry a semi-rigid inspection boat on the stern. Both departed the U.K. for Kenya 29-3-88. They constitute Squadron 86.

Disposal note: Brooke Marine 32-meter-class guided-missile patrol craft *Madaraka* (P 3121) and Brooke Marine 37.5-m guided-missile patrol craft *Mamba* (P 3100) were retired during 2000.

PATROL CRAFT [PC]

♦ **2 Shupavu class**
Bldr: Construnaves-CNE, Gondan, Spain

	Laid down	L	In serv.
P 6129 Shupavu	. . .	. . .	1998
P 6130 Shujaa	. . .	. . .	1998

Shujaa (P 6130) Brian Morrison, 2-01

Shujaa (P 6130) Mritunjoy Mazumdar, 2-01

D: 480 tons (fl) **S:** 22 kts **Dim:** 58.0 × 8.2 × 2.8
A: 1 76-mm 62-cal. OTOBreda SuperRapid DP; 1 20-mm 90-cal. Oerlikon AA
Electronics: Radar: 1 Furuno . . . nav.; 1 Furuno . . . surf. search
M: . . . diesels; 2 props; . . . bhp
Range: . . ./. . . **Crew:** 24 tot.

Remarks: Ordered 3-97. Intended for offshore patrol duties. Are equipped with two rigid inflatable inspection launches and a handling crane. Were delivered without armament early in 1998. An electro-optical director for the 76-mm gun is fitted above the pilothouse.

PATROL BOATS [PB]

♦ **5 ex-Spanish P 101 class**
Bldr: ARESA, Arenys del Mar, Barcelona (In serv. 1978-82)

P 943 P 944 P 945 P 946 P 947

D: 16.9 tons (21.7 fl) **S:** 26 kts **Dim:** 15.90 (13.70 pp) × 4.36 × 1.33
A: 1 12.7-mm mg **Electronics:** Radar: 1 Decca 110 nav.
M: 2 Baudouin-Interdiesel DNP-8 MIR diesels; 2 props; 768 bhp
Electric: 12 kVA tot. **Range:** 430/18 **Fuel:** 2.2 tons
Crew: 2 officers, 4–5 enlisted

Remarks: Former Spanish Navy units purchased in 1995. GRP construction. May be assigned to the customs service rather than the navy.

AMPHIBIOUS WARFARE SHIPS

♦ **2 Galana-class medium landing ships [LSM]**
Bldr: Construnaves-CNE, Gondan, Spain (In serv. 2-94)

L 38 Galana L 39 Tana

D: 1,400 tons (fl) **S:** 12.5 kts (12.9 on trials) **Dim:** 63.5 × 13.3 × 2.4
A: none **Electronics:** Radar: 1 Decca . . . nav.
M: 2 MTU-Izar . . . . . . diesels; 2 props; 2,700 bhp—bow-thruster
Range: . . ./. . . **Crew:** 30 tot.

AMPHIBIOUS WARFARE SHIPS *(continued)*

Remarks: Ordered by Galway, Ltd., for commercial service but taken over by the navy prior to completion. Have a 4-m-wide bow ramp capable of supporting 70-ton loads and also have a portside vehicle loading ramp.

SERVICE CRAFT

♦ **1 large harbor tug [YTB]**
Bldr: James Lamont, Port Glasgow, U.K.

NGAMIA (In serv. 1969)

D: . . . **S:** 14 kts **Dim:** 35.3 × 9.3 × 3.9 **M:** diesels; 1 prop; 1,200 bhp

Remarks: 298 grt. Transferred to the Kenyan Navy from the Mombasa Port Authority in 1-83.

Disposal note: Vosper 110-ft. training craft and former patrol craft *Simba* (P 3110) was stricken during 2000.

Note: The customs service operates 12 12-m German-built patrol boats delivered 1989–90; the Netherlands-built, 55-ton pilot boat *Kiongozi* (in serv. 1983); 17-m workboats *M'Chunguzi* and *M'Linzi;* and an 18-m, a 14-m, and two 12-m launches, the 12-m launches for service on Lake Victoria.

KIRIBATI

Note: Ship names are preceded by RKS (Republic of Kiribati Ship).

PATROL CRAFT [PC]

♦ **1 ASI 315 class**
Bldr: Transfield ASI Pty, Ltd., South Coogee, Western Australia (In serv. 22-1-94)

301 TEANOAI

Teanoai (301) LSPH Shaun Hibbitt, 1-94

D: 165 tons (fl) **S:** 21 kts (20 sust.)
Dim: 31.50 (28.60 wl) × 8.10 × 2.12 (1.80 hull)
A: provision for 1 12.7-mm mg
Electronics: Radar: 1 Furuno 1011 (I/J-band) nav.
M: 2 Caterpillar 3516 diesels; 2 props; 2,820 bhp (2,400 sust.)
Electric: 116 kw (2 × 50-kw Caterpillar 3304 diesels; 1 × 16 kw)
Range: 2,500/12 **Fuel:** 27.9 tons **Endurance:** 8–10 days
Crew: 3 officers, 14 enlisted

Remarks: Ordered in late 1992. An Australian foreign aid program "Pacific Patrol Boat," with numerous sisters in a number of Southwest Pacific–area island nation forces. Was in refit during 2001 in Australia and is expected to serve into 2009. Carries a 5-m aluminum boarding boat and has an extensive navigational suite, including Furuno FSN-70 NAVSAT receiver, 525 HFD/F, 120 MF–HFD/F, FE-881 echo sounder, and DS-70 doppler log. The 12.7-mm machinegun is not normally mounted.

KOREA, NORTH

Democratic People's Republic of Korea

Personnel (2002): Approximately 9,000 total, plus reserves. Note: Some sources give as many as 60,000 active personnel, plus 40,000 reserves, while South Korean officials stated in 10-93 that the North had a 40,000-strong navy; both estimates seem unlikely, given the size of the fleet.

Bases: The fleet is divided between the Yellow Sea and Sea of Japan, and units do not transfer between them. The East Coast Fleet is headquartered at Toejo Dong, with major bases at Najin and Wonsan and submarines based at Chaho; minor facilities exist at Kimchaek, Ksong-up, Muchon-up, Namer-ri, Pando, Sanjin-dong, Songjon, and Yohori. The much smaller West Coast Fleet is headquartered at Nampo, with submarines based at Pipa Got and minor facilities at Chodo, Pupo-ri, Sagon-ri, Sohae-ri, Sunwi-do, Tasa-ri, and Yogampo-ri.

Naval Aviation: There is no naval aviation per se, but the air force has three regiments of highly obsolescent Il-28 Beagle bombers (82 total aircraft) that can perform torpedo attacks, plus one regiment of 20 obsolescent Su-7 Fitters and two regiments of even older MiG-19 Farmers (100 aircraft) that are configured for ground attack. There are also a small number of Su-25 Frogfoot ground-attack aircraft.

Coastal Defense: There are about a dozen coastal-defense antiship missile battalions employing fixed and mobile SS-C-2 and HY-2 Styx-type weapons. Artillery in 130-mm and smaller sizes is also emplaced around the coast, and there are a number of coastal radar stations. North Korea has been attempting to develop its own antiship cruise missile, but the degree of success is not known.

Note: Data for North Korea are only marginally reliable, due to the secrecy of the North Korean government and the reluctance of the South Korean and other governments to release accurate information. Most weapons and sensors are 1940s to 1950s equipment of Soviet or Chinese origin, except for imported Japanese commercial navigational radars. Nearly all naval ship and craft construction has now halted, and the entire fleet, while still numerous, is essentially obsolescent.

There is also reported to be a "Maritime Coastal Security Police" with several patrol boats and up to 100 small patrol launches.

ATTACK SUBMARINES [SS]

♦ **22 Soviet (Chinese version) Romeo class (Project 033)**
Bldr: See remarks (In serv. 1973–95)

D: 1,319 tons surf./1,712 tons sub. **S:** 15.2 kts surf./13 kts sub.
Dim: 76.60 × 6.70 × 4.95
A: 8 (6 fwd/2 aft) 533-mm TT (14 torpedoes or 28 mines)
Electronics:
Radar: 1 Snoop Plate nav./surf. search
Sonar: Tamir-5L active; MG-10 Feniks passive
EW: MRP-11-14-series (Stop Light) intercept (1–18 GHz)
M: diesel-electric: 2 Type 37D diesels (2,000 bhp each); 2 props; 2,700 shp—2 electric creep motors: 100 shp
Range: 14,000/9 surf.; 350/9 sub. **Endurance:** 60 days
Crew: 8 officers, 43 enlisted

Remarks: An obsolete Russian design, as modified by China. Four are of Chinese construction (with Type IZ38 diesels of 2,400 bhp each), two transferred in 1973 and two in 1974; they operate on the west coast. The others are based on the east coast and were built at Mayang Do in North Korea, completing between 1976 and 1995. One additional unit was lost off the east coast 20-2-85. Diving depth: 300 m (270 normal). Battery: 224 cells; 6,600 amp-hr.

♦ **4 Soviet Whiskey class (Project 613)** (In serv. 1949–58)

D: 1,045 tons surf./1,333 tons sub. **S:** 18.44 kts surf./13.6 kts sub.
Dim: 75.94 × 6.31 × 5.00
A: 6 (4 fwd/2 aft) 533-mm TT (12 torpedoes or 20 mines)
Electronics:
Radar: 1 Snoop Plate nav./surf. search
Sonar: Tamir-5L active MF; MG-10 Feniks passive
EW: MRP-11-14-series (Stop Light) intercept (1–18 GHz)
M: 2 Type 37D diesels (2,000 bhp each), 2 Type PG-101 electric motors; 2 props; 2,700 shp—2 Type PG-103 electric creep motors; 100 shp
Range: 2,865/18.44, 8,580/9.96 surf.; 6,000/5 snorkel; 13.8/13.6 sub.
Fuel: 119.2 tons **Endurance:** 60 days **Crew:** 9 officers, 52 enlisted

Remarks: Transferred in 1974 to replace four transferred from the USSR during the 1960s. Probably at the end of their useful lives, although the U.S. Navy stated that all were still in service as of 6-99. All are based on the west coast of North Korea, on the Yellow Sea, probably primarily for training duties. Are the last in service of some 236 built. Normal operating depth: 200 m. Have two 112-cell Type 46-SU batteries. Reserve buoyancy is 27.4%.

COASTAL SUBMARINES [SSC]

♦ **22 Sang-o class** Bldr: Bong Dao Bo SY, Singpo (In serv. 1991–97)

Sang-o-class special forces variant *Ships of the World,* 1996

COASTAL SUBMARINES [SSC] *(continued)*

D: 295 tons surf./325 tons sub. **S:** 7 kts surf./8 kts sub.
Dim: 34.0–35.5 × 3.8 × 3.2
A: armed version: 4 bow 533-mm TT (no reloads)—transport version: 16 mines in external racks
Electronics:
Radar: 1 Furuno . . . nav.
Sonar: probable passive array only
M: 1 diesel generator set (probable 300 bhp); 1 shrouded prop; 200 shp
Range: 2,700/8 snorkel
Crew: 11 tot. + 15 special forces, or 19 tot. in torpedo-armed version

Remarks: The type is sized somewhere between the midget submarines and the Romeo and Whiskey classes and, from the functional designation, the craft are apparently intended primarily for antiship, coastal defense duties and also for offensive minelaying and special forces insertion. Two or more from the total are unarmed variants equipped to carry special forces personnel. The name means "Shark" and was applied by U.S. intelligence agencies, not North Korea. Said to have been built at about two per year, but production had apparently stopped by 1999. Two, in poor condition, were sold to Vietnam in 1996.

The special forces transport version unit captured off the South Korean east coast on 17-9-96 was of crude design and manufacture and was specially configured for operation in support of North Korea's Reconnaissance Bureau of the Ministry of the People's Armed Forces, which has two other submarines of the same class under its control based at Toejo Dong; the stranded craft had what appeared to be 16 mine or external cargo canister-carrying fixtures, eight per side, above the waterline but did not have any torpedo tubes.

MIDGET SUBMARINES [SSM]

♦ **36 Yugo class** Bldr: Yukdaeso-ri SY (In serv. 1965–late 1980s)

Yugo-class special forces variant Associated Press, 8-98

Yugo-class special forces variant Associated Press, 8-98

D: 76 tons surf./90 tons sub. **S:** 10 kts surf./4 kts sub.
Dim: 20.0–22.0 × 2.0 × 1.6
A: some: 2 bow 533-mm TT (no reloads)
M: 1 MTU diesel, electric drive; 1 7-bladed prop; 160 shp—1 5-bladed freewheeling auxiliary prop for noise reduction
Range: 550/10 surf.; 50/4 sub. **Crew:** 2 + 6–7 special forces personnel

Remarks: Western nickname derives from the probably erroneous belief that Yugoslavia provided some design and technical support input to this extremely primitive design. Primarily intended for the insertion of saboteurs and other special forces personnel and operated for (and possibly by) the Reconnaissance Bureau of the Ministry of the People's Armed Forces rather than the navy proper. The oldest units have reached the ends of their useful lives, and nine or more have been discarded. One unarmed unit was caught in a fishing net off the northeast coast of South Korea on 22-8-98 and after the murder/suicide of the nine-man crew was brought into a South Korean port; the craft was not equipped with a sonar system and had no torpedo tubes. The casing and sail are made of GRP. There are 10 watertight compartments to the pressure hull. Small arms and antitank rockets are carried for the saboteur swimmers, as is a rubber boat.

FRIGATES [FF]

♦ **1 Soho class** Bldr: Najin SY (In serv. 5-82)

823

D: 1,600 tons (1,845 fl) **S:** 25 kts **Dim:** 73.8 × 15.5 × 3.8 (hull)
A: 4 P-15 Termit (SS-N-2A Styx) SSM; 1 100-mm 56-cal. B-34 DP; 2 twin 37-mm 63-cal. AA; 2 twin 30-mm 65-cal. AK-230 AA; 2 twin 25-mm 80-cal. 2M-3M AA; 2 5-round RBU-1200 ASW RL
Electronics:
Radar: 1 . . . nav.; 1 Rangout (Square Tie) missile target desig.; 1 MR-104 Rys' (Drum Tilt) gun f.c.
Sonar: MG-10 hull-mounted HF searchlight
M: 2 or 4 diesels; 2 props; approx. 16,000 bhp **Crew:** 190 tot.

Remarks: Reportedly launched in 1980. Catamaran hull. Has a helicopter platform aft. Design was evidently not a success.

CORVETTES [FFL]

♦ **2 Najin class** Bldr: Najin SY

531 (In serv. 1973)	631 (In serv. 1975)

Najin-class corvette 531—with Nampo-class personnel landing craft configured as a patrol boat in the foreground Siegfried Breyer Collection

Najin-class corvette JMSDF, 5-93

D: 1,200 tons (1,500 fl) **S:** 25 kts **Dim:** 100.0 × 10.0 × 2.7
A: 2 P-15 Termit (SS-N-2A Styx) SSM; 2 single 100-mm 56-cal. B-34 DP; 2 twin 57-mm 70-cal. AA; 2 twin 30-mm 65-cal. AK-230 AA; 4 twin 25-mm 80-cal. 2M-3 AA; 2 d.c. racks; up to 30 mines
Electronics:
Radar: 1 . . . nav.; 1 Type 351 (Pot Head) surf. search; 1 Fut-B (Slim Net) air search; 1 Rangout (Square Tie) surf. search/missile target acquisition; 1 MR-104 Rys' (Drum Tilt) gun f.c.
Sonar: probable hull-mounted HF search (Russian Tamir-11 equivalent)
EW: . . . intercept array, 6 3-round decoy RL
M: 2 diesels; 2 props; 15,000 bhp **Range:** 4,000/14 **Crew:** 180 tot.

Remarks: Very primitive design, crude in finish and appearance and not related in origin to any Chinese or Russian design. A triple 533-mm torpedo tube mount was replaced in the early 1980s by a trainable twin Termit missile launcher mount, which was subsequently replaced by fixed Styx launchers evidently removed from an Osa-class missile boat during the later 1980s; the launchers are oriented directly forward and the slightest failure during launch would spell disaster. Also added since completion are two AK-230 twin 30-mm AA mountings located centerline abaft each stack, while four twin 14.5-mm AA, two depth charge mortars, and four RBU-1200 ASW RL have been deleted.

GUIDED-MISSILE PATROL CRAFT [PTG]

♦ **12–15 Soju class** Bldr: North Korea (In serv. 1981–93)

D: approx. 220 tons (fl) **S:** 34 kts **Dim:** 43.0 × 7.5 × 1.8
A: 4 P-15 Termit (SS-N-2A Styx) SSM; 2 twin 30-mm 65-cal. AK-230 AA
Electronics:
Radar: 1 Rangout (Square Tie) surf. search/missile target acquisition; 1 MR-104 Rys' (Drum Tilt) gun f.c.
M: 3 Type M-503A diesels; 3 props; 12,000 bhp
Range: . . ./. . . **Crew:** 30–40 tot.

Remarks: North Korean version of the Russian Osa-I. The last two were delivered during 1993.

♦ **6 Sohung class** Bldr: North Korea (In serv. 1980–81)

D: 80 tons (fl) **S:** 40 kts **Dim:** 26.8 × 6.2 × 1.5
A: 2 P-15 Termit (SS-N-2A Styx) SSM; 1 twin 25-mm 80-cal. 2M-3M AA
Electronics:
Radar: 1 Rangout (Square Tie) surf. search/missile target acquisition
M: 4 M-50F-4 diesels; 4 props; 4,800 bhp **Crew:** 19–20 tot.

GUIDED-MISSILE PATROL CRAFT [PTG] *(continued)*

Remarks: Steel-hulled version of the Soviet Komar class, of which North Korea operated as many as 10 until around 1990. Considering the small number of Sohungs built, the design may not have been successful.

♦ 4 ex-Chinese Huangfeng class (Project 032)
Bldr: Jiangnan SY, Shanghai (In serv. 1960–75)

D: 167 tons (186.5 normal; 205 fl) **S:** 35 kts
Dim: 38.75 × 7.60 × 1.70 (mean hull; 2.99 over props)
A: 4 C-201 HY-1 (CSS-N-1) or P-15 Termit (SS-N-2A Styx) SSM; 2 twin 25-mm 80-cal. Type 81 AA
Electronics: Radar: 1 Type 352 (Square Tie) surf. search/target desig.
M: 3 Type 42-160 (M-503A) diesels; 3 props; 12,000 bhp
Electric: 65 kw tot. **Range:** 800/30 **Crew:** 28 tot.

Remarks: Transferred in 1982. Chinese version of the Soviet Osa-I (Project 205) design.

♦ up to 8 ex-Soviet Osa-I class (Project 205)

D: 171 tons (209.5 fl) **S:** 38.5 kts
Dim: 38.6 (37.5 wl) × 7.6 (6.3 wl) × 1.8 (hull; 2.9 props)
A: 4 P-15 Termit (SS-N-2A Styx) SSM; 2 twin 30-mm 65-cal. AK-230 AA
Electronics:
Radar: 1 Rangout (Square Tie) surf. search/target desig.; 1 MR-104 Rys' (Drum Tilt) gun f.c.
M: 3 M-503A2 diesels; 3 props; 12,000 bhp **Electric:** 200 kw tot.
Range: 500/34; 750/25 **Endurance:** 5 days **Crew:** 4 officers, 24 enlisted

Remarks: Twelve were transferred from the USSR in 1968 and four more in 1972–83, but of the total, eight or more have been discarded to date.

TORPEDO BOATS [PT]

♦ up to 98 Sin Hung class
Bldr: North Korea (In serv. 1970s)

D: 25 tons (fl) **S:** 40 kts **Dim:** 19.8 × 3.4 × 1.7
A: 2 twin 14.5-mm 93-cal. 2M-7 AA; 2 fixed 450-mm TT
Electronics: Radar: 1 Zarnitsa (Skin Head) or Type 351 (Pot Head) surf. search
M: 2 M-50F-series diesels; 2 props; 2,400 bhp **Crew:** 15–20 tot.

Remarks: A small number were transferred to foreign clients. Some built during 1981–85 are reported to have had hydrofoils fitted forward as in the Chinese Huchuan class, and some may have 533-mm torpedo tubes vice 450-mm. As many as 26 or even more may have been retired or discarded, as the craft were very lightly constructed.

♦ up to 12 Soviet P 6 (Project 183)

D: 55 tons (66.5 fl) **S:** 43 kts **Dim:** 25.40 × 6.24 × 1.24
A: 2 twin 25-mm 80-cal. 2M-3 AA; 2 fixed 533-mm TT; 8 d.c. in tilt racks
Electronics:
Radar: 1 Zarnitsa (Skin Head) or Type 351 (Pot Head) surf. search
M: 4 M-50F-4 diesels; 4 props; 4,800 bhp **Range:** 600/33; 1,000/14
Crew: 15–20 tot.

Remarks: Forty-five were transferred by the USSR during the early 1960s. Wooden construction. Some lack torpedo tubes but have additional AA guns.

PATROL CRAFT [PC]

Note: A 38-m "stealth" patrol boat with faceted hull and superstructure was said to be in service as of late 1998. The craft is said to be capable of 50 kts, to have a crew of 30, and to be armed with 57-mm and 37-mm gunmounts. No other data are available, but the unit is unlikely to have modern low-detectable features.

♦ 13 Taechong I and II class
Bldr: Najin SY (In serv. 1975–95)

D: 385 tons (410 fl) **S:** 30 kts **Dim:** 59.8 × 7.2 × 2.0
A: 1 100-mm 56-cal. B-34 DP; 1 twin 57-mm 70-cal. Type 66 AA; 1 twin 25-mm 80-cal. Type 61M; 2 twin 14.5-mm 93-cal. AA; 2 5-round RBU-1200 ASW RL; 2 d.c. racks; . . . mines
Electronics:
Radar: 1 Type 351 (Pot Head) surf. search
Sonar: Tamir-11 HF (24.5–30 kHz)
M: 4 Soviet Type 40D diesels; 4 props; 8,800 bhp **Range:** 2,000/12
Crew: 75–80 tot.

Remarks: Design strongly resembles the Chinese Hainan class, but has a lower superstructure and less freeboard to the hull. The first eight have characteristics as above; later units (Taechong II, sometimes referred to as the Mayang class) are 60.8 m o.a. and displace about 420 tons full load but are otherwise similarly equipped. One Taechong I was badly damaged by South Korean Navy gunfire on 15-6-99 in the Yellow Sea.

♦ 6 Chinese Hainan class (In serv. 1975–78)

D: 395 tons (430 fl) **S:** 30.5 kts (28 sust.) **Dim:** 58.77 × 7.20 × 2.24 (hull)
A: 2 twin 57-mm 70-cal. Type 66 AA; 2 twin 25-mm Type 61M AA; 4 5-round Type 81 ASW RL; 2 BMB-2 d.c. mortars; 2 d.c. racks; . . . mines
Electronics:
Radar: 1 Type 351 (Pot Head) surf. search
Sonar: Tamir-11 HF hull-mounted (24.5–30 kHz)
M: 4 diesels; 4 props; 8,800 bhp **Range:** 750/18; 1,800/14 **Crew:** 78 tot.

Remarks: Two were transferred in 1975, two in 1976, and two in 1978. The weapons are all Chinese versions of Soviet equipment.

♦ 14 Chinese Shanghai II class (In serv. 1967–69)

D: 122.5 tons (134.8 fl) **S:** 28.5 kts **Dim:** 38.78 × 5.41 × 1.49 (hull; 1.55 full load)
A: 2 twin 37-mm 63-cal. Type 74 AA; 2 twin 25-mm 80-cal. Type 61M AA; . . . d.c.; . . . mines
Electronics:
Radar: 1 Type 756 nav. or Type 351 (Pot Head) or Zarnitsa (Skin Head) surf. search
M: 2 M-50F-4 (1,200 bhp each) and 2 Type 12D6 (910-bhp each) diesels; 4 props; 4,220 bhp
Electric: 39 kw tot. **Range:** 750/16.5 **Endurance:** 7 days **Crew:** 36 tot.

Remarks: Transferred circa 1967–69, probably as new construction. One was stricken about 1988, and one was damaged in combat with ROKN units on 15-6-99.

♦ 3 Sariwon class
Bldr: North Korea (In serv. 1965)

D: 450 tons (490 fl) **S:** 21 kts **Dim:** 62.1 × 7.3 × 2.4
A: 2 twin 57-mm 70-cal. AA; 4 quadruple 14.5-mm 93-cal. AA
Electronics:
Radar: 1 Don-2 nav.; 1 Type 351 (Pot Head) surf. search
EW: no intercept; 4 6-round decoy RL
M: 2 diesels; 2 props; 3,000 bhp **Range:** 2,700/18 **Crew:** 65–70 tot.

Remarks: Data are approximate. Possible current pennant numbers: 725, 726, 727, 728. One reportedly serves as flagship of the Maritime Coastal Security Police fleet. Have been rearmed with Chinese-made 57-mm mounts fore and aft and 14.5-mm machinegun mounts; all ASW ordnance appears to have been removed. Similar to the *Tral*-class unit but have a more angular and higher bridge superstructure. May have mine rails.

♦ 18 Soviet S.O. 1 class (Project 215) (In serv. 1957–68)

D: 190 tons (215 fl) **S:** 28 kts **Dim:** 42.0 × 6.1 × 1.9
A: 6 Soviet version: 2 twin 25-mm 80-cal. 2M-3M AA; 4 5-round RBU-1200 ASW RL; 2 d.c. racks (24 tot. d.c.); . . . mines—12 North Korean version: 1 85-mm 52-cal. DP; 2 single 37-mm 63-cal. AA; 2 twin 14.5-mm 93-cal. 2M-7 AA
Electronics:
Radar: 1 Don-2 nav. or 1 Type 351 (Pot Head) surf. search
Sonar: Soviet version: 1 Tamir-11 searchlight-type (24.5–30 kHz)
M: 3 Type 40D diesels; 3 props; 7,500 bhp **Range:** 1,100/13 **Crew:** 30–40 tot.

Remarks: Six were transferred from the USSR in antisubmarine configuration during 1957–61; the remainder were built in North Korea for patrol purposes and were all in service by 1968. Design was considered cramped by the Soviets, and the craft are bad rollers and very noisy. These are the last operated by any navy.

♦ 1 ex-Soviet Tral class (Project 59)
Bldr: Sevastopol' Navy Yard (In serv. 1938)

671

Tral-class patrol craft 671 JMSDF, 5-93

D: 441 tons (476 fl) **S:** 18 kts **Dim:** 62.00 × 7.10 × 2.39
A: 1 85-mm tank gun; 2 twin 37-mm 63-cal. V47-M AA; 4 quadruple 14.5-mm 93-cal. AA; up to 30 mines
Electronics:
Radar: 1 . . . nav.; 1 Type 351 (Pot Head) surf. search
EW: no intercept; 4 6-round decoy RL
M: 2 diesels; 2 props; 2,800 bhp tot.
Range: 2,700/18; 4,100/14 **Fuel:** 96 tons **Crew:** 60 tot.

Remarks: Former minesweeper, transferred in 1955 along with one sister that, as of 1995, had been relegated to museum service. Soviet units transferred were *Strela* (T.1) and *Paravan* (T.5). Thought to have been discarded over a decade ago, one of the two reappeared during 5-93 in support of the last North Korean ballistic-missile test firings into the Sea of Japan. That this relic was still in operational use indicates the primitive state of technology in the North Korean Navy.
Combat systems: Retains some mechanical minesweeping equipment, including the cable drum and winch, floats, and depressors. No ASW or EW intercept equipment is fitted. The tank turret has replaced the 100-mm 51-cal. low-angle mount originally installed on the forecastle, and the decoy rocket launchers are mounted on forecastle deck extensions at the break.

PATROL BOATS [PB]

♦ 18 Sinpo class (In serv. 1970s–80s)

D: 60 tons (70 fl) **S:** 43 kts **Dim:** 25.40 × 6.24 × 1.35
A: 2 single 37-mm 63-cal. AA; 4 d.c. in tilt racks
Electronics:
Radar: 1 Zarnitsa (Skin Head) or Type 351 (Pot Head) surf. search
M: 4 M-50F-4 diesels; 4 props; 4,800 bhp **Range:** 600/30, 900/14
Crew: 15–20 tot.

Remarks: Built on a steel version of the P-6 torpedo boat hull. Some may also have one or two twin 25-mm 2M-3M AA mounts, making them badly overloaded and unsteady gun platforms.

♦ 51 Chong Jin class
Bldr: North Korea (In serv. 1975–. . .)

D: 82 tons (fl) **S:** 40 kts **Dim:** 27.7 × 6.4 × 1.8
A: 1 85-mm 52-cal. tank gun; 2 twin 14.5-mm 93-cal. 2M-7 AA
Electronics:
Radar: 1 . . . nav. or Zarnitsa (Skin Head) or Type 351 (Pot Head) surf. search

PATROL BOATS [PB] *(continued)*

M: 4 Soviet M-50-series diesels; 4 props; 4,800 bhp
Range: 325/19 **Crew:** 24 tot.

Remarks: A variant of the Chaho class, differing primarily in armament. One was sunk by South Korean naval forces on the west coast on 14-6-99.

♦ 52 Chaho class Bldr: North Korea (In serv. 1974–late 1970s)

D: 82 tons (fl) **S:** 40 kts **Dim:** 27.7 × 6.4 × 1.8
A: 2 twin 14.5-mm 93-cal. 2M-7 AA; 1 40-round 122-mm BM-21 artillery RL (40 reloads)
Electronics:
Radar: 1 . . . nav. or Zarnitsa (Skin Head) or Type 351 (Pot Head) surf. search
M: 4 Soviet M-50-series diesels; 4 props; 4,800 bhp
Range: 325/19 **Crew:** 24 tot.

Remarks: Based on the P-6 torpedo boat design, but with a steel hull. Three transferred to Iran in 4-87 had a twin 23-mm AA mount aft and no gunmount forward; some or all of the North Korean examples may now be similarly armed. The rockets are primarily intended to be expended at surface ship targets, although they may have a secondary shore bombardment function.

♦ 10 or more TB-11PA class Bldr: . . ., North Korea (In serv. 1980s)

D: 8 tons (fl) **S:** 35 kts **Dim:** 11.2 × 2.7 × 1.0
A: 1 14.5-mm 93-cal. mg **Electronics:** Radar: 1 Type 24 nav.
M: 2 DOHC diesels; 2 props; 520 bhp **Range:** 200/15 **Crew:** 4 tot.

Remarks: GRP hull-construction. Used for harbor patrol by the Maritime Coastal Security Police. There is also a larger version known as the "TB 40A," of which six or more may be in service. The "Type 24" radar is probably a Japanese commercial import.

♦ . . . infiltration craft Bldr: . . ., North Korea

D: 5 tons (fl) **S:** 35 kts **Dim:** 9.3 × 2.5 × 1.0
A: 1 14.5-mm 93-cal. mg **Electronics:** Radar: 1 Furuno 701 nav.
M: 1 8-cyl. OHC diesel; 260 bhp **Crew:** 2 tot. + 4–6 infiltrators

Remarks: Above characteristics are typical of the large number of craft built over the last 30 years to infiltrate saboteurs into South Korea. Most have had wooden hulls and are distinguished by a very low freeboard to avoid being detected.

MINE COUNTERMEASURES CRAFT

♦ 23 Yukto I and II–class minesweeping boats [MSB]
Bldr: . . ., North Korea

D: 60 tons (fl) **S:** 12 kts **Dim:** 24.0 × 4.0 × . . .
A: 1 twin 14.5-mm 93-cal. 2M-7 AA; 4 mines
M: 2 diesels; 2 props; 300 bhp **Crew:** 16–20 tot.

Remarks: Characteristics are estimated. Built during the 1980s as replacements for the 1950s-supplied Soviet KM-4 class. The Yukto II class, of which only four are said to be in service, is reportedly 21.0 m o.a. All are of wooden construction and are capable of sweeping only moored mechanical mines.

AMPHIBIOUS CRAFT

♦ 10 Hantae-class utility landing craft [LCU] (In serv. 1980s)

D: 350 tons (fl) **S:** 12 kts **Dim:** 48.0 × 6.5 × 2.0
A: 4 twin 25-mm 80-cal. 2M-3M AA
M: 2 diesels; 2 props; 4,350 bhp **Range:** 2,000/12 **Crew:** 40 tot.

Remarks: All data are estimated. Can transport three tanks and up to 350 unsheltered troops for short distances.

♦ 7 Hanchon-class medium landing craft [LCM]
Bldr: North Korea

D: 145 tons (fl) **S:** 10 kts **Dim:** 35.7 × 7.9 × 1.2
A: 1 twin 14.5-mm 93-cal. AA
Electronics: Radar: 1 Zarnitsa (Skin Head) surf. search
M: 2 Soviet 3D12 diesels; 600 bhp **Range:** 600/6 **Crew:** 16 tot.

Remarks: Data are estimated. Believed capable of carrying two tanks or 200 troops for short distances. Two others have been retired.

♦ 18 Hungnam-class vehicle landing craft [LCM]
Bldr: North Korea (In serv. 1970s)

D: 70 tons (fl) **S:** 8 kts **Dim:** 17.0 × 4.4 × 1.2
A: 2 twin 14.5-mm 93-cal. 2M-7 AA
M: 2 diesels; 2 props; 400 bhp **Crew:** 4–8 tot.

Remarks: Data are estimated. Probably based on Chinese designs. Can probably carry about 35 tons of vehicle cargo or up to 100 unsheltered troops for short distances.

♦ 7 U.S. Hand Grenade–series fast infiltration launches [LCP]
Bldr: Fountain Powerboat Industries, Beaufort County, N.C. (In serv. 1993)

Remarks: Ordered between 11-92 and 3-93 were three 11.6-m, one 14.3-m, and three 14.6-m high-speed boats allegedly for racing purposes but actually for saboteur infiltration. All are said to be capable of speeds greater than 100 kts and are powered by diesel engines producing 2,000 bhp (although they are said to require intensive maintenance and to have engines that easily self-destruct). The craft are radar-equipped and probably carry small arms. The total cost was $1.71 million. The American agent who purchased the craft was belatedly indicted in 11-98 under the Trading with the Enemy Act, but by then the craft had been delivered.

♦ up to 95 Nampo-class assault landing craft [LCP]
Bldr: North Korea

D: 82 tons (fl) **S:** 40 kts **Dim:** 27.7 × 6.1 × 1.8
A: 2 twin 14.5-mm 93-cal. AA
Electronics:
Radar: 1 Zarnitsa (Skin Head) or Type 351 (Pot Head) surf. search
M: 4 M-50F-4 diesels; 4 props; 4,800 bhp **Range:** 325/19 **Crew:** 19 tot.

Remarks: Some were exported as patrol boats with the bow door welded up, and some may be in a similar status in North Korea. The steel hull is essentially that of the Chaho/Sin Hung series, using the forward compartment to accommodate about 30 troops but no vehicles. Troops debark via a narrow gangway over the bow. After a sustained voyage with the craft planing, the troops would probably be in no condition to conduct combat operations.

♦ 135 Kong Bang–series surface-effect personnel landing craft [LCPA] Bldr: North Korea (In serv. mid-1980s to 1992)

Remarks: Probably based on an imported British Hovercraft SRN-6 prototype. Aside from the 25-m Mod. 1 prototype, there are about 55 twin-engine, 21-m Mod. 2 and 79 single-engine, 18-m Mod. 3. Each variant can probably transport not more than one squad of fully equipped troops, and ranges (assuming they are meant to return) are probably not more than 120–150 n.m. in loaded condition, at around 40–45 kts. Material condition is probably already declining, and many may no longer be operable.

♦ . . . saboteur infiltration submersibles [LSDV]

D: 10 tons sub. **S:** 40–50 kts surf./4–6 kts sub. **Dim:** 12.8 × . . . × . . .
M: 3 gasoline outdrive engines; 3 props
Range: . . ./. . . **Crew:** 4 crew + 2–5 swimmers

Remarks: Can fully submerge to a depth of about 3 m. Based on the east coast at Impo-ri. A craft of this type was sunk by gunfire on 18-12-98, the four-man crew having committed suicide. May be of GRP construction. Like the Cluster Osprey class, this design is launched by a 50- to 100-ton mother ship disguised as a fishing boat.

♦ 8 or more Cluster Osprey–class semi-submersible saboteur infiltration launches [LSDV] Bldr: . . . SY, Wonsan (In serv. 1985–. . .)

Cluster Osprey semi-submersible—artist's impression *Ships of the World,* 3-99

D: 5 tons **S:** 50 kts (surf.) **Dim:** 9.3 × 2.50 × . . .
M: 3 gasoline outdrive engines; 3 props **Crew:** 6 tot.

Remarks: Intended for saboteur delivery to South Korea, traveling surfaced until near the insertion point and then ballasting down to run in awash.

Note: Also said to be in use for sabotage and infiltration missions are several two-man submersibles capable of diving to 5–8 m depth.

AUXILIARIES

♦ 1 Kowan-class submarine rescue ship [ASR]
Bldr: Najin SY(In serv. late 1980s)

5992

Kowan-class submarine rescue ship 5992 Boris Lemachko Collection

D: approx. 2,100 tons (fl) **S:** 12–14 kts **Dim:** 84.0 × 14.3 × 3.9
A: 6 twin 14.5-mm 93-cal. 2M-7 AA
Electronics: Radar: 1 . . . nav.
M: 4 diesels; 2 props; 8,000 bhp **Crew:** 160 tot.

Remarks: Catamaran hull, presumably intended to straddle a sunken submarine, although there is no sign of heavy lift gear or even a rescue bell.

Note: There are said to be eight oceangoing cargo ships adapted for use as midget submarine mother ships [AS], with names reported to be *Choong Seong-Ho No. 1, Choong Seong-Ho No. 2, Choong Seong-Ho No. 3, Dong Hae-Ho, Geon Ae Gook-Ho, Hae Gum Gang-Ho, Song Rim-Ho,* and *Soo Gun-Ho;* no data available. Converted fishing craft are believed by South Korea to be used as intelligence collection vessels [AGI].

SERVICE CRAFT

Remarks: There are undoubtedly a large number of small service craft for use as stores carriers, personnel ferries, and so forth, but no data are available. The civilian hydrographic service operates four coastal survey craft.

KOREA, SOUTH

Republic of Korea

Personnel (2001): 63,000 total, including 33,000 naval (about 5,200 officers) and 24,000 marines (1,800 officers); of the total of 56,000, 17,000 enlisted are conscripts. There are about 5,000 civilian employees, and about 9,000 naval and marine reserves are available.

Bases: Fleet headquarters is at Chinhae. First Fleet headquarters is at Donghae, with lesser facilities at Kojin, Kisamun, Pohang, Chukpyon, and Kuryonpo. Second Fleet headquarters is at Pyongtaek, with lesser facilities at Daechung Do, Ochong Do, Ijak Do, and Yong Pyong Do. Third Fleet headquarters is at Pusan, with repair and submarine facilities at Chinhae, repair facilities at Pusan and Ulsan, and lesser facilities at Kadok Do, Yokchi Do, Komun Do, Hansan Do, Cheja Do, Cheju Do, Mokpo, and Geoje Do. Air bases are at Chinhae and Pohang. Pyongtaek replaced Inchon as Second Fleet headquarters in 12-99.

Naval Aviation: Fixed wing: 8 P-3C Update III Orion (with AGM-84C Harpoon SSM) and 8 S-2C/E Tracker maritime patrol aircraft and 5 Reims-Cessna F-406 Caravan II target-services aircraft. Helicopters: 17 AgustaWestland Super Lynx Mk 99 and 13 Super Lynx Mk 100 helicopters for shipboard service, 6 AS.316B and AS.319B Alouette-III helicopters assigned to the marine corps, 10 UH-60 Blackhawk and 10 UH-1 Huey utility helicopters, and 2 OH-58 Kiowa training helicopters. ROK Air Force F-16 fighters are equipped to launch U.S.-supplied AGM-84C Harpoon antiship missiles, of which 36 were ordered during 1995. The radars in the P-3C Orion aircraft have been upgraded from APS-134(V)6 to APS-137(V)6, adding an inverse synthetic aperture (ISAR) capability for tracking and identifying targets.

South Korean Super Lynx Mk 100—aboard destroyer *Kwanggaeto-Daewang* (DD 971) Mitsuhiro Kadota, 2-01

Coastal Defense: Three batteries of shore-based RGM-84 Harpoon antiship missiles were ordered early in 1987. There are radar surveillance sites at frequent intervals along the coast.

Weapons and Sensors: Most systems still in use are of U.S. or European origin, although Korean electronics firms such as GoldStar and Samsung are manufacturing European electronics under license. GoldStar is developing the White Shark heavyweight wire-guided submarine torpedo based on the U.S. Alliant NT-37 series, and the lightweight Blue Shark ASW torpedo is also under development. The standard ASW torpedo is the U.S. Mk 46 Mod. 1 or Mod. 2, although a few earlier KT-44 (a license-built U.S. Mk 44 of 1960s vintage) may still be available.

On 19-7-00, 110 Standard SM-2 Block IIIA missiles and related equipment were requested from the U.S.A., at a cost of $159 million.

South Korean destroyers and patrol craft employ a locally built gatling AA mount using the G.E. M197 three-barreled 20-mm Vulcan gun. Daewoo Shipyard developed and manufactures the Nobong, a twin powered mounting for Bofors 40-mm 60-cal. AA guns; the mount incorporates an enclosed local control station.

An antiship missile similar to the U.S. Harpoon but with a range of 200 km is in development; it was planned to enter service in 2003 but will probably be delayed. Shipboard Super Lynx helicopters are equipped with Sea Skua antiship missiles, of which up to four can be carried.

The marine corps acquired 28 U.S. SMAW (Shoulder-launched Multipurpose Assault Weapon) launchers in 10-98, with plans to acquire 200 more later; the Mk 153 Mod. 1 launcher can fire either Mk 6 Mod. 0 HEAA (High-Explosive Anti-Armor) or HEDP (High-Explosive Dual-Purpose) rockets to a range of 500 m.

Note: Pennant numbers are subject to change at unspecified intervals. The numerals 0 and 4 are considered unlucky and are not used.

Although preliminary plans to construct a 12,000-ton "aircraft carrier" date to 1994, there do not appear to be any plans to build the ship in the foreseeable future.

ATTACK SUBMARINES [SS]

♦ **0 (+ 3) German Type 214**
Bldr: Hyundai Shipyard, Ulsan

	Laid down	L	In serv.
S	. . .	. . .	2007
S	. . .	. . .	2008
S	. . .	. . .	2009

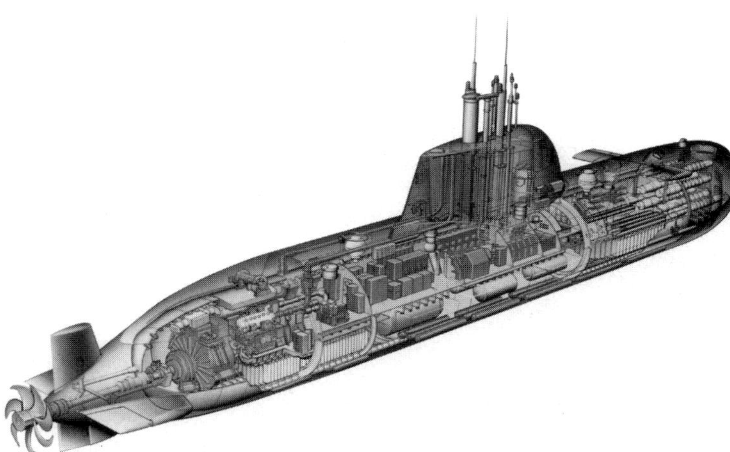

Type 214 submarine—U.S. Navy submarine *Helena* (SSN 725) in background HDW, 2000

D: 1,700 tons surf./1,860 tons sub.
S: . . . kts surf./. . . kts sub. (2–6 kts sub. on fuel cells)
Dim: 65.00 × 6.30 × . . .
A: 8 bow 533-mm TT (16 tot. wire-guided torpedoes and UGM-84C Harpoon missiles)
Electronics:
Radar: 1 . . . nav./surf. search
Sonar: cylindrical MF bow passive array; LF through MF passive flank array; towed LF linear passive array; passive ranging array; active range and bearing array
EW: . . . intercept; Sonartech Atlas torpedo-detection and tracking syst.
M: 2 MTU 16V 396–series diesel generator sets (1,000+ kw each), 1 Siemens Permasyn motor; . . . shp—2 × 120-kw Siemens PEM fuel-cell auxiliary propulsion units
Range: 12,000/. . . surf.; 8,000/8 snorkel; 1,248/4 sub. (on fuel cells; 420/8 on battery)
Endurance: 50 days **Crew:** 27 tot. (accomm. for 35)

Remarks: Design was selected 3-11-00. The submarines will be built in South Korea with the technical assistance of Howaldtswerke, which will also assist South Korean designers in preparing a follow-on 3,000-ton submarine design. The German government approved the delivery of the necessary $590 million worth of production equipment on 6-5-01. There were originally to have been six second-generation submarines ordered. The Type 214 is an expanded version of the German-Italian Type 212 design; three others have been ordered for the Greek Navy.
Hull systems: Inner and outer hulls are of austenitic steel. The submarines are to have 10% reserve buoyancy. Battery set to develop 600–900 V. Are to have the hydrogen peroxide Siemens Polymer Electrolite Membrane (PEM) fuel-cell air-independent auxiliary propulsion system.
Combat systems: May employ the STN Atlas Elektronik ISUS 90 combat data system. The sonar array is to include a cylindrical MF passive array forward, an MF/LF passive flank system (with three arrays per side), a towed LF passive array, an active ranging set, and a bow-mounted active mine-avoidance set. A Zeiss SERO 400 optronic, non-hull-penetrating periscope will be used. Four of the eight weapons tubes will have expulsion systems to enable launching antiship missiles; the others will be of the swim-out variety.

Note: A Russian offer of two to six Kilo-class (Project 636) submarines, made during 5-98, was formally declined late during 10-00.

♦ **9 German Type 209/1200**
Bldr: Daewoo SY, Okpo (SS 061: Howaldtswerke, Kiel)

	L	In serv.	
SS 061 Jang Bogo	18-6-92	2-6-93	
SS 062 Lee Chun	12-10-92	30-4-94	
SS 063 Choi Museon	7-8-93	27-2-95	
SS 065 Park Wi	21-5-94	3-2-96	
SS 066 Lee Jongmu	17-5-95	29-8-96	
SS 067 Jeong Un	5-5-96	3-98	(del. 29-8-97)
SS 068 Lee Sunsin	21-5-98	2-00	(del. 31-1-00)
SS 069 Na Daeyong	6-99	11-00	
SS 071 Lee Eokgi	26-5-00	11-01	(del.)

D: 1,100 tons surf./1,285 tons sub. **S:** 11 kts surf./22 kts sub.
Dim: 56.10 × 6.20 (7.60 over stern planes) × 5.50 (surf.)
A: 8 bow 533-mm TT (14 STN Atlas Elektronik SUT Mod. 2 torpedoes or 28 mines)

ATTACK SUBMARINES [SS] *(continued)*

Choi Museon (SS 063) U.S. Navy, 10-00

Park Wi (SS 065) Brian Morrison, 6-00

Jang Bogo (SS 061) *Ships of the World,* 2000

Electronics:
Radar: 1 . . . multimode
Sonar: STN Atlas Elektronik CSU-83 suite
EW: G.T.E. Ferret intercept (1–40 GHz); ArgoSystems AR-700 intercept
M: 4 MTU 12V493 AZ 80 diesels (800 bhp each), 4 Siemens 405-kw generator sets, 1 electric motor; 1 prop; 5,000 shp
Range: 7,500/8 surf.; 11,300/4 snorkel; 28/20, 230/8, 466/4 sub. **Fuel:** 85 tons
Endurance: 50 days **Crew:** 8 officers, 27 enlisted (accomm. for 39)

Remarks: SS 061 was built in Germany and handed over 15-10-92, while the next two were assembled in South Korea using components shipped from Germany. Phase II units were assembled in Korea, with a steadily increasing proportion of all-Korean materials and components, but some critical structures and all sensor and machinery equipment continued to be imported. The first three were ordered during 2-88, to standard IKL design; a second group of three was ordered during 1991. The third increment was ordered by 5-95, but a planned fourth trio was dropped. SS 061 left Kiel 16-4-93 aboard the dock ship *Dock Express 11.* Average cost was said to be $186 million. SS 063 was named for Admiral Choi Museon, who defeated 500 Japanese ships in 1326.
Hull systems: Are reportedly the quietest-yet Type 209 submarines, due to the use of advanced sound-damping rafting of the machinery. Maximum diving depth is 320 m, with a 250-m working depth. Have four 120-cell, 11,500-amp-hr batteries weighing a total of 257 tons.
Combat systems: Equipped with the STN Atlas Elektronik ISUS 83 (Integrated Sensor Underwater System) combat data system, with four display consoles. Have the Ferranti FMS-15 acoustic processor for a towed passive linear hydrophone system and also the Ferranti AP2000 autopilot. Reported to have an ArgoSystems intercept system with a Deutsche Aerospace USK 800/1 periscope-mounted antenna. Only 96 SUT torpedoes were ordered, the intention being to switch to an indigenous weapon made by South Korea's GoldStar. SS 068 and later were to employ nonpenetrating optronic sensor masts. SS 069 and SS 071 are equipped to launch UGM-84 Harpoon antiship missiles, but no missiles have been ordered.

MIDGET SUBMARINES [SSM]

♦ 3 or more Italian-designed S.X. 756 class
Bldrs: First unit: COS.M.O.S., Livorno; others: Hanjin Industrial SB, Masan (In serv. 1988–. . .)

D: 78 tons surf./83 tons sub. **S:** 8.5 kts surf./6 kts sub. **Dim:** 25.20 × 2.02 × . . .
A: 2 533-mm torpedoes in drop gear or 6–8 mines or 40 limpet mines
M: diesel-electric: 1 diesel generator set; 1 prop; . . . shp—bow-thruster
Range: 1,600/7 surf.; 60/4.5 sub. **Endurance:** 20 days
Crew: 6 tot. + 8 commandos

Remarks: The design was originated by COS.M.O.S. and was built under license or possibly from prefabricated kits. Can operate at up to 100-m depth. Have one fixed and one telescoping periscope. A passive sonar transducer array surrounds the small sail.

♦ 3 KSS-1 (Dolgorae) class Bldr: Hyundai SY, Ulsan

SSM 051 (In serv. 1-3-85)
SSM 052 (In serv. 8-11-90)
SSM 053 (In serv. 10-12-91)

D: 150 tons surf./175 tons sub. **S:** 6 kts surf./9 kts sub. **Dim:** . . . × . . . × . . .
A: 2 bow 533-mm TT (no reloads)
Electronics: Sonar: STN Atlas Elektronik active set and passive array
M: 1 diesel generator set; 1 prop; . . . shp **Crew:** 6 tot. + 8 combat swimmers

Remarks: Reportedly the first was delivered in 1983, the others in 1988. May not be assigned to the ROKN proper. Photos show a broad hull, a bulbous bow sonar installation, and a small sail incorporating a folding snorkel mast. There is a single periscope. Are supported by the tender *Dadohae* (ASL 50).

DESTROYERS [DD]

Note: In addition to the new destroyer classes listed, three KDX-III guided-missile destroyers of 7,000 ton std. displacement are to be ordered between 2000 and 2004 for a total of $2.31 billion. They would be equipped with the Lockheed Martin SPY-1-series Aegis, BAE Systems Sampson, or Thales APAR principal radar system (a decision was expected on 20-7-01 but had not been announced as of 9-01); the first would be launched by 2008 and the third commissioned in 2011. All are to be built by Hyundai Shipyard, Ulsan. Another three may be built later. Detailed design was started by Hyundai during 2001.

♦ 0 (+ 3) KDX-II class
Bldr: Daewoo Shipbuilding, Okpo

	Laid down	L	In serv.
975	. . .	12-00	mid-2003
976	. . .	. . .	. . .
977	. . .	. . .	mid-2005

D: 4,200 tons (5,000 fl) **S:** 30+ kts **Dim:** 154.4 × 16.9 × 4.3 (hull)
A: 8 RGM-84C Harpoon SSM; 4 8-cell Mk 41 vertical launch modules (32 Standard SM-2 MR Block IIIA missiles and Vertical-Launch ASROC ASW missiles); 1 21-round RAM Mk 31 Mod. 1 point-defense SAM syst.; 1 127-mm 62-cal. U.S. Mk 45 Mod. 4 DP; 1 30-mm Goalkeeper CIWS; 2 single 20-mm M61A1 Vulcan gatling AA; 2 triple 324-mm Mk 32 ASW TT (Blue Shark or Mk 46 Mod. 2 torpedoes); 2 Super Lynx Mk 99 ASW helicopters
Electronics:
Radar: 1 . . . nav.; 1 Thales-GoldStar MW-08 surf./air search; 1 Raytheon SPS-49(V)5 air search; 2 Thales-GoldStar STIR 2.4 f.c.; 2 Raytheon OT-134 missile illuminators; 1 Thales Goalkeeper f.c.
Sonar: STN Atlas Elektronik DSQS-21 hull-mounted LF; Daewoo . . . towed linear passive array
EW: . . . intercept/jamming; Mk 36 SRBOC decoy syst. (4 6-round Raytheon Mk 137 RL); Daewoo towed torpedo decoy syst.
M: CODOG: 2 G.E. LM-2500 gas turbines (32,480 shp each), 2 MTU 20V956 TB92 diesels (5,140 bhp each); 2 Bird-Johnson CP props; 64,960 shp max.
Electric: 3,200 kw tot. (4 × 800-kw diesel sets)
Range: 4,500/18 **Crew:** 15 officers, 170 enlisted (286 tot. accomm.)

Remarks: Follow-on to KDX-I design, with improved armament. Expected to cost $385 million each. Originally there were to have been six, but in 3-97 it was reported that only three would be built to this design so as to advance the introduction of the more-capable KDX-III class.
Combat systems: To have the BAE Systems–Samsung KDCOM combat data system with 10 display consoles, Thales databus, and U.S. WDS Mk 14 weapon-direction system. The Link 11–equivalent Korean Naval Tactical Datalink Sytem (KNTDS) will be carried.

♦ 3 Kwanggaeto-Daewang (KDX-I) class
Bldr: Daewoo Shipbuilding, Okpo

	Laid down	L	In serv.
DD 971 Kwanggaeto-Daewang	10-95	28-10-96	27-7-98
DD 972 Ulchimundok	. . .	15-10-97	1-9-99
DD 973 Yang Manchun	1997	10-98	6-00

Kwanggaeto-Daewang (DD 971) John Mortimer, 1-01

D: 3,181 tons light (3,855 fl) **S:** 33 kts (18 on diesels)
Dim: 135.4 × 14.2 × 4.3 (hull)
A: 8 RGM-84C Harpoon SSM; 1 Mk 48 Mod. 2 vertical missile launch syst. (16 Sea Sparrow RIM-7M SAM); 1 127-mm 54-cal. OTOBreda DP; 2 30-mm Goalkeeper gatling CIWS; 2 triple 324-mm ASW TT; 2 Super Lynx helicopters (Sea Skua ASM and Mk 46 Mod. 2 ASW torpedoes)

DESTROYERS [DD] *(continued)*

Kwanggaeto-Daewang (DD 971) Mitsuhiro Kadota, 2-01

Ulchimundok (DD 972) Brian Morrison, 6-00

Ulchimundok (DD 972) Brian Morrison, 6-00

Electronics:
- Radar: 1 ISC-Cardion SPS-55M surf. search; 1 Thales MW-08 surveillance; 1 Raytheon SPS-49(V)5 air search; 2 Thales STIR 1.8 f.c.; 2 Thales Goalkeeper f.c. sets
- Sonar: STN Atlas Elektronik DSQS-21BZ hull-mounted; provision for Thales towed linear passive hydrophone array
- EW: ArgoSystems APECS-II/AR-700 intercept/jammer suite; 2 330- to 340-round Matra Défense Dagaie Mk 2 decoy RL syst.; SLQ-25 Nixie towed acoustic torpedo decoy syst.

M: CODOG: 2 G.E. LM-2500 gas turbines (29,500 shp each), 2 MTU 20V956 TB92 diesels (5,140 bhp each); 2 Bird-Johnson CP props; 59,000 shp max.
Electric: 3,200 kw tot. (4 × 800-kw diesel sets)
Range: 4,500/18 **Crew:** 15 officers, 170 enlisted (286 tot. accomm.)

Remarks: Totals as high as 17–20 had originally been planned, but only three were built. The first unit is named for the 19th monarch of the Koguryo Dynasty, who ruled from 391 to 413 A.D. over most of what is now North Korea.
Hull systems: Have a constant-pressure sealed NBC warfare protective citadel.
Combat systems: The BAE Systems–Thales SSCS Mk 7 system (similar to that in the British Type 23 frigate class), with two Thales multifunction weapons-control consoles and eight fiber optic–linked operator consoles, is fitted; more than 100 distributed microprocessors are employed. Have Warner UPX-27 IFF interrogation for the Mk 10 IFF system. The listed passive towed-array sonar system may be added later but was not aboard as of 1999.

♦ 3 ex-U.S. Gearing FRAM I class
Bldr: Consolidated Steel, Orange, Texas (DD 922: Federal SB, Newark, N.J.)

	Laid down	L	In serv.
DD 919 Daejeon (ex-*New,* DD 818)	14-4-45	18-8-45	5-4-46
DD 921 Kwangju (ex-*Richard E. Kraus,* DD 849)	31-7-45	2-3-46	23-5-46
DD 922 Kangwon (ex-*William R. Rush,* DD 714)	19-10-44	8-7-45	21-9-45

Daejeon (DD 919) and Kwangju (DD 921)—with *Cheju* (APD 822) *Ships of the World,* 10-98

D: 2,425 tons (3,500 fl) **S:** 30 kts
Dim: 119.03 (116.74 wl) × 12.52 × 4.45 (6.4 sonar)
A: 8 RGM-84C Harpoon SSM; 2 twin 127-mm 38-cal. Mk 30 DP; 1 twin 40-mm 60-cal. Nobong AA; 2 single 20-mm G.E. Vulcan gatling AA; 2 triple 324-mm Mk 32 ASW TT; 1 Mk 9 d.c. rack (12 Mk 9 d.c.); 1 Super Lynx Mk 99 ASW helicopter
Electronics:
- Radar: 1 Raytheon SPS-10 surf. search; 1 Thales DA-08 air search; 1 Western Electric Mk 25 f.c.
- Sonar: Raytheon DE 1191 hull-mounted (5–7 kHz)
- TACAN: SRN-15
- EW: WLR-1 intercept; 2 decoy RL; T Mk 6 Fanfare acoustic torpedo decoy

M: 2 sets General Electric geared steam turbines; 2 props; 60,000 shp
Boilers: 4 Babcock & Wilcox; 39.8 kg/cm^2, 454° C **Electric:** 1,200 kw tot.
Range: 975/32; 2,400/25; 4,800/15 **Fuel:** 640 tons **Crew:** 274 tot.

Remarks: DD 919 and 921 were purchased 25-2-77 and DD 922 on 1-7-78. DD 919 is based at Chinhae, DD 921 at Inchon, and DD 922 at Donghae.
Disposals: *Kyonggi* (DD 923; ex-*Newman K. Perry,* DD 883) was stricken in 1998. *Jeonju* (DD 925; ex-*Rogers,* DD 876) was stricken during 2000 and is now a memorial at Tonghae.
Combat systems: Have one director for the Mk 37 f.c.s. for the 127-mm guns and a Mk 51 Mod. 2 lead-computing director for the 40-mm mount. The U.S. Mk 1 Mod. 2 40-mm AA mount added forward between the ASW torpedo tubes was replaced with a powered Nobong mounting. Korean-designed mountings for the Vulcan gatling guns are located amidships on the Harpoon ships and on the former helicopter deck on DD 925. Harpoon missiles were added amidships during 1979. The obsolete U.S. Mk 29 radars were replaced by DA-08 during the mid-1990s.

♦ 1 ex-U.S. Gearing FRAM II class
Bldr: Bath Iron Works, Bath, Maine

	Laid down	L	In serv.
DD 915 Chungbuk (ex-*Chevalier,* DD 805)	12-6-44	29-10-44	8-9-44

D: 2,400 tons (3,500 fl) **S:** 30 kts **Dim:** 119.17 × 12.45 × 5.80
A: 8 RGM-84C Harpoon; 3 twin 127-mm 38-cal. Mk 30 DP; 2 single Vulcan gatling AA; 2 single 20-mm 70-cal. Oerlikon Mk 10 AA; 2 triple Mk 32 ASW TT (Mk 46 Mod. 2 torpedoes); 2 24-round Mk 11 Hedgehog ASW spiggot mortars; 1 Mk 9 d.c. rack (12 Mk 9 d.c.); 1 Super Lynx Mk 99 helicopter
Electronics:
- Radar: 1 Raytheon SPS-10 surf. search; 1 Lockheed SPS-40 air search; 1 Western Electric Mk 25 f.c.
- Sonar: Sangamo SQS-29 series hull-mounted MF
- TACAN: SRN-15
- EW: WLR-1 intercept; 2 decoy RL; T Mk 6 Fanfare acoustic torpedo decoy

M: 2 sets G.E. geared steam turbines; 2 props; 60,000 shp
Boilers: 4 Babcock & Wilcox; 39.8 kg/cm^2, 454° C **Electric:** 1,200 kw tot.
Range: 2,400/25; 4,800/15 **Fuel:** 640 tons **Crew:** 14 officers, 260 enlisted

Remarks: Transferred on loan 5-7-72 and purchased outright 31-1-77. Based at Donghae. Sister *Jeonbuk* (DD 916; ex-*Everett F. Larson,* DD 830) was stricken during 2000 and now serves as a memorial.
Combat systems: Has one director for the Mk 37 f.c.s. for the 127-mm guns. Harpoon missiles were added and the flight deck was widened and strengthened during 1979.

FRIGATES [FF]

♦ 9 Ulsan (HDF 2000) class

	Bldr	L	In serv.
FF 951 Ulsan	Hyundai SY, Ulsan	8-4-80	1-1-81
FF 952 Seoul	Korea SB, Pusan	24-4-84	30-6-85
FF 953 Chungnam	Hanjin Industrial SB, Masan	26-10-84	1-6-86
FF 955 Masan	Daewoo SB & Heavy Mach., Okpo	26-10-84	20-7-85
FF 956 Keongbuk	Korea SB, Pusan	15-1-86	30-5-86
FF 957 Jeonnam	Hyundai SY, Ulsan	19-4-88	17-6-89
FF 958 Cheju	Daewoo SB & Heavy Mach., Okpo	3-5-88	1-1-90
FF 959 Pusan	Daewoo SB & Heavy Mach., Okpo	20-3-92	1-1-93
FF 961 Cheongju	Hyundai, Ulsan	18-2-92	1-6-93

FRIGATES [FF] *(continued)*

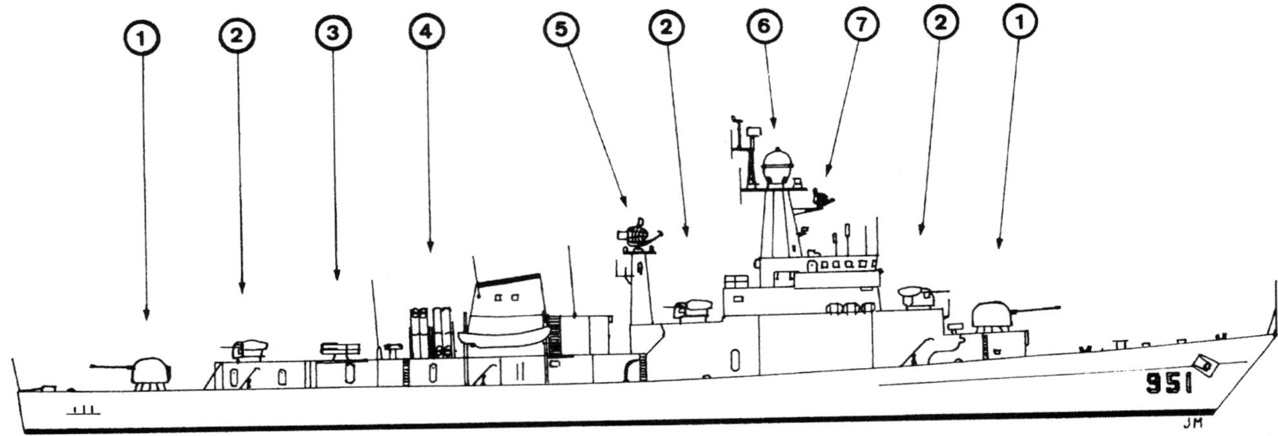

Ulsan (FF 951) 1. 76-mm OTOBreda Compact DP gun 2. 30-mm twin Emerlec AA 3. triple 324-mm ASW TT 4. Harpoon SSM launch canisters 5. DA-05 surface/air-search radar 6. WM-25 track-while-scan fire-control radar 7. ZW-06 surface-search radar
Drawing by Jean Moulin, from *Flottes de Combat*

Cheongju (FF 961)—with radome for Samsung-Marconi surface/air-search radar at the masthead and two twin 40-mm on raised deckhouse aft   John Mortimer, 1-01

Jeonnam (FF 957)—note depth charge racks in centerline slot at the stern and twin openings for the Nixie torpedo decoy system on the starboard side of the transom
Brian Morrison, 6-00

Ulsan (FF 951)—the original version of the class   H&L Van Ginderen, 8-00

Cheongju (FF 961)   Mitsuhiro Kadota, 2-01

D: 1,600 tons (1,940 normal; 2,180 fl) **S:** 35+ kts (18 on diesels)
Dim: 105.00 (98.00 pp) × 12.00 × 3.50
A: 8 RGM-84C Harpoon SSM; 2 single 76-mm 62-cal. OTOBreda Compact DP—FF 951–955: 4 twin 30-mm 75-cal. Emerlec EX-30 AA—FF 956–961: 3 twin 40-mm 70-cal. OTOBreda Compact AA—all: 2 triple 324-mm Mk 32 ASW TT; 2 Mk 9 d.c. racks (6 d.c. each)
Electronics:
Radar: FF 951–956: Thales ZW-06 surf. search; 1 Thales DA-05 air search; 1 Thales WM-25 track-while-scan f.c.—FF 957–961: 1 SPS-10 surf. search; 1 Samsung-Marconi 1810 surf./air search; 1 Thales DA-05 air search; 1 Samsung-Marconi ST-1802 f.c.
Sonar: Raytheon DE 1167 hull-mounted MF
TACAN: SRN-15
EW: GoldStar ULQ-11K intercept; Mk 36 SRBOC decoy syst. (4 6-round Mk 137 RL); SLQ-25 Nixie towed acoustic torpedo decoy syst.
M: CODOG: 2 G.E. LM-2500 gas turbines (27,200 shp each), 2 MTU 12V956 TB82 diesels (3,600 bhp each); 2 CP props; 54,400 shp each
Electric: 1,600 kw tot. (4 × 400-kw diesel sets)
Range: 900/35; 4,000/18 **Crew:** 16 officers, 134 enlisted

Remarks: First South Korean design of a major combatant. FF 953's builder was originally named the Korea-Tacoma Shipbuilding Corp. FF 951 and 953 are based at Chinhae; 952, 957, 958, and 961 at Inchon; and 955, 956, and 959 at Donghae.
Hull systems: Have stern-wedge hullform to improve fuel efficiency and maximum speed. Steel hull and aluminum superstructure.
Combat systems: Have two Thales LIOD optronic standby gun directors in the first five units. FF 955–958 employ three twin OTOBreda 40-mm AA in lieu of the four 30-mm mounts on the first three ships; FF 957 and later have a radar fire-control system in addition for the after two 40-mm mounts, which are mounted a deck higher than in the other ships. All received a Litton Data Systems computerized combat data/control system, beginning in 1992. The PHS-32 sonars in the first six units had been replaced by the DE 1167 system by 1999.

CORVETTES [FFL]

♦ 24 Pohang (KCX) class

	Bldr	In serv.	Based at
PCC 756 Pohang	Korea SB & Eng., Pusan	18-12-84	Donghae
PCC 757 Kunsan	Hanjin Industrial SB, Masan	18-12-84	Donghae
PCC 758 Keongju	Hyundai SY, Ulsan	1986	Donghae
PCC 759 Mokpo	Daewoo SB & Hvy. Mach., Okpo	1988	Donghae
PCC 761 Kimchon	Korea SB & Eng., Pusan	5-85	Donghae
PCC 762 Chung Ju	Hanjin Industrial SB, Masan	5-85	Donghae
PCC 763 Jinju	Hyundai SY, Ulsan	1986	Donghae
PCC 765 Yeosu	Daewoo SB & Hvy. Mach., Okpo	1986	. . .
PCC 766 Chinhae	Korea SB & Eng., Pusan	2-89	Inchon
PCC 767 Sunchon	Hanjin Industrial SB, Masan	6-89	Inchon
PCC 768 Yeeree	Hyundai SY, Ulsan	1989	Donghae
PCC 769 Wonju	Daewoo SB & Hvy. Mach., Okpo	8-89	Donghae
PCC 771 Andong	Hanjin Industrial SB, Masan	11-89	Donghae
PCC 772 Cheonan	Korea SB & Eng., Pusan	11-89	Inchon
PCC 773 Seongnam	Daewoo SB & Hvy. Mach., Okpo	5-89	Inchon
PCC 775 Bucheon	Hyundai SY, Ulsan	4-89	Inchon
PCC 776 Jecheon	Hanjin Industrial SB, Masan	5-89	Inchon
PCC 777 Daecheon	Korea SB & Eng., Pusan	4-89	Inchon
PCC 778 Sokcho	Hanjin Industrial SB, Masan	2-90	Inchon
PCC 779 Yeongju	Hyundai SY, Ulsan	3-90	Inchon
PCC 781 Namwon	Daewoo SB & Hvy. Mach., Okpo	4-90	Pusan
PCC 782 Kwangmyeong	Korea SB & Eng., Pusan	7-90	Pusan
PCC 783 Sinheung	Hanjin Industrial SB, Masan	3-93	Chinhae
PCC 785 Gongju	Daewoo SB & Hvy. Mach., Okpo	28-2-94	Chinhae

D: 950 tons (1,220 fl) **S:** 31 kts (15 on diesels)
Dim: 88.30 (83.47 wl) × 10.00 (9.80 wl) × 3.00 (hull)
A: PCC 756–759: 2 MM 38 Exocet SSM; 1 76-mm 62-cal. OTOBreda Compact DP; 2 twin 30-mm 75-cal. Emerlec AA; 2 triple 324-mm Mk 32 ASW TT; 2 Mk 9 d.c. racks (6 Mk 9 d.c. each)—PCC 761 and later: 2 single 76-mm 62-cal. OTOBreda Compact DP; 2 twin 40-mm 70-cal. OTOBreda Compact AA; 2 triple 324-mm Mk 32 ASW TT; 2 Mk 9 d.c. racks (6 Mk 9 d.c. each)

CORVETTES [FFL] *(continued)*

Mokpo (PCC 759)—early unit with two MM 38 Exocet missile canisters aft and twin 30-mm AA mounts forward and on fantail John Mortimer, 10-98

Seongnam (PCC 773)—late unit, with optronic director forward atop small deckhouse on pilothouse roof John Mortimer, 10-98

Chinhae (PCC 766)—with Marconi search and fire-control radars John Mortimer, 10-98

Jinju (PCC 763)—with two single 76-mm mounts and two twin 40-mm mounts, but no antiship missiles John Mortimer, 10-98

Electronics:
Radar: PCC 756–765: 1 Raytheon SPS-64(V) nav.; 1 Thales WM-28 track-while-scan f.c.—PCC 766 and later: 1 Raytheon SPS-64(V) nav.; 1 Marconi ST 1802 surf./air search; 1 Marconi S 1810 f.c.
Sonar: Thales PHS-32 hull-mounted MF
EW: GoldStar ULQ-12K intercept/jammer—PCC 756–759: Mk 36 SRBOC decoy syst. (2 6-round Raytheon Mk 137 RL)—761 and later: 4 9-round Protean decoy RL
M: CODOG: 1 G.E. LM-2500 gas turbine (27,200 or 27,800 shp), 2 MTU 12V956 TB82 diesels (3,130 bhp each); 2 CP props
Electric: 800 or 1,200 kw tot. **Range:** 800/31 (turbine); 4,000/15 (diesel)
Crew: 10 officers, 85 enlisted

Remarks: The weapons and electronics suites evolved over the course of construction of this series. The original name for Hanjin Industrial Shipbuilding Corp. was Korea-Tacoma Shipbuilding Corp.
Hull systems: The gas turbine of the first four was rated at 27,200 shp, that of the later units at 27,800 shp. PCC 766 and later may have substituted two SEMT-Pielstick 12 PA6 V280 diesels (4,800 bhp each) for the two MTU 12V956 TB82 diesels listed. Daewoo advertised only two 400-kw diesel generators on its version, but the other ships may have three.
Combat systems: The first four have the Thales SEWACO ZK combat data system; the others have the Ferranti WSA 423. Only the first four have antiship missiles; they also have a manned twin 30-mm AA mount on the fantail in place of the after 76-mm mount. Units through PCC 765 are equipped with one Thales LIROD optronic director for the 76-mm guns, with their 30-mm weapons being essentially locally controlled. PCC 766 and later have two twin OTOBreda 40-mm AA and no SSM, mount the Marconi 1810 radar at the masthead, and have two Rademac 2400 optronic directors for their 40-mm guns. All carry Motorola MX 1105 NAVSAT.

♦ 4 Donghae (HDC 800) class

	Bldr	In serv.
PCC 751 Donghae	Korea SB & Eng., Pusan	8-82
PCC 752 Suwon	Hanjin Industrial SB, Masan	10-83
PCC 753 Kangreung	Hyundai SY, Ulsan	30-11-83
PCC 755 Anyang	Daewoo SB & Heavy Machinery, Okpo	12-83

Anyang (PCC 755) H&L Van Ginderen, 1-00

Donghae (PCC 751) 9-90

D: 800 tons (1,076 fl) **S:** 31 kts
Dim: 78.50 × 10.00 (9.60 wl) × 2.60 (mean hull)
A: 1 76-mm 62-cal. OTOBreda Compact DP; 1 twin 40-mm 60-cal. Bofors AA (U.S. Mk 1 Mod. 2 mount); 2 twin 30-mm 75-cal. Emerlec AA; 2 triple 324-mm Mk 32 ASW TT; 2 Mk 9 d.c. racks (6 Mk 9 d.c. each)
Electronics:
Radar: 1 Raytheon SPS-64(V) nav.; 1 Thales WM-28 track-while-scan f.c.
Sonar: EDO 786 hull-mounted MF
EW: . . . intercept; Mk 34 RBOC II decoy syst. (2 6-round Mk 135 RL)
M: CODOG: 1 G.E. LM-2500 gas turbine (27,800 shp), 2 MTU 12V956 TB82 diesels (3,120 bhp each); 2 CP props
Range: 800/31; 4,000/15 **Endurance:** 21 days **Crew:** 10 officers, 85 enlisted

Remarks: A more heavily armed version of a similar class built for the South Korean Coast Guard. Distinguished from the *Pohang* class by a narrower superstructure, lattice mast, and less distance between the mast and stack. All four are based at Chinhae.
Combat systems: There is a Thales LIOD optronic director for the 76-mm gun. The 40-mm twin AA is of World War II design and is controlled by an electro-optical director or U.S. Mk 51 gun f.c.s.

GUIDED-MISSILE PATROL BOATS [PTG]

♦ 8 Paekku (PSMM-5) class

Bldrs: PGM 581–583: Tacoma Boatbuilding Co., Tacoma, Wash.; others: Hanjin Industrial SB, Chinhae

	In serv.		In serv.
PGM 581 Paekku 52	14-3-75	PGM 586 Paekku 57	1977
PGM 582 Paekku 53	14-3-75	PGM 587 Paekku 58	1977
PGM 583 Paekku 55	1-2-76	PGM 589 Paekku 59	1977
PGM 585 Paekku 56	1-2-76	PGM 591 Paekku 61	1978

Paekku 56 (PGM 585)—with old pennant number French Navy, 7-91

GUIDED-MISSILE PATROL BOATS [PTG] *(continued)*

D: 240 tons (268 fl) **S:** 40 kts **Dim:** 53.68 (50.30 pp) × 8.00 × 1.63
A: PGM 581–585: 2 Standard ARM SSM box launchers (4 missiles); 1 76.2-mm 50-cal. U.S. Mk 34 DP; 2 single 12.7-mm mg—PGM 586–591: 4 RGM-84A Harpoon SSM; 1 76-mm 62-cal. OTOBreda Compact DP; 1 twin 30-mm 75-cal. Emerlec AA; 2 single 12.7-mm M2 mg
Electronics:
Radar: PGM 581–585: 1 Canadian Marconi LN-66 HP nav.; 1 Western Electric SPG-50 f.c.—PGM 586–591: 1 Canadian Marconi LN-66 HP nav.; 1 HC 75 surf. search; 1 Lockheed SPS-58 air search; 1 Westinghouse W-120 f.c.
EW: Mk 34 RBOC II decoy syst. (2 6-round Mk 135 RL)
M: 6 AVCO TF-35 gas turbines; 2 CP props; 16,800 shp
Range: 2,400/18 **Crew:** 5 officers, 27 enlisted

Remarks: *Paekku* means "Seagull." May have been renumbered again as PKM 286, 275, 332, 287, 289, 278, 219, and 315.
Hull systems: Have three gas turbines per shaft, geared in as necessary to produce the desired speed range. Hullform is derived from that of the U.S. Navy's *Asheville* (PG 84) class.
Combat systems: Korean-built units have Westinghouse M-1200 fire-control systems, using inputs from the LN-66 HP radar and a Kollmorgen optical director. PGM 581–583 have the U.S. Mk 63 gun f.c.s. with SPG-50 radar and two Standard ARM SSM launchers (each with one reload).

PATROL CRAFT [PC]

♦ 86 Sea Dolphin series
Bldrs: Hanjin Industrial SB, Chinhae, and Korea SB & Eng., Masan (In serv. 1970s–1980s)

44 PKM 201 series:

PKM 215	PKM 236	PKM 256	PKM 266	PKM 282	PKM 295
PKM 216	PKM 237	PKM 257	PKM 267	PKM 283	PKM 296
PKM 221	PKM 238	PKM 258	PKM 268	PKM 285	PKM 298
PKM 222	PKM 239	PKM 259	PKM 269	PKM 288	PKM 299
PKM 223	PKM 251	PKM 261	PKM 273	PKM 291	
PKM 227	PKM 252	PKM 262	PKM 276	PKM 292	
PKM 228	PKM 253	PKM 263	PKM 279	PKM 293	
PKM 233	PKM 255	PKM 265	PKM 281	PKM 294	

42 PKM 301 series:

PKM 311	PKM 321	PKM 329	PKM 339	PKM 358	PKM 367
PKM 312	PKM 322	PKM 331	PKM 351	PKM 359	PKM 368
PKM 313	PKM 323	PKM 333	PKM 352	PKM 361	PKM 369
PKM 316	PKM 325	PKM 335	PKM 353	PKM 362	PKM 371
PKM 317	PKM 326	PKM 336	PKM 355	PKM 363	PKM 372
PKM 318	PKM 327	PKM 337	PKM 356	PKM 365	PKM 373
PKM 319	PKM 328	PKM 338	PKM 357	PKM 366	PKM 375

PKM 301–series PKM 372—with enclosed 40-mm AA forward, two enclosed 20-mm gatling guns aft Lt. Cdr. Liza Stephenson, RAN, 10-98

PKM 201–series PKM 282—with twin 30-mm AA mount forward H&L Van Ginderen, 5-97

PKM 201–series PKM 227—early version with twin 30-mm AA forward, open 40-mm AA mount aft, and two single 20-mm AA mounts atop the superstructure NAVPIC-Holland, 8-94

D: 113 tons (144 fl) **S:** 34 kts **Dim:** 33.10 (31.25 wl) × 6.92 × 1.75 (2.45 props)
A: early PKM 201 series: 1 40-mm 60-cal. Bofors Mk 3; 1 twin 30-mm 75-cal. Emerlec EX-30; 2 single 20-mm 70-cal. Mk 10 Oerlikon AA—late PKM 201 series: 1 twin 30-mm 75-cal. Emerlec EX-30 AA; 1 or 2 single 20-mm Vulcan gatling AA; 2 single 12.7-mm mg—PKM 301 series: 1 40-mm 60-cal. Bofors AA; 2 single 20-mm Vulcan gatling AA; 2 single 12.7-mm M2 mg
Electronics: Radar: 1 Raytheon 1645 nav./surf. search
M: 2 MTU 16V538 TB90 diesels; 2 props; 10,800 bhp (9,000 sust.)
Electric: 100 kw tot. (2 × 50-kw diesel sets)
Range: 500/32; 1,000/20 **Fuel:** 15 tons **Crew:** 5 officers, 26 enlisted

Remarks: Five units from the PKM 201 series were transferred to the Philippines 15-6-95 and another five were stricken the same year; two of the latter were donated to Bangladesh during 4-00.
Hull systems: Designed for 38 kts; can make 32 kts continuous. Daewoo offered the design for export as the DW 150P, or Dangpo, class at 150 tons full load, 37 m o.a., with a top speed of 37 kts and a range of 600 n.m. at 20 kts.
Combat systems: Later units, with 301-series hull numbers, have an enclosed, manned 40-mm mount on the forecastle and enclosed gatling gun mountings atop the superstructure and often also on the fantail; the 40-mm mounts use Mauser GRP enclosures. Most 201-series units have an Emerlec manned, power-operated twin 30-mm mount on the forecastle, and a few older units have an open 40-mm mount on the fantail.

MINE WARFARE SHIPS

♦ 1 Wonsan-class minelayer [MM]
Bldr: Hyundai SY, Ulsan

	Laid down	L	In serv.
MLS 560 Wonsan	12-94	9-96	9-97

Wonsan (MLS 560) John Mortimer, 10-98

D: 3,300 tons (fl) **S:** 22 kts **Dim:** 103.75 (98.00 pp) × 15.20 × 4.15
A: 1 76-mm 62-cal. OTOBreda Compact DP; 2 twin 40-mm 70-cal. OTOBreda Fast Forty AA; 2 triple 324-mm Mk 32 ASW TT; up to 300 mines
Electronics:
Radar: 1 Raytheon SPS-64(V) nav.; 1 Samsung-Marconi 1810 surf./air search; 1 Thales DA-05 air search; 2 Samsung-Marconi ST-1802 f.c.
Sonar: . . . bow-mounted MF
EW: . . . intercept; Mk 36 SFBOC decoy syst. (2 6-round Raytheon Mk 137 RL)
M: 4 SEMT-Pielstick 12 PA6–series diesels; 2 props; 17,200 bhp
Range: 4,500/15 **Crew:** 160 tot.

Remarks: Ordered 10-94, with an option for two more that was not taken up. In addition to minelaying, is able to act as a minehunter and also as a training ship and ASW escort. Has a helicopter landing platform aft for aircraft up to CH-53E size, an extensive EW suite, and optronic backup directors for guns. Carries an LCVP landing craft to port.

♦ 1 (+ 11) Yangyang-class minehunters [MHC]
Bldr: Kangnam SB, Pusan

	L	In serv.
MHC 571 Yangyang	2-99	2000?
MHC 572	. . .	. . .
MHC 573	. . .	. . .
MHC 575	. . .	. . .
MHC 576	. . .	. . .
MHC 577	. . .	. . .
MHC 578	. . .	. . .

D: 500 tons (730 fl) **S:** 15 kts **Dim:** . . . × . . . × . . .
A: 1 20-mm Vulcan gatling AA; 2 single 7.62-mm mg
Electronics:
Radar: 1 . . . nav.
Sonar: Raytheon SQQ-32 variable-depth HF minehunting
M: 2 . . . diesels; 2 props; . . . bhp
Range: . . ./. . . **Crew:** . . . tot.

Remarks: Combination minehunter/minesweepers to replace the remaining U.S.-built mine countermeasures craft. Design began in 1992. Have an Alliant SLQ-48 remotely operated minehunting and disposal submersible. Engine control systems for the second and third units were ordered from CAE, Canada, 3-8-01.

♦ 6 SK 5000–class minehunters [MHC]
Bldr: Swallowcraft, Kangnam SB, Pusan

	In serv.		In serv.
MHC 561 Kangkyeong	12-86	MHC 565 Kimpo	4-93
MHC 562 Kangjin	5-91	MHC 566 Kochang	10-93
MHC 563 Koryeong	11-91	MHC 567 Kumwha	4-94

MINE WARFARE SHIPS *(continued)*

Kangjin (MHC 562) John Mortimer, 10-98

Kangjin (MHC 562) H&L Van Ginderen, 1-00

D: 470 tons (520 fl) **S:** 15 kts **Dim:** 50.0 × 9.6 (8.31 wl) × 2.6
A: 1 20-mm 70-cal. Oerlikon Mk 10 AA; 2 single 7.62-mm mg
Electronics:
Radar: 1 Raytheon SPS-64(V)-series nav.
Sonar: Thales Type 193M Mod. 1 hull-mounted (see remarks)
M: 2 MTU . . . diesels; 2 Voith-Schneider vertical cycloidal props; 1,600 bhp—bow-thruster
Range: 2,500/12 **Crew:** 5 officers, 39 enlisted + 4 mine-disposal divers

Remarks: Design based on the Italian *Lerici* design, but not built under license from the *Lerici* builder, Intermarine. Second and third ordered in 1987, final three in 1989.
Hull systems: Single-skin, glass-reinforced plastic construction.
Combat systems: Carry two Gaymarine Pluto Plus mine-disposal vehicles and are equipped with Racal-Decca MAINS plotting gear. Sonar transducer body incorporates Type 2048 Speedscan forward-looking component; the sixth and last Type 193M set was delivered during 11-92; later units carry the Type 193M Mod. 3 or the Type 2093.

♦ 5 U.S. MSC 289–class coastal minesweepers
Bldr: Peterson Bldrs, Sturgeon Bay, Wis.

	In serv.
MSC 555 Namyang (ex-MSC 295)	8-63
MSC 556 Hadong (ex-MSC 296)	11-63
MSC 557 Samkok (ex-MSC 316)	7-68
MSC 558 Yeongdong (ex-MSC 320)	2-10-75
MSC 559 Okcheon (ex-MSC 321)	2-10-75

Samkok (MSC 557)—with original pennant number U.S. Navy, 4-68

D: 315 tons (380 fl) **S:** 14 kts **Dim:** 44.32 × 8.29 × 2.7
A: 1 twin 20-mm 70-cal. Oerlikon Mk 24 AA; 3 single 12.7-mm mg
Electronics:
Radar: 1 Decca . . . nav.
Sonar: UQS-1 or Thales 2022 hull-mounted HF
M: 4 G.M. 6-71 diesels; 2 props; 1,020 bhp **Electric:** 1,260 kw tot.
Range: 2,500/14 **Fuel:** 33 tons **Crew:** 40 tot.

Remarks: Wooden construction. Built under the U.S. Military Aid Program. Have a gas-turbine sweep generator and a lower superstructure than on the MSC 268 class. MSC 556–559 may have been reequipped with Thales 2022 minehunting sonars.

♦ 3 U.S. MSC 268–class coastal minesweepers
Bldr: Harbor Boat Building, Terminal Island, Calif.

	In serv.
MSC 551 Kumsan (ex-MSC 284)	6-59
MSC 552 Koheung (ex-MSC 285)	8-59
MSC 553 Kumkok (ex-MSC 286)	10-59

D: 320 tons (370 fl) **S:** 14 kts **Dim:** 43.0 (41.5 pp) × 7.95 × 2.55
A: 1 twin 20-mm 70-cal. Oerlikon Mk 24 AA; 3 single 12.7-mm mg
Electronics: Radar: 1 Decca 45 nav. —Sonar: UQS-1 hull-mounted HF
M: 2 G.M. Electromotive Div. 8-268A diesels; 2 props; 1,200 bhp
Range: 2,500/16 **Fuel:** 40 tons **Crew:** 40 tot.

Remarks: Built under the U.S. Military Aid Program. Wooden construction.

AMPHIBIOUS WARFARE SHIPS

Note: Plans to lay down a 10,000-ton dock landing ship in 2002 for delivery in 2005 were announced 17-1-00. The ship was to carry 700 troops, 10 helicopters, and about a dozen landing craft. No contract has been announced, however.

♦ 4 (+ 5) HDL 4000–class landing ships [LST]
Bldr: Hanjin Industrial SB, Masan

	L	In serv.
LST 681 Kojoonbong	9-92	24-3-94
LST 682 Birobong	12-96	1-12-97
LST 683 Hyangrobong	10-98	8-99
LST 685 Seonginbong	2-99	11-99

Kojoonbong (LST 681) Lt. Cdr. Liza Stephenson, RAN, 10-98

Seonginbong (LST 685)—with enclosed Fast Forty gunmount forward H&L Van Ginderen, 2-00

D: 4,278 tons (fl) **S:** 16 kts **Dim:** 106.90 × 15.40 × 3.00
A: 1 twin 40-mm 60-cal. Nobong (LST 683, 685: 70-cal. OTOBreda Fast Forty) AA; 2 single 20-mm Vulcan gatling AA
Electronics:
Radar: 1 Raytheon SPS-64(V)9 nav.; 1 Raytheon SPS-64(V)6 nav.
TACAN: SRN-15A
E/O: AESN NA-18 optronic gun f.c.
M: 2 SEMT-Pielstick 16 PA6 V280 diesels; 2 props; 12,800 bhp
Electric: 750 kw tot. **Range:** 7,500/13; 10,000/12
Crew: 14 officers, 106 enlisted

Remarks: First two ordered 6-90 to begin replacement of the LST 1 and LST 542 classes. A total of nine is planned, but no further construction contracts have been announced.
Hull systems: Have a helicopter deck aft and resemble LSTs built in South Korea for Venezuela and Indonesia, except that they have a drive-through tank deck and stern ramp. Are able to carry up to 1,800 tons of cargo (690 tons maximum beaching load) and about 200 troops; up to 17 main battle tanks can be accommodated. The articulating bow ramp extends to 14.5 m and is 4.5 m wide; the articulating stern ramp extends to 10.9 m and is 4.9 m wide. A 6.1-m-diameter turntable is fitted at the forward end of the tank deck, and there is a 9 × 4–m elevator to the upper deck.

♦ 6 ex-U.S. LST 1*– and U.S. LST 542–class landing ships [LST]

	Bldr	L	In serv.
LST 671 Unbong (ex-LST 1010)	Bethlehem, Fore River	29-3-44	25-4-44
LST 675 Gaebong (ex-LST 288)*	American Bridge, Pa.	7-11-43	20-12-43
LST 676 Weebong (ex-*Johnson County,* LST 849)	American Bridge, Pa.	30-12-43	16-1-44
LST 677 Suyeong (ex-*Kane County,* LST 853)	Chicago Bridge, Seneca, Ill.	17-11-44	11-12-44
LST 678 Bukhan (ex-*Lynn County,* LST 900)	Dravo, Pittsburgh	9-12-44	28-12-44

D: 1,653 tons (4,080 fl) **S:** 10 kts **Dim:** 99.98 (96.32 wl) × 15.24 × 4.29
A: 2 twin 40-mm 60-cal. Bofors Mk 1 Mod. 2 AA; 4 single 40-mm 60-cal. Bofors Mk 3 AA; 2 single 20-mm 70-cal. Oerlikon Mk 10 AA
Electronics: Radar: 2 . . . nav.

AMPHIBIOUS WARFARE SHIPS *(continued)*

Suyeong (LST 677) French Navy, 1990

M: 2 G.M. Electromotive Div. 12-567A or 12-278A diesels; 2 props; 1,800 bhp
Electric: 300 kw tot. **Range:** 15,000/9 **Fuel:** 569 tons **Crew:** 70 tot.

Remarks: Transferred 1955–58; all purchased outright 15-11-74.
Disposals: *Tukbong* (LST 672, ex-LST 227) was stricken during 1989 after grounding; *Bibong* (LST 673; ex-*Berkshire County,* LST 218) had been stricken by 2-99; and *Hwasan* (LST 679; ex-*Pender County,* LST 1080) was stricken during 2000 and serves as a memorial in Chung Chong Province.
Hull systems: The LST 1 class had an elevator from the upper deck to the tank deck, but all now have ramps, like the later LST 542–class ships. Can carry a maximum of 1,230 tons of cargo (815 tons for beaching), plus up to 350 troops.

♦ 2 ex-U.S. LSM 1–class medium landing ships [LSM]
Bldr: Brown SB, Houston, Texas

	Laid down	L	In serv.
LSM 657 Wolmi (ex-LSM 57)	30-6-44	21-7-44	17-8-44
LSM 658 Kirin (ex-LSM 19)	24-4-44	14-5-44	14-6-44

D: 520 tons (1,095 fl) **S:** 13 kts **Dim:** 62.0 × 10.52 × 2.53
A: 1 twin 40-mm 60-cal. Bofors Mk 1 Mod. 2 AA; 4 single 20-mm 70-cal. Oerlikon Mk 10 AA
Electronics: Radar: 1 . . . nav.
M: 2 Fairbanks-Morse 38D8Q × 10 diesels; 2 props; 2,880 bhp
Electric: 240 kw tot. **Range:** 5,000/7 **Fuel:** 160 tons **Crew:** 75 tot.

Remarks: Transferred in 1956. Cargo: 350 tons (165 tons for beaching), plus 48 troops.
Disposals: *Taecho* (LSM 651, ex-U.S. LSM 546) and *Tyoto* (LSM 652, ex-U.S. LSM 268) were stricken during 1982; *Gadeok* (LSM 653, ex-U.S. LSM 462) during 1995; and *Pungto* (LSML 650, ex-U.S. LSM 54), which was capable of laying mines, *Keomun* (LSM 655, ex-U.S. LSM 30), *Pian* (LSM 656, ex-U.S. LSM 96), *Nungra* (LSM 659, ex-U.S. LSM 84), *Sinmi* (LSM 661, ex-U.S. LSM 316), and *Ulreung* (LSM 662, ex-U.S. LSM 17) during 1998.

♦ 1 U.S. Crosley-class former high-speed transport [LPA]
Bldr: Charleston Naval Shipyard, Charleston, S.C.

	Laid down	L	In serv.
APD 822 Cheju (ex-828; ex-*William M. Hobby,* APD 95, ex-DE 236)	15-11-43	11-2-44	4-4-45

D: 1,650 tons (2,130 fl) **S:** 23.6 kts **Dim:** 93.13 × 11.3 × 3.20
A: 1 127-mm 38-cal. Mk 30 DP; 3 twin 40-mm 60-cal. Bofors Mk 1 Mod. 2 AA; 2 triple 324-mm Mk 32 ASW TT; 2 Mk 9 d.c. racks (6 Mk 9 d.c. each)
Electronics: Radar: 1 SPS-5D surf. search—Sonar: QCU-2 HF scanning
M: 2 sets G.E. geared turbines, turboelectric drive; 2 props; 12,000 shp
Boilers: 2 Foster-Wheeler "D" Express-type; 30.6 kg/cm^2, 399° C
Range: 2,300/22; 4,800/12 **Crew:** approx. 200 tot. + 160 troops

Remarks: Former fast amphibious warfare transport, thought to have been retired in 1988 but still in service in 10-98, probably as a special forces transport. Loaned by the U.S. during 8-67 and purchased 15-11-74. Has been equipped with a helicopter platform over the stern. Retains Welin davits amidships for two LCVP-type landing craft. May retain one Mk 52 director to control the 127-mm gun and three Mk 51 lead-computing directors for the 40-mm mounts. See the photograph with the destroyers *Daejon* (DD 919) and *Kwangju* (DD 921).

♦ 9 Mulkae-class utility landing craft [LCU]
Bldr: Hanjin Industrial SB, Masan

	In serv.		In serv.		In serv.
LCU 72	1979	LCU 76	1980	LCU 79	30-9-97
LCU 73	1979	LCU 77	1981	LCU 81	31-10-97
LCU 75	1980	LCU 78	1981	LCU 82	31-11-97

D: 220 tons (415 fl) **S:** 12 kts **Dim:** 41.07 × 9.07 × 2.08
A: 2 single 20-mm 70-cal. Oerlikon Mk 10 AA **Electronics:** Radar: 1 . . . nav.
M: 4 G.M. 6-71 diesels; 2 Kort-nozzle props; 1,200 bhp
Range: 560/11 **Crew:** 2 officers, 12 enlisted

Remarks: Copies of the U.S. LCU 1610 design, with a higher pilothouse; built with imported equipment. *Mulkae* means "Fur Seal." Cargo capacity: 143 tons. Cargo deck: 30.5 × 5.5 m.

Note: An order for an initial U.S. LCAC 1–class air-cushion landing craft was planned for 1998 but has not yet been placed.

♦ 1 Modified U.S. LCAC 1–class air-cushion landing craft [LCUA]
Bldr: . . . (In serv. 1997)

LSF 611 Solgae

D: approx. 80 tons light (182 max. fl) **S:** 54 kts (40 when loaded)
Dim: 26.8 (24.7 hull) × 14.3 (13.1 hull) × 0.9 (at rest)
A: 2 single 12.7-mm mg **Electronics:** Radar: 1 . . . nav.
M: 4 Avco TF40B gas turbines (2 for lift); 2 3.58-m-dia. shrouded airscrews, 4 centrifugal 1.60-m-dia. lift fans; 15,820 shp
Electric: 120 kw tot. (2 × 60-kw Turbomach T-62 gas turbine APU)
Range: 223/48 (light); 300/35 (loaded) **Fuel:** 6.2 tons (7,132 gallons)
Crew: 5 tot. + 25 troops

Remarks: Design based closely on the U.S. Navy version, but with a slightly modified pilothouse arrangement.
Hull systems: Uses the same propulsion plant as the USN LCAC 1 class. Cargo capacity: 60 tons normal. Bow and stern ramps are fitted. Operator, engineer, navigator, and nine troops travel in starboard side compartments, and deck hand, assistant engineer, load master, and vehicle crew travel in portside compartments.

Note: The ROKN also has at least one air-cushion personnel landing craft resembling a British Hovercraft design; no data available.

♦ 10 ex-U.S. Army LCM(8)-class landing craft [LCM]

D: 58.8 tons light (116 fl) **S:** 9.2 kts (loaded)
Dim: 22.40 × 6.42 × 1.40 (mean) **M:** 2 G.M. 6-71 diesels; 2 props; 600 bhp
Range: 150/9.2 (loaded) **Fuel:** 2.4 tons **Crew:** 2–4 tot.

Remarks: Transferred 9-78. Data apply to the final 96 built—the Mod. 1—delivered late 1960s–1972. Earlier Army LCM(8) Mod. 0 were rated at 57.8 tons light/111.4 full load. Mod. 1 carries up to 57.4 tons cargo, the Mod. 0, 53.5 tons. Can also carry troops for short distances.

Note: South Korea also builds glass-reinforced plastic–hulled versions of the U.S. LCVP landing craft. A small troop-carrying prototype air-cushion landing craft has been completed, and as many as 30 may be built. For use by the ROK Marines, there are 24 LVTP-7A and 53 LVTP-7 troop-carrying, 1 LVTC-7A1 and 5 LVTC-7 command, and 3 LVTR-7 recovery armored tracked amphibious landing vehicles. Current plans call for acquiring 57 improved AAV-7A and upgrading the current fleet.
The ROK Army has 192 aluminum-construction British FBM Marine–designed river bridging craft in service, with 56 delivered 1995–96 by Hanjin Industrial Shipbuilding, Masan. Characteristics include:

D: . . . tons **S:** 24 kts **Dim:** 8.38 (6.98 wl) × 2.49 × 0.66 (loaded)
M: 2 diesels; 2 waterjets; 424 bhp **Fuel:** 170 liters

AUXILIARIES

♦ 3 Cheonji-class replenishment oilers [AOR]
Bldr: Hyundai SY, Ulsan

	L	In serv.
AOE 57 Cheonji	29-12-90	1-92
AOE 58 Daecheong	1-97	31-3-98
AOE 59 Hwacheon	7-97	31-8-98

Daecheong (AOE 58)—with twin Fast Forty AA mounts fore and aft
Mitsuhiro Kadota, 2-01

Daecheong (AOE 58) John Mortimer, 2-01

D: 9,000 tons (fl) **S:** 20 kts **Dim:** 133.0 (122.5 pp) × 17.8 × 6.5
A: 2 twin 40-mm 70-cal. OTOBreda Fast Forty (AOE 57: 30-mm 75-cal. Emerlec) AA; 2 single 20-mm Vulcan gatling AA
Electronics: Radar: 2 . . . nav.
M: AOE 57: 2 SEMT-Pielstick 16 PA6 V280 diesels; 2 CP props; 15,600 bhp (see remarks)
Electric: 725 kw tot. **Range:** 4,500/15 **Crew:** . . . tot.

AUXILIARIES *(continued)*

Cheonji (AOE 57)—with twin 30-mm AA mounts fore and aft
H&L Van Ginderen, 10-97

Remarks: First unit ordered in 6-90, second two in 5-95. Builder's HDA 8000 design, a reduced version of the *Endeavour* built for New Zealand. A near-sister was ordered for Venezuela in 7-99.
Hull systems: Cargo: 4,200 tons fuels, 450 tons stores. Two replenishment stations on each beam, one for liquids and one for solid cargo transfer; also able to refuel over the stern. Has a helicopter platform and hangar aft. AOE 58 and AOE 59 have newer-model diesels than those in AOE 57.
Combat systems: AOE 58 and AOE 59 have enclosed twin 40-mm AA mounts fore and aft, with remote directors.

♦ 2 ex-U.S. Edenton-class salvage-and-rescue ships [ARS]
Bldr: Brooke Marine, Lowestoft, U.K.

	Laid down	L	In serv.
ARS 27 Pyongtaek (ex-*Beaufort,* ATS 2)	19-2-68	20-12-68	22-1-72
ARS 28 Kwangyang (ex-*Brunswick,* ATS 3)	5-6-68	14-11-69	19-12-72

Pyongtaek (ARS 27)—when still in U.S. Navy service
Piet Sinke, 3-91

D: 2,650 tons (3,200 fl) **S:** 16 kts **Dim:** 88.0 (80.5 pp) × 15.25 × 4.6
A: 2 single 12.7-mm mg
Electronics: Radar: 1 Sperry SPS-53 nav.; 1 Raytheon SPS-64(V)9 nav.
M: 4 Paxman 12 YLCM, 900-rpm diesels; 2 Escher-Wyss CP props; 6,000 bhp
Electric: 1,200 kw tot. **Range:** 10,000/13 **Crew:** 7 officers, 110 enlisted

Remarks: Both were decommissioned to reserve from the U.S. Navy 8-3-96, sold to South Korea 29-8-96, delivered 7-2-97, and commissioned in the ROKN 20-2-97.
Hull systems: Can tow ships up to 50,000-ton size. Have 272-ton dead lift over the bow. There is a 20-ton crane aft and a 10-ton boom forward. Can support divers to 260 m. Powerful pumps and complete firefighting equipment. Equipped with a bow-thruster.

♦ 1 midget-submarine tender [AS]

ASL 50 Dadohae

Remarks: No data available. Is used to support (and possibly to deploy) the midget submarines of the S.X. 756 and KSS-1 classes.

♦ 1 submarine rescue ship [ASR]
Bldr: Daewoo SB & Heavy Machinery, Okpo

	Laid down	L	In serv.
ARS 21 Chonghaejin	12-94	17-10-95	3-97

D: 4,330 tons (fl) **S:** 18.5 kts (15 sust.) **Dim:** 102.8 × 16.4 × 4.6
A: 6 single 12.7-mm M2 mg
Electronics: Radar: 1 . . . nav.—Sonar: hull-mounted HF—TACAN: . . .
M: 4 M.A.N. 16V 28/32 diesels (2,950 bhp each), electric drive: 2 motors; 2 CP props; 5,440 shp—3 bow-thrusters, 2 stern-thrusters
Electric: 5,600 kw tot. (2 × 2,000-kw shaft generators, 4 × 400-kw diesel sets)
Range: 9,500/15 **Crew:** 130 tot. (accomm.)

Remarks: Offered for export by Daewoo as its DW 4000R or Koje class. One unit of this design was also ordered in 1992 to support the new ROKN submarine force.

Chonghaejin (ARS 21)
John Mortimer, 10-98

Hull systems: Carries a deep-submergence (300-m) submarine rescue vehicle, handled by an A-frame crane at the stern. Extensive diving systems furnished; has a nine-man rescue diving bell and a large decompression chamber. Has dynamic positioning system and four-point mooring system. The rudders are of the "flapped" type to enhance low-speed maneuverability. Has a helicopter platform and two electrohydraulic, telescoping cranes. Able to provide battery charging, provisions, fuel, oxygen, and water services to submarines. Carries two LCVP-type workboats.

SERVICE CRAFT

♦ 1 weapons systems trials craft [YAGE]
Bldr: Hyundai SY, Ulsan (In serv. 4-93)

AGS 11 Seonjin

D: 310 tons (fl) **S:** 21 kts **Dim:** 34.5 × 15.0 × 3.5
A: none **Electronics:** Radar: 1 . . . nav.
M: 2 MTU 16V396 TE diesels; 2 props; 2,680 bhp
Range: 600/16 **Crew:** 5 tot. + 20 technicians

Remarks: Ordered 6-91 for the Defense Development Agency and is civilian operated. Has an aluminum-alloy hull with a SWATH twin-hullform. Used for trials with towed linear passive hydrophone sensors, navigational systems, and an indigenous torpedo development program. Has stern A-frame for torpedo recovery.

♦ 1 ex-U.S. 174-foot-class harbor tanker [YO]

	Bldr	L	In serv.
YO 6 . . . . . . (ex-YO 179)	Smith SY, Pensacola, Fla.	24-11-44	26-5-45

D: 440 tons light (1,390 fl) **S:** 9 kts **Dim:** 53.04 × 9.75 × 3.96 (loaded)
A: 2 single 20-mm Oerlikon Mk 10 AA **Electronics:** Radar: 1 . . . nav.
M: 1 Union diesel; 1 prop; 560 bhp **Electric:** 80 kw tot.
Range: 2,000/8 **Fuel:** 25 tons **Crew:** 36 tot.

Remarks: Transferred 9-71. Cargo: 900 tons liquid (6,570 bbl fuel oil). Sister *Kuyong* (YO 1, ex-YO 118) was stricken in 1997.

Note: There are also nine or more harbor tugs, including YTL 13 (ex-USN YTL 550), YTL 22 (ex-Army ST 2097), YTL 23 (ex-Army ST 2099), YTL 25 (ex-Army ST 2106), YTL 26 (ex-Army ST 2065), YTL 30 (ex-Army ST 2101), and YTL 38 (ex-Army ST . . .). All were transferred 1968–72. About 25 other yard and service craft are also in use.

ROKN large harbor tug [YTB] OI-62—of local construction; OI-53 and OI-55 are sisters
H&L Van Ginderen, 1999

MARITIME POLICE

The former Republic of Korea Coast Guard has been combined with the Maritime Police. There are about 4,000 personnel, most in shore billets. Patrol ships and craft are painted with blue hulls and white superstructures, while the large seagoing salvage ships are painted all white; the word "Police" is lettered in Korean and English on the side of the superstructure or, on the larger vessels, on the hull sides, and there

MARITIME POLICE *(continued)*

is a green stack stripe with the Maritime Police seal centered on it; rescue ships additionally have a red-yellow-blue diagonal stripe set on the hull side, with a larger shield superimposed.

Aviation: In use are an unknown number of Kamov Ka-27 Helix-series rescue and firefighting helicopters. Bombardier, Canada, won an order for a single Challenger 604 maritime surveillance aircraft on 16-6-99, for delivery in 2001; additional units may later be ordered.

PATROL SHIPS [WPS]

♦ **1 1,650-ton class** Bldr: Daewoo SB, Okpo (L: 22-1-99)

PC 1006 Seomjinkang

Seomjinkang (PC 1006) *Ships of the World,* 7-00

D: 1,650 tons (fl) **S:** 21 kts **Dim:** 84.0 × 10.4 × 3.6
A: 1 20-mm Vulcan gatling AA—4 single 12.7-mm mg
Electronics: Radar: 1 . . . nav.; 1 Kelvin-Hughes . . . surf. search
M: 2 Wärtsilä-Nohab 16V25 diesels; 2 props; 10,000 bhp
Range: 4,500/18 **Crew:** 7 officers, 50 enlisted

Remarks: Ordered in 1997. Intended for seagoing patrol, salvage, and rescue duties.

♦ **1 HDC 1150 class** Bldr: Korea SB & Eng., Pusan (In serv. 12-85)

PC 1005 Hankang

Hankang (PC 1005) *Ships of the World,* 1997

D: 980 tons (1,150 fl) **S:** 31 kts **Dim:** 87.84 × 10.0 × 2.36
A: 1 76-mm 62-cal. OTOBreda Compact DP; 1 40-mm 60-cal. Bofors Mk 3 AA; 2 single 20-mm Vulcan gatling AA
Electronics: Radar: 1 Raytheon SPS-64(V) nav.; 1 Thales WM-28 f.c.
M: CODOG: 1 G.E. LM-2500 gas turbine (27,800 shp), 2 MTU 12V956 TB 82 diesels (6,260 bhp each); 2 CP props
Range: 4,000/15 **Endurance:** 21 days **Crew:** 11 officers, 61 enlisted

Remarks: A lower-powered and more lightly armed version of the *Pohang*-class frigates built for the navy. Has the Rademac System 2400 optronic director and a visual backup to supplement the Thales WM-28 detection/tracking radar.

♦ **3 HDP 1000 class**
Bldr: Hanjin SB & Eng., Pusan (PC 1002 by Hyundai SY, Ulsan)

PC 1001 Mazingga (In serv. 29-11-81) PC 1003 . . . . . . (In serv. 31-8-83)
PC 1002 . . . . . . (In serv. 31-8-82)

Mazingga (PC 1001) Korea SB & Eng., 1981

D: 1,200 tons (1,450 fl) **S:** 21.5 kts **Dim:** 81.50 × 9.80 × 3.15
A: 1 40-mm 60-cal. Bofors Mk 3 AA; 2 twin 20-mm 70-cal. Oerlikon Mk 24 AA
Electronics: Radar: 2 . . . nav.
M: 2 Niigata–SEMT-Pielstick 12 PA6 280 diesels; 2 props; 9,600 bhp
Range: 7,000/18 **Crew:** 11 officers, 58 enlisted

Remarks: Ordered 7-11-80. PC 1001 acts as maritime police flagship. Have passive tank stabilization system. Engines were built in Japan under license.

♦ **6 Sea Whale class**

	Bldr	In serv.
PC 501	Hanjin Industrial SB, Chinhae	25-12-78
PC 502	Hanjin Industrial SB, Chinhae	1979
PC 503	Hanjin Industrial SB, Chinhae	5-5-79
PC 505	Korea SB & Eng., Pusan	31-5-80
PC 506	Hyundai SY, Ulsan	28-9-81
PC 507	Hanjin Industrial SB, Chinhae	31-7-82

Sea Whale–class PC 503 Official photo, 7-94

D: 410 tons (500 fl) **S:** 24 kts **Dim:** 60.80 × 8.00 × 2.29
A: 1 40-mm 60-cal. Bofors Mk 3 AA; 2 single 20-mm 70-cal. Oerlikon AA; 2 single 7.62-mm mg
Electronics: Radar: 2 . . . nav.
M: 2 Niigata-Pielstick 12 PA6 V280 diesels; 2 props; 9,600 bhp
Range: 1,500/25; 2,400/20 **Crew:** 11 officers, 28 enlisted

Remarks: Intended for rescue and inspection duties. Flume-type passive tank roll stabilization is on one unit, with an AA gun in the same position on the others. PC 503 has two 5,440-bhp Wärtsilä-Nohab diesels.

PATROL CRAFT [WPC]

♦ **4 32.2-meter class** Bldr: Hyundai SY, Ulsan (In serv. 1997)

PC 118 and 3 others

D: 110 tons (fl) **S:** 25 kts **Dim:** 32.2 × 6.0 × 1.4
A: 1 20-mm 70-cal. Oerlikon Mk 10 AA; 2 single 12.7-mm mg
Electronics: 1 . . . nav.
M: 2 . . . diesels; 2 props; . . . bhp **Crew:** 19 tot.

♦ **430-ton class** Bldr: Hyundai SY, Ulsan (PC 301: Daewoo SY, Okpo)

	In serv.		In serv.		In serv.
PC 300	10-4-94	PC 302	15-12-90	PC 402	12-91
PC 301	20-4-90	PC 303	20-12-91	PC 403	1993

430-ton-class PC 301 H&L Van Ginderen, 8-00

D: 300 tons light (430 fl) **S:** 19 kts **Dim:** 55.50 (53.70 pp) × 7.40 × 2.48
A: 1 or 2 single 20-mm Vulcan gatling AA; 4 single 12.7-mm M2 mg
Electronics: Radar: 1 or 2 . . . nav.
M: 2 MTU 16V396 TB83 diesels; 2 props; 4,392 bhp
Range: 2,100/15 **Crew:** 4 officers, 35 enlisted

Remarks: Equipped for search-and-rescue service and for towing. Previously listed as two different classes, but photography shows them to be virtually identical.

♦ **4 Bukhansan class**
Bldrs: Hyundai SY, Ulsan, and Daewoo SB & Heavy Machinery, Okpo (In serv. 1989–90)

PC 278 PC 279 PC 281 PC 282

D: 350 tons (380 fl) **S:** 28+ kts **Dim:** 53.10 (47.8 pp) × 7.10 × 2.40
A: 1 twin 40-mm 70-cal. OTOBreda Fast Forty AA; 1 20-mm Vulcan gatling AA; 2 single 12.7-mm mg
Electronics: Radar: 1 . . . nav. **M:** 2 MTU diesels; 2 props; 8,300 bhp
Electric: 260 kw tot. (2 × 130-kw diesel sets)
Range: 2,500/15 **Crew:** 3 officers, 32 enlisted

MARITIME POLICE PATROL CRAFT [WPC] *(continued)*

Bukhansan-class PC 278 Hyundai, 1989

Remarks: A development of the Sea Wolf/Sea Shark series; Daewoo referred to the design as the DW 300P or Salsu class. PC 278 may bear the name *Bukhansan* and PC 279 the name *Cheolmasan.* Have an optronic director for the 40-mm mount, as well as a target-designation sight. PC 278 is armed with a twin OTOBreda 40-mm Compact gunmount forward; the others appear to have Rheinmetall single Bofors 40-mm weapons.

♦ 1 PC 277 class
Bldr: Hanjin Industrial SB, Chinhae (In serv. 10-12-86)

PC 277

D: 250 tons **S:** 28 kts **Dim:** 47.75 × 7.10 × 2.35
A: 1 40-mm 60-cal. Bofors Mk 3 AA; 1 20-mm Vulcan gatling AA; 2 single 12.7-mm mg
Electronics: Radar: 1 . . . nav.
M: 2 MTU 20V538 TB91 diesels; 2 props; 9,000 bhp
Range: 2,400/25 **Crew:** 3 officers, 32 enlisted

♦ 23 Sea Shark/Sea Wolf class
Bldrs: Hyundai SY, Ulsan; Daehau SB; and Hanjin Industrial SB, Masan (In serv. 1979–82)

Sea Shark/Sea Wolf–class PC 123—with single 20-mm gatling gun forward H&L Van Ginderen, 8-00

Sea Shark/Sea Wolf–class PC 127—with raised pilothouse and a probably 20-mm Oerlikon AA mount forward H&L Van Ginderen, 8-00

D: 250 tons (280 fl) **S:** 28 kts **Dim:** 47.75 × 7.10 × 2.12 (2.50 over props)
A: 2 twin, or 1 twin and 2 single 20-mm 70-cal. Oerlikon AA; 2 single 12.7-mm mg
Electronics: Radar: 1 . . . nav.
M: 2 MTU 16V538-series diesels; 2 props; 7,320 bhp
Range: 1,600/20; 3,300/15 **Crew:** 5 officers, 24 enlisted

Remarks: Some have a raised platform aft, and there are numerous small differences, depending on when built and by whom. Units from Hyundai are known as the Sea Shark class, those from Hanjin as the Sea Wolf. Range is also given as 2,000 n.m. at 17 kts. Pennant numbers appear to have been changed to the 100 series; as completed, they ran from PC 251 through PC 276.

PATROL BOATS [WPB]

♦ 3 18.7-meter class
Bldrs: Kangan SY and Miwon SY (In serv. 1992–93)

D: 28 tons (fl) **S:** 35 kts **Dim:** 18.70 × 4.40 × 0.90
A: 1 12.7-mm mg **Electronics:** Radar: 1 . . . nav.
M: 2 MTU 12V183 TE92 diesels; 2 Hamilton waterjets; 2,000 bhp
Electric: 48 kw tot. **Range:** 250/28 **Crew:** 7 tot.

♦ . . . Swallow class
Bldr: Korea SB & Eng., Pusan (In serv. 1980s)

Swallow-class P 387 H&L Van Ginderen, 3-99

D: 32 tons (fl) **S:** 25 kts **Dim:** 20.0 × 4.7 × 1.3
A: 1 12.7-mm mg; 1 7.62-mm mg
M: 2 G.M. 12V71 TI diesels; 2 props; 1,060 bhp
Range: 500/20 **Crew:** 8 tot.

Remarks: Glass-reinforced plastic construction.

♦ 18 Sea Gull class
Bldr: Korea SB & Eng., Pusan (In serv. early 1970s)

D: 80 tons **S:** 30 kts **Dim:** 24.0 × 5.5 × . . .
A: 1 or 2 single 20-mm 70-cal. Oerlikon AA
M: 2 MTU diesels; 2 props; 3,920 bhp **Range:** 950/20 **Crew:** 18 tot.

AUXILIARIES

♦ 1 Taepyeongyang II–class ocean salvage tender [WARS]
Bldr: Hyundai, Ulsan

	Laid down	L	In serv.
3002 Taepyeongyang II	. . .	. . .	11-98

Taepyeongyang II (3002) *Ships of the World,* 7-00

D: 3,900 tons (5,000 fl) **S:** 18 kts **Dim:** 110.50 × 15.40 × . . .
A: 1 20-mm Vulcan gatling AA; 6 single 12.7-mm mg
Electronics: Radar: 2 . . . nav.
M: 4 Sangyong–Burmeister & Wain 16V 28/32 diesels; 2 CP prop; 11,800 bhp—bow- and stern-thrusters
Electric: 1,950 kw tot. (2 × 800 kw; 1 × 350 kw)
Range: 8,500/15 **Fuel:** 825 m^3 **Crew:** 120 tot.

Remarks: Has firefighting, towing, oil-spill containment, and salvage equipment. Equipped with a helicopter deck. Hull sides are heavily reinforced with rubbing strakes. Painted white, with "Police" prominently visible on the hull sides.

♦ 1 Taepyeongyang I–class ocean salvage tender [WARS]
Bldr: Hyundai, Ulsan

	Laid down	L	In serv.
3001 Taepyeongyang I	2-91	10-91	18-2-93

Taepyeongyang I (3001) *Ships of the World,* 7-00

MARITIME POLICE AUXILIARIES *(continued)*

D: 3,200 tons (4,300 fl) **S:** 21 kts **Dim:** 104.70 × 15.00 × 5.20
A: 1 20-mm Vulcan gatling AA; 6 single 12.7-mm mg
Electronics: Radar: 2 . . . nav.
M: 4 Sangyong–Burmeister & Wain 16V 28/32 diesels; 2 CP prop; 11,800 bhp—3 bow- and 2 stern-thrusters
Electric: 1,950 kw tot. (2 × 800 kw; 1 × 350 kw)
Range: 8,500/15 **Fuel:** 825 m^3 **Crew:** 121 tot.

Remarks: 4,300 grt. Has firefighting, towing, oil-spill containment, and salvage equipment. Equipped with a helicopter deck. Bow is equipped with sheaves for cable laying and repair. Can lay and recover a four-point moor for salvage purposes. Hull sides are heavily reinforced with rubbing strakes. Painted white, with "Police" prominently visible on the hull sides.

♦ **1 salvage ship [WARS]** Bldr: Hyundai, Ulsan (In serv. 11-88)

1503 . . . . . .

Salvage ship 1503 H&L Van Ginderen, 8-00

D: 3,900 tons (4,200 fl) **S:** 18 kts **Dim:** 110.5 × 15.4 × 4.9
A: 2 single 20-mm Vulcan gatling AA; 6 single 12.7-mm mg
Electronics: Radar: 2 . . . nav./surf. search
M: 2 . . . diesels; 2 props; . . . bhp
Range: . . ./. . . **Crew:** 120 tot.

Remarks: Ordered in 1996. Has a large helicopter deck aft but no hangar. Intended for ocean patrol and salvage duties.

♦ **1 salvage ship [WARS]**

	Bldr	L	In serv.
1502 Jaemin II	Hyundai SY, Ulsan	15-7-95	4-96

Jaemin II (1502) *Ships of the World,* 7-00

D: 2,500 tons (fl) **S:** 20 kts **Dim:** 88.0 × 14.50 × 4.60
A: 1 20-mm Vulcan gatling AA **Electronics:** Radar: 2 . . . nav.
M: 2 MTU . . . diesels; 2 KaMeWa CP props; 12,662 bhp—bow- and stern-thrusters
Range: 4,500/15 **Crew:** 81 tot.

Remarks: Ordered 12-93. An enlarged version of the *Jaemin I* (1501); distinguishable by twin side-by-side stacks. Painted white, with red-white-blue diagonal stripe on hull side, which also bears the legend "Police." Is equipped for firefighting, towing, ocean patrol, rescue, and salvage duties.

♦ **1 salvage ship [WARS]** Bldr: Daewoo, Okpo (In serv. 28-12-92)

1501 Jaemin I

D: 2,072 tons (fl) **S:** 18 kts **Dim:** 77.58 × 13.50 × 4.20
A: 1 20-mm Vulcan gatling AA **Electronics:** Radar: 2 . . . nav.
M: 2 MTU 16V1163 TB62 diesels; 2 CP props; 8,000 bhp
Range: 4,500/12 **Crew:** 72 tot.

Remarks: Modeled after the U.S. *Bolster* class but is much larger. Has telescoping hydraulic cranes fore and aft. Can lay and recover a four-point mooring. Carries two LCVP-type workboats. Equipped for ocean towing. Hull sides are heavily reinforced with rubbing strakes.

Jaemin I (1501) Daewoo, 12-92

SERVICE CRAFT

♦ **3 pollution-control craft [WYAG]** Bldr: Wuri SB Industries

. . . . . . (In serv. 10-92) . . . . . . (In serv. 30-10-92) . . . . . . (In serv. 9-93)

Unidentified Maritime Police pollution-control ship—with large reels aft to deploy an oil-spill containment boom; the ship is unarmed but has two firefighting monitors *Ships of the World,* 7-00

D: 220 tons (fl) **S:** 12 kts **Dim:** 31.10 × 8.50 × 1.54
Electronics: Radar: . . .
M: 2 Cummins KTA 19M diesels; 1 prop; 1,000 bhp **Electric:** 144 kw tot.
Range: 700/10 **Fuel:** 26 m^3 **Crew:** 11 tot.

♦ **1 16-ton bollard-pull tug [WYTB]**
Bldr: Wuri SB Industries (In serv. 5-93)

D: 320 tons (fl) **S:** 11.5 kts **Dim:** 27.50 × 7.60 × 2.40
M: 2 Cummins VTA 28M diesels; 2 Aquamaster azimuth drives; 1,450 bhp
Electric: 236 kw tot. **Range:** 500/10.5 **Fuel:** 27 m^3 **Crew:** 6 tot.

Note: The customs service also operates an unknown number of patrol boats, at least some of them armed with 20-mm Oerlikon guns.

KUWAIT

State of Kuwait

KUWAITI NAVY

Personnel (2002): Approx. 2,200 total (about 380 officers)

Base: Ras al Qalayah

Naval Aviation: The air force has four AS.332F Super Puma helicopters that can be armed with AM 39 Exocet antiship missiles, and its 40 F/A-18 Hornet fighters are eventually to be able to conduct maritime strikes. Plans for the acquisition of antiship missile–armed helicopters for the navy appear to have come to naught.

CORVETTES [FFL]

Note: Plans to acquire 3–5 corvettes of about 1,200 tons displacement appear to have been put on hold.

GUIDED-MISSILE PATROL BOATS [PTG]

♦ **8 P37 BRL class** Bldr: CMN, Cherbourg

	Laid down	L	In serv.
P 3711 Um Almaradim	11-94	27-2-97	31-7-98
P 3713 Ouha	2-95	29-5-97	31-7-98
P 3715 Failaka	5-95	29-8-97	19-12-98
P 3717 Maskan	8-95	6-1-98	19-12-98
P 3719 Al Ahmadi	11-95	2-4-98	1-7-99
P 3721 Al Fahaheel	2-96	16-6-98	1-7-99
P 3723 Al Yarmook	5-96	3-3-99	7-6-00
P 3725 Garoh	8-96	4-6-99	7-6-00

GUIDED-MISSILE PATROL BOATS [PTG] *(continued)*

Al Fahaheel (P 3721) Bernard Prézelin, 8-00

Garoh (P 3725)—note the canister launchers for four Sea Skua missiles at the stern Bernard Prézelin, 8-00

Al Ahmadi (P 3719) Bernard Prézelin, 8-00

D: 225 tons (247 fl) **S:** 38 kts (30 sust.)
Dim: 42.00 (37.50 pp) × 8.50 (8.20 waterline) × 1.98 (hull; 2.80 max.)
A: 4 Sea Skua SSM; 1 40-mm 70-cal. OTOBreda Fast Forty AA; 1 20-mm 90-cal. GIAT Type 15A AA; 2 single 12.7-mm M2HB mg
Electronics:
Radar: 1 Racal-Decca 20V90 nav.; Thales-Matra MRR (TRS-5204) 3-D air search; 1 Marconi Avionics Seaspray 3000 missile target-acquisition and tracking
EW: Thales DR-3000S1 Compact intercept (1–18 GHz); . . . IR detection syst.; provision for 1 330- to 340-round Matra Défense Dagaie Mk 2 decoy RL
E/O: Matra Défense Najir Mk 2 gun f.c. and surveillance
M: 2 MTU 16V538 TB93 diesels; 2 KaMeWa waterjets; 8,000 bhp
Electric: 420 kw tot. **Range:** 1,350/14; 1,700/12 **Fuel:** 30 tons
Endurance: 7 days **Crew:** 5 officers, 19 enlisted

Remarks: Referred to locally as the *Garoh* class. Ordered 27-3-95. P 3711 began sea trials in 4-97. Each unit was to have two complete crews. The first four craft arrived in Kuwaiti waters 15-8-99, and the second quartet departed France 17-8-00 for arrival in 11-00. The class took considerably longer to build and deliver than had been planned.
Hull systems: Steel hull, aluminum superstructure. Have fin stabilizers.
Combat systems: Have the Thales NCCS combat system, a version of the TAVITAC-NT weapons-control system with three Matra Défense Calisto multifunction display consoles and a Model "Y" datalink to other units of the class. The Seaspray radar/Sea Skua missile suite is a stand-alone system not integrated into the main weapons-control system. The Matra Défense Najir M42 optronic director with IR, daylight t.v., and laser rangefinder sensors controls the 40-mm AA, which has a 450-rpm firing rate. Plans to install a Sadral SAM launcher and a Salamandre jammer have been dropped, but the systems may be acquired later. A Marconi Hazeltine TPX-54(V) Mk XII IFF transponder is fitted.

♦ 1 FPB 57 class (in reserve)
Bldr: Lürssen, Bremen-Vegesack, Germany (In serv. 9-8-83)

P 5702 *Istiqlal*

Istiqlal (P 5702) U.S. Navy, 11-90

D: 353 tons (398 fl) **S:** 36 kts **Dim:** 58.10 (54.40 wl) × 7.62 × 2.83
A: 4 MM 40 Exocet SSM; 1 76-mm 62-cal. OTOBreda DP; 1 twin 40-mm 70-cal. OTOBreda AA; 2 single 7.62-mm mg
Electronics:
Radar: 1 Decca 1226C nav.; 1 Ericsson Sea Giraffe 50HC surf./air search; 1 Saab 9LV 228 f.c.
EW: Racal RDL-2 intercept; Racal Cygnus jammer; 1 330- to 340-round Matra Défense Dagaie decoy RL
M: 4 MTU 16V956 TB91 diesels; 4 props; 18,000 bhp
Electric: 405 kw (3 × 135 kw) **Range:** 1,300/30 **Fuel:** 90 tons
Crew: 4 officers, 35 enlisted

Remarks: Two ordered in 1980 to function as leaders for the six TNC-45 class. Name means "Freedom." Sister *Sabhan* (P 5704) was captured by Iraqi forces in 8-90 and sunk by UN Coalition forces 29-1-91. A preliminary contract for an extensive refit at CMN, Cherbourg, was signed in 8-94, but the ship is still laid up in Kuwait awaiting repair.

♦ 1 TNC-45 class
Bldr: Lürssen, Bremen-Vegesack, Germany

	L	In serv.
P 4505 Al Sanbouk (ex-*Jalboot*)	5-82	26-4-84

Al Sanbouk (P 4505)—with *Istiqlal* (P 5702) in background U.S. Navy, 11-90

D: 231 tons (259 fl) **S:** 41.5 kts **Dim:** 44.90 (42.30 wl) × 7.00 × 2.40
A: 4 MM 40 Exocet SSM; 1 76-mm 62-cal. OTOBreda DP; 1 twin 40-mm 70-cal. OTOBreda AA; 2 single 7.62-mm mg
Electronics:
Radar: 1 Decca 1226 nav.; 1 Ericsson Sea Giraffe 50 surf./air search; 1 Saab 9LV 200 f.c.
EW: Racal RDL-2 intercept
M: 4 MTU 16V538 TB92 diesels; 4 props; 15,600 bhp (15,000 sust.)
Electric: 369 kw tot. (3 × 123 kw) **Range:** 500/38.5; 1,500/16
Crew: 5 officers, 27 enlisted

Remarks: Ordered in 1980. Refitted by Lürssen in 1995–96.
Losses: Five were captured by invading Iraqi forces in 8-90 and subsequently sunk by UN Coalition forces (one on 18-1-91 and one on 30-1-91; dates for the others uncertain): *Al Boom* (P 4501, ex-*Werjiya*), *Al Betteen* (P 4503, ex-*Mashuwah*), *Al Saadi* (P 4507, ex-*Istiqlal*), *Al Ahmadi* (P 4509), and *Al Abdali* (P 4511, ex-*Al Mubareki*).
Combat systems: Carries 250 rounds of 76-mm and 1,800 rounds of 40-mm ammunition. Has a Matra Défense Lynx optronic gun director for the 40-mm mount, a Saab 9LV 200 control system for the 76-mm gun and missiles, and a flare rocket launcher amidships.

PATROL BOATS [PB]

Note: In addition to the units listed below, about a dozen other small ex-Iraqi or former private craft have been pressed into service for patrol or utility duties. The 12 Manta-clsss patrol boats ordered 6-98 as replacements for the unsatisfactory dozen Star Naja SM460 class units procured from the same builder in 1994 were also found to be unsatisfactory and were also returned to the builder.

MINE COUNTERMEASURES SHIPS

Note: Although an impending order for three Tripartite-class minehunters to be built in France was announced in 9-92, no contract has been signed, and the program has apparently been canceled. Negotiations were reported under way during 11-95 with the U.S. company Textron Marine for 4–6 surface-effect craft for use as mine countermeasures units, but again no contract resulted.

SERVICE CRAFT

♦ 2 Hadiya-class logistics support lighters [YFU]
Bldr: Vosper Pty, Singapore (In serv. 1979)

HADIYA CERIFF

D: 320 tons (fl) **S:** 9 kts **Dim:** 32.3 × 7.5 × 2.5
A: none **Electronics:** Radar: 1 Decca . . . nav.
M: 2 Rolls-Royce CBM-410 diesels; 2 props; 750 bhp
Range: 1,500/8 **Crew:** 1 officer, 6 enlisted

Remarks: Captured by Iraq during 1990–91 and returned in poor condition in 1993; since then, refitted for local logistic support duties. An unusual design, with a stern vehicle ramp intended to allow them to back onto shore to load or unload cargo.

♦ 1 logistics support lighter [YFU]
Bldr: Vosper Pty, Singapore (In serv. 1975)

55 FAREED

D: 170 tons (fl) **S:** 10 kts **Dim:** 27.0 × 6.9 × 1.3
A: none **Electronics:** Radar: 1 . . . nav.
M: 2 Rolls-Royce C8M-410 diesels; 2 props; 750 bhp
Range: 1,500/9 **Crew:** 9 tot.

Remarks: Captured by Iraq and returned in poor condition in 1993. Has been rehabilitated and is used to supply offshore islands. Can carry 40 tons of vehicles or dry cargo on deck, plus liquid cargo of 24,224 liters fuel and 35,579 liters of potable water. Has a bow ramp.

♦ 1 Sawahil 35–class self-propelled barracks craft [YPB]
Bldr: Inchon SB & Eng., South Korea (In serv. 1986)

S 5509 QARQ (ex-*Sawahil 35*)

Qarq (S 5509) Peter Voss, 11-92

D: approx. 1,800 tons (fl) **S:** 8 kts **Dim:** 55.00 × 20.0 × 2.0
A: 2 12.7-mm mg **Electronics:** Radar: 1 Decca . . . nav.
M: 2 diesels; 2 props; 2,400 bhp **Crew:** 40 tot.

Remarks: 545 dwt. The name has also been transliterated as *Qaruh.* Built for the Kuwait Shipbuilding and Repair Ministry for use as oilfield barracks. Escaped capture during the 1990–91 war and operated in support of Free Kuwaiti naval forces as a supply tender, carrying food, fuel, water, and ammunition. Refitted in 1996–97. Has a 20 × 20–m helicopter deck. Sisters *Sawahil 40* and *Sawahil 43* were lost during the war, and *Sawahil 50* served the Kuwaiti Coast Guard until recently.

COAST GUARD

Personnel (2002): Approx. 500 uniformed personnel, plus 600 civilians

Bases: Shuwaikh and Umm al-Hainan

Note: Most of the craft built by Cougar Marine listed below were ordered in 1-91 by the then government-in-exile and were delivered post-hostilities. All craft are painted dark gray and have a bright red paired diagonal stripe on either beam.

PATROL CRAFT [WPC]

♦ 4 Al Shaheed class
Bldr: OCÉA, St. Nazaire, France

	In serv.		In serv.
P 305 AL SHAHEED	6-97	P 307 DASMAN	10-5-01
P 306 BAYAN	6-4-99	P 308	. . .

Dasman (P 307) Bernard Prézelin, 5-01

Bayan (P 306)—note cutout to the port side of the hull amidships to facilitate access for rescuees Bernard Prézelin, 5-99

D: 90 tons (110 fl) **S:** 30 kts **Dim:** 33.30 × 7.00 × 1.15
A: 1 12.7-mm mg
Electronics: Radar: 1 Decca 20V90 nav.; 1 Decca C 252/8 nav.
M: 2 MTU 12V396 TE94 diesels; 2 waterjets; 4,400 bhp

Remarks: P 307 ran trials in 6-01, and a fourth was on order for delivery by the end of 2001.

♦ 4 ASI OPV 310 class
Bldr: Transfield ASI Pty, South Coogie, Australia (In serv. 11-92)

	In serv.		In serv.
P 301 INTTISAR	20-1-93	P 303 MAIMON	30-6-93
P 302 AMAN	20-1-93	P 304 MOBARK	30-6-93

Mobark (P 304) U.S. Navy, 9-95

D: 148 tons (165 fl) **S:** 28 kts
Dim: 32.60 (31.50 hull; 28.60 wl) × 8.20 × 1.60 (hull)
A: 1 12.7-mm mg; 2 single 7.62-mm mg
Electronics: Radar: 1 . . . nav.
M: 2 MTU 16V396 TB94 diesels; 2 props; . . . bhp—1 MTU 8V183 TE62 diesel for loiter; 1 Hamilton 422 waterjet; . . . bhp
Electric: 116 kw (2 × 50-kw Caterpillar 3304 diesels; 1 × 16 kw)
Range: 300/28; 2,500/12 **Fuel:** 27.9 tons **Endurance:** 8–10 days
Crew: 3 officers, 8 enlisted

Remarks: Ordered 8-91. Modified standard Australian foreign aid patrol boat design, with less draft and fuel and a third engine added centerline for cruising. Carry a 5-m rigid inflatable boarding boat. Builder has an option for a third pair. Sisters serve the Hong Kong Police.

PATROL BOATS [WPB]

♦ 4 . . . class
Bldr: FB Design, Italy (In serv. 2001)

D: 4.5 tons light **S:** 54 kts **Dim:** 13.00 × 2.7 × . . .
A: 2 single 12.7-mm mg **M:** 2 Yanmar . . . diesels; 2 5-bladed props; 420 bhp
Range: 300/40; 480/25 **Fuel:** 260 gallons **Crew:** 4 tot.

Remarks: Deep-vee hull formed of Kevlar composite over a balsawood core. The machinegun mounts are side-by-side forward of the amidships conning position.

♦ 6 Enforcer 40 Mk 2B class
Bldr: Cougar Marine, Warsash, U.K. (In serv. 6-96 to 11-99)

D: 5.5 tons light **S:** 45 kts **Dim:** 12.19 × 2.74 × 0.76
A: 2 single 7.62-mm mg **Electronics:** Radar: 1 . . . nav.
M: 2 Ford Sabre 380S diesels; 2 Arneson ASD 8 outdrives with Rolla props; 760 bhp
Range: 300/35 **Fuel:** 818 liters **Crew:** 4 tot.

Remarks: Monohull form, constructed of GRP and Kevlar over a foam and plywood core. Can accommodate up to 300 kg of weapons.

COAST GUARD PATROL BOATS [WPB] *(continued)*

Kuwaiti Coast Guard Enforcer 40 Mk 2B–class unit 465
Cougar Marine, 1996

♦ **23 28-foot class** Bldr: Al-Shaali Marine, Dubai (In serv. 7-92)

Remarks: GRP construction, ordered in early 1992. Powered by two Yamaha 200-bhp outboard engines. Have an APELCO navigational radar. No other details available.

♦ **10 33-foot class** Bldr: Al-Shaali Marine, Dubai (In serv. 7-92—. . .)

Remarks: GRP construction. Powered by two Yamaha 200-bhp outboard engines. Have an APELCO navigational radar. No other details available.

♦ **3 UFPB 1300 class** Bldr: Cougar Marine, Washington, U.K. (In serv. 6-91)

D: . . . tons (fl) **S:** . . . kts **Dim:** 13.0 × . . . × . . . **A:** . . .
M: 2 Ford Sabre 380C diesels; 2 Arneson surface-piercing props; 760 bhp

♦ **4 UFPB 1200 class** Bldr: Cougar Marine, Washington, U.K. (In serv. 6-91)

D: . . . tons (fl) **S:** . . . kts **Dim:** 12.0 × . . . × . . . **A:** . . .
M: 2 Ford Sabre 380C diesels; 2 Arneson surface-piercing props; 760 bhp

♦ **3 UFPB 1100 Predator-class GRP-hulled**
Bldr: Cougar Marine, Washington, U.K. (In serv. 6-91)

D: . . . tons (fl) **S:** . . . kts **Dim:** 11.0 × . . . × . . . **A:** . . .
M: 2 Yamaha 200B gasoline outboards; 400 bhp

♦ **3 UFPB 1000–class GRP-hulled**
Bldr: Cougar Marine, Washington, U.K. (In serv. 4-91)

D: . . . tons (fl) **S:** . . . kts **Dim:** 10.0 × . . . × . . . **A:** . . .
M: 2 Yamaha 200B gasoline outboards; 400 bhp

♦ **3 Cat 900–class catamarans**
Bldr: Cougar Marine, Washington, U.K. (In serv. 5-91)

D: 2 tons (fl) **S:** 35 kts **Dim:** 9.0 × . . . × . . . **A:** . . .
M: 2 Yamaha 200B gasoline outboards; 400 bhp

SERVICE CRAFT

♦ **1 PVF 512 Sea Truck–class launch [WYFL]**
Bldr: RTK Marine, Poole, U.K. (In serv. 6-94)

D: 9 tons (fl) **S:** 26 kts **Dim:** 12.7 × 3.2 × . . .
Electronics: Radar: 1 . . . nav.
M: 2 Yamaha diesels; 2 outdrive props; . . . bhp
Crew: 2 tot. + 14 passengers

Remarks: Ordered 2-94 with an option for a second (not yet taken up). GRP construction. Can be beached to disembark passengers.

♦ **2 Al Tahaddy–class logistics support craft [WYFU]**
Bldr: Singapore SB & Eng., Johore (L: 15-4-94; in serv. 7-94)

L 401 Al Tahaddy L 402 Al Soumood

Al Soumood (L 402) Maritime Photographic, 1-99

D: 215 tons (fl) **S:** 13 kts **Dim:** 43.0 × 10.0 × 1.5 **A:** . . .
Electronics: Radar: 1 Decca . . . nav.
M: 2 MTU . . . . . . diesels; 2 props; . . . bhp

Remarks: Utility landing craft–typed craft. Capable of transporting vehicle and dry cargo up to 80 tons total. Have a bow ramp and a firefighting monitor atop the pilothouse.

♦ **2 Loadmaster Mk II logistics support landing craft [WYFU]**
Bldr: Fairey Marine, Cowes (In serv. 1984–85)

L 101 Al Saffar L 103 Jalbout

D: 175 tons light; 320 tons normal (420 fl) **S:** 10.5 kts (10.0 sust.)
Dim: 33.00 (30.00 pp) × 10.20 × 1.75
A: none **Electronics:** Radar: 1 Decca . . . nav.
M: 2 Caterpillar 3412 DITA, V-12 diesels; 2 Kort-nozzle props; 1,214 bhp (1,010 sust.)
Electric: 72 kw tot. **Range:** 1,000/10 **Fuel:** 30 tons
Crew: 1 officer, 6 enlisted

Remarks: Ordered in 1983. Captured by Iraqi forces, 8-90; recovered postwar, rehabilitated, and reactivated in 1992. Cargo includes 150 tons on deck, or 90 tons on deck and 60 tons liquid cargo. Can accommodate two 60-ton tanks. Sisters *Al Seef* (L 102) and *Al Badani* (L 104) were lost during the Iraqi war.

LAOS

Lao People's Democratic Republic

ARMY MARINE SECTION

Personnel (2002): Approx. 400 total

PATROL BOATS [WPB]

♦ **approx. 40 river patrol craft**

Remarks: Reported by the press to have been a gift of the USSR in 1985. No other data available.

Note: Also possibly in service are four small landing craft. There are probably other locally built riverine craft in use as well.

LATVIA

Latvian Republic

LATVIAN NAVY
(Latvijas Juras Speki)

Personnel (2001): Approx. 800 total (including Coast Guard)

Bases: Headquarters at Riga; bases at Liepaja, Bolderaja, and Ventspils

Organization: The fleet is divided into three coast guard divisions: the First Coast Guard Division, headquartered at Liepaja; the Second Coast Guard Division, headquartered at Bolderaja; and the Third Coast Guard Division at Ventspils. The First Division incorporates the coast guard ship division at Bolderaja and a coast defense company with rifle and communications platoons; another rifle platoon is at Ainazi. The Second Division incorporates a combat ship division at Liepaja, a coast guard ship division at Liepaja, and the coast defense battalion (with companies at Kolka, Liepaja, and Pavilosta). The newly created (1998) Third Division operates a single craft at Ventspils, along with a coast defense battalion company.

The Latvian Coast Guard is subordinated to the navy and shares personnel and base resources. Craft of the former Center for Search and Rescue Coordination were to be transferred to the navy in 2001, and the first craft to transfer was the *Astra,* a former Finnish rescue ship purchased in 1996 and transferred to the navy 13-3-01.

PATROL CRAFT [PC]

♦ **1 ex-East German Osa-I class (Project 205)**

	Original in serv.	Transferred	In serv.
P-01 Zibens (ex-*Josef Schares,* 753)	6-10-71	30-8-93	7-8-94

D: 165 tons light (200 fl) **S:** 42 kts **Dim:** 38.60 × 7.60 × 1.80
A: 1 twin 30-mm 65-cal. AK-230 AA; 1 twin 23-mm 87-cal. Wrobel ZSU-23 AA
Electronics: Radar: 1 Rangout (Square Tie) surf. search
M: 3 M-503A diesels; 3 props; 12,000 bhp
Range: 800/30; 1,800/14 **Fuel:** 40 tons **Crew:** 26 tot.

PATROL CRAFT [PC] *(continued)*

Zibens (P-01) Jaroslaw Cislak, 6-98

Remarks: Donated by Germany along with sisters ex-*Heinrich Dorrenbach* (711), ex-*Fritz Gast* (714), and ex-*Otto Tost* (731). The *Tost,* although given pennant P-03, was cannibalized and scrapped 1993–94, and the *Gast* was initially renamed *Gauja* (P-02) but was not placed in service and remains afloat as a cannibalization hulk at Liepaja. One further unit of the class, ex-*Paul Wiezcorek* (754), was towed from Peenemünde 27-6-95 for cannibalization in Latvia. All were stripped of missile armament and two twin AK-230 30-mm AA mounts while still in Germany. P-01 was armed in 1996, with a Russian 30-mm mount forward and a twin 23-mm mount from *Imanta* (M-02) aft. Will probably soon be retired. Based at Liepaja.

♦ 3 ex-Norwegian Storm class
Bldr: Bergens Mekaniske Verksted, Bergen (L: P-04: 18-11-66)

P-02 Lode (ex-. . .) P-04 Bulta (ex-*Traust,* P 973)
P-03 Linga (ex-. . .)

Bulta (P-04) Dieter Wolf, 6-00

D: 105 tons (125 fl) **S:** 37 kts **Dim:** 36.53 × 6.3 × 1.55
A: P-04: 1 40-mm 60-cal. Bofors Mk 3 AA—others: 1 76.2-mm 50-cal. Bofors low-angle; 1 40-mm 70-cal. Bofors L70 AA
Electronics: Radar: P-04: Decca TM 1226 nav.—others: 1 Furuno . . . nav.
M: 2 Maybach MB 872A (MTU 16V538 TB90) diesels; 2 props; 7,200 bhp
Range: 550/36 **Crew:** . . . tot.

Remarks: P-04 was stricken from the Norwegian Navy during 1993, rehabilitated during 1994, transferred 13-12-94 with the armament systems deleted, and recommissioned 1-2-95. An old Bofors hand-operated 40-mm AA was mounted aft during 1998. P-02 and P-03 were recommissioned 11-6-01 after transfer from Norway; their original gun armament was retained, along with a Bofors TVT300 optical director without the WM-22 gun fire-control system. All three are based at Liepaja. Another unit, also transferred during 6-01, was for cannibalization use only.

MINE COUNTERMEASURES SHIPS

♦ 1 ex-German Type 331B minehunter [MHC]

	Bldr	L	In serv.
M-03 Nemejs (ex-*Völklingen,* M 1087)	Burmester, Bremen	20-10-59	21-5-60

D: 388 tons (402 fl) **S:** 16.5 kts
Dim: 47.45 × 8.5 × 2.8 (3.68 with sonar extended)
A: 1 40-mm 70-cal. Bofors AA
Electronics:
Radar: 1 Raytheon SPS-64(V) nav.
Sonar: DSQS-11A HF minehunting
M: 2 MTU 16V538 TB90 diesels; 2 CP props; 5,000 bhp **Electric:** 220 kw tot.
Range: 1,400/16; 3,950/9 **Crew:** 5 officers, 29 enlisted + 6 divers

Remarks: Stricken from the German Navy 23-3-99, transferred 24-3-99, and formally commissioned at Riga 1-10-99 after an extensive refit in Germany.
Hull systems: Wooden construction, with nonmagnetic engines. Minehunting speed is 6 kts on two 50-kw electric motors.
Combat systems: Six divers and two French PAP-104 remote-controlled minehunting devices can be carried. Has no mechanical sweep gear. The 40-mm gun is controlled by a lead-computing optical director on the bridge.

Nemejs (M-03) Curt Borgenstam, 6-01

♦ 2 ex-East German Kondor-II-class (Project 89.2) minesweepers [MSC]
Bldr: VEB Peenewerft, Wolgast

	Original in serv.	Transferred	In serv.
M-01 Viesturs (ex-*Kamenz,* 351)	24-7-71	30-8-93	4-94
M-02 Imanta (ex-*Röbel,* 324)	1-12-71	30-8-93	5-94

Viesturs (M-01)—with new AA guns abreast the stack Findler & Winter, 6-01

D: 414 tons (479 fl) **S:** 18 kts **Dim:** 56.52 × 7.78 × 2.46
A: 1 twin 23-mm 87-cal. Wrobel ZSU-23-2 AA; 2 single 20-mm 90-cal. Rh-202 AA
Electronics: Radar: TSR-333 nav.
M: 2 Type 40DM diesels; 2 CP Kort-nozzle props; 4,400 bhp
Electric: 625 kw tot. (5 × 125-kw diesel sets)
Range: 2,000/15 **Endurance:** 10 days **Crew:** 6 officers, 24 enlisted

Remarks: Transferred 21-7-93 and delivered 31-8-93 at Riga after removal of all armament and portable mine countermeasures equipment. Had been out of service in reserve since 1-12-81 and 3-10-90, respectively. The similar former East German Kondor-class torpedo retriever *Libben* (V 662) was acquired in mid-1995 for cannibalization to support these two units. M-02 was initially armed with three Polish-supplied gunmounts; two have now been distributed to other units. Both received German 20-mm AA mounts during 2000. Surplus German sweep gear was acquired for both in 1996. Based at Liepaja.

SERVICE CRAFT

♦ 1 Soviet Nyryat'-I-class diving tender [YDT]
Bldr: . . . . . . (In serv. ca. 1960)

A-51 Lidaka (ex-*Gefests,* A 101)

Lidaka (A-51) Hartmut Ehlers, 9-96

SERVICE CRAFT *(continued)*

D: 92 tons (116.1 fl) **S:** 11 kts **Dim:** 28.58 × 5.20 × 1.70
A: 1 12.7-mm mg **Electronics:** Radar: 1 SNN-7 nav.
M: 1 Type 6CSP 28/3C diesel; 1 prop; 450 bhp
Range: 1,500/10 **Crew:** 1 officer, 5 enlisted

Remarks: Ex-civilian unit of the class, based at Ventspils and taken over in 1992, not a former Russian Navy unit. Based at Liepaja.

♦ **1 ex-Polish Goliat-class (Project H300/II) small harbor tug [YTL]** Bldr: Gdynska Stocznia Remontowa Nauta, Gdynia (In serv. 20-1-63)

A-18 PERKONS (ex-H 18)

Perkons (A-18) Hartmut Ehlers, 4-95

D: 112 tons (fl) **S:** 10 kts **Dim:** 21.4 × 5.8 × 2.1
M: 1 Buckau-Wolf 8NVD36 diesel; 1 prop; 300 bhp
Range: 300/9 **Crew:** 3 officers, 9 enlisted

Remarks: Donated by Poland 16-11-93. Based at Liepaja.

Note: Also taken over were two Soviet Army pontoon bridge erection boats, renumbered RK-104 and RK-105; one is in land storage and the other acts as a painting float. A former Soviet PO-2 (Project 376) utility launch named *Roze* was transferred to the navy from the Latvian Maritime Board at Ventspils for possible future activation.

COAST GUARD

(Latvijas Kara Flotes)

Note: The coast guard is subordinate to the navy, and its personnel totals are included in the naval listing above.

PATROL CRAFT [WPC]

♦ **1 Ribnadzor-4-class fisheries protection patrol boat** Bldr: Rybinsk Sudostroitel'niy Zavod (In serv. 1979)

KA-03 KOMETA (ex-103, ex-*Ribnadzor*-2)

Kometa (KA-03) Hartmut Ehlers, 9-96

D: 143 tons (173.3 fl) **S:** 15 kts **Dim:** 34.40 × 5.80 × 2.45
A: 1 12.7-mm mg **Electronics:** Radar: 1 Mius (Spin Trough) nav.
M: 1 Type 40DM-M3 diesel; 1 prop; 2,200 bhp **Range:** . . ./. . .
Crew: 4 officers, 13 enlisted

Remarks: Taken over and recommissioned for naval use 5-5-92. Based at Bolderaja. Sister *Spulga* (KA-02) went aground at Karlskrona 2-11-00 and sank while under tow on 6-11-00.

PATROL BOATS [WPB]

♦ **5 ex-Swedish Coast Guard Kbv 236 class** (In serv. 1970)

	Transferred	Base
KA-01 KRISTAPS (ex-Kbv 244)	5-2-93	Bolderaja
KA-06 GAISMA (ex-Kbv 249)	9-11-93	Bolderaja
KA-07 AUSMA (ex-Kbv 260)	9-11-93	Liepaja
KA-08 SAULE (ex-Kbv 256)	27-4-94	Ventspils
KA-09 KLINTS (ex-Kbv 250)	27-4-94	Bolderaja

Saule (KA-08) H&L Van Ginderen, 10-00

Klints (KA-09)—with larger pilothouse Hartmut Ehlers, 4-95

D: 17 tons (fl) **S:** 22 kts **Dim:** 19.2 × 4.0 × 1.3
A: small arms **Electronics:** Radar: 1 . . . nav.
M: 2 Volvo Penta TAMD 120A diesels; 2 props; 700 bhp
Crew: 1 officer, 2 enlisted

Remarks: Sisters transferred to Estonia and Lithuania also. KA-07 has a slightly higher pilothouse, while KA-09 has a larger pilothouse with a second (Furuno) radar atop it. All carry a rigid inflatable inspection dinghy aft.

♦ **1 ex-Russian Aist-class (Project 1398) patrol launch** Bldr: Svetenskiy Zavod, Kokue (In serv. 1975–86)

KA-12 GRANATA

Granata (KA-12) Hartmut Ehlers, 4-95

D: 3.55 tons (5.8 fl) **S:** 20 kts **Dim:** 9.50 × 2.60 × 0.50
A: small arms **Electronics:** Radar: none
M: 1 3D-20 diesel; 1 prop; 235 bhp **Fuel:** 0.37 tons **Crew:** . . . tot.

Remarks: Transferred in 1994. Had been used by Russian Maritime Border Guard. Refitted in Latvia prior to recommissioning circa 5-95. Based at Liepaja.

♦ **2 former Russian Navy officers launches (Project 371U)**

KA-10 KA-11

COAST GUARD PATROL BOATS [WPB] *(continued)*

KA-11—KA-10 has a smaller cockpit aft and a smaller pilothouse
Hartmut Ehlers, 9-96

D: 9.41 tons (fl) **S:** 13.5 kts **Dim:** 12.61 × 3.23 × 0.6 (1.00 over prop)
A: small arms **Electronics:** Radar: 1 Furuno . . . nav.
M: 1 Type 3D6S diesel; 1 prop; 150 bhp **Range:** 140/13.5
Crew: 1 officer, 2 enlisted

Remarks: Built during the early 1950s. Both had been used by the DOSAAF (Soviet Communist Youth League) Technical Center for Diving at Riga. KA-11 was refitted at Riga in 1995. Both are based at Bolderaja. Have steel hulls and wooden superstructure, with KA-11 having had the cover over the after cockpit and the pilothouse enlarged while in Soviet service.

LEBANON

Republic of Lebanon

Personnel (2001): 47 officers, 1,203 enlisted total, including 100 Marines

Bases: Beirut and Jounieh

PATROL BOATS [PB]

♦ **7 Tracker Mk II class** Bldr: Fairey Allday Marine, Hamble, U.K.

	In serv.
301 Trablous (ex-*Attacker,* P 281)	11-3-83
302 Jounieh (ex-*Fencer,* P 283)	21-3-83
303 Batroun (ex-*Safeguard*)	1978
304 Jebail (ex-*Chaser,* P 282)	11-3-83
306 Saïda (ex-*Striker,* P 285)	7-83
307 Sarafand (ex-*Swift*)	1978
309 Arz (ex-*Hunter,* P 284)	21-3-83

Trablous (301) French Navy, 5-96

D: 34.54 tons (fl) **S:** 21 kts **Dim:** 20.0 (19.25 wl) × 5.18 × 1.50
A: 3 single 12.7-mm mg **Electronics:** Radar: 1 Decca 1216 nav.
M: 2 G.M. 12V71 TI diesels; 2 props; 1,300 bhp **Electric:** 30 kw tot.
Range: 650/20 **Crew:** 11 tot.

Remarks: The five former Royal Navy units were purchased in 7-92, having been paid off in 1991–92. GRP hull construction. *Batroun* and *Sarafand* were purchased in 3-94 after retirement from the British Customs Service; they have Decca 2690 radars and have been fitted with twin 23-mm AA mounts on the bow.

♦ **27 ex-U.S. Bridge Erection Boats** (14 in reserve)
Bldr: Fairey Marintechnik, Cowes, U.K. (In serv. 1980s)

D: 6 tons (fl) **S:** 22 kts **Dim:** 8.2 × 2.5 × 0.6
A: 2 single 7.62-mm mg **M:** 2 Ford Sabre 212 diesels; 2 waterjets; 424 bhp
Range: 154/22 **Crew:** 3 tot.

Remarks: Transferred 1-94, but 14 remain in land storage. Originally intended for freshwater service on European rivers in support of pontoon bridge erection units, but used by Lebanon for inshore patrol duties. Aluminum construction. No radar.

AMPHIBIOUS WARFARE CRAFT

♦ **2 French EDIC-III-class utility landing craft [LCU]**
Bldr: SFCN, Villeneuve-la-Garenne

21 Sour (In serv. 1-85) 22 Damour (L: 11-12-84)

Damour (22) French Navy, 5-96

D: 375 tons (712 fl) **S:** 10 kts **Dim:** 59.00 (57.00 pp) × 11.90 × 1.67 (1.10 light)
A: 2 single 20-mm 70-cal. Oerlikon Mk 10 AA; 1 81-mm mortar
Electronics: Radar: 1 Decca 1226 nav.
M: 2 SACM MGO 175-V12-A diesels; 2 props; 1,040 bhp
Range: 1,800/10 **Fuel:** 35 tons **Crew:** 18 tot. + 33 troops

Remarks: Ordered 30-7-83 as aid from the French government. *Sour* replaced an earlier EDIC (L 9096) of the same name that had been loaned 7-11-83. Can carry 11 trucks or 5 armored personnel carriers.

Note: Also in use is the yacht *Imanuella* (501), a captured drug runner; no details available. The customs service operates two Tracker Mk II patrol boats, the *Erez-II* and the *Lebanon-II,* with the same characteristics data as those for the naval units.

LIBYA

Socialist People's Libyan Arab Jamahiriya

Personnel (2002): Approx. 3,000 total, including special forces, naval infantry, and coast guard (beach patrol)

Bases: Ships based at Al Khums, Ras Hilal, and Tobruq; naval air base at Al Girdabiyah; naval infantry at Sidi Bilal

Naval Aviation: About five AS.316B Alouette-III helicopters

Coastal Defense: Some truck-mounted batteries with twin launchers for Russian P-20 Termit (SS-C-3) antiship missiles may still be operable. There is also an extensive force of beach patrol troops under naval control.

SUBMARINES [SS]

Note: Although the hulks of Soviet-supplied Foxtrot-class (Project 641) diesel submarines *Al Ahad* (313), *Al Mitraqah* (314), *Al Khyber* (315), and *Al Hunayn* (316) remain more or less afloat at Tobruq, none has operated even on the surface since 1995, and the last known submergence by a Libyan submarine took place 17 or more years ago. Sister *Al Badr* (311) sank alongside in harbor in 1993 and has not been repaired, while *Al Fateh* (312) was sent to the Baltic in 1987 for an overhaul and was later scrapped in Russia. Montenegrin technicians were said to be traveling to Libya to attempt repair and activation of one or more submarines as of late 7-99, but such vital components as batteries would be very difficult to obtain, and the boats are almost certainly beyond repair.

FRIGATES [FF]

♦ **2 Soviet Modified Koni class (Project 1159TR)** (1 in *reserve*)
Bldr: Krasniy Metallist Zavod, Zelnodol'sk, Russia

	Laid down	L	In serv.
212 Al Hani	10-1-85	27-4-85	28-6-86
213 *Al Ghardabia*	18-4-85	27-4-86	24-10-87

Al Hani (212)—with dark gray camouflage striping H&L Van Ginderen, 7-91

FRIGATES [FF] *(continued)*

D: 1,440 tons light; 1,596 tons normal (1,676 fl)
S: 27 kts (29.67 on trials; 22 on diesels)
Dim: 96.51 × 12.55 × 4.12 (mean hull; 5.72 over sonar)
A: 4 P-20/21 Termit (SS-N-2C Styx) SSM; 1 2-rail Osa-M (SA-N-4) SAM syst. (20 9M-33 Gecko missiles); 2 twin 76.2-mm 59-cal. AK-726 DP; 2 twin 30-mm 65-cal. AK-230 AA; 1 12-round RBU-6000 ASW RL (60 RGB-60 rockets); 4 fixed 400-mm ASW TT
Electronics:
Radar: 1 Don-2 nav.; 1 MR-302 (Strut Curve) surf./air search; 1 Koral-E (Plank Shave) surface target detection/desig.; 1 MPZ-301 (Pop Group) SAM f.c.; 1 MR-105 Turel' (Hawk Screech) 76.2-mm gun f.c.; 1 MR-104 Rys' (Drum Tilt) 30-mm gun f.c.
Sonar: MG-322T hull-mounted MF; HF f.c.
EW: 2 Bizan'-series (Watch Dog) intercept; 1 Cross Loop-A MFD/F; 2 16-round PK-16 decoy RL
M: CODAG: 1 M-813 gas turbine (18,000 shp), 2 Type 68B diesels (9,000 bhp each); 3 props; 36,000 hp
Range: 4,546/14.98 **Crew:** 96 tot.

Remarks: Were the 11th and 12th units built of this export class; 213 has been inactive for several years. These were the only version of the Koni (NATO "Koni-III") to be built with antiship missiles and ASW torpedoes, at the expense of one ASW rocket launcher.
Hull systems: The deckhouse amidships is continuous in order to accommodate additional air-conditioning equipment. The centerline propeller is of fixed pitch, while the outboard propellers are controllable pitch.
Combat systems: The Koral-E radar acts as surface search and acquisition for the Termit missiles and can also function in the passive intercept mode. The MPZ-301 track-while-scan radar controls the Osa-M SAMs; the MR-105 Turel' (with two pedestal-type optical target designators) handles the 76.2-mm guns; and the MR-104 Rys' radar director (again with two visual backup directors) serves the 30-mm guns.

Note: The Vosper Mk 7 frigate *Dat Assawari* (211), removed from a Genoese shipyard while partially finished with an overhaul, was returned to Tripoli in 1992 and is a nonoperational training hulk along with the Vosper Mk 1B corvette *Tobruk* (411).

GUIDED-MISSILE PATROL COMBATANTS [PGG]

♦ 2 Nanuchka-II class (Project 1234E)

Bldr: Sudostroitel'noye Obyedineniye "Almaz," Petrovskiy SY, St. Petersburg, Russia

	Laid down	L	In serv.
416 Tariq-ibn Ziyad (ex-*Ain Mara;* ex-MPK-9)	21-4-79	10-1-81	27-5-81
418 Ain Zaara (ex-MPK-25)	27-5-81	21-7-82	19-1-83

Tariq-ibn Ziyad (416) H&L Van Ginderen, 7-91

D: 560 tons (660 fl) **S:** 30 kts **Dim:** 59.3 × 12.6 × 2.4 (3.1 max.)
A: 6 P-20/21 Termit (SS-N-2C Styx) SSM; 1 2-rail Osa-M (SA-N-4) SAM syst. (20 9M-33 Gecko missiles); 1 twin 57-mm 70-cal. AK-727 DP
Electronics:
Radar: 1 Don-2 nav.; 1 Rangout (Square Tie) surf. missile target detection/desig.; 1 MPZ-301 (Pop Group) SAM f.c.; 1 MR-103 Bars (Muff Cob) radar-E/O gun f.c.
EW: 1 Bell Tap intercept; 2 16-round PK-16 decoy RL
M: 3 M-521 diesels; 3 props; 25,996 bhp
Range: 900/30; 2,500/12 (on 1 engine) **Endurance:** 10 days
Crew: 7 officers, 42 enlisted

Remarks: Sister *Ain Zaquit* (419) was sunk 24-3-86 by U.S. aircraft. 416, damaged the next day by U.S. aircraft, was sent to the Baltic for an extensive repair/overhaul in 1990, returning to Libya in 2-91. *Ain al Gazala* (417) was cannibalized during the 1990s to keep the other two marginally operable.
Hull systems: Considered to be poor sea boats by some customers, with unreliable propulsion plants (M-521 is a tropicalized version of the M-507, which is a paired M-504 42-cylinder radial diesel sharing a common gearbox).
Combat systems: The MR-103 radar director for the 57-mm gunmount has a t.v. adjunct. The Rangout radar's antenna is mounted within the radome named Band Stand by NATO and can also function in a passive mode as a target radiation intercept system.

GUIDED-MISSILE PATROL CRAFT [PTG]

Note: The surviving French-built Combattante II–class guided-missile patrol boats were nonoperational by 1992 but as of fall 2001, seven were operational again. See addenda for names and characteristics data.

♦ 5 Soviet Osa-II class (Project 205EM)

513 Al Zuara 523 Al Fikah 531 Al Bitar
515 Al Ruha 525 Al Sakab

Al Zuara (513)—in dry dock at Malta H&L Van Ginderen, 1986

D: 184 tons (226 normal fl, 245 overload) **S:** 40 kts (35 sust.)
Dim: 38.6 (37.5 wl) × 7.6 (6.3 wl) × 2.0 (hull; 3.1 props)
A: 4 P-15M/20/21 Termit (SS-N-2B/C Styx) SSM; 2 twin 30-mm 65-cal. AK-230 AA
Electronics:
Radar: 1 Rangout (Square Tie) surf. search/target detection; 1 MR-104 Rys' (Drum Tilt) gun f.c.
M: 3 M-504 or M-504B diesels; 3 props; 15,000 bhp **Electric:** 400 kw tot.
Range: 500/34; 750/25 **Endurance:** 5 days **Crew:** 4 officers, 24 enlisted

Remarks: Probably built at Rybinsk. One delivered in 1976, four in 1977, one in 1978, three in 1979, one in 4-80, one in 5-80, and the twelfth in 7-80. Reportedly, the original order was reduced from 24 to 12. Names and numbers above represent the latest available listing; numbers are changed from time to time. The survivors rarely put to sea. During 1993, they were repainted with blue hulls and white superstructures.
Disposals: By 1998, *Al Katum* (511), *Al Baida* (517), *Al Nabha* (519), *Al Safra* (521), *Al Mosha* (527), *Al Mathur* (529), and *Al Sadad* (533) had relegated to cannibalization spares.
Combat systems: The Rangout radar can probably also be operated in the passive mode to detect target radiations. Can carry 2,000 rounds of 30-mm ammunition. The reliability of any remaining P-15M missiles is suspect.

Note: Of the upwards of 125 radio-controlled, GRP-hulled suicide boats of Libyan, Swedish, and Cypriot construction acquired during the early 1980s for coast defense service, most are probably no longer operable. No details are available except that speeds of 30 kts were attainable and that the Cyprus-built craft were 7.92 m long and those built in Sweden were 9.45 m o.a.

MINE WARFARE SHIPS

Note: Libya has laid several minefields, apparently employing the roll-on/roll-off cargo ships *Garyounis, El Temsah,* and *Ghat* (qq.v.).

♦ 5 Soviet Natya-class (Project 266ME) fleet minesweepers [MSF]

Bldr: Sudostroitel'noye Obyedineniye "Almaz" (Sredniy Neva), Kolpino

111 Al I'sar (ex-*Ras el Gelais*) 119 Ras al Oula
113 Al Tayyar (ex-*Ras Hadad*) 123 Ras Massad
117 Ras al Falluga

MINE WARFARE SHIPS *(continued)*

Libyan Navy Natya—painted with blue hull and white superstructure 1993

D: 750 tons std., 804 tons normal (873 max.) **S:** 17.6 kts (16 sust.)
Dim: 61.00 (57.6 wl) × 10.20 × 2.98 (hull)
A: 2 twin 30-mm 65-cal. AK-230 AA; 2 twin 25-mm 80-cal. 2M-3 AA—123 only: 2 4-round SA-N-8 SAM syst. (18 Igla-1 missiles)—all: 2 5-round RBU-1200 ASW RL (60 RGB-12 rockets); 2 mine rails (8 UDME mines)
Electronics:
Radar: 1 Don-2 nav.; 1 MR-104 Rys' (Drum Tilt) f.c.
Sonar: MG-89 HF hull-mounted
M: 2 M-503B-3E diesels: 2 shrouded CP props; 5,000 bhp (4,500 sust.)
Electric: 600 kw tot. (3 × 200-kw DGR-200/1500 diesel sets)
Range: 1,800/16; 3,000/12; 5,200/10 **Fuel:** 87 tons **Endurance:** 10–15 days
Crew: 8 officers, 59 enlisted

Remarks: Survivors of 12, the first pair delivered 3-81, the second pair in 2-83, the fifth unit 3-9-83, the sixth during 2-84, the seventh 20-1-85, and the last five in 10-86. Names on the first two were changed after delivery but not, apparently, the remainder. Are used primarily for coastal patrolling and rarely, if ever, exercise their mine warfare capabilities. Were repainted with blue hulls and white superstructures around 1993. 123 conducted a cadet training cruise during 1997.
Disposals: *Ras al Hamman* (115), *Ras al Dawar* (121), and *Ras al Hani* (125) had been hulked by 1998 as cannibalization spares sources and are not likely to operate again.
Hull systems: Like the units built for India, they lack the ramp at the stern found on Soviet units. Stem is cut back sharply below the waterline. Have a low-magnetic-signature, aluminum-steel alloy hull and a DGR-450/1500P diesel-driven degaussing system. The engines are a derated version of the same high-speed, multirow diesels that power the Osa-class guided-missile patrol boats. Have enhanced air-conditioning capacity over their Russian Navy sisters and also have about 100 kw more generator capacity. Carry 45 tons of water but do not have distilling equipment. Navigational equipment includes a GKU-2 gyrocompass, NELMZB echo sounder, Rumb MFD/F, Pirs-1M receiver for Decca radio navaid, and AP-4 automatic position plot. Khmel-1 infrared position-keeping and signaling equipment is carried.
Combat systems: The RBU-1200 ASW rocket launchers are also used for detonating mines. Sweep gear includes GKT-2 mechanical, AT-2 acoustic, and TEM-3 magnetic arrays. The sonar incorporates a downward-looking, high-frequency, bottomed-mine detection component with a range of 350–400 m. Some 2,149 rounds are carried for each 30-mm gunmount.

AMPHIBIOUS WARFARE SHIPS

Disposal note: Of the two *Ibn Ouf*–class tank landing ships, *Ibn Ouf* (132) was sold or transferred to the Libyan government–controlled General National Maritime Transportation Co. around 3-99 and was to be refitted in Italy for commercial service, while *Ibn Harissa* (134) was under refit at Kraljevica Shipyard, Croatia, during 2001, either for return to naval service or for adaptation for commercial use. Of the three Polnocny-C-class (Project 773KL) medium landing craft delivered 1977–79, *Ibn al Qyis* (113) was lost on 14-9-78 or 15-9-78 through fire while at sea, and *Ibn al Hadrani* (112), *Ibn el Omayar* (116), and *Ibn el Farat* (118) had ceased to be functional by 1999, although perhaps one could be reactivated; they remain afloat.

♦ 3 or 4 Turkish Ç 107–class utility landing craft [LCU]
Bldrs: Taskizak SY, Istanbul, and Gölçük Naval SY

130 Ibn al Idrissi (ex-Ç 130) 132 Ras el Hillel (ex-Ç 132)
131 Ibn Marwhan (ex-Ç 131) 133 El Kobayat (ex-Ç 133)

D: 280 tons (600 fl) **S:** 10 kts (8.5 loaded) **Dim:** 56.56 × 11.58 × 1.25
A: 2 single 20-mm 70-cal. Oerlikon AA
Electronics: Radar: 1 . . . nav.
M: 3 G.M. Detroit Diesel 6-71TI diesels; 3 props; 900 bhp
Range: 600/10; 1,100/8 **Crew:** 15 tot.

Remarks: Former Turkish Navy units transferred 7-12-79. As many as 50 were to be acquired, with two Turkish yards each building 25, but it now appears that only the initial increment was ever received. Design follows that of the World War II–era British LCT(4) class. Cargo: up to 350 tons (five heavy tanks, up to 100 troops). Cargo deck: 28.5 × 7.9 m. One of the above may have been discarded, and the others seldom operate.

AUXILIARIES

♦ 1 oceanographic research ship [AGOR]
Bldr: C.N. Auroux, Arcachon, France (In serv. 1970)

Nour (ex-*Cryos*)

Nour Hartmut Ehlers, 4-93

D: approx. 1,100 tons (fl) **S:** 13.5 kts **Dim:** 48.70 (41.48 pp) × 10.01 × 4.01
M: 2 Duvant 6-cyl. diesels; 1 CP prop; 1,380 bhp
Electric: 509 kw tot. (1 × 264-kw, 1 × 176-kw, 1 × 69-kw diesel sets)
Range: . . ./. . . **Fuel:** 164 tons **Crew:** . . .

Remarks: A 598-grt former stern-haul fisheries research trawler, purchased from the French government Institut Français de Recherche pour l'Exploitation de la Mer in 1993. Has three cargo holds and an ice-strengthened hull. While the ship may actually be used for legitimate research, it would also be useful as a transport for special forces personnel or for intelligence collection duties.

♦ 1 support ship for small combatants [AGP]

	Bldr	Laid down	L	In serv.
711 Zeltin	Vosper Thornycroft, Woolston	1967	29-2-68	23-1-69

D: 2,200 tons (2,470 fl) **S:** 15 kts **Dim:** 98.72 (91.44 wl) × 14.64 × 3.05
A: 2 single 40-mm 60-cal. Bofors Mk 7 AA
Electronics: Radar: 1 Decca 1226 nav.
M: 2 Paxman Ventura 16YJCM diesels; 2 props; 4,000 bhp (3,500 sust.)
Electric: 800 kw tot. **Range:** 3,000/14 **Crew:** 15 officers, 86 enlisted

Remarks: Was originally intended to act as a tender and mobile repair dock for small combatants, but is of limited utility due to the small size of the docking well and poor material condition. No longer able to put to sea.
Hull systems: The 41 × 12–m well deck can receive small craft that draw up to 2.3 m. Has a hydraulically controlled stern gate. A movable crane with 3-ton loading capacity is available for the well deck, and a 9-ton crane on the port side supports the 418 m^2 of workshops amidships. Has accommodations for a flag officer and staff.

Note: The three following ships are registered as merchant vessels and operate for the Libyan government–controlled General National Maritime Transportation Co., homeported at Tripoli; all three, however, have performed both overt and covert military missions and can thus be said to be military vessels in fact if not in name.

♦ 1 vehicle transport [AK]
Bldr: Naikai SB & Eng., Setoda, Japan (In serv. 1973)

Garyounis (ex-*Mashu*)

D: approx. 15,000 tons (fl) **S:** 20.5 kts **Dim:** 166.53 (155.00 pp) × 24.36 × 6.47
Electronics: Radar: . . .
M: 2 Nippon Kokan-Pielstick 16 PC2 5V400 diesels; 2 props; 20,800 bhp—bow-thruster
Electric: 1,860 kw (3 × 620 kw) **Range:** . . ./. . . **Crew:** . . .

Remarks: 6,561 grt/2,593 dwt. Former Ro/Ro passenger ferry with accommodations for up to 679 passengers. Employed as a naval cadet training ship during 1989. The stern ramp can be used for minelaying.

♦ 1 Ro/Ro vehicle carrier [AK]
Bldr: Nystads Varv A/B, Nystad, Finland (In serv. 1-75)

Ghat

D: approx. 6,200 tons (fl) **S:** 18 kts **Dim:** 118.60 (106.79 pp) × 16.13 × 5.57
M: 2 Wärtsilä-Pielstick 8 PC2 2L400 diesels; 2 CP props; 8,000 bhp—bow-thruster
Electric: 1,560 kw tot. (3 × 520-kw diesel sets)
Range: . . ./. . . **Fuel:** 461 tons heavy oil/75 tons diesel **Crew:** . . .

Remarks: 2,412 grt/3,266 dwt. Stern door only. Has been used to transport military cargoes and to lay mines. Can carry several hundred mines on temporary rails in the vehicle deck or several hundred troops. Has side vehicle doors and can carry up to 300 automobiles.

♦ 1 Ro/Ro vehicle carrier [AK]
Bldr: C.N. Luigi Orlando, Livorno, Italy (In serv. 1971)

El Temsah (ex-*Espresso Veneto*)

D: approx. 5,600 tons (fl) **S:** 19 kts
Dim: 105.36 (96.55 pp) × 19.51 (17.51 wl) × 5.11
M: 2 Fiat B300.16V diesels; 2 CP props; 8,000 bhp
Electric: 520 kw tot. (4 × 130-kw diesel sets)
Range: . . ./. . . **Fuel:** 199 tons **Crew:** . . .

Remarks: 4,567 grt/2,926 dwt. Acquired in 1972; in addition to commercial ventures, has been used to transport military cargoes and to lay mines. Was burned out in a 1986 accident but has been restored to active service. Has a 20-m-long stern vehicle ramp, which is also useful for laying mines, and there are a total of 720 m of vehicle parking lanes and two side-loading vehicle doors.

♦ 1 Yugoslav Spasilac-class training ship [AXT]
Bldr: Tito SY, Belgrade (In serv. 1982)

722 Al Munjed (ex-Yugoslav *Zlatica*)

AUXILIARIES *(continued)*

D: 1,590 tons (fl) **S:** 13.4 kts **Dim:** 55.50 × 12.00 × 3.84 (4.34 max.)
A: 4 twin 14.5-mm 93-cal. mg **Electronics:** Radar: 1 . . . nav.
M: 2 diesels; 2 Kort-nozzle props; 4,340 bhp **Electric:** 540 kVA
Range: 4,000/13.4 **Crew:** 53 tot. (72 accomm.)

Remarks: Acquired in 1982. Resembles an oilfield supply vessel, with low freeboard aft. Sister *Aka* was in the Iraqi Navy, and another is in reserve in Croatia. Was used as submarine support ship when the Foxtrots were operational, then was laid up until used in 1998 for a cadet training cruise; has not been reported at sea since then, however.
Hull systems: Equipped for underwater cutting and welding, towing, salvage lifting, fire fighting, and other salvage tasks. Can carry up to 250 tons of deck cargo, transferring 490 tons of cargo fuel, 48 tons of cargo water, and 5 tons of lube oil. Can support divers to 300 m with a three-section decompression chamber. Also has the capability to support a small rescue submersible. Has a bow-thruster and can lay a four-point moor.

SERVICE CRAFT

♦ **1 Soviet Yelva-class (Project 535M) diving tender [YDT]**
Bldr: Gorokhovtse Zavod (In serv. 19-12-77)

Al Manoud (ex-VM 917)

D: 279 tons (300 fl) **S:** 12.4 kts **Dim:** 40.90 (37.00 pp) × 8.00 × 2.02
Electronics: Radar: 1 Mius (Spin Trough) nav.—Sonar: MGA-1 HF
M: 2 Type 3D12A diesels; 2 props; 600 bhp **Electric:** 200 kw tot.
Range: 1,870/12 **Endurance:** 10 days **Crew:** 24 tot.

Remarks: Can support seven hard-hat divers working at 60 m and has a submersible decompression chamber supported by a 2.5-ton derrick. Relegated to harbor service by the mid-1990s.

♦ **1 small floating dry dock [YFDL]**
Bldr: Blohm + Voss, Hamburg (In serv. 1984)

Lift capacity: 3,200 tons **Dim:** 105.20 × 26.00 × 6.40

Remarks: Ordered 20-2-84, laid down 17-4-84.

♦ **1 Soviet Poluchat-I-class torpedo retriever [YPT]**

723

D: 84.7 tons (92.8 fl) **S:** 21.6 kts **Dim:** 29.60 × 5.98 × 1.56 (hull)
A: 1 twin 14.5-mm 93-cal. 2M-7 AA
Electronics: Radar: 1 Mius (Spin Trough) nav.
M: 2 M-50F-4 diesels; 2 props; 2,400 bhp **Electric:** 14 kw tot.
Range: 250/21.6; 550/14; 900/10 **Crew:** 3 officers, 12 enlisted

Remarks: Delivered 20-5-85. Has a stern ramp for torpedo recovery. May no longer be operational.

♦ **4 Ras El Helal–class large harbor tugs [YTB]**
Bldr: Mondego, Foz, Portugal

	In serv.		In serv.
Ras El Helal	22-10-77	Al Shweiref	17-2-78
Al Keriat	17-2-78	Al Tabkah	29-7-78

D: 200 grt **S:** 14 kts **Dim:** 34.8 × 9.0 × 4.0 (molded depth)
M: 2 diesels; 2 props; 2,300 bhp

♦ **3 harbor tugs [YTM]**
Bldr: Jonker & Stans SY, the Netherlands (In serv. 1980)

A 33 A 34 A 35

D: 150 grt **S:** . . . **Dim:** 26.60 × 7.90 × 2.48
M: 2 diesels; 2 Voith-Schneider vertical cycloidal props; . . . bhp

Note: Two 17.00 × 6.25 × 2.75–m harbor tugs were delivered at the same time as A 33–A 35. All the tugs listed serve naval and commercial vessels at Libyan ports.

Note: The Libyan customs service operates up to four Swedish-built Boghammar patrol launches of 5.5 tons displacement and may still have six Yugoslav PB 90–class 90-ton patrol boats in service.

LITHUANIA

Lithuanian Republic

LITHUANIAN REPUBLIC NAVAL FLOTILLA

(Lietuvos Respublikas Karines Juru Pajegos)

Personnel (2001): 670 total (about 100 officers), plus 1,350 troops of the 7th Dragoon "Iron Wolf" coast defense naval infantry battalion (45 officers). Included in the navy total are the personnel of the Coastal Radar Service.

Base: Klaipeda, with Coastal Radar Service stations at Klaipeda, Nida, and Palanga

CORVETTES [FFL]

♦ **2 Grisha-III class (Project 1124M)** Bldr: Zelenodol'sk Zavod

	In serv.
F 11 Zemaitis (ex-MPK-108, *Komsomolets Latviy*)	1-10-81
F 12 Aukstaitis (ex-MPK-44)	15-8-80

Zemaitis (F 11) Findler & Winter, 6-01

Aukstaitis (F 12) Findler & Winter, 6-01

D: 860 tons light, 954 tons normal (990 fl)
S: 32 kts (21 on gas turbine alone; 16 on diesels)
Dim: 71.20 (66.90 wl) × 10.15 (9.50 wl) × 3.40 (hull)
A: 1 twin-rail Osa-2M (SA-N-4) SAM syst. (20 9M-33 Gecko missiles); 1 twin 57-mm AK-725 DP; 1 30-mm 54-cal. AK-630M gatling AA; 2 12-tubed RBU-6000 ASW RL (96 RGB-60 rockets)
Electronics:
Radar: 1 Terma Scanter Mil 009 nav.; 1 Decca RM 1290 nav.; 1 MR-302 (Strut Curve) air/surf. search; 1 MPZ-310 (Pop Group) SAM f.c.; 1 MR-123 Vympel (Bass Tilt) gun f.c.
Sonar: MGK-335MC Pirhana (Bull Nose) hull-mounted MF, Argun' (Elk Tail) MF through-hull dipping
EW: Vympel-R2 intercept, with 2 Bizan'-4 (Watch Dog) (2–18 GHz)
M: CODAG: 1 M-88 gas turbine (18,000 shp), 2 Type M507A diesels (10,000 bhp each); 3 props; 38,000 hp—2 maneuvering propellers
Electric: 1,000 kw (1 × 500-kw, 1 × 300-kw, 1 × 200-kw diesel sets)
Range: 950/27; 2,750/14; 4,000/10 **Fuel:** 130 tons + 13 tons overload
Endurance: 9 days **Crew:** 5 officers, 43 enlisted (accomm. for 83)

Remarks: Transferred and commissioned 6-11-92. Are planned to remain in service to 2007–10.
Combat systems: The torpedo tubes were removed from F 12 in 1995 and F 11 in 1996 as Lithuanian waters are too shallow for successful use of torpedoes (of which none had been furnished by the Russians, anyway). Reported to carry 1,000 rounds of 57-mm and 2,000 rounds of 30-mm gun ammunition. Depth charge racks have been removed, and there are no mines available for the deck rails. A Danish radar replaced the original Don-2 navigational/surface-search set in 1998.

PATROL CRAFT [PC]

♦ **3 ex-Norwegian Storm class**
Bldr: Bergens Mekaniske Verksted, Bergen

	L
P 31 Dzúkas (ex-*Glimt,* P 962)	27-9-65
P 32 Selis (ex-. . .)	. . .
P 33 Skalvis (ex-. . .)	. . .

Dzúkas (P 31)—prior to installation of 40-mm AA forward French Navy, 1995

D: 105 tons (125 fl) **S:** 37 kts **Dim:** 36.53 × 6.30 × 1.55
A: P 31: 1 40-mm 60-cal. Bofors Mk 3 AA; 1 12.7-mm mg—others: 1 76.2-mm 50-cal. Bofors low-angle; 1 40-mm 70-cal. Bofors L70 AA
Electronics: Radar: P 31: 1 Decca TM 1226 nav.—others: 1 Furuno . . . nav.
M: 2 Maybach MB 872A (MTU 16V538 TB90) diesels; 2 props; 7,200 bhp
Range: 550/36 **Crew:** 3 officers, 15 enlisted

PATROL CRAFT [PC] *(continued)*

Remarks: P 31 was stricken from the Norwegian Navy in 1993, rehabilitated during 1994, and transferred 11-12-94 with the armament systems deleted. P 32 and P 33 were transferred (along with a third unit to be used for cannibalization) and recommissioned 21-6-01; their original WM-22 radar gun f.c.s. was deleted. On P 31, a hand-operated 40-mm gun replaced the 12.7-mm mg on the bow in 1998; the machinegun was remounted atop the pilothouse.

PATROL BOATS [PB]

♦ 1 former Russian Navy officers launch (Project 371U)

VYTIS-01

D: 9.41 ton (fl) **S:** 13.5 kts **Dim:** 12.61 × 3.23 × 0.6 (1.00 over prop)
A: small arms **Electronics:** Radar: 1 Furuno . . . nav.
M: 1 Type 3D6S diesel; 1 prop; 150 bhp **Range:** 140/13.5
Crew: 1 officer, 2 enlisted

Remarks: Same type of launch once carried aboard Soviet *Sverdlov*-class cruisers and also used as personnel launches at naval bases. Sister *Vytis-02* serves the Lithuanian Border Police (see photograph at that entry), and two sisters are in Latvian service.

MINE COUNTERMEASURES SHIPS

♦ 2 ex-German Type 331B minehunters [MHC]

Bldr: Burmester, Bremen

	L	In serv.
M 51 KURSIS (ex-*Marburg,* M 1080)	4-8-58	11-6-59
M 52 SŪDUVIS (ex-*Koblenz,* M 1071)	6-5-57	8-7-58

Kursis (M 51) Findler & Winter, 3-01

Sūduvis (M 52) Findler & Winter, 11-99

D: 388 tons (402 fl) **S:** 16.5 kts **Dim:** 47.45 × 8.5 × 2.8 (3.68 with sonar extended)
A: 1 40-mm 70-cal. Bofors AA
Electronics:
Radar: 1 Raytheon SPS-64(V) nav.
Sonar: EFS DSQS-11A HF minehunting
M: 2 MTU 16V538 TB90 diesels; 2 CP props; 5,000 bhp **Electric:** 220 kw tot.
Range: 1,400/16; 3,950/9 **Crew:** 5 officers, 29 enlisted + 6 divers

Remarks: M 52 was decommissioned from the German Navy 22-6-99, donated and transferred in 9-99, and commissioned on 4-12-99. M 51, decommissioned from German service 25-5-00, was donated during 11-00 and recommissioned in 4-01 after a refit at Krögerwerft, Rendsburg.
Hull systems: Wooden construction, with nonmagnetic engines. Minehunting speed is 6 kts on two 50-kw electric motors.
Combat systems: Have no mechanical sweep gear. Six divers and two French PAP-104 remote-controlled minehunting devices are carried. The 40-mm gun is controlled by a lead-computing optical director on the bridge.

AUXILIARIES

♦ 1 ex-Soviet Valerian Uryvayev–class training ship [AXT]

Bldr: Khabarovsk Shipyard (In serv. 1977)

A 41 VĖTRA (ex-*Rudolf Samoylovich*)

Vétra (A 41) H&L Van Ginderen, 5-00

D: 1,050 tons (fl) **S:** 11.75 kts **Dim:** 55.66 × 9.53 × 4.16
A: 2 single 12.7-mm mg; 2 single 45-mm KM-21 saluting cannon
Electronics: Radar: 1 Decca RM 1290 nav.
M: 1 Deutz–Karl Liebnecht 6NVD48A-2U diesel; 1 CP prop; 875 bhp
Electric: 450 kw tot. **Range:** 10,000/11 **Endurance:** 40 days
Crew: 8 officers, 26 enlisted

Remarks: 694 grt/350 dwt. Transferred to Lithuanian control in 11-91 from the USSR Hydrometeorological Service, which had operated her from St. Petersburg. Belongs to the Ministry of the Environment but is leased by the Lithuanian Navy; initially used as a fisheries protection and inspection vessel, she is now employed as fleet training ship and also for coastal survey work. Has an ice-strengthened hull, a bow-thruster, and two 1.5-ton derricks serving a small hold aft. Sister *Vėjas* (ex-Soviet *Lev Titov*) is operated by the Ministry of the Environment.

SERVICE CRAFT

♦ 1 coastal survey craft [YGS]

H 21 VILNELE (ex-HK 21)

Vilnele (H 21) H&L Van Ginderen, 4-96

D: 88 tons (fl) **S:** 12 kts **Dim:** 23.1 × 5.8 × 1.8
A: 1 12.7-mm mg **Electronics:** Radar: 1 . . . nav.
M: 2 diesels; 2 props; 600 bhp **Crew:** 1 officer, 6 enlisted

Remarks: A former pilot boat acquired in 1992. Served until 1994 as tender to the *Vėtra* and later as a patrol launch. Now used mostly as an inshore survey craft. Pennant number was changed in 2001.

♦ 1 ex-Swedish Navy small harbor tug [YTL]

Bldr: . . . (In serv. 1975)

H 22 (ex-*Atlas,* A 330)

D: 35 tons (fl) **S:** 9 kts **Dim:** . . . × . . . × . . .
M: 1 . . . diesel; 210 bhp

Remarks: Donated by Sweden in 2000; had been laid up at Karlskrona since 1995.

STATE BORDER POLICE
(Pasienio Policija)

Note: Established in 1996 to serve as a form of coast guard.

Personnel (2001): Approx. 80 total

SURFACE-EFFECT PATROL BOATS [WPBA]

♦ 1 Type 2000TDX Mk 2

Bldr: Griffon Hovercraft, Southampton, U.K. (In serv. 2000)

CHRISTINA

STATE BORDER POLICE SURFACE-EFFECT PATROL BOATS [WPBA] *(continued)*

D: 5 tons (fl) **S:** 40 kts **Dim:** 12.6 × 6.1 × . . .
Electronics: Radar: 1 Furuno 100C nav.
M: 1 Deutz BF8L diesel; 1 CP shrouded prop; 355 bhp **Crew:** 3 tot.

Remarks: Ordered in 1999 for inshore and shallow-water patrol duties.

PATROL BOATS [WPB]

♦ 1 ex-Finnish Tiira class
Bldr: Valmet-Laivateollisuus, Turku

	Laid down	L	In serv.
003 KIHU	7-4-86	7-86	17-12-86

D: 65 tons (fl) **S:** 25+ kts **Dim:** 26.80 (24.20 pp) × 5.50 × 1.40 (1.85 props)
A: none **Electronics:** Radar: 1 . . . nav.
M: 2 MTU 8V396 TB82 diesels; 2 props; 2,286 bhp **Electric:** 62 kVA tot.
Fuel: 8 tons **Crew:** 2 officers, 4 enlisted

Remarks: Donated late in 1997 from the Finnish Frontier Guard. Aluminum construction, with hard-chine hullform. Sonar was removed prior to transfer.

Disposal note: The nine ex-Polish Border Guard Project S-3 (Szkwal) patrol launches donated on 5-8-96 were never put into service and were discarded in 2000.

♦ 1 ex-Swedish Kbv 041–class former oil-spill cleanup boat
Bldr: Karlstad Varv, Karlstad (In serv. 1972)

041 MADELEINE (ex-Kbv 041)

Madeleine (041) Hartmut Ehlers, 9-96

D: 70 tons (fl) **S:** 11 kts **Dim:** 18.4 × 5.4 × 1.3
M: 2 diesels; 2 props; 450 bhp **Crew:** 8 tot.

Remarks: Transferred in 4-95 for use in patrolling Coronian Lagoon, near Klaipeda. Was originally to have gone to the navy as P 41. Carries a rigid inflatable inspection boat.

♦ 1 ex-Swedish Kbv 101 class
Bldr: Karlskronavarvet (In serv. 1969)

101 LILIAN (ex-Kbv 101)

Lilian (101) Stefan Marx, 1998

D: 50 tons (fl) **S:** 22 kts **Dim:** 24.90 × 5.00 × 1.10
Electronics: Radar: 1 . . . nav.
M: 2 MTU 8V331 TC82 diesels; 2 props; 1,866 bhp **Electric:** 60 kVA tot.
Range: 1,000/15 **Fuel:** 11 tons **Crew:** 7 tot.

Remarks: Donated by the Swedish Coast Guard in 6-96. Has a small, high-frequency, hull-mounted sonar.

♦ 1 former Russian Navy officers launch (Project 371U)

VYTIS-02

Vytis-02 Hartmut Ehlers, 9-96

D: 9.41 ton (fl) **S:** 13.5 kts **Dim:** 12.61 × 3.23 × 0.6 (1.00 over prop)
A: small arms **Electronics:** Radar: 1 Furuno . . . nav.
M: 1 Type 3D6S diesel; 1 prop; 150 bhp **Range:** 140/13.5
Crew: 1 officer, 2 enlisted

Remarks: Same type of launch once carried aboard Soviet *Sverdlov*-class cruisers and also used as personnel launches at naval bases. Sister *Vytis-01* serves the Lithuanian Navy, and two sisters are in Latvian service.

♦ 1 ex-Danish Home Guard patrol boat
Bldr: Gillelje (In serv. 1941)

LOKYS (ex-*Apollo,* MHV 56)

D: 30 tons (35 fl) **S:** 10 kts (9 sust.) **Dim:** 18.4 (17.0 pp) × 6.0 × 2.2
A: 2 single 7.62-mm mg **Electronics:** Radar: 1 Decca RM 1290S nav.
M: 1 Alpha diesel; 1 prop; 165 bhp **Crew:** 7 tot.

Remarks: Donated 7-97. Wooden-hulled former fishing boat.

Note: The Lithuanian Fisheries Inspection Service operates the former Swedish Coast Guard Kbv 236–class patrol boat *Victoria* (245, ex-Kbv 245), transferred 16-2-93.

MADAGASCAR

Democratic Republic of Madagascar

MALAGASY AERONAVAL FORCE

Personnel (2001): 430 total, including a 120-strong marine infantry company. The former navy and air force were united in 1991 as the Malagasy Aeronaval Force.

Bases: Principal base at Diego-Suarez, with minor facilities at Fort Dauphin, Majunga, Manakara, Nossi-Be, Tamatave, and Tulear.

AMPHIBIOUS WARFARE CRAFT

♦ 1 French EDIC-class utility landing craft [LCU]
Bldr: C.N. Franco-Belges (In serv. 1964)

AINA VAO VAO (ex-EDIC L 9082)

D: 250 tons (670 fl) **S:** 8 kts **Dim:** 59.00 × 11.95 × 1.30 (1.62 max.)
A: 1 12.7-mm mg **Electronics:** Radar: 1 Decca 1226 nav.
M: 2 MGO diesels; 2 props; 1,000 bhp **Range:** 1,800/8 **Crew:** 17 tot.

Remarks: Transferred 27-9-85, having been laid up at Tahiti since being stricken from the French Navy in 1981. Can carry 11 trucks. Given a minor refit by French Navy personnel during 3-96.

AUXILIARIES

♦ 1 Chamois-class local support tender [AG]
Bldr: Ch. de la Perriere, Lorient

	L	In serv.
MATSILO (ex-*Chamois,* A 767)	30-4-76	24-9-76

D: 305 tons light (500 fl) **S:** 14.5 kts **Dim:** 41.60 (36.96 pp) × 7.5 × 3.18
A: 2 single 12.7-mm mg **Electronics:** Radar: 1 Decca 1226 nav.
M: 2 SACM-Wärtsilä UD30 V16M3 diesels; 2 CP Kort-nozzle props; 2,800 bhp
Range: 7,200/12 **Fuel:** 92 m^3 **Crew:** 2 officers, 8 petty officers, 10 ratings

Remarks: Stricken from the French Navy 1-9-95 and transferred to Madagascar 5-96 as a general-purpose cargo transport, patrol, and training ship. Has a 5.6-ton crane and a 50-ton stern gallows crane. Can carry 100 tons of dry cargo on deck, or 125 tons of fuel and 40 tons of water, or 65 tons of fuel and 125 tons of water. Has two rudders and an 80-hp bow-thruster. The stern winch has a 28-ton bollard pull. Can also be used as transport for 28 passengers.

AUXILIARIES *(continued)*

Matsilo CF Stephen A. Frebourg, 10-97

Martin-Pecheur ***(left)*** **and Engoulvent** CF Stephen A. Frebourg, 10-97

SERVICE CRAFT

♦ **1 coastal tug [YTB]**
Bldr: SECREN, Antsiranana (In serv. 1982)

TROZONA

Trozona CF Stephen A. Frebourg, 10-97

D: 400 tons (fl) **S:** 11.5 kts **Dim:** 30.0 (27.0 pp) × 8.0 × 4.5
A: 1 12.7-mm mg **Electronics:** Radar: 1 Decca 110 nav.
M: 1 SACM-Wärtsilä UD30 V16 ASHR diesel; 1 prop; 1,000 bhp
Electric: 120 kw tot. **Range:** 5,000/9.5
Crew: 3 officers, 9 petty officers, 14 ratings

Remarks: Acquired in 1995, refitted, and commissioned 10-97. Employed on patrol duties. Bollard pull: 17.5 tons. A firefighting monitor is mounted atop the pilothouse.

♦ **3 ex-French Aigrette-class small harbor tugs [YTL]**

ENGOULVENT (ex-Y 723) TOURTERELLE (ex-Y 643)
MARTIN-PECHEUR (ex-Y 675)

D: 56 tons (fl) **S:** 9 kts **Dim:** 18.4 × 5.7 × 2.5
M: 1 Poyaud diesel; 1 prop; 250 bhp **Range:** 1,700/9 **Crew:** 5 tot.

Remarks: *Tourterelle,* donated in 1995, had been out of service since 1980. The other two were donated in 1996. Bollard pull: 10 tons. Sister *Bouleau* had been stricken by 1997. Have no armament and no radars.

MALAWI

Republic of Malawi

MALAWI POLICE

Personnel (2002): Approx. 220 total

Base: Monkey Bay, Lake Malawi; a small facility is available on Lake Nyasa

PATROL BOATS [WPB]

Note: *Antares*-class patrol boat *Kasungu* (P 703, ex-*Chikala*), which has been out of service since 1993, is still afloat at Monkey Bay and may eventually be repaired.

♦ **1 Namicurra-class launch**
Bldr: Tornado Products, South Africa (In serv. 1980–81)

P 704 KANING'A (ex-Y 1520)

Kaning'a (P 704) Malawi Police, 1997

D: 4 tons light (5.2 fl) **S:** 30 kts **Dim:** 9.5 × 2.5 × 0.8
A: 1 12.7-mm mg; 1 twin 7.62-mm mg; 1 shotgun
Electronics: Radar: 1 . . . nav.
M: 2 BMW inboard-outboard gasoline engines; 2 props; 380 bhp **Crew:** 4 tot.

Remarks: Donated to Malawi 29-10-88 by South Africa. Radar-equipped, GRP-hulled, catamaran harbor craft, which can be land-transported by trailer. When fitted, the 7.62-mm twin mount is positioned aft in the cockpit, while the 12.7-mm mg is located at the aft edge of the pilothouse; normally only the 12.7-mm mg is carried, in the aft position. Refitted in 1997.

SERVICE CRAFT

♦ **12 Buccaneer Legend RIB personnel launches [WYFL]**
Bldr: Buccaneer Inflatables, Glenvista, South Africa (In serv. 1993)

D: 1.2 tons light (3.5 tons fl) **S:** 37 kts **Dim:** 8.00 × 2.60 × . . .
A: 1 12.7-mm mg **M:** 1 Cummins . . . diesel; 1 prop; 320 bhp
Crew: 4 + 18 troops

Remarks: Ordered in late 1992. Have semi-rigid aluminum lower hull with flexible upper collar.

MALAYSIA

Lekiu (30) Brian Morrison, 11-99

ROYAL MALAYSIAN NAVY

(Tentera Laut Diraja)

Personnel (2001): 15,400 total (including 1,450 officers), plus 3,945 reserves (with reserves planned to expand to about 7,000 by end-2002). Included in the total are an unknown number of PASKAL special forces troops.

Bases: KD *Malaya,* at Perak on Telok Muroh, is headquarters and base for Lumut Headquarters, Area 1. The headquarters and base for Area 2 is at Labuan. Small facilities are located at Kuantan on the east coast of the Malay Peninsula, KD *Sri Sandakan* on the Sulu Sea coast of Borneo, Sungei Antu in Sarawak on Borneo, and Layang-Layang in the Spratly Islands (with smaller detachments on Ubi and Mantanani Islands). A new patrol boat base is being built at Teluk Sepanggar, near Kota Kinabulu in Sabah, to replace the Labuan Island facility. An air station is to be built at Sitiawan, Perak. The principal naval dockyard at Lumut was sold to Penang Shipbuilding Corp. on 8-12-95. A new recruit training facility at Tanjung Pengelih was to have been opened by the end of 2000. If acquisition of submarines comes to pass, an underground base will be built at Teluk Sepanggar, Sabah.

Naval Aviation: The Naval Air Wing, 499 Squadron, operates six AS.355MN Fennec helicopters based at Lumut. Six AgustaWestland Super Lynx Series 300 helicopters were ordered 7-9-99 for delivery in 2003; they will employ Honeywell–Rolls-Royce LHTEC CTS800-4N turboshaft engines. The last four Wasp helicopters were retired during 5-01. Six more AS.555SN Fennec helicopters were ordered 13-10-01 for delivery at the end of 2003. On 11-10-01, Sea Skua antiship missiles were ordered for use with the Super Lynx 300 helicopters.

The Royal Malaysian Air Force operates four Beech Super King Air B200T coastal maritime surveillance aircraft. For maritime strike duties, 18 Hawk 200 single-seat and 10 two-seat Hawk 100 light fighters are equipped with Sea Eagle missiles. Eight AGM-84C Harpoon–equipped F/A-18D fighter-bombers are also capable of maritime strike; some 25 missiles are available.

Note: Warship names are prefixed by KD (*Kapal DiRaja,* or King's Ship).

Lekiu (30)—note the helicopter hangar and the very low freeboard at the stern
Brian Morrison/H&L Van Ginderen, 11-99

ATTACK SUBMARINES [SS]

Note: Although the Netherlands Rotterdamse Droogdok Maatschappij (RDM) transported its two former Netherlands Navy *Zwaardvis*-class submarines to Lumut on 20-10-00 (arriving 14-12-00) with the intent of having them overhauled at Lumut as training submarines for the Malaysian Navy, as of 10-01 no contract had been signed. The Malaysian Ministry of Defense was also looking at a French offer to transfer two used *Agosta*-class submarines (later to be replaced by new-construction Scorpène-class boats); a German-Turkish offer to transfer two Turkish Navy Type 209/1200 submarines (with two Type 214s later to be built in Turkey); an offer by Daewoo Shipyard of South Korea to build three Type 209/1200 submarines; and a Pakistani offer to sell Malaysia one of its navy's indigenously built Agosta-90B submarines and to build another. The Dutch proposal included later construction of two Moray-class boats. A decision was expected in 10-01 but may have been delayed indefinitely due to financial and policy pressures.

FRIGATES [FF]

♦ 2 Yarrow Frigate 2000 class
Bldr: GEC-Yarrow SB, Scotstoun, Glasgow, Scotland

	Laid down	L	In serv.
30 Lekiu	3-94	3-12-94	7-10-99
29 Jebat	11-94	27-5-95	18-11-99

D: 1,845 tons (2,270 fl) **S:** 28.5 kts (27 sust.)
Dim: 105.50 (97.50 pp) × 12.75 × 3.80 (hull)
A: 8 MM 40 Exocet Block 2 SSM; 1 16-cell Sea Wolf SAM vertical-launch group; 1 57-mm 70-cal. Bofors SAK 57 Mk 2 DP; 2 single 30-mm MSI DS30B REMSIG AA; 2 triple 324-mm WASS B-515/3 ASW TT (Stingray torpedoes); 1 AS.355MN Fennec helicopter

Electronics:
Radar: 1 Decca . . . nav.; 1 Ericsson Sea Giraffe 150HC surf./air search; 1 Thales DA-08 air search; 2 GEC-Marconi Type 1802 SW f.c.
Sonar: Thales Spherion hull-mounted MF
EW: Marconi Mentor-2(V)1 intercept; Thorn-EMI Scimitar jammer; 2 12-round Wallop SuperBarricade decoy RL; Graseby Sea Siren torpedo decoy syst.
E/O: 1 Rademac System 2400 optronic f.c. and surveillance; 1 GEC-Marconi Type V3901 IR surveillance
M: 4 MTU 20V1163 TB 93 diesels; 2 CP props; 40,000 hp (33,300 sust.)
Range: 5,000/14 (diesel) **Crew:** 19 officers, 127 enlisted

Remarks: Ordered 31-3-92; first steel cut for first unit 3-93. Were originally to have been commissioned 2-96 and 5-96, respectively, but experienced significant weapons-control system integration problems. Both are named for warriors of the Melaka Empire; 29, although newer, has the lower number as she is intended to be the senior ship.
Hull systems: Special attention was paid to shaping the hull and superstructure to reduce radar signature, but there are no special radar-absorption coatings.
Combat systems: Have the GEC-Marconi Nautis-F weapons-control system and EADS HF/VHF/UHF integrated communications suite. The Thales ITL 70 launch-control system is fitted for the Exocet missiles. The Rademac System 2400 electro-optical director is mounted atop the pilothouse as backup control for the 57-mm gun, which also has a local control system. Have Thales Link Y Mk 2 combat datalink capabilities. The 30-mm guns are in remotely operated mountings using inputs from the main gun fire-control system and the Rademac electro-optical director.

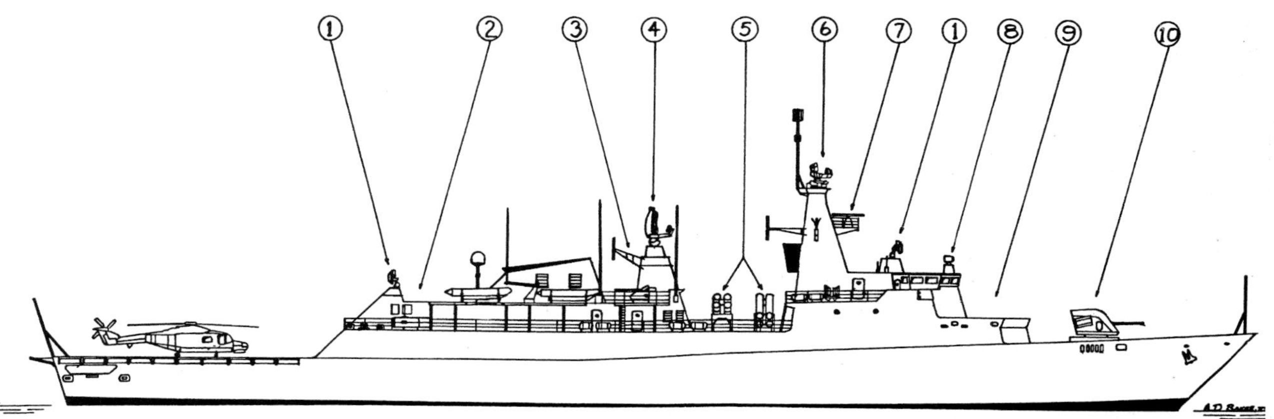

Lekiu (30) 1. Type 1802 SW radar f.c. directors 2. triple 324-mm ASW TT 3. 30-mm AA 4. DA-08 air-search radar 5. MM 40 Exocet SSM canister launchers 6. Sea Giraffe 150HC surface/air-search radar 7. navigational radar 8. System 2400 optronic f.c. director 9. Sea Wolf SAM vertical-launch group 10. 57-mm 70-cal. Bofors DP gun
Drawing by A. D. Baker III

FRIGATES [FF] *(continued)*

Jebat (29) Brian Morrison, 2-01

♦ 2 Kasturi class (Type FS-1500) Bldr: Howaldtswerke, Kiel

	Laid down	L	In serv.
25 Kasturi	31-1-83	14-5-83	15-8-84
26 Lekir	31-1-83	14-5-83	15-8-84

Lekir (26) Brian Morrison, 11-99

Kasturi (25) RAN, 3-95

D: 1,690 tons (1,900 fl) **S:** 28 kts **Dim:** 97.30 (91.80 pp) × 11.30 × 3.50 (hull)
A: 4 MM 38 Exocet SSM; 1 100-mm 55-cal. Creusot-Loire Compact DP; 1 57-mm 70-cal. Bofors SAK 57 Mk 1 DP; 2 twin 30-mm 75-cal. Emerlec AA; 1 2-round 375-mm Bofors ASW RL; 1 AS.355MN Fennec helicopter
Electronics:
Radar: 1 Decca TM 1226C nav.; 1 Thales DA-08 air search; 1 Thales WM-22 f.c.
Sonar: STN Atlas Elektronik DSQS-21 hull-mounted MF
EW: Racal Rapids intercept; Racal Scimitar jammer; EADS Telegon-8 HFD/F; 2 330- to 340-round Matra Défense Dagaie decoy RL
E/O: 2 Thales LIOD optronic gun directors
M: 4 MTU 20V1163 TB92 diesels; 2 CP props; 21,460 bhp
Electric: 1,392 kVA tot. **Range:** 3,600/18; 7,000/14 **Fuel:** 200 tons
Crew: 13 officers, 111 enlisted

Remarks: Ordered 10-6-81 and arrived in Malaysia 23-11-84. Are rated by Malaysia as corvettes. Four similar, but slightly smaller and differently equipped, near-sisters were built for Colombia. 25 is being used in trials of "smart ship" concepts to increase automation and reduce crew requirements.

Hull systems: Can make 23 kts on two diesels. There is no hangar, although provision was made to install a telescoping one. Have proven poor sea boats in anything above a State 2 sea due to the low bow freeboard, and maintenance access is poor.

Combat systems: Have the Thales SEWACO MA combat data system and are equipped for Link 5 and Thales Link Y Mk 1 datalink. The SEWACO system was to be updated during their 1999 and later refits. There are flare rocket launchers on the sides of the 57-mm mount. The 100-mm guns were upgraded to Mk 2 configuration, with improved reliability, during 1994. In the EW suite, RAPIDS = Radar Passive Identification System, and SCIMITAR = System for Countering Interdiction Missiles and Target Acquisition Radars. The MM 38 Exocet missiles will shortly be time-expired.

Modernization: Both are planned to be updated with improved antiair and ASW capabilities to serve past 2010, funds permitting. A CIWS system and a medium-range SAM system would be added, and the ASW rocket launcher would be replaced with ASW torpedo tubes, while the EW system, internal communications system, and datalinks would be replaced; the 100-mm and 30-mm guns may be replaced as well. No contracts had been signed as of 8-01.

♦ 1 Yarrow Frigate class
Bldr: Yarrow Shipbuilders, Scotstoun, Glasgow, Scotland

	Laid down	L	In serv.
24 Rahmat (ex-*Hang Jebat*)	2-66	18-12-67	31-8-71

Rahmat (24) Gilbert Gyssels, 5-90

D: 1,290 tons (1,600 fl) **S:** 27 kts (16.5 on diesel)
Dim: 93.97 × 10.36 × 3.05
A: 1 114-mm 45-cal. Vickers Mk 6 DP; 3 single 40-mm 70-cal. Bofors AA; 1 3-round Mk 10 Limbo ASW mortar
Electronics:
Radar: 1 Decca 626 nav.; 1 GEC-Marconi MS 32 surf. search; 1 Thales M-22 f.c.
Sonar: Graseby Type 170B hull-mounted MF search; Graseby Type 174 hull-mounted attack (15 kHz)
EW: UA-3 intercept; Plessey FH-4 HFD/F
M: CODOG: 1 Rolls-Royce Olympus TM-1B gas turbine (19,500 shp), 1 Crossley-Pielstick SPC2V diesel (3,850 bhp); 2 CP props
Electric: 2,000 kw tot. **Range:** 1,000/26; 5,200/16.5
Crew: 12 officers, 128 enlisted

Remarks: Ordered 11-2-66 and arrived in Malaysia 23-12-72. A major refit was completed in 6-93, during which some of the electronics systems were updated.

Hull systems: Planned to be re-engined with Stork-Wärtsilä SW28 diesels, as in the training ship *Hang Tuah,* if funds become available. Has fin stabilizers.

Combat systems: Has the Thales SEWACO combat control system and the same firm's Link Y datalink system; the Thales LW-02 air-search radar had been removed by 1997. The M-22 fire-control radar atop the mast is for the 114-mm gun. The ASW mortar, which has a range of 900 m and fires a 92-kg projectile, is covered by a MacGregor hatch that serves as a platform for a light helicopter; the Limbo mortar reportedly was no longer usable as of 1997, and the sonar suite is probably also nonoperational. The Sea Cat SAM system and its radar director were replaced by a third

FRIGATES [FF] *(continued)*

40-mm AA gun during a 1981–82 refit, but plans to replace the 114-mm mount with a French 100-mm Compact were canceled. Both the 114-mm mount and the after 40-mm mount have 103-mm U.K. Mk 1 flare rocket launch rails on either side.

PATROL SHIPS [PS]

♦ 0 (+ 6 + 21) MEKO 100 RMN class

Bldrs: Blohm + Voss, Hamburg, and PSC-Naval Dockyard Sdn Bhd (PSC-NDSB), Lumut, Perak

	Start	L	In serv.
....	15-11-01	...	6-04
....	21-12-01	...	...
....	...	...	...
....	...	...	...
....	...	...	...
....	...	...	4-08

MEKO 100 RMN design—computer rendering — Blohm + Voss, 2001

D: 1,650 tons (fl) **S:** 22+ kts
Dim: 91.10 (82.80 wl) × 12.85 (11.80 waterline) × 3.40 (mean hull)
A: 1 76-mm 62-cal. OTOBreda DP; 1 30-mm 80-cal. OTOBreda-Mauser AA; 2 single 12.7-mm mg; 1 Super Lynx 300 or AS.355MN Fennec helicopter
Electronics:
Radar: 1 . . . nav.; 1 EADS TRS-3D 3-D/16ES surf./air search
Sonar: WDS 3060 obstacle-avoidance
EW: . . . intercept/jamming syst.; ALEX decoy syst.
E/O: TMEO electro-optical gun f.c. director
M: 2 Caterpillar 3616 diesels; 2 CP props; 16,000 bhp (14,600 sust.)
Electric: 1,600 kw tot. (4 × 400 kw; Caterpillar 3412A diesels driving)
Range: 6,050/12 **Endurance:** 21 days **Crew:** 78 tot. (accomm. for 93)

Remarks: Referred to as the New-Generation Patrol Vessel (NGPV) and intended for use in offshore patrol, antipollution, oil-spill cleanup, and search-and-rescue duties. On 13-10-97, a consortium of Blohm + Voss Industrie GmbH, Howaldtswerke Deutsche Werft AG (HDW), Thyssen Rheinstahl Technik GmbH, and Ferrostaal AG was selected, but the letter of intent to order was not signed until 27-2-99 for an initial six units with an option for 21 more; the construction contract was not signed until 11-00. The total program cost is to be $1.42 billion. First steel was cut 7-6-01 at Blohm + Voss. In mid-2003, Blohm + Voss is to provide the first two ships; later units will be assembled in Malaysia, with the next four to be built primarily by PSC-NDSB with German technical assistance; prime contractorship will devolve on PSC-NDSB for any units past the first six. The full 27-unit program is expected to take place over 15 years.
Hull systems: Either diesel can drive either or both propellers. Fin stabilizers are fitted. The hull and superstructure have been shaped to reduce radar signature. A hangar and flight deck large enough to accommodate a Sikorsky S-70 (SH-60)-series helicopter are fitted, and there will be a landing and deck-traversing system.
Combat systems: STN Atlas Elektronik is providing technical assistance with combat systems integration; the combat data system is to be the Oerlikon-Contraves COSYS 110 M1, and a standard MICE/DAIL databus interface is to be employed. Are to have a Thales-AESN Link Y Mk 2 datalink system. The EW suite will be of Argo-Systems, Elettronica, GEC-Marconi (Type UAG), or Litton-Racal (Sceptre X) manufacture. Rhode & Schwarz will provide communications systems. Although an official Malay Navy announcement on 1-3-01 stated that ASW torpedo tubes would be fitted, it does not appear that they will be aboard initially, and no ASW sonar equipment is planned. Provision has been made for later installation of two MM 40 Exocet antiship missiles, and a 21-round Mk 49 launcher for the U.S. RIM-116 RAM SAM system may later be installed forward of the bridge.

♦ 2 Musytari class

	Bldr	L	In serv.
160 Musytari	Korea SB & Eng., Pusan, South Korea	19-7-84	19-12-85
161 Marikh	Malaysian SY & Eng., Pasir Gudang	21-1-85	8-12-87

D: 1,000 tons (1,300 fl) **S:** 22 kts **Dim:** 75.00 × 10.80 × 3.70
A: 1 100-mm 55-cal. Creusot-Loire Compact Mk 2 DP; 1 twin 30-mm 75-cal. Emerlec AA
Electronics:
Radar: 1 Decca TM 1226 nav.; 1 Thales DA-05 air search; 1 CelsiusTech 9GA 600 f.c.
EW: Racal Cutlass intercept; DaimlerChrysler Telegon-4 HFD/F

Musytari (160) — NAVPIC-Holland, 8-95

Marikh (161) — Maritime Photographic, 4-97

M: 2 SEMT-Pielstick diesels; 2 props; 12,720 bhp
Range: 6,000/20 **Crew:** 10 officers, 66 enlisted

Remarks: Ordered 6-83. A planned third unit was canceled. Intended to patrol the 200-n.m. economic zone. Names mean "Jupiter" and "Mars."
Combat systems: The CelsiusTech 9LV 230 radar/electro-optical combat system for the 100-mm gun has both a target detection and designation radar atop the foremast and a radar/electro-optical director atop the pilothouse to control the 100-mm gun. Have a large helicopter deck aft but no hangar. The 100-mm guns were upgraded to Mk 2 configuration, with improved reliability, during 1994.

GUIDED-MISSILE PATROL COMBATANTS [PGG]

♦ 4 ex-Iraqi Wadi M'ragh class

Bldr: Fincantieri, Muggiano, Italy

	Laid down	L	In serv.
134 Laksamana Hang Nadim (ex-*Kalid ibn al Walid,* F 216)	3-6-82	5-7-83	28-7-97
135 Laksamana Tun Abdul Gamil (ex-*Saad ibn abi Wakkad,* F 218)	17-8-82	30-12-83	28-7-97
136 Laksamana Muhammad Amin (ex-*Abdullah ibn abi Serh,* F 214)	22-3-82	5-7-83	7-99
137 Laksamana Tun Pusman (ex-*Salah Aldin Ayoobi,* F 220)	17-9-82	30-3-84	7-99

Laksamana Tun Abdul Gamil (135) — Brian Morrison, 11-99

Laksamana Tun Pusman (137) — Ralph Edwards, 3-01

D: 630 tons (705 fl) **S:** 37.5 kts **Dim:** 62.30 (57.80 pp) × 9.30 × 2.80 (hull)
A: 6 Otomat Mk 2 Block IV SSM; 1 4-round Albatros SAM syst. (12 tot. Aspide missiles); 1 76-mm 62-cal. OTOBreda SuperRapid DP; 1 twin 40-mm 70-cal. OTOBreda Dardo AA; 2 triple 324-mm ILAS-3 ASW TT

GUIDED-MISSILE PATROL COMBATANTS [PGG] *(continued)*

Laksamana Hang Nadim (134) Brian Morrison, 12-99

Electronics:
Radar: 1 Kelvin-Hughes 1007 nav.; 1 AESN RAN-12L/X surf./air search; 1 AESN Orion RTN-10X f.c.
Sonar: STN Atlas Elektronik ASO 84-41 hull-mounted (11–13 kHz)
EW: Elettronica INS-3B intercept; 1 20-round OTOBreda SCLAR decoy RL
M: 4 MTU 20V956 TB92 diesels; 4 props; 24,400 bhp (20,400 sust.)
Electric: 650 kw tot. (3 × 200-kw, 1 × 50-kw diesel sets)
Range: 1,200/31; 4,000/18 **Fuel:** 126 tons **Endurance:** 5 days **Crew:** 51 tot.

Remarks: Ordered for Iraq during 2-81, along with two helicopter-equipped half-sisters; completed in 1987 and laid up after trials. 134 and 135 were purchased by Malaysia 27-10-95 and refitted at La Spezia beginning in 1-96. The other two were purchased 20-2-97 and handed over 31-7-99 after overhauls. 136 had been used as a demonstrator for the sale of the class by Fincantieri and was actually complete as of 1987, while 137 had never been entirely completed before work had been suspended. The first firing of an Otomat Mk 2 missile by one of this class took place 8-6-00.
Combat systems: Combat data system was upgraded to the IPN-20 system in the first two, with two CO 3 optronic backup directors and two radar directors; funding shortfalls left the original IPN-10 system in the second pair. The reload Aspide missiles can only be placed in the quadruple launcher by a manually operated shipboard crane. During the reactivation refit, the 76-mm gun was upgraded, access to the 40-mm mount was improved, Link Y replaced the original combat datalink, UHF ship-to-ship communications and Inmarsat UHF SATCOM gear were added, and a GPS receiver was added. They normally operate with only two Otomat missiles aboard.

GUIDED-MISSILE PATROL BOATS [PTG]

♦ 4 Spica-M class Bldr: Karlskrona Varvet, Karlskrona, Sweden

	Laid down	L	In serv.
3511 Handalan	24-5-77	11-11-78	26-10-79
3512 Perkasa	27-6-77	11-11-78	26-10-79
3513 Pendikar	15-7-77	11-11-78	26-10-79
3514 Gempita	21-10-77	11-11-78	26-10-79

Gempita (3514) Brian Morrison, 11-99

Handalan (3511) Brian Morrison/H&L Van Ginderen, 12-99

D: 240 tons (268 fl) **S:** 37.5 kts (34.5 sust.)
Dim: 43.62 (41.00 pp) × 7.00 × 2.40 (aft)
A: 4 MM 38 Exocet SSM; 1 57-mm 70-cal. Bofors SAK 57 Mk 1 DP; 1 40-mm 70-cal. Bofors AA
Electronics:
Radar: 1 Decca 1226 nav.; 1 CelsiusTech 9LV 200 Mk 2 syst. (9LV 212 tracker, 9GR 600 search radar)
EW: Decca RDL or Cutlass intercept; MEL SUSIE-1 analyzer
M: 3 MTU 16V538 TB91 diesels; 3 props; 10,800 bhp **Electric:** 400 kVA tot.
Range: 1,850/14 **Fuel:** 80 tons **Crew:** 6 officers, 34 enlisted

Remarks: Ordered 13-8-76, arriving together in Malaysia 26-10-79. 3511 is the squadron flagship. Have 103-mm rocket flare launchers on the 57-mm mount and 57-mm RL on the 40-mm mount. The tracking radar at the masthead has a stabilized antenna. The Simrad SU scanning sonar has been removed. The MM 38 Exocet missiles will shortly be time-expired.

♦ 4 French Combattante II 4AL class Bldr: CMN, Cherbourg

	L	In serv.		L	In serv.
3501 Perdana	31-5-72	21-12-72	3503 Ganas	26-10-72	28-2-73
3502 Serang	22-12-71	31-2-73	3504 Ganyang	16-3-72	20-3-73

Ganyang (3504) Chris Sattler/H&L Van Ginderen, 1-00

Ganyang (3504) Brian Morrison/H&L Van Ginderen, 12-99

D: 234 tons (265 fl) **S:** 36.5 kts **Dim:** 47.00 × 7.10 × 2.50 (fl)
A: 2 MM 38 Exocet SSM; 1 57-mm 70-cal. Bofors SAK 57 Mk 1 DP; 1 40-mm 70-cal. Bofors AA
Electronics:
Radar: 1 Decca 626 nav.; 1 Thales Triton THD1040 surf./air search; 1 Thales Pollux f.c.
EW: Thales DR-2000 intercept
M: 4 MTU MB 870 diesels; 4 props; 14,000 bhp
Range: 800/25; 1,800/15 **Fuel:** 39 tons **Crew:** 4 officers, 26 enlisted

Remarks: All left France for Malaysia 2-5-73. Have steel hulls and aluminum-alloy superstructure. Six 103-mm rocket flare launchers on the 57-mm mount, four 57-mm RL on the 40-mm mount. Have the Thales Vega gun fire-control system. There are long-term plans to upgrade their missile systems, but the craft are nearing the end of their useful lives (and the MM 38 missiles will shortly be time-expired).

PATROL CRAFT [PC]

♦ 6 Jerong class Bldr: Hong Leong–Lürssen, Butterworth

	L	In serv.		L	In serv.
3505 Jerong	28-7-75	23-3-76	3508 Yu	17-7-76	15-11-76
3506 Tudak	16-3-76	16-6-76	3509 Baung	5-10-76	11-7-77
3507 Paus	2-6-76	18-8-76	3510 Pari	1-77	23-3-77

D: 210 tons (255 fl) **S:** 32 kts **Dim:** 44.90 × 7.00 × 2.48 (props)
A: 1 57-mm 70-cal. Bofors SAK Mk 1 DP; 1 40-mm 70-cal. Bofors AA
Electronics: Radar: 1 Decca 1226 nav.
M: 3 MTU MB 870 diesels; 3 props; 10,800 bhp **Electric:** 384 kVA tot.
Range: 700/31.5; 2,000/15 **Crew:** 5 officers, 31 enlisted

Remarks: Lürssen FPB 45 design. Rocket flare launchers are fitted on both gunmounts. Have a Matra Défense Naja electro-optical director for the 57-mm gun. Fin stabilizers are fitted. Reassigned to Naval Area 2 in 1995 and based at Sandakan. All six may be refitted and modernized at St. Petersburg, Russia, under a 10-01 agreement.

PATROL CRAFT [PC] *(continued)*

Pari (3510) H&L Van Ginderen, 5-90

Tudak (3506) Mike Louagie, 5-90

♦ 18 Vosper 103-foot class

Bldr: Vosper Ltd., Portsmouth, U.K.

	L		L
Third group:			
34 Kris	11-3-66	42 Panah	10-10-66
36 Sundang	22-5-66	43 Kerambit	20-11-66
37 Badek	8-5-66	44 Baladau	11-1-67
38 Renchong	22-6-66	45 Kelewang	31-1-67
39 Tombak	20-6-66	46 Rentaka	15-3-67
40 Lembing	22-8-66	47 Sri Perlis	26-5-67
41 Serampang	15-9-66	49 Sri Johor	21-8-67
Second group:			
3144 Sri Sabah	30-12-63	3146 Sri Negri Sembilan	17-9-64
3145 Sri Sarawak	20-1-64	3147 Sri Melaka	2-11-64

Baladau (44)—third group of Vosper 103-foot patrol craft Piet Sinke, 8-95

Sri Melaka (3147)—second group of Vosper craft; note different 40-mm shield configurations, fore and aft Piet Sinke, 9-94

D: 96 tons (109 fl) **S:** 27 kts **Dim:** 31.39 (28.95 pp) × 5.95 × 1.65
A: 2 single 40-mm 70-cal. Bofors L70 AA; 2 single 7.62-mm mg
Electronics: Radar: 1 Decca 616 nav.
M: 2 Bristol-Siddeley or Maybach MD 655/18 diesels; 2 props; 3,550 bhp
Range: 1,400/14 (3144–3147: 1,660/14) **Crew:** 3 officers, 19–20 enlisted

Remarks: Welded hulls. Vosper antiroll stabilizers. Second group was ordered in 3-63, third group in 1965. Of the original group ordered in 9-61, *Sri Kegah* (3138) and *Sri Pahang* (3141) were stricken in 1976; *Sri Perek* (3140) foundered in 1-84; and *Sri Selangor* (3139), *Sri Kelantan* (3142), and *Sri Trengganu* (3143) were stricken 1995–96. The survivors have all been refitted for further service but are long overdue for replacement. 3147 is detached to Sabah, and eight others are based at Sandakan. Five (40, 43, 44, 47, and 48) are assigned to training duties.

MINE WARFARE SHIPS

♦ 4 Italian Lerici-class coastal minehunters [MHC]

Bldr: Intermarine, Sarzana

	L	In serv.		L	In serv.
11 Mahamiru	24-2-83	11-12-85	13 Ledang	14-7-83	11-12-85
12 Jerai	8-12-83	11-12-85	14 Kinabulu	19-3-83	11-12-85

Ledang (13) Brian Morrison, 11-99

Kinabulu (14) Chris Sattler/H&L Van Ginderen, 12-99

D: 578 tons (610 fl) **S:** 16 kts **Dim:** 51.00 (46.50 pp) × 9.56 × 2.85
A: 1 40-mm 70-cal. Bofors AA
Electronics: Radar: 1 Decca 1226 nav.—Sonar: Thales TSM 2022
M: 2 MTU 12V396 TC82 (DB512) diesels; 2 CP props; 2,630 bhp (2,394 sust.)—2 electric retractable auxiliary props; 240 shp (for 7-kt sweep speed)
Electric: 1,000 kw (4 MTU V396 TC52 gen. sets)
Range: 1,400/14; 2,000/12 **Fuel:** 46 tons **Endurance:** 14 days
Crew: 5 officers, 37 enlisted

Remarks: Ordered 2-81 and arrived in Malaysia 28-3-86. Also used for patrol duties. Are based two-each at Labuan and Lumut to provide mine countermeasures services on both coasts of the Malay Peninsula. Plans to acquire four more have been canceled, but these four are planned to be updated with a more modern tactical data system.
Hull systems: Glass-reinforced plastic construction. Have a different main engine, armament, and sonar than their Italian Navy sisters. Range at 12 kts can be extended to 4,000 n.m. by using the passive antirolling tanks to carry fuel.
Combat systems: The Thales IBIS II minehunting system and TSM 2060 autopilot are fitted. Have two PAP-104 remote-controlled minehunting devices, good in depths up to 300 m, and U.K. Oropesa Mk 4 mechanical sweep gear. A Draeger Duocom decompression chamber is fitted for embarked mine disposal divers. Decoy or illumination rocket launchers are mounted on the sides of the 40-mm AA gunmount.

AMPHIBIOUS WARFARE SHIPS

Note: A dock landing ship, possibly a former U.S. Navy unit, is planned for acquisition.

♦ 1 ex-U.S. Newport-class tank landing ship [LST]

Bldr: National Steel SB, San Diego

	Laid down	L	In serv.
1505 Sri Inderapura (ex-*Spartanburg County*, LST 1192)	7-2-70	11-11-70	1-9-71

AMPHIBIOUS WARFARE SHIPS *(continued)*

Sri Inderapura (1505) H&L Van Ginderen, 5-95

D: 4,975 tons light (8,576 fl) **S:** 22 kts (20 sust.)
Dim: 159.2 (171.3 over horns) × 21.18 × 5.3 (aft; 1.80 fwd)
A: 1 20-mm Mk 15 Phalanx gatling CIWS; 4 single 12.7-mm mg
Electronics:
Radar: 1 Raytheon SPS-64(V)9 nav.; 1 Raytheon SPS-10F surf. search
EW: no intercept; Mk 36 RBOC decoy syst. (2 6-round Mk 137 RL)
M: 6 Alco 16-251 diesels; 2 CP props; 16,500 bhp
Range: 14,250/14 **Fuel:** 1,750 tons
Crew: 13 officers, 174 enlisted + troops: 20 officers, 294 enlisted (+ 72 emergency accomm.)

Remarks: Decommissioned 16-12-94 from the USN and purchased for $18.7 million, transferring the same date and commissioning in the Malaysian Navy 31-1-95. Given a major refit at Johor Baharu before entering service in 1998. The ship's name was misspelled in previous editions. The 1998 USN offer to sell sister *Barbour County* (LST 1195) was not accepted.
Hull systems: Can transport 2,000 tons of cargo, or 500 tons for beaching, on 1,765 m^2 of deck space. A side-thruster propeller forward helps when marrying to a causeway. There is a 34-m-long, 75-ton-capacity mobile aluminum ramp forward, which is linked to the tank deck by a second from the upper deck. Aft is a 242-m^2 helicopter platform and a stern door for loading and unloading vehicles. The tank deck, which has a 75-ton-capacity turntable at both ends, can carry 29 M 48 tanks or 41 2.5-ton trucks, while the upper deck can accept 29 2.5-ton trucks. Carries three LCVPs and one LCP in Welin davits. Has two 10-ton cranes. Carries 141,600 gallons of vehicle fuel.
Combat systems: The Mk 63 radar gunfire-control systems were removed 1977–78, and the two twin 76.2-mm guns were removed prior to transfer.

Note: The two multipurpose ships of the *Sri Indera Sakti* class can also be used for amphibious warfare purposes.

♦ 1 rigid inflatable personnel special forces craft [LCP]
Bldr: Mara Shipyard & Engineering, Terengganu (In serv. 1999)

D: 3.7 tons (fl) **S:** 48 kts (37 cruising) **Dim:** 7.62 (5.80 wl) × 2.72 × 0.60
A: 1 7.62-mm mg; small arms
Electronics: Radar: 1 Furuno FR-1721 Mk II nav.
M: 2 Yamaha gasoline outboards; 400 bhp
Range: 150/37 **Fuel:** 600 liters **Crew:** 3 tot. + 12 troops

Remarks: Composite hull structure. Painted black to reduce visibility. Troops are carried in six rows of two seats abaft the cockpit, while the gunner is seated forward. Additional units may be ordered.

♦ 8 (+ 38) Swedish CB 90H personnel landing craft [LCP]
Bldr: Dockstavarvet, Sweden (In serv. 1998–99; . . .)

451 through 458

CB 90H landing craft 458 Brian Morrison, 12-99

CB 90H landing craft 458 Brian Morrison, 12-99

D: 14.5 tons light (19 fl) **S:** 40+ kts (35 loaded)
Dim: 14.90 (13.00 wl) × 3.80 × 0.84 **A:** 1 12.7-mm mg; 2 mine rails
Electronics: Radar: 1 Decca BridgeMaster RD 360 nav.
M: 2 Saab Scania 8V DSI-14 diesels; 2 KaMeWa FF 410 waterjets; 1,256 bhp
Range: 260/20 **Fuel:** 2.5 tons **Crew:** 4 tot. + 20 troops

Remarks: The plan to procure 100 or more of the larger Enforcer CB 90NEX–class patrol boats designed by Storebro and to have been built by Perusahaan Sadur Timah in Malaysia for the navy and national maritime police has not gone forward on schedule due to the financial situation, but by 11-99, five were in service with the navy as special forces insertion craft. Twelve more were ordered at the end of 2000, with 29 additional units planned. They are used primarily as patrol and logistic support craft operating from Borneo.
Hull systems: Can maintain 20 kts in 1.5-m seas, and the hull can withstand at least 25 groundings without significant damage. In lieu of troops, can carry up to 2.8 tons of cargo.

AUXILIARIES

♦ 2 multipurpose support ships [AG]

	Bldr	Laid down	L	In serv.
1503 Sri Indera Sakti	Bremer-Vulcan, Bremen, Germany	15-2-80	1-7-80	24-10-80
1504 Mahawangsa	Korea-Tacoma, Masan, South Korea	. . .	. . .	16-5-83

Sri Indera Sakti (1503) Brian Morrison, 11-99

Mahawangsa (1504)—note the higher helicopter platform
Maritime Photographic, 4-97

D: 2,000 tons light (4,300 fl) **S:** 16.8 kts **Dim:** 100.00 (91.20 pp) × 15.00 × 4.75
A: 1 57-mm 70-cal. Bofors SAK 57 Mk 1 DP
Electronics: Radar: 1 Decca TM 1226 nav.; 1 . . . surf. search
M: 2 Deutz-KHD SBV 6M540 diesels; 2 CP props; 5,986 bhp—bow-thruster
Electric: 1,200 kw tot. **Range:** 14,000/15 **Fuel:** 1,350 tons (max.)
Endurance: 60 days **Crew:** 14 officers, 122 enlisted + 75 passengers

Remarks: 1,800 dwt. 1503 ordered 10-79, 1504 in 2-81. Intended to perform a variety of tasks, including providing support (including up to 1,300 tons of fuel and 200 tons of water) to deployed small combatants or mine countermeasures ships; acting as flagships; performing as vehicle and troop transports in amphibious operations; and acting as cadet training ships.
Hull systems: 1504 is 103.00 m o.a., draws 5.00 m, displaces 5,000 tons (fl), and can reach 15.5 kts; she is configured to carry 410 tons of ammunition. The ship lacks a funnel, thus effectively doubling the area of the helicopter deck, which is also positioned higher than on 1503. Both have 1,000 m^3 of cargo space for spare parts, and 10 standard 20-ft. cargo containers can be carried on deck amidships. They can carry 17 tanks, while 1504 can also stow 11 3-ton trucks on deck beneath the helicopter platform. Vehicle holds aft are reached by ramps on either side of the stern. They can carry 600 troops on the 680-m^2 vehicle deck. Extensive repair facilities and divers' support equipment are provided. Provisions spaces total 300 m^3, including 100 m^3 of refrigerated stores. A 16-ton crane is installed amidships.
Combat systems: The stern-mounted second 57-mm gun was removed from 1504 by 4-97, and both no longer carry the two 20-mm AA originally fitted. Have a Matra Défense Naja optical gun director. Chaff and illumination rocket launchers are mounted on the sides of the gunmount. Can embark a Malaysian Army Sikorsky S-61 helicopter. Have been fitted with an S-band surface-search radar and a commercial SATCOM system.

AUXILIARIES *(continued)*

Disposal note: U.S. LST 542–class support ship and former landing ship *Sri Banggi* (1501; ex-*Henry County,* LST 824) was stricken during 2000; sister *Rajah Jarom* (1502; ex-*Sedgewick County,* LST 1123) was stricken 9-9-99.

♦ **1 hydrographic survey ship [AGS]**
Bldr: Hong Leong–Lürssen, Butterworth (In serv. 12-10-98)

153 PERANTAU

Perantau (153)—white hull, buff stack and mast, pennant number not worn
Brian Morrison, 11-99

D: 1,996 tons (fl) **S:** 16.3 kts **Dim:** 67.80 (62.40 pp) × 13.28 × 4.00
A: none
Electronics:
Radar: 2 . . . . . . nav.
Sonar: STN Atlas Elektronik Fansweep and Hydrosweep multibeam mapping
M: 2 Deutz SBV8 M628 diesels; 2 Berg CP props; 4,760 bhp—1 Schottel 3-ton-thrust bow-thruster
Electric: 1,950 kw (3 × 600-kw MWM V8616 diesel-driven sets; 1 × 150 kw)
Range: 6,000/10 **Crew:** 17 officers, 77 enlisted

Remarks: 506 dwt. Ordered in fall 1996 for delivery 8-97—a very tight schedule that was not met. The ship is capable of producing high-precision underwater topography charts. Design by Krögerwerft, Germany. A near-sister was completed in 1997 for the German Hydrographic Institute.
Hull systems: STN Atlas Elektronik provided the NACOS 55 integrated navigation system, Hydrosweep MD-2 multibeam sonar, and Hydromap hydrographic evaluation system. Other survey equipment includes differential GPS, medium-range and short-range radio position-fixing systems, combined side-scan sonar and bottom-profiling system, deep-sea echo sounders, acoustic doppler current profilers, gravity corer and bottom sampling equipment, recording current meters, tide gauges, and an underwater camera. Has two 8-ton cranes aft. Carries two survey launches (with Fansweep 20 portable survey sounders), two general-purpose launches, and two rigid inflatables.

♦ **1 oceanographic research and hydrographic survey ship [AGS]**
Bldr: Hong Leong–Lürssen, Butterworth (In serv. 12-1-78)

152 MUTIARA

Mutiara (152)—does not wear her pennant number H&L Van Ginderen, 5-90

D: 1,905 tons (fl) **S:** 16 kts **Dim:** 70.0 (64.0 pp) × 13.0 × 4.0
A: 2 twin 20-mm 70-cal. Oerlikon Mk 24 AA
Electronics: Radar: 1 Decca 1226 nav.; 1 Decca 1229 nav.
M: 1 Deutz SBA-12M-528 diesel; 1 CP prop; 2,000 bhp
Range: 4,500/16 **Crew:** 14 officers, 141 enlisted

Remarks: Ordered in 1975. Carries six small survey launches and has a small helicopter platform aft. White hull, buff stack.

♦ **1 British-built training ship [AXT]**
Bldr: Yarrow Shipbuilders, Scotstoun, Glasgow

	Laid down	L	In serv.
76 HANG TUAH (ex-*Mermaid*)	1965	29-12-66	16-5-73

Hang Tuah (76) Brian Morrison, 11-99

D: 2,300 tons (2,520 fl) **S:** 22 kts **Dim:** 103.40 × 12.20 × 4.80
A: 1 57-mm 70-cal. Bofors SAK 57 Mk 1 DP; 2 single 40-mm 70-cal. Bofors L70 AA; 1 3-round Limbo Mk 10 ASW mortar (51 projectiles)
Electronics:
Radar: 1 Decca 1226 nav.; 1 Plessey AWS-1 air search
Sonar: Graseby Type 174 hull-mounted (14–22 kHz) search; Graseby Type 170 hull-mounted attack (15 kHz)
EW: none
M: 2 Stork-Wärtsilä 12SW28 diesels; 2 CP props; 9,928 bhp
Electric: . . . kw tot. (3 × . . . kw, Wärtsilä 12V UD 25 diesels driving)
Range: 4,800/15 **Fuel:** 230 tons **Crew:** 210 tot.

Remarks: Former frigate, used as fleet training ship after a 1991–92 refit. Ordered for Ghana in 1964 as a frigate-cum-yacht. Because of a change in government in Ghana, the ship was not delivered and at the end of 1971 she was purchased by the British government. Was sold to Malaysia in 5-77 and delivered 8-77 after a refit. Extensively upgraded, rearmed, and re-engined during a 1995 to 2-97 refit at Malaysian SB & Eng., Johor Baharu.
Hull systems: Has a helicopter pad but no hangar. Fin stabilizers are fitted. Originally had the same machinery (eight Admiralty Standard Range-I diesels, totaling 14,400 bhp) and has the same below-waterline hullform as the British *Leopard-* and *Salisbury*-class frigates; was given three new diesel generators during the 1995 to 2-97 refit.
Combat systems: The twin 102-mm 45-cal. Vickers Mk 19 gunmount was removed from the forecastle during the 1995–97 refit and replaced with the after 57-mm mounting from *Mahawangsa* (1504). The original 40-mm 60-cal. Mk 6 AA mounts were replaced with Bofors L70 weapons. All three gunmounts have fixed rocket flare launchers on their sides, and the 57-mm mount is controlled by a Matra Défense Naja optical director. The Limbo ASW mortar has a range of 400–914 m and fires a pattern of three 177-kg time-fuzed projectiles. The sonar suite may have been updated, although one source states that the Limbo mortar is no longer operational.

SERVICE CRAFT

Disposal note: Diving tender [YDT] *Duyong* (1109) was retired during 2000.

♦ **5 miscellaneous launches [YFL]**

KEMPONG MANGKASA PATAK SELLAR TEPURUK

Remarks: No data available.

♦ **2 Lang Tiram–class large harbor tugs [YTB]**
Bldr: Penang SY, Pulau Jerejah (In serv. 1981–82)

LANG TIRAM LANG SIPUT

D: . . . **S:** 12.5 kts **Dim:** 29.0 × 7.0 × 2.0
M: 2 Ruston-Paxman diesels; 2 props; 1,800 bhp

Remarks: Sisters *Lang Hindek* and *Lang Kangok* were transferred to Malaysian Marine Department in 1992.

♦ **3 Tunda Satu 1–class large harbor tugs [YTB]**
Bldr: Ironwood SY, Malaysia (In serv. 1978–79)

A 1 TUNDA SATU 1 A 2 TUNDA SATU 2 A 3 TUNDA SATU 3

Tunda Satu 1 (A 1) H&L Van Ginderen, 5-90

D: 150 tons **S:** . . . **Dim:** 26.0 × . . . × . . .
M: 1 Cummins diesel; 1 prop; . . . bhp

SERVICE CRAFT *(continued)*

◆ **8 miscellaneous tugs [YTB/TYM/YTL]**

A 4 Penyu (ex-*Salvigilant*)	A 8 Kepah (ex-*Arctic Supplier*)
A 5 Kupang	A 9 Siput
A 6 Sotong (ex-*Asiatic Charm*)	A 10 Teritup
A 7 Ketam	A 11 Belankas

Sotong (A 6) H&L Van Ginderen, 5-90

Remarks: A 4 is a 398-grt salvage tug, built in 1976 and purchased in 1980. A 6 is a 233-grt tug, built in 1976 and purchased in 1980. A 7 is a salvage and firefighting tug. A 8 is a 432-grt tug, built in 1974 and purchased in 1980.

◆ **1 sail-training brigantine [YTS]**
Bldr: Brooke Marine, Lowestoft, U.K.

	Laid down	L	In serv.
A 13 Tunas Samadura	1-12-88	4-8-89	16-10-89

Tunas Samadura (A 13)—white-painted and without pennant number
Brian Morrison, 8-95

D: 239 tons (fl) **S:** 10 kts power/14 kts sail **Dim:** 44.00 (35 pp) × 7.8 × 4.0
M: 2 Perkins diesels; 2 props; . . . bhp **Crew:** 6 officers, 21 enlisted + 24 trainees

Remarks: Operated by the navy, but trains all Malaysian sea services. Foremast is 30 m high, mainmast 32.6 m. Steel construction hull.

MALAYSIAN ARMY

LANDING CRAFT [LCP]

◆ **165 Damen 540 class**
Bldrs: 65 by Damen, Gorinchem, Netherlands; 100 by Limbougan Timor, Kuala Trengganu (In serv. 1986–87)

D: . . . **S:** 25–30 kts **Dim:** 5.4 × 1.83 × . . .
M: 1 40-bhp outboard **Crew:** 2 crew, 10 troops

Remarks: Ordered 10-85. Transferred from the navy in 1993. About 250–300 other small river-crossing assault boats are available.

ROYAL MALAYSIAN MARINE POLICE

Note: Planned acquisitions include three 40-m patrol boats equipped with helicopter platforms and four 32-m patrol boats.

PATROL CRAFT [WPC]

◆ **6 Brooke Marine 29-meter design**
Bldr: Penang SY, Pulau Jerejah (In serv. 1982–83)

PX 28 Sangitan	PX 30 Sri Dungun	PX 32 Sri Tumpar
PX 29 Sabahan	PX 31 Sri Tioman	PX 33 Segama

Sri Tioman (PX 31) NAVPIC Holland, 9-94

D: 114 tons **S:** 36 kts **Dim:** 29.0 (26.5 pp) × 6.0 × 1.7
A: 1 20-mm 70-cal. Oerlikon AA; 2 single 7.62-mm mg
Electronics: Radar: 1 . . . nav.
M: 2 Paxman Valenta 16 RP 200M diesels; 2 props; 8,000 bhp
Range: 1,200/24 **Crew:** 4 officers, 14 constables

Remarks: Ordered in 1980. Design evolved from that of the PX 26 class. Carry 2,000 rounds of 20-mm ammunition.

◆ **14 PZ class**
Bldr: Hong Leong–Lürssen, Butterworth (In serv. 1981–83)

PZ 1 Lang Hitan	PZ 6 Berlian	PZ 12 Harimau Akar
PZ 2 Lang Malam	PZ 7 Kurita	PZ 13 Parangan
PZ 3 Lang Leban	PZ 8 Serangan Batu	PZ 14 Marsusi
PZ 4 Lang Kuik	PZ 9 Harinan Bintang	PZ 15 Alu Alu
PZ 5 Balong	PZ 11 Harinan Belang	

Lang Hitan (PZ 1) Brian Morrison, 12-99

Harinan Bintang (PZ 9) Chris Sattler/H&L Van Ginderen, 12-99

D: 188 tons (205 fl) **S:** 34 kts **Dim:** 38.50 (36.00 wl) × 7.00 × 2.20
A: 1 40-mm 70-cal. Bofors AA; 1 20-mm 70-cal. AA; 2 single 7.62-mm mg
Electronics: Radar: 1 Kelvin-Hughes 14/9 nav.
M: 2 MTU 20V538 TB92 diesels; 2 props; 9,000 bhp **Electric:** 130 kVA tot.
Range: 550/31.5; 1,100/16 **Crew:** 4 officers, 34 constables

Remarks: Lürssen FPB 38 design. Ordered in 1979; first delivered 8-81. Sister *Harimau Kumbang* (PZ 10) has been stricken. Have two rocket flare launchers. Carry 1,000 rounds of 40-mm and 2,000 rounds of 20-mm ammunition. A near-sister was delivered to Bangladesh in 1999.

PATROL BOATS [WPB]

◆ **4 Stan Patrol 1500 class**
Bldr: . . . . . ., Malaysia (In serv. 1998–99)

Remarks: Netherlands Damen design, built at two Malaysian yards. About 15 m o.a. and powered by two diesel engines; no other data available.

MARINE POLICE PATROL BOATS [WPB] *(continued)*

♦ 1 Swedish SRC 90E class
Bldr: Storebro Bruks AB, Storebro (In serv. 1997)

D: 6.5 tons (8.5 fl) **S:** 40 kts (37 loaded) **Dim:** 11.88 (10.80 wl) × 2.90 × 0.79
M: 2 Saab Scania DSI-14 diesel; 1 FF-Jet FF-410 waterjet; 560 bhp (at 3,800 rpm; 340 bhp sust.)
Range: . . ./. . . **Fuel:** 600 liters **Crew:** 2 tot.

Remarks: Acquired for trials purposes. Hull is constructed of carbon-fiber-reinforced vinyl ester sandwich.

♦ . . . 9.65-meter class
Bldr: DMS, Johor Baharu (In serv. 1990s)

D: . . . tons (fl) **S:** 61 kts **Dim:** 9.65 × . . . × . . .
A: 2 single 7.62-mm mg **M:** 3 MerCruiser outboards; 3 props; 415 bhp
Crew: . . .

♦ 1 prototype Swiss-built
Bldr: Friedrich Fassmer Werft, Berne/Motzen (In serv. 12-96)

PX . . .

D: 44 tons (fl) **S:** 35 kts **Dim:** 21.0 × . . . × . . .
A: small arms **Electronics:** Radar: 1 . . . nav.
M: 2 MWM TBD616V16 diesels; 2 props; 3,000 bhp
Range: . . ./. . . **Crew:** . . . tot.

Remarks: Aluminum alloy construction.

♦ 23 Simonneau SM 465 class
Bldr: Hong Leong–Lürssen, Butterworth (In serv. 1992–93)

PC 6 through PC 28

Simonneau SM 465–class PC 6 Maritime Photographic, 4-97

D: 18 tons (at half load) **S:** 40+ kts **Dim:** 14.00 × 4.00 × 0.75
A: 2 single 12.7-mm mg **Electronics:** Radar: 1 Furuno . . . nav.
M: 2 MTU 12V183 TE92 diesels; 2 props; 2,000 bhp
Fuel: 2,000 liters **Crew:** 6 tot.

Remarks: Aluminum construction. Have one diesel generator and are air-conditioned. Carry an outboard-powered inspection craft.

♦ 6 or more 7.5-meter class
Bldr: Destination Marine, Johor Baharu (In serv. 1990–91)

D: . . . tons (fl) **S:** 45 kts **Dim:** 7.5 × 2.5 × 1.0
A: 2 single 7.62-mm mg **M:** 2 gasoline outboards; 550 bhp **Crew:** . . .

Remarks: Ordered 6-89 for antipiracy duties. Six were intended for service at Sabah.

♦ 3 PX 25 class
Bldr: Hong Leong–Lürssen, Butterworth (In serv. 1973–74)

PX 25 Sri Gaya PX 26 Sri Kudat PX 27 Sri Tawau

D: 92.5 tons **S:** 25 kts **Dim:** 28.0 × 5.4 × 1.6
A: 1 20-mm 70-cal. Oerlikon Mk 10 AA; 2 single 7.62-mm mg
Electronics: Radar: 1 Furuno . . . nav.
M: 2 MTU MB820Db diesels; 2 props; 2,460 bhp
Range: 1,050/15 **Crew:** 2 officers, 17 constables

Remarks: An improved version of the PX 21 class, with increased range.

♦ 4 PX 21 class
Bldr: Vosper Pty, Singapore (In serv. 1973–74)

PX 21 Kuala Trengganu PX 23 Sri Menanti
PX 22 Johore Bahru PX 24 Kuching

D: 92 tons (fl) **S:** 25 kts **Dim:** 27.3 × 5.8 × 1.5
A: 2 single 20-mm 70-cal. Oerlikon Mk 10 AA; 2 single 7.62-mm mg
Electronics: Radar: 1 Furuno . . . nav.
M: 2 MTU MB820Db diesels; 2 props; 2,460 bhp
Range: 750/15 **Crew:** 2 officers, 17 constables

♦ 12 PX 1 class
Bldr: Vosper Pty, Singapore (In serv. 1963–69)

PX 5 Maharajelela PX 11 Sangsetia PX 17 Sri Gumantong
PX 6 Pahlawan PX 12 Laksmana PX 18 Sri Labuan
PX 9 Pertanda PX 15 Kuala Kangsar PX 19 Alor Star
PX 10 Shahbandar PX 16 Arau PX 20 Kota Bahru

Kota Bahru (PX 20) NAVPIC Holland, 8-96

D: 85 tons (fl) **S:** 25 kts **Dim:** 26.29 × 5.70 × 1.45
A: 1 20-mm 90-cal. Oerlikon GAM-B01 AA; 2 single 7.62-mm mg
Electronics: Radar: 1 Furuno . . . nav.
M: 2 MTU MB820Db diesels; 2 props; 2,460 bhp
Range: 550/20; 700/15 **Crew:** 2 officers, 13 constables

Remarks: Sisters *Mahkota* (PX 1), *Temenggong* (PX 2), *Hulubalang* (PX 3), *Maharajesetia* (PX 4), *Bentara* (PX 7), *Periwa* (PX 8), *Pekan* (PX 13), and *Kelang* (PX 14) were stricken during 1992–93, and some of the above may have also since been retired.

SERVICE CRAFT

♦ 2 miscellaneous personnel ferries [WYFB]
Bldr: Brooke Dockyard, Sarawak (In serv. 1985)

PT 1 Penjaga PT 2 Margherita

Remarks: Are about 30 m long and appear to be intended primarily for riverine service. PT 2 is the more modern and may be somewhat smaller than PT 1. Also in service are smaller transports PLC 1–PLC 4, completed in 1980 by Pasir Gudang, and large personnel launches PA 39 and PA 53.

Note: The Royal Malaysian Marine Police also operate a large number of smaller patrol and support craft, as do the customs service, fisheries protection service, and Marine Transportation Department; see previous editions for details.

Waterjet-driven small police launch PSC 2—no data available
Brian Morrison, 12-99

SARAWAK MARINE DEPARTMENT

Note: The Malaysian state of Sarawak retains its own police forces and has a small maritime patrol and search-and-rescue service.

PATROL BOATS [WPB]

♦ 6 Melabing class
Bldrs: *Melabing* and *Bako:* Sarawak Slipways, Miri; *Melano* and one other: Ironwoods SY, Kuching; other two: Kiong Hong DY, Sibu (First three in serv. 1999)

Melabing Melano . . .
Bako . . . . . .

D: 33 tons (fl) **S:** 35 kts (at half load; 25 loaded)
Dim: 18.30 (15.30 wl) × 4.80 × 0.95
A: small arms **Electronics:** Radar: 1 Furuno FR-1932 nav.
M: 2 M.A.N. D2842 LE 401 diesels; 2 Vospower 170 waterjets; 1,972 bhp
Electric: 44 kVA tot. (2 × 22-kVA Leroy Somer gen., Yanmar 4TNE84 diesels driving)
Range: 600/35 **Fuel:** 6,000 liters **Crew:** 8 tot.

Remarks: Six were ordered, of which the first three had been delivered by 12-99. Designed by Camarc, in the U.K., for local construction in Sarawak. Have a Furuno FE-4300 echo sounder, GP-30 GPS plotter, and GR-80 digital GPS terminal, plus two Furuno FM-2510 VHF radios. Carry two 10-person Zodiac launches.

MALDIVE ISLANDS

Republic of Maldives

COAST GUARD

Personnel (2001): Approx. 400 total, including shore-based constabulary

Base: Male

Note: The digits in the pennant numbers all add up to 7.

PATROL BOATS [WPB]

♦ **1 Israeli Shaldag class**
Bldr: Colombo Dockyard, Colombo, Sri Lanka (In serv. 1998–99)

700 ISKANDHAR

D: 40 tons (56 fl) **S:** 46 kts **Dim:** 24.37 (20.07 pp) × 6.00 × 1.15 (1.26 max.)
A: 2 single 12.7-mm mg
Electronics: Radar: 1 Koden Mk 2 nav.
M: 2 Paxman . . . diesels; 2 waterjets; 4,250 bhp
Electric: 50 kw tot. (2 × 25-kw, 440-V a.c. diesel sets)
Range: 850/16 **Endurance:** 2–3 days **Crew:** 18 tot.

Remarks: Ordered in 1997. A second unit is planned to be ordered. Has a deep-vee, aluminum-construction hull and five watertight compartments. Air-conditioned.

♦ **1 21-meter Tracker class**
Bldr: Fairey Marine, Cowes, U.K. (In serv. 4-87)

106 NIROLHU

Nirolhu (106) H&L Van Ginderen, 4-94

D: 35 tons (38 fl) **S:** 25 kts **Dim:** 21.00 × 5.18 × 1.45
A: 1 12.7-mm M2 mg; 1 7.62-mm FN mg
Electronics: Radar: 1 Koden Mk 2 nav.
M: 2 G.M. 12V71 TI diesels; 2 props; 1,300 bhp
Range: 450/20 **Endurance:** 7 days **Crew:** 10 tot.

Remarks: Ordered 6-85. Used for fisheries protection. GRP construction.

♦ **3 ex-U.K. Tracker II class**
Bldr: Fairey Marine, Hamble (In serv. 1978–79)

133 KAANI 142 KUREDHI 151 MIDHILI

Kaani (133)—with Dagger-class launch *Funa* (124) and Tracker-class *Nirolhu* (106) in the background Laurent Morlion, via Paolo Marsan, 2000

D: 31 tons (34.5 fl) **S:** 21 kts **Dim:** 20.00 (19.30 pp) × 5.18 × 1.45
A: 1 12.7-mm M2 mg; 1 7.62-mm FN mg
Electronics: Radar: 1 Koden Mk 2 nav.
M: 2 G.M. 12V71 TI diesels; 2 props; 1,300 bhp **Electric:** 30 kw tot.
Range: 650/20 **Endurance:** 7 days **Crew:** 10 tot.

Remarks: Transferred by the U.K. in 7-89; left for the Indian Ocean via heavy-lift ship. Formerly operated by H.M. Customs and Excise as *Active, Challenge,* and *Champion,* but correlation to the new names is not available. GRP hull construction. The radar has been removed from 142.

♦ **1 17-meter class**
Bldr: Cheverton, Cowes, U.K. (In serv. 1984)

115 BUREVI (ex-7)

D: 22 tons (24 fl) **S:** 23.6 kts **Dim:** 17.00 × 4.50 × 1.20
A: 1 12.7-mm M2 mg; 1 7.62-mm FN mg
Electronics: Radar: 1 Koden Mk 2 nav.
M: 2 G.M. 8V71 TI diesels; 2 props; 850 bhp
Range: 790/18; 1,000/12 **Crew:** 9 tot.

Remarks: Originally completed in 1980 for Kiribati, but not delivered. Purchased in 1984 for the Maldives. GRP hull and aluminum superstructure.

♦ **1 Dagger class**
Bldr: Fairey Marine, Cowes, U.K. (In serv. 1982)

124 FUNA

D: 20 tons (fl) **S:** 35 kts **Dim:** 11.2 × 3.4 × 1.2
A: 1 7.62-mm mg **Electronics:** Radar: 1 Furuno . . . . nav.
M: 2 Ford Sabre diesels; 2 props; 660 bhp **Crew:** 6 tot

Remarks: GRP construction.

SERVICE CRAFT

♦ **1 Kandula-class utility landing craft [WLCU]**
Bldr: Colombo Dockyard, Sri Lanka (In serv. 1998)

. . . . . .

D: 200 tons (268 fl) **S:** 8 kts **Dim:** 33.00 (30.00 pp) × 8.00 × 1.50
A: none **Electronics:** 1 . . . nav.
M: 2 Caterpillar 3408 TA diesels; 2 props; 1,524 bhp
Range: 1,800/8 **Crew:** 12 tot. + 54 passengers

Remarks: Original design by Vosper Pty, Singapore. Sisters operate in the Sri Lanka Navy.

MALI

Republic of Mali

Personnel (2001): About 60 total

PATROL BOATS [PB]

♦ **2 Yugoslav-built, for the Niger River**

Remarks: Transferred in 1974 via Libya. Based, as are the craft below, at Bamako, Segou, Mopti, and Timbuktu. Current operating condition is unknown.

♦ **3 smaller river patrol craft**

Remarks: No details available.

MALTA

Republic of Malta

MARITIME SQUADRON

Personnel (2001): 9 officers, 211 enlisted

Organization: The Maritime Squadron is a part of the 2nd Regiment of the Armed Forces of Malta, which also includes the Air Flight and the Air Defense Battery.

Base: Valletta

Aviation: The Aviation Flight, 2nd Regiment, Armed Forces of Malta operates 2 Pilatus-Britten-Norman BN-2B-26 twin-engine light maritime patrol aircraft, 5 ex-RAF Bulldog T.1 light observation aircraft, and 1 Agusta-Bell AB-206A JetRanger, 2 Nardi-Hughes NH-500M (H.396M), 4 Agusta-Bell AB-47G-2, and 5 Aérospatiale AS.316B/D Alouette-III helicopters. Two Italian Air Force Agusta-Bell AB-212 helicopters are stationed on Malta for training and search-and-rescue duties. The fifth Bulldog was acquired during 7-01.

PATROL CRAFT [PC]

♦ 3 ex-German Kondor-I class
Bldr: VEB Peenewerft, Wolgast

	Laid down	L	In serv.
P 29 (ex-*Boltenhagen,* BG 31, ex-GS 09)	8-10-69	22-5-70	19-9-70
P 30 (ex-*Ueckermünde,* GS 01, ex-G 411)	20-8-68	27-2-69	27-6-69
P 31 (ex-*Pasewalk,* GS 05, ex-G 423)	12-12-68	18-6-69	18-10-69

P 30 A. A. de Kruijf, 6-01

P 29—outboard P 31 Dieter Wolf, 4-00

D: 339 tons (361 fl) **S:** 20 kts **Dim:** 51.98 × 7.12 × 2.30
A: 1 quadruple 14.5-mm 93-cal. AA
Electronics: Radar: 1 Furuno FR 80310 nav.; 1 Decca 1229 nav.
M: 2 Kolomna Type 40DM diesels; 2 CP props; 4,408 bhp (4,000 sust.)
Range: 1,800/15 **Crew:** 20 tot.

Remarks: After the unification of Germany, had been incorporated in the German Maritime Border Guard (*Bundesgrenzschutz-See*) but were not used operationally. P 30 and P 31 transferred to Malta in 7-92. P 29 was transferred 24-7-97; the reported name *La Vallette* is in error. The 23-mm gunmount has an on-mount lead-computing sight and replaced two single 12.7-mm mg in 1999.

PATROL BOATS [PB]

Note: A single U.S. Coast Guard Marine Protector-class (87 ft.) patrol boat was ordered from Bollinger Shipyards, Lockport, La., on 30-7-01 for delivery on 15-11-02.

♦ 2 ex-Swedish M 501 class
Bldr: . . . (In serv. 1969–71)

P . . . P . . .

D: 15 tons (fl) **S:** 14 kts **Dim:** 14.60 × 4.20 × 0.90
A: . . . **Electronics:** Radar: 1 Decca RM 914C nav.
M: 2 diesels; 2 props; . . . bhp **Crew:** 7 tot.

Remarks: Former Swedish Coastal Artillery Service minelaying launches. Delivered 8-00. Aluminum alloy hulls. May not have entered maritime squadron service.

♦ 2 ex-German Bremse (GB 23) class
Bldr: VEB Yachtswerf, Berlin (In serv. 1971–72)

P 32 (ex-GS 20, ex-G 733) P 33 (ex-GS 22, ex-G 722)

P 33 Jim Sanderson, 2001

D: 25 tons light (48 fl) **S:** 17 kts **Dim:** 22.59 (20.97 wl) × 4.70 × 1.60
A: 1 12.7-mm mg **Electronics:** Radar: 1 Furuno FR 80310 nav.
M: 1 Motorenwerke Rosslau Type 6VD 18/15 AL 1 diesel; 1 prop; 510 bhp
Range: 300/12 **Fuel:** 485 liters **Crew:** 6 tot.

Remarks: Former East German Border Guard patrol craft acquired from the German Sea Border Guard (*Bundesgrenzschutz-See*) in 7-92.

♦ 2 ex-U.S. Swift Mk II class
Bldr: Sewart Seacraft, Berwick, La. (In serv. 1968)

P 23 (ex-U.S. 50NS6823) P 24 (ex-U.S. 50NS6824)

P 23—with Bremse-class patrol boats P 32 and P 33 and a Kondor-class patrol craft in the background; note the canvas-covered former twin 12.7-mm mount tub and the Adcock-type VHFD/F atop the pilothouse Dieter Wolf, 4-00

D: 22.5 tons (fl) **S:** 25 kts **Dim:** 15.6 × 4.12 × 1.5
A: 1 12.7-mm mg **Electronics:** Radar: 1 Furuno FR 80310 nav.
M: 2 G.M. Detroit Diesel 12V71T diesels; 2 props; 960 bhp **Electric:** 6 kw tot.
Range: 400/22 **Endurance:** 24–36 hr **Crew:** 6 tot.

Remarks: Donated in 1-71. The twin 12.7-mm mg mount atop the pilothouse is no longer carried, the combination mortar/12.7-mm mount aft has been reduced to a single 12.7-mm mount, the radar has been replaced, and an Adcock-type VHFD/F antenna has been added.

Disposal note: U.S.-donated launch P 26 was sold in 2000 for use as a fishing boat.

SERVICE CRAFT

♦ 1 ex-U.S. Navy LCVP Mk 7 utility launch [WYFL]
Bldr: Gulfstream Corp. (In serv. 1965)

L 1 (ex-36VP6564)

L 1 Dieter Wolf, 4-00

D: 13.5 tons (fl) **S:** 9 kts **Dim:** 10.90 × 3.21 × 1.04 (aft)
M: 1 G.M. Gray Marine 64HN9 diesel; 1 prop; 225 bhp
Range: 110/9 **Crew:** 4 tot.

Remarks: Donated by the U.S. Navy in 1-87. GRP construction. Can carry 36 personnel or 3.5 tons of cargo in the 5.24 × 2.29–m cargo well, which has a bow ramp. Used for local transportation at Valletta. Was in poor condition by 1-99 but has been refurbished and returned to service.

Note: The Maltese Protezzjoni Civili, based at Valletta, operates sister 12.5-ton, 33-kt, self-righting search-and-rescue lifeboats *Melita I* and *Melita II* and small outboard-powered runabouts RDT I and RDT II. Also based at Valletta are government-operated pollution cleanup craft *Pupilla, Ambjent,* and *Monka* and the service craft *Miggi.*

MARSHALL ISLANDS

Republic of the Marshall Islands

GOVERNMENT OF THE MARSHALL ISLANDS MARITIME AUTHORITY

Personnel (2001): 30 total

Base: Majuro

Note: Ship names are preceded by RMIS (Republic of the Marshall Islands Ship)

PATROL BOATS [WPB]

♦ **1 ASI 315 design**
Bldr: Transfield ASI Pty, South Coogie, Western Australia (In serv. 29-6-91)

03 Lomor (ex-*Ionmeto 3*)

Lomor (03) W. D. Souter, 12-92

D: 165 tons (fl) **S:** 21 kts **Dim:** 31.50 (28.60 wl) × 8.10 × 2.12
A: 3 single 12.7-mm mg **Electronics:** Radar: 1 Furuno 1011 nav.
M: 2 Caterpillar 3516 diesels; 2 props; 2,820 bhp **Electric:** 116 kw tot.
Range: 2,500/12 **Fuel:** 27.9 tons **Endurance:** 10 days
Crew: 3 officers, 14 enlisted

Remarks: "Pacific Patrol Boat" design winner for the Australian foreign aid program. Ordered in 1989. Sisters are in Papua New Guinea, Vanuatu, Fiji, Western Samoa, and Solomon Islands service. Guns not normally mounted. Is to be refitted in Australia during 2006 to extend service to 2014.

Note: Former U.S. Navy landing craft–type ferries YFU 76 and YFU 77 were acquired 1-12-87 from the U.S. Department of the Interior (which received them from the USN on 1-12-84) for use by a Marshall Islands government civil agency for interisland public transportation. Also in use by the civil agency are former LCU 1552 and LCM(8)-class LCMs 6057 and 15967. The U.S. Coast Guard donated White (133-ft.)-class navaids tender *White Lupine* (WLM 546) to the private Marshall Islands Diabetics Reversal Program in 1998–99. The U.S. Army maintains Halter Marine Interceptor 41–class patrol craft HSPC 1 and HSPC 2 in the Marshall Islands to patrol its facilities there.

MAURITANIA

Islamic Republic of Mauritania

Personnel (2001): Approx. 500 total (40 officers), including 220 naval infantry

Bases: Headquarters and dockyard at Port Friendship, Nouakchott, with minor facilities at Port Etienne, Nouadhibou, and several coastal radar stations

Maritime Aviation: Two Piper Cheyenne II twin-turboprop aircraft were delivered in 1981 for coastal surveillance duties. Capable of 7-hour, 1,525-n.m. patrols, they have a belly-mounted Bendix RDR 1400 radar.

PATROL CRAFT [PC]

♦ **1 French PATRA class** Bldr: C.N. Auroux, Arcachon

	Laid down	L	In serv.
P-411 El Nasr (ex-*Dix Juillet;* ex-*Rapière,* P 674)	15-2-81	3-6-81	1-11-81

El Nasr (P-411) Y. Kerautret, 3-98

D: 115 tons (148 fl) **S:** 26.3 kts **Dim:** 40.70 (35.40 wl) × 5.90 × 1.55
A: 1 40-mm 60-cal. Bofors AA; 1 20-mm 70-cal. Oerlikon Mk 10 AA; 2 single 12.7-mm mg
Electronics: Radar: 1 Decca 1226 nav.
M: 2 Wärtsilä UD 33V12 diesels; 2 CP props; 5,000 bhp (4,340 sust.)
Electric: 120 kw tot. **Range:** 750/20; 1,500/15; 1,750/10
Crew: 2 officers, 18 enlisted (accomm. for 27 tot.)

Remarks: Built on speculation, acquired by French Navy 1-11-81, and then sold to Mauritania, commissioning 14-5-82. Renamed in 1988. Overhauled and re-engined in 1993–94.

PATROL BOATS [PB]

♦ **4 Indian Mandovi class** Bldr: Garden Reach DY, Calcutta (In serv. 1990)

D: 15 tons (fl) **S:** 24 kts **Dim:** 15.0 × 3.6 × 0.8
A: 1 7.62-mm mg **Electronics:** Radar: 1 Furuno FR 8030 nav.
M: 2 MWM TD-232 VI 2 diesels; 2 Hamilton waterjets; 750 bhp
Range: 240/12 **Crew:** 8 tot.

Remarks: Same basic design was also built for Mauritius by the designer, Mandovi Marine.

MINISTRY OF FISHERIES
(Délégation à la Surveillance des Pêches et au Contrôle en Mer)

Note: The ships are painted gray and carry the words "Surveillance Maritime" in large black letters on either side amidships.

FISHERIES PATROL SHIPS [WPS]

♦ **1 Arguin class**
Bldr: Fassmer Werft, Berne/Motzen, Germany (In serv. 17-7-00)

Arguin

Arguin Fassmer, 7-00

D: approx. 1,000 tons (fl) **S:** 16 kts (13.6 on one engine)
Dim: 54.50 (48.00 pp) × 10.60 × 4.90 (max.)
M: 2 MaK 6M20 diesels; 1 Lips CP prop; 2,736 bhp—200-shp Schottel bow-thruster
Electric: 522 kw tot. (3 × 174 kw, Caterpillar 3306 DI diesels driving)
Range: 15,000/. . . **Endurance:** 22 days
Crew: 13 tot. (accomm. for 32)

Remarks: Ordered 10-98; hull subcontracted to Yantar Verf, Kaliningrad, Russia. Has a 9.8 × 3.4–m, 25-kt Fassmer Type MP990 "daughter boat" inspection launch on a centerline ramp at the stern; the craft is propelled by two 230-bhp diesels driving waterjets. Based at Nouadhibou. Special sand filters are fitted to protect the machinery. Is equipped for fire fighting with a 200-m^3/min firepump.

♦ **1 Jura class** Bldr: Hall Russell & Co., Aberdeen, Scotland (In serv. 1975)

N'Madi (ex-*Criscella,* ex-*Jura*)

D: 778 tons (1,285 fl) **S:** 16.5 kts **Dim:** 59.6 × 10.7 × 4.4
A: small arms **Electronics:** Radar: 2 Decca . . . nav.
M: 2 British Polar SP112VS-F diesels; 1 CP prop; 4,200 bhp
Endurance: 18 days **Crew:** 28 tot.

Remarks: 885 grt. Former Department of Agriculture and Fisheries for Scotland fisheries protection ship, sold commercial to J. Marr, Ltd., in 1-88 and chartered to Mauritania in 7-89 for fisheries protection and offshore patrol vessel duties. Purchased by the German government and donated outright to Mauritania in 1991. Same design (with different engines) is employed for the Royal Navy's Island-class offshore patrol vessels. Has a passive tank stabilization system.

FISHERIES PATROL SHIPS [WPS] *(continued)*

N'Madi—as *Jura;* now painted with a dark gray hull and light gray superstructure
H&L Van Ginderen, 10-81

♦ **1 ex-Spanish former submarine rescue ship**
Bldr: Izar, La Carraca, Cadiz

	Laid down	L	In serv.
B-551 VOUM-LEGLEITA (ex-*Poseidón,* A 12; ex-AS 01; ex-BS 1; ex-RA 6)	28-11-61	21-3-62	8-8-64

D: 951 tons (1,107 fl) **S:** 15 kts **Dim:** 55.90 (49.80 pp) × 10.00 × 4.80
A: 2 single 20-mm 70-cal. Oerlikon Mk 10 AA
Electronics: Radar: 2 Decca TM 626 nav.
M: 2 Izar-Sulzer 6MG42 diesels; 1 CP prop; 3,200 bhp tot.
Range: 4,640/14 **Fuel:** 190 m^3 **Crew:** 6 officers, 54 enlisted (in Spanish service)

Remarks: Former submarine rescue ship, salvage ship, and diving tender, retired from the Spanish Navy in 1997. Transferred 1-00 after a refit for use as an offshore patrol vessel and fisheries patrol ship. Is equipped for fighting fires aboard other ships and has an ocean towing capability and salvage pumps.

FISHERIES PATROL CRAFT [WPC]

♦ **1 French modified Espadon 50 class**
Bldr: Leroux & Lotz, Lorient (In serv. 3-94)

ABU BEKR BEN AMER

Abu Bekr ben Amer Bernard Prèzelin, 8-01

D: 290 tons (360 fl) **S:** 22 kts **Dim:** 54.00 (48.50 pp) × 9.80 × 2.30 (2.75 props)
A: 2 single 12.7-mm mg **Electronics:** Radar: 1 Decca 2690 ARPA nav.
M: 2 SACM-RVR UD 33V 12M6 diesels; 2 CP props; 5,700 bhp—2 90-kw electric auxiliary propulsion motors; 250 shp (7.5 kts)
Electric: 370 kw tot. (2 × 150-kw, 1 × 70-kw diesel-driven sets)
Range: 1,400/23; 4,500/12; 14,000/7.5 (electric power)
Fuel: 55 tons **Endurance:** 21 days
Crew: 4 officers, 9 petty officers, 6 ratings (39 tot. accomm.)

Remarks: Ordered 8-92. Known colloquially as the *"Abba."* Commercial design, employing a deep-vee hullform capable of operating at speed in a State 4 sea. Originally ordered for the French Navy, but construction was delayed by the closing of the original contract yard and the transfer of part of the contract to CMN, which also acquired the design rights. Refitted in 2001 at DCN, Lorient. Former pennant number P-541 is no longer carried.
Hull systems: Has a stern embarkation ramp for an EDL 700 7-m, rigid inflatable, waterjet-propelled inspection boat capable of 30 kts. Can also carry up to 22 passengers. A 400-m^3/hr firefighting monitor is installed, and there are two 7-m^3 capacity spill recovery holding tanks.

Note: The customs service operates the 20.5-ton, 14-m Amgram 14–class patrol boat *Dah Ould Bah,* delivered in 3-96.

MAURITIUS

NATIONAL COAST GUARD ORGANIZATION

Personnel (2001): 750 total, including personnel manning the coastal observation stations; authorized strength was 950 total. Most officers are seconded from the Indian Navy. The organization is subordinated to the national police.

Base: Port Louis, plus 21 small coastal observation stations

Maritime Aviation: One Hindustan Aeronautic–built Dornier Do-228 with MEL surveillance radar and one Pilatus-Britten-Norman Defender are in use for coastal surveillance. One Eurocopter AS.350B Écureuil light helicopter was acquired in 1997 for use aboard the *Vigilant,* and India has provided three Chetak light helicopters, the third of which arrived during 4-99.

Note: All patrol craft and boats have the words "Coast Guard" painted in large white letters on their sides. Pennant numbers are no longer worn. India is providing assistance with the establishment of a coastal radar surveillance system.

PATROL SHIP [WPS]

♦ **1 Vigilant class** Bldr: ASMAR, Talcahuano, Chile

	Laid down	L	In serv.
VIGILANT	7-94	6-12-95	10-5-96

Vigilant Brian Morrison, 2-01

D: 1,350 tons (1,650 fl) **S:** 18 kts
Dim: 75.00 (70.50 wl; 67.50 pp) × 14.00 × 3.90
A: 1 twin 40-mm 60-cal. Mk 5 Bofors AA; 2 single 12.7-mm M2 mg; 1 AS.350B Écureuil helicopter
Electronics: Radar: 2 Kelvin Hughes . . . nav.
M: 4 Caterpillar 3516 diesels; 2 CP props; 11,780 bhp—670-shp azimuthal bow-thruster
Electric: 1,625 kw tot. (3 × 500 kw, Caterpillar 3412 diesels driving; 1 × 125 kw, Caterpillar 3306 diesel driving; all 380 V, 50 Hz)
Range: 8,000/19 **Endurance:** 30 days
Crew: 8 officers, 45 enlisted + 2 aircrew + 20 passengers or 100 survivors

Remarks: Ordered in spring 1994 for $14.6 million, with an option for a second and plans for a possible additional two; constructed in cooperation with Western Canada Marine Group. No further order had been placed as of 12-98, however. Designed by Polar Associates, Canada. Intended for fisheries and economic exclusion zone patrol, search-and-rescue duties, pollution control, and emergency towing. A half-sister was built in Ireland for the Irish Navy in 1998–99. Refitted at Mumbai Naval Dockyard, India, from 12-99 to 11-4-00 to correct propeller shaft problems and other engineering deficiencies; shaft seals were again repaired at Mumbai from 3-01 to 9-01.
Hull systems: Has a deep-vee hullform with twin rudders and a signature-reduction superstructure shape to reduce radar signature when ship is coming toward the radar. There are a hangar and flight deck for one small helicopter, although the hangar is said to be cramped. Two fire monitors are atop the hangar, with a single 600-m^3/hr firepump. Has a Flume-type stabilization system and a four-berth sick bay. Was originally intended to achieve 22 kts but can reach only 18.
Combat systems: The 40-mm gunmount was donated by India and is locally controlled.

PATROL CRAFT [WPC]

♦ **1 ex-Indian SDB Mk 3 class**
Bldr: Garden Reach Dockyard, Calcutta (In serv. 1984)

GUARDIAN (ex-*Ajay,* T . . .)

Guardian Arjun Sarup, 4-99

D: 167 tons (210 fl) **S:** 30 kts (28 sust.) **Dim:** 37.80 (32.20 pp) × 7.50 × 1.85
A: 2 single 40-mm 60-cal. Bofors Mk 3 AA
Electronics: Radar: 1 Bharat 1245 nav.
M: 2 MTU 16V 538 TB92 diesels; 2 props; 6,820 bhp **Crew:** 32 tot.

Remarks: Donated in 1993 by India. May also have a centerline cruise diesel engine, as on earlier Indian Navy craft of this general type. Refitted in 2001.

PATROL BOATS [WPB]

♦ 4 Heavy Duty Boat RIB patrol launches
Bldr: M/S Praga Marine, India (In serv. 2000)

HDB 01 HDB 02 HDB 03 HDB 04

D: 5 tons (fl) **S:** 45 kts **Dim:** 8.90 × 3.50 × 0.45
M: 2 Johnson gasoline outboards; 400 bhp
Range: 300/35 **Crew:** 4 tot. + 4 passengers

Remarks: Are used for search-and-rescue and patrol/interception duties. Painted bright orange. An option exists for the purchase of six more.

♦ 1 leased Indian P-2000 class
Bldr: Anderson Marine Pty, Kadras/Goa SY (In serv. 16-10-97)

Observer (ex-C 139)

Observer Arjun Sarup, 4-01

D: 49 tons (fl) **S:** 40 kts **Dim:** 20.80 (18.00 pp) × 5.80 × 1.00
A: 1 7.62-mm mg **Electronics:** Radar: 1 Furuno . . . I-band nav.
M: 2 Deutz-MWM TBD 234 V12 diesels outboard (823 bhp each), 1 Deutz-MWM TBD 234 V8 550-bhp loiter diesel centerline; 3 Hamilton 402-series waterjets; 2,200 bhp
Range: 600/15 **Crew:** 4 officers, 6 enlisted

Remarks: Leased and recommissioned in 4-01 as an "Interceptor Boat." One of 10 ordered in 9-90 for the Indian Coast Guard. Built in cooperation with Seaking Industries, with design services from Amgram, Ltd., Sussex, U.K. GRP hulls laid up by Anderson Marine employ molds originally built by Watercraft, Shoreham, U.K., for the Royal Navy *Archer* class.

♦ 2 Soviet Zhuk class (Project 1400M) (In serv. 3-12-89)

Rescuer Retriever

Retriever—outboard the *Guardian* Arjun Sarup, 4-99

D: 35.9 tons (39.7 fl) **S:** 30 kts
Dim: 23.80 (21.70 wl) × 5.00 (3.80 wl) × 1.00 (hull)
A: 2 twin 12.7-mm 79-cal. Utës-M mg
Electronics: Radar: 1 Furuno . . . nav.
M: 2 M-401B diesels; 2 props; 2,200 bhp
Electric: 48 kw total (2 × 21-kw, 1 × 6-kw diesel sets)
Range: 500/13.5 **Endurance:** 5 days **Crew:** 3 officers, 10 enlisted

Remarks: Were a gift of the Soviet Union originally offered in the early 1980s. Only one engine was operable on the *Rescuer* as of 4-01, and both are to be docked and overhauled.

♦ 5 Mandovi class Bldr: Garden Reach SY, Calcutta (In serv. 1989–90)

Barracuda Castor Marlin Polaris Sirius

D: 15 tons (fl) **S:** 24 kts **Dim:** 15.0 × 3.6 × 0.8
A: 1 7.62-mm mg **Electronics:** Radar: 1 Furuno FR 8030 nav.
M: 2 Deutz-MWM TD-232 V-12 diesels; 2 Hamilton waterjets; 750 bhp
Range: 240/12 **Crew:** 8 tot.

Remarks: Nine were ordered 24-7-87; two were delivered during 1-89, the rest 19-1-90. Designed by Mandovi Marine Private, Ltd. Resemble oilfield crewboats and have "Coast Guard" painted on sides. By late 1998, only five remained in inventory, and of those, two were inactive for lack of spares.

Note: Also in service are two Rover 663 FPC RIB launches donated by Australia, and 30 other outboard-powered, Avon, Halmatic, and Zodiac RIBs for search-and-rescue duties.

MEXICO

United Mexican States

MARINA NACIONAL

Personnel (2002): 37,000 total, including 8,600 marines

Bases/Organization: The Mexican Navy is divided between the Gulf of Mexico and Pacific Commands, with headquarters at Veracrúz and Acapulco, respectively. Within the two commands are three naval regions, each further divided into zones and sectors.

The Gulf Command consists of the North Naval Region at Veracrúz, with Naval Zone I at Ciudad Madero (sectors at Matamoros and La Pesca) and Naval Zone III at Veracrúz (sectors at Tuxpan and Coatzacoalos); the Eastern Naval Region at Frontera, with Naval Zone V at Frontera and Naval Zone VII at Lerma (sectors at Champotón and Ciudad del Carmen); and the Caribbean Naval Region at Chetumal, with Naval Zone IX at Yucalpetén (sector at Progreso) and Naval Zone XI at Chetumal (sectors at Isla Mujeres and Cozumel).

The Pacific Command includes the Northwest Naval Region at Mazatlán, with Naval Zone II at Ensenada, Naval Zone IV at La Paz (with sectors at Puerto Cortés and Santa Rosalia), Naval Zone VI at Guaymas (sector at Puerto Peñasco), and Naval Zone VIII at Mazatlán (sector at Topolobampo); the Western Naval Region at Lázaro Cárdenas, with Naval Zone X at San Blas, Naval Zone XII at Puerto Vallarta, Naval Zone XIV at Manzanillo (sector at Isla Socorro), and Naval Zone XVI at Lázaro Cárdenas; and the Southwestern Naval Region at Acapulco, with Naval Zone XVIII at Acapulco (sector at Ixtapa-Zihuatanejo), Naval Zone XX at Salina Cruz (sector at Puerto Angel), and Naval Zone XXII at Puerto Madero. Naval air bases are located at Mexico City, Campeche, Las Bajadas, Tulúm, Chetumal, Puerto Cortés, Isla Mujeres, La Paz, Salina Cruz, and Tapachula. The three separately administered naval bases are at Tuxpan (Veracrúz), Ensenada (Baja California), and Lázaro Cárdenas (Michoacán).

Marines: Headquarters for the marines is at Mexico City. Reorganized again in 1998, the marine corps now has three infantry brigades, each with three battalions: the 1st Brigade, headquartered at Veracrúz; the 2nd, headquartered at Acapulco; and the 4th, headquartered at Manzanillo. In addition, there are nine infantry battalions assigned one-each at Mexico City (the Guardias Presidenciales 24th Battalion), Ensenada, La Paz, Guaymas, Lerna, Mazatlán, Yucalpetén, Chetumal, and Lázaro Cárdenas. There is also the 1st Parachute Naval Fusilier Brigade at Mexico City and a Coastal Defense Group headquartered at Veracrúz with its 1st Artillery Battalion at Frontera and 2nd Artillery Battalion at Puerto Madero.

Naval Aviation: The Mexican Navy operates 8 CASA 212-200 coastal surveillance aircraft (one equipped as a VIP transport), 1 De Havilland DHC-5D Buffalo, 1 Fokker F-27, 2 Antonov An-32, and 43 light fixed-wing aircraft, including 1 Learjet 24D, 12 Beech B-55, 1 Cessna 402, 1 Beech King Air 90, 4 Rockwell Turbo-Commander 1000, 1 Piper Aztec, 1 Grumman HU-16 Albatross amphibian, 1 Cessna 337G, 1 Beech D590, 1 Cessna 206A, 1 Cessna 441, 13 Maule MX-7-180, 3 Beech T-34 Mentor, and 2 Mexican-designed Tonatiuh II. Helicopters include 10 MD Helicopters MD 90 Explorer, 12 Mil Mi-8/17, 4 Mil Mi-2 Hoplite, 4 Eurocopter AS.355 Fennec, 11 MBB BO-105CB, 4 McDonnell-Douglas MD 500E and 1 MD 500, 3 Hughes 269A, 2 Aérospatiale Alouette-III, 1 Robinson R44 Clipper, and 2 Bell UH-1H, plus 10 Aérospatiale AS.315 Lama helicopters for search-and-rescue duties and two float-equipped Robinson R22 Mariner and one RotorWay International Exec 162F trainers.

A naval "Cessna 183" was lost in a crash on 27-6-00 during an antidrug patrol. An additional 12 Mi-8 and/or Mi-17 helicopters are to be procured from Russia, and 10 more MD 90 Explorers may be purchased. All Explorers are to be armed with 70-mm rocket pods and 12.7-mm gatling machineguns.

A Bombardier DHC-8 Q200 turboprop transport (with an option for a second) was ordered 9-00 for delivery 9-01; the aircraft will be based at Mexico City. On 1-3-01, Embraer was awarded a contract for one EMB-145 AWACS aircraft (with Ericsson Erieye radar) and two EMB-145 maritime patrol aircraft for the Mexican Air Force.

During 12-01, Mexico requested 14 surplus SH-2G Super SeaSprite helicopters and three surplus P-3B Orion maritime patrol aircraft from the U.S.A.

Mexican Navy Mi-17 helicopter Mexican Navy, 1994

Mexican Navy MD 90 Explorer helicopter MD Helicopters, 1999

Naval aviation is organized into six operational squadrons, a search-and-rescue squadron, and three training squadrons. Air bases are located at Mexico City, Las Bajadas, Tulúm, Campeche, Chetumal, Puerto Cortés, Isla Mujeres, La Paz, Salina Cruz, and Tapachula, with detachments of two Mil Mi-2 Hoplite SAR helicopters each at Acapulco and Veracrúz. Aircraft are organized as follows:

1st Grupo Aeronaval at Veracrúz:
- 1 EAEPM *(Escuadrón Aeronaval Embarcado de Patrulla Aeronaval):* BO-105CB and AS.355 Fennec helicopters
- 3 EA *(Escuadrón Aeronaval):* King Air 90, CASA 212, and PA-23 Aztec light transports
- 1 EATL *(Escuadrón de Apoyo Táctico y Logistico):* Mi-8MTV-1 helicopters
- EBS *(Escuadrón de Búsqueda y Salvamento):* BO-105CB SAR helicopters

2nd Grupo Aeronaval at Chetumal:
- 1 EA: CASA 212, PA-23 Aztec, Maule M-6, Aero Commander 680T, Tonatiuh II
- 3 EATL: Mi-8MTV-1 helicopters
- 4 EBR *(Escuadrón de Búsqueda y Rescate):* UH-1H, MD 500 helicopters

Independent detachments:
- 2 EA, Mexico City: Learjet 24D VIP transports, CASA 212-200, King Air 90, DHC-5D, and Turbo-Commander 1000 light transports
- 2 EATL, Teacapan: Mi-8MTV-1 helicopters
- 4 EA, La Paz: Cessna 182, Cessna 206, Cessna 210, Cessna 337G, B-55 Baron, CASA 212, and Twin Bonanza light transports; BO-105CB, AS.319B Alouette-III helicopters; 1 HU-16 Albatross amphibian
- 5 EA, Campeche: CASA 212, Cessna 402B, Cessna 404 light transports
- 6 EA, Tapachula: B-55 Baron light transports

Escuela de Aviación Naval, Veracrúz:
- *Escuadrón Primario:* Maule MX-7-180
- *Escuadrón Basico:* F33A/C Bonanza fixed-wing, MD 500E and UH-12E helicopters
- *Escuadrón Avanzado:* B-55 Baron

Coastal Defense: The Mexican Navy and Marine Corps are responsible for coast defense. U.S.-supplied 20-mm Mk 68 AA guns are mounted on Gama Goat vehicles and surplus 40-mm Bofors AA on M35 trucks to provide coastal region defenses. To defend naval bases, the marines have eight OTOBreda M56 howitzers and FIROS 6 rocket launchers mounted on trucks.

Note: During a 4-01 conference, Mexico and Venezuela agreed to coordinate their naval shipbuilding efforts.

The two *Gearing*-class destroyers have been retyped as patrol ships for this edition, due to their greatly reduced speed and the loss of their ASW capabilities.

FRIGATES [FF]

♦ 4 ex-U.S. Knox class

Bldrs: F-211: Lockheed SB, Seattle; F-213: Avondale SY, Westwego, La.; others: Todd SB, Seattle

	Laid down	L	In serv.
F-211 Ignacio Allende (ex-E-50; ex-*Stein,* FF 1065)	1-6-70	19-12-70	8-1-72
F-212 Mariano Abasolo (ex-E-51; ex-*Marvin Shields,* FF 1066)	12-4-68	23-10-69	10-4-71
F-213 Guadalupe Victoria (ex-E-52; ex-*Pharris,* FF 1094)	11-2-72	16-12-72	26-1-74
F-214 . . . . . . (ex-*Whipple,* FF 1062)	24-4-67	12-4-68	22-8-70

Ignacio Allende (F-211)—the only *Knox*-class frigate in service with a SAM launcher, although the system is not operational; photo shows old number *Ships of the World,* 8-99

Mariano Abasolo (F-212)—with old pennant number *Ships of the World,* 8-99

D: 3,130 tons light (4,260 fl) **S:** 27+ kts
Dim: 134.00 (126.49 wl) × 14.33 × 4.77 (7.83 over sonar)
A: 1 127-mm 54-cal. Mk 42 DP; 2 paired, fixed 324-mm Mk 32 Mod. 9 ASW TT; 1 . . . helicopter
Electronics:
Radar: 1 Raytheon SPS-64(V)9 nav.; 1 Raytheon SPS-10 surf. search; 1 Lockheed SPS-40B air search; 1 Western Electric SPG-53F gun f.c.
Sonar: EDO-G.E. SQS-26CX bow-mounted LF
TACAN: SRN-15A
EW: Raytheon SLQ-32(V)2 intercept; Mk 36 SRBOC decoy syst. (2 6-round Mk 137 RL); T Mk 6 Fanfare towed acoustic torpedo decoy
M: 1 set Westinghouse geared steam turbines; 1 prop; 35,000 shp
Boilers: 2 Combustion Engineering VsM, M-Type (F-211, F-214: Babcock & Wilcox D-Type); 84 kg/cm^2, 510° C
Electric: 3,000 kw tot. (3 × 750-kw turbogenerators, 1 × 750-kw diesel set)
Range: 4,300/20 **Fuel:** 750 tons max. **Crew:** 20 officers, 268 enlisted

Remarks: In late 1996, the U.S. Congress approved the transfer by sale of the first two during U.S. FY 97; they had been in reserve since 19-3-92 and 2-7-92, respectively. The two were formally transferred for $7 million each on 29-1-98 and underwent reactivation refits in Mexico. Mexico declined the offer of sister *Roark* (FF 1053) late in 1998; instead, the *Pharris,* in reserve since 15-4-92, was purchased on 2-2-00 and towed to Manzanillo, arriving 8-3-00 for reactivation in Mexico. The *Whipple,* placed in reserve on 14-2-92 by the U.S. Navy, was offered to Mexico in 1999 and transferred late in 2001, but before her transfer had to undergo some $437,000 in repairs for damage incurred during the making of the movie *Pearl Harbor;* the ship will also be activated in Mexico. With their relatively light effective armament, the ships are essentially gunboats. Redesignated *Fragatas* in 2001.
Hull systems: Bow bulwarks and a spray strake have been added forward to reduce deck wetness, a problem in this class; the addition added 9.1 tons and extended the overall length from the original 133.59 m. Antirolling fin stabilizers fitted. The Prairie/Masker bubbler system is fitted to hulls and propellers to reduce radiated noise.
Combat systems: Carry a Mk 68 gunfire-control system with SPG-53F radar. SLQ-32(V)1—later upgraded to (V)2—replaced WLR-1C as the EW suite. The Mk 15 Phalanx CIWS was not transferred with the ships. Instead, on F-211 only, a Mk 128 octuple launcher for the no-longer-operational U.S. Mk 25 Basic Point Defense System Sea Sparrow SAM was installed on the fantail in its place, and the equally obsolete radar director was reinstalled atop the hangar; the system is not operational, and no missiles were transferred. Although the Mk 112 octuple missile launcher for the ASROC ASW missile system was retained, no missiles were acquired for it, rendering it essentially useless. The ASW torpedo tubes are fixed, in the forward end of the hangar superstructure, aimed outboard at an angle of 45°. Have the Mk 114 ASW fire-control system. F-213 has the Mk 68 Mod. 13 gun f.c.s.; the others have Mk 68 Mod. 11.

♦ 2 ex-U.S. Bronstein class Bldr: Avondale SY, New Orleans

	Laid down	L	In serv.
F-201 Nicolás Bravo (ex-E-40; ex-*McCloy,* FF 1038)	15-9-61	9-6-62	21-10-63
F-202 Hermenegildo Galeana (ex-E-42; ex-*Bronstein,* FF 1037)	16-5-61	31-5-62	16-6-63

Hermenegildo Galeana (F-202)—note 57-mm DP gun added on the fantail; photo shows old number 1998

Nicolás Bravo (F-201)—prior to addition of the 57-mm gunmount and change of pennant number Mexican Navy, 1994

FRIGATES [FF] *(continued)*

D: 2,360 tons (2,650 fl) **S:** 24 kts **Dim:** 113.23 (106.68 wl) × 12.34 × 7.00
A: 1 twin 76.2-mm 50-cal. Mk 33 DP; 1 57-mm 70-cal. Bofors Mk 3 DP; 2 triple 324-mm Mk 32 ASW TT
Electronics:
Radar: 1 . . . nav.; 1 . . . surf. search; 1 Raytheon SPS-10F surf. search; 1 Lockheed SPS-40D air search; 1 Mk 35 f.c.
Sonar: SQS-26AXR bow-mounted LF
EW: removed
M: 1 set de Laval geared steam turbines; 1 prop; 20,000 shp
Boilers: 2 Foster-Wheeler; 42.2 kg/cm^2, 440° C
Range: 3,900/15 **Fuel:** 480 tons **Crew:** 17 officers, 190 enlisted

Remarks: First offered to Mexico in 1991; transferred 16-11-93 primarily for training duties. Had been decommissioned from the USN on 13-12-90 and 14-12-90, respectively. Redesignated *Fragatas* in 2001.
Hull systems: The portside Welin davit and boat have been removed.
Combat systems: The 76.2-mm gunmount is controlled by a Mk 56 gun fire-control system. Plans to install a Bofors 57-mm 70-cal. DP gun aft were not carried out. The helicopter facility on both is hampered by the lack of a full-sized hangar. Have a Mk 114 Mod. 7 ASW weapons-control system, but the ASW features have not been activated, as the SQS-26CX sonar was an early, developmental model of the system and is no longer supportable; the Mk 112 ASROC ASW missile launchers remain aboard, however, and there are probably no torpedoes available for the two triple mountings. WLR-1 and WLR-3 intercept equipment, the Mk 34 RBOC decoy rocket system, and the T Mk 6 Fanfare homing torpedo decoy system have been removed. Two modern navigation and search radars have been added to supplement the U.S. system aboard at transfer.

PATROL SHIPS [PS]

Note: The four U.S. *Abnaki*-class oceangoing tugs [ATA] are also used for ocean patrol work; see data under Auxiliaries.

♦ 4 Durango class
Bldrs: PO-151, PO-153: Tampico Naval SY No. 1, Tamanlipas; others: Salina Cruz Naval SY No. 8, Salina Cruz

	Laid down	L	In serv.
PO-151 Durango (ex-*Miguel Lerdo de Tejada*)	3-99	. . .	. . .
PO-152 Sonora (ex-*Melchior Ocampo*)	3-99	. . .	. . .
PO-153 Guanajuato	. . .	13-12-01	. . .
PO-154 Veracrúz	. . .	17-12-01	. . .

D: 1,135 tons (1,340 fl) **S:** 18 kts **Dim:** 74.4 × 10.5 × 2.90 (3.5 over props)
A: 1 57-mm 70-cal. Bofors Mk 3 DP; 1 40-mm 60-cal. AA
Electronics:
Radar: 1 . . . nav. (X-band); 1 . . . surf./air search (S-band)
E/O: 1 Saab Dynamics EOS-450 optronic f.c. for 57-mm gun
M: 2 Caterpillar 3616 V16 diesels; 2 props; 12,394 bhp
Range: 3,830/18 **Fuel:** 227.4 tons **Endurance:** 20 days
Crew: 11 officers, 65 enlisted + 16 passengers

Remarks: An improved version of the *Sierra* class; the differences are not yet available, but the above data are approximately correct. Four Bofors 57-mm Mk 3 DP gunmounts were ordered early in 2000. Have no helicopter facilities. PO = *Patrulla Oceánica.*

♦ 4 Sierra (Holzinger 2000) class
Bldrs: PO-141, PO-143: Tampico Naval SY No. 1, Tamanlipas; others: Salina Cruz Naval SY No. 8, Salina Cruz

	Laid down	L	In serv.
PO-141 Justo Sierra Méndez (ex-C-2001)	19-1-98	1-6-98	9-99
PO-142 Benito Juárez (ex-C-2002, ex-*Rosas Coria*)	19-1-98	23-7-98	9-99
PO-143 Guillermo Prieto	1-6-98	3-99	2001?
PO-144 Matias Romero	23-7-98	3-99	2001?

Benito Juárez (PO-142)—with old pennant number
Mexican Navy, via Julio Montes, 1999

D: 1,135 tons (1,340 fl) **S:** 18 kts **Dim:** 74.4 × 10.5 × 2.90 (3.5 over props)
A: 1 57-mm 70-cal. Bofors Mk 3 DP; 1 MD-902 Explorer helicopter
Electronics:
Radar: 1 . . . nav. (X-band); 1 . . . surf./air search (S-band)
E/O: 1 Saab Dynamics EOS-450 optronic f.c. for 57-mm gun
M: 2 Caterpillar 3616 V16 diesels; 2 props; 12,394 bhp
Range: 3,830/18 **Fuel:** 227.4 tons **Endurance:** 20 days
Crew: 11 officers, 65 enlisted + 16 passengers

Remarks: Ordered in spring 1997. Planned class total was 16 but has been reduced to eight, with the second group of four now considered to be a separate class. PO = *Patrulla Oceánica.*
Hull systems: Essentially a repeat of the Águila class but with a flush-decked hull of slightly greater beam and greater freeboard and a superstructure with a shape intended to reduce radar signature. The boats are carried in pockets on either beam, and fin stabilizers are fitted. A Boston Whaler Piranha-class chase boat is to be carried at the stern. Have the Vosper VT300 fin stabilization system. The first unit was some 165 tons heavier at completion than designed.
Combat systems: The first two were equipped with Bofors 40-mm Mk 1 Mod. 2 guns and Elsag electro-optical directors.

♦ 4 Águila class
Bldrs: PO-131, PO-133: Tampico Naval SY No. 1; others: Salina Cruz Naval SY No. 20

	Laid down	L	In serv.
PO-131 Sebastián José Holzinger (ex-C-01, ex-*Capitán de Navio Sebastián José Holzinger, ex-Uxmal*)	1-6-86	1-6-88	23-11-91
PO-132 Blas Godinez (ex-C-02, ex-*Capitán de Navio Blas Godinez Brito,* ex-*Mitla*)	7-86	1-6-88	21-4-92
PO-133 José María de la Vega Gonzalez (ex-C-03, ex-*Brigadier José María de la Vega Gonzalez,* ex-*Peten*)	. . .	22-3-92	6-3-94
PO-134 Gral. Felipe Berriozabal (ex-C-04, ex-*Anahuac*)	. . .	21-4-91	5-5-93

José María de la Vega Gonzalez (PO-133)—with old pennant number
Mexican Navy, 1994

Sebastián José Holzinger (PO-131)—with old pennant number
Ships of the World, 7-00

D: 1,022 tons (1,290 fl) **S:** 22 kts **Dim:** 74.4 (70.0 pp) × 10.35 × 3.4 (max.)
A: 1 twin 40-mm 60-cal. Mk 1 Mod. 2 Bofors AA; 1 BO-105CB helicopter
Electronics: Radar: 2 Raytheon SPS-64(V)6A nav.
M: 2 MTU 20V956 TB92 diesels; 2 props; 13,320 bhp (10,140 sust.)
Range: 3,830/18 **Fuel:** 227.4 tons **Endurance:** 20 days
Crew: 11 officers, 64 enlisted + 16 passengers

Remarks: A smaller variant of the Spanish-built Halcón design, with higher speed. Plans announced 23-6-83 called for construction of nine units at four naval shipyards, but the total was reduced to four in 10-84. PO = *Patrulla Oceánica.*
Hull systems: Have a smaller helicopter deck than the Halcón class, less topweight, and two engine rooms (vice one). Displacement grew by 115 tons during construction. PO-133 and PO-134 have fin stabilization systems.

PATROL SHIPS [PS] *(continued)*

Combat systems: Were to have had an AESN NA-18 optronic fire control system and Bofors 57-mm 70-cal. DP gun, but weight considerations forced installation of an older, locally controlled weapon and the 57-mm guns have since been mounted on destroyers.

♦ 6 Halcón class

Bldr: Izar (formerly E.N. Bazán), San Fernando, Cadiz, Spain

	Laid down	L	In serv.
PO-121 VIRGILIO URIBE (ex-C-11, ex-*Cadete Virgilio Uribe Robles*)	1-7-81	13-12-81	10-9-82
PO-122 JOSÉ AZUETA (ex-C-12, ex-*Teniente José Azueta Abad*)	7-9-81	29-1-82	15-10-82
PO-123 PEDRO SAINZ DE BARBRANDA (ex-C-13, ex-*Capitán de Fragata Pedro Sainz de Barbranda Borreyo*)	22-10-81	26-2-82	3-83
PO-124 CARLOS CASTILIO BRETÓN (ex-C-14, ex-*Comodoro Carlos Castilio Bretón Barrero*)	11-11-81	26-2-82	9-6-82
PO-125 OTHÓN P. BLANCO (ex-C-15, ex-*Vice Almirante Othón P. Blanco Nuñez de Caceres*)	18-12-81	26-3-82	24-2-83
PO-126 ANGEL ORTIZ (ex-C-16, ex-*Contralmirante Angel Ortiz Monasterio*)	30-12-81	23-4-82	24-3-83

Othón P. Blanco (PO-125)—with BO-105 helicopter on deck aft; photo shows old pennant number H&L Van Ginderen, 6-94

Othón P. Blanco (PO-125)—with old pennant number H&L Van Ginderen, 6-94

D: 845 tons (988 fl) **S:** 21 kts **Dim:** 67.00 (63.00 pp) × 10.50 × 3.50 (max.)
A: 1 40-mm 70-cal. Bofors AA; 1 BO-105CB liaison helicopter
Electronics:
Radar: 1 Decca AC 1226 nav.
TACAN: SRN-15
E/O: 1 Matra Défense Naja optronic gun f.c.
M: 2 MTU 20V956 TB91 diesels; 2 props; 13,320 bhp **Electric:** 710 kw
Range: 5,000/18 **Crew:** 10 officers, 42 enlisted

Remarks: Ordered in late 1980 for use in patrolling the 200-n.m. economic zone. Generally identical to ships built for Argentina, but with more-powerful engines and a longer helicopter deck. Names were revised in 1993. Commissioning of PO-124 was delayed by an accident; originally completed 4-11-82. Pennant numbers were changed from GH-01 through GH-06 in 1992 and from the C (*Corbeta*) series in 2001. PO = *Patrulla Oceánica.*

♦ 2 ex-U.S. Gearing FRAM I class

Bldr: Bethlehem Steel, Staten Island, N.Y.

	Laid down	L	In serv.
D-101 QUETZALCÓATL (ex-*Ilhuaicamina,* E-10; ex-*Quetzalcóatl,* E-03; ex-*Vogelgesang,* DD 862)	3-8-44	15-1-45	28-4-45
D-102 NETZAHUALCÓYOTL (ex-E-11; ex-E-04; ex-*Steinaker,* DD 863)	1-9-44	13-2-45	26-5-45

Netzahualcóyotl (D-102)—with old pennant number Larry R. Coté, 9-94

Netzahualcóyotl (D-102)—with old pennant number H&L Van Ginderen, 10-96

D: 2,448 tons light (3,690 fl) **S:** approx. 15 kts
Dim: 119.03 × 12.52 × 4.60 (6.55 sonar)
A: 2 twin 127-mm 38-cal. Mk 30 DP; 1 57-mm 70-cal. Bofors SAK 70 Mk 2 DP
Electronics:
Radar: 1 Kelvin-Hughes 17/9 nav.; 1 Raytheon SPS-10 surf. search; 1 Lockheed SPS-40B (D-102: Westinghouse SPS-37) air search; 1 Western Electric Mk 25 f.c.
EW: WLR-1 intercept
M: 2 sets G.E. geared steam turbines; 2 props; 60,000 shp
Boilers: 4 Babcock & Wilcox; 43.3 kg/cm², 454° C **Electric:** 1,200 kw tot.
Range: 1,500/31; 5,800/12 **Fuel:** 650 tons **Crew:** approx. 275 tot.

Remarks: Transferred to Mexico by sale 24-2-82, as intended replacements for the then-two *Fletcher*-class destroyers. Both were renumbered in 1993, and D-101 was also renamed. Have unusual heat signature-suppressant stack caps. After FRAM conversion, could make 30 kts, but have lost a great deal of speed in recent years, probably due to boiler problems. Names and pennant numbers were again changed during 2001. D = *Destructore.*
Combat systems: Have the Mk 37 gun fire-control system with one radar director to control the 127-mm guns. A modern Bofors 57-mm gun was added forward of the bridge during the early 1990s, and the Mk 112 ASROC ASW missile launcher and two triple Mk 32 ASW torpedo tube sets had been removed by 9-94. The helicopter facility is no longer used.

Disposal note: U.S. *Fletcher*-class patrol ship (ex-destroyer) *Cuitlahuac* (E-01; ex-*John Rodgers,* DD 574) was stricken 16-7-01. U.S. *Charles Lawrence*-class patrol ship *Coahila* (E-21; ex-*Vincente Guerrero;* ex-*Coahila,* B-07; ex-*Barber,* APD 57, ex-DE 161) was also stricken 16-7-01, along with U.S. *Crosley*-class patrol ships *Usumacinta* (E-20; ex-*Miguel Hidalgo;* ex-*Usumacinta,* B-06; ex-*Don O. Woods,* APD 118, ex-DE 721) and *Chihuahua* (E-22; ex-*José María Morelos y Pavon;* ex-*Chihuahua,* B-08; ex-*Rednour,* APD 102, ex-DE 529).

♦ 17 ex-U.S. Auk-class former fleet minesweepers

Bldrs: A: Pennsylvania Shipyard, Beaumont, Texas; B: Savannah Machine & Foundry Co., Savannah, Ga.; C: General Engineering and Drydock Co., Alameda, Calif.; D: Associated Shipbuilders; E: Gulf Shipbuilding; F: J. H. Mathis, Camden, N.J.; G: Winslow Marine Railway and Shipbuilding, Seattle, Wash.

	Bldr	L
P-101 LEANDRO VALLE (ex-C-70; ex-*Pioneer,* MSF 105)[1]	A	26-7-42
P-102 JUAN DE LA BARRERA (ex-C-71; ex-*Guillermo Prieto;* ex-*Symbol,* MSF 123)[2]	B	2-7-42
P-103 MARIANO ESCOBEDO (ex-C-72; ex-*Champion,* MSF 314)[3]	C	12-12-42
P-104 MANUEL DOBLADO (ex-C-73; ex-*Defense,* MSF 317)[3]	C	18-2-43
P-105 SEBASTIÁN LERDO DE TEJADA (ex-C-74; ex-*Devastator,* MSF 318)[3]	C	19-4-43
P-106 SANTOS DEGOLLADO (ex-C-75; ex-*Gladiator,* MSF 319)[3]	C	7-5-43
P-107 IGNACIO DE LA LLAVE (ex-C-76; ex-*Spear,* MSF 322)[2]	D	25-2-43
P-108 JUAN N. ALVAREZ (ex-C-77; ex-*Ardent,* MSF 340)[3]	C	22-6-43
P-109 MANUEL GUTIÉRREZ ZAMORA (ex-C-78; ex-*Melchior Ocampo,* G-10; ex-*Roselle,* MSF 379)[4]	E	29-8-45

PATROL SHIPS [PS] *(continued)*

	Bldr	L
P-110 Valentín Gómez Farias (ex-C-79; ex-*Starling,* MSF 64)[5]	C	15-2-42
P-111 Ignacio Manuel Altamirano (ex-C-80; ex-*Sway,* MSF 120)[2]	F	29-9-42
P-112 Francisco Zarco (ex-C-81; ex-*Threat,* MSF 124)[2]	B	15-8-42
P-113 Ignacio L. Vallarta (ex-C-82; ex-*Velocity,* MSF 128)[2]	E	19-4-42
P-114 Jésus Gonzalez Ortega (ex-C-83; ex-*Chief,* MSF 315)[3]	C	5-1-43
P-115 Felipe Xicoténcatl (ex-C-84; ex-*Melchior Ocampo;* ex-*Gutierrez Zamora;* ex-*Scoter,* MSF 381)[4]	E	26-9-45
P-116 Juan de Aldama (ex-C-85; ex-*Pilot,* MSF 104)[1]	A	5-7-42
P-117 Mariano Matamoros (ex-C-86; ex-*Hermenegildo Galeana;* ex-*Sage,* MSF 111)[1]	G	21-11-42

Sebastián Lerdo de Tejada (P-105)—with old pennant number
IJsbrand Plokker, 8-98

Jésus Gonzalez Ortega (P-114)—with old pennant number
H&L Van Ginderen, 10-97

Sebastián Lerdo de Tejada (P-105)—moored outboard *Jésus Gonzalez Ortega* (P-114)
H&L Van Ginderen, 3-98

D: 890 tons (1,250 fl) **S:** 17 kts **Dim:** 67.4 (65.5 wl) × 9.8 × 3.28
A: 1 76.2-mm 50-cal. U.S. Mk 22 DP; 2 twin 40-mm 60-cal. Mk 1 Mod. 2 Bofors AA—some also: 2 single 20-mm 70-cal. Oerlikon Mk 10 AA
Electronics: Radar: 1 Kelvin-Hughes 14/9 nav.
M: 2 diesels, electric drive (see remarks); 2 props; 2,976, 3,118, or 3,532 bhp
Electric: 300–360 kw tot. **Range:** 4,300/10 **Fuel:** 216 tons
Crew: 9 officers, 96 enlisted

Remarks: All transferred in 1973. All ASW and all minesweeping gear except the winch has been removed. Sister *Ponciano Arriaga* (G-04; ex-*Competent,* MSF 316) was stricken in 1988. One other unit, *Mariano Matamoros* (ex-*Herald,* MSF 101), was converted for use as a surveying ship and has since been stricken. Some have a small deckhouse between the stacks; some have no main deck bulwarks. New radars have been added. Names and hull numbers were revised in 1993; they had been numbered G-01 through G-19. P-103, P-104, and P-110 have been modernized with a helicopter platform aft; these units now also carry a 9-ton, 12.2-m patrol craft capable of 26 kts, carrying a crew of 5, and armed with two 12.7-mm mg and a U.S. Mk 19 40-mm grenade launcher.
Propulsion systems: The superscript numbers after the ships' names refer to five different diesels used in the propulsion plants: 1 = Busch-Sulzer 539; 2 = G.M. 12-278; 3 = Baldwin VO-8; 4 = G.M. 12-278A; 5 = Alco 539. Diesels 1 and 5 produce 3,118 bhp total, 2 and 4 produce 3,532 bhp, and 3 produces 2,976 bhp. The modernized units have been re-engined.

Disposal note: Of the units of the U.S. *Admirable* class listed in the previous edition, *General Miguel Negrete* (C-50; ex-DM 01; ex-*Jubilant,* MSF 255), *General Felipe Xicoténcatl* (C-53; ex-DM 06; ex-*Scuffle,* MSF 298), *Cadete Augustin Melgar* (C-54; ex-DM 11; ex-*Device,* MSF 220), *Teniente Juan de la Barrera* (C-55; ex-DM 12; ex-*Ransom,* MSF 283), *Cadete Juan Escutia* (C-56; ex-DM 13; ex-*Knave,* MSF 256), and *Cadete Francisco Marquez* (C-59; ex-DM 17; ex-*Diploma,* MSF 221) were stricken during 2000. *General Manuel E. Rincon* (C-52; ex-DM 04; ex-*Specter,* MSF 306), *Cadete Fernando Montes de Oca* (C-57; ex-DM 14; ex-*Rebel,* MSF 284), and *General Ignacio Zaragoza* (C-60; ex-DM 18; ex-*Invade,* MSF 254) were stricken 16-7-01, as was training ship–designated *Cadete Vicente Suarez* (A-06; ex-C-61; ex-DM 19; ex-*Intrigue,* MSF 253). *Guanajuato*-class gunboat *Guanajuato* (C-07) was also stricken 16-7-01; sisters *Potosi* and *Queretaro* had been scrapped during the mid-1970s.

♦ 1 ex-U.S. Edsall-class training patrol ship [PST]
Bldr: Brown SB, Houston, Texas

	Laid down	L	In serv.
D-111 Comodoro Manuel Azueta Perillos (ex-E-30; ex-*Manuel Azueta,* A-06; ex-*Hurst,* DE 250)	27-1-43	14-4-43	30-8-43

Comodoro Manuel Azueta Perillos (D-111)—with old pennant number
H&L Van Ginderen, 5-96

D: 1,200 tons (1,590 fl) **S:** 18 kts **Dim:** 93.26 × 11.15 × 3.73
A: 3 single 76.2-mm 50-cal. U.S. Mk 26 DP; 2 twin 40-mm 60-cal. Bofors Mk 1 Mod. 2 AA; 4 single 40-mm 60-cal. Bofors Mk 3 AA; 2 single 20-mm 70-cal. Oerlikon Mk 10 AA; 2 single 37-mm saluting cannon
Electronics: Radar: 1 Kelvin-Hughes 14/9 nav.; 1 Kelvin-Hughes 17/9 nav.
M: 4 Fairbanks-Morse 38D8⅛-10 diesels; 2 props; 6,000 bhp **Electric:** 680 kw tot.
Range: 13,000/12 **Fuel:** 258 tons **Crew:** 15 officers, 201 enlisted

Remarks: Transferred 1-10-73. Former destroyer escort, used as training ship for the Gulf Fleet. Pennant number was changed in 2001. D = *Destructore.*
Combat systems: In 1994, three Mk 26 single-fire 76.2-mm guns were removed and replaced with a 76-mm 62-cal. OTOBreda Compact, controlled by an electro-optical director; a quadruple 40-mm AA mount replaced the superfiring 76.2-mm DP forward. The original armament layout, however, was restored by 1998. The Mk 52 radar director for the 76.2-mm guns, three Mk 51 Mod. 2 directors for the 40-mm AA, and all antisubmarine equipment have been removed, leaving all weapons locally controlled.

PATROL CRAFT [PC]

♦ 1 Centenary class
Bldr: Varadero Nacional No. 6, Guaymas, Sonora

	Laid down	L	In serv.
PC-241 Demócrata (ex-C-101)	1997	16-10-97	9-7-98

Demócrata (PC-241)—with old pennant number H&L Van Ginderen, 10-99

D: 400 tons (450 fl) **S:** 30 kts **Dim:** 52.50 × 9.00 × 2.60
A: 1 twin 40-mm 60-cal. Bofors Mk 1 Mod. 2 AA
Electronics: Radar: 3 . . . nav./surf. search
M: 2 MTU 20V956 TB92 diesels; 2 props; 12,238 bhp (11,700 sust.)
Range: . . ./. . . **Crew:** 13 officers, 23 enlisted

Remarks: Intended to be a series production class to replace the obsolescent *Auk* and *Admirable* class, but only one has been ordered thus far. Carries a Boston Whaler Piranha-class armed inspection launch and two rescue RIBs. Pennant number was changed in 2001. PC = *Patrulla Costera.*

PATROL CRAFT [PC] *(continued)*

♦ 30 Azteca class

Bldrs: A: Ailsa SB Co., Troon; B: Scott & Sons, Bowling; C: J. Lamont; D: Veracrúz NSY; E: Salina Cruz NSY

	Bldr	In serv.
P-201 Andrés Quintana Roo (ex-*Azteca,* P-01; ex-*Andres Quintana Roo*)	A	1-11-74
P-202 Matias de Cordova (ex-*Guayacura,* P-02; ex-*Matias de Cordova*)	B	22-10-74
P-203 Manuel Ramos Arizpe (ex-*Nahuatl,* P-03; ex-*Miguel Ramos Arizpe*)	A	23-12-74
P-204 José María Izazago (ex-*Totoran,* P-04; ex-*José María Izazago*)	A	19-12-74
P-205 Juan Bautista Morales (ex-*Papago,* P-05; ex-*Juan Bautista Morales*)	B	19-12-74
P-206 Ignacio López Rayón (ex-*Tarahumara,* P-06; ex-*Ignacio López Rayón*)	A	19-12-74
P-207 Manuel Crescencio Rejón (ex-*Tepehuan,* P-07; ex-*Manuel Crescencio Rejón*)	A	4-7-75
P-208 Antonio de la Fuente (ex-*Mexica,* P-08; ex-*Antonio de la Fuente*)	A	4-7-75
P-209 León Guzmán (ex-*Zapoteca,* P-09; ex-*León Guzmán*)	B	7-4-75
P-210 Ignacio Ramírez (ex-*Huasteca,* P-10; ex-*Ignacio Ramírez*)	A	17-7-75
P-211 Ignacio Mariscal (ex-*Mazahua,* P-11; ex-*Ignacio Mariscal*)	A	23-9-75
P-212 Heriberto Jara Corona (ex-*Huichol,* P-12; ex-*Heriberto Jara Corona*)	A	7-11-75
P-213 José María Mata (ex-*Seri,* P-13; ex-*José María Mata*)	C	13-10-75
P-214 Felix Romero (ex-*Yaqui,* P-14; ex-*Felix Romero*)	B	23-6-75
P-215 Fernando Lizardi (ex-*Tlapaneco,* P-15; ex-*Fernando Lizardi*)	A	24-12-75
P-216 Francisco J. Múgica (ex-*Tarasco,* P-16; ex-*Francisco J. Múgica*)	A	21-11-75
P-217 Pastor Rouaix José María (ex-*Acolhua,* P-17; ex-*Pastor Rouaix José María*)	B	7-11-75
P-218 José María del Castillo Velasco (ex-*Otomi,* P-18; ex-*José María del Castillo Velasco*)	C	14-1-75
P-219 Luis Manuel Rojas (ex-*Mayo,* P-19; ex-*Luis Manuel Rojas*)	C	3-4-76
P-220 José Natividad Macias (ex-*Pimas,* P-20; ex-*José Natividad Macias*)	C	2-9-76
P-222 Ignacio Zaragoza (ex-*Chontal,* P-22; ex-*General Ignacio Zaragoza*)	D	1-6-76
P-223 Tamaulipas (ex-*Mazateco,* P-23; ex-*Tamaulipas*)	D	18-5-77
P-224 Yucatán (ex-*Tolteca,* P-24; ex-*Yucatán*)	D	3-7-77
P-225 Tabasco (ex-*Maya,* P-25; ex-*Tabasco*)	E	1-1-79
P-226 Veracrúz (ex-*Cochimie,* P-26; ex-*Veracrúz*)	D	1-1-79
P-227 Campeche (ex-*Cora,* P-27; ex-*Campeche*)	D	1-3-80
P-228 Puebla (ex-*Totonaca,* P-28; ex-*Puebla*)	E	1-6-82
P-229 Margarita Maza de Juárez (ex-*Mixteco,* P-29; ex-*Margarita Maza de Juarez*)	E	29-11-76
P-230 Leona Vicario (ex-*Olmeca,* P-30; ex-*Leona Vicario*)	D	1-5-77
P-231 Josepha Ortiz de Dominguez (ex-*Tlahica,* P-31; ex-*Josepha Ortiz de Dominguez*)	E	1-6-77

Ignacio Zaragoza (P-222)—with 40-mm gun forward and old pennant number H&L Van Ginderen, 4-99

José María Izazago (P-204)—with old pennant number GEC-Alstom, 1994

D: 115 tons (165 fl) **S:** 23 kts **Dim:** 36.50 (30.94 pp) × 8.6 × 2.0
A: 1 40-mm 60-cal. Bofors Mk 3 AA *or* 1 7.62-mm mg
Electronics: Radar: 1 . . . nav.
M: 2 Ruston–Paxman-Ventura 12-cyl. diesels; 7,200 bhp **Electric:** 80 kw
Range: 2,500/12 **Crew:** 2 officers, 22 enlisted

Remarks: Original order for 21 placed 27-3-73 with Associated British Machine Tool Makers, Ltd., which subcontracted the actual construction in the U.K. and later assisted with the construction of another 10 in Mexico. The 21 built in the U.K. were rehabilitated in Mexico with British assistance for 10 more years' service, beginning in 1987. Very lightly constructed. All were renamed for Mexican tribal groups during 1993, but the original names were restored and pennant numbers changed during 2001. P = *Patrulla.*
Disposals: *Esteban Baca Calderón* (P-221; ex-*Chichimeca,* P-21; ex-*Esteban Baca Calderón*) was apparently stricken during 2001.
Combat systems: The original armament, where fitted, consisted of one 40-mm 60-cal. AA and one 20-mm 70-cal. AA; most now have only the single light machinegun.

♦ 3 ex-U.S. Coast Guard Cape class

Bldr: Coast Guard Yard, Curtis Bay, Md.

	In serv.	Recommissioned
P-271 Corrientes (ex-*Cabo Corrientes,* P-42; ex-*Jalisco;* ex-*Cape Carter,* WPB 95309)	7-12-53	1-4-90
P-272 Corzo (ex-*Cabo Corzo,* P-43; ex-*Nayarit;* ex-*Vanguard;* ex-*Cape Hedge,* WPB 95311)	21-12-53	21-4-90
P-273 Catoche (ex-*Cabo Catoche,* P-44; ex-*Cape Hattaras,* WPB 95305)	28-7-53	18-3-91

Mexican Navy Cape-class patrol craft—with Olmeca-class patrol boat *Arrecife Anegada de Adentro* (PC-309, formerly P-98) outboard H&L Van Ginderen, 6-96

D: 87 tons (106 fl) **S:** 20 kts **Dim:** 28.96 × 6.10 × 1.55
A: 1 20-mm 70-cal. Oerlikon Mk 10 AA; 2 single 12.7-mm mg
Electronics: Radar: 1 SPS-64(V)1 nav.
M: 2 G.M. 16V 149TI diesels; 2 props; 2,470 bhp **Electric:** 60 kw
Range: 550/20; 1,900/11.5 **Endurance:** 5 days **Crew:** 1 officer, 14 enlisted

Remarks: Re-engined during the 1980s. P-272 had been transferred to the U.S. Navy as a pilot boat after being stricken from the U.S. Coast Guard 7-1-87 and was transferred to Mexico in 1-90. P-271 was stricken 19-1-90 from U.S. Coast Guard and transferred 2-90. P-273 transferred after striking from the U.S. Coast Guard in 1991. "*Cabo*" was dropped from the names during 2001, when the pennant numbers were again changed. P = *Patrulla.*

PATROL BOATS [PB]

♦ 40 Stridsbåt 90H class

Bldrs: Dockstavarvet, Docksta, and Gotlands Varvet (In serv. 2-00 to 12-01)

PI-1101 Polaris
PI-1102 Sirius
PI-1103 Capella
PI-1104 Canopus
PI-1105 Vega
PI-1106 Achernar
PI-1107 Rigel
PI-1108 Arcturus
PI-1109 Alpheratz
PI-1110 Procyón
PI-1111 Avior
PI-1112 Deneb
PI-1113 Fomalhaut
PI-1114 Póllux
PI-1115 Régulus
PI-1116 Acrux
PI-1117 Spica
PI-1118 Hadar
PI-1119 Shaula
PI-1120 Mirfak
PI-1121 Ankaa
PI-1122 Bellatrix
PI-1123 Elnath
PI-1124 Alnilán
PI-1125 Peacock
PI-1126 Betelgeuse
PI-1127 Adhara
PI-1128 Alioth
PI-1129 Rasalhague
PI-1130 Nunki
PI-1131 Hamal
PI-1132 Suhail
PI-1133 Dubhe
PI-1134 Denebola
PI-1135 Alkaid
PI-1136 Alphecca
PI-1137 Eltanin
PI-1138 Cochab
PI-1139 Enif
PI-1140 Schedar

Mexican Navy Stridsbåt 90-class Alpheratz (PI-1109) Dockstavarvet, 2000

D: 13.2 tons light (18.7 fl) **S:** 45 kts **Dim:** 15.90 (13.00 wl) × 3.80 × 0.80
A: 1 12.7-mm mg **Electronics:** Radar: 1 Decca Bridgemaster-E nav.
M: 2 Caterpillar 3406E diesels; 2 KaMeWa waterjets; 1,582 bhp
Electric: 8 kw tot. (1 × 8-kw Onan set)
Range: 160/40; 240/20 **Fuel:** 1.5 tons **Crew:** 4 tot. + 21 troops

PATROL BOATS [PB] *(continued)*

Remarks: First four were built by the Gotlands Varvet division of Djupviks, which was to build another 12; the others are to be built by Dockstavarvet. Twelve were ordered 15-4-99, eight on 29-7-99, and 20 on 1-2-00. Intended to combat smugglers. PI = *Patrulla Interceptora.* Pennant numbers were changed from I-101 through I-140 and they were named during 2001.
Hull systems: Aluminum construction. Have a 14-m^3 troop compartment (with disembarkation ramp over the bow). Have a Simrad compass, log, and echo sounder. A Transas Navi Sailor electronic chart system is fitted.

♦ 40 or more 35-foot Interceptor class
Bldr: . . . . . ., Mexico (In serv. 1998–. . .)

C-101-01 series

D: . . . tons **S:** 50 kts **Dim:** 10.67 × . . . × . . .
A: 2 single 7.62-mm mg
M: 2 MTU . . . diesels; 2 HamiltonJet HJ 321 waterjets; . . . bhp

Remarks: Locally designed and built. Intended to intercept narcotics in inshore waters. Their subordination is not certain; they may belong to the army or the coast guard, but are said to be operated by "troops." Forty are based in the Baja California Peninsula and Gulf of California and the rest in the Yucatan Peninsula area. Operate under control of mobile four-wheel vehicles on land. Date above refers to ceremonial inauguration of the program, for which many of the boats had actually become operational some time earlier. No further information available. No radar is fitted. The guns are mounted in cockpits recessed into bow and atop the pilothouse, facing aft.

Note: An antidrug force of "144" craft was inaugurated 8-5-99; the craft may include the class above, plus the Piranha class below and an unknown number of Sea Force 730 rigid inflatable boats acquired in 1995–96. Also in use are an unknown number of 8.8-m Mako Marine (Miami, Fla.)–built patrol launches with two 200-bhp Mercury gasoline outboard engines.

♦ 4 XFPB class
Bldr: Trinity-Equitable, New Orleans (In serv. 1993–94)

	Laid down	L	In serv.
P-1201 Isla Coronado (ex-P-51)	1-93	6-93	9-93
P-1202 Isla Lobos (ex-P-52)	3-93	9-93	11-93
P-1203 Isla Guadalupe (ex-P-53)	8-93	12-93	1-94
P-1204 Isla Cozumel (ex-P-54)	8-93	3-94	3-94

Isla Coronado (P-1201)—with no fixed armament aboard and old pennant number H&L Van Ginderen, 4-99

D: 52 tons (fl) **S:** 50 kts (40 sust.) **Dim:** 25.00 × 5.48 × 1.33
A: 1 12.7-mm M2HB mg; 2 single 7.62-mm M60 mg
M: 3 G.M. Detroit Diesel 16V92TA diesels; 3 Arneson outdrives with Rolla surface-piercing props; 4,350 bhp
Electric: 50 kw tot. (2 × 25-kw diesel sets)
Range: 500/35; 1,200/30 **Fuel:** 8,667 liters **Crew:** 1 officer, 8 enlisted

Remarks: First three ordered in 11-92, fourth in 5-93. Similar to six sisters built for Sri Lanka. Specifically intended for antidrug interception. All are based in the Caribbean at Isla Mujeres. Pennant numbers were changed during 2001. P = *Patrulla.*
Hull systems: Kevlar-reinforced GRP hull can be operated in up to Sea State 3. Have a 220-gallon/day potable water generator.
Combat systems: P-1204 was tested with a twin launcher for Aérospatiale MM 15 missiles at the time of completion, but the weapon was not procured. Were planned to be rearmed with one 40-mm 60-cal. Bofors Mk 3 and one 20-mm 70-cal. U.S. Mk 68 AA gun, but the change has yet to be made.

♦ 36 U.S. Piranha-class riverine patrol launches
Bldr: Boston Whaler, Edgewater, Fla. (In serv. 1990–. . .)

G-01 through G-36

D: 1.6 tons **S:** 37 kts **Dim:** 6.40 × 2.30 × 0.30
A: 1 7.62-mm mg; 1 40-mm Mk 19 grenade launcher
Electronics: Radar: 1 . . . nav.
M: 2 Johnson gasoline outboards; 280 bhp
Range: 144/28 **Crew:** 2 tot. + 4 passengers

Remarks: Original plans called for procuring a total of 50. GRP construction. Outfitted at the Acapulco Naval Shipyard and intended to be carried aboard Halcón-, Águila-, *Auk-*, and *Admirable*-class patrol ships, as well as serving as local patrol craft in various ports. Are equipped with GPS receivers.

Mexican Navy Piranha-class patrol launch—in davits aboard patrol ship *José Maria de la Vega Gonzalez* (PO-133, formerly C-03) Julio Montes, 1997

♦ 13 Olmeca class
Bldr: Acapulco NSY (In serv. 1979–84)

PC-301 Arrecife Alacran (ex-P-90; ex-AM 11; ex-F-21)
PC-302 Arrecife Sisal (ex-P-91; ex-AM 12; ex-F-22)
PC-303 Arrecife Tanuijo (ex-P-92; ex-AM 13; ex-F-23)
PC-304 Arrecife Cabezo (ex-P-93; ex-AM 14; ex-F-24)
PC-305 Arrecife Santiaguillo (ex-P-94; ex-AM 15; ex-F-25)
PC-306 Arrecife Palancar (ex-P-95; ex-AM 16; ex-F-26)
PC-307 Arrecife La Galleguilla (ex-P-96; ex-AM 17; ex-F-27)
PC-308 Arrecife La Blanquilla (ex-P-97; ex-AM 18; ex-F-28)
PC-309 Arrecife Anegada de Adentro (ex-P-98; ex-AM 19; ex-F-29)
PC-310 Arrecife Rizo (ex-P-99; ex-AM 20; ex-F-30)
PC-311 Arrecife Pajaros (ex-P-100; ex-AM 21; ex-F-31)
PC-312 Arrecife de Enmedio (ex-P-101; ex-AM 22; ex-F-32)
PC-313 Arrecife de Hornos (ex-P-102; ex-AM 23; ex-F-33)

Olmeca-class Arrecife Cabezo (PC-304)—with since-stricken Lago-class patrol boat *Lago de Janitzio* (P-83) at left Leo Van Ginderen, 1-01

D: 18 tons (fl) **S:** 20 or 25 kts **Dim:** 16.7 × 4.4 × 2.4
A: 1 12.7-mm mg **Electronics:** Radar: 1 Raytheon 1900 nav.
M: first six: 2 Cummins UT-series diesels; 800 bhp—others: 2 G.M. Detroit Diesel 8V92 TI diesels; 2 props; 1,140 bhp
Range: 460/15 **Crew:** 2 officers, 13 enlisted

Remarks: GRP construction. Last unit of the initial six with Cummins diesels was delivered 22-2-83. Five additional, with G.M. diesels, were ordered 23-6-83 and delivered by end-1984. Have a firefighting water monitor forward. All were renumbered and renamed for Mexican reefs during 1993. Pennant numbers were again changed during 2001. PC = *Patrulla Costera.*

♦ 2 ex-U.S. Coast Guard Point class
Bldr: Coast Guard Yard, Curtis Bay, Md.

	In serv.
PC-281 Punta Morro (ex-P-60; ex-*Point Verde,* WPB 82311)	15-3-61
PC-282 Punta Mastún (ex-P-61; ex-*Point Herron,* WPB 82318)	14-6-61

D: 64 tons (67 fl) **S:** 23.7 kts **Dim:** 25.30 × 5.23 × 1.95
A: 2 single 12.7-mm mg **Electronics:** Radar: 1 SPS-64(V)1 nav.
M: 2 Cummins VT-12-M diesels; 2 props; 1,600 bhp
Range: 490/23.7; 1,500/8 **Fuel:** 5.7 tons **Crew:** 1 officer, 7 enlisted

Remarks: Donated by the U.S. government for antidrug patrol duties, PC-281 on 19-7-91 and PC-282 on 26-7-91. The engines are controlled from the bridge. Are equipped for towing. Were renumbered from P-45 and P-46, respectively, during 1993. Pennant numbers were again changed during 2001. PC = *Patrulla Costera.*

PATROL BOATS [PB] *(continued)*

♦ **3 Polimar class**
Bldrs: Ast. de Tampico (PC-292: Iscacas SY, Guerrero)

	In serv.
PC-291 Laguna de Tamiahua (ex-P-70, ex-*Poluno,* ex-*Polimar-I*)	1-10-62
PC-292 Laguna de Lagartos (ex-P-71, ex-*Poldos,* ex-*Polimar-II*)	1968
PC-293 Laguna de Cuyutlan (ex-P-73, ex-*Polcinco,* ex-*Polimar-IV*)	28-7-53

Laguna de Cuyutlan (PC-293)—with old pennant number   Jim Dobbins, 5-95

D: 57 tons (fl) **S:** 16 kts **Dim:** 20.5 × 4.5 × 1.3
A: 1 twin 12.7-mm mg **M:** 2 diesels; 2 props; 456 bhp

Remarks: All were given new names and hull numbers during 1993; they had been F-01 through F-05. Pennant numbers were again changed during 2001. PC = *Patrulla Costera.* Have small navigational radars. Sisters *Laguna de Kana* (P-72, ex-*Poltres,* ex-*Polimar-III*) and *Villalpando* (ex-*Laguna de Mandinga,* P-74; ex-*Aspirante José V. Rincon*) were stricken 16-7-01.

♦ **3 Lago class**
Bldr: Ast. de Tampico and Veracrúz NSY (L: 1959–61, except P-84: 1981)

PC-321 Lago de Pátzcuaro (ex-P-80, ex-AM 04)
PC-322 Lago de Chapala (ex-P-81, ex-AM 05)
PC-323 Lago de Cuitzeo (ex-P-84, ex-AM 08)

D: 37 tons (fl) **S:** 6 kts **Dim:** 17.7 × 5.0 × . . .
A: small arms **Electronics:** Radar: 1 . . . nav.
M: 1 diesel; 1 prop; 320 bhp **Crew:** 5 tot.

Remarks: Riverine patrol craft with low freeboard and bulwarks surrounding hull. Sisters AM 01–AM 03 and AM 09 had been stricken by 1986, AM 10 in 1988. The survivors were renumbered in 1993; they had been F-14 through F-18. Pennant numbers were again changed during 2001. PC = *Patrulla Costera.* Sisters *Lago de Texcoco* (P-82, ex-AM 06) and *Lago de Janitzio* (P-83, ex-AM 07) were stricken 16-7-01.

♦ **2 ex-U.S. 64-foot Distribution Box (L-Type) Boat class**

PC-294 Laguna de Alvarado (ex-P-75, ex-*Polsiete,* ex-. . .)
PC-295 Laguna de Catemaco (ex-P-76, ex-*Polocho,* ex-. . .)

D: 72.3 tons (fl) **S:** 9.5 kts **Dim:** 19.58 × 5.72 × 1.83
A: 2 single 12.7-mm mg **Electronics:** Radar: 1 . . . nav.
M: 1 G.M. Detroit Diesel 64HN11 diesel; 1 prop; 165 bhp **Range:** 110/9.5

Remarks: Acquired 1-1-89 and 15-12-90, with one having been used by the U.S. Marines as a recreational craft under the name *Retreat Hell.* Were built to set and recover mine distribution boxes for controlled minefields but are now used as general-purpose tenders and patrol boats. Had a 2.5-ton crane forward, now replaced by a machinegun. Built during the early 1950s. Pennant numbers were changed during 2001. PC = *Patrulla Costera.*

Note: The Mexican Navy also employs a number of locally built, shallow-draft launches driven by air-screw propellers as "Chase Boats" to pursue smugglers in shallow, vegetation-choked coastal waters and rivers; they normally have a crew of two.

AUXILIARIES

♦ **1 oceanographic research ship [AGOR]**
Bldr: Ochida Zosen, Ise, Japan (In serv. 1978)

BI-02 Onjuku (ex-H-04)

Onjuku (BI-02)—with old pennant number   H&L Van Ginderen, 4-99

D: 494 tons (fl) **S:** 10.5 kts **Dim:** 36.91 (33.15 pp) × 8.01 × 3.55
Electronics: Radar: 1 Furuno . . . nav.
M: 1 Yanmar 6UA-UT diesel; 1 CP prop; 700 bhp **Electric:** 240 kw tot.
Range: 5,645/10.5 **Crew:** 4 officers, 16 enlisted

Remarks: 282 grt/263 dwt. Former stern-haul trawler, acquired in 1987. Equipped with a Furuno fish-finding sonar. Intended primarily for fisheries research; retains fishing gear. Based at Ciudad del Carmen. Pennant number was changed during 2001. BI = *Buque de Investigación.*

♦ **1 oceanographic research ship [AGOR]**
Bldr: J. G. Hitzler Schiffswerft und Maschinenfabrik, Lauenburg, Germany (In serv. 1970)

BI-01 Alejandro de Humboldt (ex-H-03)

D: 585 tons (700 fl) **S:** 12.5 kts **Dim:** 42.27 (34.55 pp) × 9.61 × 3.25
M: 1 M.A.N. 8-cyl. diesel; 1 CP prop; 1,150 bhp **Electric:** 251 kw tot.
Crew: 4 officers, 16 enlisted

Remarks: 459 grt. Former German stern-haul trawler, acquired in 1982 and commissioned 22-6-87 for hydrographical and acoustic properties research. Homeported at Mazatlán. Pennant number was changed during 2001. BI = *Buque de Investigación.*

♦ **1 ex-U.S. oceanographic research ship [AGOR]**
Bldr: Halter Marine, New Orleans (In serv. 1966)

BI-06 Río Ondo (ex-H-08; ex-*Deer Island,* YAG 62)

Río Ondo (BI-06)—with old pennant number   H&L Van Ginderen, 4-99

D: approx. 400 tons (fl) **S:** 10.5 kts **Dim:** 36.58 × 8.53 × 2.13
Electronics: Radar: 2 . . . nav. **M:** 2 diesels; 2 props; . . . bhp
Range: 6,200/10.5 **Crew:** 20 tot.

Remarks: 172 grt/117 nrt. Purchased 2-8-96, having been stricken in 1995 from the U.S. Navy, which used her in support of sound-quieting trials. Former tug/supply vessel acquired by the USN 15-3-83. Pennant number was changed during 2001. BI = *Buque de Investigación.*

♦ **1 ex-U.S. Robert D. Conrad–class oceanographic research ship [AGOR]** Bldr: Christy Corp., Sturgeon Bay, Wis.

	L	In serv.
BI-03 Altair (ex-H-05; ex-*James M. Gillis,* AGOR 4)	19-5-62	5-11-62

Altair (BI-03)—with old pennant number   George R. Schneider, 10-85

D: 1,200 tons (1,380 fl) **S:** 13.5 kts **Dim:** 63.7 (58.30 pp) × 11.37 × 4.66
Electronics: Radar: 1 Raytheon TM 1600/6X; 1 TM 1660/123
M: 2 Caterpillar D-378 diesels; electric drive; 1 prop; 2,000 bhp—bow-thruster
Electric: 850 kw tot. **Range:** 10,000/12 **Fuel:** 211 tons
Crew: 12 officers, 14 enlisted + 18 scientists

Remarks: 965 grt/355 dwt. Returned to the U.S. Navy by the University of Miami in 1980 and laid up until leased to Mexico 15-6-83; Mexico bore the expense of subsequent reactivation. The large stack contains a 620-shp gas-turbine generator to drive the main shaft at speeds up to 6.5 kts for experiments requiring "quiet" sea conditions. Also has a retractable electric bow-thruster/propulsor, which can drive the ship to 4.5 kts. Refitted and recommissioned 27-11-84. Pennant number was changed during 2001. BI = *Buque de Investigación.*

AUXILIARIES *(continued)*

♦ 1 ex-U.S. YW 83–class oceanographic research ship [AGOR]
Bldr: Zenith Dredge Co., Duluth, Minn.

	Laid down	L	In serv.
BI-05 Río Suchiate (ex-H-07; ex-A-27; ex-*Monob One,* YAG 61; ex-IX 309; ex-YW 87)	1-12-42	3-4-43	11-11-43

Río Suchiate (BI-05)—as *Monob One* (YAG 61) Dr. Giorgio Arra, 2-94

D: 1,390 tons (fl) **S:** 11 kts **Dim:** 58.5 × 10.1 × 4.8
Electronics: Radar: 1 . . . nav.
M: 1 Caterpillar D 398 diesel; 1 Harbormaster swiveling prop; 580 bhp
Range: 2,500/9 **Crew:** . . . tot.

Remarks: Purchased 2-8-96. Former U.S. Navy water lighter, modified in 1959 to support the ballistic-missile submarine silencing program. In USN service, had four laboratories totaling 279 m^2. Stern was extended to support the new propulsion plant. Had been stricken from U.S. service 4-4-95. Pennant number was changed during 2001. BI = *Buque de Investigación.*

♦ 1 ex-U.S. Kellar-class hydrographic survey ship [AGS]
Bldr: DeFoe SB, Bay City, Mich.

	Laid down	L	In serv.
BI-04 Antares (ex-H-06; ex-*Samuel P. Lee;* ex-*S. P. Lee,* T-AG 192, ex-T-AGS 31)	27-6-66	19-10-67	2-12-68

Antares (BI-04)—as *S. P. Lee* (T-AGS 31) U.S. Navy, 10-68

D: 1,297 tons (fl) **S:** 13.5 kts **Dim:** 63.50 (58.00 pp) × 11.90 × 4.32
M: 2 Caterpillar D-378 diesels; electric drive; 1 prop; 2,000 shp
Fuel: 211 tons **Crew:** 12 officers, 22 enlisted

Remarks: Until retirement and transfer to Mexico on 7-12-92, had been on loan to the Pacific Branch, U.S. Geological Survey, since 27-2-74; prior to that, performed survey work and acoustic research for the U.S. Navy. The Mexican Navy has added a large charting laboratory built from beam to beam at the aft end of the forecastle deck. Pennant number was changed during 2001. BI = *Buque de Investigación.*

♦ 1 cargo ship [AK]
Bldr: Solversborgs Varv A/B, Solversborg, Sweden (In serv. 1962)

ATR-03 Tarasco (ex-*Río Lerma,* A-22; ex-*Tarasco,* A-25; ex-*Sea Point;* ex-*Tricon;* ex-*Marika;* ex-*Arneb*)

D: 1,970 tons (approx. 3,200 fl) **S:** 14.5 kts **Dim:** 86.01 × 12.60 × 4.69
M: 1 Klöckner-Humboldt-Deutz diesel; 1 prop; 2,100 bhp
Range: . . ./. . . **Crew:** . . .

Remarks: 2,969 grt/2,500 dwt. Former commercial dry cargo vessel, acquired in 1990 and commissioned 1-3-90 without significant modification. A three-hold dry cargo ship with two electric cranes and superstructure aft. Cargo capacity: 780 tons. Renamed and renumbered during 1993 and again in 2001, when retyped ATR *(Auxiliar Transporte).*

♦ 1 cargo ship [AK]
Bldr: . . . . . . (In serv. 1962)

ATR-01 Maya (ex-*Río Nautla,* A-20; ex-*Maya,* A-23)

D: 924 tons (fl) **S:** 12 kts **Dim:** 48.8 × 11.8 × 4.9
M: 1 M.A.N. diesel; 1 prop; . . . bhp **Crew:** 8 officers, 7 enlisted

Remarks: Former lighthouse supply vessel, taken over in 1988 and commissioned 1-6-88. Renamed and renumbered during 1993 and again in 2001, when retyped ATR *(Auxiliar Transporte).*

Disposal note: Transport tanker [AOT] *Portrero del Llano* (A-42, ex-*Avaro Obregon*) was stricken 16-7-01.

♦ 2 Huasteco-class transports [AP]
Bldr: Ast. de la Secretaud de Marina, Guaymas

	In serv.
AMP-01 Huasteco (ex-*Río Usumacinta,* A-10; ex-*Huasteco,* A-21)	21-5-86
AMP-02 Zapoteco (ex-*Río Coatzacoalcos,* A-11; ex-*Zapoteco,* A-22)	1-6-86

Huasteco (AMP-01)—with old pennant number H&L Van Ginderen, 1988

D: 1,854 tons (2,650 fl) **S:** 17 kts **Dim:** 72.3 (69.2 pp) × 12.8 × 5.5
A: 1 40-mm 60-cal. Mk 3 Bofors AA **Electronics:** Radar: 2 . . . nav.
M: 1 G.M. Electromotive Division EMD-series diesel; 1 prop; 3,600 bhp
Range: 5,500/14 **Crew:** 57 ship's company + up to 300 troops

Remarks: Ordered in 1984 as troop transports, vehicle carriers, and transports for construction materials, food, and hospital equipment and to act as floating infirmaries and civil disaster relief ships. Helicopter platform can accept a BO-105CB. Renamed and renumbered during 1993 and again in 2001, when retyped AMR *(Auxiliar Multipropósito).*

♦ 1 ex-U.S. Newport-class transport [AP]
Bldr: Philadelphia NSY, Philadelphia

	Laid down	L	In serv.
A-411 Papaloapan (ex-*Sonora,* A-04; ex-*Newport,* LST 1179)	1-11-66	3-2-68	7-6-69

D: 4,975 tons light (8,576 fl) **S:** 23 kts (20 sust.)
Dim: 159.2 (171.3 over horns) × 21.18 × 5.3 (aft; 1.80 fwd)
A: 4 single 12.7-mm mg
Electronics:
Radar: 1 Raytheon SPS-64(V)9 nav.; 1 Raytheon SPS-10F surf. search
M: 6 G.M. Electromotive Div. 16-645-E5 diesels; 2 CP props; 16,500 bhp—bow-thruster
Electric: 2,250 kw tot. (3 × 750 kw, Alco 251-E diesels driving; 450 V, 60 Hz a.c.)
Range: 14,250/14 **Fuel:** 1,750 tons
Crew: 15 officers, 247 enlisted + troops: 20 officers, 294 enlisted + 72 emergency accomm.

Remarks: Sold to Mexico 18-1-01 and transferred 23-5-01. Name and pennant number were changed after delivery. A = *Anfibia.* Had been decommissioned 30-9-92 and turned down earlier by several other countries. Primarily intended as a transport.
Hull systems: Can transport 2,000 tons of cargo (500 tons for beaching) on 1,765 m^2 of deck space. There is a 34-m-long, 75-ton-capacity mobile aluminum ramp forward, which is linked to the tank deck by a second from the upper deck. Aft is a 242-m^2 helicopter platform and a stern door for loading and unloading vehicles. The tank deck, which has a 75-ton-capacity turntable at both ends, can carry 23 armored personnel carriers or 29 light tanks or 41 2.5-ton trucks, while the upper deck can accept 29 2.5-ton trucks. Can carry three LCVPs and one LCP in Welin davits. Has two 10-ton cranes. Can carry 141,600 gallons of vehicle fuel.
Combat systems: The Mk 63 radar gunfire-control systems were removed 1977–78 and the two twin 76.2-mm DP gunmounts during the early 1990s. No Phalanx CIWS mount was transferred with the ship.

Disposal note: Small transport [AP] *Río Tehuantepec* (A-24; ex-*Zacatecas,* B-02) was stricken 16-7-01.

♦ 1 ex-U.S. Fabius-class transport [AP]
Bldr: American Bridge Co., Ambridge, Pa.

	Laid down	L	In serv.
A-403 Vicente Guerrero (ex-*Río Grijalva,* A-03; ex-*General Vicente Guerrero,* A-05; ex-*Megara,* ARVA 6; ex-LST 1095)	22-1-45	25-3-45	27-6-45

Vicente Guerrero (A-403)—with old pennant number H&L Van Ginderen, 7-84

AUXILIARIES *(continued)*

D: 4,100 tons (fl) **S:** 11.6 kts **Dim:** 100.0 (96.3 wl) × 15.24 × 3.4
A: 2 quadruple 40-mm 60-cal. Mk 2 Bofors AA
Electronics: Radar: 1 . . . nav.
M: 2 G.M. 12-567A diesels; 2 props; 1,700 bhp **Electric:** 520 kw
Range: 10,000/10 **Fuel:** 474 tons **Crew:** 28 officers, 85 enlisted

Remarks: Transferred 1-10-73. Originally one of two U.S. Navy tank landing ships converted while under construction to act as airframe repair ships. Has one 10-ton boom and two Mk 51 Mod. 2 gun f.c.s. for the 40-mm AA. Normally carries two U.S. LCVP personnel landing craft. Renamed and renumbered during 1993 and again in 2001, when she was also renumbered. A = *Anfibia.* Used primarily as a transport.

♦ 2 ex-U.S. LST 542–class transports [AP]
Bldrs: A-401: Bethlehem Steel, Hingham, Mass.; A-402: Chicago Bridge & Iron, Seneca, Ill.

	L	In serv.
A-401 Río Panuco (ex-A-01; ex-*Park County,* LST 1077)	9-3-44	31-3-44
A-402 Río Papaloapan (ex-A-02; ex-*Manzanillo,* ex-*Clearwater County,* LST 602)	18-4-45	8-5-45

D: 1,625 tons (4,080 fl) **S:** 11.6 kts **Dim:** 100.00 (96.30 pp) × 15.24 × 3.40
A: A-401 only: 2 twin 40-mm 60-cal. Bofors Mk 1 Mod. 2 AA; 4 single 40-mm 60-cal. Bofors Mk 3 AA
Electronics: Radar: 2 . . . nav.
M: 2 G.M. 12-567A diesels; 2 props; 1,800 bhp **Electric:** 300 kw tot.
Range: 6,000/11 **Crew:** 130 tot.

Remarks: Former tank landing ships, transferred 20-9-71 and 25-2-72, respectively. Were to have been retired on completion of the transports *Huasteco* (AMP-01) and *Zapoteco* (AMP-02) but have been retained for search-and-rescue and disaster relief work. A-402 was transferred unarmed and had been used by the U.S. Military Sealift Command as an Arctic area supply ship; her waterline forward was reinforced, and two cargo derrick kingposts were stepped during MSC service. The decks amidships have been reinforced to accept a helicopter. Were renumbered in 2001. A = *Anfibia.*

♦ 6 Iztaccihuatl-class seagoing tugs [ATA]
Bldr: . . .

ARE-05 Iztaccíhuatl (ex-R-60)
ARE-06 Popocatépetl (ex-R-61)
ARE-07 Citlaltépetl (ex-R-62)
ARE-08 Xinantécatl (ex-R-63)
ARE-09 Matlalcueye (ex-R-64)
ARE-10 Tláloc (ex-R-65)

Remarks: No data available. ARE = *Auxiliar Remolcador.* May not all be of the same class.

♦ 4 ex-U.S. Abnaki-class fleet tugs [ATA]
Bldr: Charleston SB & DD, Charleston, S.C. (ARE-01: United Engineering, Alameda, Calif.)

	Laid down	L	In serv.
ARE-01 Otomi (ex-*Kukulkan,* R-52, ex-A-52; ex-*Otomi,* A-17; ex-*Molala,* ATF 106)	26-7-42	23-12-42	29-9-43
ARE-02 Yaqui (ex-*Ehactl,* R-53, ex-A-53; ex-*Yaqui,* A-18; ex-*Abnaki,* ATF 96)	28-11-42	22-4-43	15-11-43
ARE-03 Seri (ex-*Tonatiuh,* R-54, ex-A-54; ex-*Seri,* A-19; ex-*Cocopa,* ATF 101)	23-5-43	5-10-43	25-3-44
ARE-04 Cora (ex-*Chac,* R-55, ex-A-55; ex-*Cora,* A-20; ex-*Hitchiti,* ATF 103)	24-8-43	29-1-44	27-5-44

Seri (ARE-03)—as *Tonatiuh* (R-54) French Navy, 3-3-99

D: 1,325 tons (1,675 fl) **S:** 10 kts **Dim:** 62.48 × 11.73 × 4.67
A: 1 76.2-mm 50-cal. Mk 22 DP; 2 single 20-mm 70-cal. Oerlikon Mk 10 AA
Electronics: Radar: 1 Canadian Marconi LN-66 nav.
M: 4 Caterpillar D-399 diesels, electric drive; 1 prop; 3,000 shp
Electric: 400 kw **Range:** 7,000/15; 15,000/8 **Fuel:** 304 tons
Crew: 75 tot.

Remarks: ARE-01 was purchased 1-8-78, the others on 30-9-78. Were unarmed on delivery. Used on patrol duties and as rescue tugs. Radar may have been replaced. Renamed and renumbered during 1993; reverted to the original names in 2001. ARE = *Auxiliar Remolcador.* Were re-engined in the 1970s while in U.S. service; originally had Busch-Sulzer BS-539 diesels.

Disposal note: U.S. 143-ft. ATA-class fleet tugs *Quetzalcoatl* (A-50; ex-*Mayo,* A-12; ex-R-2; ex-. . .) and *Huitilopochtli* (A-51; ex-*Mixteco,* A-13; ex-R-3; ex-. . .) were stricken 16-7-01. These ships had been misidentified as the former U.S. Maritime Commission V-4 tugs *Montauk* and *Point Vicente,* which, although transferred to Mexico in 1968, had been replaced by the early 1980s by two former commercially owned tugs.

♦ 1 sail-training ship [AXT]
Bldr: Ast. y Talleres Celaya, Bilbao, Spain

	Laid down	L	In serv.
BE-01 Cuauhtémoc (ex-A-07)	27-4-81	1-82	11-12-82

Cuauhtémoc (BE-01)—white-painted, without pennant number
Maritime Photographic, 8-01

D: 1,200 tons (1,800 fl) **S:** 15 kts **Dim:** 90.0 (67.0 pp) × 10.6 × 4.2
M: 1 G.M. Detroit Diesel 12V149 diesel; 1 prop; 750 bhp—2,368 m^2 max. sail area
Crew: 20 officers, 165 enlisted + 90 cadets

Remarks: Ordered in 1980. Three-masted bark. Equipped with commercial SATCOM gear. BE = *Buque Escuela.*

♦ 1 ex-U.S. Admirable-class training ship [AXT]
Bldr: Willamette Iron & Steel, Oreg.

	Laid down	L	In serv.
BE-02 Aldebarán (ex-*General Pedro María Anaya,* A-08; ex-H-02; ex-*Oceanográfico;* ex-DM 20; ex-*Harlequin,* MSF 365)	3-8-43	3-6-44	28-9-45

Aldebarán (BE-02)—with old number H&L Van Ginderen, 4-99

D: 615 tons (910 fl) **S:** 15 kts **Dim:** 56.24 (54.86 wl) × 10.06 × 2.80
A: 1 76.2-mm 50-cal. U.S. Mk 22 DP; 2 single 40-mm 60-cal. Bofors Mk 3 AA; 4 single 20-mm 70-cal. Oerlikon Mk 10 AA
Electronics: Radar: 1 Kelvin-Hughes 14/9 nav.; 1 . . . nav.
M: 2 Cooper-Bessemer GSB-8 diesels; 2 props; 1,710 bhp
Electric: 280 kw tot. **Range:** 4,300/10 **Fuel:** 138 tons
Crew: 12 officers, 50 enlisted

Remarks: Former fleet minesweeper, converted 1976–78 for use as an oceanographic research ship, with armament deleted, oceanographic winches and davits installed, and space at the end of the forecastle employed for portable research containers. Named during 1993. Reclassified as a training ship during the late 1990s and rearmed. Was confused with the stricken DM 15 (ex-*Crag,* MSF 214) in previous editions.

Note: Also in use as a training ship is the *Moctezuma II* (BE-03, ex-A-09); no data available.

Disposal note: Training ship [AXT] *Durango* (B-01) was stricken 16-7-01.

SERVICE CRAFT

Note: The former U.S. Navy ocean construction platform *Seacon* (ex-YFNB 33), although transferred to Mexico on 2-99, does not appear ever to have left U.S. waters.

SERVICE CRAFT *(continued)*

♦ **1 ex-U.S. pile driver [YAG]** (Leased 8-68)

. . . . . . (ex-YPD 43)

♦ **7 ex-U.S. floating cranes [YD]**

(ex-YD 156)	(ex-YD 179)	(ex-YD 183)	(ex-YD 203)
(ex-YD 157)	(ex-YD 180)	(ex-YD 194)	

Remarks: Transferred 1964–71; purchased 7-78 (except ex-YD 179 and ex-YD 194).

♦ **2 ex-U.S. ARD 12–class floating dry docks [YFDL]**
Bldr: Pacific Bridge, Alameda, Calif.

	In serv.
ADI-03 (ex-AR-15, ex-ARD 15)	1-44
ADI-04 (ex-AR-16; ex-*San Onofre,* ARD 30)	1945

Lift capacity: 3,500 tons **Dim:** 149.87 × 24.69 × 1.73 (light)

Remarks: ADI-03 was transferred in 4-71 on loan and purchased in 1981. ADI-04 was offered for sale to Mexico in 1999 and purchased 20-3-01. Were renumbered in the ADI *(Auxiliar Dique Flotante)* series in 2001.

♦ **2 ex-U.S. ARD 2–class floating dry docks [YFDL]**
Bldr: Pacific Bridge, Alameda, Calif.

	In serv.
ADI-01 (ex-DF 01, ex-ARD 2)	4-42
ADI-02 (ex-DF 02, ex-ARD 11)	10-43

Lift capacity: 3,500 tons **Dim:** 148.0 × 21.64 × 1.6 (light)

Remarks: Transferred 8-63 and 6-74. Were renumbered in the ADI *(Auxiliar Dique Flotante)* series in 2001.

♦ **1 ex-U.S. small auxiliary floating dry dock [YFDL]**
Bldr: Doullut & Ewin, Mobile, Ala. (Transferred 1-73)

. . . . . . (ex-AFDL 28) (In serv. 8-44)

Lift capacity: 1,000 tons **Dim:** 60.96 × 19.51 × 1.04 (light)

Remarks: May have been discarded, as she does not appear on an official fleet list for 2001.

♦ **1 general-purpose tender [YFU]**
Bldr: Ast. Angulo Ciudad del Carmen (In serv. 27-2-85)

ATR-02 Progreso (ex-*Río Tonala,* A-21; ex-*Progreso,* A-24)

D: 152 grt **S:** 10 kts **Dim:** 22.4 × 6.5 × 1.5
A: 1 20-mm 70-cal. Oerlikon AA **M:** 1 diesel; 1 prop; . . . bhp

Remarks: Acquired in 1988 and recommissioned 27-3-89. Can carry 57 tons of package cargo and a small number of passengers. Has a fishing boat hull. Renamed and renumbered in 1993 and again in 2001, when retyped ATR *(Auxiliar Transporte).*

♦ **6 Laguna-series miscellaneous dredges [YM]**

ADR-12 Laguna Farrallón (ex-D-26)
ADR-13 Laguna de Chairel (ex-D-27)
ADR-14 Laguna de San Andrés (ex-D-28)
ADR-15 Laguna de San Ignacio (ex-D-29)
ADR-16 Laguna de Términos (ex-D-30)
ADR-17 Laguna de Teculapa (ex-D-31)

Remarks: Acquired in 1994 from a Spanish builder; no data available. The Mexican Navy is responsible for dredging and aids-to-navigation maintenance. Received new pennant numbers in the ADR *(Auxiliar Draga)* series in 2001.

♦ **11 Bahía-series miscellaneous dredges [YM]**

ADR-01 Bahía de Banderas (ex-D-01; ex-*Chiapas,* A-30)
ADR-02 Bahía Magdalena (ex-D-02; ex-*Cristobol Colón,* A-32)
ADR-03 Bahía Kino (ex-D-03, ex-. . .)
ADR-04 Bahía Yavaros (ex-D-04, ex-. . .)
ADR-05 Bahía Chamela (ex-D-05, ex-. . .)
ADR-06 Bahía Tepoca (ex-D-06)
ADR-07 Bahía Todos Santos (ex-D-07; ex-*Mazatlán,* A-31)
ADR-08 Bahía Asunción (ex-D-22; ex-*Isla del Carmen,* A-33)
ADR-09 Bahía Almejas (ex-D-23; ex-*Isla Azteca,* A-34)
ADR-10 Bahía de Chacagua (ex-D-24)
ADR-11 Bahía de Coyuca (ex-D-25)

Remarks: Acquired in 1985. Five were renamed in 1993. No data available.

♦ **2 ex-U.S. 174-foot-class fuel lighters [YO]**
Bldrs: ATQ-01: J. H. Mathis, Camden, N.J.; ATQ-02: George Lawley, Neponset, Mass.

	L	In serv.
ATQ-01 Aguascalientes (ex-*Las Chopas,* A-45; ex-*Aguascalientes,* A-03; ex-YOG 6)	3-4-43	15-11-43
ATQ-02 Tlaxcala (ex-*Amatlan,* A-46; ex-*Tlaxcala,* A-04; ex-YO 107)	3-11-43	27-11-43

D: 440 tons (1,480 fl) **S:** 8 kts **Dim:** 53.0 × 9.75 × 2.5
A: 1 20-mm 70-cal. Oerlikon Mk 10 AA
M: 1 Fairbanks-Morse 38D8½ diesel; 1 prop; 500 bhp
Crew: 5 officers, 21 enlisted

Remarks: Purchased in 8-64 and commissioned in 11-64. Cargo capacity: 980 tons (6,570 bbl). Both were renamed and renumbered during 1993 and again in 2001. ATQ = *Auxiliar Tanque.*

♦ **2 yard tugs [YTL]**

Patron Pragmar

Remarks: Bought in 1973. No data available.

♦ **10 shallow-draft push-tugs [YTL]**

Remarks: No data available. Entered service in 1994 for use in swampy and shallow water service.

COAST GUARD

Note: The Mexican Coast Guard is essentially a customs service. Ten U.S. Mako 295–class patrol launches built by Mako Marine International, Miami, are in service, with the first four having been shipped 28-11-95 and the remainder 15-12-95; they are powered by Mercury gasoline outboard engines.

ARMY

♦ **144 25 Sport–class special forces craft**
Bldr: Pro-Line Boats, Crystal River, Fla. (In serv. 2001)

D: 1.63 kg hull only (approx. 2.2 tons fl) **S:** 40+ kts **Dim:** 7.75 × 2.59 × 0.36
A: small arms **Electronics:** Radar: . . .
M: 2 Mercury gasoline outboard motors; 400 bhp
Range: . . ./. . . **Fuel:** 545 liters **Crew:** 4 tot.

Remarks: GRP-construction open sport fishing boats, known as the "240 Sport" model when ordered late in 2000. Assigned to the 36th Grupo Anfibios de Fuerzas Especiales. Sixty operate from San Felipe and the others from Tampico, all painted olive green. Have 7.66 m^2 of cockpit area. Were delivered along with 144 Dodge Ram pickup trucks and boat tow-trailers.

Note: Also in service are 108 rigid inflatable launches with outboard motors of between 40 and 105 bhp.

MICRONESIA

Federated States of Micronesia

DIVISION OF SURVEILLANCE ATTORNEY GENERAL'S OFFICE

Personnel (2002): Approx. 120 total

Bases: Principal facility at Kolonia, with outposts at Kosral, Moen, and Takatik

Note: Micronesia, which became independent on 10-5-89, consists of the Caroline Islands archipelago islands of Kosrae, Pohnpei, Truk, and Yap. The United States retains the responsibility to provide defense against external threat. Ship names are preceded by FSS (Federated States Ship).

PATROL CRAFT [WPC]

♦ **3 ASI-315 Pacific Forum class**
Bldr: Transfield ASI Pty, Ltd., South Coogie, Western Australia

	Laid down	L	In serv.
FSM 01 Palakir	19-6-89	. . .	28-4-90
FSM 02 Micronesia	22-1-90	. . .	3-1-90
FSM 05 Independence	. . .	. . .	22-5-97

Palakir (FSM 01) RAN, 5-90

PATROL CRAFT [WPC] *(continued)*

D: 165 tons (fl) **S:** 21 kts **Dim:** 31.50 (28.60 wl) × 8.10 × 2.12 (1.80 hull)
A: 2 single 12.7-mm mg **Electronics:** Radar: 1 Furuno 1011 nav.
M: 2 Caterpillar 3516 diesels; 2 props; 2,820 bhp (2,400 sust.)
Electric: 116 kw (2 × 50 kw, Caterpillar 3304 diesel sets; 1 × 16 kw)
Range: 2,500/12 **Fuel:** 27.9 tons **Endurance:** 8–10 days
Crew: 3 officers, 14 enlisted

Remarks: First two arrived at Port Kolonia on 7-6-90 and 25-1-91, respectively. The third was ordered in 1996. Standard Australian foreign aid patrol boat design. FSM 02 was refitted during 1998–99 and the other two are to begin minor refits in 2003.
Hull systems: Carry a 5-m rigid inflatable boarding boat. Have an extensive navigational suite, including Furuno FSN-70 NAVSAT receiver, Furuno 525 HFD/F, Furuno 120 MF–HFD/F, FE-881 echo sounder, Furuno 500 autopilot, DS-70 doppler log, and a Weatherfax receiver. Differ from earlier units of the class in having a spray strake forward on the hull sides.

♦ **2 ex-U.S. Coast Guard Cape class**
Bldr: Coast Guard Yard, Curtis Bay, Md.

	In serv.
FSM 03 Paluwlap (ex-*Cape Cross,* WPB 95321)	20-8-58
FSM 04 Constitution (ex-*Cape Corwin,* WPB 95326)	14-11-58

D: 87 tons (106 fl) **S:** 20 kts **Dim:** 28.96 × 6.10 × 1.55
A: provision for 2 single 12.7-mm M2 mg
Electronics: Radar: 1 Raytheon SPS-64(V)9 nav.
M: 2 G.M. 16V 149TI diesels; 2 props; 2,470 bhp **Electric:** 60 kw tot.
Range: 550/20; 1,900/11.5 **Endurance:** 5 days **Crew:** 1 officer, 14 enlisted

Constitution (FSM 04)—stack painted blue, with four white stars
Ships of the World, 2-98

Remarks: Transferred by the U.S. government 30-3-90 as Grant-Aid. Planned transfer of a third unit, the ex-*Cape George* (WPB 95306), was canceled, and the craft went to Palau as FSM 05. Both were re-engined and otherwise modernized, completing 16-4-82 and 15-10-82, respectively; the original four Cummins VT-12-M-700 diesels produced 18 kts from 2,324 bhp. Can make 24 kts, but are restricted due to likelihood of hull damage at speeds over 20 kts. The craft normally do not carry armament.

MONTSERRAT

Crown Colony of Montserrat

MONTSERRAT POLICE FORCE

Base: Plymouth

PATROL BOATS [WPB]

♦ **1 M 160 class**
Bldr: Halmatic, Havant, U.K. (In serv. 16-1-90)

Shamrock

Shamrock—with Montserrat's Pacific 22–class RIB at left P. H. Nargeolet, 1998

D: 17.3 tons (light) **S:** 27 kts **Dim:** 15.40 (12.20 pp) × 3.86 × 1.15
A: 1 7.62-mm mg **Electronics:** Radar: 1 Decca 370 BT nav.
M: 2 G.M. Detroit Diesel 6V92 TA diesels; 2 props; 1,100 bhp (770 sust.)
Range: 300/20; 500/17 **Fuel:** 2,700 gallons **Crew:** 6 tot.

Remarks: GRP construction, provided by the U.K. as a replacement for patrol craft *Emerald Star,* lost by grounding 6-1-87. Has semi-rigid inflatable rescue dinghy at stern. Sister to Anguilla's *Dolphin,* the British Virgin Islands' *St. Ursula,* and the Turks and Caicos' *Sea Quest.*

SERVICE CRAFT

♦ **1 Pacific 22–class rigid inflatable launch [YFL]**
Bldr: Osborne, U.K (In serv. 2-96)

D: 1.75 tons light **S:** 30 kts **Dim:** 6.8 × . . . × . . .
M: 2 gasoline outboard motors; 120 bhp
Range: 85/26 **Crew:** 2 tot. + up to 12 personnel

MOROCCO

Kingdom of Morocco

MARINE ROYALE MAROCAINE

Personnel (2002): Approx. 7,800 total, including 1,500 marines

Bases: Principal base at Casablanca, with facilities at Agadir, Al Hoceima, Dakhla, Kenitra, Safa, and Tangier

Maritime Aviation: Two AS.565MA Panther helicopters are assigned to naval liaison duties. The Ministry of Fisheries and Merchant Marine operates 11 Pilatus-Britten-Norman BN2T Defender light maritime patrol aircraft for economic exclusion zone patrol.

FRIGATES [FF]

♦ **1 Spanish Descubierta class**
Bldr: Izar (formerly E.N. Bazán), El Ferrol

	Laid down	L	In serv.
501 Lieutenant Colonel Errhamani	20-3-79	26-2-82	28-3-83

Lieutenant Colonel Errhamani (501) Brian Morrison, 2-01

D: 1,270 tons (1,479 fl) **S:** 26 kts **Dim:** 88.88 (85.8 pp) × 10.4 × 3.25 (3.7 fl)
A: 1 8-round Albatros SAM syst. (24 Aspide missiles); 1 76-mm 62-cal. OTOBreda Compact DP; 2 single 40-mm 70-cal. Bofors L70 AA; 1 2-round 375-mm Bofors SR 375 ASW RL (24 Erika rockets); 2 triple 324-mm U.S. Mk 32 Mod. 5 ASW TT (Mk 46 Mod. 2 torpedoes)
Electronics:
Radar: 1 . . . nav.; 1 Thales ZW-06 surf. search; 1 Thales WM-25 Mod. 41 f.c.
Sonar: Raytheon DE 1160B hull-mounted MF
EW: Elettronica ELT 715 intercept/jammer; 2 330- to 340-round Matra Défense Dagaie decoy RL
M: 4 Izar-MTU 16MA956 TB91 diesels; 2 CP props; 18,000 bhp
Electric: 1,810 kw tot. **Range:** 4,000/18 (one engine) **Fuel:** 150 tons
Crew: 10 officers, 110 enlisted

FRIGATES [FF] *(continued)*

Lieutenant Colonel Errhamani (501) Brian Morrison, 2-01

Remarks: Ordered 14-6-77. Refitted fall 1995 in Spain, when a towing winch was added at the stern. Has fin stabilizers.
Combat systems: Has the Thales Nederland SEWACO-MR combat data system, but the combat information center is now equipped primarily as VIP quarters. Provision was made to carry four MM 38 Exocet missiles, but they were never installed. The 40-mm guns have been enclosed with Mauser mountings of the type employed on German Type 148 missile boats and are controlled by a single optical director; a second optical director serves as backup for the WM-25 system. Can carry 600 rounds of 76-mm ammunition. The DA-05 surface/air-search radar was removed during 1997 but restored in 1999, and a small navigational radar is now carried on a pole mast atop the pilothouse. A commercial SATCOM terminal is fitted.

PATROL SHIPS [PS]

♦ 0 (+ 2) Floréal class
Bldr: Chantiers de l'Atlantique, St. Nazaire, France

	Laid down	L	In serv.
611 Mohammed V	10-00	9-3-01	2002
612 Hassan II	2001	7-12-01	2002

D: 2,600 tons (2,950 fl) **S:** 20 kts **Dim:** 93.50 (85.20 pp) × 14.00 × 4.40
A: 2 MM 38 Exocet SSM; 1 76-mm 62-cal. OTOBreda Compact DP; single 20-mm 90-cal. GIAT F2 AA; 1 AS.565MA Panther helicopter
Electronics:
Radar: 1 Decca BridgeMaster-E ARPA nav.; 1 Thales DRBV-21A surf./air search; Thales WM-25 track-while-scan f.c.
M: 4 SEMT-Pielstick 6 PA6 L280 BTC diesels; 2 CP props; 9,600 bhp—250-kw bow-thruster
Electric: 1,770 kw (3 × 590-kw sets, 3 Baudouin 12 P15 2SR diesels driving)
Range: 10,000/15 **Fuel:** 390 tons **Endurance:** 50 days
Crew: 11 officers, 109 enlisted

Mohammed V (611)—fitting out at St. Nazaire Bernard Prézelin, 11-01

Remarks: Ordered 26-10-98. Intended primarily for economic exclusion zone patrol, fisheries protection, and maritime policing duties. Were originally to have been delivered in 10-00 and 6-01, but that goal has since slipped considerably. Six sisters serve in the French Navy. Seatrials for 611 began during 12-01.
Hull systems: Constructed to Veritas commercial standards. Has an emphasis on seaworthiness, with helicopter operations possible up to Sea State 5. Equipped with fin stabilizers. Have accommodations for 123 personnel total. The 23 × 14–m flight deck can accommodate a 9-ton helicopter and has a Samahé landing and deck transit system; there is also a hangar.
Combat systems: There is no combat data system. One of the two Decca radars is mounted aft for helicopter control. The Exocet missiles, 76-mm gun, and WM-25 radar are to come from units of the *Lazaga* class and were to be installed at Casablanca.

PATROL COMBATANTS [PG]

♦ 5 OPV 64 class
Bldr: Lorient Naval Industries, Lanester, France

	Laid down	L	In serv.
318 Raïs Bargach	11-94	9-10-95	14-12-95
319 Raïs Britel	. . .	19-3-96	14-5-96
320 Raïs Charkaoui	. . .	26-9-96	15-12-96
321 Raïs Maaninou	. . .	7-3-97	21-5-97
322 Raïs al Mounastiri	. . .	15-10-97	17-12-97

Raïs al Mounastiri (322) Mike Welsford, 5-00

Raïs Bargach (318) H&L Van Ginderen, 11-99

D: 580 tons (650 fl) **S:** 25 kts (22 sust.)
Dim: 64.00 (59.00 pp) × 11.42 × 3.00 (over props)
A: 2 single 20-mm 90-cal. AA; 2 single 12.7-mm mg
Electronics:
Radar: 1 Decca 2090-series BridgeMaster I-band nav.; 1 Decca 2090-series BridgeMaster-E ARPA nav.
M: 2 Wärtsilä-Nohab 16V25 diesels (900 rpm); 2 KaMeWa CP props; 10,000 bhp—2 160-shp Leroy-Somer electric auxiliary drives (8 kts max.)
Electric: 480 kw tot. (2 × 200 kw, Wärtsilä UD19 L6 diesels driving; 1 × 80 kw, Wärtsilä UD16 L6 diesel driving)
Range: 4,000/12 **Endurance:** 10 days
Crew: 6 officers, 10 petty officers, 30 nonrated (accomm. for 54 tot.)

Remarks: First two ordered from Leroux & Lotz (now LNI/Lorient Naval Industries) in late 1993 for delivery by end-1994, but the program was delayed. The other three were ordered in 10-94. Intended for fisheries patrol duties. Are somewhat less capable than the version originally offered.
Hull systems: Hullform features a double chine forward. There are eight watertight compartments. Flume-type passive stabilization tanks are fitted fore and aft. Have a helicopter platform on the stern and a stern recovery/deployment ramp for an internally stowed rigid inflatable inspection craft. Has electric drive to both propellers for low-speed operations (6–8 kts). Equipped with a 400-m^3/hr firefighting water monitor driven by a 200-kw diesel engine. For pollution control, have two 5-m^3 dispersant tanks and two 8-m-long dispersant booms. Navigation equipment includes a GPS receiver and autopilot.
Combat systems: One 40-mm gun was to have been added in Morocco from existing stocks but has not yet been installed.

♦ 4 Osprey 55 class
Bldr: Danyard A/S, Frederikshavn, Denmark

	L	In serv.		L	In serv.
308 El Lahiq	7-87	11-87	316 El Hamiss	4-90	8-90
309 El Tawfiq	10-87	2-88	317 El Karib	7-90	12-90

El Hamiss (316)—at Lorient for overhaul Bernard Prézelin, 4-01

D: 420 tons (500 fl) **S:** 19 kts (18 sust.)
Dim: 54.75 (51.83 pp) × 10.50 (9.15 wl) × 2.75
A: 1 40-mm 70-cal. Bofors AA; 2 single 20-mm 90-cal. AA

PATROL COMBATANTS [PG] *(continued)*

El Lahiq (308)—in France for overhaul; note door centerline at stern for small boat launching ramp H&L Van Ginderen, 11-99

Electronics: Radar: 2 Decca . . . nav.
M: 2 M.A.N.–Burmeister & Wain Alpha 12V.23/30 DVO diesels; 2 CP props; 4,960 bhp
Electric: 268 kw/316 kVA tot. (2 MWM TD232-V8 diesels driving)
Range: 4,500/16 **Fuel:** 95 tons **Crew:** 15 tot. + 16 passengers

Remarks: First two ordered early in 1986 for fisheries protection and search-and-rescue duties; second pair ordered 30-1-89. A third pair was reportedly ordered in 6-90, but the contract was not consummated. Similar ships are in Greek, Myanmar, Namibian, and Senegalese service. No armament was mounted at time of delivery. 317 carries the Danyard Oil Containment System with Desmi skimmer capable of accumulating 40–70 m³/hr of oil contaminant. All have a stern ramp and door for launching a 6.5-m rigid inflatable rescue/inspection craft. 308 is equipped with U.S.-made mapping sonars and navigational equipment and has conducted hydrographic surveys between Jorf las Par and Casablanca and between Rabat and Tangier. All can carry 27 tons of fresh water.

PATROL CRAFT [PC]

♦ 6 Vigilance class
Bldr: Izar (formerly E.N. Bazán), Cadiz

	L	In serv.
310 Lieutenant de Vaisseau Rabhi	23-9-87	16-9-88
311 Errachiq	23-9-87	16-12-88
312 El Akid	29-3-88	4-4-89
313 El Maher	29-3-88	20-6-89
314 El Majid	21-10-88	26-9-89
315 El Bachir	21-10-88	19-12-89

D: 307 tons (425 fl) **S:** 22 kts **Dim:** 58.1 (54.4 pp) × 7.60 × 2.70
A: 1 40-mm 70-cal. Bofors AA; 2 single 20-mm 90-cal. Oerlikon AA
Electronics: Radar: 2 Decca . . . nav.
M: 2 MTU 16V956 TB82 diesels; 2 props; 7,600 bhp (sust.)
Range: 3,800/12 **Endurance:** 10 days
Crew: 4 officers, 32 enlisted + 15 passengers

El Bachir (315) Leo Dirkx, 8-01

Remarks: Three ordered 2-10-85, with an option for three more taken up shortly thereafter. "Series P200/D" design, a reduced-power version of the *Lazaga* design for 200-n.m. economic zone patrol. Have a Matra Défense Naja optronic director for the 40-mm gun.

♦ 2 Spanish Lazaga class
Bldr: Izar (formerly E.N. Bazán), Cadiz

	In serv.
306 Commandant el Harti	25-2-82
307 Commandant Azouggarh	2-8-82

D: 303 tons (420 fl) **S:** 29.6 kts **Dim:** 57.40 (54.4 pp) × 7.60 × 2.70
A: 1 76-mm 62-cal. OTOBreda DP; 1 40-mm 70-cal. Bofors-OTOBreda AA; 2 single 20-mm 90-cal. Oerlikon GAM-B01 AA
Electronics:
Radar: 1 Decca . . . nav.; 1 Thales ZW-06 surf. search; 1 Thales WM-25 track-while-scan f.c.
M: 2 Izar-MTU MA16V956 TB91 diesels; 2 props; 7,780 bhp
Electric: 405 kVA **Range:** 700/27; 3,000/15 **Crew:** 41 tot.

Commandant el Harti (306) Winter & Findler, 7-96

Remarks: Ordered 14-6-77; first unit launched 21-7-80. Have added fuel capacity over the former Spanish Navy version.
Disposals: *Commandant al Khattabi* (304) and *Commandant Boutouba* (305) were to have been stricken during 2001.
Combat systems: Were originally equipped to carry four MM 38 Exocet antiship missiles but normally carried only two; since the mid-1990s, they have carried none at all, and the operational missiles are being rehabilitated and transferred to the new *Floréal*-class patrol ships, which will also receive the 76-mm guns from the first two units of this class. Can carry 300 rounds of 76-mm, 1,472 rounds of 40-mm, and 3,000 rounds of 20-mm ammunition. Have a Matra Défense Naja optical director aft for the 40-mm gun. The 40-mm mounting has been enclosed and a small navigational radar has been added.

♦ 2 French Type PR 72
Bldr: SFCN, Villeneuve-la-Garenne

	L	In serv.		L	In serv.
302 Okba	10-10-75	16-12-76	303 Triki	2-2-76	12-7-77

Triki (303)—with the 76-mm gunmount missing forward French Navy, 3-97

D: 370 tons (440 fl) **S:** 28 kts (at 413 tons) **Dim:** 57.0 (54.0 pp) × 7.6 × 2.5
A: 1 76-mm 62-cal. OTOBreda Compact DP; 1 40-mm 70-cal. Bofors AA; 2 single 12.7-mm mg
Electronics:
Radar: 1 Decca 1226 nav.; 1 . . . nav.
E/O: 2 Matra Défense Panda optronic f.c. directors
M: 4 SACM AGO 195V16 SZSHR diesels; 2 props; 11,040 bhp
Electric: 360 kw tot. **Range:** 2,500/16 **Crew:** 5 officers, 48 enlisted

Remarks: Ordered in 6-73. A second navigational radar has been added.

PATROL BOATS [PB]

♦ 6 French Type P 32
Bldr: CMN, Cherbourg

	L	In serv.		L	In serv.
203 El Wacil	12-6-75	9-10-75	206 El Khafir	21-1-76	16-4-76
204 El Jail	10-10-75	3-12-75	207 El Haris	31-3-76	30-6-76
205 El Mikdam	1-12-75	30-1-76	208 Essahir	2-6-76	16-7-76

El Haris (207) Carlo Martinelli, 9-96

D: 89.5 tons (fl) **S:** 29 kts **Dim:** 32.20 (30.00 pp) × 5.35 × 1.85
A: 2 single 20-mm 70-cal. Oerlikon Mk 10 AA
Electronics: Radar: 1 Decca . . . nav.
M: 2 SACM-Wärtsilä UD30 V16 diesels; 2 props; 2,700 hp
Range: 1,200/12 **Crew:** 12 tot.

Remarks: Ordered 2-74. Have a GRP-sheathed, laminated wood-construction hull. The customs service operates sisters *Erraid* (209), *Erracel* (210), *El Kaced* (211), and *Essaid* (212), all ordered during 6-85; they carry only one gun, forward.

AMPHIBIOUS WARFARE SHIPS AND CRAFT

♦ 1 ex-U.S. Newport-class tank landing ship [LST]
Bldr: National Steel Shipbuilding, San Diego

	Laid down	L	In serv.
407 Sidi Mohammed ben Abdallah (ex-*Bristol County,* LST 1198)	13-2-71	4-12-71	5-8-72

Sidi Mohammed ben Abdallah (407) French Navy, 10-98

D: 4,975 tons light (8,576 fl) **S:** 22 kts (20 sust.)
Dim: 159.2 (171.3 over horns) × 21.18 × 5.3 (aft; 1.80 fwd)
A: 1 20-mm Mk 15 Phalanx gatling CIWS; 4 single 12.7-mm mg
Electronics:
Radar: 1 Decca . . . nav.; 1 Raytheon SPS-64(V)9 nav.; 1 Raytheon SPS-10F surf. search
M: 6 Alco 16-251 diesels; 2 CP props; 16,500 bhp—bow-thruster
Range: 14,250/14 **Fuel:** 1,750 tons
Crew: 13 officers, 174 enlisted + troops: 20 officers, 294 enlisted (+ 72 emergency accomm.)

Remarks: After decommissioning 15-7-94 from the U.S. Navy, was transferred 16-8-94 as a gift under the Grant-Aid program. Based at Casablanca. Refitted in fall 1995 in Spain.
Hull systems: Can transport 2,000 tons of cargo (500 tons max. for beaching) on 1,765 m^2 of deck space. A side-thruster propeller forward helps when marrying to a causeway. There is a 34-m-long, 75-ton-capacity mobile aluminum ramp forward, which is linked to the tank deck by a second from the upper deck. Aft is a 242-m^2 helicopter platform and a stern door for loading and unloading vehicles. The tank deck, which has a 75-ton-capacity turntable at both ends, can carry 229 M 48 tanks or 41 2.5-ton trucks, while the upper deck can accept 29 2.5-ton trucks. Normally carries three LCVPs and one LCP in Welin davits. Has two 10-ton cranes. Can carry 141,600 gallons of vehicle fuel.

♦ 3 French Champlain-class medium landing ships [LSM]
Bldr: Dubigeon, Normandy

	In serv.
402 Daoud ben Aicha	28-5-77
403 Ahmed es Sakali	9-77
404 Abou Abdallah el Ayachi	12-78

D: 750 tons (1,305 fl) **S:** 16 kts **Dim:** 80.0 (68.0 pp) × 13.0 × 2.4 (mean)
A: 2 single 40-mm 70-cal. Bofors AA; 2 single 12.7-mm mg; 2 single 81-mm mortars
Electronics: Radar: 1 Decca 1226 nav.; 1 . . . nav.
M: 2 SACM V-12 diesels; 2 CP props; 3,600 bhp
Range: 4,500/13 **Crew:** 30 officers, 54 enlisted

Remarks: First two ordered 12-3-75, third on 19-8-75. 402 refitted in France during 1995. Can carry 133 troops and about 12 vehicles; has a 330-ton beaching capacity. Can also carry 208 tons of potable water in ballast tanks. Have a helicopter platform aft.

Ahmed es Sakali (403) H&L Van Ginderen, 8-97

Daoud ben Aicha (402) French Navy, 1997

♦ 1 French EDIC-class utility landing craft [LCU]
Bldr: C.N. Franco-Belges (In serv. 1965)

401 Lieutenant Malghagh

Lieutenant Malghagh (401)—with old pennant number 1977

D: 292 tons (642 fl) **S:** 8 kts **Dim:** 59.0 × 11.95 × 1.3 (1.62 fl)
A: 2 single 20-mm 70-cal. Oerlikon AA; 1 120-mm mortar
Electronics: Radar: 1 Decca 1226 nav.
M: 2 MGO diesels; 2 props; 1,000 bhp **Range:** 1,800/8 **Crew:** 16 tot.

Remarks: Ordered in 1963. Can carry 11 trucks in the open vehicle well; has a bow ramp.

♦ 1 ex-French LCM(8)-class landing craft [LCM]
Bldr: CMN, Cherbourg

. . . . . . (ex-CTM 2)

D: 56 tons light (150 fl) **S:** 9.5 kts **Dim:** 23.80 × 6.35 × 1.25
A: 2 single 12.7-mm mg **Electronics:** Radar: 1 . . . nav.
M: 2 Poyaud 520 V8 diesels; 2 props; 480 bhp **Range:** 380/8
Fuel: 3.4 tons **Endurance:** 48 hr (at half power) **Crew:** 6 tot.

Remarks: Transferred 5-99. Cargo capacity: 90 tons.

AUXILIARIES

♦ 1 Robert D. Conrad–class oceanographic research ship [AGOR]
Bldr: Northwest Marine, Portland, Ore.

	L	In serv.
702 Abou el Barakat al Barbari (ex-*Bartlett,* T-AGOR 13)	24-3-66	15-4-69

Abou el Barakat al Barbari (702) H&L Van Ginderen, 11-99

D: 1,088 tons light (1,643 fl) **S:** 13.5 kts
Dim: 63.7 (59.7 pp) × 11.4 × 4.9 (6.3 max. over sonar domes)
Electronics: Radar: 1 Raytheon 1650/SX nav.; 1 Raytheon 1660/12S nav.
M: 2 Cummins diesels, electric drive; 1 prop; 1,000 shp—1 350-shp JT700 Omnithruster (4.5 kts)
Electric: 850 kw tot.
Range: 9,000/12; 8,500/9.5 **Fuel:** 211 tons **Endurance:** 45 days
Crew: 9 officers, 17 enlisted + 15 scientists/technicians

Remarks: Transferred 26-7-93. Renamed for a famous 12th-century Arab navigator. Formerly operated by MAR, Inc., of Rockville, Md., under contract to the U.S. Military Sealift Command. The large stack contains a 620-hp gas-turbine generator set used to drive the main shaft at speeds up to 6.5 kts for experiments requiring "quiet" conditions. Sisters and near-sisters serve in Chile, Portugal, New Zealand, Tunisia, Brazil, and Mexico.

♦ 1 vehicle cargo ship [AK]
Bldr: LNI (Lorient Naval Industries), Lanester, France (In serv. 1-8-97)

408 Ad Dakhla

D: 1,105 tons light (2,160 fl) **S:** 12.5 kts (12 sust.)
Dim: 69.00 (64.00 wl) × 11.50 × 4.20 **A:** 2 12.7-mm mg
Electronics:
Radar: 1 Decca BridgeMaster C181/6 nav.; 1 Decca BridgeMaster C324/8 nav.
M: 1 Wärtsilä-Nohab 8V25 diesel; 1 CP prop; 2,693 bhp
Electric: 600 kVA tot. (2 × 300-kVA Leroy alternators, Wärtsilä-Scania UD19 L06 S4D diesels driving)
Range: 4,300/12 **Fuel:** 165 tons **Crew:** 24 tot. (accomm. for 46)

Remarks: 1,500 dwt. Ordered in 1995 to replace older support ships. The stern was built at the former Leroux & Lotz yard at St. Malo and the bow at Lanester; launched 6-97 at St. Malo, the ship was fitted out at Lorient.

AUXILIARIES *(continued)*

Ad Dakhla (408) Bernard Prézelin, 7-97

Hull systems: Cargo: 800 tons max., including cargo fuel in the lower tanks. Has two folding hatch covers to permit carrying containerized cargo and can also load vehicles. Has one 17-ton electrohydraulic crane, mounted to starboard between the two cargo hatches. The hold has a continuous deck just above the waterline that is served by a 3.5-m-wide by 2.5-m-high vehicle door to starboard; vehicles can also be carried in the two lower holds. Carries 50 tons of fresh water (75 in emergencies).

♦ **1 former Danish cargo ship [AK]**
Bldr: Frederikshavn Værft & Tjrdok, Frederikshavn

405 El Aigh (ex-*Merc Caribe*) (In serv. 1972)

D: approx. 2,000 tons (fl) **S:** 12 kts **Dim:** 76.61 × 12.30 × 3.47
A: 2 single 20-mm 70-cal. Oerlikon AA
Electronics: Radar: 2 . . . nav.
M: Burmeister & Wain Alpha, 10-cyl. diesel; 1 prop; 1,250 bhp
Range: . . . **Crew:** . . .

Remarks: 499 grt/326 nrt/1,327 dwt. Has an ice-strengthened hull with pronounced bulbous bow, two holds, and four 5-ton cranes. Acquired in 1981 to provide logistic support for operations along Saharan coast. Originally built for Per R. Henriksen P/R, Copenhagen. Bought in 1981 by the Moroccan Ministry of Travel and Commerce, then transferred to the navy. Sister *El Dakhla* (406; ex-*Anglian Merchant;* ex-*Merc Nordia*) was stricken during 1996.

SERVICE CRAFT

♦ **1 diving tender [YDT]**

14 . . .

Remarks: Former small stern-haul fishing trawler, used for diver support and stores transport duties; no data available.

♦ **1 floating dry dock [YFDL]** (Acquired from France in 1990)

Lift capacity: 4,500 tons **Dim:** 126.00 × 28.75 × . . .

♦ **1 royal yacht [YFL]** Bldr: C.N. Pise, Italy (In serv. 1981)

Oued Eddahab (ex-*Akhir*)

♦ **1 Spanish Y 171–class medium harbor tug [YTM]**
Bldr: Izar (In serv. 12-93)

. . .

D: . . . tons **S:** 9 kts **Dim:** 9.5 × 3.1 × 0.9
M: 2 diesels; 2 waterjets; 400 bhp **Range:** 440/9

♦ **2 miscellaneous sail training craft [YTS]**

Al Massira Boujdour

CUSTOMS SERVICE

Note: The Moroccan Customs Service cooperates with the navy in performing coastal patrol duties.

PATROL BOATS [WPB]

♦ **4 French Type P 32** Bldr: CMN, Cherbourg

	Laid down	L	In serv.
209 Erraid	4-86	26-12-87	18-3-88
210 Erracel	30-6-86	21-1-88	15-4-88
211 El Kaced	1-12-86	10-3-88	16-6-88
212 Essaid	. . .	19-5-88	4-7-88

Essaid (212) Carlo Martinelli, 9-96

D: 24 tons light (88.7 fl) **S:** 29 kts
Dim: 32.00 (30.09 pp) × 5.35 (4.92 wl) × 1.42 (hull)
A: 1 20-mm 90-cal. Oerlikon GAM-B01 AA
Electronics: Radar: 1 . . . nav.
M: 2 SACM-Wärtsilä UD30 V16 M7 diesels; 2 props; 2,540 bhp
Range: 1,200/12 **Crew:** 12 tot.

Remarks: Ordered 6-85. Wooden construction. Six near-sisters serve in the navy. One 20-mm AA has been removed, and the forward mount has been replaced by a newer weapon.

♦ **18 Arcor 46 class**
Bldr: Arcor, C.N. d'Aquitane, La Teste, France (In serv. 1987–88)

D 01 through D 18

Arcor 46–class D 08 Carlo Martinelli, 9-96

D: 12.3 tons (15.1 fl) **S:** 33 kts **Dim:** 14.50 × 4.00 × 1.20
A: 1 12.7-mm mg **Electronics:** Radar: 1 Furuno 701 nav.
M: 2 Poyaud-Wärtsilä UD18 V8 diesels; 2 props; 1,120 bhp
Range: 300/20 **Crew:** 6 tot.

Remarks: Ordered 6-85. Glass-reinforced plastic construction.

SERVICE CRAFT

♦ **3 Assa-class search-and-rescue craft [WYFL]**
Bldr: Schweers, Bardenfleth (In serv. 1991)

Assa Haouz Tariq

D: 40 tons (fl) **S:** 20 kts **Dim:** 19.4 × 4.8 × 1.3
M: 2 . . . . . . diesels; 2 props; 1,400 bhp **Crew:** 6 tot.

♦ **5 Arcor 17 launches [WYFL]**
Bldr: Arcor, C.N. d'Aquitaine, La Teste, France (In serv. 1989–90)

D: . . . **S:** 50 kts **Dim:** 5.5 × 2.2 × 0.8
A: 1 7.62-mm mg **M:** . . .

Note: The gendarmerie also operates 15 Arcor 55–class patrol boats delivered in 1992–95. Similar to the smaller customs service Arcor 43–class, the boats are painted with green hulls and white superstructures and are armed with a single 7.62-mm machinegun.

MOZAMBIQUE

People's Republic of Mozambique

MARINHA MOÇAMBIQUE

Personnel (2002): Approx. 100 total, including one company of marines *(Fuzileiros)*

Bases: Headquarters at Maputo, with minor facilities at Beira, Nacala, and Pemba and at Metangula on Lake Malawi

Note: By 1998, only a handful of launches remained operational on Lake Malawi, and all of the craft donated by the former Soviet Union had either flooded and sunk or been sold. There are no immediate prospects for acquisition of new craft.

In 12-95, Portugal donated the new 11.2-m fisheries patrol and research launch *Alcantara Santos* for use by a government agency other than the navy; the craft has a beam of 3.69 m and a draft of 0.7 m and is powered by two Volvo Penta 63P diesels of 375 bhp each for speeds of up to 33 kts.

MYANMAR

Socialist Republic of the Union of Myanmar (formerly Burma)

TAMDAW LAY

Personnel (2002): Approx. 5,000, including 800 naval infantry. There is also a reserve force with about 2,000 personnel available.

Bases: Headquarters at Yangon (formerly Rangoon), with facilities at Bassein, Hanggyi Island, Kyaukphu Island, Zadetkale (St. Luke's) Island, Mergui, Moulmein, Seikyi, and Sinmalaik. A Chinese-made maritime surveillance radar set was installed at Zadetkale Island during 2001.

Note: Press reports of the explosion and loss of a naval vessel named *Khakhwe* (207) on 16-11-00 cannot be correlated to any known unit or class; personnel losses of eight dead and three missing indicate that the craft was quite small. Many of the various radar systems listed on the ships and craft described below are probably no longer operational.

PATROL SHIPS [PS]

♦ **1 ex-U.S. Admirable class**
Bldr: Willamette Iron & Steel, Portland, Ore.

	Laid down	L	In serv.
42 Yan Gyi Aung (ex-*Creddock,* MSF 356)	10-11-43	22-7-44	18-12-45

Yan Gyi Aung (42) NAVPIC Holland, 7-98

D: 650 tons (905 fl) **S:** 14 kts **Dim:** 56.24 (54.86 wl) × 10.08 × 2.87
A: 1 76.2-mm 50-cal. Mk 26 DP; 2 single 40-mm 60-cal. Bofors Mk 3 AA; 2 twin 20-mm 70-cal. Oerlikon Mk 24 AA
Electronics: Radar: 1 . . . nav.
M: 2 Busch-Sulzer Type 539 diesels; 2 props; 1,710 bhp **Electric:** 280 kw tot.
Range: 9,300/10 **Fuel:** 140 tons **Crew:** 100 tot.

Remarks: Minesweeping gear was removed prior to transfer on 21-3-67 and the ASW equipment was subsequently removed. Reportedly was placed in reserve in 1994, but was active as of 9-98 on coastal patrol duties.

Disposal note: U.S. PCER 848–class patrol ship *Yan Taing Aung* (41; ex-*Farmington,* PCER 894) was laid up in unmaintained reserve in 1994 and has almost certainly deteriorated to the point of no return; characteristics can be found in the 2000–01 and earlier editions. The former British River-class frigate *Mayu* (ex-*Fal*), acquired in 1947 and retired in 1979, is maintained on land as a museum and training facility at the Yangon Naval Base.

PATROL COMBATANTS [PG]

♦ **1 Danish Osprey class**
Bldr: Danyard AS, Frederikshavn (In serv. 5-80)

55 In Daw

D: 385 tons (505 fl) **S:** 20 kts **Dim:** 49.95 (45.80 pp) × 10.5 (8.8 wl) × 2.75
A: 1 40-mm 60-cal. Bofors AA; 2 single 20-mm 70-cal. Oerlikon AA
Electronics: Radar: 1 . . . nav.
M: 2 Burmeister & Wain Alpha 16V23L-VO diesels; 2 CP props; 4,640 bhp
Electric: 359 kVA tot. **Range:** 4,500/16 **Crew:** 5 officers, 15 enlisted

In Ya (57)—since stricken NAVPIC Holland, 3-94

Remarks: Operated by the navy for the People's Pearl and Fisheries Ministry on fisheries protection and economic exclusion zone patrol. Sister to the Namibian *Tobias Hainyeko.* Was armed in Myanmar. The helicopter flight deck aft is now cluttered with equipment and apparently not used. A rescue launch is recessed into the inclined ramp at stern.
Disposal note: Sister *In Ma* (56) sank in 1987 and was not raised, and *In Ya* (57) was in unmaintained reserve at Yangon as of 1998, in poor condition.

GUIDED-MISSILE PATROL CRAFT [PTG]

♦ **6 Chinese Houxin (Type 343M or 037-II)**
Bldr: Qiuxin SY, Shanghai (In serv. 1996–. . .)

471 Maga	473 Duwa	475 . . . . . .
472 Saittra	474 Zeyda	476 . . . . . .

Myanmar Houxin-class missile craft 475 or 476—during delivery voyage; note that the antiship missile racks at the stern do not have canister launchers fitted
92 Wing Det. A, RAAF, 4-97

Duwa (473)—moored with Hainan-class *Yan Aye Aung* (449) and *Yan Zwe Aung* (450)
NAVPIC Holland, 10-98

Maga (471)—moored with repair tender *Yan Long Aung* (200)
NAVPIC Holland, 8-98

GUIDED-MISSILE PATROL CRAFT [PTG] *(continued)*

D: 430 tons (478 fl) **S:** 32 kts **Dim:** 62.00 × 7.20 × 2.24 (mean hull)
A: 4 C-801 SSM; 2 twin 37-mm 63-cal. Type 76A AA; 2 twin 14.5-mm 93-cal. Type 61 AA
Electronics:
Radar: 1 Type 756 nav./surf. search; 1 Type 352C (Square Tie) missile targeting; 1 Type 341 (Rice Lamp) gun f.c.
M: 4 diesels; 4 props; 13,200 bhp **Range:** 750/18; 2,000/14 **Crew:** . . . tot.

Remarks: Two delivered early in 1996, two in 11-96, and two in 4-97. Are named for stars. The unsophisticated design is based on the obsolescent Haizhu-class subchaser/patrol boat. 475 was reportedly damaged in a collision during builder's trials in 8-96. Were not delivered with missiles aboard, and missiles may not have been provided.

PATROL CRAFT [PC]

♦ 2 45-meter gunboats
Bldr: Naval Dockyard, Yangon (In serv. 1996?)

D: 213 tons (fl) **S:** 30 kts **Dim:** 45.0 × 7.0 × 2.5
A: 2 single 40-mm 70-cal. Bofors AA
M: 2 MTU . . . . . . diesels; 2 props; . . . bhp
Range: . . ./. . . **Crew:** 7 officers, 27 enlisted

Remarks: Construction status uncertain; reported begun in 1991. Steel-hulled craft.

♦ 10 Chinese Hainan class (Project 037) (In serv. 1964–87)

441 Yan Sit Aung	446 Yan Min Aung
442 Yan Myat Aung	447 Yan Paing Aung
443 Yan Nyein Aung	448 Yan Win Aung
444 Yan Khwinn Aung	449 Yan Aye Aung
445 Yan Ye Aung	450 Yan Zwe Aung

Yan Nyein Aung (443)—moored with a sister and repair tender *Yan Long Aung* (200) NAVPIC Holland, 8-98

Yan Khwinn Aung (444) NAVPIC Holland, 3-94

D: 375 tons (392 fl) **S:** 30.5 kts **Dim:** 58.77 × 7.20 × 2.20 (hull)
A: 2 twin 57-mm 70-cal. DP; 2 twin 25-mm 80-cal. 2M-3M AA; 4 5-round RBU-1200 ASW RL; 2 BMB-2 d.c. mortars; 2 d.c. racks
Electronics:
Radar: 1 Type 756 nav.; 1 Pot Head surf. search
Sonar: Tamir-11 hull-mounted HF
M: 4 Type 12VEZ3025/Z diesels; 4 props; 8,800 bhp
Range: 2,000/14 **Crew:** 70 tot.

Remarks: Six delivered in 1-91 were refurbished PLAN units rather than new construction, and they were in poor material condition. Four additional, equally decrepit units were transferred in 3-94. All systems are obsolescent.

♦ 5 PGM 412 class
Bldr: Naval Dockyard, Yangon (In serv. 1983–88)

412 413 414 415 416

D: 128 tons (fl) **S:** 16 kts **Dim:** 33.5 × 6.7 × 2.0
A: 2 single 40-mm 60-cal. Bofors Mk 3 AA; 2 single 12.7-mm mg
M: 2 Deutz SBA 16MB216 LLKR diesels; 2 props; 2,720 bhp
Range: 1,400/14 **Crew:** 17 tot.

Remarks: Design was heavily influenced by the U.S.-built PGM 43 class, but they have a hull knuckle at the bow. Two additional units, completed 27-6-93 by the Myanmar Shipyard and named *Thihayarsar I* and *Thihayarsar II,* were assigned to the customs service.

♦ 2 U.S. 105-foot Commercial Cruiser aluminum patrol craft
Bldr: Swiftships, Morgan City, La.

422 (In serv. 31-3-79) 423 (In serv. 28-9-79)

D: 103 tons (111 fl) **S:** 24 kts **Dim:** 31.5 × 7.2 × 2.1
A: 2 single 40-mm 60-cal. Mk 3 Bofors AA; 2 single 20-mm 70-cal. Oerlikon Mk 10 AA; 2 single 12.7-mm mg
Electronics: Radar: 1 . . . nav.
M: 2 MTU 12V331 TC81 diesels; 2 props; 1,920 bhp
Range: 1,200/18 **Fuel:** 21.6 tons **Crew:** 25 tot.

Remarks: Reportedly acquired via Vosper Pty, Singapore. Aluminum construction. Had a Raytheon 1500 Pathfinder navigational radar at delivery in 1980. Sister 421 was lost at sea in the early 1990s.

♦ 6 U.S. PGM 43 class
Bldrs: Marinette Marine, Marinette, Wis. (405, 406: Peterson Bldrs, Sturgeon Bay, Wis.)

	In serv.		In serv.
401 (ex-PGM 43)	8-59	404 (ex-PGM 46)	9-59
402 (ex-PGM 44)	8-59	405 (ex-PGM 51)	6-61
403 (ex-PGM 45)	9-59	406 (ex-PGM 52)	6-61

U.S.-built PGM 43–class unit in Myanmar service NAVPIC Holland, 10-98

D: 100 tons (141 fl) **S:** 17 kts **Dim:** 30.81 × 6.45 × 2.30
A: 1 40-mm 60-cal. Mk 3 Bofors AA; 2 twin 20-mm 70-cal. Mk 24 Oerlikon AA; 2 single 12.7-mm M2 mg
Electronics: Radar: 1 EDO 320 (405, 406: Raytheon 1500 Pathfinder) nav.
M: 8 G.M. 6-71 diesels; 2 props; 2,040 bhp
Range: 1,000/16 **Fuel:** 16 tons **Crew:** 17 tot.

♦ 2 improved Y 301–class riverine patrol craft
Bldr: Similak, Burma (In serv. 1967)

Y 311 Y 312

D: 250 tons (fl) **S:** 14 kts (12 sust.) **Dim:** 37.0 × 7.3 × 1.1
A: 2 single 40-mm 60-cal. Bofors Mk 3 AA; 2 single 20-mm 70-cal. Oerlikon Mk 10 AA
M: 2 MTU–Mercedes-Benz diesels; 2 props; 1,000 bhp **Crew:** 37 tot.

Remarks: Differ in appearance from the Y 301 class in not having a funnel and in carrying both 40-mm AA on the main deck. All gunmounts have bulletproof shields.

♦ 10 Y 301–class riverine patrol craft
Bldr: Uljanik SY, Pula, Yugoslavia (In serv. 1957–60)

Y 301 through Y 310

Y 301 class

D: 120 tons (150 fl) **S:** 13 kts **Dim:** 32.0 × 7.25 × 0.9
A: 2 single 40-mm 60-cal. Bofors Mk 3 AA
M: 2 Mercedes-Benz diesels; 2 props; 1,100 bhp **Crew:** 29 tot.

Remarks: At least one (Y 304) has a Vickers 2-pdr. (40-mm 45-cal.) AA on the forecastle vice one 40-mm Bofors. Do not have a radar.

PATROL BOATS [PB]

♦ 6 Carpentaria-class fisheries patrol boats
Bldr: De Havilland Marine, Homebush Bay, Sydney, Australia (1979–80)

112 113 114 115 116 117

D: 27 tons (fl) **S:** 27 kts **Dim:** 16.0 × 5.0 × 1.2
A: 1 20-mm 70-cal. Oerlikon Mk 10 AA or 12.7-mm mg
Electronics: Radar: 1 Decca 110 nav.
M: 2 G.M. 12V71 TI diesels; 2 props; 1,120 bhp **Range:** 700/22 **Crew:** 10 tot.

Remarks: Operated by the navy for the People's Pearl and Fisheries Ministry. Ordered 12-78. Sisters are in Indonesian and Solomon Islands forces. Aluminum construction.

PATROL BOATS [PB] *(continued)*

Carpentaria-class patrol boat in Myanmar service H&L Van Ginderen, 1980

♦ 4 18.3-meter-class riverine patrol boats
Bldr: Naval Dockyard, Yangon (In serv. 11-4-90)

Remarks: Displace 37 tons and are armed with three single 12.7-mm mg; no further data available.

♦ 3 Yugoslav PB-90-class riverine patrol boats
Bldr: Brodotehnika, Belgrade (In serv. 1990)

424 425 426

D: 80 tons (90 fl) **S:** 32 kts (26 sust.) **Dim:** 27.35 × 6.55 × 1.15 (2.20 props)
A: 2 quadruple 20-mm 90-cal. M-75 AA
Electronics: Radar: 1 Decca 1226 nav.
M: 3 diesels; 3 props; 4,350 bhp
Range: 400/25 **Endurance:** 5 days **Crew:** 17 tot.

Remarks: Have four illumination/chaff RL on the foredeck.

♦ 9 30-ton class riverine patrol boats
Bldr: Naval Dockyard, Yangon, Myanmar (In serv. 1980s)

11 12 13 14 15 16 17 18 19

D: 30 tons (37 fl) **S:** 10 kts **Dim:** 15.2 × 4.3 × 1.1
A: 1 20-mm 70-cal. Oerlikon Mk 10 AA
M: 2 Thornycroft RZ 6 diesels; 2 props; 250 bhp
Range: 400/8 **Crew:** 8 + 30–40 troops

Remarks: Low-freeboard-aft, high-forecastle craft capable of carrying a squad of troops.

♦ 6 U.S. PBR Mk II–class GRP-hulled patrol boats
Bldr: Uniflite, Bellingham, Wash. (In serv. 1978)

211 212 213 214 215 216

D: 8.9 tons (fl) **S:** 24 kts **Dim:** 9.73 × 3.53 × 0.81
A: 1 twin and 1 single 12.7-mm mg; 1 60-mm mortar
Electronics: Radar: 1 Raytheon 1900 nav.
M: 2 G.M. GV53N diesels; 2 waterjets; 430 bhp
Range: 150/23 **Crew:** 4–5 tot.

♦ 8 miscellaneous fisheries protection boats

511 520 521 522 523 901 905 906

Naval modified fishing boat patrol boat 511 NAVPIC Holland, 9-98

Remarks: Typical Burmese fishing boats. 901 is of about 200 tons displacement, while the others are of about 50–80 tons. Carry at least one machinegun.

AMPHIBIOUS WARFARE CRAFT

♦ 4 Aiyar Maung–class utility landing craft [LCU]
Bldr: Yokohama Yacht, Japan (L: 3-69)

604 Aiyar Mai 606 Aiyar Min Tha Mee
605 Aiyar Maung 607 Aiyar Min Thar

Aiyar Maung (605) Yokohama Yacht, 1959

D: 250 tons (fl) **S:** 10 kts **Dim:** 38.25 × 9.14 × 1.4
M: 2 Kubota diesels; 2 props; 560 bhp **Cargo:** 100 tons **Crew:** 10 tot.

♦ 2 Sinde-class utility landing craft [LCU]
Bldr: Yokohama Yacht, Japan (In serv. 1978)

601 Sinde 602 Htonbo

Sinde (601) Yokohama Yacht, 1968

D: 220 tons (fl) **S:** 10 kts **Dim:** 29.50 × 6.72 × 1.4
M: 2 Kubota diesels; 2 props; 300 bhp **Cargo:** 50 tons, 30 passengers

♦ 1 U.S. LCU 1610–class utility landing craft [LCU]
Bldr: Southern SB (In serv. 10-67)

603 Aiyar Lulin (ex-U.S. LCU 1626)

D: 190 tons (342 fl) **S:** 11 kts **Dim:** 41.00 × 9.0 × 2.0
A: 2 single 20-mm 70-cal. Oerlikon Mk 10 AA
M: 4 G.M. Detroit Diesel 12007T diesels; 2 props; 1,000 bhp
Range: . . ./. . . **Fuel:** 10 tons **Crew:** 14 tot.

Remarks: Used as a transport. Transferred on completion; one of only two ships built to this design. Cargo capacity: 170 tons. Has bow and stern ramps.

♦ 10 ex-U.S. LCM(6) Mk 2 class landing craft [LCM]

701 through 710

LCM(6) landing craft in Myanmar Navy service NAVPIC Holland, 8-98

D: 24 tons (64 fl) **S:** 10.2 kts (light) **Dim:** 17.07 × 4.37 × 1.22 (fwd; 1.52 aft)
M: 2 G.M. Gray Marine 64HN9 diesels; 2 props; 330 bhp
Range: 140/10 (loaded) **Crew:** 4–5 tot.

Remarks: Origins unknown. Can carry 34 tons of cargo or 80 fully equipped troops for short distances in the 11.43 × 3.35–m cargo well, which has a total area of 38.37 m^2 of usable space. Not discarded in 1996 as reported earlier.

♦ 8 riverine troop ferries [LCP]
Bldr: . . . . . ., Yangon (In serv. 1960s)

Saban Seinma Setyahat Shwethida
Sagu Sethaya Shwepazun Sinmin

D: 99 tons (fl) **S:** 12 kts **Dim:** 28.8 × 6.7 × 1.4 **A:** see remarks
M: 1 Crossley ERL-6 diesel; 1 prop; 160 bhp **Crew:** 23–32 + . . . troops

AMPHIBIOUS WARFARE CRAFT *(continued)*

Remarks: *Seinma, Shwethida,* and *Sinmin* carry one 20-mm Oerlikon AA; *Sagu* is equipped with three single 20-mm AA and differs from the others in lacking a full permanent awning above the upper deck. Typical riverine passenger vessels, with low freeboard and open superstructure (with many sections protected by light plating).

AUXILIARIES

♦ 1 coastal hydrographic survey ship [AGS]
Bldr: Miho Zosen, Shimizu, Japan (In serv. 20-6-69)

802 . . . . . . (ex-*Changi*)

D: approx. 900 tons (fl) **S:** 13 kts **Dim:** 47.0 × 8.7 × 3.6
A: 2 single 20-mm 70-cal. Oerlikon Mk 10 AA
M: 1 Niigata diesel; 1 prop; . . . bhp **Crew:** 35 tot.

Remarks: 387 grt/118 dwt. Former Singapore-registry stern-haul fisheries research trawler, arrested 8-4-74 and commissioned for service as a survey vessel.

♦ 1 hydrographic survey ship [AGS]
Bldr: Tito SY, Belgrade, Yugoslavia (In serv. 1965)

801 Thu Tay Thi

Thu Tay Thi (801) [No date or credit]

D: 1,100 tons (1,271 fl) **S:** 15 kts **Dim:** 62.21 (56.80 pp) × 11.00 × 3.60
A: 2 single 40-mm 60-cal. Bofors Mk 3 AA; 2 single 20-mm 70-cal. Oerlikon Mk 10 AA
M: 2 MB820Db diesels; 2 props; 1,710 bhp **Crew:** 7 officers, 92 enlisted

Remarks: Carries two inshore survey craft. Armament had been added by 6-93, with one mount in the center of what had been intended as a helicopter platform.

♦ 1 coastal cargo ship [AK]
Bldr: A/S Nordsøværftet, Ringkobing, Norway (In serv. 1975)

. . . Pyi Daw Aye

Pyi Daw Aye (. . .) NAVPIC Holland, 8-98

D: approx. 850 tons (fl) **S:** 11 kts **Dim:** 49.71 (44.46 pp) × 8.34 × 3.46
M: 1 . . . . . . diesel; 1 prop; 600 bhp **Crew:** 12 tot.

Remarks: 300 grt/699 dwt. Has two cargo holds and two light cargo derricks. Was in very poor condition as of 1998 but still in commission.

♦ 1 coastal tanker [AOT]
Bldr: Shimoda Dockyard, Shimoda, Japan (In serv. 1974)

609 . . . . . . (ex-*Seria Maru*)

Myanmar Navy tanker 609 NAVPIC Holland, 10-98

D: approx. 2,600 tons (fl) **S:** 10 kts **Dim:** 68.66 × 11.00 × 5.00
M: 1 Daihatsu diesel; 1 prop; 1,300 bhp
Range: . . ./. . . **Crew:** . . . tot.

Remarks: 972 grt/2,034 dwt. Former Japanese coastal fuels tanker, acquired around 1986.

♦ 1 coastal tanker [AOT]
Bldr: Watanabe Zosen K.K., Hakata, Japan (In serv. 1969)

608 . . . . . . (ex-*Inter Bunker,* ex-*Shamrock Ace,* ex-*Bunker SPC VI,* ex-*Naniwa Maru No. 33*)

Myanmar Navy tanker 608 NAVPIC Holland, 10-98

D: approx. 2,800 tons (fl) **S:** 11.5 kts **Dim:** 70.69 (65.00 pp) × 11.00 × 4.93
M: 2 Daihatsu 8-cyl. diesels; 1 prop; 1,860 bhp
Electric: 128 kw tot (2 × 64-kw diesel sets)
Range: 5,400/11.5 **Fuel:** 98.5 tons **Crew:** 15 tot.

Remarks: 992 grt/2,209 dwt. Honduran-registry commercial vessel owned by Thai company Suphachal Chareonsri, arrested 10-91 and taken over for Myanmar Navy service. No underway replenishment capability. Has cargo expansion trunk over cargo tank area.

SERVICE CRAFT

♦ 1 presidential yacht [YAG]
Bldr: . . . . (In serv. 1980s)

Ya Dana Bon

Remarks: Three-decked, white-painted riverine transport for use on the Irrawaddy River. Operated by the navy. Reported to carry two single 7.62-mm mg.

♦ 1 diving and repair tender [YDT]
Bldr: . . . , Japan (In serv. 1967)

200 Yan Long Aung

Yan Long Aung (200)—alongside a Hainan-class patrol craft NAVPIC Holland, 10-98

D: 536 tons (fl) **S:** 12 kts **Dim:** 54.6 × 9.1 × 2.4
A: 1 40-mm 60-cal. Mk 3 Bofors AA; 2 single 12.7-mm mg
M: 2 . . . . . . diesels; 2 props; . . . bhp **Crew:** 88 tot.

Remarks: Formerly a torpedo retriever and torpedo boat tender. Carries a landing craft–type workboat on the starboard quarter.

♦ 25 30- to 40-ton river launches [YFL]
Bldr: Yugoslavia (In serv. 1965)

Naval personnel launch 053 NAVPIC Holland, 10-98

Remarks: No data available. There are likely also numerous locally built launches and service craft for which no information is available.

SERVICE CRAFT *(continued)*

♦ **1 riverine hydrographic survey boat [YGS]**
Bldr: Netherlands (In serv. 1957)

807 Yay Bo

D: 108 tons (fl) **S:** 10 kts **Dim:** 30.0 × 6.8 × 1.5
A: 1 12.7-mm mg **M:** 2 . . . . . . diesels; 2 props; . . . bhp
Crew: 2 officers, 32 enlisted

NAMIBIA

FISHERIES PROTECTION SERVICE

Bases: Walvis Bay and Lüderitz

Maritime Aviation: Five ex-U.S. Air Force Cessna O-2A observation aircraft, transferred 26-6-94, operate from Eros Airport, Windhoek, as maritime surveillance and antipoaching patrol assets.

Note: Reports that patrol ships or patrol boats would be acquired from Brazil have been officially denied, although Brazilian sources indicate that an agreement to transfer an old *Imperial Marinheiro*–class patrol ship and several new-construction patrol craft, either of the *Graúna* or AVINPA-21 class, was to have been concluded during 2001 but was deferred at the last moment. All ships and craft carry "Fisheries Patrol" on the sides of their superstructures.

PATROL COMBATANTS [WPG]

♦ **0 (+ 1) Norwegian new-construction fisheries protection ship**
Bldr: Moen Slip A/S, Kolvereid, Norway (In serv. 4-02)

. . . . . .

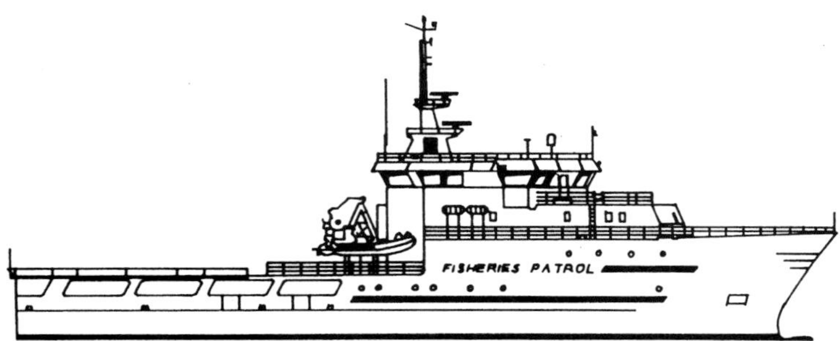

Namibia's new Norwegian-built fisheries protection ship
Drawing by A. D. Baker III

D: . . . tons **S:** 17 kts **Dim:** 57.6 × 12.5 × . . .
A: 1 12.7-mm mg **Electronics:** Radar: 2 . . . nav./surf. search
M: 2 . . . diesels; . . . props; 2,040 bhp

Remarks: Ordered 9-99. Financed by the Norwegian development aid agency NORAD. Has a helicopter deck aft and carries two RIB inspection craft.

♦ **1 Danish Osprey-class fisheries protection ship**
Bldr: Danyard A/S, Frederikshavn (In serv. 1979)

Tobias Hainyeko (ex-*Havørnen*)

Tobias Hainyeko French Navy, 9-97

D: 320 tons (506 fl) **S:** 18 kts **Dim:** 49.98 (45.80 pp) × 10.50 × 2.75
A: 1 12.7-mm mg
Electronics:
Radar: 1 Furuno FRM 64 nav.; 1 Furuno FR 1525 ARPA surf. search
M: 2 Burmeister & Wain Alpha 16V23L-VO diesels; 2 CP props; 4,640 bhp
Range: 4,500/16 **Crew:** 15 tot. (accomm. for 35)

Remarks: Donated by the Danish government and transferred in fall 1993. Had been operated since completion by the Danish Ministry of Fisheries. Has a stern hangar and ramp for a 6.5-m rubber inspection dinghy. Built to mercantile specifications. Has a helicopter deck, but the original hangar has been blanked off. Five Danish naval officers formed part of the complement through 1998. Was unarmed in Danish service.

PATROL CRAFT [WPC]

♦ **1 fisheries patrol craft/yacht**
Bldr: Burmester Yacht und Bootswerft, Bremen, Germany (In serv. 5-75)

Oryx (ex-*S To S*)

D: 406 tons (fl) **S:** 14 kts **Dim:** 45.67 (40.95 p.p.) × 9.12 × 2.94
A: 1 12.7-mm mg
Electronics: Radar: 1 Furuno FR 1525 ARPA nav.; 1 Furuno FR 805D nav.
M: 2 Deutz RSBA16M528 diesels; 1 CP prop; 2,000 bhp—bow-thruster
Electric: 184 kw tot. (2 × 92-kw diesel sets)
Range: 4,100/11 **Crew:** 6 officers, 14 enlisted

Remarks: 454 grt. Transferred at independence from the South African government and is based at Walvis Bay and used for fisheries patrol. Formerly the yacht of the managing director of Fiat, Italy. Bow built by Abeking & Rasmussen, Lemwerder. Machinery is aft.

AUXILIARIES

♦ **1 fisheries research ship [WAGOR]**
Bldr: Barens SB, Durban, South Africa (In serv. 10-68)

Benguela

D: approx. 850 tons (fl) **S:** 12 kts **Dim:** 44.20 (37.50 pp) × 9.48 × 3.67
M: 2 Burmeister & Wain Alpha 406-26VO diesels; 1 CP prop; 1,200 bhp—2 bow-thrusters
Electric: 500 kw tot. (2 × 250-kw diesel sets)
Range: . . ./. . . **Fuel:** 122 tons **Crew:** . . . tot.

Remarks: 486 grt/142 dwt. Transferred by the government of South Africa at independence and is based at Walvis Bay and used for fisheries patrol. Stern-haul trawler design.

Note: Other small government fisheries research craft, for which no data are available, include the *Kuiseb, Nautilus II,* and *Welwitschia.*

SERVICE CRAFT

♦ **2 Buccaneer Legend rigid inflatable launches [WYFL]**
Bldr: Buccaneer Inflatables, Glenvista, South Africa (In serv. 1993)

D: 1.2 tons light (3.5 tons fl) **S:** 37 kts **Dim:** 8.00 × 2.60 × . . .
A: 1 12.7-mm mg **M:** 1 Cummins . . . diesel; 1 prop; 320 bhp

Remarks: Ordered in late 1992 for rescue and patrol duties. Have a semi-rigid aluminum lower hull with flexible upper collar.

NATO

North Atlantic Treaty Organization

Note: The oceanographic research ships described below are the only vessels "owned" jointly by the NATO nations. There is, however, a NATO Standing Force (StanNavForLant) of frigates and destroyers, which would be augmented in time of war by warships from the major signatory nations, and a NATO standing mine countermeasures force was established during 5-99, primarily for service in the Mediterranean area.

AUXILIARIES

♦ **1 Alliance-class research ship [WAGE]**

	Bldr	L	In serv.
A 1956 Alliance	Fincantieri, Muggiano	9-7-86	6-5-88

Alliance (A 1956)—white painted, with buff-colored stacks and foremast; does not wear pennant number Takatoshi Okano, 4-01

AUXILIARIES *(continued)*

D: 2,466 tons (3,180 fl) **S:** 17 kts (16.3 sust.)
Dim: 93.00 (82.00 pp) × 15.20 × 5.10
Electronics:
Radar: 2 Qubit–Kelvin-Hughes Nucleus 6000 nav. (X- and S-band)
Sonar: STN Atlas Elektronik Hydrosweep mapping (50 kHz)
M: 2 GMT B.230.12M diesels, AEG CC 3127 generators, electric drive: 2 AEG 1,470-kw motors; 2 props; 4,000 shp—side-thrusters fore and aft
Electric: 1,850 kw tot. (including 1 1,605-kw Kongsberg gas-turbine set)
Range: 8,000/12 **Crew:** 10 officers, 17 unlicensed + 23 scientists

Remarks: 3,200 grt/533 dwt. Based at Naples and operated for the NATO ASW Research Center, La Spezia, by U.K. Denholm SERCO Ship Management, with German Naval Auxiliary Service officers and multinational nonrated personnel. Flies the German flag. Sister *Ta Kuan* was delivered to Taiwan in 1995, and a near-sister, configured as an intelligence collector, is to be built for the Italian Navy.
Hull systems: Has 6,100 m^2 of total working deck space and 400 m^2 of lab space. Has a towing winch, with 20-ton bollard pull, and 6,000 m of 50-mm cable. Also has a 1,000-kg oceanographic crane with telescopic arm. Special attention was paid to quieting. Has Flume-type passive tank stabilization. Pennant number (not borne) is from a block assigned to the German Navy. During 1991, began trials with a 64-hydrophone vertical-array towed passive sonar system. An STN Atlas Elektronik Hydrosweep MD multibeam echo sounder was ordered for the ship during 3-93; it covers a swath 2 km wide in waters up to 1 km deep. Other modernizations effected were substitution of Qubit–Kelvin-Hughes radars and installation of a Magnavox precision navigation system, Qubit–Kelvin-Hughes TRAC integrated navigation and information management systems, two GPS receivers, two Loran-C receivers, and a Decca radio-navigation chain receiver; the modernization was completed during 4-95. Trials were conducted 1995 with a 4-tonne, dual-frequency (200 Hz, 4 kHz) Towed Vertically Directive Source developed by the U.S. Office of Naval Research and Naval Undersea Warfare Center. The Ultra Electronics Deployable Undersea Sensing System (DUSS) will begin trials in the ship in mid-2002; the system employs an active transmitter combined with a number of receive buoys linked by the Globalstar SATCOM array and wideband terrestrial communications.

SERVICE CRAFT

♦ **0 (+ 1) oceanographic tender [YAGE]**
Bldr: McTay Marine, U.K. (In serv. 4-02)

LEONARDO

D: . . . tons (fl) **S:** . . . kts **Dim:** 28.00 × . . . × . . .
M: 2 Cummins . . . diesels, electric drive; 2 Schottel azimuthal props; . . . shp—azimuthal bow-thruster
Crew: 10 max., including scientific party

Remarks: Ordered 19-12-00. The hull is being built in Poland by Remontowa Ship Repair, Gdansk, for fitting out in the U.K. An A-frame gallows crane is installed at the stern. Replaces the *Manning* (ex-U.S. Army T-514), which was to be retired early in 2002. Used for studies of the effect of the sea floor on acoustic energy, propagation studies, and demonstration projects. Is actually owned by the Italian Ministry of Defense.

NETHERLANDS

Kingdom of the Netherlands

Personnel (2001): 9,220 tot. navy, plus 2,933 marines and 5,500 civilian employees

Bases: Headquarters at The Hague, with the main naval base at Den Helder. Minor facilities are found at Vlissingen (to close in 2005) and at Curaçao in the Caribbean. The Belgian naval staff was formally integrated with that of the Netherlands at Den Helder on 28-3-95. Fixed-wing aircraft are based at Valkenberg (to close in 2010) and helicopters at De Kooij Naval Air Station, near Den Helder.

Naval Aviation: Principal types include 12 Lockheed P-3C Update II Orion (equipped to launch AGM-84 Harpoon missiles) and 21 Westland SH-14D Lynx helicopters. Fixed-wing training is conducted at the National Flying School with a Beech 200 light transport, while helicopter training is conducted by Heliholland at Curaçao with one Eurocopter AS.355 and one Schweizer helicopter. The two Fokker F-27-200MRA maritime reconnaissance aircraft flown by 336 Sqn. from Hato, Curaçao, were replaced by a single P-3C Orion in 2000. The P-3s are to transfer to De Kooij Naval Air Station in 2010. The first of three P-3C Orions to be retired was stricken during 11-01; the second was to follow in 2-02 and the third in the fall of 2003. One SH-14D Lynx was lost early in 2-02 from *Abraham van der Hulst* (F832) in the Caribbean; it was to be replaced by a Belgian Navy Alouette-III.

Three P-3C Orion maritime patrol squadrons are based at Valkenberg (2 Sqn. for training and 320 Sqn. and 321 Sqn. operational) and two SH-14D helicopter squadrons (860 Sqn. and 861 Sqn.) at De Kooij Naval Air Station.

Up to 20 NH-90 helicopters are to be ordered to replace the Lynx, with initial deliveries coming in 2007 rather than 2003 as originally planned. Of the 13 Orions, three are to be retired by 2006 and seven are to be further updated; for those not planned for retirement, U.S. APS-137B(V)5 replacement radars were ordered on 28-9-00 for delivery by end-2002.

Seven Netherlands Army 300 Sqn. Cougar helicopters have been adapted for use from the *Rotterdam* (L 800).

Netherlands Navy P-3C Orion Rob Cabo, 7-01

Royal Netherlands Marines: Bases at Rotterdam, Doorn, and Texel (where landing craft are maintained) and training facilities at Amsterdam. Detachment at Aruba. Organized into four combat battalions, one combat support battalion (with two motorized companies, one landing craft company, and a Special Boat Section), and one logistic support battalion.

SH-14D Lynx Rob Cabo, 4-01

WEAPONS AND SYSTEMS

A. MISSILES

♦ **Surface-to-air missiles**

U.S. SM-1 MR Standard on the two *Jacob Van Heemskerck*–class frigates. U.S. RIM-7M Sea Sparrow on the *Karel Doorman*–, *Jacob Van Heemskerck*–, and *Kortenaer*-class frigates. RIM-7P Evolved Sea Sparrow in the *De Zeven Provinciën*–class frigates. Data for all can be found in the U.S.A. section.

♦ **Surface-to-surface missiles**

U.S. RGM-84 Harpoon on the *Jacob Van Heemskerck, Kortenaer,* and *Karel Doorman* classes. Sub-Harpoon was not acquired for the submarines.

B. GUNS

127-mm 54-cal. OTOBreda DP: On the new *De Zeven Provinciën*–class guided-missile frigates. These are refurbished mountings previously used aboard the Canadian Tribal class. See the Italy section for data.

76-mm OTOBreda Compact: On the *Kortenaer*- and *Karel Doorman*–class frigates. Upgraded to fire at 100 rds/min. See the Italy section for further data.

30-mm SGE-30 Goalkeeper: Uses the U.S. General Electric GAU-8A 30-mm gatling gun and EX-30 mounting, co-mounted with a Thales Nederland (formerly Hollandse Signaal-Apparaaten/H.S.A.) track-while-scan radar fire-control system. The latter uses independent I-band search/acquisition and I/K-band tracking radars. The seven-barreled gatling gun has a 4,200-rd/min maximum rate of fire; 1,190 rounds are carried on-mount. Muzzle velocity is 1,021 m/sec. Total weight, with ammunition, is 6,372 kg.

20-mm 90-cal. Oerlikon AA: In modern GIAT 20F-2 mountings on mine countermeasures vessels; old Oerlikon 70-cal. weapons in U.S.-style Mk 10 pintle mountings on frigates, minesweepers, and auxiliaries.

C. ANTISUBMARINE WEAPONS

U.S. Mk 46 Mod. 5 torpedoes on ships and aircraft, and U.S. NT-37C/D/E (reworked Mk 37) and Mk 48 Mod. 4 torpedoes on submarines.

D. RADARS

All designed and manufactured by Thales Nederland (formerly the Hollandse Signaal-Apparaaten [H.S.A.] division of Thomson-CSF). Thales Nederland and the multinational EADS established ET Marinesysteme GmbH on 19-4-01 to maintain existing H.S.A. combat systems on German and Dutch naval units, develop the combat system for the German Type 130 corvette program, continue development of the APAR radar, and cooperate on development of a joint Maritime Tactical Ballistic Missile Defence system.

Name	*Type*	*Band*
ZW-06	Nav./surf. search	I
ZW-07	Submarine nav./surf. search	I
LW-02/03	Long-range air search	D
LW-04	Long-range air search	D

WEAPONS AND SYSTEMS *(continued)*

Name	*Type*	*Band*
LW-08	Long-range air search	D
DA-05, 05A	Combined surveillance	F
DA-08	Medium-range air search	E/F
SPS-01	3-D air search	F
WM-20/25	Missile and gunfire control	K
MR-05	Medium-range air search	D (12–14 GHz)
MW-08*	Air search, multitrack	G
SEAPAR**	ESSM Sea Sparrow f.c.	X (I/J-band)
Scout	Low-interceptable nav./search	X; 1 mw to 1 w output
SMART*	3-D air search	L (F)
STING	Lightweight automatic f.c.	I/K dual-freq.
STIR***	Missile and gunfire control	I/K (X + Ka)
Surf	Low-interceptable air/surf. search	4-watt max. output; 30-km range
LIROD-8	Radar, optronic weapon control	K

***SMART-L (Signaal Multi-beam Acquisition Radar for Targeting, L-band):** Plan to deliver 20 successor SMART-L sets at the rate of two per year beginning in 1995. Range against an air target is 400 km, and up to 1,000 targets can be tracked. MW-08 is essentially a G-band variant and can detect and track up to 20 air and 10 surface contacts simultaneously.

****SEAPAR (Self-defense ESSM Active Phased-Array Radar):** Being developed by a Raytheon/Thales Nederland consortium for the NATO Sea Sparrow Project Office for availability in 2006 as a fire-control radar to take advantage of the longer-range ESSM version of the Sea Sparrow missile. It will employ technology developed for Raytheon's SPY-3 and the Thales Nederland APAR radar.

*****STIR (Separate Tracking and Illumination Radar):** Has 1.8- or 2.9-m-dia. parabolic dish antennas and a co-mounted t.v. camera.

APAR (Active Phased Array Radar): Under development in cooperation with Canada and Germany for use on future frigates. As APAR STIR, it would employ four fixed faces and act as part of the weapons-control system.

Seven Thales Squire battlefield surveillance radar sets were ordered for the Royal Netherlands Marines late in 2000.

E. ELECTRO-OPTICAL DEVICES

IRSCAN: Omnidirectional passive surveillance system by Thales Nederland. Rotates at 78 rpm and has a range of 15 km against aircraft and 12 km against missiles. Total system weighs only 560 kg.

Mirador: Developed by Thales Nederland for use in detecting, tracking, and identifying targets in poor visibility. Can perform three-dimensional target acquisition and tracking using two daylight t.v. cameras, a thermal imager, a laser rangefinder, and a low-light t.v. camera, all on a common mounting.

F. SONARS

DUBM-21: Thales HF minehunting array
DUUX-5: Thales Fenelon passive-ranging
Octopus: Active/passive submarine array on the *Walrus* class, derived from the Thales TSM-2272 Eledone
PHS-32, MF: Export sonar, hull-mounted or VDS (9.3, 10.5, or 11.7 kHz)
PHS-36, MF: License-built Canadian SQS-509 on the *Jacob Van Heemskerck–* and *Karel Doorman–*class frigates (5.5, 6.5, 7.5 kHz)
SQS-505, MF: License-built Canadian sonar on the *Kortenaer*-class frigates
Type 2026: British passive linear towed hydrophone array for submarines

G. ELECTRONIC WARFARE

In use are the British Scimitar J-band deception and jamming system, Rapids I 18-GHz passive intercept array, and Ramses I/J-band passive and deceptive repeater equipment. Boeing Argo Systems APECS-2/AR-700 intercept equipment is installed on *Karel Doorman–*class frigates.

ATTACK SUBMARINES [SS]

♦ **4 Walrus class** Bldr: Rotterdamse Droogdok Maatschappij, Rotterdam

	Laid down	L	Trials	In serv.
S 802 Walrus	11-10-79	28-10-85	12-9-90	25-3-92
S 803 Zeeleeuw	24-9-81	20-6-87	28-10-88	25-4-90
S 808 Dolfijn	12-6-86	25-4-90	10-9-91	29-1-93
S 810 Bruinvis	14-4-88	25-4-92	5-3-93	5-7-94

Walrus (S 802) Bernard Prézelin, 4-00

Dolfijn (S 808) H&L Van Ginderen, 7-99

D: 1,900 tons light, 2,465 tons surf./2,800 tons sub.
S: 13 kts surf./21 kts sub. **Dim:** 67.73 × 8.40 × 7.00
A: 4 bow 533-mm TT (20 Mk 48 Mod. 4 and NT-37D torpedoes or 40 mines)
Electronics:
Radar: 1 ZW-07 (Decca Type 1001) nav./surf. search
Sonar: Thales Octopus (TSM 2272 Eledone) active/passive; GEC Avionics Type 2026 linear clip-on passive array; Thales DUUX-5 Fenelon passive-ranging
EW: Boeing ArgoSystems AR 700 intercept
M: 3 SEMT-Pielstick 12 PA4V 200VG (S 808, S 810: Brons-Werkspoor 0-RUB 215X121) diesels (2,300 bhp each), 3 Holec Type 304 980-kw alternators, 1 Holec motor; 1 7-bladed prop; 3,950 shp surf./5,430 shp sub.
Range: 10,000/9 (snorkel) **Fuel:** 310 tons **Endurance:** 60 days
Crew: 7 officers, 45 enlisted

Remarks: First two were ordered 19-6-78 and 17-12-79, respectively. Second pair was authorized 5-1-84, with S 808 ordered 16-10-84 and S 810 on 16-8-85. Construction of the first pair was delayed by the need to lengthen the hull after the keels had been laid in order to accommodate larger diesel generator sets. S 802 was severely damaged by fire 14-8-86, returned to land 2-5-87 for repairs, and relaunched 13-9-89. Plans to construct two more units were canceled in 7-88. Active units operate at sea about 120 days per year. Hairline cracks in the inboard section of diesel-exhaust piping caused a halt to submerged operations during 10-00; S 808 was returned to full service on 25-11-00, S 810 in 12-00, and S 802 in mid-2001, while S 803 completed a refit in 2-01. Are planned to receive midlife modernizations, possibly with a section added to contain an air-independent auxiliary propulsion plant, starting in 2009. S 810 was damaged in a collision with a surface ship on 25-10-01.
Hull systems: Propulsion plant is on resilient mountings to reduce noise emissions. Each Holec ac/dc generator has built-in rectifiers and produces 980 kw. There are three 140-cell batteries. Diving depth: 300 m; periscope depth: 18 m. Has X-configuration stern control surfaces and sail-mounted bow planes. Hull construction is of MAREL steel, with single-hull midbody and double-hull ends; reserve buoyancy is 12%. S 803 was equipped with an enlarged snorkel exhaust defuser at the aft end of the sail during a 1996 yard period; the others now have it as well.
Combat systems: First two have the SEWACO VIII combat data system with seven-console GIPSY *(Geïntegreerd In Formatie en Presentatie Systeem)* data display system; the second pair have the SEWACO VII data system with SMR-MV data processor. All are equipped with the Sperry Mk 29 Mod. 2A inertial navigation system and receivers for GPS and have NATO Link 11 datalink capabilities, using a 450-m floating wire antenna. Torpedo tubes are of the U.S. Mk 67 "water-slug" type, capable of launching at any operational depth. They are fitted to launch UGM-84-series Sub-Harpoon antiship missiles, but none have been procured. The Eledone sonar suite includes a medium-range active sonar, flank passive arrays, and a sonar intercept array. Have Kollmorgen Model 76 search and attack periscopes, with integral ranging radar and intercept antennas.

Note: Of the two submarines of the *Zwaardvis* class, *Zwaardvis* (S 806) was decommissioned 13-7-94 and placed in land preservation at Rotterdam, and sister *Tijgerhaai* (S 807) was decommissioned 12-8-95. Both were purchased 12-12-95 by their builder and were delivered to Malaysia in 12-00 with the intent of refitting them locally and leasing them to the Malaysian Navy.

GUIDED-MISSILE FRIGATES [FFG]

♦ **0 (+4) De Zeven Provinciën class**
Bldr: Schelde Shipbuilding, Vlissingen

	Laid down	L	In serv.	Fully operational
F 802 De Zeven Provinciën	1-9-98	8-4-00	18-4-02	12-03
F 803 Tromp	3-9-99	7-4-01	3-03	7-04
F 804 De Ruyter	1-9-00	4-02	3-04	7-05
F 805 Evertsen	6-9-01	4-03	3-05	7-06

De Zeven Provinciën (F 802) A. A. de Kruijf, 9-01

GUIDED-MISSILE FRIGATES [FFG] *(continued)*

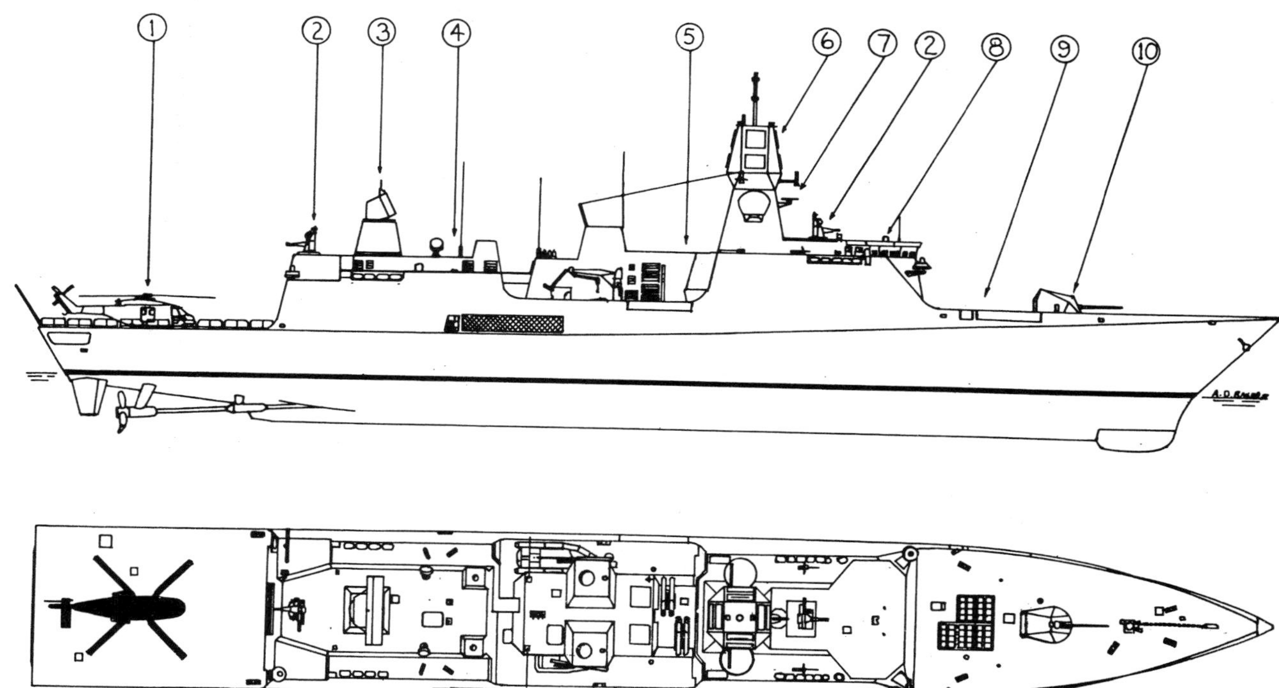

DE ZEVEN PROVINCIEN (F802)

De Zeven Provinciën (F 802) 1. NH-90 helicopter 2. 30-mm Goalkeeper CIWS 3. SMART-L early-warning radar 4. paired ASW torpedo tubes (on main deck, within the small opening in the hull side) 5. Harpoon SSM, in quadruple sets, behind radar reflection reduction paneling (see plan view) 6. APAR 3-D phased-array target-designation and tracking radar 7. Scout navigational radar 8. SIRIUS infrared surveillance and tracking sensor 9. Mk 41 VLS (40 cells) 10. 127-mm 54-cal. OTOBreda DP gun

Drawing by A. D. Baker III

De Zeven Provinciën (F 802) Rob Cabo, 9-01

De Zeven Provinciën (F 802) Ben Stans, 9-01

D: 5,864 tons (6,048 fl) **S:** 30 kts (19 on diesels)
Dim: 144.24 (130.20 pp) × 18.82 (17.15 wl) × 5.18 (mean hull)
A: 8 RGM-84F Harpoon Block ID SSM; 40-cell Mk 41 VLS (32 Standard SM-2 Block IIIA and 32 RIM-7P Evolved Sea Sparrow SAM); 1 127-mm 54-cal. OTOBreda DP; 2 30-mm Goalkeeper CIWS; 2 single 20-mm 90-cal. Oerlikon AA; four fixed, paired 324-mm Mk 32 Mod. 9 ASW TT (Mk 46 Mod. 5 torpedoes); 1 SH-14D Lynx helicopter
Electronics:
Radar: 1 Thales Scout nav./surf. search.; 1 Thales APAR 3-D phased-array target desig. and tracking; 1 Thales SMART-L early warning
Sonar: STN Atlas Elektronik DSQS-24C hull-mounted LF; provision for active towed linear array
TACAN: Thales Vesta
EW: Racal Spectre (U.K. UAT) intercept (0.5–18 GHz)/jamming (7.5–18 GHz); Mk 36 SRBOC decoy syst. (4 6-round Raytheon Mk 137 RL); 4 twin Nulka offboard jammer RL; SLQ-25A Nixie towed acoustic torpedo decoy
E/O: Thales Mirador-FD surveillance, tracking, and gun f.c.; Thales SIRIUS surveillance
M: CODOG: 2 Rolls-Royce SM-1C Spey gas turbines (26,140 shp each), 2 Stork-Wärtsilä 16V6ST diesels (5,630 bhp each); 2 CP props
Electric: 6,600 kw tot. (4 × 1,650-kw sets, 4 GEC-Alstom Paxman 12VP185 diesels driving)
Range: 5,000/18 **Endurance:** 21 days
Crew: F 802, 803: 32 officers, 47 petty officers, 123 ratings (232 accomm.)—F 804, 805: 182 tot.

Remarks: Were to be a cooperative venture with Germany and Spain under an agreement signed 27-1-94, but the German ship design differs and Spain later withdrew. First two are designated LCF (*Luchtverdedigings en Commando Fregat,* or Air-Defense and Command Frigate) and were ordered 3-6-95; they were to cost $829 million for both. Authorization for a second pair was granted by the parliament 24-10-96, and they were ordered 2-5-97 for $375 million each. The total four-ship procurement is expected to cost $1.61 billion. While the LCFs will have accommodations for one flag officer and staff, the second pair will be styled NLF *(Nieuw Luchtverdedigings Fregat)* and will not have the full command facilities of the first two. The building yard was purchased 30-5-00 by Damen Shipyards for one guilder but will retain its current name.
Hull systems: The final displacement for the first two may reach 6,200 tons full load. Employ twin rudders with rudder roll stabilization. Ship's boats are rigid inflatables stowed behind bulwarks. Reduced radar and infrared signature measures have been extensively employed. Electrical power is 220- and 115-V, 60-Hz a.c., and 24- and 28-V, 400-Hz a.c. Have six "autonomous internal zones" divided by PriMa flexible, watertight, blast- and fragmentation-resistant bulkheads.
Combat systems: The combat system is the Thales SEWACO IX, with Link 11 and 16 datalink capability; 36 Protec-II reconfigurable display and operations consoles per ship are installed. The SMART-L radar will be able to maintain up to 1,000 tracks, while APAR can maintain 200 tracks and provide guidance illumination for more than 30 (the combat system allows for 16 air targets to be attacked at once, along with two surface and two subsurface contacts). The orientation of the four phased-array faces of the APAR radar was changed late in 1997 to fore and aft, port and starboard, rather than at 45° off the centerline as originally intended.

Each Mk 41 VLS cell can hold one Standard or four Sea Sparrow missiles. Standard SM-2 Block IVA missiles are to be acquired after 2009 to give the ships a theater ballistic missile defense capability. The forward Goalkeeper CIWS may be replaced later by a U.S. RAM point-defense missile system with RIM-116 missiles.

The hull-mounted sonar was ordered 5-98, with the towed array decision to be made in 1999 between the STN Atlas Elektronik ATASS, Honeywell Low Frequency Active Towed Array, and Thales Combined Active-Passive Towed Array systems after competitive trials; but no order has been announced.

GUIDED-MISSILE FRIGATES [FFG] *(continued)*

The first two were originally to have had twin 120-mm gunmounts recycled from the *Tromp* class (and before that aboard the destroyer *Gelderland*). The OTOBreda mounts for the first two ships were ordered 12-12-96 (with an option for two more) in order to take advantage of planned developments in U.S. 127-mm extended range guidance munitions (ERGM); all four are refurbished ex-Canadian mountings from the Tribal class. The helicopter will carry ASW and antiship weapons, and the magazines will stow up to 24 ASW torpedoes and 12 antiship missiles; the DCN Samahé helicopter landing system will be installed on the 27-m-long flight deck. Terma, Denmark, is installing the SRBOC system, which will incorporate an on-mount round identification system. The Mirador E/O sensor is also referred to as the TEOOS (Trainable Electro-Optical Observation System), and the sensor mount has two daylight t.v. cameras, an Albatross thermal-imaging camera, and a low-light t.v. camera.

The Rhode & Schwarz integrated communications suite will include UHF/SHF SATCOM, an integrated message-handling and control system (IMUS), and cryptographic equipment. Navigational equipment will include two NAVSAT terminals, two inertial navigational systems (MINS), and a weather satellite receiver.

♦ 2 Jacob Van Heemskerck class

Bldr: Schelde Shipbuilding, Vlissingen

	Laid down	L	In serv.
F 812 Jacob Van Heemskerck (ex-*Pieter Florisz*)	21-1-81	5-11-83	15-1-86
F 813 Witte de With	15-12-81	25-8-84	17-9-86

Jacob Van Heemskerck (F 812) Mike Welsford, 4-01

Witte de With (F 813) Rob Cabo, 6-01

Witte de With (F 813) Bernard Prézelin, 6-01

D: 3,000 tons (3,750 fl) **S:** 30 kts (20 on cruise engines)
Dim: 130.20 (121.8 pp) × 14.40 × 4.23 (6.0 props)
A: 8 RGM-84C Harpoon SSM; 1 single-rail Mk 13 Mod. 4 missile launcher (40 Standard SM-1 MR missiles); 1 8-round Mk 29 missile launcher (24 RIM-7M Sea Sparrow missiles); 1 30-mm Goalkeeper gatling CIWS; 2 single 20-mm 70-cal. Oerlikon Mk 10 AA; 4 fixed, paired 324-mm Mk 32 Mod. 9 ASW TT (Mk 46 Mod. 5 torpedoes)
Electronics:
Radar: 1 Thales Scout nav./surf. search; 1 Thales ZW-06 surf. search; 1 Thales SMART-S air search; 1 Thales LW-08 early warning; 1 Thales STIR-18 gun f.c.; 2 Thales STIR-24 missile f.c.; 1 Thales 1 Goalkeeper f.c. array
Sonar: PHS-36 (SQS-509) hull-mounted MF
EW: Thales Sphinx intercept; Thales Ramses active (with SRR03/100 jammer); Mk 36 SRBOC decoy syst. (2 6-round Raytheon Mk 137 RL); SLQ-25 Nixie acoustic torpedo decoy syst.
M: COGOG: 2 Rolls-Royce Olympus TM-3B gas turbines (25,800 shp each); 2 Rolls-Royce Tyne RM-1C cruise gas turbines (4,900 shp each); 2 Lips CP props; 51,600 shp max.
Electric: 3,000 kw tot. **Range:** 4,700/16 (on 1 Tyne turbine)
Crew: 23 officers, 174 enlisted + 20 flag staff

Remarks: Were built as replacement hulls for a pair of *Kortenaer*-class frigates with the same pennant numbers (and same original names) that was sold to Greece. Have the basic *Kortenaer* design, modified to replace the helicopter facility with the U.S. Standard missile system. Equipped to act as flagships. Major modernizations planned for the pair were canceled in 6-96 in favor of building two additional *De Zeven Provinciën*–class LCF units (q.v.). F 812 ran aground on the Isle of Scalpay, Scotland, on 15-9-99 but was towed off by *De Ruyter* (F 806); the ship completed extensive repairs at Den Helder at the end of 11-00 and completed a refit in 1-01. They are scheduled for retirement in 2010 and 2012, respectively.
Combat systems: Have the SEWACO II data system and Link 11 datalink capability. During a 1992–93 refit, F 812 had the onion-shaped radomes for the Electrospace SHF SATCOM system installed forward of the stack. Both were backfitted with the Thales pulse-doppler S-band SMART-S 3-D radar in place of the DA-08 radar, and Scout in place of Decca 1226 during 1995–96 refits; at the same time, the STIR-18 radar was modified to permit its use as a third fire-control channel for the SM-1 missiles, U.S. OE-82 antennas were added for the WSC-3 UHF SATCOM system, a U.S. JMCIS (Joint Maritime Command Information System) terminal was added, and new software was substituted in the missile fire-control system. Two hand-served 20-mm AA have been added just abaft the bridge.

Disposal note: Of the two *Tromp*-class guided-missile frigates, the *Tromp* (F 801) was retired 12-11-99 and sold for scrapping during 2000, while the *De Ruyter* (F 806), which was to have operated until 2003, was instead retired on 3-10-00 and was also to be scrapped.

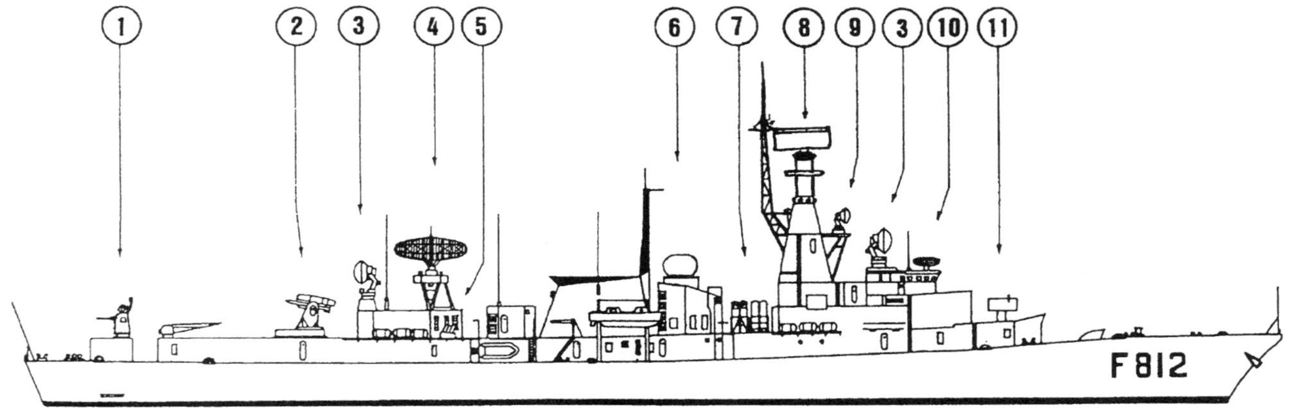

Jacob Van Heemskerck (F 812) 1. 30-mm Goalkeeper CIWS 2. Mk 13 Mod. 4 launcher for Standard SM-1 MR missiles 3. Modified STIR-24 radar illuminators for SM-1 missiles 4. LW-08 early-warning radar 5. Mk 137 launchers for Mk 36 SRBOC decoy system 6. Electrospace SHF SATCOM antenna radomes 7. Harpoon SSM 8. SMART-S air-search radar 9. STIR-18 radar illuminator for Sea Sparrow missiles 10. ZW-06 surface-search radar 11. 8-round Mk 29 launcher for Sea Sparrow missiles

Drawing by Robert Dumas, from *Flottes de Combat*

FRIGATES [FF]

Note: A follow-on class of "Q-class" small frigates had been planned to begin entering service around 2008, with the first to be ordered in 2004. The ships may be designed and procured jointly with Belgium and Germany as replacements for the *Wielingen* and Type 122 *(Bremen)* classes. No design details have been released, and the program may have been delayed or canceled for financial reasons.

♦ 8 Karel Doorman class

Bldr: Schelde Shipbuilding, Vlissingen

	Laid down	L	In serv.
F 827 Karel Doorman	26-2-85	20-4-88	31-5-91
F 829 Willem Van Der Zaan	6-11-85	21-1-89	28-11-91
F 830 Tjerk Hiddes	28-10-86	9-12-89	26-2-93
F 831 Van Amstel	3-5-88	19-5-90	27-5-93
F 832 Abraham Van Der Hulst	8-2-89	7-9-91	15-12-93
F 833 Van Nes	10-1-90	16-5-92	24-6-94
F 834 Van Galen	7-6-90	21-11-92	1-12-94

Van Nes (F 833) Mike Welsford, 6-01

D: 2,800 tons light (3,320 fl) **S:** 29 kts (21 on diesels)
Dim: 122.25 (114.40 pp) × 14.37 (13.10 wl) × 4.30 (6.05 sonar)
A: 4 RGM-84A/C Harpoon SSM; 16-cell Mk 48 Mod. 1 VLS (16 RIM-7M NATO Sea Sparrow SAM); 1 76-mm 62-cal. OTOBreda DP; 1 30-mm Goalkeeper gatling CIWS; 2 single 20-mm 70-cal. Oerlikon Mk 10 AA; 4 fixed, paired 324-mm Mk 32 Mod. 9 ASW TT (Mk 46 Mod. 5 torpedoes); 1 SH-14D Lynx ASW helicopter
Electronics:
Radar: 1 Decca 1690/9 nav.; 1 Thales Scout nav./surf. search; 1 Thales SMART-S 3-D air search; 1 Thales LW-08 early warning; 2 Thales STIR-18 missile f.c.; 1 Thales Goalkeeper f.c. array
Sonar: PHS-36 (SQS-509) hull-mounted MF—last four also: provision for Thales Anaconda (DSBV-61A) towed array
EW: ArgoSystems APECS-II intercept and AR-740 jammer; Mk 36 SRBOC decoy syst. (2 6-round Raytheon Mk 137 RL); SLQ-25 Nixie towed acoustic torpedo decoy syst.
M: CODOG: 2 Stork-Wärtsilä 12 SWD 280 V-12 cruise diesels (4,225 bhp each), 2 Rolls-Royce Spey RM-1A or C gas turbines; 2 CP props; 48,252 (F 827: 37,530) shp max.
Electric: 2,720 kw (4 × 650-kw diesel sets, Stork-Wärtsilä DRo 218K diesels driving; 1 × 120-kw diesel set)
Range: 5,000+/18 **Endurance:** 30 days
Crew: 16 officers, 138 enlisted (163 max. accomm.)

Karel Doorman (F 827)—with portable electronics vans on helicopter deck
Findler & Winter, 6-00

Abraham Van Der Hulst (F 832)—note the protective plating now carried over the vertical-launch SAM system on the port side of the helicopter hangar
Findler & Winter, 6-01

Tjerk Hiddes (F 830) Bernard Prézelin, 6-01

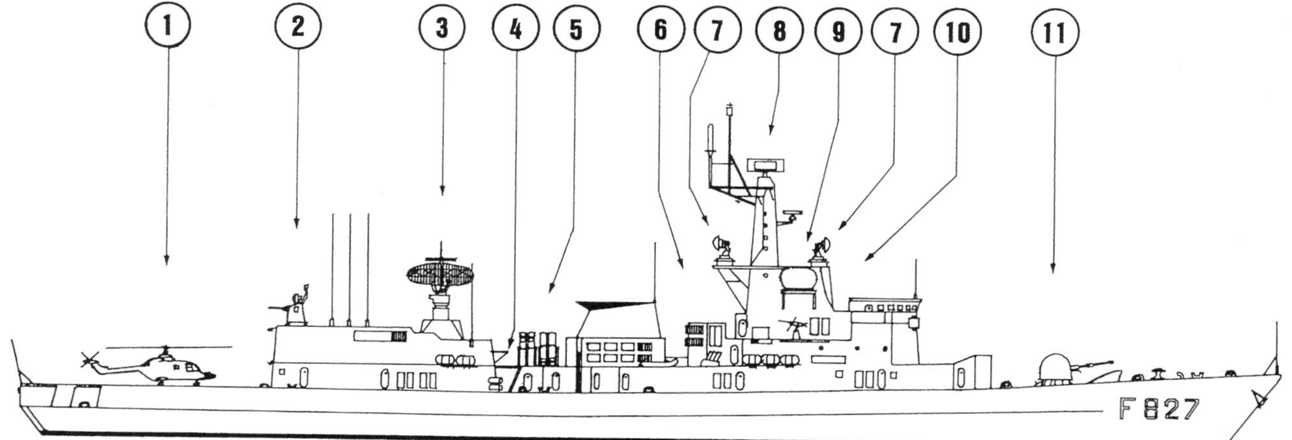

Karel Doorman (F 827) 1. SH-14D Lynx helicopter 2. 30-mm Goalkeeper CIWS atop hangar 3. LW-08 early-warning radar 4. fixed, paired Mk 32 Mod. 9 ASW TT 5. Harpoon SSM 6. Mk 137 launchers for the Mk 36 SRBOC decoy system 7. STIR-18 weapons-control radar 8. SMART-S 3-D air-search radar 9. Electrospace SHF SATCOM radomes 10. 20-mm Oerlikon AA 11. OTOBreda 76-mm DP gun
Drawing by Robert Dumas, from *Flottes de Combat*

FRIGATES [FF] *(continued)*

Willem Van Der Zaan (F 829) Rob Cabo, 6-01

Remarks: Originally known as the "M"-class. First four were ordered 29-2-84, three years earlier than planned, to help the shipbuilding industry, and the second group of four was ordered 10-4-86; four more were originally projected. Accommodations for female crew members are incorporated, plus bunks for 30 marines. Originally to have been named *Groningen, Friesland, Utrecht, Noord Brabant, Limburg, Overijssel, Drenthe,* and *Gelderland.* The names were again changed 18-3-87 to move *Van Speijk* from second to last.
Hull systems: Have a computer-controlled rudder roll-stabilization system instead of fins. Carry three RIBs. F 827 has Spey RM-1A gas turbines operating at 18,765 shp each; the remainder have the 24,126-shp RM-1C, to be backfitted in F 827.
Combat systems: Have the Thales DAISY VII/SEWACO VII(B) data system with full Link 10, 11, and 16 capability. The 76-mm gun fires at up to 100 rds/min. F 830 conducted trials with the class-standard IMCS (Integrated Monitoring and Control System) during 1992. Beginning with F 831, the onion-shaped radomes for the Electrospace SHF SATCOM system were installed abreast the bridge area; they are now backfitted to all. The planned towed linear-array sonar system has yet to be added. Are slowly being updated with radar reflection-reducing panels outboard of the vertical missile launchers, Thales Scout low-probability-of-intercept surface-search radars (with the Decca navigational radar relocated atop the pilothouse), and Inmarsat commercial SATCOM added. The long-range LR-IRSCAN infrared surveillance and tracking system is to be installed on all.

♦ 2 Kortenaer class
Bldr: Wilton-Fijenoord, Schiedam

	Laid down	L	In serv.
F 823 Philips Van Almonde	1-10-77	11-8-79	2-12-81
F 824 Bloys Van Treslong	27-4-78	15-11-80	5-11-82

Philips Van Almonde (F 823) Rob Cabo, 1-01

Bloys Van Treslong (F 824) A. A. de Kruijf, 6-00

Bloys Van Treslong (F 824) H&L Van Ginderen, 6-00

D: 3,000 tons (3,786 fl) **S:** 30 kts (20 on 2 Tyne turbines)
Dim: 130.2 (121.8 pp) × 14.4 × 4.4 (6.0 props)
A: 4 RGM-84A/C Harpoon SSM; 1 8-round Mk 29 missile launcher (24 NATO Sea Sparrow SAM); 1 76-mm 62-cal. OTOBreda DP; 1 30-mm Goalkeeper gatling CIWS; 2 single 20-mm 70-cal. Oerlikon Mk 10 AA; 2 single 12.7-mm mg; 4 fixed, paired 324-mm Mk 32 Mod. 9 ASW TT (Mk 46 Mod. 5 torpedoes); 1 SH-14D Lynx ASW helicopter
Electronics:
Radar: 1 Thales ZW-06 nav./surf. search; 1 Thales LW-08 early warning; 1 Thales WM-25 f.c.; 1 Thales STIR-18 f.c.; 1 Thales Goalkeeper f.c.
Sonar: PHS-36 (SQS-509) hull-mounted MF
EW: Thales Sphinx intercept; Thales Ramses jammer; Mk 36 SRBOC decoy syst. (2 6-round Raytheon Mk 137 RL); SLQ-25 Nixie towed acoustic torpedo decoy syst.
M: COGOG: 2 Rolls-Royce Olympus TM-3B gas turbines (25,800 shp each), 2 Rolls-Royce Tyne RM-1C cruise gas turbines (4,900 shp each); 2 LIPS CP props; 51,600 shp max.
Electric: 3,000 kw tot. (4 × 750 kw, SEMT-Pielstick PA4 diesels driving; 450-V, 3-phase, 60-Hz a.c.)
Range: 4,700/16 (on 1 Tyne turbine) **Crew:** 18 officers, 182 enlisted

Remarks: Survivors of 10 built for Netherlands service. Ordered 29-12-76. F 824 collided with and sank fireboat L 9522 on 1-9-98 at Den Helder. F 823 is to be retired during 5-02. F 824 is to be stationed in the West Indies during 5-02 on a two-year deployment, with portions of the reduced crew to rotate home at six-month intervals; she will then be retired.
Disposals: The original *Pieter Florisz* (F 812) and *Witte de With* (F 813) of this class were sold to Greece in 1981. Three were sold to Greece 9-11-92 for transfer: *Banckert* (F 810) on 14-5-93, *Callenburgh* (F 808) on 30-3-94, and *Van Kinsbergen* (F 809) on 1-3-95. *Kortenaer* (F 807) was decommissioned 15-2-96, sold to Greece 3-6-97, and handed over when stricken on 15-12-97. *Piet Heyn* (F 811) was decommissioned in 1-95 and stricken 29-6-98, and *Abraham Crijnssen* (F 816) was decommissioned in 6-96 and stricken 31-10-97; both were sold to the United Arab Emirates 2-4-96. *Pieter Florisz* (F 826, ex-*Willem Van Der Zaan*) was decommissioned 24-1-01, sold to Greece 7-6-01, and transferred 14-12-01. *Jan Van Brakel* (F 825) was retired 12-10-01 and was to be purchased by Greece.
Hull systems: The hull is divided by 15 watertight bulkheads. One pair of Denny-Brown nonretracting fin stabilizers is fitted. Have berthing for 25 female crew members. All ships have the Sperry Mk 29 Mod. 1 inertial navigation system. The engineering plant is distributed in four compartments—forward to aft: auxiliaries; Olympus gas turbines; Tyne gas turbines plus reduction gears; and auxiliaries. There are two auxiliary boilers and two evaporators.
Combat systems: All have the Thales SEWACO II data system. In peacetime, only one Lynx helicopter is carried, but a second can be accommodated in the hangar. Normally, only two or four Harpoon SSM are carried, but up to eight can be accommodated. Both are fitted with the Electrospace SHF SATCOM system and also carry Inmarsat commercial UHF SATCOM.

MINE WARFARE SHIPS

♦ 12 Alkmaar ("Tripartite")-class coastal minehunters [MHC]
Bldr: Van der Giessen de Noord, Alblasserdam

	Ordered	Laid down	L	In serv.
M 853 Haarlem	23-1-79	16-6-81	9-7-83	12-1-84
M 854 Harlingen	31-3-81	30-11-81	9-7-83	12-4-84
M 855 Scheveningen (ex-*Hellevoetsluis*)	31-3-81	24-5-82	2-12-83	18-7-84
M 856 Maassluis	16-12-81	7-11-82	5-5-84	12-12-84
M 857 Makkum	16-12-81	28-2-83	27-9-84	13-5-85
M 858 Middelburg	21-7-82	11-7-83	18-2-85	10-12-86
M 859 Hellevoetsluis (ex-*Scheveningen*)	21-7-82	12-12-83	18-7-85	20-2-87
M 860 Schiedam	5-12-83	6-5-84	26-4-86	9-7-86
M 861 Urk	5-12-83	30-9-84	4-10-86	10-12-86
M 862 Zierikzee (ex-*Veere*)	3-7-84	25-2-85	4-10-86	7-5-87
M 863 Vlaardingen	3-7-84	6-5-86	6-8-88	15-3-89
M 864 Willemstad	3-7-84	3-10-86	27-1-89	20-9-89

Vlaardingen (M 863) Bernard Prézelin, 7-01

D: 510 tons (540 fl) **S:** 15 kts (7 hunting)
Dim: 51.6 (47.1 pp) × 8.96 × 2.45 (2.6 max.)
A: 1 20-mm 90-cal. GIAT 20F-2 AA

MINE WARFARE SHIPS *(continued)*

Hellevoetsluis (M 859) Findler & Winter, 5-00

Scheveningen (M 855) Rob Cabo, 7-01

Electronics:
Radar: 1 Decca TM 1229C or Consilium Selesmar NN 950 nav.
Sonar: Thales DUBM-21B
M: 1 Brons-Werkspoor A-RUB 215 × 12 diesel; 1 CP prop; 1,900 bhp—2 75-shp bow-thrusters; 2 120-shp ACEC active rudders
Electric: 880 kw tot. (3 × 270 kw, gas-turbine driven; 1 × 160-kw diesel set)
Range: 3,500/10 **Endurance:** 15 days **Crew:** 34–42 tot.

Remarks: Same basic design as the Tripartite minehunters for France and Belgium. The original *Vlaardingen* (M 863) and *Willemstad* (M 864) were sold to Indonesia while under construction in 1985 and were replaced with later units. M 858 and M 859 were to have been transferred to Egypt as *Mecca* and *Medina,* but the transaction was never completed.
Disposals: Of the first three completed, *Alkmaar* (M 850) was retired 12-5-01, *Delfzijl* (M 851) on 19-6-01, and *Dordrecht* (M 852) on 5-7-01; they may be made available for foreign purchase.
Hull systems: Hull is made of a compound of glass fiber and polyester resin. Have active tank stabilization. The 5-ton modular van abaft the superstructure can contain a decompression station, communications equipment, drone control gear, and so forth.
Combat systems: Mine countermeasures equipment includes two PAP 104 Mk 4 remote-controlled submersibles, the EVEC 20 plot table, autopilot, Toran and Sydelis radio navaids, and the Decca HiFix Mk 6 precision navigation system. Can also tow a mechanical drag sweep and carry OD-3 mechanical sweep gear. The DUBM-21B sonar can detect mines in waters up to 80-m depth, at slant ranges up to 500 m. Are being fitted with new Consilium Selesmar NN 950 navigational radars, commencing in 1999.
Modernization: It was announced in 11-93 that three would be converted to serve as control vessels for four remote-controlled mine countermeasures drones each and that four others would have their sonar suites upgraded with propelled variable-depth buried seabed mine detection sonars to permit them to be employed as deepwater minehunters. The replacement sonar to be fitted in the deep-sea minehunting conversions may be a production variant of the EPMDS (Experimental Parametric Mine Detection Sonar) in the Thales PVDS (Propelled Variable Depth Sonar) body (which currently uses a Bofors-Sutec Double Eagle ROV equipped with the Thales TSM 2022 Mk 3 high-frequency [165 and 400 kHz] sonar and low-light-level t.v.; the device can operate at 5 kts up to 600 m ahead of the control ship and at depths to 200 m, and it weighs 400 kg); if rival candidate STN Atlas Elektronik prevails, however, the existing sonars will be updated with German technology. Originally to have been completed by 1998, the program has yet to be funded, and no contracts had been let by 8-01. The updates are now planned to be completed by 2008.

♦ 0 (+ 1 + 8 + 3) drone mine countermeasures craft [MSD]
Bldr: Royal Schelde, Vlissingen

D: 270 tons (fl) **S:** . . . kts **Dim:** 40.0 × 5.9 × . . .
M: . . .
Endurance: 144 hr unattended **Crew:** 2 (for transit)

Remarks: A prototype drone minehunter was to be begun during 2001, with sea trials to commence during 2003, but no order had been placed as of 8-01. If trials are successful, eight more will be ordered, with an option for another three, to bring the class total to 12. Four per year are planned be delivered, beginning in 2004. The craft will be controlled by Tripartite-class units, with each control ship handling four drones. Hull construction will be of low-magnetic steel alloy.

AMPHIBIOUS WARFARE SHIPS AND CRAFT

♦ 0 (+ 1) ATS-2-class Amphibious Transport Ship [LPD]
Bldr: Royal Schelde, Vlissingen

	Laid down	L	In serv.
L 801 Johan de Witt	2003	. . .	2007

D: . . . tons **S:** 19 kts **Dim:** 178.0 × 26.0 (24.26 wl) × 5.30
A: 2 single 30-mm Goalkeeper CIWS; 4 single 20-mm 70-cal. Oerlikon AA; up to 6 Netherlands Army Cougar helicopters
Electronics:
Radar: . . .
EW: . . .
M: 4 Stork Werkspoor 12SW28 diesel generator sets (3,650 kw each), 2 Holec electric motors; 2 fixed-pitch props; 16,628 shp—2 600-shp electric motors for slow-speed operations—248-shp bow-thruster
Electric: . . .
Range: . . . **Crew:** 146 tot. + 400 staff

Remarks: What had been intended as a repeat *Rotterdam* will now be a larger vessel intended to transport logistic and combat support elements of a Royal Netherlands Marines battalion, whereas the earlier *Rotterdam* would carry the combat units when both ships are available. The ATS-2 will have facilities for 400 flag and force command personnel, and will also be used for humanitarian operations, disaster relief, and emergency evacuations. Plans are to order during 4-02, with sea trials to take place in 2006.
Hull systems: Design will be an enlarged version of the *Rotterdam* and will be able to dock British LCU Mk 10 landing craft and operate heavy-lift helicopters. The docking well will be 1 m broader but considerably shorter than the one in *Rotterdam,* while the superstructure is to be enlarged to accommodate the command facilities; two LCU-1-class landing craft will be stowed in davits and two in the docking well. A large medical complex, including an operating theater, will be fitted.

♦ 1 Rotterdam-class Amphibious Transport Ship [LPD]
Bldr: Schelde Shipbuilding, Vlissingen (hull by B.V. De Merwede, Hardinxveld-Giessendam)

	Laid down	L	In serv.
L 800 Rotterdam	23-2-96	22-2-97	18-4-98

Rotterdam (L 800) Douglas A. Cromby, 2-00

D: 10,800 tons (12,750 fl) **S:** 19 kts
Dim: 166.20 (142.4 wl; 139.55 pp) × 25.0 (23.26 wl) × 5.23 (5.90 max.)
A: 2 single 30-mm Goalkeeper CIWS; 4 single 20-mm 70-cal. Oerlikon Mk 10 AA; up to 6 Netherlands Army Cougar helicopters
Electronics:
Radar: 2 Thales Pilot nav.; 1 Thales DA-08 surf./air search; 2 Thales Goalkeeper f.c.
TACAN: Thales Vesta transponder
EW: . . . intercept; Mk 36 SRBOC decoy syst. (4 6-round Raytheon Mk 137 RL); SLQ-25A Nixie acoustic torpedo decoy syst.
E/O: Thales IRSCAN surveillance and tracking
M: 4 Stork Werkspoor 12SW28 diesel generator sets (3,650 kw each), 2 Holec electric motors; 2 fixed-pitch props; 16,628 shp—2 600-shp electric motors for slow-speed operations—248-shp bow-thruster

AMPHIBIOUS WARFARE SHIPS AND CRAFT *(continued)*

Rotterdam (L 800)—with one SH-14D Lynx helicopter, nine trucks, and other equipment on deck while on deployment in the Mediterranean Findler & Winter, 2-01

Rotterdam (L 800) A. A. de Kruijf, 7-01

Electric: 3,650 kw from main generators; 1,000-kw diesel-driven harbor set (see remarks)
Range: 6,000/12
Fuel: 830 tons + 200 tons aviation and vehicle fuel + 50 tons for landing craft
Endurance: 30 days (with embarked troops)
Crew: 13 officers, 23 chief petty officers, 77 other enlisted + marines: 41 officers, 156 senior petty officers, 414 other enlisted (+ 150 additional for 24 hours)

Remarks: The final design, prepared by Schelde and Spain's Izar (formerly E.N. Bazán), was approved late in 5-93, with two sisters also built in Spain. Ordered 25-4-94. Up to 20% of the crew can be female.
Hull systems: Built to merchant marine standards but has degaussing coils and a gas-tight citadel. Ballast tanks (to flood down the docking well) accommodate 4,000 tons of seawater. Carries 300 tons of potable water. Is able to operate in Sea State 6. The main diesel generator system provides both propulsion and ship's service power. Hospital facilities include two operating rooms, 100 beds, and 10 intensive-care berths.
Combat systems: Has a dual helicopter hangar totaling 510 m^2 and two landing spots on the 60 × 25–m helicopter deck. There is 903 m^2 of internal vehicle parking space and the 885-m^2 docking well can also be used for additional vehicles; further vehicles can be carried on the 1,340-m^2 helicopter deck. Has 627 m^3 of general stores capacity (130 m^3 refrigerated), 630 m^3 of marine equipment capacity, and 320 m^3 of ammunition storage. One 25-ton and one 2.5-ton capacity crane are fitted. Is able to carry up to 30 Leopard-2 battle tanks or 160 armored personnel carriers. Two Leopard tanks have been altered to function as Beach Armored Recovery Vehicles for use with the ship, which also can carry two portable road-layers. Vehicles can be moved from below decks to the helicopter deck by a 25-ton-capacity elevator. The docking well can accommodate six LCVP Mk 3 or four Dutch LCU-1 or four British LCU Mk 9 or four U.S. LCM(8) landing craft. There are three side doors per side, with the forward door usable for vehicle loading and debarking. To support ASW helicopters, the magazine accommodates 30 Mk 46 torpedoes and 300 sonobuoys.

Embarked troop Stinger shoulder-launched SAMs are expected to contribute to ship defenses. Has SHF military SATCOM capability and Inmarsat commercial SATCOM facilities and over 40 radio transceivers and receivers. NATO Link 11 and Link 14 datalinks are fitted. The DA-08 radar uses the antenna from a DA-05 set and was recycled from one of the *Jacob Van Heemskerck*–class frigates.

♦ 5 LCU-1-class utility landing craft [LCU]
Bldr: Visser, Den Helder

	Laid down	L	In serv.
L 9525	28-4-97	9-8-97	7-4-98
L 9526	28-9-98	25-6-99	31-7-99
L 9527	28-9-98	30-8-99	24-9-99
L 9528	. . .	22-10-99	17-12-99
L 9529	. . .	12-11-99	20-12-99

L 9529—in olive-green paint Rob Cabo, 4-01

D: 200 tons (fl) **S:** . . . kts **Dim:** 27.30 (23.80 wl) × 6.84 × 1.55
A: 2 single 12.7-mm mg **Electronics:** Radar: 1 Furuno . . . nav.
M: 2 Caterpillar 3412C D1-T diesels driving Stamford 543.F1 generators (565 kVA each), 2 Alconza D.400.M6 electric motors (400 kw each); 2 Schottel SJP.82.T vertical-cycloidal props; 1,400 shp
Electric: 70 kw tot. (1 × 70 kw, Perkins T4.236 diesel driving)
Range: 400/8 **Endurance:** 14 days **Crew:** 5 tot. + 130 troops

Remarks: Four were ordered 18-4-97 for use with *Rotterdam* (L 800), with an option for the fifth later taken up. Originally were to have had hulls built in Romania, but the hulls were instead built at Roermond and fitted out at Den Helder. Visser is a subsidiary of the Damen group. Assigned directly to the Royal Netherlands Marine Corps. Painted green, they are based at Texel.
Hull systems: Unusually deep 4.4-m molded depth to hull, which has vehicle ramps fore and aft. Able to carry 130 troops or three 4-ton trucks or two 10-ton trucks or four BV 206 tracked personnel carriers or 6–8 jeeps or two Warrior armored fighting vehicles; can also carry one beach armored recovery vehicle (BARV). Ballast tanks aft are used to alter the hull trim for beaching. The propellers are mounted fore and aft. Electric power is taken from one of the main generators, and there is also a Perkins diesel-powered emergency set. L 9526 and later have improved machinery arrangements. The articulating radar mast is raised or lowered pneumatically.

L 9526 A. A. de Kruijf, 9-99

♦ 6 LCA Mk 3 landing craft [LCVP]
Bldr: Van der Giessen de Noord, Alblasserdam

	In serv.		In serv.		In serv.
L 9536	16-10-90	L 9538	26-11-91	L 9540	13-3-92
L 9537	12-12-92	L 9539	10-4-92	L 9541	19-10-92

D: 23 tons (28.5 fl) **S:** 18 kts (light; 13 loaded) **Dim:** 16.90 × 4.77 × 1.10
A: 2 single 7.62-mm FN FAL mg **Electronics:** Radar: 1 Furuno . . . nav.
M: 2 DAF-Turbo DKS-1160M diesels; 2 Schottel swiveling props; 520 bhp
Range: 220/13 **Crew:** 3 tot. + 34 troops

Remarks: Ordered 10-12-88. L 9536 laid down 10-8-89, L 9540 on 16-5-91, and L 9541 on 4-9-91. GRP construction. Can carry 7 tons of cargo or two Land Rover light trucks or a BV 202E Snowcat tracked vehicle. The cargo deck is covered with GRP segments that slide aft for stowage.

AMPHIBIOUS WARFARE SHIPS AND CRAFT *(continued)*

L 9536 A. A. de Kruijf, 7-00

L 9536—note machineguns on the port quarter and atop the troop compartment A. A. de Kruijf, 7-01

♦ 6 LCA Mk 2 landing craft [LCVP]

Bldr: Naval Shipyard, Den Helder

	In serv.		In serv.		In serv.
L 9530	10-10-84	L 9532	4-7-85	L 9534	13-12-85
L 9531	20-12-84	L 9533	13-12-85	L 9535	5-1-86

L 9535 Rob Cabo, 7-01

D: 8.5 tons (13.6 fl) **S:** 11 kts **Dim:** 16.0 × 4.4 × 1.3
A: 1 7.62-mm FN FAL mg **Electronics:** Radar: 1 Furuno . . . nav.
M: 1 DAF-Turbo diesel; 1 Schottel swiveling prop; 260 bhp
Range: 220/11 **Crew:** 3 tot. + 25 troops

Remarks: GRP construction. Were originally to have been a dozen. Can carry a Land Rover truck or a BV 202E Snowcat tracked snow vehicle in place of the 25 troops. The machinegun is mounted to port of the ramp at the bow. L 9533 has been equipped as a fireboat at Den Helder; she is painted red and has been disarmed.

♦ 23 U.S. Whaler assault craft [LCP]

Bldr: Boston Whaler, Edgewater, Fla. (In serv. 10-3-92)

WM9-9201 through WM9-9223

D: 2 tons (fl) **S:** 30 kts **Dim:** 6.50 × 2.35 × . . .
A: . . . M: 2 gasoline outboards; 140 bhp
Range: 100/30 **Crew:** 8 marines

Remarks: WM = Watertransport Motor. Purchased in 1992. Foam-core GRP construction. Also accepted for service on the same date were three 13-ft. Boston Whalers (WM9-9224 through WM9-9226) for use by the Dutch Marines in the West Indies.

Netherlands Marines Boston Whaler assault launch H&L Van Ginderen, 7-97

♦ 30 RIB assault launches [LCP]

Bldr: Mulder & Rijke, IJmuiden (In serv. 2-89 through 1-2-96)

WM8-8801, WM8-8803, WM8-8804, WM8-8902 through WM8-8909, WM8-9001 through WM8-9009, WM8-9101, WM8-9102, WM8-9201, WM8-9202, WM8-9501 through WM8-9505

Rigid inflatable assault launch WM8-8905 Rob Cabo, 4-01

D: 1.62 tons **S:** 26 kts **Dim:** 7.00 × 2.60 × 0.80
M: 1 Volvo Penta TAMD 32A diesel outboard; 110 bhp

Remarks: WM = Watertransport Motor. For transport aboard frigates, etc., and used by Dutch marines. WM8-8700 was transferred to Pakistan in 7-94, and WM8-8802 and WM8-8901 were transferred to Greece in 1995.

Note: The Royal Netherlands Marines also employ a number of smaller Zodiac RIBs capable of carrying four armed commandos in addition to the coxswain. One-man assault paddle-kayaks are also available.

Royal Netherlands Marines in a Zodiac assault RIB Piet Sinke, 6-96

AUXILIARIES

♦ 1 support ship for the Netherlands Antilles [AG]

Bldr: Vindholmen Offshore A/B, Arendal, Norway (In serv. 1984)

A 801 Pelikaan (ex-*Kilindoni*)

Pelikaan (A 801) Royal Netherlands Navy

D: 505 tons (fl) **S:** 12 kts (10 sust.) **Dim:** 46.23 (41.61 pp) × 10.61 × 2.48
A: 2 single 12.7-mm mg
Electronics: Radar: 1 Decca 1226 nav.; 1 Decca TM1229 nav.

AUXILIARIES *(continued)*

M: 2 Caterpillar 3412T diesels; 2 props; 1,040 bhp
Crew: 15 tot.

Remarks: 505 grt. Former oilfield supply-tug acquired 28-5-90 from the Tanzania Coastal Shipping Line, Arendal, Norway, and refitted at Curaçao. Commissioned 5-7-90 for use as a general-purpose tender/supply ship in the Netherlands Antilles and for transporting marines, as required, using five portable accommodations containers. Has a large electrohydraulic crane amidships that can handle small assault boats stowed on deck. Restricted from carrying passengers late in 2001 and is to be replaced soon.

♦ **1 torpedo-trials ship [AGE]**
Bldr: Schelde Shipbuilding, Vlissingen

	Laid down	L	In serv.
A 900 Mercuur	6-11-85	25-10-86	21-8-87

Mercuur (A 900) Bernard Prézelin, 7-00

D: 1,200 tons (1,500 fl) **S:** 14 kts **Dim:** 64.85 × 12.00 × 4.30
A: 2 fixed, underwater 533-mm TT; mines
Electronics:
Radar: 1 Decca TM 1229 nav.
Sonar: SQR-01 bow-mounted active and passive
M: 2 Brons-M.A.N. 61-20/27 diesel generator sets (650 kw each), electric drive; 2 props; 1,100 shp—bow-thruster
Crew: 6 officers, 30 enlisted + 3 trials personnel

Remarks: Ordered 13-6-84. An ASW escort version of the design was unsuccessfully offered commercially. Has a helicopter vertical-replenishment deck above the torpedo workshop. The sonar array is in a large bow-mounted dome that protrudes well below the keel; the two underwater torpedo tube muzzles exit near the bow. Two 20-mm Oerlikon Mk 10 AA originally fitted have been removed, as has been the triple 324-mm ASW torpedo tube mounting.

♦ **0 (+ 2) Snellius-class hydrographic survey ships [AGS]**
Bldr: Damen–Royal Schelde, Vlissingen

	Laid down	L	In serv.
A . . . Snellius	2001	. . .	2003
A . . . Luymes	2001	. . .	2003

D: 1,850 tons (fl) **S:** . . . kts **Dim:** . . . (75.0 pp) × 12.8 × 4.0
Electronics: . . .
M: diesel-electric drive; 1 prop; . . . shp—bow-thruster
Crew: 12 tot. + 6 hydrographers (accomm. for 42)

Remarks: Intended to replace *Tydeman* (A 906) and *Buyskes* (A 904). Formal contract to be let early in 2001 for about $46 million for the pair. Will reportedly each have three crews to permit near-continuous operations. Are to be used in home waters and in the Netherlands Antilles and will also perform surveillance and coast guard duties. The hulls are being built at Damen SY Galati, in Romania.

♦ **1 Tydeman-class hydrographic survey ship [AGS]**
Bldr: B.V. De Merwede, Hardinxveld-Giessendam

	Laid down	L	In serv.
A 906 Tydeman	29-4-75	18-12-75	10-11-76

Tydeman (A 906) Rob Cabo, 9-00

D: 2,977 tons (fl) **S:** 15 kts **Dim:** 90.15 × 14.43 × 4.75
Electronics:
Radar: 1 Decca 1226 nav.; 1 Decca TM1229 nav.
Sonar: Kelvin-Hughes hull-mounted side-scan; Klein towed side-scan; Elac bow-mounted HF wreck-location; 2 STN Atlas Elektronik DESO-25 precision echo sounders

Tydeman (A 906) A. A. de Kruijf, 9-00

M: 3 Stork-Werkspoor 8-FCHD-240 diesels, electric drive; 1 prop; 2,730 shp—2 bow-thrusters; 1 active rudder
Electric: 1,400 kw tot. **Range:** 10,300/13.5; 15,700/10.3
Crew: 8 officers, 54 enlisted + 15 scientists/technicians

Remarks: Constructed as a general-purpose oceanographic research and hydrographic survey ship. After a 1992 refit, has been employed as a support ship for mine countermeasures systems trials. Was to be stricken in 1999 but continues to operate, primarily in testing towed sonar systems; as of 2-00, was scheduled to be retired in 2003.
Hull systems: The hangar and flight deck, intended to support one Lynx helicopter, are now used for equipment stowage. Has a passive tank stabilization system. Eight laboratories, two in portable 20-ft. containers, are fitted. Any two of the three main diesels power the propulsion motors; the other then provides ship's service power. Has the COMPLOT charting system and the Decca HiFix Mk 6 radio precision navigation system. Carries one 10-ton and one 4-ton crane, plus several A-frame oceanographic cranes. Survey launches WM2-7601 and WM2-7602 are stowed abreast the stack.
Trials systems: Conducted trials 1994–97 with the TNO-FEL/Thomson-Sintra ALF Active Low-Frequency sonar, which uses a 2.5-m-high, omnidirectional, towed, body-mounted sound source (under 1 kHz) and two towed, 130-m receiver arrays, each with 32 hydrophones and a number of nonacoustic sensors, to detect targets out to the first convergence zone (30–60 km range). Data derived from the array are transmitted to the ship by fiber-optic cable for processing by a Sun 4/470 computer.

♦ **1 Blommendal-class hydrographic survey ship [AGS]**
Bldr: Boele's Scheepswerven en Machinefabriek BV, Bolnes

	Laid down	L	In serv.
A 904 Buyskes	31-1-72	11-7-72	9-3-73

Buyskes (A 904)—with orange-painted survey launch WM2-8902 aboard H&L Van Ginderen, 5-00

D: 867 tons (1,025 fl) **S:** 14 kts **Dim:** 58.80 × 11.13 × 3.70
Electronics:
Radar: 1 Decca TM 1226 nav.; 1 Decca 1229 nav.
Sonar: Thales Bathyscan hull-mounted HF side-scanning; 2 STN Atlas Elektronik DESO-25 precision echo sounders
M: 3 Paxman 12 RPHCZ7 diesels (742 bhp each), Smit electric drive; 1 prop; 1,100 shp
Electric: 745 kw tot. **Range:** 7,000/10 **Crew:** 6 officers, 37 enlisted

Remarks: Sister *Blommendal* (A 905) was retired 16-12-99, and A 904 is to retire in 2003. Is used in wreck surveys, equipped with wire-drag equipment and carrying two chain-clearance drag boats. Has an automated data-logging system. Operates mainly in the North Sea. Carries survey launch WM2-8902: completed 1989–90; 9.5 × 3.8 m; 1 Volvo Penta diesel; 170 bhp for 15 kts.

Note: Damen Polycat harbor launch Y 8200 is used for inshore survey work.

♦ **1 (+ 1) Patiño-class underway replenishment ships [AOR]**
Bldr: Schelde Shipbuilding, Vlissingen (hull by B.V. De Merwede, Hardinxveld-Giessendam)

	Laid down	L	In serv.
A 836 Amsterdam	25-5-92	11-9-93	2-9-95

Amsterdam (A 836) Bernard Prézelin, 6-01

AUXILIARIES *(continued)*

Amsterdam (A 836) Rob Cabo, 1-01

D: 17,040 tons (fl) **S:** 21 kts (20 sust.)
Dim: 165.84 (156.00 wl) × 23.70 (22.00 wl) × 8.00
A: 1 30-mm Goalkeeper CIWS; 2 single 20-mm 70-cal. Oerlikon Mk 10 AA; 2–3 helicopters (see remarks)
Electronics:
Radar: 2 Kelvin-Hughes . . . F-band nav.; 1 Kelvin-Hughes Type 1007 nav.
TACAN: Thales Vesta beacon
EW: Ferranti AWARE-4 radar warning; Mk 36 SRBOC decoy syst. (4 6-round Raytheon Mk 137 RL); SLQ-25 Nixie towed acoustic torpedo decoy syst.
E/O: Thales IRSCAN surveillance syst.
M: 2 Izar–Burmeister & Wain V16V-40/45 diesels; 1 5-bladed, 5.7-m-dia. CP prop; 26,240 shp
Electric: 4,000 kw tot. (4 × 1,000-kw Izar–Burmeister & Wain sets)
Range: 13,440/20 **Endurance:** 30 days
Crew: 23 officers, 137 enlisted + 70 spare berths

Remarks: A 836 was ordered during 10-91 to replace *Poolster;* the order for a planned second ship has been delayed several times. Joint design between Netherlands' Nevesbu and Spain's E.N. Bazán (now Izar) design bureaus. Twenty percent of the crew can be women. Commenced sea trials 3-4-95 and was accepted for service 10-7-95. A decision on whether to order a second ship of the class has been postponed until 2004.
Hull systems: Has four 2-ton-capacity dual-purpose and two 250-kg solid-stores alongside replenishment stations on each side and a VERTREP position forward. Cargo deadweight: 10,300 tons, including 6,700 tons fuel, 1,660 tons aviation fuel, 178.8 tons fresh water, 180.9 tons ammunition, 18.6 tons sonobuoys, 83.3 tons provisions, and 9 tons spare parts. Fuel transfer rate is 1,000 m^3 per hour to port and 600 m^3 per hour to starboard, and 200 m^3 per hour for aviation fuel on either beam; there is provision for fueling astern at 450 m^3/hr. There are repair shops to assist other vessels. Crew figure above includes 24 aviation complement. Is able to carry three SH-14D Lynx or two Merlin/Sea King–size helicopters. Has a gas-tight citadel. Capable of operating in up to Sea State 6. Equipped for NATO Link 11.

♦ 1 improved Poolster-class underway replenishment ship [AOR]
Bldr: Verolme, Alblasserdam

	Laid down	L	In serv.
A 832 Zuiderkruis	16-7-73	15-10-74	27-6-75

Zuiderkruis (A 832) Rob Cabo, 5-00

D: 17,357 tons **S:** 21 kts **Dim:** 169.59 (157.00 pp) × 20.3 × 8.4 (max.)
A: 1 30-mm Goalkeeper gatling CIWS; up to SH-14D Lynx helicopters
Electronics:
Radar: 2 Decca TM 1226C nav.; 1 Thales Scout nav./surf. search; 1 Decca 2459 surf. search
EW: Ferranti AWARE-4 radar warning; Mk 36 SRBOC decoy syst. (4 6-round Raytheon Mk 137 decoy RL)
E/O: Thales IRSCAN surveillance and tracking
M: 2 Werkspoor TM 410 16-cyl. diesels; 1 prop; 21,000 bhp
Electric: 3,000 kw tot. **Crew:** 17 officers, 249 enlisted

Remarks: As of 2-01, was to remain in service until 2010.
Hull systems: Cargo capacity: 9,000 tons fuel, 400 tons JP-5 aviation fuel, 200 tons fresh water, spare parts, ammunition. Can carry ASW torpedoes and other stores to support ASW helicopters. Has two fueling stations per side, amidships, and one sliding-stay, constant-tension, solid transfer station each side, forward.

SERVICE CRAFT

♦ 1 trials barge [YAGEN]
Y 8100 (In serv. 14-7-95)

Remarks: Ordered 31-8-94. Non-self-propelled. No data available.

Trials barge Y 8100 H&L Van Ginderen, 7-97

♦ 1 floating boathouse barge [YAGN]
Y 8066 (In serv. 1994)

♦ 1 work platform barge [YC]
Bldr: Rijkswerf, Den Helder (In serv. 11-8-95)

Y 8119 Neelte Jans

Remarks: Ordered 31-8-94 and laid down 2-1-95. Non-self-propelled.

♦ 3 work platform barges [YC]
Bldr: . . . . . . (In serv. 1995)

Y 8116 Y 8117 Y 8118

Work platform barge Y 8116 A. A. de Kruijf, 4-99

Remarks: Ordered 11-94. Non-self-propelled.

♦ 13 miscellaneous deck-cargo barges [YC] (In serv. 1900–92)
Y 8322, Y 8331, Y 8332, Y 8334, Y 8337–Y 8341, Y 8343–Y 8345, Y 8377

Deck-cargo barge Y 8340—being used as a landing stage H&L Van Ginderen, 7-99

Remarks: Y 8377 is ex-Army RV 141, transferred in 10-89 for use by marines in ship-to-shore transits. Y 8345 is used as a dirty water–receiving craft.

♦ 26 miscellaneous mooring pontoons [YC]

Y 8578 (In serv. 20-10-87)
Y 8595 (In serv. 1956)
Y 8597 (In serv. . . .)
Y 8598 (In serv. 1971)
Y 8599 (In serv. 1977)
Y 8600–8603 (In serv. 3-2-81 to 1984)
Y 8604–8610 (In serv. 1983–85)
Y 8611–8613 (In serv. 23-6-86)
Y 8614–8617 (Acquired 25-9-86)
Y 8712–8714 (In serv. 1940)

Remarks: Y 8597, Y 8598, Y 8599, and Y 8600 through Y 8603 are used with submarines. Y 8711 was stricken 4-12-96. Y 8713 carries extra accommodations huts and is moored with accommodations barge *Thetis* (A 887).

SERVICE CRAFT *(continued)*

Mooring pontoon Y 8713 H&L Van Ginderen, 7-99

♦ 1 towed-array cable pontoon [YC]

Y 8577 (In serv. 18-12-92)

Towed-array cable pontoon Y 8577 Dieter Wolf, 7-00

Remarks: Employed to replace towed linear hydrophone sonar arrays in frigates.

♦ 1 miscellaneous barge [YC]

Y 8715 (In serv. 1983)

♦ 1 floating crane [YD]

Y 8514 (In serv. 1974)

♦ 4 Cerberus-class diving tenders [YDT]

Bldr: Scheepswerf Visser, Den Helder

	Laid down	L	In serv.
A 851 Cerberus	15-4-91	18-12-91	28-2-92
A 852 Argus	16-9-91	14-3-92	2-6-92
A 853 Nautilus	16-3-92	10-6-92	18-9-92
A 854 Hydra	11-6-92	11-9-92	20-11-92

Cerberus (A 851) Rob Cabo, 7-01

D: 200 tons (233 fl) **S:** 10.25 kts
Dim: 27.30 (26.00 pp) × 8.76 (8.50 wl) × 1.50—see remarks
Electronics: Radar: 1 Decca . . . nav.
M: 2 Volvo Penta TAMD-122A diesels; 2 props; 760 bhp
Electric: 144 kVA tot. (2 × 72 kVA, DAF DH-825 MGK diesels driving)
Range: 750/10 **Crew:** 2 officers, 6 unlicensed + 6 divers

Remarks: First three ordered 29-11-90, the fourth later. Have an electrohydraulic crane with 8-m max. reach and 2-ton max. capacity aft to tend divers and a rigid inflatable boat. Can support two hard-hat divers simultaneously at 50 m. Crews are civilian. Between 2-8-97 and 12-3-98, A 854 was lengthened by 10.5 m under a 26-5-97 contract by Visser SY, Den Helder, to provide increased accommodations; she was relaunched 5-3-98 and recommissioned 13-3-98 and now displaces about 310 tons (fl).

Hydra (A 854)—as lengthened, alongside the *Argus* (A 852) H&L Van Ginderen, 7-99

♦ 6 miscellaneous diving pontoons [YDTN]

Y 8579 (In serv. 30-5-86)
Y 8580 (In serv. 18-12-85)
Y 8581 (In serv. 2-4-86)
Y 8582 (In serv. 28-5-86)
Y 8583 (In serv. . . .)
Y 8590 (In serv. 1952)

Remarks: Y 8584, 8588, and 8592 were transferred to the Sea Scouts in 1993. Y 8586 was stricken 22-2-95, and Y 8585 and 8589 had been discarded by 1999.

♦ 6 Polycat-class harbor launches [YFL]

Bldr: Mulder & Rijke, IJmuiden

Y 8200 (In serv. 15-11-89)
Y 8201 (In serv. 8-12-89)
Y 8202 (In serv. 16-2-90)
Y 8203 (In serv. 16-3-90)
WM1-9001 Jonge Prins 3 (In serv. 27-4-90)
WM1-9002 (In serv. 8-12-90)

Polycat launch Y 8201—note life raft on quick-release rack at stern A. A. de Kruijf, 7-01

D: 4.75 tons (fl) **S:** 14.5 kts **Dim:** 9.50 × 3.70 × 1.45
Electronics: Radar: 1 Furuno . . . nav.
M: 1 Volvo Penta TAMD 41 diesel; 1 waterjet; 170 bhp **Crew:** 4–6 tot.

Remarks: First four ordered 12-1-89; fifth and sixth later. Damen Polycat glass-reinforced plastic hulls. Y 8200 is used for inshore survey work.

♦ 1 public relations launch [YFL]

Bldr: Akerboom, Leiden (In serv. 1972)

Y 8005 Nieuwediep (ex-*Spido 11*)

Nieuwediep (Y 8005) A. A. de Kruijf, 7-01

SERVICE CRAFT *(continued)*

D: approx 50 tons (fl) **S:** . . . kts **Dim:** 17.75 × 3.75 × 1.45
Electronics: Radar: 1 Furuno . . . nav.
M: 2 Volvo Penta diesels; 2 props; 300 bhp **Crew:** 4 tot. + 50 passengers

Remarks: Acquired 10-2-92 and stationed at Den Helder to provide transportation for public visitors.

♦ 4 WM7-class personnel launches [YFL]
Bldr: Victoria

	In serv.		In serv.
WM7-9301 Plancius	1993	WM7-9303 Douwes	1993
WM7-9302 Waghenaer	1993	WM7-9501 Fortuin II	1995

D: 3.0 tons **S:** . . . kts **Dim:** 8.55 × 2.72 × 1.60
M: 1 . . . diesel; 1 prop; . . . bhp

Remarks: WM = Watertransport Motor. Polyester construction.

♦ 10 WM4-class personnel launches [YFL]
Bldr: Rijkswerf Den Helder

	In serv.		In serv.
WM4-6601 Rhvd	1966	WM4-7403	1974
WM4-6902 Cmmadam	1969	WM4-7502 Rhvd	1975
WM4-7301 Cmmrdam	1973	WM4-7567	1975
WM4-7303	1973	WM4-9802 (ex-WM4-7001)	1970
WM4-7402 Zuiderkruis	1974	WM4-9901 (ex-WM4-7501)	1975

WM4-series launch WM4-7502—original configuration Rob Cabo, 1-01

Rebuilt WM4-series launch WM4-9901 A. A. de Kruijf, 6-00

D: first four: 6.26 tons—others: 5.98 tons **S:** . . . kts **Dim:** 11.18 × 3.27 × 1.84
M: 1 . . . diesel; 1 prop; . . . bhp

Remarks: WM = Watertransport Motor. Polyester plastic hulls. WM4-7402 is carried aboard the replenishment oiler *Zuiderkruis* (A 832); the others are assigned to shore stations. All are receiving a CUP (Capability Update Program) refit to keep them in service through 2010, with new numbers being assigned as they are completed (e.g., WM4-9802); WM4-9901 completed the CUP update 28-5-99.

♦ 18 miscellaneous personnel launches [YFL]
13 WM2-7303 class: WM2-7402 through WM2-7404, WM2-7501, WM2-7502, WM2-7603, WM2-7605 through WM2-7608, WM2-7610, WM2-7901, WM2-7903
5 miscellaneous: WM1-8405, WM1-9001 Jonge Prinz, WM3-8001 Tjarda, WR1-8802, WR1-8804

WM2-7303-class launch WM2-7608 Rob Cabo, 7-98

Remarks: WM = Watertransport Motor. No data available. Completed in the years signified by the first two digits of the second set of numbers.

♦ 4 survey launches [YGS]
WM2-7601 WM2-7602 WM2-8901 WM2-8902

Remarks: First two carried by *Tydeman* (A 906), WM2-8901 formerly aboard *Blommendal* (A 905), and WM2-8902 aboard *Buyskes* (A 904). Last two are 9.5 × 3.8 m, with 1 Volvo Penta diesel (170 bhp for 15 kts).

♦ 5 fast self-propelled target craft [YGT]
Bldr: . . . . . . (In serv. Y 8704: 5-86; Y 8699: 1994; Y 8695: 1995)

Y 8695 Y 8696 Y 8698 Y 8699 Y 8704

Remarks: Sister Y 8697 transferred to Pakistan in 7-94.

♦ 2 target barges [YGTN]
Y 8700 Y 8705

♦ 1 fuel lighter [YO]
Bldr: Scheepswerf DeHoop B.V., Schiedam

	Laid down	L	In serv.
Y 8760 Patria	10-7-97	10-11-97	9-4-98

Patria (Y 8760) Rob Cabo, 7-00

D: . . . tons **S:** 8 kts **Dim:** 44.25 (42.00 pp) × 6.50 × 2.50
Electronics: Radar: 1 . . . nav.
M: 1 Volvo Penta TAMD 122A diesel; 1 prop; 375 bhp—1 147-shp azimuthal bow-thruster
Electric: 41 kw tot. (1 diesel set) **Crew:** 2 tot.

Remarks: Ordered 26-6-97 for service at Den Helder. The hull was assembled by Made Shipyard in two sections that were towed to DeHoop's facility on 10-10-97 and 30-10-97.
Hull systems: Carries 250 m^3 of fuel in four tanks and 175 m^3 of potable water; three 10-m^3 tanks can carry oil sludge or spoil-water from submarines. Pumping rate is 150 m^3/hr, with the same diesel engine that powers the bow-thruster also being employed to drive the pump. Hull molded depth is 2.80 m.

♦ 1 non-self-propelled accommodations barge [YPBN]
Bldr: Koninklijke Maatschappij de Schelde, Vlissingen (In serv. 27-6-85)

A 887 Thetis

Thetis (A 887)—with barge Y 8713 alongside Rob Cabo, 7-01

D: 1,000 tons (fl) **Dim:** 68.47 (62.85 pp) × 12.82 × 1.60

Remarks: Launched 1-83. Three floating fenders, delivered in 1986, served with A 887: Y 8611, Y 8612, and Y 8613. Also alongside were pontoon barges Y 8580–8582. Stationed at Den Helder.

♦ 1 ex-German Type 430 torpedo recovery craft [YPT]
Bldr: Burmester, Bremen

	Laid down	L	In serv.
Y . . . (ex-TF 1; Y 851, ex-W 70)	4-1-65	13-10-65	24-3-66

D: 56 tons (63.5 fl) **S:** 17 kts **Dim:** 25.22 (23.50 pp) × 5.40 (5.00 wl) × 1.60
Electric: 36 kw tot. (2 × 18-kw diesel sets)
M: 1 MWM 12-cyl. diesel; 1 prop; 1,000 bhp **Crew:** 6 tot.

Remarks: Stricken from the German Navy 24-5-95 and sold to the Netherlands in 1998. Wooden construction. Has a stern ramp for torpedo recovery.

SERVICE CRAFT *(continued)*

♦ 2 sludge barges [YRG]
Bldr: Scheepswerf DeHoop B.V., Lobith (Both in serv. 3-9-86)

Y 8351 Y 8352

Sludge barge Y 8352—in light condition H&L Van Ginderen, 7-99

D: approx. 460 tons (fl) **Dim:** 25.25 × 6.24 × 3.30

Remarks: Ordered 14-2-86 and laid down 4-4-86.

♦ 5 Linge-class coastal tugs [YTB]
Bldr: Delta SY, Sliedrecht (hulls for A 874, A 875 by Scheepswerf Bijlsma B.V., Wartena; hull for A 878 by Made Scheepswerf, Made)

	Laid down	L	In serv.
A 874 Linge	12-6-86	15-11-86	20-2-87
A 875 Regge	23-6-86	10-1-87	6-5-87
A 876 Hunze	17-12-86	9-6-87	20-10-87
A 877 Rotte	17-12-86	23-6-87	20-10-87
A 878 Gouwe	13-5-96	25-11-96	21-2-97

Regge (A 875) A. A. de Kruijf, 7-01

D: approx. 500 tons (fl) **S:** 12.5 kts **Dim:** 27.45 (26.30 pp) × 8.30 × 3.80
Electronics: Radar: 1 Decca TM 1229 nav.
M: 2 Stork-Werkspoor Type DRO 218 K (A 878: Caterpillar . . .) diesels; 2 Kort-nozzle props; 1,632 bhp
Electric: 192 kw **Fuel:** 55 tons **Crew:** 7 tot.

Remarks: First two ordered 16-4-86. All based at Den Helder. A 878, ordered 9-5-96, replaced *Westgat* (A 872); she was originally launched 12-9-96 and then returned to the building slip for further work.

♦ 2 Breezand-class harbor tugs [YTM]
Bldr: Deltawerf, Sliedrecht

Y 8018 Breezand (In serv. 12-89) Y 8019 Balgzand (In serv. 12-1-90)

D: approx. 90 tons (fl) **S:** 10 kts **Dim:** 16.52 × 5.32 × 1.80
Electronics: Radar: 1 . . . nav.
M: 2 Volvo Penta TAMD-122A diesels; 2 props; 760 bhp

Remarks: Ordered 5-12-88. Y 8018 was launched 22-11-89, Y 8019 on 27-12-89.

Breezand (Y 8018) Rob Cabo, 7-01

♦ 5 DT-2750-class steel tug/workboats [YTL]
Bldr: Deltawerf, Sliedrecht

Y 8055 Schelde (In serv. 18-2-87)
Y 8056 Wierbalg (In serv. 18-2-87)
Y 8057 Malzwin (In serv. 24-12-86)
Y 8058 Zuidwal (In serv. 5-12-86)
Y 8059 Westwal (In serv. 29-12-86)

Zuidwal (Y 8058) Guy Schaeffer, via Paolo Marsan, 6-00

D: approx. 35 tons (fl) **S:** . . . **Dim:** 10.80 × 3.76 × 1.60
M: 1 DAF diesel; 1 prop; 115 bhp

Remarks: Y 8058 is based at Vlissingen, the others at Den Helder.

♦ 1 LCA Mk 2 fireboat [YTR]
Bldr: Naval Shipyard, Den Helder (In serv. 13-12-85)

L 9533

D: 8.5 tons (13.6 fl) **S:** 11 kts **Dim:** 16.0 × 4.4 × 1.3
Electronics: Radar: 1 Furuno . . . nav.
M: 1 DAF-Turbo diesel; 1 Schottel swiveling prop; 260 bhp
Range: 220/11 **Crew:** 3 tot.

Remarks: Replaced the older L 9515 as fireboat at Den Helder in 2000; painted red. Glass-reinforced plastic construction.

♦ 1 sail-training ketch [YTS]
Bldr: Haarlemse Scheepsbouw Mij., Haarlem

	L	In serv.
Y 8050 Urania (ex-*Tromp*)	1929	23-4-38

D: 76.4 tons (fl) **S:** 5 kts (10 under sail) **Dim:** 23.94 × 5.29 × 3.15
M: 1 Kromhout diesel; 1 prop; 65 bhp—625 m^2 sail area **Crew:** 17 tot.

Note: There are also 24 small sport and training oar-and-sail boats with hull numbers in the WR1 series under naval control.

SERVICE CRAFT *(continued)*

Urania (Y 8050) Piet Sinke, 6-95

♦ **1 seamanship training craft [YXT]**
Bldr: Vervako SY, Heusden

	Laid down	L	In serv.
A 902 Van Kinsbergen	5-11-98	23-4-99	2-11-99

Van Kinsbergen (A 902)—painted white with yellow mast and stack
IJsbrand Plokker, 9-00

D: . . . tons **S:** . . . kts **Dim:** 41.51 (35.87 pp) × 9.20 × 3.30
Electronics: Radar: . . .
M: 2 . . . diesels; 2 props; . . . bhp—bow-thruster

Remarks: Ordered 15-6-98 as a replacement for *Zeefakkel* (A 903). Fitted out by Damen at Gorinchem after launching.

♦ **1 seamanship training craft [YXT]** Bldr: J. & K. Smit, Kinderijk

	Laid down	L	In serv.
A 903 Zeefakkel	28-11-49	21-7-50	16-3-51

Zeefakkel (A 903)—painted white with yellow stack and mast
IJsbrand Plokker, 9-99

D: 303 tons (384 fl) **S:** 12 kts **Dim:** 45.38 × 7.50 × 2.20
Electronics: Radar: 1 Decca . . . nav.
M: 2 Smit-M.A.N. diesels; 2 props; 640 bhp **Crew:** 26 tot.

Remarks: Former pilot boat, used for seamanship training at Den Helder. Re-engined in 1980. Was to be retired in 1999 but is instead being kept in service.

Note: Also used for training at Den Helder are at least eight WM1-8401-series launches, propelled either by 12 oarsmen or sails rigged from two masts.

ROYAL NETHERLANDS ARMY

AMPHIBIOUS WARFARE CRAFT

♦ **1 RV 40–class tank landing craft [WLCU]**
Bldr: Grave B.V. (In serv. 22-11-79)

RV 40

RV 40—with naval berthing barge *Thetis* (A 887) in background at left
A. A. de Kruijf, 7-01

D: 815 tons **S:** 9.4 kts **Dim:** 45.8 × 9.5 × 2.20
M: 2 Mercedes-Benz OM404 diesels; 2 props; 654 bhp **Crew:** 4 tot.

♦ **58 Type ASA-540 aluminum river assault boats [WLCP]**
Bldr: Damen, Gorinchem (In serv. 1980s)

D: 1.8 tons (fl) **S:** 25–30 kts **Dim:** 5.40 × 1.83 × 0.10
M: 1 25- to 40-bhp diesel outboard **Crew:** 4–8 tot.

♦ **49 or more Type 700 Bridge Support Boats [WLCP]**
Bldr: Damen, Gorinchem

D: 6 tons (fl) **S:** 8.6 kts **Dim:** 7.00 × 2.90 × 0.75
M: 1 Deutz BF 8L 513 diesel; 2 props; 250 bhp

Remarks: Steel construction, intended to be carried by DAF YGZ 2300 trucks and used in assembling and positioning pontoon bridges. Have 2.6-ton bollard pull. Props are full-swiveling and ducted.

SERVICE CRAFT

♦ **1 diving tender [WYDT]**
Bldr: Werf Vervaco, Heusden (In serv. 3-11-89)

RV 50

D: approx. 400 tons (fl) **S:** 9 kts **Dim:** 37.00 × 9.00 × 1.50
Electronics: Radar: 1 AP Mk 4 nav.
M: 2 . . . . . . diesels; 2 props; 476 bhp **Crew:** 21 tot.

Remarks: Launched 8-9-89. Has a "moonpool" aft beneath the gantry for a 50-m-depth-capable diving bell. Equipped with a decompression chamber.

ROYAL CORPS OF MILITARY POLICE
(Koninklijke Marechaussee)

PATROL BOATS [WPB]

♦ **3 RV 165 class** Bldr: Damen, Gorinchem

RV 165 (In serv. 1975) RV 166 (In serv. 1984) RV 169 (In serv. 1975)

RV 169 Piet Sinke, 4-00

D: . . . **S:** 17.5 kts **Dim:** 17.30 (15.30 pp) × 5.00 × 1.30
M: 2 G.M. diesels; 2 props; 700 bhp

Remarks: RV = *Rijksvaartug.* Steel construction.

Note: Also in service are 15 smaller riverine patrol boats, including the *Keysersplaat* (RV 168), *Aerdt* (RV 174), RV 176, and *Klovenier* (RV 177).

MILITARY POLICE PATROL BOATS [WPB] *(continued)*

Keysersplaat (RV 168) H&L Van Ginderen, 7-99

COAST GUARD

The Netherlands Coast Guard, established 26-2-87, has no vessels of its own but employs ships, boats, and craft supplied by other services: the Royal Netherlands Navy (which provides two lifeboat commanding officers and, since 1-6-95, exercises operational control over the organization), the National Constabulary, the Ministry of Transport, the Corps of Military Police, the Fisheries Inspection Service, and Scheveningen Radio. Units in coast guard use continue to carry their original markings while adding diagonal red, white, and blue stripes, the Netherlands Coast Guard shield, and the word "Kustwacht" on their hull sides. The Coast Guard Operations Center was collocated with the combined Belgian-Netherlands Maritime Headquarters at Den Helder in 1997, with a staff of 30. The Netherlands Antilles Coast Guard is described separately with that country.

NETHERLANDS ANTILLES AND ARUBA

COAST GUARD

Personnel (2002): Approx. 160 total

Organization: Formally established 1-1-98. Headquartered at the Royal Netherlands Perera Naval Base at Curaçao, the Netherlands Antilles and Aruba (NAA) Coast Guard is intended primarily to combat the drug trade in the Caribbean. Smaller facilities are maintained at Aruba and St. Maarten. The Royal Netherlands Navy supplies 23 of the personnel total. The coast guard is subordinate to the Royal Netherlands Navy, reporting to the senior naval commander in the area. The Netherlands Antilles and Aruba remain colonial possessions of the Netherlands, with Aruba enjoying increasing autonomy.

Maritime Aviation: Heliholland, at Curaçao, provides one Eurocopter AS.355 and one Schweizer helicopter for SAR duties as requested; they are normally engaged in training Royal Netherlands Navy helicopter pilots. One Dutch Navy P-3 Orion patrol aircraft based at Curaçao is seconded to the NAA Coast Guard.

Note: Craft are painted gray, with a broad yellow hull diagonal stripe followed by narrow blue, white, and red diagonals on the hull sides. In 1999, the crest of the Netherlands Antilles was added on the yellow diagonal.

PATROL CRAFT [WPC]

♦ **3 Patrol 4100 class**
Bldr: Damen Shipyards, Gorinchem, the Netherlands

	Laid down	L	In serv.
P 810 Jaguar	18-8-97	31-3-98	2-11-98
P 811 Panter	20-9-97	19-5-98	18-1-99
P 812 Poema	5-1-98	7-1-99	14-3-99

D: 170 tons light (204.7 tons fl) **S:** 26 kts (27.8 on trials; 24 sust.)
Dim: 42.80 (40.00 wl; 39.00 pp) × 6.71 (5.99 wl) × 2.52 (props)
A: 1 12.7-mm mg
Electronics:
Radar: 1 Kelvin-Hughes Type 1007 nav.; 1 Thales Scout nav./surf. search
EW: VHF–UHFD/F

Poema (P 812) Piet Sinke, 2-99

Jaguar (P 810) Mike Welsford, 1-99

M: 2 Caterpillar 3516 DI-TA diesels; 2 Lips CP props; 5,600 bhp—bow-thruster
Electric: 262 kVA tot. (2 × 131 kVA, 2 Caterpillar 3304B DI-T diesels driving)
Range: 600/23; 2,000/12 **Fuel:** 27.15 m^3 **Endurance:** 7 days
Crew: 3 officers, 8 enlisted + 6 constable officer passengers

Remarks: Ordered 1-5-97 for $23 million. P 810 ran trials on 14/15-10-98 and was handed over about five months behind schedule; she left for the Caribbean during 1-99. P 810 suffered a serious fire on 23-5-99 and was returned to the builder for repairs. Are stationed at Curaçao, Aruba, and St. Maarten, respectively.
Hull systems: Are able to operate in State 4–5 seas. Carry a video camera, audio recording equipment, chemical and gas sensors, and firefighting equipment (including a firefighting monitor on the forecastle and a 2.68-m^3 foam tank). Thermal-imaging and image-intensification sensors, a secure communications suite, and a gas-tight citadel are fitted. The six-man inspection RIB is carried on an inclined ramp at the stern and can achieve 45 kts on its inboard diesel/waterjet propulsion plant; also carried is a 3.8-m dory with a 25-bhp outboard.
Combat systems: Have a variant of the Thales SEWACO combat data system to coordinate the various sensor data.

PATROL BOATS [WPB]

♦ **4 PB 1 class** Bldr: Schottel, Warmond (In serv. 1970s)

PB 1 PB 2 PB 3 PB 4

PB 2—with original number Hartmut Ehlers, 11-90

D: 50 tons (fl) **S:** 18 kts **Dim:** 17.48 × 4.77 × 1.6
A: 1 12.7-mm mg **Electronics:** Radar: 1 Decca . . . nav.
M: 2 MTU 12V183 TC91 diesels; 2 props; 1,190 bhp **Crew:** 6 tot.

Remarks: Former police craft previously assigned to the Curaçao area. Were originally numbered P 1 through P 4.

♦ **6 Ribsea 700DOB-class rigid inflatable launches**
Bldr: Mulder & Rijke, IJmuiden (In serv. 13-9-97)

D: 3.1 tons (fl) **S:** 50 kts (40 sust.) **Dim:** 7.20 × 2.60 × 0.42
A: small arms **M:** 2 Mercury gasoline outboards; 400 bhp
Range: 180/. . . **Crew:** 2 tot. + 4 passengers

Remarks: Were acquired with one trailer each and a total of three towing vehicles. Are used for inshore patrol duties. Stationed at Aruba and St. Maarten.

NEW ZEALAND

Dominion of New Zealand

Personnel (20-6-01): 396 officers, 1,497 enlisted, and 507 civilian employees. Also assigned to the Royal New Zealand Navy (RNZN) were 10 Army and 5 Royal New Zealand Air Force (RNZAF) personnel. The Royal New Zealand Navy Volunteer Reserve (RNZNVR) included 104 officer and 263 enlisted active and 21 officer and 18 enlisted inactive personnel. Of the active-duty uniformed personnel, 72 officers and 286 enlisted were female. The commercial management of Babcocks (NZ), Ltd., employs about 550 other civilians.

Bases: Joint armed services headquarters was established 1-7-01 at Trentham, where a new maritime coordination center is to be built. The former naval headquarters at HMNZS *Wakefield,* Wellington, has been closed. Ships are based at HMNZS *Philomel,* Devonport Naval Base, Auckland, where there are repair facilities (operated by Babcocks [UK] since 1994); since 20-11-00, HMNZS *Philomel* has also incorporated the naval college. Training is also conducted at the naval college communications facility at HMNZS *Irirangi,* Waiouru. RNZNVR divisions are located at HMNZS *Ngapona,* Auckland (167 personnel); HMNZS *Olphert,* Wellington (85); HMNZS *Pegasus,* Christchurch (67); and HMNZS *Toroa,* Dunedin (62). Ammunition is stored and supported at RNZN Armament Depot Kauri Point. HMNZS *Tamaki,* Auckland, was disestablished on 20-11-00.

Naval Aviation: Helicopters are flown by RNZN crews but maintained by six-man RNZAF detachments. Four new Kaman SH-2G Super SeaSprite helicopters were ordered 11-3-97 to replace the interim SH-2Fs; a fifth was ordered during 7-99, and the first flight was conducted on 2-8-00 in the U.S.A. The first two SH-2G(NZ) helicopters arrived at Auckland 6-6-01. The SH-2G(NZ) is optimized for surface surveillance and surface attack duties and carries AGM-65D(NZ) Maverick antiship missiles or two Mk 46 torpedoes or two Mk 11 depth charges; they are also equipped with a single 7.62-mm MAG58 machinegun but do not have any ASW sensors. The last of four SH-2F SeaSprite helicopters was retired during 11-01.

Five Lockheed P-3K Orion maritime patrol aircraft belong to No. 5 Sqn., RNZAF; a sixth Orion, an ex-RAAF P-3B, has not yet been updated. The final Project Kestrel rewinging and structural update was completed 21-8-01. Planned further updates to the fleet were canceled in 8-00; as of 6-01, it was planned to acquire U.S. AGM-84 Harpoon antiship missiles for the Orions but to inactivate their ASW capabilities. Two leased Beech King Air B200 light transports are used for training and transport. The RNZAF's remaining 17 A-4K Skyhawks and 17 Aermacchi jet trainers were to be retired under a decision announced 8-5-01.

RNZN SH-2G(NZ) Super SeaSprite—with AGM-65D(NZ) Maverick missile Kaman, 2001

Weapons and Sensors: Obsolescent U.S. Mk 44 antisubmarine torpedoes were replaced by Alliant Techsystems Mk 46 Mod. 5 torpedoes, and current Mk 46 Mod. 2 torpedoes are being upgraded to Mod. 5. New ASW torpedoes are to be purchased, with the Eurotorp MU-90, Raytheon Mk 54, and Bofors Weapons System 90 under consideration.

FRIGATES [FF]

♦ **2 ANZAC frigate (MEKO 200 ANZ) class**
Bldr: Transfield Shipbuilding, Williamstown and Newcastle, N.S.W., Australia

	Laid down	L	In serv.
F 77 TE KAHA	19-9-94	22-7-95	22-7-97
F 111 TE MANA	18-5-96	10-5-97	10-12-99

Te Kaha (F 77) Maritime Photographic, 9-01

D: 3,200 tons (3,500 fl) **S:** 28 kts (20 on diesel)
Dim: 117.50 (109.50 pp) × 14.80 (13.80 wl) × 5.99 (4.12 hull)
A: 1 Mk 41 Mod. 5 8-celled VLS module (8 RIM-7P Sea Sparrow missiles); 1 127-mm 54-cal. Northern Ordnance Mk 45 Mod. 2 DP; 1 20-mm Mk 15 Phalanx Block I CIWS; six single 12.7-mm mg; 1 SH-2G Super SeaSprite helicopter

Te Mana (F 111)—with SH-2F SeaSprite helicopter aboard and Phalanx CIWS atop the hangar A. A. de Kruijf, 11-00

Te Mana (F 111)—note the faceted gunhouse for the 127-mm gun RNZN, 1999

Te Kaha (F 77) RNZN, 2000

Electronics:
Radar: 1 STN Atlas Elektronik 9600-M ARPA nav.; 1 Ericsson Sea Giraffe 150HC target desig.; 1 Raytheon SPS-49(V)8 early warning; 1 CelsiusTech 9LV 200 Sea Viking f.c.
Sonar: Thales Spherion-B hull-mounted (7 kHz)
EW: Racal-Thorn Sceptre XL intercept; EADS Telegon-10/Maigret HFD/F; Mk 36 Mod. 1 SRBOC decoy syst. (4 6-tubed Mk 137 RL); SLQ-25 Nixie towed acoustic torpedo decoy syst.
M: CODOG: 2 MTU 12V1163 TB83 diesels (4,420 bhp each), 1 G.E. LM-2500-30 gas turbine (30,152 shp); 2 CP props
Electric: 2,480 kw (4 × 620-kw MTU 8V396 TE54 diesels driving Siemens generator sets; 400 V, 60 Hz)
Range: 900/27 (gas turbine); 6,000/18, 10,000/13 (1 diesel) **Fuel:** 423 tons
Crew: 22 officers, 118 enlisted

Remarks: Contract was awarded 14-8-89 for eight sisters for the Royal Australian Navy, with options for two or four more for New Zealand, which decided in 9-89 initially to order only two, at a cost of about $420 million (U.S.) each. The New Zealand government decided in 11-97 not to order two additional units. Early during 1-98, the Minister of Defence indicated a desire to order at least one more during 1998 for completion in 2005, but this was again reversed in 11-98; the decision is to be examined again in 2002. *Te Kaha* means "The Strength" and *Te Mana* "The Power" in Maori. F 111 is to be homeported at Hamilton, in the Waikato region.
Hull systems: Were originally to have had two G.E. LM-2500 gas turbines and a maximum speed of 31.75 kts; the starboard turbine was eliminated to save money. Either diesel can drive either or both shafts. Fin stabilizers are fitted. Endurance is considerably greater than in other countries' units of this class, due to the enhanced fuel supply. Carry 29 m^3 of dry provisions, 26 m^3 of refrigerated provisions, and 54 tons of fresh water. Infrared-absorbent exterior paint is employed.
Combat systems: Have the CelsiusTech 9LV 453 Mk 3 combat data/fire-control system, with only one Ceros 200 director (although space for a second is present); the director has television and infrared tracking, as well as a J-band radar and a laser rangefinder. There are seven dual-screen Type IIA combat system displays, and the 9LV 453 system employs no less than 55 Motorola 6820 and 68040 processors using Ada software. Also carried is an N-FOCSS command decision support system. The ships have NATO Link 11 data-sharing. The G-band Sea Giraffe radar employs a CelsiusTech 9GA XYZ antenna. The SPS-49(V)8 radar's antenna mounts the antenna for the Cossor IFF interrogator. The Spherion-B sonar has "triple-rotation direct transmission" to increase the radiated sound level by 6 dB and incorporates a torpedo warning feature. The Dowty FMS 15 towed linear hydrophone sonar system may be added later. ASW torpedo tubes will probably be added after delivery, and the ships will probably be fitted to carry several 12.7-mm machineguns. Have Raytheon Mk 73 con-

FRIGATES [FF] *(continued)*

trol system for the SAM installation. There is space for a second vertical-launch Sea Sparrow module. The U.S. Mk 15 CIWS from *Wellington* (F 69) was fitted to F 77 early in 1999. RIM-7PTC Evolved Sea Sparrow missiles are to replace the present RIM-7P missiles around 2005, potentially quadrupling the missile load. Employ a harpoon-type helicopter haul-down system but do not have a deck-traversing system. Are equipped with Plessey GPS satellite receivers and have two Sperry Mk 49 inertial navigational systems. The 127-mm gun on F 111 has a radar-cross-section-reduction gunhouse, the first of its type on a Mk 45 gunmount in any navy. Two Ferranti FMS 15/2 towed passive sonar arrays and U.S. Whittaker Corp. DLS (Data Link Set), originally ordered for the *Leander*s below, may later be installed in these ships, but as of mid-1999, it was planned to add an active low-frequency towed array. Also planned for both are an E/O surveillance system and a UHF SATCOM terminal. As of 4-01, consideration was being given to acquiring U.S. RGM-84 Harpoon or Kongsberg Penguin missiles for the ships to give them an antiship capability.

♦ 1 U.K. Broad-Beam Leander class

	Bldr	Laid down	L	In serv.
F 421 Canterbury	Yarrow, Scotstoun	12-4-69	6-5-70	22-10-71

Canterbury (F 421)—with an SH-2F SeaSprite hovering above stern RNZN, 4-99

Canterbury (F 421) Brian Morrison, 9-01

D: 2,470 tons light (3,638 fl) **S:** 25 kts (see remarks)
Dim: 113.38 (109.73 pp) × 13.12 × 5.49
A: 1 twin 114-mm 45 cal. Mk 6 DP; 6 single 12.7-mm mg; 2 triple 324-mm Mk 32 Mod. 5 ASW TT (U.S. Mk 46 Mod. 2 torpedoes); 1 SH-2F SeaSprite helicopter
Electronics:
Radar: 1 Kelvin-Hughes Type 1006 nav.; 1 Thales LW-08 early warning; 1 Plessey Type 994 air/surf. search; 1 Lockheed Martin R76C5 f.c. for 114-mm guns; 1 General Dynamics Mk 90 Phalanx f.c.
Sonar: Graseby Type 184M hull-mounted MF; Kelvin-Hughes Type 162M hull-mounted HF bottomed-target classification
EW: ArgoSystems Phoenix AR-700 intercept-jammer suite; EADS Telegon PST 1288 HFD/F; Mk 36 Mod. 1 SRBOC decoy syst. (2 6-tubed Mk 137 RL)
M: 2 sets White-English Electric geared steam turbines; 2 5-bladed props; 30,000 shp
Boilers: 2 Babcock & Wilcox 3-drum; 38.7 kg/cm^2, 450° C Superheat
Electric: 2,500 kw tot. **Range:** 4,500/12 **Fuel:** 500 tons
Crew: 23 officers, 221 enlisted

Remarks: Sister *Wellington* (F 69) had been used primarily for training since 1-11-98; she was laid up 11-7-99 in order to provide additional crew for *Te Mana* (F 111) and was stricken 5-5-00. F 421 will continue in service until 2005. A refit to have ended in 2-01 was extended by three months due to the discovery of severe steam pipe corrosion.
Hull systems: Gearbox problems restrict maximum speed to 25 kts, although the ship made 30 kts on trials when new. Has two steam turbogenerators and two diesel generator sets. Two U.S. Omnipure waste processing plants are fitted. Infrared-absorbent exterior paint is employed.
Combat systems: During a 11-87 to 1990 refit, the MRS.3 gunfire-control system was replaced by the RCA R76C5 system and the Type 965 radar by a Thales LW-08 set. Added were a Marconi NTC-1 communications suite, Mk 32 ASW TT, and U.S. Mk 36 Super RBOC decoy RL; the Limbo ASW mortar was removed. The ship received the Siemens-Plessey NAUTIS (Naval Autonomous Intelligent System) tactical data-handling system during an early 1990s refit. NATO Link 11 monitoring capability and a Norden Systems target track management system for radar data fusion were added, along with an upgrade to the HF radio suite. During a further refit completed 9-98, the hangar and flight deck were enlarged to permit handling an SH-2F/G helicopter, a harpoon-type landing system was installed, and the U.S. Phalanx 20-mm gatling CIWS was substituted for the obsolete Sea Cat SAM system, which had been removed in 1994. During 2000, the Phalanx was removed and transferred to F 111.

PATROL SHIPS [PS]

Note: As a result of the new defense policy issued in 5-01, the RNZN is studying the purchase of a single ship to perform both the offshore patrol mission (to replace the frigate *Canterbury* [F 421]) and the military sealift mission (to replace the recently sold *Charles Upham* [A 02]). On 22-12-01, the government approved funding $500 million for the patrol ship, two seagoing patrol craft, and four inshore patrol boats. The patrol ship will be able to carry troops and to operate in Antarctic waters.

PATROL CRAFT [PC]

♦ 4 Moa-class naval reserve training/mine warfare craft
Bldr: Whangarei Engineering Co., Auckland

	L	In serv.		L	In serv.
P 3553 Moa	16-7-83	19-2-84	P 3555 Wakakura	29-10-84	26-3-85
P 3554 Kiwi	7-5-84	2-9-84	P 3556 Hinau	8-5-85	4-10-85

Wakakura (P 3555) RNZN, 1999

D: 91.5 tons light (112.2 fl) **S:** 12 kts **Dim:** 26.82 (24.38 wl) × 6.10 × 2.18
A: provision for 1 12.7-mm Browning M2 mg
Electronics: Radar: 1 Decca 916 nav.—Sonar: Klein 595 Tracpoint side-scan
M: 2 Cummins KT-1150M diesels; 2 props; 710 bhp
Range: 1,000/11 **Fuel:** 11 tons **Crew:** 5 officers, 13 enlisted

Remarks: Ordered 11-2-82. Design derived from that of an Australian 88-ft. torpedo retriever; the training craft [YXT] *Kahu* and the now-stricken survey craft *Takapu* and *Tarapunga* were built to the same basic design. Based as follows for naval reserve training: P 3553 at HMNZS *Toroa,* Dunedin; P 3554 at HMNZS *Pegasus,* Christchurch; P 3555 at HMNZS *Olphert,* Wellington; and P 3556 at HMNZS *Ngapona,* Auckland. In 1991, they received side-scan sonars and enhanced navigation equipment to permit use as "Q-route" (cleared passage) mine survey boats, and are planned to receive influence mine countermeasures gear at a later date. On 1-1-96 were assigned to the new Maritime Mine Warfare Force. P 3553 had the first female RNZN commanding officer, in spring 1998.

AUXILIARIES

Note: A review of the status of naval hydrography was under way during 2001, with the possibility that the effort would be privatized.

♦ 1 ex-U.S. Stalwart-class hydrographic survey ship [AGS]
Bldr: Halter Marine, Moss Point, Miss.

	Laid down	L	In serv.
A 14 Resolution (ex-*Tenacious,* T-AGOS 17; ex-*Intrepid*)	26-2-88	17-2-89	29-9-89

Resolution (A 14)—as modified, with tripod mainmast aft removed, new tripod mast added atop the pilothouse, and RIB launches added aft to starboard and amidships to port; the ship is painted white, with yellow mast and stacks, and does not wear her pennant number Brian Morrison, 9-01

D: 1,600 tons light (2,300 fl) **S:** 11 kts
Dim: 68.28 (62.10 wl) × 13.10 × 4.54 (6.54 over sonar)

AUXILIARIES *(continued)*

Electronics:
Radar: 2 Raytheon . . . nav.
Sonar: STN Atlas Elektronik Hydrosweep MD-2-30 multibeam mapping (30 kHz); Swath-E multibeam echo sounder; Ferranti Marine FMS 15/2 towed passive array
M: 4 Caterpillar D398B 800-bhp diesels, G.E. electric drive; 2 4-bladed props; 2,200 shp (1,600 sust.)—550-hp bow-thruster
Electric: 1,500 kVA from main generators + 265-kw emergency set
Range: 15,000/11 **Fuel:** 904 tons **Endurance:** 98 days
Crew: 7 officers, 14 enlisted + 30 scientific party

Remarks: 1,486 grt/786 dwt. Had been in reserve since 14-2-95 at San Diego. Was purchased 10-10-96 for $22.1 million and refitted at Portland, Ore., between 21-10-96 and 20-12-96; commissioned 13-2-97, departing U.S. waters 17-2-97 and arriving in Auckland 29-3-97; and reconfigured as a survey vessel between 7-97 and 9-2-98. Became fully operational as of 7-98 and was "rededicated" on 27-11-98. She is intended to be used some 300 days per year (130 days in survey work, 60 days on acoustic research, 50 days of unspecified naval tasking, and 60 days for other agencies) and is expected to serve until 2020.
Hull systems: Has a flat-chine hullform without bilge keels, which are planned to be added later in New Zealand. Has passive tank roll stabilization. There are outstanding endurance and recreational facilities for the crew. Main-engine motor/generator sets also supply ship's service power. Inshore survey craft and an enlarged charthouse have been fitted for the survey role.
Electronics systems: The UQQ-2 SURTASS (Surveillance Towed Array Sensor) has been removed, as has its associated WSC-6 satellite communications datalink system. The multibeam mapping sonar was added between 05-98 and 06-98, along with an Atlas Hydromap data system and Hydromap Caris geographic data management and processing system. The mapping sonar, with transducers mounted in a large pod below the hull, covers a swath 4,000 m wide in 1,000-m-deep water and can be employed in waters up to 5,000 m deep. A differential GPS system, the inshore survey launch *Adventure,* and additional davits and winches were also added. Late in 1998, she was fitted to tow an FMS 15 linear passive acoustic array for trials purposes. Other navigational and mission equipment includes a TSS POS/MV 320 motion sensor, Trimble 4000SE positioning equipment, Trimble Centurion nine-channel GPS, and OmniSTAR wide-area differential GPS.

♦ 1 small replenishment oiler [AOR] Bldr: Hyundai SY, Ulsan, S. Korea

	Laid down	L	In serv.
A 11 ENDEAVOUR	10-4-87	8-87	8-4-88

Endeavour (A 11) RNZN, 2000

D: 7,300 tons (12,390 fl) **S:** 14 kts **Dim:** 138.05 (128.00 pp) × 18.40 × 7.20 (4.50 light)
A: provision for 2 single 20-mm 70-cal. Oerlikon AA
Electronics:
Radar: 1 Decca-Racal RM-1290A/9 nav.; 1 Decca-Racal ARPA-1690S nav.
M: 1 Hyundai–Burmeister & Wain 12V-32/36 diesel; 1 CP prop; 5,300 bhp—Lips 600-shp bow-thruster
Electric: 1,920 kw tot. (3 × 600-kw alternators, 3 Daihatsu 6DL-20 890-bhp diesels driving; 1 × 120-kw Cummins diesel-driven emergency set)
Range: 8,000/14 **Fuel:** 400 tons **Crew:** 11 officers, 39 enlisted

Remarks: 8,400 dwt/6,990 grt. Ordered 28-7-86. Launch and completion dates were delayed by shipyard labor and machinery problems; was to have delivered 20-1-88. Left Ulsan 14-4-88 and arrived in New Zealand 25-5-88. Has operated with as few as 30 in the crew. Was given a four-month refit during 2001, during which the engine and generators were overhauled, safety measures improved, and the ship's launch relocated to the container deck.
Hull systems: Cargo: 7,500 tons fuel, 100 tons aviation fuel, and 100 tons water in five tanks. Has deck storage for four 20-ft. refrigerated cargo containers. There are single fueling stations to port and starboard, plus an over-the-stern fueling rig. Has a Magnavox 2290 NAVSAT receiver. Helicopter hangar is incorporated within the starboard side of the superstructure; the hangar may not be able to accommodate the new SH-2F/G helicopter, however.

Disposal note: Under a decision announced 8-5-01, the troop and vehicle transport *Charles Upham* (A 02, ex-*Mercandian Queen II*), which had been on charter to Spanish operator Contenemar S.A. since 25-6-98, was to be sold to the charterer on 16-7-01 for $8 million.

♦ 1 salvage ship [ARS]
Bldr: Alexander Cochrane SB, Selby, Yorkshire, U.K. (In serv. 5-79)

A 09 MANAWANUI (ex-*Star Perseus*)

D: 911 tons (fl) **S:** 10.7 kts **Dim:** 43.97 (38.25 pp) × 9.86 × 3.31 **A:** none
Electronics:
Radar: 2 Decca . . . nav.
Sonar: Klein 595 Tracpoint towed side-scan
M: 2 Caterpillar D379TA diesels; 2 CP props; 1,130 bhp—1 55-ton-thrust bow-thruster

Manawanui (A 09) RNZN, 2000

Range: 5,000/10.7; 8,000/10 **Endurance:** 130 days
Crew: 2 officers, 22 enlisted

Remarks: 480 grt/396 dwt. Oilfield service and diving tender, purchased 3-88 from Star Offshore Service Marine, Ltd., and commissioned in the RNZN 5-4-88 for use as a seagoing diving tender. On 1-1-96, was assigned to the Maritime Mine Warfare Force.
Hull systems: Capable of four-point mooring. Can support three divers working at 76 m and has a triple-lock decompression chamber. Has an electrohydraulic 13-ton crane on the after deck and can carry 150 tons of deck cargo. There is a divers' stage to starboard. A 1994 refit saw the installation of the side-scan sonar, a GPS receiver, Inmarsat satellite communications equipment, and an MCIAS data recording system. During a 1997 refit was equipped with oceanographic equipment, including a U-frame gantry, winches, and additional capstans.

SERVICE CRAFT

♦ 1 air-support training craft [YFL]
Bldr: Naval DY, HMNZS *Philomel,* Auckland (In serv. 4-84)

MATUA

D: 8 tons **S:** 14 kts **Dim:** 12.0 × . . . × . . .
M: 2 Perkins diesels; 2 props; . . . bhp
Range: 200/14 **Crew:** 2–4 tot.

Remarks: Plywood hull. Used for parachute recovery, helicopter winch training, diver support, patrol, and rescue duties at Naval Air Support Unit, Hobsonville. The same organization also operates two 12.2-m, 16-kt crash boats and one 10-m, 8-kt personnel launch.

♦ 1 personnel launch [YFL] (In serv. 1966)

MATAMUA

D: . . . tons **S:** 9 kts **Dim:** 15.9 × 4.8 × . . . **M:** 1 diesel; . . . bhp

Remarks: Employed as a liberty launch. Sister *Mahanga* has been discarded.

♦ 1 catamaran inshore survey launch [YGS]
Bldr: Bladerunner Boats, Kumeu (In serv. 11-99)

ADVENTURE

Adventure—unpainted RNZN, 11-99

D: 6.5 tons (fl) **S:** 25 kts **Dim:** 9.70 × . . . × . . .
Electronics: Radar: 1 . . . nav.—Sonar: 1 multibeam echo sounder
M: . . . **Crew:** 5 tot.

Remarks: All-aluminum-construction catamaran. Intended to operate with the *Resolution* (A 14), which will process the data obtained and stored by the small boat's multibeam echo sounder. Is also employed on commercial harbor survey work and is assigned to the Hydrographic Business Unit.

SERVICE CRAFT *(continued)*

Disposal note: Inshore survey craft *Takapu* (A 07) and *Tarapunga* (A 08) were stricken during 9-00, with A 07 sold commercial on 25-9-00.

♦ **4 Chico-40-class sail-training sloops [YTS]** (L: 21-5-90)

6911 Paea II   6912 Mako II   6913 Manga II   6914 Haku II

D: 7.3 tons (fl) **S:** 7 kts (under power) **Dim:** 12.00 (9.80 wl) × 3.90 × 2.00
M: 1 diesel; 1 prop; . . . bhp—80 m^2 sail area **Crew:** 10 max.

Remarks: Kept at Auckland for seamanship proficiency training and recreation.

♦ **1 basic-training boat [YXT]** Bldr: Whangarei Eng. Ltd.

	L	In serv.
A 04 Kahu (ex-*Manawanui*)	8-12-78	28-5-79

Kahu (A 04) RNZN, 1999

D: 91.5 tons (110 fl) **S:** 12 kts **Dim:** 26.82 (24.38 wl) × 6.10 × 2.20
Electronics: Radar: 1 Decca 916 nav.
M: 2 Cummins KT 1150M diesels; 2 props; 730 bhp
Range: 1,000/12 **Crew:** 16 max.

Remarks: Built as a diving tender; renamed and reassigned as a basic navigational and maneuvering training craft at HMNZS *Taranaki* training center on acquisition of the "new" *Manawanui* (A 09) in 1988. Same basic design as the *Moa*-class patrol/training craft and the stricken survey craft *Takapu* and *Tarapunga,* but has a light tripod mast and derrick aft.

Note: The New Zealand Customs Service received a Hawk IV–class patrol boat for smuggling interdiction purposes in 1999; the 14.9 × 5.0–m, 24-kt craft has twin Saab Scania 400-bhp diesel engines and an endurance of 1,000 n.m. at 15 kts.

NICARAGUA

Republic of Nicaragua

FUERZA NAVAL-EJERCITO DE NICARAGUA

Personnel (2002): Approx. 750 total

Bases: The fleet is organized into an Atlantic Naval District, with headquarters at Bluefields, and a Pacific District, with headquarters at Puerto Corinto. Atlantic bases include Puerto Cabezas and El Bluff, and in the Pacific are Puerto Corinto and San Juan del Sur.

PATROL BOATS [PB]

♦ **2 Soviet Zhuk class (Project 1400)**

GC-301   GC-302

D: 35.9 tons (39.7 fl) **S:** 30 kts
Dim: 23.80 (21.70 wl) × 5.00 (3.80 wl) × 1.00 (hull)
A: 2 twin 12.7-mm 60-cal. Utës-M mg **Electronics:** Radar: 1 Lotsiya nav.
M: 2 M-401B diesels; 2 props; 2,200 bhp
Electric: 48 kw total (2 × 21-kw, 1 × 6-kw diesel sets)
Range: 500/13.5 **Endurance:** 5 days **Crew:** 1 officer, 9 enlisted

Remarks: Survivors of 11 units. First unit transferred in 4-82 via Algeria; the second unit was delivered 24-7-83, the third in 1984, the fourth and fifth early in 1986, the sixth through eighth between late 1986 and early 1987, and the last three in 9-89 from Cuba. Have side-by-side, enclosed machinegun mountings. The listed radar may have been replaced with a Western commercial set. Both are based on the Atlantic Coast at El Bluff.

♦ **3 ex-Israeli Dabur class**
Bldr: Israeli Aircraft Industries, Be'er Sheva (In serv. 1973–77)

GC-201   GC-203   GC-305

Dabur-class GC-201 Fuerza Naval, via Julio Montes, 1-01

D: 25 tons (35 fl) **S:** 19 kts **Dim:** 19.8 × 5.8 × 0.8
A: 2 twin 23-mm ZSU-23 AA; 2 single 14.5-mm 93-cal. AA
Electronics: Radar: 1 Decca Super 101 Mk 3 nav.
M: 2 G.M. Detroit Diesel 12V71 TI diesels; 2 props; 960 bhp
Electric: 20 kw tot. **Range:** 1,200/17 **Crew:** 2 officers, 7 enlisted

Remarks: Three former Israeli Navy units were acquired during 11-95, delivered after overhaul in 6-96, and recommissioned on 13-8-96. Two survivors of a group of four sisters delivered in 5-78, GC-231 and GC-235, were refitted in Cuba in 1995 but had been discarded by 1998. Aluminum construction. Could make 25 kts when new. Range may have been reduced to 450 n.m. at 13 kts. The twin 14.5-mm mg mount was added on the bow in 1998. All three are based at El Bluff.

♦ **2 ex-North Korean Sin Hung class**
Bldr: . . ., North Korea (In serv. 1960s)

GC-408   GC-412

Sin Hung–class GC-410—now out of service, flanked by two sisters
Julio Montes, 2-96

D: 25 tons **S:** . . . kts **Dim:** 18.3 × 3.4 × 1.7
A: 2 twin 14.5-mm 93-cal. 2M-7 AA **Electronics:** Radar: 1 Furuno . . . nav.
M: 2 MTU . . . . . . diesels; 2 props; . . . bhp **Crew:** 10 tot.

PATROL BOATS [PB] *(continued)*

Remarks: Survivors of 10, of which two were delivered in 10-83, two in 1984, and six in 3-89. Former torpedo boats, delivered without the tubes. Had been discarded around 1998, but in 2000 two of the boats were reactivated, with their M-50-series high-speed diesels replaced by MTU truck diesels. Have a lightly built, stepped-hydroplane, aluminum-alloy hull.

♦ 54 Eduardoño class
Bldr: . . ., Colombia (In serv. . . .)

Two Eduardoño-class armed launches—no pennant numbers are worn, and the craft are painted in green and tan camouflage Julio Montes, 6-01

A camouflaged Eduardoño and its heavily armed crew of seven
Fuerza Naval, via Julio Montes, 9-00

D: approx. 4 tons (fl) **S:** . . . kts **Dim:** . . . × . . . × . . .
A: 1 14.5-mm 93-cal. mg; 2 single 7.62-mm mg
M: 2 gasoline outboard motors; 2 props; 300 bhp

Remarks: Ex-drug runners captured by the government, 8 in 1998 and another 46 by the end of 2000. Do not carry pennant numbers. They are in two sizes, with one version being 10.0 m overall. Some have been equipped with Furuno navigational radars and/or GPS terminals.

Note: Also in use are five captured Miami-built "Cigarette Boats" (two others are used by the Nicaraguan Police).

♦ 12 locally built GRP-hulled patrol launches
Bldr: . . . . . ., Nicaragua

L/E-016 and others

Locally built GRP launch L/E-016 Julio Montes, 9-00

Remarks: Prototype was completed in 1994 to begin replacement of earlier wooden-hulled craft. Use a glass-reinforced plastic hull supplied by Cuba, are powered by a single 150-bhp gasoline outboard, and are armed with one 12.7-mm mg. Have yellow, green, brown, and mauve camouflage. All have been relegated to secondary duties with the acquisition of large numbers of captured drug craft.

Disposal note: The 11 wooden-hulled launches listed in the previous edition have been retired.

MINE WARFARE CRAFT

♦ 2 Soviet Yevgenya-class (Project 1258) inshore minesweepers [MSI]
Bldr: Sudostroitel'noye Obyedineniye "Almaz" (Sredniy Neva), Kolpino

BM-501 BM-510

Yevgenya-class BM-510 Julio Montes, 2-96

D: 88.5 tons light; 94.5 tons normal (97.9 fl)
S: 11 kts **Dim:** 26.13 × 5.90 × 1.40
A: 1 twin 25-mm 80-cal. 2M-3M AA; 1 7-round MRG-1 grenade launcher; 4 d.c. (+ 8 emergency stowage)
Electronics: Radar: 1 Mius (Spin Trough) nav.—Sonar: MG-7 HF dipping
M: 2 Type 3D12 diesels; 2 props; 600 bhp—hydraulic slow-speed drive
Electric: 100 kw tot. (2 × 50-kw diesel sets)
Range: 400/10 **Fuel:** 2.7 tons **Endurance:** 3 days
Crew: 1 officer, 9 enlisted (+ 2–3 clearance divers)

Remarks: Two were delivered via Cuba in 10-84, two later. Sister BM-503 was lost in a hurricane in 1989, and one other has since been cannibalized. GRP hull. Employed primarily as patrol craft. Both are based on the Pacific Coast.

SERVICE CRAFT

♦ 1 medium harbor tug [YTM]
Bldr: . . . . . ., U.S.A. (In serv. 13-8-96)

XV Aniversario

D: 110 tons (fl) **S:** 13 kts **Dim:** 22.0 × 6.1 × . . .
A: 2 single 7.62-mm mg **Electronics:** Radar: 1 Furuno . . . nav.
M: 2 G.M. Detroit Diesel 6-71-series diesels; 2 props; 600 bhp **Crew:** 8 tot.

Remarks: Is naval-operated but is also employed for commercial tug duties.

NIGERIA

Republic of Nigeria

Personnel (2001): 650 officers, 4,950 enlisted in the navy and coast guard, plus 1,600 port security police at Lagos

Bases: The Western Naval Command has its base at NNS *Olokin,* Apapa, Lagos, with dockyard facilities at Wilmot Point, Victoria Island, near Lagos. The Eastern Naval Command base is at NNS *Anansa,* Calabar. Minor facilities exist at NNS *Okemini,* Okemini; NNS *Akaso,* Port Harcourt; and NNS *Umalokun,* Warri. Principal training facilities are located at NNS *Quorra,* Lagos. A new base is planned to be built at Bonny to combat unrest and piracy in Bayelsa.

Naval Aviation: Two Lynx Mk 89 ASW helicopters with Gem 3, 1,128-hp turbines for use aboard *Aradu* (F 89), two armed AgustaWestland A-109 for shore-based patrol, and two BO-105 light helicopters for shore-based liaison. The air force has 3 Fokker F 27 Maritime patrol aircraft, delivered 1983–84 for coastal surveillance; 14 Dornier Do-128-6MPA twin-engine aircraft used for coastal patrol and smuggling interdiction; and 12 MBB BO-105C light helicopters that can be used for search-and-rescue work. The Lynx Mk 89 shipboard helicopters have been out of service since around 1997; both were to be returned to the U.K. for refurbishment, and a third may be acquired in 2002.

Note: The current material condition of virtually all Nigerian Navy ships and craft is at best poor, and none have fully operational combat systems. Ship names are prefixed by NNS (Nigerian Naval Ship).

FRIGATES [FF]

♦ 1 MEKO 360 class (Nonoperational)
Bldr: Blohm + Voss, Hamburg

	Laid down	L	In serv.
F 89 *Aradu* (ex-*Republic*)	1-12-78	25-1-80	20-2-82

Aradu (F 89)—in better days, on builder's trials — Blohm + Voss, 1982

D: 3,360 tons (fl) **S:** 30.5 kts (18 on diesels)
Dim: 125.90 (119.00 pp) × 15.00 (14.00 wl) × 4.32 (5.80 props)
A: 1 8-round Albatros Mk 2 Mod. 9 SAM syst. (8 Aspide missiles; probably nonoperational); 1 127-mm 54-cal. OTOBreda DP; 4 twin 40-mm 70-cal. OTOBreda Dardo AA; 2 triple 324-mm STWS-1B ASW TT (18 A-244S torpedoes); 1 d.c. rack (6 d.c.); 1 Lynx Mk 89 helicopter
Electronics:
Radar: 1 Decca 1226 nav.; 1 Plessey AWS-5D surf./air search; 1 Thales STIR-18 SAM f.c.; 1 Thales M 25 gun f.c.
Sonar: STN Atlas Elektronik EA80 hull-mounted MF
TACAN: Thales Vesta beacon
EW: Decca RDL-2 intercept; Decca RCM-2 jammer; 2 20-round OTOBreda 105-mm SCLAR trainable decoy RL
M: CODOG: 2 Rolls-Royce Olympus TM-3B gas turbines (25,440 shp each), 2 MTU 20V956 TB92 diesels (5,210 bhp each); 2 KaMeWa CP props; 50,880 bhp max.
Electric: 4,120 kVA tot. **Range:** 4,500/18; 6,500/15 **Fuel:** 440 tons
Crew: 26 officers, 169 enlisted

Remarks: Ordered 3-11-77. Renamed 1-11-80 (the name means "Thunder"). Ran aground in the Congo River during 7-87, collided with a pier in 8-87 at Lagos, and also suffered a collision at sea that same year. Refitted at Victoria Island Naval Dockyard, Lagos, from 10-90 to 2-94 but by 1995 was again inoperable and was employed primarily as a brothel. Went to sea briefly in 1995 and again in 1998, when she was stranded for two months in Liberia by engine failures. Builder reported assisting with repairs in 1998–99, but few, if any, of the sensors and combat systems function, and, of the engineering plant, only one propulsion diesel was operating as of 1998, since which she has been in refit at Lagos.
Combat systems: Has the Thales SEWACO combat data system. Although the launch canister racks remain aboard, the eight Otomat Mk 1 antiship missiles long ago became time-expired and have not been replaced. Can carry 460 rounds of 127-mm and 10,752 rounds of 40-mm ammunition and 120 rounds for the decoy launchers.

PATROL COMBATANTS [PG]

♦ 2 Erin'mi class (Vosper Mk 9) (Nonoperational)
Bldr: Vosper Thornycroft, Portsmouth, U.K.

	Laid down	L	In serv.
F 83 *Erin'mi*	14-10-75	20-1-77	29-1-80
F 84 *Enymiri*	11-2-77	9-2-78	2-5-80

Enymiri (F 84) — H&L Van Ginderen, 5-82

D: 850 tons (fl) **S:** 27 kts **Dim:** 69.0 (64.0 pp) × 9.6 × 3.0 (3.6 max.)
A: 1 76-mm 62-cal. OTOBreda DP; 1 40-mm 70-cal. Bofors AA; 2 single 20-mm 70-cal. Oerlikon Mk 10 AA; 1 2-round 375-mm Bofors ASW RL
Electronics:
Radar: 1 Decca TM 1226 nav.; 1 Plessey AWS-2 air search; 1 Thales WM-24 f.c.
Sonar: Plessey PMS-26 hull-mounted MF (10 kHz)
EW: Decca Cutlass intercept; 2 Protean decoy RL
M: 4 MTU 20V956 TB92 diesels; 2 CP props; 20,512 bhp
Electric: 889 kw (3 × 260-kw MTU 6V51 sets, 1 × 109-kw emergency set)
Range: 2,200/14 **Endurance:** 10 days **Crew:** 90 tot.

Remarks: By 1989, F 83 was in marginal condition with many systems inoperative, and by 1993, she was unseaworthy; the ship was refitted in 1994–95 and participated in a 12-95 exercise at sea. By 1997, F 83 was again out of service; she was said to have been at sea once in 1998, but probably not since. F 84 had been considered beyond repair by 1996 but was in refit at Lagos during 2000.
Hull systems: Could sustain 20 kts on two diesels. Funnel was heightened after initial trials. Have Vosper gyro-controlled fin stabilizers.
Combat systems: Can carry 750 rounds of 76-mm ammunition and 24 ASW rockets. Have two 50-mm flare rocket launchers. The Sea Cat point-defense missile system (with lightweight triple launcher and 15 total missile magazine capacity) is inoperable, and replacement missiles are unavailable; the sonar set and ASW rocket launcher system are also likely to be beyond repair.

PATROL CRAFT [PC]

♦ 2 Combattante IIIB class (1 *nonoperational*)
Bldr: CMN, Cherbourg, France

	Laid down	L	In serv.
P 182 *Ayam*	7-9-79	10-11-80	11-6-81
P 183 *Ekun*	14-11-79	11-2-81	18-9-81

Ekun (P 183) — French Navy, 5-97

D: 376 tons light (430 fl) **S:** 37 kts
Dim: 56.0 (53.0 pp) × 8.16 (7.61 wl) × 2.15 (hull)
A: 1 76-mm 62-cal. OTOBreda DP; 1 twin 40-mm 70-cal. OTOBreda-Bofors AA; 2 twin 30-mm 75-cal. Emerlec EX-30 AA
Electronics:
Radar: 1 Decca 1226 nav.; 1 Thales Triton surf./air search; 1 Thales Castor-II f.c.
EW: Decca RDL intercept
M: 4 MTU 16V956 TB92 diesels; 4 props; 20,840 bhp (17,320 sust.)
Range: 2,000/15 **Crew:** 42 tot.

Remarks: Three were ordered 11-77. Remained at Cherbourg until 9-5-82 because of a payment dispute. Official commissioning date was 6-2-82 for all. Refitted 1986–88 by builder, but the ships remained in France through 9-92 because of nonpayment for the work. Sister *Siri* (P 181) was again inoperable by 1995 and was cannibalized to maintain the others. As of 1997, only P 183 was operational.
Combat systems: Have the Thales Vega gun and missile f.c.s., with two Matra Défense Panda gun directors also fitted. The U.S.-made 30-mm guns have a range of 6 km and fire at 1,200 rds/min per mount. Although they are capable of carrying four MM 38 Exocet missiles, all of Nigeria's Exocets have exceeded their shelf lives and are unusable.

♦ 3 FPB 57 class (Nonoperational)
Bldr: Friedrich Lürssen Werft, Bremen-Vegesack, Germany

	Laid down	L	In serv.
P 178 *Ekpe*	17-2-79	17-12-79	8-80
P 179 *Damisa*	17-2-79	27-3-80	4-81
P 180 *Agu*	17-2-79	7-11-80	4-81

D: 373 tons light (436 fl) **S:** 35 kts **Dim:** 58.1 (54.4 wl) × 7.62 × 2.83 (props)
A: 1 76-mm 62-cal. OTOBreda DP; 1 twin 40-mm 70-cal. OTOBreda-Bofors AA; 2 twin 30-mm 75-cal. Emerlec EX-30 AA
Electronics:
Radar: 1 Decca TM 1226C nav.; 1 Thales WM-28 track-while-scan f.c.
EW: Decca RDL intercept
M: 4 MTU 16V956 TB92 diesels; 4 props; 20,840 bhp (17,320 sust.)
Electric: 405 kVA tot. **Range:** 1,600/32; 3,000/16 **Crew:** 40 tot.

PATROL CRAFT [PC] *(continued)*

Damisa (P 179)—outboard *Agu* (P 180) Gilbert Gyssels, 6-81

Note: Of the three German-built FPB 57–class guided-missile patrol craft, P 180 was cannibalized in the early 1990s to provide spares for the other two. P 178 and 179 were refitted at Lagos in 1995 but by 1997 had again become inoperable. P 178 made a deployment to Sierra Leone in 1997 but broke down en route. During 9-01, the builder received a contract to overhaul all three in Germany. The four time-expired Otomat Mk 2 antiship missiles have been removed.

PATROL BOATS [PB]

♦ **7 . . . . . class** Bldr: Modant Marine, . . ., Nigeria (In serv. 1999–2000)

D: 10 tons **S:** 25 kts **Dim:** 12.0 (19.00 wl) × 5.80 × 1.50
A: small arms **Electronics:** Radar: . . .
M: 2 Caterpillar 3208TA SR/R diesel; 1 prop; . . . bhp
Range: . . ./. . . **Crew:** . . .

Remarks: Ordered in 1998. GRP construction. Designed by Amgram Ltd., U.K. Intended for use in oil-rig crew transfer and patrol duties around oil rigs and moored gas carriers. Operated by the Nigerian Navy. Status of the program is uncertain, but those operational are probably Nigeria's most effective naval craft.

MINE COUNTERMEASURES SHIPS

♦ **2 Italian Lerici-class minehunters [MHC]** (Nonoperational)
Bldr: Intermarine, Sarzana

	Laid down	L	Del.	In serv.
M 371 *Ohue*	23-7-84	22-11-85	28-5-87	4-88
M 372 *Maraba*	11-3-85	6-6-86	25-2-88	4-88

Maraba (M 372) Carlo Martinelli, 6-87

D: 470 tons (550 fl) **S:** 15.5 kts **Dim:** 51.00 (46.50 pp) × 9.56 × 2.80
A: 1 twin 30-mm 75-cal. Emerlec EX-30 AA; 2 single 20-mm 90-cal. Oerlikon GAM-B01 AA
Electronics:
Radar: 1 Decca 1226 nav.
Sonar: Thales TSM 2022 variable-depth HF
M: 2 MTU 12V396 TC83 diesels; 2 Turbomeccanica PG2000 waterjets; 2,840 bhp
Electric: 600 kw (2 × 300 kw, MTU 6V396 TC diesels driving)
Range: 2,500/12 **Endurance:** 14 days **Crew:** 5 officers, 45 enlisted

Remarks: First ship was ordered 9-4-83, the second in 5-84; an option for two more was not taken up. Difficulties in obtaining an export license delayed delivery. Both were out of service by 1996 but began refits at Lagos during 1999 and could be operational again by 2002.
Hull systems: GRP construction throughout. For free running, the swiveling waterjets are locked centerline, and twin rudders are used for steering; when minehunting, the waterjets are swiveled for steering. Range at 12 kts can be extended to 4,000 n.m. by using the passive roll stabilization tanks as fuel tanks.
Combat systems: Can support 6–7 mine-disposal divers. Carry two Gaymarine Pluto remote-controlled minehunting submersibles, Oropesa Mk 4 mechanical sweep gear, and the Thales IBIS-V minehunting control system. Have Galeazzi two-man decompression chambers for mine-disposal divers.

AMPHIBIOUS WARFARE SHIPS

♦ **2 German Type-502 medium landing ships [LSM]** (1 *inoperable*)
Bldr: Howaldtswerke, Hamburg

	Laid down	L	In serv.
L 1312 Ambe	3-3-78	7-7-78	11-5-79
L 1313 *Ofiom*	15-9-78	7-12-78	7-79

Ambe (L 1312) French Navy, 5-97

D: 1,190 tons light; 1,470 tons normal (1,750 fl) **S:** 17 kts
Dim: 86.9 (74.5 pp) × 14.0 × 2.30
A: 1 40-mm 70-cal. OTOBreda AA; 2 single 20-mm 90-cal. Oerlikon GAM-B01 AA
Electronics: Radar: 1 Decca 1226 nav.
M: 2 MTU 16V956 TB92 diesels; 4 props; 7,000 bhp
Electric: 900 kw tot. **Range:** 5,000/12
Crew: 6 officers, 53 enlisted + 540 troops (1,000 for short distances)

Remarks: The design was originally prepared for the German Navy, which did not order any. L 1313 went aground in 1992 and was not immediately repaired; a 1999 contract to repair and reactivate the ship was canceled in 4-01 when only 50% complete, due to major cost overruns. L 1312 remains marginally operational but can no longer be beached.
Hull systems: Cargo: 400 tons of vehicles plus troops (typically five 40-ton tanks or seven 18-ton tanks plus four 45-ton trucks). Have an articulated bow ramp (now welded shut) and a short stern ramp for loading from a pier. Each engine drives two props.

AUXILIARIES

♦ **1 U.K. Bulldog-class survey ship [AGS]**
Bldr: Brooke Marine Ltd., Lowestoft, U.K.

	Laid down	L	In serv.
A 498 Lana	5-4-74	4-3-76	15-7-76

D: 800 tons (1,100 fl) **S:** 15 kts **Dim:** 60.95 (57.80 pp) × 11.43 × 3.70
A: 2 single 20-mm 70-cal. Oerlikon Mk 10 AA
Electronics: Radar: 1 Decca 1226 nav.
M: 4 Lister-Blackstone ERS-8-M diesels; 2 KaMeWa CP props; 2,640 bhp
Electric: 880 kw tot. **Range:** 4,000/12 **Crew:** 5 officers, 34 enlisted

Remarks: Although reported as out of service and irreparable by the late 1990s, the ship was reported to be in "reasonable condition" as of 2001 and had probably been overhauled at Lagos. Has a passive-tank stabilization system and can carry one 8.7-m survey launch.

SERVICE CRAFT

♦ **2 Commander Apayi Joe–class large harbor tugs [YTB]**
Bldr: Scheepswerf de Wiel BV, Asperen, the Netherlands

A 499 Commander Apayi Joe (In serv. 9-83)
A 500 Commander Rudolf (In serv. . . .)

Commander Rudolf (A 500) H&L Van Ginderen, 7-84

D: 310 tons (fl) **S:** 11 kts **Dim:** 23.17 × 7.19 × 2.91
M: 2 M.A.N. diesels; 2 props; 1,510 bhp

Remarks: 130 grt. *Commander Rudolf* was completed but not paid for and was retained by the builder for commercial use; by 1995, however, the craft had been delivered. Their operational status is unknown, but at least one is probably capable of getting to sea.

♦ **1 water lighter [YW]**

Water Barge One

Remarks: Self-propelled. Current status unknown.

SERVICE CRAFT *(continued)*

Disposal note: The training craft Ruwan Yaro (A 497; ex-*Ogina Bereton*) was scuttled at sea on 1-12-01.

Note: There were also 44 service launches built by Fairey Marine, Hamble, U.K.: 2 of 10 m, 22 of 7 m, 15 of 6.7 m, and 5 of 5.5 m. Four Cheverton 8.2-m launches are also in use. Eight Flight Refueling Sea Flash 8.5-m, radio-controlled target boats were delivered in 1987. Two 11.75-m torpedo retrievers were delivered by Crestitalia, Ameglia, Italy, in 1986. Damen SY, Gorinchem, the Netherlands, delivered two 27-m fuel lighters and two small PushyCat 46 tugs early in 1986 for naval use. The operational status of all of these craft is unknown.

NIGERIAN COAST GUARD

Note: The coast guard is under the operational control of the navy, and naval personnel man its craft. One source reports that none of the craft listed below remain operational.

PATROL BOATS [WPB]

♦ **6 Type SM-500**
Bldr: Simonneau, Fontenay-le-Comte, France (In serv. 1986–87)

P 233 P 234 P 235 P 236 P 237 P 238

P 234 Simmoneau, 1986

D: 22 tons (25 fl) **S:** 33 kts **Dim:** 15.80 (14.05 wl) × 4.60 × 0.90 (1.80 props)
A: 2 single 7.62-mm mg **Electronics:** Radar: 1 Decca 976 nav.
M: 2 MTU 6V396 TC82DE diesels; 2 props; 2,400 bhp
Range: 375/25 **Fuel:** 2,500 liters **Crew:** 6 tot.

Remarks: Aluminum construction. The first delivered in 5-86, the second in 6-86.

♦ **2 Stan Pat 1500 patrol craft**
Bldr: Damen, Gorinchem, the Netherlands

From among:
P 227 through P 229 (In serv. 4-86) P 230 through P 232 (In serv. 6-86)

P 230 Damen, 7-86

D: 16 tons (fl) **S:** 32 kts **Dim:** 15.11 (13.57 wl) × 4.45 × 1.40 (0.75 mean hull)
A: 1 7.62-mm mg **Electronics:** Radar: 1 Decca . . . nav.
M: 2 MTU 6V331 TC82 diesels; 2 props; 2,250 bhp **Fuel:** 2 m^3 **Crew:** 6 tot.

Remarks: As of 1997, only two were fully operational.

Note: The civilian marine police organization, with approximately 1,600 personnel, is headquartered at Lagos and operates a number of launches on the Niger River and Lake Chad. Ten 7.62-m, 35-kt, aluminum-hulled launches (PAD. 42 through PAD.51) were delivered for police use by Abels Boatyard, Bristol, U.K., on 19-10-99; the boats are powered by two 80-bhp Yamaha gasoline outboards. The customs service also has several small launches.

NORWAY

Kingdom of Norway

NORSKE MARINE

Personnel (2001): 6,000 tot. (including 800 in the coast guard), plus 2,100 civilians. The Coast Artillery has an additional 2,000 personnel. There are around 17,000 non-drilling reservists, and the Home Guard has about 8,000 personnel who would operate some 200 privately owned local craft if mobilized.

Bases: Headquarters, Eastern District, is at *Karl Johans* Vern (base), Horten. Headquarters, Western District, is at Haakonsvern, Bergen. Other district bases are located at Ramsund, Harstad, and at Olasvern, Tromsø. Submarine repair and maintenance are carried out at Laksevag. The Olasvern facility is to be closed, along with six other facilities, during 2002–05.

Organization: Command of naval forces and coastal artillery forts is divided between Commander, Naval Forces South Norway (with naval district commands Østlandet, Sørlandet, Rogaland, Vestlandet, and Trøndelag), and Commander, Naval Forces North Norway (with naval district commands Halogaland and Tromsø). Naval forces are subordinate to Commanders, Allied Forces South Norway and North Norway, who are in turn subordinate to the Chief of Defense Norway. The present Naval Forces and Naval Defense Districts are to be disestablished by 31-12-04 and consolidated.

Maritime Aviation: The Royal Norwegian Navy itself operates no aircraft. Six WG-13 Lynx helicopters are used by the coast guard; replacements are to be ordered in 2000, and the order may include an additional 12 to 14. The Royal Norwegian Air Force can use its F-16 fighters in a maritime strike role, using Penguin Mk 3 missiles. For maritime surveillance duties, four P-3C Update III Orions are operated by Royal Norwegian Air Force 333 Sqn.; the aircraft began an Update Improvement Program in 1-98, receiving APS-137(V)5 inverse synthetic aperture radars, OASIS-III (Over-the-Horizon Airborne Sensor Information System) and SATCOM gear, upgrades to the AAR-36 infrared detection system, ARN-151 GPS, AAR-47 missile warning gear, and the ALE-47 decoy system. In addition, the air force operates eight Mk 43, one Mk 43A, and two Mk 43B Westland Sea King and 20 Bell UH-1D helicopters in search-and-rescue duties. Earlier Sea King variants are being updated to Mk 43B configuration with roof-mounted Bendix RSR 1500 radar, nose-mounted Bendix RDR 1300 radar, and FLIR 2000. On 13-9-01, 14 NH-90 helicopters were ordered for shipboard service, six to be configured for naval ASW and the others for Coast Guard use; all are to be delivered between 2005 and 2008.

The maritime squadrons of the Royal Norwegian Air Force are:

Aircraft	*Squadron*	*Bases*
Sea King	330 Sqn.	Banak, Bodø, Ørland, Sola
Orion	333 Sqn.	Andøya
Lynx	337 Sqn.	Bardufoss
UH-1D	719 Sqn.	Bodø
UH-1D	720 Sqn.	Rygge

Coast Artillery: Norway's coastline near important ports and harbors is heavily fortified. Existing facilities employ 127-mm guns of German World War II–era manufacture, 75-mm 60-cal. Bofors guns acquired during the 1960s, shore-mounted torpedo tubes, Penguin antiship missiles, and Swedish RBS-70 surface-to-air missiles. The Bofors 120-mm automatic ERSTA coast defense gun was ordered in 1981 and first firings took place at Trondheim in 1991; the weapon has a 27-km range and fires 24.5- or 24.6-kg shells at 25 rds/min. Bofors Weapon Systems is to supply up to 400 RBS-17 Hellfire coast defense missiles and 60 launchers to equip 12 mobile missile batteries under a 1-96 contract; the missiles replaced old German fixed 105-mm coast defense guns. Shore-mounted artillery was to be discarded between 2002 and 2005, but the parliament *(Storting)* required on 3-7-01 that nine coastal forts be retained in "mothballed" condition. The nine Hellfire mobile batteries and their support boats are being reorganized into a "Coastal Ranger" force.

Note: Names to naval ships are prefixed by KNM *(Kgl. Norske Marine),* while those of coast guard vessels are prefixed by K/V *(Kystvakt).* Kværner Mandal shipyard was sold to Umø A/S early in 2000.

WEAPONS AND SYSTEMS

The name of the principal Norwegian armaments and military electronics manufacturer was restored to Kongsberg A/S in mid-1995; from 1987, the company was known as Norsk Fortvartechnologi A/S (NFT).

The Norwegian Navy uses mostly British, American, and Swedish weapons and systems, but it has built two systems of its own, the Terne automatic ASW rocket system and the Penguin surface-to-surface missile, which are described below. The French Mistral point-defense SAM was selected for fleet-wide use in 1-93. Six launchers and 200 RIM-116 RAM point-defense missiles were requested from the United States in 1996 for use on the five new frigates.

Submarines are equipped with Swedish Tp 617 (45 kts, 20,000-m range) or American NT-37C (20,000-m range) and Mk 37 Mod. 2 wire-guided torpedoes. On 16-12-91, 146 German DM-2A3 wire-guided torpedoes were ordered for the *Ula*-class submarines. Some 190 British Stingray ASW torpedoes were delivered in 1990–92 for

WEAPONS AND SYSTEMS *(continued)*

use on P-3C Orion aircraft. Norway has also developed its own radar and electro-optical gun and missile fire-control systems. Sonars are manufactured by Kongsberg Simrad Mesotech, which has exported a number of small, high-frequency sets for naval use.

Terne-3 Mk 10 (ASW): Mfr: Kongsberg Defence & Aerospace A/S (KDA). Developed by Kongsberg, the sextuple launcher mount weighs a little less than 3 tons and ripple-launches its rockets at 45° to 75° elevation, the latter for minimum range. Reloads automatically in 40 seconds. The rocket is 1.97 m in length, 0.2 m in diameter, and 120 kg in weight (warhead: 48 kg), and has a combination timed and proximity fuze. Employed on the *Oslo* class. Received "Mk 10" upgrade 1991–93. Maximum range: 900 m.

NSM (Nytt Sjomalsmissil): Mfr: Kongsberg Defence & Aerospace A/S (KDA). A new-generation, subsonic, turbojet-powered, infrared-homing replacement for the Penguin series; in development. The decision was made in 1995 not to go ahead with a coast-defense, land-launched version, but that may be reversed later. Contract was let 24-12-96 for the research and development program; Kongsberg was working in co-operation with Aérospatiale under a 1-9-97 agreement but teamed with Germany's DaimlerChrysler Aerospace (now EADS) and TDW in 5-00 for the development of the missile. The launch canister is 4.0 m long and 81 × 80 cm in cross section. The missile airframe incorporates signature-reduction measures. First launch was on 24-10-00, and deliveries are planned for 2004–05. Service life is to be 30 years, with overhauls at 10-year intervals.

Length: 3.95 m (with booster) **Wingspan:** 1.4 m (0.7 folded)
Weight: 412 kg (with 65-kg booster) **Warhead:** 120 kg
Propulsion: Microturbo TRI-40 turbofan **Speed:** high subsonic
Max. range: 250+ km **Guidance:** imaging infrared

Penguin Mk 1: Mfr: Kongsberg Defence & Aerospace A/S (KDA). The missile is protected by a fiberglass container that also serves as a launcher. No longer in production, and most, if not all, have been removed from the ships and craft that carried them.

Length: 2.95 m **Diameter:** 0.28 m **Wingspan:** 1.42 m
Weight: 330 kg **Speed:** Mach 0.7
Max. range: 20,000 m **Guidance:** Infrared homing

Penguin Mk 2: Mfr: Kongsberg Defence & Aerospace A/S (KDA). A Mk 2 Mod. 7 helicopter-launched version was developed for the U.S. Navy.

Length: 3.00 m **Diameter:** 0.28 m **Wingspan:** 1.42 m
Weight: 340 kg **Warhead:** 120-kg Bullpup Mk 19 (50-kg explosive)
Speed: Mach 0.8
Max. range: 26,000 m **Guidance:** Infrared homing

Penguin Mk 3 (air-launched): Mfr: Kongsberg Defence & Aerospace A/S (KDA). Penguin Mk 3 can be launched at altitudes of 150 to 30,000 ft.

Length: 3.20 m **Diameter:** 0.28 m **Wingspan:** 1.00 m
Weight: 360 kg (400 with launcher)
Warhead: 120 kg (50-kg explosive) **Speed:** Mach 0.8
Max. range: 40,000+ m **Guidance:** Infrared homing

Note: Norway's Kongsberg was one of two competitors given a contract in late 1992 to develop a NATO LCAW (Low-Cost ASW Weapon), a rocket-assisted, air-launched torpedo for use against shallow-water targets. No production orders have resulted.

Mines: Existing Mk 2 and Mk 51 controlled mines have been modernized with new fuzing and a command-and-control system linked to shore-based surveillance radars under Project Ida. The Project 6033 New Independent Mine was approved 7-92 and may result in a deepwater rising mine; BAE Systems in the UK, Bofors Underwater Systems, and Kongsberg are competing to design the system, in conjunction with other partners. Initial production model deliveries would come after 2004.

Mine countermeasures: Kongsberg Simrad Mesotech, Norway, has developed the SM 2000, a 200-kHz, multibeam, obstacle-avoidance sonar that can also be employed in a mine-countermeasures role. Its range is 400 m, and the system can be used at speeds up to 4 kts. Six sets for shipboard use were to be delivered in 1999–2000.

ATTACK SUBMARINES [SS]

♦ 0 (+ 4) Viking class
Bldr: . . .

D: 1,650 tons sub. **S:** . . . kts **Dim:** 60.0 × 6.7 × . . .
A: 6 bow 533-mm TT (18 torpedoes, antiship and antiair missiles, mines, and/or UAVs)
Electronics:
Radar: . . .
Sonar: bow conformal passive array; flank passive array; towed passive array
EW: . . .
M: diesel-electric, with Stirling-cycle AIP auxiliary cruise propulsion
Crew: 22 tot.

Note: Four replacement submarines of a new design are planned. In 2-99, Norway signed an agreement with Denmark and Sweden to cooperate in the Viking (formerly Submarine 2000) program. If funding is not available, however, the four remaining *Kobben* class submarines will be given an additional life-extension overhaul to permit them to remain in service to 2012.

The joint Viking Submarine Corp. was founded in 3-00 by Kockums, Kongsberg, and Odense Staalskipværft to design and, eventually, construct the submarines; at that time, Denmark was expected to acquire four, with the first to deliver in 2005; Sweden was to receive two, the first in 2010; and Norway was to receive four, with the first delayed to 2015. Norway is to review its participation in the Viking program in 2002, and all three countries may settle on the German Type 214 design as a compromise.

The Norwegian version will be 10 m longer than the Swedish variant and will displace 300 tons more submerged in order to carry additional AIP power units. Will carry 533- and 400-mm diameter decoys, and a diver lockout chamber will be incorporated.

♦ 6 Ula class (Project 6071/German Type 210)
Bldr: Thyssen Nordseewerke, Emden

	Laid down	L	In serv.
S 300 Ula	29-1-87	28-7-88	27-4-89
S 301 Utsira	15-6-90	21-11-91	30-4-92
S 302 Utstein	6-12-89	25-4-91	14-11-91
S 303 Utvaer	8-12-88	19-4-90	8-11-90
S 304 Uthaug	15-6-89	18-10-90	7-5-91
S 305 Uredd	23-6-88	22-9-89	3-5-90

Uredd (S 305) Findler & Winter, 5-01

Uthaug (S 304) H&L Van Ginderen, 3-00

Utvaer (S 303) Curt Borgenstam, Jr., 8-00

D: 940 tons std.; 1,040 tons surf./1,150 tons sub.
S: 11 kts surf./23 kts sub. **Dim:** 59.00 × 5.40 × 4.60
A: 8 bow 533-mm TT (14 DM-2A3 Seehake wire-guided torpedoes)
Electronics:
Radar: 1 Kelvin-Hughes Type 1007 nav./surf. search
Sonar: STN Atlas Elektronik DBQS-21F (CSU-83) suite; Thales passive conformal arrays
EW: Racal Sealion intercept
M: 2 MTU 16V652 MB diesels (1,260 bhp each), 2 × 870-kw, 3-phase NEBB generator sets, 1 Siemens electric motor; 1 prop; 6,000 shp
Range: 5,000/8 snorkel **Fuel:** 100 tons **Endurance:** 40 days
Crew: 3 officers, 15–17 enlisted

Remarks: Six were ordered 30-9-82; an option to order two more was later dropped. Reportedly, the ships were plagued with noisy machinery and weapons system control problems and were initially the source of considerable dissatisfaction. S 300 was to commission 4-90 after one year of trials, which began 27-4-89; she was hit by a practice torpedo 11-11-89 with minor damage. S 300 was placed in reserve 15-11-91 to 1994, pending delivery of torpedoes. S 304 collided with an uncharted rock while submerged 2-12-94, and grounded later the same day while returning to port. Only four are active at any given time, with the others decommissioned for overhaul.
Hull systems: Normal operating depth: 250 m. Have Anker batteries. All but S 300 have pressure hulls built by Kværner Brug, Oslo. Have X-form stern control surfaces.
Combat systems: The Kongsberg MSI-90U torpedo f.c.s. are being updated under a 5-95 contract, with completions between 1998 and 2005. Fitted with the Carl Zeiss SERO 40 periscope suite, with SERO 14 optronic search periscope and SERO 15 attack periscope with laser rangefinder; also have a GPS terminal. Use Riva Calzoni Trident non-pressure-hull-penetrating radio masts. A LOFAR (Low-Frequency Active Ranging) sonar system is to be added.

♦ 4 modernized German Type 207
Bldr: Rheinstahl-Nordseewerke, Emden

	Laid down	L	In serv.	Mod. completed
S 306 Skolpen	1-11-65	24-3-66	17-8-66	10-89
S 308 Stord	1-4-66	2-9-66	9-2-67	26-10-90
S 309 Svenner	8-9-66	27-1-67	1-7-67	10-93
S 319 Kunna	3-3-64	16-7-64	1-10-64	12-91

ATTACK SUBMARINES [SS] *(continued)*

Stord (S 308) Werner Schiefer, 12-98

D: 469 tons surf./524 tons sub. **S:** 12 kts surf./17 kts sub.
Dim: 47.41 (S 309: 48.41) × 4.60 × 3.80
A: 8 bow 533-mm TT (8 Bofors Tp 61 or DM-2A3 Seehake wire-guided torpedoes)
Electronics:
Radar: 1 Kelvin-Hughes Type 1007 nav.
Sonar: STN Atlas Elektronik DBQS-21F (CSU-83) suite (active and passive)
EW: ArgoSystems AR 700 intercept
M: 2 MTU 12V493 AZ 80 GA31L diesels (600 bhp each), 2 405-kw generators, 1 1,100-kw motor; 1 2.3-m-dia. prop; 1,700 shp
Range: 5,000/8 snorkel; 14/17, 141/6 sub. **Crew:** 5 officers, 13 enlisted

Remarks: Originally a class of 15, financed by the United States. Modernized by Mjellum and Karlsen, Urivale, Bergen (completion dates listed above). S 309 is configured for training duties. S 306 was in a collision with the British merchant ship *Solena* on 13-10-97 while operating submerged, with only minor damage. Were to be retired over the 2002–05 period, but are now to be transferred to Poland, two during 2002, one in 2003, and one in 2004.
Disposals: *Kinn* (S 316; ex-*Ula,* S 300) was returned to U.S. custody for disposal on 23-5-91. *Stadt* (S 307), which was to have gone to Denmark, was damaged by grounding in spring 1987 and stricken; she was replaced by *Kya* (S 317). Also transferred to Denmark were *Utvaer* (S 303) and *Uthaug* (S 304); *Kaura* (S 315) was transferred to Denmark in 10-91 for spares. The unmodernized *Utsira* (S 301) and *Utstein* (S 302) were stricken at the end of 1991. The modernized *Sklinna* (S 314, ex-S 305) and *Kobben* (S 318), in reserve since 1998, were approved for disposal in 6-99.
Hull systems: Design is based on the German Type 205, but these are deeper diving. Were lengthened 2 m and re-engined during modernization. Operating depth: 190 m. S 309 was built 1 m longer than her sisters and is equipped with a second Pilkington CK 30 periscope for training; she displaces about 14 tons additional.
Combat systems: During modernization, received MSI-90U combat data systems in place of MSI-70U, new sonar and communications suites, Thorn-EMI D-3 data-distribution systems, new radar, and new EW gear. The MSI-90U systems have been modified to permit the submarines to launch the DM-2A3 torpedo.

FRIGATES [FF]

♦ 0 (+ 5) Fridtjof Nansen class (Project 6088)
Bldrs: Izar-. . ., Spain, and Mjellem & Karlsen, Bergen

	Laid down	L	In serv
F 310 Fridtjof Nansen	2001	2004	2005 (del.)
F 311 Roald Amundsen	. . .	. . .	. . .
F 312 Otto Sverdrup	. . .	. . .	. . .
F 313 Helge Ingstad	. . .	. . .	. . .
F 314 Thor Heyerdahl	. . .	. . .	2009

Fridtjof Nansen (F 310)—official model Norman Friedman, 10-00

Fridtjof Nansen (F 310) Norman Friedman, 10-00

D: 4,681 tons (5,121 fl) **S:** 27 kts (18 cruise on diesels)
Dim: 132.00 (120.39 wl) × 16.80 (15.90 wl) × 4.90 (mean hull)
A: 8 NSM SSM; 8-cell Mk 41VLS (32 RIM-7P ESSM Sea Sparrow missiles); 1 76-mm 62-cal. OTOBreda SuperRapid DP; 4 single 12.7-mm mg; 4 fixed, paired 324-mm ASW TT (Stingray torpedoes); 1 or 2 d.c. racks; 1 . . . helicopter

Fridtjof Nansen (F 310)—artist's rendering Izar, 2000

Electronics:
Radar: 3 Decca BridgeMaster . . . ARPA nav. (2 X-band, 1 S-band); 1 Lockheed Martin SPY-1F 3-D tracking, target desig., and weapons control; 2 Raytheon SPG-62 target illuminators
Sonar: Thales TSM 2633 (MRS 2000) Spherion hull-mounted MF; Thales CAPTAS Mk 2(V)1 active/passive towed linear array
EW: Condor CS-3701 active/passive suite; 2 . . . offboard active decoy launchers; 2 . . . trainable decoy RL; . . . torpedo decoy syst.; EADS COLDS laser countermeasure
E/O: Sagem VIGY 20 IR and optical surveillance and tracking syst.
M: CODAG: 2 Izar Bravo 12-cyl. diesels (6,000 bhp each), 1 G.E. LM-2500 gas turbine (25,750 shp); 2 CP props; 37,750 hp max.—1 1,340-shp retractable bow-thruster
Electric: 3,600 kw tot. (4 × 900-kw alternators, MTU 12V 396 diesels driving)
Range: 4,500/16 **Crew:** 120 tot. (accomm. for 146)

Remarks: Spain's Empresa Nacional Bazán (now Izar), teamed with Lockheed Martin Government Systems, won the design competition in 5-99, with the selection of the Bazán offer confirmed 29-2-00, permission to go ahead with the program given by the parliament 31-5-00, and the construction contract signed 23-6-00. The program is expected to cost $1.92 billion. Some of the armament and sensor systems may be transferred from the *Oslo* class. Mjellem & Karlsen will provide hull sections for all five ships and will perform final assembly for units 4 and 5 in Norway (Umoe Sterkoder, Kristiansund, was replaced in this role on 30-6-00). While having sophisticated sensor and combat data systems, the ships will be very lightly armed.
Hull systems: Steel hull and superstructure. Hull is to have 13 watertight compartments. To be able to operate with no personnel in the engine rooms, with the plant operated from the bridge or main engineering control room. There will be two 690-V main and two 450-V ship's service electric switchboards, with two 690/450-V, 2,000-kVA transformers. Signature-reduction measures include topside shaping, acoustically hooded machinery and equipment, an IR suppression system, a wet-down spray system, degaussing, propeller shaft grounding, and a flexible drive train. There will be four damage-control stations and a complete NBC warfare defense system. Are to remain mobile with two compartments flooded. The originally planned electric drive system was eliminated to save costs, and the electrical generation plant is considerably less powerful than the 8,200 kw total originally envisaged.
Combat systems: Lockheed Martin will perform combat systems integration in conjunction with Kongsberg; the Aegis combat system will have Kongsberg SC 3100 and SC 3200 operator consoles instead of the UYQ-70 terminals used by the U.S. Navy. To be equipped to operate with Link 11, with provisions for Link 16 and Link 22 when available. The Kongsberg-Thales MSI-2005F ASW weapons-control system will be integrated into the main system. The COLDS (Common Opto-electronic Laser Detection System) detects missile laser seekers and directs a laser beam of equivalent pulse repetition frequency against a safe spot on the ocean to spoof the missile. Space and weight are reserved for a second eight-cell Mk 41 VLS, but there are no immediate plans to incorporate the Standard SM-2 missile, although the Mk 41 cells are long enough to accommodate it. As delivered, will not have any decoy launching system, and there will be two positions for close-in AA defense weapons to be added later. Either Sikorsky Seahawk or NH-90-series helicopters are expected to be procured for the ships, and accommodations are provided for a 10-strong aviation personnel group.

♦ 3 Oslo class
Bldr: Marinens Hovedverft (Naval Dockyard), Horten

	Laid down	L	In serv.	Mod. completed
F 301 Bergen	1963	23-8-65	15-5-67	4-4-90
F 302 Trondheim	1963	4-9-64	2-6-66	30-11-87
F 304 Narvik	1964	8-1-65	30-11-66	21-10-88

Trondheim (F 302) Boris Lemachko, 8-00

FRIGATES [FF] *(continued)*

Narvik (F 304) A. A. de Kruijf, 9-01

Trondheim (F 302) Mike Welsford, 11-00

D: 1,670 tons (1,970 fl) **S:** 25 kts
Dim: 96.62 (93.87 pp) × 11.17 × 4.52 (5.62 over prop)
A: 1 8-round Mk 29 SAM launcher (24 RIM-7M Sea Sparrow missiles); 1 twin 76.2-mm 50-cal. U.S. Mk 33 DP; 1 40-mm 70-cal. Bofors AA; 1 6-round Terne-3 Mk 10 ASW RL; 2 triple 324-mm Mk 32 Mod. 5 ASW TT (6 Stingray torpedoes); 1 d.c. rack (6 d.c.)
Electronics:
Radar: 1 Decca . . . nav.; 1 Decca TM 1226 nav./surf. search; 1 Siemens-Plessey AWS-9(2D) air search; 1 CelsiusTech 9LV 200 Mk 2 gun f.c.; 1 Raytheon Mk 95 SAM f.c.
Sonar: Thales TSM 2633 (Spherion Mk 1) hull-mounted and VDS (7 kHz); Kongsberg Terne-3 hull-mounted HF attack
EW: ArgoSystems APECS intercept; Nera SR-1A intercept; 2 . . . decoy RL
M: 1 set Laval-Ljungstrom PN 20 geared steam turbines; 1 prop; 20,000 shp
Boilers: 2 Babcock & Wilcox; 42.18 kg/cm², 454° C **Electric:** 1,100 kw tot.
Range: 4,500/15 **Crew:** 11 officers, 19 senior petty officers, 90 other enlisted

Remarks: Half of the construction cost was financed by the United States. Rebuilt during the late 1970s with the Penguin antiship missile, NATO Sea Sparrow point-defense SAM, and ASW torpedo tubes. All modernized again (dates of completion above).
Disposals: Sister *Oslo* (F 300) ran aground 24-1-94 and sank the next day after having been pulled off the shore. *Stavanger* (F 303) was placed in reserve pending disposal in 4-99 and is not likely to see further active service.
Hull systems: Design is based on the U.S. *Dealey* class, but with higher freeboard forward and many European subsystems. Due to excessive weights aft and resultant hull cracking, the stern of F 304 was strengthened during an overhaul completed in late 1994, adding some 200 tons to the displacement; the alteration was made to the other two and restrictions on their open-ocean operations were lifted. They are equipped with UFAS Sjøbjørn-25-class aluminum-hulled, rigid inflatable personnel launches powered by a 350-bhp Yanmar 6LY-UTE diesel driving a Hamilton 273 waterjet for speeds up to 33 kts.
Combat systems: By the end of 1998, all had received Siemens-Plessey AWS-9 (2-D) air-search radars in place of the previous Siemens MPDR-45 sets; also installed was the Siemens-Plessey ODIN command and fire-control system as a subsystem to the existing NFT MSI-3100 combat control system. Have NATO Link 11 and Link 14 datalink capability. Two 20-mm 90-cal. Rheinmetall AA have been removed from the after superstructure, and Penguin antiship missiles are no longer carried. Use the Raytheon Mk 91 Mod. 0 control system for the NATO Sea Sparrow SAM system, with a twin-antenna Mk 95 radar director (mounted on a pylon atop the missile-reload magazine). Mounted just forward of the Mk 29 missile launcher is a TVT-300 lead-computing optronic director for the 40-mm AA gun.

AIR-CUSHION GUIDED-MISSILE PATROL BOATS [PTGA]

♦ 1 (+ 5) Skjold class (Project 6081)
Bldr: P 960: Kværner Mandal A/S, Mandal; others: . . .

	Laid down	L	In serv.
P 960 SKJOLD	8-97	22-9-98	17-4-99
P	. . .	. . .	. . .
P	. . .	. . .	. . .
P	. . .	. . .	. . .
P	. . .	. . .	. . .
P	. . .	. . .	. . .

Skjold (P 960)—during trials with OTOBreda 76-mm gun aboard KNM Tordenskjold, 9-99

Skjold (P 960)—note how much larger the newer ship is than the three *Hauk*-class missile craft moored alongside Eivind Rodlie, 10-99

D: 260 tons (fl) **S:** 55 kts (57.1 on trials)
Dim: 46.79 (41.50 pp) × 13.50 × 2.25 (0.83 on cushion)
A: provision for: 4 NSM SSM; 1 76-mm 62-cal. OTOBreda SuperRapid DP; 1 2-round Simbad point-defense SAM launcher (Mistral missiles)
Electronics:
Radar: 1 Ericsson Sea Giraffe surf./air search; 1 CelsiusTech CEROS 200 f.c.
EW: . . . . . . intercept
E/O: SAGEM VIGY 20 optronic f.c.
M: CODOG: 2 Rolls-Royce–Allison 571-KF9 gas turbines (8,160 shp each), 2 MTU 6R183 TE92 auxiliary diesels (500 bhp each); 2 KaMeWa 80S2 waterjets; 16,320 shp—2 MTU 12V183 TE92 diesels (985 bhp each) driving lift fans
Electric: 456 kw tot. (2 MTU 6R183 TE52 diesels driving)
Range: . . ./. . . **Endurance:** 14 days **Crew:** 4 officers, 11 enlisted

Remarks: *Skjold* means "Shield." Originally to have been a class of 24 to replace the *Storm* and *Snögg* classes. Her trials successfully completed, *Skjold* was in layup, without armament, as of 3-01. Kværner Mandal received the $30 million prototype contract on 30-8-96, and five to seven production versions were to have been ordered in 1999 after 15 months of trials (with the prototype later to refit to production standard); the final unit would have been delivered in 2004. The start for the production version was delayed to 2006 in 1-97 but was restored to 2000 in mid-1998 to preserve industrial capabilities; then the order for six was eliminated from the 1999 budget. The navy then announced a desire to order the seven additional units in 2003, but the program was recommended for cancellation by the chief of defense in 6-00 and the prototype was to have been stricken during 2002; instead, however, the U.S. Navy has leased the craft and the services of a Norwegian crew for a year, starting in 9-01, and during 6-01 the Norwegian Parliament convinced the government to fund construction of five more.
Hull systems: GRP-construction, rigid-sidewall surface effect ship, with infrared and radio energy shielding molded into the structure to reduce signature. Automatic ride control system. Production versions may have a different propulsion system with Rolls-Royce–Allison 571KF11 gas turbines of up to 16,400 kw total output to sustain 55 kts. The prototype was to be able to sustain 44 kts in a State 3 sea. Can operate in waters as shallow as 1 m.
Combat systems: The SENIT 2000 combat system, ordered 26-6-97, is to be made by a consortium of Kongsberg and Simrad with DCN, France, and will be a variant of DCN's SENIT 8 system; there are six display consoles. The principal radar is to be a two-dimensional system vice the originally planned 3-D radar. The communications system includes HF through UHF radios, cryptographic systems, and Link 11. The missile launchers are to be recessed into the stern area, and decoy rocket launchers are to be recessed into the bow area. Aboard in 9-99 was an experimental, reduced radar reflectivity OTOBreda 76-mm mount; the mount was returned to OTOBreda early in 10-99.

GUIDED-MISSILE PATROL CRAFT [PTG]

♦ 14 Hauk class

Bldrs: Bergens Mekaniske Verksteder (last four: Westamarin A/S, Alta)

	In serv.		In serv.
P 986 Hauk	17-8-78	P 993 Lom	15-1-80
P 987 Ørn	19-1-79	P 994 Stegg	18-3-80
P 988 Terne	13-3-79	P 995 Falk	30-4-80
P 989 Tjeld	25-5-79	P 996 Ravn	20-5-80
P 990 Skarv	17-7-79	P 997 Gribb	10-7-80
P 991 Teist	11-9-79	P 998 Geir	16-9-80
P 992 Jo	1-11-79	P 999 Erle	10-12-80

Ravn (P 996)—note the absence of Penguin missile canisters Findler & Winter, 5-00

Erle (P 999) Findler & Winter, 5-00

D: 130 tons (155 fl) **S:** 35 kts **Dim:** 36.53 × 6.3 × 1.65
A: provision for 4 Penguin Mk 2 SSM—fitted with: 1 40-mm 70-cal. Bofors AA; 1 2-round Simbad point-defense SAM launcher (Mistral missiles); 2 fixed 533-mm TT (2 Bofors Tp 61 wire-guided torpedoes)
Electronics:
Radar: 1 Decca TM 1226 nav., 1 . . . surf. search
Sonar: Simrad SQ3D/SF hull-mounted HF
EW: Racal Matilda radar intercept
E/O: MSI-80S director
M: 2 MTU 16V538 TB92 diesels; 2 props; 7,340 bhp
Range: 440/34 **Crew:** 6 officers, 18 enlisted

Remarks: As of 1999, were planned to be retained in service until 2010–15, but in 6-00, the chief of defense recommended their more or less immediate retirement; the parliament *(Storting),* however, in 7-01 required that all 14 be retained. A modernization program at Umoe-Mandal Shipyard remains ongoing, with P 991, P 992, and P 994 redelivered on 9-11-01; the others planned to be completed by the end of 2003. Crews include nine conscripts; some women also serve aboard. P 992 ran hard aground at 25 kts early in 2-02 but was to be repaired.
Hull systems: P 989 has been fitted with a wave-piercing bow to provide a 0.5-kt speed increase and improved fuel efficiency.
Combat systems: Have the Kongsberg MSI-80S fire-control system, which uses two Decca radars plus a Phillips TVT-300 electro-optical tracker and an Ericsson laser rangefinder. Have two 50-mm flare RL. During 1992–94 refits, received one Simbad twin-launcher for Mistral surface-to-air missiles in place of the 20-mm AA gun. The torpedoes have a 25-km range. Penguin missiles are not normally carried.
Modernization: The modernization program includes substituting the SENIT 2000 combat system chosen for the *Skjold* class, replacing the MSI-80S optronic director with a SAGEM VIGY 20, upgrading the 40-mm gun with an autoloader system, replacing the radar and EW system, installing new decoy rocket launchers, and adding a new communications suite with a NATO Link 11 capability.

MINE WARFARE SHIPS

♦ 2 Vidar-class minelayers [MM]

Bldr: Mjellem & Karlsen, Bergen

	Laid down	L	In serv.
N 52 Vidar	1-3-76	18-3-77	21-10-77
N 53 Vale	1-2-76	5-8-77	10-2-78

D: 1,500 tons (1,722 fl) **S:** 15 kts **Dim:** 64.80 (60.00 pp) × 12.00 × 4.00 (hull)
A: 2 single 40-mm 70-cal. Bofors AA; 1 2-round Simbad point-defense SAM launcher (Mistral missiles); 320 mines
Electronics:
Radar: 2 Decca TM 1226 nav.
Sonar: Simrad SQ3D hull-mounted HF

Vidar (N 52) Piet Sinke, 6-01

Vale (N 53) Winter & Findler, 4-98

M: 2 Wichmann 7AX diesels; 2 props; 4,200 bhp—425-shp bow-thruster
Electric: 1,000 kw tot. **Range:** . . ./. . . **Fuel:** 247 tons **Crew:** 50 tot.

Remarks: Ordered 11-6-75. Capable of serving as minelayers (mines carried on three decks, with electric elevators to first platform deck and upper deck, and three minelaying rails), torpedo-recovery ships, personnel and cargo transports, fisheries-protection ships, and ASW escorts. Have TVT-300 optronic directors for the 40-mm AA. N 52 was modified 5-98 with additional command-and-control facilities as flagship of NATO's ComStanNavForLant. Antisubmarine armament of two triple Mk 32 ASW TT and two d.c. racks has been removed. N 52 is to operate until 2008 as fleet logistics support ship, but N 53 will be retired by the end of 2004.

♦ 1 controlled minefield tender [MM]

Bldr: Voldnes Skipsverft A/S, Fosnavåg (In serv. 1981)

N 50 Tyr (ex-*Standby Master*)

Tyr (N 50) Eivind Rodlie, 4-98

D: 495 tons (650 fl) **S:** 13 kts **Dim:** 42.25 (36.02 pp) × 10.10 × 4.20
A: . . . mines
Electronics: Radar: 1 Furuno FR711 nav.; 1 Furuno 1011 nav.
M: 2 Deutz SBA12M816 diesels; 1 CP prop; 1,370 bhp—1 650-shp azimuth thruster forward—1 250-shp thruster aft
Electric: 685 kw tot. (2 × 320-kw shaft generators, 1 × 44-kw diesel set)
Range: . . ./. . . **Fuel:** . . . tons **Crew:** 7 officers, 15 enlisted

Remarks: 497 grt. Former oilfield standby safety and pollution control ship, acquired 12-93 from K/S Strand Sea Service A/S, Ålesund, for conversion from 1994 to 1-95 by Mjellum & Karlsen, Bergen, as a replacement for the controlled minefield tender *Borgen* (N 51); received a new crane, additional superstructure to accommodate mines being transported or repaired, a remotely operated submersible (ROV) and its control system, a new bow-thruster, and a workboat. Commissioned 7-3-95. The parliament *(Storting)* specifically required active retention of this ship on 3-7-01.

Note: The Norwegian Navy also intends to employ civilian passenger/vehicle ferries as minelayers in wartime. As an example, the 1,435-grt, 841-dwt ferry *Stavanger,* delivered 31-3-90 by Myklebust Mekaniske Verksted, is intended for wartime use in such a role.

MINE WARFARE SHIPS *(continued)*

♦ **9 Oksøy/Alta-class minehunter/minesweepers [MHC/MSC]**
Bldr: Kværner Mandal A/S, Mandal

	In serv.		In serv.
4 Minehunters [MHC]:			
M 340 Oksøy	15-8-94	M 342 Måløy	24-3-95
M 341 Karmøy	9-1-95	M 343 Hinnøy	8-9-95
5 Minesweepers [MSC]:			
M 350 Alta	12-1-96	M 353 Orkla	4-4-97
M 351 Otra	8-11-96	M 354 Glomma	1-7-97
M 352 Rauma	2-12-96		

Otra (M 351)—minesweeper variant ANBw/FAFIO, 4-00

Hinnøy (M 343)—minehunter variant Findler & Winter, 10-01

Måløy (M 342)—minehunter variant Bernard Prézelin, 7-01

D: 275 tons light; 343 tons std. (375 fl) **S:** 30 kts (20.5 cruising)
Dim: 55.20 (52.00 pp) × 13.55 (13.30 wl) × 2.15 (0.87 on cushion)
A: 12-round Simbad SAM syst. (Mistral missiles); 2 single 20-mm 90-cal. Rheinmetall AA; 2 single 12.7-mm M2 mg
Electronics:
Radar: 2 Decca RN 88 nav. with DB-2000 ARPA displays
Sonar: minesweepers: Simrad SA-950 hull-mounted mine-avoidance (95 kHz)—minehunters: Thales TSM-2023N variable-depth HF
M: 2 MTU 12V396 TE94 propulsion diesels (2,040 bhp each), 2 MTU 8V396 TE54 diesels for lift fans (940 bhp each); 2 Kværner Eureka waterjets; 4,160 bhp—jet-vane bow-thruster

Måløy (M 342)—minehunter variant Bernard Prézelin, 7-01

Electric: 500 kw tot. (2 MTU 12V183 TE51 diesels driving)
Range: 1,500/20 **Fuel:** 73,000 liters
Crew: minehunters: 12 officers, 26 enlisted—minesweepers: 10 officers, 22 enlisted

Remarks: Approved 3-8-87 by the Ministry of Defense and ordered 9-11-89. M 340 was laid down 1-12-90, launched 8-3-93, and declared fully operational in 5-95. Entire program is said to have cost $437.5 million, including a $156.3 million overrun. One of the minesweepers is to be retired or placed in reserve under the 6-00 Defence Analysis 2000 plan.
Hull systems: Rigid-sidewall air-cushion vehicle design. The cushion area is 48.50 × 10.00 × 2.35 (high) m. Have hydraulic drive for low-speed operations. Design limits rolling to 2°–3° in Sea State 3. All machinery is installed on the main deck, which reduces the magnetic and acoustic signatures. Have Cirrus automated air-cushion ride control and Simrad Albatross dynamic positioning system. One-ton-thrust air jets near the bow provide precise maneuvering capability. The lift fan capacity is inadequate, limiting their endurance. There is a two-man divers' decompression chamber. The standard of accommodations is very high.
Combat systems: The minehunters carry two Gayrobot Pluto Plus 41 submersibles and are equipped with the Thales/ASM/Simrad MICOS minehunting system. On both versions, the sonar transducers are mounted on pivoting arms mounted between the hulls. All have Seatex GPS receivers. The minesweepers are able to tow the Agate high-speed acoustic array with air-gun and transducer noisemakers; they also have Elma magnetic sweep gear and Oropesa size 4 wire sweep arrays but do not carry mine disposal divers.

AMPHIBIOUS WARFARE CRAFT

♦ **3 Reinøysund-class utility landing craft [LCU]**
Bldr: Mjellem & Karlsen, Bergen

	In serv.		In serv.
L 4503 Sørøysund	5-72	L 4506 Tjeldsund (ex-*Borgsund*)	2-73
L 4504 Maursund	9-72		

Tjeldsund (L 4506) Eivind Rodlie, 10-97

Maursund (L 4504) Eivind Rodlie, 10-99

D: 850 tons (fl) **S:** 11.5 kts **Dim:** 60.50 × 10.30 × 1.85
A: 3 single 20-mm 90-cal. Rheinmetall AA; rails for 120 mines
Electronics: Radar: 1 Decca TM 1226 nav.; 1 . . . nav.
M: 2 Deutz TBD 234 V12 diesels; 2 props; 1,350 bhp
Crew: 2 officers, 8 enlisted

Remarks: Modernized, re-engined, and lengthened in lieu of new construction during 1995–97. L 4506 was renamed in 1995. Unconverted sisters *Reinøysund* (L 4502) and *Rotsund* (L 4505) were converted to diver support craft [YDT] during 1999. Were

AMPHIBIOUS WARFARE CRAFT *(continued)*

recommended in 6-00 for retirement and were to be placed in reserve during 2001, but the parliament required their continued employment.
Hull systems: Original length was 51.40 m and displacement 590 tons. Have a double-folding bow-ramp door and covered vehicle cargo well. The vehicle deck was lengthened to project over the stern, where it is covered by a visor-type door. Cargo capacity: 7 Leopard tanks, 200 troops. The superstructure was greatly enlarged during reconstruction to provide enhanced accommodations.

♦ 21 CB-90N-class landing craft [LCP]
Bldrs: Dockstavarvet, Sweden; Mjellem & Karlsen, Norway; and Westamarin, Norway (In serv. 7-96 to 1998)

KA 1 Trondernes	KA 13 Stangnes	KA 20 Nidaros
KA 2 Hysnes	KA 14 Kjøkøy	KA 21 Brettingen
KA 3 Hellen	KA 15 Mørvika	KA 22 Løkhaug
KA 4 Torås	KA 16 Kopås	KA 23 Sørviknes
KA 5 Møvik	KA 17 Tangen	KA 31 Osternes
KA 11 Skrolsvik	KA 18 Oddane	KA 32 Fjell
KA 12 Kråkenes	KA 19 Malmøya	KA 33 Lerøy

Lerøy (KA 33) Eivind Rodlie, 6-01

D: 14.5 tons light (19 fl) **S:** 40+ kts (35 loaded)
Dim: 14.90 (13.00 wl) × 3.80 × 0.84
A: 2 twin and 1 single 12.7-mm mg; provision for RBS-17 Hellfire SSM, 1 81-mm mortar, 4 mines, or 6 d.c.
Electronics: Radar: 1 Decca BridgeMaster RD 360 nav.
M: 2 Saab Scania 8V DSI-14 diesels; 2 KaMeWa FF 450C or FF 410 waterjets; 1,104 or 1,256 bhp (see remarks)
Electric: 5 kw tot. (1 × 5-kw diesel set; 230/400V a.c.)
Range: 260/20 **Fuel:** 2.5 tons **Crew:** 4 tot. + 20 troops

Remarks: First four were ordered in 11-95 and delivered between 7-96 and 10-96 by the Swedish design yard for trials; three more were delivered in 1997, 13 during 1998, and two more early in 1999. *Bjørgvin* (KA 30) was no longer listed as of 1-02 and may have been lost to accident. An option for 14 more has not been exercised. Intended as transports for Coastal Artillery mobile RBS-17 Hellfire coast-defense missile batteries. Same basic design is used as Sweden's Stridsbåt-90H (Combat Boat 90H) class. Organized into four-boat battery groups, each with three launcher boats (each with four missiles and one launcher) and one command boat.
Hull systems: Can maintain 20 kts in 1.5-m seas, and the hull can withstand at least 25 groundings without significant damage. In lieu of troops, can carry up to 2.8 tons of cargo. Fuel capacity was increased over the Swedish version. KA 5 and later have uprated engines (1,256 bhp tot.) and employ KaMeWa FF 410 waterjets. Navigation equipment includes two GPS receivers, Seapath 200/M and Sealog 100/M computer navaids, a Simrad EQ30 log, and an echo sounder. There are two radar displays. The troop compartment is higher than in the Swedish Artillery Service units to permit standing.

Note: Norwegian special forces employ several high-speed, waterjet-driven RIB assault landing craft equipped with a small Raytheon radar but not armed; no other data available. The Norwegian Army has six M.A.N. GHH MLC 60 bridging ferries of 26-m span, propelled by Schottel pumpjets; the craft are named *Håling-I* through *Håling-VI*.

AUXILIARIES

Note: The 14,989-grt auto/passenger ferry *Peter Wessel* was acquired by the government in 9-85 for conversion to a casualty evacuation ship with a medical staff of 450 and facilities for 800 seriously wounded and 1,200 lightly wounded troops; she is not under naval control and normally operates in commercial service.

♦ 1 general-purpose operational support ship [AG]
Bldr: Ulstein Hatlo A/S, Ulsteinvik (In serv. 1981)

A 535 Valkyrien (ex-*Far Senior,* ex-*Stad Senior*)

D: approx. 3,000 tons (fl) **S:** 16 kts **Dim:** 68.03 (59.02 pp) × 14.71 × 4.77
A: none **Electronics:** 2 Furuno . . . nav.
M: 4 Bergens Normo KVMB-12 diesels, electric drive; 2 CP props; 11,600 shp (10,560 sust.)—2 800-shp bow-thrusters—1 800-shp stern-thruster
Electric: 3,000 kw (2 × 1,256-kw shaft generators, 2 × 244-kw diesel sets)
Range: 10,000/10 **Fuel:** 1,000 tons **Crew:** 13 tot. (accomm. for 23)

Valkyrien (A 535) Maritime Photographic, 9-98

Valkyrien (A 535)—with containerized cargo on the working deck Dieter Wolf, 5-00

Remarks: 491 grt/1,112 dwt. Former anchor-handling tug/supply vessel, purchased 12-93 from Sverre Farstad & Co., A/S, Ålesund. Converted during 1994 to 1-95 to perform such varied duties as torpedo recovery, ocean towing, target towing, transportation of troops and cargo to naval exercises, training for civilian crews of merchant vessels likely to be taken up from trade in an emergency, target service, search and rescue, support to small combatants, and pollution control; in wartime will also be able to act as a minelayer. Has an ice-strengthened hull and extensive navigational aids. Is equipped with oil-recovery gear and pollution-control equipment and can carry up to 700 tons of cargo on the open after deck. Bollard pull: 128 tons.

Note: A new repair tender for the *Fridtjof Nansen*–class frigates has been proposed; the ship would enter service after 2008.

♦ 1 royal yacht [AG]
Bldr: Camper & Nicholson's, Gosport, U.K. (L: 17-2-37)

A 533 Norge (ex-*Philante*)

Norge (A 533)—white hull, yellow funnel, pennant number not worn Walter Sartori, 7-95

D: 1,786 tons (fl) **S:** 17 kts **Dim:** 76.27 × 8.53 × 4.65
Electronics: Radar: 2 Decca . . . nav.
M: 2 Bergen KRMB-8 diesels; 2 props; 4,850 bhp **Electric:** 300 kw tot.
Range: 9,900/17 **Fuel:** 175 tons **Crew:** 18 officers, 32 enlisted

Remarks: Built as a yacht for aviation pioneer T. O. M. Sopwith, then used by the British Royal Navy as an ASW escort 1940–43, then as a training ship; purchased by Norway in 1948. Can carry 50-passenger royal party. Had a severe fire 8-3-85; was repaired by summer 1986.

♦ 1 intelligence collection ship [AGI]
Bldr: Tangen Verft A/S (In serv. 11-93)

Marjata

D: 5,300 tons (7,560 fl) **S:** 15 kts **Dim:** 81.50 (72.00 pp) × 39.90 × 6.00
Electronics: Radar: 2 . . . nav.—EW: various intercept arrays
M: 2 MTU 16V396 TE diesels, 2 Siemens generators, electric drive; 2 Schottel SRP 3030 azimuth props aft; 8,160 shp—1 bow Schottel azimuthal prop (2,720 shp)

AUXILIARIES *(continued)*

Marjata Piet Sinke, 6-01

Electric: 7,200 kw tot. (2 × 3,600-kw Dresser Rand gas turbine sets)
Crew: 14 crew + 31 technicians

Remarks: Owned by the Ministry of Defense vice the navy proper. Built under subcontract from Langsten Slip og Båtbyggeri A/S. Aerial A/S, Horten, Ramform M7 design. Replaced a smaller vessel of the same name completed in 1976. Will have three large radomes covering collection antennas and a sonar installation at the stern. Has an unusual wedge-shaped hullform of extraordinary relative beam to provide stability in the rough seas in which she will operate. Has a large helicopter deck aft. Originally painted with gray hull, white superstructure, and yellow masts, but now painted all white. The civilian geophysical research ship *Ramform Challenger* is a sister that differs in having a raised helicopter deck aft and a much smaller antenna array.

♦ 1 logistics support ship [AGP] Bldr: Horten Verft, Horten

	Laid down	L	In serv.
A 530 Horten	28-1-77	12-8-77	9-6-78

Horten (A 530) H&L Van Ginderen, 8-99

D: 2,500 tons (fl) **S:** 16.5 kts **Dim:** 87.0 (82.0 pp) × 13.7 × . . .
A: 2 single 40-mm 70-cal. Bofors AA; mines
Electronics: Radar: 3 Decca . . . nav.
M: 2 Wichmann 7AX diesels; 2 props; 4,200 bhp **Crew:** 86 tot.

Remarks: Supports submarines and small combatants. Can accommodate up to 45 additional personnel and has messing facilities for 190 additional. Has a helicopter deck and a bow-thruster. Was recommended in 6-00 for retirement but no date has been set.

SERVICE CRAFT

Note: Until 1-98, smaller service craft were identified by a pennant number system employing three letters to identify their naval district subordination, plus a one- or two-digit number. They are now identified by function: HD for diving tenders, HM for multirole tenders, HP for personnel launches, HR for rescue craft, HS for tugs, and HT for torpedo retrievers.

♦ 1 relic/training tender [YAG] Bldr: Fisher Boat Works, Detroit, Mich.

	Laid down	L	In serv.
HP 15 Hitra (ex-U.S. SC 718)	22-9-42	31-3-43	25-5-43

D: 95 tons light (148 fl) **S:** 21 kts (when new)
Dim: 33.80 (32.77 wl) × 5.18 × 1.98
A: 1 40-mm Mk 3 AA; 2 single 20-mm Oerlikon Mk 10 AA
Electronics: Radar: 1 . . . nav.
M: 2 G.M. Electromotive Div. 16-184A diesels; 2 props; 1,540 bhp
Fuel: 16 tons **Crew:** . . .

Remarks: Survivor of the ships and craft that served Free Norwegian naval forces during World War II. Reacquired 8-5-87 for restoration to operational service as a cadet training craft and museum ship; the original engines were located and reinstalled. Operational during the summer months. Wooden construction. Does not carry a pennant number. In original World War II configuration, she had a third 20-mm gun aft and was also fitted with two Mk 20 Mousetrap ASW RL, two Mk 6 d.c. mortars, and two d.c. racks.

Hitra (HP 15) Eivind Rodlie, 5-91

♦ 2 Reinøysund-class diving tenders [YDT]
Bldr: Mjellem & Karlsen, Bergen

	In serv.		In serv.
L 4502 Reinøysund	1-72	L 4505 Rotsund	11-72

D: 590 tons (fl) **S:** 11.5 kts **Dim:** 51.40 × 10.30 × 1.85
A: 3 single 20-mm 90-cal. Rheinmetall AA; rails for 120 mines
Electronics: Radar: 1 Decca TM 1226 nav.; 1 . . . nav.
M: 2 Deutz TBD 234 V12 diesels; 2 props; 1,350 bhp
Crew: 2 officers, 8 enlisted

Remarks: Converted as diver support craft during 1999. Three lengthened and modernized sisters remain in use as landing craft (q.v.).

♦ 2 small miscellaneous diving tenders [YDT]

HD 1 Rya (In serv. 1977) HD 2 Viken (In serv. 1984)

Remarks: HD 1 can reach 10 kts. HD 2 can also carry 4 tons of general cargo or up to 40 passengers.

♦ 5 Torpen-series stores tenders [YF]

	Bldr	In serv.
HM 1 Rotvaer (ex-NSD 35)	Båtservice Verft, Mandal	3-78
HM 2 Krøttøy (ex-HSD 15)	Voldnes Skipsverft, Fosnavåg	6-78
HM 3 Torpen (ex-VSD 4)	Båtservice Verft, Mandal	15-12-77

Torpen (HM 3) Eivind Rodlie, 4-99

D: typical: 215 tons (300 fl) **S:** 11 kts **Dim:** 29.0 × 6.4 × 2.57
A: 1 12.7-mm mg **Electronics:** Radar: 1 Decca 1226 nav.
M: 1 MWM TBD 601-6K diesel; 1 CP prop; 530 bhp
Range: 1,200/11 **Fuel:** 11 tons **Crew:** 6 enlisted + 100 passengers

Remarks: Basically similar craft, tailored to a variety of duties, including logistics support, ammunition transport, personnel transport (31 to 75, depending on configuration), and divers' support. Cargo capacity: 80 to 100 tons. Sisters *Wisting* (ØSD 2) and *Viken* (VSD 5) had been stricken by 1-98, and by 1-02, *Tautra* (HM 5, ex-TSD 5) and *Ramnes* (HM 6, ex-ROS 23) were no longer in service. Sister *Arnøy* (HP 9) is rated as a personnel ferry [YFL] (q.v.).

♦ 1 logistics support tender [YF] (In serv. 1969)

HM 7 Kjeøy

D: 190 tons **S:** 10.7 kts **Dim:** 20.90 × . . . × . . . **M:** 1 diesel; . . . bhp

Remarks: Generally similar to the craft of the *Torpen* series. Can carry 80 tons of cargo and 30 passengers.

SERVICE CRAFT *(continued)*

♦ 1 Hysnes-class personnel launch [YFL]
Bldr: . . . (In serv. 1985)

HP 3 Hysnes (ex-*Øysprint*)

Hysnes (HP 3) Eivind Rodlie, 5-00

D: approx. 38 tons (fl) **S:** 32 kts (26 cruise) **Dim:** 15.54 × 4.88 × 1.10
Electronics: Radar: 2 Decca . . . nav.
M: 2 Saab Scania DSI 14 diesels; 2 props; 1,250 bhp
Crew: 2 tot. + 30 passengers

Remarks: Acquired by late 1999. GRP construction. Had been re-engined in 1991.

♦ 1 HP 20–class harbor personnel launch [YFL]

HP 20 Ellida

Remarks: A request for contract tenders for one harbor personnel transport capable of breaking light ice was issued in 3-98; HP 20 was in service by 7-99. Has small bow ramp for mating to a pier, and there is a small crane forward of the passenger cabin, which can seat 24 persons. Can achieve 24 kts. No other data available.

♦ 1 Welding-class personnel launch [YFL]
Bldr: Fjellstrand, Omastrand (In serv. 1-11-74)

HP 8 Welding (ex-ØSD 1)

D: 27.5 tons **S:** 17 kts **Dim:** 16.3 × 5.3 × 1.2
A: 1 12.7-mm mg **Electronics:** Radar: 1 Decca . . . nav.
M: 2 G.M. Detroit Diesel 6V-71 diesels; 2 props; 800 bhp
Crew: 4 tot. + 14 passengers

Remarks: Sister *Brimse* (RSD 23, ex-TSD 1) was stricken during 1998.

♦ 8 miscellaneous personnel launches [YFL]

	In serv.	Kts	Passengers
HP 1 Mågøy (ex-HSD 10)	1989	20	12
HP 2 Fjøløy	1993	16	26
HP 4 Odin (ex-TSD 3, ex-ØSD 6)	1989	17	9
HP 5 Ramnes	1994	12	35 (+ 120 tons cargo)
HP 6 Wisting (ex-*Oscarsborg,* ØSD 11)	1968	9	75
HP 7 Nordep I (ex-ØSD 15)	1987	12.5	60 (+ 6 tons cargo)
HP 9 Arnøy (ex-ØSD 5)	1978	13.5	50
HP 14 Marsteinen (ex-VSD 6)	1994	12	7

Arnøy (HP 9)—with old pennant number H&L Van Ginderen, 10-90

Remarks: HP 9 is a sister to the *Torpen*-series YFs. No data are available for the others, except that HP 6 displaces 23 tons. *Folden* (HP 10, ex-ØSD 10) and *Gleodden* (HP 13, ex-SSD 3) were no longer in service as of 1-01.

♦ 4 miscellaneous rescue launches [YFL]

HR 1 Marinej 1 HR 2 Marinej 2 HR 3 HR 4

Remarks: No data available. Are probably RIBs assigned to shore stations.

♦ 1 torpedo retriever and oil-spill cleanup ship [YPT]
Bldr: Fjellstrand, Hardinger (In serv. 10-78)

HT 1 Vernøy (ex-VSD 1)

Vernøy (HT 1)—with old pennant number Lt. Arild Engelsen, R.Nor.N., 6-87

D: 150 grt **S:** 12 kts **Dim:** 31.30 × 6.67 × 2.00
M: 2 MWM diesels; 2 Schottel azimuthal props; . . . bhp **Crew:** 5 tot.

Remarks: Is also equipped for fire fighting. Has an articulating electrohydraulic crane aft to handle torpedoes.

♦ 1 small torpedo retriever [YPT]
Bldr: P. Høivolds, Kristiansand (In serv. 7-78)

HT 3 Karlsøy (ex-TRSD 4)

Remarks: Can also be employed to transport 87 tons of general cargo and 31 passengers. Capable of 11.5 kts.

♦ 1 large harbor tug [YTB]
Bldr: Haugesund Slip, Haugesund (In serv. 1979)

HS 1 Kvarven (ex-VSD 2, ex-*Oscar Tybring*)

Kvarven (HS 1)—with old pennant number Lt. Arild Engelsen, R.Nor.N., 3-88

D: approx. 170 tons (fl) **S:** 11 kts **Dim:** 22.50 × 6.30 × . . .
M: 1 G.M. Detroit Diesel 16V-149 diesel; 1 prop; 1,175 bhp (900 sust.)

Remarks: 97 grt. Acquired in 1988. Built originally as a rescue ship. Can carry 12 passengers.

♦ 2 miscellaneous medium harbor tugs [YTM]

HS 2 Bogøy (ex-VSD 10) HS 3

Remarks: HS 2 is capable of 10.5 kts and can carry 4 tons of general cargo; completed in 1993. HS 3, built in 1967, can achieve 9 kts. No other data available.

♦ 2 navigational training craft [YXT]
Bldr: Fjellstrand, Omastrand (In serv. 1-78)

P 358 Hessa (ex-*Hitra;* ex-*Marsteinen,* VSD 2)
P 359 Vigra (ex-*Kvarven,* VSD 6)

Hessa (P 358) Eivind Rodlie, 8-99

SERVICE CRAFT *(continued)*

D: 40 tons (fl) **S:** 22 kts **Dim:** 23.20 × 5.00 × 1.10
A: 1 12.7-mm mg **Electronics:** Radar: 1 Decca . . . nav.
M: 2 G.M. 12V71 diesels; 2 props; 1,800 bhp **Crew:** 5 crew + 13 cadets

Remarks: Aluminum construction. For use at the naval academy. Renamed and renumbered in 1981. P 358 was again renamed in 5-87 to free the name for the relic/training tender *Hitra* (HP 15). Gun is not usually mounted.

COAST GUARD
(Kystvakt)

The Norwegian Coast Guard was established in 4-77 to perform fisheries-protection duties, patrol the waters in the vicinity of offshore oil rigs, and maintain surveillance over the 200-n.m. economic zone. The civilian-manned, semiautonomous Fishing Equipment Patrol *(Bruksvakt)* operates smaller units to inspect fishing gear. The Inner Coastal Surveillance System (SIKO) was established 1-1-97.

Bases and Organization: Coast Guard Squadron North is based at Sortland, and Coast Guard Squadron South at Håkonsvern, near Bergen.

Coast Guard Aviation: The Royal Norwegian Air Force operates six WG-13 Lynx Mk 86 helicopters and two Lockheed P-3N Orion maritime patrol aircraft in support of the coast guard. Three additional helicopters are sought.

Norwegian Coast Guard Lynx A. D. Baker III, 4-95

Note: Ships of the Coast Guard proper have W-series pennants, while the Inner Coastal Surveillance System units have pennants in the KV-series. In some instances, a dash connects the "W" and the number in the pennants. All ships and craft carry the word *Kystvakt* (Coast Guard) on their sides. The old 40-mm 60-cal. Mk 3 Bofors AA guns are being replaced by 40-mm 70-cal. Bofors L70 mounts removed from stricken Norwegian Navy units.

PATROL SHIPS [WPS]

♦ 0 (+ 1) Svalbard class
Bldr: Tangen Verft, Krager, division of Langsten Slip & Båtbyggeri A/S, Tomrefjord

	L	In serv.
W 303 Svalbard	2-01	. . .

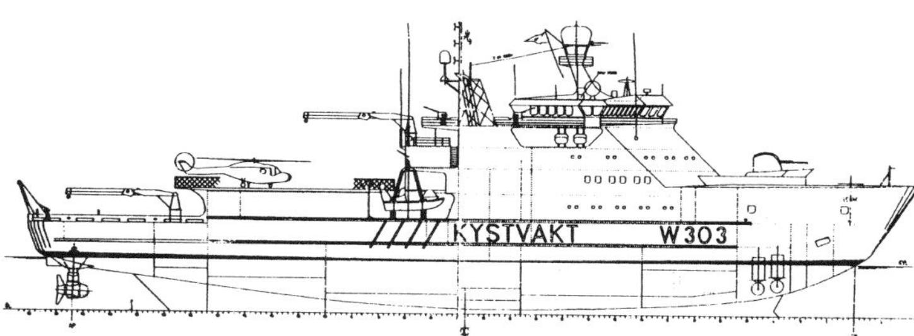

Svalbard (W 303) R.Nor.N., 1996

D: 6,100 tons (fl) **S:** 18 kts (17 sust.) **Dim:** 103.70 × 19.10 × 6.50
A: 1 57-mm 70-cal. Bofors DP; 1 2-round Simbad SAM syst. (Mistral missiles)
Electronics: Radar: . . .
M: 4 diesels, electric drive; 2 CP azimuthal props; 10,700 shp—2 bow tunnel-thrusters
Range: 10,000/13 **Crew:** 56 tot.

Remarks: Ordered 7-1-00. Intended for northern service and was to have an ice-breaker hull able to break 1-m ice. Has a helicopter deck and hangar and passive tank stabilization. Will be operated with two crews to ensure maximum sea time. Will employ an EDO combat system like that being backfitted to the *Norkapp* class.

♦ 3 Norkapp (Type 320) class

	Bldr	L	In serv.
W 320 Norkapp	Bergens Mek. Verksted, Bergen	2-4-80	25-4-81
W 321 Senja	Horten Verft, Horten	16-3-80	8-3-81
W 322 Andennes	Haugesund Verksted, Haugesund	21-3-81	30-1-82

D: 2,201 tons light (3,276 fl) **S:** 23 kts **Dim:** 105.00 (97.50 pp) × 13.85 × 4.55
A: 1 57-mm 70-cal. Bofors DP; 1 2-round Simbad SAM system (Mistral missiles); 3 single 20-mm 90-cal. Rheinmetall AA; 1 d.c. rack (6 d.c.); 1 WG-13 Lynx helicopter—provision for 2 triple 324-mm Mk 32 Mod. 5 ASW TT

Norkapp (W 320) M. Bonnin, 7-99

Andennes (W 322) Eivind Rodlie, 10-99

Electronics:
Radar: 2 Decca TM 1226 nav.; 1 Decca RM 914 nav.; 1 Plessey AWS-4 air search; 1 CelsiusTech 9LV 218 f.c.
Sonar: Simrad SS105 hull-mounted MF (14 kHz)
EW: . . . . . . intercept; 2 . . . decoy RL
EO: Thorn-EMI SM 8312 infrared surveillance syst.
M: 4 Wichmann 9-AXAG diesels; 2 CP props; 14,400 bhp
Electric: 1,600 kw tot. **Range:** 7,500/15 **Fuel:** 350 tons
Crew: 42 ship's company + 6 helicopter crew (109 tot. accomm.)

Remarks: Program was delayed by design changes and lack of funding; four additional units were canceled. W 321 was used in trials of a two-crew operational concept in 1994–95.
Hull systems: Carry three 300-m^3/hr water cannon for fire fighting and have meteorological reporting gear. Have fin stabilizers. Carry one UFAS Sjøbjørn 25–class, aluminum-hulled, rigid inflatable personnel launch powered by a 350-bhp Yanmar 6LY-UTE diesel driving a Hamilton 273 waterjet for speeds up to 33 kts. Also have one Yanmar Searaider (85 bhp outboard) rigid inflatable inspection boat.
Combat systems: In time of conflict, six Penguin Mk 2 antiship missiles can be added. The Kongsberg MSI-80S NAVKIS data system with MFC 2000S display consoles is fitted. The weapons-control system was updated in 1996–97 by adding the Thorn-EMI Marine Electro-Optical Surveillance System (MEOSS). The Simbad point-defense SAM launch position is mounted on a raised pedestal in place of the starboard aft 20-mm mounting atop the hangar.
Modernization: EDO is supplying a new command-and-control system for the class under a 7-98 contract; included are a DRS Technologies SPS-67(V)3 surface-search radar, IFF system, integrated E/O f.c. and surveillance sensor, hull-mounted sonar, and integrated bridge control and display suite. The combat data system will employ 4–6 multifunction display consoles. Installations were to begin during 2001.

♦ 1 Tromsø-class leased fisheries patrol vessel
Bldr: Naval Shipyard Gdynia, Gdynia, Poland (In serv. 4-96)

W 313 Tromsø

Tromsø (W 313) Eivind Rodlie, 10-99

D: 2,100 tons (fl) **S:** 17 kts **Dim:** 70.0 (51.40 pp) × 12.40 × 5.50
A: 1 40-mm 70-cal. Bofors L70 AA **Electronics:** Radar: 2 . . . nav.
M: 1 . . . diesel; 1 CP prop; 3,600 bhp—690-shp azimuthal bow thruster—400-shp stern side-thruster
Electric: 2,100 kw tot. (1 × 1,000-kw shaft generator, 2 × 500-kw diesel sets, 1 × 100-kw emergency diesel set)
Range: . . ./. . . **Fuel:** 400 m^3
Crew: 5 officers, 10 enlisted, 5 civilians (26 tot. accomm.)

COAST GUARD PATROL SHIPS [WPS] *(continued)*

Remarks: Ordered 11-95 and operated under 10-year charter (with option to purchase after 5 years) from Tromsø Dampskibsselskab, using owner's crews in part. Has two crews. Intended to operate around northern Norway; has an ice-strengthened hull and helicopter deck. An 800-m^3-total oil recovery/seawater ballast tankage system is included, and the ship is equipped for fire fighting. Carries 150 m^3 of fresh water. Equipped with a rigid inflatable boarding boat and an inspection launch and has a 3.5-ton-capacity (at 12-m radius) electrohydraulic crane aft. Has an environmental cover for the 40-mm gun.

♦ 1 Ålesund-class leased fisheries patrol vessel
Bldr: Myklebust Mek. Verksted, Gurskebotn (In serv. 4-96)

W 312 Ålesund

Ålesund (W 312) Peter Voss, 7-01

D: 1,470 tons (fl) **S:** 18 kts **Dim:** 63.20 (57.00 pp) × 11.50 × 4.67
A: 1 40-mm 70-cal. Bofors L70 AA
Electronics: Radar: 1 . . . nav.; 1 . . . nav.
M: 1 Wichmann 8V28B diesel; 1 Wichmann PR 82/4I CP prop; 3,600 bhp—bow- and stern-thrusters
Electric: . . . kw tot. (1,440-kw main shaft generator, 2 × . . .-kw emergency sets)
Range: 20,600/13 **Endurance:** 200 days
Crew: 5 officers, 15 enlisted, 3 civilians (32 tot. accomm.)

Remarks: Ordered 11-95 and operated under 10-year charter (with option to purchase after 5 years) from Remøy Shipping. Construction contracted to Myklebust Mek. Verksted, which subcontracted the forward portion of hull to Voldnes Skipsverft and the stern to Ulstein Vannylven. Has a stern-haul trawler hullform with bulbous forefoot. Uses two alternating crews. Helicopter facilities are fitted. Two semi-rigid inflatable inspection boats are carried, with the Springer 25 to port capable of 36 kts and a 120 n.m. range on its Hamilton waterjet propulsion system; both are handled by an electrohydraulic crane. Has a 37-ton-bollard-pull hydraulic towing winch. There is an 800-ton-capacity spilled oil recovery tank. The crew is berthed in 12 single and 10 two-person cabins.

♦ 1 leased fisheries patrol vessel
Bldr: Mjellem & Karlsen A/S, Bergen (In serv. 1967)

W 318 Nysleppen (ex-*Strill Guard,* ex-*Optinor,* ex-*Hydrograf*)

D: approx. 500 tons (fl) **S:** 13.2 kts **Dim:** 38.97 × 7.83 × 2.94
A: 1 40-mm 60-cal. Mk 3 Bofors AA
M: 1 8-cyl. Caterpillar diesel; 1 prop; 800 bhp—bow-thruster
Electric: 100 kw (2 × 50-kw diesel sets)
Range: 3,100/13 **Fuel:** 38 tons **Endurance:** 10 days **Crew:** . . .

Remarks: 343 grt/351 dwt. Chartered 8-97 from Egil Arne Petterson, Hammerfest. Carries a RIB inspection dinghy to port and an elderly lifeboat to starboard. Has a crow's-nest lookout position.

♦ 1 leased hydrographic research vessel
Bldr: Sterkoder Mek. Verksted, Kristiansund (In serv. 1978)

W 311 Lance

Lance (W 311) Mike Louagie, 10-88

D: approx. 2,200 tons (fl) **S:** 14 kts **Dim:** 60.71 (53.57 pp) × 12.65 × 5.70
M: 1 MaK 9M453AK, 9-cyl. diesel; 1 CP prop; 3,200 bhp
Electric: 1,240 kw tot. (1 × 640-kw, 2 × 300-kw diesel sets)
Crew: 12 naval, 5 civilians

Remarks: 1,162 grt/975 dwt. Leased from the Mapping Agency of the Norwegian Ministry of the Environment for 10 months each year, beginning in 1994; during the other two months, serves as a hydrographic research vessel. Used on fisheries patrol and as a supply vessel. Built as a stern-haul fishing trawler and acquired 6-80 by the Ministry of the Environment. Has an ice-strengthened hull and is equipped with one 10-ton derrick. When on coast guard service, may be armed with one 40-mm 60-cal. Mk 3 Bofors gun.

♦ 1 leased stern-haul purse seiner
Bldr: Brødrene Lothes, Haugesund (In serv. 7-78)

W 317 Lafjord

Lafjord (W 317) Lt. Arild Engelsen, R.Nor.N., 2-88

D: approx. 1,800 tons (fl) **S:** 14.5 kts **Dim:** 55.40 (48.11 pp) × 9.86 × 6.18
A: 1 40-mm 60-cal. Mk 3 Bofors AA **Electronics:** Radar: . . .
M: 1 Wichmann 7AXA diesel; 1 prop; 2,100 bhp
Electric: 419 kw tot. (2 × 160-kw, 1 × 99-kw diesel sets)
Range: 7,700/14.5 **Fuel:** 189.5 tons heavy oil, 36 tons diesel **Crew:** . . . tot.

Remarks: 814 grt/1,000 dwt. Chartered in 1980 from K/S Lafjord & Co., Bergen. Has side-thrusters fore and aft and an ice-strengthened hull.

Note: Also in use is W 316, name not available, a large, modern stern-haul trawler with a single 40-mm AA forward; no further information is yet available.

♦ 1 leased stern-haul purse seiner
Bldr: Smedvik Mek. Verksted A/S, Tjørvåg (In serv. 4-78)

W 315 Nordsjøbas

Nordsjøbas (W 315) H&L Van Ginderen, 3-97

D: approx. 1,780 tons (fl) **S:** 13.5 kts **Dim:** 52.05 (44.73 pp) × 10.01 × 6.37
A: 1 40-mm 60-cal. Mk 3 Bofors AA **Electronics:** Radar: . . .
M: 1 MaK 6M453AK diesel; 1 CP prop; 2,400 bhp
Electric: 920 kw tot. (1 × 752-kw, 1 × 168-kw diesel sets)
Range: 8,300/13.5 **Fuel:** 180 tons **Crew:** . . . tot.

Remarks: 814 grt/1,087 dwt. Chartered in 1980 from Nordsjøbas A/S, Ålesund. Has side-thrusters fore and aft.

♦ 1 leased purse seiner
Bldr: Beliard, Crighton & Cie., Ostend, Belgium (In serv. 1955)

W 314 Stålbas (ex-*Trålbas,* ex-*Commandant Charcot,* ex-*Jean Charcot*)

Stålbas (W 314) Lt. Arild Engelsen, R.Nor.N., 2-88

COAST GUARD PATROL SHIPS [WPS] *(continued)*

D: approx. 1,400 tons (fl) **S:** 12 kts **Dim:** 58.76 (52.43 pp) × 9.43 × 4.64
A: 1 40-mm 60-cal. Mk 3 Bofors AA **Electronics:** Radar: . . .
M: 1 Wärtsilä Vasa 12V22 diesel; 1 CP prop; 2,180 bhp
Electric: 816 kw tot. (3 × 272-kw diesel sets) **Range:** . . ./. . . **Crew:** . . . tot.

Remarks: 913 grt/472 dwt. On charter from Remøy Management, Ålesund. Side-thrusters are fitted fore and aft. Originally built as a trawler.

Disposal note: Former naval fisheries protection ship *Nornen* (W 300) was retired during 2000.

AUXILIARIES

♦ **1 H. U. Sverdrup II–class ocean surveillance ship [WAGI]**
Bldr: Kaldnes Industrier A/S, Tønsberg (completed by Sigbj. Iversen A/S, Flekkefjord, 6-90)

H. U. Sverdrup II

H. U. Sverdrup II H&L Van Ginderen, 9-90

D: 1,387 grt **S:** . . . kts **Dim:** 55.00 × 13.00 × 5.38
M: 1 Bergens 8-cyl. diesel; 1 prop; 2,000 bhp

Remarks: Operated for the Forsvarets Forskingsinstitut (Military Research Institute) by the coast guard. White hull, red pilothouse and masts, red-blue-red diagonal hull stripe. Equipped with Marisat satellite communications equipment, stern-haul trawl equipment, and a large oceanographic crane aft. Russian official sources have referred to this ship (probably erroneously) as an intelligence collector.

INNER COASTAL SURVEILLANCE SYSTEM

An organization formed on 1-1-97 to provide closer-in patrol of Norwegian offshore interests. Its unarmed ships and craft carry the word *Kystvakt* on their sides, and the organization is subordinate to the main coast guard.

	In serv.	Tonnage
KV 1 Titran	1992	184 grt
KV 2 Kongsøy	1958	331 grt
KV 3 Sture Gøran	1969	193 grt
KV 4 Ice Lady	1959	442 grt
KV 5 Agder	1974	140 grt
KV 6 Garsøy	1988	195 grt
KV 7 Åhav	1987	50 grt

Garsøy (KV 6) Eivind Rodlie, 6-01

Remarks: KV 6 can make 20 kts on two 1,142-bhp Deutz-MWM TBD 04 V8 diesels and is 34.00 (o.a.) × 6.00 × 1.80 m (KV 1 is similar); the ship has one X-band and one S-band navigational radar. KV 7 can reach 25 kts on two 1,100-bhp G.M. diesels and is 27.00 (o.a.) × 5.80 × 1.50 m.

Åhav (KV 7) H&L Van Ginderen, 8-99

FISHING EQUIPMENT PATROL
(Bruksvakt)

Also subordinated to the coast guard is the unarmed Fishing Equipment Patrol, which operates eight chartered former fishing craft and oilfield support craft, all repainted a uniform naval gray:

	In serv.	Tonnage
KV 21 Polarvakt	1965	290 grt
KV 22 Barentshav	1957	318 grt
KV 23 Norvakt	1959	197 grt
KV 24 Lofothav	1954	271 grt
KV 25 Sjøveien	1966	339 grt
KV 27 Sjøfareren	1966	180 grt
KV 28 Nysleppen	1967	343 grt

Norvakt (KV 23) H&L Van Ginderen, 8-99

Sjøfareren (KV 27) A. A. de Kruijf, 4-00

Remarks: KV 27 can make 12 kts on her one G.M. 16V149 TI, 1,200-bhp diesel and is 28.36 × 7.71 × 3.70 m. *Havkyst* (KV 26) had left the service by 1-1-01.

MINISTRY OF THE ENVIRONMENT

(Kystverket)

The Ministry of the Environment has a fleet of seven ships and craft operated by its own personnel: *Sjøtroll* (80 tons, in serv. 1976), *Johan Hjort* (2,000 tons, in serv. 12-90), the tug/supply vessel *Geofjord* (1,615 grt, ex-*Aldona,* acquired 11-91 as an oil-spill recovery ship), and the pollution-control tenders *Oljevern 01* through *Oljevern 04* (completed in 1978, 200 tons, with crews of 2 officers and 6 unlicensed personnel each). A new oceanographic and seismic research ship was ordered from Flekkefjord in 12-00 for delivery in 2003 to the National Oceanographic Institute.

OMAN

Sultanate of Oman

ROYAL NAVY OF OMAN

Personnel (2002): Approx. 4,500 total, plus about 1,300 civilian employees. All personnel are volunteers.

Bases: Headquarters at Muaskar al Murtafa'a. The principal base is at Qa'Adat Said bin Sultan Albahria Base, Wudam, with lesser facilities at Minah Rasyut and Jazorat Ghanam, Musandam. The Wudam facility was placed under foreign commercial management in 1998 under a five-year contract that is also intended to expand shipbuilding and repair facilities at the base.

Maritime Aviation: Two Royal Omani Air Force Dornier Do-228-100 light maritime surveillance aircraft are used for coastal patrol. Air force Super Puma and Sea King helicopters can land aboard platforms on several of the larger ships. Two AgustaWestland Super Lynx 300 helicopters were ordered for shipboard use on 11-1-02.

Note: Ship and craft names are prefixed RNOV (Royal Navy of Oman Vessel).

CORVETTES [FFL]

Note: As many as three offshore patrol vessels may be ordered to enter service by 2005 to improve further Oman's ability to control its territorial waters.

♦ **2 Vigilance class (Project Muheet)**
Bldr: Vosper Thornycroft, Woolston, Southampton, U.K.

	Laid down	L	In serv.
Q 31 Qahir al Amwaj	17-5-93	21-9-94	3-9-96
Q 32 Al Mua'zzar	4-4-94	26-9-95	26-11-96 (accepted)

Qahir al Amwaj (Q 31) Brian Morrison, 2-01

Al Mua'zzar (Q 32) Omani Navy, 1998

D: 1,185 tons (1,450 fl) **S:** 31 kts **Dim:** 83.70 (78.50 pp) × 11.50 × 3.50 (hull)
A: 8 MM 40 Exocet Block 2 SSM; 1 8-round Crotale NG SAM syst. (16 Crotale VT-1 missiles); 1 76-mm 62-cal. OTOBreda SuperRapid DP; 2 single 20-mm 90-cal. Oerlikon GAM-B01 AA; 2 single 7.62-mm mg
Electronics:
Radar: 1 Kelvin-Hughes Type 1007 nav.; 1 Thales MW-08 3-D surf./air search; 1 Thales Castor-IIJ MRR (TRS-5204) f.c.; 1 Thales Sting f.c.
Sonar: see remarks
EW: Thales DR-3000S1 Compact intercept (1–18 GHz); Furuno FD527 comms D/F; 2 12-round Wallop SuperBarricade decoy RL
E/O: Thales IRSCAN surveillance/tracking

Qahir al Amwaj (Q 31) John Mortimer, 2-01

M: 4 Crossley–SEMT-Pielstick 16 PA6 V280 STC diesels; 2 KaMeWa CP props; 32,000 bhp (28,160 sust.)
Electric: 1,200 kw tot. (3 × 400-kw MTU RV183 TF51 diesel-powered sets; 1 × 70-kw MTU 6V 183 AA51 diesel emergency set)
Range: 5,500/12 **Fuel:** 156 tons **Crew:** 14 officers, 62 enlisted (accomm.)

Remarks: Ordered 5-4-92. Names mean "Conqueror of the Waves" and "The Supported," respectively. Q 31 departed for Oman 18-6-96 and Q 32 on 20-3-97. Are being operated with crews totaling around 60 each.
Hull systems: Have fin stabilizers. The aluminum alloy superstructure is shaped to reduce radar signature and has been coated with radar-absorbent materials. Stack has an infrared-suppressant system. Have a helicopter deck but no hangar. Carry 19 tons of fresh water.
Combat systems: Have the Thales SEWACO-FD combat system (based on the TACTICOS C2 system). The Thales SINCOS communications suite is fitted. The Sting radar-E/O gun director incorporates radar, laser rangefinder, and low-light-level t.v. sensors. Planned installation of a towed active linear sonar array and two sets of ASW torpedo tubes did not take place, and the ships have no ASW capability.

PATROL SHIPS [PS]

♦ **1 Al Mabrukah class** Bldr: Brooke Marine, Lowestoft, U.K.

	L	In serv.
Q 30 Al Mabrukah (ex-A 1, ex-*Al Said*)	7-4-70	1971

Al Mabrukah (Q 30) Omani Navy, 1996

D: 785 tons (930 fl) **S:** 17 kts **Dim:** 61.47 (55.63 pp) × 10.70 × 3.05
A: 1 40-mm 70-cal. Bofors AA; 2 single 20-mm 90-cal. RO-Oerlikon GAM-B01 AA
Electronics:
Radar: 1 Decca TM 1226 nav.; 1 Decca . . . nav.
EW: Racal Cutlass radar intercept; 2 9-round Wallop Barricade decoy RL
M: 2 Paxman Ventura 12YJCM diesels; 2 props; 2,580 bhp
Electric: 50 kw tot. (2 × 250-kw diesel sets)
Crew: 11 officers, 23 enlisted + 37 passengers/trainees

Remarks: 990 grt/290 dwt. Renamed and converted from royal yacht to fleet training ship at builders, 1-83 to 4-84; received new accommodations arrangements, communications suite, and armament and the helicopter deck was enlarged. Had increasingly been used on patrol duties and was formally redesignated as a "corvette" in 1997.

GUIDED-MISSILE PATROL CRAFT [PTG]

♦ **4 Province class** Bldr: Vosper Thornycroft, Portchester, U.K.

	Laid down	L	In serv.
B 10 Dhofar	30-9-80	14-10-81	7-8-82
B 11 Al Sharquiyah	10-81	2-12-82	5-12-83
B 12 Al Bat'nah	9-12-81	11-82	18-1-84
B 14 Mussandam	8-10-87	19-3-88	31-3-89

Al Bat'nah (B 12) French Navy, 1995

GUIDED-MISSILE PATROL CRAFT [PTG] *(continued)*

Mussandam (B 14) French Navy, 4-93

D: 311 tons light (394 fl) **S:** 40 kts **Dim:** 56.70 (52.00 pp) × 8.20 × 2.40 (hull)
A: 6 or 8 MM 40 Exocet SSM; 1 76-mm 62-cal. OTOBreda Compact DP; 1 twin 40-mm 70-cal. OTOBreda AA; 2 single 12.7-mm mg
Electronics:
Radar: B 11: 1 Decca 1226 nav.; 1 Plessey AWS-4 air search—others: 1 Decca TM 1226 nav.; 1 Plessey AWS-6 air search; 1 CelsiusTech 9LV 300 f.c. syst.
EW: Racal 242 suite (Cutlass intercept, Scorpion jammer, Sadie processor); 2 9-round Wallop Barricade decoy RL
M: 4 Paxman Valenta 18RP200 diesels; 4 props; 17,900 bhp (15,000 sust.)—2 80-hp electric outdrives
Electric: 420 kw tot. **Range:** 2,000/15 **Fuel:** 45.5 tons
Crew: 5 officers, 40 enlisted + 14 trainees

Remarks: B 10 was ordered in 1980, B 11 and B 12 in 1-81, and B 14 on 3-1-86. B 10 sailed for Oman 21-10-82. Similar ships are operated by Egypt and Kenya, and the U.S. Navy has acquired 14 variants of the design with greatly reduced armament.
Combat systems: B 10 has the Sperry Sea Archer Mk 2 gun fire-control system, with two optical trackers. The other three can carry eight MM 40 Exocets in two sets of four but usually carry only six; they also have the CelsiusTech 9LV 300 f.c.s. with I-band search radar and J-band radar/electro-optical fire-control director forward and a separate t.v./IR director aft for the 40-mm AA. The Exocet launchers have now been "boxed-in" with metal heat shielding.

PATROL CRAFT [PC]

♦ 3 Vigilante 400 class (Project Mawj)
Bldr: CMN, Cherbourg

	Laid down	L	In serv.
B 1 Al Bushra	16-2-94	14-3-95	15-6-95
B 2 Al Mansoor	12-4-94	3-5-94	10-8-95
B 3 Al Najah	27-6-94	5-3-96	5-96

Al Najah (B 3) Ralph Edwards, 2-01

Al Najah (B 3) Brian Morrison, 2-01

D: 373 tons (477 fl) **S:** 24 kts (22 sust.)
Dim: 54.50 (50.00) × 8.00 (7.70 wl) × 2.54
A: 1 76-mm 62-cal. OTOBreda Compact DP; 2 single 20-mm 90-cal. RO-Oerlikon GAM-B01 AA; 2 single 12.7-mm M2 mg
Electronics:
Radar: 1 Kelvin-Hughes Type 1007 ARPA nav.
E/O: CelsiusTech 9LV 207 optronic director
M: 2 MTU 16V538 TB93 diesels; 2 CP props; 8,400 bhp
Electric: 360 kw tot. (3 × 120 kw) **Range:** 2,400/15 **Fuel:** 73 tons
Endurance: 15 days **Crew:** 3 officers, 21 enlisted + 20 passengers

Remarks: Ordered 1-9-93; another five to be equipped with ASW weapons and sensors were proposed but not ordered. Names repeat those of the stricken 37.5-m-class patrol boats. Fitting out was completed at the Royal Dockyard, Muscat. First two arrived in Oman 28-9-95, B 3 on 29-6-96. Have two 35-m³ cargo holds.
Combat systems: The 76-mm guns were to have been taken from the gunboats of the Brooke Marine 37.5-m class, but new mounts were instead provided to replace the French 40-mm mountings installed at launch. Provision was made for later installation of up to eight MM 15 short-range antiship missiles, four fixed 324-mm ASW torpedo tubes, and the Thales ATAS towed active sonar array, but the plan to give them an ASW capability has been canceled. Also omitted was the planned Thales DR-3000S1 Compact intercept system and two 9-round Wallop Barricade decoy rocket launchers.

PATROL BOATS [PB]

♦ 4 Al Seeb class
Bldr: Vosper Pty, Singapore (In serv. 15-3-81)

B 20 Al Seeb B 21 Al Shinas B 22 Al Sadah B 23 Al Khasab

Al Seeb (B 20) Omani Navy, 1996

D: 60.7 tons (75 fl) **S:** 26 kts **Dim:** 25.00 (23.00 pp) × 5.80 × 1.50
A: 1 20-mm 90-cal. Oerlikon GAM-B01 AA; 2 single 7.62-mm mg
Electronics: Radar: 1 Decca 1226 nav.
M: 2 MTU 12V331 TC92 diesels, plus 1 Cummins N855M cruise diesel (197 bhp); 3 props; 3,072 bhp
Range: 750/14; 2,300/8 **Crew:** 13 tot.

Remarks: Ordered 24-4-81. Craft had been completed in 1980 on speculation by builder. Glass-reinforced plastic hulls. Have five spare berths. Maximum speed on cruise diesel is 8 kts.

AMPHIBIOUS WARFARE SHIPS AND CRAFT

Note: The large troop and vehicle transport *Fulk al Salamah* is subordinated to the Royal Yacht Squadron (q.v.).

♦ 1 Nasr al Bahr–class landing ship [LST]
Bldr: Brooke Marine, Lowestoft, U.K.

	L	In serv.
L 2 Nasr al Bahr	16-5-84	13-2-85

Nasr al Bahr (L 2) French Navy, 3-95

D: 2,500 tons (fl) **S:** 15.5 kts **Dim:** 93.00 (80.00 pp) × 15.50 × 2.3 (mean)
A: 2 twin 40-mm 70-cal. OTOBreda Dardo AA; 2 single 20-mm 90-cal. Oerlikon GAM-B01 AA
Electronics:
Radar: 1 Decca 1226 nav.; 1 Decca 1290 nav.
EW: . . . intercept; 2 18-round Wallop Super Barricade decoy RL
M: 2 Paxman Valenta 18RP200CM diesels; 2 CP props; 7,800 bhp
Range: 4,000/13 **Endurance:** 28 days (10 with troops)
Crew: 13 officers, 16 chief petty officers, 52 other enlisted + 240 troops: 13 officers, 16 noncommissioned officers, 211 other enlisted

Remarks: Ordered 18-3-82. Two sisters were built for Algeria. Name means "Sea Lion."
Hull systems: Vehicle deck is 75 × 7.4 m, with a 30 × 7–m cargo hatch; bow ramp is 18 m long by 4.5 m wide and stern ramp is 5 × 4 m. Intended to land 450 tons of cargo or seven main battle tanks on a gradient of up to 1:40. Two Sea Truck LCVPs carried. Has a helicopter deck for one Sea King/Commando or Super Puma helicopter. A traveling 16-ton crane spans the cargo deck forward. Max. cargo: 650 tons. A new, taller funnel was fitted during a 1997 refit.
Combat systems: Has the CelsiusTech 9LV 200 weapons-control system with one Matra Défense Lynx electro-optical gun director. Carries 2,000 rounds of 40-mm and 2,450 rounds of 20-mm ammunition and 244 chaff rounds.

Disposal note: Logistic support landing ship *Al Munassir* (L 1), placed in reserve during the mid-1990s, is no longer considered to be a reactivatable asset.

AMPHIBIOUS WARFARE SHIPS AND CRAFT *(continued)*

♦ 3 Saba al Bahr–class utility landing craft [LCU]
Bldr: Vosper Pty, Singapore

	Laid down	L	In serv.
L 8 Saba al Bahr	. . .	30-6-81	17-9-81
L 9 Al Doghas	9-7-82	12-11-82	10-1-83
L 10 Al Temsah	8-9-82	15-12-82	12-2-83

Al Temsah (L 10) Omani Navy, 1996

D: 230 tons (fl) **S:** 8 kts **Dim:** 33.0 (27.84 pp) × 8.18 × 1.51
A: none **Electronics:** Radar: 1 Furuno 701 nav.
M: 2 Caterpillar 3408TA diesels; 2 props; 762 bhp
Electric: 180 kw tot. **Range:** 1,800/8 **Crew:** 11 tot.

Remarks: L 8: 170 grt/100 dwt; L 9, 10: 191 grt/155 dwt. The first was ordered 24-4-81, the others in 7-82. Cargo: 100 tons of vehicles or stores, or 45 tons of deck cargo plus 50 tons of fresh water (and 35 tons of water ballast). L 8 is 30.00 m o.a./24.85 pp. Pennant numbers were changed from C-series to L-series in 2000.

♦ 1 landing craft [LCM]
Bldr: Lewis Offshore, Stornaway, Scotland (In serv. 1979)

L 7 Al Neemran

Al Neemran (L 7) Omani Navy, 1994

D: approx. 140 tons (fl) **S:** 8 kts (7 loaded) **Dim:** 25.5 × 7.4 × 1.8
A: none **Electronics:** Radar: 1 Furuno . . . nav.
M: 2 . . . diesels; 2 props; 300 bhp **Crew:** 6 tot.

Remarks: 85 dwt. Cargo: approx. 75 tons. Pennant changed from C 7 to L 7 in 2000.

AUXILIARIES

♦ 1 dry cargo ship [AK]
Bldr: Scheepswerf G. Bijlsma & Zn. B.V., Wartena, the Netherlands

	L	In serv.
S 2 Al Sultana (ex-A 2)	18-5-75	4-6-75

D: approx. 1,700 tons (fl) **S:** 11.25 kts **Dim:** 65.69 (59.90 pp) × 10.83 × 4.13
A: none **Electronics:** Radar: 1 Decca TM 1226 nav.
M: 1 Mirrlees-Blackstone ESL8 Mk 2 diesel; 1,120 bhp
Electric: 192 kw tot. (2 × 76-kw, 1 × 40-kw diesel sets)
Fuel: 82.5 tons **Crew:** 20 tot.

Remarks: 909 grt/1,495 dwt. A traveling 1-ton crane straddles the 33.6 × 7.7–m hatch to one continuous 40.4-m-long hold. Was replaced in the training role by *Al Mabrukah* (Q 30). Refitted 1992 and given a new pennant number in 1997.

Al Sultana (S 2) Carlo Martinelli, 4-97

SERVICE CRAFT

♦ 1 Sea Truck–type divers' support launch [YDT]
Bldr: Rotork, U.K. (In serv. 1991)

R 1

D: 13 tons (fl) **S:** 20 kts **Dim:** 18.0 × 3.8 × 1.1
A: 2 single 7.62-mm mg **Electronics:** Radar: none
M: 2 Volvo Penta AQD70D diesels; 2 props; 430 bhp **Crew:** 4 tot.

Remarks: Supports combat swimmers rather than hard-hat divers. Sister *Zahra 27* serves the Royal Oman Police.

♦ 11 miscellaneous workboats [YFL]
Bldr: Cheverton, Cowes, U.K. (In serv. 4-75)

W 4 W 5 W 7 through W 11 WF 41 through WF 44

D: 3.5 tons **S:** 25 kts **Dim:** 8.28 × 2.7 × 0.8 **M:** 2 diesels

Remarks: WF 41 through WF 44 are 12.0 m overall and displace about 5.5 tons (fl).

♦ 1 inshore survey craft [YGS] Bldr: Watercraft, U.K. (In serv. 4-81)

H 1 Al Rahmanniya

Al Rahmanniya (H 1) Omani Navy, 1996

D: 23.6 tons (fl) **S:** 13.5 kts **Dim:** 15.5 (14.0 pp) × 4.0 × 12.5
Electronics: Radar: 1 Decca 101 nav.
M: 2 Volvo TMD 120A diesels; 2 props; 520 bhp **Electric:** 25 kVA
Range: 500/12 **Crew:** 10 tot.

Remarks: Glass-reinforced plastic construction. Raytheon DE 719B and Kelvin-Hughes MS 48 echo sounders, a Decca DMU transponder and Sea Fix receiver, and a Hewlett-Packard 9815A data-storage computer are fitted.

Note: Two small U.S. Navy survey launches from the survey ship *Harkness* (T-AGS 32) were left in Oman during 11-92 but do not seem to have been put into service.

♦ 1 or more Sea Flash radio-controlled target boats [YGT]
Bldr: Flight Refuelling, U.K. (In serv. 1987)

♦ 2 PushyCat 1500–class small tugs [YTL]
Bldr: Scheepswerf Damen B.V., Gorinchem, the Netherlands (In serv. 1990)

T 2 T 3

Remarks: Dimensions: 15.0 × 4.75 × 1.90. Sister T 1 was lost overboard on delivery voyage and was replaced by T 3.

SERVICE CRAFT *(continued)*

PushyCat tug T 3 Hartmut Ehlers, 10-92

♦ **1 sail-training craft [YTS]**
Bldr: Hard & MacKenzie, Buckie, Scotland (In serv. 1971)

S 1 Shabab Oman (ex-*Captain Scott*)

Shabab Oman (S 1) Carlo Martinelli, 7-94

D: 386 tons (fl) **S:** 10 kts (on diesels) **Dim:** 43.90 × 8.59 × 4.65
M: 2 Gardner 8-cyl. diesels; 2 props; 460 bhp
Crew: 5 officers, 15 enlisted + 3 officer/instructors, 24 trainees

Remarks: 264 grt. Three-masted, wooden-hulled barkentine, purchased in 1977 in the U.K. for training Omani youth in seamanship; commissioned in 1979. Operated by the navy for the Ministry of Youth Affairs. Name means "Youth of Oman."

Disposal note: Brooke Marine 37.5-m patrol craft *Al Wafi* (B 4) and *Al Fulk* (B 5) were placed in reserve in 1995 with the intent of reactivating the pair eventually for use as training craft; the plan did not come to fruition, and the craft are now probably beyond reclamation. Their sisters *Al Mujahid* (B 6) and *Al Jabhar* (B 7) were stricken during 1994.

ROYAL YACHT SQUADRON

Note: An entirely separate organization from the navy, the Royal Yacht Squadron bases its ships at Mina al Qaboos. In addition to the two large, modern units below, the squadron also operates the elegant wooden-hulled, three-masted, lateen-rigged sailing dhow *Zinat al Bihar.*

♦ **1 royal yacht [WAG]** Bldr: C.N. Picchiotti, Viareggio, Italy (In serv. 7-82)

Al Said

Al Said Peter Voss, 9-94

D: 3,250 tons (fl) **S:** 18 kts **Dim:** 103.82 (85.91 pp) × 16.24 × 4.72
Electronics: 1 Decca TM 1226C nav.; 1 Decca ACS 1230C nav.
M: 2 GMT A420.6L diesels; 2 CP props; 8,400 hp—bow-thruster
Electric: 2,142 kw tot. (3 × 714-kw diesel sets) **Crew:** 16 officers, 140 enlisted

Remarks: 4,442 grt/1,320 dwt. Replaced former *Al Said* (now training ship *Al Mabrukah* [Q 30]). Has a helicopter pad aft, VHF SATCOM, and fin stabilizers. Carries one Rotork LCVP and three Puma-C-class personnel launches.

♦ **1 troop and vehicle transport [WAP]**
Bldr: Bremer-Vulkan, Bremen-Vegesack, Germany

	Laid down	L	In serv.
Fulk al Salamah (ex-*Ghubat al Salamah,* ex-*Tulip*)	17-1-86	29-8-86	3-4-87

Fulk al Salamah French Navy, 7-96

D: approx. 10,000 tons (fl) **S:** 19.5 kts **Dim:** 136.33 (125.02 pp) × 21.04 × 5.30
A: none **Electronics:** Radar: 2 Decca . . . nav.
M: 4 G.M.T. A420.6 diesels; 2 CP props; 16,800 bhp
Electric: 3,780 kw tot. (3 × 1,260-kw diesel sets)
Range: . . . . **Crew:** . . .

Remarks: 10,864-grt/5,186-nrt combination attack transport/logistic support vessel. Has VHF SATCOM equipment, a hangar and flight deck for two AS.332C Super Puma transport helicopters, two Sea Truck landing craft in davits below the helicopter deck, a large cargo hold forward with a 22.4 × 7.0–m hatch, accommodations for at least 240 troops, and a large vehicle loading door to starboard (plus four personnel/stores doors through the hull sides). *Tulip* was the cover name assigned while the ship was building. Was attached to UNESCO during 1991 as an "investigation ship."

ROYAL OMAN POLICE

Bases: Principal base at Mina al Qaboos, with craft also stationed at Sidab

Aviation: Two Pilatus Porter light transports for search-and-rescue duties, delivered in 4-84

Note: Some 15 new patrol boats from 11 to 15 m in length were to have been ordered in 1996 but had not been delivered as of 6-99; these may be intended for fisheries protection duties, a responsibility that may be transferred from the Royal Omani Navy to the police, but most of the existing patrol boat inventory is in need of replacement.

PATROL BOATS [WPB]

♦ **2 Type D 59116, GRP-hulled**
Bldr: Yokohama Yacht, Japan (In serv. 1988)

Dheeb al Bahar II Dheeb al Bahar III

Dheeb al Bahar II and Dheeb al Bahar III Hartmut Ehlers, 10-92

D: 65 tons (fl) **S:** 36 kts **Dim:** 23.00 × 5.20 × 1.20
A: 1 12.7-mm mg
Electronics: Radar: 1 Furuno FR-711-2 nav.; 1 Furuno 2400 nav.
M: 2 MTU 12V396 TB93 diesels; 2 props; 3,260 bhp
Range: 420/30 **Crew:** 11 tot.

♦ **1 P 2000 class** Bldr: Watercraft Ltd., Shoreham, U.K. (In serv. 12-84)

Dheeb al Bahar I

D: 80 tons (fl) **S:** 38 kts **Dim:** 20.80 (18.00 pp) × 5.80 × 1.50
A: 1 20-mm 90-cal. Oerlikon GAM-B01 AA; 2 single 7.62-mm mg
Electronics: Radar: 1 Furuno FR-701 nav.
M: 2 MTU 12V396 TB93 diesels; 2 props; 3,920 bhp (3,260 sust.)
Range: 423/35; 660/22 **Crew:** 8 tot.

Remarks: GRP construction with aluminum superstructure. Equipped with a navigational satellite receiver and an MFD/F loop.

ROYAL OMAN POLICE PATROL BOATS [WPB] *(continued)*

♦ 1 Type PT 1903 Mk III patrol craft
Bldr: Le Comte, Vianen, the Netherlands (In serv. 8-81)

HARAS VIII

D: 30 tons (33 fl) **S:** 30 kts **Dim:** 19.27 × 4.95 × 1.25
A: 2 single 12.7-mm mg **Electronics:** Radar: 1 Decca 1226C nav.
M: 2 MTU 8V331 TC92 diesels; 2 props; 1,770 bhp
Range: 1,650/17; 2,300/12 **Crew:** 10 tot.

♦ 3 CG 29 class Bldr: Karlskrona Varvet, Karlskrona, Sweden

HARAS VII (In serv. 6-81) HARAS X (In serv. 14-4-82)
HARAS IX (In serv. 1982)

Haras X Omani Navy, 1998

D: 84 tons (fl) **S:** 25 kts **Dim:** 28.9 × 5.4 × 1.3
A: 2 single 20-mm 90-cal. Oerlikon GAM-B01 AA
Electronics: Radar: 1 Decca 1226C nav.
M: 2 MTU 8V331 IC82 diesels; 2 props; 1,866 bhp
Range: 600/15 **Crew:** 13 tot.

Remarks: GRP construction. Enlarged version of a design built for Liberia. *Haras IX* has also been reported to have MTU 12V396 diesels.

♦ 1 CG 27–class GRP-hulled Bldr: Karlskrona, Sweden (In serv. 1980)

HARAS VI

D: 53 tons (fl) **S:** 27 kts **Dim:** 24.0 × 5.5 × 1.0
A: 1 20-mm 90-cal. Oerlikon GAM-B01 AA
Electronics: Radar: 1 Decca 1226C nav.
M: 2 MTU 12V331 diesels; 2 props; 2,800 bhp **Crew:** 11 tot.

♦ 5 Haras I–class GRP-hulled Bldr: Vosper Pty, Singapore

HARAS I through HARAS IV (In serv. 22-12-75) HARAS V (In serv. 11-78)

Haras II Hartmut Ehlers, 10-92

D: 45 tons (50 fl) **S:** 24.5 kts **Dim:** 22.9 × 6.0 × 1.5
A: 1 20-mm 90-cal. Oerlikon GAM-B01 AA
Electronics: Radar: 1 Decca 101 nav.
M: 2 Caterpillar D348 diesels; 2 props; 1,450 bhp
Range: 600/20; 1,000/11 **Crew:** 11 tot.

♦ 2 Zahra 18 class
Bldr: Emsworth SY, U.K. (In serv. 1987)

ZAHRA 18 ZAHRA 21

D: 18 tons (21 fl) **S:** 22 kts **Dim:** 16.0 × 4.2 × 1.2
A: 1 or 2 single 7.62-mm mg **Electronics:** Radar: 1 Decca 101 nav.
M: 2 Cummins VTA-903M diesels; 2 props; 643 bhp
Range: 700/20; 510/22 **Crew:** 6 tot.

Remarks: GRP hulls molded by Watercraft, Shoreham, and completed by Emsworth.

Zahra 18 Hartmut Ehlers, 10-92

♦ 3 Zahra 14 class
Bldr: Watercraft, Shoreham (In serv. 1981)

ZAHRA 14 ZAHRA 15 ZAHRA 17

Zahra 17—alongside *Zahra 14* Hartmut Ehlers, 10-92

D: 17.25 tons (fl) **S:** 22 kts **Dim:** 13.9 (12.6 wl) × 4.3 × 1.1
A: 1 or 2 single 7.62-mm mg **Electronics:** Radar: 1 Decca 101 nav.
M: 2 Cummins VTA-903M diesels; 2 props; 643 bhp
Range: 700/20; 510/22 **Crew:** 6 tot.

Remarks: The GRP hulls were molded to a standard Keith Nelson pilot/patrol boat design. *Zahra 17* has a higher pilothouse than the others.

SERVICE CRAFT

♦ 1 Zahra 16–series diving tender [WYDT]
Bldr: Rotork, U.K. (In serv. 1981)

ZAHRA 27

Zahra 27 Hartmut Ehlers, 10-92

D: 11 tons (23 fl) **S:** 20 kts **Dim:** 18.0 × 3.0 × 0.5
A: 2 single 7.62-mm mg
M: 2 Volvo Penta AQD 70/750 diesel outdrives; 430 bhp **Crew:** 4 tot.

Remarks: Sisters *Zahra 16, Zahra 20,* and *Zahra 22* have been retired. Sister R 1 serves the navy.

PAKISTAN

Islamic Republic of Pakistan

Personnel (2001): 2,300 officers (75 assigned to the Maritime Security Agency), 22,800 enlisted (including about 900 assigned to the Maritime Security Agency), and 5,000 reservists. The marine corps commando unit has 1,200 personnel. The navy also operates all customs service patrol boats.

Bases: Major base and repair facilities at Karachi and Ormara; minor facilities at Gwadar and Port Qasim

Naval Aviation: The Naval Air Arm consists of 2 P-3C Orion, 3 Atlantic Mk 1, and 1 Fokker F-27-400M maritime patrol aircraft; 3 Westland Lynx HAS.3 and 7 AS.316 Alouette-III shipboard helicopters; 5 Westland Sea King Mk 45 and Sea King Mk 45C land-based helicopters armed with AM 39 Exocet antiship missiles; 4 Fokker F-27-200 and 2 HAMC Y-12-II transports; and 2 Cessna liaison aircraft.

All naval aircraft are based at PNS *Mehran* and are assigned to the following squadrons: Sea Kings to 111 Sqn., Lynxes to 222 Sqn., Alouettes to 333 Sqn., Orions to 28 Sqn., and Atlantics to 29 Sqn.

Thales Ocean Master radars have been installed in the Atlantic Mk 1s; one Fokker F-27-200 has also been equipped with Ocean Master, plus DR-3000A intercept equipment. All five Sea King helicopters have been fitted with GEC-Marconi AQS-928G acoustic processors and Type 2069 dipping sonars. Three ex-French Navy Atlantic Mk 1 reconnaissance aircraft donated during 1996 have been used for cannibalization spares. An operational Atlantic Mk 1 was shot down by Indian aircraft on 10-8-99; 16 aircrew were lost. A P-3C Orion crashed 29-10-99, killing the crew of 21. Twelve air force Mirage-V fighters are equipped to launch AM 39 Exocets for maritime strike missions.

Pakistani Navy P-3C Orion Lockheed Martin, 1993

Pakistani Navy Atlantic Mk 1 U.S. Navy, 5-95

Weapon and Sensors: Italian WASS heavyweight torpedoes are on order to replace older French torpedoes.

Note: Ship names are preceded by PNS (Pakistani Naval Ship).

ATTACK SUBMARINES [SS]

♦ 1 (+ 2) French Agosta-90B class
Bldr: DCN, Cherbourg (S 139: Karachi NSY)

	Laid down	L	In serv.
S 137 Khalid	15-7-95	8-8-98	21-12-99
S 138 Saad	6-98	. . .	2-02
S 139 Hamza	3-1-97	2005	2006

Khalid (S 137) DCN, 1999

Khalid (S 137) Pakistani Navy, 2000

D: 1,250 tons std.; 1,570 tons surf./1,760 tons sub. **S:** 12.5 kts surf./20 kts sub.
Dim: 67.57 × 6.80 × 5.40
A: 4 bow 550-mm TT (16 F 17P Mod. 2 torpedoes and/or SM 39 Exocet SSM)
Electronics:
Radar: 1 Kelvin-Hughes Type 1007 nav./surf. search
Sonar: Thales: TSM 2233 Advanced Eledone active/passive; DUUX-5 (TSM 2055) passive ranging; TSM 2933 towed linear passive array
EW: Thales DR-3000U intercept
M: 2 SEMT-Pielstick A16 PA4 185 diesels (850 kw each), Jeumont-Schneider electric motor; 1 prop; 3,000 shp—1 23-hp cruise motor—S 139 only: MESMA air-independent auxiliary power system (200 kw)
Range: 7,900/10 snorkel; 178/3.5 sub. **Fuel:** 200 tons
Endurance: 68 days **Crew:** 7 officers, 29 enlisted

Remarks: Ordered 21-9-94. The first unit was built entirely in France. The three prefabricated sections for S 138 were fabricated in France between 9-95 and 5-98 and were shipped to Karachi 29-4-98 for outfitting and assembly. The third is being constructed and fitted out at Karachi (where the program was officially inaugurated 3-1-97 by the Pakistani president), with about 20% of the components and material coming from France, where hull section fabrication had begun on 13-2-99. The officially projected completion dates for the second and third units are probably optimistic. Program is to cost $950 million total, plus another $100 million for the SM39 Exocet missiles. Pakistan has offered to provide S 139 to Malaysia, with a replacement to be built for the Pakistani Navy; during 6-01, it was claimed by the Pakistani Navy C-in-C that Pakistan does not need French technical assistance or permission to build additional units of the class for export. S 137 was delivered in France 13-9-99, arrived at Karachi 16-12-99, and is assigned to Submarine Squadron 5.
Hull systems: Agosta-90B is an updated version of the original *Agosta* with smaller crew, greater automation, an inertial navigation system, an integrated weapon system with optronic periscope, and the French MESMA *(Module d'Énergie Sous-Marine Autonome)* air-independent propulsion system (which is to be installed in the third unit in an 8-m extra section to the pressure hull and backfitted to the other two later). MESMA burns ethanol and oxygen in a high-pressure combustion heat generating loop, transferring the heat to a secondary Rankine-cycle heat transference loop. The complete MESMA system weighs some 30 tons but produces only 200 kw of electricity. The hull sections to accommodate the MESMA system were fabricated in France, with the first completed 6-00; trials with the complete system were to be conducted in France in 2001 and the sections then shipped to Pakistan for installation in S 139.

The pressure hulls are built of HLES 80 (*Haute Limite Elastique Soudable,* a U.S. HY 100–equivalent steel. The batteries are supplied by CEAC. Operating functions will be controlled by a SAGEM SS Mk 1 control system. The integrated navigational suite includes Minicin Mod. 3 inertial navigation, radio navigation receivers, CGM 5 gyro, and LH 92 automatic log. Safare Crouzet provided a self-noise monitoring system. Normal maximum operating depth: 320 m.
Combat systems: The sonar sets are an integral function of the UDS International SUBTICS (Submarine Tactical Information and Command System) weapons control system, which is similar to the French Navy's SET *(Système d'Exploitation Tactique)* and has 6 two-screen display consoles. SOPELEM search and attack periscopes are fitted, as is an "electromagnetic detection system." S 137 launched an SM 39 Exocet missile on 10-3-01 while submerged.

♦ 2 French Agosta class
Bldr: Dubigeon, Nantes

	Laid down	L	In serv.
S 135 Hashmat (ex-*Astrant*)	15-9-76	14-12-77	17-2-79
S 136 Hurmat (ex-*Adventurous*)	18-9-77	1-12-78	18-2-80

Hurmat (S 136) 92 Wing Det. A, RAAF, 1998

ATTACK SUBMARINES [SS] *(continued)*

D: 1,230 tons std.; 1,480 tons surf. (max.)/1,725 tons sub.
S: 12.5 kts surf./20.5 kts sub. **Dim:** 67.90 × 6.80 × 5.40
A: 4 bow 550-mm TT (20 F 17P torpedoes and UGM-84A Harpoon SSM)
Electronics:
Radar: 1 Thales DRUA-33 nav./surf. search
Sonar: Thales DUUA-2A/B active/passive search/attack (8 kHz); Thales DSUV-2H passive; Thales DUUX-2A passive-ranging
EW: ARUR intercept; ARUD intercept
M: 2 SEMT-Pielstick A16 PA4 185 diesels, electric drive; 1 prop; 4,600 shp—1 23-hp cruise motor
Range: 7,900/10 snorkel; 178/3.5 sub. **Fuel:** 200 tons
Crew: 7 officers, 47 enlisted

Remarks: Originally ordered for South Africa, but the sale was canceled in 1977 due to the arms embargo and completion slowed. Sold to Pakistan in 11-78. Very quiet, highly automated submarines. Diving depth: 300 m. Battery capacity is twice that of the *Daphné* class. Were fitted to launch U.S. Sub-Harpoon antiship missiles in 1984–85, but the missiles are now past their shelf lives. Are assigned to Submarine Squadron 5.

♦ 4 French Daphné class

	Bldr	Laid down	L	In serv.
S 131 Hangor	Naval Arsenal, Brest	1-12-67	30-6-69	12-1-70
S 132 Shushuk	C.N. Ciotat, Le Trait	1-12-67	30-7-69	12-1-70
S 133 Mangro	C.N. Ciotat, Le Trait	8-7-68	7-2-70	8-8-70
S 134 Ghazi (ex-*Cachalote*)	Dubigeon, Nantes	27-10-66	16-2-68	25-1-69

Ghazi (S 134) U.S. Navy, 10-95

D: 700 tons std.; 870 tons surf. (max.)/1,045 tons sub.
S: 13.5 kts surf./16 kts sub. **Dim:** 57.75 × 6.75 × 4.56
A: 12 550-mm TT (8 fwd, 4 aft, no reloads; E 15 torpedoes and UGM-84A Harpoon SSM)
Electronics:
Radar: 1 Thales DRUA-31 nav./surf. search
Sonar: Thales DUUA-1 active/passive search/attack; Thales DSUV-2F passive search
EW: ARUR intercept; ARUD intercept
M: 2 SEMT-Pielstick 12 PA4 135 450-kw diesel generator sets, 2 Jeumont-Schneider 800 shp (1,300 for short periods) electric motors; 2 props
Range: 2,700/12.5 surf.; 4,300/7.5 snorkel **Crew:** 7 officers, 47 enlisted

Remarks: S 134 was purchased from Portugal in 12-75. S 131 sank the Indian frigate *Khukri* in 1971. Diving depth: 300 m. Two of the class will be retired on delivery of the second and third Agosta-90B submarines, but the others are planned to remain in service through 2010. Are assigned to Submarine Squadron 5.
Combat systems: U.S. Sub-Harpoon capability was added in 1985–86, but the missiles are now past their shelf lives. The eight forward tubes can be accessed from within the submarine; the four aft-facing tubes are externally loaded and are mounted above the pressure hull. The E 15 torpedoes have a range of 6.6 n.m. at 25 kts and have a 300-kg warhead.

MIDGET SUBMARINES [SSM]

♦ 2 MG-110-class midget submarines
Bldr: Pakistan NDY, Karachi (In serv. 1988–. . .)

Pakistani Navy MG-110 midget submarine French Navy, 1994

D: 110 tons surf./130 tons sub. **S:** 9 kts surf./7 kts sub.
Dim: 27.8 × 2.02 × 5.60 (high)
A: 2 533-mm SUT wire-guided torpedoes or 8 Mk 414 300-kg mines in drop gear
M: 1 diesel generator set, 1 electric motor; 1 3-bladed prop; . . . shp
Range: 1,600/7 surf.; 8.5/6, 60/4.5 sub. **Endurance:** 20 days
Crew: 6 crew + 8 combat swimmers

Remarks: Assembled with components supplied by COS.M.O.S., Livorno, Italy. A lengthened version of the same builder's S.X. 756 class. Began delivery in 1988 to replace the earlier S.X. 404–class midget subs, which have all been retired; a third MG-110 was lost in 1995, and further construction was abandoned. Diving depth: 150 m max. Have a Pilkington CK 39 periscope. A number of COS.M.O.S. CF2 FX60, two-man swimmer delivery vehicles ("chariots") from the same builder are also in service, and two can be carried in lieu of torpedoes or mines on each MG-110.

FRIGATES [FF]

Note: Plans to purchase up to four Chinese-built frigates, possibly of the Jiangwei-II class, were made public in 3-95. An agreement to build four frigates, the first in China and the other three at Karachi Shipyard and Engineering Works, was signed with China 12-4-00, but the $500 million funding needed was not available. In 1-01, it was again announced that an existing Chinese-built unit of the class would be acquired for $63 million and that Pakistan would build three more by 2010, but again no funds were provided in the 2001 budget. Ukraine also hopes to attract Pakistani funds for the construction of frigates.

♦ 6 ex-U.K. Amazon class (Type 21)
Bldr: Yarrow (Shipbuilders) Ltd., Scotstoun, Glasgow, Scotland (D 182, 185: Vosper Thornycroft, Woolston)

	Laid down	L	In serv.
D 181 Tariq (ex-*Ambuscade,* F 172)	1-9-71	18-1-73	5-9-75
D 182 Babur (ex-*Amazon,* F 169)	6-11-69	26-4-71	11-5-74
D 183 Khyber (ex-*Arrow,* F 173)	28-9-72	5-2-74	29-7-76
D 184 Badr (ex-*Alacrity,* F 174)	5-3-73	18-9-74	2-7-77
D 185 Tippu Sultan (ex-*Active,* F 171)	23-7-71	23-11-72	17-6-77
D 186 Shahjahan (ex-*Avenger,* F 185)	30-10-74	20-11-75	119-7-78

Tippu Sultan (D 185)—with *Daphné*-class submarine *Shushuk* (S 132) alongside; note the Chinese sextuple SAM launcher forward of the bridge on D 185
Arjun Sarup, 3-01

Khyber (D 183)—with Chinese SAM system forward and Phalanx CIWS aft; note the single 400-mm ASW torpedo tube abreast the Phalanx mount, aimed aftward
Pakistani Navy, 2000

Shahjahan (D 186)—with Harpoon launch canisters forward of the bridge
Steve Zaloga, 3-01

D: 3,210 tons (3,710 fl) **S:** 30 kts
Dim: 117.04 (109.70 pp) × 12.7 × 4.8 (6.4 over sonar)
A: D 181, 183, 185: 1 6-round LY-60N SAM syst.; 1 114-mm 55-cal. Vickers Mk 8 DP; 1 20-mm Mk 15 Phalanx gatling CIWS—D 183 only: 2 fixed 400-mm ASW TT (Bofors Tp 43X2 torpedoes); 1 Lynx helicopter—D 182, 184, 186: 4 RGM-84 Harpoon SSM; 1 114-mm 55-cal. Vickers Mk 8 DP; 1 20-mm Mk 15 Phalanx gatling CIWS—D 184, 186 only: 2 triple 324-mm STWS.1 ASW TT (U.S. Mk 46 torpedoes)—D 182 only: 2 fixed 400-mm ASW TT (Bofors Tp 43X2 torpedoes); 1 Lynx helicopter
Electronics:
Radar: 1 Kelvin-Hughes Type 1006 nav.; 1 Marconi Type 992R (D 181, 183, 185: Thales DA-08) surf./air search—D 182, 184, 186 only: 1 AESN RTN-10X Orion gun f.c.; General Dynamics Mk 90 Phalanx f.c.—D 181, 183, 185 only: 1 LL-1 f.c. (with laser and IR sensors)
Sonar: Graseby Type 184P hull-mounted search; Kelvin-Hughes Type 162M bottomed-target classification (50 kHz); Type 185 underwater telephone
EW: Thales DR-3000S1X intercept; FH-12 HFD/F; 2 8-round Corvus decoy RL—D 183, 185 also: 4 4-round decoy RL—all: Type 182 towed acoustic torpedo decoy
E/O: 1 Matra Défense Najir Mk 2 optronic f.c.

FRIGATES [FF] *(continued)*

Badr (D 184)—with Harpoon missiles forward and Phalanx CIWS atop the hangar Pakistani Navy, 2000

Tariq (D 181)—note the antenna for the DA-08 air-search radar atop the foremast and the prominent hull stiffening strake amidships Brian Morrison, 11-99

M: COGOG: 2 Olympus TM-3B gas turbines (25,000 shp each), 2 Tyne RM-1A gas turbines (4,250 shp each); 2 CP props; 50,000 shp max.
Electric: 3,000 kw tot. (4 × 750-kw diesel sets; 450 V, 3-phase, 60-Hz a.c.)
Range: 1,200/30; 4,500/17 **Endurance:** 60 days **Crew:** 13 officers, 164 enlisted

Remarks: D 181 transferred 28-7-93 and formally commissioned at Karachi 20-11-93. D 182 retired from the Royal Navy 30-9-93 and transferred same date, commissioning 18-1-94. D 183 and D 184 were transferred 1-3-94, D 185 on 29-7-94, and D 186 on 23-9-94. Designed jointly by Vosper Thornycroft and Yarrow under a 27-2-68 contract. In British service, sister *Ardent* (F 184) was lost on 21-5-82 and *Antelope* (F 170) on 24-5-82. All are assigned to Destroyer Squadron 25. In 1-01, it was announced that the class would be retired by 2010.
Hull systems: The ships have been criticized for fragility and vulnerability and for being overloaded and top-heavy; permanent ballast had to be added, and in RN service, none could carry the full originally intended weapon and sensor suite. The hulls were strengthened during the early 1980s, due to cracking during the Falklands War; doubler plates were added amidships and other work added some 350 tons to displacement and cost at least 2 kts in maximum speed. New equipment added in Pakistan has not helped their stability. Remote control of the engine room is accomplished from the bridge. Have retractable fin stabilizers.
Combat systems: As transferred, had the CAAIS DBA-2 combat data system and a Ferranti WSA.4 digital fire-control system employing two Selenia RTN-10X radar directors (U.K. Type 912) for the 114-mm gun and the since-removed Sea Cat SAM system; the after radar director has been removed in all, and the forward one has been replaced by a Chinese LL-1 set in D 181, 183, and 185. The CAAIS DBA-2 combat data system is a separate entity whose data are automatically transmitted to the WSA.4; both use a single FM-1600B computer.

CelsiusTech of Sweden received a contract on 16-9-94 to reequip four of the ships (probably D 181, 182, 183, and 185) with the 9LV Mk 3 combat system, but the work does not appear to have been done; the same four ships were to receive tubes for Bofors Tp 43X2 ASW torpedoes, but only D 183 is *confirmed* to have received the tubes, mounted one on either side of the hangar at the forecastle deck level and aimed aft. Two Thales/BAE Systems ATAS (Active Towed Acoustic System) sets were ordered in 11-93 for these ships, but, again, the equipment has not been installed.

Four Thales DR-3000S EW systems were ordered to replace the original UAA-1 intercept arrays. The Thales LW-08 radar was selected to replace the Type 992R air-search radar in 9-94, but only the three ships with the Chinese SAM system have it; in those ships, the Chinese LL-1 radar director controls both the gun and the missiles. All six ships were to receive the Matra Défense Najir Mk 2 electro-optical backup 114-mm gun director. Chinese-made twin 25-mm AA were mounted just abaft the bridge on D 182, 184, and 186, but they were later removed, as have been the two single 20-mm Oerlikon Mk 4 mountings from all. D 185 (and possibly others) has an additional navigational radar set. All six have been modified to accept a 20-mm Phalanx gatling CIWS atop the helicopter hangar; the mounts are moved from ship to ship, as there are not enough for all of them.

♦ 2 ex-U.K. Broad-Beam Leander class

Bldr: Yarrow, Scotstoun, Glasgow, Scotland

	Laid down	L	In serv.
F 262 ZULFIQUAR (ex-*Apollo,* F 70)	1-5-69	15-10-70	28-5-72
F 263 SHAMSHER (ex-*Diomede,* F 16)	30-1-68	15-4-69	2-4-71

Shamsher (F 263) Brian Morrison, 8-95

Shamsher (F 263) Brian Morrison, 8-95

D: 2,660 tons (3,120 fl) **S:** 27 kts
Dim: 113.38 (109.73 pp) × 13.12 × 4.50 (5.49 props)
A: 1 twin 114-mm 45-cal. Vickers Mk 6 DP; 3 twin 25-mm 80-cal. Type 61M AA; 1 3-round Limbo Mk 10 ASW mortar; 1 AS.319B Alouette-III helicopter
Electronics:
Radar: 1 . . . nav.; 1 Kelvin-Hughes Type 1006 nav.; 1 Plessey Type 994 surf./air search; 1 Marconi Type 965 early warning; 1 Plessey Type 903 gun f.c.
Sonar: Graseby Type 184P hull-mounted MF search; Graseby Type 170B hull-mounted HF attack; Kelvin-Hughes Type 162M bottomed-target classification
EW: UA-8/9 intercept; Type 668 jammers—F 262 only: UA-13 VHFD/F—F 263 only: FH-12 HFD/F—both: 2 8-round Corvus decoy RL; Type 182 towed acoustic torpedo decoy
M: 2 sets White–English Electric geared steam turbines; 2 5-bladed props; 30,000 shp
Boilers: 2 Babcock & Wilcox 3-drum; 38.7 kg/cm^2, 450° C
Electric: 2,500 kw tot. **Range:** 4,500/12 **Fuel:** 500 tons
Crew: 15 officers, 220 enlisted

FRIGATES [FF] *(continued)*

Remarks: F 262 was decommissioned and sold to Pakistan 14-10-88, and F 263 was decommissioned 7-7-88 and sold 15-7-88. Although among the newest Royal Navy *Leanders*, they had not been modernized. F 263 carried 39 officers and 288 enlisted on a visit to Indonesia in mid-1995. The ships are to be retired by 2010 or sooner, as their engineering systems are proving difficult to maintain. Are assigned to Destroyer Squadron 18 and used primarily for training.
Combat systems: By 1994, both had lost their Sea Cat point-defense SAM systems, including the associated Type 904 radar director; the 20-mm gunmounts had been removed, and twin Chinese 25-mm gunmounts had been substituted for them just abaft the pilothouse and on the former Type 904 radar director platform atop the helicopter hangar. A second navigational radar antenna has been stepped on a pole mast atop the pilothouse, to port.

GUIDED-MISSILE PATROL CRAFT [PTG]

♦ 3 Jalalat class
Bldr: Karachi NDY

	L	In serv.
P 1029 Jalalat (ex-P 1022)	17-11-96	15-8-97
P 1030 Shujaat	6-3-99	30-9-99
P	6-00	3-01

Jalalat (P 1029) Pakistani Navy, 2000

D: 150 tons (185 fl) **S:** 23 kts **Dim:** 39.0 × 6.7 × 1.8
A: 4 C-801 (CSS-N-4 Sardine) SSM; 1 twin 37-mm 63-cal. Type 76A AA
Electronics:
Radar: 1 Type 756 nav.; 1 Type SR-47A/R missile target detection and tracking; 1 Type 47G gun f.c.
EW: . . . radar threat warning; 4 4-round decoy RL
M: 2 MTU . . . diesels; 2 props; 5,984 bhp
Range: 2,000/17 **Crew:** 3 officers, 28 enlisted

Remarks: Design is based on that of the patrol craft *Larkana* (q.v.), but with Chinese-supplied armament and sensors. The second and any later units were to carry C-802 missiles and will have intercept and jamming equipment. P 1024 was laid down during 6-98. Are assigned to Patrol Squadron 10.

♦ 3 ex-Chinese Huangfeng class (Chinese Project 21)
Bldr: Jiangnan SY, Shanghai (In serv. 1960–75)

P 1026 Deshat P 1027 Himmat P 1028 Quwwat

Deshat (P 1026) H&L Van Ginderen, 8-94

D: 175 tons light; 186.5 normal (205 fl)
S: 35 kts **Dim:** 38.75 × 7.60 × 1.70 (mean hull)
A: 4 C-201 (CSS-N-1 Styx) SSM; 2 twin 25-mm 80-cal. Type 61M AA
Electronics: Radar: 1 Type 352 (Square Tie) surf. search/target acquisition
M: 3 Type 42-160 (M-503A) diesels; 3 props; 12,000 bhp (8,025 sust.)
Electric: 65 kw tot. **Range:** 800/30 **Crew:** 28 tot.

Remarks: Arrived at Karachi 27-4-84 as deck cargo; are probably ex-Chinese navy units rather than new construction. The Chinese copies of the Soviet-designed M-503A multirow radial diesels are difficult to maintain and offer only about 600 hours between overhauls. Unlike the original Soviet Project 205 design (Osa-I), they have hull portholes. Sister *Azmat* (P 1025) was stricken during 1998. Are assigned to Patrol Squadron 10.

PATROL CRAFT [PC]

♦ 1 Larkana class Bldr: Karachi Naval Dockyard (L 6-6-94)

P 157 Larkana

Larkana (P 157) French Navy, 9-97

D: 150 tons (180 fl) **S:** 24 kts **Dim:** 39.0 × 6.7 × 1.7
A: 1 twin 37-mm 63-cal. Type 74 AA; 2 twin 25-mm 80-cal. Type 61M AA; 2 Mk 64 d.c. racks
Electronics: Radar: 1 Type 756 nav.
M: 2 MTU . . . diesels; 2 props; 5,984 bhp
Range: 2,000/17 **Crew:** 3 officers, 22 enlisted

Remarks: First combatant built in Pakistan; keel laid 1991. Three more were being built as *Jalalat*-class guided-missile patrol craft (q.v.). Hull lines enlarged from those of the *Rajshahi* (P 140).

♦ 1 32-meter class Bldr: Brooke Marine, Lowestoft, U.K. (In serv. 1965)

P 140 Rajshahi

D: 115 tons (143 fl) **S:** 24 kts **Dim:** 32.62 (30.48 pp) × 6.10 × 1.55
A: 2 single 40-mm 60-cal. Bofors Mk 9 AA; 2 single 14.5-mm 93-cal. AA
Electronics: Radar: 1 . . . nav.
M: 2 MTU 12V538 diesels; 2 props; 3,400 bhp **Crew:** 19 tot.

Remarks: Last survivor of a class of four. A sister operates in the Bangladeshi Navy.

MINE WARFARE SHIPS

♦ 3 Tripartite-class minehunters [MHC]
Bldr: DCN Lorient (M 163: fitted out by Karachi NDY)

	Laid down	L	In serv.
M 166 Munsif (ex-*Sagittaire*, M 650)	13-11-85	9-11-88	27-7-89
M 163 Muhafiz (ex-M 654, ex-*Moshad*)	7-4-94	8-7-95	15-5-96
M 164 Mujahid (ex-*Mahmoud*)	8-4-94	28-1-97	9-7-98

Mujahid (M 164) Pakistani Navy, 2000

D: 535 tons (605 fl) **S:** 15 kts (on main engine; 7 while hunting)
Dim: 51.6 (47.1 pp) × 8.96 × 2.49 (hull; 3.50 max.)
A: 1 20-mm 90-cal. GIAT 20F2 AA; 2 single 12.7-mm mg
Electronics:
Radar: 1 Kelvin-Hughes Type 1007 (M 166: Decca 1229) nav.
Sonar: Thales DUBM-21D (M 166: DUBM-21B)
M: 1 Brons-Werkspoor A RUB 215V12 diesel; 1 CP prop, 1,900 bhp—2 ACEC electric maneuvering props (120 shp each)—bow-thruster
Electric: 750 kw tot. **Range:** 3,000/12
Crew: 5 officers, 23 petty officers, 21 ratings

Remarks: Ordered 17-1-92; an option for three additional was not taken up. The first ship was transferred from the French Navy in 9-92 and left for Pakistan 27-11-92, the second was built at Lorient and arrived in Pakistan 18-9-96, and the hull for the third was shipped to Karachi 19-4-95 for fitting out with French assistance. Are assigned to Minesweeper Squadron 21.

MINE WARFARE SHIPS *(continued)*

Hull systems: Built of glass-reinforced polyester plastic. Have a six-man portable decompression chamber module at the aft end of the forecastle deck.
Combat systems: Have one mechanical drag sweep, and may also have the AP-4 acoustic sweep. Have an EVEC 20 automatic plotting table, Decca HiFix and Sydelis radio precision navigation equipment, and two PAP-104 remote-controlled mine-hunting submersibles. M 163 and M 164 have the digital DUBM-21D sonar, with hybrid circuitry, Mustang computer, higher-definition displays, built-in test equipment, and integration into the tactical system; they also have the Thales TSM 2061 Mk II tactical data system and the Finnish Elesco Family of Integrated Minesweeping Systems (FIMS) sweep array with MRK-960 three-electrode magnetic sweep and MKR-400 pipe-type noncontrollable noisemaker.

AUXILIARIES

Note: Auxiliaries are assigned to Auxiliary Squadron 42. Plans to acquire a new-construction hydrographic survey ship for $70–75 million were announced in 1-01.

♦ 1 oceanographic research ship [AGOR]

	Bldr	Laid down	L	In serv.
Behr Paima	Ishikawajima Harima, Tokyo	16-2-82	. . .	17-12-82

D: approx. 1,400 tons (fl) **S:** 13.75 kts **Dim:** 61.02 (55.00 pp) × 11.82 × 3.71
M: 2 Daihatsu 6DSM-22 diesels; 2 CP props; 2,000 bhp—bow-thruster
Electric: 960 kw tot. (3 × 320-kw, 410-V, 50-Hz a.c. diesel sets)
Range: 5,400/12 **Crew:** 16 officers, 68 enlisted

Remarks: 1,183 grt./400 dwt. Ordered 15-4-81. Operated by the navy for the Ministry of Communications, Ports, and Shipping. Carries two hydrographic survey launches. White painted.

♦ 1 Chinese Fuqing-class replenishment oiler [AOR]

	Bldr	L	In serv.
A 47 Nasr	Dalian SY	. . .	31-7-87

Nasr (A 47)—with Phalanx CIWS visible abaft the stack — Brian Morrison, 11-99

Nasr (A 47)—note telescoping hangar in extended position — Brian Morrison, 8-95

D: 14,600 tons (21,740 fl) **S:** 18.6 kts **Dim:** 160.82 (157.00 pp) × 21.80 × 9.40
A: 2 twin 37-mm 63-cal. Type 74 AA; 1 20-mm Mk 15 Phalanx CIWS gatling AA; 2 single 14.5-mm 93-cal. AA
Electronics: Radar: 2 Decca 1226 nav.; 1 General Dynamics Mk 90 Phalanx f.c.
M: 1 Dalian-Sulzer 8 RLB 66 diesel; 1 prop; 17,400 bhp (15,000 sust.)
Electric: 2,480 kw tot. **Range:** 18,000/14.6 **Crew:** 26 officers, 120 enlisted

Remarks: Has equipment similar to U.S. Navy transfer systems: two liquid replenishment stations per side, with constant-tension solid transfer stations each side just forward of the stack. Helicopter deck can accommodate a Sea King or Alouette-III, but there is no hangar. Four electric cranes and two derricks for cargo handling. Can carry 11,000 tons of fuel oil, 1,000 tons of diesel fuel, 200 tons of feedwater, 200 tons of potable water, and 50 tons of lube oil. A U.S. Phalanx antimissile gun system was added abaft the funnel in 1995; the mount was probably removed from the discarded County-class destroyer *Babur.* Was rammed by the commercial tanker *Sun Marsat* at Karachi on 21-10-98, with minor damage.

♦ 1 ex-Dutch Poolster-class replenishment oiler [AOR]
Bldr: Rotterdamse Droogdok Maatschappij, Rotterdam

	Laid down	L	In serv.
A 20 Moawin (ex-*Poolster,* A 835)	18-9-62	16-10-63	10-9-64

D: 16,836 tons (fl) **S:** 21 kts **Dim:** 168.41 (157.00 pp) × 20.33 × 8.24
A: 2 single 20-mm 70-cal. Oerlikon Mk 10 AA; 1 d.c. rack (8 d.c.)
Electronics:
Radar: 1 Decca TM 1229 nav.; 1 Decca 2459 surf. search
Sonar: 1 CWE-610 hull-mounted MF (probably nonoperational)
EW: SLQ-32(V)1 intercept; Mk 36 SRBOC decoy syst. (4 6-round Raytheon Mk 137 RL)

Moawin (A 20) — SAN, 4-97

M: 2 sets geared steam turbines; 1 prop; 22,500 shp **Boilers:** 2
Electric: 2,100 kw **Crew:** 17 officers, 183 enlisted

Remarks: Purchased 22-6-94, transferred 27-7-94, and departed Dutch waters 3-8-94. Officially recommissioned on 15-9-94. Is also a combat supply ship capable of participating effectively in antisubmarine warfare. For short distances, she can carry 300 troops.
Hull systems: Cargo capacity: 10,300 tons, including 8,000 tons of fuel. Has a hangar for three small helicopters or one Sea King helicopter.
Combat systems: U.S. EW equipment has been substituted in Pakistan for the Netherlands Navy Ferranti AWARE-4 array.

SERVICE CRAFT

♦ 1 degaussing tender [YDG]
Bldr: Karachi SY & Eng. Wks. (In serv. 1979)

D: 260 tons (fl) **S:** 10 kts **Dim:** 35.22 (34.0 wl) × 7.00 × 2.4
M: 1 diesel; 1 prop; 375 bhp **Crew:** 5 tot.

Remarks: Built with French technical assistance and very similar in design to French Navy's Y 732. Wooden hull.

♦ 1 floating dry dock [YFDL]
Bldr: Karachi SY & Eng. Wks. (In serv. 1995)

. . . . . .

Lift capacity: 4,000 tons **Dim:** 166.0 × 28.0 × . . .

Remarks: Four-section dock, with last module launched 31-12-94.

♦ 1 floating dry dock [YFDL]
Bldr: Karachi SY & Eng. Wks. (In serv. 1981)

. . . . . .

Lift capacity: 2,000 tons

♦ 1 U.S. ARD 2–class floating dry dock [YFDL]
Bldr: Pacific Bridge, Alameda, Calif. (In serv. 4-43)

Peshawar (ex-ARD 6)

Lift capacity: 3,500 tons **Dim:** 148.03 × 21.64 × 1.6 (light)

Remarks: Transferred 6-61. May have been replaced by the new 4,000-ton dock.

♦ 1 1,200-ton-capacity floating dry dock [YFDL] (In serv. 1974)
FC II

♦ 2 utility launches [YFL]
Bldr: Karachi SY & Eng. Wks. (In serv. 1991)

427 428

D: 57 grt **S:** . . . kts **Dim:** 19.96 (17.63 pp) × 5.04 (4.88 wl) × 1.50
M: 2 G.M. 8V71 TI diesels; 2 props; 680 bhp **Electric:** 44 kw

♦ 2 logistics craft [YFL]
Bldr: Le Comte, Vianen, the Netherlands (In serv. 18-2-82)

D: 13 tons (fl) **S:** 21 kts **Dim:** 18.1 × 3.8 × 0.9
M: 2 Volvo Penta AQAD 40 diesels; 2 outdrives; 520 bhp

Remarks: GRP-hulled landing craft. Names and numbers not known.

♦ 2 Gwadar-class liquid cargo lighters [YO/YW]
Bldr: Karachi SY & Eng. Wks.

A 49 Gwadar (In serv. 1984) A 21 Kalmat (In serv. 29-8-92)

Gwadar (A 49)—note Maritime Security Agency ship *Nazim* (D 156) and patrol craft *Barkat* (P 1060) and *Vehdat* (P 1063) in background — Pakistani Navy, 2000

SERVICE CRAFT *(continued)*

D: approx. 1,400 tons (fl) **S:** 10 kts **Dim:** 62.84 (57.92 pp) × 11.31 × 3.03
A: 2 single 14.5-mm 93-cal. mg **Electronics:** Radar: 2 Decca . . . nav.
M: 1 Sulzer diesel; 1 prop; 550 bhp **Crew:** 25 tot.

Remarks: A 49 (831 grt) is configured to carry fuel, while A 21 (885 grt) is a water tanker. Both carry about 350 m^3 of liquid cargo and also have an electrohydraulic crane to permit carrying dry cargo on deck. A 21 was laid down 23-2-90 and launched 11-6-91. A 21 has a simplified superstructure with freestanding stack, while A 49's stack fairs into the pilothouse structure.

♦ **1 Attock-class liquid cargo lighter [YO]**
Bldr: . . ., Trieste, Italy (In serv. 1957)

A 40 Attock (ex-U.S. YO 249)

D: 600 tons light (1,225 fl) **S:** 8 kts **Dim:** 54.0 × 9.8 × 4.6
M: 2 GMT diesels; 2 props; 800 bhp **Crew:** 18 tot.

Remarks: Built with U.S. Mutual Defense Assistance Program funds. Cargo: 6,500 bbl (about 550 tons). Two single 20-mm AA and the navigational radars have been removed. Sister *Zum Zum* (A 44), configured as a water tanker, was stricken during 1996.

♦ **1 ex-U.K. O-class accommodations barge hulk [YPBN]**
Bldr: John Brown & Co., Clydebank

	Laid down	L	In serv.
A 260 (ex-*Tippu Sultan,* ex-*Onslow,* ex-*Pakenham*)	1-7-40	31-3-41	8-10-41

D: approx. 2,000 tons (fl) **Dim:** 105.16 (103.18 pp) × 10.67 × . . .

Remarks: Transferred to Pakistan 30-9-49 as a destroyer and later converted to a Type 16 antisubmarine frigate with U.S. funds. Had two sets Parson geared turbines (40,000 shp) and two Admiralty three-drum boilers, the latter probably still in use to provide hotel services. Used since deactivation in 1980 as a berthing hulk, small combatant support ship, and supply barge at Gwadar.

♦ **2 Bholu-class harbor tugs [YTB]**
Bldr: Damen, Hardinxveld, the Netherlands (In serv. 4-91)

A 44 Bholu A 45 Gama

D: 265 tons (fl) **S:** 12 kts **Dim:** 26.00 (24.36 pp) × 6.81 × 2.15
Electronics: Radar: 1 . . . nav.
M: 2 Cummins KTA-38M diesels; 2 props; 1,900 bhp
Fuel: 36 tons **Crew:** 6 tot.

Remarks: Replaced two former U.S. small harbor tugs with the same names. Equipped for fire fighting.

♦ **2 large harbor tugs [YTB]**
Bldr: Karachi SY & Eng. Wks.

Delair (In serv. ca. 2000) Janbaz (In serv. 1990)

D: 282 grt **S:** . . . kts **Dim:** 35.01 (32.62 pp) × 9.30 × 3.90
M: 2 Niigata diesels; 2 props; . . . bhp

Remarks: *Janbaz* has also been reported to be a fuel lighter, and the two may be of differing designs.

♦ **1 small pusher tug [YTL]**
Bldr: Karachi SY & Eng. Wks. (In serv. 11-1-83)

Goga

Remarks: No data available. Also in service is the small tug *Jhara.*

MARITIME SECURITY AGENCY

Note: The Maritime Security Agency (MSA) was established 1-1-87 to patrol the maritime exclusion zone. Its personnel were transferred from the navy, to which it is subordinated. The MSA's ships and boats are painted white, with red and blue diagonal stripes and "MSA" on the side. Most craft operate from Karachi.

Personnel (1999): 75 officers, 900 enlisted (all seconded from the navy)

Aviation: Two Pilatus-Britten-Norman BN-2T Maritime Defender light maritime reconnaissance aircraft assigned to 93 Sqn. at PNS *Mehran* are dedicated to fisheries patrol and search-and-rescue work; the second was delivered in mid-1994.

Maritime Security Agency BN-2T Maritime Defender U.S. Navy, 1-96

DESTROYERS [WDD]

♦ **1 ex-U.S. Gearing FRAM I class** Bldr: Todd Pacific SY, Seattle

	Laid down	L	In serv.
D 156 Nazim (ex-*Tughril,* D 167; ex-*Henderson,* DD 785)	27-10-44	28-5-44	4-8-45

D: 2,425 tons (3,460 fl) **S:** 30 kts **Dim:** 119.00 × 12.45 × 5.80 (max.)
A: 1 twin 127-mm 38-cal. Mk 30 DP; 4 quadruple 14.5-mm 93-cal. ZPU-4 AA
Electronics:
Radar: 1 Decca 1226 nav.; 1 Raytheon SPS-10B surf. search; 1 Lockheed SPS-40 air search; 1 Western Electric Mk 25 gun f.c.
EW: ArgoSystems APECS-II suite with AR 700 intercept
M: 2 sets G.E. geared steam turbines; 2 props; 60,000 shp
Boilers: 4 Babcock & Wilcox; 43.3 kg/cm², 454° C **Electric:** 1,300 kw tot.
Range: 2,400/25; 4,800/15 **Fuel:** 600 tons **Crew:** 27 officers, 247 enlisted

Remarks: Transferred from the Pakistani Navy in 1998 to replace the identically named and numbered unit resubordinated in 1993 (ex-*Tuppu Sultan,* D 168; ex-*Damato,* DD 871). Serves as flagship of the Maritime Security Agency and seldom, if ever, moves under her own power. The quadruple machinegun mounts are not always installed. The helicopter facility aft remains usable. The Harpoon missiles, Phalanx CIWS, and torpedo tubes were removed, and the sonar is probably nonoperational, as is the Mk 112 ASROC ASW missile launcher amidships. The after twin 127-mm gunmount has been deleted.

PATROL CRAFT [WPC]

♦ **4 Barkat class** Bldr: Huangpu SY, China

	In serv.		In serv.
P 1060 Barkat	1-90	P 1062 Nusrat	8-90
P 1061 Rehmat	1-90	P 1063 Vehdat	8-90

Vehdat (P 1063) and a sister—moored alongside the previous *Nazim* (D 156) French Navy, 1996

D: 390 tons (435 fl) **S:** 27 kts **Dim:** 58.77 × 7.20 × 2.40 (mean hull)
A: 1 twin 37-mm 63-cal. Type 74 AA; 2 twin 14.5-mm 93-cal. AA
Electronics: Radar: 2 Fujitsu OPS-9 or Anritsu ARC-32A nav.
M: 4 MTU 16V396 TB93 diesels; 4 props; 8,720 bhp
Range: 1,500/12 **Crew:** 5 officers, 45 enlisted

Remarks: First two were delivered 29-12-89 for commissioning in Pakistan. Are built on Hainan-class naval patrol boat hulls. Sisters operate in Chinese police and customs forces.

♦ **4 Chinese Shanghai-II class**

P 65 Pishin (ex-P 145) P 68 Rafaqat
P 66 Sabqat P 69 Bahawalpur (ex-P 149)

Sabqat (P 66) French Navy, 1995

D: 122.5 tons normal (134.8 fl) **S:** 28.5 kts **Dim:** 38.78 × 5.41 × 1.55 (hull)
A: 2 twin 37-mm 63-cal. Type 74 AA; 2 twin 25-mm 80-cal. Type 61M AA
Electronics: Radar: 1 Anritsu ARC-32A nav.
M: 2 Type L12-V180 (M-50F-4) diesels (1,200 bhp each), 2 L12-180Z (12D6) diesels (910 bhp each); 4 props; 4,220 bhp
Electric: 39 kw tot. **Range:** 750/16.5 **Endurance:** 7 days **Crew:** 36 tot.

Remarks: Transferred from China in 1972 or 1973. P 66 and P 68 were commissioned in the Maritime Security Agency during 4-92, and P 65 and P 69 were transferred from the navy in 1998. Have been renovated and given new electronics. Sisters *Quetta* (P 141), *Bannu* (P 154), *Kalat* (P 156), and *Sahival* (P 160), officially in reserve since 1982, were renovated and transferred to the MSA on 1-1-87 but stricken in 1990.

COAST GUARD

Note: The coast guard, organized in 1985, is manned by Pakistani Army personnel and subordinated to the Ministry of the Interior. All of the craft listed below have GRP hulls.

COAST GUARD *(continued)*

PATROL BOATS [WPB]

♦ **1 Swallow class**
Bldr: Swallowcraft/Kangnam SB, Pusan, South Korea (In serv. 3-86)

Saif

D: 32 tons (fl) **S:** 25 kts **Dim:** 20.0 × 4.7 × 1.3
A: 2 single 12.7-mm mg
M: 2 G.M. Detroit Diesel 12V71 TI diesels; 2 props; 1,060 bhp
Range: 500/20 **Crew:** 8 tot.

♦ **4 Italian MV 55 class** Bldr: Crestitalia, Ameglia (In serv. 1987)

Burq Sadd Shabaz Waqir

D: 22.8 tons (fl) **S:** 35 kts **Dim:** 16.50 × 5.20 × 0.88
A: 1 20-mm AA **Electronics:** Radar: 1 . . . nav.
M: 2 MTU diesels; 2 props; 2,200 bhp **Range:** 425/25 **Crew:** 5 tot.

CUSTOMS SERVICE

Note: Pakistani Customs Service craft are naval-manned and would come under naval control in wartime. The service operates 18 MV 55–class patrol boats, P 551 through P 568, which are identical to the Maritime Security Agency units of that class, except that they have a single 14.5-mm machinegun and are powered by two 800-bhp diesels for 30-kt maximum speed.

PALAU

Republic of Palau

BUREAU OF PUBLIC SAFETY DIVISION OF LAW ENFORCEMENT

Note: The Republic of Palau in the western Caroline Islands consists of 343 islands and became fully independent on 1-10-94. Craft are identified by a broad blue and narrow yellow diagonal hull stripe abreast the pilothouse. Craft names are preceded by PSS (Palau State Ship).

PATROL CRAFT [WPC]

♦ **1 Australian ASI 315 class**
Bldr: Transfield ASI Pty, Ltd., South Coogie, W.A. (In serv. 25-7-96)

001 President H. I. Remeliik

President H. I. Remeliik (001) ABPH Darren Yates, RAN, 5-96

D: 148 tons (165 fl) **S:** 21 kts **Dim:** 31.50 (28.60 wl) × 8.10 × 2.12 (1.80 hull)
A: 2 single 7.62-mm mg **Electronics:** Radar: 1 Furuno 1011 nav.
M: 2 Caterpillar 3516 diesels; 2 props; 2,820 bhp (2,400 sust.)
Electric: 116 kw (2 × 50-kw Caterpillar 3304 diesel sets; 1 × 16 kw)
Range: 2,500/12 **Fuel:** 27.9 tons **Endurance:** 8–10 days
Crew: 3 officers, 12 enlisted + 7 Marine Patrol Police constables

Remarks: Standard Australian foreign aid patrol boat design. Named for Haruo I. Remeliik, Palau's first president. Ran trials in 5-96. To be given a refit during 2003 and a major refit during 2011 in Australia.
Hull systems: Carries a 5-m rigid inflatable boarding boat. Has an extensive navigational suite, including Furuno FSN-70 NAVSAT receiver, Furuno 525 HFD/F, Furuno 120 MH–HFD/F, FE-881 echo sounder, Furuno 500 autopilot, DS-70 doppler log, and Weatherfax receiver. Differs from earlier units of the class in having a spray strake forward on the hull sides.

PANAMA

Republic of Panama

NATIONAL MARITIME SERVICE

Personnel (2001): 620 total

Base: Flamenco Island, Colón. There are repair facilities at Coco Solo and a small facility at Quebrada de Piedra. In mid-1996, construction began on a new base, repair, and training facility at Remo Largo, Cativa, Colón; it had not been finished as of 1999.

Maritime Aviation: The air force operates a number of aircraft with a secondary maritime patrol role, including 2 DHC Twin Otter, 3 CASA C-212, 1 Pilatus-Britten-Norman BN-2T Islander, 2 Cessna U-17, and 1 Cessna 172. Air force helicopters include 8 Bell UH-1B, 9 UH-1H, and 4 UH-1N. Larger fixed-wing transports include 1 L-188 Electra, 4 C-47s, 1 Shorts Skyvan, and 1 Falcon 20 for VIP transport. Aircraft are based at Quebrada de Piedra, and a small airport facility is being built at Kuna Yala.

PATROL CRAFT [WPC]

♦ **2 U.K. Vosper 103-foot class**
Bldr: Vosper Thornycroft, Portsmouth (In serv. 3-71)

P-301 Panquiaco (ex-GC 10) P-302 Ligia Elena (ex-GC 11)

Ligia Elena (P-302) H&L Van Ginderen, 4-97

D: 96 tons (123 fl) **S:** 18 kts **Dim:** 31.25 × 6.02 × 1.98
A: 2 single 7.62-mm mg **Electronics:** Radar: 1 Raytheon 2600 nav.
M: 2 G.M. Detroit Diesel 16V71 TI diesels; 2 props; 2,500 bhp
Electric: 80 kVA tot. **Range:** 1,400/14 **Crew:** 3 officers, 14 enlisted

Remarks: Launched 22-7-70 and 25-8-70, respectively. P-302 was sunk by U.S. forces during the 12-89 invasion and P-301 had been discarded by late 1991, but both began extensive overhauls in Panama in 9-92 (including re-engining) and have been returned to service. Have Vosper fin stabilizers, steel hulls, and aluminum alloy superstructures. Both are assigned to the Pacific coast.

♦ **1 former oceanographic research support craft**
Bldr: Equitable Equipment Co., New Orleans (In serv. 1965)

P-303 Naos (ex-*Erline,* 105UB821; ex-M/V *Orrin*)

Naos (P-303) Panamanian Navy, 12-98

D: 96 tons (120 fl) **S:** 10 kts **Dim:** 32.00 × 6.31 × 1.80
A: 2 single 7.62-mm mg **Electronics:** Radar: 1 Raytheon 920 nav.
M: 2 Caterpillar . . . diesels; 2 props; approx. 1,000 bhp
Range: 550/8 **Crew:** 2 officers, 9 enlisted

Remarks: Former offshore crew boat, acquired in 1967 and operated by the U.S. Naval Underwater Systems Center at Tudor Hill, Bermuda, until transferred to Panama in 7-92. Commissioned in 12-92 after an overhaul and employed in local patrol duties, based on the Pacific coast. Re-engined in 1997.

♦ **1 former drug runner**
Bldr: . . . (In serv. . . .)

P-305 Escudo de Verguas (ex-*Aun Sin Nombre,* ex-*Kathyuska Kelly*)

D: 158 tons (fl) **S:** 10 kts **Dim:** 27.6 × 7.3 × 1.9
A: 1 12.7-mm mg **Electronics:** Radar: 1 Raytheon . . . nav.
M: 2 G.M. Detroit Diesel 12V71 TI diesels; 1,020 bhp (840 sust.)
Crew: 2 officers, 8 enlisted

Remarks: Confiscated in 1996. Operates in the Caribbean. Resembles a fishing boat.

PATROL CRAFT [WPC] *(continued)*

Escudo de Verguas (P-305) Panamanian Navy, 11-98

♦ **1 ex-U.S. mine route survey craft** (In serv. . . .)

P-304 Flamenco (ex-103WB 831; ex-*Scherazade,* CT-3; ex-*Scherazade*)

Flamenco (P-304)—as *Scherazade* (CT-3) H&L Van Ginderen, 8-88

D: 220 tons (fl) **S:** 9 kts **Dim:** 30.8 × 7.6 × 2.1
A: 2 single 7.62-mm mg **Electronics:** Radar: 1 Furuno 1411 nav.
M: 2 Caterpillar diesels; 2 props; . . . bhp **Crew:** 2 officers, 9 enlisted

Remarks: Transferred 22-7-92. Wooden-hulled former shrimp boat, later used for U.S. Naval Reserve COOP (Craft Of Opportunity Program) mine route survey work and then as a workboat. Had been acquired for USN service 28-6-85.

PATROL BOATS [WPB]

♦ **3 ex-U.S. Sea Spectre PB Mk IV class**
Bldr: Atlantic Marine, Ft. George Island, Fla.

	Laid down	L	In serv.
P-841 Chiriqui (ex-68PB841)	24-12-84	23-9-85	2-1-86
P-842 Veraguas (ex-68PB842)	25-3-85	11-11-85	2-1-86
P-843 Bocas del Toro (ex-68PB843)	17-6-85	31-12-85	15-2-86

D: 42.25 tons (46 fl) **S:** 20 kts **Dim:** 120.85 × 5.50 × 1.07 (hull; 1.80 props)
A: 2 single 7.62-mm mg **Electronics:** Radar: 1 Furuno 1411 nav.
M: 3 G.M. 12V71 TI diesels; 3 props; 1,950 bhp **Endurance:** 3 days
Range: 450/26; 2,000/. . . **Crew:** 1 officer, 6 enlisted

Remarks: Transferred without armament as grant-aid in 3-98. Aluminum construction. Were able to reach 30 kts when new. Had intricate camouflage paint schemes as of late 1998.

♦ **1 U.S. Swiftships 65-foot class**
Bldr: Swiftships, Morgan City, La. (In serv. 7-82)

P-201 General Esteban Huertas (ex-*Comandante Torrijos,* GC 16)

General Esteban Huertas (P-201)—with old pennant number U.S. Navy, 1983

D: 31.1 tons (35 fl) **S:** 23 kts (13 sust.) **Dim:** 19.81 (17.90 wl) × 5.64 × 1.83
A: 2 single 7.62-mm mg **Electronics:** Radar: 1 Raytheon . . . nav.
M: 2 G.M. Detroit Diesel 12V71 TI N75 diesels; 2 props; 1,020 bhp
Electric: 20 kw tot. **Range:** 500/8 **Fuel:** 6 tons **Crew:** 2 officers, 8 enlisted

Remarks: Badly damaged in the 12-89 invasion, but has been restored to service. Sister *Presidente Porras* (P-202) was sunk. Aluminum construction. Operates in the Caribbean.

♦ **1 former oilfield crew boat**
Bldr: . . .

P-203 Cacique Nome (ex-*Negrita*)

Cacique Nome (P-203)—on land for overhaul Panamanian Navy, 12-98

D: 68 tons (fl) **S:** 13 kts **Dim:** 24.4 × 4.6 × 1.8
A: 2 single 7.62-mm mg **Electronics:** Radar: 1 Raytheon 1900 nav.
M: 2 G.M. Detroit Diesel 12V 71-series diesels; 2 props; 1,680 bhp
Range: 250/10 **Crew:** 2 officers, 6 enlisted

Remarks: Typical oilfield crew boat of U.S. construction. Refitted at Coco Solo and commissioned 5-5-93. Operates on the Pacific coast.

♦ **5 U.S. Coast Guard 82-foot Point class**
Bldr: J. Martinac SB, Tacoma, Wash. (P-206, P-207: U.S. Coast Guard Yard, Curtis Bay, Md.)

	In serv.
P-204 3 de Noviembre (ex-*Point Barrow,* WPB 82348)	4-10-66
P-206 28 de Noviembre (ex-*Point Huron,* WPB 82357)	17-2-67
P-207 10 de Noviembre (ex-*Point Francis,* WPB 82356)	3-2-67
P-208 4 de Noviembre (ex-*Point Winslow,* WPB 82360)	3-3-67
P-209 . . . . . . (ex-*Point Hannon,* WPB 82355)	23-1-67

D: 64 tons (69 fl) **S:** 23.7 kts **Dim:** 25.30 × 5.23 × 1.95
A: 2 single 12.7-mm mg
Electronics:
Radar: 1 Raytheon SPS-64(V)1 (P-208, P-209: Hughes-Furuno SPS-73(V)) nav.
M: P-204: 2 Cummins VT-12-M diesels; 2 props; 1,600 bhp—others: 2 Caterpillar 3412 diesels; 2 props; 1,480 bhp
Range: 490/23; 1,500/8 **Fuel:** 5.7 tons **Crew:** 1 officer, 9 enlisted

Remarks: P-204 was transferred 7-6-91, P-206 and P-207 on 22-4-99, P-208 on 20-9-00, and P-209 on 11-1-01. Well-equipped with navigational and salvage equipment; can tow smallcraft. P-204 operates in the Caribbean.

♦ **1 ex-U.S. MSB 29–class former minesweeping boat**
Bldr: John Trumpy, Annapolis, Md. (In serv. 1954)

P-205 Punta Mala (ex-MSB 29)

D: 80 tons (fl) **S:** 12 kts **Dim:** 25.0 × 5.8 × 1.7
A: 2 single 7.62-mm mg **Electronics:** Radar: 1 Raytheon 1900 nav.
M: 2 Packard 2D850 diesels; 2 props; 600 bhp
Range: 1,500/10 **Crew:** 2 officers, 9 enlisted

Remarks: Transferred to Panama 3-3-93 for use as a patrol craft. Wooden construction. Was the only unit of its class. Operates on the Pacific coast.

♦ **2 ex-U.S. LCPL Mk 11 class**

P-101 Panama P-102 Calamar (ex-PC-3602)

D: 9.75 tons light (13 fl) **S:** 19 kts (15 sust.) **Dim:** 10.98 (9.26 pp) × 3.97 × 1.13
A: 1 7.62-mm mg **Electronics:** Radar: none
M: 1 G.M. 8V71 TI diesel; 350–425 bhp
Range: 160/12 **Fuel:** 630 liters **Crew:** 5 tot.

Remarks: Former U.S. Navy personnel landing craft. P-101 was acquired in 2-98 and P-102 in 12-92. GRP construction. Can also carry up to 2 tons of cargo or 15 passengers. Sisters *Barracuda* (PC-3601) and *Centollo* (PC-3603) were stricken in 1997.

♦ **6 19-foot Guardian-class patrol launches**
Bldr: Boston Whaler, Edgewater, Fla. (In serv. 11-95 through 12-98)

BPC-1801 through BPC-1806

D: 0.79 tons light (1.59 fl) **S:** 35 kts **Dim:** 5.64 × 2.18 × 0.25
A: 1 7.62-mm mg **M:** 2 Johnson gasoline outboard motors; 150 bhp
Fuel: 239 liters **Crew:** 4 tot.

Remarks: GRP foam-core construction. No radar fitted.

♦ **5 22-foot Pirana-class patrol launches**
Bldr: Boston Whaler, Edgewater, Fla. (In serv. 6-91 through 10-92)

BPC-2201 through BPC-2205

D: 1.5 tons (2 fl) **S:** 35 kts **Dim:** 6.81 × 2.26 × 0.60
A: 1 7.62-mm mg **M:** 2 Johnson gasoline outboard motors; 360 bhp
Range: 167/40 **Crew:** 4 tot.

Remarks: GRP foam-core construction. No radar fitted.

PATROL BOATS [WPB] *(continued)*

♦ **10 BPC-3201-class patrol launches**
Bldr: . . . . . . (In serv. 6-95 to 10-98)

BPC-3201 through BPC-3210

D: 7 tons (fl) **S:** 35 kts **Dim:** 10.2 × 2.3 × 0.6
A: 1 7.62-mm mg **Electronics:** Radar: none
M: 2 Yamaha gasoline outboards; 400 bhp **Crew:** 4 tot.

Remarks: Skiff-hulled craft of GRP construction. All serve in the Caribbean.

Note: Also used for patrol are the open launches BPC-2902 and BPC-2903, 9-m craft that operate in the Pacific and were acquired during the mid-1990s.

AUXILIARIES

Note: U.S. Coast Guard seagoing buoy tender *Sweetgum* (WLB 309) has been offered for transfer on 19-9-02.

SERVICE CRAFT

♦ **2 ex-U.S. MSB 5–class logistics support craft [WYF]**

L-16 Nombre de Dios (ex-MSB 28) L-17 Bastimentos (ex-MSB 41)

D: 30 tons light (44 fl) **S:** 12 kts **Dim:** 17.45 × 4.83 × 1.2
A: 1 7.62-mm mg **Electronics:** Radar: 1 Raytheon . . . nav.
M: 2 G.M. Detroit Diesel 6-71 diesels; 2 props; 600 bhp
Crew: 1 officer, 5 enlisted

Remarks: Survivors of a class of 47 minesweeping boats built between 1952 and 1956. Have wooden hulls and nonmagnetic machinery. Transferred to Panama 3-3-93 and used in logistic support duties on the Pacific coast. Armament, all sweep gear, and radar were removed. Sister *Santa Clara* (L-15, ex-MSB 25) was stricken during 1996.

♦ **1 logistic support craft [WYF]**

L-11 Trinidad (ex-*Endeavour*)

D: 120 tons (fl) **S:** 12 kts **Dim:** 22.9 × 4.3 × 2.1
Electronics: Radar: 1 Furuno . . . nav.
M: 1 Caterpillar . . . diesel; 1 prop; 365 bhp **Crew:** 1 officer, 6 enlisted

Remarks: Acquired in 9-91 and entered service in 5-92.

♦ **5 miscellaneous support launches [WYFL]**

BA-051 Bucaro (ex-*Orient Express*)
BA-054 Orca
BA-055 Dorado I
BA-056 Dorado II
BA-057 Anguilla

Remarks: BA-051, employed for training, is a former drug-running, 19-m sailing sloop captured in 1996. BA-054, acquired in 1997, is used for rescue duties on the Pacific coast. BA-055 and BA-056, acquired in 2-98, are 40-kt, outboard-powered open launches used for logistics support. BA-057 is another former drug runner, put in service in 11-98, and is capable of 50 kts.

Note: The Panamanian Customs Service received 16-m, Dutch-built (Delta, Sliedrecht) launches *Hornerito* and *Surubi* in 9-95; no other data available.

PAPUA NEW GUINEA

DEFENCE FORCE MARITIME ELEMENT

Personnel (2002): Approx. 400 total

Bases: Headquarters at Port Moresby. One patrol boat each is deployed to Buka and Alotau. There is also a facility at Lombrun on Manus Island.

Maritime Aviation: The Papua New Guinea Defence Force operates 4 Nomad N.22B light transports, 1 Beech Super King Air 200, and 1 Gulfstream-II transport for coastal patrol and logistics duties.

Note: Ship names are preceded by HMPNGS (Her Majesty's Papua New Guinea Ship).

PATROL CRAFT [PC]

♦ **4 ASI 315 class**
Bldr: Transfield ASI Pty, Ltd., South Coogie, Western Australia

	Laid down	L	In serv.
P 01 Tarangau	. . .	. . .	16-5-87
P 02 Dreger	12-1-87	7-9-87	29-10-87
P 03 Seeadler	21-3-88	21-9-88	28-10-88
P 04 Basilisk	19-10-88	. . .	1-7-89

D: 165 tons (fl) **S:** 21 kts (20 sust.)
Dim: 31.50 (28.60 wl) × 8.10 × 2.12 (1.80 hull)
A: 1 20-mm 90-cal. Oerlikon GAM-B01 AA; 2 single 12.7-mm M2 mg
Electronics: Radar: 1 Furuno. . . nav.
M: 2 Caterpillar 3516TA diesels; 2 props; 2,820 bhp (2,400 sust.)
Electric: 116 kw (2 × 50-kw Caterpillar 3304 diesels; 1 × 16 kw)
Range: 2,500/12 **Fuel:** 27.9 tons **Endurance:** 8–10 days
Crew: 3 officers, 14 enlisted

Basilisk (P 04) LSPH W. McBride, RAN, 7-89

Remarks: First two ordered 19-3-85, the other pair 3-10-85. Australian foreign aid program Pacific Patrol Boat, with sisters in a number of Southwest Pacific–area island nation forces. Carry a 5-m aluminum boarding boat. Have an extensive navigational suite, including Furuno FSN-70 NAVSAT receiver, Furuno 525 HFD/F, Furuno 120 MF–HFD/F, FE-881 echo sounder, and DS-70 doppler log. The original Furuno radar was replaced in all during 1997 refits in Australia; the navigational systems were also updated.

AMPHIBIOUS WARFARE SHIPS

♦ **2 ex-Australian Balikpapan-class utility landing craft [LCU]**
Bldr: Walkers Ltd., Maryborough

31 Salamaua (In serv. 19-10-73) 32 Buna (In serv. 7-12-73)

Salamaua (31) Gilbert Gyssels, 1980

D: 316 tons (503 fl) **S:** 8 kts **Dim:** 44.5 × 10.1 × 1.9
A: 2 single 12.7-mm M2 mg **Electronics:** Radar: 1 Decca RM 916 nav.
M: 3 G.M. Detroit Diesel 12V71 diesels; 3 props; 675 bhp
Range: 1,300–2,280/10 (depending on load) **Crew:** 2 officers, 11 enlisted

Remarks: In service in 1972 and transferred in 1975. Cargo: 140–180 tons. Refitted 1985–86.

SERVICE CRAFT

♦ **1 ex-Australian small harbor tug [YTL]**
Bldr: Perrin Eng., Brisbane (In serv. 1972)

HTS 503

D: 47.5 tons **S:** 9 kts **Dim:** 15.4 × 4.6 × 1.1
M: 2 G.M. Detroit Diesel 3-71 diesels; 2 props; 340 bhp
Range: 710/9 **Crew:** 3 tot.

Remarks: Transferred in 1974. Retains Royal Australian Navy pennant number.

PARAGUAY

Republic of Paraguay

ARMADA NACIONAL DE PARAGUAY

Personnel (2001): 1,677 total, including 50 naval aviation, 450 marines, and the coast guard *(Prefectura General Naval),* the last a nonwaterborne force

Bases: On the Río Paraguay: Base Naval de Bahía Negra (BNBN). On the Río Parana: Base Naval Ciudad del Este (BNCE), Base Naval de Encarnación (BNE), Base Naval de Salto del Guairá (BNSG), and Base Naval de Ita-Piru (BNIP). Repairs and maintenance are performed at the Arsenal de Marina, Puerto Sajonia, near Asunción.

Organization: The principal commands include the Cuartel General, Comando de la Flota, Comando de la Infantería de Marina, Comando de la Aviación Naval, Comando de Apoyo de Combate, Comando de Institutos Navales de Ensenanza, Prefectura General Naval, Dirección de Apoyo de Servicio, and Dirección del Material.

Naval Aviation: Fixed wing assets include 2 Cessna 310, and 1 Cessna 150M light utility aircraft. Helicopters include 2 Helibras AS.350B Esquilo (referred to locally as HB-350, or UH-50). Fixed-wing aircraft are based at Asunción International Airport and helicopters at Puerto Sajonia, near Asunción. Four Robinson R-44 light helicopters are to be ordered.

Paraguayan Navy AS.350B Esquilo helicopter Hartmut Ehlers, 5-00

PATROL COMBATANTS [PG]

♦ 1 Brazilian Roraima class
Bldr: Ars. de Marinha do Rio de Janeiro

	Laid down	L	In serv.
P 05 Itaipú	3-3-83	16-3-84	2-4-85

Itaipú (P 05)—alongside a unit of the *Bouchard* class Hartmut Ehlers, 5-00

D: 220 tons light (384 fl) **S:** 14.5 kts **Dim:** 46.3 (45.0 pp) × 8.45 × 1.42 (max.)
A: 1 40-mm 60-cal. Bofors Mk 3 AA; 2 single 12.7-mm M2 mg; 2 81-mm mortar/12.7-mm mg combination mounts
Electronics: Radar: 1 . . . nav.
M: 2 M.A.N. V6V 16/18 TL diesels; 2 props; 1,824 bhp (1,732 sust.)
Range: 4,500/11 **Endurance:** 30 days
Crew: 9 officers, 31 enlisted + 30 marines

Remarks: Order was announced 11-4-83. Has small helicopter deck and can accommodate one of the AS.350 helicopters. Carries medical personnel for civic action duties.

♦ 2 ex-Argentinian Bouchard class
Bldr: Rio Santiago NY, Argentina

	L	In serv.
P 02 Nanawa (ex-*Bouchard*)	20-3-36	16-5-37
P 04 Teniente Farina (ex-*Py*)	31-3-38	1-7-38

Nanawa (P 02) Hartmut Ehlers, 5-00

D: 450 tons (650 fl) **S:** 16 kts **Dim:** 59.5 × 7.3 × 2.6
A: 2 twin 40-mm 60-cal. Bofors AA; 2 single 12.7-mm mg
Electronics: Radar: 1 . . . nav.
M: 2 M.A.N. diesels; 2 props; 2,000 bhp **Range:** 3,000/12 **Crew:** 70 tot.

Remarks: Former ocean minesweepers. P 02 was donated in 1-64 and P 04 was purchased 6-3-68. Sister *Capitán Meza* (P 03, ex-M 2, ex-*Seaver*) is now employed as an immobile barracks hulk.

♦ 2 Paraguay class (1 in *reserve*)
Bldr: Cantieri Odero, Genoa, Italy (In serv. 5-31)

C 1 Paraguay (ex-*Comodoro Meyo*)
C 2 *Humaitá* (ex-*Capitán Cabral*)

Paraguay (C 1) Hartmut Ehlers, 5-00

Humaitá (C 2) Monika Wolforth, 5-00

D: 636 tons light; 745 normal (856 fl) **S:** 17.5 kts **Dim:** 70.15 × 10.70 × 1.65
A: C 1: 2 twin 120-mm 50-cal. Ansaldo Model 1926 low-angle; 3 single 76-mm 40-cal. Odero-Terni Model 1917 AA; 2 single 40-mm 39-cal. Odero-Terni Model 1928 2-pdr. AA
Electronics: Radar: 1 . . . nav.
M: 2 sets Parsons geared steam turbines; 2 props; 3,800 shp **Boilers:** 2
Range: 1,700/16 **Fuel:** 170 tons **Crew:** 86 tot.

Remarks: Configuration has changed very little from that when first delivered nearly 70 years ago. Have light armor: 12.7-mm to sides and 7.6-mm to decks. The boilers have become unreliable, and the propulsion plant may eventually be replaced with diesel engines. C 2 was relegated to floating museum status on 6-9-00 but remains on the official force list.
Combat systems: The 120-mm mounts were developed for use on late-1920s Italian destroyer classes. An optical rangefinder serves each of the two 120-mm gunmounts. The 76-mm guns are not U.S. mounts as previously listed but are instead high-angle mounts of Italian origin. The 40-mm AA on C 1 are the last of their type on an active warship in any navy; the inactive C 2 has two single 40-mm 60-cal. Bofors AA and two single Oerlikon 20-mm AA.

♦ 1 former tug Bldr: Werf Conrad, Haarlem, the Netherlands (In serv. 1908)

P 01 Capitán Cabral (ex-*Triunfo,* ex-*Adolfo Riquelme*)

Capitán Cabral (P 01) Hartmut Ehlers, 5-00

D: 180 tons (206 fl) **S:** 8 kts **Dim:** 34.50 (30.00 pp) × 7.10 × 1.71
A: 1 40-mm 60-cal. Mk 3 Bofors AA; 2 single 20-mm 70-cal. Oerlikon AA; 2 single 12.7-mm M2 mg

PATROL COMBATANTS [PG] *(continued)*

Electronics: Radar: 1 . . . nav.
M: 1 Caterpillar 3408 diesel; 1 prop; 336 bhp **Crew:** 25 tot.

Remarks: Steel or iron hull (not wood as previously reported). Originally reciprocating steam-powered, she was re-engined and rearmed in the late 1980s. Operates from Puerto Sajonia, Asunción.

PATROL BOATS [PB]

Note: Two Rodman 101–class and five Rodman 55–class patrol launches ordered from Spain 19-9-95 were never delivered due to payment problems; the craft were eventually sold to Surinam by the builder.

♦ 2 Yhaguy class Bldr: . . ., Taiwan (In serv. 23-6-99)

P 08 Yhaguy P 09 Tebicuary

Tebicuary (P 09) Hartmut Ehlers, 5-00

D: 20 tons (fl) **S:** 40 kts **Dim:** 16.5 × . . . × . . .
A: 2 single 12.7-mm mg **Electronics:** Radar: 1 . . . nav.
M: 2 gasoline inboard engines; 800 bhp **Crew:** 12 tot.

Remarks: Donated by Taiwan. GRP construction.

♦ 13 P 07 class Bldr: Arsenal de Marina, Asunción

	L		L		L		L
P 07	9-89	P 11	12-9-91	P 15	9-93	P 19	9-95
P 08	10-9-90	P 12	9-92	P 16	9-94		
P 09	10-9-90	P 13	9-92	P 17	9-94		
P 10	12-9-91	P 14	9-93	P 18	9-95		

D: 18 tons (fl) **S:** 12 kts **Dim:** 14.70 × 3.06 × 0.85
A: 2 single 12.7-mm mg **Electronics:** Radar: none
M: 2 G.M. 6-71 diesels; 2 props; 340 bhp **Range:** 240/12 **Crew:** 4 tot.

Remarks: Steel construction units, designed by the Paraguayan Navy and built at its own facilities to save funds. Replaced six small patrol craft delivered by the U.S. in 1967–71.

♦ 2 ex-Taiwanese Tzu Chiang class
Bldr: China Shipbuilding Corp., Kaohsiung (In serv. 31-12-77)

P 06 Capitán Ortiz (ex-FABG 3) P 07 Teniente Robles (ex-FABG 4)

Capitán Ortiz (P 06)—outboard *Teniente Robles* (P 07) Hartmut Ehlers, 5-00

D: 47 tons (fl) **S:** 38 kts **Dim:** 22.86 × 5.49 × 0.94 (1.82 props)
A: 1 20-mm 70-cal. Oerlikon AA; 1 12.7-mm mg
Electronics: Radar: 1 Decca 926 nav.
M: 3 MTU 12V331 TC81 diesels; 3 props; 4,020 bhp
Electric: 30 kw tot. (1 × 30-kw Ford diesel set)
Range: 700/32; 1,200/17 **Crew:** 12 tot.

Remarks: Former prototype guided-missile patrol boats, with a design based on the Israeli Dvora class but with slightly different hullform, three engines, and a tall pylon mast. Were decommissioned in 1994, disarmed, and donated to Paraguay in 11-94. Aluminum construction.

♦ 2 LP 101 class Bldr: Sewart Seacraft, Berwick, La. (In serv. 12-67)

LP 101 LP 102

LP 102 Hartmut Ehlers, 5-00

D: 15 tons (fl) **S:** 20 kts **Dim:** 13.1 × 3.9 × 0.9
A: 2 single 12.7-mm mg **Electronics:** Radar: none
M: 2 G.M. Detroit Diesel 6-71 diesels; 2 props; 500 bhp **Crew:** 7 tot.

Remarks: Survivors of six delivered 1967–71 and stricken during the early 1990s. These two had been restored to operations by 12-97, and the others (LP 103–LP 106) may have followed. Aluminum construction.

AMPHIBIOUS WARFARE CRAFT

♦ 3 U.S. LCVP Mk 7 class [LCVP]
Bldr: . . . . . ., Ladario, Brazil (In serv. 1980s)

EDVP 01 EDVP 02 EDVP 03

EDVP 03 Hartmut Ehlers, 5-00

D: 9 tons (13 fl) **S:** 8 kts **Dim:** 10.90 × 3.21 × 1.04 (aft)
M: 1 Saab Scania D11 diesel; 157 bhp

Remarks: GRP hulls. Can carry 36 troops or 3.5 tons of cargo. Cargo deck is 5.24 × 2.29 m, with a 2.00-m-wide access through the bow ramp.

AUXILIARIES

Disposal note: Ex-U.S. LSM 1–class headquarters ship *Boqueron* (BC 1, ex-*Teniente Pratt Gil,* ex-*Corrientes,* ex-LSM 86) had been removed from service by 12-97 but remains afloat as a hulk, pending disposal. Cargo and training ship *Guarani,* owned by the navy, is on charter to a commercial operator and operates between Asunción, Buenos Aires, and Montevideo; as of 5-00, the ship had been stripped of much of the cargo-handling gear but remained in service with a naval crew.

SERVICE CRAFT

♦ 1 river transport [YF] Bldr: Arsenal de Marina, Asunción (In serv. 1964)

T 1 Teniente Herreros (ex-*Presidente Stroessner*)

D: 420 tons (fl) **S:** 10 kts **Dim:** 37.8 × 9.0 × 2.2
M: 2 MWM diesels; 2 props; 330 bhp

Remarks: 150 grt. Cargo: 120 tons. Has a single 1-ton electrohydraulic crane amidships and superstructure near the stern. There are also several very small stores carriers in service.

♦ 1 U.S. LCU 501–class ferry [YFB]
Bldr: Bison Shipbuilding Corp., Buffalo, N.Y. (In serv. 13-4-44)

BT 1 (ex-YFB 82, ex-LCU 1040)

BT 1—under reconstruction Hartmut Ehlers, 5-00

SERVICE CRAFT *(continued)*

D: 143 tons light (309 fl) **S:** 10 kts **Dim:** 36.8 (32.00 wl) × 9.96 × 1.2 (aft)
M: 3 G.M. Gray Marine 64YTL diesels; 3 props; 675 bhp

Remarks: Former U.S. Navy landing craft, adapted as a personnel and vehicle ferry and transferred to Uruguay during 6-70. Had been stricken by 12-97, along with sister BT 2 (ex-U.S. YFB 86), but as of 5-01 was being reconstructed at Asunción, employing materials and equipment from the original craft. The "new" BT 1 has a much larger superstructure than the original and may have an enlarged, barge-type hull. The characteristics data above apply to the craft as originally completed and may no longer be applicable.

♦ 1 ex-U.S. floating dry dock [YFDL]
Bldr: Doullut & Ewin, Mobile, Ala. (In serv. 6-44)

DF 1 (ex-AFDL 26)

DF 1 Hartmut Ehlers, 5-00

Lift capacity: 1,000 tons **Dim:** 60.96 × 19.5 × 1.04 (light)

Remarks: Transferred in 3-65.

♦ 1 presidential yacht [YFL]
3 de Febrero

3 de Febrero Hartmut Ehlers, 5-00

Remarks: Low-freeboard, white-painted craft operated by the navy. No data available.

Disposal note: Navigational aids tender B 1 is now assigned to the Obras Publicas y Comunicaciones.

♦ 1 riverine survey launch [YGS] Bldr: . . . (In serv. 1957)
4 de Mayo

Remarks: Displaces 50 tons and has crew of 1 officer and 9 enlisted. Formerly listed as the *Lancha Ecografa,* which was her type designation, not her name.

♦ 1 survey launch [YGS]
LH 1 S/O R. Lesme

S/O R. Lesme (LH 1) Hartmut Ehlers, 5-00

Remarks: No information available. Resembles a U.S. Coast Guard 40-ft. utility boat of 1950s vintage but appears to be larger.

Note: The four miscellaneous dredges, *Asunción* (RP 1), *Progreso* (D 1), *Draga* (D 2), and D 3 are no longer part of the navy but are assigned to the Obras Publicas y Comunicaciones.

♦ 1 ex-U.S. YTL 422–class tug
Bldr: Gunderson Bros. Eng. Corp., Portland, Ore.

	Laid down	L	In serv.
R 4 Triunfo (ex-YTL 567)	5-3-45	17-8-45	30-10-45

Triunfo (R 4) Hartmut Ehlers, 5-00

D: 85 tons (fl) **S:** 9 kts **Dim:** 20.17 × 5.18 × 1.50
M: 1 Scania DSI 14 M03 diesel; 1 prop; 357 bhp **Crew:** 5 tot.

Remarks: Date of transfer unknown, but was apparently during the mid-1970s. Had been reported stricken, but was noted in service during 2000. May have been re-engined and modified as per the *Angostura* (R 5).

♦ 1 ex-U.S. YTL 131–class tug [YTL]
Bldr: Robert Jacob, Inc., Staten Island, N.Y.

	Laid down	L	In serv.
R 5 Angostura (ex-YTL 211)	26-12-41	20-6-42	21-8-42

Angostura (R 5)—at right, with two R 2–class tugs; note the extended funnel and new pilothouse atop the old on the *Angostura* Hartmut Ehlers, 12-97

D: 82 tons **S:** 9 kts **Dim:** 20.2 (19.5 wl) × 5.5 × 2.4
M: 1 Scania DSI 14 M03 diesel; 1 prop; 357 bhp **Crew:** 5 tot.

Remarks: Transferred by lease in 3-65. Has been re-engined in Paraguay, and a pilothouse has been added above the original pilothouse.

♦ 2 R 2–class small tugs [YTL]
R 6 Stella Maris R 7 Esperanza

R 2–class tug Esperanza (R 7) Hartmut Ehlers, 5-00

Remarks: Locally built, 20-ton craft. Sister R 2 had been retired by end-2000.

Note: An open-launch dockyard tug, the *Arsenal 1* (A 1), is also in service, and the Prefectura General Naval operates a few waterborne craft, including the outboard motor–propelled PGN 214.

PERU

Republic of Peru

MARINA DE GUERRA DEL PERÚ

Personnel (2001): 2,300 officers, 25,000 enlisted (including the 5,000 officers and enlisted of the Naval Infantry)

Bases: Callao (with dockyard), San Lorenzo (submarines), Chimbote, Paita, and San Juan, with river bases at Iquitos and on the Río Madre de Dios and the Lake Titicaca base at Puno. Minor bases are located at El Salto, Bayovar, Pimental, Pacasmayo, Salaverry, Mollendo, Matarani, Ilo, Inambari, Pucallpa, and El Estrecho. The naval academy is located at La Punta, Callao.

Organization: Organized into two commands: Pacific Naval Force, headquartered at Callao, and Amazon River Force, headquartered at Iquitos. The Pacific Naval Force is subdivided into five naval forces: Surface, Submarine, Naval Aviation, Infantry, and Special Operations. Planning for a reorganization was under way during 2001. Operations are geographically divided into five naval zones: I Zone at Piura, II Zone at Callao, III Zone at Arequipa, IV Zone at Pucallpa, and V Zone at Iquitos.

Naval Aviation: Fixed-wing, land-based aircraft include 5 Beech Super King Air 200T maritime patrol aircraft; 1 Fokker F-27-200, 1 Fokker F-27-500, 1 Fokker F-27-600, and 2 Antonov An-32B transports; 3 Beech T-34C trainers; and 1 Cessna 206 light liaison aircraft. Helicopters include 3 AM 39 Exocet SSM–equipped ASH-3D Sea King, 5 Agusta-Bell AB-212AS, 4 Bell 206B JetRanger, 1 Bell 205A, and 3 Mil Mi-8T Hip.

Peruvian Fokker F-27-500 Peruvian Navy, 2000

Peruvian ASH-3D Sea King—aboard frigate *Mariategui* (FM 54) Peruvian Navy, 4-01

Peruvian Agusta-Bell AB-212AS—aboard frigate *Carvajal* (FM 51) Peruvian Navy, 6-01

Peruvian Bell 206B JetRanger Peruvian Navy, 2001

Peruvian Mil Mi-8T Hip Peruvian Navy, 2001

Marines: The 5,000-strong naval infantry force is headquartered at Ancón and is divided into the *Guarnición de Marina* 1st Battalion and *Guardia Chalaca* 2nd Battalion at Ancón; *Punta Malpelo* 3rd Battalion at Tumbes; and *Ucayali* 4th Battalion at Pucallpa. The force is equipped with armored cars and with light amphibious vehicles.

Weapons Systems: The navy's Centro de Fabricación de Armas (CEFAR) division of the SIMA shipyard group has designed and deployed the MGP-86 *(Marina de Guerra del Perú)* quadruple SAM launcher, which employs manned, open launchers similar to those developed for the Russian Navy to launch 9M-39 Igla (NATO SA-16 Gimlet) heat-seeking SAMs purchased from Nicaragua in 1994. The same launcher is also being deployed in land-based batteries.

Note: Ship names are preceded by BAP (*Buque Armada Peruana,* or Peruvian Naval Ship).

ATTACK SUBMARINES [SS]

♦ 6 German Type 209/1200 Bldr: Howaldtswerke, Kiel

	L	In serv.
SS 31 Angamos (ex-*Casma*)	31-8-79	19-12-80
SS 32 Antofagasta	19-12-79	14-3-80
SS 33 Pisagua (ex-*Blume*)	19-5-81	8-4-82
SS 34 Chipana (ex-*Pisagua*)	7-8-81	12-7-83
SS 35 Islay	11-10-73	23-1-75
SS 36 Arica	5-4-74	4-4-75

Arica (SS 36) Peruvian Navy, 1999

Arica (SS 36)—sail area Peruvian Navy, 1999

ATTACK SUBMARINES [SS] *(continued)*

D: 1,000 tons surf. std.; 1,180 tons fl/1,285 tons sub.
S: 11 kts surf./12 kts snorkel/21 kts sub. (for 5 min) **Dim:** 55.90 × 6.30 × 5.50
A: 8 bow 533-mm TT (14 tot. German SST-4 Mod. 0 wire-guided torpedoes)
Electronics:
Radar: 1 Thales Calypso nav./surf. search
Sonar: S 31, 32: STN Atlas Elektronik CSU 3-Z active; PRS 3-4 passive—SS 33–36: STN Atlas Elektronik CSU-83 active/passive suite—all: Thales DUUX-2C intercept
EW: . . . . . . intercept
M: 4 MTU Type 12V493 AZ80 GA31L diesels, each linked to a 450-kw Siemens alternator, 1 Siemens electric motor; 1 prop; 4,600 shp
Range: 11,300/4 surf.; 28/20, 460/4 sub. **Fuel:** 63 tons
Endurance: 40 days **Crew:** 5 officers, 30 (SS 35, 36: 26) enlisted

Remarks: SS 31 and SS 32 were ordered 12-8-76, two others in 3-77. Delivery of SS 33 was delayed by a collision 2-4-82. SS 32 completed an overhaul at SIMA, Callao, in 10-96. SS 31 was renamed on 19-8-98. Planning for a modernization for the entire class was under way during 2001.
Hull systems: SS 33 and later are 56.1 m o.a., 1,185 tons surf./1,290 tons sub. Diving depth: 250 m. The battery has four groups of 120 cells, weighs 257 tons, and produces 11,500 amp-hr.
Combat systems: All now have the Sepa Mk 3 torpedo fire-control system.

CRUISERS [CL]

♦ 1 ex-Dutch De Ruyter–class light cruiser
Bldr: Wilton-Fijenoord, Schiedam

	Laid down	L	In serv.
CLM 81 ALMIRANTE GRAU (ex-*De Ruyter*, ex-*De Zeven Provinciën*)	5-9-39	24-12-44	18-11-53

D: 9,681 tons (12,165 fl) **S:** 32 kts **Dim:** 187.32 (182.4 pp) × 17.25 × 6.72
A: 8 Otomat Mk 2 SSM; 4 twin 152-mm 53-cal. Bofors DP; 2 twin 40-mm 70-cal. OTOBreda AA; 4 single 40-mm 70-cal. Bofors AA
Electronics:
Radar: 1 Decca 1226 nav.; 1 Thales DA-08 surf. search; 1 Thales LW-08 early warning; 1 Thales WM-25 track-while-scan gun/missile f.c.; 1 Thales STIR-24 SAM illuminator; 2 Thales LIROD-8 gun f.c.
EW: Thales Rapids intercept; CME Scimitar deceptive jammer; 1 Matra Défense Sagaie decoy RL; 2 Matra Défense Dagaie decoy RL
M: 2 sets Parsons geared steam turbines; 2 props; 85,000 shp
Boilers: 4 Yarrow-Werkspoor, three-drum **Electric:** 4,000 kw tot.
Range: 2,100/32; 6,900/12 **Crew:** 49 officers, 904 enlisted

Remarks: Purchased 7-3-73, recommissioned 23-5-73. Completion of refitting at Amsterdamse Droogdok Maatschappij planned for 26-3-85 to 1987 was delayed by shipyard bankruptcy and Peruvian payment difficulties. During refit, was known as "Proyecto 01." Left the Netherlands 22-1-88 and was officially recommissioned 7-89 in Peru, but without many of the weapons and systems planned for her modernization. The modernization was eventually completed in 1994 at SIMA, Callao. Currently active as flagship of the Fuerza de Superficie. Is the world's last operational gun cruiser and carries the largest naval guns currently in service.

Almirante Grau (CLM 81) Peruvian Navy, 4-01

Hull systems: Armor consists of a 76- to 102-mm belt and 20 to 25 mm on two decks; the 152-mm gunhouses are lightly armored.
Combat systems: During modernization, was fitted with the H.S.A. (now Thales) SEWACO-PE combat system. Four twin 57-mm Bofors DP were removed prior to departure for Europe; these and eight single 40-mm AA removed during her period in the Netherlands were sent to Sweden for rehabilitation; the 57-mm guns have not been remounted, but in 1994 eight single 40-mm weapons and eight Otomat cruise missile containers were installed. The four forward 40-mm single mounts were replaced in 1995 by the two twin OTOBreda Dardo mountings removed from the *Daring*-class destroyer *Palacios.* Was to have received two octuple Albatros SAM launchers for Aspide SAMs during the refit in the Netherlands, but although the foundations were added, the launchers were not, and the after position now accommodates the radome housing a SHF SATCOM antenna. Can carry 3,250 rounds of 152-mm and 16,000 rounds of 40-mm ammunition. The original CWE-10N sonar was removed during modernization. The antenna for a Panamax SATCOM system is mounted in a larger radome on the after superstructure.

DESTROYERS [DD]

♦ 1 ex-U.K. Daring class
Bldr: Yarrow, Scotstoun, Glasgow

	Laid down	L	In serv.
DM 74 FERRÉ (ex-*Decoy*)	22-9-46	29-3-49	28-4-53

D: 2,819 tons (3,592 fl) **S:** 32 kts
Dim: 121.60 (111.55 pp) × 13.10 × 4.60 (5.50 max.)
A: 8 MM 38 Exocet SSM; 3 twin 114-mm 45-cal. Mk V DP; provision for 2 4-round MGP-86 SAM syst. (9M39 Igla missiles); 2 twin 40-mm 70-cal. OTOBreda Dardo AA
Electronics:
Radar: 1 Decca 250 HC nav.; 1 Plessey AWS-1 air search; 1 Thales Triton surf./air search; 4 AESN RTN-10X f.c.
Sonar: removed
EW: F0417-501 intercept

Almirante Grau (CLM 81) Peruvian Navy, 4-01

DESTROYERS [DD] *(continued)*

Ferré (DM 74) Peruvian Navy, 11-00

Ferré (DM 74) Peruvian Navy, 4-01

M: 2 sets English Electric geared steam turbines; 2 props; 54,800 shp
Boilers: 2 Babcock & Wilcox (45.7 kg/cm^2; 454° C superheat)
Range: 3,500/15 **Fuel:** 584 tons **Crew:** 17 officers, 205 enlisted

Remarks: Purchased in 1969 and refitted by Cammell Laird in the U.K., completing in 1973. Modernized again during 1977–78. Was to have been retired in 1999 but was still in service as of fall 2000. Sister *Palacios* (DM 73, ex-*Diana*) was stricken in 1993.

Combat systems: Has the AESN NA-10 gun fire-control system, with radar directors atop the bridge, abaft the after stack, and port and starboard near the 40-mm gunmounts. A helicopter platform is fitted at the stern.

FRIGATES [FF]

♦ 4 Italian Lupo class

Bldrs: FM 51, 52: Fincantieri, Riva Trigoso; FM 53, 54: SIMA, Callao

	Laid down	L	In serv.
FM 51 Carvajal	8-10-74	17-11-76	5-2-79
FM 52 Villavisencio	6-10-76	7-2-78	25-6-79
FM 53 Montero	16-6-76	8-10-82	29-7-84
FM 54 Mariategui	13-8-76	8-10-84	28-12-87

D: 2,208 tons (2,500 fl) **S:** 32 kts **Dim:** 108.4 (106.0 pp) × 11.28 × 3.66
A: 8 Otomat Mk 2 SSM; 1 127-mm 54-cal. OTOBreda DP; 1 8-round Albatros SAM syst. (8 Aspide missiles); provision for 2 4-round MGP-86 SAM syst. (9M-39 Igla missiles); 2 twin 40-mm 70-cal. OTOBreda Dardo AA; 2 triple 324-mm Mk 32 ASW TT (WASS A-244 torpedoes); 1 AB-212 (FM 51, 54: ASH-3D Sea King with AM 39 Exocet missiles) ASW helicopter

Carvajal (FM 51)—with AB-212AS helicopter on the lengthened flight deck aft
Peruvian Navy, 2000

Villavisencio (FM 52)—with the original short-length helicopter deck
Peruvian Navy, 6-01

Mariategui (FM 54)—with ASH-3D Sea King on lengthened helicopter deck
Peruvian Navy, 4-01

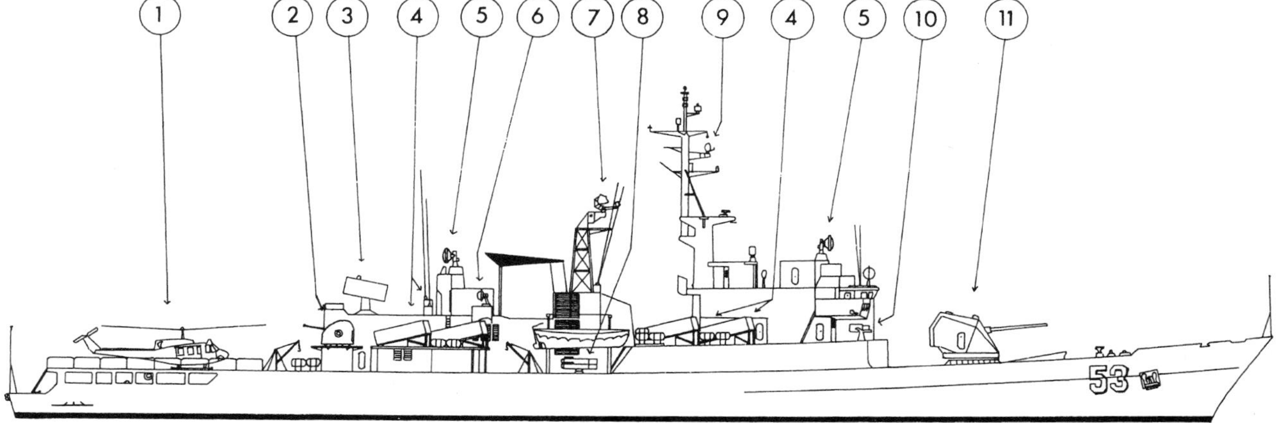

Montero (FM 53) 1. AB-212AS helicopter on original-length helicopter platform 2. twin 40-mm OTOBreda Dardo AA 3. 8-round Albatros system SAM launcher 4. Otomat Mk 2 antiship missile launch canisters 5. RTN-10X gun (forward) and RTN-30X SAM f.c. radars 6. RTN-20X radar gun f.c. directors port and starboard for 40-mm AA 7. RAN-10S air-search radar 8. triple ASW torpedo tubes 9. RAN-11LX surface-search radar 10. 20-round SCLAR decoy rocket launcher 11. 127-mm 54-cal. OTOBreda DP gun
Drawing by Robert Dumas, from *Flottes de Combat*

FRIGATES [FF] *(continued)*

Montero (FM 53)—with USS *Rodney M. Davis* (FFG 60) in foreground — Peruvian Navy, 7-01

Electronics:
Radar: 1 S.M.A. 3RM20 nav.; 1 AESN RAN-11LX surface search; 1 AESN RAN-10S air search; 1 AESN RTN-10X f.c.; 2 AESN RTN-20X f.c.; 1 AESN RTN-30X f.c.
Sonar: EDO 610E hull-mounted (6, 7, 8 kHz)
EW: Elettronica Lambda intercept; 2 20-round 105-mm OTOBreda SCLAR decoy RL
M: CODOG: 2 Fiat-G.E. LM-2500 gas turbines (25,000 shp each), 2 GMT A230-20M diesels (3,900 bhp each); 2 CP props
Electric: 3,120 kw tot.
Range: 900/35 (on gas turbines); 3,450/20.5 (on diesels)
Crew: 20 officers, 165 enlisted

Remarks: Italian technicians assisted in the building of FM 53 and FM 54 at Callao. Differ from the Italian Navy's version in having a fixed (vice telescoping) hangar and a step down to the hull at the stern; the Dardo 40-mm mounts are one deck higher, and the SAM fire-control system also differs. Planning for a modernization for the entire class was under way during 2001.
Combat systems: Selenia IPN-10 data system is fitted. There are no reloads for the Albatros SAM system. The helicopter provides over-the-horizon targeting and mid-course guidance for the Otomat missiles. In 1989, were fitted with equipment to permit refueling hovering Sea King helicopters. One unit was used in trials during 1996 with a single MGP-86 manned SAM launcher for Russian 9M-39 Igla (NATO SA-16 Gimlet) missiles, and the others have since been backfitted to accept the launchers, two of which are installed during periods of crisis. FM 51 and 54 were modified at SIMA, Callao, in 1997–98 with helicopter decks extended right to the stern to accommodate a Sea King helicopter; the hangars remained unaltered, however.

GUIDED-MISSILE PATROL COMBATANTS [PGG]

♦ 6 French PR-72-560 class

Bldr: SFCN, Villeneuve-la-Garenne (hulls of CM 21, 23, 25 by Arsenal de Lorient)

	L	In serv.
CM 21 Velarde	16-9-78	25-7-80
CM 22 Santillana	11-9-79	25-7-80
CM 23 De los Heros	20-5-79	17-11-80
CM 24 Herrera	16-2-79	26-2-81
CM 25 Larrea	20-5-79	16-6-81
CM 26 Sanchez Carrion	28-6-79	14-9-81

D: 470 tons light; 560 tons normal (610 fl) **S:** 37 (CM 21–23: 34) kts
Dim: 64.0 (59.0 pp) × 8.35 × 2.60 (max.)
A: 4 MM 38 Exocet SSM; 1 76-mm 62-cal. OTOBreda Compact DP; 1 twin 40-mm 70-cal. OTOBreda-Bofors AA; provision for 1 4-round MGP-86 SAM launcher (9M-39 Igla/SA-16 Gimlet missiles); 2 single 7.62-mm mg
Electronics:
Radar: 1 Decca TM 1226 nav.; 1 Thales THD 1040 Triton air/surf. search; 1 Thales Castor-II f.c.
EW: Thales DR-2000 intercept
M: CM 21–23: 4 MTU 12V595-series diesels; 4 props; 17,424 bhp—CM 24–26: 4 SACM AGO 240 V-16 M7 diesels; 4 props; 22,000 bhp
Electric: 560 kw tot. **Range:** 1,200/30; 2,500/16 **Crew:** 36 tot. (accomm. for 46)

Santillana (CM 22) — Peruvian Navy, 5-01

Sanchez Carrion (CM 26) — Peruvian Navy, 6-01

Remarks: Originally were numbered P 101–P 106. Under a late 1998 contract, are being refitted and re-engined and given new engine controls and monitoring systems; three had been completed as of 7-01.
Hull systems: A helicopter VERTREP (Vertical Replenishment) station is painted on the fantail, to starboard.
Combat systems: Have the Thales Vega weapons-control system, with a Matra Défense Panda backup optical gun director. During modernization refits, are being fitted to accept the portable, Peruvian-developed MGP-86 point-defense SAM launcher, which uses 9M-39 Igla missiles purchased secondhand from Nicaragua in 1994.

PATROL CRAFT [PC]

♦ 2 Marañon-class river gunboats

Bldr: John I. Thornycroft, Woolston, U.K.

	Laid down	L	In serv.
CF 13 Ucayali (ex-CF 401)	4-50	7-3-51	3-10-51
CF 14 Marañon (ex-CF 402)	4-50	23-4-51	3-10-51

PATROL CRAFT [PC] *(continued)*

Marañon (CF 14) Peruvian Navy, 1999

D: 350 tons (365 fl) **S:** 12 kts **Dim:** 47.22 × 9.75 × 1.22
A: 1 76.2-mm 50-cal. U.S. Mk 26 DP; 2 single 40-mm 60-cal. Bofors Mk 3 AA; 2 single 20-mm 70-cal. Oerlikon Mk 10 AA
Electronics: Radar: 1 . . . nav.
M: 2 British Polar M441 diesels; 2 props; 800 bhp
Range: 5,000/10 **Crew:** 4 officers, 36 enlisted

Remarks: Based at Iquitos for service on the upper Amazon. Steel hulled with aluminum-alloy superstructures. The after 76.2-mm mount was replaced by a second 40-mm mounting, and the twin 20-mm mounts have been replaced by singles.

♦ **2 Amazonas-class river gunboats**
Bldr: Electric Boat Co., Groton, Conn. (In serv. 1934)

CF 11 Amazonas (ex-CF 403) CF 12 Loreto (ex-CF 404)

Amazonas (CF 11) Peruvian Navy, 1999

D: 250 tons **S:** 15 kts **Dim:** 46.7 × 6.7 × 1.2
A: 1 76.2-mm 50-cal. U.S. Mk 26 DP; 3 single 40-mm 60-cal. Mk 3 Bofors AA; 2 single 20-mm 70-cal. Oerlikon AA
M: 2 diesels; 2 props; 750 bhp **Range:** 4,000/10 **Crew:** 5 officers, 30 enlisted

Remarks: Based at Iquitos on the upper Amazon. The 40-mm AA mounts have shields, and a third 40-mm mount has replaced the after 76.2-mm weapon. Do not have radars.

Note: The old river gunboat *America* (15), nonoperational since 1981, is retained as a museum at Iquitos. The former U.S. *Cannon*-class frigate *Castilla* (ex-*Bangust,* DE 739) is hulked at Iquitos on the upper Amazon as headquarters and training ship for the Amazon Flotilla.

PATROL BOATS [PB]

♦ **6 U.S. 40-foot Dauntless class**
Bldr: SeaArk, Monticello, Ark. (In serv. 6-00 through 11-00)

D: 12.25 tons (fl) **S:** 28 kts
Dim: 12.19 (11.13 wl) × 4.27 × 1.32 (max.; 0.69 hull)
A: 2 single 12.7-mm mg; 2 single 7.62-mm mg
Electronics: Radar: 1 Furuno 821 nav.
M: 2 Caterpillar 3208TA diesels; 2 props; 870 bhp (720 sust.)

Two Peruvian 40-ft. Dauntless-class patrol boats—in Guardacosta colors Peruvian Navy, 2001

Electric: 10 kw tot. (1 × 10-kw generator; 220 V, 60 Hz a.c.)
Range: 200/30; 400/22 **Fuel:** 500 gallons **Crew:** 5 tot.

Remarks: Ordered 2-00 by the U.S. DoD for the Peruvian Riverine Program for use on the upper Amazon for patrol and drug interdiction, but on delivery they were found to have too deep a draft for riverine work; they were reassigned to the Pacific Naval Force early in 2001, but pennant numbers and names had not been assigned as of 8-01. Have C. Raymond Hunt, “Deep-Vee” aluminum-construction hull and superstructure, with bunks for four. Magellan 315 GPS and Motorola Astro Spectra VHF radio are fitted.

Note: For use on the upper Amazon, a number of locally built, aluminum-hulled patrol launches are employed. These displace between 2.3 and 6.5 tons and are powered either by twin Yamaha outboards or by one Volvo Penta outdrive diesel. Most of the craft carry two 7.62-mm mg and, in addition to crews of four, can accommodate 10 or more troops.

Upper Amazon River patrol launch Peruvian Navy, 1994

AMPHIBIOUS WARFARE SHIPS

♦ **4 ex-U.S. Terrebonne Parish–class tank landing ships [LST]**
Bldr: Ingalls SB, Pascagoula, Miss. (DT 144: Bath Iron Works, Bath, Maine)

	L	In serv.
DT 141 Paita (ex-*Walworth County,* LST 1164)	18-5-53	26-10-53
DT 142 Pisco (ex-*Waldo County,* LST 1163)	17-3-53	17-9-53
DT 143 Callao (ex-*Washoe County,* LST 1165)	14-7-53	30-11-53
DT 144 Eten (ex-*Traverse County,* LST 1160)	3-10-53	19-12-53

Pisco (DT 142) Peruvian Navy, 2-01

D: 2,590 tons (6,225 fl) **S:** 13 kts
Dim: 117.35 × 16.76 × 3.70 (mean; 5.18 max. aft)
A: 5 40-mm 60-cal. Bofors AA (2 twin U.K. Mk 5 or U.S. Mk 1 Mod. 2; 1 U.S. Mk 3)
Electronics: Radar: 1 . . . nav.
M: 4 G.M. 16-278A diesels; 2 CP props; 6,000 hp **Electric:** 600 kw tot.
Range: 6,000/9 **Fuel:** 1,060 tons **Crew:** 116 tot.

Remarks: Leased from the U.S.A. for five years on 7-8-84; this was extended another five years on 8-8-89, again through 8-94, and again through 8-99, when it was again extended. Reactivated from Maritime Administration reserve by Todd SY, San Francisco, Calif., and delivered mid-10-84; all were officially recommissioned 4-3-85. As of 1993, DT 142 was being used for cannibalization spares but has since been restored to full service.

AMPHIBIOUS WARFARE SHIPS *(continued)*

Hull systems: Have a bow ramp and accommodations for 395 troops. Cargo: approx. 2,200 tons, carried in the tank deck and on the upper deck, forward (with a ramp to the lower deck).
Combat systems: Having been in Military Sealift Command service from 1972 until deactivated, they were unarmed at time of transfer; formerly carried three dual 76.2-mm DP with two Mk 63 gun f.c.s. Received 40-mm AA after arrival in Peru. DT 142 has twin U.S. Mk 1 Mod. 2 40-mm mountings forward vice the twin, shielded Mk 5 mounts on others of the class.

AUXILIARIES

♦ 1 oceanographic research ship [AGOR]
Bldr: SIMA, Callao

	Laid down	L	In serv.
Humboldt	3-1-77	13-10-78	1980

Humboldt—red hull and masts, cream-colored superstructure
Peruvian Navy, 2001

D: 1,200 tons (1,980 fl) **S:** 14 kts **Dim:** 76.21 (66.02 pp) × 12.68 × 4.40
A: none **Electronics:** Radar: 2 . . . nav.
M: 2 Burmeister & Wain Alpha 10V23L-VO diesels; 2 CP props; 3,000 bhp
Crew: 53 tot.

Remarks: 1,731 grt/600 dwt. Modified stern-haul factory trawler design, well-equipped for oceanographic and fisheries research.

♦ 1 ex-Netherlands Dokkum-class survey ship [AGS]
Bldr: Gusto/F.A. Smulders, Schiedam

	Laid down	L	In serv.
AH 171 Carrasco (ex-*Abcoude,* M 810; ex-MSC 176)	10-11-53	2-9-55	18-5-56

Carrasco (AH 171)
Peruvian Navy, 3-01

D: 373 tons (453 fl) **S:** 15 kts **Dim:** 46.62 × 8.75 × 2.28
A: 2 single 20-mm 70-cal. Mk 10 Oerlikon AA
Electronics: Radar: 1 Decca TM 1229C nav.
M: 2 Fijenoord-M.A.N. V 64 diesels; 2 props; 2,500 bhp
Range: 2,500/10 **Crew:** 27–36 tot.

Remarks: Former minesweeper, decommissioned from the Netherlands Navy 5-11-93, stricken 16-7-94, and purchased 12-7-94, departing Dutch waters on delivery voyage 20-7-94. Typed as a *Buque Hidrográfico* and employed both in hydrographic survey and training duties. Wooden construction. Funded by the United States, hence the MSC-series hull number assigned during building. Reports that sisters *Drachten* and *Naaldwijk* were purchased in 1996 were in error.

♦ 1 Ilo-class cargo ship [AK]
Bldr: SIMA, Callao (In serv. 15-12-71)

ATC 131 Mollendo (ex-*Ilo*)

Mollendo (ATC 131)
Peruvian Navy, 6-01

D: 18,400 tons (fl) **S:** 15.6 kts **Dim:** 153.88 (144.56 pp) × 20.48 × 9.39
M: 1 Burmeister & Wain 6K47EF diesel; 1 prop; 11,600 bhp
Electric: 1,140 kw (3 × 380-kw diesel sets) **Crew:** 60 tot.

Remarks: 8,621 grt/13,450 dwt. Typed as a *Buque Transporte de Carga,* ATC 131 (renamed 10-3-00) is used primarily to carry commercial cargo by the Oficina Naviera Comercial. Engine room flooded 1-91 off the Spanish coast while carrying 11,000 tons of sugar, and she has had numerous engineering problems since. Sister *Rimac* is in commercial service for the state shipping company.
Hull systems: Has five holds with a total of 19,563 m^3 grain and 18,082 m^3 bale capacity. Has five hatches (of 7.0, 12.8, 12.8, 18.2, and 10.4 × 6.5 m, respectively), one 3-ton crane, and two 50-ton, six 10-ton, and six 5-ton derricks.

♦ 1 ex-U.S. Sealift-class oiler [AO]
Bldr: Bath Iron Works, Bath, Maine

	L	In serv.
ATP 153 Lobitos (ex-*Santa Chiara;* ex-*Sealift Caribbean,* T-AOT 174)	8-6-74	6-11-74

Lobitos (ATP 153)
Maritime Photographic, 6-01

D: 33,000 tons (fl) **S:** 16 kts **Dim:** 178.92 (170.80 pp) × 25.61 × 10.50
Electronics: Radar: 1 Raytheon TM 1650/6X nav.; 1 Raytheon TM 1645 nav.
M: 2 Colt-Pielstick 14 PC2 V400, 14-cyl., 520-rpm diesels; 1 CP prop; 14,000 bhp—bow-thruster
Electric: 2,000 kw tot.
Range: 12,000/16 **Fuel:** 3,440 tons **Crew:** . . . tot.

Remarks: 17,157 grt/27,217 dwt. Purchased from commercial operator Santa Sopia S.A., Panama, in 2-98; had been stricken from U.S. Military Sealift Command service on completion of a 20-year charter in 10-95, during which time the ship had been operated in freighting service by commercial contract crews. Is typed as a *Buque Transporte de Petroleo.* Was provided with an underway refueling capability in a refit completed in 11-98 and is also operated in revenue commercial service. Cargo: 225,154 barrels liquid. In U.S. MSC service, was operated with a crew of 9 officers and 17 unlicensed personnel.

Note: The acquisition of a fleet replenishment oiler was under consideration as of 2001.

♦ 1 Talara-class transport oiler [AOT]
Bldr: SIMA, Callao

	Laid down	L	In serv.
ATP 152 Talara	1975	9-7-76	23-1-78

Talara (ATP 152)
Peruvian Navy, 2000

D: 30,000 tons (fl) **S:** 16.25 kts **Dim:** 171.18 (161.55 pp) × 25.38 × 9.53
M: 1 Burmeister & Wain 6K 47EF diesel; 1 prop; 11,600 bhp
Electric: 1,890 kw tot. **Crew:** . . . tot.

Remarks: 16,633 grt/25,648 dwt. Cargo: 35,642 m^3. Typed as a *Buque Transporte de Petroleo.* Sister *Trompeteros* is operated by Petroperu, the state fuel monopoly, which transferred this ship to the navy's Oficina Naviera Comercial upon completion.

♦ 1 ex-U.S. Sotoyomo-class ocean tug [ATA]
Bldr: Levingston SB Co., Orange, Texas

	Laid down	L	In serv.
AMB 160 Unanue (ex-*Wateree,* ATA 174)	5-1-43	18-11-43	20-7-44

AUXILIARIES *(continued)*

Unanue (AMB 160) Peruvian Navy, 1999

D: 835 tons (fl) **S:** 13 kts **Dim:** 43.59 (40.70 pp) × 10.31 × 3.96
A: none **Electronics:** Radar: 2 . . . nav.
M: 2 G.M. Electromotive Div. 12-278A diesels, electric drive; 1 prop; 1,500 shp
Electric: 120 kw tot. **Range:** 8,000/8 **Fuel:** 158 tons **Crew:** 45 tot.

Remarks: Purchased from the U.S.A. in 11-61 and employed on salvage and search-and-rescue duties. Typed *Buque Madrina de Buzos.*

♦ **1 ex-U.S. Cherokee-class ocean tug [ATA]**
Bldr: Cramp SB, Philadelphia

	Laid down	L	In serv.
ARA 123 Guardian Rios (ex-*Pinto,* ATF 90)	10-8-42	5-1-43	1-4-43

Guardian Rios (ARA 123) Peruvian Navy, 1999

D: 1,235 tons (1,675 fl) **S:** 16.5 kts **Dim:** 62.48 (59.44 pp) × 11.73 × 4.67
A: 4 single 20-mm 70-cal. Oerlikon AA **Electronics:** Radar: 2 . . . nav.
M: 4 G.M. 12-278 diesels, electric drive; 1 prop; 3,000 shp
Electric: 260 kw tot. **Range:** 6,500/16; 13,000/10 **Crew:** 99 tot.

Remarks: Loaned in 12-60 and purchased outright 17-5-74. Used for salvage and rescue duties.

SERVICE CRAFT

♦ **1 riverine supply craft [YF]**

Remarks: One 35-m, self-propelled supply lighter is employed on the upper Amazon. The craft displaces about 230 tons (fl) and can carry about 50 troops in addition to around 80 tons of supplies.

♦ **1 floating dry dock [YFDM]** Bldr: SIMA, Callao (In serv. 2-91)

ADF 104

Lift capacity: 4,500 tons **Dim:** 115.8 × 30.1 × 12.5 (max., flooded)

Remarks: Launched 12-12-90. Designed by Senermar, Spain. Intended for use at Callao. Internal dimensions: 99.8 × 23.8 m. Is also used for commercial repair work.

♦ **1 ex-U.S. ARD 2–class floating dry dock [YFDM]**
Bldr: Pacific Bridge Co., Alameda, Calif. (In serv. 8-43)

ADF 107 (ex-WY 20, ex-ARD 8)

Lift capacity: 3,500 tons **Dim:** 148.03 × 21.64 × 1.60 (light)

Remarks: Transferred in 2-61 and purchased outright in 1981; not stricken in 1991 as reported in previous editions. Is also used for commercial repair work.

♦ **1 small floating dry dock [YFDL]**
Bldr: John I. Thornycroft, Southampton (In serv. 1951)

ADF 108

Small floating dry dock ADF 108—with patrol craft *Ucayali* (CF 13) aboard Peruvian Navy, 2001

Lift capacity: 600 tons **Dim:** 59.13 × 18.7 × . . .

Remarks: Serves the Amazon Flotilla at Iquitos, assigned to SINAI *(Servicio Industrial de la Marina-Iquitos).*

♦ **1 ex-U.S. AFDL 7–class floating dry dock [YFDL]**
Bldr: Foundation Co., Kearny, N.J. (In serv. 10-44)

ADF 106 (ex-WY 19, ex-AFDL 33)

Lift capacity: 1,900 tons **Dim:** 87.78 × 19.51 × 0.99 (light)

Remarks: Transferred in 7-59.

♦ **2 ABC 360–class Amazon River cargo barges [YFN]**
Bldr: SIMA, Iquitos

ABC 360 ABC 361

Remarks: Classified as *Barcazas de Carga.* No data available.

♦ **2 Dutch Van Straelen–class inshore survey craft [YGS]**
Bldr: De Vries–Leutsch, Amsterdam

	Laid down	L	In serv.
AH 175 Carrillo (ex-*Icaro;* ex-*Van Hamel,* M 871)	27-4-59	28-5-60	14-10-60
AH 176 Melo (ex-*Van der Wel,* M 878)	30-5-60	3-5-61	6-10-61

Carrillo (AH 175) Peruvian Navy, 1999

D: 151 tons (171 fl) **S:** 13 kts **Dim:** 33.08 (30.30 wl) × 6.88 × 1.80
A: 1 20-mm 70-cal. Oerlikon Mk 10 AA
Electronics: Radar: 1 Decca TM 1226 nav.
M: 2 G.M. Detroit Diesel 16V92N diesels; 2 props; 1,400 bhp
Crew: 2 officers, 15 enlisted

Remarks: Former inshore minesweepers, purchased 23-2-85 for conversion in Peru to inshore survey duties. Received the Interplot 200 survey system and new engines. Wooden construction. Bridge on AH 175 has been modified and enlarged.

♦ **1 coastal survey craft [YGS]** Bldr: SIMA, Chimbote (In serv. 1982)

EH 174 Macha

D: 49 tons (53 fl) **S:** 13 kts **Dim:** 19.8 × 5.2 × 0.9
M: 2 Caterpillar 3406-TA diesels; 2 props; 534 bhp
Range: 533/10.5 **Crew:** 2 officers, 4 enlisted

Remarks: Has side-looking sonar for bottom mapping to 1,200-m depths. EH = *Embarcación Hidrográfica.*

♦ **1 river survey craft [YGS]**
Bldr: MacLaren, Niteroi, Brazil (In serv. 1981)

AH 172 Stiglich

D: 230 tons (250 fl) **S:** 9 kts **Dim:** 31.40 × 8.00 × 1.54
Electronics: Radar: 1 . . . nav.
M: 2 Caterpillar 3304 diesels; 2 props; 250 bhp
Range: 8,000/9 **Crew:** 2 officers, 20 enlisted

Remarks: Operates on the Amazon from Iquitos. White-painted. Classed as a *Buque Hidrográfico.*

SERVICE CRAFT *(continued)*

Stiglich (AH 172) Peruvian Navy, 1991

♦ 1 river survey craft [YGS] Bldr: SIMA, Iquitos (In serv. 1981)

AEH 173

D: 12 tons (fl) **S:** 7 kts **Dim:** 10.0 × 3.7 × 1.4
M: 2 Volvo Penta AQD-series diesels; 2 props; . . . bhp

Remarks: GRP construction. Operates on the Amazon from Iquitos. White-painted. Classed as a *Buque Hidrográfico.*

Note: Also reported in use for riverine survey duties is the 5-ton, 40-kt launch AH 177.

♦ 1 hospital craft for Amazon service [YH]
Bldr: SIMA, Iquitos (In serv. 13-5-76)

ABH 302 MORONA

Morona (ABH 302) Peruvian Navy, 1999

D: 150 tons (fl) **S:** 12 kts **Dim:** 30.0 × 6.0 × 0.6
M: diesels; . . . bhp **Range:** 5,864/6.4 **Crew:** . . . tot.

Remarks: Based at Iquitos on the upper Amazon. Refitted mid-1990s with enlarged superstructure. There are also several smaller hospital launches on the Amazon.

♦ 1 hospital craft for Lake Titicaca service [YH]
Bldr: Cammell-Laird, Birkenhead, U.K. (In serv. 1879)

ABH 306 PUNO (ex-*Yapura*)

Puno (ABH 306) Peruvian Navy, 2000

D: 500 grt **S:** . . . kts **Dim:** 38.10 × 6.10 × 3.96
Electronics: Radar: 1 Raytheon 1500B Pathfinder nav.
M: 1 Paxman-Ricardo V-12 gasoline engine; 1 prop; 410 bhp

Remarks: Reacquired by the navy 17-3-76 and converted to a hospital ship. Sister *Chuquito* (ARB 19, ex-*Yavari*) was stricken in 1990 after 119 years' service and is now used as a museum ship.

♦ 1 coastal light fuels tanker [YO]
Bldr: Gerhard Voldnes A/S Skps, Fosnavåg, Norway (In serv. 1965)

ACP 157 SUPE (ex-*Taxiarchis,* ex-*Cryla,* ex-*Gevotank*)

Supe (ACP 157) Maritime Photographic, 6-01

D: 1,400 tons (fl) **S:** 10 kts (9 loaded) **Dim:** 66.81 (63.68 pp) × 9.53 × 3.95
A: none **Electronics:** Radar: 2 . . . nav.
M: 1 MaK 6-cyl. diesel; 1 CP prop; 1,100 bhp
Electric: 128 kw tot. (2 × 56-kw, 1 × 16-kw emergency diesel sets; 220 V a.c.)
Range: . . ./. . . **Fuel:** 38 tons **Crew:** 17 tot.

Remarks: 497 grt/1,138 dwt. Former commercial vegetable oil tanker, acquired 29-8-95 and intended for revenue-producing service, delivering parcel cargoes to coastal ports and fueling fishing fleets at sea. Has an ice-strengthened hull. Cargo: 1,200 tons (1,437 m^3) liquid in eight tanks. Typed as a *Buque Transporte de Petroleo.*

♦ 2 ex-U.S. 174-foot-class yard oilers [YO]
Bldrs: ACP 118: Jeffersonville Boat & Mach., Ind.; ACP 119: RTC Shipbuilding, Camden, N.J.

	Laid down	L	In serv.
ACP 118 NOGUERA (ex-YO 221)	15-1-45	22-5-45	31-8-45
ACP 119 GAUDEN (ex-YO 171)	18-3-44	20-7-44	15-11-44

Noguera (ACP 118) Peruvian Navy, 1999

D: 440 tons light (1,390 fl) **S:** 10 kts (9 loaded) **Dim:** 53.04 × 9.75 × 3.96
A: none **Electronics:** Radar: 1 Raytheon . . . nav.
M: 2 G.M. diesels; 2 props; 540 bhp **Electric:** 80 kw tot.
Range: 2,000/8 **Crew:** 20 tot.

Remarks: ACP 118 transferred in 2-75; ACP 119 was purchased 26-1-81. Sisters ex-YO 220 and ex-YOG 88, both stricken from the U.S. Navy 19-5-97, were offered for purchase early in 1999 but not accepted. Cargo: approximately 900 tons (6,570 barrels). Typed as *Buques Cisterna de Petroleo.* Have black hulls and dark gray superstructures.

♦ 4 Río Comaina–class Amazon River fuel lighters [YO]
Bldr: SIMA, Iquitos (In serv. 1975–76)

ABP 336 RÍO COMAINA　ABP 338 RÍO CHINGANAZA
ABP 337 RÍO HUAZAGA　ABP 339 RÍO CENEPA

D: approx. 165 tons (fl) **S:** 7.5 kts **Dim:** 30.0 × 6.0 × 1.0
M: 2 Caterpillar D 3304 diesels; 2 props; 250 bhp

Remarks: Typed as *Cisternas de Petroleo,* as are the five Peruvian YONs.

♦ 2 ABP 342–class Amazon River fuel barges [YON]
Bldr: SIMA, Iquitos (In serv. 1974)

ABP 342　ABP 343

D: approx. 210 tons (fl) **Dim:** 60.3 × 12.1 × 0.3

♦ 1 ABP 344–class Amazon River fuel barge [YON]
Bldr: Conrad Industries, Morgan City, La. (In serv. . . .)

ABP 344

D: approx. 150 tons (fl) **Dim:** 42.6 × 12.1 × 0.3

♦ 1 ABP 345–class Amazon River fuel barge [YON]
Bldr: SIMA, Iquitos (In serv. 1974)

ABP 345

D: approx. 270 tons (fl) **Dim:** 48.7 × 12.0 × 0.3

SERVICE CRAFT *(continued)*

♦ 1 ABP 346–class Amazon River fuel barge [YON]
Bldr: Conrad Industries, Morgan City, La. (In serv. . . .)

ABP 346

D: approx. 320 tons (fl) **Dim:** 45.7 × 12.1 × 0.6

♦ 1 floating forward riverine base [YPL]
Bldr: SIMA, Iquitos (In serv. 7-98)

ABF 401 (ex-B6-01)

Forward riverine base ABF 401 Peruvian Navy, 7-98

Remarks: Designed by the U.S. Army Corps of Engineers to provide a floating accommodations, command, and logistics support base for Peruvian National Police, Navy, and Coast Guard personnel on the 10,000-km Peruvian Amazon basin network. Resembles a two-deck houseboat. No data available.

♦ 1 torpedo retriever [YPT]
Bldr: Friedrich Lürssen Werft, Vegesack, Germany (In serv. 18-7-81)

ART 322 San Lorenzo

San Lorenzo (ART 322) Peter Voss, 9-81

D: 51.5 tons (65.5 fl) **S:** 19 kts **Dim:** 25.35 (23.47 pp) × 5.62 × 1.68
M: 2 MTU 8V396 TC82 diesels; 2 props; 1,590 bhp
Range: 500/15 **Fuel:** 14 tons **Crew:** 9 tot.

Remarks: Can stow four long or eight short torpedoes on the ramp aft. Typed as a *Lancha de Rescate de Torpedos.*

♦ 1 ex-U.S. YR 24–class floating workshop [YR]
Bldr: DeKom SB, Brooklyn, N.Y.

	Laid down	L	In serv.
ART 105 (ex-YR 59)	3-11-43	22-4-44	24-8-44

D: 520 tons (770 fl) **Dim:** 45.72 × 10.36 × 1.8
Electric: 220 kw tot. **Fuel:** 75 tons **Crew:** 47 tot.

Remarks: Transferred 8-8-61. Typed as a *Taller Flotante de Reparaciones.*

♦ 1 large harbor tug [YTB]
Bldr: . . . . . ., U.S.A. (In serv. 1984)

ARB 126 Dueñas

D: 869 tons (fl) **S:** 11 kts **Dim:** 40.99 × 11.58 × . . .
M: 2 Fairbanks 38D81/8 × 10 diesels; . . . props; 3,400 bhp

Remarks: Acquired in 1984 from Belco Petroleum Co. and put into service 6-5-85. Typed as a *Remolcador de Bahía.* Based at Callao.

♦ 2 Selendon-class harbor tugs [YTM]
Bldr: Ruhrorter, Duisburg, Germany (In serv. 1967)

ARB 128 Olaya ARB 129 Selendon

D: 80 grt **S:** 10 kts **Dim:** 18.7 × 6.2 × 2.3
M: 1 diesel; 1 prop; 600 bhp **Range:** 1,500/12; 2,000/8

Selendon (ARB 129) Peruvian Navy, 1999

♦ 2 Mejia-class small harbor tugs [YTL]
Bldr: Fabrimet, Callao (In serv. 1974)

ARB 120 Mejia ARB 121 Huerta

Mejia (ARB 120) Peruvian Navy, 1999

D: 19.9 tons (fl) **S:** 10 kts **Dim:** . . . × . . . × . . .
M: 1 G.M. Detroit Diesel 6H-12-V71 diesel; 1 prop; 340 bhp
Range: 850/8; 1,000/6 **Crew:** . . . tot.

Remarks: Typed as *Remolcadores de Bahía.* Are also equipped to transport personnel locally. Based at Callao.

♦ 1 Tapuima-class riverine push-tug [YTL]
Bldr: Gonzales SY, Houston, Texas (In serv. 1973)

AER 180 Tapuima

D: approx. 60 tons (fl) **S:** . . . kts **Dim:** 13.1 × 5.5 × 1.2
M: 2 G.M. Detroit Diesel 8V71 diesels; 2 props; 600 bhp

Remarks: Serves on the upper Amazon. Acquired in 1982.

♦ 2 Gaudin-class riverine push-tugs [YTL]
Bldr: SIMA, Iquitos

AER 186 Gaudin (In serv. 1975) AER 187 Zambrano (In serv. 1977)

D: approx. 45 tons (fl) **S:** 5 kts **Dim:** 16.2 × 6.5 × 1.2
M: 2 Caterpillar D334 6-cyl. diesels; 2 props; 450 bhp

Remarks: Serve on the upper Amazon. Less than 50 tons displacement.

♦ 1 sail training craft [YTS]
Bldr: Hattaras Yachts, High Point, N.C.

ALY 311 Neptuno

D: 26 tons **S:** 19 kts **Dim:** 16.1 × 4.7 × 3.4
M: 2 G.M. Detroit Diesel 6V71 TI diesels; . . . bhp

Remarks: Although typed as an *Embarcación de Instrucción,* is used more as a yacht. No information available on rig or sail area.

♦ 1 sail training craft [YTS]
Bldr: James O. Rasborough, Halifax, Canada (In serv. 1974)

ALY 313 Marte

Marte (ALY 313) Peruvian Navy, 2000

SERVICE CRAFT *(continued)*

D: 55 tons **S:** 8 kts **Dim:** 20.30 × 5.18 × 1.95
Electronics: Radar: 1 Furuno . . . nav.
M: 2 Perkins 130C 6-cyl. diesels; 2 props; 260 bhp
Endurance: 7 days **Crew:** 2 officers, 3 enlisted, 21 cadets

Remarks: Used for cadet instruction at the naval academy.

♦ **1 ex-U.S. 174-foot water tanker [YW]**
Bldr: Leatham D. Smith, Wis.

	Laid down	L	In serv.
ACA 111 Caloyeras (ex-YW 128)	9-4-45	22-5-45	28-7-45

D: 440 tons (1,390 fl) **S:** 7 kts **Dim:** 53.04 × 9.75 × 4.0
M: 1 G.M. diesel; 1 prop; 640 bhp **Fuel:** 25 tons **Crew:** 23 tot.

Remarks: Purchased 26-1-81. Cargo: 930 tons. Sister *Mantilla* (ACA 110, ex-YW 122) was stricken in 1997. Strongly resembles the 174-ft.-class yard oilers *Noguera* (ACP 118) and *Gauden* (ACP 119), illustrated above.

♦ **1 water barge [YWN]** Bldr: SIMA, Iquitos (In serv. 1972)

ABA 332

Remarks: 330 tons (fl). Serves at the Base Naval del Callao. Typed as a *Barcaza Cisterna de Agua.*

COAST GUARD
(Guardacosta)

Note: The Peruvian Coast Guard was established in 1975 and is intended to patrol to the extent of the 200-n.m. economic zone. Pennant numbers are prefaced by letter designations indicating subordination to the Coastal Patrol (PC), Lake Patrol (PL), Port Patrol (PP), or River Patrol (PF). Plans were announced during 10-00 to build one oceangoing and four coastal patrol boats at the SIMA yard, Callao; this was changed in 2001 to two oceangoing and 12 coastal craft. Larger craft carry a red-white-red diagonal striping on the hull side.

Maritime Aviation: One de Havilland Twin Otter DHC-6-100 floatplane transport (transferred from the navy)

Peruvian Coast Guard DHC-6-100 Twin Otter floatplane Peruvian Navy, 2001

PATROL CRAFT [WPC]

♦ **5 Río Cañete class** Bldr: SIMA, Chimbote

	In serv.		In serv.
PC 243 Río Nepeña	1-12-81	PC 246 Río Huarmey	8-10-82
PC 244 Río Tambo	10-3-82	PC 247 Río Zaña	12-2-85
PC 245 Río Ocoña	14-7-82		

Río Zaña (PC 247) Peruvian Navy, 1999

D: 296 tons (fl) **S:** 22 kts (17 sust.) **Dim:** 50.98 (49.10 pp) × 7.40 × 1.70
A: 1 20-mm 70-cal. Oerlikon Mk 10 AA; 2 single 12.7-mm mg
Electronics: Radar: 1 JRC 5256 nav.—EW: . . . intercept
M: 4 Izar-MTU V8V 16/18 TLS diesels; 2 props; 5,640 bhp
Electric: 170 kw tot. **Range:** 3,000/17 **Endurance:** 20 days
Crew: 4 officers, 26 enlisted

Remarks: Have steel hulls and aluminum superstructures. Class prototype *Río Cañete* (PC 248) was stricken in 1990. The 40-mm gun formerly mounted aft has been removed. PC 245 completed a one-year overhaul at SIMA in 1996, in which a distilling plant was installed, as was a VHF/UHF SATCOM transceiver; the others followed in 1996–98.

♦ **1 U.S. PGM 71 class** Bldr: SIMA, Callao (In serv. 5-9-71)

PC 223 Río Chira (ex-PGM 11)

Río Chira (PC 223) Peruvian Navy, 1999

D: 130 tons (145 fl) **S:** 17 kts **Dim:** 30.80 (30.20 wl) × 6.40 × 1.85 (2.31 props)
A: removed **Electronics:** Radar: 1 JRC 5256 nav.
M: 8 G.M. Detroit Diesel 6-71 diesels; 2 props; 2,200 bhp
Electric: 120 kw tot. **Range:** 1,500/10 **Crew:** 4 officers, 18 enlisted

Remarks: Transferred from the navy in 1975. Built with U.S. aid and equipment but did not receive a U.S. hull number. U.S.-built sister *Río Sama* (PC 222, ex-U.S. PGM 78) has been stricken. The armament of one 40-mm 60-cal. Bofors Mk 3, three single 20-mm Oerlikon, and two 12.7-mm machineguns has been removed.

PATROL BOATS [WPB]

♦ **2 Cougar 42–class port patrol launches**
Bldr: Cougar Marine, Miami, Fla. (In serv. 1992–93)

PP 210 Río Supe PP 211 Río Vitor

Río Supe (PP 210) or Río Vitor (PP 211) Peruvian Navy, 1999

D: 2.5 tons (fl) **S:** 40 kts **Dim:** 12.80 × 3.60 × 1.80
A: small arms **Electronics:** Radar: 1 . . . nav.
M: 2 Volvo Penta TAMD 62A outdrive diesels; 2 props; 500 bhp
Range: 240/. . . **Crew:** 6 tot.

Remarks: Typed as *Patrulleras Interceptoras.* Resemble U.S. "cigarette boat" racing launches. GRP construction.

♦ **3 Cougar 25–class port patrol launches**
Bldr: Cougar Marine, Miami, Fla. (In serv. 1992–93)

PP 212 Mancora PP 213 Huara PP 214 Quilca

D: 1.5 tons (fl) **S:** 35 kts **Dim:** 6.80 × 2.20 × 0.40
A: small arms **Electronics:** Radar: 1 . . . nav.
M: 1 Volvo Penta AD 41B outdrive diesel; 1 prop; 200 bhp
Range: 207/. . . **Crew:** 3 tot.

Remarks: GRP construction. Typed as *Patrulleras de Puerto.* No data available.

♦ **1 Pucusana-class port patrol launch**
Bldr: Construcciones Nauticas, Callao (In serv. . . .)

PP 215 Pucusana

D: 3.5 tons (fl) **S:** 30 kts **Dim:** 9.10 × 3.30 × 1.10
A: small arms **Electronics:** Radar: . . .
M: 1 Volvo Penta KAD 42PA outdrive diesel; 1 prop; 230 bhp
Range: 500/. . . **Crew:** 6 tot.

♦ **8 Cougar 22–class harbor patrol launches**
Bldr: Cougar Marine, Miami, Fla. (In serv. 1992–93)

DCB 350 La Cruz	DCB 353 Samanco	DCB 356 Ancón
DCB 351 Cabo Blanco	DCB 354 Besique	DCB 357 Paracas
DCB 352 Colan	DCB 355 Salinas	

COAST GUARD PATROL BOATS [WPB] *(continued)*

D: 1.5 tons (fl) **S:** 30 kts **Dim:** 6.60 × 2.20 × 0.90
A: small arms **Electronics:** Radar: . . .
M: 1 Evinrude gasoline outboard; 200 bhp
Range: 120/. . . **Crew:** 4 tot.

Remarks: GRP construction. Typed as *Embarcaciones de Control de Bahía.* No data available.

♦ 1 La Punta–class harbor patrol launch
Bldr: Construcciones Nauticas, Callao (In serv. . . .)

DCB 358 La Punta

D: 1.2 tons (fl) **S:** 25 kts **Dim:** . . . × . . . × . . .
A: small arms **Electronics:** Radar: . . .
M: 1 Evinrude SE 450 EXPO gasoline outboard; 150 bhp
Range: 87/. . . **Crew:** 4 tot.

Remarks: GRP construction. Typed as a *Deslizador de Control de Bahía.*

♦ 2 Río Majes–class port patrol launches
Bldr: Construcciones Nauticas, Callao (In serv. 1981–82)

PP 232 Río Santa PP 233 Río Majes

D: 15 tons (fl) **S:** 25 kts **Dim:** 10.4 × 3.1 × 1.9
A: small arms **Electronics:** Radar: 1 Furuno . . . nav.
M: 2 Evinrude BE 200CXCM gasoline outboards; 400 bhp
Range: 90/. . . **Crew:** 6 tot.

♦ 2 Río Viru–class port patrol launches
Bldr: Camcraft, U.S.A. (In serv. 1981–82)

PP 235 Río Viru PP 236 Río Lurin

Río Lurin (PP 236) Peruvian Navy, 2001

D: 14 tons (fl) **S:** 15 kts **Dim:** 13.1 × 3.8 × 1.9
A: small arms **Electronics:** Radar: 1 Raytheon . . . nav.
M: 2 G.M. Detroit Diesel 6-71 diesels; 2 props; 500 bhp
Range: 240/. . . **Crew:** 6 tot.

Remarks: The above four craft were mistakenly reported in the previous edition to have been built in Brazil and to be of the same class.

Disposal note: The patrol launch named *Río Surco* (PP 237) is no longer in service.

♦ 1 Yacila-class port patrol launch
Bldr: Recona, Callao (In serv. . . .)

DCM 365 Yacila

D: 6.5 tons (fl) **S:** 15 kts **Dim:** 9.2 × 3.3 × 1.5
M: 1 G.M. Detroit Diesel . . . diesel; 1 prop; 108 bhp
Range: 270/. . . **Crew:** 5 tot.

♦ 4 Río Santiago–class riverine patrol boats
Bldr: SIMA, Iquitos (In serv. . . .)

PF 260 Río Huallaga PF 262 Río Putumayo
PF 261 Río Santiago PF 263 Río Nanay

D: 4.2 tons (fl) **S:** 25 kts **Dim:** 10.00 × 2.55 × 1.55
A: 2 single 12.7-mm mg
M: 1 Volvo Penta KAD 42B outdrive diesel; 230 bhp
Range: 470/. . . **Crew:** 4 tot.

Remarks: Aluminum construction. PF 263 has an Evinrude engine of 150 bhp and is consequently slower. Typed as *Patrulleras Fluviales.*

♦ 4 Río Napo–class riverine patrol boats
Bldr: SIMA, Iquitos (In serv. . . .)

PF 264 Río Napo PF 266 Río Matador
PF 265 Río Yavari PF 267 Río Pachitea

D: 1.8 tons (fl) **S:** 35 kts **Dim:** 6.75 × 2.28 × 0.60
A: small arms
M: 2 Evinrude SE-150 WTPLY outboards; 300 bhp
Range: 200/. . . **Crew:** 5 tot.

Remarks: Aluminum construction. Typed as *Patrulleras Fluviales.*

♦ 4 Río Itaya–class riverine patrol boats
Bldr: SIMA, Iquitos (In serv. . . .)

PF 270 Río Itaya PF 272 Río Zapote
PF 271 Río Patayacu PF 273 Río Chambira

D: 0.8 tons (fl) **S:** 20 kts **Dim:** 5.80 × 2.10 × 1.00
A: small arms **M:** 1 Evinrude SE-150 WTPLY outboard; 150 bhp
Range: 140/. . . **Crew:** 4 tot.

Remarks: Aluminum construction. PF 271 has two engines for 300 bhp total. Typed as *Patrulleras Fluviales.*

♦ 1 Río Tambopata–class riverine patrol boat
Bldr: SIMA, Iquitos (In serv. . . .)

PF 274 Río Tambopata

D: 1.5 tons (fl) **S:** 40 kts **Dim:** 8.30 × 2.20 × 0.90
A: small arms **M:** 1 Evinrude SE-200 WTPLG outboard; 200 bhp
Range: 360/. . . **Crew:** 5 tot.

Remarks: Aluminum construction. Typed as *Patrulleras Fluviales.* Operates on the Río Madre de Dios.

♦ 8 Contamana-class riverine patrol boats
Bldr: SIMA, Iquitos (In serv. . . .)

PF 250 Contamana PF 254 Poyeni
PF 251 Nueva Requena PF 255 Aguaytia
PF 252 Atalaya PF 256 Puerto Inca
PF 253 Zorrillos PF 257 San Alejandro

Remarks: Aluminum construction. Typed as *Patrulleras Fluviales.* No data available.

♦ 3 P 33 class
Bldr: American Shipbuilding & Designs, Miami, Fla.

PL 290 Río Ramis (In serv. 15-9-82) PL 292 Río Azangaro (In serv. 4-2-83)
PL 291 Río Ilave (In serv. 20-11-82)

Río Ramis (PL 290) American Shipbuilding, 1982

D: 4.8 tons (fl) **S:** 27 kts **Dim:** 10.06 (9.19 pp) × 3.35 × 0.76
A: 1 or 2 single 12.7-mm mg
Electronics: Radar: 1 Raytheon 2800 nav.
M: 2 Perkins ST-6-354-4M diesels; 2 props; 480 bhp
Range: 450/27 **Crew:** 4 tot.

Remarks: GRP construction with Kevlar armor. Employed on Lake Titicaca.

♦ 1 Río Zarumilla class
Bldr: Korody Marine, Viareggio, Italy (In serv. 5-9-60)

PC 242 Río Piura

D: 37 tons (fl) **S:** 18 kts **Dim:** 20.00 × 5.20 × 1.10
A: 1 20-mm 70-cal. Oerlikon Mk 10 AA; 1 12.7-mm mg
Electronics: Radar: 1 Raytheon 1900 Pathfinder nav.
M: 2 G.M. Detroit Diesel 8V71 diesels; 2 props; 1,200 bhp
Range: 1,000/14 **Crew:** 1 officer, 7 enlisted

Remarks: Sister *Río Zarumilla* (PC 240) was stricken in 1990 and *Río Tumbes* (PC 241) in 1994. The forward 40-mm gunmount was replaced by the 20-mm weapon in 1992, and the after mounting has been replaced by the 12.7-mm mg.

SERVICE CRAFT

♦ 1 Largato-class ferry boat [WYFB]

MD 147 Lagarto

D: 30 tons (fl) **S:** . . . kts **Dim:** 16.0 × 9.0 × 1.2
M: 2 Harbormaster azimuthal drive diesels; 150 bhp

Remarks: Transferred from the Ministerio de Transportes y Comunicaciones during 3-79. Used as a ferry at Puerto Maldonado on the Río Madre de Dios.

PHILIPPINES

Republic of the Philippines

Personnel (2001): Approx. 17,900 total, including 10,300 navy and 7,600 marines. There are in the neighborhood of 18,000 reserves (12,000 in ready-reserve status); the reserve force is planned to be enlarged to 70,000 by 2012. As of 1998, there were 88 Navy-Affiliated Reserve Units, which used local fishing craft for training.

Organization and Bases: Headquarters at Manila. Principal base and repair facilities at Cavite on Manila Bay. In 1995, the navy was reorganized into a naval base at Cavite, plus four naval force bases: Naval Force North, headquartered at Cagayan; Naval Force West, at Palawan; Naval Force South, at Tawi-Tawi; and Naval Force Central, at Mactan. The Naval Station San Miguel, Zambales, is used for training. Naval Reservation Ternate is used for marine corps headquarters and training. Smaller outposts are located at Bonifacio, Cebu, Davao, Legaspi, Poro, and Zamboanga.

Naval Aviation: Seven Philippine-assembled Pilatus-Britten-Norman BN-2 Defender light maritime patrol aircraft and seven MBB BO-105 helicopters. The air force has two Fokker F-27 Maritime patrol aircraft. Two of four refurbished former RAF C-130K Hercules transports ordered in 3-01 from Lockheed Martin for the Philippine Air Force will be equipped with portable "interim long-range patrol" modules for coastal patrol and SAR missions.

Marine Corps: The force of three brigades and 10 battalions was reduced to two brigades and six battalions in 1995. Headquarters is at Ternate on Manila Bay, with major forces deployed to Mindanao and Palawan Islands. The marine corps operates 51 U.S.-supplied LVTP-7 armored amphibious personnel carriers; 25 were to have been rehabilitated by 2000.

Note: Ship names are preceded by BRP (*Barko ng Republika ng Pilipinas,* or Ship of the Republic of the Philippines). New acquisition plans have been largely thwarted by a lack of available funding.

PATROL SHIPS [PS]

Note: Plans to acquire three to five new-construction offshore patrol vessels, announced in 1996, are on hold for lack of funding. The ships were to have been of around 1,200 tons displacement and capable of 24 kts. An offer of three virtually free retired *D'Estienne d'Orves*–class (A 69) corvettes from France was turned down in 2000.

♦ 1 ex-U.S. Cannon class
Bldr: Federal SB & DD Co., Newark, N.J.

	Laid down	L	In serv.
PF 11 Rajah Humabon (ex-*Hatsuhi;* ex-*Atherton,* DE 169)	14-1-43	27-5-43	29-8-43

Rajah Humabon (PF 11) John Mortimer, 5-98

D: 1,240 tons (1,620 fl) **S:** 20 kts **Dim:** 93.27 (91.44 wl) × 11.15 × 3.56 (hull)
A: 3 single 76.2-mm 50-cal. Mk 26 DP; 3 twin 40-mm 60-cal. Mk 1 Mod. 2 AA; 6 single 20-mm 70-cal. Oerlikon Mk 10 AA; 4 single 12.7-mm mg
Electronics: Radar: 1 Raytheon SPS-64(V)11 nav.; 1 . . . nav.; 1 . . . nav.
M: 4 G.M. Electromotive Div. 16-278A diesels, electric drive; 2 props; 6,000 shp
Electric: 680 kw tot. **Range:** 11,600/11 **Fuel:** 260 tons **Crew:** 165 tot.

Remarks: Stricken in 1993 but restored to service at Cavite Dockyard in 1995, recommissioning during 1-96. Had been transferred to Japan from the USN on 14-6-55 and stricken 6-75, reverting to U.S. ownership. Sold to the Philippines 23-12-78, she remained laid up in Japan until towed to South Korea for overhaul in 1979. Sister *Datu Kalantiaw* (PS 76; ex-*Booth,* DE 170) was lost in a typhoon 21-9-81 and *Datu Sikatuna* (ex-*Amick,* DE 168) was stricken and discarded in 1989.
Combat systems: The entire ASW suite, with EDO SQS-17B hull-mounted sonar, a Mk 10 Hedgehog spiggot mortar, six Mk 6 depth charge mortars, and one Mk 9 depth charge rack, was removed prior to 1995. The 76.2-mm guns originally had a Mk 52 radar director (with Mk 26 radar) for AA control and a Mk 41 optical rangefinder for surface fire, but the obsolescent control systems have all been removed and all guns are locally controlled using ringsights. As of 1998, it was planned to add antiship missiles to this aged unit, but none have been purchased to date.

♦ 2 ex-U.S. Auk-class former minesweepers
Bldrs: PS 70: Associated SB, Seattle; PS 74: Savannah Machinery & Foundry, Savannah, Ga.

	Laid down	L	In serv.
PS 70 Quezon (ex-*Vigilance,* MSF 324)	28-11-42	5-4-43	28-2-44
PS 74 Rizal (ex-PS 69; ex-*Murrelet,* MSF 372)	24-8-44	29-12-44	21-8-45

D: 890 tons (1,250 fl) **S:** 18 kts **Dim:** 67.39 (65.53 wl) × 9.80 × 3.28
A: 2 single 76.2-mm 50-cal. Mk 26 DP; 2 twin 40-mm 60-cal. Mk 1 Mod. 2 AA; 2 single 20-mm 70-cal. Oerlikon Mk 4 AA; 4 single 12.7-mm mg
Electronics: Radar: 1 Raytheon SPS-64(V)11 nav.; 1 . . . nav.; 1 . . . nav.

Quezon (PS 70) John Mortimer, 5-98

Rizal (PS 74) NAVPIC Holland, 11-00

M: 4 G.M. Electromotive Div. 12-278 diesels, electric drive; 2 props; 3,532 shp
Electric: 360 kw tot. **Range:** 4,300/10 **Fuel:** 216 tons **Crew:** 100 tot.

Remarks: PS 74 was transferred 18-6-65 and PS 70 on 19-8-67. Had been stricken at the end of 1994, but both were refitted at Cavite Dockyard during 1995. PS 74 completed restoration in 1-96 and was renumbered prior to recommissioning; PS 70 completed a rehabilitation overhaul in 4-96. They differ visually in that PS 70 has bulwarks to the hull sides amidships, while PS 74 does not. PS 74 sank a Chinese fishing boat in a collision on 23-5-99 off Scarborough Bank.
Combat systems: All ASW equipment has been removed. As of 1998, it was planned to add antiship missiles to these ships. The machineguns are mounted on the fantail and bridge wings; the remaining 20-mm mounts are before the pilothouse. There is no weapons-control system, and all guns are ringsight aimed.

♦ 6 ex-U.S. PCE 827 and PCER 848 classes
Bldrs: PS 19, 23: Pullman Standard Car Co., Chicago; PS 28: Albina Eng. & Machine Wks., Portland, Ore.; others: Willamette Iron & Steel Corp., Portland, Ore.

	Laid down	L	In serv.
PS 19 Miguel Malvar (ex-*Ngoc Hoi;* ex-*Brattleboro,* EPCER 852)	28-10-43	1-3-44	26-5-44
PS 22 Sultan Kudarat (ex-*Dong Da II;* ex-*Crestview,* PCE 895)	2-12-42	18-5-43	30-10-44
PS 23 Datu Marikudo (ex-*Van Kiep II;* ex-*Amherst,* PCER 853)	16-11-43	18-3-44	16-6-44
PS 28 Cebu (ex-PCE 881)	11-8-43	10-11-43	31-7-44
PS 31 Pangasinan (ex-PCE 891)	28-10-42	24-4-43	15-6-44
PS 32 Iloilo (ex-PCE 897)	16-12-42	3-8-43	6-1-45

Miguel Malvar (PS 19) NAVPIC Holland, 11-97

PATROL SHIPS [PS] *(continued)*

Cebu (PS 28)—with *Miguel Malvar* (PS 19) in background; note the differences in the bridge superstructure configurations Alexandre Sheldon-Duplaix, 12-97

D: 903 tons (fl) **S:** 15 kts **Dim:** 56.24 (54.86 wl) × 10.08 × 2.87
A: 1 76.2-mm 50-cal. Mk 26 DP—PS 19 only: 2 twin 40-mm 60-cal. Mk 1 Mod. 2 AA—others: 3 single 40-mm 60-cal. Bofors Mk 3 AA; 4 single 20-mm 70-cal. U.S. Mk 68 AA; 4 single 12.7-mm mg
Electronics: Radar: 1 SPS-64(V)11 nav.; 1 SPS-64(V). . . nav.
M: PS 22, 23, 32: 2 G.M. 12-278A diesels; 2 props; 2,000 bhp—PS 19, 28, 31: 2 G.M. 12-567A diesels; 2 props; 1,800 bhp
Electric: 240–280 kw tot. **Range:** 9,000/10 **Fuel:** 125 tons
Crew: 7 officers, 70 enlisted

Remarks: PS 28 through PS 32 were transferred 7-48; one of these, *Leyte* (PS 30, ex-PCE 885), was lost by grounding in 1979. PS 19, 22, and 23 were transferred to South Vietnam 11-7-66, 29-11-61, and 6-70, respectively, and escaped Vietnam in 5-75; PS 19 and 22 were sold to the Philippines in 11-75, PS 23 on 5-4-76. PS 19 and PS 23 were built with longer forecastles as rescue ships. Sister *Negros Occidental* (PS 29, ex-U.S. PCE 884) was discarded during 1995 but remains afloat and could later be refitted for further service.
Combat systems: PS 19, 22, 31, and 32 completed two-year rehabilitations 1990–92 with revised armament and new radars and communications gear; PS 23 and PS 28 were refitted to the same standard in 1992–93. There is no weapons-control system; all guns are ringsight aimed.

♦ 1 ex-U.S. Admirable-class former minesweeper
Bldr: Winslow Marine Railway, Seattle

	Laid down	L	In serv.
PS 20 Magat Salamat (ex-*Chi Lang;* ex-*Gayety,* MSF 239)	14-11-43	19-3-44	23-9-45

Magat Salamat (PS 20) Philippine Navy, 1997

D: 650 tons light (905 fl) **S:** 14 kts **Dim:** 56.24 (54.86 wl) × 10.06 × 2.87
A: 1 76.2-mm 50-cal. Mk 26 DP; 2 single 40-mm 60-cal. Mk 3 AA; 4 single 20-mm 70-cal. Mk 68 AA; 4 single 12.7-mm mg
Electronics: Radar: 1 SPS-64(V)11 nav.
M: 2 . . . . . . diesels; 2 props; 1,710 bhp **Electric:** 280 kw tot.
Range: 9,000/10 **Fuel:** 140 tons **Crew:** 7 officers, 70 enlisted

Remarks: Rehabilitated at Cavite Dockyard beginning late in 1995. Had been transferred to Vietnam in the mid-1960s, escaping to the Philippines in 4-75, and was formally acquired 11-75. The original Copper-Bessemer GSD-8 diesels have probably been replaced.
Combat systems: There is no weapons-control system; all guns are ringsight aimed. The 76.2-mm gunmount has been provided with a shield.

PATROL COMBATANTS [PG]

♦ 3 ex-U.K. Peacock class
Bldr: Hall Russell, Aberdeen, Scotland

	Laid down	L	In serv.
PS 35 Emilio Jacinto (ex-*Peacock,* P 239)	29-1-82	1-12-82	12-10-83
PS 36 Apolinario Mabini (ex-*Plover,* P 240)	13-5-82	12-4-83	20-7-84
PS 37 Artemio Ricarte (ex-*Starling,* P 241)	9-9-82	7-9-83	10-8-84

Artemio Ricarte (PS 37) Leo Dirkx, 5-99

Apolinario Mabini (PS 36) Brian Morrison, 11-99

Emilio Jacinto (PS 35) Takatoshi Okano, 10-98

D: 664 tons (712 fl) **S:** 28+ kts (25 sust.) **Dim:** 62.60 (60.00 pp) × 10.00 × 2.72
A: 1 76-mm 62-cal. OTOBreda Compact DP; 4 single 7.62-mm mg
Electronics: Radar: 1 Kelvin-Hughes Type 1006 nav.
M: 2 APE-Crossley SEMT-Pielstick 18 PA6 V280 diesels; 2 3-bladed props; 14,188 bhp—1 Schottel S103 LSVEST drop-down, shrouded loiter prop; 181 shp
Electric: 755 kw tot. **Range:** 2,500/17 **Fuel:** 44 tons
Crew: 6 officers, 25 enlisted (44 tot. accomm.)

Remarks: Purchased 4-97 for about $20 million total, with turnover on 1-8-97 and recommissioning 4-8-97. Had been built for service at Hong Kong and became surplus when the colony was handed back to China on 30-6-97. Sisters *Swallow* (P 242) and *Swift* (P 243) returned to U.K. 3-9-88 and were paid off and sold to Ireland 8-10-88.
Hull systems: Carry two Avon Searaider 5.4-m, 30-kt, 10-man semi-rigid rubber inspection dinghies and a small "fast patrol craft." Have two rudders. Reported to be bad rollers, requiring deeper bilge keels to be fitted.
Combat systems: Some 450 rounds of 76-mm ammunition can be carried, with the gun controlled by a GSA7 Sea Archer Mk 1 electro-optical director, to which a G.E.C. V3800 thermal imager was added in 1987. Have two 50-mm rocket flare projectors. The Philippine Navy plans to add some sort of antiship missile to the ships, but due to topweight problems, it would have to be a lightweight system such as Sea Skua; no missiles have been ordered to date.

PATROL CRAFT [PC]

♦ 2 (+ 2 + 3) Gen. Emilio Aguinaldo class
Bldr: Cavite NSY

	Laid down	L	In serv.
PG 140 Gen. Emilio Aguinaldo	. . .	23-6-84	21-11-90
PG 141 Gen. Antonio Luna	2-12-90	23-6-92	1999
PG 142	14-2-94	. . .	. . .

PATROL CRAFT [PC] *(continued)*

Gen. Antonio Luna (PG 141)—being moved by two Philippine Navy tugs while still not quite complete
Leo Dirkx, 5-99

D: 215 tons (279 fl) **S:** 18 kts **Dim:** 44.0 × 6.2 × 1.6
A: 2 single 40-mm 60-cal. Bofors Mk 3 AA; 2 single 20-mm 70-cal. Oerlikon AA; 4 single 12.7-mm mg
Electronics: Radar: 1 . . . nav.
M: 4 G.M. Detroit Diesel 12V92 TA diesels; 4 props; 2,040 bhp
Range: 1,100/18 **Crew:** 6 officers, 52 enlisted

Remarks: PG 140 was originally to have carried antiship missiles; press reports indicate she was not finally commissioned until 6-92, and no missiles have been carried since. PG 141 was launched as indicated but did not begin fitting out until 1994 budget funding was provided; she has yet to be commissioned. PG 142 was officially begun 23-6-92, but little work has been accomplished. Three more are planned, and if funds are available, their armament would be changed to one 76-mm OTOBreda Compact DP and an OTOBreda twin 25-mm AA; due to the extensive superstructure and its attendant topweight, however, the installation of additional armament does not seem practicable. The design is overloaded and underpowered; the basic hull design was evolved from that of the *Katapangan* class.

♦ 3 Katapangan class

	Bldr	In serv.
P 101 Kagitingan	W. Müller, Hameln, Germany	9-2-79
P 102 Bagong Lakas	W. Müller, Hameln, Germany	9-2-79
P 103 Katapangan	Cavite NSY	1982

D: 132 tons (150 fl) **S:** 16 kts **Dim:** 37.0 × 6.2 × 1.7
A: 1 twin 30-mm 75-cal. Emerlec EX-31 AA; 4 single 12.7-mm mg; 2 single 7.62-mm mg
Electronics: Radar: 1 . . . nav.
M: 2 MTU MB 12V493 TZ60 diesels; 2 props; 2,050 bhp
Crew: 4 officers, 26 enlisted

Remarks: Unsuccessful design that could not approach designed speed of 28 kts. Had been discarded by 1992, but were rehabilitated under the 1994 budget. A fourth unit, *Bagong Silang,* was never completed at Cavite.

♦ 5 ex-South Korean Sea Dolphin class (PKM 200 series)

Bldrs: Korea-Tacoma SY, Chinhae, and Korea SB & Eng., Masan (In serv. 1970s–80s)

PG 110 Tomas Batillo
PG 111 Boni Serrano
PG 112 Bienvenido Salting
PG 114 Salvador Abcede
PG 115 Ramon Aguirre

Sea Dolphin–class unit in South Korean service—Philippine Navy version has an open 40-mm mount on fantail, a twin 30-mm mount forward (as here), and single 20-mm mounts on bridge wings; the masts have also been changed to four-legged lattice structures
H&L Van Ginderen, 5-97

D: 113 tons (143 fl) **S:** 38 kts **Dim:** 33.10 (31.25 wl) × 6.92 × 1.75 (2.45 props)
A: 1 40-mm 60-cal. Bofors Mk 3 AA; 1 twin 30-mm 90-cal. Emerlec AA; 2 single 20-mm 70-cal. Oerlikon Mk 10 AA; 2 single 7.62-mm M2 mg
Electronics: Radar: 1 Raytheon 1645 nav./surf. search
M: 2 MTU 16V538 TB90 diesels; 2 props; 10,800 bhp (9,000 sust.)
Electric: 100 kw tot. (2 × 50-kw diesel sets)
Range: 500/32; 1,000/20 **Fuel:** 15 tons **Crew:** 5 officers, 26 enlisted

Remarks: Five units from the PKM 200 series—the former PKM 225, 226, 229, 231, and 235—were transferred to the Philippines 15-6-95 and arrived 8-95. After refurbishment, PG 110–114 were recommissioned 22-5-96. Two more were employed as cannibalization spares. Designed for 38 kts; can now make only 32 kts continuous.

PATROL BOATS [PB]

♦ 22 U.S. 78-foot class

Bldrs: PG 370–381 and five others: Trinity-Equitable SY, New Orleans; others: Marine Division, Atlantic, Gulf & Pacific Co. (AG&P SY), Manila

	In serv.
PG 370 Jose Andrada	8-90
PG 371 Enrique Jurado	24-6-91
PG 372 Alfredo Peckson	24-6-91
PG 374 Simeon Castro	24-6-91
PG 375 Carlos Albert	1-92
PG 376 Heracleo Alano	1-92
PG 377 Liberato Picar	1-92
PG 378 Hilario Ruiz	1-6-95
PG 379 Rafael Pargas	1-6-95
PG 380 Nestor Reinoso	1-6-95
PG 381 Dioscoro Papa	1-6-95
PG 383 Ismael Lomibao	1995
PG 384 Leovigildo Antioque	22-5-96
PG 385 Federico Martir	22-5-96
PG 386 Filipino Flojo	22-5-96
PG 387 Anastacio Cacayorin	1996
PG 388 Manuel Gomez	1996
PG 389 Teotimo Figuracion	1996
PG 390 José Loor Sr.	1997
PG 392 Juan Magluyan	3-98
PG 393 Florenca Nuño	5-98
PG 395 Felix Apolinario	1999

Florenca Nuño (PG 393)—with 25-mm gun forward
H&L Van Ginderen/C. Delgoffe, 5-00

Hilario Ruiz (PG 378) H&L Van Ginderen/Brian Morrison, 5-98

D: 56.4 tons (fl) **S:** 28 kts **Dim:** 23.66 × 6.06 × 1.01 (hull; 1.76 props)
A: five or more: 1 25-mm 75-cal. Mk 38 Mod. 0 Bushmaster low-angle—all: 2 or 4 single 12.7-mm M3 mg; 2 single 7.62-mm mg
Electronics: Radar: 1 Raytheon SPS-64(V)11
M: 2 G.M. 16V92 TAB diesels; 2 props; 2,800 bhp
Electric: 70 kw (2 × 35-kw diesel sets) **Range:** 600/24, 1,200/12
Fuel: 18,950 liters **Endurance:** 5 days **Crew:** 2 officers, 8 enlisted

Remarks: First four were ordered in 9-89 for $9.4 million; the fifth was ordered in 4-90 and three more in 8-90. In 3-93, Halter received a $36.2 million (U.S.) contract to build four more in the U.S.A., provide four kits to a yard in the Philippines, and assist in the construction of three more in a Philippine yard; in 6-94, another 12 were ordered for $27.5 million, with seven to be built by AG&P Shipyard in the Philippines. DF 379 and 380 were launched 29-4-95 by AG&P. The original goal was 35 total, but that has been curtailed for lack of funds. Were originally intended to operate in flotillas of seven, each attached to a larger patrol boat acting as leader.
Hull systems: Aluminum construction. A 4-m rigid inflatable boat powered by a 40-bhp outboard motor is stowed amidships.
Combat systems: The design made provision to install a 40-mm Mk 3 gun on the foredeck and an 80-mm mortar aft, but current plans call for eventual installation of a 25-mm mount forward on all, with many still lacking the weapon as of 2001; as of 2000, PG 381, 384, 389, 390, and 393 had the 25-mm mount. Carry 4,000 rounds of 12.7-mm and 2,000 rounds of 7.62-mm ammunition. Usually carry two "big eyes" binoculars on tripod mounts, one on the forecastle and one just abaft the mast. Some have a second navigational radar.

♦ 4 U.S. Swift Mk III class

Bldr: Peterson Bldrs, Sturgeon Bay, Wis. (In serv. 1975–76)

PCF 351 PCF 352 PCF 353 PCF 354

D: 28 tons (36.7 fl) **S:** 30 kts **Dim:** 19.78 × 5.5 × 1.8
A: 1 twin and 2 single 12.7-mm mg **Electronics:** Radar: 1 Koden . . . nav.
M: 3 G.M. 8V71 TI diesels; 3 props; 1,950 bhp **Range:** 500/30 **Crew:** 8 tot.

Remarks: Aluminum construction. Pilothouse offset to starboard. Ten sisters serve in the Philippine Coast Guard.

PATROL BOATS [PB] *(continued)*

PCF 351—with guns temporarily dismounted H&L Van Ginderen/Brian Morrison, 5-98

♦ 10 South Korean Schoolboy/Sea Hawk class

Bldrs: Korea SB & Eng., Masan, and Korea-Tacoma SY, Chinhae (In serv. 1974–79)

PG 841 CONRADO YAP	PG 847 LÉOPOLDO REGIS
PG 842 TEDORICO DOMINADO, JR.	PG 848 LÉON TADINA
PG 843 COSME ACOSTA	PG 849 LORETO DANIPOG
PG 844 JOSÉ ARTIAGA, JR.	PG 851 APOLLO TIANO
PG 846 NICANOR JIMENEZ	PG 853 SULPICIO FERNANDEZ

D: 72 tons (80 fl) **S:** 40 kts **Dim:** 25.37 × 5.40 × 1.20
A: 1 40-mm/60-cal. Bofors Mk 3 AA; 2 single 20-mm 70-cal. Oerlikon Mk 10 AA; 2 single 12.7-mm mg; 2 single 7.62-mm mg
Electronics: Radar: 1 Raytheon 1645 nav.
M: 2 MTU 16V538 TD90 diesels; 2 props; 5,200 bhp
Range: 500/20; 600/17 **Crew:** 6 officers, 19 enlisted

Remarks: Transferred to the Philippines as the result of an agreement reached in late 5-93 for a token $100 each. Eight were commissioned in the Philippines 23-6-93, the others on 23-6-94. Have been rearmed with spare weapons from Philippine Navy inventory. Two sisters, to have been numbered PG 845 and PG 852, have not yet been reactivated and were probably employed as cannibalization spares.

♦ 2 ex-U.S. Coast Guard 82-foot Point class

Bldr: J. Martinac SB, Tacoma, Wash. (PG . . .: U.S. Coast Guard Yard, Curtis Bay, Md.)

	In serv.
PG 394 ALBERTO NAVARET (ex-*Point Evans,* WPB 82354)	10-1-67
PG 396 ABRAHAM CAMPO (ex-*Point Doran,* WPB 82375)	1-6-70

D: 64 tons (66 fl) **S:** 23.7 kts **Dim:** 25.3 × 5.23 × 1.95
A: 2 single 12.7-mm M2 mg
Electronics: Radar: 1 Hughes-Furuno SPS-73 nav.
M: 2 Cummins VT-12-M diesels; 2 props; 1,600 bhp—*or* 2 Caterpillar 3412 diesels; 2 props; 1,480 bhp
Range: 490/23.7; 1,500/8 **Fuel:** 5.7 tons **Crew:** 1 officer, 7 enlisted

Remarks: PG 394 was transferred by donation 1-12-99 and PG 396 on 6-3-01 (and recommissioned on 5-12-01). Mild steel hull. High-speed diesels are controlled from the bridge. PG 3. . . displaces 69 tons (fl), can achieve 22.6 kts, and has a range of 320 n.m. at 22.6 kts or 1,200 n.m. at 8 kts. The armament listed is that aboard in USCG service; it may be augmented with additional 12.7-mm and/or 7.62-mm mg in Philippine service.

AMPHIBIOUS WARFARE SHIPS

♦ 2 U.S. Army Gen. Frank S. Besson–class vehicle landing ships [LST]

Bldr: Halter Marine–Moss Point Marine, Escatawpa, Miss.

	In serv.
LC 550 BACOLOD CITY	3-12-93
LC 551 DAGUPAN CITY (ex-*Cagayan de Oro*)	23-6-94

Dagupan City (LC 551) Takatoshi Okano, 10-98

D: 1,678 tons light (4,265 fl) **S:** 12 kts (11.6 sust.)
Dim: 83.14 (78.03 pp) × 18.28 (18.16 wl) × 3.66 (max.)
A: 2 single 20-mm 70-cal. Oerlikon Mk 10 AA; 2 single 12.7-mm M2 mg
Electronics: Radar: 1 Raytheon SPS-64(V)2 nav.; 1 Raytheon SPS-64(V)2 nav.
M: 2 G.M. EMD 16-645-E2 diesels; 2 props; 3,900 bhp—bow-thruster (250 shp)
Electric: 500 kw (2 × 250-kw diesel sets) **Range:** 8,358/11
Fuel: 524 tons **Endurance:** 38 days **Crew:** 6 officers, 24 enlisted

Bacolod City (LC 550) John Mortimer, 5-98

Remarks: Ordered 3-4-92, under the U.S. Aid Program, with the contract administered by the U.S. Army. Design is based on the Australian roll-on/roll-off beachable cargo ship *Frances Bay.* Built to commercial specifications.
Hull systems: Can transport up to 1,815 metric tons of vehicles or cargo containers on the 975-m^2 cargo deck; beaching load is 900 tons on a 1:30 gradient. Can also carry up to 122 tons of potable water. Have a bow ramp of 8.23-m width, but no stern ramp as on U.S. Army examples; instead, the pair have a helicopter deck and accommodations for 150 troops aft. Carry two LCVP landing craft in davits amidships.

♦ 5 ex-U.S. LST 1 and LST 542–class landing ships [LST]

Bldrs: LT 86, 87: Bethlehem Steel, Hingham, Mass.; LT 501: American Bridge, Ambridge, Pa.; LT 504: Missouri Valley Bridge & Iron Co., Evansville, Ind.; LT 516: Dravo Corp., Pittsburgh, Pa.

	In serv.
LT 86 ZAMBOANGA DEL SUR (ex-*Marion County,* LST 975)	3-2-45
LT 87 COTABATO DEL SUR (ex-THI NAI; ex-*Cayuga County,* LST 529)	28-2-44
LT 501 LAGUNA (ex-T-LST 230)	3-11-43
LT 504 LANAO DEL NORTE (ex-T-LST 566)	29-5-44
LT 516 KALINGA APAYO (ex-AE 516; ex-*Can Tho;* ex-*Garrett County,* AGP 786, ex-LST 786)	28-8-44

Lanao del Norte (LT 504) C. Schaefer, 3-97

D: 1,620 tons (4,080 fl) **S:** 11 kts **Dim:** 99.98 (96.32 wl) × 15.24 × 4.29
A: LT 86, 87, 516 only: 2 twin 40-mm 60-cal. Mk 1 Mod. 2 Bofors AA; 2 single 40-mm 60-cal. Bofors Mk 3 AA—all: 4 single 20-mm 70-cal. Oerlikon AA
Electronics: Radar: 1 Raytheon SPS-64(V)11 nav.
M: 2 G.M. 12-567A diesels; 2 props; 1,700 bhp **Electric:** 300 kw tot.
Range: 15,000/9 **Fuel:** 570 tons **Crew:** 60–100 tot.

Remarks: LT 86 was transferred 15-10-76; later deactivated, she was recommissioned 21-11-90. LT 87 escaped from South Vietnam (to which she had been transferred in 12-63) in 4-75 and was officially transferred to the Philippines 17-11-75; stricken in 1993, she was restored to service in 1995 and is now configured as a command center for disaster relief operations. LT 501 and LT 504 were purchased in 1976, having previously been stricken by the USN and laid up in Japan. LT 516 was transferred to South Vietnam in 4-71, escaped in 4-75, and was purchased by the Philippines 13-9-77. LT 501 and LT 504 were rehabilitated during 1992–93; none of the other survivors is in good condition.
Disposals: Stricken have been *Agusan del Sur* (LT 54; ex-*Nha Trang;* ex-*Jerome County,* LST 848), *Mindoro Occidental* (LT 93, ex-T-LST 222), *Suragao del Norte* (LT 94, ex-T-LST 488), *Suragao del Sur* (LT 95, ex-T-LST 546), *Maquindanao* (LT 96; ex-*Caddo Parish,* LST 515), *Cagayan* (LT 97; ex-*Hickman County,* LST 825), *Ilocos Norte* (LT 98; ex-*Madeira County,* LST 905), *Tarlac* (LT 500, ex-T-LST-47), *Samar Oriental* (LT 502, ex-T-LST 287), *Lanao del Sur* (LT 503, ex-T-LST 491), *Leyte del Sur* (LT 505, ex-T-LST 607), *Davao Oriental* (LT 506; ex-*Oosumi;* ex-*Daggett County,* LST 689), *Aurora* (LT 508; ex-*Harris County,* T-LST 822), *Samar del Norte* (LT 510; ex-*Shiretoko;* ex-*Nansemond County,* LST 1064), *Cotabato del Norte* (LT 511; ex-*Orleans Parish,* T-LST 1069, ex-MCS 6, ex-LST 1069), and *Tawi-Tawi* (LT 512, ex-T-LST 1072). The *Sierra Madre* (LT 57; ex-AL 57; ex-*Dumaguet;* ex-South Vietnamese *My Tho;* ex-U.S. *Harnett County,* AGP 821, ex-LST 821) ran aground in 1999 on the Spratley Islands, where the hulk is now employed as an observation station. *Benguet* (LT 507; ex-*Davies County,* T-LST 692) grounded on Scarborough Shoal in the South China Sea 3-11-99; she was pulled off on 30-11-99 but found not worth repairing and stricken during 2000.
Hull systems: LT 516 was converted during the mid-1960s to serve as a smallcraft tender; she retains operational bow doors, but much of the cargo deck is filled with repair shops and bins for spare parts. The ship has a helicopter deck amidships and a 10-ton derrick tending an enlarged hatch.

AMPHIBIOUS WARFARE SHIPS *(continued)*

♦ 7 U.S. LCM(8)-class landing craft [LCM]

LCM 260 through LCM 266

D: 118 tons (fl) **S:** 9 kts **Dim:** 22.43 × 6.42 × 1.4 (aft)
M: 4 G.M. 6-71 diesels; 2 props; 600 bhp **Range:** 140/9 **Crew:** 3 tot.

Remarks: Transferred 19-3-75. Cargo capacity: 54 tons or 120 troops. LCM 260 sank during a typhoon 13-11-90 but was restored to service.

♦ 11 ex-U.S. LCM(6)-class landing craft [LCM]

D: 24 tons (56 fl) **S:** 10 kts **Dim:** 17.07 × 4.37 × 1.17 (aft)
M: 2 G.M. Gray Marine 64HN9 diesels; 2 props; 330 bhp
Range: 130/9 **Crew:** 3 tot.

Remarks: Transferred 1955–75. Cargo capacity: 30 tons or 80 troops. Sixty-nine others have been discarded or converted to service craft.

♦ 7 U.S. Mini-ATC class [LCP]

Bldr: Tacoma BY, Tacoma, Wash. (In serv. 1978)

D: 9.3 tons light (13 fl) **S:** 28.5 kts **Dim:** 10.97 × 3.89 × 0.30
A: up to 4 single 12.7-mm mg; 1 40-mm Mk 19 grenade launcher; 1 60-mm M 60 mortar
M: 2 G.M. 8V53N diesels; 2 Jacuzzi 14Y waterjets; 566 bhp
Range: 37/28 **Crew:** 2 tot. + 15 troops

Remarks: Aluminum construction; rectangular planform. Can carry small radar. Very quiet in operation. Three others have been discarded.

♦ 2 Aquatrack amphibious vehicles [LCP]

Bldr: GKN Defence, Telford, U.K. (In serv. 1995)

D: 13.5 tons (fl) **S:** 6 kts in water/40 kph on land
Dim: 9.21 × 3.20 × 3.15 (high)
M: 1 Deutz BF8L513 diesel; 2 CP props; 315 bhp
Range: 500 km/40 kph (on land) **Crew:** 2 tot. + 2 passengers

Remarks: Operated by the Philippine Marines for the Mount Pinatubo Rescue Team. Running gear duplicates that of an M 113 armored personnel carrier, and the tracks contribute to afloat propulsion. Able to beach through 3-m seas. Can operate in Sea State 5. Has a 4.3 × 2.6–m open cargo deck and stern ramp aft, capable of carrying 5 tons of cargo or a light truck.

AUXILIARIES

♦ 1 ex-U.S. Alamosa-class cargo ship [AK]

Bldr: Froemming Bros., Milwaukee, Wis. (In serv. 22-9-45)

AC 90 Mactan (ex-TK 90; ex-*Kukui,* WAK 186; ex-*Colquitt,* AK 174)

Mactan (AC 90) Douglas A. Cromby, 9-92

D: 4,900 tons (7,450 fl) **S:** 12 kts **Dim:** 103.18 (97.54 pp) × 15.24 × 6.43
A: 2 single 20-mm 70-cal. Oerlikon Mk 10 AA; 2 single 12.7-mm mg
Electronics: Radar: 1 Raytheon SPS-64(V)11 nav.; 1 . . . nav.
M: 1 Nordberg TSM6 diesel; 1 prop; 1,750 bhp **Electric:** 500 kw tot.
Fuel: 350 tons **Crew:** 85 tot.

Remarks: 6,071 dwt. Built for the U.S. Maritime Commission, taken over by the U.S. Navy on completion, then transferred to the U.S. Coast Guard 24-9-45. Transferred on loan to the Philippines 1-3-72 and purchased outright 1-8-60. Was to have been stricken during 1994 but remains in commission. The first platform deck in the cargo hold was converted to passenger accommodations while the ship was in USCG service. Is employed as a military transport, supply ship, and lighthouse tender and normally stows one LCM(6) or LCVP landing craft amidships for use as a supply tender.

♦ 1 troop transport [AP]

Bldr: Ishikawajima-Harima, Tokyo (In serv. 1959)

AT 25 Ang Pangulo (ex-TP 777, ex-*The President,* ex-*Roxas,* ex-*Lapu-Lapu*)

D: 2,239 tons (2,727 fl) **S:** 18 kts **Dim:** 83.84 (78.50 pp) × 13.01 × 6.4
A: 2 single 20-mm 70-cal. Oerlikon Mk 10 AA—2 single 12.7-mm mg
Electronics: Radar: 2 . . . nav.
M: 2 Mitsui–Burmeister & Wain DE 642 VBF 75 diesels; 2 props; 5,000 bhp
Electric: 820 kw tot. **Range:** 6,900/15
Crew: 8 officers, 73 enlisted + 48 passengers

Ang Pangulo (AT 25) Leo Dirkx, 5-99

Remarks: Built as part of Japan's war reparations. Initially employed as a presidential yacht and command ship. Was in Hong Kong for sale in 1986 and remained away from the Philippines during the initial period of former President Marcos's exile. On return to Philippine waters was redesignated a troop transport, a role for which she is not particularly well equipped. As of 5-96, she was again being referred to as the presidential yacht.

♦ 1 ex-U.S. Achelous-class repair ship [AR]

Bldr: Chicago Bridge & Iron Co., Seneca, Ill.

	L	In serv.
AD 617 Yakal (ex-AR 517; ex-*Satyr,* ARL 23; ex-LST 852)	13-11-44	24-11-44

D: 3,960 tons (fl) **S:** 11.6 kts **Dim:** 99.98 (96.32 wl) × 15.24 × 3.71
A: 1 quadruple 40-mm 60-cal. Bofors Mk 2 AA; 5 twin 20-mm 70-cal. Oerlikon Mk 24 AA
Electronics: Radar: 1 Raytheon SPS-64(V)11 nav.
M: 2 G.M. 12-567A diesels; 2 props; 1,800 bhp **Electric:** 420 kw tot.
Fuel: 620 tons **Crew:** 250 tot.

Remarks: Transferred 24-1-77. Was converted during construction to serve as a repair ship, with shops installed in the former tank deck and wing compartments.
Disposals: *Kamagong* (AR 67; ex-*Aklan;* ex-*Romulus,* ARL 22; ex-LST 926) was discarded during 1989 and *Narra* (AR 88; ex-*Krishna,* ARL 38; ex-LST 1149) during 1992.
Hull systems: Has a 60-ton capacity A-frame lift boom to port, one 10-ton derrick, and one 20-ton derrick. The bow doors have been welded shut.

Note: Two small vessels described as "research ships" were acquired in 1993: *Fort San Antonio* (AM 700) and *Fort Abad* (AM 701); no data available.

SERVICE CRAFT

♦ 1 ex-U.S. YCV 3–class former aircraft transport barge [YC]

Bldr: Pearl Harbor NSY (In serv. 25-11-43)

YB 206 (ex-YCV 7)

Dim: 33.53 × 9.14 × . . . **Cargo capacity:** 250 tons

Remarks: Transferred 5-63. Used as a general-purpose barge.

♦ 2 ex-U.S. Navy barges [YC]

	Transferred		Transferred
YC 227 (ex-YC 1402)	8-59	YC 301 (ex-YC 1403)	8-71

Dim: 24.38 × 8.73 × 1.22

♦ 1 ex-U.S. 30-ton-capacity floating crane [YD]

	In serv.	Transferred
YU 206 (ex-YD 163)	12-5-46	1-71

D: 650 tons (fl) **Dim:** 36.58 × 13.72 × 2.13

♦ 1 ex-U.S. 60-ton-capacity floating crane [YD]

	In serv.	Transferred
YU 207 (ex-YD 191)	3-52	8-71

D: 920 tons (fl) **Dim:** 36.58 × 18.24 × 2.13

♦ 1 ex-U.S. Army 230-class 100-ton-capacity floating crane [YD]

	L	Transferred
YD 202 (ex-BCL 1791)	1943	7-49

D: 2,100 tons (fl) **Dim:** 64.0 × 12.5 × 3.4

♦ 2 ex-U.S. AFDL floating dry docks [YFDL]

Bldr: V.P. Loftis, Wilmington, N.C. (In serv. 1944–45)

YD 205 (ex-AFDL 44, ex-ARDC 11) YD . . . (ex-AFDL 40)

Lift capacity: 2,800 tons **Dim:** 118.6 × 25.6 × 3.1 (light)

Remarks: YD 205 was transferred during 9-69 and purchased outright on 1-8-80. Ex-AFDL 40 was purchased on 30-6-90.

♦ 2 ex-U.S. AFDL 1–class floating dry docks [YFDL]

	Bldr	In serv.
YD 200 (ex-AFDL 24)	Doullet & Ewin, Mobile, Ala.	1-44
YD 204 (ex-AFDL 20)	G. D. Auchter, Jacksonville, Fla.	6-44

SERVICE CRAFT *(continued)*

Lift capacity: 1,000 tons **Dim:** 60.96 × 19.51 × 1.04 (light)

Remarks: YD 200 was transferred during 7-48. YD 204 was loaned during 10-61 and purchased 1-8-80.

♦ 1 Ang Pinuno–class presidential yacht [YFL]
Bldr: Vosper Pty., Singapore (In serv. 12-77)

TP 77 Ang Pinuno

D: 150 tons **S:** 28.5 kts **Dim:** 37.9 × 7.2 × . . .
M: 3 MTU 12538 TB91 diesels; 3 props; 7,500 bhp

Remarks: Stricken in 1995 but restored to service in 1998–99 at Cavite. Are painted white.

♦ 1 or more converted LCM(6) personnel launches [YFL]
286 and others

D: 24 tons (56 fl) **S:** 10 kts **Dim:** 17.07 × 4.37 × 1.17 (aft)
M: 2 G.M. Gray Marine 64HN9 diesels; 2 props; 330 bhp
Range: 130/9 **Crew:** 3 tot.

Remarks: Former U.S.-built landing craft, with the tank deck enclosed to accommodate seated passengers and the bow ramp plated up.

♦ 1 dredge [YMN]
SDP-1

Naval dredge SDP-1 Leo Dirkx, 5-99

Remarks: No data available. Non-self-propelled.

♦ 2 ex-U.S. 174-foot YOG-class small tanker [YO]
Bldr: Puget Sound NSY, Bremerton, Wash.

	Laid down	L	In serv.
AF 72 Lake Taal (ex-YO 72, ex-YOG . . .)	. . .	. . .	14-4-45
AF 78 Lake Buhi (ex-YO 78, ex-YOG 73)	15-12-43	23-2-44	28-11-44

D: 445 tons light (1,420 fl) **S:** 8 kts **Dim:** 53.04 × 10.01 × 4.27
A: 1 20-mm 70-cal. Mk 10 Oerlikon AA **Electronics:** Radar: 1 . . . nav.
M: 2 G.M. 8-278A diesels; 2 props; 640 bhp **Fuel:** 25 tons
Crew: 5 officers, 25 enlisted

Remarks: Transferred 7-67; had been used as gasoline tanker by the U.S. Navy. Ex-U.S. YOG 33 and YOG 80, which escaped from Vietnam, were used for cannibalization spares. Cargo capacity: 985 tons. Sister *Lake Mainit* (YO 35) was stricken during 1979 and *Lake Naujan* (YO 43, ex-YO 173) in 1989.

♦ 1 ex-U.S. Savage-class barracks barge [YPB]
Bldr: Brown Shipbuilding, Houston, Texas

	Laid down	L	In serv.
PS 4 Rajah Lakandula (ex-*Tran Hung Dao;* ex-*Camp,* DER 251)	27-1-43	16-4-43	16-9-43

D: 1,590 tons light (1,850 fl) **Dim:** 93.27 × 11.15 × 4.27 (max.)
M: nonoperational: 4 Fairbanks-Morse 38D8⅛ × 10 diesels; 2 props; 6,080 bhp
Electric: 580 kw tot. **Range:** 11,500/11 **Fuel:** 300 tons **Crew:** . . .

Remarks: Former radar picket destroyer escort, transferred to Vietnam 6-1-71 and, after escape in 1975, sold to the Philippines 5-4-75. Was stricken during 1988 but has remained afloat as a barracks barge at Cavite. Armament at time of retirement was two single 76.2-mm 50-cal. Mk 34 DP, 2 twin 20-mm AA, and two triple ASW TT. She is unlikely to be reactivated for further service.

♦ 1 ex-U.S. Barnegat-class barracks barge [YPB]
Bldr: Lake Washington SY, Houghton, Wash.

	Laid down	L	In serv.
PS 7 Andres Bonifacio (ex-*Ly Thuong Kiet;* ex-*Chincoteague,* WHEC 375; ex-AVP 24)	23-7-41	15-4-42	12-4-43

D: 1,766 tons light (2,800 fl) **Dim:** 95.72 (91.44 wl) × 12.55 × 4.27 (max.)
A: nonoperational: 1 127-mm 38-cal. Mk 30 DP; 2 twin 40-mm 60-cal. Bofors Mk 1 Mod. 2 AA; 2 single 20-mm 70-cal. Oerlikon Mk 10 AA
M: nonoperational: 4 Fairbanks-Morse 38D8⅛ × 10 diesels; 2 props; 6,080 bhp
Electric: 600 kw tot. **Range:** 18,000/15 **Fuel:** 400 tons **Crew:** . . .

Remarks: Built as a seaplane tender and used by the U.S. Coast Guard as an ocean patrol cutter after transfer in 1946. Transferred to Vietnam in 1971 and escaped in 1975 to the Philippines, which purchased the ship and three sisters on 5-4-76. Stricken in 1993 but remains afloat in use as a barracks barge and as a possible reactivation asset. Some of the armament listed above may have been removed for use on other ships and craft. Could make 17 kts when operational.

♦ 1 or more medium harbor tugs [YTM]
YQ . . . Lilimbon

Lilimbon—tug assigned to the Philippine Navy Seabees Leo Dirkx, 5-99

Remarks: No characteristics data available. Is attached to the Philippine Navy Construction Corps (Seabees).

♦ 2 ex-U.S. YTL 442–class small harbor tugs [YTL]
Bldr: Everett-Pacific Co., Everett, Wash.

YQ 223 Tagbanua (ex-YTL 429) YQ 225 Ilongot (ex-YTL 427)

YTL 442–class tug—renumbered 2000 and equipped for firefighting H&L Van Ginderen/Brian Morrison, 5-98

D: 70 tons (80 fl) **S:** 9 kts **Dim:** 20.17 × 5.18 × 1.5
M: 1 Hamilton 685A diesel; 300 bhp

Remarks: Built 1944–45; transferred 5-63 and 8-71. At least one is now equipped as a fireboat; renumbered 2000 in 1998, the craft has two firefighting monitors.

♦ 1 ex-U.S. YTM 764–class fireboat [YTR] (In serv. 1945)
YQ . . . Fire Tug (ex-*Hiamonee,* YTM 776)

Fire Tug—the former U.S. *Hiamonee* (YTM 776), still without a Philippine Navy pennant number H&L Van Ginderen/Brian Morrison, 5-98

D: 260 tons (350 fl) **S:** 11 kts **Dim:** 30.8 × 8.5 × 3.7
M: 2 Enterprise diesels; 1 prop; 1,270 bhp **Crew:** 8 tot.

Remarks: Purchased 30-6-90; had been stricken from the U.S. Navy 30-11-86. Is employed as a fireboat and general-purpose tug, although only one firefighting monitor is fitted, atop the pilothouse.

♦ 2 ex-U.S. 174-foot YW-class water tankers [YW]
Bldrs: AW 33: Marine Iron & SB Co., Duluth, Minn.; AW 34: Leatham D. Smith SB, Sturgeon Bay, Wis.

	Laid down	L	In serv.
AW 33 Lake Buluan (ex-YW 111)	30-9-44	16-12-44	1-8-45
AW 34 Lake Paoay (ex-YW 130)	14-5-45	24-6-45	28-8-45

D: 440 tons light (1,390 fl) **S:** 8 kts **Dim:** 53.04 × 10.01 × 4.0
A: 1 40-mm 60-cal. Bofors Mk 3 AA; 1 20-mm 70-cal. Oerlikon AA
Electronics: Radar: 1 . . . nav.
M: 2 G.M. 8-278A diesels; 2 props; 640 bhp **Electric:** 80 kw
Fuel: 25 tons **Crew:** 5 officers, 25 enlisted

SERVICE CRAFT *(continued)*

Lake Paoay (AW 34)—with patrol boat *Teotimo Figuracion* (PG 389) alongside NAVPIC Holland, 12-97

Remarks: Transferred 16-7-75. Cargo capacity: 930 tons. Sister *Lake Lanao* (YW 42, ex-U.S. YW 125) was stricken during 1989.

COAST GUARD

Note: Given autonomous status from the Philippine Navy and transferred from the Department of National Defense to the Department of Transportation and Communication on 23-11-96, the size of the Philippine Coast Guard has fluctuated widely since its establishment in the early 1970s. At one time, it had responsibility for maintaining navigational aids and included many of the tenders now returned to the navy. Up to 60 new patrol craft are desired, but funds are lacking. The coast guard has eight districts comprising a total of 60 stations. In addition to the units listed, many adapted wooden-hulled native smallcraft are employed for local logistic and patrol service; no characteristics are available for these. There are also a number of powered fishing craft and coastal commercial craft enrolled in the Philippine Coast Guard Auxiliary.

Personnel (2002): Approx. 3,000 active, plus 4,000 ready reserve

PATROL CRAFT [WPC]

♦ 0 (+ 4 + 10) Bay class
Bldr: Tenix Defense Systems, South Coogie, Australia

Remarks: Approved 10-12-01 and to be constructed during 2001–04 for $150 million, with an option for 10 more. Based on the Australian Customs Service design.

♦ 2 (+ 2) San Juan–class search-and-rescue craft
Bldr: Tenix Defense Systems, South Coogie, Australia

AU 001 San Juan (In serv. 21-7-00) AU 002 Don Emilio (In serv. 12-00)

San Juan (AU 001) Tenix, 7-00

D: 540 tons (fl) **S:** 24.5 kts **Dim:** 56.00 (51.00 wl) × 10.55 × 2.50 (max.)
A: small arms **Electronics:** Radar: 2 Furuno . . . nav.
Electronics: . . .
M: 2 Caterpillar 3612 diesels; 2 CP props; 10,890 bhp
Electric: 690 kw tot. (2 × 260 kw, Caterpillar 3406 diesels driving; 1 × 170 kw, Caterpillar 3306T diesel driving; 60 Hz a.c.)
Range: 1,000/24; 2,000/15 **Fuel:** 88 tons + 3 tons helicopter fuel
Crew: 8 officers, 30 enlisted + 300 survivors

Remarks: Built with Australian government financial assistance. Two more were authorized on 10-12-01. AU 002 was launched 4-10-00. AU 001 is based at Manila and AU 002 at Cebu City. Have medical facilities and carry a medical officer. Helicopter deck can accept a Sikorsky S-76 or Bell UH-1H, but there is no hangar. Navaids include Furuno FS-1800 GPS set and Furuno Felcom-81A Inmarsat commercial SATCOM. Employ a single-chine planing hull. Carry a 6.5-m rescue RIB on the stern launch/recovery ramp and four 4.5-m RIBs handled by two cranes. A divers' recompression chamber is fitted, and the ships are equipped with pollution-control gear. Delivered unarmed, but will probably be fitted with 12.7-mm mg. Are painted white.

♦ 2 Bessang Pass–class search-and-rescue craft (1 *nonoperational*)
Bldr: Sumidagawa, Tokyo (In serv. 1976–77)

AU 75 *Bessang Pass* (ex-SAR 99) AU 100 Tirad Pass (ex-SAR 100)

Bessang Pass (AU 75)—with old pennant number H&L Van Ginderen, 1986

D: 275 tons (fl) **S:** 30 kts (27.5 sust.) **Dim:** 44.0 × 7.4 × 1.5
A: 2 twin 12.7-mm mg **Electronics:** Radar: 1 . . . nav.
M: 2 MTU 12V538 TB82 diesels; 2 props; 4,030 bhp
Range: 2,300/14 **Crew:** 32 tot.

Remarks: Although AU 75 was reported to have run aground and been lost in 9-83, she was to have been refitted and returned to service as of 8-98, although she was still nonoperational in 2001. AU 100 has also been refitted for antipiracy patrol duties. Similar craft were constructed for the Indian Coast Guard. Are painted white.

♦ 4 ex-U.S. PGM 39 class Bldr: Tacoma Boat, Tacoma, Wash.

	In serv.
PG 61 Agusan (ex-PGM 39)	3-60
PG 62 Catanduanes (ex-PGM 40)	3-60
PG 63 Romblon (ex-PGM 41)	3-60
PG 64 Palawan (ex-PGM 42)	6-60

D: 122 tons **S:** 17 kts **Dim:** 30.6 × 6.4 × 2.1 (props)
A: 2 single 20-mm 70-cal. Oerlikon Mk 10 AA
Electronics: Radar: 1 Raytheon 1500 nav.
M: 2 MTU 12V493 TY57 (MB 820) diesels; 2 props; 1,900 bhp
Range: 1,400/11 **Crew:** 15 tot.

Remarks: Transferred from Philippine Navy service by 1992.

PATROL BOATS [WPB]

♦ 11 CGC 103–class patrol launches
Bldr: Cavite NY (In serv. 1984–. . .)

CGC 103 CGC 115 CGC 129 CGC 132 CGC 134 CGC 136
CGC 110 CGC 128 CGC 130 CGC 133 CGC 135

D: 13 tons (fl) **S:** 28 kts **Dim:** 12.2 × 4.1 × 0.9
A: 1 12.7-mm mg; 1 7.62-mm mg **Electronics:** Radar: none
M: 2 G.M. Detroit Diesel 6-71 diesels; 2 props; 560 bhp
Range: . . ./. . . **Crew:** 5 tot.

Remarks: Used for harbor police work. GRP construction. One was stricken in 1994.

♦ 3 Mk II design Bldr: Cavite NY (In serv. 7-85 to 1986)

DF 314 DF 315 DF 316

D: 24.6 tons (fl) **S:** 36 kts **Dim:** 16.7 × 5.0 × 1.3
A: . . . **Electronics:** Radar: 1 . . . nav.
M: 2 MTU 8V396 TB93 diesels; 2 props; 2,400 bhp

Remarks: Improved version of the DB 411 class. GRP hull. There were to have been 55 built under the 18-6-82 order, but by 1986 only four hulls were ready and no more were built.

♦ 10 DB 411 class Bldr: Marcelo Fiberglass Corp., Manila (In serv. 1975–76)

DB 411 DB 417 DB 422 DB 429 DB 432
DB 413 DB 419 DB 426 DB 431 DB 433

DB 431 RAN, 6-82

COAST GUARD PATROL BOATS [WPB] *(continued)*

D: 15 tons (21.75 fl) **S:** 20 kts **Dim:** 14.07 × 4.32 × 1.04 (1.48 props)
A: 1 twin and 1 single 12.7-mm mg
Electronics: Radar: 1 Canadian Marconi LN-66 nav.
M: 2 MTU 8V-331 TC80 diesels; 2 props; 1,800 bhp **Electric:** 7.5 kVA tot.
Range: 200/36 **Crew:** 6 tot.

Remarks: Eighty were ordered in 8-75, but of 25 hulls completed during 1975, 12 were destroyed by fire and the program was terminated. Since then, at least two others have been discarded. The twin machinegun mount is recessed into the forecastle. Later examples employ Cummins diesels. Were originally intended to achieve 46 kts. Formerly numbered in the PC series.

♦ 6 Australian fiberglass-hulled
Bldr: De Havilland Marine, Sydney (In serv. 20-11-74 to 8-2-75)

DF 318 DF 321 DF 326 DF 328 DF 330 DF 331

DF 318 Leo Dirkx, 5-99

D: 16.5 tons (fl) **S:** 25 kts **Dim:** 14.0 × 4.6 × 1.0
A: 2 single 12.7-mm mg **M:** 2 Caterpillar D348 diesels; 2 props; 740 bhp
Range: 500/12 **Crew:** 8 tot.

Remarks: Design very similar to the U.S. Patrol Boat Mk 1 class.

♦ 14 U.S. Swift Mk III class
Bldr: Peterson Bldrs, Sturgeon Bay, Wis. (In serv. 1975–76)

DF 325 through DF 332 DF 347 DF 352 DF 354
DF 334 DF 351 DF 353

DF 334—painted white H&L Van Ginderen/Brian Morrison, 5-98

D: 28 tons (36.7 fl) **S:** 30 kts **Dim:** 19.78 × 5.5 × 1.8
A: 1 twin and 2 single 12.7-mm mg
Electronics: Radar: 1 Canadian Marconi LN-66 nav.
M: 3 G.M. 8V71 TI diesels; 3 props; 1,950 bhp
Range: 500/30 **Crew:** 8 tot.

Remarks: Aluminum construction. Pilothouse offset to starboard. Sisters PCF 351 though PCF 354 serve in the Philippine Navy, and three others have been discarded. DF 347, and possibly others, has had the twin 12.7-mm mg position atop the pilothouse removed.

♦ 12 ex-U.S. Swift Mk I and Mk II class
Bldr: Sewart Seacraft, Berwick, La. (In serv. 1966–70)

Mk I: DF 300, DF 301, DF 302, DF 303
Mk II: DF 305, DF 307 through DF 313

D: 22.5 tons (fl) **S:** 25 kts **Dim:** 15.6 × 4.12 × 1.5
A: 1 twin 12.7-mm mg; 1 combination 81-mm mortar/12.7-mm mg
Electronics: Radar: 1 Canadian Marconi LN-66 nav.
M: 2 G.M. 12V71T diesels; 2 props; 960 bhp **Electric:** 6 kw tot.
Range: 400/22 **Endurance:** 24–36 hr **Crew:** 6–8 tot.

Remarks: Aluminum construction. Data apply to Mk II version; Mk I is 15.2 m o.a. and has a flush-decked hull, while the Mk II has a low forecastle to improve seaworthiness. Formerly numbered in the PCF series. Six others, including the Philippine-built, ferroconcrete-hulled PCF 317, have been discarded.

AUXILIARIES

Note: Acquisition of a new 56.9-m navigational aids tender was authorized during 1997, but funding has not yet been made available. The U.S. Navy offered for sale during FY 99 one *Stalwart*-class ocean surveillance ship, *Triumph* (T-AGOS 4), which would have been adapted for the role, but the offer was not accepted.

♦ 1 Corregidor-class navigational aids tender [WAGL]
Bldr: Niigata Eng., Niigata, Japan

	Laid down	L	In serv.
AG 891 CORREGIDOR	8-7-97	5-11-97	2-3-98

Corregidor (AG 891) Leo Dirkx, 5-99

D: approx. 1,130 tons (fl) **S:** 13.4 kts **Dim:** 56.92 (50.00 pp) × 11.00 × 3.75
A: none **Electronics:** Radar: 1 . . . nav.
M: 2 Niigata . . . diesels; 2 props; . . . bhp **Range:** 4,000/11.7
Fuel: 87.1 m^3 **Endurance:** 15 days **Crew:** 37 tot. (+ 8 spare)

Remarks: 835 grt/731 dwt. Lighthouse and buoy tender. Has a 418.8-m^3 buoy hold and 87.6-m^3 cargo hold. Carries 106 m^3 of fresh water and up to 383 m^3 of ballast water. Crew includes a maintenance team from the Department of Transportation and Communications. Is painted white.

♦ 1 ex-U.S. Coast Guard Balsam-class navigational aids tender [WAGL]
Bldr: Marine Iron & SB Corp., Duluth, Minn. (In serv. 2-5-44)

AG 89 KALINGA (ex-TK 89; ex-*Redbud,* WAGL 398, ex-T-AKL 398, ex-AG 398)

Kalinga (AG 89) 1977

D: 935 tons (1,020 fl) **S:** 13 kts **Dim:** 54.86 × 11.28 × 3.96
A: 1 12.7-mm mg **Electronics:** Radar: 1 . . . nav.
M: 2 . . . diesels, electric drive; 1 prop; 1,200 shp
Range: 3,500/7.5 **Crew:** 53 tot.

Remarks: Built for the U.S. Coast Guard, then transferred to the U.S. Navy on 25-3-49 as AG 398 and to the Military Sealift Command in 10-49 as T-AKL 398, and returned to the U.S. Coast Guard 20-11-70. Transferred to the Philippines 1-3-72. Has a 20-ton buoy derrick. Refitted at Cavite Dockyard in 1995, recommissioning 11-95; the original Cooper-Bessemer GSD-8 diesels were replaced. Has a helicopter platform and an ice-breaking bow.

♦ 2 ex-U.S. Army FS 381–class navigational aids tenders [WAGL]
Bldr: Ingalls, Pascagoula, Miss. (In serv. 1943–44)

AE 71 MANGYAN (ex-AS 71; ex-*Miho,* ex-FS 524)
AE 79 LIMASAWA (ex-TK 79; ex-*Nettle,* WAK 169, ex-FS 396)

D: 473 tons light (950 fl) **S:** 12 kts **Dim:** 53.8 (50.27 pp) × 9.75 × 3.05
A: 2 single 12.7-mm mg **Electronics:** Radar: 1 . . . nav.
M: 2 G.M. 6-278A diesels; 2 props; 1,000 bhp **Electric:** 225 kw tot.
Range: 3,700/11; 4,150/10 **Fuel:** 67 tons **Crew:** 50 tot.

Remarks: AE 79 was loaned in 1-68 and purchased outright 31-8-78. AE 71 was purchased 24-9-76 after having served in the Japanese Navy as a mine countermeasures support ship; she was refitted and recommissioned during 1979. Both serve as buoy tenders and lighthouse supply ships. Cargo capacity: 345 tons. Speed reduced to 8 kts in AE 71; AE 79 has been overhauled and the engines renewed. Sister *Badjao* (AE 59, ex-AS 59; ex-Japanese *Nasami;* ex-U.S. Army FS 408) was stricken during 1996.

♦ 1 ex-U.S. Army FS 330–class navigational aids tender [WAGL]
Bldr: Higgins, Inc., New Orleans (In serv. 1944)

AE 46 CAPE BOJEADOR (ex-TK 46, ex-FS 203)

D: 420 tons (742 fl) **S:** 10 kts **Dim:** 51.77 (48.77 pp) × 9.75 × 2.43
A: 2 single 12.7-mm mg **Electronics:** Radar: 1 . . . nav.

COAST GUARD AUXILIARIES *(continued)*

M: 4 Buda-Lanova 6 DHMR-1879 diesels; 2 props; 680 bhp
Electric: 225 kw tot. **Range:** 3,830/10 **Fuel:** 50 tons **Crew:** 50 tot.

Remarks: Decommissioned in 1988 but refitted for further service and recommissioned 21-11-90; may have been re-engined as well, as obtaining parts for the engines listed above would be extremely difficult. Had been transferred from the U.S.A. in 2-50. Cargo capacity: 150 tons. Sister *Lauis Ledge* (TK 45, ex-FS 185) was stricken in 1988.

Coast Guard auxiliary Sarangani (101-21) Leo Dirkx, 5-99

SERVICE CRAFT

♦ **2 ex-U.S. YTL 442–class small harbor tugs [WYTL]**
Bldrs: YQ 222: Winslow Marine Railway & SB, Winslow, Wash.; YQ 226: Everett-Pacific Co., Everett, Wash.

YQ 222 Igorot (ex-YTL 572) YQ 226 Tasaday (ex-YTL 425)

D: 70 tons (80 fl) **S:** 9 kts **Dim:** 20.17 × 5.18 × 1.5
M: 1 Hamilton 685A diesel; 300 bhp

Remarks: Built 1944–45. YQ 222 was transferred during 7-48 by grant. YQ 226 was transferred on loan in 12-69 and purchased outright 1-8-80. Two sisters serve in the Philippine Navy proper.

Note: Also in use for logistic services are two large landing craft (B 124, B 244), LCM(6)-class landing craft BM 270, LCVP BV 182, and around 80 "Banca"-type native launches with outboard propulsion.

The Ministry of Defense operates the ships and craft of the Coast and Geodetic Survey, including *Hydrographer Ventura* (1,169 grt; completed in 1999 in Spain); *Atyimba* (686 tons fl; completed in 1969); and 245-ton sisters *Arinya* (completed in 1962) and *Alunya* (completed in 1964). An environmental patrol and fisheries protection patrol boat, *Bantay Kalikasan,* commissioned 2-2-95, may also be operated by this agency, as may the sister "research ships" *Fort San Antonio* (AM 700) and *Fort Abad* (AM 701), which were acquired in 1993.

POLAND

Republic of Poland

POLSKA MARYNARKA WOJENNA

Personnel (1999): 17,123 total (2,643 officers, 1,920 warrant officers, 1,880 noncommissioned officers, 1,300 other enlisted, 200 contract enlisted, 9,180 conscripts), plus 250 naval cadets

Organization and Bases: The major commands are the two coastal defense flotillas, one warship flotilla, and the naval air brigade. They are subordinated and based as follows: Captain Boreslaw Romanowski 3rd Warship Flotilla at Gdynia-Oksywie, VADM Kazimierz Prembski 8th Coast Defense Flotilla at Świnoujście, and RADM Wlodzimierz Steyer 9th Coast Defense Flotilla at Hel. Ships of the Hydrographic Protection Squadron are based at Gdynia-Oksywie. The naval academy and the warrant officers school are at Gdynia, while the career noncommissioned officers school is at Ustka. The 1st Naval Regiment of Riflemen *(Morski Pulk Strzelcow)* is based at Gdynia-Witomin and the 11th Naval Communications Regiment *(11 Pulk Lacznosci MW)* at Wejherowo. The 7th Naval Hospital is at Gdańsk-Oliwa and the 115th Military Hospital on the Hel Peninsula.

Naval Aviation: The Naval Aviation Brigade *(Brygada Lotnictwa Marynarki Wojennej)* operates 6 TS-11Rbis DF Iskra reconnaissance jets, 12 TS-11bis D/DF Iskra jet trainers, 5 An-2 Colt light transports, 3 An-28 transports, 6 An-28B-1R Bryza maritime surveillance aircraft, 4 SH-2G SeaSprite shipboard ASW helicopters, 6 Mi-2RM utility helicopters, 10 Mi-14PL land-based ASW helicopters, 3 Mi-14PS SAR helicopters, 2 W-3 Sokol transport helicopters, and 3 W-3RM Anakonda SAR helicopters (with 4 more on order).

Aviation elements are the 7th Special Air Force Regiment at Siemirowice, 34th Fighter Regiment at Gdynia-Babie Doly, and 40th Helicopter Squadron for Combating Submarines and Rescue at Darlowo.

It had been planned to begin receiving an ASW version of the Anakonda helicopter to be called the W-3U-1 Alligator, but lack of funding has delayed the order. Two ex-U.S. Navy SH-2G helicopters were transferred late in 2000 and two more during early 2001; they are equipped to launch A-244S and MU-90 Impact torpedoes. Some 27 Iryada combat training aircraft, completed in 1996 but stored, may be acquired and completed to the Oryada Orkan M-93 configuration as replacements for the 21 MiG-21bis and 5 MiG-21UM fighters transferred to the Polish Air Force during 2001.

Trials with an updated Mi-14PL helicopter began in 2000; the aircraft has an updated mission suite called Kryl-lot, a new tactical information distribution system, a Krab acoustic signal processor, an updated Oka-2M dipping sonar, and Mniszka MAD gear. Two more updated Mi-14PL were to be completed in 2001, and all 10 are to have been updated by 2004 and will carry A-244S Mod. 3 ASW torpedoes.

TS-11Rbis Iskra reconnaissance aircraft Jaroslaw Cislak, 2000

An-28B-1R Bryza maritime surveillance aircraft Findler & Winter, 7-00

An-28 light transport Jaroslaw Cislak, 2000

Mi-2RM utility helicopter Jaroslaw Cislak, 2000

Mi-14PL ASW helicopter Jaroslaw Cislak, 2000

W-3RM Anakonda SAR helicopter Jaroslaw Cislak, 2000

W-3 Sokol transport helicopter Jaroslaw Cislak, 2000

Coastal Defense: In use to defend major ports and naval facilities are long-range artillery and SS-C-3 Styx truck-mounted antiship missiles. The 1st Naval Regiment of Riflemen (*Morski Pulk Strzelcow,* or Marine Rifle Regiment) is based at Gdynia-Witomin, while the 8th Coastal Defense Flotilla is protected by the 8th Anti-Aircraft Artillery Battalion at Miedzyzdroje and the 9th Coastal Defense Flotilla is protected by the 7th Anti-Aircraft Artillery Battalion and the 55th ABC Defense Company at Ustka. The 8th Kolobrzkeski Sappers Battalion and 4th Minelaying Battalion at Dziwnow carry out engineering tasks in support of the 8th Flotilla. CRM-100 naval covert coastal surveillance radars built by Przemyslowy Instytut Telekomuniacji (PIT), Warsaw, began delivery late in 1999; they have a range of about 24 n.m. and are linked to the Leba automated command and control system (the radar may later be adapted for surface ships and for use on offshore platforms).

WEAPONS AND SENSORS

While most weapon and sensor systems are of Soviet origin, Poland manufactures some under license and has introduced its own navigational radars as a result of its extensive merchant ship and fishing boat construction industry. A naval gun-mount manufactured by the Cenzin Foreign Trade Enterprise is the twin 23-mm Wrobel-2MR, a water-cooled variant of the Soviet ZU-23-2 mount that can also be equipped to carry two 9K-32M Strela heat-seeking missiles:

Length: 2.608 m **Bore:** 23 mm
Mount weight: 2,500 kg **Muzzle velocity:** 970 m/sec
Rate of fire: 1,600–2,000 rds/mount/min (800 practical)
Effective range: 2,000 m **Effective altitude:** 1,500 m

On-mount ammunition supply is 200 rounds per barrel. The 9K-32M missiles have a length of 1.440 m and a diameter of 72 mm and have a cruise velocity of 500 m/sec; the infrared seeker has a 40° field of view. Also available from the same manufacturer are the 12.7-mm Drop and Ohar naval heavy machinegun mountings.

Current torpedoes, all of Soviet-era manufacture, are the Type 53-56, Type 53-65K oxygen-powered, SET-53 and SET-53M electric ASW homing; and TEST-71 wire-guided electric ASW—all of 533-mm diameter. During 2000, 10 A-244S ASW torpedoes were acquired from Italy for use with Mi-14 PL helicopters. Some 30 Eurotorp MU-90 Impact ASW torpedoes were to be ordered in 2001.

The Polish T.MMD-2 mine weighs 640 kg (warhead: 240 kg) and is some 1.815 m long and 572 mm in diameter. As of 2-01, 252 operational and 15 exercise versions had been ordered for the Polish Navy (with an option for 248 more), and the U.S. Navy had ordered 100.

Note: All ship names are prefixed by ORP (*Okret Rzeczpospolitej Polskiej,* or Ship of the Republic of Poland).

ATTACK SUBMARINES [SS]

Note: As replacements for the Foxtrot-class submarines, Norway is transferring the Type 207 submarines *Skolpen* (S 306), *Stord* (S 308), *Svenner* (S 309), and *Kunna* (S 319), two during 2002, one in 2003, and one in 2004. See pp. 521–522 for characteristics and appearance.

♦ 1 Soviet Kilo class (Project 877E)

Bldr: United Admiralty SY, St. Petersburg (In serv. 29-4-86)

291 ORZEL (ex-B-800)

D: 2,325 tons surf. (2,460 with emergency fuel)/3,180 tons sub.
S: 10 kts surf./9 kts snorkel/17 kts sub.
Dim: 72.60 (70.0 wl) × 9.90 (12.80 over stern planes) × 6.60 (fwd; 6.20 mean)
A: 6 bow 533-mm TT (18 Type 53-65K and TEST-71ME torpedoes, or up to 24 Type MDT mines); 1 Fasta-M shoulder-launched SAM position (8 9K-32M Strela-2M missiles)

Orzel (291) Dieter Wolf, 6-97

Electronics:
Radar: 1 MRK-50 Tobol (Snoop Tray-2) nav./search
Sonar: MGK-400 Rubikon (Shark Gill) LF active/passive suite; MG-53 passive hull array; MG-519 Arfa (Mouse Roar) HF active classification/mine avoidance; MG-553 sound-velocity measuring; MG-512 own-ship cavitation detection
EW: MRP-25 Ankier intercept; Type 6701E Iva (Quad Loop) HFD/F

M: 2 Type 4-2DL42M diesels driving 30DG generator sets (1,825 bhp/1,500 kw at 700 rpm); electric drive: 1 PG-141 motor; 1 6-bladed prop; 5,900 shp—1 130-shp PG-142 electric low-speed motor on main shaft—2 PG-140 low-speed maneuvering motors; 2 ducted props; 204 shp (3 kts)
Range: 6,000/7 snorkel; 400/3 sub. **Fuel:** 172 tons
Endurance: 45 days **Crew:** 16 officers, 44 enlisted

Remarks: *Orzel* was the first Kilo to be exported from the then-USSR. Additional units were planned to complete replacement of the quartet of Whiskey-class submarines then in service, but lack of funds forced the leasing of two Foxtrots (q.v.) instead. Based at Gdynia-Oksywie. Communications and data-sharing systems were updated in 1999–2000 to allow the ship to operate with NATO forces, and the submarine was thoroughly overhauled for continued service.
Hull systems: Propulsion plant is on isolation mounts for silencing. Hull has 32% reserve buoyancy at surfaced displacement. At rest on the surface, the submarine trims down 0.4 m by the bow. Maximum diving depth is 300 m, normal maximum operating depth 240 m, and periscope depth 17.5 m. Has an anechoic hull coating. Two Type 446 batteries, each with 120 cells, provide 9,700 kwh and weigh 446 tons total. Hull has six watertight compartments.
Combat systems: Combat system, designated Murena or MVU-110EM, has two operator consoles and can conduct two simultaneous attacks while tracking three other targets manually. The SAM launch position is located in the after portion of the sail. Only two of the torpedo tubes can accept wire-guided torpedoes.

♦ 2 ex-Soviet Foxtrot class (Project 641K)

Bldrs: Admiralty/Sudomekh SY, St. Petersburg; Severodvinsk SY (In serv. 1957–68)

	Laid down	L	In serv.
292 WILK (ex-B-38)	30-10-61	31-1-62	30-9-62
293 DZIK (ex-B-40)	24-9-65	16-11-65	6-9-66

D: 1,957 tons surf./2,203 tons surf. (max.)/2,484 tons sub.
S: 15.5 kts surf./10 kts snorkel/18 kts sub.
Dim: 91.30 (89.70 wl) × 7.50 × 6.06 (surf.)

Dzik (293) Maritime Photographic, 6-99

Wilk (292) Adam Smigielski, 2000

ATTACK SUBMARINES [SS] *(continued)*

A: 10 533-mm TT (6 fwd, 4 aft; 22 Type 53-56WA and SET-53M torpedoes, or 32 Type AMD-1000 or MDT mines and 6 torpedoes)
Electronics:
Radar: 1 RKL-101 Flag nav./search
Sonar: MG-10M Gerkules HF active; MG-200 Arktika MF passive; MG-15 Tuloma underwater telephone; MG-13 Svyet-M sonar intercept
EW: MRP-25 Nakat-M (Stop Light) intercept; Type 6701E Iva (Quad Loop) HFD/F
M: 3 Type 37D diesels (2,000 bhp each), 3 electric motors (1 × 2,700-shp PG-102, 2 × 1,350-shp PG-101); 3 props; 5,400 shp (sub.)—140-shp PG-104 electric low-speed motor on centerline shaft
Range: 20,000/8 surf.; 11,500/8 snorkel; 36/18, 380/2 sub.
Fuel: 360 tons **Endurance:** 70 days **Crew:** 12 officers, 61 enlisted

Remarks: Commissioned in Polish service on 3-11-87 and 7-12-88, respectively; purchased from Russia outright during 1993 and are to be retained in service until 2002–03. 292 was refitted during 1993. Both are based at Gdynia-Oksywie.
Hull systems: Have four 112-cell German Varta batteries. Can dive in as little as 45–60 seconds and have 527 tons reserve buoyancy in surfaced condition. The pressure hull has seven watertight compartments. Operating depth is 240 m, maximum depth 280 m.
Combat systems: Torpedo fire control by the Leningrad-641 system.

GUIDED-MISSILE DESTROYERS [DDG]

♦ 1 ex-Soviet Modified Kashin class (Project 61MP)
Bldr: 61 Kommunara, Nikolayev

	Laid down	L	In serv.
271 Warszawa (ex-*Smel'yy*)	15-11-66	6-2-68	27-11-69

Warszawa (271) Jaroslaw Cislak, 2000

D: 4,010 tons std. (4,975 fl) **S:** 32 kts
Dim: 146.20 (134.50 wl) × 15.80 (14.00 wl) × 4.87 (max. hull)
A: 4 P-20/21 Termit (SS-N-2C Styx) SSM (4 KT-97M-BRK launchers); 2 W-601M Volna SAM syst. (2 twin-rail ZIF-101 launchers; 32 V-600 Goa missiles); 2 twin 76.2-mm 59-cal. AK-726 DP; 4 single 30-mm 54-cal. AK-630M gatling AA; 1 quadruple 533-mm Type PTA-53-61 TT (5 SET-53M and Type 53-56WA torpedoes); 2 12-round RBU-6000 Smerch 213-mm ASW RL (192 RGB-60 rockets); 2 single 45-mm saluting cannon
Electronics:
Radar: 1 Tamirio SRN-207 nav.; 1 Volga nav.; 2 Tamirio SRN-7534 Nogat surf. search; 1 MR-310A Angara-M (Head Net-C) air search; 1 MR-500U Kliver (Big Net) early warning; 2 Yatagan (Peel Group) SAM f.c.; 2 MR-105 Turel' (Owl Screech) 76.2-mm f.c.; 2 MR-123 Vympel (Bass Tilt) 30-mm f.c.
Sonar: MGK-336 Platina hull-mounted MF; MG-311 Vychegda hull-mounted HF f.c.; LGS-3P Vega (Mare Tail) MF VDS
EW: MP-401 Start (2 Bell Squat, 2 Bell Shroud) intercept array; PK-16 decoy syst. (4 16-round KL-101 RL; 128 rockets)
E/O: 2 Type 9 Sz-33 (Tee Plinth) t.v.; 4 WPB-425 (Watch Box) periscopes
M: Type M-8Je plant: 4 Type DE-59 gas turbines; 2 3.9-m-dia. props; 96,000 shp (72,000 sust.)
Electric: 2,800 kw tot. (4 × 600-kw Type GTU-6 gas turbine sets, 2 × 200-kw diesel sets)
Range: 1,520/32; 4,500/14.5 **Fuel:** 940 tons **Endurance:** 25 days
Crew: 29 officers, 286 enlisted

Remarks: Transferred on 9-year lease during 12-87 and commissioned 9-1-88; purchased outright during 1993. Was to be stricken on commissioning of the second ex-USN FFG, but may be retained. Now rarely, if ever, operates. Is attached to the 3rd Flotilla and based at Gdynia.
Hull systems: The additional topweight over the standard Project 61 design required the addition of more than 100 tons of metal ballast and requires retention of a fuel reserve. Had been rebuilt in the USSR, completing in 1975, with a variable-depth sonar in a new stern that extended the hull length by 2 m, a helicopter platform atop the VDS housing, four Styx missiles replacing two RBU-1000 ASW RL, and the forward superstructure enlarged to increase officer accommodations.
Combat systems: Carries 2,400 rounds of 76.2-mm and 12,000 rounds of 30-mm ammunition. The twin turret for the 76.2-mm guns is a ZIF-67. SAM systems are reportedly no longer functional.

GUIDED-MISSILE FRIGATES [FFG]

♦ 1 (+ 1) ex-U.S. Oliver Hazard Perry class

	Bldr	Laid down	L	In serv.
272 Gen. K. Pulaski (ex-*Clark,* FFG 11)	Bath Iron Works, Bath, Maine	17-7-78	24-3-79	9-5-80
273 Gen. T. Kosciuszko (ex-*Wadsworth,* FFG 9)	Todd Shipyards, San Pedro, Calif.	13-7-77	29-7-78	28-2-80

Gen. K. Pulaski (272) Jürg E. Kürsener, 5-01

Gen. K. Pulaski (272) Dieter Wolf, 6-00

D: 2,769 tons light (3,658 fl) **S:** 29 kts (30.6 on trials)
Dim: 135.64 (125.9 wl) × 13.72 × 5.8 (6.7 max.)
A: 1 Mk 13 Mod. 4 launcher (4 Harpoon and 36 Standard SM-1 MR Block VIB missiles); 1 76-mm 62-cal. Mk 75 DP; 1 20-mm Mk 15 Phalanx gatling CIWS; 2 triple 324-mm Mk 32 Mod. 7 ASW TT (6 A-244 Mod. 3 torpedoes); 1 SH-2G Super SeaSprite ASW helicopter (A-244Z and/or MU-90 Impact torpedoes)
Electronics:
Radar: 1 Cardion SPS-55 surf. search; 1 Raytheon SPS-49(V)4 air search; 1 Raytheon Mk 92 Mod. 4 missile/gun f.c.; 1 Lockheed STIR missile/gun f.c.
Sonar: SQQ-89(V)2 (273: SQQ-89(V)9) suite: Raytheon SQS-56 hull-mounted LF
TACAN: URN-25
EW: Raytheon SLQ-32(V)2 intercept; Mk 36 SRBOC decoy syst. (2 6-round Raytheon Mk 137 launchers); SLQ-25 Nixie towed acoustic torpedo decoy
M: 2 G.E. LM-2500 gas turbines; 1 5.5-m-dia., CP, 5-bladed prop; 41,000 shp (40,000 sust.)—2 drop-down electric propulsors; 720 shp
Electric: 3,000 kw tot. (3 × 1,000 kw, diesels driving)
Range: 4,200/20; 5,000/18 **Fuel:** 587 tons + 64 tons helicopter fuel
Crew: 16 officers, 198 enlisted

Remarks: 272 was transferred 15-3-00 as a gift and recommissioned in Poland on 25-6-00, the 80th anniversary of the establishment of the Polish Navy; the full name (not borne on the nameplate) is *General Kazimierz Pulaski.* 273 was to transfer on 28-6-02. Both ships are named for Polish officers who assisted in the American Revolution.
Hull systems: Has 19-mm aluminum-alloy armor over the magazine spaces, 16-mm steel over the main engine-control room, and 19-mm Kevlar plastic armor over vital electronics and command spaces. Because of a hull twisting problem, doubler plates have been added over the hull sides amidships just below the main deck. Speed on one turbine alone is 25 kts. The auxiliary power system uses two retractable pods located well forward and can drive the ships at up to 6 kts. Have fin stabilizers. No helicopter haul-down and deck traversal system is fitted.
Combat systems: The ships have the Mk 13 weapons-direction system. The Mk 92 Mod. 4 fire-control system controls missile and 76-mm gun fire; it uses a STIR (modified SPG-60) antenna amidships and a U.S.-built version of the Hollandse Signaal Apparaaten (H.S.A., now Thales) WM-28 radar forward and can track four separate targets, while there are two missile illumination channels.

Delivered with 272 were 18 Standard SM-1 MR Block VI missiles (one a dummy training round), two RGM-84 Harpoon Block IG antiship missiles, and six ASW torpedoes. The Mk 75 gun is a license-built version of the OTOBreda Compact. Two Mk 24 optical missile and gun target designators are mounted in tubs atop the pilothouse. A total of 24 ASW torpedoes can be carried for helicopters and the shipboard tubes. The SQQ-89(V) sonar suite incorporates a UYQ-25A sonobuoy processor; the towed linear passive hydrophone arrays were not transferred with the ships.

FRIGATES [FF]

♦ 0 (+ 7) MEKO A-100 class (Project 621)
Bldrs: Stocznia Marynarki Wojennej, Gdynia

	Laid down	L	In serv.
241	28-10-01	. . .	2004
242	2003	. . .	. . .
243	2005	. . .	. . .
244	2007	. . .	. . .
245	2009	. . .	. . .
246	2011	. . .	2013
247	2013	. . .	2015

FRIGATES [FF] *(continued)*

Project 621 (MEKO A-100) *Okrety Wojenne,* 2000

D: 1,650 tons (2,050 fl) **S:** 30+ kts
Dim: 95.20 × 13.25 (12.32 wl) × 3.35 (hull mean)
A: 8 Saab Bofors RBS-15 Mk 3 SSM; 1 8-cell Mk 41 VLS (32 RIM-7P Evolved Sea Sparrow or 8 RIM-7M Sea Sparrow missiles); 1 21-round RAM Mk 31 SAM syst. (RIM-116A Block 0 missiles); 1 76-mm 62-cal. OTOBreda SuperRapid DP; 2 triple 324-mm ASW TT; 2 6-round Bofors ASW-610 ASW mortars; 1 . . . helicopter
Electronics:
Radar: 1 . . . nav.; 1 EADS MRS-3D 3-D search; 2 . . . f.c.
Sonar: . . .
EW: . . . . intercept; 2 . . . decoy RL
M: COGAG: 1 . . . . . . gas turbine (18,800 shp), 2 . . . . . . diesels (8,000 bhp each); 2 CP props
Range: 4,000/15 **Crew:** 74–90 tot.

Remarks: Offered as a cooperative program in place of the original Polish Navy concept of building up to seven modified versions of the *Kaszub* class (Project 620 II). Plans are to order one every two years, with deliveries at two-year intervals. No contract had been signed as of 8-01, however, putting the above construction schedule in doubt.
Combat systems: CTM, Gdynia, and PIT, Warsaw, would perform combat system integration for the class. The ships would have a Thales TACTICOS combat system compatible with NATO weapon and sensor systems. MOC Mk 3 combat system operator consoles will be fitted.

CORVETTES [FFL]

♦ **1 Kaszub class (Project 620)** Bldr: Stocznia Północna, Gdańsk

	Laid down	L	In serv.
240 KASZUB	11-5-85	4-10-86	15-3-87

Kaszub (240) Findler & Winter, 6-01

Kaszub (240) Jaroslaw Cislak, 2000

D: 1,051 tons (1,183 fl) **S:** 26.2 kts
Dim: 82.34 (77.83 pp) × 10.00 × 2.93 (hull; 4.9 over sonar)
A: 1 76.2-mm 59-cal. AK-176 DP; 2 4-round Fasta-4M SAM syst. (16 9K-32M Strela-2M missiles); 3 twin 23-mm 87-cal. ZU-23-2M Wrobel-1 AA; 2 12-round RBU-6000 Smerch ASW RL (98 RGB-60 rockets); 2 twin 533-mm DTA 53-620 TT (SET-53M torpedoes); 2 d.c. racks (6 B-1 or B-2 d.c. each); 2 mine rails (4–20 tot. Type 08/39, AGSB, or JaM mines)
Electronics:
Radar: 1 Tamirio SRN-741XT nav.; 1 Tamirio SRN-7453 Nogat surf. search; 1 MR-302 Rubka (Strut Curve) surf./air search
Sonar: MG-322T Argun hull-mounted MF; MG-329M Shelon HF dipping (at stern); MG-16 underwater telephone
EW: no intercept; 1 122-mm Jastrzab-2 decoy RL; 2 9-round 81-mm Derkacz-2 decoy RL
M: 4 Cegielski-Sulzer 16ASV25/30 diesels; 2 CP, 250-rpm props; 16,890 bhp
Electric: 800 kw tot. (4 × 200-kw diesel sets)
Range: 840/26; 2,000/18; 3,480/14 **Crew:** 9 officers, 71 enlisted

Remarks: First seagoing combatant designed and built in Poland since prior to World War II. Work began 9-6-84. Was not a success; she was found to have a warped hull and shafts after launch and had to be repaired at the Gdynia naval yard. Was loaned to the border guard in fall 1990 for use as a flagship; returned to naval service 1-91. Communications and data-sharing systems were updated in 1999–2000 to allow the ship to operate with NATO forces. Is attached to the 11th Patrol Boat Squadron.
Combat systems: The helicopter-type dipping sonar is located in the cabinet at the extreme stern; the ship must be dead in the water to use it. Main gun forward was not mounted until 9-91 and still lacks a fire-control director; it is locally controlled. During foreign port visits, has carried two 45-mm saluting cannon on the forecastle. Carries three smoke floats each side at the stern. Has the Drakon torpedo fire-control system for the two torpedo tube sets, which train out several degrees to fire.

GUIDED-MISSILE PATROL CRAFT [PTG]

♦ **3 ex-East German Sassnitz class (Project 660)**
Bldr: VEB Peenewerft, Wolgast

	Laid down	L	In serv.
421 ORKAN	13-9-89	29-9-90	18-9-92
422 PIORUN	10-7-90	7-7-90	11-3-94
423 GROM (ex-*Huragan*)	18-9-89	11-12-90	28-3-95

Piorun (422)—prior to conversion, with USS *Vicksburg* (CG 69) in background
Jaroslaw Cislak, 6-00

Grom (423) and Piorun (422) Jaroslaw Cislak, 6-98

D: 330 tons (326 fl) **S:** 38.5 kts **Dim:** 48.90 (45.00 pp) × 8.65 × 2.20
A: to receive: 8 RBS-15 Mk 3 SSM; 1 76.2-mm 59-cal. AK-176 DP; 1 30-mm 54-cal. AK-630M gatling AA; 1 4-round FAM-14 SAM syst. (8 9K-32M Strela-2M missiles)
Electronics:
Radar: 1 Tamirio SRN-443XTA nav.; 1 Tamirio NUR-27XA surf. search; 1 MR-123 Vympel-AME (Bass Tilt) gun f.c.
EW: 1 10-round, 122-mm Jastrzab-2 decoy RL; 8 9-round, 81-mm Derkacz-2 decoy RL
M: 3 M-520T diesels; 3 props; 16,183 bhp (14,570 sust.)
Electric: 366 kw (1 × 183-kw, 2 × 128-kw diesel sets)
Range: 1,619/38; 1,600/18; 2,400/13 **Endurance:** 5 days
Crew: 4 officers, 32 enlisted

Remarks: East German project number was 151A. Were purchased incomplete without engines or armament just prior to the unification of Germany; transferred 3-10-90. This class was originally to have been built in Poland as well, supplanting the canceled indigenous Project 665 missile boat design. Name for 423 was changed in 1994. 421 had her communications and datalink systems updated during 1999–2000 to allow her to operate with NATO forces. All three are being modernized (see below). Are attached to the 3rd Flotilla Patrol Boat Squadron, based at Gdynia-Oksywie.

GUIDED-MISSILE PATROL CRAFT [PTG] *(continued)*

Hull systems: Each "star radial" M-520 diesel has eight rows of seven cylinders. Have steel hulls and aluminum superstructures.
Combat systems: A Polish-made surface-search radar was substituted for the originally planned Russian antiship missile targeting radar. The ships were originally intended to carry eight Kh-35 Uran (SS-N-25 Switchblade) antiship missiles.
Under a $15.5 million contract signed 29-6-01, the three are to be modernized by Thales Nederland and Stocznia Marynarki Wojennej, Gdynia, with the Thales TACTICOS combat data system, Sting radar/electro-optical gun fire-control system, Focon digital fiber-optic data network, and NATO Link 11 capability added. Will retain their German Rhode & Schwarz radio communications gear. The search radar will be replaced by the Ericsson Sea Giraffe AMB 3-D system, and the Przemyslowy Instytut Telekomuniacji (PIT) ESM system and PIT's CRM-200 navigational radar will be substituted for current equipment. The three will be fitted to launch eight Saab RBS-15 Mk 3 antiship missiles, although RBS-15 Mk 2 missiles will be temporarily substituted until they are replaced after 2004. Work began on 422 during 7-01 for completion before the end of 2002.

♦ 4 Soviet Tarantul-I (Russian Molnaya-1) class (Project 1241RE)
Bldr: Volodarskiy SY 341, Rybinsk

	In serv.		In serv.
434 Górnik	28-12-83	436 Metalowiec	13-2-88
435 Hutnik	31-3-84	437 Rolnik	4-2-89

Górnik (434) Findler & Winter, 6-00

Rolnik (437) Findler & Winter, 6-01

D: 385 tons light, 420 tons normal (455 fl) **S:** 43 kts
Dim: 56.90 (49.50 pp) × 10.20 (9.40 wl) × 2.14 (hull; 3.59 props)
A: 4 P-20/21 Termit (SS-N-2C Styx) SSM (KT-138E launchers); 1 76.2-mm 59-cal. AK-176 DP; 1 4-rail MTU-40S (SA-N-8) SAM syst. (12 9K-32M Strela-2 missiles); 2 single 30-mm 54-cal. AK-630 gatling AA
Electronics:
Radar: 1 Kivach-2 (436, 437: Pechora) nav.; 1 Garpun-E (Plank Shave) targeting; 1 MR-123 Vympel-A (Bass Tilt) f.c.
EW: 2 PK-16 decoy syst. (2 16-round KL-101 RL)
M: M-15E COGAG plant: 2 DMR-76 cruise gas turbines (4,000 shp each), 2 PR-77 boost gas turbines (12,000 shp each); 2 props; 32,000 shp
Electric: 500 kw tot. (2 × 200-kw, 1 × 100-kw diesel sets)
Range: 400/43; 2,200/14 **Fuel:** 50 tons (122,634 liters)
Endurance: 10 days **Crew:** 6 officers, 40 enlisted

Remarks: Names mean "Miner," "Steelworker," "Metalworker," and "Farmer," respectively. All four are based at Gdynia-Oksywie.
Hull systems: Stainless-steel-alloy, seven-watertight-compartment hull with aluminum alloy superstructure, decks, and internal bulkheads. Very strongly constructed. Have difficulty maneuvering below 10 kts. Range has also been stated to be 2,350 n.m. at 12–13 kts (at 34° C), with a maximum speed of 43 kts at 15° C (35 kts at 34° C).
Combat systems: Carry 252 ready-service rounds and another 150 in reserve for the 76.2-mm gun. The Zvezdochka-1241RE weapons system employs digital computers and has many backup features. The target-designation radar can be used in the passive mode to provide target bearings and threat warning. A PMK-453 lead-computing backup optical director can control the 30-mm guns, and the 76.2-mm mount can be locally controlled.

♦ 5 Soviet Osa-I (Russian Moskit) class (Project 205)

	In serv.		In serv.
427 Puck	26-10-67	432 Dziwnów	27-1-75
430 Darlowo	20-1-72	433 Wladyslawowo	13-11-75
431 Świnoujście	13-1-73		

Świnoujście (431) Jaroslaw Cislak, 2000

D: 165 tons light, 209.5 normal (220 fl)
S: 38.5 kts (36 sust.) **Dim:** 38.6 × 7.6 × 1.73
A: 4 P-15U Termit (SS-N-2A Styx) SSM; 1 4-round Fasta-4M SAM syst. (8 Strela-2M missiles); 2 twin 30-mm 65-cal. AK-230 AA
Electronics:
Radar: 1 Tamirio SRN-207M nav.; 1 Rangout (Square Tie) surf. search/target desig.; 1 MR-104 Rys' (Drum Tilt) gun f.c.
M: 3 M-503A2 diesels; 3 props; 12,000 bhp
Range: 400/34; 750/25 **Crew:** 4 officers, 18 enlisted

Remarks: Built in the USSR during the early 1960s and transferred on the dates listed above. All are named for coastal cities and are based at Gdynia-Oksywie.
Disposals: *Hel* (421), *Gdańsk* (422), and *Kolobrzeg* (430) have been discarded, the latter on 18-9-92. *Ustka* (428) and *Oksywie* (429) were stricken 2-10-00. Sisters *Gdynia* (423), *Szczecin* (425), and *Elblag* (426) were converted as patrol boats for the border guard beginning in 1989 and have since been stricken.

PATROL CRAFT [PC]

Note: A 700-ton Project 924 antisubmarine patrol combatant class is in the project definition phase as a replacement for the *Grożny*-class patrol craft.

♦ 8 Grożny (Modified Obluze) class (Project 912M)
Bldr: Stocznia Marynarki Wojennej, Gdynia (In serv. 1970–72)

	Laid down	L	In serv.
351 Grożny	...	29-11-69	8-2-70
352 Wyterwaly	3-1-69	12-6-69	8-2-70
353 Zręczny	...	...	30-12-70
354 Zwinny	...	12-6-70	30-12-70
355 Zawzięty	...	...	10-10-71
356 Zwrotny	11-4-70	...	4-7-71
357 Niegięty	...	...	7-7-72
358 Czujny	...	25-9-72	30-9-72

Zwrotny (356) Jaroslaw Cislak, 2000

D: 212 tons (235 fl) **S:** 24 kts **Dim:** 41.26 (39.50 pp) × 6.29 × 1.95 (hull)
A: 2 twin 30-mm 65-cal. AK-230 AA; 4 d.c. racks (2 topside; 2 through stern; 24 total Type B-1 and B-2 d.c.) *or* 2 short mine rails in lieu of topside d.c. racks (4 AMD-1000 mines)
Electronics:
Radar: 1 Tamirio SRN-231 nav.—all except 351, 352, 356: 1 MR-104 Rys' (Drum Tilt) gun f.c.
Sonar: MG-11-265 Tamir-11 hull-mounted HF searchlight (23–30 kHz)
M: 2 Type 40DM diesels; 2 props; 4,400 bhp **Electric:** 150 kw tot. (2 × 75 kw)
Range: 410/23.7; 1,200/16 **Fuel:** 25 tons **Endurance:** 12 days
Crew: 27 tot. + 4 spare berths

Remarks: Names mean "Persistent," "Formidable," "Obstinate," "Nimble," "Agile," "Adroit," "Inflexible," and "Vigilant," respectively. The radar gun f.c. director was never installed on 351 and 352 and had been removed from 356 by mid-1999; a lead-computing sight is available as a backup. All are operated by the 11th Chaser Squadron of the 9th Coastal Defense Flotilla, based at Hel. The Polish Maritime Brigade operates Project 912 sisters.

♦ 11 KP-166 (Pilica) class (Project 918M)
Bldr: Stocznia Marynarki Wojennej, Gdynia

	In serv.		In serv.		In serv.
KP-166	23-4-77	KP-170	7-8-80	KP-174	22-9-82
KP-167	28-1-78	KP-171	8-1-82	KP-175	7-1-83
KP-168	28-1-78	KP-172	7-5-82	KP-176	24-2-83
KP-169	10-2-79	KP-173	22-7-82		

PATROL CRAFT [PC] *(continued)*

KP-171 Jaroslaw Cislak, 2000

D: 85.62 tons std., 86.88 tons normal (93.03 normal fl; 100 max. fl)
S: 27.8 kts (25 cruise) **Dim:** 28.85 × 5.76 × 1.36 (hull)
A: 1 twin 23-mm 87-cal. ZU-23-2M Wrobel-1 AA; 2 fixed 533-mm OTAM-53 TT (2 SET-53M homing torpedoes)
Electronics:
Radar: 1 Tamirio SRN-301 nav.
Sonar: MG-329M portable dipping set; SP-4301 echo sounder
M: 3 M-50F-5 diesels; 3 props; 3,600 bhp **Range:** 340/25; 1,160/11.4
Endurance: 5 days **Crew:** 3 officers, 9–11 enlisted

Remarks: Transferred to the navy in 1991 from the Ministry of the Interior's border guard. Now considered to be ASW patrol boats. All are based at Kolobrzeg in the 16th ASW Division, 8th Coastal Defense Flotilla.
Disposals: KP-161 through KP-165 were returned to the coast guard in 1992 as SG-161 through SG-165.
Hull systems: Have steel hull, aluminum alloy superstructure, and GRP mast.
Combat systems: Carry 2–4 Type MDS smoke floats at the stern. Two different torpedo tube mounts, removed from discarded P-6-class torpedo boats, were installed; they are angled 7° outboard. The original Soviet twin 25-mm 2M-3M gunmounts were replaced 1986–90.

MINE WARFARE SHIPS

♦ 0 (+ 5 + 2) Project 257 coastal minehunters [MHC]
Bldr: Stocznia Marynarki Wojennej, Gdynia

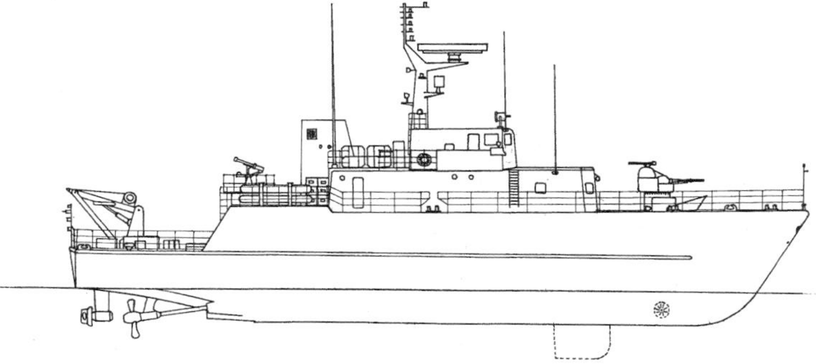

Project 257 coastal minehunter Jerzy Lewandowski, *Okrety Wojenne,* 2000

D: . . . tons **S:** . . . kts **Dim:** . . . × . . . × . . .
A: 1 twin 23-mm 87-cal. ZU-23-2MR Wrobel-2MR AA; 1 4-round Fasta-4M SAM syst. (8–12 tot. 9M-32M Strela-2M missiles)
Electronics:
Radar: 1 Decca BridgeMaster-E ARPA nav.
Sonar: AkMor SHL-100AM hull-mounted HF; AkMor SHL-200M-1 towed side-scan VHF
M: . . . diesels; 1 prop—active rudder stern-thruster—bow-thruster
Range: . . ./. . . **Crew:** . . .

Note: Detail design work on a new GRP-hulled minehunter [MHC] class was to begin after 6-01. The hull-mounted sonar dome is to be retractable.

♦ 3 Krogulec-class (Project 206FM) minehunters [MHC]
Bldr: Stocznia imeni Komuny Pariskej, Gdynia

	Laid down	L	In serv.
621 Flaming	. . .	5-5-65	11-11-66
623 Mewa	18-7-66	22-12-66	9-5-67
624 Czajka	12-9-66	17-12-66	17-6-67

D: 426 tons light; 472.1 tons normal (507 fl) **S:** 18 kts
Dim: 60.00 (58.20 pp) × 7.97 (7.70 wl) × 2.14 (hull)
A: 1 twin 23-mm 87-cal. ZU-23-2MR Wrobel-2MR AA (4 9M-32M Strela-2M SAM on mount); 2 Fasta-4M SAM launchers (16 tot. 9M-32M Strela-2M missiles); 2 d.c. racks (12 B-1 or B-2 d.c. tot.); 2 mine rails (8 AMD-1000 or 16 08/39 mines)

Czajka (624) Jaroslaw Cislak, 2000

Mewa (623) Jaroslaw Cislak, 2000

Electronics:
Radar: 1 Decca BridgeMaster-E ARPA nav.
Sonar: AkMor SHL-100AM hull-mounted HF; AkMor SHL-200M-1 towed side-scan VHF
EW: PIT Bren intercept; 6 9-round Derkach 81-mm decoy RL
M: 2 Sulzer-Cegielski ATL25/30 diesels; 2 Lips-Schelde CP props; 3,740 bhp
Electric: 160 kw tot. (4 × 40-kw [55 kw max.] Leyland–Huta Stalowa Wola SW 400 diesel generator sets)
Range: 2,000/12 **Fuel:** 45 tons **Endurance:** 12 days
Crew: 5 officers, 48 enlisted (incl. 5 mine-disposal divers)

Remarks: Named for birds. Have been extensively overhauled and modernized, with communications and datalink systems updated to allow them to operate with NATO forces; work on 623 was completed 16-5-99, and the ship was recommissioned during 12-99. 624 completed modification 26-5-99, and 621 was under conversion during 2000 for delivery during 2001. The trio are planned to operate through 2010.
Disposals: *Orlik* (613), *Krogulec* (614), *Jastrzab* (615), and *Kormoran* (616) were stricken during 6-93; *Czapla* (617) and *Pelikan* (619) during 12-93; *Albatros* (618) during 1995; and *Tukan* (620) on 2-10-00. *Rybitwa* (622) is employed as an accommodations hulk.
Combat systems: Are now equipped with the Pstrokosz integrated mine countermeasures command, control, and communications system and carry Polish-designed Ukwial remotely operated sonar- and t.v.-equipped submersibles and new sonars to enable them to act as minehunters. They are also fitted with the MT-2 mechanical sweep with Bofors explosive cutters and have had the TEM-PE-2M magnetic sweep gear updated so that it can operate concurrently with a new BGAT acoustic sweep gear set, with both handled by a new, smaller sweep winch. A two-compartment decompression chamber and semi-rigid inflatable launch were added for the mine-disposal divers, and 10 ZNH-230 sonobuoys are also carried. They can detect moored mines at a range of 1,600 m and bottom mines at 600 m. NATO-compatible Suprasl IFF systems and the Pstroksz precision navigation system are fitted. During modernization, they also received a new degaussing system, overhauled engines, a new NBC warfare protection system, and NATO-compatible fueling connections. The Polish Navy hopes to acquire Russian Igla SAMs to replace the Strela-2Ms.

♦ 17 Notec-class (Project 207D, 207P, and 207M) coastal minehunter/minesweepers [MHC]
Bldr: Stocznia Marynarki Wojennej, Gdynia

	L	In serv.		L	In serv.
630 Goplo	16-4-81	13-3-82	639 Necko	21-11-88	9-5-89
631 Gardnó	23-6-83	31-3-84	640 Naklo	29-5-89	2-3-90
632 Bukowo	28-7-84	23-6-85	641 Drużno	29-11-89	21-9-90
633 Dąbie	24-5-85	11-5-86	642 Hańcza	9-7-90	1-3-91
634 Jamno	11-2-86	11-10-86	643 Mamry	20-9-91	25-9-92
635 Mielno	27-6-86	9-5-87	644 Wigry	28-11-92	14-5-93
636 Wicko	20-3-87	12-10-87	645 Śniardwy	20-6-93	28-1-94
637 Resko	1-10-87	26-3-88	646 Wdzydze	24-6-94	2-12-94
638 Sarbsko	10-5-88	12-10-88			

MINE WARFARE SHIPS *(continued)*

Drużno (641)—Project 207P Jaroslaw Cislak, 2000

Jamno (634)—Project 207P Findler & Winter, 6-01

D: 208 tons light; 213 tons normal (225 fl) **S:** 14.5 kts
Dim: 38.46 (36.50 pp) × 7.35 (7.15 molded breadth) × 1.78 (hull)
A: 1 twin 23-mm 87-cal. ZU-23-2MR Wrobel-2MR AA; 2 d.c. racks (12 d.c. tot.); 2 mine rails (6–24 mines, depending on type)
Electronics:
Radar: 1 Tamirio SRN-302 nav.
Sonar: AkMor SHL-100 Flaming-A; AkMor SHL-200 hull-mounted HF mine-location
M: 2 Type M-401A diesels; 2 Kort-nozzle 5-bladed, CP, 241-rpm props; 2,000 bhp (1,600 sust.)—1 150-kw, 514-rpm tunnel-thruster fwd
Electric: 60 kw tot. (2 × 30-kw Wola 71H6 diesel-driven sets)
Range: 950/14; 1,100/9 **Endurance:** 5 days
Crew: 4 officers, 6 warrant officers, 20 enlisted

Remarks: Named for lakes. 630 (Project 207D) is used as a trials ship for sweep gear and sonars and is based at Gdynia-Oksywie. Project 207P units 631–642 are assigned to the 12th Division, 8th Coastal Defense Flotilla, Świnoujście. Project 207M units 643–646 are assigned to the 13th Minesweeping Division, 9th Coastal Defense Flotilla, Hel. Plans for a fifth Project 207M unit were canceled in 1993. 643 had communications and datalink systems updated during 1999–2000 to allow her to operate with NATO forces.
Hull systems: Have 20-mm-thick GRP hull-construction. All are capable of hunting for or sweeping mines in waters 5–20 m deep in conditions up to Sea State 3 and winds at 4–5 Beaufort. The Project 207M quintet have a longer pilothouse. The final four have 230 kVA total alternator capacity from two Wola 71H6 diesel-driven, 400-V, 50-Hz alternator sets; also fitted are two 30-kw dc sweep current generators. Normally carry crews of only 24 total.
Combat systems: SHL-100 Flaming-A is a forward-looking mine-avoidance sonar, while SHL-200 is a side- and aft-looking mine-location set operating at 100 kHz. The ships are equipped with mechanical, acoustic, and magnetic sweep gear. The first two were initially fitted with the Type 23-2PM gunmount until the Wrobel-2MR mount was available; the SAM-launching feature of the gunmounts is not used in these ships. Are to be equipped with more modern sweep gear. The depth charge racks are bolted to the mine rails when installed.

♦ 2 Leniwka-class (Project B-410S-IVS) minesweeping boats [MSI]
Bldr: Stocznia imeni E. Kwiatkowskiego, Ustka (In serv. 12-10-83)

625 TR-25 626 TR-26

D: 245 tons (269 fl) **S:** 11 kts **Dim:** 25.67 × 7.22 × 3.25
A: none **Electronics:** Radar: 1 Tamirio SRN-311 nav.
M: 1 Sulzer-Puck 6AL20/24 diesel; 1 CP prop; 570 bhp
Range: 3,200/10 **Crew:** 8–10 tot. (16 accomm.)

Remarks: Conversions of Project B-410, 192-grt, 79-dwt trawlers to tow line-charges—an effective but dangerous mine countermeasures technique. Are also capable of towing MT-3U, SEMT-1, and BAT-2 sweep arrays and are used for naval reservist training. Large numbers of civilian sisters are available for emergency use. Both are based at Świnoujście.

TR-25 (625)—outboard TR-26 (626) Jaroslaw Cislak, 2000

AMPHIBIOUS WARFARE SHIPS

♦ 5 Lublin-class (Project 767) minelayer/landing ships [LSM]
Bldr: Stocznia Północna, Gdańsk

	L	In serv.		L	In serv.
821 Lublin	12-7-88	12-10-89	824 Poznań	5-1-90	8-3-91
822 Gniezno	7-12-88	23-2-90	825 Toruń	8-6-90	24-5-91
823 Kraków	7-3-89	27-6-90			

Gniezno (822) Jaroslaw Cislak, 2000

Kraków (823) H&L Van Ginderen, 7-00

D: 1,210 tons std.; 1,350 tons normal (1,675 fl) **S:** 16.5 kts
Dim: 95.80 (91.20 hull; 81.00 pp) × 10.80 × 2.40
A: 4 twin 23-mm 87-cal. ZU-23-2MR Wrobel-2MR combination AA/SAM syst. (24 Strela-2M missiles); 12 . . .-mm multibarrel beach-clearing RL; up to 134 mines on tank deck
Electronics:
Radar: 1 Tamirio SRN-7453 nav.; 1 Tamirio SRN-443XTA surf. search
EW: no intercept; 12 9-round, 81-mm Derkach-2 decoy RL
M: 3 Sulzer-Cegielski 6ATL25D diesels; 3 Kort-nozzle props; 5,400 bhp
Electric: 750 kVA tot. (3 × 250-kVA, ZMiN-Wola, 400-V, 50-Hz diesel sets)
Range: 850–1,400/16.25 (depending on load) **Endurance:** 5 days
Crew: 5 officers, 2 warrant officers, 8 petty officers, 22 other enlisted + 135 troops

Remarks: 465 dwt. Officially retyped as minelayers in mid-1992, but remain configured primarily for an amphibious role. A planned sixth unit was canceled. 821 has been employed as a combat diver support ship since at least 1998. Two were refitted in 1998.
Hull systems: The 600-m^2 open cargo deck can accommodate nine 45-ton tanks in one row or two rows of 2.5-m-wide vehicles for a maximum vehicle load of 465 tons; maximum cargo load is 536 tons. Have hydraulic-snub cargo tie-down system. Vehicle deck has 4.2-m clearance at the ends, and the two-part folding bow ramp is 20 m long when extended. Equipped with an automated ballast system for use when discharging or loading cargo off a beach. Have Decca AD-2 and BRAS radio navaid receivers.

AMPHIBIOUS WARFARE SHIPS *(continued)*

Combat systems: In the minelaying role, a mezzanine deck can be added in the vehicle cargo space to increase stowage. 824 was initially equipped with ZU-23-2 Wrobel-1 gunmounts vice the combination gun/missile mounting. Each 23-mm mount has 200 ready-service rounds.

♦ 3 Deba-class (Project 716) utility landing craft [LCU]

Bldr: Stocznia Marynarki Wojennej, Gdynia

851 KD-11 (In serv. 7-8-88) 853 KD-13 (In serv. 3-5-91)
852 KD-12 (In serv. 2-1-91)

KD-13 (853)—outboard KD-11 (851) Jaroslaw Cislak, 2000

D: 164 tons normal (176 fl) **S:** 20 kts
Dim: 37.23 (33.60 wl) × 7.27 (6.27 wl) × 1.67
A: 1 twin 23-mm 87-cal. ZU-23-2 Wrobel-1 AA; 2 PW-LWO line-charge RL; mines
Electronics: Radar: 1 Tamirio SRN-207A nav.
M: 3 M-401A diesels; 3 props; 3,150 bhp
Electric: 104 kVA tot. (2 × 52-kVA diesel alternator sets; 400 V, 50 Hz)
Range: 500/16 **Fuel:** 9.4 tons **Crew:** 12 tot. + 50 troops

Remarks: Built as landing craft but redesignated as patrol boats during 1992, although they remain configured for amphibious warfare. Originally plans to build 12 were reduced to five and finally to three; three new units were delivered to Yemen during 2001. Are based at Świnoujście.
Hull systems: Can carry a 20-ton payload (one armored personnel carrier and 50 troops).

AUXILIARIES

♦ 3 Mrówka-class (Project 208) degaussing/deperming tenders [ADG]

Bldr: Stocznia Marynarki Wojennej, Gdynia

SD-11 (In serv. 10-10-71) SD-12 (In serv. 25-6-72) SD-13 (In serv. 16-12-72)

SD-13 IJsbrand Plokker, 9-99

D: 550 tons (600 fl) **S:** 9.5 kts **Dim:** 44.23 × 8.12 × 2.54
A: SD-12: 1 twin 23-mm 87-cal. ZSU-23-2 AA—others: 1 twin 25-mm 80-cal. 2M-3 AA
Electronics: Radar: 1 Tamirio RN-231 nav.
M: 1 Wola 6ND36 diesel; 1 prop; 335 bhp
Range: 1,000/9.5 **Endurance:** 14 days **Crew:** 25 tot.

Remarks: SD = *Stacja Demagnetyzacyjna* (degaussing station). Names "*Wrona,*" associated with SD-11, and "*Rys',*" associated with SD-12, are unofficial. Can deperm ships of up to 6,000 tons.

Disposal note: The Polnocny-B (Project 771A) former medium landing ship *Cedynia* (810), used in recent years as a munitions and cargo transport [AE], was stricken 7-4-01 for scrapping.

♦ 1 Bereza (SR-28)-class (Project 130Z Malz) fleet support ship [AG]

Bldr: Stocznia Północna, Gdańsk

	L	In serv.
511 Kontradmiral X. Czernicki (ex-SR-253)	16-11-00	1-9-01

Kontradmiral X. Czernicki (511) *Okrety Wojenne,* 2001

D: 2,049 tons (2,290 fl) **S:** 13.8 kts (12 sust.) **Dim:** 72.90 × 13.80 × 4.50
A: 1 twin 23-mm 87-cal. ZU-23-2MR Wrobel-2MR AA; provision for 2 4-round WM-4 launchers for Strela-2M point-defense SAMs
Electronics:
Radar: 1 Decca BridgeMaster C341 ARPA nav.; 1 Tamirio SRN-. . . surf. search; 1 Tamirio . . . air search
EW: Jastrzab intercept; ORLO laser detector; 4 9-round, WNP 81/9, 81-mm Jastrzab decoy RL
M: 2 Zgoda-Sulzer 8AL25D, 750-rpm diesels; 2 CP Kort-nozzle props; 2,896 bhp—bow-thruster
Electric: 1,185 kVA + 1,550 kw tot. (2 × 480 kVA, 1 × 225 kVA; 2 × 645 kw, 1 × 260 kw)
Range: 2,500/12 **Endurance:** 30 days (14 with troops aboard)
Crew: 8 officers, 6 warrant officers, 8 senior petty officers, 33 ratings + 140 troops

Remarks: Originally ordered as the 19th Project 130 deperming tender [ADG] for the Soviet Navy and left incomplete when the Russians were unable to continue payments; significantly reconfigured and completed as a troop or military cargo ship, underway support ship, and intelligence collection vessel (using special containerized equipment in the latter role). Project name means "Mollusk." Work began 16-8-00. Based at Świnoujście and assigned to the 2nd Transport-Mineship Squadron, 8th Coast Defense Flotilla, at Świnoujście.
Hull systems: Has been reconfigured to carry 140 troops with full equipment, 10 20-ft. cargo containers (150 tons max. total), or four 20-ft. containers and six Star 266 trucks. A 16-ton hydraulic crane is fitted, and there is a ramp at the stern for vehicles. A 20 × 12–m helicopter deck for one Anakonda-size helicopter is fitted above the fantail, and helicopter fueling facilities are provided. Has NBC warfare protection equipment and a GPS navigational aid. Achieved 14.1 kts on trials in light condition.
Combat systems: The LN-10 Leba command and communication system is fitted, as are a SATCOM terminal and a RADWAR Suprasl IFF interrogator. For intelligence collection missions, the ship can carry a PIT Srokosz modular communications and signals intercept system mounted in a 20-ft. container positioned on the helicopter deck.

♦ 1 Polnocny-C-class (Project 776) command ship [AGF]

	Bldr	L	In serv.
811 Grunwald	Stocznia Północna, Gdańsk	16-9-72	21-4-73

Grunwald (811) Jaroslaw Cislak, 2000

D: 1,060 tons light; 1,233 tons normal (1,314 fl) **S:** 16.3 kts
Dim: 81.30 (76.00 pp) × 9.30 × 1.20 (fwd/2.60 aft)
A: 2 twin 30-mm 65-cal. AK-230 AA; 2 4-round Fasta-4M SAM syst. (Strela-2M missiles); 2 18-round 140-mm MW-18M RL
Electronics:
Radar: 1 Tamirio SRN-207 nav.; 1 Tamirio SRN-433XTA nav.; 1 Tamirio SRN-7453 Nogat surf. search; 1 MR-104 Rys' (Drum Tilt) f.c.
M: 2 Type 40DM diesels; 2 props; 4,400 bhp
Range: 1,200/16; 2,600/12 **Endurance:** 30 days
Crew: 45 tot. + 54 command staff and vehicle crew

Remarks: The only unit of her type built, the ship is currently command ship for the 8th Flotilla but is used primarily for hydrographic survey work. Ships of this general design serve in the Russian Navy in landing-ship configuration (Project 773), and a modified version with helicopter deck ("Polnocny-D" Projects 773K, 773 KL, and 773IM) was built for export to Iraq, Libya, and India. Based at Świnoujście.
Hull systems: The normal belowdecks vehicle deck was configured with permanent command and accommodations facilities, with space left at the forward end only to transport one 15-ton armored personnel carrier or two light trucks or jeeps. Hull has a sharp, reinforced "beak" at the bow to facilitate beaching. The upper deck cannot be used to carry cargo.

♦ 2 modified Moma-class (Project 863) intelligence collectors [AGI]

Bldr: Stocznia Północna, Gdańsk (In serv. 1975–76)

262 Nawigator (In serv. 17-2-75) 263 Hydrograf (In serv. 8-5-75)

D: 1,467 tons std. (1,675 fl) **S:** 17 kts
Dim: 73.30 × 12.00 (11.20 wl) × 3.82 (4.20 max.)
A: provision for 4 twin 25-mm 80-cal. 2M-3 AA

AUXILIARIES *(continued)*

Nawigator (262) Jaroslaw Cislak, 2000

Electronics:
Radar: 1 Tamirio SRN-623 nav.; 1 Tamirio SRN-7453 Nogat surf. search
EW: . . . intercept; . . . jammer
M: 2 Zgoda-Sulzer 6TD48 diesels; 2 CP props; 3,600 bhp
Range: 8,700/11 **Endurance:** 30 days **Crew:** 87 tot.

Remarks: At one time, were euphemistically described as "navigational training ships," but are now openly listed as radioelectronic collection ships *(okret dozoru radioelektronicznego)*. Based at Gdynia-Oksywie. Crane is omitted, superstructure is lengthened, and lattice mainmast is as on *Piast* class. In 262, the forecastle is the original length, and the radome is cylindrical; in 263, the forecastle has been extended aft to the bridge face and the radome atop the pilothouse has a rounded top.

♦ **2 Heweliusz-class (Project 874) hydrographic survey ships [AGS]** Bldr: Stocznia Północna, Gdańsk

	Laid down	L	In serv.
265 Heweliusz	5-6-81	20-11-81	27-11-82
266 Arctowski	5-6-81	20-11-81	27-11-82

Arctowski (266) Hartmut Ehlers, 5-00

Heweliusz (265) Jaroslaw Cislak, 2000

D: 1,145 tons std. (1,218 fl) **S:** 13.7 kts (12 sust.)
Dim: 61.60 × 11.20 (10.80 wl) × 3.50
Electronics: Radar: 1 SRN-743X nav.; 1 SRN-7453 Nogat surf. search
M: 2 Cegielski-Sulzer 6AL25/30 diesels; 2 1.9-m-dia., 320-rpm CP props; 1,920 bhp—2 140-kw electric auxiliary drive motors—bow-thruster
Electric: 675 kVA tot. **Range:** 5,900/11 **Crew:** 10 officers, 39 enlisted

Remarks: 751 grt/250 dwt. Modified version of the Finik-class built for the Soviet Navy. Named for an astronomer and an explorer. Civilian sisters *Planeta* (launched 21-5-82) and *Zodiak* (launched 28-8-82) are subordinated to the Maritime Agency, Szczecin. The two naval units are based at Gdynia-Oksywie.
Hull systems: Are able to link via chain drag for clearance surveys. Have four precision echo sounders. Unlike their Russian Navy sisters, have forecastle extended nearly to stern (providing additional accommodations spaces) and no buoy-handling capability. Carry two small survey launches aft. An STN Atlas Elektronik DESO 20 precision echo sounder, RALOG 20 radio navigation receiver, and DOLOG 12D doppler log are fitted.

♦ **1 Soviet Moma-class (Project 861K) hydrographic survey ship [AGS]** Bldr: Stocznia Północna, Gdańsk (In serv. 20-2-71)

261 Kopernik

Kopernik (261) Jaroslaw Cislak, 2000

D: 1,250 tons (1,506 fl) **S:** 17.3 kts **Dim:** 73.32 × 11.20 × 3.77
Electronics:
Radar: 1 Tamirio SRN-743X nav.; 1 Tamirio SRN-7453 Nogat surf. search
M: 2 Sulzer-Zgoda 6TD48 diesels; 2 CP props; 3,600 bhp
Range: 8,700/11 **Endurance:** 35 days
Crew: 8 officers, 12 enlisted + 40 survey party

Remarks: Operated for the Academy of Science and based at Gdynia-Oksywie. Named for the astronomer Copernicus. Sisters are in the Bulgarian, Russian, and Croatian navies. *Piast*-class salvage ships and *Wodnik*-class training ships are very similar. Two others, the *Nawigator* (262) and *Hydrograf* (263), serve as intelligence collectors. 261 has 35 m^2 of laboratory deck area and has been modified for use in seismic survey and oil exploration work. The buoy crane was removed in 1983.

♦ **1 ZP-1200-class small replenishment oiler [AO]**
Bldr: Stocznia Marynarki Wojennej, Gdynia (In serv. 11-3-91)

Z-1 Baltyk

Baltyk (Z-1) ANBw, 10-00

D: 1,984 tons (2,984 fl) **S:** 15.7 kts
Dim: 84.70 (79.00 pp) × 13.10 (12.80 wl) × 4.80
A: 2 twin 23-mm 87-cal. ZU-23-2 Wrobel-1 AA
Electronics:
Radar: 1 Tamirio SRN-443XTA nav.; 1 Tamirio SRN-7453 Nogat surf. search
M: 2 Sulzer-Cegielski 8ASL25D diesels; 2 props; 4,025 bhp
Range: 4,250/12 **Endurance:** 20 days **Crew:** 4 officers, 28 enlisted

Remarks: Based at Gdynia-Oksywie. Was originally to have been the first of a class of four. Communications and datalink systems were updated during 1999–2000 to allow operations with NATO forces.
Hull systems: Has replenishment stations port and starboard and is also able to conduct astern refueling. Z = *Zbiornikowiec* (tanker). Cargo capacity: 1,184 tons fuel in seven tanks, 97.5 tons lube oil in four tanks, 26 tons residual oil, and 28 tons used oil.

♦ **3 Moskit-class (Project B-199 and ZW-2) coastal oilers [AO]**

	Bldr	Laid down	L	In serv.
Z-3	Stocznia Rzeczna, Wrocław	12-67	22-7-69	23-9-70
Z-8	Stocznia Rzeczna, Wrocław	. . .	14-9-69	23-7-70
Z-9	Stocznia Wisła, Gdańsk	. . .	1-8-70	15-5-71

Z-8 Jaroslaw Cislak, 2000

AUXILIARIES *(continued)*

D: 700 tons light (1,225 fl, except Z-9: 1,180 tons fl) **S:** 10 kts
Dim: 57.7 (55.87 wl) × 9.50 (9.30 wl) × 3.32 (Z-9: 3.60)
A: 2 twin 23-mm 87-cal. ZU-23-2 (Z-9: 25-mm 80-cal. 2M-3M) AA; provision for 2 4-round Fasta-4M SAM syst. (Strela-2M missiles)
Electronics: Radar: 1 Tamirio SRN-206 nav.
M: 1 Magdeburg (Z-9: Model 6NVD 48A-ZU) diesel; 1 CP prop; 845 (Z-9: 1,054) bhp
Range: 1,200/12 **Endurance:** 10 days **Crew:** 2 officers, 21 enlisted

Remarks: Z = *Zbiornikowiec* (tanker). The names associated with these ships, *"Krab," "Meduza,"* and *"Slimak,"* are unofficial. Z-9 is considered to be of a separate class: ZW-2. Based at Świnoujście, Hel, and Gdynia-Oksywie, respectively. Wrobel-1 mounts have replaced the twin 25-mm 2M-3 mounts previously installed, except in Z-9, which retains the 25-mm mounts. The gunmounts are not always fitted, and the missile systems do not seem yet to have been mounted. Cargo: Z-3, Z-8: 656.5 tons; Z-9: 598.6 tons.

♦ **2 Piast-class (Project 570) salvage ships [ARS]**
Bldr: Stocznia Północna, Gdańsk

281 Piast (In serv. 26-1-74) 282 Lech (In serv. 30-11-74)

Piast (281)—with helicopter deck over stern area Jaroslaw Cislak, 2000

Lech (282) Jaroslaw Cislak, 6-98

D: 1,697 tons std. (1,887 fl) **S:** 15.5 kts
Dim: 72.64 (67.20 pp) × 12.00 (11.60 wl) × 4.60
A: 2 4-round Fasta-4M SAM launchers (8 Strela-2M missiles)—provision for: 2 twin 25-mm 80-cal. 2M-3 AA; 2 twin 23-mm 87-cal. ZU-23-2 Wrobel-1 AA
Electronics: Radar: 2 Tamirio SRN-7453 Nogat nav./surf. search
M: 2 Sulzer-Zgoda 6TD48, 225-rpm diesels; 2 CP, 225-rpm props; 3,600 bhp
Electric: 900 kVA tot. (3 × 300-kVA diesel sets)
Range: 3,000/12 **Endurance:** 25 days **Crew:** 8 officers, 49 enlisted + 12 divers

Remarks: Variation of the Moma design for salvage and rescue duties. Based at Gdynia-Oksywie. 282 had her communications systems updated during 1999–2000 to allow her to operate with NATO forces. Sister *Vanguardia* (ex-East German *Otto von Guericke*) is in the Uruguayan Navy.
Hull systems: Have extensive firefighting facilities: three foam/water monitors, two firepumps, and two portable firefighting pumps; total pump capacity is 1,960 m^3/hour. Capable of ocean-towing. Have a 60-m-capable, three-person diving bell and a six-place decompression chamber. 281 deployed with UN Coalition forces to the Mideast 12-90 to 20-5-91, armed with four twin 25-mm AA and equipped with a Navstar 2000 GPS receiver, Navtex facsimile receiver, and Kelvin-Hughes collision avoidance system. Both have been refitted with a dynamic positioning system with heavier anchors forward and two anchors mounted aft in order to provide a four-point mooring capability. 281 has a light helicopter platform mounted atop the salvage equipment aft.

♦ **2 Wodnik-class (Project 888) training ships [ATS]**
Bldr: Stocznia Północna, Gdańsk

	L	In serv.		L	In serv.
251 Wodnik	29-11-75	28-5-76	252 Gryf	13-3-76	26-9-76

D: 1,489 tons (1,745 fl) **S:** 15.5 kts **Dim:** 72.24 × 12.00 (11.60 wl) × 4.13
A: 2 (252: 1) twin 30-mm 65-cal. AK-230 AA; 2 twin 23-mm 87-cal. ZU-23-2MR Wrobel-2MR combination AA/SAM syst. (Strela-2M missiles)
Electronics: Radar: 1 Tamirio SRN-7453 Nogat nav./surf. search
M: 2 Sulzer-Cegielski 6TD48 diesels; 2 CP props; 3,600 bhp **Range:** 7,800/15
Endurance: 30 days **Crew:** 24 officers, 32 enlisted + 13 instructors, 87 cadets

Remarks: Nearly identical to the former East German *Wilhelm Pieck* and similar to the *Luga* and *Oka* in the Soviet Navy. Based at Gdynia-Oksywie. Names mean "Water Elf" and "Griffin." From 12-90 to 5-91, 251 operated as an unarmed hospital ship in support of UN Coalition forces in the Mideast, reconverting to training ship on return. 251 had communications and other systems updated during 1999–2000 to allow her to operate with NATO units.

Wodnik (251)—with helicopter deck aft John Mortimer, 2-01

Gryf (252)—with a second twin 30-mm AA aft Jaroslaw Cislak, 2000

Hull systems: Developed from the Moma navigational aids tender design. Have the latest navigational systems from the West and Russia. As a hospital ship, 251 had berths for 84 patients (plus facilities for 30–50 ambulatory patients) and carried 10 medical personnel in addition to an operating crew of 63; to assist her deployment, she received new radios, a Navstar 2000 GPS receiver, a Navtex facsimile receiver, and Kelvin-Hughes collision avoidance equipment.
Combat systems: The MR-104 Rys' (Drum Tilt) gun fire-control radar formerly carried at the top of the lattice mast has been removed from both, and the 30-mm guns are now controlled by individual ringsight directors. A helicopter deck added aft on 251 in 1991 and has been retained in place of the 30-mm mount originally fitted there.

SERVICE CRAFT

♦ **1 pollution control lighter [YAG]**
Bldr: Stocznia Północna, Gdańsk (In serv. 14-7-61)

B-7 (ex-Z-7)

B-7 H&L Van Ginderen, 8-99

D: 615 tons (fl) **S:** 8 kts **Dim:** 44.2 × 7.6 × 3.1 (max.)
M: 1 Wola diesel; 1 prop; 300 bhp **Crew:** 12–18 tot.

Remarks: Former Project 500 fuel lighter, converted as an oil-spill collection craft by Nauta Repair Yard, Gdynia.

♦ **1 Grom-class destroyer relic [YAG]**
Bldr: J. Samuel White, Cowes, U.K.

	Laid down	L	In serv.
H-34 Blyskawica	1-10-35	1-10-36	1-10-37

Blyskawica (H-34) H&L Van Ginderen, 8-99

SERVICE CRAFT *(continued)*

D: 2,011 tons light; 2,660 tons std. (3,383 fl) **S:** 35 kts
Dim: 114.00 × 11.00 × 3.30
A: 4 twin 102-mm 45-cal. Vickers Mk 19 DP; 4 twin and 2 single 37-mm 63-cal. AA; 1 triple 533-mm TT; 4 BMB-1 d.c. mortars; 2 d.c. racks
Electronics: Radar: 1 Don nav.; 1 Ball End nav.; 1 Type 291 air search
M: 2 sets Parsons geared steam turbines; 2 props; 54,000 shp
Boilers: 3 3-drum type; 331° C **Range:** 1,700/14.2 **Fuel:** 376 tons
Crew: 193 tot. (when operational)

Remarks: Ordered 29-3-35. Was the world's fastest destroyer as completed. After service as the postwar Polish Navy flagship, was decommissioned in 1974 and made into a nonoperational memorial at Gdynia in 1976; she is painted in her World War II colors and with her wartime pennant number. Was refitted in late 1997 at Nauta Ship Repair Yard. Receives about 4 million visitors annually. Sister *Grom* was lost 5-5-40.

♦ 1 B-600-class cargo lighter [YF]

B-9 (In serv. 9-10-70)

B-9 Jaroslaw Cislak, 2000

Remarks: B = *Barka* (dumb-barge or self-propelled lighter for dry or liquid cargo). Is self-propelled and has a small navigational radar; no further data available.

Disposal note: Miscellaneous barges B-5 and B-6 were reportedly removed from service by 6-98.

♦ 2 Project KH-K-class communications launches [YFL]
Bldr: Wroclawska Stocznia Rzeczna, Wrocław

K-20 (In serv. 15-5-89) K-21 (In serv. 19-2-90)

D: 12.25 tons (fl) **S:** 8.4 kts **Dim:** 9.00 × . . . × . . .

Remarks: Also capable of light towing. K = *Kuter* (general-purpose craft).

♦ 3 Project 4142–class passenger launches [YFL]
Bldr: Tczewska Stocznia Rzeczna, Tczewie

K-5 (In serv. 15-2-88) K-7 (In serv. 15-12-88) K-9 (In serv. 25-9-89)

K-9 Jaroslaw Cislak, 2000

D: 45 tons (50 fl) **S:** 9.1 kts **Dim:** 18.88 × 4.42 × 1.60
M: 1 Wola diesel; 1 prop; 100 bhp **Range:** 85/8 **Crew:** 4 tot.

Remarks: Similar to survey launches K-4 and K-10. K = *Kuter* (general-purpose craft).

♦ 3 Project B-574 passenger launches [YFL]
Bldr: Wroclawska Stocznia Rzeczna, Wrocław

K-12 (In serv. 26-7-78) K-13 (In serv. 26-7-78) K-14 (In serv. 17-12-78)

D: 45 tons (50 fl) **S:** 9.1 kts **Dim:** 18.88 × 4.42 × 1.60
M: 1 Wola diesel; 1 prop; 100 bhp **Range:** 85/8 **Crew:** 4 tot.

Remarks: Similar to Project 4142, but with wooden hulls. Can also be used as tugs. K = *Kuter* (general-purpose craft).

K-13 H&L Van Ginderen, 8-99

♦ 2 Project B-447 passenger launches [YFL]
Bldr: Wroclawska Stocznia Rzeczna, Wrocław

K-1 (In serv. 11-4-76) K-2 (In serv. 11-7-76)

D: 45 tons (50 fl) **S:** 9.1 kts **Dim:** 18.88 × 4.42 × 1.60
M: 1 Wola diesel; 1 prop; 100 bhp **Range:** 85/8 **Crew:** 4 tot.

Remarks: Similar to Project B-574. Also usable as inshore survey craft. K = *Kuter* (general-purpose craft).

♦ 1 SMK-75-class multipurpose launch [YFL]
Bldr: Stocznia Marynarki Wojennej, Gdynia (In serv. 15-2-86)

M-41

D: . . . tons (fl) **S:** . . . kts **Dim:** 6.35 × . . . × . . .

Remarks: M = *Motorwka* (general-purpose harbor-service motorboat).

♦ 6 M-35/MW-class multipurpose launches [YFL]
Bldr: Tczewska Stocznia Rzeczna, Tczewie

	In serv.		In serv.		In serv.
M-5	10-7-84	M-21	29-12-83	M-29	1-7-85
M-12	12-10-83	M-22	10-11-84	M-30	25-12-85

M-22 Jaroslaw Cislak, 2000

D: 28.66 tons (fl) **S:** 8.3 kts **Dim:** 10.75 × 4.0 × 1.5
M: 3 diesels; 3 props; 450 bhp **Crew:** 3 tot.

Remarks: One sister was delivered to the coast guard in 1991 as SG-036. M = *Motorwka* (general-purpose harbor-service motorboat).

♦ 1 MG-600/MW-class multipurpose launch [YFL]
Bldr: Stocznia Wisła, Gdańsk (In serv. 20-4-77)

M-32

M-32 Jaroslaw Cislak, 2000

D: 40 tons (fl) **S:** 14.7 kts **Dim:** 20.61 × . . . × . . .

Remarks: M = *Motorwka* (general-purpose harbor-service motorboat).

SERVICE CRAFT *(continued)*

♦ **2 Project B-306 multipurpose launches [YFL]**
Bldr: Stocznia Marynarki Wojennej, Gdynia

M-2 (In serv. 7-6-73) M-28 (In serv. 31-1-74)

M-28 Jaroslaw Cislak, 2000

D: 35 tons (41 fl) **S:** 9.6 kts **Dim:** 17.8 (15.2 pp) × 4.4 × 1.6
M: 1 Wola DM 150 diesel; 1 prop; 150 bhp **Crew:** 6 tot.

Remarks: General-purpose launches that can be used as mooring buoy tenders, small tugs, personnel launches, and inshore survey craft. Sister M-27 was stricken in 1996. M = *Motorwka* (general-purpose harbor-service motorboat).

♦ **2 Project Delfin motor launches [YFL]**
Bldr: Stocznia Ustka, Ustka (In serv. 8-3-71)

M-25 M-26

D: . . . tons **S:** . . . kts **Dim:** 8.52 × . . . × . . .

Remarks: M = *Motorwka* (general-purpose harbor-service motorboat).

♦ **1 Project MS-3600 commander-in-chief's yacht [YFL]**
Bldr: Stocznia Marynarki Wojennej, Gdynia

	Laid down	L	In serv.
M-1	10-9-69	25-2-70	26-6-70

M-1—blue hull, white superstructure as commander-in-chief's yacht
Jaroslaw Cislak, 2000

D: 74.4 tons (fl) **S:** 27.6 kts **Dim:** 28.70 × 5.80 × 1.20
M: 3 Soviet M-50-FS diesels; 3 props; 3,600 bhp **Crew:** 8 tot. + 30 passengers

Remarks: Has a steel hull and aluminum superstructure. M = *Motorwka* (general-purpose harbor-service motorboat).

♦ **1 Project M-600/II staff motorboat [YFL]**
Bldr: Stocznia Marynarki Wojennej, Gdynia (In serv. 2-2-67)

M-3

M-3—blue hull, white superstructure Jaroslaw Cislak, 2000

D: 35 tons (fl) **S:** 16.3 kts **Dim:** 20.11 (19.57 pp) × 4.47 × 1.00
M: 2 Wola 300 diesels; 2 props; 600 bhp **Crew:** 4 tot. + 12 passengers

Remarks: M = *Motorwka* (general-purpose harbor-service motorboat).

♦ **1 M-150-class motor launch [YFL]**
Bldr: Stocznia Marynarki Wojennej, Gdynia (In serv. 29-1-66)

M-6

D: 10 tons (fl) **S:** 12.3 kts **Dim:** 13.95 × . . . × . . .

Remarks: M = *Motorwka* (general-purpose harbor-service motorboat).

♦ **2 Russian Kometa-M-class (Project 342 MT) passenger hydrofoils [YFLH]** Bldr: Serge Ordzhonikidze Zavod, Poti

Pogwizd (In serv. 5-11-86) Zodiak (In serv. 10-4-84)

Zodiak Jaroslaw Cislak, 2000

D: 60 tons (fl) **S:** 32 kts **Dim:** 35.1 × 6.0 × 3.6 (1.7 on foil)
M: 2 M-50-series diesels; 2 props; 1,800 bhp **Crew:** 6 tot. + 116 passengers

Remarks: Operate between Hel and Oksywie. Sister *Zefir* has been stricken.

♦ **2 Project 4234 inshore survey craft [YGS]**
Bldr: Stocznia Wisła, Gdańsk

K-4 (ex-KH-121) (In serv. 25-9-89) K-10 (ex-KH-122) (In serv. 6-2-89)

K-4 Jaroslaw Cislak, 2000

D: 45 tons (50 fl) **S:** 9.1 kts **Dim:** 18.88 × 4.42 × 1.60
Electronics: Radar: 1 Tamirio SRN-207A nav.
M: 1 Wola DM 150 diesel; 1 prop; 165 bhp
Range: 85/8 **Crew:** 10 tot. + 4 passengers

Remarks: Similar to passenger launches K-5, K-7, and K-9. GRP construction. K = *Kuter* (general-purpose craft).

♦ **5 MH-111-class hydrographic launches [YGS]**
Bldr: Tczewska Stocznia Rzeczna, Tczewie

	In serv.		In serv.		In serv.
M-35	12-7-84	M-38	18-1-84	M-40	24-10-84
M-37	18-1-84	M-39	18-1-84		

M-40—in land storage with M-39, M-38, and M-37 Jaroslaw Cislak, 2000

D: 9.1 tons (10 fl) **S:** 8.6 kts **Dim:** 10.72 × 4.06 × 0.60
Electronics: Radar: 1 Tamirio SRN-207A nav.
M: 1 Puck-Rekin SW 400/MZ diesel; 95 bhp
Range: 184/8.4 **Crew:** 4 tot. + 8 survey party

SERVICE CRAFT *(continued)*

Remarks: Resemble cabin cruisers. Project 306 launches M-2 and M-28 and Project 447 launches K-1 and K-2 (qq.v.) can also be used for inshore survey work. M = *Motorwka* (general-purpose harbor-service motorboat).

♦ 3 45-meter fuel barges [YON]
Bldr: Tczewska Stocznia Rzeczna, Tczewie

B-11 (In serv. 31-12-79) B-12 (In serv. 1-8-80) B-13 (In serv. 20-6-81)

B-11 Dieter Wolf, 8-95

Remarks: B = *Barka* (dumb-barge or self-propelled lighter for dry or liquid cargo).

♦ 1 Project PR-5 fuel barge [YON]
Bldr: Stocznia Północna, Gdańsk (in serv. 2-2-55)

B-2

B-2 Jaroslaw Cislak, 2000

D: 423 tons (fl) **Dim:** 30.2 × . . . × . . .

Remarks: B = *Barka* (dumb-barge or self-propelled lighter for dry or liquid cargo). Sister B-1 has been hulked.

♦ 1 Project BPZ-500A/MW fuel barge [YON]
Bldr: Tczewska Stocznia Rzeczna, Tczewie (In serv. 25-7-88)

B-3

Remarks: Length: 35 m o.a. B = *Barka* (dumb-barge or self-propelled lighter for dry or liquid cargo). Based at Kolobrzeg.

♦ 2 Pajak-class (Project Kormoran) torpedo retrievers [YPT]
Bldr: Stocznia Marynarki Wojennej, Gdynia

	L	In serv.
K-8	26-8-70	3-7-71
K-11	23-6-71	11-12-71

K-11—note slot in stern for torpedo retrieval ramp Maritime Photographic, 6-99

D: 110 tons light; 133 tons std. (149 fl) **S:** 21 kts (19.3 sust.)
Dim: 34.92 (33.70 wl) × 6.60 (6.02 wl) × 1.72
A: 1 twin 23-mm 87-cal. ZU-23-2 Wrobel-1 AA
Electronics: Radar: 1 Tamirio SRN-206 nav.
M: 2 M-50F-5 diesels; 2 props; 2,370 bhp
Range: 256/17.5; 660/9.5 **Endurance:** 5 days **Crew:** 18 tot.

Remarks: The names associated with these ships, *"Kormoran-I"* and *"Kormoran-II,"* are unofficial. K = *Kuter* (general-purpose craft). Both are based at Gdynia-Oksywie. Have a 3-ton-capacity crane with 8-m radius and a stern recovery ramp. Can stow eight 533-mm torpedoes on deck.

Disposal note: Self-propelled floating workshop W-2 had been stricken by the end of 1998.

♦ 2 Zbyszko-class (Project B-823) salvage tenders [YRS]
Bldr: Stocznia Ustka, Ustka

	Laid down	L	In serv.
R-14 Zbyszko	5-90	12-90	8-11-91
R-15 Maćko	10-90	2-91	20-3-92

Maćko (R-15) H&L Van Ginderen, 8-99

D: 380 tons (fl) **S:** 11 kts **Dim:** 35.00 (30.00 pp) × 8.00 × 3.00
Electronics: Radar: 1 Tamirio SRN-402X nav
M: 1 Sulzer-Cegielski 6AL20/24D diesel; 1 Kort-nozzle, CP, 458-rpm, 1.58-m-dia. prop; 750 bhp (530 sust.)
Electric: 144 kw tot (3 × 48-kw Wola SW400 diesel sets)
Range: 3,000/10 **Crew:** 15 tot.

Remarks: Operated by the Naval Rescue and Salvage Service. R = *Okret Ratownicz* (salvage tug, salvage craft, or diving tender). Able to support two divers to 45 m simultaneously and have 100-m depth decompression chambers. Equipped with two DWP-16 firefighting water cannon. Based at Kolobrzeg.

♦ 3 Pluskwa-class (Project R-30) salvage tugs [YRS]
Bldr: Stocznia Marynarki Wojennej, Gdynia

R-11 Gniewko (In serv. 29-9-81) R-13 Semko (In serv. 9-5-87)
R-12 Bolko (In serv. 7-11-82)

Gniewko (R-11) Jaroslaw Cislak, 2000

D: 321 tons (369 fl) **S:** 12 kts **Dim:** 32.38 (28.50 pp) × 9.00 (8.20 wl) × 3.06
Electronics: Radar: 1 Tamirio SRN-823 nav.
M: 1 Sulzer-Cegielski 6AL25/30 diesel; 1 Kort-nozzle prop; 1,470 bhp
Electric: 363 kw tot. (3 × 121 kw; 3 Wola H-6 165-bhp diesels driving)
Range: 4,600/7 **Fuel:** 43 tons **Endurance:** 6 days
Crew: 18 tot. (incl. 5 divers)

Remarks: R-11 was launched 26-10-80 and commenced sea trials 7-7-81. R = *Okret Ratownicz* (salvage tug, salvage craft, or diving tender). All three are attached to the 41st Salvage and Rescue Division, R-11 based at Hel and the others at Świnoujście. Can recover objects from depths up to 60 m and are equipped to support salvage divers and conduct fire fighting.

♦ 2 Project H-960-class large harbor tugs [YTB]
Bldr: Gdynska Stocznia Remontowa Nauta, Gdynia

H-6 (In serv. 25-9-92) H-8 (In serv. 19-3-93)

SERVICE CRAFT *(continued)*

H-8 Jaroslaw Cislak, 2000

D: 310 tons (332 fl) **S:** 12 kts **Dim:** 27.80 × 8.40 (8.00 wl) × 3.00
Electronics: Radar: 1 Tamirio SRN-401XA nav.
M: 1 Sulzer-Cegielski 6ATL25D diesel; 1 Kort-nozzle, CP, 247-rpm prop; 1,280 bhp
Range: 1,150/12 **Crew:** 1 officer, 16 enlisted

Remarks: Ordered in 1988. H-6 was launched 11-5-91, H-8 on 15-11-92. H = *Holownik* (tug). H-6 is based at Hel, H-8 at Gdynia-Oksywie.

♦ 2 Motyl-class (Project 1500) large harbor tugs [YTB]
Bldr: Stocznia Północna, Gdańsk

H-12 (In serv. 13-1-64) H-20 (In serv. 12-9-64)

H-12 Jaroslaw Cislak, 5-95

D: 390 tons std. (439 fl) **S:** 12 kts **Dim:** 31.85 (28.60 pp) × 8.70 × 3.90
Electronics: Radar: 1 Tamirio SRN-206 nav.
M: 1 Sulzer-Zgoda 5TD48 diesel; 1 prop; 1,500 bhp **Electric:** 150 kw tot.
Range: 1,500/12 **Fuel:** 20 tons **Crew:** 22 tot.

Remarks: Were to be replaced by Project H-960 tugs during 1993, but remain in service, H-12 at Świnoujście and H-20 at Gdynia-Oksywie. H = *Holownik* (tug). Sister H-19 was stricken circa 1993.

♦ 2 Project B-820 medium harbor tugs [YTM]
Bldr: Stocznia Ustka, Ustka

H-9 (In serv. 27-6-93) H-10 (In serv. 24-6-93)

H-10—outboard a Project H-800/IV tug Jaroslaw Cislak, 2000

D: 149.3 tons (fl) **S:** 10.8 kts **Dim:** 22.01 (18.50 pp) × 6.40 × 2.30
M: 1 Cegielski-Sulzer 6AL20/24 diesel; 1 CP prop; 570 bhp
Endurance: 4 days **Crew:** 4-6 tot.

Remarks: 75 kilonewton bollard pull. H = *Holownik* (tug). Further units were planned at one time.

♦ 4 Bucha-class (Project H-900/II) medium harbor tugs [YTM]
Bldr: Stocznia Remontowa Nauta, Gdynia

H-3 (In serv. 3-12-79) H-5 (In serv. 15-6-81)
H-4 (In serv. 10-2-80) H-7 (In serv. 19-7-81)

H-7 Jaroslaw Cislak, 2000

D: 220 tons (310 fl) **S:** 12 kts **Dim:** 26.30 (25.40 pp) × 7.10 × 2.80
Electronics: Radar: 1 Tamirio SRN-206 nav.
M: 1 Cegielski-Sulzer 6AL20/24H diesel; 1 CP prop; 760 bhp
Electric: 76 kw tot. **Fuel:** 20 tons **Crew:** 15 tot.

Remarks: Class was also built for civil use. H = *Holownik* (tug). Bollard pull: 10 tons. H-3 is based at Hel, H-4 at Świnoujście, and H-5 and H-7 at Gdynia-Oksywie. Also known by NATO class name "Bucha."

♦ 2 Project H-800/IV medium harbor tugs [YTM]
Bldr: Stocznia Remontowa Nauta, Gdynia

H-1 (In serv. 30-12-70) H-2 (In serv. 28-2-79)

H-2 Peter Froud, 6-98

D: 218 tons (fl) **S:** 11 kts **Dim:** 25.6 × 6.8 × 2.8
Electronics: Radar: 1 Tamirio SRN-206 nav.
M: 1 Magdeburg 6NVD48 diesel; 1 Kort-nozzle prop; 800 bhp
Range: 1,500/9 **Crew:** 17 tot.

Remarks: Bollard pull: 12 tons. H = *Holownik* (tug).

♦ 1 Project B-79/II sail-training craft [YTS]

	Bldr	Laid down	L	In serv.
Iskra	Stocznia Gdańska	11-11-81	6-3-82	11-8-82

D: 381 tons (498 fl) **S:** 10.2 (under power)
Dim: 49.00 (42.70 hull; 36.00 pp) × 8.00 × 3.70
Electronics: Radar: 1 Tamirio SRN-206 nav.
M: 1 Wola 68H12 diesel; 1 CP, 356-rpm, 1.5-m-dia. prop; 310 bhp—sail area: 1,038 m^2 max.; 960 m^2 normal
Crew: 5 officers, 8 petty officers, 50 cadets

Remarks: The three-masted barkentine's name means "Spark." Has 63 total berths. Can also be used for oceanographic research. Is operated by the Polish Naval Academy *(Akedemia Marynarki Wojennej)*. Circumnavigated the globe in 1995–96. Sister *Pogoria* is civilian subordinated, as is the much larger sail-training ship *Dar Mlodziezy*, also completed in 1982. Sister *Kaliakra* is operated by Bulgaria. The old naval sail-training ship *Iskra*, renamed *Iotka*, survives as a civilian youth training craft.

SERVICE CRAFT *(continued)*

Iskra Maritime Photographic, 8-98

♦ 4 Bryza-class (Project OS-1) navigational training craft [YXT]

Bldr: Stocznia Wisła, Gdańsk

	In serv.		In serv.
K-18 Bryza	10-1-65	712 Kadet	19-7-75
711 Podchorąży	30-11-74	713 Elew	5-3-76

Kadet (712) Jaroslaw Cislak, 2000

D: 146.7 tons (fl) **S:** 11 kts **Dim:** 28.82 × 6.85 × 1.85
Electronics: Radar: 2 Tamirio SRN-743X nav.
M: 2 Wola DM-150 diesels; 2 props; 300 bhp **Electric:** 84 kw tot.
Range: 1,100/10 **Endurance:** 5 days **Crew:** 11 tot. + 26 students

Remarks: K-18, with a less elaborate superstructure, displaces 135.5 tons (fl) and her dimensions are 26.82 × 6.00 × 1.80; she is now used only as a personnel launch and the name is unofficial. This class was also widely employed by Soviet naval schools and merchant marine schools for navigation and seamanship training. K-18 and 713 are based at Gdynia-Oksywie, 711 at Hel, and 712 at Świnoujście.

MINISTRY OF THE INTERIOR
POLISH BORDER GUARD
(Straz Graniczna Rzeczpospolitej Polskiej)

Established 19-5-91 under the Ministry of the Interior from the assets of the former Sea Border Brigade, which had earlier been known as the Border Guard *(Wojska Ochrony Pogranicza)* and several other maritime agencies. Ships and craft are marked "*Straz Graniczna RP,*" and their dark blue hulls carry a red diagonal stripe with a yellow edge. Pennant numbers begin with SG *(Strazy Granicnej)*. Most ships are based at Gdańsk. The fleet is organized into two squadrons, the Kaszubski Dywizjon Strazy Granicznej (Kashubian Squadron of the Border Guard) and the Pomorski Dywizjon Strazy Granicznej (Pomeranian Squadron). The Baltycki Dywizjon Strazy Granicznej (Baltic Squadron) was disestablished on 1-1-00.

Maritime Aviation: Four PZL-104M Wilga 2000 light observation aircraft and one PZL M20 Mewa (license-built Piper PA 34 Seneca-II) light patrol aircraft

Construction Program: As of 5-00, plans called for the construction of two 400- to 500-ton, 50- to 60-m-long, 25-kt patrol craft armed with a 25-mm gun and equipped with a helicopter platform. Also planned are two more SAR 1500 rescue launches, two air-cushion craft, and five smaller support launches.

PATROL CRAFT [WPC]

♦ 2 SKS-40-class fisheries patrol boats

Bldr: Stocznia Wisła, Gdańsk

SG-311 Kaper-1 (In serv. 21-1-91) SG-312 Kaper-2 (In serv. 1-10-94)

Kaper-1 (SG-311) Jaroslaw Cislak, 2000

D: 470 tons (fl) **S:** 17.6 kts
Dim: 42.60 (38.76 pp) × 8.38 (7.70 wl) × 2.80 (3.00 max.)
A: 2 single 7.62-mm mg
Electronics: Radar: 1 Decca . . . nav.; 1 Tamirio SRN-231 nav.
M: 2 Sulzer-HCP 8ATL25D diesels; 2 CP, 1.65-m-dia., 493-rpm props; 4,790 bhp
Electric: 290 kw tot. (2 × 145 kw, Wola 72H6 diesels driving)
Range: 2,800/14 **Endurance:** 8 days **Crew:** 11 crew + 2 inspectors

Remarks: 376 grt. Begun for the Maritime Office of Inspections *(Urzed Morski)* but incorporated instead into the new border patrol agency. *Kaper* means "Privateer." SG-312 was launched 3-4-92. As of 4-02, SG-311 was attached to the Kashubian Squadron and based at Gdańsk, while SG-312 was attached to the Pomeranian Squadron and based at Kolobrzeg. SG-311 carries Project M-4500 RIB SG-027 on deck aft.

♦ 2 Obluze class (Project 912)

Bldr: Stocznia Marynarki Wojennej, Gdynia

SG-323 Zefir (In serv. 10-6-67) SG-325 Tęcza (In serv. 31-1-68)

Zefir (SG-323) H&L Van Ginderen, 8-99

D: 212 tons (237 fl) **S:** 24 kts **Dim:** 41.40 (39.50 pp) × 5.80 × 1.90 (hull)
A: 2 twin 30-mm 65-cal. AK-230 AA; 4 d.c. racks (2 internal, 2 on deck aft; 24 tot. d.c.); 4 AMD-1000 mines in lieu of topside d.c. racks
Electronics:
Radar: 1 Tamirio SRN-207 nav.
Sonar: Tamir-11 hull-mounted HF searchlight
M: 2 Type 40DM diesels; 2 props; 4,000 bhp **Electric:** 150 kw
Range: 1,220/12 **Fuel:** 25 tons **Crew:** 20 tot.

Remarks: Names mean "Zephyr" and "Rainbow," respectively. Five additional units with more-powerful engines and fire-control radars for the 30-mm AA serve in the Polish Navy. Both are attached to the Pomeranian Squadron and based at Kolobrzeg.
Disposals: *Fala* (SG-321) and *Szkwal* (SG-322) were stricken 16-2-96, with *Fala* destined to become a museum ship. *Zorza* (SG-324) was stricken 22-10-98.

PATROL BOATS [WPB]

♦ 2 SAR-1500SG patrol launches

Bldr: Alu International, Gdańsk (hulls), and Damen Shipyard Polska, Gdynia (fitting out)

SG-211 Strażnik-1 (In serv. 29-4-00) SG-212 Strażnik-2 (In serv. 9-7-00)

BORDER GUARD PATROL BOATS [WPB] *(continued)*

Strażnik-1 (SG-211) Jaroslaw Cislak, 2000

D: . . . tons **S:** 35 kts **Dim:** 15.20 (14.6 hull; 11.80 wl) × 5.39 (4.20 hull) × 0.90
A: 1 7.62-mm PKMS mg **Electronics:** Radar: 1 Decca BridgeMaster-E ARPA nav.
M: 2 M.A.N. 2848LE 401 diesels; 2 waterjets; 1,340 bhp
Range: 170/20 **Fuel:** 1.56 m^3 **Crew:** 1 officer, 3 enlisted + 8 passengers

Remarks: Ordered 5-10-99, with the pair laid down 7-10-99 and 5-11-99, respectively. Two more may be procured. SG-211 is attached to the Kashubian Squadron and based at Gdańsk; SG-212 is attached to the Pomeranian Squadron. Have aluminum hulls with an inflated collar surrounding the hull. Design is based on the Dutch SAR 1500 lifeboat *Graf Van Bylandt.* Can carry up to 75 rescuees in an emergency.

♦ 2 Pilica class (Project 918M)
Bldr: Stocznia Marynarki Wojennej, Gdynia

SG-161 (In serv. 6-6-73) SG-164 (In serv. 3-10-74)

SG-164—with RIB alongside aft Jaroslaw Cislak, 2000

D: 79.7 tons (86.9 fl) **S:** 28 kts **Dim:** 28.59 × 5.76 × 1.30
A: 1 twin 23-mm 87-cal. Wrobel-2M AA
Electronics: Radar: 1 Tamirio RN-231 nav.
M: 3 M-50F-4 diesels; 3 props; 3,600 bhp **Crew:** 13 tot.

Remarks: Differ from the eight naval-subordinated units in lacking torpedo tubes and in having an A-frame gantry crane aft to assist in towing and rescue work. SG-161 is attached to the Kashubian Squadron and based at Gdańsk; SG-164 is attached to the Pomeranian Squadron and based at Świnoujście. Sisters SG-162, SG-163, and SG-164 were stricken 19-2-99.

♦ 6 Wisloka class (Project 90)
Bldr: Stocznia Wisła, Gdańsk

	In serv.		In serv.		In serv.
SG-142	20-1-74	SG-145	27-7-75	SG-150	23-4-77
SG-144	1-2-75	SG-146	24-10-75	SG-152	5-8-77

SG-150—outboard a sister Jaroslaw Cislak, 2000

D: 42 tons (50 fl) **S:** 12 kts **Dim:** 22.8 × 5.0 × 1.2
A: 1 twin 12.7-mm M1 mg **Electronics:** Radar: 1 Tamirio SRN-207 nav.
M: 2 Wola 31 ANM28 H12A diesels; 2 props; 1,006 bhp
Range: 500/18 **Crew:** 9 tot.

Remarks: SG-142 and SG-150 are attached to the Kashubian Squadron and based at Gdańsk, the others to the Pomeranian Squadron, based at Świnoujście. Sister SG-141 was stricken 19-2-99, while SG-147, SG-148, SG-149, and SG-151 had already been stricken by that date. SG-150 carries Project MR-4800 RIB SG-025 on deck aft.

SERVICE CRAFT

♦ 2 MI-6-class launches [WYFL]
Bldr: Stocznia Wisła, Gdańsk (In serv. 1988–90)

SG-006 SG-008

SG-006 Jaroslaw Cislak, 2000

D: 13.8 tons (17.9 fl) **S:** 11 kts **Dim:** 14.05 (13.00 pp) × 3.52 × 1.20

Remarks: Sister SG-015 was stricken 19-2-99, and SG-016 and SG-017 on 25-6-99. SG-006 is attached to the Pomeranian Squadron and based at Świnoujście, and SG-008 to the Kashubian Squadron, based at Gdańsk.

♦ 1 M-35/MW-class launch [WYFL]
Bldr: Tzcewska Stocznia Rzeczna, Tzcewcie (In serv. 25-12-85)

SG-036

SG-036 Jaroslaw Cislak, 2000

D: 28.66 tons (41 fl) **S:** 8.3 kts **Dim:** 10.75 × 4.4 × 1.6
M: 1 Wola DM 150 diesel; 1 prop; 150 bhp **Crew:** 4 tot.

Remarks: Six sisters serve in the Polish Navy. Attached to the Kashubian Squadron and based at Gdańsk.

♦ 1 MG 600–class launch [WYFL]
Bldr: Stocznia Wisła, Gdańsk (In serv. 4-76)

SG-011

D: 40 tons (fl) **S:** 16 kts **Dim:** 20.61 × 4.38 × 1.15
A: small arms **M:** 2 3D12 diesels; 2 props; 600 bhp

Remarks: Assigned to the Kashubian Squadron and based at Gdańsk.

Note: Also in service are 14 RIBs: four Project S-7500 and S-7500/K: SG-002, SG-003, SG-004, and SG-005; seven Project MR-4800 and MR-4800/B: SG-020 through SG-026; and three Project M-4500: SG-027, SG-029, and SG-030. Sail-training craft *Galeon* (in serv. 29-7-86) and *Karawela II* (in serv. 15-7-81) of, respectively, Conrad 46– and Conrad 45–type are also in service.

BORDER GUARD SERVICE CRAFT *(continued)*

Project S-7500 launch SG-004—with pilothouse and Koden radar; SG-005 does not have either feature H&L Van Ginderen, 8-99

Project MR-4800 RIB SG-022—on travel trailer, with 50-bhp Johnson outboard motor installed Jaroslaw Cislak, 2000

Disposal note: The final Project B-306 launch, SG-082, had been retired by 4-00, as had been Project MT-8 launches SG-101 and SG-014.

PORTUGAL

Portuguese Republic

MARINHA PORTUGUESA

Personnel (2001): 11,600 (1,690 officers); included in the total are 1,460 marines *(Corpo de Fuzileiros)* and 420 naval police. There are about 5,000 civilian employees.

Bases: Principal base at Alfeite, which also has a well-equipped dockyard; smaller facilities at Ponta Delgada, Portimão, Porto, and Funchal (Madeira)

Naval Aviation: Five Lynx Mk 95 ordered 10-90 were delivered during 1993 to form a naval aviation organization (three are new construction, the other two are rebuilt, ex-RN HAS.3s); the helicopters carry Bendix 1500 radars and AQS-18 dipping sonars. Naval aircraft are based at Montijo, near Lisbon.

Eight Air Force CASA 212-200 Aviocar light transports (four with photo equipment) are equipped for maritime reconnaissance and fisheries protection duties. Six ex-Australian P-3B-II Orions are operated by Esquadra de Reconhecimento Maritimo 601 from Montijo; between 2002 and 2008, they are to be upgraded by Lockheed Martin to extend their service lives by 25 years. Five C-130H Hercules transports and 12 AS.330C Puma helicopters are used for search and rescue. Two CASA 212-300s were ordered in early 1993 for fisheries patrol duties to begin replacement of the CASA 212-200s. A dozen AgustaWestland EH.101 helicopters were ordered on 3-12-01 to replace the Pumas.

Portuguese Navy Lynx Mk 95—aboard *Vasco da Gama* (F 330) Findler & Winter, 6-00

Marines: The *fuzileiros* are formed into a Light Landing Battalion *(Batalhão Ligeiro de Desembarque)* that can be integrated into a joint Dutch-British-Portuguese amphibious brigade. The naval police have been separated from the former Fuzileiros 1st Battalion to create an independent Unidade de Polícia Naval of about 420 personnel. The fuzileiros received Milan antitank missiles during 1996.

Note: Ship names are preceded by NRP *(Navio Republicano Portugues).*

ATTACK SUBMARINES [SS]

Note: Replacements for the *Daphné*-class submarines were requested in the 1992–98 defense plan, and funding of about $540 million was to have been included in the 1997 budget. Three submarines of about 1,500 tons submerged displacement are desired. A requirement was that the submarines be able to launch UGM-84 Sub-Harpoon missiles. The Franco-Spanish Scorpène and a German Submarine Consortium design were short-listed in 1998, and an order was expected in 1999, but no funds have been made available for the project to date.

♦ 2 French Daphné class Bldr: Dubigeon-Normandy, Nantes

	Laid down	L	In serv.
S 164 Barracuda	19-10-65	24-4-67	4-5-68
S 166 Delfim	14-5-67	23-9-68	1-10-69

Delfim (S 166) Ben Sullivan, 10-00

Barracuda (S 164) Rob Cabo, 6-01

D: 746 tons std.; 868 tons surf./1,038 tons sub.
S: 13.5 kts surf./15 kts sub. **Dim:** 57.78 × 6.75 × 4.62
A: 12 550-mm TT (8 fwd, 4 aft; 12 ECAN E 14 or E 15 torpedoes—no reloads)
Electronics:
Radar: 1 Kelvin-Hughes Type 1007 nav./search
Sonar: Thales DUUA-2 active (8.4 kHz); Thales DSUV-2 passive
EW: ARUR and ARUD intercept
M: diesel-electric propulsion: 2 SEMT-Pielstick 12 PA1 diesels, 2 × 450-kw generator sets, 2 Jeumont-Schneider 800-shp (1,300 shp for short periods) motors; 2 props
Range: 2,710/12.5, 9,430/. . . surf.; 2,130/10, 4,300/7.5 snorkel
Crew: 5 officers, 45 enlisted

Remarks: A replacement program has not been decided upon, but an order is now expected during 2002.
Disposals: *Cachalote* (S 165) was purchased by the Pakistani Navy in 1975. *Albacora* (S 163) was stricken 14-7-00.
Hull systems: Operating depth was originally 300 m, but they probably do not attempt that now.
Combat systems: The sonar suite has been updated, but not to the extent performed on sisters in other navies. The after torpedo tubes are external to the pressure hull. Were to be modernized under the 1992–95 budgetary period, probably with French sonars, but funds were not available, although they did receive new radars in 1994.

FRIGATES [FF]

♦ 3 MEKO 200 class

	Bldr	Laid down	L	In serv.
F 330 Vasco da Gama	Blohm + Voss, Hamburg	2-2-89	26-6-89	20-11-90
F 331 Alvares Cabral	Howaldtswerke, Kiel	2-6-89	2-5-90	18-1-91
F 332 Corte Real	Howaldtswerke, Kiel	20-10-89	2-5-90	22-11-91

D: 2,920 tons (3,200 fl) **S:** 31.75 kts (18 on diesel)
Dim: 115.90 (109.00 pp) × 14.80 (13.80 wl) × 5.97 (4.10 hull)
A: 8 RGM-84C Harpoon SSM; 1 8-round Mk 29 SAM launcher (8 RIM-7M Sea Sparrow missiles); 1 100-mm 55-cal. Model 1968 CADAM DP; 1 20-mm Mk 15 Phalanx gatling CIWS; 2 single 20-mm 70-cal. Oerlikon Mk 4 AA; 2 triple 324-mm Mk 32 Mod. 5 ASW TT (U.S. Mk 46 Mod. 5 torpedoes); 1 Lynx Mk 95 ASW helicopter

FRIGATES [FF] *(continued)*

Vasco da Gama (F 330) Curt Borgenstam Jr., 8-00

Alvares Cabral (F 331) Findler & Winter, 5-01

Corte Real (F 332) Mike Welsford, 6-01

Electronics:
Radar: 1 Kelvin-Hughes Type 1007 nav.; 1 Thales MW-08 Mod. 3 3-D surf./air search; 1 Thales DA-08 early warning; 2 Thales STIR-18 f.c.; 1 General Dynamics Mk 90 Phalanx f.c.
Sonar: Computing Devices Canada SQS-510(V) hull-mounted (6.4–8.0 kHz)
EW: ArgoSystems APECS-II/AR-700 intercept/jammer suite; Mk 36 Mod. 1 SRBOC decoy syst. (2 6-round Raytheon Mk 137 RL); SLQ-25 Nixie towed acoustic torpedo decoy syst.
M: CODOG: 2 MTU 12V1163 TB83 diesels (4,420 bhp each), 2 G.E. LM-2500-30 gas turbines (30,000 shp each); 2 Escher-Weiss CP props
Electric: 2,480 kw (4 × 620-kw diesel sets)

Range: 900/31.75; 4,100/18 (2 diesels) **Fuel:** 300 tons
Crew: 23 officers, 44 petty officers, 115 ratings (incl. 4 officers, 5 petty officers, and 9 ratings in helicopter detachment) + 16 flag staff

Remarks: Ordered 25-7-86. Financed 60% by the U.S., Canada, West Germany, Norway, and the Netherlands and 40% by Portugal. Equipped to accommodate a flag officer staff. F 330 completed a 6-month overhaul at the Arsenal do Alfeite on 19-4-01, with all electronics systems overhauls under a contract with Thales Nederland; the other two ships were to follow.
Hull systems: Have fin stabilizers and the NAUTOS propulsion control system.
Combat systems: Have Thales SEWACO (Sensor Weapon, Control and Command System), STACOS tactical command system, and Vespa datalink transponder. NATO Link 11 and Link 14 datalinks, the Sicom 200 integrated communications suite, and an MNS 2000 navigation suite are fitted. Are fitted for later installation of a towed linear hydrophone array (TASS). One set of UHF SATCOM equipment, using the British SCOT system, is rotated among the three.

♦ **3 French Commandant Riviere class** Bldr: A.C. de Bretagne, Nantes

	Laid down	L	In serv.
F 480 Comandante João Belo	6-9-65	22-3-66	1-7-67
F 481 Comandante Hermengildo Capelo	13-5-66	29-11-66	26-4-68
F 483 Comandante Sacadura Cabral	18-8-67	15-3-68	25-11-69

Comandante João Belo (F 480) Carlo Martinelli, 6-98

Comandante Hermengildo Capelo (F 481) B. Laffont, 3-96

D: 1,760 tons (2,250 fl) **S:** 25 kts (26.6 on trials)
Dim: 102.70 (98.00 pp) × 11.80 × 3.80 (hull; 4.35 max.)
A: 2 single 100-mm 55-cal. Model 1953 DP; 2 single 40-mm 60-cal. Bofors AA; 2 triple 324-mm Mk 32 Mod. 5 ASW TT (Mk 46 Mod. 5 torpedoes)
Electronics:
Radar: 1 Kelvin-Hughes Type 1007 nav.; 1 Thales DRBV-22A air search; 1 Thales DRBV-50 surf./air search; 1 Thales DRBC-31D f.c.
Sonar: Computing Devices Canada SQS-510(V) hull-mounted
EW: ArgoSystems APECS-II/700 intercept/jamming suite; Mk 36 SRBOC decoy syst. (2 6-round Raytheon Mk 137 RL); SLQ-25(V) Nixie acoustic torpedo decoy syst.
M: 4 SEMT-Pielstick 12 PC2.2 V400 diesels; 2 props; 16,000 bhp

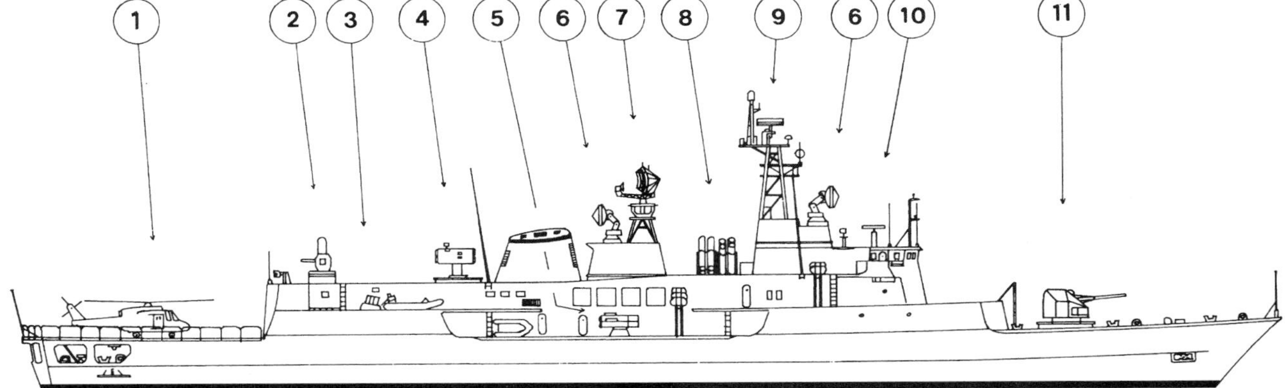

Vasco da Gama (F 330) 1. Lynx Mk 95 helicopter 2. Mk 15 Phalanx CIWS 3. Mk 137 launchers for the Mk 36 SRBOC decoy system 4. 8-round Mk 29 launcher for Sea Sparrow missiles 5. triple Mk 32 Mod. 5 ASW TT. 6. STIR-18 fire-control/illumination radars 7. DA-08 early-warning radar 8. RGM-84 Harpoon SSM 9. MW-08 surface/air-search radar 10. Type 1007 navigational radar 11. 100-mm 55-cal. Model 1968 CADAM DP gun Drawing by Robert Dumas, from *Flottes de Combat*

FRIGATES [FF] *(continued)*

Electric: 1,280 kw tot. (4 × 320-kw diesel sets)
Range: 2,300/25; 7,500/15 **Fuel:** 210 tons **Crew:** 14 officers, 183 enlisted

Remarks: As completed, were generally similar to sisters built for the French Navy. They were modernized under the 1992–1995 budget to keep them in service through 2006; F 481 completed the first modernization refit 10-95, with accommodations for 15 female personnel added. Sister *Comandante Roberto Ivens* (F 482) was to have been adapted for cadet training duties but was instead stricken during 1997; the hulk remained at Alfeite Arsenal through 1-01.
Combat systems: Modernization included installing the Thales SEWACO-FD-derived combat data system, adding a NATO Link 11 datalink capability, and substituting the Computing Devices Canada SQS-510(V) sonar for the original SQS-17A and DUBA-3 suite, U.S. Mk 32 Mod. 5 tubes and Mk 46 Mod. 5 torpedoes for the French 550-mm tubes, and the ArgoSystems APECS-II/700 EW suite for ARBR-10. The U.S. SLQ-25 Nixie towed torpedo decoy system was added, while the 305-mm mortar and after, superfiring, 100-mm gunmount were removed. A planned helicopter platform addition was omitted.

PATROL SHIPS [PS]

Note: A new class of 10 offshore patrol vessels, referred to as the NPO 2000 project, is sought to replace the *Baptiste de Andrade–* and *João Coutinho–*class patrol ships and the *Cacine*-class patrol craft, if financial assistance can be secured from the European Union. The ships, to be built at the Arsenal do Alfeite, would be used for EEZ patrol and SAR duties. Armed with a single, 40-mm, hand-worked AA, they would have a helicopter deck aft. It was hoped to order the class late in 2001, with the first to enter service in 2003.

♦ 4 Baptiste de Andrade class
Bldr: Izar (formerly E.N. Bazán), Cartagena, Spain

	Laid down	L	In serv.
F 486 Baptiste de Andrade	1-9-72	13-3-73	19-11-74
F 487 João Roby	1-12-72	3-6-73	18-3-75
F 488 Afonso Cerquiera	10-3-73	6-10-73	26-6-75
F 489 Oliveira e Carmo	1-6-73	22-2-74	28-10-75

Baptiste de Andrade (F 486) Winter & Findler, 8-98

Oliveira e Carmo (F 489) Winter & Findler, 8-98

D: 1,252 tons (1,348 fl) **S:** 21 kts **Dim:** 84.59 (81.0 pp) × 10.3 × 3.3
A: 1 100-mm 55-cal. Model 1968 DP; 2 single 40-mm 60-cal. Bofors AA
Electronics:
Radar: 1 Decca TM 626 nav.; 1 Plessey AWS-2 air search; 1 Thales Pollux f.c.
Sonar: removed—EW: none
M: 2 OEW-Pielstick 12 PC2 V400 diesels; 2 props; 10,560 bhp
Electric: 1,100 kVA **Range:** 5,900/18 **Crew:** 11 officers, 111 enlisted

Remarks: Developed version of the *João Coutinho* class, with more modern weapons and electronics. F 488 began stripping in mid-12-93 for striking 3-1-94 but was given a refit in 1997 and returned to service. Since 1999, the class has been employed for "public interest tasks" (i.e., fisheries patrol) and the ASW capability has been deleted, as in the *João Coutinho* class.
Combat systems: Have a Thales Vega gun-control system with Pollux radar and a backup C.S. Défense Panda optical director for the 100-mm gun and two lead-computing directors for the 40-mm AA. Have a helicopter deck fitted atop after deckhouse, but no landing aids or hangar. The Thales Diodon hull-mounted sonar and two triple Mk 32 ASW torpedo tube sets were removed during 1999–2000; the air-search radar may also have been deleted. Data about fisheries activities are exchanged via SIFICAP satellite communications system to a shore database.

♦ 6 João Coutinho class
Bldrs: F 475–477: Blohm + Voss, Hamburg; others: Izar (formerly E.N. Bazán), Cartagena, Spain

	Laid down	L	In serv.
F 471 Antonio Enes	10-4-68	16-8-69	18-6-71
F 475 João Coutinho	24-12-68	2-5-69	7-3-70
F 476 Jacinto Candido	10-2-68	16-6-69	10-6-70
F 477 General Pereira d'Eca	21-4-69	26-7-69	10-10-70
F 484 Augusto de Castilho	15-10-68	4-7-69	14-11-70
F 485 Honorio Barreto	20-2-68	11-4-70	15-4-71

Augusto de Castilho (F 484) ABBw/FAFIO, 5-00

Honorio Barreto (F 485) H&L Van Ginderen, 7-97

D: 1,252 tons (1,401 fl) **S:** 24.4 kts **Dim:** 84.59 (81.0 pp) × 10.30 × 3.30
A: 1 twin 76.2-mm 50-cal. U.S. Mk 33 DP; 1 twin 40-mm 60-cal. Bofors AA
Electronics:
Radar: 1 Decca RM 1226C nav.; 1 Kelvin-Hughes . . . surf. search
Sonar: removed—EW: none
M: 2 OEW-Pielstick 12 PC2 V280 diesels; 2 props; 10,560 bhp
Electric: 900 kw tot. **Range:** 5,900/8 **Crew:** 9 officers, 68 enlisted

Remarks: Former corvettes. Primarily used for fisheries patrol duties, with ASW capabilities deleted, resulting in a saving of 23 enlisted personnel billets. Can also carry 34 marines.
Hull systems: F 475 made 25 kts on original trials. The helicopter deck has a removable hatch.
Combat systems: ASW armament of one Mk 10 Hedgehog mortar, 2 Mk 6 d.c. mortars, and 2 d.c. racks had been deleted by 1987. During the early 1990s, the obsolete MLA-1B air-search radar was replaced by a Kelvin-Hughes surface-search set. The SPG-34 gunfire-control radar and Mk 63 Mod. 21 gun f.c.s. had been removed by 1994, leaving the 76.2-mm mount dependent on local control. The 40-mm mount has an associated Mk 51 Mod. 2 lead-computing director just abaft the stack. Can carry 1,200 rounds of 76.2-mm ammunition. Data about fisheries activities are exchanged via SIFICAP satellite communications system to a shore database.

PATROL CRAFT [PC]

♦ 8 Cacine class
Bldrs: P 1140–1147: Arsenal do Alfeite; others: Est. Nav. do Mondego

	In serv.		In serv.
P 1140 Cacine	5-69	P 1146 Zaire	11-70
P 1141 Cunene	6-69	P 1147 Zambeze	1-71
P 1144 Cuanza	30-5-69	P 1160 Limpopo	9-4-73
P 1145 Geba	5-70	P 1161 Save	5-73

Cunene (P 1141) H&L Van Ginderen, 11-99

D: 292.5 tons (310 fl) **S:** 20 kts **Dim:** 44.00 × 7.67 × 2.20
A: 1 40-mm 60-cal. Bofors AA; 1 20-mm 70-cal. Oerlikon AA
Electronics: Radar: 1 Kelvin-Hughes Type 1007 nav.
M: 2 MTU 12V538 TB80 diesels; 2 props; 4,400 bhp (3,750 sust.)
Range: 4,400/12 **Crew:** 3 officers, 30 enlisted

Remarks: P 1160 and P 1161, built by Estalieros Navais do Mondego, have low bulwarks at the bow; the others do not. All carry radio signal direction-finding equipment. Rigid inflatable inspection dinghies, tended by a small electrohydraulic crane, have replaced the after 40-mm gun and two d.c. racks. The original Maybach 12V528 diesels have been replaced.
Disposals: *Mandovi* (P 1142) was retired in 1997; five more were to be stricken starting in 1999, but with the exception of *Rovuma* (P 1143), stricken during 2000, the others remain operational, as no funds for replacements have been available.

PATROL BOATS [PB]

♦ 4 Centaro class
Bldrs: P 1157, 1158: CONAFIL, Vila Real de Santo Antonio; others: Arsenal do Alfeite

	In serv.		In serv.
P 1157 Centaro	9-00	P 1159 Pegaso	10-00
P 1158 Orion	9-00	P 1160 Sagitario	10-00

D: 82 tons (94 fl) **S:** 26 kts (28 on trials) **Dim:** 28.40 × 5.95 × 1.45
A: 1 20-mm 70-cal. Oerlikon Mk 4 AA **Electronics:** Radar: 1 . . . nav.
M: 2 Cummins KTA50-M2 diesels; 2 props; 3,600 bhp
Electric: 150 kw tot. (2 × 75 kw, Cummins 6BT5.9D(M) diesels driving)
Range: 640/20 **Crew:** 2 officers, 8 enlisted

Remarks: Ordered in 1998 as an improved version of the *Argos* class for use in fisheries protection, search and rescue, and general inshore patrol work. Aluminum construction. A 4-m inspection and rescue launch is carried on a launch and recovery ramp at the stern.

♦ 1 river patrol boat
Bldr: Arsenal do Alfeite (In serv. 1-8-91)

P 370 Rio Minho

Rio Minho (P 370) H&L Van Ginderen, 8-94

D: 57 tons (72 fl) **S:** 10 kts **Dim:** 22.4 (20.0 pp) × 5.5 × 0.8
A: 1 7.62-mm mg **Electronics:** Radar: 1 Furuno FR-1505 DA nav.
M: 2 Deutz diesels; 2 Schottel waterjets; 664 bhp
Range: 420/7 **Crew:** 1 officer, 7 enlisted

Remarks: Replaced the patrol craft *Atria* (P 360) as Rio Minho patrol craft.

♦ 5 Argos class
Bldrs: CONAFIL, Vila Real de Santo Antonio, and Arsenal do Alfeite

	In serv.		In serv.
P 1150 Argos	2-7-91	P 1153 Cassiopeia	11-11-91
P 1151 Dragão	18-10-91	P 1154 Hidra	18-12-91
P 1152 Escorpião	26-11-91		

Hidra (P 1154) Leo Van Ginderen, 1-01

D: 84 tons (94 fl) **S:** 28 kts **Dim:** 27.20 (25.20 pp) × 5.90 × 1.40
A: 2 single 12.7-mm mg **Electronics:** Radar: 1 Furuno FR-1505 DA nav.
M: 2 MTU 12V396 TE84 diesels; 2 props; 3,700 bhp
Range: 1,350/15; 200/28 **Crew:** 1 officer, 8 enlisted

Remarks: Hulls for first two were delivered to Arsenal do Alfeite early in 1991 for fitting out; the other three were built entirely at Alfeite. *Geba* (P 1145) collided with P 1150 on 7-7-95, causing severe damage.
Hull systems: GRP construction with seven watertight compartments. Have a ramp at the stern for a 4.0-m rigid inflatable inspection boat. Have Tayo VHF-Plus radio D/F.

♦ 6 Albatroz class
Bldr: Arsenal do Alfeite

	In serv.		In serv.
P 1162 Albatroz	9-12-74	P 1165 Aguia	28-2-75
P 1163 Acor	9-12-74	UAM 630 Condor (ex-P 1166)	23-4-75
P 1164 Andorhina	20-12-74	P 1167 Cisne	31-3-76

Albatroz (P 1162) Leo Van Ginderen, 1-01

D: 45 tons (fl) **S:** 20 kts **Dim:** 23.6 (21.88 pp) × 5.25 × 1.6
A: 1 20-mm 70-cal. Oerlikon AA; 2 single 12.7-mm mg
Electronics: Radar: 1 Decca 316P nav.
M: 2 Cummins diesels; 2 props; 1,100 bhp
Range: 450/18; 2,500/12 **Crew:** 1 officer, 7 enlisted

Remarks: *Condor* was relegated to harbor duties in 1992 and no longer carries fixed armament; she is operated by the naval police.

Note: Units with UAM-series pennants are all assigned to harbor patrol duties and are assigned to the naval police. UAM = *Unitad Auxiliaria da Marinha* (Naval Auxiliary Unit).

♦ 8 Spanish Bazán 39–class harbor patrol boats
Bldr: Rodman-Polyships, Vigo

	In serv.		In serv.
UAM 642 Calmaria	30-11-93	UAM 646 Suão	9-94
UAM 643 Cirro	30-11-93	UAM 647 Macareo	9-94
UAM 644 Vendeval	18-1-94	UAM 648 Preia-Mar	10-94
UAM 645 Moncão	8-94	UAM 649 Baixa-Mar	11-94

Calmaria (UAM 642) Guy Schaeffer, 8-98

D: 12 tons (15.7 fl) **S:** 32 kts **Dim:** 11.9 × 3.8 × 0.7
A: 1 7.62-mm mg **Electronics:** Radar: 1 Furuno 1830 nav.
M: 2 Izar-M.A.N. D2866 LXE diesels; 2 waterjets; 881 bhp
Range: 275/20 **Crew:** 3 tot.

Remarks: Ordered 8-1-93 to the same design as the Spanish Guardia Civil del Mar boats for use by the Brigada Fiscal (Customs Brigade) for drug control work. GRP construction. Design is also known as the Saeta 12 10T.

♦ 4 Surriada-class harbor patrol boats
Bldr: Cheverton, Cowes, U.K. (In serv. 1982)

UAM 602 Surriada	UAM 612 Bonança
UAM 605 Mareta	UAM 613 Mar Chão

Mareta (UAM 605) Leo Van Ginderen, 1-01

PATROL BOATS [PB] *(continued)*

D: 9 tons (fl) **S:** 20 kts **Dim:** 12.0 × 3.6 × 1.0
A: small arms **Electronics:** Radar: 1 Decca 110 nav.
M: 2 Volvo Penta TAMD 66B outdrive diesels; 2 props; 426 bhp **Crew:** 4 tot.

Remarks: First pair delivered in 5-82, the others in 7-82. Intended to patrol on the Tagus in the Lisbon area. GRP hulls. Have service craft pennant numbers.

♦ 30 miscellaneous harbor patrol boats

UAM 611 Bolina

D: 15 tons (fl) **S:** 14 kts **Dim:** 12.57 × 3.64 × 1.10
M: 2 Rolls-Royce Sabre 212 diesels; 2 props; 424 bhp

UAM 608 Maresia

D: . . . **S:** . . . **Dim:** 12.0 × 2.7 × 1.8
M: 2 Rolls-Royce Sabre 212 diesels; 2 props; 424 bhp

UAM 631 Levante

D: . . . **S:** . . . **Dim:** 12.0 × 3.8 × . . .
M: 2 Volvo Penta diesels; 2 props; 520 bhp

UAM 636 Ventante

Ventante (UAM 636) Guy Schaeffer, via Paolo Marsan, 9-98

D: 7.8 tons (fl) **S:** 32 kts **Dim:** 12.0 × 3.8 × 0.5
Electronics: Radar: 1 Decca . . . nav.
M: 2 AIFO 8361/SR diesels; 2 Castoldi 06 waterjets; 580 bhp
Range: 224/28 **Fuel:** 0.6 tons **Crew:** 5 tot.

UAM 601 Baluarte
UAM 603 Melides
UAM 604 Mar de Sesibra
UAM 607 Roaz
UAM 610 Colfinho
UAM 614 Balanço
UAM 616 Satitante
UAM 617 Tenebrosa
UAM 618 Teresa Paula
UAM 619 Perraria
UAM 620 Capitania
UAM 621 San Lourenço
UAM 622 Salga
UAM 623 Serreta
UAM 624 Diogo de Teive
UAM 625 Comandante Newton
UAM 626 Espalamaca
UAM 627 Carça
UAM 628 Marvão
UAM 629 Mar da Barca
UAM 632 Arrábida
UAM 633 Santa Catarina
UAM 634 Sirocco
UAM 635 Brisa
UAM 639 Tufão
UAM 640 Ciclone

Satitante (UAM 616) Leo Van Ginderen, 1-01

Remarks: UAM 636 is a sister to the Italian Customs Service's V.5500 class, built by Crestitalia, Ameglia, around 1980 and is of GRP construction. UAM 611 is a typical U.K. Keith Nelson GRP-hulled pilot launch. No data available for the other units. All are attached to various port and harbor facilities.

MINE COUNTERMEASURES SHIPS

Note: Portugal was to have been a participant in the Belgian-Dutch deep-sea minesweeper program, but when the Netherlands canceled participation in 1993, Portuguese interest ended. Although there is a formal requirement for four new mine countermeasures units, funds are not available for their procurement. The German offer of the retired Type 331B minehunter *Tübingen* (M 1074) in 1998 was not accepted.

AMPHIBIOUS WARFARE SHIPS AND CRAFT

Note: Although long-term plans call for the acquisition of a major amphibious warfare unit to carry peacekeeping forces, funds are not available. The offer of the U.S. landing ship *Newport* (LST 1179) was not accepted, and plans to acquire the Australian landing ship *Tobruk* (L 50) did not come to fruition. Negotiations with Schelde of the Netherlands were under way in late 2000 for the possible construction of a modified *Amsterdam*-class dock landing ship [LPD].

♦ 1 Bombarda-class utility landing craft [LCU]

Bldr: Arsenal do Alfeite (In serv. 1985)

LDG 203 Bacamarte

Bacamarte (LDG 203) H&L Van Ginderen/F. Heine, 1-00

D: 285 tons (652 fl) **S:** 11 kts (9.5 loaded) **Dim:** 59.0 (52.88 pp) × 11.91 × 1.6
A: 2 single 20-mm 70-cal. Oerlikon AA
Electronics: Radar: 1 Decca RM 316P nav.
M: 2 MTU MD 225 diesels; 2 props; 910 bhp
Range: 1,800/8 **Crew:** 3 officers, 18 enlisted

Remarks: Design based on the French EDIC series. Cargo: 350 tons. Sisters *Bombarda* (LDG 201) and *Alabarda* (LDG 202) were retired during 1997.

AUXILIARIES

Note: All survey ships and craft are subordinated to the Hydrographic Institute *(Instituto Hidrográfico)*.

♦ 2 ex-U.S. Stalwart-class survey ships [AGS]

Bldr: Tacoma Boat, Tacoma, Wash.

	Laid down	L	In serv.
A 522 Dom Carlos I (ex-*Audacious,* T-AGOS 11; ex-*Dauntless*)	29-2-88	28-1-89	12-6-89
A 523 Almirante Gago Coutinho (ex-*Assurance,* T-AGOS 5)	31-5-84	12-1-85	1-5-85

Almirante Gago Coutinho (A 523) George R. Schneider, 1-00

D: 1,600 tons light (2,285 fl) **S:** 11 kts **Dim:** 68.28 (62.10 wl) × 13.10 × 4.57
Electronics: Radar: 2 . . . nav.
M: 4 Caterpillar-Kato D-398B 800-bhp diesels, G.E. electric drive; 2 4-bladed props; 2,200 shp (1,600 sust.)—550-hp bow-thruster
Electric: 1,500 kVA from main generators + 265-kw emergency set
Range: 3,000/11 + 6,480/3 **Fuel:** 834 tons **Endurance:** 98 days
Crew: 6 officers, 6 petty officers, 19 junior enlisted + 15 technicians

Remarks: 1,472 grt/786 dwt. Built as an ocean surveillance ship to tow a long linear passive hydrophone array and placed in reserve by the U.S. Navy on 30-11-95, A 522 was transferred 9-12-96 as Grant-Aid for use as a hydrographic survey ship to replace *Almeida Carvalho;* she was recommissioned 28-2-97 and was in refit and conversion through mid-1998 in Portugal. A 523 was transferred 28-10-99 and recommissioned 26-1-00; the ship is employed primarily for oceanographic research.
Hull systems: Have a flat-chine hullform without bilge keels. Have passive tank roll stabilization. Originally intended to conduct 60- to 90-day patrols and to be at sea 292 days per year, they have outstanding endurance and recreational facilities for crews but are considered to be rough-riding vessels during the winter months in higher latitudes. Main-engine motor/generator sets also supply ship's service power.

AUXILIARIES *(continued)*

Mission systems: The UQQ-2 SURTASS (Surveillance Towed Array Sensor) was removed prior to transfer, as was the WSC-6 satellite communications system. Are now equipped with survey and oceanographic sensors, wet and dry laboratories, a chartroom, a survey launch, new cranes, and space to accept a portable container.

♦ 2 Andromeda-class hydrographic survey ships [AGS]
Bldr: Arsenal do Alfeite

	Laid down	L	In serv.
A 5203 Andromeda	1984	12-12-85	1-2-87
A 5205 Auriga	6-84	1986	1-7-87

Andromeda (A 5203) H&L Van Ginderen, 8-97

D: 230 tons (270 fl) **S:** 12 kts **Dim:** 31.50 (28.00 pp) × 7.74 × 2.50
Electronics: Radar: 1 Racal-Decca RM 914C nav.
M: 1 MTU 12V396 TC 82 diesel; 1 prop; 1,200 bhp (1,030 sust.)
Electric: 160 kw (1 × 100-kw diesel set, 1 × 60-kw shaft generator)
Range: 1,100/12; 1,980/10 **Fuel:** 35.5 tons **Crew:** 3 officers, 14 enlisted

Remarks: Intended to replace the U.K. Bay-class survey ship *Alfonso de Albuquerque* (A 526), stricken in 1983. Also used for oceanographic research. A 5205 carries a Phantom S2 remotely piloted submersible and a Klein towed side-scan sonar.

♦ 1 U.K. Rover-class oiler [AO] Bldr: Swan Hunter, Hebburn-on-Tyne

	Laid down	L	In serv.
A 5210 Bérrio (ex-*Blue Rover,* A 270)	18-1-69	11-11-69	15-7-70

Bérrio (A 5210) Maritime Photographic, 4-00

D: 4,763 tons light (11,585 fl) **S:** 19.25 kts (17 sust.)
Dim: 140.62 (131.07 pp) × 19.26 × 7.14
A: 2 single 20-mm 70-cal. Oerlikon Mk 7A AA
Electronics:
Radar: 1 Kelvin-Hughes Type 1006 nav.; 1 Decca TM 1226 nav.; 1 Decca 1229 nav.
M: 2 Crossley-Pielstick 16 PA4 diesels; 1 CP prop; 15,360 bhp—bow-thruster
Electric: 2,720 kw tot. (8 × 340-kw diesel sets)
Range: 14,000/15 **Fuel:** 965 tons heavy oil + 123 tons diesel
Crew: 7 officers, 11 petty officers, 36 ratings

Remarks: 7,513 grt/7,042 dwt. Purchased and transferred 31-3-93. Sisters operate in Indonesian and British service.
Hull systems: Has 13 cargo tanks totaling 8,155 m^3 and one 387-m^3 dry cargo hold. Cargo capacity includes 4,500 tons of fuel, 460 tons of aviation fuel, 325 tons of water, 10 tons of lube oil, 120 tons of stores, and 25 tons of munitions. Has a helicopter deck but no hangar. Re-engined in 1973–74. Has two stern anchors.

♦ 1 lighthouse tender and seagoing tug [ATA]
Bldr: Arsenal do Alfeite

	Laid down	L	In serv.
A 521 Schultz Xavier	2-70	1972	14-7-72

D: 900 tons (fl) **S:** 14 kts **Dim:** 56.1 × 10.0 × 3.8
M: 2 diesels; 1 prop; 2,400 bhp **Range:** 3,000/12.5
Crew: 4 officers, 50 enlisted

Schultz Xavier (A 521) H&L Van Ginderen, 3-91

♦ 1 ex-German Horst Wessel–class sail-training ship [AXT]
Bldr: Blohm + Voss, Hamburg

	L	In serv.
A 520 Sagres (ex-*Guanabara,* ex-*Albert Leo Schlageter*)	30-10-37	1-2-38

Sagres (A 520) A. D. Baker III, 6-00

D: 1,725 tons (1,940 fl) **S:** 10.5 kts (18 under sail)
Dim: 90.00 (75.90 hull; 70.40 pp) × 11.90 × 5.30
A: 2 single 47-mm saluting guns **Electronics:** Radar: 2 Decca . . . nav.
M: 2 MTU 12V183 TE92 diesels; 1 prop; 750 bhp—sail area: 2,355 m^2 max.
Range: 5,450/7.5 (under power) **Crew:** 12 officers, 150 enlisted + . . . cadets

Remarks: Acquired by the U.S. Navy as war reparations in 1945; was sold to Brazil in 1948 and then to Portugal in 1962, commissioning 2-2-62. Height of mainmast: 43.3 m. Sisters are U.S. Coast Guard's *Eagle,* Romania's *Mircea,* Germany's *Gorch Fock,* and Russian merchant training vessel *Tovarisch.* Was refitted and the hull renewed at Arsenal do Alfeite 2-87 to 1988 and again refitted in 1991–92, when she was also re-engined.

♦ 1 sail-training schooner [AXT]
Bldr: . . . . . ., Lisbon (In serv. 1937)

UAM 201 Creoula

D: 818 tons (1,055 fl) **S:** . . . kts **Dim:** 67.4 × 9.9 × 4.2
M: 1 MTU 8V183 TE92 diesel; 1 prop; 480 bhp **Crew:** . . .

Remarks: Former four-masted Grand Banks fishing schooner, acquired in 1976 as a museum by the Portuguese Department of Fisheries; turned over to the navy and commissioned for active seagoing training in 1987. Refitted and re-engined in 1992, when accommodations were also improved.

AUXILIARIES *(continued)*

Creoula (UAM 201) H&L Van Ginderen, 9-91

SERVICE CRAFT

Note: UAM stands for *Unitad Auxiliaria da Marinha* (Naval Auxiliary Unit). Harbor patrol boats with UAM-series pennant numbers are listed above under patrol boats.

♦ 2 environmental protection launches [YAG]
Bldr: Aqua-Guard, Vancouver, Canada (In serv. 1994)

UAM 886 Vazante UAM 688 Enchente

D: 14 tons (fl) **S:** 10 kts **Dim:** 8.84 × 3.00 × 0.96
M: . . . diesels; . . . props; . . . bhp **Range:** 60/5 **Crew:** 2 tot.

Remarks: Bought through the European Community ENVIREG (Environmental Regulation) program and used in the Lisbon area. Transport floating pollution barriers and can extract debris from the water.

♦ 1 sailing frigate relic [YAG]
Bldr: . . . (In serv. . . .)

Dom Fernando II e Glória

Remarks: Nineteenth-century sailing frigate, rehabilitated at Aveiro and maintained by the navy at the Portuguese Naval Museum after exhibition at the Universal Expo 98 world fair.

♦ 2 miscellaneous ammunition lighters [YE]

UAM 304 Marateca UAM 305 Mouro

Mouro (UAM 305) H&L Van Ginderen, 3-91

♦ 1 yacht/tender [YFL] Bldr: Halmatic, U.K. (In serv. 10-84)

UAM 901 Alva

D: 6.5 tons (fl) **S:** 20 kts **Dim:** 10.62 (9.37 wl) × 3.50 × 0.84
M: 2 Volvo TAMD 60C diesels; 2 props; 420 bhp

Remarks: GRP construction. Based at Lisbon and used as commander-in-chief's yacht. Carries 12 passengers.

Alva (UAM 901) H&L Van Ginderen, 3-91

♦ 9 miscellaneous harbor personnel transports [YFL]

UAM 907 Coura	UAM 910 Tamega	UAM 913 Zezere
UAM 908 Paiva	UAM 911 Tua	UAM 915 Nabão
UAM 909 Sorraia	UAM 912 Vascão	UAM 916 Muge

Coura (UAM 907)—*Paiva* (UAM 908) is identical Bernard Prézelin, 3-98

Remarks: Attached to the Lisbon Naval Base. The Portuguese Air Force also operates at least one personnel ferry, F-A 1, in the Lisbon area.

♦ 3 miscellaneous personnel launches [YFL]

UAM 831 Tainha UAM 905 Caia UAM 906 Corgo

Remarks: Employed as flag officers' barges at Lisbon. UAM 831 was completed 6-12-93.

♦ 2 dockyard service craft [YFL]

UAM 851 Cordoaria UAM 853 Romeira

Remarks: Attached to the Arsenal do Alfeite. No data available.

♦ 1 aquarium service craft [YFL]

UAM 852 Albacora II

Albacora II (UAM 852) H&L Van Ginderen, 6-00

Remarks: Attached to the Vasco da Gama Aquarium *(Aquário Vasco da Gama)*. No data available.

♦ 1 catamaran river navigational aids tender [YGL]
Bldr: San Jacinto, Aveiro (In serv. 30-1-85)

UAM 676 Guia

D: 70 tons **S:** 8.5 kts **Dim:** 22.0 × 7.9 × 2.2
M: 1 Deutz SBA 6M 816U diesel; 1 Schottel prop; 350 bhp—1 Harbor Master 50 F76 maneuvering unit (3.5 kts)

Remarks: Subordinated to the Lighthouse Service *(Direcção de Faróis)*.

SERVICE CRAFT *(continued)*

Guia (UAM 676) Mike Louagie, 3-91

♦ 6 miscellaneous navigational aids tenders [YGL]

UAM 675 Berlenga
UAM 677 Esteiro
UAM 678 Bugio
UAM 679 Giralta
UAM 681 São Vicente
UAM 780 Santa Maria II

Navigational aids tender Esteiro (UAM 677) Leo Van Ginderen, 1-01

♦ 3 Coral-class inshore survey/lighthouse tenders [YGS]

UAM 801 Coral
UAM 802 Atlanta (ex-*Hidra*)
UAM 805 Fisália

Remarks: GRP construction. Are 36 tons (fl). Launched in 1980. UAM 805 has a larger, glassed-in cabin forward of the pilothouse. No other data available.

Disposal note: Inshore lighthouse tender/survey craft *Savel* (UAM 630), *Actinia* (UAM 803), and *Sicandra* (UAM 804) were stricken during 2000.

♦ 28 miscellaneous port lifeboats [YH]

UAM 650 Aguda
UAM 651 Almirante Jaime Afreixo
UAM 652 Almirante Ferreira do Amaral
UAM 655 Commandante Couceiro
UAM 656 Patrão Ezequiel Seabra
UAM 657 Gomes de Amorim
UAM 658 Nossa Senhora de Conceição
UAM 659 Patrão António Faustino
UAM 660 Patrão Quirino Lopes
UAM 661 Patrão Rabumba
UAM 662 Patrão Chalandra
UAM 663 Rainha Don Amélia
UAM 664 Rei Don Carlos I
UAM 665 Santa Maria
UAM 667 Patrão António Simóes
UAM 668 Patrão João Rangel
UAM 669 Vila Chã
UAM 670 Patrão Henrique Faleiro
UAM 671 Patrão Cesar Martins
UAM 672 Patrão João da Silva
UAM 673 Patrão Joaquim Casaca
UAM 674 Patrão Joaquim Lopes
UAM 682 Patrão Arnaldo dos Santos
UAM 685 Patrão José André dos Santos
UAM 689 Rainha D. Amelia
UAM 690 Patrão Moisés Macatrão
UAM 691 Nossa Senhora da Boa Viagem
UAM 692 Duque da Ribeira

Remarks: Subordinated to the Naval Rescue Service *(Instituto de Socorros a Náufragos)*. Painted white and orange and have *"Salva-Vidas"* (Life-Saving) on the side. UAM 690 was completed 18-4-97: built of GRP, she displaces 11.12 tons, can achieve 21 kts (18 sust.), is 13.5 (11.8 pp) × 3.8 × 0.62, and is based at Ribeira da Foz. UAM 689, UAM 690, UAM 691 (in serv. 1997), and UAM 692 (in serv. 17-5-98) are 17 m long and have a 350-bhp diesel engine. No further data available.
Disposals: *Sota Patrão António Crista* (UAM 666) had been discarded by 1-01.

Patrão Cesar Martins (UAM 671) Guy Schaeffer, via Paolo Marsan, 9-98

Patrão Moisés Macatrão (UAM 690)—UAM 691 and UAM 692 are sisters
Guy Schaeffer, via Paolo Marsan, 9-98

♦ 1 accommodations barge [YPB]

UAM 854 Barrocas

Remarks: Attached to the Arsenal do Alfeite. No data available.

♦ 1 ex-U.S. Army Design 3004 medium harbor tug [YTM]

Bldr: . . . . . . (In serv. 1954)

UAM 914 Nisa (ex-RB 2, ex-ST 1996)

D: 100 tons light (122 fl) **S:** 12 kts **Dim:** 21.31 × 5.94 × 2.50
M: 1 diesel; 1 prop; 600 bhp
Range: 3,500/12 **Fuel:** 15 tons **Crew:** 6 tot.
Remarks: Transferred 2-3-62. Sister RB 1 was stricken in 1984.

♦ 1 sail-training sloop [YTS]

A 5201 Vega (ex-*Arreda*)

D: 60 tons **S:** . . . **Dim:** 19.8 × 4.3 × 2.5

♦ 1 sail-training yacht [YTS]

A 5204 Polar (ex-*Anne Linde*)

Polar (A 5204) Carlo Martinelli, 7-96

SERVICE CRAFT *(continued)*

D: 70 tons **S:** . . . **Dim:** 22.9 × 4.9 × 2.5

Remarks: Acquired in trade for the large sail-training ship *Sagres I,* now a museum ship at Hamburg. Both A 5204 and *Vega* (A 5201) have Raytheon commercial navigational radar sets.

♦ 3 Rodman 700–class seamanship training craft [YXT]
Bldr: Rodman Polyships, Vigo, Spain (In serv. 1996)

UAM . . . Mindelo UAM . . . Cacheu UAM . . . Niassa

D: 2 tons **S:** 22 kts **Dim:** 6.98 × 2.80 × 0.70
M: 1 Volvo Penta AQAD 40 diesel; 1 prop; 130 bhp
Range: . . ./. . . **Fuel:** 200 liters **Crew:** . . . tot.

Remarks: Acquired for the naval school to teach trainees from Portuguese-speaking African nations. GRP construction.

♦ 1 Chinese-style motor lorcha [YXT]
Bldr: . . ., Macao (In serv. 1988)

UAM 202 Macau

Macau (UAM 202)—the only Chinese junk in a NATO navy *Ships of the World,* 1995

D: approx. 200 tons (fl) **S:** . . . kts **Dim:** 34.10 (26.5 wl) × 6.6 × 3.6
M: 1 diesel; 1 prop; . . . bhp—auxiliary sails

Remarks: Wooden-construction, modified Chinese junk used for training and administrative duties at Macao. Painted chocolate brown, with yellow-ocher upperworks.

Note: The Portuguese Customs Brigade *(Brigada Fiscal)* operates a considerable number of small harbor launches without fixed armament. To replace older units, a dozen 45-kt, 16.36-m, GRP construction launches were ordered from CONAFIL, Vila Real de Santo Antonio, early in 2000, with deliveries having started during 9-00.

QATAR

State of Qatar

Personnel (2002): Approx. 1,800 total, including the marine police

Bases: Principal base at Doha, with a small facility at Halul Island

Maritime Aviation: Eight Agusta-built SH-3D Sea King helicopters of the Air Force's No. 8 Squadron are in service for search-and-rescue duties; of these, two are equipped to launch AM 39 Exocet missiles. Twelve Air Force Mirage F.1EDA and two F.1DDA can also launch AM 39 Exocets.

Coastal Defense: There are two truck-mounted batteries of MM 40 Exocet antiship missiles, with four missiles per truck.

Note: Ship names are prefixed by QENS (Qatari Emiri Navy Ship).

CORVETTES [FFL]

Note: Initial plans are being made for the acquisition of two 1,400-ton air-defense corvettes to be used in protecting offshore gas fields; funds are currently unavailable, however.

GUIDED-MISSILE PATROL CRAFT [PTG]

♦ 4 Vita class Bldr: Vosper Thornycroft, Portchester, U.K.

	L	In serv.		L	In serv.
Q 04 Barzan	1-4-95	9-5-96	Q 06 Al Udeid	21-3-96	16-12-96
Q 05 Huwar	15-7-95	6-6-96	Q 07 Al Debeel	31-8-96	3-7-97

Huwar (Q 05) French Navy, 1998

Al Debeel (Q 07)—with *Al Udeid* (Q 06) in background Vosper Thornycroft, 1997

D: 376 tons light (480 fl) **S:** 38 kts (35 sust.)
Dim: 56.50 (52.00 wl) × 9.00 (8.2 wl) × 2.25 (hull; 2.50 max.)
A: 4 MM 40 Exocet SSM; 1 76-mm 62-cal. OTOBreda SuperRapid DP; 1 6-round Sadral point-defense SAM syst. (Mistral missiles); 1 30-mm Goalkeeper SGE-30 CIWS; 2 single 12.7-mm mg
Electronics:
Radar: 1 Kelvin-Hughes Type 1007 nav.; 1 Thales MRR 3-D surf./air search; 1 Thales Sting gun f.c.; 1 Thales Goalkeeper f.c.
EW: Thales DR-3000S1 Compact intercept (1–18 GHz); Dassault Salamandre jammer; 1 330- to 340-round Matra Défense Dagaie decoy RL
E/O: Thales IRSCAN surveillance and tracking
M: 4 MTU 20V538 TB93 diesels; 4 props; 18,800 bhp (15,020 sust.)
Electric: 780 kw tot. (3 × 260-kw Stansfield alternators, 3 MWM TB234V-8 diesels driving—412 bhp each)—135-kw emergency set
Range: 1,800/12 **Fuel:** 44 tons **Crew:** 7 officers, 24 enlisted, 4 trainees

Remarks: Design derived from Vosper Thornycroft's "Vita" concept. Ordered 4-6-92. First two departed for Qatar 18-7-97, the second pair 30-4-98.
Hull systems: Have accommodations for a total of 47 personnel. Equipped with fin stabilizers.
Combat systems: Have the Thales SEWACO-FD combat data system. The Sting radar gun director has radar and television sensors. Employ C.S. Défense Sidewinder EW suite control system, and use the Thorn-EMI shipboard data distribution system. The MRR radar operates in G band and is used for close- and medium-range target detection and designation.

♦ 3 French Combattante III class Bldr: CMN, Cherbourg

	Laid down	L	In serv.
Q 01 Damsah	6-5-81	17-6-82	10-11-82
Q 02 Al Ghariyah	26-8-81	23-9-82	10-2-83
Q 03 Rbigah	27-10-81	22-12-82	11-5-83

Damsah (Q 01) CMN, 1982

D: 395 tons (430 fl) **S:** 38.5 kts
Dim: 56.00 (53.00 pp) × 8.16 × 2.15 (hull; 2.50 max.)
A: 8 MM 40 Exocet SSM; 1 76-mm 62-cal. OTOBreda Compact DP; 1 twin 40-mm 70-cal. OTOBreda AA; 2 twin 30-mm 75-cal. Emerlec EX-30 AA
Electronics:
Radar: 1 Decca 1226 nav.; 1 Thales Pollux search; 1 Thales Castor-II gun f.c.
EW: Racal Cutlass intercept; 1 330- to 340-round Matra Défense Dagaie decoy RL
M: 4 MTU 20V538 TB93 diesels; 4 props; 19,300 bhp (15,020 sust.)
Range: 2,000/15 **Crew:** 6 officers, 41 enlisted

GUIDED-MISSILE PATROL CRAFT [PTG] *(continued)*

Remarks: Ordered 10-80. Very similar in appearance and equipment to the three Nigerian units of the class. Arrived at Doha in 7-83. Refitted 1996–98.
Combat systems: Have the Thales Vega weapons-control system, with two Matra Défense Panda optical backup gun directors. During planned refits, the 30-mm AA are to be replaced by two Simbad twin launchers for Mistral infrared-homing SAMs and the intercept array is to be replaced by the Thales DR-3000 system.

PATROL CRAFT [PC]

Note: Although a letter of agreement was signed on 16-11-96 with Vosper Thornycroft, U.K., for the construction of two 46-m patrol craft, lack of funds and later offers from other shipyards have prevented a final contract from being signed to date.

♦ **4 Vosper 103-foot class** Bldr: Vosper Thornycroft, Portchester, U.K.

	In serv.		In serv.
Q 13 That Assuari	3-10-75	Q 15 Fateh al Khatab	22-1-76
Q 14 Al Wussail	28-10-75	Q 16 Tariq	1-3-76

That Assuari (Q 13)—with a sister in the background L. V. Bonneau, 2001

D: 120 tons (fl) **S:** 27 kts **Dim:** 32.40 (31.10 pp) × 6.30 × 1.60 (hull)
A: 1 twin 30-mm 75-cal. Oerlikon GCM-A03-2 AA; 1 single 20-mm 70-cal. Oerlikon AA
Electronics: Radar: 1 Decca 1226 nav.
M: 2 Paxman Ventura 16RP200 diesels; 2 props; 6,250 bhp **Crew:** 25 tot.

Remarks: Were to have been retired upon arrival of the new Vita-class missile craft but were still active as of early 2001. Sisters *Barzan* (Q 11) and *Huwar* (Q 12) were stricken in 1996. The original twin 30-mm gunmounts were replaced by single 20-mm mounts during early 1990s refits but had been restored by 2001. Probably can no longer make the indicated maximum speed.

PATROL BOATS [PB]

♦ **up to 3 Polycat 1450 class**
Bldr: Damen, Gorinchem, the Netherlands (In serv. 1980)

Q 31 series

D: 18 tons (fl) **S:** 26 kts **Dim:** 14.5 × 4.7 × 1.5
A: 1 12.7-mm mg **Electronics:** Radar: 1 Decca . . . nav.
M: 2 G.M. Detroit Diesel 12V71 TI diesels; 2 props; 1,300 bhp
Range: 650/20 **Crew:** 11 tot.

Remarks: Ordered 2-83. GRP construction. Of the original six, one was out of service in 1997 and two more by 1999.

♦ **up to 12 Spear-class craft Mk I and Mk II launches**
Bldr: Fairey Marine, Hamble, U.K. (In serv. 1974–77)

From among Q 71 through Q 95

D: 4.3 tons **S:** 26 kts **Dim:** 9.1 × 2.8 × 0.8
A: 3 single 7.62-mm mg **M:** 2 diesels; 2 props; 290 bhp **Crew:** 4 tot.

Remarks: Thirteen others had been cannibalized or discarded by 1999.

SERVICE CRAFT

♦ **1 logistics landing craft [YFU]** Bldr: . . . , Singapore (In serv. 1987)

Rabha

D: . . . **S:** 9–10 kts **Dim:** 48.8 × . . . × . . .
M: 2 diesels; 2 props; . . . bhp

Remarks: Reportedly capable of transporting three tanks and 110 troops.

♦ **1 inshore survey craft**
Bldr: . . . . . . (In serv. 2000)

Mukhtabar Albihar

Note: The marine police, with a total of about 800 personnel, operate nine patrol boats:

- **3 M 160 class** (In serv. 12-96): 19 tons (fl), 24 kts, 1 12.7-mm mg
- **4 MV 45 class** (In serv. 1989): 17 tons (fl), 32 kts, 2 single 7.62-mm mg
- **2 P 1200 class** (In serv. 1980): 12.7 tons (fl), 29 kts, 2 single 7.62-mm mg

There is also a customs service patrol launch force.

Qatari Marine Police M 160–class patrol boat Halmatic, 12-96

LA RÉUNION

French Overseas Department

POLICE

PATROL BOATS [WPB]

♦ **1 ex-French Navy Type V 14**
Bldr: DCN, Lorient (In serv. 7-5-87)

Vétiver (ex-P 790)

D: 16 tons (20 fl) **S:** 20 kts **Dim:** 14.60 (13.20 wl) × 4.60 × 1.90 (1.20 hull)
A: 1 12.7-mm mg; 1 7.62-mm mg **Electronics:** Radar: 1 Decca 060 nav.
M: 2 Baudouin 12 F 11S diesels; 2 props; 800 bhp
Range: 360/18 **Crew:** 7 tot.

Remarks: Transferred to the local government at Mayotte in 1997 on completion of the new 32-m patrol boat *Jasmin* (P 723) for the French Navy for service at La Réunion. Has a plastic hull. Designed by DCN Cherbourg. Carries a rigid inflatable inspection dinghy on davits at the stern.

ROMANIA

Republic of Romania

Personnel (2000): 20,144 total (12,081 conscripts), including the IX Naval Division of regular Romanian Army troops, organized into two brigades, each with 10 battalions. The force total is planned to be reduced to around 8,200 by 2010. The Border Guard *(Granaceri)* has an additional 700 troops.

Organization: To be reorganized into two maritime commands and one riverine flotilla command by 2004. Command facilities will be at Bucharest, with the maritime flotillas coming under two territorial divisions. Separate fleet air commands and two antiaircraft defense units are to be disbanded.

Bases: Headquarters, principal base, and training facilities at Mangalia, with small combatants and naval aviation based at Constanta. On the Danube River system, the headquarters is at Giurgiu, with other facilities at Tulcea, Galati, and Sulina. Border guard bases are at Constanta and at Ursova on the Danube.

Naval Aviation: Six Soviet Mi-14PL Haze-A land-based ASW helicopters and six Romanian-built IAR-316 Alouette-III shipboard helicopters are in service, operated by the air force. Seventeen IAR-330L Puma helicopters are assigned to the search-and-rescue role and carry the legend "Coast Guard" on their sides.

Naval Infantry: The 10,247-strong IX Naval Division incorporates two mechanized, one motorized, and one artillery brigade, with one air-defense regiment, an antitank battalion, and a reconnaissance battalion. Equipment includes 138 artillery pieces, 120 TR-580 heavy tanks, and 208 armored personnel carriers.

Coastal Defense: There is one battalion of SS-C-3 Styx truck-mounted antiship missiles and 10 battalions with towed 130-mm guns; these are subordinated to the IX Naval Division of the Romanian Army.

Programs: A 20-year program was instituted in 2000 to enable the Romanian Navy to operate more effectively with the NATO navies. Useful ships are to be overhauled and modernized and older ones retired, but as yet there is no discussion of new construction. The destroyer *Marasesti,* the frigates, and some auxiliaries are to be fitted for receiving underway replenishment; GPS navaids are to be acquired; Inmarsat terminals will be placed aboard *Marasesti* and the frigates; new HF, VHF, and UHF voice and continuous-wave communications gear is to be added, allowing better coordination with the Romanian Air Force; and Global Maritime Distress (GMDSS) system gear is to be bought.

ATTACK SUBMARINES [SS]

♦ **1 Soviet Kilo class (Project 877E)** (Nonoperational)
Bldr: United Admiralty SY, St. Petersburg (In serv. 12-86)

521 *Delfinul*

Delfinul (521) *Ships of the World,* 1998

D: 2,325 tons surf.; 2,450 tons with emergency fuel/3,076 tons sub.
S: 10 kts surf./17 kts sub.
Dim: 72.60 (70.0 wl) × 9.90 (12.80 over stern planes) × 6.60 (fwd; 6.20 mean)
A: 6 bow 533-mm TT (18 torpedoes or 24 mines); 1 Fasta-4 SAM shoulder-launched SAM syst. (8 9K-32M Strela missiles)
Electronics:
Radar: 1 MRK-50 Tobol (Snoop Tray-2) nav./search
Sonar: MGK-400 Rubikon (Shark Gill) LF active/passive suite; passive hull array; MG-519 Arfa (Mouse Roar) HF active classification/mine avoidance; MG-553 sound-velocity measuring; MG-512 cavitation detection
EW: Brick Pulp or Squid Head intercept; 6701E (Quad Loop) D/F
M: 2 Type 4-2DL42M diesel generator sets (1,825 bhp/1,500 kw at 700 rpm), electric drive: 1 motor; 1 6-bladed prop; 5,900 shp—1 130-shp low-speed motor—2 low-speed maneuvering motors; 2 ducted props; 204 shp (3 kts)
Range: 6,000/7 snorkel; 400/3 sub. **Fuel:** 172 tons **Endurance:** 45 days
Crew: 12 officers, 41 enlisted

Remarks: Named for Romania's first submarine, which was commissioned in 1936. Is said to be in need of a major overhaul and has not been operational since at least mid-1996.
Hull systems: Propulsion plant is suspended for silencing. Hull has 32% reserve buoyancy at 2,350 m^3 surfaced displacement. At rest on the surface, the submarine trims down 0.4 m by the bow. Maximum diving depth is 300 m, normal depth 240 m, and periscope depth 17.5 m. Has an anechoic hull coating. Two batteries, each with 120 cells, provide 9,700 kwh. Hull has six watertight compartments.
Combat systems: The combat system, designated Murena or MVU-110EM, can conduct two simultaneous attacks while tracking three other targets manually. The SAM launch position is located in after portion of the sail. Weapons carried can include Type E-53 wire-guided, E-53-60 and E-53-85 wake-homing, and E-53-67 acoustic homing torpedoes and KMD-500, KMD-1000, KMD-II-500, KMD-II-1000, and UMD mines.

DESTROYERS [DD]

♦ **1 Muntenia class** Bldr: Santierul Naval 2 Mai, Mangalia

	Laid down	L	In serv.
111 Marasesti (ex-*Muntenia*)	1979	4-81	5-8-85

Marasesti (111) Antonio Pintos, 7-95

Marasesti (111) Carlo Martinelli, 11-95

D: 5,400 tons (5,790 fl) **S:** 27 kts **Dim:** 144.60 (139.00 pp) × 14.80 × 4.90 (hull)
A: 4 twin P-20/21 Termit (SS-N-2C Styx) SSM launchers; 2 twin 76.2-mm 59-cal. AK-726 DP; 4 single 30-mm 54-cal. AK-630 gatling AA; 2 quadruple SA-N-5 Grail SAM launchers (9K-32M Strela short-range missiles); 2 triple 533-mm TT (Russian 53-65 wake-homing torpedoes); 2 12-tubed RBU-6000 ASW RL; 2 IAR-316 Alouette-III helicopters; 1 IAR-330 Puma helicopter
Electronics:
Radar: 1 Nayada nav.; 1 MR-302 Rubka (Strut Curve) air/surf. search; 1 Garpun (Plank Shave) missile target desig.; 1 Fut-B (Hawk Screech) 76.2-mm gun f.c.; 2 MR-104 Rys' (Drum Tilt) 30-mm gun f.c.
Sonar: . . . MF hull-mounted search; . . . HF f.c.
EW: . . . intercept; 2 16-tubed PK-16 decoy RL
M: 4 6-cyl. diesels; 4 3-bladed props; 32,000 bhp
Range: . . ./. . . **Crew:** 25 officers, 245 enlisted

Remarks: Reportedly was laid down in 1981 and launched by 1983. Laid up in 6-88, shortly after completion, she may never have operated in her original configuration; major modifications were completed 15-8-92, after which she made several Mediterranean cruises. A planned second unit does not seem to have been laid down. The ship was offered for sale in 2-93 but remains in commission. Has elaborate flag/head-of-state accommodations. The original Romanian type designation, *Destrugator* (Destroyer), was changed to *Fregate* (Frigate) in 3-01. Based at Mangalia.
Hull systems: When advertised for sale, was said to be all-diesel, but one source indicates that she has two Russian boost gas turbines, and another says that there are four propeller shafts. Although much topweight was removed during post-completion modifications, she retains excess topweight.
Combat systems: During the reconstruction, the four twin antiship missile launchers were re-sited one deck lower and the original tower masts were replaced by lighter and lower lattice masts in order to improve stability; in addition, the two quintuple-tubed RBU-1200 ASW rocket launchers were replaced by RBU-6000 launchers mounted forward of the bridge. Combat systems are mostly autonomous, without a central combat control center. Four radomes of differing sizes for probable EW intercept antennas are mounted on the foremast; these replaced the original Bizan'-series (Watch Dog) arrays. The manned SAM launchers flank the base of the foremast. The Garpun (Plank Shave) antiship missile target designation radar has its antenna mounted on the foremast; the device can also be employed as a passive receiver for target emissions.
During the 2000–2020 program, is to be given GPS navigation gear, an underway replenishment capability, and new communications equipment (including Inmarsat SATCOM); the radar and sonar systems are to be integrated with a combat data system, using a locally developed system employing commercial computers running a Windows NT program.

FRIGATES [FF]

♦ **0 (+ 2) ex-U.K. Boxer-class (Type 22 Batch 2) ASW**
Bldrs: Swan Hunter (Shipbuilders) Ltd., Wallsend-on-Tyne

	Laid down	L	In serv.
. . . . . . (ex-*London,* F 95)	23-2-82	27-10-84	5-6-87
. . . . . . (ex-*Coventry,* F 98)	29-3-84	8-4-86	24-10-88

D: 4,250 tons (4,850 fl) **S:** 30 kts (18 on cruise engines)
Dim: 148.10 (140.00 pp) × 14.75 × 4.30 (hull; 6.00 max.)
A: 4–8 . . . SSM; 2 sextuple Sea Wolf GWS.25 Mod. 3 SAM syst.; 1 . . .-mm DP; 2 twin 30-mm 75-cal. Oerlikon GCM-A03-2 AA; 2 single 20-mm 90-cal. Oerlikon GAM-B01 AA; 2 triple 324-mm STWS.2 ASW TT; 1–2 . . . helicopters
Electronics:
Radar: 1 Kelvin-Hughes Type 1007 nav.; 1 Marconi Type 967M-968 surf./air search; 2 Marconi Type 911 f.c.
Sonar: Plessey Type 2016 hull-mounted (4.5–7.5 kHz)
EW: Racal UAA(2) intercept; DLB decoy RL syst. (4 6-round RL); Type 2070 towed torpedo decoy
M: COGAG: 2 Rolls-Royce Spey SM-1A gas turbines (18,770 shp each), 2 Rolls-Royce Tyne RM-1C gas turbines (5,340 shp each); 2 CP props; 48,220 shp max.
Electric: 4,000 kw (4 × 1,000-kw Paxman Valenta 12PA 200CZ diesel-driven sets)
Range: 7,000/18; 12,000/14 (one shaft) **Fuel:** 700 tons + 80 tons aviation fuel
Crew: 19 officers, 246 enlisted (accomm. for 320 tot.)

Remarks: Negotiations were under way during 9-01 for the purchase of these two ships, which would be given major refits prior to transfer; in addition, they would be fitted with a new combat data system, new antiship missiles, and a medium-caliber gun. Data above are for the ships in U.K. service. *London* was decommissioned 11-6-99, and *Coventry* was scheduled to be retired at the end of 2001.
Hull systems: Two auxiliary boilers and two 50-ton/day flash evaporators are installed. Water-displacement fuel tanks are used.
Combat systems: In U.K. service, had the CACS-1 data system, with 26 operators and 16 displays. Are NATO Link 11 and Link 14 compatible. The Type 275(2) jammers were deactivated or removed by the end of 2000.

♦ **2 Tetal-II class (Project 1048M)**
Bldr: Santierul Naval 2 Mai, Mangalia

	L	In serv.
264 Contre-Amiral Eustatiu Sebastian	1988	30-12-89
265 Contre-Amiral Horia Macellariu	1991	29-9-96

Contre-Amiral Eustatiu Sebastian (264) Cem D. Yaylali, 7-95

Contre-Amiral Horia Macellariu (265) Arsenalul Armatei, 1999

FRIGATES [FF] *(continued)*

D: 1,540 tons (1,660 fl) **S:** 24 kts **Dim:** 92.42 (89.40 pp) × 11.40 × 3.75
A: 1 twin 76.2-mm 59-cal. AK-176 DP; 2 single 30-mm 59-cal. AK-630 gatling AA; 2 twin, trainable 533-mm ASW TT; 2 12-tubed RBU-6000 ASW RL; 2 d.c. racks; 1 IAR-316B Alouette-III helicopter
Electronics:
Radar: 1 Nayada nav.; 1 MR-302 Rubka (Strut Curve) surf./air search; 1 MR-123 Vympel (Bass Tilt) f.c.
Sonar: hull-mounted MF search and HF f.c.; HF dipping sonar at stern
EW: 2 Bizan'-4 (Watch Dog) intercept (2–18 GHz); 2 16-tubed PK-16 decoy RL
M: 4 . . . diesels; 4 props; 17,612 bhp (13,140 sust.)
Electric: 700 kw tot. (4 × 175-kw diesel sets)
Range: 1,500/. . . **Endurance:** 10 days **Crew:** 7 officers, 70 enlisted

Remarks: Employ same hull and propulsion as the original Tetal-I variant but substitute a helicopter deck (with no hangar or haul-down system) for the after 76.2-mm gunmount and have improved weapons. The "M" in the project number stands for *Modernizata.* A planned third unit was reportedly laid down, but work seems to have been canceled. Are based at Constanta.
Combat systems: Although listed as being of the AK-630 model, the 30-mm gatling guns, which are mounted abreast the stack, may be of the lighter-weight AK-306 model. There are Kolonka-2 manned ringsight directors for the AK-230 AA mounts, and the 76.2-mm mount can be controlled locally. The MR-123 director can control the 76.2-mm and AK-630/306 gunmounts.

♦ 4 Tetal-I class (Project 1048)
Bldr: Santierul Naval 2 Mai, Mangalia

	L	In serv.
260 Amiral Petre Barbuneanu	1981	4-2-83
261 Vice-Amiral Vasile Scodrea	1982	3-1-84
262 Vice-Amiral Vasile Urseanu	1983	3-1-85
263 Vice-Amiral Eugeniu Rosca	1985	23-4-87

Amiral Petre Barbuneanu (260) Cem D. Yaylali, 9-98

Vice-Amiral Vasile Urseanu (262) Romanian Navy, 1995

D: 1,480 tons (1,600 fl) **S:** 24 kts **Dim:** 92.42 (89.40 pp) × 11.40 × 3.60
A: 2 twin 76.2-mm 59-cal. AK-726 DP; 2 twin 30-mm 65-cal. AK-230 AA; 4 twin 14.5-mm 93-cal. AA; 2 16-tubed RBU-2500 ASW RL; 2 twin, trainable 533-mm TT; 2 mine rails
Electronics:
Radar: 1 Nayada nav.; 1 MR-302 Rubka (Strut Curve) surf./air search; 1 Fut-B (Hawk Screech) f.c.; 1 MR-104 Rys' (Drum Tilt) f.c.
Sonar: . . . . . . hull-mounted MF
EW: 2 Bizan'-4 (Watch Dog) intercept (2–18 GHz); 2 16-tubed PK-16 decoy RL
M: 4 . . . . . . diesels; 4 props; 17,612 bhp
Electric: 700 kw tot. (4 × 175-kw diesel sets)
Range: 1,500/. . . **Endurance:** 10 days **Crew:** 7 officers, 70 enlisted

Remarks: "Tetal" is the NATO code name for this class, which is entirely of Romanian design. First unit was laid down in 1980; program was slowed by economic problems. Are operating undermanned, with as few as 7 officers, 7 warrant officers, and 37 enlisted. Romanian ship-type designation: *Fregate* (Frigate). All are based at Constanta.
Hull systems: Have also been reported as having four 3,250-bhp diesels.
Combat systems: The Fut-B (Hawk Screech) radar director for the 76.2-mm gunmounts has two associated manned target designators on the bridge wings. The MR 104 Rys' (Drum Tilt) radar director controls both 30-mm mounts, and Kolonka-1 ringsight backup directors are carried on platforms flanking the mast. The torpedo tubes can probably accommodate both antiship and antisubmarine torpedoes. Are planned to be updated with NATO-compatible communications and IFF systems, an E/O adjunct to the weapons-control system, and, possibly, improved weapons and other sensors.

GUIDED-MISSILE PATROL BOATS [PTG]

♦ 3 Soviet Tarantul I class (Project 1241E)
Bldr: Volodarskiy Zavod, Rybinsk

188 Zborul (In serv. 12-90)
189 Pescarusul (In serv. 12-91)
190 Lastunul (In serv. 12-91)

D: 385 tons light (455 fl) **S:** 43 kts
Dim: 56.10 (49.50 pp) × 10.20 (9.40 wl) × 2.14 (hull; 3.59 props)
A: 4 P-20/21 Termit (SS-N-2C Styx) SSM; 1 76.2-mm 59-cal. AK-176 DP; 1 4-round MTU-40S (SA-N-8) SAM syst. (12 9K-32M Strela missiles); 2 single 30-mm 54-cal. AK-630 gatling AA

Lastunul (190) Romanian Navy, 1995

Electronics:
Radar: 1 Kivach-2 nav.; 1 Garpun (Plank Shave) targeting; 1 MR-123 Vympel (Bass Tilt) f.c.
EW: 2 16-round PK-16 decoy RL
M: M-15E COGAG plant: 2 DMR-76 cruise gas turbines (4,000 shp each), 2 PR-77 boost gas turbines (12,000 shp each); 2 props; 32,000 shp
Electric: 500 kw tot. (2 × 200-kw, 1 × 100-kw diesel sets)
Range: 760/43; 1,400/13 **Fuel:** 50 tons (122,634 liters)
Endurance: 10 days **Crew:** 7 officers, 32 enlisted

Remarks: Romanian ship-type designation: *Nave Purtatoare de Racchete* (Missile-carrying Ship). Based at Mangalia.
Hull systems: Stainless-steel-alloy, seven-watertight-compartment hull with aluminum alloy superstructure, decks, and internal bulkheads. Very strongly constructed and rugged. Have difficulty maneuvering below 10 kts, due to small size of the rudders.
Combat systems: Do not have a combat system per se; each weapons system is independently controlled by analog computers, although there are backup control systems for each. Carry 152 ready-service rounds and can carry another 150 in reserve for the 76.2-mm gun, which can be operated in local mode as well as under director control. Normally carry two infrared-homing and two radar-homing antiship missiles. The Plank Shave radar can be used in the passive mode to determine target bearing. There is otherwise no intercept system other than a small MFD/F.

♦ 3 ex-Soviet Osa-I class (Project 205)
Bldr: Volodarskiy SY, Rybinsk (199: Santierul Naval 2 Mai, Mangalia)

	In serv.		In serv.
195 Vulturul	3-11-64	199 Albatrosul	25-2-81
198 Eretele	1-1-65		

Eretele (198) Romanian Navy, 1991

D: 171 tons (209.5 fl) **S:** 38.5 kts **Dim:** 38.60 × 7.60 × 1.80 (hull; 2.90 props)
A: 4 P-20/21 Termit (SS-N-2C Styx) SSM; 2 twin 30-mm 65-cal. AK-230 AA; 1 4-round SA-N-5/8 SAM syst. (4 9K-32M Strela missiles)
Electronics:
Radar: 1 Rangout (Square Tie) surf. search/target desig.; 1 MR-104 Rys' (Drum Tilt) gun f.c.
M: 3 M-503A2 diesels; 3 props; 12,000 bhp (8,025 sust.) **Electric:** 200 kw tot.
Range: 500/34; 750/25 **Endurance:** 5 days **Crew:** 4 officers, 24 enlisted

Remarks: Delivered new, except 199, which was assembled in Romania and replaced an earlier transferred unit. Romanian ship-type designation: *Vedete Purtatoare de Rachete* (Missile-carrying Boat). Sisters *Soimul* (194), *Uliul* (196), and *Acvila* (197) were cannibalized for spares in 1997–98.

TORPEDO BOATS [PT]

♦ **12 Naluca class** Bldr: Santierul Naval 2 Mai, Mangalia

	In serv.		In serv.
201 Naluca	19-5-79	207 Fulgerul	30-12-80
202 Smeul	25-10-79	208 Vintul	25-5-81
203 Viforul	14-1-80	209 Vulcanul	26-10-81
204 Vijelia	7-2-80	210 Furtuna	13-1-82
205 Viscolul	30-4-80	211 Trasnetul	15-6-82
206 Virtejul	1-9-80	212 Tornada	5-10-82

Vintul (208) Romanian Navy, 1995

D: 215 tons (fl) **S:** 38 kts **Dim:** 38.60 × 7.60 × 1.85 (hull)
A: 2 twin 30-mm 65-cal. AK-230 AA; 4 fixed 533-mm TT
Electronics:
Radar: 1 Baklan (Pot Drum) nav./surf. search; 1 MR-104 Rys' (Drum Tilt) f.c.
M: 3 M-503A2 diesels; 3 props; 12,000 bhp (8,025 sust.) **Electric:** 200 kw tot.
Range: 500/34; 750/25 **Endurance:** 5 days **Crew:** 4 officers, 18 enlisted

Remarks: Design is based on Osa class, essentially an Osa-I with torpedo tubes substituted for the missile launchers. NATO nickname for the class was "Epitrop." Romanian ship-type designation: *Vedete Torpiloare Mari* (Large Torpedo Boat). All are based at Mangalia, and some may be in reserve.

♦ **14 Chinese Huchuan-class (Project 834) semi-hydrofoils**
Bldrs: Dobreta SY, Turnu, and Santierul Naval 2 Mai, Mangalia
(In serv. 1973–83, 1988–90)

From among: 51 through 74, 320 through 325

Huchuan-class 67—on foil Romanian Navy, 1995

Huchuan-class 320—outboard three sisters Arsenalul Armatei, 1999

D: 37 tons (43 fl) **S:** 52 kts **Dim:** 22.50 × 6.26 (3.80 deck) × 1.15 (1.11 foiling)
A: 2 twin 14.5-mm 93-cal. Type 81 AA; 2 fixed 533-mm TT; 4 d.c. in tilt racks
Electronics: 1 Type 756 nav.
M: 3 Type L-12V-180 diesels; 3 props; 3,600 bhp **Electric:** 5.6 kw tot.
Range: 500/30 **Endurance:** 2 days **Crew:** 11 tot.

Remarks: Romanian ship-type designation: *Vedete Torpiloare Mici* (Small Torpedo Boat). Three others, built in China, were later deleted, as have been nine Romanian-built craft. 320–325 were completed 1988–90 by Santierul Naval 2 Mai, Mangalia. Sisters *Jupiter* and *Marte* had the torpedo tubes and hydrofoils removed and were assigned for use as search-and-rescue craft [YH]. All use Chinese-made, side-by-side, powered gunmounts. The diesel engines are a Chinese version of the Russian M-50F-4. All are based at Mangalia, and some of them may be in reserve.

MINE WARFARE SHIPS

♦ **2 Cosar-class minelayers [MM]**
Bldr: Santierul Naval 2 Mai, Mangalia

	In serv.
271 Vice-Amiral Ioan Murgescu	30-12-80
274 Vice-Amiral Constantin Balescu	16-11-81

Vice-Amiral Ioan Murgescu (271)—with helicopter deck aft
Romanian Navy, 1995

D: 1,450 tons (fl) **S:** 19 kts **Dim:** 79.0 × 10.6 × 3.6
A: 1 57-mm 70-cal. DP; 2 twin 30-mm 65-cal. AK-230 AA; 2 twin 14.5-mm 93-cal. Type 81 AA; 2 5-round RBU-1200 ASW RL; 2 mine rails (200 mines)
Electronics:
Radar: 1 Nayada nav.; 1 MR-302 Rubka (Strut Curve) surf./air search; 1 MR-103 Bars (Muff Cob) f.c.; 1 MR-104 Rys' (Drum Tilt) f.c.
Sonar: probable Tamir-11 (MG-11)-derivative hull mounted searchlight (25–30 kHz)
EW: 2 Bizan'-4 (Watch Dog) intercept (2–18 GHz)
M: 2 . . . . . . diesels; 2 props; 6,400 bhp **Crew:** 75 tot.

Remarks: "Cosar" is the NATO nickname. Romanian ship-type designation: *Puitoare de Mine* (Minelayer). Also useful as ASW escorts. Share the same hull as the oceanographic research ship *Grigore Antipa* and intelligence collection ship *Emil Racovita*.
Combat systems: The MR-105 radar/electro-optical director controls the semiautomatic 57-mm gun; the MR-104 radar f.c.s. controls the 30-mm AA, for which there are also Kolonka-1 backup ringsight directors on platforms on the lattice mast. There is a helicopter platform above the minelaying deck aft on 271, but it appears more intended for ceremonial functions than actual use by aircraft; on 274 there is reportedly a crane in its stead.

♦ **4 Musca-class oceangoing minesweepers [MSF]**
Bldr: Cala de Adocare, Mangalia

	Laid down	L	In serv.
24 Locotenant Remus Lepri	1984	. . .	23-4-87
25 Locotenant Lupu Dinescu	. . .	8-86	6-1-89
29 Locotenant Dimitrie Nicolescue	1985	. . .	7-12-89
30 Sublocotenant Alexandru Axente	. . .	. . .	7-12-89

Locotenant Remus Lepri (24)—with Bulgarian minesweeper *Iskar* (31) at right
French Navy, 1997

Locotenant Dimitrie Nicolescue (29) Romanian Navy, 1995

D: 710 tons (790 fl) **S:** 17 kts **Dim:** 60.80 (59.20 wl) × 9.50 × 2.70
A: 2 twin 30-mm 65-cal. AK-230 AA; 4 quadruple 14.5-mm 93-cal. AA; 2 4-round SA-N-5 SAM syst. (. . . 9K-32M Strela missiles); 2 5-round RBU-1200 ASW RL; 2 mine rails (50 mines)

MINE WARFARE SHIPS *(continued)*

Electronics:
Radar: 1 Nayada nav.; 1 Kivach nav.; 1 MR-104 Rys' (Drum Tilt) f.c.
Sonar: Tamir-11 (MG-11)-derivative hull-mounted HF searchlight
M: 2 . . . diesels; 2 props; 4,800 bhp **Range:** . . . **Crew:** 60 tot.

Remarks: Romanian ship-type designation: *Dragoare Maritime* (Seagoing Minesweeper). Steel-hulled. Carry an unusually large number of danbuoy swept channel markers and may have magnetic and acoustic sweep gear in addition to mechanical sweeping equipment. The point-defense SAM launchers are mounted abaft the forward 30-mm mount on the forecastle and just abaft the stack.

♦ **4 German M-40-class minesweepers [MSF]**
Bldr: Galati SY

	In serv.
13 Vice-Amiral Mihai Gavrilescu (ex-*Democratia*)	1954
14 Vice-Amiral Ioan Balanescu (ex-*Descatusaria*)	1954
15 Vice-Amiral Emil Grescescu (ex-*Desrobiriea*)	1955
16 Vice-Amiral Ioan Georgescu (ex-*Dreptatia*)	1956

Vice-Amiral Mihai Gavrilescu (13) Romanian Navy, 1995

D: 543 tons light; 637 tons std. (775 fl) **S:** 17 kts
Dim: 62.30 (57.60 pp) × 8.90 (8.50 wl) × 2.62
A: 2 twin and 1 single 37-mm 63-cal. AA; 2 twin 14.5-mm 93-cal. Type 81 AA; 2 4-round SA-N-5 SAM syst. (. . . 9K-32M Strela missiles); 2 5-round RBU-1200 ASW RL; 2 mine rails (50 mines)
Electronics:
Radar: 1 Don-2 nav.
Sonar: Tamir-11-derivative hull-mounted HF searchlight
M: 2 diesels; 2 props; 2,500 bhp
Range: 4,000/10 **Fuel:** 156 tons **Crew:** 80 tot.

Remarks: Begun for the German Navy as coal-burning, reciprocating-steam-powered ships. Launched postwar. Romanian ship-type designation: *Dragoare de Baza* (Base Minesweeper), indicating subsidiary status. Converted to burn fuel oil on completion. Modernized during 1976–83 with new superstructures, diesel engines in place of the original steam plant, and updated ASW ordnance. Retain their mechanical minesweeping equipment. None has been fitted with helicopter facilities.

Disposal note: Soviet-supplied T-301-class (Project 255) coastal minesweepers *Locotenant Alexandru Pompilian* (9), *Commodore Dumitry Lupascu* (17), *Commodore Vasile Toescu* (18), *Commodore Constantin Micoescu* (19), *Captain Adrian Vasiliu* (26), *Captain Constantin Istrate* (27), and *Captain Alexandru Constantinescu* (28) were retired during 1999–2000; sisters *Captain Constantin Dumitrescu* (4), *Locotenant Constantin Virtosu* (5), *Locotenant Gheorrghe Niculescu* (6), *Locotenant Moise Pauta* (7), and *Locotenant Nicolae Stoicescu* (8) were cannibalized and stricken between 1996 and 1998.

AUXILIARIES

♦ **1 ex-French Friponne-class general-purpose support ship [AG]**
Bldr: Brest Dockyard (In serv. 1920)

ND 113 Sublocotenant Ion Ghiculescu (ex-*Impatiente*)

D: 330 tons (443 fl) **S:** 12 kts **Dim:** 60.9 × 7.0 × 2.5
A: 1 37-mm 63-cal. AA; 2 twin 14.5-mm 93-cal. Type 81 AA; 2 5-round RBU-1200 ASW RL
Electronics:
Radar: 1 . . . nav.
Sonar: Tamir-11M (MG-11) searchlight-type hull-mounted HF
M: 2 Sulzer diesels; 2 props; 900 bhp
Range: 3,000/10 **Fuel:** 30 tons **Crew:** 50 tot.

Remarks: Modernized during the 1980s with streamlined superstructure, new armament, and so forth. Painted white. Sister *Dumitrescu* (ND 111, ex-*Friponne*) was stricken during the early 1980s, and *Lieutenant Commander Eugen Stihi* (ND 112, ex-*Mignonne*) had been retired by 1995, although the hull remains as a hulk at Constanta. Had been employed as a hydrographic survey ship, but now appears to be used primarily as a ceremonial vessel.

♦ **1 intelligence collection ship [AGI]**
Bldr: Drobeta Severin SY (In serv. 30-10-77)

Emil Racovita

D: 1,900 tons (fl) **S:** 11 kts **Dim:** 70.1 × 10.0 × 3.0
M: 1 diesel; 1 prop; 3,285 bhp **Crew:** 80 tot.

Remarks: Although designed as an oceanographic research ship, is used primarily as an intelligence collector. Based at Constanta. Other sources list this unit as a near-sister to the salvage and oceanographic research ship *Grigore Antipa* (q.v.).

♦ **2 Croitor-class small-combatant tenders [AGP]**
Bldr: Santierul Naval Braila, Braila

281 Constanta (In serv. 15-9-80) 283 Midia (In serv. 26-2-82)

Midia (283) H&L Van Ginderen, 8-99

Constanta (281) Guy Schaeffer, via Paolo Marsan, 6-01

D: 2,850 tons (fl) **S:** 16 kts **Dim:** 108.0 × 13.5 × 3.8
A: 1 twin 57-mm 70-cal. DP; 2 4-round SA-N-5 SAM syst (16 9K-32M Strela missiles); 2 twin 30-mm 65-cal. AK-230 AA; 2 twin 14.5-mm 93-cal. AA; 2 5-round RBU-1200 ASW RL; 1 IAR-316 Alouette-III helicopter
Electronics:
Radar: 1 Kivach nav.; 1 MR-302 Rubka (Strut Curve) surf./air search; 1 MR-103 Bars (Muff Cob) f.c.; 1 MR-104 Rys' (Drum Tilt) f.c.
Sonar: Tamir-11 (MG-11) derivative hull-mounted HF searchlight
EW: 2 Bizan'-series (Watch Dog) intercept (2–18 GHz)
M: 2 diesels; 2 props; 6,500 bhp **Crew:** 150 tot.

Remarks: "Croitor" is the NATO nickname. Have a helicopter hangar and flight deck aft. Crane forward of bridge tends the magazine for torpedoes and Termit-series antiship missiles. The SA-N-5 rack launchers are mounted atop the helicopter hangar.

♦ **1 Dolj-class general cargo ship [AK]**
Bldr: Santierul Naval Braila, Braila (L: 1977)

Albatros (ex-*Dej*)

D: 8,750 tons (fl) **S:** 16 kts (15.5 sust.)
Dim: 130.8 (121.21 pp) × 17.71 × 8.10 (max.; 6.60 normal)
Electronics: . . .
M: 1 Cegielski-Sulzer 5RD68 diesel; 1 prop; 6,100 bhp
Electric: 600 kw tot. (3 × 200-kw diesel sets)
Range: . . ./. . . **Fuel:** 1,148 tons heavy oil **Crew:** . . . tot.

Remarks: 4,399 grt/6,253 dwt. Acquired 6-95 from Intreprinderea de Exploratore a Floti Maritime NAVROM, Constanta. Has been largely inactive. Has an ice-strengthened hull, four holds, and five 3-ton cranes. Grain capacity is 11,980 m^3, bale capacity 11,067 m^3.

♦ **1 small seagoing tanker [AO]**
Bldr: Tulcea SY (In serv. 24-12-92)

TM 532

TM 532—note bulbous bow form French Navy, 8-96

D: 2,170 tons (fl) **S:** 16 kts **Dim:** 76.3 × 12.5 × 5.0
A: 1 twin 30-mm 65-cal. AK-230 AA; 2 twin 14.5-mm 93-cal. AA
Electronics: Radar: 1 . . . nav.
M: 2 diesels; 2 props; 4,800 bhp **Crew:** . . . tot.

Remarks: A second was reported under construction, but work may have halted for lack of funds, although the number 201 has been reported. Has one replenishment station per side. Cargo: 1,200 tons.

AUXILIARIES *(continued)*

♦ **2 coastal tankers [AO]**
Bldr: Santierul Naval Braila, Braila (In serv. 15-6-71)

TM 530 TM 531

D: 1,042 tons (fl) **S:** 12.5 kts **Dim:** 55.2 × 9.4 × 4.1
A: 1 37-mm 63-cal. AA; 2 single 12.7-mm mg
M: 2 diesels; 2 props; 1,800 bhp **Cargo:** 500 tons

♦ **1 submersible tender/salvage ship [ARS]**
Bldr: Cala de Adocare, Mangalia (In serv. 25-5-80)

Grigore Antipa

Grigore Antipa—white-painted and with no pennant number
Romanian Navy, 1995

D: 1,450 tons (fl) **S:** 19 kts **Dim:** 79.0 × 10.6 × 3.6
A: none **Electronics:** Radar: 1 Nayada nav.
M: 2 diesels; 2 props; 6,400 bhp **Crew:** 75 tot.

Remarks: Employs same hull and propulsion plant as the Cosar-class minelayers. Carries the SM358 manned salvage submersible at the stern and a submersible decompression chamber beneath a quadrantial gantry to starboard, aft. Equipped to lay a four-point mooring. Based at Constanta and may also be employed in intelligence collection. Painted white, with deck equipment in red. Has a commercial SATCOM terminal.

♦ **2 Grozavu-class ocean tugs [ATA]**
Bldr: Olteniza SY

RM 501 Grozavu (In serv. 29-6-93) RM 502 Hercules (In serv. 29-9-96)

Grozavu (RM 501) *Ships of the World,* 1998

D: 3,600 tons (fl) **S:** 12 kts **Dim:** 64.8 × 14.6 × 5.5
A: 1 twin 30-mm 65-cal. AK-230 AA; 4 twin 14.5-mm 93-cal. AA
M: 2 diesels; 2 props; 5,000 bhp **Crew:** . . .

Remarks: RM = *Remorcher de Mare* (Seagoing Tug). Also capable of salvage duties.

♦ **1 German Horst Wessel–class sail-training ship [AXT]**
Bldr: Blohm + Voss, Hamburg

	Laid down	L	In serv.
Mircea	15-4-38	22-9-38	29-3-39

D: 1,604 tons (fl) **S:** 12 kts (13 under sail)
Dim: 81.28 (67.84 o.a. hull; 62.80 wl) × 12.50 × 5.02
Electronics: Radar: 1 Decca 202 nav.; 1 Nayada nav.
M: 1 MaK 6M 451 AK diesel; 1 prop; 1,100 bhp—max. sail area: 5,739 m^2
Range: 5,000/13 (on sail and engine); 3,000/12 (engine alone)
Crew: 5 officers, 17 warrant officers, 38 enlisted + 120–140 cadets

Remarks: Three-masted bark. Fore- and mainmast are 44 m above the waterline, the mizzenmast 39 m. Can carry a total of 23 sails (4 jibs, 6 staysails, 10 square sails, and 3 gaff sails). Sister to U.S. Coast Guard *Eagle,* Russian merchant training vessel *Tovarisch,* German *Gorch Fock,* and Portuguese *Sagres.* Navigation equipment includes a Rumb-16 D/F loop, MEL-25 log, and DT-700 echo sounder. Refitted by builder, 1966–67. Based at Constanta.

Mircea H&L Van Ginderen, 1997

SERVICE CRAFT

♦ **4 degaussing tenders [YDG]**

	Bldr	In serv.
Automatice	Santierul Naval Braila, Braila	9-12-72
Electronica	Santierul Naval Braila, Braila	6-8-73
Energerica	Santierul Naval Braila, Braila	20-10-73
Magnetica	Santierul Naval 2 Mai, Mangalia	18-12-89

D: 160 tons (fl) **S:** 12.5 kts **Dim:** 38.0 × 5.5 × 1.4
A: 1 twin 14.5-mm 93-cal. AA; 2 single 12.7-mm 79-cal. mg
M: 1 diesel (800-bhp) generator set, electric motor; 1 prop; 600 shp

Remarks: *Magnetica* is larger: 299 tons (fl); 40.8 × 6.6 × 3.2 (molded depth). All are capable of providing deperming services to ships of up to 3,000 tons displacement.

♦ **1 commander-in-chief's yacht [YFL]**

Rindunica

Rindunica U.S. Navy, 1992

D: 40 tons (fl) **S:** 28 kts **Dim:** 24.0 × 5.0 × 1.1
Electronics: Radar: 1 . . . nav.
M: 2 M-50F-series diesels; 2 props; 2,200 bhp **Crew:** 6 tot.

♦ **1 Chinese Huchuan-class semi-hydrofoil rescue craft [YH]**
Bldr: Dobreta SY, Turnu (In serv. 14-1-80)

Jupiter

D: 39 tons (45 fl) **S:** 50 kts **Dim:** 22.50 × 6.26 (3.80 deck) × 1.15 (1.11 foiling)
A: 2 twin 14.5-mm 93-cal. Type 81 AA **Electronics:** 1 Type 756 nav.
M: 3 Type L-12V-180 diesels; 3 props; 3,600 bhp **Electric:** 5.6 kw tot.
Range: 500/30 **Crew:** 9 tot.

Remarks: Built as search-and-rescue craft. The diesel engines are a Chinese version of the Russian M-50F-4. Sister *Marte* had been stricken by 1996.

♦ **4 small fuel lighters [YO]**
Bldr: Braila SY (In serv. 1986–87)

MM 132 MM 133 MM 136 MM 137

D: 190 tons (fl) **S:** 10 kts **Dim:** 29.6 × 6.9 × 2.5
M: 2 Type 3D6 diesels; 2 props; 300 bhp Cargo: 80 tons

Remarks: Sister MM 131 was retired during 2001.

♦ **5 small harbor tugs [YTL]**

SRS 570 SRS 571 SRS 572 SRS 577 SRS 675

Tug SRS 570 French Navy, 9-94

Remarks: Carry one twin and one single 14.5-mm mg. No further data available.

DANUBE FLOTILLA

RIVER MONITORS [PM]

♦ **3 (+ 1) Mihail Kogalniceanu class (Project 1310)**
Bldr: Santierul Naval Turnu Severin, Mangalia (In serv. 1993–98)

45 Mihail Kogalniceanu (L: 19-12-93)
46 I. C. Bratianu (L: 28-12-94)
47 Lascar Catargiu (In serv. 1998)

Mihail Kogalniceanu (45) Romanian Navy, 1991

D: 474 tons (550 fl) **S:** 18 kts **Dim:** 62.00 × 7.60 × 1.60
A: 2 single 105-mm tank guns; 1 quadruple and 2 twin 14.5-mm 93-cal. AA; 2 4-round SA-N-5 SAM syst (16 9K-32M Strela missiles); 2 40-round 122-mm BM-21 artillery RL (. . . reloads)
Electronics: Radar: 1 Mius (Spin Trough) nav.
M: 2 . . . diesels; 2 props; 3,800 bhp **Crew:** 52 tot.

Remarks: Romanian ship-type designation: *Minitoare* (Monitor). Carry inspection dinghies on stern. The BM-21 rocket launchers retract within the superstructure for reloading. There are no mine rails. All are based at Braila. A fourth unit is said to be under construction.

♦ **5 Brutar-II class** Bldr: Santierul Naval 2 Mai, Mangalia

	In serv.		In serv.
176 Rahova	14-4-88	179 Posada	14-5-92
177 Opanez	24-7-90	180 Rovine	30-7-93
178 Smardan	24-7-90		

Rahova (176) Siegfried Breyer Collection

D: 370 tons (fl) **S:** 16 kts **Dim:** 50.7 × 8.0 × 1.5
A: 1 105-mm tank gun; 1 twin 23-mm AA; 2 quadruple and 2 twin 14.5-mm AA; 1 4-round SA-N-5 SAM syst. (. . . 9K-32M Strela missiles); 2 40-round 122-mm BM-21 artillery RL (. . . reloads); 2 mine rails (. . . mines)
Electronics: Radar: 1 . . . nav.
M: 2 diesels; 2 props; 2,700 bhp

Remarks: "Brutar" is the NATO nickname. Romanian ship-type designation: *Vedete Blindante Mari* (Large Armored Boat). Very low-lying craft, with armored tank turret and machinegun turrets. They are about 5 m longer than the *Grivita* (94) and also feature sloped armor on the sides in the region of the artillery rocket launchers, increasing their maximum beam by about 1 m. The BM-21 rocket launches are retracted into the hull for reloading. Four of the 14.5-mm mg mounts are mounted in twin armored turrets abreast the tank turret; the others are in standard Romanian open quadruple mountings. The mine rails are considerably longer than in the *Gravita*.

♦ **1 Brutar-I class**
Bldr: Santierul 2 Mai, Mangalia (In serv. 21-11-86)

94 Grivita

D: 320 tons (fl) **S:** 18 kts **Dim:** 45.7 × 8.00 × 1.5
A: 1 105-mm tank gun; 2 twin 14.5-mm 93-cal. AA; 2 4-round SA-N-5 SAM syst. (. . . 9K-32M Strela missiles); 2 40-round 122-mm BM-21 artillery RL; 2 mine rails (. . . mines)
Electronics: Radar: 1 . . . nav.
M: 2 M-50-series diesels; 2 props; 2,400 bhp

Remarks: Has virtually no superstructure but is equipped with two periscopes and a conning station forward of and below the armored turret. The BM-21 rocket launches are retracted into the hull for reloading.

♦ **18 VB 76 class** Bldr: Dulcea SY (In serv. 1974–77)

VB 76 Mr. Constantin Ene
VB 77 Mr. Gheorghe Sontu
VB 78 Cpt. Ganescu
VB 79 Cpt. Ion Grigore Nastase
VB 80 Cpt. Nicolae Lazar Bogdan
VB 81 Locotenant Bordeianu
VB 82 Locotenant Stanescu
VB 83 Locotenant Stoicescu
VB 84 Sublocotenant Elefterescu
VB 85 Sublocotenant Izvoranu
VB 86 Locotenant Alexandrescu
VB 87 Locotenant Dumitrescu
VB 88 Cpt. Marcineanu
VB 89 Locotenant Calinescu
VB 90 Mr. Ion
VB 91 Mr. Giurescu
VB 92 Cpt. Romano
VB 93 Locotenant Paraschivescu

VB 76–class Cpt. Ion Grigore Nastase (VB 79)—note monitor *Grivita* (94) in background at right; the ship has no identifiable pilothouse structure
Siegfried Breyer Collection

VB 76–class Cpt. Nicolae Lazar Bogdan (VB 80) Romanian Navy, 1991

D: 127 tons (fl) **S:** 17 kts **Dim:** 32.4 × 4.8 × 0.9
A: 1 76-mm low-angle; 2 twin 14.5-mm 93-cal. AA; 2 single 81-mm mortars
M: 2 diesels; 2 props; 1,700 bhp **Crew:** 25 tot.

Remarks: Romanian ship-type designation: *Vedeta Blindante Mici* (Small Armored Boat); the "VB" prefix is no longer painted on with the hull numbers. "Mr." is the Romanian contraction for "Major."

PATROL BOATS [PB]

♦ **3 U.S. 27-foot Vigilant class**
Bldr: Boston Whaler, Edgewater, Fla. (In serv. 4-93)

D: 2.27 tons light (4.0 fl) **S:** 36 kts **Dim:** 8.10 × 3.05 × 0.48
A: 1 7.62-mm mg **Electronics:** Radar: 1 Furuno . . . nav.
M: 2 Evinrude gasoline outboards; 450 bhp **Fuel:** 545 liters **Crew:** 3 tot.

Remarks: Transferred for use in enforcing the UN embargo against Serbia on the Danube. Foam-core GRP "unsinkable" hulls.

Note: A small, locally designed air-cushion vehicle [PBA] was completed for the Danube River Flotilla in 1998 by the shipyard at Mangalia; no data available.

MINE WARFARE CRAFT

♦ **25 river minesweepers [MSI]** Bldr: Turnu-Severin SY (In serv. 1975–84)

VD 141 through VD 165

River minesweeper VD 148—alongside a sister Romanian Navy, 1991

D: 97 tons (fl) **S:** 13 kts **Dim:** 33.3 × 4.0 × 0.89
A: 2 twin 14.5-mm 93-cal. Type 81 AA; 2 mine rails (6 mines)
Electronics: Radar: 1 Nayada nav. **M:** 2 diesels; 2 props; 870 bhp

Remarks: Resemble the VB 76–class monitors. Seven based at Galati, four at Giurgiu, three at Sulina, four at Tulcea, and seven at Turnu-Severin.

SERVICE CRAFT

♦ **1 headquarters ship [YAG]**

Republica

Remarks: A very old side-wheel paddle boat of about 300 tons (fl).

♦ **8 Braila-class vehicle ferries [YFB]** Bldr: Braila SY (In serv. 1967–70)

203 205 207 208 415 416 419 420

D: 240 tons (fl) **S:** 4 kts **Dim:** 38.3 × 8.9 × 1.0
M: 2 Type 3D 6 diesels; 2 props; 300 bhp

Remarks: Primarily employed carrying civilian vehicles and cargo on the river system. Were formerly numbered C 414 et seq. Have barge-like hulls with extendable bow vehicle ramps. There is a single cargo derrick and two smaller cranes. Engines and superstructure are aft. Can carry 160 tons of cargo.

DANUBE FLOTILLA SERVICE CRAFT *(continued)*

♦ 9 SM 165-class patrol/utility launches [YFL]

SM 161 through SM 169

D: 22 tons **S:** 12 kts **Dim:** 12.2 × 3.0 × 0.9

♦ 5 SD 200–class patrol/utility boats [YFL]

SD 270 SD 274 SD 275 SD 277 SD 278

♦ 3 accommodations barges [YPL]

IALOMITA OLTUL SIRETUL

Note: Also in service at the Danube River facilities at Turnu-Severin and at the naval base at Constanta are non-self-propelled barges of the *Tulcea* class: *Bega, Delta, Jiuz, Prahova, Siretul, Timis,* and *Tismana.* They are used for stores, berthing, and minor repair duties.

RUSSIA

Russian Federation

ROSIYSKIY VOENNOMORSKIY FLOT

Personnel (2002): 125,000 total. About 12,000 additional personnel are assigned to the Naval Forces of the Federal Border Guard Service, including seagoing and shore personnel; this already small force is to be reduced by 8,500. In 5-91, a new organization called the "Coastal Force" was created to incorporate three understrength former Red Army motorized battalions transferred to the navy in 1990, the 12,100-man naval infantry, and the 400-strong Coastal Missile and Artillery Force (which was reduced from 7,000 during 2001). Of some 20,000 civilian employees, about 3,000 serve in seagoing positions in the Naval Auxiliary Service. On 1-11-01, it was announced that the Baltic Fleet would be cut from 35,000 to 30,000 personnel.

Organization and Bases: Naval headquarters is in Moscow. The headquarters for the Northern Fleet is at Severomorsk in the Kola Inlet, and other major ship bases in the Northern Fleet area are located at Gadzhgiyevo, Gremikha, Nerpich'ya Guba, Andreeva Guba, Bol'shaya Lopatka Guba, Mal'aya Lopatka Guba, Olenya Guba, Sayda Guba, Ara Guba, Pala Guba, Yokanga, Polyarnyy (not closed as had been previously planned), Murmansk (Rosta shipyard), and Arkhangel'sk (naval infantry). Late in 2000, mention began to be made of a separate "Kola Fleet" assigned to the protection of the Barents Sea and charged with protecting ships and submarines deploying beyond local waters, with its units based at Severomorsk and Polyarnyy. Pacific Fleet headquarters is at Vladivostok (which also has the major repair yards for the area), with major facilities at Petropavlovsk-na-Kamchatskiy and Sovetskaya Gavan and minor facilities at Komsomol'sk for the Amur River Flotilla; there are numerous detachments elsewhere in the area (the Magadan facility has been closed, and the major submarine base at Fokino, near Vladivostok, was to be closed in 2001). The Baltic Fleet headquarters is at Kaliningrad, with the principal bases at Bal'tiysk in the Kaliningrad oblast and at Kronshtadt Island, west of St. Petersburg; minor facilities are located at Lomonosov, Primorsk, and Vyborg. The former Leningrad Naval Base command was incorporated into the Baltic Fleet command structure during 1993. The Black Sea Fleet headquarters remains at Sevastopol', with smaller facilities at Novorossiysk (which is to be expanded) and at Temryuk. The Caspian Flotilla headquarters was removed to Astrakhan during 1992, but most ships are based at Makhachkala.

Russia continues to keep a ship on station in Syria, although its navy now only rarely appears in the Mediterranean. The formerly significant (but recently all-but-abandoned) Russian naval base at Cam Ranh Bay, Vietnam, may be closed during 2002 due to Russian inability to pay the rent.

As a result of a senior-level inspection conducted during 1-02, all remaining active Pacific Fleet submarines are to be consolidated at Sovetskaya Gavan, near Vladivostok.

The major St. Petersburg naval shipbuilding yards—Admiralty, Baltic, and Northern—are to be combined into a single new shipbuilding facility on the site of the current Northern Shipyard, with work to start in 2000 and complete in 2005–06. Ship repair facilities at St. Petersburg's Kronshtadtskiy Morskoy Zavod are to be reorganized into separate naval and commercial ship repair facilities.

Coastal Defense: During 2001, the remaining coastal missile defense forces were to have been placed in cadre status, with only 50 troops manning the missile regiments in each of the major fleets. The P-20/21 Rubezh-A (SSC-3) and P-35 Redut (SSC-1B) missiles and their transporters were placed in a state of preservation, although there are plans to conduct one test firing per fleet per year for each system type.

Future Programs: A Russian Navy long-term plan released 20-5-00 called for a force with 12 SSBNs, 20 SSGN/SSNs, 35 SSs, and about 70 principal surface combatants, but it was stated that, as the Russian Navy is only receiving 11–12% of the defense budget and would need 25% to achieve its goals, the plan is unlikely to be realized.

Note on ship names and types: Prior to 1991, the pennant numbers on the sides of Russian combatants were temporary tactical numbers denoting administrative subordination and were changed wholesale from time to time for security reasons. Since that time, however, the numbers have been relatively stable, and for that reason they are now included here, prefixing warship names and/or the alphanumeric names applied to small combatants, mine warfare units, and amphibious warfare units. Submarines normally do not wear pennant numbers.

The class names used herein are for the most part those used by NATO, with Russian class nicknames following in parentheses and the official permanent project number assigned to the design following the class name. The Russian Navy has a number of unique ship-type classifications; these are translated, where applicable, in the individual class entries.

WEAPONS AND SYSTEMS

Note: Nuclear warheads were widely deployed in the past on Soviet Navy missiles and other ordnance, especially submarine-deployed weapons. In 1991 in response to an initiative by U.S. President Bush, it was announced that tactical nuclear weapons would be removed from Soviet warships, with the intent that only strategic ballistic submarines would have nuclear warheads in the future.

The navy announced in 1-01 that two of seven "missile systems," four of seven air-defense missile systems, and three of seven shipboard artillery systems in use would be retired by the end of the year, which should lead to further significant reductions in numbers and classes of ships and craft.

Dates in parentheses following system names below are for acceptance into service.

A. MISSILES

♦ Submarine-launched ballistic missiles

Note: CEP = Circular Error Probable (i.e., half of all missiles launched will fall within this radius). The RSM-series designations for ballistic missile systems are apparently used only in diplomatic negotiations.

SS-N-18 Stingray (Russian RSM-50/R-29DU Volna) (8-77)

Two-stage missile employed on the Delta-III class. CEP is estimated at 1,100 m (Mod. 1). In 10-91, 224 remained in operational service. Mods. 2 and 3 are no longer in service. Production designation was 4K-75DU. Overall missile system designation is D-9DU. Designed by the Makeyev Bureau. The proposed commercial space-booster variant has the program name Volna. Capable of depressed-trajectory firing, which reduces detectability; test firings were to be conducted in that mode during 2000. The missiles employ an astral-radio correction flight trajectory, employing data from navigational satellites to correct the inertially set flight path while in flight.

Length: 14.10 m **Diameter:** 1.80 m **Weight:** 35,300 kg
Range: 3,510 n.m. (3 × 550-kg MIRV warheads)

SS-N-20 Sturgeon (Russian R-39) (. . .)

Cover designation RSM-52 was used for diplomatic purposes; production designation for the missile was 3M-20. Now carried only by one active Project 941 (Typhoon)-class submarine. Solid-fueled missile using liquid-fueled thrusters to alter flight trajectory, based on inputs to the inertial guidance system from navigational satellites. Each missile carries 10 warheads.

Length: 16.0 m **Diameter:** 2.40 m
Weight: 90,000 kg (incl. 6,000 kg launch-assist device and 2,500 kg reentry vehicle)
Range: 4,480 n.m. (10 × 255-kg MIRV warheads)

SS-N-23 Skiff (Russian RSM-54/R-29RM) (2-86)

Three-stage weapon, originally with a payload of up to 10 (Mod. 1) or four (Mod. 2) MIRV warheads, carried by the six Delta-IV class SSBNs. Designed by the Makeyev Bureau. As of 10-91, 940 Mod. 2 missiles were in operational service. CEP is estimated at 500 m. The first stage weighs 22,300 kg at launch. Overall missile system designator: D-9RM. The commercial space-booster variant has the program name Shtil. Production was restarted under a 1999 order. A new 10-warhead version nicknamed Sineva is planned to be in production from 2002 to 2007.

Length: 14.8 m **Diameter:** 1.90 m **Weight:** 40,300 kg
Range: 4,860 nm (4 × 700-kg MIRV warheads)

SS-N-. . . (Russian Bulava) (2007)

The solid-fueled Makeyev Bureau SS-NX-28 (Russian R-39UTTKh Grom or 3M-91 Izdelie) missile was formally canceled early in 1998 after three unsuccessful flights. A smaller successor missile was to be designed by another agency for use with the incomplete SSBN *Yuriy Dolgorukiy* and the modernized Project 941–class TK-208; it will be a navalized version—known as Bulava (Mace)—of the new Topol-M, which entered service late in 1998 with land-based rocket forces. The planned naval version is intended to enter service by about 2007, but as of 12-01 there had been no test launches announced. The missile is claimed to be capable of defeating any U.S. ballistic missile defense system, probably indicating that it will employ decoys. Data for the land-based version of the three-stage, solid-fueled Topol-M include:

Diameter: 1.86 m **Length:** 22.7 m **Weight:** 47,200 kg **Range:** 11,000 km

♦ Surface-to-surface cruise missiles

SS-N-2A/SS-N-2B Styx (Russian P-15/P-15U Termit) (1960/1965)

P-15, the original fixed-wing missile, is dubbed SS-N-2A by NATO and uses the hooded 4S-30 launcher; the P-15U Termit-U, with folding wings, is called SS-N-2B and uses the cylindrical KT-67B or KT-67ER launcher. Production designation for the P-15 was 4K-40 or 4K-40T, while for P-15U it was 4K-40U. Liquid-propulsion rocket with solid booster. I-band active radar guidance in targeting, with infrared *or* radar homing. Altitude can be preset at 100, 150, 200, 250, or 300 m. Installed in Osa-I and Osa-II guided-missile boats. No longer used by the Russian Navy, but still in foreign service. Designed by MKB Raduga.

Length: 6.665 m **Diameter:** 0.8 m **Wingspan:** 2.5 m
Weight: 2,523 kg **Warhead:** 480 kg **Speed:** Mach 1.3 (320 m/sec)
Range: 80 km max (50–60 effective)/8 km min.

WEAPONS AND SYSTEMS *(continued)*

SS-N-2C Styx (Russian P-15M Termit-M; export: P-20/21/22 Rubezh) (1972)

The basic weapon, the P-15M, has folding wings and an improved radar seeker. The P-20 Rubezh series export versions included the basic radar-homing P-20; the P-20K, with an improved radar altimeter to permit lower cruise flight; and the P-20M, with range extended to 45 n.m. The P-21 is an infrared-homing version of the P-20, and the P-22 is an infrared-homing version of the extended-range P-20M. In order to employ fully the over-the-horizon maximum range of the SS-N-2C, it is necessary to have a forward observer. The SS-N-2C is carried by Tarantul-I and -II guided-missile patrol craft, using KT-138 launchers. Missile production designation is 4K-40M. Widely exported. A land-based version, the SSC-3, is carried in pairs on special truck launchers.

Length: 6.5 m **Diameter:** 0.8 m **Wingspan:** 2.5 m
Weight: 2,500 kg **Warhead:** 500 kg armor-piercing **Speed:** Mach 1.3

SS-N-2D Styx (Russian P-27 Termit-R) (1980s?)

The latest variant of the Styx family, equipped with a new L-band seeker and, like the P-20M, capable of 45-n.m. flights. Missile production designation is 3M-51; the overall system is the 4K-51. Made by the Progress airframe plant, Khabarovsk, but no longer in production. It is uncertain whether it was ever used by the Russian Navy, which has almost no craft left that could launch it.

Note: With the retirement of the last warship equipped to launch it, the SS-N-3B Shaddock (Russian P-6 Progress) has effectively been retired.

SS-N-9 Siren (Russian P-120 Malakhit) (1972)

Features inertial guidance, with active radar or infrared homing to the target. Has a 500-kg conventional or nuclear warhead. Developed by the Chelomey Bureau (now NPO Mashinostroeniya) and installed in Nanuchka-I- and -III-class guided-missile patrol combatants. A submerged-launch version (P-120L) was carried by Charlie-II submarines. Missile production designation is 4K-85, and the launcher is designated KT-84.

Length: 8.84 m **Diameter:** 0.80 m **Wingspan:** 1.6 m
Weight: 5,400 kg **Speed:** Mach 0.9
Range: 30 n.m. (64.8 n.m. with a forward observer or video datalink)

SS-N-12 Sandbox (Russian P-500 Bazal't) (1975)

Has a 1,000-kg conventional or nuclear warhead. Developed by the Chelomey Bureau. Now carried only by *Slava*-class cruisers. Missile production designation: 4K-80.

Length: 12.4 m **Diameter:** 0.88 m **Wingspan:** 1.8 m
Weight: 4,800 kg **Speed:** Mach 2.5 **Range:** 300 n.m.

Note: The SS-N-14 Silex, a dual-purpose antisubmarine and antiship missile, is described in the antisubmarine weapon section.

SS-N-19 Shipwreck (Russian P-700 Granit) (1981)

Designed by the Chelomey (OKB-52, now Mashinostroeniya) design bureau and carried by the *Kirov*-class cruisers and Oscar-class nuclear-powered submarines (from which it is submerged launched). The missile's manufacturing designation is 3M-45, and it is also referred to as the P-50 missile. Originally intended to be launched by salvo against aircraft carriers detected and tracked via the datalinked, nuclear-powered Legenda radar surveillance satellite system, which is no longer in use, nor is the missile version with the original 500-kiloton nuclear warhead. A rear-mounted solid-fuel booster is employed for the submerged launch, with a KR-93 turbojet engine providing sustained flight (ramjet propulsion has also been reported, and the external configuration would support either method). Has double-folding wings and folding tail surfaces.

Length: 10.5 m **Diameter:** 0.88 m **Wingspan:** 2.6 m
Weight: 7,000 kg **Warhead:** 750 kg
Speed: Mach 2.5 max. **Range:** 550 km

SS-N-21 Sampson (RPK-55 Granat) (1988)

A torpedo-tube-launched strategic land target weapon similar in concept to the U.S. Tomahawk. It was withdrawn from service in 1991, but numerous examples remain in land storage. Developed by the Novator Bureau. Submerged launched from submarines. Employ a terrain-following, low-altitude (190–200 m) flight pattern. Production designation was 3M-10. Has a nuclear warhead. A "stealth"-type nosecone fairing is fitted. The turbojet sustainer engine is extended from the lower, aft end of the missile after launch. The projected land-launch variant was designated SSC-4 Slingshot by NATO, although it does not seem to have entered production.

Length: 8.09 m (8.39 with canister) **Diameter:** 0.51 m (0.65 with canister)
Wingspan: 0.30 m **Weight:** 1,700 kg (2,440 with canister)
Speed: Mach 0.7 **Range:** 1,620 n.m.

SS-N-22 Sunburn (Russian P-270 Moskit/P-100 Moskit-M) (1984)

Missile production designation: 3M-80; export version: 3M-80E. Designed by Raduga OKB, with production integration by Altair State Research and Development Corp. and production by the Progress airframe plant, Khabarovsk. A successor to the SS-N-9, but not used by submarines. At launch, climbs to 32–70 m altitude. Descends to 10–15 m (20 m for export versions) at 17 km after launch. At 7.5 km from the predesignated target, climbs to 20 m to activate its radar seeker. At 1 km from the target, pops up to 24 m in active mode or descends to 3 m in passive mode. Can be programmed to pull 15-g., 200-m-radius evasive turns until 7 km from the target. Capable of being launched up to 60° off target azimuth and at 5-second intervals. Minimum range is 7 km.

Carried by *Sovremennyy*-class destroyers and Tarantul-III- and Dergach-class guided-missile patrol combatants. The design has been sold to Boeing for target drone use by the U.S. Navy. Some 841 were said to be in Russian and Ukrainian hands as of 6-94, when production had probably ceased. In 7-98, 48 new Moskit-M surface-launched missiles were ordered for China (the only export customer to date) to keep the Progress plant in operation, but funding was not provided until 5-99; all had been delivered by 1-01.

Propulsion is rocket-ramjet, with an internal rocket booster that is ejected through the exhaust as the ramjet sustainer ignites. The P-100 Moskit-M version (of which only a few were made for Russian Navy use) has a 129-km range. An air-launched version, the Kh-41, was first launched during 1998 but has not yet entered service.

Length: 9.385 m **Diameter:** 0.52 m (1.3 over folded fins)
Wingspan: 2.10 m (1.30 folded)
Weight: 3,950 kg **Warhead:** 300 kg (150 kg of explosive)
Speed: Mach 2.5 **Range:** 100 km

SS-N-25 Switchblade (Russian Kh-35 Uran) (1997)

A Harpoon- or Exocet-size antiship weapon intended to be booster-launched from canisters mounted in quadruple nests; the design was originally intended for air launch. Design bureau: Zvezda OKB. Only one Russian Navy combatant, Matka-class trials craft R-44, has launched the weapon. The missile has been purchased by India, where it entered service in 1998. Cruise altitude is 5–10 m, descending to 3–5 m during final approach. Production designation: 3M-24 (3M-24E for export). The 3Ts-25E target-seeker radar can be used in active and passive modes and can detect and home on a 10,000-m^2 target at a range of 40–45 km in normal conditions, 85–90 km under ideal conditions, and up to 260 km under radar ducting conditions.

Length: 3.75 m (4.7 with booster) **Diameter:** 470 mm
Wingspan: 930 mm
Weight: 603 kg (incl. 120-kg booster) **Warhead:** 145 kg
Speed: Mach 0.9 (280–300 m/sec) **Range:** 5–130 km

An improved version, the 3M-24M1, with a GPS receiver and a range of 250 km is planned, and another variant with an infrared seeker may be developed. The proposed, highly mobile Bal coast-defense version, known to NATO as the SSC-X-6, is described below under coast-defense missiles, but it is now unlikely ever to be produced.

SS-NX-26 Yakhont/Sapless (Russian P-800 Oniks/3M-55) (1999)

Offered by NPO Mashinostroeniya (successor to the Chelomey Bureau) is the ramjet-powered P-800 Oniks, which makes its Mach-2.5 terminal attack at 5- to 15-m sea-skimming height. Production designation: 3M-55. Can be vertically launched from a submerged submarine, launched horizontally from 650-mm-diameter torpedo tubes, or launched by aircraft (two per Mig-29, three per Su-27, and eight per Tu-142) or land batteries. It employs an integral solid-rocket booster. A longer-range version with solid-fuel propulsion, Yashma, was offered for development for export in 6-95, but apparently fostered no interest. Yakhont is evidently the export name, with Oniks the name of the domestic version. The export version was said to be ready for production as of 8-99, but in 11-00 was being offered for production beginning in 2002. The radar seeker has a range of 75 km and is said to be able to distinguish targets by position and radar cross section or to home on electromagnetic radiation. The proposed Bastion coast-defense version has been designated SSC-5 by NATO. Data for the submarine- and ship-launched versions are:

Length: 8.90 m **Diameter:** 650 mm (container)
Weight: 3,900 kg (2,550 air-launched) **Warhead:** 200 kg
Speed: Mach 2.0–2.5 **Range:** 120 km low/300 km high
Cruise altitude: 5–14,000 m

A longer-range (300-km) variant of the Yakhont is in development as the Brahmos. Capable of vertical launch from surface ships and submarines or of being launched by aircraft, the Brahmos is to have a warhead weight of up to 300 kg, a maximum altitude of 15,000 m, and a length of 9.0 m.

SS-N-27 Novator Al'fa (Russian P-10 Biryuza/3M-54) (. . .)

Novator Design Bureau offers the Biryuza antiship missile for air launch, for submarine launch (via capsule), in a shipboard-launch version, or in a six-tube mobile land launcher (as the Al'fa system). At the onset of terminal run-in, beginning about 60 km from the target, the missile ejects a terminal-homing, Mach-2.5, rocket-powered payload vehicle that travels at about 10 m altitude. The weapon is still in competition with the P-800 Oniks for possible Russian Navy service but is being sold in quantity to the Indian Navy as the 3M-54E Club for surface ship (3M-54E) and submarine (3M-54TE) use. Data for the original version include:

Length: 8.22 m **Diameter:** 533 mm
Weight: 1,900 kg (2,500 with solid booster) **Warhead:** 200 kg
Speed: Mach 0.6–0.8 (3.0 attack) **Range:** 220 km

The subsonic 3M-54E1 variant of the system employs an airframe derived from that of the RPK-55 Granat (NATO SS-N-21) and resembles the U.S. Tomahawk. Both 3M-54E and 3M-54E1 employ the same 400- to 500-kg-thrust Baranov TRDD-50 turbojet cruise engine. The 3M-54E1 is intended to fit in a standard 533-mm torpedo tube. Cruise altitude is 10–15 m, and during terminal phase, it flies at 5 m altitude; there is no detaching terminal-phase vehicle. Trials had not been completed as of 3-01, and no export sales have yet been announced:

Length: 6.20 m **Diameter:** 533 mm
Weight: 1,780 kg (at launch) **Warhead:** 450 kg
Speed: Mach 0.6–0.8 (180–240 m/sec) **Range:** approx. 300 km

An ASW version designated 91RE1 is in development for launch from 533-mm submarine torpedo tubes at depths to 150 m and with the submarine traveling at speeds up to 15 kts; it would weigh 2,050 kg (including a homing torpedo payload) and have a range of 35 km. The 91RE2 ASW version would be fired from surface ships and would have a weight of 1,200 kg and a range of 40 km; it would be launchable from vertical tubes or inclined canister launchers.

Note: Further development of the NPO Mashinostroeniya Al'fa missile has apparently been terminated.

WEAPONS AND SYSTEMS *(continued)*

Vikhr' (. . .)

Vikhr' is an adaptation of a helicopter-borne antitank missile system. Offered for export, a full system would consist of four missile canisters co-mounted on a standard AK-306 or AK-630 gatling gun mount and controlled by an electro-optical director. Range is about 8–10 km.

♦ Coast-defense missiles

Note: When the Coastal Missile and Artillery regiments were placed in cadre status during 2001, only the Redut and Rubezh-A systems had been deployed. The other systems listed below existed only as export offerings or prototypes that have not yet entered production and are now unlikely to do so for Russian employment.

SSC-1B Sepal (Russian P-35 Redut)

A truck-mounted member of the SS-N-3 family. Uses an eight-wheel SPU-35V vehicle (ZIL-135MB chassis) with one missile. A separate command, control, and communications trailer with radar target detection and tracking radar is required. The missile has a range of between 25 and 270 km and can be set to cruise at 100-, 4,000-, and 7,000-m altitudes. The vehicle has a crew of five and can travel 500 km at a maximum of 40 kph. All remaining launchers and missiles assigned to Russian coastal missile regiments were placed in preservation during 2001.

SSC-3 Styx (Russian P-20/21 Rubezh-A)

A truck-launched variant of the SS-N-2C/D family (which see for details). Carried two per launch vehicle, with target determination radar mounted on the 3S-51 vehicle. All remaining launchers and missiles assigned to Russian coastal missile regiments were placed in preservation during 2001.

Note: The SSC-4 Slingshot (Russian S-10 Granat), a truck-mounted version of the SS-N-21 strategic cruise missile with either a nuclear or conventional warhead, did not enter production, although it was apparently tested.

SSC-X-5 Yakhont (Russian . . . Bastion)

A land-launched system employing the SS-NX-26 Yakhont supersonic ramjet missile (q.v.), still in development but offered for potential export. The land-launch system had not yet entered production when the Coastal Missile and Artillery regiments stood down in 2001.

SSC-X-6 (Russian Bal)

The land-launch system for the Kh-35 Uran (NATO SS-NX-25) antiship missile, offered for development as an integrated truck-mounted system with eight missiles and a target detection and tracking radar. It had not yet entered production when the Coastal Missile and Artillery regiments stood down in 2001. A complete battery would require 46 personnel and would include two self-propelled command, control, and communications vehicles, four launch vehicles, and four missile transporter/reloader vehicles, for a total of 64 weapons. The vehicles would have a top speed of 60 kph and a range of up to 800 km. Time to set up and launch would be only 10 minutes. Missile characteristics are as for SS-NX-25.

Note: Land-based S-300PS (SA-12) surface-to-air missiles were used in an antiship role during an 8-99 exercise. Also used for coast defense were fixed and mobile guns of up to 130-mm bore, but apparently none remained in service as of 2001. The latest system was the 130-mm Bereg single self-propelled gun, which used the same gun as the naval twin AK-130 system; a battery was to consist of one central command and control station with radar and electro-optical fire-control equipment (mounted on an eight-wheeled MAZ-543M chassis), four to six mobile gun vehicles with backup optical fire-control systems, and one or two support vehicles. Range for the gun is said to be more than 22 km, with a semiautomatic rate of fire of 10 rds/min, but it never proceeded beyond prototype testing, and Ukraine confiscated the sole prototype.

The KBM Engineering Design Bureau's 9M-120 Ataka antitank missile is also offered in a naval short-range antiship variant; it has a range of about 6 km. It had not yet entered production when the Coastal Missile and Artillery regiments stood down in 2001.

♦ Surface-to-air missiles

SA-N-1 Goa (Russian M-1 Volna system) (1962)

A naval version of the land-based SA-3. Now fitted on one Kashin-class destroyer and one Kynda-class cruiser in the Russian Navy and on five Kashin-class destroyers in the Indian Navy. Also has a surface-to-surface capability. Uses Yatagan (Peel Group) radar directors and the ZIF-101 or ZIF-102 cross-level stabilized twin-launcher. The M-1 Volna system uses V-600 (4K-90) missiles, and the M-1M Volna-M and M-1P Volna-P systems use the V-601 (4K-91) missile; all versions have 16 missiles per magazine. Can handle aerial targets at speeds of 100–600 m/sec. System reaction time is 16–18 seconds. Designed by the Fakel Engineering Design Bureau with system integration by the Altair Bureau. Is obsolescent and reportedly was never considered satisfactory in service; probably one of the missile systems planned to be dropped at the end of 2000.

Length: 5.948 m overall (1st stage: 1.871 m; 2d stage: 4.131 m)
Diameter: 1st stage: 552 mm; 2d stage: 390 mm
Weight: 960 kg (1st stage: 532 kg; 2d stage: 428 kg) **Warhead:** 72 kg
Speed: 730 m/sec
Range: 24 km slant range (3.5 min.); 17 km surface-to-surface
Altitude: 0.1–14 km

SA-N-3 Goblet (Russian M-11 Shtorm system) (1967)

Twin Type B-187 or Type B-192A launcher with V-611 (4K-60 and 4K-65) missiles. Guidance is via radar/command by Head Lights–series (Grom) radar director. Now fitted only on one Kara-class destroyer. Has an anti-surface target capability. Designed by Fakel Engineering Design Bureau, with Altair Bureau providing system integration. Minimum range is 7 km. System reaction time is 25 seconds, and the missile can be used against targets traveling up to 700 m/sec.

Weight: 550 kg **Warhead:** approx. 60 kg
Speed: Mach 2.5 **Range:** 30 km **Altitude:** 300–80,000 ft.

SA-N-4 Gecko (Russian Osa-M, Osa-2M, and Osa-MA systems) (1968)

The twin ZIF-122 (also known as the 4S-33) launcher elevates from a cylindrical magazine holding 20 9M-33M missiles on four rings of five. The missile was designed by Fakel Engineering Design Bureau, with Altair State Research and Development Corp. providing system integration. All versions of the system are designated RZ-13 by the navy, but production numbers assigned were 4K-33 for the original Osa-M system, 4K-33M for the Osa-2M (which can also use 9M-33M3 or 9M-33M5 missiles), and 4K-33M for the Osa-MA system on the Koni-class export frigates (with 9M-33M missiles). Guidance is radar/command via Pop Group (MPZ-301) radar director. Has a conventional warhead. Fitted in *Kirov-class* cruisers, Kara-class destroyers, Krivak-series frigates, Grisha-series corvettes, Nanuchka-series guided-missile patrol combatants, and *Ivan Rogov*–class landing ships. The system reaction time is 20 seconds, and only one target can be engaged at a time by each director. Can be used against surface targets.

Length: 3.16 m **Diameter:** 0.21 m **Weight:** 126 kg
Warhead: 14.2 kg **Range:** 1.2–10 km **Altitude:** 80–16,400 ft.

SA-N-5 Grail (Russian Strela-2 and Strela-2M systems) (1969)

A naval version of the SA-7 Grail (Russian 4K-32 or 4K-32M Strela) missile. Formerly carried on Pauk- and Tarantul-class small combatants, landing ships, some minesweepers, and many auxiliaries. Either employs a four-missile launch rack with operator or is shoulder-launched singly from a 9P-53 or 9P-58 launch/storage tube. East German–built quadruple launchers were designated the Fasta-4M system, with the launcher apparently designated the MTU-4US. The Grail is IR homing and visually aimed. Strela-2M entered service in 1974. Both variants have been almost entirely superseded in naval service by the Strela-3 series (SA-N-8), but some may remain in foreign navies.

Length: 1.44 m **Weight:** 15 kg (with launch tube)
Speed: 500 m/sec **Range:** 4.4 km **Altitude:** up to 7,800 ft.

SA-N-6 Grumble (Russian S-300F Fort and S-300FM Fort-M) (1983)

A navalized version of the land-based SA-10. The export naval version is known as Rif; an updated version of the system, the Rif-M, was announced 9-4-01. Designer: Fakel Engineering Design Bureau, with system integration by the Altair State Research and Development Corp. Range is up to 100 km, depending on the type of missile launched; altitude is up to 90,000 ft. Range against incoming missiles at 25-m altitude is 25 km; targets at 2,000 m and higher can be engaged to 90 km. Can handle targets moving at up to 2,268 kts (4,200 km/hr). The initial version on cruisers *Azov* and *Admiral Ushakov* used hot launch, but all current missiles employ vertical cold-launch from eight-missile 3S-41 rotating magazines (with the missiles in individual containers) and use track-via-missile guidance via the Top Dome (3P-41 Volna) radar system; each Top Dome can reportedly track six targets simultaneously, directing two missiles per target, provided they are within the same 60° arc. Launch interval is 3 seconds. Carried by *Kirov-* and *Slava*-class cruisers. Also has an antiship capability. Land-based S-300 version has been exported. Three different missiles are used: 5V-55K with a range of 45 km; 5V-55RM with a 75-km range; and the new 5V-55U missile (equivalent to the land-based S-300PMU) with 100-km range (the missile has also been referred to as the 48N6E2 and in the Fort-M version on *Petr Velikiy* is said to have a range of 150 km).

Data for the 5V-55RM missile include:

Length: 7.25 m **Diameter:** 508 mm **Wingspan:** 1.124 m
Weight: 1,664 kg **Warhead:** 133 kg
Speed: 2,000 m/sec **Range:** 5–75 km **Altitude:** 25–25,000 m

SA-N-7 Gadfly (Russian M-22 or ZR-90 Uragan system) (1981)

A navalized version of the land-based Buk-1M (SA-11), employing MS-196 single-armed launchers. Designer: Novator Bureau, with system integration by Altair State Research and Development Corp. Used on *Sovremennyy*-class and Indian Navy Project 15 destroyers and Indian Project 11356 frigates only. The export version is referred to as the Shtil (Stiletto) system. Has 24 single-stage Type 9M-38M1 or 9M-38M13 single-stage missiles per magazine, 12 each on two side-by-side rings (only the prototype ZS-90 launchers had a ring of eight missiles surrounded by a ring of 12). Each launcher group requires a crew of 19 and weighs 49 tons. The launcher elevates to 70° maximum. The missiles can maneuver at up to 20 g. and employ semi-active homing guidance via Front Dome (OP-3) radar illuminators. The missiles can handle aircraft targets traveling 420–830 m/sec and missiles moving 330–830 m/sec, and the system probably has a secondary antiship capability. System reaction time is 16–19 seconds, and advertised kill percentage is 81–96% for a two-missile salvo. The similar but improved and longer-range 9M-38E1 Yozh missile for the land-based Buk-2M/Ural (SA-X-17 Grizzly) is believed to be used on the 16th-built and later units of the *Sovremennyy* class; it was to replace the 9M-30-series missiles on earlier ships of the class, but funding was not available.

Length: 5.55 m **Diameter:** 400 mm **Wingspan:** 860 mm
Weight: 690 kg **Warhead:** 70 kg **Speed:** Mach 3.0 (830 m/sec)
Range: 25 km max./3 km min. against aircraft; 3.5–12 km against missiles
Altitude: 15–15,000 m against aircraft; 10–10,000 m against missiles

SA-N-8 Gremlin (Russian Strela-3) (1986?)

A navalized version of the SA-14 (Russian 9M-36 Strela-3), the cooled-seeker successor to the SA-7 Grail. Developed by KBM, Kolomna. Uses either the same Fasta-4M system with MTU-4US, four-round manned launcher as the Strela-2/2M (SA-N-5) or a shoulder-launcher. A twin, manned lightweight launcher nicknamed the Dzhigit is on offer for export but has not been seen on Russian warships. Has slightly greater

WEAPONS AND SYSTEMS *(continued)*

range than the SA-N-5, from which it is virtually indistinguishable while in the launch tube, which has a slightly larger control section than that of the SA-N-5 launch tube. Weight: 9.9 kg; length: 1.3 m. The launchers are also able to employ the SA-16 Igla-I (9M-313) missile, an improved version of the SA-14 that entered service around 1985, and can also accept the SA-18 Grouse (9M-39 Igla).

SA-N-9 Gauntlet (Russian Kinzhal) (1984)

A vertically launched, short-range system intended as a successor to SA-N-4; naval variant of the SA-15 Tor. Export name is Klinok. Designer: Fakel Engineering Design Bureau, with system integration by Altair State Research and Development Corp. The 9M-330 (naval production designation: 3M-95) missiles are carried in groups of eight in 2-m-diameter 3S-95 launch cylinders aboard *Udaloy*-class destroyers, carriers *Admiral Gorshkov* and *Admiral Flota Sovetskogo Soyuza Kuznetsov,* and other new-construction ships. Maximum flight time is 20 seconds, with a 10-second max. motor burn. Can be used against targets traveling at up to 700 m/sec. Response time is 8 to 24 seconds, and one missile can be launched every 3 seconds. Uses a gas-ejection launch system, with the missile engines igniting when the missiles are about 20 m above the launcher. Each system can track and attack four targets within a 60°-wide by 60°-high field. Command guided by Cross Sword radar directors, which have a co-mounted target detection and designation radar, an illumination radar, and an electro-optical backup feature and can control two missiles simultaneously. The control system may be designated ZR-90. Missile appears to have had developmental problems, as the first ships to carry it were completed as much as eight years before it was available for installation. Each Kinzhal installation weighs 41 tons and requires a crew of 13.

Weight: 165 kg **Warhead:** 15 kg
Speed: 850 m/sec **Range:** 1.5–15 km **Altitude:** 32–19,700 ft.

SA-N-11 Grison close-in weapons system (Russian Kortik) (1988)

A naval version of the land-based Tunguska (2S-6) system. *Kortik* means "dagger." The export version is known as Kashtan ("Chestnut Tree"). Referred to by NATO as the CADS-1 (Close Air Defense System-1). Designer: KB Priborstroyeniye, Tula, with shipboard system integration by Altair State Research and Development Corp. Carried on the carrier *Admiral Flota Sovetskogo Soyuza Kuznetsov,* cruisers *Admiral Nakhimov* and *Petr Velikiy,* frigate *Neustrashimyy,* and one Tarantul-II-class guided-missile craft (for trials). Uses the radar-guided 9M-311 Vikhr'-K missile (a navalized SA-19), launched from a disposable tube. Mount carries up to eight missiles, two 30-mm Type GSH-6-30L gatling AA guns (each with 500 rounds in a linkless feed system), and an on-mount Hot Flash (3P-87) search-and-track radar system with electro-optical backup; a separate Pozitiv-M-series target detection and tracking radar is normally associated with the system. Missiles can be auto-reloaded from a belowdecks magazine that holds 48 missiles per mount. The 30-mm gatling guns are essentially the same as those used in the AK-630 mount, except for provision of a water cooling jacket and flash shield. They can be used against targets at up to 3,000 m altitude and ranges from 500 to 1,500 m (4,000 m max. range); rate of fire is 2,500 rds/min/barrel, and muzzle velocity is 960 m/sec (1,100 m/sec for armor-piercing rounds). The entire Kortik/Kashtan mount weighs 13,500 kg, is 2.25 m high, and sweeps a 2.76-m radius. Production ceased in 1993. The Kashtan-M, with 100–200% improved system reliability and reduced reaction time, was offered for export in 2000. Characteristics for the 9M-311 Vikhr'-K missile include:

Length: 2.562 m **Diameter:** 170 mm **Wingspan:** 225 mm
Weight: 43.6 kg **Warhead:** 9 kg
Speed: 900 m/sec initial; 600 m/sec in sustained flight after 800 m
Range: 1.5–10 km **Altitude:** 15–6,000 m

Note: The similar Paltash CIWS, under development in 1995 at Tochmash Central Scientific Research Institute, Klimovsk, would have had two 30-mm cannon with a combined rate of fire of 10,000 rds/min; the on-mount radar antenna was to be housed in a spherical radome. There is no indication that a prototype was ever tested, however. France's Thales is teamed with the Russian Fakel design bureau to develop a vertical-launch version of the VT-1 Crotale point-defense missile, using a cold-launch gas generator ejection system; it was to have been available for production by 2001–02, but no tests have been announced, and the project may have languished.

The Arena anti–cruise missile defense system for warships was said to be in development as of 2-01. Based on a reactive armor concept developed for armored vehicles, Arena would be a kind of reactive skin to vital sections of a ship that would detonate or slow armor-piercing missile warheads. It would probably be too heavy and too expensive to cover more than a small percentage of the surface of a warship.

♦ Air-to-surface missiles

AS-4 Kitchen (Russian Kh-22) (1967)

Developed by the Raduga MKB. The Kh-22M missile uses a 1,000-kg conventional warhead; the Kh-22N had a nuclear warhead. The Kh-22MP variant was an antiradar weapon. Uses inertial guidance with radar-terminal homing. Was in service on Backfire-B aircraft. Has reportedly been put back into production, possibly in expectation of sales to India.

Length: 11.1 m **Diameter:** 0.87 m **Wingspan:** 4.8 m
Weight: 6,400 kg **Speed:** Mach 2.5–3.5
Range: 240 n.m. high-launch/146 n.m. low-launch

AS-7 Kerry (Russian Kh-23M Grom) (late 1970s)

A tactical weapon, designed by Zvezda OKB. Uses solid-fuel propulsion and has command guidance and a 110-kg conventional warhead. Can be carried by the land-based Su-25 Frogfoot; was formerly used on carrier-based Yak-38 Forger aircraft. The updated Grom-M version is designated Kh-66; an antiradar version was designated Kh-24. Now used primarily for training.

Length: 3.5 m **Diameter:** 305 mm **Wingspan:** 0.95 m
Weight: 287 kg **Speed:** 1,895 kts **Range:** 1–6 n.m.

Note: The AS-9 Kyle (Russian Kh-28 and Kh-28E) missile system is believed to have been retired from service by 2001.

AS-11 Kilter (Russian Kh-58 series) (1985)

Variants include Kh-58A, -58E, and -58U. Designed by Raduga MKB. Has passive home-on-electromagnetic-emissions (ARM) guidance with a shutdown memory feature but is not tunable in flight. Flies a modified ballistic flight path. Roughly comparable to the U.S. AGM-88 HARM.

Weight: 780 kg **Warhead:** 170 kg
Speed: 2,008 kts **Range:** 70–180 km

AS-13 Kingbolt (Russian Kh-59 Ovod) (. . .)

Similar to the U.S. Maverick in concept; uses electro-optical control with lock-on-after-launch capability. Designed by Zvezda OKB. Used with the APK-9 datalink pod for maximum range. Usable only in clear-air, daylight conditions.

Weight: 875 kg **Warhead:** 250 kg
Speed: . . . kts **Range:** 32 n.m.

AS-14 Kedge (Russian Kh-29 series) (. . .)

Made in three versions: the television-guided Kh-29T, laser-guided Kh-29ML, and home-on-electromagnetic-radiation (ARM) Kh-29P. Designed by Molniya OKB. Flies a modified ballistic flight path. Kh-29T is usable in daylight only. The Kh-29MP probably uses the same seeker as the AS-12 Kegler and requires the use of a belly-mounted guidance pod.

Weight: 680 kg **Warhead:** 320 kg
Speed: 660 kts **Range:** 4.3–5.4 n.m. (Kh-29MP: 18.9 n.m.)

AS-16 Kickback (Russian Kh-15P/S) (1992)

Short-range, inertially guided, rocket-powered missile with an active millimeter-wave terminal seeker. Designed by Raduga OKB. Equivalent to the U.S. Air Force SRAM, which it somewhat resembles. Carried by Tu-22M3 Backfire-C bombers. The terminal-homing antiship version is the Kh-15S; the Kh-15P has a passive antiradar seeker. Has a Mach 5 terminal dive.

Length: 4.78 m **Diameter:** 455 mm **Wingspan:** 0.92 m
Weight: approx. 1,200 kg **Warhead:** 150 kg

AS-17 Krypton (Russian Kh-31A/P) (1993?)

Ramjet-powered missile with alternate antiship or anti–land target seekers. Designed by Zvezda OKB. Also used by Russian Air Force in a radiation-seeking variant. The Kh-31A variant is 5.23 m long. Data for Kh-31P:

Length: 5.20 m **Diameter:** 0.36 m **Wingspan:** 779 mm
Weight: 600 kg **Warhead:** 90 kg
Speed: Mach 2.9 **Range:** 70 n.m.

AS-X-18 Kazoo (Russian Kh-59M Ovod-M) (. . .)

Turbojet-powered, t.v.-command-guided antiship weapon with 7–1,000 m preset cruise altitude. Another design by the Zvezda OKB. Derived from the Kh-59 (AS-13). Has not yet entered active service.

Length: 5.1–5.3 m **Weight:** 850 kg (air-launched)/1,000 kg (ship-launched)
Warhead: 315-kg armor-piercing or 280-kg canister
Speed: Mach 0.9 **Range:** 150 km max.

AS-20 Kayak (Russian Kh-35 Uran) (1998–99?)

Air-launched version of the Kh-35 Uran (SS-N-25 Switchblade). Designed by Zvezda OKB. Has been offered for export for several years but does not seem to have entered service yet in Russia. Was on offer to India as of 6-00.

Note: Laser-guided and conventional free-fall bombs in 500-, 750-, and 1,000-kg sizes are also available.

♦ Air-to-air missiles

AA-10 Alamo (Russian R-27) (. . .)

Carried by Su-27K/Su-33 Flanker-D shipboard fighters. Available in active, semiactive, and passive-homing versions. Developer: Vympel Bureau, in cooperation with Artem, Ukraine. The R-27P1 passive-homing variant has a maximum range of 80 km and the 347-kg passive-homing R-27EP1 has range of 110 km; both home on radiations from the target aircraft.

AA-11 Archer (Russian R-73, R-73M) (. . .)

Carried by Su-27K/Su-33 Flanker-D shipboard fighters. Developer: Vympel Bureau.

AA-12 Adder (Russian R-77) (1993)

A medium-range weapon that is also being developed in vertical-launched land and shipboard versions. Can be used by naval Su-27K/Su-33 Flanker-D carrier aircraft. Equivalent to the U.S. AMRAAM. All versions use the Belotsevkovskiy folding "Vene-

WEAPONS AND SYSTEMS *(continued)*

tian blind" control surfaces. A longer-range rocket-ramjet-powered version is in development. Developer: Vympel Bureau.

Weight: 175 kg **Warhead:** 18 kg
Speed: 1,721 kts **Range:** 43.2 n.m.

Note: Novator Design Bureau offers the 400-km-range KS-172 Al'fa AAM with active radar homing and midcourse correction capability for antimissile and anti-AWACS use. The two-stage missile is 7.4 m long, including the 1.4-m booster; seven can be carried by an Su-33 Flanker-D, but the system has not yet been procured for the Russian Navy. Development status is uncertain.

B. ARTILLERY ROCKET SYSTEMS

140-mm Ogon

Made by Start Zavod, Yekaterinburg, and used only on the Zubr (NATO Pomornik) surface-effect landing craft class (Project 12322). Employs 22-tube, autoloading, retractable launchers that, when closed, have a cover that fits flush with the upper deck of the launch craft. A truck-mounted coast-defense version of the system is offered for export as the Daraba.

140-mm UMS-73 Grad-M

Employed only on a few Ropucha- and Alligator-class tank landing ships and the *Ivan Rogov*–class dock landing ships. A twin-armed launcher hoists two 20-round magazine clips from below decks for salvo launching.

122-mm WM-18

A manually loaded system employed on Polnocny-series landing ships. Each launcher holds 18 rockets.

C. GUNS

130-mm/54-caliber twin, dual-purpose (Russian AK-130)

A fully automatic gun for surface, shore-bombardment, and aerial targets. Fitted on *Sovremennyy* and *Admiral Chabanenko*–class destroyers, *Slava*-class cruisers, and later *Kirov*-class cruisers. Made by Yurga Engineering Plant, Yurga. Water cooled. Uses a modified Kite Screech (MR-184) dual-band radar director with electro-optical (t.v. and laser rangefinder) backup or local control by on-mount operator. The export version has a reduced firing rate of 35–60 rounds per mount per minute. Can train and elevate at 25°/sec. Uses AR-32 influence and DVM-60M time-fuzed AA ammunition as well as high-explosive surface-target projectiles. There are 180 ready-service rounds per mount. The fire-control system is designated T-91. A single-barreled, mobile coast-defense system, Bereg, using the same gun, is offered for export.

Mount weight: 98 metric tons without ammunition
Projectile weight: 32 kg (+ 21-kg cartridge)
Muzzle velocity: 950 m/sec **Rate of fire:** 60+ rds/min/barrel max.
Arc of elevation: −15° to +85° **Max. range for surface fire:** 28,000 m

100-mm/55-caliber single-purpose (Russian U-5 TS)

An armored T-55 tank turret-mounted gun carried on Yaz-class and Vosh-class river monitors.

Muzzle velocity: 780 m/sec **Rate of fire:** 4 rds/min max.
Arc of elevation: −4° to +17° **Max. range:** 4,800 m

100-mm/59-caliber automatic dual-purpose (Russian AK-100)

A single-barreled, water-cooled gun in an enclosed, manned mounting found on *Udaloy*-class destroyers and *Neustrashimyy*-, Krivak-II-, and Krivak-III-class frigates. Designed by Ametist Central Design Bureau and made by Topaz. Uses a Kite Screech (MR-145 Lev) radar director (75-km range) with electro-optical backup or local control by on-mount operator. Fires high-explosive shells with impact, proximity, or time fuzing. The ZIF-91 mount carries 175 ready-service rounds and can traverse through ±200°. System weight is 8 metric tons, and the gunhouse is armored. The gun mounting is designated the A-190.

Mount weight: 49 tons empty **Projectile weight:** 15.6 kg
Muzzle velocity: 880 m/sec **Rate of fire:** 60 rds/min
Arc of elevation: −10° to +85° **Training speed:** 30°/sec
Elevation speed: 20°/sec **Max. theoretical range:** 21,500 m

76.2-mm/59-caliber single automatic dual-purpose (Russian AK-176)

A fully automatic gun with on-mount crew, designed as the A-221 by Burevestnik Central Scientific Research Institute and since manufactured by Topaz. Entered service on 22-6-79. The AK-176M version has an armored gunhouse; used on larger ships, it is outwardly identical to the AK-176. Carried by Grisha-V- and Parchim-II-class corvettes; Nanuchka-III-, Pauk-, and Tarantul-class guided-missile patrol combatants; Matka-class guided-missile hydrofoils, and others. Requires a crew of six, with two on mount. Employs Bass Tilt (MR-123 or MR-123-02 Vympel/Koral) radar/electro-optical director or Rakurs electro-optical director or local, on-mount control. The automatic magazine below the gun rotates with the mount and holds 152 rounds. Fires high-explosive shells with impact or proximity fuzing.

Weight: 11.2 tons empty, 13.1 tons with ready-service ammunition
Projectile weight: 5.9 kg **Muzzle velocity:** 850 m/sec
Rate of fire: 120 rds/min **Arc of elevation:** −15° to +85°
Training speed: 35°/sec **Elevation speed:** 30°/sec
Theoretical max. range for surface fire: 15,500 m
Practical range for antiaircraft fire: 6,000–7,000 m

76.2-mm/59-caliber twin dual-purpose (Russian AK-726)

Installed on Kara- and Kashin-class destroyers, Krivak-I-class frigates, *Smol'nyy*-class training ships, and *Ivan Susanin*–class patrol icebreakers. Employs an Owl Screech (MR-105 Turel'), Hawk Screech (Fut-B), or Kite Screech-A (MR-114 Yakhont) radar director, with Fut-B used in conjunction with a separate ringsight target designator. The twin gunmount is designated ZIF-67 and has 5-mm bulletproof plating. In larger ships, the normal ammunition allowance is 300 rounds per barrel. The normal gun crew is nine per mount.

Mount weight: 26,000 kg **Projectile weight:** 12.8 kg
Muzzle velocity: 980 m/sec **Rate of fire:** 90–107 rds/min/barrel
Arc of elevation: −10° to +85°
Max. range for surface fire: 15.7 km (13.2 effective)
Max. range for antiaircraft fire: 11,000 m (6,000–7,000 effective)

76.2-mm/48-caliber single-purpose (Russian D-56 TM)

Tank turret–mounted weapon used on Shmel'-class river gunboats (same mount and turret as used by PT-76 amphibious tank).

Muzzle velocity: 680 m/sec **Rate of fire:** 15 rds/min max.
Arc of elevation: −4° to +30° **Max. effective range:** 800 m

57-mm/70-caliber twin automatic dual-purpose (Russian AK-725)

Automatic weapon with no on-mount crew, installed on Grisha-II- and -III-class corvettes, Nanuchka-I guided-missile patrol combatants, and Ropucha-series LSTs. Has water-cooled barrels. The mount is designated ZIF-72. Employs a Muff Cob (MR-103 Bars) radar/electro-optical or Bass Tilt (MR-123 Vympel/Koral) radar director. Barrels have a life of 1,500 rounds. Maximum range is 12.7 km, but the shells self-destruct at 6.7 km.

Mount weight: 14,500 kg **Rate of fire:** 200 rds/min/barrel max.
Max. effective range: 6,700 m

Note: The twin, manned 57-mm/70-cal. open ZIF-31B mounting is still found on Alligator-class landing ships and one Don-class submarine tender. It can be locally controlled. Maximum effective range: 8,400 m.

37-mm/63-caliber twin AA (Russian V-11M)

No longer in Soviet service but is still found on foreign ships, particularly Chinese-built version, Type 74. Uses either hand-cranked cross-leveling or power cross-leveling. Control by on-mount lead-computing sight.

Muzzle velocity: 880 m/sec **Rate of fire:** 160 rds/min/barrel max.
Arc of elevation: 0° to +85° **Max. range:** 9,500 m (2,500 effective)

30-mm/54-caliber single gatling AA (Russian AK-630 and AK-630M)

Designed to fire a great number of rounds at an extremely high rate in order to intercept a cruise missile at a relatively short distance. Manufactured by Mashzavod imeni Ryabakov, Tula. In service on numerous classes, installed in mounts similar to those of the 30-mm AK-230 double-barreled automatic guns. The GSh-6-30K gatling gun has six 30-mm barrels; 2,000 rounds are carried on-mount, with another 1,000 per mount normally maintained in reserve. Nicknamed the "Metallorezka." The system cannot engage targets flying below 10 m in altitude. The often-used incorrect designation "ADMG-630" is an early NATO nickname.

The AK-630M is an updated variant with an improved magazine feed. A version known as AK-213M with a different magazine shape apparently never entered production. An over-and-under, twin gatling mount was offered in 1993 as the AK-630M1-2 Roy, but only one was built and it was installed only in one Matka-class trials ship; its data are similar to the AK-630 and AK-630M, except for higher weight (2.5 tons empty, 6.5 loaded) and greater rate of fire (4,000 rds/min). Maximum burst duration for AK-630 and AK-630M1-2 mounts is 400 rounds.

In 1997, a new twin variant was offered as the Palma, using two AO-18KD guns mounted on either side of a central pedestal that also carries an E/O tracker. The guns would have an 1,100-m/sec muzzle velocity, and a full 10,000 rounds of ammunition per mount (6.9 tons) would be carried. Palma would have a 3- to 5-second response time and would employ an MR-700-series Fregat target-designation radar and MR-123 Vympel fire-control radar.

AK-630-series mounts are normally controlled by a Bass Tilt (MR-123-02 Vympel) radar director, with an SP-521 Rakurs (NATO Kolonka-2) remote manned backup director (on the carrier *Admiral Flota Sovetskogo Soyuza Kuznetsov,* the gun is controlled by the Hot Flash radar system on nearby Kortik gun/missile close-in-defense systems). Data for the basic AK-630 are:

Mount weight: 3,814 kg complete **Projectile weight:** 0.834 kg
Muzzle velocity: 880–900 m/sec **Rate of fire:** 4,000–5,000 rds/min max.
Arc of elevation: −12° to +88°
Traverse rate: 70°/sec **Elevation rate:** 50°/sec
Max. range for antiaircraft fire: 4,000–5,000 m

30-mm/54-caliber single lightweight gatling AA (Russian AK-306)

Lightweight version of the AK-630 series, using the electrically driven AO-18L gun with a rate of fire of 600–1,000 rds/min. Has 500 rounds on mount. Elevates to 85°. Used on late-construction Natya (Project 266ME), all Sonya, and all Lida-class minesweepers and some riverine combatants. Mount weighs 1,000 kg empty, vice the 1,850 kg of the heavyweight version, and has no cooling system.

30-mm/65-caliber twin automatic AA (Russian AK-230)

Manufactured by Mashzavod imeni Ryabakov, Tula. Installed on many classes of ships—cruisers, destroyers, guided-missile boats, supply ships, and so on. Widely exported. Employs Drum Tilt (MR-104 Rys') radar director or Kolonka-1 remote ringsight director. Replaced in production by the AK-630/306 gatling gun system.

Mount weight: 1,905 kg **Muzzle velocity:** 1,050 m/sec
Rate of fire: 1,000 rds/min/barrel max.
Max. range for antiaircraft fire: 4,000 m

WEAPONS AND SYSTEMS *(continued)*

25-mm/80-caliber twin AA (Russian 2M-3M)

Still found on exported ships and a few Russian Navy units, the manned mount employs two superimposed guns, with an on-mount ringsight for control. Widely employed on Chinese and other former Soviet-client naval ships. The twin 2M-8 version of this mount was used on submarines in the 1950s, and the 2M-3 was an early, unpowered mounting.

Muzzle velocity: 900 m/sec **Rate of fire:** 150–200 rds/min/gun max.
Arc of elevation: −10° to +83° **Max. range:** 3,000 m

14.5-mm/93-caliber twin machine gun (Russian 2M-7)

Found in over-and-under twin open mountings.

Muzzle velocity: 1,000 m/sec **Rate of fire:** 150 rds/min/gun
Arc of elevation: −5° to +90° **Max. range:** 7,000 m

Note: Also still in use are 1930s-design, twin, over-and-under 12.7-mm 79-cal. 2M-1 machinegun mounts and the Utës-M twin 12.7-mm 60-cal. manned side-by-side mounting on Zhuk-class patrol boats, river monitors, and surface-effect amphibious craft; Utës-M has a combined 1,200 rds/min. rate of fire. The original Utës version has a single 12.7-mm mg.

For saluting purposes, old Type 21KM 45-mm guns have been adapted and are installed semipermanently in larger combatants.

D. ANTISUBMARINE WEAPONS

♦ Missiles

SS-N-14 Silex (Russian URPK-3/4 Metel'/URK-5 Rastrub) (1973/1984)

Two versions of this missile entered service, both given the same basic designation by NATO. The original URPK-3 system employed the Type 83R Metel' ("Snowstorm") missile with a 450-mm AT-1 (NATO E45-70A) homing torpedo payload carried below the fuselage. The AT-1 was replaced by the 533-mm AT-2UM (NATO 53-72) torpedo in 1973 and the missile was redesignated the Type 84R Metel'-M; the new torpedo had a range of 8 km with a 23-kt search speed and 40-kt attack speed and was effective to 400-m depths. The URPK-3 employed fixed quadruple KT-100M launchers and the Grom-M (NATO Head Lights-B) control radar for guidance. The URPK-4 version for the Krivak-series (Project 1135) frigates employed a quadruple trainable KTM-100-1135 launcher and was controlled by the MR-212 Drakon (NATO Eye Bowl) radar.

The original URPK-3 and URPK-4 were superseded in 1984 by the URK-5 Rastrub ("Bell") system, which used a "universal missile," the Type 83R, against either submarines or surface targets; for the latter mission, the missile body itself was fitted with a warhead. The homing torpedo payload is the UMGT-1 (NATO E45-75A), with an operating depth to 500 m, a maximum speed of 41 kts, and a range of 8 km. In the ASW mode, the missile cruises at 400-m altitude at Mach 0.95; in the antiship mode, the missile descends to 15 m in the terminal phase to deliver a 185-kg shaped hollow-charge warhead (in addition to the 60-kg warhead within the torpedo). The missile uses two solid drop-off boosters and a solid rocket sustainer and has folding wings and fins. The Type 85RUS variant is also equipped with an infrared terminal seeker. Also offered for export was a *shore*-launched version. The data below refer to the URK-5 system/Type 85R missile version:

Length: 7.205 m **Diameter:** 0.574 m (upper body) **Height:** 1.35 m
Weight: 3,930 kg **Speed:** 290 m/sec **Range:** 5–50 km

SS-N-15a/b Starfish (Russian RPK-6 Vodopod/Vodoley) (1981)

Antisubmarine missile very similar in concept and design to the former U.S. Navy UUM-44 SUBROC. Designed by Novator Bureau, Sverdlovsk. Submerged-launched from 533-mm submarine torpedo tubes on the Victor, Akula, and Sierra-series submarines and from torpedo tubes on later *Kirov*-class cruisers and on the frigate *Neustrashimyy.* Also usable against surface targets. The RPK-6 Vodopod ("Waterfall") uses Type 83R and 83RN (SS-N-15a) missiles, while the surface-launch version, referred to as Vodoley, uses Type 84R and nuclear-warhead 84RN (SS-N-15b) missiles. Launch depth is 50–150 m for the Vodopod, and launch preparations for both versions take only 10 seconds.

Length: 8.166 m **Diameter:** 533 mm **Weight:** 2,445 kg
Payload: 742-kg UMGT-1 homing torpedo with 100-kg warhead
Range: 10–35 km

Note: The weapon originally assigned the SS-N-15 Starfish designation by NATO was the now-retired RPK-2 V'yuga, which used the Type 81R missile and carried a 200-kT nuclear depth charge to a range of 10–35 km; V'yuga entered service in 1969.

SS-N-16a/b Stallion (Russian/RPK-7 Veter/Vodopod-MK) (1984)

Derived from the SS-N-15 system but uses 650-mm tubes and has roughly twice the range. Employs the Type 86R (B-255) missile to transport a 742-kg UMGT-1 acoustic homing torpedo, which has a range of 8 km, a maximum speed of 41 kts, a 100-kg warhead, and a sensor range of up to 1,500 m. Has a range of around 100 km, and the course reportedly can be command-changed in flight. Can be launched between 50 and 350 m depth. RPK-7 Veter is 11 m long. The Type 88R version (SS-N-16b) carries a nuclear depth bomb.

SS-NX-29 Medvedka (Russian Medvedka)

A small-ship antisubmarine missile system developed by Moscow Thermal Engineering Institute and under trial in the now-retired prototype Babochka-class hydrofoil *Aleksandr Kunakhovich* beginning in 1994; as of 10-00, funds were said to be unavailable to complete state trials for the missile, which has not yet entered production. Would be manufactured by Votinsky Zavod. Launches a rocket with a 2.8-m-long, 320-mm-diameter parachute-retarded homing Gidropribor Central Research Institute UTST-95 Kolibri thermal-propulsion torpedo payload. The rocket has a variable-thrust solid-fuel motor to variable ranges. Prototypes are four-tube, elevatable mountings, but the system is also offered in twin-tube and four-tube fixed launchers and rotatable two- or four-tube installations for larger ships. The fire-control system, developed by Granit Research and Production Association, electronically compensates for ship stabilization errors. A Mach 2 antiship variant is offered for development that would employ a two-stage solid rocket with active or passive terminal seeker and a range of 50 km. The launcher, with four missiles, weighs 9,500 kg.

Length: 5.35 m **Diameter:** 400 mm **Weight:** 750 kg
Range: 8–23 km **Depth of target:** 15–500 m

SS-NX-. . . (Russian Type 91RE2)

Offered for export by the Novator Experimental Machine-Design Bureau in 5-99. Designed for vertical or inclined launch. Has a solid-fueled APR-3ME torpedo payload. Would employ booster for launch and use a parachute to lower the torpedo after separation. The torpedo is 3.2 m long by 350 mm in diameter and weighs 450 kg, with a 76-kg warhead; it has a target-detection range of 2,000 m and a maximum attack depth of 800 m. Up to four missiles could be directed at one target. Missile data include:

Length: 6.20 m **Diameter:** 51.4 cm **Weight:** 1,200 kg **Range:** 40 km

♦ Rockets

Note: RBU = *Raketnaya Bombometnaya Ustanovka* (Rocket Depth-charge Launcher)

RPK-5 Liven' (1982)

A 10-tube weapon system similar in configuration to the RBU-6000 but launching a considerably larger Type 89R rocket with a range of up to 3,000 m (100 m minimum range) against submarines at down to 600-m depths. Manufacturer: Splav Research Enterprise, Tula. The export system is referred to as the UDAV-1 and the system has been referred to by NATO—inaccurately—as the RBU-12000. Primarily an antitorpedo system, with secondary ASW and antiswimmer functions. Launcher designation is KT-153. Found to date on the carriers *Admiral Gorshkov* and *Admiral Flota Sovetskogo Soyuza Kuznetsov,* and the *Kirov*-class cruisers *Admiral Nakhimov* and *Petr Velikiy.* Original trials were in a six-tube variant on Grisha-class corvette MRK-5. Primarily intended as a torpedo countermeasure launcher, with UDAV-1M-system projectiles in Type 111SZ simple explosive (232.5 kg each), 111SG acoustic-fuzed, or 111SO decoy rockets (201 kg each); the decoy rockets are fired in pairs, followed by the floating barrage rocket and simple barrage rockets. The system is said to have a reaction time of 15 seconds. The rockets are 300 mm in diameter, and the launcher weighs 6,600 kg.

RBU-6000 Smerch-2/RPK-8 Zapad

The 3,100-kg mount has 12 barrels, 2.00 m in length and 212 mm in diameter, arranged in a horseshoe and normally fired in paired sequence. Has a vertical automatic loading system, loading barrel by barrel. Can be trained and elevated. Maximum range: 6,000 m. Normal allowance is 192 rockets for each pair of two. Installed in *Slava* and *Kirov* cruisers; *Udaloy-,* Kara-, and Kashin-class guided-missile destroyers; Krivak and *Neustrashimyy*-class frigates; and Grisha-class corvettes. Uses the PUS-B Burya fire-control system and requires three personnel: one operator and two to load hoists in the magazine. The standard RGB-60 round is 1,830 mm long and weighs 110 kg; the warhead weighs 25 kg and has impact and time/impact fuzes. Can also be employed as a torpedo countermeasure, using RPK-8 rounds.

The RPK-8 Zapad antisubmarine rocket system uses the same launcher as the RBU-6000 system, but with the 90R missile, a 112.5-kg, 212-mm-diameter acoustic-homing round made by Splav State Research and Production Association that can detect targets up to 130 m away and can deflect from its ballistic descent after striking the water; the 90R has a 19-kg warhead and is said to be able to attack submarines at 1,000-m depths or defeat torpedoes at depths of up to 10 m. The 90R rocket, said to be 80% effective and eight times more effective than the RGB-60, has been bought by India and Algeria and is said to be in production for the Russian Navy.

RBU-2500

Made up of two horizontal rows of eight barrels each, approximately 1.6 m in length, which can be trained and elevated. Manual reloading. Range: 2,500 m. Has a 21-kg warhead. Now carried only by two *Smol'nyy*-class training ships and a handful of ships in foreign navies. Probably also usable as a torpedo countermeasure launcher.

RBU-1200 Uragan

Made up of two horizontal rows of short, superimposed barrels, three atop two. Tube diameter: 253.5 mm; length: 1.380 m. The 71.5-kg (34-kg warhead) rocket is 1.228 m long and 252 mm in diameter. Range: 1,200 m. Early installations were fixed in train and their tubes had to be manually loaded at 40° elevation, but systems in Natya and Pauk classes can be trained for firing and must be trained 90° outboard for loading from deckhouse magazines.

RBU-1000 Smerch-3

Primarily a torpedo countermeasure launcher, but can be used against submarines operating at up to 500-m depth, submarine countermeasures, and even frogmen. The stabilized 1,800-kg launcher is made up of six barrels arranged in two vertical rows of three and fired in order at 1-second intervals, with vertical automatic loading. Installed in Kara-, *Sovremennyy-,* and Kashin-class destroyers. Uses the PUS-B Burya fire-control system. Trainable. Tube diameter: 300 mm. Length: 2.165 m. Range: 1,000 m. Rocket weighs 195 kg (100-kg warhead). Normal allowance is 24 rounds per launcher.

DP-64

Handheld rocket-grenade launcher. A twin-barreled weapon launching 0.65-kg FG-45 high-explosive or SG-45 marker grenades to a range of 400 m. Said to have a 14-m destructive radius with the 0.18-kg explosive in the FG-45. Intended for use on classes of ships and submarines and also by shore personnel against combat swimmers.

WEAPONS AND SYSTEMS *(continued)*

DP-65

Lightweight rocket-grenade launcher. A 10-barreled launcher for 55-mm-diameter RG-55 rocket grenades, with a range of 5–500 m. Can be remotely aimed and elevated and uses acoustic target cueing to detect combat swimmers.

MRG-1

Seven-barreled, pedestal-mounted portable rocket grenade launcher intended for use by surface ships and harbor defenses against combat swimmers. Has a range of 50–500 m and employs 55-mm-diameter RG-55 grenades. Firing is cued by acoustic sensors.

♦ Depth charges

The successor to the long-standard PLAB depth bomb is the S3V (or KAB-250PL), which weighs 94 kg (with 50 kg of explosive) and has a length of 1.30 m and a diameter of 211 mm. The weapon has an active sonar fuzing system and can change its underwater trajectory by up to 60° off the initial path, sinking to a depth of 600 m in 16.2 seconds, at which point it can be up to 520 m offset from the original drop point. The S3V sinks at the rate of 16.2 m/sec. The PLAB-10K (RBK-11) is a cluster depth bomb with six small depth charges.

Note: Many of the weapons described in the Mines section are intended for use against submarines as well as surface ships.

E. TORPEDOES

Note: Although a great many different torpedoes have been produced over the past 40 years for submarine, surface-ship, and aircraft use, the number actually in widespread service is not as great, and many of those offered for export since 1990 exist only as paper designs or in prototype status. The listing below contains both service and export models but may not be exhaustive.

DST-90: Long-range, wake-homing torpedoes for submarine use. Maximum firing depth is 100 m, and the torpedo runs at a depth of 20 m. The gas-turbine propulsion system is fueled by a mix of kerosene and high-test hydrogen peroxide. May be related to SET-92K and APSET-92 torpedoes. Probably only a prototype system.

Diameter: 650 mm **Length:** 11.000 m **Weight:** 4,750 kg
Warhead weight: 557 kg **Speed/range:** 35 kts/50 km

DT: Long-range, submarine-launched export torpedo with active acoustic homing, although the illustration in a brochure showed it being used in what appeared to be a wake-homing mode (as well as in a preprogrammed mode against a harbor). Gas turbine; wakeless propulsion. Offered for export in 1993, although Russia does not export submarines with 650-mm torpedo tubes! May be only a paper project.

Diameter: 650 mm **Length:** 11.000 m **Weight:** 4,500 kg
Warhead weight: 445 kg **Speed/range:** 50 kts/50 km; 30 kts/100 km

65-76: Wake-homing weapon made by Dvigatel Zavod, St. Petersburg, and launched from Victor-III and all later submarines with 650-mm tubes. Probably available originally in both conventional and nuclear-warhead versions. The standard 650-mm long-range, wake-homing torpedo aboard Russian Navy nuclear-powered attack submarines. Entered service in 1957. The latest version, with hydrogen peroxide fuel, was removed from service in 2-02 as a result of the *Kursk* disaster. The torpedo is known as the "Kit" (Kite).

Diameter: 650 mm **Length:** 9.140 m
Warhead weight: 900 kg **Speed/range:** 50 kts/50 km; 30 kts/100 km

UMGT-1: Antisubmarine torpedo made by Dvigatel Zavod, St. Petersburg, and used as payload for RPK-6 Vodopod and RPK-7 Veter submarine missiles. An acoustic-homing weapon with a range of 8 km at 41 kts, a sensor range of 1,500 m, and a 100-kg warhead. Can be launched at depths up to 150 m.

UGST: Antisurface torpedo with pumpjet propulsor and unitary-fueled reciprocating engine. In development by Region and Mortep since the 1980s and offered for export; may not have entered production for Russian Navy use. Can attack submarines at depths to 500 m. Has magnetic and acoustic fuzes. Also offered with a television, wire-guided homing system for use against surface ships.

Diameter: 534.4 mm **Length:** 7.200 m **Weight:** 2,200 kg
Warhead weight: 200 kg **Speed/range:** 35–50 kts/20–35 km

TEST-71M: Wire-guided antisubmarine and antisurface torpedo from Dvigatel Zavod, St. Petersburg. Electrical propulsion. Has both acoustic proximity and contact fuzes. The silver-zinc battery has a 1-year shelf-life aboard submarines. Available for export in a 7.935-m-long version as TEST-71ME and TEST-71MVE, the latter for antisubmarine use. A practice variant weighing 1,480 kg or 1,445 kg is also available. Can be used against submarines operating down to 400 m in depth. Related to the SET-65E. The latest variant, TEST-71MK, remains in service and incorporates a wire-guidance feature.

Diameter: 534.4 mm **Length:** 8.260 m
Weight: 1,840 kg **Warhead weight:** 205 kg
Speed/range: 40 kts/20 km max. (cruise speed: 24 kts)

TEST-96: Multipurpose ship- and submarine-launched wire-guided export torpedo with active/passive homing, impact and proximity fuzes, and electric propulsion.

Diameter: 533 mm **Length:** 8.000 m **Weight:** 1,800 kg
Warhead weight: 250 kg **Speed/range:** . . ./. . .

ET-80A: Wire-guided, improved version of the SET-65 with 400-m depth capability. Electric propulsion. For use by submarines and surface ships.

Diameter: 533 mm **Length:** 7.800 m
Warhead weight: 272 kg **Speed/range:** 35 kts/15 km; . . ./12 km

53-68: Modernized, nuclear-warhead version of the 53-65 with 100-m launch depth and 300-m maximum operating depth. Straight runner with wakeless HTP fuel propulsion. No longer deployed, but may be retained in storage at land depots.

Diameter: 533 mm **Length:** 7.200 m
Warhead: 20 kT nuclear **Speed/range:** 45 kts/14 km

53-65K: Wake-homing anti–surface ship weapon with a closed-cycle turbine engine. Runs at 4- to 14-m depths and can successfully attack ships moving at up to 35 kts. Operational in 1968. Export version is 53-65KE. The practice version has a range of 12 km.

Diameter: 533.4 mm **Length:** 7.945 m **Weight:** 2,100 kg
Warhead weight: 300 kg **Range:** 55 kts/19 km; 40 kts/24 km

SET-65: Submarine torpedo with passive acoustic homing and electric propulsion and 400-m operating capability, operational in 1967. The practice version weighs 1,362 kg. A 2001 Russian brochure gives the SET-65E export version's speed as 40 kts and its maximum range as 16 km.

Diameter: 533.4 mm **Length:** 7.800 m **Weight:** 1,738 kg
Warhead weight: 205 kg **Speed/range:** 35 kts/10 km; 24 kts/15 km

53-83: Thermal engine–propelled, surface- and submarine-launched wake-homing weapon. Other than its diameter (533 mm), no data are available.

ET-80(66): Nuclear-warhead submarine torpedo with silver-zinc battery electric propulsion and a 300-m operating depth. Straight runner. No longer deployed, but may be retained in storage at land depots.

Diameter: 533 mm **Length:** 7.700 m
Warhead: 20 kT nuclear **Speed/range:** 35 kts/10 km; 20 kts/40 km

SAET-50/SAET-60M/USET-80: Referred to by NATO as the ET-80A. Entered service in 1961 as the first Soviet passive acoustic homing torpedo, intended for use by submarines against surface targets; runs at 5- to 14-m depths. The initial Soviet designation was probably SAET-50, while SAET-60 is a higher-performance version that appeared around 1966 and has a range of 15 km at 35 kts; both weapons use a 46-cell battery. The current version, known as the USET-80, is said to be only 10% reliable, although it is the most widely deployed torpedo on Russian submarines; it may have been the cause of the demise of the submarine *Kursk*.

Diameter: 534.4 mm **Length:** 7.800 m **Weight:** 1,855 kg
Warhead weight: 205 kg **Speed/range:** SAET-50: 23.3 kts/7.3 km

E53-75, E53-79: Electric torpedoes for air and missile delivery. May no longer be in use.

53-66: Electric-propelled straight and pattern-running torpedo for surface ship and submarine use. May no longer be in use.

53-57: Antiship torpedo for surface ships, introduced in 1957. May no longer be in use.

Diameter: 533 mm **Length:** . . .
Warhead weight: 300 kg **Speed/range:** 45 kts/18 km

53-56V, VA: Standard export torpedo boat weapon, either straight or pattern running with reciprocating air/steam propulsion. Entered service during the 1950s. A nuclear-warhead version with a 15-kT warhead was developed for Soviet submarine use but is no longer deployed.

Diameter: 533 mm **Length:** 7.000 m
Warhead weight: 400 kg **Speed/range:** 51 kts/4 km; 41 kts/8 km

SET-53M: Active acoustic antisubmarine torpedo, introduced in 1953 for use in surface ships. Probably long out of service in Russia but still may appear in foreign fleets.

Diameter: 533 mm **Length:** . . .
Warhead weight: 100 kg **Speed/range:** 29 kts/14 km

E45-75A: An improved E45-70 with a 300-m operating depth and electric propulsion, for delivery by SS-N-14 or aircraft. A modified, 4.6-m-long version is also in use that presumably has a longer range. E45-75A replaced the slower E45-70A.

Diameter: 450 mm **Length:** 3.900 m
Warhead weight: 90 kg **Range:** 38 kts/8 km

APSET-95: Russian Navy designation: UMGT-1 (NATO E40-79). Air-dropped ASW torpedo usable against 2- to 400-m-deep submarine targets. Parachute retarded. Uses active/passive homing and electric propulsion. An improved version, APSET-96, has also been offered for export.

Diameter: 400 mm **Length:** 3.845 m **Weight:** 650–720 kg
Warhead weight: 60 kg **Speed/range:** 24 or 40 kts/up to 20 km

USET-95 (Mod. 3): Multipurpose ship-, aircraft-, and submarine-launched export torpedo with active/passive acoustic homing for use against submarine and surface targets. Electric propulsion. Can be launched from 534.4-mm tubes using liners.

Diameter: 400 mm **Length:** 4.700 m **Weight:** 650–720 kg
Warhead weight: 60 kg **Speed/range:** 50 kts/. . .

SET-40: Active/passive-acoustic-homing, surface-launched antisubmarine torpedo with battery power. Seeker range is 585 m. Entered service around 1960 and has largely been succeeded by the SET-65. Also serves as the payload of the PMT-1 moored antisubmarine mine.

Diameter: 400 mm **Length:** 4.500 m **Weight:** 530 kg
Warhead weight: 80 kg **Speed/range:** 28 kts/8 km
Depth of target: up to 200 m

APR-2: Intended for dropping by helicopters and aircraft against submarines at depths of up to 600 m and moving at up to 43 kts. Has a solid-rocket propulsion system that continues to function underwater, and employs active acoustic homing with a range of 1,500 m. In effect, it is a cross between a homing torpedo and a self-propelled depth charge.

Diameter: 350 mm **Length:** 3.7 m **Weight:** 575 kg
Warhead: 100 kg Trotyl equivalent
Speed: 62 kts **Endurance:** 1–2 min

APR-3: A developmental, updated version of the APR-2 under development that will use pumpjet propulsion vice the APR-2's rocket; it will be effective to 800-m depths. The APR-3E is offered for export. For both, the seeker sensor is a multichannel active sonar with 1.5–2.0° bearing accuracy, and the guidance system employs two-plane adaptive lead-angle computation. The APR-3 searches in an 1,800- to 2,000-m-diameter circle and has a 2,000-m detection range. It is offered as the payload for the Type 91RE2 antisubmarine missile system (see description under antisubmarine missiles).

WEAPONS AND SYSTEMS *(continued)*

Diameter: 350 mm **Length:** 3.20 m **Weight:** 450 kg
Warhead: 76 kg TNT equivalent
Speed: 65 kts search, 100 kts attack **Endurance:** . . .

GPD-3: Decoy device designed to be carried two per torpedo tube. Russian designation: MG-74. Nickname: "Impostor." Each 3.9-m-long, 533-mm-diameter, 797-kg device can be instructed to perform noise jamming, selective jamming of active sonars, or echo simulation and can be used at up to 250-m depths. Developed by Gidropribor Central Research Institute. A 400-mm-diameter, 4.5-m-long decoy device with a weight of 497 kg is also still in use.

VA-111 Shkval: A 533-mm-diameter, 195-kt, rocket-propelled weapon that travels in a supercavitating vacuum bubble. Made by Region. Its maximum range is only 7–10 km. Probably intended as a countermeasure against torpedo attack, using a nuclear warhead to destroy not only the enemy torpedoes but also the launch platform. Entered service in 1977 but was removed from service in 1991 and stored for possible future use. A version with a speed of 300 kts is in development, with initial sea trials conducted in spring 1998; a Shkval-E variant with a 210-kg-TNT warhead is offered for export, and the new version is equipped with a target sensor of unspecified variety. The weapon's diameter would preclude its being launched from a conventional 533-mm torpedo tube, thus limiting its use to the Russian Navy. Shkval-E uses both a contact and a probable laser fuse. The Kazakhstani factory in 1999 sold China a number of Shkvals but not the fire-control system, rendering them useless. The earlier RAT-52 air-dropped rocket torpedo has been retired. Data for the export Shkval-E include:

Diameter: 534.4 mm **Length:** 8.2 m
Weight: 2,700 kg **Warhead:** 210 kg TNT equivalent
Speed: 90–100 m/sec **Max. effective range:** 10 km

Note: For launching 400-mm-diameter torpedoes from surface ships, single 402-mm OTA-40 fixed tubes are employed; the tubes are 4.90 m long and weigh 475 kg empty. They employ gunpowder ejection. For surface ships with 533-mm weapons, the 536-mm-diameter, 8.525-m-long PTA-series trainable or fixed tubes are used; they also employ gunpowder ejection and are electrically trained.

F. MINES

Russia has a vast inventory of air-, surface-, and submarine-launched mines, using mechanical (contact), acoustic, magnetic, and possibly pressure fuzing. Older mines still available include the M12, M16, M26, M31, KB1, MAG, AMAG1, PLT-G, PL-150, KRAB, MIRAB, MKB-3, MAG, and MYaM. Specific details are unavailable for the modern systems, such as the KMD and AMD, which have 300-kg explosive charges, and the rocket-propelled rising mines known by NATO as "Cluster Bay" and the deep-water "Cluster Gulf," which have 230 kg of explosives. The RMZ and YaRM mines are small antimine countermeasures and anti-invasion weapons. There may also be stocks of nuclear-armed mines.

Mines offered for export in 2-93 at the IDEX-93 arms show included:

KPM: Surface ship–launched moored anti-invasion beach defense mine designed to be laid by smallcraft moving at up to 6 kts. Weighs 745 kg, has a 480-kg TNT-equivalent warhead, and can be moored in waters 5–20 m deep. Length: 1.40 m; width: 0.7 m; height: 0.745 m.

MDM-1: Electromagnetic and acoustic influence bottom mine launched by submarines traveling at up to 8 kts or surface ships moving at up to 15 kts. Weighs 960 kg and has an explosive charge equivalent to 1,120 kg of TNT. Measures 2.860 m long by 533 mm in diameter. Can be emplaced in waters 12–120 m deep.

MDM-2: Surface-launched bottom mine with three-channel acoustic exploder, detonation delay setting, ship counter, and self-destruction feature. Weight: 1,413 kg with 950-kg TNT-equivalent warhead. Measures 2.30 m long by 790 mm in diameter (atop cart). Can be laid in waters 12–35 m deep (125 m for use as an antisubmarine mine).

MDM-3: Aircraft- or surface-launched three-channel fuzed (acoustic/electromagnetic/pressure) bottom mine. In the surface-launched version, the device weighs 635 kg with cart and is 1.525 m long; air launched (at up to 540 kts), it weighs 525 kg and is 1.58 m long. Both variants carry 300-kg-TNT-equivalent warheads. Can be emplaced in waters up to 35 m deep.

MDM-4: Aircraft- or surface-launched three-channel fuzed (acoustic/electromagnetic/pressure) bottom mine. In the surface-launched version, the device weighs 1,420 kg with cart and is 2.30 m long; air launched (at up to 540 kts), it weighs 1,370 kg and is 2.785 m long. Both variants carry 950-kg-TNT-equivalent warheads. Can be emplaced in waters up to 50 m deep (125 m surface-launched or 250 m air-dropped as an antisubmarine mine).

MDM-5: Aircraft- or surface-launched three-channel fuzed (acoustic/electromagnetic/pressure) bottom mine. In the surface-launched version, the device weighs 1,470 kg with cart and is 2.40 m long; air launched (at up to 540 kts), it weighs 1,500 kg and is 3.055 m long. Both variants carry 1,350-kg-TNT-equivalent warheads. Can be emplaced in waters up 60 m deep (300 m for use as an antisubmarine mine).

MDM-6: Offered in 3-94, it can be launched by surface ships traveling 4–15 kts or submarines traveling 4–8 kts, can be laid in waters as shallow as 12 m or as deep as 120 m, and has a 1-year in-water life. Seeker is similar to that of the larger MDM-5. Weighs 960 kg and is 2.860 m long by 533 mm in diameter.

MDS: Mobile bottom mine laid by submarines. Resembles a torpedo and has contra-rotating propellers. Employs an influence sensor and can be laid in waters more than 8 m deep. Weight: 1,380 kg; length: 7.9 m; diameter: 534 mm.

MShM: A 4.00-m-long export rising mine, said also to be torpedo tube–launched and to be intended for emplacement in waters 60–300 m deep. The payload is rocket driven, with the rocket ejected from the cylindrical, 533-mm-diameter capsule. The entire weapon weighs 820 kg, and the rocket has a 250-kg warhead. The rocket uses an acoustic target sensor, and one is capable of covering an area of 882,000 m^2.

RMK-1: A 1,850-kg, 7.83-m-long by 533-mm-diameter, tethered antisubmarine mine moored in depths from 200 to 400 m. Releases a rocket-powered homing device with a 350-kg warhead. Offered for export as the RMR-2. Entered service in 1983 as a replacement for the RMT-1. It can be emplaced from air, surface, or submarine platforms.

RMT-1: Moored antisubmarine mine that releases a SET-40 homing torpedo, equivalent to the U.S. Navy's CAPTOR system and said to be superior in performance. Entered service in 1972. The torpedo, at the top of the array, is launched horizontally.

RM-2: Rocket-assisted submarine- or ship-laid moored mine with influence sensors; the activated mine launches the stabilized, solid-fuel rocket, which has both impact and influence fuzing. Can be laid in depths up to 450 m. Weight: 870 kg; length: 3.850 m; diameter: 534 mm.

SMDM: Submarine torpedo tube–launched mine. Version 1 is 533 mm in diameter, weighs 7,900 kg, has a 480-kg warhead, and can be emplaced in waters 4–100 m deep. Version 2 is 650 mm in diameter, weighs 5,500 kg, has an 800-kg warhead, and can be emplaced in waters 8–150 m deep. Propelled by a torpedo afterbody to a predetermined location. An "SMDM-4," offered in 3-94, can be emplaced in waters as shallow as 4 m or as deep as 150 m and has an explosive weight equivalent to 480 kg of TNT and a working life of 1 year.

UDM/UDM-2/UDM-500: Antisurface and antisubmarine magnetic influence mines intended for air drop or surface launch. Usable in waters more than 8 m deep. UDM and UDM-2 have fin stabilizers, while UDM-500 has a braking parachute. UDM weighs (surface launch/aircraft launch) 1,420/1,320 kg and is 2.100/2.785 m long by 790/630 mm in diameter. UDM-2 weighs 1,470/1,500 kg and is 2.400/3.055 m long by 630 mm in diameter. UDM-500 weighs 635/575 kg and is 1.525/1.500 m long by 600/450 mm in diameter.

G. RADARS

Note: Radars are listed by their NATO names, although because those names were based on appearance rather than performance characteristics, there is not always a direct correlation to the actual Russian designation and name, which, where known, are given. In the ship listings, the Russian designations and names are given first, with the NATO names in parentheses. For some radars, there appears to be more than one nickname; while this may be a case of there being both domestic and export system names, it may also indicate that there are capability and/or configurational differences as well.

♦ Navigational

The most widely used are the X-band Don-2, Mius (Spin Trough), Volga (Don-Kay), and MR-212/201 Vaygach and Vaygach-U (Palm Frond). Kivach-3, and MR-312 Nayada are Russian designators (also used by NATO) for small sets used on recent small combatants and auxiliaries. Many ships carry two or three navigational sets (port-and-starboard antennas normally operate together with a single display).

♦ Surface search

Submarines carry the MRK-50 Albatros/Tobol series (Snoop Tray, Snoop Slab, Snoop Plate, or Snoop Pair), all operating in the X band. Submarines also carry ranging radars mounted on their attack periscopes.

♦ Long-range air search

Big Net: Russian designation: MR-500 Kliver ("Jib"). A large L-band (850-MHz) radar fitted on the two surviving Kashin destroyers. Its detection range on an aircraft is probably more than 100 miles.

Flat Screen: Russian MR-700 Podberezovik. Made by Salyut, Moscow, and offered for export as the Podberezovik-ET1 and -ET2. C-band, planar array, rotating 3-D long-range air-search radar found only aboard the Kara-class destroyer *Kerch'*. Has 300-km range against a 7-m^2 target at 1,500-m altitude, with a 5-km minimum range. Can track a 500-m^2 surface target at 30 km. Rotates at 12 rpm. System weighs 13 tons with a 3-ton antenna and requires 110 kw.

Half Plate: Russian MR-755 Fregat-MA. Made by Salyut Moscow Production Association. Single-antenna, phased array set on two modernized Krivak-I frigates and some Grisha-V corvettes. Said to have a range of 150 km against air targets within a 55° vertical swath. Rotates at 15 rpm and has a system weight of 6,500 kg.

Head Net-C: Russian MR-310U Angara-M. S-band radar with an antenna consisting of two Head Net-A antennas mounted back to back, one in a horizontal plane, the other tilted about 30°. Once widely used on cruisers and destroyers. The Head Net–series radars use a band that gives a 60- to 70-mile detection range on an attack bomber flying at high altitude.

Peel Cone: Russian Reyd. Small air/surface-search combined radar used on Maritime Border Guard Muravey-, Stenka-, and Pauk-class patrol craft and on naval Pauks and Mukha-class hydrofoils.

Plate Steer: Russian M-700-series Fregat-M. S band. Top Steer and Strut Curve antennas combined in a back-to-back array on two early *Sovremennyy*-class destroyers and the carrier *Admiral Flota Sovetskogo Soyuza Kuznetsov.*

Sky Watch: Russian Mars-Passat. The Russian Navy's first fixed, planar-array, early-warning radar, employing four arrays. Apparently unsuccessful and probably not operational (provision was made for it on the carrier *Kuznetsov,* but it does not seem to have been installed).

Slim Net: Russian Fut-N. An early-model S-band radar fitted on Petya-class corvettes and no longer in Russian Navy service.

Strut Curve: Russian MR-302 Rubka. S-band set on early Grisha-series corvettes. Widely exported.

Strut Pair: Russian MR-320M Topaz/Topaz-M/V. S band. Mounted on the carrier *Kuznetsov,* early *Udaloy*-class destroyers, and early Grisha-V corvettes. Employs pulse compression. The antenna is essentially two Strut Curve reflectors back to back. Manufactured by Typhoon Instrument Building Plant, Kaluga.

Top Pair: Russian MR-800 Flag or Voskhod. C/F-band, 3-D radar using a Top Sail and a Big Net antenna mounted back to back. Used on the *Kirov* and *Slava* classes, always accompanied by a Top Steer backup radar. Said to have a range of 500 km against aerial targets. Antenna rotates at 3–12 rpm, and system weight is 43,500 kg.

Top Plate: Russian MR-750 Fregat-MA; the version on the frigate *Neustrashimyy* is designated MR-760 and Top Plate-B (Russian MR-710 Fregat-MA) is on the *Slava*-

WEAPONS AND SYSTEMS *(continued)*

class cruisers *Varyag* and *Admiral Flota Lobov*. MR-750 is an E-band radar with identical back-to-back, phased-array, 3-D radar antennas on *Udaloy*-class destroyers *Marshal Vasilevskiy, Admiral Zakharov,* and later. Can detect a 7-m^2 target at a range of 130 km at 5,000 m altitude or a 300-m^2 ship at 30 km. Rotates at 15 rpm. Requires 30 kw of 380-V, 50-Hz current. System weighs 7.5 tons with a 2.2-ton antenna. Associated with the Poima-E data processor, which can track 20 targets simultaneously. Export version is Fregat-MAE. Related to the single-antenna MR-755 Fregat-MA (Half Plate).

Top Sail: Russian MR-600 Voskhod ("Dawn"). S-band, 3-D radar now installed only on two Kara-class destroyers. Uses a very large, heavy, stabilized antenna.

Top Steer: Russian MR-700 Fregat. S-band, back-to-back, 3-D radar antenna using one Top Steer and one Top Plate antenna, on later *Sovremennyy*-class destroyers.

♦ Missile tracking and control

Band Stand: Russian Monolit (although the nickname "Mineral" appears to be applied when the dome is associated with the SS-N-22 missile system and "Titanit" when it is associated with SS-N-9). On *Sovremennyy* destroyers and Tarantul-II and Nanuchka guided-missile combatants, the radome covers an L-band, tropospheric-scatter radar for antiship missile target acquisition, tracking, and control. Housed in a large radome. In export ships (and possibly some Russian installations), "Band Stand" covers a Square Tie missile target acquisition radar, associated with the SS-N-2 Styx family; later classes may have Band Stand radomes over Plank Shave antiship missile target-designation radars.

Cross Dome: Russian MR-352 Pozitiv series. Manufactured by Typhoon Instrument Building Plant, Kaluga. Separate target detection and tracking radar for the Kortik/Kashtan gun-and-missile CIWS, with antennas mounted in a hemispherical radome. Export versions are Pozitiv-E, Pozitiv-E1.1, etc. Three-dimensional system with a range from 15 to 110 km and capable of tracking 30 targets simultaneously.

The Pozitiv-ME1.2 version does not employ a radome and is a true 3-D radar. Employing a mechanically stabilized, rotating, single-pane phased-array antenna with IFF interrogation antenna on the lower edge, the radar is tailored to act as the target detection and designation set for the Kashtan CIWS. The first customer was Algeria.

Cross Sword: Russian MR-350 or MR-360 Podkat. Manufactured by Typhoon Instrument Building Plant, Kaluga. Ku- and X-band, multiarray missile guidance director for the SA-N-9 SAM system. Incorporates both detection/tracker radar and illuminator/tracker antennas. Probably has an electro-optical backup. Can track and attack four targets simultaneously within a 60°-wide by 60°-high field.

Eye Bowl: Russian MR-212 Drakon or Musson. F band. A smaller version of the command antenna component of Head Lights, installed in *Udaloy*-class destroyers and Krivak-series frigates (which do not have Head Lights). Command radar for the SS-N-14 antisubmarine/antiship missile system.

Front Dome: Russian OP-3. X-band target illuminator for the SA-N-7 SAM system in the *Sovremennyy*-class destroyers (which have six) and on Indian Navy Project 15 destroyers and Project 1135 frigates. Resembles the gun fire-control radar Bass Tilt and is very compact. Each director can track two targets simultaneously if the targets are reasonably close together.

Head Lights-C: Russian Grom. F-, G-, H-, and D-band antenna now mounted only on two Kara-class guided-missile destroyers. Similar to Peel Group, with an assembly of tracking radar for the target and guidance radar for the missile. Used for guidance for the Goblet missile of the SA-N-3 system and for the surface-to-underwater missiles of the SS-N-14 system. Formerly found in several versions, designated Head Lights-A, -B, and -C, the last being equipped to provide tracking and control of SS-N-14 missiles.

Hot Flash: Russian 3P-87. Multiantenna radar weapons-control system found on the Kortik combined SA-N-11 SAM/twin 30-mm gatling AA close-in defense system mounting. Controls the guns and provides target designation to the missiles.

Peel Group: Russian Yatagan. Now found only on the two surviving Kashin-series destroyers. The antenna assembly is made up of two groups of large and small reflectors, in both horizontal and vertical orientation, with parabolic design (S-band tracker; X-band tracker). Maximum range is approximately 30–40 miles. Used for guidance of the Goa missile in the SA-N-1 system.

Plank Shave: Russian 3Ts-25 Garpun ("Harpoon"), designed by the Granit Central Research Institute and manufactured by Typhoon Instrument Building Plant, Kaluga. Employed as an active and passive target detection and designation system for shorter-range antiship missile systems of the Termit (SS-N-2) and Kh-35 Uran (SS-N-25) series; it is also capable of being employed as a surface- and air-search radar. A successor to Square Tie, acting as air/surface search and missile target acquisition and tracking radar. The latest export variant is known as Garpun-Bal E1 (3Ts-25E1) and is said to have a range of 45 km in active mode and 70–500 km in passive intercept mode; the system has a 0.2–1.5° bearing accuracy in passive mode and 1° bearing accuracy when active and can track six targets simultaneously.

Pop Group: Russian MPZ-301 Baza (export name: Korund). F-, H-, and I-band missile guidance set for the SA-N-4 system. Upper component rotates independently and serves as a target acquisition radar; lower portion is used for missile control and can handle two missiles at once. Latest version appears to have an electro-optical backup.

Square Tie: Russian Rangout. Employed for SS-N-2-series missile target detection and designation. Also acts as a surface-search radar and probably can be used as a passive radar intercept receiver. Found on exported Osa-series small missile combatants and also used by the Chinese Navy.

Top Dome: Russian Volna. X-band director associated with the SA-N-6 vertically launched SAM system in the *Kirov*- and *Slava*-class cruisers. Employs a 4-m-diameter hemispheric radome, fixed in elevation but mechanically steerable in azimuth. Three smaller dielectric radomes are mounted on the face of its mounting pedestal, and there is also a smaller hemispheric radome below it. Can reportedly track six targets at once, although probably only if all are within about a 60° cone.

Trap Door-C: Russian Argon. Used for tracking the SS-N-12 missiles on the *Slava*-class cruisers (with the Argon-1164 antenna mount fixed on the mast).

♦ Gunfire control

Bass Tilt: Russian MR-123 Vympel; export name: Koral-E. X(I)-band radar director used with paired AK-630 gatling guns fitted in *Kiev* carriers and Kara cruisers, as well as in Grisha-III corvettes, where it also controls the twin 57-mm, and in Nanuchka-III corvettes and Matka guided-missile patrol craft, where it also controls the 76.2-mm gun. Tracking ranges are up to 45 km (30 km with MTI). Peak power output: 250 kw with 1.8° beamwidth. Normally rotates at 15 rpm until going into target tracking mode. System weight: 5.2 tons. The latest version, MR-123-02, incorporates a television camera and laser rangefinder.

Drum Tilt: Russian MR-104 Rys'. C- and X-band radar director installed on ships and craft fitted with 30-mm AK-230 twin-barrel AA.

Hawk Screech: Russian Fut-B. X-band director for 76.2-mm DP guns; always found in conjunction with optical director/target designators. Obsolescent.

Kite Screech-A, -B, -C: Russian MR-114, MR-145, and MR-184 Lev. X- and Ka-band director to control 100-mm AK-100 and 130-mm AK-130 twin DP. There is a television backup and laser rangefinder adjunct in Kite Screech-B. Can track targets to 75 km and tracks its own shells for correction, employing a digital computer. Elevates to 75°. System weight: 8.0 tons. Has MTI and ECCM features. Beamwidth: 1° in X band and 0.25° in Ka band. Peak output power: 300 kw in X band, 25 kw in Ka band. MR-184 Kite Screech-C is used with 130-mm guns, while MR-145 Kite Screech-B is used with 100-mm mounts in recent classes and MR-114 Kite Screech-A was found only in the Krivak-II-class frigates.

Muff Cob: Russian MR-103 Bars. C-band director for 57-mm AA twin automatic guns. Has a television camera attachment.

Owl Screech: Russian MR-105 Turel'. X-band director for 76.2-mm DP guns. An improved version of Hawk Screech, without the associated manned target designators.

Note: A new radar gunfire-control system nicknamed Laska was offered for export in 4-97 by the Topaz Moscow State Industrial Complex.

♦ Datalink antennas

Light Bulb: Russian Pricep. Spherical radomes found only on SS-N-22 Sunburn antiship missile–equipped *Sovremennyy*-class destroyers (two antennas) and Tarantul-III missile boats (one antenna). Apparently performs a datalink function with the missiles.

Note: The Russian Navy also employs numerous other datalink systems, for which details are unavailable. Such datalinks include systems permitting aircraft to provide targeting data to surface ships and submarines for over-the-horizon launching of antiship missiles. Some of the Bell-series radomes usually associated with EW functions may actually house directional datalink antennas tailored to specific weapons systems or functions such as ASW.

H. SONARS

Until the late 1950s, the Soviet Navy showed little interest in antisubmarine warfare or, of course, submarine detection. Most of its ships were equipped with HF sonars (Tamir-11 or -11M, Pegas, Herkules) of World War II–era concept. New or modernized ships have much-improved sensors. Where known, actual Russian nomenclature is employed in the ship data sections; most sonars have alphanumeric designators beginning with "MG-."

♦ For surface ships

MG-7: Used on Yevgenya (Project 1258) inshore minesweepers and as a static swimmer and chariot detection set, lowered on a cable while at moorings. HF (above 100 kHz).

MG-11 Tamir-11 (NATO Stag Ear): HF (24.5–30 kHz) searchlight set, no longer used by the Russian Navy but still found in smaller export craft in Third World fleets

MG-26 Khrom, Khrom-K, or Khrom-2M: standard underwater telephone set

MG-35 Shtil: MF underwater communications set used in the Kara and Krivak-III classes and on most submarine classes. MG-35E is an export version offered by the Akhtuba Instrumentation Plant; it has 6-kw transmission power.

MG-69 and -69M: Made by Priboy. Mine countermeasures sonars, with the MG-69M (offered for export in 2000) having a bottom-mine detection capability and incorporating digital technology and a new signal processor.

MG-79 Mizen: A further improvement on the MG-16 Lany (NATO Stag Ear), used in Natya-class minesweepers. Range against bottom mines in up to 100 m of water is said to be as much as 400 m, with 1.5° bearing accuracy.

MG-89 and -89M Serna: Made by Priboy. Combined MF/HF set used in late and export Natyas for minehunting and mine avoidance. Range: 1,500 m against moored mines or 500 m against bottom mines, with 1.5° bearing accuracy. MG-89M, offered for export in 2000, employs digital technology and a new signal processor.

MG-311 Vychegda (NATO Wolf Paw): Used in the Kashin, Koni, and Petya classes for ASW search

MG-312 Titan (NATO Bull Nose): MF ASW set in the Kashin and Koni classes

MG-322: Possible designation for the search component of the set in the one Bulgarian Koni. MG-322T is used in the Parchim-class units now in Indonesian service.

MG-325 Vega (NATO Mare Tail): VDS on older major combatants

MG-332 Titan-2 (NATO Bull Nose): Hull or bow mounted; the main search set in the Kara class

MG-335 Platina (NATO Bull Horn): In the *Kuznetsov, Slava,* and *Sovremennyy* classes

MG-335M Argun': Hull-mounted LF set used in Grisha-series corvettes and the nuclear-powered intelligence collector *Ural*

MG-509 Radian (NATO Mouse Roar): Mine-avoidance sonar fitted on submarines with the Kerch and Rubin sonar suites

MG-519 Arfa: Mine-avoidance sonar fitted to submarines with the Rubikon or Skat-series sonar suites

MG-747 Amulet: HF dipping sonar on the nuclear-powered intelligence collector *Ural* and possibly other units

MGK-345 Bronza: Said to have a range of 4.6 km hull-mounted, 5.5 km as a towed VDS, and 7 km in the dipping version. Operates at center frequencies of 6.5, 7.0, and 7.5 kHz, with 1% range accuracy and 0.7° bearing accuracy. Has range scales up to 32 km. A component of the Zvezda M-1 sonar suite (NATO Rat Tail).

WEAPONS AND SYSTEMS *(continued)*

MGK-335MS Pirhana: May be the designation for the VDS version of Platina used on Krivak-I and -II. The VDS version can be towed at up to 150-m depths.
MGK-355 Polinom (NATO Horse Jaw/Horse Tail): Active bow-mounted and VDS suite on the *Kirov*-class cruisers and *Udaloy*-class destroyers
MGK-365 Zvezda M-1 (NATO Ox Yoke/Ox Tail): LF active/passive bow array on the carrier *Kuznetsov,* frigate *Neustrashimyy,* and two Krivak frigates. The destroyer *Admiral Chabanenko* has the Zvezda M-2 variant.

♦ For submarines

Systems currently employed include:

MGK-400 Rubikon: Sonar suite on Tango- and Kilo-class diesel submarines and Delta-III SSBNs
MGK-503 Skat-KS (NATO Shark Gill): Sonar suite on Victor-III and Sierra-I SSNs. SKAT-BDRM is on the Delta-IV-class SSBNs. An upgraded version of the basic MGK-500 Skat. The system includes passive detection arrays, sound intercept warning system, communications system, MG-512 self-noise measurement set, MG-518 upward-beam echo sounder for ice navigation, MG-519 mine-detection/avoidance active set, MR-553 sound-velocity measurement device, NOR-1 ice-free lane detection set, and NOK-1 safe-surfacing set to detect overhead obstacles.
MGK-540 Skat-3 (NATO Shark Gill): Sonar suite on Akula-I, Akula-II, and Sierra-II SSNs and Oscar-II SSGNs; the first Russian all-digital sonar system
MGK-. . . Lira: New sonar suite for the Lada-class SS
MGK-. . . Irtysh Amfora: Sonar suite for the *Severodvinsk*-class SSN; uses a spherical bow array
MGS-30: Emergency pinger for sunken submarines, effective to 6,000 m and with a range of 10 km; can be interrogated up to nine months after sinking

♦ For aircraft

Ka-27PL Helix ASW helicopters carry dipping sonars, which are also used aboard smaller ASW patrol craft such as the Turya and Stenka classes. Land-based maritime patrol/ASW aircraft (Bear-F, May) carry an extensive family of sonobuoys.

♦ Fixed sea-based

Numerous fixed hydrophone arrays are installed to protect Soviet naval bases and harbors. The Cluster Lance planar arrays are used in the Pacific area.

I. ELECTRONIC WARFARE

The large number of radomes of every description that can be seen on Soviet ships, especially on the newest and most important types (helicopter and guided-missile cruisers, for example) is an indication of the attention the Russian Navy gives to electronic warfare. NATO code names for the antenna arrays for intercept or jamming radars include the Side Globe intercept/jamming; Top Hat-A intercept; Top Hat-B jamming; Bell Thump/Bell Bash intercept/jamming; Bell Shroud/Bell Squat intercept; Rum Tub intercept; Bell Clout intercept; Cage Pot intercept; Sprat Star VHF intercept; Grid Crane VHF–UHF intercept; Site Crane VHF intercept; and Watch Dog intercept. Literally hundreds of antennas have received NATO nicknames, and it is not possible to list them all here; the individual antennas are listed by name and correlated to Russian system names (where known) on the ship data pages.

Submarine EW systems employ the following NATO-designated antenna arrays:

Bald Head: Russian Bukhta system. Large radome combined with Snoop Head radar array on Oscar-II-class SSGNs.
Brick Pulp: Russian MRP-10 Zaliv-P or Buleva system. Plain radome on Delta-III and Delta-IV SSBNs and Victor-III SSNs.
Rim Hat: Truncated conical radome combined with Snoop Pair radar on Akula- and Sierra-class SSNs
Squid Head: Russian MRM-25EM system. Thimble radome atop ring of small disc antennas on the Kilo and Tango classes.
Stop Light-A: Russian Nakat. Older system (1–18 GHz) on export Kilo-class SSs.

Russian designations for EW systems offered for export (but not correlated to NATO-designated system nicknames) include:

MR-401S/MP-401MS: Integrated intercept and jamming system for surface ships, with a 7–30° bearing accuracy, five operating personnel, and a system weight of 6,100 kg
MR-405: Integrated intercept/jamming system that also cues launch of decoys from the PK-16 weapons system. The active component offers repeater, masking, spot, and barrage jamming and provides 360° coverage. The system weighs 2,000 kg and requires two operators.
MR-407: Integrated intercept/jamming system that also cues decoy launch from PK-2 and PK-16 launchers. The system weighs 6,500 kg and has three operators. May equate to NATO Foot Ball radome array on *Sovremennyy*-class destroyers.

Three types of decoy rocket launchers are employed:

PK-2: Twin-tube, autoloading 140-mm ZIF-121 launcher, mechanically elevated and trained, with AZ-TSP-47 (36.1-kg chaff), AZ-TST-47 (37.5-kg infrared), and AZ-TSO-47 (38.5-kg combined chaff/IR) rounds; all varieties are 1.105 m long. Entering service is the AZ-TSTV-47 round, which floats and dispenses a 6,000-m-long aerosol cloud to defeat laser rangefinders. Each system weighs 15,000 kg, and 100 rounds per launcher are carried. Can fire at 15 rds/min. Requires a crew of five to seven personnel. Used on Maritime Border Guard Amur River Flotilla Yaz-class monitors as an artillery device, firing antipersonnel grenades.
PK-10: Ten-tube, 120-mm, fixed elevation and train, with SR-50 (25.5-kg chaff), SOM-50 (25-kg infrared- and laser-fuzed decoy), and SK-50 (25-kg chaff/IR/laser combined) rounds; all rounds are 1.226 m long. The system first appeared on a *Udaloy* in 1989 and is now widely deployed. The launcher itself, which weighs 205 kg, is designated KT-216; as many as 16 can be controlled from one console on a large ship.
PK-16: East German–designed, 16-round, 82-mm bore, fixed-train, mechanically elevated, with TSP-60U (8.3-kg chaff) and TSP-60U (8.5-kg infrared) rounds; both varieties are 653 mm long. The launcher designation is KT-101. A 32-round version, PK-32, was installed on East German–built *Sassnitz*-class patrol boats.

TACAN systems include the large cylindrical Cake Stand array on aircraft carriers, and the various forms of the paired cylindrical Privod (NATO Round House) array on the *Kirov, Udaloy,* and other classes. A variety of microwave automatic aircraft landing system arrays are used on modern carriers, cruisers, destroyers, and *Neustrashimyy*-class frigates.

J. COMMUNICATIONS

All Russian Navy warships are equipped to transmit and receive MF through VHF communications, while submarines have a VLF capability (using towed buoy antennas) and UHF equipment is coming into wider use in surface ships. VHF antennas in use include: Cage Bare, Cage Cone, Cage Stalk, and the older Straight Key. Major warships usually have a Pop Art VHF antenna. Submarines rely on VLF, using towed wire and/or towed buoy antennas, and a land-based ELF submarine communications alerting station entered service in the early 1990s. Tu-142 Bear-J aircraft were equipped with a trailing wire antenna strategic submarine communications system analogous to the U.S. TACAMO system.

K. SATELLITES

The Russians had hoped to maintain an ocean surveillance ELINT satellite system whose data was to be transmitted either to ground stations or directly to ships equipped with the SS-N-12 and SS-N-19 cruise-missile systems, but recent economic problems have made it difficult to sustain the necessary satellite constellation; the system is thus only intermittently operational at best. The receiving antenna is mounted in a large cylindrical radome termed Punch Bowl. Many other ships can apparently also employ Russian and Western commercial communications and navigational satellites.

L. INFRARED AND ELECTRO-OPTICAL SYSTEMS

Cod Eye: Radiometric sextant used on ballistic-missile submarines for precision navigation
Half Cup: Russian Spektr-F. A laser detection system seen increasingly on combatants and intelligence collection ships. The fixed devices are normally installed in pairs and have a 20- to 25-km range against the infrared emissions from an incoming missile. Made by the Industrial Amalgam Zagorskiy Optika-Mekhanichevkyy Zauro.
Squeeze Box: Installed on *Sovremennyy*-class destroyers and on *Ivan Rogov*- and Alligator-class landing ships with 140-mm artillery rocket launchers. A lightweight version is used on Pomornik-class surface-effect landing craft. Believed to incorporate television, laser rangefinder, and infrared sensors and used in artillery rocket fire control.
Tee Plinth: Russian MT-45. Heavyweight television sensor installed in large ships in the 1960s and 1970s.

Note: Also in use are smaller, fixed television surveillance devices such as Tilt Pot and periscopes mounted atop pilothouses to permit operations in biological or chemical warfare conditions and poor weather. The "Tall View" periscope in the *Sovremennyy* class probably provides the commanding officer with his own view when he is in the command center during combat operations; there are similar "CIC periscopes" in other large combatants. All combatant submarines carry both a wide-field-of-view search periscope and a higher-magnification, narrow-view attack periscope, the latter probably fitted with a laser and/or radar rangefinder.

GUIDED-MISSILE AIRCRAFT CARRIERS [CVG]

♦ 1 Kuznetsov (Orel) class (Project 11435)

Bldr: Chernomorskiy (Nosenko) SY 444, Nikolayev (Mikolayiv), Ukraine

	Laid down	L	In serv.
063 Admiral Flota Sovetskogo Soyuza Kuznetsov (ex-*Tbilisi,* ex-*Leonid Brezhnev,* ex-*Riga*)	1-9-82	4-12-85	29-1-91

Admiral Flota Sovetskogo Soyuza Kuznetsov (063)—during 1996 Mediterranean deployment, with six Su-33 fighters and two Su-25UTG trainers on deck
Norman Polmar, via *Ships of the World*

GUIDED-MISSILE AIRCRAFT CARRIERS [CVG] *(continued)*

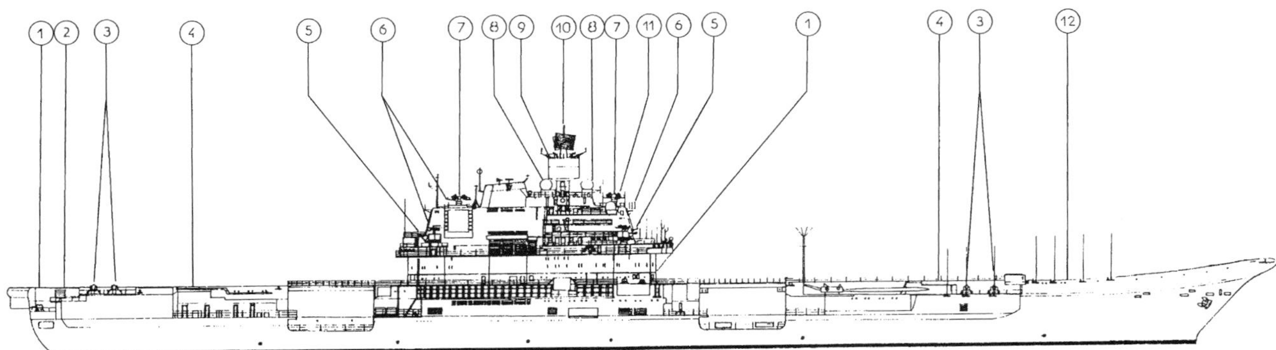

Admiral Flota Sovetskogo Soyuza Kuznetsov (063) 1. 30-mm AK-630M gatling AA 2. RPK-5 Liven' ASW RL 3. Kortik CIWS (with twin 30-mm gatling AA and 8 SAM rails per mount) 4. Kinzhal SAM system silos 5. MR-360 Podkat radar directors for the Kinzhal system 6. Mars-Passat early-warning radar arrays (nonoperational) 7. MR-320M Topaz-M surface/air-search radars 8. Low Ball SATCOM antenna radomes 9. Cake Stand TACAN antenna array 10. MR-710 Fregat-MA 3-D air-search radar 11. Punch Bowl radar surveillance datalink antenna radomes (nonoperational) 12. P-700 Granat antiship missile launchers (recessed into the flight deck)
Drawing by Lucien Gassier, from *Flottes de Combat*

Admiral Flota Sovetskogo Soyuza Kuznetsov (063)—at sea, with four Su-33 fighters and one Ka-27 helicopter on deck TASS, 2000

Admiral Flota Sovetskogo Soyuza Kuznetsov (063)—snow-covered at her operating base Boris Lemachko, 11-00

D: 43,000 tons light; 55,000 tons std. (59,100 fl; 65,000 max.) **S:** 29 kts
Dim: 306.45 (270.00 wl) × 72.30 (68.5 flight deck; 35.41 wl) × 9.14 (10.00 max.)
Air group: 12 Su-33 Flanker-D interceptors; 14 Ka-27PL Helix-A ASW helicopters; 3 Ka-29RLD AEW helicopters; 2 Ka-27PS Helix-C SAR helicopters
A: 12 P-700 Granit (SS-N-19 Shipwreck) SSM; 24 Kinzhal (SA-N-9) VLS SAM syst. (192 9M-330 Gauntlet missiles); 8 Kortik CIWS (256 tot. 9M-311/SA-N-11 Grison missiles, plus 2 single 30-mm gatling AA per mount); 6 single 30-mm 54-cal. AK-630 gatling AA; 2 10-round RPK-5 Liven' (UDAV-1) ASW/antitorpedo RL (60 tot. rockets)
Electronics:
Radar: 3 MR-212/201 Vaygach-U (Palm Frond) nav.; 2 MR-320M Topaz-M (Strut Pair) air search; 1 Mars-Passat (Sky Watch) 3-D early warning (nonoperational); 1 MR-710 Fregat-MA (Top Plate-B) 3-D air search; 4 MR-360 Podkat (Cross Sword) f.c.; 8 3P-87 (Hot Flash) f.c. (on Kortik mounts); 2 Fly Trap CAC
Sonar: MGK-365 Zvezda M-1 hull-mounted LF; MG-35 underwater telephone

Admiral Flota Sovetskogo Soyuza Kuznetsov (063) M.O.D. U.K., 3-96

TACAN: Cake Stand
EW: Sozbezie-BR suite: 8 Wine Glass, 4 Flat Track, 8 Bell Push, and 4 Bell Nip intercept/jamming; 3 Cross Loop D/F; 2 twin PK-2 decoy RL; 10 fixed 10-round PK-10 decoy RL
E/O: 1 Bob Tail telescoping; 3 Tin Man t.v./IR/laser; 5 fixed t.v.; 4 optical periscopes; 4 or more Spektr-F (Half Cup) laser warning
M: 4 sets TV12-4 geared steam turbines; 4 props; 200,000 shp
Boilers: 8 KVG-4 turbopressurized, 64 kg/cm^2
Electric: 22,500 kw tot. (9 × 1,500 kw turboalternators, 6 × 1,500 kw diesel sets)
Range: 3,850/29; 8,500/18; 12,000/10 **Fuel:** 3,100 tons
Endurance: 45 days (provisions limited)
Crew: 518 officers, 1,442 enlisted ship's company + 626 air group + 40 flag staff

Remarks: Design began in 1974, with the ship intended primarily to carry interceptor fixed-wing aircraft with no ground or ship attack role. The original name was

GUIDED-MISSILE AIRCRAFT CARRIERS [CVG] *(continued)*

changed to *Leonid Brezhnev* 26-11-82, to *Tbilisi* 11-8-87, and for the third time 4-10-90. Deployed without an air group from the Black Sea bound for the Northern Fleet to serve as flagship 2-12-91. Is homeported at Kolskiy Ostrov (Bay). Refitted 2-95 to 18-9-95 by Sevmorput, Rosta, during which four of eight boilers were retubed. Deployed to the Mediterranean 12-95 to 3-96 with about 14 fixed-wing pilots. Refitted again at Rosta 7-96 to 1-7-98 and officially rejoined the Northern Fleet 3-11-98. An Indian Ocean deployment was planned for 9-99 but was not carried out, and, despite occasional short trips to sea, the ship has been assigned to the Sevmorput repair yard at Severodvinsk since 1995, with the work expected to complete summer 2000. As of 11-00, 25 simulator-trained pilots were available to fly the 279th Air Fighter Regiment's Su-33 fighters from the ship, but only 10 aircraft were available as of 11-01. Was briefly at sea during 6-99 to conduct carrier compatibility tests with the Sukhoi Su-27KUB two-seat trainer and again in 9-00. As of 4-00, consideration was being given to re-engining the ship with a nuclear power plant, according to the Russian Defense Ministry, but the necessary funds are not likely to become available. As of 4-01, the ship was badly in need of a refit, including reboilering, the tubes having already been replaced three times.

The second ship of the class (Project 1143.6), *Varyag,* also initially named *Riga,* was laid down 6-12-85 and launched 6-12-88. Fitting out had ceased by 11-92, and the ship was stricken 30-7-93. The largely stripped hulk was sold by Ukraine and left Mikolayiv 14-6-00 for China for scrapping; not until 4-11-01, however, was the tow permitted to pass through the Bosporus.

Hull systems: The propulsion plant is essentially a duplicate of that used in the *Kiev* class, with standard vertical turbopressurized boilers upgraded to produce up to 115 tons/hr of steam. There are 3,857 compartments within the hull and island. Has 27 decks from keel up. Trims down by the stern by about 2 m. Has the Kaskad automatic degaussing system.

Aviation systems: Is rated to carry a maximum of 52 aircraft (36 Su-33 fighters, 16 Ka-27 ASW helicopters, and 5 other helicopters), but the nominal actual combat air group is not large: two 12-plane squadrons of Su-33 Flanker interceptor aircraft (only 20 Su-33 were ordered in the first production batch, and they are not equipped to conduct strike missions) and 12 Helix-series helicopters, four of which will eventually be of the early-warning radar variant and two for search and rescue. During the ship's 12-95 to 3-96 deployment, only 12 Su-33 and two Su-25UTG fixed-wing aircraft were carried. Originally, 16 of the since-canceled Yak-141 V/STOL fighters were to be carried in lieu of 12 Su-33 or MiG-29K fighters. The single Su-27KUB-1 two-seat shipboard trainer can also be operated. The Ka-27PL ASW helicopters are planned to be replaced by the newer Helix model Ka-31.

Flight deck area totals 14,700 m^2. The aircraft landing system employs four cross-deck wires spaced at 14-m intervals near the after end of the 220-m, 5.5°-angled deck, and aircraft are guided to the deck by an automatic radar-controlled landing system employing two Fly Trap-B microwave automatic landing control devices; there is also a Luna-3 mirror landing system. Aircraft take off up the 15° ramp from any of three detent positions (two with a 105-m run and one to port with a 195-m run), where they are held firmly in check until full engine afterburner thrust is developed. A great many objects protrude above the flight deck, including decoy rocket launchers, a fixed navigational light mast to starboard, and a number of firefighting foam cannon. There are but two aircraft elevators, 20 m long by 15 m wide and capable of lifting about 40 tons each. Belowdecks aircraft accommodations are limited by the 153-m-long by 26.0-m-wide by 7.2-m-high hangar and by the installation of 12 inclined launch tubes for antiship missiles that take up space that could have been employed for additional aircraft stowage; there are very few flight deck aircraft tiedown positions, and all aircraft are intended to be hangared. The hangar is equipped with four fore-and-aft tracks for maneuvering and securing aircraft. Carries 2,500 tons aviation fuel.

Combat systems: The shipboard armament suite, aside from the dozen antiship missiles, is strictly for short-range self-defense and is the heaviest such ever installed on any ship. The six individual AK-630 gatling guns are controlled by the Kortik CIWS fire-control systems or by remote backup optical directors. In all, 24,000 rounds of 30-mm ammunition are carried for the AK-630 mounts and 48,000 rounds for the Kortik mountings. The SA-N-9 rotating silo launchers are arranged in groups of six, and the Kortik CIWS systems are paired to cover the four "corners" of the ship. The RPK-5 Liven ASW rocket launchers are installed aft, primarily as torpedo countermeasures launchers.

The Mars-Passat (Sky Watch) four-panel fixed planar array three-dimensional air-search radar in *Kuznetsov* was not a success and is not operational. The communications suite is called Buran-2. Satellite communications antenna systems include two Low Ball communications arrays and two Punch Bowl over-the-horizon targeting data reception antennas, although the associated radar satellites are no longer operating. Navigational equipment includes Kurs-10A-1 and 10A-2 gyrocompasses; an ILE-1 electrodynamic log; a Beysur navigation system; an RYu-02 radionavigation aid; GEL-3, NEL-M1, and NEL-M2 echo sounders; and an AP-5 automatic plot.

Disposal note: The Modified *Kiev*-class (Project 11434) VTOL aircraft carrier *Admiral Gorshkov* (ex-*Baku*), inoperable since 1991, was to be donated to India in 2001, although the expected contract was not signed when the Indian prime minister visited Moscow early in 11-01; if the intended transfer does not go through, the ship will probably be scrapped. Of the three aviation cruisers [CVHG] of the *Kiev* class, *Kiev* was stricken 31-8-94 and began a tow to China for scrapping 21-5-00. *Minsk* and *Novorossiysk* were stricken 30-7-93 and sold to a South Korean corporation in 1994 for scrapping; *Minsk* departed for South Korea during 11-95 and *Novorossiysk* on 29-12-95, but after several years lying derelict near Pusan, *Novorossiysk* was sold to an Indian breaker, while the stripped hulk of the *Minsk* was sold to a Chinese firm in 9-98 for use as a floating exhibition and theme park near Hong Kong.

MARITIME AVIATION *(Morskaya Aviatsiya)*

Naval aviation is an integral part of the Russian Navy. Organization and ranks are the same as those of the Russian Air Force. The Russian Navy as of 1999 had been given the responsibility for the development of its own aircraft. Current first-line active aircraft totals are estimated as follows: *fixed-wing:* about 48 Backfire-C bombers (not all flyable), 17 Su-33 Flanker-D shipboard interceptors (10 operational as of 11-01), 35 Su-17 Fencer-C and -D land-based strike fighters, 3 Il-20 Coot-A and -B and 4–8 An-12 Cub electronic surveillance, 9 Tu-142M3 Bear-F maritime reconnaissance and ASW, and 35 Il-18 May medium-range maritime reconnaissance and ASW; *helicopters:* 65 Ka-27PL Helix-A ASW (includes an unknown number of the Ka-27RTs targeting variant), 2 Ka-27RLD Helix aerial surveillance, 16 Ka-29TB Helix-B assault, and 12 Ka-27PS Helix-D SAR/utility. There are also an unknown number of training and transport aircraft.

COMBAT AIRCRAFT

Note: In the following entries, the "operational radius" is roughly 60% of the maximum radius given by half of the range. The aircraft are arranged alphanumerically by design bureau designation.

Fixed-wing aircraft:

♦ 35 Il-38 May antisubmarine patrol aircraft Design Bureau: Ilyushin

Il-38 May maritime patrol aircraft 1994

IOC: 1969 **Wingspan:** 37.40 m **Length:** 39.60 m **Height:** 10.2 m
Weight: 33.70 tons empty (66.00 max.) **Wing area:** 140 m^2
Speed: 372 kts max. (354 cruise, 162–216 during patrol)
Engines: 4 Ivechenko AI-20M turboprops (4,250 shp each)
Ceiling: 26,000–33,000 ft. **Range:** 7,100 km ferry; 6,500 km normal patrol
Operational radius: 1,700 km (11 hr) **Fuel:** 35,153 liters (all internal)
Armament: 8,000 kg weapons, flares, and sonobuoys (2 AT-1 or AT-2 torpedoes and 10 PLAB-250-120 d.c. or 8 AMD-2-500 mines
Avionics: TSV-264 (Wet Eye) surveillance radar, MAD boom, sonobuoy processor, etc.

Remarks: Development began in 1960, using the airframe from the Il-18D transport with the wings moved 3 m forward on fuselage to offset the weight of the radar, additional fuel tanks, and Berkut-38 combat system. Conducted first flight 27-9-61; entered service 17-1-69. Crew of seven. Znamya Truda (now MiG-MAPO) built 57 total, of which five were later sold to India. Although only 35 were flying as of 2001, another 15 airframes were said to be available for refurbishment and updating for Russian or export use. One other Il-38 is employed for magnetic and gravimetric mapping in the Arctic region.

Are equipped with the Put-4B-2K navigational aid system, AP-6E autopilot, and ARK-B radio compass. Sonobuoys carried normally include 144 RGB-1 passive nondirectional, 10 RGB-2 passive directional, and 3 RSB-3 active/passive. Takeoff distance is 1,200 m, landing distance 850 m. One received a modular, weapons-bay-mounted aerial refueling capability and Korshun combat data system in 1972; the program was halted in 1976 with no further aircraft converted.

The prototype Il-38N conversion update first flew early in 2001 and was to be equipped with a chin-mounted FLIR and a new EW intercept array mounted in a large pod on stilts atop the forward fuselage. The modernized aircraft carries the Novella combat data system in place of the original Berkut. Production modification Il-38N update aircraft would be flown until 2010–12.

♦ 35 Su-24 Fencer maritime fighter-bombers
Design Bureau: Sukhoi-Beriev

Russian Navy Su-24 Fencer-D strike fighter 1990

IOC: 1985 **Wingspan:** 17.63 m (10.36 m fully swept) **Length:** 22.67 m
Height: 5.92 m **Weight:** 39,700 kg max. (35,910 normal)
Speed: 1,320 kts at sea level; 1,550 kts at 36,000 ft. (Mach 1.35)
Engines: 2 Lyulka AL-21F-3 turbojets (11,200 kg thrust each)
Ceiling: 36,000 ft. **Range:** 2,750 km ferry
Operational radius: 3,390 km low-low-low; 1,300 km high-low-high
Fuel: 9,850 kg internal; 14,900 kg with three external tanks **Crew:** 2
Armament: 4 Kh-25L, 3 Kh-29L/T, 2 Kh-31P, or 2 Kh-59 missiles or up to 8 tons KAB-500KR or KAB-1500L guided bombs; 1 23-mm cannon (500 rds)

Remarks: Fencer-A, -B, and -D strike fighters were transferred from the Soviet Air Force in 1989–90 to avoid CFE limitations. Variable-geometry, swing-wing design (with four positions: 16°, 35°, 45°, and 69°). Takeoff run: up to 1,400 m from a concrete runway; landing run: 950 m. Twenty-two Su-24K aircraft are said to be based in the Crimea.

♦ 4 Su-25UTG Frogfoot shipboard trainers
Design Bureau: Sukhoi-Beriev

IOC: 1978 **Wingspan:** 14.36 m **Length:** 15.55 m
Weight: 12.7 tons max. **Speed:** Mach 0.8 (520 kts)
Engines: 2 Tumanskiy R-195 turbojets (4,500 kg thrust each)
Ceiling: 7,000 m **Operational radius:** 280 km (900 with four external tanks)

COMBAT AIRCRAFT *(continued)*

Su-25UTG Frogfoot shipboard trainer 1990

Remarks: A navalized carrier familiarization variant of the two-seat Su-28 Frogfoot trainer, the Su-25UTG, was tested aboard the carrier *Admiral Flota Sovetskogo Soyuza Kuznetsov* in 11-89; five of the 10 completed were transferred to Ukraine, and one Russian unit was lost at the end of 1992. An Su-25UTG equipped for reconnaissance and fitted with a Pastel-K side-scan radar and air-to-air missile capability was to be delivered to the Russian Navy in 10-98. The 11th Su-25UTG trainer was delivered in 9-97, but the 10 delivered in 1989–90 are now mostly nonoperational.

♦ 17 Su-33 Flanker-D shipboard interceptors
Design Bureau: Sukhoi-Beriev

Su-33 Flanker-D shipboard fighter

Wingspan: 14.70 m (10.00 folded) **Length:** 21.93 m **Height:** 5.90 m
Wing area: 62 m^2 **Speed:** Mach 2.35 (1,550 kts) max.; 702 kts at sea level
Engines: 2 Lyulka AL-31F turbofans (7,598 kg thrust each; 12,500 kg with afterburning)
Altitude: 56,000 ft. **Operational radius:** 1,500 km (4,000 max.)
Armament: 10 AA-10 Alamo and/or AA-11 Archer AAM (6,500 kg max.); 1 30-mm GSh-301 gatling gun (150 rds)
Avionics: track-while-scan, look-down/shoot-down radar with 130-km range

Remarks: Design bureau designation is Su-27K. In addition to 20 production aircraft delivered 1993–95 (out of 24 originally ordered), five prototypes had been produced by end-1991, including a single side-by-side, Su-27IB two-seat trainer version. Shipboard acceptance trials for the production aircraft were conducted in 7-94. Only 10 Su-33s were available for carrier compatibility training at Nitka, Ukraine, during 11-01.

The navalized Flanker has folding wings and an upward-folding radome for carrier stowage, canard winglets, a shorter "stinger" radome protruding from the aft end, a tailhook (which eliminates one stores position), upgraded engines, 10 tons of internal fuel capacity for 4,000-km ferry range, and aerial refueling capability. The Su-33 weighs 2,500 kg more than the land-based version of the aircraft in light condition. Landing speed is 240 kph. The folding portion of the wing was intended to have six stores positions. The Su-33 has been shown carrying the "ASM-MSS" air-to-ground missile, an apparent air-launched version of the SS-N-22.

The commander of the carrier *Kuznetsov*'s fighter air group was lost with his aircraft 17-6-96, a second aircraft was lost 13-5-00, and the deputy commander of Russian Naval Aviation was lost in the crash of another 17-7-01. As of 11-99, only 12 were fully operational, with others undergoing refurbishment and being modified for air-to-ground attack operations.

The first Su-27KUB *(Korabel'niy Uchebno-Boyevoy)* side-by-side shipboard trainer was first flown 29-4-99 and was tested briefly aboard the *Kuznetsov* during 10-99; the aircraft is fully combat capable, and two additional units were building as of 11-99. The wing of the Su-27KUB has a greater span than that of the Su-33 and 8 m^2 more area; it also incorporates a higher proportion of composites. The Su-27KUB, if it enters production, is to employ the Al-31FP engine and a Fazotron N-014 radar. The Russian Navy designation for the trainer version is Su-38, and the manufacturer has also referred to it as the Su-33UB.

♦ about 48 Tu-22M3 Backfire-C medium-range bombers
Design Bureau: Tupolev

IOC: 1984 **Wingspan:** 34.28 m (23.30 fully swept)
Length: 42.60 m **Height:** 11.60 m **Weight:** 124.0 tons max.
Speed: Mach 2.0 (2,000 kph) at 50,000 ft. max.; Mach 1.3 at 3,000 ft.
Engines: 2 Samara NK-25 turbojets (30,000-kg/245-kN thrust each)
Ceiling: 46,000 ft. service
Operational radius: (with/without refueling) 3,485/2,250 km supersonic, 6,300/5,320 km subsonic (6,000 kg load)
Fuel: 53.0 tons max. **Crew:** 4

Tu-22M3 Backfire-C bomber

Armament: 24,000 kg bombs; or 3 AS-4, 6 AS-6, or 6 AS-9 missiles; or mines; 2 23-mm cannon (twin)
Avionics: Down Beat navigation and bombing radar; optical bombsight; Fan Tail tailgun radar; ECM/ECCM suite

Remarks: Has variable-geometry swept wings, which sweep to three positions only: 20°, 30°, and 65°. The Backfire-C has raked engine air inlets and more powerful engines than the preceding Backfire-B, all of which are believed to have been retired from naval service. Naval Aviation units carry no refueling probes, and very little flight time has been accomplished in recent years. Takeoff speed is 200 kts with a 2,000–2,100 m run; landing speed is 154 kts with a 1,200–1,300 m run at 88 tons landing weight. Cruising speed is said to be 486 kts. External weapons loads can consist of 2 FAB-3000, 8 FAB-1500, 42 FAB-500, or 69 FAB-250 or FAB-100 bombs or 8 1,500-kg or 18 500-kg mines.

♦ 9 Tu-142M3 Bear-F maritime reconnaissance and ASW aircraft
Design Bureau: Tupolev

Tu-142 Bear-F ASW aircraft U.S. Navy

IOC: 1975 **Wingspan:** 51.10 m **Length:** 49.50 m **Height:** 12.12 m
Weight: 185 tons max. (91.8 empty) **Speed:** 462 kts (397 cruise)
Engines: 4 Kuznetsov NK-12MV turboprops (15,000 shp each); 4 8-bladed AV-60K counterrotating props
Ceiling: 36,000 ft. **Operational radius:** 4,000 km
Endurance: 16.75 hrs unrefueled **Fuel:** 86 tons
Armament: 2 23-mm cannon (twin); 9,000 kg (max.) torpedoes; air-dropped stores
Avionics: Wet Eye (Berkut or Korshun-K) surveillance radars; ECM/ECCM suite

Remarks: The Bear-F (Tu-142M) ASW patrol aircraft has also been exported to India. Length over the refueling probe is 53.088 m. The wings are swept at 33° 33′ and have an area of 289.9 m^2. Takeoff run at maximum load is 2,530 m. The current version of the Bear-F said to be able to find and track submarines operating 800 m below the surface; a crew of 10 can be carried. The nine surviving Tu-142M3 aircraft are planned to be retained until at least 2016. All Bear-J communications relay aircraft are believed to have been retired.

♦ Tu-204 maritime reconnaissance aircraft
Design Bureau: Tupolev

Remarks: The Tupolev Bureau is developing a maritime reconnaissance version of its Tu-204 medium-range commercial transport, which first flew in 1989 (and has yet to find a commercial buyer). If ordered in quantity, the aircraft would have a magnetic anomaly detector (MAD) stinger and would probably employ the indigenous PS-90 turbofan engine. Avionics and weapons systems for the proposed military variant remain in the definition stage.

Helicopters:

♦ 65 Ka-27PL Helix-A antisubmarine helicopters
Design Bureau: Kamov

IOC: 1982 **Rotor diameter:** 15.90 m **Length:** 11.30 m (12.23 rotors deployed)
Weight: 11,500 (Ka-32T: 12,600) kg max.

COMBAT AIRCRAFT *(continued)*

Ka-27PL Helix-A ASW helicopter NAVPIC-Holland, 10-01

Ka-29TB Helix-B shipboard assault helicopter Rozvoorouzhenie, 1995

Ka-29RLD AEW helicopter prototype—with radar antenna deployed 1995

Speed: 143 kts (124 with 5,000-kg payload)
Engines: 2 Isotov TV3-117VK turboshafts (2,200 shp each) (Ka-28PL: TVZ-117MA, 2,350 shp each; Ka-29TB: TV3-117VK, 2,400 shp each; Ka-32: 2,225 shp each)
Ceiling: 2,950 m hovering; 6,000 m max. **Range:** 540 n.m. max.
Operational radius: 375 km (2.0–2.5 hr) (Ka-32: 800 km/4.5 hr)
Fuel: 3,270 liters (internal)
Armament: 800 kg max: 2 ASW torpedoes or PLAB-250-120 d.c. or OMAB bombs; 2 UV-26 countermeasures dispensers (32 decoys each)—Ka-29TB: 1 7.62-mm gatling gun; 8 AT-6 Spiral antitank missiles; 2 80-mm rocket pods (20 each) or 57-mm rocket pods (32 each); 8–10 troops
Avionics: Osminog radar; VGS-3 Ros-V dipping sonar; NKV-252 navigation system; PKV-252 flight control system

Remarks: Prototype first flew in 12-74. Various versions, by maker's designation, have included the Ka-27L transport, Ka-27PL ASW (Helix-A), Ka-27PS utility (Helix-C), Ka-27PSD search and rescue (Helix-D), Ka-28 export version of Ka-27PL, Ka-29TB naval infantry transport (Helix-B), Ka-31 export aerial surveillance, Ka-32T civil transport/naval utility, and Ka-32S civilian search and rescue. The Ka-27PL can cover 1,200 km^2 of ocean during an operational sortie. Maximum payload is 800 kg and maximum endurance is 5.2 hours. Several Ka-27 airframes were equipped to provide targeting services for antiship missile–launching cruisers and destroyers and are designated Ka-27RTs. The Ka-27PS utility variant can carry 5,000 kg of cargo internally, while the Ka-27PSD SAR variant has a 300-kg electric hoist and carries 4,830 kg of internal fuel.

The Ka-28PL export variant (two sold to Syria, two to Yugoslavia, several to Vietnam, and six to date to China) carries 4,770 liters of fuel and has a 50-minute-longer mission endurance than the Ka-27PL. An updated ASW variant (designated Ka-31 or Ka-32A7) began flight trials in 1995 and a production prototype was begun during 1-02. It incorporates a new radar capable of detecting up to 200 air and seaborne targets and tracking 20 of them at ranges of 100–150 km for airborne and 250 km for surface targets and can be equipped to carry two antiship missiles. Production had not commenced as of 2001.

The Ka-29TB armed combat transport variant can carry 16 fully equipped troops or 10 stretchers. It is equipped with FLIR and low-light television sensors. The Ka-29TB has a maximum takeoff weight of 11,500 kg and a combat payload of 1,800 kg. Its ferry range is 740 km (with two 500-liter fuel tanks in the weapons bay in lieu of torpedoes) and maximum speed is 151 kts (130 cruise). Some 59 were built, but only about 16 remain in service. On 24-5-01, Kamov announced a new variant, the Ka-32-10, with an enlarged cabin for 24 passengers and a cargo capacity of 4 tons within the cabin and 7 tons slung beneath; the aircraft would be built at Kuretau and could enter production in three years if an order is received.

Two prototype Ka-29RLD (*Radio Lokatsionnogo Dozora,* or Radar Control) aerial surveillance versions had been completed by early 1993; its E-801 radar's antenna deploys from beneath the fuselage. The Ka-29RLD (Kamov's "Ka-31" or "Ka-252RLD") was to be produced in small numbers for use on the carrier *Admiral Flota Sovetskogo Soyuza Kuznetsov* but has not yet entered production. The Ka-29RLD/Ka-31 weighs 12,500 kg max. takeoff and has a cruising speed of 220 kts; it can hover at up to 3,500 m altitude for 2.5 hours and can detect aircraft targets to 100–150 n.m. and surface contacts to the radar horizon. A crew of two is carried.

Note: During 9-01, the two-seat Kamov Ka-226U training helicopter was selected for procurement for the Russian Navy, although no planned production figures were released.

SUBMARINES

Note: Current Russian submarines have an anechoic hull coating that absorbs the emissions of sonars and thus reduces the intensity of reflected echoes. The rubber-compound anechoic tiles come in several thicknesses, and individual tiles are frequently seen to be missing, accounting for the odd random rectangular depressions seen on the outer hulls of many Russian submarines. The inside surfaces of the outer hulls also likely have coatings, as do the outsides of the pressure hulls, with the latter coating probably intended to reduce the noise radiated by the submarine itself. Modern Russian submarine classes employ pneumatic antivibration and sound isolation mountings for machinery and may also use active sound cancellation systems. Magnetic signatures have been reduced to about 15% of their 1970s levels.

NUCLEAR-POWERED BALLISTIC-MISSILE SUBMARINES [SSBN]

(RPKSN = *Raketnyy Podvodnyy Kreyser Strategicheskogo Naznacheniya,* or Strategic Missile Submarine Cruiser; formerly PLARB = *Podvodnaya Lodka Atomnaya Raketnaya Ballisticheskaya,* or Nuclear-Powered Ballistic-Missile Submarine)

Note: A spring 1999 decision by the Russian government to reduce the percentage of its strategic nuclear warheads from 50% launched by submarines to 25% bodes ill for the future of the SSBN force. Henceforth, the goal is to have 50% of the missiles land-launched and 25% air-launched from the aging strategic bomber fleet.

♦ 0 (+ 1 + . . .) Borey class (Project 955)

Bldr: Sevmashpredpriyatiye, Severodvinsk (Severodvinsk SY 402)

	Laid down	L	Trials	In serv.
K-. . . Yuriy Dolgorukiy (ex-*Sankt Petersburg*)	2-11-96	. . .	2005?	2006?

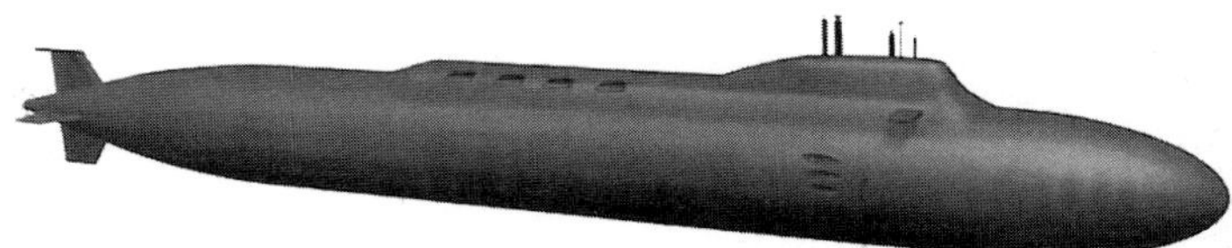

Borey-class (Project 955) original configuration—artist's conjecture U.S. Navy, 1996

D: 14,720 tons surf./19,400 tons sub. **S:** 15 kts surf./29 kts sub.
Dim: 170.00 × 13.50 × 9.00
A: 12 Bulava ballistic missiles; 4 533-mm TT (12 tot. UGST and SAET-60M torpedoes, Type 86R/SS-N-16 Stallion ASW missiles); 1 shoulder-launched SAM system (8 Igla-M missiles)
Electronics:
Radar: . . .
Sonar: MGK-540 Skat-3M suite with towed array
M: 2 OK-650B pressurized-water nuclear reactors (190 Mw each), 2 Type OK-9 steam turbines; 2 7-bladed props; 98,000 shp—2 500-shp dc electric emergency props
Electric: 7,400 kw tot. (2 × 3,200-kw turboalternators, 2 × 500-kw diesel sets)
Endurance: 100 days **Crew:** 55 officers, 52 enlisted

Remarks: Program commenced in 1982 under chief designer Vladimir N. Zdornov of the Rubin Central Naval Technology Design Bureau (TsKB-18). The original reported project nickname, Grom ("Thunder"), was applied to the missile system. The overall project name is Borey ("Cold Northern Wind"). The first unit is named for the founder of Moscow, "George Long-Arm." Was to have been the 1,001st submarine built in Russia since the Soviet Revolution of 1917. However, was only 2–3% complete as of mid-1998 by which time construction had halted. No construction funds were provided during 1997–2000, although the submarine was then said to be 47% complete. New funding was provided in 12-00 to resume work, and on 22-2-01, Admiral Kravchenko stated that work was on schedule for completion in 2005. The associated SS-N-28 Grom missile program was canceled early in 1998, and the design of the submarine had to be recast to accommodate a new, smaller missile.
Hull systems: Diving depth: 380 m normal, 450 m maximum operational. A detachable crew rescue chamber is built into the central portion of the sail. The hullform incorporates a Double Hogner stern, as in the Delta-IV SSBNs and the retired Papa-class SSGN. The overall design was very conservative and appears to have evolved from that of Project 667BDRM (the Delta-IV class).
Combat systems: Was to have had the Omnibus combat direction system, the Molnaya-M communications suite, and the Medveditsa-M navigation systems suite. The planned SS-N-28 Grom ballistic missile, an improved version of the SS-N-20, is to be replaced by the smaller Bulava, a submerged launch–capable variant of the SS-25 Topol-M (NATO SS-25 Sickle).

NUCLEAR-POWERED BALLISTIC-MISSILE SUBMARINES [SSBN] *(continued)*

♦ 6 Delta-IV (Del'fin) class (Project 667BDRM)

Bldr: Sevmashpredpriyatiye, Severodvinsk (Severodvinsk SY 402)

	Laid down	L	Del.	In serv.	Fleet
K-51 VERKHOTUR'E (ex-*Imeni XXVI Sezda KPSS*)	23-2-81	2-84	28-12-84	29-12-85	Northern
K-84 YEKATERINBURG	9-81	1-85	30-12-85	7-87	Northern
K-114 TULA	3-84	3-12-86	14-11-87	22-4-88	Northern
K-117 BRYANSK	3-85	12-87	17-10-88	3-90	Northern
K-18 KARELIYA	7-2-86	3-2-89	17-6-89	11-10-89	Northern
K-407 NOVOMOSKOVSK	3-87	14-2-90	30-12-90	20-2-92	Northern

D: 11,740 tons surf./15,500 tons sub. **S:** 14 kts surf./24 kts sub.
Dim: 167.00 (158.0 wl) 11.70 × 8.80
A: 16 R-29RM (SS-N-23 Skiff) ballistic missiles; 4 bow 533-mm TT (12 torpedoes and/or Type 86R/SS-N-15 Starfish missiles)

Kareliya (K-18) Boris Lemachko, 7-99

Kareliya (K-18)—at left, with *Verkhotur'e* (K-51) at right Boris Lemachko, 8-00

Electronics:
Radar: 1 Albatros'-series (Snoop Tray) nav./surface search
Sonar: MGK-500-series Skat-BDRM (Shark Gill) LF active/passive suite: MGK-519 active mine-avoidance; Pelamida towed passive array; MG-512 cavitation monitor; MG-518 upward-looking echo sounder; MG-519 mine detection; MG-533 sound-velocity measurement; NOR-1 active ice-lane detector; NOK-1 active surface warning
EW: MRP-10 Zaliv-P (Brick Pulp) intercept; Park Lamp D/F
E/O: Cod Eye radiometric sextant; 2 periscopes

M: 2 VM-4SG pressurized water nuclear reactors (90 Mw each), 2 sets Type OK-700A geared steam turbines; 2 7-bladed props; 60,000 shp—2 306-shp electric low-speed motors
Electric: 6,920 kw tot. (2 × 3,000-kw turbogenerators; 2 × 460-kw diesel sets)
Endurance: 80 days **Crew:** 41 officers, 94 enlisted

Remarks: The ultimate expansion of the original Yankee (Project 667A) design. All are in the Northern Fleet, based at Gadshievo, on the Olen'ya Guba. At least two additional units were being built when production was halted by order of President Yeltsin. Designed at TsKB Rubin under S. N. Kovalev. On 7-12-89, K-84 attempted to launch 16 missiles in succession while in the White Sea; the third launch failed and 13 of the crew were injured, apparently by the falling missile. One unit was damaged 20-3-93 in a collision with the U.S. submarine *Grayling.* K-407 was employed to launch a commercial-configured RSM-54 missile with a German Tubsat-M telecommunications satellite on 8-7-98. The only unit yet to have been given a recoring overhaul, K-51, was refitted from 1993 to 12-99 at Zvezdochka Verf, Severodvinsk, and was to operate until 2005–07; during 5-00, however, it was announced that six units of the class would have to operate until 2015. K-84 has been overdue for a refit since 1996 and may not be fully operational. K-18 was named in 8-96, K-114 was named on 12-10-97, K-407 was renamed on 17-9-97, and K-51 and K-84 were renamed during 4-99. K-18 successfully launched two missiles 12-9-00, although no new/rotation missiles may have been loaded on any Russian SSBN since 2-99, when all shoreside missile-handling cranes were declared unsafe.
Disposals: The unnamed K-64, the third Delta-IV completed, was declared for scrap during 2-01.
Hull systems: The design was initially distinguishable from the Delta-III class by markedly fewer limber holes at the base of the missile tube "hump," the presence of a towed passive hydrophone array dispenser tube atop rudder, and, on K-51 only, a pyramidal housing at the aft end of the missile turtledeck; many of the surviving Delta-IIIs, however, have now been backfitted with towed array fittings and have had the limber hole openings covered in the missile bay area. Capable of operating under the Arctic ice pack and breaking through to launch weapons. Normal operating depth: 380 m; maximum: 450 m. Have bow and stern side-thrusters. May have a detachable crew escape chamber abaft the missile tubes. Hull beam also reported as 12.2 m, surfaced displacement as 9,210 tons, and submerged displacement as 11,740 tons. The enveloped volume submerged displacement figure is about 18,200 tons.
Combat systems: The ballistic-missile launch complex is known as D-9RM. Have a Pert Spring antenna for the Tsunami SATCOM system, a Tobol-M navigational system, and the Molnaya-M communications suite. The missiles are launched while the submarine is at 55-m depth, traveling at up to 6 kts. All missiles now employ four warheads. Were to have been adapted to launch the now-canceled SS-N-28 Grom ballistic missile.

♦ 3 Typhoon (Akula) class (Projects 941 and 941U*)

(2 nonoperational)
Bldr: Sevmashpredpriyatiye, Severodvinsk (Severodvinsk SY 402)

	Laid down	L	In serv.	Fleet
TK-208 *DMITRIY DONSKOY**	3-3-77	23-9-80	14-12-82	Northern
TK-13	5-1-84	30-4-85	29-12-85	Northern
TK-20 SEVERSTAL'	6-1-86	7-88	4-9-89	Northern

Delta-IV-class (Project 667BDRM) SSBN Boris Lemachko, 7-00

NUCLEAR-POWERED BALLISTIC-MISSILE SUBMARINES [SSBN] *(continued)*

Two Project 941 Typhoon-class SSBNs at their Northern Fleet base
Boris Lemachko

Typhoon-class SSBN *Ships of the World*

A Typhoon surfaced in the ice pack—with four missile tube outer doors open
Siegfried Breyer Collection

TK-17 (at left, with cylindrical missile tube inspection device on deck) and TK-12—laid up at Severodvinsk, awaiting scrapping 8-01

D: 23,200 tons surf./33,800 tons sub. (see remarks)
S: 12 kts surf./25 kts sub. **Dim:** 172.8 (165.0 wl) × 23.2 × 11.5
A: TK-20: 20 R-39 (SS-N-20 Sturgeon) ballistic missiles—TK-208: provision for 20 Bulava ballistic missiles—all: 6 bow 533-mm TT (22 Type 53-65K, SET-65, and SAET-60M torpedoes and Type 83RN and 84RN/SS-N-15 Starfish missiles); 1 shoulder-launched SAM syst. (8 Igla-M missiles)

Electronics:
Radar: 1 Albatros'-series (Snoop Pair) nav./search
Sonar: Skat-series (Shark Gill) LF active/passive suite; MG-519 Alfa active mine avoidance; MG-518 Sever echo sounder
EW: Nakat-M (Rim Hat) intercept (on Tobol mast); Park Lamp D/F
E/O: Cod Eye radiometric sextant; 2 periscopes

M: 2 OK-650 pressurized-water nuclear reactors (190 Mw each), 2 sets steam turbines; 2 shrouded 7-bladed props; 100,000 shp—2 516-shp low-speed electric motors on main shafts; 2 1,020-shp drop-down emergency propulsors (bow and stern)
Electric: 14,300 kw tot. (4 × 3,200-kw turbogenerators, 2 × 750-kw diesel sets)
Endurance: 120 days **Crew:** 52 officers, 85 warrant officers, 42 enlisted

Remarks: Submarine class code name is Akula ("Shark") in Russia; Tayfun is the overall project code name for the submarine *and* its missiles. Designed at TsKB Rubin, St. Petersburg, under Sergei N. Kovalev. These are the world's largest submarines by a considerable margin, intended to operate beneath the Arctic ice pack, breaking through to launch missiles. The first built, TK-208 (named during 10-00), commenced modernization at Severodvinsk in 10-90 to carry SS-N-28 Grom missiles but is now officially stated to have been altered instead to carry the smaller Bulava missile; the ship was named during 10-00 but remains in a building hall at Severodvinsk. TK-13 has been in reserve since 1997 and is in need of a refit but has not yet been stricken. On 20-6-00, the fully operational TK-20 was named for a major industrial company; the boat's most recent operational deployment commenced 28-9-01.
Disposals: The incomplete TK-210 was broken up on the ways in 1990. TK-202 and TK-12 (the second and third built) were discarded 31-7-96 for lack of funds to refit them; with U.S. financial and technical assistance, TK-202 began scrapping in 1999. TK-17, the fifth constructed, inactive since 1998, began scrapping late in 8-01.
Hull systems: Maximum safe diving depth is 400 m. The volume within the outer hull and appendages is 49,800 m^3. Surfaced displacement has also been reported as being 28,500 tons. Design incorporates two parallel 8.5-m-diameter (6.0 forward) pressure hulls within the outer hull, with the massive sail being an additional pressure vessel; another pressure vessel centerline forward accommodates the torpedo tubes, while a fifth, small one is located centerline at the stern for the rudder and sternplane machinery. There are 19 watertight compartments. Flanking the sail are two cylindrical crew escape modules. Hull has massive bilge keels to reduce rolling, an unusual feature in a modern submarine. On TK-208 only, abaft the communications buoy hatches were pyramidal protrusions that probably served as flow trim devices; these may now have been removed. Telescoping masts from fore to aft include two periscopes, radio sextant, radar, radio, and D/F. Officers live in two- and four-man cabins, and crew amenities include a gymnasium, solarium, swimming pool, sauna, and pet facilities.
Combat systems: The forward location of the missile tubes between two parallel pressure hulls is unique. All have two large hatches abaft the sail for deploying towed communications buoys. The Rim Hat EW intercept array surrounds the base of the back-to-back radar antenna, which also has a directional EW mode. Have the Tobol-941 navigation system. The ballistic-missile launch complex in TK-20, in which the missiles are suspended from rings around their upper ends, is known as D-19; all missiles now carry 10 warheads. The solid-fueled R-39 missiles employ liquid-fuel thrusters for in-flight course correction. The torpedo tubes are arranged two abreast and three high, above the bow active/passive sonar array; they are stated to be able to launch mines, and one official source indicates that at least two are of 650-mm diameter. Have the Molnaya-L1 communications suite (with Tsunami SATCOM) and Symfoniya navigational suite. The MTK-100 underwater television system is fitted. Were all to have been adapted to launch the now-canceled SS-N-28 Grom ballistic missile; during 3-01, TK-208 was officially stated to be converting to carry the new Bulava ballistic missile.

♦ 7 Delta-III (Kal'mar) class (Project 667BDR) (2 *nonoperational*)
Bldr: Sevmashpredpriyatiye, Severodvinsk (Severodvinsk SY 402)

	Laid down	L	In serv.	Fleet
K-487 Podol'sk	4-75	4-77	25-12-77	Northern
K-496 Borisoglebsk	7-75	8-77	28-10-78	Northern
K-506 Zelenograd	11-75	12-77	8-12-78	Pacific
K-223 Kizlovodsk	2-77	4-79	3-12-79	Pacific
K-180 Petropavlovsk-Kamchatskiy	8-77	1-80	2-12-80	Pacific
K-433 Svyatoy Giorgiy Pobedonosets	8-78	6-80	19-12-80	Pacific
K-44 Ryazan	6-79	1-82	14-12-82	Northern

Delta-III class (Project 667BDR) Boris Lemachko, 2-01

D: 10,600 tons surf./13,050 tons sub. **S:** 14 kts surf./24 kts sub.
Dim: 155.00 × 11.70 × 8.70
A: 16 R-29DU (SS-N-18 Stingray) SLBM; 4 533-mm bow TT (12 torpedoes and/or Type 83RN and 84RN/SS-N-15 Starfish missiles); 2 402-mm OTA-40 bow TT (4 MG-14 or MG-44 active decoys)

NUCLEAR-POWERED BALLISTIC-MISSILE SUBMARINES [SSBN] *(continued)*

Delta-III class—note towed array sonar dispenser port at top of vertical stabilizer at the stern and the numerous freeing ports at the base of the long fairing over the missile tubes Siegfried Breyer Collection

Electronics:
Radar: 1 MRK-50-series (Snoop Tray) nav./search
Sonar: MGK-400 Rubikon LF active/passive suite: MGK-519 active mine avoidance; Pelamida towed passive array; MG-512 cavitation monitor; MG-518 upward-looking echo sounder; MG-533 sound-velocity measurement; NOR-1 active ice-lane detector; NOK-1 active surface warning
EW: MRP-10 Zaliv-P (Brick Pulp) intercept; Park Lamp D/F
E/O: Cod Eye radiometric sextant; 2 periscopes

M: 2 VM-4S pressurized-water nuclear reactors (89.2 Mw each), 2 Type OK-700A steam turbines; 2 5-bladed props; 52,000 shp—2 306-shp electric low-speed motors on main shafts
Electric: 6,920 kw tot. (2 × 3,000-kw a.c. alternators, 2 × 460-kw diesel sets)
Endurance: 80 days **Crew:** 40 officers, 90 enlisted

Remarks: Survivors of 18 completed. All Pacific Fleet ballistic-missile submarines were named on 1-7-98, but the following names have not yet been correlated to the K-series hull numbers: *Dmitrov, Krasnogorsk, Noginsk, Serpukhov,* and *Voskresensk.* K-44 was named on 19-3-98 and K-496 on 11-1-99. K-496 was the submarine from which a failed launch attempt to place a solar monitoring satellite in orbit occurred during 7-01. A press report on 19-7-99 stated that only one or two of the Pacific Fleet units, all of which are based at Petropavlovsk-na-Kamchatskiy, could go to sea. K-487 launched an exercise missile on 18-9-01. According to a 23-4-99 statement by Russian Navy C-in-C Fleet Admiral Kuroyedov, all Pacific Fleet units were to be retired by 2005, but during 7-99, he said that all surviving units of the class would be extended in service indefinitely.
Disposals: K-424, the class prototype, was stricken in 1996, along with the second unit, K-441 (named *Imeni XXVI Sezda K.P.S.S.* until 8-92). Three more Pacific Fleet units had been stricken by 1998. Northern Fleet unit K-129, the 13th unit of the class, which had suffered bow damage in a collision in 1993 and was reported to have been stricken 1-9-95, was instead converted to a submersible tender and relaunched 29-12-00; see under [SSAN]. Pacific Fleet units K-211, K-449, K-455, and K-498 had ceased to function by late 2001.
Hull systems: Has a higher turtledeck than the Delta-II to accommodate longer ballistic-missile tubes. The pressure hull is 9.8 m in diameter, has 211 external frames, and has 11 watertight compartments; the missile compartment is 45 m long. Height from keel to top of sail is 17.65 m. Primary ship's service electric power is delivered at 380 V/50 Hz. Test diving depth is 580 m, normal operating depth 320 m. The bow planes rotate to vertical in order to facilitate breaking through ice; the submarines normally break through up to 0.9 m of ice but can surface through 1.8 m ice in an emergency. Have bow and stern side-thrusters. Crew amenities include a gymnasium and solarium.
Combat systems: The Molnaya-M communications suite incorporates towed VLF communications buoys and a Pert Spring antenna for the Tsunami SATCOM system, and there is a towed communications buoy stowed beneath a hatch just abaft the missile tubes. The navigational suite is known as Tobol-M. Were being backfitted with towed passive linear sonar arrays, as on the Delta-IV class, from which they were becoming difficult to distinguish, but the updating program has probably ended. Some are fitted with the MGK-400 Rubikon active sonar. The ballistic-missile launch complex is known as D-9R. The surviving units were to have been adapted to launch the now-canceled SS-N-28 Grom ballistic missile. All remaining R-29DU missiles employ three warheads.

Disposal note: The four Delta-II (Murena-M)-class (Project 667BD) ballistic-missile submarines were discarded from the Northern Fleet 31-7-96: K-182 (ex-*Shestidesyatiletie Velikogo Oktyabrya*), commissioned 4-11-77; K-92, commissioned 17-12-75; K-193, commissioned 30-12-75; and K-421, commissioned 30-12-75. K-421 began scrapping at Zvezdochka Verf, Severodvinsk, during 2-00.
Of the 18 units of the Delta-I (Murena) class (Project 667B), class prototype K-279 was stricken 24-1-91; Pacific Fleet unit K-477 on 5-7-94; Northern Fleet units K-450, K-385, K-453, K-460, K-472, and K-475 and Pacific Fleet units K-171, K-417, K-497, K-512, and K-523 on 31-3-95; and Northern Fleet units K-447 and K-457 in 1998. Pacific Fleet K-500 (ex-*60 Letiye Velikogo Oktyabrya*) and K-530 were reportedly still in commission as of 8-00, but all Delta-I SSBNs were to have been retired by the end of 2001.

NUCLEAR-POWERED CRUISE-MISSILE ATTACK SUBMARINES [SSGN]

(PLARK = *Podvodnaya Lodka Atomnaya Raketnaya Krylataya,* or Nuclear-Powered Cruise-Missile Submarine)

♦ 10 (+ 2) Oscar-II (Antey-II) class (Project 949A) (1 in *reserve*)

Bldr: Sevmashpredpriyatiye, Severodvinsk (Severodvinsk SY 402)

	Laid down	L	In serv.	Fleet
K-148 KRASNODAR (ex-*Vologda*)	1982	1985	7-86	Northern
K-132 IRKUTSK	1983	1986	1987	Pacific
K-119 VORONEZH	1984	1986	1988	Pacific
K-173 *KRASNOYARSK*	1985	1987	1988	Pacific
K-410 SMOLENSK	1986	1988	1990	Northern
K-442 CHELYABINSK	1987	1989	29-12-90	Pacific
K-456 VILYUCHINSK (ex-*Kasatka*)	1988	1990	1991	Pacific
K-266 ORËL' (ex-*Severodvinsk*)	1989	22-5-92	12-92	Northern
K-186 OMSK	1990	8-5-93	15-12-93	Pacific
K-150 TOMSK	1993	18-7-96	28-2-97	Pacific
K-139 BELGOROD (ex-*Pskov*)	1994	9-99	. . .	. . .
K-135 VOLGOGRAD	1995?	. . .	. . .	. . .

Irkutsk (K-132) JMSDF, 11-01

Orël' (K-266)—sail detail; note the intricate pattern of anechoic tiles covering the outer hull TASS, 9-01

Chelyabinsk (K-442) *Ships of the World,* 2000

D: 14,700 tons surf./19,400 tons sub. **S:** 15 kts surf./31 kts sub.
Dim: 154.0 × 18.2 (20.1 over stern planes) × 9.2
A: 24 P-700 Granit (SS-N-19) SSM; 4 bow 533-mm and 4 bow 650-mm TT (24 Type 86R and/or 88R/SS-N-16 Stallion and Type 83RN and 84RN/SS-N-15 Starfish missiles and/or 65-76, USET-80, and Shkval torpedoes, and 4 MG-14 or MG-44 programmable torpedo decoys)
Electronics:
Radar: 1 Albatros'-series (Snoop Pair) nav./search
Sonar: MGK-540 Skat-3 (Shark Gill) LF active/passive suite: Pelamida towed passive array; MG-512 cavitation monitor; MG-518 upward-looking echo sounder; MG-519 active mine detection; MG-533 sound-velocity measurement; NOR-1 ice-lane detector; NOK-1 surface warning
EW: Bald Head intercept; . . . D/F

M: 2 OK-650B pressurized-water reactors (190 Mw each), 2 sets Type OK-9 steam turbines; 2 7-bladed props; 98,000 shp—2 electric low-speed motors for speeds up to 5 kts
Electric: 6,780 kw tot. (2 × 3,200-kw turboalternators, 2 × 190-kw diesel sets)
Endurance: 120 days **Crew:** 52 officers, 55 enlisted

NUCLEAR-POWERED CRUISE-MISSILE ATTACK SUBMARINES [SSGN] *(continued)*

Remarks: Type designation: *Atomnie Podvodnie Kreysery 1 Ranga* (Nuclear-powered Submarine Cruiser, 1st Class). Lengthened version of Oscar-I, on which design development began in 1967 at the Rubin Design Bureau under P. O. Pustyntsev (later I. L. Baranov). There were originally to have been 20 units. Work on *Belgorod* ceased around 1996–97, but the submarine was launched in 9-99, possibly just to clear the ways; the shipyard is self-funding a small continuing construction effort on the *Belgorod,* which was launched without sail or missile tube covers. A 13th unit, to have been named *Pskov* (K-160, later to have been named *Barnaul*), was canceled in 1996, although the ship was "dedicated" in 5-96 and was probably partially assembled. The 13th hull was said to be about 75% ready for launch as of 10-00, while sections for another unit were partially assembled; K-132 began a minor overhaul at Vladivostok during 12-01.

K-456 was renamed on 4-5-97. K-150 transited under the polar icecap to the Pacific Fleet, arriving at Petropavlovsk-na-Kamchatskiy 24-9-98. K-132 and K-173, the latter out of service since 1995, are laid up with skeleton crews awaiting funding for recoring and refit.

Losses: The newest Northern Fleet unit, *Kursk* (K-141), sank on 12-8-00 in the Barents Sea after a Type 65-76 exercise torpedo exploded, with the loss of 118 crew. The submarine had made a cruise to the Mediterranean in the fall of 1999. The Dutch Mammoet-Smit consortium raised all but the bow of the submarine in the fall of 2001, and it was to be scrapped.

Hull systems: The enveloped volume submerged displacement is 23,860 tons. The missile tubes provide a 3.5-m standoff between the outer hull and pressure hull. Maximum operational diving depth is 500 m. There are 10 watertight compartments within the pressure hull. All machinery employs two-stage sound isolation mountings. Crew amenities include a gymnasium, solarium, swimming pool, sauna, and pet facilities. The additional length over that of the two stricken Project 949 Oscar-I-class units is employed for combat data systems and improved degaussing systems.

Combat systems: The missile tubes are arranged in two rows of 12 flanking the pressure hull and fixed at an elevation of about 40°; six doors cover each row of 12. To achieve their maximum combat usefulness, the submarines were intended to employ their Punch Bowl antennas to receive radar satellite targeting data from a system that never went into service, but they can employ ELINT-derived target data from the US-PU-series satellites of the Legend system, whose final satellite was launched 21-12-01. They also have a Pert Spring antenna for the Molnaya-M SATCOM system. The 650-mm torpedo tubes may be used to launch the RPK-7 Veter (or Vodopod-MK) system's Type 88R antisubmarine missiles. All have a towed linear passive hydrophone array, with the cable deploying from the top of the vertical stabilizer at the stern. A towed VLF communications buoy is housed in the hump abaft the sail; it is deployed via a double-doored 7.5 × 2.5–m hatch. The integrated navigational system is termed Symfoniya-U, and the communications suite designation is Tsunami. The Rim Hat EW intercept array surrounds the base of the search radar radome.

Disposal note: Modified Charlie-II (Skat-M/Project 0674040) cruise-missile trials submarine *Novogord Velikiy* (B-452; ex-*Berkut,* K-452), retained in commission in reserve for more than 5 years, was to be retired "by 2002"; the submarine had been reconfigured to launch the Oniks (Yakhont) supersonic antiship cruise missile, but it is unclear whether any at-sea launches were ever carried out. The other five units of the Charlie-III class were discarded 1992–95: B-458 (in serv. 29-12-75), B-479 (in serv. 29-9-77), B-503 (in serv. 31-12-78), B-508 (in serv. 15-3-80), and B-209 (in serv. 31-12-80 and stricken 1-9-95).

♦ 1 Yankee Notch (Grusha) class (Project 667AT)

Bldr: Sevmashpredpriyatiye, Severodvinsk (Severodvinsk SY 402) (In serv. 5-12-69)

	Laid down	L	In serv.
K-395	4-9-67	28-7-69	9-1-70

D: 8,880 tons surf./9,684 tons sub. **S:** 16 kts surf./26 kts sub.
Dim: 141.7 × 12.80 × 8.30
A: 14 533-mm TT (6 fwd, 8 amidships; 32 RPK-55 Granat/SS-N-21 Sampson strategic cruise missiles amidships; 12 tot. RPK-6 Vodopod/SS-N-15a ASW missiles; and/or USET-80 and 53-65K torpedoes or MG-74 Impostor torpedo decoys)
Electronics:
Radar: 1 RLK-101 Albatros' nav./search
Sonar: MGK-300 Rubin active/passive array; MG-509 active mine avoidance
EW: MRP-10 Zaliv-P intercept; . . . D/F
M: 2 VM-4T pressurized water reactors (72 Mw each), 2 OK-700 steam turbines; 2 5-bladed props; 51,000 shp—2 260-shp low-speed electric motors
Electric: 6,200 kw tot. (2 Type TMV-32, 2,600-kw a.c. turboalternators; 2 × 500-kw diesel sets)
Endurance: 80 days **Crew:** 40 officers, 81 enlisted

Remarks: One of three converted to launch the Granat missile, with a new amidships section incorporating four 533-mm tubes per side. Converted between 24-6-88 and 30-12-91 and recommissioned 11-2-92. Sisters K-236 and K-408 (conversions completed 1997–98) were stricken during 4-96, but K-395 has been kept operational despite the intended missiles having been placed in land storage in 1991. Conversion of three others was canceled. The ship was undergoing a minor overhaul as of 3-00 and is based in the Northern Fleet, more likely as a training asset than an operational combatant, since in 1991 the Russian government agreed not to use nuclear-armed land-attack versions of the Granat missile.

Hull systems: The sail was lengthened by 3 m to 20 m overall during conversion, and the overall length was also increased. Normal maximum operating depth: 320 m (400 m max.).

Combat systems: One source credits the submarine with two 402-mm (for eight SET-73 homing torpedoes) and four 533-mm torpedo tubes (for 12 53-65K and SET-65 torpedoes) forward and only four 533-mm tubes amidships (and a total of 24 Granat missiles).

Disposal note: Oscar-I (Antey)-class (Project 949) units *Arkhangel'sk* (K-525) and *Murmansk* (K-206, ex-*Minskiy Komsomolets*) were stricken 7-11-99 and 7-1-98, respectively. Although the pair's impending scrapping was announced in 11-98, work did not begin on defueling the *Murmansk* until 20-7-01.

The inactive, experimental Yankee Sidecar–class (Project 667) cruise-missile submarine KS-420 remained afloat and in commission at Sayda Guba as late as 4-99 but is unlikely to see further service.

The single Papa-class (Project 661) nuclear-powered cruise-missile submarine, K-162, was decommissioned during 1991 and is stored at Severodvinsk, officially in reserve. The world's fastest submarine, K-162 achieved a sustained speed of 44.9 kts during trials on the power from two 88.7-Mw reactors.

Of the 11 Charlie-I (Skat)-class (Project 670) cruise-missile submarines, K-429 sank 1-6-83 in the Pacific and was subsequently raised, but sank again 13-8-85 and was not returned to service; another, leased to India 5-1-88 for three years under the name *Chakra,* was returned to the Soviet Pacific Fleet in 1-91 and discarded; Pacific Fleet units B-201 and B-320 were stricken 5-7-94; and the last to be retired, B-212, was stricken from the Pacific Fleet 1-9-95.

NUCLEAR-POWERED ATTACK SUBMARINES [SSN]

(PLA = *Podvodnaya Lodka Atomnaya,* or Nuclear-Powered Submarine)

Note: A further nuclear-powered attack submarine design is said to be under development at the Malakhit Central Design Bureau, St. Petersburg, with the first unit originally intended for completion before around 2005; as no new ships or submarines are to be ordered until at least 2003, however, it may be well into the second decade of the 21st century before a new SSN class enters service.

♦ 0 (+ 1 + 6) Severodvinsk (Yasen') class (Project 885)

Bldr: Sevmashpredpriyatiye, Severodvinsk (Severodvinsk SY 199)

	Laid down	L	In serv.
K-329 Severodvinsk	21-12-93	. . .	. . .

Severodvinsk (Project 885)—artist's conjecture, showing a bow-mounted Irtysh-Amfora sonar array, amidships torpedo tubes, and standard propeller at the stern
U.S. Navy, 1996

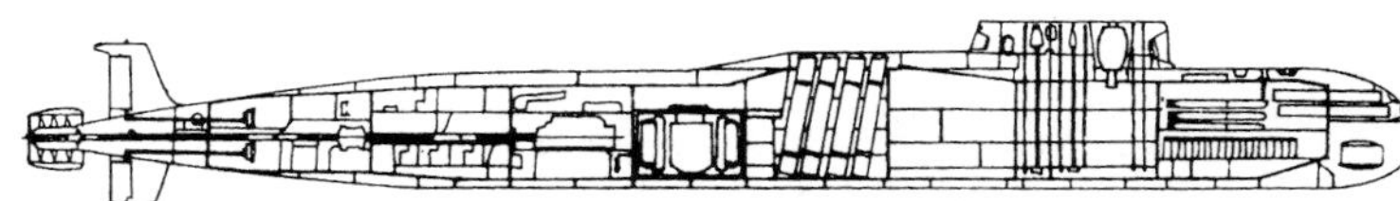

Severodvinsk (Project 885)—internal arrangement drawing, showing an older-type cylindrical sonar array beneath the bow-mounted torpedo tubes and a pumpjet propulsor aft; note also the slightly angled missile tubes abaft the sail
A. S. Pavlov, *Voennie Korabli Rossie,* 1997–98

D: 9,500 tons surf./11,800 tons sub. **S:** 16 kts surf./31 kts sub.
Dim: 120.00 × 15.0 × 10.0
A: 6 multipurpose inclined launch tubes (up to 24 Oniks antiship missiles); 8 bow 533-mm TT (24 tot. Type 83RN and 84RN/SS-N-15 Starfish missiles, USET-80 and UGST torpedoes, MDM-6 and MShM mines, etc.)
Electronics:
Radar: 1 MRK-50 Albatros'-series (Snoop Pair) nav./search
EW: . . . intercept; 6 533-mm external tubes for 12 MG-104 and/or MG-114 decoys (2 per tube)
Sonar: Irtysh-Amfora system, with bow-mounted spherical active/passive array or Skat-3 syst. with cylindrical bow array; active arrays; flank array; towed linear passive array
M: 1 OK-650KPM pressurized-water nuclear reactor (200 Mw), 2 sets steam turbines; 1 pumpjet prop; 50,000 shp
Electric: . . . tot. (2 × . . . turboalternators, 1 × 700-kw diesel set, 1 × 300-kw diesel set)
Endurance: 100 days **Crew:** 32 officers, 53 enlisted

Remarks: A total of seven was reportedly planned. Work on the first, which was ordered 22-1-93, had halted as of 2-11-96; at that time, only fabrication of the sternmost third of the hull had been accomplished. The Russian Navy C-in-C, however, claimed during 6-01 that work was still under way on the *Severodvinsk.* A second boat was not begun. Designed by Malakhit Central Design Bureau 16 (TsKB-16) under V. N. Pyalov. Crew was originally to have been 22 officers and 28 enlisted, indicating that some planned degree of automation was later sacrificed.

Hull systems: Propulsion plant is said to be substantially the same as in the Project 971 (Akula SSN) submarines but was probably to have had enhanced noise-reduction features. One published Russian report stated in 4-96 that the submarine would have a maximum speed between 35 and 40 kts and a maximum quiet-operating speed of 20 kts (implying that the quiet-operating speed of the previous Akula series is less than that). The normal maximum operating depth was to be 520 m, with a maximum of 600 m.

Combat systems: Speculation as to what might be carried in the vertical launch tubes includes possible stowage of the Novator Al'fa (SS-N-27) antiship cruise missile, although it can also be accommodated by normal 533-mm torpedo tubes, or the supersonic, ramjet-propelled Yakhont export antiship missile system (domestic nickname: Oniks), a competitor to the Al'fa.

The Irtysh-Amfora bow sonar array is expected to resemble the array of the U.S. BQQ-2, in which a spherical active/passive array is flanked by passive receiving hydrophone arrays, but a drawing of the ship published in 1996 showed a standard Russian-style cylindrical bow array (the system dubbed Skat-3) with the torpedo tubes above it. Resource constraints may have forced Russia to abandon the more complex spherical array, which is installed in Yankee Big-Nose trials submarine *Kazan* (KS-403); see under [SSAN]. Locating a spherical sonar array at the bow requires the torpedo tubes to be relocated further aft, angled outboard, as in U.S. submarine designs since the late 1950s; if the design has been altered to employ a cylindrical array, however, then the tubes will likely have been relocated at the bow. Was to have the Medveditsa-M navigation suite and the Paravan towed communications buoy.

NUCLEAR-POWERED ATTACK SUBMARINES [SSN] *(continued)*

♦ 2 (+ 2) Akula-II class (Project 09710)

Bldr: Sevmashpredpriyatiye, Severodvinsk (Shipyard 402)

	Laid down	L	In serv.	Fleet
K-157 VEPR' ("Wild Boar")	16-6-90	10-12-94	25-11-96	Northern
K-335 GEPARD ("Cheetah")	1991	18-9-99	4-12-01	Northern
K-337 KUGUAR ("Cougar")	1993	. . .	. . .	Northern
K-333 RYS'	1993?	. . .	. . .	. . .

Vepr' (K-157)—the first Akula-II SSN
SPMBM Malachite, via Norman Polmar, 1996

Vepr' (K-157) M.O.D. U.K., via Norman Polmar, 7-96

Gepard (K-335)—just after launch; note the lack of a pod atop the vertical stabilizer aft 9-99

Gepard (K-335)—the sail on this unit is longer than that on the *Vepr'* to accommodate the towed array winch TASS, 2001

D: 9,830 tons surf./. . . tons sub. **S:** 10 kts surf./33–35 kts sub.
Dim: 114.30 × 13.60 (15.40 over stern planes) × 9.68
A: 4 bow 650-mm TT (Type 86R and 88R/SS-N-16 Stallion missiles and/or Type 65-76 or UGST torpedoes); 4 bow 533-mm TT (Type 83R and 84R/SS-N-15 Starfish and RPK-55 Granat/SS-N-21 Sampson missiles; USET-80 torpedoes; mines); 1 shoulder-launched SAM syst. (18 Strela-2M or Igla-M missiles)
Electronics:
Radar: 1 MRK-50 Albatros'-series (Snoop Pair) nav./search
Sonar: MGK-540 Skat-3 (Shark Gill) suite: MGK-503 LF active/passive; passive flank array; MG-519 HF active mine avoidance; large-aperture towed passive LF linear hydrophone array
EW: Amber Light intercept; Rim Hat intercept; Park Lamp D/F; 6 533-mm external bow tubes for 12 MG-104 and/or MG-114 programmable torpedo decoys (2 per tube)
M: 1 OK-9BM pressurized-water nuclear reactor (190 Mw), steam turbines; 1 7-bladed prop; 47,600 shp—2 410-shp dc electric low-speed motors (3–4 kts)
Electric: 1,500 kw (2 × 750-kw diesel emergency sets)
Endurance: 100 days **Crew:** 31 officers, 22 enlisted

Remarks: Designed by Firma Malakhit, St. Petersburg, under G. N. Chernishov. The lengthened Akula-II class incorporates further quieting measures and a greater degree of automation over the Improved Akula-I (Project 971U). Work on K-335 (with reactor installed and fueled and a crew assigned since 1998), K-337, and K-333 at Severodvinsk had ceased by early 1997, but construction on the then-80% complete K-335 was restarted in 9-97, builder's trials began 15-9-00, and acceptance trials started 7-12-00. K-337, then 30% complete, was offered to India for delivery in 2004 on a five-year lease, but the offer was rejected on 8-2-02; K-333 will probably not be completed.

Hull systems: Enveloped volume submerged displacement for the Akula-II version is 12,770 tons. K-157 appears to be about 4 m longer than the Akula-I series between the after edge of the sail and the towed communications buoy hatch; with the additional length being in the engineering area abaft the probable reactor spaces, it is most likely associated with further quieting measures in the main engine suspension system. See also the hull systems remarks under the Akula-I class.
Combat systems: Both have nonacoustic submarine detection system arrays mounted on the forward edge of the sail and on the casing forward of the sail. K-335 lacks the towed array pod atop the vertical stabilizer at the stern (the towed array is streamed from a small tube at the top of the vertical stabilizer, with the winch and drum relocated within the lengthened sail). A total of 40 torpedo tube–launched weapons can be carried. See also the combat systems remarks under the Akula-I class.

♦ 10 (+ 2) Akula-I (Shchuka-B) class (Projects 971 and 971U*) (2 *nonoperational*)

Bldrs: A: Zavod imeni Leninskiy Komsomol (Shipyard 199), Komsomol'sk-na-Amur; B: Sevmashpredpriyatiye, Severodvinsk (Shipyard 402)

	Bldr	Laid down	L	In serv.	Fleet
From among:					
K-263 DEL'FIN	A	1981	15-7-84	12-85	Pacific
K-322 *KASHALOT*	A	1982	1985	1986	Pacific
K-391 BRATSK (ex-*Kit*)	A	1982	1985	1987	Pacific
K-331 NARVAL (ex-*Rys'*)*	A	1983	1986	1989	Pacific
K-480 *AK-BARS* (ex-*Kazan*, ex-*Bars*)	B	1986	16-4-88	31-12-88	Northern
K-317 PANTERA*	B	6-11-86	5-90	30-12-90	Northern
K-461 VOLK*	B	1986	11-6-91	27-1-92	Northern
K-419 KUZBASS (ex-*Morzh*)	A	1984	11-6-91	1992	Pacific
K-328 LEOPARD*	B	26-10-88	28-6-92	15-12-92	Northern
K-154 TIGR*	B	1989	26-6-93	5-1-94	Northern
K-267 SAMARA (ex-*Drakon*)	A	1985	15-7-94	28-7-95	Pacific
K-152 NERPA*	A	1986	. . .	. . .	Pacific
K-. . . KABAN	A	1992	. . .	. . .	Pacific

Improved Akula-I class (Project 971U)—note the covers over the decoy launching tubes, three on either side of the torpedo-loading hatch fairing at the bow
M.O.D. U.K., via Norman Polmar, 1994

D: 8,140 tons surf./. . . tons sub. **S:** 10 kts surf./33–35 kts sub.
Dim: 110.30 × 13.60 (15.40 over stern planes) × 9.68
A: 4 bow 650-mm TT (Type 86R and 88R/SS-N-16 Stallion missiles and/or Type 65-76 torpedoes); 4 bow 533-mm TT (Type 83RN and 84RN/SS-N-15 Starfish and RPK-55 Granat/SS-N-21 Sampson missiles; USET-80 torpedoes; mines); 1 shoulder-launched SAM syst. (18 Strela-2M or Igla-M missiles)

NUCLEAR-POWERED ATTACK SUBMARINES [SSN] *(continued)*

Akula-I class (Project 971)—note the nonacoustic ASW sensors on the casing forward of the sail U.S. Navy, 1994

Electronics:
Radar: 1 MRK-50 Albatros'-series (Snoop Pair) nav./search
Sonar: MGK-540 Skat-3 (Shark Gill) suite: MGK-503 LF active/passive; passive flank array; MG-519 HF active mine avoidance; large-aperture towed passive LF linear hydrophone array
EW: Amber Light intercept; Rim Hat intercept; Park Lamp D/F—K-419 and later: 6 533-mm external tubes for MG-104 and MG-114 programmable torpedo decoys (2 per tube)
M: 1 OK-9BM pressurized-water nuclear reactor (190 Mw), steam turbines; 1 7-bladed prop; 47,600 shp—2 410-shp dc electric low-speed motors (3–4 kts)
Electric: 1,500 kw (2 × 750-kw diesel emergency sets)
Endurance: 100 days **Crew:** 33 officers, 40 enlisted

Remarks: Designed by Firma Malakhit, St. Petersburg, under G. N. Chernishov. In 8-98, the local government of Samara pledged funds for the completion of K-267, which although delivered in late 1995 had not yet been fully paid for; in return for a 2-year sponsorship, the boat was renamed *Samara.* K-154 was in refit at Sevmashpredpriyatiye in 2000 and was expected to complete by the end of the year. K-322 had been laid up by the end of 1998 for lack of funds to recore her. The crew of K-331 has requested yet another renaming, to *Magadan.* K-317 began a refit at Sevmashpredpriyatiye late in 2000 for completion in 2001, allowing the submarine to operate for an additional 5–8 years.

Komsomol'sk-built units are all to the original design. Severodvinsk-built K-331 and later have significant sound quieting improvements over the earlier boats and are referred to by NATO as the Improved Akula-I class and by Russia as Project 971U. Two Improved Akula-I units laid down in 1986 and 1987 remain incomplete within the building hall at Komsomol'sk, with K-152 82% finished and having already had the reactor installed and fueled and *Kaban* about 25% complete; work had ceased around 9-95 on both due to lack of payments, and the two were unsuccessfully offered by the building yard to India and China during 1999. During 1-00, however, the government provided funds for further work on K-152, which was 82% complete at that time.

A Russian offer to deliver the 70% complete K-152 to India during 2004 on a five-year lease was turned down on 8-2-02. K-317 arrived at Severodvinsk 6-9-00 for a refueling overhaul.

Disposals: The unnamed class prototype K-284, commissioned in the Pacific Fleet only on 31-12-88 after a protracted series of trials, was reportedly stricken in 12-95; the hulk remains afloat.

Hull systems: Akulas differ in appearance from the Sierras in having a longer, much more streamlined sail. They also have a steel pressure hull vice titanium on the Sierra. A detachable crew-escape compartment is located within the sail. Maximum operating depth is 520 m, with normal operating depth of 400–450 m and crush depth reported as 900 m. Sound-quieting measures on all include double isolation of mechanical noise sources; all machinery is mounted on isolated foundations which are in turn mounted on rafts isolated from the inner hull structure by rubber pneumatic blocks. There are six main watertight compartments and four internal decks in the ship control space area (Compartment II) and auxiliary machinery spaces (Compartment III). The propulsion plant includes four steam generators, with two circulating pumps for the first and fourth loops and three pumps for the third; the steam turbine plant includes two a.c. turboalternators, each with two feed and two condensor pumps. Sufficient diesel fuel is available to operate the two diesel generator sets for 10 days. There are two electric battery groups. Class prototype K-284 had a 190-Mw OK-650M.01 reactor.

Combat systems: The combat system is named Omnibus and the navigation suite Medveditsa-971. The Snoop Pair radar and Rim Hat intercept array are on the same telescoping mast, with the Rim Hat array surrounding the base of the radar antenna. All have a pod-mounted towed linear hydrophone array dispenser atop the vertical stabilizer. There are a total of 40 weapons stowed in the torpedo tubes and internal reload racks. K-419 and later units have six external horizontal tubes flanking the loading hatch atop the pressure hull at the bow; each tube holds two programmable torpedo decoys. The earlier units probably carry up to four MG-74 decoys internally in lieu of weapons. All are said to be able to accommodate 28 RPK-55 Granat strategic cruise missiles, a subsonic weapon with a 200-kT nuclear warhead that was supposed to have been placed in land storage after an agreement with the U.S.A. in 1991.

All except K-284 have nonacoustic submarine detection system arrays mounted on the forward edge of the sail and on the casing forward of the sail. The sonar hydrophone array includes a massive active/passive cylindrical bow array beneath the torpedo tubes, large rectangular conformal arrays on either side of the hull forward of the sail, a smaller linear flank array on either beam between the sail and the stern, passive arrays on the forward and after edges of the sail, an active array in the sail, and a towed passive linear array housed in the pod atop the vertical fin at the stern. The Molnaya-M communications suite includes a towed antenna buoy. Have a Pert Spring SATCOM antenna. K-284 and K-322 lack hydroacoustic countermeasures systems.

♦ 2 Sierra-II (Kondor) class (Project 945A) (1 *nonoperational*)
Bldr: Krasnoye Sormovo Zavod 112, Nizhniy Novgorod

	Laid down	L	In serv.	Fleet
K-534 *Nizhniy Novgorod* (ex-*Zubatka*)	6-86	6-88	28-12-90	Northern
K-336 Pskov (ex-*Okun'*)	5-90	6-92	12-8-93	Northern

Pskov (K-336) TASS, 2000

Nizhniy Novgorod (K-534)—note the large, broad-topped sail with sensor masts offset to starboard and nonacoustic ASW sensors on the projection to starboard at the forward end of the sail M.O.D. U.K., 1992

D: 6,470 tons surf./8,500 tons sub. **S:** 12 kts surf./33.6 kts sub.
Dim: 110.50 × 12.22 (16.50 over horizontal stabilizers) × 9.40
A: 6 bow 533-mm TT (40 Type 83RN and 84RN/SS-N-15 Starfish ASW missiles; VA-111 Shkval rocket torpedoes; USET-80 torpedoes; or up to 42 mines in lieu of other weapons); 1 shoulder-launched SAM syst. (8 Strela-2M or Igla-M missiles)
Electronics:
Radar: 1 MRK-50 Albatros'-series (Snoop Pair) nav./search
Sonar: MGK-540 Skat-3 (Shark Gill) LF suite; passive flank arrays; MG-519 active HF mine avoidance; large-aperture towed passive hydrophone array
EW: Rim Hat intercept; Park Lamp D/F
M: 1 pressurized-water OK-650B nuclear reactor (190 Mw), 1 steam turbine; 1 7-bladed prop; 48,000 shp—2 496-shp auxiliary propulsion motors—2 185-shp retractable electric maneuvering propulsors
Electric: 4,700 kw tot. (2 × 1,600-kw turboalternators, 2 × 750-kw diesel generator sets)
Endurance: 100 days **Crew:** 32 officers, 29 enlisted

Remarks: Designed by Lazurit Central Design Bureau 112. Both are in the Northern Fleet, with K-336 based at Ara Guba and K-534 at Litsa Guba, where she has been lying in commission but nonoperational since 6-97, in need of overhaul and recoring. The incomplete hull of K-536, a modified Project 945B (Project Mars) variant, was canceled during 7-92 and scrapped in 1993.

Hull systems: Have seven watertight compartments in the pressure hull, vice six in the earlier Sierra-I (Project 945), to incorporate improved sound quieting and crew amenities. The Sierra-II is 5 m longer than the Sierra-I and has a 6-m-longer sail that is also broader, with a conspicuously blunt forward edge; the Sierra-II sail has the telescoping masts mounted on the starboard side, while the port side appears to incorporate two detachable crew buoyant rescue chambers. Like Sierra-I, Sierra-IIs have titanium pressure hulls. Maximum depth: 600 m; normal operating depth: 520 m. The propulsion plant includes four steam generators, with two circulating pumps for the first and fourth loops and three pumps for the third; the steam turbine plant includes two a.c. turboalternators, each with two feed and two condensor pumps. Sufficient diesel fuel is available to operate the two diesel generator sets for 10 days. There are two electric battery groups. Two retractable underhull maneuvering propulsors are fitted.

Combat systems: Two additional 533-mm torpedo tubes were added to the original design, in part to be able to launch the Granat (SS-N-21) strategic cruise missile but also because the larger bow cylindrical sonar transducer array precluded installation of 650-mm tubes. The sonar suite includes the cylindrical bow array, three active planar arrays (two flank, one in the sail), and large vertical Shark Rib passive flank arrays. In addition to the hydroacoustic arrays, also carry a nonacoustic antisubmarine sensor system incorporating some 12 probes, nine on the forward edge of the sail and three on a protrusion to starboard from the forward end of the sail. The combat system is called Omnibus, the communications suite Molnaya-MTs, and the navigation suite Symfoniya.

NUCLEAR-POWERED ATTACK SUBMARINES [SSN] *(continued)*

♦ 2 Sierra-I (Barrakuda) class (Project 945) (1 in *reserve*)

Bldr: Krasnoye Sormovo Zavod 112, Nizhniy Novgorod

	Laid down	L	In serv.	Fleet
K-239 KOSTROMA (ex-*Karp*)	8-5-82	29-7-83	21-9-84	Northern
K-276 KRAB	8-83	4-84	9-87	Northern

Kostroma (K-239)—trimmed down aft while running on the surface Russian Navy, 2000

Sierra-I class (Project 945) Norwegian Air Force

D: 6,300 tons surf./8,300 tons sub. **S:** 12 kts surf./33.6 kts sub.
Dim: 107.00 × 12.22 (16.50 over stern stabilizers) × 8.80
A: 2 bow 650-mm and 4 bow 533-mm TT (40 Type 83RN and 84RN/SS-N-15 Starfish and Type 86R and 88R/SS-N-16 Stallion ASW missiles; VA-111 Shkval rocket torpedoes; and/or USET-80 and 65-76 torpedoes; or up to 42 mines in lieu of other weapons)
Electronics:
Radar: 1 MRK-50 Albatros'-series (Snoop Pair) nav./search
Sonar: MGK-503 Skat-KS (Shark Gill) suite; Paravan towed passive hydrophone array
EW: Rim Hat intercept, Park Lamp D/F
M: 1 OK-650A pressurized-water nuclear reactor (180 Mw), 1 steam turbine; 1 7-bladed prop; 43,000 shp—2 496-shp auxiliary propulsion motors
Electric: 3,800 kw tot. (2 × 1,600-kw turboalternators; 2 × 300-kw diesel generator sets, 750-bhp diesels driving)
Endurance: 90 days **Crew:** 31 officers, 28 warrant officers

Remarks: Design initiated 3-72 at TsKB-122 Lazarit Design Bureau under N. I. Kvash. The submarines were transferred via river/canal system to Severodvinsk for final fitting out. K-239, renamed during 1996, was in a collision with the U.S. submarine *Baton Rouge* 11-2-92 and has been laid up at Ara Guba since 1998 awaiting funding for a recoring overhaul. The identities of the pair had been confused in earlier editions.
Hull systems: Sierras differ from Akulas in having a significantly blunter sail shape, although the Sierra-I has a smaller and more streamlined sail than does the later Sierra-II. K-239 has a low extension to the after end of the sail not found on the K-276. Normal operating depth is 480 m, maximum 550 m. The propulsion plant includes four steam generators, each with two circulating pumps for the first and fourth loops and three pumps for the third; the steam turbine plant includes two a.c. turboalternators, each with two feed and two condensor pumps. Sufficient diesel fuel is available to operate the two diesel generator sets for 10 days. There are two electric battery groups. Maximum speed is also reported to be 35.5 kts. They probably do not have the crew escape pod system incorporated in the later Sierra-II pair.
The titanium pressure hull has a yield strength of 70–72 kg/mm^2, a hemispheric end cap, and six watertight compartments. The use of titanium for the pressure hull was intended to reduce the magnetic signature and to permit a lighter, river-transportable submarine. A solid-fuel pyrotechnic gas generator system can be used to blow the two main ballast tanks in an emergency.
Combat systems: Carry environmental sensors on the sail for nonacoustic submarine detection and are equipped with a mast-mounted Pert Spring communications satellite antenna. The combat system is called Omnibus, the communications suite Molnaya-MTs, and the navigation suite Symfoniya. Are not equipped with a portable SAM system like the later Sierra-II.

♦ 5 Victor-III class (Project 671RTMK/671.7) (1 in *reserve*)

Bldr: Admiralteiskiye Verfi 194, St. Petersburg

	Laid down	L	In serv.
K-292	15-4-86	29-4-87	27-11-87
K-388	8-5-87	3-6-88	30-11-88
K-138	7-12-88	5-8-89	10-5-90
K-414 DANIIL MOSKOVSKIY	1-12-88	31-8-90	30-12-90
K-448 TAMBOV'	31-1-91	17-10-91	24-9-92

Victor-III class (Project 671RTMK)—at Severodvinsk Boris Lemachko, 8-99

Victor-III class—note the slab-sided outer hull casing amidships and the several missing anechoic tiles Boris Lemachko, 2-01

D: 4,950 tons light surf.; 6,990 tons normal surf./7,250 tons sub.
S: 11.6 kts surf./31 kts sub.
Dim: 107.20 × 10.78 (16.48 over stern planes) × 7.90 (fwd; 7.80 aft)
A: 2 bow 650-mm TT (8 Type 88R/SS-N-16 Stallion missiles and/or Type 65-76 torpedoes); 4 bow 533-mm TT (16 Type 83RN and 84RN/SS-N-15 Starfish and Type 53-65K and USET-80 torpedoes, VA-111 Shkval rocket torpedoes, MG-74 Korund and Siren decoys, or up to 36 mines)
Electronics:
Radar: 1 MRK-50 Albatros'-series (Snoop Tray-2) nav./search
Sonar: MGK-503 Skat-KS (Shark Gill) suite: LF active/passive; passive flank array; Barrakuda towed passive linear array; MT-70 active ice avoidance (see remarks)
EW: MRP-10 Zaliv-P/Buleva (Brick Pulp) intercept; Park Lamp D/F
M: 2 VM-4P pressurized-water nuclear reactors (75 Mw each), 2 sets OK-300 steam turbines; 1 7-bladed prop; 31,000 shp at 290 shaft rpm—2 low-speed electric cruise motors; 2 small props on stern planes; 1,020 shp at 500 rpm
Electric: 4,460 kw tot. (2 × 2,000-kw, 380-V, 50-Hz a.c. OK-2 turbogenerators, 1 × 460-kw diesel emergency set)
Endurance: 80 days **Crew:** 27 officers, 34 warrant officers, 35 enlisted

Remarks: Survivors of 26 Project 671–series units; as of 7-00, four were active in the Northern Fleet and none in the Pacific, where the one remaining unit, K-292, was laid up at Strelok. Project 671RTM was approved in 6-75. Launchings resumed at St. Petersburg in 7-85 with the 22nd Project 671 unit, modified as Project 671RTMK (or 671.7) to enable launching Granat strategic cruise missiles. Hull number prefixes were originally "B," but were changed to "K" on 29-8-91 when the class was redesignated Large Nuclear-Powered Submarines, First Rank. A Northern Fleet unit of this class suffered a gas leak accident in 1-98, killing the commanding officer and injuring four enlisted personnel. K-448 was named on 10-4-95. Northern Fleet unit K-388 conducted trials in carrying commercial cargo in the Arctic region in 1995.
Disposals: Among the 21 Project 671RTM units deactivated and/or stricken due to the lack of overhaul and recoring funds were K-182 (stricken 31-7-96), K-218, *50 Let Komsomol'skiy na Amur* (K-242) (stricken 30-5-98), K-251 (stricken 30-5-98), K-254, K-298, K-305 (stricken 30-5-98), K-324, K-355 (stricken 30-5-98), K-358 (ex-*Murmanskiy Komsomolets*), K-360 (stricken 30-5-98), K-412 (stricken 31-7-96), K-492 (stricken 31-7-96), *Volgograd* (K-502), K-507 (stricken 30-5-98), K-524 (ex-*60 Let Sheftstva V.L.K.S.M.*), and K-527.
Hull systems: Pressure hull is fabricated from AK-29 steel. Initially employed an unusual eight-bladed propeller, consisting of two tandem four-bladed props oriented 22.5° apart and co-rotating; all survivors have a standard seven-bladed prop. Diving depth is 400 m normal/600 m maximum operational. Are more highly automated than earlier versions of the Victor series, permitting smaller crews, although complements have grown as new systems have been added. There are two 112-cell battery groups with 8,000 Amp-hr capacity. Reserve buoyancy is 28%.
Combat systems: The late-construction Project 671RTMK Victor-IIIs employed the Varyag command system, which has four computers, four command consoles, three combat data consoles, three sonar operator consoles, and three weapons/countermeasures consoles; they were the only units equipped to launch the RPK-55 Granat (SS-N-21 Sampson) strategic cruise missile, now no longer in service. One periscope is Type PZKG-10. The ASW missile system is known as the RPK-6 Vodopod or RPK-7 Veter, depending on whether 533-mm-diameter Type 86R or 650-mm Type 88R missiles are carried (presumably, both can be). VA-111 Shkval rocket-powered torpedoes, with nuclear warheads, were meant as "revenge" weapons against submarines

NUCLEAR-POWERED ATTACK SUBMARINES [SSN] *(continued)*

that had fired on Soviet boats and are probably no longer carried, since tactical nuclear weapons were removed from Russian warships in 1991. Torpedoes can be launched at depths up to 250 m.

The standard communications suite is the Molnaya-L, with Kiparis, Anis, and Sintez antennas and the Paravan towed VLF wire antenna, which is deployed from the casing abaft the sail. The Tsunami-B SATCOM system (with Pert Spring antenna) is fitted to all. The navigation suite is designated Medveditsa-671RTM.

The Project 671RTMK units have Skat-series sonar suites with the Barrakuda LF active/passive bow array (with a nominal range of 230 km), Akula flank arrays, Chanel passive sonar intercept, a passive ranging array, the Pithon towed array, an active HF fire-control set, a mine-avoidance active set, and an underwater telephone. Also carried on a few is a nonacoustic wake-sensing system with sensors mounted on the starboard side of the sail.

ATTACK SUBMARINES [SS]

(PL = *Podvodnaya Lodka,* or Submarine)

♦ 0 (+ 2 + 1) Lada class (Projects 677 and 677E*)

Bldr: Admiralteiskiye Verfi 194, St. Petersburg

	Laid down	L	In serv.
B-100 Sankt Peterburg	26-12-97	2002?	2003?
B-. . . . .*	26-12-97	. . .	. . .
B-.	. . .	. . .	. . .

Lada class (Project 677) Firma Rubin

D: 1,765 tons surf. normal/2,700 tons sub. **S:** 11 kts surf./22 kts sub.
Dim: 67.00 × 7.20 × 4.40
A: 6 bow 533-mm TT (16 tot. P-10 Biyuza antiship missiles, Type 91RE1 Klub ASW missiles, SET-80 torpedoes, VA-111 Shkval rocket torpedoes, or up to 22 DM-1 and/or RM-2G mines)
Electronics:
Radar: 1 . . . nav./search
EW: . . . intercept
Sonar: Lira suite: bow active; bow and flank passive; towed linear passive array; active bow mine-avoidance set; passive rangefinding array; self-noise measurement
M: 2 Type 2D-42-series diesel generator sets, 1 2,000-kw electric motor generator; 1 7-bladed prop; 2,700 shp—possible Kristal-27E fuel-cell auxiliary propulsion syst.; 400 shp
Range: 6,000/. . . snorkel; 650/3 sub. **Endurance:** 50 days
Crew: 41 tot. (34 on Project 677E)

Remarks: B-100 was ordered in 8-97 for the Russian Navy, while a similar Project 677E (Amur 1650) unit was financed as an export demonstrator by the Korskaya Tekhika financial consortium (Rubin Design Bureau, Admiralty Shipyard, National Reserve Bank, Amur Shipyard, Zvezdochka State Engineering Co., the Ministry of Defense First Central Research Institute, and Rosvoorouszhenie, the state military export firm). Both units are versions of the Rubin Central Design Bureau's Amur 1650, on which design work began in 1989. Project Amur is available in versions from 550 to 2,000 tons surfaced displacement (see table below). B-100 was said to be about 30% complete as of 1-00, while the export boat was only 7% complete, but after a renewal of Indian interest in the submarine, the latter's pressure hull was said to have been completed as of 12-00. Negotiations were under way for a contract to build a second Project 677 for the Russian Navy as of 7-00.

Hull systems: Modern Russia's first single-hulled submarine, the Lada is a conservative design, with sail-mounted bow planes and cruciform stern control surfaces. Intended to operate 10 years between overhauls. Will have two battery groups. Said to be "8–10 times" quieter than the Project 877 Kilo and will have an anechoic hull coating. To use brushless generators to reduce noise. Will have an inertial navigational system. Crew figure given is with three-section watch; with a two-section watch, the crew can be reduced to 34. Accommodations are in separate cabins. All waste products will be retained aboard until return to port. Normal operating depth limit is 200 m, with 250-m maximum. The proposed air-independent propulsion system would use two vertical cryogenic pressure containers, one for hydrogen and one for oxygen; it is uncertain whether it will be aboard B-100.

Combat systems: The attack periscope is to have night-vision features and a laser rangefinder. The search periscope will be non-hull-penetrating. Will have a trailing-wire communications antenna. The radar and intercept antennas will be on the same mast, and the radar will have a low-power mode for concealed operations.

Variants offered: Amur 1450, the export variant about which most information has been published (as it would be expected to offer the greatest chance for foreign purchase interest), would have one 2,000-kw electric motor developing 2,700 shp, a range of 4,000 n.m. on snorkel and 300 n.m. at 3 kts submerged, and an endurance of 30 days and would carry a crew of 34–41. The Amur 1850 variant would have more battery capacity than the Amur 1450 and a more powerful electric motor; its endurance would also be extended. The Amur 1650 variant announced in 1997 appears to have been tailored to Indian requirements. Basic data for the variants offered to date include:

Amur variant	*550*	*750*	*959*	*1450*	*1650*	*1850*
Displacement (m^3)						
Normal surfaced	550	750	950	1,450	1,765	1,850
Full, submerged	700	900	1,300	2,100	2,300	2,600
Length (m)	46	48	56	58	67	68
Beam (m)	4.4	5.0	5.6	7.2	7.1	7.2
Normal depth (m)	200	200	250	250	250	250
Armament						
Tubes/dia. (mm)	4/400	4/400	4/533	6/533	6/533	6/533
Total weapons	8	16	12	16	18	16
Speed, sub. (kts)	18	17	19	17	21	22
Range (n.m.)						
Submerged (at 3 kts)	250	250	350	300	650	500
Snorkeling	1,500	3,000	4,000	4,000	6,000	6,000
Endurance (days)	20	20	30	30	40	50
Crew (tot.)	18	21	21	34	. . .	37

Note: In 1998, the Rubin Design Bureau announced the development of the Project 636M design, said to be the third generation of the basic Kilo concept. Project 636M would feature a "missile complex," an inertial navigational system, a night-vision periscope with television and laser rangefinder, a towed VLF and ELF communications antenna, a "more powerful" sonar suite, and a battery with 2.5 times the service life of current Russian submarine batteries (which are short-lived in comparison with foreign submarine batteries). Project 636M is intended to be competitive in the export market through 2010 and will be able to accept further new systems as they are developed. No customers have materialized to date, although it may be this version that was unsuccessfully offered to South Korea in 1999.

♦ 8 Improved Kilo class (Project 636) (4 *nonoperational*)

Bldrs: A: Krasnoye Sormovo Zavod 199, Nizhniy Novgorod; B: Zavod imeni Leninskiy Komsomol 112, Komsomol'sk-na-Amur

	Bldr	Laid down	L	In serv.	Fleet
B-401 Novorossiysk	A	6-88	8-89	4-1-90	Northern
B-402 Vologda	A	11-88	9-89	1990	Northern
B-425 Almatyevsk	A	6-89	5-90	7-91	Northern
B-437 (ex-*Magnitogorskiy Komsomolets*)	A	9-89	8-90	1991	Northern
B-459 Vladikavkaz	A	3-90	15-7-91	2-92	Northern
B-187	B	3-10-90	10-91	1-93	Pacific
B-190	B	10-91	8-5-92	12-94	Pacific
B-459	B	5-92	6-10-93	. . .	Pacific

Improved Kilo–class Vologda (B-402)—arriving at Faslane
A. Love, *Ships of the World,* 2001

D: 2,350 tons surf./3,126 tons sub. **S:** 11 kts surf./19.8 kts sub.
Dim: 73.80 × 9.90 × 6.60 (max. surf.)
A: 6 bow 533-mm TT (18 Type 86R/SS-N-16 Stallion missiles, torpedoes, and/or up to 24 mines); 1 shoulder-launched SAM syst. (6 Igla-M missiles)
Electronics:
Radar: MRK-50 Albatros' (Snoop Tray-2) nav./search
Sonar: MGK-400 Rubikon (Shark Gill) LF active/passive suite: passive hull array; MG-519 active object avoidance; MG-553 sound-velocity measurement; MG-512 self-cavitation measurement
EW: MRM-25EM (Squid Head) intercept
M: 2 Type 4-2AA-42M turbocharged diesel generator sets (1,500 kw each at 700 rpm), 2 PG-141M electric motors; 1 7-bladed prop; 5,500 shp—1 MT-140 electric low-speed motor (183 shp)—2 MT-168 internal electric creep/maneuvering motors; 2 ducted props; 204 shp (for 3 kts)
Range: 7,500/7 snorkel; 400/3 sub. **Endurance:** 45 days
Crew: 13 officers, 12 warrant officers, 12 petty officers, 15 nonrated

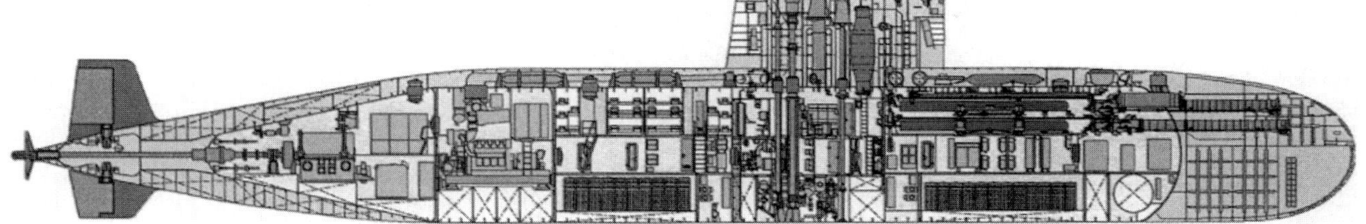

Lada class (Project 677) Firma Rubin

ATTACK SUBMARINES [SS] *(continued)*

An Improved Kilo–class (Project 636) unit, possibly B-437—during a visit to the U.K. Paul C. Clift, 5-94

A Project 636 Improved Kilo, possibly B-437—note the chopped-off deck casing at the stern, characteristic of this class Paul C. Clift, 5-94

Remarks: An across-the-board improvement over the standard Project 877–series Kilo that has been offered for foreign sale as the Project 636 since 1993 but is also in service with the Russian Navy. Two export Type 636 Kilos were built for China at Admiralty Shipyard, St. Petersburg. Both formerly active Pacific Fleet units were laid up as of 1999 for lack of funds to provide new batteries; at least one had only 17 crewmembers assigned as of 3-01.

Hull systems: Have improved sound quieting over the earlier Project 877 series and a greater degree of automation. The electric propulsion motor is mounted on a flexible raft, and the maximum shaft rpm has been halved to 250 rpm. Maximum snorkeling speed is 8–10 kts. The bow has been reshaped to improve flow and some auxiliary machinery has been moved aft from the bow compartment to reduce noise interference with the passive bow sonar array. A more efficient model of the diesel generator set has been employed. The 7.2-m-diameter pressure hull has been lengthened to 53.0 m to accommodate the rafted main engines and also allowing tankage for additional diesel fuel. Pressure hull thickness is 24–27 mm, except in some reinforced areas, where it is 30–35 mm thick. There are three 614-mm-diameter access hatches. The outer hull is coated with 0.8-m-square rubber anechoic tiles, attached with glue over special studs. The stern planes, rudder, and bow planes mounted just forward of the sail are controlled by a Pirit-23 hydraulic system. The two maneuvering propellers are mounted in internal ducts just forward of the stern planes, with the shafts to the motors protruding directly aft through the after pressure bulkhead. The export version of Project 636 has been offered with an air-independent propulsion system in a lengthened hull.

There are two attack periscopes with 1.5× and 6× magnification. Have two 120-cell Type 446 lead-acid batteries. Height from keel to the top of the 5-m-high sail is 14.7 m. Diving depth is 240 m normal/300 m maximum, and periscope depth is 17.5 m. Require 120 seconds to submerge. The hull has 30% reserve buoyancy in surfaced condition.

Combat systems: Only the two outer torpedo tubes in the lower row can accommodate TEST-71ME wire-guided torpedoes, while all tubes can launch 53-65KE, 53-56B, 53BA, and SET-53ME torpedoes; an automatic reload system permits reloading within 3 minutes. Torpedoes can be launched down to 240-m depth. With 12 in the torpedo tubes and 12 in the racks, 24 Type AM-1 mines can be carried in lieu of some torpedoes; mines can be laid only with the submarine at a depth of not more than 50 m.

The combat system is the digital MVU-110EM, which has three computer/processors; five targets can be tracked simultaneously (two automatically). The MGK-400 sonar suite is said to be able to detect submarines at a range of 16–20 km and surface ships at 60–80 km. Radio communication gear fitted includes two P-654-MP transmitters, three P-680-1 HF/VHF receivers, one P-683-1 LF receiver, one P-625 UHF transceiver, and one P-608H portable set. The MPM-25EM intercept array incorporates the transponder for the Khrom-K IFF system.

♦ 16 Kilo (Paltus) class (Projects 877 and 877KM) (13 *nonoperational*)

Bldrs: A: Zavod imeni Leninskiy Komsomol 112, Komsomol'sk-na-Amur; B: Krasnoye Sormovo Zavod 199, Nizhniy Novgorod

	Bldr	Laid down	L	In serv.	Fleet
10 Project 877:					
B-248	A	6-79	12-9-80	4-82	Pacific
B-260	A	9-80	19-8-81	10-81	Pacific
B-227	A	9-81	1-9-82	11-82	Baltic
B-229	A	6-82	8-83	10-83	Pacific
B-404 (ex-*Tyumanskiy Komsomolets*)	A	9-82	9-83	11-83	Pacific
B-871*	B	1-83	1-3-84	6-84	Black Sea
B-405	A	9-83	9-84	10-84	Pacific
B-177 Lepetsk	B	11-84	1-9-85	29-9-00	Northern
B-806	B	9-85	7-86	8-87	Baltic
B-354	B	8-87	7-88	16-2-89	Northern

*Converted to Project 877VD

	Bldr	Laid down	L	In serv.	Fleet
6 Project 877KM:					
B-470	A	9-84	8-85	9-85	Pacific
B-439	A	9-85	7-86	8-86	Pacific
B-445	A	10-86	8-87	10-87	Pacific
B-394 (ex-*Komsomolets Tadzhikistan*)	A	9-87	9-88	10-88	Pacific
B-464	A	11-88	9-89	6-91	Pacific
B-496	A	10-89	10-90	10-91	Pacific

B-227—the active Baltic Fleet Project 877 Kilo Boris Lemachko, 7-00

B-871—the Black Sea Fleet's pumpjet-equipped Project 877VD Kilo Hartmut Ehlers, 7-00

A Northern Fleet Project 877 Kilo M.O.D. U.K.

D: 2,325 tons surf. (2,450 with emergency fuel)/3,076 tons sub.
S: 10 kts surf./17 kts sub.
Dim: 72.60 (70.0 wl) × 9.90 (12.80 over stern planes) × 6.60 (fwd; 6.20 mean)
A: 6 533-mm bow TT (18 Type 86R/SS-N-16 Stallion missiles, torpedoes, and/or up to 24 mines); 1 shoulder-launched SAM syst. (6 Igla-M missiles)
Electronics:
Radar: 1 MRK-50 Albatros' (Snoop Tray-2) nav./search
Sonar: MGK-400 Rubikon (Shark Gill) LF active/passive suite; passive hull array; MG-519 Arfa (Mouse Roar) HF active target classification/mine avoidance; MG-553 sound-velocity measuring; MG-512 cavitation detection—some also: MG-53 sonar intercept
EW: MRM-25EM (Squid Head) intercept; 6701E (Quad Loop) D/F
M: 2 Type 4-2DL42M diesel generator sets (1,825 bhp/1,500 kw at 700 rpm), electric drive: 1 motor; 1 6-bladed prop (B-871: pumpjet); 5,900 shp—1 130-shp low-speed motor; 2 low-speed maneuvering motors; 2 ducted props; 204 shp (3 kts)

ATTACK SUBMARINES [SS] *(continued)*

Range: 6,000/7 snorkel; 400/3 sub. **Fuel:** 172 tons
Endurance: 45 days **Crew:** 12 officers, 41–45 enlisted

Remarks: Informally known as the Warshavyanka class, as they were originally intended to be built in numbers for the Warsaw pact navies; Paltus is the official project code name. Begun in 1974 at Firma Rubin, the design effort was headed by Yu. N. Kormilitsyn. B-177 was completed in 1991 but was placed in reserve until commissioned on 29-9-00. Black Sea Fleet unit B-871 began an overhaul and conversion at Sevastopol' on 9-9-90 and has been fitted with a pumpjet propulsor; the submarine remained nonoperational until 7-99 for lack of batteries but returned to sea during 2000 as that fleet's only active submarine. Baltic Fleet unit B-227 was given new batteries late in 2000; the boat is used primarily to train foreign crews. B-806 was in refit at St. Petersburg as of 10-01.

All Pacific Fleet units were laid up in 1998 for lack of funds to provide new batteries. Two Pacific Fleet submarines of this class, presumably from Russian Navy assets, were offered to South Korea in 3-99 for delivery by the end of the year; South Korea declined the offer. In 5-99 a Russian official stated that two inactive Pacific Fleet units of the class would be made available for foreign sale after refurbishment and updating at Amur Zavod, Komsomol'sk under the direction of the Rubin Central Design Bureau.

Exports: Foreign customers (Projects 877E and 877EKM) have been India (10), Algeria (2), Poland (1), Romania (1), Iran (3), and China (2). Export models on offer have included Projects 877M with six 533-mm internal tubes; 877EM, 73.2 m long with two tubes capable of firing wire-guided torpedoes; 877MK, with an improved combat data system; and 877EKM, with all tubes capable of launching wire-guided torpedoes. Export-configured units have had a longer walking deck abaft the sail than the Russian Navy version.

Hull systems: Propulsion plant is suspended for silencing. Hull has 32% reserve buoyancy at 2,350 m^3 surfaced displacement and 26% at 2,450 m^3. Surfaced draft at 2,450 tons with emergency fuel and antisonar coating installed is 6.60 m forward, 6.70 m aft. Enveloped volume submerged is 4,200 m^3. Maximum diving depth is 300 m, normal depth 240 m, and periscope depth 17.5 m; can submerge in 120 seconds. Can sustain 8 kts on surface in the heaviest sea conditions and can achieve 400 n.m. submerged at 3 kts if the air-conditioning system is off. Have an anechoic hull coating like larger nuclear submarines. Two battery groups, each with 120 cells, provide 9,700 kw-hr at 100 Amp. The 51.8-m-long pressure hull has six watertight compartments. The air regeneration system provides enough breathable atmosphere for 260 hours of operations with a full crew. Carry 10 tons of lube oil, 8.5 tons of provisions, 19.3 tons of fresh water, and 4 tons of distilled water. Have the Pirit-2E automated maneuvering system.

Combat systems: The combat system, designated MVU-110EM, can conduct two simultaneous attacks while tracking three other targets manually. The sonar suite is supplemented by MG-519 active mine-avoidance set, MG-553 sound velocity meter, and MG-512 own-ship cavitation detector. The shoulder-fired SAM launch position is located in the after portion of the sail. Torpedo tube–launched weapons carried can include TEST-71M wire-guided, E53-65K and SET-53M wake-homing, and E53-56B acoustic homing torpedoes; KMD-500, KMD-1000, KMD-II-500, KMD-II-1000, and UMD mines; and Type 83R and 84R (SS-N-15 Starfish) antisubmarine missiles. Full mine load is carried two in each tube plus 12 in the torpedo reload compartment. Can launch torpedoes via compressed air in waters up to 240 m deep. On the six Project 877KM units, the lower, outboard tubes are equipped to launch wire-guided torpedoes, of which up to six may be carried. Torpedoes are launchable by the Murena-M torpedo launch system within 2 minutes of alert; reload of all six tubes takes only 5 minutes. There are two PZKG periscopes. Communications equipment includes Type IVA-MV for shortwave and Type ANIS-M-B for VHF and UHF.

♦ 3 Tango (Som) Class (Project 641B) (2 *nonoperational*)

Bldr: Krasnoye Sormovo Zavod 112, Nizhniy Novgorod (ex-Gorkiy) (In serv. 1975–82)

	In serv.
B-307	1981
B-437 MAGNETOGORSK (ex-*Magnetogorskiy Komsomolets*)	1979
B-515	1981

A typical Project 641B Tango-class unit U.S. Navy

D: 2,770 tons surf./3,556 tons sub. **S:** 13 kts surf./16 kts sub.
Dim: 90.20 × 8.60 × 5.70
A: 6 bow 533-mm TT (24 Type 86R/SS-N-16 Stallion missiles, torpedoes, and/or mines)
Electronics:
Radar: 1 MRK-50-series Albatros' (Snoop Tray-1 or -2) search
Sonar: MGK-400 Rubikon LF active/passive suite: MG-14 MF active; MG-519 Arfa (Mouse Roar) mine detection; passive hull array; MG-553 sound-velocity measurement; MG-512 cavitation detector—B-437 also: towed passive array
EW: MRM-25EM (Squid Head) Quad Loop D/F
M: 3 Type 2D-42 diesels (1,825 bhp each), 3 PG-102 electric motors; 2 5-bladed props; 6,256 shp—2 140-shp electric low-speed motors
Range: 20,000/11 surf.; 14,000/7 snorkel; 15/15, 450/2.5 sub.
Fuel: 410–420 tons **Crew:** 17 officers, 61 enlisted

Magnetogorsk (B-437)—with towed sonar array dispenser fairing at the stern U.S. Navy, 1994

Remarks: Project number has also been reported as 641BUKI. Project name, Som, means Sheatfish. The design team at TsKB 18, Firma Rubin, was led by Igor D. Spasskiy, with Z. A. Deribin (succeeded by Yu. N. Kormilitsyn) as chief project designer. The first unit, B-380, was delivered 20-5-73, and roughly two per year were built. As of 1996, none were operational, due to the lack of replacement battery sets. By 5-00, however, Northern Fleet unit B-437, with a towed sonar array, was operating from Polyarnyy; the other two commissioned survivors are inactive in the Northern Fleet.

Disposals: Northern Fleet units B-290, B-303, and B-519, at Kronshtadt for overhauls, were stricken 1-9-95. B-319 and B-386 were stricken from the Northern Fleet 31-7-96 (with B-386 becoming a museum exhibit at Severodvinsk on 12-1-01). Baltic Fleet unit B-312 was deactivated 1-5-98 and stricken during 1999; Baltic Fleet unit B-307 had been stricken earlier. Baltic Fleet unit B-303 was towed away for scrap 1-7-99 and B-519 and B-290 two days later. Black Sea Fleet unit B-380 (ex-*Gor'hovskiy Komsomolets*) was inactivated 10-1-96 and was turned down by Ukraine for transfer; the submarine remains afloat at Sevastopol', however, but is unlikely to be refitted and reactivated. B-30, B-97, B-215, B-504, and B-546 remain afloat at various Northern Fleet bases but are out of commission and unlikely to return to service.

Hull systems: Hull is sheathed in an anechoic sonar-absorbent rubber compound. Have significantly greater battery capacity than the Foxtrot class and their greater internal volume provides more space for weapons reloads. Diving depth: 300 m maximum, 240 m normal operating. Total volume enveloped by outer hull, the sail, and all appendages is 4,600 m^3.

Combat systems: Have the Most-641B navigation/data system and the Uzel combat data system with Vol'fram torpedo f.c. computer and Pirit autopilot. EW arrays vary; some had the later Squid Head array. B-437 was fitted with a towed linear passive sonar array at Kronshtadt during the mid-1990s, with the cable reel in a drum forward of the sail and the array exiting a tube above the stern; a second unit was supposed to have received it, but the work was not completed.

NUCLEAR-POWERED AUXILIARY SUBMARINES [SSAN]

♦ 2 (+ 1) Uniform (Kashalot) class (Project 1910) (1 *nonoperational*)

Bldr: Admiralteiskiye Verfi 196 (Sudomekh Division), St. Petersburg

	Laid down	L	In serv.
AS-13	20-10-77	25-11-82	31-12-86
AS-15	23-2-83	29-4-88	30-12-91
AS-12	16-7-90	26-8-95	. . .

Uniform class (Project 1910) M.O.D. U.K., 1992

D: 1,390 tons surf./1,580 tons sub. **S:** 10 kts surf./30 kts sub.
Dim: 69.0 × 7.0 × 5.2 **A:** none
Electronics: Radar: Snoop Slab search—Sonar: HF active arrays
M: 1 1.5-Mw pressurized water nuclear reactor; 1 prop; 10,000 shp
Crew: 36 tot.

NUCLEAR-POWERED AUXILIARY SUBMARINES [SSAN] *(continued)*

Remarks: Apparently intended for research or special operations on the ocean floor. The first Soviet single-hulled nuclear-powered submarines. Fitting-out work on AS-12, of a possible Project 10831 modified design, had ceased by 10-98.
Hull systems: Titanium-construction, single-hulled design with an operating diving depth of up to 700 m. Have fairings on the hull side abreast the sail house maneuvering thrusters.

♦ 2 Paltus (Nelhma) class (Project 1851)
Bldr: Admiralteiskiye Verfi 196 (Sudomekh Division), St. Petersburg

	Laid down	L	In serv.
AS-21	26-12-84	29-4-91	28-12-91
AS-35	20-12-89	29-9-94	12-10-95

D: 730 tons sub. **S:** 6 kts sub. **Dim:** 53.0 × 3.8 × 5.3
M: 1 10-Mw pressurized water reactor, 1 diesel generator set; 1 prop; 300 shp
Crew: 14 tot. (all officers)

Remarks: Other sources give the Paltus class as Project 1083.1. Reportedly yet another small submarine intended for special operations on the sea floor. Equipped with two manipulators forward and maneuvering thrusters abreast the sail. Operating depth said to be 1,000 m. Work on a reported third unit had ceased by 10-98 (and probably well before that).

♦ 1 Delta Stretch class (Project . . .)
Bldr: Sevmashpredpriyatiye, Severodvinsk (Severodvinsk SY 402)

	Laid down	L	In serv.
BS-129 (ex-K-129)	2-79	3-81	19-11-81

D: 10,600 tons surf./13,050 tons sub. **S:** 14 kts surf./24 kts sub.
Dim: . . . × 11.70 × 8.70 **A:** probably none
Electronics:
Radar: 1 MRK-50-series Albatros' (Snoop Tray) nav./search
Sonar: MGK-500-series Skat-2 (Shark Gill) LF active/passive suite: MGK-519 (Mouse Roar) active mine avoidance; MG-512 cavitation monitor; MG-518 active upward-looking echo sounder; MG-519 mine detection; MG-533 sound-velocity measurement; NOR-1 ice-lane detector; NOK-1 surface warning
EW: MRP-10 Zaliv-P (Brick Pulp) intercept; Park Lamp D/F
M: 2 VM-4S pressurized-water nuclear reactors (89.2 Mw each), 2 Type OK-700A steam turbines; 2 5-bladed props; 52,000 shp—2 306-shp electric low-speed motors on main shafts
Electric: 6,920 kw tot. (2 × 3,000-kw a.c. alternators, 2 × 460-kw diesel sets)
Endurance: 80 days **Crew:** . . . tot.

Remarks: Relaunched 29-12-00 after undergoing conversion since 1995 at Severodvinsk as a *Sverkhmalaya Podvodnavy Lodka* ("Super-Small Submarine") tender for the Paltus class (Project 1851). Had been in a collision with a U.S. submarine during 1993 and was then considered for conversion as a civilian oceanographic research submarine.
Hull systems: The 32.5-m mid-body, originally intended for a second Yankee Stretch conversion, replaced the original 45-m-long ballistic-missile section, but the new overall dimension is not known and could be as long as the 162.5 m of the Yankee Stretch. The pressure hull is 9.8 m in diameter. Primary ship's service electric power is delivered at 380 V/50 Hz. Test diving depth is 580 m, normal operating depth 320 m. Has bow and stern side-thrusters. Is probably able to accommodate a Paltus SSAN within the new mid-body.
Combat systems: The Molnaya-M communications suite incorporates towed VLF communications buoys and a Pert Spring antenna for the Tsunami SATCOM system.

♦ 1 Yankee Stretch conversion (Project 09774)
Bldr: Sevmashpredpriyatiye, Severodvinsk (Severodvinsk SY 402)
(In serv. 31-8-70)

	Laid down	L	In serv.
BS-411 Orënburg (ex-KS-411, ex-K-411)	25-5-68	16-1-70	31-8-70

D: 9,408 tons surf./11,685 tons sub. **S:** 16 kts surf./27 kts sub.
Dim: 162.50 × 11.70 × 8.30 **A:** none
Electronics:
Radar: 1 RLK-101 Albatros' (Snoop Tray-1) nav./search
Sonar: MGK-300 Rubin active/passive array; MG-509 mine avoidance
EW: MRP-10 Zaliv-P intercept
M: 2 VM-4T pressurized water reactors (72 Mw each), 2 OK-700 steam turbines; 2 5-bladed props; 51,000 shp—2 260-shp low-speed electric motors
Electric: 6,200 kw tot. (2 Type TMV-32 2,600-kw a.c. turboalternators, 2 × 500-kw diesel sets)
Endurance: 80 days **Crew:** 42 officers, 64 enlisted

Remarks: Known in Russia as the "SMPL/AS" conversion, with SMPL probably standing for *Sverkhmalaya Podvodnavy Lodka* ("Super-Small Submarine"). Officially stated to be a "Nuclear Submarine Carrier of Deepwater Automated Apparatus." Like the Delta Stretch, is intended to support units of the Paltus class. Converted at Severodvinsk between 20-10-83 and 30-12-90. Based in the Northern Fleet. Although a mid-body for use in a second Yankee Stretch conversion was fabricated, the conversion was never made, and the section was later employed on the Delta Stretch.

BS-411—the "Yankee Stretch" (Project 09774) French Navy, 8-92

♦ 1 Yankee Big Nose (Akson-2) conversion (Project 09780)
Bldr: Sevmashpredpriyatiye, Severodvinsk (Severodvinsk SY 402)

	Laid down	L	In serv.
KS-403 Kazan	1970	1971	20-8-71

Kazan (KS-403)—the "Yankee Big Nose" (Project 09780) sonar trials conversion
A. S. Pavlov, *Voennie Korabli Rossie,* 1997–98

D: 8,675 tons surf./9,190 tons sub. **S:** 16 kts surf./27 kts sub.
Dim: 151.80 × 11.70 × 7.90 **A:** probably removed
Electronics:
Radar: 1 MRK-50 Albatros' (Snoop Tray-1) nav./search
EW: . . .
Sonar: probable Irtysh-Amfora trials suite; MG-509 mine avoidance
M: 2 VM-4G pressurized water reactors (89.2 Mw each), 2 OK-700 steam turbines; 2 5-bladed props; 52,000 shp—2 260-shp low-speed electric motors on main shafts
Electric: 6,120 kw tot. (2 Type TMV-32 2,600-kw a.c. turboalternators, 2 × 460-kw diesel sets)
Endurance: 100 days **Crew:** 57 officers, 43 enlisted

Remarks: Former ballistic-missile submarine, converted 1978–80 and lengthened by 5 m to 134 m under Project 667AK to accommodate Skat low-frequency sonar suite under Project 09774, Akson-1 (NATO nickname Yankee Pod). The ship was equipped with a variety of submarine sensor systems for trials purposes, including a pod atop the vertical stabilizer to accommodate a towed linear passive hydrophone array; there was also a second towed array dispenser tube just below the pod. Mounted on either side of the forward edge of the sail were what appeared to be fixed torpedo front-end bodies, indicating possible use for trials of torpedo seeker systems. Diving depth: 380 m normal operating, 450 m maximum.

Refitted 1993 to 23-10-96 under Project 09780, Akson-2, with a greatly extended bulbous bow intended to house the prototype of the spherical hydrophone array of the Irtysh-Amfora suite for the *Severodvinsk* class (Project 885). The sail was also lengthened, and the pod atop the vertical stabilizer was replaced by a standard internal towed array dispenser tube. The submarine is assigned to the Morfizpribor sonar research and design institute and is based in the Northern Fleet.

AUXILIARY SUBMARINES [SSA]

Disposal note: The sole Beluga (Russian Makrel')-class (Project 1710) trials submarine, SS-533, inactive at Sevastopol' since 1997, was planned to be stricken during late 2001. The submarine did not have the name *Forel,* as incorrectly listed in earlier editions.

AUXILIARY SUBMARINES [SSA] *(continued)*

Of the four Bravo (Kefal')-class (Project 690) target submarines, Northern Fleet unit BS-368 was stricken 3-7-92; Black Sea Fleet unit SS-256, stricken 10-1-96 and offered to Ukraine (which did not accept her), was towed to Kerch' for scrapping 29-10-99; and Black Sea Fleet unit SS-226 was flooded out and foundered 17-1-99 but was later refloated, leaving only SS-310, used as a stationary training device at Sevastopol', remaining on the fleet list but unlikely to be returned to service.

Of the two India (Lenok)-class (Project 940) salvage submarines, Pacific Fleet unit BS-486 (ex-*Komsomolets Uzbekhistana*) was stricken 17-11-94 and was towed away for scrap 20-9-00. The Northern Fleet's India, BS-257, has been immobilized since 1990 in need of a major overhaul but is still considered a unit of the fleet, although unlikely ever to operate again.

MIDGET SUBMARINES [SSM]

Disposal note: Losos (Pirhana)-class (Project 865) combatant midget submarines MS-520 and MS-521, in reserve since 7-92, were stricken during 1997, but one may have been retrieved during 1999–2000 and upgraded to serve as a technology and sales demonstrator by the St. Petersburg Maritime Machine-Building Bureau, which is offering variants of the design for export with submerged displacements of 130, 170, 220, 400, 550, and 750 tons; gas turbine–powered generators are offered, and a crew of nine plus six combat swimmers could be carried.

Swimmer-delivery vehicles are discussed in the amphibious warfare section under [LSDV]. Salvage and research submarines [YSS] are listed with service craft.

NUCLEAR-POWERED GUIDED-MISSILE CRUISERS [CGN]

♦ **4 Kirov (Orlan) class (Projects 1144* and 1144.2)** (3 *nonoperational*)
Bldr: Ob'yedineniye Baltiyskiye Verf (Baltic Yard), St. Petersburg, Russia

	Laid down	L	In serv.	Fleet
090 Admiral Ushakov* (ex-*Kirov*)	27-3-74	27-12-77	30-12-80	Northern
015 Admiral Lazarev (ex-*Frunze*)	27-7-78	26-5-81	31-10-80	Pacific
080 Admiral Nakhimov (ex-*Kalinin*)	17-5-83	25-4-86	30-12-88	Northern
099 Petr Velikiy (ex-*Yuri Andropov*)	25-4-86	24-4-89	18-4-98	Northern

Petr Velikiy (099) *Ships of the World,* 8-00

Petr Velikiy (099)—launching a 9M-330 Gopher SAM Boris Lemachko, 8-00

D: 24,300 tons std., 24,500 tons normal (26,396 fl, except *Ushakov:* 25,860 fl)
S: 32 kts (17 on conventional steam power)
Dim: 251.20 (228.00 wl) × 28.50 (24.00 wl) × 9.10 (mean hull; 10.33 max.)

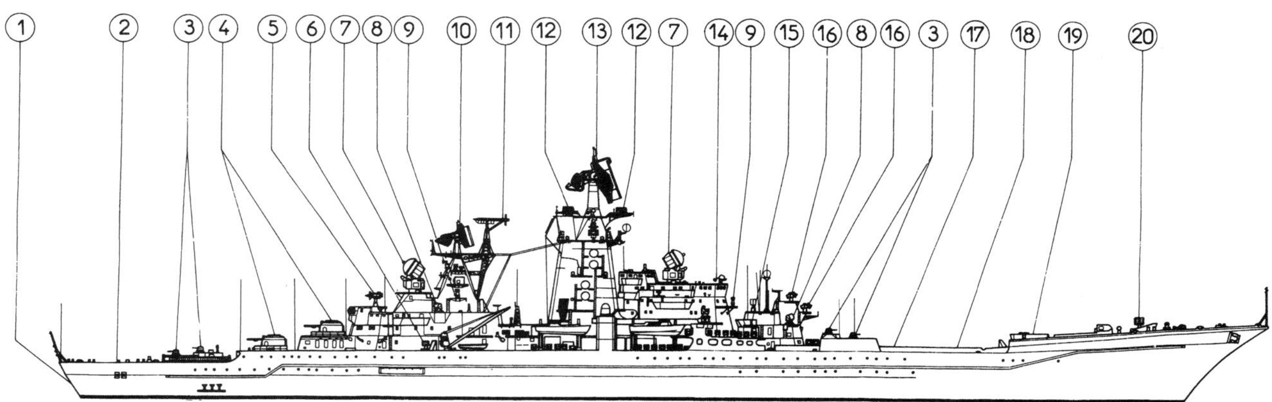

Admiral Ushakov (090) 1. VDS housing 2. helicopter pad 3. 30-mm AK-630 gatling AA 4. 100-mm DP 5. MR-114 Lev radar director for 100-mm guns 6. RBU-1000 ASW and antitorpedo RL 7. Volna radar director for Fort SAM system 8. MR-123 Vympel radar director for 30-mm AA 9. Tin Man optronic sensor 10. MR-700 Fregat 3-D air-search radar 11. Vee Tube HF comms antenna 12. Privod TACAN 13. MR-800 Voskhod 3-D early-warning radar 14. MR-212/201 Vaygach-U navigational radar 15. Osa-M SAM system. 16. Drakon radar director for URK-5 Rastrub ASW/antiship missile system 17. P-700 Granit antiship missile launchers (recessed into deck) 18. Fort SAM VLS (recessed into deck) 19. RBU-6000 ASW RL
Drawing by Louis Gassier, from *Flottes de Combat*

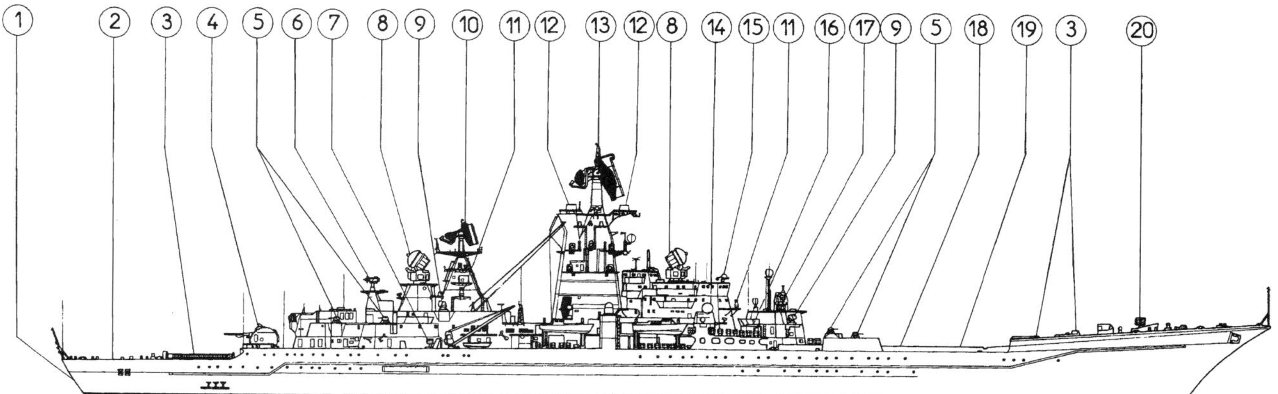

Admiral Lazarev (015) 1. VDS housing 2. helicopter pad 3. planned location for Kinzhal SAM system (never installed) 4. twin 130-mm AK-130 DP gunmount 5. 30-mm AK-630M gatling AA 6. MR-184 Lev radar director for 130-mm gunmount 7. RBU-1000 ASW/torpedo countermeasures RL 8. Volna radar director for Fort SAM system 9. MR-123 Vympel radar director for 30-mm AA 10. MR-700 Fregat 3-D air-search radar 11. Tin Man optronic sensor 12. Privod-B TACAN 13. MR-800 Voskhod 3-D early-warning radar 14. Big Ball SATCOM antenna radome 15. MR-212/201 Vaygach-U navigational/surface-search radars 16. Osa-M SAM system launchers 17. MPZ-301 Baza radar directors for the Osa-M SAM system. 18. P-700 Granit antiship missile launchers (recessed into deck) 19. Fort SAM VLS 20. RBU-6000 ASW RL
Drawing by Louis Gassier, from *Flottes de Combat*

NUCLEAR-POWERED GUIDED-MISSILE CRUISERS [CGN]
(continued)

Admiral Nakhimov (080) Boris Lemachko, 2-00

Admiral Ushakov (090)—when laid up at Severomorsk *Ships of the World,* 1999

Admiral Lazarev (015)—when still active, showing former pennant number 1990

A: *Ushakov:* 20 P-700 Granit (SS-N-19 Shipwreck) SSM (20 inclined SM-233 launch tubes); 12 6-round Fort (SA-N-6) SAM syst. (96 5V-55RM/Grumble missiles; 12 B-203A vertical launchers); 2 twin-rail Osa-M (SA-N-4) SAM syst. (40 9M-33/Gecko missiles); 2 single 100-mm 59-cal. AK-100 DP (2,000 rounds); 8 single 30-mm 54-cal. AK-630M gatling AA (48,000 rounds); 1 2-round URK-5 Rastrub (SS-N-14 Silex) ASW missile syst. (20 Type 83RUS Veter missiles); 2 quintuple 533-mm TT (20 torpedoes); 1 12-round RBU-6000 ASW RL (96 RGB-60 rockets); 2 6-round RBU-1000 ASW RL (72 rockets); 2 Ka-27PL Helix-A ASW helicopters; 1 Ka-27RTs Helix-A targeting helicopter

Lazarev: 20 P-700 Granit (SS-N-19 Shipwreck) SSM (20 inclined SM-233 launch tubes); 12 6-round Fort (SA-N-6) SAM syst. (96 5V-55RM/Grumble missiles; 12 B-203A vertical launchers); 2 twin-rail Osa-M (SA-N-4) SAM syst. (40 9M-33/Gecko missiles); 1 twin 130-mm 70-cal. AK-130 DP (840 rounds); 8 single 30-mm 54-cal. AK-630M gatling AA (48,000 rounds); 2 quintuple 533-mm TT (20 torpedoes and/or Type 86R Vodopod-MK/SS-N-16 Stallion missiles); 1 12-round RBU-6000 ASW RL (60 rockets); 2 6-round RBU-1000 ASW RL (102 rockets); 2 Ka-27PL Helix-A ASW helicopters; 1 Ka-27RTs Helix-A targeting helicopter

Nakhimov: 20 P-700 Granit (SS-N-19 Shipwreck) SSM (20 inclined SM-233 launch tubes); 12 6-round Fort (SA-N-6) SAM syst. (96 5V-55U/Grumble missiles; 12 B-203A vertical launchers); 2 twin-rail Osa-M (SA-N-4) SAM syst. (9M-33/Gecko missiles); 1 twin 130-mm 70-cal. AK-130 DP (840 rounds); 6 Kortik CIWS, each with 8 missile rails and 2 30-mm gatling AA (192 9M-311/SA-N-11 Grison missiles; 24,000 30-mm rounds); 2 quintuple 533-mm TT (20 torpedoes and/or Type 86R Vodopod-MK/SS-N-16 Stallion missiles); 1 10-round RPK-5 Liven' ASW RL (40 rockets); 2 6-round RBU-1000 ASW RL (102 rockets); 2 Ka-27PL Helix-A ASW helicopters; 1 Ka-27RTs Helix-A targeting helicopter

Petr Velikiy: 20 P-700 Granit (SS-N-19 Shipwreck) SSM (20 inclined SM-233 launch tubes); 12 6-round S-300F/FM Fort/Fort-M (SA-N-6) SAM syst. (48 48N6E and 48N6E2/Grumble missiles; 12 B-203A vertical launchers); 16 8-round Kinzhal (SA-N-9) SAM syst. (128 9M-330/Gopher missiles); 6 Kortik CIWS, each with 8 missile rails and 2 30-mm gatling AA (192 9M-311/SA-N-11 Grison missiles; 24,000 30-mm rounds); 1 twin 130-mm 70-cal. AK-130 DP (840 rounds); 2 quintuple 533-mm TT (20 torpedoes and/or Type 86R Vodopod-MK/SS-N-16 Stallion missiles); 1 10-round RPK-5 Liven' ASW RL (40 rockets); 2 6-round RBU-1000 ASW RL (102 rockets); 2 Ka-27PL Helix-A ASW helicopters; 1 Ka-27RTs Helix-A targeting helicopter

Electronics:

Ushakov:

Radar: 3 MR-212/201 Vaygach-U (Palm Frond) nav.; 1 MR-800 Voskhod (Top Pair) 3-D early warning; 1 MR-700 Fregat-M (Top Steer) 3-D air search; 2 Volna (Top Dome) SA-N-6 f.c.; 2 MPZ-301 Baza (Pop Group) SA-N-4 f.c.; 2 Drakon (Eye Bowl) SS-N-14 f.c.; 1 MR-114 Lev (Kite Screech-A) 100-mm f.c.; 4 MR-123 Vympel (Bass Tilt) 30-mm f.c.; 1 Fly Screen microwave landing aid

Sonar: Zvezda-M1 suite: MGK-335 Platina (Horse Jaw) bow-mounted LF; Orion (Horse Tail) LF VDS; MG-35 underwater telephone; MGK-355TA torpedo detection

TACAN: 2 Privod (Round House)

EW: 8 MR-401 Gruzhor (Side Glove) intercept; 4 MR-404 (Rum Tub) jammers; 10 Bell-series intercept and/or jammers; 2 PK-2 decoy syst. (2 twin ZIF-121M RL; 400 rockets)

E/O: 4 Tin Man stabilized multisensor surveillance

Lazarev:

Radar: 3 MR-212/201 Vaygach-U (Palm Frond) nav.; 1 MR-800 Voskhod (Top Pair) 3-D early warning; 1 MR-700M Fregat (Top Steer) 3-D air search; 2 Volna (Top Dome) SA-N-6 f.c.; 2 MPZ-301 Baza (Pop Group) SA-N-4 f.c.; 1 MR-184 Lev (Kite Screech-C) 130-mm f.c.; 4 MR-123 Vympel (Bass Tilt) 30-mm f.c.; 1 Fly Screen landing aid

Sonar: MGK-355 Polinom suite: MGK-335 Platina (Horse Jaw) hull-mounted HF; Orion (Horse Tail) LF VDS; MG-35 underwater telephone; MGK-355TA torpedo detection

TACAN: 2 Privod-B (Round House)

EW: Kantata-M suite: 8 Wine Flask; 10 Bell series; 2 PK-2 trainable decoy syst. (2 twin ZIF-121 RL; 400 rockets)

E/O: 4 Tin Man stabilized multisensor surveillance

Nakhimov:

Radar: 3 MR-212/201 Vaygach-U (Palm Frond) nav.; 1 MR-800 Voskhod (Top Pair) 3-D early warning; 1 MR-710 Fregat-MA (Top Plate-B) 3-D air search; 2 Volna (Top Dome) SA-N-6 f.c.; 2 MPZ-301 Baza (Pop Group) SA-N-4 f.c.; 1 MR-184 Lev (Kite Screech-C) gun f.c.; 6 3P-87 (Hot Flash) Kortik CIWS f.c.; 1 Fly Screen landing aid

Sonar: MGK-355 Polinom suite: MGK-335 Platina (Horse Jaw) hull-mounted HF; Orion (Horse Tail) LF VDS; MG-35 underwater telephone; MGK-355TA torpedo detection

TACAN: 2 Privod-B (Round House)

EW: Kantata-M suite: 8 Foot Ball intercept; 4 Bell Bash jammers; 4 Bell Nip; 4 Bell Push; 4 Bell Thumb; 2 PK-2 decoy syst. (2 twin ZIF-121RL; 400 rockets)

E/O: 4 Tin Man stabilized multisensor surveillance

Petr Velikiy:

Radar: 3 MR-212/201 Vaygach-U (Palm Frond) nav.; 2 MR-320M Topaz-M (Strut Pair) surf./air search; 1 MR-800 Voskhod (Top Pair) 3-D early warning; 1 MR-710 Fregat-MA (Top Plate-B) 3-D air search; 1 Volna (Top Dome) SA-N-6 f.c.; 1 F1M (Tomb Stone) SA-N-6 f.c.; 2 Podkat (Cross Sword) SA-N-9 f.c.; 1 MR-184 (Kite Screech-C) 130-mm gun f.c.; 6 3P-87 (Hot Flash) Kortik CIWS f.c.; 1 Fly Screen landing aid

Sonar: MGK-355 Polinom suite: MGK-335 Platina (Horse Jaw) hull-mounted HF; Orion (Horse Tail) LF VDS; MG-35 underwater telephone; MGK-355TA torpedo detection

TACAN: 2 Privod (Round House)

EW: Kantata-M suite: 8 Foot Ball intercept; 4 Bell Bash jammers; 4 Bell Nip; 4 Bell Push; 4 Bell Thumb; 2 PK-2 decoy syst. (2 twin ZIF-121 RL; 400 rockets); 12 10-round PK-10 fixed decoy RL

E/O: 4 Tin Man stabilized multisensor surveillance; . . . Spektr-F (Half Cup) laser warning

M: CONAS (Combined Nuclear and Steam): 2 KN-3 nuclear reactors (300 Mw each) + 2 oil-fired boilers, steam turbines; 2 4-bladed props; 140,000 shp

Electric: 15,000 kw tot. (4 × 3,000-kw turboalternators, 4 × 1,500-kw diesel sets)

Range: 14,000/30 (on nuclear plant); 1,300/17 (on steam plant)

Fuel: 1,120 tons + 58 tons aviation fuel **Endurance:** 60 days

Crew: 105 officers, 550 enlisted (accomm. for 120 officers, 640 enlisted)—*Lazarev:* 304 tot. while in reserve

Remarks: The type-designation applied has been RKR (*Raketnyy Kreyser,* Missile Cruiser) or, on occasion, *Atomnaya Raketnyy Kreyser.* Designed under Gennadiy Starshinov. A 6-96 Russian technical paper stated that these ships have only one-twentieth the combat potential of a single U.S. nuclear-powered aircraft carrier. The names were changed under a 27-5-92 decree by President Yeltsin.

Status: *Admiral Ushakov,* the former *Kirov,* which had a minor nuclear power–related accident while on a Mediterranean deployment in 1-90 and did not again deploy, was stricken 17-10-98 for cannibalization; on 14-1-99, the Russian Duma requested that she be saved and refitted under the 1999–2002 Repair Plan at the expense of 50% of the funding for repair of other Northern Fleet units. The Russian Navy reinstated the ship during 3-99, but the $250–400 million needed for the refit was not available, and the ship had already been significantly stripped of useful materials and equipment; when the navy failed to raise the necessary funds through public donations, the ship was again prepared for striking. However, funds were finally provided early in 2000 to at least begin the repairs and reactivation at Severodvinsk, with the intent to complete the work in 2003 (although little or no work had been accomplished as of 10-01).

Admiral Lazarev, which arrived in the Pacific Fleet 9-10-85, was reported in the Russian press to be for sale for scrap in 7-94, and a formal decision to decommission the ship for disposal was reportedly made 10-12-94; in 2-95, however, the Russian Navy vigorously denied that the ship was for sale, although admitting that she had not gone to sea in 5 years. Late in 1997, it was announced that the *Lazarev* would be decommissioned shortly, which finally happened 18-6-99; in 2000, however, funds were provided to begin repairs, and some work had commenced by 6-00.

Admiral Nakhimov underwent a short refit during mid-1996 at Rosta but was said to be unable to go to sea as of 6-98; a further refit was to start at Severodvinsk in 12-98, using components scavenged from the *Ushakov,* but the ship did not arrive at Severodvinsk to begin the work until 21-8-99 and remained there into 10-01 with little or no work accomplished.

Petr Velikiy began sea trials 8-6-96. During subsequent sea trials in the Baltic on 27-10-96, a steam pipe ruptured, killing four personnel. The ship departed the Baltic late in 11-96 for further trials in the Barents Sea but was laid up on arrival 24-11-96 and remained inactive until late 1997. When finally commissioned, she was placed in the Northern Fleet rather than the Pacific, as originally intended. The ship was dry docked for minor overhaul as of 8-01 but was fully active during 9-01.

Construction of a fifth unit, to have been named *Admiral Flota Sovetskogo Soyuza Kuznetsov* (following initial plans to name her *Dzerzhinskiy* and then *Oktyabrskaya Revolutsiya*), was authorized 31-12-88, but the ship was officially canceled 4-10-90 shortly after the keel had been laid; scrapping began during 11-89.

NUCLEAR-POWERED GUIDED-MISSILE CRUISERS [CGN]
(continued)

Hull systems: A long, raised strake down either side of the hull on all four acts as an external hull stiffener, as on some smaller Russian warship classes. The helicopter hangar is beneath the forward portion of the fantail, with an elevator delivering the aircraft to the flight deck. The steeply raked stern has a 9-m-wide centerline recess for the VDS installation. Two solid-stores replenishment stations are fitted: one amidships to port and one folding station forward to port, abreast the SA-N-6 system; both employ the sliding-stay, constant-tension concept. Oil and water replenishments are handled at stations on either beam abreast the Kite Screech gun f.c. radar. The forward reload missile transfer equipment is considerably more compact on *Lazarev* and later units than it was on *Ushakov.* Have 100-mm armor on the reactor compartment's sides and 35-mm on its ends, 70-mm on the sides and 50-mm on the upper deck of the steering machinery compartment, and 80-mm on the conning position. Amenities include a sauna with 6-m pool, a saloon and billiard room for the officers, and a 200-seat enlisted "club" that converts to a gymnasium. The ships have their own television studio and printing plant and are equipped with a two-deck clinic. Firefighting capabilities are said to be deficient.

Propulsion systems: The two circular reactor access hatches can be seen amidships, just abaft the enormous twin exhaust uptakes for the unusual CONAS (Combined Nuclear and Steam) propulsion system. The oil-fired boilers provide steam to completely separate turbines, which are geared to the same drive shafts as the nuclear-supplied turbines. The starboard stack uptake serves the oil-fired boilers, while the port uptake serves to ventilate the reactor spaces.

Combat systems: The combat direction system is called Lesorub 44. The launch tubes for the 20 P-700 antiship missiles are buried within the hull at a fixed elevation angle of 40–45°, in four rows of five, forward of the superstructure. Before these are the 12 vertical launchers for the long-range SAM system; each has a door, beneath which is a rotating magazine containing eight missiles. Targeting data for the P-700 missile, with its 300-n.m. maximum range, was to come either from land-based aircraft, a helicopter embarked on the ship, or radar satellites via the Punch Bowl satellite communications antennas on either side of the ship (but the satellite system never became operational). The gatling gun mounts on the first two are paired and located so as to cover all four quadrants; each pair is served by a Bass Tilt radar director and a manned, SP-521 Rakurs (Kolonka-2) ringsight backup director.

On *Lazarev* and *Nakhimov,* eight SA-N-9 launchers were intended to be fitted within the forecastle, while eight more were to be located flanking the helicopter elevator, four per side (the gatling guns are mounted on the after superstructure); they have never been installed. The intended two Cross Sword directors for SA-N-9 were never mounted; they were to have been positioned abaft the Kite Screech aft and between the two Pop Group directors forward. The two MR-320M Topaz-M (Strut Pair) radars in *Petr Velikiy* provide target designation services to the two Cross Sword radar tracker/directors for the SA-N-9 SAM system. *Nakhimov* and *Petr Velikiy* have the new RPK-5 Liven' ASW/countertorpedo rocket launcher vice the RBU-6000 and mount the new Kortik combined twin long-barrel 30-mm gatling gun and octuple, reloadable SA-N-11 missile system vice the 30-mm AK-630 mounts.

Petr Velikiy initially had two Top Dome radar directors for the Fort (SA-N-6) surface-to-air missile system, but by 7-96, the forward one had been replaced by a modified Tomb Stone director adapted from a mobile land-based system; one Russian publication stated that a different missile variant is used with each director.

As might be expected, the communications antenna array is extensive and diverse and includes satellite communications equipment and long-range HF gear. The first two were given the Tsunami-BM SATCOM system and the later pair the Kristall-BK system. *Petr Velikiy* has two large, thimble-shaped radomes for the Legenda SATCOM system on pylons forward of the boat davits amidships and two smaller Punch Bowl spherical radomes just below the Korall-BN (Low Ball) SATCOM radomes. The four stabilized Tin Man electro-optical sensors cover all four quadrants, and there are also several smaller remote t.v. cameras. Two Bob Tail radiometric sextant antennas are housed in spherical enclosures. The Fly Screen microwave landing-approach radar is mounted on a starboard platform on the after tower mast. The VDS employs a lens-shaped "fish" about 4 m in diameter to house the transducer and has a twin boom-mounted empennage with horizontal and vertical control surfaces. In addition to an LF bow-mounted sonar, there is probably an MF set for fire-control purposes (including depth determination) for the ASW rocket launchers (which also have a torpedo countermeasures function). The EW devices listed here as Wine Flask have also been referred to as Modified Foot Ball; they appear to be combined receiver/jammers.

GUIDED-MISSILE CRUISERS [CG]

♦ **3 Slava (Atlant) class (Project 1164)**
Bldr: 61 Kommunara SY 445, Nikolayev, Ukraine

	Laid down	L	In serv.	Fleet
121 Moskva (ex-*Slava*)	5-11-76	27-7-79	7-2-83	Black Sea
055 Marshal Ustinov (ex-*Admiral Flota Lobov*)	5-10-78	25-2-82	21-9-86	Northern
011 Varyag ("Viking") (ex-*Chervona Ukraina*)	27-7-79	28-8-83	25-12-89	Pacific

D: 9,380 tons std. (11,280 normal fl; 11,490 max. fl) **S:** 32.5 kts (30 sust.)

Dim: 186.40 (170.00 wl) × 20.80 (19.20 wl) × 6.23 (mean hull; 8.40 over sonar dome)

A: 16 P-500 Bazal't (SS-N-12 Sandbox) SSM (4K-80 missiles); 8 8-round Fort (SA-N-6) vertical-launch SAM groups (64 S-300MPU/3R-41 or 5V-55/Grumble missiles; 8 B-203A rotating vertical launchers); 2 twin-rail Osa-MA SAM syst. (40 9M-33M5/Gecko missiles); 1 twin 130-mm 70-cal. AK-130 DP (600 rounds); 6 single 30-mm 54-cal. AK-630M gatling AA (48,000 rounds); 2 quintuple 533-mm TT; 2 12-round RBU-6000 ASW RL (144 rockets); 1 Ka-27PL ASW or Ka-2RTs Helix targeting helicopter

Marshal Ustinov (055) *Ships of the World,* 2000

Moskva (121)—at Toulon Alexandre Sheldon-Duplaix, 9-01

Varyag (011) Boris Lemachko, 9-00

Moskva (121)—amidships details Alexandre Sheldon-Duplaix, 9-01

Varyag (011) *Ships of the World,* 2000

GUIDED-MISSILE CRUISERS [CG] *(continued)*

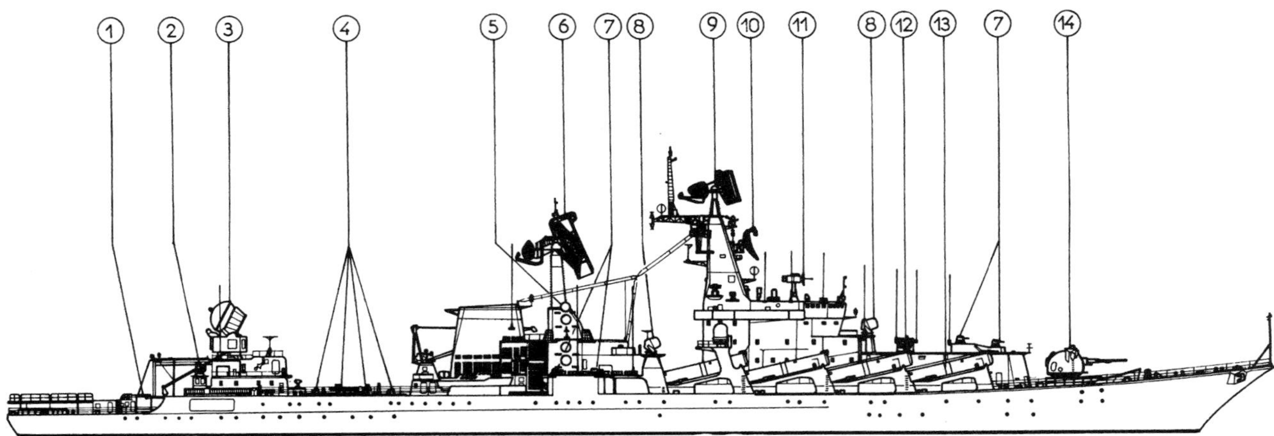

Moskva (121) 1. Osa-MA SAM launchers (port and starboard, flanking helicopter hangar) 2. MPZ-301 Baza director for Osa-M system 3. Volna radar director for Fort SAM system 4. Fort SAM VLS (recessed into deck) 5. Gurzhor-A and -B EW antennas 6. MR-600 Voskhod 3-D early-warning radar 7. 30-mm AK-630M gatling AA 8. MR-123 Vympel radar directors for 30-mm gatling AA 9. MR-700 Fregat 3-D air-search/target-designation radar 10. Argon-1164 tracking and telemetry array for P-500 Bazal't missiles 11. MR-184 Lev radar director for 130-mm gunmount 12. RBU-6000 ASW RL 13. four twin launchers per side for P-500 Bazal't antiship missile system 14. twin 130-mm AK-130 DP gunmount — Drawing by Louis Gassier, from *Flottes de Combat*

Ukrayina—fitting out — Boris Lemachko, 1998

Electronics:
Radar: 3 MR-212/201 Vaygach-U (Palm Frond) nav.; 1 MR-600 Voskhod (Top Pair) 3-D early warning; 1 MR-700 Fregat (Top Steer) (*Varyag:* MR-710 Fregat-MA/Top Plate-B) 3-D air search; 1 Volna (Top Dome) SA-N-6 f.c.; 2 MPZ-301 Baza (Pop Group) SA-N-4 f.c.; 1 MR-184 Lev (Kite Screech-C) 130-mm gun f.c.; 3 MR-123 Vympel (Bass Tilt) 30-mm f.c.; 1 Argon-1164 (Front Door-C) SS-N-12 tracking and telemetry
Sonar: Bull Nose hull-mounted LF; Platina (Horse Tail) MF VDS
EW: *Moskva, Ustinov,* and *Varyag:* Kol'cho suite: 8 MR-401 Gurzhor-A and -B (Side Globe) intercept; 4 MR-404 Ograda (Rum Tub) jammers; 2 Bell Crown; 2 Bell Push; . . . Bell-series; 2 PK-2 decoy syst. (2 twin ZIF-121 trainable RL; 400 rockets)—*Varyag* also: 12 10-round PK-10 fixed decoy RL—*Lobov:* 2 MP-405M Start-2 syst: MRP-11M/12M (Bell Shroud) intercept; 2 Bell Squat; 4 Foot Ball-B; 2 PK-2 trainable decoy syst. (2 twin ZIF-121 trainable launchers; 400 rockets); 12 10-round PK-10 fixed decoy RL
E/O: *Moskva* only: 2 Tee Plinth stabilized t.v. surveillance
M: COGOG M-21 plant: 4 M8KF boost gas turbines (22,500 shp each); 2 M-70 cruise gas turbines (10,000 shp each); 2 exhaust-gas cruise turbines (1,500 shp each); 2 props; 113,000 shp
Electric: 8,250 kw tot. (3 × 1,500-kw, 3 × 1,250-kw gas turbine sets)
Range: 2,200/32; 8,070/18 **Fuel:** . . . tons + 17.5 tons aviation fuel
Endurance: 30 days **Crew:** 62 (*Moskva:* 66) officers, 64 michmen, 355 enlisted

Remarks: Initially referred to by the NATO code name "BLK-COM-1" and later, briefly, as the "Krasina" class. Typed *Raketnyy Kreyser* (Missile Cruiser) by the Russian Navy. Chief designer was V. Mutikhin. Fitted as flagships, in which role they carry up to 27 additional officers and 24 additional enlisted. Are unusual in having considerable equipment that was not the latest of its type in Soviet service even when the class was introduced.

Status: *Moskva* (named *Slava* until 14-7-95) began an overhaul in 12-90 at 61 Kommunara Zavod, Nikolayev; the work was 70% complete as of 7-98 but was not completed due to nonpayment of debts by Russia. The ship was returned to Russian Navy control 16-7-99 for further work at Sevastopol' before recommissioning during 4-00; she became flagship of the Black Sea Fleet 26-10-00. A missile from the *Moskva* hit a Ukrainian passenger ship during 4-00.

Marshal Ustinov entered the Baltic for an overhaul in 1994 and reentered service 13-1-98, returning to the Northern Fleet. *Varyag* (name changed 9-2-96) remains in commission with a reduced crew.

The fourth ship of the class, the *Ukrayina,* was the last combatant warship to be built by 61 Kommunara Shipyard and was delayed in completion by the economic turmoil in Russia and Ukraine. As of 1-4-93, when the ship was taken over by Ukraine, it was reported that she would be completed for the Ukrainian Navy, but an agreement was reached during 8-95 (at which time she was said to be 94.2% complete) for the ship to be completed for the Russian Navy as the *Admiral Flota Lobov.* Lack of funds, however, again precluded any work being done, and the ship remained Ukrainian property. Ukrainian President Kuchma then decreed on 17-2-99 that she would be completed for the Ukraine Navy, and the Ukrainian flag was raised aboard her 17-6-99. By 8-00, however, work on completing the ship had again halted for lack of funds, and on 28-9-01, Kuchma offered to sell her to Russia, which a week later accepted for the price of $200 million.

A fifth, revised Project 11641 unit, to have been named *Rossiya* (later changed to *Oktyabrskaya Revolutsiya*), and a sixth, to have been named *Admiral Flota Sovetskogo Soyuza Gorshkov,* were canceled 4-10-90. The pair would have displaced an additional 200 tons, would have been 6 m longer than the earlier group, and would have had the Platina sonar system (without towed array) and the canceled R-1000 Vulcan missile system.

Hull systems: Have retractable fin stabilizers. Each of the paired stack uptakes on the first three incorporates one cruise-turbine exhaust, two boost-turbine exhausts, and two gas-turbine generator exhausts. Gas turbine exhaust waste-heat boilers provide steam to two auxiliary turbines to improve cruising range by about 12%. Unlike the first three ships of the class, the *Admiral Flota Lobov* has a single large stack uptake, with a smaller crane offset to starboard. Officer accommodations are opulent by Western standards, even to the extent of installing a waterfall-equipped belowdecks swimming pool and sauna, but enlisted quarters are Spartan; in general, the ships contain a great deal of flammable material and appear to lack adequate damage control features. A one-man elevator is installed to take the commanding officer from the central command post to the bridge. Have operated with as few as 38 officers.

Combat systems: Only one director is provided for the Fort SAM system, limiting its flexibility and restricting target tracking to six aircraft at a time, all within a 60° bearing. The torpedo tubes are mounted behind shutters in the ship's sides, near the stern. The hangar floor is one half-deck below the flight deck, which is reached via an inclined ramp, the helicopter being maneuvered by a chain-haul system. In *Varyag,* the Top Steer paired radar was replaced by Top Plate, and 10 PK-10 fixed decoy rocket launchers were added. Two Punch Bowl antennas for the Korvet-5 satellite targeting datalink system are fitted. *Lobov* has the radomes for two Korvet-5 SATCOM system antennas, but may not have the actual system; the ship's EW suite is simplified from that of the three earlier ships.

♦ 1 Kynda (Project 58) class *(Nonoperational)*

Bldr: Severnyy Zavod, St. Petersburg

	Laid down	L	In serv.	Fleet
118 ADMIRAL GOLOVKO (ex-*Doblestnyy*)	20-4-60	18-8-62	1-5-64	Black Sea

Admiral Golovko (118) — Hartmut Ehlers, 7-00

D: 4,300 tons std.; 4,825 tons normal (5,350 fl) **S:** 34 kts
Dim: 142.70 × 16.20 (15.20 wl) × 4.73 (5.30 over sonar)
A: 2 4-round SM-70 trainable launch groups for P-35 Progress-M (SS-N-3 Shaddock) SSM (16 4K-44 missiles; see remarks); 1 twin-rail Volna-M (SA-N-1) SAM syst. (ZIF-101 launcher; 16 missiles); 2 twin 76.2-mm 59-cal. AK-726 DP (2,400 rounds); 4 single 30-mm 54-cal. AK-630M gatling AA; 2 12-round RBU-6000 ASW RL (96 RGB-90 rockets); 2 triple 533-mm TTA-53-57 TT
Electronics:
Radar: 2 Don-2 nav.; 2 MR-300 Angara (Head Net-A) surf./air search; 2 Binom (Scoop Pair) SSM tracking; 1 Yatagan (Peel Group) SAM f.c.; 1 MR-105 Turel' (Hawk Screech) gun f.c.; 2 MR-123 Vympel (Bass Tilt) 30-mm f.c.
Sonar: GAS-372 Gerkules-2M hull-mounted HF
EW: Konuhs syst.: 2 Zaliv 11-12 intercept; 1 Zaliv 13-14 intercept; 1 Zaliv 15-16 intercept; MR-262 Ograda jammer
E/O: 4 MT-45 stabilized t.v. cameras; 2 VBP-452 periscopes
M: 2 sets TV-12 geared steam turbines; 2 props; 91,000 shp
Boilers: 4 KVN-95/64 turbopressurized (470° C, 64 kg/cm^2)
Electric: 2,500 kw tot. (2 × 750-kw TD-750 turbogenerators, 2 × 500-kw DG-500 diesel sets)
Range: 1,500/34; 6,000/14 **Endurance:** 10 days
Crew: 25 officers, 279 enlisted

GUIDED-MISSILE CRUISERS [CG] *(continued)*

Remarks: Ordered 6-12-56. Despite the diminutive size, has always been considered a cruiser by the Soviet and Russian Navies and has always had a captain first rank as commanding officer. Survivor of a group of four; 10 were originally planned. Modernized from 4-6-82 to 1-3-89 at Sevastopol'. Was employed as flagship of the Black Sea Fleet 1995–2000. The ship was to begin a refit and boiler repairs during fall 2000 at Lazarevskoye Admiraleystvo Ship Repairing Plant, Sevastopol', for completion late in 2001, but the work was not started, and as of summer 2001, only a cadre crew of 30 was aboard. Although plans call for retaining her until 2005, she may be retired sooner.
Disposals: Baltic Fleet sister *Groznyy* was stricken 24-6-91; the Pacific Fleet's *Varyag* (ex-*Soobrazitel'niy*) was laid up 29-4-90 and stricken 21-5-91; and Pacific Fleet unit *Admiral Fokin* (ex-*Vladivostok,* ex-*Steregushchiy*) was stricken 30-7-93 and scrapped in India in 1995.
Hull systems: Was the first Russian warship class with turbopressurized boilers. Has fin stabilizers. Hull block coefficient is 0.492 and amidships molded depth is 10.0 m. As built, displacement was 4,250 tons standard, 4,790 normal, and 5,315 full load. There was no armor plating. Fuel consumption as built was 845 kg/n.m. at full power, and maximum propeller rpm is 300.
Combat systems: Although the ship launched at least one Progress (SS-N-3) missile during an exercise on 17-4-98, the antiship missile system is not believed to be combat ready. The reloads for the SS-N-3 missiles were carried in the superstructure deckhouses immediately adjacent to the two trainable, elevatable quadruple launchers, and missiles were launched and controlled via the system's Binom (Scoop Pair) dual radar set, with their onboard seekers relaying information back to the ship via the two Uspekh-U (Plinth Net) antennas mounted on the forward side of the after tower mast. The four AK-630 gatling AA guns were fitted during a 1980s refit. The Volna-M SAM system employs the ZIF-101 dual, triaxially stabilized launcher, V-600 missile storage and delivery system, and the 4R-90 Yatagan launch system. There is a helicopter platform on the fantail, but no hangar, and only 5 tons of helicopter fuel can be carried. Two 45-mm 21-KM saluting cannon are normally carried. The torpedoes could be launched against surface targets with inputs from the MR-105 radar; for ASW use, the Zummer ASW torpedo-control system was connected to the ship's Burya ASW fire-control system. Has the Parol' IFF system.

Note: Black Sea Fleet *Sverdlov*-class gun cruiser *Admiral Kutusov,* the only remaining Soviet-era gun cruiser, was being prepared for use as a museum exhibit at Sevastopol' as of 8-00.

GUIDED-MISSILE DESTROYERS [DDG]

♦ 10 Sovremennyy (Sarych) class (Projects 956 and 956A)
(2 *nonoperational*)
Bldr: Severnaya Verf 190, St. Petersburg

	Laid down	L	In serv.	Fleet
Project 956:				
720 Boyevoy ("Militant")	26-3-82	4-8-84	28-9-86	Pacific
778 Burnyy ("Fiery")	4-11-83	30-12-86	30-9-88	Pacific
429 Gremyashchiy ("Thunderous") (ex-*Vedushchiy*)	23-11-84	30-5-87	14-1-89	Northern
715 Bystryy ("Speedy")	29-10-85	28-11-87	30-9-89	Pacific
420 *Rastoropnyy* ("Prompt")	15-8-86	4-6-88	30-12-89	Northern
754 *Bezboyaznennyy* ("Intrepid")	8-1-87	18-2-89	23-12-90	Pacific
406 Bezuderzhanyy ("Tenacious")	24-2-87	30-9-89	25-6-91	Northern
Project 956:				
620 Bespokoynyy ("Restless")	18-4-87	22-2-92	29-12-93	Baltic
610 Nastoychivyy ("Persistent") (ex-*Moskovskiy Komsomolets*)	7-4-88	15-2-92	27-3-93	Baltic
434 Besstrashnyy ("Fearless")	16-4-88	31-12-92	17-4-94	Northern

D: 6,500 tons light, 7,940 tons normal (8,480 fl) **S:** 33.4 kts (32.7 sust.)
Dim: 156.37 (145.00 wl) × 17.19 (16.30 wl) × 5.99 (mean hull; 7.85 max.)
A: 8 P-270 Moskit or P-100 Moskit-M (SS-N-22 Sunburn) SSM (3M-80 or 3M-82 missiles); 2 ZR-90 Uragan (SA-N-7) SAM syst. (2 single-rail MS-196 launchers; 48 9M-38 Buk-M1 or 9M-38M1 Smerch/Gadfly missiles); 2 twin 130-mm 54-cal. AK-130 DP (2,000 rounds); 4 single 30-mm 54-cal. AK-630M gatling AA (16,000 rounds); 2 twin 533-mm DTA-53 TT; 2 6-round RBU-1000 ASW RL (48 RGB-10 rockets); 2 mine rails (up to 40 tot. mines); 1 Ka-27PL Helix-A ASW or Ka-27RTs targeting helicopter

Nastoychivyy (610)—Project 956A Jaroslaw Cislak, 6-00

Bespokoynyy (620)—with Helix helicopter aboard Jaroslaw Cislak, 6-01

Bezboyaznennyy (754)—in reserve at Vladivostok Boris Lemachko, 2000

Electronics:
Radar: 3 MR-212/201 Vaygach-U (Palm Frond) nav.; 1 MR-760MA Fregat-MA (Top Plate-B) 3-D air search; 6 OP-3 (Front Dome) SA-N-7 f.c.; 1 MR-184M Lev (Kite Screech-C) 130-mm f.c.; 2 MR-123 Vympel (Bass Tilt) 30-mm f.c.; 1 Mineral surf. target tracking and desig.
Sonar: MG-335MS Platina-S (Bull Horn) MF bow-mounted; MG-7 (Whale Tongue) HF f.c.

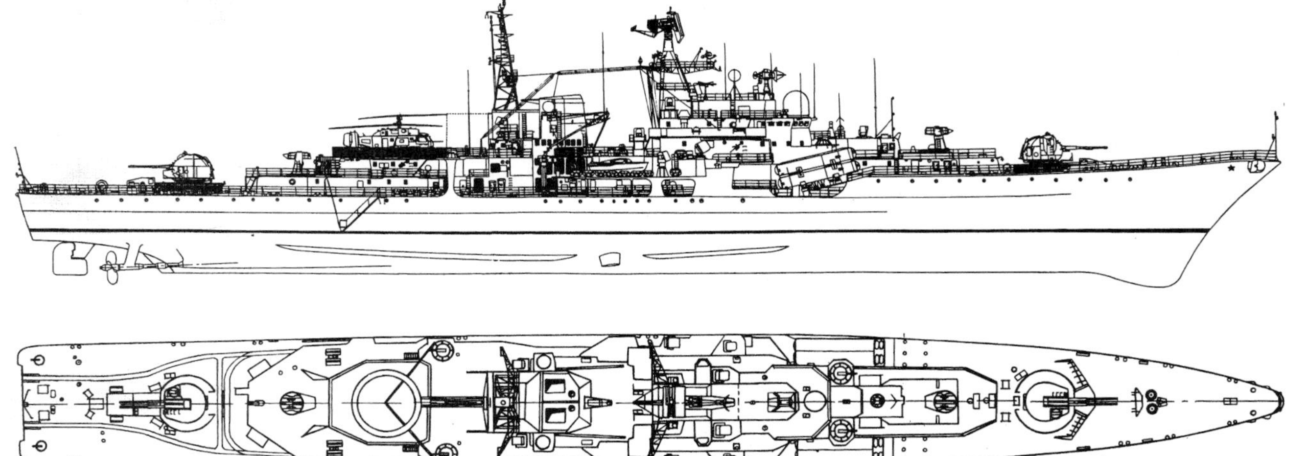
Sovremennyy class (Project 956) Rozvoorouzhenie, 2000

GUIDED-MISSILE DESTROYERS [DDG] *(continued)*

Bespokoynyy (620)—Project 956A Martin Mokrus, 6-01

Burnyy (778)—a Pacific Fleet Project 956 unit *Ships of the World,* 2000

EW: MP-405M Start-2 or MR-401 intercept syst.: 2 MRP-11M/12M (Bell Shroud); 2 Bell Squat; 4 Foot Ball-B; MR-407 jamming syst.; 2 PK-2M trainable decoy syst. (2 twin-tube ZIF-121 launchers; 200 rockets)—all except *Boyevoy:* 8 10-round PK-10 fixed decoy RL

E/O: 2, 4, or 8 Spektr-F (Half Cup) laser warning; 1 Squeeze Box multisensor; 1 Tall View periscope; 2 Watch Box bridge periscopes

M: 2 sets TV-12 geared steam turbines; 2 4-bladed props; 110,000 shp (99,500 sust.)

Boilers: 4 turbopressurized Type KVN-98/64, 640 kg/cm^2, 500° C

Electric: 4,900 kw tot. (2 × 1,250-kw turboalternators, 4 × 600-kw diesel sets)

Range: 1,345/32.7; 3,920/18 (5,340/18.4 with overload fuel)

Fuel: 1,740 tons + 5 tons aviation fuel **Endurance:** 30 days

Crew: 25 officers, 271 enlisted (accomm. for 38 officers, 330 enlisted)

Remarks: Type designation: EM (*Eskhadrennyy Minonosets,* Destroyer). Project name, Sarych, means "Buzzard." Chief designer was I. Rubis. Design derived from the Kresta-I and -II series built at the same shipyard; uses a similar hullform and the same propulsion plant. Formerly called the "BAL-COM-2" class by NATO. Primarily intended for surface warfare tasks, including antiship, shore bombardment, and antiair defense; the minimal ASW capability is primarily for self-defense. At one time it was planned to provide one unit of this class to Cuba in 1990–91. Two units were ordered from 61 Kommunara Zavod, Nikolayev: *Vnushitel'nyy* ("Imposing") was laid down in 1982 and launched 17-10-87 but never completed (the hulk has been used as a floating storage barge), and the second unit was not begun. *Bespokoynyy,* the first of the Project 956A variant (see below), suffered a serious fire at Baltiysk 13-8-92, delaying her departure for the Pacific; she was instead assigned to the Baltic Fleet at Baltiysk with *Nastoychivyy.* Two of the above units were to be sold to China, according to a 3-00 announcement, but no contract announcement had been made as of 10-01. *Rastoropnyy* entered the Baltic at the end of 11-00 and proceeded to Svernyy Werf, St. Petersburg, reportedly to undergo a major overhaul and modernization. Pacific Fleet unit *Bystryy,* placed in reserve early in 1999 with three of her boilers unserviceable, entered Dalzavod Shipyard during 5-00 for a refit. *Bezboyaznennyy* was placed in "1st Category Reserve" during 1999.

The first planned Project 956U unit, to have carried the Kortik point-defense system, was the scrapped 20th hull and was to have been named *Vechniy.* A total of 28 of all versions of the basic design was to have been completed. Instead, it was announced in 8-95 that only 19 would be completed, with components assembled for later units, including the 20th, *Buynyy,* to be discarded. In 1-96, however, with no funds available for further work on the class, it was announced that two units of the class, the 18th, *Yekaterinburg* (ex-*Vazhniy*), and 19th, *Aleksandr Nevskiy* (ex-*Vdumchivyy*), would be sold to China.

Disposals: *Sovremennyy,* which began a never-completed overhaul at Rosta in 1988, was allocated for cannibalization in 8-98 and stricken during 11-98; she remains afloat at Rosta as a spares source. The disarmed and partially stripped *Otlichnyy* was placed in technical reserve at Severomorsk in 11-94 under constant pumping to control flooding; she was stricken in 1998 and later scrapped. Pacific Fleet unit *Otchayannyy* and Northern Fleet units *Otlichniy* and *Okrylennyy* were stricken 16-8-97, with the latter being scrapped beginning 10-00 at Murmansk. Northern Fleet unit *Bezuprechniy* began a yard period at Rosta in 1992 but was laid up 1-11-93; in 8-94, the ship was sent to Severnaya Werf, St. Petersburg, for conversion to Project 956A configuration, but the work never commenced and she is now essentially derelict, having been stripped of useful parts to assist in outfitting the two sold to China. Pacific Fleet unit *Stoikiy* flooded and capsized during spring 1999 while in reserve; a sailor had stolen the flooding valve castings. Pacific Fleet unit *Osmotritel'nyy,* in reserve for some years, was under consideration for scrapping as of 1999.

Hull systems: The propulsion plant is essentially the same as that of the preceding Kresta-I and -II classes and employs turbopressurized boilers. Retractable fin stabilizers are fitted. Export versions are offered with a propulsion plant said to produce 73,500 kw (98,578 shp).

Combat systems: The combat system is named Sapfir-U. Early units, now stricken, had a variety of radar installations, but the survivors are more standardized.

The helicopter hangar is partially telescoping, extending aft from the stack structure, and the helicopter facilities are less elaborate than in other contemporary Russian classes, with no support or weapons stowage for an ASW helicopter provided. The Ka-25RTs Hormone-B helicopter (which was seldom carried) could provide targeting data for the Moskit (SS-N-22) missiles, and the ships also have the large Monolit (Band Stand) radome associated with missile targeting. In recent years, when a helicopter has been aboard, it has been either a Ka-27PL ASW or a utility version of the Helix. There are also two small spherical Pricep (Light Bulb) datalink radomes on the sides of the stack that are associated with the Moskit missile system, which uses quadruple KT-190 fixed launchers. The twin-tube, trainable launchers for the PK-2 decoy systems are at the extreme stern, and all except *Boyevoy* have eight additional 10-round PK-10 fixed launchers (six on the bridge level, two aft).

The MS-196 SAM launchers are apparently limited to launch arcs within 30° of the centerline. Maximum launch rate is five rounds per minute per launcher. The 130-mm guns, in ZIF-94 mountings, are of a fully automatic, water-cooled model, capable of AA or surface fire; they are restricted to firing arcs of 40° each side of the centerline. The AK-630 guns are restricted to firing arcs of −5° (off the centerline) through 160° for the forward mounts and 15° off centerline forward through 170° for the after mounts. The Lev-series radar gun directors in the final three units have laser rangefinder attachments.

Squeeze Box is an optronic gun fire-control director combining a laser rangefinder, low-light-level television, and infrared devices. *Nastoychivyy* appears to substitute two Soup Cup EW antennas for two Foot Ball-B and also has a Trawl Net intercept antenna and a Long Head IFF transponder. *Bezboyaznennyy* and *Nastoychivyy* have two Chop Dish small SATCOM antennas.

Bespokoynyy and later are designated Project 956A and have longer cruise-missile tubes to accept the extended-range P-100 Moskit-M system's 3M-82 missile; Project 956A ships are also said to carry a naval version of the 9M-38E1 Yozh (NATO SA-17 Grizzly) land-based SAM vice the Uragan system's original 9K-37 Smerch missiles.

Offered for export construction is an 8,700-ton variant with 16 Kh-35 Uran (SS-N-25 Switchblade) antiship missiles in place of the eight SS-N-22 missiles, two Kortik CIWS flanking the aft end of the helicopter deck, and omission of the AK-630 gatling guns. A 9,000-ton variant has also been offered with 24 unidentified vertically launched antiship missiles replacing the aft 130-mm gunmount and four Kortik mounts (the forward pair would replace the tube-launched cruise missile launcher installations abreast the bridge). Export versions are also offered with the SSN-137 towed sonar array.

♦ 1 Kara (Berkut-B) class (Project 1134B)

Bldr: 61 Kommunara SY 445, Nikolayev, Ukraine

	Laid down	L	In serv.	Fleet
713 Kerch'	30-4-71	21-7-72	25-12-74	Black Sea

GUIDED-MISSILE DESTROYERS [DDG] *(continued)*

Kerch' (713) Hartmut Ehlers, 7-00

D: 6,590 tons light (8,470 normal fl, 8,825 max. fl)
S: 32.7 kts (30 sust., 18 on cruise turbines)
Dim: 173.40 (162.00 wl) × 18.50 (16.80 wl) × 6.35 (max.; 5.74 max. hull)
A: 8 URK-5 Rastrub (SS-N-14 Silex) ASW/antiship SSM (2 4-round KT-100 launchers, 8 Type 83R and 83RUS missiles); 2 twin-rail M-11 Shtorm (SA-N-3) SAM syst. (80 V-611/Goblet missiles); 2 twin-rail Osa-M (SA-N-4) SAM syst. (40 9M-33/Gecko missiles); 2 twin 76.2-mm 59-cal. AK-726 DP (2,400 rounds); 4 single 30-mm 54-cal. AK-630M gatling AA (8,000 rounds); 2 quintuple 533-mm TT; 2 12-round RBU-6000 ASW RL (144 RGB-60 rockets); 2 6-round RBU-1000 ASW RL (60 RGB-10 rockets); 1 Ka-27PL Helix-A helicopter
Electronics:
Radar: 1 Don-2 or MR-212/201 Vaygach-U (Palm Frond) nav.; 2 Volga (Don-Kay) nav.; 1 MR-700 Podberezovik (Flat Screen) 3-D early warning; 1 MR-310U Angara-M (Head Net-C) air search; 2 Grom (Head Lights-C) cruise missile f.c.; 2 MPZ-301 Baza (Pop Group) SA-N-4 f.c.; 2 MR-105 Turel' (Owl Screech) 76.2-mm f.c.; 2 MR-123 Vympel (Bass Tilt) 30-mm f.c.
Sonar: MG-332 Titan-2T (Bull Nose) hull-mounted MF; MG-325 Vega (Mare Tail) MF VDS
EW: Kol'cho-series suite: 8 MR-401 Gurzhor-A/B (Side Globe) intercept; 4 MR-404 (Rum Tub) jammers; 2 PK-2 trainable decoy syst. (2 twin ZIF-121 RL)
E/O: 2 Tee Plinth t.v. surveillance
M: COGOG M-5 plant: 4 M-8E (GTU-12A) boost gas turbines, 20,000 shp each; 2 M-62 cruise gas turbines, 6,000 shp each; 2 props; 92,000 shp max.
Electric: 5,600 kw tot. (4 × 1,250-kw, 1 × 600-kw gas turbine sets)
Range: 2,270/32.7; 7,100/18; 9,000/14
Fuel: 1,830 tons + 16.8 tons aviation fuel **Endurance:** 30 days
Crew: 47 officers, 47 warrant officers, 286 enlisted

Remarks: Type designation: BPK (*Bol'shoy Protivolodochnyy Korabl',* Large Antisubmarine Ship), a type considered by the Russian Navy to be more in the destroyer than cruiser category; the commanding officers have normally been commander-equivalents. Visited Italy and France during 11-98 but was in marginal operating condition. The pennant number was changed from 711 to 713 between 1999 and mid-2000. While undergoing refit during 2001, two of the ship's main turbines and the cruise turbines were replaced by engines from the Ukrainian Navy frigate *Sevastopol'.*
Disposals: Pacific Ocean Fleet units *Nikolayev* and *Tashkent* returned to the Black Sea for overhauls in the late 1980s; both were stricken 3-7-92 and sold for scrap during 1994, with the *Nikolayev* having sunk in the Red Sea while under tow to India and the *Tashkent* being scrapped at Alang, India, in 12-94. *Vladivostok* (ex-*Tallin*), in reserve at Sevastopol' since the early 1990s, was stricken on 5-7-94 and scrapped 12-94 at Alang. Pacific Fleet unit *Petropavlovsk* was stricken on 17-11-94. The Modified Kara–class Black Sea Fleet destroyer *Azov* (Project 1134.7BF) was stricken 10-12-98, already having been stripped of useful equipment. The *Ochakov* suffered a shipyard fire at Sevmorzavod, Sevastopol', on 9-2-93 while in an overhaul that was to have been completed by the end of 1996; the Moscow local government agreed to fund completion of the overhaul in 1999, probably employing components cannibalized from the stricken *Azov,* but little or no work had been accomplished by 10-01, and the ship has apparently been abandoned.
Hull systems: Have retractable active fin stabilization systems.
Combat systems: The missile systems all can also be used against surface targets, and the RBU weapons have a countertorpedo capability. The helicopter hangar is at main-deck level, the helicopter being raised to the flight deck by means of an inclined elevator. Six ASW torpedoes are carried for the helicopter. Received the new MR-700 Podberezovik (Flat Screen) rotating, phased planar array, 3-D air-search radar in place of MR-600 Voskhod (Top Sail) during a late-1980s overhaul; the radar has not been fitted to any other class.

♦ 1 Kashin class (Project 61)
Bldrs: 61 Kommunara Zavod 445, Nikolayev, Ukraine

	Laid down	L	In serv.	Fleet
810 Smetlivyy ("Intelligent")	26-8-67	15-6-68	21-10-69	Black Sea

Smetlivyy (810)—the two sets of quadruple antiship missile launchers were removed by the end of 2000 Hartmut Ehlers, 7-00

D: 3,550 tons std.; 4,030 tons normal (4,510 fl) **S:** 34 kts (35.5 on trials)
Dim: 144.00 (132.20 wl) × 15.80 (14.00 wl) × 4.45 (hull; 6.0 max.)
A: 2 twin-rail SA-N-1 Volna SAM syst. (2 ZIF-101 launchers; 32 V-601/Goa missiles); 1 twin 76.2-mm 59-cal. AK-726 DP; 1 quintuple 533-mm PTA-53-61 TT; 2 12-round RBU-6000 ASW RL (192 RGB-60 rockets); 2 mine rails (. . . mines)
Electronics:
Radar: 2 Volga (Don-Kay) or Vaygach-U (Palm Frond) nav.; 1 MR-310U Angara-M (Head Net-C) air search; 1 MR-500 Kliver (Big Net) early warning; 1 Yatagan (Peel Group) SA-N-1 f.c.; 1 MR-105 Turel' (Owl Screech) gun f.c.
Sonar: MIK-300 suite: MG-332 Titan-2 bow sonar and MG-325 Vega VDS (see remarks)
EW: 2 Start-1 (Bell Shroud) intercept; 2 . . . (Bell Squat) jammers; 4 16-round PK-16 fixed decoy RL; 2 10-round PK-10 fixed decoy RL
E/O: 2 trainable Tee Plinth t.v.; 4 Tilt Pot fixed t.v.; 2 Watch Box bridge periscopes
M: COGAG M-3 plant: 4 Type M-8E gas turbines, 2 3-bladed props (300 rpm max.); 96,000 shp (72,000 sust.)
Electric: 2,800 kw tot. (4 × 600-kw gas turbine sets, 2 × 200-kw diesel sets)
Range: 1,000/35; 2,000/30; 3,500/18 **Fuel:** 940 tons + 6 tons aviation fuel
Crew: 22 officers, 266 enlisted

Remarks: Program initiated 8-56; design completed 11-59. Was in overhaul and modification 1987–96; after departing the yard, was briefly laid up for lack of funds to complete the final 5% of the overhaul, which included a new sonar suite, the addition of antiship missiles, and improved EW equipment. Is assigned to the Black Sea Fleet. Was demoted from *Bol'shoy Protivolodochnyy Korabl'* (Large Antisubmarine Ship) to *Storozhevoy Korabl'* (Patrol Ship) in 1992.
Disposals: Class prototype *Komsomolets Ukrainyy* was laid down 15-9-59, launched 31-12-60, and commissioned 31-12-62. Of 20 originally completed during 1962–73, six were converted or completed to the "Modified Kashin" design (Projects 61M and 61MP). *Otvazhnyy* (ex-*Orel*) sank 20-8-74 after a SAM magazine explosion and fire. *Provornyy* was converted during the 1970s as trials ship for the SA-N-7 SAM system and was stricken in 10-90. *Komsomolets Ukrainyy* was stricken 24-1-91, *Soobrazitel'ny* on 3-7-92, and *Odarennyy, Steregushchiy,* and *Strogiy* on 30-7-93. *Sposobnyy* returned to the Black Sea 30-7-87 for a refit and conversion as Project 01091 sonar trials ship at Sevmorzavod, Sevastopol', but was officially stricken 6-1-93 and towed away for scrap 2-4-95 (in 4-93, Ukraine had made a claim to the ship but was rebuffed by Russia). *Obratsovyy* was stricken 30-7-93 and *Krasnyy Krym* on 24-6-91. *Reshitel'niy,* long out of service, was not stricken until 16-8-97 and was scrapped in Turkey in 1999. *Krasny Kavkaz* was stricken 26-5-98 and *Skoryy* by mid-1999.
Hull systems: Original displacement was 3,400 tons standard, 4,390 full load. There are 14 main watertight compartments, including five main engineering compartments: forward and after paired main engine compartments (each with one main engine, two gas turbine generators, and a diesel generator) and an auxiliary compartment. The service life of the main engines is nominally 3,000 hours. Were among the world's first ships to pay attention to sound and heat radiation reduction, and the superstructure and stacks were shaped to reduce radar return; stack effluent temperature is 180° C at full power. Superstructure and masts were built of AMG-5V light alloy. Hull has a double bottom over 80% of length. Manned spaces are pressurized against NBC warfare attack; the washdown system supplies 700 tons/hr of salt water. Has retractable fin stabilizers. Original provisions endurance was only 10 days; 70 tons of fresh water are carried.
Combat systems: Can carry 2,400 rounds of 76.2-mm ammunition; the twin 76.2-mm guns are in a ZIF-67 mounting. The Volna SAM system, which uses ZIF-101 triaxially stabilized twin-armed launchers, has never been considered satisfactory and may no longer be operational. During 1990s refit, the RBU-1000 ASW rocket launchers were replaced by racks port and starboard for quadruple Kh-35 Uran (SS-N-25) missile launchers (not actually installed until 2000 and then removed again after a port visit to Turkey), a variable-depth sonar was added at the stern, and the after 76.2-mm gunmount and its associated f.c. radar were deleted. Other changes included the installation of a modern EW suite and increased officer accommodations within the forward superstructure block, but planned replacement of the 533-mm torpedo tube mount by a seven-tube 402-mm OTA-40 mounting was not carried out.

Disposal note: The remaining Modified Kashin (Project 61M), the Black Sea Fleet's *Sderzhannyy,* began stripping of armament and antennas for later disposal on 29-5-01. *Smel'yy* was transferred to Poland during 12-87; *Ognevoy* was scrapped in Turkey in 10-90; *Slavnyy* was stricken 24-6-91; *Stroynyy* was scrapped in Turkey in 1-91; and *Smyshlennyy* was stricken 22-2-93.

DESTROYERS [DD]

♦ 1 Admiral Chabanenko ("Udaloy-II") class (Project 11551)
Bldr: Yantar Zavod 820, Kaliningrad

	Laid down	L	In serv.	Fleet
650 Admiral Chabanenko (ex-*Admiral Basistiy*)	28-2-89	14-12-92	28-1-99	Northern

Admiral Chabanenko (650) Boris Lemachko, 7-99

D: 7,750 tons (8,950 fl) **S:** 29.5 kts
Dim: 163.0 (150.0 wl) × 19.3 (17.8 wl) × 6.2 (8.0 max.)

DESTROYERS [DD] *(continued)*

Admiral Chabanenko (650)—with trials pennant
M.O.D. Bonn, via Siegfried Breyer, 10-96

Admiral Chabanenko (650)—note the one twin 130-mm gunmount forward in place of the two single 100-mm mountings carried on the similar *Udaloy* class
M.O.D. Bonn, via Siegfried Breyer, 9-95

A: 8 P-100 Moskit-M (SS-N-22 Sunburn) SSM (2 quadruple KT-190M launchers); Kinzhal (SA-N-9) SAM syst. (8 8-round PU 4S-95 VLS; 64 9M-330 Tor-M1/Gauntlet missiles); 1 twin 130-mm 70-cal. AK-130 DP; 2 Kortik CIWS (each with 8 missile tubes and 2 30-mm GSH-6-30L gatling AA; 64 tot. 9M-311 Vikhr'-K/SA-N-11 Grison missiles); 2 10-round RPK-5 Liven' ASW RL; 2 quadruple 533-mm TT (Type 86R Vodopod-NK [SS-N-16] ASW missiles and torpedoes); 2 mine rails (. . . mines); 1 Ka-27PL Helix-A ASW helicopter; 1 Ka-27RTs Helix targeting helicopter

Electronics:

Radar: 3 MR-212/201 Vaygach-U (Palm Frond) nav.; 1 MR-760 Fregat-MA (Top Plate) 3-D air search; 1 MR-320M Topaz-V (Strut Pair) surf./air search; 1 MR-184 Lev (Kite Screech-C) 130-mm f.c.; 1 Garpun-BAL (in Monolit/Band Stand radome) antiship missile targeting; 2 MR-360 Podkat (Cross Sword) SA-N-9 f.c.; 2 3P-87 (Hot Flash) Kortik CIWS f.c.; 1 Fly Screen-B helicopter landing aid

Sonar: Zvezda M-2 suite: . . . (Ox Yoke) bow-mounted LF; MGK-345 Bronza (Rat Tail) LF VDS

TACAN: 2 Privod-B (Round House)

EW: Start-series suite: 2 Wine Glass intercept; 2 MP-401 (Bell Shroud) intercept; 2 Bell Squat; 2 PK-2 decoy syst. (2 twin, trainable ZIF-121 RL); 10 10-round PK-10 fixed decoy RL

E/O: 4 Spektr-F (Half Cup) laser detection

M: COGAG M-9 plant: 2 M-8KF boost gas turbines (22,500 shp each), 2 M-62 cruise gas turbines (7,500 shp each); 2 props; 60,000 shp max.
Electric: 6,000 kw tot. (4 × 1,500-kw gas turbine sets)
Range: 5,700/18 **Fuel:** 2,000 tons **Endurance:** 30 days
Crew: 32 officers, 264 warrant officers and enlisted

Remarks: Two ships of this design were originally intended for the KGB Maritime Border Guard but after the 1991 revolution were bequeathed to the navy. Completion of the first was delayed by the economic and social turmoil within Russia, and the second, *Admiral Kucharov* (or, according to other sources, *Admiral Basistiy*) was scrapped in 3-94, prior to launch. *Chabanenko* was handed over to the Russian Navy in 10-96 but was not commissioned for two additional years; she departed Baltiysk 24-2-99 and arrived at Severomorsk 10-3-99 for duty with the Northern Fleet. As of 12-00, the ship was assigned to the "Kola Fleet" and based at Severomorsk.
Hull systems: Hull and propulsion plant essentially duplicate those of the *Udaloy* class, although the forecastle deck has been extended further aft. One source indicates that the gas turbine engines are uprated over those in the *Udaloys*, producing a total output of 65,000 shp and an unlikely maximum speed of 32 kts. Maximum propeller rpm is 327.
Combat systems: Electronics equipment not listed above includes two Chop Dish SATCOM antennas mounted abreast the hangar and two Pricep (Light Bulb) datalink antennas, associated with the Moskit missile system. The sonar suite probably duplicates that of the frigate *Neustrashimyy;* the bow-mounted sonar dome is unusually long, extending aft to beneath the 130-mm mount and containing a second, possibly flank, transducer array, but one source indicates that a planned, even larger array was not installed. The torpedo tubes are mounted behind shutters in the hull sides, and there may be a complete set of reloads. Carries 350 rounds of 130-mm and 12,000 rounds of 30-mm gun ammunition. The RBU-6000 rocket launchers are described as being intended primarily as antitorpedo countermeasures in this ship. The 130-mm gun fire-control radar is a dual-frequency set with laser rangefinder and television adjuncts. The Type 2S95 vertical SAM launchers provide up to a 24 launch/min rate of fire.

♦ 9 Udaloy (Fregat) class (Project 1155R)

Bldrs: A: SevernayaVerf 190, St. Petersburg; B: Yantar Zavod 820, Kaliningrad

	Bldr	Laid down	L	In serv.	Fleet
400 Vitse-Admiral Kulakov	A	4-11-77	16-5-80	10-1-82	North.
687 Marshal Vasil'yevskiy	A	22-4-79	29-12-81	8-12-83	North.
564 Admiral Tributs	A	19-4-80	26-3-83	30-12-85	Pac.
543 Marshal Shaposhnikov	B	8-5-83	30-12-84	30-12-85	Pac.
619 Severomorsk (ex-*Simferopol'*, ex-*Marshal Zhukov*, ex-*Marshal Budenniy*)	B	12-6-84	24-12-85	30-12-87	North.
605 Admiral Levchenko (ex-*Khabarovsk*)	A	27-1-82	21-2-85	30-9-88	North.
572 Admiral Vinogradov	B	5-2-86	4-6-87	30-12-88	Pac.
678 Admiral Kharlamov	B	7-8-86	29-6-88	30-12-89	North.
548 Admiral Panteleyev	B	28-4-88	7-2-90	19-12-91	Pac.

Admiral Panteleyev (548)—a Pacific Fleet unit, at speed Chris Sattler, 2-01

Severomorsk (619)—at Baltiysk, prior to returning to the Northern Fleet after overhaul Boris Lemachko, 7-00

Marshal Vasil'yevskiy (687)—at Severomorsk, prior to overhaul; note the twin hangars and the VDS housing door, and that the ship still lacked the MR-320M Topaz-V air-search radar antenna atop the foremast Boris Lemachko, 7-00

Admiral Tributs (564)—visiting Japan Mitsuhiro Kadota, 9-01

Marshal Shaposhnikov (543)—laid up at Vladivostok but in commission
Boris Lemachko, 8-00

DESTROYERS [DD] *(continued)*

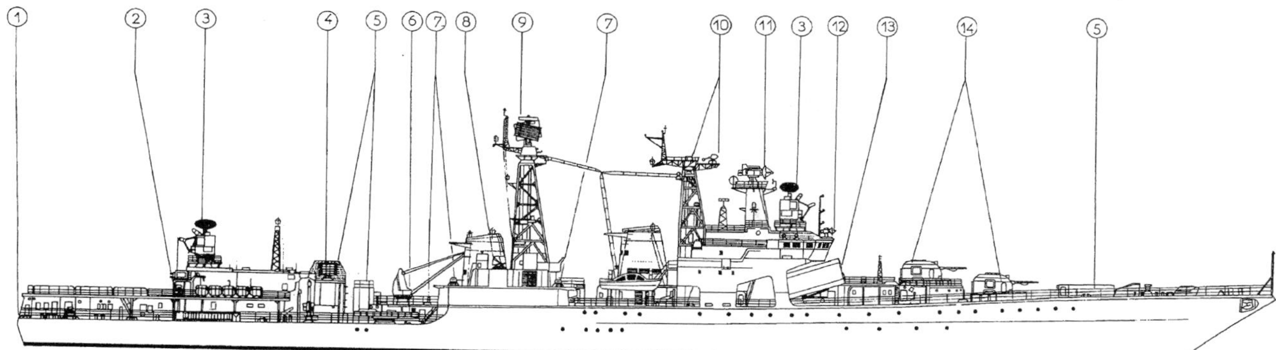

Udaloy class 1. VDS housing beneath helicopter flight deck 2. dual helicopter hangars 3. MR-360 Podkat radar director for Kinzhal SAM system 4. RBU-6000 ASW RL 5. rotating vertical launch cells for Kinzhal SAM system 6. quadruple 533-mm TT (port and starboard) 7. 30-mm AK-630M gatling AA 8. MR-123 Vympel radar director for 30-mm AA 9. MR-760MA Fregat-MA 3-D air-search radar 10. MR-212/201 Vaygach-U navigational/surface-search radars (the platform above these is now occupied by the antenna for the MR-320M Topaz-V surface/air-search radar) 11. MR-145 Lev radar director for the 100-mm guns 12. Drakon radar director/trackers for URK-5 Rastrub ASW/antiship missiles 13. quadruple launch containers for URK-5 ASW/antiship missiles 14. 100-mm AK-100 DP guns Drawing by Lucien Gassier, from *Flottes de Combat*

Admiral Vinogradov (572)—a Pacific Fleet unit Brian Morrison, 2-01

D: 6,930–6,945 tons std.; 7,570–7,585 tons normal (8,404 max. fl)
S: 29.5 kts (29 sust.)
Dim: 163.50 (145.00 wl) × 19.00 (17.20 wl) × 5.19 (hull; 7.80 max.)
A: 8 URK-5 Rastrub (SS-N-14 Silex) ASW and antiship SSM (2 quadruple KT-100 launchers; 8 Type 83R and 83RUS missiles); 8 Kinzhal (SA-N-9) SAM syst. (8 8-round PU 4S-95 VLS; 64 9M-330 Tor M1/Gauntlet missiles); 2 single 100-mm 70-cal. AK-100 DP (1,200 tot. rounds); 4 single 30-mm 54-cal. AK-630M gatling AA (12,000 rounds); 2 12-round RBU-6000 ASW RL (96 RGB-12 rockets); 2 quadruple 533-mm CLTA-53-1155 TT; 2 mine rails (. . . mines); 2 Ka-27PL Helix-A ASW helicopters

Electronics:

Radar: 3 MR-212/201 Vaygach-U (Palm Frond) nav.—all but *Shaposhnikov:* 1 MR-320M Topaz-V (Strut Pair) surf./air search; 1 MR-760MA Fregat-MA (Top Plate) 3-D air search; 2 Drakon (Eye Bowl) f.c. for ASW/antiship missiles; 1 MR-145 Lev (Kite Screech-B) 100-mm f.c.; 2 MR-360 Podkat (Cross Sword) SAM f.c.; 2 MR-123 Vympel (Bass Tilt) 30-mm f.c.; 1 . . . (Fly Screen-B) microwave helicopter landing aid

Sonar: MGK-355 Polinom suite: MGK-335 Platina (Horse Jaw) hull-mounted HF; Orion (Horse Tail) LF VDS; MG-35 underwater telephone; MGK-355TA torpedo detection

TACAN: 2 Privod (Round House)

EW: 2 Start-2 (Bell Shroud); 2 Bell Squat; 4 Bell Crown; 2 twin PK-2 decoy RL (ZIF-121 launchers; 400 rockets)—later ships also: 10 10-round PK-10 fixed decoy RL

E/O: later ships: 6 Spektr-F (Half Cup) laser warning

M: COGAG M-9 plant: 2 M-8KF boost gas turbines (22,500 shp each); 2 M-62 cruise gas turbines (7,500 shp each); 2 5-bladed props; 60,000 shp max.
Electric: 5,000 kw tot. (4 × 1,250-kw gas turbine sets)
Range: 2,550/29; 7,700/18; 6,882/14 **Fuel:** 1,500 tons + 40 tons aviation fuel
Endurance: 30 days **Crew:** 29 officers, 191 enlisted

Remarks: Class initially had the NATO nickname "BAL-COM-3." Type designation is BPK (*Bol'shoy Protivolodochnyy Korabl',* Large Antisubmarine Ship). Project name Fregat means "Frigate bird." The first three built lacked SAM systems and were Project 1155; the survivors are Project 1155R (the two groups are also sometimes referred to as Projects 1155A and 1155B). This class saw relatively little operational use during the 1990s because of the difficulty in obtaining spare gas turbines, which have had to be imported from Ukraine; the Rybinsk Motors factory began repairing the existing engines in 1999 and is developing the capability to manufacture replacements. Increased funding has permitted an increasing number of refits and ships of the class are now much more extensively employed in operations.

Status: *Admiral Tributs* had a serious shipyard fire at Vladivostok 18-7-91 and was placed in reserve in 1995; she had another fire in 9-95 and began repairs during 1-98 at Dalzavod Shipyard, Vladivostok, where she remained through 2001. The Russian press reported in late 1993 that *Simferopol'* would have to be decommissioned for lack of available crew, but the ship was active in 1996; the name was changed to *Severomorsk* 21-1-96. She began a major refit at Severnaya Verf, St. Petersburg, arriving in 7-98 but with work not commencing until fall 1999 and completing 30-8-00; her departure for the Northern Fleet was delayed by a fire at St. Petersburg in 9-00, and the ship left Baltiysk 5-11-00. *Admiral Levchenko* arrived in 2-00 at the same yard for refit and replacement of engines and returned to the Northern Fleet at the end of 9-01, and *Admiral Kharlamov* was refitted at Northern Fleet area facilities during 1998–99. *Marshal Vasil'yevskiy* was refitting at Sevmashpredpriyatiye, Severodvinsk, during 2001 and was expected to return to service in 2002. The refit of *Vitse-Admiral Kulakov,* at Kronshtadt since 1992, was moved to Severnaya Verf, St. Petersburg, in 6-00 and resumed for completion in 2002.

Disposals: Class prototype *Udaloy* was stricken from the Northern Fleet 31-8-98. *Admiral Zakharov,* completed in 1983, suffered an engine room explosion and fire 17-2-92, was stricken 29-9-94, and was later scrapped in South Korea. *Admiral Spiridonov,* placed in 2nd class reserve at Vladivostok 31-8-98 after several years of inactivity, is being used as a spare parts source and is not likely to return to service.

Hull systems: Were originally to have had a more-powerful propulsion plant totaling 72,000 shp, but the intended boost turbine component was not developed. Either cruise turbine can drive either or both shafts via a common gearbox. Maximum propeller rpm is 327. Have automated controls for the propulsion and auxiliary plants. Fitted with retractable fin stabilizers. The sonar dome is 30 m long and 5.1 m wide and imposes a considerable performance penalty. In overload condition, up to 1,700 tons of fuel can be carried.

Combat systems: The combat system is named Lesorub-5. Four vertical launchers for the Kinzhal SAM system have a combined rate of fire of up to 24 per minute and are located on the raised portion of the forecastle, two more are disposed athwartships in the small deckhouse between the torpedo tubes, and two are arranged fore and aft in the deckhouse between the RBU-6000 ASW RL mounts; each rotating cylinder holds eight missiles. All normally carry four antiship and four antisubmarine torpedoes in the 533-mm tubes; there are no reloads.

The two hangars are side by side and use inclined elevator ramps to raise the aircraft to the flight deck; the hangar roofs slide forward in two segmented sections to clear the rotors. From the third unit on, the helicopter deck was wider, extending to the sides of the ship. Two Privod (Round House) TACAN radomes are mounted on yards on the after mast, while the Fly Screen microwave landing-control radar is beside the starboard hangar. Four ASW torpedoes, 72 air-dropped rocket-propelled depth charges, and 20 standard depth charges can be carried for the helicopters.

DESTROYERS [DD] *(continued)*

The EW suite is incomplete, with several empty platforms on the after mast, except for *Severomorsk,* which has four Foot Ball (Start-series) radomes on the after mast. *Kulakov* was to have had the radar suite updated to later class standard during her current, protracted overhaul. *Marshal Shaposhnikov* still lacks the antenna for the MR-320M Topaz-V air-search radar atop the foremast.

FRIGATES [FF]

♦ 0 (+ 4) Project 20380

Bldr: Severnaya Verf, St. Petersburg

	Laid down	L	In serv.
. . . STEREGUSHCHIY	21-12-01	. . .	2005
. . . . . .	. . .	. . .	. . .
. . . . . .	. . .	. . .	. . .
. . . . . .	. . .	. . .	2010

D: 1,850 tons (2,100 fl) **S:** 30 kts **Dim:** 104.8 (94.00 pp) × 13.6 × 3.4 (mean hull)
A: 12 3M-54E Club vertically launched SSM; 3 Kinzhal (SA-N-9) SAM syst. (3 8-round PU 4S-95 VLS; 24 9M-330 Tor M1/Gauntlet missiles); 2 4-rail Fasta-4M point-defense SAM syst. (24 Igla-M/Gremlin missiles); 1 100-mm 59-cal. A-190 DP; 2 single 30-mm 54-cal. AK-630M AA; 4 fixed 400-mm OTA-40 TT (paired); 1 Ka-27PL Helix-A ASW helicopter
Electronics:
Radar: 1 FR-2130S nav.; 2 MR-212/201-1 Vaygach-U (Palm Frond) nav./surf. search; 1 Fregat-MA 3-D air search; 1 Garpun surface-target desig.; 1 MR-360 Podkat (Cross Sword) SAM f.c.
Sonar: Platina-MS hull-mounted LF
EW: ASOR-ME intercept; 2 10-round PK-10 fixed decoy RL
M: 2 or 4 . . . . . . diesels; 2 CP props; 38,428 bhp—drop-down electric azimuthal bow-thruster
Electric: 2,000 kw tot. (4 × 500-kw diesel sets)
Range: 3,600/. . . **Endurance:** 15 days **Crew:** 117 tot. (with aircrew)

Remarks: Are initially to be used in the Caspian Flotilla, according to statements by the commander-in-chief of the Russian Navy, Adm. Kuroyedov, and the chief of the Main Navy Staff, Adm. Kravchenko. The design was approved by the Russian Navy during 2-01, at which time a unit cost of $50 million was expected. The construction contract was given to Severnaya Verf on 25-5-01. Although the goal is 25 ships in the class and the Russian Navy C-in-C announced that 10 were in the original order, the number was reduced to four as of 15-6-01, and the price had risen to about $120 million each. During 10-01, an export version, Project 20282, was offered to Iran for $150 million.
Hull systems: Will have fin stabilizers and bow bulwarks. No hangar is to be fitted, but there will be a helicopter weapons reload and fueling capability. The hull and superstructure do not appear to have had much radar signature reduction effort. The boat to starboard and RIB to port are carried behind low bulwarks.
Combat systems: The 30-mm gatling guns appear to have only lead-computing ringsight directors. The Klinok SAM launcher sets are recessed into the deck just forward of the helicopter platform, while the 3M-54E Club missiles are vertically launched from a set of 12 cells just abaft the 100-mm gun. One press source reported that the ships would have two Kashtan CIWS each and that they would carry the Kh-35 Uran antiship missile rather than the more potent Club, so it is possible that the design has not yet been finalized.

Disposal note: The cancellation of the construction of the frigate *Novik* (Project 12441) at Yantar Zavod, Kaliningrad, was announced 30-10-01. The ship had been laid down 26-7-97, but no further work was done and she was canceled on 22-1-98. Some $3.16 million was provided in the FY 01 defense budget to restart construction, however, but the age of the design and the projected expense to complete the one ship evidently caused the second termination.

♦ 0 (+ 1) Gepard class (Project 11660)

Bldr: Zelenodol'sk Zavod, Kazan, Tatarstan

	Laid down	L	In serv.	Fleet
TATARSTAN (ex-*Yastreb*, ex-SKR-200)	15-9-92	7-93	2002?	. . .

Tatarstan—fitting out *Sudostroinie,* via Siegfried Breyer, 1996

Tatarstan—fitting out Zelenodol'sk Zavod, 1996

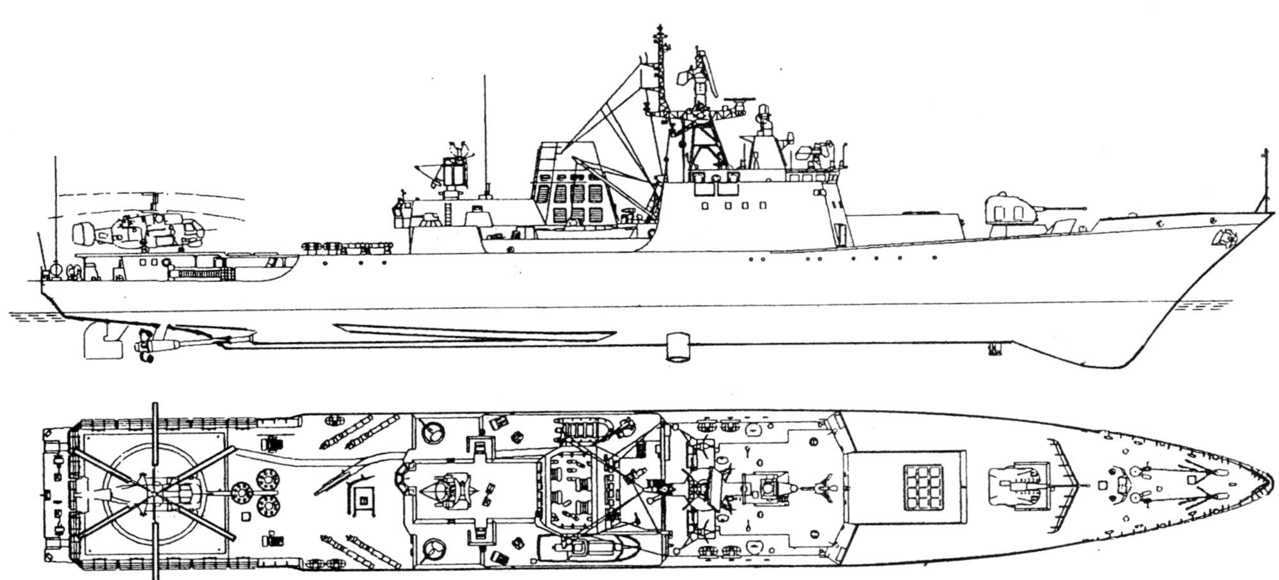

Project 20380 frigate Severnoye Design Bureau, 2001

FRIGATES [FF] *(continued)*

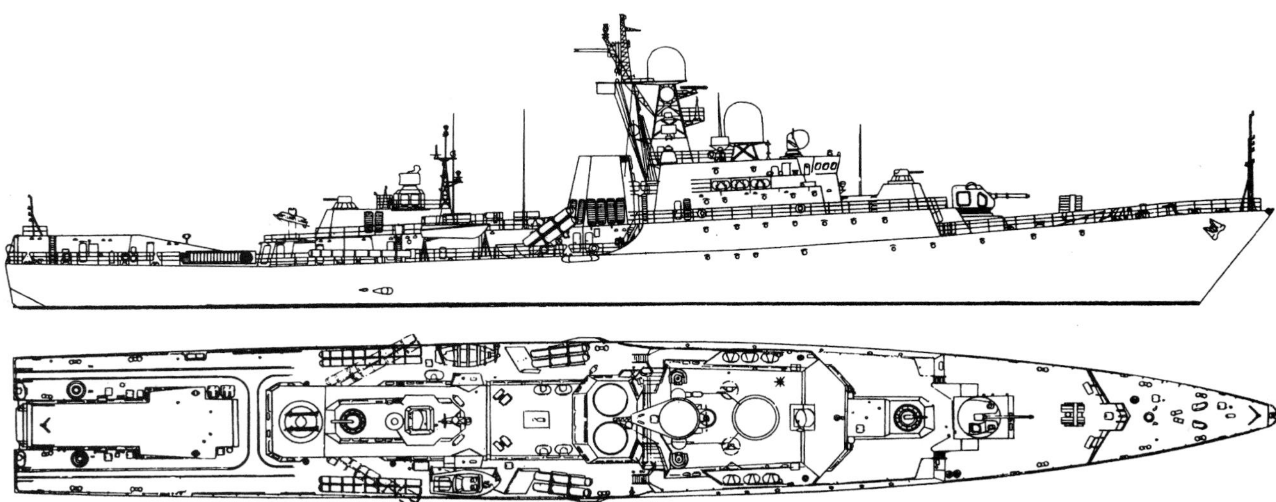

Tatarstan (Project 1166.1) Rozvoorouzhenie, 1993

D: 1,500 tons (1,930 fl) **S:** 28 kts (20 on diesel)
Dim: 102.14 (93.50 wl) × 13.09 × 3.60 (5.30 over sonar dome)
A: 8 Kh-35 Uran (SS-N-25 Switchblade) SSM; 1 twin-rail Osa-M (SA-N-4) SAM syst. (20 9M-33/Gecko missiles); 1 76.2-mm 59-cal. AK-176 DP; 2 single 30-mm 54-cal. AK-630 gatling AA; 2 twin 533-mm TT; 1 12-round RBU-6000 ASW RL; 2 mine rails (12–20 mines)
Electronics:
Radar: 1 . . . nav.; 1 MR-352 Pozitiv (Cross Dome) surf./air search; 1 MPZ-301 Baza (Pop Group) SA-N-4 missile f.c.; 1 Monolit (Band Stand) cruise missile target desig.; 1 MR-123 Vympel (Bass Tilt) 30-mm f.c.
Sonar: Zarnitsa suite: . . . MF hull mounted; . . . MF VDS
EW: 2 Bell Shroud intercept; 2 Bell Squat jammers; 4 16-round PK-16 fixed decoy RL
M: CODOG: 2 gas turbines (29,300 shp each), 1 Type 61D diesel (8,000 bhp); 2 props
Electric: 1,800 kw tot. (3 × 600-kw, 380-V, 50-Hz a.c. diesel alternator sets)
Range: 950/27; 3,500/14; 4,000/10 (5,000/10 at overload displacement)
Endurance: 15 days **Crew:** 15 officers, 94 enlisted (accomm. for 131 tot.)

Remarks: Has also been listed as Project 1159.1. Characteristics above are for the basic Project 11660 version, of which the first, *Tatarstan,* was essentially complete by late 1995. *Burevestnik* was to be of a modified design, optimized for patrol duties, and was to have a helicopter hangar if completed. Funds had reportedly been found during 12-99 to complete three ships, which were said at that time to be 93%, 67%, and 40% complete, but as of 2-02, it was reported that the second and third hulls had been scrapped. Funding for completion of the first unit was requested from Tatarstan, and the ship was said to be intended for delivery to the Baltic Fleet (possibly to the border guard rather than the navy) during 6-01—but as of 10-01, the *Tatarstan* remained at the builder's yard, with her new eventual fleet assignment said to be the Caspian Flotilla.

The design is offered for export in the following variations: Gepard 1, with a helicopter platform (but no hangar) atop a deckhouse at the stern replacing the VDS housing; Gepard 2, with a helicopter hangar in place of the SA-N-4 SAM system and VDS deleted; Gepard 3, with greater beam (13.8 m) and displacement (2,100 tons fl), a Kortik CIWS in place of the forward 30-mm gatling gun, the other gatling guns eliminated, the missile tubes raised one deck, the torpedo tubes moved near the stern, and a helicopter deck and hangar above a VDS housing; Gepard 4, configured as a rescue ship with no armament (although mounting positions as in the basic design would be fitted forward) and with a hangar and flight deck as in the Gepard 2; and Gepard 5, with helicopter deck, no hangar, and reduced gun armament (one 76.2-mm and two 30-mm gatling) as a patrol ship, with extended range (6,000 n.m. at 10 kts) but reduced speed of 23 kts from two 8,000-bhp diesels and no gas turbine.
Hull systems: Molded depth amidships: 7.25 m; height above waterline: 25.00 m. Capable of employing weapons in up to Sea State 5. Steel hull and superstructure, with some use of aluminum-magnesium alloy in the upper superstructure. To carry 13 10-man life rafts. Hull is equipped with fin stabilizers and has twin rudders. Either the gas turbines or the diesel is used for propulsion, but not all together; in an emergency, the diesel can drive one shaft and one gas turbine the other.
Combat systems: To carry a sonobuoy receiver/processor for working with ASW aircraft. A tactical data system is planned. The hull-mounted sonar dome is located below and just forward of the bridge. The large Monolit (Band Stand) radome atop the pilothouse probably contains a target detection and designation radar for the Kh-35 Uran antiship missiles. The sonar dome is mounted below and just forward of the bridge. To carry 500 rounds of 76-mm and 4,000 rounds of 30-mm ammunition.

♦ 1 Neustrashimyy (Yastreb) class (Project 11540)

Bldr: Yantar Zavod 820, Kaliningrad

	Laid down	L	In serv.	Fleet
712 Neustrashimyy ("Fearless")	25-3-87	25-5-88	24-1-93	Baltic

D: 3,210 tons light; 3,590 tons std. (4,350 fl) **S:** 29 kts (31+ on trials)
Dim: 129.63 (123.00 wl) × 15.60 (14.30 wl) × 4.26 (mean hull; 8.35 over sonar dome)
A: 4 Kinzhal (SA-N-9) SAM syst. (4 8-round PU 4S-95 VLS; 32 9M-330 Tor-M1/Gauntlet missiles); 1 100-mm 59-cal. AK-100 DP (350 rounds); 2 Kortik CIWS (each with 8 missile tubes and 2 30-mm GSH-6-30L gatling AA; 64 tot. 9M-311 Vikhr'-K/SA-N-11 Grison missiles); 6 fixed 533-mm fixed TT (12 RPK-6 Vodopod/SS-N-16 missiles and/or SET-65 and 53-65K torpedoes); 2 12-round RBU-6000 ASW RL (96 RGB-60 rockets); 1 Ka-27PL Helix-A helicopter; 2 mine rails (. . . mines)

Neustrashimyy (712) Winter & Findler, 6-95

Neustrashimyy (712) Winter & Findler, 6-95

Electronics:
Radar: 1 MR-312 Nayada nav.; 1 MR-212/201 Vaygach-U (Palm Frond) nav.; 1 MR-760MA Fregat-MA (Top Plate) 3-D air search; 1 MR-352 Pozitiv (Cross Dome) target desig.; 1 MR-360 Podkat (Cross Sword) SAM f.c.; 1 MR-145 Lev (Kite Screech-B) 100-mm f.c.; 2 3P-87 (Hot Flash) Kortik f.c.
Sonar: MGK-365 Zvezda M-1 suite: . . . (Ox Yoke) bow-mounted LF; MGK-345 Bronza (Rat Tail) LF VDS; MG-35 underwater telephone
EW: MR-407 Vympel-R2 suite: 2 . . . (Foot Ball-A) intercept; 2 . . . (Half Hat-B) intercept; 2 . . . (Cage Flask) intercept; 2 . . . (Bell Squat) jammer; 2 16-round PK-16 fixed decoy RL (400 rockets); 8 10-round PK-10 fixed decoy RL
M: COGAG: 2 M-70 cruise gas turbines (9,000 shp each), 2 M-90 boost gas turbines (19,500 shp each); 2 props; 57,000 shp max.
Electric: 3,050 kw tot. (1 × 1,250-kw and 1 × 600-kw gas turbine sets, 2 × 600-kw diesel sets; 380 V a.c.)
Range: 700/30; 2,900/18 **Fuel:** 580 tons **Endurance:** 30 days
Crew: 35 officers, 34 warrant officers, 141 enlisted

Remarks: Ordered 3-2-97. Began sea trials during 12-89 but was not commissioned until more than three years later, after a number of alterations had been performed. Has been largely inactive since 1995 but completed a three-month refit at Yantar Zavod, Kaliningrad, during 7-00. The design is optimized for ASW and was originally intended to be a successor to the much smaller Grisha series. At least four were planned, with the fourth, *Nepokornyy* ("Unruly"), to have been of a modified design (Project 1154.1). *Yaroslav Mudryy* (ex-*Nepristupnyy*) was laid down 27-5-88 and launched during 5-91; she and unlaunched sister *Tuman* were stricken 22-10-98. *Mudryy* began scrapping in 2001, while the *Tuman* was launched 6-11-98 only to clear the ways for merchant ship repair work and began scrapping on 29-3-99. As of 2-02, however, the yard was said to be working on the *Mudryy* in hopes of selling her either for export or to the Russian Navy.
Hull systems: Is of steel construction, with very little use of light alloys in the superstructure. Special care has been taken in the design to reduce radar and infrared emissions. The above-water hullform has a flat flare over its entire length, while the low superstructure has each level broken by flat convex planes to disperse radar returns. The stacks feature complex eductors and are shaped to reduce radar returns; the after stack (just abaft the mainmast) was originally so low as to be barely higher

FRIGATES [FF] *(continued)*

than the hangar. Between initial trials and 10-91, baffle plates were added abreast the stack exhausts, the eight exhausts in the forward stack were raised slightly and angled aftward, and the formerly flat door covering the variable-depth sonar housing was given a sawtooth angular surface—all to reduce infrared signature further. Most of the superstructure is sheathed in radar-absorbent material; the effectiveness of the signature-reduction effort is spoiled somewhat, however, by the design of the lattice mast and a plethora of bulky antennas. Has fin stabilizers, and flow fins have been added to the hull bottom just outboard the propellers. The generator plant has also been described as consisting of five diesel sets with a total output of 3,500 kw.
Combat systems: The combat system is designated Tron and was reportedly the first fully integrated Russian Navy computerized system. The six torpedo tubes flanking the hangar are fixed at about a 15° outboard angle and can launch the Type 86R antisubmarine missiles of the RPK-6 Vodopod system as well as wire-guided torpedoes. The designation Zvezda M-1 applies to the entire hull-mounted and variable depth sonar suite; there is no provision for a towed linear passive hydrophone array. The sonar dome projects well ahead of the keel and extends aft nearly as far as the RBU-6000 ASW rocket launcher, indicating the likely presence of passive flank arrays. The RBU-6000 ASW rocket launcher can function as a torpedo countermeasure system. The ASW weapons-control system name is Purga. There are none of the bridge periscopes found in other modern Russian designs. Amidships there are provisions for later installation of four quadruple launchers for the Kh-35 Uran (NATO SS-N-25 Switchblade) antiship missile system. The communications suite is referred to as Buran-6.

Note: The Krivak-III-class frigates are described in the Federal Border Guard section.

♦ 4 Krivak-II (Burevestnik-M) class (Project 1135M)
(2 nonoperational) Bldr: Yantar Zavod 820, Kaliningrad

	Laid down	L	In serv.	Fleet
916 *Rezvyy* ("Lively")	10-12-73	30-5-75	30-12-75	Northern
731 Neukrotimyy ("Invincible") (ex-*Komsomolets Litviy*, ex-*Neukrotimyy*)	22-1-76	27-6-77	30-12-77	Baltic
662 *Revnostnyy* ("Roaring")	27-6-79	23-4-80	27-12-80	Pacific
808 Pytlivyy ("Inquisitive")	27-6-79	16-4-81	30-11-81	Black Sea

Pytlivyy (808) Siegfried Breyer Coll., 1996

D: 2,945–3,075 tons light; 3,305 tons normal (3,505 max. fl) **S:** 30.6 kts
Dim: 123.10 (113.00 wl) × 14.20 (13.2 wl) × 4.57 (mean hull; 7.3 over sonar dome)
A: 4 URK-5 Rastrub (SS-N-14 Silex) SSM (1 quadruple KT-106 launcher; 4 Type 83R and 83RUS missiles); 2 twin-rail Osa-M (SA-N-4) SAM syst. (40 9M-33/Gecko missiles); 2 single 100-mm 59-cal. AK-100 DP (1,200 rounds); 2 12-round RBU-6000 ASW RL (144 RGB-60 rockets); 2 quadruple 533-mm UTA-53-1135 TT (4 SET-65 and 4 53-65K torpedoes); 2 mine rails (12–20 mines)
Electronics:
Radar: 1 MR-212/201 Vaygach-U (Palm Frond) or Volga (Don-Kay) nav.; 1 Mius (Spin Trough) or Don-2 nav.; 1 MR-310U Angara-M (Head Net-C) air search; 2 . . . Drakon (Eye Bowl) SS-N-14 f.c.; 2 MPZ-301 Baza (Pop Group) SA-N-4 f.c.; 1 MR-114 Lev (Kite Screech-A) 100-mm gun f.c.
Sonar: MGK-332MC Titan-2 (Bull Nose) hull-mounted MF; MG-325 Vega (Mare Tail) MF VDS; MG-26 underwater telephone

Neukrotimyy (731) H&L Van Ginderen 4-97

EW: Smerch suite: 2 Bell Shroud intercept; 2 Bell Squat jammer; 4 16-round PK-16 fixed decoy RL (128 rockets); 2 towed torpedo decoys—*Revnostnyy* and possibly others also: 4 10-round PK-10 fixed decoy RL
E/O: some: 2 Spektr-F (Half Cup) laser warning
M: COGAG M-7 plant: 2 M-62 cruise gas turbines (7,475 shp each), 2 M-8K boost gas turbines (20,000 shp each); 2 props; 54,950 shp tot.
Electric: 3,000 kw (5 × 600-kw diesel sets)
Range: 640/30; 4,000/14 **Endurance:** 30 days
Crew: 23 officers, 28 warrant officers, 130 enlisted (accomm. for 194 tot.)

Remarks: Type designation: SKR (*Storozhevoy Korabl',* Patrol Ship), formerly BPK (*Bol'shoy Protivolodochnyy Korabl',* Large Antisubmarine Ship). The VDS housing at the stern is somewhat larger than on the Krivak-I, but the principal difference between the two classes is the substitution of two single 100-mm for the two twin 76.2-mm guns. *Neukrotimyy* was renamed in 1988 for the Communist Youth League of Lithuania but renamed again in 1990 when that country demanded independence. Repairs on *Neukrotimyy* were suspended in mid-1995 when 90% complete and were not completed until 2000. A refit of the *Revnostnyy* was at a standstill at Dalzavod repair yard in 5-00, with 80% of the work complete; the ship appears to be in very poor condition but remains in commission.
Disposals: *Gordelivyy* was reported in mid-1992 to have begun an overhaul that could not be completed for lack of funds; the ship was instead placed in reserve and stricken 5-7-94. Pacific Fleet unit *Grozyashchiy* was stricken 17-11-94 and *Rezkiy* on 1-9-95. Black Sea Fleet unit *Razitel'nyy* was stricken from the Black Sea Fleet 10-1-96 and was to have been transferred to Ukraine 1-4-96, but was not transferred until 6-97. Pacific Fleet unit *R'yannyy* and Northern Fleet units *Gromkiy* and *Bessmennyy* were stricken 16-8-98.
Hull systems: Were designed to be 2,870 tons standard, 3,430 tons full load, but one source indicates that displacements have grown to 3,170 tons standard and 3,670 tons full load. There are 14 watertight compartments. The superstructure is built of aluminum-magnesium alloy, welded to the hull with bimetallic inserts. Type UKA-135 fin stabilizers are fitted. The propulsion plant originally delivered 45,570 shp normal/51,200 shp max. total (with the cruise turbines operating at 6,000 shp each and the boost turbines at 18,000 each), but the output was later increased. Hull block coefficient is 0.46, very fine for this type of vessel. For slow speeds, any one of the engines can drive both propellers.
Combat systems: The combat system is known as Planshet-35 and the ASW weapons control system as Purga. Carry 1,200 rounds of 100-mm ammunition. The chaff/decoy rocket launchers were moved from the stern to the 01 level, abreast the aft SA-N-4 launcher. *Revnostnyy* has four four-tube decoy RL mounted between the torpedo tubes, in addition to her normal chaff RL system. Can carry 12 KSM, 14 KRAB, or 16 IGDM-500 mines. The bow sonar initially installed was designated MG-332T. The hoist gear for the VDS is designated POUKB-1.

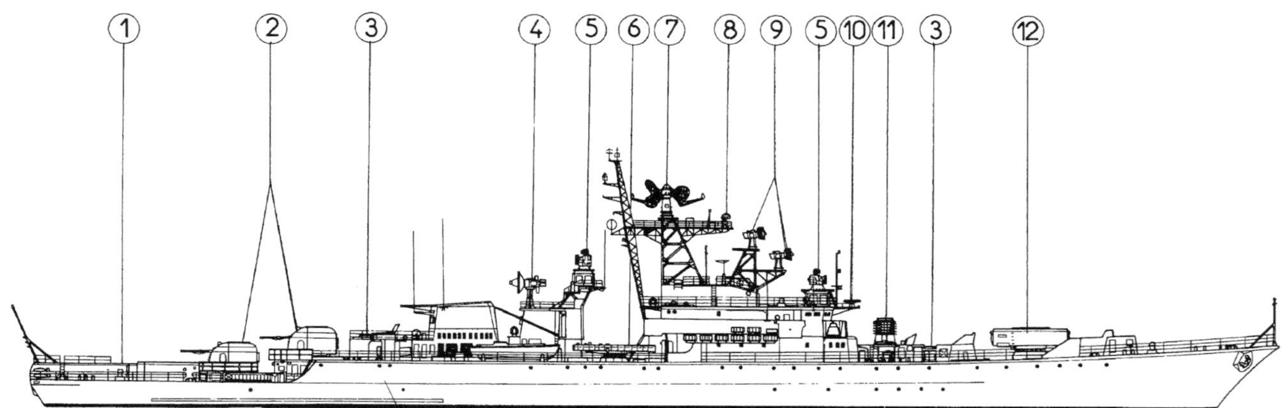

Krivak-II class 1. VDS housing 2. 100-mm AK-100 DP guns 3. launchers for Osa-M SAM system (shown retracted) 4. MR-114 Lev radar director for 100-mm guns 5. MPZ-301 Baza radar director for Osa-M SAM system 6. quadruple 533-mm TT 7. MR-310U Angara-M surface/air-search radar 8. Volga or Vaygach-U navigational/surface-search radar 9. Drakon radar directors for URK-5 Rastrub ASW/antiship missile system 10. Mius navigational radar 11. RBU-6000 ASW RL 12. quadruple KT-106 launcher for URK-5 Rastrub missiles
Drawing by Lucien Gassier, from *Flottes de Combat*

FRIGATES [FF] *(continued)*

♦ **2 Modified Krivak-I class (Project 11352)**
Bldr: Severnaya Verf 190 (ex-Zhdanov Zavod 190), St. Petersburg

	Laid down	L	In serv.	Converted	Fleet
930 Legkiy ("Light") (ex-*Leningradskiy Komsomolets*)	22-4-76	1-4-77	29-9-77	12-87 to 3-90	Northern
702 Pylkiy ("Ardent")	6-5-77	20-8-78	28-12-78	1990 to 17-3-94	Baltic

Pylkiy (702) French Navy, 3-96

Pylkiy (702) Boris Lemachko, 7-00

Legkiy (930)—showing how the enlarged VDS housing severely restricts arcs of fire for the after twin 76.2-mm gunmount *Ships of the World,* 1997

D: 3,175 tons (3,675 fl) **S:** 30.6 kts
Dim: 126.0 (116.9 wl) × 14.2 (13.2 wl) × 4.7 (mean hull; 8.0 over sonar)
A: 4 URK-5 Rastrub-B (SS-N-14 Silex) SSM (1 quadruple KT-106 launcher; Type 83R and 83RUS missiles); 2 twin-rail Osa-M (SA-N-4) SAM syst. (40 9M-33/Gecko missiles); 2 twin 76.2-mm 59-cal. AK-726 DP; 2 quadruple 533-mm UTA-53-1135 TT (4 SET-65 and 4 53-65 torpedoes); 2 mine rails (12–16 mines)
Electronics:
Radar: 2 MR-212/201 Vaygach-U (Palm Frond) nav.; 1 MR-755 Fregat-M2 (Half Plate) surf./air search; 2 . . . Drakon (Eye Bowl) SS-N-14 f.c.; 2 MPZ-301 Baza (Pop Group) SA-N-4 f.c.; 1 MR-105 Turel' (Owl Screech) gun f.c.
Sonar: MGK-365 Zvezda M-1 suite: MGK-335S Platina-C hull-mounted LF; MGK-345 Bronza LF VDS; MG-35 underwater telephone
EW: 2 Start-2 (Bell Shroud) intercept; 2 MP-401 Start (Bell Squat-A/B) jammer; 4 16-round PK-16 fixed decoy RL (128 rockets); 2 towed torpedo decoys; 3 sets corner-reflector decoys
E/O: 6 Spektr-F (Half Cup) laser warning
M: COGAG M-7 plant: 2 M-62 cruise gas turbines (7,475 shp each), 2 M-8K boost gas turbines (20,000 shp each); 2 props; 54,950 shp tot.
Electric: 3,000 kw (5 × 600-kw diesel sets)
Range: 640/30; 4,000/14 **Endurance:** 30 days
Crew: 22 officers, 198 warrant officers and enlisted

Remarks: This modernization program was initiated in 1985–86 for the original version of the Krivak class, but lack of funds halted the program with only two units fully converted. It had originally been intended to construct new Project 1135 units to the modified design. *Legkiy* was modernized to Project 11352 configuration at Severnaya Verf, St. Petersburg, followed by *Pylkiy* at Yantar Zavod 820, Kaliningrad, completed during 1994. Krivak-I-class *Letuchiy* was to have begun a similar modernization in 3-87 for completion 4-90 at the Far East Shipbuilding Plant 202, Vladivostok, but the work was not performed. *Pylkiy* began a refit at Yantar Zavod, Kaliningrad, fall 2000, and was in dry dock at Baltiysk during 6-01.
Hull systems: One semiofficial source gives the revised displacement as 3,000 tons standard and 3,350 tons full load. The bow appears to have been lengthened by about 3 m to accommodate the new bow-mounted sonar. See the remarks under the Krivak-I class for additional information.
Combat systems: The full conversion provided an improved sonar suite (with enlarged VDS housing), while the RBU-6000 ASW rocket launchers replaced by as-yet-vacant racks for two quadruple Kh-35 Uran (SS-N-25) antiship cruise missile launchers, the Angara-M (Head Net-C) air-search radar was replaced by Fregat-M2 (Half Plate) atop a new lattice foremast with an additional deckhouse level at its base, and eight 10-tube fixed decoy rocket launchers were added to the four 16-tube launchers already mounted; also added were the six Spektr-F laser detectors. The communications suite was updated to Buran-6 standard. The ASW weapons-control system name is Purga.

♦ **6 Krivak-I (Burevestnik) class (Projects 1135 and 11353*)** (2 *nonoperational*)
Bldrs: A: Yantar Zavod 820, Kaliningrad; B: Severnaya Verf 190 (ex-Zhdanov Zavod 190), St. Petersburg; C: Zaliv Zavod 532, Kerch', Ukraine

	Bldr	Laid down	L	In serv.	Fleet
663 *Storozhevoy* ("Guarding")	A	20-7-72	21-3-73	30-12-73	Pacific
937 *Zharkiy** ("Passionate")	A	16-4-74	3-11-75	29-6-76	Northern
754 Druzhnyy ("Amicable")	A	12-10-73	30-5-75	30-9-75	Baltic
661 Letuchiy ("Flying")	B	9-3-77	19-3-78	20-8-78	Pacific
955 Zadornyy ("Provocative")	B	10-11-77	25-3-79	31-8-79	Baltic
801 Ladnyy ("Friendly")	C	25-5-79	7-5-80	29-12-80	Black Sea

Ladnyy (801) Hartmut Ehlers, 7-00

Druzhnyy (754) Winter & Findler, 6-98

Zharkiy (937)—the only Krivak-I with enlarged VDS housing; note the twin 76.2-mm gunmounts Boris Lemachko

D: 2,810 tons std.; 3,200 tons normal (3,420 fl) **S:** 30.6 kts (32.5 on trials)
Dim: 123.00 (113.00 wl) × 14.20 (13.20 wl) × 4.48 (hull; 7.30 max.)
A: 4 URK-5 Rastrub (SS-N-14 Silex) SSM (1 quadruple KT-106 launcher; 4 Type 83R and 83RUS missiles); 2 twin-rail SA-N-4 Osa-M SAM syst. (ZIF-122 launchers; 40 9M-33/Gecko missiles); 2 twin 76.2-mm 59-cal. AK-726 DP (2,000 rounds); 2 12-round RBU-6000 ASW RL (144 RGB-60 rockets); 2 quadruple 533-mm UTA-53-1135 TT (4 SET-65 and 4 53-65 torpedoes); 2 mine rails (12–16 mines)
Electronics:
Radar: 1 Don-2 or Mius (Spin Trough) nav.; 1 Volga (Don-Kay) or MR-212/201 Vaygach-U (Palm Frond) nav.; 1 MR-310U Angara-M (Head Net-C) air search; 2 . . . Drakon (Eye Bowl) SS-N-14 f.c.; 2 MPZ-301 Baza (Pop Group) SA-N-4 f.c.; 1 MR-105 Turel' (Owl Screech) gun f.c.
Sonar: MG-332 Titan-2 (Bull Nose) hull-mounted MF; MG-325 Vega (Mare Tail) MF VDS; MG-26 underwater telephone; NEL-5 echo sounder
EW: 2 Start-2 (Bell Shroud) intercept; 2 MP-401 Start (Bell Squat-A/B) jammer; 4 16-round PK-16 fixed decoy RL (128 rockets); 2 towed torpedo decoys; 3 sets corner-reflector decoys
E/O: some: Spektr-F (Half Cup) laser warning
M: COGAG M-7 plant: 2 M-62 cruise gas turbines (7,475 shp each), 2 M-8K boost gas turbines (20,000 shp each); 2 props; 54,950 shp tot.
Electric: 3,000 kw tot. (5 × 600-kw diesel sets)
Range: 1,290/30; 4,995/14 **Fuel:** 348 tons normal (515 max.)
Endurance: 30 days **Crew:** 22 officers, 23 warrant officers, 145 enlisted

FRIGATES [FF] *(continued)*

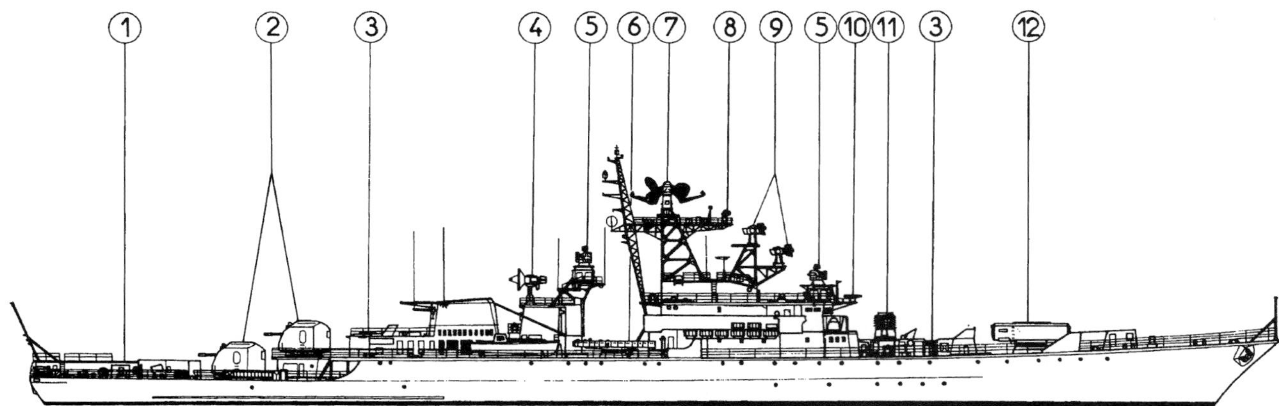

Krivak-I class 1. VDS housing 2. twin 76.2-mm DP gunmounts 3. launchers for Osa-M SAM system (shown retracted) 4. MR-105 Turel' radar director for 76.2-mm guns 5. MPZ-301 Baza radar directors for Osa-M SAM system 6. quadruple 533-mm TT 7. MR-310U Angara-M surface/air-search radar 8. Volga or Vaygach-U navigational/surface-search radar 9. Drakon radar directors for URK-5 Rastrub ASW/antiship missile system 10. Mius navigational radar 11. RBU-6000 ASW RL 12. quadruple KT-106 launcher for the URK-5 Rastrub missile system — Drawing by Lucien Gassier, from *Flottes de Combat*

Remarks: Designed at Northern Planning and Design Office (TsKB-53) by a team headed by Prof. V. Yukhnin, with Nikolay Pavlovich Sobelev as chief designer. Keel for class prototype *Bditel'nyy* was laid 21-7-68. In 1978, the Krivak-I and Krivak-II classes were rerated from second-class BPK (*Bol'shoy Protivolodochnyy Korabl',* Large Antisubmarine Ship) to SKR (*Storozhevoy Korabl',* Patrol Ship), a demotion prompted perhaps by their limited endurance at high speeds, speed, and size.

Status: *Letuchiy* was to have been modernized to the same configuration as the Project 11352 (Modified Krivak-I)–class *Legkiy* and *Pylkiy,* but the work was not performed. *Storozhevoy* completed a 6-year overhaul at Vladivostok late in 1994 and returned to her base at Petropavlovsk, where she was found to need further repairs. *Zharkiy* has not operated since the early 1990s and at one point was offered for scrap, but seems still to be at least nominally in service. *Druzhnyy* completed a refit during 2000. *Ladnyy* was under overhaul at Sevastopol' during 2001.

Disposals: Pacific Fleet sister *Razyashchiy* and Northern Fleet unit *Doblestnyy* were stricken 3-7-92, with the former towed away for scrap 8-93 and the latter in 12-96. Northern Fleet unit *Dostoynyy* was stricken 22-2-93, Baltic Fleet units *Sil'nyy* and *Svirepyy* on 30-7-93, and *Bditel'nyy* and *Bodryy* on 31-7-96 (scrapped at Kiel, Germany, beginning on 14-10-97, and at Yantar Zavod, Kaliningrad, in 1998, respectively). Pacific Fleet unit *Poryvistyy* was relegated to service as a museum ship during 1995 and sister *Retivyy* was stricken 1-9-95. Black Sea Fleet sister *Deyatel'nyy* was stricken 5-7-94 and was towed through the Bosporus bound for scrapping during 5-97. Black Sea Fleet units *Bezzavetnyy* and *Bezukoriznennyy* (both stricken 10-1-96) were to have been transferred to Ukraine 1-4-96, but the transfer was not carried out until 6-97; they have since been stricken. Pacific Fleet unit *Razumnyy* had been stricken by 1998.

Hull systems: Were designed to be 2,735 tons standard, 3,100 tons full load, but one source reports that displacements have grown to 3,075 tons standard and 3,575 tons full load. There are 14 watertight compartments. The superstructure is built of aluminum-magnesium alloy, welded to the hull with bimetallic inserts. Type UKA-135 fin stabilizers are fitted. The propulsion plant originally delivered 45,570 shp normal/51,200 shp max. total (with the cruise turbines operating at 6,000 shp each and the boost turbines at 18,000 each), but the total output was later increased. Hull block coefficient is 0.46, very fine for this type of vessel. For slow speeds, any one of the engines can drive both propellers. All have UKA-135 retractable fin stabilizers and a single rudder.

Combat systems: The combat system is designated Planshet-35. The bow sonar operates at 4.5, 5.0, or 5.5 kHz, with a 380-Hz bandwidth; pulse repetition rates are 30, 60, or 120 msec, and the set employs rotating directional transmission (RDT), with either CW or FM transmission. The VDS is apparently an independent system, and its towed "fish" is said to suffer from directional instability. There is a separate high-frequency tilting-stave sonar linked to the Purga fire-control system to provide targeting for the RBU-6000 ASW rocket launchers. *Zharkiy* was modified during the mid-1980s with a new VDS housing and possible new bow sonar, an installation that probably duplicates that in the two Modified Krivak-I-class frigates. All can carry 2,000 rounds of 76.2-mm ammunition, and the two mine rails can accommodate 12 KSM, 14 KRAB, or 16 IGDM-500 mines.

CORVETTES [FFL]

Note: Most of the Russian "corvette" classes are under the normal 1,000-ton full-load displacement figure differentiating patrol combatants [PG] from corvettes [FFL]. They are nonetheless retained here in the corvette category by convention, as their displacements had originally been considerably overestimated by NATO intelligence agencies.

♦ 12 Parchim-II class (East German Project 133.1M)

Bldr: VEB Peenewerft, Wolgast, Germany

	Laid down	L	In serv.
247 MPK-192	26-2-85	29-8-85	11-4-86
311 MPK-205 Kazanets	4-1-85	28-12-85	11-4-86
301 MPK-67	28-3-85	19-4-86	30-6-87
308 MPK-99	25-6-85	12-8-86	28-12-87
245 MPK-105	30-12-85	20-11-86	16-3-88
222 MPK-213	8-4-86	28-2-87	29-7-88
258 MPK-216	22-6-86	25-6-87	30-9-88
209 MPK-219	7-11-86	30-9-87	23-12-88
218 MPK-224	28-2-87	30-3-88	31-3-89
233 MPK-227	2-9-87	16-8-88	20-2-89
244 MPK-228 Bashkortostan	20-11-87	31-10-88	20-2-89
255 MPK-229 Kalmykiya	23-2-88	30-1-89	20-2-89

MPK-67 (301) — Boris Lemachko, 6-00

MPK-67 (301) — Boris Lemachko, 6-00

CORVETTES [FFL] *(continued)*

MPK-105 (245) Jaroslaw Cislak, 7-01

D: 790 tons light; 865 tons normal (935 fl) **S:** 24.5 kts
Dim: 75.20 (69.00 pp) × 9.78 (8.50 wl) × 2.80 (hull; 4.55 max.)
A: 1 76.2-mm 59-cal. AK-176 DP; 1 30-mm AK-630 gatling AA; 2 4-round Strela-3 (SA-N-8) SAM syst. (24 Gremlin missiles); 2 twin 533-mm TT; 2 12-round RBU-6000 ASW RL (96 RGB-60 rockets); 2 d.c. racks (12 d.c. tot.); 2 mine rails
Electronics:
Radar: 1 Mius (Spin Trough) nav.; 1 MR-352 Pozitiv (Cross Dome) air search; 1 MR-123 Vympel (Bass Tilt) gun f.c.
Sonar: MGK-335MC (Bull Horn) hull-mounted (3 kHz); Ros'-K HF dipping
EW: Vympel-R2 suite: 2 Bizan'-4 (Watch Dog) intercept (2–18 GHz); 2 16-round PK-16 fixed decoy RL
M: 3 Type M-504A-3 diesels; 3 props (centerline only: CP); 14,250 bhp
Electric: 900 kw tot. (1 × 500-kw, 2 × 200-kw diesel sets)
Range: 1,200/20; 2,200/12 **Endurance:** 10 days **Crew:** 9 officers, 71 enlisted

Remarks: Type designation: MPK (*Malyy Protivolodochnyy Korabl',* Small Antisubmarine Ship). An improved version of the former East German Navy's *Parchim* class (all of whose members are now in the Indonesian Navy), with later armament, a more powerful sonar, and a new 75-n.m.-range MR-352 Pozitiv radar. As this design was inferior in most respects to the contemporary Grisha-V, its acquisition may have been a form of aid to the East German shipbuilding industry. Commenced refitting in order of construction during 9-94 at the building yard in Germany, with all completed by 10-95. All are in the Baltic Fleet. MPK-229 was named during 12-96 under an agreement whereby the Kalmyk Republic would provide financial assistance and draftees to the Baltic Fleet. MPK-205 was named on 10-2-98. MPK-228 was damaged by fire during 1999 but has been repaired. The three ships with 300-series pennant numbers are based at Kronshtadt, while the others are based at Baltiysk.
Hull systems: Due to engine cooling problems, these ships can only operate for 30 minutes at speeds between 8 and 12 kts.
Combat systems: The dipping sonar deploys through the forwardmost of the two doors on the starboard side of the main deck superstructure. The d.c. racks exit through ports in the stern. The ASW weapons-control system name is Drakon. The first 10 did not initially carry the antenna for the MR-352 radar within the large masthead radome due to developmental problems; the antenna was later backfitted.

♦ 23 Grisha-V class (Projects 1124MEh, 1124MU, and 1124.4)

Bldrs: A: Leninskaya Kuznitsa SY No. 302, Kiev; B: Zelenodol'sk Zavod No. 340, Kazan; C: Khabarovsk SY No. 368, Khabarovsk

	Bldr	Laid down	L	In serv.	Fleet
064 MPK-134 Muromets (ex-*Kievskiy Komsomolets,* ex-MPK-64)	A	5-80	5-82	10-12-82	Black Sea
071 MPK-118 Suzdalets (ex-*Komsomolets Moldaviy*)	A	1-8-81	27-3-83	30-10-83	Black Sea
129 MPK-139	A	8-4-82	18-2-84	2-8-84	Northern
055 MPK-199 (ex-*Komsomolets Armenii*)	A	20-2-84	7-12-85	7-10-86	Black Sea
171 MPK-113	A	2-11-85	31-7-87	5-8-88	Northern
053 MPK-207	A	12-6-86	6-5-88	3-4-89	Black Sea
054 MKP-217 Eysk	A	16-3-87	12-4-89	26-12-89	Black Sea
. . . MPK-125	A	20-8-87	30-3-90	29-9-90	Pacific
375 MPK-82	A	20-4-89	20-4-91	26-9-91	Pacific
250 MPK-194 Brest (ex-*Brestkiy Komsomolets*)	B	11-5-87	30-7-88	27-9-88	Northern
. . . MPK-196	B	11-5-87	30-7-88	30-12-88	Northern
106 MPK-197	B	27-10-87	8-4-89	25-10-89	Northern
187 MPK-203 Yunga	B	26-3-88	19-7-89	28-12-89	Northern
138 MPK-130 (ex-*Arkhangelskiy Komsomolets*)	B	17-8-88	9-3-90	28-9-90	Northern
. . . MPK-56	B	12-4-89	30-6-90	29-12-90	Northern
. . . MKP-10	B	19-3-90	27-7-91	28-12-91	Northern
108 MPK-14 Monchegorsk	B	27-3-91	6-6-92	31-5-93	Northern
196 MPK-59	B	20-11-90	22-5-93	12-8-94	Northern
390 MPK-222	C	7-1-87	27-4-89	20-12-89	Pacific
396 MPK-28	C	2-9-87	9-9-89	27-12-89	Pacific
332 MPK-107 (ex-*Irkutskiy Komsomolets*)	C	22-2-88	5-6-90	14-12-90	Pacific
323 MPK-64	C	4-1-88	2-10-90	31-12-90	Pacific
362 MPK-17	C	22-1-90	28-8-91	30-12-91	Pacific

D: 876–930 tons std. (1,030–1,070 fl)
S: 32 kts (21 on gas turbine; 16 on diesels)
Dim: 71.20 (66.90 wl) × 10.15 (9.50 wl) × 3.54–3.72 (hull)
A: 1 twin-rail Osa-M (SA-N-4) SAM system (20 9M-33/Gecko missiles); 1 76.2-mm 59-cal. AK-176 DP (304 rounds); 1 30-mm 54-cal. AK-630M gatling AA (3,000 rounds); 2 shoulder-launched Strela-3 (SA-N-8) SAM positions (20–24 Gremlin shoulder-launched missiles); 2 twin 533-mm TT; 1 12-round RBU-6000 ASW RL (48 RGB-60 rockets; see remarks); 2 d.c. racks (6 d.c. each) or up to 18 mines

MPK-134 Muromets (064)—an early Grisha-V with MR-320 Topaz-M search radar
Boris Lemachko, 2000

MPK-17 (362)—the newest Grisha-V, with MR-755 Fregat-M2 search radar
Boris Lemachko, 2000

MPK-107 (332)—exercising with Japanese naval ships
JMSDF, via *Ships of the World,* 9-00

Electronics:
Radar: 1 MR-312 Nayada nav.; 1 MR-320 Topaz-M (Strut Pair) (late units: MR-755 Fregat-M2/Half Plate-B) surf./air search; 1 MPZ-301 Baza (Pop Group) SA-N-4 f.c.; 1 MR-123 Vympel (Bass Tilt) gun f.c.
Sonar: MGK-335MC Platina (Bull Horn) hull-mounted (3 kHz); Shelon' (Elk Tail) dipping (7.5 kHz)
EW: 2 Bizan'-4B (Watch Dog) intercept (2–18 GHz); 2 16-round PK-16 fixed decoy RL—some also: 4 10-round PK-10 fixed decoy RL
E/O: some: 4 Spektr-F (Half Cup) infrared detectors
M: CODAG: 1 M-8M gas turbine (18,000 shp), 2 Type M-507A diesels (10,000 bhp each); 3 props; 38,000 hp—2 maneuvering propellers
Electric: 1,000 kw tot. (1 × 500-kw, 1 × 300-kw, 1 × 200-kw diesel sets)
Range: 950/27; on diesels alone: 2,500/14; 4,000/10 **Fuel:** 143 tons
Endurance: 9 days **Crew:** 9 officers, 77 enlisted

Remarks: Type designation: MPK (*Malyy Protivolodochnyy Korabl',* Small Antisubmarine Ship). Sister *Stelyak* was built for the Federal Border Guard. MPK-194 was named *Brest* during 7-00. MPK-217 was named on 9-9-99, MPK-203 on 2-2-90, and MPK-14 on 17-8-99. One as-yet unidentified Northern Fleet unit was named *Yekatarinskiy Gavan* during 7-00.
Disposals: Northern Fleet units MPK-69, MPK-142, MPK-190, MPK-198, and MPK-202 were stricken 16-3-98; Pacific Fleet unit MPK-89 on 17-7-97, and MPK-20 on 20-8-92 while building at Khabarovsk. *Lutsk* was transferred to Ukraine 12-2-94 while building at Kiev.
Hull systems: There are two drop-down harbor maneuvering propulsors at the extreme stern, as in the now-stricken Petya class (Project 159 series). Carry 10.5 tons of lube oil and 27.2 tons of fresh water. Maximum propeller rpm is 585 on the diesels.
Combat systems: This final production variant of the basic Grisha design substituted the MR-320M Topaz-M (Strut Pair) radar for MR-302 Rubka (Strut Curve) and a 76.2-mm gun for the twin 57-mm mount, with one RBU-6000 ASW RL removed as weight compensation (the surviving mount is carried in the port position). Beginning in the late 1980s, the MR-755 Fregat-M2 (Half Plate-B) radar (whose antenna consists of one half of the back-to-back Top Plate 3-D radar) was substituted for MR-320M on new-construction units.

Two launch positions for shoulder-fired point-defense SAMs have been added at the break of the 01 level superstructure, just forward of the stack. Just abaft the mast is a manned SP-521 Rakurs (Kolonka-2) backup ringsight director for the 30-mm gun. The ships can carry 550 rounds of 76-mm and 2,000 rounds of 30-mm ammunition. The torpedo tubes have been modified to launch wire-guided torpedoes. The dipping sonar is housed in the after superstructure, lowering through the hull between the starboard and centerline propeller shafts. The d.c. racks are mounted atop the mine rails and must be removed to carry mines (which is rarely—if ever—done).

CORVETTES [FFL] *(continued)*

♦ **4 Grisha-III class (Projects 1124M and 1124MP)** (1 in *reserve*)
Bldrs: A: Khabarovsk SY No. 368, Khabarovsk; B: Leninskaya Kuznitsa SY No. 302, Kiev; C: Zelenodol'sk Zavod No. 340, Kazan

	Bldr	Laid down	L	In serv.	Fleet
314 MPK-178	A	30-11-82	8-5-84	21-12-84	Pacific
369 MPK-191	A	30-11-82	7-5-85	21-12-85	Pacific
078 *MPK-127* (ex-*Komsomolets Gruziy*)	B	16-9-74	10-7-76	27-12-76	Black Sea
059 MPK-49	C	23-3-80	14-2-82	31-8-82	Black Sea

MPK-49 (059)—note the 57-mm mount aft, distinguishing the Grisha-III variant from the Grisha-V   Boris Lemachko, 7-00

MPK-178 (314)   Boris Lemachko, 8-99

D: 860 tons light; 954 tons normal (990 fl)
S: 34 kts (21 on gas turbine alone; 16 on diesels)
Dim: 71.20 (66.90 wl) × 10.15 (9.50 wl) × 3.40 (hull)
A: 1 twin-rail Osa-M (SA-N-4) SAM syst. (20 9M-33/Gecko missiles); 1 twin 57-mm AK-725 DP (1,100 rounds); 1 30-mm 54-cal. AK-630M gatling AA (2,000 rounds); 2 12-round RBU-6000 ASW RL (96 RGB-60 rockets); 2 twin 533-mm TT; 2 d.c. racks (12 d.c.) or up to 18 mines
Electronics:
Radar: 1 Don-2 nav.; 1 MR-302 Rubka (Strut Curve) surf./air search; 1 MPZ-301 Baza (Pop Group) SA-N-4 f.c.; 1 MR-123 Vympel (Bass Tilt) gun f.c.
Sonar: MGK-335M Argun' (Bull Nose) hull-mounted MF; Shelon' (Elk Tail) MF through-hull dipping
EW: 2 Bizan'-4B (Watch Dog) intercept (2–18 GHz)
M: CODAG: 1 M-8M gas turbine (18,000 shp), 2 Type M-507A diesels (10,000 bhp each); 3 props; 38,000 hp—2 maneuvering propellers
Electric: 1,000 kw (1 × 500-kw, 1 × 300-kw, 1 × 200-kw diesel sets)
Range: 950/27; on diesels alone: 2,750/14; 4,000/10
Fuel: 130 tons + 13 tons overload **Endurance:** 9 days
Crew: 9 officers, 74 enlisted

Remarks: Russian type: MPK (*Malyy Protivolodochnyy Korabl',* Small Antisubmarine Ship). Survivors of 22 built for the Soviet Navy. Although considered to be in commission, MPK-127 had only a seven-man cadre crew and was laid up at Tuapse as of 2001. Sisters *Bezuprechniy, Zorkiy,* and *Smelyy* are in service with the Federal Border Guard in the Pacific area.
Disposals: Pacific Fleet units: MPK-81 was stricken 11-2-94, MPK-122 and MPK-155 on 5-7-94, MPK-143 and MPK-4 on 17-7-97, MPK-37 and MPK-145 on 4-8-95, MPK-170 on 31-7-96, and MPK-101 (ex-*Zaporozhkiy Komsomolets*) on 16-3-98. Northern Fleet: MPK-138 was stricken 3-7-92, MPK-40 on 25-1-94, and MPK-141 and MPK-152 on 5-7-94. Baltic Fleet: MPK-44 (ex-*Komsomolets Latvii*) and MPK-108 were stricken 28-4-93 and transferred to Lithuania. Black Sea Fleet: MPK-6 was stricken 16-3-98 and scrapped at Inkerman beginning 9-12-98.
Hull systems: Have retractable fin stabilizers. Said to consume 450 kg of fuel per hour at 14 kts on diesel propulsion. Maximum propeller rpm is 585 on the diesels.
Combat systems: The MR-123 Vympel (Bass Tilt) fire-control radar, which is atop a small deckhouse to port on the aft superstructure, was substituted for the MR-103 Bars (Muff Cob) fire-control radar fitted in earlier variants of the Grisha series, while a gatling gun was mounted in the space occupied by MR-103 in the Grisha-I and -II. Some may have two Strela-3 (SA-N-8) SAM launch positions, as on the Grisha-V. Can carry 1,000 rounds of 57-mm and 2,000 rounds of 30-mm gun ammunition. The d.c. racks are mounted atop the mine rails and must be removed to carry mines (which is rarely—if ever—done).

Note: All Grisha-II-class units are assigned to the Federal Border Guard and are described in that section.

Disposal note: The sole Grisha-IV-class (Project 1124K) unit, MPK-104, was stricken from the Black Sea Fleet 16-3-98. The last two of 15 Grisha-I (Albatros)-class units, MPK-33 and MPK-31, were stricken 7-2-95.

GUIDED-MISSILE PATROL COMBATANTS (AIR-CUSHION) [PGGA]

♦ **2 Dergach (Sivuch)-class (Project 1239) surface-effect ships**
Bldr: Zelenodol'sk Zavod, Kazan

	In serv.	Fleet
615 MRK-27 Bora ("Wind")	12-5-97	Black Sea
575 MRK-17 Samum ("Fiery Wind")	26-2-00	Baltic

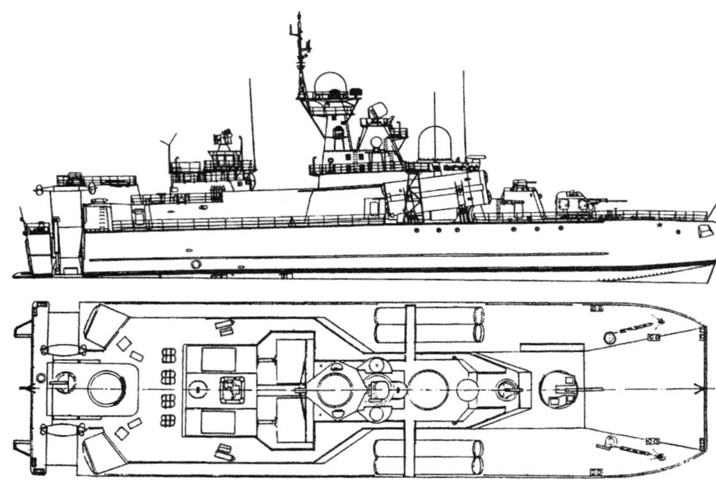
Dergach class (Project 1239)   Rozvoorouzhenie, 1995

MRK-27 Bora (615)—in black-and-gray-toned camouflage   Hartmut Ehlers, 7-00

MRK-17 Samum (575)—in gray paint, with stern area painted black to cover exhaust staining   Boris Lemachko, 7-00

D: 850 tons light; 910 tons std. (1,050 fl) **S:** 53 kts (45 sust.; 20 hullborne)
Dim: 65.60 (63.90 hull) × 17.20 × 3.05 (1.70 on cushion)
A: 8 P-270 Moskit (SS-N-22 Sunburn) SSM (2 quadruple KT-190 launchers); 1 twin-rail Osa-MA 1 (SA-N-4) SAM syst. (20 9M-33M/Gecko missiles); 1 76.2-mm 59-cal. AK-176M DP (345 rounds); 2 single 30-mm 54-cal. AK-630 gatling AA (6,000 rounds)
Electronics:
Radar: 1 SRN-207 Ekran (Curl Stone-B) nav.; 1 MR-352 Pozitiv (Cross Dome) surf./air search; 1 Monolit-M (Band Stand) active/passive surf. target detection, tracking, and targeting; 1 MPZ-301 Baza (Pop Group) SA-N-4 f.c.; 1 MR-123-1 Vympel-AM (Bass Tilt) gun f.c.
EW: Vympel-R2 suite: 2 MRP-11/12M intercept; 2 MP-405 intercept; 1 Rumb MFD/F; 2 10-round PK-10 fixed decoy RL; 2 16-round PK-16 decoy RL
M: CODOG M-10 plant: 2 M-10-1 gas turbines for propulsion (20,000 shp each); 2 Zvezda M-511A diesels (10,000 bhp each) for hullborne operations; 2 Zvezda M-504 diesels (rated at 3,300 bhp each) for lift fans; 2 4-bladed tandem props (on Z-drive pylons) for on-cushion propulsion, 2 4-bladed props for hullborne propulsion
Electric: 800 kw tot. (4 × 200-kw diesel sets)
Range: 800/45 on cushion; 2,500/12 hullborne
Endurance: 10 days **Crew:** 9 officers, 59 enlisted

GUIDED-MISSILE PATROL COMBATANTS (AIR-CUSHION) [PGGA] *(continued)*

Aboard the Samum (575)—the decks are painted light green
Boris Lemachko, 7-00

Remarks: Project nickname is Sivuch ("Beaver"). Chief designer was L. V. El'skiy of the Almaz Design Bureau, succeeded by Valery I. Korolkov. A programmed third unit was canceled. Intended for 15-year service lives, the ships are said to be expensive to operate, mechanically unreliable, and plagued by vibration at high speeds. Both were named on 18-3-92. Program authorized 24-12-80. MRK-27 was delivered 30-12-89 but not accepted for operational service until 1997; the ship is homeported at Sevastopol'. MRK-17, launched 12-10-92, was delivered to the Baltic Fleet 31-12-95 but remained uncommissioned for more than four years. On 26-1-01, it was announced that MRK-17 might be returned to the Black Sea Fleet. During a 2-01 visit to the building yard, the Russian Navy C-in-C hinted that more ships of the class might be built.
Hull systems: Rigid sidewall–type surface-effect ships, the largest ever built, with semirigid bow and stern seals that did not need replacement during the mere 1,250 hours the *Bora* operated 1989–2000. Have an aluminum-magnesium alloy hull. The propellers are mounted in tandem at the end of struts that can be swung completely out of the water; there are diesel-powered hull-mounted propellers for harbor maneuvering. One set of propulsion engines must be stopped before the other can be engaged. The M-511A is a twin variant of the M-504 radial diesel. Using the cushion pressurization engines alone, the air exhausting from the stern can produce speeds of 3 kts for local maneuvering. The commanding officer has a BCh-5 automated shipboard equipment monitoring display console.
Combat systems: The ships have a Monolit-M (Band Stand) radome and two Pricep (Light Bulb) datalink radomes, equipment associated with the Moskit supersonic, sea-skimming missile system; Monolit can operate in either active or passive intercept mode. All eight antiship missiles can be salvoed within 35 seconds. The control system for the Osa-M SAM system has also been referred to as the 4R-33A. The Vympel radar director can control the 76-mm and/or 30-mm guns simultaneously against a single target; there are two manned SP-521 Rakurs (Kolonka-2) ringsight backup directors for the gatling guns. The communications suite is named Buran-7.

Disposal note: Of the two Utka (Lun')-class (Project 903) wing-in-ground-effect craft, the missile-armed unit, MD-160, was no longer in service as of 1999, while the search-and-rescue-configured *Spasatel'* had not been completed and has probably been abandoned.

GUIDED-MISSILE PATROL COMBATANTS [PGG]

Note: Tarantul-class variants are listed under Guided-Missile Patrol Craft [PTG], as all but one variant built to date displace less than 500 tons full load.

♦ 17 Nanuchka-III and -IV* class (Project 1234.1 and 1234.7*)
(2 in *reserve*)
Bldrs: Sudostroitel'noye Obyedineniye "Almaz," Petrovskiy SY, St. Petersburg; Vladivostokskiy Sudostroitel'nyy Zavod (Ulis),Vladivostok

	Laid down	L	In serv.	Fleet
512 Aysberg ("Iceberg")	11-11-76	20-4-79	1-12-79	Northern
566 Burun ("Front")	1975	1977	17-2-78	Baltic
555 Geyzer ("Geyser")	21-12-87	28-8-89	28-2-90	Baltic
551 Liven' ("Downpour")	28-9-88	8-5-91	11-2-92	Baltic
590 Meteor ("Meteor")	13-11-84	16-9-87	19-2-88	Baltic
617 Mirazh ("Mirage")	30-8-83	19-8-86	24-2-87	Black
409 Moroz ("Frost")	17-2-85	23-9-89	28-2-90	Pacific
526 Nakat* ("Counter-recoil")	4-11-82	16-4-87	30-12-87	Northern
570 Passat ("Tradewind")	27-5-88	13-6-90	14-3-91	Baltic
562 Priliv ("Tide Surge")	29-4-82	26-4-85	7-1-86	Baltic
520 Rassvet ("Dawn")	29-9-86	22-8-88	1-3-89	Northern
450 *Razliv* ("Flooding")	1-11-86	24-8-91	11-2-92	Pacific
620 Shtil' ("Stiletto") (ex-*Komsomolets Mordovii*, ex-*Zyb'*)	28-6-76	23-10-78	16-2-79	Black
423 *Smerch* ("Waterspout")	16-11-81	16-11-84	4-3-85	Pacific
533 Tucha ("Stormcloud")	4-5-77	29-4-80	24-10-80	Northern
505 Urugan ("Hurricane")	1-8-80	27-5-83	15-12-83	Northern
. . . Zyb' ("Long Swells")	26-8-86	28-2-89	31-10-89	Baltic

Meteor (590)—in the Nanuchka-III class, the large radome for the Titanit targeting sensor is mounted atop the pilothouse
Jaroslaw Cislak, 7-01

Urugan (505)—with antiship missile tube doors open
Siegfried Breyer Collection, 2000

Nakat (526)—the Nanuchka-IV-class (Project 1234.7) trials ship, with the Osa-M SAM launcher in raised position; note the sextuple rack for cruise missiles abreast the bridge
Boris Lemachko, 7-96

D: 610 tons light; 639 tons std. (730 fl; 790 max.) **S:** 34 kts
Dim: 59.30 (54.85 wl) × 11.80 (8.86 wl) × 3.08 (normal)
A: 6 P-120 Malakhit (SS-N-9 Siren) SSM (2 triple KT-84 launchers); 1 twin-rail Osa-M (SA-N-4B) SAM syst. (20 9M-33M5/Gecko missiles); 1 76.2-mm 59-cal. AK-176 DP (304 rounds); 1 30-mm 65-cal. AK-630 gatling AA (3,000 rounds)
Electronics:
Radar: 1 or 2 MR-312 Nayada nav. (not in all); 1 Dubrava (Peel Pair) nav./surf. search (not in all); 1 Titanit (Band Stand) target desig.; 1 MPZ-301 Baza (Pop Group) SAM f.c.; 1 MR-123 Vympel (Bass Tilt) gun f.c.
EW: Vympel-R2 suite: 2 Half Hat-B intercept; 2 Foot Ball-A intercept; 2 16-round PK-16 decoy RL; 4 10-round PK-10 decoy RL
M: 3 M-521 diesels; 3 props; 30,000 shp
Electric: 700 kw tot. (2 × 300-kw, 1 × 100-kw diesel sets)
Range: 415/34; 2,100/18; 3,500/12 (1 engine)
Fuel: 132 tons **Endurance:** 10 days
Crew: 7 officers, 42 enlisted (accomm. for 10 officers, 55 enlisted)

Remarks: Type designation: MRK (*Malyy Raketnyy Korabl',* Small Missile Ship). *Burun,* the first built, was commissioned 17-2-78. One Northern Fleet unit, *Nakat,* sometimes referred to as the Nanuchka-IV (Project 1234.7), was modified while under construction with two sextuple racks for P-800 Oniks (SS-NX-26 Sapless/Yakhont) antiship missiles in place of the SS-N-9 SSM. *Moroz* acted as host to Japanese ships visiting Petropavlovsk-na-Kamchatka during 9-00.
Disposals: Black Sea Fleet unit *Mirazh* was not transferred to Ukraine in 1997 as reported in the last edition. Pacific Fleet unit *Purga,* Northern Fleet unit *Priboi,* and Black Sea Fleet unit *Iney* (ex-*XX Syezd V.L.K.S.M.*) had been stricken by late 1998. A unit named *Perekat,* laid down in 1988, was broken up in 1992. Northern Fleet unit *Veter* was stricken 4-8-95. The hull of another (to have been named *Koreyets*) was broken up before completion on the ways at the Petrovskiy facility in 1991.
Combat systems: The single 76.2-mm DP was substituted for the Nanuchka-II's twin 57-mm AA aft, the gatling gun is in the position occupied by Muff Cob in the Nanuchka-I, and Bass Tilt is situated atop a new deckhouse abaft the mast. The 30-mm gatling gun is off centerline to starboard. Two Fish Bowl or Pricep (Light Bulb) radomes on the mast are believed to house SS-N-9 missile datalink antennas. Intercept arrays vary considerably: early units had a Peel Pair target-designation and tracking radar atop the mast, while later units lack the Peel Pair, add two Light Bulb missile datalink antenna radomes on the sides of the mast, and have one or two MR-312 Nayada navigational radars. Late units also had four 10-round PK-10 fixed decoy rocket launchers in addition to the two 16-round launchers.

GUIDED-MISSILE PATROL COMBATANTS [PGG] *(continued)*

♦ 2 Nanuchka-I (Ovod) class (Project 1234)
Bldr: Sudostroitel'noye Obyedineniye "Almaz," Petrovskiy SY, St. Petersburg

	Laid down	L	In serv.	Fleet
595 Molniya	30-9-71	27-8-73	7-2-74	Baltic
621 Zarnitsa	27-7-70	28-4-73	26-10-73	Black Sea

Zarnitsa (621)—the surviving Black Sea Fleet Nanuchka-I; note the 57-mm gunmount aft and the large radome for the Titanit targeting sensor mounted abaft the pilothouse Hartmut Ehlers, 7-00

D: 610 tons light; 639 tons std. (700 fl; 760 max.) **S:** 35 kts
Dim: 59.30 (54.00 wl) × 11.80 (8.86 wl) × 3.02 (normal)
A: 6 P-120 Malakhit (SS-N-9 Siren) SSM (2 triple KT-84 launchers); 1 twin-rail Osa-M (SA-N-4) SAM syst. (20 4K-33/Gecko missiles); 1 twin 57-mm 70-cal. AK-725 DP (1,100 rounds)
Electronics:
Radar: 1 Dubrava (Peel Pair) nav./surf. search; 1 Titanit (Band Stand) missile target desig.; 1 MPZ-301 Baza (Pop Group) SA-N-4 f.c.; 1 MR-103 Bars (Muff Cob) gun f.c.
EW: Zaliv suite: 4 . . . intercept; 2 16-round PK-16 decoy RL
M: 3 M-507A diesels; 3 props; 30,000 bhp
Electric: 750 kw tot. (2 × 300-kw, 2 × 75-kw diesel sets)
Range: 900/30; 2,500/12 (1 engine) **Fuel:** 132 tons **Endurance:** 10 days
Crew: 7–10 officers, 42–50 enlisted

Remarks: Survivors of a class of 17. Design approved 17-8-65. Type designation: MRK (*Malyy Raketnyy Korabl',* Small Missile Ship). *Zarnitsa* is assigned to the 166th Novorossiysk Red Banner Small Rocket Ship Division of the 41st Fast Rocket Craft Brigade.
Disposals: Pacific Fleet unit *Musson* sank 16-4-87 after being hit by a target drone; 39 were killed. Black Sea Fleet unit (and class prototype) *Burya* was stricken 24-6-91. Also stricken have been Pacific Fleet unit *Briz* and Black Sea Fleet unit *Groza* on 3-7-92; *Bora* and *Grom* on 5-7-94; *Volna* and *Zarya* on 31-7-96; Baltic Fleet sisters *Grad, Raduga, Shkval,* and *Shtorm* on 5-7-94, 10-12-95, 1-9-95, and 16-3-98, respectively; Pacific Fleet units *Vikhr* on 5-7-94, *Tsiklon* on 17-11-94, and *Tayfun* on 1-9-95; and Northern Fleet unit *Metel'* on 16-3-98.
Hull systems: Are reported to be very bad seaboats, with pronounced heaving motion, but are nonetheless claimed to be operable in seas up to State 5 (State 4 for weapons operations). Engines are reported to be unreliable.
Combat systems: In this class, the Band Stand radome contains the antenna for the Titanit SSM target-designation system. The communications system can maintain seven circuits simultaneously.

GUIDED-MISSILE PATROL CRAFT [PTG]

♦ 0 (+ . . .) Katran class (Project 20970)
Bldr: . . .

D: 284 tons (fl) **S:** 35 kts **Dim:** 46.1 × 8.2 × 2.0
A: 8 Kh-35 Uran-E (3M-24E) antiship missiles; 1 Kashtan CIWS (2 30-mm GSH-6-30L gatling AA and 32 9M-311 Vikhr'-K missiles); 2 single 30-mm 54-cal. AK-630M gatling AA
Electronics:
Radar: . . . nav.; 1 Pozitiv-E1.1 (Type 3C-25E) target detection and tracking
EW: . . .
M: 3 M-520 diesels; 3 props; 14,400 bhp
Electric: . . .
Range: 2,200/14 **Endurance:** . . . days **Crew:** . . .

Remarks: Offered for export in 10-00 as a replacement for the 1950s-design Project 205 Osa series. Would employ hull and superstructure shaping to reduce radar reflectivity. The Almaz design bureau foresees sales of perhaps 150 units to former Project 205 customers. A prototype may be laid down in 2002 or 2003. The AK-630M mounting will also carry two launch rails for point-defense or anti-smallcraft missiles.

♦ 0 (+ 1 + . . .) Skorpion class (Project 12300)
Bldr: Vympel Zavod, Rybinsk

D: 470 tons (fl) **S:** 40 kts **Dim:** 56.8 × 10.3 (10.8 over walkways) × . . .
A: 4 P-800 Oniks (SS-NX-26 Sapless) SSM; 1 76.2-mm 59-cal. AK-176 DP; 2 Kashtan CIWS (2 30-mm GSH-6-30L gatling AA and 32 9M-311 Vikhr'-K/SA-N-11 Grison missiles each; 6,000 total rounds 30-mm)
Electronics:
Radar: 1 Pozitiv-ME1.1 search radar; 1 Monument-E1 surface target tracking and datalink; 1 Puma-E gun f.c.
Sonar: Anapa hull-mounted
EW: . . . intercept; 4 10-round PK-10 decoy RL

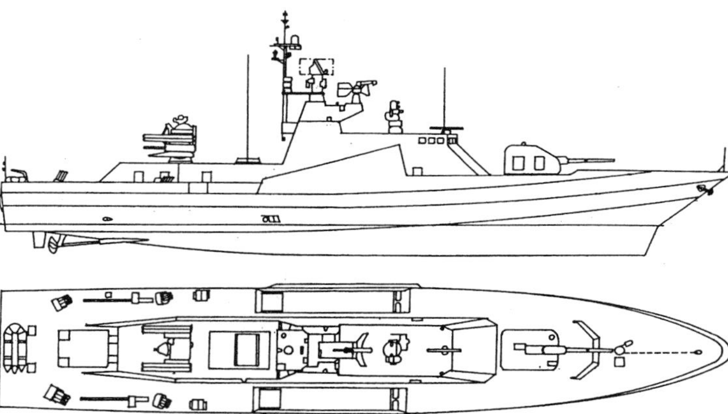

Skorpion (Project 12300) design concept *Voenniy Parad,* 1-00

M: CODAG: 1 M-70FR gas turbine (16,000 shp), 2 MTU 16V4000 M-90 diesels; 3 props; 20,900 hp max.
Range: 1,500 (2,200 with overload fuel)/12 **Endurance:** 10 days
Crew: 37 tot.

Remarks: A "stealth" design by the Central Maritime Design Office. A privately funded prototype was laid down 5-6-01, with the craft to be ready for trials by 2005. Also offered is the Project 12301 variant with Kh-35 Uran antiship missiles, and Project 12301P for potential Russian Federal Border Guard purchase. The price is said to be about $35 million per boat, and the builder hopes to sell 10 to the Russian Navy, 10 to the Federal Border Guard, and 28 abroad.
Combat systems: Will have vertical launchers for the SSMs. The Sigma combat system, Gorizont-25 integrated navigational system, and Buran-6E automatic communications suite will be fitted.

♦ 1 (+ . . .) Tarantul-IV class (Project 12421)
Bldr: Vympel Zavod, Rybinsk (In serv. 26-2-00)

. . . R-5

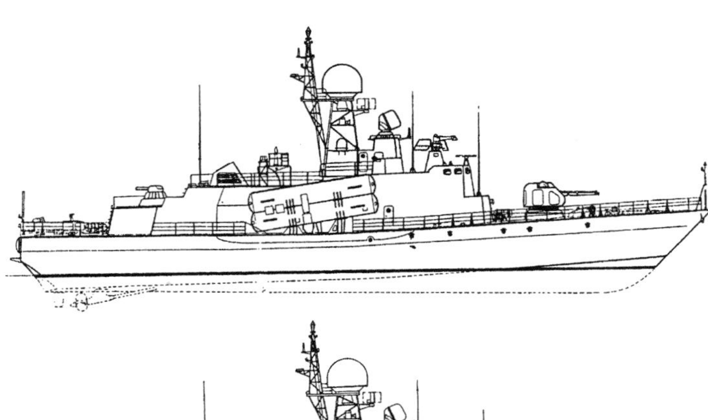

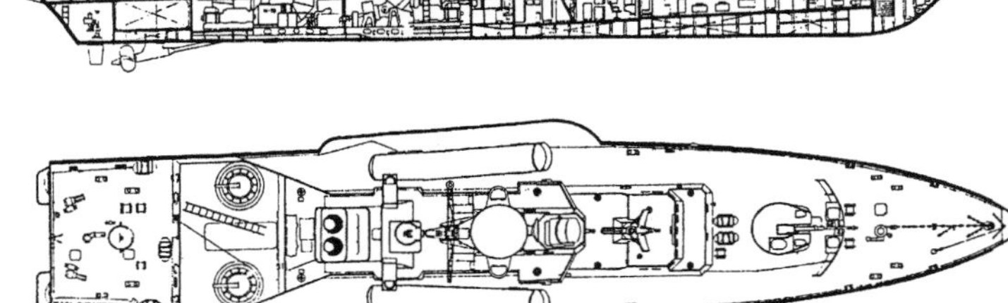

R-5—the Tarantul-IV (Project 12421) Rozvoorouzhenie, 1995

D: 450 tons (550 fl) **S:** 38 kts (35 sust.)
Dim: 56.9 × 13.00 (max.; 8.75 wl) × 2.65 (hull; 4.51 props)
A: 4 P-270 Moskit (SS-N-22 Sunburn) SSM; 1 76.2-mm 59-cal. AK-176 DP; 1 4-round Fasta-4M (SA-N-8) SAM syst. (12 Igla-M/Gremlin missiles); 2 single 30-mm 54-cal. AK-630M gatling AA
Electronics:
Radar: 1 Kivach-3 nav.; 1 MR-352 Pozitiv surf./air search; 1 Garpun-Bal target detection/desig.; 1 MR-123-02 Vympel (Bass Tilt) gun f.c.
EW: 2 Half Hat-B intercept; 2 Foot Ball-A intercept; 2 10-round PK-10 decoy RL
M: 2 gas turbines (16,000 shp each); 2 props; 32,000 shp
Electric: 455 kw tot (2 × 180-kw, 1 × 95-kw, 380-V, 50-Hz diesel sets)
Range: 1,700/. . .; 2,400/12–13 **Crew:** 44 tot.

Remarks: Prototype of the latest export offering in the basic Tarantul series, with addition of MR-352 Pozitiv surface- and air-search radar set and the elimination of the cruise diesels. Launched in 9-97. May be owned by the Almaz design bureau as

GUIDED-MISSILE PATROL CRAFT [PTG] *(continued)*

an export demonstrator rather than the Russian Navy itself, although it was said to have been assigned to the Baltic Fleet as of 5-00. No further units have been ordered. Missile-firing trials were to begin during 10-99. Although *Molnaya* ("Lightning") has been given as the actual name for the craft, it may be a reference to the overall project name, which is also Molnaya. The same basic design is offered with 16 Kh-35 Uran (SS-N-25) antiship missiles as Project 12418.
Hull systems: Maximum speed listed is achievable in 15° C air temperature.
Combat systems: The Garpun-Bal radar system can track 15 targets simultaneously and can also be used in passive mode to track and target emitting platforms.

♦ 20 Tarantul-III (Molnaya-M) class (Project 1241.1RZ)

Bldrs: Sudostroitel'noye Obyedineniye "Almaz," Petrovskiy SY, St. Petersburg, and Sredniy Neva SY, Kolpino; Vladivostokskiy Sudostroitel'nyy Zavod (Ulis), Vladivostok

	In serv.		In serv.
940 R-11	9-91	953 R-239	1989
924 R-14	12-91	832 R-240	1988
937 R-18	9-92	943 R-261	1988
978 R-19	12-92	909 R-271	1989
921 R-20	12-93	825 R-291	1991
946 R-24	1994	874 R-293	1992
819 R-47 (ex-*Tamborvskiy Komsomolets*)	1987	951 R-297	1990
		971 R-298	1990
955 R-60	1987	954 R-334 IVANOVETS	12-89
952 R-109	1990	907 R-442	12-89
814 R-187	1989		

R-239 (953)—at Sevastopol' Boris Lemachko, 2000

R-298 (971)—at Vladivostok Boris Lemachko, 2000

R-240 (832) Jaroslaw Cislak, 7-01

D: 436 tons light (493 fl) **S:** 38 kts (41 light)
Dim: 56.10 (49.50 pp) × 10.20 (8.74 wl) × 2.47 (hull; 4.33 props)
A: 4 P-270 Moskit (SS-N-22 Sunburn) SSM (3M-80 missiles); 1 76-mm 59-cal. AK-176 DP (152 rounds); 1 4-round Fasta-4M (SA-N-8) SAM syst. (16 9M-36 Strela-3M/Gremlin missiles); 2 single 30-mm 54-cal. AK-630M gatling AA (4,000 rounds)
Electronics:
Radar: 1 Kivach-3 nav.; 1 Mineral (Band Stand) missile target detection/desig.; 1 MR-123-02 Vympel (Bass Tilt) gun f.c.
EW: MP 405-1 Vympel-R2 suite: 2 Half Hat-B intercept; 2 Foot Ball-A intercept; 2 16-round PK-16 decoy RL; 2 or 4 10-round PK-10 decoy RL
M: CODAG: 2 M-70 (PR-76) gas turbines (12,000 shp each), 2 Type M-510 diesels (5,000 bhp each; 4,000 sust.); 2 props; 34,000 hp max.
Electric: 500 kw tot. (2 × 200-kw, 1 × 100-kw diesel sets)
Range: 400/36; 1,600/20; 2,400/12 **Fuel:** 50 tons **Endurance:** 10 days
Crew: 8 officers, 33 enlisted

Remarks: Although a prototype Tarantul configured with four SS-N-22 supersonic sea-skimming missiles appeared in the early 1980s, not until 1987 was what appears to be a production version sighted. The original program goal was 44 units. Four are in the Baltic Fleet based at Baltiysk, three are assigned to the Caspian Flotilla, and there are also units in the Pacific (including R-297 and R-298) and Black Sea Fleets (including R-60, R-239, and R-334).
Disposals: R-63 (ex-*Kuybyshevskiy Komsomolets*) had been transferred to Ukraine by 8-97 and has since been scrapped. Five others, mostly from the Black Sea Fleet, have been retired for lack of overhaul funds.
Hull systems: The propulsion system differs from that of earlier Tarantuls in that diesels were substituted for the cruise turbines to improve cruising range.
Combat systems: A single Pricep (Light Bulb) missile datalink antenna radome is located atop a vertical lattice mast. The antenna within the Band Stand radome provides active and passive targeting for the antiship missiles; the EW suite is integrated with the active radars and can track 15 targets simultaneously to 120 km actively and 500 km passively. There is a backup lead-computing optical director for the six-barrel, 30-mm gatling guns. Carry a total of 152 rounds of 76.2-mm and 4,000 rounds of 30-mm ammunition (including 2,000 rounds of 30-mm ready-service on-mount). The communications suite permits maintaining seven circuits simultaneously.

♦ 6 Tarantul-II (Molnaya) class (Project 1241.1/2 or 12411M)

Bldrs: Sudostroitel'noye Obyedineniye "Almaz," Petrovskiy SY, St. Petersburg, and Sredniy Neva SY, Kolpino; Vladivostokskiy Sudostroitel'nyy Zavod (Ulis), Vladivostok

	In serv.		In serv.
944 R-42	1983	820 R-255 (ex-*Kronshtadtskiy Komsomolets*)	1981
962 R-71	1985	705 R-. . .	. . .
714 R-101	1985		
852 R-129	1985		

Tarantul-II pennant 705—at Astrakhan Boris Lemachko, 7-00

R-71 (962)—trials unit with MR-352 Pozitiv radar in the large radome atop the mast pylon and a modified Kortik CIWS with no missile reload facilities aft in place of the normal two AK-630 gatling guns; atop the mast is a radome-mounted antenna for the Pricep datalink system Hartmut Ehlers, 7-00

D: 329 tons light; 436 std. (469 fl) **S:** 42 kts
Dim: 56.10 (49.50 pp) × 10.20 (8.74 wl) × 2.38 (hull; 4.15 props)
A: 4 P-15M Termit (SS-N-2C Styx) SSM; 1 76.2-mm 59-cal. AK-176 DP; 1 Fasta-4M (SA-N-8) SAM syst. (16 9M-36 Strela-3M/Gremlin missiles)—all except R-71: 2 single 30-mm 54-cal. AK-630M gatling AA—R-71 only: 1 Kortik CIWS (with 8 missile tubes and 2 30-mm GSH-6-30L gatling AA; 8 tot. 9M-311 Vikhr'-K/SA-N-11 Grison missiles—see remarks)
Electronics:
Radar: 1 Kivach-3 nav.; 1 Monolit (Band Stand) missile target detection and tracking; 1 MR-123 Vympel (Bass Tilt) gun f.c.—R-71 also: MR-352 Pozitiv (Cross Dome) surf./air search; 1 3P-87 (Hot Flash) Kortik f.c.
EW: no intercept; 2 16-round PK-16 decoy RL
M: COGAG M-15 plant: 2 M-75 (DMR-76) cruise gas turbines (5,000 shp each), 2 M-70 (PR-77) boost gas turbines (12,000 shp each); 2 props; 32,000 shp (23,700 shp at 34° C air and 30° C water temperature)
Electric: 700 kw tot. (2 × 200-kw, 1 × 300-kw diesel sets)
Range: 760/43; 1,400/13 **Fuel:** 50 tons **Endurance:** 10 days
Crew: 5 officers, 36 enlisted

Remarks: The initial large-scale production variant of the Tarantul design for the Soviet Navy. The considerably modified R-71 is a trials ship (Project 1241.7) in the Black Sea Fleet, the unit with pennant number 705 is assigned to the Caspian Flotilla, and R-255 and possibly two others are assigned to the Baltic Fleet and based at Baltiysk.

GUIDED-MISSILE PATROL CRAFT [PTG] *(continued)*

Disposals: Caspian Flotilla sister *Poltavskiy Komsomolets* and one Black Sea Fleet unit were transferred to Bulgaria in 1992. One Baltic Fleet unit had been stricken by 7-96 at Kronshtadt, and three others are believed to have been retired as well. Pacific Fleet unit R-46 was stricken 5-7-94. Black Sea Fleet unit R-54 (ex-*Krasnodarskiy Komsomolets*) was transferred to Ukraine in 6-97. Pacific Fleet units R-45, R-66, and R-69 were stricken 1-9-95, R-76 and R-158 on 31-7-96, and R-113 and R-230 during 1997. Another five had been retired by 1999, mostly from the Black Sea Fleet.
Hull systems: The cruise gas turbines exhaust through a stack, while the high-speed turbines exhaust through the transom stern, adding their residual thrust to the propulsive power; all four engines are employed simultaneously for maximum power. One unit of the class is said to have had the same CODAG propulsion plant as the Tarantul-III variant.
Combat systems: A Pricep (Light Bulb) cruise missile datalink antenna has been added at the masthead, while the Band Stand radome conceals a missile target acquisition and tracking radar that can also be employed in passive mode. There are four unoccupied positions for EW antennas. Some 152 rounds of 76.2-mm and 4,000 rounds of 30-mm ammunition are normally carried, although there is emergency stowage for an additional 162 rounds of 76-mm ammunition. R-71 has been equipped with a Kortik twin 30-mm cannon/9M-311 missile launcher (with missile racks but without missile reload facilities) and an MR-352 Pozitiv surface/air-search target detection, designation, and tracking radar set.

Disposal note: Of the two Tarantul-I-class (Project 1241.1) guided-missile craft retained in Russian Navy service, Baltic Fleet unit R-26 (860), the last remaining unit, appears to have been retired in 2000; others were built for export to Poland (4), East Germany (5), India (5, plus others built indigenously), and Vietnam (2).

♦ 2 Matka (Vikhr')-class (Project 206MR) semi-hydrofoil
Bldr: Sudostroitel'noye Obyedineniye "Almaz" (Sredniy Neva), Kolpino

701 R-27 (In serv. 1977) 966 R-44 (In serv. 1978)

R-44 (966)—at Sevastopol', with the two quadruple launchers for Kh-35 Uran antiship missiles temporarily removed; they were restored early in 2001
Boris Lemachko, 2000

R-27 (701)—at Astrakhan Boris Lemachko, 7-00

D: 230 tons (257 fl; 268 max.) **S:** 42 kts
Dim: 38.60 (37.50 wl) × 12.5 (7.6 hull; 5.9 wl) × 2.10 (hull; 3.26 over foils)
A: R-27: 2 P-15 Termit (SS-N-2C Styx) antiship missiles; 1 76.2-mm 59-cal. AK-176 DP; 1 30-mm 54-cal. AK-630M gatling AA—R-44: 8 Kh-35 Uran (SS-N-25 Switchblade) SSM; 1 76.2-mm 59-cal. AK-176 DP; 1 twin 30-mm 54-cal. AK-630M1-2 Roy gatling AA
Electronics:
Radar: 1 Cheese Cake nav.; 1 Garpun (Plank Shave) target detection/tracking; 1 MR-123 Vympel-AM (Bass Tilt) gun f.c.
M: 3 M-520TM5 diesels; 3 props; 16,200 bhp (14,400 sust.)
Electric: 300 kw tot. (1 × 100-kw DGF-2A-100/1500 and 1 × 200-kw DRGA-2A-200/1500 diesel sets; 380 V, 50 Hz a.c.)
Range: 600/35; 1,200/22–24; 1,800/10–12 **Fuel:** 38 tons max., overload
Endurance: 8 days **Crew:** 25–28 tot.

Remarks: Essentially a missile-armed version of the Turya-class hydrofoil torpedo boat, with larger superstructure, a 76.2-mm gun forward, and missiles and gatling gun aft. Designed by the Almaz Bureau. Black Sea Fleet unit R-44 is equipped for trials and sales demonstration work with Kh-35 Uran antiship missiles and is based at Karanhinnaya Bay, Sevastopol'. R-27 retains the original armament and is based in the Caspian Sea at Astrakhan.
Disposals: At least four Baltic Fleet units had been discarded by 1995 (including R-254 on 5-7-94), and R-25, R-27, R-30, R-50, and R-221, which had been in storage at Kronshtadt since the mid-1990s, are now derelict. Four Black Sea Fleet units (R-251, R-260, R-262, and R-265) were transferred to Ukraine 10-1-96 and another, R-15, on a later date. The unmodified R-161 is in reserve in the Black Sea Fleet and probably will not return to service.
Hull systems: Steel hull with aluminum/magnesium alloy superstructure. Appear to be overloaded, and construction ceased in favor of the Tarantul series. As with Turya class, the stern planes on the surface while the bow is supported by the hydrofoils at high speeds. Both the foils and the transom stern flap are remotely controlled via a Baza 02065 gyro system to improve the ride. In colder waters (below 25° C), the craft could make 43–45 kts on foil.
Combat systems: In 1987–88, R-44 had her P-15M Termit (SS-N-2B Styx) missile launchers replaced with two quadruple tubes for Kh-35 Uran (SS-N-25 Switchblade) antiship missiles; the ship also carries the prototype AK-630M1-2 twin 30-mm gatling gun mounting in place of the original AK-630M and has small portable deckhouses just forward of the Kh-35 installation. R-44's missile tubes were temporarily removed during 2000 and put aboard the destroyer *Smel'yy* but were reinstalled at Feodosiya in spring 2001. Positions for EW intercept antennas remain empty. Carry 152 rounds of 76.2-mm and 2,000 rounds of 30-mm ammunition. SPO-3 radiation-warning equipment and the R-784 automated radio system are fitted.

TORPEDO BOATS [PT]

Disposal note: The sole Bogomol-class (Project 02065; Project Vikhr'-3) training torpedo boat, Pacific Fleet unit T-229, was offered for sale in 7-99 and is no longer in service. Turya-class (Project 206M) torpedo boats T-75 and T-118 had been retired from the Caspian Flotilla by 2001.

PATROL CRAFT, HYDROFOIL [PCH]

♦ 1 Mukha (Sokol) class (Project 11451)
Bldr: More Zavod, Feodosiya, Ukraine

	Laid down	L	In serv.
060 MPK-220 Vladimirets	12-5-84	20-8-90	14-3-91

MPK-220 Vladimirets (060)—in dry dock at Sevastopol' Hartmut Ehlers, 8-00

D: 320 tons light; 362 tons std.; 415.1 tons normal (468.1 fl)
S: 50 kts (12.2 on cruise diesels)
Dim: 49.97 (46.3 wl) × 9.9 (hull; 21.2 over foils; 9.20 wl) × 4.5 (mean hull; 7.26 over foils)
A: 1 76.2-mm 59-cal. AK-176 DP; 2 single 30-mm 54-cal. AK-630M gatling AA; 2 quadruple 224-mm TR-224 ASW TT
Electronics:
Radar: 1 Don-2 nav.; 1 Reyd (Peel Cone) nav./surf. search; 1 MR-123 Vympel (Bass Tilt) f.c.
Sonar: Zvezda-M1 through-hull variable-depth dipping sonar amidships
EW: no intercept equipment; 2 16-round PK-16 decoy RL
M: CODAG: 2 NK-12M boost gas turbines (18,000 shp each), 2 M-401 diesels (1,200 bhp each); 3 tandem 4-bladed propellers; 38,400 shp max.—2 Kort-nozzle low-speed thrusters
Electric: 400 kw tot. (2 × 200-kw diesel sets)
Range: 750/50; on one diesel: 1,200/12; 2,000/8 **Endurance:** 7 days
Crew: 5 officers, 34 enlisted

Remarks: A production version of the 1978-vintage Babochka prototype (Project 1141.1), with heavier armament and a less powerful propulsion plant. Assigned to the Black Sea Fleet. Named during 7-98. Was under refit at Sevastopol' during 2001. Sister MPK-215 (wearing pennant 056) has been stripped of armament and sensors and is derelict at Sevastopol'. A third unit, MPK-231, was not completed and was stricken 28-7-94. Three further units were being built for the Ukraine Navy, but construction was abandoned.
Hull systems: A true hydrofoil, with fixed foils fore and aft. One semiofficial source gives the displacement as 364 tons light and 475 tons full load. An export version has been offered by Ukraine with one Ukraine Central Machinery gas turbine on the centerline (4,000 shp) and two PR-77 boost gas turbines (12,100 shp each), at a cost of $25 million per ship.
Combat systems: The combat system is designated Gangut-1141 and the communications suite Buran-7. The small-diameter torpedo tubes must be trained outboard about 40° to launch; which torpedo is carried is not known.

PATROL CRAFT, HYDROFOIL [PCH] *(continued)*

Disposal note: Prototype hydrofoil antisubmarine warfare craft *Aleksandr Kunakhovich* (NATO Babochka class, Project 1141.1) had been stricken by 2001.

Note: All Muravey (Antarets)-class (Project 133) patrol hydrofoils are subordinated to the Federal Border Guard and are discussed in that section.

PATROL CRAFT [PC]

Note: See also under the Federal Border Guard for additional patrol craft and patrol boat designs.

♦ 3 Svetlyak class (Project 1041.0)

Bldrs: Vladivostokskiy Sudostroitel'nyy Zavod (Vostochnaya Verf), Ulis, Vladivostok; Sudostroitel'noye Obyedineniye "Almaz," Petrovskiy SY, St. Petersburg

	In serv.
301 AKA-235	1991
361 AKA-275	1992
. . . AKA-. . . 300 Let Rossiyskomu Flotu	1997

D: 328 tons (365 normal fl; 382 max.) **S:** 32 kts (31 sust.)
Dim: 49.50 (45.00 wl) × 9.20 × 2.14 (hull; 2.50 props)
A: 1 76.2-mm 59-cal. AK-176M DP; 1 30-mm 54-cal. AK-630M gatling AA; 16 Igla-series (SA-14/16) shoulder-launched SAM; 1 or 2 AGS-17 grenade launchers; 1 DP-64 antiswimmer grenade launcher; 2 fixed 402-mm OTA-40 ASW TT; 2 d.c. racks (6 d.c. each)
Electronics:
Radar: 1 Reyd (Peel Cone) nav./surf. search; 1 MR-123 Vympel-AM (Bass Tilt) f.c.
Sonar: Uzh HF helicopter dipping sonar at stern
EW: Slyabing intercept; MFD/F loop; 2 16-round PK-16 decoy RL
M: 3 M-520B diesels; 3 props; 15,000 bhp
Electric: 400 kw tot. (1 × 200-kw, 2 × 100-kw diesel sets; 380 V, 50 Hz a.c.)
Range: 1,500/31–32; 2,200/12–13 **Endurance:** 10 days
Crew: 4 officers, 4 warrant officers, 20 enlisted (41 tot. accomm.)

Remarks: Type designation: AKA (*Artilleriyskiy Kater,* Gunboat). Design, by Almaz Central Marine Design Bureau, was tailored to extended patrolling for Federal Border Guard use, but three have been assigned to the navy: AKA-235 in the Baltic, AKA-275 in the Black Sea, and *300 Let Rossiyskomu Flotu* ("300 Years of the Russian Navy") to the Northern Fleet. The Federal Border Guard (q.v.) operates another 28, with construction continuing.
Hull systems: Semi-planing, round-bilge hull with low spray chine forward. Propellers do not project below the keel. Have a steel hull with magnesium/aluminum alloy superstructure. Can survive with two compartments flooded. Have NBC warfare protection. The engine room is coated with vibration-damping material. The pilothouse is equipped with a centerline periscope.
Combat systems: There is an SP-521 Rakurs (Kolonka-2) ringsight backup director for the 30-mm gun, and the 76.2-mm mount can be operated in local control and has an integral electro-optical sighting system. Carry 152 rounds of 76-mm ammunition (all on-mount) and up to 3,000 rounds of 30-mm. Navigational equipment includes a NAVSAT receiver, radio navaid receiver, automatic plot, and echo sounder. There is no hull-mounted sonar; the dipping sonar is extended from a compartment to port of the centerline at the stern.

♦ 1 Tyulen'-class (Project 2035) patrol tug

Bldr: Kirova Zavod, Astrakhan (In serv. 1985)

931 PRDK-179

PRDK-179 (931)—at Astrakhan — Boris Lemachko, 1997

D: 380 tons (471.7 fl) **S:** 10.4 kts **Dim:** 39.10 × 8.10 × 2.85
A: 1 4-round Fasta-4M SAM launcher (Igla-M/Gremlin missiles); 1 twin 25-mm 80-cal. 2M-3M AA; 1 MRG-7 grenade launcher
Electronics:
Radar: 1 Mius (Spin Trough) nav.
Sonar: MG-329 hull-mounted MF; MG-7 dipping (100 kHz)
M: 1 . . . diesel; 1 prop; 578 bhp **Endurance:** 5 days **Crew:** 15 tot.

Remarks: PRDK = *Pereoborudovran v Protivodiversionniy Korabl'.* Has a tug-type hull with knuckle forward. Equipped with MFD/F and VHD/F. Appears to lack towing and rescue equipment. Assigned to Caspian Flotilla.

♦ 2 Pauk-I (Molnaya-2) class (Project 1241.2)

Bldr: Yaroslavl SY

	In serv.
316 MPK-60 (ex-*Komsomolets Bashkiriy*)	12-80
306 MPK-144	1979

MPK-144 (306)—based at Kronshtadt — Boris Lemachko, 7-00

MPK-60 (316)—with old pennant number; note the dipping sonar housing extending over the transom stern at the centerline — Hartmut Ehlers, 7-96

D: 415 tons (475 fl) **S:** 32 kts (28 sust.)
Dim: 57.60 (49.50 pp) × 10.40 (8.74 wl) × 2.14 (hull; 3.59 props)
A: 1 76.2-mm AK-176 DP; 1 4-round Fasta-4M SAM syst. (16 9M-313 Igla-M/Gremlin missiles); 1 30-mm 54-cal. AK-630 gatling AA; 2 5-round RBU-1200 ASW RL (30 RGB-12 projectiles); 4 fixed 402-mm OTA-40 ASW TT; 2 d.c. racks (6 BB-1 d.c. each)
Electronics:
Radar: 1 Mius (Spin Trough) nav.; 1 Reyd (Peel Cone) nav./surf. search; 1 MR-123 Vympel-AM (Bass Tilt) f.c.
Sonar: MGK-345 Bronza MF hull-mounted and MF dipping (6.5/7.0/7.5 kHz)
EW: Vympel-R2 suite: 2 Half Hat-B intercept; 2 16-round PK-16 decoy RL
M: 2 M-517 or M-507A twin diesels; 2 props; 20,800 bhp (16,180 sust.)
Electric: 500 kw tot. (2 × 200-kw, 1 × 100-kw diesel sets)
Range: 2,000/20; 2,600/14; 1,600/12 (normal fuel; 3,000/12 with max. fuel)
Fuel: 50 tons normal **Endurance:** 10 days
Crew: 5–7 officers, 31–32 enlisted

Remarks: Type designation MPK (*Malyy Protivolodochnyy Korabl',* Small Antisubmarine Ship). Another 20 (two of them Project 1241PE) are operated by the Federal Border Guard. This class uses same hull as the Tarantul-class missile boat but has ASW armament vice antiship missiles and an all-diesel propulsion plant vice Tarantul's COGAG/CODOG system. Both serve in the Baltic Fleet; they are the oldest units of the class.
Disposals: Black Sea Fleet units MPK-124 and MPK-146 were transferred to Bulgaria in 1990, and MPK-93 and MPK-116 were stricken 10-1-96 and later transferred to Ukraine. Federal Border Guard sisters *Gregoriy Gnatenko, Grigoriy Kuropyatnikov,* and PSKR-813 were transferred to the Ukraine Maritime Border Guard in 2-92. *Nikolay Kaplinov* (MPK-76) was scrapped in mid-overhaul at Baltiysk during 1995.
Hull systems: The large housing for the dipping sonar system projects about 1.5 m out from the stern. The large hull-mounted sonar dome is located approximately beneath the gun fire-control radar. Both have the low pilothouse common to units completed up to 1982. The hull is constructed of mild steel, while the middle part of the deck plating, some internal bulkheads, and much of the superstructure are made of aluminum-magnesium alloy.
Combat systems: The combat data system is designated SU-580. There is an SP-521 Rakurs (Kolonka-2) backup ringsight director for the single gatling AA gun; the MR-123 radar director can control both the 76.2-mm and 30-mm guns. Normal ammunition load is 152 rounds of 76-mm (all ready-service, on-mount) and 2,000 rounds of 30-mm. The sonar suite has a range of about 7 km for the dipping component, which can be lowered to 200 m; MGK-345 applies to both the hull mounted and dipping sonars.

♦ 1 Stenka (Tarantul) class (Project 205M)

Bldr: Sudostroitel'noye Obyedineniye "Almaz," Petrovskiy SY, St. Petersburg

375 AKA-232 (In serv. . . .)

D: 170 tons light; 211 tons std. (245 fl) **S:** 35 kts
Dim: 39.80 (37.50 wl) × 7.60 (5.90 wl) × 1.96
A: 2 twin 30-mm 65-cal. AK-230 AA; 4 fixed 402-mm OTA-40 TT (4 SET-40 ASW torpedoes); 2 d.c. racks (6 BB-1 d.c. each)
Electronics:
Radar: 1 Reyd (Peel Cone) nav./surf. search; 1 MR-104 Rys' (Drum Tilt) gun f.c.
Sonar: Bronza hull-mounted HF; HF helicopter dipping-type
EW: SPO-3 intercept

PATROL CRAFT [PC] *(continued)*

M: 3 M-504B or M-520 diesels; 3 props; 15,000 bhp
Range: 500/35; 800/20; 1,500/11.5 **Endurance:** 10 days
Crew: 4–5 officers, 26–27 enlisted

Remarks: The majority of the 117 built for Russia served as Project 205P in the Federal Border Guard, which still has 23 in service (which see for appearance). AKA-232 operates in the Caspian Flotilla.

PATROL BOATS [PB]

Note: Most surviving craft in this category appear to be assigned either to the Federal Border Guard or to the customs service.

♦ 5 Zhuk (Gryf) class (Project 1400 or 1400M)
Bldr: More Zavod, Feodosiya, Ukraine (In serv. 1971–86)

AKA-11 AKA-38 AKA-49 AKA-326 AKA-388

Russian Navy Zhuk pennant 043—assigned to the Caspian Flotilla
NAVPIC-Holland, 10-01

D: 35.9 tons (39.7 fl) **S:** 30 kts
Dim: 23.80 (21.70 wl) × 5.00 (3.80 wl) × 1.00 (hull; 1.90 max.)
A: 1 twin 14.5-mm 93-cal. 2M-7 AA *or* 1 twin 12.7-mm 60-cal. Utës-Ma mg
Electronics: Radar: 1 Lotsiya nav.
M: Project 1400M: 2 M-401 diesels; 2 props; 2,200 bhp—Project 1400: 2 M-50F4 diesels; 2 props; 2,400 bhp
Electric: 48 kw total (2 × 21-kw, 1 × 6-kw diesel sets)
Range: 700/28; 1,100/15 **Endurance:** 5 days **Crew:** 1 officer, 6 enlisted

Remarks: More than 110 others of this class were exported, 26 remain in Federal Border Guard service, and at least 10 were built as naval officers' yachts [YFL] (q.v.). Have an aluminum alloy hull. Capable of operating in up to Sea State 4 or 5.

♦ 1 Poluchat-I (TL-1) class (Project 368RS)
Bldr: Sosnovka Zavod (In serv. 1960–77)

156 AKA-527

AKA-527 (156) Boris Lemachko, 2000

D: 84.7 tons (92.8 fl) **S:** 21.6 kts
Dim: 29.60 × 6.10 (5.80 wl) × 1.56 (1.90 props)
A: 1 twin 25-mm 80-cal. 2M-3M AA; 1 twin 14.5-mm 93-cal. 2M-7 AA; 1 17-round 140-mm BM-14-17 PU artillery RL; 1 AGS-17 grenade launcher
Electronics: Radar: 1 Mius (Spin Trough) nav.
M: 2 M-50F-4 diesels; 2 props; 2,400 bhp **Range:** 250/21.6; 550/14
Crew: 1 officer, 2 warrant officers, 12 enlisted

Remarks: Modified torpedo retriever design, the survivor of several built for patrol duties. Operates in the Caspian Flotilla. Can carry 85 140-mm artillery rockets and 816 rounds of 25-mm and 2,352 rounds of 14.5-mm ammunition.

RIVER MONITORS [WPM]

Note: The Yaz (Project 1208)-, Pivyaka (Project 1212)-, and Vosh (Project 1248)-class river monitors are subordinated to the Federal Border Guard (q.v.).

♦ 16 Shmel' class (Project 1204)
Bldrs: Kamysh Burun Zavod, Kerch', and 61 Kommunara Zavod, Nikolayev, Ukraine (In serv. 1967–74)

AK-201	AK-223	AK-248	AK-489
AK-202	AK-224	AK-249	AK-507
AK-208	AK-245	AK-407	AK-508
AK-209	AK-247	AK-409	AK-509

Caspian Flotilla Shmel' pennant 046 Boris Lemachko, 7-00

D: 77.4 tons (fl) **S:** 24 kts **Dim:** 27.70 × 4.32 × 0.90 (2.00 molded depth)
A: 1 76.2-mm 48 cal. D-56TM low-angle (in a PT-76 tank turret); 1 twin 25-mm 80-cal. 2M-3M AA; 1 7.62-mm mg (in tank turret); 1 17-round 140-mm BM-14-17 artillery RL (36 rockets); 2 mine rails (up to 8 mines)
Electronics: Radar: 1 Donets-2 nav.
M: 2 M-50F-4 diesels; 2 props; 2,400 bhp
Electric: 50 kw tot. (2 × 25-kw DG-25 diesel sets)
Range: 240/20; 600/10 **Fuel:** 4.75 tons **Endurance:** 7 days
Crew: 1 officer, 2 warrant officers, 11 enlisted

Remarks: Survivors of 65 built for the Soviet Navy; 53 others were for the Maritime (now Federal) Border Guard. Units built at Nikolayev were prefabricated and later assembled at Khabarovsk for Border Guard use on the Amur-Ussuri River system, where 16 remain in service. Naval type designation: AK (*Artilleriyskiy Kater,* Artillery Cutter). Designed by TsKB-5 (the current Firma Almaz) design bureau under L. V. Ozimov. AK-208, -245, -247, -407, -409, -489, -507, -508, and -509 are in the Baltic Fleet (most stored ashore in reserve); the others are in the Caspian Flotilla. Two units are maintained on Lake Pripus on the Estonian border. Only two pennant numbers are available: AK-509 is 112 and AK-407 is 148.
Disposals: Four were transferred to Kampuchea 1984–85. Former Danube River Flotilla units AKA-211, -246, and -563 were transferred to Ukraine 1-5-95; other units of the Danube Flotilla, including AK-209, -223, -224, -225, -248, -397, -506, -527, -564, -582, -583, -598, -599, and -602 were also transferred to Ukraine in 1995, along with other assets of the former Russian Danube Flotilla. Pacific Fleet Amur River Flotilla units AK-354 and -587 were stricken 3-7-92 and 9-10-92, respectively, followed by sisters AKA-203, -242, -314, -316, -317, -318, -384, -387, -581, and -584 on 30-7-93 and AKA-197, -198, -205, -385, -398, -399, -408, -585, -588, and -589 on 5-7-94. AK-234 and AK-374 served in the Caspian Flotilla.
Hull systems: The screws are mounted in tunnels to reduce draft. Armor includes 10-mm over the pilothouse and gun barbettes, 8-mm over the hull and internal bulkheads, and 5-mm over the deck and pilothouse. Have a Gradus-2 gyrocompass and NEL-7 echo sounder.
Combat systems: Early units had a twin 14.5-mm machinegun mount aft that resembled a tank turret, and some have also carried up to four 30-mm BL-30 Plamya grenade launchers and four pintle-mounted 7.62-mm machineguns. The 7.62-mm machinegun is mounted coaxially with the 76.2-mm gun (for which 40 rounds are carried on-mount); up to four others fire through slits in the sides of the open-topped redoubt forward of the artillery RL. Mine loads vary from four UDM-500 or two UDM-1000 to six KPM or eight YaM mines.

MINE WARFARE SHIPS

Note: As of 6-00, Sudostroitel'noye Obyedineniye "Almaz" was planning to commence construction of the first Project Agat (Project 02668) seagoing mine countermeasures ships at its Sredniy Neva yard at Kolpino. The ship, if built, would employ 1,300-bhp, low-magnetic DRA-472 engines. From the project number, Agat appears to be yet another variant of the basic Natya design.

♦ 2 Gorya-class (Project 1266.0) minehunting ships [MHS]
Bldr: Sudostroitel'noye Obyedineniye "Almaz" (Sredniy Neva), Kolpino

	Laid down	L	In serv.
762 Vladimir Gumanenko	15-9-85	4-3-91	9-1-94
901 Zheleznyakov	28-2-85	17-7-86	30-12-88

D: 780 tons light; 1,070 std. (1,228 fl) **S:** 15.7 kts
Dim: 67.80 × 10.95 × 3.65 (4.35 over sonar)
A: 1 76.2-mm 59-cal. AK-176 DP; 1 30-mm 54-cal. AK-630M gatling AA; 2 4-round Fasta-4M (SA-N-8) SAM syst. (16 9M-39 Igla/Gremlin missiles); 8 fixed 402-mm Ketmen' special TT

MINE WARFARE SHIPS *(continued)*

Zheleznyakov (901)—with original pennant number BMVg/M.O.D. Bonn, 8-89

Vladimir Gumanenko (762) Boris Lemachko, 1998

Electronics:
Radar: 1 MR-312 Nayada nav.; 1 MR-212/201 Vaygach-U (Palm Frond) nav.; 1 MR-123 Vympel (Bass Tilt) f.c.
Sonar: Kabarga-A3 HF minehunting
EW: no intercept arrays; 2 16-round PK-16 decoy RL
M: 2 M-503B-37 diesels; 2 CP props; 5,100 bhp—bow- and stern-thrusters
Range: 1,500/12 **Endurance:** 15 days **Crew:** 7 officers, 63 enlisted

Remarks: Metal-hulled combined minehunter/minesweeper design possibly originally intended for locating and neutralizing U.S. Captor deep-laid torpedo-launching mines. Twenty were to have been built. *Zheleznyakov* was transferred to the Black Sea Fleet during 8-89 and is based at Novorossiysk. *Vladimir Gumanenko* was initially attached to the Baltic Fleet but was transferred to the Northern Fleet in 1996 or 1997, although not arriving from the Baltic until 11-00; she is assigned to the "Kola Fleet" and based at Severomorsk. Construction of a third was canceled.
Combat systems: The very cramped mine countermeasures working area accommodates several standard acoustic mine countermeasures devices, including KTK-1, TEM-3M, AT-3, and SHZ-3. The 76.2-mm gun is limited to less than 180° in horizontal train. The ship tows a remote-controlled Paltus minehunting submersible with 3,100 m of control cable. For mine disposal, two 100-kg depth bombs and 20 smaller charges are carried. The sliding doors at the 02 level on the hull sides aft cover the quadruple launch tubes for the special minehunting torpedoes, which are fired in pairs linked by a cable to engage mine anchor cables. Employ the Buran-6 communications suite.

♦ 1 Natya-II (Akvamarin-2) class (Project 266.6) minehunting ship [MHS]
Bldr: Sudostroitel'noye Obyedineniye "Almaz" (Sredniy Neva), Kolpino

960 Strelok (In serv. 1982)

Strelok (960)—with original pennant number U.S. Navy, 2-86

D: 750 tons std., 804 tons normal (873 fl) **S:** 17.6 kts (16 sust.)
Dim: 61.00 (57.60 wl; 56.00 pp) × 10.20 (9.80 wl) × 2.98 (hull; 3.45 max.)
A: 2 twin 30-mm 65-cal. AK-230M AA; 2 Fasta-4M (SA-N-8) SAM syst. (16 Strela-3 or Igla-M/Gremlin missiles)
Electronics: Radar: 1 Don-2 nav.—Sonar: MG-89 Serna HF hull-mounted
M: 2 M-503B-3E diesels; 2 CP props; 5,000 bhp
Electric: 600 kw tot. (3 × 200-kw DGR-200/1500 diesel sets)
Range: 1,800/16; 3,000/12; 5,200/10 **Fuel:** 87 tons **Endurance:** 10–15 days
Crew: 8 officers, 59 enlisted

Remarks: Single-unit prototype believed intended for trials with a minehunting system deployed from a deckhouse on the fantail; the equipment replaced the standard Natya mine countermeasures winch. Retains articulated sweep gear davits at the stern, but no countermeasures gear is visible on deck. Omitted were the normal ASW RL and two twin 25-mm AA. Transferred to the Black Sea Fleet in 7-85 and is based at Novorossiysk.

Note: A minesweeper named *Mineralnye Voda* ("Mineral Water") was said to be operating from Novorossiysk and was given the name on 1-8-00; class not known.

♦ 15 (+ 2) Natya-I (Akvamarin)-class (Project 266M and 266ME*) fleet minesweepers [MSF] (4 or more *nonoperational*)
Bldr: Sudostroitel'noye Obyedineniye "Almaz" (Sredniy Neva), Kolpino

	In serv.	Fleet
610 Svyazist	1978	Baltic
718 MT-265*	12-89	Pacific
738 MT-264*	9-89	Pacific
770 Valentin Pikul'*	20-1-02	(Northern)
806 Motorist	1976	. . .
817 Pulemetchik	1975	. . .
831 Komendor	1974	. . .
834 Dal'nomershchik	1987	. . .
838 Mashinist	1975	. . .
854 Marsoviy	1986	Pacific
855 Kontradmiral Vlasov	1972	. . .
909 Vitse-Admiral Zhukov (ex-*Ehlektrik*)	1977	Black Sea
911 *Radist* (ex-*Kharkovskiy Komsomolets*)	1973	Black Sea
912 *Turbinist*	1975	Black Sea
913 *Navodchik* (ex-*Kurskiy Komsomolets*, ex-*Navodchik*)	30-12-74	Black Sea
919 *Snayper*	1976	Black Sea
. . . Vitse-Admiral Zakhar'in*	2002?	. . .

Valentin Pikul' (770)—prior to launch but nearly complete TASS, 2000

Radist (911)—now laid up; note the early-model cranes at the stern Boris Lemachko, 6-00

D: Project 266M: 715 tons light, 735–750 tons std., 804–812 tons normal—Project 266ME: 745 tons (804 fl; 873 max.)
S: 17.6 kts (16 sust.)
Dim: 61.00 (57.60 wl; 56.00 pp) × 10.20 (9.80 wl) × 2.98 (hull; 3.60 max.)
A: Project 266M: 2 twin 30-mm 65-cal. AK-230M AA; 2 twin 25-mm 80-cal. 2M-3M AA; 2 4-round Fasta-4M (SA-N-8) SAM syst. (16 Strela or 20 Igla-M/Gremlin missiles); 2 5-round RBU-1200M ASW RL (30 RGB-12 projectiles); 1 mine rail (7 KMD-100 mines or 32 BB-1 d.c.)—Project 264ME: 2 single 30-mm 54-cal. AK-306 gatling AA; 2 4-round Fasta-4M (SA-N-8) SAM syst. (20 Strela-3 or Igla-M/Gremlin missiles); 2 5-round RBU-1200M ASW RL (30 RGB-12 projectiles); 1 mine rail (7 KMD-100 mines or 32 BB-1 d.c.)

MINE WARFARE SHIPS *(continued)*

Vitse-Admiral Zhukov (909)—with late-model cranes at stern, alongside the Natya-II *Strelok* (920) Hartmut Ehlers, 8-00

Project 266ME variant MT-264 (738)—off Hokkaido JMSDF, via *Ships of the World,* 12-00

Electronics:
Radar: 1 or 2 Don-MN (Don-2) nav.—Project 266M only: 1 MR-104 Rys' (Drum Tilt) f.c.
Sonar: Project 266M: MG-69 Lan' or MG-79 Mizen' search; MG-26 underwater telephone—Project 266ME: MG-89 minehunting; MG-35 underwater telephone; NEL-MZB echo sounder
M: 2 M-503B-3E diesels; 2 shrouded CP props; 5,000 bhp
Electric: 600 kw tot. (3 × 200-kw DGR-200/1500 diesel sets; 380 V, 50 Hz a.c.)
Range: 1,800/16; 2,700/12; 5,200/10 **Fuel:** 48 tons normal; 87 tons max.
Endurance: Project 266M: 10 days—Project 266ME: 15 days
Crew: 6 officers, 8 warrant officers, 54 enlisted

Remarks: Type designation: MT (*Morskoy Tral'shchik,* Seagoing Minesweeper). Equipped also to serve as ASW escorts, with the RBU-1200 rocket launchers also used for detonating mines. Designed under T. D. Pokhodun. Khabarovsk SY completed only five in 1972–76, of which none remain in service. The first unit, *Semen Roshal',* was completed for the Baltic Fleet in fall 1970. Post-1980 Project 266ME production was both for domestic use and for export, with one unit delivered to Syria with no ASW ordnance or minesweeping gear in 1985 as a training ship, 12 for India, eight for Libya, one for Ethiopia, and one for Yemen (the latter two to a modified design; see below). Of the active survivors, at least four are in the Northern Fleet, four or more in the Pacific Fleet, one in the Baltic Fleet, and five in the Black Sea Fleet. The *Navodchik* was again to have been renamed, as the *Kovrovets,* during 7-01, but the change does not appear to have been made; that ship, along with *Radist, Snayper,* and *Turbinist,* had been reduced to cadre crew status as of summer 2001, with only 10 crew aboard each.

Beginning in 1989, four units of a new variant with single 30-mm AK-306 gatling guns substituted for the twin 30-mm AK-230 mounts, but without 25-mm guns, Rys' (Drum Tilt) fire-control radar, or net trawl facilities, were completed; MT-264 and MT-265 were transferred from the Baltic to the Pacific Fleet, and one each was sold to Ethiopia and Yemen. Two more in the same configuration were reported under construction for export as of 1-94, and of those, *Valintin Pikul'* (launched 31-5-00 at Sredniy Neva Zavod) was to be assigned to the Northern Fleet after trials; the *Vitse-Admiral Zakhal'in,* not yet launched, may eventually be completed as well.

Disposals: Black Sea Fleet units *Ivan Maslov* and *Schitchik* and Baltic Fleet unit MT-159 have been stricken (dates unknown). Pacific Fleet units *Kontradmiral Pershin, Paravan,* and *Tral* were stricken 30-7-93; Black Sea Fleet units *Dizelist* and *Signal'shchik* and Pacific Fleet unit *Kontradmiral Khoroshkhin* on 5-7-94; Black Sea unit *Rulevoy* by 1995; Baltic Fleet unit *Semen Roshal'* on 1-9-95; and Pacific Fleet unit *Yakor'* on 1-9-95 (sunk as a missile target 25-4-96). Pacific Fleet Project 265ME unit *Zaryad* was stricken 31-7-96 after only five years' service. Sister *Torpedist* was redesignated experimental ship OS-99 in 1990 and stricken in 1995. *Zapad, Raketchik,* and Pacific Fleet unit *Zapal* were stricken during 1997. Black Sea Fleet units *Razvedchik* and *Zenitchik* were transferred to Ukraine in 1997. Baltic Fleet unit *Dmitry Lysov* was placed in reserve in 1998 and is unlikely to return to service. *Artillerist* and *Desantnik* were no longer in service as of 2001.

Hull systems: The stem is cut back sharply below the waterline, as in the earlier T-43 and Yurka classes. Have low magnetic signature, with an aluminum-steel alloy hull and the DGR-450/1500P diesel-driven degaussing system. Endurance at 12 kts with normal 48-ton fuel load is 1,500 n.m.; with 80-ton overload fuel load, 2,700 n.m. All living spaces are air-conditioned.

Combat systems: Two quadruple point-defense SAM launchers have been added to a number of units of the class (but not all), just abaft the lattice mast. Some also have an extra navigational radar atop the pilothouse, usually a Mius (Spin Trough). Sweep gear includes SEMP-3 magnetic and MPT-3 mechanical arrays and a net trawl deployed over the stern ramp. The sonar incorporates a downward-looking, HF, bottomed-mine detection component. Can deploy television minehunting equipment. Have NEL-5 echo sounders. Ships completed through 1980 had rigid 2.5-ton-capacity davits aft; later units had articulated KBG-5-TMI jib cranes in the same position. *Valentin Pikul'* is said to be equipped with an MKT-210 towed television minehunting system, BKT or AT-3, AT-5, TEM-4, PMR-2 and PMT sweep arrays, and the Mikron sweep-operating system.

♦ 38 Sonya (Yakhont)-class (Project 1265 and 1265.5*) coastal minesweepers [MSC]

Bldrs: Avangard Zavod, Petrozavodsk; Vladivostokskiy Sudostroitel'niy Zavod (Ulis),Vladivostok

	In serv.	Fleet
107 BT-88	1988	Caspian
401 BT-285 (ex-*Kolomenskiy Komsomolets*)	1978	Northern
403 BT-454	1978	Northern
405 BT-226	1986	Northern
410 BT-732 (ex-*Komsomolets Kirgiziy*)	1977	Northern
411 BT-111 Kolomna	1986	Northern
418 BT-22	1981	Northern
424 BT-15	1982	Northern
425 BT-31	1981	Northern
426 BT-241 Mineral'nie Vodi	1985	Black Sea
430 BT-202 (ex-*Khersonskiy Komsomolets*)	1976	Black Sea
433 BT-21	1980	Black Sea
435 BT-116*	1998	. . .
438 BT-40	1982	Black Sea
501 BT-212*	1988	Baltic
505 BT-. . . Aleksey Lebedev*	1989	Baltic
510 BT-230	1987	Baltic
513 BT-48	1987	Baltic
522 BT-213 Sergei Kolbas'ev	1989	Baltic
523 BT-78	1978	. . .
525 BT-232	1989	Pacific
531 BT-244	1987	Caspian
532 BT-88	1988	Caspian
533 BT-245	1989	Pacific
554 BT-96	12-83	Pacific
561 BT-115†	1993	Baltic
561 BT-256*†	1990	Pacific
565 BT-100	2-85	Pacific
568 BT-94	1983	Baltic
580 BT-132	1-81	Pacific
583 BT-44	1985	. . .
592 BT-114	11-87	Pacific
593 BT-215	1991	Pacific
598 BT-51	12-86	Pacific
. . . BT-97	1984	. . .
. . . BT-211	1985	. . .
. . . BT-109 Novoural'sk	1984	Northern
. . . BT-. . .Vladimir Polukhin*	1987	. . .

†Both ships are reported to have the same pennant number

BT-212 (501)—a Baltic Fleet Project 1265.5 Sonya with two 30-mm AK-306 gatling guns German Navy, 8-99

BT-232 (525)—a standard Project 1265 Sonya with a twin 25-mm AA mount aft, assigned to the Pacific Fleet Boris Lemachko, 1999

MINE WARFARE SHIPS *(continued)*

BT-48 (513)—with heat-seeking SAM launchers flanking the 25-mm AA mount at the forecastle break Boris Lemachko, 2000

D: 401–427 tons (430–460 fl) **S:** 14 kts
Dim: 48.80 (46.00 wl) × 10.20 (9.20 wl) × 2.40–2.50 (mean hull; 2.75–2.85 max.)
A: Project 1265: 1 twin 30-mm 65-cal. AK-230M AA; 1 twin 25-mm 80-cal. 2M-3M AA—some also: 1 or 2 4-round Fasta-4M (SA-N-8) SAM syst. (up to 15 Strela-3 or Igla-M/Gremlin missiles); up to 5 mines—Project 1265.5: 2 single 30-mm 54-cal. AK-306 gatling AA; 1 or 2 4-round Fasta-4M (SA-N-8) SAM syst. (up to 15 Strela-3 or Igla-M/Gremlin missiles); up to 5 mines
Electronics:
Radar: 1 Mius (Spin Trough) nav.
Sonar: MG-69, -79, or -89 Serna HF hull-mounted; MG-26 or -35 underwater telephone; NEL-MZB echo sounder (see remarks)
M: 2 DRA-210-A or -B diesels; 2 3-bladed CP props; 2,200 or 2,000 bhp—2 low-speed thrusters
Electric: 350 kw tot. (3 × 100-kw, 1 × 50-kw diesel sets; 380 V, 50 Hz a.c.)
Range: 1,700/10 **Fuel:** 27.1 tons **Endurance:** 15 days
Crew: 5–6 officers, 26–40 enlisted (45 tot. accomm.)

Remarks: Type designation: BT (*Basovyy Tral'shchik,* Base Minesweeper), 3rd Rank. *Yakhont,* the program name, refers to a kind of sapphire. Designed in 1968 under D. I. Rudakov and, later, Valeriy Ivanovich Nemudrov at the Western Design Bureau, St. Petersburg. Construction ceased at Vladivostok in 1991 after 22 had been built. BT-115 was the last completed at Petrozavodsk, with work on BT-116 suspended until restarted for completion in 1998. Two incompete Petrozavodsk units were sold to the Mediterranean Tourism Investment Corp., a French firm, and were to be completed starting in 6-01 as tour boats for service on the Côte d'Azur. Two new Project 1265E export units were transferred to Cuba in 1980 and two more in 1985; other new units have gone to Bulgaria (4), Syria (1), and Vietnam (2). One Northern Fleet unit has been renamed the *Yadrin.* Caspian Sea Flotilla unit BT-88 is used as a patrol craft, the reason for her combatant-series pennant number. A replacement design was planned to enter service in 1996 but has been indefinitely postponed due to financial problems. BT-88 and BT-244 may be subordinated to the Federal Border Guard; one of them was named *Vitse-Admiral German Ugrumov* around 9-01.
Disposals: Caspian Flotilla units BT-16 (ex-*Astrakhanskiy Komsomolets*), -103, and -155 were transferred to Azerbaijan 3-7-92. One Northern Fleet unit was declared for scrap in 1991, and Baltic Fleet units BT-123 and -342 were offered for scrap in 1992. Baltic Fleet units BT-77, -258, -260, -291, -320, and -324 were stricken 30-7-93. Pacific Fleet units stricken: BT-266 and -327 on 30-7-93 (BT-327 relegated to service as a berthing barge); BT-734 on 5-7-94; BT-347 and -438 on 1-9-95; BT-267 on 31-7-96; and BT-38, -56, -78, -121, and -470 on 16-8-97. Black Sea Fleet unit BT-79 (ex-*Khersonskiy Komsomolets*) was transferred to Ukraine 30-12-95, followed in mid-1997 by BT-126 (ex-*Orensburgskiy Komsomolets*), which had been stricken 10-1-96. Northern Fleet units BT-152, -206, -261, -263, -270, -294, -296, -298, -302, and -325; Baltic Fleet units BT-252, -315, -317, -328, -329, -330, and -350; and BT-343 (fleet unknown) have either been discarded or placed in unmaintained reserve since 1998 or never existed.
Hull systems: Wooden construction with glass-reinforced plastic hull sheathing. Bollard pull: 10 tons at 9 kts. Endurance is five days longer than with Project 1265E export variant, and range is 200 n.m. greater at 10 kts. Later series-construction units have the 1,000-bhp DRA-210A main propulsion diesels, which have the alternative designation 12ChPN 18/20. Early units were fitted with the older Type 9D diesel, and some have two 100-kw and one 200-kw diesel generator sets.
Combat systems: Carry AT-5 acoustic, PEMT-4 magnetic loop, and BKT-2 mechanical sweep equipment. Can tow CT-2 solenoidal magnetic minesweeping buoys and also net-sweep arrays and can lay linear mine disposal charges. Are also able to employ KIU-1 or KIU-2-2m underwater television mine location and destruction equipment. Export variants carry the GKT-2 contact sweep; ST-2, AT-2, and PEMT-2 influence sweeps; and an IT-3 mine detector/exploder. Are equipped with an underwater telephone. The 25-mm mount is aimed by the operator, while the 30-mm mount is controlled by a Kolonka-1 ringsight director; 1,000 rounds of 30-mm and 2,000 rounds of 25-mm ammunition are normally carried. The Project 1265.5 units were built with two 30-mm AK-630M gatling AA in place of the original armament; they also have MG-69 or MG-79 Mizen sonars in place of MG-89 Serna and employ two SP-521 Rakurs (Kolonka-2) 19-1 simple remote directors to control the gunmounts. The sonar dome pivots at the after end to retract within the hull in all variants. Manned launchers for point-defense missiles began to be added to these ships in the early 1980s, initially just one to port or starboard of the after gunmount, but later two, flanking the gunmount.

♦ **9 (+ 1) Lida (Sapfir)-class (Project 10750) inshore minesweepers [MSI]** Bldr: Sudostroitel'noye Obyedineniye "Almaz" (Sredniy Neva), Kolpino

	Laid down	L	In serv.
219 RT-233	20-10-88	8-7-93	9-9-94
302 RT-231	28-7-88	19-8-92	25-8-93
316 RT-57	20-10-86	29-7-87	12-12-89
330 RT-252	12-10-87	27-9-91	30-12-91
331 RT-341	15-1-87	25-4-89	30-12-89
348 RT-248	16-3-87	6-2-90	29-9-90
371 RT-249	9-4-87	27-7-90	29-12-90
372 RT-234	27-4-89	31-3-94	28-8-96
388 RT-273	29-3-88	11-12-91	30-9-92
. . . RT- . . .	. . .	. . .	2002?

RT-233 (219)—at Astrakhan Boris Lemachko, 7-00

RT-57 (316)—at St. Petersburg Rozvoorouzhenie, 7-96

D: 85 tons light; 131 tons normal (135 fl; 137 max.) **S:** 12.5 kts
Dim: 31.45 × 6.50 × 1.58
A: 1 30-mm 54-cal. AK-306 gatling AA; 5 Igla-M (SA-14/16) shoulder-launched SAMs; 2 mine rails (. . . mines)
Electronics:
Radar: 1 Liman nav.
Sonar: Kabarga-A1 HF hull-mounted minehunting
M: 3 Type 3D-12MM diesels; 3 props; 900 bhp
Electric: 150 kw tot. (3 × 50-kw diesel sets)
Range: 210/12.5; 400/10 (650/10 with overload fuel) **Endurance:** 5 days
Crew: 1 officer, 13 enlisted

Remarks: Intended as the successor to the Yevgenya class. Offered for export as Project 10750E or for coproduction. Designed by V. I. Nemudrov and A. A. Forst of the Western Design Bureau, St. Petersburg (now the Zapadnoye PKB). Intended to counter mines in waters up to 80 m deep. Although some 17–22 were to be built, the program was terminated after only nine had been completed, all for the Baltic Fleet, and a Russian press article severely criticized the design. RT-233 (formerly pennant 300) has since been transferred to the Caspian Flotilla. Three units of the class begun at Petrozavodsk Zavod prior to 1991 remained suspended at the yard as of 5-01, and one other was said to be nearing completion at Sredniy Neva, Kolpino, as of 1-02.
Hull systems: Glass-reinforced plastic construction with frames at 400-mm spacing (300 mm aft). Main and auxiliary machinery is sound mounted, and special attention has been paid to reducing acoustic and magnetic signatures. A degaussing system is fitted. Berthing spaces are air-conditioned. Navigation equipment includes NEL-M3B echo sounder, LGT-1 pressure log, and GKU-2 gyrocompass. An infrared signaling system is fitted.
Combat systems: Mine countermeasures equipment includes a towed television hunting system (as on the Yevgenya class), an AT-6 acoustic sweep, one or two mag-

MINE WARFARE SHIPS *(continued)*

netic sweeps (one an SEMT-1 coil array), and one GKT-3MO deep contact wire sweep. Have an LES-67 minesweeping winch with three drums and a bollard pull of 5.3 tons at 9 kts. Have an SP-521 Rakurs (Kolonka-2) pedestal director for the gunmount, for which 500 rounds are normally carried (1,000 in emergency).

♦ 12 Yevgenya (Korund)-class (Project 1258) inshore minesweepers [MSI] (1 or more in *reserve*)

Bldr: Sudostroitel'noye Obyedineniye "Almaz" (Sredniy Neva), Kolpino

	In serv.	Fleet		In serv.	Fleet
201 *RT-697*	1975	Black Sea	235 RT-402	1978	Black Sea
204 RT-71	1981	Caspian	239 RT-439	1972	Black Sea
206 RT-420	1979	Pacific	245 RT-588	1977	Black Sea
223 RT-348	1975	Caspian	246 RT-471	1979	Pacific
228 RT-195	1982	Caspian	259 RT-603	1973	. . .
229 RT-41	1980	Pacific	299 RT-823	1976	Black Sea

Yevgenya class—typical unit Siegfried Breyer Collection

Yevgenya RT-697 (201)—in preservation at Sevastopol' Hartmut Ehlers, 8-00

D: 88.5 tons light; 94.5 tons normal (97.9 fl) **S:** 11 kts
Dim: 26.13 (24.20 wl) × 5.90 (5.10 wl) × 1.38
A: 1 twin 14.5-mm 93-cal. 2M-7 or 1 twin 25-mm 80-cal. 2M-3M AA; 1 7-round MRG-1 grenade launcher; 4 d.c. (+ 8 emergency stowage)
Electronics:
Radar: 1 Mius (Spin Trough) or Kivach nav.
Sonar: MG-7 HF dipping
M: 2 Type 3D12 diesels; 2 props; 600 bhp—hydraulic slow-speed drive
Electric: 100 kw tot. (2 × 50-kw diesel sets)
Range: 400/10 **Fuel:** 2.7 tons **Endurance:** 3 days
Crew: 1 officer, 9 enlisted (+ 2–3 clearance divers)

Remarks: Typed RT (*Reydnyy Tral'shchik,* Roadstead Minesweeper), 4th Class. Designed under V. I. Blinov. Production totaled 52 for the Soviet Navy. Project 1258E was built for export and domestic use 1969–1985. Four were transferred to Bulgaria, 10 to Cuba, six to India, three to Iraq, three to Mozambique, four to Syria, three to Yemen, two to Vietnam, and two to Angola; a number of Cuban units were further transferred to Nicaragua.
Disposals: During 1992, Northern Fleet unit RT-437 and Baltic Fleet units RT-106, -332, and -601 were offered for sale for scrap. Caspian Flotilla units RT-136 and -437 were stricken 3-7-92 and transferred to Azerbaijan, while sister RT-278 was stricken the same date and scrapped at Baku. Two were transferred to Estonia prior to the liberation of the Baltic Republics but were not put into service; two others had been stricken at Baltiysk by 1995. Pacific Fleet unit RT-403 was stricken 30-7-93 and RT-52 on 5-7-94 (and redesignated as service craft RPV-1603). RT-214 was stricken 10-1-96 and went to Ukraine 12-3-96. Pacific Fleet unit RT-402 was stricken during 1997. Black Sea Fleet sisters RT-439, -588, -823, and -1202 were transferred to Georgia in 1998. At least one Baltic Fleet unit is in reserve at Kronshtadt.
Hull systems: Glass-reinforced plastic hull. Navigational equipment includes Girya-MA gyrocompass and NEL-7 echo sounder.
Combat systems: Can employ a Neva-1 television minehunting system useful to 30-m depths; it dispenses marker buoys to permit later disposal of mines by divers or explosive charges. The sonar is lowered via one of the stern davits. Carry VKT-1 mechanical, AT-2 acoustic, and SEMT-1 solenoid coil sweep gear. Some export units were armed with one twin 25-mm 2M-3 AA.

♦ 1 Barentsevo More–class (Project 1332) auxiliary minesweeper [MSA] (In reserve)

Bldr: Baltiya Zavod, Klaypeda, Estonia (In serv. 12-73)

844 *MT-434*

MT-434 (844)—while active Boris Lemachko, 7-93

D: 1,290 tons (1,889 fl) **S:** 13.3 kts **Dim:** 58.82 × 12.99 × 5.10
A: 2 twin 25-mm 80-cal. 2M-3M AA; 2 7-round MRG-7 grenade launchers
Electronics: Radar: 1 Don-2 nav.—Sonar: . . .
M: 1 Zgoda-Sulzer Type 6L-525 diesel; 1 CP prop; 2,200 bhp
Electric: 300 kw tot. (2 × 150-kw diesel sets)
Range: 10,000/13 **Fuel:** 231 tons **Endurance:** 36 days **Crew:** 39 tot.

Remarks: Converted in 1984 from one of 65 units of the *Barentsevo More* class as a prototype for adapting Russia's numerous fish factory trawler fleet for mine countermeasures duties in wartime. Is assigned to the Northern Fleet and was formerly operated in the White Sea in support of nuclear submarine trials. Considered to be a Seagoing Base Minesweeper. Was in reserve as of 12-98.

♦ 3 Olya (Malakhit)-class (Project 1259) minesweepers [MSB]

Bldr: Sudostroitel'noye Obyedineniye "Almaz" (Sredniy Neva), Kolpino (In serv. 12-73 to 1980)

. . . RT-139 . . . RT-141 . . . RT-254

Two Olya-class harbor minesweepers Hartmut Ehlers, 7-96

D: 62 tons (66 fl) **S:** 12 kts (10 sust.) **Dim:** 22.77 × 4.50 × 0.92 (1.40 max.)
A: 1 twin 12.7-mm 60-cal. Utës-Ma mg; . . . mines
Electronics: Radar: 1 Kivach nav.
M: 2 Type 3D-6N diesels; 2 props; 470 bhp
Electric: 100 kw tot. (2 × 50-kw diesel sets)
Range: 300/9; 400/8 **Crew:** 1 officer, 10 enlisted

Remarks: Four were built for the Soviet Navy, and the class has also been built under license in Bulgaria. The Russian units had originally been intended for Danube River service. Designed by Central Design Bureau 19 under V. V. Sidorov and V. I. Blinov. Originally served at Kronshtadt; the survivors serve as harbor minesweepers at Baltiysk Naval Base and are in marginal condition. A prototype was laid down in 1962 and completed during 1966; the first series-construction unit was begun in 1969 and the craft, RT-278, was commissioned during 12-73. GRP construction.
Combat systems: Sweep gear includes AT-6 acoustic, SEMT-1 solenoid coil, and GKT-3 mechanical arrays. The original twin 25-mm 2M-3 AA mount was replaced by the twin machinegun mount during the 1990s.

Disposal note: As of 3-00, the sole Tolya (Lazurit)-class (Project 1225.5) drone minesweeper, RT-343, had been laid up in poor condition on land at St. Petersburg. All remaining PO-2 (Yaroslavets)-class (Project 376) launches configured as riverine minesweepers had been discarded or reassigned to other duties as of 2001.

MINE WARFARE SHIPS *(continued)*

♦ 3 Tanya (Chelnok)-class (Project 1300.0) drones [MSD]
Bldr: Sudostroitel'noye Obyedineniye "Almaz" (Sredniy Neva), Kolpino

	In serv.		In serv.
324 PChT-61	1987	353 PChT-702	1986
326 PChT-344	1989		

Tanya-class PChT-61 (324)—outboard a sister, at Kronshtadt
Boris Lemachko, 2000

D: 88 tons (90 fl) **S:** 8.5 kts **Dim:** 26.20 (25.40 wl) × 4.20 (4.00 wl) × 1.90
M: 2 diesel generator sets (1 × 200 kw, 1 × 90 kw), electric drive; 4 props; 270 shp
Range: 200/8.5

Remarks: Designed at the Western Planning and Design office under V. I. Nemudrov as riverine magnetic mine countermeasures drones. The single Project 1300 prototype was completed in 1979, followed by seven Project 1300.0 production variants, which differed externally in having a tripod mast vice a pole. Steel-construction, remote-controlled craft with identical hull lines fore and aft and two propellers at both ends to improve maneuvering in narrow river channels. Can be controlled via the RTU-2T telemetry system by one operator and have a shock-mounted pilothouse for operations with personnel aboard. Designed to operate in waters up to 30-m deep and can tow EMT magnetic and AT-6 acoustic sweep gear. All surviving units are based in the Baltic.

AMPHIBIOUS WARFARE SHIPS

♦ 1 Ivan Rogov (Yedinorog)-class (Project 1174) dock landing ship [LSD]
Bldr: Yantar Pribaltiyskiy Zavod 820, Kaliningrad

	L	In serv.	Fleet
020 Mitrofan Moskalenko	1988	12-89	Northern

Mitrofan Moskalenko (020)—on delivery to the Northern Fleet
M.O.D. Bonn, 3-92

D: 8,260 tons light (11,580 without combat load; 14,060 fl) **S:** 21 kts (19 sust.)
Dim: 157.50 (149.90 wl) × 23.80 (22.00 wl) × 4.20 (6.70 flooded down)
A: 1 twin-rail Osa-M (SA-N-4) SAM syst. (20 4K-33/Gecko missiles); 1 twin 76.2-mm 59-cal. AK-726 DP; 2 4-round Fasta-4M (SA-N-8) SAM syst. (16–20 Igla-M/Gremlin missiles); 4 single 30-mm 54-cal. AK-630 gatling AA; 1 40-round 122-mm UMS-73 Grad-M artillery RL (1,320 BM-21 rockets); 4 Ka-29TB Helix-B helicopters
Electronics:
Radar: 2 MR-212/201 Vaygach-U (Palm Frond) nav.; 1 MR-710 Fregat-MA (Top Plate-A) air search; 1 MR-10 Turel' (Owl Screech) 76.2-mm gun f.c.; 1 MPZ-301 Baza (Pop Group) SAM f.c.; 2 MR-123 Vympel (Bass Tilt) 30-mm gun f.c.; 1 Fly Screen microwave helicopter landing aid
EW: no intercept or jammers; 4 16-round PK-16 decoy RL; 10 10-round PK-10 decoy RL
TACAN: Privod (Round House)
E/O: 1 Squeeze Box multisensor artillery rocket f.c. and surveillance
M: COGAG M-12 plant: 2 M-8K gas turbines; 2 props (260 rpm max.); 36,000 shp
Electric: 3,000 kw tot. (6 × 500-kw diesel sets)

Mitrofan Moskalenko (020)
Dr. Eric Grove, 3-95

Range: 4,000/18 (7,200/18 with emergency fuel); 7,500/14.5 (6,000/14 loaded)
Endurance: 30 days (15 with 500 landing force aboard)
Crew: 37 officers, 202 enlisted + troops: 46 officers, 519 enlisted

Remarks: Type designation: BDK (*Bol'shoy Desantnyy Korabl',* Large Landing Ship). Designed under N. V. Maksimov. A planned fourth unit was canceled. The ability to use helicopters, to beach, and to deploy air-cushion vehicles gave a versatility unmatched by any other Russian amphibious-warfare ship; those capabilities were combined with an organic shore fire-bombardment capability and very extensive command, control, and surveillance facilities. *Mitrofan Moskalenko,* while in commission, seldom operates.
Disposals: *Ivan Rogov* was laid up by 1994, stricken 1-9-95, and being scrapped at Vladivostok as of 5-99. *Aleksandr Nikolayev* was under refit at Vladivostok for possible sale to Indonesia in mid-1999, but the offer was not accepted and work has since halted.
Hull systems: The hull has a pronounced bulb projecting forward below the waterline. Is equipped with bow doors and a 32-m-long articulating ramp leading to a 54-m-long by 12.3-m-wide by 3-m-high vehicle cargo deck (660 m^2 total parking area) in the forward part of the hull, while a stern door provides access to a 75-m-long by 12.8-m-wide by 8.2-m-high floodable docking well intended to accommodate up to three Lebed-class (Project 1206) air-cushion landing craft (q.v.) or six Ondatra-class (Project 1176) or T-4 (Project 1785) landing craft. The massive superstructure incorporates a helicopter hangar with a steep ramp leading downward to a helicopter pad on the foredeck and doors aft that lead to a second helicopter platform over the stern. There are also hydraulically raised ramps leading from the upper deck forward of the superstructure to both the bow doors and the docking well. Cargo capacity: 2,500 tons maximum; capable of transporting an entire naval infantry battalion and its vehicles, including 53 tanks or 80 armored personnel carriers, and trucks (load reduced to 25 tanks if landing craft are carried). The normal load is 440 troops and 79 vehicles, or a tank unit with 46 main battle tanks.
Combat systems: The Grad-M rocket launcher has a range of 20 km; each rocket produces 356 shrapnel fragments. The rockets are carried in a drum magazine and automatically loaded in two packets of 20 each. A total of 1,200 rounds are carried for the twin 76.2-mm, ZIF-67 gunmount and 16,000 rounds for the 30-mm guns. The Osa-M SAM system uses the standard ZIF-122 launcher. Each Ka-29 helicopter can transport 16 fully equipped troops and provide its own fire support with rockets, missiles, and guns.

♦ 3 Ropucha-II-class (Project 775.2) tank landing ships [LST]
Bldr: Stocznia Polnocna, Gdansk, Poland

	In serv.	Fleet
077 BDK-11	2-91	Pacific
130 BDK-61 Korolev	4-91	Baltic
151 BDK-54 Azov	20-4-90	Black Sea

BDK-54 Azov (151)
Hartmut Ehlers, 7-00

BDK-11 (077)
JMSDF, 1995

AMPHIBIOUS WARFARE SHIPS *(continued)*

BDK-61 Korolev (130)—note stern vehicle ramp H&L Van Ginderen, 10-96

D: 2,768 tons light; 3,450 tons standard (4,080 fl) **S:** 17.8 kts
Dim: 112.50 (105.00 wl) × 15.00 × 3.70 (aft)
A: 1 76.2-mm 59-cal. AK-176M DP; 2 single 30-mm 54-cal. AK-630M gatling AA; 2 40-round 122-mm UMS-73 Grad-M artillery RL (320 BM-21 rockets); 2 mine rails (up to 90 1-ton mines)
Electronics:
Radar: 2 Don-2 nav.; 1 MR-352 Pozitiv (Cross Dome) surf./air search; 1 MR-123 Vympel (Bass Tilt) gun f.c.
E/O: 1 Squeeze Box surveillance/rocket f.c.; 2 bridge periscopes
M: 2 Type 16 VB40/48 16-cyl., 500-rpm diesels; 2 props; 19,200 bhp
Electric: 1,920 kw tot. (3 × 640 kw; Cegielski-Sulzer 6A25 diesels driving)
Range: 3,500/16; 6,000/12 **Endurance:** 30 days (with landing force)
Crew: 8 officers, 79 enlisted (accomm. for 17 officers, 81 enlisted) + 225 troops

Remarks: Variant of the basic Ropucha design, substituting later defensive armament and sensors. Only three were built. Hull system data for the Ropucha-I class (q.v.) apply. BDK-54 (laid down 22-11-98 and launched 19-5-89) was named on 10-12-98; the ship had visited Greece during 10-98. BDK-54 was named and renumbered from BDK-122 during 2000.

♦ 16 Ropucha-I-class (Project 775) tank landing ships [LST]
(some in *reserve*) Bldr: Stocznia Polnocna, Gdansk, Poland

	In serv.	Fleet
012 BDK-91 Olenogorskiy Gornyak	1976	Northern
016 BDK-45	5-3-85	. . .
027 BDK-182 Kondopoga	1976	Northern
031 BDK-55 Aleksandr Otrakovskiy	1978	Northern
035 BDK-183	1977	. . .
039 BDK-32	1982	. . .
066 BDK-101 Mukhtar Avezov	19-12-81	Pacific
070 *BDK-14*	31-8-81	Pacific
102 BDK-58 Kaliningrad	9-12-84	Baltic
110 BDK-100 Aleksandr Shabalin	1985	Baltic
127 BDK-43	1983	Baltic
130 BDK-122	1989	. . .
142 BDK-46	11-87	Black Sea
156 BDK-67	1988	Black Sea
158 BDK-64 Tsezar' Kunikov	1986	Black Sea
. . . BDK-105	1982	Baltic

BDK-58 Kaliningrad (102)—with bow doors open and vehicle ramp partly lowered; the frigate *Pylkiy* (702) is in the background, at left Boris Lemachko, 2000

BDK-46 (142)—at Sevastopol' Hartmut Ehlers, 7-00

D: 2,768 tons light (4,080 fl) **S:** 17.5 kts
Dim: 112.50 (105.00 wl) × 15.00 × 3.70 (aft, loaded)

BDK-101 Mukhtar Avezov (066) JMSDF, 3-94

BDK-67 (156)—one of the handful of Ropucha-I LSTs to be equipped with two artillery rocket launchers on the foredeck Hartmut Ehlers, 7-00

A: 2 twin 57-mm 70-cal. AK-725 DP—some: 4 4-round Fasta-4M SAM syst. (32 Strela-3 or Igla-M/Gremlin missiles)—some also: 2 40-round 122-mm UMS-73 Grad-M artillery RL (360 BM-21 rockets)—all: 2 mine rails (up to 92 1-ton mines)
Electronics:
Radar: 2 Don-2 or MR-212/201 Vaygach-U (Palm Frond) nav.; 1 MR-302 Rubka (Strut Curve) surf./air search; 1 MR-103 Bars (Muff Cob) gun f.c.
M: 2 Type 16ZVB 40/48 16-cyl., 500-rpm diesels; 2 props; 19,200 bhp
Electric: 1,920 kw tot. (3 × 640 kw; Cegielski-Sulzer 6A25 diesels driving)
Range: 3,500/16; 6,000/12 **Endurance:** 30 days (with landing force)
Crew: 8 officers, 79 enlisted (accomm. for 17 officers, 81 enlisted) + 150 troops

Remarks: Russian type designation: BDK (*Bol'shoy Desantnyy Korabl',* Large Landing Ship). Builder's Project B-23. BDK-64 was refitted at Varna, Bulgaria, from 1996 to 12-98; a Baltic Fleet unit of the class was refitted at Rostock, Germany, beginning in 3-98; and BDK-182 began a refit at St. Petersburg during 7-98. BDK-58, refitted at Rostock in 1999, was named on 2-7-99. Two of the class, fleet affiliation and BDK numbers unknown, have been named *Zemlyansk* and *Nikolay Korsakov.* Some 40 enlisted personnel on BDK-101 mutinied on 18-7-00 against beatings and other cruel treatment; the offending officers and warrants were arrested. Black Sea Fleet unit BDK-46, thought to have been stricken by 1999, was undergoing reactivation overhaul at Sevastopol' during 2001.
Disposals: Pacific Fleet unit BDK-48 was stricken during 1994, followed by Pacific Fleet units BDK-63, -90, -181, and -197 on 5-7-94. Baltic Fleet unit BDK-47 was stricken 1-9-95 and Northern Fleet unit BDK-200 was stricken 30-7-98. BDK-119 was transferred to South Yemen in 1979 (and stricken there by 1999), and *Konstantin Ol'shanskiy* (BDK-56) was transferred to Ukraine 12-3-96. Pacific Fleet unit *Bobryusk* (BDK-98) and one other unit had been retired by 1999.
Hull systems: The six units in the group built 1980–85 had angled hances to the corners of the main-deck superstructure, a stern ramp with no external web reinforcing, and reinforcing gussets around the forward 57-mm gun platform. The hull has a molded depth of 8.65 m amidships and is equipped with a "beak" bow projection to aid in beaching. Fully degaussed. Have a forced ventilation system with NBC warfare filters. No vehicle cargo is carried on the upper deck; the hatch serves for loading vehicles by crane and for ventilation when vehicle motors are running. Bow and stern doors permit roll-on/roll-off loading. Cargo capacity: 482 tons; usable deck space: 540 m^2 on a full-length vehicle deck that is 95 m long and 4.5 m high, with a width of 6.5 m for the forward 55 m, narrowing to 4.5 m beneath the superstructure to the stern. Alternate cargo loads are 10 41-ton tanks with 40 vehicle crew and 150 troops; 12 amphibious tanks with 36 vehicle crew; or a mix of three 41-ton tanks, three 120-mm mine throwers, three armored cars, four trucks, five light vehicles, and 123 troops. One Pacific Fleet unit had a crane on the foredeck.
Combat systems: Several received four quadruple point-defense SAM launchers, although these may later have been removed. The entire class was intended to receive two UMS-73 barrage rocket launchers on the forecastle, but only the six most recently completed actually carried the weapons, and several of these ships have been discarded; the rockets are carried in a drum magazine, are loaded in two packets of 20 each, have a range of up to 20 km, and are fired at 0.5-second intervals. Although equipped to receive the accompanying Squeeze Box electro-optical rangefinder/director, none of the ships yet has it. Some 20 smoke floats can be carried aft. Mines can only be carried when there is no amphibious cargo. The communications suite can accommodate 15 simultaneous channels.

♦ 5 Alligator (Tapir)-class (Project 1171) tank landing ships [LST]
Bldr: Yantar Zavod, Kaliningrad

	Laid down	L	In serv.	Fleet
081 BDK-104 Nikolay Vilkov	3-9-71	30-11-73	30-7-74	Pacific
119 BDK- . . . Minsk (ex-*Donetskiy Shakhter*)	5-9-68	10-3-69	31-12-69	Baltic
148 BDK-69 Nikolay Obyekov	30-8-67	29-2-68	31-12-68	Black Sea
150 BDK-65 (ex-*Voronezhskiy Komsomolets,* ex-BDK-10)	5-2-64	1-7-64	18-8-66	Black Sea
152 BDK-. . . Nikolay Fil'chenkov	30-1-74	29-3-75	30-12-75	Black Sea

AMPHIBIOUS WARFARE SHIPS *(continued)*

Minsk (119)—in refit at Baltiysk Jaroslaw Cislak, 2000

BDK-69 Nikolay Obyekov (148) Hartmut Ehlers, 7-00

BDK-65 (150)—with two cranes forward, moored with the artillery rocket launcher–equipped *Nikolay Fil'chenkov* (152) at Sevastopol' Boris Lemachko, 7-00

Nikolay Vilkov (081)—the Pacific Fleet's only Alligator; note the artillery rocket launcher on the bow JMSDF, 3-94

D: 2,760 tons light; 2,905 tons std. (4,360 fl) **S:** 16.5 kts (16 sust.)
Dim: 113.1 (105.0 pp) × 15.6 × 4.10 (mean hull; 6.15 aft, loaded)
A: 1 twin 57-mm 70-cal. ZIF-31B DP—BDK-104 and *Fil'chenkov* only: 2 twin 25-mm 2M-3M AA; 3 4-round Fasta-4M SAM syst. (24 Strela-3 or Igla-M/Gremlin missiles)—BDK-77, BDK-104, and *Fil'chenkov* only: 1 40-round 122-mm UMS-73 Grad-M artillery RL (160 rockets)
Electronics:
Radar: 2 Don-2 and/or Mius (Spin Trough) nav.
E/O: BDK-77, BDK-104, and *Fil'chenkov* only: 1 Squeeze Box multisensor surveillance/rocket f.c.
M: 2 Type 58A diesels; 2 props; 9,000 bhp
Electric: early units: 740 kw tot. (2 × 270-kw, 2 × 100-kw diesel sets)—BDK-104 and *Fil'chenkov:* 900 kw tot. (3 × 300-kw DRG300/500-1 diesel sets)
Range: 3,500/16.5; 8,000/15
Endurance: 15 days (20 for BDK-104 and *Fil'chenkov;* 10 with landing force)
Crew: 5 officers, 50 enlisted + 440 troops (313 in BDK-65)

Remarks: Soviet type designation: BDK (*Bol'shoy Desantnyy Korabl',* Large Landing Ship). The design, by TsKB-50, was initially approved 14-2-62 but evolved continually during the time these ships were built. Also known as the Nosorog class in Russia. Survivors of 14 completed; a 15th unit, to have been named *Nikolay Golubkov,* was canceled in 1975 while under construction. Although the former *Donetskiy Shakhter* had been reported stricken on 1-9-95, the ship remained in service and underwent a refit at Baltiysk during 2000–01; she is used primarily to ferry vehicles and equipment between Kaliningrad and St. Petersburg/Kronshtadt and was renamed *Minsk* 12-3-01. BDK-69 began an overhaul during 4-01.
Disposals: Black Sea unit *Il'ya Azarov* (BDK-104) was stricken 10-1-96 and transferred to Ukraine in 4-96. Black Sea unit *Krymskiy Komsomolets* (BDK-6) was stricken in 1992, Baltic Fleet unit *Krasnaya Presnaya* on 17-11-94, and Pacific Fleet units BDK-25 (ex-*Tomskiy Komsomolets,* ex-BDK-13), BDK-80 (ex-*Petr Il'ichev*), *Sergei Lazo,* and *Aleksandr Tortsev* on 17-11-94. BDK-25 was sold for scrap in 4-95. Baltic Fleet unit BDK-62 (ex-*Komsomolets Kareliy*) was stricken during 1998 and BDK-77 (ex-*50 Let Shefstva V.L.M.S.M.*) prior to 2001.
Hull systems: Have ramps fore and aft. Their cargo hoisting equipment varies (one or two 5-ton KE26TD cranes, one 7.5-ton KE29 crane): Type I unit BDK-65 has two cranes forward; later ships had one less crane. Cargo capacity is about 600 tons for beaching and 1,750 tons in freighting service; can carry 20 tanks, plus lighter vehicles on upper decks. The tank deck is 90 m long and totals 850 m^2 in area. Nominal vehicle capacity is 20 MAZ-543 or 52 ZIL-131, or 85 GAZ-66 trucks. Troops are accommodated below the tank deck under cramped conditions in the lower, No. 3 hold. The engines are Model 58A-3 in *Minsk* and Model 58A-4 in BDK-104 and *Nikolay Fil'chenkov.*
Combat systems: In Type IV pair (BDK-104 and *Fil'chenkov*), a 40-tube, 140-mm UMS-73 rocket launcher forward for shore bombardment was added; they also have two twin 25-mm AA mounts aft in addition to the other armament. The open 57-mm gun mounting is locally controlled; 1,200 rounds of ammunition are normally carried. The communications suite can handle six channels simultaneously.

♦ 1 Polnocny-C-class (Project 773) medium landing ship [LSM]
Bldr: Stocznia Polnocna, Gdansk, Poland (In serv. 1971)

. . . SDK-154

Polnocny-C class—a since-stricken Baltic Fleet unit Hartmut Ehlers, 9-93

D: 920 tons (1,192 fl) **S:** 16 kts
Dim: 81.30 (76.00 wl) × 9.30 (9.00 wl) × 1.20 (fwd; 2.60 aft)
A: 2 twin 30-mm 65-cal. AK-230 AA; 2 18-round 140-mm WM-18 barrage RL; 4 Fasta-4M (SA-N-8) SAM launchers (32 Strela-3M or Igla-M/Gremlin missiles)
Electronics: Radar: 1 Mius (Spin Trough) nav.; 1 MR-104 Rys' (Drum Tilt) gun f.c.
M: 2 Type 40DM diesels; 2 props; 4,400 bhp
Range: 900/16; 3,000/12 **Endurance:** 3 days
Crew: 5 officers, 36 enlisted + 160 troops

Remarks: Russian designation: SDK (*Sredniy Desantnyy Korabl',* Medium Landing Ship). Eight were built. Operates in the Caspian Flotilla.
Disposals: There were four Black Sea Fleet units, of which SDK-137 has been transferred to Ukraine, one now serves in the Caspian Flotilla, and SDK-82 was stricken 30-7-93. Pacific Fleet unit SDK-135 was sold in 1994 and converted to a commercial cargo vessel and renamed *Nadezhda.* Two others have been discarded, including Baltic Fleet unit SDK-156 on 1-9-95. Northern Fleet unit SDK-164 was being scrapped as of 11-01.
Hull systems: A lengthened and broadened version of the Polnocny-B, with a 53.3-m-long by 6.7-m-wide by 3.8-m-high vehicle deck. Carry up to 250 tons cargo. Differ from near-sister *Grunwald* in the Polish Navy in having a full-length tank deck and no command facilities. See Polnocny-B class entry for additional remarks.

Note: The two remaining Polnocny-B-class (Project 771) medium landing craft have been redesignated as cargo transports and can be found under [AK].

♦ 3 Pomornik (Zubr)-class (Project 1232.2) air-cushion vehicle landing craft [LCUA]
Bldr: Sudostroitel'noye Obyedineniye "Almaz," Dekabristov SY, St. Petersburg

770 MDK-118 (In serv. . . .)
782 MDK-94 (In serv. 15-10-91)
795 MDK-108 (In serv. 10-8-94)

MDK-94 (782) Boris Lemachko, 7-00

AMPHIBIOUS WARFARE SHIPS *(continued)*

MDK-94 (782)—on shore, with stern ramp down Jaroslaw Cislak, 7-01

D: 340 tons light; 415 tons normal (550 fl) **S:** 63 kts (55 sust.)
Dim: 57.3 (56.2 hull) × 25.6 (22.0 hull) × 21.9 (high)
A: 2 4-round Fasta-4M (SA-N-8) SAM syst. (32 Igla-M/Gremlin missiles); 2 single 30-mm 54-cal. AK-630M gatling AA; 2 22-round 140-mm MS-227 Ogon' retractable artillery RL (132 rockets); up to 80 mines in lieu of vehicle cargo, using portable rails
Electronics:
Radar: 1 SRN-207 Ekran (Curl Stone-B) nav.; 1 MR-123-2 Vympel (Bass Tilt) gun f.c.
E/O: 1 Quad Look multisensor surveillance and rocket f.c.
M: 5 NK-12MV (M-70) gas turbines (12,100 shp each/10,000 shp sust.; 2 to power lift fans); 3 ducted 5.5-m-dia. CP airscrew propellers, 4 NO-10 2.5-m-dia. lift fans; 36,300 shp for propulsion
Electric: 300 or 400 kw tot. (4 × 75- or 100-kw GTG-110 gas turbine sets)
Range: 300/55 with 130-ton payload; 1,000/55 light **Fuel:** 56 tons (180 m^3)
Endurance: 5 days (1 with full troop complement)
Crew: 4 officers, 7 warrant officers, 20 enlisted + 140–360 troops

Remarks: Project name is Zubr ("Bison"). Are too large for shipboard transportation and are intended for short-range independent assault operations. Hull numbers are in the MDK (*Mal'yy Desantnyy Korabl',* Small Landing Ship) category. There are apparently significant reliability problems with the design; they were originally intended to have a 16-year service life. The only remaining units serve in the Baltic Fleet, where one has been in reserve and the other operates only twice per year; they are to be refitted using the profits from the sale of two to Greece, which has purchased one new and the refurbished Baltic Fleet unit MDK-50 from Russia and two refurbished units from Ukraine. One was named *Yevgeniy Kocheschkov* early in 2002.
Disposals: Work on two others at St. Petersburg had been halted for about two years as of 7-95, and attempts were being made to sell them for commercial purposes; approval to scrap them was given early in 7-97, and one was sold to Greece during 6-99 and delivered during 9-01. The class prototype, assigned to the Baltic Fleet, had been scrapped by mid-1998, and two others followed by 1999. Black Sea Fleet units MDK-57, -93, and -123 were transferred to Ukraine 1-3-96.
Hull systems: The complex hull structure employs light alloys, some of which are flammable. The vehicle deck can hold up to 10 BTR-70 armored amphibious personnel transport vehicles or three T-80B main battle tanks plus a detachment of infantry—or up to 140 troops and 130 tons of combat cargo. Have small bow and stern ramps. Navigational equipment includes a gyrocompass, Decca radionavigation system receiver, drift indicator, and NAVSAT receiver.
Propulsion systems: Three of the gas-turbine engines are mounted on pylons and drive airscrew propellers; they are equipped with exhaust thrust diverters to enhance mobility. The two lift-fan gas turbines drive four blowers to maintain skirt pressure and are mounted near the stern in the wing compartments; they exhaust through the stern.
Combat systems: The Quad Look electro-optical device is a modified Squeeze Box that has no weather cover; there is also a television camera mounted just below the pilothouse. The navigational radar is mounted within a lozenge-shaped radome. The retractable MS-227 artillery rocket launchers are located near the bow in the hull wing-walls and are reloaded below decks. The rockets have a range of 4.5–10 km, depending on type, and are ripple fired at 0.2-second intervals; they are launched via the DVU-3 control system.

♦ 2 Aist (Dzheryan)-class (Project 1232.1) air-cushion vehicle amphibious landing craft [LCUA]
Bldr: Sudostroitel'noye Obyedineniye "Almaz," Dekabristov SY, St. Petersburg (In serv. 1970–85)

700 MDK-. . . 722 MDK-113

D: 231 tons light; 298 tons std. (355 fl) **S:** 70 kts light (50 sust., loaded)
Dim: 47.80 (45.50 hull) × 17.50 × 0.3 (1.3 at rest)
A: 2 4-round Fasta-4M (SA-N-8) SAM syst. (32 9M-36 Strela-3 or Igla-M/Gremlin missiles); 2 twin 30-mm 65-cal. AK-230 AA
Electronics:
Radar: 1 Mius (Spin Trough) nav.; 1 MR-104 Rys' (Drum Tilt) f.c.
EW: no intercept; 2 16-round PK-16 fixed decoy RL
M: 2 DT-4 gas turbines; 4 AV-70 airscrew props, 2 lift fans; 31,558 shp
Electric: 60 kw (2 × 30-kw diesel sets)
Range: 100/45; 208/40 **Fuel:** 47 tons **Endurance:** 5 days
Crew: 3 officers, 18 enlisted + up to 220 troops

MDK-113 (722)—on beaching pad at Baltiysk Hartmut Ehlers, 9-95

Remarks: Eighteen were built. Typed MDK (*Mal'yy Desantnyy Korabl',* Small Landing Ship). The designed service life was not more than 16 years. Three Black Sea Fleet units were transferred to the Federal Border Guard around 1996 and are now employed as patrol craft in the Caspian Sea. MDK-113 was active as of 7-00, based at Baltiysk, as is pennant 700.
Disposals: Baltic Fleet units VP-103 and VP-117 were for sale for scrap in 1992, and two more Baltic units were discarded during 1993.
Hull systems: Have bow and stern ramps. Cargo capacity: 74 tons (2 T-62 or T-64 tanks, or 4 PT-76 tanks, or 5 BTR-60 armored personnel carriers), plus 220 troops; normal load, however, is around 50 tons. The DT-4 gas turbines are marinized versions of the NK-12 aircraft engine. Early units had riveted aluminum hulls, later ones welded; the hull structure experienced considerable corrosion in service.
Combat systems: Carry 2,000 rounds of 30-mm ammunition. Early units did not have the point-defense SAM launchers.

♦ 14 Vydra-class (Project 106K) utility landing craft [LCU]
Bldr: Nikolayevsk-na-Amur Zavod (In serv. 1967–69)

612 MDK-23	625 MDK-181	646 MDK-190	. . . MDK-170
613 MDK-175	630 MDK-176	652 MDK-192	. . . MDK-191
622 MDK-200	639 MDK-193	653 MDK-173	
623 MDK-155	641 MDK-159	. . . MDK-168	

Vydra class—typical Russian Navy unit H&L Van Ginderen, 1995

D: 308 tons light (550 fl) **S:** 10.5 kts
Dim: 54.50 (50.00 pp) × 7.70 (7.50 wl) × 2.25 (mean hull)
Electronics: Radar: 1 Don-2 nav.
M: 2 Type 3D12 diesels; 2 Kort-nozzle props; 600 bhp
Range: 1,400/10 loaded **Endurance:** 8 days **Crew:** 12 tot.

Remarks: Type designation: MDK (*Mal'yy Desantniy Korabl',* Small Landing Craft). Retain their amphibious warfare craft alphanumeric names and pennant numbers, although most are probably primarily employed as logistic support craft. The cargo deck is 30.0 × 4.5 m and can accommodate up to 176 tons of vehicles or cargo (6 ZIL-131 or 10 GAZ-66 trucks). Survivors of 46 built for Russian use; others were built for Bulgaria (21, of which two were transferred to Georgia during 2001) and Egypt (10). One other active unit has been redesignated as a service craft (see under [YF]), and MDK-174 operates for the Federal Border Guard. Sister *Tarpan* (OS-237), employed for trials duties, was stricken 10-1-96 and transferred to Ukraine. Caspian Flotilla unit MDK-21 was converted from 12-99 to 6-00 at Astrakhan as the civilian research craft *Geofisik-4.*

♦ 3 Lebed (Kal'mar)-class (Project 1206) air-cushion landing craft [LCMA]
Bldr: Sudostroitel'noye Obyedineniye "Almaz," Dekabristov SY, St. Petersburg, or Yuzhnaya Tochka Zavod, Feodosiya, Ukraine

	In serv.		In serv.
557 D-146	1983	602 D-141	1982
600 D-457	1985		

D: 70 tons (87 fl) **S:** 70 kts max. **Dim:** 24.8 × 10.8 × 1.3 (at rest)
A: 1 twin 12.7-mm Ütes-M mg **Electronics:** Radar: 1 . . . nav.
M: 2 AL-20K gas turbines; 2 shrouded airscrew props; 20,000 shp (16,000 sust.)
Range: 100/60 **Fuel:** 12.7 tons **Crew:** 2 officers, 4 enlisted + 120 troops

Remarks: Entire class of 20 had been believed to have been retired by end-1997, but it was reported in 2000 that four remained in the Northern Fleet, of which D-454 (pennant 543) was photographed on 21-7-00 loading for transit via the canal and river system from the Northern Fleet for operations with the Federal Border Guard in the Caspian. Of the remainder, one was transferred to Vietnam and the others had been retired by the late 1990s. Can carry one or two armored personnel carriers or 120 troops or about 35 tons of cargo. Have a bow ramp only.

Note: Ten Tsaplya-class (Project 1206.1) air-cushion landing craft are operated by the Federal Border Guard (q.v.).

AMPHIBIOUS WARFARE SHIPS *(continued)*

Lebed class—typical unit, since retired from the Northern Fleet 7-94

♦ 2 Serna-class (Project 1177.0) fast landing craft [LCM]

Bldr: Volga Zavod, Nizhniy Novgorod

	In serv.		In serv.
747 DKA-67	4-5-95	. . . DKA-. . .	2001

DKA-67 (747)—with a Ropucha-class LST in the background
Hartmut Ehlers, 7-96

D: 53 tons light (105 fl) **S:** 30 kts **Dim:** 25.65 × 5.85 × 1.52 (1.30 at speed)
A: shoulder-launched Strela-3 (SA-16) SAMs; 3 single 7.62-mm PKMB mg
Electronics: Radar: 1 Liman nav.
M: 2 Zvezda M-503A-3 diesels; 2 shrouded props; 3,300 bhp
Electric: 32 kw tot (2 × 16-kw DGR-16/1,500 diesel sets)
Range: 100/30 loaded; 600/30 half-load **Crew:** 4 tot.

Remarks: Private venture design by the R. Alekseyev Central Hydrofoil Design Bureau. Five were built, two of which were sold to a commercial operator in the United Arab Emirates in 1994, one was sold to Estonia in 1994, DKA-67 was delivered to the Baltic Fleet, and a second naval unit was intended for use by the Caspian Flotilla. "Serna" is the builder's project name and is also used as the NATO nickname.
Hull systems: Have a useful load of 45–50 tons on the 13 × 4 × 2.5–m cargo deck that extends about 2 m beneath the pilothouse. A portable canopy and seats for 100 personnel can be installed on the vehicle deck. The semi-planing hull incorporates an air cavity to provide underhull lubrication. Aluminum-magnesium alloy construction. Have an articulating bow ramp. Range with half load of 600 n.m. can be achieved by using reserve void tanks to carry fuel.

♦ 23 Ondatra (Akula)-class (Project 1176) landing craft [LCM]

(In serv. 1979–91)

533 DKA-182	640 DKA-704	660 DKA-702	690 DKA-142
578 DKA-148	643 DKA-277	672 DKA-295	692 DKA-512
590 DKA-464	644 DKA-424	674 DKA-348	713 DKA-460
631 DKA-337	650 DKA-426	677 DKA-70	722 DKA-288
635 DKA-52	654 DKA-347	679 DKA-343	799 DKA-325
637 DKA-423	659 DKA-143	682 DKA-536	

DKA-460 (713)—at St. Petersburg Hartmut Ehlers, 7-96

D: 90 tons normal (107.3 fl) **S:** 11.5 kts **Dim:** 24.50 × 6.00 × 1.55
A: none **Electronics:** Radar: 1 Mius (Spin Trough) nav. (portable)
M: 2 Type 3D12 diesels; 2 props; 600 bhp **Range:** 330/10; 500/5
Endurance: 2 days **Crew:** 5 tot. (enlisted)

Remarks: Typed DKA (*Desantnyy Kater,* Landing Craft). In all, 29 were built for use aboard the *Ivan Rogov*–class landing ships. Two were transferred to Yemen in 1983, one is in Georgian service, and DK-305 and DK-455 were transferred to Ukraine in 1997. The cargo well is 13.7 × 3.9 m and can accommodate one 40-ton tank or up to 50 tons of general cargo; some 20 troops/vehicle crew can be carried.

♦ up to 73 T-4 class (Project 1785) landing craft [LCM]

Bldr: . . . (In serv. 1968–74)

T-4 class—standard-configuration, late-construction unit
H&L Van Ginderen, 1995

D: 35 tons light (93 fl) **S:** 10 kts (light) **Dim:** 20.4 × 5.4 × 1.2 (max. aft)
M: 2 Type 3D6 diesels; 2 props; 300 bhp
Range: 300/8 **Endurance:** 2 days **Crew:** 2 tot.

Remarks: Some 76 were said still to be in service as of 2001, but among those were at least three that had been redesignated for service craft duties. Can accommodate up to 50 tons of cargo on the 9.5 × 3.9–m vehicle deck. D-305 and D-455 of the Black Sea Fleet were transferred to Ukraine in 1996–97.

Note: Two other LCM designs, the Project 1733 Vostok class and Project 20150 Slavyanka class, now seem to be used only for service craft functions and are listed below under [YFU].

♦ up to 6 Gus (Skat)-class (Project 1205) air-cushion personnel landing craft [LCPA]

Bldr: Sudostroitel'noye Obyedineniye "Almaz," Dekabristov Zavod, St. Petersburg (In serv. 1969–76)

631 D-357	698 D-448	. . . D-442
634 D-732	. . . D-338	. . . D-446

Gus class—in camouflage paint scheme H&L Van Ginderen, 1992

D: 17 tons light (27.2 fl) **S:** 49 kts (loaded) **Dim:** 21.3 × 8.4 × 0.2 (at rest)
M: 2 TVD-10 turboprop engines; 2,340 shp—1 TVD-10 gas turbine lift-fan engine; 780 shp
Range: 185/50 light; 230/43 loaded **Crew:** 7 tot. + 24 troops

Remarks: Survivors of 32 built. A small number had a second control cab above and behind the normal one, for training purposes. Troops debark via two ladders on either side forward.

SWIMMER DELIVERY VEHICLES [LSDV]

♦ up to 24 Triton-II (Project 908) special forces submersibles

B-520 through B-543 series

D: 5.7 tons sub. **S:** 6 kts sub.
Dim: 9.50 × 1.90 × 1.60 **M:** 1 electric motor; 1 prop; . . . shp
Range: 60/6 **Endurance:** 12 hours **Crew:** 6 tot. combat swimmers

Remarks: Triton-II was offered for export in 1994 and is also in use by Russian special forces (Spetsnaz), who employ several different types of swimmer-delivery vehicles. Designed by Firma Malakhit, St. Petersburg, under Yu. K. Mineyev. Diving depth: 40 m.

SWIMMER DELIVERY VEHICLES [LSDV] *(continued)*

Note: LSDV designs offered for foreign sale during 1993 included the Project 907 Triton, a 1.6-ton, 5.0-m-long device with a speed of 6 kts for 6 hours and capable of carrying two combat swimmers. A total of eight Triton vehicles are said to have been constructed, B-483 through B-490. The Sirena-UME combat diver chariot can be launched from a 533-mm torpedo tube and is 11.3 m long; displacing 1.6 tons submerged, it has a range of 8 n.m. at 4 kts and can dive to 40 m.

AUXILIARIES

Note: The numbers of ships remaining within the various auxiliary and service craft classes are more difficult to determine because they tend not to be sold abroad for scrapping to the same extent as are combatants (which have the more valuable metals in greater proportion). Further, many such units are kept in commission for accommodations use but no longer perform their primary functions. Insofar as possible, the number of still commissioned but nonoperational units for the classes below, where known, is given at the end of the class header; most of these ships are being used for berthing facilities, if at all, and few will ever return to service; nonetheless, because they have not yet been formally discarded, they are recorded here.

♦ 19 Bereza (SR-28)-class (Polish Project 130) deperming ships [ADG] (3 or more in reserve)

Bldr: Stocznia Polnocna, Gdansk, Poland (In serv. 1985–90)

SR-23	SR-120	SR-253	SR-560	SR-936
SR-28	SR-137	SR-278	SR-569	SR-938
SR-59	SR-216	SR-479	SR-570	SR-939
SR-74	SR-245	SR-541	SR-933	

Black Sea Fleet Bereza SR-939 Boris Lemachko, 7-00

Caspian Flotilla Bereza SR-933 Boris Lemachko, 7-95

D: 1,850 tons (2,051 fl) **S:** 13.8 kts **Dim:** 69.50 × 13.80 × 3.99
Electronics: Radar: 1 Mius-M (Kivach) nav.
M: 2 Zgoda-Sulzer 8AL25/30, 750-rpm diesels; 2 CP Kort-nozzle props; 2,940 bhp—bow-thruster
Electric: 1,185 kVA + 1,550 kw tot. (2 × 480 kVA, 1 × 225 kVA, 2 × 645 kw, 1 × 260 kw)
Range: 1,000/13.8 **Endurance:** 30 days **Crew:** 50 tot. (civilian)

Remarks: SR = *Sudno Razmagnichivanya* (Deperming Vessel); intended for "degaussing surface ships and submarines, conducting magnetic field measurements of ships and vessels, [and] regulating ground fault neutralizers." SR-74, -216, -479, -569, and one other are assigned to the Northern Fleet; SR-23, -28, -120, -245, -479, -570, and -936 to the Baltic Fleet; SR-933 to the Caspian Flotilla; and SR-59, -137, -541, and -939 to the Black Sea Fleet.
Disposals: One sister was delivered to Bulgaria in mid-1989. Of two more that were building at the time of the collapse of the Soviet Union, one remained nearly complete at the builder's yard as of 7-98 and has been altered for Polish Navy service. Sister SR-568 was stricken from the Black Sea Fleet 10-1-96 and was in Ukraine service as of 8-97. SR-548 was no longer in service as of 2001.
Hull systems: Data listed above are from a Polish source; Russian Navy data indicate a displacement of 2,090 tons full load. Can service two ships simultaneously. Have three laboratories, a machine shop, and a cable hold. A large crane is fitted aft to handle deperming cables.

♦ 22 Pelym (SR-218)-class (Project 1799 and 1799A) deperming ships [ADG] (5 or more in reserve)

Bldr: Khabarovsk (14 units) and Gorokhovtse Shipyards (In serv. 1971–87)

SR-26	SR-180	SR-218	SR-233	SR-334	SR-409
SR-77	SR-188	SR-220	SR-276	SR-344	SR-455
SR-111	SR-203	SR-221	SR-280	SR-370	
SR-179	SR-215	SR-222	SR-281	SR-373	

Baltic Fleet Pelym-class SR-203—a mid-series unit with a tripod mast aft Boris Lemachko, 2000

Pacific Fleet Pelym-class SR-111—a late-construction unit with the forecastle deck extended to the stern Boris Lemachko, 2000

D: 1,050 tons (1,200 fl) **S:** 13.5 kts **Dim:** 64.06 × 11.71 × 3.51
Electronics: Radar: 1 Donets-2 nav.
M: 1 1,200-kw diesel generating set, 2 300-kw diesel generating sets, electric drive; 1 prop; 1,740 shp (1,536 sust.)
Range: 1,000/13.5; 2,500/12 **Endurance:** 15 days **Crew:** 43 tot. (civilian)

Remarks: SR = *Sudno Razmagnichivanya* (Deperming Vessel). Late units have a tripod mast aft to support radio antenna wires; early ships had an aerial spreader on the stack. The final variant (Project 1799A) had the forecastle deck extended right aft to the stern to provide stowage for a rectangular raft of unknown function. As of 2000, SR-215, -218, -220, -276, -280, -334, -409, and -455 were in the Northern Fleet; SR-203 in the Baltic Fleet; SR-26 and -344 in the Black Sea Fleet; and SR-77, -111, -180, -188, -221, -222, -233, -281, -370, and -373 in the Pacific.
Disposals: One was transferred to Cuba in 2-82. Pacific Fleet unit SR-191 was stricken 5-7-94, and Baltic Fleet unit SR-70 on 1-9-95. Baltic Fleet unit SR-241 sank at Kronshtadt during the winter of 1998–99, and SR-407 was stripped and readied for scrapping by 8-00; others also may have been discarded or be in reserve.

Note: The surviving Sekstan-class (Project 220) deperming tenders are listed under [YDG] in the Service Craft section.

♦ 1 Finik-class (Project 872) munitions transport [AE]

Bldr: Stocznia Polnocna, Gdansk, Poland (In serv. 1979–81)

VTR-75 (ex-OS-265, ex-GS-265)

Finik-class VTR-75—with T-43GKS-class signature-monitoring ship SFP-17 alongside Hartmut Ehlers, 7-00

D: 950 tons (1,186 fl) **S:** 13.8 kts **Dim:** 61.30 × 11.80 (10.80 wl) × 3.28
Electronics: Radar: 2 Don-2 nav.

AUXILIARIES *(continued)*

M: 2 Cegielski-Sulzer diesels; 2 CP props; 1,920 bhp—2 75-kw electric motors for quiet, 6-kt operations—130-kw bow-thruster
Electric: 675 kVA tot. **Range:** 3,000/13; 4,800/11 **Endurance:** 15 days
Crew: 5 officers, 23 unlicensed (civilian)

Remarks: Polish B-91 design. Black Sea Fleet unit built as a hydrographic survey ship and navigational aids tender, later employed as a trials ship (OS-265), and by 7-00 redesignated as a munitions carrier. Based at Sevastopol'.
Hull systems: Intended for navigational buoy-tending and hydrographic survey duties, for which four echo sounders are fitted. Up to three fiberglass 3-dwt utility landing craft can be stowed on the buoy working deck beneath the 7-ton crane.

♦ 3 Amga-class (Project 1791) ballistic-missile transports [AEM]
(1 in *reserve*)
Bldr: Krasnoye Sormovo SY, Nizhniy Novgorod

AMGA (In serv. 12-72) DAUGAVA (In serv. 30-12-80) VETLUGA (In serv. 1976)

Vetluga Boris Lemachko, 1998

Daugava—with new missile-handling crane Boris Lemachko, 2000

D: *Amga:* 3,300 tons light (4,480 fl) **S:** 15.5 (*Amga:* 14.5) kts
Dim: *Amga:* 102.00 × 17.80 × 4.50 (see remarks)
A: 2 twin 25-mm 80-cal. 2M-3M AA **Electronics:** Radar: 1 Don-2 nav.
M: 2 Type 67B (12DRPN 23/2 × 30) (*Amga:* Type 37D) diesels; 2 props; 7,500 (*Amga:* 4,000) bhp
Range: 4,500/12 (*Amga:* 4,000/12) **Endurance:** 20 days **Crew:** 56 tot.

Remarks: Have ice-reinforced hulls and one 55-ton crane with a reach of 34 m. Intended to transport ballistic missiles for strategic submarines. *Vetluga* (Project 1791M) is 109.8 m. *Daugava* (Project 1791P) is 113.2 m long and displaces 6,200 tons (fl); since delivery in 1976, she has been equipped with a new, more robust missile-handling crane boom, with solid sides. *Vetluga* and *Daugava* are in the Pacific Fleet; *Amga,* which has a lower-powered propulsion plant, is in the Northern Fleet, in reserve. An RSN-50 ballistic missile was dropped alongside the *Vetluga* at Konyushkov Bay, 60 km east of Vladivostok, on 16-6-00, causing a fire and smoke that severely injured a dozen or more personnel.

♦ 2 Lama-class (Project 323B) cruise missile transports [AEM]
Bldr: Chernomorets Zavod, Nikolayev, Ukraine

	In serv.
GENERAL RYABAKOV (ex-PRTB-13, ex-PM-873, ex-PM-877)	1979
VTR-33 (ex-PRTB-33, ex-*Voronezh,* ex-PM-874, ex-PM-873)	1972

D: 4,045 tons (5,000 fl) **S:** 13 kts **Dim:** 112.80 × 15.50 × 4.40
A: *Ryabakov* only: 1 twin 57-mm 70-cal. AK-725 DP
Electronics:
Radar: *Ryabakov:* 2 Don-2 nav.; 1 MR-302 Rubka (Strut Curve) air search; 1 MR-103 Bars (Muff Cob) f.c.—VTR-33: 2 Don-2 nav.; 1 Fut-N (Slim Net) surf./air search
M: 2 Type 1D-46 (6DN 39/45) diesels; 2 props; 2,600 bhp
Range: 2,000/10 **Endurance:** 15 days **Crew:** up to 154 civilians

General Ryabakov Hartmut Ehlers, 7-00

VTR-33—as *Voronezh* H&L Van Ginderen, 7-96

Remarks: Designation as PRTB (*Plavuchaya Raketno-Tekhnicheskaya Basa,* Floating Missile Technical Base) indicates that the ships are capable of servicing nuclear warheads. Survivors of seven Project 323–series units built. Both are stationed in the Black Sea Fleet at Sevastopol' and are operated by civilian crews. VTR-33 was most recently renamed during 8-99.
Disposals: Northern Fleet unit PRTB-15 (ex-PM-44, ex-PM-93) was offered for scrap during 1992. Pacific Fleet unit PRTB-20 (ex-. . .) was stricken 30-7-93 and PTB-24 (ex-PM-150) and PRTB-43 (ex-PM-150) on 5-7-94; PTB-8 (ex-. . .) was also stricken in 1994. *Kolomiya* (U 533, ex-PRTB-13) was transferred to Ukraine in 1996 but was later scrapped at Inkerman, beginning late in 1999.
Hull systems: VTR-33 was designed to serve small missile craft and could carry 12 Styx-series reload missiles; the ship has two 10-ton precision cranes. *General Ryabakov* has larger cranes and was originally intended to transport SS-N-3-series missiles.
Combat systems: The former armament of one twin 57-mm 70-cal. ZIF-31B DP and two twin 25-mm 2M-3M AA has been removed from VTR-33, and the armament on *Ryabakov* is probably nonoperational.

Disposal note: As of late 2000, the ballistic-missile transport *Aleksandr Brykin,* completed in 1987, was lying out of service at Rosta, with armament and life rafts removed. The ship is believed to have been stricken, as she was not flying any national ensign.

♦ 6 Mayak-class (Project 502R) provisions transports [AFT]
Bldrs: Dnepr SY, Kiev; Volgograd; Khabarovsk; and Yaroslavl (In serv. 1965–70)

LAMA MIUS NEMAN RIONI UL'MA VYTEGRA

Mius—outboard sister *Lama* Werner Globke, 8-97

D: 770 tons (950 fl) **S:** 12.1 kts (11 sust.) **Dim:** 54.3 × 9.3 × 3.6
Electronics: Radar: 1 Mius (Spin Trough) nav.
M: 1 8NVD 48AU diesel; 800 bhp **Electric:** 300 kw tot. (3 × 100-kw diesel sets)
Range: 6,000/11; 8,300/9 **Fuel:** 127 tons **Endurance:** 30 days
Crew: 29 tot. (civilian)

AUXILIARIES *(continued)*

Remarks: 690 grt. Former trawlers. Refrigerated fish holds were converted to carry provisions for deployed forces. *Rioni* and *Vytegra* are assigned to the Northern Fleet, *Neman* and *Ul'ma* to the Pacific Fleet, and *Lama* and *Mius* to the Black Sea Fleet. Some, including both Black Sea Fleet units, may be inactive.
Disposals: Pacific Fleet unit *Ishim* was stricken 1-9-95. Black Sea Fleet sister *Buzuluk* was stricken 10-1-96 and transferred to Ukraine on 1-8-97. Other naval sisters operated as intelligence collectors, and several became ASW training ships (all now stricken).

♦ 2 Tomba-class (Project 802) generator ships [AG]
(1 *nonoperational*) Bldr: A. Warski SY, Szczecin, Poland (In serv. 1978)

ENS-244 ENS-348

Tomba-class ENS-244—under tow, with an Okhtenskiy-class tug alongside aft
Boris Lemachko, 2000

D: 4,101 tons (5,411 fl) **S:** 12.5 kts **Dim:** 108.60 × 16.50 × 4.50
Electronics: Radar: 1 Don-2 nav.; 1 Mius (Spin Trough) nav.
M: 1 Zgoda-Sulzer 6TAD-48 diesel; 1 prop; 3,000 bhp
Electric: 6,400 kw tot. (8 × 800-kw diesel sets)
Range: 23,800/12 **Fuel:** 405 tons **Endurance:** 30 days
Crew: 3 officers, 46 enlisted

Remarks: ENS = *Elektrostantsiye Nativatel'noye Sudno* (Electric Power Station and Steam-Source Ship). Have two stacks and a "mack" on the forecastle, all containing diesel-engine exhausts, while the stack amidships also has the uptake from a large auxiliary boiler. Have two 1.5-ton cranes. ENS-348 is in the Pacific Fleet and may be being used to provide power to facilities ashore; ENS-244 is based at Severomorsk and appears to be nonoperational.
Disposals: Northern Fleet sister ENS-254 has been stricken and Northern Fleet unit ENS-357 was stricken 1-9-95.

♦ 3 Vytegrales-class (Project 1998) search-and-rescue ships [AG]
Bldr: Zhdanov Zavod, St. Petersburg (In serv. 1964–66)

508 Apsheron (ex-*Vagalets*) 208 Sevan (ex-*Svir'les*)
506 Dauriya (ex-*Vyborglets*)

Sevan (208)—one of two modified with enhanced helicopter facilities
F. Behling, 7-97

Dauriya (506)—largely unmodified since original conversion; note the two parabolic reflector antennas now installed abreast the signal mast atop the bridge
Hartmut Ehlers, 7-00

D: 4,760 tons (7,230 fl) **S:** 15 kts **Dim:** 126.00 (114.00 pp) × 16.70 × 5.60
Electronics:
Radar: 2 MR-212/201 Vaygach-U (Palm Frond) nav./surf. search (*Dauriya:* 2 Don-2 nav.)—*Apsheron* and *Sevan* only: 1 Fly Screen landing aid
TACAN: *Apsheron* and *Sevan* only: 2 Privod (Round House)
M: 1 Bryansk–Burmeister & Wain 950 VTBF 110 diesel; 1 prop; 5,200 bhp
Range: 7,380/14.5 **Fuel:** 462 tons **Endurance:** 60 days **Crew:** 90 tot. (naval)

Remarks: Originally built as Project 596P merchant timber carriers, then converted to space-event support ships by the addition of more communications facilities and a helicopter platform over the stern—consequently losing access to the after hold. Although they have been used as fleet supply ships and flagships, they are still considered to be search-and-rescue vessels. *Apsheron* (painted white) and *Dauriya* (with black hull and white superstructure) are assigned to the Black Sea Fleet; *Sevan* (painted white) was resubordinated to the Baltic Fleet Search and Rescue Brigade in 7-97. The previous edition confused the *Apsheron* and *Dauriya.*
Disposals: Black Sea Fleet sister *Dikson* (ex-*Vostok-3*) was further converted to a weapons trials ship (Project 59610); she was stricken 30-7-93 and scrapped in 1995. *Donbass* (ex-*Vostok-4*) was stricken 30-7-93 and towed to Turkey for scrapping in 2-95. Sister *Yamal* was reconverted to a standard commercial cargo ship during 1995 at Kaliningrad. *Baskunchak* (ex-*Kirishi*) and *Taman'* (ex-*Suzdal'*) were stricken 10-1-96 and transferred to Ukraine 12-3-96. Seven sisters, all now stricken, were converted to serve the Academy of Sciences as satellite-tracking ships.
Hull systems: A deckhouse was built over hold no. 3 forward of the superstructure in *Sevan* during the 1980s. In 1991, *Apsheron* completed an extensive refit and alteration at Sevastopol' and was equipped with a 13 × 11.5 × 6–m hangar for two helicopters and new electronics including two Vaygach-U (Palm Frond) radars in place of Don-2, Round House helicopter-control TACAN, and Fly Screen helicopter landing aid radar antennas. By 1993, *Sevan* had completed a similar refit and modernization. *Dauriya* has been given two large parabolic reflector antennas abreast the signal mast but otherwise is little altered since the original conversion.

♦ 18 Onega-class (Project 1806 and 1806.1) environmental-monitoring ships [AG] (12 *nonoperational*)
Bldr: Zelenodol'sk Zavod (In serv. 9-73 to 1996)

Akademik Isanin (ex-GKS-83)	*SFP-177*
Akademik Semenikhin	SFP-183
Georgiy Chernishev	*SFP-224*
GKS-224	SFP-283 (ex-GKS-283)
GKS-240	*SFP-288*
GKS-286	*SFP-295*
Inzhener Akulov	*SFP-372*
SFP-95 (ex-GKS-95)	*SFP-542*
SFP-173	*SFP-562*

Baltic Fleet Onega SFP-283—an early-construction unit with pylon masts and a stand-alone after deckhouse
Boris Lemachko, 2000

Black Sea Fleet Onega SFP-183—a late-construction unit with lattice masts, the stack set much further aft, and an air-sampling station emplaced abaft the stack
Hartmut Ehlers, 7-00

D: 1,300–1,350 tons (1,410–1,460 fl) **S:** 14 kts
Dim: 80.00 × 11.60 × 3.17–3.27
Electronics:
Radar: 1 Don-2 nav.—some also: 1 . . . nav.
Sonar: Arktika-M passive array; active dipping set
M: 2 diesels; 2 props; 2,800 bhp **Electric:** 800 kw tot. (4 × 200-kw diesel sets)
Range: 1,000/10 **Endurance:** 15 days **Crew:** 45 tot.

Remarks: GKS = *Gidroakusticheskoye Kontrol'noye Sudno* (Hydroacoustic Monitoring Ship); SFP (*Sudna Fizicheskiy Postroeniy,* Physical Fields Measuring Post) on later and redesignated units indicates a somewhat different mission and sensors. Officially said to be intended to "measure acoustic, magnetic, low-frequency, electromagnetic, electric, and heat fields set up by surface ships and submarines for compliance with existing standards and specifications." SFP-173 and SFP-177 were delivered in 1991. *Akademik Semenikhin,* which is in the GKS configuration, was commissioned 15-10-92 and the similar *Akademik Isanin* and *Inzhener Akulov* in 1994 and 1996, respectively; *Georgiy Chernishev* is said to have been delivered during 2000. SFP-95, GKS-240, GKS-283, SFP-562, and *Isanin* are assigned to the Northern Fleet; SFP-173, SFP-224, SFP-295, and SFP-542 to the Pacific Fleet; SFP-177 and SFP-183 to the Black Sea Fleet; and *Akulov* and *Semenikhin* to the Baltic Fleet.

AUXILIARIES *(continued)*

Disposals: Pacific Fleet unit SFP-340 was stricken in 1990 after a fire, and Pacific fleet sister SFP-343 was stricken in 9-95. Black Sea Fleet unit SFP-322 was stricken 10-1-96 and transferred to Ukraine in 1997. Baltic Fleet unit SFP-511 was derelict at Kronshtadt as of 1998. SFP-52 (ex-GKS-52) had been stricken by 2001.
Hull systems: Later ships (Project 1806.1) have the after deckhouse farther forward, abutting the stack, and have lattice vice pylon masts. SFP-designated units are usually seen with two side-by-side modular structures topped with two rectangular air vents mounted at the forward end of the after deckhouse platform (which was originally intended to be a helicopter platform); the devices may be employed in air sampling.

♦ 1 T-43GKS-class (Project 513M) signature-monitoring ship [AG]
Bldr: Leninskaya Kuznitsa Zavod, Kiev, Ukraine (In serv. 9-12-56)

SFP-17 (ex-GKS-17)

D: 490 tons (570 fl) **S:** 14.5 kts **Dim:** 58.00 (54.00 wl) × 8.50 × 2.10
Electronics:
Radar: 1 Don-2 or Mius (Spin Trough) nav.
Sonar: MG-11 Tamir-11 searchlight HF; Mars-24KI passive array
M: 2 Type 9D diesels; 2 CP props; 2,200 bhp
Range: 1,000/10 **Endurance:** 10 days **Crew:** 60 tot.

Remarks: GKS = *Gidroakusticheskoye Kontrol'noye Sudno* (Hydroacoustic Monitoring Ship). Survivor of 17 modified from a minesweeper hull design to measure the radiated noise of other ships, including submarines, by laying hydrophone arrays via the several small 800-kg-capacity davits they carried aft. Has a 124-cell battery system for operating measuring equipment under silent conditions. GKS-17, although said to have been transferred to Ukraine 12-3-96, remains at Sevastopol' and has been redesignated as a physical fields measurement ship SFP-17.
Disposals: GKS-45 was transferred to the civilian A. N. Krylov Research Institute as a research vessel. Thirteen others have been stricken: GKS-11 and -15 were stricken 24-6-91, GKS-22 had capsized and sunk at Kronshtadt by 1998, and GKS-12, -16, -18, -19, -20, -21, and -45 had been stricken by 2000.

Disposal note: Ex-German fleet tender (yacht) *Angara* (ex-*Nadir,* ex-German *Hela*) was relegated to floating barracks *(Plavuchaya Kazerne)* status in 1998 as PKZ-14. She was immobilized by an engine room fire in 1996 and is moored at Sevastopol'; see under [YPB].

♦ 5 Dobrynya Nikitich–class (Project 97 and 97AP/2*) port icebreakers [AGB]
Bldr: Admiralty SY, St. Petersburg (In serv. 1960–74)

	Laid down	L	In serv.	Fleet
Dobrynya Nikitich	20-12-59	10-5-60	31-12-60	Black Sea
Purga*	31-5-60	10-12-60	23-10-61	Baltic
Buran	21-1-66	16-5-66	24-10-66	Baltic
Sadko*	22-6-67	28-6-68	6-11-68	Pacific
Peresvet*	10-7-68	29-1-69	28-7-70	Northern

Buran—at Kronshtadt — Boris Lemachko, 1998

Sadko — U.S. Navy, 9-91

D: 2,300–2,520 tons (2,700–2,940 fl) **S:** 14.5 kts **Dim:** 67.70 × 18.30 × 5.50
Electronics: Radar: 1 or 2 Don-2 nav.
M: 3 13D100 diesels, electric drive; 3 props (1 fwd); 5,400 shp
Electric: 700 or 1,200 kw tot. **Range:** 5,500/12; 13,000/9.4
Fuel: 580 tons **Endurance:** 30 days **Crew:** 39–48 tot.

Remarks: Twenty of this class were built for the Soviet Navy and civilian service. *Peresvet, Purga,* and *Sadko* were built to Project 97AP/2 patrol and hydrographic survey configuration and were armed with one twin 57-mm ZIF-31B AA and one twin 25-mm 2M-3M AA, since removed; they displace 3,600 tons (fl) and have a range of 6,800 n.m. at 12 kts. All can carry 170 tons of fresh water and 27 tons of lubricants.
Disposals: Pacific Fleet sisters *Il'ya Muromets* and *Vyuga* were stricken on 30-7-93 and in 1991, respectively.

Disposal note: *Ivan Susanin*–class auxiliary icebreaker *Ivan Susanin* had been stricken by 2000. *Kamchatka*-class (Project 10221) sonar trials ship *Kamchatka* (SSV-679, ex-SSV-391), placed in reserve since around 1993, is not likely to be reactivated and has been dropped from this edition.

♦ 1 Potok (Smen')-class (Project 1236) torpedo trials ship [AGE]
Bldr: Zelenodol'sk SY (In serv. 1971–74)

OS-138

Potok-class OS-225—since stricken

D: 750 tons (860 fl) **S:** 17 kts **Dim:** 72.1 × 9.4 × 2.5
A: 1 533-mm TT; 1 406-mm TT **Electronics:** Radar: 1 Don-2 nav.
M: 2 Type 40-D diesels; 2 props; 4,000 bhp
Range: 2,500/12 **Endurance:** 5 days **Crew:** 30 tot.

Remarks: OS = *Opitnoye Sudno* (Experimental Vessel). The design closely resembles that of a T-58-class minesweeper, but the forecastle extends further aft, nearly to the stern. The trainable torpedo tubes are on the bow. A large crane aft is used for retrieval of expended weapons. Operated on Lake Ladoga, east of St. Petersburg. May not be active.
Disposals: Black Sea Fleet sisters OS-149 and OS-225 were stricken 1-9-95, and OS-100 was transferred to Ukraine 1-8-97.

♦ 1 Volgograd-class (Project 593) trials tender [AGE]
Bldr: . . . . . Zavod, Volgograd (In serv. 10-64)

OS-248 Volgograd

D: 1,200 tons (fl) **S:** 16 kts **Dim:** 82.40 × 13.90 × 3.55
M: 4 Type 5D-50 diesel generator sets, 2 electric motors; 2 props; 2,800 shp
Electric: 740 kw tot. (4 × 160-kw, 1 × 100-kw diesel sets)
Range: . . ./. . . **Fuel:** 68 tons **Crew:** . . . tot.

Remarks: Former passenger vessel, taken over for Caspian Sea service in 1992. Function uncertain. Has folding masts for riverine navigation.

♦ 7 Vishnaya (Meridian)-class (Project 864) intelligence collectors [AGI]
Bldr: Stocznia Polnocna, Gdansk

	In serv.
407 SSV-169 Tavriya	1986
425 SSV-175 Odograf	1988
437 SSV-201 Priazov'ye	14-6-87
756 SSV-208 Kuril'y	16-10-86
402 SSV-231 Vasiliy Tatishchev (ex-*Pelengator*)	21-8-88
411 SSV-520 Meridian	1985
761 SSV-535 Kareliya	5-6-86

Baltic Fleet Vishnaya SSV-520 Meridian (411)—with a single radome
Boris Lemachko, 7-00

D: 2,690 tons light; 3,100 tons std. (3,470 fl)—see remarks **S:** 16 kts
Dim: 94.40 (88.00 wl) × 14.60 × 4.50
A: 2 single 30-mm 54-cal. AK-630 gatling AA; 2 4-round Fasta-4M (SA-N-8) SAM (16 Igla-1M/Gremlin missiles)
Electronics:
Radar: 2 Volga (Don-Kay) nav.
Sonar: Pamyat hull-mounted array; HF dipping sonar
EW: various intercept arrays
M: 2 Cegielski-Sulzer 12AV 25/30, 750-rpm diesels; 2 CP props; 4,400 bhp—2 140-shp electric auxiliary low-speed drives
Electric: 2,000 kw tot. (4 × 500 kw) **Range:** 7,900/12.5
Endurance: 45 days **Crew:** 30 officers, 121 enlisted

AUXILIARIES *(continued)*

Black Sea Fleet Vishnaya SSV-201 Priazov'ye (437)—with two radomes Hartmut Ehlers, 7-00

Pacific Fleet Vishnaya SSV-208 Kuril'y (756)—with two spherical radomes on the mounting platforms atop the bridge JMSDF, 10-01

Remarks: SSV-208 and -535 are in the Pacific Fleet, SSV-201 is in the Black Sea Fleet, SSV-169 and -175 are in the Northern Fleet, and SSV-231 and -520 are in the Baltic Fleet. SSV-231 was renamed early in 2000. SSV-520 was sequestered at Nauta Ship Repair Yard in Poland during 1992 for nonpayment of repair fees; the ship completed a refit at Rostock NIR-Reparaturwerft, Germany, in 4-99. The ships are now only rarely deployed, and then only in local waters; as yet, they have not been photographed wearing the pennant numbers listed above. SSV-231 completed her 13th deployment, a reconnaissance voyage to the Atlantic, on 6-11-01.
Hull systems: Displacements are reported to have risen to 2,980 tons light/3,996 full load in service.
Combat systems: There are two Rakurs-series lead-computing directors for the 30-mm guns mounted forward. The point-defense SAM launchers are aft. The dipping sonar installation is mounted within the stern, deploying the transducer through a door in the transom. Two large circular radome foundations atop the forward superstructure support a variety of antennas; SSV-201 and -231 have two large radomes and SSV-175 and -520 have one, while SSV-169 has exposed parabolic-mesh antennas on the after of the two platforms and no antennas on the forward one. Neither Pacific Fleet unit has large radomes.

♦ 3 Al'pinist-class (Project 503M) intelligence collectors [AGI]
Bldr: Leninskaya Kuznetsa Zavod, Kiev, Ukraine

739 GS-7 (In serv. 1979) 317 GS-39 (In serv. 1981)
314 GS-19 (In serv. 1980)

Pacific Fleet Al'pinist GS-7—off Okinawa JMSDF, via *Ships of the World,* 8-99

D: 810 tons light (1,140 fl) **S:** 12.6 kts **Dim:** 53.70 (46.20 pp) × 10.50 × 4.10
A: GS-19 and GS-39 only: 2 Fasta-4M (SA-N-8) SAM syst. (16 Strela-2M or Igla-1M/Gremlin missiles)

Baltic Fleet Al'pinist GS-39—GS-19 is very similar Boris Lemachko, 7-00

Electronics: Radar: 1 Don-2 nav.—Sonar: Paltus-MP
M: 1 Type 8NVD48-2U diesel; 1 CP prop; 1,320 bhp
Electric: 450 kw tot. (1 × 300-kw, 1 × 150-kw diesel sets)
Range: 7,600/12.5 **Fuel:** 162 tons **Endurance:** 25 days **Crew:** 24 tot.

Remarks: Selected from a class of several hundred 322-dwt Project 503 stern-haul trawlers and modified as intelligence collectors. The Russian Navy also used an *Al'pinist* in an experimental role (OS-104, now stricken), and several have been used in civilian oceanographic research. GS-19 and GS-39 are in the Baltic Fleet, GS-7 in the Pacific Fleet, from which sister GS-8 was stricken 5-7-94. GS-7 operated in the South China Sea during summer 1998.
Hull systems: The 218-m^3 former fish hold may provide electronics and/or additional accommodations spaces. Have a bow-thruster.
Mission systems: During 1988 GS-19 and GS-39 had their forecastle decks extended to the stern, point-defense launchers added fore and aft, and their collection antenna suites greatly enhanced: a series of planar antennas surround the ships at upper deck level, and an elaborate VHFD/F array surmounts the after goalpost mast. GS-7 has had the forecastle extended, but not all the way to the stern. GS-19 is equipped with a Stop Light submarine-type intercept array, GS-39 carries two Bizan'-4-series (Watch Dog) intercept arrays, and GS-7 has a Squid Head submarine-type antenna array.

♦ 2 Bal'zam (Aziya)-class (Project 1826) intelligence collectors [AGI] (1 in *reserve*)
Bldr: Yantar Zavod 820, Kaliningrad

	In serv.		In serv.
696 SSV-80 Pribaltika	28-7-84	463 SSV-571 Belomor'ye	1986

Belomor'ye (SSV-571)—the only active Bal'zam French Navy, 5-96

D: 3,100 tons (4,900 fl) **S:** 22 kts (20 sust.) **Dim:** 105.0 × 15.5 × 5.6
A: 1 30-mm 54-cal. AK-630 gatling AA; 2 4-round Fasta-4M SAM syst. (16 Strela-series or Igla-1M missiles)
Electronics:
Radar: 2 Volga (Don-Kay) nav.
Sonar: hull-mounted MF; possible passive hull arrays; Uzh HF dipping
EW: 2 Cage Pot; 1 Twin Wheel D/F; 1 Log Maze D/F; 1 Fir Tree; 1 Wing Fold; 1 Trawl Net; 2 Sprat Star; 1 Cross Loop-A MFD/F; 1 High Ring-C HFD/F; 1 Park Plinth VHFD/F
M: 2 Type 58D (16DRPN 23/2 × 30) diesels; 2 props; 9,000 bhp
Range: 7,000/16, 10,000/14 **Endurance:** 60 days
Crew: 189 tot. (accomm. for 220)

Remarks: SSV = *Sudno Svyazyy* (Communications Vessel). These were the first built-for-the-purpose intelligence-collection and -processing ships, wholly military in concept. SSV-571 is active in the Northern Fleet, while SSV-80 is in the Pacific Fleet, where she is laid up at Vladivostok in poor condition.
Disposals: Northern Fleet sister (and class prototype) *Lira* (SSV-516) had become derelict by the end of 1996 and was stricken during 1998. Pacific Fleet unit *Aziya* (SSV-493), laid up at Vladivostok since the mid-1990s, had been stricken by 2001.
Hull systems: Equipped to refuel under way and to transfer solid cargo and personnel via constant-tension rigs on either side of the after mast.
Combat systems: There is only a remote SP-521 Rakurs (Kolonka-2) pedestal director for the gatling gun. The two spherical radomes probably house satellite transmitting and receiving antennas. Have Prim Wheel and Soup Cup satellite antennas. Russian designations for the special antennas (uncorrelated) are Prokhlada, Buksir-N, Rotor-H, Oktava, and Pamyat.

♦ 2 converted Yug-class (Project 0862.1 and 0862.2) intelligence collectors [AGI]
Bldr: Stocznia Polnocna, Gdansk

	In serv.
SSV-703 Temryuk (ex-SSV-328, ex-*Yug*)	5-78
SSV-704 (ex-*Mangyshlak*)	4-11-83

D: 1,960 tons (2,490 fl) **S:** 15.6 kts **Dim:** 82.50 (75.80 pp) × 13.50 × 3.97
A: 2 twin 12.7-mm 59-cal. Utës-M mg
Electronics:
Radar: 2 Don-2 nav.
Sonar: Uzh HF dipping
EW: 2 Bizan'-4 (Watch Dog) intercept; 1 HFD/F loop

AUXILIARIES *(continued)*

Yug-class SSV-704 J. G. Stemmelin, 5-97

M: 2 Zgoda-Sulzer 12AB 25/30 diesels; 2 CP props; 4,400 bhp (3,600 sust.)—2 125-shp electric low-speed motors—300-shp bow-thruster
Electric: 3,600 kw tot. (4 × 500-kw, 4 × 400-kw diesel sets)
Range: 4,430/17; 10,850/13 **Fuel:** 343 tons (406 max.) **Endurance:** 45 days
Crew: 4 officers, 54 enlisted

Remarks: Conversion of SSV-703 from an existing Black Sea Fleet oceanographic research ship was completed in summer 1989 and that of SSV-704 by 1990. The forecastle deck was extended to the stern and the sides plated in; the 01- and 02-level superstructures were also extended aft, presumably to allow for an increase in accommodations and for electronics spaces. Both are in the Northern Fleet. SSV-703 wore tactical pennant 700 when entering the Baltic in 10-00.
Combat systems: The machinegun mounts are mounted abaft the boats. The large radome on the cylindrical stalk between the stack and the foremast was also found on the giant *Ural* (SSV-33). There is, however, a paucity of other electromagnetic signal collection antennas, and the ships may have a more specialized intelligence collection role, perhaps in acoustics.

Disposal note: Of the six *Primor'ye*-class (Project 394B) intelligence collection ships, *Zabaykal'ye* (SSV-464), stricken 30-7-93, was scrapped in India early in 1995; *Primor'ye* (SSV-465) was stricken 5-7-94 from the Pacific Fleet; Northern Fleet unit *Zakarpat'ye* (SSV-502) was stricken 31-12-93 and scrapped during 1995; Northern Fleet unit *Zaporozh'ye* (SSV-501) was stricken 31-7-96; Black Sea Fleet unit *Krym* (SSV-590) was towed from Sevastopol' for scrapping on 26-1-00; and *Kavkaz* (SSV-591) was reassigned as a floating barracks and staff headquarters hulk during 2001.

♦ 3 Moma-class (Project 861M) intelligence collectors [AGI]
Bldr: Stocznia Polnocna, Gdansk, Poland (In serv. 1968–74)

Ekvator Kil'din Liman

Ekvator—note large HFD/F loop aft, two MFD/F loops on the mast, and the removal of the buoy crane forward Boris Lemachko, 1998

D: 1,080 tons light; 1,260 tons std. (1,560 fl) **S:** 16 kts
Dim: 73.30 (64.20 pp) × 11.20 (10.80 wl) × 3.90
A: 2 4-round Fasta-4M (SA-N-8) SAM syst. (16 Strela and/or Igla-series missiles)
Electronics: Radar: 2 Don-2 nav.—Sonar: Bronza array
M: 2 Zgoda-Sulzer 6TD48 diesels; 2 CP props; 3,600 bhp
Range: 9,700/11 **Endurance:** 35 days
Crew: *Liman* and *Kil'din:* 15 officers, 12 warrant officers, 43 enlisted

Remarks: Former survey ship/navigational buoy tenders. Black Sea Fleet navigational aids tender variant *Liman* was redesignated an intelligence collector in 1999 and deployed as such to the Adriatic in 4-99; she was relieved by Black Sea Fleet sister *Kil'din* 19-5-99 and returned to Sevastopol' 16-7-99. Another, the *Okean,* is reported to serve as SSV-518 in the Black Sea Fleet, but other sources state that she was transferred to civilian control in 1992. *Ekvator* is assigned to the Pacific Fleet.
Disposals: Northern Fleet unit *Archipelag* (SSV-512) was stricken 5-7-94. Black Sea Fleet unit *Yupiter* was stricken 10-1-96 and transferred to Ukraine 12-3-96. Pacific Fleet units *Il'men'* (SSV-472), *Pelorus* (SSV-509), and *Seliger* were stricken 30-7-93, and *Vega* (SSV-474) was stricken 1-9-95. *Nakhodka* (SSV-506) had apparently been stricken by 2001.

♦ 7 Kashtan-class (Project 141) mooring-buoy tenders [AGL]
Bldr: VEB Neptunwerft, Rostock, East Germany

Alexandr Pushkin (ex-KIL-926) (In serv. 1988)
KIL-143 (In serv. 1989)
KIL-158 (In serv. . . .)
KIL-164 (In serv. 1989)
KIL-168 (In serv. 5-10-90)
KIL-498 (In serv. 1990)
KIL-927 (In serv. 1988)

Aleksandr Pushkin Boris Lemachko, 7-00

KIL-143—near Murmansk NAVPIC-Holland, 10-01

D: 4,200 tons (5,250 fl) **S:** 13.75 kts **Dim:** 113.00 (97.82 pp) × 18.22 × 3.71
Electronics: Radar: 1 Mius (Spin Trough) nav.; 1 Don-2 nav.
M: 2 Karl Liebnecht–M.A.N. 8VDS 26/20AL-1 diesels (2,991 bhp each), 2 generator sets, electric drive; 2 props; 4,200 shp (3,000 sust.)—bow-thruster
Range: 4,000/11 **Endurance:** 45 days
Crew: 44 tot. (accomm. for 18 officers, 36 unlicensed civilians)

Remarks: 4,400 grt/1,000 dwt. *Aleksandr Pushkin* is based in the Baltic; KIL-168, KIL-498, and KIL-927 are homeported at Vladivostok; and KIL-143 and KIL-164 are homeported at Murmansk. KIL-158, reportedly transferred to Ukraine in 1993 and used in commercial service, appeared to be back in Russian Navy service as of 2000 and relieved Amur-class repair ship PM-56 as station ship at Tartus, Syria, during 9-00. The Pacific Fleet units have been employed in carrying commercial vehicle, timber, and finished lumber cargoes since 1992. KIL-926 was refitted at Rostock, Germany, during 1999; she was renamed *Aleksandr Pushkin* on completion of the overhaul on 5-6-99.
Disposals: Baltic Fleet unit KIL-140 was renamed SS-750 during 1995 and is equipped to serve as a salvage and rescue submersible tender (see under [ARS]).
Hull systems: Have a 100-ton German Stülcken heavy-lift gantry at the stern for lifting mooring buoys and for salvage assignments, a 12-ton electrohydraulic crane to starboard, and a 60-ton derrick amidships. Like the preceding Sura class (of which this design is an obvious development), these also have a 300-ton liquid-cargo capacity.

♦ 9 Sura-class mooring-buoy tenders (Project 145) [AGL]
(3 in *reserve*) Bldr: VEB Neptunwerft, Rostock, East Germany
(In serv. 1965–72, 1976–78)

KIL-1	KIL-21	*KIL-23*	KIL-27	KIL-31
KIL-2	KIL-22	KIL-25	*KIL-29*	

KIL-31 M.O.D. U.K., 5-90

AUXILIARIES *(continued)*

KIL-1 Boris Lemachko, 2000

D: 2,260 tons (3,150 fl) **S:** 13.2 kts
Dim: 87.30 (80.20 hull; 68.00 pp) × 14.80 × 5.10
Electronics: Radar: 2 Don-2 nav.
M: 4 diesels, electric drive; 2 props; 2,240 shp (1,780 sust.)
Range: 4,000/10 **Endurance:** 20 days **Crew:** 45 tot. (civilian)

Remarks: 2,366 grt. KIL = *Kilektor* (Mooring Tender). KIL-2, -22, -23, and -31 are assigned to the Northern Fleet; KIL-21 and -27 to the Pacific Fleet; KIL-25 to the Black Sea Fleet; and KIL-1 and KIL-29 to the Baltic Fleet. KIL-25 was refitted in 1996 in Bulgaria. KIL-1 was stricken 24-6-91 but was still afloat at Kronshtadt in 1998 and had been refitted and reactivated by 7-00.
Disposals: Pacific Fleet unit KIL-32 was stricken in 3-95 and sold to China, probably for scrapping. Black Sea Fleet unit KIL-33 was stricken 10-1-96 and transferred to Ukraine during summer 1997.
Hull systems: Can carry 460 tons of cargo in the hold amidships and 300 tons of cargo fuel. The stern rig, which can lift 65 tons, is used for buoy-handling and salvage. Mooring buoys are stowed amidships and moved aft for handling by the stern gallows rig via a chain-haul system. There are also a 5-ton electric crane to port and a 65-ton heavy-lift boom amidships, the latter tending the buoy stowage holds. The diesel propulsion generator plant is forward.

♦ 1 Marshal Nedelin–class (Project 1914.1) missile range instrumentation ship [AGM] Bldr: United Admiralty SY, St. Petersburg

	Laid down	L	Del.	In serv.
Marshal Krylov	24-7-82	24-7-87	31-12-89	23-2-90

Marshal Krylov Boris Lemachko, 1998

Marshal Krylov JMSDF, 7-90

D: 18,360 tons light; 23,800 tons normal (23,780 fl)
S: 22.7 kts **Dim:** 211.20 × 27.70 × 8.30
A: provision for 3 single 30-mm 54-cal. AK-630 gatling AA
Electronics:
Radar: 3 MR-212/201 Vaygach-U (Palm Frond) nav.; 1 MR-750 Fregat (Top Plate) surf./air search; 1 Fly Screen helicopter control; 1 End Tray balloon tracking; 1 Ship Globe missile tracking
Sonar: MGK-335-series Platina-S LF hull-mounted; Uzh dipping sonar
TACAN: c2 Privod-B (Round House)
M: 2 Type 68E (DGZA-6U or 18DRN 23/2 × 30) diesels; 2 props; 16,000 shp
Range: 20,000/15.5 **Endurance:** 120 days
Crew: 81 officers, 82 warrant officers, ?40 enlisted (accomm. for 106 officers, 311 enlisted)

Remarks: Was intended to begin replacement of the since-stricken *Desna-* and *Sibir'*-class range-tracking ships, but was equipped also to serve in a space-tracking and communications role. Named for a pioneer leader of the Soviet ballistic-missile program. Pacific Fleet unit *Marshal Nedelin* was reported stricken in 1997 and was towed to India for scrapping 4-4-00. A planned third ship, *Marshal Biryuzov,* was canceled. An incomplete, greatly modified, civilian-subordinated version of the class, *Akademik Nikolay Pilyugin,* was sold incomplete and converted to a cruise liner. *Marshal Krylov* was assigned to the Pacific Fleet 23-2-90.
Hull systems: Twin hangars can accommodate two Ka-32 Helix utility helicopters. Hull has a bulbous bow form. Has a swimming pool just abaft the stack.
Mission systems: Has one Quad Leaf, three Quad Wedge, four Quad Rods, and six telemetry reception arrays. Is equipped with the Tayfun-2 SATCOM and Shtorm communications suite.

♦ 2 Sibiryakov-class (Project 873) oceanographic research ships [AGOR] Bldr: A. Warski SY, Szczecin, Poland

	Laid down	L	In serv.
Sibiryakov	8-88	5-89	7-90
Romuald Mukhlevich	1988	1990	12-91

Sibiryakov H&L Van Ginderen, 3-95

Romuald Mukhlevich NAVPIC-Holland, 10-01

D: 2,280 tons light (3,450 fl) **S:** 16 kts (14 sust.)
Dim: 85.65 (75.60 pp) × 15.00 × 4.80
Electronics: Radar: 2 MR-312 Nayada nav.—Sonar: . . .
M: 2 Cegielski-Sulzer Type 12 ASV25D 1,000-rpm diesels, electric drive: 2 2,400-kw motors; 2 CP props; 6,480 shp—2 Type 6AL20D 750-rpm auxiliary diesels, 2 420-kw motors for low-speed propulsion—bow and stern tunnel-thrusters
Electric: 2,780 kVA tot. (3 Sulzer 6AL25D diesel-driven sets)
Range: 11,520/12 **Endurance:** 40 days
Crew: 58 tot. + 12 scientists/technicians

Remarks: 1,950 dwt. Ordered 1-89 to explore for mineral resources at depths up to 6,000 m. *Sibiryakov* is assigned to the Baltic Fleet and *Romuald Mukhlevich* to the Northern Fleet.
Hull systems: Can carry two 18-ton submersibles and have 14 laboratories, including hydrographic, meteorological, magnetometric, geologic, gravimetric, and photographic facilities. Model photos indicate presence of a broad-swath echo-sounder mapping system, with conformal transducer windows forward, amidships, and aft. Designed full load displacement was 3,422 tons.
Combat systems: Provision was made at the bow for a twin 30-mm AK-230 AA gunmount with optical director, and the ships have an NBC defense filter system and internal degaussing.

♦ 13 Yug-class (Project 862) oceanographic research ships [AGOR] (5 in *reserve*)

Bldr: Stocznia Polnocna, Gdansk, Poland (In serv. 5-78 to 6-9-83)

Donuzlav	*Senezh*
Gidrolog	Stvor
Gorizont	Tayga
Marshal Gelovani	Vitse-Admiral Vorontsov (ex-*Briz*)
Nikolay Matusevich	*Vizir*
Pegas	*Zodiak*
Persey	

D: 1,960 tons (2,490 fl) **S:** 15.6 kts **Dim:** 82.50 (75.80 pp) × 13.50 × 3.97
Electronics: Radar: 2 Don-2 nav.
M: 2 Zgoda-Sulzer 12AB 25/30 diesels; 2 CP props; 4,400 bhp (3,600 sust.)—2 125-shp electric low-speed motors—300-shp bow-thruster
Electric: 3,600 kw tot. (4 × 500-kw, 4 × 400-kw diesel sets)
Range: 4,430/17; 10,850/13 **Fuel:** 343 tons (406 max.) **Endurance:** 45 days
Crew: 4 officers, 54 enlisted (accomm. 8 officers, 38 unlicensed civilians, 20 scientists + 4 spare)

AUXILIARIES (continued)

Donuzlav—at Sevastopol' Hartmut Ehlers, 7-00

Gorizont NAVPIC-Holland, 10-01

Zodiak—laid up at Kronshtadt; note the unique gantry crane and extended after superstructure Boris Lemachko, 1998

Remarks: Said to be intended for "complex oceanographic research; exploration of the sea bed and sampling of soils; gravimetric studies; hydrographic and geophysical research, including the removal and implanting of oceanographic buoys; collection of navigational and hydrographic data; and inshore hydrographic surveys by [use of the] embarked two Project 727 glass-reinforced plastic-hulled cutters." *Briz* was renamed *Vitse-Admiral Vorontsov* in 1985. *Stvor* and *Donuzlav* are assigned to the Black Sea Fleet and *Gorizont* and *Vizir* to the Northern Fleet. *Nikolay Matusevich, Persey,* and *Zodiak* are laid up at Kronshtadt; and *Pegas* is active in the Pacific Fleet. *Marshal Gelovani* began a 45-day environmental survey of the Sea of Okhotsk in 10-00 under the joint Russian-German Kuriles and Sea of Okhotsk Experiment program; as of 4-00, she was the only active Pacific Fleet oceanographic research ship. Even those still nominally in commission seldom operate.
Disposals: Class name-ship *Yug* was converted to an intelligence collector by 1989, followed by *Mangyshlak* by 1990 (see under [AGI]). *Pluton* and *Strelets* of this class, previously assigned to the Baltic Fleet, were transferred to the Federal Border Guard in 8-97 and are now based at Murmansk, from where they are used to conduct economic exclusion zone (EEZ) patrols; see under [WPS]. *Gals* appears to have been discarded by 2001.
Hull systems: As completed, were 1,842 tons light, 2,435 fl. Have a quadrantial davit over the stern ramp with 4-ton lift, two 5-ton booms, several oceanographic davits, three echo sounders, and six laboratories. Have deck reinforcements for three twin 25-mm 80-cal. 2M-3M AA. *Zodiak* was fitted about 1985 with a large gantry at the stern to handle a towed object and had the main deck superstructure extended aft.

♦ 2 Akademik Krylov–class (Project 852 and 856) oceanographic research ships [AGOR] (In reserve)
Bldr: A. Warski SY, Szczecin, Poland

Admiral Vladimirskiy (In serv. 1974) *Leonid Demin* (In serv. 1979)

D: 6,580 tons (9,120 fl) **S:** 20.4 kts (19 sust.) **Dim:** 147.80 × 18.60 × 6.26–6.40
Electronics: Radar: 3 Don-2 nav.
M: 4 diesels; 2 props; 16,000 bhp
Range: 18,000/15 **Endurance:** 45 days
Crew: 90 tot. (civilian) + 80 scientists (accomm. for 250 tot.)

Leonid Demin—in the Baltic while escorting Kilo-class submarine *Yunes* to Iran M.O.D. Bonn, 12-96

Admiral Vladimirskiy—laid up at Kronshtadt as an accommodations facility for officers and their families Boris Lemachko, 1999

Remarks: Among the largest ships of their type in any navy. *Leonid Demin* escorted the third Iranian Kilo-class submarine from the Baltic to Iran between 11-96 and 1-97 but has not operated since returning to Kronshtadt. *Admiral Vladimirskiy* has not operated since at least the mid-1990s.
Disposals: Black Sea Fleet unit *Akademik Krylov* was sold to a Greek commercial operator in 1993, Baltic Fleet unit *Mikhail Krupskiy* was stricken 1-9-95, and Pacific Fleet unit *Leonid Sobelyev* was stricken 31-7-96 (and sold to India for scrap in 8-97). *Ivan Kruzhenstern* was placed in unmaintained reserve at Kronshtadt during 10-98 and has apparently since been stricken.
Hull systems: Equipped with a helicopter hangar and flight deck, two Project 726 survey launches, and 26 laboratories totaling 900 m^2. Have two cargo holds and a 7-ton cargo crane forward. *Demin,* delivered in 1978, has a pointed stern, adding about 2 m to the overall length listed above.

♦ 2 Nikolay Zubov–class (Project 850M) oceanographic research ships [AGOR]
Bldr: A. Warski SY, Szczecin, Poland

Andrey Vil'kitskiy (In serv. 1966) *Semen Dezhnev* (In serv. 1968)

Andrey Vil'kitskiy—visiting St. Petersburg H&L Van Ginderen, 1995

D: 2,674 tons (3,021–3,123 fl) **S:** 16.5 kts **Dim:** 89.70 × 13.00 × 4.80
Electronics:
Radar: *Vil'kitskiy:* 2 Don-2 nav.—*Dezhnev:* 2 MR-212/201 Vaygach-U (Palm Frond) nav.
Sonar: MG-329 hull-mounted HF; NEL-5 and NEL-6 echo sounders
M: 2 Zgoda-Sulzer 8TD-48 diesels; 2 props; 4,800 bhp
Electric: 960 kw tot. (3 × 320-kw diesel sets)
Range: 9,000/15.3; 10,000/13 **Endurance:** 40 days
Crew: 68 tot. (civilian) + up to 26 scientific party (146 tot. accomm.)

Remarks: Assigned to the Northern Fleet.
Disposals: Sister *Vasiliy Golovnin* was stricken from the Black Sea Fleet in 1991 and later taken over by Ukraine under the name *Sviatov Nikolay;* by 8-94, the ship was in derelict condition at Sevastopol'. Northern Fleet unit *Aleksey Chirikov* was stricken 30-7-93 and Pacific Fleet unit *Fedor Litke* on 31-7-96. *Faddey Bellingsgauzen, Nikolay Zubov,* and *Boris Davydov* have also been retired. Three others, now stricken, served as intelligence collectors.
Hull systems: Could originally carry four Project 727U or 338M survey launches, but now have only two. Have nine laboratories, totaling 120 m^2, along with two 7-ton and two 5-ton booms, nine 0.5- to 1.2-ton oceanographic-equipment davits, and 600 m^3 capacity total in two holds. The after platform, *not* for helicopters, was larger in the later ships.

AUXILIARIES *(continued)*

♦ 1 Modified Sorum-class (Project 1454) hydrographic survey ship [AGS] Bldr: Yaroslavl Zavod (In serv. 30-10-87)

GS-31 (ex-OS-572)

GS-31—as OS-572 M.O.D. U.K., 6-88

D: 1,250 tons (1,696 fl) **S:** 14 kts **Dim:** 59.10 (55.50 pp) × 12.60 × 4.60
Electronics: Radar: 2 Don-2 nav.
M: 2 Type 25-DB 2 (6ChN 30/38) diesels, electric drive; 1 prop; 2,500 shp (1,850 sust.)
Range: 6,700/13 **Fuel:** 322 tons **Crew:** 60 tot. (accomm.)

Remarks: Built as a trials platform for towed passive linear hydrophone (towed array) research and development. Variant of a standard ocean tug design, but with the forecastle deck extended to the stern, where a raised poop housed the array and towing winch. After several years of inactivity, was redesignated a hydrographic survey vessel in 1997 and now presumably operates in that role. Assigned to the Northern Fleet.

♦ 23 Finik-class (Project 872) hydrographic survey ships [AGS] (9 in *reserve*) Bldr: Stocznia Polnocna, Gdansk, Poland (In serv. 1979–81)

GS-44 GS-87 GS-278 *GS-301* GS-398 *GS-403*
GS-47 GS-260 *GS-280* GS-388 *GS-399* GS-404
GS-84 *GS-270* GS-294 *GS-392* *GS-400* GS-405
GS-86 GS-272 GS-297 GS-397 *GS-402*

Finik-class GS-86—at Sevastopol', with black hull and white superstructure
Hartmut Ehlers, 8-00

Finik-class GS-294—note the beachable workboat stowed athwartships abaft the buoy hatch JMSDF, 10-94

D: 950 tons (1,186 fl) **S:** 13.8 kts **Dim:** 61.30 × 11.80 (10.80 wl) × 3.28
Electronics: Radar: 2 Don-2 nav.
M: 2 Cegielski-Sulzer diesels; 2 CP props; 1,920 bhp—2 75-kw electric motors for quiet, 6-kt operations—130-kw bow-thruster
Electric: 675 kVA tot. **Range:** 3,000/13; 4,800/11 **Endurance:** 15 days
Crew: 5 officers, 23 unlicensed (civilian)

Remarks: Polish B-91 design. GS = *Gidrograficheskoye Sudno* (Hydrographic Survey Ship). Fleet assignments include GS-44, -47, -84, -270, -272, -397, and -404 in the Pacific Fleet; GS-301 in the Caspian Flotilla; and GS-87, -260, -278, -280, -297, -388, -392, -398, -399, -400, -403, and -405 in the Northern Fleet. One was built for East Germany and four for Poland (two civilian). GS-401 became Ukrainian property and is in commercial service. Black Sea Fleet unit GS-265 was redesignated OS-265 as a trials ship and now serves as ammunition transport VTR-75. Several Pacific Fleet units, including GS-47 and GS-84, have been employed carrying commercial cargoes.
Hull systems: Intended for navigational buoy-tending and hydrographic survey duties, for which four echo sounders are fitted. Up to three fiberglass 3-dwt utility landing craft can be stowed on the buoy working deck beneath the 7-ton crane. Have hydrological, hydrographic, and cartographic facilities.

Note: The Russian Navy Hydrographic Service ships of the Finik, Moma, Biya, Kamenka, Samara, and other classes are used as hydrographic survey ships and navigation tenders, handling buoys, marking channels, and so forth. They set and retrieve some 2,000 buoys and 4,000 spar buoys that are taken up for the winter months and, prior to 1992, supported and maintained 600 lighthouses, 150 noise beacons, and 8,000 navigation buoys. Most can carry from two to six navigation buoys. In addition, they are equipped to take basic oceanographic and meteorological samplings.
The two Ayristo (NATO Vinograd)-class inshore survey ships can now be found under [YGS] in the Service Craft section.

♦ 8 Biya-class (Project 871) hydrographic survey ships [AGS] (2 in *reserve*) Bldr: Stocznia Polnocna, Gdansk, Poland (In serv. 1972–76)

GS-193 GS-200 *GS-206* GS-214
GS-194 GS-202 GS-210 GS-273

Biya-class GS-273—at Sevastopol', with a Flamingo-class launch alongside
Boris Lemachko, 5-00

Biya-class GS-214—note that the buoy crane is mounted at the forecastle break in this class M.O.D. Bonn, 7-91

D: 600 tons (723 fl) **S:** 13 kts **Dim:** 54.30 × 9.56 × 2.65
Electronics: Radar: 1 Don-2 nav.
M: 2 diesels; 2 CP props; 1,100 bhp **Range:** 2,000/11
Fuel: 90 tons **Endurance:** 15 days **Crew:** 25 tot. (civilian)

Remarks: GS = *Gidrograficheskoye Sudno* (Hydrographic Survey Ship). Eighteen were originally built for Soviet Navy use. GS-202 is assigned to the Caspian Flotilla, GS-273 to the Black Sea Fleet, GS-200 and -210 to the Pacific Fleet, and the others to the Northern Fleet.
Disposals: One unit was transferred to Guinea-Bissau, one (GC-186) to Cuba in 1980, and one to Cape Verde in 1980. GS-275 was stricken from the Baltic Fleet 3-7-92 and GS-198 from the Pacific Fleet 5-7-94. GS-82 was stricken 10-1-96 and transferred to Ukraine in 1997. GS-204 and -208 were stricken during 1994 and GS-212 in 1996.
Hull systems: Similar to the Kamenka class, but with a longer superstructure and less buoy-handling space. Carry one survey launch and have one 5-ton crane. Laboratory space: 15 m^2.

♦ 11 Kamenka-class (Project 870) hydrographic survey ships [AGS] (8 in *reserve*)
Bldr: Stocznia Polnocna, Gdansk, Poland (In serv. 1968–72)

GS-66 *GS-107* *GS-194* GS-211
GS-78 *MGS-113* (ex-*Bel'bek*) *GS-198* *GS-269*
GS-103 *GS-118* GS-199

D: 590 tons (703 fl) **S:** 13.7 kts **Dim:** 53.50 × 9.40 × 2.62
Electronics: Radar: 1 Don-2 nav.
M: 2 Cegielski-Sulzer 6 NVD-48 diesels; 2 CP props; 1,765 bhp
Range: 1,720/13 **Endurance:** 15 days **Crew:** 24 tot. (civilian)

AUXILIARIES *(continued)*

Kamenka-class GS-118—laid up at Kronshtadt Boris Lemachko, 2000

Remarks: GS = *Gidrograficheskoye Sudno* (Hydrographic Survey Ship). Similar to the Biya class (Project 871), but with more facilities for stowing and handling buoys. Have no survey launch. One 5-ton crane is fitted. GS-103 is in the Black Sea Fleet; GS-66 and GS-107 in the Baltic Fleet; GS-78 and -118 in the Northern Fleet; and MGS-113 and GS-198, -199, -211, and -269 in the Pacific Fleet.
Disposals: One sister, *Buk,* formerly served in the East German Navy and now is employed by the German Water Navigation Board Maritime Police *(Schiffahrtspolizei)*. Northern Fleet unit GS-74 was stricken 5-7-94. The naval-manned Pacific Fleet unit *Astronom* was stricken 30-7-93 and sold commercial. Baltic Fleet unit GS-207 was stricken 1-9-95. Sister *Vern'er* (GS-108) was transferred to Estonia as EVA-108, and Black Sea Fleet unit GS-273 was stricken 10-1-96 and had been transferred to Ukraine by summer 1997.

♦ 11 Moma-class (Project 861) hydrographic survey ships [AGS]
(6 in *reserve*) Bldr: Stocznia Polnocna, Gdansk, Poland (In serv. 1967–74)

ANDROMEDA	*ARTIKA*	*KOLGUYEV*	*MORZHOVETS*
ANTARES	*ASKOL'D*	KRIL'ON	*TAYMYR*
ANTARKTIDA	*CHELEKEN*	MARS	

Moma-class Mars—off Murmansk NAVPIC-Holland, 10-01

Moma-class Antarktida U.S. Navy, 1-95

D: 1,140 tons (1,502 fl) **S:** 15 kts
Dim: 73.30 (64.20 pp) × 11.20 (10.80 wl) × 3.80
Electronics: Radar: 2 Don-2 nav.
M: 2 Zgoda-Sulzer 6TD48 diesels; 2 CP props; 3,600 bhp
Range: 8,000/11 **Endurance:** 25 days **Crew:** 41 tot. (civilian)

Remarks: Sisters operate in the Polish, Bulgarian, and Croatian navies. Nine others served as intelligence collectors. *Andromeda* was sequestered at Nauta Ship Repair Yard in Poland during 1992 for nonpayment of repair fees and not released until 1-95, when she returned to the Pacific Fleet.
Disposals: *Okean* (ex-SSV-518) and *Berezan'* were transferred prior to 1992 to the custody of cities in the Ukraine for use as navigational aids tenders, with the former scrapped during 7-01 and the latter transferred to the Ukrainian Navy. Sister *Sever* was stricken from the Pacific Fleet in 1988, and *Anadyr'* was stricken in 1984 after going aground. Pacific Fleet unit *Zapol'yare* was stricken 5-7-94, Northern Fleet unit *El'ton* on 1-9-95, and Pacific Fleet unit *Al'tayr* on 31-7-96. The Pacific Fleet's *Rybachiy* (ex-*Odograf*), modified with oceanographic research equipment and naval manned, was stricken 16-8-97. Sister *Liman* was redesignated as an intelligence collector in 1999.

Moma-class Cheleken—laid up at Sevastopol' Boris Lemachko, 5-00

Hull systems: Carry one survey launch and a 7-ton crane, and have four laboratories, totaling 35 m^2. *Kolguyev* has had her main deck deckhouse extended over the buoy-handling area, and her crane has been removed.

Disposal note: Of the units of the Samara (Azimut)-class of hydrographic survey ship/navaids tenders (Project 860) listed in the last edition, *Pamyat' Merkuriya,* while employed as a commercial passenger and cargo ferry, was lost in a Black Sea storm 26-1-01, and *Glubometr,* assigned to the Pacific Fleet, is believed no longer to be in service.

Note: Small, coastal, and roadstead survey craft are listed under [YGS].

♦ 3 Ob'-class (Project B-320/B-320 II) hospital ships [AH]
Bldr: A. Warski SY, Szczecin, Poland

IRTYSH (In serv. 10-8-90) SVIR' (In serv. 7-89) YENISEY (In serv. 1-81)

Svir'—at Severomorsk Boris Lemachko, 2000

Irtysh—at Vladivostok Boris Lemachko, 9-00

D: 9,430 tons (11,623–11,977 fl) **S:** 20 kts (19.8 sust.)
Dim: 152.60 (142.00 pp) × 19.40 × 6.39
Electronics: Radar: 3 Don-2 (*Irtysh:* MR-312 Nayada) nav.
M: 2 Type 12 ZV 40/48, 12-cyl., 750-rpm diesels; 2 CP props; 15,600 bhp
Electric: 5,000 kVA tot. (4 × 1,250-kVA diesel sets)
Range: 8,000/19; 10,000/14 **Fuel:** 2,125 tons **Endurance:** 40 days
Crew: 124 ship's crew + 83 medical personnel, up to 300 patients, or up to 650 passengers

Remarks: Intended to "provide medical and recreational facilities." Have also been employed as personnel transports. Have civilian crews but carry uniformed naval medical personnel. Later two are Project B-320 II, implying a modification to the basic design; external differences are minor. *Irtysh* is in the Pacific Fleet, *Svir'* in the Northern Fleet, and *Yenisey* in the Black Sea Fleet. The ships are on offer for charter for humanitarian purposes. *Svir'* had a serious fire 10-3-99, with three deaths. Were being maintained with crews of 75 in 1998.
Disposals: Class name-ship *Ob'* (commissioned 28-3-80) was stricken 16-8-97.
Hull systems: Normally have 100 sickbeds, plus 200 berths for recuperating personnel that can be converted to sickbeds; in an emergency, another 150 can be added. There are seven operating rooms and five laboratories. The ships have a decompres-

AUXILIARIES *(continued)*

sion chamber and a sauna, as well as a collapsible swimming pool that is deployed over the side. Degaussing gear and NBC warfare filters are fitted. The hangar aft can accommodate a Hormone-C or Helix-D utility helicopter. Bow-thrusters fitted, as are fin stabilizers. There are a physical therapy facility, two gymnasiums, two pools, a library, and a 100-seat auditorium. Are equipped with a Rumb radio direction-finder, M3-B echo sounder, KEL-1 automatic log, and Kurs-10A-1 gyrocompass. One source gives the radar designations as MR-212, MR-216, and MR-250.

♦ 2 Neon Antonov–class (Project 1595) cargo ships [AK]
Bldr: Nikolayevsk-na-Amur Zavod

DVINA (In serv. . . .) IRBIT (In serv. 1975)

Dvina—at Severomorsk; note the bulbous forefoot to the bow Boris Lemachko, 5-00

D: 2,420 tons light (4,040 fl) **S:** 18 kts **Dim:** 96.30 (87.20 pp) × 14.50 × 5.10
Electronics: Radar: 1 Volga (Don-Kay) nav.; 1 Mius (Spin Trough) nav.
M: 2 Type 67B (12DRPN 23/2 × 30) diesels; 1 prop; 7,500 bhp
Range: 5,000/18; 8,750/14 **Endurance:** 25 days
Crew: 45 tot. + 18 passengers

Remarks: Specialized supply ships for remote garrisons in the Pacific region. Both were chartered commercial in 1992, but *Dvina* now serves the Northern Fleet and *Irbit* has apparently been returned from the charterer. Eight sisters operate with the Federal Border Guard in the Pacific area.
Hull systems: Carry one Project 1785 logistics landing craft (36 tons light, 78.2 tons fl; 21.90 × 5.81 × 1.00 m; one 470-bhp diesel for 9.8 kts) starboard aft and a workboat port aft, with a 50-ton boat derrick to handle them. The hull has a bulbous forefoot and two cargo holds forward, tended by only two 5-ton derricks. The pilothouse is equipped with MPK-455M navigational periscopes port and starboard. Cargo capacity: 804 tons.
Combat systems: The armament of one twin 30-mm 65-cal. AK-230 AA gunmount and two twin 12.7-mm Ütes-M machinegun mounts was removed by 1992.

♦ 3 Yuniy Partizan–class (Project 740/2B) cargo ships [AK] (1 in *reserve*)
Bldr: Turnu-Severin SY and Oltenitza SY, Romania (In serv. 1975–78)

PECHORA (In serv. 1976) *TURGAY* (In serv. 1975) UFA (In serv. 30-6-77)

Ufa—carrying a commercial cargo at Maizuru, Japan Takatoshi Okano, 1-99

D: 2,800 tons std. (3,947 fl) **S:** 12.8 kts **Dim:** 88.75 (80.25 pp) × 12.80 × 4.60
Electronics: Radar: 1 Don-2 nav.
M: 1 Zgoda-Sulzer 8 TAD 36 diesel; 1 prop; 2,080 bhp **Electric:** 306 kw tot.
Range: 4,800/10 **Fuel:** 125 tons **Endurance:** 20 days **Crew:** 35 tot. (civilian)

Remarks: 2,079 grt/2,150 dwt. Sister *Pinega,* converted to a missile transport (Project 10680) and renamed *Vitse-Admiral Fomin,* was scrapped in 1995. Pacific Fleet unit *Ufa,* still naval owned, has been employed in commercial cargo-carrying since 1992. *Turgay* is laid up at Sevastopol', and *Pechora* is assigned to the Northern Fleet. Twenty sisters were constructed for civilian service.
Hull systems: Have three 10-ton cranes, one of which can be rigged to lift 28 tons. Cargo volume: 3,200 m^3. Originally intended to be able to carry 58 standard cargo containers.

Note: Cargo ships and larger dry cargo-carrying service craft are usually referred to as VTR (*Voyenyy Transport,* Military Transport).

Turgay—laid up at Sevastopol' Hartmut Ehlers, 7-00

♦ 1 Amguema-class (Project 550) icebreaking cargo ship [AK]
Bldr: Kherson SY (In serv. 9-74)

YAUZA

Yauza 1976

D: 5,118 tons light (14,470 fl) **S:** 15 kts
Dim: 133.10 (123.00 pp) × 18.80 (18.50 wl) × 7.60 (max.)
Electronics: Radar: 2 Don-2 nav.
M: 4 Type 3D-100 diesels, electric drive; 1 prop; 7,200 shp
Electric: 880 kw tot. (4 × 220-kw diesel sets) **Range:** 7,000/15
Fuel: 1,000 tons **Endurance:** 90 days **Crew:** 58 tot. (civilian)

Remarks: 6,280-dwt passenger/cargo ship, assigned to the Northern Fleet. Not sighted in many years but reportedly still in use. Can break 0.6-m ice. Two 60-ton, two 10-ton, and six 5-ton cranes. Navigational equipment includes an SRP-5 HFD/F, NEL-5 echo sounder, and Kurs-3 gyrocompass.

♦ 2 Polnocny-B-class (Project 771A) vehicle cargo ships [AK]
Bldr: Stocznia Polnocna, Gdansk, Poland (In serv. 15-6-67 to 30-11-70)

VTR-140 (ex-MDK-. . .) VTR-141 (ex-MDK-. . .)

D: 558 tons light; 640 tons std. (884 fl) **S:** 18 kts
Dim: 75.00 (70.00 wl) × 9.00 (8.60 wl) × 1.20 (fwd; 2.40 aft; 2.07 mean)
A: 1 twin 30-mm 65-cal. AK-230 AA
Electronics:
Radar: 1 Mius (Spin Trough) nav.; 1 MR-104 Rys' (Drum Tilt) gun f.c.
M: 2 Type 40DM diesels; 2 props; 4,400 bhp **Range:** 700/18; 2,000/16
Crew: 5 officers, 32 enlisted + 60–180 troops

Remarks: Former medium landing ships redesignated as cargo ships. VTR = *Voyenyy Transport,* Military Transport. Survivors of 13 Project 771 and 12 Project 771A units delivered to the Soviet Union 1967–70. Assigned to the Black Sea Fleet.
Hull systems: Differed from the Polnocny-A (Project 770D and 770MA) in having concave bow-flare. Has a door only in the bow, and the hull has a "beak" projecting forward below the waterline at the bow to aid in beaching. Hatches to the upper deck are for loading and ventilation only. Cargo: 237 tons max., including six tanks or 180 troops and their equipment; 30 vehicle crew are carried with the tank loadout. The vehicle deck is 44.3 m long, 5.3 m wide, and 3.6 m high.
Combat systems: Can carry 4,000 rounds of 30-mm ammunition.

♦ 1 Vytegrales-class (Project 1918) cargo ship [AK]
Bldr: Zhdanov Zavod, St. Petersburg (In serv. 1966)

YAMAL (ex-*Tosnolets*)

Yamal—at Kaliningrad having helicopter facilities removed Hartmut Ehlers, 9-95

AUXILIARIES *(continued)*

D: 4,900 tons (8,920 fl) **S:** 16 kts **Dim:** 121.90 (114.00 pp) × 16.70 × 6.80
Electronics: Radar: 2 Don-2 nav.
M: 1 Bryansk–Burmeister & Wain 950 VTBF 110 diesel; 1 prop; 5,200 bhp
Electric: 660 kw tot. (3 × 220-kw diesel sets)
Range: 7,380/14.5 **Fuel:** 462 tons **Crew:** 60 tot.

Remarks: Originally built as a Project 596P merchant timber carrier, then converted as a space-event support ship by the addition of more communications facilities and a helicopter platform over the stern—consequently losing access to the after hold. Converted back to a standard dry-cargo ship at Kaliningrad during 1995 and now used by the Baltic Fleet to supply naval facilities in Kaliningrad. Three sisters remain configured as astronaut rescue/command and logistics support tenders; see under [AG].

♦ 1 MP-6-class (Project 572) cargo ship [AK]
Bldr: Turnu-Severin SY, Hungary (In serv. 1959–60)

KHOPER

Khoper NAVPIC-Holland, 10-01

D: 1,247 tons (2,033 fl) **S:** 12.2 kts **Dim:** 75.40 (70.00 pp) × 11.70 × 3.98
Electronics: Radar: 1 Don-2 nav.
M: 2 Buckau-Wolff 6NVD48 (8DR) diesels; 1 prop; 1,600 bhp
Range: 2,000/11 **Endurance:** 15 days **Crew:** 5 officers, 43 enlisted

Remarks: 1,000 dwt. Former medium landing ship. The bow doors were welded shut circa 1960, when the class was adapted for use as cargo vessels. *Khoper* was subsequently further converted to transport early-model strategic ballistic missiles, with the two forward hatches combined into one and a single crane fitted. Thought to have been retired by the late 1980s, the ship was still active in the Northern Fleet as of 10-01, probably for use as a general cargo carrier. Pacific Fleet sister *Bureya* (ex-VTR-296) was sold in Japan in 1993, while Baltic Fleet *Bira* (ex-OS-10) was stricken in 1996, and *Vologda* was stricken 1-9-95 and sold for commercial service.

♦ up to 4 Keyla-class (Project 1849) cargo ships [AK]
Bldr: . . . SY, Budapest, Hungary (In serv. 1958–66)

ONEGA TERIBERKA TULOMA VIL'YANDI

D: 832 tons light (2,042 fl) **S:** 12 kts **Dim:** 78.5 (71.4 pp) × 10.5 × 4.6
Electronics: Radar: 1 or 2 Don-2 or Mius (Spin Trough) nav.
M: 1 Lang 8 LD315RF diesel; 1 prop; 1,000 bhp **Electric:** 300 kw tot.
Range: 4,200/10.7 **Fuel:** 72 tons **Crew:** 26 tot. (civilian)

Remarks: 1,296 grt/1,280 dwt. Are attached to the Northern Fleet. Typical engines-aft, two-hatch coastal cargo vessels. Can carry 1,100 tons of cargo. Have one 10-ton and six 2.5-ton cranes.
Disposals: *Tvertsa* was stricken from the Pacific Fleet 24-6-91, *Ussuri* was reportedly sold commercial during 1992, and *Mezen'* was stricken from Black Sea Fleet 10-1-96 and transferred to Ukraine. *Ritsa* was converted as a training ship for intelligence collection personnel and was derelict at Sevastopol' by mid-1997. Other units probably no longer in service include *Ponoy, Severka, Unzha,* and *Yeruslan.*

♦ 1 Kaliningradneft'-class oiler [AO]
Bldr: Rauma-Repola, Rauma, Finland (In serv. 5-83)

VYAZ'MA (ex-*Katun*)

Vyaz'ma—at Severomorsk Boris Lemachko, 2000

D: 3,150 tons light; 4,820 tons std. (8,913 fl) **S:** 14.4 kts
Dim: 115.50 (112.00 pp) × 17.00 × 7.00
Electronics: Radar: 1 Okean-A nav.; 1 Okean-B nav.
M: 1 Russkiy–Burmeister & Wain 5 DKRP 50/110-2 diesel; 1 prop; 3,850 bhp
Electric: 805 kw tot. **Range:** 5,000/14 **Fuel:** 452 tons **Endurance:** 50 days
Crew: 12 officers, 28 unlicensed (all civilians)

Remarks: 4,821 grt/5,873 dwt. One of the last two built of a class that had more than two dozen units delivered to the USSR Ministry of Fisheries 1979–82. Assigned to the Northern Fleet.
Disposals: *Argun'* (ex-*Kallevere*), which formerly operated with the Pacific Fleet, was chartered to the Far East Shipping Line during 1991 and was sold to a commercial operator in 1996; the ship was arrested at Cape Town in 1999 and auctioned to pay debts on 23-5-00.
Hull systems: Is not capable of alongside refueling but does have two over-the-stern liquid replenishment rigs, although she can refuel ships moored alongside, dead in the water. There is no provision for underway solid stores replenishment. Carries 5,750 m^3 (5,263 tons) of liquid cargo in 10 tanks and 80 m^3 of dry cargo in one hold within the forecastle. Two cargo pumps have combined 400-m^3/hr capacity. Has a 1,600-ton water ballast capacity.

♦ 2 Dubna-class oilers [AO]
Bldr: Rauma-Repola, Rauma, Finland

DUBNA (In serv. 1974) PECHENGA (In serv. 1978)

Pechenga—with all underway solid and liquid transfer equipment removed
Boris Lemachko, 6-98

Dubna—with underway replenishment equipment removed
NAVPIC-Holland, 10-01

D: 4,300 tons light (11,140 fl) **S:** 15.5 kts
Dim: 130.10 (126.30 pp) × 20.00 × 7.20
Electronics: Radar: 2 Don-2 nav.
M: 1 Russkiy Dizel 8DRPH 23/230, 8-cyl. diesel; 1 prop; 6,000 bhp
Electric: 1,485 kVA tot. **Range:** 7,000/16; 8,200/12
Fuel: 1,056 m^3 **Endurance:** 60 days **Crew:** 62 tot. (civilian)

Remarks: 6,022 grt/6,500 dwt. Soviet type designation: VTR (*Voyenyy Tanker,* Military Tanker). Pacific Fleet unit *Pechenga* had the solid stores transfer system removed during 1993–94 and is employed primarily in carrying commercial liquid cargoes. *Dubna* retains the masting but no longer carries hoses.
Disposals: Black Sea Fleet unit *Sventa* had become the Ukrainian *Kerch'* (U 758) by 8-97. Pacific Fleet unit *Irkut* was stricken 31-7-96 and sold for commercial service.
Hull systems: Cargo capacity is 5,300 tons total: 2,100 tons fuel oil, 2,080 tons diesel, 120 tons lube oil (in four grades), 900 tons fresh water, 50 tons provisions, and 50 tons spares. Have 27 cargo tanks. There are four 250-ton/hr, two 100-ton/hr, and two 20-ton/hr cargo pumps. *Dubna* (but not *Pechenga*) can transfer 1-ton loads from constant-tension stations forward. Supply liquid replenishment from one station on port and starboard, amidships, and over the stern. Additional berths are provided for "turnover crews." The original commercial Okean-series radars were replaced.

♦ 5 Boris Chilikin–class (Project 1559V and 1593*) replenishment oilers [AO] (1 in *reserve*)
Bldr: Baltic Zavod, St. Petersburg

	In serv.		In serv.
BORIS BUTOMA*	1978	SERGEY OSIPOV (ex-*Dnestr*)	1977
GENRIKH GASANOV	1975	VLADIMIR KOLYACHITSKIY	1972
IVAN BUBNOV	1974		

Vladimir Kolyachitskiy JMSDF, via *Ships of the World,* 1-01

AUXILIARIES *(continued)*

Ivan Bubnov—laid up at Sevastopol' Hartmut Ehlers, 7-00

D: 6,950 tons light (22,460 fl) **S:** 16.7 kts (16 sust.)
Dim: 162.36 (150.02 pp) × 21.41 × 9.04
Electronics: Radar: 2 Volga (Don-Kay) nav.
M: 1 Cegielski-Sulzer 6 DKRN-74/160, 6-cyl. diesel; 1 prop; 9,600 bhp
Electric: 1,200 kw tot. (1 × 500-kw gas turbine set; 2 × 300-kw, 1 × 100-kw diesel sets)
Range: 10,000/16 **Endurance:** 90 days **Crew:** 75 tot. (civilian)

Remarks: 16,300 dwt. Soviet type designation: VTR (*Voyenyy Tanker,* Military Tanker). Naval version of the merchant *Velikiy Oktyabr* class. *Dnestr* was renamed on 5-4-97 in honor of the former civilian captain of the *Genrikh Gasanov,* who died aboard his ship in 11-96 after more than 20 years aboard her. *Boris Butoma,* completed 30-10-78, differs from the others in minor detail. She and *Vladimir Kolyachitskiy* are assigned to the Pacific Fleet, *Ivan Bubnov* to the Black Sea Fleet (where she was in layup status as of 2000), and the other two to the Northern Fleet.
Disposals: Black Sea Fleet unit *Boris Chilikin* had become the Ukrainian U 757 by 8-97.
Hull systems: Equipment varies: early units had solid-stores, constant-tension rigs on both sides forward; later units had the rig only to starboard, with a liquid transfer station to port. All have port and starboard liquid-replenishment stations amidships and can replenish liquids over the stern. Cargo: 8,250 tons fuel oil, 2,050 tons diesel fuel, 1,000 tons jet fuel (kerosene), 450 tons fresh water, 450 tons boiler feedwater, 250 tons lube oil, and 220 tons dry cargo (primarily provisions). There are two 3-ton electric cranes forward.
Combat systems: *Bubnov* and *Gasanov* were the last completed and appeared in merchant colors, without two twin 57-mm automatic gunmounts, MR-302 Rubka (Strut Curve) air/surface-search radar, or MR-103 Bars (Muff Cob) fire-control radars; that equipment was removed from the other ships by the end of the 1970s, although several retained their gunhouses for a short period.

♦ 4 Altay-class (Project 160) oilers [AO]
Bldr: Rauma-Repola, Rauma, Finland

	In serv.	Fleet		In serv.	Fleet
Ilim	1971	Pacific	Prut	1972	Northern
Kola	1967	Northern	Yel'nya	1971	Baltic

Kola H&L Van Ginderen, 1-97

Ilim JMSDF, 11-95

D: 2,828 tons light (7,225 fl) **S:** 14.2 kts
Dim: 106.07 (97.00 pp) × 15.40 × 6.75
Electronics:
Radar: 2 Don-2 nav.
Sonar: MGL-25 underwater telephone; NEL-5 echo sounder
M: 1 Valmet–Burmeister & Wain BM-550 VTBN-110 diesel; 1 prop; 3,250 bhp (2,900 sust.)
Electric: 638 kw tot. (2 × 260-kw, 1 × 22-kw diesel sets; 1 × 96-kw turbogenerator)
Range: 6,000/12 **Fuel:** 264 tons **Endurance:** 20 days **Crew:** 52 tot. (civilian)

Remarks: 3,670 grt/5,045 dwt. More than two dozen sisters served in the Soviet merchant marine. *Yel'nya* was stricken in 1992 and the hulk was briefly seized by Ukrainian dissidents at Sevastopol' during 4-93; she was subsequently refitted for further service and in 7-96 transited to the Baltic Fleet and is now based at Baltiysk, from which she is primarily employed in fueling the Russian fishing fleet, although she was reported in 11-01 to be badly in need of a refit.
Disposals: Pacific Fleet unit *Yegorlik* was sold commercial in 1996. Black Sea Fleet unit *Izhora* was chartered commercial 17-7-91 but may remain naval property.
Hull systems: An A-frame kingpost forward was added to *Izhora, Ilim,* and *Prut* during the late 1970s, permitting them to refuel one ship at a time on either beam; the others could only fuel alongside while dead in the water. Transfer gear, however, has been removed from *Ilim* and probably the others as well. All are also able to replenish over the stern. Have 10 cargo tanks and were originally equipped to transport 1,300 tons of heavy oil, 2,700 tons of distilled fuel, 200 tons of water, and 100 tons of lube oil. Differ in details, heights of masts, etc. The main propulsion engine bears the Russian designation 5DKRN-50/100. They carry 95 tons potable water for own use.

♦ 2 Olekma-class oilers [AO]
Bldr: Rauma-Repola, Rauma, Finland (In serv. 1964)

Iman Olekma

Iman—at Sevastopol', alongside the water tanker *Manych* Hartmut Ehlers, 9-98

Olekma—with A-frame kingpost abaft bridge to support underway liquid transfer hoses French Navy, 4-95

D: 2,300 tons light (6,440 fl) **S:** 14 kts **Dim:** 105.40 × 14.80 × 6.20
Electronics: Radar: 1 Don-2 nav.; 1 . . . nav.
M: 1 Burmeister & Wain 550 VTBF-110 diesel; 1 prop; 2,900 bhp
Electric: 295 kw tot. (2 × 120-kw diesel sets, 1 × 55-kw emergency diesel set)
Range: 4,000/14; 6,000/10 **Fuel:** 257 tons **Endurance:** 20 days
Crew: 40 tot. (accomm. for 52)

Remarks: 3,360 grt/4,400 dwt. Assigned to the Black Sea Fleet. Near-sister *Pevek*-class *Zolotoi Rog* was stricken in 1994 and sold for scrap in Turkey.
Hull systems: *Olekma* was modernized in 1978 with an A-frame abaft the bridge to permit underway fueling of one ship at a time on either beam; can also refuel over the stern. Cargo capacity is 4,482 tons total: 1,500 tons fuel oil, 1,500 tons diesel, 150 tons lube oil, 500 tons fresh water, 50 tons dry stores. There are two 250-ton/hr cargo pumps and one 3-ton and three 1-ton cargo derricks.

♦ 6 Uda-class (Project 577) oilers [AO]
Bldr: Karamaki Zavod, Vyborg (In serv. 1962–67)

	In serv.	Fleet		In serv.	Fleet
Dunay	12-65	Pacific	Sheksna	12-62	Northern
Koida	7-66	Black Sea	Terek	7-62	Northern
Lena	12-66	Baltic	Vishera	6-67	Pacific

Lena—with extra A-frame kingpost amidships to support refueling hoses South African Navy, 4-97

AUXILIARIES *(continued)*

Koida Boris Lemachko, 8-00

D: 2,910 tons light (7,160 fl) **S:** 17 kts **Dim:** 121.2 × 15.8 × 6.3
Electronics:
Radar: 2 Don-2 nav.—*Lena* also: 1 MR-212/201 Vaygach-U (Palm Frond) nav.
M: 2 Type 58D (16DPN 23/2 × 30) diesels; 2 props; 9,000 bhp
Range: 4,000/14 **Endurance:** 30 days **Crew:** 74 tot. (civilian)

Remarks: Type designation: VTR (*Voyenyy Tanker,* Military Tanker). Three others were transferred to Indonesia during the early 1960s and later scrapped. *Lena* cruised to Cape Town and back during 1997. *Koida* was stricken 30-7-93 but was refitted late in the 1990s and is based at Sevastopol'.
Hull systems: *Dunay, Vishera,* and *Lena* have been equipped with a second A-frame kingpost amidships for underway liquid replenishment. Cargo capacity includes 2,000 tons of fuel oil, 800 tons of distillate fuel, 100 tons of lube oil, 300 tons of feedwater, 200 tons of potable water, and 100 tons of stores.
Combat systems: Equipped to carry eight 57-mm AA, but none has been mounted since the early 1960s.

Note: *Baskunchak*-class (Project 1545) tanker *Sovetskiy Pogranichnik* is assigned to the Federal Border Guard fleet (q.v.).

♦ 1 Berezina-class (Project 1833) replenishment oiler [AOR]
(Nonoperational) Bldr: Zavod imeni 61 Kommunara, Nikolayev, Ukraine

	Laid down	L	In serv.
154 *Berezina*	18-8-72	20-4-75	30-12-77

Berezina (154)—flying the Naval Auxiliary Service flag but still moored inactive at Sevastopol', with armament removed Hartmut Ehlers, 7-00

D: 13,660 tons light; 22,820 tons normal (24,956 fl) **S:** 21.3 kts
Dim: 209.70 × 25.10 × 8.32
Electronics:
Radar: 1 Donets-2 nav; 2 Volga (Don-Kay) nav./surf. search; 1 MR-302 Rubka (Strut Curve) surf./air search—probably inactive: 1 MPZ-301 (Pop Group) SAM f.c.; 1 MR-103 Bars (Muff Cob) gun f.c.; 2 MR-123 Vympel (Bass Tilt) gun f.c.
Sonar: MG-312I Titan bow-mounted MR set with HF f.c. component
EW: 2 Bell Shroud intercept; 2 Bell Squat jammers; 2 PK-2 decoy syst. (2 twin, trainable RL)
M: 2 M-8E gas turbines, 2 waste-heat turbines; 2 props; 30,000 shp
Range: 10,000/18.1 **Endurance:** 90 days
Crew: . . . tot. (civilian) (accomm. for 214 crew, 182 passengers)

Remarks: Inactive since 1990, the ship had been the Soviet/Russian Navy's only naval-manned underway replenishment oiler until stricken during 1997. By 5-98, the ship had been stripped of armament and much useful equipment at Sevastopol', but in 2000, she was recommissioned as a civilian-manned oiler, although not yet reactivated.
Hull systems: Could refuel over the stern and from two Struna 2V-400 constant-tension stations, one per side amidships. Solid replenishment is by two Struna 1V-2.5, sliding-stay, constant-tension transfer rigs on either side. Pumping rate over the stern is 40 tons/hr. Vertical replenishment could also be carried out by two utility helicopters hangared in the after superstructure. There are four 10-ton stores-handling cranes to supply ships moored alongside. Cargo: 2,500 tons fuel, 900 tons ammunition, 286 tons provisions, 1,600 tons fresh water, 120 tons potable water, and 502 tons spare parts. Accommodations were provided for 182 spare submarine crewmembers, and mooring pockets for submarines were provided low on the hull sides. The propulsion plan employs four gas turbine exhaust waste-heat boilers to produce steam to drive two small boost turbines to improve fuel economy and increase total horsepower.

Combat systems: Two twin 57-mm 70-cal. AK-725 DP gunmounts, four 30-mm AK-630 gatling AA guns, and two RBU-1000 ASW rocket launchers have been removed, and it is likely that the Osa-M (SA-N-4) SAM system has either been removed or incapacitated. All weapons-control radars, however, remain aboard, although it is likely that, if and when the ship is reactivated, only the search radars will be rendered operational. The sonar and EW systems are probably also inoperable.

♦ 2 Belyanka-class (Project 1151.0) nuclear waste–disposal ships [AOS]
Bldr: Karamaki Zavod, Vyborg

Amur (In serv. 29-11-87) Pinega (In serv. 17-7-87)

Amur Boris Lemachko, 1991

D: 6,680 tons std. (8,250 fl) **S:** 15.3 kts **Dim:** 130.3 (123.10 pp) × 17.34 × 6.95
Electronics: Radar: 2 Kivach nav.
M: 2 Type 58E (16DPN 23/2 × 30) diesels; 1 prop; 9,000 bhp
Range: 4,000/14 **Endurance:** 25 days **Crew:** 86 tot. (civilian)

Remarks: Intended as waste nuclear-reactor plant coolant-water collection and spent fuel rod transport ships. *Amur,* based at Severodvinsk, has been employed to dump radioactive waste liquids into the Kara Sea east of Novaya Zemlya. *Pinega,* based in the Pacific Fleet area, is to be converted with Japanese assistance for use in the at-sea disposal of low-level radioactive waste. A third unit was reportedly begun at Severodvinsk but was not completed.
Hull systems: Have a large electrohydraulic crane to handle containers with spent reactor rods. Cargo capacity: 1,070 tons. The 10.5 × 14.5 × 6.0–m cargo hold is tended by one KE39, 16-ton, 20-m-reach electrohydraulic crane.

♦ 4 Luza-class (Project 1541) missile fuel transports [AOS]
Bldr: Karamaki Zavod, Vyborg (In serv. 1960–62)

Alambay Barguzin Don Selenga

Don—moored at Sevastopol', alongside an Okhtenskiy-class seagoing tug Boris Lemachko, 7-00

Alambay JMSDF, 10-94

D: 926 tons light; 1,140 tons normal (1,540 fl) **S:** 12.2 kts
Dim: 62.20 × 10.00 × 3.63 **Electronics:** Radar: 1 Don-2 nav.

AUXILIARIES *(continued)*

M: 2 diesels; 2 props; 1,600 bhp **Range:** 2,000/11 **Endurance:** 10 days
Crew: 4 officers, 36 unlicensed (civilian)

Remarks: Survivors of nine built. Originally designed to carry volatile liquids, including 357 tons of oxidizer and 152 tons of missile fuel, in 10 vertical cylindrical isolation tanks. *Alambay* and *Barguzin* (refitted in 1995) are in the Pacific Fleet, *Don* in the Black Sea Fleet, and *Selenga* in the Baltic. Some of these may be inactive or may have been stricken.
Disposals: *Yenisey* was stricken in 1978 after an accident. Northern Fleet units *Aragvi* and *Kama* were stricken 1-9-95, and two others (*Oka* and *Sasima*) had been retired by the early 1990s.

♦ 4 Vala-class (Project 1783A) nuclear waste transports [AOS]

Bldrs: Karamaki Zavod, Vyborg, and . . . Zavod, Vladivostok (In serv. 1961–71)

TNT-11 TNT-19 TNT-23 TNT-29

Northern Fleet Vala-class unit—with pennant 12 NAVPIC-Holland, 10-01

D: 1,080 tons light (2,310 fl) **S:** 11 kts **Dim:** 74.40 × 11.50 × 3.95
A: provision for 2 twin 12.7-mm Utës-M mg
Electronics: Radar: 1 Don-2 nav.
M: 2 Type 1D46 (6DN 39/45) diesels; 2 props; 2,600 bhp
Range: 1,000/9 **Endurance:** 20 days **Crew:** 4 officers, 29 enlisted

Remarks: Carry up to 906 tons of waste liquids from nuclear propulsion plants and have been used for open-ocean dumping of low-level radioactive materials. TNT-23 is assigned to the Pacific Fleet and the others to the Northern Fleet. Some of these are inactive, and all are in need of replacement (and are reported to be significantly radioactive).
Disposals: Pacific Fleet unit TNT-27, which dumped radioactive materials in the Sea of Japan in 10-93, is no longer operational. TNT-25 has been derelict at Zvezdochka repair yard, Yagriy Island, Severodvinsk, since 1994, still with 450 tons of radioactive waste aboard. TNT-5, -8, -17, -22, and -42 have been stricken.

Note: Also used for nuclear waste transport and disposal are as many as three units (TNT-12, -22, and -42) of the Zeya class (Project 1783), essentially a non-self-propelled version of the Vala class, and the smaller PEK-50 class barges, which hold only 50 tons of radioactive liquid each. Most of the survivors are in poor condition, and many are radioactively contaminated.

♦ 19 Amur-class (Project 304 and 304M*) repair ships [AR] (9 *nonoperational*)

Bldr: A. Warski SY, Szczecin, Poland (In serv. 1968–78, 1981–88)

PM-10	*PM-52*	PM-69*	PM-86*	*PM-139*
PM-15	PM-56	*PM-73*	PM-97*	PM-140
PM-34	PM-59*	*PM-75*	*PM-129*	PM-156
PM-40	PM-64	*PM-82*	PM-138	

D: 4,000 tons (5,490 fl) **S:** 14 kts **Dim:** 121.70 × 17.00 × 4.63
Electronics: Radar: 1 Don-2 nav.
M: 2 diesels; 1 prop; 2,990 bhp
Range: 7,800/10; 13,200/8 **Endurance:** 40 days
Crew: 208 tot. + up to 300 passengers

Amur-class PM-138—at Sevastopol' Hartmut Ehlers, 7-00

Amur-class PM-86—a Baltic Fleet Project 304M Jaroslaw Cislak, 2000

Amur-class pennant 30—at Kronshtadt, with a Tarantul-I-class missile boat alongside H&L Van Ginderen, 7-00

Remarks: PM = *Plavuchaya Masterskaya* (Floating Workshop). Early units did not have the passenger facilities. Serve surface ships and submarines with basic repair facilities and 280 tons of spare parts. Have two 3-ton cranes and, usually, one 1.5-ton crane. The fourth series (Project 304M or NATO Amur-II), consisting of PM-59, -69, -86, -92, and -97, had an extra deckhouse atop the superstructure forward of the stack, squared-off stacks, a slightly flattened face to the forward side of the bridge superstructure, and only two, new-style cranes. There are a great many more minor variations within the class. In addition to the units listed above, a PM-30 has been photographed in the Baltic, possibly a renumbering.
Disposals: PM-94 and -164 had been stricken by 1996. Northern Fleet units PM-163 and -161 were stricken on 22-2-93 and 1-9-95, respectively, and PM-49 was derelict at Pavlowskaya Bukhta as of 10-96. Black Sea Fleet unit PM-9 was transferred to Ukraine 1-8-97. PM-5, -37, -81, and -92 (all but the latter having been nonoperational for several years) had been stricken by 2001.

♦ 7 Oskol class (Projects 300 and 303) [AR] (5 *nonoperational*)

Bldr: A. Warski SY, Szczecin, Poland (In serv. 1963–67)

PM-20	*PM-51*	*PM-63*	PM-146
PM-26	*PM-62*	*PM-68*	

Oskol-class PM-26—at Sevastopol' Hartmut Ehlers, 7-00

AUXILIARIES *(continued)*

Oskol-class PM-146—a flush-decked Project 303 unit French Navy, 1991

D: 2,034–2,100 tons (2,521–2,800 fl) **S:** 14 kts
Dim: 88.6 × 13.60 (12.00 wl) × 3.80–3.90
Electronics: Radar: 2 Don-2 nav.
M: 1 Zgoda-Sulzer 6TAD-48 diesel; 1 prop; 2,250 bhp
Range: 3,000/10 **Crew:** 60 tot. (accomm. for 137)

Remarks: PM = *Plavuchaya Masterskaya* (Floating Workshop). Thirteen were built: six Project 300 (2,078 tons std./2,690 tons fl); two armed Project 301T (2,100 tons std./2,700 tons fl); and five flush-decked Project 303 (2,034 tons std./2,521 tons fl), of which PM-146 is one. All have one or two 3-ton cranes. PM-26 is assigned to the Black Sea Fleet and is berthed in the Sovetskaya Bukhta, Sevastopol'.
Disposals: Project 303/2 sister PM-147 was stricken from the Pacific Fleet 3-7-92. Black Sea Fleet unit PM-2 was transferred to the Ministry of Shipbuilding (and offered to Ukraine in 1997 but not accepted). PM-28 had been discarded by 1996. Pacific Fleet unit PM-148 was stricken 31-7-96. The remaining armed unit, Black Sea Fleet unit PM-24, was scrapped in Turkey beginning 15-10-97. PM-21 was deployed to Yemen at Aden during the late 1980s but returned to the Black Sea in 1991 and has since been stricken.

♦ 2 Biriusa-class (Project 1175) cable layers [ARC]
(1 *nonoperational*) Bldr: Wärtsilä SY, Turku, Finland

	L	In serv.		L	In serv.
BIRIUSA	29-11-85	20-6-86	KEM'	23-11-85	24-11-86

Kem'—at Vladivostok Boris Lemachko, 2000

D: 2,370 tons (fl) **S:** 11.8 kts **Dim:** 86.10 (78.70 pp) × 12.6 × 3.10
Electronics: Radar: 2 Mius (Spin Trough) nav.
M: diesel-electric: 2 Wärtsilä Vasa 8R22 diesels; 2 Schottel azimuthal props; 1,700 shp—bow tunnel thruster
Crew: 48 tot. (civilian)

Remarks: 2,650 grt. Ordered 1-85. Both are in the Pacific Fleet. *Kem'* was overhauled in South Korea in 1994, but *Biriusa* was laid up by 1997 awaiting funding for a badly needed overhaul.
Hull systems: A lengthened version of the *Emba* class, with more-powerful engines, carrying twice as much cable (600 tons: 518 m^3 coiled, in two cable tanks), and equipped with a gantry over the bow cable. Have three 2-m-diameter bow cable sheaves and two 2-m-diameter cable drums. Propellers swivel through 360°.

♦ 2 Emba-class (Project 1172) cable layers [ARC] (1 *nonoperational*)
Bldr: Wärtsilä SY, Turku, Finland

NEPRYADVA (L: 24-4-81) SETUN' (L: 29-4-81)

Nepryadva—laid up at Lomonosov Boris Lemachko, 1999

Setun'—at Sevastopol' Hartmut Ehlers, 7-00

D: 1,443 tons (2,145 fl) **S:** 11.8 kts **Dim:** 75.90 (68.50 pp) × 12.60 × 3.10
Electronics: Radar: 2 Mius (Spin Trough) nav.
M: diesel-electric: 2 Wärtsilä Vasa 6R22 diesels; 2 shrouded Schottel props; 1,360 shp—bow tunnel thruster
Range: 7,000/7 **Endurance:** 25 days **Crew:** 38 tot. (civilian)

Remarks: 1,910 grt. Cargo: 300 tons cable. Intended for use in shallow coastal areas, rivers, and harbors. Have one 5-ton crane. *Setun'* is in the Black Sea Fleet. Baltic Fleet unit *Nepryadva* was reported sold to Estonia in 1997 but was still laid up at Lomonosov under Russian colors as of 3-99. Caspian Flotilla unit *Emba* was transferred to Azerbaijan after 1992.

♦ 5 Klaz'ma-class (Project 1112 and 1274*) cable layers [ARC]
Bldr: Wärtsilä SY, Turku, Finland

	Laid down	L	In serv.
DONETS	17-12-67	1968	1968
INGURI	21-10-76	7-10-77	1978
TAVDA	14-4-76	21-10-76	6-10-77
YANA*	4-5-61	1-11-62	9-7-63
ZEYA	1968	1969	1970

Donets Jaroslaw Cislak, 7-01

D: 3,800–3,910 tons (6,810–6,920 fl) **S:** 14 kts
Dim: 130.4 (120.0 pp) × 16.0 × 5.75 **Electronics:** Radar: 2 Don-2 nav.
M: 5 Wärtsilä 624TS diesels (1,000 bhp each), electric drive; 2 props; 2,150 shp—475-shp active rudder—640-shp bow-thruster
Range: 12,000/14 **Fuel:** 250 tons **Endurance:** 30 days
Crew: 85–118 tot. (civilian)

Remarks: Type designation: KS (*Kabel'noye Sudno,* Cable Ship). *Yana* has an all-naval crew and reportedly can be employed as a minelayer. Plans to replace these worn-out ships with eight larger, 4,000-dwt cable layers to be built in Finland foundered with the collapse of the USSR, and their present operational condition is unknown. *Donets* is assigned to the Baltic Fleet, *Tavda* to the Pacific Fleet, and the others to the Northern Fleet.
Disposals: Black Sea Fleet sister *Tsna* was stricken 10-1-96 and transferred to Ukraine between 6-97 and 8-97; she has since been stricken. Pacific Fleet units *Katun'* and *Ingul* (Project 1274) were stricken in 1995 and on 31-7-96, respectively.
Hull systems: *Yana* (Project 1274) has four 2,436-bhp diesel generator sets and a longer forecastle and is 5,645 grt/3,400 dwt (6,810 fl). All have ice-strengthened hulls. In the 5,760-grt/3,750-dwt later units (Project 1112), the diesel engines drive five 680-kw generators, which provide power for propulsion and for all auxiliary functions. All cable machinery was built by Submarine Cables, Ltd., Great Britain. *Inguri, Tavda,* and *Zeya* carry 1,850 m^3 of cable and displace 7,885 tons (fl), drawing 5.76 m. The other two have three cable tanks totaling 1,600 m^3.

♦ 3 Malina-class (Project 2020) nuclear-powered-submarine propulsion plant tenders [ARR]
Bldr: Chernomorskiy Zavod, Nikolayev, Ukraine

PT'-5 PM-63 (In serv. 6-84)
PT'-6 PM-74 (In serv. 14-9-85)
PT'-7 PM-12 (In serv. 9-90)

AUXILIARIES *(continued)*

Malina-class PM-74 (PT'-6) JMSDF, 8-95

Malina-class PM-74 (PT'-6)—note the faceted hullform U.S. Navy, 1985

D: 10,435 tons (12,983 fl) **S:** 11.5 kts **Dim:** 138.4 (123.0 wl) × 21.0 × 6.86
Electronics:
Radar: 2 MR-212/201 Vaygach (Palm Frond) nav. (PM-12: 2 MR-312 Nayada nav.)
M: 4 diesels, 4 PG-112-1 generator sets, electric drive; 1 prop; 2,700 shp
Range: 13,000/10 **Endurance:** 45 days **Crew:** 33 officers, 191 enlisted

Remarks: PM = *Plavuchaya Masterskaya* (Floating Workshop). Second unit began trials in spring 1985, the third in 11-90. A fourth, PM-16, was launched in 1-92 to clear the ways; after massive modifications, she was completed in 5-96 as the Swan Hellenic cruise liner *Minerva*. Northern Fleet units PM-12 and PM-63 are assigned to the civilian nuclear-powered icebreaker fleet at Murmansk and to Sevmash at Severodvinsk, respectively. PM-74 was delivered to the Pacific Fleet late in 1985. PM-63 completed an overhaul at Severodvinsk 17-12-94, but it was reported in 1998 that her propulsion system was inoperable. PM-12 was refitted from 8-98 to 6-10-00, using U.S. funds to improve the security of nuclear materials; she is based at Nerpa Zavod, near Murmansk.
Hull systems: The unusual hullform, with no curved surfaces, indicates that the ships were not intended to move very often. They were designed to serve nuclear-powered submarines, as evidenced by the mooring pockets along the hull sides and the two 16-ton-capacity, specialized reactor recoring cranes. Have 450 m^3 of radioactive liquid storage tankage and are capable of accommodating 1,400 fuel rods—the equivalent of six reactor recorings.

♦ 1 Khoper-class (Project 16570) salvage tug [ARS]
Bldr: Svirsk Zavod, Nikol'sk (In serv. 7-96)

SB-931

D: 1,960 tons light (2,883 fl) **S:** 12+ kts
Dim: 63.75 (57.57 pp) × 14.26 × 5.61 (max.)
A: 1 twin 25-mm 80-cal. Type 2M-3M AA
Electronics: Radar: . . .
M: 2 Type 6R32 diesels; 2 CP props; 5,900 bhp
Range: 12,000/12 **Crew:** 25 tot. (accomm. for 37)

Remarks: Prototype was laid down in 1995 as a general salvage and rescue tug design capable of supporting divers to 45-m depths and equipped for a wide variety of salvage and underwater work duties. To date, no further units have been announced. Carries a rescue lifeboat, a divers' workboat, and diver recovery and decompression systems. Also equipped for fire fighting and water-blast cleaning. Hull has seven watertight compartments and an icebreaking bow. Was initially assigned to the Northern Fleet but may now be in the Baltic.

♦ 1 Kashtan-class rescue submersible tender [ARS]
Bldr: VEB Neptunwerft, Rostock, East Germany (In serv. 1990)

SS-750 (ex-KIL-140)

D: 4,200 tons (5,250 fl) **S:** 13.75 kts **Dim:** 113.00 (97.82 pp) × 18.22 × 3.71
Electronics: Radar: 1 Mius (Spin Trough) nav.; 1 Don-2 nav.
M: 2 Karl Liebnecht–M.A.N. 8VDS 26/20AL-1 diesels (2,991 bhp each), 2 generator sets, electric drive; 2 props; 4,200 shp (3,000 sust.)—bow-thruster
Range: 4,000/11 **Endurance:** 45 days
Crew: 44 tot. (accomm. for 18 officers, 36 unlicensed civilians)

Remarks: 4,400 grt/1,000 dwt. Renamed during 1995. Is used to transport and support two salvage submersibles, AS-22 and AS-26 (see under [YSS]). Is based in the Baltic and acted as trials tender to the deep salvage submersible *Rus'* during 6-00. Seven sisters remain in service as mooring buoy tenders.
Hull systems: Has a 100-ton German Stülcken heavy-lift gantry at the stern for lifting mooring buoys and for salvage assignments, a 12-ton electrohydraulic crane to starboard, and a 60-ton derrick amidships. The external appearance was not extensively altered from the standard appearance for the class.

Kashtan-class SS-750 2000

Disposal note: Of the two *Nikolay Chiker*–class (Project 5757) salvage tugs, *Fotiy Krylov* (SB-135) was stricken 3-7-92. She was sold to Alexander G. Tsavliris & Sons, Piraeus, Greece, early in 1993 as *Tsavliris Giant;* the Russian government subsequently declared the sale to have been invalid, recovered ownership of the vessel, and then leased her to Tsavliris Salvage Group, which operates her from Singapore on charter. Sister *Nikolay Chiker* (SB-131) was long-term chartered to the same company (now trading as Tsavliris Russ) during 7-00; remaining under the Russian flag, she was refitted late in 2000 and is now stationed in the Far East.

♦ 3 Sliva-class (Project 712) salvage tugs [ARS]
Bldr: Rauma-Repola Oy, Uusikaupunki/Nystad, Finland

	Laid down	L	In serv.	Fleet
SB-406	. . .	6-7-83	20-2-84	Northern
SB-921	17-8-84	28-12-84	5-7-85	Baltic
Shakhter (ex-SB-922)	31-8-84	3-5-85	20-12-85	Black Sea

Sliva-class Shakhter—at Sevastopol' Boris Lemachko, 5-00

Sliva-class SB-921 H&L Van Ginderen, 3-90

D: 2,170 tons (2,980 fl) **S:** 16.1 kts **Dim:** 68.81 (60.13 pp) × 15.40 × 5.40
Electronics: Radar: 2 MR-312 Nayada-5 nav.
M: 2 SEMT-Pielstick/Russkiy Dizel 6 PC2.5 L400 (TS HN40/46) diesels; 2 CP props; 7,800 bhp—bow-thruster
Range: 6,120/15 **Endurance:** 30 days
Crew: 43 crew + 10 salvage party (all civilian)

AUXILIARIES *(continued)*

Remarks: 2,050 grt/810 dwt. The similar icebreaking rescue ships of the *Stroptivyy* class are civilian subordinated. SB-922 was renamed *Shakhter* ("Miner") in 1987.
Disposals: Sister SB-408 was sold to Alexander G. Tsavliris & Sons, Piraeus, Greece, and renamed *Tsavliris Challenger* early in 1993 for use as a station salvage ship based in Sri Lanka; the Russian government subsequently declared the sale to have been invalid and recovered ownership, after which she was chartered to Tsavliris, for whom she still operates.
Hull systems: Bollard pull: 90 tons. Ice-reinforced hull. Able to support divers to 60 m. Have four water monitors, one 60- and one 30-ton winch, a unique 350-m floating power cable to support vessels in distress, a 5-ton electrohydraulic crane, and two cargo holds (100 m^3 and 50 m^3).

♦ 3 Goryn'-class (Project 563S) rescue tugs [ARS]
Bldr: Rauma-Repola, Rauma, Finland (In serv. 1982–83)

SB-36 (ex-MB-36) SB-522 (ex-MB-62) SB-523 (ex-MB-64)

Goryn'-class SB-522 Boris Lemachko, 2-01

Goryn'-class SB-36—at Sevastopol' Hartmut Ehlers, 7-00

D: 1,650 tons light; 2,240 tons normal (2,600 fl) **S:** 13.5 kts
Dim: 63.50 × 14.30 (13.80 wl) × 5.20
Electronics: Radar: 2 Don-2 nav.
M: 1 Russkiy Dizel Type 67N diesel; 1 prop; 3,500 bhp
Range: 8,000/12 **Endurance:** 40 days **Crew:** 43 tot. (civilian)

Remarks: SB = *Spastel'niy Buksir* (Rescue Tug). Former fleet tugs, redesignated as salvage tugs; have also been referred to as Project 714. SB-365, -522, and -523 can be distinguished from the standard tug version by the electrohydraulic crane and small tripod mast abaft the stack, and they have probably been fitted with MG-26 underwater telephones. SB-523 is in the Northern Fleet, SB-522 in the Pacific Fleet, and SB-36 (redesignated from MB-36 prior to 7-00) in the Black Sea Fleet.
Disposals: In 1991, sister SB-521 (ex-MB-61) began operating under charter to the Kamchatskiy Shipping Co. of Petropavlovsk as the *Kremenets*. SB-524 (ex-MB-108) of the Black Sea Fleet was stricken during 1996 and transferred to Ukraine in 1997.

♦ 4 Pionier Moskvyy–class (Project 05360 and 05361*) salvage submersible tenders [ARS] (1 *nonoperational*)
Bldr: Karamaki Zavod, Vyborg

Mikhail Rudnitskiy (In serv. 1979) Giorgiy Titov (In serv. 1983)
Giorgiy Koz'min (In serv. 1980) *Sayany** (In serv. 1984)

Mikhail Rudnitskiy NAVPIC-Holland, 10-01

Sayany—Project 05361 undersea research variant, laid up at Vladivostok, with gray hull and red superstructure Boris Lemachko, 2000

D: 6,100 tons (7,960 fl) **S:** 15.75 kts **Dim:** 130.30 (119.00 pp) × 17.30 × 5.90
Electronics:
Radar: 2 Okean-M nav.
Sonar: MGA-21 (*Sayany:* MG-89 Mezen') MF/HF active; MGV-5N underwater communications
M: 1 5DKRN 62/140-3 diesel; 1 prop; 6,100 bhp
Electric: 1,500 kw tot. **Range:** 12,000/15.5 **Endurance:** 45 days
Crew: 10 officers, 12 warrant officers, 40 enlisted + 40 naval salvage/submersible operations party

Remarks: Type designation: *Sudno-baza Podvodnikh Issledovaniy* (Underwater Research Support Ship). First three carry the ensign of the Naval Salvage and Rescue Service and are named for important developers of research/salvage submersibles; *Sayany* was configured for scientific research submersible support and was laid up, although in commission, as of 2001. *Mikhail Rudnitskiy* and *Giorgiy Titov* serve in the Northern Fleet and the other two in the Pacific Fleet.
Hull systems: A modification of a standard merchant timber-carrier/container-ship design, retaining two holds. The former after hold area has two superstructure levels built over it, and the former small hold forward has been plated over. Retain two 50-ton and two 20-ton derricks and have had heavy-cable fairleads cut in the bulwarks fore and aft and a number of boat booms added to starboard; the heavy-lift system is stabilized. *Titov* has a larger superstructure built over the no. 3 hold than do the first two and carries two Pisces submersibles with 2,000-m depth capability. *Rudnitskiy* carries the Poisk-2-class (Project 1839) three-man salvage submersible [YSS] *Bester* (ARS-34), plus underwater search and exploration equipment; during 8-00, she also operated the Project 1855 rescue submersible *Priz* (AS-32). *Sayany,* painted in white and gray, has had the forecastle and poop decks extended, the deckhouse amidships raised one deck higher, and a two-level deckhouse built over the forward hold area; she appears intended for a research role and is equipped with a high-frequency sonar of the type used on Russian Navy minesweepers. All are equipped with bow- and stern-thrusters and can be attached to a four-point salvage moor.

♦ 4 Ingul (Pamir)-class (Project 1452) salvage tugs [ARS]
Bldr: United Admiralty SY, St. Petersburg

	Laid down	L	In serv.	Fleet
Alatau	23-3-82	21-4-83	29-12-83	Pacific
Altay (ex-*Karabakh*)	14-2-85	18-4-87	21-10-87	Northern
Mashuk	7-6-74	27-6-75	25-12-75	Pacific
Pamir	2-4-73	28-5-74	26-12-74	Northern

D: 3,320 tons (4,040 fl) **S:** 20 kts (18.75 cruise) **Dim:** 92.79 (80.40 pp) × 15.63 × 5.85
Electronics: Radar: 2 Don-2 or Okean nav.
M: 2 Type 58D-4R, 16-cyl. diesels; 2 CP props; 9,000 bhp
Electric: 1,300 kw (4 × 300-kw, 1 × 100-kw diesel sets)
Range: 9,000/18.7; 15,000/12 **Fuel:** 675 tons heavy oil, 155 tons diesel
Endurance: 60 days **Crew:** 70 tot. (civilian) + 18 salvage party

Remarks: Two sisters, *Yaguar* and *Bars* (2,781 grt/1,140 dwt), were built for the merchant marine and had 35-man crews, plus bunks for 50 rescued personnel; *Bars* was sold to China in 1997. *Altay* was renamed in 1994.
Hull systems: Very powerful tugs with a constant-tension highline personnel rescue system, salvage pumps, firefighting equipment, and complete diving gear, capable of supporting divers to 60-m depths from two stations. Have 94-ton bollard pull and are

AUXILIARIES *(continued)*

Altay NAVPIC-Holland, 10-01

Altay NAVPIC-Holland, 10-01

equipped with one 60-ton and one 30-ton towing winch. An NK-300 submersible television camera system is installed. Have four 500-m^3/hr firefighting pumps. Carry one-each Project 1393A, 1394A, and 338PKV motorboats. Have three cargo holds (400 m^3 aft, 300 m^3 forward, and 120 m^3 rescue equipment stowage). The hull has a large bulbous bow. *Altay* has Intelsat SATCOM equipment and may have more elaborate salvage capabilities. All can carry 182 tons of potable water.
Combat systems: Provision was made to install a twin 57-mm AA mount and two twin 25-mm AA mounts, but none has ever carried armament.

♦ 4 Okhtenskiy (Goliat)-class (Project 733S) rescue tugs [ARS]
Bldr: Petrozavod SY, St. Petersburg (In serv. 1958–early 1960s)

SB-4 Kodor   SB-5   SB-9   SB-171 Loksa

Okhtenskiy-class rescue tug SB-5 Boris Lemachko, 1997

D: 759 tons (934 fl) **S:** 13.2 kts **Dim:** 47.30 (43.00 pp) × 10.30 × 4.20
Electronics:
Radar: 1–2 Don-2 or Mius (Spin Trough) nav.
Sonar: Kama hull-mounted underwater telephone
M: diesel-electric: 2 Type D5D50 (6ChN 30/38) diesels, 2 generator sets (950 kw each); 1 prop; 1,500 shp
Electric: 340 kw tot. **Range:** 8,000/11 **Fuel:** 197 tons
Endurance: 25 days **Crew:** 51 tot. (civilian + naval diving party)

Remarks: SB = *Spastel'niy Buksir* (Rescue Tug), hence the "S" suffix to the project number. Principal characteristics are essentially identical to the general fleet-tug version, except that they are equipped to support divers and have an underwater telephone. Bollard pull is 20 tons. There is a 5-ton derrick. SB-5 deployed to the Mediterranean during 6-98 to tow home Amur-class repair ship PM-56 from Syria. SB-9 is in the Northern Fleet based at Arkhangel'sk, SB-4 and -5 are in the Black Sea Fleet, and SB-171 is in the Baltic Fleet.
Disposals: Northern Fleet sister SB-3 was for sale for scrap in 1992, Pacific Fleet unit SB-28 was stricken 3-7-92, and SB-163 (ex-MB-163) had been retired by 2001. Black Sea Fleet unit *Moshniy* (SB-6) was stricken 5-7-94. Black Sea Fleet unit SB-15 was stricken 10-1-96 and transferred to Ukraine 1-8-97. Northern Fleet unit SB-11 had reverted to fleet tug status as MB-11 by 2001.

♦ 2 Roslavl-class (Project AT-202) seagoing tugs [ARS]
Bldr: . . . SY, Riga (In serv. 1953–60)

SB-41   SB-46

Roslavl-class rescue tug SB-46 H&L Van Ginderen, 1995

D: 470 tons (625 fl) **S:** 12 kts **Dim:** 44.5 × 9.5 × 3.3
Electronics: 1 Don-2 nav. **M:** 2 diesels; 2 props; 1,200 bhp
Range: 6,000/11 **Fuel:** 86.8 tons **Crew:** 30 tot. (civilian)

Remarks: Predecessor to the Okhtenskiy class. SB-46 is assigned to the Caspian Flotilla and based at Astrakhan. The status of SB-41 is uncertain. Seven others are still in service as fleet tugs [ATA].

♦ 4 Iva-class (Polish Project B-99) firefighting tugs [ARS]
Bldr: Stocznia Polnocna, Gdansk, Poland

	L	In serv.		L	In serv.
Vikhr-5	11-5-84	30-11-84	Vikhr-8	22-12-84	31-5-85
Vikhr-6	4-9-84	28-2-85	Vikhr-9	18-6-85	29-3-86

Vikhr-5 H&L Van Ginderen, 1998

D: 2,299 tons (fl) **S:** 16 kts **Dim:** 72.30 (63.00 pp) × 14.30 × 4.56
M: 2 Cegielski-Sulzer 16 AV 25/30 diesels; 2 CP props; 5,880 bhp—2 500-shp side-thrusters
Electric: 740 kw (2 × 370-kw diesel sets) **Range:** 2,500/12 **Fuel:** 186 tons
Crew: 26 ship's company + 18 rescue team + 50 evacuees

AUXILIARIES *(continued)*

Remarks: 2008 grt/317 dwt. Eight others (all with *"Vikhr"*-series names) are civilian units serving offshore oilfields. Have water, foam, and chemical firefighting systems with a total pumping capacity of 4,000 m³/hr.
Disposals: *Vikhr-2* was transferred to Vietnam in 5-92. *Vikhr-4* was sold to the Norwegian firm Echo Shipping in 2000 as the *Echo Fighter* and placed on long-term charter to Greenpeace as the *Esperanza* as of 1-01.

♦ 4 Katun'-II (Ikar)-class (Project 1993) seagoing fireboats [ARS]
Bldr: Srednyy Neva Zavod, Kolpino, St. Petersburg (In serv. 1978–80)

PZhS-64 PZhS-92 PZhS-95 PZhS-219

D: 1,065 tons (1,255 fl) **S:** 17 kts **Dim:** 65.40 × 10.20 × 3.19
Electronics:
Radar: 1 Mius (Spin Trough) nav.
Sonar: MGA-21 HF hull-mounted object avoidance
M: 2 Type 6DR-42 diesels; 2 props; 5,000 bhp
Electric: 500 kw tot. (2 × 200-kw, 1 × 100-kw diesel sets)
Range: 2,000/17 **Endurance:** 20 days **Crew:** 38 tot.

Remarks: An enlarged version of the Katun'-I design (Project 1893). One source says only two were built. Have two 1,000-m³/hr and four 500-m³/hr fire and salvage pumps. PZhS-64 and -92 operate in the Northern Fleet, the others in the Pacific.

♦ 9 Katun'-I-class (Project 1893) seagoing fireboats [ARS]
Bldr: Srednyy Neva Zavod, Kolpino, St. Petersburg (In serv. 1970–78)

PZhS-96	PZhS-123	PZhS-209	PZhS-279	PZhS-551
PZhS-98	PZhS-124	PZhS-273	PZhS-282	

Katun'-I-class PZhS-123—at Sevastopol' Hartmut Ehlers, 8-00

Katun'-I-class PZhS-98—at Murmansk NAVPIC-Holland, 10-01

D: 883 tons (930 fl) **S:** 18 kts **Dim:** 62.60 × 10.20 × 3.19
Electronics:
Radar: 1 Mius (Spin Trough) or Don-2 nav.
Sonar: MGA-21 HF hull-mounted object avoidance
M: 2 Type 40DM (12DRN 23/30) diesels; 2 props; 4,400 bhp
Range: 1,800/12 **Endurance:** 20 days **Crew:** 32 tot. (civilian; accomm. for 45)

Remarks: Originally designated PDS (*Pozharno-Degazatsionnoye Sudno,* Firefighting and Decontamination Ship) and later revised to PZhS (*Pozharnoye Sudno,* Firefighting Ship). There are several civilian sisters, including the *General Gamidov.* Fleet assignments include PZhS-96, -124, -282, and -551 in the Baltic; PZhS-98 in the Northern; PZhS-123 in the Black Sea; PZhS-209 in the Pacific; and PZhS-273 and -279 in the Caspian Flotilla. PZhS-123 carries the local unofficial name *Dunay.*
Hull systems: Have extensive firefighting gear, including an extendable boom-mounted monitor, and can fight fires on land up to 200 m from the water. Also intended for use in decontaminating surface ships and submarines. Have an 8-ton bollard-pull towing hook. Are equipped with four 1,000-m³/hr firefighting and salvage pumps, one 1,000-m³/hr and seven 500-m³/hr firefighting monitors, high-pressure air and portable electric power supplies, a tank to hold 15 tons of foam agent, and a Project 1395 motorboat equipped with a towing hook.
Note: See also harbor fireboat entries under [YTR].
Disposal note: Ugra-class (Project 1886.1) submarine tender *Vladimir Yegorov* (ex-PB-82) was scrapped in 1993 and should not have been included in the last edition; Black Sea Fleet unit *Volga,* used in recent years as a stationary staff headquarters and accommodations hulk at Sevastopol', had been discarded by mid-2001. Pacific Fleet Don-class (Project 310) submarine tender PB-9 (ex-*Kamchatskiy Komsomolets,* ex-PKZ-124, ex-*Batur*) may still be performing a similar role as a hulk.
Modified Dnepr–class (Project 725A) submarine tenders PM-130 and PM-135 are apparently no longer in service.

♦ 1 El'brus (Osminog)-class (Project 537) submarine rescue ship [ASR]
Bldr: Zavod imeni 61 Kommunara, Nikolayev, Ukraine

	L	In serv.
ALAGEZ	1984	28-1-89

Alagez—with a Krivak-I-class frigate alongside Boris Lemachko, 7-98

Alagez H&L Van Ginderen, 2-92

D: 12,430 tons (14,300 fl) **S:** 20 kts (17 sust.)
Dim: 175.00 (156.00 wl) × 25.10 (24.80 wl) × 7.50
A: provision for 4 single 30-mm 54-cal. AK-630 or AK-306 gatling AA
Electronics:
Radar: 1 Don-2 nav.; 2 MR-212/201 Vaygach-U (Palm Frond) nav.
Sonar: MGA-6 Gamma hull-mounted HF search suite
M: 4 Type 68G (18DN 23/2 × 30) diesels (7,250 bhp each), electric drive; 2 props; 24,900 shp
Electric: 3,200 kw tot. (4 × 800-kw diesel sets)
Range: 5,000/20; 15,000/10 **Endurance:** 60 days **Crew:** 312 tot. + 106 passengers

Remarks: Far and away the world's largest and most elaborate submarine salvage-and-rescue ship. Deployed to the Pacific Fleet on completion. Was undergoing reactivation as of 10-00 as a result of the loss of the cruise-missile submarine *Kursk.* Based at Vladivostok.
Disposal: Older sister *El'brus*—which made one brief deployment from 12-81 to 1-82 and then returned to the Black Sea, emerged again briefly in 5-84, and has not deployed since—was stricken between 8-97 and 5-98 and was towed to India for scrapping in 2-00. The incomplete hull of a third unit, *Ayudag,* was launched 1-95 to clear the ways and was approved for scrapping in 8-95.
Hull systems: Has an icebreaking hull. The large hangar aft of the stack was intended to hold one Poisk-2-class (Project 1839) and two *Priz*-class (Project 1855) salvage-and-rescue submersibles [YSS], which are moved forward on rails for launching by an extendable overhead 100-ton gantry crane that can be deployed on either side in sea states up to 5. Has a hangar for one Helix helicopter, with the hangar door pivoting downward to form a ramp leading to the helicopter flight deck. Can lay and retrieve a four-point moor. The 3-ton crane on the port quarter has a very long folding arm. Has submersible decompression and observation chambers, firefighting equipment, and five 500-m³/hr salvage pumps.

♦ 1 Nepa-class (Project 530) submarine rescue ship [ASR]
(Nonoperational) Bldr: Black Sea SY, Nikolayev, Ukraine

	Laid down	L	In serv.
KARPATY	11-9-63	24-12-64	29-3-67

D: 5,180 tons (5,776 fl) **S:** 16.5 kts **Dim:** 129.50 × 18.60 × 5.50
Electronics:
Radar: 2 Don-2 nav.
Sonar: MG-16 and MGA-1 hull-mounted HF search sets; MG-26 underwater telephone
M: 4 Type 3D-100M diesels (1,800 bhp each), 4 PG-150 generator sets (1,375 kw each), electric drive; 2 props; 6,350 shp

AUXILIARIES *(continued)*

Karpaty—laid up at Kronshtadt Boris Lemachko, 2000

Electric: 1,600 kw tot. (4 × 300-kw, 2 × 200-kw diesel sets)
Range: 3,800/16.5; 8,000/12.2 **Endurance:** 45 days
Crew: 175 tot. + 76 passengers

Remarks: Has been assigned to the Baltic Fleet since beginning a 1989–93 refit at Liepaya, after which she was moored out of service at Kronshtadt with the refit incomplete, although still in commission and with at least a partial crew and apparently able to get under way. All diving and salvage equipment, however, was said to be obsolete as of 8-00. After the *Kursk* disaster, the ship began a reactivation overhaul, but insufficient funds were provided to complete the work, and it was halted.
Hull systems: Displacement was originally 5,080 tons light, 5,690 tons fl. Has a 100-ton lift hook supported by horns extending over the stern, and two others extending through the hull bottom, permitting the lifting of a 750-ton object from the sea-bottom. There are also two 60-ton derricks amidships. Is a very large all-purpose salvage ship with submarine-rescue equipment, including several rescue bells (one termed "SK-59") and observation chambers, including two stowed in the inner sides of the huge projecting lift frame at the stern. Can support divers at 60-m depths and has special diver apparatus to support a diver to 140 m. There are one 15-ton, two 5-ton, and one 3.2-ton derricks. Stated to be able to salvage submarines from depths of up to 500 m.

♦ 2 Prut-class (Project 05275* and 527M) submarine rescue ships [ASR] · Bldr: Zavod imeni 61 Kommunara, Nikolayev, Ukraine

	In serv.	Fleet
EPRON (ex-SS-26, ex-MB-26)*	29-10-59	Black Sea
SS-83 (ex-SS-24)	1961	Pacific

EPRON—at Sevastopol' Hartmut Ehlers, 7-00

D: 2,120 tons light; 2,770 tons std. (3,330–3,380 fl) **S:** 18.8 (SS-83: 17.8) kts
Dim: 89.70 (85.00 wl) × 14.30 (14.00 wl) × 5.20–5.40 (6.57 max.)
Electronics:
Radar: 2 Don-2 nav.
Sonar: MGA-6 suite (probable HF search); MG-26 underwater telephone
M: 4 3D-100M diesels (1,800 bhp each), 4 PGK-215/55 generator sets (1,250 kw each), electric drive; 2 props; 7,000 shp
Electric: 1,740 kw tot. (7 × 220-kw diesel sets)
Range: 2,500/16.5; 10,500/11.3 **Fuel:** 260.2 tons **Endurance:** 35 days
Crew: 129–135 tot.

Remarks: SS = *Spasitel'noye Sudno* (Rescue Ship). SS-83 was modernized during 1969–74 to Project 527M status. *EPRON* is an acronym for *Ekspeditskaya Podvodnik Rabot Ososbogo Nazhnacheniya,* the Russian Navy's submarine rescue service, and was assigned in 1969; the ship underwent a refit at Sevastopol' during 1999.
Disposals: Northern Fleet sister *Altay* (SS-22) burned out in 1969 and was scrapped; SS-44 was grounded and lost in 1973; SS-23 was scrapped around 1987; Black Sea Fleet unit SS-21 was stricken 7-1-92 and became the commercial *Podvodnik Marinesko;* Pacific Fleet unit *Zhiguli* (ex-SS-25) was stricken 30-7-93 and sold to China, probably for scrapping; Northern Fleet unit *Beshtau* (ex-SS-44, ex-MB-11; not the same unit as the SS-44 lost in 1973) was stricken 22-2-93; and Northern Fleet unit *Vladimir Trefol'ev* (ex-SS-87, ex-SS-28) was stricken 1-9-95.
Hull systems: Have one 12-ton derrick, two or three special carriers for rescue chambers, a submersible decompression chamber for divers, and salvage observation bells. Four anchor buoys are stowed on inclined racks on the after deck. Earlier units had tripod foremasts; these survivors have quadripod foremasts and smaller mooring buoys. Can tow ships of more than 15,000 tons displacement.

♦ 2 Neftegaz-class (Polish Project B-92) oilfield tug/supply vessels [ATA] Bldr: A. Warski SY, Szczecin, Poland (In serv. 1983–87)

Ilga (In serv. 4-11-83) Kalar

Kalar—red hull, white superstructure, black funnels, yellow mast JMSDF, 10-01

D: 3,080 tons (4,013 fl) **S:** 15 kts **Dim:** 80.70 (71.50 pp) × 16.30 (15.0 wl) × 5.00
Electronics: Radar: 2 MR-312 Nayada nav.
M: 2 Zgoda-Sulzer diesels; 2 CP props; 7,200 bhp
Electric: 1,200 kw tot. (3 × 400-kw diesel sets)
Range: 5,000/12 **Fuel:** 533 tons **Endurance:** 30 days
Crew: 23 tot. (civilian) + 12 passengers

Remarks: 2,372 grt/1,396 dwt. Survivors of a class of 43 oilfield supply tugs ordered in 1982. Cargo: up to 600 tons of dry cargo on deck, plus 1,000 m^3 of liquid cargo. Can act as tugs and have four firefighting water monitors. Have a bow-thruster. *Ilga* has carried a large missile-range telemetry tracking antenna aft and operates in the Northern Fleet, primarily in cargo service; *Kalar* is in the Pacific Fleet and is used as a rescue tug. Black Sea Fleet sister *Aleksandr Kortunov* had been discarded or sold commercial by 2002.

Disposal note: MB-331-class oceangoing tug MB-331 had either been stricken or transferred to commercial service by 2001; sister MB-330, in poor condition, was operating on charter to the Far Eastern Shipping Co. (FESCO) by 1996.

♦ 7 Goryn'-class (Project 563) seagoing tugs [ATA]
Bldr: Rauma-Repola, Finland (In serv. 1982–83)

MB-15	MB-32	MB-38	Yevgeniy Khorov (ex-MB-35)
MB-18	MB-36	MB-119 (ex-*Bilbino*)	

Goryn'-class seagoing tug MB-38 NAVPIC-Holland, 10-01

Goryn'-class MB-32 Boris Lemachko, 1999

D: 1,650 tons light; 2,240 tons normal (2,600 fl) **S:** 13.5 kts
Dim: 63.50 × 14.30 (13.80 wl) × 5.20
Electronics: Radar: 2 Don-2 nav.
M: 1 Russkiy Dizel Type 67N diesel; 3,500 bhp
Range: 8,000/12 **Endurance:** 40 days **Crew:** 43 tot. (civilian) + 18 passengers

Remarks: 1,600 grt. Russian type designation: MB (*Morskoy Buksir,* Seagoing Tug). Intended for ocean towing, salvage, and fire fighting. Four others were converted as

AUXILIARIES *(continued)*

rescue tugs (SB—*Spastel'noye Buksir*). MB-38 is in the Northern Fleet, and MB-35 (delivered 15-9-82 and renamed late in 2001) and MB-119 (delivered 20-3-78) are in the Baltic Fleet, with MB-15, MB-18, and MB-32 in the Pacific Fleet. Black Sea Fleet unit MB-36 was redesignated SB-36 prior to 7-00.
Disposals: MB-105 (ex-*Baykalsh*) was sold to Vietnam for commercial use in 8-95.
Hull systems: Early units had 35-ton bollard pull. The later units have a Type 671 diesel and produce 43 tons bollard pull. The two series can be distinguished visually by the overlapping rubbing strakes at the forecastle break in the early units and the sloping connecting strake in late units.

♦ 17 Sorum-class (Project 745) seagoing tugs [ATA]
Bldr: Yaroslavl Zavod (In serv. 1973–92)

MB-4, MB-25, MB-26, MB-28, MB-37, MB-56, MB-58, MB-61, MB-76, MB-99, MB-100, MB-106, MB-110, MB-147, MB-148, MB-196, MB-236

MB-100 NAVPIC-Holland, 10-01

Sorum-class MB-61—note circular blanking plates for installation of 30-mm guns forward of the pilothouse and the SATCOM radome on the after mast JMSDF, 3-93

D: 1,140–1,210 tons (1,512–1,656 fl) **S:** 13.8 kts
Dim: 58.30 (55.50 pp) × 12.60 × 4.60
Electronics: Radar: 2 Don-2 nav.
M: 2 Type 25-DB 2 (6ChN 30/38) diesels, electric drive; 1 prop; 2,500 shp (1,850 sust.)
Range: 6,200/11 **Fuel:** 297 tons **Endurance:** 40 days
Crew: 35 tot. (civilian) + 40 passengers/rescuees

Remarks: MB = *Morskoy Buksir* (Seagoing Tug). MB-110, the final unit, was completed 31-8-91. Armed versions of the design serve the Federal Border Guard as patrol ships [WPS] (q.v.), and another, OS-572, was a trials ship [AGE] and now operates as survey vessel GS-31. Reported fleet assignments: MB-28, -56, -58, and -100 in the Northern; MB-25, -37, -61, -76, and -148 in the Pacific; MB-31 in the Black Sea; and MB-4 in the Baltic. As many as nine of those listed above may be nonoperational.
A modified version with larger superstructure and an A-frame kingpost aft is used by the Ministry of Fisheries as a rescue tug, prominently displaying *Spastel'* ("Rescue") on the black hull sides; known as the *Almaz* class, it includes *Almaz, Ametist, Kapitan Beklemishev,* and *Neustrashimyy,* with sister *Purga* having been sold to the Turkish Navy in 1999. One unit of the class, possibly a civilian *Almaz,* has been transferred to Vietnam. Soviet Naval Auxiliary Service units are unarmed but do have blanking plates for two twin 30-mm AA mount positions forward. Most units recently sighted have a radome for a commercial SATCOM system antenna atop the after mast.
Disposals: Black Sea Fleet sisters MB-30 and -304 were stricken 10-1-96, and MB-30 was transferred to Ukraine on 1-8-97; the remaining Black Sea Fleet unit, MB-31, was sunk as a missile target during 2001. By 2001, Northern Fleet units MB-6, -13, -19, and -307 had been stricken, while sisters MB-70 and -175 had earlier been discarded or sold commercial.

♦ 24 Okhtenskiy (Goliat)-class seagoing tugs (Project 733) [ATA]
Bldr: Petrozavod SY, St. Petersburg (In serv. 1958–1966)

	Fleet		Fleet
MB-5	Northern	MB-162	Baltic
MB-8	. . .	MB-164	Northern
MB-11	Northern	MB-165 Serdity	Baltic
MB-12	Pacific	MB-166	Pacific
MB-16	Pacific	MB-169	. . .
MB-21	Northern	MB-172	Northern
MB-23	Black Sea	MB-173 50 Let Oktyabrskiy	Black Sea
MB-52	Northern	MB-175	Pacific
MB-86	. . .	MB-176	. . .
MB-95	Pacific	MB-178 Saturn	Baltic
MB-157	. . .	RB-187 (ex-MB-. . .)	. . .
MB-160	Black Sea	RB-196 (ex-MB-. . .)	. . .

Okhtenskiy-class MB-21—a Northern Fleet unit NAVPIC-Holland, 10-01

Okhtenskiy-class MB-173—still named *50 Let Oktyabrskiy* ("50th Anniversary of the Revolution") Boris Lemachko, 1998

D: 717 tons (890 fl) **S:** 13.3 kts **Dim:** 47.30 (43.0 pp) × 10.30 × 4.14
Electronics: Radar: 1 or 2 Don-2 or Mius (Spin Trough) nav.
M: diesel-electric: 2 Type D5D50 (6ChN 30/38) diesels, 2 generator sets (950 kw each); 1 prop; 1,500 shp
Electric: 340 kw tot. **Range:** 6,000/13; 7,800/7 **Fuel:** 197 tons
Endurance: 30 days **Crew:** 31 tot. (civilian) + 40 passengers/rescuees

Remarks: MB = *Morskoy Buksir* (Seagoing Tug); sisters designated SB (*Spastel'noye Buksir,* Rescue Tug) are listed under [ARS]. Two have been demoted to *Rednyy Buksir* (Roadstead Tug) status, but their former MB-numbers are not known. Most units with names vice MB-series nomenclature were civilian, but the names listed above are applied to naval units.
Disposals: A number of the 40 naval (including eight Project 733S rescue tugs [ARS]) and 23 civilian units completed have been stricken. Pacific Fleet sister *Alatyr',* laid up in 1990, was stricken 5-9-94. Black Sea Fleet units *Tyulen* (MB-171) and *Volkhov* were stricken 5-7-94 and 31-7-96, respectively. Pacific Fleet units MB-24 and -170 were stricken 31-7-96 for commercial employment. Others known to have been retired are *Stoikiy, Strogiy,* MB-2, MB-24, MB-64, MB-151, and *Sil'niy* (MB-152). One Pacific Fleet unit was transferred to Vietnam in 5-92, and MB-51 was transferred to Ukraine on 1-8-97.
Hull systems: Bollard pull: 27 tons initial/17 tons sustained. Have a 5-ton derrick.

♦ 7 Roslavl-class (Project 730) seagoing tugs [ATA]
Bldr: Dalyan' Zavod, Riga (In serv. 1953–60)

MB-45, MB-69, MB-95, MB-102, MB-134, MB-145, MB-147

D: 470 tons (625 fl) **S:** 12 kts **Dim:** 44.5 × 9.5 × 3.5
Electronics: Radar: 1 Don-2 nav.
M: 2 Type 6DR-30/50 diesels; 2 props; 1,200 bhp
Electric: 125 kw tot. (1 × 100-kw, 1 × 25-kw diesel sets) **Range:** 6,000/11
Fuel: 86.8 tons **Endurance:** 10 days **Crew:** 30 tot. (civilian)

Remarks: Predecessor to the Okhtenskiy class; project number has also been said to be A-202. Two others, SB-41 and SB-46, remain in service as rescue tugs, and two, named *Bodriy* and *Nevel'skoy,* are assigned to another government agency. Two others were built in Romania. MB-102 is assigned to the Northern Fleet and MB-145 to the Caspian Flotilla; fleet assignments for the others are not available.

AUXILIARIES *(continued)*

Roslavl-class MB-145—at Makhachkala on the Caspian Sea
Boris Lemachko, 1997

Disposals: Black Sea Fleet unit *Dzhambul* and MB-158 were stricken 3-7-92. Baltic Fleet units MB-91 and MB-94 were stricken 22-2-93 and 1-9-95, respectively. Northern Fleet unit MB-116 was stricken 22-2-93, and MB-125 has either been discarded or never existed.

♦ 1 Manych-class (Project 1549) water tanker [AW]
Bldr: Karamaki Zavod, Vyborg (In serv. 1972)

MANYCH

Manych—with munitions carrier *General Ryabakov* in the background
Hartmut Ehlers, 7-00

D: 3,065 tons light (5,800 fl) **S:** 17 kts **Dim:** 114.5 × 15.9 × 5.8 (max.)
A: provision for 2 twin 57-mm 70-cal AK-725 DP
Electronics:
Radar: 2 Volga (Don-Kay) nav.; 1 MR-302 Rubka (Strut Curve) surf./air search; 2 MR-103 Bars (Muff Cob) gun f.c. (nonfunctional)
M: 2 Type 58D diesels; 2 props; 9,000 bhp
Range: 6,000/14 **Endurance:** 30 days **Crew:** 79 tot.

Remarks: Refitted in Bulgaria in the mid-1990s. Is in service, based at Sevastopol', although the ship has not been known to get under way for some time. Retains fire-control radars, but the two twin 57-mm DP gunmounts were removed in 1981. Sister *Tagil* was discarded from the Pacific Fleet in 1996.
Hull systems: Cargo capacity: 1,800 tons potable or boiler water, 20 tons distilled water, and 180 tons provisions.

♦ 4 Voda (MVT-6)-class (Project 561) water tankers [AWT]
Bldr: Yantar Zavod, Kaliningrad (In serv. 1953–60)

MVT-16 MVT-20 MVT-136 (ex-*Vodoley-21*) MVT-148

Voda-class MVT-136—a Pacific Fleet unit Boris Lemachko, 5-96

D: 982 tons light (2,255 fl) **S:** 12 kts **Dim:** 81.30 × 11.40 × 3.44 (1.65 light)
Electronics: Radar: 1 Don-2 or Mius (Spin Trough) nav.
M: 2 Russkiy Dizel 8DR30/50 diesels; 2 props; 1,600 bhp
Electric: 150 kw tot. (1 × 100-kw, 1 × 50-kw diesel sets; 380 V, 50 Hz)
Range: 2,900/10; 3,500/7 **Endurance:** 15 days **Crew:** 38 tot.

Remarks: 1,000 grt. Seventeen were completed, of which several were equipped with working decks to permit their use as underway water replenishment ships for deployed steam-powered warships. The five above were still in limited use in the late 1990s.

Disposals: Baltic Fleet unit MVT-138 was stricken 3-7-92. Black Sea Fleet unit *Abakan* (ex-MVT-9) was stricken 30-7-93 (but remains hulked at Sevastopol'); sister *Sura* (ex-MVT-19) was stricken 10-1-96 and transferred to Ukraine in 1997. Pacific Fleet unit MVT-135 (ex-*Vodoley-12*) was stricken 31-7-96 for scrapping but may be the unit now in Vietnamese Navy service. Also reported discarded between 1989 and 1997 were MVT-6, -10, -17, -18, -134, and -428.
Hull systems: Cargo: 700 tons feedwater, 300 tons potable water. Have one 3-ton derrick for hose handling.

♦ 2 Smol'nyy class (Project 887) [AXT]
Bldr: A. Warski SY, Szczecin, Poland (In serv. 1976–78)

200 PEREKOP (In serv. 1-1-78) 210 SMOL'NYY (In serv. 1976)

Smol'nyy (210) A. A. de Kruijf, 7-01

Perekop (200) Hartmut Ehlers, 7-96

D: 5,659 tons light; 6,120 tons std. (7,270 fl) **S:** 20 kts
Dim: 138.00 × 17.20 × 5.53
A: 2 twin 76.2-mm 59-cal. AK-726 DP; 2 twin 30-mm 65-cal. AK-230 AA; 2 12-round RBU-2500 ASW RL (128 RGB-25 rockets); 2 45-mm Type 21-KM saluting cannon
Electronics:
Radar: 1 Volga (Don-Kay) nav.; 2 Don-2 nav.; 1 Mius (Spin Trough) nav.; 1 MR-310 Angara-M (Head Net-C) surf./air search; 1 MR-105 Turel' (Owl Screech) f.c.; 1 MR-104 Rys' (Drum Tilt) AA f.c.
Sonar: Shelon hull-mounted MF search; searchlight HF attack
EW: 2 Bizan'-4 (Watch Dog) intercept (2–18 GHz)
M: 2 16-cyl. diesels; 2 props; 16,000 bhp
Electric: 2,560 kw tot. (4 × 640-kw diesel sets; 400 V, 50 Hz)
Range: 10,870/14 **Fuel:** 1,050 tons **Endurance:** 40 days
Crew: 12 officers, 121 enlisted + 30 instructors and 300 cadets

Remarks: Built to relieve the *Sverdlov*-class cruisers that were formerly used for cadet training. Both are based at Kronshtadt. *Smol'nyy* began a refit at Rostock, Germany, 6-4-98. Most weapon and sensor equipment is obsolescent.
Disposals: *Khasan* was decommissioned 1-10-95, stricken 31-10-98, and scrapped at Yantar Shipyard, Kaliningrad, beginning in 11-99.
Hull systems: Carry six rowboats aft for exercising the cadets. Have numerous duplicate navigational training facilities for training purposes. Carry 396 tons of potable water, 35 tons of lubricating oil, and 61.2 tons of provisions. Also said to carry 14 instructors and 330 cadets.
Combat systems: Carry 700 rounds of 76.2-mm and 4,000 rounds of 30-mm ammunition.

Disposal note: *Luga*-class cadet-training ship *Luga,* laid up at Kronshtadt since the mid-1990s, had reached derelict condition by 2000 and is unlikely to see further service. Sister *Oka* was based at the now-Azerbaijani port of Baku in the Caspian to support the Kirov Naval Academy and was transferred to Azerbaijan in 1992 or 1993.

SERVICE CRAFT

Note: Classes listed below are those for which data have been published. There are additionally large numbers of yardcraft in such categories as floating cranes [YD], floating dry docks [YFDB, YFDM, YFDL], covered and open barges [YC, YFN], and fuel barges [YON] and innumerable small launches [YFL]; illustrations for examples of some of these are provided, where available.

SERVICE CRAFT *(continued)*

♦ **10 Razvedchik-class (Project 1388M) environmental monitoring craft [YAG]** Bldr: Sosnovka Zavod (In serv. 1983–87)

KRKh-321	KRKh-559	KRKh-1374	KRKh-1884
KRKh-528	KRKh-579	KRKh-1668	
KRKh-536	KRKh-959	KRKh-1821	

Razvedchik-class KRKh-536 NAVPIC-Holland, 10-01

D: 220 tons (270 fl) **S:** 31 kts **Dim:** 46.0 × 6.0 × 2.1
Electronics: Radar: 1 Mius (Spin Trough) nav.
M: 2 M-504-series diesels; 2 props; 9,000 bhp
Range: 1,500/10 **Endurance:** 10 days **Crew:** 14 tot.

Remarks: Intended for radiological and environmental pollutant monitoring. A variant of the NATO-designated Shelon'-class (Project 1388) torpedo retriever, with a full-height after deckhouse containing laboratory spaces and no torpedo retrieval ramp. KRKh-536, -559, and -959 are in the Northern Fleet; KRKh-321 is in the Black Sea Fleet; KRKh-1821 is in the Baltic Fleet; and KRKh-528 and -579 are in the Pacific Fleet. KRKh-213 has been reconfigured as officer's yacht KSV-213. Sister KRKh-1208 was derelict at Kronshtadt in 1999.

♦ **1 fleet staff support craft [YAG]**

AZERBAYZHAN

Azerbayzhan H&L Van Ginderen, 5-95

Remarks: No data available. A large river passenger craft adapted to serve as the flagship for the Caspian Flotilla.

♦ **1 historical relic, former armored cruiser [YAG]**

	Bldr	Laid down	L	In serv.
AVRORA	New Admiralty SY, St. Petersburg	6-1897	5-1900	1903

Avrora H&L Van Ginderen, 7-93

D: 6,732 tons normal (7,271 fl) **S:** 19 kts
Dim: 126.83 (123.47 wl) × 16.63 × 7.30 (max.)
A: 14 single 130-mm low-angle; 5 single 45-mm AA
M: 3 sets vertical triple-expansion steam; 3 props; 13,000 ihp (nonoperational)
Boilers: 20 Belleville-Dolgolenko watertube (nonoperational)

Remarks: Famous as the ship that fired the signal starting the Bolshevik Revolution on 25-10-17. Used for training between World Wars I and II; damaged during World War II. Has served as a museum since 1948. Underwent massive restoration at Severnaya Verf 190, St. Petersburg, essentially receiving a new 32-mm hull plating intended to last for several centuries; she was refloated in early 1987 and rededicated 25-10-87. Data above pertain to the ship in 1941.

♦ **2 Muna-class trials craft [YAGE]**
Bldr: . . . SY, Nikolayev, Ukraine (In serv. 1966–85)

OS-114 (ex-MBSS-. . .) OS-220 (ex-MBSS-. . .)

Muna-class trials craft OS-220 Hartmut Ehlers, 9-98

D: 457 tons (688 fl) **S:** 11 kts **Dim:** 51.50 × 8.40 × 2.70
A: OS-220 only: 2 bow . . .-mm TT (underwater)
Electronics: Radar: 1 Mius (Spin Trough) nav.
M: 1 Type 6DR 30/50 diesel; 1 prop; 600 bhp
Range: 1,700/10 **Endurance:** 15 days **Crew:** 15 tot. (+ 7 passengers)

Remarks: Former munitions carriers reconfigured for trials service. OS-220, based at Balaklava in the Black Sea Fleet, is equipped to launch and recover torpedoes.
Hull systems: Have a single 3.2-ton-capacity electric crane.

♦ **1 missile trials barge [YAGE]**

BGP-60

Submersible missile-trials platform BGP-60 Hartmut Ehlers, 9-98

Remarks: No data available. Was in storage at Balaklava as of 9-98. Appears to be a roughly square barge complete with a vertical launch tube for ballistic missiles, covered by a partial section of submarine outer hull structure. A tower structure on one corner provides an observation post. The craft is submersible. Moored with the craft was another test barge, possibly configured for launching cruise missiles.

SERVICE CRAFT *(continued)*

♦ . . . miscellaneous floating cranes [YD]

Remarks: The Russian Navy and the Ministry of Shipbuilding have a large number of floating cranes, most equipped with auxiliary propulsion systems to permit local movement at bases and in harbors.

Floating crane PK-21500—with Flamingo-class workboat RK-290 alongside
Hartmut Ehlers, 9-95

♦ 4 Sekstan-class (Project 220) deperming tenders [YDG]

Bldr: Laivateolissus SY, Turku, Finland (In serv. 1953–57)

SR-127 SR-144 SR-151 SR-154

Sekstan-class SR-154—alongside Bereza-class deperming tender SR-137 at Sevastopol'
Werner Globke, 8-97

D: 280 tons (400 fl) **S:** 9 kts **Dim:** 40.6 × 9.3 × 4.3
Electronics: Radar: 1 Don-2 or Mius (Spin Trough) nav.
M: 1 diesel; 1 prop; 400 bhp
Range: 8,000/9 **Endurance:** 37 days **Crew:** 24 tot.

Remarks: Survivors of 72 built as war reparations. Several were transferred abroad and others were converted as cargo lighters. Wooden construction. Among recent disposals, Baltic Fleet unit SR-176 was stricken 22-2-93 and SR-160 and SR-171 were abandoned in Latvia in 2-94. SR-144 is in the Northern Fleet, SR-154 in the Black Sea Fleet, and the other two in the Pacific Fleet.

♦ 0 (+ . . .) new-construction diving tenders (Project . . .) [YDT]

Bldr: Sudostroitel'nyy Zavod "Slip," Rybinsk (In serv. . . .)

D: approx. 300 tons (fl) **S:** 11 kts **Dim:** 38.00 × 7.70 × 1.90
Electronics: Radar: 1 . . . nav.
M: 2 diesels; 2 props; 600 bhp **Electric:** 150 kw tot. (3 × 50-kw diesel sets)
Range: 500/11 **Endurance:** 5 days **Crew:** 16 tot. (incl. 6 divers)

Remarks: The first unit was to have been completed in 1996, if funds for construction had been made available, but there have been no reports of any actual construction progress. Intended to begin replacement of the remaining Project 376 and 1415 diving tenders. Will be able to support divers to depths of 60 m.

♦ 28 Flamingo (Tanya)-class (Project 1415.1 and 1415.2) diving tenders [YDT]

Bldrs: Sosnovka Zavod, Rybinsk; Yaroslavl Zavod; and others (In serv. 1976–90s)

RVK-114	RVK-557	RVK-1209	RVK-1390	RVK-1893	RVK-2058
RVK-125	RVK-576	RVK-1250	RVK-1405	RVK-1943	RVK-2059
RVK-187	RVK-615	RVK-1251	RVK-1480	RVK-1944	RVK-2072
RVK-344	RVK-717	RVK-1254	RVK-1886	RVK-2029	
RVK-511	RVK-1080	RVK-1376	RVK-1887	RVK-2048	

Flamingo-class diving tender RVK-2059—with bulwarks at bow and stern
Hartmut Ehlers, 7-96

Flamingo-class diving tender RVK-1250—with hull bulwarks forward only; some diving-tender units have continuous bulwarks running from bow to stern
H&L Van Ginderen, 7-00

D: 42 tons (54 fl) **S:** 11 kts **Dim:** 21.20 × 3.93 × 1.40
Electronics: Radar: 1 Lotsiya nav. (not always fitted)
M: 1 Type 3D-12A or 3D-12L diesel; 1 prop; 300 bhp
Electric: 12 kw tot. (DGR 1A-16/1500 generator)
Range: 200/11 **Endurance:** 5 days **Crew:** 3 tot. + 5 divers

Remarks: Designed by Redan Central Design Bureau. RVK probably stands for *Rednyy Vodolanyy Kater* (Roadstead Diving Cutter). Can support divers to 45 m. Up to 50 sisters are assigned to the Federal Border Guard as patrol boats and are known in Russia as the Kulik class (q.v.). Others are equipped as workboats [YFL] or inshore survey craft [YGS]. The bulwarks around the hull vary in extent, with some having full bulwarks, others various cut-outs, and others bulwarks only at the bow and stern.

♦ 28 Yelva (Krab)-class (Project 535M) diving tenders [YDT]

Bldr: Gorokhovtse Zavod (In serv. 1971–83)

VM-20	VM-250	VM-409	VM-420	VM-809	VM-915
VM-72	VM-263	VM-413	VM-425	VM-907	VM-916
VM-146	VM-268	VM-414	VM-429	VM-908	VM-919
VM-153	VM-270	VM-415	VM-725	VM-909	
VM-154	VM-277	VM-416	VM-807	VM-910	

Yelva-class diving tender VM-416—off Sevastopol'; note gantry for submersible diver's decompression chamber to port at the aft end of the superstructure
Boris Lemachko, 2000

Yelva-class diving tender VM-72—off Murmansk NAVPIC-Holland, 10-01

D: 279 tons (300 fl) **S:** 12.4 kts **Dim:** 40.90 (37.00 pp) × 8.00 × 2.02
Electronics: Radar: 1 Don-2 or Mius (Spin Trough) nav.—Sonar: MGA-1 HF
M: 2 Type 3D-12A diesels; 2 props; 600 bhp **Electric:** 200 kw tot.
Range: 1,870/12 **Endurance:** 10 days **Crew:** 24 tot. + 4 divers

Remarks: Can support two divers at once to 60 m. Have a built-in decompression chamber; some (but not all) also have a submersible decompression chamber. Have

SERVICE CRAFT *(continued)*

one 2.5-ton-capacity derrick. Endurance has also been reported as 1,500 n.m. at 10 kts. Additional units are in civilian service. Known fleet assignments: VM-153, -277, -414, -425, -429, -725, -809, -908, -915, and -916 in the Northern; VM-146, -263, -270, -409, -415, -420, -807, and -910 in the Pacific; VM-250, -268, and -909 in the Baltic; and VM-154, -413, and -416 in the Black Sea. Some are probably nonoperational.
Disposals: Baltic Fleet units VM-143 and -266 were stricken 22-2-93 and Pacific Fleet unit VM-251 on 5-7-94. VM-152 was stricken from the Black Sea Fleet 10-1-96 and transferred to Ukraine. Several were exported, including VM-917 to Libya in 1973 and two to Cuba (in 1973 and 1978; one later lost).

♦ up to 55 Nyryat'-1-class (Project 522) diving tenders [YDT] (In serv. 1955 to mid-1960s)

From among:

VM-1	VM-72	VM-88	VM-122	VM-153	VM-203
VM-7	VM-73	VM-89	VM-125	VM-155	VM-260
VM-9	VM-74	VM-91	VM-126	VM-159	VM-261
VM-10	VM-75	VM-93	VM-129	VM-189	VM-277
VM-33	VM-76	VM-99	VM-142	VM-191	
VM-34	VM-77	VM-103	VM-147	VM-192	
VM-48	VM-79	VM-107	VM-148	VM-193	
VM-65	VM-80	VM-113	VM-149	VM-194	
VM-70	VM-82	VM-115	VM-150	VM-195	
VM-71	VM-87	VM-116	VM-151	VM-201	

Black Sea Fleet Nyryat'-1-class diving tender VM-125—with enclosed pilothouse added atop the original position Boris Lemachko, 2000

D: 105.4 tons (115 fl) **S:** 10 kts **Dim:** 28.50 × 5.50 × 1.70
Electronics: Radar: 1 Mius (Spin Trough) nav. or none
M: 1 Type 6CSP 28/3C diesel; 1 prop; 450 bhp
Range: 900/9 **Endurance:** 10 days **Crew:** 15–22 tot.

Remarks: VM = *Vodolaznyy Morskoy* (Seagoing Diving Tender). Survivors of about 60 built for Soviet Navy. Same hull was used for the GPB-480-class inshore survey craft. Others were built for export. The commanding officer is usually an experienced *michman* (warrant officer). Can support hard-hat divers to 20-m depths. As built, could be equipped with one 12.7-mm mg. Black Sea Fleet unit VM-122 bears the name *Udomlya.*
Disposals: Northern Fleet units VM-105 and -121 were offered for scrap in 1992. VM-84, -106, and -127 were stricken from the Baltic Fleet 22-2-93. VM-5, -14, -114, and -230 were stricken from the Black Sea Fleet 10-1-96 and transferred to Ukraine. VM-125 was mistakenly accidentally attacked and sunk by Syrian aircraft during 1989, but the craft was evidently salvaged, as she was listed as active as of 2000.

♦ . . . Nyryat'-2 (Yaroslavets)-class (Project 376) diving tenders [YDT]

Bldrs: Yaroslavl Zavod (In serv. 1950s–90) and Sosnnovskiy Sudostroitel'nyy Zavod (1995–. . .)

From among:

RVK-220 through RVK-257	RVK-1159
RVK-259 through RVK-500	RVK-1349
RVK-617	RVK-1446
RVK-667	RVK-1893
RVK-780 through RVK-790	RVK-1947
RVK-850 through RVK-900	RVK-2081
RVK-920	

D: 32.2 tons (38.2 fl) **S:** 9–10 kts **Dim:** 21.00 × 3.90 × 1.40 (max.; 1.26 mean)
Electronics: Radar: 1 Spin Trough nav. or none
M: 1 Type 3D-6S1 diesel; 1 prop; 150 bhp
Electric: 10 kw tot. (1 × 10-kw DGPN-8/1500 diesel driving)
Range: 1,600/8 **Fuel:** 1.5 tons **Endurance:** 5 days
Crew: 10 tot. as diving tender

Remarks: More than 600 Project 376 launches have been built to the same general design for military and civilian use, of which 400 were said still to be in military service as of 1998. Nyryat'-2 was a NATO nickname applied to PO-2 class workboats configured as diving tenders with bow or full-length bulwarks (see under [YFL]), but some diving tenders do not have any bulwarks at all. Can support hard-hat divers to 20-m depths. All-steel construction. Can be operated safely in Force 8 winds and 2-m seas and can break light ice.

Black Sea Fleet Nyryat'-2-class diving tender RVK-617—with the characteristic bulwarks from bow to stern that distinguish this variant of the ubiquitous Project 376 launch; the cruiser *Admiral Golovko* is in the background
Hartmut Ehlers, 7-00

♦ 20 Muna-class (Project 1823, 1823B, 1824B, and 1824T) ammunition lighters [YE]

Bldrs: . . . SY, Nikolayev, Ukraine, and Nakhodka SY (In serv. 1966–85)

VTR-6	VTR-48	VTR-82	VTR-87	VTR-92
VTR-28	VTR-76	VTR-83	VTR-89	VTR-94
VTR-32	VTR-77	VTR-85	VTR-90	VTR-97
VTR-39	VTR-81	VTR-86	VTR-91	VTR-148

Muna-class munitions lighter H&L Van Ginderen, 7-00

D: 457 tons (688 fl) **S:** 11 kts **Dim:** 51.50 × 8.40 × 2.70
Electronics: Radar: 1 Mius (Spin Trough) nav.
M: 1 Type 6DR 30/50 diesel; 1 prop; 600 bhp
Range: 1,700/10 **Endurance:** 15 days **Crew:** 15 tot. + 7 passengers

Remarks: Built in several different configurations: some as torpedo transports, others to carry surface-to-air missiles. The newest, VTR-76, was completed 17-12-85. Originally carried MBSS (*Morskaya Barzha Samokhodnaya Sukhogruznaya,* Seagoing Self-Propelled Dry Cargo Lighter)-series pennants but now have VTR (*Voyennyy Transport,* Military Transport)-series pennants. Two others were converted into coastal survey ships (since stricken) and another two into trials craft [YAGE] OS-114 and OS-220 (q.v.). VTR-77 is assigned to the Baltic Fleet, while VTR-76, -85, -87, -89, -90, -and -91 are assigned to the Pacific; VTR-94 remains in Black Sea Fleet service, and subordination of the others listed is not available. The Federal Border Guard operates four others.
Disposals: VTR-93 was stricken 10-1-96 and was in Ukraine Navy service as of 8-97.
Hull systems: Usually have a single 3.2-ton-capacity electric crane positioned between two or four small holds. Deadweight cargo capacity is 175 tons.

♦ 1 Vydra-class (Project 106K) cargo lighter [YF]

Bldr: . . . . . . (In serv. 1967–69)

BSS-705200 (ex-MDK-. . .)

D: 308 tons light (550 fl) **S:** 10.5 kts
Dim: 54.50 (50.00 pp) × 7.70 (7.50 wl) × 2.25 (mean hull)
Electronics: Radar: 1 Don-2 nav.
M: 2 Type 3D-12 diesels; 2 Kort-nozzle props; 600 bhp
Range: 1,400/10 (loaded) **Endurance:** 8 days **Crew:** 12 tot.

Remarks: The only current unit to have been redesignated as a service craft out of 15 survivors of the 46 built for Russian use as utility landing craft (see entry for this class under utility landing craft [LCU] for illustration). Assigned to the Black Sea Fleet. The cargo deck is 30.0 × 4.5 m and can accommodate up to 176 tons of vehicles or cargo (6 ZIL-131 or 10 GAZ-66 trucks).

♦ 1 or more SMB-1-class (Project 106) cargo lighters [YF]

Bldr: . . . . . . (In serv. 1958–65)

MBSS-233200

SERVICE CRAFT *(continued)*

SMB-1-class cargo lighter MBSS-233200 Boris Lemachko, 1999

D: 180 tons light; 280 tons std. (356 fl) **S:** 10.5 kts
Dim: 48.20 (44.40 pp) × 6.70 (5.50 wl) × 1.90 (mean hull)
M: 2 Type 3D-12 diesels; 2 props; 600 bhp
Range: 1,200/10 (loaded) **Endurance:** 5 days **Crew:** 12 tot.

Remarks: Former utility landing craft employed as local-service supply craft, the survivors of 20 built. At least one is operational in the Caspian Flotilla and others in the Black Sea. The cargo deck is 25.0 × 4.0 m and can accommodate up to 176 tons of vehicles or cargo (6 ZIL-131 or 10 GAZ-66 trucks).

♦ 12 Project 411B dry cargo lighters [YF]
Bldr: Vyborg Zavod (In serv. 1958–61)

MBSN-405250	MBSN-449250	MBSN-465250	MBSN-804250
MBSN-430250	MBSN-452250	MBSN-466250	MBSN-815250
MBSN-437250	MBSN-454250	MBSN-802250	MBSN-818250

Project 411B dry cargo lighters MBSN-454250 and MBSN-452250—modified to drop four drum-shaped buoys to establish a four-point moor, probably in support of salvage work Boris Lemachko, 1999

D: 320 tons (fl) **S:** 9 kts **Dim:** 35.0 × . . . × . . .
M: 1 Type 3D-12 diesel; 1 prop; 300 bhp **Range:** 1,150/9 **Crew:** 8 tot.

Remarks: Either the above list is incomplete or some of these craft have had their pennant numbers changed over the years (as evidenced by the photo of an MBSN-4532250).

♦ 2 Lentra (Logger)-class cargo lighters [YF]
Bldr: Leningradskaya Kuznitsa Zavod, Kiev, Ukraine (In serv. 10-55)

Alma Pakhra

Lentra-class cargo lighter Alma Hartmut Ehlers, 7-00

D: 250 tons (479 fl) **S:** 10 kts **Dim:** 39.20 × 7.30 × 2.80
Electronics: Radar: 1 Mius (Spin Trough) nav.
M: 1 Type 8 NVD-36 diesel; 1 prop; 300 bhp
Range: 6,900/9 **Fuel:** 41.7 tons **Crew:** 21 tot.

Remarks: Modified fishing craft employed as local cargo transports, *Pakhra* in the Caspian Flotilla and *Alma* in the Black Sea Fleet. Can carry up to 55 tons of liquid cargo in addition to solid stores stowed in two holds.

♦ 1 or more Shalanda (BSS-53150)-class (Project 431) cargo lighters [YF]
Bldr: . . . . . (In serv. 1951 to late 1950s)

MNS-30150

Shalanda-class lighter MNS-30150—at Sevastopol' Boris Lemachko, 7-00

D: 158 tons light (326 fl) **S:** 8.2 kts **Dim:** 36.00 × 6.90 × 2.00
M: 1 Type 3D-12 diesel; 1 prop; 300 bhp
Range: 500/8 **Endurance:** 10 days **Crew:** 8 tot.

Remarks: Although many have been discarded, a few of the 60 built may still be in service. The standard version could carry 150 tons of dry cargo and was normally equipped with one 3-ton electric crane. Some were configured as slaked lime transports in support of the now-discarded Quebec-class (Project A615), Kreislauf-cycle submarines.

MAB-50250—one of a large class of non-self-propelled barges found in most fleet areas; the Black Sea Fleet craft has two cargo holds, with a crane mounted between them and a small pilothouse at the stern Hartmut Ehlers, 7-00

Note: Some 150 floating dry docks served the Soviet Navy at the end of the 1980s (of which all but about 30 were the property of the Ministry of Shipbuilding), but only five of them had capacities of 25,000 tons or more; many of the older ones have since been abandoned, but newer units are listed below. Most Russian floating dry docks were built in Yugoslavia. PD = *Plavuchiya Dok* (Floating Dry Dock). See also [YRD] for specialized transport docks. An unfinished 13,500-ton-capacity floating dock was purchased from the Kherson Shipyard during 7-97 for use in scrapping discarded nuclear-powered submarines in the Northern Fleet area; the craft has steel sidewalls and a reinforced concrete pontoon hull.

Medium floating dry dock PD-0002—under tow in the Sea of Japan JMSDF, 1994

♦ 1 PD-50-class large floating dry dock [YFDB]
Bldr: Götaverken, Arendal, Sweden (In serv. 1980)

PD-50

Capacity: 80,000 tons **Dim:** 330.00 × 67.00 × 6.10

Remarks: Assigned to the Northern Fleet. Has been employed for docking aircraft carriers and was to be used for docking the salvaged hulk of the submarine *Kursk.* Has one 50-ton and one 30-ton traveling crane. Flooded draft over blocks is 15 m. Has a crew of about 175 tot.

♦ 1 PD-41-class large floating dry dock [YFDB]
Bldr: Ishikawajima-Harima Heavy Industries, Tokyo (In serv. 10-78)

PD-41

Capacity: 80,000 tons **Dim:** 305.00 × 67.00 × 6.00

Remarks: Assigned to the Pacific Fleet and has been employed for docking aircraft carriers. Has two 30-ton traveling cranes. Flooded draft over blocks is 15 m. Has a crew of about 175 tot.

SERVICE CRAFT *(continued)*

♦ 2 PD-81-class large floating dry docks [YFDB]
Bldr: . . . . . . (In serv. 1979–80)

PD-81 PD-. . .

Capacity: 29,300 tons **Dim:** 250.00 × 38.30 × 5.20

Remarks: One is assigned to the Pacific Fleet at Vladivostok. Have one 20-ton and one 15-ton traveling crane. Flooded draft over blocks is 11.4 m.

♦ 1 Project 2121 large floating dry dock [YFDB]
Bldr: . . . . . . (In serv. 1980)

SUKHONA

Capacity: 25,000 tons **Dim:** 199.0 × 42.0 × 7.0

Remarks: Assigned to the Northern Fleet and has been employed for docking *Kiev*-class aircraft carriers. Has two 25-ton traveling cranes. Flooded draft over blocks is 13 m and distance between wing walls is 27 m.

♦ 1 Shilka-class (Project 1780) medium floating dry dock [YFDM]
Bldr: Amur Shipyard (In serv. . . .)

SHILKA

Capacity: 12,000 tons
Dim: 180.00 × 35.00 (24.00 dock floor width) × 16.80 (max.)

Remarks: Covered, climate-controlled dock built for Russian Navy Pacific Fleet submarine use on the Kamchatka Peninsula. Has 10-m maximum water depth above keel blocks when flooded. There are two 10-ton, two 8-ton (2.3 ton at maximum reach), and three 0.5-ton cranes. Diesel generators are fitted. The design is also offered for export.

♦ . . . Project 1760 medium floating dry docks [YFDM]
Bldr: . . . . . . (In serv. . . .)

Capacity: 8,500 tons **Dim:** 155.0 × 32.4 × 4.5

Remarks: Concrete construction. Have two 5-ton traveling cranes. Flooded draft over blocks is 7.0 m and width between wing walls is 23.4 m.

♦ 3 Project 823 medium floating dry docks [YFDM]
Bldr: . . . . . . (In serv. 1965–. . .)

PD-3 . . . . . .

Project 823 medium floating dry dock PD-3—under tow in the Sea of Japan; note the extensive superstructure atop one side of the dockwall and the traveling crane on the other; stowed horizontally atop the long superstructure is a tall, slender vent stack, an indication that the dock is intended to service nuclear-powered submarines JMSDF

Capacity: 6,500 tons **Dim:** 155.0 × 31.0 × 5.0

Remarks: Concrete construction. Have two 5-ton traveling cranes. Flooded draft over blocks is 8.5 m and width between wing walls is 22.5 m.

♦ 2 Project 122A medium floating dry docks [YFDM]
Bldr: . . . . . .

PD-27 (In serv. 1954) . . . (In serv. 1960)

Capacity: 6,000 tons **Dim:** 140.0 × 32.0 × 4.4

Remarks: Have two 5-ton traveling cranes. Flooded draft over blocks is 7.0 m and width between wing walls is 21.3 m.

♦ 1 Project 782 medium floating dry dock [YFDM]
Bldr: . . . . . . (In serv. 1954)

PD-45

Capacity: 8,000 tons **Dim:** 120.0 × 37.4 × 4.3

Remarks: Steel construction. Has two 3-ton traveling cranes. Flooded draft over blocks is 8.0 m and width between wing walls is 24.4 m.

Note: The following three dock classes were typed PDE (expansion not known) and were better equipped to perform more complex repairs.

♦ 1 Project 13560 medium repair floating dry dock [YFDM]
Bldr: . . . . . . (In serv. 1985)

PD-. . .

Capacity: 8,500 tons **Dim:** 148.7 × 35.0 × 5.2

Remarks: Concrete construction. Has two 12-ton and two 10-ton traveling cranes. Flooded draft over blocks is 10.0 m and width between wing walls is 20.0 m.

♦ 1 Project 1780 medium repair floating dry dock [YFDM]
Bldr: . . . . . . (In serv. 1977)

PD-71

Capacity: 13,400 tons **Dim:** 180.0 × 35.0 × 6.2

Remarks: Steel construction. Has two 10-ton and four 8-ton traveling cranes. Flooded draft over blocks is 10.0 m and width between wing walls is 20.6 m.

♦ 3 Project 1777 medium repair floating dry docks [YFDM]
Bldr: . . . . . . (In serv. 1973–78)

PD-73 . . . . . .

Capacity: 9,100 tons **Dim:** 160.0 × 32.4 × 7.3

Remarks: Concrete construction. Have two 10-ton and two 8-ton traveling cranes. Flooded draft over blocks is 9.1 m and width between wing walls is 21.4 m.

♦ . . . Project 1758 small floating dry docks [YFDL]
Bldr: . . . . . . (In serv. 1970s)

Capacity: 4,500 tons **Dim:** 118.0 × 29.6 × 3.3

Remarks: Concrete construction. Have two 5-ton traveling cranes. Flooded draft over blocks is 6.3 m and width between wing walls is 20.0 m.

♦ 1 Project 765 small floating dry dock [YFDL]
Bldr: . . . . . . (In serv. 1967)

PD-6

Capacity: 2,000 tons **Dim:** 91.0 × 15.0 × 6.0

Remarks: Steel construction. Has two 5-ton traveling cranes. Flooded draft over blocks is 6.5 m.

♦ 45 Flamingo (Tanya)-class (Project 1415.1) workboats [YFL]
Bldrs: Sosnovka Zavod, Rybinsk; Yaroslavl Zavod; and others (In serv. 1976–90s)

6 BSK-series:

BSK-2 BSK-12 BSK-15
BSK-3 BSK-14 BSK-16

17 RK (Rednyy Kater, *Roadstead Cutter)-series:*

RK-78 RK-676 RK-963 RK-1206 RK-1394 RK-1886
RK-340 RK-931 RK-994 RK-1214 RK-1403 RK-1978
RK-413 RK-962 RK-995 RK-1243 RK-1664

18 PRDKA (Protivodiversionniye Kater, *Counterswimmer Cutter)-series:*

PRDKA-316 PRDKA-391 PRDKA-407 PRDKA-1356
PRDKA-331 PRDKA-400 PRDKA-409 PRDKA-1376
PRDKA-333 PRDKA-402 PRDKA-419 PRDKA-1978
PRDKA-372 PRDKA-404 PRDKA-838
PRDKA-376 PRDKA-405 PRDKA-885

4 named units:

H. BEZHLIVTSEV M. NAUMOV
I. PASKIREV N. RUDENKO

Flamingo-class workboat RK-1206—at Vyborg; the bulwarks have been cut away in two places to aid personnel in boarding and debarking Boris Lemachko, 1999

D: 42 tons (54 fl) **S:** 11 kts **Dim:** 21.20 × 3.93 × 1.40
Electronics: Radar: 1 Lotsiya nav. (not always fitted)
M: 1 Type 3D-12A or 3D-12L diesel; 1 prop; 300 bhp
Electric: 12 kw tot. (DGR 1A-16/1500 generator)
Range: 200/11 **Endurance:** 5 days **Crew:** 4 tot. + 27 passengers

Remarks: Designed by Redan Central Design Bureau. RK *(Reydnyy Kater)* workboat version has a capacity for 27 passengers or 17 tons of cargo. Others are equipped as diving tenders [YDT] and inshore survey craft [YGS] (qq.v.), while additional units are assigned to the border guard as patrol boats, and one, TS-581, is used by the customs service. The numbers painted on the craft may change with varying assignments or changes of basing, as few photos show craft with any of the numbers listed above.

♦ 0 (+ 5) flag officers' yachts [YFL]
Bldr: Severnaya Verf, St. Petersburg (In serv. 3-02)

D: 85 tons (fl) **S:** 25+ kts **Dim:** 32.0 (27.4 pp) × 6.5 (6.2 wl)
Electronics: Radar: 1 . . . nav.
M: 1 Zvezda . . . diesel; 1 prop; . . . bhp
Crew: 6 tot. + 20 passengers

Remarks: A contract for two was announced in 9-00, later increased to five. Will replace aging craft now in use as flag officer barges and are known as "parade motorboats." The first two will be assigned to the Kronshtadt Naval Base, which placed the initial building order. The first unit, however, was not laid down until 28-4-01.

♦ 1 Razvedchik-class (Project 1388M) flag officers' yacht [YFL]
Bldr: Sosnovka Zavod (In serv. 1983–87)

KSV-213

SERVICE CRAFT *(continued)*

Officers' yacht KSV-213 NAVPIC-Holland, 10-01

D: 220 tons (270 fl) **S:** 31 kts **Dim:** 46.0 × 6.0 × 2.1
Electronics: Radar: 1 Mius (Spin Trough) nav.
M: 2 M-504-series diesels; 2 props; 9,000 bhp
Range: 1,500/10 **Endurance:** 10 days **Crew:** 14 tot.

Remarks: KSV = *Katera Svyazi* (Communications Cutter). Adapted from the version of Project 1388 configured as a radiological monitoring craft [YAG]. Has a full-height after deckhouse and no torpedo retrieval ramp.

♦ 14 Project 14670 officers' yachts [YFL]
Bldr: Yuzhnaya Tochka Zavod, Feodosiya, Ukraine (In serv. 1985–88)

KSV-9 Sokol	KSV-1499	Chaika
KSV-316 Gurzuf	KSV-1537	Kronshtadt
KSV-1135 Berkut	KSV-1594	Lastochka
KSV-1380	KSV-1754	Lebed'
KSV-1460	Burun	

Project 14670 officers' yacht KSV-1754—at Sevastopol' Boris Lemachko, 2000

D: 38 tons (49 fl) **S:** 31 kts **Dim:** 24.0 × 5.2 × 1.9
A: none **Electronics:** Radar: 1 . . . nav.
M: 2 M-50F-series diesels; 2 props; 2,400 bhp
Range: 700/29; 1,100/15 **Endurance:** 5 days **Crew:** 12 tot.

Remarks: KSV = *Katera Svyazi* (Communications Cutter); used for local control and liaison activities. One source says only eight were built, so the named units may duplicate known KSV numbers. Design is based on the Zhuk-class (Project 1400) patrol boat hull. KSV-1537, *Lebed',* and *Kronshtadt* are in the Baltic Fleet; KSV-1594 is in the Caspian Flotilla; and the other three fleets are said to have one or two each. Sister *Pogranichnik* ("Border Guardsman") is assigned to the Federal Border Guard.

♦ 4 Project 360 flag officers' yachts [YFL]
Bldr: Sudostroitel'noye Obyedineniye "Almaz," Petrovskiy SY, St. Petersburg (In serv. 1961–64)

KSV-11 KSV-12 KSV-21 Shtorm

D: 136.7 tons (149.6 fl) **S:** 35.6 kts **Dim:** 37.15 × 7.50 × 2.41
Electronics: Radar: 1 . . . nav.
M: 2 M-503-series radial diesels; 2 props; 6,600 bhp
Range: 460/26 **Endurance:** 5 days **Crew:** 13 tot.

Remarks: KSV = *Katera Svyazi* (Communications Cutter). Yacht version of the Project 205–series (NATO Osa-class) missile boat design. KSV-11 is in the Baltic Fleet and *Shtorm* in the Pacific Fleet; the subordination of the others is not available. Black Sea Fleet sister *Merkuriy* was transferred to Georgia during 1998 and is now used as a patrol boat.

♦ 4 Al'batros-class (Project 183Sh) flag officers' yachts [YFL]
Bldr: Sudostroitel'noye Obyedineniye "Almaz," Petrovskiy SY, St. Petersburg (In serv. circa 1964–75)

Shkval Tayfun Tsiklon Uragan

D: 56.6 tons (68 fl) **S:** 39 kts **Dim:** 23.7 × 6.1 × 1.3
Electronics: Radar: 1 . . . nav.
M: 4 M-50F-1 diesels; 4 props; 4,800 bhp
Range: 320/32 **Fuel:** 7.2 tons **Endurance:** 5 days **Crew:** 11 tot.

Remarks: Able to accommodate about 40 personnel for short trips. The hullform is derived from that of the wooden-hulled P-6 torpedo boat. *Shkval* is in the Northern Fleet, the others in the Pacific Fleet.
Disposals: Baltic Sea Fleet unit *Al'batros,* Black Sea Fleet unit *Burevestnik,* and Northern Fleet units *Chayka* and *Sokol* (KSV-9) have been stricken since 1999; *Sokol* was subsequently transferred to Ukraine. *Berkut* (ex-KSV-1135) was stricken in 1994 and is now in private hands at Balaklava.

Project 183Sh flag officers' yacht Shkval NAVPIC-Holland, 10-01

♦ 49 Polish Bryza-class (Project 772) personnel ferries [YFL]
Bldrs: Stocznia Wisla, Gdansk, Poland, and Neftegaz Zavod (In serv. 1967–79)

MK-199	MK-537	PSK-52
MK-320 through MK-336	PSK-46	PSK-55
MK-501 through MK-525	PSK-49	

Bryza-class MK-537—at Sevastopol' Boris Lemachko, 7-99

D: 134 tons (144.5 fl) **S:** 10.5 kts **Dim:** 28.82 × 6.30 × 2.00
Electronics: Radar: 2 . . . nav.
M: 2 Type 3-D6 or Wola DM-150 diesels; 2 props; 300 bhp
Electric: 84 kw tot. **Range:** 1,100/10 **Crew:** 11 tot. + . . . passengers

Remarks: Six others of the slightly different Project 772U are employed as training craft [YXT] (q.v.). Two with local names, *Mechta* and *Nadezhda,* are based at Sevastopol'.

♦ 37 Nazhimovets-class (Project 286) personnel ferries [YFL]
Bldr: . . . . . . (In serv. 1954–64)

MK-31	PSK-1993 (ex-PK-1)
MK-38	PSK-2005 (ex-MK-22)
MK-45 through MK-60	PSK-2006
PK-6 through PK-19	PSK-2007
PSK-1991 (ex-MK-4)	

Nazhimovets-class personnel ferry 1679—at Murmansk NAVPIC-Holland, 10-01

D: 87 tons (105 fl) **S:** 11.2 kts **Dim:** 26.90 × 5.30 × 1.85
M: 1 Type 3D-12 diesel; 1 prop; 300 bhp
Endurance: 5 days **Crew:** 5 tot. + 123 passengers

Remarks: Several have local names. Most seem to have been assigned to the Pacific Fleet, from which PSK-12 was stricken in 1995.

SERVICE CRAFT *(continued)*

♦ **. . . PO-2 (Yaroslavets)-class (Project 376) workboats [YFL]**
Bldrs: Yaroslavl Zavod (In serv. 1950s–90) and Sosnovskiy Sudostroitel'nyy Zavod (In serv. 1995–. . .)

P-376	RK-45	RK-518	RK-1116	and others
RK-25	RK-162	RK-778	RK-1818	

PO-2-class workboat RK-25—at Sevastopol' Hartmut Ehlers, 7-00

D: 32.2 tons (38.2 fl) **S:** 9–10 kts **Dim:** 21.00 × 3.90 × 1.40 (max.; 1.26 mean)
Electronics: Radar: 1 Mius (Spin Trough) nav. or none
M: 1 Type 3D-6S1 diesel; 1 prop; 150 bhp
Electric: 10 kw tot. (1 × 10-kw DGPN-8/1500 diesel driving)
Range: 1,600/8 **Fuel:** 1.5 tons **Endurance:** 5 days
Crew: 4–6 tot. as utility craft

Remarks: RK = *Reydniy Kater* (Roadstead Cutter). More than 600 have been built to the same general design for military and civilian use, of which 400 were said still to be in military service as of 2001; some were configured as Nyryat'-2-class diving tenders [YDT] and others as survey craft [YGS] and training craft [YXT] (q.v.). All-steel construction. Can be operated safely in Force 8 winds and 2-m seas and can break light ice. Are rail-transportable. The craft remain under construction at Sosnovka for military and civil use. P-376 is used as a patrol boat in the Pacific Fleet and may mount a 12.7-mm 2M-1 or 14.5-mm 2M-7 twin machinegun.

♦ **up to 65 Admiralets-class (Project 371bis and 371U) workboats [YFL]** Bldr: . . . . . . (In serv. 1956–. . .)

P-721 through P-730	RK-1101	RK-1351	RK-1781
RK-1009	RK-1107	RK-1513	RK-1821
RK-1048	RK-1119	RK-1585	RK-2084
RK-1049	RK-1159	RK-1645	RK-2101
RK-1050	RK-1189	RK-1709	RK-2113
RK-1056	RK-1194	RK-1728	RK-2271
RK-1070	RK-1238	RK-1733	RK-2323
RK-1088	RK-1341	RK-1757	

D: 9.41 tons (fl) **S:** 13.5 kts **Dim:** 12.61 × 3.23 × 1.10
M: 1 3D-6 diesel; 1 prop; 150 bhp **Range:** 140/13 **Crew:** 2 tot.

Remarks: Units with P-series pennants are probably used for harbor patrol duties; the others are *Reydniy Katera* (Roadstead Cutters) used as general utility launches.

Note: Also in service in 2001 were up to 82 harbor utility craft of Projects T-63, 73, 351, and 433; all had Type 3D-6 diesel engines of 150 bhp, but no further information is available.

♦ **up to 32 Slavyanka-class (Project 20150) harbor utility craft [YFU]** Bldr: . . ., Slavyanka (In serv. 1979–98)

Slavyanka-class harbor utility craft BSS-050 Hartmut Ehlers, 7-96

D: 36 tons light (78.2 fl) **S:** 9.8 kts **Dim:** 21.90 × 5.81 × 1.00
M: 1 diesel; 1 prop; 470 bhp **Crew:** 2 tot.

Remarks: Resemble vehicle landing craft and have a bow ramp. Used for local stores transport. Some have BSS-series pennants (including BSS-74050) and others have pennants in the RBK series (including RBK-2019).

♦ **up to 35 Vostok-class (Project 1733) harbor utility craft [YFU]**
Bldr: . . . (In serv. 1969–80)

D: 18.56 tons light (38.9 fl) **S:** 8.2 kts **Dim:** 16.50 (pp) × 4.78 × 1.00
M: 1 diesel; 1 prop; 235 bhp **Crew:** 2 tot.

Remarks: Resemble vehicle landing craft and have a bow ramp. The open vehicle/cargo compartment forward is 9.5 m long by 3.9 m wide.

♦ **2 BGK-1701-class (Project 16611) inshore survey craft [YGS]**
Bldr: Vympel Zavod, Rybinsk (In serv. 1996)

GS-438 (In serv. 1996) GS-439 (In serv. 1997)

BGK-1701-class survey craft GS-439—at Kronshtadt; note the extendible, side-looking, bottom-mapping sonar support boom in stowed position, folded aft along the side of the craft, which has a black hull and white superstructure
Boris Lemachko, 1998

D: 310 tons light (384.7 fl) **S:** 11.5 kts
Dim: 39.80 (37.76 wl) × 7.80 (9.80 over survey sonar supports) × 2.20
Electronics: Radar: 1 . . . nav.
M: 2 DRA-525 diesels; 2 Kort-nozzle props; 400 bhp—bow-thruster
Range: . . ./. . . **Endurance:** 10 days **Crew:** 22 tot.

Remarks: Intended for sea bottom surveys in coastal regions and probably to have been a replacement for the GPB-480 design. Are equipped with booms on either beam to support towed mapping sonar arrays; when extended, the array is 42.6 m wide and permits surveying at 6 kts. No further construction has been reported.

♦ **2 Vinograd (Ayristo)-class coastal survey ships [YGS]**
Bldr: Rauma-Repola SY, Savonlinna, Finland

GS-525 (In serv. 12-11-85) GS-526 (In serv. 17-12-85)

Vinograd-class survey craft GS-525—in refit at Rostock, Germany
Hartmut Ehlers, 6-98

D: 372 tons light (499 fl) **S:** 10 kts (8.5 sust.)
Dim: 32.30 (28.60 pp) × 9.60 × 2.60
Electronics: Radar: 1 Mius (Spin Trough) nav.
M: 2 Baykal 300 diesels; 2 CP props; 598 bhp
Range: 1,000/6 **Endurance:** 10 days **Crew:** 19 tot. (civilian)

Remarks: Have small side-scan sonars that lower from recesses on the hull sides amidships. Data are processed and recorded by electronic computer, the first such system on a Russian survey ship class. GS-525 is in the Baltic Fleet, GS-526 in the Northern Fleet. GS-525 was refitted at Neptunwerft, Rostock, during 1998.

SERVICE CRAFT *(continued)*

♦ 26 Flamingo (Tanya)-class (Project 1415.2) inshore survey craft [YGS]

Bldrs: Sosnovka Zavod, Rybinsk; Yaroslavl Zavod; and others (In serv. 1976–90s)

BGK-193	BGK-817	BGK-1512	BGK-1627	BGK-1938
BGK-326	BGK-1373	BGK-1515	BGK-1631	BGK-1939
BGK-498	BGK-1416	BGK-1554	BGK-1641	
BGK-585	BGK-1417	BGK-1557	BGK-1642	
BGK-717	BGK-1506	BGK-1567	BGK-1919	
BGK-799	BGK-1507	BGK-1596	BGK-1937	

Flamingo-class survey craft BGK-1631—at St. Petersburg, with a surveyors' reference pole lashed to the mast Boris Lemachko, 2000

D: 42 tons (54 fl) **S:** 11 kts **Dim:** 21.20 × 3.93 × 1.40
Electronics: Radar: 1 Lotsiya nav. (not always fitted)
M: 1 Type 3D-12A or 3D-12L diesel; 1 prop; 300 bhp
Electric: 12 kw tot. (DGR 1A-16/1500 generator)
Range: 200/11 **Endurance:** 5 days **Crew:** 4 tot.

Remarks: BGK = *Bol'shoye Gidrograficheskoye Kater* (Large Hydrographic Cutter). Designed by Redan Central Design Bureau. Have hull bulwarks cut down amidships. Others of this class are configured as diving tenders [YDT] and workboats [YFL] and as patrol boats for the Federal Border Guard.

♦ up to 68 GPB-480-class (Project 1896 and 1896U) inshore survey craft [YGS]

Bldr: Vympel Zavod, Rybinsk (In serv. 1955–60s)

From among:

BGK-53	BGK-171	BGK-310	BGK-597	BGK-697	BGK-794
BGK-54	BGK-172	BGK-312	BGK-613	BGK-705	BGK-795
BGK-73	BGK-185	BGK-327	BGK-625	BGK-716	BGK-796
BGK-74	BGK-188	BGK-333	BGK-626	BGK-752	BGK-835
BGK-77	BGK-191	BGK-359	BGK-627	BGK-754	BGK-885
BGK-102	BGK-192	BGK-462	BGK-628	BGK-755	BGK-886
BGK-137	BGK-193	BGK-478	BGK-629	BGK-767	BGK-1505
BGK-140	BGK-197	BGK-480	BGK-632	BGK-768	BGK-1511
BGK-161	BGK-209	BGK-487	BGK-635	BGK-775	BGK-1529
BGK-162	BGK-210	BGK-498	BGK-652	BGK-785	BGK-1550
BGK-163	BGK-212	BGK-551	BGK-663	BGK-786	BGK-1554
BGK-167	BGK-214	BGK-574	BGK-682	BGK-789	UK-231
BGK-168	BGK-218	BGK-586	BGK-683	BGK-792	
BGK-169	BGK-244	BGK-596	BGK-685	BGK-793	

D: 92 tons (116.1 fl) **S:** 12.5 kts (11.8 sust.) **Dim:** 28.58 × 5.20 × 1.70
Electronics: 1 SNN-7 nav.
M: 1 Type 6CSP 28/3C diesel; 1 prop; 450 bhp (300 sust.)
Range: 1,500/10 **Endurance:** 10 days **Crew:** 14–15 tot.

Remarks: BGK = *Bol'shoye Gidrograficheskoye Kater* (Large Hydrographic Cutter). Also referred to as the GS-204 class. Were earlier numbered in the GPB (*Gidrograficheskoye Pribezhnyy Bot,* Coastal Hydrographic Survey Boat) series. BGK-218, -632, -685, and -886 are in the Caspian Flotilla; BGK-171, -214, -312, -613, -767, -1511, and -1529 in the Baltic Fleet; BGK-77, -244, -333, -635, -697, and -775 in the Black Sea Fleet; BGK-73, -137, -172, -191, -192, -193, -197, -212, -310, -327, -462, -478, -487, -551, -574, -596, -597, -625, -626, -663, -754, -755, -768, -835, -885, -1505, -1550, and -1554 in the Northern Fleet; and BGK-53, -54, -74, -102, -140, -161, -162, -163, -167, -168, -169, -185, -188, -209, -210, -359, -480, -586, -627, -628, -629, -652, -682, -683, -705, -752, -785, -786, -789, -792, -795, and -796 and training unit UK-231 in the Pacific Fleet.

GPB-480-class BGK-462—at Murmansk NAVPIC-Holland, 10-01

Disposals: Several others have been stricken, including Pacific Fleet units BGK-362, -481, -508, and -788 (the last on 5-7-94) and Black Sea Fleet units BGK-247, -716, -186, -631, -930, and -1629 (the last four on 30-7-93). BGK-37, -246, -248, -334, -650, -714, and -1589 were stricken 10-1-96 and later transferred to Ukraine.
Hull systems: There are a 6-m^2 charthouse/laboratory and two 1.5-ton derricks. Most employ a dual side-looking mapping sonar system using transducers mounted on swinging-arm davits amidships. Displacements have grown with age, and some are as much as 98 tons light, 126 full load.

♦ 3 Gornostai-class (Project . . .) inshore survey craft [YGS]

BGK-22 BGK-28

Gornostai-class survey craft BGK-22—at Sevastopol' Hartmut Ehlers, 8-00

Remarks: No data available. Modified fishing boats, resembling smaller versions of the GPB-480 class. BGK-22 is in the Black Sea Fleet, BGK-28 in the Baltic Fleet.

♦ 20 GPB-710 (Kayra)-class (Project 1403A) survey launches [YGS]

Bldr: . . . (In serv. 1969–. . .)

MGK-252	MGK-710	MGK-760	MGK-954	MGK-1273
MGK-352	MGK-749	MGK-771	MGK-1001	MGK-1659
MGK-657	MGK-751	MGK-840	MGK-1002	MGK-1804
MGK-678	MGK-753	MGK-879	MGK-1099	MGK-1805

D: 7 tons (fl) **S:** 10 kts **Dim:** 11.0 × 3.0 × 0.7
M: 1 diesel; 1 prop; 90 bhp **Range:** 150/10 **Endurance:** 2 days **Crew:** 6 tot.

Remarks: MGK = *Mal'yy Geografischeskoye Kater* (Small Hydrographic Cutter). GRP construction. For use either independently or transported aboard larger hydrographic survey ships.
Disposals: MGK-150, -175, -258, -912, -913, and -1098 were transferred to Ukraine 10-1-98.

♦ 16 MGK-1019 (Drofa)-class (Project 16830) survey launches [YGS]

Bldr: . . . . . . (In serv. . . .)

MGK-1019	MGK-1782	MGK-2106
MGK-1236	MGK-2075	and others

D: 5.5 tons (fl) **S:** 7.5 kts **Dim:** 9.1 × 2.90 × 0.70
M: 1 Type 6CHSP-9.5/11 diesel; 1 prop; 65 bhp
Range: 150/7.5 **Endurance:** 1 day **Crew:** 2 tot.

Remarks: MGK = *Mal'yy Geografischeskoye Kater* (Small Hydrographic Cutter). All serve in the Caspian Flotilla. Two others, MGK-112 and MGK-1889, were transferred to Ukraine 10-1-98.

♦ . . . PO-2 (Yaroslavets)-class (Project G-376) survey launches [YGS]

Bldr: Yaroslavl Zavod (In serv. 1958–90)

BGK-11 BGK-466 BGK-747 and others

D: 32.2 tons (38.2 fl) **S:** 9–10 kts **Dim:** 21.00 × 3.90 × 1.40 (max.; 1.26 mean)
Electronics: Radar: 1 Mius (Spin Trough) nav. or none
M: 1 Type 3D-6S1 diesel; 1 prop; 150 bhp
Electric: 10 kw tot. (1 × 10-kw DGPN-8/1500 diesel driving)
Range: 1,100/8 **Fuel:** 1 ton **Endurance:** 3 days **Crew:** 4–6 tot.

SERVICE CRAFT *(continued)*

PO-2-class survey launch BGK-11 H&L Van Ginderen, 7-00

Remarks: More than 600 have been built to the same general design for military and civilian use. Are rail-transportable. All-steel construction. Have reduced range compared with other PO-2 variants (see under [YFL] and [YXT] and under the Nyryat'-2 class [YDT]). Were originally numbered in the MGK-511 through MGK-726 series. Baltic Fleet units BGK-466 and BGK-747 have bulwarks extending from the bow to just forward of the pilothouse.

♦ 6 Burunduk-class (Project 1392V) target-control boats [YGT]

Bldr: Zelenodol'sk Zavod (In serv. 1966–70)

KVM-119 KVM-332 KVM-543 KVM-684 KVM-702 KVM-732

Burunduk-class target-control boat KVM-702 H&L Van Ginderen, 10-91

D: 160 tons (200 fl) **S:** 17 kts **Dim:** 38.60 (37.50 wl) × 7.80 (6.30 wl) × 1.44 (hull)
Electronics: Radar: 1 Rangout (Square Tie) surf. search/target detection
M: 3 M-50F-series diesels; 3 props; 3,600 bhp
Range: 300/17 **Endurance:** 5 days **Crew:** 12 tot.

Remarks: Are from among the 49 Osa (Project 205) hulls adapted for target service use. In this configuration, they are employed to operate unmanned Project 1392 target craft via the Fialka radio control system. Black Sea Fleet KVM-702 was reportedly stricken on 30-7-93 but was reported to be operational in the Black Sea Fleet again as of 1-99.
Disposals: Baltic Fleet unit KVM-659 was stricken 1-9-95.

♦ 12 Lotsman-class (Project 1392B) missile targets [YGT]

Bldr: Zelenodol'sk Zavod (In serv. 1966–70)

KM-76 KM-159 KM-447 KM-593 KM-654 KM-731
KM-102 KM-330 KM-541 KM-594 KM-730 KM-897

Lotsman-class target craft KM-593—as KTs-593 H&L Van Ginderen, 1995

D: 160 tons (200 fl) **S:** 17 kts **Dim:** 38.6 (37.5 wl) × 7.8 (6.3 wl) × 1.44 (hull)
M: 3 M-50-Fseries diesels; 3 props; 3,600 bhp
Range: 300/17 **Endurance:** 5 days **Crew:** 12 tot. (see remarks)

Remarks: Formerly designated KTs (*Kontrol'naya Tsel',* Controlled Target); designation was changed to KM (expansion not available) by 1-99. Survivors of 20 built. Employ the Osa (Project 205) missile boat hull but have a much less powerful propulsion plant. Crew disembarks when the craft is in operation. Can be equipped with radar corner reflectors to attract radar-homing missiles and two heat-generator chimneys to attract infrared-homing missiles. KM-593 and KM-731 are in the Black Sea Fleet.
Disposals: Black Sea Fleet units KTs-895 and -1207 were stricken 3-7-92 and KTs-332 on 30-7-93. KTs-543 and -896 had been discarded or sunk by 2001. Some or all of the above may by now have been stricken as well.

Note: The Russian Navy also employs large numbers of non-self-propelled target barges, all specially constructed for the role. Two variants predominate: the 107-m missile-target design with a tapered, ship-like hull; and the 64-m catamaran-hulled gunnery-target barge.

♦ 14 SK-620 (Drakon)-class ambulance craft [YH]

Bldr: Stocznia Wisla, Gdansk, Poland (In serv. 1978–84)

MK-391 MK-1408 PSK-405 SN-126 SN-1320
MK-1303 MK-1409 PSK-673 SN-128 SN-1520
MK-1407 PSK-382 PSK-1411 SN-401

SK-620-class PSK-673—at Murmansk NAVPIC-Holland, 10-01

D: 306.6 tons light (341 fl) **S:** 11.2 kts **Dim:** 39.41 (36.00 pp) × 8.40 × 2.15
Electronics: Radar: 1 or 2 Mius (Spin Trough) nav.
M: 2 Wola 56ANM30-H12, 1,600-rpm diesels; 2 props; 620 bhp
Electric: 156 kVA tot. (3 × 52 kVA, Wola SW400/E53 diesel-driven)
Range: 1,000/10 **Endurance:** 6 days (with 32 persons aboard)
Crew: 14 tot. + 3 medical personnel and 15 patients (25 in emergency)

Remarks: A total of 35 was built. Pennant numbers were initially in the SK-600 series (SK = *Sanitarnyy Kater,* Clinical Cutter); the 12 later units were designated MK (*Mestaya Kater,* . . . Cutter). Those with PSK-series pennants have been used as personnel ferries. Ambulance craft are white painted and have NBC warfare defensive measures, a sick bay with 12 berths, an isolation space with two berths, an operating room, a disinfection chamber, a first-aid station, and medical equipment storerooms. Very similar to the slightly smaller Petrushka-class training craft by the same builder.

♦ 30 Toplivo-2 (Kair)-class (Project 1844 and 1844D*) liquid cargo lighters [YO]

Bldrs: Kherson SY; Khabarov SY; Alexandria SY, Egypt (In serv. 1958–84)

MNS-35500 VTN-34 VTN-46 VTN-66 VTN-82*
PUS-1 VTN-35 VTN-48 VTN-68 VTN-95
VTN-24 VTN-36 VTN-53 VTN-71 VTN-96
VTN-26 VTN-37 VTN-58 VTN-72 VTN-98
VTN-28 VTN-39 VTN-60* VTN-75 VTN-99
VTN-30 VTN-45 VTN-64 VTN-78 VUS-22

Toplivo-2-class fuel lighter VTN-28 Boris Lemachko, 7-01

D: 466–547 tons (1,140–1,180 fl) **S:** 10 kts
Dim: 54.26 (49.40 pp) × 7.40 × 3.10–3.44
Electronics: Radar: 1 Mius (Spin Trough) or Don-2 nav.
M: 1 Russkiy Dizel 6 DR30/50-5-2 diesel; 1 prop; 600 bhp **Electric:** 250 kw tot.
Range: 1,500/10 **Fuel:** 19 tons **Endurance:** 20 days **Crew:** 20–24 tot.

Remarks: 308 grt/508 dwt. The series built in Egypt was terminated by Soviet expulsion. VTN-64, -66, and -96 are assigned to the Black Sea Fleet; VTN-28, -37, -60, and -82 to the Pacific Fleet; VTN-24 and -30 to the Baltic Fleet; VTN-45 and -95 to the Caspian Flotilla; and the others to the Northern Fleet. VTN-60 and -82 (completed 16-7-84) are of Project 1844D, differences unknown. PUS-1 and VUS-22 serve as special liquid cargo lighters. MNS-35500 has for some reason been relegated to harbor service.
Disposals: Black Sea Fleet sisters VTN-38 and -81 were stricken 10-1-96 and transferred, probably in 6-97, to Ukraine. Pacific Fleet unit VTN-43 was stricken 31-7-96 and sold for commercial use. Baltic Fleet unit VZS-431 had been stricken by 1994 and is used as a fuel barge at Admiralty Shipyard, Sudomekh division.

SERVICE CRAFT *(continued)*

Hull systems: Have four cargo tanks, totaling 606 m^2. As fuel lighters, can carry up to 495 tons fuel oil. Fully seagoing, if required. Have one 0.5-ton hose-handling crane.

♦ up to 13 Khobi-class (Project 437M) base tankers [YO]
Bldr: . . . SY, St. Petersburg (In serv. 1957–59)

From among:

	Fleet		Fleet
Cheremsha	Northern	Shacha	Northern
Indiga	Black Sea	Shelon'	Pacific
Khobi	Caspian	Sisola	Northern
Metan	Northern	Sos'va	Baltic
Moksha	Pacific	Tartu	Northern
Orsha	Baltic	Tunguska	Pacific
Seyma	Black Sea		

Khobi-class Seyma—at Sevastopol' Boris Lemachko, 7-00

D: 690 tons light; 768 tons std. (1,520 fl) **S:** 13 kts
Dim: 67.40 (63.20 pp) × 10.10 × 3.63
Electronics: Radar: 1 Don-2 nav.
M: 2 Type 8DR 30/50 diesels; 2 props; 1,600 bhp
Range: 2,000/10 **Endurance:** 10 days **Crew:** 33 tot.

Remarks: Although antiquated, a number of this class reportedly remain in local service. Baltic Fleet sister *Lovat'* was stricken 1-9-95. Three others were built for Indonesia and two for Albania. Cargo is either 700 tons fuel oil or 550 tons diesel fuel, although in recent years at least one has been used as a sludge lighter: the *Cheremsha* was used to steal 1,197.5 tons of fuel from Northern Fleet ships during 1996–97 while supposedly pursuing her normal activity of collecting waste water.

Disposal note: The following vessels, all listed in the previous edition, are no longer in service: *Irtysh*-class base tanker *Narva; Konda*-class base tankers *Konda, Sayaniy,* and *Yakhroma;* and *Nercha*-class (Project 931) base tankers *Klyaz'ma* and *Nercha.*

♦ 1 ex-German Dora-class base tanker [YO]
Bldr: D. W. Kramer Sons, Elmshorn, Germany (In serv. 1941)

Istra (ex-German *Elsa*)

Istra—at Sevastopol' Boris Lemachko, 7-00

D: 973 tons (1,200 fl) **S:** 12 kts **Dim:** 61.00 (56.65 pp) × 9.00 × 2.75
A: none **Electronics:** Radar: 1 . . . nav.
M: 2 M.A.N. 6-cyl. diesels; 2 3-bladed props; 900 bhp
Range: 1,200/12 **Crew:** 20 tot.

Remarks: Former German Luftwaffe aviation fuel lighter, captured by Great Britain in 5-45 and assigned to Russia as war reparations in 1946. Cargo: 331 tons liquid, 17.5 tons dry stores. Baltic Fleet sister *Izhma* (ex-*Empire Togonto,* ex-*Dora*) had been stricken by 2001, and two others were stricken several decades ago.

♦ approx. 30 Toplivo-3-class harbor fuel lighters [YO]
Bldr: . . . . . . (In serv. 1950s)

VTN-3 VTN-24 and others

Toplivo-3-class fuel lighter VTN-3—alongside icebreaker *Purga* at Lomonosov Boris Lemachko, 1999

D: 1,200 tons (fl) **S:** 9 kts **Dim:** 52.7 × 10.0 × 3.0
M: 1 3D-12 diesel; 1 prop; 300 bhp

Remarks: Low freeboard, low superstructure harbor craft. A number of the 47 built have been discarded, including Northern Fleet units VTN-1, -7, -22, and -35 on 1-9-95.

♦ 2 Bolva-series (Project 5-Ya) accommodations barges [YPB]
Bldr: Valmet Oy, Helsinki, Finland (In serv. 1983)

IPKZ-100 Imatra Miass

Imatra (IPKZ-100)—moored at Sevastopol' Hartmut Ehlers, 8-00

D: 2,500 tons (3,573 fl) **Dim:** 113.50 (110.90 pp) × 13.80 × 2.80
Endurance: 30 days **Crew:** 40 tot. + 394 passengers

Remarks: 4,448 grt/1,000 dwt. Of the total of 48 built, only two late units went to naval service. The first series of eight Bolva-I units were built 1960–63; the second series of 30 Bolva-IIs, built 1963–72, had a hangar-like auditorium built atop the superstructure aft; and the Bolva-IIIs were built 1971–. . . , with 10 completed. The last three civil units were ordered in 1983. IPKZ-100 is stationed at Sevastopol', *Miass* at Kaliningrad.

♦ 2 Volna-class accommodations barges [YPB]

S-920 Volna

Remarks: Have been used to accommodate crews of submarines fitting out at Admiralty Shipyard, St. Petersburg, since the 1960s. They have at least four diesel generator sets but do not appear to have been fitted with propulsion systems.

SERVICE CRAFT *(continued)*

Volna—at Admiralty Shipyard, St. Petersburg H&L Van Ginderen, 7-00

♦ **1 ex-German accommodations hulk [YPB]**
Bldr: H. C. Stülcken Sohn, Hamburg

	Laid down	L	In serv.
PKZ-14 (ex-*Angara,* ex-*Nadir,* ex-*Hela*)	23-11-37	28-12-38	16-10-40

PKZ-14—at Sevastopol' Hartmut Ehlers, 7-00

D: 2,113 tons (2,520 fl)
Dim: 99.80 (92.50 wl) × 12.70 (12.20 wl) × 3.70 (4.05 max.)

Remarks: Built as fleet tender (i.e., yacht) for the German Navy. Assigned to Russia in 1946 as war reparations. Assigned as yacht and floating headquarters for C-in-C Black Sea Fleet. A major engineering space fire in the early 1990s left her immobile, and she was reclassified as a floating barracks *(Plavuchiya Kazerna)* in 1998, remaining at her usual mooring at Sevastopol'. When operational, could make 19.3 kts on 8,360 bhp from two M.A.N. W9Vu 40/46 diesels, with a range of 2,000 n.m. at 15 kts. Has accommodations for 224.

Note: Retired combatant ships employed as floating barracks are common in the Russian Navy. All bear hull numbers in the PKZ (*Plavuchiya Kazerna,* Floating Barracks) series. Many of the larger oceanographic research ships have been employed as floating quarters for officers and their families.

♦ **24 Shelon' (TL-1127)-class (Project 1388) torpedo retrievers [YPT]** Bldr: Sosnovka Zavod (In serv. 1978–84)

TL-270	TL-1003	TL-1134	TL-1536	TL-1666
TL-287	TL-1004	TL-1271	TL-1551	TL-1717
TL-288	TL-1126	TL-1302	TL-1596	TL-2021
TL-289	TL-1127	TL-1474	TL-1597	TL-2023
TL-704	TL-1128	TL-1478	TL-1603	

Shelon'-class torpedo retriever TL-287 Werner Globke, 8-97

D: 270 tons (fl) **S:** 30 kts **Dim:** 46.0 × 6.0 × 2.0
Electronics: Radar: 1 Kuban nav.—Sonar: Oka-1 HF dipping
M: 2 M-504 diesels; 2 props; 10,000 bhp
Range: 1,500/10 **Endurance:** 10 days **Crew:** 20 tot.

Remarks: Have a high-speed hull with a covered torpedo-recovery ramp aft. Eight others were completed 1983–87 as Razvedchik-class (Project 1388M) environmental monitoring ships [YAG] (q.v.). TL-1128 is equipped with a twin 25-mm 80-cal. 2M-3M gunmount on the forecastle, and the others have a pedestal on which to place the gunmount. Fleet assignments include: TL-270, -1003, -1004, -1126, -1128, -1474, -1478, -1536, -1596, and -1666 in the Northern; TL-287 in the Black Sea; TL-1127, -1603, and -1717 in the Baltic; and TL-1134, -1302, -1551, -2021, and -2023 in the Pacific.
Disposals: Black Sea Fleet units TL-1374, -1476, and -1602 were stricken 3-7-92, and sisters TL-1005 and -1616 were stricken 10-1-96 and transferred to Ukraine in 1997. Black Sea Fleet unit TL-1626 was stricken for disposal 31-7-96. Pacific Fleet unit TL-827 was stricken 8-2-98. One unit was reportedly transferred to Azerbaijan during 1992.

♦ **13 Poluchat-I (TL-1)-class (Project 368T) torpedo retrievers [YPT]** Bldrs: Sosnovka Zavod and Nikolayevsk-na-Amure Zavod (In serv. 1960–77)

TL-119	TL-720	TL-843	TL-980	TL-998
TL-184	TL-826	TL-854	TL-994	
TL-373	TL-842	TL-923	TL-997	

Poluchat-I-class torpedo retriever TL-997 Boris Lemachko, 5-00

D: 84.7 tons (92.8 fl) **S:** 21.6 kts
Dim: 29.60 × 6.10 (5.80 wl) × 1.56 (1.90 props)
Electronics: Radar: 1 Don-2 or Mius (Spin Trough) nav.
M: 2 M-50F-4 diesels; 2 props; 2,400 bhp **Range:** 250/21.6; 550/14
Crew: 1 officer, 2 warrant officers, 12 enlisted

Remarks: TL = *Torpedolov* (Torpedo Retriever). Have a recovery ramp aft. Export units had lower-powered M-50-series diesels and could achieve only 18 kts. One other is configured as patrol boat AKA-527 in the Caspian Flotilla, and at least one other has been converted as an officers' yacht. Large numbers have been retired in recent years. Have a Gira-KM gyrocompass and NEL-3 echo sounder. The hull has seven watertight bulkheads.

Note: The classes that follow under the [YRD] designation were all intended to transport new warships (primarily submarines) from inland yards through the extensive Soviet river and canal network to coastal facilities with sufficient water depth to permit them to be floated for final fitting out. All of them were of steel construction, and all were characterized by having the forward end enclosed, as in the World War II–era U.S. ARD classes. They are not equipped with cranes, and they are proportionately much narrower than normal floating dry docks. Often a small superstructure to house the tow crew is fitted at the forward, enclosed end. The Russian designation is TPD, wherein the "T" stands for "Transport" and the "PD" for *Plavuchiya Dock* (Floating Dock).

♦ **1 Project 20230 transport dock [YRD]**
Bldr: . . . . . . (In serv. 1983)

Oka-2

Capacity: 5,200 tons **Dim:** 135.4 × 14.0 × 3.6

Remarks: Flooded draft over blocks is 9.0 m and width between wing walls is 11.2 m.

♦ **1 Project 1767 transport dock [YRD]**
Bldr: . . . . . . (In serv. 1972)

TPD-70

Capacity: 4,700 tons **Dim:** 134.6 × 14.0 × 3.6

Remarks: Flooded draft over blocks is 8.8 m and width between wing walls is 12.0 m.

♦ **3 Project 1757 transport docks [YRD]**
Bldr: . . . . . . (In serv. 1969–75)

TPD-59 2 others

Capacity: 8,500 tons **Dim:** 165.0 × 23.5 × 3.9

Remarks: Flooded draft over blocks is 10.6 m and width between wing walls is 14.5 m.

♦ **7 Project 1753 transport docks [YRD]**
Bldr: . . . . . . (In serv. 1963–67)

TPD-9 6 others

Capacity: 3,600 tons **Dim:** 135.0 × 14.0 × 3.2

Remarks: Flooded draft over blocks is 7.6 m and width between wing walls is 1.4 m.

♦ **2 Project 769A transport dock [YRD]**
Bldr: . . . . . . (In serv. 1964)

TPD-14 1 other

Capacity: 4,500 tons **Dim:** 144.0 × 18.4 × 3.8

SERVICE CRAFT *(continued)*

Remarks: Flooded draft over blocks is 8.9 m and width between wing walls is 13.2 m.

Note: Examples of some of the older transport docks that may still be available include: Project 769 (three built; characteristics as for Project 769A except only 131 m long and 3,700 tons capacity); Project 768 (1,300 tons capacity, 77.2 m long); Project 764 (three built 1956–59, 1,700 tons capacity, 110.0 m long).

♦ 1 Landysh-class nuclear waste–processing barge [YRRN]
Bldr: . . . . . ., Japan (In serv. 16-8-00)

LANDYSH

Remarks: Rectangular barge, with a processing plant capable of handling 7,000 m^3 of nuclear waste per year. Built for the Pacific Fleet with Japanese financial and technical assistance. Placed in operation at Zvezda Zavod, Bol'shoy Kamen, near Vladivostok, on 22-11-01, the facility also includes several buildings and can treat up to 7,000 m^3 of nuclear waste water annually.

♦ 1 nuclear support barge [YRRN]
Bldr: Rauma-Repola, Savonlinna, Finland (In serv. 9-86)

ROSTA-1

D: 1,700 tons (fl) **Dim:** 63.00 × 12.00 × 2.30

Remarks: Launched 21-3-86. Intended to provide radiation-hazard disposal, decontamination, laboratory services, and refit assistance to nuclear-powered ships at Murmansk.

♦ 2 PM-124-class (Project 326 or 326M) nuclear support barges [YRRN]
Bldr: . . . (In serv. 1960–. . .)

PM-78 PM-125

D: 3,300 tons (4,000 fl) **Dim:** 92.00 × 13.40 (12.00 wl) × 4.50
Endurance: 15 days **Crew:** 59 tot.

Remarks: Originally constructed as non-self-propelled freight barges for war reparations in the early 1950s; adapted from 1960 on to support nuclear submarine construction and repair. Employ the same hull as the Vyn-class accommodations barges. Two were Project 326 and six were Project 326M. Have two 12-ton recoring cranes and storage space for 560 used nuclear fuel rods. Northern Fleet unit PM-124 has been discarded. Pacific Fleet units PM-48, -80, and -133 were contaminated with nuclear radiation and have been discarded, and Northern Fleet unit PM-78 was said to be contaminated as of 9-00 but was still being used for used nuclear fuel rod storage. Pacific Fleet unit PTB-24 was stricken 5-7-94.

♦ 1 salvage lifting ship [YSD]
Bldr: De Schelde, Vlissingen, the Netherlands

	Laid down	L	In serv.
KOMMUNA (ex-*Volkhov*)	1912	30-11-13	27-7-15

Kommuna—at Sevastopol' Hartmut Ehlers, 8-00

D: 2,450 tons (fl) **S:** 10.2 kts **Dim:** 96.0 × 20.4 × 4.7
A: none **Electronics:** 1 . . . nav.
M: 2 diesels; 2 props; 1,200 bhp **Range:** 1,700/6 **Fuel:** 82 tons
Crew: 250 tot. (when manned)

Remarks: Although "retired" during 1978, was refitted 1980–84 and remains in service at Sevastopol' to support submersibles. Catamaran hulled. Intended to raise sunken submarines by means of four 250-ton-capacity lifting rigs above and between the hulls.

♦ 0 (+ 1) submarine scrapping support barge [YSDN]
Bldr: Palada Zavod, Kherson, Ukraine (In serv. . . .)

Remarks: A large barge was ordered in 1996, intended to provide support during the scrapping of nuclear-powered submarines. As of 30-8-00, it was 98.5% complete, but the Russian government had not found a satisfactory way to pay for it and was trying to obtain delivery by promising to pay for half the work; no reports of a delivery have been received.

♦ 0 (+ 1) submarine rescue submersible [YSS]
Bldr: Rybinskiy Zavod, Rybinsk (In serv. 2002)

Remarks: Laid down in 1993, but by 11-00 was only 20% complete. The work pace increased in response to the loss of the submarine *Kursk,* but funding shortages halted work during 2-01. No data are available, but she is said to be able to work in depths to 100 m and to be used for repairs on external, underwater features of surface ships and submarines as well as to rescue submariners. Has a crew of 16, plus six divers in repair mode.

♦ 2 Rus'-class (Project 1681) salvage submersibles [YSS]
Bldr: Admiralty Shipyard, St. Petersburg

	Laid down	L	In serv.
RUS'	1-6-92	20-5-00	2000
KONSUL	1997	. . .	12-00

D: 24 tons (surf.) **S:** 3 kts **Dim:** 8.0 × 2.1 × 3.7 (high)
M: 6 electric maneuvering motors
Endurance: 80 hrs **Crew:** 2–3 tot.

Remarks: Designed by the Malakhit Desigh Bureau. Capable of diving to 6,000 m. Crew is carried in a 2.1-m-diameter titanium alloy sphere. The sonar system can detect objects to 750-m ranges, and the manipulator can lift objects weighing up to 400 kg. Sea trials for *Rus'* began from Baltiysk during 10-99. *Rus'* was to be used to dive on the Yankee-class (Project 667AU) SSBN K-219, which sank 6-10-86 east of Bermuda. *Konsul* was to have been completed by 12-00, but no reports to that effect have been received and the craft may still be undelivered.

♦ 5 Priz-class (Project 1855) salvage submersibles [YSS]
Bldr: Rauma-Repola, Finland (In serv. 1987–. . .)

MIR-1 through MIR-5 (one is now AS-32 PRIZ)

D: 18.7 tons sub. **S:** . . . kts **Dim:** 7.8 × 2.9 × 3.2 (high)

Remarks: Intended for salvage and bottom work. Carried by the *El'brus*-class submarine rescue ship *Alagez* and the civilian research ship *Akademik M. Keldysh.* Diving depth: 6,100 m. Have a titanium pressure hull and two manipulators. One unit, renumbered AS-32, is named *Priz* and took part in the unsuccessful rescue attempts for the submarine *Kursk* during 8-00; the craft was painted with red and white vertical stripes and operated from the salvage ship *Mikhail Rudnitskiy.*

♦ 4 Sever-class (Project 1832) research submersibles [YSS]
Bldr: Admiralteiskiye Verfi 196 (Sudomekh Division), St. Petersburg

LS-8 LS-17 LS-28 LS-34

D: 28 tons surf./40 tons sub. **S:** 4 kts sub. **Dim:** 12.5 × 2.7 × 3.8 (high)
Crew: 5 tot.

Remarks: Capable of diving to 2,000 m. Some may have been discarded.

♦ 18 Poisk-2-class (Project 1839 and 1839.2) rescue and salvage submersibles [YSS]
Bldr: Admiralteiskiye Verfi 196 (Sudomekh Division), St. Petersburg

ARS-1	ARS-7	ARS-13	ARS-29	ARS-35
ARS-2	ARS-9	ARS-14	ARS-30	ARS-36
ARS-3	ARS-10	ARS-15	ARS-31	
ARS-4	ARS-12	ARS-16	ARS-34 BESTER	

D: 46 tons sub. **S:** 3.9 kts sub. **Dim:** 13.60 × 3.49 × 4.87 (high)
Electronics:
Sonar: MGA-8 search; MGS-29 noisemaking beacon; MGA-2 underwater telephone (8.2 kHz); MGV-55 underwater telephone (34.5–39.9 kHz)
M: electric motors; 1 prop—2 vertical thrusters—2 horizontal thrusters
Range: 16/2 **Endurance:** 48 hours **Crew:** 3 tot.

Remarks: Can be carried by the rescue ship *Alagez* and several other salvage and rescue ships. Diving depth: 500 m. ARS = *Avtonomiy Rabochniy Snaryad* (Autonomous Utility Craft). Have an SP-200M battery complex with three groups of 116 cells at 220 V and four groups of 14 cells at 27 V. Have two periscopes and four viewing ports and are equipped with an MGP-30/600 underwater manipulation system. There are also three anchors. ARS-34, which took part in the unsuccessful rescue attempts on the submarine *Kursk* during 8-00, is named *Bester;* the craft operated from the salvage ship *Mikhail Rudnitskiy.*

♦ up to 9 Project 1837 and 1837K rescue and salvage submersibles [YSS]
Bldr: Admiralteiskiye Verfi 196 (Sudomekh Division), St. Petersburg

AS-5 AS-11 AS-18 AS-20 through AS-27 series

D: 45 tons sub. **S:** 3.6 kts sub. **Dim:** 12.7 × 3.9 × 5.4 (high)
Electronics:
Sonar: MGA-5 search; MGS-29 noisemaking beacon; MGA-2 underwater telephone (8.2 kHz); MGV-55 underwater telephone (34.5–39.9 kHz)
M: 6 electric motors; 2 props—2 vertical thrusters—2 horizontal thrusters
Range: 16.5/2 **Endurance:** 48 hours (10 with rescued personnel aboard)
Crew: 3 tot.

Remarks: Can (or could) carry up to 11 personnel and were used for rescue duties. Normal operating depth: 500 m. Pressure hull is constructed of AK-29 steel. SP-200M lead-acid battery complex has three groups of 16 cells at 220 V and four groups with 27 V output. Have three periscopes and an RSU-1D radio set. Equipped with a bow manipulator and two sets of lifting pistons. In the Black Sea Fleet, were based with old rescue ship *Kommuna,* the rescue ship *El'brus,* and the trials craft OS-3; were also carried by India (Project 940) salvage submarines. Several of the total of 12 built have been discarded: Pacific Fleet sister A-3 was stricken 30-7-93 and AS-14 and AS-19 on 31-7-96.

Note: Also in service are (or were) four Poisk-class (Project 1806) rescue and salvage submersibles (AGS-6, -17, -37, and -38) with a diving depth of 4,000 m.

♦ 3 OT-2400-class (Project N-3291) large riverine push-tugs [YTB]
Bldr: Obuda SY, Budapest, Hungary (In serv. 1988)

RB-346 RB-347 RB-348

D: 725 tons (923 fl) **S:** 13 kts **Dim:** 51.5 × 12.0 × 2.3
Electronics: Radar: 1 . . . nav.
M: 2 Type G-70 diesels; 2 props; 2,400 bhp **Range:** . . ./. . .
Fuel: 200 tons **Endurance:** 15 days **Crew:** 16 tot. (civilian)

Remarks: Employed as push-tugs for submarine transportation docks and barges on the canal system linking the St. Petersburg area with the Northern Fleet. Assigned to the Baltic Fleet. Have rectangular barge-like hulls with twin barge push-pylons at the bow.

SERVICE CRAFT *(continued)*

OT-2400-class river tug RB-346 Boris Lemachko, 1999

♦ **9 Stividor (MB-70)-class (Project 192 and 192A*) large harbor tugs [YTB]** Bldr: . . . . . ., Yugoslavia (In serv. 1970–89)

RB-22* RB-108 RB-136 RB-280* RB-326
RB-40 RB-109 RB-167 RB-325

Northern Fleet Stividor-class tug RB-108 NAVPIC-Holland, 10-01

D: 451 tons (575 fl) **S:** 13 kts **Dim:** 35.7 × 9.5 × 4.6
M: 2 ASL-25D diesels; 2 Kort-nozzle props; 2,520 bhp—bow-thruster
Electric: 340 kw tot. (2 × 125-kw, 2 × 45-kw diesel sets)
Range: . . ./. . . **Fuel:** 76 tons **Endurance:** 10 days **Crew:** . . . tot.

Remarks: Bollard pull: 35 tons. Carry 14 tons of potable water, 3.6 tons of lubricants. Have three firefighting water monitors. Late-construction units RB-22 (in serv. 1989) and RB-280 are Project 192A, differences unknown (there are no external differences). The engines were built in the former East Germany. RB-40, -108, and -109 are in the Northern Fleet; RB-22, -280, -325, and -326 in the Pacific; and RB-136 in the Black Sea.

♦ **19 Prometey (Anton Mazin)-class (Project 498, 04983, and 04985) large harbor tugs [YTB]**
Bldrs: Petrozavod SY, St. Petersburg; Gorokhovets SY (In serv. 1973–83)

RB-1 RB-158 RB-202 RB-265 RB-360
RB-7 RB-173 RB-217 RB-296 RB-362
RB-57 RB-179 RB-239 RB-314
RB-98 RB-201 RB-262 RB-327

Prometey-class large harbor tug RB-158 NAVPIC-Holland, 10-01

D: 257 tons light; 305 tons normal (364 fl) **S:** 11 kts
Dim: 29.30 (28.2 pp) × 8.30 × 3.20
Electronics: Radar: 1 Mius (Spin Trough) nav.
M: 2 6DR 30/50 diesels; 2 Kort-nozzle props; 1,200 bhp (see remarks)
Electric: 50 kw tot. **Range:** 1,800/12 **Fuel:** 30 tons **Crew:** 3–5 tot.

Remarks: More than 100 were built since 1971, most of which went into civilian service. Some have been exported. Known fleet subordinations: RB-7, -173, -179, -217, and -239 are in the Pacific Fleet; RB-68 and -158 in the Northern Fleet; RB-314 and -327 in the Baltic Fleet; and RB-98 and -201 in the Black Sea Fleet.
Disposals: RB-69, -295, and -308 of this class were stricken from the Black Sea Fleet 10-1-96 and later transferred to Ukraine.
Hull systems: Have a 14-ton bollard pull and an ice-strengthened hull. The more powerful Project 498T (or 04983) series (of which RB-239 is one) have two 800-bhp Type 8ChNP-25/30 diesels and displace 319 tons full load; they are 29.80 m long and draw 3.40 m. RB-217 is of the later Project 04985, differences unknown.

♦ **35 Sidehole-I and -II (Peredovik)-class (Project 737K and 737M) medium harbor tugs [YTM]**
Bldr: Petrozavod SY, St. Petersburg (In serv. 1973–83)

BUK-600 RB-25 RB-49 RB-194 RB-233 RB-248
RB-2 RB-26 RB-51 RB-197 RB-237 RB-250
RB-5 RB-29 RB-52 RB-198 RB-240 RB-256
RB-17 RB-43 RB-168 RB-199 RB-244 RB-310
RB-20 RB-44 RB-192 RB-212 RB-246 RB-311
RB-23 RB-46 RB-193 RB-232 RB-247

Sidehole-II-class tug RB-198 NAVPIC-Holland, 10-01

Northern Fleet Sidehole-I-class tug RB-51 NAVPIC-Holland, 10-01

D: 183 tons (206 fl) **S:** 10 kts **Dim:** 24.2 × 7.0 × 3.4
Electronics: Radar: 1 Mius (Spin Trough) nav.
M: 2 Type 6 ChN25/34 diesels; 2 vertical cycloidal props; 900 bhp
Electric: 37 kw tot. (1 × 37-kw diesel set)
Range: 130/9.5 **Fuel:** 17.4 tons **Endurance:** 6 days **Crew:** 4 tot.

Remarks: Others are employed in civil use. Bollard pull: 10.5 tons. Naval units have RB (*Rednyy Buksir,* Roadstead Tug) pennants, except BUK-600, whose designation

SERVICE CRAFT *(continued)*

indicates "Tug-Cutter." The NATO nickname "Sidehole" derived from the distinctive cutout in the sides of the first level of the superstructure abreast the side-by-side stacks in the initial production variant. Known fleet assignments include: RB-232, -233, -240, -310, and -311 and BUK-600 in the Pacific; RB-248 and -256 in the Caspian Flotilla; RB-44, -193, -199, -237, -244, and -247 in the Black Sea; and RB-2, -29, -43, -49, -50, -168, -246, and at least one other in the Northern.
Disposals: Northern Fleet unit RB-290 was stricken 3-7-92. Black Sea Fleet units RB-245 and -255 were stricken 5-7-94, and the same fleet's RB-27 was stricken 10-1-96 and later transferred to Ukraine.
Hull systems: Twenty-six early Project 737 units displaced 150 tons light (178 fl) and were powered by 300-bhp 6 Ch-25/34 diesels; some of the units listed above are probably of that variant. Can carry 3.6 tons potable water and 0.5 tons lube oil.

Disposal note: All remaining units of the Tugur-class (Project 730) medium harbor tugs had been stricken by 2001, as had been the former German tug RB-65.

♦ 30 Project 1496 small harbor tugs [YTL]
Bldr: Sovetskaya Govan' Zavod, Azove (In serv. 1966–80)

BUK-1393 RB-10 RB-158 RB-222 RB-288 RB-293
MB-301 RB-14 RB-179 RB-243 RB-290 RB-297
MB-315 RB-51 RB-185 RB-254 RB-303 RB-298
MB-317 RB-63 RB-195 RB-259 RB-312 RB-399
MB-322 RB-66 RB-215 RB-263 RB-313 RB-410

Project 1496 tug-cutter designated BUK-1240 Boris Lemachko, 1995

D: 91.3 tons (108.5 fl) **S:** 10.5 kts **Dim:** 23.40 × 5.87 × 1.87
Electronics: Radar: 1 Lotsiya nav.
M: 1 Type 8 ChSN 18/22-1 diesel; 1 shrouded prop; 315 bhp
Electric: 18 kw tot. **Range:** 1,450/10.5 **Fuel:** 8.3 tons
Endurance: 6 days **Crew:** 8 tot.

Remarks: Eleven others serve the Federal Border Guard in the Pacific region. Most are designated RB (*Rednyy Buksir,* Roadstead Tug); four are designated MB (*Morskoy Buksir,* Seagoing Tug) and one BUK, which stands for "Tug-Cutter." All are in the Northern Fleet, except RB-259 in the Caspian Flotilla, and MB-301, RB-14, and RB-399 in the Pacific Fleet.

Disposals: RB-83, -139, -161, -197, and -270 have been stricken since 1999.

Note: Illustrated are examples of two classes of small naval tugs for which no data are available. Some PO-2 (Project 376) general-purpose launches, including BUK-45 at Sevastopol', are also numbered in the BUK series, with the acronym standing for "Tug-Cutter."

BUK-1241—a Baltic Fleet tug-cutter of unknown class Boris Lemachko, 2000

BUK-407—a smaller Baltic Fleet tug-cutter Hartmut Ehlers, 7-96

♦ . . . Vyun-class (Project 1664.0) firefighting launches [YTR]
Bldr: . . . USSR (In serv. 1995–. . .)

D: 67.4 tons (fl) **S:** 19.4 kts **Dim:** 30.80 × 5.00 × 0.81 (fwd; 0.75 aft)
Electronics: Radar: 1 . . . nav.
M: 2 Type M-419A diesels; 2 waterjets; 2,170 bhp
Fuel: 3 tons **Crew:** 2 tot. + 6 firemen

Remarks: Firefighting launch, designed by Vympel Joint Stock Co., with at least one prototype *(Vyun-I)* completed by 1997. Has four PN-60B main firepumps of 60-liter/sec capacity each and three 216-m^3/hr-capacity fire monitors, plus two portable firepumps, a water curtain system, and foam blanket–generating equipment. Intended for harbor, lake, and riverine service. It is not known if any are in naval service, but the design could serve as a replacement for earlier such craft.

♦ 16 Morkov-class (Project 14611) fireboats [YTR]
Bldr: Vympel Zavod, Rybinsk (In serv. 1984–92)

PZhK-415 PZhK-1296 PZhK-1544 PZhK-1560
PZhK-417 PZhK-1378 PZhK-1545 PZhK-1680
PZhK-638 PZhK-1514 PZhK-1546 PZhK-1859
PZhK-900 PZhK-1515 PZhK-1547 PZhK-2055

Morkov-class fireboat PZhK-2055—outboard sister PZhK-1378 at Severomorsk
Boris Lemachko, 2000

D: 280 tons (320 fl) **S:** 12.5 kts **Dim:** 41.00 (36.53 pp) × 7.80 × 2.14
Electronics: Radar: 1 Mius (Spin Trough) nav.
M: 2 Barnaul' 3KD 12N-520 diesels; 2 CP props; 1,040 bhp—bow-thruster
Electric: 400 kw tot. **Range:** 250/12.5 **Endurance:** 5 days **Crew:** 15 tot.
Remarks: PZhK-900 is based at St. Petersburg, and PZhK-415 and -1680 are also in the Baltic Fleet. Other fleet assignments include PZhK-1296, -1378, -1545, -1546, and -2055 in the Northern; PZhK-417, -1515, -1544, -1547, -1560, and -1859 in the Pacific; and PZhK-638 in the Caspian Flotilla. Four similar Mars-class (Project 14613) craft had been completed by 1996, and three more have been built for Turkey, but none seem to have entered Russian Navy service to date. Sister PZhK-1819 was stricken from the Black Sea Fleet 10-1-96 and later transferred to Ukraine.
Hull systems: Have four firefighting water monitors, two with 220-m^3/hr capacity and two of 500 m^3/hr, driven by two 750-m^3/hr diesel-powered pumps; in some, there are four 720-m^3/hr fire monitors. Have both foam and Freon extinguishing systems, with 20 tons of foaming agent carried. Can spray a water curtain to protect themselves. Can also be used for towing.

♦ up to 26 Pozharnyy-I (PZhK-1)-class (Project 364) fireboats [YTR]
Bldrs: Volodarskogo Zavod, Rybinsk; Kirova Zavod, Khabarovsk; and Nikolayevsk-na-Amure (In serv. 1954–67)

PZhK-3 PZhK-36 PZhK-46 PZhK-59 PZhK-84
PZhK-5 PZhK-37 PZhK-47 PZhK-64 PZhK-86
PZhK-17 PZhK-41 PZhK-49 PZhK-66
PZhK-30 PZhK-42 PZhK-53 PZhK-68
PZhK-31 PZhK-43 PZhK-54 PZhK-79
PZhK-32 PZhK-44 PZhK-55 PZhK-82

SERVICE CRAFT *(continued)*

Pozharnyy-I-class fireboat PZhK-5 H&L Van Ginderen, 7-00

D: 145.9 tons (179–181 fl) **S:** 15.7 kts
Dim: 34.90 (31.90 wl) × 6.50 (6.20 wl) × 1.84
Electronics: Radar: 1 Mius (Spin Trough) or Don-2 nav. or none
M: 2 Type M-50F-1 diesels (900 bhp each), 1 Type . . . diesel (450 bhp); 3 props; 2,250 bhp
Range: 284/15.7; 1,050/10 **Fuel:** 12 tons **Endurance:** 5 days **Crew:** 26 tot.

Remarks: As many as 84 were built, some for civilian organizations.
Disposals: Black Sea Fleet unit PZhK-50 sank during a storm while in port in 1992. Known strikes include PZhK-45 in 1991. PZhK-4, PDK-15, PDK-71, PZhK-429, and PZhK-432 were transferred to other agencies. PZhK-12 and -170 were stricken from the Baltic Fleet 3-7-92. PZhK-20 and -38 were stricken 10-1-96 and later transferred to Ukraine. One other was built for export to Iraq.

♦ 1 Modified Toplivo-2–class (Project 1844.4) water lighter [YW]
Bldr: Khabarovsk SY (In serv. 1993)

MVT-17

MVT-17—at Vladivostok Boris Lemachko, 1998

D: 625 tons (1,204 fl) **S:** 10 kts **Dim:** 54.54 × 9.70 × 3.51
A: none **Electronics:** Radar: 1 . . . nav.
M: 1 6-DR-series diesel; 1 prop; 600 bhp
Range: 1,000/10 **Endurance:** 15 days **Crew:** 21 tot.

Remarks: Final variant of the numerous Toplivo-2 series. Assigned to the Pacific Fleet and given a seagoing water tanker pennant, probably indicating use in transporting potable water to offshore facilities. Differs in external appearance from earlier units primarily in having an enlarged superstructure aft. No further sisters have been built.

♦ 8 Project 1580 harbor water lighters [YW]
Bldr: . . . . . . SY, Yugoslavia (In serv. 1988–91)

PPSK-10	PPSK-16	PPSK-20	PPSK-27
PPSK-15	PPSK-18	PPSK-25	PPSK-28

D: 447 tons (553 fl) **S:** 11 kts **Dim:** 45.0 × 8.0 × 2.1
M: 1 . . . diesel; 1 prop; 600 bhp **Endurance:** 5 days **Crew:** 21 tot.

Remarks: Sister PPSK-17 has been stricken from the Baltic Fleet.

♦ up to 30 Toplivo-1-class (Project 5) water lighters [YW]
Bldr: Lenin Shipyard, Gdansk, Poland (In serv. 1959–62)

MNS-8240 MNS-8250 MNS-25250 and others

D: 420 tons (600 fl) **S:** 10 kts **Dim:** 34.40 (33.00 pp) × 7.00 × 3.10
M: 1 Type 3D-12 diesel; 1 prop; 300 bhp **Fuel:** 6 tons **Crew:** . . . tot.

Remarks: Harbor water lighters. Hull numbers in the MNS series. A number have been discarded, and some may have been converted to transport fuel. MNS-8250 is based at Kronshtadt and MNS-25250 at Sevastopol'.

Toplivo-1-class water lighter MNS-8240—at Kronshtadt Boris Lemachko, 1999

♦ 12 Petrushka-class (Project TS-39 or UK-3) training cutters [YXT]
Bldr: Stocznia Wisla, Gdansk (In serv. 1978–84)

MK-157	MK-207	MK-1277	PSK-1519	PSK-1562	UK-216
MK-194	MK-288	PSK-1304	PSK-1556	PSK-2017	UK-240

Petrushka-class training cutter—with local fleet pennant number
H&L Van Ginderen, 7-00

D: 338.2 tons normal (345.4 fl) **S:** 12 kts **Dim:** 39.27 (36.00 pp) × 8.60 × 2.55
Electronics: Radar: 2 Mius (Spin Trough) nav.
M: 2 Wola H12, 1,000-rpm diesels; 2 props; 610 bhp
Electric: 180 kw tot. (2 × 90 kw; Wola H6 diesels driving)
Range: 1,000/10 **Crew:** 13 tot. + 30 instructors and students

Remarks: Hull numbers were all originally in the UK (*Uchebniy Kater,* Training Cutter) series. The first delivery of a second series, ordered during 4-91, was halted by the collapse of the Soviet Union. Have two classrooms and a navigational training facility on the bridge, and an MFD/F loop on a short mast aft. Are equipped with NBC warfare defense measures. Very similar to the SK-620-class ambulance craft from the same builder. Have an echo sounder, gyrocompass, MFD/F, and electromagnetic log. Two 23-person-capacity workboats are carried. UK-230 of this class was transferred to the Brigantina youth training organization during 1999. PSK-designated units are used as personnel ferries; the function of the MK-designated units is not available.

♦ 6 Polish Bryza-class (Project 772U) training cutters [YXT]
Bldrs: Stocznia Wisla, Gdansk, Poland; Neftegaz Zavod (In serv. 1967–79)

UK-214 UK-222 UK-230 UK-232 UK-236 UK-687

Bryza-class training cutter UK-537—since stricken Boris Lemachko, 1998

D: 135 tons (142 fl) **S:** 10.5 kts **Dim:** 28.82 × 6.60 × 1.86
Electronics: Radar: 2 . . . nav.
M: 2 Type 3-D6 or Wola DM-150 diesels; 2 props; 300 bhp
Electric: 84 kw tot. **Range:** 1,100/10 **Crew:** 11 tot. + 28 students

Remarks: Used at naval training centers for basic navigation and maneuvering training. Some 49 others remain in service as personnel ferries [YFL] with numbers in the MK and PSK series (q.v.). All are in the Baltic Fleet except UK-687, which is in the Caspian Flotilla.
Disposals: Black Sea Fleet unit UK-190 was stricken 5-7-94 and transferred to Ukraine.

SERVICE CRAFT *(continued)*

♦ up to 20 PO-2 (Yaroslavets)-class (Project 376U) training launches [YXT] Bldr: Yaroslavl Zavod (In serv. 1950s–90)

UK-190 through UK-193 UK-195 through UK-210

D: 32.2 tons (38.2 fl) **S:** 9–10 kts **Dim:** 21.00 × 3.90 × 1.40 (max.; 1.26 mean)
Electronics: Radar: 1 Mius (Spin Trough) nav. or none
M: 1 Type 3D-6S1 diesel; 1 prop; 150 bhp
Electric: 10 kw tot. (1 × 10-kw DGPN-8/1500 diesel driving)
Range: 1,600/8 **Fuel:** 1.5 tons **Endurance:** 5 days
Crew: 4–6 tot. + . . . trainees

Remarks: More than 600 have been built to the same general design for military and civilian use (see under [YFL] and [YGS] and under the Nyryat'-2 class [YDT]). Can be operated safely in Force 8 winds and 2-m seas and can break light ice. The Project 376U variant is employed for navigational and maneuvering training duties.

Note: In use as immobile training hulks are a number of former combatants. They can be distinguished by the use of UTS *(Uchebnoye / Trenoye Sudno)*-series hull numbers. Former T-43-class minesweeper UTS-306 was refitted at Kaliningrad in 1995, early-model sister UTS-415 was still in use at Sevastopol' as of 2000, and long-hull T-43 training barge UTS-433 was moored at Donuzlav in 2000.

T-43-class UTS-415—a former fleet minesweeper employed for training at Sevastopol'
Boris Lemachko, 7-00

FEDERAL BORDER GUARD

(Naval Forces of the Federal Border Guard Service)

The former KGB Maritime Border Service fleet was reorganized in 1994 as the Naval Forces of the Federal Border Guard Service with the assigned duties of defending Russia's borders, defending the Russian Economic Exclusion Zone (EEZ), providing fisheries protection services (in conjunction with the Ministry of Fisheries), and providing protection to the resources of the Far North and continental shelves of Russian territory (in conjunction with the Ministry of Ecology and Natural Resources). The Federal Border Guard is attempting to evolve into more of a coast guard–like organization, although it continues to have the mission of protecting the security of Russia's maritime borders. Its officers are trained at the regular naval academies, and its enlisted personnel are almost all conscripts. In wartime, the organization's ships and craft would come under the control of the navy, which in peacetime has been accused of not providing the necessary support to maintain their combat systems. The fisheries patrol ships and craft of the Ministry of Fisheries were taken over by the Federal Border Guard in 8-98.

Personnel (2002): Approx. 12,000 total, including the seagoing and shore establishments. The total is to be reduced to 8,500 over the next year or two. Ships and craft are operating with 50% crew complements.

Organization: There are two Maritime Regional Directorates, Arctic and Pacific, to which are subordinated 10 Coastal Border Guard Regions, as follows: the 1st, Murmansk; 2nd, Arkhangelsk; 3rd, St. Petersburg; 4th, Kaliningrad; 5th, Novorossiysk; 6th, Caspian Sea; 7th, Nakhodka; 8th, Sakhalin Island; 9th, Kuril Islands; and 10th, Kamchatka. Each region is divided into sectors dependent on the numbers and types of ships and craft assigned. Ships and craft are categorized by descending size and capability as 1st class, EEZ patrol ships; 2nd class, coastal border guard ships; 3rd class, ships and boats for port and roadstead patrol; 4th class, ships and boats for river and lake patrol; and 5th class, support craft. By 2010, the Federal Border Guard hopes to have 300 patrol ships, 650 smaller boats of all types, and 50 support ships and craft—probably a hopelessly unattainable goal.

Maritime Aviation: The Federal Border Guard operates Ka-27 Helix helicopters, Be-12PSS Mail SAR amphibians, and An-26 and An-72P Coaler maritime surveillance aircraft. As of 5-96, only 48% of the border guard aircraft inventory was flyable, and of 27 total new aircraft requested in 1995 and 1996, only six had been procured. All border guard Mi-8 and Mi-24 helicopters and Tu-134 and An-24 transports were retired in 1997–98. The approximately 25 border guard Be-12PSS *(Poiskovo Spasatelnyi)* Mail amphibians have had their weapons systems and submarine detection gear removed. Plans call for adding helicopter decks to the larger ("1st through 3rd Rate") ships to accommodate rescue helicopters.

Coastal Defense: Troop detachments are stationed at various island and mainland coastal locations considered vulnerable to assault. Coastal surveillance radar systems cover most areas, with the Gorizont Nayada-5 radar in the process of being replaced by the Nayada-5PV.

Note: While "naval" ship and craft types carry pennant numbers, those ships and craft transferred from the Ministry of Fisheries do not. Most units now carry diagonal stripes of red, blue, and white on the hull sides, but on some the red stripes lead, while on other units the blue stripes lead.

FRIGATES [WFF]

Note: Future plans call for the acquisition of an unspecified number of the ocean patrol version of the naval Gepard-class (Project 1166.0) small frigate (see under Russian Navy section).

♦ 7 Krivak-III (Nerey) class (Project 11351BPB) (1 or more *nonoperational*) Bldr: Zaliv Zavod 532, Kerch', Ukraine

	Laid down	L	In serv.
116 Menzhinskiy	14-8-81	31-12-82	29-12-83
158 Dzerzhinskiy	11-1-84	2-3-84	29-12-84
156 Orël (ex-*Yuriy Andropov*, ex-*Imeni XXVII S'yezda K.P.S.S.*)	26-9-83	2-11-85	30-9-86
175 Pskov (ex-*Imeni 70 Letiya VchK-KGB*)	. . .	. . .	30-12-87
060 Anadyr (ex-*Imeni 70 Letiya Pogranvoysk*)	22-10-87	28-3-88	16-8-89
103 Kedrov	5-11-88	30-4-89	20-11-90
059 Vorovskiy	20-2-90	28-7-90	29-12-90

Orël (156)—active at Vladivostok after a refit, with a new air-search radar
Boris Lemachko, 1999

Kedrov (103) French Navy, 10-90

D: 3,274 tons std.; 3,458 tons normal (3,642 fl; 3,774 max.) **S:** 31 kts (30 sust.)
Dim: 122.98 (113.00 pp) × 14.20 (13.2 wl) × 4.72 (hull; 6.20 over sonar dome)
A: 1 twin-rail Osa-MA (SA-N-4) SAM syst. (20 9M-33/Gecko missiles); 1 100-mm 59-cal. AK-100 DP (2,000 rounds); 2 single 30-mm 54-cal. AK-630M gatling AA (12,000 rounds); 1 . . . grenade launcher; 2 12-round RBU-6000 ASW RL (96 RGB-60 rockets); 2 quadruple 533-mm UTA-53-1135 TT (4 SET-65 and 4 53-65K torpedoes); 1 Ka-27PS Helix-A helicopter
Electronics:
Radar: 1 Vaygach-U (Palm Frond) nav.; 1 Volga (Don-Kay) or Nayada-1 nav.; 1 Nayada-2 helicopter control; 1 MR-760 Fregat-MA (Top Plate) 3-D (*Menzhinskiy:* MR-310U Angara-M/Head Net-C) air search; 1 MPZ-301 Baza (Pop Group) missile f.c.; 1 MR-114 Bars (Kite Screech-A) 100-mm f.c.; 1 MR-123 Vympel (Bass Tilt) 30-mm f.c.
Sonar: MGK-335S Platina-C hull-mounted LF; MG-345 Bronza LF VDS; MG-26 underwater telephone
EW: 2 Start-2 (Bell Shroud) intercept; 2 MP-401 Start (Bell Squat A/B) jammer; 4 16-round PK-16 fixed decoy RL (128 rockets); 2 towed torpedo decoys; 3 sets floating corner-reflector decoys
E/O: . . . Spektr-F (Half Cup) laser warning
M: COGAG M-7 plant: 2 M-62 cruise gas turbines (7,475 shp each), 2 M-8K boost gas turbines (20,000 shp each); 2 props; 54,900 shp max.
Electric: 2,500 kw tot. (5 × 500-kw diesel sets)
Range: 1,146/30; 3,636/14 **Fuel:** . . . tons + 22 tons aviation fuel
Endurance: 30 days
Crew: 26 officers, 29 warrant officers, 143 enlisted (incl. 12 in aviation group)

Remarks: Revised version of basic Krivak design for Federal Border Guard service in the Far East. Design approved 6-80. Typed PSKR (*Pogranichnyy Storozhevoy Korabl',* Border Patrol Ship). First two are named for prominent KGB "heroes." The original name for the *Orël* ("Eagle") meant "In Honor of the 27th Congress of the Communist Party of the Soviet Union," and that of the *Pskov* "In Honor of the 70th Anniversary of the KGB." The sixth is named for Mikhail Sergeyevich Kedrov (1878–1941), a pioneer member of the NKVD and later a member of the Soviet supreme court; and the seventh is named for a World War II–era KGB leader. The eighth unit, to have been named *Kirov* and then (after the 1991 revolution) *Latsis,* was taken over in 3-93 by Ukraine and completed as *Hetman Sagaidachnyy.* A ninth, begun as the *Krasniy Vympel* ("Red Banner") was to be completed for Ukrainian service as *Hetman Vyshnevetsky,* but work ceased. *Dzerzhinskiy* completed a modernization overhaul at Vladivostok in 1999. The ships are seldom operated, due to the expense, and not all of their combat systems are operational; full crews are not carried.

BORDER GUARD FRIGATES [WFF] *(continued)*

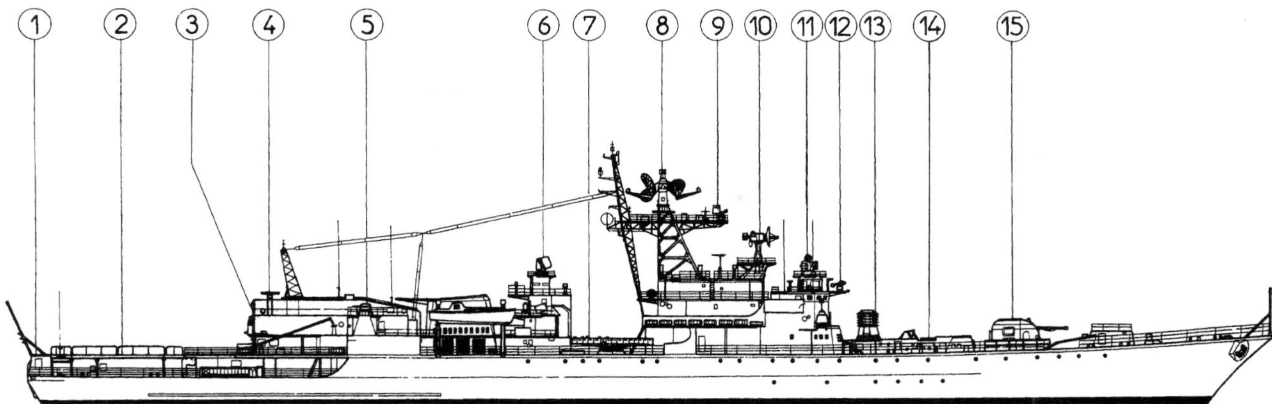

Krivak-III Menzhinskiy (116) 1. VDS sonar housing 2. helicopter platform 3. helicopter hangar 4. Nayada-2 radar for helicopter landing and takeoff control 5. 30-mm AK-630M gatling AA 6. MR-123 Vympel radar director for 30-mm guns 7. quadruple 533-mm TT 8. MR-310U Angara-M (MR-760 Fregat-MA on others of the class) air-search radar 9. Volga navigational and surface-search radar 10. MR-114 Bars radar director for 100-mm gun 11. MPZ-301 radar director for Osa-M SAM system 12. Nayada-1 navigational radar 13. RBU-6000 ASW RL 14. Osa-M SAM launcher (shown retracted) 15. 100-mm AK-100 DP gun Drawing by Lucien Gassier, from *Flottes de Combat*

Hull systems: There are 14 watertight compartments. The superstructure is built of aluminum-magnesium alloy, welded to the hull with bimetallic inserts. Type UKA-135 fin stabilizers are fitted. The propulsion plant originally delivered 45,570 shp normal/51,200 shp max. total (with the cruise turbines operating at 6,000 shp each and the boost turbines at 18,000 shp each), but the output was later increased. Hull block coefficient is 0.46, very fine for this type of vessel. For slow speeds, any one of the engines can drive both propellers.
Combat systems: The combat system is designated Sapfir-U7, the ASW weapons control system name is Purga, the antisubmarine missile control system is called Musson, and the communications suite is the Tayfun-3. The addition of a helicopter facility (with simple deck-transit system) and helicopter weapons reload magazines cost two gunmounts and one SA-N-4 position aft, while the Krivak-I/II SS-N-14 dual-purpose missile system was replaced by a 100-mm gun, more useful for the patrol mission of these ships. Two six-barrel gatling guns were added to improve close-in defense. The Nayada-2 radar mounted atop the helicopter hangar serves in flight control.

CORVETTES [WFFL]

♦ 1 Grisha-V class (Project 1124MU)
Bldr: Shipyard No. 368, Khabarovsk

	Laid down	L	In serv.
. . . Stelyak (ex-MPK-221)	8-2-85	29-4-87	29-12-87

D: 930 tons std. (1,070 fl) **S:** 32 kts (21 on gas turbine; 16 on diesels)
Dim: 71.20 (66.90 wl) × 10.15 (9.50 wl) × 3.72 (hull)
A: 1 twin-rail Osa-M (SA-N-4) SAM syst. (20 9M-33/Gecko missiles); 1 76.2-mm 59-cal. AK-176 DP (304 rounds); 1 30-mm 54-cal. AK-630M gatling AA (3,000 rounds); 2 point-defense shoulder-launched SAM positions (20–24 Igla-M missiles); 2 twin 533-mm TT; 1 12-round RBU-6000 ASW RL (48 RGB-60 rockets); 2 d.c. racks (6 d.c. each) or up to 18 mines
Electronics:
Radar: 1 MR-312 Nayada nav.; 1 MR-755 Topaz-2B (Half Plate-B) surf./air search; 1 MPZ-301 Baza (Pop Group) SAM f.c.; 1 MR-123 Vympel (Bass Tilt) gun f.c.
Sonar: MGK-335MC Platina (Bull Nose) hull-mounted (3 kHz); Shelon' (Elk Tail) dipping (7.5 kHz)
EW: 2 Bizan'-4B (Watch Dog) intercept (2–18 GHz); 2 16-round PK-16 fixed decoy RL
M: CODAG: 1 M-8M gas turbine (18,000 shp), 2 M-507A diesels (10,000 bhp each); 3 props; 38,000 hp
Electric: 1,000 kw tot. (1 × 500-kw, 1 × 300-kw, 1 × 200-kw diesel sets)
Range: 950/27; on diesels alone: 2,500/14; 4,000/10 **Fuel:** 143 tons
Endurance: 9 days **Crew:** 9 officers, 77 enlisted

Remarks: Assigned to the Federal Border Guard on completion. Operates in the Pacific region. A reported second unit of this design named *Poryvistry* apparently never existed.
Hull systems: There are two drop-down harbor maneuvering propulsors at the extreme stern, as in the now-stricken Petya (Project 159-series) class. Carries 10.5 tons of lube oil and 27.2 tons of fresh water.
Combat systems: Two launch positions for shoulder-fired point-defense SAMs have been added at the break of the 01 level superstructure, just forward of the stack. Just abaft the mast is an SP-521 Rakurs (Kolonka-2) backup ringsight director for the 30-mm gun. The torpedo tubes have been modified to launch wire-guided torpedoes. The dipping sonar is housed in the after superstructure, lowering through the hull between the starboard and centerline propeller shafts.

♦ 3 Grisha-III class (Projects 1124M and 1124MP)
Bldr: Vladivostokskogo SSZ, Novolitovsk

	Laid down	L	In serv.
. . . Bezuprechniy	7-79	5-81	19-12-81
058 Zorkiy	15-2-80	2-11-81	29-10-82
061 Smel'yy	18-3-81	7-5-83	15-12-83

D: 860 tons light; 954 tons normal (990 fl)
S: 32 kts (21 on gas turbine; 16 on diesels)
Dim: 71.20 (66.90 wl) × 10.15 (9.50 wl) × 3.40 (hull)

Smel'yy (061)—with old number; a second boat has been added to port of the stack on this unit U.S. Navy, 1985

A: 1 twin-rail Osa-M (SA-N-4) SAM syst. (20 9M-33/Gecko missiles); 1 twin 57-mm AK-725 DP (1,100 rounds); 1 30-mm 54-cal. AK-630M gatling AA (2,000 rounds); 2 12-round RBU-6000 ASW RL (96 RGB-60 rockets); 2 twin 533-mm TT; 2 d.c. racks (6 d.c. each)
Electronics:
Radar: 1 Don-2 nav.; 1 MR-302 Rubka (Strut Curve) surf./air search; 1 MPZ-301 Baza (Pop Group) SAM f.c.; 1 MR-123 Vympel (Bass Tilt) gun f.c.
Sonar: MGK-. . . Argun' (Bull Nose) hull-mounted MF; Shelon' (Elk Tail) MF through-hull dipping
EW: 2 Bizan'-4B (Watch Dog) intercept (2–18 GHz)
M: CODAG: 1 M-8M gas turbine (18,000 shp), 2 M-507A diesels (10,000 bhp each); 3 props; 38,000 hp—2 maneuvering propellers
Electric: 1,000 kw (1 × 500-kw, 1 × 300-kw, 1 × 200-kw diesel sets)
Range: 950/27; 2,750/14; 4,000/10 **Fuel:** 130 tons + 13 tons overload
Endurance: 9 days **Crew:** 9 officers, 74 enlisted

Remarks: Survivors of five built for the KGB Border Guard. All serve in the Pacific region.
Disposals: *Bditel'nyy* and *Reshitel'nyy* were stricken 13-6-98; three others, *Bravyy, Vernyy,* and *Strogiy,* were stricken 10-2-92 and broken up while under construction. *Bezuprechniy* may also no longer be in service.
Hull systems: Have retractable fin stabilizers. Said to consume 450 kg of fuel per hour at 14 kts. *Smel'yy* has had an extra boat added to port of the stack, stowed on an 01-level platform.
Combat systems: The d.c. racks are mounted on the aft end of the mine rails. Some may have two SAM launch positions, as on the Grisha-V.

♦ 4 Grisha-II class (Project 1124P)
Bldrs: Zelenodolsk Zavod 340, Kazan (In serv. 1973–. . .)

	Laid down	L	In serv.
. . . Izumrud	8-2-73	3-2-74	28-12-74
. . . Predaniy	18-3-82	16-4-83	30-9-83
. . . Nadezhnyy	19-9-82	25-2-84	20-9-84
. . . Dozorniy	28-6-83	1985	26-12-85

Northern Fleet area Grisha-II class M.O.D. U.K., 9-87

BORDER GUARD CORVETTES [WFFL] *(continued)*

Northern Fleet area Grisha-II class M.O.D. U.K., 5-90

D: 890 tons (1,010 fl) **S:** 32 kts
Dim: 71.10 (66.90 wl) × 10.15 (9.50 wl) × 3.60 (hull)
A: 2 twin 57-mm AK-257 DP (2,200 rounds); 2 12-round RBU-6000 ASW RL (96 RGB-60 rockets); 2 twin 533-mm DTA-53-1124 TT; 2 d.c. racks (20 tot. d.c.) or mines
Electronics:
Radar: 1 Don-2 nav.; 1 MR-302 Rubka (Strut Curve) surf./air search; 1 MR-103 Bars (Muff Cob) f.c.
Sonar: MGK-355M Argun' (Bull Nose) hull-mounted (3 kHz); Shelon' (Elk Tail) through-hull dipping (7.5 kHz)
EW: 2 Bizan'-4B (Watch Dog) intercept (2–18 GHz)
M: CODAG: 1 M-8M (M-813) gas turbine (18,000 shp), 2 M-507A diesels (10,000 bhp each); 3 props; 38,000 hp—2 maneuvering propellers
Electric: 1,000 kw (1 × 500-kw, 1 × 300-kw, 1 × 200-kw diesel sets)
Range: 950/27; 2,750/14; 4,000/10
Fuel: 130 tons + 13 tons overload (see remarks) **Endurance:** 9 days
Crew: 9 officers, 70 enlisted

Remarks: Survivors of 12 built for the KGB Maritime Border Guard. All are active in the Northern Fleet, although probably not for much longer. The names *Korund, Malachit,* and *Primernyy* associated with this class were apparently in error.
Disposals: *Brilliant* was stricken 13-3-95, *Zhemchug* on 4-10-95, *Rubin* on 15-6-92, *Ametist* on 23-5-97, *Sapfir* on 13-6-98, and *Provorniy* on 4-8-98. Black Sea Fleet units *Dnepr* and *Izmail* were transferred to Ukraine 26-11-92.
Hull systems: Can achieve 7 kts on one diesel, 16 kts on both diesels, and 22 kts on gas turbine alone. Fin stabilizers are fitted. There is tankage for 22.2 tons of fresh water and 10.5 tons of lube oil.
Combat systems: A second twin 57-mm gun (with 500 rounds per mount) was substituted for the Osa-M SAM system forward, and the missile-control radar was not installed.

PATROL SHIPS [WPS]

Note: In order to carry out its new fisheries patrol duties, the Federal Border Guard has taken over an unknown number of patrol ships from the Ministry of Fisheries; most would fit in the Patrol Ship [WPS] category. In addition to the classes described below, a Northern Fleet–area unit named *Syktyvkar* was taken over in 8-98 from the Ministry of Fisheries; no data available. A fisheries protection ship named *Berkut* was added to the Baltic-area fleet 1-7-98; again, no data available. A Pacific-area fisheries patrol craft named *A. Pyn'ko* has been named in the press.

♦ 8 Al'pinist class (Project 503POS)
Bldr: Volgograd Zavod (*Argal, Bars:* Khabarovsk; two new units: Yaroslavl Zavod)

	In serv.		In serv.		In serv.
Antias	1997	Diana	2000	. . .	9-01
Argal	1998	Paliya	1998	. . .	12-01
Bars	1989	Parella	1999		

D: 810 tons light (1,140 fl) **S:** 12.6 kts **Dim:** 53.70 (46.20 pp) × 10.50 × 4.10
Electronics: Radar: 2 Don-2 nav.
M: 1 Type 8NVD48-2U diesel; 1 CP prop; 1,320 bhp—bow-thruster
Electric: 450 kw tot. (1 × 300-kw, 1 × 150-kw diesel sets)
Range: 7,000/12.5 **Fuel:** 162 tons **Endurance:** 25 days **Crew:** 44 tot.

Remarks: A standard 704-grt/308-dwt long-lines fishing trawler design, acquired and adapted for use as fisheries patrol ships. The Russian Navy uses three sisters as intelligence collectors. *Antias* had a confrontation with a U.S. Coast Guard cutter in Bering Sea waters during 1999. *Bars* was transferred to Federal Border Guard control in 1998 and operates in the Pacific, as will the two new units ordered from Yaroslavl Zavod during 10-00.

♦ 4 Komandor-class fisheries protection ships
Bldr: Danyard, Frederikshavn, Denmark

	L	In serv.
Komandor	. . .	8-89
Shkiper Gek	4-89	20-12-89
Kherluf Bidstrup	8-89	2-90
Manchzur	4-5-90	6-7-90

D: 2,425 tons (fl) **S:** 20 kts (19.2 cruising)
Dim: 88.90 (82.20 wl) × 13.60 × 4.70 (mean)
A: none; 1 Ka-32S Helix-D SAR helicopter
Electronics: Radar: 3 . . . nav. (1 Furuno)
M: 2 Russkiy Dizel–Pielstick 6 PC2.5 L400 diesels; 1 4-bladed CP prop; 7,786 bhp—1 500-shp bow-thruster
Electric: 1,840 kw (1 × 600-kw shaft generator, 2 × 620-kw diesel sets)
Range: 7,000/19.2 **Crew:** 42 tot.

Remarks: 2,800 grt/534 dwt. Ordered 11-11-87. Operated for and by the Ministry of Fisheries in the Northern Pacific area until 8-98 when transferred to the Federal Border Guard. The helicopter is stored in a two-deck-high hangar beneath the flight deck, which is 14 m long and has folding sides to increase its width. Have Blohm + Voss folding fin stabilizers. Carry two unsinkable GRP lifeboats and two rigid inflatables—one of which is for inspection duties.

Kherluf Bidstrup Boris Lemachko, 3-01

Manchzur—with a commercial vehicle cargo; note that the engine exhaust stack is near the stern in this class, abaft the helicopter deck JMSDF, 4-94

♦ 1 Akademik Fersman class (Project B-93)
Bldr: A. Warski SY, Szczecin, Poland

	L	In serv.
Spastel' Proconchik (ex-*Akademik Fersman*)	24-1-85	5-86

Akademik Sel'skiy—a sister to the *Spastel' Proconchik* JMSDF, 4-94

D: 3,250 tons (fl) **S:** 14.5 kts **Dim:** 81.87 (73.51 pp) × 14.83 × 5.00
Electronics: Radar: 2 . . . nav.
M: 1 Zgoda-Sulzer 6 ZL 40/48 diesel; 1 Kort-nozzle CP prop; 4,200 bhp—bow-thruster
Electric: 2,208 kw tot. (1 × 1,200-kw shaft alternator, 2 × 504-kw diesel sets)
Range: 12,000/14.5 **Fuel:** 700 m^3 heavy oil, 170 m^3 diesel
Crew: 31 tot. + 29 passengers (as research ship)

Remarks: 2,833 grt/1,283 dwt. Sold to the Russian government early in 1997 by the Yuzhmorneftegeofizika trust, which had used her as a seismic research ship. The new name indicates employment in search-and-rescue service, for which her long range is well suited.

♦ 2 Yug class (Project 862)
Bldr: Stocznia Polnocna, Gdansk, Poland (In serv. 1978–83)

Pluton Strelets

Strelets—while still in naval service Hartmut Ehlers, 7-93

BORDER GUARD PATROL SHIPS [WPS] *(continued)*

D: 1,960 tons (2,490 fl) **S:** 15.6 kts **Dim:** 82.50 (75.80 pp) × 13.50 × 3.97
A: probably none
Electronics: Radar: 2 Don-2 nav.
M: 2 Zgoda-Sulzer 8TD48.2 diesels; 2 CP props; 4,400 bhp (3,600 sust.)—2 100-kw low-speed electric motors—300-shp bow-thruster
Electric: 1,920 kVA tot.
Range: 9,000/13 **Fuel:** 343 tons **Endurance:** 40 days
Crew: 8 officers, 38 unlicensed (civilian), 20 scientists + 4 spare

Remarks: Built as oceanographic research and hydrographic survey vessels. Transferred to the Federal Border Guard in 1997, arriving at Murmansk, where they are now based, in 8-97. Are used to conduct EEZ patrols. Thirteen sisters remain in the Russian Navy configured as oceanographic research ships, and two others were converted as intelligence collection ships.
Hull systems: Have a quadrantial davit over stern ramp with 4-ton lift, two 5-ton booms, several oceanographic davits, three echo sounders, and six laboratories. Have deck reinforcements for three twin 25-mm AA. Carry two Project 727 GRP-hulled inshore survey launches.

♦ 6 Ivan Susanin–class (Project 97P/8) patrol icebreakers
Bldr: Admiralty SY, St. Petersburg (In serv. 1975–81)

	Laid down	L	In serv.	Fleet area
150 Aysburg	17-10-73	27-4-74	26-12-74	Pacific
173 Anadyr' (ex-*Imeni XXV S'yezda K.P.S.S., ex-Dnepr*)	16-7-75	14-2-76	30-9-76	. . .
018 Murmansk (ex-*Dunay*)	24-12-76	5-8-77	30-12-77	Pacific
170 Neva	23-11-77	28-7-78	29-12-78	Pacific
183 Volga	27-2-79	19-4-80	26-12-80	Pacific
036 Irtysh (ex-*Imeni XXVI S'yezda K.P.S.S.*)	22-4-80	3-7-81	25-12-81	Pacific

Irtysh (036)—when still named *Imeni XXVI S'yezda K.P.S.S.* M.O.D. U.K., 5-90

Volga (183) U.S. Navy, 5-90

D: 2,785 tons (3,710 fl) **S:** 14 kts **Dim:** 70.0 (62.0 pp) × 18.1 (17.5 wl) × 6.60
A: 1 twin 76.2-mm 59-cal. AK-276 DP; 2 single 30-mm 54-cal. AK-630 gatling AA
Electronics:
Radar: 2 Volga (Don-Kay) nav.; 1 MR-302 Rubka (Strut Curve) surf./air search; 1 MR-105 Turel' (Owl Screech) 76.2-mm gun f.c.
M: 3 Type 13D-100 diesels, electric drive; 2 props; 4,800 shp
Electric: 1,200 kw tot. **Range:** 5,500/14.5; 13,000/9.4 **Fuel:** 580 tons
Endurance: 50 days **Crew:** 9 officers, 33 enlisted (accomm. for 123 tot.)

Remarks: Built for KGB Maritime Border Service use and designated PSKR (*Pogranichnyy Storozhevoy Korabl'*, Border Patrol Ship). Sisters *Ivan Susanin* and *Ruslan* have been stricken. *Anadyr'* and *Irtysh* were given their current names in 11-4-92 and *Murmansk* in 5-96; the latter was refitted from 7-97 to 1-00.
Hull systems: Can carry 170 tons of fresh water and 27 tons of lubricants. The hull is divided into eight watertight compartments. The bow propeller was omitted in this variant and the motor compartment used to accommodate two diesel generator sets.
Combat systems: The 30-mm gatling AA guns are controlled only by two SP-521 Rakurs (Kolonka-2) ringsight directors. Have a helicopter deck aft but no hangar. *Murmansk* and *Neva* also have two positions for shoulder-launched surface-to-air missiles.

♦ 20 (+ 1) Sorum-class (Project 745P) armed tugs
Bldr: Yaroslavl Zavod (In serv. 1974–. . .)

	In serv.	Fleet
010 Ural	30-9-86	Northern
016 Ladoga	. . .	Northern
021 Vitim (ex-*Yan Berzin*)	30-9-80	Baltic
022 Zapolyare	29-9-82	Northern
030 Yenisey	5-11-87	Northern
035 Vyatka (ex-*Viktor Kingisepp*)	30-9-88	Baltic
043 Amur	. . .	Pacific
067 Chukotka	1981	Pacific
073 Zabaykal'ye	1979	Pacific
101 General Armii Matrosov (ex-*Taymir*)	1992	Caspian
103 Don	24-10-97	Baltic
105 Baykal	. . .	Baltic
106 Brest	. . .	Pacific
110 Kareliya	30-9-83	Northern
142 Aldan (ex-*Bug*)	25-11-85	Pacific
159 Primor'ye	. . .	Pacific
185 Sakhalin	. . .	Pacific
198 Kamchatka	. . .	Pacific
. . . Nevel'sk	1998–99	Pacific
. . . Stavropol	1998	Caspian
. . . . . .	. . .	. . .

Ladoga (016) NAVPIC-Holland, 10-01

Zabaykal'ye (073)—with paint in disrepair Boris Lemachko, 2000

D: 1,210 tons (1,656 fl) **S:** 14 kts **Dim:** 58.3 (55.5 pp) × 12.6 × 4.6
A: *Don, Sakhalin, Stavropol,* and *Vyatka:* 2 single 20-mm 54-cal. AK-306 gatling AA—others: 2 twin 30-mm 65-cal. AK-230 AA
Electronics: Radar: 2 Don-2 nav.
M: 2 Type 5-2D42 (6 ChN 30/38) diesels, 2 generators (950 kw each), electric drive; 1 prop; 2,500 shp (1,850 sust.)
Range: 6,750/13 **Fuel:** 297 tons **Endurance:** 40 days
Crew: 3 officers, 37 enlisted

Remarks: Typed PSKR (*Pogranichnyy Storozhevoy Korabl'*, Border Patrol Ship). Armed units of a standard naval/commercial Project 745 seagoing tug, used by the Federal Border Guard for patrol duties. Because these ships are inexpensive to operate and can accommodate deck cargo, they are widely used by the border guard, especially in the Pacific region. Retain all towing, firefighting, and salvage facilities. A new series of five was ordered during 5-94. Two more were ordered fall 1998. *Vitim* was renamed in 1997. *Don* was laid down 18-12-91 but not launched until 8-96; the keel for another was laid down in 5-97. Pacific area unit *Neman* was stricken 16-7-96.
Hull systems: The output of the propulsion plant is listed as less than that of the Project 745 ocean tug version, which is credited with 3,000 shp. Carry 89 tons of potable water.
Combat systems: On all, the guns are controlled by a single SP-521 Rakurs (Kolonka-2) manned director.

PATROL CRAFT, HYDROFOIL [WPCH]

♦ 9 Muravey (Antarets) class (Project 133)
Bldr: Yuzhnaya Tochka Zavod, Feodosiya, Ukraine (In serv. 1983–92)

062 P-118	095 P-106	. . . P-109
072 P-107	138 Tuapse (P-104)	. . . P-110
076 P-117	. . . Del'fin (P-101)	. . . P-111

BORDER GUARD PATROL CRAFT, HYDROFOIL [WPCH]
(continued)

Black Sea Muravey-class pennant 136 French Navy, 1997

Black Sea Muravey-class pennant 025

D: 180 tons light; 195 tons std. (220 fl) **S:** 65 kts (60 sust.)
Dim: 40.30 (39.60 hull; 34.40 wl) × 8.00 (12.0 over foils; 7.30 wl) × 1.90 (hull; 4.55 over foils)
A: 1 76.2-mm 59-cal. AK-176 DP; 1 30-mm 54-cal. AK-630 gatling AA; 2 fixed 402-mm OTA-40 ASW TT; 1 d.c. rack (6 d.c.); 1 55-mm grenade launcher (70 projectiles)
Electronics:
Radar: 1 Reyd (Peel Cone) nav./surf. search; 1 MR-123 Vympel (Bass Tilt) gun f.c.
Sonar: Ros'-K HF dipping at stern
M: COGAG M-20 plant: 2 M-70 gas turbines; 2 props; 22,600 shp (20,000 sust.)
Range: 410/45–50 **Endurance:** 5 days **Crew:** 5 officers, 20 enlisted

Remarks: Thirteen were built for the KGB Maritime Border Service. Designed under B. F. Orlov at Alekseyev Central Hydrofoil Design Bureau. One of the units listed above may have been renamed *Riba.* Of the survivors, P-107, -117, and -118 (commissioned 8-3-91) serve in the Baltic, the others in the Black Sea. Commercial versions equipped to carry 150 passengers and six automobiles or 300 passengers are offered for export.
Disposals: Black Sea sisters P-103, -105, and -108 were stricken 5-7-94 after having been transferred to Ukraine in 4-94; P-115 was in Ukraine service by 1997. Black Sea unit P-102 was stricken for disposal on 23-9-94.
Hull systems: Foil system uses fixed, fully submerged bow and stern sets, with an automatically adjusted amidships surface-piercing set beneath the bridge to control the ride. There is a single step to the hull aft. Both propeller shafts are sharply angled downward and are supported by the stern foil struts assembly. Can maintain 50 kts in Sea State 4 and operate hullborne in up to Sea State 7. Hull is hard-chine in form and made of aluminum-magnesium alloy.
Combat systems: The dipping sonar deploys through a hatch in the transom stern. There is an SP-521 Rakurs (Kolonka-2) ringsight backup director for the 30-mm gatling gun aft. The d.c. rack is on the starboard quarter. The grenade launcher is intended to combat underwater swimmers.

PATROL CRAFT [WPC]

♦ 0 (+ 3) Merkuriya class (Project 14232)
Bldr: Volga Zavod, Nizhniy Novgorod

AL'BATROS (ex-*Sokzhoi*) (In serv. 22-1-02) . . . . . .

D: 90 tons (99 fl) **S:** 50 kts **Dim:** 35.40 × 8.30 × 2.00 (props)
A: 1 30-mm 54-cal. AK-306 gatling AA; 1 14.5-mm AA; 1 Kornet or Metis-M SAM syst. (4 missiles; see remarks)
Electronics:
Radar: 1. . . nav.
EW: . . . intercept; 1 10-round PK-10 decoy RL
M: 2 Zvezda M-504B-4 diesels; 2 props; 9,980 bhp
Range: 500/30 **Endurance:** 5 days **Crew:** 16 tot.

Remarks: Typed as a "4th Rank Border Guard Ship" and referred to as the *Sokzhoi* class in recent literature. Designed by Alekseyev Central Hydrofoil Design Bureau, Nizhniy Novgorod, for the customs service, for which the prototype *Petr Matveyev* (TS-100) and *Pavel Vereshchagin* (TS-101) operate; they were built by Yaroslavskiy Shipbuilding. *Sokzhoi* was laid down at Volga Zavod 31-5-95 and a second unit on 2-4-95; although a delivery date of 30-9-97 was at one time announced, it appears that the first craft was not launched until 23-6-00 and did not complete trials until mid-6-01. The *Sokzhoi* is assigned to the Astrakhan Brigade and operates in the Caspian Sea. See photo of *Petr Matveyev* in the customs section for general appearance. The design is also offered for export as a high-speed yacht with MTU 16V396 TV94 diesels as an alternative propulsion plant.

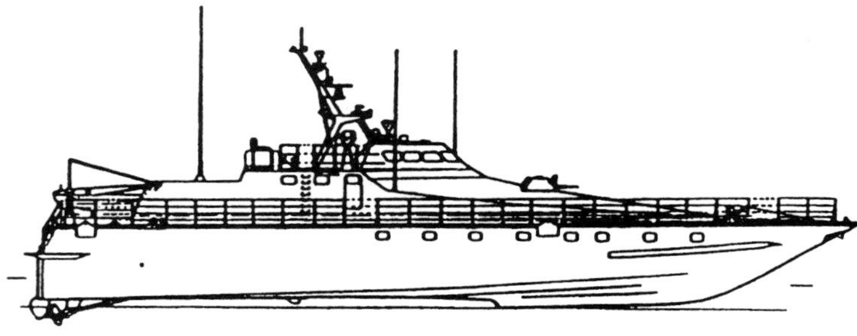

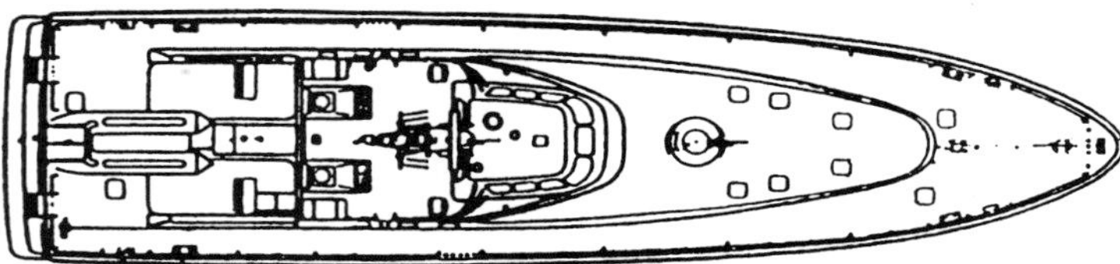
Merkuriya class—armed Border Guard variant (Project 14232) Aleksey Bureau

Hull systems: Originally reported to displace 102 tons full load. Range is also given as 800 n.m. Uses an air cavity beneath the aluminum-magnesium alloy hull to enhance planing lift. Can operate in State 6 seas and at 30 kts in 1.5-m waves.
Combat systems: The 30-mm gun is controlled by a Kolonka-219 lead-computing ringsight director. The design is also offered for export with a 7.62-mm mg added to the 30-mm mount, firing coaxially, plus two to four antiship missiles of unspecified type, while six Igla shoulder-launched SAMs can supplement or replace the Kornet or Metis-M system (for which no data are available; they may have been programs that have not reached production stage).

♦ 1 (+ 2 + . . .) Mirazh class (Project 14310)
Bldr: Vympel Zavod, Rybinsk

PK-500 (In serv. 12-9-01) PK-501 PK-502

Mirazh class—official model Rozvoorouzhenie, 1996

D: 109 tons light; 120 tons normal (121.1 fl) **S:** 50 kts
Dim: 34.95 × 6.79 (6.60 wl) × 2.10 (hull; 2.70 props)
A: 1 30-mm 54-cal. AK-306 gatling AA; 1 twin 14.5-mm mg; 2 triple 9M-114 Shturm SSM launchers (6 9M-120 Ataka or 9M-121 Vikhr' short-range missiles); 1 twin point-defense SAM launcher position (8 Igla-M missiles); 1 DP-64 handheld grenade launcher
Electronics: Radar: 1 Decca BridgeMaster C181/4 AT nav.
M: 2 Zvezda M-520 diesels; 2 props; 10,800 bhp
Electric: 124 kw tot. (2 × 50-kw, 1 × 25-kw, 380-V, 50-Hz diesel sets)
Range: 1,500/8 **Fuel:** 16.2 tons **Endurance:** 5 days
Crew: 2 officers, 3 warrant officers, 7 enlisted

Remarks: Offered for export in 2-93; construction of three was authorized in 1993, but only one was launched, in 1988. After lack of success in selling the craft, the yard presented it to the Federal Border Guard on 18-7-01 for service in the Caspian Sea, where it was commissioned into the Astrakhan Brigade. Another boat was laid down on 8-1-01. Designed by Firma Almaz, St. Petersburg. Funds permitting, the border guard would like to acquire 20 additional units.
Hull systems: Have an aluminum-magnesium alloy hull, with a stepped design and the hull bottom equipped with "interceptors" to minimize roll and improve the hull planing effect. Underhull air lubrication reduces the lift-to-drag ratio by between 5% and 30%. Can operate in Sea State 5. Fully armed, the craft would displace 126 tons full load. Equipped with the tropicalized M-520 TM5 engine, the craft would have a maximum speed of 48 kts.
Combat systems: Said to be able to carry 500 rounds of 30-mm ammunition and 2,000 rounds of machinegun ammunition. The export version was offered with six 9M-120 Ataka (NATO AT-6 Spiral) missiles; these were originally designed for antitank use and have a range of 6 km. The 30-mm gunmount has 500 rounds on-mount.

BORDER GUARD PATROL CRAFT [WPC] *(continued)*

♦ 28 (+ . . .) Svetlyak class (Project 1041.0)

Bldrs: Vladivostokskiy Sudostroitel'nyy Zavod (Vostochnaya Verf), Ulis, Vladivostok (In serv. 1988–. . .); Sudostroitel'noye Obyedineniye "Almaz," Petrovskiy SY, St. Petersburg (In serv. 1991–. . .); Yaroslavskiy SB, Yaroslavl (6 units, in serv. 1990–95)

	In serv.
011 PSKR-921 Otvazhniy	1995
012 PSKR-922	1995
013 PSKR-914 Korsakov	1992
017 PSKR-920 Podol'sk	1994
023 PSKR-915 Nevel'sk	1993
026 PSKR-918 Yuzhno-Sakhalinsk	1994
028 PSKR-906 Sochi	8-2-92
042 PSKR-911 Siktivkar	1991
044 PSKR-917	1994
065 PSKR-908 Briz	1990
069 PSKR-907	. . .
076 PSKR-919 Storoshevik	12-6-00
088 PSKR-903 Kholmsk	1989
100 PSKR-902 Staropol'	1989
102 PSKR-931 Kizlyar	23-12-97
106 PSKR-912 Derbent	1994
109 PSKR-905	1991
112 PSKR-932	1997
132 PSKR-910	1993
137 PSKR-916	1993
141 PSKR-909 Vyborg	1992
143 PSKR-913 Almaz	15-10-93
144 PSKR-904	1990
162 PSKR-901	1988
165 PSKR-930	1996
174 PSKR-923	1996
. . . PSKR-. . . Valentin Pikul'	27-6-01
. . . . . .	4-00

PSKR-909 Vyborg (141)—a Baltic Svetlyak Boris Lemachko, 6-00

PSKR-918 Yuzhno-Sakhalinsk (026)—visiting Japan Mitsuhiro Kadota, 4-00

PSKR-915 Nevel'sk (023)—on a visit to Japan; note the dipping sonar housing at the centerline of the stern Mitsuhiro Kadota, 5-01

A new Svetlyak with AK-630 gatling guns fore and aft—fitting out at Ulis Boatyard, Vladivostok Boris Lemachko, 4-00

D: 328 tons light (365–375 normal fl, 382–390 max.) **S:** 32 kts (31 sust.)
Dim: 49.50 (45.00 wl) × 9.20 × 2.14 (hull; 2.50 props)
A: 1 76.2-mm 59-cal. AK-176M DP (not in PSKR-931, *Pikul',* and unnamed unit); 1 (PSKR-913, *Pikul',* and unnamed unit: 2) single 30-mm 54-cal. AK-630M gatling AA; 1 or 2 AGS-17 grenade launchers; 1 DP-64 antiswimmer grenade launcher; 2 fixed 402-mm OTA-40 ASW TT (4 SET-40 torpedoes); 2 d.c. racks (6 BB-1 d.c. each)
Electronics:
Radar: 1 Reyd (Peel Cone) and/or Mius (Spin Trough) nav./surf. search; 1 MR-123 Vympel-AM (Bass Tilt) f.c.
Sonar: Uzh HF helicopter dipping sonar at stern (not in PSKR-931, *Pikul',* and one other)
EW: Slyabing intercept; . . . MFD/F loop; 2 16-round PK-16 fixed decoy RL
M: 3 Zvezda M-520B diesels; 3 props; 15,000 bhp
Electric: 400 kw tot. (1 × 200-kw, 2 × 100-kw diesel sets; 380 V, 50 Hz a.c.)
Range: 1,500/31–32; 2,200/12–13 **Endurance:** 10 days
Crew: 4 officers, 4 warrant officers, 20 enlisted (41 tot. accomm.)

Remarks: Design, by Almaz Central Marine Design Bureau, is tailored to extended patrolling. Three sisters serve in the Russian Navy. The NATO nickname means "Firefly." The initial Project 1041.0-series units were built for service in the Far East. The first Petrovskiy-built unit (Probably PSKR-913) was launched 28-7-92 and delivered 25-2-93; the same yard launched its seventh unit 10-12-96, the only naval surface combatant launched in Russia that year. PSKR-906 was delivered by Almaz 27-5-99 and is assigned to the Black Sea. The *Valentin Pikul'* was launched at St. Petersburg 25-5-00 and commissioned 26-6-01 for assignment during 8-01 to the Astrakhan Brigade of the Federal Border Guard, based at Kaspiysk; the Almaz yard had wanted the ship to be named *Anatoly Korolyov,* in honor of the former head of the firm, who died 27-3-01. Two sisters may have been ordered by Vietnam.

Project 1041.2 is offered as an export version without ASW equipment. The design is also offered as Project 1041.1 at 390 tons full load, with a 30-kt maximum speed and eight SS-N-25 missiles. The patrol version has been offered to Sri Lanka and to Equatorial Guinea at $25 million per unit.

Hull systems: Semi-planing, round-bilge hull with low spray chine forward. Propellers do not project below the keel. Have a steel hull with aluminum-magnesium alloy superstructure. Can survive with two compartments flooded. Have NBC warfare protection. The engine room is coated with vibration-damping material. The pilothouse is equipped with a centerline periscope.

Combat systems: There is an SP-521 Rakurs (Kolonka-2) ringsight backup director for the 30-mm gun; the 76.2-mm mount can be operated in local control and has an integral electro-optical sighting system. Carries 152 rounds of 76-mm (all on-mount) and up to 3,000 rounds of 30-mm ammunition. Navigational equipment includes a NAVSAT receiver, radio navaid receiver, automatic plot, and echo sounder. The design is also offered with a quadruple SAM launcher (and 16 Igla-series heat-seeking missiles) atop an enlarged dipping sonar housing at the stern, but none has yet been seen with the feature installed; the dipping sonar is extended from a compartment to port of the centerline at the stern, and there is no hull-mounted set. Some also have an additional Vaygach or MR-312 Nayada navigational radar. PSKR-931, *Pikul',* and a unit fitting out at Vladivostok during 2000 received a 30-mm AK-630M gatling gun forward instead of the standard 76-mm mount.

♦ 2 Modified Pauk class (Project 1241PE)

Bldr: Yaroslavskiy SB, Yaroslavl

	Laid down	L	Del.	In serv.
093 Novorossiysk (ex-MPK-291)	11-4-90	23-4-91	30-3-97	12-5-97
. . . Kuban' (ex-MPK-292)	20-7-90	. . .	31-12-97	9-4-98

Modified Pauk Novorossiysk (093)—prior to delivery 1991

D: 425 tons (495 fl) **S:** 32 kts (28 sust.)
Dim: 58.5 (49.5 pp) × 10.2 (9.4 wl) × 2.16 (hull; 3.61 props)
A: 1 76.2-mm 59-cal. AK-176 DP; 1 4-round Fasta-4M SAM syst. (16 Igla-M/Gremlin missiles); 1 30-mm 54-cal. AK-630 gatling AA; 2 5-round RBU-1200 ASW RL (30 RGB-12 rockets); 4 fixed 533-mm TT (2 SET-65E ASW and 2 Type 53-65KE antiship torpedoes); 2 d.c. racks (6 BB-1 d.c. each)

BORDER GUARD PATROL CRAFT [WPC] *(continued)*

Novorossiysk (093) and Kuban'—at their builder's, prior to delivery Yaroslavskiy Zavod, 10-96

Electronics:
Radar: 1 Pechora nav.; 1 MR-352 Pozitiv (Cross Dome) air/surf. search; 1 MR-123 Vympel-AM (Bass Tilt) gun f.c.
Sonar: MGK-345 MF hull-mounted and MF dipping system
EW: 2 16-round PK-16 fixed decoy RL
M: 2 M-521-TM5 diesels; 3 props; 17,330 bhp
Range: 2,000/20; 3,000/12 **Fuel:** 50 tons **Endurance:** 10 days
Crew: 7 officers, 32 enlisted

Remarks: Are of the export Pauk-II variant of the type delivered to India (4) and Cuba (1); they were originally intended for delivery to Iraq, along with MPK-293, which was not completed. They differ from the standard Russian Navy version in having a larger pilothouse, incorporating Cross Dome radar, and using 533-mm torpedo tubes (which are able to carry antiship as well as ASW torpedoes) vice 402-mm ASW TT. MPK-291 was named on 24-8-96 and MPK-292 on 10-9-97 when they were transferred to the Border Guard; they operate in the Black Sea.
Hull systems: The large housing for a dipping sonar system projects 1.5 m out from the stern. The large hull-mounted sonar dome is located approximately beneath the gun fire-control radar. The hull is constructed of mild steel, while the middle part of the deck plating, some internal bulkheads, and much of the superstructure are made of aluminum-magnesium alloy. Range with normal fuel allowance is only 1,600 n.m. at 12 kts.
Combat systems: The combat data system is designated SU-580E. There is an SP-521 Rakurs (Kolonka-2) backup ringsight director for the single gatling AA gun. Bass Tilt can control both the 76.2-mm and 30-mm guns. The normal ammunition load is 152 rounds of 76-mm (all ready-service, on-mount) and 2,000 rounds of 30-mm. The torpedo tubes must be trained out to launch. The sonar suite is nicknamed Bronza; MGK-345 applies to both the hull-mounted and dipping sonars, and the dipping sonar transducer can be lowered to 200 m.

♦ 2 Bogomol (Vikhr'-III) class (Project 2061)
Bldr: Vladivostokskiy Sudostroitel'nyy Zavod, Ulis, Vladivostok

070 PSKR-900 (In serv. 1988) 075 PSKR-907 (In serv. 1989)

D: 215 tons (251 fl) **S:** 36 kts **Dim:** 40.15 × 7.60 × 2.80
A: 1 76.2-mm 59-cal. AK-176M DP; 1 30-mm 54-cal. AK-306M AA
Electronics:
Radar: 1 MR-102 (Pot Drum) surf. search; 1 MR-123 Vympel (Bass Tilt) f.c.
EW: Nakat intercept; SPO-3 jammer
M: 3 M-520TM-5 diesels; 3 props; 14,400 bhp
Electric: 300 kw tot. (1 × 200-kw, 1 × 100-kw diesel sets)
Range: 400/36; 1,700/12 (2,500/12 with emergency fuel stowage)
Endurance: 9 days **Crew:** 5 officers, 32 enlisted

Remarks: Originally ordered for Iraq, but retained for use in the Pacific area, initially to train foreign crews, and then transferred to the Federal Border Guard in 1997. One was numbered T-229 in Russian Navy service.

♦ 18 Pauk-I (Molnaya-2) class (Project 1241.2P)
Bldrs: Yaroslavl Zavod; Vladivostokskiy Sudostroitel'nyy Zavod, Ulis, Vladivostok

	In serv.		In serv.
021 PSKR-804 Tol'yatti	1984	065 PSKR-806 Minsk (ex-*Yaguar*)	1984
023 PSKR-818 Nakhodka	1986	077 PSKR-815 Nikolay Kaplunov (ex-*Sobol'*)	1985
024 PSKR-802 Kaliningrad (ex-*Kunitsa*)	1982	130 PSKR-803 Kondor	1983
031 PSKR-810 Yaroslavl	1986	132 PSKR-801 Voron	1982
037 PSKR-816 Yastreb	1992	134 PSKR-809 Krechet	1987
040 PSKR-811 Sarych	...	136 PSKR-800 Berkut	1981
041 PSKR-808 Grif	1986	152 PSKR-807 Kobchik	1985
042 PSKR-814 Orlan	1989	182 PSKR-805 Korshun	1984
052 PSKR-817 Cheboksary	1992		
063 PSKR-812 Sokol	1989		

PSKR-809 Krechet (134)—off Nadhodka in the Pacific Boris Lemachko, 1998

PSKR-807 Kobchik (152)—in the Pacific U.S. Navy, 10-95

D: 415 tons (475 fl) **S:** 32 kts (28 sust.)
Dim: 57.60 (49.50 pp) × 10.40 (8.74 wl) × 2.14 (hull; 3.59 props)
A: 1 76.2-mm AK-176 DP; 1 4-round Fasta-4M (SA-N-8) SAM syst. (16 9M-313 Igla/Gremlin missiles); 1 30-mm 54-cal. AK-630 gatling AA; 2 5-round RBU-1200 ASW RL (30 RGB-12 projectiles); 4 fixed 402-mm OTA-40 ASW TT (4 SET-40 torpedoes); 2 d.c. racks (6 BB-1 d.c. each)
Electronics:
Radar: 1 Mius (Spin Trough) nav.; 1 Reyd (Peel Cone) nav./surf. search; 1 MR-123 Vympel-AM (Bass Tilt) f.c.
Sonar: MGK-345 Bronza MF hull-mounted and MF dipping (6.5/7.0/7.5 kHz)
EW: Vympel-R2 suite: 2 Half Hat-B intercept (not in all); 2 16-round PK-16 fixed decoy RL—some also: 2 10-round PK-10 fixed decoy RL
M: 2 Zvezda M-517 or M-507A twin diesels; 2 props; 20,800 bhp (16,180 sust.)
Electric: 500 kw tot. (2 × 200-kw, 1 × 100-kw diesel sets)
Range: 2,000/20; 2,600/14; 1,600/12 (3,000/12 with max. fuel)
Fuel: 50 tons normal **Endurance:** 10 days **Crew:** 5–7 officers, 31–32 enlisted

Remarks: Uses the same hull as the Tarantul-class missile corvette but has ASW armament vice antiship missiles and an all-diesel propulsion plant vice the Tarantul's COGAG/CODOG system. Another two are operated by the Russian Navy. PSKR-802, -804, -810, -815, and -817 serve in the Baltic area; PSKR-808 and -814 in the Black Sea; and the others in the Pacific.
Disposals: Federal Border Guard sisters *Gregoriy Gnatenko, Grigoriy Kuropyatnikov* (PSKR-806), and PSKR-813 were transferred, probably on loan, to the Ukraine Maritime Border Service in 2-92; they were permanently transferred during 4-94 but not officially stricken until 5-7-94.
Hull systems: A large housing for a dipping sonar system projects about 1.5 m out from the stern. The large hull-mounted sonar dome is located approximately beneath the gun fire-control radar. The hull is constructed of mild steel, while the middle part of the deck plating, some internal bulkheads, and much of the superstructure are made of aluminum-magnesium alloy.
Combat systems: The combat data system is designated SU-580. There is an SP-521 Rakurs (Kolonka-2) backup ringsight director for the single gatling AA gun. The Bass Tilt radar director can control both the 76.2-mm and 30-mm guns. The normal ammunition load is 152 rounds of 76-mm (all ready-service, on-mount) and 2,000 rounds of 30-mm. The sonar suite has a range of about 7 km for the dipping component; MGK-345 applies to both the hull-mounted and dipping sonars, and the dipping sonar transducer can be lowered to 200 m.

♦ 1 Project 1330 fisheries protection craft
Bldr: Vympel Joint Stock Co., Rybinsk (In serv. 1983)

Zogotitsa

D: 124.7 tons (183.1 fl) **S:** 9.5 kts **Dim:** 26.40 × 6.50 × 2.70
M: 1 diesel; 1 prop; 225 bhp **Range:** 1,800/9.5 **Crew:** 11 tot.

Remarks: Standard small fishing boat design adapted by the Ministry of Fisheries as a fisheries inspection craft.

♦ 19 Stenka (Tarantul) class (Project 205P)
Bldrs: Sudostroitel'noye Obyedineniye "Almaz," Petrovskiy SY, St. Petersburg; Yaroslavl Zavod; and . . ., Vladivostok (In serv. 1977–90)

014 PSKR-714	053 PSKR-718	097 PSKR-712	135 PSKR-727
035 PSKR-724	057 PSKR-653	113 PSKR-665	137 PSKR-631
044 PSKR-660	074 PSKR-701	126 PSKR-657	139 PSKR-659
047 PSKR-700	078 PSKR-717	129 PSKR-690	143 PSKR-723
048 PSKR-715	082 PSKR-726	133 PSKR-641	

Stenka-class PSKR-659 (139) JMSDF, 1994

BORDER GUARD PATROL CRAFT [WPC] *(continued)*

Stenka-class PSKR-727 (135) H&L Van Ginderen, 10-96

D: 170 tons light; 211 tons std. (245 fl) **S:** 35 kts
Dim: 39.80 (37.50 wl) × 7.60 (5.90 wl) × 1.96
A: 2 twin 30-mm 65-cal. AK-230 AA; 4 fixed 402-mm OTA-40 TT (4 SET-40 ASW torpedoes); 2 d.c. racks (6 BB-1 d.c. each)
Electronics:
Radar: 1 Baklan (Pot Drum) or Peel Cone nav./surf. search; 1 MR-104 Rys' (Drum Tilt) gun f.c.
Sonar: Bronza hull-mounted HF; HF helicopter dipping-type
EW: SPO-3 intercept
M: 3 M-504B or M-520 diesels; 3 props; 15,000 bhp
Range: 500/35; 800/20; 1,500/11.5 **Endurance:** 10 days
Crew: 4–5 officers, 26–27 enlisted

Remarks: Survivors of some 117 built for the KGB Maritime Border Service 1967–90. Construction continued for more than 20 years, although at a low rate in later years, and new units continued to enter service to replace early craft being discarded until the early 1990s. Late-construction units had Peel Cone navigational radar vice Pot Drum. Only a small number were exported: four to Cuba, four to Cambodia, two to Azerbaijan in 7-92 (ex-Russian AK-234 and AK-374), and several to Vietnam. PSKR-698, -712, -714, and -718 operate in the Baltic; PSKR-660, -700, -715, -717, and -723 are in the Black Sea; PSKR-690 and -692 are in the Pacific; and PSKR-631, -641, -657, -659, and -665 are in the Caspian (as is the one naval unit, AKA-232).
Disposals: From the Pacific Fleet, PSKR-680 and -691 were stricken 31-1-91; PSKR-681 through -684 on 10-9-92; P-685, -686, -687, -699, and -698 on 30-7-93; and P-693 and -705 on 5-7-94 for disposal. In 2-92, 13 Black Sea area units (PSKR-635, -636, -637, -639, -642, -650, -702, -709, -720, -722, and two others) were transferred on loan to Ukrainian control; three more (probably PSKR-629, -630, and -643) were offered but not accepted and were stricken on 5-7-94 along with several others. Black Sea unit PSKR-651 was stricken in 1998 at Novorossiysk. Baltic-region units PSKR-667 and -699 were awaiting scrapping as of late 1998. PSKR-638 and -692 were transferred to Georgia late in 1999. Stricken since 1999 have been PSKR-694, -704, and -725.

AIR-CUSHION PATROL BOATS [WPBA]

♦ 4 (+ . . .) Chilim class (Project 20910)
Bldr: Yaroslavskiy Sudostroitelniy Zavod

. . . (In serv. 20-9-00) . . . .

Chilim-class patrol hovercraft FPS RF, via M. Schiele, 2001

D: 8.6 tons (9.4 fl) **S:** 37.8–43.2 kts (light) **Dim:** 12.0 × 5.6 (5.9 over skirts) × . . .
A: 1 7.62-mm PKMB mg (600 rounds); 1 RPG-7 grenade launcher; 1 . . .-mm OKM mg; 7 AK-47 rifles; . . . Igla-M shoulder-launched SAMs
Electronics: Radar: 1 . . . nav.
M: 2 Deutz BF8M513 diesels; 2 lift fans and two airscrew propellers; 506 bhp (430 sust.)
Electric: 9 kw tot. (2 × 3-kw shaft generators, 1 × 3-kw diesel set)
Range: 162/38 (calm water; 350/38 with ferry fuel load)
Fuel: 425 kg normal **Crew:** 2 tot. + 6 troops

Remarks: Ordered in fall 1997 for delivery by mid-1998 but delayed by funding problems; first unit was laid down 24-2-98 and ran trials on the Volga 25-1-00. Designed by Almaz Central Marine Construction Bureau under W. A. Abramovskiy. Have GPS receivers, a radar, an MK-69-M2 magnetic compass, two IFF transponders, and an infrared detector. Can maintain 27–32 kts in a State 3 sea. Originally were to have been engined with Deutz BF6M1013 engines of 215 bhp each. Payload is 800 kg maximum.

PATROL BOATS [WPB]

♦ 1 (+ 9) Mangust class (Project 12150)
Bldr: Vympel Joint Stock Co., Rybinsk (In serv. 20-8-01 to . . .)

MANGUST

Mangust-class patrol boat—official model Rozvoorouzhenie

D: 27.2 tons (fl) **S:** 53 kts **Dim:** 19.45 × 4.40 × 1.20 (max.; 1.13 hull)
A: 2 single 14.5-mm mg; 1 Igla-M shoulder-launched SAM launch position; 2 single AGS-17 grenade launchers; 1 DP-64 antiswimmer grenade launcher
Electronics: Radar: 1 . . . nav.
M: 2 Zvezda M-470K diesels; 2 props; 3,000 bhp
Range: 230/35–40 **Endurance:** 48 hours **Crew:** 6 tot.

Remarks: Design was first announced in the early 1990s; the prototype, TS-300, was completed in 1998 for the customs service. The first unit completed for the Federal Border Guard was assigned to the Caspian Sea region. A second unit was launched during 8-01, and the builder has the capacity to build five per year. Design name *Mangust* means "Mongoose." GRP construction. Has a SATCOM terminal.

♦ 3 (+ . . .) Teryer class (Project 14170)
Bldr: Zelenodol'sk Zavod

TERYER-1 (In serv. 16-9-00) TERYER-2 TERYER-3

D: 8.3 tons **S:** 32 kts **Dim:** 11.52 × 3.14 × 0.56
A: small arms **Electronics:** Radar: 1 . . . nav.
M: 2 . . . diesels; 2 waterjets; 464 bhp
Range: 120/30 **Crew:** 6 tot.

Remarks: *Teryer* means "Terrier." Prototype ran trials in 1998 but was not accepted by the border guard until 9-00. Zelenodol'sk Marine Design Bureau is developing a more powerful version with two 300-bhp diesels and a range of 480 n.m.

♦ 6 Sobol' class (Project 12200)
Bldr: Sosnovka Zavod, Rybinsk (In serv. 1999–2001)

BSK-4 BSK-5 BSK-6 BSK-7 BSK-8 BSK-9

D: 54 tons (fl) **S:** 50 kts **Dim:** 27.70 × 5.60 × 1.10
A: 1 30-mm 54-cal. AK-306 gatling AA; . . . shoulder-launched Igla-M SAMs; 1 30-mm AGS-17 Plamya grenade launcher
Electronics: Radar: 1 . . . nav.
M: 2 diesels; 2 props; 3,700 bhp **Range:** 700/40 **Crew:** 6 tot.

♦ 1 Mustang-2 class (Project 18623)
Bldr: Yaroslavskiy SB, Yaroslavl (In serv. 2000)

BSK-19

D: 35.5 tons (fl) **S:** 40 kts **Dim:** 20.0 × 4.5 × 1.1
A: 1 14.5-mm 93-cal. AA; 1 30-mm AGS-17 Plamya grenade launcher
Electronics: Radar: 1 . . . nav.
M: 2 Zvezda M-470 diesels; 2 KaMeWa FF-550 waterjets; 2,950 bhp
Range: 250/30 **Crew:** 6 tot.

Remarks: Originally intended for police duties and ordered by the Ministry of Fisheries, whose fisheries patrol duties were absorbed by the Federal Border Guard in 8-98. Aluminum alloy hull. Made 48 kts on trials. Can operate in a State 5 sea. Designed by Redan Bureau, St. Petersburg.

♦ 2 Mustang class (Project 18627)
Bldr: Yaroslavskiy SB, Yaroslavl

PMK-1 (In serv. 1999) PMK-2 (In serv. 2000)

D: 18 tons (21.2 fl) **S:** 40 kts **Dim:** 15.80 × 3.80 × 0.70
A: 1 14.5-mm 93-cal. AA; 2 shoulder-launched Igla-M SAMs; 1 30-mm AGS-17 Plamya grenade launcher
Electronics: Radar: 1 . . . nav.
M: 1 Zvezda M-470 diesel; 1 KaMeWa FF-550 waterjet; 1,500 bhp
Range: 500/37 **Crew:** 1–2 tot.

Remarks: Originally intended for police duties and ordered by the Ministry of Fisheries, whose fisheries patrol duties were absorbed by the Federal Border Guard in 8-98. First unit launched 7-7-97. Aluminum alloy hull. Made 48 kts on trials. Can operate in a State 5 sea. Designed by Redan Bureau, St. Petersburg.

BORDER GUARD PATROL BOATS [WPB] *(continued)*

♦ 1 Mustang-99 class (Project 18629)
Bldr: Yaroslavskiy SB, Yaroslavl (In serv. 12-99)

PMK-3

D: 30.8 tons (fl) **S:** 50 kts **Dim:** 19.60 × 3.90 × 0.90
A: 1 14.5-mm 93-cal. AA **Electronics:** Radar: 1 . . . nav.
M: 2 . . . diesels; 2 KaMeWa waterjets; 3,200 bhp
Range: 350/45 **Crew:** 4 tot.

♦ 1 (+ 11) Ogonek class (Project 12130)
Bldr: Khabarovskiy Sudostroytel'niy Zavod, Khabarovsk (In serv. 4-12-98 to . . .)

. . . Sretenets

D: 91 tons (98 fl) **S:** 25.2 kts **Dim:** 33.40 × 4.20 × 0.81
A: 1 30-mm 65-cal. AK-306 gatling AA; 1 4-round Fasta-4M (SA-N-8) SAM syst. (. . . Igla-M missiles); 1 14.5-mm AA
Electronics: Radar: . . .
M: 2 . . . diesels; 2 props; 2,200 bhp
Range: 270/20 **Crew:** 2 officers, 1 warrant officer, 14 enlisted

Remarks: Intended to patrol the Amur and Ussuri River borders with China. Two or three more of the class were to be built after 2000, and up to 12 may ultimately be constructed. The enclosed 14.5-mm mg mount is mounted aft and the 30-mm gatling gun forward.

♦ 5 or more (+ . . .) Yastreb class (Project 1226.0)
Bldr: Yaroslavskiy Shipbuilding Plant OJSC, Yaroslavl

	Laid down	L	In serv.
Rus'	3-1-97	22-5-97	19-9-97
. . .	3-97	. . .	4-98
. . .	3-7-97	. . .	10-98
. . .	29-10-97	. . .	11-98
. . .	. . .	. . .	1998

Yastreb-class Rus' Yaroslavskiy Zavod, 9-97

D: 9.75 tons (fl) **S:** 40 kts
Dim: 13.50 (12.97 pp) × 3.42 (3.20 wl) × 0.85 (0.66 hull)
A: 1 7.62-mm mg **Electronics:** Radar: 1 . . . nav.
M: 2 diesels; 2 KaMeWa waterjets; 880 bhp
Range: 200/35 **Endurance:** 1 day **Crew:** 2 tot. + 6 troops

Remarks: GRP construction. First craft may have been built on speculation. The design, by Almaz Central Design Bureau, is also offered for export.

♦ 3 (+ . . .) Boyets class (Project 13987)
Bldr: Redan Joint Stock Co., St. Petersburg (In serv. 7-96 to . . .)

S-1 S-2 S-3

D: 5.9 tons (6.6 fl) **S:** 40 kts **Dim:** 10.20 × 3.10 × 0.51
A: small arms **Electronics:** Radar: 1 . . . nav.
M: 2 Volvo Penta TAMD 63L diesels; 2 KaMeWa waterjets; 630 bhp
Range: 250/40 **Crew:** 2 tot. + 8 passengers

Remarks: S-1 is used as part of the security service for the Russian president. The craft are intended for riverine, lake, and coastal service. Can mount a 12.7-mm mg. GRP construction.

♦ 17 Kulik class (Project 1415PV)
Bldrs: Sosnovka Zavod, Rybinsk; Yaroslavl Zavod; and others (In serv. 1976–90s)

PSKA-200 through PSKA-250 series

D: 42 tons (54 fl) **S:** 10.8 kts **Dim:** 21.20 × 3.93 × 1.40
A: small arms **Electronics:** Radar: 1 Lotsiya nav. (not always fitted)
M: 1 Type 3D-12A or 3D-12L diesel; 1 prop; 300 bhp
Electric: 12 kw tot. (DGR 1A-16/1500 generator)
Range: 200/11 **Endurance:** 5 days **Crew:** 4 tot.

Remarks: Assigned as harbor patrol and utility craft for the Federal Border Guard; some 95 others serve as naval service craft, where they are known as the Tanya (NATO Flamingo) class. Designed by the Redan Central Design Bureau. Are rail transportable. The craft do not wear their PSKA numbers; some have pennant numbers in the BGK series, while others wear only a number, without the BGK prefix.

Kulik-class BGK-1631—at Kronshtadt Boris Lemachko, 7-00

♦ 23 Zhuk (Gryf) class (Project 1400 or 1400M)
Bldr: More Zavod, Feodosiya, Ukraine (In serv. 1971–86)

637 PSKA-545	648 PSKA-51	661 PSKA-576	671 PSKA-530
639 PSKA-513	652 PSKA-500	662 PSKA-577	679 PSKA-532
640 PSKA-516	657 PSKA-510	663 PSKA-128	. . . PSKA-52
641 PSKA-553	658 PSKA-520	664 PSKA-139	. . . PSKA-548
642 PSKA-554	659 PSKA-525	665 PSKA-109	. . . PSKA-560
643 PSKA-563	660 PSKA-559	666 PSKA-111	

Zhuk-class PSKA-545 (637)—with Russian Navy Moma-class survey ships in the background French Navy, 1997

D: 35.9 tons (39.7 fl) **S:** 30 kts
Dim: 23.80 (21.70 wl) × 5.00 (3.80 wl) × 1.00 (hull; 1.90 max.)
A: 1 twin 14.5-mm 93-cal. 2M-7 AA *or* 1 twin 12.7-mm 60-cal. Utës-Ma mg
Electronics: Radar: 1 Lotsiya nav.
M: Project 1400: 2 M-50F-4 diesels; 2 props; 2,400 bhp—Project 1400M: 2 M-401 diesels; 2 props; 2,200 bhp
Electric: 48 kw total (2 × 21-kw, 1 × 6-kw diesel sets)
Range: 700/28; 1,100/15 **Endurance:** 5 days **Crew:** 1 officer, 6 enlisted

Remarks: Ten operated by the Soviet GRU military intelligence service had hull numbers and, in several cases, names, including *Sokol* (KSV-9), KSB-12, *Chayka* (KSV-485), *Berkut* (KSV-1135), *Gurzuf* (KSV-1499), and KSV-1754. Twenty-three Black Sea–area Federal Border Guard units (PSKA-53, -54, -125, -141, -501 through -512, -517, -519, -523 through -526, and -534) were stricken 5-7-94 and transferred to the Ukraine Border Guard, and P-527 was transferred to the Ukraine Navy. One Caspian area unit was to have transferred to Kazakhstan in 1996. One semiofficial source states that only 30 were built for the Federal Border Guard. More than 110 others have been exported. At least 10 others were built as naval (vice border guard) officers' yachts (Project 14670) [YFL] (q.v.).
Hull systems: Aluminum alloy hull. Capable of operating in up to Sea State 4 or 5. Range also reported as 700 n.m. at 28 kts and 1,100 n.m. at 15 kts.
Combat systems: Most export units were armed with two 12.7-mm 60-cal. Utës-M, side-by-side turreted gunmounts; earlier nonexport units have one (or occasionally two) over-and-under 14.5-mm 93-cal. 2M-7 gunmounts, while many retained for border guard service now have the twin 12.7-mm Utës-M machinegun mounting forward and a searchlight aft.

♦ 30 Saygak class (Projects 14081 and 14081M)
Bldrs: Kama Zavod, Perm; . . ., Moscow (In serv. 1986–99)

PSKA-400 through PSKA-429

D: 11.5 tons (13 fl) **S:** 38 kts (35 sust.) **Dim:** 14.05 × 3.50 × 0.65
A: small arms **Electronics:** Radar: 1 . . . nav.
M: 1 Zvezda M-401B (12CHSN18/20) diesel; 1 waterjet; 1,000 bhp
Electric: 8 kw (1 Type DGK8/1500 diesel driving; 27 V)
Range: 135/35 **Fuel:** 1.15 tons **Crew:** 2 tot. + 4–8 police personnel

Remarks: Offered for foreign sale in 1993 and typical of current Russian small personnel launch design. Rail transportable, the craft are intended for riverine and lake use and in coastal waters in seas up to Sea State 3. Aluminum alloy construction. Sisters TS-501 through TS-505 are used by the customs service (q.v.). One additional unit was built as a prototype radio-controlled target (Project 14082) and two have been built in Kazakhstan.

BORDER GUARD PATROL BOATS [WPB] *(continued)*

Saygak-class PSKA-419 (652)—in camouflage paint scheme
Boris Lemachko, 5-98

♦ 30 Aist-class (Project 1398) launches
Bldr: Svetenskiy Zavod, Kokue (In serv. 1975–86)

PMK-18 PMK-21 PMK-50 PMK-51 and others

D: 3.55 tons (5.8 fl) **S:** 20 kts **Dim:** 9.50 × 2.60 × 0.50
A: small arms **Electronics:** Radar: none
M: 1 3D-20 diesel; 1 waterjet; 235 bhp **Fuel:** 0.37 tons **Crew:** . . . tot.

Remarks: Employed on the Amur-Ussuri River network in the Russian Far East. Rail transportable. One former Maritime Border Service unit was transferred to Latvia in 1995, four are operated by the Georgian Navy, and others are used by the customs service. Designed by Redan Central Design Bureau, St. Petersburg, in 1968.

♦ 15 PO-2 (Yaroslavets) class (Project P-376)
Bldrs: Yaroslavl Zavod (In serv. 1958–90); Sosnovskiy Sudostroitel'nyy Zavod (In serv. 1995–. . .)

PSKA-580	PSKA-586	PSKA-591	PSKA-594	PSKA-597
PSKA-581	PSKĄ-587	PSKA-592	PSKA-595	PSKA-598
PSKA-582	PSKA-590	PSKA-593	PSKA-596	PSKA-599

D: 32.2 tons (38.2 fl) **S:** 9–10 kts **Dim:** 21.00 × 3.90 × 1.40 (max.; 1.26 mean)
A: 1 twin 12.7-mm 79-cal. mg
Electronics: Radar: 1 Mius (Spin Trough) nav. or none
M: 1 Type 3D-6S1 diesel; 1 prop; 150 bhp
Electric: 10 kw tot. (1 × 10 kw, DGPN-8/1500 diesel driving)
Range: 1,600/8 **Fuel:** 1.5 tons **Endurance:** 5 days
Crew: 2 warrant officers, 6 enlisted

Remarks: More than 600 have been built to the same general design for military and civilian use. Are rail transportable and all-steel construction. Can be operated safely in Force 8 winds and 2-m seas and can break light ice. The majority of the Federal Border Guard units are in the Pacific region, most on the Amur-Ussuri River network.

RIVER MONITORS [WPM]

♦ 2 Yaz' (Slepen') class (Project 1208)
Bldr: Khabarovsk Zavod

	Laid down	L	In serv.
066 Blagoveshchensk (ex-*60 Let VChK*)	14-10-76	15-10-77	28-6-79
106 Shkval (ex-MAK-11)	27-2-79	28-10-80	30-5-81

Yaz'-class Blagoveshchensk (066)
H&L Van Ginderen, 5-95

D: 390 tons light; 423 tons std. (447 fl) **S:** 24.3 kts (23 sust.)
Dim: 55.20 (53.30 wl) × 9.14 (8.48 wl) × 1.44
A: 2 single 100-mm D-10T2S low-angle (in T-55 tank turrets); 2 single 30-mm 54-cal. AK-630M gatling AA; 2 twin 12.7-mm 60-cal. Utës-M mg; 2 single 7.62-mm mg (in 100-mm turrets); 1 twin 140-mm ZIF-121M Sneg artillery RL; 2 30-mm BP-30 Plamya grenade launchers; shoulder-launched point-defense SAMs
Electronics:
Radar: 1 Mius (Spin Trough) or Kivach nav.; 1 MR-123 Vympel (Bass Tilt) f.c.
M: 3 M-512B diesels; 3 props; 11,400 bhp
Range: 550/20; 1,000/10 **Endurance:** 10 days **Crew:** 4 officers, 28 enlisted

Remarks: Low-freeboard monitors, designed at TsKB-5 under M. V. Koshkin. Some were reportedly assembled at Vladivostok. Both survivors are assigned to the Amur-Ussuri River network.

Disposals: Since the late 1990s, *Groza* (ex-MAK-2), *Smerch* (ex-MAK-6), *Tayfun* (ex-MAK-4), *Imeni 60 Letiya Oktyabr* (ex-*Khabarovsk*, ex-MAK-8), *Imeni 60 Letiya Pogranvoysk*, *Shtorm* (ex-MAK-7), *Vikhr'* (ex-*Khabarovsk*, ex-MAK-8), *Vyuga* (ex-MAK-11), and *Uragan* (ex-MAK-3) have been placed in disposal reserve. MAK-1 was discarded in 1992.
Hull systems: Have cutaway bows to improve navigation in light ice. The three propellers and three rudders are mounted in a "tunnel" to reduce the draft. Are extensively armored, with 35-mm armor on the superstructure, pilothouse, and weapons-control stations; 8- to 20-mm side plating; 100- to 200-mm on the citadel; and 35-mm decks.
Combat systems: The ZIF-121M rocket launcher amidships is essentially the same autoloading device employed on major seagoing combatants as a decoy rocket launcher; in these ships, it reportedly launches artillery rockets, although it may also be used for illumination rockets. The 7.62-mm machineguns are coaxially mounted with the 100-mm cannon. Do not have mine rails.

♦ 5 Vosh (Moskit) class (Project 1248.1)
Bldr: Svetenskiy Zavod, Kokue (In serv. 1988–91)

018 PSKR-482	131 PSKR-484	166 PSKR-483
121 PSKR-485	164 PSKR-486	

Vosh-class unit—possibly named *Vasiliy Pozharkov*
Boris Lemachko, 6-01

D: 150 tons light; 213 tons std. (223–230 fl) **S:** 17.5 kts
Dim: 38.90 (37.50 wl) × 6.1 × 1.27
A: 1 100-mm D-10T2S low-angle (in a T-55 tank turret); 1 30-mm 54-cal. AK-630M gatling AA; 1 twin 12.7-mm 60-cal. Utës-M mg; 1 twin 140-mm ZIF-21M Sneg artillery RL; 1 30-mm BP-30 Plamya grenade launcher
Electronics: Radar: 1 Mius (Spin Trough) nav.
M: 3 M-401B diesels; 3 props; 3,300 bhp
Range: 500/10 **Endurance:** 7 days **Crew:** 3 officers, 31 enlisted

Remarks: Employed on the Amur and Ussuri River borders with China. Also known as the PSKR-300 class. One may have been named *Vasiliy Pozharkov.* The 100-mm gun is mounted coaxially with a 7.62-mm machinegun in an armored turret salvaged from a T-55 tank. Do not have mine rails. Have 100- to 200-mm armor over vital areas. Naval sisters AKA-313, -320, -440, -459, -467, and -469 have been stricken.

♦ 8 Piyavka class (Project 1249)
Bldr: Khabarovsk Zavod (In serv. 1979–84)

013 PSKR-55	093 Kazak Ussuriyskiy (ex-PSKR-56)	123 PSKR-58
058 PSKR-57		146 PSKR-54
065 PSKR-53	117 PSKR-52	189 PSKR-59

Piyavka-class PSKR-57 (058)
Boris Lemachko, 1997

D: 150 tons light; 216 tons std. (229 fl) **S:** 17.5 kts
Dim: 41.90 (40.00 wl) × 6.1 × 1.23
A: 1 30-mm 54-cal. AK-630M gatling AA; 1 twin 12.7-mm 60-cal. Utës-M mg; 1 30-mm BP-30 Plamya grenade launcher
Electronics: Radar: 1 Mius (Spin Trough) nav.
M: 3 M-401B diesels; 3 props; 3,300 bhp **Range:** 500/10 **Endurance:** 7 days
Crew: 2 officers, 26 enlisted + 12 troops

Remarks: Like the Vosh class, are intended for duty on the Amur-Ussuri River system to police the border with China, but are configured to carry a dozen constabulary personnel in addition to the crew and can also carry up to 12 tons of supplies. Are not armored. PSKR-56 was named in 1996.

♦ 16 Shmel' class (Project 1204)
Bldrs: Kamysh Burun Zavod, Kerch' (98 units), and 61 Kommunara Zavod, Nikolayev, Ukraine (In serv. 1967–74)

019 PSKR-341	080 PSKR-347	094 PSKR-365	149 PSKR-374
033 PSKR-358	085 PSKR-355	107 PSKR-375	179 PSKR-366
034 PSKR-359	089 PSKR-357	113 PSKR-346	181 PSKR-342
049 PSKR-377	091 PSKR-350	147 PSKR-376	187 PSKR-367

BORDER GUARD RIVER MONITORS [WPM] *(continued)*

Shmel'-class PSKR-374 (149)—at Blagoveshchensk, with a border guard PO-2 patrol launch in the background Boris Lemachko, 1998

D: 77.4 tons (fl) **S:** 24 kts **Dim:** 27.70 × 4.32 × 0.90 (2.00 molded depth)
A: 1 76.2-mm 48-cal. D-56TM (in a PT-76 tank turret); 1 twin 25-mm 80-cal. 2M-3M AA *or* 1 twin 14.5-mm 93-cal. 2M-7 AA; 1 7.62-mm mg (in tank turret); 2 mine rails (up to 4 mines each)
Electronics: Radar: 1 Donets-2 nav.
M: 2 M-50F-4 diesels; 2 props; 2,400 bhp
Electric: 50 kw tot. (2 × 25-kw diesel sets)
Range: 240/20; 600/10 **Fuel:** 4.75 tons **Endurance:** 7 days
Crew: 1 officer, 2 warrant officers, 11 enlisted

Remarks: Survivors of 53 built for the KGB Border Guard; 16 of the 65 built for the Soviet Navy are also still in service. Designed by TsKB-5 (the current Firma Almaz) design bureau under L. V. Ozimov. Units built at Nikolayev were prefabricated and later assembled at Khabarovsk. Three former Federal Border Guard units based on Lake Peipus in western Russia (including PSKR-389) are now in Belorussian hands, while four others may be in Ukrainian service. Danube Flotilla units AKA-506, -564, -583, and -602 were stricken 31-7-96 and scrapped. All remaining Federal Border Guard units operate on the Amur-Ussuri River border between China and Russia.
Hull systems: The screws are mounted in tunnels to reduce draft. Armor includes 10-mm over the pilothouse and gun barbettes, 8-mm over the hull and internal bulkheads, and 5-mm over the deck and pilothouse. Have a Gradus-2 gyrocompass and NEL-7 echo sounder.
Combat systems: Some have also carried up to four 30-mm Plamya grenade launchers and four pintle-mounted 7.62-mm machineguns. One 7.62-mm machinegun is mounted coaxially with the 76-mm gun (for which 40 rounds are carried on-mount). Mine loads vary from four UDM-500 or two UDM-1000 to six KPM or eight YaM mines.

AMPHIBIOUS WARFARE CRAFT

♦ 3 Aist (Dzheryan)-class (Project 1232.1) air-cushion landing craft [WLCUA]

Bldr: Sudostroitel'noye Obyedineniye "Almaz," Dekabristov SY, St. Petersburg (In serv. 1970–85)

D: 231 tons light; 298 tons std. (355 fl) **S:** 70 kts (light; 50 sust., loaded)
Dim: 47.80 (45.50 hull) × 17.50 × 0.3 (1.3 at rest)
A: 2 4-rail Fasta-4M (SA-N-8) SAM syst. (32 9M-36 Strela-3/Gremlin missiles); 2 twin 30-mm 65-cal. AK-230 AA
Electronics:
Radar: 1 Mius (Spin Trough) nav.; 1 MR-104 Rys' (Drum Tilt) f.c.
EW: no intercept; 2 16-round PK-16 fixed decoy RL
M: 2 DT-4 gas turbines; 4 AV-70 airscrew props, 2 lift fans; 31,558 shp
Electric: 60 kw (2 × 30-kw diesel sets)
Range: 100/45; 208/40 **Fuel:** 47 tons **Endurance:** 5 days
Crew: 3 officers, 18 enlisted + up to 220 troops

Remarks: Typed MDK (*Mal'yy Desantnyy Korabl',* Small Landing Ship). The designed service life was not more than 16 years. Transferred to the border guard from the Black Sea Fleet in 1995–96 and now employed as Caspian Sea patrol craft, operating from Makhachkala. Three others survive as amphibious warfare craft in the Russian Baltic Fleet.
Hull systems: Have bow and stern ramps. Cargo capacity: 74 tons (two T-62 or T-64 tanks or four PT-76 tanks or five BTR-60 armored personnel carriers) plus 220 troops; the normal load, however, is around 50 tons. The DT-4 gas turbines are marinized versions of the NK-12 aircraft engine. Early units had riveted aluminum hulls, later ones welded; the hull structure has experienced considerable corrosion in service.
Combat systems: Carry 2,000 rounds of 30-mm ammunition.

♦ 1 Vydra-class (Project 106KM) utility landing craft [WLCU]

Bldr: . . . . . . (In serv. 1967–69)

610 MDK-174

D: 308 tons light (550 fl) **S:** 10.5 kts
Dim: 54.50 (50.00 pp) × 7.70 (7.50 wl) × 2.25 (mean hull)
Electronics: Radar: 1 Don-2 nav.
M: 2 Type 3D-12 diesels; 2 Kort-nozzle props; 600 bhp
Range: 1,400/10 (loaded) **Endurance:** 8 days **Crew:** 1 officer, 11 enlisted

Remarks: Assigned to the Amur-Ussuri River network as a supply craft. The cargo deck measures 30.0 × 4.5 m and can accommodate up to 176 tons of vehicles or cargo (6 ZIL-131 or 10 GAZ-66 trucks). Bulgaria received 21 sisters and Egypt 10.

♦ 8 Tsaplya (Murena)-class (Project 1206.1) air-cushion vehicle landing craft [WLCMA]

Bldrs: Yuzhnaya Tochka SY, Feodosiya; Ussuri SY, Khabarovsk

	In serv.		In serv.
659 D-143	1992	680 D-285	1988
665 D-259	9-10-87	688 D-458	2-4-87
668 D-453	1985	690 D-142	1991
670 D-323	1990	699 D-447	1989

Tsaplya-class D-142 (690) Siegfried Breyer Collection

Tsaplya-class D-323 (670) H&L Van Ginderen, 5-95

D: 80 tons light; 104 tons std. (135 normal; 149 fl)
S: 55 kts (empty; 50 with 24-ton load)
Dim: 31.60 (over skirt) × 12.90 (14.80 over skirt) × 1.6 (at rest)
A: 2 single 30-mm 54-cal. AK-306 gatling AA; 1 shoulder-launched SAM position (. . . Igla-M missiles); 1 twin 12.7-mm Utës-M mg; 2 40-mm BP-30 Plamya grenade launchers (1,800 grenades); 10–24 mines in lieu of vehicles
Electronics: Radar: 1 SRN-207 Ekran (Curl Stone-B) nav.
M: 2 PR-77 gas turbines; 2 3.5-m-dia. airscrew props; 8,000 shp—2 2.2-m-dia. axial lift fans (powered by main engines)
Range: 500/50; with 24-ton payload: 200/55 **Endurance:** 1–3 days
Crew: 3 officers, 8 enlisted + 80–130 troops

Remarks: Rated as DKA (*Desantny Kater,* Landing Craft), 3rd class. Design is essentially that of a lengthened Lebed (Project 1206); intended for riverine service. Are operated on the Amur-Ussuri River system in the Far East. The design has been offered for foreign sale without artillery rockets as Project 1206.1E. A mine warfare variant, Pelikan (Project 1206T), was also built, but both units have been discarded. Although one source reported that 10 were built, the total may only have been the eight still in service as of 2001.
Hull systems: Cargo: 24 tons of cargo under normal conditions, but up to 40–42 tons with a 10-kt speed reduction: one amphibious tank plus 80 troops, or 25 tons of stores and 160 soldiers, or 225 soldiers. Other cargo: one T-72M or T-80 tank or two PT-76 amphibious tanks or three BTR-70 armored personnel carriers. The bow ramp is 5.5 m long by 5.0 m wide. The cargo deck has about 130 m^2 of useful space. Light alloy hull with detachable, rubberized, flexible cloth skirts that are cylindrical in section. Can maintain 50 kts in Sea State 2 or 30 kts in Sea State 3. The gas turbine plant is also reported as two MT-70R installations; the engines drive an integrated lift/propulsion plant with one axial lift fan and one airscrew propeller on either side. Can cross 1-m obstacles and ditches up to 4–5 m wide.
Combat systems: The gatling guns are controlled by SP-521 Rakurs (Kolonka-2) ringsight directors on platforms abaft the pilothouse. The grenade launchers flank the bow ramp. May also carry "AGS-17" rockets. Carry 1,000 rounds of 30-mm and 1,000 rounds of 12.7-mm ammunition.

♦ 1 Lebed (Kal'mar)-class (Project 1206) air-cushion landing craft [WLCMA]

Bldr: Sudostroitel'noye Obyedineniye "Almaz," Dekabristov SY, St. Petersburg, or Yuzhnaya Tochka Zavod, Feodosiya, Ukraine (In serv. 1984)

543 D-454

D: 70 tons (87 fl) **S:** 70 kts (max.) **Dim:** 24.8 × 10.8 × 1.3 (at rest)
A: 1 12.7-mm Ütes-M mg **Electronics:** Radar: 1 . . . nav.
M: 2 AL-20K gas turbines; 2 shrouded airscrew props; 20,000 shp (16,000 sust.)
Range: 100/60 **Fuel:** 12.7 tons **Crew:** 2 officers, 4 enlisted + 120 troops

Remarks: The entire class had been reported retired by the end of 1997, but it was reported in 2000 that four remained in the Northern Fleet, of which D-454 was photographed on 21-7-00 loading for transit via the canal and river system from the Northern Fleet for operations with the Federal Border Guard in the Caspian. Used for patrolling oil fields and shallow waters. Can carry one or two armored personnel carriers or 120 troops or about 35 tons of cargo. Has a bow ramp only.

BORDER GUARD AUXILIARIES

♦ 8 Neon Antonov–class (Project 1595) cargo ships [WAK]

Bldr: Nikolayevsk-na-Amur Zavod (In serv. 1978–87)

115 Ivan Lednev	119 Nikolay Starshinov
105 Ivan Yevteyev	143 Sergey Sudyeskiy
184 Mikhail Konovalov	154 Vasiliy Sutsov
090 Nikolay Sipyagin	176 Vyacheslav Denisov

Mikhail Konovalov (184) JMSDF, 10-94

Vyacheslav Denisov (176)—at Vladivostok Boris Lemachko, 2000

D: 2,420 tons light (4,040 fl) **S:** 18 kts **Dim:** 96.30 (87.20 pp) × 14.50 × 5.10
A: 1 twin 30-mm 65-cal. AK-230 AA; 2 twin 12.7-mm 60-cal. Utës-M mg
Electronics:
Radar: 2 Vaygach-U (Palm Frond) *or* 1 Volga (Don-Kay) and 1 Mius (Spin Trough) or Don-2 nav.
M: 2 Type 67B (12DRPN 23/2 × 30) diesels; 1 prop; 7,500 bhp
Range: 5,000/18; 8,750/14
Endurance: 25 days **Crew:** 45 tot. + 18 passengers

Remarks: Specialized supply ships for remote garrisons of the Federal Border Guard in the Pacific area. Built in the Far East. Some may be nonoperational. Sisters *Dvina* and *Irbit* are assigned to the Russian Navy Pacific Fleet. The initial ship of the class was named *Neon Antonov;* either the ship has been stricken or one of the units listed above is that ship renamed.
Hull systems: Carry one Project 1785 logistics landing craft aft to starboard (36 tons light/78.2 tons fl; 21.90 × 5.81 × 1.00 m; one 470-bhp diesel for 9.8 kts) and a workboat to port, aft, with a 50-ton boat derrick to handle them. The hull has a bulbous forefoot. There are two cargo holds forward, tended by only two 5-ton derricks. The pilothouse is equipped with MPK-455M navigational periscopes port and starboard. Cargo capacity: 804 tons.
Combat systems: The 30-mm gunmount is controlled by a Rakurs-series (Kolonka-1) remote ringsight director mounted in an enclosed shelter, which must limit its effectiveness. The machineguns are in enclosed mounts like those mounted on Zhuk-class patrol craft.

♦ 1 Baskunchak-class (Project 1545) oiler [WAO]

Bldr: Zaliv Zavod, Kerch' (In serv. 1966–68)

102 Sovetskiy Pogranichnik

Sovetskiy Pogranichnik (102)—at Vladivostok Boris Lemachko, 4-01

D: 1,260 tons light (2,940 fl) **S:** 13.2 kts **Dim:** 83.60 (74.00 pp) × 12.00 × 3.80
Electronics: Radar: 1 Don-2 nav.
M: 1 Type 8DR 43/61W diesel; 1 prop; 2,220 bhp (2,000 sust.)
Electric: 325 kw tot. **Range:** 5,000/12 **Fuel:** 124 tons **Crew:** 30 tot.

Remarks: 1,768 grt/1,660 dwt. The name means "Soviet Border Guardsman" and has not yet been changed. Operates in the Pacific, primarily employed in transporting fuels to outlying Federal Border Guard outposts. Sister *Ivan Golubets* had been discarded by 2001 and replaced with the new, smaller *Ishim* (see under [WYO]). One sister, *Usedom,* was formerly in the East German Navy; 16 others served in the Soviet merchant marine. Has an ice-reinforced hull. Cargo: 1,490 tons (9,993 bbl) of up to four different types.

♦ 2 Okhtenskiy (Goliat)-class (Project 733) patrol tugs [WATA]

Bldr: Petrozavod SY, St. Petersburg (In serv. 1958–66)

PB-187 PB-196

Border Guard Okhtenskiy-class seagoing tug pennant 033—with a cargo of five automobiles and vans on deck aft JMSDF, 12-95

D: 717 tons (890 fl) **S:** 13.3 kts **Dim:** 47.30 (43.0 pp) × 10.30 × 4.14
A: small arms
Electronics: Radar: 1 or 2 Don-2 or Mius (Spin Trough) nav.
M: diesel-electric: 2 Type D5D50 diesels; 1 prop; 1,500 shp **Electric:** 340 kw
Range: 6,000/13; 7,800/7 **Fuel:** 197 tons **Endurance:** 30 days
Crew: 31 tot. (civilian) + 40 passengers/rescuees

Remarks: Standard seagoing tug design, of which five were assigned to the KGB Maritime Border Guard in the Far East (including ex-MB-36 and ex-MB-163) and were at one time armed with a twin 57-mm ZIF-31B gunmount forward. Sister PSKR-3 (ex-MB-. . .) was stricken 5-7-94. Bollard pull: 27 tons initial/17 sustained. Have a 5-ton derrick. A number of naval sisters remain in service as tugs and as rescue tugs.

SERVICE CRAFT

♦ 1 command staff craft [WYAG]

Karl Marx

Karl Marx H&L Van Ginderen, 1994

Remarks: Elderly, steam-powered, sidewheel passenger craft, operated on the Amur-Ussuri River network. Has two shielded probable 76-mm or 85-mm guns of truly ancient origin. No other information is available. Retention of the name *Karl Marx* indicates a certain suspension of current realities.

♦ up to 4 Muna-class (Project 1823) ammunition lighters [WYE]

Bldr: Nakhodka SY (In serv. 1966–85)

036 PSKR-451 . . . PSKR-452 . . . PSKR-454 . . . PSKR-460

Muna-class PSKR-451 (036)—alongside *Neon Antonov*–class cargo ship *Ivan Yevteyev* at Vladivostok Boris Lemachko, 5-98

D: 457 tons (688 fl) **S:** 11 kts **Dim:** 51.50 × 8.40 × 2.70
Electronics: Radar: 1 Mius (Spin Trough) nav.
M: 1 Type 6DR 30/50 diesel; 1 prop; 600 bhp
Range: 1,700/10 **Endurance:** 15 days **Crew:** 15 tot. + 7 passengers

BORDER GUARD SERVICE CRAFT *(continued)*

Remarks: Munitions lighters, adapted as local cargo transports. PSKR-451 is based at Vladivostok, and the others, if still in service, probably also operate in the Far East region.
Hull systems: Have a single 3.2-ton-capacity electric crane positioned between two small holds. Cargo capacity: 175 tons.

♦ 0 (+ 2) . . .-class (Project . . .) cargo lighters [WYF]
Bldr: Sudoverf, Rybinsk (In serv. . . .)

D: 114 tons (fl) **S:** 9 kts **Dim:** 24.00 × 5.20 × 1.52
Electronics: . . .
M: 2 . . . diesels; 2 azimuthal, Kort-nozzle props; 296 bhp

Remarks: Ordered during 7-00 for local river ferry and coastal service. Have a 12.5 × 3.6–m cargo deck suitable for carrying two 25-ton trucks and have a bow ramp. Can be used to tow barges. The yard was previously known as Rybinsk Shipyard.

♦ 8 Kanin-class (Project 16900A) cargo lighters [WYF]
Bldr: Zvezdochka State-Run Machine Building Enterprise, Severodvinsk

	In serv.		In serv.
PSKR-490 Kanin	1994	PSKR-. . . Urengoy	9-98
PSKR-491 . . .	1995	PSKR-. . . Ogra	1998
PSKR-. . . Khanty-Mansiysk	28-3-97	PSKR-. . . Arkhangel'sk	1999
PSKR-. . . Yurga	12-97	PSKR-.	2000?

Kanin (PSKR-490)—at Gelendzhik Boris Lemachko, 7-00

D: 748 tons (920 fl) **S:** 9.5 kts **Dim:** 45.45 × 8.80 × 2.50
Electronics: Radar: 1 . . . nav.
M: 2 . . . diesels; 1 prop; 800 bhp
Range: 2,200/8 **Endurance:** 10 days **Crew:** 22 tot.

Remarks: 396 dwt. Originally completed for commercial service but acquired for the Federal Border Guard after completion. *Khanty-Mansiysk* is assigned to the Black Sea, PSKR-490 and one other to the Barents Sea area. Bows are reinforced for Arctic navigation. Have two holds and a single electrohydraulic crane. Three sisters were under construction for merchant service in 1998. The shipyard is also known as the Zvezdochka Scientific Industrial Association.

♦ 1 Chaika-class (Project 1360) presidential yacht [WYFL]
Bldr: Sudostroitel'noye Obyedineniye "Almaz," Petrovskiy SY, St. Petersburg (In serv. 1980)

Kavkaz

D: 158 tons (220 fl) **S:** 32 kts **Dim:** 45.50 × 8.0 × 2.50 (mean hull)
M: 2 M-503A radial diesels; 2 props; 8,000 bhp
Range: 500/35 **Fuel:** 40 tons **Crew:** 32 tot.

Remarks: Built on the Osa (Project 205) missile-boat hull but with a two-level, streamlined superstructure. Operated in the Black Sea by the Federal Border Guard. White painted. A refit by the builder is scheduled for completion 1-6-02. To be replaced in 2007. Sister *Krym* was transferred to Ukraine 1-5-95.

♦ 1 Project 14670 officers' yacht [WYFL]
Bldr: . . . . . . (In serv. 1985–88)

Pogranichnik

Pogranichnik—at Kronshtadt, with memorial submarine D-2 in the background Boris Lemachko, 2000

D: 38 tons (49 fl) **S:** 31 kts **Dim:** 24.0 × 5.2 × 1.9
A: none **Electronics:** Radar: 1 . . . nav.
M: 2 M-50F-series diesels; 2 props; 2,400 bhp
Range: 700/29; 1,100/15 **Endurance:** 5 days **Crew:** 12 tot.

Remarks: Some 13 sisters serve naval officers. The design is a variant of the Zhuk-class patrol boat.

♦ 1 Project 12210 fuel lighter [WYO]
Bldr: Zvenigov Zavod, . . . (In serv. 2001)

. . .

D: 2,350 tons (fl) **S:** 10 kts **Dim:** 72.30 × 12.00 × 4.30
M: 2 diesels; 2 props; 2,800 bhp **Range:** 1,500/10 **Crew:** 7 tot.

Remarks: Probably intended for riverine service in the Far East.

♦ 1 Project 15010 fuel lighter/supply ship [WYO]
Bldr: Nikolayevske-na-Amur Zavod (In serv. 2001)

Ishim

D: 960 tons light (2,450 fl) **S:** 14 kts **Dim:** 80.00 × 12.00 × 3.70
M: 1 diesel; 1 prop; 2,800 bhp **Crew:** 35 tot.

Remarks: Intended to support offshore and coastal bases. Cargo: 1,115 tons distillate fuel, 600 tons kerosene, 430 tons gasoline, 80 tons lube oil, 75 tons potable water, and 50 tons of provisions.

♦ 5 Bis-class (Project 1481) riverine fuel lighters [WYO]
Bldr: Sventenskiy Zavod, Kokue (In serv. 1974–76)

VNS-180150 VNS-182150 VNS-. . .
VNS-181150 VNS-183150

Three Bis-class fuel lighters—note the extremely shallow draft Boris Lemachko, 10-00

D: 600 tons (fl) **S:** 10 kts **Dim:** 57.8 × 9.5 × 1.2
M: 2 Type 3D-12 diesels; 2 props; 600 bhp
Endurance: 6 days **Crew:** 7 tot.

Remarks: Operate on the Amur and Ussuri Rivers. Have sufficient communications facilities to be used as command ships.

♦ 27 Project 1496 small harbor tugs [WYTL]
Bldr: Sovetskaya Govan' Zavod, Azove (In serv. 1966–80)

600 PSKA-272	620 PSKA-582	648 PSKA-585	663 PSKA-589
603 PSKA-584	621 PSKA-594	651 PSKA-588	664 PSKA-597
604 PSKA-583	624 PSKA-274	654 PSKA-278	671 PSKA-590
608 PSKA-599	626 PSKA-277	655 PSKA-275	673 PSKA-282
614 PSKA-595	633 PSKA-586	656 PSKA-279	681 PSKA-273
615 PSKA-581	636 PSKA-592	657 PSKA-276	697 PSKA-587
617 PSKA-580	642 PSKA-591	659 PSKA-281	

Project 1496 tug PSKA-591 (642)—at Nakhodka Boris Lemachko, 5-97

D: 91.3 tons (108.5 fl) **S:** 10.5 kts **Dim:** 23.40 × 5.87 × 1.87
Electronics: Radar: 1 or 2 Lotsiya and/or Mius (Spin Trough) nav.
M: 1 Type 8 ChSN 18/22-1 diesel; 1 shrouded prop; 315 bhp
Electric: 18 kw tot.
Range: 1,450/10.5 **Fuel:** 8.3 tons **Endurance:** 6 days **Crew:** 8 tot.

Remarks: All serve in the Pacific region as tugs and local stores and personnel transports. Another 35 are in naval service (q.v.). Have a NEL-10 echo sounder. Carry 4.4 tons potable water.

CUSTOMS SERVICE

Note: Little information is available about the structure or composition of the Russian Federation Customs Service, but it has become apparent that it operates patrol craft independent of the Russian Navy and the Federal Border Guard. Known classes are listed below.

CUSTOMS SERVICE PATROL CRAFT [WPC]

♦ **2 (+ . . .) Merkuriya class (Project 14232)**
Bldr: Yaroslavskiy SB, Yaroslavl

TS-100 Petr Matveyev (L: 10-96)
TS-101 Pavel Vereshchagin (In serv. 5-11-00)

Customs Service patrol craft Pavel Vereshchagin (TS-101)
Boris Lemachko, 10-00

D: 90 tons (99.3 fl) **S:** 50 kts **Dim:** 35.40 × 8.30 × 2.00 (props)
A: 1 14.5-mm AA; 2 single 7.62-mm mg
Electronics: Radar: 1 . . . nav.
M: 2 M-504B-4 diesels; 2 props; 9,980 bhp (8,000 sust.)
Range: 600/30 **Endurance:** 5 days **Crew:** 16 tot.

Remarks: Designed by Alekseyev Central Hydrofoil Design Bureau, Nizhniy Novgorod, for the customs service, replacing the initial Ikar project. The design is also offered for export as a high-speed yacht, with MTU 16V396 TV94 diesels as an alternative propulsion plant. Uses an air cavity beneath the aluminum-magnesium alloy hull to enhance planing lift. Can operate in State 6 seas and at 30 kts in 1.5-m waves. Armament can also be a coaxial dual 14.5-mm and 7.62-mm machinegun mount, as on the prototype, or a 30-mm AK-306 lightweight gatling gunmount. The prototype was to be delivered to Vladivostok in 12-96 for use as a customs service patrol craft from Novorossiysk. A modified and more heavily armed sister named *Al'batros* (ex-*Sokzhoi*) was completed for the Federal Border Guard.

PATROL BOATS [WPB]

♦ **1 (+ . . .) Mangust class (Project 1215.0)**
Bldr: Yaroslavskiy SB, Yaroslavl (In serv. 1998–. . .)

TS-300

D: 26.1 tons (27.2 fl) **S:** 53 kts **Dim:** 19.50 (17.10 wl) × 4.60 (4.40 wl) × 1.15
A: 2 Igla shoulder-launched SAMs; 1 14.5-mm mg; 1 7.62-mm mg; 1 30-mm AGS-17 Plamya grenade launcher
Electronics: Radar: 1 . . . nav.
M: 2 M-470K diesels; 2 Arneson outdrive props; 1,500 bhp
Electric: 16 kw tot. (1 × 16-kw diesel set)
Range: 350/40; 430/37 **Fuel:** 3.5 tons **Endurance:** 2 days **Crew:** 6 tot.

Remarks: GRP construction. First craft may have been built on speculation, but has been assigned to the customs service. The design, by Almaz Central Design Bureau, is also offered for export. Constructed of aluminum-magnesium alloy. The propulsion drive system is made in the U.S.A. See entry for this class in the Federal Border Guard section for appearance.

Customs Service patrol launch TS-589—class not known
Boris Lemachko, 2000

♦ **5 Saygak class (Projects 1408.1 and 1408M)**
Bldr: Kama Shipyard, Perm (Permskiy Sudostroitel'nyy Zavod) (In serv. 1986–. . .)

TS-501 TS-502 TS-503 TS-504 TS-505

D: 13 tons (fl) **S:** 38 kts (35 sust.) **Dim:** 14.05 × 3.50 × 0.65
A: small arms **Electronics:** Radar: 1 . . . nav.
M: 1 M-401B (12CHSN18/20) diesel; 1 waterjet; 1,000 bhp
Electric: 8 kw (1 Type DGK8/1500 diesel driving; 27 V)
Range: 135/35 **Fuel:** 1.15 tons **Crew:** 2 tot. + 4–8 police personnel

Remarks: Offered for foreign sale in 1993 and typical of current Russian small personnel launch design. Rail-transportable, the craft are intended for riverine and lake use and in coastal waters in seas up to Sea State 3. Aluminum alloy construction. TS-505 is assigned to Kaliningrad. The Moscow Shipyard (Moskovskiy Sudostroitel'nyy Zavod) is also to build the design, if demand warrants, and two are being built in Kazakhstan. See entry for this class in the Federal Border Guard section for appearance.

ST. HELENA

British Territory

Note: One 607-class rigid inflatable launch was delivered in 1996 by RTK Marine, Poole, U.K., for diving support, rescue, and general workboat duties; no data available.

ST. KITTS

State of Saint Christopher–Nevis

ST. CHRISTOPHER–NEVIS COAST GUARD

Personnel (2001): 45 total

Base: Basseterre

Note: Nevis declared its independence from the joint State of Saint Christopher–Nevis on 14-10-97, but a follow-up referendum failed and the islands remain united.

PATROL CRAFT [WPC]

♦ **1 U.S. 110-foot Commercial Cruiser design**
Bldr: Swiftships, Morgan City, La. (In serv. 7-85)

C 253 Stalwart

Stalwart (C 253) Mike Louagie, 1995

D: 99.8 tons (fl) **S:** 24 kts (21 cruise) **Dim:** 33.53 × 7.62 × 2.13
A: 2 single 12.7-mm M2 mg; 2 single 7.62-mm mg
Electronics: Radar: 1 Raytheon . . . nav.
M: 4 G.M. Detroit Diesel 12V71 TI diesels; 4 props; 2,400 bhp (1,680 sust.)
Range: 1,800/15 **Fuel:** 31,608 liters **Crew:** 11 tot.

Remarks: Aluminum construction. Acquired with U.S. financial assistance. The weapons are normally not mounted.

PATROL BOATS [WPB]

♦ **1 U.S. Dauntless 40-foot class**
Bldr: SeaArk Marine, Monticello, Ark. (In serv. 8-8-95)

C 421 Ardent

D: 15 tons (fl) **S:** 28 kts **Dim:** 12.19 (11.13 wl) × 3.86 × 0.69 (hull)
A: 1 7.62-mm mg **Electronics:** Radar: 1 Raytheon R40X nav.
M: 2 Caterpillar 3208TA diesels; 2 props; 850 bhp (720 sust.)
Range: 200/30; 400/22 **Fuel:** 250 gallons **Crew:** 4 tot.

Remarks: Ordered 4-94. Aluminum construction. C. Raymond Hunt, "Deep-Vee" hull design.

PATROL BOATS [WPB] *(continued)*

Ardent (C 421) SeaArk, 8-95

♦ **1 Spear class**
Bldr: Fairey Marine, U.K. (In serv. 10-9-74)

RANGER I

D: 4.3 tons (fl) **S:** 20 kts **Dim:** 9.1 × 2.8 × 0.8
A: 2 single 7.62-mm mg
M: 2 Ford Mermaid diesels; 2 props; 360 bhp **Crew:** 2 tot.

Remarks: GRP construction. Does not have a radar.

SERVICE CRAFT

♦ **2 Whaler utility launches [WYFL]**
Bldr: Boston Whaler, Rockland, Mass. (In serv. 5-88)

C 087 ROVER I C 078 ROVER II

D: 1.5 tons light (2 fl) **S:** 35 kts **Dim:** 6.81 × 2.26 × 0.60
M: 1 Johnson V6-2500CC gasoline outboard; 223 bhp
Range: 70/35 **Crew:** 2 tot.

Remarks: U.S. government funded. Foam-core GRP construction.

ST. LUCIA

State of Saint Lucia

COAST GUARD

Note: The coast guard is subordinated to the Comptroller of Customs and Excise.

Personnel (2001): 49 total

Base: Castries

PATROL BOATS [WPB]

♦ **1 U.S. Dauntless 40-foot class**
Bldr: SeaArk Marine, Monticello, Ark. (In serv. 9-10-95)

P-04 PROTECTOR

Protector (P-04) SeaArk, 10-95

D: 15 tons (fl) **S:** 28 kts **Dim:** 12.19 (11.13 wl) × 3.86 × 0.69 (hull)
A: 1 7.62-mm mg **Electronics:** Radar: 1 Raytheon R40X nav.
M: 2 Caterpillar 3208TA diesels; 2 props; 850 bhp (720 sust.)
Range: 200/30; 400/22 **Fuel:** 250 gallons **Crew:** 5 tot.

Remarks: Ordered in 4-94 under the U.S. Foreign Military Sales aid program. Aluminum construction. C. Raymond Hunt, "Deep-Vee" hull design.

♦ **1 U.S. 65-foot Commercial Cruiser design**
Bldr: Swiftships, Morgan City, La. (In serv. 3-5-84)

P-02 DEFENDER

D: 35 tons (fl) **S:** 23 kts **Dim:** 19.96 × 5.59 × 1.52
A: small arms **Electronics:** Radar: 1 Raytheon 1210 nav.
M: 2 G.M. Detroit Diesel 12V71 TI diesels; 2 props; 1,350 bhp
Electric: 20 kw **Range:** 500/18 **Crew:** 5 tot.

Remarks: Ordered 9-11-83 with U.S. financial aid. Aluminum construction with a blue hull and white superstructure.

Defender (P-02) Maritime Photographic, 11-93

♦ **1 ex-U.S. Coast Guard 82-foot Point class**
Bldr: J. Martinac SB, Tacoma, Wash. (In serv. 14-4-67)

P-01 ALPHONSE REYNOLDS (ex-*Point Turner,* WPB 82365)

D: 64 tons (69 fl) **S:** 23 kts **Dim:** 25.3 × 5.23 × 1.95
A: 2 single 12.7-mm M2 mg
Electronics: Radar: 1 Raytheon SPS-64(V)1 nav.
M: 2 Caterpillar 3412 diesels; 2 props; 1,480 bhp
Range: 490/23.7; 1,500/8 **Fuel:** 5.7 tons **Crew:** 1 officer, 7 enlisted

Remarks: Decommissioned from U.S. Coast Guard service 3-4-98 and donated to St. Lucia 15-4-98. Is in excellent condition and was re-engined early in the 1990s.
Hull systems: Hull in mild steel. High-speed diesels are controlled from the bridge. Well-equipped for salvage and towing.

Note: Also in service are Mako Marine–built, GRP-hulled launches P-06 and P-07 and the 35-kt, rigid inflatable Hurricane search-and-rescue launch P-05.

ST. VINCENT

State of Saint Vincent and the Grenadines

COAST GUARD

Note: Formerly named the Marine Wing of the State of Saint Vincent and the Grenadines Police Force. The prefix SVG in pennant numbers stands for "St. Vincent Government."

Personnel (2001): 60 total

Base: Calliaqua

PATROL CRAFT [WPC]

♦ **1 120-foot Commercial Cruiser class**
Bldr: Swiftships, Morgan City, La.

	L	In serv.
SVG-01 CAPTAIN MULZAC	6-6-86	13-6-87

Captain Mulzac (SVG-01) Alexandre Sheldon-Duplaix, 1-92

PATROL CRAFT [WPC] *(continued)*

D: 101 tons light (. . . fl) **S:** 21 kts **Dim:** 35.56 × 7.62 × 2.10
A: 2 single 12.7-mm M2 mg; 2 single 7.62-mm mg
Electronics: Radar: 1 Furuno 1411 Mk II nav.
M: 4 G.M. Detroit Diesel 12V71 TI diesels; 4 props; 2,700 bhp
Range: 1,800/15 **Crew:** 4 officers, 10 enlisted

Remarks: Former oilfield pipe carrier, converted for patrol duties. Ordered in 8-86 with U.S. financial aid. Aluminum construction.

PATROL BOATS [WPB]

♦ 1 U.S. Dauntless 40-foot class
Bldr: SeaArk Marine, Monticello, Ark. (In serv. 8-6-95)

SVG-04 HAIROUN

D: 15 tons (fl) **S:** 28 kts **Dim:** 12.19 (11.13 wl) × 3.86 × 0.69 (hull)
A: 1 7.62-mm mg **Electronics:** Radar: 1 Raytheon R40X nav.
M: 2 Caterpillar 3208TA diesels; 2 props; 850 bhp (720 sust.)
Range: 200/30; 400/22 **Fuel:** 250 gallons **Crew:** 4 tot.

Remarks: Ordered in 4-94. Aluminum construction. C. Raymond Hunt, "Deep-Vee" hull design.

♦ 1 U.K.-built
Bldr: Vosper Thornycroft, Portchester (In serv. 23-3-81)

SVG-05 GEORGE MCINTOSH

George McIntosh (SVG-05) H&L Van Ginderen, 3-81

D: 70 tons (fl) **S:** 24.5 kts **Dim:** 22.86 × 7.43 × 1.64
A: 1 20-mm 90-cal. Oerlikon AA
Electronics: Radar: 1 Furuno 1411 Mk II nav.
M: 2 Caterpillar 12V D348 TA diesels; 2 props; 1,840 bhp (1,450 sust.)
Electric: 24 kw tot. **Range:** 600/21; 1,000/11 **Crew:** 3 officers, 8 enlisted

Remarks: GRP, Keith Nelson–design hull.

♦ 2 8.2-meter patrol launches
Bldr: Buhlers Yachts, Ltd.

SVG-06 LARIKAI SVG-07 BRIGHTON

D: 6 tons (fl) **S:** 23 kts **Dim:** 8.20 × 2.95 × 0.90
M: 2 Johnson V-6, 2.5-liter gasoline outboards; 310 bhp **Crew:** 3 tot.

Remarks: The original Perkins diesel was removed in 1989–90 when the craft were converted to use gasoline outboards, gaining 4 kts maximum speed.

Note: Also used for local service are the U.S.-supplied Zodiac rigid inflatable launch SVG-03 and the 1994-vintage, Boston Whaler–built launch *Chatham Bay* (SVG-08).

SAMOA

Independent State of Samoa

Base: Apia Harbor

Note: The name of the country was changed from Western Samoa during 8-97.

PATROL CRAFT [PC]

♦ 1 Australian ASI 315 class
Bldr: Transfield-ASI, South Coogie, W.A., Australia

	Laid down	L	In serv.
NAFANUA	20-5-87	18-2-88	19-3-88

D: 165 tons (fl) **S:** 20 kts **Dim:** 31.5 (28.6 wl) × 8.1 × 2.12
A: small arms **Electronics:** Radar: 1 Furuno 1011 nav.
M: 2 Caterpillar 3516 diesels; 2 props; 2,820 bhp **Electric:** 116 kw tot.
Range: 2,500/12 **Fuel:** 29 tons **Crew:** 3 officers, 14 enlisted

Remarks: Provided under the Australian Defence Cooperation Program; sisters have been built for other Southwest Pacific nations. Ordered 3-10-85. To begin a major life-extension refit in Australia during 2003. Has an extensive navigational suite, including a Furuno FSN-70 NAVSAT receiver, 525 HF/DF, 120 MF–HFD/F, FE-881 echo sounder, and DS-70 doppler log.

Nafanua H&L Van Ginderen, 1-96

Note: The Samoan government also operates the *Lady Samoa II,* a small utility landing craft employed for local cargo and personnel transport. The craft was built by Yokohama Yacht in Japan and was launched 28-7-88.

SÃO TOME AND PRINCIPE

Republic of São Tome and Principe

Personnel (2002): 50–75 total

PATROL BOATS [PB]

♦ 1 U.S. 2810-V Protector class
Bldr: SeaArk Marine, Monticello, Ark. (In serv. 11-1-92)

FALCÃO

D: . . . tons (fl) **S:** 38 kts **Dim:** 8.69 × 3.56 × 0.56
A: small arms **Electronics:** Radar: 1 Furuno . . . nav.
M: 2 Volvo AQAD 41/290 outdrive diesels; 2 props; 400 bhp **Crew:** 4 tot.

Remarks: U.S. donation. Aluminum construction. Formally dedicated 20-1-92. A unit of the same design is employed by the U.S. Coast Guard on Lake Champlain.

Disposal note: Two Russian Zhuk-class (Project 1400) patrol boats delivered in 1983 are no longer in service.

Note: Also in use is a 6.7-m riverine patrol craft equipped with a 12.7-mm mg and capable of 13 kts.

SAUDI ARABIA

Kingdom of Saudi Arabia

Personnel (2002): Approx. 13,500 total, including 1,500 marines

Bases: Headquarters at Riyadh. Principal bases at Jiddah (Red Sea) and Al Jubail (Persian Gulf). Minor facilities at Al Qatif, Al Wajh, Duba, Haqi, Qizan, Ras al-Mishab, Ras Tanura, and Yanbu' al-Bahr. The Technical Institute for Naval Training remains at Al Dammam, but ships are no longer based there. Construction on a new major base at Jizan on the Red Sea was started in 1996.

Naval Aviation: Eighteen AS.365F/AS Dauphin-2 for ship- and shore-based ASW and ship attack, and four AS.365N Dauphin-2 configured for search-and-rescue duties with Omera DRB-32 search radar. The Frontier Force, Border Guard, and Police Division of the Ministry of the Interior share six AS.332F1 Super Puma helicopters equipped with AM 39 Exocet antiship missiles or a 20-mm cannon. Also available are six AS.332B1 troop transports, six AS.565 Panther SAR helicopters, and up to 40 Agusta Bell 412EP utility and SAR helicopters (three are configured as VIP transports).

♦ AS.365 Dauphin-2 helicopter

Rotor diameter: 13.29 m **Length:** 11.41 m (fuselage) **Height:** 4 m
Weight: 1,850 kg (light; 3,900 max.) **Speed:** 130 kts max.
Propulsion: 2 Turbomeca Arriel 1C turbines; 710 bhp each
Radius of action: 100 n.m. with 4 AS 15; 140 n.m. with 2 AS 15
Endurance: 2 hr with 4 AS 15; 3 hr with 2 AS 15
Armament: 2 or 4 Aérospatiale AS 15 antiship missiles or 2 Mk 36 ASW torpedoes

Saudi Navy AS.365 Dauphin-2 French Navy, 1996

Remarks: The AS 15 missile has a range of 15 km, weighs 96 kg, and is 2.16 m long. The helicopter carries an Agrion-15 frequency-agile, pulse-doppler radar to provide missile targeting and to permit the helicopter to provide midcourse guidance update information to the ship-launched Otomat Mk 2 (Erato) missiles, which have a range of 90 n.m., weigh 780 kg , and carry a 210-kg warhead.

Coastal Defense: Several batteries of truck-mounted Otomat Mk 2 (Erato) antiship missiles are reportedly available.

ATTACK SUBMARINES [SS]

Note: Saudi Arabia has had long-term plans to purchase between 6 and 10 submarines, and initial bids were requested by 12-86. Designs being considered were the Dutch *Walrus/Zeeleeuw* and *Moray* classes, the Vickers Type 2400, the West German IKL 2000, the Swedish Kockums Type 471, a French design, and an Italian design. The *Moray* design had reportedly been chosen by late 1989, but no contracts were let. Reports that Saudi Arabia had actually ordered small submarines and/or midget submarines from South Korea are incorrect. There are no immediate prospects for the ordering of submarines.

GUIDED-MISSILE FRIGATES [FFG]

♦ 0 (+ 3) Al Riyadh (F-3000S) class Bldr: DCN, Lorient

	Laid down	L	Del.	In serv.
812 Al Riyadh	29-9-99	1-8-00	7-02	4-03
814 Makkah	25-8-00	20-7-01	7-03	...
816 Dammam	26-8-01	25-4-02	3-04	...

D: 3,800 tons normal (4,650 fl) **S:** 25 kts
Dim: 133.00 (128.00 pp) × 17.00 (13.80 wl) × 4.40 (hull)
A: 8 MM 40 Exocet Block 2 SSM; 2 8-cell Sylver A43 vertical-launch SAM group (16 Aster-15 missiles); 1 76-mm 62-cal. OTOBreda SuperCompact DP; 2 single 20-mm 90-cal. GIAT F2 AA; 2 single 12.7-mm mg; 4 fixed 533-mm ASW TT (F 17P wire-guided heavyweight ASW torpedoes); 2 AS.365F/AS Dauphin-2 helicopters (with AS 15 antiship missiles)
Electronics:
Radar: 2 Decca 20V90 nav.; 1 Thales DRBV-26D Jupiter early warning; 1 Thales Arabel missile f.c.; 1 Thales Castor-IIJ/C gun f.c.
Sonar: Thales Spherion bow-mounted; Thales CAPTAS 20 towed array
EW: Thales DR-3000S2 intercept (1–18 GHz); Dassault Salamandre B2 jammer; Altesse communications intercept and D/F; TRC 281 comms jammer; 2 330- or 340-round Matra Défense Dagaie Mk 2 decoy RL
E/O: 2 Matra Défense Najir target desig./f.c.

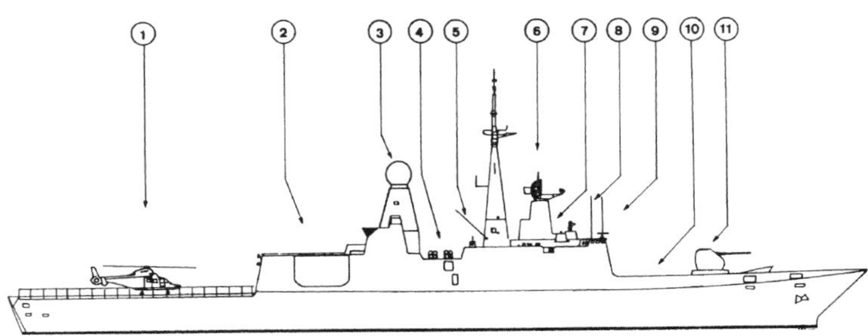

Al Riyadh (812) 1. Dauphin-2 helicopter 2. helicopter hangar with boat pocket abreast 3. Arabel target detection and tracking 4. MM 40 Exocet antiship missiles 5. 20-mm F2 AA 6. DRBV-26D early-warning radar 7. Dagaie Mk 2 decoy launcher 8. Castor-IIJ/C gun f.c. radar 9. Decca 20V90 nav./surface-search radar 10. Sylver vertical launch system for Aster-15 missiles 11. 100-mm GIAT Compact DP gun
Drawing by Jean Moulin, from *Flottes de Combat*

Al Riyadh (812) Bernard Prézelin, 9-01

Al Riyadh (812)—note that boat pockets flank the single helicopter hangar
Bernard Prézelin, 9-01

Al Riyadh (812)—on sea trials, with 100-mm gun temporarily mounted forward Bernard Prézelin, 9-01

GUIDED-MISSILE FRIGATES [FFG] *(continued)*

M: 4 SEMT-Pielstick 16 PA6 BTC diesels; 2 CP props; 31,800 bhp—drop-down, azimuthal bow-thruster
Electric: 3,000 kw (3 × 1,000-kw diesel sets)
Range: 7,000/15; 8,000/12 **Fuel:** . . . tons **Endurance:** 50 days
Crew: 25 officers, 155 enlisted (accomm. for 190 tot.)

Remarks: A project definition contract was granted to France on 11-6-89, but a letter of agreement was not signed until 22-11-94 and then for only two ships under the "Sawari-2" program, which also called for the construction of a fully equipped naval training center and major technical support services in addition to the two frigates. The third unit was ordered 21-5-97. 812 began sea trials during 9-01.
Hull systems: A particular effort has been made to reduce the ships' signatures; the diesel propulsion engines are mounted in pairs on isolation platforms, and the superstructure, masts, and forecastle are covered with a radar-absorbent GRP-resin compound. All chocks and bollards are covered to reduce radar reflectivity. In addition, boats are stowed in superstructure recesses covered with sliding doors and vertical hull and superstructure surfaces are slanted at ±10° to reduce radar reflectivity. They are also fitted with degaussing equipment and extensive NBC warfare protection. The superstructure is built primarily of steel. Special steel armor is provided for the magazines; the hull plating is 10-mm steel. Employ modified deep-vee hullform, fin stabilizers, and rudder-controlled roll reduction to improve seaworthiness. There are two rudders, and the hullform incorporates twin skegs aft. Hull has 11 watertight compartments. The helicopter can be launched and recovered in up to Sea State 6, and the SAMAHE deck traversing and landing system is fitted.
Combat systems: The SENIT 7 (Thales TAVITAC 2000) combat-control system with nine Vista display consoles and two tactical plotting tables is installed. The ships have Link 11 connectivity with Saudi AWACS aircraft. The first two were originally to have had Crotale-NG SAM systems as an interim measure until the Aster-15 system was available, but delays in the start of the program have permitted all three to be built with the same equipment. Provision has been made for doubling the number of Sylver vertical missile launch cells, and the ships may eventually carry the longer-ranged Aster-30 missile as well as the Aster-15. 812 was completed with a GIAT 100-mm Compact gunmount, but it was to be replaced during a summer 2004 refit at Lorient; the other two will have the 76-mm mount installed during construction; the associated Castor-IIJ/C radar director also has IR and low-light-level television sensors. The planned two Sadral point-defense SAM systems have been dropped from all three.

FRIGATES [FF]

♦ 4 Al Madinah class

	Bldr	Laid down	L	In serv.
702 AL MADINAH	Arsenal de Lorient	15-10-81	23-4-83	4-1-85
704 HOFOUF	CNIM, La Seyne	14-6-82	24-6-83	31-10-85
706 ABHA	CNIM, La Seyne	7-12-82	23-12-83	4-4-86
708 TAIF	CNIM, La Seyne	1-3-83	25-5-84	29-8-86

D: 2,000 tons (2,250 normal; 2,610 fl) **S:** 30 kts
Dim: 115.00 (106.50 pp) × 12.50 (wl) × 3.40 (4.65 over sonar)
A: 8 Otomat Mk 2 Erato SSM; 1 8-round Crotale EDIR SAM syst. (26 missiles); 1 100-mm 55-cal. Compact DP; 2 twin 40-mm 70-cal. OTOBreda Dardo AA; 4 fixed 533-mm ASW TT (F 17P wire-guided torpedoes); 1 AS.365F Dauphin-2 helicopter

Taif (708) Rob Cabo, 1-00

Taif (708) Rob Cabo, 1-00

Electronics:
Radar: 2 Decca TM 1226 nav.; 1 Thales Sea Tiger (DRBV-15) air search; 1 Thales Castor-IIC gun f.c.; 1 Thales DRBC-32E missile f.c.
Sonar: Thales TSM 2630 (Diodon) hull-mounted; Thales TSM 2630 (Sorel) VDS
EW: Thales DR-4000S intercept syst.; Thales Janet jammer; EADS Telegon-6 D/F; 2 330- or 340-round Matra Défense Dagaie Mk 2 decoy RL
E/O: 1 Contraves LSEOS Mk II gun f.c.; 2 Matra Défense Naja gun f.c.
M: 4 SEMT-Pielstick 16 PA6 BTC diesels; 2 props; 32,500 bhp
Electric: 2,560 kw (4 × 480-kw, 2 × 320-kw diesel sets)
Range: 6,500/18; 8,000/15 **Fuel:** 370 tons **Endurance:** 30 days
Crew: 15 officers, 50 petty officers, 114 other enlisted

Remarks: Ordered in 10-80 as part of the Sawari program. Under a 2-94 agreement, they were given extensive overhauls in France under the Mouette program. Work began in France in 12-95 with 702, which departed for Saudi Arabia 8-4-97; 704 arrived in Toulon 1-10-96, 706 completed in summer 1999, and 708 finished 21-3-00. All are based at Jiddah.
Hull systems: Have an NBC warfare defense citadel. There are 13 main watertight bulkheads to the hull, which is equipped with retractable fin stabilizers. During refits, the NBC defense system was improved, as were self-maintenance capabilities.

Taif (708)—on postmodernization trials Rob Cabo, 2-00

FRIGATES [FF] *(continued)*

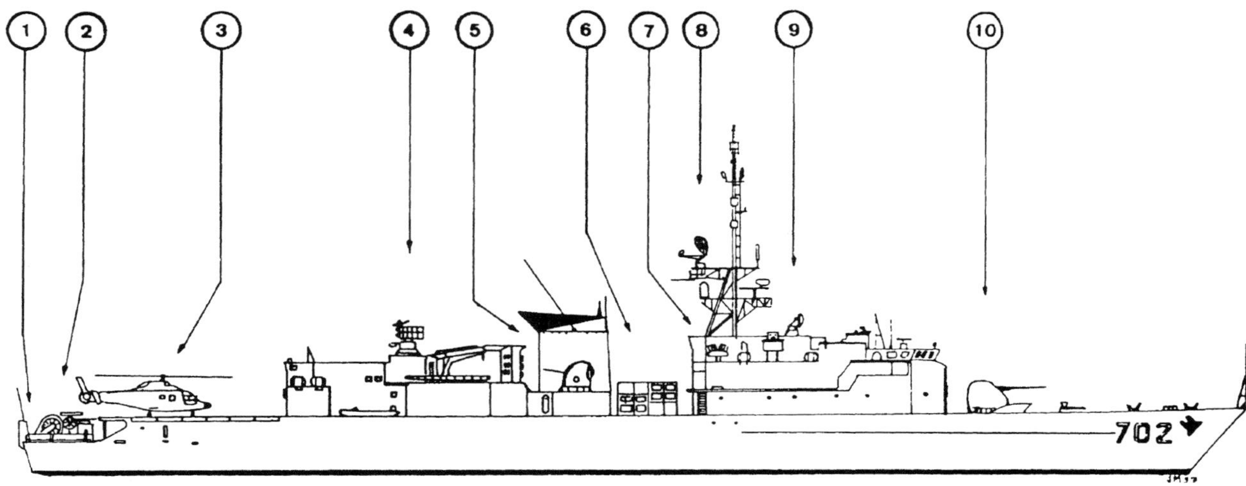

Al Madinah (702) 1. stern 533-mm torpedo tubes 2. Sorel variable-depth sonar 3. Dauphin-2 helicopter 4. Crotale EDIR SAM launcher 5. twin 40-mm OTOBreda AA 6. Otomat antiship missiles 7. Dagaie Mk 2 decoy RL 8. Sea Tiger (DRBV-15) air-search radar 9. Castor-IIC gun f.c. radar 10. 100-mm Compact DP gun

Drawing by Jean Moulin, from *Flottes de Combat*

Combat systems: Have the Thales TAVITAC computer data system, with two Type 15M 125F computers, nine BarcoView Texen Vista display consoles (one on the bridge), and two E7000 tactical tables; the combat datalink operates with NATO Link 11 and Royal Saudi Air Force aircraft. The Otomat missiles have the Erato (Extended Range Automated Targeting) feature, using the combat data system and helicopter-derived target data. Have the Alcatel Type DLA torpedo f.c.s. Sorel is a VDS version of the Diodon sonar; both operate at 11, 12, or 13 kHz. Carry 500 rounds of 100-mm and 6,300 rounds of 40-mm ammunition. During the modernization refits, the fire-control radars were updated, and the original helicopter deck-handling system was replaced by the DCN SAMAHE system; the Otomat Mk 2 Erato missiles were also overhauled. Are equipped with Matra Défense Sylosat NAVSAT receivers.

CORVETTES [FFL]

♦ **4 U.S. PCG class** Bldr: Tacoma Boatbuilding, Tacoma, Wash.

	Laid down	L	In serv.
612 Badr (ex-PCG 1)	30-5-79	26-1-80	28-9-81
614 Al Yarmook (ex-PCG 2)	13-12-79	13-5-80	10-5-82
616 Hitteen (ex-PCG 3)	19-5-80	5-9-80	12-10-82
618 Tabuk (ex-PCG 4)	22-9-80	18-6-81	10-1-83

Al Yarmook (614)—with frigate *Taif* (708) in background

A. A. Alleyne, U.S. Navy, 1998

Al Yarmook (614) H&L Van Ginderen, 2-97

D: 903 tons (1,038 fl) **S:** 30 kts on gas turbine; 21 kts on diesels
Dim: 74.68 × 9.60 × 2.59 (hull)
A: 8 RGM-84C Harpoon SSM; 1 76-mm 62-cal. U.S. Mk 75 DP; 1 20-mm Mk 15 Block 0 Phalanx CIWS; 2 single 20-mm 70-cal. Oerlikon AA; 1 81-mm mortar; 2 single 40-mm Mk 19 grenade launchers; 2 triple 324-mm Mk 32 Mod. 5 ASW TT (Mk 46 Mod. 2 torpedoes)
Electronics:
Radar: 1 Cardion SPS-55 nav./surf. search; 1 Lockheed Martin SPS-40B air search; 1 Sperry Mk 92 Mod. 5 f.c.; 1 General Dynamics Mk 90 Phalanx f.c.
Sonar: SQS-56 (Raytheon DE-1160B) hull-mounted (5.6, 7.5, 8.4 kHz)
EW: SLQ-32 (V)1 intercept; Mk 36 SRBOC decoy syst. (2 6-round Mk 137 RL)
E/O: Safire infrared surveillance and tracking
M: CODOG: 1 G.E. LM-2500 gas turbine (23,000 shp), 2 MTU 12V652 TB91 diesels (3,058 bhp tot.); 2 CP props
Electric: 1,200 kw tot. **Range:** 4,000/20 **Crew:** 7 officers, 51 enlisted

Remarks: Ordered 30-8-77. Program was completed well behind schedule, with the ships considerably overweight. Have fin stabilizers. There is one Mk 24 optical target designation transmitter. The Mk 309 ASW f.c.s. is fitted. Were given a commercial combat information datalink system (Link W) during the late 1990s. All are based at Al Jubail on the Persian Gulf and are supported by U.S. contractors.

GUIDED-MISSILE PATROL COMBATANTS [PTG]

♦ **9 U.S. PGG class** Bldr: Peterson Builders, Sturgeon Bay, Wis.

	Laid down	L	In serv.
511 As Siddiq (ex-PGG 1)	30-9-78	22-9-79	15-12-80
513 Al Farouq (ex-PGG 2)	12-3-79	17-5-80	22-6-81
515 Abdul Aziz (ex-PGG 3)	19-10-79	23-8-80	3-9-81
517 Faisal (ex-PGG 4)	4-3-80	15-11-80	23-11-81
519 Khalid (ex-PGG 5)	27-6-80	28-3-81	11-1-82
521 Amr (ex-PGG 6)	21-10-80	13-6-81	21-6-82
523 Tariq (ex-PGG 7)	10-2-81	23-9-81	16-8-82
525 Oqbah (ex-PGG 8)	8-5-81	12-12-81	18-10-82
527 Abu Obaidah (ex-PGG 9)	4-9-81	3-4-82	6-12-82

Khalid (519) Leo Dirkx, 11-98

D: 425 tons (495 fl) **S:** 34 kts on gas turbine; 16 kts on diesels
Dim: 58.02 × 8.08 × 1.95 (hull)
A: 4 RGM-84C Harpoon SSM; 1 76-mm 62-cal. U.S. Mk 75 DP; 1 20-mm Mk 15 Block 0 Phalanx CIWS; 2 single 20-mm 70-cal. Oerlikon AA; 1 81-mm mortar; 2 single 40-mm Mk 19 grenade launchers
Electronics:
Radar: 1 Cardion SPS-55 nav./surf. search; 1 Sperry Mk 92 Mod. 5 f.c.; 1 General Dynamics Mk 90 Phalanx f.c.
EW: SLQ-32 (V)1 intercept; Mk 36 SRBOC decoy syst. (2 6-round Mk 137 RL)
E/O: Safire infrared surveillance and tracking

GUIDED-MISSILE PATROL COMBATANTS [PTG] *(continued)*

Oqbah (525) H&L Van Ginderen, 1-00

M: CODOG: 1 G.E. gas turbine (23,000 shp), 2 MTU 12V652 TB91 diesels (3,058 bhp tot.); 2 CP props
Electric: 800 kw **Range:** 600/30; 2,900/14 **Crew:** 5 officers, 33 enlisted

Remarks: Ordered 16-2-77. Delivered behind schedule and considerably over designed displacement. Have fin stabilizers. There is one Mk 24 optical target designation transmitter. Were given a commercial combat information datalink system (Link W) during the late 1990s. 521 and 523 are based at Jiddah on the Red Sea, the others on the Persian Gulf at Al Jubail.

PATROL BOATS [PB]

♦ 17 U.S. 78-foot PCF class
Bldr: Trinity-Equitable SY, New Orleans (In serv. 1-93)

52 through 68

D: 56.4 tons (fl) **S:** 28 kts **Dim:** 23.66 × 6.06 × 1.01 (hull; 1.76 props)
A: 2 single 25-mm 87-cal. U.S. Mk 38 low-angle chain guns; 2 single 7.62-mm mg
Electronics: Radar: 1 Raytheon SPS-64(V)1 nav.
M: 2 G.M. Detroit Diesel 16V92 TAB diesels; 2 props; 2,800 bhp
Electric: 70 kw (2 × 35 kw) **Range:** 600/24, 1,200/12 **Fuel:** 18,950 liters
Endurance: 5 days **Crew:** 2 officers, 6 enlisted

Remarks: Ordered in 12-90. Referred to locally as PCF Fast Patrol Craft. Aluminum construction. A 4-m rigid inflatable boat powered by a 40-bhp outboard motor is stowed amidships. Even-numbered boats serve on the Red Sea coast, with six at Jiddah and three at Jizen; the other eight are based at Jubail on the Persian Gulf coast. Sisters serve in the Philippine Navy.

♦ 40 Naja ASD 12 class
Bldr: Simonneau Marine, Fontenay-le-Comte, France (In serv. 1988–89, 1991)

Naja ASD 12 class—on trials Simonneau, 1988

D: 7.5 tons (fl) **S:** 50 kts **Dim:** 12.80 (10.20 pp) × 4.00 × 0.50
A: 1 20-mm 90-cal. GIAT F2 AA; 2 single 7.62 GIAT mg
Electronics: Radar: 1 Furuno . . . nav.
M: 4 OMC gasoline outboard motors; 1,200 shp
Range: 350/35 **Fuel:** 1,700 liters **Crew:** 4 tot.

Remarks: First group of 20 was ordered 6-6-88, second group in 10-90. Of the first, one was lost during shipment but was replaced by the builder. Aluminum construction. Employed by naval special forces personnel.

MINE WARFARE SHIPS

♦ 3 U.K. Sandown-class minehunters [MHC]
Bldr: Vosper Thornycroft, Woolston

	Laid down	L	In serv.
420 Al Jawf (ex-*Inverness*)	. . .	2-8-89	21-12-91
422 Shaqra	14-5-90	15-5-91	8-2-93
424 Al Kharj	4-90	9-2-93	9-94

D: 378 tons light (465 fl) **S:** 15 kts (13 sust.; 6.5 hunting)
Dim: 52.50 (50.00 pp) × 10.50 (9.00 wl) × 2.30
A: 1 twin 30-mm 75-cal. Emerlec EX-74
Electronics:
Radar: 1 Kelvin-Hughes Type 1007 nav.
Sonar: 1 Plessey-MUSL 2093 variable-depth minehunting
EW: Thales Shiploc intercept; Mk 36 RBOC decoy syst. (2 6-round Mk 137 RL)
E/O: Oerlikon-Contraves Sea Hawk Mk 2 TMEO optronic surveillance/f.c.

Shaqra (422) Maritime Photographic, 5-96

Al Kharj (424) Maritime Photographic, 3-96

M: 2 Paxman-Valenta 6 RPA 200-E diesels; 2 Voith-Schneider 16 G.S. 5-bladed vertical cycloidal props; 1,500 bhp (1,360 sust.)—2 200-shp electric motors (7 kts max.)—2 Schottel electric bow-thrusters
Electric: 750 kw (3 × 250-kw Mawdsley generators); 3 Perkins V8-250G diesels driving (335 bhp each)
Range: 3,000/12 **Crew:** 7 officers, 40 enlisted

Remarks: Ordered 3-12-88. A planned second batch of three has not been ordered. 420 did not depart for Saudi Arabia until 3-11-95, four years after completion; 422 departed 1-12-96 and 424 on 7-8-97 after completion of vibration trials.
Hull systems: GRP construction. Cramped internally.
Combat systems: The Plessey NAUTIS-M navigation/minehunting data system is fitted. The sonar uses a variable depth, vertical lozenge-shaped towed body lowered beneath the hull; it has search, depth-finder, classification, and route survey modes. All have the RN Remote-Controlled Mine Disposal System Mk 2, using two French PAP-104 Mk 5 submersibles, and carry mine disposal divers. They also have Racal Hyperfix, QM 14, and Navigator Mk 21 radio navaids. Are capable of dealing with mines to 200-m depths.

♦ 4 U.S. MSC 322–class minesweepers [MSC]
Bldr: Peterson Builders, Sturgeon Bay, Wis.

	Laid down	L	In serv.
412 Addiriyah (ex-MSC 322)	12-5-76	20-12-76	6-7-78
414 Al Quysumah (ex-MSC 323)	24-8-76	26-5-77	15-8-78
416 Al Wadeeah (ex-MSC 324)	28-12-76	6-9-77	7-9-78
418 Safwa (ex-MSC 325)	5-3-77	7-12-77	20-10-78

Al Quysumah (414) H&L Van Ginderen, 1996

D: 320 tons (407 fl) **S:** 14 kts **Dim:** 46.63 × 8.29 × 4.06 (max.)
A: 1 20-mm 70-cal. Mk 67 AA
Electronics:
Radar: 1 Cardion SPS-55 nav./surf. search
Sonar: G.E. SQQ-14 VDS minehunting HF
M: 2 Waukesha L1616 diesels; 2 props; 1,200 bhp
Electric: 2,150 kw tot. (1 × 1,750-kw a.c. sweep generator, 2 × 200 kw; all diesel)
Crew: 4 officers, 35 enlisted

MINE WARFARE SHIPS *(continued)*

Remarks: Ordered 30-9-75. Longer than other standard U.S. export coastal minesweepers of the period. Wooden construction. Used primarily as patrol boats and played very little part in clearing Iraqi-laid mines during and after the Persian Gulf War. 412 is based at Jiddah, the others at Al Jubail.

AMPHIBIOUS WARFARE CRAFT

♦ 4 U.S. LCU 1646–class utility landing craft [LCU]
Bldr: Newport SY, Newport, R.I. (In serv. 1976)

212 Al Qiaq (ex-SA 310) 216 Al Ula (ex-SA 312)
214 As Sulayel (ex-SA 311) 218 Afif (ex-SA 313)

D: 173 tons light (375 fl) **S:** 11 kts **Dim:** 41.07 × 9.07 × 2.00
A: 2 single 20-mm 70-cal. U.S. Mk 67 AA
Electronics: Radar: 1 Canadian Marconi LN-66 nav.
M: 4 G.M. Detroit Diesel 6-71 diesels; 2 Kort-nozzle props; 900 bhp
Electric: 80 kw tot. **Range:** 1,200/10
Crew: 2 officers, 12 enlisted + 20 passengers

Remarks: Standard units of the class, with cargo capacity rated at 168 tons on the open 30.5 × 5.5–m cargo deck. Have ramps fore and aft. Are used as logistics transports, based at Al Jubail.

♦ 4 U.S. LCM(6)-class landing craft [LCM]
Bldr: Marinette Marine, Marinette, Wis. (In serv. 7-80)

220 Dhuba 222 Umlus 224 Al Leeth 226 Al Quonfetha

D: 24 tons (57.5 fl) **S:** 13 kts **Dim:** 17.07 × 4.37 × 1.14
A: 2 single 40-mm Mk 19 grenade launchers
M: 2 G.M. Detroit Diesel 6V71 diesels; 2 props; 450 bhp
Range: 130/9 (loaded) **Crew:** 5 tot.

Remarks: Four others received in 7-77 have been cannibalized. Cargo: 30 tons or 80 troops, in the 11.9 × 3.7–m cargo well.

AUXILIARIES

♦ 2 underway replenishment oilers [AOR]
Bldr: C.N. la Ciotat, Marseilles

	Laid down	L	In serv.
902 Boraida	13-4-82	22-1-83	29-2-84
904 Yunbou	9-10-83	20-10-84	29-8-85

Boraida (902) Carlo Martinelli, 3-97

Yunbou (904) Bernard Prézelin, 3-99

D: 10,500 tons (trials) **S:** 20.5 kts **Dim:** 135.0 × 18.7 × 7.0
A: 2 twin 40-mm 70-cal. OTOBreda Dardo AA
Electronics:
Radar: 2 Decca TM 1226 nav.
E/O: 2 Matra Défense Naja optical f.c.s.
M: 2 SEMT-Pielstick 14 PC2.5 V400 diesels; 2 CP props; 13,200 bhp
Electric: 3,400 kw tot. **Range:** 7,000/17 **Endurance:** 30 days
Crew: 140 tot. + 55 cadets

Remarks: Ordered in 10-80 as part of the Sawari program. Design is a reduced version of the French *Durance* class. 902 left France for Saudi Arabia 3-8-84. Act as training ships as well as replenishment vessels. 902 began a refit at Toulon during 3-96, completing in 5-97; 904 was refitted from 5-97 to 3-99. Both are based at Jiddah.
Hull systems: Cargo includes 4,350 tons of diesel fuel, 350 tons of aviation fuel, 140 tons of potable water, 100 tons of provisions, 100 tons of munitions, and 70 tons of spares. Have one replenishment station per side, plus over-the-stern refueling. Can transfer 1.7-ton solid loads. Have electrical, mechanical, and metal workshops.
Combat systems: The two AS.365N Dauphin-2 helicopters can also carry ASW and antiship weapons.

SERVICE CRAFT

♦ 2 U.S. YTB 760–class tugs [YTB] (In serv. 15-10-75)

EN 111 Tuwaig (ex-YTB 837) EN 112 Dareen (ex-YTB 838)

D: 291 tons (356 fl) **S:** 12 kts **Dim:** 33.22 × 9.30 × 4.14
A: 2 single 20-mm 70-cal. Mk 67 AA
Electronics: Radar: 1 Canadian Marconi LN-66 nav.
M: 1 Fairbanks-Morse 38D8Q diesel; 1 prop; 2,000 bhp
Electric: 120 kw tot. **Range:** 2,000/10 **Crew:** 4 officers, 8 enlisted

Remarks: Bollard pull: 25 tons. Intended for target towing, fire fighting, torpedo recovery, and local patrol duties. EN 111 is based at Al Jubail, EN 112 at Jiddah (to assist the yacht squadron).

ROYAL YACHT SQUADRON

Note: The Royal Yacht Squadron is considered a separate command, but personnel are drawn from the navy. The yachts are based at Jiddah.

AUXILIARIES

♦ 1 ex-Iraqi presidential yacht [AG]
Bldr: Elsinore SB & Eng., Denmark (L: 10-80; in serv. 1981)

Al Yamana (ex-*Qadissayat Saddam*)

Al Yamana Elsinore SB, 1980

D: 1,660 tons (fl) **S:** 19.3 kts **Dim:** 82.00 × 13.00 × 3.30
M: 2 MTU 12V1163 TB82 diesels; 2 CP props; 6,000 bhp **Electric:** 1,095 kVA

Remarks: 2,282 grt. Because of the Iran-Iraq War, was never delivered to Saddam Hussein, who gave it as a present to King Fahd in 1987. Can carry 56 passengers (74 additional on short cruises). Has Sperry retractable fin stabilizers and a 300-hp bowthruster. There is a helicopter deck aft above the swimming pool.

♦ 1 royal yacht [AG]
Bldr: Helsingor Værft, Denmark (In serv. 12-83)

Abdul Aziz

Abdul Aziz Wallesfoto, 6-84

D: approx. 5,200 tons (fl) **S:** 22 kts **Dim:** 147.00 (126.00 pp) × 18.00 × 4.90
M: 2 Lindholmen-Pielstick 12 PC2.5 V400 diesels; 2 props; 15,600 bhp
Fuel: 640 tons **Crew:** 65 tot. + 4 royals + 60 passengers

Remarks: Delivered in 4-83 by the builders to Vosper Shiprepairers, Southampton, for final fitting out; ran post-outfitting trials 15-5-84. Has a swimming pool, a helicopter hangar forward beneath the forecastle, and a stern ramp leading to a vehicle garage.

♦ 1 Jetfoil-type hydrofoil royal yacht tender [AG]
Bldr: Boeing, Seattle (In serv. 8-85)

Al Aziziah

D: 115 tons (fl) **S:** 46 kts
Dim: 27.4 (foils down) × 9.1 × 1.9 (hull; 5.2 foils down at rest; 2.0 foiling)
A: 2 single 20-mm G.E. Sea Vulcan gatling AA, with 2 Stinger missiles co-mounted
Electronics: Radar: 1 . . . nav.
M: 2 Allison 501-KF20A gas turbines; 2 Rocketdyne R-20 waterjet pumps; 9,000 shp (7,560 sust.)—2 G.M. 8V92 TI diesels; 2 props; 900 bhp for hullborne cruise
Range: 890/40; 1,500/15 (hullborne) **Fuel:** 33 tons **Crew:** . . .

Remarks: Aluminum construction. Subcontracted to Boeing by Lockheed. Has a Kollmorgen HSV-20NCS electro-optical GFCS with Mk 35 Mod. L3 electro-optical sight for the gunmounts. Acts as tender and escort craft for the larger yachts.

MINISTRY OF THE INTERIOR
BORDER GUARD

Personnel (2002): Approx. 5,400 total

Bases: Headquarters at Azizah, with minor facilities at Al Qatif, Al Sharmah, Al Wajh, Dammam, Haqi, Qizan, Ras al-Mishab, Ras Tanura, and Yanbu' al-Bahr.

BORDER GUARD PATROL CRAFT [WPC]

♦ 4 Al Souf class

Bldr: Blohm + Voss, Hamburg

	In serv.		In serv.
351 Al Jouf	15-6-89	353 Hail	20-8-89
352 Turaif	15-6-89	354 Najran	20-8-89

Turaif (352) Gilbert Gyssels, 6-89

D: 210 tons (fl) **S:** 38 kts **Dim:** 38.80 (36.20 pp) × 7.90 × 1.90
A: 2 single 20-mm 90-cal. Oerlikon GAM-B01 AA; 2 single 12.7-mm mg
Electronics:
Radar: 1 Decca RM 1290A nav.; 1 Decca ARPA S-1690 surf. search
M: 3 MTU 16V538 diesels; 3 props; 11,260 bhp **Electric:** 321 kVA tot.
Range: 1,900/15 **Crew:** 4 officers, 16 enlisted

Remarks: Ordered in 9-86. Have steel hulls and aluminum superstructures. A 300-liter/min firefighting monitor is fitted. Carry a radio direction-finder. Two are based at Jiddah on the Red Sea and two at Al Dammam on the Persian Gulf.

PATROL BOATS [WPB]

♦ 2 Sea Guard SM742 class

Bldr: Simonneau Marine, Fontenay-le-Comte, France (In serv. 4-92)

304 Al Riyadh 305 Zulurab

Zulurab (305)—in missile trials configuration Simonneau, 1992

D: 52.5 tons (fl) **S:** 35+ kts **Dim:** 22.50 × 5.60 × 1.70
A: 1 20-mm 90-cal. GIAT F2 AA; 2 single 7.62 GIAT mg
Electronics: Radar: 1 Furuno . . . nav.
M: 2 MTU 12V396 TB92 diesels; 2 props; 2,920 bhp
Range: . . ./. . . **Fuel:** 6,500 liters **Crew:** 10 tot.

Remarks: Ordered in 1992. Aluminum construction. Used for wire-guided missile trials in France before delivery, but Saudi Arabia did not buy the missile system. Based at Jiddah.

♦ 30 SM 331 Tom Cat–class patrol launches

Bldr: Simonneau Marine, Fontenay-le-Comte, France (In serv. 1992)

D: 4.65 tons (fl) **S:** 40 kts **Dim:** 9.30 × 3.04 × 0.45
A: 1 7.62-mm mg **Electronics:** Radar: 1 Furuno . . . nav.
M: 2 Johnson 6-cyl. gasoline outboards; 500 bhp **Fuel:** 500 liters **Crew:** 4 tot.

Remarks: Aluminum construction.

SM 331 Tom Cat class Simonneau

♦ 2 CGV-26 Explorer class

Bldr: Abeking & Rasmussen, Lemwerder, Germany

	Laid down	L	In serv.
Al Jubatel	1-3-86	3-87	4-87
Salwa	1-3-86	3-87	4-87

Al Jubatel Abeking & Rasmussen, 1987

D: 80 tons (95 fl) **S:** 34 kts **Dim:** 26.60 (23.00 pp) × 6.50 × 1.80 (props)
A: 2 single 20-mm 90-cal. Oerlikon GAM-B01 AA; 2 single 12.7-mm mg
Electronics: Radar: 1 Decca AC 1290 nav.
M: 2 MTU 16V396 TB94 diesels; 2 props; 6,340 bhp
Range: 1,100/25 **Crew:** 4 officers, 8 enlisted

Remarks: Ordered 11-8-85. Steel construction. Based at Qizan and Al Wajh, respectively.

♦ 10 Scorpion class

Bldrs: Bayerische Schiffsbau, Erlenbach, Germany (20 units of the original 25); Arminias Werft, Bodenwerder, Germany (5 units) (In serv.: first 15: 1979; last 10: 28-2-81)

From among: 139 through 164

Scorpion-class 153 Leo Dirkx, 11-98

BORDER GUARD PATROL BOATS [WPB] *(continued)*

D: 33 tons (fl) **S:** 25 kts **Dim:** 17.14 (15.6 pp) × 4.98 × 1.40
A: 2 single 7.62-mm mg **Electronics:** Radar: 1 Decca RM 914 nav.
M: 2 G.M. 12V71 TI diesels; 2 props; 1,300 bhp (1,050 sust.)
Range: 200/20 **Crew:** 7 tot.

Remarks: Fifteen sisters have already been discarded, despite brief service. Aluminum construction.

♦ 12 Rapier class
Bldr: Halter Marine, New Orleans (In serv. 1976–77)

127 through 138

D: 26 tons (fl) **S:** 28 kts **Dim:** 15.24 × 4.57 × 1.35
A: 2 single 7.62-mm mg **Electronics:** Radar: 1 . . . nav.
M: 1 G.M. 12V71 TI diesels; 2 props; 1,300 bhp **Electric:** 20 kw tot.
Crew: 1 officer, 8 enlisted

♦ 60 Whaler patrol launches
Bldr: Boston Whaler, Rockland, Mass. (In serv. 1980s)

D: 1.5 tons light (2 fl) **S:** 30 kts **Dim:** 8.30 × 2.00 × 0.60
M: 2 Johnson V-6, 2.5-liter gasoline outboards; 310 bhp
Range: 70/35 **Crew:** 2 tot.

Note: Also in service for local patrol and transportation duties are up to 475 Task Force Boats (U.K.) 5.25-m launches delivered in 1976; 50 6.5-m launches built in Greece by Cytra in the 1970s; 4 14-m launches built in Greece circa 1974; 10 12.8-m launches from the same builder; 2 Bertram (Miami) Enforcer-class 9.4-m launches delivered in the 1980s; 8 6.4-m catamarans; 4 5.1-m Viper launches; and 2 3.9-m Cobra launches.

AUXILIARIES

♦ 1 training ship [WAXT]
Bldr: Bayerische Schiffsbau, Erlenbach, Germany (In serv. 12-77)

TEBUK

D: 600 tons (750 fl) **S:** 20 kts **Dim:** 60.0 (55.5 pp) × 10.0 × 2.50
A: 1 20-mm Oerlikon GAM-B01 AA
Electronics: Radar: 1 Decca TM 1226 nav.
M: 2 MTU 16V538 TB81 diesels; 2 props; 5,260 bhp (4,800 sust.)
Electric: 1,040 kVA tot. **Range:** 2,400/18; 3,900/12
Crew: 24 tot. + 36 trainees

SERVICE CRAFT

♦ 5 (+ . . .) Type 8000TD(M) hovercraft launches [WYFLA]
Bldr: Griffon Hovercraft, Woolston, U.K.

D: 27 tons (fl) **S:** 42 kts **Dim:** 21.15 (19.85 hull) × 11.30 (8.70 hull) × . . .
A: 1 12.7-mm mg **Electronics:** Radar: 1 . . . nav.
M: 2 MTU 12V183 TB32 diesels; 2 ducted CP airscrew props; 1,600 bhp
Range: 365/42; 500/. . . **Fuel:** 2,000 liters **Crew:** 4 tot. + 16 passengers

Remarks: Ordered in 10-00. Maximum hover height: 1.25 m. Can make 50 kts in light condition, can carry an 8-ton payload, and can be operated on one engine. A 1-ton crane and a single firefighting monitor are fitted. The vehicle well forward can accommodate a jeep or Land Rover. Three are based on the Red Sea coast and two on the Persian Gulf coast.

♦ 3 Type SAH-2000 hovercraft launches [WYFLA]
Bldr: Slingsby, U.K. (In serv. 1991–92)

D: . . . tons **S:** 40 kts **Dim:** 10.6 × 4.2 × . . . **A:** 1 7.62-mm mg
M: 1 Deutz BF6L913C diesel for lift and propulsion; 1 ducted airscrew; 190 bhp
Range: 500/40 **Crew:** 2 tot. + 16 passengers

Remarks: Have Kevlar armor.

♦ 3 ramped personnel launches [WYFL]
Bldr: Rotork, U.K. (In serv. 1991)

AL FAISAL AL HAMZA AL HASSHIM

D: 9 tons (fl) **S:** 28 kts **Dim:** 12.7 × 3.2 × 0.9
M: 2 diesels; 2 props; 240 bhp **Crew:** 3 tot. + 28 troops

♦ 1 yacht [WYFL]

AL TAIF

D: 75 tons (fl) **S:** 15 kts **Dim:** 21.4 × 5.8 × 1.7
Electronics: Radar: 1 Decca 101 nav.
M: 2 Deutz SBF 12M716 diesels; 2 props; . . . bhp

Remarks: Used primarily for training. Based at Jiddah.

♦ 3 fuel lighters [WYO]

AL FORAT AL NIL DAJLAH

D: 233 tons (fl) **S:** 12 kts **Dim:** 28.70 (27.00 pp) × 6.50 × 2.10
Electronics: Radar: 1 Decca 110 nav.
M: 2 Caterpillar D343 diesels; 2 props; . . . bhp
Range: 500/12 **Crew:** . . . tot.

Remarks: *Al Nil* is based at Azizah, the others at Jiddah.

♦ 3 harbor tugs [WYTM]

D: 210 tons (fl) **S:** 13 kts **Dim:** 25.7 × 7.2 × 2.9
M: 1 Deutz SBA 16M816 diesel; 1 prop; . . . bhp **Range:** 1,200/12

♦ 3 fireboats [WYTR]
Bldr: Vosper Pty, Singapore (In serv. 1982)

JUBAIL 1 JUBAIL 2 JUBAIL 3

Jubail 2 H&L Van Ginderen, 1-97

D: approx. 210 tons (fl) **S:** 18 kts (17 sust.) **Dim:** 32.4 × 7.2 × 2.0
Electronics: Radar: 1 Decca 090 nav.
M: 2 MWM TBD 603 V16 diesels; 2 props; . . . bhp
Range: 950/16 **Fuel:** 25 tons **Crew:** 10 tot. (accomm. for 13)

Remarks: 183 grt. Have six firefighting monitors; the largest, atop the pilothouse, has a volume of 16,000 liters/min, while three atop the mast can pump 5,000 liters/min each and two aft can each pump 8,000 liters/min. The craft are protected by spray screens and carry foam and Halon spray facilities. They can also support divers and have portable salvage pumps. An extensive navigational equipment suite is provided.

SENEGAL

Republic of Senegal

Personnel (2002): Approx. 600 total

Bases: Headquarters, principal base, and dockyard at Dakar, with facilities also on the Casamance River
Maritime Aviation: The air force operates one Canadian de Havilland DHC-6-300M Twin Otter for maritime patrol.

Note: Due to maintenance problems, only the landing craft *Faleme-II* was fully operational as of early 2001.

PATROL SHIPS [PS]

♦ 0 (+ 1) ex-U.S. Coast Guard Balsam class

D: 697 tons light (1,038 fl) **S:** 12.8–13 kts **Dim:** 54.9 (51.8 pp) × 11.3 × 4.0
A: 2 single 12.7-mm mg **Electronics:** Radar: 1 Hughes-Furuno SPS-73 nav.
M: 2 diesels, electric drive; 1 prop; 1,200 shp **Electric:** 400 kw tot.
Range: 8,000/12; 23,500/7.5 **Crew:** 6 officers, 47 enlisted

Remarks: One unit, as yet unidentified, is planned for transfer during 2003. Very robustly constructed vessel that should still have a number of years' service remaining despite advanced age. Has a 20-ton derrick and icebreaking hull.

PATROL COMBATANTS [PG]

♦ 1 Osprey 55 design
Bldr: Danyard, Frederikshavn, Denmark

	Laid down	L	In serv.
FOUTA	11-86	3-87	1-6-87

D: 500 tons (fl) **S:** 20.2 kts (19 sust.)
Dim: 54.75 (50.83 pp) × 10.50 (9.15 wl) × 2.55 (hull)
A: 1 40-mm 70-cal. Bofors AA; 1 20-mm 90-cal. GIAT F2 AA
Electronics: Radar: 1 Furuno FR-1411 nav.; 1 Furuno FR-1221 nav.
M: 2 M.A.N.–Burmeister & Wain Alpha 12V.23/30-DVO diesels; 2 CP props; 4,960 bhp
Electric: 359 kw tot. **Range:** 4,500/16 **Fuel:** 95 tons
Crew: 4 officers, 34 enlisted + 8 trainees

Remarks: Ordered early in 1986, financed by the Ministry of Equipment. Thornycroft-Giles "short, fat ship" hull. Near-sisters are in Mauritanian, Moroccan, Greek, and Myanmar service. Used for 200-n.m.-economic-zone and fisheries patrol. Were armed after delivery. Have no helicopter facility. There are berths for 20 rescued personnel. A stern docking well holds a 6.5-m Watercraft RI-22 inspection/rescue boat. Carries 27 tons of fresh water.

PATROL COMBATANTS [PG] *(continued)*

Fouta Bernard Prézelin, 2-01

PATROL CRAFT [PC]

♦ 1 French PR 72 MS class Bldr: SFCN, Villeneuve-la-Garenne

	Laid down	L	In serv.
Njambuur	5-80	23-12-80	2-83

Njambuur Bernard Prézelin, 12-98

D: 381 tons light (451 fl) **S:** 30 kts **Dim:** 58.70 (54.0 pp) × 8.22 × 2.18
A: 2 single 76-mm 62-cal. OTOBreda Compact; 2 single 20-mm 90-cal. GIAT F2 AA
Electronics:
Radar: 1 Decca 1226 nav.; 1 Furuno 1421 nav.
E/O: 2 Matra Défense Naja optical f.c.
M: 4 SACM AGO 195V16 RVR diesels; 4 props; 12,800 bhp (11,760 sust.)
Range: 2,500/16 **Crew:** 39 tot. + 7 passengers

Remarks: Ordered in 1979. No longer carries pennant P 773. Was towed to Lorient, France, late in 2001 for a major overhaul and modernization that is to be completed late in 2003.

♦ 3 PR-48 class Bldr: SFCN, Villeneuve-la-Garenne

	Laid down	L	In serv.
Saint Louis	20-4-70	5-8-70	1-3-71
Popenguine	12-73	22-3-74	10-8-74
Podor	12-75	20-7-76	13-7-77

Popenguine—with two sisters and the *Njambuur* in the background
Bernard Prézelin, 2-01

D: 240 tons (avg.) **S:** 23 kts **Dim:** 47.5 (45.5 pp) × 7.1 × 2.5
A: 2 single 40-mm 70-cal. Bofors AA; 2 single 12.7-mm mg
Electronics: Radar: 1 Furuno 1421 nav.
M: 2 AGO V12 CZSHR diesels; 2 props; 6,240 bhp
Range: 2,000/16 **Crew:** 3 officers, 22 enlisted

Remarks: Steel construction. Are in very poor material condition.

PATROL BOATS [PB]

♦ 2 U.S. 51-foot class
Bldr: Peterson Bldrs, Sturgeon Bay, Wis.

	In serv.
Matelot Alioure Samb	28-10-93
Matelot Oumar Ndoye	4-11-93

Matelot Alioure Samb French Navy, 6-97

D: 22 tons (24 fl) **S:** 24 kts **Dim:** 15.54 × 4.47 × 1.30
A: 1 twin 12.7-mm M2 mg; 2 single 7.62-mm mg
Electronics: Radar: 1 Furuno . . . nav.
M: 2 G.M. Detroit Diesel 6V-92TA diesels; 2 props; 900 bhp **Electric:** 15 kw tot.
Range: 500/20 **Fuel:** 800 gallons **Crew:** 6 tot.

Remarks: Are from among a group of five ordered 25-9-92 by the U.S. Navy for transfer to African countries. Cost $925,000 each. Aluminum construction. Carry a 4.27-m rigid inflatable inspection craft (with 50-bhp outboard motor) on the stern.

♦ 3 Interceptor class
Bldr: Turbec, St. Catharines, Ont., Canada

Casamance 2 Sénégal 2 Siné Saloum 2

Sénégal 2 Bernard Prézelin, 2-01

D: 52 tons (61.7 fl) **S:** 32 kts **Dim:** 26.5 × 5.81 × 1.60
A: 1 20-mm 90-cal. GIAT F2 AA **Electronics:** Radar: 1 JRC 3610 nav.
M: 2 diesels; 2 props; 2,700 bhp **Crew:** . . .

Remarks: In service 10-79, 2-79, and 7-79, respectively. Used for fisheries protection patrol.

AMPHIBIOUS WARFARE CRAFT

♦ 1 French EDIC 700–class tank landing craft [LCU]
Bldr: SFCN, Villeneuve-la-Garenne

	Laid down	L	In serv.
Karabene	23-4-85	6-3-86	23-6-86

Karabene—with missile craft *Njambuur* in background at left
Bernard Prézelin, 2-01

AMPHIBIOUS WARFARE CRAFT *(continued)*

D: 410 tons light (730 fl) **S:** 12 kts
Dim: 59.00 (52.90 pp) × 11.90 × 1.69 (max.)
A: 2 single 20-mm 90-cal. GIAT F2 AA; 1 81-mm mortar
Electronics: Radar: 1 Furuno RDP 118 nav.
M: 2 UNI UD30.V12 (SACM-MGO 175 V12 ASH) diesels; 2 props; 1,400 bhp (1,040 sust.)
Range: 1,800/8 **Crew:** 18 tot.

Remarks: Ordered 3-6-85; arrived during 8-86. Cargo: 340 tons (11 trucks or five light tanks), carried in a 28.50 × 8.0–m vehicle well.

♦ 1 French EDIC-class tank landing craft [LCU]
Bldr: SFCN, Villeneuve-la-Garenne (L: 30-3-67)

Faleme-II (ex-*Javeline,* L 9070)

Faleme-II Bernard Prézelin, 2-01

D: 280 tons light (670 fl) **S:** 8 kts (loaded)
Dim: 59.00 × 11.95 × 1.30 (1.62 max. fl)
A: 2 single 20-mm 70-cal. Oerlikon AA **Electronics:** Radar: 1 Decca 1229 nav.
M: 2 SACM-MGO 175 V12 ASH diesels; 2 props; 1,040 bhp
Range: 1,800/8 **Crew:** 5 petty officers, 12 ratings (in French service)

Remarks: Stricken from the French Navy in 1998 and transferred to Senegal 12-1-00. EDIC = *Engins de Débarquement pour Infantrie et Chars.* Can carry 11 trucks or five armored personnel carriers.

♦ 1 ex-French LCM(8)-class landing craft [LCM]
Bldr: CMN, Cherbourg

. . . (ex-CTM 5)

Ex-CTM 5—without new name or number Bernard Prézelin, 2-01

D: 56 tons light (150 fl) **S:** 9.5 kts **Dim:** 23.80 × 6.35 × 1.25
A: 2 single 12.7-mm mg **Electronics:** Radar: 1 . . . nav.
M: 2 Poyaud 520 V8 diesels; 2 props; 480 bhp **Range:** 380/8
Fuel: 3.4 tons **Endurance:** 48 hours at half power **Crew:** 6 tot.

Remarks: Transferred from the French Navy in 5-99. Cargo capacity: 90 tons. The machineguns are usually not mounted.

SERVICE CRAFT

♦ 1 small oceanographic research ship [YAG]
Bldr: . . . . . ., Japan (In serv. 2001)

Itaf Deme

Remarks: No data available, but appears to be of the same size and general design as the *Louis Sauger,* which she was intended to supplement. A modified purse-seiner used mainly for fisheries research. Ordered during 2000. Naval crewed.

Itaf Deme Bernard Prézelin, 2-01

♦ 1 small oceanographic research ship [YAG]
Bldr: Narasaki Zosen, Muroran, Japan (In serv. 1985)

Louis Sauger

Louis Sauger Bernard Prézelin, 12-98

D: approx. 450 tons (fl) **S:** 9 kts **Dim:** 36.63 (30.51 pp) × 8.03 × 2.94
M: 1 Yanmar diesel; 1 CP prop; 800 bhp

Remarks: 56 grt. Modified purse-seiner intended primarily for fisheries research. Naval crewed.

♦ 1 French Oiseau-class small harbor tug [YTL]
Cheik Oumar Fall (ex-*Olivier,* Y 719)

Cheik Oumar Fall Bernard Prézelin, 2-01

D: 56 tons **S:** 9 kts **Dim:** 18.4 × 5.7 × 2.5
M: 1 Poyaud diesel; 1 prop; 250 shp **Range:** 1,700/9 **Crew:** 4 tot.

SERVICE CRAFT *(continued)*

Remarks: On loan from the French Navy; arrived in 1990. Bollard pull: 3.5 tons. Renamed in 2000. Sister *Ibis* has been discarded, and *Aigrette,* on loan since 1990, was stricken in 1998.

Note: The customs service operates six Spanish-built patrol launches: four 3.4-ton LVI 85S class (*Djibril, N'diaye, Gorée,* and *Djilor*), completed in 1987, and two 26-ton DS-10 class (DS-01 *Dialore-01* and DS-02 *Dialore-02*), completed in 1-82. The latter were in very poor condition as of 2001.

Former U.S. Coast Guard lifeboat 44311—aboard USS *Anchorage* (LSD 36) for shipment to the Seychelles George R. Schneider, 7-00

SEYCHELLES

Republic of Seychelles

SEYCHELLES COAST GUARD

Personnel (2002): Approx. 300 total, including 80 air wing and 100 naval infantry

Base: Port Victoria, Mahé

Maritime Aviation: One Britten-Norman BN-42 B/T Maritime Defender

Note: The Seychelles People's Navy and People's Air Force were combined into a single coast guard service during 12-92.

PATROL CRAFT [WPC]

♦ **1 FPB 42 class**
Bldr: C.N. Picchiotti, Viareggio, Italy (In serv. 10-1-83)

605 Andromache

Andromache (605)—note that the 20-mm gun formerly mounted on the bow has been removed French Navy, 2-96

D: 240 tons (268 fl) **S:** 28 kts **Dim:** 41.80 × 8.00 × 2.50 (props; 1.70 hull)
A: 2 single 7.62-mm mg **Electronics:** Radar: 2 Furuno . . . nav.
M: 2 Paxman-Valenta 16 RP200 CM diesels; 2 props; 6,800 bhp (5,700 sust.)
Range: 3,000/16 **Crew:** 3 officers, 19 enlisted

Remarks: Ordered 8-10-81; a planned second unit was not ordered. Also used as a personnel transport. Refitted during 1985–86 in Italy. The 20-mm Oerlikon AA mounting formerly on the bow has been removed.

Disposals: Russian-built Turya-class (Project 206ME) hydrofoil torpedo boat *Zoroaster* (606), in reserve since 1992, has been deleted in this edition due to the unlikelihood of spares being obtainable to repair her; she remains afloat as a training hulk, with the 57-mm gunmount, fire-control radar, and torpedo tubes removed. The remaining Russian-donated Zhuk-class (Project 1400M) patrol boat, *Fortune* (604), had been retired by mid-2000.

SERVICE CRAFT

♦ **5 ex-U.S. Coast Guard 44-foot Motor Life Boat–class lifeboats [WYH]** Bldr: USCG Yard, Curtis Bay, Md. (In serv. 31-3-61 to 8-5-73)

D: 14.9 tons light (17.7 fl) **S:** 13 kts (11.8 sust.) **Dim:** 13.44 × 3.87 × 1.19
Electronics: Radar: 1 JRC . . . nav.
M: 2 G.M. Detroit Diesel 6V53 diesels; 2 props; 372 bhp
Range: 185/11.8; 200/11 **Fuel:** 1.2 tons **Crew:** 4 tot.

Remarks: Transferred in 7-00; are the former U.S. Coast Guard 44305, 44311, 44336, 44347, and 44393. "Unsinkable" design. Can carry up to 21 rescued personnel.

Note: Also operated by the coast guard are the small presidential yacht *Gemini* and a sailing schooner with auxiliary propulsion, *Arc en Ciel,* which is used as a local logistics support craft. The 855-ton (fl) logistics landing craft *Cinq Juin* is operated by the Ministère de la Cooperation in commercial service but is available for government cargoes.

SIERRA LEONE

Republic of Sierra Leone

Personnel (2002): Approx. 100 total

Base: Freetown

PATROL CRAFT [PC]

♦ **1 Chinese Haizhui class** (Nonoperational)
Bldr: Guijian SY (In serv. 1-1-97)

PB 103

D: 150 tons (170 fl) **S:** 29 kts **Dim:** 41.0 × 5.41 × 1.80
A: 1 twin 37-mm 63-cal. Type 76 AA; 1 twin 25-mm 80-cal. Type 81 AA; 2 twin 14.5-mm 93-cal. AA
Electronics: Radar: 1 Anritsu 726 UA nav./surf. search
M: 4 Type L12-180Z diesels; 4 props; 4,800 bhp (4,400 sust.)
Range: 750/16 **Crew:** 4 officers, 24 enlisted

Remarks: A new-construction unit transferred in 11-96 to replace the inoperable Shanghai-II-class patrol boats *Moa* and *Naimbana,* which in turn had been transferred in 3-87 as replacements for a trio of Shanghai-IIs delivered in 1976. Was inoperable by 1998 but may since have been repaired. Has gyro-controlled fin stabilizers. Sisters operate in the Sri Lankan Navy.

Disposal note: The U.S. 110-ft. Commercial Cruiser–class patrol craft *Farandugu* had been hulked by 2000 and is probably beyond repair. Two Cougar Cat 900S patrol launches acquired in 1998 quickly became inoperable and will probably not be returned to service.

AMPHIBIOUS WARFARE CRAFT

♦ **1 Chinese Yuhai-class utility landing craft [LCU]** (Nonoperational)
Bldr: Wuhu SY (In serv. 1-1-97)

104 *Tiwai Island*

Tiwai Island (104)—aboard Chinese commercial dock-ship *Developing Road* 92 Wing, Det. A, RAAF, 2-97

D: 799 tons (fl) **S:** 14 kts **Dim:** 58.4 × 10.4 × 2.7
A: 2 twin 14.5-mm 93-cal. Model 81 AA **Electronics:** Radar: 1 Type 756 nav.
M: 2 M.A.N. 8L 20/27 diesels; 2 props; 4,900 bhp
Range: 1,000/12 **Crew:** 56 tot.

Remarks: Transferred in 11-96 and formally commissioned 1-1-97. By 2001, may have become nonoperational for lack of maintenance and spares. Has a bow ramp only. Cargo capacity: two tanks and 250 troops, or up to 150 tons of miscellaneous cargo. Misidentified as a unit of the Yunnan class in the last edition.

SINGAPORE

Republic of Singapore

Personnel (2002): Approx. 4,500 total (including 900 conscripts); 5,000 reservists are also available in emergency

Bases: Headquarters is at Bukit Gombak and principal base at Tuas, Jurong, on the Johore Strait. A base at Woodlands used jointly with Malaysia for training reverted to Singaporean control in 1997. Work began in 1-98 on a new base at Changi, near the eastern end of the Johore Strait; an adjacent facility is to open in 2003 to house the Training Command's maritime warfare, naval technology, and marine engineering training programs. The former operational base at Brani closed 12-10-00.

Organization: Operational missile combatants and the latest patrol craft are assigned to the 1st Flotilla, while antisubmarine patrol craft and the tank landing ships are assigned to the 3rd Flotilla. The Naval Logistics Command (NALCOM) is responsible for repairs, maintenance, and supply. Base defense is handled by Base Defence Squadrons, medical care by Medical Centers, and materiel and personnel transportation by the Naval Material and Transport Base. There is also a Coastal Command (COSCOM) to manage naval operations in the Singapore Strait; six inshore patrol craft and the mine countermeasures units are assigned to it. The Training Command (TRACOM) is responsible for all training and for the Institute of Naval Technology and Operations, Institute of Maritime Systems, Institute of Maritime Warfare at Tuas, and Tactical Training Centers at Brani and Tuas.

Maritime Aviation: There is no naval-subordinated aviation arm. The Singapore Air Force 125 Sqn. has 66 helicopters available for maritime support missions: 22 AS.332M Super Puma helicopters equipped for ASW and troop carrying, 18 Bell UH-1H helicopters, 6 AS.350B Écureuil light helicopters, and 20 AS.550 Fennec attack helicopters (10 with Helitow antitank/antiship missiles and 20-mm rocket pods, 10 in utility configuration). Five Fokker 50 Maritime Enforcer maritime patrol aircraft are assigned to 121 Sqn.; they have APS-134 surveillance radars, Honeywell P-650 weather radar, AQR-185(V) sonobuoy receivers, GEC V00-1069 infrared sensors, ASQ-504(V) magnetic anomaly detectors, an extensive EW suite, and Litton LTN-92 inertial navigation systems, and their weapons can include two fuselage-mounted Harpoon antiship missiles and four wing-mounted ASW torpedoes. Four other Fokker 50 aircraft serve in logistic support roles. Eight new helicopters are to be ordered for delivery by 2008 for service aboard the new frigates.

The Singapore Air Force also operates four E-2C Hawkeye radar surveillance aircraft and some 50 A-4 Skyhawk fighter-bombers capable of maritime strike. Eight F-16A/B fighters were delivered in 1988. In addition to tracking aerial contacts, the Hawkeyes are capable of providing over-the-horizon targeting data for Harpoon missiles aboard naval units.

Note: The name of the principal local warship builder, Singapore SB & Eng., has been changed to Singapore Technologies Marine. Ship names are prefixed by RSS (Republic of Singapore Ship). Pennant numbers no longer are preceded by a type-letter when painted on the ships, but the prefixes remain in effect for administrative purposes.

ATTACK SUBMARINES [SS]

♦ 4 ex-Swedish Sjöormen class (Type A-11B)

Bldr: Kockums AB, Malmö (*Challenger:* Karlskronavarvet)

	Laid down	L	In serv.
S . . . Centurion (ex-*Sjöormen*)	1965	25-1-67	31-7-67
S . . . Challenger (ex-*Sjöhästen*)	1966	9-1-68	15-9-69
S . . . Chieftain (ex-*Sjöhunden*)	1966	21-3-68	25-6-69
S . . . Conqueror (ex-*Sjölejonet*)	1966	29-6-67	16-12-68

Conqueror Brian Morrison, 8-00

Conqueror Brian Morrison, 8-00

D: 1,130 tons surf./1,400 tons sub. **S:** 10 kts surf./20 kts sub.
Dim: 50.5 × 6.1 × 5.1
A: 4 bow 533-mm TT (8 Tp 613 torpedoes or mines); 2 bow 400-mm TT (4 Tp 431 ASW torpedoes)

Challenger Curt Borgenstam Jr., 9-97

Electronics:
Radar: 1 Terma . . . search
Sonar: STN Atlas Elektronik CSU-83 suite
EW: . . .
M: diesel-electric: 4 Hedemora-Pielstick PV/12 PA2, 525-bhp diesel generator groups (600 kw each), 1 ASEA electric motor; 1 5-bladed prop; 1,500 shp
Endurance: 21 days **Crew:** 7 officers, 21 enlisted

Remarks: The contract announced 23-9-95 to acquire the *Sjöhunden* called for transfer in 4-96 for use in training submariners in Swedish waters; the submarine was refitted at Karlskrona from 2-96 to 26-9-97 and originally was to have left for Singapore late in 2-98 but has been retained in Sweden for training (along with *Challenger*) until 2003. On 31-7-97, three more former Swedish Navy units were ordered under Project Riken, all to be refurbished at Kockums, Malmö, for delivery 1999–2001. *Conqueror* and *Centurion* were officially transferred 28-5-99 to begin their refit and tropicalization modifications. The remaining unit of the class, *Sjöbjornen,* was also purchased, for cannibalization. The active four are not expected to be fully combat-ready until 2003, at which point they will be nearly 35 years old. *Conqueror* was commissioned in Singapore 2-7-00 as the first unit of 171 Squadron and *Chieftain* was relaunched 23-5-01 for arrival in Singapore late in 2001.
Hull systems: Maximum diving depth: 150 m. Have four battery compartments. The stern planes are in X-configuration; bow planes are on the sail. During modifications for Singapore service, piping and valves were replaced for operations in higher-salinity waters, and the air-conditioning system was enhanced.
Combat systems: *Challenger* was modernized 1984–85 with the Ericsson IBS-A17 combat data/fire-control system with a Cesnor 932 computer and two operator consoles; the other units may retain the older IBS-A12 system, but a French UDS International SUBTICS (Submarine Tactical Integrated Combat System) may be substituted in Singapore. The extent of upgrades made during activation and alteration for Singapore service has not been reported.

FRIGATES [FF]

♦ 0 (+ 6) Souverainte class (NGPV Project)

Bldrs: first unit: DCN, . . .; others: Singapore Technologies Marine, Jurong

	Laid down	L	In serv.
. . . . . .	. . .	. . .	2008
. . . . . .	. . .	. . .	. . .
. . . . . .	. . .	. . .	. . .
. . . . . .	. . .	. . .	. . .
. . . . . .	. . .	. . .	. . .
. . . . . .	. . .	. . .	. . .

D: 3,000 tons (fl) **S:** 31 kts **Dim:** 110.0 × . . . × . . .
A: 8 RGM-84C Harpoon SSM; 4 Barak VLS SAM groups (32 missiles); 1 57-mm 70-cal. Bofors SAK 57 Mk 3 or OTOBreda 76-mm 62-cal. SuperRapid DP; 4 fixed 533-mm TT (Tp 61 wire-guided torpedoes); 1 . . . helicopter
Electronics:
Radar: 1 . . . nav., 1 Thales Herakles 3-D surf./air search and f.c.
Sonar: bow-mounted LF; MF VDS; towed passive array
EW: . . .
M: . . . diesels, electric drive; 2 props; . . . shp
Range: 4,000/. . . **Crew:** 60 tot.

Remarks: NGPV = New Generation Patrol Vessel. Originally planned to be ordered in late 1997 or early 1998 as a class of eight 1,000-ton missile corvettes, the program was delayed to incorporate new technologies from abroad, and the ship size has grown from 75–90 m overall to as large as 110 m, placing it in the frigate category. A contract to design the class and build the first unit was given to DCN, France, 3-3-00.
Hull systems: Was originally to have employed a trimaran hull constructed of GRP, with Kevlar armor, but as the size has nearly tripled, will be a monohull built of conventional materials, with considerable effort made at signature reduction.
Combat systems: The combat system is to be provided by Singapore Technologies Electronics and will incorporate an integrated ship command and operation system, fiber-optic data transfer, multifunction operating consoles, an integrated communications suite, and automation of functions to reduce personnel requirements. Reloads are planned for the fixed torpedo tubes. The Matra Aster-15 SAM system, using Sylver VLS, may have been selected instead of Barak.

GUIDED-MISSILE PATROL COMBATANTS [PGG]

♦ 6 Victory (MGB 62) class

Bldr: Singapore Technologies Marine, Jurong (P 88: Lürssen, Vegesack, Germany)

	L	In serv.
P 88 Victory	8-6-88	18-8-90
P 89 Valour	10-12-88	18-8-90
P 90 Vigilance	27-4-89	18-8-90
P 91 Valiant	22-7-89	25-5-91
P 92 Vigour	1-2-89	25-5-91
P 93 Vengeance	23-2-90	25-5-91

Valiant (P 91) Brian Morrison, 8-00

Vengeance (P 93) John Mortimer, 8-01

Vigour (P 92) John Mortimer, 8-01

D: 550 tons normal (600 fl) **S:** 35 kts **Dim:** 62.95 (59.90 pp) × 9.30 × 2.60
A: 8 RGM-84C Harpoon SSM; 2 Barak VLS SAM groups (16 missiles); 1 76-mm 62-cal. OTOBreda SuperRapid DP; 4 single 12.7-mm mg; 2 triple 324-mm ILAS-3 ASW TT (WASS A-244S torpedoes)
Electronics:
Radar: 1 Kelvin-Hughes Type 1007 nav.; 1 Ericsson Sea Giraffe 150HC surf./air search; 2 Elta EL/M-2221 GM STGR f.c.
Sonar: Thales Salmon VDS
EW: Rafael SEWS 1101 intercept; MBAT/RAN-1010 jammer; Alenia-Marconi Shield III decoy syst. (2 6-round RL); Mk 36 RBOC decoy syst. (2 6-round Mk 137 RL)
M: 4 MTU 20V538 TB93 diesels; 4 props; 18,740 bhp (15,020 sust.)
Electric: 408 kw tot. **Range:** 700/34; 4,000/16 **Crew:** 8 officers, 41 enlisted

Remarks: First unit ordered in 6-86. Transferred in 10-91 to the new Coastal Command for antipiracy, fisheries protection, and search-and-rescue duties. They constitute 188 Squadron, 1st Flotilla.
Hull systems: Same hull as a pair built for Bahrain, but without helicopter facilities. Received the Van Rieetschoten & Houwens ARSA (Adaptive Rudder-roll Stabilizing Autopilot) rudder roll-stabilization system during 1992. Have experienced stability problems due to the weight of the large tower mast structure.
Combat systems: Have the CelsiusTech 9LV 200 combat system and Israeli NATACS command system. The navigation radar incorporates a combat data plotting system. The EW suite intercept band covers 1–18 GHz, and the jammer covers 7.5–18 GHz, using two stabilized antennas. There is also a communications D/F capability. Barak point-defense missile systems were ordered for all in 4-96 after successful trials in P 89; the two 8-cell launch groups are recessed into the main deck on either side near the stern, and a second weapons-control radar has been added abaft the tower mast. Normally, only two Harpoon missiles are aboard.

PATROL COMBATANTS [PG]

♦ 12 Fearless class

Bldr: Singapore Technologies Marine, Jurong

	L	In serv.
P 94 Fearless	18-2-95	5-10-96
P 95 Brave	9-9-95	5-10-96
P 96 Courageous	9-9-95	5-10-96
P 97 Gallant	27-4-96	3-5-97
P 98 Daring	27-4-96	3-5-97
P 99 Dauntless	23-11-96	3-5-97
P 82 Resilience	23-11-96	7-2-98
P 83 Unity	19-7-97	7-2-98
P 84 Sovereignty	19-7-97	7-2-98
P 85 Justice	18-10-97	7-2-98
P 86 Freedom	18-10-97	22-8-98
P 87 Independence	4-98	22-8-98

Independence (P 87)—gunboat variant John Mortimer, 6-01

Fearless (P 94)—ASW variant, with VIGY-10 optronic surveillance sensor on new mast platform Brian Morrison, 8-00

Brave (P 95)—ASW variant, now with triple torpedo tube mounts port and starboard; note the pipe guards over the waterjet exhausts at the stern Brian Morrison, 8-00

PATROL COMBATANTS [PG] *(continued)*

D: 500 tons (fl) **S:** 36 kts **Dim:** 55.0 × 8.60 × 2.20 (hull)
A: 1 2-round Sadral point-defense SAM syst. (. . . Mistral missiles); 1 76-mm 62-cal. OTOBreda SuperRapid DP; 4 single 7.62-mm mg—P 94–99 only: 2 triple 324-mm ILAS-3 ASW TT (WASS A-244S torpedoes)
Electronics:
Radar: 1 Kelvin-Hughes Type 1007 nav.; 1 Elta EL/M-2228X surveillance/f.c.
Sonar: P 94–99 only: Thales TSM-2362 Gudgeon MF hull-mounted
EW: Elisra NS-9010C intercept; Alenia-Marconi Shield III decoy syst. (2 6-round RL)
E/O: Elbit MSIS optronic gun f.c.
M: 2 MTU 12V595 TE90 diesels; 2 KaMeWa waterjets; 8,430 bhp
Range: . . ./. . . **Crew:** 5 officers, 22 enlisted

Remarks: The contract for the first six was assigned to Singapore Shipbuilding and Engineering in mid-1994; an order for the second six was announced 18-2-94. *Courageous* was originally to have been named *Unity.* P 94–99 constitute 189 Squadron, while P 82–87 comprise 82 Squadron. P 94–99 are designated APV (Antisubmarine Patrol Vessels), while the others are OPV (Offshore Patrol Vessels). P 83 is used to test new equipment as the "naval technology evaluation ship."
Combat systems: Have the Elbit ST 3100 WCS combat data system. The second group of six was to carry four to six Gabriel-II antiship missiles in lieu of antisubmarine torpedo tubes, but they were completed without the missiles and they are no longer planned to be added. The sonar is derived from Thales's Spherion series; it has a retractable transducer. All 12 carry a rigid inflatable inspection launch aft; in P 82–87, it is handled by a large electrohydraulic crane. P 94 had been fitted with a Sagem VIGY-10 electro-optical surveillance system by mid-2000, with the sensor mounted on a new platform on the mast.

GUIDED-MISSILE PATROL CRAFT [PTG]

♦ 6 Sea Wolf (FPB 45) class
Bldrs: P 76, P 77: Lürssen, Vegesack, Germany; others: Singapore Technologies Marine, Jurong

	In serv.		In serv.
P 76 Sea Wolf	1972	P 79 Sea Tiger	1974
P 77 Sea Lion	1972	P 80 Sea Hawk	1975
P 78 Sea Dragon	1974	P 81 Sea Scorpion	29-2-76

Sea Wolf (P 76)—with four Harpoon and two Gabriel-I antiship missile canisters aboard Brian Morrison, 8-00

Sea Dragon (P 78)—in the more normal configuration, with only two of four possible Harpoon launch canister positions filled H&L Van Ginderen, 1-00

D: 226 tons (254 fl) **S:** 35 kts **Dim:** 44.90 (42.30 wl) × 7.00 × 2.48
A: 2 or 4 RGM-84C Harpoon SSM; 2 Gabriel-I SSM; 1 57-mm 70-cal. Bofors SAK 57 Mk 1 DP; 1 2-round Simbad point-defense SAM syst. (. . . Mistral missiles); 2 single 12.7-mm mg
Electronics:
Radar: 1 Decca TM 626 nav.; 1 Thales WM-28 f.c.
EW: Rafael SEWS 1101 intercept/jammer suite; Mk 36 RBOC decoy syst. (4 6-round Mk 137 RL)
M: 4 MTU 16V538 TB92 diesels; 4 props; 14,400 bhp (13,640 sust.)
Range: 950/30; 2,000/15 **Crew:** 7 officers, 33 enlisted

Remarks: Ordered in 1970. Class constitutes 185 Squadron, 1st Flotilla. Are to be maintained active until at least 2004. Are somewhat overloaded.
Combat systems: Four Harpoon SSMs replaced the former Gabriel triple, trainable SSM mount aft, but normally only two are carried; in 1988, P 80 was the first to complete modernization, with P 76, the last, completing her update early in 1991. The remaining two fixed Gabriel launchers will be removed when the missiles have reached the end of their shelf lives. Two multiple 57-mm flare launchers are carried on the 57-mm mount. Carry 504 rounds of 57-mm ammunition. The Simbad manned launcher for Mistral missiles has replaced the 40-mm mount formerly on the fantail; the decoy rocket launchers flank the Simbad launcher. Intercept equipment on tripod topmast was added in 1980–81.

PATROL BOATS [PB]

♦ 12 FB-series inshore patrol craft (In reserve)
Bldr: Singapore Technologies Marine, Jurong (In serv. 1990–91)

FB 31 through *FB 42*

FB 35 NAVPIC-Holland, 5-95

D: 20 tons (fl) **S:** 30 kts **Dim:** 14.5 × 4.1 × 1.1
A: 1 7.62-mm mg **Electronics:** Radar: 1 Decca . . . nav.
M: 2 MTU 12V183 TC91 diesels; 2 Hamilton waterjets; 1,200 bhp **Crew:** 4 tot.

Remarks: Similar to the Police Coast Guard PT 12 class, they were formerly based at Brani as part of 186 Coastal Patrol Squadron but have been retained in land storage at Tuas for several years.

MINE WARFARE SHIPS

♦ 4 Swedish Landsort-class minehunters [MHC]
Bldr: Karlskronavarvet, Karlskrona (see remarks)

	Laid down	L	In serv.
M 105 Bedok	17-10-91	24-6-93	7-10-95
M 106 Kallang	. . .	29-1-94	7-10-95
M 107 Katong	. . .	8-4-94	7-10-95
M 108 Punggol	. . .	16-7-94	7-10-95

Kallang (M 106) Douglas A. Cromby, 6-00

Punggol (M 108)—note mine-clearance swimmer access platform recessed into the port side of the transom stern Brian Morrison, 8-00

MINE WARFARE SHIPS *(continued)*

D: 310 tons (360 fl) **S:** 15 kts **Dim:** 47.50 (45.00 pp) × 9.60 × 2.30
A: 1 40-mm 70-cal. Bofors L70 AA; 4 single 7.62-mm mg; portable mine rails
Electronics:
Radar: 1 Norcontrol DB 2000 nav.; 1 Thales WM-20 gun f.c.
Sonar: Thales TSM 2022 variable-depth HF minehunting
E/O: CelsiusTech 9LV 100 optronic gun f.c.
M: 4 Saab-Scania DSI-14 diesels; 2 Voith-Schneider vertical cycloidal props; 1,440 bhp
Electric: 585 kVA tot. **Range:** 2,500/12 **Crew:** 7 officers, 32 enlisted

Remarks: Two were ordered in 4-91, with an option for two more. M 105 was built entirely in Sweden; the hulls for the others were built in Sweden and outfitted in Singapore by Singapore Technologies Marine, Jurong, with M 108 leaving Sweden 17-8-93 as deck cargo. M 106 began sea trials during 11-94. All were commissioned together as 194 Mine Countermeasures Squadron, based at Tuas under the Coastal Command.
Hull systems: GRP construction. Have two 225-kVA and one 135-kVA diesel generator sets, all mounted on the upper deck to reduce noise signature.
Combat systems: Have the Thales TSM 2061 mine countermeasures information system with IBIS plot. Carry two PAP 105 Mk 5 remote-controlled mine-disposal vehicles. The Y-shaped portable mine rail arrangement provides a single laying point. Are equipped with a Racal precision navigation system and a Magnavox GPS system.

AMPHIBIOUS WARFARE SHIPS AND CRAFT

♦ 4 Endurance-class tank landing ships [LST]
Bldr: Singapore Technologies Marine, Jurong

	L	In serv.
L 207 ENDURANCE	14-3-98	18-3-00
L 208 RESOLUTION	1-8-98	18-3-00
L 209 PERSISTENCE	13-3-99	7-4-01
L 210 ENDEAVOUR	13-2-00	7-4-01

Persistence (L 209) Brian Morrison, 10-01

Endeavour (L 210) Brian Morrison, 8-01

D: 6,000 tons (8,500 fl) **S:** 15+ kts **Dim:** 141.0 × 21.0 × 5.0 (mean)
A: 2 twin-rail Simbad point-defense SAM syst. (. . . Mistral missiles); 1 76-mm 62-cal. OTOBreda SuperRapid DP; 2 single 12.7-mm mg
Electronics:
Radar: 1 Kelvin Hughes Type 1007 ARPA nav.; 1 Ericsson Sea Giraffe 150HC surf./air search
EW: Rafael RAN 1101 intercept; . . . jammer; Alenia-Marconi Shield III decoy syst. (2 6-round RL)
E/O: 1 Matra Défense Najir 2000 optronic director and surveillance
M: 2 Ruston 16RK270 diesels, electric drive; 2 KaMeWa CP props; 13,400 shp—bow-thruster
Electric: 2,800 kw tot (4 × 700-kw, 875-kVA diesel sets)
Range: 5,000+/15; 10,400/12 **Crew:** 65 tot. (accomm. for 100) + 350 troops

Remarks: Ordered in 8-96 as replacements for the U.S.-built LSTs for use in logistics support duties. L 207 was laid down 26-3-97. Builder's class name is "STEM 1400 LST." Designed in cooperation with Ingalls Shipbuilding, Pascagoula, Miss. They form the 3rd Flotilla's 191 Squadron and operate from Tuas Naval Base.
Hull systems: Have a 60-ton-capacity, 4.05-m-wide, 16.8-m-long bow ramp; a stern docking capacity for up to four landing craft on the main vehicle deck; and two 22-ton-capacity, 18-m-long, 6-m-wide internal elevators between the vehicle deck and the upper deck. The stern door is 15.6 m wide by 8 m high and swings down to form a 7-m, 66-ton-capacity vehicle ramp. Two 25-ton cranes are fitted. Cargo capacity includes up to 18 tanks, 20 other vehicles, and 350 troops, for a total of more than 1,080 tons. Four EP 02–class landing craft [LCVP] and two RIBs are carried in quadrantial davits. Have an integrated bridge system to enable one operator to control ship speed and direction. There is a prominent bow bulb, which may interfere with beaching. The engine rooms are designed for full-time unmanned operation. Twin rudders are fitted.

Endurance (L 207) Singapore Technologies Marine, 1999

Combat systems: Were originally to have had two 8-cell vertical launchers for Barak SAMs; a planned twin 40-mm OTOBreda Compact and 30-mm Goalkeeper SGE-30 CIWS were also omitted from the armament suite. A twin helicopter landing and deck traversing system is installed on the flight deck, and two AS.332M Super Puma helicopters can be carried. An integrated communications system with fiber-optic local area network is fitted, and there is an integrated combat information center.

Note: British *Sir Lancelot*–class vehicle cargo ship *Perseverance* (L 206) was decommissioned during 10-01 in preparation for her conversion into a submarine support ship; see entry under [AS].

Disposal note: LST 542–class vehicle landing ships *Excellence* (L 202, ex-T-LST 629) and *Intrepid* (L 203, ex-T-LST 579) were decommissioned and stricken 23-11-00. They, along with sisters *Endurance* (L 201; ex-*Holmes County,* LST 836) and *Persistence* (L 205, ex-T-LST 613), which were stricken during 1998, remain afloat.

♦ 6 RPL 60–class utility landing craft [LCU]

	Bldr	Laid down	L	In serv.
RPL 60	North SY, Singapore	. . .	11-85	1986
RPL 61	North SY, Singapore	. . .	11-85	1986
RPL 62	Singapore Technologies Marine	5-85	10-85	2-11-85
RPL 63	Singapore Technologies Marine	5-85	10-85	2-11-85
RPL 64	Singapore Technologies Marine	. . .	. . .	1993
RPL 65	Singapore Technologies Marine	. . .	. . .	1993

RPL 60 John Mortimer, 8-01

D: 151 tons (approx. 330 fl) **S:** 10 kts **Dim:** 36.0 (33.0 pp) × 8.5 × 1.8
A: none **Electronics:** Radar: 1 . . .
M: 2 Deutz-M.A.N. D2540MLE diesels; 2 Schottel vertical cycloidal props; 860 bhp
Crew: 6 tot.

AMPHIBIOUS WARFARE SHIPS AND CRAFT *(continued)*

Remarks: First four were ordered 28-2-85. Units differ in detail, by builder. Cargo capacity: 110 tons max. Can carry 450 standing troops or two AMX13 tanks. Cargo deck: 26.5 × 6.6 m. Painted green and assigned to the Naval Logistics Command.

♦ 30 EP 02–class vehicle and personnel landing craft [LCVP]
Bldr: Singapore Technologies Marine, Jurong (In serv. 1993–. . .)

EP 02–class landing craft 357 Brian Morrison, 8-00

D: 38 tons (fl) **S:** 20 kts **Dim:** 21.0 × 5.6 × 0.7
A: 2 single 12.7-mm mg
M: 2 M.A.N. D2866 LE diesels; 2 KaMeWa waterjets; 880 bhp
Range: 100/20 **Crew:** 4 tot. + 30 troops

Remarks: Enlarged version of EP 01 class, with greater freeboard and an 18-ton cargo capacity. Numbered in the 300 series.

♦ 10 U.S. 22-foot Whaler class [LCP]
Bldr: Boston Whaler, Rockland, Mass. (In serv. 1989)

D: 1.5 tons light (2.25 fl) **S:** 40 kts **Dim:** 6.81 × 2.26 × 0.36
A: 1 12.7-mm mg; 1 40-mm Mk 19 grenade launcher
M: 2 Johnson OMC gasoline outboard engines; 360 bhp
Range: 167/40; 750/. . . **Fuel:** 243 liters **Crew:** 3 tot.

Remarks: GRP-hulled open launches. Used by Naval Diving Unit combat swimmer group. To be replaced by new 12-m craft not yet ordered.

♦ 100 EP 01–class personnel landing craft [LCP]
Bldr: Singapore Technologies Marine, Jurong (In serv. 1980s–90s)

EP 01–class landing craft L 210-1—assigned to the landing ship *Endeavour* (L 210) Brian Morrison, 10-01

D: 4 tons (fl) **S:** 20 kts **Dim:** 13.6 × 3.7 × 0.6
M: 2 M.A.N. D2866 LE diesels; 2 Hamilton 362 waterjets; 816 bhp
Range: 100/20 **Crew:** 2 tot. + 30 troops

Remarks: Typed "Fast Craft, Equipment and Personnel." Aluminum construction craft, with a cargo well and bow ramp. Can carry one platoon of troops or a light vehicle. Are assigned to 195 Squadron. Now are numbered in the 500 and 800 series, except for those carried aboard the larger tank landing ships, which wear the same pennant number as their hosts.

Rigid inflatable boat operated by Singapore Navy to carry eight special forces personnel in shock-mounted seats—one of at least two such craft in service; note the sound-shrouded outboard motors beneath the radar installation at the stern NAVPIC-Holland, 10-98

Note: The Singapore Army (q.v.) possesses some 450 small personnel landing boats.

AUXILIARIES

♦ 1 U.K. Sir Lancelot–class submarine tender [AS]
Bldr: Fairfield SB & Eng. Co., Govan, Scotland

	Laid down	L	In serv.
L 206 PERSEVERANCE (ex-*Lowland Lancer;* ex-*Sir Lancelot,* L 3029)	3-62	25-6-63	16-1-64

Perseverance (L 206)—prior to modification to serve as a submarine tender Brian Morrison, 8-00

D: 3,270 tons (5,674 fl) **S:** 17.25 kts (15 sust.)
Dim: 126.45 (111.66 pp) × 17.68 × 3.95
A: 2 2-round Simbad SAM syst. (. . . Mistral missiles); 1 40-mm 70-cal. Bofors L70 AA; 6 single 12.7-mm mg
Electronics:
Radar: 1 Norcontrol DB 2000 nav.; 1 . . . nav.
EW: Thales DR-2000 intercept
M: 2 Denny-Sulzer 12MH51 diesels; 2 props; 9,520 bhp—bow-thruster
Electric: 1,400 kw tot. (4 × 350-kw diesel sets)
Range: 8,000/15 **Fuel:** 811 tons **Crew:** 65 tot.

Remarks: 6,390 grt/2,215 dwt. Purchased in 10-92 from Lowline, Ltd., and delivered to Singapore 21-11-92 to begin conversion at Singapore Shipbuilding & Engineering as a fleet support ship, the first replacement for the five former U.S. Navy LSTs. Had served as a British Royal Fleet Auxiliary from completion until put up for sale 31-3-89 and sold commercial 1-6-90. Was decommissioned in 10-01 in preparation for conversion into a submarine support ship; details of the conversion have not yet been released. The pennant number may be changed to the A series.
Hull systems: Beaching cargo capacity is 340 tons, using the bow ramp; both bow and stern ramps serve the two interior vehicle cargo decks. Cargo tanks can accommodate 120 tons of vehicle fuel. In RFA service, had accommodations for 402 troops and could carry 534 in an emergency. Equipped with two 20-ton- and two 3-ton-capacity cranes. Has helicopter landing areas on a platform aft and amidships. Carries two EP 01–class LCPs in davits aft. A Marisat SATCOM terminal is fitted.

SERVICE CRAFT

♦ 2 floating dry docks [YFDL]
Bldr: Singapore Technologies Marine, Jurong (In serv. 1994)

FD 1 FD 2

FD 1 and FD 2 NAVPIC-Holland, 4-94

Remarks: Capacity: 600 tons. FD 1 is based at Tuas, FD 2 at Brani.

♦ 2 ALC-1800-class personnel launches [YFL]
Bldr: Le Comte, Vianen, the Netherlands (L: 16-10-85; in serv. 1-11-85)

FL 1 FL 2

Remarks: No data available. Ordered 10-4-85 and laid down 12-6-85 and 4-7-85, respectively.

♦ 1 route survey craft/diving tender [YGS]
Bldr: Singapore Technologies Marine, Jurong

	L	In serv.
A 102 JUPITER	3-4-90	1-6-90

D: 170 tons (fl) **S:** 14.25 kts **Dim:** 35.70 (33.50 wl) × 7.10 × 2.30 (props)
A: 1 20-mm Oerlikon GAM-B01 AA; 2 single 12.7-mm mg
Electronics: Radar: 1 Decca 1226 nav.
M: 2 Deutz-MWM TBD 234 V12 diesels; 2 props; 1,360 bhp—azimuth thruster
Electric: 345 kw tot. (3 × 115-kw diesel-driven sets)

SERVICE CRAFT *(continued)*

Jupiter (A 102) H&L Van Ginderen, 4-98

Range: 200/14.5; 288/4 on steerable thruster
Crew: 5 officers, 28 enlisted + divers

Remarks: Sophisticated multipurpose craft capable of performing mine clearance route survey work, acting as a diving tender, or assisting in salvage operations. Carries a towed side-scan high resolution sonar and has an underwater data logging system and precision navigation equipment. To assist divers, has a two-man decompression chamber and two high-pressure compressors. Carries a 10-man rigid inflatable dinghy with a 60-bhp engine, handled by a 1.5-ton crane. Also employed to carry remotely operated vehicles to assist in developing minehunting techniques. Designed with German assistance. Assigned to 194 Squadron, 3rd Flotilla.

♦ **1 fuel lighter [YO]**
Bldr: Siong Huat SY, Singapore (In serv. 1-9-87)

Jolly Rodger II

D: 800 dwt **S:** . . . **Dim:** . . . × . . . × . . .
M: 2 MWM TPK-6K diesels; 2 props; 2,060 bhp

Remarks: Laid down 8-6-87, launched 11-8-87.

POLICE COAST GUARD

PATROL BOATS [WPB]

Note: Under a 1999 contract for the Southerly 18-m-class small patrol boats, two 20-m, 30-kt command boats are also to be constructed; no data yet available. Also to be acquired are six rigid inflatable patrol launches.

♦ **0 (+ 20 + 20) Southerly 10.5-meter-class small patrol RIBs**
Bldr: Asia-Pacific Shipyards, Singapore (In serv. 2001–. . .)

D: . . . tons **S:** 52 kts **Dim:** 10.80 × 3.05 × . . .
M: 3 Yamaha gasoline outboards; 3 props; 750 bhp
Range: . . ./. . . **Fuel:** 880 liters **Crew:** 2 tot. + 8 constables

Remarks: The first 20 were ordered in fall 2000, with an option for 20 more later. Being produced in cooperation with Australian Motor Yachts, Coomera. Have an aluminum alloy core structure.

♦ **25 Southerly 18-meter-class small patrol boats**
Bldr: Asia-Pacific Shipyards, Singapore (In serv. 1998–2000)

PT 20 Manta Ray
PT 21 . . . . . . Rat
PT 22 . . . . . . Ray
PT 23 Bull Ray
PT 24 Butterfly Ray
PT 25 Cownose Ray
PT 26 . . . . . . Ray
PT 27 Electric Ray
PT 28 . . . . . . Ray
PT 29 . . . . . . Ray
PT 30 Eagle Ray
PT 31 Giant Reef Ray
PT 32 River Ray
PT 33 . . . . . . Ray
PT 34 . . . . . . Ray
PT 35 . . . . . . Ray
PT 36 . . . . . . Ray
PT 37 . . . . . . Ray
PT 38 . . . . . . Ray
PT 39 . . . . . . Ray
PT 40 . . . . . . Ray
PT 41 . . . . . . Ray
PT 42 . . . . . . Ray
PT 43 . . . . . . Ray
PT 44 . . . . . . Ray

Manta Ray (PT 20)—command craft, with larger pilothouse
Brian Morrison, 8-00

River Ray (PT 32)—standard-configuration Southerly 18-m-class unit
Brian Morrison, 8-00

D: . . . tons **S:** 40+ kts **Dim:** 18.0 × 5.4 × 0.9
A: 1 7.62-mm mg **Electronics:** Radar: 1 . . . nav.
M: 2 . . . diesels; 2 waterjets; 400 bhp **Crew:** 5 tot.

Remarks: Contract for 18 units was awarded in 9-97 to Geraldton Boat Builders, Geraldton, W.A., Australia, which built the boats at Asia-Pacific's Singapore yard; a contract for the other units was issued during 1-00. Aluminum construction. Can reach 40 kts on 80% power. Two, P 20 and P 30, were configured as command and control boats. Were to replace the earlier PX-series patrol boats.

♦ **4 White Marlin–class fast interceptors**
Bldr: . . . . . .

PK 21 White Marlin
PK 22 Silver Marlin
PK 23 Striped Marlin
PK 24 Black Marlin

White Marlin (PK 21) Brian Morrison, 8-00

Remarks: No data available.

♦ **5 (+ . . .) Fish-class fast interceptors**
Bldr: Greenbay Marine, Green Bay, Wis. (In serv. 5-95 to . . .-96)

PK 10 Sailfish
PK 20 Spearfish
PK 30 Billfish
PK 40 Swordfish
PK 50 Spikefish

Sailfish (PK 10) Brian Morrison, 8-00

D: . . . tons **S:** 50 kts **Dim:** 12.8 × 3.2 × 0.5
A: 1 7.62-mm mg **Electronics:** Radar: 1 Furuno . . . nav.
M: 3 MerCruiser 502 Magnum diesel outdrive engines; . . . bhp

Remarks: Designed by Philip Curran. No longer carry the standard white-red-white diagonal hull striping of the Singapore Police Coast Guard, in order to reduce their visibility.

♦ **12 PT 12 class** Bldr: Singapore Technologies Marine, Jurong

	In serv.		In serv.
PT 12	2-87	PT 18	3-89
PT 13	2-87	PT 19 Dorado	3-89
PT 14	21-1-89	PT 20	4-89
PT 15 Todak	21-1-89	PT 21	4-89
PT 16	21-1-89	PT 22	. . .
PT 17 Striped Marlin	3-89	PT 23	. . .

COAST GUARD PATROL BOATS [WPB] *(continued)*

Striped Marlin (PT 17) Douglas A. Cromby, 6-00

D: 21 tons (fl) **S:** 30+ kts **Dim:** 14.80 × 4.23 × 1.20
A: 2 single 7.62-mm mg **Electronics:** Radar: 1 Decca . . . nav.
M: PT 12–15: 2 M.A.N. D2840 LE diesels; 2 props; 1,252 bhp—PT 16–23: 2 MTU 12V183 TC 91 diesels; 2 props; 1,182 bhp
Range: 310/22 **Fuel:** 2,000 liters **Crew:** 4 tot.

Remarks: Updated version of the PT 1 class. The final two are configured as command boats and have air-conditioned seating for 10 passengers. All have names.

♦ 11 PT 1 class Bldr: Singapore SB & Eng., Jurong

	Laid down	L	In serv.
PT 1	21-7-83	19-12-83	14-1-84
PT 2	25-7-83	6-1-84	17-2-84
PT 3	28-7-83	16-1-84	13-3-84
PT 4	1-8-83	23-3-84	6-4-84
PT 5 Cosby	15-9-83	23-4-84	15-5-84
PT 6 Dolphin	30-9-83	14-5-84	1-6-84
PT 7 Leatherjacket	11-10-83	30-5-84	19-6-84
PT 8	14-10-83	16-6-84	5-7-84
PT 9	21-12-83	4-7-84	1-8-84
PT 10 Pari Burong	6-1-84	23-7-84	24-8-84
PT 11 Piranha	19-1-84	10-8-84	5-9-84

Leatherjacket (PT 7) Brian Morrison, 8-00

D: 20 tons **S:** 30 kts **Dim:** 14.54 × 4.23 × 1.20 (props)
A: 1 7.62-mm mg **Electronics:** Radar: 1 Decca . . . nav.
M: 2 M.A.N. D2542 MLE diesels; 2 props; 1,076 bhp
Range: 310/22 **Fuel:** 2,600 liters **Crew:** 7 tot.

Remarks: Aluminum construction. Four near-sisters (CE 5–CE 8) were built for Singapore Customs (delivered 6-2-87) and seven for Brunei.

♦ 12 Swift class
Bldr: Singapore Technologies Marine, Jurong (In serv. 20-10-81)

PH 50 Hammerhead Shark (ex-*Swift Lancer,* P 12)
PH 51 Mako Shark (ex-*Swift Swordsman,* P 14)
PH 52 White Shark (ex-*Swift Archer,* P 16)
PH 53 Blue Shark (ex-*Swift Combatant,* P 18)
PH 54 Tiger Shark (ex-*Swift Knight,* P 11)
PH 55 Basking Shark (ex-*Swift Warrior,* P 15)
PH 56 Sandbar Shark (ex-*Swift Conqueror,* P 21)
PH 57 Thresher Shark (ex-*Swift Chieftain,* P 23)
PH 58 Whitetip Shark (ex-*Swift Warlord,* P 17)
PH 59 Blacktip Shark (ex-*Swift Challenger,* P 19)
PH 60 Goblin Shark (ex-*Swift Cavalier,* P 20)
PH 61 School Shark (ex-*Swift Centurion,* P 22)

Mako Shark (PH 51) Brian Morrison, 8-00

D: 45.7 tons (fl) **S:** 33 kts (31 sust.) **Dim:** 22.7 (20.0 pp) × 6.2 × 1.6 (3.0 props)
A: 1 20-mm 90-cal. Oerlikon GAM-B01 AA; 2 single 7.62-mm mg
Electronics: Radar: 1 Decca 1226 ARPA nav.
M: 2 Deutz SBA-16M816 diesels; 2 props; 2,660 bhp
Range: 550/20; 900/10 **Fuel:** 8.6 tons **Crew:** 3 officers, 9 enlisted

Remarks: First unit was launched 8-6-80. On 15-2-93, the first four were transferred to the Police Coast Guard; four more followed in 1994, and the final four were transferred and recommissioned 22-1-97.
Hull systems: Design based on the Australian de Havilland Capricornica design. Aluminum construction. Carry 2 tons of fresh water and have two generator sets.

Disposal note: The 24 patrol launches of the PX 1 class were to have been retired during 2000–01 with the delivery of the new Southerly 18-m-class patrol boats.

♦ 37 PC 32–class patrol launches
Bldr: Vosper Thornycroft, Singapore (In serv. 1978–79, . . .)

PC 32 through PC 65 PC 100 series

PC 32–class unit PC 110 NAVPIC-Holland, 4-95

D: 2 tons (fl) **S:** 35 kts **Dim:** 6.5 × 2.5 × 0.46
A: small arms **Electronics:** Radar: 1 Furuno . . . nav.
M: 2 Johnson outboards; 280 bhp **Crew:** 4 tot.

Remarks: PC 32–51 were delivered in 1978–79. The second series began building in the late 1980s.

Note: There are additional Police Coast Guard launches in service, including at least four in the PL series. Also in operation are a number of service craft, including the push-tug *Pilot Whale.*

Singapore Police Coast Guard push-tug Pilot Whale NAVPIC-Holland, 5-95

SINGAPORE ARMY

♦ **450 assault-personnel landing craft [LCP]**
Bldr: Singapore Technologies Marine, Jurong (In serv. 1980s)

D: . . . **S:** 12 kts **Dim:** 5.3 × 1.8 × 0.7 (molded depth)
M: 1 outboard motor; 50 shp **Crew:** 12 troops

Remarks: Man-portable craft.

CUSTOMS AND EXCISE SERVICE

Note: The Singapore Customs and Excise Service operates at least 28 patrol launches, including the large CE 8; 20-ton sisters CE 5 through CE 7; four CE 1–class launches, CE 1 through CE 4; and 20 or more C 70–class launches. Customs and excise craft are painted gray. The five large units can mount a single 7.62-mm mg. A new class of 12-m, 50-kt fast patrol RIB launches powered by four Yamaha 250-bhp gasoline outboards began delivery during 2001 from Lita Ocean, Singapore, employing prefabricated kits supplied by Marine Kits Australia.

Customs and Excise patrol boat CE 7 NAVPIC-Holland, 9-98

Customs and Excise patrol boat CE 3 Chris Sattler, 8-00

Customs and Excise patrol launch C 78 NAVPIC-Holland, 8-98

SINGAPORE PORTS AUTHORITY

Note: The Singapore Ports Authority operates 18 GP 50–class pilot launches, the hydrographic survey craft *Mata Ikan* (103 tons, built 1967), and survey launches *Discovery* and *Investigator* (31 tons, built 1980).

SLOVENIA

Slovene Republic

SLOVENE NATIONAL POLICE

(Nasi Mornarji)

Note: Officially formed 30-1-93 at the time of the launch of the first ship built for it, the training vessel *Sinji Galeb,* Slovenia's maritime force was officially referred to as the 430th Coastal Defense Unit of the Slovene Army, but in mid-1996, the entire organization was transferred to the Slovene National Police.

Personnel (2002): Approx. 60 total

Base: Isola, near Koper

PATROL BOATS [WPB]

♦ **1 Israeli Super Dvora Mk II class**
Bldr: RAMTA–Israeli Aircraft Industries, Be'er Sheva (In serv. 1-8-96)

HPL 21 Ankaran (ex-P 112)

D: 48 tons (54 fl) **S:** 42 kts **Dim:** 22.40 × 5.49 × 1.00
A: 2 single 20-mm 70-cal. Oerlikon Mk 10 AA; 2 single 12.7-mm mg
Electronics: Radar: 1 Koden MD 3220 nav.—E/O: 1 Elop MSIS surveillance
M: 2 MTU 8V396 TE94 diesels; 2 props; 3,000 bhp
Electric: 30 kw **Range:** 700/14 **Crew:** 3 officers, 9 enlisted

Remarks: Ordered in 9-95. Aluminum construction. Negotiations to purchase a second were under way as of 11-97, but no order followed.

♦ **1 GC 20 class** Bldr: Aviotechnica, Viareggio, Italy (In serv. 21-6-95)

P 111 Ladse

Ladse (P 111) H&L Van Ginderen, 1998

D: 44 tons (fl) **S:** 40 kts **Dim:** 19.86 × 5.00 × 0.90 (hull)
A: 1 7.62-mm mg **Electronics:** Radar: 2 Furuno . . . nav.
M: 2 MTU 8V396 TE84 diesels; 2 props; 2,400 bhp
Electric: 32 kw tot. (2 × 16-kw sets) **Range:** 270/35 **Crew:** 9 tot.

Remarks: Aluminum-magnesium alloy hull and superstructure. Not considered suitable for open-sea work.

SERVICE CRAFT

♦ **1 training launch [WYXT]** Bldr: . . . . . . (In serv. 30-1-93)

P 101 Sinji Galeb

Sinji Galeb (P 101) H&L Van Ginderen, 1998

Remarks: A 12-m, GRP-construction cabin cruiser; no other data available.

Note: Several small patrol boats and rigid inflatable patrol launches are in service. There is also a Slovene Customs Service, which also operates several small patrol boats.

SOLOMON ISLANDS

Republic of the Solomon Islands

ROYAL SOLOMON ISLANDS POLICE SERVICE

Personnel (2001): 14 officers, 46 constables

Note: Vessel names are prefaced by RSIPV (Royal Solomon Islands Police Vessel).

PATROL CRAFT [WPC]

♦ **2 ASI 315 design**
Bldr: Transfield ASI Pty, South Coogee, W.A., Australia

	Laid down	L	In serv.
03 Lata	12-9-87	19-5-88	3-9-88
04 Auki	23-1-91	. . .	2-11-91

Lata (03) H&L Van Ginderen, 10-94

Auki (04) H&L Van Ginderen, 1-94

D: 165 tons (fl) **S:** 21 kts **Dim:** 31.50 (28.60 wl) × 8.10 × 2.12
A: 3 single 12.7-mm mg **Electronics:** Radar: 1 Furuno 1011 nav.
M: 2 Caterpillar 3516 diesels; 2 props; 2,820 bhp **Electric:** 116 kw tot.
Range: 2,500/12 **Fuel:** 27.9 tons **Endurance:** 10 days
Crew: 1 officer, 4 noncommissioned, 9 constables

Remarks: Pacific Patrol Boat design for the Australian foreign aid program. First unit was ordered 3-10-85. 03 is to be refitted in 2003, 04 in 2006. Carry a 5-m aluminum boarding boat. Have an extensive navigational suite, including a Furuno FSN-70 NAVSAT receiver, 525 HFD/F, 120 MF–HFD/F, FE-881 echo sounder, and DS-70 doppler log. Sisters are in service in Fiji, Papua New Guinea, Samoa, and Vanuatu.

DEPARTMENT OF FISHERIES

PATROL BOATS [WPB]

♦ **1 Carpentaria class**
Bldr: De Havilland Marine, Homebush Bay, Australia (In serv. 30-3-79)

01 Tulagi

D: 27 tons (fl) **S:** 27 kts **Dim:** 16.0 × 5.0 × 1.2
A: 2 single 7.62-mm mg **Electronics:** Radar: 1 Decca 110 nav.
M: 2 G.M. Detroit Diesel 12V71 TI diesels; 2 props; 1,120 bhp
Range: 700/22 **Crew:** 10 tot.

Remarks: Operated by the Department of Fisheries for fisheries patrol.

Disposal note: Oceanographic research craft *Solomon Atu* and *Solomon Kariqua* are operated by other Solomon Islands government agencies, as are the utility landing craft *Ligumo III* and *Ulushaghe.*

Tulagi (01) H&L Van Ginderen, 1989

SOUTH AFRICA

Republic of South Africa

Personnel (2002): 5,050 uniformed personnel and about 1,600 civilians. There were also 2,984 naval reserves.

Bases: Headquarters at Pretoria. Operational command and principal base at Simon's Town, with missile boats based at SAS *Scorpion,* Salisbury Island, Durban. Operational command center at Silvermine, near Cape Town. Officer training is conducted at Gordon's Bay and enlisted basic training at Saldanha Bay. During 2002, SAS *Scorpion* is to be scaled back to the status of naval station, and the government-owned ARMSCOR agency is to take over the management of Simon's Town Dockyard.

Naval Aviation: A South African Air Force detachment is available to assist the navy and can provide eight AS.316 Alouette-III and 51 Oryx (Cougar Mk 1) helicopters for shipboard operations. Five C-47TP transports are used for maritime surveillance, and two SafAir L-100 Hercules commercial transports have been chartered for search-and-rescue and pollution-control duties. Four to six EADS (ex-CASA) CN-235 maritime patrol aircraft may be procured to replace the aged C-47TP aircraft. A plan to procure four GKN Westland Super Lynx 300 helicopters for service on the new frigates has been deferred; during 6-01, the U.S. Navy offered to donate four SH-2G Super SeaSprite shipboard helicopters.

Weapons and Sensors: Most equipment is of European or Israeli origin. Stocks of U.S.-supplied Mk 44 ASW torpedoes are being upgraded as the A44, fitted with a 61-kg Sochem directed-energy warhead and a new homing head; a running time of 6 minutes at 32 kts is claimed. As of 10-00, only a dozen French-made E 14/15 torpedoes remained serviceable.

The twin 35-mm 35DP6 gunmount is under development as an antiaircraft weapon; mounting two Vektor GA 35 guns with a 1,175-m/sec muzzle velocity and a firing rate of 550 rounds per gun per minute, the mount will also have a t.v./infrared sight, and the guns may be adapted to fire the Oerlikon-Contraves AHEAD (Advanced Hit Efficiency and Destruction) round. The weapons are planned to be mounted on the new frigates.

The Skorpioen antiship missile is a license-built version of the Israeli Gabriel-II. A new warhead for backfitting to existing missiles has been developed by Sochem; it consists of a steel casing containing 35 self-forging-fragment explosive charges, with the voids filled with PBX explosive. The warhead weighs 150 kg, of which 99 kg is explosive. As of 10-00, only 36 missiles remained serviceable.

The SAMCON 600 naval mine is offered for export and may be purchased for domestic use. It can be launched by aircraft, submarines, and surface ships.

Denel announced late in 1998 the development of the Umkhonto vertically launched shipboard SAM for service entry around 2002. Intended for use on the new South African Navy frigates, the missile will initially employ heat-seeking guidance but may later incorporate active radar homing and a larger rocket motor. Missiles are to be carried in groups of four launchers. Data for the Umkhonto, the design of which is based on the Crotale NG, include:

Length: 3.30 m **Diameter:** 180 mm **Wingspan:** 400 mm
Weight: 125 kg **Warhead:** 20 kg blast/fragmentation
Speed: Mach 3.5 **Range:** 800 m min./12,000 m max.

Note: Ship names are prefaced by SAS (South African Ship).

ATTACK SUBMARINES [SS]

♦ **0 (+ 3) German Type 209/1400 MOD class**
Bldr: German Submarine Consortium

	Laid down	L	In serv.
S	. . .	. . .	7-05
S	. . .	. . .	7-06
S	. . .	. . .	7-07

D: 1,472 tons surf./1,594 tons sub. **S:** 11.0 kts surf./21.5 kts sub.
Dim: 62.00 × 6.20 (7.60 over stern planes) × 5.50
A: 8 bow 533-mm TT (14 torpedoes and/or mines)
Electronics:
Radar: . . .
Sonar: STN Atlas Elektronik CSU-90 suite
EW: Grintek . . .
M: 4 MTU 12V493 A280 AG diesels (800 bhp each), 4 405-kw generator sets, 1 Siemens electric motor; 1 prop; 5,000 shp

ATTACK SUBMARINES [SS] *(continued)*

Range: 10,000/8 snorkel; 25/21.5, 230/8, 390/4 sub. **Endurance:** 45 days
Crew: 30 tot. + 5 trainees

Remarks: Design selected 12-11-98 to replace the *Daphné* class; an agreement to purchase the submarines from the German Submarine Consortium (consisting of Howaldtswerke Deutsche Werft, Thyssen Nordseewerke, and Ferrostaal) for 4.5 billion rand (about $750 million) was concluded 16-6-99, with the final contract signed 7-7-00. Construction on the first unit was begun by HDW 22-5-01, and fabrication of the first stern section was begun by Kockums during 4-01.
Hull systems: Normal operating depth: 200 m max.
Combat systems: Will have the STN Atlas Elektronik ISUS-90-45 combat system, non-hull-penetrating Zeiss OMS 100 optronic sensor mast, Zeiss SERO 400 electro-optic periscope system, and Grintek Communications comms equipment.

♦ **3 French Daphné class** (1 in *reserve*)
Bldr: Dubigeon, Nantes

	Laid down	L	In serv.
S 97 *Spear* (ex-*Maria Van Riebeeck*)	14-3-68	18-3-69	24-7-70
S 98 Umkhonto (ex-*Emily Hobhouse*)	18-11-68	24-10-69	26-2-71
S 99 Assegaai (ex-*Johanna Van Der Merwe*)	24-4-69	21-7-70	27-8-71

Umkhonto (S 98)—as *Emily Hobhouse* H&L Van Ginderen, 4-97

D: 755 tons std.; 869 tons surf./1,040 tons sub. **S:** 13.5 kts surf./16 kts sub.
Dim: 57.78 × 6.90 × 5.23 (max.)
A: 12 550-mm TT (8 fwd, 4 aft; 12 E 14/15 and L 3 torpedoes—no reloads)
Electronics:
Radar: Thales Calypso-II search
Sonar: Thales DUUA-2 active (8.4 kHz); Thales DUUX-2 passive ranging; Thales DSUV-2 passive search
EW: S 98, 99: Grinaker . . . intercept (2–19 GHz)—S 97: Thomson-CSF ARUD intercept
M: 2 SEMT-Pielstick 8 PA4 135 diesels, 2 450-kw generator sets, electric drive: 2 Jeumont-Schneider 800-shp (1,300-shp for short periods) dual-armature motors; 2 props
Range: 2,700/12.5 surf.; 4,300/7.5 snorkel **Crew:** 6 officers, 45 enlisted

Remarks: Ordered 10-2-67. Sequential modernization of the class began in 1986 at Simon's Town Dockyard with a South African–developed command system, installation of air-conditioning and a freshwater distiller, and new sonar and combat data systems by Trivetts-UEC, Durban; S 98 completed 1-89, S 99 on 12-12-90, and S 97 on 13-3-92. S 98 completed a further modernization/overhaul in 3-95. New communications suites, periscopes, and new data displays are being added during refits that began with S 99 in 1996; S 99 was recommissioned 22-5-99, when all three were given new names. S 98 was in overhaul from 5-99 to 26-1-01, while S 97 has been in reserve since 1996.
Hull systems: Diving depth: 300 m. Have two 80-cell batteries, totaling 80 tons. There is berthing for only 34 personnel.
Combat systems: Torpedo tubes employ hydraulic ram-launching. The SOPELEM M41 search and ST3 attack periscopes have had their optics upgraded by Eloptro; the search periscope now has low-light-level television, and both now have passive rangefinding features. The sonar suite listed above is that originally installed. The DUUA-2 has been upgraded with new signal processing capabilities during modernizations, while the long-range passive set, passive ranging set, and intercept sonar are being replaced with UEC Projects–developed equipment. The Trivetts-UEC DCSC-2 torpedo fire-control system was installed during modernizations. In the active pair, the original ARUD intercept equipment has been replaced by a Grinaker system employing an omnidirectional antenna array and two color displays. The SEACOM 1 communications suite, which covers the HF, VHF, and UHF bands and also has an Inmarsat-C receiver, has been substituted, and S 99 now has a GPS receiver. During 1-99, African Defence Systems received a contract to install new combat systems and Denel a contract for new periscopes for S 98 and S 99.

FRIGATES [FF]

♦ **0 (+ 4) MEKO A-200SAN frigates**
Bldrs: A: Blohm + Voss, Hamburg; B: HDW, Kiel

	Bldr	Laid down	L	Del.	In serv.
F	A	2-8-01	. . .	12-02	8-04
F	B	. . .	. . .	6-03	12-04
F	A	. . .	. . .	28-11-03	4-05
F	B	. . .	. . .	6-04	6-05

D: 3,590 tons (fl) **S:** 28 kts **Dim:** 121.00 (105.20 wl) × 16.34 × 4.40 (hull mean)
A: 8 MM 40 Exocet Block 2 SSM; 16 Denel Umkhonto VLS SAM—1 76-mm 62-cal. OTOBreda DP; 1 twin 35-mm . . . Denel AA; 2 single 20-mm 90-cal. Rheinmetall AA; . . . 533-mm TT; 1 or 2 Super Lynx 300 or SH-2G Super SeaSprite helicopters (with Mokapa antiship missiles)

MEKO A-200SAN frigate—computer rendering Blohm + Voss, 3-00

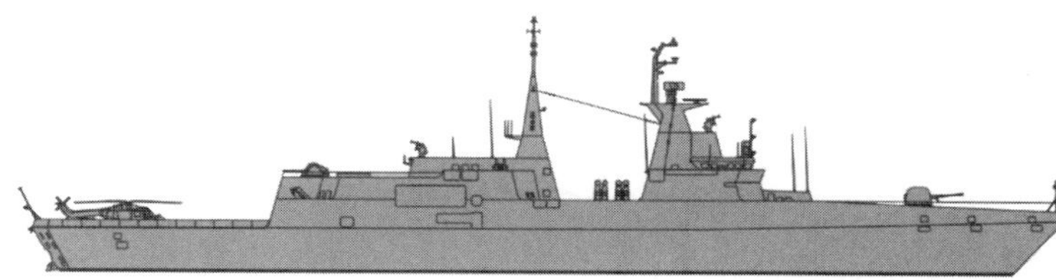
MEKO A-200SAN frigate Blohm + Voss, 3-00

Electronics:
Radar: 1 Thales Scout nav.; 1 Thales MRR 3-D search; 2 Reutech ORT RTS-6400 f.c.
Sonar: Thales Kingklip hull-mounted LF
TACAN: Thales Vesta beacon
EW: Avitronics Shrike electronic and laser signal warning; 2 Wallop-Grintek UltraBarricade decoy syst. (2 24-round trainable RL)
E/O: 1 Reutech . . . tracking; 2 M-Tek target-desig. sights
M: CODAG: 1 G.E. LM-2500 gas turbine (26,824 shp), 2 MTU 16V1163 TB93 diesels (7,940 bhp each); 1 KaMeWa waterjet centerline, 2 Lips CP props outboard
Electric: 2,200 kw tot. (4 × 550-kw, MTU . . . diesels driving)
Range: 7,000/. . . **Endurance:** 28 days
Crew: 92 ship's company + 8 aircrew (124 tot. accomm.)

Remarks: The Blohm + Voss design was selected 12-11-98 and ordered 3-12-99. Work began on the first unit 28-2-01 and on the third 28-8-01. The program is known as Project Sitron. The ships will be outfitted and weapons integration performed after delivery in South Africa.
Hull systems: Hull is shaped to reduce radar signature. Have fin stabilizers. The propulsion system is described as CODAG-WARP (Combined Diesel and Gas Turbine—Waterjet and Refined Propellers), with the cross-connected diesels driving the two CP props and the gas turbine the waterjet. One diesel can drive both propeller shafts for economic cruising at up to 20 kts. The gas turbine and diesels exhaust out the stern of the ship, providing some residual thrust and signature-reduction benefits. Twin rudders are fitted. The helicopter hangar will accommodate one Oryx or two smaller helicopters.
Combat systems: Will have a Thales Tavitac combat data system. The 76-mm guns are to be recycled from older SAN ships. The Umkhonto missiles will be carried in four quadruple vertical-launch modules. The decoy launchers carry 24 102-mm Wallop SuperPallisade and SuperStockade decoy rockets, with two tubes for larger decoys. No EW jamming system will be carried. Two indigenously made 25-mm LIW GA35 guns are to replace the 20-mm mounts later. Will have the locally developed Grinaker Seacon-1 external and Thales FOKON internal communications suites. The Kentron Mokapa antiship missile for the helicopters has a range of 12 n.m.

GUIDED-MISSILE PATROL CRAFT [PTG]

♦ **7 Israeli Reshev ("Warrior") class** (3 in *reserve*)
Bldrs: P 1562–1563: Israeli SY, Haifa; others: Sandock Austral SY, Durban

	L	In serv.
P 1562 *Shaka* (ex-*P. W. Botha*)	9-9-77	2-12-77
P 1563 Adam Kok (ex-*Frederick Creswell*)	15-1-78	6-4-78
P 1564 *Sekhukhuni* (ex-*Jim Fouche*)	18-9-78	22-12-78
P 1565 Isaac Dyobha (ex-*Franz Erasmus*)	16-3-79	27-7-79
P 1567 Galeshewe (ex-*Hendrik Mentz*)	26-3-82	11-2-83
P 1568 *Job Masego* (ex-*Kobie Coetsee*)	3-9-82	11-2-83
P 1569 Makhanda (ex-*Magnus Malan*)	27-3-86	4-7-86

Adam Kok (P 1563) H&L Van Ginderen, 4-00

GUIDED-MISSILE PATROL CRAFT [PTG] *(continued)*

Makhanda (P 1569) H&L Van Ginderen, 11-97

D: 415 tons (450 fl) **S:** 34.5 kts (32 sust.)
Dim: 58.10 (54.10 pp) × 7.62 × 2.35 (fwd; 2.69 aft)
A: 6 Skorpioen SSM; 2 single 76-mm 62-cal. OTOBreda Compact DP; 2 single 20-mm 90-cal. Oerlikon GAM-B01 AA; 4 single 12.7-mm mg
Electronics:
Radar: 1 Thales THD-1040 Neptune surf./air search; 1 Alenia RTN-10X Orion f.c.
EW: P 1563: Grintek MN-21 intercept; Systel Kondor comms intercept; ADS signal warning and analysis processor; ADS decoy control syst.—others: Elta MN-53 intercept; Elta EA-2118 comms intercept; Elta Rattler jammer—all: 4 ACDS decoy RL
M: 4 MTU 16V538 TB91 diesels; 4 props; 12,000 bhp
Electric: 352 kw tot. (4 × 88 kw) **Range:** 1,500/30; 3,000/20; 5,000/15
Endurance: 10 days **Crew:** 8 officers, 44 enlisted

Remarks: Six were ordered in late 1974; a second sextet was ordered 15-11-77, three of which were never laid down, although equipment, including weapons and electronics, had been bought for them. Originally referred to as the "Minister" class and named for former ministers of defense, the ships were renamed on 1-4-97 after South African military heroes, and the official class name was also altered. P 1563 completed an electronics equipment upgrade early in 1997, and P 1567 was refitted from 1997 to 3-98, but without the electronics upgrade. Based at SAS *Scorpion,* Salisbury Island, Durban. The last of the class is to be stricken in 2008.

Disposals: *Jan Smuts* (P 1561) was decommissioned to reserve 20-3-98 but has been stripped of useful equipment and will not likely be returned to service. *René Sethren* (P 1566, ex-*Oswald Pirow*) was stricken 12-10-01.
Hull systems: Have a water washdown system to permit operating in NBC warfare conditions. Engines exhaust either above or below the waterline, the latter employed to reduce infrared signature. Have six spare berths for trainees. P 1567 and later have strengthened hulls and some changes in the electronics suite, but the entire class has been severely stressed by the heavy seas off South Africa's coast.
Combat systems: The Skorpioen antiship missile is a license-built version of the Israeli Gabriel-II; its range is 20 n.m. at Mach 0.7. Carry 500 rounds of 76-mm ammunition. The Project Calaban modernization program was to incorporate a new communications suite, improved EW, a modern target-designation system using a computerized combat data system, a weapons-control update, and new fuzing for the 76-mm ammunition, but apparently only P 1563 received the entire package.

PATROL BOATS [PB]

♦ 28 Namicurra class
Bldr: Tornado Products, South Africa (In serv. 1980–81)

Y 1501 through Y 1505 Y 1521 through Y 1530
Y 1507 through Y 1519

Namicurra-class Y 1527 Brian Morrison, 2-01

D: 4 tons light (5.2 fl) **S:** 30 kts **Dim:** 9.5 × 2.7 × 0.8
A: 1 12.7-mm mg; 1 twin 7.62-mm mg; 1 shotgun
Electronics: Radar: 1 Furuno . . . nav.
M: 2 BMW or Yamaha inboard-outboard gasoline engines; 2 props; 380 bhp
Range: 180/20 **Crew:** 4 tot.

Remarks: Radar-equipped, GRP-hulled, catamaran harbor craft that can be land-transported on trailers. Sister Y 1520 was transferred to Malawi 29-10-88, and Y 1506 was lost off Port Elizabeth (date not available). When fitted, the 7.62-mm twin mount is positioned aft in the cockpit, while the 12.7-mm mg is located at the aft edge of the pilothouse; normally only the 12.7-mm mg is carried, in the aft position. Now carry only the letter "Y" and the last two digits of the pennant number on each side of the pilothouse.

MINE WARFARE SHIPS

♦ 4 River-class coastal minehunters [MHC]
Bldrs: First two: Abeking & Rasmussen, Lemwerder, Germany; others: Sandock Austral SY, Durban

	In serv.
M 1499 Umkomaas (ex-*Navors I*)	13-2-81
M 1213 Umgeni (ex-*Navors II*)	23-3-81
M 1142 Umzimkulu (ex-*Navors III*)	30-10-81
M 1212 Umhloti (ex-*Navors IV*)	26-11-81

Umhloti (M 1212) H&L Van Ginderen, 4-00

Umzimkulu (M 1142) H&L Van Ginderen, 4-00

D: 380 tons (fl) **S:** 16.5 kts **Dim:** 48.10 (44.50 pp) × 8.45 × 2.10 (fwd; 2.50 aft)
A: 1 20-mm 90-cal. Oerlikon GAM-B01 AA; 2 single 12.7-mm mg
Electronics:
Radar: 1 Decca . . . nav.
Sonar: 1 Simrad . . . hull-mounted HF; 1 Klein towed side-looking HF
M: 2 MTU 12V652 TB81 diesels; 2 Voith-Schneider vertical cycloidal props; 3,156 bhp—2 85-kw electric motor/shaft generators for minehunting operations (7 kts max.)
Electric: 618 kw tot. (2 × 165-kw, 12-cyl. diesel sets; 1 × 118-kw diesel set; 2 × 85-kw shaft generators)
Range: 2,000+/13 **Fuel:** 55 tons **Crew:** 7 officers, 33 enlisted

Remarks: Ordered in 1978. The first two hulls were built in West Germany, ostensibly as "hydrological and geophysical research ships," and delivered to Sandock Austral Shipyard, Durban, in 1980 for outfitting. The last unit launched 31-7-81. All were originally painted with blue hulls and white superstructures; they were repainted gray during 1-82, but were not officially acknowledged as naval vessels until 28-1-88. Sufficient equipment was purchased to outfit a total of 12, but no work has begun on building additional units. They form the Mine Countermeasures Squadron, at Simon's Town. They are to serve through 2010.
Hull systems: Wooden construction, with GRP hull sheathing below the waterline. Have four rudders.
Combat systems: Have Minehunting System Mk 2, including two French PAP-104 remote-controlled submersibles per ship. Were designed to carry the Thales DUBM-21 minehunting sonar, but a Simrad retractable two-frequency set was fitted instead. Navigational equipment includes an MRD1 precision radionavigation set, gyrocompass, doppler log, and echo sounder. Have a mine disposal divers' rigid inflatable boat aft and a decompression chamber for the six-man mine disposal diver team. Thales–African Defence Systems data plotting and recording systems are being installed under a 5-99 contract.

♦ 4 ex-German Type 351 minesweepers [MSC]
Bldr: Burmester, Bremen

	L	In serv.
M . . . Tshwane (ex-*Schleswig,* M 1073)	2-10-57	30-10-58
M . . . Kapa (ex-*Düren,* M 1079)	12-6-58	22-4-59
M . . . Egoli (ex-*Konstanz,* M 1081)	30-9-58	23-7-59
M . . . Thekwini (ex-*Wolfsburg,* M 1082)	10-12-58	8-10-59

Six German Type 351 minesweepers on a barge, en route to South Africa
Findler & Winter, 1-01

MINE WARFARE SHIPS *(continued)*

D: 488 tons (fl) **S:** 16.5 kts **Dim:** 47.50 × 8.50 × 2.75
A: 1 40-mm 70-cal. Bofors AA
Electronics: Radar: 1 STN Atlas Elektronik TRS-N nav.—Sonar: DSQS-11A
M: 2 MTU MD 871 UM/1D diesels; 2 CP props; 3,300 bhp
Range: 2,200/16 **Electric:** 195 kw tot. **Crew:** 4 officers, 40 enlisted

Remarks: Transferred 15-1-01; departed 19-1-01 for Simon's Town on a pontoon barge under tow with sisters *Paderborn* (M 1076, stricken 24-11-99) and *Ulm* (M 1083, stricken 21-9-99), which were transferred for cannibalization but may instead be activated. The first two were recommissioned 5-9-01, and the second pair were to be recommissioned early in 2002. Locally referred to as the "City" class, they carry the tribal names for Pretoria, Kapstadt, Johannesburg, and Durban, respectively. They are former Type 320 minesweepers, each converted to control three F-1 Troika drone magnetic/acoustic minesweepers, completing on 19-3-81, 7-11-83, 24-5-82, and 4-3-82, respectively. South Africa also requested two Seehund drones, but Germany was not able to oblige; the ships are thus initially of little use except as patrol craft, although additional mine countermeasures equipment may be installed in South Africa. They are expected to operate for about 10 years before replacement by newer ships.
Hull systems: Wooden construction, with original nonmagnetic engines.
Combat systems: As transferred, could carry and tow an Oropesa sweep rig and stow numerous channel-marking (dan) buoys. Were each intended to be able to control three German Seehund-type minesweeping drones. The 40-mm gun is controlled by a remote lead-computing optical director.

Disposal note: Of the former U.K. "Ton"-class minesweeper/minehunters operated by South Africa, *Kaapstad* (P 1557, ex-M 1142, ex-*Hazleton,* ex-*Blue Firefly*) was laid up in 12-85 and sold during 1989; *Pretoria* (P 1556, ex-M 1144, ex-*Dunkerton*, ex-*Golden Firefly*) was laid up and dedicated as a museum ship at Hout Bay 5-12-87; *Johannesburg* (M 1207, ex-*Castleton*) was sold for scrap in 9-88; *Port Elizabeth* (M 1212, ex-*Dumbleton*) was laid up in 9-85 and sold for scrap during 9-88; *Mosselbaai* (M 1213, ex-*Oakington*) was laid up in 11-81 and sold for scrap during 9-88; *Durban* (M 1499) was paid off 23-10-85 and dedicated as a museum ship at Durban 5-5-88; *Walvisbaai* (M 1214, ex-*Pachington*) and *East London* (M 1215, ex-*Chilton*) were retired 5-9-01; and *Kimberley* (M 1210, ex-*Stratton*) and *Windhoek* (M 1498), in reserve since 1999, were to be discarded early in 2002.

AMPHIBIOUS WARFARE CRAFT

♦ 8 Delta 80–class personnel landing craft [LCP]
Bldr: . . . (In serv. mid-1980s)

L 21 through L 28

Delta 80–class L 22—aboard the *Drakensberg* (A 301) Peter Froud, 4-97

D: 5.5 tons (fl) **S:** 37 kts **Dim:** 8.32 × 3.05 × 0.90
A: small arms **M:** 2 gasoline outboard motors; 350 bhp
Range: 150/35 **Crew:** 5 tot.

Remarks: GRP construction. Carried aboard *Drakensberg* (A 301) and *Outeniqua* (A 302) for use by special forces personnel.

AUXILIARIES

♦ 1 ex-Ukrainian Ivan Papanin–class fleet supply ship [AF]
Bldr: Kherson Zavod, Ukraine (In serv. 8-6-93)

A 302 Outeniqua (ex-*Juvent,* ex-*Aleksandr Sledzak*)

Outeniqua (A 302) Capt. A. F. A. Pearson, 4-97

Outeniqua (A 302) Marc Fabre, 4-97

D: 21,025 tons (fl) **S:** 17.1 kts (16.75 sust.)
Dim: 166.31 (156.44 pp) × 22.96 × 9.00
A: 4 single 20-mm 90-cal. Oerlikon GAM-B01 AA; 6 single 12.7-mm M2 mg; 2 Army AS.330H/J Puma helicopters
Electronics: Radar: 3 Decca . . . nav. (one aft)
M: 1 Bryansk–Burmeister & Wain 8DKRN 60/195 diesel; 1 CP prop; 17,516 bhp
Electric: 2,400 kw tot. **Range:** 8,000/16.75 loaded; 14,000/16.75 light
Fuel: 2,280 m^3 **Endurance:** 60 days
Crew: 17 officers, 109 enlisted + up to 600 troops

Remarks: 14,184 grt/10,125 dwt. Keel laid in 6-91. Originally ordered as the icebreaking roll-on/roll-off and general cargo ship *Aleksandr Sledzak* for the Murmansk Steamship Co., but taken over by Ukraine and operated commercially by the shipyard as *Juvent.* Purchased on 18-2-93 for around $13.2 million, arriving at Simon's Town 24-2-93 and commissioning 8-6-93. After an initial operational period, was refitted with improved helicopter facilities at Durban in 1994; refitted again from 5-96 to 9-96 and again in 5-97 to 9-97. Also serves as Antarctic research support ship to supplement the Department of Transport–operated *S.A. Aguilhas.* Reportedly has not been a success in service.
Hull systems: Is able to carry and deploy two Namicurra-class patrol craft or four 37-kt Delta 80 assault craft. Has five holds (four hatches) and a side-loading door and ramp for vehicles; total cargo hold capacity is 16,900 m^3. Fitted with two twin 25-ton cranes (the after pair) and two 12-ton cranes (forward pair) amidships. During a 1997 refit, was equipped with liquid and solid transfer-at-sea capabilities (one each per side), a SEACOM-1 military communications suite, Decca radar for helicopter flight control, improvements to the helicopter facilities (including a roll-indicator bar, deck lighting, and flight-deck restraints), improvements to the accommodations, and installation of a full combat data system. The ship is equipped with a 60-berth portable berthing module for use during midshipman training cruises. A hospital facility is fitted.

♦ 1 U.K. Hecla-class hydrographic survey ship [AGS]

	Bldr	Laid down	L	In serv.
A 324 Protea	Yarrow, Scotstoun	20-7-70	14-7-71	23-5-72

Protea (A 324)—white hull, buff funnel and mast, pennant number not displayed SAN, 4-97

D: 1,930 tons (2,750 fl) **S:** 14 kts **Dim:** 79.25 (71.63 pp) × 14.94 × 4.57
A: 2 single 20-mm 70-cal. Oerlikon AA; 2 single 12.7-mm mg
Electronics:
Radar: 1 Kelvin-Hughes Type 1006 nav.
Sonar: STN Atlas Elektronik Hydrosweep MD multibeam mapping; STN Atlas Elektronik Deso 25 survey echo sounder; EG&G side-scan mapping
M: 3 MTU . . . . . . diesels (1,280 bhp each), 3 generator sets, 1 motor; 1 CP prop; 2,000 shp—bow-thruster
Range: 12,000/11 **Fuel:** 560 tons
Crew: 18 officers, 114 enlisted + 4 aircrew

Remarks: Ordered 7-11-69. Equipped during a 1983 refit for electronic surveillance duties and carries an extensive communications suite. Re-engined during a refit in 1995–96 and is now expected to operate until at least 2009. White painted, with buff stack and mast.
Hull systems: Hull is reinforced for navigating in ice. Bow-thruster and antiroll tanks are fitted. During the 1996 refit, the air-conditioning and refrigeration plants were upgraded and a new steam boiler and evaporators were fitted.
Mission systems: Has the Polaris survey system, with automated data storage, both for the ship and for the two survey launches. Navigational equipment includes an STN Atlas Elektronik Dolog 22 doppler log, a ship-motion sensor, a bathymetric probe,

AUXILIARIES *(continued)*

an automated tide gauge, Racal Hyderlink long-range radio position fixing, Del Norte transponder short-range radio position fixing, and differential GPS. Both survey launches have GPS and Deso 25 echo sounders; each can tow the side-scan mapping sonar. Also carried is a suite of land survey equipment. Can carry an Alouette-III helicopter for aerial survey work and buoy and transponder placement. Communications intercept equipment was removed during the 1996 refit.

♦ 1 fleet replenishment ship [AOR]
Bldr: Dorbyl Marine, Durban

	Laid down	L	In serv.
A 301 Drakensberg	3-8-84	24-4-86	11-11-87

Drakensberg (A 301) Ralph Edwards, 2-01

Drakensberg (A 301)—note second helicopter spot forward Chris Sattler, 2-01

D: 6,000 tons light (12,500 fl) **S:** 20+ kts **Dim:** 146.30 × 19.50 × 7.90
A: 4 single 20-mm 90-cal. Oerlikon GAM-B01 AA; 6 single 12.7-mm M2 mg; 2 AS.330H/J Puma helicopters
Electronics: Radar: 2 . . . nav.
M: 2 12-cyl. SEMT-Pielstick diesels; 1 CP prop; 16,320 bhp—bow-thruster
Range: 8,000/. . . **Endurance:** 90 days
Crew: 10 officers, 86 enlisted + 10 SAAF aviation complement + 22 trainees

Remarks: Ordered 22-9-84. The largest ship ever built in South Africa; builder was formerly known as Sandock Austral. Is used for patrol and SAR duties and is, by default, currently South Africa's most capable naval ship.
Hull systems: Can carry 5,500 tons of cargo fuel, 208 tons of potable water, 100 tons of dry provisions, 33 tons of frozen foods, 230 tons of containerized cargo, and 1,000 tons of palletized and general cargo and munitions. There are helicopter decks fore and aft but a hangar aft only; when Puma helicopters are embarked, 10 SAAF personnel are aboard. One dual refueling/solid transfer station is located on each beam, and the ship is also capable of over-the-stern refueling. Equipped with tunnel-thruster in the pronounced bulbous bow. Has five generator sets. Four desalinization plants can produce 70,000 liters of potable water per day. Has davits port and starboard to handle 37-kt Delta 80 assault boats. Has additional navigational training equipment and an extensive infirmary and can accommodate more than 200 additional personnel, if required. Two rigid inflatable boats, two landing craft, and two diving service boats are carried. The helicopter deck traversing system has been removed.

SERVICE CRAFT

♦ 1 diving tender and torpedo-recovery craft [YDT]

	Bldr	Laid down	L	In serv.
P 3148 Fleur	Dorman Long, Durban	2-69	30-6-69	3-12-69

D: 220 tons (302 fl) **S:** 15.5 kts **Dim:** 37.41 (35.0 wl) × 7.30 × 2.20
A: 2 single 12.7-mm Browning mg; 2 single 7.62-mm mg
Electronics: Radar: 1 Decca . . . nav.
M: 2 Paxman-Ventura 12 YJCM diesels; 2 props; 2,614 bhp
Range: 2,477/12.5 **Crew:** 4 officers, 23 enlisted

Remarks: The first naval ship designed and built in South Africa. Has a ramp at the stern for torpedo recovery, covered by a curved roller-door. Has a six-person divers' decompression chamber. The passive tank stabilization is said not to work effectively. Refitted in the late 1970s, with the forecastle deck cut back to enlarge the fantail and new, lower stacks added. Refitted 6-80 to 2-81, receiving a hydraulic crane amidships and diver's equipment crane aft. Acts as support and safety tender to the submarines.

Fleur (P 3148) Marc Fabre, 4-97

♦ 2 personnel launches [YFL]

Escombe (ex-*Sunbird*) Forerunner (ex-*Tarentaal*)

Remarks: Employed at Durban. Displace 25 tons and can carry 80 seated personnel. Built in 1972 for commercial service and acquired by the SAN in 11-85. No other data available.

♦ 3 Coastguard T 2212–class hydrofoil rescue craft [YHH]
Bldr: T-Craft International, Cape Town (In serv. 1992)

P 1552 Tobie (In serv. 6-92) P 1554 Tekane (In serv. 12-96)
P 1553 Tern (In serv. 6-96)

Tekane (P 1554) SAN, 4-97

D: 23 tons (45 fl) **S:** 41 kts **Dim:** 22.00 × 7.00 × 0.90
A: 1 12.7-mm mg **Electronics:** Radar: 1 . . . nav.
M: 2 MTU 12V183 TE92 diesels; 2 Castoldi waterjets; 2,000 bhp
Range: 525/30 **Crew:** 4 tot. + 15 passengers

Remarks: Trials with a prototype were undertaken during summer 1991 under temporary pennant number T 2201. Three production versions were ordered in 10-91, but one was initially rejected. As of 3-95, two were in land storage at Simon's Town, but both participated in the 4-97 naval review. Were intended to serve as air-sea rescue craft in support of the South African Air Force, based at Saldanha Bay. The South African Police Coast Guard also uses units of this design, and three were sold to Israel in 11-97.
Hull systems: Have an unusual catamaran hullform with hydrofoils between the hulls. GRP construction. There are accommodations for 16 but they can be operated with as few as four personnel. Were intended to be able to maintain 37 kts in Sea State 5. Carry a 3.4-m rigid inflatable rescue boat aft in a recess between the hulls.

Disposal note: Air-sea rescue craft P 1551 (ex-R 31), in reserve since 1997, is unlikely to see further active service and has been dropped from this edition.

♦ 1 large harbor tug [YTB]
Bldr: . . . . . ., Singapore (L: 1995)

K 230 Umalusi (ex-*Golden Energy*)

D: 490 tons (fl) **S:** 13 kts **Dim:** 30.00 (28.84 wl) × 10.00 × 4.90 (max.)
Electronics: Radar: 1 Furuno 1941 nav.
M: 2 Caterpillar 3516TA diesels; 2 Aquamaster Model 1401 Kort-nozzle 4-bladed azimuth props; 3,620 bhp
Electric: 212 kVA tot. (2 × 106-kVA Caterpillar 3304T diesel sets driving)
Range: . . ./. . . **Fuel:** 60 m^3 **Crew:** 12 tot.

Remarks: Large firefighting harbor tug, purchased from Tai Kong Trading Co., Singapore, in 3-97, for $4.48 million to replace the *De Noord.* The new name, the subject of a public contest, means "Shepherd" in Bantu.
Hull systems: Has a 42-ton bollard pull capacity and is equipped with an 80-ton double-drum towing winch, two 13,000-liter/min fire monitors, and a 50-m^3/hr oil dispersant system with a 7.6-m^3 capacity.

♦ 1 large harbor tug [YTB]

	Bldr	L	In serv.
De Mist	Dorman Long, Durban	21-12-78	23-12-78

D: 275 tons (fl) **S:** 12.5 kts **Dim:** 34.3 (32.3 pp) × 7.8 × 3.4
M: 2 Mirrlees-Blackstone ESL-8-MGR diesels; 2 Voith-Schneider vertical cycloidal props; 2,440 bhp
Crew: 5 officers, 6 unlicensed (civilian)

SERVICE CRAFT *(continued)*

De Mist—black hull, buff superstructure Peter Froud, 4-97

Remarks: Bollard pull: 25 tons. Has two firefighting monitors and carries 20,000 liters lightwater foam. Based at Simon's Town Dockyard. Is fully seagoing, if required.

♦ 1 large harbor tug [YTB]

	Bldr	Laid down	L	In serv.
De Neys	Globe Eng. Works, Cape Town	7-67	7-69	23-7-69

De Neys French Navy, 4-97

D: 282 tons (fl) **S:** 11.5 kts **Dim:** 28.65 (27.0 wl) × 8.23 × 4.72
M: 2 Lister-Blackstone ERS-8-M diesels; 2 Voith-Schneider vertical cycloidal props; 1,268 bhp
Crew: 10 tot. (civilian)

Remarks: 180 grt. Bollard pull: 14-ton max. Steel construction, with wooden decks. Based at Simon's Town Dockyard. Has a single firefighting monitor.

♦ 3 miscellaneous dockyard tugs [YTM]

DL 2 DL 4 E. L. S. Sylvester DL 5

DL 2 Peter Froud, 4-97

Remarks: All three are used at Simon's Town Dockyard. DL 2 was built around 1940 in Scotland, DL 4 was launched 5-2-73 at Simon's Town, and DL 5 was built during the 1960s in South Africa at Globe Engineering Works. No further data available.

E. L. S. Sylvester (DL 4) Peter Froud, 4-97

POLICE COAST GUARD
(Kuswag)

Note: The South African Police Water Wing was renamed the Police Coast Guard in 1995 and is equipped with a number of miscellaneous small craft and launches and at least one T-Craft catamaran hydrofoil launch of the type used by the navy (q.v.). Hulls are painted red and superstructures white, and either diagonal hull stripes or stack stripes of blue-yellow-blue are carried.

♦ 1 seagoing salvage tug [WARS]
Bldr: James Brown & Hamer, Durban (L: 11-76)

John Ross

John Ross Piet Sinke, 1982

D: . . . **S:** 21 kts **Dim:** 94.65 (85.65 pp) × 15.85 × 7.52
Electronics: Radar: . . .
M: 2 Mirrlees-Blackstone 16-cyl. diesels; 1 prop; 19,200 bhp—800-shp bow-thruster
Range: 22,000/21 **Fuel:** 1,697 tons **Crew:** . . . tot.

Remarks: 2,822 grt/275 nrt. Leased for salvage and rescue duties from and operated by Smit-Pentow Marine. Has 210-ton bollard pull.

S.A. Kuswag IV Marc Fabre, 4-97

Note: The 5,353-grt/3,035-dwt, Department of Transport–operated Antarctic survey and supply ship *S.A. Agulhas* has not been operated by the navy since 1989. Other government-owned vessels include the fisheries research ships *Africana, Algoa,* and *Sardinops* and fisheries protection ships *Jasus, Patella,* and *Pelagus.*

DEPARTMENT OF ENVIRONMENTAL AFFAIRS AND TOURISM

The South African Department of Environmental Affairs and Tourism is responsible for fisheries and environmental protection. Bids for three 45-m and one 80-m fisheries protection ships were requested 15-6-01 and received 18-10-01 from Appledore Shipbuilders, U.K.; Austal Ships, Australia; Blohm + Voss, Germany (for the larger ship only); Farocean Marine, South Africa (small ships only); Fincantieri, Italy (small ships only); Southern African Shipyards; and Vosper Thornycroft.

The 80-m offshore patrol ship will cover the entire South African economic exclusion zone and the waters off the Prince Edward Islands. With a range of 7,500 n.m. at 15 kts, an endurance of 45 days or more, and a maximum speed of 20 kts, the vessel is expected to be at sea 250–300 days per year. The ship will have a hospital and

DEPARTMENT OF ENVIRONMENTAL AFFAIRS AND TOURISM *(continued)*

helicopter deck, but no hangar, and the crew will include seven fisheries control officers and four cadets. The three smaller ships are to be able to operate up to 200 n.m. offshore but will mostly operate within 50–80 miles of the coast; they are to have a range of 3,500 n.m. at 15 kts and a 25-kt maximum speed and will carry two fisheries control officers in addition to the crew. All four ships will also have the capability to deal with oil spills. Contracts are planned to be let in spring 2002, with the first ship to deliver in 05-03 or 06-03 and the final ship a year later.

SPAIN

Spanish State

ARMADA ESPAÑOLA

Personnel (2001): 22,863 total (2,670 officers), plus 8,895 naval infantry/*Tercio de Armada* (491 officers), and about 8,300 civilians. As of the end of 1999, 1,003 women served in the navy.

Bases: The fleet is divided into four zones, with the overall fleet command headquarters at Rota and zone headquarters and subsidiary facilities as follows:

- Cantabrian Zone: Headquarters at Ferrol Arsenal, with logistics support at La Graña, electronics school at Vigo, and naval school at Marin
- Straits Zone: Headquarters at La Carraca Arsenal, Cádiz, with naval air base and fleet command center at Rota and amphibious warfare base at Puntales
- Mediterranean Zone: Headquarters at Cartagena Arsenal, support bases at Mahón on Minorca and Porto Pi on Majorca (which also has a submarine weapons school), and submarine school at La Algameca
- Canaries Zone: Headquarters at Las Palmas Arsenal

Naval Aviation: Eight EAV-8B Harrier V/STOL fighter-bombers and eight EAV-8B+ Harriers are in service for use on the carrier *Príncipe de Asturias;* the EAV-8Bs are being re-equipped as EAV-8B+ with the APG-65 radar. Spanish Harriers carry AIM-120 AMRAAM and AIM-9L Sidewinder air-to-air missiles; additional AIM-120 missiles, plus AGM-65F Maverick and AGM-88 HARM air-to-ground missiles, were to be purchased during 1999. Three EAV-8Bs have been lost in accidents, the latest in 2-98. Under a 29-1-01 contract, Boeing, St. Louis, Mo., is to upgrade two EAV-8B to EAV-8B+ by 7-03, with an option to upgrade the others.

The Arma Aerea de la Armada also operates 6 SH-60B Seahawk, 10 Agusta-Bell AB-212 (three equipped with Elettronica "Gufo" 2000 EW intercept gear and five with a datalink), 8 Sikorsky SH-3D Sea King, 3 SH-3D AEW conversions, and 10 Hughes 369-HM(500M) Cayuse helicopters, plus 3 Cessna 550 Citation-II liaison aircraft. The Sea King ASW helicopters are to be upgraded to SH-3H configuration with the CESELSA NAT-5 combat system, new radio and navigational aids, and AQS-18(V) dipping sonar added, and the engine transmissions, rotors, stabilization system, and other dynamic systems rehabilitated. Six additional SH-60B Block I helicopters were ordered 17-9-99 for use with the F-100 frigates, and the first was completed 5-12-01; all 12 SH-60Bs are to be equipped to launch Kongsberg Penguin Mk 2 Mod. 7 antiship missiles, 20 of which were ordered in 6-00. After 2005, the remaining AB-212 and SH-3 helicopters are planned to be replaced with Sikorsky H-60 Seahawk variants, and the existing SH-60Bs may be upgraded to the U.S. Navy's MH-60R configuration. An SH-3D was lost at sea on 13-7-99.

The Grupo Aeronaval Alfa has six squadrons, all based at Rota: 3 Sqn. (10 AB-212 helicopters), 4 Sqn. (3 Citation-II light transports), 5 Sqn. (9 SH-3D ASW helicopters and 3 SH-3D AEW helicopters), 6 Sqn. (10 Cayuse training helicopters), 9 Sqn. (16 EAV-8B Harriers), and 10 Sqn. (6 SH-60B Seahawk ASW helicopters).

Spanish Navy EAV-8B Harrier Bernard Prézelin, 4-00

Spanish Navy EAV-8B+ Harrier Bernard Prézelin, 4-00

Spanish Navy SH-3D Sea King Camil Busquets i Vilanova, 1-99

The Spanish Air Force performs the maritime surveillance mission, using two P-3A, five P-3B, and four P-3C Orions; the seven A- and B-model aircraft are being updated with five multifunction data display stations each and new weapons and ASW sensor management systems under a 6-99 contract with CASA, with the first to be completed early in 2002. Five P-3Bs are receiving modernizations by EADS/CASA, with the first to complete in 2002; a new radar, ESM, IFF interrogator, Link 11 capability, inertial navigation, GPS receiver, communications suite, and ground support center are being procured for the aircraft.

Eight Air Force CASA C-212 Aviocar aircraft with APS-128 radar, four Fokker F-27-200MPA fixed-wing aircraft, and 15 AS.332B Super Puma helicopters are used for search-and-rescue work. Air Force F/A-18 Hornet fighter-bombers are equipped for maritime strike with AGM-84F Harpoon missiles. The search-and-rescue service *(Servicio de Busqueda y Salvamento)* has nine AS.332F Super Puma helicopters for rescue duties and two configured as VIP transports.

The CASA CN-235M is Spain's current-production maritime surveillance aircraft and has been widely exported. The version delivered to the Irish Air Corps in 11-94 had these characteristics:

Wingspan: 25.8 m **Length:** 21.3 m **Weight:** 13,600 kg max.
Wing area: 60 m^2 **Speed:** 282 kts (cruise)
Engines: 2 G.E. CT7-9C turboprops; 3,500 shp tot.
Range: 1,038 n.m. **Crew:** 6 tot.
Avionics: Litton APS-504(V)5 INS, FLIR, radar

Marine Corps: The Tercia de Armada (TEAR) was re-formed in 1968 from the Grupo Especial de Infantería de Marina, which had been established in 1957. Its head is a major general who reports directly to the naval chief of staff. The TEAR consists of an amphibious assault force stationed at San Fernando, near Cádiz, and a defense/security force of three regiments stationed at Ferrol, San Fernando, and Cartagena, with smaller detachments at Madrid and at Las Palmas in the Canary Islands. Artillery support consists of one battery of six U.S. M 109 self-propelled 155-mm guns and two batteries of six 105-mm towed howitzers. Also available are 16 M 60A3 medium tanks and 17 Alvis Scorpion FV-101 light tanks. There are 35 other armored vehicles, 12 amphibious trucks, 13 bulldozers, 17 special vehicles, 461 other wheeled vehicles (including 123 U.S. HUMVEE light trucks), and 257 trailers. For amphibious assault, there are 19 AAVP-7A1 tracked armored personnel vehicles, all updated from LVTP-7-series configuration between 11-97 and mid-2000. Antitank equipment consists of 12 TOW and several Dragon missile launchers, while 12 Mistral lightweight SAM systems (50 missiles total) provide air defense. Air support to the TEAR is supplied by the 10 AB-212 helicopters from the Navy's 3 Sqn.

Coastal Defense: A Mobile Coastal Artillery Group was formed by the Spanish Army during 1-01, using six E.N. Santa Barbara towed 155-mm 52-cal. APU SBT howitzers. The weapon uses base-bleed ammunition to achieve ranges of up to 40 km, and the carriage employs a diesel engine to provide hydraulic power to the carriage wheels.

WEAPONS AND SYSTEMS

Except for naval guns, which are domestically manufactured, most of the weapon systems in use are of American or French manufacture. In use are U.S. RGM-84A and -84C Harpoon antiship missiles and Mk 46 Mod. 5 antisubmarine torpedoes. Spanish Air Force F/A-18 Hornets can carry AGM-84C Harpoon missiles for maritime strikes. In 5-99, 44 AGM-65F Maverick missiles were ordered for use with AV-8B+ Harrier aircraft.

The Meroka antiaircraft/antimissile point-defense system consists of two rows of six 20-mm Oerlikon guns:

Length: 120 calibers **Projectile Weight:** 102 gr. (320 gr. all-up)
Muzzle velocity: 1,200 m/sec **Rate of fire:** 9,000 rds/min max.
Maximum effective range: 2,000 m

Meroka employs a Lockheed Martin VPS-2 Sharpshooter I-band monopulse radar on the mount, with target designation by the ship's AESN RAN-12L/X dual-frequency search radar and an AESN PDS-10 TDS console. The 20 Mod. 2A mounts procured carry 720 rounds each and have a thermal imager; the later Mod. 2B version has 2,160 rounds. In 1993, three Mod. 2B mounts with digital data processors; automatic target acquisition; improved performance against sea-skimming targets; a more powerful, PRF-agile AESN RTN-30X radar using moving-target indication (MTI); and built-in test equipment were procured, and all Mod. 2A mounts are being upgraded to the same standard.

Under development for use on the F-100- and succeeding F-110-class frigates is the Bazán-FABA DORNA *(Dirección de Tiro Optrónica y Radárica Naval)* gun fire-control system with comounted K-band radar and laser rangefinder; it can be used independently of the main weapons control system to control 40-, 76-, and 127-mm guns.

WEAPONS AND SYSTEMS *(continued)*

Mines made by SAES, Madrid, include:

- MILA-6B: Limpet mine with time fuze; also usable as a demolition charge
- MIM-90: Cylindrical submarine-laid mine with same detection systems as the MO-90
- MO-90: 1,000-kg moored mine (with 300-kg HBX-3 charge) capable of being laid in depths of 15 to 350 m at speeds of up to 30 kts by surface craft. Height: 1.90 m; width: 1.10 m. Lethal to 40-m range. Has minesweeping countermeasures features and can be programmed to sterilize in 0 to 720 days. First deliveries: 12-92.

There are two fixed ground stations for the SECOMSAT *(Sistema Español de Comunicaciones Militares por Satélite)* military SATCOM system, which employs the commercial Hispisat communications satellite constellation. Shipboard terminals had been installed by early 1997 in the carrier *Príncipe de Asturias*, the frigate *Navarra,* and the transport *Aragón,* and the marines have a mobile terminal; the other *Perry*-class frigates are also to receive the system. Twenty Leica GPS MX 412B 12-channel differential GPS sets were delivered early in 1998 for shipboard use.

Note: Pennant numbers on all seagoing ships have been toned down to a dark gray. The major state-owned shipyards Astilleros Españoles S.A. (AESA) and E.N. Bazán were combined in 7-00, with the new firm known as Izar.

V/STOL AIRCRAFT CARRIERS [CVV]

♦ 1 modified U.S. Sea Control Ship design

Bldr: Izar, Ferrol

	Laid down	L	In serv.
R 11 PRÍNCIPE DE ASTURIAS (ex-*Canarias,* ex-*Almirante Carrero*)	8-10-79	22-5-82	30-5-88

Príncipe de Asturias (R 11) Camil Busquets i Vilanova, 5-00

Príncipe de Asturias (R 11) Bernard Prézelin, 4-00

D: 15,912 tons (17,188 fl) **S:** 26 kts
Dim: 195.1 (187.5 pp) × 24.4 (30.0 flight deck) × 6.7 (9.4 over prop)
Air group: 6–8 EAV-8B Harrier V/STOL fighters; 2 SH-60B, 6–10 SH-3D/G, and 2–4 AB-212 helicopters
A: 4 12-barrel 20-mm Meroka Mod. 2A CIWS
Electronics:
Radar: 1 Cardion SPS-55 surf. search; 1 Hughes SPS-52C 3-D air search; 1 ITT SPN-35A air control; 1 Selenia RAN-11L/X target desig.; 4 Lockheed VPS-2 f.c. (on Meroka mounts)
TACAN: URN-25
EW: Elettronica Nettunel intercept; Mk 36 Mod. 2 SRBOC decoy syst. (6 6-round Mk 137 RL); SLQ-25 Nixie towed torpedo decoy syst.
M: 2 G.E. LM-2500 gas turbines; 1 CP prop; 46,400 shp—2 800-shp retractable Pleuger electric auxiliary props (4.5 kts)
Electric: 7,500 kw (3 Allison 501-K17 gas turbine–driven, 2,500-kw sets)
Range: 6,500/20
Crew: 90 officers, 465 enlisted + 201 air group + 7 flag staff

Remarks: Ordered 29-6-77. Design is essentially that of the final version of the U.S. Navy's canceled Sea Control Ship concept, with a 12° ski-jump bow added. Serves as flagship of Grupo Aeronaval Alfa and is based at Rota.
Hull systems: Has two pair Denny-Brown fin stabilizers. The U.S. Prairie/Masker hull and propeller air bubble system is installed to reduce radiated noise. Boats include two LCVP-type landing craft. Has been modified to accommodate female crewmembers.

Príncipe de Asturias (R 11) Camil Busquets i Vilanova, 5-00

V/STOL AIRCRAFT CARRIERS [CVV] *(continued)*

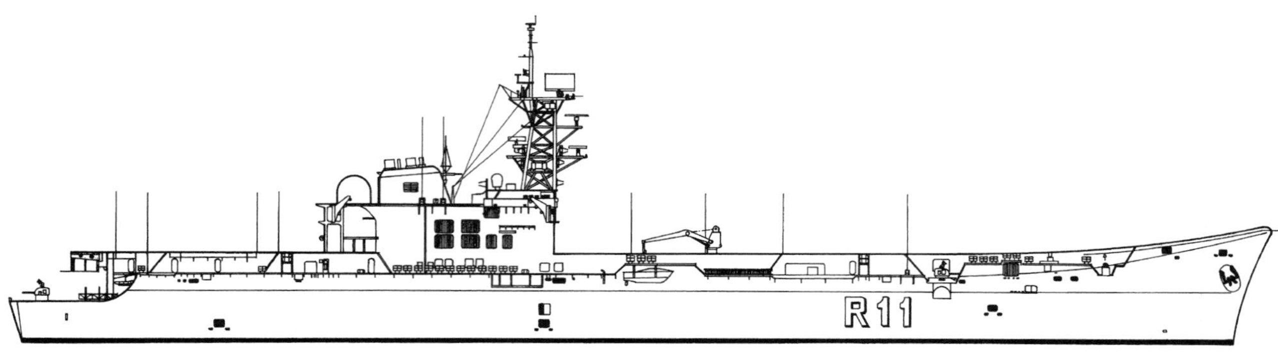

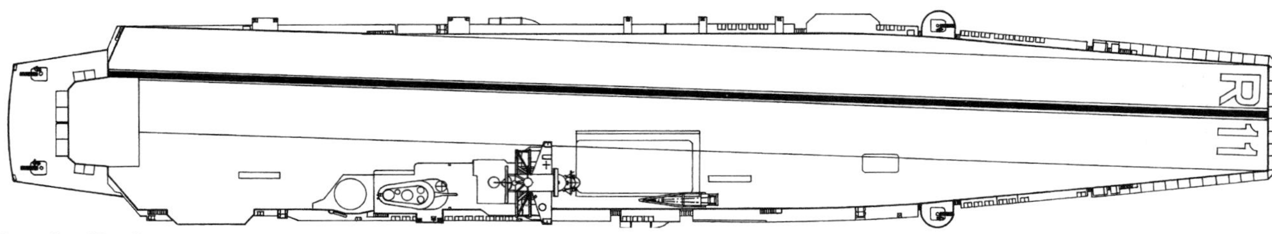

Príncipe de Asturias (R 11) *Ships of the World*

Aviation systems: The flight deck measures 175.3 × 29 m and is served by two elevators, one at the extreme aft end and the other to starboard of the flight path, forward of the island. The takeoff pattern from the 12° ski jump is angled to starboard. The hangar provides a total of 2,300 m^2 of parking space. In a 1990 refit, a parallel fuel distribution system with 37,000-m^3 tank capacity was installed to permit carrying a fuel load of 40% aviation fuel/60% DFM propulsion fuel; at the same time, the island superstructure was enlarged to port at its aft end to incorporate a briefing room, the flying control central was enlarged, and accommodations for six additional officers and 30 additional enlisted were added. A Marconi Deck Approach Projector Sight (DAPS) has been added to facilitate Harrier landings.
Combat systems: The Tritan combat data system employs two Unisys UYK-43 and two UYK-20 computers; Link 11 and Link 14 datalink and U.S. FLEETSATCOM are installed, as are the Saturn 3S and SECOMSAT *(Sistema Español de Comunicaciones Militares por Satélite)* SATCOM system, both of which share two SCOT radome-covered dish antennas. Has U.S. UPX-25 and UPX-28 IFF equipment, the Raylass navigation system with Magnavox MX1105 NAVSAT/Omega receiver, and two Sperry HK inertial navigation systems (SINS). The SPS-52C radar was updated to SPS-52D in 1990. Two Rheinmetall 37-mm saluting cannon are mounted on the fantail.

ATTACK SUBMARINES [SS]

♦ 0 (+ 2–4) Scorpène (S 80) program Bldr: Izar, Cartagena

	Laid down	L	In serv.
S	. . .	. . .	. . .
S	. . .	. . .	. . .
S	. . .	. . .	. . .
S	. . .	. . .	. . .

D: 1,265 tons std.; 1,425 tons surf./1,565 tons sub.
S: 12 kts surf./20 kts sub. **Dim:** 61.70 × 6.20 × . . .
A: 6 bow 533-mm TT (18 tot. F 17 Mod. 2 torpedoes and UGM-84 Harpoon or SM 39 Exocet missiles)
Electronics: Radar: . . .—Sonar: . . .
M: 2 × 1,100-kw diesel generator sets, 1 electric motor; 1 prop; 3,800 shp
Range: 6,500/8 snorkel; 40/20, 550/4 sub. **Endurance:** 50 days
Crew: 32–35 tot.

Remarks: Intended to replace the *Daphné* class. A cooperative design effort between Izar and DCN, France. The first unit is now hoped to be ordered in 2002.
Hull systems: If an air-independent auxiliary propulsion (AIP) variant of the Scorpène design is selected, the submarines would be 1,465 tons standard, 1,670 tons surfaced full load, and 1,815 tons submerged and be 8 m longer; range on the Rankine-cycle AIP system (probably Bertin's MESMA system) would be 750 n.m. at 4 kts. Diving depth: 300–350 m.
Combat systems: Are planned to employ the Kongsberg Defence and Aerospace MSI-90U combat data system, using multifunction flat-screen displays.

♦ 4 French Agosta (S 70) class Bldr: Izar, Cartagena

	Laid down	L	In serv.
S 71 Galerna	5-9-77	5-12-81	22-1-83
S 72 Siroco	27-11-78	13-11-82	5-12-83
S 73 Mistral	30-5-80	14-11-83	5-6-85
S 74 Tramontana	18-12-81	30-11-84	27-1-86

D: 1,230 tons std.; 1,490 tons surf./1,750 tons sub.
S: 12 kts surf./20.5 kts sub. **Dim:** 67.90 × 6.80 × 5.40

Galerna (S 71) Camil Busquets i Vilanova, 5-01

Tramontana (S 74) Camil Busquets i Vilanova, 6-00

Siroco (S 72)—in refit at Cartagena Dieter Wolf, 1-01

A: 4 bow 550-mm TT (20 ECAN F 17 Mod. 2, E 18, and L 5 Mods. 3 and 4 torpedoes, or up to 19 mines with 9 torpedoes)
Electronics:
Radar: 1 DRUA-33C search/nav.
Sonar: S 71, 72, and 74: Thales DUUX-2A passive ranging; Thales DUUX-5 passive ranging—S 73: Thales DUUA-2A/2B active; Thales DSUV-22 passive search and attack; SOLARSUB towed passive linear array
EW: Thorn-EMI Manta-E intercept
M: 2 SEMT-Pielstick 16 PA4 185 diesel generator sets (850 kw each); 1 prop; 4,600 shp (main engine)—1 32-shp cruising engine
Range: 8,500/9 snorkel; 17.5/17.5, 350/3.5 sub. **Fuel:** 185 tons
Endurance: 45 days **Crew:** 6 officers, 48 enlisted

ATTACK SUBMARINES [SS] *(continued)*

Remarks: Built with technical assistance from DCN, France. First two were ordered 9-5-75, second pair on 29-6-77. S 73 may now not receive the new equipment added to the others. All are based with the Flotilla de Submarinos at Cartagena.
Hull systems: Can dive to 300 m. During recent modernizations to all but S 73, the periscopes were modified for night vision, new tubular-plate batteries were substituted, new diesel engine exhaust valves were fitted, and noise-reduction measures were undertaken.
Combat systems: All but S 73 have received midlife "ACRUX" refits, beginning in 3-93 with S 71; in addition, the DLA-2A (CIMSA 15/Mitra-125) torpedo fire-control system was modified to launch the F 17 Mod. 2 torpedo, and the sonar suites were upgraded. S 73 ran trials during spring 1991 with the Thales clip-on DSUV-62 towed passive linear hydrophone array, but it was not purchased; instead, the SOLARSUB (*Sonar de Largo Alcance Remolcado Submarino;* or Long-Range Towed Sonar, Submarine) is being developed, and trials began with S 73 on 26-2-98. The prototype SOLARSUB used Australian Thales Narama towed components.

♦ **4 Daphné (S 60) class** Bldr: Izar, Cartagena

	Laid down	L	In serv.
S 61 Delfín	13-8-68	25-3-72	3-5-73
S 62 Tonina	2-3-70	3-10-72	10-7-73
S 63 Marsopa	19-3-71	15-3-74	12-4-75
S 64 Narval	24-4-72	14-12-74	22-11-75

Narval (S 64) Mike Welsford, 1-01

Tonina (S 62)—ashore for refit Camil Busquets i Vilanova, 5-01

D: 869 tons surf./1,043 tons sub. **S:** 13.2 kts surf./15.5 kts sub.
A: 12 550-mm TT (8 fwd, 4 aft; 12 ECAN F 17 Mod. 2 wire-guided and E 14, E 15, and L 5 Mod. 3/4 active/passive-homing torpedoes, or 12 mines in lieu of torpedoes)
Electronics:
Radar: 1 DRUA-33A search/nav.
Sonar: Thales DUUA-2A and DUUA-1D active; Thales DSUA-22 passive search and attack (see remarks)
EW: Thorn-EMI Manta-E intercept
M: 2 SEMT-Pielstick PA1 450-kw diesel generator sets, 2 800-shp (1,300-shp for short periods) electric motor; 2 props
Range: 2,710/12.5 surf.; 4,300/7.5 snorkel **Crew:** 6 officers, 41 enlisted

Remarks: Built with technical assistance from DCN, France, under an agreement signed 16-7-66. Are to remain in service to at least 2003. S 64, in reserve since 6-93, completed a reactivation refit at Cartagena in 2-96. S 61 commenced a much-delayed refit in 2-97. S 62 is no longer planned to receive further updates. All are based with the Flotilla de Submarinos at Cartagena.
Hull systems: Normal operating depth: 300 m.
Combat systems: Beginning with S 61, were refitted during the late 1980s with DUUA-2A forward (they retain DUUA-1D aft), DSUV-22 passive sonar, and an updated DLT-D-3A torpedo fire-control system; they now have a large bow sonar dome. S 63, which completed a refit at Cartagena in 4-93, has been equipped with a Thales DSUV-62C towed passive hydrophone array and the U.S. Prairie/Masker radiated-noise-suppression bubbler system.

GUIDED-MISSILE FRIGATES [FFG]

Note: Preliminary design work is also ongoing for a follow-on F-110 guided-missile ship design that would have many features and systems similar to those of the F-100 but with additional gun firepower.

♦ **0 (+ 4) F-100 design** Bldr: Izar, Ferrol

	Laid down	L	In serv.
F 101 Álvaro de Bazán	14-6-99	27-10-00	10-02
F 102 Almirante Juan de Borbón (ex-*Roger de Lauria*)	27-10-00	28-2-02	11-03
F 103 Blas de Lezo	3-02	7-03	1-05
F 104 Méndez Nuñez	7-03	9-04	2-06

Álvaro de Bazán (F 101)—computer rendering Izar, 2001

Álvaro de Bazán (F 101)—on trials Izar, 2-02

D: 4,555 tons (5,802 fl) **S:** 28.5 kts (27 sust.)
Dim: 146.72 (133.20 pp) × 18.60 (17.50 wl) × 4.75 (4.84 at full load)
A: 8 RGM-84F Harpoon Block ID SSM; 48-cell Mk 41 VLS syst. (32 Standard SM-2 Block IV and 64 RIM-7PTC Evolved Sea Sparrow SAM); 1 127-mm 54-cal. Mk 45 Mod. 2 DP; 1 12-barrel 20-mm Meroka-2B CIWS; 2 single 20-mm 90-cal. AA; 4 fixed 324-mm Mk 32 Mod. 9 ASW TT; 1 SH-60B Seahawk LAMPS III Block II ASW helicopter
Electronics:
Radar: 1 Thales Scout nav./surf. search; 1 Raytheon SPS-67(V)4 surf. search; 1 Lockheed Martin SPY-1D 3-D tracking, target-desig., and weapons control; 2 Raytheon SPG-62 target illuminators; 1 AESN RAN-30L/X Meroka f.c.; 1 FABA DORNA gun f.c.

GUIDED-MISSILE FRIGATES [FFG] *(continued)*

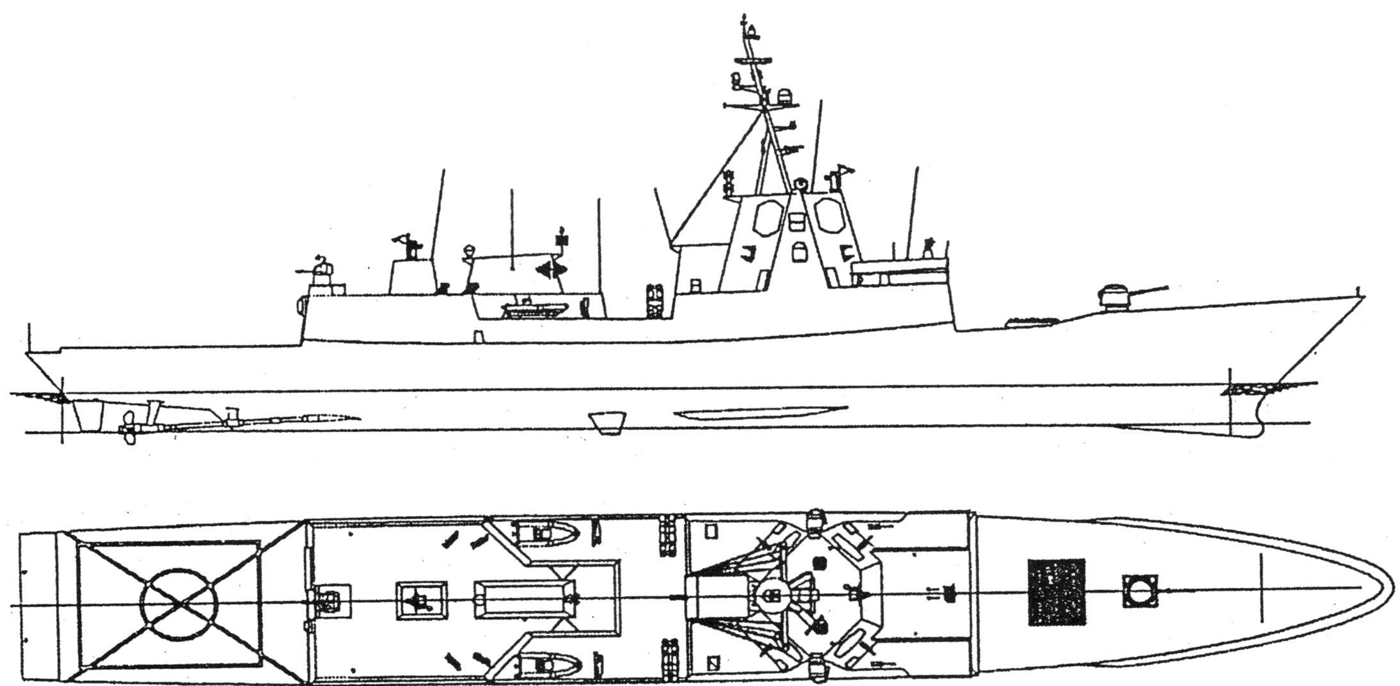

Álvaro de Bazán (F 101) Izar, 1996

Álvaro de Bazán (F 101)—fitting out Camil Busquets i Vilanova, 5-01

Sonar: ENOSA-Raytheon DE 1160LF (I) hull-mounted; EDO UQN-4 deepwater echo sounder; EDO Model 5400 underwater telephone; provision for active/passive towed linear hydrophone array

EW: Indra SLQ-380 Aldebarán intercept/jammer suite; CESELSA Elnath Mk 9000 comms intercept; . . . laser detection and countermeasure syst.; Mk 36 Mod. 2 SRBOC decoy RL syst. (4 6-round Mk 137 RL); SLQ-25A Enhanced Nixie acoustic torpedo decoy syst.

E/O: Thales Sirius optronic surveillance; FABA DORNA radar/optronic f.c.s.

M: CODOG: 2 G.E. LM-2500 gas turbines (23,324 shp each), 2 Bazán-Caterpillar 3600-series low-rpm diesels (6,000 shp each); 2 LIPS 4.65-m-dia., 5-bladed CP props; 46,648 shp max.

Electric: 4,400 kw tot. (4 × 1,100-kw Bazán-MTU 12C396 diesel sets)

Range: 5,000/18 **Endurance:** 21 days

Crew: 35 officers, 215 enlisted (incl. 11 air unit) (accomm. for 250, incl. 16 flag group)

Remarks: Were to have been constructed under a 27-1-94 cooperative venture with the Germany and the Netherlands; Spain, however, withdrew from the radar and weapons-control portions of the agreement on 6-6-95. Authority to construct four was granted by the Council of Ministers 24-1-97, the contract was placed 31-1-97, and fabrication of modules began during 11-97. Sea trials for F 101 were to start in 1-02. Are to cost about $540 million each. Intended to serve for 30 years. The Standard SAM system will provide AAW coverage out to 150 km. Will be based at Rota.

Hull systems: Have fin stabilizers. The ships are to be able to operate in 100-kt winds. A design growth margin of 450 tons is provided; the maximum permissible displacement will be 6,250 tons. The hull has four internal decks and is built of AH-36 high-tensile steel. The hangar can accommodate two SH-60-size helicopters, but only one will be assigned to each ship; the flight deck will be 26.4 m long. Fireproof internal paneling is employed, and special efforts have been made to reduce radar, acoustic, and heat signatures. Are to have Sperry MarineWQN-2 doppler speed and motion logs.

Combat systems: The SPY-1D Aegis radar system has the Lockheed Martin Distributed Advanced Naval Combat System with much the same Aegis Baseline 5 Phase III system used on current-construction U.S. *Arleigh Burke*–class destroyers, but the Spanish version will have a federated data distribution architecture, giving it some features of the later Aegis Baseline 6 Phase I on the first two ships and Baseline 7 Phase I on the latter two. Hardware and software requirements are being defined by Fábrica de Artillería de Bazán (FABA) so as to integrate Spanish and U.S.-origin equipment, via a redundant local area net. Hewlett-Packard 743 VME processors are being used. There are 14 SAINSEL CONAM2000 color command consoles and two integrated command display consoles. The ships will have NATO Link 11 and Link 16 datalink and UHF and SHF SATCOM.

Also incorporated in the combat system is FABA's DORNA optronic and radar naval fire-control system. The torpedo fire-control system will be the SAINSEL DLT 309. SAINSEL, CESELSA, and ENOSA are all part of the Indra Electronics Group. The U.S. UPX-29 fixed-array IFF interrogation system with Sanders OE-120/UPX electronically steered interrogation antenna is installed, as is the Lucent UYS-2A(V) DEM E electronic and acoustic intercept signal-processing system. Space is provided for later installation of a towed linear sonar array.

The point-defense RIM-7PTC Evolved Sea Sparrow Missiles will be carried in "quad packs," four per Mk 41 launch cell, and Standard SM-2 Block IIIA missiles will be used for area air defense. May later be equipped to carry U.S. BGM-109C Tomahawk land-attack missiles. The 127-mm guns are surplus U.S. Navy mountings from *Tarawa*-class LHAs upgraded to Mod. 2 by Izar's FABA armament division. Plans to install ABCAS ASW mortars have been canceled. The Aegis system will provide target cueing for the CIWS. The ships will have a full LAMPS-III ASW helicopter capability, with the SQQ-28 LAMPS-III electronics package and SRQ-4 datalink.

♦ 6 U.S. Oliver Hazard Perry class Bldr: Izar, Ferrol

	Laid down	L	In serv.
F 81 Santa María	22-5-82	24-11-84	12-10-86
F 82 Victoria	16-8-83	23-7-86	11-11-87
F 83 Numancia	8-1-86	29-1-87	17-11-89
F 84 Reina Sofia (ex-*América*)	12-10-87	19-7-89	30-10-90
F 85 Navarra	15-4-91	23-10-92	30-5-94
F 86 Canarias	15-4-92	21-6-93	14-12-94

Reina Sofia (F 84)—with SATCOM radomes added abreast the mainmast Camil Busquets i Vilanova, 5-00

D: F 81–84: 2,851 tons light, 3,610 tons std. (4,017 fl)—F 85, 86: 4,107 tons (fl)

S: 29 kts max. **Dim:** 138.80 (125.90 wl) × 14.30 × 4.52 (6.60 sonar dome)

GUIDED-MISSILE FRIGATES [FFG] *(continued)*

Navarra (F 85)—with SATCOM equipment Jaroslaw Cislak, 7-01

Victoria (F 82)—without SATCOM equipment Ben Sullivan, 4-01

Numancia (F 83) Bernard Prézelin, 5-00

A: 1 Mk 13 Mod. 4 missile launcher (8 RGM-84C Harpoon SSM and 32 Standard SM-1 MR Block V SAM); 1 76-mm 62-cal. U.S. Mk 75 DP; 1 20-mm Meroka Mod. 2A or 2B CIWS; 2 triple 324-mm Mk 32 Mod. 5 ASW TT (Mk 46 Mod. 5 torpedoes); 1 SH-60B Seahawk LAMPS-III ASW helicopter

Electronics:

Radar: 1 Raytheon 1650/9xR nav.; 1 Cardion SPS-55 nav./surf. search; 1 Raytheon SPS-49(V)4 or (V)5 air search; 1 Lockheed Martin Mk 92 Mod. 2 or 6 CAS track-while-scan gun/missile f.c.; 1 Raytheon STIR Mk 54 Mod. 0 missile target illumination; 1 AESN RAN-12L/X Meroka CIWS target desig.; 1 Lockheed Martin VPS-2 CIWS f.c.

Sonar: Raytheon DE 1160 hull-mounted MF; Gould SQR-19(V)2 TASS

TACAN: URN-25

EW: Elettronica Nettunel Mk 3000 active/passive suite; Mk 36 SRBOC decoy syst. (2 6-round Mk 137 RL); SLQ-25 Nixie torpedo decoy syst.

M: 2 Fiat-G.E. LM-2500 gas turbines; 1 CP prop; 41,000 shp—2 350-shp, retractable, rotatable electric auxiliary propulsion motors

Electric: 4,000 kw (4 × 1,000-kw Kato-Allison 114-DOOL diesel sets)

Range: 5,000/18 **Fuel:** 587 tons **Crew:** 13 officers, 210 enlisted

Remarks: First three were ordered 29-6-77, the fourth on 19-6-86, and the fifth and sixth 26-10-89. F 85 began sea trials in 10-93. They form the 41st Escort Squadron and are assigned to Aviation Group Alfa, based at Rota.

Hull systems: All have the longer hull used in U.S. units FFG 36–61. The last two were built with accommodations for female crewmembers, and the others were similarly modified. The U.S. Prairie/Masker bubble noise reduction system is fitted, as are fin stabilizers. F 85 and F 86 have had hydrodynamic flow fins added at the waterline aft to improve fuel economy by about 6%.

Combat systems: Have NATO Link-11 datalink and Saturn 3S SATCOM gear. The hull-mounted sonar is essentially the same as the U.S. Navy's SQS-56. Have the RAST helicopter deck-handling system to handle SH-60B LAMPS-III helicopters. F 83 and later were completed with the SSQ-28 LAMPS-III datalink, and it was backfitted to the others. Although twin hangars can accommodate two SH-60B, only one per ship is carried. F 81–84 have Mk 92 Mod. 4 f.c.s. and SPS-49(V)4 radars; the other two, with the CORT update, have Mk 92 Mod. 6 f.c.s. and SPS-49(V)6 radars. F 85 and 86 also have the improved Mod. 2B Meroka CIWS, SAINSEL-CESELSA-INISEL three-operator CONAM combat data display systems, and an integrated GPS/inertial navigation system. F 83 and 86 had terminals for the Hispisat SATCOM system installed by 1997, and the others are to be similarly backfitted; F 85 received Matra-Marconi SCOT antennas for the Hispisat SHF SATCOM system in 1998.

Modernization: All may receive the INISEL-FABA DORNA *(Dirección de Tiro Optrónica y Radárica Naval)* weapons direction system, with the Thales Nederland Sting radar tracker, infrared camera, laser rangefinder, and high-definition t.v. in place of the original U.S. Mk 92 systems; trials commenced with a containerized system on the helicopter deck of F 83 in 4-96. All are also to receive the Ensa Elnath communications intercept system. The original VPS-2 radars for the Meroka system were to be replaced by an AESN RTN-30X radar, but none had it as of 2001.

♦ 5 Baleares class Bldr: Izar, Ferrol

	Laid down	L	In serv.
F 71 Baleares	31-10-68	20-8-70	24-9-73
F 72 Andalucía	2-7-69	30-3-71	23-5-74
F 73 Cataluña	20-8-70	3-11-71	16-1-75
F 74 Asturias	30-3-71	13-5-72	2-12-75
F 75 Extremadura	3-11-71	21-11-72	10-11-76

Baleares (F 71) Curt Borgenstam, Jr., 8-00

Cataluña (F 73) Luciano Grazioli, 3-00

Extremadura (F 75)—note door for VDS at centerline at the stern Bernard Prézelin, 9-01

D: 3,015 tons light; 3,350 tons std. (4,177 fl) **S:** 28 kts

Dim: 133.59 (126.5 pp) × 14.33 × 4.6 (7.01 over sonar)

A: 4 RGM-84C Harpoon SSM; 1 single-rail Mk 22 guided-missile launcher (16 Standard SM-1 MR Block V SAM); 1 127-mm 54-cal. Mk 42 Mod. 10 DP; 2 12-barrel 20-mm Meroka Mod. 2A CIWS; 2 single 12.7-mm mg; 1 Mk 16 Mod. 8 ASROC ASW RL syst. (1 8-round Mk 112 launcher, plus 18 reloads); 4 fixed 324-mm Mk 32 Mod. 9 ASW TT (Mk 46 Mod. 5 torpedoes)

GUIDED-MISSILE FRIGATES [FFG] *(continued)*

Electronics:
Radar: 1 Decca 1226 nav.; 1 Raytheon SPS-10 surf. search; 1 Lockheed Martin SPS-52B 3-D air search; 1 AESN RAN-12L/X Meroka target desig.; 2 Lockheed Martin VPS-2 Meroka f.c.; 1 Raytheon SPG-51C SAM f.c.; 1 Westinghouse SPG-53B gun/SAM f.c.
Sonar: Raytheon DE 1160C bow-mounted MF (3.5 kHz); Edo SQS-35A VDS
TACAN: SRN-15A
EW: Elettronica Nettunel Deneb Mk 1500 intercept and Mk 1600 jammer; Mk 36 SRBOC decoy syst. (4 6-round Mk 137 RL); SLQ-25 Nixie torpedo decoy syst.

M: 1 set Westinghouse geared steam turbines; 1 prop; 35,000 shp
Boilers: 2 Combustion-Engineering; 84 kg/cm², 510° C **Electric:** 3,000 kw tot.
Range: 4,500/20 **Fuel:** 750 tons **Crew:** 15 officers, 241 enlisted

Remarks: Built with American aid under an agreement of 31-5-66 as U.S. DEG 7 to DEG 11. Form the 31st Escort Squadron and are based at Ferrol. To be retired 2003–08 with the deliveries of the F-100 class.
Hull systems: The boilers have been renovated and converted to burn diesel fuel. Have fin stabilizers and the Prairie/Masker air bubbler system to reduce noise radiated through hull and propeller. Accommodations have been modified for female crewmembers.
Combat systems: An initial modernization completed in all by 1987 saw the addition of Harpoon missiles, SRN-15A TACAN, Tritan-1 combat data system, upgraded missile fire-control with Mk 152 digital computer, and NATO Link 11 capability. The second round of modernizations completed 1988–91 added two Meroka CIWS and their AESN RAN-12 target-detection radar, updated the EW suite (including the addition of decoy RL), and substituted the Raytheon DE 1160B sonar for the original SQS-23; the SQS-35A variable-depth sonar and the Tritan-1 combat data system were also updated (see entry for the carrier *Príncipe de Asturias*). All now have the Saturn 3S SATCOM system and the Deneb EW system. The Mk 74 missile fire-control system can use both the Mk 73 director (with SPG-51C radar) and Mk 68 director (with SPG-53B) to control two Standard missiles; the Mk 68 system is also used to control the 127-mm gun. The ships have the Mk 114 digital ASW computer to control ASROC and ASW torpedo firing. The Mk 32 torpedo tubes are built into the port and starboard sides of the after superstructure and are oriented to a 45° angle outboard of the centerline. The two Mk 25 tubes for Mk 37–series torpedoes originally built into the stern, facing aft, were removed during mid-1990s refits, and the space was adapted to accommodate female personnel. Can accommodate eight Harpoon SSM, but normally carry only four and sometimes fewer.

Vencedora (F 36) Bernard Prézelin, 4-00

Cazadora (F 35)—in refit; note sonar dome Camil Busquets i Vilanova, 5-01

FRIGATES [FF]

♦ 4 Descubierta (F-30) class

Bldr: Izar, Cartagena (F 35, 36: Izar, Ferrol)

	Laid down	L	In serv.
F 33 INFANTA ELENA	26-1-76	14-9-76	12-4-80
F 34 INFANTA CRISTINA	14-9-76	19-4-77	24-11-80
F 35 CAZADORA	14-12-77	17-10-78	20-7-81
F 36 VENCEDORA	1-5-78	27-4-79	27-3-82

Vencedora (F 36) NAVPIC-Holland, 10-00

Infanta Elena (F 33) Camil Busquets i Vilanova, 12-99

D: 1,428 tons (1,640 fl) **S:** 26 kts **Dim:** 88.88 (85.80 pp) × 10.40 × 3.95
A: 2 or 4 RGM-84A/C Harpoon SSM; 1 8-round Mk 29 SAM launcher (24 RIM-7H Sea Sparrow and Aspide missiles); 1 76-mm 62-cal. OTOBreda DP; 2 single 40-mm 70-cal. Bofors AA; 1 2-round 375-mm Bofors ASW RL; 2 triple 324-mm Mk 32 ASW TT (Mk 46 Mod. 5 torpedoes)
Electronics:
Radar: 1 . . . nav.; 1 Thales ZW-06/2 surf. search; 1 Thales DA-05/2 surf./air search; 1 Thales WM-25 track-while-scan f.c.
Sonar: Raytheon DE 1160C hull-mounted MF
EW: Elsag Deneb Mk 1600 intercept; CESELSA Canopus Mk 1600 jammer; Mk 36 SRBOC decoy syst. (2 6-round Mk 137 RL); SLQ-25 Nixie torpedo decoy syst.
M: 4 MTU-Bazán 16MA956 TB91 diesels; 2 CP props; 18,000 bhp
Electric: 1,810 kw tot. **Range:** 6,100/18; 7,500/12 **Fuel:** 250 tons
Crew: 10 officers, 108 enlisted + 30 marines

Remarks: F 33 and 34 were ordered 7-12-73, the other two 25-5-76. Sisters *Centinella* (F 37) and *Serviola* (F 38) were sold to Egypt in 1982, prior to completion; another sister was built for Morocco. They form the 21st Escort Squadron and are based at Cartagena. Sister *Diana* (F 32) was converted in 2000 at Cartagena to serve as a mine countermeasures support ship; see under [MCS]. *Descubierta* (F 31) was converted during 2000 to serve as a fisheries patrol ship; see under [PS].
Hull systems: Have fin stabilization, plus the U.S. Prairie/Masker bubbler system to reduce radiated noise below the waterline. Can accommodate 30 troops. An auxiliary gas turbine generator set has been added amidships for use during passive sonar search. Have been modified to accommodate female crewmembers.
Combat systems: Have the Tritan IV command system, integrated with Deneb ESM interface for Elsag Mk 1000 ESM equipment. The WM-25 radars are being upgraded with new front-end amplifiers and signal processors. Plans for backfitting Raytheon Type 1167 VDS and Meroka CIWS have been abandoned. Carry 600 rounds of 76-mm ammunition. Are equipped with Saturn 3S SATCOM transceivers.

PATROL SHIPS [PS]

♦ 1 Arnomendi-class fisheries patrol ship

Bldr: Construcciones Navales P. Freire, Vigo (In serv. 20-1-01)

P 63 ARNOMENDI

D: 1,500 tons (fl) **S:** 16.02 kts (trials) **Dim:** 66.50 × 10.50 × 4.35
A: 1 12.7-mm mg **Electronics:** Radar: 1 . . . nav.
M: 1 MaK 8M-25 diesel; 1 CP prop; 3,265 bhp—bow-thruster
Range: 22,000/16 **Crew:** 44 tot. (naval and civilian)

Remarks: Built for the Secretaría General de Pesca Marítima but transferred to the navy 17-1-01 by the Ministerio de Agricultura, Pesca, y Alimentación. Carries Ministry of Agriculture, Fisheries, and Food civilian personnel for inspection duties. Based at Las Palmas, Canary Islands.
Hull systems: Has a helicopter platform but no hangar. Is equipped with a hook for towing and carries two 6.2-m RIBs, each with two waterjet engines. Two fire monitors are located atop the foremast, and the ship is equipped to support divers. There are two electric generators.

PATROL SHIPS [PS] *(continued)*

Arnomendi (P 63) Ralph Edwards, 8-01

♦ 1 Alborán-class fisheries patrol ship

Bldr: Construcciones Navales P. Freire, Vigo (In serv. 8-1-97)

P 62 Alborán

Alborán (P 62) Dieter Wolf, 2-99

D: 1,356 tons (1,848 fl) **S:** 15 kts (13 sust.)
Dim: 65.92 (57.00 pp) × 10.50 × 4.35 **A:** 1 12.7-mm mg
Electronics: Radar: 1 Furuno FAR-2825 nav.; 1 Furuno FR-2130S nav.
M: 1 MaK 6M 453C diesel; 1 CP prop; 3,000 bhp (2,447 sust.)—electric emergency propulsion syst.; 350 shp (5 kts)—bow-thruster
Electric: 1,040 kw tot (1 × 400-kw, 2 × 320-kw diesel sets)
Range: 20,000/11 **Fuel:** 575 tons + 15 tons JP-5 aviation fuel
Crew: 7 officers, 30 enlisted + 14 passengers (see remarks)

Remarks: New-construction, 1,123-grt/900-dwt stern-haul trawler hull, taken over for use as an oceangoing fisheries protection ship. Funded by the *Subsecretaria de la Marine Mercante* for the Ministry of Agriculture, Fisheries, and Food (MAPA). Is based at Cartagena and operates primarily in the Mediterranean. The normal passenger complement includes two physicians and four fisheries inspectors.
Mission systems: Is equipped with an Inmarsat SATCOM terminal. The helicopter deck, large enough to accommodate an AB-212, is built over the stern and is 10.53 m above the normal waterline. A recreational gymnasium is fitted. Navigational equipment includes a TD-L 1620 MFD/F and FD-160 VHFD/F, Furuno FE-881 Mk II echo sounder, Furuno FCV-780 underwater television, Robertson RGC-11 gyrocompass, DS-70 doppler log, AP-9 Mk II-GA automatic pilot, FAX-208 meteorological fax, and two Furuno GPS receivers. Has 670 m^3 of stores capacity, including 20 m^3 refrigerated.

♦ 4 Serviola class (Type B-215) Bldr: Izar, Ferrol

	Laid down	L	In serv.	Based at
P 71 Serviola	7-10-89	10-5-90	22-3-91	Ferrol
P 72 Centinela	19-1-90	30-10-90	24-9-91	Las Palmas
P 73 Vigía	6-6-90	12-4-91	24-3-92	Cádiz
P 74 Atalaya	30-10-90	22-11-91	29-6-92	Ferrol

D: 826 tons light (1,270 fl) **S:** 20 kts **Dim:** 68.65 (63.00 wl) × 10.40 × 3.40
A: 1 76.2-mm 50-cal. U.S. Mk 26 DP; 2 single 12.7-mm mg
Electronics: Radar: 1 Decca 2690BT ARPA nav.; 1 Decca 2459F/I nav.
M: 2 Bazán-MTU 16V956 TB91 diesels; 2 CP props; 7,500 bhp
Electric: 468 kw tot. (3 Bazán-M.A.N. R6V 16/18 diesel sets)
Range: 8,000/12 **Fuel:** 247 tons **Endurance:** 30 days
Crew: 8 officers, 34 enlisted + 6 spare berths

Remarks: Ordered in 2-89 for use as offshore patrol vessels; a planned fifth unit was not ordered. Design is based on the Águila class for the Mexican Navy. Originally referred to as the Milano class while under construction.
Hull systems: Have a platform for an AB-212-size helicopter, but no hangar. Have nonretractable fin stabilizers. Carry two rigid inflatable inspection boats and have three 80-m^3/hr firefighting pumps. Are being modified to accommodate female crewmembers.

Vigía (P 73) Camil Busquets i Vilanova, 1-99

Combat systems: The 76.2-mm gun, from surplus stocks, is controlled by an Alcor-C optronic director or locally. P 73 has been equipped with an MSP-4000 optronic surveillance device for trials. Can carry 200 rounds of 76.2-mm and 7,000 rounds of 12.7-mm ammunition. Are equipped with Saturn 3S SATCOM transceivers.

♦ 1 Chilreu-class fisheries patrol ship

Bldr: Naval Gijón, S.A., Gijón (L: 2-5-88)

P 61 Chilreu (ex-*Pescalonso 2*)

Chilreu (P 61) Camil Busquets i Vilanova, 5-01

D: 1,157 tons (2,101 fl) **S:** 15 kts (12.5 sust.)
Dim: 67.78 (57.82 pp) × 11.02 × 4.66
A: 1 12.7-mm mg **Electronics:** Radar: 2 Decca . . . nav.
M: 1 MaK 6M 453AK diesel; 1 CP prop; 2,460 bhp
Electric: 1,040 kw tot (1 × 400-kw, 2 × 320-kw diesel sets)
Range: 15,000/12 **Endurance:** 90 days **Crew:** 6 officers, 26 enlisted

Remarks: 1,316 grt/1,080 dwt. Former commercial stern-haul trawler, transferred from the Ministry of Agriculture, Fisheries, and Food and commissioned into the Spanish Navy 30-3-92. Retains the refrigerated cargo hold and is equipped with an Inmarsat terminal. Based at Ferrol.

♦ 1 Descubierta-class fisheries patrol ship Bldr: Izar, Cartagena

	Laid down	L	In serv.
P 75 Descubierta (ex-F 31)	16-11-74	8-7-75	18-11-78

Descubierta (P 75) Ralph Edwards, 8-01

D: 1,418 tons (1,630 fl) **S:** 26 kts **Dim:** 88.88 (85.80 pp) × 10.40 × 3.90
A: 1 76-mm 62-cal. OTOBreda DP; 2 single 12.7-mm mg
Electronics: Radar: 1 . . . nav.; 1 Thales ZW-06/2 surf. search
M: 4 MTU-Bazán 16MA956 TB91 diesels; 2 CP props; 18,000 bhp
Electric: 1,810 kw tot. **Range:** 6,100/18; 7,500/12 **Fuel:** 250 tons
Crew: 10 officers, 108 enlisted + 30 marines

PATROL SHIPS [PS] *(continued)*

Remarks: Ordered 7-12-73. Converted during 2000 to serve as a fisheries patrol and "standby" ship, operating from Las Palmas in the Canary Islands. Renumbered to P 75 on 5-6-00.
Hull systems: Has fin stabilization. Can accommodate 30 troops and has been modified to accommodate female crewmembers.
Combat systems: Carries 600 rounds of 76-mm gun ammunition. All other armament, most of the sensors, and the EW equipment were removed during conversion, but 12.7-mm mg were added forward of the bridge and abaft the stack.

PATROL CRAFT [PC]

♦ 10 Anaga class Bldr: Izar, San Fernando, Cádiz

	L	In serv.		L	In serv.
P 21 Anaga	14-2-80	14-10-80	P 26 Medas	15-12-80	16-10-81
P 22 Tagomago	14-2-80	30-1-81	P 27 Ízaro	15-12-80	9-12-81
P 23 Marola	. . .	4-6-81	P 28 Tabarca	15-12-80	30-12-81
P 24 Mouro	. . .	14-7-81	P 29 Deva	24-11-81	3-6-82
P 25 Grosa	15-12-80	15-9-81	P 30 Bergantín	24-11-81	30-7-82

Ízaro (P 27) Dieter Wolf, 1-01

Deva (P 29) Camil Busquets i Vilanova, 6-00

D: 296.5 tons (350 fl) **S:** 20 kts **Dim:** 44.4 (40.0 pp) × 6.6 × 2.6
A: 1 76.2-mm 50-cal. U.S. Mk 22 DP; 1 20-mm 70-cal. Oerlikon Mk 10 AA
Electronics: Radar: 2 Decca 1226 nav.
M: 1 Bazán-MTU 16V956 SB90 diesel; 1 CP prop; 4,800 bhp (4,000 sust.)
Range: 4,000/13 **Crew:** 3 officers, 22 enlisted

Remarks: Ordered 22-7-78; P 21 was laid down in 4-79. P 30 was originally numbered PVZ 210 and the others PVZ 21–PVZ 29. Named for small islands. Carry rescue and firefighting equipment. Intended primarily as fisheries protection patrol craft. Two 7.62-mm mg can also be mounted.

♦ 6 Barceló class
Bldrs: P 11: Lürssen, Vegesack, Germany; others: Izar, La Carraca, Cádiz

	L	In serv.
P 11 Barceló	6-10-75	26-3-76
P 12 Laya	16-12-75	23-12-76
P 13 Javier Quiroga	16-12-75	1-4-77
P 14 Ordóñez	10-9-76	7-6-77
P 15 Acevedo	10-9-76	14-7-77
P 16 Candido Perez	3-3-77	25-11-77

D: 110 tons (134 fl) **S:** 36.5 kts **Dim:** 36.2 (43.2 pp) × 5.8 × 1.75 (2.15 props)
A: 1 40-mm 70-cal. Bofors AA; 1 20-mm 70-cal. Oerlikon Mk 10 AA; 2 single 12.7-mm mg
Electronics: Radar: 1 Raytheon 1620/6 nav.
M: 2 Bazán-MTU 16V538 TB90 diesels; 2 props; 7,320 bhp (6,120 sust.)
Electric: 220 kVA tot. **Range:** 600/33.5; 1,200/16 **Fuel:** 18 tons
Crew: 3 officers, 16 enlisted

Remarks: Lürssen FPB 36 design. Carry 750 rounds of 40-mm and 2,500 rounds of 20-mm ammunition. A Matra Défense optical director is fitted for the 40-mm gun.

Barceló (P 11) Leo Dirkx, 4-01

Javier Quiroga (P 13) Camil Busquets i Vilanova, 3-00

PATROL BOATS [PB]

♦ 4 Conejera class Bldr: Izar, San Fernando, Cádiz

	L	In serv.
P 31 Conejera (ex-LVE 1)	9-81	31-12-81
P 32 Dragonera (ex-LVE 2)	9-81	31-12-81
P 33 Espalmador (ex-LVE 3)	11-1-82	10-5-82
P 34 Alcanada (ex-LVE 4)	10-2-82	10-5-82

Alcanada (P 34) Camil Busquets i Vilanova, 5-01

D: 85 tons (fl) **S:** 25 kts **Dim:** 32.15 (30.0 pp) × 5.30 × 1.42
A: 1 20-mm 70-cal. Oerlikon Mk 10 AA; 1 12.7-mm mg
Electronics: Radar: 1 Furuno . . . nav.
M: 2 Bazán-M.A.N. V8V16/18 TLS diesels; 2 props; 2,800 bhp (2,450 sust.)
Range: 1,200/15 **Crew:** 12 tot.

Remarks: Ordered in 1978; first two laid down 20-12-79. Jointly funded by the navy and the Ministry of Commerce for fisheries patrol duties. Aluminum construction. A planned further six were not built.

PATROL BOATS [PB] *(continued)*

Espalmador (P 33) Findler & Winter, 2-01

♦ 2 small fisheries patrol boats
Bldr: Astilleros Viudes, Barcelona

P 81 Toralla (In serv. 29-4-87) P 82 Formentor (In serv. 23-6-89)

Toralla (P 81) Dieter Wolf, 1-01

D: 56 tons (78 fl) **S:** 19.75 kts **Dim:** 28.50 (25.00 wl) × 6.50 × 1.45
A: 1 12.7-mm mg
Electronics: Radar: 1 Decca RM 1070 nav.; 1 Decca RM 270 nav.
M: 2 Bazán-MTU 8V396 TB93 diesels; 2 props; 2,200 bhp
Range: 1,000/12 **Crew:** 13 tot.

Remarks: GRP-sheathed wooden hulls. A planned third was not ordered.

♦ 1 P 101 class
Bldr: Aresa, Arenys del Mar, Barcelona (In serv. 1981–88)

P 114 (ex-Y 528, ex-P 111, ex-LVC 11)

D: 16.9 tons (21.7 fl) **S:** 27 kts **Dim:** 15.90 (13.7 pp) × 4.36 × 1.33
A: 1 12.7-mm mg **Electronics:** Radar: 1 Decca 110 nav.
M: 2 Baudouin-Interdiesel DNP-8 MIR diesels; 2 props; 1,024 bhp
Electric: 12 kVA tot. **Range:** 430/18 **Fuel:** 2.2 tons
Crew: 2 officers, 4–5 enlisted

Remarks: Ordered 13-5-77. Jointly funded by the navy and the Ministry of Commerce. GRP construction. Seven other P 101–class units, reclassified as personnel launches (see under [YFL]), are also in service; of those, three operate on the Río Miño as patrol boats.
Disposals: Sister P 103 was stricken in 1990. P 115 was damaged by fire late in 1991 but not stricken until 1-5-93. Eighteen others were stricken during 1993. Y 528 was again redesignated P 114 on 15-2-96 to replace P 104, which was stricken that date.

♦ 1 Cabo Fradera–class river patrol boat
Bldr: Izar, La Carraca, Cádiz (In serv. 11-1-63)

P 201 Cabo Fradera (ex-PVI 01, ex-V 22)

D: 21 tons (28 fl) **S:** 10 kts **Dim:** 17.80 × 4.20 × 0.82
A: 1 7.62-mm mg **Electronics:** Radar: 1 Furuno . . . nav.
M: 2 diesels; 2 props; 280 bhp **Crew:** 9 tot.

Remarks: Based at Tuy on the Río Miño border with Portugal.

Disposal note: The last P 202–class patrol launch, P 221, was stricken 24-5-00.

MINE WARFARE SHIPS

♦ 1 Descubierta-class mine countermeasures support ship [MCS]
Bldr: Izar, Cartagena

	Laid down	L	In serv.
M 11 Diana (ex-F 32)	18-7-75	26-1-76	30-6-79

Diana (M 11) Camil Busquets i Vilanova, 11-00

D: 1,408 tons (1,620 fl) **S:** 26 kts **Dim:** 88.88 (85.80 pp) × 10.40 × 3.90
A: 1 76-mm 62-cal. OTOBreda Compact DP
Electronics:
Radar: 1 . . . nav. (X-band); 1 . . . nav. (S-band)
Sonar: removed
EW: removed
M: 4 MTU-Bazán 16MA956 TB91 diesels; 2 CP props; 18,000 bhp
Electric: 1,810 kw tot. **Range:** 6,100/18; 7,500/12 **Fuel:** 250 tons
Crew: 10 officers, 108 enlisted

Remarks: Ordered on 7-12-73 as a small frigate; converted in 2000 at Cartagena to serve as a mine countermeasures support ship and renumbered M 11 on 15-6-00.
Hull systems: Has fin stabilization, plus the U.S. Prairie/Masker bubble system to reduce radiated noise below the waterline.
Combat systems: During conversion, the Albatros SAM system, two 40-mm AA, all ASW and ESM equipment, Harpoon missiles, and some radars were removed. Additional navigational radars were added, along with a diver's decompression chamber and foundations for four portable mine countermeasures repair shop modules. Is equipped with a Saturn 3S SATCOM transceiver.

♦ 4 (+ 2 + 2) Segura-class minehunters (M-3 program) [MHC]
Bldr: Izar, Cartagena

	Laid down	L	In serv.
M 31 Segura	30-5-95	25-7-97	27-4-99
M 32 Sella	12-96	6-7-98	28-5-99
M 33 Tambre	12-97	5-3-99	18-2-00
M 34 Turia	11-98	22-11-99	6-12-01
M 35	. . .	. . .	5-04
M 36	. . .	. . .	5-04
M 37	. . .	. . .	. . .
M 38	. . .	. . .	. . .

Tambre (M 33) Camil Busquets i Vilanova, 12-00

Turia (M 34) Camil Busquets i Vilanova, 12-00

D: 520 tons (550 fl) **S:** 14.5 kts **Dim:** 54.00 (51.00 pp) × 10.70 × 2.15
A: 1 20-mm 85-cal. Oerlikon GAM-B01 AA
Electronics:
Radar: 1 Kelvin-Hughes 1007 nav.
Sonar: Indra–Raytheon–Thomson-Marconi SQQ-32(SP) variable-depth minehunting (HF)
E/O: Alcor-C optronic gun director
M: 2 MTU 12V396 TB84 diesels; 2 Voith-Schneider vertical cycloidal props; 1,120 bhp—2 168-shp electric motors for 7-kt hunting speeds—2 74-shp bow-thrusters
Electric: 810 kw tot. (3 × 270-kw diesel sets)
Range: 2,000/12 **Crew:** 7 officers, 26 enlisted (40 tot. accomm.)

MINE WARFARE SHIPS *(continued)*

Remarks: Construction of the first four enlarged versions of the British *Sandown*-class minehunter design at Izar, Cartagena, was initially authorized 26-10-92 and confirmed by the Spanish cabinet 7-5-93. Two more minehunters were ordered 29-12-00, and another two are to be ordered later. Plans to order the second group of four as minesweepers have apparently been canceled. Construction technology assistance was provided by France's DCN under a 12-93 contract.
Combat systems: The SMYC CM *(Sistema de Mando y Control para Cazaminas)* minehunting data and command system is based on the GEC-Marconi NAUTIS-M; it has three CM-1 operator consoles and is integrated with the FABA PN/UDDB navigation system. Carry two Gayrobot Pluto Plus mine detection and disposal vehicles. A FABA ICCS 4 integrated communications system is fitted.

Disposal note: The four ex-U.S. Navy *Aggressive*-class minesweepers transferred to Spain in 1971 have been retired: *Guadalete* (M 41; ex-PVZ 41; ex-M 41; ex-*Dynamic,* MSO 432) on 15-7-98, *Guadiana* (M 44; ex-*Vigor,* MSO 473) in 1999, *Guadalquivir* (M 43; ex-*Persistent,* MSO 491) on 13-10-00, and *Guadalmedina* (M 42; ex-*Pivot,* MSO 463) on 2-4-00.

♦ 4 ex-U.S. MSC 268– and Redwing*-class coastal minesweepers [MSC]

	Bldr	L	In serv.
M 22 Ebro (ex-M 26, ex-MSC 269)	Bellingham SY, Bellingham, Wash.	8-11-57	19-12-58
M 25 Genil (ex-M 31, ex-MSC 279)	Tacoma Boat, Tacoma, Wash.	8-8-58	11-9-59
M 26 Odiel (ex-M 32, ex-MSC 288)	Tampa Marine, Tampa, Fla.	3-9-58	9-10-59
M 27 Sil (ex-PVZ 55; ex-M 29; ex-*Redwing,* MSC 200)*	Tampa Marine, Tampa, Fla.	29-4-54	16-6-59

Ebro (M 22) Camil Busquets i Vilanova, 5-01

Genil (M 25) Dieter Wolf, 1-01

D: 355 tons (384 fl) **S:** 12 kts
Dim: M 27: 44.45 (44.06 wl) × 8.51 (7.95 wl) × 2.85 (max.)—others: 43.90 × 8.51 × 2.85 (max.)
A: 1 twin 20-mm 70-cal. Oerlikon Mk 24 AA
Electronics:
Radar: 1 Decca TM 626 or RM 914 nav.
Sonar: UQS-1D hull-mounted (100 kHz)
M: M 27: 2 G.M. Electromotive Div. 8-268A diesels; 2 props; 1,760 bhp—others: 4 G.M. Detroit Diesel 6-71 diesels; 2 props; 1,200 bhp
Electric: 720 kw tot. (2 × 300 kw, 2 × 60 kw)
Range: 1,625/13.6; 3,900/7 **Fuel:** 25.3 tons **Crew:** 4 officers, 35 enlisted

Remarks: Originally a group of 12, transferred under the U.S. Military Assistance Plan: two in 1954, one in 1955, three in 1956, one in 1958, two in 1959, and three in 1960. Are attached to the Fuerza de Medidas contra Minas and based at Cartagena; they will be retired in 2004 after 45 years' service.

Disposals: Ex-U.S. *Adjutant*-class units *Duero* (M 23; ex-M 28; ex-*Spoonbill,* MSC 202) and *Miño* (M 28, ex-PVZ 53, ex-M 25, ex-MSC 266) were retired during 1999. *Adjutant*-class *Júcar* (M 21, ex-M 23, ex-MSC 220) and MSC 268–class *Tajo* (M 24, ex-M 30, ex-MSC 287) were retired during 12-01.

AMPHIBIOUS WARFARE SHIPS

♦ 2 (+ 1) Rotterdam-class dock landing ships [LPD]
Bldr: Izar, Ferrol

	Laid down	L	In serv.
L 51 Galicia	31-5-96	21-7-97	30-4-98
L 52 Castilla	11-12-97	14-6-99	26-6-00

Galicia (L 51) Camil Busquets i Vilanova, 5-00

Galicia (L 51) Camil Busquets i Vilanova, 5-00

Castilla (L 52)—note search radar and SATCOM radomes above the bridge *Ships of the World,* 2001

D: 9,500 tons std.; 11,200 tons normal (13,815 fl) **S:** 20 kts
Dim: 163.12 (145.00 wl; 142.2 pp) × 25.00 (23.26 wl) × 5.23 (5.90 props)
Air group: 6 helicopters
A: 2 twin 20-mm 70-cal. Oerlikon Mk 24 AA; provision for 2 20-mm Meroka Mod. 2B CIWS
Electronics:
Radar: 3 Kelvin-Hughes . . . ARPA nav.; 2 Lockheed VPS-2 Meroka f.c.—L 52 also: DaimlerChrysler TRS-3D/16-ES 3-D air/surf. search and target desig.
EW: Indra SLQ-380 Aldebarán intercept; Mk 36 SRBOC decoy syst. (4 6-round Mk 137 RL)

AMPHIBIOUS WARFARE SHIPS *(continued)*

M: 4 Bazán–M.A.N.–Burmeister & Wain 40/54A diesels; 2 props; 19,000 shp—2 680-shp side-thrusters
Electric: 6,800 kw tot. (4 × 1,500-kw diesel sets; 2 × 400-kw emergency diesel sets)
Range: 6,000/12
Fuel: 800 tons + 200 tons aviation and vehicle fuel + 50 tons for landing craft
Crew: L 51: 13 officers, 100 enlisted + troops: 41 officers, 570 enlisted (L 52: 179 crew + 65 marine corps staff + 404 troops)

Remarks: L 51 was ordered during 8-94 for $169 million. Approval to construct L 52 was granted by the Council of Ministers 9-5-97. The design was prepared by Royal Schelde and Spain's Izar. Sister *Rotterdam* was built for Netherlands Navy service, and similar ships are on order for the U.K., with others possibly to be ordered by Belgium and Germany. L 52 has enhanced command and control capabilities for service as an amphibious force flagship; this is to result in fewer troops but a larger staff being accommodated. Consideration was being given to construction of a third unit modified with a full-length flight deck and starboard-side island superstructure, but work would not begin until perhaps 2004. Are based at Rota.
Hull systems: Built to merchant marine standards but have degaussing coils and a gas-tight citadel. The Spanish Navy version has straight diesel propulsion, whereas the Dutch version has a diesel-electric propulsion plant and different weapon and sensor systems. L 51 has accommodations for up to 127 ship's company. Have a dual helicopter hangar (510 m^2 tot.) and two landing spots on the 60 × 25–m (1,340 m^2) helicopter deck; can carry up to six helicopters in the hangars. Have 1,010 m^2 of internal vehicle parking space and can use the 885-m^2 (55 × 16–m) docking well for additional vehicles; further vehicles can be carried on the helicopter deck and in the helicopter hangar. Normal vehicle load is expected to be 5 M 60A3 tanks, 3 LVTP-7 amphibious armored personnel carriers, 10 trucks with trailers, 31 light vehicles with trailers, 2 ambulances, 1 crane, 1 push-truck, and 1 forklift; 33 M 60 tanks alone could be carried. Maximum cargo is 2,488 tons. The docking well can accommodate four LCM(8) landing craft (up to 347 tons) or up to 818 tons of vehicles. Carry 300 tons potable water. Ballast tanks (to flood down the docking well) accommodate 4,000 tons of seawater. Troop cargo includes 400 m^3 total equipment stowage plus 30 m^3 (about 112 tons) of ammunition storage. Hospital facilities in L 51 include two operating rooms, 100 beds, and 10 intensive care berths.
Combat systems: Have an infrared surveillance system and some form of combat data system. Are NATO Link 11 compatible. To permit use as secondary ASW platforms, are equipped with a sonobuoy and weapons storage compartment capable of accommodating 25 tons of stores. L 52 has the SICOA *(Sistema de Mando y Control para Operaciones Anfibias)* command-and-control system and enhanced communications and support facilities for a 65-person marine staff (at the expense of some troop berthing) and an enhanced radar suite.

♦ 2 ex-U.S. Newport-class tank landing ships [LST]
Bldr: National Steel SB, San Diego

	Laid down	L	In serv.
L 41 HERNÁN CORTÉS (ex-*Barnstable County,* LST 1197)	19-12-70	2-10-71	27-5-72
L 42 PIZARRO (ex-*Harlan County,* LST 1196)	7-11-70	24-7-71	8-4-72

Pizarro (L 42) Guy Schaeffer, via Paolo Marsan, 6-98

Hernán Cortés (L 41) H&L Van Ginderen, 11-98

D: 4,975 tons light; 6,800 tons std. (8,550 fl) **S:** 22 kts (20 sust.)
Dim: 159.2 (171.3 over horns) × 21.18 × 5.3 (aft; 1.80 fwd)
A: 1 20-mm Mk 15 Phalanx gatling CIWS; 2 single 20-mm 85-cal. Oerlikon GAM-B01 AA; 4 single 12.7-mm mg
Electronics:
Radar: 1 Canadian Marconi LN-66 nav.; 1 Raytheon SPS-10 surf. search
M: 6 Alco 16-251 diesels; 2 CP props; 16,500 bhp—bow-thruster
Range: 14,250/14 **Fuel:** 1,750 tons
Crew: 15 officers, 25 petty officers, 215 nonrated + 374–431 troops

Remarks: L 41 was transferred 26-8-94 and L 42 on 14-4-95, both on 50-month leases with an option to purchase. Are attached to the Grupo Anfibio Delta and based at Rota.
Hull systems: Can transport 2,000 tons of cargo, or, for beaching, 500 tons, on 1,765 m^2 of deck space. There is a 34-m-long, 75-ton-capacity mobile aluminum ramp forward, which is linked to the tank deck by a second from the upper deck. Aft is a 242-m^2 helicopter platform and a stern door for loading and unloading vehicles. Four pontoon causeway sections can be carried on the hull sides. The tank deck, which has a 75-ton-capacity turntable at both ends, can carry 23 AAV-7A1 armored personnel carriers or 29 M 48 tanks or 41 2.5-ton trucks, while the upper deck can accept 29 2.5-ton trucks. Now carry two LCVPs and two LCPs in Welin davits. Have two 10-ton cranes. Carry 141,600 gallons of vehicle fuel. Transferred with six pontoon sections each, two of them powered. In an emergency situation, can transport up to 1,610 troops for a brief time, in lieu of vehicles.
Combat systems: Both are now equipped with Saturn 3S SATCOM systems. The Phalanx CIWS is said to be nonoperational in both. They are operated with three AB-212 helicopters each, although there is no hangar.

Disposal note: Ex-U.S. *Paul Revere*–class amphibious transport *Aragón* (L 22; ex-*Francis Marion,* LPA 249; ex-*Prairie Mariner*) was stricken 17-11-00; sister *Castilla* (ex-*Paul Revere,* LPA 248; ex-*Diamond Mariner*) was stricken 16-6-98.

Note: The EDIC-class utility landing craft were redesignated as auxiliaries (q.v.) in 1986.

♦ 2 ex-U.S. LCU 1466–class utility landing craft [LCU]
Bldr: Kingston Dry Dock Const. Co., Kingston, N.Y. (L: 4-55)

L 71 (ex-LCU 11, ex-LCU 1, ex-U.S. LCU 1471)
L 72 (ex-LCU 12, ex-LCU 2, ex-U.S. LCU 1491)

D: 180 tons (347 fl) **S:** 8 kts **Dim:** 35.08 × 10.36 × 1.60 (aft)
A: 2 single 20-mm 70-cal. Oerlikon Mk 10 AA **Electronics:** Radar: 1 . . . nav.
M: 3 Gray Marine 64YTL diesels; 3 props; 675 bhp **Electric:** 40 kw tot.
Range: 1,200/6 (700/7 loaded) **Fuel:** 11 tons **Crew:** 6 crew + 8 troops

Remarks: Transferred in 6-72. Cargo: 160 tons. Both are attached to the Grupo Anfibio Delta and are based at Puntales, Cádiz; they are used locally as ferries and no longer participate in amphibious warfare activities.

♦ 8 LCM 1E–class landing craft
Bldr: Izar, La Carraca, San Fernando (In serv. 2001)

	In serv.		In serv.		In serv.
L 601	19-2-01	L 604	2001	L 607	2001
L 602	9-3-01	L 605	2001	L 608	2001
L 603	2001	L 606	2001		

D: 52 tons light (108 fl) **S:** . . . kts **Dim:** 23.30 × 6.40 × 1.04 (loaded)
M: 2 Bazán-MTU . . . diesels; 2 waterjets; 2,200 bhp
Range: 160/. . . **Crew:** 3 tot.

Remarks: Intended to be carried by the new *Rotterdam*-class dock landing ships. Steel construction. Have 56-ton capacity (100 tons in overload condition) on a 100-m^2 vehicle deck. Bow and stern ramps are fitted.

♦ 2 amphibious warping tugs [LCM]
Bldr: . . . (In serv. 19-10-95)

L 91 L 92

Remarks: U.S.-type tug pontoons, powered by modular diesel outdrives. Assigned with six ex-U.S. pontoon sections to the Grupo Naval de Playa at Puntales Naval Base, Cádiz, for use aboard the two *Newport*-class LSTs. No data available.

♦ 8 U.S. LCM(8)-class landing craft [LCM]
Bldrs: L 81–86: Oxnard Boat, Calif. (In serv. 1975); others: Izar, La Carraca, San Fernando (In serv. 1988)

L 81 (ex-LCM 81) through L 86 (ex-LCM 86) L 87 L 88

D: 58.8 tons (116 fl) **S:** 10 kts **Dim:** 22.40 × 6.42 × 1.83 (aft)
M: 2 G.M. Detroit Diesel 6-71 diesels; 2 props; 600 bhp
Range: 150/9.2 (loaded) **Fuel:** 2.4 tons **Crew:** 5 tot.

Remarks: First six were transferred between 7-75 and 9-75; the other two were built in Spain. Carry up to 53.5 tons of cargo. Assigned to the Grupo Naval de Playa at Puntales Naval Base, Cádiz.

♦ 16 LCM(6)E-class landing craft [LCM]
Bldr: Izar, San Fernando

L 161 through L 167 L 261 through L 267 L 601 L 602

D: 24 tons (56 fl) **S:** 10.2 kts **Dim:** 17.07 × 4.37 × 1.52 (props)
M: 2 Gray Marine 64HN9 or G.M. 6V71 diesels; 2 props; 330 bhp
Range: 130/10 **Crew:** 3 tot. + 80 troops

Remarks: L 601 was completed 28-12-84, L 602 on 1-2-85, and the others in 1985–89. Cargo: 34 tons.

♦ 4 LCVP Mk 7E landing craft [LCVP]
Bldr: Astilleros y Talleres Ferrolanos (In serv. 1987)

D: 11.77 tons (fl) **S:** . . . **Dim:** . . . × . . . × . . . **M:** . . .

Remarks: One is attached to the carrier *Príncipe de Asturias* (R 11).

♦ up to 14 ex-U.S. LCVP [LCVP]

D: 13 tons (fl) **S:** 9 kts **Dim:** 10.90 × 3.21 × 1.04 (aft)
M: 1 Gray Marine 64HN9 diesel; 225 bhp **Range:** 110/9

AMPHIBIOUS WARFARE SHIPS *(continued)*

Remarks: Survivors of 20 transferred with larger ships. Have GRP hulls. Can carry 36 troops or 3.5 tons of cargo. The cargo deck measures 5.24 × 2.29 m, with 2.00-m-wide access through the bow ramp.

AUXILIARIES

♦ 1 stores transport [AFT]

Bldr: Eriksbergs M/V, Göteborg, Sweden (In serv. 5-53)

A 01 CONTRAMAESTRE CASADO (ex-*Thanasis K.,* ex-*Fortuna Reefer,* ex-*Bonzo,* ex-*Bajamar,* ex-*Leeward Islands*)

Contramaestre Casado (A 01)—with portable tracking array on the helicopter platform aft
Bernard Prézelin, 5-00

D: approx. 5,300 tons (fl) **S:** 16 kts **Dim:** 104.20 (96.12 pp) × 14.36 × 6.11
A: 2 single 20-mm 70-cal. Oerlikon Mk 10 AA
Electronics: Radar: 1 Decca 626 nav.; 1 Decca TM 1226 nav.
M: 1 Eriksberg 7-cyl. heavy-oil diesel; 1 prop; 3,600 bhp **Electric:** 660 kw tot.
Range: 18,600/16 **Fuel:** 727 tons **Crew:** 72 tot.

Remarks: 2,272 grt/2,743 dwt. Former commercial refrigerated cargo ship, impounded for smuggling and turned over to the Spanish Navy to supply the Canary Islands; commissioned 15-12-82. Has four cargo holds, two 5-ton derricks, and a helicopter platform at the stern. The guns are mounted on the main deck, abreast the forward cargo crane.

♦ 1 ex-German Darss-class intelligence collector [AGI]

Bldr: VEB Schiffswerft Neptun, Rostock (In serv. 6-85)

A 111 ALERTA (ex-*Jasmund,* D 41)

Alerta (A 111) Camil Busquets i Vilanova, 5-01

Alerta (A 111) Dieter Wolf, 1-01

D: 2,292 tons (fl) **S:** 12 kts **Dim:** 76.52 × 12.37 × 4.15
A: 2 single 12.7-mm mg **Electronics:** Radar: 1 Decca . . . nav.
M: 1 12-cyl. Kolomna Type 40 DM diesel; 1 CP Kort-nozzle prop; 2,200 bhp
Electric: 520 kw (4 × 130 kw)
Range: 1,000/12 **Endurance:** 14 days **Crew:** 60 tot.

Remarks: Purchased in late 1992 and commissioned 6-12-92 prior to sailing to Spain for a refit. Begun as a cargo vessel, but converted for use as an intelligence collector by the former East German Volksmarine. Five sisters, all now stricken, served as cargo vessels in the Volksmarine and Bundesmarine. Transferred without intelligence equipment, which was developed by Spain; is also used for trials with new radar and EW equipment. Has a Saturn 3S SATCOM terminal.

♦ 1 Antarctic oceanographic research ship [AGOR]

Bldr: Izar, San Fernando

	Laid down	L	In serv.
A 33 HESPÉRIDES (ex-*Mar Antártico*)	1989	12-3-90	1991

Hespérides (A 33)—red hull, white superstructure, orange foremast and stacks
Camil Busquets i Vilanova, 5-00

D: 1,983 tons (2,750 fl) **S:** 15 kts **Dim:** 82.48 (77.74 pp) × 14.33 × 4.48
A: none
Electronics:
Radar: 1 Decca 2690 ARPA nav.; 1 Decca 2690 ACS nav.
Sonar: all Simrad: EM-12 deep-sea multibeam echo sounder (13 kHz/11,000-m depth); EM-1000 multibeam echo sounder (95 kHz/5,800-m depth); EK-500 fisheries research echo sounder (38, 120, and 200 kHz); EA-500 hydrographic echo sounder (12 and 200 kHz); SL-490 obstacle-avoidance sonar (49 kHz); and VD-280 towed transducer platform
M: 2 Bazán–M.A.N.–Burmeister & Wain 14V 20/27 diesels (1,904 bhp each) and 2 Bazán–M.A.N.–Burmeister & Wain 7L 20/27 diesels (884 bhp each) in two generator set pairs; 2 AEG 1,400-kw electric motors; 1 prop; 3,800 shp—350-shp bow- and stern-thrusters
Range: 12,000/13 **Endurance:** 120 days
Crew: 9 officers, 30 enlisted + 30 scientists

Remarks: Ordered in 7-88. Paid for by the Ministry of Foreign Affairs; operated by the navy and subordinated to the Straits Zone. Intended for geophysical, magnetic, and biological research. Hull painted red and superstructure white.
Hull systems: Has an icebreaker bow for duties in support of Spain's Livingston Island, Antarctica, station. Has a helicopter deck and telescopic hangar for one Agusta-Bell 212. Can support divers to 200 m. The 12 laboratories total 330 m^2. In addition to the main generator complexes, also has a 120-kw emergency diesel generator set. All of the sonar equipment, except the towed transducer, has transducers mounted in a 12 × 3–m keel dome. There is a complete automated data reduction and storage system.

♦ 2 Malaspina-class hydrographic survey ships [AGS]

Bldr: Izar, La Carraca, Cádiz

	L	In serv.		L	In serv.
A 31 MALASPINA	14-8-73	21-2-75	A 32 TOFIÑO	22-12-73	23-4-75

Tofiño (A 32)—white-painted Dieter Wolf, 1-01

D: 820 tons (1,090 fl) **S:** 15 kts **Dim:** 57.7 (51.4 pp) × 11.7 × 3.64
A: 2 single 20-mm 70-cal. Oerlikon Mk 10 AA
Electronics:
Radar: 1 Raytheon 1620/6XB nav.
Sonar: STN Atlas Elektronik DESO-10 AN 1021 echo sounders; Burnett 538-2 deep-sounding echo sounder; Egg Mk 8 side-scanning mapping sonar
M: 2 San Carlos–MWM TbRHS-345-6I diesels; 2 CP props; 2,700 bhp—active rudder with electric motor for slow-speed operations
Electric: 780 kVA tot. **Range:** 3,140/14.5; 4,000/12
Crew: 9 officers, 54 enlisted

Remarks: Formerly AH 31 and AH 32, redesignated in 1986. Have a Magnavox Transit satellite navigation system, Omega, Raydist, and Hewlett-Packard 2100AC computer.

AUXILIARIES *(continued)*

Tofiño (A 32) Camil Busquets i Vilanova, 5-00

♦ **4 Castor-class survey ships [AGS]**
Bldr: Izar, La Carraca, Cádiz

	L	In serv.		L	In serv.
A 21 CÁSTOR	5-11-64	1-12-66	A 23 ANTARES	5-3-73	21-11-74
A 22 PÓLLUX	5-11-64	15-12-66	A 24 RIGEL	5-3-73	21-11-74

Póllux (A 22) Dieter Wolf, 1-01

D: 354.5 tons (383.4 fl) **S:** 11.5 kts **Dim:** 38.36 (33.84 pp) × 7.60 × 3.10 (max.)
A: none **Electronics:** Radar: 1 Raytheon 1620 nav.
M: 1 Echevarría–Burmeister & Wain Alpha 408-26VO (A 21, 22: Sulzer) diesel; 1 prop; 800 (A 21, 22: 720) bhp
Range: 3,000/11.5 **Fuel:** 52.9 tons **Crew:** 4 officers, 34 enlisted

Remarks: Redesignated from AH 21–24 in 1986. Were produced in pairs, the later units having full main-deck bulwarks and the earlier pair a cleared fantail to allow use of Oropesa floats to support towed side-looking mapping sonar arrays. Have Raydist navigation system, Omega receivers, three echo sounders, and a Hewlett-Packard 2100A computer. Subordinated to the Straits Zone.

♦ **1 roll-on/roll-off vehicle and container carrier [AK]**
Bldr: Cia. Comercio e Navegação Maua, Niterói, Brazil (In serv. 10-84)

A 05 EL CAMINO ESPAÑOL (ex-*Cindya,* ex-*Mercantil Mage,* ex-*Araguary*)

El Camino Español (A 05) Dieter Wolf, 1-01

D: 4,560 tons (fl) **S:** 15 kts (12.4 sust.) **Dim:** 93.53 (80.02 pp) × 18.24 × 4.61
A: none **Electronics:** Radar: 2 . . . nav.
M: 2 M.A.N.-Sulzer 6L25/30 diesels; 2 props; 6,482 bhp—bow-thruster
Electric: 600 kw tot. (3 × 200-kw, 220/440-V, 50-Hz sets)
Range: . . ./. . . **Fuel:** 382.5 tons heavy oil, 106.5 tons diesel **Crew:** . . . tot.

Remarks: 1,329 grt/3,502 dwt. Acquired 5-3-98 from Scheepvaartmij Unidor N.V., Willemstad, Netherlands Antilles, to carry military vehicles and cargo for the Spanish Army. Commissioned 27-9-99. The officers are naval personnel and the enlisted personnel army.
Hull systems: Combination vehicle, heavy-lift, and container carrier, with a cargo deck and a single 8.0-m-long, 11.5-m-wide, combination stern door/vehicle ramp aft. Has two internal vehicle cargo decks (40.2 and 39.0 m long, both 12.5 m wide and 6.1 m high, with a total lane-length of 344 m). Can also be used to carry up to 260 standard 20-ft. cargo containers and has two 25-ton-capacity cranes mounted on the port side.

♦ **1 vehicle carrier [AK]**
Bldr: Soc. Met. Duro Felguera, Gijón, Spain (In serv. 1973)

A 04 MARTÍN POSADILLO (ex-ET 02, ex-*Cala Portals,* ex-*Rivanervión*)

Martín Posadillo (A 04) Dieter Wolf, 1-01

D: 1,920 tons (fl) **S:** 14 kts **Dim:** 75.01 (68.03 pp) × 13.01 × 4.27
A: none **Electronics:** Radar: . . . nav.
M: 1 MWM RHS345AU diesel; 1 prop; 2,400 bhp
Electric: 264 kw tot. (2 × 132-kw diesel-driven sets; 380 V, 50 Hz a.c.)
Range: . . ./. . . **Crew:** 18 tot.

Remarks: 684 grt/1,283 dwt. Former commercial vehicle ferry, acquired by the Spanish Army (*Ejército Español,* hence the former army pennant number ET 02) to support troops at Ceuta and Melilla in North Africa. Commissioned 15-2-00. Although she remains an army-owned ship, the vessel is naval crewed and operated.
Hull systems: Cargo: up to 42 trucks and 25 jeeps. Has a single, nonslewing centerline vehicle ramp at the stern and two cargo decks.

Note: A second Spanish Army vehicle transport, the *Santa Teresa de Avila* (ET 01), may now operate in Spanish Navy service or may have been sold; the craft was much smaller than the other naval AKs, being only 17.6 m overall, 6.3 m in beam, and 2.3 m molded depth.

♦ **1 replenishment oiler [AO]** Bldr: Izar, Ferrol

	Laid down	L	In serv.
A 11 MARQUÉS DE LA ENSENADA (ex-*Mar del Norte*)	16-11-89	3-10-90	3-6-91

Marqués de la Ensenada (A 11) Bernard Prézelin, 5-01

D: 13,592 tons (fl) **S:** 16 kts **Dim:** 123.21 (115.00 pp) × 19.50 × 7.98
A: 2 single 7.62-mm mg
Electronics: Radar: 1 Decca 2690/9 ARPA nav.; 1 Decca 2459 surf. search
M: 1 Bazán-M.A.N. 18V40/54A diesel; 1 prop; 11,250 bhp
Electric: 2,520 kw tot. (4 × 630-kw Bazán-MTU V8V 16/18 TL diesels driving)
Range: 10,000/15 **Crew:** 11 officers, 69 enlisted

Remarks: A commercial-design tanker, ordered in 12-88 initially as an interim replacement for the retired *Teide* until the *Patiño* (A 14) was available. Based at Las Palmas.
Hull systems: Has a helicopter platform aft and VERTREP positions fore and aft. Cargo: 7,498 tons distillate fuel, 1,746 tons JP-5, 2,878 tons water, and 10 tons spares, plus six 20-ft. refrigerated containers. Can accept 1,000 tons of additional cargo fuel in an emergency. Liquid supply stations port and starboard can transfer 680 m^3 per hour, while solid transfer stations port and starboard can handle 250-kg loads. Has three 120-m^3/hr cargo pumps and an 18-ton/day distiller. Medical facilities are provided.
Combat systems: Provision was made for later installation of a Meroka CIWS aft and four Mk 137 decoy RL.

♦ **1 Patiño-class replenishment oiler [AOR]** Bldr: Izar, Ferrol

	Laid down	L	In serv.
A 14 PATIÑO (ex-*Mar del Sur*)	1-7-93	22-6-94	16-6-95

AUXILIARIES *(continued)*

Patiño (A 14) Bernard Prézelin, 4-00

D: 17,045 tons (fl) **S:** 21 kts (20 sust.)
Dim: 165.84 (156.00 wl) × 23.70 (22.00 wl) × 8.00
A: 2 single 20-mm 85-cal. Oerlikon GAM-B01 AA; up to 3 SH-3D Sea King helicopters
Electronics:
Radar: 1 . . . nav.; 2 Decca 2690 nav. and helicopter control
TACAN: URN-25A
EW: Indra SLQ-380 Aldebarán intercept; Mk 36 SRBOC decoy syst. (6 6-round Mk 137 RL); SLQ-25A Nixie towed torpedo decoy syst.
M: diesel-electric: 4 Bazán-M.A.N. V16V-40/45 diesels, 2 motors; 2 props; 26,240 shp
Range: 13,500/20 **Endurance:** 30 days
Crew: 143 tot. + 19 air complement + 20 spare berths

Remarks: Ordered 26-12-91. Officially rated as a *Buque de Aprovisionamiento de Combate* (Combat Supply Vessel) and also known as the AOR 90 class. Was a joint design between the Netherlands' Nevesbu and Spain's Bazán design bureaus under an agreement signed in 11-88; sister *Amsterdam* (A 836) was built in the Netherlands and operates in the Netherlands Navy. A 14 is based at Rota.
Hull systems: Has four 2-ton-capacity, dual-purpose and two 250-kg solid stores alongside-replenishment stations and a VERTREP position forward and can refuel over the stern at 450 m³/hr. Cargo deadweight: 10,300 tons, including 6,700 tons ship fuel, 1,660 tons JP-5, 180 tons water, 20 tons ammunition, 100 tons dry stores, 25 tons sonobuoys, and 9 tons spare parts. Has repair and medical facilities. Can accommodate up to 50 female crewmembers.
Combat systems: As of 2001, the planned Meroka Mod. 2B CIWS had not been installed. Four decoy launchers are mounted abreast the stack on the after superstructure and two more atop the pilothouse.

♦ 1 salvage and rescue tug [ARS]
Bldr: Duro Felguera, Gijón (In serv. 24-3-75)

A 101 MAR CARIBE (ex-*Amatista*)

Mar Caribe (A 101) Camil Busquets i Vilanova, 5-00

D: 1,860 tons (fl) **S:** 13.5 kts **Dim:** 58.48 (52.61 pp) × 11.86 × 4.21
A: none **Electronics:** Radar: 2 . . . nav.
M: 2 Echevarría–Burmeister & Wain Alpha 18V 23/30 diesels; 2 props; 4,860 bhp—bow-thruster
Electric: 660 kw (3 × 220-kw diesel sets)
Range: 6,000/10 **Fuel:** 361 tons **Crew:** 44 tot.

Remarks: Former oilfield supply tug, purchased and commissioned 14-12-88. Assigned to the amphibious forces. Sister *Mar Rojo* (A 102, ex-*Amapola*) was redesignated a submarine rescue ship in 1997 and renamed *Neptuno* (A 20) in 1999; see under [ASR].
Hull systems: Has 80-ton bollard pull.

♦ 1 submarine rescue ship [ASR]
Bldr: Duro Felguera, Gijón (In serv. 24-3-75)

A 20 NEPTUNO (ex-*Mar Rojo,* A 102; ex-*Amapola*)

Neptuno (A 20) Camil Busquets i Vilanova, 11-00

D: 1,860 tons (fl) **S:** 13.5 kts **Dim:** 58.48 (52.61 pp) × 11.86 × 4.21
A: none **Electronics:** Radar: 2 . . . nav.
M: 2 Echevarría–Burmeister & Wain Alpha 18V 23/30 diesels; 2 props; 4,860 bhp—bow-thruster
Electric: 660 kw (3 × 220-kw diesel sets)
Range: 6,000/10 **Fuel:** 361 tons **Crew:** 44 tot.

Remarks: Former oilfield supply tug, purchased and commissioned 14-12-88. Replaced the *Poseidón* (A 12) as submarine rescue ship in 1997 and was renamed and renumbered during 1999.
Hull systems: Has 80-ton bollard pull. Completed conversion at Cartagena Navy Yard as a diving tender and diving training ship in 1-91; has been equipped to support divers to 200 m and carries a 600-m-capable Vosma submersible that will later be replaced by a deep submergence submarine rescue vehicle. Also equipped with a dynamic positioning system and an HF object avoidance sonar.

♦ 1 ex-commercial seagoing tug [ATA]
Bldr: Astilleros Luzuriaga, Pasajes, San Sebastián (In serv. 1982)

A 53 LA GRAÑA (ex-Y 119, ex-*Punta Amer*)

D: 480 tons (fl) **S:** 14 kts **Dim:** 31.24 (29.00 pp) × 8.40 × 3.16
M: . . . diesels; 2 Voith-Schneider vertical cycloidal props; 3,240 bhp
Range: 1,750/12 **Crew:** 28 tot.

Remarks: 292 grt/205 dwt. Redesignated as a seagoing tug during 1994. Sister Y 120 was stricken during 1993.

♦ 2 Mahón-class seagoing tugs [ATA]
Bldr: Astilleros Atlantico, Santander (In serv. 1978)

A 51 MAHÓN (ex-*Circos*) A 52 LAS PALMAS (ex-*Somiedo*)

Mahón (A 51) French Navy, 9-97

Las Palmas (A 52)—with red hull and white upperworks Ralph Edwards, 8-01

D: 1,437 (A 52: 1,450) tons (fl) **S:** 14 kts **Dim:** 41.0 × 11.6 × 5.5
A: 2 single 12.7-mm mg **Electronics:** Radar: 2 Decca . . . nav.
M: 2 AESA-Sulzer 16 ASV 25/30 diesels; 2 props; 7,744 bhp
Range: A 52: 27,000/12 **Crew:** 8 officers, 25 enlisted

AUXILIARIES *(continued)*

Remarks: 700 dwt. Former oilfield support tugs purchased from Compañía Hispano Americana de Offshore and commissioned 30-7-81. Redesignated from AR 51 and AR 52 in 1986. A 52 was modified in 1988 to serve as an Antarctic exploration ship, with her bow strengthened, space for two scientific vans on the fantail, additional fuel tankage, and accommodations for 22 scientists; she was relieved during 1992 in that role by *Hespérides* (A 33) and is now based at Las Palmas as a general-purpose ocean tug, although she is still painted in high-visibility colors.

♦ **1 Cádiz-class ocean tug [ATA]** Bldr: Izar, La Carraca, Cádiz

	L	In serv.
A 43 FERROL (ex-AR 43, ex-AR 45, ex-RA 5)	14-9-62	11-4-64

Ferrol (A 43) Ralph Edwards, 8-01

D: 951 tons (1,069 fl) **S:** 15 kts **Dim:** 55.90 (49.80 pp) × 10.00 × 4.50 (max.)
A: 2 twin 20-mm 70-cal. Oerlikon Mk 24 AA
Electronics: Radar: 1 Decca . . . nav.
M: 2 Bazán-Sulzer 6MG42 diesels; 1 CP prop; 3,200 bhp
Range: 4,640/15 **Fuel:** 190 m^3 **Crew:** 48 tot.

Remarks: Can carry and lay 24 mines. Sister *Cádiz* (A 42) was stricken 1-5-93, and A 43 will likely soon follow.

♦ **1 sail-training ship [AXT]** Bldr: Astilleros Echevarrieta, Cádiz

	Laid down	L	In serv.
A 71 JUAN SEBASTIÁN DE ELCANO	24-11-25	5-3-27	17-8-28

Juan Sebastián de Elcano (A 71)—at Valparaiso, Chile Leo Dirkx, 4-98

D: 3,420 tons (3,754 fl) **S:** 10 kts **Dim:** 94.11 (82.00 pp) × 13.6 × 6.95
A: 2 single 37-mm saluting cannon
Electronics: Radar: 2 Decca TM 626 nav.
M: 1 Deutz-MWM RBV 6M diesel; 1 prop; 1,500 bhp—2,467 m^2 max. sail area
Range: 10,000/9.5; 13,000/8 **Fuel:** 230 tons **Crew:** 224 tot. + 80 cadets

Remarks: Four-masted topsail schooner. Renumbered from A 01 in 1986, but the pennant number is not borne. Re-engined in 1992. Based at Cádiz.

SERVICE CRAFT

♦ **29 miscellaneous barges [YC]**

Y 302–304, 307–321, 323, 331, 341–344, 346, 351–354

♦ **2 YGR 23–class floating cranes [YD]** (In serv. 1954)

Y 383 (ex-YGR 22) Y 384 (ex-YGR 23)

D: 470–490 tons (fl) **Dim:** 22.5 × 14.0 × 3.0 **Capacity:** 30 tons

♦ **1 miscellaneous floating crane [YD]** (In serv. 1953)

Y 385 (ex-YGR 31)

D: 272 tons **Dim:** 19.0 × 11.7 × 2.4 **Capacity:** 15 tons

♦ **1 Nereida-class diving tender [YDT]**
Bldr: Izar, Cartagena (In serv. 13-4-81)

Y 563 PROSERPINA (ex-YBZ 12)

D: 103.5 tons (fl) **S:** 9 kts **Dim:** 21.5 × 5.9 × 2.9
M: 1 Sulzer diesel; 1 prop; 200 bhp **Crew:** 6 tot.

Remarks: Sister *Nereida* (Y 562, ex-YBZ 11) was stricken during 6-98.

♦ **2 small diving tenders [YDT]**
Bldr: Astilleros y Talleres Ferrolanos, La Graña (In serv. 6-86)

Y 583 (ex-YBZ 83) Y 584 (ex-YBZ 84)

♦ **1 small diving tender [YDT]** Bldr: . . . (In serv. 9-9-82)

Y 579 (ex-YBZ 61)

D: 8 tons **S:** 12 kts **Dim:** 11.0 × 4.0 × 0.8 **M:** diesels; waterjets

♦ **1 small diving tender [YDT]** (In serv. 15-6-83)

Y 580 (ex-YBZ 71)

D: 13.7 tons **S:** 7 kts **Dim:** 10.9 × 3.8 × 0.8 **M:** 1 diesel; 70 bhp

♦ **5 ammunition lighters [YE]**
Bldr: Cartagena NDY (In serv.: Y 365: 1986; others: 1991)

Y 365 Y 421 Y 422 Y 423 Y 424

Ammunition lighter Y 424 Ralph Edwards, 8-01

Ammunition lighter Y 365 Camil Busquets i Vilanova, 5-01

D: 53 tons light (140 fl) **S:** . . . kts **Dim:** 22.3 × 8.7 × 0.8
M: 2 Harbormaster diesel azimuthal outdrive engines; 600 bhp

Remarks: The data do not apply to the slightly smaller Y 365, which was ordered 30-12-85 and launched 25-9-86. All have rectangular barge-like hulls, a single hold, and an articulating electrohydraulic crane.

♦ **7 P 101–class harbor patrol launches [YFL]**
Bldr: ARESA, Arenys del Mar, Barcelona (In serv. 1978–82)

Y 521 (ex-P 102) Y 524 (ex-P 122) Y 526 (ex-P 118)
Y 522 (ex-P 107) Y 525 (ex-P 101) Y 527 (ex-P 119)
Y 523 (ex-P 121)

D: 16.9 tons (21.7 fl) **S:** 26 kts **Dim:** 15.90 (13.70 pp) × 4.36 × 1.33
A: 1 12.7-mm mg **Electronics:** Radar: 1 Decca 110 nav.
M: 2 Baudouin-Interdiesel DNP-8 MIR diesels; 2 props; 768 bhp
Electric: 12 kVA tot. **Range:** 430/18 **Fuel:** 2.2 tons
Crew: 2 officers, 4–5 enlisted

Remarks: Ordered 13-5-77; funded jointly by the navy and Ministry of Commerce. Redesignated late in 1993 from patrol craft to "Small Transport Craft" but retain a port patrol function; sister Y 528 was again redesignated, to P 114, on 15-2-96. Three operate on the Río Miño. Originally numbered in the LVC series.
Hull systems: Y 523 and 524 have supercharged engines producing 1,024 bhp total and a maximum speed of 27 kts. GRP hull construction.

SERVICE CRAFT *(continued)*

P 101–class patrol launch Y 525—white-painted Guy Schaeffer, 9-98

♦ 4 P 202–class harbor patrol craft [YFL]
Bldr: Rodman-Polyships, Vigo (In serv. 1978–80)

Y 545 (ex-P 202) Y 547 (ex-P 211)
Y 546 (ex-P 204) Y 548 (ex-P 220)

D: 3 tons (4.2 fl) **S:** 18 kts **Dim:** 9.0 × 3.1 × 0.8
A: 1 7.62-mm mg **Electronics:** Radar: see remarks
M: 2 Ebro MH-58 inboard/outboard diesels; 2 props; 240 bhp
Range: 120/18 **Crew:** 6 tot.

Remarks: Retyped "Small Transport Craft" from patrol craft late in 1993, but are still used in harbor patrol work. GRP construction. Originally numbered in the PVI series. May have Decca 060 navigational radars. Sister P 221 was stricken 24-5-00.

♦ 5 Y 531–class personnel launches [YFL]
Bldr: Rodman, Vigo (In serv. 1980–81)

Y 531 (ex-QF 01) through Y 535 (ex-QF 05)

Y 531–class personnel launch Y 533—outboard LCP(L) Mk 11E launch Y 505
H&L Van Ginderen, 5-94

D: 3 tons (4.2 fl) **S:** 17 kts **Dim:** 9.0 × 3.1 × 0.8
M: 2 Volvo-Penta inboard/outboard diesels; 2 props; 240 bhp **Range:** 120/18

Remarks: GRP construction. Similar to the P 202 class.

♦ 12 ex-U.S. LCP(L) Mk 11E personnel launches [YFL]

Y 501 through Y 512

D: 9.75 tons light (13 fl) **S:** 19 kts **Dim:** 10.98 (9.26 pp) × 3.97 × 1.13
Electronics: Radar: 1 SPS-59 (Canadian Marconi LN-66) nav.
M: 1 G.M. 8V71 TI diesel; 1 prop; 350–425 bhp
Range: 150/19 **Fuel:** 630 liters **Crew:** 3 tot. + 17 passengers

Remarks: Former control landing craft, now used for miscellaneous local duties. GRP construction. Can carry 2 tons of cargo. Y 502 is based at Port Mahon, Minorca, and Y 505 at Porto Pi, Majorca.

♦ 4 miscellaneous personnel launches [YFL]

Y 515 Y 519 Y 529 Y 530

Remarks: Different designs, ranging from 2.9 to 17.5 tons (fl). Flag-officer launch Y 537 (ex-LVC 79, ex-*Cynosure*) was stricken during 2001.

♦ 2 EDIC-class logistics support craft [YFU]
Bldr: Izar, La Carraca, Cádiz

	L	In serv.		L	In serv.
A 06 (ex-LCT 6)	10-11-65	6-12-66	A 08 (ex-LCT 8)	10-11-66	30-12-66

EDIC-class A 06 H&L Van Ginderen, 11-99

D: 279 tons (710 fl) **S:** 9.5 kts **Dim:** 59.00 (52.9 pp) × 11.90 × 1.86
A: 1 20-mm 70-cal. Oerlikon Mk 10 AA; 2 single 12.7-mm mg
Electronics: Radar: 1 Decca 404 nav.
M: 2 Bazán-M.A.N. R6V16/18 TLS diesels; 2 props; 1,060 bhp
Electric: 25 kw tot. **Range:** 1,500/9.5 **Crew:** 17 tot.

Remarks: Licensed version of the French EDIC type utility landing craft. Redesignated as logistics support craft in 1986; originally numbered BDK 6 and BDK 8. Cargo: 300 tons. Armament may have been removed. Sister A 07 (ex-LCT 7) was stricken during 1998.

♦ 1 suction dredge [YM] Bldr: IHC, the Netherlands (In serv. 2-12-81)

Y 441 (ex-YDR 11)

Suction dredge Y 441 Camil Busquets i Vilanova, 1-99

D: 150 tons (fl) **S:** . . . **Dim:** 25.2 × 5.8 × 1.0 **M:** 1 diesel; 530 bhp

♦ 1 antisubmarine net-laying barge [YNG] (In serv. 1960)

Y 361 (ex-YDS 01)

D: 53 tons light (140 fl) **S:** . . . kts **Dim:** 22.3 × 8.7 × 0.8
M: 2 diesels; 2 Harbormaster azimuthal props; . . . bhp

Remarks: Sister YDS 03 was stricken in 1984, and Y 362 (ex-YDS 02), Y 363 (ex-YDS 04), and Y 364 (ex-YDS 05) in 1995.

♦ 1 fuel lighter [YO] Bldr: Izar, San Fernando (In serv. 1980)

Y 231 (ex-YPF 21, ex-PP 6)

Fuel lighter Y 231 Camil Busquets i Vilanova, 1-99

D: 523 tons (fl) **S:** 10.8 kts **Dim:** 24.0 × 7.0 × 3.0
M: 2 Harbormaster diesel azimuthal outdrive units; 600 bhp

Remarks: Cargo: 300 tons.

SERVICE CRAFT *(continued)*

♦ **1 fuel lighter [YO]** Bldr: Izar, San Fernando (In serv. 1980)

Y 232 (ex-YPF 31, ex-PP 23)

D: 830 tons (fl) **S:** 10.7 kts **Dim:** 42.8 × 8.4 × 3.1
M: 1 diesel; 1 prop; 600 bhp **Cargo:** . . . tons

Note: Also in service is fuel lighter Y 221, a rectangular barge hull with two Harbormaster diesel outdrives for propulsion; no other data available.

Fuel lighter Y 221 Camil Busquets i Vilanova, 1-99

♦ **1 diesel-fuel lighter [YO]** Bldr: Izar, Cartagena (In serv. 1981)

Y 254 (ex-YPG 41)

D: 214 grt **S:** 10.7 kts **Dim:** 24.0 × 5.5 × 2.2
M: 1 M.A.N. diesel; 1 prop; 400 bhp **Cargo:** 100 tons

♦ **1 diesel-fuel lighter [YO]** Bldr: Izar, Cádiz (In serv. 1980)

Y 255 (ex-YPG 51)

D: 520 grt **S:** . . . **Dim:** 34.0 × 7.0 × 2.9
M: 1 diesel; 1 prop; . . . bhp **Cargo:** . . .

♦ **3 YPG 21–class diesel-fuel lighters [YO]**
Bldr: Izar, Cádiz (In serv. 1963–65)

Y 237 (ex-YPG 22) Y 252 (ex-YPG 21) Y 253 (ex-YPG 23)

D: 337 grt **S:** 10.7 kts **Dim:** 34.3 × 6.2 × 2.3
M: 1 diesel; 1 prop; 220 bhp **Cargo:** 100 tons

♦ **2 YPG 01–class diesel-fuel lighters [YO]**
Bldr: Izar, Ferrol (In serv. 1956, 1959)

Y 236 (ex-YPG 13, ex-YPG 03) Y 251 (ex-YPG 11, ex-YPG 01)

D: 200 grt **S:** 10 kts **Dim:** 34.0 × 6.0 × 2.7
M: 1 diesel; 1 prop; . . . bhp **Cargo:** 193 tons

Remarks: Formerly numbered in the PB series. Sister YPG 02 was stricken in 1982.

♦ **2 non-self-propelled fuel oil barges [YON]** (In serv. . . .)

Y 202 (ex-YPFN 31) Y 211 (ex-YPGN 01)

♦ **1 oil-spill recovery storage barge [YOSN]**

Y 411

Remarks: No data available. Sister Y 412 was stricken in 1994.

♦ **1 barracks barge [YPB]**
Bldr: Pullman Std. Car Co., Chicago (In serv. 1944)

Y 601 (ex-YFCN 01, ex-LSM 329 or 331)

D: 1,095 tons (fl) **Dim:** 62.03 (59.89 wl) × 10.52 × 2.54

Remarks: Former medium landing ship, transferred 5-60. Hulked and employed as an accommodations ship at Ferrol.

♦ **2 Y 122–class coastal tractor tugs [YTB]**
Bldr: Izar, Ferrol (In serv. 1991)

Y 122 Y 123

D: 423 tons (fl) **S:** 12 kts **Dim:** 29.50 (28.00 pp) × 11.00 × 4.00
Electronics: 1 Decca RM 770 nav.
M: 2 Caterpillar diesels; 2 Voith-Schneider Type 26 II/165 vertical cycloidal props; 3,000 bhp
Range: 1,000/12 **Fuel:** 58.3 tons **Crew:** 8 tot.

Remarks: Bollard pull: 35 tons. Have two 1,200-m^3/hr firefighting monitors and a 1-ton crane.

Tug Y 123 Camil Busquets i Vilanova, 5-00

♦ **2 Y 118–class large harbor tugs [YTB]**
Bldr: Izar, . . . (In serv. 1988–91)

Y 118 Y 121

Tug Y 121 Camil Busquets i Vilanova, 1-99

D: 220 tons (236 fl) **S:** 14 kts **Dim:** 22.5 × 7.5 × . . .
M: 2 MTU diesels; 2 Voith-Schneider 21 Gil/135 vertical cycloidal props; 1,768 bhp (1,560 sust.)
Range: 1,560/14

Remarks: Are equipped with two firefighting water monitors. Have an electrohydraulic crane on the fantail for torpedo recovery.

♦ **2 coastal tugs [YTB]**
Bldr: Izar, Ferrol

Y 116 (ex-YRR 21, ex-YRR 71) (In serv. 10-4-81)
Y 117 (ex-YRR 22, ex-YRR 72) (In serv. 1-6-81)

D: 422 tons (fl) **S:** 12.4 kts **Dim:** 28.0 × 8.0 × 3.8
M: 2 diesels; 2 Voith-Schneider vertical cycloidal props; 1,500 bhp
Range: 3,000/10

Disposal note: YRR 53–class coastal tug Y 115 (ex-YRR 16, ex-YRR 55, ex-RR 55) was stricken during 1998 and sister Y 114 (ex-YRR 15, ex-YRR 54, ex-RR 54) during 2001.

♦ **2 large harbor tugs [YTB]**
Bldr: Izar, Ferrol (In serv. 1983)

Y 144 (ex-*Procyon*) Y 145 (ex-. . . . . .)

Tug Y 145 Camil Busquets i Vilanova, 1-99

SERVICE CRAFT *(continued)*

D: . . . tons **S:** 11 kts **Dim:** . . . × . . . × . . .
M: 2 diesels; 2 props; 2,030 bhp

Remarks: 195 grt. Former merchant tugs. Have been equipped with roller fenders on the superstructure to permit coming alongside the carrier *Príncipe de Asturias* (R 11).

♦ 3 Y 141–class large harbor tugs [YTB]
Bldr: Izar, Cartagena (In serv. 1981)

Y 141 Y 142 Y 143

D: 195 tons (229 fl) **S:** 12 kts **Dim:** 28.0 × 7.5 × 3.4
M: 2 diesels; 1 prop; 950 bhp **Range:** 2,030/11

♦ 1 submarine-support push-tug [YTM]
Bldr: Izar, La Carraca (In serv. 1-99)

Y 174

Submarine-support push-tug Y 174—just prior to launch
Camil Busquets i Vilanova, 1-99

D: 17 tons (fl) **S:** 9 kts **Dim:** 8.40 × 3.80 × 0.70
M: 2 Guascor H74TA diesels; 2 Hamilton waterjets; 536 bhp
Range: 75/8 **Crew:** 2 tot.

Remarks: First of a new series intended to replace earlier, less-powerful push-tugs (listed under [YTL]).

♦ 1 medium harbor tug [YTM]
Bldr: Izar, San Fernando (In serv. 14-4-87)

Y 147

Medium harbor tug Y 147 Ralph Edwards, 8-01

D: . . . tons **S:** 10 kts **Dim:** 16.5 × . . . × . . .
M: 1 diesel; 1 prop; 400 bhp **Range:** 400/10

Remarks: 87 grt. Ordered 18-12-85; launched 25-2-87. Has one water monitor for firefighting. Based at Las Palmas, Canary Islands.

♦ 1 medium harbor tug [YTM]
Bldr: S. España d. C.N. Cádiz (In serv. 1965)

Y 146 (ex-YRP 61)

D: 173 tons (fl) **S:** 10 kts **Dim:** 23.3 × 6.0 × 2.9
M: 1 diesel; 1 prop; 825 bhp **Range:** 830/10

Remarks: Entered naval service 27-10-83.

Disposal note: YRR 50–class coastal tug Y 111 (ex-YRR 11, ex-YRR 31, ex-RR 50) was retired during 2001.

♦ 1 U.S. Army Design 3004 medium harbor tug [YTM]
(In serv. 27-12-61)

Y 143 (ex-YRP 41, ex-RP 40, ex-. . .)

D: 111 tons light (133 fl) **S:** 12 kts **Dim:** 21.31 × 5.94 × 2.50
M: 1 diesel; 1 prop; 600 bhp **Range:** 600/10 **Fuel:** 15 tons **Crew:** 6 tot.

♦ 9 YRP 01–class small harbor tugs [YTL]
Bldr: Izar, La Carraca (In serv. 1965–67)

Y 131–135, Y 137–140 (from among ex-YRP 01–09, 012)

D: 65 tons (fl) **S:** 9 kts **Dim:** 18.45 (16.75 pp) × 4.72 × 1.57 (max.)
M: 1 diesel; 1 Kort-nozzle prop; 200 bhp **Range:** 200/8 **Crew:** 6 tot.

Remarks: Sister YRP 10 was stricken 11-6-84, YRP 11 on 6-7-82, and Y 136 in 1992.

♦ 3 submarine-support push-tugs [YTL]

Y 171 (ex-YRS 01) (In serv. 3-11-82)
Y 172 (ex-YRS 02) (In serv. 5-85)
Y 173 (ex-YRS 03) (In serv. 6-85)

Submarine-support push-tug Y 171—on land for maintenance
Camil Busquets i Vilanova, 5-01

D: 9.8 (Y 171: 10.5) tons (fl) **S:** 11 kts **Dim:** 9.5 (Y 171: 8.3) × . . . × . . .
M: 2 diesels; 2 waterjets; 400 bhp **Range:** 440/11

♦ 4 miscellaneous sail training craft [YTS]

	In serv.	D (tons fl)	Rig
A 72 Arosa	1-4-81	52	ketch
A 74 La Graciosa (ex-*Dejá Vu*)	1931	. . .	schooner
A 75 Sisargas	19-9-95	90	ketch
A 76 Giralda	10-9-93	25	ketch

Sail training craft Sisargas (A 75) Camil Busquets i Vilanova, 5-01

SERVICE CRAFT *(continued)*

Remarks: All are attached to the Naval Academy *(Escuela Naval Militar)*. A 72, 22.84 m o.a., was built in Portsmouth, U.K., by Inglaterra. A 75 is on loan from a private individual. A 76 was donated by King Juan Carlos I on 23-8-93; built in the U.K. by Morris & Mortimer, Argull, she is 25.0 × 6.0 m, has two 114-bhp Gardner diesels, and can achieve 14 kts. Sloop *Hispania* (A 73) was stricken 5-7-01.

♦ 1 large water lighter [YW]
Bldr: Izar, San Fernando (In serv. 16-10-81)

A 66 Condestable Zaragoza (ex-AA 41, ex-AA 32, ex-A 32)

Condestable Zaragoza (A 66)—with old pennant number — Spanish Navy, 1984

D: 895 tons (fl) **S:** 10.8 kts **Dim:** 48.8 (42.85 pp) × 8.40 × 3.35
M: 1 diesel; 1 prop; 700 bhp **Cargo:** 600 tons **Crew:** 16 tot.

♦ 1 large water lighter [YW]
Bldr: Izar, San Fernando

	L	In serv.
A 65 Marinero Jarano (ex-AA 31, ex-A 31)	1-7-81	16-3-81

Marinero Jarano (A 65) — Ralph Edwards, 8-01

D: 535 tons (fl) **S:** 10.8 kts **Dim:** 34.0 × 7.0 × 3.03
M: 1 diesel; 1 prop; 600 bhp **Cargo:** 300 tons

♦ 1 A 7–class large water lighter [YW]
Bldr: Izar, La Carraca, San Fernando

	L	In serv.
A 63 Torpedista Hernández (ex-AA 22, ex-A 10)	27-10-58	26-9-62

Torpedista Hernández (A 63) — H&L Van Ginderen, 7-94

D: 589 tons (610 fl) **S:** 10 kts **Dim:** 44.78 (41.00 pp) × 7.55 × 3.10 (max.)
M: 1 diesel; 1 prop; 700 bhp **Range:** 1,000/9 **Crew:** 17 tot.

Remarks: Cargo: 350 tons. Named in 1982. Sisters *Maquinista Maciás* (A 62) and *Fogonera Bañobre* (A 64) were stricken in 1993.

♦ 5 Guardiamarina Barrutia–class navigational training tenders [YXT]
Bldr: Izar, Cartagena

	L	In serv.
A 81 Guardiamarina Barrutia	27-5-82	14-9-82
A 82 Guardiamarina Salas	26-1-83	10-5-83
A 83 Guardiamarina Godínez	9-5-83	4-7-83
A 84 Guardiamarina Rull	19-1-84	11-6-84
A 85 Guardiamarina Chereguini	29-3-84	11-6-84

Guardiamarina Barrutia (A 81) — Spanish Navy, 1992

D: 90 tons (fl) **S:** 12.5 kts **Dim:** 21.89 × 5.10 × 1.52
A: none **Electronics:** Radar: 1 Halcón 948 nav.
M: 2 MTU diesels; 2 props; 800 bhp
Range: 1,000/. . . **Crew:** . . . tot. + 1 instructor, 12–21 cadets

Remarks: Tenders to the Escuela Naval Militar (naval academy). Have a Magnavox NAVSAT receiver and Decca 21 Navigator. Were formerly numbered YE 01–05 and AI 01–05. A 81 has an "operations center."

AIR FORCE

The Spanish Air Force operates three 11-m Rodman 38–class GRP air/sea rescue boats built by Polyships at Vigo in 1991. Launch EA 01 is assigned to the Puerto Pollenca airbase.

Note: All Spanish Army logistics support craft have either been transferred to the navy or disposed of.

GUARDIA CIVIL SERVICIO MARÍTIMO

Originally subordinated to the Spanish Army, the Guardia Civil has been given port security and antiterrorist responsibilities and plans to expand its afloat forces to a total of 12 30-m, 36 18-m, and 39 12-m patrol boats, supported by some 2,000 personnel. In wartime, the organization would come under the Ministry of Defense. The initial units were established in 9-91 with 194 men and 6 women at Corunna, Santander, Murcia, and Barcelona; facilities have since been added at Algeciras, Almeira, Malaga, and Pontevedra. Craft are painted green and white, with a red-yellow-red diagonal abaft the green-painted bows. The Guardia Civil also operates a number of MBB BO-105 light SAR helicopters. Plans to transfer the six naval *Barceló*-class patrol craft and a dozen smaller naval patrol boats were canceled.

Personnel (2001): Approx. 1,600 total

PATROL BOATS [WPB]

Note: The first of a new class of patrol boats for the Guardia Civil, the *Seriola,* was awaiting delivery during 5-01; no data yet available. The craft has a stern ramp for the launch and recovery of a small RIB inspection and rescue launch.

Seriola — Camil Busquets i Vilanova, 5-01

♦ 15 Bazán 39 class
Bldr: Izar, Cartagena (In serv. 1993–94)

L 01 through L 15

GUARDIA CIVIL PATROL BOATS [WPB] *(continued)*

Bazán 39–class L 11 Leo Dirkx, 9-01

D: 14 tons (fl) **S:** 38 kts **Dim:** 11.9 × 3.8 × 0.7
A: 1 7.62-mm mg **Electronics:** Radar: 1 Ericsson . . . nav.
M: 2 M.A.N. D2848 LXE diesels; 2 Hamilton waterjets; 1,360 bhp
Range: 300/25 **Crew:** 4 tot.

Remarks: GRP hulls. The design is based on that of the civil Saetta-II yacht. Twenty-four more were planned.

♦ **14 Rodman 55 class** Bldr: Rodman-Polyships, Vigo (In serv. 1992–96)

M 01 through M 14

Rodman 55–class M 10 Findler & Winter, 2-01

D: 15.7 tons (fl) **S:** 40 kts **Dim:** 16.5 × 3.8 × 0.7
A: 1 12.7-mm mg **Electronics:** Radar: 1 Ericsson . . . nav.
M: 2 Bazán-M.A.N. D2848 LXE diesels; 2 Hamilton waterjets; 1,360 bhp
Range: 500/25 **Crew:** 7 tot.

Remarks: Five were completed in 1992, three in 1993, and six in 1995–96. GRP construction. Have a VHFD/F array. Five similar craft were ordered for Paraguay in 1995.

Note: The Guardia Civil also employs an unreported number of RIB patrol and inspection launches.

CUSTOMS SERVICE

(Servicio de Vigilancia Aduanera)

Note: Ships and craft have very dark blue hulls and white narrow-broad-narrow diagonal hull stripes superimposed with the customs service shield. Smaller units carry *"Aduanas"* (Customs) on their hull sides.

Aviation: Four MBB BO-105CB helicopters (Argos I-IV) and one BO-117 helicopter. The six CASA 212-200 Aviocar maritime patrol aircraft were transferred to the air force in 1997.

Ships and craft in service include:

	In serv.	D	S (kts)	Bhp	Dim
Águila	1974	80	29	2,750	32.00 × 5.75 × 1.60
Albatros III	1-7-70	84.7	29	2,700	32.25 × 5.86 × 1.85
Alca I, III	1989	24	35	2,000	16.98 × 4.70 × 0.79
Alcaraván I–V	1984–87	71.5	28	3,920	28.50 × 6.50 × 1.80
Cárabo	1978	60.3	17	1,350	24.4 × 5.15 × . . .
Cóndor V	1992	. . .	35	1,300	14.00 × 4.00 × . . .
Cormorán	20-2-90	22	65	2,970	17.00 × 4.00 × 1.00
Gavilán I–IV	1976–87	65	22.5–31	2,750	28.00 × 5.15 × 1.30
Gerifalte I and II	8-01	87	35	5,520	31.36 × 6.00 × 1.10
Halcón II and III	1980, 83	73	28	3,200	24.50 × 6.08 × . . .
HJ I, III–XIII	1986–90	20	45–50	2,970	14.00 × 3.80 × 0.70
IMP I–III	1989–90	5	65–70	400	9.60 × 2.85 × . . .
IPP I–III	1989	2	65–70	400	6.35 × 2.40 × . . .
Neblí I	15-1-93	50.5	50	6,960	22.55 × 6.47 × 1.65
Petrel	1994	1,600	12	1,200	72.5 × 12.0 × . . .
VA II–V	1984–85	23.7	28	1,400	15.7 × 4.1 × 1.2

VA II–series customs launch VA-III—renamed *La Restinga*
Camil Busquets i Vilanova, 10-99

SOCIETY FOR MARITIME RESCUE AND SAFETY

(Sociedad de Salvamento y Seguridad Marítima)

Established in 1995 by the Spanish Government to coordinate the existing rescue system. Employs chartered salvage and rescue units, and the fleet changes composition frequently. Ships and craft are painted a brilliant red-orange and have one broad and one narrow diagonal hull stripe. In 1998, 9 large seagoing salvage tugs, 14 small all-weather rescue craft, 4 harbor pollution cleaning craft, and 4 SH-3 Sea King helicopters were in service. As of 2000, the three-digit pennant numbers formerly applied to salvage tugs had been replaced by two-digit numbers prefixed by BS-, while smaller rescue craft bore ES-series numbers.

Salvage and rescue tug Alonso de Chaves (BS-11)—1,549 grt, 8,650 bhp, based at Santander Bernard Prézelin, 1-00

Salvage and rescue tug Ibaizabal-Dos—based at Bilbao
Bernard Prézelin, 1-00

SOCIETY FOR MARITIME RESCUE AND SAFETY *(continued)*

RIB rescue craft ES-28 Leo Dirkx, 9-01

RIB rescue craft ES-34 Leo Dirkx, 9-01

GALICIAN STATE FISHERIES PROTECTION SERVICE

(Servicio de Inspección e Vigilancia Pesqueira)

Operated by the Xunta de Galacia, with bases at Vigo, Portonovo, Vilaxoán, Riveira, Portosín, Sada, and Celeiro; additional bases are to be built on the Costa da Morte. Similar organizations operate craft in Andalucía, Catalunya, Asturias, and the Basque area; no data available. Craft are painted with an aquamarine blue bow, dark blue stern, and aquamarine and white superstructures. As of 2000, the Galician State Fisheries Protection Service operated 19 small launches, only two of which displaced more than 10 tons full load.

SRI LANKA

Republic of Sri Lanka

Personnel (2001): 18,343 total, including 1,036 officers, plus 1,943 total Sri Lanka Volunteer Naval Force (143 officers) and Naval Reserve of 227 (10 officers)

Bases: The fleet is divided into four Area Commands: North, East, South, and West. The principal base and repair facility is at Trincomalee, and there are minor facilities at Colombo, Kalpitya, Kankesanthuri, Karainagar, Tangalla, and Welisra.

Maritime Aviation: Plans to establish a naval air wing with three Indian Chetak helicopters, announced in 12-00, were canceled in 8-01. One Beech Super King Air was acquired in 1986 by the air force for maritime surveillance, which also operates six Bell 214 helicopters for land-based maritime patrol and attack duties.

Note: Ship names are prefaced by SLNS (Sri Lanka Naval Ship). Tamil rebel forces operate a large number of very small, outboard-powered craft for raiding purposes; no details are available. A midget submarine intended for Tamil rebel forces was discovered under construction at Seacraft Shipyard, Phuket, Thailand, on 9-4-00 by Thai police forces. An unidentified "transport capable of carrying 400 troops" was sunk by Tamil forces at Trincomalee on 23-10-00.

PATROL SHIPS [PS]

♦ **1 ex-Indian Sukanya class**
Bldr: Hindustan SY, Vishakhapatnam

	Laid down	L	In serv.
P 620 Sarayu (ex-*Sharada,* P 55)	9-88	22-8-90	27-10-91

Sarayu (P 620) Brian Morrison, 8-01

Sarayu (P 620) Brian Morrison, 8-01

D: 1,650 tons (1,890 fl) **S:** 21.7 kts **Dim:** 101.95 (96.00 pp) × 11.50 × 3.40
A: 3 single 40-mm 60-cal. Bofors Mk 3 AA; 4 single 12.7-mm mg
Electronics:
Radar: 1 Bharat 1245 nav.; 1 . . . nav.; 1 Decca 2459 surf. search
EW: . . . intercept
M: 2 Kirloskar–SEMT-Pielstick 16 PA6 V280 diesels; 2 props; 12,800 bhp
Range: 7,000/15 **Fuel:** 300 tons + 40 tons aviation fuel **Endurance:** 60 days
Crew: 10 officers, 60 enlisted (accomm. for 16 officers, 141 enlisted)

Remarks: Purchased for $20 million and transferred 9-12-00. Plans for a second, new-construction unit of the class were canceled during 7-01. The pennant number is not carried.
Hull systems: Has fin stabilizers and a towing capability. Carries 60 tons of fresh water and 9 tons of lube oil. Some helicopter-related equipment was removed prior to transfer.
Combat systems: The 40-mm guns are simple Mk 3 powered mountings with local control only; two additional mounts were added abreast the hangar after delivery. Also added were a third navigational radar and a radar intercept array. Has a helicopter hangar and flight deck, but no naval helicopters are available.

GUIDED-MISSILE PATROL CRAFT [PTG]

♦ **2 Reshev (Sa'ar IV) class** Bldr: Israel SY, Haifa

	L	In serv.
P 701 Nandimithra (ex-*Moledet*)	22-3-79	5-79
P 702 Suranimila (ex-*Komemiyut*)	19-7-79	8-80

D: 415 tons (450 fl) **S:** 32 kts **Dim:** 58.10 × 7.62 × 2.40
A: 4 Gabriel-II SSM; 2 single 76-mm 62-cal. OTOBreda Compact DP; 2 single 20-mm Rafael Typhoon gatling AA
Electronics:
Radar: 1 Thales Neptune TH-D 1040 surf./air search; 1 Alenia Orion RTN-10X gun f.c.
EW: Elisra NS 9003/5 intercept/jammer suite
E/O: Elop MSIS IR/t.v. surveillance and tracking
M: 4 MTU 16V956 TB91 diesels; 4 props; 14,000 bhp (10,680 sust.)
Range: 1,650/30; 4,000/17.5 **Crew:** 45 tot.

Remarks: Purchased during 2000 and recommissioned in Sri Lanka 9-12-00.
Hull systems: Quarters are air-conditioned.
Combat systems: The original missile armament was seven fixed Gabriel launchers. The 76-mm guns have been specially adapted for shore bombardment. The armament was revised prior to delivery.

PATROL CRAFT [PC]

Note: In 7-99, it was reported that negotiations were under way with Russia for the purchase of a Svetlyak-class patrol craft, a Bogomol-class torpedo boat, and a Pauk-I-class antisubmarine patrol craft; the discussions, however, came to nothing. In 1-00, talks began with Israel for the purchase of two craft of unknown class, plus a training package.

♦ **2 Chinese Lushun class (Project 062-1-G)**
Bldr: Lushun Dockyard, China (In serv. 2-3-98)

P 340 Prathpa P 341 Udara

PATROL CRAFT [PC] *(continued)*

D: 212 tons (fl) **S:** 28 kts **Dim:** 45.50 × 6.40 × 1.70
A: 2 twin 37-mm 63-cal. Type 76 AA; 2 twin 14.5-mm 79-cal. Type 81 AA
Electronics: Radar: 1 Decca RM 1070A nav.
M: 4 Type Z12V 190 BCJ diesels; 4 props; 4,800 bhp
Range: 750/16 **Crew:** 3 officers, 27 enlisted

♦ 1 Chinese Haiqing class (Project 037-I)
Bldr: Qingdao SY (In serv. 22-5-96)

P 351 Parakramabahu

Parakramabahu (P 351) Sri Lankan Navy, 5-96

D: 440 tons (478 fl) **S:** 28 kts **Dim:** 62.0 × 7.20 × 2.24 (hull)
A: 2 twin 57-mm Type 66 AA; 2 twin 14.5-mm 79-cal. Type 81 AA; 4 5-round Type 87 ASW RL; 2 BMB-2 d.c. mortars; 2 d.c. racks; 2 mine rails
Electronics: Radar: 1 Anritsu RA 273 nav./surf. search—Sonar: HF hull-mounted
M: 4 PR 230ZC diesels; 4 props; 13,200 bhp
Range: 750/18; 1,300/15 **Crew:** 70 tot.

Remarks: Delivered new 13-12-95 but not commissioned until later. Acquisition of two more was canceled. Has an optical f.c. director. Range can be extended to 1,800 n.m. by using void tankage.

♦ 1 Jayesagara class Bldr: Colombo DY

	Laid down	L	In serv.
P 601 Jayesagara	5-82	26-5-83	9-12-83

Jayesagara (P 601) Mike Louagie, 5-90

D: 315 tons (330 fl) **S:** 15 kts **Dim:** 39.80 × 7.00 × 2.20
A: 1 twin 25-mm 80-cal. Type 61 AA; 1 twin 14.5-mm 79-cal. Type 81 AA
Electronics: Radar: 1 Anritsu RA 273 nav./surf. search
M: 2 M.A.N. 8L 20/27 diesels; 2 props; 2,040 bhp **Electric:** 220 kw tot.
Range: 3,000/11 **Endurance:** 30 days **Crew:** 4 officers, 48 enlisted

Remarks: Two were ordered 31-12-81; three more were authorized in 8-84 but were not built. Sister *Sagarawardene* (P 602) was sunk by two Tamil Tiger insurgent suicide explosive boats on 19-9-94. The 25-mm gunmount is to be replaced by a more modern weapon.

♦ 7 (+ 2) Chinese Haizhui class
Bldr: Guijian SY (P 317–319: Qinxin SY)

	In serv.		In serv.
P 322 Ranarisi	14-7-92	P 318 . . .	8-98
P 330 Ranajaya	9-9-96	P 319 . . .	8-98
P 331 Ranadeera	9-9-96	P	2001
P 332 Ranawickrema	9-9-96	P	2001
P 317 . . .	8-98		

Ranajaya (P 330)—as deck cargo on heavy-lift ship *Gajah Borneo* 92 Wing Det. A, RAAF, 8-95

D: 150 tons (170 fl) **S:** 29 kts **Dim:** 41.0 × 5.41 × 1.80
A: P 322–332: 1 twin 37-mm 63-cal. Type 76 AA; 1 twin 25-mm 80-cal. Type 81 AA; 2 twin 14.5-mm 93-cal. AA—P 317–319: 2 twin 20-mm 75-cal. Oerlikon–Royal Ordnance GCM-A03-2 AA; 2 twin 14.5-mm 93-cal. AA
Electronics:
Radar: P 322–332: 1 Anritsu 726 UA nav./surf. search—P 317–319: 1 Koden MD 3220 Mk 2 nav.; 1 Furuno 825 nav.
M: 4 Type L12-180Z diesels; 4 props; 4,800 bhp (4,400 sust.)
Range: 750/16 **Crew:** 4 officers, 24 enlisted

Remarks: P 322, delivered during 11-91, is of a slightly different design, closer to the original Shanghai-II in appearance. Sister *Ranasura* (P 320) was lost on 13-4-95 and *Rana Viru* (P 321) was sunk by Tamil forces on 19-7-96. P 330–332 were delivered by Chinese heavy-lift ships between 9-95 and 22-5-96 and have a flush-faced leading edge to the superstructure, which in both earlier variants includes an enclosed pilothouse. P 330–332 have fin stabilizers. Two more were ordered during 12-00. The third group, P 317–319 (presumably including the pair ordered in 12-00), have twin British-made AA mountings fore and aft and twin Chinese semi-enclosed 14.5-mm mg mountings amidships.

♦ 3 Chinese Shanghai-II class

P 311 Weeraya (ex-P 3141) P 315 Jagatha (ex-P 3145)
P 312 Ranakami (ex-P 3142)

Weeraya (P 311)—with twin 25-mm AA mount forward, twin 37-mm mount aft, and two twin 14.5-mm mounts amidships Sri Lankan Navy, 1990

D: 122.5 tons (135 fl) **S:** 28.5 kts **Dim:** 38.78 × 5.41 × 1.55
A: 2 twin 20-mm 90-cal. Royal Ordnance GCM-A03 AA; 2 twin 14.5-mm 93-cal. Type 81 mg
Electronics: 1 Furuno FR 8250 nav.
M: 2 Type L12-180 diesels (1,200 bhp each), 2 Type L12-180Z diesels (910 bhp each); 4 props; 4,220 bhp
Electric: 39 kw **Range:** 750/16.5 **Endurance:** 7 days **Crew:** 34 tot.

Remarks: The first two (and three others since stricken or lost) were transferred in 2-72 and in 1975; P 315 was transferred in 1980 and commissioned 30-11-80.
Disposals: Of the original group, *Daksaya* was stricken during 1983, *Balawitha* (P 3144) was stricken during 1991, *Suraya* (P 310) was lost 13-4-95, and *Rakshaka* (P 316), damaged the same date, was stricken during 1996.
Hull systems: The L12-180 diesel is a copy of the Russian M-50F-4 engine, and the L12-180Z is a copy of the 12D6 engine.
Combat systems: The original group was delivered armed with two twin 37-mm AA and two twin 25-mm AA and equipped with Pot Head radars.

PATROL BOATS [PB]

♦ 5 Mk V-A Pegasus class
Bldr: Halter Marine Equitable SY, New Orleans (In serv. 1997)

P 480 P 481 P 483 P 484 P 485

Mk V-A Pegasus class Sri Lankan Navy, 11-96

PATROL BOATS [PB] *(continued)*

D: 57 tons (68 fl) **S:** 47 kts (40 sust.) **Dim:** 24.99 × 5.33 × 1.32
A: 2 single 20-mm 90-cal. Oerlikon AA; 2 single 12.7-mm M 2 mg; 2 single 7.62-mm M 60 mg; 1 40-mm Mk 19 grenade launcher
Electronics: Radar: 1 Raytheon R 1210 nav.
M: 2 MTU 16V396 TE94 diesels; 2 Arneson outdrives with Rolla surf.-piercing props; 4,570 bhp
Electric: 50 kw tot. (2 × 25-kw diesel sets)
Range: 500/35; 1,200/30 **Fuel:** 8,667 liters **Crew:** 12 tot.

Remarks: Three were ordered in 3-96, with an option for three more taken up in 12-96. The first two were delivered 8-11-96, the third during 12-96, and the last three in 9-97. Five more were to be ordered early in 2001 at $3.8 million each, but the order was not placed. P 482 was lost to Tamil sabotage on 7-4-00, and another may have been damaged. Similar craft operate in the U.S. Navy. Kevlar-reinforced GRP hull. Have a 220-gallon/day potable water generator. Heavier armament is to be added later, probably to include U.S. 25-mm Bushmaster guns in place of one or both 20-mm mounts.

♦ 11 Israeli Shaldag class
Bldrs: P 470–472, 1 other: Israel Shipyards, Haifa; others: Colombo DY

	In serv.		In serv.
P 470 (ex-P 491)	5-90	P 454	1997
P 471 (ex-P 492)	20-7-96	P 455	1997
P 472	16-2-00	P 495	1998
P 451 (ex-P 494)	1997	P 497	1999
P 452 (ex-P 495)	1997	P . . .	5-1-02
P 453	1998		

Shaldag-class P 470—Israeli-built version — Sri Lankan Navy, 1996

Shaldag class—Sri Lankan–built, "Colombo-class" version — Sri Lankan Navy, 1996

D: 40 tons (56 fl) **S:** 46 kts **Dim:** 24.37 (20.07 pp) × 6.00 × 1.15 (1.26 max.)
A: 1 20-mm Rafael Typhoon gatling AA; 1 20-mm 90-cal. Oerlikon; 4 single 7.62-mm mg; 4 40-mm Mk 19 grenade launchers
Electronics: Radar: 1 Furuno FR 8250 or Koden Mk 2 nav.
M: P 470–472: 2 Deutz-MWM TBD 604 B V16 diesels; 2 waterjets; 5,000 bhp—others: 2 MTU 12V396 TE94 diesels; 2 waterjets; 4,570 (3,260 sust.) bhp
Electric: 50 kw tot. (2 × 25-kw, 440-V a.c. diesel sets)
Range: 850/16 **Endurance:** 2–3 days **Crew:** 15 tot.

Remarks: P 470 was a builder-funded prototype that was not accepted by the Israeli Navy; trials by the U.S. Navy, mandated by the U.S. Congress, found the craft unacceptable as well. Sri Lanka bought the prototype on 24-1-96, along with P 471; a third Israeli-built unit, P 472, was acquired in 2000. The Sri Lankan–built units, known locally as the Colombo class, are a modified version with improved hull strength, a smaller superstructure, and different engines, built with Israeli technical assistance at Colombo Dockyard; two were also built at Colombo for the Maldive Islands.
Disposals: P 494 and P 496 were lost to Tamil rebel forces 5-6-00 with 21 dead, and several others have been damaged, some severely.
Hull systems: Have a deep-vee, aluminum-construction hull and five watertight compartments. Are air-conditioned. The range for P 470 and 471 has also been reported as 640 n.m. at 45 kts.
Combat systems: The armament above was seen on several units of the class as of 2000; some may retain the original 20-mm Oerlikon gun on the bow.

♦ 4 Sea Sentinel 508 class
Bldrs: Simonneau Marine, Fontenay-le-Comte, France (In serv. 1993–95)

P 410 (ex-P 483) P 412 (ex-P 485)
P 411 (ex-P 484) P 413 (ex-P 486)

Sea Sentinel 508–class P 410—with original pennant number — French Navy, 1993

D: 28 tons (fl) **S:** 45 kts (42 sust.) **Dim:** 17.3 × 4.9 × . . .
A: 1 20-mm 90-cal. GIAT F2 AA; 1 12.7-mm mg; 2 single 7.62-mm mg
Electronics: Radar: 1 . . . nav.
M: 2 MTU 12V183 TE93 diesels; 2 Hamilton waterjets; 2,300 bhp
Range: 500/35 **Crew:** 8 tot.

Remarks: Ordered in 3-93, with the first two completed 11-93 and 12-93 and the second pair of hulls fitted out at Colombo. Nine more, referred to as the UFAC (Ultra-Fast Attack Craft) class, were ordered in 1996 from Colombo Dockyard, but they were later canceled, as was a plan to build up to an additional 96. Aluminum construction.

♦ 3 Killer class
Bldr: Korea SB & Eng., Pusan (In serv. 2-88)

P 430 (ex-P 473) P 431 (ex-P 474) P 432 (ex-P 475)

Killer-class P 430—with original pennant number — Sri Lankan Navy, 1996

D: 56 tons (fl) **S:** 40 kts **Dim:** 23.0 × 5.4 × 1.8
A: 2 single 20-mm 90-cal. Oerlikon AA; 2 single 12.7-mm mg
Electronics: Radar: 1 Decca 926 nav.
M: 2 MTU 8V396 TB93 diesels; 2 props; 3,260 bhp **Crew:** 12 tot.

Remarks: Ordered in 10-86. A planned additional three were not ordered.

♦ 7 Israeli Super Dvora class
Bldr: RAMTA–Israeli Aircraft Industries, Be'er Sheva (In serv. 1987–97)

	In serv.		In serv.
P 440 (ex-P 465)	1987	P 460 (ex-P 441)	5-11-95
P 441 (ex-P 466)	1987	P 461 (ex-P 496)	30-4-96
P 442 (ex-P 467)	1987	P 462 (ex-P 497)	22-6-96
P 443 (ex-P 468)	1987		

Super Dvora–class P 441 — Sri Lankan Navy, 1996

D: 48 tons (54 fl) **S:** 36 (P 460–462: 46) kts **Dim:** 22.40 × 5.49 × 1.00
A: 2 single 20-mm 70-cal. Oerlikon AA; 2 single 12.7-mm mg
Electronics: Radar: 1 Decca 926 (P 460–462: Koden MD 3220) nav.
M: 2 MTU 12V396 TB93 or TB94 diesels; 2 props; 3,260 bhp—see remarks
Electric: 30 kw tot. **Range:** 700/14 **Crew:** 1 officer, 9–11 enlisted

Remarks: An improved version of the basic Dvora design. The first four are from a group ordered in 10-86. The second group (P 460–462) are of the Mk II version with slightly more-powerful engines and an improved fire-control and surveillance system.
Disposals: P 464 was lost 29-8-93 and P 463 on 29-8-95. On 20-3-01, one was sunk by Sri Lankan Air Force fire and another to Tamil Rebel action.
Hull systems: Engines in P 460–462 are rated at 2,285 bhp each, producing a top speed of around 46 kts, while the engines in the first four produce speeds of about 36 kts.
Combat systems: P 460–462 have an Elop MSIS optronic director.

♦ 3 Israeli Dvora class
Bldr: Israeli Aircraft Industries, Be'er Sheva (In serv. 1984–86)

P 420 (ex-P 453) P 421 (ex-P 454) P 422 (ex-P 455)

PATROL BOATS [PB] *(continued)*

Dvora-class P 457—lost on 25-10-96 Sri Lankan Navy, 8-91

D: 47 tons (fl) **S:** 36 kts **Dim:** 21.62 × 5.49 × 0.94 (1.82 props)
A: 2 single 20-mm 70-cal. Oerlikon AA; 2 single 12.7-mm mg
Electronics: Radar: 1 Decca 926 nav.
M: 2 MTU 12V331 TC81 diesels; 2 props; 2,720 bhp
Electric: 30 kw **Range:** 700/32; 1,200/17 **Crew:** 12 tot.

Remarks: Six were ordered in late 1984. Aluminum construction.
Disposals: P 456 was lost 29-8-95, P 458 on 30-3-96, and P 457 on 25-10-96. Two others had been lost earlier. One Dvora or Super Dvora was sunk 18-10-97.

♦ **4 P 445 class** Bldr: Colombo DY

	L	In serv.		L	In serv.
P 241	...	20-9-82	P 244	27-8-82	1982
P 242	...	17-9-82	P 245	20-9-82	1982

P 445–class P 241 Sri Lankan Navy, 1993

D: 40 tons (44 fl) **S:** 22 kts **Dim:** 20.0 (18.3 pp) × 5.1 × 1.3
A: 1 20-mm 70-cal. Oerlikon AA; 2 single 12.7-mm mg
Electronics: Radar: 1 Furuno FR 2010 nav.
M: 2 G.M. Detroit Diesel 12V71 TI diesels; 2 props; 1,300 bhp (840 sust.)
Range: 1,200/14 **Fuel:** 10 tons **Endurance:** 14 days
Crew: 1 officer, 9 enlisted

Remarks: Steel construction. Sister P 243 was lost to a limpet mine on 11-6-96.

♦ **4 P 201 class** Bldr: Colombo DY

P 201 (In serv. 1981) P 211 (In serv. 6-86) P 214 P 215

D: 15 tons (22 fl) **S:** 20 kts **Dim:** 13.73 × 3.63 × 0.90
A: 1 12.7-mm mg **Electronics:** Radar: 1 Furuno FR 2010 nav.
M: 2 G.M. Detroit Diesel 8V71 TI diesels; 2 props; 800 bhp (460 sust.)
Electric: 1 kw **Range:** 450/14 **Fuel:** 2.5 tons **Crew:** 1 officer, 5 enlisted

Remarks: Also employed for customs inspection. Sister P 203 sank during 1989.

♦ **4 Belikawa class**
Bldr: Cheverton, Cowes, U.K. (In serv. 4-77 to 10-77)

P 221 P 222 P 223 P 224

D: 22 tons (fl) **S:** 23.6 kts **Dim:** 17.0 × 4.5 × 1.2
A: 1 12.7-mm mg **Electronics:** Radar: 1 Decca 110 nav.
M: 2 G.M. Detroit Diesel 8V71 TI diesels; 2 props; 800 bhp
Range: 790/18; 1,000/12.2 **Crew:** 7 tot.

Remarks: GRP construction. Initially intended for customs duties but used as patrol craft. Originally named *Belikawa, Diyakawa, Korawakka,* and *Seruwa,* respectively, with hull numbers P 421–424. Sister *Tarawa* (P 225, ex-P 425) has been discarded.

♦ **25 P 151 class**
Bldrs: P 151, 152: TAOS Yacht, Colombo (In serv. 1991); others: Blue Star Marine, Colombo (In serv. 1994–95, 1997–98)

P 151	P 161 through P 173	P 189 through P 194
P 152	P 180	P 196 through P 198

D: 7 tons (9 fl) **S:** 33 kts **Dim:** 9.8 × 2.1 × 0.5
A: 1 12.7-mm mg **Electronics:** Radar: 1 Furuno 1941 nav.
M: 2 Cummins 6BTA5.9-M2 diesels; 2 waterjets; 584 bhp
Range: 330/25 **Crew:** 5 tot.

P 151–class P 161 Sri Lankan Navy, 1996

Remarks: GRP construction. Sister P 174 was lost early in 1999 and P 183 was lost during 2000. More were to be built, but the program seems to have ceased by the end of 1998.

♦ **6 P 140 class** Bldr: Blue Star Marine, Colombo (In serv. 1988)

P 144 P 145 P 146 P 147 P 148 P 149

P 140–class P 149 Sri Lankan Navy, 1990

D: 3.5 tons (5 fl) **S:** 30 kts **Dim:** 12.8 × 2.4 × 0.5
A: 1 12.7-mm mg **Electronics:** Radar: none
M: 2 gasoline outboard motors; 280 bhp **Crew:** 4 tot.

Remarks: Designed to operate from the "deckship" command vessels. Sister P 150 was lost to a mine in 8-91, P 143 was lost in 1996, and three others have been lost or discarded. These six may also have been stricken.

♦ **3 P 111 class**
Bldr: Consolidated Marine Eng., Sri Lanka (In serv. 1988–94)

P 111 P 112 P 113

P 111–class P 112 Sri Lankan Navy, 1996

D: 3.5 tons (5 fl) **S:** 26 kts **Dim:** 13.4 × 3.0 × 0.5
A: 1 12.7-mm mg **Electronics:** Radar: none
M: 2 Yamaha D343 K diesels; 2 props; 324 bhp **Crew:** 4–5 tot.

Remarks: Nine were delivered in 1988, four in 1992, and two in 1994. Designed to operate from the "deckship" command vessels. Wooden construction. A dozen have been lost in action or discarded, and these three may no longer be in service.

♦ **4 Cougar Cat 900 patrol craft**
Bldr: Cougar Marine, Netley, U.K. (In serv. 1984–85)

P 101 P 102 P 107 P 109

Cougar Cat 900–class P 106—since stricken Sri Lankan Navy, 1990

D: 4.5 tons (7.4 fl) **S:** 30 kts **Dim:** 10.40 × 2.89 × 0.78 (0.48 at speed)
A: 1 12.7-mm mg **Electronics:** Radar: none
M: 2 Ford Sabre diesels; 2 Type 290P outdrives; 500 bhp
Range: 150/32 **Crew:** 3–8 tot.

PATROL BOATS [PB] *(continued)*

Remarks: The first unit, purchased in 1984 for evaluation in operations from mother ships, was 9.20 m o.a. GRP construction. Eight more were ordered in 1-85 and delivered by 10-85. At least five have been lost or discarded.

AMPHIBIOUS WARFARE CRAFT

Note: Two additional "tank landing ships" were ordered during 12-00 from China; these may be additional units of the Yuhai class. A chartered transport named *Pride of the South* was being used to carry 1,200 troops when attacked and damaged by rebels 17-9-01.

♦ 1 Chinese Yuhai-class utility landing craft [LCU]
Bldr: Wuhu SY (In serv. 22-5-96)

L 841 Shakhti

Shakhti (L 841) Sri Lankan Navy, 5-96

D: 799 tons (fl) **S:** 14 kts **Dim:** 58.4 × 10.4 × 2.7
A: 5 twin 14.5-mm 93-cal. Model 81 AA; 6 single 12.7-mm mg
Electronics: Radar: 1 Type 756 nav.
M: 2 M.A.N. 8L 20/27 diesels; 2 props; 4,900 bhp
Range: 1,000/12 **Crew:** 56 tot.

Remarks: Delivered 13-12-95. A reported second unit was for a different country. Essentially an enlarged LCU; appears to have been designed for commercial rather than military service. Has a bow ramp only. Cargo capacity is two tanks and 250 troops, or up to 150 tons of miscellaneous cargo. The 12.7-mm mg were added in Sri Lanka.

♦ 2 Kandula-class utility landing craft [LCU]
Bldr: Colombo DY

	In serv.
L 839 Ranagaja (ex-*Gajasingha*)	15-11-91
L 836 Ranavijaya	21-7-94

D: 200 tons (268 fl) **S:** 8 kts **Dim:** 33.00 (30.00 pp) × 8.00 × 1.50
A: 4 14.5-mm 93-cal. AA; 2 12.7-mm mg
Electronics: Radar: 1 Furuno FCR 1421 nav.
M: 2 Caterpillar 3408 TA diesels; 2 props; 1,524 bhp
Range: 1,800/8 **Crew:** 2 officers, 10 enlisted + 54 troops

Remarks: Vosper Singapore–built sisters *Kandula* (A 537) and *Pabbatha* (L 838, ex-A 538) were lost during 1992 and on 24-2-98, respectively; a second landing craft (class unspecified) was also lost on the latter date. L 839 was begun for a civilian customer and taken over for the navy; the craft was badly damaged by gunfire during 10-95, with 54 personnel casualties.

♦ 1 M-10-class air-cushion landing craft [LCMA]
Bldr: Vosper Thornycroft, Portchester, U.K. (In serv. 6-98)

A 530

M-10-class hovercraft A 530 ABS Hovercraft, 6-98

D: . . . tons **S:** 35 kts (loaded) **Dim:** 18.84 × 8.80 × 0.35 (at rest)
A: 1 12.7-mm mg **Electronics:** Radar: 1 . . . nav.
M: 2 Deutz BF12L513C diesels; 2 lift fans, 2 airscrew props; 1,050 bhp
Range: 600/30 **Fuel:** 4,600 liters **Crew:** 1 officer, 2 enlisted + 56 troops

Remarks: Designed by ABS Hovercraft, U.K. Arrived in Sri Lanka during 12-98. Is capable of carrying one tracked vehicle, 56 seated troops, one 20-ft. cargo container, or 20 stretcher cases. The hull is constructed of GRP, with a GRP/foam sandwich deck and Kevlar-reinforced superstructure. Can clear 1-m obstacles and operate in 2.5-m seas.

♦ 2 Chinese Yuqin-class landing craft [LCM]

L 820 (In serv. 6-91) L 821 (In serv. 5-95)

Yuqin-class landing craft L 820 Sri Lankan Navy, 1992

D: 60 tons light (110 fl) **S:** 11.5 kts (9.5 loaded) **Dim:** 24.1 × 5.2 × 1.1
A: 2 twin 14.5-mm 93-cal. AA **Electronics:** Radar: 1 Fuji . . . nav.
M: 2 Type 12V50 diesels; 2 props; 600 bhp
Range: 500/10 **Crew:** 2 officers, 10 enlisted

Remarks: Cargo capacity: 46 tons.

♦ 2 catamaran personnel transports [LCP]
Bldr: International Catamarans, Hobart, Tasmania, Australia (In serv. 20-12-87)

A 540 Hansaya (ex-*Offshore Pioneer*)
A 541 Lihinaya (ex-*Offshore Pride*)

Lihinaya (A 541) Sri Lankan Navy, 1990

D: 153.2 tons (fl) **S:** 32 kts **Dim:** 30.00 × 11.20 × 2.34
A: 1 20-mm 70-cal. Oerlikon AA; 2 single 12.7-mm mg
Electronics: Radar: 1 Furuno 1012 nav.
M: 2 MTU diesels; 2 props; 3,560 bhp **Crew:** 2 officers, 10 enlisted

Remarks: 169 grt. Cargo: 60 tons of stores or 120 troops. Acquired in 1-86 and converted by Sing Koon Seng SY, Singapore, where they were lengthened 5 m and had additional superstructure added. Originally built as oilfield supply boats.

SERVICE CRAFT

♦ 1 fuel lighter [YO]

Madera Oya

MARINE POLICE

Note: The Sri Lanka police organization announced plans in 8-98 to order five patrol boats for operation on the country's northern and eastern coasts; no data available.

SUDAN

Republic of the Sudan

Personnel (2002): Approx. 400 total

Bases: Kosti, Flamingo Bay, for Red Sea units; Khartoum for Nile River units

Aviation: Two CASA Aviocar C-212-200

Note: Due to operating conditions and the withdrawal of traditional sources of aid, the material condition of the units of the Sudanese fleet is seriously deficient. A number of patrol craft are no longer operable, and all auxiliaries have been discarded. Iran has supplied several small patrol craft and some technical aid. Although it was announced in 3-95 that Iran and Sudan were to establish a joint naval base on the Red Sea coast, none has been established.

PATROL BOATS [PB]

♦ **8 Iranian Ashoora-I-class patrol launches**
Bldr: IRI Marine Industries, Iran (In serv. 1992)

D: 3 tons (fl) **S:** 42 kts **Dim:** 8.1 × 2.4 × 0.5 **A:** 1 14.5-mm 93-cal. mg
M: 2 Yamaha gasoline outboards; 400 bhp **Crew:** 3 tot.

Remarks: GRP construction. Based on the Red Sea coast at Kosti.

Disposal note: The two remaining ex-Iranian 70-ton patrol boats, *Kader* (129, ex-*Shahpar*) and *Karari* (130, ex-*Shakram*), have been inoperable at Flamingo Bay since 1995 and are unlikely to see further service.

♦ **4 Yugoslav Type 15 riverine patrol launches**
Bldr: . . . (In serv. 18-5-89)

502 Kurmuk 503 Qaysan 504 Rumbek 505 Mayom

D: 19.5 tons (fl) **S:** 16 kts **Dim:** 16.87 × 3.90 × 0.65 (0.70 props)
A: 1 20-mm 90-cal. Hispano-Suiza M-71 AA; 2 single 7.62-mm mg
Electronics: Radar: none **M:** 2 diesels; 2 props; 330 bhp
Range: 160/12 **Crew:** 6 tot.

Remarks: Design originally intended for riverine and lake use by Yugoslavia. Were a gift, intended for use on the White Nile. Based at Khartoum.

♦ **4 ex-Iranian U.S. 40-foot Commercial Cruiser class**
Bldr: Sewart Seacraft, Berwick, La. (In serv. 1963)

1161 Maroub 1162 Fijab 1163 Salak 1164 Halote

D: 10 tons **S:** 30 kts **Dim:** 12.2 × 3.4 × 1.1
A: 1 12.7-mm mg **Electronics:** Radar: none
M: 2 G.M. Detroit Diesel 6-71 diesels; 2 props; 348 bhp

Remarks: Donated by Iran in 1978 and thought to have been stricken circa 1990, but at least three were said to be in service on the Red Sea in 1992 and all four were operable as of 1998.

AMPHIBIOUS WARFARE CRAFT

♦ **5 Yugoslav DC 101–class personnel landing craft [LCVP]**
Bldr: Vela Luca, Korcula Island, Yugoslavia

D: 5.5 tons light (11 fl) **S:** 25 kts (20 sust.) **Dim:** 11.30 × 3.10 × 0.32
A: 1 7.62-mm mg **Electronics:** Radar: 1 Decca 101 nav.
M: 2 diesels; 2 waterjets *or* 2 outdrives; 260 bhp
Range: 100/15 **Crew:** 2 tot.

Remarks: Delivered by air in 1991 and assembled in Sudan. Based at Kosti, Flamingo Bay. GRP construction. Misidentified as Type 11 landing craft in earlier editions. Can carry two jeeps or 30 troops, for a total of 4.8 tons.

SURINAM

Republic of Surinam

Personnel (2001): 25 officers, 215 enlisted

Base: Kruktu Tere, Paramaribo

Naval Aviation: The air force uses two CASA C-212-400 transports for coastal patrol and also has one Cessna 172 trainer. Aircraft operate from Zorg-en-Hoop airbase and Paramaribo-Zanderij Airport.

PATROL BOATS [PB]

♦ **3 Rodman 101 class**
Bldr: Rodman-Polyships, Vigo, Spain (In serv. 2-99 to 4-99)

P 01 Jarrabakka P 02 Spari P 03 Gramorgu

D: 46 tons (fl) **S:** 33 kts **Dim:** 30.00 (24.96 pp) × 6.51 (6.00 wl) × 1.50
A: 1 12.7-mm mg **Electronics:** Radar: 1 Furuno . . . nav.
M: 2 MTU 12V2000 diesels; 2 Hamilton HM-571 waterjets; 2,900 bhp (2,760 sust.)
Electric: 42 kw (2 × 21-kw diesel sets) **Range:** 800/25 **Crew:** 9 tot.

Remarks: Ordered in 12-97. GRP construction.

♦ **5 Rodman 55 class**
Bldr: Rodman-Polyships, Vigo, Spain (In serv. 10-98 to 4-99)

P 04 P 05 P 06 P 07 P 08

D: 15.7 tons (fl) **S:** 25 kts **Dim:** 16.50 × 3.80 × 0.7
A: 1 7.62-mm mg **Electronics:** Radar: 1 Decca . . . nav.
M: 2 Bazán-M.A.N. D2848 LXE diesels; 2 Hamilton waterjets; 1,360 bhp (1,216 sust.)
Range: 500/25 **Crew:** 7 tot.

Remarks: Ordered in 12-97; had originally been ordered for Paraguay. GRP construction.

SERVICE CRAFT

♦ **2 hydrographic survey craft [YGS]**

Coeroeni Litani

Remarks: Owned by the Ministry of Economic Affairs and operated by the navy. *Coeroeni,* launched in 1962, displaces 80 tons; *Litani,* launched in 1958, displaces 70 tons.

Note: The Surinam Fisheries Department has a 15-person fisheries inspection team and operates a 14-m patrol launch.

SWEDEN

Kingdom of Sweden

SVENSKA MARINEN

Personnel (2001): 9,500 total (2,700 officers), including 6,000 draftees. The total includes 3,900 personnel assigned to the Coastal Artillery Service. There are also about 1,300 civilian employees, with some crewing service craft and auxiliaries. About 6,000 reservists (1,600 officers) are available for the navy and coastal artillery (about 3,000 total for the latter).

Organization: The fleet is divided into the Eastern and Southern Commands. Serving the commands are three helicopter squadrons, three surface flotillas, one submarine flotilla, three mine warfare squadrons, six amphibious battalions, one heavy coastal missile battery, and three mobile coastal artillery battalions. The 18th Fast Patrol Boat Squadron, Karlskrona, was retired on 1-7-01, leaving only smallcraft based on Sweden's western coast.

Bases: Principal base at Muskö, with minor facilities at Göteborg and Härnösand. Training facilities are located at Härsförden.

Coastal Defense: The Coastal Artillery Service is organized into three coastal artillery battalions (750 personnel and eight Bofors 120-mm 55-cal. KARIN/CD 80 mobile guns each), six amphibious battalions (800 personnel each), a coastal missile battalion (200 personnel, with six missile trucks, each with four RBS-15 Mk 2 launchers), and two mobile coastal artillery brigade headquarters. The artillery and missile battalions may be eliminated and the amphibious strength cut to three active and one reserve battalions. The first of three Mowag wheeled armored vehicles was delivered from Switzerland 30-6-97. New self-propelled Bofors TriKA 40-mm AA batteries and associated Ericsson ARTE 740 (Giraffe CD) radars were ordered in mid-1998 for the Coastal Artillery Service, with the prototype system to be delivered in 2001 and production versions in 2002. The fixed 75-, 120-, and 152-mm gun batteries are being retired.

Naval Aviation: 350 personnel. 24 helicopters: 10 Agusta Bell 206-A JetRanger (HKP-6) and 14 Vertol 107-II-4 (3 HKP-4B for minesweeping and 11 HKP-4C for rescue and ASW, with six depth charges or up to four Tp 422 torpedoes, plus AS-380 dipping sonar). Of three CASA C-212-200 Aviocar light transports ordered 16-12-85, two were for the coast guard, and one was for the navy as a TP-89 maritime surveillance aircraft. The Swedish Air Force employs six Fairchild Metro-III light transports with Ericsson Erieye side-looking radars for maritime surveillance. Twelve AS.332M1 Super Puma (HKP-10) helicopters are used by the Swedish Air Force for search-and-rescue duties. The 14 HKP-4 helicopters were refitted and given new doppler navigation systems by late 2001.

On 18-9-01, a contract was placed for 20 AgustaWestland A-109 Power helicopters (Swedish designation: HKP-15), with five to be equipped for shipboard operations; the aircraft will be used for liaison, ASW, SAR, medical evacuation, and training, and the airframes will be built by Denel in South Africa.

WEAPONS AND SYSTEMS

Note: Saab AB announced plans to acquire CelsiusTech in 11-99, and the evolution was completed 8-3-00. The former CelsiusTech-owned Bofors Weapons Systems was sold to United Defense Industries of the U.S.A. in 6-00, but the Bofors Missiles division was not included in the package; Bofors will remain in Sweden.

A. MISSILES

RBS-12: The infrared-homing Norwegian Kongsberg Penguin Mk 2 missile, in use on board the *Kaparen*-class guided-missile patrol boats.

Length: 3.0 m **Diameter:** 280 mm **Wingspan:** 1.4 m
Weight: 340 kg **Warhead weight:** 120 kg **Speed:** Mach 0.7
Max. range: 30 km at an altitude of 60–100 m

RBS-15: Made by Saab Dynamics. Became operational in 1985. Has a solid rocket booster and a turbojet sustainer. A sea-skimmer, it has a terminal-homing guidance system. The RBS-15F is launched from air force Viggen jet fighters. Under a 1994 contract, all missiles were upgraded to Mk 2 status by the end of 1997. A submarine-launched version is being studied. The Mk 3 version has a range of 200 km, programmable flight waypoints, reduced radar cross-section, a reattack capability, a 200-kg warhead, greater maneuverability, and greater resistance to countermeasures, and it can be used for land attack. Data for the Mk 2 version:

Length: 4.350 m **Diameter:** 0.500 m
Wingspan: 0.85 m folded/1.4 extended
Weight: 598 kg (770 with booster) **Speed:** Mach 0.8
Range: 80–100 km at an altitude of 10–20 m

RBS-17: A version of the U.S. Laser-Hellfire, procured for use by 25 Coastal Artillery Service battalions.

Length: 1.625 m **Weight:** 48 kg (71 with launcher) **Range:** 5+ km

RBS-70: Shoulder-launched SAM made by Bofors. Entered development in 1983 as a weapon for surface combatants in a version known as the RBS-70 SLM. Replaced army and coastal artillery 40-mm AA during 1990–92.

WEAPONS AND SYSTEMS *(continued)*

Length: 1.735 m **Diameter:** 152 mm
Weight: 25 kg **Launcher weight:** 150 kg (loaded)
Range: 5–6 km **Altitude:** 3 km

RBS-90: Basically a longer-range RBS-70 Mk 2 with a night sight. It is offered with a remote-controlled octuple launcher. Range is 8 km and altitude 5 km.

B. GUNS

Note: All guns are manufactured by Saab AB under its Bofors trademark.

57-mm single-barrel automatic SAK 57 Mk 3: Employs a shaped GRP gunhouse, lengthened to conceal the gun barrel at low depression and reduce radar signature and incorporates fold-out decoy rocket launchers. There are 120 rounds on-mount, with 40 ready to fire. Uses cassettes to reduce reload time to 8 seconds. As with the other 57-mm mounts, it has a backup local control capability. The 57-mm 3P (Prefragmented, Programmable, Proximity-fuzed) round weighs 2.4 kg, with 2,400 tungsten pellets and 0.46 kg of Octol explosive as payload. The HCER-BB (High Capacity Extended Range–Base-Bleed) round, with a range of 21 km and muzzle velocity of 950 m/sec, is also available.

57-mm single-barrel automatic SAK 57 Mk 2: Entered service in 1985. Carries 120 rounds ready service within the low, streamlined gunhouse, automatically loading clips of 20 rounds each. Can be upgraded to the Mk 3 version (q.v.).

Mount weight: 6 tons
Shell weight: AA: 5.8 kg (projectile: 2.4 kg); surface fire: 6.8 kg
Muzzle velocity: 1,020 m/sec **Max. rate of fire:** 220 rds/min
Arc of elevation: −10° to +85° **Training speed:** 55°/sec
Range: 14,000 m max. horizontal

57-mm single-barrel automatic SAK 57 Mk 1: Installed on the *Kaparen*-class missile boats and Spica-II torpedo boats.

Mount weight: 6 tons (without ammunition)
Max. rate of fire: 200 rds/min **Arc of elevation:** −10° to +75°
Training speed: 55°/sec **Elevation speed:** 20°/sec

40-mm single-barrel semi-automatic L70—The 40-mm, 70-cal., 3.7-ton Trinity mounting has a 1,025-m/sec muzzle velocity, a 4-km range, and a 330-rd/min firing rate from a 100-round magazine. Fitted with an integral radar, the Trinity fires a 0.975-kg, 3P (Prefragmented, Preprogrammable, Proximity-fuzed) round with 1,000 tungsten pellets. The Basic Trinity version, the E1, has on-mount radar and laser rangefinder; the E1 Optronic version lacks the radar and the S1 variant uses a remote-control director and has no on-mount operator. A Mk 3 version, using the Trinity mount but without the fire-control system, is being developed. Characteristics for the standard Bofors L70 gunmount include:

Length of barrel: 70 calibers
Mount weight: 2.8–3.3 tons (without ammunition)
Muzzle velocity: 1,005–1,025 m/sec **Arc of elevation:** −10° to +90°
Training speed: 85°/sec **Effective range:** 4 km

C. TORPEDOES

Note: All torpedoes are produced by Saab Bofors Underwater Systems AB, Motala (formerly Bofors Sutec; formerly Underwater Division, Swedish Ordnance; and formerly FFV Ordnance).

Tp 62 (Torpedo 2000): New-generation heavyweight torpedo to follow the Tp 61 series. The first order was placed 17-12-97 and the first example delivered 12-6-01. The weapon is wire guided, with active, passive, and combined active/passive homing modes. It has eight interchangeable modules, is powered by a hydrogen peroxide–fueled engine, and has contact and influence fuzes. Maximum operating depth: 500 m. Has also been ordered by Brazil. An Autonomous Underwater Vehicle (AUV 62) surveillance version is under study.

Diameter: 533.4 mm **Length:** 5.990 m **Weight:** 1,450 kg
Warhead: . . . **Speed:** 60 kts max. **Range:** 45 km max.

Tp 61 series: The wire-guided Tp 61 is used for antisurface duties from surface ships and submarines. It entered service in 1977 and is now employed in the Tp 613 version, with a wakeless hydrogen peroxide engine. The Tp 617 is a 6.98-m-long export version weighing 1,850 kg and having a 20,000-m range. Characteristics for the Tp 613:

Diameter: 533.4 mm **Length:** 7.025 m
Weight: 1,765 kg **Warhead:** 240 kg **Range:** 30 km

Tp 46 Grampus: New lightweight torpedo in development to replace the Tp 42/45 series.

Tp 45: Evolved from the Tp 431 program and formerly known as Tp 43X2, the Tp 45 was to enter service in the mid-1990s.

Diameter: 400 mm **Length:** 2.800 m **Weight:** 310 kg **Range:** 20 km

Note: Due to the delay in the availability of the Tp 45, 50 Whitehead A-244 lightweight torpedoes were ordered from Italy in 1990.

Tp 42/43 series: The lightweight Tp 42 torpedo, for use against submarines by submarines, surface ships, and aircraft, is wire guided and has acoustic homing. It was developed from the similar Tp 41. The Tp 422 entered Swedish service in 1983; a reduced-charge warhead is available for peacetime use against intruders. Data for the Tp 422 include:

Diameter: 400 mm
Length: 2.600 m (2.440 without wire-guidance attachment)
Weight: 298 kg **Warhead:** 50 kg **Range:** 20 km (10 at high speed)

D. ASW WEAPONS

ALECTO: Under development by Saab Bofors Dynamics for use on the *Visby* class. Has a six-barrel, trainable, 127-mm launcher capable of firing ASW, passive torpedo-defense, and offboard air-defense decoy rounds. Range originally was to be 150–1,200 m, but as of 2000, the planned range was to be as much as 6,000 m, and torpedo countermeasure, ECM, and sonobuoy payloads are foreseen.

ASW 600: A Saab Bofors Dynamics–made rocket launcher firing 100-mm-dia. M83 charges to ranges of 350–400 m in patterns of 9, 18, 27, or 36 grenades when installed in the normal four-unit suite. Formerly named Elma LLS-920. Each grenade weighs 4.2 kg and has a shaped-charge warhead. A shallow-water (10 m minimum) version entered service in 1986, followed by chaff and IR decoy rounds. A 600-m-range hard-kill version of the ASW 600 round, the M90, with a larger rocket engine, is now available, as is a decoy round called EWS-900E. The current missile system is officially known as RBS-12. The ASW 601 system, which used a trainable launcher, was not put into production.

Bofors 375-mm ASW rocket launcher: No longer in Swedish Navy service, was once widely used in foreign navies in 2-, 4-, or 6-tube versions. Two types of rockets were furnished: the Erika, with ranges from 600 to 1,600 m, and the Nelli, with ranges from 1,600 to 3,600 m. The SR-375 twin-tube launcher has a 24-round autoloading magazine.

Note: During 1992, Saab Missiles announced a new depth charge with a Dowty active acoustic sensor (100–200 kHz) and control fins; charges missing a target by more than 5 m would sink without detonating. Helicopters can employ the Malin ASW depth charge.

E. MINES

Submarines employ the Saab Bofors Underwater Systems Mine 42, a 533-mm-diameter converted Tp 27 straight-running heavyweight torpedo equipped with influence fuzing; these are launched from 533-mm torpedo tubes. Also used by submarines are portable mine-belt mine containers, two per submarine, each holding 22 influence mines.

F. SENSORS

The Ericsson Sea Giraffe 150–series C-band radars are offered for export in various models and provide for air and surface search via two separate channels. The digital, pulse-compression radar is offered at 15- to 60-kw power with differing antenna gains. A new variant with agile, multibeam transmission was offered in 1997; it can track 100 targets at up to 70° elevation and has new ECCM features. Five Sea Giraffe AMB sets were ordered in 1-98 for the *Visby* class; the radar is based on the variant used with the land-based RBS-23 Bamse air-defense missile system.

Seven sets of U.S. Klein side-scan high-frequency sonars were purchased in 1984 to assist in locating intruding submarines.

Saab Bofors Dynamics offers a mobile underwater acoustic, magnetic, pressure, and electric field data acquisition system; data are sent to a portable land evaluation station via fiber-optic cable, and there is also a television camera to permit monitoring the area above the array.

Note: In the ship name and hull number lists below, a three-letter condensed form of the ship's name used when pennant numbers have been painted out is also given.

ATTACK SUBMARINES [SS]

Note: Swedish submarine builder Kockums was taken over by Howaldtswerke Deutsche Werft (HDW), Kiel, on 21-9-99, but the trademark is maintained.

♦ 0 (+ 2) Viking class

Bldr: . . .

D: 1,350 tons surf. **S:** . . . kts **Dim:** 50.0 × 6.7 × . . .
A: 6 bow 533-mm TT (18 torpedoes, antiship and antiair missiles, mines, and/or UAVs)
Electronics:
Radar: . . .
Sonar: bow conformal passive array; flank passive array; towed passive array
M: 2 Hedemora V12A/15-Ub (VA 185) diesels (1,300 bhp each), 2 generators, 1 electric motor; 1 7-bladed prop; 1,800 shp—2 Stirling V4-275R Mk II 75-kw air-independent generator sets
Crew: 22 tot.

Remarks: An initial concept design contract was let to Kockums in late 1994 for completion by mid-1997. In 2-99, Denmark signed an agreement with Norway and Sweden to cooperate in the program. The joint Viking Submarine Corp. was founded in 3-00 by Kockums of Sweden, Kongsberg of Norway, and Odense Staalskibsværft of Denmark to design and eventually construct the submarines; at that time, Sweden was expected to receive two, with the first to deliver in 2010; Denmark to acquire four (two possibly ex-Swedish submarines on loan), with the first to deliver in 2005; and Norway to receive four, with the first delayed to 2015. As of 2001, however, consideration was being given to adopting the German Type 214 design rather than spending large sums to develop further an all-new design with similar capabilities, and Norway was in any case considering leaving the program, with a decision to be made during 2002.

Combat systems: Intended to carry land-attack and antiship missiles, mines, 53- and 40-cm-diameter self-propelled jammers and decoys, subsurface-to-air missiles, "smart" mines, and 53-cm-dia. surveillance vehicles. Provision will be made to carry a Hugin 3000 swimmer delivery vehicle (capable of operating to a depth of 3,000 m), and there will be a combat swimmer lockout chamber. The navigation suite is to include GPS, SINS, a speed log, an underwater terrain navigation system, and a Loran-C receiver. The communications suite will cover the LF through VHF bands and will employ communications buoys, an expendable antenna system, and SATCOM. The sonar suite is to include own-noise analysis, passive ranging, a towed array, a flank array, a conformal array, navigation and mine avoidance arrays, and an acoustic intercept system. A nonpenetrating optronic periscope system with integral electronic intercept antennas will be used.

ATTACK SUBMARINES [SS] *(continued)*

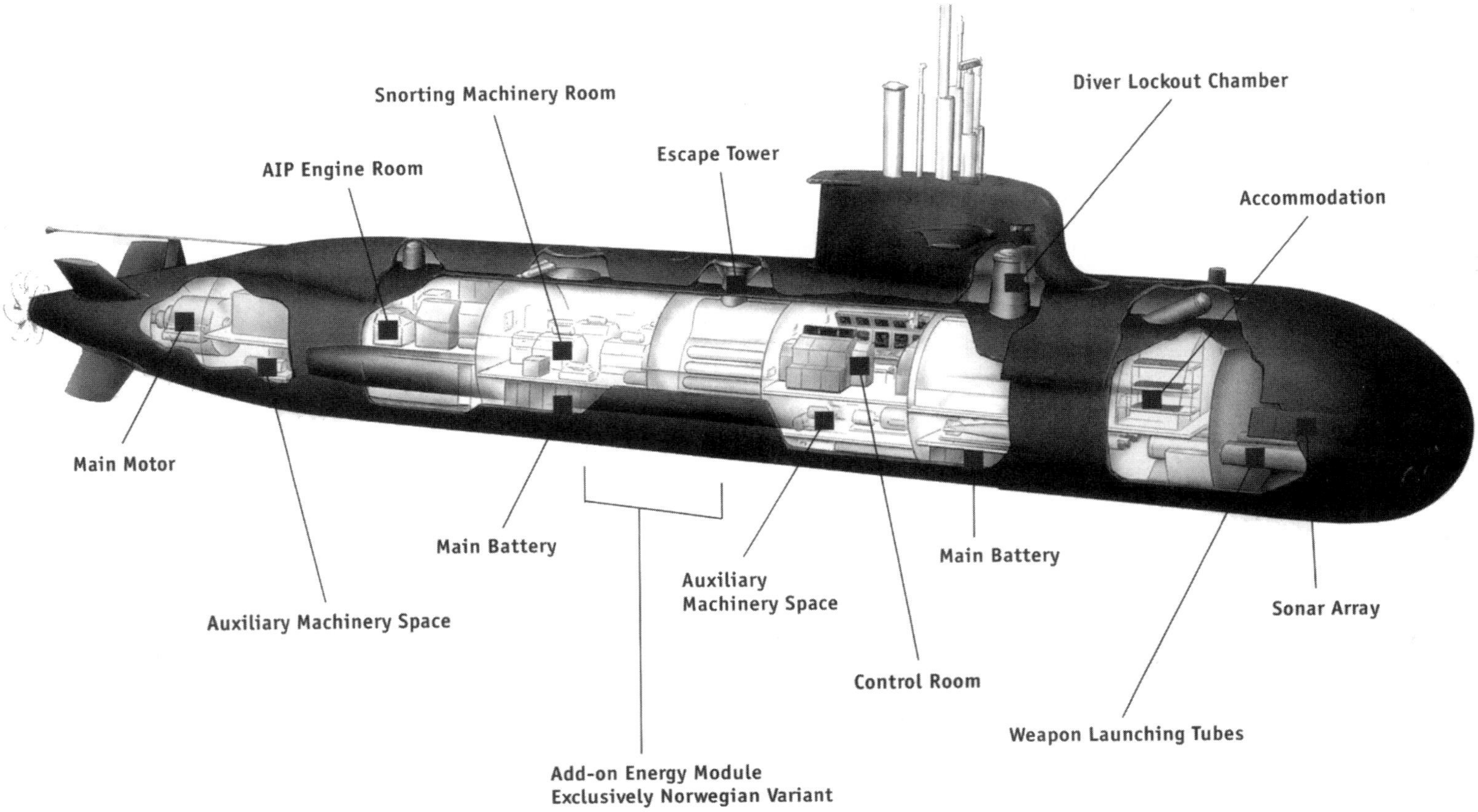

Viking design concept Viking Submarine Corp., 2001

♦ **3 Gotland class (Type A-19)** Bldr: Kockums, Malmö

	Symbol	Laid down	L	Trials	Del.	In serv.
Gotland	Gld	27-11-92	2-2-95	1-7-95	2-9-96	9-99
Uppland	Upd	14-1-94	9-2-96	1-8-96	1-5-97	9-99
Halland	Hnd	7-94	27-9-96	15-3-97	1-10-97	9-99

Uppland (Upd) Jaroslaw Cislak, 6-01

Halland (Hnd) Bernard Prézelin, 10-00

D: 1,384 tons surf./1,494 tons sub. **S:** 10 kts surf./10 kts snorkel/20 kts sub.
Dim: 60.60 × 6.06 × 5.60 (surf.)
A: 4 bow 533-mm TT (12 Tp 613 or Tp 62 torpedoes); 2 bow 400-mm TT (4 Tp 422 or Tp 45 ASW torpedoes); 22 Tp 42 mines in external belt
Electronics:
Radar: 1 Terma . . . nav./surf. search
Sonar: STN Atlas Elektronik CSU-90-2 suite: PRS 3-15 panoramic passive ranging; FAS 3-1 LF flank arrays
EW: Thorn-EMI Manta intercept

M: 2 Hedemora V12A/15-Ub (VA 185) diesels (1,300 bhp each), 2 Jeumont-Schneider 760-kw generators, 1 ASEA electric motor; 1 7-bladed prop; 1,800 shp—2 Stirling V4-275R Mk II 75-kw air-independent generator sets
Range: . . ./. . . **Crew:** 23 tot.

Remarks: Ordered 28-3-90, although not funded until the 1992 budget. An order change was placed 5-9-91 to incorporate Stirling-cycle external-combustion engines, resulting in a 200-ton increase in displacement and 7.5-m increase in length; the original displacement was to have been 1,240 tons surfaced, 1,350 tons submerged. Plans to construct two more were abandoned. *Halland* was equipped during 2001 with improved air-conditioning and enhanced communications systems to permit her to operate with foreign navies in "warmer" waters; the submarine had made a very successful cruise to the Mediterranean during 2000, the first-ever visit there by a Swedish submarine.

Hull systems: Design is essentially an updated Type A-17 with Stirling-cycle air-independent auxiliary low-speed propulsion and improved electronics. The Stirling engines, which can operate the submarines at up to 6 kts, are extremely quiet running, radiating less noise than a household appliance; about 24 tons of liquid oxygen are carried for the engines, which also burn standard diesel fuel. Employ Varta batteries. The hull has a rubberized anechoic coating. Normal diving depth: 200 m. Employ a SAGEM gyrocompass, differential GPS receiver, and inertial navigation system and have a Polyamp-FMV magnetic sensor to permit automatic control adjustment of the degaussing system to deal with local magnetic field variations.

Combat systems: Have the Saab 9SCS Mk 3 submarine command, control, communications, and weapons-control system (Swedish Navy designation SESUB 940A) with three Terma Type IID multifunction operator consoles; the system is a variant of the 9LV Mk 3 and can track 95 targets simultaneously. The data system was updated starting in 1998 to permit employment of the new Tp 62 torpedo, and the Tp 45 lightweight torpedo is to replace the Tp 431 initially carried. Have one Kollmorgen Model 76 periscope and one CK083 periscope, the latter upgraded by Thales Optronics with a thermal imager and an enhanced image intensifier. Torpedo tubes are of the swim-out configuration, and two torpedoes per tube are carried in the 400-mm tubes. A VLF communications set is fitted. There are no plans to fit a towed array sonar but an active mine-avoidance sonar is to be added. U.S. Signal Processing Systems acoustic intercept arrays and signal analysis systems have been added.

♦ **4 Västergötland class (Type A-17)** (2 in *reconstruction*)
Bldrs: Kockums, Malmö, and Karlskronavarvet, Karlskrona (see remarks)

	Symbol	Laid down	L	In serv.
Västergötland	Vgd	10-1-83	17-9-86	27-11-87
Hälsingland	Hgd	1-1-84	31-8-87	20-10-88
Södermanland	Söd	1985	12-4-88	21-4-89
Östergötland	Ögd	1986	9-12-88	10-1-90

D: 990 tons light; 1,070 tons surf./1,143 tons sub.
S: 11 kts surf./20 kts sub. **Dim:** 48.50 × 6.06 × 5.60 (surf.)
A: 6 bow 533-mm TT (12 Tp 613 torpedoes); 3 bow 400-mm TT (6 Tp 422 or Tp 45 torpedoes); 22 mines in external portable containers
Electronics:
Radar: 1 Terma . . . nav./surf. search
Sonar: STN Atlas Elektronik CSU-83 suite: DBQS-21 active/passive; FAS 3-1 flank arrays; towed array
EW: ArgoSystems AR-700-S5 intercept

ATTACK SUBMARINES [SS] *(continued)*

Östergötland (Ögd)—prior to modernization Mike Welsford, 4-01

Västergötland (Vgd) H&L Van Ginderen, 5-00

Hälsingland (Hgd) H&L Van Ginderen, 10-99

M: 2 Hedemora V12A/15-Ub (VA 185) diesels (1,080 bhp each), 2 Jeumont-Schneider 760-kw generators, 1 ASEA electric motor; 1 5-bladed prop; 1,800 shp
Endurance: 45 days **Crew:** 5 officers, 15 enlisted (25 accomm.)

Remarks: Design by Kockums under a 17-4-78 contract. Ordered 8-12-81, with Kockums building the mid-bodies and Karlskronavarvet the bows and sterns. *Södermanland* and *Östergötland* are being given Stirling Mk 3 air-independent auxiliary engines and lengthened by 10 m under an 11-99 contract with Kockums; the other two are to be retired in 2004 when the refitted pair return to service.
Hull systems: Can operate at 300 m. Have only 7% reserve buoyancy. Employ sail-mounted forward control planes and cruciform stern control surfaces. Have six berthing compartments, with five spare berths for trainees. Two Tudor 84-cell lead-acid battery sets are fitted. Have a Sperry Mk 29 gyrocompass, two main watertight compartments, and an anechoic hull coating. There is a single crew escape chamber, fitted with a mating coaming for rescue submersibles or diving bells.
Combat systems: The torpedo tubes are arranged with the six 533-mm tubes in a row above the three short 400-mm tubes. Use the Ericsson IPS-17 combat data/fire-control system (Swedish Navy designation SESUB 900A). Two Barr & Stroud CK038 periscopes are fitted. *Västergötland* has a prototype t.v. mounted on a telescoping mast in lieu of one periscope. U.S. Signal Processing Systems acoustic intercept arrays and signal analysis systems are being added to *Östergötland* and *Södermanland,* which are also to receive active mine-avoidance sonars. Plans to add a land-attack missile-launching capability appear to have been dropped.

Disposal note: Of the three units of the *Näcken* class (Type A-14), the AIP-equipped *Näcken* was leased to Denmark on 13-2-02 for four years, with an option for Denmark to purchase the submarine or extend the lease in 2005, and *Neptun* was placed in storage reserve in 1998 and *Najad* in 1999, with both being theoretically capable of being reactivated in an emergency.

Of the five units of the *Sjöormen* class, *Sjöhunden* was sold to Singapore 23-9-95 for training purposes and *Sjöormen* (stricken in 1996), *Sjöljonet,* and *Sjöhästen* were sold to Singapore 31-7-97 for refurbishment and delivery in 1999–2001, along with the *Sjöbjornen,* which was cannibalized in Sweden for spares.

MIDGET SUBMARINES [SSM]

♦ **1 intruder simulator** Bldr: K. A. Johanssons AB (L: 19-6-90)

Spiggen

Spiggen Curt Borgenstam, Jr., 8-97

D: 12 tons surf./14 tons sub. **S:** 6 kts surf./3–5 kts sub.
Dim: 11.00 × 1.70 × 2.70 (high) **A:** none
M: 1 Volvo Penta diesel, electric drive; 1 prop; . . . shp
Range: 27/5 sub. **Endurance:** 2 days **Crew:** 2 tot.

Remarks: Intended to simulate the foreign submarines long believed to have been operating in Swedish waters. Named for a British X-craft midget submarine acquired by the Swedish Navy after World War II. Began trials in 1-91. Refitted by Kockums during 1995. Diving depth: 100 m.

Note: Swimmer delivery vehicles *Stor Klas* (R 2) and *Lill Klas* (R 1) are described under [LSDV]. Submarine rescue submersible *URF* is described in the service craft section under [YSS].

GUIDED-MISSILE PATROL COMBATANTS [PGG]

Note: Long-range planning calls for construction of a 200- to 300-ton surface-effect craft, guided-missile patrol boat class capable of 40–45 kts; the first would complete after 2010. Also foreseen is a 110-m seagoing warship.

♦ **0 (+ 5) Visby (YS 2000)-class multipurpose**
Bldr: Karlskronavarvet, Karlskrona

	Laid down	L	In serv.
K 31 Visby	17-12-96	8-6-00	1-05
K 32 Helsingborg	. . .	26-6-03	7-05
K 33 Härnösand	. . .	21-4-04	1-06
K 34 Nyköping	. . .	17-2-05	7-06
K 35 Karlstad	. . .	17-11-05	1-07

Visby (K 31)—at launch, with dummy gunmount Karlskronavarvet, 6-00

Visby (K 31)—fitting out Curt Borgenstam, Jr., 7-01

GUIDED-MISSILE PATROL COMBATANTS [PGG] *(continued)*

Visby (K 31)—computerized ghost internal view Karlskronavarvet, 2000

Sundsvall (K 24)—in standard dark camouflage Mike Welsford, 4-00

D: 620 tons (fl) **S:** 38 kts (34 sust.; 15 on diesels)
Dim: 72.80 (63.00 wl; 61.50 pp) × 10.40 × 2.40
A: fitted with 1 57-mm 70-cal. Bofors SAK 57 Mk 3 DP—provision for: 8 RBS-15 Mk 3 SSM; 4 fixed 400-mm ASW TT (4 Tp 45 torpedoes); 2 6-round 127-mm ALECTO ASW RL; 1 HKP-15 helicopter
Electronics:
Radar: 1 . . . X-band nav.; 1 . . . S-band surf. search; 1 Ericsson Sea Giraffe AMB 3-D C-band surveillance; 1 Saab CEROS 200 radar/E/O f.c.
Sonar: CDC Hydra suite: . . . hull-mounted; . . . two-frequency variable-depth; . . . towed linear passive array
EW: Condor Systems CS-3701 intercept (2–18 GHz); . . . comms intercept; 127-mm passive torpedo and antimissile decoys launched by the ALECTO launchers
E/O: . . . IRST
M: CODOG: 4 Honeywell-Vericor TF50A gas turbines (5,365 shp each), 2 MTU 16V 2000 N90 diesels (1,740 bhp each); 2 KaMeWa 125 SII waterjets; 21,460 shp max.—bow-thruster
Electric: 810 kw tot. (3 × 270-kw Isotta Fraschini V1308 T2ME-1550 diesel alternator sets)
Range: . . ./. . . **Crew:** 21 officers, 20 enlisted + small flag staff

Remarks: YS stands for *Ystridfartyg;* they are also known as the YSM class. Funding was requested in 8-93 for the first four; the program was delayed two years in 10-93 but reinstated in 9-6-94. The contract was reduced to two with an option for two more when let on 12-10-95; the second pair was ordered 17-12-96 and a third pair early in 9-99. The first four will be delivered in a mine countermeasures configuration, with the third pair to be equipped with eight antiship missiles. The original class total was to have been 20, which was reduced to 14 in 1996 and then six; the sixth unit, *Uddevalla* (K 36), was canceled during 9-01 due to significant program cost overruns, although an option to build the ship later remains. The design grew by several hundred tons in the final contract version, and the launch date for K 31 has slipped a year from the originally announced 4-6-99; the builder's sea trials began on 7-12-01, and the ship was to be handed over to the navy by 4-02 for further trials expected to last into 2005.
Hull systems: Measures were taken during design and construction to reduce the radar cross-section; infrared, magnetic, hydroacoustic, visual, airborne acoustic, laser, and electrical signatures; hydroacoustic target strength; wake; and directionally emitted signals. Although initially planned to be rigid-sidewall air-cushion vehicles, these ships are instead conventional monohulls. The multi-axial, carbon-reinforced, glass-and-carbon-fiber-sandwich plastic construction will provide low radar and magnetic signature and will be composed of patent MAX-CF HS carbon/glass hybrid reinforcement with vinylester-polyester matrix and ductile PVC foam. The helicopter hangar is below the flight deck, but K 33 will be the first to be capable of operating helicopters. Fin stabilizers are fitted. Will have carbon-fiber power shafts.
Combat systems: Will employ the Saab 9LV CETRIS combat system, which is based on the 9LV Mk 3E; there are to be 16 multipurpose display/action terminals. The Danish INFOCOM ICS2000 integrated communications system will be employed. Weight and space are reserved for a point-defense SAM system. Will have GPS navigation capability and will use external target location sensor information datalinked to the ships. The 57-mm gun will employ Bofors 3P (Prefragmented, Programmable, Proximity-fuzed) ammunition.

The first four will carry a minehunting sonar and two Bofors Double Eagle mine-location ROVs and two STN Atlas Elektronik Seafox ROVs for mine disposal; the ROVs will be deployed through doors in the side of the hull amidships, and a third, Swedish-developed ROV-S reconnaissance submersible will also eventually be carried. In K 35, the mine countermeasures submersible installation will be replaced by four belowdecks launchers for antiship missiles per side; the Bamsea navalized version of the low-signature RBS-23 Bamse missile and the Raytheon ESSM are under consideration and may be backfitted into the original four beginning in 2005. Will have an infrared scanner and two weapons-control directors. The Hydra sonar suite will be supported by a Computing Services Canada NECTA (Naval Environmental Command Tactical Aid) underwater environment modeling system with 3-D color displays. The Computer Devices Canada integrated hull-mounted and towed array sonar suite, ordered 29-9-97, will be used for both ASW and mine countermeasures. An active radar jammer may be fitted later.

GUIDED-MISSILE PATROL CRAFT [PTG]

♦ 4 Göteborg class (KKV-90 design) Bldr: Karlskronavarvet, Karlskrona

	Symbol	Laid down	L	In serv.
K 21 Göteborg	Gbg	10-2-86	12-4-89	15-2-90
K 22 Gävle	Gle	10-9-88	12-8-89	1-2-91
K 23 Kalmar	Kmr	10-9-88	1-11-90	1-9-91
K 24 Sundsvall	Svl	10-3-89	29-11-91	7-7-93

D: 380 tons (425 fl) **S:** 32 kts **Dim:** 57.0 (50.0 wl) × 8.0 (7.3 wl) × 1.93
A: 8 RBS-15 SSM; 1 57-mm 70-cal. Bofors SAK 57 Mk 2 DP; 1 40-mm 70-cal. Bofors L70 AA; 4 fixed 400-mm ASW TT (Tp 45 torpedoes); 4 9-round Saab ASW 600 ASW RL; 2 mine rails (40 or more mines)

Kalmar (K 23)—in new light-toned camouflage Ben Sullivan, 5-01

Göteborg (K 21) Mike Welsford, 5-01

Electronics:
Radar: 1 Terma PN-612 nav.; 1 Saab Pilot surf. search; 1 Ericsson Sea Giraffe 150HC surf./air search; 2 Saab 9GR 400 f.c.
Sonar: Simrad SS 304 Spira hull-mounted (34 kHz); Thales TSM 2643 Salmon dismountable VDS (MF)
EW: ArgoSystems AR-700 intercept/deception syst.; IR detector; Saab 9CM 300 decoy syst. (2 36-round RL)
M: 3 MTU 16V396 TB94 diesels; 3 KaMeWa 80-S62/6 waterjets; 8,640 bhp (6,390 sust.)—K 22 only: bow-thruster
Electric: 855 kVA tot. (3 × 285-kVA diesel alternator sets)
Range: . . ./. . . **Crew:** 7 officers, 36 enlisted (46 tot. accomm.)

Remarks: Ordered 1-12-85; two others, to have been named *Helsingborg* and *Härnösand,* were not ordered. Considered to be corvettes. Modernization refits began in late 1998 with K 22. Under a 28-6-01 contract, the class is to have communications suites, combat data systems, and after fire-control directors upgraded.
Hull systems: Have steel hulls, aluminum superstructures, and fin stabilizers. Infrared, radar, and noise signature-suppression measures are incorporated. K 22 during modernization had radar signature-suppression measures added, including reconfiguring the deckhouse, replacing the lifelines with nonreflective ones, and extension of the bridge wings; the others are to be similarly updated.
Combat systems: Have the Saab 9LV Mk 3 weapons-control system with six multifunction operator consoles. The Saab 9LV 450 gunfire-control system uses the ARTE-726E gun-control, RCI-400 missile fire-control, TORPE torpedo-control, 9AU 300 ASW fire-control and 9CM 300 EW-control systems. The EW suite includes an Argo Systems CAROL intercept receiver and deception transmitter, with Thorn-EMI Sceptre XL analyzer. The two optronic weapons directors have co-mounted television, IR, laser, and 9GR 400 radars. The four fixed ASW TT are mounted with two firing aft

GUIDED-MISSILE PATROL CRAFT [PTG] *(continued)*

and two forward on the starboard-side mine rails for wire-guided Tp 45 ASW torpedoes. GEC-Marconi AQS-928G/SM acoustic processors are fitted and can monitor up to eight LOFAR passive omnidirectional and four DIFAR or VLAD passive directional, two DICASS (active directional), and one bathythermograph buoys simultaneously. The PN-612 navigational radar is the same equipment as the Scanter Mil 009 radar used by the Danish Navy. K 22 has been used since 1995 in trials with an STN Atlas Elektronik passive towed linear sonar array, with the winch and drum mounted to starboard of the VDS installation; after the 1998–2001 refit, K 22 has a new gunhouse for the 40-mm mount, shortened mine rails, and a new ESM suite. One ship of this class tested the Thales IRSCAN infrared search-and-track system during 1999–2000.

♦ 2 Stockholm class (Spica-III/YA-81 design)
Bldr: Karlskronavarvet, Karlskrona

	Symbol	Laid down	L	In serv.
K 11 Stockholm	Sto	1-8-82	24-8-84	1-3-85
K 12 Malmö	Mmö	14-3-83	21-3-85	10-5-85

Stockholm (K 11)—"before and after" computerized drawing showing *Stockholm* in the foreground prior to modernization and as modified in the background
Karlskronavarvet, 2001

Stockholm (K 11)—prior to start of modernization Hartmut Ehlers, 6-00

D: 310 tons (335 fl) **S:** 30 kts (20 on diesels)
Dim: 50.5 (46.6 wl) × 7.5 (6.8 wl) × 2.0 (hull)
A: 8 RBS-15 SSM; 1 57-mm 70-cal. Bofors SAK 57 Mk 2 DP; 4 fixed 400-mm ASW TT (Tp 45 torpedoes); 2 6-round 127-mm ALECTO ASW RL; 2 mine rails (40 or more mines)
Electronics:
Radar: 1 Terma PN-612 nav.; 1 Ericsson Sea Giraffe 50HC surf./air search; 1 Saab 9LV 200 Mk 2 f.c.
Sonar: Simrad SS 304 Spira hull-mounted (34 kHz); Thales TSM 2642 Salmon dismountable MF VDS
EW: Saab-Scania EWS-905 intercept; 2 36-round Saab Philax decoy RL
M: CODAG: 1 Vericor TF50 gas turbine (5,364 shp), 2 MTU 16V396 TB94 diesels (2,095 bhp each); 3 CP props
Electric: 648 kw tot. **Range:** . . . **Crew:** 7 officers, 23 enlisted

Remarks: Ordered in 9-81. Both are undergoing midlife modernizations under an 11-99 contract with Kockums, with the work to be completed at Karlskrona by the end of 2002.
Hull systems: The original Allison 570KF gas turbine (7,170 shp max./6,000 shp sust.) was replaced by a TF50 engine during modernization, K 12 in 9-01 and K 11 a month later; the gearbox was also changed and newer versions of the diesel engines were substituted. The superstructure configuration has been significantly altered to reduce radar and infrared signatures, and a pylon mast is replacing the original lattice structure.
Combat systems: As completed, had the Ericsson MARIL 880 weapons-control system, with an SRA Censor 932E computer, but a new system based on the Saab 9LV Mk 3 is being installed during modernization. The 9LV 300 gunfire-control system incorporates a 9LV 200 radar director forward and a 9LV 100 optronic director on the aft face of the main mast. During modernization, the 40-mm 70-cal. Bofors AA mount aft is being removed, as is the provision to launch wire-guided Tp 61 antiship torpedoes; four 400-mm fixed ASW torpedo tubes may be incorporated in the modified design.

♦ 9 Kaparen class
Bldr: Bergens Mekanske Verksted, Bergen, Norway

	Symbol	L	In serv.
P 153 Magne	Mag	9-1-78	12-10-78
P 159 Kaparen	Kap	8-8-79	7-8-80
P 160 Väktaren	Väk	12-12-79	19-9-80
P 161 Snapphanen	Sna	18-3-80	14-1-81
P 162 Spejaren	Spe	13-5-80	21-3-81
P 163 Styrbjörn	Syb	8-80	26-10-81
P 164 Starkodder	Sta	1-81	24-8-81
P 165 Tordön	Tön	3-2-81	26-10-81
P 166 Tirfing	Tir	17-9-81	21-1-82

Spejaren (P 162) Jürg Kürsener, 6-00

Tordön (P 165) A. A. de Kruijf, 6-00

Kaparen (P 159)—note VDS installation at stern H&L Van Ginderen, 6-00

D: 140 tons (170 fl) **S:** 32–34 kts **Dim:** 36.53 (33.6 pp) × 6.30 × 1.70
A: 2 or 4 RBS-12 (Penguin Mk 2) SSM; 1 57-mm 70-cal. Bofors SAK 57 Mk 1 DP; 4 9-round Saab ASW 600 ASW RL; 24 mines or 2 d.c. racks in lieu of missiles
Electronics:
Radar: 1 Terma Scanter 009 nav.; 1 Saab 9LV 200 Mk 2 f.c.
Sonar: Simrad SA-950 HF hull-mounted; Simrad ST-240 HF VDS (not in P 153)
EW: Saab-Scania EWS-905 intercept
M: P 153: 2 MTU 20V672 TB90 diesels; 2 props; 7,200 bhp—others: 2 MTU 16V396 TB94 diesels; 2 props; 6,400 bhp; hydraulic-drive low-speed propulsion
Electric: 200 kVA tot. **Range:** 550/35 **Crew:** 8 officers, 12 enlisted

Remarks: P 159–166 are former *Hugin*-class guided-missile craft that were modernized as general-purpose patrol units between 1992 and 1994. Class prototype *Jägaren* (V 150, ex-P 150, ex-P 151) was reclassified as a patrol craft in 1989. The unmodified *Hugin* (P 151), *Munin* (P 152), P 153, and *Mode* (P 154) were to have been redesignated as patrol boats and retired circa 1996–97, but instead retained their missile armament.
Disposals: *Vale* (P 155), *Mjölner* (P 157), and *Mysing* (P 158) were stricken in 1995 and *Hugin* (P 151), *Munin* (P 152), *Mode* (P 154), and *Vidar* (P 156) on 1-7-01. The remaining nine are to be retired during 2002–04.

GUIDED-MISSILE PATROL CRAFT [PTG] *(continued)*

Hull systems: All originally had two MTU 20V672 TB90 diesels (3,600 bhp each) reclaimed from discarded *Plejad*-class torpedo boats. P 159–166 were re-engined during modernizations and provided with hydraulic drive for low-speed loiter operations; they also received the Roll-Nix rudder roll-control system and their electrical distribution, air-conditioning, and accommodations were improved.
Combat systems: Carry 103-mm rocket flare launchers on either side of the 57-mm gunmount. The Saab 9LV 200 Mk 2 fire-control system employs separate search and tracking radars. Saab-Scania EWS-905 "Doughnut" passive intercept EW systems have been added, with the toroidal radome mounted just below the stabilized search antenna for the 9LV 200 radar f.c.s. As part of the modernization suite, a 24-kHz Simrad ST.240 Toadfish variable-depth sonar set and a Simrad SA.950 hull-mounted replacement sonar have been installed (the latter replacing a Simrad SQ.3D/SF, 24-kHz searchlight sonar), and the longer-range ASW 600 ASW rocket launcher has replaced the earlier launchers. The craft normally carry only two Penguin missiles.

♦ 6 Spica-II class Bldr: Karlskronavarvet, Karlskrona

	Symbol	L	In serv.
R 131 Norrköping	Nkg	16-11-72	5-11-73
R 132 Nynäshamn	Nyn	24-4-73	8-9-73
R 138 Piteå	Pit	12-5-73	13-9-75
R 139 Luleå	Lul	19-8-75	28-11-75
R 140 Halmstad	Hsd	28-11-75	9-4-76
R 142 Ystad	Ysd	3-9-76	10-12-76

Halmstad (R 140) Curt Borgenstam, 6-00

Piteå (R 138) Findler & Winter, 6-01

Nynäshamn (R 132) Findler & Winter, 6-01

D: 190 tons (230 fl) **S:** 40.5 kts **Dim:** 43.6 × 7.1 × 1.6 (2.4 props)
A: RBS-15 SSM; 1 57-mm 70-cal. Bofors SAK 57 Mk 1 DP; 2 fixed 533-mm TT (Tp 613 wire-guided torpedoes)
Electronics:
Radar: 1 Terma Scanter 009 nav.; 1 Ericsson Sea Giraffe 50HC surf./air search; 1 Saab 9LV 200 Mk 1 f.c.s.
EW: ArgoSystems AR-700 intercept; 2 36-round Saab Philax decoy RL
M: 3 Rolls-Royce Proteus gas turbines; 3 props; 12,900 shp
Crew: 7 officers, 20 enlisted

Remarks: R 142 was modernized between 3-95 and 12-96 at Karlskronavarvet; R 132 completed a midlife refit at Karlskronavarvet in 8-98, and three others had been completed by 4-99, with the remaining unit to follow by 8-99. The six were to have served until 2010, but are now to be retired between 2002 and 2004 due to funding cuts ordered in 10-98.
Disposals: Stricken in 1998 were the *Norrtälje* (R 133), *Varberg* (R 134), *Västerås* (R 135), *Umeå* (R 137), and *Strömstad* (R 141). R 135 is being preserved at the Naval Museum in Karlskrona.
Hull systems: The gas turbines exhaust through the transom to provide residual thrust for added speed. The six survivors were originally to have been re-engined with a different gas turbine plant, but funding was not available.
Combat systems: Have the MARIL 880 (SRA) combat system, which permits over-the-horizon targeting data to be received from a helicopter. All were re-equipped to employ the Saab RBS-15 cruise missile during 1982–85. Four missiles are normally carried, along with two 533-mm torpedo tubes for wire-guided Tp 61 torpedoes, but up to eight missiles can be carried or, with the missiles removed, four more torpedo tubes can be installed aft. Mines can be substituted for the missiles and the torpedo tubes, the forwardmost pair of which must be swung out several degrees before firing. The ESM suite includes a Thorn-EMI SUSIE analyzer (2–18 GHz). All have six rails for 103-mm rocket radar flares on the 57-mm gunmount. The ships no longer carry Simrad ST-240 portable variable-depth sonars or ASW rocket launchers.

PATROL CRAFT [PC]

♦ 1 modified Hugin class
Bldr: Bergens Mekanske Verksted, Bergen, Norway (In serv. 8-6-72)

V 150 Jägaren (ex-P 150, ex-P 151)

Jägaren (V 150) ANBw/FAFIO, 5-00

D: 120 tons (150 fl) **S:** 20 kts **Dim:** 36.53 (33.6 pp) × 6.20 × 1.60
A: 1 40-mm 70-cal. Bofors L70 AA; 2 mine rails
Electronics: Radar: 1 Terma Scanter 009 nav.
M: 2 Cummins KTA 50-M diesels; 2 props; 2,800 bhp
Electric: 200 kVA tot. **Crew:** 3 officers, 12 enlisted

Remarks: Was prototype for the *Hugin* class but carried Penguin Mk 1 missiles only briefly. Was re-engined and rearmed during 1988 and relegated to patrol and trials duties.

PATROL BOATS [PB]

♦ 3 Dalarö class Bldr: Djupviks, Rönnäng

	Symbol	In serv.		Symbol	In serv.
V 09 Dalarö	Dal	21-9-84	V 11 Östhammar	Öst	1-3-85
V 10 Sandhamn	San	5-12-84			

Östhammar (V 11) H&L Van Ginderen, 4-99

D: 50 tons (fl) **S:** 30 kts **Dim:** 23.40 × 5.10 × 1.05
A: 1 20-mm 70-cal. Oerlikon AA; 2 single 7.62-mm mg; mines
Electronics: Radar: 1 Terma Scanter 009 nav.; 1 Terma TM 610 nav.
M: 2 MTU 8V396 TB83 diesels; 3 props; 2,100 bhp
Electric: 60 kw tot. **Crew:** 3 officers, 4 enlisted + 3 passengers

Remarks: Ordered 28-2-83 in lieu of further torpedo-boat-to-patrol-boat conversions (all since stricken). Are equipped with G.E.C. AQS-928 sonobuoy processors. The 20-mm gun is not normally installed. Have a fitting for a single portable mine rail at the stern.

Note: Numerous other patrol craft serve in the Coastal Artillery Service (q.v.).

MINE WARFARE SHIPS

Note: The Coastal Artillery Service (q.v.) has a large number of specialized minelayers and amphibious warfare units capable of laying mines. Most surface combatants and all submarines can also be used to lay mines.

♦ 1 fleet minelaying/training ship Bldr: Karlskronavarvet, Karlskrona

	Symbol	Laid down	L	In serv.
M 04 Carlskrona (ex-*Karlskrona*)	Ckr	1980	28-5-80	19-3-82

Carlskrona (M 04) Arjun Sarup, 4-01

Carlskrona (M 04) Camil Busquets i Vilanova, 5-00

D: 3,300 tons (3,550 fl) **S:** 20 kts **Dim:** 105.70 (97.50 pp) × 15.2 × 4.00
A: 2 single 57-mm 70-cal. Bofors SAK 57 Mk 1 DP; 2 single 40-mm 70-cal. Bofors L70 AA; 105 large mines
Electronics:
Radar: 1 Terma Scanter 009 nav.; 1 Raytheon . . . nav.; 1 Ericsson Sea Giraffe 50HC surf./air search; 2 Saab 9LV 200 Mk 2 f.c. (9LV 400 syst.)
EW: ArgoSystems AR-700 intercept; 2 36-round Saab Philax decoy RL
M: 4 Nohab-Polar F212-D825, 12-cyl. diesels; 2 CP props; 10,560 bhp—bow-thruster
Electric: 2,570 kVA tot.
Crew: as training ship: 43 officers, 40 cadets, 92 enlisted + accomm. for 46 instructors, 136 cadets

Remarks: Ordered 25-11-77. The name spelling was changed to honor the current Swedish king. Intended to act as a mine countermeasures ship support tender and submarine torpedo hard target in peacetime, when not conducting the annual cadet training cruise. If used as a minelayer, the ship would carry 118 personnel total.
Hull systems: Reinforced below the waterline to permit exercise torpedo hits. There are 14 watertight compartments. Has Roll-Nix rudder roll control, providing a 40% reduction in roll.
Combat systems: Has extensive navigational systems. A helicopter deck is raised above the fantail. There are two lead-computing optical directors to control the 40-mm AA, and two radar/optronic 9LV 200 Mk 2 directors for the 57-mm guns. The Simrad SQ3-D/SF hull-mounted sonar has been removed. A large radome was added abaft the after gun director for the ship's 2000 cruise; it contains the antenna for a SATCOM system.

♦ 1 Älvsborg-class minelayer Bldr: Karlskronavarvet, Karlskrona

	Symbol	Laid down	L	In serv.
M 03 Visborg	Vbg	16-10-73	22-1-75	6-2-76

D: 2,450 tons (fl) **S:** 16 kts **Dim:** 92.4 (83.3 pp) × 14.7 × 4.0
A: 3 single 40-mm 70-cal. Bofors SAK 40/48 AA; up to 300 mines
Electronics:
Radar: 1 Terma Scanter 009 nav.; 1 Raytheon . . . nav.; 1 Ericsson Sea Giraffe 50HC surf./air search; 1 Saab 9LV 200 f.c.
EW: ArgoSystems AR-700 intercept; 2 36-round Saab Philax decoy RL
M: 2 Nohab-Polar 112VS, 12-cyl. diesels; 1 CP prop; 4,200 bhp—350-shp bow-thruster
Electric: 1,200 kw tot. **Crew:** 20 officers, 70 enlisted + 158 flag staff accomm.

Visborg (M 03) Jaroslaw Cislak, 6-99

Remarks: Equipped as flagship of the Coastal Fleet. Has a helicopter deck. Two triple 103-mm flare rocket launchers are installed. Sister *Älvsborg,* laid up at the end of 1993, was sold to Chile in 10-96.

♦ 1 Kbv 171–class mine countermeasures support ship [MCS]
Bldr: Karlskronavarvet, Karlskrona

	L	In serv.
A 262 Skredsvik (ex-M 70, ex-Kbv 172)	13-9-80	10-81

Skredsvik (A 262) H&L Van Ginderen, 12-94

D: 335 tons (375 fl) **S:** 20 kts **Dim:** 49.90 (46.00 pp) × 8.52 × 2.40
A: none
Electronics:
Radar: 1 Decca . . . nav.
Sonar: Simrad Subsea hull-mounted HF searchlight-type
M: 2 Hedemora V16A/15 diesels; 2 KaMeWa CP props; 4,480 bhp—bow-thruster
Electric: 340 kVA **Range:** 500/20; 3,000/12 **Crew:** 14 tot.

Remarks: Former Swedish Coast Guard class "A" cutter, laid up in 1990 and leased to the navy in 1991. Refitted from 12-92 to 2-93 to act as a mine clearance divers' support ship and command vessel for mine countermeasures operations. Sister Kbv 171 was sold to Belgium in 1998.
Hull systems: GRP sandwich hull construction, originally developed for the unbuilt M 70–class naval minesweeper. The former helicopter platform is now used to stow rigid inflatable divers' workboats. Has the Roll-Nix rudder roll-control system. A fire-fighting water monitor is located on the 01 level, forward of bridge.

♦ 1 mine-countermeasures support ship [MCS]
Bldr: Drypool Group, Cochrane SY, Selby, Scotland (In serv. 1973)

A 261 Utö (ex-*Smit Manila,* ex-*Seaford,* ex-*Seaford Challenger*)

Utö (A 261) Curt Borgenstam, Jr., 5-99

D: 1,800 tons (fl) **S:** 14 kts **Dim:** 55.91 (49.00 pp) × 12.27 (11.80 wl) × 4.57
A: 2 single 20-mm 70-cal. Oerlikon AA
Electronics: Radar: 1 Terma Scanter 009 nav.
M: 2 Mirrlees Blackstone EZ SL 16M diesels; 2 CP props; 5,000 bhp
Electric: 600 kw (3 × 200-kw diesel sets)
Crew: 35 officers, 30 enlisted (incl. mine warfare staff of 33)

Remarks: Former 791-grt/1,040-dwt oilfield support tug/salvage and diving tender, converted as a mine-countermeasures craft tender and command ship for mine countermeasures operations by Pan-United Shipyard, Singapore. Commissioned in 4-89.

MINE WARFARE SHIPS *(continued)*

♦ 7 Landsort (M 80)-class coastal minesweeper/hunters [MHC]
Bldr: Karlskronavarvet, Karlskrona

	Symbol	Laid down	L	In serv.
M 71 Landsort	Ldo	5-10-81	22-11-82	19-3-84
M 72 Arholma	Arh	13-2-82	10-10-84	23-11-84
M 73 Koster	Ksr	1-9-84	16-1-86	30-5-86
M 74 Kullen	Kln	1-1-85	15-8-86	3-7-87
M 75 Vinga	Vin	27-4-86	14-8-87	22-11-87
M 76 Ven	Ven	15-5-87	18-8-88	12-12-88
M 77 Ulvön	Uln	2-1-88	10-89	9-10-92

Ven (M 76) Curt Borgenstam, Jr., 5-97

Arholma (M 72) Curt Borgenstam, Jr., 4-95

D: 310 tons (360 fl) **S:** 15 kts **Dim:** 47.50 (45.00 pp) × 9.60 × 2.30
A: 1 40-mm 70-cal. Bofors SAK 40/48 AA; . . . RBS-70 shoulder-launched SAMs; 2 single 7.62-mm mg; 4 9-round Saab ASW 600 ASW RL; . . . mines (portable rails)
Electronics:
Radar: 1 Terma Scanter 009 nav.
Sonar: Thales TSM 2022 variable-depth minehunting (250–525 kHz)
EW: . . . Matilde intercept; 2 36-round Saab Philax decoy RL
M: 4 Saab-Scania DSI-14 diesels; 2 Voith-Schneider vertical cycloidal props; 1,456 bhp
Electric: 468 kw tot. (2 × 180-kw, 1 × 108-kw alternators)
Range: 2,000/12 **Crew:** 12 officers, 14 enlisted

Remarks: First pair ordered 25-2-81, next four on 31-1-84, and one more in 10-88; plans to order an eighth were canceled. Four sisters were built for Singapore.
Hull systems: GRP construction, using the same mold as the Swedish Coast Guard's patrol cutter Kbv 171. The diesel generator sets are all mounted on the upper deck to reduce the noise signature.
Combat systems: Have the 9MJ 400 computerized integrated navigational/mine system and a Saab 9LV 100 gun control system with TVT-100 optronic director for the 40-mm gun. Carry two Sutec Sea Owl remote-controlled mine-disposal vehicles, as well as controlling up to three GRP, self-propelled, magnetic/acoustic catamaran SAM minesweeping devices. The EW intercept gear is a Swedish-built variant of the Thorn-EMI Matilda. Have a Y-shaped portable mine rail arrangement, with a single laying point.
M 77 was used in 9-95 to demonstrate the Bofors-Sutec Ibis VII Propelled Variable-Depth Sonar system, which uses a Sutec Double Eagle remotely operated vehicle and a Thales TSM 2022 Mk 3 sonar. One unit has been equipped for trials with the Finnish Elesco Family of Integrated Minesweeping Systems (FIMS) sweep array with MRK-960 three-electrode magnetic sweep and MKR-400 pipe-type noncontrollable noisemaker; the data processing system is Elesco's SSCP, with differential GPS.

♦ 4 (+ 4 + 4) Styrsö-class inshore minesweeper/minehunters [MHI]
Bldr: Karlskronavarvet, Karlskrona

	L	In serv.		L	In serv.
M 11 Styrsö	8-3-96	20-9-96	M 13 Skaftö	20-1-97	13-6-97
M 12 Spårö	30-8-96	21-2-97	M 14 Sturkö	27-6-97	19-12-97

Sturkö (M 14) Curt Borgenstam, Jr., 5-01

Skaftö (M 13) Curt Borgenstam, Jr., 8-97

D: 175 tons (200 fl) **S:** 13 kts
Dim: 36.00 (33.00 wl; 32.00 pp) × 7.90 × 2.20 (2.00 hull)
A: 2 12.7-mm mg—mines
Electronics:
Radar: Decca BridgeMaster ARPA nav./surf. search
Sonar: Terma RESON hull-mounted mine-avoidance; EG&G DF-1000 towed side-looking; Tritech SE 500 (in ROV)
M: 2 Saab-Scania DSI-14 diesels; 2 fixed-pitch props; 728 bhp—bow-thruster
Electric: 818 kw tot. (2 × 414-kw diesel sets)
Range: 1,500/12 **Fuel:** 20 m^3 **Endurance:** 7 days
Crew: 7 officers, 8 enlisted + 2 spare berths

Remarks: YSB = *Ystridfartyg Bevakning* (Surface Combat Vessel). Can also be employed as coastal patrol craft. First four were ordered 11-2-94, with work on first actually begun during 7-93. Are capable of minesweeping as well as minehunting. The first of two planned additional batches of four was to be equipped for minehunting and would have carried mine disposal divers; a third batch of four was planned to replace the existing mine disposal diver support ships. No further contracts have been placed, however.
Hull systems: Employ GRP construction and "stealth" signature-reduction features tested in the trials ship *Smyge,* but with conventional monohulls. Have full NBC protection system, including sprinkler systems and a filtered citadel.
Combat systems: The Erisoft ERIMIS (Erisoft Maritime Information System) mine countermeasure command system employs six multifunction command modules, with inputs from the sonar suite, radar, GPS receiver, laser rangefinder, gyro, and log. The mine countermeasures suite includes two Bofors Sea Eagle remotely operated submersibles equipped with a television camera and the Tritech SE 500 high-definition sonar. Much of the sweep gear comes from discarded units of the *Arkö* class; included is AK-90 acoustic sweep and EL-90 magnetic sweep gear. A 40-mm gun can be retrofitted, and RBS-70 SAMs may later be carried. The ships are able to control SAM-series mine countermeasures drones.

♦ 1 Viksten-class inshore minesweeper [MSI]

	Symbol	Bldr	L	In serv.
M 33 Viksten	Vsn	Karlskronavarvet, Karlskrona	18-4-74	1-7-74

D: 115 tons (130 fl) **S:** 11 kts **Dim:** 25.3 × 6.6 × 2.5
A: 1 20-mm 70-cal. Oerlikon AA
Electronics: Radar: 1 Terma Scanter 009 nav.
M: 1 diesel; 1 prop; 460 bhp **Crew:** 9 tot.

Remarks: Hull is made of glass-reinforced plastic. Was intended to serve as the prototype for a new class of 300-ton, 43-m coastal minesweepers that were not built.

Disposal note: *Gillöga*-class inshore minesweepers [MSI] *Gillöga* (M 47) and *Svartlöga* (M 49) were stricken during 1997 and sister *Rödlöga* (M 48) during 1998. *Gåssten*-class inshore minesweeper [MSI] *Gåssten* (M 31) was stricken during 2000 and sister *Norsten* (M 32) was sold in 1998–99 for use as a fishing boat.

MINE WARFARE SHIPS *(continued)*

Viksten (M 33) H&L Van Ginderen, 8-93

♦ 1 Danish MRD-STOR-class drone minesweeper [MSD]
Bldr: Danyard, Aalborg (In serv.12-01)

. . .

D: 102 tons (125 fl) **S:** 12 kts (11 sust.)
Dim: 26.50 (24.15 wl; 23.90 pp) × 7.00 × 2.20
Electronics: Radar: 1 . . . nav.—Sonar: Thales STS 2054 towed side-scan HF
M: 2 Saab Scania DSI 14.74.M diesels; 2 Schottel SPJ.82T azimuthal waterjets; 960 bhp—bow-thruster
Range: 420/10 **Crew:** 3–4 tot. (for transits; accomm. for 11 tot.)

Remarks: Ordered in 2-01 for comparative trials with the canceled Swedish SAM-II class. GRP construction. Can be operated by crews as inshore minehunter/minesweepers or by remote control. The Danish Navy operates four configured as minehunting drones and plans to acquire more equipped as patrol craft.
Combat systems: Employs the IN-SNEC sonar and television datalink and INFOCOM low-rate craft command datalink. Uses containerized mine countermeasures equipment. Can be used to deploy Sutec Double Eagle mine location and disposal ROVs or to stream sweep gear. Has a 7-kN bollard pull at 8.5 kts.

Note: In development by Karlskrona is a follow-on catamaran minehunting drone, NYSAM ("New SAM") of some 50 tons displacement and with a 15-kt transit speed and 11-kt sweeping/hunting speed. Much of the same equipment would be used as with the SAM-II air-cushion vehicle concept.

♦ 5 SAM 01–class radio-controlled mine countermeasures craft [MSD]
Bldr: Karlskronavarvet, Karlskrona

SAM 01 (In serv. 29-3-83)
SAM 02 (In serv. 29-3-83)
SAM 03 Sammy (In serv. 1992)
SAM 04 Paddington (In serv. 26-5-83)
SAM 05 Samanta (In serv. 1992)

Paddington (SAM 04) Curt Borgenstam, Jr., 8-93

D: 15 tons (20 fl) **S:** 8 kts **Dim:** 18.0 × 6.10 × 0.70 (1.60 prop)
M: 1 Volvo-Penta TAMD 70D diesel; 1 Schottel shrouded prop; 210 bhp
Range: 330/7

Remarks: Have catamaran hulls. Can also automatically lay eight swept-channel danbuoy markers. An eventual total of 20 was planned at one time. Two sisters—the original SAM 03 and SAM 05—were sold to the U.S. Navy for use in the Persian Gulf in 3-91; replacements *Sammy* and *Samanta* were completed in 1992. Six others were delivered to Japan during 1998–99.

♦ 1 mine warfare diver support tender [MSS]
Bldr: Båtservice, Mandal, Norway (In serv. 1984)

A 212 Ägir (ex-*Bloom Surveyor*)

D: 240 tons (fl) **S:** 11 kts **Dim:** 24.35 (21.50 pp) × 7.60 × 1.28
A: none **Electronics:** Radar: 1 Terma Scanter 009 nav.; 1 . . . nav.
M: 2 G.M. Detroit Diesel diesels; 2 props; 1,540 bhp

Remarks: 117 grt. Acquired in 1989 from a Norwegian oilfield company. Has a portable decompression chamber, a stern diver-support gallows crane, extensive communications gear, and a bow-thruster. Reclassified from diving tender to mine warfare tender at the end of 1996.

Disposal note: *Hisingen*-class mine countermeasures diver support craft [MSS] *Hisingen* (M 43), *Blackan* (M 44), *Dämmen* (M 45), and *Galten* (M 46) were stricken during 2000.

Ägir (A 212) Curt Borgenstam, Jr., 8-94

♦ 5 M 15–class mine countermeasures diver support craft [MSS]
Bldr: . . . (L: 1941)

M 20 (ex-*Skuld,* A 242) M 21 M 22 M 24 M 25

M 22 H&L Van Ginderen, 10-96

D: 70 tons (93 fl) **S:** 12–13 kts **Dim:** 27.7 × 5.05 × 1.4 (2.0 props)
A: fitted for 1 20-mm 70-cal. Oerlikon AA **Electronics:** Radar: none
M: 2 diesels; 2 props; 320–430 hp **Crew:** 10 tot.

Remarks: Wooden hulls. M 21, 22, and 25 are used as tenders for mine clearance divers. All were to be replaced by the *Styrsö* class, but they remain in service. The gun is not normally mounted. M 20 was returned to the mine countermeasures category in 1993 after having served as a trials tender; the craft retains an additional deckhouse abaft the pilothouse.
Disposals: M 15, M 16, *Lommen* (A 231, ex-M 17), and *Spoven* (A 232, ex-M 18) were stricken during 1984; M 23 and M 26 were stricken during 1989.

AMPHIBIOUS WARFARE CRAFT

Note: Swedish surface amphibious warfare craft are subordinated to the Coastal Artillery Service (q.v.).

♦ 1 Mala-class swimmer delivery vehicle [LSDV]
Bldr: Brodosplit, Split, Yugoslavia (In serv. 1-85)

R 2 Stor Klas

D: 1.4 tons **S:** 4.4 kts sub. **Dim:** 4.90 × 1.22 × 1.32 (high; 1.70 over fins)
A: 2 50-kg limpet mines **M:** 1 electric motor; 1 prop; 6 shp
Range: 18/4.4; 23/1.7 **Crew:** 2 tot.

Remarks: Aluminum and Plexiglas free-flooding hull. Diving depth: 60 m max. Also purchased was a two-man chariot, *Lill Klas* (R 1), with a range of 8 n.m. at 2.5 kts; the device is 3.7 m long and weighs 145 kg without riders. Both craft are intended to assist in the search for submarine intruders and to act as training targets.

AUXILIARIES

Note: In addition to the naval-subordinated units listed in this section, the Swedish Navy also crews and operates icebreakers, hydrographic survey ships, and navigational aid tenders for other Swedish government agencies; those units are listed in the appropriate sections.

♦ 1 intelligence collection ship [AGI]
Bldr: Karlskronavarvet, Karlskrona

	Symbol	Laid down	L	In serv.
A 201 Orion	Ori	23-4-82	30-11-83	7-6-84

D: 1,400 tons (fl) **S:** 15 kts **Dim:** 61.3 × 11.0 × 4.2 **A:** none
Electronics: Radar: 1 Terma Scanter 009 nav.; 1 Raytheon . . . nav.—EW: . . .
M: 2 Hedemora V8A/135 diesels; 1 CP prop; 1,840 bhp **Crew:** 35 tot.

AUXILIARIES *(continued)*

Orion (A 201) Curt Borgenstam, Jr., 7-01

Orion (A 201) Flottenkommando, 8-99

Remarks: Ordered 25-6-81. Expected to last 30 years. Has signals collection antennas beneath a large GRP radome atop the full length of the superstructure. Has a commercial SATCOM antenna atop after lattice mast and a helicopter platform at the stern.

♦ **1 ex-Russian Modified Akademik Shuleykin–class patrol boat tender [AGP]** Bldr: Laivateollisuus, Turku, Finland

	L
A 264 Trossö (ex-*Livonia,* ex-*Ar'nold Veymer*)	14-2-88

Trossö (A 264) Findler & Winter, 6-01

D: 2,554 tons (fl) **S:** 14 kts **Dim:** 74.50 (64.3 pp) × 14.70 × 4.50
Electronics: Radar: 1 Okean-M4 nav.; 1 Okean-B nav.
M: 2 SEMT-Pielstick 6 PC2.5 L400 diesels; 2 CP props; 3,500 bhp—200-shp bow-thruster
Electric: 600 kVA tot.
Range: 14,000/12 **Endurance:** 50 days **Crew:** 64 tot.

Remarks: 1,650 grt/600 dwt. Purchased around 9-96 from the Estonian Marine Institute. Originally configured for general oceanography, the ship was subordinated to the Estonian S.S.R. Academy of Sciences. The ship was transferred to Estonia in 1991 under the name *Livonia* and was adapted as a pollution patrol and cleanup vessel and for use in fisheries protection duties before being assigned to the Estonian Marine Institute. Was converted in Sweden during 1997 to serve as a depot and headquarters ship for the surface attack flotilla based at Karlskrona. A second ship was to be acquired during 2000 as tender to the surface attack flotilla at Berga Naval Base, but no announcement has yet been made.
Hull systems: Has Decca Arkas autopilot, Rumb MFD/F loop, NEL-M2B echo sounder, ELAC ENIF deep echo sounder, ELAC bottom profiler, Furuno doppler log, EL-2 electromagnetic log, and Furuno FSN-200 NAVSAT receiver, and can be fitted with Intelsat SATCOM. The radars may have been replaced during the 1997 refit.

♦ **1 patrol craft tender [AGP]**
Bldr: Sterkoder M/V, Kristiansund, Norway

A 263 Gålö (ex-*Herjolfur*)

Gålö (A 263) Curt Borgenstam, Jr., 5-01

D: approx. 1,600 tons (fl) **S:** 14 kts **Dim:** 60.36 (53.01 pp) × 12.01 × 4.55
A: none **Electronics:** Radar: 1 . . . nav.
M: 1 Wichmann 9AXA diesel; 1 CP prop: 2,400 bhp—bow- and stern-thrusters
Range: . . ./. . . **Crew:** . . . tot.

Remarks: 1,037 grt/200 dwt. Former Ro/Ro vehicle cargo and passenger ferry, purchased in 1993 from Herjolfur H/f, Vestmannæyjar, Iceland, for conversion as a patrol boat tender. Has one 5-ton crane. As a ferry, had 17 cabins with 34 total berths.

♦ **1 general-purpose cargo transport [AK]**
Bldr: Mjellem & Karlsen, Bergen, Norway (In serv. 1980)

A 343 Sleipner (ex-*Ardal*)

Sleipner (A 343) Curt Borgenstam, Jr., 8-00

D: 1,049 tons (fl) **S:** 12 kts **Dim:** 49.66 (45.12 pp) × 11.03 × 3.55
A: provision for 2 single 20-mm 70-cal. Oerlikon AA
Electronics: Radar: 2 . . . nav.
M: 1 Bergens Normo LDM-8 diesel; 1 prop; 1,300 bhp—bow-thruster
Electric: 236 kw tot. (2 × 118-kw diesel sets)
Range: . . ./. . . **Crew:** 12 tot.

Remarks: 448 grt/825 dwt. Former Ro/Ro vehicle cargo and container carrier, purchased in 1992 from Fylkesbåtane i Sogn og Fjordane, Florø, Norway, for use as a general-purpose supply ship. Has an ice-strengthened hull, 45 m of vehicle cargo lane (8.0 m wide and 2.3 m high), 1 cargo hold (with a 6.4 × 2.9–m hatch), one 10-ton electrohydraulic crane, and one 20-ton derrick. There is a stern ramp for vehicle loading, plus one side door. Cargo capacity: 1,130 m^3 bale.

♦ **1 submarine rescue and salvage ship [ASR]**
Bldr: Scheepswerf de Hoop, Lobith, the Netherlands (In serv. 1985)

A 214 Belos (ex-*Energy Supporter*) (Bel)

D: approx. 5,600 tons (fl) **S:** 13.26 kt **Dim:** 104.91 (85.91 pp) × 18.45 × 5.10
A: fitted for 2 single 20-mm 70-cal. Oerlikon AA
Electronics:
Radar: . . .
Sonar: . . . hull-mounted HF; . . . towed side-scan
M: electric drive: 5 Brons-M.A.N. 9LV 25.30 diesels (2,250 bhp each), 5 generators, 2 motors; 2 Azimuth props; 5,110 shp—3 CP bow-thrusters
Electric: main generators + 1 × 304-kw emergency diesel set
Range: . . ./. . . **Fuel:** . . . tons
Crew: 25 ship's company + up to 40 salvage party, including divers

AUXILIARIES *(continued)*

Belos (A 214)—note helicopter platform at the bow Curt Borgenstam, Jr, 4-00

Belos (A 214)—with rescue submersible *URF* on deck Curt Borgenstam, Jr., 4-00

Remarks: 5,069 grt. Former oilfield-supply, firefighting, and diver maintenance support vessel purchased 2-4-92 from Italian company S.A.N.A. and refitted at Rio de Janeiro before proceeding to Sweden and commissioning 15-10-92. Has medical and berthing facilities for 35 rescued submariners.
Hull systems: A dynamic positioning system is fitted. Has a 22-m helicopter deck raised above the forecastle. Hull has two moonpool calm-water diving accesses through the hull bottom. A Mantis one-man tethered submersible, handled by an A-frame crane to starboard, is used to reconnoiter bottomed submarines and has a 760-m max. depth; the Mantis can also be used as a remotely operated vehicle. The ship also carries a three-man diving bell capable of operating in depths up to 1,500 m, a divers' "wet bell" usable to 60-m depths, and Sea Owl remotely operated submersibles. There are a six-man and an eight-man decompression chamber for divers and a 35-man hyperbaric chamber for rescued submariners.

SERVICE CRAFT

♦ 4 Ejdern-class sonobuoy monitoring boats [YAG]
Bldr: Djupviks, Tjörn

B 01 Ejdern (In serv. 23-4-91) B 03 Svärtan (In serv. 1991)
B 02 Krickan (In serv. 1991) B 04 Viggen (In serv. 1992)

Ejdern (B 01) Curt Borgenstam, Jr., 5-97

D: 34 tons (36 fl) **S:** 15 kts **Dim:** 19.00 (17.40 pp) × 4.98 × 1.00
A: provision for 1 20-mm 70-cal. Oerlikon AA
Electronics: Radar: 1 . . . nav.
M: 2 Volvo Penta TAMD-122A diesels; 2 props; 800 bhp
Crew: 3 officers, 7 enlisted

Remarks: Aluminum construction. Equipped to deploy six recoverable hydrophones for use in detecting intruders in Swedish waters. Have G.E.C. AQS-928 sonobuoy acoustic data processors. The gun is not normally mounted.

♦ 2 Hanö-class service craft [YAG]
Bldr: Karlskronavarvet, Karlskrona (In serv. 1953)

V 53 Tjurkö V 54 Sturkö

Sturkö (V 54) H&L Van Ginderen, 4-92

D: 280 tons **S:** 13 kts **Dim:** 42.0 × 7.0 × 3.0
A: none **Electronics:** Radar: 1 . . . nav.
M: 2 Nohab diesels; 2 props; 910 bhp **Crew:** 25 tot.

Remarks: Built as minesweepers. Had been redesignated as patrol boats in 1979 and deactivated in the late 1980s. Were reactivated early in 1993 for use as utility tenders.

♦ 1 trials craft [YAGE] (L: 1929; in serv. 1970)

A 241 Urd (ex-*Capella*)

D: 63 tons (90 fl) **S:** 8 kts **Dim:** 27.0 × 5.6 × 2.8
M: 1 diesel; 1 prop; 200 bhp

Remarks: Former fishing boat.

♦ 1 diving tender [YDT] Bldr: . . ., Sweden (L: 1983)

A 213 Nordanö (ex-*Sjöjungfrun*)

D: approx. 240 tons (fl) **S:** 10 kts **Dim:** 24.4 × 7.6 × 2.7
A: none **Electronics:** Radar: none
M: 2 Volvo Penta TAMD diesels; 2 props; 767 bhp **Crew:** . . . tot.

Remarks: 148 grt. Acquired in 1992.

♦ 3 diving tenders [YDT] Bldr: Storebro Bruks, Storebro (In serv. 1980)

D: 7 tons (fl) **S:** 24 kts **Dim:** 10.35 × 3.30 × 1.0
Electronics: Radar: 1 Decca 091 nav.
M: 2 Volvo Penta TAMD 60C diesels; 2 props; 370 bhp

Remarks: Have a fold-down door at the stern. Useful load: 1.7 tons.

♦ 1 Loke-class ferry [YFB] Bldr: Oskarshamms (In serv. 1994)

A 344 Loke

Loke (A 344) H&L Van Ginderen, 10-96

D: 455 tons (fl) **S:** 12.5 kts **Dim:** 35.90 × 9.00 × 2.68
A: none **Electronics:** Radar: 1 Terma Scanter 009 nav.
M: 2 Saab-Scania . . . diesels; 2 props; . . . bhp **Crew:** 8 tot.

Remarks: Was to have been the first of a new class of coastal transports for the Coastal Artillery Service, but no additional units were ordered. Is equipped with a bow ramp for vehicle cargo and an electrohydraulic crane amidships for cargo pallets. Can carry 50 personnel for short voyages or 200 persons in local harbor service. Cargo capacity is 50 tons on deck. Not equipped for minelaying.

SERVICE CRAFT *(continued)*

♦ **1 Stridsbåt 90H–class senior officer's launch [YFL]**
Bldr: Dockstavarvet, Docksta (In serv. 1999)

BLÅTUNGA

Blåtunga Curt Borgenstam, Jr., 6-00

D: 18 tons light (fl) **S:** 40 kts **Dim:** 15.90 (13.00 wl) × 3.80 × 0.80
Electronics: Radar: 1 Decca RD 360 nav.
M: 2 Saab-Scania 8V DSI-14 diesels; 2 FF Jet 450 waterjets; 1,256 bhp
Range: 160/40; 240/20 **Fuel:** 1.5 tons **Crew:** 4 tot. + 21 troops

Remarks: Has flag officer and staff accommodations in the space occupied by the troop compartment in the boats of this class built for the Coastal Artillery Service. Aluminum construction.

♦ **1 personnel ferry [YFL]** Bldr: . . ., Gryt (In serv. 1984)

RÖDNÄBBA (ex-*Långvik*)

Remarks: Former coastal passenger vessel, acquired in 1990 for use in local transportation of naval personnel.

♦ **2 range safety boats [YFL]**
Bldr: Storebro Bruks, Storebro (In serv. 1980)

D: 5.5 tons (7 fl) **S:** 24 kts **Dim:** 10.35 × 3.30 × 1.0
Electronics: Radar: 1 Decca 091 nav.
M: 2 Volvo Penta TAMD 60C diesels; 2 props; 370 bhp

Remarks: Have a fold-down door at the stern. Useful load: 1.7 tons.

♦ **3 personnel launches [YFL]**
Bldr: Storebro Bruks, Storebro (In serv. 1980)

1298 1300 1310

Personnel launch 1298 Gilbert Gyssels, 8-90

D: 5.5 tons (7 fl) **S:** 24 kts **Dim:** 9.30 × 3.30 × 1.0
Electronics: Radar: 1 Decca 091 nav.
M: 2 Volvo Penta TAMD 60C diesels; 2 props; 370 bhp

Remarks: Builder's Type 31 design. GRP construction. Can carry 25 personnel or six stretchers. Can reach 27 kts in light condition.

♦ **7 603-class utility craft [YFU]**
Bldrs: Djupviks, Tjörn; Oskarhamms; Marinvarvet, Fårösund (In serv. 1986–87)

652 ALMÖ	654 . . .	656 . . .	658 . . .
653 DONSÖ	655 . . .	657 BOLLÖ	

D: 20 tons (53 fl) **S:** 8–10 kts **Dim:** 21.0 (20.0 pp) × 7.2 × 0.7
A: none **Electronics:** Radar: 1 Decca RM 914C nav.
M: 2 Saab-Scania DSI-11/40-M20 diesels; 2 Schottel props; 340 bhp
Cargo: 25 tons deck cargo or 30 tons liquid **Crew:** . . .

Remarks: Classified as *Trossbåt* (Support Boat). The prototype (since discarded) was delivered in 1978. The Coastal Artillery Service operates sisters 603 through 612 as landing craft. Have a stores-handling crane and bow ramp and can be beached.

Disposal note: Harbor fuel lighter *Eldaren* (A 229, ex-*Brotank*) was stricken during 2000.

Almö (652) Curt Borgenstam, Jr., 8-94

♦ **1 torpedo- and missile-recovery craft [YPT]**
Bldr: Lunde Varv & Verkstads, Kramfors

	Symbol	L	In serv.
A 248 PINGVINEN	PIN	26-9-73	3-75

Pingvinen (A 248) Werner Schiefer, 10-96

D: 191 tons (fl) **S:** 13 kts **Dim:** 33.0 × 6.1 × 1.8
Electronics: Radar: 1 Terma Scanter 009 nav.
M: 2 MTU 12V493 diesels; 2 props; 1,040 bhp **Crew:** 14 tot.

♦ **1 torpedo- and missile-recovery craft [YPT]**
Bldr: Djupviks, Rönnäng (L: 9-63)

A 247 PELIKANEN (PEL)

Pelikanen (A 247) Jaroslaw Cislak, 9-98

D: 130 tons **S:** 15 kts **Dim:** 33.0 × 5.8 × 1.8
Electronics: Radar: 1 Terma Scanter 009 nav.
M: 2 MTU 12V493 diesels; 2 props; 1,040 bhp **Crew:** 14 tot.

♦ **1 salvage and rescue submersible [YSS]**
Bldr: Kockums, Malmö (L: 17-4-78)

URF

D: 52 tons surf. **S:** 3 kts **Dim:** 13.9 × 43.2 × 2.9 **Crew:** 3 tot.

Remarks: URF is an acronym for *Ubåts Räddnings Farkost* (Submarine Rescue Craft). Two projected sisters were not built. Sweden and Norway signed an agreement in early 1995 for the *URF* to provide rescue services for Norwegian submarines. Based at the Naval Diving Center, Berga. The submarine rescue ship *Belos* (A 214) acts as tender and transport. *URF* can mate while submerged with the British submarine rescue craft LR5.
Hull systems: Can be towed at up to 10 kts to the scene of an accident. Has a depth capability of 460 m and lockout capability to support two divers to 300 m. Can accommodate up to 25 persons rescued from a bottomed submarine. Pressure hull of HY-130 steel; collapse depth is 900 m.

SERVICE CRAFT *(continued)*

URF—suspended from the dynamic-positioning stern crane of the *Belos* (A 214) Jaroslaw Cislak, 9-98

Note: Kockums in 5-01 announced development of a second-generation *URF* capable of rescuing up to 35 persons from a submarine bottomed at a depth of 700 m and listing as much as 45°. There is no immediate customer for the craft.

♦ **1 Achilles-class icebreaking tug [YTB]**
Bldr: Åsiverken, Åmål (L: 1962)

A 251 Achilles

Ajax (A 252)—since stricken; *Achilles* (A 251) is identical Royal Swedish Navy, 1992

D: 450 tons **S:** 12 kts **Dim:** 35.5 (33.15 pp) × 9.5 × 3.9
Electronics: Radar: 1 or 2 Decca 1226C nav.
M: 1 diesel; 1 prop; 1,650 bhp **Crew:** 12 tot.

Remarks: Capable of light icebreaking. Sister *Ajax* (A 252) was stricken in 1994.

♦ **2 Herkules-class icebreaking tugs [YTM]**
Bldr: Åsiverken, Åmål

A 323 Herkules (L: 1969) A 324 Hera (L: 1971)

D: 127 tons **S:** 11.5 kts **Dim:** 21.4 × 6.9 × 3.7 **M:** diesels; 615 bhp

Hera (A 324) Gilbert Gyssels, 8-90

♦ **2 Hermes-class icebreaking tugs [YTM]** (L: 1953–57)

A 253 Hermes (Hem) A 322 Heros (Her)

Hermes (A 253) Curt Borgenstam, Jr., 6-94

D: 185 tons **S:** 11 kts **Dim:** 24.5 (23.0 pp) × 6.8 × 3.6 **M:** diesel; 600 bhp

Remarks: Sister *Hector* (A 321) was stricken during 1991.

♦ **6 small harbor tugs/tenders [YTL]**
Bldr: Lunde Varv & Verkstads, Kramfors (In serv. 1978–79)

A 751	A 753 Ran	A 755 . . . . .
A 752 Willy	A 754 Björkö	A 756 . . . . .

Willy (A 752) Curt Borgenstam, Jr., 8-97

D: 42 tons (fl) **S:** 9.5 kts **Dim:** 15.5 × 5.0 × 2.7 **M:** 1 diesel

Remarks: Can break thin ice. Carry 40 passengers. Sisters 701–705 are used by the Coastal Artillery Service.

♦ **2 sail-training schooners [YTS]**
Bldr: Naval Dockyard, Stockholm (L: 1947–48)

S 01 Gladan (Gad) S 02 Falken (Fak)

D: 220 tons **S:** 6 kts **Dim:** 42.5 (34.4 hull; 28.3 pp) × 7.27 × 4.2
M: 1 diesel auxiliary; 1 prop; 220 bhp—max. sail area: 711 m^2
Crew: 8 officers, 8 enlisted + 28 cadets

SERVICE CRAFT *(continued)*

Gladan (S 01) Jaroslaw Cislak, 8-95

♦ **1 Arkö-class training craft [YXT]**
Bldr: Karlskronavarvet, Karlskrona (In serv. 1964)

M 67 Nämndö

D: 285 tons (300 fl) **S:** 14.5 kts **Dim:** 44.4 × 7.5 × 2.5 (3.0 props)
A: none **Electronics:** Radar: 1 . . . nav.
M: 2 MTU 12V 493 diesels; 2 props; 1,000 bhp **Crew:** . . . tot.

Remarks: Former minesweeper, converted during the early 1990s for use as a navigational training tender. Stack was raised to keep exhaust from the open bridge area. Wooden construction.

COASTAL ARTILLERY SERVICE

The Coastal Artillery Service *(Kustartilleriet)* has 3,900 active personnel (2,800 conscripts) and 3,000 reservists. In addition to the craft described below, it operates 120-mm Bofors Karin mobile artillery and RBS-15 and RBS-17 antiship missiles. Organized into five regiments and subordinated to the Swedish Navy, the coastal artillery also has a 265-man ranger battalion. A major expansion and reorganization into six amphibious coastal defense squadrons, each with 800 personnel, was canceled in 2-91 but has been reinstated. Each squadron is to operate 2 CB-90L command boats, 33 Stridsbåt 90H fast personnel landing craft, 13 SRC 90E personnel landing craft, 4 vehicle landing craft, 26 G-boat assault boats, 13 smaller assault boats, and 19 canoes.

PATROL BOATS [PB]

♦ **12 Tapper class (Bevakningsbåt 2000 or Type 80)**
Bldr: Djupviks, Tjörn

	In serv.		In serv.		In serv.
81 Tapper	4-2-93	85 Trygg	1995	89 Stolt	6-97
82 Djärv	1993	86 Modig	1995	90 Ärlig	12-97
83 Dristig	1994	87 Hurtig	12-95	91 Munter	1998
84 Händig	1994	88 Rapp	12-96	92 Orädd	5-99

Munter (91) *Ships of the World,* 1999

D: 54 tons (60 fl) **S:** 28 kts (25 sust.) **Dim:** 21.85 (19.73 pp) × 5.40 × 1.05
A: 2 single 12.7-mm mg; 4 9-round Saab ASW 600 ASW RL; 8 d.c. in individual racks; 1 mine rail
Electronics:
Radar: 2 Decca . . . nav.
Sonar: Simrad . . . HF hull-mounted searchlight
M: 2 MWM TBD 234 V16 diesels; 2 waterjets; 2,440 bhp (2,090 sust.)—bow-thruster
Electric: 40 kVA tot. **Crew:** 8 tot

Remarks: The first seven were ordered in 1991 to begin replacement of the Type 72 class; five more were ordered in 1994. Design is based on the same builder's Kbv 290 for the Swedish Coast Guard. Aluminum alloy construction. Have a GPS navigational system. Normally carry a Phantom HD-2 remotely operated submersible equipped with a Tritech ST 525 HF imaging sonar for sea-bottom surveillance.

♦ **7 Type 72 class**

63 Ekeskär	70 Hojskär	76 Hamnskär
65 Gråskär	73 Häradsskär	
68 Altarskär	74 Bredskär	

Ekeskär (63) H&L Van Ginderen, 9-90

D: 28 tons (30 fl) **S:** 18 or 22 kts **Dim:** 21.1 × 4.6 × 1.3
A: 1 20-mm 70-cal. Oerlikon AA; 8 d.c.; mines
Electronics: Radar: 1 Decca RM 914C nav.
M: 3 diesels; 3 props; . . . bhp

Remarks: Built in two series, 61 through 70 in 1959–61 and 71 through 77 in 1966–68; the second group could achieve 22 kts on their more-powerful engines. All survivors except 68 have been modernized with a new pilothouse, taller tripod mast, and radar antenna relocated to a short mast atop the pilothouse; they also carry sonars to permit them to act as inshore antisubmarine units. 76 was given a new, larger pilothouse.
Disposals: Stricken by 1995 had been *Torskär* (61), *Väderskär* (62), *Örskär* (66), *Sprängskär* (75), and *Huvudskär* (77), 75 having been one of the modernized units. *Häradsskär* (73) was also stricken, but was restored to service in 1997 after a modernization refit. *Äggskär* (69) and *Flaggskär* (72) were stricken in 1997. *Getorskär* (71) was sold to a youth organization for a token sum in 1998. *Skifteskär* (64) was sold in 1999–2000 for private use, and *Vitaskär* (67) was discarded during 2000.

MINE WARFARE SHIPS

♦ **1 MUL 20–class minelayer [MM]** Bldr: Åsiverken, Åmål

	Symbol	L	In serv.
MUL 20 Furusund	Fur	16-12-82	10-10-83

Furusund (MUL 20) Royal Swedish Navy, 1984

D: 225 tons (245 fl) **S:** 11 kts **Dim:** 32.4 (30.0 pp) × 8.4 × 1.8
A: 1 20-mm 70-cal. Oerlikon AA; 2 7.62-mm mg; . . . mines
Electronics: Radar: 1 Decca RM 1226C nav.
M: 2 Saab-Scania GASI-14 diesels (335 bhp each), ASEA 300-kVA electric drive; 2 props; 420 shp—1 125-hp maneuvering prop
Electric: 73 kw tot. **Crew:** 24 tot. (10 in peacetime)

Remarks: Ordered 23-6-81. Nine more were planned, but the builder went bankrupt after only one was completed and no more were ordered. Can carry up to 24 tons of mines on two deck rails.

COASTAL ARTILLERY SERVICE MINE WARFARE SHIPS
(continued)

♦ 6 MUL 12–class mine planters [MM] (In serv. 1952–56)

MUL 12 Arkösund (Ark)
MUL 13 Kalmarsund (Ksd)
MUL 15 Grundsund (Gru)
MUL 17 Skramsösund (Smd)
MUL 18 Fårösund (ex-*Öresund*)
MUL 19 Bårösund (Bår)

Kalmarsund (MUL 13) Curt Borgenstam, Jr., 8-94

D: 200 tons (245 fl) **S:** 10.5 kts **Dim:** 31.18 (29.0 pp) × 7.62 × 3.1
A: 2 single 12.7-mm mg; . . . mines
Electronics: Radar: 1 Decca RM 1226C nav.
M: 2 Nohab or Saab-Scania diesels; 2 props; 460 bhp **Crew:** 24 tot.

Remarks: These craft are used for placing and maintaining controlled minefields. They were given names in 1985–86. Sister *Fårösund* (MUL 16) was sold to a commercial operator in the U.S.A. in spring 1995 but has since been laid up in the U.K. *Alnösund* (MUL 14) was stricken during 1996. MUL 17 is now considered to be an auxiliary and no longer has a primary minelaying role. Can carry up to 26 tons of mines on two deck rails.

♦ 1 coastal mine planter [MM] (L: 1946)

MUL 11 Kalvsund (Kvd)

Kalvsund (MUL 11) H&L Van Ginderen, 4-93

D: 200 tons (fl) **S:** 10 kts **Dim:** 30.1 (27.0 pp) × 7.21 × 3.65
A: 2 single 12.7-mm mg; . . . mines
Electronics: Radar: 1 Terma Scanter 009 nav.
M: 2 Atlas diesels; 1 prop; 300 bhp **Crew:** 9 tot.

Remarks: Reclassified as an auxiliary in 1993, but the original hull number was retained. Can carry up to 21 tons of mines on two deck rails.

♦ 6 small minelaying launches [MM] Bldr: Marinvarvet, Fårösund

1879, 1880, 1881 (In serv. 4-7-83)
1882, 1883, 1884 (In serv. 23-1-84)

Remarks: Displace 2.5 tons. Waterjet powered for 20 kts. Ordered 27-11-82.

Disposal note: Of the 42 M 501–class minelaying launches listed in the last edition, corrected information indicates that only 16 ever existed (M 501 through M 516) and that, as of 2000, only one was known to be in use. Two were sold to Malta in 2000 and the others were sold for commercial employment.

Note: Most of the larger amphibious warfare craft can also be employed to lay mines.

AMPHIBIOUS WARFARE CRAFT

♦ 3 Grim-class utility landing craft [LCU]
Bldr: Åsiverken, Åmål

Bore Grim Heimdal

Grim—with typical vehicle ferry bow Curt Borgenstam, Jr., 8-97

Bore—with helmet-type bow door Curt Borgenstam, Jr., 6-01

D: 340 tons (fl) **S:** 12 kts **Dim:** 36.0 × 8.5 × 2.6
A: provision for 2 single 20-mm 70-cal. Oerlikon AA
Electronics: Radar: 1 . . . nav.
M: 2 diesels; 2 props; 800 bhp **Crew:** . . . tot. + 325 troops

Remarks: *Grim* was launched in 1962, *Bore* and *Heimdal* in 1967. Of car-ferry design: the bow hinges upward on *Bore* and *Heimdal* to permit extending ramp. Drive-through superstructure. Can be adapted to lay mines. One 20-mm AA can be installed atop the pilothouse and another abaft the stacks.

♦ 1 (+ 3) M-10X-class air-cushion landing craft [LCMA]
Bldrs: Karlskronavarvet, Karlskrona, and ABS Hovercraft, U.K.
(In serv.: one 26-6-98, others in 2000)

M-10X prototype Curt Borgenstam, Jr., 6-98

D: 26 tons (fl) **S:** 50 kts (light; 35 loaded) **Dim:** 20.6 × 8.80 × 0.35 (at rest)
A: 1 12.7-mm mg **Electronics:** Radar: 1 . . . nav.
M: 2 Deutz BF12L513C diesels, 2 lift fans; 2 airscrew props; 1,050 bhp
Range: 600/30 **Fuel:** 4,600 liters **Crew:** 1 officer, 2 enlisted

Remarks: Designed by ABS Hovercraft, which also provided the machinery and skirts. Three more were ordered during 11-01, but cannot yet be started, as the yard lacks the necessary resources.
Hull systems: Capable of carrying one tracked vehicle, 50 seated troops, one 20-ft. cargo container, or 20 stretcher cases. The hull is constructed of GRP carbon fiber and vinyl laminate, with a GRP/foam sandwich deck and Kevlar-reinforced superstructure. Can clear 1-m obstacles and operate in 2.5-m seas.

♦ 26 Trossbåt-class vehicle/personnel landing craft [LCM]
Bldrs: First two: Homsvarvet (In serv. 1-91 and late 1993); others: Djupviks, Tjörn (In serv. 1996 to 19-3-97, . . . to . . .)

661 through 686

COASTAL ARTILLERY SERVICE AMPHIBIOUS WARFARE CRAFT *(continued)*

Trossbåt 673—at speed — Eivind Rodlie, 2001

Trossbåt 662—the bow swings upward to permit the vehicle ramp to be extended — Curt Borgenstam, Jr., 9-00

D: 30 tons (45 fl) **S:** 30 kts (23 loaded) **Dim:** 24.00 × 5.40 × 1.20
A: 1 12.7-mm mg; mines (on portable rails)
Electronics: Radar: 1 Terma Scanter 009 nav.
M: 3 Saab-Scania 8V DSI-14 diesels; 3 Alumina FF450 waterjets; 1,380 bhp
Range: 150/15 (loaded) **Fuel:** 15,000 liters **Crew:** 4 tot. + 17 troops

Remarks: *Trossbåt* means "Support Boat." Aluminum construction. Cargo: 15 tons on the 14.0 × 4.5–m deck area, or 2 m^3 of water and 9 tons of cargo, or 8 m^3 of diesel fuel or 7 m^3 of water and no deck cargo. Have a folding bow ramp and small crane. Considered to be capable of operating in light ice. A dozen sisters were ordered 22-1-01 for the United Arab Emirates Navy.

♦ 10 603-class vehicle landing craft [LCM]

Bldrs: Djupviks, Tjörn; Oskarhamms; Marinvarvet, Fårösund (In serv. 1984–87)

603 through 612

603-class landing craft 610 — Curt Borgenstam, Jr., 7-94

D: 20 tons (53 fl) **S:** 8–10 kts **Dim:** 21.0 (20.0 pp) × 7.2 × 0.7
A: none **Electronics:** Radar: 1 Decca RM 914C nav.
M: 2 Saab-Scania DSI-11/40-M20 diesels; 2 Schottel props; 340 bhp
Cargo: 25 tons deck cargo or 30 tons liquid **Crew:** . . .

Remarks: The prototype (since discarded) was delivered in 1978. Classified as *Trossbåt* ("Support Boat"). 603 was delivered 2-4-84 by Marinvarvet; 604 and 605 by Djupviks on 1-10-84. 607 was in service 1-9-86, 608 on 22-9-86, 609 on 12-3-87, and 610 on 27-4-86. 612 was delivered in 1987. The navy proper operates seven sisters as service craft.

♦ 2 (+ 12) Transportbåt 2000–class personnel landing craft [LCP]

Bldr: Djupviks, Tjörn (In serv. 11-98 to 1-99)

451 452

Transportbåt 2000–class 452 — Eivind Rodlie, 2001

D: 43 tons (fl) **S:** 25 kts (loaded) **Dim:** 23.5 × 5.1 × 1.0
A: 2 single 12.7-mm mg; 2 mine rails
Electronics: Radar: 1 Terma . . . nav.
M: 451: 3 Saab-Scania DSI 14 diesels; 3 FF Jet 450 waterjets; 1,194 bhp—452: 2 Volvo Penta 163 diesels; 3 KaMeWa K40 waterjets; . . . bhp
Range: . . ./. . . **Crew:** 3 tot.

Remarks: Two aluminum-hulled prototypes were ordered in 9-97 to evaluate a proposed program for about 12 additional craft to deliver 2003–10, but no further orders have been announced. One is configured to carry 45 fully equipped troops or 10 tons of stores and the other as a mobile brigade headquarters. The production version may be built of GRP and have a different propulsion system. The first unit was to complete in 11-98, the second in 1-99. The machineguns are carried on training rings above the bridge and on the stern.

♦ 145 (+ 27) Stridsbåt 90H–class fast personnel landing craft [LCP]

Bldrs: Dockstavarvet, Docksta; Gotlands Varvet (In serv. 10-12-92 to 1-03)

801 through 945

Stridsbåt 90H–class 854 — Jürg Kürsener, 3-01

Stridsbåt 90H–class 909—with 18 sisters, at Vaxholm — Jürg Kürsener, 3-01

D: 13.2 tons light (18 fl) **S:** 40 kts **Dim:** 15.90 (13.00 wl) × 3.80 × 0.80
A: 2 fixed and 1 flexible 12.7-mm mg—provision for: RBS-17 Hellfire SSM; 1 81-mm mortar; 4 mines (2.8 tons); or 6 d.c.
Electronics:
Radar: 1 Decca RD 360 (final 27: Decca BridgeMaster-E ARPA) nav.
M: 2 Saab-Scania 8V DSI-14 diesels; 2 FF Jet 450 waterjets; 1,256 bhp
Range: 160/40; 240/20 **Fuel:** 1.5 tons **Crew:** 4 tot. + 21 troops

Remarks: The first batch of 12 was begun during 9-90 by Dockstavarvet; the Batch II order, placed 23-1-92, was shared by the two yards above (Gotlands Varvet is a subsidiary of Djupviks), with the final 27 being delivered 2001–03. The basic design has also been an export success, with 22 sold to Norway, 17 to Malaysia, and 40 to Mexico. A near-sister operates as the VIP launch *Blåtunga* for the Swedish Navy.
Hull systems: Aluminum construction. 801's hull has a 20° deadrise to vee-bottom; the others have a 26° deadrise. There is a 14-m^3 troop compartment (with a disembarkation ramp over bow). 801 has a lower-power propulsion plant (1,080 bhp) and can achieve only 35 kts.

COASTAL ARTILLERY SERVICE AMPHIBIOUS WARFARE CRAFT *(continued)*

Combat systems: The 30-mm fixed cannon of prototypes 801 and 802 was replaced by a pair of 12.7-mm machineguns; the single 12.7-mm mg (which can be replaced by a 40-mm grenade launcher) is mounted on a ring atop the troop compartment. Two units completed in 1993 and four more of the batch converted in 1995–96 are designated CB-90L and are configured as Battalion Command Centers; they have two 7.5-kVA generator sets and 220/380-V, 48-Hz electrical installations to support nine workstations and a unit commander in the reconfigured troop compartment; 10 additional radio antennas are fitted. 801 was fitted with a Patria Vammas–Hägglunds AMOS (Advanced Mortar System) twin 120-mm mortar in an armored turret mounted abaft the pilothouse late in 1999 for trials; additional units may be similarly converted. The final 27 have Transas Scandinavia Navsystem 3000 automated navigations systems and Decca BridgeMaster-E radars.

♦ **52 (+ 20) SRC 90E–class ambulance craft [LCP]**
Bldr: Storebro Bruks, Storebro (In serv. 15-8-95 to end-1998)

103 through 154

SRC 90E–class 103 Storebro, 1995

D: 6.5 tons light (9.5 fl) **S:** 40 kts (37 loaded)
Dim: 11.88 (10.88 hull) × 2.90 × 0.70
M: 2 Saab-Scania DSI-14 V-8 diesels; 1 KaMeWa FF-410 waterjet; 560 bhp (at 3,800 rpm; 340 sust.)
Range: 215/40 **Fuel:** 650 liters **Crew:** 2 tot.

Remarks: Capable of carrying 1 ton of cargo in addition to 10 troops or seated casualties or 4–5 stretcher cases. Prototypes 101 and 102 were delivered in 1994. The first series order for 39 came in 11-94; 13 more were ordered early in 1997, and eventual force level of 72 was at one time planned. At least one (Kbv 414) was also procured for the coast guard. A further prototype for an improved version capable of 50 kts was launched 28-10-98.
Hull systems: Hulls are constructed of carbon-fiber-reinforced vinyl ester sandwich with a foam core. Cabin and piloting station are vibration-isolated from the rest of the hull. The bow folds down to become a step.

♦ **70 200-class large personnel landing craft [LCP]**
Bldrs: Lunde Varv & Verkstads, Kramfors; Marinteknik, Öregrund (In serv. 1957–77)

207, 208, 211–217, 219–226, 228, 230–239, 241–277, 280–284

200-class 258 H&L Van Ginderen, 1-98

200-class 99—reason for out-of-sequence pennant not known Jürg Kürsener, 3-01

D: 31 tons (fl) **S:** 17 kts **Dim:** 21.4 × 4.2 × 1.3
A: 2 or 3 6.5-mm mg; mines
Electronics: Radar: 1 Decca RM 914C nav.
M: 3 Saab-Scania 6 DS-11 diesels; 3 props; 705 bhp
Crew: 5 tot. + 40 troops

Remarks: Have a patrol boat–like bow that opens to permit extension of a ramp from the troop compartment below decks. There is a twin machinegun to port, plus a single mount aft in some. Mine rails can be laid from the pilothouse over the stern. 266–269 have Volvo Penta diesels. 210 was re-engined in 1984 by Djupviks in a pilot program for a class-wide rehabilitation, receiving two Saab-Scania DSI-14 diesels and two steerable hydraulic drives (950 hp); 35 were refitted during 1990–93 and another 17 during 1997–98. Numbers missing in the 200–284 sequence have been stricken.

♦ **100 G-båt raiding launches [LCP]**
Bldr: Marine Alutech Oy, Teijo, Finland (In serv. 1993–99)

G-båt raiding launch Stefan Marx, 1998

D: 1.75 tons (3 fl) **S:** 30 kts **Dim:** 8.10 (6.50 pp) × 2.10 × 0.50
M: 1 Volvo TAMD 42WJ diesel; 1 FF Jet waterjet; 230 bhp (at 3,800 rpm; 170 sust.)
Fuel: 250 liters **Crew:** 1 + 8 troops

Remarks: Designed by FMV. Aluminum construction. Typed *Gruppbåt.* The 53rd unit was completed in 6-94 and the 100th during 1999. Cargo capacity: 1 ton.

♦ **56 outboard-powered canoes [LCP]**

Remarks: Intended for the amphibious battalion *(Amfibiebatalion).* Are actually more of a kayak design than canoe.

Two-man raiding canoe Royal Swedish Navy

SERVICE CRAFT

♦ **1 501-class launch [YFL]** (L: 1969–71)

509

D: 15 tons (fl) **S:** 14 kts **Dim:** 14.6 × 4.2 × 0.9
Electronics: Radar: 1 Decca RM 914C nav.
M: 2 diesels; 2 props; . . . bhp **Crew:** 3 tot.

Remarks: One of 12 (not 42 as previously listed) former minelaying launches. Now used as a tender at Karlskrona Naval Base. The other 11 have been sold for commercial use or discarded.

♦ **5 support tugs [YTL]** Bldr: Djupviks, Tjörn (In serv. 1982–85)

701 702 703 704 705

D: 42 tons **S:** 9.5 kts **Dim:** 15.5 × 5.0 × 2.7
M: 1 diesel; 1 prop; . . . bhp

Remarks: Can be used to transport cargo or personnel, to plant mines, or as tugs. Bulwarks at the bow open to permit debarking personnel over a beach. Several sisters serve the Swedish Navy proper.

COASTAL ARTILLERY SERVICE SERVICE CRAFT *(continued)*

Support tug 702 Curt Borgenstam, Jr., 6-94

NATIONAL SWEDISH ADMINISTRATION OF SHIPPING AND NAVIGATION

(Svenska Staten Sjöfartsverk)

AUXILIARIES

Note: All Swedish icebreakers are owned by the National Swedish Administration of Shipping and Navigation but are manned and administered by the Swedish Navy, which also crews the other units listed in this section. In 1984, it was decided to arm seagoing icebreakers permanently. Svenska Staten Sjöfartsverk ships and craft have black hulls and buff-colored superstructures; the stacks are white and bear the organization's seal.

♦ 1 Oden-class icebreaker [WAGB] Bldr: Götaverken, Arendal

	Laid down	L	In serv.
Oden	19-10-87	5-8-88	29-1-89

Oden—with the three armed *Urho*-class icebreakers in the background H&L Van Ginderen, 8-98

D: 10,300 tons (12,900 fl) **S:** 17 kts (free; 3 through 1.8-m ice)
Dim: 107.80 (93.20 pp) × 31.00 (max.; 29.40 over reamers; 25.00 wl) × 7.00 (8.50 max.)
A: provision for: 4 single 40-mm 70-cal. Bofors L70 AA; . . . mines
Electronics: Radar: 2 . . . nav.
M: 4 Cegielski-Sulzer 8ZAL-40S diesels, geared drive; 2 shrouded CP props; 24,480 bhp—bow- and stern-thrusters
Electric: 4,800 kw (4 NEBB 1,200-kw alternators; Sulzer AT-25H diesels, 1,750 bhp each, driving)
Range: 30,000/13 **Fuel:** 2,917 tons heavy oil; 854 tons diesel
Crew: 32 tot. + 17 spare berths

Remarks: 9,436 grt/4,906 dwt. Ordered in 1-87. Is available for Arctic-service commercial charter in summer and was commercially crewed for a North Pole expedition in 1996. A second unit, to be named *Thule,* is planned but has not yet been funded.
Hull systems: The unique hullform, designed by Canadian Marine Drilling Co., is nearly rectangular in planform and has a barge-like bow with beam-wise extensions. Has a 150-ton towing winch, 10-ton crane, and 390-m^2 helicopter deck aft. Carries up to 3,650 m^3 of ballast water and has a heeling pump system, hull wash, and jet-mister to assist in ice conditions.
Combat systems: The 40-mm guns can be mounted at the corners of the superstructure. Can be equipped as a minelayer.

♦ 3 Finnish Urho-class icebreakers [WAGB]
Bldr: Wärtsilä, Helsinki

	Laid down	L	In serv.
Atle	10-5-73	27-11-73	21-10-74
Frej	. . .	3-6-74	30-9-75
Ymer	12-2-76	3-9-76	26-10-77

D: 7,900 tons (9,500 fl) **S:** 18.5 kts
Dim: 104.70 (96.02 pp) × 23.86 (22.5 wl) × 8.40
A: 4 single 40-mm 70-cal. Bofors L70 AA; 3 mine rails

Atle—with guns aboard H&L Van Ginderen, 5-95

M: 5 Wärtsilä-Pielstick 12 PC2.5 V400 diesels (4,650 bhp each), 5 generators, 4 Strömberg electric motors; 2 fixed-pitch props fwd, 2 CP props aft; 22,000 shp
Crew: 16 officers, 38 enlisted

Remarks: 6,844 grt. Has a helicopter platform. All personnel live and normally work above the main deck. *Frej* was given permanent gun armament, mine rails, and fuel facilities for two helicopters in 10-83 and the others in 1984. The guns are mounted atop the hangar and forward of the pilothouse.

♦ 1 Ale-class lake icebreaker [WAGB]
Bldr: Wärtsilä, Helsinki, Finland

	L	In serv.
Ale	1-6-73	12-12-73

Ale H&L Van Ginderen, 9-98

D: 1,550 tons (fl) **S:** 14 kts **Dim:** 46.0 × 13.0 × 5.0
A: provision for 1 40-mm 70-cal. Bofors L70 AA (not normally aboard)
M: 2 diesels, electric drive; 2 props; 4,750 shp **Crew:** 8 officers, 24 enlisted

Remarks: Built for service on Lake Vänern in central Sweden. Also used for hydrographic surveys in summer.

Note: In addition to the above, three 3,000-dwt commercial combination icebreaker/oilfield anchor-handling tugs ordered in 7-98 for delivery in 2000–01 will be employed from January to March for 15 years by the Board of Navigation as icebreakers in Swedish waters. Ordered by Bylock & Nordsjofrakt, Sweden, and Viking Supply Ships, Norway, under the consortium name B&N Viking Icebreaking & Offshore AS, the ships are being built by Kvaerner Kleven Leirvik, Norway. The ships will have a bollard pull of 200 tons on 18,500 bhp and will be able to break 1-m ice at 3 kts continuous.

Disposal note: Modified *Tor*-class icebreaker *Njord* and *Tor*-class icebreaker *Tor* were retired in 1998–99 and were converted in Quebec during 2000–01 for commercial use as Arctic cruise liners, the former renamed *Polar Star.*

♦ 2 Baltica-class harbor icebreaker/navigational tenders [WAGL]
Bldr: Åsiverken, Åmål

Baltica (In serv. 26-2-82) Scandica (In serv. 27-1-83)

D: 1,238 tons (fl) **S:** 15 kts **Dim:** 54.92 (50.12 pp) × 12.04 × 2.70
Electronics: Radar: 1 Decca ARPA; 1 Decca Clearscan nav.
M: 2 Hedemora V16A/10 diesels; 1 CP prop; 3,520 bhp—300-shp bow and stern tunnel-thrusters
Electric: 1,100 kw tot. (5 × 220-kw diesel sets) **Fuel:** 140 tons **Crew:** 12 tot.

Remarks: 856 grt/350 dwt. Have a 12-ton electrohydraulic crane serving a combination buoy hold/workshop. Can tow at 50-ton bollard pull. Capable of operating in light ice conditions. Civilian manned.

SHIPPING AND NAVIGATION ADMINISTRATION AUXILIARIES
(continued)

Scandica—black hull, cream upperworks Curt Borgenstam, Jr., 6-00

♦ **1 lighthouse supply ship [WAGL]**
Bldr: Åsiverken, Åmål (In serv. 22-1-81)

Fyrbjörn

D: . . . tons **S:** 12.5 kts **Dim:** 40.05 (39.50 pp) × 10.50 × 3.30
M: 1 Hedemora V12A/13.5 diesel; 1 prop; 1,360 bhp

Remarks: 430 grt. Molded depth of hull: 4.9 m.

♦ **1 lighthouse supply ship [WAGL]**
Bldr: Sigbjörn Iversens Mek. Verkstads, Flekkefjord, Norway (In serv. 14-12-76)

Fyrbyggaren

Fyrbyggaren Curt Borgenstam, Jr., 5-99

D: . . . tons **S:** . . . kts **Dim:** 41.8 × 10.0 × . . .
M: 1 Wichmann 5AX diesel; 1 prop; 1,500 bhp **Crew:** 8 tot.

Remarks: 499 grt. Molded depth of hull: 4.9 m.

SERVICE CRAFT

♦ **1 catamaran-hulled hydrographic survey craft [WYGS]**
Bldr: Oskarshamms Varv (In serv. 28-6-85)

Nils Strömkrona (Nsa)

D: 175 tons **S:** 12 kts **Dim:** 30.00 (27.61 pp) × 10.0 × 1.60
M: 4 Saab-Scania 8-cyl. diesels; 2 CP props; 1,729 bhp—bow- and stern-thrusters
Range: . . ./. . . **Fuel:** 17 tons **Crew:** 5 officers, 9 enlisted

Remarks: 311 grt. Built to replace an 1894-vintage unit with the same name. Each aluminum-construction hull has 3.9-m beam. Based at Norrköping.

Nils Strömkrona Curt Borgenstam, Jr., 8-93

♦ **1 coastal survey boat [WYGS]** Bldr: Djupviks, Rönnäng (In serv. 10-82)
Jacob Hägg (Jhä)

Jacob Hägg Jaroslaw Cislak, 5-98

D: 130 tons (fl) **S:** 16.5 kts **Dim:** 36.50 × 7.50 × 1.65
M: 4 Saab-Scania DSI-14 diesels; 2 props; 1,684 bhp (1,300 sust.)

Remarks: Aluminum construction. The same builder also delivered a 42-ton, 400-hp hydrographic survey launch in 1983.

Note: Also operated by the National Swedish Administration of Shipping and Navigation are the geological research ship *Altair* and the fisheries research ship *Argos.* The polar support ship *Stena Arctica* (ex-*Columbialand*) has on occasion been chartered for Arctic research. The 509-grt catamaran submersible support ship *Ocean Surveyor* is owned by the Swedish Geological Institute *(Sveriges Geologiska Institut Undersokning).*

COAST GUARD

The Swedish Coast Guard, organized in 1638, became independent from the Swedish Customs Service on 1-7-88. It now is responsible for fisheries regulation, customs patrol, pollution and dumping monitoring and cleanup and other environmental considerations, and merchant traffic regulation. All units now have dark blue-painted hulls with a yellow diagonal stripe and white superstructures. None are armed. All boat pennants were changed during 7-88 from a "Tv" (*Tullverket,* or Central Customs Office) prefix to "Kbv" (*Kustbevakning,* Coast Guard).

Personnel (2002): About 600 total

Organization: The coast guard fleet is organized into four regions, with a total of 15 districts; each district has two to four stations, with craft based at 30 locations.

Maritime Aviation: Four CASA C-212-200 Aviocar patrol aircraft with side-looking radar (SLAR), one Cessna 402C liaison aircraft, and four BO-105 helicopters

PATROL SHIPS [WPS]

♦ **1 modified Finnish Tursas class**
Bldr: Rauma Oy, Uusikaupunki, Finland

Kbv 181 Gotland (In serv. 30-11-90)

Gotland (Kbv 181) Hartmut Ehlers, 6-96

COAST GUARD PATROL SHIPS [WPS] *(continued)*

D: 800 tons (fl) **S:** 16 kts **Dim:** 56.00 (49.80 pp) × 10.20 × 4.00
Electronics:
Radar: 2 Decca . . . nav.
Sonar: Simrad Subsea hull-mounted HF searchlight-type
M: 2 Wärtsilä-Vasa 8R22 diesels; 2 props; 3,800 bhp—bow-thruster
Electric: 700 kw tot. **Range:** 2,800/15; 6,100/8 **Fuel:** 82 m^2 **Crew:** 11 tot.

Remarks: Ordered in 10-89 as flagship and command vessel for search-and-rescue and oil-spill cleanup operations. Lengthened over the Finnish prototype in order to accommodate a second hold to stow oil-spill cleanup gear. Can be armed with one 20-mm 70-cal. Oerlikon AA. Able to make 12 kts through 0.2-m ice. Equipped in 1994 with a Russian GLONASS navigational satellite receiver.

PATROL CRAFT [WPC]

♦ 1 (+ 2) Kbv 201 class Bldr: Kockums, Karlskrona

Kbv 201 (In serv. 10-01) Kbv 202 (In serv. 10-01) Kbv 203 (In serv. . . .)

Kbv 201—at builder's Curt Borgenstam, Jr., 9-01

D: 468 tons (fl) **S:** 22 kts (20 sust.) **Dim:** 52.0 (50.0 pp) × 8.6 × 2.3
Electronics: Radar: 1 . . . nav.; 1 . . . nav.
M: 2 MWM 620-series 16-cyl. diesels; 2 props, 2 CP props; 7,500 bhp—2 bow-thrusters
Range: 2,000/16 **Endurance:** 5 days **Crew:** 8 tot.

Remarks: Two were ordered in 9-98, with an option for two more taken up in 1999. Design was prepared by Marintek, Norway. Have a spilled-oil recovery system with two storage tanks totaling 100 tons capacity. A ramp is incorporated in the stern for a high-speed RIB. A towing winch is installed aft, and there is a firefighting monitor on the forecastle. There are two flapped rudders, and fin stabilizers are fitted. Cabins are provided for each crewmember. There are integrated bridge controls for maneuvering, navigation, and communications. Are capable of breaking 30-cm ice.

PATROL BOATS [WPB]

♦ 11 Kbv 301 class
Bldr: Karlskronavarvet, Karlskrona (Kbv 301: Djupviks, Tjörn/Rönnäng) (In serv. 1993–97)

Kbv 301 through Kbv 311

Kbv 301 H&L Van Ginderen, 2-95

D: 34 tons light (47 fl) **S:** 38 kts (34 sust.) **Dim:** 19.95 × 4.65 × 1.02
Electronics: Radar: 1 Furuno FR 7010 nav.; 1 Furuno 2011 surf. search
M: 2 MTU 12V183 TE92 diesels; 2 KaMeWa waterjets; 2,000 bhp
Range: 250/34; 500/. . . **Crew:** 3–4 tot.

Remarks: Design evolved from Kbv 290. Aluminum alloy construction. Prototype Kbv 301 was completed in 1993, with 10 more ordered in 12-93; Kbv 302 was completed 17-2-95 and Kbv 306 on 22-8-96, with later units completing during 1997. Navigational equipment includes a Furuno FCV 561 echo sounder, Robertson RGC50 gyro, GPS receiver, Decca Navigator radio navaid receiver, autopilot, and data-recording computer. An image-intensifier surveillance device is fitted.

♦ 1 Kbv 290 class Bldr: Djupviks, Tjörn/Rönnäng (In serv. 6-12-90)

Kbv 290

Kbv 290 H&L Van Ginderen, 12-97

D: 45 tons (51 fl) **S:** 28 kts **Dim:** 21.85 (19.73 pp) × 5.40 × 1.05
Electronics: Radar: 1 . . . nav.
M: 2 MWM TBD 234 V16 diesels; 2 props; 2,120 bhp
Range: 400/. . . **Fuel:** 5,000 liters **Crew:** 4 tot.

Remarks: Aluminum construction. Intended as the prototype for a new class to replace older patrol craft; the production version became the Kbv 301 class (q.v.).

♦ 2 Kbv 288 class Bldr: Djupviks, Tjörn/Rönnäng (In serv. ca. 1990)

Kbv 288 Kbv 289

Kbv 288 H&L Van Ginderen, 1-95

D: 53 tons (fl) **S:** 24 kts **Dim:** 21.85 × 5.40 × 1.80
Electronics: Radar: 1 Furuno FR2011 nav.; 1 Furuno FR7040R nav.
M: 2 Cummins KTA 38M diesels; 2 props; 2,080 bhp
Electric: 60 kVA tot. **Range:** 300/. . . **Crew:** 5 tot.

Remarks: An improved version of the Kbv 281 class with lower superstructure. Have a Plath gyrocompass and autopilot, Furuno FCV 665 and FUS 200 echo sounders, Decca Mk 53 radio navaid receiver, Furuno GP500 GPS receiver, Wesmar S5400 imaging sonar, and fax and television receivers in a navigational suite typical of those fitted in modern Swedish Coast Guard patrol boats.

♦ 7 Kbv 281 class Bldr: Djupviks, Tjörn/Rönnäng

	In serv.		In serv.		In serv.
Kbv 281	1979	Kbv 284	30-1-84	Kbv 287	12-2-87
Kbv 282	. . .	Kbv 285	2-5-84		
Kbv 283	1980	Kbv 286	21-8-86		

Kbv 285 Curt Borgenstam, Jr., 6-98

D: 37 tons (42 fl) **S:** 30+ kts **Dim:** 21.85 × 5.00 × 1.70
Electronics: Radar: 1 Furuno FR2011 nav.; 1 Furuno FR7040R nav.
M: 2 Cummins KTA 38M diesels; 2 props; 2,100 bhp **Crew:** 5 tot.

Remarks: Class B cutters. Aluminum construction. Kbv 286 and 287 were ordered 1-9-85. Kbv 286 was launched 14-6-86 and Kbv 287 on 25-1-87; they lack the flying bridge atop the pilothouse of the other five.

♦ 2 Kbv 102 class Bldr: Djupviks, Tjörn (In serv. 1972–73)

Kbv 104 Kbv 105

COAST GUARD PATROL BOATS [WPB] *(continued)*

Kbv 103—since stricken H&L Van Ginderen, 8-98

D: 53 tons (fl) **S:** 22 kts **Dim:** 26.72 × 5.23 × 1.13
M: Kbv 102, 104: 2 MTU 8V331 TC82 diesels; 2 props; 1,866 bhp
Electric: 60 kVA **Range:** 1,000/15 **Fuel:** 11 tons **Crew:** 6 tot.

Remarks: Class A cutters. Aluminum construction. Three sisters were built for the Liberian Coast Guard. Kbv 105 was re-engined in 1987 with two Cummins KTA 38M diesels. Sisters Kbv 102 and 103 had been retired by the end of 2001.

SERVICE CRAFT

♦ **1 Class A pollution-control depot ship [WYAG]**
Bldr: Lunde Varv & Verkstads, Ramvik (L: 24-3-85)

Kbv 006

D: 450 tons (fl) **S:** 15 kts **Dim:** 37.35 (33.70 pp) × 8.80 × . . .
M: 2 Cummins KTA-2300M diesels; 2 rudder props; 2,100 bhp
Fuel: 30.5 tons **Crew:** 6 tot.

Remarks: Similar to the Kbv 004 design. Ordered in 12-84.

♦ **1 Class A pollution-control depot ship [WYAG]**
Bldr: Lunde Varv & Verkstads, Ramvik (In serv. 1980)

Kbv 004

D: 450 tons (fl) **S:** 12 kts **Dim:** 35.5 × 8.0 × 3.0
M: 2 diesels; 2 props; 1,200 bhp **Electric:** 224 kVA **Crew:** 10 tot.

Remarks: Has a helipad on the fantail, a 200-hp bow-thruster, a 30-kt workboat, 80 m^3 of oil-containment tanks, 500 m^3 of containment boom stowage, oil-spill skimming equipment, firefighting gear, and salvage diver support capabilities.

♦ **1 Class A pollution-control depot ship [WYAG]**
Bldr: . . . . . . (In serv. 1960)

Kbv 003 Rivöfjord (ex-*Rangoon*)

Rivöfjord (Kbv 003) H&L Van Ginderen, 7-94

D: 477 tons (fl) **S:** 11 kts **Dim:** 40.0 × 6.46 × 3.52 **M:** . . .

Remarks: Bought in 1973 and rebuilt by Djupviks. Was lengthened 6.0 m and given a bow bulb in 1987 by Dockstavarvet, Docksta. Has salvage diver support capabilities.

♦ **2 Kbv 050–class Class B Sea Truck pollution-control craft [WYAG]** Bldr: Lunde Varv & Verkstads, Ramvik (In serv. 20-9-83 and 6-83)

Kbv 050 Kbv 051

D: 340 tons (fl) **S:** 9.5 kts **Dim:** 39.15 × 8.50 × 2.40
M: diesels **Range:** 2,000/9 **Crew:** . . .

Remarks: An enlarged version of the Kbv 045 class. Have bow ramps and can beach.

Kbv 051 H&L Van Ginderen, 5-00

♦ **5 Kbv 045–class Class B Sea Truck pollution-control craft [WYAG]** Bldr: Lunde Varv & Verkstads, Ramvik (In serv. 1980–83)

Kbv 045 Kbv 046 Kbv 047 Kbv 048 Kbv 049

Kbv 048 H&L Van Ginderen, 6-99

D: 133 tons (230 fl) **S:** 11 kts **Dim:** 28.9 (24.80 pp) × 6.5 × 1.9
M: 2 Saab-Scania DST-11 diesels; 2 props; 540 bhp
Electric: 300 kw **Fuel:** 18 tons **Crew:** 4 tot.

Remarks: Resemble landing craft, with bow ramp. Have an endless belt-type oil-recovery device, with 110 m^3 of total tankage for recovered oil and stowage for 800-m oil-spill containment booms. Have hydraulic thrusters fore and aft. Kbv 045 was lengthened to 36.4 m o.a. by Öregrund Marinteknik Verkstad during 1993 to increase the recovered waste capacity to 150 m^3; she now displaces 340 tons full load.

♦ **1 Class B Sea Truck–type oil-spill cleanup boat [WYAG]**
Bldr: Djupviks, Rönnäng (In serv. 1976)

Kbv 044

Kbv 044 H&L Van Ginderen, 5-96

D: 76 tons (100 fl) **S:** 12 kts **Dim:** 25.0 × 6.0 × 1.5
M: 2 Volvo Penta diesels; 2 props; 580 bhp

Disposal note: Oil-spill cleanup craft Kbv 059 and the Kbv 041–class cleanup craft Kbv 041 and Kbv 043 were out of service by 1999.

♦ **1 Kbv 010–class Class C oil-spill cleanup base craft [WYAG]**
Bldr: Lunde Varv & Verkstads, Ramvik (In serv. 1985)

Kbv 010

D: 400 tons (fl) **S:** 12 kts **Dim:** 46.10 × 8.60 × 3.50
M: 2 . . . diesels; 2 props; . . . bhp

COAST GUARD SERVICE CRAFT *(continued)*

Kbv 010 Curt Borgenstam, Jr., 6-00

♦ **1 Class D1 catamaran oil-spill cleanup craft [WYAG]**
Bldr: Djupviks, Tjörn (In serv. 8-6-82)

Kbv 020

D: 60 tons (fl) **S:** 27 kts **Dim:** 27.6 × 9.2 × 1.5
M: 2 MTU 12V396 TB82 diesels; 2 props; 2,600 bhp

Remarks: A drum-type skimmer mounted forward between the hulls can recover up to 40 tons/hr, or a belt-type cleaner can recover 10–20 tons/hr. The design is Westermoen of Norway's Type 88.

♦ **1 Kbv 015–class Class C oil-spill cleanup base craft [WYAG]**

Kbv 015 (In serv. 1971)

D: 140 tons (fl) **S:** . . . **Dim:** 23.0 × 5.5 × . . .

♦ **3 miscellaneous Class D2 catamaran oil-spill cleanup craft [WYAG]**

	In serv.	D	Dim
Kbv 021, 022	1973	30 tons (fl)	14.0 × 7.0
Kbv 023	1975	30 tons (fl)	16.5 × 7.5

♦ **6 Class E Skerry-boat shore-cleaning boats [WYAG]**
(In serv. 1979–82)

From among: Kbv 701 through Kbv 712

D: 9 tons **S:** . . . **Dim:** 9.0 × 3.1 × . . .

♦ **1 or more SRC 90E–class personnel launches [WYFL]**
Bldr: Storebro Bruks, Storebro (In serv. . . .)

Kbv 414

Kbv 414 Storebro

D: 6.5 tons light (9.5 fl) **S:** 40 kts (37 loaded)
Dim: 11.88 (10.88 hull) × 2.90 × 0.70
M: 2 Saab-Scania DSI-14 V-8 diesels; 1 KaMeWa FF-410 waterjet; 560 bhp (at 3,800 rpm; 340 sust.)
Range: 215/40 **Fuel:** 650 liters **Crew:** 2 tot. + 10 passengers

Remarks: Sister to a large group being procured for the Coastal Artillery Service, but is used by the coast guard for personnel transportation and SAR duties.
Hull systems: Hulls are constructed of carbon-fiber-reinforced vinyl ester sandwich with a foam core. The cabin and piloting station are vibration-isolated from the rest of the hull. Capable of carrying four stretchers and/or 10 seated casualties.

♦ **1 Kbv 416–class launch [WYFL]**
Bldr: Aluminumbåtar, Gryt (In serv. 1981)

Kbv 416

D: 6.8 tons (fl) **S:** 33 kts **Dim:** 10.20 × 3.15 × . . .
Electronics: Radar: 1 Anritsu . . . nav.
M: 2 Volvo Penta AQAD 41 diesel outdrives; 2 props; . . . bhp

Remarks: Is equipped with a Shipmate RS 5700 GPS receiver.

♦ **8 Kbv 401–class launches [WYFL]**

Kbv 401 through Kbv 408

♦ **22 miscellaneous speedboats [WYFL]** (In serv. 1962–92)

Kbv 314, 317, 318, 321, 341, 365, 366, 368, 369, 371–373, 381–385, 389, 391–394

♦ **1 Bussjö 650–class Class K workboat [WYFL]** (In serv. . . .)

Kbv 079

D: 1.7 tons (fl) **S:** 25 kts **Dim:** 6.56 × 2.53 × 0.46
M: 1 Volvo Penta AQAD 40 diesel outdrive; 130 bhp

♦ **3 2000 TDX–class air-cushion vehicles [WYFLA]**
Bldr: Griffon Hovercraft, Salisbury Green, Southampton, U.K.

Kbv 891 (In serv. 1992) Kbv 892 (In serv. 1992) Kbv 893 (In serv. 10-9-93)

D: 6.75 tons (fl) **S:** 35 kts **Dim:** 11.04 × 4.60 × 0.52
Electronics: Radar: 1 Furuno . . . nav.
M: 1 Deutz BF8L-513 diesel driving lift fan and 1 CP airscrew; 320 bhp
Fuel: 284 liters **Crew:** 3 tot.

♦ **8 miscellaneous Class G oil-spill storage lighters [WYON]**

	In serv.	D	Dim
Kbv 061	1974	300 tons (fl)	28.8 × 6.3 × . . .
Kbv 062	1975	140 tons (fl)	12.0 × 6.0 × . . .
Kbv 063	1974	250 tons (fl)	28.8 × 6.3 × . . .
Kbv 064	1981	. . .	. . .
Kbv 065	1983	450 dwt	33.0 × 10.0 × 2.15
Kbv 066	. . .	440 dwt	30.0 × 10.0 × 2.15
Kbv 068	1979	400 tons (fl)	30.6 × 6.8 × . . .
Kbv 069	1980	360 tons (fl)	30.6 × 6.7 × . . .

Remarks: Kbv 065 at Göteborg is a former tank barge, has 15 cargo tanks, and can carry vehicles on deck; she was built by Kalmar Fartygsreparationer, Kalmar.

SWITZERLAND

Swiss Confederation

SWISS ARMY

PATROL BOATS [WPB]

♦ **11 Patrouillenboat 80 class** Bldr: Müller AG, Spiez (In serv. 1978–84)

A 462001 Antares
A 462002 Aquarius
A 462003 Castor
A 462004 Mars
A 462005 Orion
A 462006 Perseus
A 462007 Pollux
A 462008 Saturn
A 462009 Sirius
A 462010 Uranus
A 462011 Venus

Perseus (A 462006) H&L Van Ginderen, 3-98

D: 5.2 tons (5.9 fl) **S:** 30 kts **Dim:** 10.7 × 3.3 × 0.9 (0.6 hull)
A: 2 single 12.7-mm mg **Electronics:** Radar: 1 JFS Electronic 364 nav.
M: 2 Volvo Penta KAD 42 diesels; 2 props; 460 shp **Crew:** 8 tot.

Remarks: GRP construction, with wooden superstructure. Replaced a group of wooden-hulled craft built in 1942. Employed on Lakes Constance, Geneva, and Maggiore. A 462002 was completed in 1978, A 462007 in 1984, and the rest in 1981. Are being modernized from 1998 on, receiving diesels in place of the original gasoline engines at the cost of about 5 kts maximum speed.

Note: Swiss police agencies operate six 10-m and one 12-m patrol launches. The Geneva Police operate launches GE 4001 and GE 4002, the latter named *Rudevent.*

SYRIA

Syrian Arab Republic

Personnel (2002): Approx. 3,200 total, plus 2,500 reserves

Bases: Principal base at Tartus, with minor facilities at Al Mina al Bayda, Baniyas, and Latakia

Naval Aviation: Two Kamov Ka-28PL Helix-A ASW and 12 Mi-14PL Haze-A ASW helicopters

Coastal Defense: Twelve batteries of SSC-1B Shaddock (possibly no longer operational) and SSC-3 Styx missiles were transferred from the former USSR; they are located in mobile batteries at Tartus, Baniyas, and Latakia. Coast defense artillery includes 36 130-mm and 12 100-mm guns, served by a network of radar surveillance and radar fire-control equipment.

CORVETTES [FFL]

♦ 2 ex-Soviet Petya-I class (Project 159E)
Bldr: Khabarovsk Zavod

	Laid down	L	In serv.
1/508 . . . . . . (ex-12, ex-SKR . . .)	. . .	. . .	. . .
2/508 Al Hirasa (ex-14, ex-SKR-95)	10-3-67	15-5-68	13-3-69

Al Hirasa (2/508) H&L Van Ginderen, 9-81

D: 938 tons (1,077 fl) **S:** 29 kts
Dim: 81.80 (78.00 pp) × 9.20 (8.90 wl) × 2.85 (hull)
A: 2 twin 76.2-mm 59-cal. AK-276 DP; 4 12-round RBU-2500 ASW RL; 1 triple 533-mm TT; 2 d.c. racks (6 d.c. each); 2 mine rails
Electronics:
Radar: 1 Don-2 nav.; 1 Fut-N (Slim Net) air/surf. search; 1 Fut-B (Hawk Screech) gun f.c.
Sonar: Titan hull-mounted MF; Vychegda HF searchlight attack
M: CODOG: 1 Type 61-D3 diesel (6,000 bhp), 2 M-2 gas turbines (15,000 shp each); 3 props (centerline CP)—2 75-kw auxiliary electric motors (3 kts)
Range: 450/29; 4,800/10 **Crew:** 8 officers, 84 enlisted

Remarks: Transferred in 7-75 and 3-75, respectively. Based at Tartus. Both were operational in 2001, although how much longer that can be maintained is questionable.

GUIDED-MISSILE PATROL CRAFT [PTG]

♦ 8 ex-Soviet Osa-II class (Project 205ME)

33 34 35 36 37 38 39 40

Syrian Osa-II French Navy, 1983

D: 184 tons (226 fl; 245 overload) **S:** 40 kts (35 sust.)
Dim: 38.6 (37.5 wl) × 7.6 (5.9 wl) × 2.01 (hull)
A: 4 P-15M Termit (SS-N-2C Styx) SSM; 2 twin 30-mm 65-cal. AK-230 AA; 1 4-round Fasta-M point-defense SAM syst.
Electronics:
Radar: 1 Rangout (Square Tie) surf. search/target detection; 1 MR-104 Rys' (Drum Tilt) gun f.c.
EW: 2 16-round PK-16 decoy RL

M: 3 M-504B diesels; 3 props; 15,000 bhp **Electric:** 400 kw tot.
Range: 500/34; 750/25 **Endurance:** 5 days **Crew:** 4 officers, 24 enlisted

Remarks: Two transferred in 1978, four in 1979, two in 1982, two in 5-84, and two in 1985; four had been stricken by 1987. The pair delivered in 1984 were each equipped with two 16-tube PK-16 decoy rocket launchers and a Grail point-defense SAM launcher; the others have presumably been backfitted. All are based at Latakia.

PATROL BOATS [PB]

♦ 5 ex-Polish Szkwal-class (Project S-3) harbor patrol launches
Bldr: Stocznia Wisla, Gdansk (In serv. 1990)

. . . (ex-SG-111 through SG-115, ex-K-111 through K-115)

D: 21 tons (fl) **S:** 37 kts **Dim:** 11.67 (10.50 pp) × 4.56 × 0.88
A: 2 single 7.62-mm mg **Electronics:** Radar: 1 Koden MD 3400 nav.
M: 2 . . . diesels; 2 props; 2,000 bhp **Crew:** 4 tot.

Remarks: Harbor patrol craft with GRP hulls. An unsuccessful design. All five had previously served in the Polish Coast Guard and, before that, the Polish Navy. Transferred in 4-95.

♦ 8 Soviet Zhuk (Gryf) class (Project 1400M)

1/8 2/8 3/8 4/8 5/8 6/8 7/8 8/8

D: 35.9 tons (39.7 fl) **S:** 30 kts
Dim: 23.80 (21.70 wl) × 5.00 (3.80 wl) × 1.00 (hull; 1.90 max.)
A: 2 twin 12.7-mm 60-cal. Utës-M mg **Electronics:** Radar: 1 Lotsiya nav.
M: 2 M-401 diesels; 2 props; 2,200 bhp
Electric: 48 kw total (2 × 21-kw, 1 × 6-kw diesel sets)
Range: 500/13.5 **Endurance:** 5 days **Crew:** 1 officer, 9 enlisted

Remarks: Three delivered new in 12-83, three in 12-84, and three in 1-85; one has been stricken. Based at Tartus.
Hull systems: Aluminum alloy hull. Capable of operating in up to Sea State 4 or 5. Range is also reported as 700 n.m. at 28 kts and 1,100 n.m. at 15 kts.

MINE WARFARE SHIPS AND CRAFT

Disposal note: T-43-class fleet minesweeper *Hittin* (504) remains afloat at Latakia as an accommodations hulk and base ship but is no longer operational. Vanya-class (Project 257DME) coastal minesweepers *Kadisia* (775) and *Yarmouk* (776) had been stricken by 1997.

♦ 1 Soviet Sonya-class (Project 1265E) coastal minesweeper [MSC]
Bldr: Avangard Zavod, Petrozavodsk

532

D: 401 tons (430 fl) **S:** 14 kts
Dim: 48.80 (46.00 wl) × 10.20 (9.20 wl) × 2.40–2.50 (mean hull; 2.75–2.85 max.)
A: 1 twin 30-mm 65-cal. AK-230 AA; 1 twin 25-mm 80-cal. 2M-3M AA; 1 4-round Fasta-M point-defense SAM syst.; up to 5 mines
Electronics:
Radar: 1 Mius (Spin Trough) nav.
Sonar: MG-89 Serna HF hull-mounted; MG-35 underwater telephone; NEL-MZB echo sounder (see remarks)
M: 2 DRA-210-A or -B diesels; 2 3-bladed CP props; 2,200 or 2,000 bhp—2 low-speed thrusters
Electric: 350 kw tot. (3 × 100-kw, 1 × 50-kw diesel sets; 380 V, 50 Hz a.c.)
Range: 1,700/10 **Fuel:** 27.1 tons **Endurance:** 15 days
Crew: 5–6 officers, 26–40 enlisted (45 tot. accomm.)

Remarks: Arrived in Syria in 1-86. Based at Tartus.
Hull systems: Wooden construction with GRP hull sheathing. Bollard pull: 10 tons at 9 kts.
Combat systems: Carries acoustic, loop and towed solenoidal magnetic, and net-sweep and mechanical sweep equipment and can lay linear mine disposal charges. Carries GKT-2 contact sweep; ST-2, AT-2, and PEMT-2 influence sweeps; and an IT-3 mine detector/exploder. The 25-mm mount is aimed by the operator, while the 30-mm mount is controlled by a Kolonka-1 ringsight director. The point-defense SAM launcher is mounted to port of the 25-mm mount. Normally carries 1,000 rounds of 30-mm and 2,000 rounds of 25-mm ammunition. The sonar dome pivots at the after end to retract within the hull.

♦ 3 Soviet Yevgenya-class (Project 1258) inshore minesweepers [MSI]
Bldr: Sudostroitel'noye Obyedineniye "Almaz" (Sredniy Neva), Kolpino

6/507 7/507 8/507

D: 88.5 tons light; 94.5 tons normal (97.9 fl) **S:** 11 kts
Dim: 26.13 (24.20 wl) × 5.90 (5.10 wl) × 1.38
A: 1 twin 25-mm 80-cal. 2M-3M AA; 4 d.c. (+ 8 emergency stowage)
Electronics: Radar: 1 Mius (Spin Trough) nav.—Sonar: MG-7 HF dipping
M: 2 Type 3D12 diesels; 2 props; 600 bhp—hydraulic slow-speed drive
Electric: 100 kw tot. (2 × 50-kw diesel sets)
Range: 400/10 **Fuel:** 2.7 tons **Endurance:** 3 days
Crew: 1 officer, 9 enlisted (+ 2–3 clearance divers)

Remarks: First unit transferred in 1978, the second in 1981; the third and fourth arrived 15-2-85 and the fifth on 19-1-86. Sisters 4/507 and 5/507 had been stricken by the end of 1997. Based at Tartus.
Hull systems: GRP hull. Navigational equipment includes a Girya-MA gyrocompass and NEL-7 echo sounder. The last two delivered had tripod masts.
Combat systems: Can employ a Neva-1 television minehunting system, useful to 30-m depths, which dispenses marker buoys to permit later disposal of mines by divers or explosive charges. The sonar is lowered via one of the stern davits. Carry VKT-1 mechanical, AT-2 acoustic, and SEMT-1 solenoid coil sweep gear.

AMPHIBIOUS WARFARE SHIPS AND CRAFT

♦ 3 Soviet Polnocny-B-class (Project 771) medium landing ships [LSM] Bldr: Stocznia Polnocna, Gdansk, Poland

1/114 2/114 3/114

D: 558 tons light; 640 tons std. (884 fl) **S:** 18 kts
Dim: 75.00 (70.00 wl) × 9.00 (8.60 wl) × 1.20 (fwd; 2.40 aft; 2.07 mean)
A: 1 or 2 twin 30-mm 65-cal. AK-230 AA; 2 18-round 140-mm WM-18 barrage RL (180 rockets); 2 or 4 4-round Fasta-M point-defense SAM syst.
Electronics: Radar: 1 Mius (Spin Trough) nav.; 1 MR-104 Rys' (Drum Tilt) f.c.
M: 2 Type 40DM diesels; 2 props; 4,400 bhp
Range: 700/18; 2,000/16 **Crew:** 5 officers, 32 enlisted + 60–180 troops

Remarks: One transferred from the USSR 15-1-84, two in 2-85. Based at Tartus and used primarily as coastal logistics support transports.
Hull systems: Have a bow door only. The hull has a "beak" projecting forward below the waterline at the bow to aid in beaching. Hatches to the upper deck are for loading and ventilation only. Cargo: 237 tons max., including six tanks, or 180 troops and their equipment; 30 vehicle crew are carried with tank loadout. The vehicle deck is 44.3 m long, 5.3 m wide, and 3.6 m high.

AUXILIARIES

♦ 1 modified Soviet Natya-class (Project 266E) oceanographic research ship [AGOR]
Bldr: Sudostroitel'noye Obyedineniye "Almaz" (Sredniy Neva), Kolpino (In serv. 1985)

642

Syrian Natya 642—prior to conversion from training ship to oceanographic research vessel French Navy, 1985

D: 750 tons std.; 804 tons normal **S:** 17.6 kts (16 sust.)
Dim: 61.00 (57.6 wl) × 10.20 × 2.98 (hull) **A:** removed
Electronics: Radar: 1 Don-2 nav.; 1 MR-104 Rys' (Drum Tilt) f.c.
M: 2 M-503B-3E diesels; 2 shrouded CP props; 5,000 bhp
Electric: 600 kw tot. (3 × 200-kw DGR-200/1500 diesel sets)
Range: 1,800/16; 3,000/12; 5,200/10 **Endurance:** 10–15 days
Crew: 8 officers, 59 enlisted

Remarks: Built specifically as a training ship, with no ASW ordnance or mine countermeasures systems. Arrived from the USSR in 1-85. Was converted to serve as an oceanographic research ship during the early 1990s and is now painted white.
Hull systems: Low-magnetic-signature, aluminum-steel alloy hull.
Combat systems: Delivered armed, with two twin 30-mm AK-230 and two twin 25-mm 2M-3M AA mounts, now removed; retains the MR-104 Rys' radar associated with the 30-mm mounts.

♦ 1 training ship/transport [AXT]
Bldr: Stocznia Polnocna SY, Gdansk (In serv. 1989)

Al Assad

Al Assad Camil Busquets i Vilanova, 7-01

D: approx. 7,500 tons (fl) **S:** 16 kts **Dim:** 115.90 (106.93 pp) × 18.02 × 6.01
A: none **Electronics:** Radar: 2 . . . nav.
M: 2 Zgoda-Sulzer 6ZL 40/48 diesels; 2 props; 8,700 bhp—bow-thruster
Electric: 1,512 kw tot. (3 × 504-kw diesel sets; 400 V, 50 Hz a.c.)
Range: 12,500/15 **Crew:** 56 tot. + 140 trainees

Remarks: 7,191 grt/3,459 dwt. Ordered at the beginning of 1984 and launched 8-2-87. A combination naval and merchant marine training ship and vehicle and personnel transport. Can carry 60 standard 20-ft. cargo containers and has a bale cargo capacity of 3,606 m^3. Has a stern ramp for vehicle cargo. Based at Latakia.

SERVICE CRAFT

Disposal note: Soviet-provided Sekstan-class degaussing tender 153 had ceased to be used by 2000.

♦ 1 Soviet Nyryat-1-class (Project 522) diving tender [YDT]

D: 105.4 tons (115 fl) **S:** 10 kts **Dim:** 28.50 × 5.50 × 1.70
Electronics: Radar: 1 Mius (Spin Trough) nav.
M: 1 Type 6CSP 28/3C diesel; 1 prop; 450 bhp
Range: 900/9 **Endurance:** 10 days **Crew:** 22 tot.

Remarks: Transferred in 9-67. Based at Al Mina al Bayda. Can support hard-hat divers to 20-m depths.

♦ 3 survey launches [YGS] Bldr: ARCOR, La Teste, France (In serv. 1985)

D: 9 tons (fl) **S:** 25 kts **Dim:** 9.80 (8.50 pp) × 3.40 × 0.90
M: 2 Volvo Penta AQAD-40 diesels; 2 props; 310 bhp
Range: 300/. . . **Crew:** 4 tot.

Remarks: Ordered in 12-84. GRP construction.

TAIWAN

Republic of China

Personnel (2001): 41,000 total navy and 14,500 marines, plus 32,500 naval and 35,000 marine reservists. The future force is to be 56,000 total, including 15,000 marines.

Bases: Organized into three naval districts: First Naval District, with headquarters at Tsoying and naval shipyard at Kaohsiung; Second Naval District, with headquarters and naval shipyard at Makung in the Pescadores; and Third Naval District, with headquarters and naval shipyard at Keelung. Other naval facilities are located at Anping, Hualien, Suao, and Wuchi, and a new naval base is under construction near Taiting. Antisubmarine assets are organized into two districts, the Eastern and Southern.

Naval Aviation: The Naval Aviation Command, established formally on 1-4-99 at Sheng Uing Naval Air Station, Hualien, has 22 S-2T Tracker land-based ASW aircraft (11 nonoperational), 12 MD-500/ASW shipboard helicopters, and 21 S-70C(M)-1 Thunderhawk helicopters. The marines also have several light liaison aircraft and helicopters.

Naval Helicopter Group has 12 McDonnell Douglas MD-500/ASW and 19 Sikorsky S-70C(M)-1 Thunderhawk helicopters for land-based use (the MD-500s occasionally are deployed aboard destroyers and frigates). The S-70C(M)-1 helicopters are assigned to No. 701 "Thunder Hawk" and No. 702 "Magic Hawk" squadrons. The S-70C(M)-1 is an export version of the U.S. Navy SH-60B Seahawk and is equipped with APS-128PC radar, ASN-150 tactical navigation system, ALR-606 ESM gear, one or two ARR-84 99-channel sonobuoy receivers, and MAD gear. Two Thunderhawks have been reconfigured as SIGINT collectors. The MD-500s have ASQ-81(V)2 MAD gear and can lift one torpedo. Eleven S-70C(M)-2 helicopters configured for shipboard service were ordered 26-6-97 for use in the new *La Fayette*–class frigates. Negotiations to acquire a dozen ex-USN SH-2F SeaSprite shipboard helicopters for service aboard the *Knox* class have been under way for at least five years, without result. A dozen ex-USN MH-53E mine countermeasures helicopters may be acquired.

The Grumman S-2E Trackers of the 439th Composite Wing of the Republic of China Air Force (ROCAF) were transferred to the Republic of China Navy (ROCN) on 1-7-98; they continue to constitute the 33rd and 34th Squadrons and are based at Pintung. Two Trackers were modernized in 1991 by Grumman to S-2T standard, with Garrett TPE-331-15AW turboprops (1,640 shp each), an AQS-902F digital sonobuoy processor, an ARR-84 99-channel sonobuoy receiver, DIFAR and CODAR capability, Litton APS-504 radar, ASQ-504 MAD, and AAS-40 FLIR (in place of the former searchlight); 18 other aircraft were modernized by the Chung-Shan Institute of Science and Technology at Taichung. Two S-2Es are fitted for EW vice ASW duties. On 24-4-01, the U.S. announced that it would sell a dozen surplus P-3C Orion maritime reconnaissance and ASW aircraft to Taiwan to replace the Trackers, but the offer may have to be withdrawn and another aircraft type substituted due to an alleged lack of available Orions.

The ROCAF operates four Grumman E-2T Hawkeye airborne early warning and air control aircraft equipped with APS-145 radar. Fifty single-seat A-3B and two-seat AT-3B Lui-Meng jet trainers of the ROCAF are equipped for a maritime strike role with Hsiung Feng-II air-to-surface missiles. In 9-98, the U.S.A. sold Taiwan 58 air-launched AGM-84 Harpoon antiship missiles for launch from ROCAF F-16 fighters.

S-2T Tracker *DTM,* 1-01

S-70C(M)-1 Thunderhawk *DTM,* 7-00

MD-500/ASW—with torpedo and MAD gear aboard *DTM,* 1-01

Marine Corps: Formerly organized into two combat divisions with a total of 30,000 active personnel, the ROC Marine Force has been reduced by half and now has only one full-strength division. The marine corps has some 717 U.S.-built LVT-5 tracked amphibious vehicles (in troop-carrying, command, and beach salvage variants), plus U.S. M 109 tracked artillery and M 60 tanks. The U.S.A. offered in 2001 to transfer 54 AAV-7A1 amphibious tracked personnel carriers.

Coastal Defense: Land-based mobile batteries with Hsiung Feng-II antiship missiles are maintained on the islands of the Pescadores, Tung-Ying, Chu-Kwang, Tsoying, and Shiao Liuchiu. Naval 127-mm guns in mountings removed from discarded ex-USN destroyers and frigates are also emplaced for shore defense.

Fleet Modernization: Under the six Kuang Hua major modernization programs, the ROCN plans to spend a total of $12 billion on new-construction ships to update the fleet:

- Kuang Hua I: 7 *Oliver Hazard Perry*–class guided-missile frigates for $4.6 billion
- Kuang Hua II: 6 *La Fayette*–class frigates built in France for $3.4 billion
- Kuang Hua III: 12 500-ton *Jing Chiang*–class patrol combatants for $326 million
- Kuang Hua IV: 10 to 12 1,000- to 1,500-ton guided-missile corvettes for $1.85 billion
- Kuang Hua V: 20 large harbor tugs for $74 million
- Kuang Hua VI: 50 guided-missile patrol craft for $370 million

WEAPON AND SENSORS

♦ Surface-to-surface missiles

Gabriel-II: An unknown number of Israeli-provided Gabriel-II antiship missiles remain in inventory. They can be launched by the same launchers used for the Hsiung Feng-I system.

Harpoon (RGM-84): Imported U.S. weapon for launch from U.S.-supplied *Knox*-class frigates; 41 RGM-84A were purchased in 1993, 58 AGM-84A air-launched variants were ordered in 1998 for the air force, and 71 RGM-84L Block II variants of the missile were requested during 9-00, along with six training missiles and 10 launch command sets, for use on the PFG-2 class. See data in U.S. section.

Hsiung Feng-I: Indigenously developed and based on the Gabriel-II, with numerous improvements. *Hsiung Feng* means "Mighty Wind."

Length: 3.43 m **Diameter:** 0.34 m **Wingspan:** 1.366 m
Weight: 537.5 kg **Warhead:** 180 kg
Speed: Mach 0.7 **Range:** 36–40 km **Altitude:** 1–3 m

Hsiung Feng-II: Developed by the Chung-Shan Institute of Science and Technology. Powered by a turbojet, it has a midcourse guidance provision and an active X-band radar seeker *plus* IR seekers. The weapon is capable of air, surface, and land launch and may be adapted for submarine launch. The first air launches were made in 1993, using an AT-3 jet trainer to carry the missile and an F-104 fighter to provide targeting. Shipboard launches are from quadruple box launchers oriented athwartships. Powered by a Microturbo 078 turbojet. Missiles being produced as of 2001 have a range of 170 km, an improved imaging infrared seeker, and a self-forging fragmentation warhead. Mobile land launchers for the missile were to enter service in 2002.

Length: 4.845 m **Diameter:** 0.4 m **Wingspan:** 1.15 m
Weight: 695 kg **Warhead:** 190 kg
Speed: Mach 0.85 **Range:** 150–170 km **Altitude:** 5–7 m

Note: A 300-km-range, land-attack version of Hsiung Feng-II is under development, as is a supersonic antiship version to be known as Hsiung Feng-III.

♦ Surface-to-air missiles

RAM: In 2-93, it was announced that the U.S. was planning to sell the RIM-116A RAM point-defense SAM system to Taiwan, possibly for use aboard the planned new class of medium-size patrol ships; no mounts have been ordered to date, however.

Sea Chaparral: Manned, quadruple launcher for the MIM-72F adaptation of the heat-seeking AIM-9D Sidewinder AAM. Originally developed during Vietnam War for the U.S. Navy. Used on ROCN frigates, amphibious ships, and auxiliaries. The normal outfit is 16 missiles per launcher.

Length: 2.908 m **Diameter:** 0.127 m **Wingspan:** 0.701 m
Weight: 85.7 kg **Warhead:** 11.34 kg
Speed: Mach 1.7–2.5 **Range:** 1.2–9.4 km **Altitude:** 4,755 m max.

Standard SM-1 MR: U.S.-made surface-to-air missiles used aboard *Gearing*-class DDGs and PFG-2-class FFGs. In 1989, 88 Standard SM-1s were acquired for use aboard modernized *Gearings*, and in 1992, 204 SM-1 Block VI missiles were ordered for use aboard the new frigates.

♦ Shipboard guns

U.S.-made guns in use include 127-mm Mk 42 Mod. 9 single DP; 76.2-mm Mk 33 twin DP; 76-mm Mk 75 DP (or the original Italian-made OTOBreda version); 40-mm 60-cal. Bofors AA in single Mk 3, twin Mk 1 Mod. 2, and quadruple Mk 2 mountings; 20-mm Mk 15 Mod. 11 Block 0 Phalanx close-in weapons systems (CIWS); and a few 20-mm 70-cal. Oerlikon AA in U.S. Mk 10 single or Mk 24 twin mountings. The indigenously developed, 580-kg T 75 AA mounting employs 20-mm 68-cal. M39A2 or M39A3 aircraft cannon, which have a 2,000-m practical range when used on ships.

The Taiwanese Mk 62 gun f.c.s. uses existing U.S. Mk 51 Mod. 2 and Mk 52 f.c.s. with stabilization added to enable them to be employed against surface targets; a total of 38 systems were manufactured in the 1960s, and these have been recycled to newer ships. Other weapons-control systems are of U.S. or French origin.

♦ Torpedoes

In use are U.S.-made Mk 44 and Mk 46 antisubmarine torpedoes and German SUT submarine torpedoes. In 9-98, 131 Alliant Mk 46 Mod. 5A(S) ASW torpedoes were ordered from the U.S.A., primarily for use with helicopters; another 41 were ordered during 3-99. Taiwan's Wang Siang Guan underwater ordnance laboratory is working on the Kang Lung ("Proud Dragon") heavyweight 533-mm wire-guided torpedo project.

♦ ASW ordnance

The U.S. Mk 16 Mod. 8 ASROC system, with eight-cell Mk 112 launchers, is installed on *Knox*-class frigates, and missiles with Mk 45 Mod. 5 torpedo payloads have been acquired. Many ships are equipped with U.S. Mk 9–design racks for Mk 9 quick-sinking depth charges (154.2 kg, with an 88.45-kg explosive payload). The cylindrical Mk 6 depth charge is also still in use (190.5 kg, with a 136.1-kg explosive payload).

♦ Mines

Mk 6 Mod. 14: Bottom-moored, spherical, mechanical contact mine of U.S. design. Diameter: 105.41 cm; weight: 635 kg with Mk 6 Mod. 5 or Mod. 16 anchor and 136 kg of explosives. Some are equipped with a contact buoy tethered to the top of the mine casing.

WSM 110: Air-dropped or surface-launched, cylindrical, bottom influence mine. Length: 1.690 m; diameter: 485 mm; weight: 635 kg, with a 295-kg explosive payload.

WSM 111: A moored, rocket-assisted rising mine for antisubmarine use. In development in 2001 by the Chung-Shan Institute of Science and Technology.

WSM 210: Spindle-shaped bottom influence mine with a 295-kg explosive payload. Intended for launch from surface ships; can be laid in waters 30–120 m deep. WS-II-series mines made after 1990 have a microprocessor, use multi-influence sensors, and can be laid in shallower water.

♦ Sensors and countermeasures

To date, most shipboard equipment has been of U.S. or French design and manufacture. Locally developed have been the Tacheng combat datalink system (also known as "Link T"), which is hosted on an off-the-shelf Acer personal computer system, and the CR-201 King Feng 127-mm countermeasures rocket launcher, which uses a 16-tube trainable launcher. Litton WD-2A radar-warning equipment (equivalent to ALR-66 aircraft gear) is being employed on smaller combatants and auxiliaries, and the U.S. Mk 36 Mod. 1 and 2 SRBOC (Super Rapid Blooming Offboard Countermeasures) launch system is used on newer ships. The French Matra Défense Dagaie Mk 2 decoy launcher is aboard the *La Fayette*–class frigates, along with French/European sensors.

Note: China Shipbuilding Corp., with yards at Kaohsiung and Keelung, was for sale as of 6-00 but continues to operate.

ATTACK SUBMARINES [SS]

Note: U.S. President George W. Bush announced on 24-4-01 that the U.S. would provide eight conventionally powered diesel-electric submarines for Taiwan, but almost immediately the governments of the Netherlands and Germany, in order to appease China, declared that their submarine builders could not participate. Bids for eight submarines were requested by the U.S. government on 16-10-01, with the contract to be let around 4-02, but the first boat would not be laid down until 2004 nor delivered until 2010. The U.S. Navy was to present four "preferred concept" options for the program during 3-02.

♦ 2 Hai Lung class

Bldr: Wilton Fijenoord, Schiedam, the Netherlands

	Laid down	L	Del.	In serv.
793 Hai Lung	12-82	4-10-86	9-10-87	9-10-87
794 Hai Hu	12-82	20-12-86	9-4-88	4-7-88

ATTACK SUBMARINES [SS] *(continued)*

Hai Lung (793) *Taiwan Defense Review,* 8-98

Hai Lung (793) *Ships of the World*

D: 2,370 tons surf. (max.)/2,657 tons sub. **S:** 11 kts surf./20 kts sub.
Dim: 66.92 × 8.40 × 6.70
A: 6 bow 533-mm TT (28 German SUT wire-guided torpedoes)
Electronics:
Radar: 1 Thales ZW-06 nav./surf. search
Sonar: Thales SIASS-Z integrated passive/active suite
EW: Elbit Timnex 4CH(V)2 intercept (2–18 GHz)
M: 3 Brons/Stork-Werkspoor 12 ORUB 215 diesels (1,350 bhp each), 2 922-kw Holec DG.110/47/90 alternator groups, 1 Holec 3,800-kw motor; 1 5-bladed prop; 5,100 shp sub./1,400 shp surf.
Range: 10,000/9 surf. **Fuel:** 310 tons **Crew:** 8 officers, 59 enlisted

Remarks: Ordered in late 1980, over mainland China's protests. The design, which is based closely on that of the Dutch *Zwaardvis* class, is also referred to as the Sea Dragon class, as the names mean "Sea Dragon" and "Sea Tiger," respectively. A request for two more (and an option for a fifth and sixth) was turned down by the Dutch government in 1984 due to Chinese pressure. A highly automated design. 794 ran aground while submerged early in 10-01 but was not seriously damaged.
Hull systems: Have two 196-cell batteries. Normal operational diving depth: 240 m.
Combat systems: Have SINBADS-M, an eight-target track data system, and the Sperry Mk 29 Mod. 2A inertial navigation system. A submerged-launch variant of the Hsiung Feng-II antiship missile is in development for use by these and any later submarines. Have the Carl Zeiss SERO 40 periscope suite, with AS 40 attack and BS 40 attack periscopes.

AUXILIARY SUBMARINES [SSA]

♦ 2 ex-U.S. GUPPY II class

	Bldr	Laid down	L	In serv.
791 Hai Shih (ex-*Cutlass,* SS 478)	Portsmouth NSY, Portsmouth, N.H.	22-7-44	5-11-44	17-3-45
792 Hai Pao (ex-*Tusk,* SS 426)	Cramp SB, Philadelphia	23-8-43	8-7-45	11-4-46

D: 1,517 tons std.; 1,870 tons surf./2,440 tons sub.
S: 18 kts surf./16 kts sub. **Dim:** 93.57 × 8.33 × 5.18
A: 10 533-mm TT (6 fwd, 4 aft; 22 torpedoes—but may have none)
Electronics:
Radar: 1 SS-2 search
Sonar: BQR-2B passive; BQS-4C active (7 kHz); DUUG-1B sonar intercept
EW: WLR-1G; WLR-3 intercept
M: diesel-electric: 4 Fairbanks-Morse 38D8Q diesels, 2 electric motors; 2 props; 4,610 bhp surf./5,200 shp sub.
Range: 10,000/10 surf.; 95/5 sub. **Fuel:** 330 tons
Crew: 11 officers, 70 enlisted

Remarks: Transferred 12-4-73 and 18-10-73, for ASW training. Have four 126-cell batteries. The source of torpedoes, if any, is uncertain: they may use old Japanese or U.S. Mk 14 World War II–era straight-runners, Indonesian-supplied German SUT, or U.K. Mk 24 Tigerfish. The tubes were welded shut at the time of delivery but may have been made operational again. Diving depth was originally limited to 122 m but is probably much less now. New propeller shafts were ordered from the U.S. for both in 1999, indicating an intention to keep them in service.

Hai Pao (792) Raymond Cheung, 1996

GUIDED-MISSILE DESTROYERS [DDG]

♦ 0 (+ 4) ex-U.S. Kidd class

Bldr: Northrup Grumman Ingalls SB, Pascagoula, Miss.

	Laid down	L	In serv.
. . . . . . (ex-*Kidd,* DDG 993; ex-*Kourush*)	26-6-78	11-8-79	27-6-81
. . . . . . (ex-*Callaghan,* DDG 994; ex-*Daryush*)	23-10-78	1-12-79	29-8-81
. . . . . . (ex-*Scott,* DDG 995; ex-*Nader*)	12-2-79	1-3-80	24-10-81
. . . . . . (ex-*Chandler,* DDG 996; ex-*Andushirvan*)	7-5-79	24-5-80	13-3-82

Chandler (DDG 996)—in U.S. Navy service H&L Van Ginderen, 3-98

Callaghan (DDG 994)—in U.S. Navy service 93 Wing Det. A, RAAF, 3-94

GUIDED-MISSILE DESTROYERS [DDG] *(continued)*

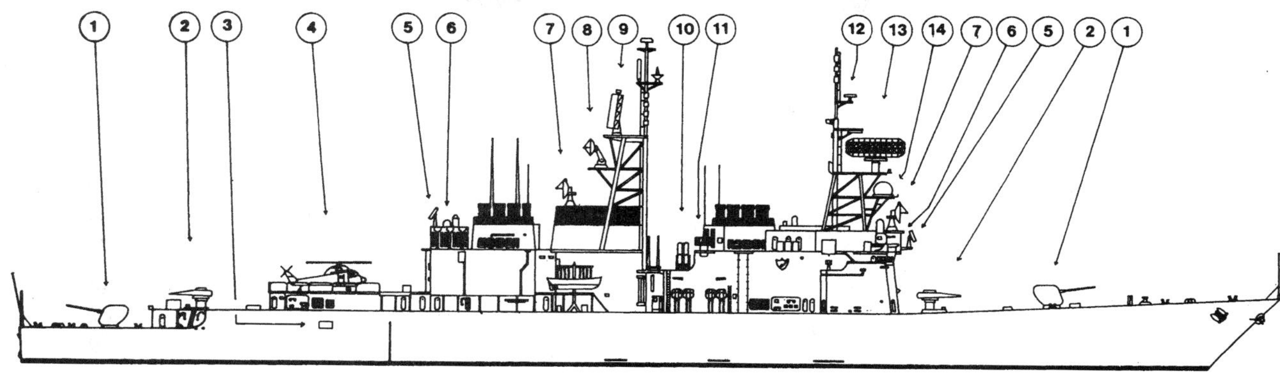

Kidd class in U.S. Navy service 1. 127-mm 54-cal. Mk 45 DP 2. Mk 26 twin SAM launch system 3. triple Mk 32 ASW TT (behind shutters in hull sides) 4. helicopter platform 5. antennas for SATCOM system 6. 20-mm Mk 15 Phalanx CIWS 7. SPG-51D missile illuminators 8. SPG-60 gun f.c. and missile illumination radar 9. SPS-48E 3-D early-warning radar 10. Harpoon antiship missile launch canisters

Drawing by Robert Dumas, from *Flottes de Combat*

Chandler (DDG 996)—in U.S. Navy service David Broecker, 4-99

D: 7,326 tons light (9,950 fl) **S:** 30+ kts
Dim: 171.70 (161.23 fl) × 16.76 × 7.01 (10.06 over sonar)
A: 2 twin-rail Mk 26 missile launchers (68 Standard SM-2 MR Block II missiles); 8 RGM-84 Harpoon SSM; 2 single 127-mm 54-cal. Mk 45 Mod. 1 DP; 2 20-mm Mk 15 Phalanx gatling CIWS; 2 triple Mk 32 Mod. 5 ASW TT (24 Mk 46 Mod. 5 torpedoes); 1 . . . helicopter
Electronics:
Radar: 1 Raytheon SPS-64(V)9 nav.; 1 Cardion SPS-55 surf. search; 1 Raytheon SPS-49(V)5 air search; 1 ITT SPS-48E 3-D early warning; 2 Raytheon SPG-51D missile illumination; 1 Lockheed Martin SPG-60 illumination/gun f.c.; 1 Lockheed Martin SPQ-9A surf. gun f.c.; 2 General Dynamics Mk 90 Phalanx f.c.
Sonar: EDO-G.E. SQS-53A bow-mounted LF
TACAN: URN-25
EW: Raytheon SLQ-32(V)5 passive, with Sidekick jammer; Mk 36 SRBOC decoy syst. (4 6-round Mk 137 RL); SLQ-25 Nixie towed torpedo decoy syst.
M: 4 G.E. LM-2500 gas turbines; 2 5-bladed props; 86,000 shp (80,000 sust.)
Electric: 6,000 kw tot. (3 × 2,000-kw Allison 501K gas turbine–driven alternators; 360–400 Hz)
Range: 3,300/30; 6,000/20 **Fuel:** 1,534 tons + 72 tons aviation fuel
Crew: 28 officers, 320 enlisted

Remarks: Offered by the U.S. on 1-1-01. The ROCN decided to request them on 2-10-01, and a formal request to the U.S.A. was expected by early 2002. Reactivation, refit, and transfer is to cost $760.8 million, with the first to be delivered during 2004 and the last during 2006. Even unmodernized, these ships are superior to the *Sovremennyy*-class destroyers acquired by China. The characteristics and equipment listed above describe the ships in U.S. Navy service; they may be considerably altered during reactivation, including the substitution of Mk 41 vertical launch systems for the outmoded Mk 26 launchers.

Six ships of this class were originally ordered for Iran in 1974; two were canceled during 6-76 and a construction contract for four was let 23-3-78. Ex-DDG 993 and ex-DDG 994 were canceled by the new Iranian government on 3-2-79 and the other two on 31-3-79. The U.S. Congress authorized their completion for the U.S. Navy, and the ships were formally acquired 25-7-79 for about $510 million each. Ex-DDG 993 was decommissioned from the USN 12-3-98, ex-DDG 994 on 31-3-98, ex-DDG 995 on 15-12-98, and ex-DDG 996 on 24-9-99. Ex-DDG 993 and ex-DDG 995 were stored at Philadelphia and the other two at Bremerton, Wash.

Hull systems: Larger-capacity air-intake filter systems than those on the similar *Spruance* class were installed in order to handle the dust and sand prevailing in the Persian Gulf area. Extensive use of Kevlar and aluminum armor raised their displacements by around 1,000 tons.

Combat systems: All four received the New Threat Upgrade improvements between 1988 and 1990 and are equipped with the Mk 14 weapons-direction system. They also have the Naval Tactical Data System (NTDS), with Links 4A, 11, and 14. Two Mk 74 missile fire-control systems employ the two SPG-51D missile illuminators and the SPG-60 gun fire-control radar to enable attacking three aerial targets simultaneously; there are four SYR-1 missile telemetry receivers. The Mk 86 Mod. 5 gun f.c.s. uses the SPQ-9A radar for surface fire and the SPG-60 radar for AA fire. The Mk 116 underwater f.c.s. handles ship-launched ASW torpedo launching (and formerly ASROC ASW missile launching).

♦ 7 ex-U.S. Gearing FRAM-I-class Wu Chin III conversions

	Bldr	Laid down	L	In serv.
912 Chien Yang (ex-*James E. Kyes,* DD 787)	Todd Pacific SY, Seattle	27-12-44	4-8-45	8-2-46
921 Liao Yang (ex-*Hanson,* DD 832)	Bath Iron Works, Bath, Maine	7-10-44	11-3-45	11-5-45
923 Shen Yang (ex-*Power,* DD 839)	Bath Iron Works, Bath, Maine	26-2-45	30-6-45	13-9-45
925 Te Yang (ex-*Sarsfield,* DD 837)	Bath Iron Works, Bath, Maine	15-1-45	27-5-45	31-7-45
927 Yun Yang (ex-*Hamner,* DD 718)	Federal SB, Newark, N.J.	5-4-45	24-11-45	11-7-46
928 Chen Yang (ex-*Johnston,* DD 821)	Consolidated Steel, Orange, Texas	6-5-45	19-10-45	10-10-46
929 Shao Yang (ex-*Hollister,* DD 788)	Todd Pacific SY, Seattle	18-1-45	9-10-45	29-3-46

Chien Yang (912) *Ships of the World,* 7-01

Chen Yang (928) *Ships of the World,* 7-01

D: 2,500 tons (3,540 fl) **S:** 27 kts
Dim: 119.03 (116.74 wl) × 12.52 × 4.65 (6.54 over sonar)
A: 4 Hsiung Feng-II SSM; 2 triple and 2 paired, fixed SAM launchers (10 Standard SM-1 MR SAM/SSM); 1 76-mm 62-cal. OTOBreda DP; 2 single 40-mm 70-cal. Bofors AA; 1 20-mm Mk 15 Phalanx CIWS; 1 8-round Mk 16 ASROC ASW syst. (Mk 112 launcher; no reloads); 2 triple 324-mm Mk 32 ASW TT (Mk 46 Mod. 5 A/S torpedoes); 1 MD-500 helicopter

GUIDED-MISSILE DESTROYERS [DDG] *(continued)*

Chen Yang (928) *Ships of the World,* 7-01

Yun Yang (927) *Ships of the World,* 7-01

Electronics:
Radar: 1 Goldstar . . . nav.; 1 Raytheon SPS-58A surf./air search; 1 Thales DA-08/2 air search; 1 Thales STIR-18 missile f.c.; 1 Westinghouse HW-160 gun f.c.; 1 General Dynamics Mk 90 Phalanx f.c.
Sonar: Raytheon DE-1191 hull-mounted (4.5/5.0/5.5 kHz)
TACAN: SRN-15
EW: Chang Feng III active/passive suite; AS-899A D/F; 4 16-round King Fen VI decoy RL; T Mk 6 Fanfare towed acoustic torpedo decoy
E/O: Thales LIOD gun f.c. and tracking
M: 2 sets G.E. geared steam turbines; 2 props; 60,000 shp
Boilers: 4 Babcock & Wilcox; 43.3 kg/cm^2, 454° C **Electric:** 1,200 kw tot.
Range: 1,500/31; 5,800/12 **Fuel:** 720 tons **Crew:** 275 tot.

Remarks: 912 and 921 were transferred 18-4-73, 923 and 925 on 1-10-77, and 927 and 928 on 27-2-81; 929 was purchased 17-4-83. All have been extensively modernized and completely rearmed to act as air-defense ships. 921 and 925 are assigned to the 124th Frigate Squadron, the others to the 146th Frigate Squadron; all are to be retained in service until the *Kidd*-class ships are transferred.
Combat systems: Under Project Wu Chin III, the ships received Honeywell H 930 weapons-control systems (with UYK-19 computer), with a Thales STIR-18 fire-control radar substituted for the original Mk 37 director and Mk 25 radar; the system can track 24 air, surface, and underwater targets simultaneously while controlling attacks on four, with an 8-second response time. All 127-mm mounts were deleted, and an OTOBreda 76-mm mount was substituted forward. On the fantail, two sets of triple fixed box launchers for U.S. Standard SM-1 MR surface-to-air missiles (which can also be used against surface targets) are positioned fore and aft of a U.S. Mk 15 CIWS; two twin Standard box launchers are located forward of the bridge. The DA-08/2 air-search radar (which uses the antenna for the LW-05 radar) is located atop the foremast, and the SPS-58A radar (which uses an SPS-10 radar antenna) is located on the former air-search radar platform. A new lattice aftermast carries the HW-160 radar and the various arrays for the Chang Feng III EW suite, which was derived from the Hughes SLQ-31. The 40-mm AA are mounted to port at the aft corner of the hangar structure (necessitating deletion of the ASROC reload magazine) and on a raised platform forward of the whaleboat to starboard. The Raytheon DE-1191 sonar is a digital, transistorized update to the SQS-23. They also received a Taiwanese-made SATCOM system and the Ta Chen combat information datalink system. A quadruple Hsiung Feng-II SSM launch group aimed athwartships to starboard had been added amidships on all by 1995. 912 had received two new, unidentified radomes for a probable new EW system by 4-01, and several others of the class had been given platforms above the bridge window area to support the antennas.

DESTROYERS [DD]

Disposal note: Of the U.S. *Gearing* FRAM-I class, Wu Chin II conversion *Kai Yang* (924; ex-*Richard B. Anderson,* DD 786) was stricken 16-11-99; the unmodified *Tsu Yang* (930; ex-*Hawkins,* DD 873) on 16-10-98 (the superstructure being removed and assembled at the naval academy as a training facility); Wu Chin II conversion *Lai Yang* (920; ex-*Shelton,* DD 790) on 16-3-99; Wu Chin I conversion *Han Yang* (915; ex-*Herbert J. Thomas,* DD 833) on 16-8-99; and *Sui Yang* (926; ex-*Leonard K. Mason,* DD 852) during 2-00. Another FRAM-I unit, *Chao Yang* (916; ex-*Rowan,* DD 782), was lost 22-8-77 while under tow to Taiwan for activation.
U.S. *Gearing* FRAM-II-class *Fu Yang* (907; ex-*Ernest G. Small,* DD 838) was stricken 16-12-99 and sister *Dang Yang* (911; ex-*Lloyd Thomas,* DD 764) on 16-3-99.
Of the two ex-U.S. *Allen M. Sumner* FRAM-II-class Wu Chin I–conversion destroyers, *Lo Yang* (914; ex-*Taussig,* DD 746) was stricken 16-2-00 and *Nan Yang* (917; ex-*John W. Thomason,* DD 760) on 16-1-00. The only *Allen M. Sumner*–class Wu Chin I–conversion destroyer, *Huei Yang* (906; ex-*English,* DD 696) was stricken 16-8-99. The final active *Allen M. Sumner*–class Tien Shi–conversion destroyer, *Yueh Yang* (905; ex-*Haynsworth,* DD 700), was stricken 16-1-99; sisters *Heng Yang* (902; ex-*Samuel N. Moore,* DD 747) and *Hua Yang* (903; ex-*Bristol,* DD 857) were stricken during 5-95. Two additional Tien Shi units had been stricken earlier: *Hsiang Yang* (901; ex-*Brush,* DD 745) around 1984 and *Po Yang* (910; ex-*Maddox,* DD 731) around 1985 for use as a training device at the Naval Weapons School.
Of the four ex-U.S. *Fletcher*-class destroyers, *Kwei Yang* (908; ex-*Twining,* DD 540) and *Chiang Yang* (909; ex-*Mullany,* DD 528) were stricken 16-7-99, *An Yang* (918; ex-*Kimberly,* DD 521) on 16-9-99, and *Kun Yang* (919; ex-*Yarnall,* DD 541) on 16-10-99.

GUIDED-MISSILE FRIGATES [FFG]

♦ 7 (+ 1) PFG-2 class (Kuang Hua I program)
Bldr: China SB, Kaohsiung

	Laid down	L	In serv.
1101 Cheung Kung	2-12-90	27-10-91	7-5-93
1103 Cheng Ho	21-12-91	15-10-92	28-3-94
1105 Chi Kuang	4-10-92	27-9-93	4-3-95
1106 Yueh Fei	5-9-93	26-8-94	7-2-96
1107 Tzu I	8-94	13-7-95	9-1-97
1108 Pan Chao	7-95	3-7-96	16-12-97
1109 Chang Chien	6-96	5-97	1-12-98
1110 Tian Dan	4-01	5-02	3-04

Cheng Ho (1103) Chris Sattler, via H&L Van Ginderen, 5-99

Cheung Kung (1101) H&L Van Ginderen, 1-99

Pan Chao (1108) *DTM,* 1-00

D: 3,207 tons light (4,104 fl) **S:** 27.5 kts
Dim: 138.07 (125.90 wl) × 14.31 (13.72 wl) × 5.70 (8.60 max.)
A: 8 Hsiung Feng-II SSM; 1 Mk 13 Mod. 4 guided-missile launch syst. (40 Standard SM-1 MR SAM and RGM-84L Harpoon SSM); 1 76-mm 62-cal. OTOBreda DP; 2 single 40-mm 70-cal. Bofors AA; 1 20-mm Mk 15 Phalanx gatling CIWS; 3 single 20-mm 68-cal. Type 75 AA; 2 triple Mk 32 Mod. 5 ASW TT (Mk 46 Mod. 5 torpedoes); 1 S-70C(M)-2 Thunderhawk ASW helicopter

GUIDED-MISSILE FRIGATES [FFG] *(continued)*

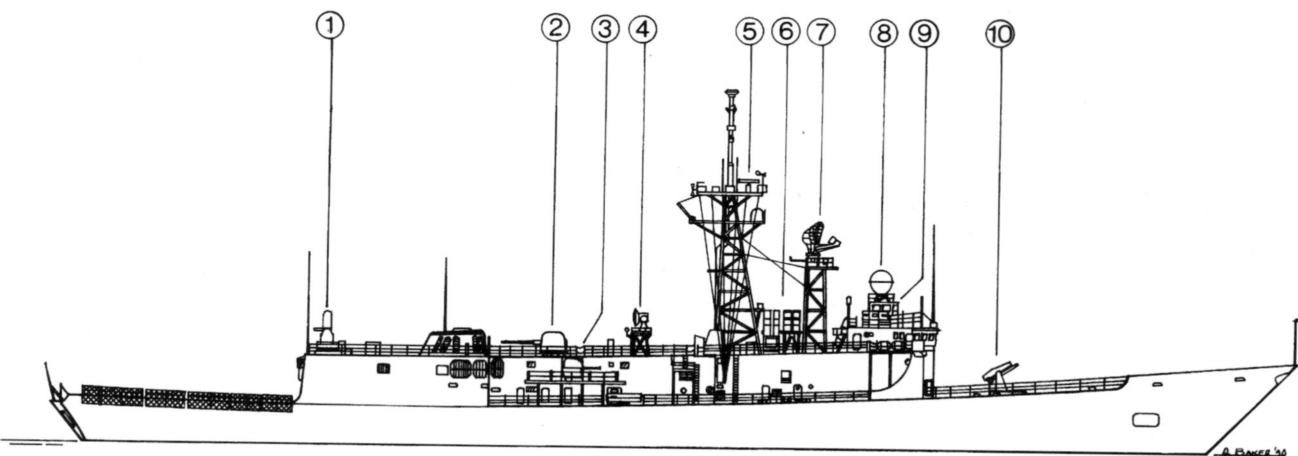

Cheung Kung (1101) 1. 20-mm Mk 15 Phalanx CIWS 2. 76-mm 62-cal. OTOBreda DP 3. 40-mm 70-cal. Bofors AA 4. STIR-24 weapons-control radar 5. SPS-55 surface-search radar 6. Hsiung Feng-II antiship missile launch canisters (to be removed) 7. SPS-49(V)5 air-search radar 8. Mk 92 Mod. 6 weapons-control radar 9. Chang Feng IV/SLQ-32(V)5 EW system antenna group 10. Mk 13 Mod. 4 missile launcher

Drawing by A. D. Baker III

Yueh Fei (1106) South African Navy, 4-97

Electronics:

Radar: 1 Cardion SPS-55 surf. search; 1 Raytheon SPS-49(V)5 air search; 1 Raytheon Mk 92 Mod. 6 f.c.; 1 Thales STIR-24 missile f.c.; 1 General Dynamics Mk 90 Phalanx f.c.

Sonar: Raytheon DE-1160B hull-mounted MF; provision for EDO SQR-18A(V)2 towed passive linear hydrophone array or Thales ATAS/Lamproie towed passive/active linear hydrophone array

EW: Chang Feng IV suite (SLQ-32(V)5 intercept, Sidekick jammer); Mk 36 SRBOC decoy syst. (2 6-round Mk 137 RL); SLQ-25A Nixie towed acoustic torpedo decoy syst.

M: 2 G.M. LM-2500 gas turbines; 1 CP prop; 40,420 shp—2 drop-down electric propulsors; 720 shp

Electric: 4,000 kw tot. (4 × 1,000-kw diesel alternator sets)

Range: 4,200/20; 5,000/18 **Fuel:** 587 tons + 64 tons helicopter fuel

Crew: 13 officers, 193 enlisted + 19 air group

Remarks: Ordered 8-5-89. Design is a slightly modified version of the "long-hulled" U.S. Navy *Oliver Hazard Perry* class. Named for Chinese maritime heroes. Construction of the first two was aided by "kits" supplied by Bath Iron Works, Bath, Maine, which also provided technical assistance in constructing the others. Detail design by Gibbs & Cox. Originally only four were to have been built to the basic design, but development of the phased-array radar and vertically launched SAM for the Batch II updated variant lagged, and the Batch II program was canceled altogether in 10-94. Are all assigned to the 124th Frigate Squadron. Funds to construct the eighth unit were provided in the 1999 budget; the ship had been canceled in 10-94 and was to be reordered during 1-99, but the actual contract was delayed to 12-00.

Hull systems: Have fin stabilizers, rudder roll-control, and the Prairie/Masker acoustic sound-signature-reduction air-bubble generation system.

Combat systems: The U.S. Norden Systems SYS-2(V)2 sensor data fusion system is installed, as is the Vitro Cando off-the-shelf computerized data system, which assists the Mk 92 weapons-control system. A RAST helicopter hold-down and transfer system is fitted. 1105 was the first of the class to have a datalink, which was backfitted into the earlier pair. The Hsiung Feng-II missiles are carried in box launchers atop the superstructure, abaft the bridge; they are launched by a U.S. Hughes-supplied missile-control system that can also control the 40-mm guns. The 40-mm mounts cannot be manned when the 76-mm gun is firing, due to blast effects. The 20-mm guns are modified M 39 aircraft cannon and are mounted atop the hangar (flanking the Phalanx) and forward of the Mk 92 f.c.s. radome. The towed sonar array will not be installed until later; the EDO system offered would incorporate an AMSP2 processor, while the Thales system would have both active and passive capabilities. To be used by the Mk 13 launcher, 71 RGM-84L Harpoon Block II missiles were requested from the U.S.A. for this class in 9-00; they will replace the Hsiung Feng-II launchers, which will be mounted ashore for coastal defense and aboard *Jing Jiang*–class patrol combatants.

FRIGATES [FF]

♦ 6 La Fayette class (Project Kuang Hua II)

Bldr: DCN, Lorient

	Laid down	L	In serv.
1202 Kang Ting	1-9-93	12-3-94	24-5-96
1203 Hsi Ning	28-3-94	5-11-94	12-10-96
1205 Kun Ming	7-11-94	13-5-95	26-2-97
1206 Ti Hua	1-7-95	25-11-95	14-8-97
1207 Wu Chang	1-7-95	25-11-95	16-12-97
1208 Cheng De	27-12-95	26-7-96	9-3-98

Kang Ting (1202) Chris Sattler, 6-00

Wu Chang (1207) and Ti Hua (1206) *DTM,* 10-98

D: 3,680 tons (fl) **S:** 28 kts **Dim:** 125.00 × 15.40 (13.80 wl) × 4.00 (hull)

A: 8 Hsiung Feng-II SSM; 1 4-round Sea Chaparral SAM syst. (16 MIM-72F missiles); 1 76-mm 62-cal. U.S. Mk 75 DP; 2 single 40-mm 70-cal. Bofors AA; 1 20-mm Mk 15 Mod. 11 Block IA Phalanx CIWS; 2 triple 324-mm Mk 32 Mod. 5 ASW TT (Mk 46 Mod. 5 torpedoes); 1 S-70C(M)-1 Thunderhawk ASW helicopter

FRIGATES [FF] *(continued)*

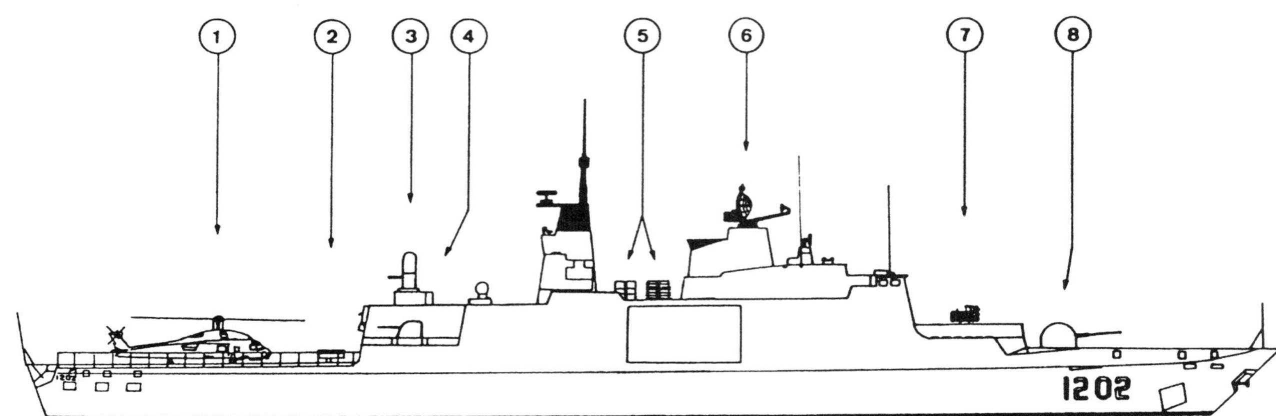

Kang Ting (1202) 1. S-70C(M)-1 Thunderhawk helicopter 2. triple Mk 32 ASW TT 3. 20-mm Mk 15 Phalanx CIWS 4. 40-mm 70-cal. Bofors AA 5. Hsiung Feng-II antiship missiles 6. Jupiter air-search radar 7. launcher for Sea Chaparral SAM system 8. 76-mm 62-cal. OTOBreda DP — Drawing by Jean Moulin, from *Flottes de Combat*

Hsi Ning (1203) — Chris Sattler, 6-00

Electronics:
Radar: 2 Decca 20V90 nav.; 1 Thales Triton-G surf. search; 1 Thales Jupiter air search; 2 Thales Castor-IIC f.c.; 1 General Dynamics Mk 90 Phalanx f.c.
Sonar: Thales TSM 2633 Spherion-B hull-mounted (MF); provision for Thales ATAS (V)3 ALOSE/Lamproie active towed linear array (3 kHz)
EW: . . . . . . intercept/jamming; 2 330- to 340-round Matra Défense Dagaie Mk 2 decoy RL
E/O: 2 Matra Défense Najir target-desig. and gun f.c.
M: 4 SEMT-Pielstick 16 PA6 BTC diesels; 2 CP props; 31,800 bhp
Electric: 2,250 kw tot. (3 × 750-kw diesel alternator sets)
Range: 7,000/15; 9,000/12 **Fuel:** . . . **Endurance:** 50 days
Crew: 20 officers, 156 enlisted

Remarks: Also referred to by Taiwan as the PF class and by the builders as the FL-3000 class or MOP-1 class. A project definition contract was granted to France 11-6-89, with the construction contract signed 27-9-91. Originally, France was to deliver the first six hulls without weapons or sensors to Taiwan for fitting out (earlier, it had been proposed to deliver the hulls in prefabricated sections); in mid-1993, however, it was decided to build the six ships under contract entirely in France, saving about $120 million. In 1-94, France and the People's Republic of China announced that no more orders would be accepted, but that was later clarified to mean no more beyond the total of 14 on option, although no more have been ordered. The ships are named for the capital cities of mainland Chinese provinces. 1202 arrived 18-5-96 and required only a week to outfit with armament prior to commissioning. They constitute Frigate Squadron 131 and are based at Keelung.
Hull systems: Particular effort has been made to reduce the ships' signatures: The diesel propulsion engines are mounted in pairs on isolation platforms and the superstructure, masts, and forecastle are covered with radar-absorbent GRP-resin compound. Much of the superstructure is built of glass-reinforced plastic. The vertical hull and superstructure surfaces are slanted at ±10° and all chocks, bollards, and boat recesses are covered to reduce radar reflectivity. The ships are also fitted with degaussing equipment and extensive NBC warfare protection.
Special armor is provided for the magazines. Employ a modified deep-vee hullform, fin stabilizers, and rudder-controlled roll reduction to improve seaworthiness. There are two rudders, and the hullform incorporates twin skegs aft. Hull has 11 watertight compartments. The French SAMAHE helicopter deck downhaul and deck transiting system turned out to be incompatible with the S-70C(M)-1 helicopter and has been modified; the helicopter can be launched and recovered in up to Sea State 6. One Taiwanese source states that SEMT-Pielstick 12 PA6 V280STC diesels are installed, for a total of 21,000 bhp and a maximum speed of only 25 kts.
Combat systems: The ships have the Thales TAVITAC 2000 fully distributed combat data system with five Vista display consoles and a Precilec DHS plotting table. The Sea Chaparral SAM system, while obsolescent, is reliable. The 76-mm guns were made by OTOBreda, but to the U.S. Mk 75 pattern. The Jupiter radar employs the antenna from the Thales LW-08 radar. 1207 has a Taiwanese-developed EW system for trials. At least one unit had what appeared to be the French ARBB-33 Salamandre active jamming system in 1999, but none has yet been fitted with the planned SLQ-32(V)5 suite, a torpedo decoy system, or the planned ATAS (Active Towed-Array Sonar) active/passive linear hydrophone array with Mustang acoustic processor. In 1999, negotiations were under way with France for the installation of six-round Sadral launch systems (with Mistral IR missiles) in place of the 40-mm mounts.

♦ 8 ex-U.S. Knox class

Bldr: Avondale SY (now Northrop Grumman SB), Westwego, La. (932: Lockheed SB, Seattle)

	Laid down	L	In serv.
932 Chi Yang (ex-*Robert E. Peary,* FFT 1073; ex-*Conolly,* FF 1073)	20-12-70	23-6-71	23-9-72
933 Feng Yang (ex-*Brewton,* FF 1086)	2-10-70	24-7-71	8-7-72
934 Fen Yang (ex-*Kirk,* FF 1087)	4-12-70	25-9-71	9-9-72
935 Lan Yang (ex-*Joseph Hewes,* FFT 1078)	15-5-69	7-3-70	24-4-71
936 Hae Yang (ex-*Cook,* FF 1083)	20-3-70	23-1-71	18-12-71
937 Hwai Yang (ex-*Barbey,* FF 1088)	5-2-71	4-12-71	11-11-72
938 Ning Yang (ex-*Aylwin,* FF 1081)	13-11-69	29-8-70	18-9-71
939 Yi Yang (ex-*Valdez,* FF 1096)	30-6-72	24-3-73	27-7-74

D: 3,075 tons light; 3,877 tons std. (4,260 fl) **S:** 27.5 kts
Dim: 134.0 (126.5 wl) × 14.33 × 4.60 (7.55 over sonar)—see remarks
A: 4 RGM-84A Harpoon SSM (from ASROC launcher); 1 127-mm 54-cal. Mk 42 Mod. 9 DP; 1 20-mm Mk 15 Phalanx CIWS; 4 single 20-mm 68-cal. T 75 AA; 2 single 12.7-mm M2 mg; 1 8-round Mk 16 ASROC ASW syst. (Mk 112 launcher; 12 reloads); 4 paired, fixed 324-mm Mk 32 Mod. 9 fixed TT (Alliant Mk 46 Mod. 5 torpedoes); 1 MD-500 helicopter

FRIGATES [FF] *(continued)*

Yi Yang (939) William H. Clarke, 7-99

Hae Yang (936) ROCN, 1996

Feng Yang (933) *Ships of the World,* 1998

Hwai Yang (937) *DTM,* 1998

Electronics:
Radar: 1 Raytheon SPS-64(V)9 nav.; 1 Raytheon SPS-10F (937, 939: Norden SPS-67(V)1) surf. search; 1 Lockheed SPS-40B air search; 1 Western Electric SPG-53F gun f.c.; 1 General Dynamics Mk 90 Phalanx f.c.
Sonar: SQS-26CX hull-mounted (3.5 kHz); SQS-35 VDS (see remarks); EDO SQR-18A(V)1 towed linear passive hydrophone array
TACAN: SRN-15
EW: SLQ-32(V)1 or (V)2 intercept; Mk 36 SRBOC decoy syst. (2 6-round Mk 137 RL), T Mk 6 Fanfare towed acoustic torpedo decoy
M: 1 set Westinghouse geared steam turbines; 1 prop; 35,000 shp
Boilers: 2 Combustion Eng. (932: Babcock & Wilcox) D-Type; 84 kg/cm^2, 510° C
Electric: 3,000 kw tot. (3 × 750-kw turboalternators, 1 × 750-kw diesel set)
Range: 2,750/27.5; 4,300/20 **Fuel:** 750 tons
Crew: 17–20 officers, 255–265 enlisted

Remarks: The first three were transferred on lease upon decommissioning from the USN 7-8-92, 23-7-92, and 6-8-93, respectively. The lease cost only $14.5 million, but the complete training, overhaul, modification, and technical support package came to $236.19 million. They arrived at Tsoying 27-9-93 and were commissioned 6-10-93. 935 was transferred on decommissioning from the USN 30-6-94, while 936 (in reserve since 30-4-92) and 937 (in reserve since 19-3-92) were transferred 31-5-94 and 21-6-94, respectively; all three left U.S. waters 2-7-95 and were formally recommissioned 4-8-95. Permanent transfer by sale for the first six was approved under the U.S. Defense Authorization Act for FY 99. The six constitute Frigate Squadron 168, based at Chung Cheng Naval Base, Suao; 935 is flagship.

A third group of three was planned for acquisition by sale during 1996; all had been in reserve for several years and needed reactivation refits prior to delivery, and the final arrangement, made in 1998, resulted in the purchase of 938 and 939 on 28-4-98. After activation refits at Detjens SY, Charleston, S.C., they arrived in Taiwan 4-10-99 and were commissioned 18-10-99. The offer of a third, the *Pharris* (FF 1094), was declined. 938 and 939 had been in reserve since 15-5-92 and 15-12-91, respectively. In 7-97, the U.S. Congress authorized the sale of *Whipple* (FF 1062) and *Downes* (FF 1070) to Taiwan for use as cannibalization spares, but the offer was declined.

Hull systems: Nonretractable antirolling fin stabilizers are fitted in all. The Prairie/Masker bubbler system is fitted to hulls and propellers to reduce radiated noise.

Combat systems: All have the C-STEM tactical data plotting system. The ASROC system has an automatic reloading magazine beneath the bridge; the two starboard cells and corresponding reload magazine positions are employed for Harpoon missiles. The ships have the SWG-1A Harpoon firing system. The ASW torpedo tubes are fixed, in the forward end of the hangar superstructure, aimed outboard at an angle of 45°. The SQS-35 towed VDS was restored to service prior to transfer, but it is apparently now used only to stream the SQR-18A(V)1 towed array. All carry a Mk 68 gunfire-control system with SPG-53A, -53D, or -53F radar. 937 tested the CS/MPQ-78 fire-control system in 1999 as a possible replacement for the Mk 68 system; the device is based on the Contraves Skyguard system. Have the Mk 114 ASW fire-control system. All received the ASWTDS (ASW Tactical Data System) during the 1980s. 935–937 were equipped with latest-model Mk 15 Mod. 11 Block IA Phalanx CIWS, with a 4,500-rpm firing rate and additional on-mount ammunition; they also carry a Tai Yang Technologies commercial SATCOM system. 938 and 939 were fitted with McDonnell Douglas Astronautics Mast-Mounted Sight (a modified helicopter electro-optical device) during their reactivations in the U.S.A.: the spherical antennas are mounted on the forward face of the pilothouse.

CORVETTES [FFL]

Note: Under the Kuang Hua V program, announced in 7-96, the ROCN planned to construct 10 to 12 guided-missile-equipped corvettes of around 2,000 tons displacement, but the entire program appears to have been halted.

GUIDED-MISSILE PATROL COMBATANTS [PGG]

♦ 12 Jing Chiang class (Project Kuang Hua III)

Bldr: China SB, Kaohsiung (603: United [Lien-Ho] SB, Kaohsiung)

	Laid down	L	In serv.
603 Jing Chiang	18-8-93	27-6-94	1-12-94
605 Dang Chiang	1-9-97	18-6-98	7-9-99
606 Sing Chiang	1-9-97	14-8-98	7-9-99
607 Feng Chiang	1-98	22-10-98	. . .
608 Tzeng Chiang	1-98	12-98	. . .
609 Kao Chiang	6-98	3-99	11-99
610 Jin Chiang	6-98	13-5-99	. . .
611 Hsiang Chiang	10-98	7-99	5-00
612 Tze Chiang	10-98	9-99	21-7-00
613 Po Chiang	3-99	11-99	21-7-00
615 Chang Chiang	3-99	3-00	21-7-00
617 Chu Chiang	3-99	5-00	21-7-00

Jing Chiang (603)—with Hsiung Feng-I missiles *DTM*

Feng Chiang (607)—outboard *Sing Chiang* (606) *DTM,* 1-00

Hsiang Chiang (611)—outboard a sister *DTM,* 7-00

D: 500 tons light (680 fl) **S:** 25.1 kts **Dim:** 61.41 × 9.50 × 2.5
A: 1 40-mm 70-cal. Bofors AA; 1 20-mm 68-cal. T 75 AA; 2 single 12.7-mm mg; 2 d.c. racks (4 Mk 6 d.c. each); 2 mine rails (8 tot. mines)—603 only: 4 Hsiung Feng-I SSM (see remarks)
Electronics:
Radar: 1 Decca BridgeMaster 250 (603: CS/UPS-60X) nav.—605 and later: Terma Scanter Mil 009 surf. search—603 only: 1 CS/SPG-21A missile f.c.
Sonar: Simrad SS-247 hull-mounted HF (24 kHz active/passive)
EW: Litton WD-2A intercept; DLT-6 130-mm decoy syst. (2 6-round RL)
E/O: all except 603: Contraves Brashear LSEOS Mk IIA f.c.—603 only: El-Op Sea Eye FLIR
M: 2 MTU 16V1163 TB93 diesels; 2 props; 15,020 bhp (12,800 sust.)
Range: 3,600/15 **Crew:** 7 officers, 25 enlisted (accomm. for 50 tot.)

Remarks: Prototype 603 was ordered 25-6-93 and work commenced 18-8-93 as part of the naval Kuang Hua III (Second Generation Combatant III) program. Was to have been a class of 12 naval patrol boats for the planned Coastal Patrol Administration, which was never organized, but in mid-1995, it was announced that the remaining 11 would be built after all. The contract was tendered 19-6-96, then canceled over alleged financial irregularities; it was reinstated 26-6-97. Cost for first unit was $19 million, and the remaining 11 were to cost about $15 million each. All are named for Taiwanese rivers. The failure of the U.S.-made gun fire-control system to pass trials delayed the commissioning of the first five units into 9-99. A sister is operated by the coast guard as the *Taipei* (116).
Hull systems: Fin stabilizers are fitted. 605 and later have Sperry Mk 39 ring-laser gyros and SRD-331M doppler speed logs.
Combat systems: Most armament and other combat systems on 603 were recycled from a retired destroyer. 603 carries two inspection boats and is equipped with two firefighting water cannon. The surface-search radar on 603 is a license-built version of the Canadian Marconi LN-66. While 603 is normally equipped with four missiles, the others had only weight and space provision; as of 2001, however, it was planned to mount Hsiung Feng-II antiship missiles removed from PFG-2-class frigates. The E/O fire-control system in 605 and later controls the 40-mm AA gun and has a low-light t.v., infrared sensors, and a laser rangefinder on the stabilized director. 603 has a Kollmorgen Mk 985 periscopic backup gun director, but the gun is primarily locally controlled. German Buck Mk 245 Giant IR and Mk 214 Sea Gnat radar decoy rockets are used with Danish-made decoy system.

GUIDED-MISSILE PATROL CRAFT [PTG]

♦ 0 (+ 1 + 29) Kuang Hua VI project

Bldr: first unit: Tsoying Logistics Command, Kaohsiung (in serv. 4-03); others: China SB, Kaohsiung, with Jong Shyn SB and Ching Fu SB

Kuang Hua VI project—official model of the original, smaller concept *DTM,* 1996

D: 180 tons (fl) **S:** 30–36 kts **Dim:** 40.0 × 7.0 × . . .
A: 4 Hsiung Feng-II missiles; 1 40-mm 70-cal. Bofors L70 AA
Electronics: Radar: . . .
M: 3 diesels; 3 outdrive CP props; . . . bhp **Range:** 1,000/30 **Crew:** . . . tot.

Remarks: The program was approved in 7-96, and the design is in development as a one-for-one replacement for the Hai Ou class, but with only 30 to be built; all were to be completed by 2003 at a total cost of more than $3 billion, but as of late 1998, plans called for building and testing a prototype before committing to series production. During 4-99 it was announced that only the prototype would be ordered initially. On 5-1-01, production of the prototype was approved, but as of 11-01, the final design still had not been completed nor the main engines selected. The design, developed by the ROCN's Ship Development Center, will employ stealth techniques to reduce radar and infrared signatures and has been enlarged in 1997 from the original 34.5-m, 150-ton concept.
Combat systems: Will employ the Taiwanese-developed Ta-Cheng tactical data system and a ship-to-shore datalink. A new stand-alone fire-control system for the missiles, with a single display and command console, is to be employed. The antiship missiles are to be mounted in pairs athwartships behind sloped bulwarks to reduce radar signature. The 40-mm mount is to be placed forward but may be replaced by another weapon; at the stern, either a 20-mm T 75S AA gun or a point-defense SAM system may be installed.

♦ 47 Hai Ou class

Bldrs: China SB, Kaohsiung (In serv. 1980–84)

FABG 7 through FABG 12
FABG 14 through FABG 21
FABG 23 through FABG 30
FABG 32 through FABG 39
FABG 41 through FABG 57

Hai Ou–class FABG 52 *Ships of the World,* 1-98

D: 47 tons (56 fl) **S:** 40 kts **Dim:** 22.87 × 5.50 × 1.00 (2.02 props)
A: 2 Hsiung Feng-I SSM; 1 20-mm 68-cal. T 75 AA; 2 single 12.7-mm mg
Electronics:
Radar: 1 CS/UPS-60X nav.; 1 Lockheed Martin HR-76C5 (CS/SPG-21A) missile target-desig.
EW: Litton WD-2A intercept; 2 paired AV-2 decoy RL
M: 2 MTU 12V331 TC92 diesels; 2 props; 2,605 bhp **Electric:** 30 kw tot.
Range: 700/32 **Crew:** 2 officers, 8 enlisted

Remarks: Design is based closely on an original pair of imported Israeli Dvora class. Class name means "Seagull." All are attached to the Hai Chiao ("Sea Dragon") division, homeported at Makung, Tsoying, Anping, Wuchi, Keelung, and Suao. Two similar, earlier craft of Taiwanese design and construction were disarmed and transferred to Paraguay in 11-94.
Hull systems: Aluminum construction. Made 45 kts light on trials but are now capable of only 25–30 kts maximum speed. Hullform differs from that of the Dvora class and provides greater speed on less horsepower.

GUIDED-MISSILE PATROL CRAFT [PTG] *(continued)*

Hai Ou–class FABG 10 *DTM,* 10-98

Combat systems: The fire-control radar is a variant of the HR-76 C2 used on destroyers and it is accompanied by a Kollmorgen Mk 35 optical sight projecting through the pilothouse roof. Early units had a pylon mast and the missile launchers situated near the stern; later units (the majority) have a lattice mast and the missile launchers located closer to amidships. Shoulder-launched Stinger point-defense SAMs may also be carried. FABG 11 has Israeli-made missile-control equipment and an Israeli fire-control radar.

♦ 2 Israeli Dvora class

Bldr: Israeli Aircraft Industries, Be'er Sheva (In serv. ca. 1980)

FABG 5 FABG 6

D: 47 tons (56 fl) **S:** 36 kts **Dim:** 21.62 × 5.49 × 0.94 (1.82 props)
A: 2 Gabriel-II SSM; 1 20-mm 68-cal. T 75 AA; 2 single 12.7-mm mg
Electronics:
Radar: 1 Decca 926 nav.; 1 Elta EL/M-2221 missile f.c.
E/O: Elop optical missile f.c.
M: 2 MTU 12V331 TC82 diesels; 2 props; 2,860 bhp **Electric:** 30 kw tot.
Range: 700/32; 1,200/17 **Crew:** 2 officers, 8 enlisted

Remarks: Procured as prototypes for the later Hai Ou variant, but equipped with a standard Israeli weapon and sensor fit (the 20-mm gun was added later and has a Mk 62 remote director).

♦ 2 Lung Chiang class

	Bldr	In serv.
601 Lung Chiang	Tacoma Boatbldg, Tacoma, Wash.	15-5-78
602 Sui Chiang	China SB Corp., Kaohsiung	6-83

Sui Chiang (602) *Ships of the World,* 1996

D: 218 tons (240 fl) **S:** 36.2 kts
Dim: 50.14 (46.94 pp) × 7.26 × 1.65 (hull; 3.05 max.)
A: 4 Hsiung Feng-I SSM; 1 76-mm 62-cal. OTOBreda DP; 1 40-mm 70-cal. Bofors L70 AA; 2 single 12.7-mm mg
Electronics:
Radar: 1 Goldstar . . . nav.; 1 Raytheon SPS-58C surf./air search; Lockheed Martin HR-76 f.c.
EW: WD-2A intercept; 2 paired AV-2 (602: SMOC-4) decoy RL
M: CODOG: 3 G.M. 12V149 TI diesels (1,800 bhp each), 3 AVCO-Lycoming TF-40A gas turbines (5,000 shp each); 3 CP props; 15,000 shp max.
Range: 700/36 (gas turbines); 1,900/30 (3 diesels); 2,700/12 (1 diesel)
Fuel: 14,869 gallons **Crew:** 6 officers, 32 enlisted

Remarks: Design is a variation of the Tacoma Boatbuilding (U.S.) PSMM Mk-5 design. The second unit is of a revised design with fin stabilizers; a planned six additional were canceled. Both had been brought up to the same standard of equipment by 1990. 601 is to be decommissioned soon and may be transferred abroad.
Combat systems: The HR-76 radar for the H-930 Mod. 2 weapons-control system is mounted in a radome atop the mainmast, and the antenna for the SPS-58A radar is on a stub mast forward of the exhaust stack. The original twin Emerlec 30-mm AA mount has been replaced by a 40-mm mount.

PATROL CRAFT [PC]

♦ 8 32-meter class

Bldr: China SB, Kaohsiung (In serv. 1987–90)

PCL-1 Ning Hai PCL-5 . . . Hai PCL-8 . . . Hai
PCL-2 Ann Hai PCL-6 . . . Hai PCL-9 . . . Hai
PCL-3 . . . Hai PCL-7 . . . Hai

PCL-8 *DTM,* 8-99

D: 100 tons (143 fl) **S:** 40 kts **Dim:** 32.10 × 8.99 × 1.80
A: 1 40-mm 60-cal. Bofors AA; 1 20-mm 68-cal. T 75 AA; 2 d.c. racks (4 d.c. each)
Electronics: Radar: 1 Decca . . . nav.—Sonar: . . . hull-mounted HF
M: 3 MTU 12V396 TB93 diesels; 3 props; 5,880 bhp
Range: . . . **Fuel:** 36 tons **Crew:** 3 officers, 13 enlisted

Remarks: Designed by Vosper-QAF, Singapore. Intended for harbor and coastal patrol service. They are assigned to the Coastal Patrol Command under the tactical control of various naval bases and have a Gemini dinghy on davits aft. *Hai* means "sea." The 40-mm gun is on a locally made power-driven mounting. A 20-mm mount was added on the fantail around 1994 in place of the original two single 12.7-mm mg.

Note: At least six small, GRP-hulled armed launches were in use for escort duties in the Matsu Island region as of 4-01. Armed with either a 40-mm Mk 19 grenade launcher or a 12.7-mm mg and crewed by two or three, the white-painted craft are powered by two gasoline outboard engines and have a JRC navigational radar.

MINE WARFARE SHIPS

Note: An indigenously developed follow-on class based on the MWW 50 class was reported to be under construction as of 7-96; the ships were said to be of 588 tons full load displacement, 49.9 m overall by 9.4 m beam, and intended to employ an "automatic" minehunting system, but no actual ship has materialized. Also under consideration is construction of a small mine countermeasures craft with a design based on that of a commercial fishing boat.

♦ 4 MWW 50–class coastal minehunters [MHC]

Bldr: Abeking & Rasmussen, Lemwerder, Germany

	Laid down	L	In serv.
1301 Yung Feng (ex-*Explorer-I*)	26-4-90	29-10-90	12-7-91
1302 Yung Chia (ex-*Explorer-II*)	26-4-90	29-10-90	12-7-91
1303 Yung Nien (ex-*Explorer-III*)	22-10-90	2-5-91	12-7-91
1305 Yung Shun (ex-*Explorer-IV*)	22-10-90	2-5-91	12-7-91

Yung Feng (1301) *DTM,* 1998

D: 464.5 tons (558.3 fl) **S:** 15 kts **Dim:** 49.90 × 10.80 (9.80 wl) × 2.80
A: 1 20-mm 68-cal. T 75 AA; 2 single 12.7-mm mg
Electronics:
Radar: 1 Decca . . . nav.
Sonar: Thales TSM 2022 through-hull VDS
M: 2 MTU 8V396 TB 93 diesels; 2 props; 2,180 bhp
Range: 2,500/12 **Crew:** 5 officers, 40 enlisted

Remarks: Two were ordered 14-9-88 and two on 23-3-89. Were delivered without armament or mine countermeasures equipment in a blue hull/white superstructure paint scheme and lettered "CPC Offshore" on their sides for the China Petroleum Corporation, which had ostensibly ordered them as "multipurpose offshore vessels" intended for "support to oil rigs, oceanographic research, fire fighting, pollution control, and search and rescue." Were not formally commissioned until 3-95. A planned order for up to eight more was canceled due to a procurement scandal over spare parts for the first four, which have proven difficult to maintain. A Taiwanese press report gave the name of 1302 as *Yung Pei.*

MINE WARFARE SHIPS *(continued)*

Yung Shun (1305) *DTM,* 1998

Hull systems: Wooden hull construction. At least one has suffered from mechanical problems.
Combat systems: Have the Thales IBIS-V mine countermeasures data system. Each can carry one Pinguin A1 search/classification and one Pinguin B3 mine localization and disposal ROV. In 6-97, a 20-mm AA replaced the firefighting monitor formerly mounted on the foredeck.

♦ 4 ex-U.S. Aggressive-class minehunter/minesweepers [MHS]
Bldr: J. M. Martinac, Tacoma, Wash. (1306: Wilmington Boat Works, Wilmington, Calif.)

	Laid down	L	In serv.
1306 Yung Yang (ex-*Implicit,* MSO 455)	29-10-51	1-8-53	10-3-54
1307 Yung Tzu (ex-*Conquest,* MSO 488)	26-3-53	20-5-54	20-7-55
1308 Yung Ku (ex-*Gallant,* MSO 489)	21-5-53	4-6-54	14-9-55
1309 Yung Teh (ex-*Pledge,* MSO 492)	24-6-54	20-7-55	20-4-56

Yung Ku (1308) *DTM,* 1998

Yung Tzu (1307) C. Chung, 7-96

D: 716 tons light; 857 tons std. (920 fl) **S:** 14 kts **Dim:** 52.42 × 10.97 × 4.2
A: 2 single 12.7-mm M2 mg
Electronics:
Radar: 1 Raytheon SPS-64(V)9 nav.
Sonar: SQQ-14 variable-depth minehunting (350 kHz)
M: 4 Waukesha L-1616 diesels; 2 CP props; 2,400 bhp
Range: 3,300/10 **Fuel:** 48 tons **Crew:** 10 officers, 68 enlisted

Remarks: 1307–1309 were transferred 3-8-94 and 1306 on 30-9-94. All had outer hull planking replaced prior to delivery in Taiwan; they were formally commissioned at Kaohsiung 1-3-95.
Hull systems: Wooden construction and nonmagnetic, stainless-steel machinery. All were given very thorough rehabilitations during the early to mid-1970s, receiving semi-enclosed bridges, enlarged superstructures abaft the bridge, SQQ-14 minehunting sonars, new communications gear, and upgraded accommodations.
Combat systems: Have the SLQ-37(V) magnetic sweep system, incorporating A Mk 4(V) and A Mk 6(B) acoustic arrays and the SLQ-38 wire sweep. Hoist machinery for the SQQ-14 minehunting sonar occupies the position of the former 40-mm AA gun. Plans to update their mine countermeasures systems have not reached fruition.

♦ 1 U.S. MSC 289–class coastal minesweeper
Bldr: Dorchester SY, Dorchester, N.J.

	Laid down	L	In serv.
161 Yung Lo (ex-MSC 306)	26-6-64	23-10-65	10-6-66

D: 335 tons (392 fl) **S:** 13.6 kts **Dim:** 44.32 × 8.29 × 2.59 (hull)
A: 1 twin 20-mm 70-cal. Mk 24 Oerlikon AA
Electronics:
Radar: 1 Decca 1226 nav.
Sonar: UQS-1D hull-mounted (100 kHz)
M: 2 Waukesha L-1616 diesels; 2 props; 1,200 bhp
Range: 2,500/10; 3,500/7 **Fuel:** 40 tons **Crew:** 6 officers, 35 enlisted

Remarks: Departed U.S. waters 7-7-66 but did not arrive at Tsoying until 20-2-67. Wooden construction. The sonar is primarily intended for detecting moored mines and is of little or no use against bottomed mines. Carries the A Mk 4(V) acoustic mine countermeasure. Sister *Yung Hsin* (160, ex-MSC 302) was stricken during 5-95.

♦ 3 ex-Belgian Adjutant and U.S. MSC 268*–class coastal minesweepers [MSC]

	Bldr	In serv.
158 Yung Chuan (ex-MSC 278)*	Tacoma Boat, Tacoma, Wash.	10-6-59
167 Yung Ching (ex-*Eekloo,* ex-MSC 101)	Hodgdon Bros., Maine	5-53
168 Yung Chen (ex-*Maaseick,* ex-MSC 78)	Adams Yacht, Quincy, Mass.	7-53

Yung Chuan (158) *DTM,* 4-98

D: 167, 168: 337 tons (385 fl); 158: 335 tons (378 fl) **S:** 13.6 kts
Dim: 167, 168: 43.92 (41.50 wl) × 8.26 × 2.17 (2.62 max.)—158: 44.45 × 8.50 × 2.59 (max.)
A: 1 twin 20-mm 70-cal. Oerlikon Mk 24 AA
Electronics:
Radar: 1 Decca 707 nav.
Sonar: Simrad SA950 hull-mounted (95 kHz)
M: 167, 168: 2 G.M. 8-268A diesels; 2 props; 1,200 bhp—158: 4 G.M. Detroit Diesel 6-71 diesels; 2 props; 890 bhp)
Range: 2,500/12; 3,500/7 **Fuel:** 40 tons **Crew:** 6 officers, 35 enlisted

Remarks: Wooden hulls. 158 was transferred on completion; the others were transferred between 7-69 and 11-69. Have been modernized and rehabilitated under the Fu Yung program: 158 in 1983–84 and the others by 1987. 158 has a lower bridge structure than the others. Carry A Mk 4(V) acoustic mine countermeasures.
Disposals: Sister *Yung Ping* (156, ex-MSC 140) was stricken in 1982 and *Yung Chi* (166, ex-*Charleroi,* ex-MSC 152) and *Yung Nien* (479, ex-MSC 277) by 1991. *Yung Ju* (159, ex-MSC 300) ran aground off the west coast of Taiwan and was stricken in 1992. *Yung Sui* (164; ex-*Diksmuide,* ex-MSC 65) had been stricken by 1994 and *Yung Fu* (162, ex-*Diest,* ex-MSC 77), *Yung Shan* (165, ex-MSC 63), and *Yung Jen* (163, ex-MSC 64) were stricken during 5-95.

AMPHIBIOUS WARFARE SHIPS

♦ 1 command ship/tank landing ship [LCC]
Bldr: Dravo Corp., Neville Island, Pittsburgh, Pa.

	L	In serv.
LCC 1 Kaohsiung (ex-219; ex-*Chung Hai,* LST 229; ex-*Dukes County,* LST 735)	11-3-44	26-4-44

D: 1,653 tons (3,675 fl) **S:** 11 kts **Dim:** 99.98 × 15.24 × 4.27
A: 2 twin 40-mm 60-cal. Bofors Mk 1 Mod. 2 AA; 2 single 40-mm 60-cal. Bofors Mk 3 AA; 2 single 20-mm 68-cal. T 75 AA; 4 single 12.7-mm mg
Electronics:
Radar: 1 CS/UPS-60 nav.; 1 Raytheon SPS-10 surf. search; 1 Lockheed Martin (R.C.A.) SPS-6C air search
M: 2 G.M. 12-567A diesels; 2 props; 1,700 bhp
Electric: 300 kw tot. **Range:** 15,000/9 **Crew:** 11 officers, 100 enlisted

Remarks: Transferred 21-5-57; converted to a command ship in 1964, with additional communications gear and radars. Is assigned to the 205th Squadron. Retains bow doors. An SPS-6C radar antenna has replaced the original SPS-12; the actual set installed may be a variant of the SPS-58. Has one Taiwanese Mk 62 and two U.S. Mk 51 optical gun f.c. directors.

AMPHIBIOUS WARFARE SHIPS *(continued)*

Kaohsiung (LCC-1) *DTM,* 1998

♦ 1 ex-U.S. Anchorage-class dock landing ship [LSD]
Bldr: General Dynamics, Quincy, Mass.

	Laid down	L	In serv.
193 Shui Hai (ex-*Tan Hai;* ex-*Pensacola,* LSD 38)	12-3-69	11-7-70	27-3-71

Shui Hai (193) William H. Clarke, 4-00

D: 8,200 tons light (13,680 fl) **S:** 22 kts
Dim: 168.66 (162.80 wl) × 25.90 × 5.60 (6.10 max.)
A: 2 20-mm Mk 15 Phalanx gatling CIWS; 6 single 12.7-mm M2 mg
Electronics:
Radar: 1 Raytheon SPS-64(V)9 nav.; 1 Raytheon SPS-10F surf. search; 1 Lockheed Martin SPS-40D air search
EW: Raytheon SLQ-32(V)1 intercept; Mk 36 SRBOC decoy syst. (4 6-round Mk 137 RL); SLQ-25 Nixie towed torpedo decoy syst.
M: 2 sets de Laval geared steam turbines; 2 props; 24,000 shp
Boilers: 2 Foster-Wheeler; 42.3 kg/cm^2, 467° C
Range: 14,800/12 **Fuel:** 2,750 tons
Crew: 18 officers, 303–304 enlisted + troops: 25 officers, 311 enlisted

Remarks: Transferred 22-9-99. Assigned to the new Fast-Response Amphibious Group on 1-5-00, prior to arrival on 2-6-00. Sister *Ft. Fisher* (LSD 40) was offered to Taiwan for transfer but was not accepted; the ROCN nonetheless still desires to acquire a second ship of the class.
Hull systems: Can accommodate (with or without portable mezzanine deck installed) 1–3 LCU, 6–9 LCM(8), 12–18 LCM(6), or 50 LVT in the 131.06 × 15.24-m well deck. One LCM(6), one LCP, and two LCPLs can be stowed on deck, handled by the two 50-ton cranes. Has 1,115 m^2 of vehicle parking space forward of the docking well. The helicopter deck is removable and has one landing spot. Carries 90 tons of JP-5 fuel for helicopters.
Combat systems: Mk 56 and Mk 63 gun directors were removed in 1977, as were two twin 76.2-mm gunmounts by 1990 and the remaining 76.2-mm mounts in 1993–94.

♦ 1 ex-U.S. Cabildo-class dock landing ship [LSD]
Bldr: Newport News SB & DD, Newport News, Va.

	Laid down	L	In serv.
191 Chung Cheng (ex-*Comstock,* LSD 19)	3-1-45	28-4-45	2-7-45

D: 4,790 tons (9,375 fl) **S:** 15.6 kts **Dim:** 139.52 (138.38 wl) × 22.0 × 5.49
A: 1 4-round Sea Chaparral point-defense SAM syst. (16 MIM-72F missiles); 4 quadruple 40-mm 60-cal. Bofors Mk 2 AA
Electronics:
Radar: 1 Canadian Marconi LN-66 nav.; 1 Raytheon SPS-5 surf. search
M: 2 sets geared steam turbines; 2 props; 9,000 shp
Boilers: 2 single-drum; 17.5 kg/cm^2 **Range:** 8,000/15; 16,675/9.5
Fuel: 1,758 tons **Crew:** 17 officers, 230 enlisted + up to 1,200 troops

Chung Cheng (191) H&L Van Ginderen, 1-97

Remarks: Acquired in 1985 from a scrap dealer for cannibalization, but was found to be in good condition and was recommissioned during 9-2-86, followed by a refit that ended in 1-87. Took the name and number of the former *Ashland*-class LSD *White Marsh* (LSD 8), which had been transferred on loan 17-11-60 and purchased outright during 5-76. Is employed in resupply service to Pratas Reef islands in South China Sea. Sister *Chen Hai* (LSD 192; ex-*Fort Marion,* LSD 22), transferred by sale on 15-4-77, was stricken 1-6-99.
Hull systems: Has a helicopter platform over the 119.5 × 13.4–m docking well, which can accommodate three LCUs, 18 LCMs, or 32 amphibious armored troop carriers. The boilers do not have superheat.
Combat systems: Has four U.S. Mk 51 and one Taiwanese Mk 62 lead-computing gun f.c.s., with the latter employing stabilization and range information from the surface-search radar for use against surface and shore targets.

♦ 2 ex-U.S. Newport-class tank landing ships [LST]
Bldr: Philadelphia Naval Shipyard

	Laid down	L	In serv.
232 Chung Ho (ex-*Manitowoc,* LST 1180)	1-2-67	4-6-69	24-1-70
233 Chung Ping (ex-*Sumter,* LST 1181)	14-11-67	13-12-69	20-6-70

Chung Ho (232) Chris Sattler, 6-00

Chung Ho (232) Chris Sattler, 6-00

D: 4,975 tons light (8,576 fl) **S:** 22 kts (20 sust.)
Dim: 159.2 (171.3 over horns) × 21.18 × 5.3 (aft; 1.80 fwd)
A: 2 twin 40-mm 60-cal. Bofors Mk 1 Mod. 2 AA; 1 20-mm Mk 15 Phalanx CIWS; 2 single 12.7-mm mg
Electronics:
Radar: 1 Raytheon SPS-64(V)9 nav.; 1 Raytheon SPS-10F surf. search
TACAN: SRN-15A
M: 6 G.M. Electromotive Div. 16-645-E5 diesels; 2 CP props; 16,500 bhp—bow-thruster
Electric: 2,250 kw tot. (3 × 750 kw, Alco 251-E diesels driving; 450 V, 60 Hz a.c.)
Range: 14,250/14 **Fuel:** 1,750 tons
Crew: 13 officers, 174 enlisted + troops: 20 officers, 294 enlisted + 72 emergency accomm.

Remarks: Were to transfer on lease 7-1-95 but their reactivation for transfer was not begun until mid-1996 at Newport News Shipbuilding & Dry Dock, Virginia; they had been decommissioned 30-6-93 and placed in reserve on 30-9-93. The official transfer took place on 18-4-97 at Guam, and the ships were formally commissioned on 8-5-98 at their base at Tsoying. Both were purchased outright 29-9-00. They were assigned to the new Fast-Response Amphibious Group on 1-5-00. Taiwan turned down the offer of a third unit, *Newport* (LST 1179), in 1997, and the offer of the *Schenectady* (LST 1185) was rejected during 2000.
Hull systems: Can transport 2,000 tons of cargo, or, for beaching, 500 tons, on 1,765 m^2 of deck space. A side-thruster propeller forward helps when marrying to a causeway. There is a 34-m-long, 75-ton-capacity mobile aluminum ramp forward, which is linked to the tank deck by a second from the upper deck. Aft is a 242-m^2 helicopter platform and a stern door for loading and unloading vehicles. Four pontoon causeway sections can be carried on the hull sides. The tank deck, which has a 75-ton-capacity turntable at both ends, can carry 23 AAV-7A1 armored personnel carriers, 29 M 48 tanks, or 41 2.5-ton trucks, while the upper deck can accept 29 2.5-ton trucks. Normally carry three LCVPs and one LCP in Welin davits. Have two 10-ton cranes. Carry 141,600 gallons vehicle fuel.

AMPHIBIOUS WARFARE SHIPS *(continued)*

Combat systems: The Mk 63 radar gunfire-control systems were removed during 1977–78, but unlike other units of their class, they retained the two twin 76.2-mm gunmounts on delivery; by 10-98, 233 had had the 76.2-mm mounts replaced by two twin 40-mm 60-cal. AA mounts. A TACAN antenna has been added atop the mainmast.

♦ 11 ex-U.S. LST 1- and LST 542–class tank landing ships [LST]
(3 in reserve)

	Bldr	In serv.
201 Chung Hai (ex-LST 755)	American Br., Ambridge, Pa.	29-7-44
205 Chung Chien (ex-LST 716)	Jeffersonville B & M, Ind.	18-8-44
208 Chung Shun (ex-LST 732)	Dravo, Pittsburgh, Pa.	10-4-44
216 Chung Kuang (ex-LST 503)	Jeffersonville B & M, Ind.	14-12-43
217 Chung Suo (ex-*Bradley County,* LST 400)	Newport News SB & DD, Va.	7-1-43
218 Chung Chi (ex-LST 279)	American Br., Ambridge, Pa.	25-10-43
221 Chung Chuan (ex-*Wan Tu,* ex-LST 640)	Chicago Bridge & Iron, Seneca, Ill.	18-9-44
226 Chung Chih (ex-*Sagadohoc County,* LST 1091)	American Br., Ambridge, Pa.	6-4-45
227 Chung Ming (ex-*Sweetwater County,* LST 1152)	Dravo, Pittsburgh, Pa.	13-4-45
230 Chung Pang (ex-LST 578)	Missouri Valley Bridge & Iron, Evansville, Ind.	15-7-44
231 Chung Yeh (ex-*Sublette County,* LST 1144)	Chicago Bridge & Iron, Seneca, Ill.	28-5-45

Chung Pang (230)—with two pair of Welin davits per side, aft *DTM,* 1-98

Chung Suo (217)—with unique lattice mast aft *DTM,* 1996

D: 1,653 tons (4,080 fl) **S:** 11.6 kts **Dim:** 99.98 × 15.24 × 3.40
A: 2 twin 40-mm 60-cal. Bofors Mk 1 Mod. 2 AA; 2 single 40-mm 60-cal. Bofors Mk 3 AA; 2 or 4 single 20-mm 68-cal. T 75 AA; 2 or 4 12.7-mm mg
Electronics: 1 CS/UPS-60X nav.
M: 2 G.M. 12-567A diesels; 2 props; 1,700 bhp **Electric:** 300 kw tot.
Range: 15,000/9 **Fuel:** 569 tons **Crew:** 100–125 tot.

Remarks: 201 was transferred 29-5-46, 205 on 12-6-46, 208 on 29-5-46, 216 on 4-4-55, 217 and 218 on 30-6-55, 221 on 29-5-46, 226 on 21-10-58, 227 on 24-10-58, 230 on 21-9-58, and 231 on 21-9-61. All were re-engined and extensively rebuilt during the late 1960s, in many cases becoming almost new ships. From 1992 on, a further modernization under the Chung Hsing program provided new engines, generators, and air-conditioning systems, plus rebuilt bridge superstructures. 226 was to have been converted as a command ship (LCC 2) and did receive the same large lattice mast as LCC 1 (q.v.).
Combat systems: Have two U.S. Mk 51 and one Taiwanese Mk 62 gun f.c.s., with the latter employing stabilization and range information from the surface-search radar for use against surface and shore targets. Most have four sets of Welin davits, while 226 has six and 205 has two; each set handles one LCVP landing craft. All carry Tai Yang Co. commercial SATCOM telephone equipment.
Disposals: *Chung Cheng* (224; ex-*Lafayette County,* LST 859) was stricken during 1989. Between 1984 and 1991, six others were laid up at Kaohsiung: *Chung Ting* (203, ex-LST 537), *Chung Chi* (206, ex-LST 1017), *Chung Lien* (209, ex-LST 1050), *Chung Chiang* (225; ex-*San Bernardino County,* LST 1110), *Chung Shu* (228, ex-LST 520), and *Chung Wan* (229, ex-LST 535); all were discarded during 1993. *Chung Sheng* (222, ex-LST(H) 1033) ran aground near Keelung on 5-10-95 and was stricken and scrapped on site. Stricken for scrap on 8-11-97 were *Chung Hsing* (204, ex-LST 557), *Ching Yung* (210, ex-574), and *Chung Fu* (223; ex-*Iron County,* LST 840).

♦ 4 ex-U.S. LSM 1–class medium landing ships [LSM]

	Bldr	L	In serv.
341 Mei Chin (ex-LSM 155)	Charleston NY, S.C.	19-6-44	26-7-44
347 Mei Sung (ex-LSM 457)	Western Pipe & Steel, San Pedro, Calif.	28-1-45	28-3-45
353 Mei Ping (ex-LSM 471)	Brown SB, Houston, Texas	17-2-45	23-2-45
356 Mei Lo (ex-LSM 362)	Brown SB, Houston, Texas	9-12-44	11-1-45

Mei Ping (353) *DTM,* 10-98

D: 513 tons light; 743 tons std. (1,095 fl) **S:** 12.5 kts
Dim: 62.03 (59.89 wl) × 10.52 × 2.20 (2.54 max.)
A: 2 twin 40-mm 60-cal. Bofors Mk 1 Mod. 2 AA; 4 single 20-mm 68-cal. T 75 AA; 4 single 12.7-mm mg
Electronics: Radar: 1 CS/UPS-60X nav.
M: 2 G.M. Electromotive Div. 16-278A (353, 356: 2 Fairbanks-Morse 38D8⅛ × 10) diesels; 2 props; 2,800 bhp
Electric: 240 kw tot. **Range:** 5,000/7 **Fuel:** 165 tons
Crew: 8–13 officers, 35–56 enlisted

Remarks: 341 and 347 were transferred in 1946, 353 in 11-56, and 356 in 5-62. Have been extensively modernized, the original cylindrical pilothouse and bridge replaced with larger, rectangular structure and a twin 40-mm AA mount added aft. Have one U.S. Mk 51 and one Taiwanese Mk 62 gun f.c.s., with the latter employing stabilization and range information from the surface-search radar for use against surface and shore targets. Pennant numbers were changed from the 600 series during modernizations.

♦ 2 U.S. LCU 1610–class utility landing craft [LCU]
Bldr: China SB Corp., Kaohsiung (In serv. 1979)

LCU-497 LCU-498

LCU-497 *DTM,* 1998

D: 190 tons (390 normal, 437 fl) **S:** 11 kts **Dim:** 41.07 × 9.07 × 2.08
A: 2 single 20-mm 68-cal. T 75 AA; 2 single 12.7-mm mg
Electronics: Radar: 1 CS/UPS-60X nav.
M: 4 G.M. Detroit Diesel 6-71 diesels; 2 Kort-nozzle props; 1,200 bhp
Electric: 40 kw tot.
Range: 1,200/8 **Fuel:** 13 tons **Crew:** 4 officers, 15 enlisted

Remarks: Built under license from the United States. Do not have names. Cargo capacity: 180 tons; cargo space: 36.9 × 7.62 m max. (with a 4.5-m-wide bow ramp). Up to 400 troops can be accommodated for short periods on deck. Their drive-through feature permits marrying bow and stern to other landing craft or causeways. Have kedging anchor starboard side aft to assist in extraction from beaches.

♦ 6 ex-U.S. LCU 1466–class utility landing craft [LCU]
Bldr: Ishikawajima-Harima, Japan (In serv. 3-55)

LCU-488 Ho Shan (ex-LCU 1596)
LCU-489 Ho Chuan (ex-LCU 1597)
LCU-490 Ho Seng (ex-LCU 1598)
LCU-491 Ho Meng (ex-LCU 1599)
LCU-492 Ho Mou (ex-LCU 1600)
LCU-493 Ho Shou (ex-LCU 1601)

Ho Chuan (LCU-489) *DTM,* 1998

D: 180 tons light (347 fl) **S:** 8 kts **Dim:** 35.08 × 10.36 × 1.60 (aft)
A: 2 single 20-mm 68-cal. T 75 AA; 2 single 12.7-mm mg
Electronics: Radar: 1 CS/UPS-60X nav.
M: 3 G.M. Gray Marine 64 YTL diesels; 3 props; 675 bhp **Electric:** 40 kw tot.
Range: 1,200/6 (700/7 loaded) **Fuel:** 11 tons **Crew:** 4 officers, 15 enlisted

Remarks: Built under the U.S. Offshore Procurement Program. Cargo: 150 tons or 300 troops on the 15.8 × 9.0–m deck, with a 4.3-m-wide bow ramp.

AMPHIBIOUS WARFARE SHIPS *(continued)*

♦ 14 ex-U.S. LCU 501 (LCT(6))–class utility landing craft [LCU]

	In serv.
LCU-401 Ho Chi (ex-LCU 1212)	16-8-44
LCU-402 Ho Huei (ex-LCU 1218)	25-8-44
LCU-403 Ho Yao (ex-LCU 1244)	22-9-44
LCU-405 Ho Feng (ex-LCU 1397)	26-10-44
LCU-406 Ho Chao (ex-LCU 1429)	8-12-44
LCU-407 Ho Teng (ex-LCU 1452)	20-10-44
LCU-481 Ho Shun (ex-LCU 1225)	4-9-44
LCU-482 Ho Tsung (ex-LCU 1213)	17-8-44
LCU-484 Ho Chung (ex-LCU 849)	7-8-44
LCU-485 Ho Chang (ex-LCU 512)	7-9-43
LCU-494 Ho Chun (ex-LCU 892)	27-7-44
LCU-495 Ho Yung (ex-LCU 1271)	19-8-44
LCU-496 Ho Chien (ex-LCU 1278)	22-7-44
SB 1 Ho Chie (ex-LCU 700)	18-4-44

Ho Chun (LCU-494) *Ships of the World,* 2001

D: 158 tons (286 fl) **S:** 10 kts **Dim:** 36.3 (32.0 wl) × 9.96 × 1.27 (max. aft)
A: 2 single 20-mm 68-cal. T 75 AA; 2 single 12.7-mm mg
Electronics: Radar: 1 CS/UPS-60X nav.
M: 3 G.M. 6-71 diesels; 3 props; 675 bhp **Electric:** 20 kw tot.
Fuel: 10.5 tons **Crew:** 4 officers, 15 enlisted

Remarks: Six were transferred between 1946 and 1948, the others in 1958 and 1959. SB 1 has served in an auxiliary role since delivery, and one of the other units has been redesignated SB 2. Sister *Ho Deng* (LCU-404, ex-LCU 1367) sank after a collision in Makung Harbor during a typhoon on 22-8-86, and *Ho Cheng* (LCU-486, ex-LCU 1145) ran aground and was lost 13-2-70. LCU-485 has an enlarged deckhouse on the poop deck.

Note: Taiwan is said to be interested in purchasing U.S.-built LCAC 1–class air-cushion landing craft, funded by the army for use in resupply of army contingents on the Matsu and Quemoy Islands.

♦ 250 U.S. LCM(3)- and LCM(6)-class landing craft [LCM]
Bldrs: U.S. and Taiwan

LCM(6) 2228—with transport *Yuen Feng* (AP 524) in background *DTM,* 5-00

D: 26.7 tons light (62.35 fl) **S:** 9 kts **Dim:** 17.07 × 4.37 × 1.52 (max. aft)
A: 1 or 2 single 12.7-mm mg in some
M: 2 G.M. Gray Marine 64HN9 diesels; 2 props; 450 bhp
Range: 130/9 **Crew:** 5–9 tot.

Remarks: LCM(3) craft displace 56 tons (fl), measure 15.28 m o.a., and carry a cargo of 30 tons and a crew of 4–5. LCM(6) craft can carry 34 tons.

♦ about 100 U.S. LCVP class [LCVP]

LCVP—from the now-stricken landing ship *Chung Fu* (223) C. Chung

D: 13 tons (fl) **S:** 9 kts **Dim:** 10.9 × 3.21 × 1.04
A: 2 single 7.62-mm mg **M:** 1 G.M. Gray Marine 64HN9 diesel; 225 bhp
Range: 110/9 **Crew:** 3 tot.

Remarks: Wooden construction. Cargo: 36 troops or 4 tons. Some 25 to 30 of the total, known as Type 272, were built in Taiwan in the 1970s. Some are equipped with radar and two 7.62-mm mg for use as beach reconnaissance craft. Many are assigned to the LSTs.

♦ . . . U.S. LCPR class [LCP]

LCPR 1902 *DTM,* 1998

D: 8.39 tons light (12 fl) **S:** 10 kts (loaded) **Dim:** 10.69 × 10.79 × 1.00
A: 2 single 7.62-mm mg **M:** 1 G.M. Gray Marine 64HN9 diesel; 225 bhp
Range: 110/9 (loaded) **Crew:** 3 tot. + 36 troops

Remarks: Of uncertain origin, but at least eight remained in service as of the late 1990s; they may have been transferred with since-stricken ex-U.S. Navy APDs. Are probably GRP-hulled versions of the original U.S. World War II–era design. Differ from the similar LCVP in having a smaller cargo well and bow ramp and in mounting the machineguns forward.

♦ . . . M2A2 UDT/patrol launches [LCP]

Remarks: Can achieve 40 kts, carry a 12.7-mm mg, have a crew of 3 or 4, and are equipped with a GPS set. No further data available.

Note: Also in service are several M8-class UDT/patrol launches, built of GRP; they have a speed of 40–45 kts, carry a crew of 8, and are armed with one 12.7-mm and one 7.62-mm mg.

Still in use are 20 or more ARP 2001–class and 15 or more ARP 3001–class UDT/patrol launches [LCP] intended to carry underwater demolition teams to beachheads and to act as patrol craft during amphibious landings; both designs are built of GRP, are powered by a DaimlerChrysler 115 gasoline outboard motor of 115 bhp, and can carry 4–6 commandos. The ARP 3001 is slightly longer, and both designs can be equipped with one 7.62-mm mg. Thirty ARP 3001–class sisters were donated to Honduras in 1996.

For over-the-beach service, some 717 U.S.-made LVT-5 tracked amphibious armored personnel carriers are in use by the marines. Troop-carrying, command, and beach salvage variants are in service.

ARP 2001–*(right)* and ARP 3001–class commando launches—the ARP 2001 series have blunt bows and are slightly longer C. Chung, 1994

AUXILIARIES

♦ 1 Alliance-class oceanographic and hydrographic research ship [AGOR] Bldr: Fincantieri, Muggiano, La Spezia, Italy

	Laid down	L	In serv.
AGS 1601 Ta Kuan	8-4-94	17-12-94	26-9-95

D: 2,466 tons (3,180 fl) **S:** 17 kts (16.3 sust.)
Dim: 93.00 (82.00 pp) × 15.20 × 5.10 **A:** none
Electronics:
Radar: 1 Sperry Marine . . . nav.; 1 . . . nav.
Sonar: Simrad EM 1200

AUXILIARIES *(continued)*

Ta Kuan (AGS 1601) ROCN, via *DTM,* 8-97

M: 2 GMT B.230.12M diesels, AEG CC 3127 generators, electric drive: 2 AEG 1,470-kw motors; 2 props; 4,000 shp—side-thrusters fore and aft
Electric: 1,850 kw tot. (incl. 1 1,605-kw gas-turbine set)
Range: 12,000/15.5 **Crew:** 82 tot. (incl. 20 scientists)

Remarks: Ordered 10-6-93 for use by the Ministry of Transport and Communications. Design is closely based on that of the NATO research ship *Alliance* but is capable of Arctic operations. Is employed primarily in oceanographic research in support of antisubmarine warfare at the underwater sound range off Suao, eastern Taiwan.
Hull systems: Has about 6,100 m^2 of working deck space total and 400 m^2 of lab space. Has a towing winch and 20-ton bollard pull, with 6,000 m of 50-mm cable. Also has a 1,000-kg oceanographic crane with telescopic arm. Special attention was paid to quieting. Has Flume-type passive tank stabilization.

♦ 1 underway-replenishment ship [AOR] Bldr: China SB, Keelung

	Laid down	L	In serv.
AOE 530 Wu Yi	25-6-88	4-3-89	23-6-90

Wu Yi (AOE 530) H&L Van Ginderen/Chris Sattler, 5-99

Wu Yi (AOE 530) Chris Sattler, 5-99

D: 7,700 tons light (17,000 fl) **S:** 20.8 kts **Dim:** 162.12 × 22.00 × 8.60
A: 1 4-round Sea Chaparral SAM syst. (16 MIM-72F missiles); 2 single 40-mm 60-cal. Bofors Mk 3 AA; 2 single 20-mm 68-cal. T 75 AA; 4 single 12.7-mm mg
Electronics:
Radar: 1 GoldStar . . . nav.; 1 CS/UPS-60X nav.; 1 . . . nav.
TACAN: SRN-15
M: 2 Mitsubishi-M.A.N. 14-cyl. diesels; 2 props; 25,000 bhp
Range: 8,000/17.5 **Crew:** 18 officers, 146 enlisted

Remarks: Designed in the U.S.A. by Rosenblatt & Son. The helicopter deck at the stern is capable of handling two CH-47 or S-70C-size helicopters. Capable of underway replenishment on both sides; has four fueling and two solids transfer stations. Carries 9,300 tons of fuel and water and 600 tons of munitions and provisions. The largest naval unit yet built in Taiwan. Reportedly, the hull was found to be warped after launch and has a permanent list, the ship is underpowered, and there are gearbox and steering equipment problems.
Combat systems: The original Bofors L70 AA mounts (which were locally controlled) were replaced by elderly, hand-operated 40-mm 60-cal. mountings in 1999.

♦ 2 ex-U.S. Patapsco-class transport tankers [AOT]
Bldr: Cargill, Savage, Minn.

	Laid down	L	In serv.
AOG 507 Chang Bai (ex-*Elkhorn,* AOG 7)	7-9-42	15-5-43	12-2-44
AOG 517 Hsing Lung (ex-*Pecatonia,* AOG 57)	6-12-44	17-3-45	28-11-45

Chang Bai (AOG 507) *Ships of the World,* 1996

D: 1,850 tons light (4,335 fl) **S:** 14 kts **Dim:** 94.72 (89.0 wl) × 14.78 × 4.78
A: 2 twin 40-mm 60-cal. Bofors Mk 1 Mod 2 AA; 2 single 20-mm 68-cal. T 75 AA; 4 single 12.7-mm mg
Electronics: Radar: 1 CS/UPS-60X nav.
M: 2 G.M. 16-278A diesels; 2 props; 3,300 bhp **Electric:** 460 kw tot.
Range: 4,880/14; 6,940/10 **Fuel:** 314 tons **Crew:** 76 tot.

Remarks: Former gasoline tankers, now used for supplying offshore islands. Cargo: 2,040 tons. 507 was transferred 1-7-72. Both were purchased outright 19-5-76. Sister *Lung Chuan* (515; ex-New Zealand *Endeavour;* ex-*Namakagon,* AOG 53) has been stricken.
Combat systems: Have one U.S. Mk 51 and one Taiwanese-developed Type 62 gun f.c.s. for the 40-mm guns.

♦ 3 Yuen Feng–class transports [AP]
Bldr: Tsoying NSY

	Laid down	L	In serv.
AP 524 Yuen Feng	16-12-81	6-4-82	10-9-82
AP 525 Wu Gang	26-10-83	26-4-84	9-10-84
AP 526 Hsin Kang	. . .	. . .	11-88

Hsin Kang (AP 526) *DTM*

Yuen Feng (AP 524) *Ships of the World,* 2000

D: AP 524: 2,070 tons light; 3,040 tons std. (4,600 fl)—others: 2,804 tons (4,845 fl)
S: 20 (AP 524: 20.4) kts **Dim:** 101.78 × 16.46 (AP 524: 18.0) × 4.57
A: 1 4-round Sea Chaparral point-defense SAM syst. (16 MIM-72F missiles); 2 single 40-mm 60-cal. Bofors Mk 3 AA; 4 single 12.7-mm mg
Electronics:
Radar: 1 Goldstar . . . nav.
EW: Litton WD-2A intercept; Mk 36 SRBOC decoy syst. (2 6-round Mk 137 RL)
M: 2 diesels; 2 props; . . . bhp—bow-thruster
Range: 5,600/16 (AP 524: 5,600/18) **Crew:** 11 officers, 50 (AP 524: 84) enlisted

Remarks: Transports to serve the Quemoy and Matsu Island garrisons, replacing stricken LSTs. Stern was truncated to fit a small berthing area; they do *not* have stern vehicle ramp. AP 524 can carry 500 passengers; AP 525 and 526 can carry more than 600 and have smaller cargo cranes. 526 was hit aft by a South Korean merchant ship at Kaohsiung on 21-3-97; the severe damage was repaired by 13-5-97. Although they had been ordered, AP 527 through 529 may have been canceled in 1998 when the government directed the ROCN to use commercial vessels to transport troops and supplies whenever possible; there is no evidence of their completion.

AUXILIARIES *(continued)*

♦ 1 Wan An–class transport [AP]

Bldr: China SB, Keelung

	Laid down	L	In serv.
AP 523 Wan An	5-5-78	22-7-78	26-1-79

Wan An (AP 523) *DTM,* 1998

D: 2,591 tons (4,262 fl) **S:** 17 kts **Dim:** 101.77 × 16.46 × 4.57
A: 2 single 20-mm 68-cal. T 75 AA; 2 single 12.7-mm mg
Electronics: Radar: 1 Goldstar . . . nav. **M:** 1 6-cyl. diesel; 1 prop; . . . bhp
Range: 5,000/15 **Crew:** 11 officers, 50 enlisted

Remarks: Passenger/cargo ship with accommodations for 500 troops. Has small cargo holds fore and aft. Was involved in a collision with merchant ship *Sunny Gas* on 28-3-97.

♦ 1 Tai Wu–class transport [AP]

Bldr: China SB, Keelung

	Laid down	L	In serv.
AP 518 Tai Wu	6-6-71	17-9-71	6-1-72

Tai Wu (AP 518) *DTM,* 1998

D: 2,591 tons light (4,262 fl) **S:** 17 kts **Dim:** 101.77 × 16.46 × 4.57 (max.)
A: 2 single 40-mm 60-cal. Bofors Mk 3 AA; 2 single 20-mm 68-cal. T 75 AA; 2 single 12.7-mm mg
Electronics: Radar: 1 Goldstar . . . nav. **M:** 1 6-cyl. diesel; 1 prop; . . . bhp
Range: 5,000/15 **Crew:** 11 officers, 55 enlisted

Remarks: 2,510 dwt/3,040 grt. Can carry 500 troops.

♦ 1 ex-U.S. Bolster-class salvage ship [ARS]

Bldr: Basalt Rock Co., Napa, Calif.

	Laid down	L	In serv.
ARS 550 Ta De (ex-*Recovery,* ARS 43)	6-1-45	4-8-45	15-5-46

D: 2,045 tons (fl) **S:** 14.8 kts **Dim:** 65.08 (63.09 wl) × 13.40 × 4.11
A: 2 single 20-mm 68-cal. T 75 AA
Electronics: Radar: 1 Raytheon 3400 nav.; 1 SPS-10F surf. search
M: 4 Caterpillar D-399 diesels, electric drive; 2 props; 3,060 shp (2,440 sust.)
Electric: 460 kw tot. **Range:** 9,000/14; 20,000/7 **Fuel:** 300 tons
Crew: 6 officers, 97 enlisted (in USN service)

Remarks: Transferred by sale 30-9-98; had been decommissioned from the USN 30-9-94. The reported transfer of sister *Hoist* (ARS 40) in 1999 as the *Ta Peng* (ARS 49) was incorrect. The *Conserver* (ARS 39) was offered for transfer during U.S. FY 00 but was not accepted. Differs from the *Diver* class in having slightly greater beam.

♦ 1 ex-U.S. Diver-class salvage ship [ARS]

Bldr: Basalt Rock Co., Napa, Calif.

	Laid down	L	In serv.
ARS 552 Tai Hu (ex-*Grapple,* ARS 7)	8-9-42	31-12-42	16-12-43

D: 1,478 tons (1,745 fl) **S:** 14.8 kts **Dim:** 65.08 (63.09 wl) × 12.40 (11.89 wl) × 4.11
A: 2 single 20-mm 68-cal. T 75 AA **Electronics:** Radar: 1 CS/UPS-60X nav.
M: 4 Caterpillar D-399 diesels, electric drive; 2 props; 3,000 shp
Electric: 460 kw tot. **Range:** 9,000/13; 14,700/7 **Fuel:** 283 tons **Crew:** 85 tot.

Remarks: Transferred 1-12-77.

Tai Hu (ARS 552) H&L Van Ginderen, 1-99

♦ 5 ex-U.S. Cherokee-, Abnaki*-, and Achomawi†-class fleet tugs [ATA]

Bldrs: ATF 551: United Eng., Alameda, Calif.; ATF 555: Cramp SB & DD, Philadelphia; others: Charleston SB & DD, Charleston, S.C.

	Laid down	L	In serv.
ATF 551 Ta Wan (ex-*Apache,* ATF 67)	8-11-44	8-5-45	12-12-45
ATF 553 Ta Mo (ex-*Tawakoni,* ATF 114)*	19-5-43	28-10-43	15-9-44
ATF 554 Ta Tu (ex-*Achomawi,* ATF 148)†	15-1-44	10-9-44	11-11-44
ATF 555 Ta Feng (ex-*Narragansett,* ATF 88)	31-2-42	8-8-42	15-1-43
ATF 563 Ta Tai (ex-*Shakori,* ATF 162)†	9-5-45	9-8-45	20-12-45

Ta Feng (ATF 555)—*Cherokee* class *DTM,* 1998

Ta Tu (ATF 554)—*Achomawi* class *DTM,* 1998

D: ATF 554, 563: 1,640 tons (2,130 fl)—others: 1,235 tons (1,731 fl) **S:** 15 kts
Dim: 62.48 (59.44 wl) × 11.73 × 4.93 (max.; ATF 554, 563: 5.18 max.)
A: 1 40-mm 60-cal. Bofors Mk 3 AA; 2 single 12.7-mm mg (see remarks)
Electronics: Radar: 1 CS/UPS-60X nav.
M: 4 G.M. 12-278 (ATF 553: Caterpillar D399; ATF 554: G.M. 12-278A) diesels, electric drive; 1 prop; 3,000 shp
Electric: 260 or 400 kw tot. **Range:** 6,500/16; 15,000/8 **Fuel:** 295 tons
Crew: 11 officers, 76–78 enlisted

Remarks: ATF 551 was transferred 30-6-74 and ATF 553 on 1-9-78. The others were purchased unarmed 20-6-91 from the U.S. Maritime Administration, along with the ex-*Wenatchee* (ATF 118), which was to be used for cannibalization spares. ATF 551 went aground 15-3-87 but was salvaged for further service. Sister *Ta Tung* (ATF 548; ex-*Chickasaw,* ATF 83) was stricken 16-7-99.
Combat systems: As of early 1999, ATF 563 had 20-mm 70-cal. AA mounts vice the 12.7-mm mg listed.

SERVICE CRAFT

Note: The following entries are by no means an exhaustive listing of the Taiwanese service craft inventory, but precise details are unavailable.

SERVICE CRAFT *(continued)*

♦ **1 ex-U.S. medium auxiliary floating dry dock [YFDM]**
Bldr: Everett Pacific, Calif. (In serv. 6-44)

Fo Wu 7 (ex-*Competent,* AFDM 6, ex-YFD 62)

Dim: 189.6 × 37.8 (28.3 clear width) × 1.9 (16.1 max flooded)
Capacity: 18,000 tons

Remarks: Transferred by sale during 1999. Had been retired from the USN during 7-97 at Pearl Harbor.

♦ **1 ex-U.S. ARD 12–class floating dry dock [YFDL]**
Bldr: Pacific Bridge, Alameda, Calif.

Fo Wu 6 (ex-*Windsor,* ARD 22)

Dim: 149.86 × 24.69 × 1.73 (light) **Capacity:** 3,500 tons

Remarks: In service 4-44, transferred on lease 19-5-76, and purchased outright in 1996.

♦ **1 ex-U.S. ARD 2–class floating dry dock [YFDL]**
Bldr: Pacific Bridge, Alameda, Calif.

Fo Wu 5 (ex-ARD 9)

Dim: 148.03 × 21.64 × 1.75 (light) **Capacity:** 3,500 tons

Remarks: In service 9-43, transferred 12-1-77, and purchased outright in 1981.

♦ **2 ex-U.S. floating dry docks [YFDL]**
Bldr: V. P. Loftis, Wilmington, N.C.

Han Jih (ex-AFDL 34) Hay Tan (ex-AFDL 36)

Dim: 73.15 × 19.69 × 1.3 (light) **Capacity:** 1,000 tons

Remarks: In service 6-44 and 5-44 and transferred in 7-59 and 3-47, respectively.

♦ **1 ex-U.S. floating dry dock [YFDL]**

Kim Men (ex-AFDL 5)

Dim: 60.96 × 19.5 × 1.04 **Capacity:** 1,000 tons

Remarks: Built in 1944 and transferred in 8-58.

♦ **1 personnel ferry [YFL]** Bldr: . . .

	Laid down	L	In serv.
. . . . . .	16-10-96	27-3-97	15-5-97

D: 339 tons (fl) **S:** 12 kts **Dim:** 41.15 × . . . × . . .
Electronics: Radar: 1 Goldstar . . . nav.
M: . . . diesels; . . . props; . . . bhp
Range: 1,200/12 **Crew:** 10 tot. + 350 passengers

♦ **1 German Seahorse-class research submersible [YSS]**
Bldr: . . . . . ., Germany (In serv. 1984)

D: 52 tons sub. **S:** 5 kts sub. **Dim:** 14.5 × 2.3 × . . .
M: battery-powered electric motor; 1 prop; 107 shp
Range: 400/5 sub. **Crew:** 4 tot. + 2 divers

Remarks: Delivery of a second was canceled by the German government. Ostensibly intended for underwater research, but probably employed in clandestine operations.

♦ **0 (+ 4 + 4–5) YTB 50–class large harbor tugs [YTB]**
Bldr: Chung Fu SB, Kaohsiung

	In serv.		In serv.
YTB 50	15-7-99	YTB . . .	13-9-99
YTB . . .	15-8-99	YTB . . .	15-10-99

YTB 50 *DTM,* 6-00

D: approx. 360 tons (fl) **S:** 10.5 kts **Dim:** 28.0 × 8.0 × 3.8
M: 2 Cummins V12 KTA38M2 diesels; Ulstein azimuthal props; 2,400 bhp
Crew: 10–12 tot.

Remarks: Four were ordered in 7-98 to begin replacement of the remaining U.S.-built harbor tugs; four or five more are planned under the Kuang Hua V program, with another 10 possibly to be built later. Are equipped for fire fighting (with a telescoping mast to support a firefighting monitor) and oil-spill recovery. Have a 23-ton bollard pull capability.

♦ **1 or more YTB 48–class large harbor tugs [YTB]**
Bldr: . . . . . . (In serv. . . .)

YTB 48

YTB 48 *DTM,* 1998

D: 286 tons (356 fl) **S:** 12.5 kts **Dim:** 33.05 × 9.30 × 4.14
M: 1 Fairbanks-Morse 38D8⅛ × 12 diesel; 1 prop; 2,000 bhp
Electric: 120 kw tot. **Range:** 2,000/12 **Crew:** 12 tot.

♦ **3 YTL 41–class medium harbor tugs [YTM]**
Bldr: . . ., Taiwan (In serv. 1990–91)

YTL 41 YTL 43 YTL 45

YTL 43 C. Chung, 2-93

Remarks: No data available. Replaced former U.S. Navy small harbor tugs with the same numbers that had been transferred in 1963–64. Are equipped for fire fighting, with a monitor atop the mast, two atop the pilothouse, and one on the after superstructure.

♦ **3 ex-U.S. Army Design 3004 medium harbor tugs [YTM]**

YTL 34 (ex-ST-2002) YTL 36 (ex-ST-2004) YTL 38 (ex-ST-2008)

D: 100 tons light (122 fl) **S:** 12 kts **Dim:** 21.31 × 5.94 × 2.50
M: 1 diesel; 1 prop; 600 bhp **Range:** 3,500/12 **Fuel:** 15 tons **Crew:** 6 tot.

Remarks: Built around 1954 and transferred in 3-62.

MARITIME SECURITY POLICE COASTAL PATROL COMMAND

Established in 1990 under the Ministry of the Interior Civil Police to patrol coastal waters, harbors, and river mouths. Also referred to as the 7th Peace Preservation Police Corps. In time of war, would switch to naval subordination. Duties include interdiction of illegal immigrants, countering smuggling, and fisheries protection within territorial waters. On 8-12-92, the Coastal Patrol Command was given responsibility for coastal defense and received a number of troops from the army and military police. The entire organization may soon be combined with the new coast guard.

MARITIME SECURITY POLICE *(continued)*

Personnel (1998): 1,000 total

Organization: Northern Group headquarters at Takshui, with squadrons at Hualien, Suao, Keelung, and Hsinchu; Southern Group headquarters at Kaohsiung, with squadrons at Anping, Kenting, Makung, and Wuchi. There is also a special operations team, equipped with several helicopters.

PATROL CRAFT [WPC]

♦ **6 PP-901 class** Bldr: Lung Teh SB, Kaohsiung (In serv. 9-96 to 1-97)

PP-6001 PP-6002 PP-6003 PP-6005 PP-6006 PP-6007

PP-6002—note rigid inflatable fender around hull *Ships of the World,* 2001

D: 91 tons (102 fl) **S:** 42 kts
Dim: 30.50 (28.00 pp) × 6.20 × 1.30 (2.40 over props)
A: 2 single 12.7-mm mg **Electronics:** Radar: 2 . . . nav.
M: 2 Paxman 12VP185 diesels; 4-bladed props; 6,552 bhp
Electric: 96 kw tot. (2 × 48-kw Alsthom sets, diesel driven)
Range: 600/25 **Fuel:** 17 m^3 **Crew:** 12 tot.

Remarks: Ordered in 10-95. Kevlar structure with deep-vee hullform. Have an X-band navigational radar, video plot, GPS receiver, D/F, and echo sounder. Carry a 6.5-m RIB inspection craft. Are also reported to have a propulsion plant of two MTU diesels of 3,070 bhp each for a maximum of 30 kts (28 sust.) and to have been constructed of steel, with aluminum superstructures by TMMC Shipyard, Kaohsiung.

♦ **12 PP-1001 class** Bldr: . . . . . . (In serv. 8-12-92 to 11-98)

PP-1001 PP-1002 PP-1003 PP-1005 PP-1006 PP-1007 PP-1008 PP-1009 PP-10010 PP-10011 PP-10012 PP-10013

PP-10011 *Ships of the World,* 2001

D: 140 tons (fl) **S:** 30 kts **Dim:** 27.40 × 8.70 × 1.60
A: 2 single 12.7-mm mg **Electronics:** Radar: 1 Decca . . . nav.
M: 2 MTU diesels; 2 props; 6,000 bhp **Crew:** 12 tot.

Remarks: The first two were built for the ROCN and transferred to the new Maritime Security Police on completion.

Note: Also in service are two or more 25-m patrol craft in the PP-5000 pennant number series; capable of 32 kts, they appear to be of recent construction.

PP-5025—PP-5017 is identical *Ships of the World,* 2001

PATROL BOATS [WPB]

♦ **3 or more PP-3551 class**
Bldr: . . . (In serv. . . .)

PP-3551 PP-3552 PP-3553

PP-3553 *Ships of the World,* 2001

D: 55.7 tons (fl) **S:** 28 kts **Dim:** 20.0 × . . . × . . .
A: 2 single 12.7-mm mg **M:** 2 . . . diesels; 2 props; . . . bhp

♦ **7 PP-701 class** Bldr: Lung Teh SB (In serv. 12-94 to . . .-95)

PP-701 PP-702 PP-703 PP-705 PP-706 PP-707 PP-708

D: 29 tons (fl) **S:** 45 kts **Dim:** 20.00 × 4.80 × 0.72
A: . . . small arms **Electronics:** Radar: 1 . . . nav.
M: 3 M.A.N. . . . diesels; 3 Servogear 4-bladed props; 3,320 bhp
Range: 400/30 **Crew:** 8 tot.

Remarks: Have a single-skin, GRP, deep-vee hull using a PVC core with Kevlar and E-glass reinforcement; a semi-rigid inflatable fender surrounds the hull. Capable of maintaining 30 kts in 2-m waves and Force 8 winds. Intended for antismuggling patrol off the northeast coast of Taiwan.

♦ **23 PP-501 class**
Bldr: China SB, Kaohsiung (prototype: Vosper Pty, Singapore) (In serv. 1989–. . .)

PP-501 PP-502 PP-602 PP-603 PP-605 PP-606 PP-607 PP-609 PP-610 PP-611 PP-612 PP-613 PP-615 PP-616 PP-618 PP-619 PP-620 PP-621 PP-623 PP-625 PP-627 PP-628 PP-630

PP-501 *Ships of the World*

D: 28 tons (fl) **S:** 40+ kts **Dim:** 21.00 (16.60 wl) × 4.80 × 1.00
A: 2 single 12.7-mm mg **Electronics:** Radar: 1 Decca 170 nav.
M: 2 G.M.–Stewart & Stevenson 16V92 TMAB diesels; 2 Arneson ASD 14 surf.-piercing outdrives; 2,700 bhp
Electric: 18 kw tot. **Range:** 400/. . . **Crew:** 8 tot.

Remarks: Aluminum construction. Previously referred to as the PBC 3501 class.

♦ **10 PP-820 class** Bldr: China SB, Kaohsiung (In serv. 1989–91)

PP-820 PP-821 PP-822 PP-823 PP-825 PP-826 PP-827 PP-828 PP-829 PP-830

D: 100 tons (fl) **S:** 30 kts **Dim:** 27.4 (26.2 wl) × 8.7 × 1.8
A: 2 single 12.7-mm mg **Electronics:** Radar: 1 . . . nav.
M: 3 Isotta Fraschini diesels; 3 Castoldi waterjets; 3,000 bhp

Remarks: Used mainly for fisheries patrol and counterinsurgency missions. Have a large searchlight atop the pilothouse.

MARITIME SECURITY POLICE PATROL BOATS [WPB] *(continued)*

♦ 12 PP-801 class Bldr: China SB, Kaohsiung

PP-801	PP-803	PP-808	PP-810	PP-812	PP-815
PP-802	PP-807	PP-809	PP-811	PP-813	PP-816

D: 55 tons (fl) **S:** 25 kts **Dim:** . . . × . . . × . . .
A: 2 single 12.7-mm mg **M:** 2 diesels; waterjet drive

Remarks: Were built around 1971. Aluminum construction. Sister PP-805 was lost during 11-97.

♦ 22 Type 42 class Bldr: . . ., Taiwan (In serv. 1970s)

D: 10.5 tons (fl) **S:** 32 kts **Dim:** 12.8 × . . . × . . .
A: 1 12.7-mm mg **Electronics:** Radar: 1 . . . nav.
M: 2 G.M. diesels; 2 Arneson surf.-piercing outdrives; 1,300 bhp **Range:** 400/. . .

Remarks: GRP construction. C. Raymond Hunt design.

♦ 20 M-4 Jet-Boat riverine patrol craft

PP-301 series

Remarks: Employed for harbor and river-mouth antismuggling patrol. Gasoline outboard propelled.

COAST GUARD

The Coast Guard was established on 28-1-00, when the eight largest ships of the customs service were transferred to the new agency. During 2001, the Coast Guard was effectively combined with the National Police Administration, the National Fire Administration, and the Fisheries Administration, and the agency name may be changed to the Marine Development Ministry. Although permission was given during 2-01 for the coast guard to establish an air arm, no progress had been made by 9-01.

Personnel (2001): 2,100 total

PATROL SHIPS [WPS]

♦ 2 Ho Hsing class Bldr: China SB, Keelung

Ho Hsing (In serv. 1992) Wei Hsing (In serv. 1992)

Wei Hsing *Ships of the World,* 2000

D: 1,795 tons (fl) **S:** 22 kts **Dim:** 82.29 × 11.59 × 4.14
A: 2 single 12.7-mm mg **Electronics:** Radar: 2 Decca . . . nav.
M: 2 MTU 16V1163 TB93 diesels; 2 CP props; 13,122 bhp—bow-thruster
Electric: 1,050 kw tot. (3 × 350-kw diesel alternator sets)
Range: 7,000/16 **Fuel:** 290 tons **Crew:** 18 officers, 62 enlisted

Remarks: Ordered 11-1-90. Plans to deliver both 1-7-91 were delayed by a German embargo on the engines. The nearly complete *Ho Hsing* capsized 18-8-91 in a typhoon but was salvaged. Were taken over from the customs service during 1-00. Have accommodations for two senior personnel in addition to the listed crew. Are very similar to U.S. Coast Guard *Bear*-class, 270-ft. cutters, but carry no heavy armament and substitute four high-speed interceptor craft in individual davits (two per side) for a helicopter facility; the eight interceptor craft were delivered in 7-91 from Hood Military Vessels of the U.S.: 12.19 m o.a., two 300-bhp Cummins diesels driving Arneson outdrives for 35 kts, range of 382 n.m. at 35 kts or 466 n.m. at 30 kts, and a crew of 6.

FISHERIES PATROL SHIPS [WPS]

Note: The ships and craft in this category were taken over by the Maritime Security Police in 4-93 from the Ministry of Agriculture. Currently in use are the *Shun Hu No. 1* (785 tons; 58.8 m o.a.; 16 kts), *Shun Hu No. 2* and *Shun Hu No. 3* (496 tons; 45.2 m o.a.; 16 kts), *Shun Hu No. 5* (131 tons; 31.5 m o.a.; 20 kts), and *Shun Hu No. 6* (200 tons); no other data are available for these units.

Shun Hu No. 3 *Ships of the World,* 2001

Shun Hu No. 1 Mitsuhiro Kadota, 9-01

Shun Hu No. 5 *Ships of the World,* 2001

PATROL COMBATANTS [WPG]

♦ 4 Hsiung Hsing class Bldr: Ching-Fu SB, Kaohsiung

	In serv.		In serv.
117 Hsiung Hsing	20-1-01	119 Ting Hsing	5-01
118 Kuo Hsing	3-01	120 Chu Hsing	30-6-01

Hsiung Hsing (117) *Ships of the World,* 2001

D: 500 tons (630 fl) **S:** 30 kts **Dim:** 63.50 × 9.28 × 2.70
A: 1 20-mm 68-cal. T 75 AA
Electronics: Radar: 1 JRC . . . X-band nav.; 1 JRC . . . S-band surf. search
M: 2 MTU 16V1163 TB93 diesels; 2 props; 15,608 bhp
Range: 2,400/18 **Crew:** 9 officers, 37 enlisted

♦ 1 Jing Chiang class Bldr: China SB, Kaohsiung (In serv. . . .)

116 Taipei

Taipei (116) *Ships of the World,* 2001

COAST GUARD PATROL COMBATANTS [WPG] *(continued)*

D: 500 tons light (680 fl) **S:** 30.9 kts **Dim:** 61.41 × 9.50 × 2.5
A: 2 single 12.7-mm mg
Electronics: Radar: 1 Decca BridgeMaster 250 nav.; 1 Terma Scanter Mil 009 surf. search
M: 2 MTU 16V1163 TB93 diesels; 2 props; 15,020 bhp (12,800 sust.)
Range: 3,600/15 **Crew:** 7 officers, 25 enlisted

Remarks: Differs from naval sisters (q.v.) in having only light machinegun armament and in carrying two RIB inspection/rescue aft in davits.

♦ **2 Mou Hsing class** Bldr: Wilton-Fijenoord, Schiedam, the Netherlands

	L	In serv.		L	In serv.
Mou Hsing	13-2-88	14-6-88	Fu Hsing	13-2-88	14-6-88

Mou Hsing Fu S. Mei, 1-93

D: 700 tons light (917 fl) **S:** 28 kts (25 sust.) **Dim:** 66.10 × 9.60 × 3.22
A: 2 single 12.7-mm mg **Electronics:** Radar: 2 . . . nav.
M: 3 MTU 16V538 TB93 diesels; 3 props; 13,200 bhp (11,040 sust.)
Range: 4,500/12 **Crew:** 54 tot.

Remarks: Ordered in 4-86. Taken over from the customs service during 1-00.

♦ **1 Yun Hsing class** Bldr: China SB, Keelung (In serv. 28-12-87)

Yun Hsing

Yun Hsing H&L Van Ginderen, 5-97

D: 900 tons (964 fl) **S:** 24 kts **Dim:** 65.0 × 10.0 × 2.9
A: 2 single 12.7-mm mg **Electronics:** Radar: 2 JRC . . . nav.
M: 2 M.A.N.-Sulzer 12 VSA 25/30 diesels; 2 props; 7,200 bhp **Crew:** 67 tot.

Remarks: Taken over from the customs service during 1-00. Carries two U.S. 26-ft. motor whaleboats as inspection boats.

♦ **2 Chin Hsing class** Bldr: China SB, Keelung

Chin Hsing (In serv. 23-5-85) Pao Hsing (In serv. 11-86)

D: 550 tons (fl) **S:** 24 kts **Dim:** 57.8 × 7.8 × 2.1
A: 2 single 12.7-mm mg **Electronics:** Radar: 2 JRC . . . nav.
M: 2 M.A.N. 12V 25/30 diesels; 2 props; 7,200 bhp **Crew:** 40 tot.

Remarks: A flush-decked design resembling the South Korean Coast Guard's Sea Whale class, but somewhat smaller. *Chin Hsing* was launched 26-12-84. Former armament of one 40-mm and two single 20-mm AA has been removed.

PATROL CRAFT [WPC]

Note: Twelve 560-ton offshore patrol boats are planned to improve anti-infiltration and antismuggling capabilities.

♦ **1 Hsun Hsing class** Bldr: China SB, Kaohsiung (In serv. 15-12-86)

Hsun Hsing

D: 239 tons (264 fl) **S:** 28 kts **Dim:** 44.5 × 7.5 × 1.7
A: 3 single 12.7-mm mg **Electronics:** Radar: 2 . . . nav.
M: 3 MTU 16V396 TB93 diesels; 3 props; 8,160 bhp **Crew:** 41 tot.

CUSTOMS SERVICE

The Customs Service is subordinated to the Ministry of Finance in peacetime and to the navy in time of war. Its ships and craft are painted white, and seagoing units bear the legend "Customs Preventive Ship" on their sides in English. All ships and craft of more than 100 tons full load displacement were transferred to the new coast guard on 28-1-00.

TANZANIA

United Republic of Tanzania

Personnel (2001): 1,050 total (including coast guard)

Bases: Headquarters, principal base, and repair facilities at Dar es Salaam; coast guard base at Zanzibar; and inland bases at Mtwara and Mwanza on Lake Victoria and Kigoma on Lake Tanganyika

Coastal Defense: There is a battery of mobile 85-mm artillery.

PATROL CRAFT [PC]

♦ **2 Chinese Shanghai-II class**

JW 9867 Mzizi JW 9868 Mzia

Tanzanian Shanghai-II—one of the now-stricken group delivered 1970–71 H&L Van Ginderen, 1984

D: 122.5 tons (134.8 fl) **S:** 28.5 kts **Dim:** 38.78 × 5.41 × 1.49 (hull; 1.554 fl)
A: 2 twin 37-mm 63-cal. Type 74 AA; 2 twin 25-mm 80-cal. Type 61M AA
Electronics: Radar: 1 Type 756 nav.
M: 2 Type L12-180 (M-50F-4) diesels (1,200 bhp each), 2 Type 12D6 diesels (910 bhp each); 4 props; 4,200 bhp
Electric: 39 kw tot. **Range:** 750/16.5 **Endurance:** 7 days **Crew:** 36 tot.

Remarks: Delivered in 6-92; were probably refurbished ex-Chinese Navy units rather than new construction. Of seven other new units delivered in 1970–71, the last was out of service by early 1992. The 910-bhp diesels are used for cruising.

TORPEDO BOATS [PT]

♦ **2 Chinese Huchuan class (Project 026)**
Bldr: Hudung SY, Shanghai

JW 9843 JW 9844

Huchuan-class JW 9842—since stricken 1976

D: 39 tons (45.8 fl) **S:** 50 kts **Dim:** 22.50 × 3.80 × 1.146
A: 2 fixed 533-mm TT; 2 twin 14.5-mm 93-cal. Type 81 mg
Electronics: Radar: 1 Skin Head nav.
M: 3 M-50F-4 diesels; 3 props; 3,600 bhp **Electric:** 5.6 kw
Range: 500/30 **Crew:** 11 tot.

Remarks: Survivors of four delivered new in 1975. Unlike most Chinese Navy Huchuans, these craft had no hydrofoils. Are late-model Project 026 units with one gunmount forward and one aft. All four were operational in 1993, having undergone overhauls at Dar es Salaam in 1991–92, but by 1998, JW 9841 and JW 9842 had been stricken to provide a source of spares for the other two; the operational units are based on Lake Tanganyika at Kigoma, where there are few, if any, targets for their torpedoes (assuming any are still operable), and the radars are probably no longer functioning.

PATROL BOATS [PB]

♦ **1 Yugoslav Type 16 class** (In serv. late 1980s)

D: 23 tons (fl) **S:** 15 kts **Dim:** 17.00 × 3.60 × 0.85 (mean)
A: 1 20-mm 90-cal. AA; 2 single 7.62-mm mg
Electronics: Radar: 1 Decca 110 nav.
M: 2 diesels; 2 props; 464 bhp **Range:** 340/15 **Crew:** 7 tot.

Remarks: Steel hull, wooden decking. Can transport up to 30 troops for short distances.

AMPHIBIOUS WARFARE CRAFT

♦ **2 Chinese Yuchin-class (Type 069) landing craft [LCM]**
Bldr: Kailing SY, Zhoushen (L: 8-4-95)

L 08 Pono L 09 Kibua

Kibua (L 09) M.O.D. Bonn, 4-97

D: 85 tons (fl) **S:** 11.5 kts **Dim:** 24.1 × 5.2 × 1.2
M: 2 M.A.N. . . . diesels; 2 props; 600 bhp
Range: 700/11.5 (light) **Crew:** 8 tot.

Remarks: A new export version of the design, with greater molded depth to improve cargo capacity, an improved steering system, and air-conditioning. Intended primarily for logistics support. Based at Dar es Salaam.

COAST GUARD

PATROL BOATS [WPB]

♦ **2 70-ton class** Bldr: Vosper Thornycroft, Portchester, U.K.

D: 70 tons **S:** 24.5 kts **Dim:** 22.9 × 6.0 × 1.5
A: 2 single 20-mm 90-cal. Oerlikon GAM-B01 AA
Electronics: Radar: 1 Furuno . . . nav.
M: 2 diesels; 2 props; 1,840 bhp **Range:** 800/20 **Crew:** 11 tot.

Remarks: The first two of four units were delivered 6-7-73, the others during 1974; one was retired around 1997, and one was inoperable as of 1999. GRP construction. Keith Nelson hull design. Both are assigned to Zanzibar.

THAILAND

Kingdom of Thailand

Personnel (2001): 24,000 total (including 1,150 in the naval air arm), plus 11,000 marines and Coast Defense Command personnel; the total force is to be reduced to 17,000

Organization: There are three area commands: the First Naval Area Command, with headquarters at Sattahip; the Second Naval Area Command, with headquarters at Bangkok; and the Third Naval Area Command, with headquarters at Phang-Nga on the Andaman Sea coast.

Bases: Fleet headquarters, dockyard, and principal base at Bangkok; other bases at Phang-Nga, Sattahip, and Songkhla. A dockyard is being developed at Sattahip, and a small base is being constructed on Phuket Island.

Naval Aviation: The First Air Wing is located at Utapai and the Second Air Wing at Songkhla. Aircraft available include 6 AV-8S Matador V/STOL fighters and 2 TAV-8A Harrier V/STOL trainers, all of 301 Sqn.; 14 A-7E and 4 TA-7C Corsair-II land-based attack aircraft; 11 Summit Sentry O2-377 Sentry light attack aircraft; 3 P-3B Orion, 2 Fokker F-27-400M and 3 Fokker F-27-200 Marine, 6 Dornier Do-228-212, 8 S-2F Tracker, and 9 GAF N-24L Searchmaster for maritime surveillance; 1 UP-3T Orion, 2 Fokker F-27-400M, and several C-47 transports; 10 Cessna O-1G Bird Dog observation aircraft; 14 U-17B Skywagon utility aircraft; 2 CL-215-III firefighting amphibians; 2 Lake L-A4 Skimmer training amphibians; 1 EC-47 ELINT aircraft; and 6 Sikorsky S-70B-7 Seahawk, 6 Sikorsky S-76B, and 2 Bell UH-1H (Bell 212) helicopters. One Bell UH-1H was lost during a SAR attempt on 26-5-01.

The F-27-200 patrol aircraft are equipped to launch AGM-84C Harpoon missiles and Stingray ASW torpedoes. Two AgustaWestland Super Lynx 300 helicopters were ordered 1-8-01 for shipboard drug-trade interdiction duties; they will be powered by two Honeywell–Rolls-Royce LHTEC CTS800-4N turboshafts each.

Thai Navy AV-8S Matador Royal Thai Navy, 1996

Coast Defense Command: The Royal Thai Marines have two divisions stationed in the eastern coastal area of the country for coastal defense duties. Emplaced artillery includes 155- and 130-mm guns. For air defense, 76-, 40-, 37-, and 20-mm AA are available. Also used by the Coast Defense Command are Chinese-supplied PL-9B shoulder-launched SAMs and 10 mobile batteries of MM 38 Exocet antiship missiles.

Weapons and Sensors: The fleet operates a wide variety of equipment from a large number of national suppliers, complicating logistics and tactical employment.

Note: Ship names are preceded by HTMS (His Thai Majesty's Ship).

AIRCRAFT CARRIERS, V/STOL [CVV]

♦ **1 Chakri Naruebet class**
Bldr: Izar (formerly E.N. Bazán), Ferrol, Spain

	Laid down	L	In serv.
911 Chakri Naruebet	12-7-94	20-1-96	10-8-97

Chakri Naruebet (911) Royal Thai Navy, 8-97

Chakri Naruebet (911) Izar, 1997

Chakri Naruebet (911)—with container ship visible over the bow in the background Royal Thai Navy, 8-97

AIRCRAFT CARRIERS, V/STOL [CVV] *(continued)*

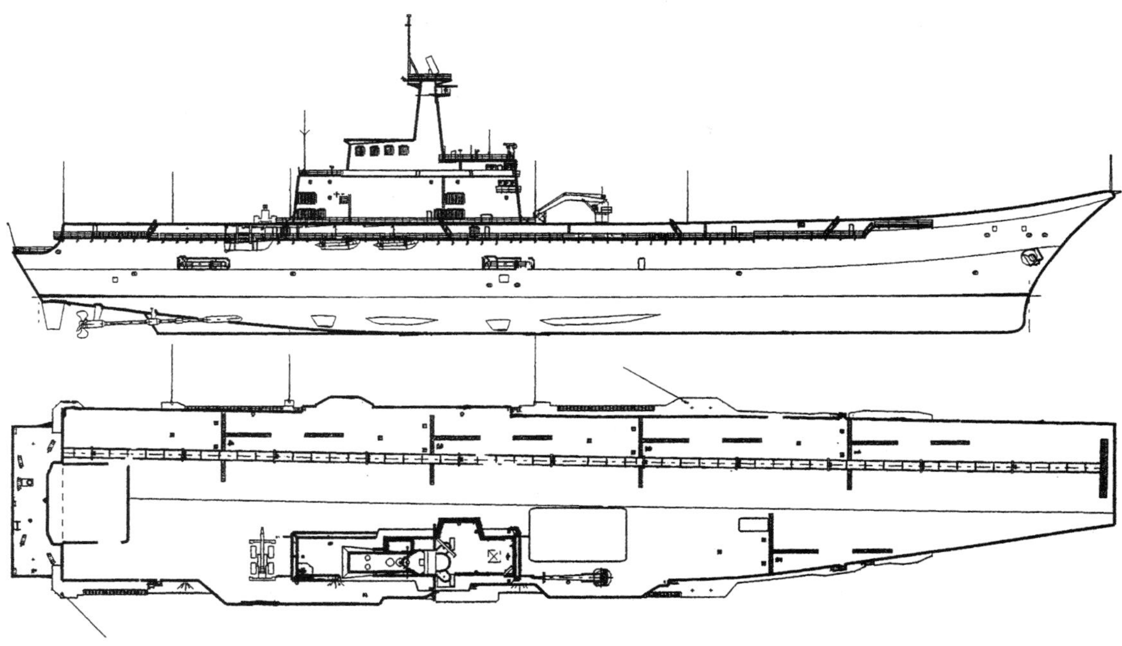

Chakri Naruebet (911) Izar, 1995

D: 11,486 tons (fl) **S:** 27.5 kts (26.2 sust.; 17.2 on diesels)
Dim: 182.65 (174.10 flight deck; 164.10 pp) × 30.50 (22.50 wl) × 6.12
Air group: 6 AV-8S Matador V/STOL fighters; 4 S-70B-7 Seahawk helicopters (up to 18 tot. helicopters)
A: 3 6-round Sadral point-defense SAM syst. (. . . Mistral missiles); 2 single 20-mm AA; 2 single 12.7-mm mg
Electronics:
Radar: 2 Kelvin-Hughes 1007 nav.; 1 Hughes SPS-52C 3-D air search; 1 Kelvin-Hughes . . . air control
EW: none (see remarks)—TACAN: SRN-15A

M: CODOG: 2 Bazán-MTU 16V1163 TB83 diesels (5,600 bhp each), 2 G.E. LM-2500 gas turbines (22,125 shp each); 2 5-bladed CP props; 44,250 shp max.
Electric: 4,800 kw tot. (4 × 1,200-kw M.A.N. diesel alternator sets)
Range: 7,150/16.5; 10,000/12
Crew: 62 officers, 393 enlisted + up to 146 aircrew + up to 675 troops

Remarks: Ordered 28-3-92; delivered 27-3-97. Builder's BSAC 160 design. Name means "In Honor of the Chakri Dynasty." Intended for disaster relief duties in peacetime; was originally to have had a civilian crew. Due to funding shortages, the ship is being operated only one day per month—within the confines of the naval base at Sattahip—to exercise the air group; planned further equipment and armament additions are on hold, and 78% of the crew has been transferred to other units. Negotiations were reportedly under way late in 2001 for lease to the Indian Navy.
Hull systems: The hull has 14 watertight compartments, and the ship is built to Lloyd's RS commercial standards. Has two pairs of fin stabilizers. The hullform includes a wedge at the stern to improve speed and economy. The normal troop accommodation total is 455. Has accommodations for the Thai royal family. There is stowage for 99 m^3 of refrigerated and 300 m^3 of dry stores, 60 tons of aviation fuel, and 100 tons of aviation ordnance. Evaporators producing 90 tons of water per day are fitted. There are two rudders.
Aviation systems: Up to five CH-47 Chinook-size helicopters can be accommodated on the after portion of the flight deck. The 100 × 20.5–m hangar below will be able to hold 10 Sea Harrier V/STOL fighters, 15 Sea King–size helicopters, or 30 or more personnel carriers. The 165 × 30.5–m flight deck is served by two 13.5 × 13.5–m, 20-ton elevators (one centerline at the stern) and a 16-ton crane. There are two weapons elevators.
Combat systems: The combat data and control system is based on the Spanish Tritan, with UYK-3 and UYK-20 computers. Provision has been made for later installation of a long-range 2-D air-search radar set, an EW system (including the SLQ-32(V)3 intercept/jammer and four U.S. Mk 137 decoy launchers), and a hull-mounted sonar. The planned 8-cell U.S. Mk 41 vertical SAM launcher group has not been fitted, but three sextuple Sadral launchers for Mistral heat-seeking SAMs had been added by 2001. The navigational suite includes a Magnavox MX 1105 GPS-and-Omega receiver.

ATTACK SUBMARINES [SS]

♦ 0 (+ 2) German IKL 500 class Bldr: Vickers Ltd., Barrow, U.K.

From among:	Laid down	L	In serv.
. . . (ex-*Gal*)	1973	2-12-75	12-76
. . . (ex-*Tanin*)	1974	25-10-76	6-77
. . . (ex-*Rahav*)	1975	1977	12-77

D: 420 tons light; 540 tons surf./600 tons sub.
S: 11 kts surf./17 kts sub. **Dim:** 48.50 × 4.80 × 4.30
A: 8 bow 533-mm TT (10 U.S. NT-37E torpedoes)
Electronics:
Radar: Kelvin-Hughes Type 1006 nav./surf. search
EW: Elbit Timnex 4CH(V)1 intercept (2–18 GHz)
Sonar: STN Atlas Elektronik CSU-3 panoramic passive array; STN Atlas Elektronik IC-80 intercept

M: 2 MTU 12V493 AZ80 diesels (600 bhp each), 2 AEG 405-kw generators, 1 Siemens motor; 1 prop; 1,800 shp
Range: 3,600/11 surf.; 5,000/6 snorkel; 200/5 sub. **Fuel:** 30 tons
Crew: 30 tot.

Remarks: It was announced 6-9-01 that Thailand would acquire at least two units of this class on a hire-purchase basis for $30.3 million each; the third may also be acquired as a spares source, although a South African company was said to be interested in acquiring the boat as a tourist attraction. Originally ordered in 4-72 and built under license from IKL in Germany as the Vickers Type 540. Were extensively overhauled commencing in 1994, and they were laid up in the late 1990s.
Hull systems: Have three battery groups totaling 360 cells, one air compressor, two hydraulic pumps, one main line pump, and a seawater evaporator. As in German Type 206 and 209 submarines, the bow planes are fixed in pitch and are extended to starboard to rise or to port to descend. All three were lengthened by 3.5 m during the late 1980s; the pressure hull is now 32 m long.
Combat systems: Have the TIOS fire-control system. Are equipped with a Magnavox SATNAV receiver, a GPS receiver, an electromagnetic log, and two gyrocompasses. U.S. Sub-Harpoon missiles were provided and the fire-control systems altered in 1983. Carried U.S. NT-37E torpedoes in Israeli service, with eight in the tubes and two spares. The torpedo tubes are of the swim-out variety. Have Kollmorgen Type 901 attack and Type 902 search periscopes.

FRIGATES [FF]

♦ 2 Chinese Type 25T Bldr: Zhonghua SY, Shanghai

	Laid down	L	In serv.
421 Naresuan	11-91	7-93	15-12-94
422 Taksin	1991	23-7-94	28-9-95

Taksin (422) Takatoshi Okano, 7-98

Naresuan (421) Takatoshi Okano, 6-00

FRIGATES [FF] *(continued)*

Naresuan (421) Brian Morrison, 10-01

Naresuan (421) Brian Morrison, 10-01

D: 2,590 tons (2,980 fl) **S:** 32 kts **Dim:** 120.50 × 13.40 × 3.85 (hull)
A: 8 RGM-84A Harpoon SSM; 1 127-mm 54-cal. U.S. Mk 45 Mod. 2 DP; 2 twin 37-mm 76-cal. Type 76A AA; 2 triple 324-mm Mk 32 Mod. 5 ASW TT (Mk 46 Mod. 5 torpedoes); 1 helicopter (see remarks)
Electronics:
Radar: 1 Raytheon SPS-64(V)15 nav.; 1 Raytheon SPS-64(V)5 helicopter control; 1 Chinese Type 360 surf./air search; 1 Thales LW-08 air search; 1 Thales STIR-18 gun and SAM f.c.; 1 Chinese Type 347G gun f.c. (for 37-mm AA)
Sonar: Chinese SJD-7 bow-mounted (MF)
EW: Chinese Mirage NRJ-5 intercept and Model 945 GPJ passive jammer; . . . active jammer; 4 26-round Type 945 decoy RL
E/O: JM-83H optronic gun f.c.
M: CODOG: 2 G.E. LM-2500 gas turbines (27,500 shp each), 2 MTU 20V1163 TB83 diesels (8,000 bhp each/7,385 bhp sust.); 2 CP props; 55,000 shp max.
Electric: 1,760 kw tot. (4 × 440 kw, MTU 12V396 TM53 diesels driving)
Range: 4,000/18 **Endurance:** 15 days **Crew:** 24 officers, 144 enlisted

Remarks: Ordered 21-9-89. The first unit was handed over 15-12-94 for final fitting out with Western-supplied electronics and weapons in Thailand, completing in 10-95; only the Chinese-made armament and electronic equipment listed above was aboard at time of delivery. Very lightly built, with firing of the 127-mm gun causing structural damage forward.
Hull systems: Have fin stabilizers. Damage control is considerably improved over earlier Chinese designs.
Combat systems: There is a helicopter hangar, and two Super Lynx 300 helicopters were ordered for use with the ships during 2001. One source indicates that the Mirage EW system is a copy of the Elettronica Newton-Beta system. There is one Chinese JM-83H optical backup director for the 37-mm guns, mounted atop the after edge of the helicopter hangar; the Type 347G radar director is said to be a license-built version of the Selenia RTN-20S. The Raytheon DE-1160C hull-mounted LF (5.6/7.5/8.4 kHz) sonar may be substituted later for the Chinese set installed at delivery. Acquisition of the planned eight-cell VLS launch group forward of the bridge area has had to be deferred. Space exists for a second STIR-18 radar weapons director antenna aft.

♦ 4 Chinese Jianghu-III class (Project 053T and 053HT)
Bldr: Zhonghua SY, Shanghai

	Laid down	L	In serv.
455 Chao Phraya	4-89	24-6-90	5-4-91
456 Bangpakong	1989	24-7-90	20-7-91
457 Kraburi	1990	28-12-90	16-1-92
458 Saiburi	1990	29-6-91	4-8-92

Chao Phraya (455)—with two 100-mm gunmounts John Mortimer, 10-01

D: 1,676 tons (1,924 fl) **S:** 31 kts (30 sust.) **Dim:** 103.20 × 10.83 × 3.10 (hull)
A: 4 C-801 SSM; 1 (455, 456: 2) twin 100-mm 56-cal. DP; 4 twin 37-mm 63-cal. Type 74 AA; 2 5-round Type 86 ASW RL
Electronics:
Radar: 1 Decca RM 1290A/D ARPA nav.; 1 Type 354 (MX-902/Eye Shield) air search; 1 Type 352C (Square Tie) missile target acquisition and tracking; 1 Type 343 (Sun Visor) gun f.c.; 1 Type 341 (Rice Lamp) gun f.c.
Sonar: Type SJD-5A bow-mounted searchlight (HF)
EW: Elettronica Newton-Beta suite (Type 211 intercept, Type 318 noise jammer, Type 521 deception jammer); 2 26-round Type 945 decoy RL

Bangpakong (456) Brian Morrison, 2-01

Saiburi (458)—with helicopter deck aft Takatoshi Okano, 6-00

FRIGATES [FF] *(continued)*

Bangpakong (456) Ralph Edwards, 2-01

M: 4 MTU 20V1163 TB83 diesels; 2 CP props; 26,750 bhp (sust.)
Electric: 1,600 kw (4 × 400-kw MTU 8V396-series diesel-driven sets)
Range: 3,500/18 **Endurance:** 15 days
Crew: 22 officers, 146 enlisted (accomm. for 24 officers, 182 enlisted)

Remarks: First two were ordered 18-7-88, the second pair in 8-89. Are employed primarily for antipiracy and marine police functions. Plans to modernize the ships with Western weapons and sensors have been dropped.
Hull systems: Said to be flimsily constructed and to have very poor damage-control features. Have a fin stabilization system. May be able to reach only 28 kts.
Combat systems: The EW suite employs Type 923 omnidirectional antennas (for the Type 521 deception jammer) and Type 981 omnidirectional and Type 929 directional antennas, all mounted on the mast and superstructure sides; the equipment is of Italian design, license-built in China. The 100-mm guns are controlled by the Wok Won director atop the pilothouse (with integral Type 343 Sun Visor radar), while the Type 341 radar aft provides range inputs to the 37-mm guns, which are aimed via ringsights and are arranged to cover one quadrant for each mount. The 100-mm guns have a rate of fire of 25 rds/min and a range of 16 km and employ a French-designed autoloader. 457 and 458 have a helicopter platform raised above the fantail at the forecastle level and omit the after twin 100-mm gunmount, but there is no hangar; Bell UH-1N helicopters can be accommodated.

♦ 1 Yarrow Frigate class
Bldr: Yarrow, Scotstoun, Glasgow, Scotland

	Laid down	L	In serv.
433 Makut Rajakumarn	11-1-70	18-11-71	7-5-73

Makut Rajakumarn (433) Takatoshi Okano, 7-98

Makut Rajakumarn (433) *Ships of the World,* 7-98

D: 1,650 tons (1,900 fl) **S:** 26 kts on gas turbines; 18 kts on diesel
Dim: 97.56 (92.99 pp) × 10.97 × 5.5 (over sonar)
A: 2 single 114-mm 55-cal. Vickers Mk 8 DP; 1 twin 40-mm 70-cal. OTOBreda Compact AA; 2 single 12.7-mm mg; 2 triple 324-mm PMW 49A ASW TT (6 Stingray torpedoes); 1 d.c. rack (6 d.c.)
Electronics:
Radar: 1 Decca . . . nav.; 1 Thales ZW-06 surf. search; 1 Thales DA-05 surf./air search; 1 Thales WM-22 Mod. 61 f.c.
Sonar: STN Atlas Elektronik DSQS-21C hull-mounted MF
EW: Elettronica Newton intercept; FH-4 HFD/F
M: CODOG: 1 Rolls-Royce Olympus TBM-3B gas turbine (23,125 shp), 1 Crossley-Pielstick 12 PC2 V diesel (6,000 bhp); 2 CP props
Electric: 2,200 kw tot. **Range:** 1,000/25; 4,000/18
Crew: 16 officers, 124 enlisted

Remarks: Ordered 21-8-69. Similar to the Malaysian *Rahmat* but longer and more heavily armed. Used primarily as a training ship. Modernized during 1985–88 after a serious fire in 2-84: a new sonar and air-search radar were fitted, and the engineering plant was renewed.
Combat systems: During a 1993 refit, the Sea Cat missile launcher and director were deleted and replaced with two single 40-mm AA. In 1997, two sets of ASW TT (with U.K. Stingray torpedoes) replaced the single 40-mm mounts, a new EW suite was fitted, and a twin 40-mm AA mount with an optical director was situated aft. The original Limbo triple ASW mortar remains aboard but is nonoperational. Has a Thales SEWACO TH combat data system. The WM-22 track-while-scan radar controls the 114-mm guns, and there are two optical backup directors.

♦ 2 ex-U.S. Knox class
Bldr: Avondale Marine (now Northrop Grumman SB), Westwego, La.

	Laid down	L	In serv.
461 Phuttha Yotfa Chulalok (ex-*Truett,* FFT 1095)	27-4-72	3-2-73	1-6-74
462 Phuttha Loetla Naphalai (ex-*Ouellet,* FF 1077)	15-1-69	17-1-70	12-12-70

Phuttha Loetla Naphalai (462) H&L Van Ginderen, 8-98

Phuttha Yotfa Chulalok (461) *Ships of the World,* 1998

D: 3,130 tons light (4,260 fl) **S:** 29 kts
Dim: 134.00 (126.49 wl) × 14.33 × 4.77 (7.83 over sonar)
A: 4 RGM-84C Harpoon SSM (using Mk 112 ASROC launcher syst.); 1 127-mm 54-cal. Mk 42 Mod. 10 DP; 1 20-mm Mk 15 Phalanx CIWS; 4 single 12.7-mm M2 mg; 1 8-round Mk 16 Mod. 8 ASROC ASW syst. (Mk 112 launcher); 4 fixed 324-mm Mk 32 Mod. 9 ASW TT (Mk 46 Mod. 5 torpedoes); 1 . . . helicopter
Electronics:
Radar: 1 Raytheon SPS-64(V)9 nav.; 1 Raytheon SPS-10F surf. search; 1 Lockheed Martin SPS-40D air search; 1 Western Electric SPG-53F gun f.c.; 1 General Dynamics Mk 90 Phalanx f.c.
Sonar: G.E. SQS-26CX bow-mounted LF; EDO SQR-18(V) (462: SQR-18(V)2) towed linear passive array
TACAN: SRN-15A
EW: SLQ-32(V)2 intercept; Mk 36 SRBOC decoy syst. (4 6-round Mk 137 RL); T Mk 6 Fanfare towed acoustic torpedo decoy
M: 1 set Westinghouse geared steam turbines; 1 prop; 35,000 shp
Boilers: 2 Combustion Engineering V2M M-Type (462: Babcock & Wilcox D-Type); 84 kg/cm^2, 510° C
Electric: 3,000 kw tot. (3 × 750-kw turbogenerators, 1 × 750-kw diesel set)
Range: 4,300/20 **Fuel:** 750 tons max. **Crew:** 17 officers, 271 enlisted

Remarks: 461 was transferred upon decommissioning from the USN 31-7-94; 462, in reserve since 6-8-93, was leased 27-11-96 and transferred 5-98 after reactivation and refit by Cascade General at Portland, Ore., arriving in Thailand during 11-98. Both were on 5-year lease, but 461 was donated outright during U.S. FY 00.
Hull systems: Bow bulwarks and a spray strake were added forward to reduce deck wetness, a problem in this class; the addition added 9.1 tons and extended the overall length from the original 133.59 m. 461 has a TEAM (SM-5) computer system for the continual monitoring of the ship's electronic equipment. Antirolling fin stabilizers are fitted to both. The Prairie/Masker bubbler system is fitted to the hull and propellers to reduce radiated noise.
Combat systems: The ASROC system has an 18-weapon automatic reloading magazine beneath the bridge; it is also used to stow the Harpoon missiles, which are launched from the starboard pair of eight launcher cells. The ASW torpedo tubes are fixed, in the forward end of the hangar superstructure, aimed outboard at an angle of 45°; a total of 24 Mk 46–series torpedoes can be carried, including those intended to be carried by the helicopter. Both have the Mk 114 Mod. 6 ASW fire-control system and a Mk 68 Mod. 3 gunfire-control system with SPG-53F radar. During the

FRIGATES [FF] *(continued)*

reactivation overhaul, 462 was equipped with what is now the world's only SQR-18(V)2 Towed Array Sonar System (TASS); 461 retains the SQR-18(V) system, which uses the winch and VDS "fish" from the inactivated SQS-35 VDS system to tow the linear array. A Marisat SATCOM system has replaced the WSC-3 UHF SATCOM system in both.

Note: *Cannon*-class frigate *Pin Klao* (413) has been retyped as a training ship [AXT] (q.v.).

CORVETTES [FFL]

♦ 2 U.S. PFMM Mk 16 class

Bldr: Tacoma Boatbuilding, Tacoma, Wash.

	Laid down	L	In serv.
441 Ratanakosin	6-2-84	11-3-86	26-9-86
442 Sukhothai	26-3-84	20-7-86	19-2-87

Ratanakosin (441) H&L Van Ginderen, 8-98

Sukhothai (442) RAN, 3-95

D: 840 tons normal (960 fl) **S:** 26 kts **Dim:** 76.82 × 9.55 × 2.44 (hull)
A: 8 RGM-84A Harpoon SSM; 1 8-round Albatros SAM syst. (24 Aspide missiles); 1 76-mm 62-cal. OTOBreda Compact DP; 1 twin 40-mm 70-cal. OTOBreda Compact AA; 2 single 20-mm 90-cal. Oerlikon GAM-B01 AA; 2 triple 324-mm Mk 32 Mod. 5 ASW TT (6 Stingray torpedoes)
Electronics:
Radar: 1 Decca 1226 nav.; 1 Thales ZW-06 surf. search; 1 Thales DA-05 surf./air search; 1 Thales WM-25 Mod. 41 f.c.
Sonar: STN Atlas Elektronik DSQS-21C hull-mounted MF
EW: Elettronica Newton intercept; 1 330- or 340-round Matra Défense Dagaie Mk 2 decoy RL
E/O: Thales LIROD-8 f.c.
M: 2 MTU 20V1163 TB83 diesels; 2 props; 16,000 bhp (14,730 sust.)
Range: 3,000/16 **Crew:** 15 officers, 72 enlisted

Remarks: Ordered 9-5-83. Plans to build a third ship in Thailand were canceled. An enlarged version of U.S.-built Saudi Arabian PCG class. Have the Thales Mini-SADOC weapons-control system. The LIROD-8 optronic backup director for the 76-mm gun has radar, infrared, and low-light-level t.v. sensors.

♦ 2 ex-U.S. PF 103 class

Bldrs: 431: American SB, Toledo, Ohio; 432: Norfolk SB & DD, Norfolk, Va.

	Laid down	L	In serv.
431 Tapi (ex-PF 107)	1-4-70	17-10-70	1-11-71
432 Khirirat (ex-PF 108)	18-2-72	2-6-73	10-8-74

D: 893 tons light (1,172 fl) **S:** 20 kts **Dim:** 84.04 × 10.06 × 3.05 (4.27 sonar)
A: 1 76-mm 62-cal. OTOBreda Compact DP; 1 40-mm 70-cal. Bofors L70 AA; 2 single 20-mm 90-cal. Oerlikon GAM-B01 AA; 2 single 12.7-mm mg; 2 triple 324-mm Mk 32 Mod. 5 ASW TT (6 Mk 46 Mod. 2 torpedoes); 1 Mk 9 d.c. rack (7 Mk 9 d.c.)
Electronics:
Radar: 1 Raytheon . . . nav.; 1 Westinghouse SPS-6C air search; 1 Thales WM-22 Mod. 61 f.c.
Sonar: STN Atlas Elektronik DSQS-21C hull-mounted MF
M: 2 Fairbanks-Morse 38TD8⅛ × 10 diesels; 2 props; 5,300 bhp
Electric: 750 kw tot. **Range:** 2,400/18 **Fuel:** 110 tons
Crew: 15 officers, 120 enlisted

Remarks: Ordered 27-6-69 and 26-6-71, respectively. Four sisters were also built for the Iranian Navy. 431 completed modernization in 1983 with the OTOBreda gun replacing the forward U.S. 76.2-mm mount, a Bofors 40-mm on a raised bandstand replacing the aft 76.2-mm mount, two single 20-mm AA replacing the original twin 40-mm mount, an H.S.A. WM-22 track-while-scan radar director mounted above the bridge, and a new sonar in place of the original U.S. SQS-17A; the Hedgehog ASW spiggot mortar was removed. 432 received a similar modernization in 1985–87, and both received further updates to their communications suites in 1988–89. The main engines are turbopressurized.

Khirirat (432) Arjun Sarup, 4-01

PATROL SHIPS [PS]

♦ 0 (+ 2 + 2–10) new construction

Bldr: China SB Trading or Australian Submarine Corp. and Bangkok DY

	Laid down	L	In serv.
. . . . . .	. . .	. . .	2003
. . . . . .	. . .	. . .	2004

D: 1,000–1,500 tons (fl) **S:** 23 kts **Dim:** 80.0–90.0 × . . . × . . .
A: . . .; 1 . . . helicopter
M: . . . diesels; 2 props; . . . bhp

Remarks: Intended to replace retired offshore patrol vessels and supplement existing patrol assets, with the first unit to deliver in 2003 and an eventual 12-unit construction program possible. China Shipbuilding Trading secured the $71 million contract for the first two during 8-01, although no design details were announced and a final contract was still pending; due to irregularities with the original contract, Australian Submarine Corp. was allowed to rebid on 30-10-01, and a new decision was to be made 30-11-01.

Disposal note: U.S. *Tacoma*-class patrol ships *Tachin* (411; ex-*Glendale,* PF 36) and *Prasae* (412; ex-*Gallup,* PF 47) were retired during 2000 after more than 55 years' service each.

GUIDED-MISSILE PATROL BOATS [PTG]

♦ 3 Ratcharit class

Bldr: C.N. Breda, Venice, Italy

	L	In serv.
321 Ratcharit	30-7-78	10-8-89
322 Witthayakom	2-9-78	12-11-79
323 Udomet	28-9-78	21-2-80

Witthayakom (322)—with old pennant number *DTM,* 1995

D: 235 tons light (270 fl) **S:** 36 kts **Dim:** 49.80 (47.25 pp) × 7.50 × 1.68 (hull)
A: 4 MM 38 Exocet SSM; 1 76-mm 62-cal. OTOBreda Compact DP; 1 40-mm 70-cal. OTOBreda AA

GUIDED-MISSILE PATROL BOATS [PTG] *(continued)*

Electronics:
Radar: 1 Decca 1226 nav.; 1 Thales WM-25 track-while-scan f.c.
EW: Decca RDL-2 intercept
M: 3 MTU MD20 V538 TB91 diesels; 3 CP props; 13,500 bhp
Electric: 440 kw tot. **Range:** 650/36; 2,000/15 **Crew:** 7 officers, 38 enlisted

Remarks: Were formerly numbered 4–6. Ordered 23-7-76. Builder's BMB 230 design. Can make 30 kts on two engines.

♦ 3 Prabrarapak class
Bldr: Singapore Technologies Marine, Jurong, Singapore

	L	In serv.
311 Prabrarapak	29-7-75	28-7-76
312 Hanhak Sattru	28-10-75	6-11-76
313 Suphairin	20-2-76	1-2-77

Hanhak Sattru (312)—with old pennant number — Giorgio Arra, 1981

D: 224 tons (260 fl) **S:** 41 kts **Dim:** 44.9 × 7.0 × 2.1 (2.46 props)
A: 5 Gabriel-I SSM (2 fixed, 1 triple trainable launchers); 1 57-mm 70-cal. Bofors Mk 1 DP; 1 40-mm 70-cal. Bofors L70 AA; 2 single 12.7-mm mg
Electronics:
Radar: 1 Decca TM 626 nav.; 1 Thales WM-28 Mod. 5 track-while-scan f.c.
EW: Decca RDL-2 intercept
M: 4 MTU 16V538 TB92 diesels; 4 props; 14,000 bhp **Electric:** 405 kVA tot.
Range: 500/38.5; 1,500/16 **Crew:** 5 officers, 36 enlisted

Remarks: Built under license from Friedrich Lürssen Werft, Germany, and are similar to the Singapore Navy's Sea Wolf–design boats. The missiles are no longer mounted and may have become time-expired; a replacement system is being sought. Six 103-mm rocket flare launch rails are mounted on the sides of the 57-mm mount.

PATROL COMBATANTS [PG]

♦ 3 Hua Hin class
Bldr: Asia Marine, Samut Prakau (543: Bangkok Naval DY)

	Laid down	L	In serv.
541 Hua Hin	3-97	3-3-99	25-3-00
542 Klaeng	5-97	19-4-99	2001
543 Si Racha	12-97	6-9-99	2001

Hua Hin (541) — A. D. Baker III, 1997

D: 645 tons (fl) **S:** 25 kts **Dim:** 62.0 (56.7 pp) × 8.9 × 2.7 (hull)
A: 1 76-mm 62-cal. OTOBreda Compact DP; 1 40-mm 70-cal. Bofors L70 AA; 2 single 20-mm 90-cal. Oerlikon GAM-B01 AA; 2 single 12.7-mm mg
Electronics: Radar: 1 Sperry SM5000 APAR nav.; 1 Sperry RASCAR nav.
M: 3 Paxman 12VP 185 diesels; 3 props (CP on centerline); 10,372 bhp (sust.)
Range: 2,500/15 **Crew:** 11 officers, 34 enlisted

Remarks: Ordered in 9-96 from Silkline, but the contract was canceled for lack of performance and reissued as above. Very similar to the *Khamronsin* design but lack ASW equipment. A single optical director is fitted for the 76-mm gun; the 40-mm mount is locally controlled.

♦ 3 Khamronsin class

	Bldr	Laid down	L	In serv.
531 Khamronsin	Italthai, Bangkok	15-3-88	15-8-89	29-7-92
532 Thayanchon	Italthai, Bangkok	20-4-88	7-12-89	5-9-92
533 Longlom	Royal Thai Naval DY, Bangkok	15-3-88	8-8-89	2-10-92

Longlom (533) — Brian Morrison, 10-01

Thayanchon (532) — Chris Sattler, 11-99

Longlom (533) — Brian Morrison, 10-01

D: 362 light (475 half load; approx. 630 fl) **S:** 25 kts
Dim: 62.0 (56.7 pp) × 8.26 × 2.50 (hull)
A: 1 76-mm 62-cal. OTOBreda Compact DP; 1 twin 30-mm 70-cal. OTOBreda AA; 4 single 12.7-mm mg; 2 triple 324-mm BAE Systems PMW-49A ASW TT (Stingray torpedoes); 2 d.c. mortars; 1 d.c. rack; . . . mines
Electronics:
Radar: 1 Decca 1226 nav.; 1 BAE Systems AWS-4 surf./air search
Sonar: STN Atlas Elektronik DSQS-21C hull-mounted MF
M: 2 MTU 12V1163 TB93 diesels; 2 CP props; 7,340 bhp
Range: 2,500/15 **Fuel:** . . . **Crew:** 6 officers, 51 enlisted

Remarks: Ordered 29-9-87; a fourth in a simplified version was ordered in 9-89 for the marine police (q.v.).
Combat systems: Have a BAE Systems Sea Archer 1A Mod. 2 optronic (t.v./IR/laser) gun f.c.s. and the BAE Systems (ex-Plessey) NAUTIS-P combat data system. Are unusual among modern warships in having depth charge mortars installed (on the fantail, forward of the single centerline depth charge rack, which is flanked by short mine rails).

♦ 3 MV 400 design
Bldr: C.N. Breda, Porto Marghera, Venice, Italy

	Laid down	L	In serv.
331 Chonburi	15-8-81	7-6-82	22-2-83
332 Songkhla	15-9-81	6-9-82	16-7-83
333 Phuket	15-12-81	3-2-83	13-1-84

D: 400 tons (450 fl) **S:** 30 kts **Dim:** 60.40 (57.50 pp) × 8.80 × 1.95 (hull)
A: 2 single 76-mm 62-cal. OTOBreda Compact DP; 1 twin 40-mm 70-cal. OTOBreda-Bofors AA; 2 single 12.7-mm mg
Electronics:
Radar: 1 Thales ZW-06 surf. search; 1 Thales WM-22 Mod. 61 track-while-scan f.c.
EW: Elettronica Newton intercept; Mk 36 SRBOC decoy syst. (4 6-round Mk 137 RL)

PATROL COMBATANTS [PG] *(continued)*

Phuket (333) Brian Morrison, 10-01

M: 2 MTU 20V538 TB92 diesels; 3 CP props; 15,000 bhp (12,600 sust.)
Electric: 800 kw tot. **Range:** 900/29; 2,500/18 **Crew:** 7 officers, 35 enlisted

Remarks: Ordered in 11-79. Have a steel hull and aluminum-alloy superstructure. Able to accommodate antiship missiles, but none have been installed. Have a Thales LIROD-8 optronic backup director for the 76.2-mm guns.

PATROL CRAFT [PC]

♦ 3 PC 30 class Bldr: Silkline International, Pranburi

	Laid down	L	In serv.
T 81	3-97	. . .	7-99
T 82	. . .	1999	. . .
T 83	. . .	1999	29-8-00

T 81—on trials Silkline, 3-99

D: 105 tons (120 fl) **S:** 27 kts (25 sust.) **Dim:** 31.00 (28.00 pp) × 6.50 × 1.80
A: 1 40-mm 60-cal. Bofors Mk 3 AA; 1 20-mm 90-cal. Oerlikon GAM-B01 AA; 2 single 12.7-mm mg
Electronics: Radar: 1 Sperry SM5000 nav.
M: 2 MTU 16V2000 N90 SR diesels; 2 props; 3,600 bhp
Electric: 160 kw (2 × 80-kw diesel sets)
Range: 1,300/15 **Fuel:** 26,000 liters **Endurance:** 7 days
Crew: 3 officers, 26 enlisted

Remarks: Ordered in 9-96; 15 more were planned, but the builder went bankrupt and no more have been ordered. Designed and constructed in partnership with Australian Submarine Corp. Are used for economic exclusion zone patrol. The "T" in the pennant number is rendered in Sanskrit. Aluminum construction.

♦ 6 Sattahip class Bldr: Italthai SY, Samutprakarn, Bangkok

	L	In serv.		L	In serv.
521 Sattahip	27-7-83	16-9-83	524 Kantang	26-10-84	14-10-85
522 Klongyai	9-3-84	7-5-84	525 Thepa	1985	17-4-86
523 Takbai	25-5-84	18-7-84	526 Thai Muang	12-85	17-4-86

Thepa (525)—with old 76.2-mm Mk 22 gun forward NAVPIC-Holland, 2-97

D: 270 tons (300 fl) **S:** 22 kts **Dim:** 50.14 (47.22 wl) × 7.30 × 1.58 (1.80 props)
A: 521–523: 1 76-mm 62-cal. OTOBreda Compact DP; 1 40-mm 70-cal. Bofors L70 AA; 2 single 20-mm 90-cal. Oerlikon GAM-B01 AA; 2 single 12.7-mm mg—524–526: 1 76.2-mm 50-cal. U.S. Mk 22 DP; 1 40-mm 60-cal. Bofors Mk 3 AA; 2 single 20-mm 90-cal. Oerlikon GAM-B01 AA; 2 single 12.7-mm mg

Sattahip (521)—with 76-mm OTOBreda gun forward NAVPIC-Holland, 8-96

Electronics: Radar: 1 Decca 1226 nav.
M: 2 MTU 16V538 TB91 diesels; 2 props; 6,840 bhp **Electric:** 420 kw tot.
Range: 2,500/15 **Fuel:** 80 tons **Crew:** 56 tot.

Remarks: The first four were ordered 9-9-81, the others on 27-12-83 and 31-8-84 to a Lürssen design. The first three have Italian NA 18 optronic director for the 76-mm gun. The 76.2-mm guns in the final three came from discarded U.S.-built ships.

♦ 7 T 93 class Bldr: Royal Thai Naval DY, Bangkok

	In serv.		In serv.		In serv.
T 93	1973	T 96	1982	T 99	5-87
T 94	16-9-81	T 97	16-9-83		
T 95	1981	T 98	1984		

T 93–class T 96 Brian Morrison, 10-01

T 93–class T 99 Brian Morrison, 11-99

D: 117 tons (125 fl) **S:** 25 kts **Dim:** 34.00 (32.00 wl) × 5.70 × 1.40 (1.65 props)
A: 2 single 40-mm 60-cal. Bofors Mk 3 AA; 2 single 12.7-mm mg
Electronics: Radar: 1 Decca . . . nav.
M: 2 MTU 12V538 TB81 diesels; 2 props; 3,300 bhp **Crew:** 23–25 tot.

Remarks: A revised version of the T 91 design. T 99 has a 20-mm gun aft and has a BAE Systems Sea Archer Mk 1A optronic director for the 40-mm gun, which is a Bofors 70-cal. power-operated weapon. The "T" in the pennant number is rendered in Sanskrit.

♦ 2 T 91 class Bldr: Royal Thai Naval DY, Bangkok

T 91 (L: 1965) T 92 (L: 1973)

T 91—with high superstructure NAVPIC-Holland, 9-96

PATROL CRAFT [PC] *(continued)*

T 92—with low superstructure NAVPIC-Holland, 12-96

D: 87.5 tons (100 fl) **S:** 25 kts **Dim:** 31.8 × 5.36 × 1.5
A: T 91: 1 40-mm 60-cal. Bofors Mk 3 AA; 1 20-mm 90-cal. Oerlikon GAM-B01 AA—T 92: 2 single 40-mm 60-cal. Mk 3 AA
Electronics: Radar: 1 Decca . . . nav.
M: 2 MTU diesels; 2 props; 3,300 bhp **Range:** 700/21 **Crew:** 21 tot.

Remarks: T 91 has a longer superstructure and lower spray strakes on the hull sides forward. Both were refitted in 1984–85. The "T" in the pennant number is rendered in Sanskrit.

♦ 10 ex-U.S. PGM 71 class Bldr: Peterson Bldrs, Sturgeon Bay, Wis.

	L	In serv.
T 11 (ex-PGM 71)	22-5-65	1-2-66
T 12 (ex-PGM 79)	18-12-65	1967
T 13 (ex-PGM 107)	13-4-67	28-8-67
T 14 (ex-PGM 113)	3-6-69	18-8-69
T 15 (ex-PGM 114)	24-6-69	18-8-69
T 16 (ex-PGM 115)	24-4-69	12-2-70
T 17 (ex-PGM 116)	3-6-69	12-2-70
T 18 (ex-PGM 117)	24-6-69	12-2-70
T 19 (ex-PGM 123)	4-5-70	25-12-70
T 110 (ex-PGM 124)	22-6-70	10-70

PGM 71–class T 17 NAVPIC-Holland, 2-97

D: 130 tons (144 fl) **S:** 17 kts **Dim:** 30.81 × 6.45 × 2.30
A: 1 40-mm 60-cal. Mk 3 Bofors AA; 1 twin 20-mm 70-cal. Oerlikon Mk 24 AA; 2 single 12.7-mm M2 mg; 1 81-mm mortar
Electronics: Radar: 1 Decca 202 (T 11, 12: Decca 303) nav.
M: 8 G.M. Detroit Diesel 6-71 diesels; 2 props; 2,040 bhp
Range: 1,000/12 **Crew:** 23–25 tot.

Remarks: The twin 20-mm mount on the fantail has been replaced by an 81-mm mortar. The "T" in the pennant number is rendered in Sanskrit.

HYDROFOIL PATROL BOATS [PBH]

♦ 1 Hysucat 18 catamaran hydrofoil
Bldr: Tecnautic, Prapradaeng, Bangkok (L: 21-9-86)

T 231

T 231—with original armament Tecnautic, 1986

D: 41 tons (fl) **S:** 31 kts **Dim:** 18.25 × 6.57 × 1.61 (props)
A: 1 20-mm 90-cal. Oerlikon GAM-B01 AA
Electronics: Radar: 1 . . . nav.
M: 2 MWM TBD 234 V-12 diesels; 2 props; 1,640 bhp
Range: 500/36 **Crew:** 2 officers, 8 enlisted

Remarks: Was ordered 23-9-85 after trials with a 6.5-m, 85-hp prototype. The design was assisted by Friedrich Lürssen Werft, Bremen-Vegesack. Exceeded the designed displacement by 5.5 tons due to water seepage between the Kevlar outer sheathing and foam-core inner hull wall and failed to make 36-kt contract speed; plans to acquire 12 more were canceled. The design employs catamaran hulls with fixed foils mounted between them. The original U.S. 20-mm G.E. Vulcan 20 gatling gun, Kollmorgen-G.E. SV-20NCS gun f.c.s., and Mk 35 Mod. L3 periscopic sight were removed in 1988 and replaced with the 20-mm Oerlikon. Two near-sisters were completed in 3-95 for the marine police and later loaned to the customs service.

PATROL BOATS [PB]

♦ 18 T 213 class Bldr: Italthai Development Co., Bangkok

	In serv.		In serv.		In serv.
T 213	29-8-80	T 219	16-9-81	T 225	28-3-84
T 214	29-8-80	T 220	16-9-81	T 226	28-3-84
T 215	29-8-80	T 221	16-9-81	T 227	1984
T 216	26-3-81	T 222	16-9-81	T 228	1984
T 217	26-3-81	T 223	16-9-81	T 229	1990
T 218	26-3-81	T 224	19-11-81	T 230	1991

T 220 Brian Morrison, 10-01

D: 34 tons (approx. 50 fl) **S:** 22 kts (18 sust.) **Dim:** 19.8 × 5.3 × 1.5
A: 1 20-mm 90-cal. Oerlikon GAM-B01 AA; 1 12.7-mm mg/81-mm mortar combination
Electronics: Radar: 1 Decca 110 nav.
M: 2 MTU 8V396-series diesels; 2 props; 1,300 bhp
Crew: 1 officer, 7 enlisted

Remarks: Aluminum construction. Intended for fisheries protection duties. The U.S.-made combined mortar/machinegun mount is on the fantail. The "T" in the pennant number is rendered in Sanskrit or not displayed.

♦ 3 ex-U.S. Sea Spectre PB Mk III class
Bldr: Peterson Bldrs, Sturgeon Bay, Wis. (In serv. 1975)

T 210 T 211 T 212

D: 28 tons (36.7 fl) **S:** 30 kts (22 sust.) **Dim:** 19.78 × 5.50 × 1.80 (props)
A: 2 20-mm 70-cal. Mk 67 Oerlikon AA; 2 single 12.7-mm mg; 2 single 7.62-mm mg; 1 81-mm mortar
Electronics: Radar: 1 Raytheon 1500B Pathfinder nav.
M: 3 G.M. Detroit Diesel 8V71 TI diesels; 3 props; 1,800 bhp
Range: 450/20 **Endurance:** 3 days **Crew:** 1 officer, 8 enlisted

Remarks: Transferred in 1975. Aluminum construction. The "T" in the pennant number is rendered in Sanskrit or not displayed.

♦ 9 ex-U.S. Swift Mk II class Bldr: Swiftships, Morgan City, La.

T 21 through T 29

Swift Mk II–class T 26—outboard a sister Paolo Marsan, 8-98

D: 22.5 tons (fl) **S:** 25 kts (20 sust.) **Dim:** 15.64 × 4.14 × 1.06
A: 1 twin 12.7-mm mg; 1 12.7-mm mg/81-mm mortar combination
Electronics: Radar: 1 Raytheon 1500B Pathfinder nav.
M: 2 G.M. Detroit Diesel 6V53 N diesels; 2 props; 860 bhp
Range: 400/24 **Crew:** 1 officer, 7 enlisted

PATROL BOATS [PB] *(continued)*

Remarks: Transferred in 1968–70. Aluminum construction. Two are assigned to the Riverine Squadron and operate on the upper Mekong River. The "T" in the pennant number is rendered in Sanskrit.

♦ 90+ assault boats
Bldr: . . ., Thailand (In serv. late 1980s)

D: 0.4 tons (fl) **S:** 24 kts **Dim:** 5.0 × 1.9 × 0.4
A: 1 7.62-mm mg **M:** 1 gasoline outboard; . . . bhp **Crew:** 2 tot. + 4 troops

Remarks: Locally built, GRP, foam-core-hull craft employed by the Riverine Squadron on the upper Mekong River.

♦ 13 U.S. PBR Mk II class
Bldr: Uniflite, Bellingham, Wash.

T 240 series

PBR Mk II class Royal Thai Navy, 1996

D: 8.9 tons (fl) **S:** 14 kts **Dim:** 9.73 × 3.53 × 0.81
A: 1 twin and 1 single 12.7-mm mg; 1 60-mm mortar
Electronics: Radar: 1 Raytheon 1900 (SPS-66) nav.
M: 2 G.M. 6V53N diesels; 2 Jacuzzi waterjets; 420 bhp
Range: 150/23 **Crew:** 4 tot.

Remarks: Survivors of 37: 20 transferred in 1966–67, 10 in 1972, and 7 in 1973. Have GRP-construction hulls with some Kevlar armor. Employed by the Riverine Squadron on the upper Mekong River. Are all over-age, worn out, and in need of replacement; could originally make 24 kts. The "T" in the pennant number is rendered in Sanskrit.

MINE WARFARE SHIPS

♦ 1 mine countermeasures support ship [MCS]

	Bldr	L	In serv.
621 THALANG	Royal Thai Naval DY, Bangkok	. . .	4-8-80

Thalang (621) Maritime Photographic, 11-01

D: 1,000 tons (fl) **S:** 12 kts **Dim:** 55.7 × 10.0 × 3.1
A: 1 40-mm 60-cal. Mk 3 Bofors AA; 2 single 20-mm 70-cal. Oerlikon Mk 10 AA; 2 single 12.7-mm M2 mg; . . . mines
Electronics: Radar: 1 Decca TM 1226 nav.
M: 2 MTU diesels; 2 props; 1,310 bhp **Crew:** 77 tot.

Remarks: Designed by Ferostaal, Essen, Germany. Has two 3-ton cranes on the stern and carries four sets of spare mine countermeasures equipment for transfer to minesweepers. Also capable of use as a minelayer and can stream a mechanical minesweeping array.

♦ 2 Gaeta-class minehunter/minesweepers [MHC]
Bldr: Intermarine, Sarzana, Italy

	Laid down	L	In serv.
633 LADYA	11-96	30-3-98	3-99
634 THA DIN DAENG	9-97	31-10-98	1-00

D: 665 tons (697 fl) **S:** 14.3 kts **Dim:** 52.45 (46.50 pp) × 9.87 × 2.95
A: 1 30-mm Royal Ordnance DS-30B AA
Electronics:
Radar: 1 STN Atlas Elektronik 9600M ARPA nav.
Sonar: STN Atlas Elektronik DSQS-11H

Ladya (633) John Mortimer, 5-99

M: 2 MTU 396 TE74K diesels; 2 Voith-Schneider Type 18 GH/135 vertical cycloidal props; 1,610 bhp—2 180-shp hydraulic motors for quiet running to 6 kts—180-shp bow-thruster
Electric: 900 kw tot. **Range:** 1,500/14; 2,500/12 **Fuel:** 49 tons
Crew: 8 officers, 42 enlisted

Remarks: Ordered 19-9-96; a planned third unit was not ordered. Sisters operate in the Italian and Australian navies.
Hull systems: GRP, foam-core-hull construction. Carry a two-man decompression chamber and are fitted with passive tank stabilization (using tanks for fuel, range can be extended by 1,500 n.m. at 12 kts). Crew listing includes seven mine disposal divers.
Combat systems: Use the STN Atlas Elektronik MWS-80 mine countermeasures operations-control system. Carry two Gayrobot Pluto Plus remotely operated vehicles. Are able to stream Oropesa Mk 4 mechanical sweep gear and have the Australian Defence Industries Mini Dyad and Bofors MS 106 influence sweep systems. Plans call for the sonar to be upgraded to the more effective DSQS-11M version.

♦ 2 M 48–class minehunter/minesweepers [MHC]
Bldr: Friedrich Lürssen Werft, Vegesack, Germany

631 BANGRACHAN (In serv. 29-4-87) 632 NHONGSARHAI (In serv. 17-11-87)

Nhongsarhai (632) John Mortimer, 6-01

D: 414 tons light (444.3 fl) **S:** 18 kts **Dim:** 48.00 (45.70 pp) × 9.30 × 2.75
A: 3 single 20-mm 90-cal. Oerlikon GAM-B01 AA; mine rails
Electronics:
Radar: 1 Decca 1229 nav.
Sonar: STN Atlas Elektronik DSQS-11H hull-mounted
M: 2 MTU 16V396 TB83-DB51L diesels; 2 CP props; 3,223 bhp—auxiliary diesel low-speed propulsion (7 kts)
Electric: 620 kw tot. **Range:** 3,100/12 **Crew:** 7 officers, 33 enlisted

Remarks: 631 was ordered 31-8-84, 632 on 5-8-85; an option for two more was not exercised. Used primarily as patrol boats. Have had problems with stability, and the ineffective sonar system may be replaced with the STN Atlas Elektronik DSQS-11M.
Hull systems: Composite hull construction: nonmagnetic metal framing with wooden skin. Have Becker flap rudders, the Motorola MiniRanger navigational positioning system, and a Draeger portable decompression chamber for mine disposal divers.
Combat systems: Have the STN Atlas Elektronik MWS-80R mine countermeasures system. Carry two Gaymarine Pluto remote-controlled minehunting/disposal submersibles, plus mechanical, magnetic, and acoustic sweep gear. Use a removable generator module when sweeping and carry SDG 31 mechanical sweep gear. Carry 7,600 rounds of 20-mm ammunition and 30 mine-disposal charges.

♦ 2 ex-U.S. MSC 289–class minesweepers [MSC]

	Bldr	In serv.
612 BANGKEO (ex-MSC 303)	Dorchester SB, Camden, N.J.	9-7-65
613 DON CHEDI (ex-MSC 313)	Peterson Bldrs, Sturgeon Bay, Wis.	17-9-65

D: 330 tons (384 fl) **S:** 13 kts **Dim:** 44.32 × 8.29 × 2.70
A: 1 20-mm 70-cal. Oerlikon Mk 10 AA
Electronics:
Radar: 1 Decca 1226 nav.
Sonar: UQS-1D hull-mounted (100 kHz)
M: 4 G.M. Detroit Diesel 6-71 diesels; 2 props; 1,000 bhp (880 sust.)
Range: 2,500/10 **Crew:** 7 officers, 36 enlisted

Remarks: Transferred upon completion. Wooden construction. Were re-engined and reactivated from reserve in 1987–88, but now need replacement. Sister *Tadindeng* (7, ex-U.S. MSC 301) was stricken in 1992 and *Ladya* (635, ex-MSC 297) in 1995. Carry U.S. Mk 4(V), Mk 6, and Type Q2 mine countermeasures equipment. The original twin 20-mm AA mount has been replaced by a single mount.

MINE WARFARE SHIPS *(continued)*

Don Chedi (613)—outboard *Bangkeo* (612) Maritime Photographic, 11-01

♦ 7 MSB 11–class minesweeping launches [MSB]
Bldr: . . ., Thailand (In serv. 1994–98)

MSB 11 through MSB 17

D: 25 tons (fl) **S:** 8 kts **Dim:** 15.29 × 4.01 × 1.35
A: 2 single 7.62-mm mg
M: 1 G.M. Gray Marine 64 HN9 diesel; 1 prop; 165 bhp
Range: . . ./. . . **Crew:** 10 tot.

Remarks: Wooden construction design, patterned on the U.S.-built 50-ft. class but with the hull decked over forward and a pilothouse added. Equipped with a generator for the magnetic sweep array and able to sweep moored mechanical mines. No radar is fitted, but they have a large corner reflector on the mast to permit tracking by land-based radars.

♦ 5 ex-U.S. 50-foot motor-launch minesweepers [MSB]

MLM 6 (ex-MSB 1) through MLM 10 (ex-MSB 5)

D: 21 tons (fl) **S:** 8 kts **Dim:** 15.29 × 4.01 × 1.31
A: 2 single 7.62-mm mg **M:** 1 Navy DB diesel; 1 prop; 85 bhp
Range: 150/8 **Crew:** 6 tot.

Remarks: Transferred in 1963–64. Formerly numbered MLMS 6–10. Wooden-hulled former personnel launches, converted before transfer. Employed on the Chao Phraya River.

AMPHIBIOUS WARFARE SHIPS

♦ 2 PS 700–class tank-landing ships [LST]

	Bldr	L	In serv.
721 Sichang	Italthai SY, Bangkok	14-4-87	9-10-87
722 Surin	Bangkok Dock Co.	12-4-88	16-12-88

Sichang (721)—with *Kolum* (765) alongside Maritime Photographic, 11-01

D: 721: 3,540 tons (4,235 fl)—722: 4,520 tons (fl) **S:** 16 kts
Dim: 721: 103.00 (91.65 pp) × 15.65 × 3.52—722: 109.00 o.a.
A: 1 (722: 2) single 40-mm 70-cal. Bofors L70 AA; 2 single 20-mm 90-cal. Oerlikon GAM-B01 AA; 2 single 12.7-mm mg
Electronics: Radar: 1 Decca 1226 nav.
M: 2 MTU 20V1163 TB62 diesels; 2 CP props; 9,600 bhp
Range: 4,000/14; 7,000/12 **Crew:** 52 crew + 339 (722: 354) troops

Remarks: 2,045 dwt. License-built French Normed design, built with technical assistance from Korea Tacoma SY. Six units were originally planned; a third was ordered during 1987 but later canceled. 722 was not fully operational until 1992.
Hull systems: 722 was delayed after launch to include a 6-m hull "plug" to provide sufficient space for the ship to accommodate a 354-man Thai troop battalion. Cargo: 850 tons (up to 13 50-ton tanks, 6 2-ton trucks). Have a 17-m bow ramp. Beaching draft is 2.88 m at 1,162 dwt. The helicopter deck aft in 722 is one deck higher, and the ship is flush decked, whereas 721 has a forecastle.

Surin (722)—note the lack of a forecastle Maritime Photographic, 11-01

Combat systems: Have the BAE Systems Sea Archer Mk 1A Mod. 2 optronic (low-light t.v./laser/IR) f.c.s. for the 40-mm guns. The additional 40-mm mount in 722 is mounted aft atop a helicopter flight deck control station.

♦ 5 ex-U.S. LST 542–class tank-landing ships [LST]

	Bldr	L	In serv.
711 Anthong (ex-LST 294)	American Bridge Co., Ambridge, Pa.	15-12-43	8-1-44
712 Chang (ex-*Lincoln County*, LST 898)	Dravo, Pittsburgh	25-11-44	29-12-44
713 Pangan (ex-*Stark County*, LST 1134)	Chicago Bridge & Iron, Ind.	16-3-45	7-4-45
714 Lanta (ex-*Stone County*, LST 1141)	Chicago Bridge & Iron, Ind.	18-4-45	9-5-45
715 Prathong (ex-*Dodge County*, LST 722)	Jeffersonville Br. & Mach. Co., Ind.	21-8-44	13-9-44

Lanta (714) Maritime Photographic, 11-01

Chang (712) Maritime Photographic, 11-01

D: 1,625 tons (4,080 fl) **S:** 11 kts **Dim:** 99.98 × 15.24 × 4.36
A: 711–713: 2 twin 40-mm 60-cal. Bofors Mk 1 Mod. 2 AA; 4 single 40-mm 60-cal. Bofors Mk 3 AA; 4 single 12.7-mm mg—712 also: 2 single 20-mm 70-cal. Oerlikon Mk 10 AA—714: 6 single 40-mm 60-cal. Bofors Mk 3 AA—715: 2 single 40-mm 60-cal. Bofors Mk 3 AA
Electronics: Radar: 1 Decca 1229 nav.; 1 Decca 1226 nav.
M: 2 G.M. 12-567A diesels; 2 props; 1,700 bhp **Electric:** 300 kw tot.
Range: 15,000/9 **Fuel:** 569 tons **Crew:** 80 tot. + 348 troops
Remarks: 711 was purchased in 10-47. 712 was transferred in 8-62, 713 in 5-66, 714 on 12-3-70 (purchased 1-3-79), and 715 on 17-12-75. 711 had been discarded by 1978, but the hulk was restored to service in 1994–95.
Hull systems: Cargo: 1,230 tons max./815 tons beaching. All but 713 carry a tracked 10-ton mobile crane on the upper deck. 712 has a reinforced bow and waterline, originally intended for Arctic navigation.
Combat systems: Two Mk 51 Mod. 2 lead-computing directors for twin 40-mm AA have been removed.

AMPHIBIOUS WARFARE SHIPS *(continued)*

♦ 2 ex-U.S. LSM 1–class medium landing ships [LSM]

Bldrs: 731: Pullman Std. Car Mfg. Co., Chicago; 732: Brown SB, Houston, Texas

	Laid down	L	In serv.
731 Kut (ex-LSM 338)	17-8-44	5-12-44	10-1-45
732 Kram (ex-LSM 469)	27-1-45	17-2-45	17-3-45

Kut (731) NAVPIC-Holland, 9-96

D: 743 tons (1,095 fl) **S:** 12.5 kts **Dim:** 62.03 × 10.52 × 2.54
A: 1 twin 40-mm 60-cal. Bofors Mk 1 Mod. 2 Bofors AA; 4 single 20-mm 70-cal. Oerlikon Mk 10 AA
Electronics: Radar: 1 Decca 1226 nav.
M: 2 Fairbanks-Morse 38D8⅛ × 10 diesels; 2 props; 2,800 bhp
Range: 2,500/12 **Crew:** 6 officers, 85 enlisted + 50 troops

Remarks: Formerly numbered 1 and 3. 731 was transferred in 10-46, 732 on 25-5-62. Have a Mk 51 Mod. 2 optical lead-computing director for the 40-mm mount. Cargo: 452 tons. Sister *Phai* (2, ex-LSM 333) was stricken during 1990.

♦ 1 ex-U.S. LSSL 1–class support landing craft [LCFS]

Bldr: Commercial Iron Works, Portland, Ore.

	Laid down	L	In serv.
751 Nakha (ex-*Himiwari*, ex-LSSL 102)	13-1-45	3-2-45	17-2-45

Nakha (751) NAVPIC-Holland, 1-97

D: 233 tons (387 fl) **S:** 14 kts **Dim:** 48.16 × 10.52 × 2.54
A: 1 76.2-mm 50-cal. Mk 22 DP; 2 twin 40-mm 60-cal. Bofors Mk 1 Mod. 2 AA; 3 single 20-mm 70-cal. Oerlikon Mk 10 AA; 2 single 12.7-mm M2 mg
Electronics: Radar: 1 Decca . . . nav.
M: 8 G.M. Detroit Diesel 6051-71 diesels; 2 CP props; 1,320 bhp
Electric: 120 kw **Range:** 3,500/12.5 **Fuel:** 84 tons **Crew:** 60 tot.

Remarks: Transferred to Japan in 7-59 and to Thailand in 10-66 on return to U.S. control from Japan. Used mainly as a tender and headquarters ship for small patrol craft. The armament has been slightly reduced, and the gunmounts have locally fabricated shielding. The last of a once-numerous class.

♦ 2 ex-U.S. LCI(L) 351–class infantry landing craft [LCP]

Bldrs: 741: George Lawley & Sons, Neponset, Mass.; 742: Commercial Iron Works, Portland, Ore.

	Laid down	L	In serv.
741 Prab (ex-LCI(M) 670)	21-3-44	28-3-44	1-4-44
742 Satakut (ex-LCI(M) 739)	30-1-44	27-2-44	6-3-44

D: 231 tons light (387 fl) **S:** 14.4 kts **Dim:** 48.46 (46.63 wl) × 7.21 × 1.73
A: 741: 1 76.2-mm 50-cal. Mk 22 DP—742: 1 40-mm 60-cal. Bofors Mk 3 AA—both: 2 single 20-mm 70-cal. Oerlikon Mk 10 AA
Electronics: Radar: 1 Raytheon 1500B Pathfinder (SPS-53) nav.
M: 8 G.M. 6051-71 diesels; 2 CP props; 1,320 bhp **Electric:** 40 kw tot.
Range: 5,600/12.5 **Fuel:** 113 tons **Crew:** 7 officers, 42 enlisted + 76 troops

Remarks: 741 was built in only 11 days. Transferred to Thailand in 10-46. Completed with four 4.2-in. (107-mm) chemical mortars and with the normal raised forecastle deleted, but were reconfigured to carry troops by Thailand. 741 had been out of service for several years before a refit circa 1991–92; her forecastle has been removed,

Prab (741)—with old pennant number Ross Gillett, 8-89

and the 76.2-mm gun is located on the foredeck. 742 was refitted for further service during the mid-1990s and carries the 40-mm gun atop the original forecastle. Can carry 101 tons cargo. They and the LSSL 1–class *Nakha* (751) are the last of more than 1,100 ships built to this general design.

♦ 0 (+ 3) Man Nok–class utility landing craft [LCU]

Bldr: Silkline-ASC (Australian Submarine Corp) Joint Venture Co., Prandari

	L	In serv.
780 Man Nok	4-8-01	. . .
781 Man Nai	1-5-01	. . .
782 Man Klang	5-7-01	. . .

D: 550 tons (fl) **S:** 12 kts **Dim:** 52.40 (48.00 pp) × 11.20 × 1.20
A: 2 single 20-mm 70-cal. Oerlikon Mk 10 AA
Electronics: Radar: 1 Raytheon 1900 Pathfinder nav.
M: 2 Caterpillar 3412DITA diesels; 2 Kort-nozzle props; 1,440 bhp
Range: 1,500/10 **Crew:** 3 officers, 30 enlisted

Remarks: Ordered in 10-97 for delivery within 36 months, but program was well behind schedule when the original builder defaulted. Have bow and stern vehicle ramps, and the bridge is offset to starboard. Have one diesel generator set.

♦ 4 Thong Kaeo–class utility landing craft [LCU]

Bldr: Royal Thai Naval DY, Bangkok

771 Thong Kaeo (In serv. 23-12-82)
772 Thonglang (In serv. 19-4-83)
773 Wang Nok (In serv. 16-9-83)
774 Wang Nai (In serv. 11-11-83)

Wang Nai (774)—alongside *Surin* (722) Maritime Photographic, 5-97

D: 193 tons (396 fl) **S:** 10 kts **Dim:** 41.0 × 9.0 × 2.1
A: 2 single 20-mm 90-cal. Oerlikon GAM-B01 AA; 2 single 7.62-mm mg
Electronics: Radar: 1 Decca . . . nav.
M: 2 G.M. Detroit Diesel 16V71N diesels; 2 props; 1,400 bhp
Range: 1,200/10 **Crew:** 3 officers, 29 enlisted

Remarks: Formerly numbered 7–10. Based on the U.S. LCU 1626–class design. Ordered in 1980; a fifth unit was ordered in 1984 but never completed. Cargo: 143 tons, with a 30.5 × 5.5–m vehicle deck.

♦ 6 ex-U.S. LCU 501–class utility landing craft [LCU]

	Bldr	L	In serv.
761 Mataphon (ex-LCU 1260)	Quincy Barge, Ill.	29-7-44	8-9-44
762 Rawi (ex-LCU 800)	Mt. Vernon Br. Co., Ohio	14-6-44	16-6-44
763 Adang (ex-LCU 861)	Darby, Kansas City, Kans.	15-2-44	22-2-44
764 Phe Tra (ex-LCU 1089)	Quincy Barge, Ill.	10-5-44	10-6-44
765 Kolum (ex-LCU 904)	Missouri Valley Bridge & Iron	13-5-44	11-3-44
766 Talibong (ex-LCU 753)	Quincy Barge, Ill.	30-3-44	10-5-44

D: 134 tons (309 fl) **S:** 10 kts **Dim:** 36.3 × 9.96 × 1.14
A: 2 twin 20-mm 70-cal. Oerlikon Mk 24 AA
Electronics: Radar: 1 Raytheon 1500B (SPS-53) Pathfinder nav.
M: 3 G.M. 6051-71 diesels; 3 props; 675 bhp
Range: 1,200/7 **Fuel:** 10.5 tons **Crew:** 13 tot.

Remarks: Transferred between 10-46 and 11-47. Used as logistics transports on the Chao Phraya River. Cargo: 150 tons. 765, stricken in 1984, had been rehabilitated for further service by 1993.

AMPHIBIOUS WARFARE SHIPS *(continued)*

Talibong (766) Maritime Photographic, 11-01

♦ 24 ex-U.S. LCM(6)-class landing craft [LCM]

L 14, L 15, L 16, L 61 through L 68, L 71 through L 78, L 81, L 82, L 85, L 86, L 87

D: 24 tons (56 fl) **S:** 9 kts **Dim:** 17.11 × 4.27 × 1.17
M: 2 G.M. Gray Marine 64HN9 diesels; 2 props; 330 bhp
Range: 130/9 **Crew:** 5 tot.

Remarks: Transferred between 2-65 and 4-69. Cargo capacity: 34 tons.

♦ 12 ex-U.S. LCVP-class landing craft [LCVP]

L 51 through L 59 L 510 through L 512

D: 12 tons (fl) **S:** 9 kts **Dim:** 10.9 × 3.21 × 1.04
M: 1 G.M. Gray Marine 64HN9 diesel; 1 prop; 225 bhp
Range: 110/9 **Crew:** 3 tot. + 39 troops

Remarks: Transferred during 3-63. Are carried aboard the Thai LSTs.

♦ 4 armored riverine personnel transports [LCP]
Bldr: Bangkok Dock Co. (In serv. 1984)

L 40 L 41 L 42 L 43

D: 10 tons (fl) **S:** 25 kts **Dim:** 12.0 × 3.0 × 1.0
M: 2 Ford Sabre diesels; 2 Castoldi Mod. 06 waterjets, ; . . . bhp
Crew: . . . tot. + 35 troops

Remarks: Based on a GRP-hulled prototype constructed in 1968.

♦ 3 Type 1000 TD hovercraft personnel transports [LCPA]
Bldr: Griffon Hovercraft, Salisbury Green, U.K. (In serv. 1990)

D: 4.9 tons (fl) **S:** 33 kts (27 loaded) **Dim:** 8.80 × 3.93 × 2.50 (high)
M: 1 Deutz BF 6L913C diesel; 1 shrouded airscrew/1 lift-fan; 192 bhp
Range: 200/27 **Crew:** 2 tot. + 10 troops or 1,000 kg cargo

Remarks: Used primarily for search-and-rescue duties.

AUXILIARIES

♦ 1 navigational buoy tender [AGL]
Bldr: Royal Thai Naval DY, Bangkok (In serv. 18-1-79)

821 Suriya

Suriya (821) Maritime Photographic, 11-01

D: 690 tons light (960 fl) **S:** 12 kts **Dim:** 54.2 (47.3 pp) × 10.0 × 3.0
A: 2 single 20-mm 70-cal. Oerlikon Mk 10 AA
Electronics: Radar: 1 Decca . . . nav.
M: 2 MTU diesels; 1 prop; 1,310 bhp **Electric:** 300 kw tot.
Range: 3,000/12 **Crew:** 12 officers, 48 enlisted

Remarks: One 10-ton derrick serves a short, very-low-freeboard working deck forward. Cargo capacity: 270 tons.

♦ 1 oceanographic research ship [AGOR]
Bldr: C. Melchers, Bremen, Germany

	Laid down	L	In serv.
811 Chandhara	27-9-60	17-12-60	1961

Chandhara (811) NAVPIC-Holland, 7-01

D: 870 tons (997 fl) **S:** 13 kts **Dim:** 70.0 (61.0 pp) × 10.5 × 3.0
A: 2 single 40-mm 60-cal. Bofors Mk 3 AA
Electronics: Radar: 1 Decca . . . nav.
M: 2 Klöckner-Humboldt–Deutz diesels; 2 props; 1,090 bhp
Range: 10,000/10 **Crew:** 8 officers, 60 enlisted

Remarks: Built as a training ship and has also served as a royal yacht.

♦ 1 oceanographic research and survey ship [AGS]
Bldr: Royal Thai Naval DY, Bangkok

	Laid down	L	In serv.
812 Suk	27-8-79	16-9-81	3-9-82

Suk (812) H&L Van Ginderen, 5-99

D: 1,400 tons (1,526 fl) **S:** 15 kts **Dim:** 62.9 × 11.0 × 4.1
A: 2 single 20-mm 70-cal. Oerlikon Mk 10 AA; 2 single 7.62-mm mg
Electronics: Radar: 1 Decca TM 1226 nav.
M: 2 MTU diesels; 2 props; 2,400 bhp **Crew:** 20 officers, 66 enlisted

Remarks: Used primarily in oceanographic research, for which a stern gallows crane and five oceanographic cranes are fitted.

♦ 1 small oiler [AO]

	Bldr	L	In serv.
831 Chula	Singapore Slipway & Eng.	24-9-80	1981

Chula (831)—with former pennant number Royal Thai Navy, 1996

D: 2,000 tons (fl) **S:** 14 kts **Dim:** 67.00 × 9.50 × 4.35
A: 2 single 20-mm 90-cal. Oerlikon GAM-B01 AA
Electronics: Radar: 1 Decca 1226 nav.
M: 2 MTU 12V396 TC62 diesels; 2 props; 2,400 bhp
Crew: 7 officers, 32 enlisted

Remarks: 960 dwt. Formerly numbered 2. Cargo: 800 tons, transferred by means of an electrohydraulic boom supporting the hose.

♦ 1 Chinese-built Project R22T replenishment oiler [AOR]
Bldr: . . . SY, Dalien

	Laid down	L	In serv.
871 Similan	12-94	9-11-95	12-8-96

D: 22,000 tons (fl) **S:** 20 kts (19 sust.) **Dim:** 171.40 × 24.16 × 9.00
A: 4 single 20-mm 90-cal. Oerlikon GAM-B01 AA
Electronics: Radar: 1 Decca 1290 ARPA nav.
M: 2 SEMT-Pielstick 16 PC2 6V400 diesels; 2 KaMeWa CP props; 24,000 bhp
Range: 10,000/15 **Crew:** 19 officers, 138 enlisted + 26 passengers

AUXILIARIES *(continued)*

Similan (871) Royal Thai Navy, 1997

Remarks: Ordered 29-9-93. A much-modified, flush-deck version of the Fuqing class built for the Chinese Navy and merchant marine and for the Pakistani Navy; layout resembles a French *Durance*-class ship.
Hull systems: Has a hangar for one Sikorsky S-70 helicopter to provide vertical replenishment of solid stores. There are two refueling stations on either beam. Carries 11,400 tons of cargo, including 7,900 tons of diesel fuel, 2,500 tons of aviation fuel, 250 tons of fresh water, 70 tons of lube oil, and 680 tons of dry cargo, ammunition, and stores.
Combat systems: The planned Chinese-made armament of four twin 37-mm Model 76A AA and their associated Type 341 Rice Lamp radar f.c. director were not mounted, nor was the Type 354 (Eye Shield) search and target-designation radar.

♦ 1 British Algerine-class training ship [AXT]
Bldr: Redfern Const. Co., Toronto, Canada

	Laid down	L	In serv.
415 PHOSAMTON (ex-*Minstrel*)	27-6-44	5-10-44	9-6-45

Phosamton (415) Maritime Photographic, 11-01

D: 1,040 tons (1,335 fl) **S:** 16 kts **Dim:** 68.58 × 10.82 × 3.28
A: 1 76.2-mm 50-cal. U.S. Mk 22 DP; 1 40-mm 60-cal. Bofors Mk 3 AA; 2 single 20-mm 70-cal. Oerlikon Mk 10 AA
Electronics: Radar: 1 Raytheon 1500B Pathfinder nav.
M: 2 sets triple-expansion reciprocating steam; 2 props; 2,400 ihp
Boilers: 2 × 3-drum **Range:** 10,000/10 **Fuel:** 235 tons **Crew:** 103 tot.

Remarks: The world's last active reciprocating steam-propelled warship. Former fleet minesweeper, transferred in 4-47. Was given a refit during late 1984 and remains in service, although mostly pierside. Mechanical minesweeping gear was removed and replaced by a deckhouse on the fantail to increase accommodations when she was relegated to training duties.

♦ 1 ex-U.S. Cannon-class training ship [AXT]
Bldr: Western Pipe & Steel, Los Angeles, Calif.

	Laid down	L	In serv.
413 PIN KLAO (ex-*Hemminger,* DE 746)	8-5-43	27-12-43	30-5-44

D: 1,240 tons (1,620 fl) **S:** 20 kts **Dim:** 93.27 (91.44 wl) × 11.15 × 3.56 (hull)
A: 3 single 76.2-mm 50-cal. Mk 22 DP; 3 twin 40-mm 60-cal. Mk 2 Mod. 5 AA; 2 triple 324-mm Mk 32 Mod. 5 ASW TT (6 Mk 46 Mod. 2 torpedoes); 1 24-round Mk 10 Hedgehog fixed ASW spiggot mortar; 8 Mk 6 d.c. mortars (3 Mk 9 d.c. each); 2 Mk 9 d.c. racks (7 Mk 9 d.c. each)
Electronics:
Radar: 2 . . . nav.; 1 Westinghouse SPS-6C air search
Sonar: SQS-11 hull-mounted MF
M: 4 G.M. 16-278A diesels, electric drive; 2 props; 6,000 shp
Electric: 680 kw tot. **Range:** 11,600/11 **Fuel:** 260 tons
Crew: 14 officers, 178 enlisted

Remarks: Transferred in 7-59 and purchased 6-6-75, after which the ship underwent an extensive overhaul at Guam. Relegated to cadet training service in 1991 and has made several Asian training cruises since. The Mk 52 AA radar gun director for the 76.2-mm guns has been removed, as have one Mk 63 radar director and two Mk 51 Mod. 2 lead-computing directors for the 40-mm guns, but the optical rangefinder for the 76.2-mm guns has been retained.

Disposal note: *Tachin*-class training ship *Maeklong* (414) was retired in 1997 after 60 years' service and has been embedded in concrete as a museum ship after restoration to her pre–World War II appearance.

Pin Klao (413)—with old pennant number *Ships of the World,* 4-92

SERVICE CRAFT

♦ 2 inshore survey craft [YGS]
Bldr: Lürssen, Vegesack, Germany (In serv. 1956)

OCEANOGRAPHIC II (In serv. 1956) OCEANOGRAPHIC III (In serv. 1972)

D: 90 tons (96 fl) **S:** 12 kts **Dim:** 29.0 × 5.5 × 1.5
M: 1 diesel; 1 prop; . . . bhp **Crew:** 2 officers, 9 enlisted

♦ 3 Samed-class harbor oilers [YO]
Bldr: Royal Thai Naval DY, Bangkok

834 PROET (In serv. 16-1-70) 842 CHIK (In serv. 1970)
835 SAMED (In serv. 15-12-70)

Samed (835) NAVPIC-Holland, 7-96

D: 360 tons (485 fl) **S:** 9 kts **Dim:** 39.0 (36.6 pp) × 6.1 × 2.8
A: none **Electronics:** Radar: 1 . . . nav.
M: 1 G.M. 8-268A diesel; 500 bhp **Crew:** 20 tot.

Remarks: Formerly numbered 9–11. Were designed to mount two single 20-mm AA but do not carry them. Cargo: 210 tons.

♦ 1 ex-U.S. YO 57–class fuel lighter [YO]
Bldr: Albina Engineering and Mechanical Works, Portland, Ore. (In serv. 1944)

832 SAMUI (ex-YOG 60)

Samui (832) NAVPIC-Holland, 3-95

D: 445 tons light (1,420 fl) **S:** 8 kts **Dim:** 53.03 × 9.75 × 4.27
A: 2 single 20-mm 70-cal. Oerlikon Mk 10 AA
Electronics: Radar: 1 Raytheon 1500B Pathfinder (SPS-53) nav.
M: 1 Union diesel; 1 prop; 560 bhp **Fuel:** 25 tons **Crew:** 29 tot.

Remarks: Transferred post–World War II. 832 had been hulked during 1980s but was restored to service circa 1991 after a refit; a flying bridge has been added above the original pilothouse. Cargo: 985 tons.

SERVICE CRAFT *(continued)*

♦ **1 Prong-class fuel lighter [YO]** Bldr: . . . (In serv. 1938)

833 Prong

D: 150 tons (fl) **S:** 10 kts **Dim:** 29.0 × 5.5 × 2.3
M: 1 diesel; 1 prop; 150 bhp **Crew:** 14 tot.

Remarks: Had been hulked many years ago but was reported restored to service by 1995.

♦ **2 Samaesan-class firefighting large harbor tugs [YTB]**
Bldr: Oakwell Engineering, Bangkok (In serv. 28-2-95)

855 Samaesan 856 Raet

Raet (856) Royal Thai Navy, 1994

D: 300 tons (fl) **S:** 10 kts **Dim:** 25.00 × 8.50 × 2.40
A: none **Electronics:** Radar: 1 . . . nav.
M: 2 Caterpillar 3512TA diesels; 2 Aquamaster US 901 azimuthal props; 2,350 bhp
Range: . . ./. . . **Crew:** 6 tot.

Remarks: Formerly numbered 7 and 8. Ordered 23-9-92 and launched 12-93. Have twin stacks and an all-around-view pilothouse. Have two water monitors atop the pilothouse and a third atop the tall mast. Serve at the Sattahip Naval Base.

♦ **2 Rin-class coastal tugs [YTB]**
Bldr: Singapore SB & Eng. (In serv. 9-80)

853 Rin (L: 14-6-80) 854 Rang (L: 12-6-80)

Rang (854) NAVPIC-Holland, 9-96

D: 250 tons (300 fl) **S:** 12 kts **Dim:** 32.3 × 9.0 × . . .
M: 1 MWM TBD 441V/12K diesel; 1 prop; 2,100 bhp **Electric:** 233 kw
Range: 1,000/10 **Crew:** 16 tot.

Remarks: Formerly numbered 5 and 6. Bollard pull: 22 tons. Have four firefighting monitors, including one atop the unusually tall mast.

♦ **2 ex-Canadian small harbor tugs [YTL]**
Bldr: Central Bridge Co., Trenton, Ontario (In serv. 1943–44)

851 Klueng Baden 852 Marin Vichai

D: 63 grt **S:** 8 kts **Dim:** 19.8 × 5.0 × 1.8 **M:** 1 diesel; 240 bhp

Remarks: Formerly numbered 2 and 3. Acquired in 1953.

Note: There is also reported to be a tug named *Kret Kaew* (861); no data available.

Klueng Baden (851)—outboard fuel lighters *Prong* (833) and *Proet* (834)
Maritime Photographic, 11-01

♦ **1 Charn-class water lighter [YW]**
Bldr: Royal Thai Naval DY, Bangkok (L: 14-1-65)

841 Chuang

Chuang (841) Maritime Photographic, 5-97

D: 355 tons (485 fl) **S:** 11 kts **Dim:** 42.0 × 7.5 × 3.1
M: 1 G.M. diesel; 500 bhp **Crew:** 29 tot.

Remarks: Formerly numbered 5. Can carry one 20-mm AA. No radar is fitted.

Note: In addition to the larger service craft listed and described here, the Royal Thai Navy operates numerous small personnel launches, stores transports, and fuel and water lighters in local, base-support service.

ROYAL THAI ARMY

A series of 24 vehicle landing craft of some 100 tons full load displacement was to be delivered in 1996–97 by Marsen Co., Ltd., Samut Phraken, to the Royal Thai Army; no details available.

ROYAL THAI MARINE POLICE

Performing duties analogous to those of a coast guard, the Royal Thai Marine Police has absorbed the former customs service fleet, although customs craft are still labeled as such. The organization operates a number of aircraft and helicopters, including a CASA CN-235-200 maritime reconnaissance/transport aircraft delivered 9-2-96.

PATROL CRAFT [WPC]

♦ **1 modified Khamronsin class**
Bldr: Italthai Marine, Bangkok (In serv. 4-92)

1804 Srinakarin

D: 362 light (475 fl) **S:** 25 kts **Dim:** 62.0 (56.7 pp) × 8.26 × 2.50 (hull)
A: 1 30-mm 82-cal. OTOBreda AA; 2 single 20-mm 90-cal. Oerlikon GAM-B01 AA
Electronics: Radar: 1 Decca 1226 nav.
M: 2 Deutz-M.W.M. BV 16M 628 diesels; 2 CP props; 9,980 bhp
Range: 2,500/15 **Fuel:** . . . **Crew:** 6 officers, 51 enlisted

Remarks: A simplified version of the Thai Navy *Khamronsin*-class patrol craft design. Ordered in 9-89; a second was ordered in 1991, but was later cancelled.

♦ **2 Damrong Rachanuphat class** Bldr: Schiffwerft Hameln, Germany

	In serv.
1802 Damrong Rachanuphat	3-1-69
1803 Lopburi Ramas	10-12-72

D: 430 tons (fl) **S:** 23 kts **Dim:** 56.7 × 8.1 × 2.4
A: 1 twin 30-mm 75-cal. Oerlikon GCM-A03 AA; 2 single 20-mm 90-cal. Oerlikon GAM-B01 AA
Electronics: Radar: 1 Decca 1226 nav.; 1 Decca . . . nav.
M: 4 MTU diesels; 2 props; 4,400 bhp **Crew:** 45 tot.

Remarks: The original armament has been recently updated.

MARINE POLICE PATROL CRAFT [WPC] *(continued)*

Lopburi Ramas (1803) H&L Van Ginderen, 2-88

♦ 2 Chasanyabadee class Bldr: Sumidigawa, Tokyo, Japan

1101 Chasanyabadee (In serv. 8-72) 1103 Phromyothee (In serv. 5-73)

Chasanyabadee (1101)—alongside *Srinakarin* (1804) Maritime Photographic, 5-97

D: 130 tons (fl) **S:** 32 kts **Dim:** 34.0 × 5.8 × 2.8
A: 2 single 20-mm 70-cal. Oerlikon Mk 10 AA
Electronics: Radar: 1 Decca . . . nav.
M: 3 Ikegai diesels; 3 props; 4,050 bhp

♦ 1 Chawengsak Songkram class
Bldr: Yokohama Yacht, Japan (In serv. 13-4-73)

1102 Chawengsak Songkram

D: 190 tons (fl) **S:** 32 kts **Dim:** 37.0 (35.5 pp) × 6.80 × 1.50
A: 2 single 20-mm 70-cal. Oerlikon Mk 10 AA
Electronics: Radar: 1 . . . nav.
M: 4 Ikegai diesels; 2 props; 5,400 bhp **Crew:** 4 officers, 12 enlisted

Remarks: Unnamed sister 1201 is assigned to customs duties.

PATROL BOATS [WPB]

♦ 1 Sriyanont class Bldr: Italthai Marine, Bangkok (In serv. 12-6-86)

901 Sriyanont

Sriyanont (901)—outboard *Phromyothee* (1103) and *Lopburi Ramas* (1803) Maritime Photographic, 5-97

D: 52 tons light (approx. 90 fl) **S:** 23 kts **Dim:** 27.4 × 4.9 × 2.0
A: 1 20-mm 90-cal. Oerlikon GAM-B01 AA; 2 single 7.62-mm mg
Electronics: Radar: 1 Decca . . . nav.
M: 2 Deutz SBA 16M 816CH diesels; 2 props; 2,680 bhp **Crew:** 14 tot.

♦ 3 U.S. Cutlass class Bldr: Halter Marine, New Orleans (In serv. 9-3-69)

807 Phra Ong Chao Khamrop 809 Ram Inthra
808 Picharn Pholakit

Picharn Pholakit (808)—outboard *Phra Ong Chao Khamrop* (807) NAVPIC-Holland, 8-96

D: 34 tons (fl) **S:** 25 kts **Dim:** 19.66 × 5.18 × 1.12
A: 1 20-mm 70-cal. Oerlikon Mk 10 AA; 2 single 7.62-mm mg
M: 3 G.M. Detroit Diesel 12V71 TI diesels; 2 props; 1,530 bhp
Fuel: 2.7 tons **Crew:** 15 tot.

♦ 3 27-meter class Bldr: Tecnautic, Bangkok (In serv. 1984)

810 811 812

810 and 812—with 18-meter-class 619 alongside Maritime Photographic, 5-97

D: 50 tons (fl) **S:** 27 kts **Dim:** 27.00 × 5.85 × 1.90
A: 1 20-mm 90-cal. Oerlikon GAM-B01 AA; 2 single 7.62-mm mg
M: 3 Isotta-Fraschini diesels; 3 Castoldi 07 waterjets; 2,500 bhp

♦ 4 24.6-meter class Bldr: Marsun, Bangkok (In serv. 27-3-91–. . .)

632 633 634 635

635—outboard *Damrong Rachanuphat* (1802) Maritime Photographic, 11-01

D: 60 tons (fl) **S:** 38 kts **Dim:** 24.60 × 6.00 × 1.10
A: 1 12.7-mm mg **Electronics:** Radar: 1 . . . nav.
M: 2 G.M. Detroit Diesel 16V149 TI diesels; 2 props; 4,000 bhp **Crew:** 12 tot.

Remarks: Kevlar/GRP sandwich hull. Launched 11-2-91. There may also be a 630 and 631 of this design.

♦ 5 19.5-meter class Bldr: Italthai Marine, Bangkok (In serv. 1987–90)

625 626 627 628 629

D: 42 tons (fl) **S:** 27 kts **Dim:** 19.5 × 5.3 × 1.5
A: 1 12.7-mm mg **Electronics:** Radar: 1 . . . nav.
M: 2 M.A.N. D2842LE diesels; 2 props; 1,520 bhp

Remarks: Sisters are also operated by the Fisheries Patrol Service.

MARINE POLICE PATROL BOATS [WPB] *(continued)*

629 John Bouvia, 1990

♦ **17 18-meter class** Bldr: Tecnautic, Bangkok (In serv. 1983 to 19-2-86)

608 through 624

619—outboard the larger 810 and 812 Maritime Photographic, 11-01

D: 30 tons (fl) **S:** 27 kts **Dim:** 18.30 × 4.45 × 0.90
A: 1 12.7-mm mg **Electronics:** Radar: 1 . . . nav.
M: 2 Isotta-Fraschini ID 368V diesels; 2 Castoldi 07 waterjets; 1,930 bhp

♦ **2 17.4-meter class** Bldr: Marsun, Bangkok (In serv. 26-3-86)

539 540

539—outboard a 16.6-meter patrol boat Maritime Photographic, 5-97

D: 30 tons (fl) **S:** 25 kts **Dim:** 17.4 × 4.9 × 0.9
A: 1 12.7-mm mg **Electronics:** Radar: 1 . . . nav.
M: 2 G.M. Detroit Diesel 12V71 TI diesels; 2 props; 1,500 bhp **Crew:** 8 tot.

♦ **26 16.6-meter class**
Bldrs: 513–533: Sumidigawa, Tokyo, Japan; others: Captain Co., Bangkok (In serv. 1978–79)

513 through 538

D: 18 tons (fl) **S:** 23 kts **Dim:** 16.5 × 3.8 × 0.70
A: 1 12.7-mm mg **M:** 2 Cummins diesels; 800 bhp

526 Maritime Photographic, 11-01

♦ **26 12.2-meter class** Bldr: Camcraft, Crown Point, La.

415 through 440

435 NAVPIC-Holland, 8-96

D: 13 tons (fl) **S:** 25 kts **Dim:** 12.2 × 3.7 × 1.0
A: small arms **M:** 2 G.M. Detroit Diesel 6-71 diesels; 2 props; 540 bhp

♦ **1 11.5-meter GRP-hulled prototype**
Bldr: SEAT Co., Bangkok (In serv. 1990)

339

339 Maritime Photographic, 5-97

D: approx. 5 tons (fl) **S:** 60 kts (57 sust.) **Dim:** 11.58 × 2.73 × . . .
M: 5 gasoline outboard motors; 1,000 bhp

♦ **38 11.3-meter river patrol boats** Bldr: . . .

301 through 338

333 NAVPIC-Holland, 8-96

MARINE POLICE PATROL BOATS [WPB] *(continued)*

D: 5 tons (fl) **S:** 25 kts **Dim:** 11.3 × 3.4 × . . .
A: small arms **M:** 2 . . . diesels; 2 props; . . . bhp

♦ 22 Typhoon-class rigid inflatable boats
Bldr: Task Force Boats, U.K. (In serv. 1990–91)

Remarks: Has two 225-bhp Johnson gasoline outboards and can make 50 kts (40 with 12 police aboard).

Note: The Thai Marine Police also use numerous outboard-powered launches.

CUSTOMS

The Thai Customs Service is subordinate to the Thai Marine Police but has its own fleet of patrol craft and launches, for which no fleet list is available. The largest unit is the *Customs 1201,* a sister to the Thai Marine Police patrol craft *Chawengsak Songkram.* Hysucat 18 patrol boats *Customs 610* and *Customs 611* are on loan from the Thai Marine Police.

Customs 1201 Maritime Photographic, 5-97

Hysucat 18–class Customs 610—alongside sister *Customs 611*
NAVPIC-Holland, 3-95

FISHERIES PATROL SERVICE
(Truatpramong)

The Fisheries and Agriculture Department's Fisheries Patrol Service employs a number of small patrol boats that are painted a deep blue and have a broad white and narrow blue and gold diagonal hull stripe. At least two units, *Fisheries Patrol 609* and *Fisheries Patrol 617,* are sisters to Thai Marine Police units of the 19.5-m class and 630 series, respectively. The Fisheries and Agriculture Department operates white-painted fisheries patrol and research units, which are generally typical examples of locally built fishing craft designs.

TOGO

Republic of Togo

Personnel (2001): 105 total

Base: Lomé

PATROL BOATS [PB]

♦ 2 wooden-hulled Bldr: C.N. de l'Estérel, Cannes, France

P 761 Kara (L: 18-5-76) P 762 Mono (L: 1976)

Mono (P 762) French Navy, 12-96

D: 80 tons (fl) **S:** 30 kts **Dim:** 32.00 × 5.80 × 1.50
A: 1 40-mm 60-cal. Mk 3 Bofors AA; 1 20-mm 70-cal. Oerlikon Mk 10 AA
Electronics: Radar: 1 Furuno . . . nav.
M: 2 MTU 12V493 TY60 diesels; 2,700 bhp **Range:** 1,500/15
Crew: 1 officer, 17 enlisted

Remarks: Wooden construction. The 20-mm gun is on the forecastle, the 40-mm gun aft.

Note: There are also two smaller patrol launches in service; no data available.

TONGA

Kingdom of Tonga

TONGAN DEFENCE SERVICE
MARITIME DEFENCE DIVISION

Personnel (2001): 118 total (19 officers), plus Royal Tongan Marines: 4 officers, 46 enlisted

Base: HMNB *Masefield,* Touliki Base, on Nuku'alofa

Maritime Aviation: The Tongan Defence Service's Air Force Division has one modernized Beech 18 maritime patrol aircraft, received in mid-1996, and a Champion Citabria, acquired in mid-1999 for training and patrol duties.

Note: Ship names are preceded by VOEA *(Vaka Oe Ene Afio).*

PATROL CRAFT [PC]

♦ 3 ASI 315 design Bldr: Transfield-ASI, South Coogie, W.A., Australia

	Laid down	L	In serv.
P 201 Neiafu	30-1-89	. . .	30-10-89
P 202 Pangai	2-10-89	. . .	30-6-90
P 203 Savea	2-90	. . .	23-3-91

Savea (P 203) H&L Van Ginderen, 9-99

D: 165 tons (fl) **S:** 21 kts **Dim:** 31.50 (28.60 wl) × 8.10 × 2.12
A: 2 single 12.7-mm mg **Electronics:** Radar: 1 Furuno 1101 nav.
M: 2 Caterpillar 3516 diesels; 2 props; 2,820 bhp **Electric:** 116 kw tot.
Range: 2,500/12 **Fuel:** 27.9 tons **Endurance:** 10 days
Crew: 4 officers, 9 enlisted

Remarks: Of the Australian government's "Pacific Patrol Boat" grant-aid design, examples of which have been donated to a number of Southwest Pacific island states. P 203 was refitted from 5-99 to 8-99 by Port Macquerie Slipways, Australia.
Hull systems: Aluminum construction. Carry a 5-m aluminum boarding boat. Have an extensive navigational suite, including Furuno FSN-70 NAVSAT receiver, 525 HFD/F, 120 MF–HFD/F, FE-881 echo sounder, and DS-70 doppler log. P 203 is additionally equipped to perform hydrographic survey work.

SERVICE CRAFT

♦ 1 royal yacht [YFL]

TITILUPE

Titilupe H&L Van Ginderen, 8-99

D: 10 tons (fl) **S:** 8 kts **Dim:** 10.4 × 3.0 × 1.0
M: 1 Ford Sabre diesel; 1 prop; . . . bhp

Remarks: GRP construction. Also used in patrol work.

♦ 6 4.90-meter aluminum utility launches [YFL]

Remarks: Powered by 30-bhp outboard motors.

♦ 1 Australian-built U.S. LCM(8)-class landing craft [YFU]
Bldr: North Queensland Eng., Cairns

C 315 LATE (ex-Australian Army 1057)

Late (C 315) H&L Van Ginderen, 1-94

D: 34 tons light (116 fl) **S:** 12 kts **Dim:** 22.70 × 6.41 × 1.37
A: 1 7.62-mm mg **Electronics:** Radar: 1 Koden MD 305 nav.
M: 2 G.M. Detroit Diesel 12V71 diesels; 2 props; 600 bhp
Range: 480/10 **Crew:** 5 tot.

Remarks: Transferred to Tonga 1-9-82. Cargo: 55 tons. Has been fitted with a pilothouse and navigational radar and is used for interisland logistic support.

Note: The Tonga Marine and Wharf Department operates the 1,119-grt/2,889-dwt tanker *Lomipeau* (ex-French Navy *Punaruu,* A 632; ex-Norwegian merchant chemical tanker *Bow Cecil*), transferred from the French Navy on 28-9-95; initially, the ship had a Tongan Navy crew and wore pennant A 301, but the intent was to transfer to civilian mariner operation by 1998. The 5.4-ton Sea Truck logistic landing craft *Fangailifuka* and *'Alo-i-Talau* are operated by the governors of Ha'apaik and Vavau Islands, respectively, but can be recalled for Tongan Navy service if necessary.

TRINIDAD AND TOBAGO

Republic of Trinidad and Tobago

COAST GUARD

Personnel (2001): 55 officers, 595 enlisted

Bases: Headquarters at Staubles Bay, Chauguaramas; stations at Hart's Cut, Port Fortin, Tobago, Point Galeota (Mayaro), and Piarco International Airport (Trinidad)

Aviation: The coast guard operates one Cessna 402B light transport for maritime surveillance and has two Piper Navajo, two C-26, and one Cessna 310-II aircraft for liaison and training. The private National Helicopter Services, Ltd., which supports search-and-rescue service, provides one BO-105 helicopter in support of the Trinidad and Tobago Police Service and the armed forces and also has available two S-76, one S-76A+, and three other BO-105 helicopters available.

Coastal Defense: A coastal surveillance radar system is being installed with U.S. assistance.

Note: Ship names are preceded by TTS (Trinidad and Tobago Ship).

PATROL SHIPS [PS]

♦ 1 ex-U.K. Island-class offshore patrol vessel
Bldr: Hall Russell, Aberdeen

	L	In serv.
CG 20 NELSON (ex-*Orkney,* P 299)	29-6-76	25-2-77

Nelson (CG 20) Ben Sullivan, 1-01

D: 998 tons (1,280 fl) **S:** 16.5 kts **Dim:** 61.10 (51.97 pp) × 11.00 × 4.27
A: 1 20-mm 90-cal. Oerlikon GAM-B01 AA; 2 single 7.62-mm mg
Electronics:
Radar: 1 Kelvin-Hughes Type 1006 nav.
Sonar: Simrad SU "Sidescan"
M: 2 Ruston 12RK3CM diesels (750 rpm); 1 CP prop; 5,640 bhp (4,380 sust.)
Electric: 536 kw tot. (3 × 162-kw, 1 × 50-kw diesel sets; 440 V a.c.)
Range: 11,000/12 **Fuel:** 310 tons
Crew: 4 officers, 29 enlisted (accomm. for 57 tot.)

Remarks: Retired from the Royal Navy 27-5-99 and transferred to Trinidad and Tobago 18-12-00, recommissioning 22-2-01.
Hull systems: Has fin stabilizers and can maintain 12–15 kts in a Force 8 gale. Two Avon Searaider semi-rigid dinghies are carried for inspection purposes. Can carry 28.6 tons of detergent (a 6-hr supply) for oil-spill cleanup.
Combat systems: The Racal CANE DEA-1 combat data system is fitted. The 30-mm gun was removed prior to transfer, but a 20-mm gun may have been substituted.

PATROL CRAFT [WPC]

♦ 2 CG 40 class (Nonoperational)
Bldr: Karlskronavarvet, Karlskrona, Sweden (In serv. 15-6-80)

CG 5 *BARRACUDA* CG 6 *CASCADURA*

Cascadura (CG 6) Maritime Photographic, 1-94

D: 210 tons (fl) **S:** 32 kts (27 sust.) **Dim:** 40.60 × 6.70 × 1.70
A: 1 40-mm 70-cal. Bofors L70 AA; 1 20-mm 90-cal. Oerlikon GAM-B01 AA
Electronics: Radar: 1 Decca TM 1226 nav.
M: 2 Paxman-Valenta 16RP200 CM diesels; 2 props; 8,000 bhp (6,700 sust.)
Range: 2,200/15 **Crew:** 22 tot. + 9 spare berths

Remarks: Ordered in 8-78. Have an optronic f.c.s. for the 40-mm AA. A rescue dinghy is carried on the stern. Have HF and VHF D/F gear and pollution spill control equipment. Refitted in 1988–89. Both were placed ashore for refits during 1999, but as of 4-01, only CG 6 was nearing completion.

PATROL BOATS [WPB]

♦ 3 U.S. Dauntless class
Bldr: SeaArk, Monticello, Ark. (In serv. 14-6-95)

CG 38 Soldado CG 39 Mayaro CG 40 Roxborough

Soldado (CG 38) SeaArk, 5-95

D: 11 tons (15 fl) **S:** 28 kts **Dim:** 12.19 (11.13 wl) × 3.86 × 0.69 (hull)
A: 1 7.62-mm mg **Electronics:** Radar: 1 Raytheon R40X nav.
M: 2 Caterpillar 3208TA diesels; 2 props; 850 bhp (720 sust.)
Range: 200/30; 400/22 **Fuel:** 250 gallons **Crew:** 5 tot.

Remarks: Ordered in 4-94. The last unit was completed in 4-95, and all were delivered together as part of a U.S. aid package. Based at Cedros, Tobago, and Galeota, respectively. Aluminum construction. C. Raymond Hunt, "Deep-Vee" hull design.

♦ 2 31-foot Interceptor class
Bldr: Bowen Boats, Port-of-Spain (In serv. 5-91)

CG 001 CG 002

D: . . . tons **S:** 46 kts **Dim:** 9.45 × . . . × . . .
A: small arms **Electronics:** Radar: 1 Raytheon . . . nav.
M: 2 gasoline outboards; . . . bhp **Crew:** 2–3 tot.

Remarks: Aluminum construction. Attached to the Special Squadron for anti-drug work.

♦ 2 Wasp 20-meter class
Bldr: W. A. Souter & Sons, Cowes, U.K. (In serv. 12-82)

CG 31 Kairi (ex-*Sea Bird*) CG 32 Moriah (ex-*Sea Dog*)

Moriah (CG 32) Trinidad & Tobago C.G., 1989

D: 32 tons (fl) **S:** 36 kts (30 sust.) **Dim:** 20.0 × 5.0 × 1.5
A: 2 single 7.62-mm mg **Electronics:** Radar: 1 Decca 150 nav.
M: 2 G.M. 16V92 TI diesels; 2 props; 2,400 bhp
Range: 450/30 **Crew:** 2 officers, 4 enlisted

Remarks: Ordered 30-9-81. Transferred from the police in 6-89. Aluminum hulls. Both had fallen into disrepair by the mid-1990s but were refurbished and restored to service during 1999.

♦ 4 Wasp 17-meter-class patrol craft
Bldr: W. A. Souter & Sons, Cowes, U.K. (In serv. 27-8-82)

CG 27 Plymouth CG 29 Galeota
CG 28 Caroni CG 30 Moruga

D: 19.25 tons (fl) **S:** 28 kts (25 sust.) **Dim:** 16.76 (13.90 wl) × 4.20 × 1.40
A: 2 single 7.62-mm mg **Electronics:** Radar: 1 Decca 150 nav.
M: 2 G.M.–Stewart & Stevenson 8V92 MTAB diesels; 2 props; 1,470 bhp
Range: 500/18 **Crew:** 2 officers, 4–6 enlisted

Remarks: GRP construction. Ordered in 8-81. Sister *Cedros* (CG 35, ex-Marine Police *Sea Erne*) was stricken in 1997. CG 28, 29, and 30, after lying ashore in neglect during the mid-1990s, were refurbished and returned to service during 1999.

Disposal note: Patrol launch *Carenage* (CG 37, ex-Sea Dragon) was stricken during 1999.

Plymouth (CG 27) H&L Van Ginderen, 2-94

♦ 1 aluminum-hulled
Bldr: SeaArk Marine, Monticello, Ark. (In serv. 5-79)

CG 33 Matelot (ex-*Sea Scorpion*)

Matelot (CG 33) Maritime Photographic, 1-94

D: 15.5 tons (fl) **S:** 28 kts **Dim:** 13.7 × 4.1 × 1.3
A: 1 7.62-mm mg **Electronics:** Radar: 1 . . . nav.
M: 2 G.M. Detroit Diesel 8V92 diesels; 2 props; 850 bhp
Range: 500/20 **Crew:** 6 tot.

Remarks: Transferred from the police 30-6-89. Refitted during 1998. Sister *Mathura* (CG 34, ex-*Sea Spray*) was stricken in 1990.

♦ 4 ex-U.S. Coast Guard 82-foot Point class
Bldr: CG 7, 9: J. Martinac SB, Tacoma, Wash.; CG 8, CG 10: Coast Guard Yard, Curtis Bay, Md.

	In serv.
CG 7 Corozal Point (ex-*Point Bennett,* WPB 82351)	19-12-66
CG 8 Crown Point (ex-*Point Heyer,* WPB 82369)	3-8-67
CG 9 Galera Point (ex-*Point Bonita,* WPB 82347)	12-9-66
CG 10 Bacolet Point (ex-*Point Highland,* WPB 82333)	27-6-62

Crown Point (CG 8) Leo Dirkx, 9-00

D: 64 tons (69 fl) **S:** 23.7 kts **Dim:** 25.3 × 5.23 × 1.95
A: provision for 2 single 7.62-mm M2 mg
Electronics: Radar: 1 Hughes-Furuno SPS-73 nav.

PATROL BOATS [WPB] *(continued)*

M: 2 Caterpillar 3412 diesels; 2 props; 1,480 bhp
Range: 490/23.7; 1,500/8 **Fuel:** 5.7 tons **Crew:** 1 officer, 7 enlisted

Remarks: CG 7 and 8 were transferred by donation 12-2-99, having been stricken from U.S. Coast Guard service during 1998. CG 9 was donated 14-11-00 and CG 10 on 24-7-01.
Hull systems: Hull built of mild steel. High-speed diesels are controlled from the bridge. Well-equipped for salvage and towing. Although elderly, are in excellent condition but are considered to be heavy rollers.

SERVICE CRAFT

♦ 4 Hurricane 733–class rigid inflatable launches [WYFL]

CG 003 CG 004 CG 005

Remarks: Delivered in 1993 as U.S. aid. Are 25-ft., GRP-hulled craft with inflatable rubber collars powered by two Johnson V6 gasoline outboards. Equipped with Raytheon navigational radar. One other has been stricken.

♦ 1 service launch [WYFL]
Bldr: Tugs & Lighters, Ltd., Port-of-Spain (In serv. 15-8-76)

A 01 Naparima (ex-CG 26)

D: 21.4 tons **S:** 10 kts **Dim:** 15.2 × 4.9 × 2.4
M: 2 G.M. Detroit Diesel 6V71 diesels; 2 props; 460 bhp
Range: 400/10 **Crew:** 6 tot.

♦ 1 small launch [WYFL]

A 04 Reform

Remarks: Transferred from the Prison Authority in 1989.

TUNISIA

Republic of Tunisia

Personnel (2001): Approx. 4,800 total (including 800 conscripts)

Bases: Principal base and headquarters at Bizerte; additional facilities at Kilibia, La Galité, and Sfax

Maritime Aviation: The air force acquired 10 surplus ex-U.S. Navy SH-3H and HH-3E Sea King helicopters in 1995 for search-and-rescue duties.

GUIDED-MISSILE PATROL CRAFT [PTG]

♦ 3 Combattante-III class Bldr: CMN, Cherbourg, France

	Laid down	L	In serv.
P 501 La Galité	26-5-82	16-6-83	27-2-85
P 502 Tunis	28-9-82	27-10-83	28-3-85
P 503 Carthage	6-1-83	24-1-84	29-4-85

Tunis (P 502) Clark E. Castle, 4-99

D: 395 tons (425 fl) **S:** 38.5 kts
Dim: 56.80 (53.00 pp) × 8.16 × 2.15 (2.50 props)
A: 8 MM 40 Exocet SSM; 1 76-mm 62-cal. OTOBreda Compact DP; 1 twin 40-mm 70-cal. OTOBreda AA; 2 twin 30-mm 75-cal. Oerlikon AA
Electronics:
Radar: 1 Decca . . . nav.; 1 Thales Triton-S surf./air search; 1 Thales Castor-IIB gun f.c.
EW: Thales DR-2000 intercept, 1 330- or 340-round Matra Défense Dagaie decoy RL
M: 4 MTU 20V538 TB93 diesels; 4 props; 19,300 bhp **Electric:** 405 kVA tot.
Range: 700/33; 2,800/10 **Crew:** 35 tot.

Remarks: Ordered 27-6-81. Are said to be in need of refits, but all are operating.
Combat systems: Have the Thales TAVITAC combat direction system with Vega-II control system for missiles and 76- and 40-mm guns; two Matra Défense Naja optronic gun directors atop the pilothouse control the 30-mm mounts and/or the 40-mm mount. The Matra Défense Sylosat satellite navigational system is fitted.

PATROL CRAFT [PC]

♦ 3 Chinese Type 62-1 class patrol boats
Bldr: . . . (In serv. 3-94)

P 207 Utique P 208 Jerba P 209 Kuriat

Jerba (P 208) U.S. Navy, 7-96

D: 120 tons (fl) **S:** 32 kts (28 sust.) **Dim:** 35.0 × 5.4 × 1.8
A: 2 twin 25-mm 80-cal. Type 81 AA **Electronics:** Radar: 1 Type 756 nav.
M: 4 MWM TBD604 BV12 diesels; 4 props; 4,400 bhp
Range: 750/17 **Crew:** 39 tot.

Remarks: Delivered via heavy-lift ship in 1-94. A shortened version of the Shanghai-II design, with a larger superstructure, lighter armament, and German-made diesels.

♦ 3 French P 48 class Bldr: SFCN, Villeneuve-la-Garenne

	L	In serv.
P 301 Bizerte	20-11-69	10-7-70
P 302 Horria (ex-*Liberté*)	19-2-70	10-70
P 304 Monastir	25-6-74	25-3-75

Bizerte (P 301) H&L Van Ginderen/Camil Busquets i Vilanova, 7-98

D: 250 tons (fl) **S:** 22 kts **Dim:** 48.0 (45.5 pp) × 7.1 × 2.25
A: 2 twin 37-mm 63-cal. Model 74 AA; 2 4-round SS 12 wire-guided missile launchers
Electronics: Radar: 1 Decca TM 1226 nav.
M: 2 MTU 16V652 TB81 diesels; 2 props; 4,600 bhp
Range: 2,000/16 **Crew:** 4 officers, 30 enlisted

Remarks: Rearmed with guns from discarded Shanghai-II-class patrol craft in 1994. The missile system may no longer be functional; command-guided from a station on the bridge, it is considered unreliable except against large, nearby targets.

Disposal note: Vosper 103-ft. patrol craft *Tazarka* (P 205) and *Menzel Bourguiba* (P 206) were stricken during 1999–2000.

PATROL BOATS [PB]

♦ 4 French 32-meter class Bldr: C.N. de l'Estérel, Cannes

	In serv.		In serv.
P 201 Istiklal (ex-French VC 11)	1957	P 203 Al Jala	11-63
P 202 Joumhouria	1-61	P 204 Remada	7-67

Joumhouria (P 202) B. Laffont, 5-99

D: 60 tons (82 fl) **S:** 28 kts **Dim:** 31.45 × 5.75 × 1.7
A: 2 single 20-mm 70-cal. Oerlikon AA
Electronics: Radar: 1 Decca 1226 nav.
M: 2 MTU 12V493 TY70 diesels; 2 props; 2,700 bhp (2,200 sust.)
Range: 1,400/15 **Crew:** 3 officers, 14 enlisted

Remarks: Wooden construction. P 201 was launched 25-5-57 and transferred in 3-59.

♦ 6 French 25-meter class
Bldr: C.N. de l'Estérel, Cannes (In serv. 1961–63)

V 101 V 102 V 103 V 104 V 105 V 106

PATROL BOATS [PB] *(continued)*

V 101 H&L Van Ginderen, 1984

D: 38–39 tons **S:** 23 kts **Dim:** 25.0 × 4.75 × 1.25
A: 1 20-mm 70-cal. Oerlikon AA **Electronics:** Radar: 1 Decca 1226 nav.
M: 2 G.M. 12V71 TI diesels; 2 props; 940 bhp **Range:** 900/16 **Crew:** 11 tot.

Remarks: V 107 and V 108, disarmed, were transferred to the Fisheries Administration in 1971 as *Sabeq el Bahr* (T 2) and *Jaouel el Bahr* (T 3); T 3 was lost 7-7-89.

AUXILIARIES

♦ 1 buoy tender and pollution-control ship [AGL]
Bldr: Damen SY, Gorinchem, the Netherlands (In serv. 3-98)

A 802 Sidi bou Said

Sidi bou Said (A 802) *Marines*/J. Carney, 1998

D: approx. 640 tons (fl) **S:** 10.4 kts **Dim:** 38.80 × 10.25 × 2.80
A: none **Electronics:** Radar: . . .
M: 2 Caterpillar 3406C TA/B diesels; 2 props; 800 bhp
Electric: . . . kw tot. (2 × . . ., Caterpillar 3304 B/T-SR4 diesels driving)
Range: . . ./. . . **Crew:** 18 tot.

Remarks: Ordered in 12-96 as a "buoy-laying, towing, and pollution-control vessel" to Damen's Stan Carrier 3910 design. Can carry 50 tons of deck cargo and up to 200 m^3 of fuel oil and water. Bollard pull: 8 tons. Has a 20-ton deck crane and an A-frame gantry with 50-ton capacity.

♦ 1 ex-Robert D. Conrad–class oceanographic research ship [AGOR]
Bldr: Northwest Marine, Portland, Ore.

	L	In serv.
A 701 N.H.O. Salammbo (ex-*De Steiguer,* T-AGOR 12)	3-6-66	28-2-69

N.H.O. Salammbo (A 701) Luciano Grazioli, 2-01

D: 1,088 tons light (1,643 fl) **S:** 13.5 kts
Dim: 63.51 (58.32 pp) × 11.89 × 4.97 (6.3 max. over sonar domes)
Electronics: Radar: 1 Raytheon 1650/SX nav.; 1 Raytheon 1660/12S nav.
M: 2 Cummins diesels, electric drive; 1 prop; 1,000 shp—JT700 Omnithruster; 350 shp
Electric: 850 kw **Range:** 9,000/12 **Fuel:** 211 tons **Endurance:** 45 days
Crew: 9 officers, 17 unlicensed + 15 scientists/technicians (as U.S. ship)

Remarks: 1,143 grt/355 dwt. Transferred 2-11-92 and left for Tunisia 9-11-92. The new name commemorates a major oceanographic research center in Tunisia. To be used for foreign cruising as well as for oceanographic research in Tunisian waters. The large stack contains a 620-hp gas-turbine generator set used to drive the main shaft at speeds up to 6.5 kts for experiments requiring quiet conditions. Also has a retractable electric bow-thruster/propulsor, which provides up to 4.5 kts. Sisters operate in the U.S., Chilean, Mexican, and New Zealand navies.

♦ 1 ex-U.S. Silas Bent–class training ship [AXT]
Bldr: Defoe SB, Bay City, Mich.

	L	In serv.
A 700 Kheireddine (ex-*Wilkes,* T-AGS 33)	31-7-69	28-6-71

Kheireddine (A 700) Paolo Marsan, 7-99

D: 1,915 tons (2,565 fl) **S:** 15 kts **Dim:** 86.9 (80.8 pp) × 14.6 × 4.6
Electronics: Radar: 1 Raytheon RM 1650/9X nav.; 1 Raytheon TM 1660/12S nav.
M: 2 Alco diesels, electric drive: Westinghouse or G.E. motor; 1 CP prop; 3,600 shp—350-hp bow-thruster
Electric: 960 kw tot. **Range:** 5,800–6,300/14.5; 8,000/13 **Fuel:** 461 tons
Crew: 35 tot. + 26–30 scientists

Remarks: Deactivated from the U.S. Navy 8-9-95 and transferred 29-9-95 as Grant-Aid to Tunisia. Used primarily as training ship for the Tunisian Naval Academy but also performs oceanographic research work in the Mediterranean. Retains bathymetric and acoustic doppler current-profiling equipment. Sister *Wyman* (AGS 34) was offered for transfer by sale in 1998 but was not accepted.

SERVICE CRAFT

♦ 2 ex-U.S. Army LCM(8) Mod. 1–class utility craft [YFU]
(In serv. 1954)

. . . . . . (ex-LCM 8265, ex-C200779)
. . . . . . (ex-LCM 8268, ex-C200782)

D: 58.8 tons light (116 fl) **S:** 9.2 kts (loaded) **Dim:** 22.40 × 6.42 × 1.40 (mean)
M: 2 G.M. Detroit Diesel 6-71 diesels; 2 props; 600 bhp
Range: 150/9.2 (loaded) **Fuel:** 2.4 tons **Crew:** 2–4 tot.

Remarks: Former U.S. Army landing craft originally built for the U.S. Navy. Donated to Tunisia 17-11-00. Cargo: 60 tons or 150 personnel for short distances in the 12.8 × 4.3–m open well with 54.6-m^2 space. Have a bow ramp.

♦ 2 ex-U.S. Coast Guard White-class coastal buoy tenders [YGL]
Bldr: Erie Concrete & Steel Supply Co., Erie, Pa.

	Laid down	L	In serv.
A . . . Tabarka (ex-*White Heath,* WLM 545)	4-6-43	21-7-43	9-8-44
A . . . Turgueness (ex-*White Lupine,* WLM 546)	28-4-43	28-7-43	31-5-44

D: 435 tons (600 fl) **S:** 9.8 kts **Dim:** 40.49 × 9.14 × 2.67
M: 2 diesels; 2 props; 600 bhp **Electric:** 90 kw tot.
Range: 2,100/9.8; 4,500/5.1 **Fuel:** 40 tons **Crew:** 1 officer, 23 enlisted

Remarks: Former U.S. Navy self-propelled covered lighters YF 446 and YF 445, transferred to the U.S. Coast Guard on 3-9-47 and 9-8-47, respectively. They were stricken from the USCG 27-2-98 and 31-3-98 and donated to Tunisia 10-6-98 for service as navigational buoy tenders. Have one 10-ton buoy-handling derrick.

♦ 1 navigational aids tender [YGL]
Bldr: . . ., the Netherlands (In serv. 1961)

Boughrara (ex-*IJsselmeer*)

Boughrara B. Laffont, 5-99

SERVICE CRAFT *(continued)*

D: . . . tons **S:** . . . kts **Dim:** 26.60 × 5.60 × 1.50
M: 1 diesel; 1 prop; . . . bhp

Remarks: Acquired in 1996 from the Netherlands.

♦ **2 inshore survey launches [YGS]**

ALYSSA (In serv. 25-3-96) GUESETTE (In serv. 1992)

D: 8.5 tons (fl) **S:** 10 kts **Dim:** 11.0 × 3.8 × 1.1
M: 1 Perkins diesel; 1 prop; 200 bhp **Crew:** 6 tot.

Remarks: *Alyssa* is additionally configured for oceanographic research.

Note: Also in service for oceanographic research is the 200-ton *Didon;* no data available.

♦ **1 ex-U.S. Savage-class headquarters and accommodations hulk, former radar picket frigate [YPB]**
Bldr: Consolidated Steel, Orange, Texas

	Laid down	L	In serv.
E 7 INDAKH (ex-*President Bourgiba;* ex-*Thomas J. Gary,* DER 326, ex-DE 326)	15-6-43	21-8-43	27-11-43

D: 1,590 tons (1,850 fl) **Dim:** 93.27 (91.50 pp) × 11.22 × 4.27 (hull)

Remarks: Former frigate, employed as training ship and fleet flagship until a serious engine room fire on 16-4-92 forced her immobilization at Bizerte, where she now serves as fleet headquarters and accommodations ship.

♦ **1 small harbor tug**

SIDI MANSOUR

Small harbor tug Sidi Mansour B. Laffont, 5-99

NATIONAL GUARD

(Gendarmerie Nationale—Direction Maritime)

PATROL CRAFT [WPC]

♦ **6 ex-German Kondor-I-class patrol boats**
Bldr: VEB Peenewerft, Wolgast

	In serv.
601 RAS EL BLAD (ex-*Demmin,* GS 02, ex-G 422)	16-8-69
602 RAS AJDIR (ex-*Malchin,* GS 03, ex-G 441; ex-*Klütz,* G 13)	18-10-69
603 RAS EDDREK (ex-*Altentreptow,* GS 04, ex-G 414)	5-9-69
604 RAS MAMOURA (ex-*Templin,* BG 31, ex-GS 06, ex-G 442)	20-12-69
605 RAS ENGHELA (ex-*Ahrenskoop,* BG 33, ex-GS 08, ex-G 421)	8-8-70
606 RAS IFRIKIA (ex-*Warnemünde,* ex-*Bergen* . . .)	25-9-69

Ras Enghela (605)—standard configuration H&L Van Ginderen, 3-98

D: 225 tons light (339 fl) **S:** 20 kts **Dim:** 52.00 × 7.12 × 2.40
A: 1 twin 25-mm 80-cal. Type 61 AA (see remarks)
Electronics: Radar: 1 (606: 2) . . . nav.
M: 2 Type 40DM diesels; 2 CP props; 4,000 bhp (sust.)
Range: 1,900/15 **Crew:** 20 tot.

Remarks: After the unification of Germany, had been incorporated in the Maritime Border Guard *(Bundesgrenzschutz-See)* but were not used operationally. 601–604 were transferred to Tunisia in 7-92 without armament, although at least 601 had received a 25-mm mount removed from a discarded Shanghai-II-class patrol boat by 1995. 605 was transferred 5-8-97 and was not immediately armed. 606, transferred 16-5-00, had been reconfigured as a fisheries protection and research vessel during East German service and was later employed in that capacity by the German Ministry of Food and Agriculture; her superstructure had been extended nearly to the stern and the bridge moved forward.

Ras Ifrikia (606)—with enlarged and lengthened superstructure Bernard Prézelin, 6-00

PATROL BOATS [WPB]

♦ **4 Gabes class** Bldr: SBCN, Loctudy, France (In serv. 1988–89)

GABES JERBA KELIBIA TABARK

D: 12 tons (fl) **S:** 35 kts **Dim:** 12.9 × 3.8 × 0.9
A: 2 single 12.7-mm mg **Electronics:** Radar: 1 Decca . . . nav.
M: 2 . . . diesels; 2 props; 800 bhp **Range:** 250/15 **Crew:** 6 tot.

♦ **5 ex-East German Bremse class**
Bldr: VEB Yachtswerf, Berlin (In serv. 1971–72)

BULLARIJIA (ex-G 36) SELEUTA (ex-G 39) UTIQUE (ex-G 37)
SBEITLA (ex-G 32) UERKOUANE (ex-G 38)

Utique—in German service Hartmut Ehlers, 4-91

D: 25 tons light (48 fl) **S:** 17 kts **Dim:** 22.59 (20.97 wl) × 4.70 × 1.60
A: 2 single 7.62-mm mg **Electronics:** Radar: 1 Furuno FR 80310 nav.
M: 1 Motorenwerke Rosslau Type 6VD 18/15 AL 1 diesel; 1 prop; 510 bhp
Range: 300/12 **Fuel:** 485 liters **Crew:** 4 tot.

Remarks: Transferred as a gift of the German government during 5-92. Wooden hulls.

Note: The customs service operates 10 locally built *Assad ibn Fourat*–class, 32-ton patrol boats completed between 1986 and 1989. Capable of 28 kts, they are 20.5 m o.a. and are armed with one 12.7-mm and two 7.62-mm mg. Their range is 500 n.m. at 20 kts, and a crew of 8 can be carried. The craft are gray-painted and carry a broad red/narrow white/narrow red diagonal stripe on each side.

Assad ibn Fourat–class customs launch B. Laffont, 5-99

TURKEY

Republic of Turkey

TURKISH REPUBLIC NAVY

(Türkiye Cumhuriyeti Bahriyesi)

Personnel (2001): 51,000 total (4,200 officers) navy (including 900 naval aviation and 3,000 marines), plus 70,000 naval reserve

Bases: Fleet Headquarters is located at the capital, Ankara. Fleet Command was to be moved from Gölçuk to Izmir in 2002, with the Southern Sea Area Command moved from Izmir to Antalya. The main naval base and dockyard at Gölçuk is to be moved to Aksaz; work on expanding the Aksaz Naval Base began on 27-9-00. Other naval facilities as of 2000 were located at Aksaz, Büyükdere, Çanakkale, Erdek, Foça, Iskenderun, Karamürsel, and Mersin. Türkiye Gemi Sanayi A.S.'s private Pendik Shipyard at Istanbul was transferred to the Turkish Navy for new construction in 1999, with the building yard at Gölçuk reoriented to repair work. Taşkizak Naval Shipyard, Istanbul, is now used only for constructing small combatants and service craft. Black Sea forces are to be concentrated at Sinop or Samsun.

Naval Aviation: The Turkish Naval Aviation Force *(Türk Donama Havaciligi)* has one operational squadron, 351 Sqn., with 3 AB-204AS, 10 AB-212ASW, and 3 AB-212EW helicopters based at Kocaeli. Fixed-wing pilot proficiency is maintained on six SOCATA TB-20 trainers delivered in 1995. Naval air facilities are maintained at Trabzon, Sinop, Istanbul, Çanakkale, Izmir, Antalya, Iskenderun, and Cengiz Topel Naval Air Station, Kocaeli.

Four Sikorsky S-70B Seahawk ASW helicopters, equipped with AGM-114M Hellfire-II antiship missiles, HELRAS active dipping sonar, and APS-143(V) radar, were ordered 13-2-97, and another four were ordered in 2-98. The program was held up by the U.S. Congress until the first four were approved during 3-99. The first S-70B flew 18-1-01, but the start of deliveries was held up until 11-01 by software development problems. A 2-00 order for an additional eight (with an option for a total of 14) was canceled in 4-01 due to funding problems, but the Turkish Navy still plans an eventual total of 32. The aircraft are equipped with the APS-143 radar, FLIR, and a deck landing and traversing system.

Nine CASA CN-235 maritime patrol aircraft (three for the coast guard) were ordered 28-4-97, but the final contract was not signed until 10-98. The aircraft are being locally assembled by Tusas Aerospace Industries, near Ankara; the first to be delivered crashed on 18-5-01. On 14-10-97, six SAR-configured Agusta-Bell 412 helicopters were ordered for the coast guard.

Marines: The Turkish Marine Corps has three combat infantry battalions, one artillery battalion, a headquarters company, and various support units.

Note: Turkish Navy ship names are preceded by TCG (*Türkiye Cumhuriyeti Genisi,* or Turkish Republic Ship). Since 1997, submarine pennant numbers are no longer displayed, and surface ship pennants have had the white component replaced with gray to reduce the contrast and thereby assist somewhat in defeating infrared-homing missiles.

WEAPONS AND SYSTEMS

Most weapons and systems are of U.S. origin and some are from Germany or France. British Sea Skua antiship missiles have been purchased for use by the AB-212 helicopters. The Turkish Navy also has a considerable number of AGM-84A and AGM-84C Harpoon surface-launched antiship missiles and received UGM-84C Sub-Harpoon missiles during the mid-1990s. A July 1999 order for 16 Penguin Mk 2 Mod. 7 antiship missiles was canceled in 10-99, but in 7-00 Norway agreed to sell Turkey Penguin Mk 3 missiles. In 2-01, 84 AGM-114K Hellfire-II antiship missiles with blast-fragmentation warheads for antiship use from SH-60B Seahawk helicopters began delivery. Some 208 pedestal-mounted Stinger point-defense SAM launch systems from ASELSAN, Turkey, were to be delivered by the end of 2000 for use on naval ships and at shore stations.

In 1991, a license was obtained from Marconi Underwater Systems to build 40 Mk 24 Mod. 2 Tigerfish wire-guided submarine torpedoes to begin replacement of German SUT and SST-4 and U.S. Mk 37 torpedoes; 20 Tigerfish were delivered by GEC-Marconi in 1998. Ten U.S. Mk 48 submarine torpedoes were ordered in 1990.

All Turkish Navy major surface combatants are equipped to employ Link 11 datalink. Links 16 and 22 and the U.S. Cooperative Engagement Capability (CEC) may be incorporated in the future.

Sea Guard Close-In Weapons System: Mfr: Contraves/Oerlikon. Employed only by the Turkish Navy, each Sea Guard installation has three Sea Zenith quadruple 25-mm AA with a combined rate of fire of 3,200 rounds per minute per mount. With a practical range of about 2,000 m, the mountings can depress to −15° and elevate to +127°, with extremely rapid elevation and traversing. In the MEKO 200 class, the three mounts are controlled by two Siemens Albis radar/electro-optical directors. Sufficient ready-service ammunition is carried on-mount for 18 engagements.

Bora: Mfr: ASELSAN Microwave and Systems Technologies Division. A close-defense SAM system using components from the armored vehicle Pedestal-Mounted Air Defense System (PMADS) and the smaller Zipkin system. The prototype Bora, completed in 1999, carries four Stinger heat-seeking SAMs and a 12.7-mm mg, plus t.v. and infrared optical sensors and a pulse-laser rangefinder, all on a stabilized mounting. No immediate plans for shipboard installations have been announced.

V/STOL AIRCRAFT CARRIERS [CVH]

Note: Under planning first revealed during 4-98, a study was being made of the feasibility of building one or more small aircraft carriers of about 12,500 tons full load displacement at a projected cost of $400 million per ship. The ship appears nowhere in future acquisition plans through about 2020, however.

ATTACK SUBMARINES [SS]

♦ 4 (+ 4) German Type 209/1400 class

Bldr: Gölçuk NSY, Kocaeli, Izmir (S 359 and 360: Pendik NSY, Istanbul)

	Laid down	L	In serv.
S 353 Preveze	12-9-89	27-11-93	28-7-94
S 354 Sakarya	1-2-90	28-7-94	4-96 (del. 21-12-95)
S 355 18 Mart	28-7-94	25-8-97	24-7-98
S 356 Anafartalar	1-8-95	2-9-98	22-7-99
S 357 Gür	24-7-98	25-7-01	2-04
S 358 Çanakkale	22-7-99	7-02	6-04
S 359 Burakreis	25-7-01	. . .	2005
S 360	. . .	. . .	2006

D: 1,464 tons surf./1,586 tons sub. **S:** 11.0 kts surf./21.5 kts sub.
Dim: 62.00 × 6.20 (7.60 over stern planes) × 5.50
A: 8 bow 533-mm TT (14 Mk 24 Mod. 2 Tigerfish torpedoes and UGM-84C Sub-Harpoon SSM and/or mines—see remarks)

Sakarya (S 354) Cem D. Yaylali, 8-00

Preveze (S 353) Peter Froud, 5-99

Anafartalar (S 356) Mike Welsford, 4-00

Electronics:
Radar: 1 . . . nav./surf. search
Sonar: STN Atlas Elektronik CSU-83/1 suite (with flank and TAS-3 towed passive arrays)
EW: Racal Porpoise (S 357 and later: Sealion) intercept suite
M: 4 MTU 12V493 A280 AG diesels (800 bhp each), 4 405-kw generator sets, 1 Siemens electric motor; 1 prop; 5,000 shp
Range: 15,000/4 surf.; 10,000/8 snorkel; 25/21.5, 230/8, 390/4 sub.
Endurance: 50 days **Crew:** 8 officers, 27 enlisted (accomm.)

Remarks: A lengthened version of the standard IKL 1400 design. The first two of a planned six were ordered 12-11-87, and the second pair, ordered in 1993, were built with Howaldtswerke technical assistance. S 357–360 are being built under a 996 million DM agreement signed with Howaldtswerke 22-7-98 but not finalized until 3-99; S 359 is to cost $556 million. Are named for battles.
Hull systems: Diving depth: 320 m. Have 10% reserve buoyancy. There are four 120-cell batteries. Have Kollmorgen Model 76-374 search and attack periscopes, with integral ranging radar and intercept antennas.
Combat systems: All have the STN Atlas Elektronik ISUS-83-2 command-and-control system with four display consoles; it links radar, periscope t.v., ESM, Link 11, and sonar suite data. Four of the torpedo tubes can be used to launch missiles and four to lay mines. The Porpoise EW suite is an export version of the British Navy's UAC system. S 357 and later are to carry STN Atlas Elektronik DM-2A4 wire-guided torpedoes.

♦ 6 German Type 209/1200

Bldrs: First three: Howaldtswerke, Kiel; others: Gölçuk NSY, Kocaeli, Izmir

	Laid down	L	In serv.
S 347 Atilay	1-12-72	23-10-74	12-3-76
S 348 Saldiray	2-1-73	14-2-75	15-1-77
S 349 Batiray	11-6-75	24-10-77	7-11-78
S 350 Yildiray	1-5-76	20-7-77	20-7-81
S 351 Doganay	21-3-80	16-11-83	16-11-85
S 352 Dolunay	16-11-83	21-7-88	29-6-90

Yildiray (S 350) Hartmut Ehlers, 3-96

D: 1,000 tons std./1,180 tons surf./1,285 tons sub. **S:** 11.5 kts surf./22 kts sub.
Dim: 55.90 × 6.30 × 5.50
A: 8 bow 533-mm TT (14 SUT, SST-4 Mod. 0, and Mk 37 Mod. 2 wire-guided torpedoes and/or mines)

ATTACK SUBMARINES [SS] *(continued)*

Doganay (S 351) Hartmut Ehlers, 10-95

Electronics:
Radar: 1 Thales Calypso-II nav./surf. search
Sonar: STN Atlas Elektronik CSU-3 suite: AN 526 passive/AN 407AS active, DUUX-2 underwater telephone
EW: S 347, 348: Racal Sealion intercept—others: Racal Porpoise suite
M: 4 MTU 12V493 TY60 diesels (600 bhp each), 1 Siemens electric motor; 4 405-kw generator sets; 5,000 shp
Range: 7,800/8, 11,300/4 surf.; 28/20, 460/4 sub. **Fuel:** 185 tons
Endurance: 50 days **Crew:** 6 officers, 27 enlisted

Remarks: Are all to be modernized to permit retirement of the remaining ex-U.S. Navy submarines. In 2000, two submarines of this class were offered for lease to Malaysia, probably S 347 and S 348, with the pair to be replaced later by two new-construction Type 209/1400 for Malaysia.
Hull systems: Have four Hagen 120-cell lead-acid batteries, delivering 11,500 Amp-hr and weighing 257 tons. Normal operating depth: 250 m.
Combat systems: First two have the Thales M8 torpedo fire control; the others have the Thales SINBADS combat system. Have Kollmorgen Model 76-374 search and attack periscopes, with integral ranging radar and intercept antennas. The original Thales DR-2000 EW suite in the first two was replaced in 1999–2000.

♦ 2 ex-U.S. Tang class
Bldr: Portsmouth NSY, Portsmouth, N.H.

	Laid down	L	In serv.
S 342 Hizir Reis (ex-*Gudgeon,* SSAG 567)	20-5-50	11-6-52	21-11-52
S 343 Piri Reis (ex-*Tang,* SS 563)	18-4-49	19-6-51	25-10-52

Piri Reis (S 343) Cem D. Yaylali, 10-98

Hizir Reis (S 342) Hartmut Ehlers, 9-96

D: 2,050 tons surf./2,700 tons sub. **S:** 15.6 kts surf./18.3 kts sub.
Dim: 87.50 × 8.33 × 5.80
A: 8 533-mm TT (6 fwd for Mk 48 wire-guided and Mk 23 straight-running torpedoes; 2 short TT aft for Mk 37 Mod. 2 wire-guided torpedoes)
Electronics:
Radar: 1 Fairchild BPS-12 search
Sonar: EDO BQS-4 passive; Raytheon BQG-4 (PUFFS) passive-ranging; EDO BQR-2B active
EW: WLR-1 intercept
M: 3 Fairbanks-Morse 38D8⅛ × 10 diesels, 2 Westinghouse motors; 2 props; 3,430 bhp surf./5,600 shp sub.
Range: 7,600/15; 17/9 sub. **Crew:** 11 officers, 75 enlisted

Remarks: S 343 was leased for five years 8-2-80 and recommissioned 21-4-80. S 342 was leased 30-9-83 and recommissioned 30-9-83. Both were purchased outright 6-8-87. Have Mk 106 Mod. 18 torpedo f.c.s. Were transferred with Mk 48 Mod. 4 torpedoes, and additional Mk 48 Mod. 4 torpedoes were purchased later. Normal operating depth limit: more than 215 m. One sister remains in U.S. service as a drone target submarine.

♦ 1 ex-U.S. GUPPY IIA class
Bldr: Portsmouth NSY, Portsmouth, N.H.

	Laid down	L	In serv.
S 336 Murat Reis (ex-*Razorback,* SS 394)	9-9-43	27-1-44	3-4-44

Uluçalireis (S 338)—since stricken Cem D. Yaylali, 8-00

D: 1,525 tons std.; 1,848 tons surf./2,440 tons sub.
S: 17.4 kts surf./9.4 kts snorkel/14 kts sub. **Dim:** 93.36 × 8.33 × 5.04
A: 10 533-mm TT (6 fwd, 4 aft; 24 Mk 23 and Mk 37 torpedoes or 40 mines)
Electronics:
Radar: 1 SS-2A nav./surf. search
Sonar: EDO BQR-2B passive; EDO BQS-4 active; Raytheon BQG-3 passive ranging
EW: . . . intercept
M: 3 Fairbanks-Morse 38D8⅛ × 10 diesels, electric drive; 2 props; 3,430 bhp surf./5,200 shp sub.
Range: 10,000/10 surf.; 95/5 sub. **Fuel:** 330 tons
Crew: 9 officers, 76 enlisted

Remarks: Transferred in 11-70 and recommissioned 17-12-71. While in U.S. service, was equipped as a "hard" target for ASW training.
Disposals: Sisters *Oruç Reis* (S 337; ex-*Pomfret,* SS 391) and *Preveze* (S 345; ex-*Entemedor,* SS 340) were stricken in 1987, *Burak Reis* (S 335; ex-*Sea Fox,* SS 402) during 1996, *Birinci Inönü* (S 346; ex-*Threadfin,* SS 410) during 1998, and *Cerbe* (S 340; ex-*Trutta,* SS 421) on 23-7-99. *Uluçalireis* (S 338; ex-*Thornback,* SS 418), stricken 7-8-00, may become a exhibit at the Rahmi M. Koç Technical Museum, Hasköy, Istanbul.

GUIDED-MISSILE FRIGATES [FFG]

♦ 6 (+ 1) ex-U.S. Oliver Hazard Perry class

	Bldr	Laid down	L	In serv.
F 490 Gaziantep (ex-*Clifton Sprague,* FFG 16)	Bath Iron Works, Bath, Maine	30-7-79	16-2-80	21-3-81
F 491 Giresun (ex-*Antrim,* FFG 20)	Todd, Seattle	21-6-78	27-3-79	26-9-81
F 492 Gemlik (ex-*Flatley,* FFG 21)	Bath Iron Works, Bath, Maine	13-11-79	15-5-80	20-6-81
F 493 Gelibolu (ex-*Reid,* FFG 30)	Todd, San Pedro, Calif.	8-10-80	27-6-81	19-2-83
F 494 Gökçeada (ex-*Mahlon S. Tisdale,* FFG 27)	Todd, San Pedro, Calif.	19-3-80	7-2-81	13-11-82
F 495 Gediz (ex-*John A. Moore,* FFG 19)	Todd, San Pedro, Calif.	19-12-78	20-10-79	14-11-81
F 496 Gökova (ex-*Samuel Eliot Morison,* FFG 13)	Bath Iron Works, Bath, Maine	4-12-78	14-7-79	10-10-80

Gemlik (F 492) Findler & Winter, 2-01

Giresun (F 491) Mike Welsford, 9-01

D: 3,106 tons light (3,989 fl) **S:** 29 kts (30.6 on trials)
Dim: 135.64 (125.9 wl) × 13.72 × 5.8 (6.7 max.)
A: 1 Mk 13 Mod. 4 missile launcher (4 RGM-84C Harpoon and 36 Standard SM-1 MR missiles); 1 76-mm 62-cal. Mk 75 DP; 1 20-mm Mk 15 Phalanx gatling CIWS; 2 single 12.7-mm mg; 2 triple 324-mm Mk 32 Mod. 7 ASW TT (Mk 46 Mod. 5 torpedoes); 1 S-70B Seahawk helicopter

GUIDED-MISSILE FRIGATES [FFG] *(continued)*

Gaziantep (F 490) Turkish Navy

Gediz (F 495) George R. Schneider, 10-00

Electronics:

Radar: 1 . . . nav.; 1 Cardion SPS-55 surf. search; 1 Raytheon SPS-49(V)4 air search; 1 Raytheon Mk 92 Mod. 2 missile illumination/gun f.c.; 1 Lockheed Martin STIR (SPG-60 Mod.) missile illumination/gun f.c.; 1 General Dynamics Mk 90 Phalanx f.c.

Sonar: SQQ-89(V)2 suite: Raytheon SQS-56 hull-mounted LF (see remarks)

TACAN: URN-25

EW: Raytheon SLQ-32(V)2 passive; Mk 36 SRBOC decoy syst. (2 6-round Mk 137 RL); SLQ-25 Nixie towed acoustic torpedo decoy

M: 2 G.E. LM-2500 gas turbines; 1 5.5-m-dia., 5-bladed CP prop; 41,000 shp (40,000 sust.)—2 350-shp drop-down electric propulsors

Electric: 4,000 kw tot. (4 × 1,000-kw diesel-driven alternator sets)

Range: 4,200/20; 5,000/18 **Fuel:** 587 tons + 64 tons helicopter fuel

Crew: 19 officers, 121 petty officers, 79 other enlisted (214 max. accomm.)

Remarks: F 490 and 491 were transferred under the Grant-Aid program during U.S. FY 96, while F 492 was transferred on lease (but was offered for outright sale for $28 million during U.S. FY 01). F 490 had been decommissioned from the USN 2-6-95, F 491 on 8-5-96, and F 492 on 11-5-96. F 490 arrived in Turkey 16-3-98 and the other two on 13-4-98; they were formally recommissioned 24-7-98. F 493, decommissioned 25-9-98 from the USN, was transferred by sale 5-1-99. F 494, in reserve since 27-9-96, and the ex-*Duncan* (FFG 10), which was purchased as a spare parts source, departed Pearl Harbor under tow 29-1-99 for Detyens SY, Charleston, S.C.; F 494 arrived at Gölçuk 27-9-99. F 495 was transferred by sale 1-9-00 and formally recommissioned in Turkey 25-7-01. The planned fall 2001 sale to Turkey of the *Estocin* (FFG 15) has been postponed until 10-04, but FFG 13 remained on schedule for transfer 10-4-02. They are locally referred to as the "G" class and are named for Turkish towns.

Hull systems: Displacement figures above apply specifically to F 496. These ships are particularly well protected against splinter and fragmentation damage, with 19-mm aluminum-alloy armor over magazine spaces, 16-mm steel over the main engine-control room, and 19-mm Kevlar plastic armor over vital electronics and command spaces. Speed on one gas turbine is 25 kts. The auxiliary power system uses two retractable pods located well forward and can drive the ships at up to 6 kts. The two Brown Brothers fin stabilizers extend 2.36 m, have a mean chord of 2.36 m, and are located 57.9 m abaft the bow perpendicular; F 490 and 493 were the only units of the class never fitted with the stabilizers while in U.S. Navy service, and they still have not been added. All are equipped with the Prairie/Masker air bubbler system to reduce radiated machinery noise below the waterline.

The helicopter flight decks are being extended (as in later examples of the USN units of the class) by Pendik Naval Shipyard, Istanbul, to handle S-70 helicopters, with two ships already modified by the end of 2001; the modified ships will be 138.80 m o.a.

Combat systems: The Mk 92 Mod. 4 fire-control system controls missile and 76-mm gunfire; it uses a STIR (modified SPG-60) antenna amidships and a U.S.-built version of the WM-28 radar forward and can track four separate targets. The Mk 75 gun is a license-built version of the OTOBreda Compact. A Mk 13 weapons-direction system is fitted. There are two Mk 24 optical missile and gun target designators mounted in tubs atop the pilothouse. The only ship-launched ASW weapons are the Mk 46 Mod. 5 torpedoes in the two triple torpedo tubes; a total of 24 torpedoes can be carried for the tubes and the helicopter. Harpoon antiship missiles are launched via the SWG-1 launch-control system. F 490–495 were delivered without helicopters, SQQ-28 helicopter datalink, or towed passive sonar arrays, but a navigational radar was added. Upgrades to the combat-control system are planned under the Genesis program, with contractor bids due 20-10-00; existing stand-alone displays will be replaced by multifunctional operator consoles and the combat system integrated. F 496 retained the towed sonar array when transferred, as will the *Estocin* (FFG 15).

FRIGATES [FF]

♦ 0 (+ 6) TF-2000 project

Bldrs: Four by Pendik NSY, Istanbul; two by . . .

Blohm + Voss MEKO 200—official model of their design offered in the TF-2000 project competition Norman Friedman, 4-01

D: about 1,800 tons (fl) **S:** 28+ kts (26 sust.; 18 on diesels)

Dim: . . . × . . . × . . .

A: . . ./. . . SSM; . . . vertical-launch area air-defense missile syst.; . . . vertical-launch short-range air-defense missile syst.; point-defense air defense syst.; 1 or 2 . . .-mm DP guns; 2 single 25- to 40-mm AA; 2 triple 324-mm Mk 32 ASW TT (Mk 46 Mod. 5 torpedoes); 1 10-ton-class helicopter

Electronics:

Radar: 1 . . . nav.; 1. . . surf. search; 1 . . . 3-D air search

Sonar: . . . bow-mounted LF

EW: . . .

E/O: . . . missile-detection syst.; . . . t.v./low-light t.v./IR/laser director

M: CODOG: 2 gas turbines, 1 or 2 diesels; 2 CP props; . . . hp

Range: 5,000/18 **Endurance:** 30 days **Crew:** 41 officers, 201 enlisted

Remarks: Turkey plans to order six replacement frigates in the near future in a program to cover a 15-year period and to cost in excess of $3 billion. By 2025, some 14 new frigates were to be built, at a total cost of $6.070 billion, but the program was scaled back. A request for proposals was to be issued in 7-96 but was repeatedly delayed until 18-5-00, when the total of ships was raised to eight but then later again reduced to six. Four are to be built at the Pendik Navy Yard and two by a private Turkish firm. Only two bids were received on 2-1-00: one by a German consortium (Blohm + Voss, Lürssenwerft, and Abeking & Rasmussen) offering the Blohm + Voss MEKO A200 design in conjunction with local builder Rahmi Okc–RMK and the other by the Turkish Celik Trans firm, which, however, was unable to post the necessary $2 million bond. As of 11-01, no contract had been announced, and the program may be a victim of further financial constraints. It had been hoped to deliver the first ship in 2004 and the last in 2009.

♦ 4 MEKO 200TN Track II-A and -B* class

	Bldr	Laid down	L	In serv.
F 244 Barbaros	Blohm + Voss, Hamburg	4-92	26-10-93	25-3-95
F 245 Oruçreis	Gölçuk NSY, Kocaeli	23-7-92	28-7-94	10-5-96
F 246 Salihreis*	Blohm + Voss, Hamburg	16-3-95	26-9-97	17-12-98
F 247 Kemalreis*	Gölçuk NSY, Kocaeli	3-12-96	24-7-98	8-6-00

Barbaros (F 244)—MEKO 200TN Track II-A variant with Mk 29 Sea Sparrow missile launcher atop the helicopter hangar aft Camil Busquets i Vilanova, 10-99

D: F 244, 245: 3,100 tons (3,350 fl)—F 246, 247: 3,150 tons (3,400 fl)

S: 31.75 kts (22 max. on diesel)

Dim: F 244, 245: 116.72 (107.20 pp) × 14.80 (13.80 wl) × 6.12 (max.; 4.25 hull)—F 246, 247: 117.72 (108.20 pp) × 14.80 (13.80 wl) × 6.12 (max.; 4.25 hull)

FRIGATES [FF] *(continued)*

Oruçreis (F 245)—MEKO 200TN Track II-A variant; note the SATCOM antennas abaft the side-by-side exhaust stacks — Dieter Wolf, 4-00

Kemalreis (F 247)—MEKO 200TN Track II-B variant with Mk 48 vertical SAM launch system abaft the twin stacks — Mike Welsford, 8-00

A: 8 RGM-84C Harpoon SSM—F 244, 245 only: 1 8-round Mk 29 SAM launcher (24 RIM-7M Sea Sparrow SAM)—F 246, 247 only: 1 Mk 41 Mod. 8 vertical launch group (16 RIM-7P Sea Sparrow SAM)—all: 1 127-mm 54-cal. Mk 45 Mod. 2A DP; 3 4-barrel 25-mm Oerlikon GM 25-52 Sea Zenith CIWS; 2 triple 324-mm Mk 32 Mod. 5 ASW TT; 1 AB-212 ASW helicopter

Electronics:

Radar: 1 Decca 2690 BT ARPA nav.; 1 BAE Systems AWS-9 (TN) 996 air search; 1 Thales STIR-24 SAM f.c.; 1 Thales STIR-18 missile/gun f.c.; 1 Contraves TMX Dolphin CIWS target desig.; 2 Contraves TMKu CIWS f.c.

Sonar: Raytheon SQS-56 (DE 1160) hull-mounted MF

TACAN: URN-25

EW: Racal Cutlass B-1 intercept; Racal Scorpion B jammer; Mk 36 SRBOC decoy syst. (2 6-round Mk 137 RL); SLQ-25 Nixie towed torpedo decoy syst.

E/O: GEC-Marconi FLIR; Ferranti laser rangefinder

Kemalreis (F 247)—note the Sea Zenith CIWS mounts flanking the helicopter hangar — Mike Welsford, 8-00

M: CODOG: 2 MTU 16V1163 TB83 diesels (6,530 bhp each), 2 G.E. LM-2500-30 gas turbines (31,766 shp each); 2 KaMeWa CP props; 63,532 shp max.

Electric: 2,480 kw tot. (4 × 620-kw MTU 8V396-series diesel alternator sets)

Range: 900/31.75; 4,100/18 (2 diesels) **Fuel:** 300 tons

Crew: 24 officers, 156 enlisted

Remarks: The first two of a planned four were ordered 19-1-90 (although the contract did not go into effect until 13-3-91); a letter of intent for the second pair was signed 14-12-92 and the final contract signed with the Blohm + Voss/Thyssen Rheinstahl Technik GmbH consortium on 25-11-94. First steel was cut for F 244 on 5-11-91. The German subsidy for the construction of the second pair was suspended from 3-95 to 9-95 because of Turkey's intervention against Kurdish elements in northern Iraq. F 244 arrived at Gölçuk 27-6-95. An additional two were on option, to be built one-each in Turkey and Germany, but they were canceled in 10-99.

Hull systems: In addition to having a different propulsion system than the initial Turkish MEKO quartet, these ships also substitute later electronics, improved air-conditioning, and better NBC warfare protection (with a complete citadel). F 246 and 247 are 1 m longer to accommodate SH-60 helicopters more easily; they also have bulwarks fitted to the bow. All have fin stabilizers.

Combat systems: Have the Thales STACOS Mod. III FD combat data system with two Oerlikon-Contraves Ku-band radar trackers for Sea Sparrow and the Sea Guard CIWS. The first two are fitted for later substitution of the Mk 41 vertical launch group for 16 Sea Sparrow missiles in place of the octuple Mk 29 launcher; the later pair had the Mk 41 vertical launch group aft as built and have two STIR-24 tracker/illuminators; they also have command staff facilities. When available, the folding-fin Evolved Sea Sparrow SAM will be procured, allowing 24 to be carried in the eight Mk 41 Mod. 8 VLS cells. S-70B helicopters equipped to launch AGM-114M Hellfire-II antiship missiles are to replace the older AB-212 helicopters, which are equipped

Salihreis (F 246)—MEKO 200TN Track II-B — Ben Sullivan, 3-00

FRIGATES [FF] *(continued)*

to launch Sea Skua missiles. F 244 and 245 are equipped with two antennas for the Scot-1C SHF SATCOM system and a commercial SATCOM terminal, while the others have two commercial SATCOM antennas.

♦ 4 MEKO 200TN Track I class

	Bldr	Laid down	L	In serv.
F 240 Yavuz	Blohm + Voss, Hamburg	31-5-85	7-11-85	17-7-87
F 241 Turgut Reis (ex-*Turgut*)	Howaldtswerke, Kiel	20-9-85	30-5-86	4-2-88
F 242 Fatih	Gölçuk NSY, Kocaeli	1-1-86	24-4-87	22-7-88
F 243 Yildirim	Gölçuk NSY, Kocaeli	24-4-87	22-7-88	21-7-89

Yavuz (F 240) Cem D. Yaylali, 8-00

Turgut Reis (F 241) *Ships of the World,* 6-00

Yildirim (F 243) Turkish Navy

Turgut Reis (F 241) Mitsuhiro Kadota, 6-01

D: 2,414 tons (2,994 fl) **S:** 27 kts (20 cruise)
Dim: 110.50 (102.20 pp) × 14.20 (13.25 wl) × 4.10 (mean hull)
A: 8 Harpoon SSM; 1 8-round Mk 29 SAM launcher (16 RIM-7M Sea Sparrow missiles); 1 127-mm 54-cal. Mk 45 Mod. 1 DP; 3 4-barrel 25-mm Oerlikon-Contraves Sea Zenith GM 25 CIWS; 2 triple 324-mm Mk 32 Mod. 5 ASW TT (Mk 46 Mod. 5 torpedoes); 1 Agusta-Bell AB-212 helicopter with Sea Skua SSM
Electronics:
Radar: 1 Decca TM 1226 nav.; 1 BAE Systems AWS-6 (Dolphin) surf./air search; 1 Thales DA-08 air search; 1 Thales WM-25 track-while-scan missile/gun f.c.; 1 STIR-24 SAM illumination; 2 Siemens Albis TMKu radar/optronic f.c. (for Sea Zenith CIWS)
Sonar: Raytheon SQS-56 (DE 1160) hull-mounted MF
TACAN: Thales Vesta
EW: Thales Rapids/Ramses suite; Mk 36 SRBOC decoy syst. (2 6-round Mk 137 RL); SLQ-25 Nixie towed torpedo decoy syst.
M: 4 MTU 20V1163 TB93 diesels; 2 CP props; 35,940 bhp (29,940 sust.)
Electric: 1,440 kw tot. (3 × 480-kw MTU diesel-driven sets)
Range: 4,000/20 **Fuel:** 380 tons **Crew:** 26 officers, 154 enlisted

Remarks: Ordered in 4-83, with Blohm + Voss supplying technical assistance for the two constructed in Turkey. The name of F 241 was changed 14-2-88.
Hull systems: The MEKO modular concept permits rapid changeout and installation of combat systems. Have fin stabilizers.
Combat systems: Have the Thales STACOS-TU data system. Albis, by Siemens, is a laser/radar/optronic f.c. director for the Sea Zenith guns. S-70B Seahawk helicopters equipped to launch AGM-114M Hellfire-II antiship missiles are to replace the older AB-212 helicopters.

Disposal note: Of the two *Berk*-class frigates, *Berk* (D 358) was stricken 12-01-99 and sunk as a torpedo target on 9-6-00, and *Peyk* (D 359) was taken out of service during spring 2000 and stricken during 11-00.

♦ 6 ex-U.S. Knox class

Bldr: Avondale SY (now Northrop Grumman SB), Westwego, La. (F 252: Lockheed SB, Seattle)

	Laid down	L	In serv.
F 250 Muavenet (ex-*Capodanno,* FF 1093)	12-10-71	21-10-72	17-11-73
F 252 Kocatepe (ex-*Reasoner,* FF 1063)	6-1-69	1-8-70	31-1-71
F 253 Zafer (ex-*Thomas C. Hart,* FF 1092)	8-10-71	12-8-72	28-7-73
F 254 Trakya (ex-*McCandless,* FFT 1084)	4-6-70	20-3-71	18-3-72
F 255 Karadeniz (ex-*Donald B. Beary,* FFT 1085)	24-7-70	22-5-71	22-7-72
F 256 Ege (ex-*Ainsworth,* FFT 1090)	11-6-71	15-4-72	31-3-73

D: 3,130 tons light (4,260 fl) **S:** 29 kts
Dim: 134.00 (126.49 wl) × 14.33 × 4.77 (7.83 over sonar)
A: 4 RGM-84C Harpoon SSM (using Mk 112 ASROC launcher); 1 127-mm 54-cal. Mk 42 Mod. 10 DP; 1 20-mm Mk 15 CIWS; Mk 16 Mod. 8 ASROC ASW RL syst. (1 8-round Mk 112 launcher); 4 single 12.7-mm mg; 2 twin, fixed 324-mm Mk 32 Mod. 9 fixed ASW TT (Mk 46 Mod. 5 torpedoes); 1 Mk 9 d.c. rack (6 Mk 9 d.c.); 1 AB-212 helicopter

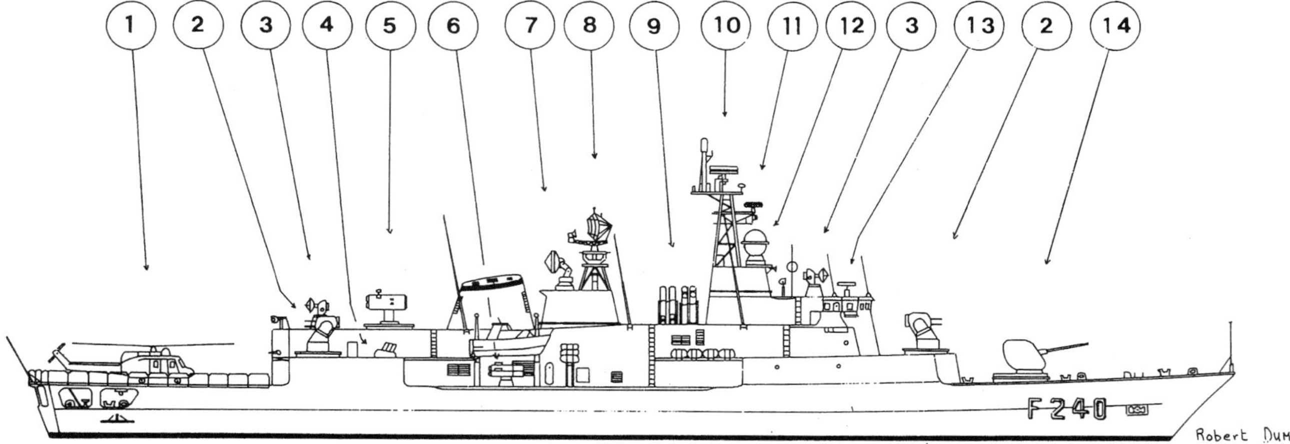

Yavuz (F 240) 1. AB-212 ASW helicopter 2. Sea Zenith 4-barrel 25-mm CIWS 3. Siemens Albis TMKu CIWS f.c. radar 4. Mk 137 rocket launchers for Mk 36 SRBOC decoy system 5. 8-round Mk 29 SAM launcher 6. Mk 32 ASW TT 7. STIR-24 tracker/illuminator radar 8. DA-08 air-search radar 9. Harpoon antiship missiles 10. WM-25 track-while-scan radar director 11. 127-mm 54-cal. DP gun
Drawing by Robert Dumas, from *Flottes de Combat*

FRIGATES [FF] *(continued)*

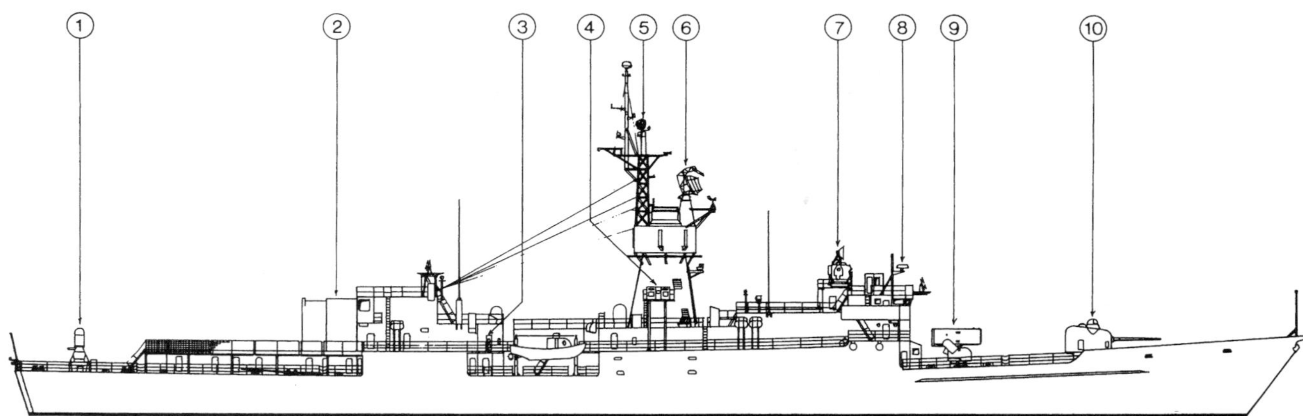

Knox class 1. 20-mm Phalanx CIWS 2. telescoping helicopter hangar 3. twin, fixed Mk 32 Mod. 9 ASW TT 4. SLQ-32(V)2 EW antenna group 5. SPS-10F surface-search radar 6. SPS-40D air-search radar 7. stabilized director for Mk 68 gun fire-control system, with SPG-53F radar 8. navigational radar 9. 8-cell Mk 112 ASROC missile launcher 10. 127-mm Mk 42 Mod. 10 DP gun
Drawing by A. D. Baker III

Kocatepe (F 252) Camil Busquets i Vilanova, 6-99

Zafer (F 253) Bernard Prézelin, 5-01

Zafer (F 253) Bernard Prézelin, 5-01

Electronics:
Radar: 1 Decca TM 1226 nav.; Raytheon SPS-10F surf. search; 1 Lockheed SPS-40D air search; 1 Western Electric SPG-53D/F gun f.c.; 1 General Dynamics Mk 90 Phalanx f.c.
Sonar: EDO-G.E. SQS-26CX bow-mounted LF
TACAN: SRN-15A
EW: Raytheon SLQ-32(V)2 intercept; Mk 36 SRBOC decoy syst. (2 6-round Mk 137 RL); T Mk 6 Fanfare towed acoustic torpedo decoy

Karadeniz (F 255)—without bow bulwarks or spray strakes Leo Dirkx, 7-01

M: 1 set Westinghouse geared steam turbines; 1 prop; 35,000 shp
Boilers: 2 Combustion Engineering (F 252: Babcock & Wilcox) V2M D-Type; 84 kg/cm², 510° C
Electric: 3,000 kw tot. (3 × 750-kw turbogenerators, 1 × 750-kw diesel set)
Range: 4,300/20 **Fuel:** 750 tons max. **Crew:** 17–20 officers, 255–267 enlisted

Remarks: Transferred on lease after decommissioning from the U.S. Navy: F 250 on 30-7-93, F 252 on 28-8-93, F 253 on 30-8-93, F 254 on 5-6-94, F 255 on 20-5-94, and F 256 on 27-5-94. The first three, plus the stricken *Adatepe* (F 251), were officially commissioned in the Turkish Navy 29-11-93 and the others on 29-7-94. F 250 and F 252 through F 255 were purchased outright during 2001–02. The former *Elmer Montgomery* (FF 1082) was also transferred as Grant-Aid on 13-12-93 as a spare parts source; the ship was scrapped beginning 12-10-99 at Aliaga. Sisters *Paul* (FF 1080), *Miller* (FF 1091), and *W. S. Sims* (FF 1059) were transferred at no cost on 31-12-98 for use as spare parts sources and were then to be scrapped in Turkey; *Miller,* delivered in 8-99, was sunk during a torpedo exercise in 2001. The Turkish Navy is reportedly not enthusiastic about these ships due to their light armament, age, and relatively poor condition.
Disposals: Sister *Adatepe* (F 251; ex-*Fanning,* FF 1076) was stricken during 11-00 after suffering severe boiler problems. *Akdeniz* (F 257; ex-*Bowen,* FFT 1079) was stricken during 2001.
Hull systems: Except on F 250 and 255, bow bulwarks and a spray strake have been added forward to reduce deck wetness, a problem in this class; the addition added 9.1 tons and extended the overall length from the original 133.59 m. All except F 252 have a TEAM (SM-5) computer system for the continual monitoring of the ship's electronic equipment. Antirolling fin stabilizers are fitted in all. The Prairie/Masker bubbler system is installed to reduce radiated noise.
Combat systems: At least four of the class have been refitted with the Sigma K-5 command-and-control system and Link 11 capability. The ASROC system has an 18-weapon, automatic-reloading magazine beneath the bridge; it is also used to stow the Harpoon missiles, which are launched from the starboard pair of launcher cells. The ASW torpedo tubes are fixed in the forward end of the hangar superstructure, aimed outboard at an angle of 45°; a total of 24 Mk 46–series torpedoes can be carried, including those intended to be carried by the helicopter. The ships have the Mk 114 Mod. 6 ASW fire-control system. In 7-93, the U.S. Congress authorized the sale of 32 Harpoon missiles, 40 ASROC ASW rockets, and 104 Mk 46 Mod. 5 ASW torpedoes to support the *Knox*-class frigates. The towed array sonars were not transferred to Turkey, and the VDS installations had been removed as well. All carry a Mk 68 Mod. 3 gunfire-control system with SPG-53D or -53F radar. The WSC-3 UHF satellite communications systems were replaced by a commercial Marisat terminal prior to transfer. The LN-66 navigational radars installed at time of transfer have been replaced.

CORVETTES [FFL]

Note: A program to construct a large number of corvettes in Turkey under the MilGem or National Vessel Project may take precedence over future frigate construction due to budget curtailments. A request to industry for proposals for the construction of eight patrol and surveillance ships was issued 18-5-00. One competitor would be a joint U.S.-Ukrainian effort using the Gibbs and Cox "Mistral-1500T" design, with systems integration by IAI, Israel, and construction technology from the Ukrainian state shipbuilding center. No announcements of a winning design or of an actual construction contract have been made, however, and the current economic situation may delay or cancel the effort; the six A 69 corvettes purchased from France are but an interim solution.

CORVETTES [FFL] *(continued)*

♦ 6 ex-French D'Estienne d'Orves class (Type A 69)

Bldr: Lorient Arsenal (DCN Lorient)

	Laid down	L	In serv.
F 500 BOZCAADA (ex-*Commandant de Pimodan,* F 787)	1-9-75	7-8-76	20-5-78
F 501 BODRUM (ex-*Drogou,* F 783)	15-12-74	31-1-76	30-9-76
F 502 BANDIRMA (ex-*Quartier-Maître Anquetil,* F 786)	1-8-75	7-8-76	4-2-78
F 503 BEYKOZ (ex-*D'Estienne d'Orves,* F 781)	1-9-72	1-6-73	10-9-76
F 504 BARTIN (ex-*Amyot d'Inville,* F 782)	11-9-73	30-11-74	13-10-76
F 505 BAFRA (ex-*Second-Maître le Bihan,* F 788)	1-11-76	13-8-77	7-7-79

Bozcaada (F 500) Bernard Prézelin, 7-01

Bozcaada (F 500) Bernard Prézelin, 7-01

Bozcaada (F 500) Bernard Prézelin, 7-01

D: 1,100 tons (1,250 fl) **S:** 23.3 kts
Dim: 80.00 (76.00 pp) × 10.30 × 3.00 (5.30 over sonar)
A: 2 MM 38 Exocet; 1 100-mm 55-cal. Model 1968 CADAM DP; 2 single 20-mm 70-cal. Oerlikon AA; 4 single 12.7-mm mg; 1 6-round 375-mm Model 1972 F1 ASW RL; 4 550-mm fixed TT for L 5 ASW torpedoes (no reloads)
Electronics:
Radar: 1 Decca 1226 nav.; 1 Thales DRBV-51A surf./air search; 1 Thales DRBC-32E f.c.
Sonar: Thales DUBA-25 hull-mounted MF
EW: ARBR-16 intercept; 2 330- or 340-round Matra Défense AMBL-1A Dagaie decoy RL; SLQ-25 Nixie towed acoustic torpedo decoy syst.
M: 2 SEMT-Pielstick 12 PC2 V400 diesels; 2 CP props; 12,000 bhp
Electric: 840 kw (2 × 320-kw, 1 × 200-kw diesel-driven sets)
Range: 4,500/15 **Endurance:** 15–20 days
Crew: 7 officers, 85 enlisted (in French service)

Remarks: Purchase for $60 million total (plus $150 million for overhauls) announced 11-00. Very economical and seaworthy ships, designed for coastal antisubmarine warfare but available for scouting missions, training, and showing the flag. The new names commemorate Turkish coastal towns. After refits at Brest, F 500 was recommissioned in the Turkish Navy 25-7-01, F 501 on 18-10-01, and F 502 on 14-12-01. F 503 and F 504 are to receive more-extensive overhauls to the engines and armament systems and will be delivered in 2002, along with the ex-F 788, which will be transferred after decommissioning from French Navy service.
Hull systems: Do not have fin stabilizers but are nonetheless excellent sea boats.
Combat systems: The control system for the 100-mm gun consists of a DRBC-32E monopulse, X-band radar and a semi-analog, semi-digital computer; there is also a Matra Défense Naja optical director. During refits in the late 1980s, the ships received a new 100-mm gun, U.S. SLQ-25 Nixie torpedo decoy, upgraded sonar, Dagaie launchers, L 5 ASW torpedo launching capability, and waste processing systems. ASW rocket launchers had been removed from all except F 503 by 11-97 but are being reinstalled prior to transfer.

GUIDED-MISSILE PATROL COMBATANTS [PGG]

♦ 3 (+ 4 + 2) Kiliç class

Bldr: Pendik NSY, Istanbul (P 330: Friedrich Lürssen Werft, Bremen-Vegesack, Germany)

	Laid down	L	In serv.
P 330 KILIÇ	. . .	6-96	24-7-98 (del. 12-2-98)
P 331 KALKAN	5-7-96	24-9-98	22-7-99 (del. 1-4-99)
P 332 MIZRAK	. . .	5-4-99	8-6-00
P 333 MELTEM	25-7-01	. . .	2003
P 334 TUFAN	4-01	. . .	. . .
P	. . .	. . .	. . .
P	. . .	. . .	2007

Kalkan (P 331)—with only two Harpoon canisters aboard Cem D. Yaylali, 8-00

Kiliç (P 330) Turkish Navy, 7-98

D: 540 tons (fl) **S:** 38 kts **Dim:** 62.4 (59.0 pp) × 8.3 × 2.8
A: up to 8 RGM-84C Harpoon SSM; 1 76-mm 62-cal. OTOBreda Compact DP; 1 twin 40-mm 70-cal. OTOBreda Compact AA; 2 single 7.62-mm mg
Electronics:
Radar: 1 Thales Scout nav./surf. search; 1 Thales MW-08 3-D air search; 1 Thales STING-EO f.c.—P 333 and later: 1 Thales LIROD f.c.
EW: Racal Cutlass C-1 intercept; Mk 36 SRBOC decoy syst. (2 6-round Mk 137 RL)
E/O: P 330–332: 1 Thales LIROD Mk 2 f.c.—all: 1 Thales target-desig. sight
M: 4 MTU 16V956 TB91 diesels; 4 props; 18,000 bhp (15,120 sust.)
Electric: 405 kVA tot. **Range:** 700/35; 1,600/32.5; 3,300/16
Endurance: 12 days **Crew:** 6 officers, 39 enlisted

Remarks: An enlarged version of the FPB 57 design, with an integrated weapons-control system and new electronics. Three were authorized early in 1993 and ordered in 3-94. P 330 departed German waters 28-3-98. Four more (with an option for another two) were ordered 19-6-00.
Hull systems: Were initially fitted with bulwarks at the bow, which were removed after the builder's trials. One Turkish source credits them with 22,000 bhp; if so, some other propulsion diesel is installed.
Combat systems: Have Thales STACOS-FD Mod. 4 combat data systems and can employ offboard targeting information via datalink. A Vesta helicopter beacon is fitted. The STING-EO fire-control system for the 76-mm gun incorporates both a radar and an E/O sensor. The LIOD (LIROD, with radar, in P 333 and later) system controls the 40-mm mount. Usually carry only two or four Harpoon missiles.

GUIDED-MISSILE PATROL CRAFT [PTG]

♦ 2 modified German FPB 57 class

Bldr: Taşkizak Naval DY, Istanbul

	L	In serv.		L	In serv.
P 348 YILDIZ	3-6-94	3-6-96	P 349 KARAYEL	20-6-95	19-9-96

Karayel (P 349) Cem D. Yaylali, 8-00

D: 387 tons (432.4 fl) **S:** 36.5 kts **Dim:** 57.84 (54.40 pp) × 7.62 × 2.83
A: up to 8 RGM-84C Harpoon SSM; 1 76-mm 62-cal. OTOBreda Compact DP; 1 twin 35-mm 90-cal. Oerlikon AA; 2 single 7.62-mm mg
Electronics:
Radar: 1 Kelvin-Hughes Type 1007 nav.; 1 BAE Systems AWS-6 (Dolphin) surf./air search; 1 Siemens Albis TMX-CW f.c.
EW: Racal Cutlass B-1 intercept; Mk 36 SRBOC decoy syst. (2 6-round Mk 137 RL)
E/O: Thales LIOD optronic director (for 35-mm mount)
M: 4 MTU 16V956 TB91 diesels; 4 props; 18,000 bhp (15,120 sust.)
Electric: 405 kVA tot. **Range:** 700/35; 1,600/32.5; 3,300/16
Endurance: 12 days **Crew:** 6 officers, 39 enlisted

Remarks: Ordered in 6-91 as an improved version of the *Dogan* series.
Hull systems: Have steel hulls, aluminum superstructures, and NBC warfare defensive citadels.
Combat systems: Have Thales STACOS-FD Mod. 4 combat data systems and can employ offboard targeting information via datalink. A Thales Vesta helicopter beacon is fitted. Can carry 300 rounds of 76-mm and 2,750 rounds of 35-mm ammunition. Usually carry only two or four Harpoon missiles.

♦ 8 German FPB 57 class

Bldr: Taşkizak Naval DY, Istanbul (P 340: Lürssen, Vegesack, Germany)

	Laid down	L	In serv.
P 340 DOGAN	2-6-75	16-6-76	15-6-77
P 341 MARTI	1-7-75	30-6-77	28-7-78
P 342 TAYFUN	1-12-75	19-7-79	19-7-79
P 343 VOLKAN	...	11-8-80	25-7-80
P 344 RÜZGAR (ex-*Gurbet*)	30-7-81	...	17-12-84
P 345 POYRAZ	...	17-12-84	7-2-86
P 346 GAYRET	...	24-7-87	22-7-88
P 347 FIRTINA	...	31-5-88	23-10-88

Dogan (P 340) Cem D. Yaylali, 8-00

Rüzgar (P 344) Hartmut Ehlers, 10-98

D: 353 tons (398 fl) **S:** 36.5 kts **Dim:** 58.1 (54.4 pp) × 7.62 × 2.83
A: up to 8 RGM-84A Harpoon SSM; 1 76-mm 62-cal. OTOBreda Compact DP; 1 twin 35-mm 90-cal. Oerlikon AA; 2 single 7.62-mm mg
Electronics:
Radar: 1 Decca TM 1226 nav.; Thales WM-28-41 f.c.
EW: MEL SUSIE-1 intercept; 2 20-round decoy RL
E/O: P 341, 346, 347: 2 Thales LIOD-series optronic gun f.c.
M: 4 MTU 16V956 TB91 diesels; 4 props; 18,000 bhp (15,120 sust.)
Electric: 405 kVA tot. **Range:** 700/35; 1,600/32.5; 3,300/16
Endurance: 12 days **Crew:** 5 officers, 33 enlisted

Remarks: The initial series order was placed 3-8-73. Have steel hulls, aluminum superstructures.
Combat systems: The 76-mm mount had a manned local-control cupola on P 340–345, since deleted. All can carry 300 rounds of 76-mm and 2,750 rounds of 35-mm ammunition. Usually carry only two or four Harpoon antiship missiles. P 340–343 are being modernized by Thales under a 9-97 contract, with the TACTICOS combat data system replacing the original system and LIOD Mk 2 (Lightweight Optronic Director) and EW intercept systems being added; P 341, the first to be completed, returned to service during 12-00. P 346 and 347 had LIOD optronic gun directors on completion.

♦ 8 Kartal-class guided-missile and torpedo boats

Bldr: Friedrich Lürssen Werft, Vegesack, Germany (In serv. 1967–71)

	In serv.		In serv.
P 321 DENIZKUŞU	9-3-67	P 326 PELIKAN	11-2-70
P 322 ATMACA	9-3-67	P 327 ALBATROS	18-3-70
P 323 ŞAHIN	3-11-66	P 328 ŞIMŞEK	6-11-69
P 324 KARTAL	3-11-66	P 329 KASIRGA	25-11-67

Denizkuşu (P 321) Cem D. Yaylali, 7-00

Kartal (P 324) Cem D. Yaylali, 10-98

D: 184 tons (210 fl) **S:** 42 kts **Dim:** 42.8 × 7.14 × 2.21
A: 2 single 40-mm 70-cal. Bofors L70 AA; 4 Penguin Mk 1 SSM; 2 fixed 533-mm TT (2 wire-guided torpedoes); 4 mines (in lieu of missiles)
Electronics: Radar: 1 Decca TM 1226 nav.—EW: . . . intercept
M: 4 MTU 16V538 diesels; 4 props; 12,000 bhp
Range: 500/39; 1,000/32 **Crew:** 39 tot.

Remarks: Have wooden planking on steel and light-metal keel and frames; the superstructure is built of aluminum alloy. Can be fitted as fast gunboats or minelayers (with four mines). All now normally carry four Penguin IR-homing antiship missiles and no longer carry spare torpedoes. Sister *Meltem* (P 325) was cut in two by the Soviet naval training ship *Khasan* 25-9-85 and stricken after salvage.

PATROL CRAFT [PC]

♦ 9 AB 25 class

Bldr: Haliç SY (P 133: Camialti SY; P 135, 136: Taşkizak NSY, Istanbul)

	In serv.		In serv.
P 125 AB 25	2-2-69	P 131 AB 31	17-11-71
P 126 AB 26	6-2-70	P 133 AB 33	15-5-70
P 127 AB 27	27-6-69	P 135 AB 35	13-4-76
P 128 AB 28	4-69	P 136 AB 36	13-4-76
P 129 AB 29	21-2-69		

AB 33 (P 133) Hartmut Ehlers, 3-96

D: 150 tons (170 fl) **S:** 22 kts **Dim:** 40.24 × 6.40 × 1.65
A: 1 40-mm 60-cal. Bofors Mk 3 AA; 1 20-mm 70-cal. Oerlikon Mk 10 AA; 2 single 12.7-mm mg; 2 4-rail Mk 20 Mousetrap ASW RL; 4 single d.c. release racks

PATROL CRAFT [PC] *(continued)*

Electronics:
Radar: 1 Decca TM 1226 nav.
Sonar: Thales PMS-26 hull-mounted HF
M: 2 SACM-AGO V16CSHR diesels; 2 props; 4,800 bhp—2 cruise diesels; 300 bhp
Crew: 3 officers, 28 enlisted

Remarks: Fourteen others are assigned to the marine police. Built with French technical assistance. P 135 and 136, delivered two years later than others, have a lower hull knuckle forward and bow bulwarks. Cruise diesels are geared to the main shafts. Hull numbers, formerly P 1225–1236, were revised 1-1-91. The forward 40-mm gun was replaced by a 20-mm mount to reduce topweight.
Disposals: AB 30 was transferred to the Georgian Navy 5-12-98, AB 32 to Kazakhstan on 3-7-99, and AB 34 to Azerbaijan on 17-7-00.

Disposal note: U.S. *Asheville*-class patrol craft *Bora* (P 339; ex-*Surprise,* PG 97) and the Turkish-built, German-designed, PB 57–class *Girne* (P 140) were retired during 11-00.

♦ 4 ex-U.S. PGM 71 class
Bldr: Peterson Bldrs, Sturgeon Bay, Wis.

	L	In serv.
P 121 AB 21 (ex-PGM 104)	4-5-67	8-67
P 122 AB 22 (ex-PGM 105)	25-5-67	9-67
P 123 AB 23 (ex-PGM 106)	7-7-67	10-67
P 124 AB 24 (ex-PGM 108)	14-9-67	5-68

AB 21 (P 121) H&L Van Ginderen, 7-95

D: 104 tons (144 fl) **S:** 17 kts **Dim:** 30.81 × 6.45 × 1.83
A: 1 40-mm 60-cal. Bofors Mk 3 AA; 2 twin 20-mm 70-cal. Oerlikon Mk 24 AA; 2 4-rail Mk 20 Mousetrap ASW RL; 2 d.c. racks (2 d.c. each)
Electronics:
Radar: 1 Raytheon 1500B nav.
Sonar: EDO SQS-17A hull-mounted MF
M: 8 G.M. Detroit Diesel 6-71 diesels; 2 props; 2,040 bhp **Electric:** 30 kw tot.
Range: 1,000/12 **Fuel:** 16 tons **Crew:** 30 tot.

Remarks: The first three were handed over during 12-67. Hull numbers, formerly P 1221–1224, were revised 1-1-91. Two single 12.7-mm mg have been removed.

♦ 3 ex-U.S. PC 1638 class
Bldr: Gunderson Bros., Portland, Ore. (P 116: Gölçuk NSY, Kocaeli)

	L	In serv.
P 113 Yar Hisar (ex-PC 1640)	14-5-64	9-64
P 114 Ak Hisar (ex-PC 1641)	14-5-64	3-12-64
P 116 Koç Hisar (ex-PC 1643)	12-64	7-65

Yar Hisar (P 113) Hartmut Ehlers, 6-98

D: 325 tons (477 fl) **S:** 19 kts **Dim:** 52.9 × 7.0 × 3.1 (hull)
A: 2 single 40-mm 60-cal. Bofors Mk 3 AA; 2 twin 20-mm 70-cal. Oerlikon Mk 24 AA
Electronics: Radar: 1 Decca TM 1226 nav.
M: 2 Alco 169 × 10AT diesels; 2 props; 4,800 bhp
Range: 5,000/10 **Fuel:** 60 tons **Crew:** 5 officers, 60 enlisted

Remarks: Design based on the U.S. PC 461 class of World War II.
Disposals: Sisters *Sultan Hisar* (P 111, ex-PC 1638), *Demir Hisar* (P 112, ex-PC 1639), and *Sivri Hisar* (P 115, ex-PC 1642) were stricken during 11-00, and the others are to be retired when the newly acquired ex-French corvettes are fully in service.
Combat systems: Until the late 1990s, were equipped with a Mk 15 trainable Hedgehog ASW spiggot mortar on the bow, four Mk 6 depth-charge mortars (with three rounds each), and one Mk 9 depth-charge rack (with nine depth charges). All ASW ordnance and the sonar have been removed, and a second 40-mm AA has replaced the Hedgehog forward.

♦ 2 ex-German Mercure-class former coastal minesweepers
Bldr: C.N. Amiot (CMN), Cherbourg, France

	Laid down	L	In serv.
P 301 Kozlu (ex-M 523; ex-*Hameln,* M 1251)	20-1-58	20-8-59	15-10-59
P 302 Kuşadası (ex-M 524; ex-*Vegesack,* M 1250)	20-12-57	21-5-59	19-9-59

D: 366 tons (383 fl) **S:** 14.5 kts **Dim:** 44.62 (42.5 pp) × 8.41 × 2.55
A: 1 twin 20-mm 70-cal. Oerlikon Mk 24 AA
Electronics:
Radar: 1 Decca 707 nav.
Sonar: Simrad . . . hull-mounted HF
M: 2 Mercedes-Benz MB-820 Db diesels; 2 KaMeWa CP props; 1,320 bhp
Electric: 816 kw tot. (2 × 320-kw, 2 × 68-kw diesel sets)
Range: 5,000/12 **Fuel:** 34.9 tons **Crew:** 40 tot.

Remarks: Built for the German Navy, placed in reserve in 1963, and stricken 31-12-73. Transferred to Turkey between 6-75 and 10-75. Converted for use as patrol craft at Taşkizak in 1999. Three sisters remain as minesweepers [MSC] (q.v. for appearance), and one other is a salvage ship [ARS]. Wooden construction.

♦ 2 ex-Canadian Bay-class former coastal minesweepers
Bldr: Davie SB, Lauzon, Que.

	L
P 530 Trabzon (ex-M 530, ex-*Gaspé*)	20-5-53
P 531 Terme (ex-M 531, ex-*Trinity*)	31-7-53

Terme (P 531)—with former pennant number prefix Hartmut Ehlers, 10-89

D: 390 tons (412 fl) **S:** 16 kts **Dim:** 50.0 (46.05 pp) × 9.21 × 2.8
A: 1 40-mm 60-cal. Bofors AA; 2 single 12.7-mm mg
Electronics: Radar: 1 Decca TM 1226 nav.
M: 2 G.M. 12-278A diesels; 2 props; 2,400 bhp
Electric: 940-kw sweep + 690-kw ship's service
Range: 4,000/10 **Fuel:** 52 tons **Crew:** 4 officers, 31 enlisted

Remarks: Transferred under the U.S. Military Aid program on 19-5-58. Redesignated as patrol boats in 1991 with their portable sweep gear removed. Sister *Tekirdag* (A 601, ex-M 533, ex-*Ungava*) has been reconfigured to act as an intelligence collector [AGI] (q.v.). Sister *Tirebolu* (P 532, ex-M 532, ex-*Comox*) was stricken 15-12-95. Wood-planked skin on steel frame. The 40-mm gun is in a World War II–era U.K. "Boffin" mounting. Do not have a sonar.

Disposal note: U.S. Coast Guard 83-ft. patrol boats LS 9 through LS 12 (P 109 through P 112) were stricken during 1999 after 47 years' service.

Note: Mine-disposal divers' tenders of the MTB 1 class and the various antisubmarine net tenders also carry patrol-series pennant numbers.

MINE WARFARE SHIPS

Note: The *Rhein*-class training ships also have mine rails, as do the *Kartal*-class guided-missile patrol boats.

♦ 1 Osman Gazi–class minelayer/landing ship [MM]
Bldr: Taşkizak NSY, Istanbul

	Laid down	L	In serv.
N^L 125 Osman Gazi	5-7-89	20-7-90	27-7-94

Osman Gazi (N^L 125) Hartmut Ehlers, 10-95

D: 3,773 tons (fl) **S:** 17 kts (15 sust.) **Dim:** 105.00 (95.50 wl) × 15.50 × 3.75
A: 2 twin 40-mm 70-cal. Bofors AA; 1 twin 35-mm 90-cal. Oerlikon AA; approx. 200 mines
Electronics: Radar: 1 Decca TM 1226 nav.
M: 4 MTU 8V396-series diesels; 2 props; 10,000 bhp
Range: 4,000/15 **Crew:** . . .

Remarks: Named for the founder of the Ottoman Empire. Construction of a second, to have been named *Orhan Gazi* (N^L 126), was canceled in 7-91. Has 50% more capacity than *Sarucabey* class, carrying 900 troops and 15 tanks. Carries four LCVP-type landing craft abreast the stack and has a helicopter platform, amphibious warfare command facilities, and full NBC warfare protection. Two ports in the stern lead to mine rails on the tank deck.

MINE WARFARE SHIPS *(continued)*

♦ 1 Sarucabey-class minelayer/landing ship [MM]
Bldr: Taşkizak NSY, Istanbul

	Laid down	L	In serv.
N^L 123 Sarucabey (ex-*Karaçebey*)	25-7-80	30-7-81	26-7-84
N^L 124 Karamürselbey	26-7-83	26-7-84	27-7-85

Sarucabey (N^L 123) Cem D. Yaylali, 4-96

Karamürselbey (N^L 124)—with pilothouse one deck lower than on N^L 123 Leo Dirkx, 7-01

D: 2,600 tons (fl) **S:** 14 kts **Dim:** 92.0 × 14.0 × . . .
A: 3 single 40-mm 70-cal. Bofors L70 AA; 2 twin 20-mm 70-cal. Oerlikon Mk 24; 2 mine rails (150 mines)
Electronics: Radar: 1 Decca TM 1226 nav.
M: 3 diesels; 3 props; 4,320 bhp **Crew:** . . .

Remarks: Have two LCVPs stowed on deck amidships, handled by large articulated crane. There are two mine embarkation ports on each side at tank-deck level that can also be used to disembark troops into craft alongside. Can carry 11 tanks, 12 trucks, and 600 troops. Minelaying ports in the stern lead to rails on the tank deck.

Disposal note: Minelayer/landing ship *Çakabey* (N^L 122) was stricken during 1999 and scrapped beginning in 7-01. Danish-built *Falster*-class minelayer *Nusret* (N 110, ex-N 108, ex-U.S. MMC 16) was stricken 7-2-01.

♦ 2 ex-German, ex-U.S. LST 542–class minelayer/tank landing ships [MM]
Bldrs: N^L 120: Missouri Valley Bridge & Iron, Evansville, Ind.; N^L 121: American Bridge Co., Ambridge, Pa.

	Laid down	L	In serv.
N^L 120 Bayraktar (ex-L 403; ex-*Bottrop;* ex-*Saline County,* LST 1101)	22-11-44	3-1-45	26-1-45
N^L 121 Sancaktar (ex-*Bochum;* ex-*Rice County,* LST 1081)	13-11-44	5-1-45	30-1-45

D: 3,640 tons (4,140 fl) **S:** 11 kts **Dim:** 101.37 × 15.28 × 3.98 (max.)
A: 2 twin 40-mm 60-cal. Bofors Mk 1 Mod. 2 AA; 2 single 40-mm 60-cal. Bofors Mk 3 AA; . . . mines
Electronics: Radar: 1 Kelvin-Hughes 14/9 nav.
M: 2 G.M. 16-567A diesels; 2 props; 1,700 bhp **Electric:** 860 kw
Range: 15,000/9 **Crew:** 60 tot.

Remarks: Both were transferred from the U.S.A. to West Germany during 8-61. N^L 120 was transferred to Turkey 13-12-72 and N^L 121 on 12-12-72. Had been converted to minelayers while in German service. Six rails on the upper deck, tapering to two at the stern, have been removed, but there remain four rails below decks, exiting through a broadened stern. Four 2-ton mine-handling cranes were added. The bow doors have been retained. Were redesignated amphibious ships in 1974–75, but were again placed in the mine warfare category in 1980. Carry four LCVPs in Welin davits aft and two small launches forward.

♦ 0 (+ 6) A-class coastal minehunters [MHC]
Bldr: First unit: Lürssen/Abeking & Rasmussen; others: Pendik NSY, Istanbul (In serv. 2003–07)

	Laid down	L	In serv.
M . . . Alanya	6-11-00	. . .	2003
M . . . Amasra	25-7-01	12-03	. . .
M	. . .	. . .	. . .
M	. . .	. . .	. . .
M	. . .	. . .	. . .
M	. . .	. . .	2007

D: . . . tons (715 fl) **S:** 14 kts **Dim:** 54.46 × 9.70 (9.56 wl) × 2.50 (3.2 props)
A: 1 30-mm 80-cal. OTOBreda/Mauser AA; 2 single 12.7-mm mg; 60 mines
Electronics:
Radar: 1 Kelvin Hughes Type 1007 nav.
Sonar: Thales Type 2093 minehunting HF VDS
EW: Thales DR-2000 intercept

A-class minehunter—artist's rendering Lürssen/Abeking & Rasmussen, 2000

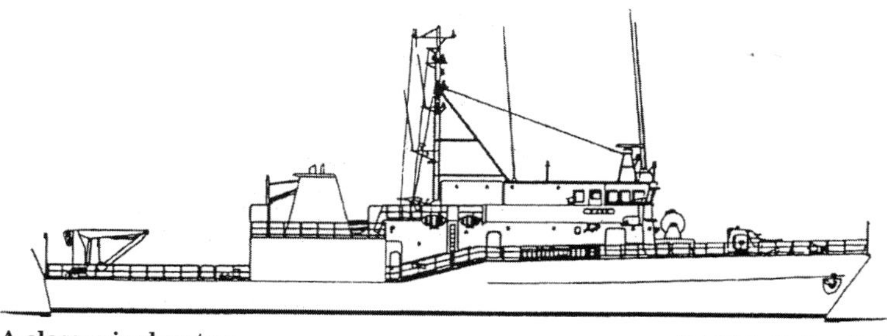

A-class minehunter *Schiff & Hafen,* 3-00

M: 2 MTU 8V396 TE84K diesels; 2 Voith-Schneider vertical cycloidal props; 3,000 bhp—2 Schottel azimuthal thrusters
Electric: 690 kw tot. (3 × 230 kw, 3 MWM 6-cyl. diesels driving)
Range: . . ./. . . **Crew:** 53 tot. accomm.

Remarks: The Friedrich Lürssen Werft–Abeking & Rasmussen design, a variant of the German Navy's Type 332, was selected 8-4-99, and the contract was signed 30-7-99. The program is to cost $625 million. Three to five additional units may be ordered later.
Hull systems: Shock mountings are provided for virtually every piece of equipment and for all crew seats. Have a less-powerful propulsion plant than their German half-sisters and are beamier. A Haux portable divers' decompression chamber will be carried.
Combat systems: Will have the Alenia-Marconi Systems Nautis-III-M command system. Are intended to carry two PAP 104 Mk 5 remote-controlled mine location/destruction submersibles and four mine-clearance divers. A single Oropesa mechanical minesweeping rig will be carried.

♦ 5 ex-French Circé-class coastal minehunters [MHC]
Bldr: CMN, Cherbourg

	Laid down	L	In serv.
M 260 Edinçük (ex-*Cybèle,* M 712)	15-9-70	2-3-72	28-9-72
M 261 Edremit (ex-*Calliope,* M 713)	4-4-70	20-10-71	28-9-72
M 262 Enez (ex-*Clio,* M 714)	4-9-69	10-6-71	18-5-72
M 263 Erdek (ex-*Circé,* M 715)	30-1-69	15-12-70	18-5-72
M 264 Ermenli (ex-*Cérès,* M 716)	2-2-71	10-8-72	8-3-73

Edremit (M 261) Leo Dirkx, 5-01

Erdek (M 263) Cem D. Yaylali, 8-00

MINE WARFARE SHIPS *(continued)*

D: 423 tons (508 fl) **S:** 15 kts **Dim:** 50.90 (46.50 pp) × 8.90 × 3.60 (max.)
A: 1 20-mm 90-cal. GIAT F2 AA
Electronics:
Radar: 1 DRBN 34A (Decca 1229) nav.
Sonar: Thales DUBM 21D HF VDS
M: 1 MTU diesel; 1 prop; 1,800 bhp—2 260-shp electric propulsors
Range: 3,000/12 **Crew:** 4 officers, 19 petty officers, 24 ratings

Remarks: Sold to Turkey under a 24-9-97 agreement; M 261 and 263 were stricken from the French Navy 13-2-97, M 262 during 3-97, M 260 on 4-7-97, and M 264 on 1-4-98. M 260 arrived in Turkey 24-8-98 and M 262 on 9-12-98; M 263 was handed over 8-12-98 and arrived in Turkey during 1-99, and M 264 was transferred during 1-99. All were formally recommissioned 22-7-99. Designed for the detection and destruction of mines laid as deep as 60 m.
Hull systems: Hull is made of laminated wood. The design stressed low magnetic signature and silent operation. Have two independent propulsion systems: one for transit, the other for minesweeping, both with remote control. Special rudders with small propellers are mounted at the base of the main rudders' after ends and powered by a 260-hp electric motor, giving a speed of 7 kts and permitting exceptional maneuverability.
Combat systems: Prior to transfer, were updated with the Thales MINETAC tactical data system (based on the SENIT 8.01 combat data system), PAP-Plus mine countermeasures submersibles, and differential GPS receivers. Mines are destroyed either by divers (six in each crew) or by the one of the two PAP-Plus wire-guided submersibles. The ships do not have minesweeping gear. They received the updated DUBM-20A sonar with coherent processing feature during mid-1980s refits; this was subsequently further updated to DUBM-20B and then to DUBM-21D prior to transfer.

♦ 3 ex-German Mercure-class coastal minesweepers [MSC]
Bldr: C.N. Amiot (CMN), Cherbourg

	Laid down	L	In serv.
M 520 Karamürsel (ex-*Wörms,* M 1253)	19-3-58	30-1-60	30-4-60
M 521 Kerempe (ex-*Detmold,* M 1252)	19-2-58	17-11-59	20-2-60
M 522 Kilimli (ex-*Siegen,* M 1254)	18-4-58	29-3-60	9-7-60

Kilimli (M 522) Hartmut Ehlers, 4-96

D: 366 tons (383 fl) **S:** 14.5 kts **Dim:** 44.62 (42.50 pp) × 8.41 × 2.55
A: 1 twin 20-mm 70-cal. Oerlikon Mk 24
Electronics: Radar: 1 Decca 707 nav.—Sonar: Simrad . . . hull-mounted HF
M: 2 Mercedes-Benz MB-820 Db diesels; 2 KaMeWa CP props; 1,320 bhp
Electric: 816 kw tot. (2 × 320-kw sweep generators, 2 × 68-kw ship's service gen.)
Range: 5,000/12 **Fuel:** 34.9 tons **Crew:** 40 tot.

Remarks: Built for the West German Navy, placed in reserve in 1963, and stricken 31-12-73. Were transferred to Turkey between 6-75 and 10-75. Sisters *Kozlu* (M 523, ex-*Hameln*) and *Kuşadasi* (M 524, ex-*Vegesack*) were converted to patrol craft at Taşkizak in 1999, and *Kemer* (M 525, ex-*Passau*) was stricken in 1998 but then adapted as salvage support ship A 582. Wooden construction. M 520 has been employed for minehunting trials since 1987 and is equipped with a minehunting sonar; the others had Simrad mine avoidance sonars added after 1988.

♦ 5 ex-U.S. MSC 289–class coastal minesweepers [MSC]
Bldrs: M 514, 515: Dorchester Bldrs, Dorchester, N.J.; others: Peterson Bldrs, Sturgeon Bay, Wis.

	L	Del.	In serv.
M 514 Silifke (ex-MSC 304)	21-11-64	9-65	21-3-66
M 515 Saros (ex-MSC 305)	1-5-65	2-66	25-10-66
M 516 Sigacik (ex-MSC 311)	12-6-64	6-65	20-12-65
M 517 Sapanca (ex-MSC 312)	14-9-64	26-7-65	20-12-65
M 518 Sariyer (ex-MSC 315)	21-4-66	8-9-67	7-12-67

D: 300 tons (392 fl) **S:** 14 kts **Dim:** 44.32 × 8.29 × 2.55 (hull)
A: 1 twin 20-mm 70-cal. Oerlikon Mk 24 AA
Electronics: Radar: 1 Decca 1226 nav.—Sonar: UQS-1D hull-mounted (100 kHz)
M: 2 Waukesha L-1616 diesels; 2 props; 1,200 bhp
Range: 2,500/10 **Fuel:** 40 tons **Crew:** 4 officers, 34 enlisted

Remarks: Provided under the U.S. Military Aid program. Wooden construction. Have a lower pilothouse and taller stack than earlier U.S.-designed minesweepers. The sonar is primarily for detecting and avoiding moored mines and has little utility against bottom mines. Are equipped with acoustic, magnetic, and wire-sweep arrays.

Saros (M 515) Flottenkommando, 2001

♦ 4 ex-U.S. MSC 268–class coastal minesweepers [MSC]
Bldr: Bellingham SY, Bellingham, Wash.

	L	Del.	In serv.
M 510 Samsun (ex-MSC 268)	6-9-57	30-9-58	3-10-58
M 511 Sinop (ex-MSC 270)	4-1-58	2-59	7-2-59
M 512 Sürmene (ex-MSC 271)	1958	27-3-59	30-3-59
M 513 Seddulbahir (ex-MSC 272)	1958	5-59	1-5-59

Seddulbahir (M 513)—outboard an MSC 289–class minesweeper
Cem D. Yaylali, 7-98

Sinop (M 511)—note that the port main deck bulwark extends much farther aft than the starboard bulwark in this class Cem D. Yaylali, 6-99

D: 300 tons (392 fl) **S:** 13 kts **Dim:** 43.0 (41.5 pp) × 7.95 × 2.55
A: 1 twin 20-mm 70-cal. Oerlikon Mk 24 AA
Electronics: Radar: 1 Decca 1226 nav.—Sonar: UQS-1D hull-mounted (100 kHz)
M: 4 G.M. Detroit Diesel 6-71 diesels; 2 props; 880 bhp (sust.)
Range: 2,500/10 **Fuel:** 40 tons **Crew:** 4 officers, 34 enlisted

Remarks: Provided under the U.S. Military Aid program. Are equipped with acoustic, magnetic, and wire-sweep arrays. The sonar is primarily for detecting and avoiding moored mines and has little utility against bottom mines.

♦ 4 ex-U.S. Cove-class inshore minesweepers [MSI]
Bldr: Peterson Bldrs, Sturgeon Bay, Wis.

	L	In serv.
M 500 Foça (ex-MSI 15)	23-8-66	8-67
M 501 Fethiye (ex-MSI 16)	7-12-66	9-67
M 502 Fatsa (ex-MSI 17)	11-4-67	10-67
M 503 Finike (ex-MSI 18)	11-67	12-67

D: 203 tons (239 fl) **S:** 12.5 kts **Dim:** 34.06 × 7.14 × 2.4
A: 2 single 12.7-mm mg **Electronics:** Radar: 1 . . . nav.
M: 4 G.M. Detroit Diesel 6-71 diesels; 2 props; 960 bhp **Electric:** 120 kw tot.
Range: 1,000/9 **Fuel:** 20 tons **Crew:** 20 tot.

MINE WARFARE SHIPS *(continued)*

Fethiye (M 501) Hartmut Ehlers, 10-98

Remarks: Transferred on completion. Wooden construction. The machinegun mounts are atop the pilothouse and abaft the stack; the actual guns are normally stowed below.

♦ 3 ex-U.S. 64-foot distribution-box minefield tenders [MSS]

Y 81 Şamandira 1 (ex-Y 1148, ex-Y 131)
Y 91 Şamandira 11 (ex-Y 1149, ex-Y 132)
Y 92 Şamandira 12 (ex-Y 1150)

Şamandira 1 (Y 81)—with old pennant number, moored alongside MTB 1–class mine warfare support tenders MTB 8 (P 318) and MTB 9 (P 319) *Ships of the World*

D: 72 tons (fl) **S:** 9.5 kts **Dim:** 19.58 × 5.72 × 1.83
A: 1 G.M. Gray Marine 64HN9 diesel; 1 prop; 225 bhp **Crew:** 6 tot.

Remarks: Transferred in 1959. Wooden construction. Y 92 was restored to service in 1994 several years after having been discarded. Are used as controlled-minefield electrical distribution box tenders. They resemble the MTB 1 class but are smaller. Two sisters operate in the Mexican Navy as patrol boats.

♦ 8 MTB 1–class mine-warfare support tenders [MSS]

Bldr: . . ., U.K. (In serv. 1942)

P 312 Dalgiç 2 (ex-MTB 2)
P 313 MTB 3
P 314 MTB 4
P 315 MTB 5
P 316 MTB 6
P 317 MTB 7
P 318 MTB 8
P 319 MTB 9

Dalgiç 2 (P 312) Antonio Scrimali, 8-97

D: 70 tons **S:** 20 kts **Dim:** 21.8 × 4.2 × 2.6
A: 1 12.7-mm mg **M:** 2 diesels; 2 props; 2,000 bhp

Remarks: P 312 was redesignated a mine clearance diver support boat in 1983; the others are used as general-purpose tender/supply craft at mine warfare bases. Sister MTB 10 was stricken in 1987. MTB 1 was converted to diving tender [YDT] *Dalgiç 1.*

♦ 2 Şamandira Motoru–class small danbuoy layers [MSS]

Y 91 Şamandira Motoru 11 Y 92 Şamandira Motoru 12

Remarks: Five others of this class are laid up in land storage. No data available.

AMPHIBIOUS WARFARE SHIPS AND CRAFT

Note: The minelayer/landing ships *Osman Gazi* ($\mathrm{N^L}$ 125), *Sarucabey* ($\mathrm{N^L}$ 123), *Karamürselbey* ($\mathrm{N^L}$ 124), *Bayraktar* ($\mathrm{N^L}$ 120), and *Sancaktar* ($\mathrm{N^L}$ 121) can also be employed in amphibious landings.

♦ 2 ex-U.S. Terrebonne Parish–class tank landing ships [LST]

Bldr: Christy Corp., Sturgeon Bay, Wis.

	L	In serv.
L 401 Ertugrul (ex-*Windham County,* LST 1170)	22-5-54	15-12-54
L 402 Serdar (ex-*Westchester County,* LST 1167)	18-4-53	10-3-54

Serdar (L 402) French Navy, 1998

Ertugrul (L 401) Turkish Navy

D: 2,590 tons (5,786 fl) **S:** 15 kts **Dim:** 117.35 (112.77 pp) × 17.06 × 5.18
A: 3 twin 76.2-mm 50-cal. Mk 33 DP
Electronics:
Radar: 1 Decca TM 1226 nav.; 1 SPS-10 surf. search; 2 Western Electric Mk 34 f.c.
M: 4 G.M. Electromotive Div. 16-278A diesels; 2 CP props; 6,000 bhp
Electric: 600 kw **Fuel:** 874 tons **Crew:** 116 tot. + 395 troops

Remarks: L 401 was leased in 6-73 and L 402 in 8-74; both were purchased 6-8-87. Cargo: 2,200 tons. Can carry four LCVPs in Welin davits. Have two Mk 63 radar gun f.c.s.

Note: The "Ç" preceding landing craft pennants stands for *Çikartma Gemisi* ("Landing Craft").

♦ 17 Ç 139–class utility landing craft [LCU]

Bldr: Taşkizak NSY, Istanbul

	L		L		L		L
Ç 139	8-84	Ç 144	25-7-85	Ç 149	21-7-90	Ç 154	7-93
Ç 140	8-84	Ç 145	21-7-89	Ç 150	7-91	Ç 155	10-93
Ç 141	9-84	Ç 146	21-7-89	Ç 151	10-91		
Ç 142	25-7-85	Ç 147	21-7-89	Ç 152	10-91		
Ç 143	25-7-85	Ç 148	21-7-90	Ç 153	7-92		

Ç 141 Hartmut Ehlers, 6-86

D: 280 tons light (600 fl) **S:** 10 kts (8.5 loaded) **Dim:** 60.16 × 11.58 × 1.25 (aft)
A: 2 single 20-mm 70-cal. Oerlikon Mk 10 AA; 2 single 12.7-mm mg
Electronics: Radar: 1 Decca TM 1226 nav.
M: 2 MTU 8V396 TE-series diesels; 2 props; 1,240 bhp
Range: 600/10 (light); 1,100/8 (loaded) **Crew:** 1 officer, 16 enlisted

Remarks: Developed from the Ç 107 design, but with greater length, greater molded depth amidships, and a larger superstructure. Can carry 100 troops and six M 48 tanks.

♦ 12 Ç 107–class utility landing craft [LCU]

Bldr: Gölçuk NSY, Kocaeli (In serv. 1973–81)

Ç 117 Ç 123 Ç 125 Ç 127 Ç 129 Ç 135
Ç 120 Ç 124 Ç 126 Ç 128 Ç 134 Ç 137

AMPHIBIOUS WARFARE SHIPS AND CRAFT *(continued)*

Ç 120 French Navy, 1998

D: 260 tons light (580 fl) **S:** 10 kts (8.5 loaded) **Dim:** 56.56 × 11.58 × 1.25 (aft)
A: 2 single 20-mm 70-cal. Oerlikon Mk 10 AA; 2 single 12.7-mm mg
Electronics: Radar: 1 Decca TM 1226 nav.
M: 3 G.M. Detroit Diesel 6-71 diesels; 3 props; 900 bhp (675 sust.)
Range: 600/10 (light); 1,100/8 **Crew:** 1 officer, 16 enlisted

Remarks: Design is based on the British LCT(4) design. Can carry 100 troops and five M 48 tanks.
Disposals: Libya received Ç 130–Ç 133 in 12-79. Ç 136 was lost in a storm 30-1-85. Ç 107 and 113 were stricken in 1992; Ç 111, 112, 115, and 116 had been deleted by 1981; and Ç 110 was stricken during 1998. Ç 108, 114, 118, 119, 121, and 122 were stricken early in 2000.

♦ 19 U.S. LCM(8)-class landing craft [LCM]
Bldr: Taşkizak NSY, Istanbul (In serv. 1965–66)

Ç 302	Ç 305	Ç 309	Ç 313	Ç 319	Ç 329–331
Ç 303	Ç 308	Ç 312	Ç 314	Ç 321–327	

D: 34 tons light (121 fl) **S:** 12 kts **Dim:** 22.43 × 6.43 × 1.35 (fwd; 1.47 aft)
A: 1 or 2 single 12.7-mm mg
M: 4 G.M. Detroit Diesel 6-71 diesels; 2 props; 590 bhp
Range: 190/12 (light); 140/9 (loaded) **Crew:** 5 enlisted

Remarks: Cargo: 60 tons or 150 troops for short distances in the 12.8 × 4.3–m open well with 54.6 m^2 space. Eleven or more sisters have been discarded, including eight in 1991, one in 1992, and Ç 316 and Ç 328 during 2000.

♦ 22 or more U.S. LCVP landing craft [LCVP]

D: 13 tons (fl) **S:** 9 kts **Dim:** 10.9 × 3.21 × 1.04
A: 2 single 7.62-mm mg **M:** 1 G.M. Gray Marine 64HN9 diesel; 225 bhp
Range: 110/9 **Crew:** 3 tot.

Remarks: Carried aboard the larger mine warfare and amphibious landing ships. Wooden construction. Cargo: 36 troops or 4 tons.

♦ 2 or more special forces fast landing craft [LCP]
Bldr: KOÇ–RMK Tersanesi, Tuzla (In serv. 2001)

New Turkish special forces craft Hartmut Ehlers, 10-00

Remarks: No data available. Appear to be of GRP construction and about 15–18 m o.a. Are powered by two diesels driving 6-bladed propellers and have stairways on both sides of the tumblehome stern to facilitate the retrieval of swimmers.

AUXILIARIES

♦ 1 ex-Canadian Bay-class intelligence collector [AGI]
Bldr: Davie SB, Lauzon, Que. (L: 12-11-51)

A 601 Tekirdag (ex-M 533, ex-*Ungava*)

Tekirdag (A 601) H&L Van Ginderen, 7-95

D: 390 tons (412 fl) **S:** 16 kts **Dim:** 50.0 (46.05 pp) × 9.21 × 2.8
A: removed
Electronics: Radar: 1 Decca TM 1226 nav.; 1 Decca . . . nav.
M: 2 G.M. Detroit Diesel 12-278A diesels; 2 props; 2,400 bhp
Electric: 690 kw tot. **Range:** 4,000/10 **Fuel:** 52 tons
Crew: 4 officers, 31 enlisted

Remarks: Former coastal minesweeper, transferred under the U.S. Military Aid program 19-5-58. Has been equipped with an EW intercept antenna array and was redesignated an auxiliary in 1991. The armament of two 12.7-mm mg on the bow and a 40-mm 70-cal. Bofors AA was removed in 1994–95. Two sisters serve as patrol craft. Wood-planked skin on steel frame.

Disposal note: Intelligence collection ship *Yunus* (A 590; ex-German *Alster,* A 50; ex-trawler *Mellum*) was stricken 6-3-00 and arrived at Aliaga for scrapping 16-11-00.

♦ 1 U.S. Adjutant-class oceanographic research ship [AGOR]
Bldr: Stephen Bros., . . . (In serv. 8-54)

Y 90 Deney (ex-*Selçuk,* M 508; ex-*Pavot;* ex-MSC 124)

D: 300 tons (392 fl) **S:** 14 kts **Dim:** 43.00 (41.50 pp) × 7.95 × 2.55
A: none **Electronics:** Radar: 1 . . . nav.
M: 2 G.M. Detroit Diesel 8-268A diesels; 2 props; 1,200 bhp
Range: 2,500/10 **Fuel:** 40 tons **Crew:** . . . tot.

Remarks: Originally was built for France, but was returned to U.S. control 23-3-70 and transferred to Turkey 4-9-70. Retired as a minesweeper in 4-98 and subsequently was converted as an oceanographic research ship. Wooden construction.

♦ 1 oceanographic research and hydrographic survey ship [AGS]
Bldr: Gölçuk NSY, Kocaeli (L: 17-11-83; in serv. 7-84)

A 594 Çubuklu (ex-Y 1251)

Çubuklu (A 594) J. G. Stemmelen, 5-97

D: 512 tons light (680 fl) **S:** 11 kts **Dim:** 40.40 (36.40 wl) × 9.60 × 3.20
A: 2 single 20-mm 70-cal. Oerlikon Mk 10 AA
Electronics: Radar: 1 Decca . . . nav.
M: 1 MWM diesel; 1 CP prop; 1,004 bhp (820 sust.)
Crew: 5 officers, 26 enlisted (39 tot. accomm.)

Remarks: Carries one survey launch to port. Forecastle side plating extends abaft the boat installation on the port side. Received a Qubit (Australia) integrated navigation data processing system in 1990–91.

♦ 2 ex-U.S. Silas Bent–class hydrographic survey ships [AGS]
Bldr: American SB, Lorain, Ohio

	L	In serv.
A 588 Çandarli (ex-*Kane,* T-AGS 27)	20-11-65	19-5-67
A 599 Çeşme (ex-*Silas Bent,* T-AGS 26)	16-5-64	23-7-65

Çandarli (A 588) Leo Dirkx, 7-01

D: 1,900 tons (2,743 fl) **S:** 15 kts **Dim:** 86.9 (80.8 pp) × 14.6 × 4.6
A: none **Electronics:** Radar: 2 Raytheon . . . nav.
M: 2 Alco diesels, electric drive: Westinghouse electric motor; 1 CP prop; 3,600 shp—350-shp electric bow-thruster
Electric: 960 kw tot. **Range:** 5,800/14.5; 8,000/13 **Fuel:** 461 tons
Crew: 40 tot. + 30 scientists

Remarks: A 599 was transferred to Turkey 28-10-99 at Singapore, having been deactivated by the U.S. Military Sealift Command the same day; the ship was formally recommissioned 8-6-00. A 588 was transferred 14-3-01 and formally recommissioned 25-7-01.

AUXILIARIES *(continued)*

♦ **3 Kanarya-class coastal cargo transports [AK]**
Bldr: Taşkizak NSY, Istanbul (In serv. 1972–74)

A 591 Şarköy (ex-Y 1156)
A 592 Karadeniz Ereglisi (ex-Y 1157)
A 593 Eceabat (ex-Y 1165)

Şarköy (A 591)—with former pennant number H&L Van Ginderen, 1991

D: 823 tons (fl) **S:** 10 kts **Dim:** 50.7 (47.4 pp) × 8.0 × . . .
A: 1 20-mm 70-cal. Oerlikon Mk 10 AA **Electronics:** Radar: 1 . . . nav.
M: 1 diesel; 1 prop; 1,440 bhp **Crew:** 3 officers, 20 enlisted

Remarks: 500 dwt. Molded depth: 3.6 m. Were redesignated auxiliaries from service craft in 1991. Cargo is about 300 tons total, in two holds, tended by two 1-ton derricks. Sister *Kanarya* (ex-Y 1155) was stricken in 1993.

♦ **1 ex-U.S. AN 103–class net tender [AN]**
Bldr: Krögerwerft, Rendsburg, Germany

	Laid down	L	In serv.
P 305 AG 5 (ex-AN 104)	1960	20-10-60	25-2-61

D: 680 tons (975 fl) **S:** 12.8 kts **Dim:** 52.50 (48.50 hull) × 10.60 × 3.70
A: 1 40-mm 70-cal. Bofors L70 AA; 3 single 20-mm 70-cal. Oerlikon Mk 10 AA
Electronics: Radar: 1 Decca TM 1226 nav.
M: 1 M.A.N. G7V 40/60 diesel; 1 prop; 1,470 bhp
Range: 6,500/10.8 **Fuel:** 134 tons **Crew:** 5 officers, 45 enlisted

Remarks: Sister to the *Thetis* in the Greek Navy. Built with U.S. Offshore Procurement funds. Can carry 1,600 rounds of 40-mm and 25,200 rounds of 20-mm ammunition.

♦ **1 ex-U.S. AN 93–class net tender [AN]**
Bldr: Bethlehem Steel, Staten Island, N.Y.

	L	In serv.
P 306 AG 6 (ex-Dutch *Cerberus,* ex-AN 93)	5-52	10-11-52

AG 6 (P 306) Hartmut Ehlers, 5-84

D: 780 tons (902 fl) **S:** 12.8 kts **Dim:** 50.29 (44.50 pp) × 10.20 × 3.20
A: 1 76.2-mm 50-cal. Mk 22 DP; 4 single 20-mm 70-cal. Oerlikon Mk 10 AA
Electronics: Radar: 1 Decca TM 1226 nav.
M: 2 G.M. 8-268A diesels, electric drive; 1 prop; 1,500 shp
Range: 5,200/12 **Crew:** 48 tot.

Remarks: Prototype of a class also built in France and Italy. Transferred to the Netherlands in 12-52; was returned 17-9-70 and transferred to Turkey the same day.

♦ **1 Modified Akar–class replenishment oilers [AO]**
Bldr: KOÇ–RMK Tersanesi, Tuzla, Istanbul

	Laid down	L	In serv.
A 595 Yarbay Kudret Güngör	5-11-93	10-94	24-10-95

Yarbay Kudret Güngör (A 595) ANBw/FAFIO, 10-99

Yarbay Kudret Güngör (A 595) Turkish Navy, 1995

D: approx. 20,000 tons (fl) **S:** 15 kts **Dim:** 145.10 × 22.80 × 8.40
A: 2 twin 35-mm 90-cal. Oerlikon AA; 1 20-mm Mk 15 Phalanx CIWS
Electronics:
Radar: 1 Decca TM 1226 nav.; 1 Decca . . . nav.; 1 General Dynamics Mk 90 Phalanx f.c.
M: 2 diesels; 1 prop; 6,500 bhp
Range: 6,000/14 **Endurance:** 90 days **Crew:** 14 officers, 189 enlisted

Remarks: 14,000 dwt. Ordered in 5-93 as the first Turkish commercial-built ship for the Turkish Navy. Began sea trials in 12-95. Is a near sister to *Akar* (A 580), as it had long been planned to build a second ship of the class, but has more-modern armament and a different cargo layout. There is a civilian sister to this vessel, delivered by the builder in 1992. The builder was formerly known as SEDEF Gemi Endustrisi A.S.
Hull systems: Cargo includes 11,300 tons of fuel oil, 80 tons of lube oil, and 2,700 tons of fresh water; refrigerated cargo capacity is 250 m^3 and dry provisions capacity 250 m^3. As in *Akar,* there is one liquid fuel underway transfer station per side; an extra cargo crane has been added forward, to port. Has a helicopter deck but no hangar.
Combat systems: The 35-mm mount was recycled from a retired destroyer and may have local-only control. The Phalanx mounting is forward and has a wide arc of fire.

♦ **1 Akar-class replenishment oiler [AO]**
Bldr: Gölçuk NSY, Kocaeli

	L	In serv.
A 580 Akar	16-11-83	24-4-87

Akar (A 580) French Navy, 2-96

D: 19,350 tons (fl) **S:** 15 kts **Dim:** 145.1 × 22.8 × 8.4
A: 1 twin 76.2-mm 50-cal. Mk 33 DP; 1 twin 40-mm 70-cal. Bofors AA; 2 single 20-mm 70-cal. Oerlikon Mk 10 AA
Electronics:
Radar: 1 Decca . . . nav.; 1 Decca 1226 nav.; 1 Western Electric Mk 34 f.c.
M: 1 diesel; 1 prop; 6,500 bhp **Crew:** 329 tot.

Remarks: 15,000 dwt. Construction was suspended for several years after launching.
Hull systems: Cargo: essentially the same as *Yarbay Kudret Güngör* (A 595), but has less capacity for solid stores. Has one underway liquid replenishment station per side and, directly forward of the bridge, two cranes to handle solid stores. Has a helicopter platform but no hangar.
Combat systems: Has a U.S. Mk 63 gun f.c.s. for the 76.2-mm guns, with the SPG-34 radar's antenna on the gunmount.

♦ **2 Albay Hakki Burak–class transport tankers [AOT]**
Bldr: KOÇ–RMK Tersanesi, Tuzla

	L	In serv.
A 571 Albay Hakki Burak	. . .	8-6-00
A 572 Yüzbazi Tolunay	21-11-99	8-6-00

Albay Hakki Burak (A 571)—in light-load condition Turkish Navy, 1999

AUXILIARIES *(continued)*

D: 2,355 tons light (. . . fl) **S:** 15 kts **Dim:** 81.3 × . . . × . . .
A: 2 single 12.7-mm mg **Electronics:** Radar: 1 . . . nav.
M: 2 . . . diesels; 2 props; 3,200 bhp

Remarks: 1,500 dwt. Transport tankers without underway replenishment capabilities. No other data available.

♦ **1 Taşkizak-class transport tanker [AOT]**
Bldr: Taşkizak NSY, Istanbul

	L	In serv.
A 570 TAŞKIZAK	28-7-83	1-8-84

Taşkizak (A 570) J. G. Stemmelen, 5-97

D: 1,440 tons (fl) **S:** 13 kts **Dim:** 64.6 × 9.4 × 3.5
A: 1 40-mm 60-cal. Bofors Mk 3 AA; 2 single 20-mm 70-cal. Oerlikon Mk 10 AA
Electronics: Radar: 1 Decca TM 1226 nav.
M: 1 diesel; 1 prop; 1,400 bhp **Crew:** 57 tot.

Remarks: Cargo capacity is 800 tons.

♦ **1 Binbaşi Saadettin Gürcan–class transport oiler [AOT]**
Bldr: Taşkizak NSY, Istanbul (L: 7-69)

A 573 BINBAŞI SAADETTIN GÜRCAN

Binbaşi Saadettin Gürcan (A 573)—in overhaul; the survey ship *Çubuklu* (A 594) is seen alongside H&L Van Ginderen, 7-95

D: 1,505 tons (4,680 fl) **S:** 16 kts **Dim:** 89.7 × 11.8 × 5.4
A: 1 40-mm 60-cal. Bofors Mk 3 AA; 2 single 20-mm 70-cal. Oerlikon Mk 10 AA
Electronics: Radar: 1 Decca TM 1226 nav.
M: 4 G.M. Electromotive Div. 16-567A diesels, electric drive; 2 props; 4,400 shp
Crew: . . . tot.

Remarks: Primarily used as a transport tanker, but is capable of delivering fuel to ships alongside while dead in the water.

♦ **1 ex-German Bodensee-class transport oiler [AOT]**
Bldr: Lindenau-Werft, Kiel

	Laid down	L	In serv.
A 575 INEBOLU (ex-*Bodensee,* ex-*Unkas*)	24-8-55	19-11-55	11-2-56

Inebolu (A 575) Hartmut Ehlers, 5-86

D: 1,237 tons (1,840 fl) **S:** 13.5 kts **Dim:** 67.1 (61.2 pp) × 9.84 × 4.27
A: 2 single 20-mm 70-cal. Oerlikon Mk 10 AA
Electronics: Radar: 1 Kelvin-Hughes 14/9 nav.
M: 1 MaK 6-cyl. diesel; 1 prop; 1,050 bhp **Electric:** 238 kVA tot.
Range: 6,240/12 **Crew:** 26 tot.

Remarks: Former merchant tanker. Acquired 26-3-59 for the West German Navy and transferred to Turkey 25-8-77. Cargo: 1,231 tons. Has one underway replenishment station, usable to either side.

♦ **1 ex-Russian Almaz-class salvage tug [ARS]**
Bldr: Okean SY, Mikolayiv, Ukraine (In serv. ca. 1974)

A 586 AKBAŞ (ex-. . .)

Russian commercial Almaz-class salvage tug Ametist—the *Akbaş* (A 586) is similar JMSDF/*Ships of the World,* 1998

D: 1,210 tons (1,656 fl) **S:** 13.25 kts (sust.)
Dim: 58.55 (51.62 pp) × 12.68 × 4.67 **A:** . . .
Electronics: Radar: 2 Don-2 nav.
M: diesel-electric: 2 Type 25-DB 2 (6ChN 30/38) diesels (1,500 bhp each), 2 generators, 1 motor; 1 prop; 2,500 shp (1,850 sust.)
Range: 6,200/11 **Fuel:** 297 tons **Endurance:** 40 days
Crew: approx. 35 tot.

Remarks: 1,074 grt/44 dwt. Purchased in 1999 from Russia; her former identity is not known, but she may have been the *Purga,* a former fishing fleet salvage tug. Design is very similar to the Russian Navy Sorum-class seagoing tug, except that the superstructure is higher and the mainmast is of A-frame configuration. Can accommodate 40 rescued personnel and is equipped for fire fighting, salvage pumping, and ocean towing. Based at Aksaz.

♦ **1 ex-French Tenace-class salvage tug [ARS]**
Bldr: Ch. de la Rochelle–Palice, France

	L	In serv.
A 576 DEGIRMENDERE (ex-*Centaure,* A 674)	8-1-74	15-11-74

Degirmendere (A 576) Bernard Prézelin, 4-99

D: 970 tons (1,440 fl) **S:** 13.5 kts **Dim:** 51.0 × 11.5 × 5.7
A: none **Electronics:** Radar: 1 Decca TM 1226 nav.
M: 2 SACM AGO 240 V12 diesels; 1 Kort-nozzle CP prop; 4,600 bhp
Electric: 766 kw tot. (3 × 227-kw, 1 × 85-kw diesel sets)
Range: 9,500/13 **Fuel:** 500 tons **Crew:** 3 officers, 34 enlisted

Remarks: Decommissioned from the French Navy and sold to Turkey 15-1-99; was transferred 16-3-99 and formally recommissioned 22-7-99. Based at Aksaz and used for salvage duties. Two sisters remain in French Navy service.
Hull systems: Pumps include one of 350 m^3/hr (serving two fire monitors with a range of 60 m) and one of 120 m^3/hr, plus numerous smaller salvage and firefighting pumps. Carries two semi-rigid inflatable boats. Bollard pull: 60 tons. Living quarters are air-conditioned.

♦ **1 ex-German Mercure-class salvage tender [ARS]**
Bldr: C.N. Amiot (CMN), Cherbourg

	Laid down	L	In serv.
A 582 KEMER (ex-M 525; ex-*Passau,* M 1255)	19-5-58	25-6-60	15-10-60

D: 366 tons (383 fl) **S:** 14.5 kts **Dim:** 44.62 (42.5 pp) × 8.41 × 2.55
A: 1 twin 20-mm 70-cal. Oerlikon Mk 24 AA

AUXILIARIES *(continued)*

Electronics: Radar: 1 Decca 707 nav.
M: 2 Mercedes-Benz MB-820 Db diesels; 2 KaMeWa CP props; 1,320 bhp
Electric: 816 kw tot. (2 × 320-kw, 2 × 68-kw diesel sets)
Range: 5,000/12 **Fuel:** 34.9 tons **Crew:** 40 tot.

Remarks: Built for the German Navy, placed in reserve in 1963, and stricken 31-12-73. Transferred to Turkey between 6-75 and 10-75. Was stricken in 1998 but then was modified as a salvage tender and recommissioned. Three sisters serve as minesweepers [MSC] (q.v. for appearance) and two as patrol craft. Wooden construction.

♦ **1 ex-U.S. Diver-class salvage ship [ARS]**
Bldr: Basalt Rock Co., Napa, Calif.

	Laid down	L	In serv.
A 589 Işin (ex-*Safeguard,* ARS 25)	5-6-43	20-11-43	31-10-44

Işin (A 589) Cem D. Yaylali, 10-97

D: 1,480 tons (1,970 fl) **S:** 14.8 kts **Dim:** 65.08 (63.09 pp) × 12.5 × 4.0
A: 2 single 20-mm 70-cal. Oerlikon Mk 10 AA **Electronics:** Radar: 2 . . . nav.
M: 4 Cooper-Bessemer GSB-8 diesels, electric drive; 2 props; 3,000 shp
Electric: 460 kw tot. **Fuel:** 300 tons **Crew:** 97 tot.

Remarks: Leased 28-9-79; purchased 6-8-87. Wooden fenders add 0.6 m to beam.

Disposal note: Submarine tender *Umurbey* (A 588, ex-German cargo ship *Dithmarschen)* was stricken 12-1-99 and arrived at Aliaga for scrapping 18-9-99. U.S. *Bluebird*-class submarine rescue ship *Kurtaran* (A 584; ex-*Bluebird,* ASR 19; ex-*Yurok,* ATF 164) was stricken 15-9-00 and sunk by aircraft during an exercise in 2001.

♦ **1 ex-U.S. Chanticleer-class submarine rescue ship [ASR]**
Bldr: Moore SB & DD Co., Oakland, Calif.

	Laid down	L	In serv.
A 585 Akin (ex-*Greenlet,* ASR 10)	15-10-41	12-7-42	29-5-43

Akin (A 585) Leo Dirkx, 7-01

D: 1,770 tons (2,321 fl) **S:** 15 kts **Dim:** 76.61 (73.15 pp) × 12.8 × 4.52
A: 1 40-mm 60-cal. Bofors Mk 3 AA; 2 twin 20-mm 70-cal. Oerlikon Mk 24 AA
Electronics: Radar: 1 Decca TM 1226 nav.
M: 4 Alco 539 diesels, electric drive; 1 prop; 3,000 shp **Electric:** 460 kw tot.
Fuel: 235 tons **Crew:** 85 tot.

Remarks: Loaned to Turkey 12-6-70 and purchased outright 15-2-73. Carries a McCann rescue diving bell and four marker buoys. Can also be used for general salvage duties.

♦ **1 Darica-class seagoing tug/torpedo retriever [ATA]**
Bldr: Taşkizak NSY, Istanbul

	L	In serv.
A 578 Darica (ex-Y 1125)	27-7-87	20-7-90

D: 750 tons (fl) **S:** 14 kts **Dim:** 40.9 × 9.8 × 3.9
A: none **Electronics:** Radar: 1 . . . nav.
M: 2 ABC diesels; 2 props; 4,000 bhp **Range:** 2,500/14

Remarks: Oilfield tug/supply-type vessel, with an open fantail for recovering and stowing torpedoes; is also equipped for fire fighting and salvage.

Darica (A 578) H&L Van Ginderen, 11-94

♦ **1 ex-U.S. Cherokee-class fleet tug [ATA]**
Bldr: United Eng. Co., Alameda, Calif.

	Laid down	L	In serv.
A 587 Gazal (ex-*Sioux,* ATF 75)	14-2-42	27-5-42	6-12-42

Gazal (A 587) H&L Van Ginderen, 7-95

D: 1,235 tons (1,675 fl) **S:** 16.5 kts **Dim:** 62.48 (59.44 pp) × 11.73 × 4.67
A: 1 76.2-mm 50-cal. Mk 22 DP; 2 single 20-mm 70-cal. Oerlikon Mk 10 AA
M: 4 G.M. 12-278 diesels, electric drive; 1 prop; 3,000 shp **Electric:** 260 kw tot.
Range: 6,500/16; 15,000/8 **Fuel:** 300 tons **Crew:** 85 tot.

Remarks: Transferred 30-10-72 and purchased outright 15-8-73. Can be used for salvage duties.

♦ **2 Van-class water tankers [AWT]**
Bldr: Gölçuk NSY, Kocaeli (In serv. 1969–70)

A 597 Van (ex-Y 1208) A 598 Ulabat (ex-Y 1209)

Van (A 597) Hartmut Ehlers, 7-95

D: 900 tons (1,250 fl) **S:** 10 kts **Dim:** 53.1 × 9.0 × 3.0
A: 1 20-mm 70-cal. Oerlikon Mk 10 AA
Electronics: Radar: 1 Decca 707 nav.
M: 1 diesel; 1 prop; 650 bhp **Crew:** . . . tot.

Remarks: Cargo: 700 tons. Reclassified as auxiliaries from service craft on 1-1-91.

♦ **3 ex-German FW 1–class water tankers [AWT]**
Bldr: Schichau, Bremerhaven (A 600: Jadewerft, Wilhelmshaven)

	Laid down	L	In serv.
A 581 Çinar (ex-*FW 1*)	5-4-63	22-7-63	30-11-63
A 598 Söğüt (ex-Y 1217, ex-*FW 2*)	5-4-63	3-9-63	4-1-64
A 600 Kavak (ex-*FW 4*)	14-6-63	14-3-64	28-7-64

AUXILIARIES *(continued)*

Kavak (A 600) Cem D. Yaylali, 4-97

D: 598 tons (647 fl) **S:** 9.5 kts **Dim:** 44.03 (41.4 pp) × 7.8 × 2.63
M: 1 MWM 12-cyl. diesel; 1 prop; 230 bhp **Electric:** 130 kVA tot.
Range: 2,150/9 **Fuel:** 15 tons **Crew:** 12 tot.

Remarks: A 598 was transferred 3-12-75, A 600 on 12-4-91, and A 581 early in 1996. Cargo: 343 tons of fresh water. A 598 was reclassified as an auxiliary from service craft on 1-1-91.

♦ 2 ex-German Rhein-class (Type 401) training ships [AXT]

	Bldr	L	In serv.
A 577 Sokullu Mehmet Paşa (ex-*Donau,* A 69)	Schlichting, Travemünde	26-11-60	23-5-64
A 579 Cezayirli Gazi Hasan Paşa (ex-*Elbe,* A 61)	Schlieker, Hamburg	5-5-60	17-4-62

Sokullu Mehmet Paşa (A 577) Hans Karr, 10-01

Cezayirli Gazi Hasan Paşa (A 579) Camil Busquets i Vilanova, 8-00

D: 2,330 tons (2,930 fl) **S:** 20 kts (22 on trials)
Dim: 98.80 (92.80 pp) × 11.80 × 3.95
A: 2 single 100-mm 65-cal. Creusot-Loire Model 1953 DP; 2 twin 40-mm 70-cal. Bofors AA; 2 mine rails (70 mines max.)
Electronics:
Radar: 1 . . . nav.; 1 Thales SGR-103 surf. search; 1 Thales SGR-105 air search; 2 Thales M45 f.c.
EW: . . . intercept
M: 6 MTU 16V TB81 (A 577: Maybach . . .) diesels; 2 CP props; 11,400 bhp
Electric: 2,250 kw tot. **Range:** 2,500/16 **Fuel:** 334 tons
Crew: 98 tot. (accomm. for 40 officers, 170 enlisted)

Remarks: Built as small combatant tenders but have been used as cadet training ships since acquired by Turkey. The current A 577 was transferred 13-3-95 as a replacement for a near-sister ship of the same name and number, the ex-*Isar* (A 54), transferred 30-9-82. Similarly, the current A 579 was decommissioned from the German Navy 17-12-92 and transferred during 1993 as a replacement for near-sister *Cezayirli Gazi Hasan Paşa* (A 579; ex-*Ruhr,* A 64). Both have two M4 radar directors for the 100-mm guns and can be employed as minelayers or escorts, if required.

SERVICE CRAFT

♦ 5 Deniz Temizleme Arac-1-class pollution-control craft [YAG]
Bldr: Y 151: . . ., Italy; others: Gölçuk NSY (In serv. 1982–95)

Y 151 Deniz Temizleme Arac-1 through Y 155 Deniz Temizleme Arac-5

D: 12.5 tons (fl) **S:** 10 kts **Dim:** 12.50 × 5.30 × . . .
M: 2 G.M. Detroit Diesel . . . diesels; 2 props; 380 bhp

Remarks: Catamaran-hulled craft with debris and oil-spill collection sweepers between the hulls. Also have one firefighting monitor.

Pollution skimmer Deniz Temizleme Arac-5 (Y 155) Hartmut Ehlers, 10-96

♦ 1 ex-U.S. floating crane [YD]
Bldr: Odenback SB, Rochester, N.Y. (In serv. 14-8-51)

Y 60 Algarna III (ex-Y 1023, ex-YD 185)

D: 1,200 tons (fl) **Dim:** 36.6 × 13.7 × 2.7

Remarks: Transferred in 9-63. Capacity: 100 tons.

♦ 1 miscellaneous floating crane [YD]

Y 59 Levent (ex-Y 1022)

Remarks: Capacity: 600 tons.

♦ 1 MTB 1–class diving tender [YDT] Bldr: . . ., U.K. (In serv. 1942)

Y . . . Dalgiç 1 (ex-MTB 1)

Dalgiç 1 (Y . . .) Cem D. Yaylali, 6-98

D: 70 tons **S:** 20 kts **Dim:** 21.8 × 4.2 × 2.6 **M:** 2 diesels; 2,000 bhp

Remarks: Sister P 312 was redesignated a mine clearance diver support boat in 1983; seven others are used as general-purpose tender/supply craft at mine warfare bases. Sister MTB 10 was stricken in 1987.

♦ 1 Cephane-class ammunition lighter [YE]

Y 97 Cephane 2 (ex-Y 1195)

Remarks: Of about 850 tons (fl). *Cephane 1* (Y 1194) was stricken during 1987 and *Cephane 3* (Y 1197) during 1992.

♦ 15 Salopa-series stores lighters [YF]

Y 21 Salopa 21 (ex-Y 1031) through Y 35 Salopa 35 (ex-Y 1045)

Salopa 33 (Y 33) Hartmut Ehlers, 11-93

Remarks: No data available; characteristics vary.

♦ 5 Layter-series stores lighters [YF]

Y 102 Layter 2 (ex-Y 1012)
Y 103 Layter 3 (ex-Y 1013)
Y 104 Layter 4 (ex-Y 1014)
Y 106 Layter 6 (ex-Y 1016)
Y 107 Layter 7 (ex-Y 1017)

Remarks: No data available. Sister *Layter 1* (Y 101, ex-Y 1011) was scrapped during 2000.

♦ 16 Mavna-series miscellaneous stores launches [YF]

Y 1 Mavna 1 (ex-Y 1181) through Y 4 Mavna 4 (ex-Y 1184)
Y 7 Mavna 7 (ex-Y 1187) through Y 13 Mavna 13 (ex-Y 1193)
Y 14 Mavna 14 (ex-Y 1198) through Y 18 Mavna 18 (ex-Y 1202)

Mavna 18 (Y 18) H&L Van Ginderen, 7-95

Remarks: Small, engines-aft, diesel-powered stores and personnel lighters.

SERVICE CRAFT *(continued)*

♦ **9 miscellaneous floating dry docks [YFDL/YFDM]**

	Capacity (tons)
Y 121 Havuz 1 (ex-Y 1081)	16,000
Y 122 Havuz 2 (ex-Y 1082)	12,000
Y 123 Havuz 3 (ex-Y 1083)	2,500
Y 124 Havuz 4 (ex-Y 1084)	4,500
Y 125 Havuz 5 (ex-Y 1085)	400
Y 126 Havuz 6 (ex-Y 1086)	3,000
Y 128 Havuz 8 (ex-Y 1088)	700
Y 129 Havuz 9 (ex-Y 1089)	3,500
Y 130 Havuz 10 (ex-Y 1090)	300

Remarks: Y 123 is a sectional pontoon dock built in 1958 by M.A.N., Blixen, Germany, with U.S. funds; she displaces 4,500 tons empty and measures 115.95 × 36.4 (30.50 clear width) × 9.0 (max.; 8.00 clear over blocks) m. Taşkizak Naval Dockyard delivered Y 130 in 7-89, and Gölçuk Naval Shipyard delivered Y 129 on 21-7-89.

♦ **1 miscellaneous personnel ferry [YFL]**

Y 46 Tersane III

Personnel ferry Tersane III (Y 46) Cem D. Yaylali, 4-98

Remarks: Small, enclosed personnel ferry employed in the Istanbul area for local transportation. There may be additional sisters or other similar craft in service.

♦ **2 miscellaneous officers' yachts [YFL]**

Y 76 Gül (ex-Y 1103) Kaplan

Kaplan Cem D. Yaylali, 5-95

Gül (Y 76) H&L Van Ginderen, 7-95

Remarks: *Kaplan* is a former U.S. "63-ft. AVR" wooden-hulled air/sea rescue craft used as a flag officer's barge and does not seem to have a Y-series number.

♦ **7 pontoon barges [YFN]**

Ponton 1 (ex-Y 1061) through Ponton 7 (ex-Y 1067)

♦ **2 inshore-survey craft [YGS]** (In serv. 1994?)

Y 35 Mesaha 1 Y 36 Mesaha 2

D: 38 tons (fl) **S:** 10 kts **Dim:** 15.9 × 4.5 × 1.3
Electronics: Radar: 1 . . . nav.
M: 2 G.M. Detroit Diesel 6-71 diesels; 2 props; 440 bhp (348 sust.)
Range: 600/10 **Crew:** 9 tot.

Mesaha 2 (Y 36)—outboard *Mesaha 1* (Y 35) Cem D. Yaylali, 9-94

Note: Steel-hulled craft that replace a pair of former U.S. Navy 52-ft. inshore survey boats with the same names and pennant numbers.

♦ **3 ex-U.S. YNG 45–class non-self-propelled gate craft [YNG]**
Bldr: Weaver SY, Orange, Texas (In serv. 1960–61)

Y 101 Kapi I (ex-YNG 45) Y 103 Kapi III (ex-YNG 47)
Y 102 Kapi II (ex-YNG 46)

D: 325 tons (fl) **Dim:** 33.5 × 10.4 × 1.5

♦ **3 H 500–class small fuel lighters [YO]**
Bldr: Taşkizak NSY, Istanbul (In serv. 1970s)

Y 140 H 500 (ex-Y 1231) Y 142 H 503 (ex-Y 1233)
Y 141 H 501 (ex-Y 1232)

Fuel lighter H 501 (Y 141)—with former pennant number Hartmut Ehlers, 3-90

D: 300 tons **S:** 11 kts **Dim:** 33.6 × 8.5 × 1.8
M: 1 G.M. Detroit Diesel 6-71 diesel; 1 prop; 225 bhp **Cargo:** 150 tons

♦ **2 ex-U.S. APL 41–class barracks barges [YPL]**
Bldrs: Y 38: Puget Sound Bridge & Dredge, Seattle; Y 39: Tampa SB, Tampa, Fla.

	L
Y 38 Yüzbaşi Nasit Öngeren (ex-Y 1204, ex-APL 47)	5-1-45
Y 39 Binbaşi Metin Sülüs (ex-Y 1205, ex-APL 53)	3-3-45

D: 2,660 tons (fl) **Dim:** 79.6 × 14.99 × 2.59 **Electric:** 300 kw **Crew:** 650 tot.

Remarks: Y 38 was leased in 10-72, Y 39 in 12-74; both were purchased 6-8-87. The pennant numbers were changed in 1991. Non-self-propelled.

♦ **1 Turkish-built torpedo retriever [YPT]**
Bldr: Gölçük NSY, Kocaeli (In serv. 1995)

Y 44 Takip-2

Takip-2 (Y 44) Cem D. Yaylali, 9-98

Remarks: No data available. Has two cranes for retrieving weapons but no recovery ramp. Appears to be about 18 m o.a. and powered by two diesels.

♦ **1 ex-U.S. 72-foot-class torpedo retriever [YPT]**
Bldr: Gölçük NSY, Kocaeli (In serv. 1961)

Y 98 Takip-1 (ex-Y 1052, ex-. . .)

D: 53 tons (fl) **S:** 18 kts **Dim:** 22.17 × 5.18 × 1.68
M: 2 G.M. diesels; 2 props; 1,000 bhp **Range:** 450/18 **Crew:** 6 tot.

Remarks: Built with U.S. aid to a U.S. standard design. Wooden construction. Can carry up to 10.8 tons of weapons retrieved via the stern ramp.

♦ **1 old torpedo retriever [YPT]**
Bldr: Gölçük NSY, Kocaeli (In serv. 1938)

Y 95 Torpido Tenderi 95 (ex-Y 1051)

D: 300 tons (fl) **S:** 10 kts **Dim:** . . . × . . . × . . .
M: 1 MWM diesel; 1 prop; 1,000 bhp **Crew:** 6 tot.

SERVICE CRAFT *(continued)*

Remarks: This craft is not the ex-TF 107 stricken from German Navy 31-8-89 and transferred to Turkey 4-9-89, which seems not to have entered service. Instead, it is a near-sister to the now-stricken munitions lighter *Bekirdere* (Y 94). Has two torpedo recovery ramps.

♦ 5 Önder-class large harbor tugs [YTB]
Bldr: Alaybey SY, Izmit (In serv.: Y 160: 22-7-99; others: 8-6-00)

Y 160 Önder . . . .

Önder (Y 160)—artist's rendering, showing propeller installation
Voith-Schneider, 2000

D: . . . tons **S:** 12 kts **Dim:** 28.0 (26.5 pp) × 9.0 × 4.4 (over props)
M: 2 . . . diesels; 2 Voith-Schneider Type 26 GII/165 vertical cycloidal props; 3,400 bhp
Range: 1,500/12 **Crew:** . . . tot.

Remarks: Equipped for fire fighting, with water monitors at the masthead and atop the pilothouse.

♦ 1 ex-East German Project 414 large harbor tug [YTB]
Bldr: Yachtwerft/Volkswerft, Stralsund (In serv. 1989)

A 583 Aksaz (ex-*Koos,* Y 1651; ex-*Delphin,* A 08)

D: 286 tons (320 fl) **S:** 10.5 kts **Dim:** 30.87 (29.30 pp) × 8.77 × 2.50
Electronics: Radar: 1 SRN-402 nav.
M: 1 SKL 6VD26/20 AL-1 diesel; 1 Kort-nozzle prop; 1,200 bhp (720 sust.)
Electric: 150 kw tot. **Range:** 1,800/10 **Crew:** 13 tot.

Remarks: 140 grt. Acquired by Germany upon unification in 10-90 as one of three completed units of a planned six-unit class. Was stricken 28-9-95 and sold to Turkey 7-10-96, departing the same date. Fitted with one water monitor for fire fighting.

♦ 2 Doganarslan-class large harbor tugs [YTB]
Bldr: Taşkizak NSY, Istanbul (In serv. 25-7-85 and 1987)

Y 52 Doganarslan (ex-Y 1123) Y 56 Özgen (ex-Y 1128)

Doganarslan (Y 52) J. G. Stemmelen, 4-97

D: 500 tons (fl) **S:** 12 kts **Dim:** . . . × . . . × . . . **M:** . . .

♦ 1 Kuvvet-class larger harbor tug [YTB]
Bldr: . . . . . . (In serv. 2-62)

Y 53 Kuvvet (ex-Y 1122)

D: 390 tons **S:** . . . kts **Dim:** 32.1 × 7.9 × 3.6 **M:** . . .

Remarks: Built in Turkey with U.S. Grant-Aid funds. Pennant number was changed during 1991.

♦ 1 U.S. Army Design 3004 medium harbor tug [YTM]
Bldr: . . . . . .(In serv. 2-62)

Y 54 Kudret (ex-Y 1229, ex-LT-. . .)

D: 100 tons light (122 fl) **S:** 12 kts **Dim:** 21.31 × 5.94 × 2.50
M: 1 diesel; 1 prop; 600 bhp **Range:** 3,500/12 **Fuel:** 15 tons **Crew:** 6 tot.

Remarks: Built in Turkey with U.S. Grant-Aid funds. Pennant number was changed during 1991.

♦ 1 ex-U.S. Army 320-design small harbor tug [YTL]

Y 64 Ersen Bayrak (ex-Y 1134, ex-LT-. . .)

♦ 1 Turkish-designed small harbor tug [YTL]
Bldr: Gölçuk NSY (In serv. 11-5-63)

Y 55 Atil (ex-Y 1132)

D: 143 tons (fl) **S:** 10 kts **Dim:** 24.40 × 6.72 × 2.70
M: 1 G.M. Electromotive Div. 8-268A diesel; 1 prop; 450 bhp

♦ 38 push-tugs [YTL]

Katir 1 through Katir 38

Katir 38 Hartmut Ehlers, 10-89

Remarks: No data available. Are not assigned Y-series pennant numbers.

♦ 3 Russian Mars-class (Project 14613) fireboats [YTR]
Bldr: Vympel Zavod, Rybinsk

	In serv.		In serv.
A 1542 Söndüren 2	8-6-00	A 1544 Söndüren 4	8-6-00
A 1543 Söndüren 3	22-7-99		

D: 385 tons (fl) **S:** 11.5 kts
Dim: 39.80 (37.76 wl; 35.20 pp) × 7.80 × 4.75 (max.)
Electronics: Radar: 1 Mius (Spin Trough) nav.
M: 2 Barnaul' 3KD 12N-520 diesels; 2 CP props; 1,018 bhp—bow-thruster
Electric: 400 kw tot.
Range: 500/11.5 **Fuel:** 12.6 tons **Endurance:** 5 days **Crew:** 13 tot.

Remarks: Ordered in 1997; two remained to be completed as of summer 1999. As many as five were originally planned. Have two 1,000-m^3/hr M827 diesel-driven pumps and four fire monitors (2 × 500 m^3/hr, 2 × 220 m^3/hr), plus two firehose distribution mains on the upper deck, a water curtain system, and chemical and powder fire-extinguishing systems. There are two foam generators, with articulating applicators mounted 15 m above the waterline. Can place water on fires at a distance of 200 m.

♦ 1 ex-U.S. firefighting tug [YTR]

Y 51 Söndüren 1 (ex-Y 1117, ex-YTL 751)

D: 70 tons (80 fl) **S:** 8 kts **Dim:** 21.34 × 5.89 × 2.21
M: 1 diesel; 1 prop; 375 bhp **Range:** 700/8 **Crew:** 4 tot.

Remarks: Transferred in 5-54.

♦ 1 water lighter [YW] Bldr: Gölçuk NSY, Kocaeli (L: 1979)

Y 140

D: 850 tons (fl) **S:** 10 kts **Dim:** 51.8 (46.8 pp) × 8.1 × . . .
M: 1 diesel; 1 prop; 480 bhp **Cargo:** 530 dwt

♦ 4 Pinar 3–class small water lighters [YW]
Bldr: Taşkizak NSY, Istanbul (In serv. ca. 1970)

Y 113 Pinar 3 Y 114 Pinar 4 Y 115 Pinar 5 Y 116 Pinar 6

Pinar 5 (Y 115) Hartmut Ehlers, 10-96

D: 300 tons **S:** 11 kts **Dim:** 33.6 × 8.5 × 1.8
M: 1 G.M. Detroit Diesel 6-71 diesel; 1 prop; 225 bhp **Cargo:** 150 tons

SERVICE CRAFT *(continued)*

♦ **1 large water lighter [YW]** Bldr: Gölçuk NSY, Kocaeli (In serv. 1958)

Y 112 Pinar 2

Pinar 2 (Y 112) Paolo Marsan, 8-97

D: 1,300 tons (fl) **S:** 10 kts **Dim:** 51.0 × 8.5 × . . .
A: none **M:** 1 diesel; 1 prop; . . . bhp **Crew:** 11 tot.

♦ **1 small water lighter [YW]**
Bldr: Meentzer SY, the Netherlands (In serv. 1938)

Y 111 Pinar 1 (ex-*Istanbul*)

D: 490 tons (fl) **S:** . . . **Dim:** . . . × . . . × . . . **M:** 1 diesel; 240 bhp

♦ **1 small water lighter [YW]**

Y 110 Mehmet Kaptan

♦ **8 E-1-class cadet training craft [YXT]**
Bldr: Bora Shipping Industry and Trading (Bora-Düzgit Tersanesi), Tuzla

	In serv.		In serv.
A 1531 E-1	22-7-99	A 1535 E-5	8-6-00
A 1532 E-2	22-7-99	A 1536 E-6	8-6-00
A 1533 E-3	8-6-00	A 1537 E-7	8-6-00
A 1534 E-4	8-6-00	A 1538 E-8	8-6-00

D: 93.5 tons (fl) **S:** 13 kts **Dim:** 28.80 × 6.00 × 1.20
Electronics: Radar: . . . **M:** 2 MTU . . . diesels; 2 props; . . . bhp
Range: 240/10 **Crew:** . . . tot.

Remarks: Ordered during 12-97 for use at the Turkish Naval Academy as seamanship and navigational training boats. The first unit was launched in 10-98, and all were to have been delivered by 8-99; the final unit was delivered in 3-00. Have aluminum hulls. Built under subcontract by Duzgit Group at Tuzla.

MINISTRY OF THE INTERIOR COAST GUARD
(Sahil Güvenlik)

Personnel (2002): Approx. 1,200 total, headed by a Turkish Navy rear admiral

Aviation: Three Agusta-Bell AB-206B helicopters and one Maule MX-7 light fixed-wing aircraft are based at Naval Air Station Topel. The aircraft are painted white with a red diagonal stripe. Three CASA CN-235 maritime patrol aircraft were ordered 28-4-97 and will be assembled in Turkey by Tusas Aerospace Industries. On 14-10-97, six search-and-rescue-configured Agusta-Bell 412 helicopters were ordered; the order was canceled during 12-98, then reconstituted during 3-99 for five AB 412s.

Note: Requests for bids to construct four 1,400-ton, helicopter-equipped search-and-rescue patrol ships were sent out during 12-01.

PATROL CRAFT [WPC]

♦ **12 SG 80 class** Bldr: Taşkizak NSY, Istanbul

	L	In serv.		L	In serv.
SG 80	3-6-94	6-96	SG 86	. . .	8-6-00
SG 81	3-6-94	5-7-96	SG 87	. . .	8-6-00
SG 82	20-4-95	5-97	SG 88	. . .	8-6-00
SG 83	20-4-95	5-97	SG 89	. . .	8-6-00
SG 84	5-7-96	1998	SG 90	. . .	8-6-00
SG 85	5-7-96	1998	SG 91	. . .	8-6-00

SG 85 Leo Dirkx, 5-01

SG 88 Cem D. Yaylali, 8-01

D: 182.4 tons (195 fl) **S:** 27 kts (25 sust.) **Dim:** 40.75 (37.00 pp) × 7.05 × 2.13
A: 1 40-mm 70-cal. Bofors L70 AA; 2 single 12.7-mm mg
Electronics: Radar: 1 Decca . . . nav.
M: 2 MTU . . . diesels; 2 props; 5,700 bhp (5,040 sust.)
Range: . . ./. . . **Crew:** 24 tot.

Remarks: Designed by Taşkizak Naval Dockyard with assistance from the Technical University of Istanbul. Have a more conventional hullform than the SG 71 and SAR-33 classes. A firefighting water monitor is mounted aft.

♦ **4 SG 71 class**
Bldr: Taşkizak NSY, Istanbul

SG 71 (In serv. 25-7-85) SG 73 (L: . . .)
SG 72 (L: 25-7-85) SG 74 (L: 24-7-87)

SG 71 Cem D. Yaylali, 8-00

D: 210 tons (fl) **S:** 40 kts (35 sust.) **Dim:** 36.60 × 8.60 × 1.90
A: 1 40-mm 60-cal. Bofors Mk 3 AA; 2 single 7.62-mm mg
Electronics: Radar: 1 Decca TM 1226 nav.
M: 3 SACM (UNI) AGO 195 V16 CSHR diesels; 3 CP props; 12,000 bhp (7,200 sust.)
Range: 450/35; 1,000/20 **Crew:** 24 tot.

Remarks: A lengthened version of the SAR-33 class, with a longer superstructure. They bury their bows at higher speeds and are not considered a success. The pilothouse windows slope forward on SG 71, backward on SG 74.

♦ **10 SAR-33 class**
Bldr: Taşkizak NSY, Istanbul (SG 61: Abeking & Rasmussen, Lemwerder, Germany) (In serv. 1978–84)

SG 61 (ex-J 61) through SG 70 (ex-J 70)

SG 62 Hartmut Ehlers, 3-99

D: 150 tons (170 fl) **S:** 40 kts **Dim:** 33.00 (29.50 wl) × 8.60 × 1.85
A: 1 40-mm 60-cal. Bofors Mk 3 AA; 2 single 76.2-mm mg
Electronics: Radar: 1 Decca TM 1226 nav.
M: 3 SACM-AGO 195 V16 CSHR diesels; 3 CP props; 12,000 bhp (7,200 sust.)
Electric: 300 kw tot. **Range:** 450/35; 1,000/20 **Fuel:** 18 tons **Crew:** 23 tot.

Remarks: SG 61 was launched 12-12-77 and SG 62 in 7-78. SG 65 through SG 67 entered service 30-7-81. Have a wedge-shaped hull design of remarkable seaworthiness and steadiness at high speeds in heavy weather. Turkey was to have built 14 units of this class for Libya, but the contract was canceled around 1986.

COAST GUARD PATROL CRAFT [WPC] *(continued)*

SG 64 Cem D. Yaylali, 9-98

♦ 14 AB 25 class Bldr: Taşkizak NSY, Istanbul (In serv. 1972–78)

SG 21 through SG 34

SG 34—with bow bulwarks and lower chine line Cem D. Yaylali, 4-97

SG 28—early version H&L Van Ginderen, 10-94

D: 170 tons (fl) **S:** 22 kts **Dim:** 40.24 × 6.4 × 1.65
A: 2 single 40-mm Bofors Mk 3 AA; 1 20-mm 70-cal. Oerlikon Mk 10 AA *or* 2 single 12.7-mm mg
Electronics: Radar: 1 Decca TM 1226 nav.
M: 2 SACM-AGO 195 V16 CSHR diesels; 2 props; 4,800 bhp—2 cruise diesels; 300 bhp
Crew: 25 tot.

Remarks: Eleven sisters are operated by the Turkish Navy and one each by Azerbaijan, Georgia, and Kazakhstan. Built with French technical assistance. SG 30–34 are of the later variant with lower hull knuckle and low bulwarks at the bow to improve seaworthiness; they have two machineguns on platforms at the aft end of the superstructure, while the earlier units have a single 20-mm AA abaft the mast.

PATROL BOATS [WPB]

♦ 10 Onuk-15 class
Bldr: Yonca Technical Investment Co. and Onuk Vehicle Ltd., Tuzla (In serv. 9-98 to 8-6-00)

SG 101 through SG 110

SG 101 A. A. de Kruijf, 9-01

D: 90 tons (fl) **S:** 45 kts **Dim:** 29.6 × 6.3 × 1.5
A: 2 single 12.7-mm mg **Electronics:** Radar: 1 . . . nav.
M: 2 MTU 16V4000 M90 diesels; 2 MJP 750 waterjets; 7,300 bhp
Range: 750/30 **Crew:** 3 officers, 8 enlisted + 7 passengers

Remarks: Also known as the Onur class; the builder's Sea Guard design. Ordered for $56 million in 5-99, with all to be delivered during 2000. The hull is built of composite materials, with replaceable armor plating. Were meant to carry a 20- or 30-mm gun forward also, but it has not yet been mounted. The low-observable design is by Kaan NZ Onuk, with noise-, electronic-, and heat-reduction measures. Also offered with an AlliedSignal TF-series gas turbine on a centerline waterjet for 55-kt maximum speeds.

♦ 4 U.S. 27-foot Vigilant-class patrol launches
Bldr: Boston Whaler, Edgewater, Fla. (In serv. 9-99)

Remarks: Foam-core GRP hull construction, claimed to be unsinkable. Powered by twin 250-bhp Mercury gasoline outboard motors for speeds in excess of 50 kts.

♦ 14 Interceptor class
Bldr: Yonca Technical Investment Co., Tuzla (In serv. 9-98 to . . .-99)

SG 4 through SG 17

SG 4 Leo Dirkx, 8-01

D: 19 tons (fl) **S:** 54 kts **Dim:** 15.40 × 4.04 × 0.92
A: small arms **Electronics:** Radar: 1 Raytheon . . . nav.
M: 2 MTU 12V183 TE93 diesels; 2 props; 2,300 bhp
Range: 300/40 **Crew:** 2 tot.

Remarks: Six were ordered in 5-97 and eight more during 10-98. Intended to intercept smugglers. The first unit was delivered mid-9-98, the next eight weeks later, and the remainder at six-week intervals. Have a GPS receiver and an echo sounder. SG 4 made 53.7 kts on trials.

♦ 10 14.6-meter class
Bldrs: Gölçük NSY, Kocaeli, and Taşkizak NSY, Istanbul

SG 50 through SG 59

SG 59 H&L Van Ginderen, 7-95

D: 25 tons (29 fl) **S:** 18 kts (15 sust.) **Dim:** 14.6 × 3.5 × 1.1
A: 1 12.7-mm mg **Electronics:** Radar: 1 Raytheon . . . nav.
M: 2 diesels; 2 props; 700 bhp **Crew:** 7 tot.

Remarks: The first three by Taşkizak were completed 20-7-90 and three others in 7-91; four were delivered by Gölçük Naval Shipyard 23-7-92. SG 102 and SG 103 are no longer in service.

Disposal note: The eight German KW 15–class patrol boats, SG 12 through SG 16 and SG 18 through SG 20, had been withdrawn from service by 2000.

♦ 1 SG 40 class

SG 43

D: 25 tons (fl) **S:** 12 kts **Dim:** 16.8 × 4.20 × 1.10
A: 1 12.7-mm mg **Electronics:** Radar: 1 Decca . . . nav.
M: 2 G.M. Gray Marine 64HN9 diesels; 2 props; 450 bhp
Range: 200/12 **Crew:** 7 tot.

Remarks: Wooden-hulled craft, probably built in Turkey, date not available. Has an enclosed pilothouse and a more raked bow than the Mk 5 Picket Boat class and appears newer. Sister SG 40 was transferred to Georgia during 2-98.

COAST GUARD PATROL BOATS [WPB] *(continued)*

♦ 4 ex-U.S. Mk 5 Picket Boat class

SG 44 SG 46 SG 48 SG 49

SG 44 Hartmut Ehlers, 6-86

D: 15 tons (fl) **S:** 18 kts **Dim:** 13.94 × 4.17 × 1.10
A: 2 single 7.62-mm mg **Electronics:** Radar: 1 Decca . . . nav.
M: 2 G.M. Gray Marine 64HN9 diesels; 2 props; 450 bhp
Range: 200/18 **Crew:** 5 tot.

Remarks: Wooden-hulled. Transferred during the 1950s. SG 48 and 49 operate from North Cyprus. SG 41 and 42 have been stricken.

♦ 1 SG 2–class harbor patrol boat Bldr: . . .

SG 2

D: 15 tons (fl) **S:** 18 kts **Dim:** 14.5 × 4.4 × 0.7
A: small arms **Electronics:** Radar: 1 . . . nav.
M: 2 diesels; 2 props; 700 bhp **Crew:** 7 tot.

Remarks: GRP-hulled cabin cruiser.

♦ 1 SG 1–class harbor patrol boat Bldr: . . .

SG 1

D: 35 tons (fl) **S:** 20 kts **Dim:** 17.0 × 5.0 × 1.0
A: small arms **Electronics:** Radar: 1 . . . nav.
M: 2 diesels; 2 props; 1,050 bhp **Crew:** 7 tot.

Remarks: GRP-hulled cabin cruiser.

TURKMENISTAN

Personnel (2001): Approx. 125 total

Bases: All craft are based at Türkmenbashy (formerly known as Krasnovodsk).

Organizations: Organized in a division of patrol "ships," one seagoing minesweeper, and two air-cushion landing craft.

PATROL BOATS [PB]

♦ 0 (+ 3) Kalkan-M class
Bldr: Morye Zavod, Feodosiya, Ukraine (In serv. 2002)

D: 7 tons (fl) **S:** 30 kts **Dim:** 10.6 × 3.3 × 0.6
M: 1 Volvo . . . diesel; 1 prop; 450 bhp **Crew:** 2 tot. + 6 passengers

Remarks: Ordered in early 2002; additional units may be ordered later.

♦ 1 ex-U.S. Coast Guard 82-foot Point class
Bldr: Coast Guard Yard, Curtis Bay, Md. (In serv. 3-8-70)

PB-129 Merjen (ex-*Point Jackson,* WPB 82378)

D: 64 tons (66–69 fl) **S:** 22.6 kts **Dim:** 25.3 × 5.23 × 1.95
A: 2 single 12.7-mm M2 mg **Electronics:** Radar: 1 Hughes-Furuno SPS-73 nav.
M: 2 Caterpillar 3412 diesels; 2 props; 1,480 bhp
Range: 320/22.6; 1,200/8 **Fuel:** 5.7 tons **Crew:** 8–10 tot.

Remarks: Transferred after striking on 30-5-00. Hull is built of mild steel. High-speed diesels are controlled from the bridge. Well-equipped for salvage and towing. Is equipped with 4.27-m Avon Searider rigid inflatable boats powered by a 40-bhp outboard engine. PB-129 is shown in the photo of Georgian sister *Tsotne Dadiani* (P 210).

Note: Several other patrol boats, classes and total unknown, are said to be in service, listed as ships.

MINE COUNTERMEASURES

Note: Turkmenistan is said to have received one seagoing mine countermeasures unit from Russia, class unknown.

AMPHIBIOUS WARFARE CRAFT

♦ 2 Skat (NATO "Gus")-class (Project 1205) air-cushion personnel landing craft [LCPA]
Bldrs: Zelenodol'sk and Feodosiya Shipyards (In serv. 1969–74)

D: 27 tons (fl) **S:** 49 kts **Dim:** 20.4 × 8.4 × 0.5 (at rest)
A: small arms **Electronics:** Radar: 1 . . . nav.
M: 2 TVD-10M gas turbines; 2 airscrew propellers; 1,560 shp—1 TVD-10 gas turbine lift engine; 780 shp
Range: 200/40 **Crew:** 7 tot. + 40 troops

Remarks: Identification is tentative, as several units of this class were assigned to the Soviet Caspian Flotilla. Three of these (of Project 1205P) were configured to recover cosmonauts who had fallen into the sea; two (of which D-441 was transferred to Turkmenistan in 1994) were based in the Caspian Sea and another in the Aral Sea.

TURKS AND CAICOS

POLICE

Base: Cockburn Harbor, Grand Turk

PATROL BOATS [WPB]

♦ 1 M 160 class Bldr: Halmatic, Havant, U.K. (In serv. 9-89)

Sea Quest

Sea Quest Maritime Photographic, 1-94

D: 17.3 tons (fl) **S:** 27+ kts **Dim:** 15.40 (12.20 pp) × 3.86 × 1.15
A: 1 7.62-mm mg **Electronics:** Radar: 1 Decca 370BT nav.
M: 2 G.M. Detroit Diesel 6V92 TA diesels; 2 props; 1,100 bhp (770 sust.)
Range: 300/20; 500/17 **Fuel:** 2,700 liters **Crew:** 8 tot.

Remarks: Sister to the British Virgin Islands' *Ursula.* Carries a rigid inflatable inspection dinghy aft.

♦ 1 Dagger class
Bldr: Fairey Marine, Cowes (In serv. 6-86)

Sea Hawk

Sea Hawk Maritime Photographic, 1-94

D: 8 tons light (12 fl) **S:** 24 kts **Dim:** 12.2 × 3.4 × 1.1
A: 1 7.62-mm mg **Electronics:** Radar: 1 Decca 370BT nav.
M: 2 Perkins T6.3544M diesels; 2 props; 440 bhp (330 sust.)
Range: 540/20 **Crew:** 6 tot.

Remarks: GRP construction.

TUVALU

TUVALU POLICE FORCE MARITIME WING

Personnel (2001): Approx. 30 total

Base: Funafuti

Note: Ship names are preceded by HMTSS (Her Majesty's Tuvalu Surveillance Ship).

PATROL CRAFT [WPC]

♦ **1 ASI 315 class**
Bldr: Transfield-ASI, South Coogie, W.A., Australia (In serv. 8-10-94)

801 Te Mataeli

Te Mataeli (801) H&L Van Ginderen, 7-94

D: 165 tons (fl) **S:** 21 kts (20 sust.)
Dim: 31.50 (28.60 wl) × 8.10 × 2.12 (1.80 hull) **A:** small arms
Electronics: Radar: 1 Furuno 1011 nav.
M: 2 Caterpillar 3516 diesels; 2 props; 2,820 bhp (2,400 sust.)
Electric: 116 kw (2 × 50-kw Caterpillar 3304 diesels; 1 × 16 kw)
Range: 2,500/12 **Fuel:** 27.9 tons **Endurance:** 8–10 days
Crew: 3 officers, 14 enlisted

Remarks: An Australian foreign aid program "Pacific Patrol Boat," with 15 sisters in a number of Southwest Pacific island nation forces (and five more on order as of 1-94). Ordered in late 1992. Name means "Knowledge-That-Brings-You-Home." Carries a 5-m aluminum boarding boat. Has an extensive navigational suite, including Furuno FSN-70 NAVSAT receiver, 525 HFD/F, 120 MF–HFD/F, FE-881 echo sounder, and DS-70 doppler log.

PATROL BOAT [WPB]

♦ **1 small patrol boat** Bldr: Richards, U.K. (In serv. 1991)

Nivanga

D: . . . tons **S:** . . . kts **Dim:** . . . × . . . × . . . **A:** . . .
M: 2 Mirrlees-Blackstone ESL-2 Mk 1 diesels; . . . props; 1,325 bhp

Remarks: Used for search-and-rescue duties. No further information available.

UGANDA

ARMY MARINE UNIT

Personnel (2002): Approx. 140 total

Bases: Headquarters at Fort Bell, Entebbe. Minor facilities at Bukakata, Gaba, Jinja, Majinji, and Sese, all on Lake Victoria.

Note: Operations by the Ugandan Army Marine Unit on Lake Victoria were said to be at a standstill as of 9-99 due to the heavy growth of hibiscus plants in the lake. The three Yugoslav Type AL8K aluminum launches were no longer operational. Some 14 GRP-hulled craft, armed with one 78.62-mm mg and powered by gasoline outboard motors, may still be available in storage; these were built by FB Marine, Italy.

UKRAINE

Personnel (2002): Approx. 9,200 total, including naval aviation and 1,500 naval infantry

Organization: Divided into the Western Maritime Operational Territory and Southern Maritime Operational Territory, headquartered at Odesa and Novoozerne, respectively. The Surface Forces are organized into brigades, basic tactical formations, and squadrons; the Submarine Force has one squadron (and one submarine); Naval Aviation has regiments subdivided into squadrons; the Shore-based Rocket-artillery Forces have brigades; and the Naval Infantry is organized into one brigade and one headquarters, two mechanized, and one paratroop battalions. In addition, special formations are established for intelligence; nuclear, chemical, and biological defense; the Radio-Technical Service; electronic warfare; the Hydrographic and Hydrometeorological Service; and engineering.

Bases: Headquarters are at Kiyiv (Kiev). The main base, naval infantry headquarters, and repair facilities are at Streletskaya and Karantynnaya Harbors, Sevastopil (Sevastopol'); the Western Maritime Operational Territory at Odesa (Odessa); the Southern Maritime Operational Territory at Novoozerne; and the River Gunboat Division at Izmayil. There are surface ship bases at Chornomorske, Donuzlav, Kerch', Mirnoye, Ochakiv, and Simferopol and aviation facilities at Saki and Ochakiv. The border guard and smaller naval units use facilities at Odesa and other Ukraine seaports. Naval repairs can be carried out at Mikolayiv Shipyard 61 Kommunara (Shipyard 444), which performed major overhauls on Soviet Navy units for many years, and also at Feodosiya and at Zaliv Shipyard, Kerch'. Training for officers is carried out at the Sevastopol' Naval Institute.

Naval Aviation: Several Su-27 Flanker land-based interceptors and Su-24 Fencer land-based maritime strike aircraft may remain flyable. Also in use are up to 11 Be-12 ASW amphibians and up to 28 Ka-25 Hormone and Ka-27 Helix-series helicopters.

Coastal Defense: An independent missile and artillery brigade was commissioned 24-2-96; using the assets of the former Black Sea Fleet 362nd Missile Regiment, the brigade was equipped with truck-mounted SS-N-2C cruise missiles (which may now no longer be operational). There are also a number of radar-equipped shore observation stations. The prototype 130-mm Bereg missile coast-defense gun system (with only one gun) was confiscated by Ukraine; see Russian section for characteristics.

Note: Names below are transliterated from the Cyrillic insofar as possible by the system preferred by the Ukraine government; in actual usage, however, a number of ship names (and even some place names) continue to be spelled and transliterated locally by the old Russian system (e.g., Sevastopol' vice Sevastopil), largely because the ships are based mostly at Crimean ports where the populace remains predominantly Russian-speaking.

ATTACK SUBMARINES [SS]

♦ **1 Foxtrot class (Project 641K)** (Nonoperational)
Bldr: Novo Admiralteiskiye Verfi 196 (Sudomekh Division), St. Petersburg, Russia

	Laid down	L	In serv.
U 01 *Zaporizhzhya* (ex-B-435)	24-3-70	29-5-70	6-11-70

Zaporizhzhya (U 01) Hartmut Ehlers, 8-00

D: 1,957 tons surf./2,485 tons sub. **S:** 15.5 kts surf./18 kts sub.
Dim: 91.30 (89.70 wl) × 7.50 × 6.06 (surf.)
A: 10 533-mm TT (6 fwd, 4 aft; 14 torpedoes or 28 AMD-1000 mines)
Electronics:
Radar: 1 MRK-50 Albatros (Snoop Tray-1) nav./search
Sonar: MG-15 Herkules active; MG-100 Arktika MF active target tracking (13–16 kHz); MG-10 Feniks-M passive array
EW: 1 Stop Light intercept; Quad Loop D/F
M: 3 Type 2D-42M diesels (1,825 bhp each), 3 electric motors (1 × 2,700 shp, 2 × 1,350 shp); 3 6-bladed props; 5,400 shp (sub.)—1 100-shp low-speed electric "creep" motor on centerline shaft
Range: 4,153/16.6, 20,000/8 surf.; 11,500/8 snorkel; 36/18, 380/2 sub.
Fuel: 360 tons **Endurance:** 70 days **Crew:** 12 officers, 70 enlisted

Remarks: Transferred and recommissioned 1-8-97. Completed a refit in 8-00, but is without batteries, which are being sought from Germany, and has not operated at sea since 1995; a 12-man caretaker crew is assigned.
Hull systems: Has four 112-cell Type 46SU battery groups. Can dive in as little as 45–60 seconds and has 527 tons of reserve buoyancy in surfaced condition. The pressure hull has seven watertight compartments. Operating depth: 250 m; maximum: 280 m. The crew size listed is maximum accommodations. One authoritative source gives the range as 30,000 n.m. at 8 kts on the surface or 17,900 n.m. at 8 kts on snorkel; this may be achievable by employing some ballast tankage for fuel stowage.
Combat systems: Uses the Leningrad mechanical analog torpedo fire-control system. The original combat load was 22 torpedoes, with eight aft; in recent years, however, the stern tubes have been loaded with countermeasures devices and berths have replaced the reload racks in the after torpedo room. Most of the combat systems were inoperative at time of transfer.

GUIDED-MISSILE CRUISERS [CG]

Note: President Leonid Kuchma offered the incomplete *Slava* (Atlant)-class guided-missile cruiser *Ukrayina* (ex-*Admiral Flota Lobov*, ex-*Ukrayina*, ex-*Vilna Ukrayina*, ex-*Bohdan Khmenytsky*, ex-*Poltava*, ex-*Admiral Flota Lobov*, ex-*Komsomolets*) to Russia on 28-9-01, and the offer was tentatively accepted a week later, only to be rejected during 1-02; work on the ship had ceased during 8-00 for lack of funds, and it was also stated that the Russians would not provide the 16 P-500 cruise missiles that were to constitute the ship's principal armament. The fate of the 94%-complete ship is now uncertain.

FRIGATES [FF]

♦ 1 Russian Krivak-III class (Project 11351)

Bldr: Kamysh-Burun Zavod 532, Kerch'

	Laid down	L	In serv.
U 130 Hetman Sahaydachniy (ex-*Poltava*, ex-*Latsis*, ex-*Kirov*)	9-7-91	29-3-92	11-7-93

Hetman Sahaydachniy (U 130) Hartmut Ehlers, 7-00

Hetman Sahaydachniy (U 130) Boris Lemachko, 2000

D: 3,274 tons std.; 3,458 tons normal (3,642 fl; 3,774 max.) **S:** 31 kts (30 sust.)
Dim: 122.98 (113.00 pp) × 14.20 (13.2 wl) × 4.72 (hull; 7.20 over sonar dome)
A: 1 twin-rail Osa-MA (SA-N-4) SAM syst. (20 9M-33/Gecko missiles); 1 100-mm 59-cal. AK-100 DP (600 rounds); 2 single 30-mm 54-cal. AK-630M gatling AA (12,000 rounds); 1 . . . grenade launcher; 2 12-round RBU-6000 ASW RL (96 RGB-60 rockets); 2 quadruple 533-mm UTA-53-1135 TT (4 SET-65 and 4 53-65K torpedoes); 1 Ka-25 Hormone or Ka-27 Helix helicopter; 2 mine rails (12–16 mines)
Electronics:
Radar: 1 MR-212/201 Vaygach-U (Palm Frond) nav.; 1 Volga (Don-Kay) nav.; 1 Nayada-2 helicopter control; 1 MR-760 Fregat-MA (Top Plate) 3-D air search; 1 MPZ-301 (Pop Group) SAM f.c.; 1 MR-114 Bars (Kite Screech-A) 100-mm f.c.; 1 MR-123 Vympel (Bass Tilt) 30-mm f.c.
Sonar: MGK-332MC Titan-2 (Bull Nose) hull-mounted MF; MG-325 Vega (Mare Tail) MF VDS; MG-26 underwater telephone
EW: Smerch suite: 2 Start-2 (Bell Shroud) intercept; 2 MP-401 Start (Bell Squat A/B) jammers; 4 16-round PK-16 fixed decoy RL (128 rockets); 2 towed torpedo decoys; 3 sets corner-reflector decoys
M: COGAG M-7 plant: 2 M-62 cruise gas turbines (7,475 shp each), 2 M-8K boost gas turbines (20,000 shp each); 2 props; 54,950 shp tot.
Electric: 2,500 kw tot. (5 × 500-kw diesel sets)
Range: 1,146/30; 3,636/14 **Fuel:** . . . tons + 22 tons aviation fuel
Endurance: 30 days **Crew:** 18 officers, 162 warrant officers and enlisted

Remarks: A revised version of the basic Krivak design for Soviet KGB Maritime Border Guard service in the Far East, where the first six now serve. U 130, the seventh unit, originally to have been named *Kirov* (and then *Latsis* after the 1991 revolution), was taken over by Ukraine and began trials, operating from Sevastopil in mid-3-93. Named for a Cossack hetman who led incursions into Crimea and Turkey during the 18th century. The eighth unit, begun as the *Krasniy Vympel* (later *Berzin*, and then *Zaliv*) was to be completed for Ukraine as the *Hetman Bayda Vyshnevetskiy* (U 131), but construction was canceled in 2-96.
Combat systems: The combat system is designated Sapfir-U7, the ASW weapons-control system name is Purga, and the communications suite is called Tayfun-3. The addition of a helicopter facility (with a simple deck-transit system) and helicopter weapons reload magazines cost two gunmounts and one SAM position aft, while the SS-N-14 dual-purpose missile system of the Krivak-I/II was replaced by a 100-mm gun, more useful for the patrol mission of these ships. Two 6-barrel gatling guns were added to improve close-in defense. The Nayada-2 radar mounted atop the helicopter hangar is intended to serve in landing control.

♦ 1 ex-Russian Krivak-II (Burevestnik-M) class (Project 1135M)

(Nonoperational) Bldr: Yantar Zavod 820, Kaliningrad

	Laid down	L	In serv.
U 132 Sevastopol' (ex-*Razitel'nyy*)	11-2-75	1-7-76	31-12-76

Sevastopol' (U 132)—in refit Hartmut Ehlers, 7-00

D: 2,945–3,075 tons std.; 3,305 normal (3,505 max. fl) **S:** 30.6 kts
Dim: 123.10 (113.00 wl) × 14.20 (13.2 wl) × 4.57 (mean hull; 7.3 over sonar dome)
A: 4 URK-5 Rastrub (SS-N-14 Silex) SSM (KT-106 launcher; 8 Type 83R and 83RUS Metel' missiles); 2 twin-rail Osa-M (SA-N-4) SAM systems (40 9M-33/Gecko missiles); 2 single 100-mm 59-cal. AK-100 DP (1,200 rounds); 2 12-round RBU-6000 ASW RL (144 RGB-60 rockets); 2 quadruple 533-mm UTA-53-1135 TT (4 SET-65 and 4 53-65K torpedoes); 2 mine rails (12–16 mines)
Electronics:
Radar: 1 MR-212/201 Vaygach-U (Palm Frond) nav.; 1 Don-2 nav.; 1 MR-310U Angara-M (Head Net-C) air search; 2 . . .Drakon (Eye Bowl) SSM f.c.; 2 MPZ-301 Baza (Pop Group) SA-N-4 f.c.; 1 MR-114 Lev (Kite Screech-A) 100-mm f.c.
Sonar: MGK-332MC Titan-2 (Bull Nose) hull-mounted MF; MG-325 Vega (Mare Tail) MF VDS; MG-26 underwater telephone
EW: Smerch suite: 2 Start-2 (Bell Shroud) intercept; 2 MP-401 Start (Bell Squat A/B) jammers; 4 16-round PK-16 fixed decoy RL (128 rockets); 2 towed torpedo decoys; 3 sets corner-reflector decoys
M: COGAG M-7 plant: 2 M-62 cruise gas turbines (7,475 shp each), 2 M-8K boost gas turbines (20,000 shp each); 2 props; 54,950 shp tot.
Electric: 3,000 kw tot. (5 × 600-kw diesel sets)
Range: 640/30; 4,000/14 **Endurance:** 30 days
Crew: 23 officers, 28 warrant officers, 130 enlisted (accomm. for 194 tot.)

Remarks: Stricken from the Black Sea Fleet 10-1-96; was to have been transferred from the Black Sea Fleet 1-4-96, but was withheld for a period. Recommissioned 24-8-97. Was in overhaul at Sevastopil during 1998–2001, with the engines removed and transferred to the Russian Kara-class destroyer *Kerch'*.
Hull systems: There are 14 watertight compartments. The superstructure is built of aluminum-magnesium alloy, welded to the hull via bimetallic inserts. The propulsion plant originally delivered 45,570 shp normal/51,200 shp max. total (with the cruise turbines operating at 6,000 shp each and the boost turbines at 18,000 each), but the output was later increased. The hull block coefficient is 0.46, very fine for this type of vessel. For slow speeds, any one of the engines can drive both propellers. Has UKA-135 fin stabilizers and a single rudder. Was designed to be 2,735 tons standard, 3,100 tons full load, but one source reports that displacements have grown to 3,075 tons standard and 3,575 tons full load.
Combat systems: The combat system is known as Planshet-35 and the ASW weapons-control system is Purga. The chaff/decoy rocket launchers were moved from the stern to the 01 level, abreast the aft SA-N-4 launcher. Can carry 12 KSM, 14 KRAB, or 16 IGDM-500 mines. The antenna for the MR-3100 air-search radar has been removed.

Disposal note: Krivak-I-class (Project 1135) frigates *Mikolayiv* (U 133, ex-*Bezukoriznennyy*) and *Dnipropetrovsk* (U 134, ex-*Bezzavetnyy*) were to be stricken and scrapped after 9-00.

CORVETTES [FFL]

♦ 1 (+ 1) Grisha-V class (Project 1124EhM)
Bldr: Leninskaya Kuznitsa SY, Kiyiv

	L	In serv.
U 200 Lutsk	22-5-93	12-2-94
U 202 Ternopil	. . .	2002?

Lutsk (U 200) Hartmut Ehlers, 8-00

Lutsk (U 200) Hartmut Ehlers, 8-00

D: 876 tons light; 930 tons std. (1,070 fl)
S: 32 kts (21 on gas turbine; 16 on diesels)
Dim: 71.20 (66.90 wl) × 10.15 (9.50 wl) × 3.72 (hull)
A: 1 twin-rail Osa-M (SA-N-4) SAM syst. (20 9M-33/Gecko missiles); 1 76.2-mm 59-cal. AK-176 DP; 1 30-mm 54-cal. AK-630M gatling AA; 2 4-round Fasta-4M (SA-N-8) SAM syst. (20–24 Strela-3/Gremlin shoulder-launched missiles); 2 twin 533-mm TT; 1 12-round RBU-6000 ASW RL (48 RGB-60 rockets); 2 d.c. racks (6 d.c. each) or up to 18 mines on the two mine rails
Electronics:
Radar: 1 MR-312 Nayada nav.; 1 MR-755 Topaz-2B (Half Plate-B) surf./air search; 1 MPZ-301 Baza (Pop Group) SA-N-4 f.c.; 1 MR-123 Vympel (Bass Tilt) gun f.c.
Sonar: MGK-335MC Platina (Bull Horn) hull-mounted (3 kHz); Shelon' (Elk Tail) dipping (7.5 kHz)
EW: 2 Bizan'-4B (Watch Dog) intercept (2–18 GHz); 2 16-round PK-16 fixed decoy RL; 4 10-round PK-10 fixed decoy RL
E/O: 4 Spektr-F (Half Cup) infrared detectors
M: CODAG: 1 M-8M (M-88) gas turbine (18,000 shp), 2 Type M-507A diesels (10,000 bhp each); 3 props; 38,000 hp—2 maneuvering propellers
Electric: 1,000 kw tot. (1 × 500-kw, 1 × 300-kw, 1 × 200-kw diesel sets)
Range: 950/27; on diesels alone: 2,500/14; 4,000/10 **Fuel:** 143 tons
Endurance: 9 days **Crew:** 9 officers, 77 enlisted

Remarks: Taken over while under construction. It was announced in 1993 that four more would be built, but work on the 85%-complete *Ternopil* (U 202) was halted from 1995 to 2001, while work on the others never commenced. U 200 was overhauled at Mikolayiv from 9-00 to 5-01.
Hull systems: There are two retracting harbor maneuvering propulsors at the extreme stern. Carries 10.5 tons of lube oil and 27.2 tons of fresh water. Maximum propeller rpm is 585 on the diesels.
Combat systems: Just abaft the mast is a Rakurs (Kolonka-2) backup ringsight director for the 30-mm gun. Carries 304 rounds of 76-mm and 2,000 rounds of 30-mm ammunition. The torpedo tubes have been modified to launch wire-guided torpedoes. The dipping sonar is housed in the after superstructure, lowering through the hull between the starboard and centerline propeller shafts. Has all of the improvements fitted to late-construction examples of the class in the Russian Navy.

♦ 1 ex-Russian Grisha-II class (Project 1124A)
Bldr: Zelenodol'sk Zavod, Kazan

	Laid down	L	In serv.
U 206 Vinnitsya (ex-*Dnepr*)	17-6-76	12-9-76	31-12-76

D: 830 tons (990 fl) **S:** 35 kts
Dim: 71.10 (66.90 wl) × 10.15 (9.50 wl) × 3.45 (hull)
A: 2 twin 57-mm AK-257 DP; 2 12-round RBU-6000 ASW RL (96 RGB-60 rockets); 2 twin 533-mm TT; 2 d.c. racks (6 d.c. each) or mines
Electronics:
Radar: 1 Don-2 nav.; 1 MR-302 Rubka (Strut Curve) surf./air search; 1 MR-103 Bars (Muff Cob) f.c.
Sonar: MGK-355M Argun' (Bull Nose) hull-mounted (3 kHz); Shelon' (Elk Tail) through-hull dipping (7.5 kHz)
EW: 2 Bizan'-4B (Watch Dog) intercept (2–18 GHz)

Vinnitsya (U 206) Hartmut Ehlers, 8-00

Vinnitsya (U 206) Hartmut Ehlers, 8-00

M: CODAG: 1 M-8M (M-813) gas turbine (18,000 shp), 2 M-507A diesels (10,000 bhp each); 3 props; 38,000 hp—2 maneuvering propellers
Electric: 1,000 kw (1 × 500-kw, 1 × 300-kw, 1 × 200-kw diesel sets)
Range: 950/27; 2,750/14; 4,000/10 **Fuel:** 130 tons + 13 tons overload
Endurance: 18 days **Crew:** 60 tot. (79 accomm.)

Remarks: Stricken from the Russian Federal Border Guard 26-11-92 and transferred to the Ukraine Maritime Border Guard 5-7-94; further transferred to the Ukraine Navy in 1-96 and renamed. Sister *Chernigiv* (U 205, ex-*Izmail*) was to be stricken after 9-00.
Hull systems: An official source states that the unsupported endurance is twice that of the former naval units of the Grisha series. Fin stabilizers are fitted.
Combat systems: A second twin 57-mm was substituted for Osa-M SAM system forward. Can carry 2,200 rounds of 57-mm ammunition.

Disposal note: Grisha-III-class corvette *Herson* (U 210, ex-MPK 52) began scrapping at Donuslav early in 2001; the reported sister *Odessa* (U 204) evidently did not exist. Grisha-I-class (Project 1124) corvette *Sumi* (U 209, ex-MPK-43) was scrapped at Il'ychevsk beginning in 7-00. Ex-Russian Petya-III-class (Project 159AE) corvette U 132 was scrapped at Inkerman in 8-96. Petya-II-class (Project 159A) SKR-112, which defected to Ukraine at Odesa on 21-7-92 and was taken over as the first combatant ship in the new Ukrainian Navy (as U 131), was decommissioned to become a memorial at Odesa on 6-4-93.

HYDROFOIL GUIDED-MISSILE PATROL CRAFT [PTGH]

♦ 3 ex-Russian Matka (Vikhr')-class (Project 206MR) semi-hydrofoils
Bldr: Sudostroitel'noye Obyedineniye "Almaz" (Sredniy Neva), Kolpino (In serv. 1979–81)

U 152 Uman' (ex-R-260) U 154 Kakhovka (ex-R-265)
U 153 Pryluky (ex-R-262)

Uman' (U 152) Hartmut Ehlers, 8-00

D: 233 tons (258 fl; 268 max.) **S:** 42 kts
Dim: 38.60 (37.50 wl) × 12.5 (7.6 hull; 5.9 wl) × 2.10 (hull; 3.26 foils)
A: 2 P-15M Termit (SS-N-2C Styx) SSM; 1 76.2-mm 59-cal. AK-176M DP; 1 30-mm 54-cal. AK-630 gatling AA; . . . SA-14/16 shoulder-launched SAMs
Electronics:
Radar: 1 . . . nav.; 1 Garpun (Plank Shave) target detection/tracking; 1 MR-123 Vympel-AM (Bass Tilt) gun f.c.
EW: no intercept equipment; 2 16-round PK-16 decoy RL
M: 3 M-520TM5 diesels; 3 props; 14,400 bhp
Electric: 300 kw tot. (1 × 100-kw DGF2A-100/1500 and 1 × 200-kw DRGA-2A-200/1500 diesel sets; 380 V, 50 Hz a.c.)
Range: 600/35; 1,200/22–24; 1,800/11–12 **Fuel:** 38 tons max. overload
Endurance: 8 days **Crew:** 25–28 tot.

HYDROFOIL GUIDED-MISSILE PATROL CRAFT [PTGH]
(continued)

Kakhovka (U 154) Boris Lemachko, 1998

Remarks: Essentially a missile-armed version of the Turya-class hydrofoil torpedo boat, with a larger superstructure, a 76.2-mm gun forward, and missiles and gatling gun aft. The three were stricken from the Black Sea Fleet 10-1-96 and transferred to Ukraine on the same date.
Disposals: *Konotop* (U 150, ex-R-15), which was transferred and recommissioned 12-8-97 but by late 1998 was inactive at Sevastopil, was transferred to Georgia in 1998. *Tsyurupynsk* (U 151, ex-R-251) was donated to a youth training school at the end of 2001 for use as a stationary training device.
Hull systems: Have a steel hull with aluminum/magnesium alloy superstructure. The stern planes on the surface while the bow is supported by the hydrofoils at high speeds. To improve the ride, both the foils and the transom stern flap are remotely controlled via a Baza 02065 gyro system. In colder waters (below 25° C), the craft can make 43–45 kts on foil.
Combat systems: The original Cheese Cake navigational radar (so called because of its flat-topped cylindrical radome) has been replaced by a small slotted-waveguide set. Positions for EW intercept antennas remain empty. Can employ weapons in Sea State 6. Carry 152 rounds of 76.2-mm and 2,000 rounds of 30-mm ammunition. Have SPO-3 radiation-warning equipment and the R-784 automated radio system.

GUIDED-MISSILE PATROL CRAFT [PTG]

Disposal note: Tarantul-III (Project 1241.1RZ) unit *Kremenchuk* (U 156, ex-R-63, ex-*Kuybyshevskiy Komsomolets*) was stricken around 9-00 and scrapped during 2001.

♦ 1 Tarantul-II (Molnaya) class (Project 1241.1/2)
Bldrs: Sudostroitel'noye Obyedineniye "Almaz," Petrovskiy SY, St. Petersburg and/or Sredniy Neva SY, Kolpino (In serv. 1981–86)

	Laid down	L	In serv.
U 155 Nikopol' (ex-R-54, ex-*Krasnodarskiy Komsomolets*)	21-4-81	18-12-82	30-12-83

Nikopol' (U 155) Boris Lemachko, 7-00

D: 329 tons light; 436 tons normal (469 fl) **S:** 42 kts
Dim: 56.10 (49.50 pp) × 10.20 (8.74 wl) × 2.25 (hull; 4.15 props)
A: 4 P-15M Termit (SS-N-2C Styx) SSM; 1 76.2-mm 59-cal. AK-176 DP; 1 4-round Fasta-4M (SA-N-8) SAM syst. (9M-36 Strela-3M/Gremlin missiles; 2 single 30-mm 54-cal. AK-630M gatling AA
Electronics:
Radar: 1 Kivach-3 nav.; 1 Monolit (Band Stand) missile target detection and tracking; 1 MR-123 Vympel (Bass Tilt) gun f.c.
EW: intercept via Band Stand; 2 16-round PK-16 decoy RL
M: COGAG M-15 plant: 2 M-75 (DMR-76) cruise gas turbines (5,000 shp each), 2 M-70 (PR-77) boost gas turbines (12,000 shp each); 2 props; 34,000 shp
Electric: 700 kw tot. (2 × 200-kw, 1 × 300-kw diesel sets)
Range: 760/43; 1,400/13 **Fuel:** 50 tons **Endurance:** 10 days
Crew: 5 officers, 36 enlisted

Remarks: Transferred 1-8-97.
Hull systems: The cruise gas turbines exhaust through a stack, while the high-speed turbines exhaust through the transom stern, adding their residual thrust to the propulsive power; all four are employed simultaneously via planetary gearing for maximum power.
Combat systems: A Pricep (Light Bulb) cruise missile datalink antenna has been added at the masthead, while the Band Stand radome conceals a missile target acquisition and tracking radar that can also be employed in passive intercept and tracking mode. There are four unoccupied positions for EW antennas. Some 152 rounds of 76.2-mm and 4,000 rounds of 30-mm ammunition are normally carried, and there is emergency stowage for an additional 162 rounds of 76-mm ammunition.

PATROL COMBATANTS [PG]

♦ 2 Russian Pauk-I (Molnaya-2) class (Project 1241.2)
Bldr: Yaroslavl SY, Russia

	In serv.
U 207 Uzgorod (ex-MPK-93)	1982
U 208 Hmelnichkiy (ex-*Morska Ochorona,* ex-MPK-116)	1985

Hmelnichkiy (U 208) Leo Dirkx, 7-01

D: 420 tons (475 fl; 534 max.) **S:** 32 kts (28 sust.)
Dim: 57.60 (49.50 pp) × 10.40 (8.74 wl) × 2.14 (hull; 3.45 max.)
A: 1 76.2-mm AK-176 DP; 1 4-round Fasta-4M (SA-N-8) SAM syst. (16 9M-313 Igla/Gremlin missiles); 1 30-mm 54-cal. AK-630 gatling AA; 2 5-round RBU-1200M ASW RL (30 RGB-12 projectiles); 4 fixed 402-mm OTA-40 ASW TT; 2 d.c. racks (12 BB-1 d.c.)
Electronics:
Radar: 1 Mius (Spin Trough) nav.; 1 Reyd (Peel Cone) nav./surf. search; 1 MR-123 Vympel-AM (Bass Tilt) f.c.
Sonar: MGK-345 Bronza MF hull-mounted and MF dipping (6.5/7.0/7.5 kHz)
EW: Vympel-R2 suite: 2 Half Hat-B intercept; 2 16-round PK-16 decoy RL
M: 2 M-507A or M-517 twin diesels; 2 props; 20,800 bhp (16,180 sust.)
Electric: 500 kw tot. (2 × 200-kw, 1 × 100-kw diesel sets)
Range: 2,000/20; 2,600/14; 1,600/12 (normal fuel; 3,000/12 with max. fuel)
Fuel: 50 tons normal **Endurance:** 10 days
Crew: 5–7 officers, 31–32 enlisted

Remarks: Were stricken from the Black Sea Fleet 10-1-96 and transferred on 12-3-96 (one source indicates that U 208's strike date was 5-7-94). U 207 may not have entered active service yet. Three sisters are in the border guard.
Hull systems: The large housing for a dipping sonar system projects about 1.5 m out from the stern. The large hull-mounted sonar dome is located approximately beneath the gun fire-control radar. The hull is constructed of mild steel, while the middle part of the deck plating, some internal bulkheads, and much of the superstructure are made of aluminum-magnesium alloy.
Combat systems: The combat data system is designated SU-580. There is an SP-521 Rakurs (Kolonka-2) backup ringsight director for the single gatling AA gun; the Bass Tilt radar director can control both the 76.2- and 30-mm guns. The normal ammunition load is 152 rounds of 76-mm (all ready-service, on-mount) and 2,000 rounds of 30-mm. The sonar suite has a range of about 7 km for the dipping component, whose sonar transducer can be lowered to 200 m; MGK-345 applies to both the hull-mounted and dipping sonars.

PATROL BOATS [PB]

♦ 1 ex-Russian Flamingo (Tanya) class (Project 1415)
Bldr: Sosnovka Zavod, Rybinsk, or Yaroslavl Zavod (In serv. 1980s)

U 240 Feodosiya (ex-P 99, ex-RVK-1403)

Feodosiya (U 240) Hartmut Ehlers, 7-00

PATROL BOATS [PB] *(continued)*

D: 42 tons (54 fl) **S:** 11 kts **Dim:** 21.20 × 3.93 × 1.40
A: small arms; 1 AK-17 grenade launcher
Electronics: Radar: 1 Lotsiya nav.
M: 1 Type 3D12A or 3D12L diesel; 1 prop; 300 bhp
Electric: 12 kw tot. (DGR 1A-16/1500 generator)
Range: 200/11 **Endurance:** 5 days **Crew:** 3 tot. + 5 divers

Remarks: Transferred in 1997. Employed as a counterswimmer harbor patrol boat *(protivodivyersionniye kater).* Differs from most Project 1415 units in having continuous bulwarks surrounding the upper deck. Several others in Ukraine service are configured as diving tenders and so forth.

♦ **1 ex-Russian Zhuk (Gryf) class (Project 1400M)**
Bldr: Morye (ex-Yuzhnaya Tochka) Zavod, Feodosiya (In serv. 1980)

U 120 Skadovs'k (ex-PSKA-527)

Skadovs'k (U 120) Hartmut Ehlers, 7-00

D: 35.9 tons (39.7 fl) **S:** 30 kts
Dim: 23.80 (21.70 wl) × 5.00 (3.80 wl) × 1.00 (hull; 1.90 max.)
A: 1 twin 12.7-mm 60-cal. Utës-Ma mg **Electronics:** Radar: 1 Lotsiya nav.
M: 2 M-401 diesels; 2 props; 2,200 bhp
Electric: 48 kw total (2 × 21-kw, 1 × 6-kw diesel sets)
Range: 500/13.5 **Endurance:** 5 days **Crew:** 1 officer, 9 enlisted

Remarks: The former identification is uncertain. Transferred from Russia around 1996–97. Nineteen others serve in the border guard.
Hull systems: Aluminum alloy hull. Capable of operating in up to Sea State 4 or 5. Range is also reported as 700 n.m. at 28 kts and 1,100 n.m. at 15 kts.

MINE COUNTERMEASURES SHIPS AND CRAFT

♦ **2 ex-Russian Natya-I (Akvamarine)-class (Project 266M) fleet minesweepers [MSF]**
Bldr: Sudostroitel'noye Obyedineniye "Almaz" (Sredniy Neva), Kolpino

	In serv.
U 310 Zhovti Vodi (ex-*Razvedchik*)	1977
U 311 Cherkasi (ex-*Zenitchik*)	1974

Cherkasi (U 311) Hartmut Ehlers, 8-00

Zhovti Vodi (U 310) Boris Lemachko, 7-00

D: 715 tons light; 735–750 tons std.; 804–812 tons normal (873 fl)
S: 17.6 kts (16 sust.)
Dim: 61.00 (57.60 wl; 56.00 pp) × 10.20 (9.80 wl) × 2.98 (hull; 3.60 max.)
A: 2 twin 30-mm 65-cal. AK-230M AA; 2 twin 25-mm 80-cal. 2M-3M AA; 2 5-round RBU-1200M ASW RL (30 RGB-12 rockets); 7 KMD-1000 mines or 32 mine disposal charges
Electronics:
Radar: 1 or 2 Don-MN (Don-2) nav.; 1 MR-104 Rys' (Drum Tilt) f.c.
Sonar: MG-69 Lan' or MG-79 Mizen' search MG-26 underwater telephone
M: 2 M-503B-3E diesels; 2 shrouded CP props; 5,000 bhp
Electric: 600 kw tot. (3 × 200-kw DGR-200/1500 diesel sets; 380 V, 50 Hz a.c.)
Range: 1,800/16; 2,700/12; 5,200/10 **Fuel:** 48 tons normal, 87 tons max.
Endurance: 10 days **Crew:** 6 officers, 8 warrant officers, 54 enlisted

Remarks: Transferred to Ukraine in 1997, with U 310 still "in reserve" in 1998 but active by 7-00. Equipped to serve also as ASW escorts, with the RBU-1200 rocket launchers also used for detonating mines. Designed under T. D. Pokhodun.
Hull systems: Have a low-magnetic-signature, aluminum-steel alloy hull. Have the DGR-450/1500P diesel-driven degaussing system. Endurance at 12 kts with a normal 48-ton fuel load is 1,500 n.m. and with 80-ton overload fuel load is 2,700 n.m. All living spaces are air-conditioned.
Combat systems: Sweep gear includes SEMP-3 magnetic and MPT-3 mechanical arrays and a net trawl deployed over the stern ramp. The sonar incorporates a downward-looking, HF, bottomed-mine detection component. Can deploy television minehunting equipment. Have NEL-5 echo sounders.

♦ **2 ex-Russian Sonya (Yakhont)-class (Project 1265) coastal minesweepers [MSC]** Bldr: Avangard Zavod, Petrozavodsk

	In serv.
U 330 Melitopol' (ex-BT-79, ex-*Sevastopol'skiy Komsomolets*)	1979
U 331 Mariupol' (ex-BT-126, ex-*Orenburgskiy Komsomolets*)	1978

Melitopol' (U 330) Igor' Stelanovich, via Boris Lemachko, 5-01

Mariupol' (U 331) Boris Lemachko, 6-00

D: 401 tons (430 fl) **S:** 14 kts
Dim: 48.80 (46.00 wl) × 10.20 (9.20 wl) × 2.40 (mean hull; 2.75 max.)
A: 1 twin 30-mm 65-cal. AK-230M AA; 1 twin 25-mm 80-cal. 2M-3M AA; 5 mines
Electronics:
Radar: 1 Mius (Spin Trough) nav.
Sonar: MG-89 Serna HF hull-mounted; MG-35 underwater telephone; NEL-MZB echo sounder
M: 2 DRA-210-B diesels; 2 3-bladed CP props; 2,000 bhp—2 low-speed thrusters
Electric: 350 kw tot. (3 × 100-kw, 1 × 50-kw diesel sets; 380 V, 50 Hz a.c.)
Range: 1,700/10 **Fuel:** 27.1 tons **Endurance:** 15 days
Crew: 5–6 officers, 26–40 enlisted (45 tot. accomm.)

Remarks: Transferred 1-10-96. *Yakhont,* the program name, refers to a kind of sapphire. Designed under Valeriy Ivanovich Nemudrov. U 331 was refitted during 1997–98.
Hull systems: Wooden construction with GRP hull sheathing. Bollard pull: 10 tons at 9 kts.
Combat systems: Carry AT-5 acoustic, PEMT-4 magnetic loop, and BKT-2 mechanical sweep equipment. Can tow CT-2 solenoidal magnetic minesweeping buoys and net-sweep arrays and can lay linear mine disposal charges. Are also able to employ KIU-1 underwater television mine location equipment. Equipped with an underwater telephone. The 25-mm mount is aimed by the operator, while the 30-mm mount is controlled by an SP-521 Rakurs (Kolonka-1) ringsight director.

MINE COUNTERMEASURES SHIPS AND CRAFT *(continued)*

♦ 1 ex-Russian Yevgenya (Korund)-class (Project 1258) inshore minesweeper [MSI]

Bldr: Sudostroitel'noye Obyedineniye "Almaz" (Sredniy Neva), Kolpino (In serv. 1970–76)

U 360 GENICHESK (ex-RT-214)

Genichesk (U 360) Boris Lemachko, 4-97

D: 88.5 tons light; 94.5 tons normal (97.9 fl) **S:** 11 kts
Dim: 26.13 (24.20 wl) × 5.90 (5.10 wl) × 1.38
A: 1 twin 14.5-mm 93-cal. 2M-7 AA; 1 7-round MRG-1 grenade launcher; 4 d.c. (+ 8 emergency stowage)
Electronics:
Radar: 1 Mius (Spin Trough) or Kivach nav.
Sonar: MG-7 HF dipping
M: 2 Type 3D12 diesels; 2 props; 600 bhp—hydraulic slow-speed drive
Electric: 100 kw tot. (2 × 50-kw diesel sets)
Range: 400/10 **Fuel:** 2.7 tons **Endurance:** 3 days
Crew: 1 officer, 9 enlisted + 2–3 clearance divers

Remarks: Transferred 12-3-96. Designed under V. I. Blinov.
Hull systems: GRP hull. Navigational equipment includes a Girya-MA gyrocompass and NEL-7 echo sounder.
Combat systems: Can employ a Neva-1 television minehunting system, useful to 30-m depths, which dispenses marker buoys to permit later disposal of mines by divers or explosive charges. The sonar is lowered via one of the stern davits. Carries VKT-1 mechanical, AT-2 acoustic, and SEMT-1 solenoid coil sweep gear.

AMPHIBIOUS WARFARE SHIPS AND CRAFT

♦ 1 ex-Russian Ropucha-I-class (Project 775) tank landing ship [LST]

Bldr: Stocznia Polnocna, Gdansk, Poland (In serv. 1985)

U 402 KONSTYANTYN OLSHANSKYY (ex-*Konstantin Ol'shanskiy,* BDK-56)

Konstyantyn Olshanskyy (U 402) Hartmut Ehlers, 7-00

Konstyantyn Olshanskyy (U 402)—with bow doors open and ramp extended Leo Dirkx, 7-01

D: 2,768 tons light; 3,450 tons normal (4,080 fl) **S:** 17.5 kts
Dim: 112.50 (105.00 wl) × 15.00 × 3.70 (aft, loaded)
A: 2 twin 57-mm 70-cal. AK-725 DP; 2 40-round 122-mm UMS-73 Grad-M artillery RL (360 BM-21 rockets); up to 92 1-ton mines
Electronics:
Radar: 2 Don-2 or Vaygach (Palm Frond) nav.; 1 MR-302 Rubka (Strut Curve) surf./air search; 1 MR-103 Bars (Muff Cob) gun f.c.
M: 2 Type 16ZVB 40/48 16-cyl., 500-rpm diesels; 2 props; 19,200 bhp
Electric: 1,920 kw tot. (3 × 640 kw; Cegielski-Sulzer 6A25 diesels driving)
Range: 3,500/16; 6,000/12 **Endurance:** 30 days (with landing force)
Crew: 8 officers, 79 enlisted (accomm. for 17 officers, 81 enlisted) + 150 troops

Remarks: Stricken from the Black Sea Fleet 10-1-96 and transferred 12-3-96. Builder's Project B-23.
Hull systems: The hull has a molded depth of 8.65 m amidships and is equipped with a "beak" bow projection to aid in beaching. Fully degaussed. Has a forced ventilation system with NBC warfare filters. No vehicle cargo is carried on the upper deck; the hatch serves for loading by crane and for ventilation when vehicle motors are running. There are both bow and stern doors, permitting roll-on/roll-off loading. Cargo capacity: 450 tons; usable deck space: 600 m^2. Alternate cargo loads are 10 41-ton tanks with 40 vehicle crew and 150 troops; 12 amphibious tanks with 36 vehicle crew; or a mix of three 41-ton tanks, three 120-mm mine-throwers, three armored cars, four trucks, five light vehicles, and 123 troops.
Combat systems: Although the entire class was intended to receive two UMS-73 barrage rocket launchers on the forecastle, only the six most recently completed (among them, U 402) actually carried the weapons. Some 20 smoke floats can be carried aft. Mines can only be carried when there is no amphibious cargo.

♦ 1 ex-Russian Alligator (Tapir) class (Project 1171) tank landing ship [LST]

Bldr: Yantar Zavod, Kaliningrad

	Laid down	L	In serv.
U 401 RIVNE (ex-*Il'ya Azarov,* BDK-104)	17-10-69	31-3-70	10-6-71

Rivne (U 401)—when in layup at Odesa Werner Globke, 8-97

D: 2,760 tons light; 2,905 tons std. (4,360 fl) **S:** 16.5 kts (16 sust.)
Dim: 113.1 (105.0 pp) × 15.6 × 4.10 (mean hull; 6.15 aft, loaded)
A: 1 twin 57-mm 70-cal. ZIF-31B DP; 1 40-round 122-mm UMS-73 Grad-M artillery RL (160 rockets)
Electronics:
Radar: 2 Don-2 and/or Mius (Spin Trough) nav.
E/O: 1 Squeeze Box multisensor surveillance/rocket f.c.
M: 2 Type 58A diesels; 2 props; 9,000 bhp
Electric: 740 kw tot. (2 × 270-kw, 2 × 100-kw diesel sets)
Range: 3,500/16.5; 8,000/15 **Endurance:** 15 days (10 with landing force)
Crew: 5 officers, 50 enlisted + 440 troops

Remarks: Transferred in 4-96, although she had been lying unmaintained and without armament at Odesa for several years. A refit had been completed as of 9-01, and the ship is again operational.
Hull systems: Cargo capacity is about 600 tons for beaching and 1,750 tons in freighting service; can carry 20 tanks, plus lighter vehicles on the upper decks. The tank deck is 90 m long and totals 850 m^2 in area. Has vehicle ramps fore and aft and one 7.5-ton KE29 crane. Nominal vehicle capacity is 20 MAZ-543, 52 ZIL-131, or 85 GAZ-66 trucks. Troops are accommodated below the tank deck, in considerable discomfort, in the lower, No. 3 hold.
Combat systems: The open 57-mm gun mounting is locally controlled; 1,200 rounds of ammunition are normally carried. The communications suite can handle six channels simultaneously.

♦ 1 ex-Russian Polnocny-C class (Project 773) medium landing ship [LSM]

Bldr: Stocznia Polnocna, Gdansk, Poland (In serv. 1971)

U 410 KIROVOGRAD (ex-SDK-137)

Kirovograd (U 410)—prior to refit and activation Werner Globke, 8-97

AMPHIBIOUS WARFARE SHIPS AND CRAFT *(continued)*

D: 920 tons (1,192 fl) **S:** 16 kts
Dim: 81.30 (76.00 wl) × 9.30 (9.00 wl) × 1.20 (fwd; 2.60 aft)
A: 2 twin 30-mm 65-cal. AK-230 AA; 2 18-round 140-mm WM-18 barrage RL; 4 Fasta-4M (SA-N-8) SAM syst. (32 Strela-3M/Grail missiles)
Electronics: Radar: 1 Mius (Spin Trough) nav.; 1 MR-104 Rys' (Drum Tilt) f.c.
M: 2 Type 40DM diesels; 2 props; 4,400 bhp
Range: 900/16; 3,000/12 **Endurance:** 3 days
Crew: 5 officers, 36 enlisted + 160 troops

Remarks: Transferred from the Black Sea Fleet in 1994 but not operated until a refit was completed during 2001. A lengthened and broadened version of the Polnocny-B, with a 53.3-m-long. 6.7-m-wide vehicle deck. Carries up to 250 tons of cargo. Differs from near-sister *Grunwald* in the Polish Navy in having a full-length tank deck and no command facilities.

♦ 2 Pomornik (Zubr)-class (Project 1232.2) air-cushion vehicle landing craft [LCUA]

Bldr: Morye (ex-Yuzhnaya Tochka) Zavod, Feodosiya

	In serv.
U 420 Donets'k	26-6-93
U 424 Artemivs'k (ex-MDK-123)	. . .

Donets'k (U 420) Boris Lemachko, 7-99

D: 340 tons light; 415 tons normal (550 fl) **S:** 63 kts (55 sust.)
Dim: 57.3 (56.2 hull) × 25.6 (22.0 hull) × 21.9 (high)
A: 2 4-round Fasta-4M (SA-N-8) SAM syst. (32 9M-36 Igla-1M/Gremlin missiles); 2 single 30-mm 54-cal. AK-630M gatling AA; 2 22-round 140-mm MS-227 Ogon' retractable artillery RL (132 rockets); up to 80 mines in lieu of vehicle cargo
Electronics:
Radar: 1 SRN-207 Ekran (Curl Stone-B) nav.; 1 MR-123 Vympel (Bass Tilt) gun f.c.
E/O: 1 DVU-3 (Quad Look) surveillance/f.c.
M: 5 NK-12MV (M-70) gas turbines (12,100 shp each/10,000 shp sust.; 2 to power lift fans); 3 ducted CP airscrew propellers, 4 NO-10 lift fans; 36,300 shp for propulsion
Electric: 300 or 400 kw tot. (4 × 75- or 100-kw GTG-110 gas turbine sets)
Range: 300/55 with 130-ton payload; 1,000/55 light **Fuel:** 56 tons (180 m^3)
Endurance: 5 days (1 with full troop complement)
Crew: 4 officers, 7 warrant officers, 20 enlisted + 140–360 troops

Remarks: U 420 was announced to be in Ukrainian service in 1993. Sister *Ivan Bohun* (U 421) was building at Morye Zavod but was left incomplete until reordered for Greece in 1999, along with *Horlivka* (U 423, ex-Russian MDK-93). U 424 was one of the three Black Sea Fleet units handed over to Ukraine at Donuzlav 1-3-96 and was recommissioned 27-3-96. Too large for shipboard transportation, they are intended for short-range independent assault operations. There are apparently significant reliability problems with the design. U 420 was badly damaged 23-5-95, requiring two months of repairs.
Disposals: Sister *Kramators'k* (U 422, ex-MDK-57) was to be stricken after 9-00. *Ivan Bohun* (U 421) and *Horlivka* (U 423, ex-MDK-93) were refurbished in 2000–01 for sale to Greece.
Hull systems: The dimensions above include the flexible skirt in inflated condition. Were originally intended to have a 16-year service life. The vehicle deck can hold up to 10 BTR-70 armored amphibious personnel transport vehicles or three T-80B main battle tanks plus a detachment of infantry—or up to 140 troops and 130 tons of combat cargo. Have small bow and stern ramps. The vehicle cargo deck has an area of 400 m^2. Navigational equipment includes a gyrocompass, Decca radio-navigation system receiver, drift indicator, and NAVSAT receiver. Three of the gas-turbine engines are mounted on pylons and drive airscrew propellers; they are equipped with exhaust thrust diverters to enhance mobility. The lift-fan gas turbines drive four blowers to maintain skirt pressure and are mounted near the stern in the wing compartments and exhaust through the stern.
Combat systems: The Quad Look electro-optical device is a modified Squeeze Box that has no weather cover; there is also a television camera mounted just below the pilothouse. The navigational radar is mounted within a lozenge-shaped radome. The retractable artillery rocket launchers are located near the bow in the hull wing-walls and are reloaded below decks by hand.

♦ 1 ex-Russian Ondatra (Akula)-class (Project 1176) landing craft [LCM]

Bldr: . . . . . . (In serv. 1975)

U 430 Svatove (ex-*Vil'*, ex-DK-305)

D: 90 tons normal (107.3 fl) **S:** 11.5 kts **Dim:** 24.50 × 6.00 × 1.55
A: none **Electronics:** Radar: 1 . . . nav.
M: 2 Type 3D12 diesels; 2 props; 600 bhp **Range:** 330/10; 500/5
Endurance: 2 days **Crew:** 6 enlisted

Remarks: Transferred 31-7-96. In all, 29 were built for use aboard the Russian *Ivan Rogov*–class landing ships. The cargo well measures 13.7 × 3.9 m and can accommodate one 40-ton tank or up to 50 tons of general cargo; some 20 troops/vehicle crew can be carried.

Svatove (U 430) Boris Lemachko, 3-99

♦ 1 T-4-class (Project 1785) landing craft [LCM]

Bldr: . . . . . . (In serv. 1970)

U . . . Tarpan (ex-DK-455)

Tarpan (U . . .)—still with Russian Navy pennant 538 Boris Lemachko, 2000

D: 35 tons light (93 fl) **S:** 10 kts (light) **Dim:** 20.4 × 5.4 × 1.2 (max. aft)
M: 2 Type 3D6 diesels; 2 props; 300 bhp
Range: 300/8 **Endurance:** 2 days **Crew:** 2–3 tot.

Remarks: Transferred to Ukraine 31-7-96; was under refit in 1997–98. Can accommodate up to 50 tons of cargo on the 9.5 × 3.9–m vehicle deck.

AUXILIARIES

♦ 1 Bereza (SR-28)-class (Polish Project 130) deperming ship [ADG]

Bldr: Stocznia Polnocna, Gdansk, Poland (In serv. 1987)

U 811 Balta (ex-SR-568)

Balta (U 811) Hartmut Ehlers, 9-98

D: 1,811 tons (2,096 fl) **S:** 13.6 kts **Dim:** 69.50 × 13.80 × 3.98
A: none **Electronics:** Radar: 1 Mius-M (Kivach) nav.
M: 2 Zgoda-Sulzer 8AL25/30, 750-rpm diesels; 2 CP Kort-nozzle props; 2,940 bhp—bow-thruster
Electric: 1,185 kVA + 1,550 kw tot. (2 × 480 kVA, 1 × 225 kVA; 2 × 645 kw, 1 × 260 kw)
Range: 1,000/13.6; 1,200/10 **Fuel:** 170 tons **Endurance:** 30 days **Crew:** 45 tot.

Remarks: Transferred 1-8-97. Intended for "degaussing surface ships and submarines, conducting magnetic field measurements of ships and vessels, [and] regulating ground fault neutralizers."
Hull systems: Can service two ships simultaneously. Has three laboratories, a machine shop, and a cable hold. A large crane is fitted aft to handle deperming cables.

AUXILIARIES *(continued)*

Disposal note: Ex-Russian Lama-class missile transport [AEM] *Kolomiya* (U 533, ex-PRTB-13) was scrapped at Inkerman, beginning in 1-00.

♦ 1 ex-Russian Muna-class (Project 1823) torpedo transport [AE]
Bldr: Vympel Zavod, Nizhniy Novgorod, Russia (In serv. 1968)

U 754 Dzhankoy (ex-VTR-93, ex-VTR-69, ex-MTB-169250)

D: 441 tons light (686 fl) **S:** 11.5 kts **Dim:** 51.50 × 8.44 × 2.70
A: none **Electronics:** Radar: 1 Mius (Spin Trough) nav.
M: 1 Type 6DR 30/50 diesel; 1 prop; 600 bhp
Range: 2,240/11.4; 4,950/9.3 **Endurance:** 15 days
Crew: 15 tot. + 7 passengers

Remarks: Stricken from the Black Sea Fleet 1-10-96 and transferred to Ukraine 1-8-97. Has a single 3.2-ton-capacity electric crane positioned between four small holds which, on this ship, are intended to accommodate torpedoes. Cargo capacity: 175 tons.

Disposal note: Mayak-class provisions transport *Yalta* (U 755, ex-*Buzuluk*) was sold to a private firm 8-12-00.

♦ 1 ex-Russian Onega-class (Project 1806) signature monitoring ship [AG] (Nonoperational)
Bldr: Zelenodol'sk Zavod, Russia (In serv. 1987)

U 812 *Severodonets'k* (ex-SFP-322)

D: 1,350 tons (1,460 fl) **S:** 14 kts **Dim:** 80.00 × 11.60 × 3.17–3.27 **A:** none
Electronics:
Radar: 1 Don-2 nav.
Sonar: Arktika-M passive array; active dipping set
M: 2 diesels; 2 props; 2,800 bhp
Range: 1,000/10 **Endurance:** 15 days **Crew:** 45 tot.

Remarks: Transferred in 1997. In Russian service, was officially said to be intended to "measure acoustic, magnetic, low-frequency, electromagnetic, electric, and heat fields set up by ships and submarines for compliance with existing standards and specifications." Said to be in need of a refit and was not active as of 1998.
Hull systems: SFP-designated units were usually seen with two side-by-side modular structures topped with two rectangular air vents mounted at the fore end of the after deckhouse platform (which was originally intended to be a helicopter platform); the devices may be employed in air sampling.

♦ 1 ex-Russian Potok (Smen')-class (Project 1236) torpedo trials ship [AGE]
Bldr: Zelenodol'sk Zavod, Russia (In serv. 1972)

U 863 Artsiz (ex-OS-100)

D: 750 tons (860 fl) **S:** 17 kts **Dim:** 72.1 × 9.4 × 2.5
A: 1 533-mm TT; 1 402-mm TT **Electronics:** Radar: 1 Don-2 nav.
M: 2 Type 40-D diesels; 2 props; 4,000 bhp
Range: 2,500/12 **Endurance:** 5 days **Crew:** 30 tot.

Remarks: Transferred 1-8-97. Current status is uncertain; may be inactive. The trainable torpedo tubes are on the bow. A large crane aft is used for retrieval of expended weapons.

Disposal note: T-43-class trials ship *Svitlovods'k* (U 861, ex-OS-35, ex-MT-811) burned out during 2-01 and was left derelict.

♦ 1 Modified Kamchatka–class (Project 12884) fleet flagship [AGF]
Bldr: Chernomorets Zavod, Mikolayiv

	Laid down	L	In serv.
U 510 Slavutych (ex-*Pridneprovye*, SSV-189)	7-88	1-90	27-7-92

Slavutych (U 510)—visiting New York City — William H. Rau, 7-00

D: 4,460 tons (5,010 fl) **S:** 14.8 kts **Dim:** 106.02 × 16.01 × 6.00
A: 1 single 30-mm AK-306 gatling AA; 2 twin 14.5-mm 93-cal. AA; 2 4-round Fasta-4M (SA-N-8) SAM syst. (16 Strela-2M/SA-14 Gremlin missiles); 2 single 45-mm saluting cannon
Electronics:
Radar: 2 Vaygach-U (Palm Frond) nav.
EW: . . . intercept; 2 16-round PK-16 decoy RL
M: 1 diesel; 1 prop; 5,236 bhp **Range:** 13,000/14
Endurance: 90 days **Crew:** 19 officers, 110 enlisted

Remarks: Said to have been begun for the Soviet navy as an intelligence collector, this ship is essentially a sister to the now-stricken *Kamchatka* of the Russian Pacific Fleet but lacks the tall and bulky tower mast amidships. Has been adapted to serve as the Ukrainian fleet flagship. Visited New York during 2000. The lightweight gatling AA guns do not have radar directors; optical SP-521 Rakurs (Kolonka-2) lead-computing directors are mounted within nearby enclosed cupolas. Based at Sevastopil.

♦ 1 ex-Russian Amur-class (Project 304) flag and staff ship [AGF]
Bldr: A. Warski SY, Szczecin, Poland (In serv. 1970)

U 803 Krasnodon (ex-PM-9)

Krasnodon (U 803)—as PM-9 — Werner Globke, 8-97

D: 4,000 tons (5,490 fl) **S:** 14 kts **Dim:** 121.70 × 17.00 × 4.63
A: none **Electronics:** Radar: 1 Don-2 nav.
M: 2 diesels; 1 prop; 3,000 bhp
Range: 7,800/10; 13,200/8 **Endurance:** 40 days **Crew:** 145 tot.

Remarks: Transferred 1-8-97. Completed an overhaul and modifications during 2001 to serve as a command and staff support ship for ships based at Sevastopil. Can serve surface ships and submarines with basic repair facilities and carry 280 tons of spare parts. Has two 3-ton cranes and one 1.5-ton crane.

♦ 1 ex-Russian Sura-class (Project 145) mooring-buoy tender [AGL]
Bldr: VEB Neptunwerft, Rostock, East Germany (In serv. 1976)

U 852 Shostka (ex-KIL-33)

Shostka (U 852) — Boris Lemachko, 5-00

D: 2,260 tons (3,150 fl) **S:** 13.2 kts
Dim: 87.30 (80.20 hull; 68.00 pp) × 14.80 × 5.10
Electronics: Radar: 2 Don-2 nav.
M: 4 diesels, electric drive; 2 props; 2,240 shp (1,780 sust.)
Range: 4,000/10 **Endurance:** 20 days **Crew:** 40 tot.

Remarks: 2,366 grt. Stricken from the Black Sea Fleet 10-1-96 and transferred to Ukraine 1-8-97.
Hull systems: Can carry 460 tons of cargo in the hold amidships and 300 tons of cargo fuel. The stern rig, which can lift 65 tons, is used for buoy handling and salvage. Mooring buoys are stowed amidships and moved aft for handling by the stern gallows rig via a chain-haul system. There is also a 5-ton electric crane to port and a 65-ton heavy-lift boom amidships, the latter tending the buoy stowage holds. The diesel propulsion generator plant is forward.

♦ 1 Kamenka-class (Project 871) hydrographic survey ship [AGS]
Bldr: Stocznia Polnocna, Gdansk, Poland (In serv. 1979–81)

U 600 GS-82

D: 590 tons (703 fl) **S:** 13.7 kts **Dim:** 53.50 × 9.40 × 2.62
Electronics: Radar: 1 Don-2 nav.
M: 2 Cegielski-Sulzer 6 NVD-48 diesels; 2 CP props; 1,765 bhp
Range: 2,000/11 **Endurance:** 15 days **Crew:** 24 tot.

Remarks: Stricken from the Black Sea Fleet 10-1-96; became Ukraine property in 12-3-96 but retains the original Russian alphanumeric name. Similar to the Biya-class units but has more facilities for stowing and handling buoys. No survey launch is carried.

♦ 1 ex-Russian Muna-class (Project 1824B) survey ship [AGS]
Bldr: Nakhodka SY (In serv. 1970–78)

U 512 Pereyaslav (ex-Uglomer, GS-13)

D: 457 tons (688 fl) **S:** 11 kts **Dim:** 51.50 × 8.40 × 2.70
Electronics: Radar: 1 Mius (Spin Trough) nav.
M: 1 Type 6DR 30/50 diesel; 1 prop; 600 bhp
Range: 1,700/10 **Endurance:** 15 days **Crew:** 22 tot.

Remarks: Former ammunition lighter, extensively converted at a Baltic-area shipyard to serve as a coastal survey ship (completed in 7-90). Stricken 10-1-96 and later transferred to Ukraine. A small deckhouse covers the former forward ammunition hold area, while two kingposts with derricks were stepped forward of the pilothouse. The original electric crane was retained.

AUXILIARIES *(continued)*

♦ **2 ex-Russian Biya-class (Project 870) hydrographic survey ships [AGS]** Bldr: Stocznia Polnocna, Gdansk, Poland (In serv. 1968–72)

U 601 GS-212 U 603 GS-273

D: 750 tons (fl) **S:** 13 kts **Dim:** 55.0 × 9.2 × 2.6
Electronics: Radar: 1 Don-2 nav.
M: 2 diesels; 2 CP props; 1,200 bhp **Range:** 4,700/11
Fuel: 90 tons **Endurance:** 15 days **Crew:** 25 tot.

Remarks: Stricken from the Black Sea Fleet 10-1-96. Retain their original Russian Navy alphanumeric names. Fourteen were originally built for Soviet Navy use. Similar to the Kamenka class, but with a longer superstructure and less buoy-handling space; carry one survey launch and have one 5-ton buoy crane. Laboratory space: 15 m^2.

♦ **1 ex-Russian Moma-class (Project 861) survey ship [AGS]** Bldr: Stocznia Polnocna, Gdansk, Poland (In serv. 1969)

U 602 Alchevsk (ex-*Berezan'*)

D: 1,140 tons (1,502 fl) **S:** 15 kts **Dim:** 73.30 (64.20 pp) × 11.20 (10.80 wl) × 3.80
Electronics: Radar: 2 Don-2 nav.
M: 2 Zgoda-Sulzer 6TD48 diesels; 2 CP props; 3,600 bhp
Range: 8,000/11 **Endurance:** 25 days **Crew:** 41 tot. (civilian)

Remarks: *Berezan'* and sisters *Liman* and *Okean* (ex-SSV-518) were transferred prior to 1992 to the custody of the cities of Kerch', Feodosiya, and Odesa, respectively, for use as navigational aids tenders. *Liman* was stricken 5-7-94, but was active again in Russian Navy service in 4-99. *Okean* reverted to Russian control and was sold for scrap during 7-01, and *Berezan'* subsequently reverted to Black Sea Fleet control, but was stricken 10-1-96 and transferred to Ukraine in 1997. Sister *Simferopol'* operates as a training ship and intelligence collector (see under [AXT]).
Hull systems: Carries one survey launch and a 7-ton crane, and has four laboratories, totaling 35 m^2.

♦ **1 ex-Russian Keyla-class (Project 740) cargo ship [AK]** Bldr: . . . SY, Budapest, Hungary (In serv. 1958–66)

U 753 Kriviy Rig (ex-*Mezen'*)

D: 854 tons light (2,178 fl) **S:** 10.7 kts **Dim:** 78.5 (71.4 pp) × 10.5 × 4.6
Electronics: Radar: 1 or 2 Don-2 or Mius (Spin Trough) nav.
M: 1 Lang 8 LD315RF diesel; 1 prop; 1,000 bhp **Electric:** 300 kw tot.
Range: 4,200/10.7 **Fuel:** 72 tons **Crew:** 26 tot.

Remarks: 1,296 grt/1,280 dwt. Stricken from Black Sea Fleet 10-1-96, transferred during 4-96, and recommissioned 1-8-97. Carries 1,100 tons of cargo. Has one 10-ton and six 2.5-ton cranes. Alternate diesel engine designation: 84RN 31.5/45.

Disposal note: Of the two Modified *Vytegrales*–class (Project 596KU) former space event support ships transferred from the Russian Black Sea Fleet during 1-96, *Chernivitsi* (U 703, ex-PSK-210, ex-*Kirishi*) and *Ivano-Frankivs'k* (U 704, ex-*Taman'*, ex-*Suzdal'*) were scrapped at Aliaga, Turkey, beginning 25-9-00 and 28-10-00, respectively. *Dubna*-class oiler *Kerch'* (U 758, ex-*Sventa*), *Boris Chilikin*–class replenishment oiler *Makiievka* (U 757, ex-*Boris Chilikin*), and Klaz'ma-class cable layer *Noviy Bug* (U 851, ex-*Tsna*) were for sale at Sevastopil as of 12-00.

♦ **1 ex-Russian Goryn'-class (Project 563S) rescue tug [ARS]** Bldr: Rauma-Repola, Finland (In serv. 1983)

U 705 Kremenets' (ex-SB-524, ex-MB-108)

Kremenets' (U 705) Leo Dirkx, 7-01

D: 1,650 tons (2,200 fl) **S:** 13.5 kts **Dim:** 63.50 × 14.30 (13.80 wl) × 5.20
Electronics: Radar: 2 Don-2 nav.
M: 1 Russkiy Dizel Type 67N diesel; 3,500 bhp
Range: 8,000/12 **Endurance:** 40 days **Crew:** 40 tot. (civilian)

Remarks: Stricken from the Black Sea Fleet 10-1-96 and transferred to Ukraine in summer 1997. Former fleet tug, redesignated as a salvage tug while in Russian service; can be distinguished from standard tug version by the electrohydraulic crane and small tripod mast abaft the stack. Probably was fitted with an MG-26 underwater telephone.

♦ **1 ex-Russian Okhtenskiy (Goliat)-class (Project 733S) rescue tug [ARS]** Bldr: Petrozavod SY, St. Petersburg (In serv. 1962)

U 706 Izyaslav (ex-SB-15)

D: 759 tons (934 fl) **S:** 13.2 kts **Dim:** 47.30 (43.00 pp) × 10.30 × 4.20
Electronics: Radar: 1 or 2 Don-2 or Mius (Spin Trough) nav.
M: diesel-electric: 2 Type D5D50 (6ChN 30/38) diesels, 2 generator sets (950 kw each); 1 prop; 1,500 shp
Electric: 340 kw tot. **Range:** 8,000/11 **Fuel:** 197 tons
Endurance: 25 days **Crew:** 51 tot. (civilian) + naval diving party

Remarks: Stricken from Black Sea Fleet 10-1-96 and transferred in 4-96. Former Russian designation was SB (*Spastel'niy Buksir,* Rescue Tug), hence the "S" suffix to the project number. Sister *Kovel'* (U 831, ex-Russian MB-51) is equipped as a standard seagoing tug [ATA] (q.v.). Principal characteristics are essentially identical to the general fleet-tug version, except that the rescue tugs were equipped to support divers and were able to act as submarine safety ships. Has a Kama hull-mounted underwater telephone. Bollard pull is 20 tons. There is a 5-ton derrick.

♦ **1 ex-Russian Sorum-class (Project 745) seagoing tug [ATA]** Bldr: Yaroslavl Zavod (In serv. 1973)

U 830 Korets' (ex-MB-30)

Korets' (U 830) Hartmut Ehlers, 8-00

D: 1,210 tons (1,620 fl) **S:** 13.8 kts **Dim:** 55.50 × 12.60 × 4.60
Electronics: Radar: 2 Don-2 nav.
M: 2 Type 2D42 (6ChN 30/38) diesels, electric drive; 1 prop; 2,500 shp
Range: 6,200/11 **Fuel:** 322 tons **Endurance:** 40 days
Crew: 35 tot. (civilian) + 40 passengers/rescuees

Remarks: Transferred from Black Sea Fleet 1-8-97. Russian and Ukrainian type designation MB means *Morskiye Buksir* (Seagoing Tug). Has blanking plates for two twin 30-mm AA mounts forward.

♦ **1 ex-Russian Okhtenskiy (Goliat)-class (Project 733) seagoing tug [ATA]** Bldr: Petrozavod SY, St. Petersburg (In serv. 1965)

U 831 Kovel' (ex-MB-51)

D: 759 tons (934 fl) **S:** 13.2 kts **Dim:** 47.30 (43.00 pp) × 10.30 × 4.20
Electronics: Radar: 1 or 2 Don-2 or Spin Trough nav.
M: diesel-electric: 2 Type D5D50 (6ChN 30/38) diesels, 2 generator sets (950 kw each); 1 prop; 1,500 shp
Electric: 340 kw tot. **Range:** 8,000/11 **Fuel:** 197 tons
Endurance: 25 days **Crew:** 35 tot.

Remarks: Transferred 1-8-98. Sister *Izyaslav* (U 706, ex-Russian SB-15) is equipped as a submarine safety ship/rescue tug [ARS] (q.v.).

♦ **1 ex-Russian Voda-class (Project 561) water tanker [AWT]** Bldr: Yantar Zavod 820, Kaliningrad (In serv. 1957)

U 756 Sudak (ex-*Sura,* ex-MVT-19)

Sudak (U 756) Hartmut Ehlers, 8-00

D: 982 tons light (2,255 fl) **S:** 12 kts **Dim:** 81.30 × 11.40 × 3.44 (1.65 light)
Electronics: Radar: 1 Don-2 or Mius (Spin Trough)
M: 2 Russkiy Dizel 8DR30/50 diesels; 2 props; 1,600 bhp
Electric: 150 kw tot. (1 × 100-kw, 1 × 50-kw diesel sets; 380 V, 50 Hz a.c.)
Range: 2,900/10; 3,500/7 **Endurance:** 15 days **Crew:** 22 tot. (40 accomm.)

Remarks: Transferred in summer 1997. Russian class name: MVT-6. Cargo: 700 tons feedwater, 300 tons potable water. Has one 3-ton derrick for hose handling.

AUXILIARIES *(continued)*

♦ **1 ex-Russian Moma-class (Project 861M) training ship [AXT]**
Bldr: Stocznia Polnocna, Gdansk, Poland (In serv. 1968–74)

U 511 SIMFEROPOL' (ex-*Yupiter*)

Simferopol' (U 511) Boris Lemachko, 7-00

D: 1,260 tons (1,600 fl) **S:** 16 kts **Dim:** 73.3 (64.2 pp) × 10.8 × 3.9
A: removed **Electronics:** Radar: 2 Don-2 nav.
M: 2 Zgoda-Sulzer 6TD48 diesels; 2 CP props; 3,600 bhp
Range: 8,000/11 **Fuel:** 220 tons **Crew:** 85 tot.

Remarks: Former intelligence collector (adapted from the standard survey/navaids tender ship design), transferred to Ukraine 1-3-96 and recommissioned the same date. In Russian service, had new superstructures added in the area forward of the bridge and new masts. The Ukraine Navy officially refers to the ship as a training vessel, although she performed in an intelligence collection role as recently as 7-97. The nameboard on the ship continues to be spelled *Simferopol',* although a strict Ukrainian transliteration would be *Simferopil.*

SERVICE CRAFT

♦ **1 ex-Russian Vydra-class (Project 106K) trials craft [YAGE]**
Bldr: Komintern Zavod, Kherson, Ukraine (In serv. 1966)

U 832 KOROSTEN' (ex-*Tarpan,* OS-237, ex-. . .)

Korosten' (U 832)—stern portion Werner Globke, 8-97

D: 308 tons light (442 fl) **S:** 10.5 kts
Dim: 54.50 (50.00 pp) × 7.70 (7.50 wl) × 2.25 (mean hull)
Electronics: Radar: 2 Don-2 nav.
M: 2 Type 3D-2 diesels; 2 Kort-nozzle props; 600 bhp
Range: 1,400/10 (loaded) **Endurance:** 8 days **Crew:** 12 tot.

Remarks: Stricken from the Black Sea Fleet 10-1-96 and transferred in 1997. One of 46 built for Russian use as utility landing craft, later employed in local service as utility cargo carriers; current function unknown. The cargo deck measures 30.0 × 4.5 m and can accommodate up to 176 tons of vehicles or cargo (6 ZIL-131 or 10 GAZ-66 trucks). Sister *Bilyaïvka* (U 904, ex-Russian MBSS-233200) is configured as a stores carrier [YF] (q.v.).

♦ **1 ex-Russian Shalanda (BSS-53150)-class (Project 431) trials craft [YAGE]** Bldr: . . . (In serv. 1958)

U 860 KAMYANKHA (ex-*Kasatka,* OS-94, ex-MBSS-155150)

D: 158 tons light (326 fl) **S:** 8.2 kts **Dim:** 36.00 × 6.90 × 2.00
Electronics: Radar: 1 . . . nav.
M: 1 Type 3D-12 diesel; 1 prop; 300 bhp
Range: 500/8 **Endurance:** 10 days **Crew:** 8 tot.

Remarks: Stricken from the Black Sea Fleet 10-1-96. A former stores lighter [YF], altered to perform a research function; is one of a group of Shalanda-class units originally configured to transport slaked lime to support Quebec-class (Project A615) closed-cycle submarines. A deckhouse has been built forward over the original hold. The standard version could carry 150 tons of cargo and was equipped with one 3-ton electric crane.

Kamyankha (U 860) Hartmut Ehlers, 9-98

♦ **1 ex-Russian Project D-9030 floating crane [YD]**
Bldr: . . . SY, Budapest, Hungary (In serv. 1983)

U 804 SARNI (ex-PK-112025)

Remarks: Transferred in 1997. Displacement: 1,060 tons (fl). Crane can lift 25 tons. No other data available.

♦ **1 ex-Russian Yelva (Krab)-class (Project 535M) diving tender [YDT]** Bldr: Gorokhovtse Zavod (In serv. 1975)

U 700 NIKISHIN (ex-VM-152)

Nikishin (U 700) Boris Lemachko, 1999

D: 295 tons (fl) **S:** 12.4 kts **Dim:** 40.90 (37.00 pp) × 8.00 × 2.07
Electronics: Radar: 1 Mius (Spin Trough) nav.
M: 2 Type 3D12A diesels; 2 props; 600 bhp **Electric:** 200 kw tot.
Range: 1,870/12 **Endurance:** 10 days **Crew:** 30 tot.

Remarks: Stricken from Black Sea Fleet 10-1-96 and transferred around 4-96. Can support seven divers at once to 60 m. Has a built-in decompression chamber and probably also a submersible decompression chamber. The name *Krab* was incorrectly ascribed to this craft in the previous edition.

♦ **3 ex-Russian Nyryat'-1-class (Project 522) diving tenders [YDT]**
(In serv. 1958–60)

U 633 . . . . . . (ex-VM-114) U . . . . (ex-VM-14)
U 707 BRODI (ex-VM-5)

D: 105.4 tons (115 fl) **S:** 10 kts **Dim:** 28.50 × 5.50 × 1.70
Electronics: Radar: 1 Mius (Spin Trough) nav.
M: 1 Type 6CSP 28/3C diesel; 1 prop; 450 bhp
Range: 900/9 **Endurance:** 10 days **Crew:** 15 tot.

Remarks: Stricken from the Black Sea Fleet 10-1-96 and transferred to Ukraine; sister VM-230 was also offered but not accepted. VM = *Vodolaznyy Morskoy* (Seagoing Diving Tender). Use the same hull as that of the GPB-480-class inshore survey craft. Can support hard-hat divers to 20-m depths. As built, could be equipped with one 12.7-mm mg.

♦ **1 ex-Russian Vydra-class (Project 106K) cargo lighter [YF]**
Bldr: Komintern Zavod, Kherson, Ukraine (In serv. 1965)

U 904 BILYAÏVKA (ex-MBSS-233200)

D: 301 tons light (543 fl) **S:** 10.5 kts
Dim: 54.50 (50.00 pp) × 7.70 (7.50 wl) × 2.25 (mean hull)
Electronics: Radar: 1 Don-2 nav.
M: 2 Type 3D12 diesels; 2 Kort-nozzle props; 600 bhp
Range: 1,400/10 (loaded) **Endurance:** 8 days **Crew:** 12 tot.

Remarks: Stricken from the Black Sea Fleet 10-1-96 and transferred later. Based at Odesa. One of 46 built for Russian use as utility landing craft, employed in local service as utility cargo carriers. This unit was formerly employed in trials service. The cargo deck measures 30.0 × 4.5 m and can accommodate up to 176 tons of vehicles or cargo (6 ZIL-131 or 10 GAZ-66 trucks). Sister *Korosten'* (U 832; ex-Russian *Tarpan,* OS-237) is configured as a trials craft [YAGE] (q.v.).

♦ **1 ex-Russian Project 1526 cargo lighter [YF]**
Bldr: Zavod 490, ... (In serv. 1959)

U . . . NOVGOROD-SIVERS'KIY (ex-MBSS-5200)

Remarks: Transferred in 1997. Displacement: 200 tons. Has two cargo holds and a small crane. No other data available.

SERVICE CRAFT *(continued)*

Novgorod-Sivers'kiy (U . . .)—pennant number not carried
Igor' Stelanovich, via Boris Lemachko, 8-00

♦ **1 ex-Russian Project 4116 cargo lighter [YF]**
Bldr: . . . . . . (In serv. 1952)

U . . . . . . (ex-MBSN-405250)

Remarks: Transferred in 1996–97; no data available.

♦ **1 ex-Russian Project 1141 medium floating dry dock [YFDM]**

U 949 Berel'nik (ex-SPD-23)

Remarks: Completed in 1960. No characteristics data available. Name also reported as *Berestechko.*

♦ **1 ex-Russian Project 1758 small floating dry dock [YFDL]**
Bldr: . . . . . . (In serv. 1970s)

U . . . (ex-PD-51)

Capacity: 4,500 tons **Dim:** 118.0 × 29.6 × 3.3

Remarks: Concrete construction. Have two 5-ton traveling cranes. Flooded draft over blocks is 6.3 m and width between wing-walls is 20.0 m.

♦ **1 ex-Russian Project 1240 small floating dry dock [YFDL]**

U 950 Khmil'nik (ex-PD-26)

♦ **3 ex-Russian Flamingo (Tanya)-class (Project 1415) harbor launches [YFL]**
Bldr: Sosnovka Zavod, Rybinsk, or Yaroslavl Zavod (In serv. 1980s)

U 721 Volodimir-Volnidskiy (ex-RVK-1075)
U 732 . . . . . . (ex-RVK-1403)
U 733 Tokmak (ex-RVK-1475)

Tokmak (U 733) Hartmut Ehlers, 7-00

D: 42 tons (54 fl) **S:** 11 kts **Dim:** 21.20 × 3.93 × 1.40
Electronics: Radar: 1 Lotsiya nav.
M: 1 Type 3D12A or 3D12L diesel; 1 prop; 300 bhp
Electric: 12 kw tot. (DGR 1A-16/1500 generator)
Range: 200/11 **Endurance:** 5 days **Crew:** 3 tot. + 5 divers

Remarks: Transferred in 1997. Employed as general-purpose launches at Kerch', Sevastopil, and Balaklava, respectively. Sister U 634 is an inshore survey craft [YGS], and *Feodosiya* (U 240, ex-P-99) is a harbor antiswimmer patrol boat.

♦ **6 ex-Russian PO-2-class (Project 376) harbor launches [YFL]**

From among:

U 731 Mirgorod (ex-RVK-493)	U . . . . . . (ex-RVK-5)
U 926 . . . . . (ex-RVK-. . .)	U . . . . . . (ex-RVK-258)
U . . . RK-1931	U . . . . . . (ex-RVK-761)
U . . . Romni (ex-RVK-155)	U . . . . . . (ex-RVK-1473)

D: 32 tons (38 fl) **S:** 9–10 kts **Dim:** 21.0 × 3.90 × 1.40 (max.; 1.26 mean)
A: when used as patrol craft: 1 twin 12.7-mm 79-cal. mg
Electronics: Radar: 1 Mius (Spin Trough) nav. or none
M: 1 Type 3D-6S1 diesel; 1 prop; 150 bhp
Electric: 10 kw tot. (1 × 10 kw, DGPN-8/1500 diesel driving)
Range: 1,600/8 **Fuel:** 1.5 tons **Endurance:** 5 days **Crew:** 4–6 tot.

PO-2-class launch U 172—note shield for twin 12.7-mm mg mount
Boris Lemachko, 2000

Remarks: Stricken from the Black Sea Fleet 10-1-96 for transfer to Ukraine. At least one of the boats listed above, now numbered BG 501, serves the border guard. RK-1931, which retained her Russian alphanumeric name into 8-00, and U 926 operate in the Sevastopil area. A unit numbered U 172, operating at Odesa, has a twin 12.7-mm mg mount forward.

♦ **1 ex-Russian Al'batros-class (Project 183Sh) flag officers' yacht [YFL]** Bldr: Sudostroitel'noye Obyedineniye "Almaz," Petrovskiy SY, St. Petersburg (In serv. ca. 1965)

U 853 . . . . . . (ex-*Sokol,* KSV-9)

D: 56.6 tons (68 fl) **S:** 39 kts **Dim:** 23.7 × 6.1 × 1.3
Electronics: Radar: 1 . . . nav.
M: 4 M-50F-1 diesels; 4 props; 4,800 bhp
Range: 320/32 **Fuel:** 7.2 tons **Endurance:** 5 days **Crew:** 11 tot.

Remarks: Transferred in 1997. Ukrainian designation: *Katera Svyazi* (Communications Cutter). Employs a P-6-class wooden torpedo boat hull and the same propulsion plant. Able to accommodate about 40 personnel for short trips. Four sisters remain active in the Russian Navy.

♦ **1 ex-Russian PSKL-16-class large cargo barge [YFNB]**
Bldr: . . . . . . (In serv. 1986)

U 855 Zolotonosha (ex-PSKL-19)

Zolotonosha (U 855) Hartmut Ehlers, 9-98

D: 2,604 tons (fl?) **Dim:** . . . × . . . × . . .

Remarks: Concrete hull construction. Equipped with generators and one electrohydraulic crane. Was at one time deployed to Alexandria, Egypt, by the Soviet Navy. No other data available.

♦ **1 ex-Russian Duna-class (Project 440) floating power barge [YFP]** Bldr: . . . . . . (In serv. 1956)

U 813 Berdichiv (ex-ENS-5)

Remarks: Non-self-propelled craft, equipped with two Type 37D diesel engines (2,000 bhp each) driving generators primarily intended for charging submarine batteries.

♦ **1 ex-Russian Flamingo (Tanya)-class (Project 1415) survey craft [YGS]** Bldr: Sosnovka Zavod, Rybinsk, or Yaroslavl Zavod (In serv. 1989)

U 634 (ex-BGK-1569)

D: 42 tons (54 fl) **S:** 11 kts **Dim:** 21.20 × 3.93 × 1.40
Electronics: Radar: 1 Lotsiya nav.
M: 1 Type 3D12A or 3D12L diesel; 1 prop; 300 bhp
Electric: 12 kw tot. (DGR 1A-16/1500 generator)
Range: 200/11 **Endurance:** 5 days **Crew:** 3 tot. + 5 divers

Remarks: Transferred in 1997. Based at Sevastopil.

SERVICE CRAFT *(continued)*

♦ **4 Nyryat (GPB-480)-class (Project 1896) inshore-survey craft [YGS]** Bldr: . . . . . ., USSR (In serv. 1974 and 1976)

U 631 (ex-BGK-697) U 633 (ex-BGK-37)
U 632 (ex-BGK-334) U 635 Skvyra (ex-BGK 650)

Skvyra (U 635) Hartmut Ehlers, 7-00

D: 92 tons (116.1 fl) **S:** 12.5 kts **Dim:** 28.58 × 5.20 × 1.70
Electronics: 1 SNN-7 nav.
M: 1 Type 6CSP 28/3C diesel; 1 prop; 450 bhp (300 sust.)
Range: 1,500/10 **Crew:** 15 tot.

Remarks: Stricken from the Black Sea Fleet 10-1-96 and later transferred. The charthouse/laboratory measures 6 m^2, and there are two 1.5-ton derricks. Most employ a dual side-looking mapping sonar system using transducers mounted on swinging-arm davits amidships. Russian sisters BGK-246, -248, -650, and -714, stricken the same date, were offered to Ukraine but were evidently not accepted.

♦ **6 GPB-710 (Kayra)-class (Project 1403A) survey launches [YGS]** Bldr: . . . (In serv. 1974–78)

. . . (ex-MGK-150) . . . (ex-MGK-258) . . . (ex-MGK-913)
. . . (ex-MGK-175) . . . (ex-MGK-912) . . . (ex-MGK-1098)

D: 7 tons (fl) **S:** 10 kts **Dim:** 11.0 × 3.0 × 0.7
M: 1 diesel; 1 prop; 90 bhp
Range: 150/10 **Endurance:** 2 days **Crew:** 6 tot.

Remarks: Designated MGK (*Mal'yy Geografischeskoye Kater,* Small Hydrographic Cutter) in Russian service. GRP construction. For use either independently or transported aboard larger hydrographic survey ships. Transferred 10-1-96; they probably do not have U-series pennant numbers.

♦ **3 MGK-1019 (Drofa)-class (Project 16830) survey launches [YGS]** Bldr: . . . . . . (In serv. 1986 and 1989)

. . . (ex-MGK-112) . . . (ex-MGK-1877) . . . (ex-MGK-1889)

D: 5.5 tons (fl) **S:** 7.5 kts **Dim:** 9.1 × 2.90 × 0.70
M: 1 Type 6CHSP-9.5/11 diesel; 1 prop; 65 bhp
Range: 150/7.5 **Endurance:** 1 day **Crew:** 2 tot.

Remarks: Were transferred to Ukraine 10-1-96.

Note: Also transferred 10-1-96 were Project 727M GRP-hulled former shipboard survey launches ex-MGK-146 and ex-MGK-1694; no data available.

♦ **3 ex-Russian non-self-propelled gunnery target barges [YGT]**

2 Project 436B: . . . (ex-22), . . . (ex-26) (In serv. 1981–83)
1 Project 454: . . . (ex-46) (In serv. 1978)

Remarks: Designated *Shchitiy Artilleriyskiye* ("Artillery Shield").

♦ **1 ex-Russian SK-620 (Drakon)-class ambulance craft [YH]** Bldr: Stocznia Wisla, Gdansk, Poland (In serv. 1983)

U 782 Sokal' (ex-PSK-1410)

Sokal' (U 782) Hartmut Ehlers, 8-00

D: 200 tons (240 fl) **S:** 10 kts **Dim:** 32.7 × 7.4 × 2.8
Electronics: Radar: 1 Mius nav.
M: 2 Wola Type 31-AMH diesels; 2 props; 620 bhp
Range: 1,000/10 **Crew:** 14 tot.

Remarks: Transferred in 1997. Ukrainian designation: *Meditsinskiy Kater.* Has a hospital ward with facilities for 12 patients. In 1998, was being used as a general-purpose launch.

♦ **1 ex-Russian Project 1430 ambulance craft [YH]** Bldr: . . . . . . (In serv. 1976)

U 783 Illichivsk (ex-PSK-658)

Remarks: Transferred in 1997. Displacement: 101 tons (fl); no other data available.

♦ **2 ex-Russian Toplivo-2 (Kair)-class (Project 1844) fuel lighters [YO]** Bldr: Komintern Zavod, Kherson, Ukraine (In serv. 1972 and 1981)

U 759 Bahmach (ex-VTN-81) U 760 Fastiv (ex-VTN-38)

Fastiv (U 760) Hartmut Ehlers, 8-00

D: 466 tons (1,180 tons fl) **S:** 10 kts **Dim:** 54.26 (49.40 pp) × 7.40 × 3.10–3.44
Electronics: Radar: 1 Mius (Spin Trough) or Don-2 nav.
M: 1 Russkiy Dizel 6 DR30/50-5-2 diesel; 1 prop; 600 bhp **Electric:** 250 kw tot.
Range: 1,500/10 **Fuel:** 19 tons **Endurance:** 20 days **Crew:** 24 tot.

Remarks: 308 grt/508 dwt. Transferred 1-8-97. Ukrainian type designation: *Maliye Morskiy Tanker* (Small Seagoing Tanker). Have four cargo tanks totaling 606 m^3 and can carry up to 495 tons fuel oil. Are fully seagoing, if required. Have one 0.5-ton hose-handling crane. U 760 was just completing an overhaul as of 8-00, and U 759 was badly in need of overhaul.

♦ **1 ex-Russian Project 14630 fuel barge [YON]** Bldr: . . . . (In serv. 1983)

U 954 (ex-MUS-482)

D: 208.8 tons

♦ **2 ex-Russian Project 1515 fuel barges [YON]** Bldr: . . . . . . (In serv. 1977 and 1973)

U . . . (ex-MUS-595) U . . . (ex-MUS-857)

Note: Former Russian oceanographic research ship *Mikhail Lomonosov* is employed as a berthing hulk [YPL] at Sevastopil.

♦ **2 ex-Russian Shelon' (TL-1127)-class (Project 1388) torpedo retrievers [YPT]** Bldr: Sosnovka Zavod, Russia (In serv. 1974 and 1987)

U 890 Malin (ex-TL-1005) U 891 Monastirishye (ex-TL-1616)

Monastirishye (U 891) Boris Lemachko, 5-00

D: 270 tons (fl) **S:** 30 kts **Dim:** 46.0 × 6.0 × 2.0
Electronics: Radar: 1 Kuban nav.—Sonar: 1 Oka-1 helicopter dipping-type
M: 2 M-504 diesels; 2 props; 10,000 bhp
Range: 1,500/10 **Endurance:** 10 days **Crew:** 20 tot.

Remarks: Stricken from the Black Sea Fleet 10-1-96 and transferred to Ukraine in summer 1997. Has a high-speed hull with a covered torpedo-recovery ramp aft. U 891 had still not had her Russian pennant number replaced as of 5-00 and may not be active.

SERVICE CRAFT *(continued)*

♦ 1 ex-Russian Project 1784 repair barge [YR]
Bldr: . . . (In serv. 1963)

U . . . . . . (ex-SM-15)

D: 920 tons (fl?) **Dim:** . . . × . . . × . . .

Remarks: Type designation SM *(Sudna-Misheni)* retained. Floating machine shop. No other data available. Probably transferred in 1997.

♦ 2 ex-Russian Prometey-class (Project 498) large harbor tugs [YTB]
Bldr: Petrozavod SY, St. Petersburg, or Gorokhovets SY, Russia (In serv. 1971–80s)

U 947 KRASNOPEREKOPS'K (ex-RB-308) U . . . . . . (ex-RB-69)

Krasnoperekops'k (U 947) Hartmut Ehlers, 7-00

D: 262 tons (308 fl) **S:** 11 kts **Dim:** 29.30 (28.2 pp) × 8.30 × 3.30
Electronics: Radar: 1 Mius (Spin Trough) nav.
M: 2 6DR 30/50 diesels; 2 Kort-nozzle props; 1,200 bhp
Electric: 50 kw tot. **Range:** 1,800/12 **Fuel:** 30 tons **Crew:** 3–5 tot.

Remarks: Stricken from the Black Sea Fleet 10-1-96 and transferred to Ukraine in 4-96. Have 14-ton bollard pull and an ice-strengthened hull. Ex-RB-69 may be of another class.

♦ 2 ex-Russian Sidehole-II-class (Project 737K) harbor tug [YTM]
Bldr: Petrozavod SY, St. Petersburg (In serv. 1970–83)

U 953 DUBNO (ex-RB-295) U . . . (ex-RB-27)

Dubno (U 953) Hartmut Ehlers, 8-00

D: 183 tons (206 fl) **S:** 10 kts **Dim:** 24.2 × 7.0 × 3.4
Electronics: Radar: 1 Mius (Spin Trough) nav.
M: 2 Type 6 CHN25/34 diesels; 2 vertical cycloidal props; 900 bhp
Range: 130/9.5 **Fuel:** 5.5 tons **Endurance:** 6 days **Crew:** 12 tot.

Remarks: Stricken from the Black Sea Fleet 10-1-96 and later transferred to Ukraine. Russian *Peredovik* class. Bollard pull: 10.5 tons.

♦ 3 ex-Russian Project T63OZh small harbor tugs [YTL]
Bldr: . . . . . . (In serv. 1954–56)

. . . (ex-BUK-239) . . . (ex-BUK-261) . . . (ex-BUK-300)

Remarks: Transferred in 1997. Type designation: *Buksiriye Kater* (Tug-Cutter). Displacement: 19 tons (fl). No other data available.

♦ 1 ex-Russian Morkov-class (Project 14611) fireboat [YTR]
Bldr: . . . USSR (In serv. 1987)

U . . . (ex-PZhK-1819)

D: 280 tons (320 fl) **S:** 12.5 kts **Dim:** 41.00 (36.53 pp) × 7.80 × 2.14
Electronics: Radar: 1 Mius (Spin Trough) nav.
M: 2 Barnaul' 3KD 12N-520 diesels; 2 CP props; 1,040 bhp—bow-thruster
Electric: 400 kw tot. **Range:** 250/12.5 **Endurance:** 5 days **Crew:** 15 tot.

Remarks: Stricken from the Black Sea Fleet 10-1-96 and later transferred to Ukraine.
Hull systems: Has four firefighting water monitors, two with 220-m^2/hr capacity and two of 500-m^3/hr, driven by two 750-m^3/hr diesel-powered pumps. Has both foam and Freon extinguishing systems, with 20 tons of foaming agent carried. Can spray a water curtain for self-protection. Can also be used for towing.

♦ 2 ex-Russian Pozharnyy-I-class (Project 364) fireboats [YTR]
Bldr: . . . (In serv. 1953–54)

U 722 BORSHCHIV (ex-PZhK-20) U 728 EVPATORIYA (ex-PZhK-38)

Borshchiv (U 722)—with minesweeper *Cherkasi* (U 311) and corvette *Lutsk* (U 200) in the background Leo Dirkx, 7-01

D: 145.9 tons (181 fl) **S:** 15.7 kts **Dim:** 34.9 × 6.2 × 1.8
Electronics: Radar: 1 Mius (Spin Trough)
M: 2 Type M-50F-1 diesels; 2 props; 2,250 bhp (1,800 sust.)
Range: 284/15.7; 1,050/10 **Fuel:** 12 tons **Crew:** 26 tot.

Remarks: Stricken from Black Sea Fleet 10-1-96 and transferred to Ukraine in 4-96. May have had a propulsion plant consisting of two 900-bhp M-50 diesels plus a centerline 450-bhp diesel. Can be armed with two twin 12.7-mm 79-cal. machinegun mounts. Both are based at Odesa.

♦ 3 Petrushka-class (Polish Project TS-39 or UK-3) training cutters [YXT]
Bldr: Stocznia Wisla, Gdansk (In serv. 1982–. . .)

U 540 CHIGIRIN U 541 SMILA U 542 DARNICYA

Petrushka-class training craft U 542 Boris Lemachko, 2000

D: 212 tons light (236 fl) **S:** 11.5 kts **Dim:** 33.00 × 7.44 × 2.44
Electronics: Radar: 2 Mius nav. (Spin Trough)
M: 2 Wola H12, 1,000-rpm diesels; 2 props; 570 bhp
Electric: 250 kVA tot. (2 × 125 kVA, Wola H6 diesels driving)
Range: 1,000/11.3 **Crew:** 13 tot. + 30 instructors and students

Remarks: U 541 was reportedly transferred in 1995, the others by 8-97; U 542 and 543 are named *Suvar* and *Akar,* but which is which is not known, nor are their former identities. Have two classrooms and a navigational training facility on the bridge. Are equipped with NBC warfare defense measures. Very similar to the slightly larger SK-620-class ambulance craft from the same builder. U 540 visited Turkey in 7-98. All three are based at Sevastopil.

♦ 2 Polish Bryza-class (Project 772) training cutters [YXT]
Bldr: Neftegaz Zavod (In serv. 1967–79)

U 543 . . . . . . (ex-. . .) U 544 VOZNESENS'K (ex-. . .)

D: 135 tons (142 fl) **S:** 10.5 kts **Dim:** 28.82 × 6.60 × 1.86
Electronics: Radar: 2 . . . nav.
M: 2 Type 3-D6 diesels; 2 props; 300 bhp **Electric:** 84 kw tot.
Range: 1,100/10 **Crew:** 11 tot. + 26 students

Remarks: Transferred in 1994–95. One is ex-Black Sea Fleet unit UK-190, stricken 5-7-94. Used for basic navigation and maneuvering training.

SERVICE CRAFT *(continued)*

Voznesens'k (U 544) H&L Van Ginderen, 1998

MARITIME BORDER GUARD

(Mors'ka Okhorona)

Note: Ships and craft were originally painted a very dark gray and had a broad yellow and narrow blue diagonal hull stripe; they are now mostly repainted with blue hull (hull areas subject to exhaust smoke staining painted black), white superstructures, and broad yellow hull stripe. Lettered on the sides is the legend "*Mors'ka Okhorona.*" The letters BG began to precede the hull numbers early in 1999, and many of the pennant numbers initially applied began to be changed at the same time.

PATROL COMBATANTS [WPG]

♦ 2 Russian Pauk-I (Molnaya-2) class (Project 1241.2)
Bldr: Yaroslavl SY, Russia (In serv. 1980–92)

BG 50 Grigoriy Kuropyatnikov (ex-BG 012, ex-PSKR-817)
BG 52 Grigoriy Gnatenko (ex-BG 014, ex-PSKR-815)

Grigoriy Kuropyatnikov (BG 50) Hartmut Ehlers, 8-00

Grigoriy Gnatenko (BG 52)—with former pennant number
Boris Lemachko, 2000

D: 425 tons (495 fl; 554 max.) **S:** 32 kts (28 sust.)
Dim: 57.60 (49.50 pp) × 10.40 (8.74 wl) × 2.14 (hull; 4.00 props)
A: 1 76.2-mm AK-176 DP; 1 Fasta-4M (SA-N-8) SAM syst. (16 9M-313 Igla/Gremlin missiles); 1 30-mm 54-cal. AK-630 gatling AA; 2 5-round RBU-1200 ASW RL (30 RGB-12 rockets); 4 fixed 402-mm OTA-40 ASW TT; 2 d.c. racks (12 BB-1 d.c.)
Electronics:
Radar: 1 Mius (Spin Trough) nav.; 1 Reyd (Peel Cone) nav./surf. search; 1 MR-123 Vympel-AM (Bass Tilt) f.c.
Sonar: MGK-345 Bronza MF hull-mounted and MF dipping (6.5/7.0/7.5 kHz)
EW: Vympel-R2 suite: 2 Half Hat-B intercept; 2 16-round PK-16 decoy RL
M: 2 M-507A or M-517 twin diesels; 2 props; 20,800 bhp (16,180 sust.)
Electric: 500 kw tot. (2 × 200-kw, 1 × 100-kw diesel sets)
Range: 2,000/20; 2,600/14; 1,600/12; with max. fuel: 3,000/12
Fuel: 50 tons normal **Endurance:** 10 days **Crew:** 5–7 officers, 31–32 enlisted

Remarks: Transferred from the Russian Federal Border Guard, from which they had been stricken 5-7-94. Both are based at Balaklava. Sister *Poltava* (BG 51, ex-BG 013, ex-PSKR-813) was reportedly stricken during 2001. Two other transferred sisters are in Ukraine Navy service.
Hull systems: The large housing for a dipping sonar system projects about 1.5 m out from the stern. The large hull-mounted sonar dome is located approximately beneath the gun fire-control radar. The hull is constructed of mild steel, while the middle part of the deck plating, some internal bulkheads, and much of the superstructure are made of aluminum-magnesium alloy.
Combat systems: The combat data system is designated SU-580. There is an SP-521 Rakurs (Kolonka-2) backup ringsight director for the single gatling AA gun; the Bass Tilt radar director can control both the 76.2- and 30-mm guns. The normal ammunition load is 152 rounds of 76-mm (all ready-service, on-mount) and 2,000 rounds of 30-mm. The sonar suite has a range of about 7 km for the dipping component, whose sonar transducer can be lowered to 200 m; MGK-345 applies to both the hull mounted and dipping sonars.

HYDROFOIL PATROL CRAFT [WPCH]

♦ 2 (+ 2) ex-Russian Muravey (Antarets) class (Project 133)
Bldr: Morye (ex-Yuzhnaya Tochka) Zavod, Feodosiya, Ukraine (In serv. 1983–89)

BG 53 . . . . . . (ex-BG 025, ex-PSKR-105)
BG 55 Galichina (ex-BG 027, ex-PSKR-115)

Galichina (BG 55) Boris Lemachko, 1999

D: 180 tons light; 195 tons std. (220 fl) **S:** 65 kts (60 sust.)
Dim: 40.30 (39.60 hull; 34.40 wl) × 8.00 (12.0 over foils; 7.30 wl) × 1.90 (hull; 4.55 over foils)
A: 1 76.2-mm 59-cal. AK-176 DP; 1 30-mm 54-cal. AK-630 gatling AA; 2 fixed 402-mm OTA-40 ASW TT; 1 d.c. rack (6 d.c.); 1 55-mm grenade launcher (70 grenades)
Electronics:
Radar: 1 Reyd (Peel Cone) nav./surf. search; 1 MR-123 Vympel (Bass Tilt) gun f.c.
Sonar: Ros'-K HF dipping at stern
M: COGAG M-20 plant: 2 M-70 gas turbines; 2 props; 22,600 shp (20,000 sust.)
Range: 410/45–50 **Endurance:** 5 days **Crew:** 5 officers, 20 enlisted

Remarks: Thirteen Project 133 units were built for the KGB Maritime Border Guard. BG 53 was transferred to Ukraine in 4-94. BG 55 was reportedly transferred in 1996, but a reported fourth unit evidently did not transfer. Sister BG 54 (ex-BG 026, ex-PSKR-108) was reportedly stricken during 2001. A late 2001 report stated that two incomplete units of the class are eventually to be finished at the Morye yard. Designed under B. F. Orlov at Alekseyev Central Hydrofoil Design Bureau. Both are based at Balaklava.
Hull systems: The foil system uses fixed fully submerged bow and stern sets, with an automatically adjusted amidships surface-piercing set beneath the bridge to control the ride. There is a single step to the hull aft. Both propeller shafts are sharply angled downward and are supported by the stern foil struts assembly. Can maintain 50 kts in Sea State 4 and operate hullborne in up to Sea State 7. Hull is hard-chine in form and made of aluminum-magnesium alloy.
Combat systems: The dipping sonar deploys through a hatch in the transom stern. There is an SP-521 Rakurs (Kolonka-2) ringsight backup director for the 30-mm gatling gun aft. The depth charge rack is on the starboard quarter. The grenade launcher is intended to combat underwater swimmers.

PATROL CRAFT [WPC]

♦ 11 Stenka (Tarantul) class (Project 205P)
Bldr: Sudostroitel'noye Obyedineniye "Almaz," Petrovskiy SY, St. Petersburg (In serv. 1967–90)

BG 019 . . . . . . (ex-PSKR-636)
BG 020 Volin (ex-PSKR-637)
BG 021 . . . . . . (ex-PSKR-642)
BG 031 Zakarpattya (ex-PSKR-648)
BG 032 Zaporiz'ka Sich (ex-PSKR-650)
BG 034 Bukovina (ex-PSKR-702)
BG 036 Podilla (ex-PSKR-709)
BG 037 Pavel Derzhavin (ex-PSKR-720)
BG 32 Donbas (ex-BG 035, ex-PSKR-705)
BG 57 Mikolayiv (ex-BG 023, ex-PSKR-722)
BG 61 Odesa (ex-BG 033, ex-PSKR-652)

D: 170 tons light; 211 tons std. (245 fl) **S:** 35 kts
Dim: 39.80 (37.50 wl) × 7.60 (5.90 wl) × 1.96
A: 2 twin 30-mm 65-cal. AK-230 AA; 4 fixed 402-mm OTA-40 ASW TT; 2 d.c. racks (12 d.c.)
Electronics:
Radar: 1 Baklan (Pot Drum) or Reyd (Peel Cone) nav./surf. search; 1 MR-104 Rys' (Drum Tilt) gun f.c.
Sonar: Bronza hull-mounted HF; Ros'-K HF helicopter dipping-type at stern
EW: SPO-3 intercept

BORDER GUARD PATROL CRAFT [WPC] *(continued)*

Donbas (BG 32) Boris Lemachko, 2000

M: 3 M-504 or M-520 diesels; 3 props; 15,000 bhp
Range: 500/35; 800/20; 1,500/12 **Endurance:** 10 days
Crew: 4–5 officers, 26–27 enlisted

Remarks: Built for the Maritime Border Guard of the KGB. Some were transferred to the Ukraine Maritime Border Guard in 2-92, possibly initially on loan. Sixteen Russian Federal Border Guard Black Sea units were stricken 5-7-94 and offered to the Ukraine Border Guard, which accepted 13, of which BG 018 (ex-PSKR-635) and BG 022 have since been stricken. BG 32 and 57 had their numbers changed after 1999, and it is likely that the others have also since been changed to two-digit numbers. Two other names for units of this class, *L'yiv* and *Kriviy Rig,* have not been correlated to pennant numbers yet.

PATROL BOATS [WPB]

♦ **0 (+ . . .) . . . class (Project 24009)**
Bldr: Morye Feodosiya Production Association (In serv. . . .)

D: 39.1 tons (fl) **S:** 40 kts **Dim:** 25.80 × 5.10 × 1.00
A: 1 20-mm AA; 2 single 12.7-mm mg **Electronics:** Radar: 1 . . . nav.
M: 2 MTU or MWM diesels; 2 MJP or KaMeWa waterjets; 2,680 bhp
Range: . . ./. . . **Fuel:** 3.2 tons **Crew:** 7 tot. + 2 passengers

Remarks: A proposed design for the Ukraine Border Guard and for export, using a deep-vee hullform with twin bilge keels and spray deflector. Aluminum-magnesium alloy construction. Would have an automated stabilization system.

♦ **10 (+ . . .) Kalkan class (Project 50030)**
Bldr: Morye Feodosiya Production Assn. (In serv. 1996–. . .)

BG 303, BG 304, BG 316, BG 318, BG 503, BG 504, BG 604, BG 618, BG 807 Matros Mikola Mushnirov, BG 808

Kalkan-class patrol launch Boris Lemachko, 2000

D: 7 tons (fl) **S:** 30 kts **Dim:** 10.6 × 3.3 × 0.6
A: small arms **Electronics:** Radar: none
M: 1 Type 457K diesel; 1 waterjet; 496 bhp (442 sust.)
Range: 254/. . . **Crew:** 2 tot. + 6 passengers

Remarks: Produced for harbor and riverine service, beginning in the mid-1990s. Have aluminum alloy hulls with GRP superstructures. A civilian version called the Krym-6 is also offered for service in sheltered waters. BG 303 operates from Sevastopil and BG 503 from Balaklava. BG 303 through BG 618 were not named, but later units seem to be. Three sisters were ordered for Turkmenistan early in 2002.

♦ **19 ex-Russian Zhuk (Gryf) class (Project 1400A or 1400M)**
Bldr: Morye Zavod, Feodosiya (In serv. 1971–86 and 1992–94)

BG 100 through BG 107, BG 109 through BG 111, BG 115 through BG 119, 3 others

D: 35.9 tons (39.7 fl) **S:** 30 kts
Dim: 23.80 (21.70 wl) × 5.00 (3.80 wl) × 1.00 (hull; 1.90 max.)
A: 1 twin 12.7-mm 60-cal. Utës-Ma mg **Electronics:** Radar: 1 Lotsiya nav.
M: Project 1400M: 2 M-401 diesels; 2 props; 2,200 bhp—Project 1400A: 2 M-50F-4 diesels; 2 props; 2,400 bhp

Zhuk-class BG 101 Boris Lemachko, 2000

Electric: 48 kw total (2 × 21-kw, 1 × 6-kw diesel sets)
Range: 500/13.5 **Endurance:** 5 days **Crew:** 1 officer, 9 enlisted

Remarks: Russian Federal Border Guard Black Sea–area units P-53, -54, -125, -141, -501 through -512, -517, -519, -523 through -526, and -534 were stricken 5-7-94 and transferred to Ukraine, but most were evidently not put into service; units previously renumbered 611, 633, 634, and 635 have been stricken since transfer. An article in the Russian magazine *Tayfun* in 2-98 stated that five were completed during 1992–94 at Morye Zavod, Feodosiya, where two were built for Vietnam in the mid-1990s. Two stationed at Yalta are used as escorts for the presidential yacht *Krym.* All were renumbered in the BG 100 series in 7-99, having previously been numbered in the BG 600 series. Nine are based at Odesa, five at Balaklava, and BG 118 and 119 at Kerch'.
Hull systems: Aluminum alloy hull. Capable of operating in up to State 4 or 5 seas. Range is also reported as 700 n.m. at 28 kts and 1,100 n.m. at 15 kts.
Combat systems: Armament seems to have been standardized at one twin 12.7-mm mount forward. Most (but not BG 102) have a searchlight mounted in the after weapons mount position.

♦ **4 ex-Russian Shmel'-class (Project 1204M) riverine**
Bldrs: Kamysh Burun Zavod, Kerch', and 61 Kommunara Zavod, Mikolayiv

	In serv.		In serv.
BG 83 Nizhin (ex-AK-563)	1968	BG 171 Lubni (ex-AK-211)	1972
BG 84 Izmayil (ex-AK-397)	1969	BG 173 Kaniv (ex-AK-246)	1971

Kaniv (BG 173) Boris Lemachko, 1999

D: 77.4 tons (fl) **S:** 24 kts **Dim:** 27.70 × 4.32 × 0.90 (2.00 molded depth)
A: 1 76.2-mm 48-cal. D-56TM low-angle gun (in a PT-76 tank turret, with a 7.62-mm mg); 1 twin 25-mm 80-cal. 2M-3M AA; 2 mine rails (up to 8 mines)
Electronics: Radar: 1 Donets-2 nav.
M: 2 M-50F-4 diesels; 2 props; 2,400 bhp
Electric: 50 kw tot. (2 × 25-kw DG-25 diesel sets)
Range: 240/20; 600/10 **Fuel:** 4.75 tons **Endurance:** 7 days
Crew: 1 officer, 2 warrant officers, 11 enlisted

Remarks: Designed in Russia by TsKB-5 (the current Almaz) design bureau under L. V. Ozimov. AKA-211, -246, and -563 were transferred to Ukraine in 8-95, along with other assets of the former Russian Danube Flotilla, while AKA-248, -327, and -397 were stricken 10-1-96 from the Black Sea Fleet and transferred later; of these, only four have been put into service. Were originally numbered in the BG 171 series by Ukraine.
Hull systems: The screws are mounted in tunnels to reduce draft. Have 10-mm armor over the pilothouse and gun barbettes, 8-mm over the hull and internal bulkheads, and 5-mm over the deck and pilothouse.
Combat systems: One 7.62-mm machinegun is mounted coaxially with the 76-mm gun (for which 40 rounds are carried on-mount). Mine loads vary from four UDM-500 or two UDM-1000 to six KPM or eight YaM mines. Have a Gradus-2 gyrocompass and NEL-7 echo sounder.

SERVICE CRAFT

♦ **1 ex-Russian riverine forces flagship [WYAG]**
Bldr: Schiffswerf Linz, Germany (In serv. 1942)

BG 80 Dunay (ex-BG 500, ex-SSV-10, ex-PS-10, ex-*Prut,* ex-German *Grafenau*)

D: 300 tons (421 fl) **S:** 11 kts (8.5 sust.) **Dim:** 48.28 (46.60 pp) × 7.20 × 1.21
A: 3 single 14.5-mm 93-cal. mg; 2 single 45-mm saluting cannon
M: 2 Deutz RVM6M545 diesels; 2 props; 1,000 bhp (820 sust.)
Range: 3,300/9.1 **Fuel:** 44 tons **Crew:** 24 tot.

BORDER GUARD SERVICE CRAFT *(continued)*

Dunay (BG 80)—with former pennant number Boris Lemachko, 1999

Remarks: Built as one of 11 German Type N river tugs for use on the Danube. Served as flagship of the Russian Danube River Flotilla from shortly after World War II until transferred to Ukraine, along with other Danube Flotilla units, on 1-5-95. Retained her Russian name. A sister serves as flagship of the Yugoslav Federation forces on the Danube.

♦ **2 or more Katran-class (Project . . .) launches [WYFL]**
Bldr: Morye Zavod, Feodosiya (In serv. late 1990s–. . .)

BG 316 BG 349

Katran-class launch BG 349 Boris Lemachko, 1999

D: 13.2 tons (fl) **S:** 38 kts **Dim:** 14.30 × 3.60 × . . .
A: small arms **Electronics:** Radar: none
M: 1 Type 6TD diesel; 1 waterjet; 1,000 bhp
Range: 270/27 **Fuel:** 1.28 tons **Endurance:** 1 day **Crew:** 3 tot.

Remarks: Intended for harbor or lake use. Three-layer GRP construction. Can carry eight passengers or police/troops.

♦ **1 Krym-class (Project 1360) yacht [WYFL]**
Bldr: Sudostroitel'noye Obyedineniye "Almaz," Petrovskiy SY, St. Petersburg (In serv. 1981)

BG 01 Krym

Krym (BG 01)—white-painted, without pennant number Boris Lemachko, 2000

D: 158 tons (220 fl) **S:** 32 kts **Dim:** 45.5 × 8.7 × 2.5 (mean hull)
M: 2 M-503A radial diesels; 2 props; 8,000 bhp
Range: 500/35 **Fuel:** 40 tons **Endurance:** 3 days **Crew:** 32 tot.

Remarks: Transferred to Ukraine 1-5-95. Employed as the presidential yacht *(prezidentskaya yakhta),* based at Yalta. Sister *Kavkaz* remains in Russian service, also on the Black Sea. Painted white.

♦ **1 ex-Russian PO-2-class (Project 376) harbor launch [WYFL]**

BG 501 (ex-602, ex-RVK-. . .)

D: 32 tons (38 fl) **S:** 9–10 kts **Dim:** 21.0 × 3.90 × 1.40 (max.; 1.26 mean)
M: 1 Type 3D-6S1 diesel; 1 prop; 150 bhp

PO-2-class launch BG 501 Boris Lemachko, 1999

Electric: 10 kw tot. (1 × 10 kw, DGPN-8/1500 diesel driving)
Range: 1,600/8 **Fuel:** 1.5 tons **Endurance:** 5 days **Crew:** 4–6 tot.

Remarks: Stricken from the Black Sea Fleet 10-1-96 for transfer to Ukraine. Operates from Balaklava.

UNITED ARAB EMIRATES

Note: Incorporating the former Defense Force Sea Wing of the Abu Dhabi National Defense Force, the U.A.E. Navy was formed 1-2-78 as part of the federated forces of Abu Dhabi, Ajman, Dubai, Fujairah, Ras al Khaimah, Sharjah, and Umm al Qaiwan. The merchant marines of these states are also combined into a single administrative unit. Several of these nation-states, including Abu Dhabi and Dubai, also operate separate customs services with their own patrol craft.

Personnel (2002): 200 officers, 2,200 enlisted

Bases: Principal base and headquarters at Taweela, midway between Abu Dhabi and Dubai. Subsidiary bases at Damla and Mina Zayed in Abu Dhabi; Mina Jebel and Mina Rashid in Dubai; and Khor Fakkan, Mina Saqr, and Mina Sultan in Sharjah. A major new base is planned to be built north of Fujairah.

Naval Aviation: Two Pilatus-Britten-Norman BN-2 Islander Maritime Defender for patrol duties, several Aérospatiale AS.565SA Panther helicopters, 7 Aérospatiale AS.332 Super Puma helicopters, and 5 Aérospatiale AS.316B Alouette-III light helicopters. The Super Puma helicopters can launch AM 39 Exocet and the Panthers AS 15 antiship missiles. WASS A-244S ASW torpedoes were selected for use with the helicopters in 1997. Four EADS C-295 maritime patrol aircraft were ordered during 3-01.

U.A.E. Navy AS.332 Super Puma Stefan Marx, 3-95

Weapons and Sensors: The U.A.E. requested 12 RGM-84L Harpoon Block II antiship missiles from the U.S.A. on 25-10-01. The package would include launch containers, maintenance training and support, shipboard equipment, test gear, and other logistics support arrangements, for a total cost of $40 million.

Coastal Defense: Dubai is said to have acquired 30 truck-launched Chinese HY-2 antiship missiles by 1995.

Note: Abu Dhabi Shipbuilding, already a partner with Newport News Shipbuilding in the U.S.A., made an alliance with the Halmatic division of Vosper Thornycroft of the U.K. in 7-01 to build and sell Halmatic's GRP-construction smallcraft in the Gulf region.

Pennant numbers were being revised during 2001, with the original four-digit numbers (the first two digits standing for the length of the ship or craft) being recast as two- or three-digit pennants.

ATTACK SUBMARINES [SS]

Note: In 10-96, the U.A.E. issued requests for data from submarine builders with the intent to order two to four small diesel submarines eventually. No contracts have resulted.

FRIGATES [FF]

Note: During the 1990s, the U.A.E. several times requested bids on between two and eight additional, new-construction frigates. A number of shipbuilders worldwide have sought the order, for which the specifications appeared to change whenever it seemed that a purchase decision might be expected. Royal Schelde, in the Netherlands, has stated that it believes it has an inside track on whatever order may eventually transpire, due to the *Kortenaer* sale, and it is offering a variant of its LCF (*Luchtverdedigings en Commando Fregat,* or Air-defense and Command Frigate) with simplified systems and a different main gun mounting. Newport News Shipbuilding and Dry Dock in the United States has offered several variants of its FF-21 design. No actual building or purchase contracts are expected in the near future.

♦ 2 Netherlands Kortenaer class

Bldr: Royal Schelde, Vlissingen

	Laid down	L	In serv.
F 01 Abu Dhabi (ex-*Abraham Crijnssen,* F 816)	25-10-78	16-5-81	26-1-83
F 02 Al Amarat (ex-*Piet Heyn,* F 811)	28-4-77	3-6-78	14-4-81

Al Amarat (F 02) Claronav Pictures, 1-98

Abu Dhabi (F 01) *Ships of the World,* 7-01

D: 3,000 tons (3,786 fl) **S:** 30 kts (20 on two Tyne turbines)
Dim: 130.2 (121.8 pp) × 14.4 × 4.4 (6.0 props)
A: 8 RGM-84L Harpoon Block II SSM; 1 8-round Mk 29 missile launcher (24 RIM-7M NATO Sea Sparrow SAM); 1 76-mm 62-cal. OTOBreda DP; 1 30-mm SGE-30 Goalkeeper CIWS; 2 single 20-mm 70-cal. Oerlikon AA; 4 fixed 324-mm Mk 32 Mod. 9 ASW TT (Mk 46 Mod. 5 torpedoes); 1 . . . . . . helicopter
Electronics:
Radar: (all Thales) 1 Scout nav.; 1 ZW-06 surf. search; 1 LW-08 early warning; WM-25 f.c.; 1 STIR-18 f.c.
Sonar: 1 Canadian Westinghouse SQS-505 hull-mounted MF
EW: Sphinx intercept; Ramses jammer; Mk 36 SRBOC decoy syst. (2 6-round Mk 137 RL); SLQ-25 Nixie towed torpedo decoy syst.
M: COGOG: 2 Rolls-Royce Olympus TM-3B gas turbines (25,800 shp each), 2 Rolls-Royce Tyne RM-1C cruise gas turbines (4,900 shp each); 2 LIPS CP props; 51,600 shp max.
Electric: 3,000 kw tot. (4 × 750 kw, SEMT-Pielstick PA4 diesels driving)
Range: 4,700/16 (on one Tyne turbine) **Crew:** 140 tot.

Remarks: Purchased 2-4-96. F 01 was transferred and recommissioned 31-10-97 and F 02 on 29-6-98 after refits at Vlissingen that commenced in summer 1996; F 02 departed for the U.A.E. 3-7-98. F 01 had been decommissioned from the Royal Netherlands Navy in 6-96 and F 02 in 1-95. As part of the purchase agreement, training and electronics overhaul facilities were built in Abu Dhabi, and two tugs to handle the ships were bought. Are being operated with far smaller crews than when in Dutch service, where they carried 18 officers and 182 enlisted.
Hull systems: The hull is divided by 15 watertight bulkheads. One pair of Denny-Brown, nonretracting fin stabilizers is fitted. Particular attention has been paid to habitability. Have the Sperry Mk 29 Mod. 1 inertial navigation system. The engineering plant is distributed in four compartments, forward to aft: auxiliaries; Olympus gas turbines; Tyne gas turbines plus reduction gears; auxiliaries. There are two auxiliary boilers and two evaporators.
Combat systems: Have the Thales SEWACO-II combat data system. Normally, only one helicopter is carried, but a second can be accommodated in the hangar. The Mk 36 SRBOC chaff system replaced the original Knebworth/Corvus RL. Thales Scout low-probability-of-intercept navigational radars were installed during the 1996–98 activation refits, and new Goalkeeper mountings were purchased for the ships. A U.A.E. request for 72 RIM-7P Sea Sparrow missiles for the ships has not been met, although 24 older RIM-7M missiles were to be furnished during 1999; France's DCN and Eurosam have proposed replacing the Mk 29 box launchers with Sylver vertical launchers for Aster-15 SAMs. The U.A.E. requested 24 RGM-84G-4 Harpoon missiles for the ships in 8-97, but none had been delivered as of mid-1999; a new request for 12 RGM-84L missiles was made 25-10-01. Both have carried eight Harpoon launch canisters since delivery, but they have probably been empty.

CORVETTES [FFL]

Note: A 90-m corvette class is planned under project LEWA-2. Requests for proposals were to be received early in 1997, but no contract had been announced as of 12-01.

GUIDED-MISSILE PATROL COMBATANTS [PGG]

♦ 0 (+ 6) Project Baynunah class

Bldrs: first unit: CMN, Cherbourg; others: Abu Dhabi SB (ADSB)

	Laid down	L	In serv.
P	. . .	. . .	. . .
P	. . .	. . .	. . .
P	. . .	. . .	. . .
P	. . .	. . .	. . .
P	. . .	. . .	. . .
P	. . .	. . .	. . .

D: approx. 650 tons (fl) **S:** 30 kts **Dim:** 70.0 × . . . × . . .
A: 8 . . . . . . SSM; 1 . . . . . . point-defense SAM syst.; 1 76-mm 62-cal. OTOBreda SuperRapid or 57-mm 70-cal Bofors SAK 57 Mk 3 DP; . . .
Electronics:
Radar: . . .
EW: . . .
M: . . .
Range: 2,000/. . . **Crew:** . . . tot.

Remarks: Proposals were requested in 11-96 but, as is all too common with U.A.E. procurement programs, the requirements were revised in 2-97, requiring inclusion of facilities for a helicopter and enhanced signature-reduction measures. Initial bids were received by 2-3-97, but a winning design from CMN, Cherbourg, was not selected until 23-3-01; a contract was to follow by the end of 2001 but none had been announced as of 11-01. The initial unit would be built in France, with subsequent production at Abu Dhabi Ship Building (a Newport News Shipbuilding and CMN partner).
Combat systems: Either Harpoon or MM 40 Exocet missiles and either the Raytheon RAM or MBD/MSI Sigma point-defense missile system will be fitted. The combat system will be either the SaabTech 9LV Mk 3E or Thales TACTICOS, and the EADS TRS-3D, Ericsson Sea Giraffe AMB, or Thales MRR search radar will be fitted. A helicopter hangar and flight deck are to be fitted.

♦ 2 German FPB 65 class

Bldr: Friedrich Lürssen Werft, Vegesack (In serv. 10-91)

CM 01 Muray Jip CM 02 Das

Muray Jip (CM 01) French Navy, 1996

Das (CM 02)—with AS.332 Super Puma on deck French Navy, 1996

D: 590 tons (660 fl) **S:** 34 kts (32 sust.)
Dim: 65.95 (62.90 pp) × 9.30 × 2.60
A: 8 MM 40 Exocet SSM; 1 8-round Crotale Modulaire SAM syst.; 1 76-mm 62-cal. OTOBreda SuperRapid DP; 1 30-mm Thales Goalkeeper gatling CIWS; 1 AS.316B Alouette-III helicopter
Electronics:
Radar: 1 Decca TM 1226 nav.; 1 Ericsson Sea Giraffe 50HC surf./air search; 1 Saab Dynamics 9LV 223 Mk 2 f.c.; 1 Thales DRBC-51C f.c.; 1 Thales Goalkeeper f.c. array
EW: Racal Cutlass RDL-2 intercept; Racal Cygnus jammer; 2 330- or 340-round Matra Défense Dagaie decoy RL

GUIDED-MISSILE PATROL COMBATANTS [PGG] *(continued)*

M: 4 MTU 16V538 TB92 diesels; 4 props; 15,600 bhp **Electric:** 408 kw tot.
Range: 4,000/16 **Fuel:** 120 tons **Crew:** 43 tot.

Remarks: Ordered in mid-1987, along with the FPB-44 class. The design is a lengthened version of the FPB-62-class ships built for Bahrain. Were launched during 1989 and completed in 11-90 and 1-91, respectively; transferred after training completed. Plans to order a third were canceled.
Combat systems: In these ships, the elaborate weapons-control array includes the Saab Dynamics 9LV 331 radar/optronic system for the 76-mm gun (which in this class is linked to the Sea Giraffe surveillance radar rather than the usual 9GA 209 search radar) and the self-contained, track-while-scan radar array of the Goalkeeper close-in weapons system; the DRBC-51C radar provides illumination for the Crotale SAMs and is also equipped with backup optronic accessories. Goalkeeper has its own target-detection/designation and tracking radars. In addition, a Matra Défense Najir optronic backup director with t.v. and infrared sensors and a laser rangefinder for the 76-mm gun is mounted on the bridge just forward of the tower mast. Have a helicopter deck with integral elevator to the hangar below, as in the similar Bahraini navy units.

GUIDED-MISSILE PATROL CRAFT [PTG]

♦ 2 German FPB-44 class
Bldr: Friedrich Lürssen Werft, Vegesack

P 41 Mubarraz (In serv. 2-91) P 42 Makasib (In serv. 2-91)

Makasib (P 42)—with former pennant number Steven J. Zaloga, 4-97

Makasib (P 42)—with former pennant number French Navy, 1-96

D: 210 tons (235 fl) **S:** 34 kts **Dim:** 44.0 (41.50 pp) × 7.0 × 2.2 (props)
A: 4 MM 40 Exocet; 1 6-round Sadral SAM syst. (. . . Mistral missiles); 1 76-mm 62-cal. OTOBreda SuperRapid DP; 2 single 20-mm 90-cal. Rheinmetall AA
Electronics:
Radar: 1 Thales Scout nav.; 1 Ericsson Sea Giraffe 50HC surf./air search; 1 Saab Dynamics 9GA 331 f.c.
EW: Racal Cutlass RDL-2 intercept; Racal Cygnus jammer; 1 330- or 340-round Matra Défense Dagaie decoy RL
M: 2 MTU 20V538 TB92 diesels; 2 props; 10,200 bhp **Electric:** 405 kVA tot.
Range: 500/38; 1,600/16 **Crew:** 5 officers, 35 enlisted

Remarks: Order placed in mid-1987; ships arrived in U.A.E. waters in 5-91. Are an enlarged version of Lürssen's FPB-38 design rather than being further units of the TNC-45 class. Were numbered P 4401 and P 4402, respectively, until 2001.
Combat systems: The combat control system is the Saab Dynamics (ex-CelsiusTech) 9LV 200 Mk 2. The Sadral installation is the first export of that French system, and, in these ships, is controlled by a Matra Défense Najir optronic director abaft the mast. In order to accommodate the point-defense SAM system and the enhanced EW suite (whose spherical radome for the Cygnus jammer is mounted on the mast), a second gun position was sacrificed. A Bofors 57-mm rocket flare/chaff launcher is mounted amidships. The original Decca 1226 navigational radars were replaced with Thales low-probability-of-intercept Scout sets during 1997–98.

♦ 6 German TNC-45 class
Bldr: Friedrich Lürssen Werft, Vegesack

	In serv.		In serv.
P 151 Baniyas	11-80	P 154 Shaheen	4-81
P 152 Marban	11-80	P 155 Saqar	6-81
P 153 Rodqum	4-81	P 156 Tarif	6-81

Shaheen (P 154) Steven J. Zaloga, 3-01

Marban (P 152)—with former pennant number French Navy, 1996

D: 231 tons (259 fl) **S:** 41.5 kts **Dim:** 44.90 (42.30 pp) × 7.00 × 2.46 (props)
A: 4 MM 40 Exocet; 1 76-mm 62-cal. OTOBreda Compact DP; 1 twin 40-mm 70-cal. Bofors-OTOBreda AA; 2 single 7.62-mm mg
Electronics:
Radar: 1 Thales Scout surf. search; 1 Ericsson Sea Giraffe 50 surf./air search; 1 Saab Dynamics 9LV 200 Mk 2 f.c.s.
EW: Racal Cutlass RDL-2 intercept; 1 330- or 340-round Matra Défense Dagaie decoy RL
M: 4 MTU 16V538 TB92 diesels; 4 props; 15,600 bhp (13,000 sust.)
Electric: 405 kVA tot. **Range:** 500/38.5; 1,600/16
Crew: 5 officers, 27 enlisted

Remarks: Ordered in late 1977. Refitted (without significant equipment modernization) by Abu Dhabi Ship Building (ADSB), with technical assistance from Newport News Shipbuilding and Dry Dock, beginning 9-96; P 151 and 152 were completed in 1998 and P 153 and 154 in 10-99, and the last two were to complete in mid-2000. Were renumbered from P 4501 through P 4506 late in 3-01.
Combat systems: The radar director is equipped with low-light-level t.v. and an infrared tracker and has an associated search radar atop the mast. There is a Matra Défense Panda optical director for the 40-mm mount. Carry 350 rounds of 76-mm, 1,800 rounds of 40-mm, and 6,000 rounds of machinegun ammunition. The original navigational radar was replaced by Scout during 1997–98. SaabTech Systems received a contract on 23-1-01 to provide new Tarif-45 combat data and control systems for the class; the installation is to be carried out at ADSB.

PATROL CRAFT [PC]

♦ 0 (+ 12) Project LEWA-3
Bldr: Abu Dhabi SB (In serv. . . .)

D: . . . **S:** . . . **Dim:** 30.0 × . . . × . . .
A: 6 Lockheed Martin Seagull SSM (see remarks); 1 25-mm Mk 38 Bushmaster low-angle gun
Electronics: . . .
M: 2 . . . diesels; . . .

Remarks: On 11-12-99, a preliminary contract was reportedly signed with DCN, France, whereby the first of 12 20-m LEWA-3 patrol craft would be built in France and the remainder by Abu Dhabi Ship Building; final contracts had not been concluded as of 11-01. No design data is available. Plans now call for using hull molds from CMN, France, with layup and outfitting to take place in Abu Dhabi.
Combat systems: The Seagull missile system employs a modified AGM-114M Hellfire-II missile with blast-fragmentation warhead and a range of about 8 km. The missiles would be mounted four fixed on the aft-mounted mast and two on the sides of the 25-mm Bushmaster chain-gun mounting.

♦ 6 U.K. 110-foot class
Bldr: Vosper Thornycroft, Portsmouth, U.K.

	L		L
P 1101 Ardhana	7-3-75	P 1104 Al Ghulian	16-9-75
P 1102 Zurara	13-6-75	P 1105 Radoom	15-12-75
P 1103 Murban	15-9-75	P 1106 Ghanadhah	1-3-76

PATROL CRAFT [PC] *(continued)*

Zurara (P 1102) Maritime Photographic, 3-95

D: 110 tons (140 fl) **S:** 29 kts **Dim:** 33.5 (31.5 pp) × 6.4 × 1.7
A: 1 twin 30-mm 75-cal. BMARC/Oerlikon A32 AA; 1 20-mm 90-cal. BMARC/Oerlikon A41A AA
Electronics: Radar: 1 Decca TM 1226 nav.
M: 2 Ruston–Paxman-Valenta RP200M diesels; 2 props; 5,400 bhp
Range: 1,800/14 **Crew:** 26 tot.

Remarks: Were originally operated by Abu Dhabi prior to the establishment of the U.A.E. fleet. Are in need of replacement. Have two U.K. 51-mm rocket flare launchers. All remained in service as of mid-2001, with previous reports of retirements having been in error. May have been renumbered P 101 through P 106 during 2001.

PATROL BOATS [PB]

♦ 0 (+ 20) Seaflyer class
Bldr: EGI-Droge SB, Rosario, Argentina (In serv. . . .)

D: . . . tons **S:** 65 kts **Dim:** 13.25 × . . . × . . .
A: . . . **Electronics:** Radar: . . .
M: 1 Seatek diesel; 1 prop; 600 bhp
Range: 500/. . . **Crew:** . . .

Remarks: Reportedly ordered late in 1997, although there are as yet no indications of any deliveries. GRP construction. Intended to combat pirates and smugglers.

♦ 3 Boghammar launches
Bldr: Boghammar, Stockholm, Sweden (In serv. 1986)

D: 5.5 tons (fl) **S:** 50 kts **Dim:** 13.00 × 2.66 × 0.90
M: 2 Volvo Penta TAMD-70E diesels; 2 outdrive props; 600 bhp
Range: 500/35 **Crew:** 3–5 tot.

Remarks: Purchased by Abu Dhabi specifically for the defense of the sultan's palace and are not part of the regular U.A.E. armed forces. Have stepped hydroplane hulls.

MINE COUNTERMEASURES SHIPS

Note: Bids were requested from shipbuilders by 10-12-97 for the construction of three minehunters for the U.A.E. Navy. Lürssenwerft and Abeking & Rasmussen jointly offered the Type 332, Vosper Thornycroft the *Sandown* class, DCN International a modernized variant of the Tripartite design, Intermarine the *Gaeta* class, Kvaerner Mandal the *Oksøy* class, and Karlskronvarvet the *Styrsö* class. No winner had been announced as of 11-01. Components for the Australian Minesweeping System (AMS) were ordered 30-11-01, however; included will be a single 16.7-m, GRP-hulled, remotely controlled launch converted to tow one AMS set.

Note: Twelve Swedish Trossbåt-class fast landing craft [LCVP] were ordered 22-1-02; see addenda for details.

AUXILIARIES

♦ 1 vehicle cargo ship [AK]
Bldr: Defence Shipyard, Abu Dhabi (In serv. 1999)

Al Feyi

D: . . . tons (fl) **S:** 12 kts **Dim:** 64.00 (56.20 pp) × 12.00 × 2.70
A: probably none **Electronics:** Radar: . . .
M: 2 Caterpillar . . . diesels; 2 props; 1,760 bhp
Electric: 284 kw tot. (2 × 142-kw diesel alternator sets)
Range: . . ./. . . **Crew:** . . . tot.

Remarks: A 700-grt/1,600-dwt ramped cargo vessel.

♦ 1 vehicle and personnel transport [AP]
Bldr: Shin Yang SB, Malaysia (In serv. 1999)

Marawah (ex-*Meranti 39*)

Remarks: 2,450 grt. No further data available.

♦ 1 seagoing tug [ATA]
Bldr: Richard Dunston, Hessle, U.K. (In serv. 4-89)

A 3501 Annad

D: 795 tons (fl) **S:** 14.4 kts **Dim:** 35.00 (31.25 pp) × 9.80 × 4.15
Electronics: Radar: 1 Decca RM 2070/4 BT nav.

Annad (A 3501) R. Van Der Hoek, 1989

M: 2 Caterpillar 3606TA diesels; 2 Liaaen CP props; 4,200 bhp—Jastrum bow-thruster (3-ton thrust)
Electric: 206 kw (2 × 103-kw Siemens–Mercedes-Benz OM421 diesel sets)
Range: 2,500/14 **Fuel:** 143 tons **Crew:** 3 officers, 10 enlisted

Remarks: 400 grt. A fully equipped berthing/coastal tug, with secondary firefighting, rescue, and salvage capabilities. Bollard pull: 55 tons. The bow-thruster is powered by a 362-bhp Caterpillar 3406TA diesel. Has a towing winch with 400 m of 40-mm cable and a 5-ton capstan, two 600-m^3/hr pumps for the three 200-m^3/hr and one 400-m^3/hr fire and foam monitors, and extensive navigational and communications systems. Can transport two standard containers on stern.

SERVICE CRAFT

♦ 1 diving tender [YDT]
Bldr: Crestitalia, Ameglia, La Spezia, Italy (In serv. 7-87)

D 1051

D 1051 Crestitalia, 1987

D: 100 tons (fl) **S:** 27 kts **Dim:** 31.35 × 6.90 × 1.20
Electronics: Radar: 1 . . . nav.
M: 2 MTU 12V396 TB93 diesels; 2 props; 3,950 bhp
Range: 432/18 **Crew:** 6 tot.

Remarks: Ordered in 12-85. A lengthened version of the *Mario Marino* class (builder's M/V 100 design) built for the Italian Navy. GRP construction. Intended to support combat swimmers, as well as providing diving support services. Has a decompression chamber.

♦ 4 (+ 3) L 6401–class logistics landing craft [YFU]
Bldr: Abu Dhabi SB (In serv.: L 64, 65: 1996; L 66, 67: 1999)

L 64 L 65 L 66 L 67

L 64 Steven J. Zaloga, 3-01

SERVICE CRAFT *(continued)*

D: . . . tons **S:** 11 kts **Dim:** 64.0 × . . . × . . .
A: none **Electronics:** . . .
M: 2 Caterpillar 3508 diesels; 2 props; . . . **Crew:** 19 tot. + 56 troops

Remarks: No other data available. Were originally numbered L 6401 through L 6404. Three more were ordered during 11-01.

♦ 3 Al Feyi–class logistics landing craft [YFU]
Bldrs: L 51: Siong Huat, Singapore (in serv. 4-8-87); others: Vosper-QAF, Singapore (L: 14-10-88, in serv. 12-88)

L 51 Al Feyi L 52 Dayyinah L 53 Jananah

D: 650 tons (fl) **S:** 11 kts **Dim:** 54.0 (50.0 pp) × 11.0 × 2.8
A: 2 single 12.7-mm mg **Electronics:** Radar: 1 . . . nav.
M: 2 MTU diesels; 2 props; 1,248 bhp **Range:** 1,800/11 **Crew:** 10 tot.

Remarks: 350 dwt. Can carry four medium tanks and can also transport fuel and water cargo. Have a large crane. Built at Argos Engineering Pty facilities, under lease. Were numbered L 5401 through L 5403 until 2001.

Disposal note: The logistics landing craft *Ghagha II* is civilian owned and operated, as are two Russian-built Serna-class high-speed landing craft.

♦ 2 PushyCat-class dockyard tugs [YTM]
Bldr: Gamen, Gorinchem, the Netherlands (In serv. 1998)

2001 Temsah 2002 Ugaab

Temsah (2001) Maritime Photographic, 1999

D: approx. 90 tons (fl) **S:** . . . kts **Dim:** 16.50 × 5.00 × 1.80
Electronics: Radar: 1 . . . nav.
M: 2 Volvo Penta TAMD-122A diesels; 2 props; 760 bhp **Crew:** . . . tot.

Remarks: Ordered in 4-96 for service at Abu Dhabi to attend the two *Kortenaer*-class frigates. Have a firefighting monitor on a platform abaft the mast.

MINISTRY OF THE INTERIOR COAST GUARD

Personnel (2002): 110 officers, 1,090 enlisted

Note: As of 2000, craft were being painted with a black hull (with red diagonal stripe) and white superstructure.

PATROL CRAFT [WPC]

♦ 2 Protector class
Bldr: FBM Marine, Cowes, U.K. (In serv. fall 1999)

P 1101 . . . . . . P 1102 . . . . . .

D: 180 tons (fl) **S:** 35 kts **Dim:** 33.00 (29.00 pp) × 6.70 × 1.90
A: 1 20-mm 90-cal. Mauser AA in Coulverine mounting; 2 single 12.7-mm mg
Electronics: Radar: 1 . . . nav.—E/O: SAGEM optronic f.c. and surveillance
M: 2 MTU 16V396 TE94 diesels; 2 props; 5,920 bhp
Electric: 160 kw tot. (2 × 80-kw Stamford generators, MTU diesels driving)
Range: . . ./. . . **Fuel:** 15 tons **Crew:** 14 tot.

Remarks: Ordered during 1-99 under Project LEWA-3. Were to be delivered in fall 1999 but have probably been delayed or canceled. Aluminum construction. A Zodiac RIB with a 25-bhp Yamaha outboard motor is carried aft.

PATROL BOATS [WPB]

♦ 1 (+ . . .) Ghantut class
Bldr: Seaspray Aluminum Boats Emirates (In serv. 2-00)

561 Ghantut

D: . . . tons **S:** 30 kts **Dim:** 17.00 (15.10 wl) × 5.66 × 1.20
A: . . . **Electronics:** Radar: 1 Decca BridgeMaster . . . nav.
M: 2 MTU 12V183 TE72 diesels; 2 props; 1,620 bhp
Range: 350/25 **Fuel:** 4,000 liters **Crew:** 5 tot.

Remarks: Intended for search-and-rescue and patrol duties. Has a Sitex 800 GPS terminal and Koden HFD/F.

Note: Emirates Marine Technologies, Abu Dhabi, has built a prototype Hurricane-50 high-speed patrol launch. It employs a Kevlar/epoxy planing hull and is equipped with a Furuno GPS terminal and VHF communications. The design is also offered with gas turbine propulsion. The prototype remains company property. Characteristics:

D: 9.8 tons (fl) **S:** 70 kts **Dim:** 15.30 × 3.50 × 0.90
A: . . . **Electronics:** Radar: 1 Simrad LCD nav.
M: Three Seatek . . . diesels; 3 Arneson outdrives with Rolla surf.-piercing props; 3,000 bhp
Range: . . ./40 **Fuel:** 1,200 liters **Crew:** 3–6 tot.

♦ 3 18.1-meter class
Bldr: C.N. Baglietto, Varazzo, Italy (In serv. 1993)

501 502 503

D: 22 tons (fl) **S:** 40 kts **Dim:** 18.1 × 4.3 × 0.7
A: 2 single 7.62-mm mg **Electronics:** Radar: 1 Decca . . . nav.
M: 2 MTU 12V183 TE 92 diesels; 2 props; . . . bhp **Crew:** 6 tot.

Remarks: Ordered in 1992. GRP construction.

♦ 6 GC 23 class
Bldr: C.N. Baglietto, Varazzo, Italy (In serv. 1986–88)

758 759 760 761 762 763

GC 23–class 758 Maritime Photographic, 3-99

D: 40 tons light; 44.50 tons std. (48 fl) **S:** 41.8 kts (38 sust.)
Dim: 23.00 (20.00 wl) × 5.50 × 1.17
A: 1 20-mm 90-cal. Oerlikon GAM-B01 AA; 2 single 7.62-mm mg
Electronics: Radar: 1 . . . nav.
M: 2 MTU 12V396 TB93 diesels; 2 props; 3,560 bhp (2,960 sust.)
Electric: 64 kVA **Range:** 700/20 **Fuel:** 7,500 liters
Endurance: 4 days **Crew:** 9 tot.

Remarks: Design derived from the Italian customs *Meattini* class. Has an aluminum-magnesium alloy hull and superstructure. The first unit, paid for by Dubai, was delivered in 3-86; the second, paid for by Abu Dhabi, in 5-86; and the third and fourth, paid for by Dubai, on 14-7-87 and during 9-87. The last two units were delivered in 1988.

♦ 12 Shark 33 class
Bldr: Al-Shaali Marine, Dubai (In serv. 1993–94)

From among: 310 through 323

Shark 33–class 310 NAVPIC-Holland, 5-96

D: . . . tons **S:** . . . kts **Dim:** 10.06 × . . . × . . .
A: 1 7.62-mm mg **Electronics:** Radar: 1 Koden . . . nav.
M: 2 Yamaha gasoline outboards; 500 bhp **Crew:** 2–4 tot.

Remarks: Ordered in 1992. An enlarged version of the Shark 28 class. Have GRP-construction hulls. Al-Shaali is the successor to Gulf Craft.

♦ 23 Shark 28 class
Bldr: Gulf Craft, Dubai (In serv. 1992–93)

200 series

Shark 28–class 299 Maritime Photographic, 3-99

COAST GUARD PATROL BOATS [WPB] *(continued)*

D: . . . tons **S:** . . . kts **Dim:** 8.53 × . . . × . . .
A: 1 7.62-mm mg **Electronics:** Radar: 1 Koden . . . nav.
M: 2 Yamaha gasoline outboards; 500 bhp **Crew:** 2–4 tot.

Remarks: Ordered in 1992. GRP construction.

♦ **16 P-63A-class** Bldr: Camcraft, New Orleans, La. (In serv. 9-78)

650 through 665

P-63A-class 660 NAVPIC-Holland, 5-96

D: 50 tons (fl) **S:** 25 kts **Dim:** 19.2 × 5.5 × 1.5
A: 1 20-mm 90-cal. Oerlikon GAM-B01 AA
M: first two: 2 G.M. 12V71 TI diesels; 2 props; 1,400 bhp—others: 2 MTU 6V396 TB93 diesels; 2 props; 1,630 bhp
Crew: 8 tot.

Note: Also in use are several aluminum-hulled, outboard-powered open launches that can be transported on road trailers (with 200-series pennants) and several wooden-hulled dhows (100-series pennants).

AMPHIBIOUS WARFARE CRAFT

♦ **1 or more Sea Spray raiding craft [WLCP]**
Bldr: Halmatic, Southampton, U.K. (In serv. 1993)

Sea Spray assault RIB Stefan Marx, 3-95

D: 4 tons (fl) **S:** 38 kts **Dim:** 9.5 × 3.0 × 0.6
A: 1 7.62-mm mg **M:** 2 Yamaha gasoline outboards; 450 bhp
Crew: 3 tot. + 11 commandos

Remarks: Ordered for counterterrorist duties in 6-92. Have GRP hulls with an inflatable collar at the gunwale.

♦ **8 Arctic-28-class rigid inflatable launches [WLCP]**
Bldr: Halmatic, Northam, U.K. (In serv. mid-1993)

D: 4 tons (fl) **S:** 38 kts **Dim:** 9.00 × 2.90 × 0.30 **A:** 1 7.62-mm mg
M: 2 OMC gasoline outboards; 450 bhp
Range: 250/. . . **Fuel:** 1,100 liters **Crew:** 1 tot. + 8 troops

Remarks: Basic hull constructed of GRP. Intended to carry commandos.

SERVICE CRAFT

♦ **2 FPB 512–class diving tenders [WYDT]** Bldr: Rotork Marine, U.K.

D: 8.8 tons (fl) **S:** 12 kts **Dim:** 12.7 × 3.2 × . . .
Electronics: Radar: 1 Decca 060
M: 2 Volvo Penta diesels; 2 Castoldi Type 06 waterjets; 430 bhp
Range: 100/12 **Crew:** 3 tot.

Remarks: Have GRP hulls and bow ramps.

♦ **2 Arun-class pilot boats [WYFL]**
Bldr: Halmatic, Havant, U.K. (In serv. 1992)

D: 34 tons (fl) **S:** 18 kts **Dim:** 15.85 × 5.34 × 1.50
M: 2 Caterpillar 3412 diesels; 2 props; 1,000 bhp **Crew:** 5 tot.

Remarks: 34 grt. Kevlar construction hull. Basic design, with low amidships freeboard, was intended for search-and-rescue duties but is also ideal for pilot boat use.

ARMY SPECIAL OPERATIONS COMMAND

SWIMMER DELIVERY VEHICLES [LSDV]

♦ **. . . Class 5**
Bldr: Eurotec Industries (Emirates Marine), Abu Dhabi (In serv. 1996–. . .)

D: 3.5 tons (light) surf. **S:** 7 kts sub. **Dim:** 9.1 × 1.15 × . . .
M: 1 Alstom/Parvex electric motor; 10.7 shp
Electronics: Sonar: 1 obstacle avoidance; 1 echo sounder
Range: 60/6 **Endurance:** 10 hr **Crew:** 2 tot.

Remarks: Have an 80-mm-thick hull composed of nine layers of GRP and carbon-fiber composite. There are two externally mounted nickel-cadmium batteries. Normal operating depth: 30 m; maximum diving depth: 50 m. Are equipped with a GPS receiver, autopilot, and magnetic compass. The obstacle-avoidance sonar has a range of 150 m. The divers ride in cockpits; their breathing system uses either onboard or personal equipment. Payload: 450 kg. The design was ordered by two Middle East countries on 20-3-01.

♦ **. . . Class 4**
Bldr: Eurotec Industries (Emirates Marine), Abu Dhabi (In serv. 1994–. . .)

D: 1.3 tons (light) surf. **S:** 7 kts sub. **Dim:** 7.35 × 0.95 × . . .
M: 1 Alstom/Parvex electric motor; 10.7 shp
Electronics: Sonar: 1 obstacle avoidance; 1 echo sounder
Range: 60/6 **Endurance:** 10 hr **Crew:** 2 tot.

Remarks: Have an 80-mm-thick hull composed of nine layers of GRP and carbon-fiber composite. There are two externally mounted silver-zinc batteries. Normal operating depth: 30 m; maximum diving depth: 50 m. Are equipped with a GPS receiver, autopilot, and magnetic compass. The obstacle-avoidance sonar has a range of 150 m. The divers ride in cockpits; their breathing system uses either onboard or personal equipment. Payload: 200 kg.

CUSTOMS SERVICES

Several of the component states of the United Arab Emirates operate their own customs service patrol craft. Dubai has two U.S. Swiftships 19.8-m Commercial Cruisers. In 1992, Abu Dhabi took delivery of two new 18.28-m pilot craft with GRP hulls molded by Tyler Boats from Berthon Boat; they each have two Caterpillar 3412-DITA diesels. In 1987, Sharjah received two 70-ton, 24-kt, 23.77-m customs patrol boats of modified oilfield crewboat design from Halter Marine, Moss Point, Miss.

Note: Dubai also has a marine police force for harbor patrol duties. It operates at least two Magellan 36 GRP-hulled, twin Yamaha outboard-powered patrol launches (Nos. 123 and 124) and at least one smaller, aluminum-construction launch (No. 007).

UNITED KINGDOM

United Kingdom of Great Britain and Northern Ireland

Personnel (1-01): 36,168 total Royal Navy (7,008 officers), 6,216 Royal Marines (677 officers), 2,290 Royal Fleet Auxiliary (820 officers), 3,121 Royal Naval Volunteer Reserve (958 officers), 17,400 Royal Naval Reserve, and 913 Royal Marine Reserve (81 officers). There are about 60,000 civilian administrative and dockyard employees.

Organization: Units of the Submarine Flotilla are assigned to the 1st Squadron at HMS *Neptune,* Faslane, Scotland, and the 2nd Squadron, HMS *Defiance,* Devonport, England. Units of the Surface Flotilla are assigned with the 3rd and 5th Destroyer Squadrons and the 45th Frigate Squadron, all based at Portsmouth, England, and the 1st, 2nd, and 6th Frigate Squadrons at Devonport. Mine Countermeasures Flotilla units are assigned to the 1st, 2nd, and 4th Squadrons at Portsmouth. Fishery Protection Squadron ships are based at Portsmouth and Surveying Squadron units at Devonport.

Bases: Operational headquarters at Joint Support Unit, Northwood, near London (but during 4-02 was to move to Whale Island, Portsmouth). Naval bases at Portsmouth (Commander-in-Chief, Naval Home Forces; Headquarters, Royal Marines; Flag Officer, Portsmouth; and Flag Officer, Surface Flotillas), Devonport (Flag Officer, Sea Training), Faslane (Flag Officer, Scotland, Northern England, and Northern Ireland), and Gibraltar (Commander, British Forces Gibraltar). Naval air stations are RNAS Yeovilton at HMS *Heron,* Yeovil, Somerset, and RNAS Culdrose at HMS *Seahawk,* Culdrose, Cornwall. Submarine training is carried out at HMS *Raleigh,* Tor Point, Cornwall. The Royal Marine Special Boat Service is based at Poole, Dorset.

The joint services Royal Hospital at Haslar is to close in 2002. The naval air station at HMS *Osprey,* Portland, was decommissioned during 3-99, and RNAS Prestwick at HMS *Gannet,* Prestwick, Scotland, is to be effectively closed by the end of 2002. The gunnery training school, HMS *Cambridge,* near Plymouth, England, was closed on 30-3-01, with training transferred to HMS *Raleigh* and HMS *Dryad,* Portsmouth.

Naval Aviation: First-line operational aircraft include 28 Sea Harrier FA.2 V/STOL fighters, 12 Merlin HM.1 and 31 Sea King HAS.5/6 ASW helicopters, 9 Sea King AEW.2A AEW helicopters, 29 Sea King HC.4 troop-carrying helicopters, 43 Lynx HAS.3/HMA.8 light shipboard helicopters, and 6 Lynx AH.7 and 9 Gazelle AH.1 assault helicopters. Land-based maritime patrol aircraft operated by the Royal Air Force (RAF) include 19 Nimrod MR.2P maritime patrol and 2 Nimrod R.2 EW aircraft. A more complete listing of aircraft, organization, and characteristics is found in the Naval Aviation section following the aircraft carrier [CV] listing.

Royal Marines: The principal operationally deployable component of the Royal Marines is 3 Commando Brigade, headquartered at Plymouth. Subordinated to it are 40, 42, and 45 Commando, which deploy with combat support and combat services elements seconded from the British Army: 29 Commando Regiment Royal Artillery, 59 Independent Commando Squadron Royal Engineers, and the Commando Logistic Regiment. The first Royal Marines armored vehicle, the 10.5-ton Viking armored personnel carrier, was unveiled during 7-01; it carries 12 personnel, including the driver.

Royal Fleet Auxiliary: Major auxiliary and supply vessels are responsible to the Royal Fleet Auxiliary (RFA), an organization manned by uniformed civil servants; the total number of personnel is being reduced to 2,050. The ships are built to the specifications of Lloyd's of London (compartmentation, damage control, and habitability) and also meet the standards of the Shipping Naval Acts of 1911 and of the Ministry of Transportation. In 1985, it was decided to reclassify all RFA ships as "government-owned vessels"; this was modified on 30-11-89 to place the vessels under the Director General of Supplies and Transport (Navy), Ministry of Defence (Navy). Since 1994, the head of the Royal Fleet Auxiliary has been a flag officer coequal with other type commanders. The ships fly the blue ensign of the reserve, rather than the white ensign.

Marine Services Agency: On 3-12-94, the Royal Maritime Auxiliary Service (RMAS) became the Marine Services Agency. On 28-2-96, the contract to perform most Marine Services Agency functions was let to SERCO-Denholm, effective 8-7-96, while some other specialized work is being carried out by a government-owned corporation based at Pembroke Dock, Wales. All craft operated by SERCO-Denholm were transferred to its control on 12-8-96 on bareboat charter and will continue to be U.K. government owned, to wear former RMAS colors, and to fly the RMAS ensign. Former RMAS craft based at Gibraltar were transferred to Commander, British Forces Gibraltar, and are operating with civilian crews under Marine Services Gibraltar.

Maritime Volunteer Service: At the time of its disestablishment on 1-4-94, the Royal Naval Auxiliary Service (RNXS) had 2,700 personnel at 64 ports in the United Kingdom, assigned to 12 vessels and 25 port headquarters. The organization was effectively reborn the same month as the non-government-funded Maritime Volunteer Service (MVS), with around 2,000 civilian volunteers in 46 units (now 50). *Loyal Moderator* (A 220), the first of a planned 16 craft, was acquired in 3-95, and the former Thames Port Health Authority tender *Londinium I* was acquired in 9-96. Former Sea Cadet ship *Appleby* was acquired in 4-99. The craft are not considered government property. Since 7-5-98, the Royal Navy has been providing informal advisory assistance, but not financial aid, to the MVS.

Shipbuilders and Major Component Manufacturers: British Aerospace (now styled BAE Systems) and GEC-Marconi Electronic Systems merged in 1999, bringing all but one major British naval shipbuilding yard under one management; BAE Systems now controls the Vickers Shipbuilding & Engineering, Ltd. (VSEL), Kvaerner Govan, and Yarrow yards and also manufactures command systems, radars, sonars, naval guns, and torpedoes; its 49.95% share in Thomson-Marconi Sonar was sold to Thales in 2001. BAE Systems also owns the former Siemens Plessey and BAeSEMA concerns under its BAE Defence Systems, Ltd. (BAeDSL).

Vosper Thornycroft, Woolston, the U.K.'s only other major naval shipbuilder, purchased Halmatic on 3-11-98 and has moved Halmatic's assets to its Portchester yard. Racal Marine was purchased by Sperry Marine (a division of Litton Industries, now Northrop Grumman) in the U.S.A. during 1998 but is retaining its corporate identity; former owner Racal Electronics became a part of France's Thales on 11-10-00.

WEAPONS AND SYSTEMS

A. MISSILES AND BOMBS

Note: The missile design, development, and manufacturing efforts of France's Aérospatiale Matra and the U.K.'s BAE Systems (including its subsidiary Alenia Marconi Systems) were combined early in 3-01 as MBDA, which stands for Matra BAE Dynamics, Alenia Marconi Systems, and Aérospatiale Matra.

♦ Strategic ballistic missiles

Trident-2 D-5 Bldr: Lockheed

A U.S. missile with a delivery vehicle and payload of British design and manufacture and an independent trajectory (MIRV) capability. The agreement for the acquisition of Trident was signed 14/15-7-80. A total of 58 Trident missiles (of an originally planned 80) were acquired, and they have British-built A-90 warheads. During 7-98, submarines on patrol were limited to a maximum of about 48 warheads each. The missiles are serviced at King's Bay, Ga., in the United States. The Royal Navy's "fewer than 200" nuclear warheads are Britain's only nuclear weapons.

♦ Surface-to-surface missiles

Since 8-77, 300 U.S. UGM-84 Sub-Harpoon antiship missiles have been acquired for submarine use. RGM-84C Harpoon Block IC, in the GWS.60 system for surface launching, is carried aboard Type 23 (Duke-class) and Type 22 (*Cornwall*-class) frigates. Additional AGM-84C Harpoons have been procured for use on RAF Nimrod aircraft. All submarine-launched Harpoons are to be retired by 2008.

All MM 38 Exocet missiles (formerly used on the Type 22 Batch I and II frigates and on trucks based at Gibraltar for coast defense) had been retired by 1999.

For the Project Horizon replacement frigate program, there is a requirement for a weapon with a 150- to 200-km range capable of inflicting mission kill on a 1,000- to 4,000-ton warship and also able to deal with "very fast, armed patrol boats." A shore-bombardment variant is also foreseen.

At the end of 2000, the navy was considering the use of a fiber-optically guided missile for use by submarines against seaborne, coastal, and aerial targets, in part to replace the Sub-Harpoon.

Tomahawk (BGM-109 Block III) Bldr: Raytheon Systems, U.S.A.

Some 65 U.S. Tomahawk BGM-109 Block III land-attack cruise missiles were ordered in 10-95 for around $280 million for use from *Swiftsure*-, *Trafalgar*-, and *Astute*-class submarines. *Splendid* (S 106) launched up to a dozen Tomahawk missiles at Serbian targets on 24-3-99 (20 replacement missiles were ordered 1-8-99), while another three were launched at terrorist targets in Afghanistan during 10-01. Another 48 missiles, Block IIIC, were requested during 10-01. See U.S. section for system details.

♦ Surface-to-air missiles

Sea Dart (GWS.30) Bldr: MBDA

A medium-range system using the Mk 30 Mod. 2 launcher on Type 42 destroyers. By 1985, 1,000 had been delivered, of which 500 had been fired by late 1986. Another 100 with G.Mk.39 A1 fragmentation warheads were ordered in 3-86. The Type 909 fire-control radars were updated under a 5-87 contract with Marconi. Plans call for refurbishing all existing airframes; an infrared fuze will be fitted, and other improvements in low-altitude capability and response time are being made. The weapons system is planned to be retired by 2015. Has a limited antiship capability.

Length: 4.40 m **Diameter:** 0.42 m **Wingspan:** 0.91 m
Weight: 550 kg **Warhead:** 22.7 kg, expanding-rod
Propulsion: solid-propellant booster, ramjet sustainer
Speed: Mach 2.5–3.0 **Range:** 35 n.m. max. **Altitude:** 100–60,000 ft.
Guidance: semiactive homing **Fire control:** Type 909 radar

Sea Wolf (GWS.25/26) Bldr: MBDA

GWS.25 is fitted on Type 22 frigates in a trainable launcher containing six missiles (total weight with missiles: 3,500 kg). Target designation is via the combined Type 967-968 radar. The GWS.25 Mod. 3 fire-control system employs the Marconi Type 911 (ex-805SW) search-and-track radar, with DN 181 Blindfire guidance, and upgraded features to the Type 967-968 radar.

The GWS.26 vertical-launch version is carried by the Type 23 frigates. By 3-95, some 950 vertical-launch versions had been ordered. Under a 2-00 contract, the third (and planned final) buy of missiles was ordered; deliveries of the Block II missiles are to begin during 2004, with the missiles having Mk 4 SWELL (Sea Wolf Enhanced Low Level) dual-action fuzes, which will also be backfitted to existing missiles starting in 2002.

Alenia Marconi Electronic Systems was selected in 9-98 (but not contracted until 12-00) to update the GWS.25 Mod. 3 and GWS.26 Mod. 1 systems; an E/O sensor is to be added to the Type 911 tracking radars, while improvements to the radar trackers will increase acquisition range and improve low-altitude performance in clutter. The upgrades will be performed between 2006 and 2011. Data for the Sea Wolf missile include:

Length: 1.9 m **Diameter:** 0.3 m **Wingspan:** 0.56 m
Weight: 82 kg **Warhead:** 13.4 kg
Speed: Mach 2.5 **Range:** 5,000 m nominal **Guidance:** radar
Fire control: Marconi Type 910 and 911 pulse-doppler radars, which permit control of two-missile salvos, or electro-optical tracker

Javelin (GWS. . . .) Bldr: Thales Air Defense (formerly Short Missile Systems)

The Royal Navy began purchase of the shoulder-launched Javelin (successor to Blowpipe) in 6-84 and conducted initial at-sea firings shortly thereafter. Its guidance is semiautonomous line-of-sight. The weapon is issued to deployed units of all types for terminal defense. The 12.7-kg Javelin missile is 1.4 m long, has a range of 4,000 m, and employs a two-stage rocket motor.

Starstreak/Seastreak (GWS. . . .)
Bldr: Thales Air Defense (formerly Short Missile Systems)

The successor to Javelin is Starstreak, a Mach-0.4, 1.27-m-long missile with a range of 7 km. The first 1,000 production Starstreak missiles were ordered during 5-95 for use by the British Army and the Royal Marines.

Note: The Royal Marines also employ mobile Rapier area-defense SAM batteries.

♦ Air-to-surface missiles

Note: A successor to Sea Skua began initial planning in 1999. In addition to the missiles listed below, RAF Nimrod aircraft can be fitted with AGM-84C Harpoon antiship missiles.

Sea Skua (CL 834) Bldr: MBDA

Developed for use by Lynx helicopters, which can carry two or four. Single-stage solid-fuel propulsion. The air-launched version has been exported to Brazil, Germany, Turkey, and South Korea. Under a 5-97 contract, existing missiles are being given life-extension overhauls. An export surface-ship version has been developed for small surface combatant use, with initial trials launches conducted in late 1988, but only one sale has been made to date, to Kuwait.

Length: 2.50 m **Diameter:** 0.25 m **Wingspan:** 0.72 m
Weight: 145 kg **Warhead:** 20 kg high explosive
Speed: Mach 0.8 **Range:** 15,000 m **Guidance:** semiactive

Sea Eagle (P3T) Bldr: MBDA

Developed from the Anglo-French, television-guided Martel, Sea Eagle uses active radar guidance and employs the French Microturbo/Toulouse TRI-60 engine for propulsion. Its first aerial launchings took place in spring 1981. Indian Navy Sea Harrier, Il-38 May, and Tu-142MKE Bear F Mod. 3 aircraft and Indian Air Force Jaguar attack aircraft carry the weapon, which has also been sold to Malaysia for use with Hawk 100 and Hawk 200 light attack aircraft. Sea Eagle was withdrawn from British use during 2-00.

Length: 4.0 m **Diameter:** 0.4 m **Wingspan:** 1.2 m
Weight: 600 kg **Speed:** Mach 0.85 **Range:** 250 km

♦ Bombs

Invincible-class aircraft carriers have 500- and 1,000-lb. conventional bombs for use by Sea Harrier fighter-bombers.

♦ Air-to-air missiles

AMRAAM (AIM-120A) Bldr: Raytheon Systems, U.S.A.

A long-range weapon used by the Sea Harrier FA.2. The first 100 were ordered in early 1993, with a total of 210 planned; first deliveries were in 1995.

Length: 3.65 m **Diameter:** 0.178 m **Weight:** 151.5 kg
Warhead: 22.7 kg **Range:** more than 74 km
Guidance: inertial midcourse, active terminal homing

WEAPONS AND SYSTEMS *(continued)*

Sidewinder-1B (AIM-9L) Bldr: Raytheon Systems, U.S.A.

An infrared-homing, solid-fuel, Mach-2.5, lightweight weapon employed by Sea Harrier FA.2 V/STOL aircraft.

Length: 2.90 m **Diameter:** 0.127 m **Wingspan:** 0.61 m
Weight: 84.4 kg **Speed:** Mach 2.5 **Range:** 12 n.m.

B. GUNS

114-mm Mk 8 Bldr: Vickers

A light, single-barrel gunmount with a glass-reinforced plastic housing installed on the Type 42 destroyers and Type 23 and Type 22 Batch 3 frigates. The mounts on the Type 23 frigates are to be upgraded to Mk 8 Mod. 1 standard, with a saving of 6 tons per ship as well as reduced space requirements below decks. The 11 guns aboard the Type 42 destroyers may be upgraded to Mk 8 Mod. 2 status and reused aboard the Project Horizon replacement program frigates; the weapons would lose the ready-service feed ring in favor of a hoist directly to the magazine. Development of an extended-range High Effect/Extended Range round weighing 20.6 kg and with a muzzle velocity of 869 m/sec was ordered from Royal Ordnance in 8-97; it will have a range of 29 km.

Length of barrel: 55 calibers **Shell weight:** 21.0 kg
Rate of fire: 25 rds/min **Arc of elevation:** −10° to +53°
Max. effective range for surface fire: 23,000 m
Max. effective range for antiaircraft fire: 6,000 m

114-mm Mk 6 Bldr: Vickers

A double-barrel, 45-cal., semiautomatic, dual-purpose gun, phased out of Royal Navy service in 1992 but still found on *Leander*-class frigates in the Indian, New Zealand, and Chilean navies. It uses variable-fuzed shells with proximity and point-detonating fuzes of variable sensitivity.

Muzzle velocity: 850 m/sec **Rate of fire:** 10–12 rds/min/barrel
Max. effective range for surface fire: 17,000 m
Max. effective range for antiaircraft fire: 6,000 m

30-mm twin Bldr: Oerlikon/Royal Ordnance

Twin GCM-A03-2 mounts. Eight mounts were procured during 1982 from BMARC (now Royal Ordnance) as emergency close-defense weapons for Type 42 destroyers, and additional mounts were acquired later. Optical lead-computing sights. Rate of fire is 500 rds/min/barrel and effective range is 2 km.

30-mm DS-30B single Bldr: Royal Ordnance

A stabilized single mounting for the Mauser-designed 30-mm gun. In 9-84, 25 were ordered for the Type 23 frigates and to begin replacement of old 40-mm mounts; by 7-90, 63 total had been ordered. There are 160 rounds ready service on-mount.

Projectile weight: 0.36 kg **Muzzle velocity:** 1,080 m/sec
Rate of fire: 650 rds/min **Effective range:** 3 km

30-mm Goalkeeper (SGE-30) CIWS Bldr: Thales Nederland

The G.E. GAU-8A, 30-mm gatling gun in an EX-30 mounting comounted with the Thales radar detect-and-track fire-control system. Fifteen mounts have been procured. For characteristics, see the Netherlands section.

20-mm Oerlikon Bldr: Royal Ordnance

Large numbers of single-barrel, British-made Oerlikon GAM-B01 mountings were procured in 1982–83 to augment close defense on a variety of classes. A 90-cal. weapon with a 1,000-rd/min firing rate and an optical, lead-computing sight on-mount, it has an effective range of 2 km.

20-mm Phalanx Mk 15 CIWS Bldr: General Dynamics (U.S.A.)

Six U.S. Mk 15 Mod. 0 CIWS (Close-In Weapon System) mounts were purchased in 5-82 for use on the *Invincible*-class carriers. Additional mountings have since been ordered for Type 42 destroyers, the amphibious warfare ships *Ocean* and *Fearless,* and the replenishment ships *Fort Victoria* and *Fort George.* It uses the six-barrel G.E. Vulcan gatling gun; see the U.S. section for details.

Note: World War II–era 20-mm 70-cal. Oerlikon Mk 7A single mounts remain aboard three Type 42 destroyers and on several auxiliaries.

7.62-mm machineguns

Standard NATO 7.62-mm light machineguns, having been found very useful during the Falklands War for disrupting low-level air attacks, were added in considerable numbers to frigates and destroyers, using simple pintle mountings.

C. ANTISUBMARINE WEAPONS

Mk 10 Mortar (Limbo)

A triple-barrel mortar, based on the Squid of World War II, that fires 177-kg time-fuzed shells, each with 94 kg of Minol explosive. Range: 400–1,000 m. It was retired from Royal Navy service in 1992, but is still aboard a small number of British-built warships in the Chilean, Indian, Indonesian, Iranian, and Pakistani navies.

Mk 11 Mod. 3 depth charge

Dropped from helicopters against shallow targets. Has also been sold to Brazil, Chile, Egypt, France, India, and Pakistan.

Length: 1.4 m **Diameter:** 280 mm **Weight:** 145 kg **Warhead:** 80 kg

D. TORPEDOES

Spearfish Bldr: BAE Systems

The heavyweight replacement for Tigerfish; began development in 1981. Has a HAP (Hydrogen-Ammonium Perchlorate)-Otto fuel system and a 900-shp turbine engine with pumpjet propulsor. One hundred preproduction models, ordered in 1982, completed delivery in 1993 after protracted development and reliability problems; the average cost was $14.6 million each. In 12-94, a 10-year, $950 million contract was placed for an additional 300 weapons; the first units were delivered in 9-99 and the last are due for delivery by late 2004.

Diameter: 533 mm **Length:** 8.50 m
Weight: 1,850 kg **Warhead:** 300 kg
Speed: 75 kts (55 sust.) **Range:** 40 km **Depth:** 900 m max.

Mk 24 Tigerfish Bldr: BAE Systems

A wire-guided weapon for submarines. It entered service in 1980; 2,000 were on order by 1986, but its total production for the Royal Navy is said to have been only about 750. Originally known as ONGAR. To improve reliability, the 600 Mod. 1 units in service were updated to Mod. 2 from 1986 to mid-1988. Licenses to assemble the weapon have been granted to Chile, Indonesia, and Turkey.

Diameter: 533 mm **Length:** 6.464 m
Weight: 1,551 kg **Warhead:** 134 kg, magnetic and impact-fuzed
Speed: 35 kts **Range:** 16 km at 35 kts; 22 km at 24 kts

NST 75 11 Stingray Bldr: BAE Systems

The lightweight antisubmarine torpedo replacement for Mk 44 and Mk 46 for use by surface ships and aircraft. It officially entered service in 1986, although it was present during the Falklands War in 1982. Electric powered, with a pumpjet propulsor. Contracts were let in 1996 to develop an improvement package to upgrade existing torpedoes; the upgraded Stingray Mod. 1 will enter service in 2004. About 3,500 Stingrays have been built for the U.K., Norway, Egypt, and Thailand.

Diameter: 325 mm **Length:** 2.60 m **Weight:** 267 kg
Warhead: 45 kg Torpex **Speed:** 45 kts max. **Range:** 8 km at 45 kts

E. MINES

Stonefish Bldr: BAE Systems

A medium-depth, modular magnetic/acoustic/pressure mine for launch by aircraft, surface ships, or submarines. The original version, described below, is being supplemented by a shorter, lighter Mk 2 version with 500 kg of PBX explosive. There is also a training version. It has been bought by Australia, Finland, the U.K., and two unnamed countries.

Length: 2.4 m (exercise version: 1.9 m) **Diameter:** 533 mm
Weight: 990 kg (exercise version: 440 kg) **Warhead:** 700 kg Torpex
Service life in water: up to 700 days **Shelf life:** 20 years

Dragonfish Bldr: BAE Systems

A lightweight, anti-invasion mine for use in waters to 30-m depths. About 85 kg in weight, it carries 80 kg of explosive and has a 200-day in-water lifetime.

Note: Also still in inventory are a number of older Mk 12, Mk 17, and Mk 28 mines (for details, see Norman Friedman, *The Naval Institute Guide to World Naval Systems, 1997–1998*), and the Vickers Versatile Exercise Mine System, a 2.71-m-long, 533-mm-diameter, 560-kg device that can be laid and recovered, simulating virtually any known type of mine for training.

F. RADARS

♦ Navigational radars

1006(1): 9,650 MHz. In submarines; a navalized Kelvin-Hughes 19/9A.
1006(2), 1006(3): 9,445 MHz. In major surface units.
1006(4): 9,425 MHz. In mine countermeasures ships.
1007: Kelvin-Hughes Series 1600, plus the Red Pac I-band (3-cm) nav. radar with manual plot. Replaces Type 1006.
1008: Racal-Decca Marine set, derived from commercial, E/F-band BridgeMaster series to supplement Type 1007 in some combatants. First orders were announced in 9-95. In 4-00, 19 BridgeMaster-E 180, X-band versions were ordered for use on support ships.

Note: Auxiliaries use a number of different commercial navigational radars, primarily the Decca 1226 and 1229 models. Smallcraft employ Decca, Raytheon, or Furuno commercial sets.

♦ Combined air- and surface-search radars

967-968: Paired back-to-back antennas, 967 in L band (1,260–1,360 MHz) and 968 in S band (2,950–3,040 MHz). Employed with the GWS.25 Sea Wolf system in Type 22 frigates. Type 967M has pulse-doppler to detect small targets. Rotates at 30 rpm. Incorporates Type 1010 interrogator for Mk XII IFF.
994: S-band. BAE Systems (ex-Plessey) AWS-4 on Castle-class patrol ships and the auxiliary *Argus.* Uses quarter-cheese antenna from the obsolete Type 993.
996: S-band (2,850–3,100 MHz). The 996/2 version is a 3-D replacement for Type 992Q in older ships. The 996/1 version is for Type 23 frigates. Also used for target designation. Has a stabilized antenna. The BAE Systems AWS-9(3D) is the current commercial version. Under a 5-99 contract with BAE Systems, are being upgraded with improved cooling systems and better target track extraction to reduce false-alarm rates.

♦ Air-search, early-warning radars

965: P-band. Long-range early warning. Still found in the Indian and Chilean navies. The AKE(2) antenna is a double-deck AKE(1). Type 965M has moving-target indicator feature.
1022: L-band. Thales Nederland LW-08 radar with a Marconi antenna, installed on the *Invincible* class and Type 42 destroyers. Incorporates the Cossor 850 IFF interrogator. Has an approximate range of 225 n.m. Rotates at 6–8 rpm.
ASTRAL (Air Surveillance and Targeting Radar, L-band): In development as a replacement for Type 1022. Uses a rotating planar array. To have 400-km range.
SAMPSON: Active phased-array radar for the canceled Project Horizon program, under development by BAE Systems. A new semispherical, two-faced rotating antenna array was introduced in 1998 to reduce wind resistance and topside weight.

WEAPONS AND SYSTEMS *(continued)*

♦ Weapons-control radars

909: For the Sea Dart system (also controls the 114-mm Mk 8 gun in the Type 42 destroyers).
911: Marconi ST805 SW for the Sea Wolf GWS.25 Mod. 3 system in Type 22 frigates and, as 911(2), for vertical-launch Sea Wolf in the Type 23 frigates. The land-based Blindfire radar uses part of the same antenna array.

♦ For aircraft

Blue Kestrel: Multifunction; for Merlin helicopters.
Blue Vixen: Multifunction; for Sea Harrier FA.2.
Searchwater: I-band. For surface search in Nimrod patrol aircraft and air and surface search in Sea King AEW.2 helicopters. Frequency-agile.
Searchwater 2000: I-band. Racal set to be installed in updated Nimrod 2000 patrol aircraft and Sea King AEW helicopters.
Sea Searcher: I-band. For use by Sea King HAS.6 ASW helicopters in interrogating the LAPADS sonobuoy system.
Sea Spray: Surface search and target designation; for Lynx helicopters.

G. SONARS

♦ For surface ships

Type	*Function/Remarks*	*Freq. (kHz) or Band*	*Maker*
185	Underwater telephone	8–9	Graseby
193M	Minehunting	100–300	Thales
2008	Underwater telephone	HF	Admiralty
2009	Underwater telephone/IFF	HF	. . .
2015	Bathythermograph	N/A	. . .
2016	Hull, 360° scan	5.5/6.5/7.5	Thales
2031(Z)	Towed passive	. . .	Thales
2034	Side-scan	110	Waverly
2048	"Speedscan," PMS 75 fwd-looking mine avoidance	HF	Thales
2050	Hull, 360° scan	4.5–7.5	Thales
2053	Side-scan mine locator	HF	. . .
2057	Towed passive Type 2031(Z) replacement	. . .	Thales
2059	Minehunting ROV tracker	HF	Mills Cross
2060	Bathythermograph	N/A	. . .
2065	Thin-line array for Type 2057	. . .	. . .
2066	Torpedo expendable countermeasure system	N/A	. . .
2068	Raypath predictor (SEPADS)	. . .	. . .
2070	U.S. SLQ-25A Nixie decoy (four sets procured in 1998)	. . .	Freq. Eng. Labs
2080	"Talisman" (joint British-French design project for surface-ship suite	LF	. . .
2087	Bistatic towed array (in development)	VLF	Thales
2093	Minehunting	HF	Thales
2095	Minehunting	HF	Thales
2193	Minehunting (to replace Type 193M from 2004 on)	HF	Thales

♦ For submarines

Type	*Function/Remarks*	*Freq. (kHz) or Band*	*Maker*
183	Underwater telephone	. . .	. . .
197	Echo sounder	HF	. . .
728	Upward-looking echo sounder	HF	. . .
780	Upward-looking echo sounder	HF	. . .
2007	Passive flank array	1–3	BAC
2008	Passive flank array		
2019	PARIS intercept	2–14	Thales
2020	Active/passive bow (submarine version of Type 2016; uses same array as Type 2001; 2020EX is an upgrade)	5.5–5.7 active/ 2–16 passive	Thales
2027	Passive ranging (uses Type 2001 and 2020 arrays)	. . .	. . .
2032	Bow array beam-former for Type 2020	VLF	. . .
2035	Sonar frequency analyzer	. . .	. . .
2039	Recording bathythermograph	N/A	. . .
2046	Processor display/50-m towed array (27 on order)	. . .	Thales
2047	16-channel processor/freq. analyzer	. . .	. . .
2066	Bandfish torpedo-countermeasure	. . .	Dowty
2071	Noise augmentation decoy	. . .	. . .
2073	Emergency pinger	. . .	A.B. Prec.
2074	Bow active/passive replacement for Type 2001/2020; uses Type 2020 array	. . .	Thales
2076	Designation for entire suite for SSNs, includes Types 2074, 2077, and 2081 (in design)	. . .	Thales
2077	Ice-navigation set for SSNs	HF	. . .
2081	Environmental sonar/nonacoustic suite	. . .	Chelsea Instr.
2082	Sonar intercept to replace Type 2019	. . .	Thales
2090	Integrated Bathymetric Information System	. . .	Dowty

Remarks: Type 2087 will be employed by surface ships and will incorporate an active, 500-Hz, LF hull sonar and a VLF passive towed array operating down to 100 Hz and weighing around 3 tons. The development contract was let in 2-95 to Babcock Defence Systems, working with Westinghouse (U.S.A.), Indal (Canada), and Systemtechnik Nord (Germany), but Thomson-Marconi is still in competition for the order, which has been delayed to spring 2001. The contract was to be let early in 2001—an 18-month delay over the original target—but it was again opened in mid-2001.

Two Type 2081 sensor packets are carried by SSNs. They measure water temperature, fluorescence, bioluminescence, and other ambient oceanographic phenomena.

♦ For helicopters

Type	*Function/Remarks*	*Band*	*Maker*
2069	Upgraded Type 195M for Sea King	HF	Thales
2095	Dipping	HF	Thales

Remarks: Type 2095 uses the FLASH (Folding Light Acoustic System for Helicopters) array in conjunction with an AQS-950 processor.

♦ Sonobuoys

In use are the Australian SSQ-981 Barra and the U.S. SSQ-904 and SSQ-906 Jezebel, SSQ-954 and -954B Miniature DIFAR, and SSQ-963A CAMBS (Command Active Multi-Beam Sonobuoy). Some 100,000 SSQ-955 HIDAR (High Instantaneous Dynamic Range) sonobuoys were ordered from Ultra Electronics for $52 million early in 1998 for delivery from 2000 through 2003.

H. DATA SYSTEMS

ADAWS 8: On the three oldest Type 42 destroyers.
ADAWS 10: Aerial and ASW defense; an update for the ADAWS 5. Fitted on the *Invincible*-class aircraft carriers.
ADIMP (ADAWS Improvement Program): Entered service on Type 42 destroyer *Manchester* in 1993; 14 total were ordered for the *Invincible* class and the final eight Type 42 destroyers. Uses two F 2420 computers to sextuple the processing power of the earlier ADAWS 7 (itself an improved ADAWS 4). Has Racal LFB and LFC automatic radar track recorders and LFD track combiner, as well as Ferranti LFA for the Type 996 radar interface. Supports NATO Link 10, 11, 14, and 16 datalinks.
CACS 1 (Computer-Assisted Command System): In the Type 22 Batch 3 frigates. Has two Ferranti FM 1600E computers and 12 Argus M700 miniprocessors.
CCA (Captain's Combat Aid): MUSL system for the *Invincible* and Type 42 classes; being added to Type 22 frigates as well.
SAGOP (Semi-Automated Gun Course Plotting Station): Installed on 18 ships equipped with 114-mm guns; was being given a naval gunfire support function as of 1998.
SSCS (Surface Ship Command System): Successor to the abortive CACS 5 for the Type 23 frigates; ordered during 10-89. Has parallel processing, modular software, and Link 11 and 14 capability.

Note: A number of other computerized command support and combat management systems are in development. The Pilot Flag Support System (PFSS) uses the U.S. JOTS I target position database software and acts as an intelligent datalink terminal; it has been installed in Type 42 Batch C destroyers. The Fleet Ocean Surveillance Product (FOSP) provides track correlation and dynamic updating of onboard databases, in conjunction with the ship's Link 11 terminal. An Admiralty Research Establishment data fusion system has undergone trials in the Type 23 frigate *Marlborough.*

I. COUNTERMEASURES

Note: The various active countermeasures systems are known as "Outfits."

♦ Surface ship and submarine systems

Electronic systems:
CXA(1): EADS Telegon-6 communications direction finder for submarines. Part of the UAP(1) suite. CXA(1) was to have been replaced by CXA(2), the EADS Telegon-12, by 12-96, but delays resulted in cancellation in 5-98; it will now be replaced by a new system to be built by either Raytheon E-Systems or Sanders.
Soothsayer: Lockheed Martin Systems Integration–Owego and Thales-Racal vehicle-mounted land system for Royal Marine use. Formerly called EW2000, it was ordered in 2000 to enter service in 2006 and will cover communications and radar frequencies in support of countermeasures.
UA-14: Racal portable radar threat warning system for use on smallcraft and helicopters.
UAA(2): Covers 1–18 GHz. Used in Type 42 destroyers, Type 22 frigates, and *Invincible*-class carriers. Made by RRDS (Racal Radar Defense Systems; now part of Thales).
UAA(3): In development to replace UAA(2).
UAD: U.S. SRD-19 direction finder portion of the Outboard suite (U.S. SSQ-108 system).
UAE: ELINT array based on the EM Systems S-3000 (0.5–18 GHz).
UAF(1): Thales Cutlass intercept suite for Type 23 frigates. Associated with Type 675 or commercial Cygnus jammers. Systems in *Illustrious* and early Type 23 frigates were upgraded in 1995–96.
UAG(1): Thales E- to J-band (2–27 GHz) intercept on the *Fort Victoria* class; Mentor 2 is the commercial name.
UAK: A component of the Outboard combat direction finding suite. Upgraded by Sanders and Siemens-Plessey during 1996–98.
UAN(1), UAN(2): Thales Guardian shipboard version of the aircraft MIR-2 Orange Crop. Covers 0.6–18 GHz and is used on Castle-class patrol ships and the helicopter ship *Argus.*
UAP(1), UAP(3): Thales suite in submarines, UAP(1) in SSNs and UAP(3) in *Vanguard*-class SSBNs.
UAR(1): Thales Matilda radar warning set. Covers 7.5–18 GHz and is aboard Hunt-class mine countermeasures ships and the repair ship *Diligence* and is on survey ships when used as mine countermeasures support ships.
UAS(1): Falcon RX-740 set added to frigates and destroyers on Persian Gulf deployment. Covers 1,000 MHz–18 GHz.
UAT(1): Made by Thales for use on Type 23 frigates. Covers 2–40 GHz, with a 360° sweep from −15° to +30°. Has a 255-track capacity and a 2,000-mode threat library. Based on Sceptre XL. UAT(2) and UAT(3) are land-based prototypes and training versions.

WEAPONS AND SYSTEMS *(continued)*

UAT(5), UAT(6): Thales variant in Type 22 frigates and Type 42 Batch 2 and 3 destroyers, with antenna Outfit UCB(1).
UAT(7): Replacement for UAF in early Type 23 frigates; also used on aircraft carriers and the helicopter carrier *Ocean* and to be in the *Albion*-class LPDs.
UBB(1): Replacement system for Type 42 destroyers and Type 22 frigates. Will cover 0.5–18 GHz. May use existing antennas.

Jammers:
RCM-3: Gate-stealing jammer by Decca. Being added to large surface combatants.

Note: The Type 670 and Type 675(2) jammers were phased out by the end of 2000, without replacement.

Decoy systems:
Bandfish: Type 2066 expendable submarine acoustic decoy.
DEC: Laser dazzling device to confuse or incapacitate aircraft pilots and infrared-homing missiles.
DLB: Hunting Engineering's six-tube, 130-mm Sea Gnat launcher, deployed in groups of four and equipped to fire Chemring Mk 214 Mod. 1 RF seduction and Royal Ordnance Mk 216 Mod. 1 RF distraction rounds and chaff mortar rounds. In some, two rear 130-mm tubes are replaced with 102-mm tubes for launching N4 broadband chaff distraction rockets. The Mk 251 Siren active decoy round was to enter service during 2001, by which time seven ships were to have been converted to employ it.
DLC: Vickers Corvus eight-tube, 102-mm launcher, often with a 50-mm flare launcher atop. Fires N4 broadband chaff distraction rockets and is mounted two per ship. No longer used by the Royal Navy, it is still found in a few foreign fleets.
DLD: U.S. Raytheon (ex-Hycor) Mk 137, six-tube launcher for the Mk 36 SRBOC system. Mounted four per ship in some auxiliaries. Fires Mk 182 chaff mortar rounds.
DLE: Thales Shield six-tube, 102-mm launcher, mounted four per ship and firing N5 broadband chaff rockets. Eleven systems were procured.
DLF(1): Irvin Aerospace Rubber Duck floating corner reflectors.
DLF(2): Irvin Replica floating reflector. Used by the U.S. Navy as SLQ-49. Can create the illusion of a 50,000-m^2 target.
DLF(3): Replacement for DLF(2). The initial order was for 16 ship sets, to include 70 buoys per ship. Can create the illusion of a 50,000-m^2 target. Uses four fixed, horizontal, tubular, compressed-air launchers. Existing sets are "cross-decked" to deploying ships.
DLH: Marconi/Dassault (now Thales) SIREN offboard, 7.5- to 17.5-GHz, active, parachute-retarded aerial jammer. Launched from 130-mm DLB and DLJ Sea Gnat countermeasures rocket launchers. Forty sets were planned but may not have been procured.
DLJ(1), DLJ(2): Decoy launcher outfits for large ships: DLJ(1) uses four DLB and four DLD; DLJ(2) uses eight DLB launchers and is on *Invincible, Illustrious, Fearless, Argus, Fort Victoria,* and *Fort George.*
DLK: Wallop Defence Systems Barricade 57-mm lightweight infrared and chaff decoy rocket launcher. By 1991, 27 sets, each with two 18-barrel launchers, were in service.

Note: Mk 8 114-mm guns can fire Chaff Charlie I- or J-band chaff rounds, and helicopters can manually drop Chaff Hotel.

Commercial equipment:
Type 242: Thales (ex-Racal) integrated intercept/jammer suite, with Cutlass, Scorpion, and Sadie processor.
Cutlass: Thales (ex-Racal) intercept. Covers 0.6–18 GHz, with 5 MHz/5° accuracy.
Matilda-E—Microwave Analysis Threat Indication and Launch Direction Apparatus; lightweight, low-cost intercept system by Thales (ex-Racal). Six portable sets were on British mine countermeasures ships by 1989.
Mentor A/B/C: BAE Systems (ex-Marconi) intercept sets. Coverage to 40 GHz. Mentor 2002, introduced in 1993, covers 1–18 GHz and incorporates a jamming system and Shield rocket decoy launchers; a Falcon DS-301A, 2- to 500-MHz communications intercept receiver is optional.
Sabre: Thales intercept for submarines. Covers 0.6–40 GHz, with 5 MHz/2° or 8° accuracy.
Sarie: BAE Systems Selective Automatic Radar Identification Equipment; an add-on for existing EW suites.
Sceptre: Thales (ex-CME, ex-Philips/Racal) intercept suite: Sceptre 0 for small ships, Sceptre X for corvettes, and Sceptre XL for large combatants.
Scimitar: Thales (ex-CME, ex-Philips/Racal) deception/jammer.
Scorpion: Thales (ex-Racal) wide-beam jammer. It can jam 5–8 targets and has 50-kw output between 7.5 and 18 GHz and a 1.5-second response time. Integrates with the Outfit UAF(1) console.
Shield: BAE Systems (ex-Siemens-Plessey) decoy rocket launcher. Shield I uses six-tube launchers. Shield III, with an improved central processor, comes in 12-, 18-, and 24-tube versions for different-sized ships. Launches P8 time-fuzed chaff rockets and P6 infrared decoy rockets.
Siren: BAE Systems (ex-Marconi) offboard jammer.
UltraBarricade: Decoy launch system offered by Wallop Defence Systems and Grintek of South Africa. Has 24 chaff and dual-band IR rocket decoys on a trainable mounting that can also accommodate two tubes for larger decoys and even small surface-to-air missiles. The control system also provides optimum course-to-steer for the ship's helmsman.

♦ Helicopter systems

Yellow Veil: Jamming equipment on Lynx HAS.3 and Sea King HAS.6 helicopters. Derived from U.S. Whitaker ALQ-167(V). Used to protect surface ships as well as the carrying aircraft.

♦ Torpedo decoys

SLQ-25A Nixie: U.S.-made torpedo decoy equipment. Four sets were purchased during 1997.
SSTD (Surface Ship Torpedo Defense System): Ultra Electronics was selected during 11-01 as the prime contractor for the British version of the SSTD, but a contract was not expected until 2002 and the system will not enter service until at least 2004 (and probably considerably later). Some 65 ships will be equipped to use SSTD, a system to detect, classify, and locate torpedoes and to assist in the use of expendable countermeasures, but only about 23 ship-sets are to be procured. SSTD will use the U.S. Frequency Engineering Laboratories SLQ-25A Nixie towed decoy, the TRAMP (Torpedo Recognition Acoustic Multibeam Processor) sonar processor, a towed passive sonar deployed with the Nixie, and a variety of expendable countermeasures that have yet to be developed.
Submarine countermeasures: Four-inch (102-mm)-diameter decoy launchers are employed: Mk 6 in the *Swiftsure* class, Mk 8 in the *Trafalgar* class, and Mk 10 in the *Vanguard* class.
Type 182: An obsolescent towed noisemaker, aboard surface combatants.

J. COMMUNICATIONS

The Royal Navy employs the Skynet super high frequency (SHF) satellite communications system in carriers, destroyers, and frigates, although since there are not sufficient sets, only units deploying or fully operational carry the twin SCOT (Satellite Communications Terminal) radomes, which are 1–2 m in diameter and operate in the 500-MHz band. Royal fleet auxiliaries, hydrographic ships, and corvettes of the Castle class carry the commercial Intelsat SATCOM system. Shipboard LF/MF/HF/VHF systems are increasingly integrated and are among the best in the world; single-sideband is extensively employed. Eight frigates are equipped with the Stand-Alone Message Processing (SAMP) system. All large combatants are Link 11 equipped, and Marconi Electronic Systems (now BAE Systems) received a contract in 9-96 to provide Link 16 interoperability for the Type 42 destroyers and *Invincible*-class carriers.

BAE Systems has developed an improved SR(S) 7392 HF broadcast multichanneling capability using digital hardware and new software to permit existing equipment to increase the number of channels in operation; the system will enter service in 2004. Alert Communications is supplying a new Outfit SEZ HF communications set that allows up to four broadcasts to share one broadcast channel for transmission; the system was in seven ships by fall 2000, including the submarine *Trafalgar,* mine countermeasures ship *Brocklesby,* and RFA oiler *Gold Rover.*

V/STOL AIRCRAFT CARRIERS [CVH]

♦ 0 (+ 2) . . . . . . class

Bldr: . . . . . .

	Laid down	L	In serv.
R	. . .	. . .	2012
R	. . .	. . .	2015

Thales concept for an angled-deck carrier with a catapult rather than a ski jump Thales, 2000

BAE Systems concept for a carrier with a ski jump takeoff and vertical landing BAE Systems, 2000

V/STOL AIRCRAFT CARRIERS [CVH] *(continued)*

BAE Systems concept for a conventional carrier with an angled deck and two catapults BAE Systems, 2000

Thales concept for a ski-jump carrier Thales, 2001

D: 40,000–60,000 tons (fl) **S:** . . . kts **Dim:** 250.0–340.0 × . . . × . . .
Air group: 40 F-35 JSF fixed-wing strike fighters and up to 10 helicopters
A: . . .
Electronics:
Radar: . . .
Sonar: . . .
EW: . . .
M: 4 Rolls-Royce WR-21 intercooled recuperative gas turbines, electric drive; 2 props; 100,000 shp
Electric: . . . kw tot.
Range: . . ./. . . **Fuel:** . . . tons **Crew:** 1,000+ tot.

Remarks: The 7-98 Defence White Paper confirmed that two conventional carriers would be built to replace the *Invincible* class. The U.S. F-35B or F-35C JSF (Joint Strike Fighter) will form the principal component of the air group. On 5-5-99, two consortia bid on the carrier development program: BAE Systems, teamed with Marconi Electronic Systems (soon thereafter owned by BAE), Rolls-Royce, and Harland & Wolff SY; and France's Thales, teamed with Lockheed Martin Naval Electronics and Surveillance Systems, Raytheon Systems, and British Marine Technology. Both consortia received preliminary design contracts on 23-11-99 and "assessment phase" design contracts on 21-11-01. The ships are to cost about $1.8 billion each. The construction contract is planned to be placed in 2004. The names *Eagle* and *Furious* have been proposed for the pair.

The ships will be built at facilities operated by Harland & Wolff, Belfast; VSEL at Birkenhead or Barrow; Kvaerner at Govan; or, pending renovations, Swan Hunter at Tyneside.
Hull systems: There is some indication that the ships may displace as much as 50,000 tons full load, and BAE Systems has offered a 53,000-ton design with a ski-jump bow and an angled deck incorporating either a steam or electromagnetic catapult. The preferred propulsion plant is four WR-21 intercooled recuperative gas turbines, with shaft-mounted electrical generators to provide propulsion and ship's service power. The ships would have inboard elevators to reduce radar signatures.
Aviation systems: Although initially said to be intended to carry the U.S. F-35C JSF V/STOL strike fighter, which would not require catapults or arrestor gear, the ships may instead be configured to handle a navalized version of the Eurofighter, the Dassault Rafale-M, or the Boeing F/A-18E/F, which would significantly reduce the number of aircraft that could be carried and increase the cost of the ships—for no particular gain in warfighting capability. A contract to design an electromagnetic catapult for potential use in the ships was to be let in 2001. They are to be able to generate 150 combat sorties per day. As yet, there are no indications that any defensive armament system is to be installed.

♦ 3 Invincible class (1 in *reserve*)

	Bldr	Laid down	L	In serv.
R 05 *Invincible*	Vickers, Barrow	20-7-73	3-5-77	11-7-80
R 06 Illustrious	Swan Hunter, Wallsend	7-10-76	14-12-78	20-6-82
R 07 Ark Royal	Swan Hunter, Wallsend	14-12-78	4-6-81	1-11-85

Ark Royal (R 07) Maritime Photographic, 8-01

Ark Royal (R 07)—note the enlarged flight deck parking area to starboard of the ski-jump ramp Royal Navy, 7-01

Ark Royal (R 07)—note the removal of the Type 909 missile directors Derek Fox, 8-01

V/STOL AIRCRAFT CARRIERS [CVH] *(continued)*

Ark Royal (R 07)—after activation refit Royal Navy, 7-01

Illustrious (R 06)—with Type 909 directors removed Maritime Photographic, 1-01

Invincible (R 05)—under way on own power at Portsmouth Douglas A. Cromby, 7-01

Invincible (R 05) Douglas A. Cromby, 7-01

D: 16,970 tons (20,710 fl) **S:** 28 kts
Dim: 210.00 (192.87 wl) × 36.0 (27.50 wl) × 6.5 (8.8 over sonar dome)
Air group: R 06: 6 Sea Harrier FA.2 Sea Harrier; 4 Harrier GR.7; 7 Sea King HAS.6; 3 Sea King AEW.2A; 2 Sea King HC.4 (see remarks)—R 07: 6 Sea Harrier FA.2; 4 Harrier GR.7; 4 (later 6) Merlin HM.1; 3 Sea King AEW.2A
A: R 05, R 06: 3 30-mm Goalkeeper gatling CIWS—R 07: 3 20-mm Mk 15 Phalanx gatling CIWS—all: 2 single 20-mm 90-cal. Oerlikon GAM-B01 AA
Electronics:
Radar: 2 Kelvin-Hughes Type 1007 nav.; 1 BAE Systems Type 996(1) surf./air search; 1 Thales Type 1022 early warning; 3 Thales Goalkeeper (R 07: General Dynamics Mk 90) f.c. suite
Sonar: BAE Systems Type 2016 hull-mounted; Type 762 echo sounder; Type 185 underwater telephone
TACAN: R 06 only: Collins AN/RN-139(V)
EW: R 05, R 07: UAT(7) intercept—R 06: UAT(8) intercept—all: UAD/UAK (U.S. SSQ-108(V)2) communications intercept and D/F; 8 6-round DLJ(2) decoy RL; Type 182 towed acoustic torpedo decoy—R 05 also: UCB(1) EW control processor
M: 4 Rolls-Royce Olympus TM-3B gas turbines; 2 props; 112,000 shp (94,000 sust.)
Electric: 14,000 kw (8 × 1,750-kw Paxman Valenta 16-RPM 200A diesel alternator sets)
Range: 7,000/18
Crew: 60 officers, 625 enlisted + air group: 80 officers, 286 enlisted

Remarks: R 05 was ordered 17-4-73, R 06 on 14-5-76, and R 07 in 12-78. They were redesignated "ASW aircraft carriers" in 1980, previously having been considered a type of cruiser. Only two are operational at any one time. The ships can embark 960 marines for short periods. All three are homeported at Portsmouth. R 07 departed Portsmouth 6-5-99 and began a $176 million reactivation and modernization overhaul at Rosyth 11-5-99; she was redelivered 13-7-01 and rededicated 22-11-01 and was to reenter operational service in spring 2002. R 05 underwent a short overhaul late in 1999; she was placed in reduced readiness reserve in 5-01 and began a refit in 11-01 in preparation for layup until commencing a modernization and reactivation overhaul in 2003. R 06 is to begin a 23-month refit in 7-02.
Hull systems: Modifications to R 06 in 1998–99 added about 160 tons to the displacement. All have the Prairie/Masker hull and propeller bubble system to reduce acoustic signature.
Aviation systems: R 05 and R 06 originally had a 7° "ski jump" to assist Sea Harrier aircraft in making rolling takeoffs at full combat load. The ramp on R 07 was inclined 12° and was 12 m longer. The ramp in R 06 is now inclined 13°, and R 07 has been

V/STOL AIRCRAFT CARRIERS [CVH] *(continued)*

altered. The 183-m-long by 13.5-m-wide flight deck was slightly angled to port to clear the now-removed Sea Dart SAM launcher. The single-level hangar has three separate bays, with the amidships bay narrower to permit passage of the gas-turbine exhaust trunks. The two 9.7 × 16.7–m hydraulic, scissors-type aircraft elevators were to be replaced by Strachan & Henshaw chain-type elevators, but funds were not provided. RAF Harrier GR.7 strike fighters form an integral part of the air groups when these ships are deployed, and all Sea Harrier FA.2 and Harrier GR.7 aircraft are now under the Joint Force Harrier command. R 07 is the first Royal Navy ship to operationally deploy the new Merlin helicopter.

As modified, R 06 is expected to carry up to a full expeditionary air group of eight Sea Harrier FA.2, eight Harrier GR.7, four Sea King AEW.2, and two Sea King HAS.6, with five other HAS.6 deployed to accompanying auxiliaries.

Combat systems: Have the ADAWS 10 combat data system, employing NATO Link 10, 11, and 14 datalinks and, in R 05 and R 06, the Link 16 JTIDS (Joint Tactical Information Distribution System). The ADIMP (ADAWS Improvement Combat Data System) fitted in R 06 and R 07 was installed in R 05 in 1999. The UAD/UAK communications intercept system employs the U.S. SSQ-108(V)2 Outboard communications intercept–D/F system, with the SRD-19 direction finder, SLR-16 intercept receiver, and OK-324/SYQ system supervisor station. Active units have two SCOT-1C antennas for the Skynet SHF SATCOM system and also have an Intelsat commercial SATCOM terminal. R 06 has a temporary TACAN capability to permit safer operation of RAF Harriers; the system was installed in 12-00 and was adapted from equipment intended for airborne use.

Modifications: The Sea Dart SAM system has been removed from all three, starting with R 06 during her 7-98 to 16-3-99 refit. R 05 was similarly altered during an 8-99 to 2-00 refit at Portsmouth, but in addition had the two Type 909 missile-control radars removed and was fitted to operate Merlin HAS.1 helicopters. The Type 909s were originally retained on R 06 but were removed late in 2000. The vacated space has been used to enlarge the parking area of the flight deck by 8% so as to better accommodate RAF Harrier GR.7 fighter-bombers, and the Sea Dart magazine space has been converted for GR.7 weapons stowage; beneath the 23 × 18–m flight deck extension are some 22 new compartments. Additionally, R 06 received Link 16 capability, UAT(8) EW suite in place of UAF(1), and addition of the UCB(1) electronic warfare control processor and an automated command decision aid.

During her reactivation overhaul at Rosyth, R 07 received the Integrated Electronic Warfare Control Processor, with UAT intercept, two Type 675 jammers (now removed), Sea Gnat, and DLH decoy equipment, as well as other modifications like those performed on R 06. The ship was also equipped to operate and maintain Merlin helicopters. The three U.S. Mk 15 Phalanx CIWS were retained and not updated.

Note: The helicopter transport/training ship *Argus* (A 135) was intended to be able to carry up to 12 Sea Harriers and to operate eight of them, although she is considered primarily to be a source of additional aircraft to act as spares for the carriers. The new "Aviation Support ship" *Ocean* has been redesignated as an assault helicopter carrier [LPH] and is discussed in the section on amphibious warfare ships.

NAVAL AVIATION

The Fleet Air Arm consists of first-line squadrons (whose designations are characterized by a group of three figures beginning with an 8) with missions of attack, ASW, or helicopter assault. Second-line squadrons (whose designations are characterized by three figures beginning with a 7) are used in schools and for tests and maintenance.

Operationally assigned aircraft of the Royal Navy included (as of 8-01):

Qty.	*Type*	*Function*	*Squadrons*
28	Sea Harrier FA.2	attack/interceptor	800, 801, 899
2	Harrier T.8N	training	899
12	Merlin HM.1	ASW	700M, 814, 824, 829
26	Sea King HAS.6	ASW, logistics	810, 820
5	Sea King HAS.5	SAR	771
29	Sea King HC.4	troop-carrying	845, 846, 848
9	Sea King AEW.2A	early warning	849
25	Lynx HAS.3	ASW, attack, transport, training	702, 815
18	Lynx HMA.8	ASW, attack, transport, training	702, 815
13	Jetstream T.2	training	750
2	Jetstream T.3	liaison	HMS *Heron* Comms. Flt.
12	Hawk T.1/T.1A	training	FSATO (ex-FRADU)*
6	Lynx AH.7	assault	847
9	Gazelle AH.1	assault	847
3	HS.125	VIP transport	RAF detachment
1	Turbine Defender	ASW research	Director General, Underwater Weapons

* RAF-owned aircraft used for a variety of attack simulation training and operated by Hunting Contract Services with civilian pilots on behalf of the Fleet Support Air Tasking Organisation (FSATO) from RNAS Culdrose, Cornwall; the unit is known as FRADU (Fleet Requirements and Air Direction Unit), its former official name. The Hawks often work with the three Falcon 20 radar signal simulation aircraft operated by FR Aviation, Bournemouth.

Note: Operational control of the Sea Harrier force came under the RN/RAF Joint Force 2000 Harrier command on 1-4-00; all operational Sea Harriers will move from Yeovilton to RAF Cottesmore in 2003 and be incorporated in No. 3 Group, RAF Strike Command (also in 2003, 899 Sqn. training will be moved to RAF Wittering, where it will be united with RAF 20R Squadron).

Eight HAS.5 aircraft of 819 Sqn., HMS *Gannet,* Prestwick, Scotland, were retired during 2001, leaving a detachment of two in SAR service at that location. Nine HAS.6 of 814 Sqn. were retired during 11-00, and the squadron was reconstituted with four (later to be six) Merlin HM.1 helicopters on 5-10-01. 829 Sqn. will stand up in 2002 to support six small-ship Merlin flights for frigates, and 820 Sqn. will stand up in 2003 to support a second carrier squadron. 824 Sqn., established 2-6-00, performs Merlin training at Culdrose.

Operated by FR Aviation, Ltd., for target and EW training are nine Dassault Falcon 20, one Beech C55 Baron, and two Cessna 441 Conquest II; the same company operates and maintains the 12 Hawk trainers of the FRADU. Seven of the Falcon 20 aircraft simulate threats using ALE-43 active emitters, BOZ-3 chaff launchers, and other EW gear; the other two have ALQ-167(V) jammer pods. Several Hawk T.1 jet trainers are used as training and support aircraft.

Basic flying training was contracted out as of 1-4-94, with Hunting Services providing 20 Slingsby T.67M Mk.II Firefly trainers for initial training of both RAF and RN pilots. Helicopter training is carried out at the triservice Defence Helicopter Flying School, RAF Shawbury and RAF Valley; employed in training RN, RAF, and British Army helicopter pilots are 9 HT.1 Griffin, 26 HT.1 Squirrel, and 12 HT.2 Squirrel helicopters (the latter at 670 Sqn., Middle Wallop). 727 Sqn. was established 6-12-01 at Plymouth to recruit future pilots and observers and offers up to 12 hours of initial flying training, using Grob light trainers and instructors contracted from VY Aerospace.

COMBAT AIRCRAFT

Fixed-wing aircraft:

Note: The U.S. Lockheed Martin F-35 Joint Strike Fighter has been selected for procurement of up to 150 examples as the Future Joint Combat Aircraft, to be operated by the RN/RAF Joint Force 2000 from land and shipboard. Whether the U.S. Navy F-35B version or the smaller-winged U.S. Marine Corps F-35C version will be procured has not yet been decided.

♦ Sea Harrier FA.2 Manufacturer: British Aerospace

Sea Harrier FA.2 Jaroslaw Cislak, 6-98

RAF Harrier GR.7 in Royal Navy colors Maritime Photographic, 3-98

Wingspan: 7.60 m **Length:** 14.50 m **Height:** 3.71 m
Weight: 10,500 kg **Speed:** Mach 0.96 (1.2 in a dive)
Propulsion: 1 Rolls-Royce Pegasus 105 vectored-thrust turbojet; 9,750 kg thrust
Ceiling: 50,000+ ft. max. **Range:** VTOL: 50 n.m.; STOL: 200 n.m.
Armament: 2,270 kg total: 6 AIM-120 AMRAAM, 2 30-mm Aden cannon, 454 kg of bombs
Avionics: Blue Vixen multimode radar

Remarks: The former FRS.2 designator was changed to FA.2 during mid-1994 to reflect the dual attack/interceptor role. As of 8-01, 28 were operationally assigned and 19 were kept as spares or were in overhaul. Thirty-three Sea Harrier FRS.1 were converted to FA.2 standard, and a further 18 FA.2 were built as such, with the last delivered 18-1-99. Five of the seven two-seat Harriers were updated to T.8N standard to support training for the FA.2, the first completed 7-7-93 and the last by end-1995. All are to be retired between 2004 and 2006 and replaced by RAF Harrier ground-attack aircraft upgraded to GR.9 configuration.

FA.2 aircraft used in the Adriatic area have been equipped with GPS receivers and ALE-40 chaff/flare dispensers and can launch Paveway II laser-designated bombs. GPS receivers are now being added to all FA.2s, and they are later to receive Sky Guardian 200 radar warning receivers. All can use NATO Link 16. Sea Eagle antiship missiles are no longer carried.

Helicopters:

♦ Merlin HM.1 Manufacturer: AgustaWestland

Merlin HM.1—aboard frigate *Lancaster* (F 229) Ben Sullivan, 9-00

COMBAT AIRCRAFT *(continued)*

Merlin HM.1 Maritime Photographic, 9-00

Rotor diameter: 18.59 m **Length:** 22.81 m (15.75 folded)
Height: 6.50 m (5.21 folded) **Weight:** 6,917 kg empty (14,600 max.)
Speed: 167 kts (150 cruise)
Propulsion: 3 Rolls-Royce/Turboméca/Piaggio RTM.322-01/8 turboshafts (2,130 shp each)
Ceiling: 15,000 ft max.
Range/endurance: 5 hr on station at 100 n.m. operating radius; 1,150 n.m. ferry range
Armament: Four Stingray torpedoes or 30 troops to 200 n.m. radius; 6,000 kg underslung to 550 n.m. range
Avionics: Marconi Electronic Systems Blue Kestrel 5000 radar; Thales Type 2095 ADS (Active Dipping Sonar) with AQS-903 acoustic processor; Racal Orange Reaper (Kestrel) ESM (0.6–18 GHz coverage)

Remarks: On 2-9-91, 44 production variants ordered from the IBM-AgustaWestland consortium at a unit cost of about £97 million each, which has since risen to £101 million ($145 million). The program was five years behind schedule as of early 1998; they were originally to have entered service in 1999 aboard frigates and carriers. The 18th was delivered in 11-99, with the last to deliver in 2002. Nine preproduction prototypes were delivered between 1984 and 1990. The Merlin is also being procured by the British Army and by Italy; a Canadian order for a SAR variant was canceled in 11-93 but reinstated in 1997. Rather late in the game, it was discovered that the aircraft is too large to fit on the elevators of the *Invincible* class and too high to fit in Type 22 frigate hangars. In 7-98, the program was limited to 44 total airframes. Requires only one pilot and one systems operator in the ASW role. An improved HM.2 variant weighing 15,500 kg max. and with more-powerful RTM.322 engines, is under consideration; to enter service around 2009, it would have an improved radar and carry the Future Air-to-Service Guided Weapon (FASGW).

♦ Lynx HAS.3, HMA.8, and AH.7

Manufacturer: AgustaWestland

Lynx HAS.3 Maritime Photographic, 7-01

Lynx HMA.8—note the distinguishing nose sensor and EW antenna array
Jaroslaw Cislak, 7-01

Rotor diameter: 12.80 m **Length:** 15.16 m **Height:** 3.60 m
Weight: 4,716 kg **Speed:** 145 kts
Propulsion: 2 Rolls-Royce Gem 4 turboshafts (1,120 shp each)
Ceiling: 12,000 ft max.
Range/endurance: 1 hr 30 min (half in transit, half hovering); 340 n.m. max.
Armament: 2 Mk 46 or Stingray torpedoes, 2–4 Sea Skua ASM

Remarks: Data above apply to the HAS.3 version. The HAS.3 has a Sea Spray radar but no dipping sonar. Some are equipped with U.S. ALQ-167(V) Yellow Veil ECM; most have MIR.2 Orange Crop EW. As of 8-01, 25 HAS.3 and 18 HMA.8 Lynx were assigned to squadrons, with the others in overhaul or storage. Another 12 HAS.3 may be upgraded to HMA.8.

Three Lynx helicopters began trials late in 1989 as prototypes for the HMA.8 update: the weight was increased to 5,125 kg with the installation of Rolls-Royce Gem 42-1 turboshafts, composite rotor blades, a chin radome for an undetermined radar, and a new tactical data system. The HMA.8 Lynx also has Sea Owl infrared search and tracking equipment, CAE-made boom-mounted MAD gear, and the Sea Spray 3000 radar upgrade (which integrates the radar with the central tactical system).

Six Lynx AH.7 serve with 847 Sqn. in support of the Royal Marines. They are equipped to launch up to eight TOW antitank missiles and have a thermal-imaging sight.

♦ Sea King HC.4, HAS.5/6, and AEW.2A/7

Manufacturer: AgustaWestland

Sea King HAS.6 Piet Sinke, 11-00

Sea King HC.4 Maritime Photographic, 9-00

Sea King AEW.2A—with radome in operating position
Maritime Photographic, 6-99

Rotor diameter: 18.90 m **Length:** 22.15 m (17.03 fuselage; 14.40 folded)
Weight: 9,750 kg max. takeoff **Speed:** 126 kts cruise
Propulsion: 2 Rolls-Royce Gnome H.1400-1 turboshafts (1,535 shp each) driving a 5-bladed rotor and a tail rotor
Ceiling: 10,000 ft. max.
Range/endurance: 3 hr 15 min, normal mission
Armament: HAS.6: up to 4 Mk 46 or Stingray torpedoes or 4 Mk 11 d.c.; 1 or 2 7.62-mm mg (HC.4: 2,727 kg stores or 22 troops)

COMBAT AIRCRAFT *(continued)*

Remarks: All surviving HAS.2 helicopters have been updated to HAS.5, and some later to HAS.6, except for 10 converted as HAS.2A (now AEW.2A) airborne early-warning aircraft with Searchwater air/surface-search radar (with its antenna in an inflating radome on a pivoting arm to starboard). HAS.6 conversions and new aircraft have ASQ-504(V) MAD gear, Type 2069 dipping sonar, and AQS-9026 sonobuoy processor. Most HAS.5/6 have the Orange Crop EW suite. All HC.4 troop transports now come under joint operational control with British Army and RAF troop-support helicopters.

All AEW.2A are being updated to AEW.7 configuration with new Searchwater 2000 pulse-doppler search radar, a JTIDS terminal to provide Link 16 commonality, and new IFF and communications gear. The first production conversion was delivered during 4-01 and is to enter service in 2003.

♦ Gazelle AH.1 Manufacturer: AgustaWestland

Royal Marine Gazelle AH.1 Maritime Photographic, 9-00

Rotor diameter: 10.80 m **Length:** 9.52 m **Height:** 2.74 m
Weight: 908 kg empty (1,700 max.) **Speed:** 164 kts (140 cruise)
Propulsion: 1 Turboméca Astazou IIIA turboshaft; 562 shp
Ceiling: 16,730 ft. max. **Range:** 190 n.m.

Remarks: All are assigned to 847 Sqn. in support of Royal Marines for reconnaissance duties. Have "fenestron"-type shrouded tail rotor, a three-bladed main rotor, and a roof-mounted optical sight for antitank missiles. Can carry five personnel, including the pilot.

C. ROYAL AIR FORCE MARITIME AIRCRAFT

The RAF Strike Command was reorganized on 1-4-00. Its No. 3 Group, under a Royal Navy officer, includes the Nimrod force, search-and-rescue helicopters, and the Joint Force 2000 RN/RAF Harrier force. Maritime Patrol Aircraft of No. 18 (Maritime) Group include 19 Nimrod MR.2P aircraft in No. 120, 201, and 206 Sqns. Also in use are two Nimrod R.1P electronics aircraft, and two additional MR.2P are in storage.

Eighteen of the 21 surviving Nimrod airframes are to be rehabilitated and upgraded to Nimrod MRA.4 (formerly Nimrod 2000) configuration under a 7-96 contract, with the first aircraft originally to redeliver in 4-03 and the last in 2006; as of 3-99, however, the program was two years behind schedule, with the first aircraft to become operational in 3-05 or later. The modernized Nimrods are being re-engined with BMW–Rolls-Royce BR710 turbofans, the Racal Searchwater 2000MR surveillance radar will be fitted, and Boeing is to supply a new tactical command system; the U.S. Joint Tactical Information Distribution System (JTIDS, Link 16) is also being fitted.

The Raytheon/Racal Astor (Airborne Stand-Off Radar) synthetic-aperture imagery and moving-target detection radar system may be adapted for maritime surveillance after its initial entry into service in 2005 on five RAF Global Express land-based aircraft.

Nimrod MR.2P Bernard Prézelin, 7-01

Nimrod MRA.4—artist's concept M.O.D., U.K., 2001

NUCLEAR-POWERED BALLISTIC-MISSILE SUBMARINES [SSBN]

Note: Royal Navy submarines do not wear their pennant numbers. The assigned numbers are included here for reference only.

♦ 4 Vanguard class

Bldr: BAE Systems (formerly Marconi Marine–VSEL, formerly Vickers SB & Eng.), Barrow-in-Furness

	Ordered	Laid down	L	In serv.
S 28 Vanguard	30-4-86	3-9-86	4-3-92	14-9-93
S 29 Victorious	6-10-87	12-4-88	29-9-93	7-1-95
S 30 Vigilant	13-11-90	16-2-91	14-10-95	2-11-96
S 31 Vengeance	7-7-92	1-2-93	20-9-98	27-11-99

Victorious (S 29) Bernard Prézelin, 9-00

Victorious (S 29)—with tug above stern in background Bernard Prézelin, 9-00

Vengeance (S 31)—note the fixed bow planes M.O.D. U.K., 11-99

D: 15,850 tons (sub.) **S:** 25 kts sub. **Dim:** 149.30 × 12.80 × 10.10
A: 16 Trident D-5 ballistic missiles; 4 bow 533-mm TT (Spearfish and Tigerfish torpedoes)
Electronics:
Radar: 1 Kelvin-Hughes Type 1007 nav./search
Sonar: Type 2054 suite: Type 2043 active/passive; Type 2044 towed array; Type 2045 acoustic intercept; Type 183 underwater telephone
EW: Racal UAP(3) intercept suite; 12 SSE Mk 10 countermeasures tubes (Type 2066 Bandfish and Type 2071 decoys)
M: 1 Vickers–Rolls-Royce PWR.2 pressurized-water reactor, W. H. Allen steam generators, GEC-Alstom steam turbines; 1 pumpjet; 27,500 shp—2 Paxman diesel alternator sets for emergency power; 2,700 shp
Crew: 14 officers, 121 enlisted

Remarks: The program to replace the *Resolution* class began with the announcement on 15-7-80 of the selection of the Trident D-5 missile with eight multiple independent reentry vehicle (MIRV) warheads, necessitating use of a U.S. *Ohio*-class midsection (although the submarines are shorter than the U.S. submarine, as eight fewer missiles are carried). Require refit and recoring only every 8–9 years. The first ship cost £1,705 million, the second £974.9 million, and the third £929 million; the fourth was expected to cost £962.6 million. S 28 was formally christened on 30-4-92, began sea trials 23-10-92, and began her first operational cruise during 12-94; S 29 followed a year later. S 31 began sea trials 28-4-99 and entered operational service 13-2-01. All are based at Faslane, on the River Clyde, at a facility officially opened 14-8-93. S 28 began a four-year overhaul at Devonport during 2-02.

Since 7-98, only one has been on patrol at a time, carrying only 48 warheads vice the 92 originally to be carried; missile launch readiness has been lowered to "days" rather than minutes of warning. In 1995, the class was given a "substrategic" role, with Trident D-5 missiles effectively replacing RAF-delivered WE 177 bombs, without alteration to the delivery payloads on the missiles. Were to have a total of five crews for the three submarines to be in commission at any one time; initially, the first two had two crews and the third and fourth a single crew.

NUCLEAR-POWERED BALLISTIC-MISSILE SUBMARINES [SSBN] *(continued)*

Vigilant (S 30) M.O.D. U.K., 1998

Hull systems: Have an anechoic hull coating. The U.S. Rockwell SINS Mk 2 inertial navigation system is installed. The two Paxman diesel alternators charge a 480-cell battery group for emergency propulsion. Bow planes are permanently extended, an unusual and vulnerable arrangement. The hull contains some 80 km of piping and more than 500 km of cabling.
Combat systems: Have the Dowty SAFS 3 fire-control system with DCC(BN) digital tactical data-handling system. Pilkington Optronics CK 51 search and CH 91 attack periscopes are fitted. A stern-arc-covering sonar system is to be installed and integrated with the Type 2054 suite; this suite had reliability problems in S 28, and the towed passive sonar array has had to be attached as a "clip-on" system in all four rather than reeled within the outer hull.

Note: All four decommissioned *Resolution*-class SSBNs are stored, defueled, at Rosyth, where they are planned to remain until at least 2012.

NUCLEAR-POWERED ATTACK SUBMARINES [SSN]

Note: The number of SSNs in service is gradually to be reduced from 12 to 10. Plans are under way for a follow-on "Future Attack Submarine" class to begin replacing the original *Trafalgar* class around 2017–20. Submerged displacement will range from 5,000 to 8,000 tons. The PWR.2 reactor, with a core that would last the expected lifetime of the submarine, would provide power via electric drive. Vertical launchers for cruise missiles and facilities for remotely operated underwater reconnaissance vehicles may be incorporated. The staff target was to be issued around 2002.

During 7-01, to meet the Future Attack Submarine requirement, Devonport Dockyard (DML), teamed with Rolls-Royce, Thales, and BMT Defence Services, offered its C4500 SSN program, under which 4,500-ton, 84-m SSNs would be assembled at Devonport from modules built elsewhere. The submarines would have crews of 55 and interchangeable weapons modules for vertical-launch weapons or special forces vehicles.

Future Attack Submarine concept M.O.D., 1999

♦ 0 (+ 3 + 3) Astute class

Bldr: BAE Systems Marine (formerly Marconi Astute Class Limited/MACL), Barrow-in-Furness

	Start	L	In serv.
S 20 Astute	31-1-01	9-04	8-05
S 21 Ambush	2001	2005	8-07
S 22 Artful	2003	2007	2-09
S	2005	. . .	2010
S	2007	. . .	2012
S	2009	. . .	2014

Astute (S 20)—artist's rendering BAE Systems, 1999

Astute (S 20)—artist's rendering BAE Systems, 1997

D: 6,690 tons surf./7,200 tons sub. **S:** 29 kts sub. **Dim:** 97.00 × 11.27 × 10.0
A: 6 bow 533-mm TT (38 tot. weapons: UGM-109C Tomahawk missiles, Spearfish and Tigerfish torpedoes, mines)
Electronics:
Radar: 1 Kelvin-Hughes Type 1007 nav./search; 1 . . . bistatic radar receiver
Sonar: Type 2076 integrated suite (with Type 2074 active/passive bow array, Type 2077 HF under-ice nav. active, Type . . . towed passive array)
EW: Thales UAP(4) intercept suite; DML CESM comms intercept (HF–UHF); . . . decoy launchers for SCAD 101 and SCAD 102 decoys and SCAD 200 sonar jammers
M: 1 modified Rolls-Royce PWR.2 pressurized-water reactor, 2 sets GEC-Alstom geared turbine drive; 1 pumpjet; 27,000 shp—2 Paxman auxiliary diesel alternators for emergency propulsion syst.; 1 retractable auxiliary electric propulsor
Crew: 12 officers, 86 enlisted (accomm. for 110 tot.)

Remarks: Originally known as the *Trafalgar* Batch 2 (B2TC) class. Requests for bids to build the class were issued to VSEL and to Marconi Electronic Systems Naval Systems on 14-7-94 for an initial three with an option for one or two more. Marconi (which formed a special subsidiary for the project and is now part of BAE Systems, as is VSEL) was the winner, and the final contract was let 17-3-97 for a total of $3.18 billion. It was announced in 7-98 that two more would be ordered after 2000. Pressure hull components for S 20 began fabrication during 10-99. In 8-00, it was announced that a sixth would be sought, as a replacement for *Trafalgar* (S 107).
Hull systems: The reactor, with Type H core, is designed to operate for 25–30 years without requiring refueling. The hullform forward will resemble that of the *Vanguard* class, with nonretracting bow planes; the stern is fuller than in previous Royal Navy submarines, in part because the pressure hull is of constant diameter throughout, and all control services are externally actuated, reducing the number of pressure hull penetrations. Will have improved accommodations over the *Trafalgar* class, although some 18 bunks will still have to be shared. Low-speed operating capabilities will also be improved, and the submarines will be capable of operating under ice and in tropical waters. Will have two 440-V, a.c. Vosper Thornycroft main electrical switchboards. The originally planned submerged displacement was 6,510 tons. Normal maximum operating depth is to be 300 m.
Combat systems: Will have many of the same systems as the *Trafalgar* class, although the towed array will be deployed from an onboard reel rather than as a clip-on, and provision for Tomahawk missiles will be built in. The BAE Systems Submarine Command System (SMCS) combat system and Thales (ex-Ferranti-Thomson) tactical weapons system data highway will be installed. Are to have Links 11 and 16 and provision for Link 22 to support surface forces. Will have provision to carry U.S.-style dry deck shelters for special forces equipment. Will not employ nonpenetrating optronic optical sensors, but will have two Pilkington Optronics CM010 non-hull-penetrating masts with periscope, optronics, and ESM antennas, permitting more room in the control spaces. Are to have a Thales Sensors (ex-Racal) bistatic, mast-mounted radar receiver system that will allow the processing of target information from noncooperative radar sets in the vicinity of the submarine, using two Type AZE-4 antenna arrays. The first three will have the UAP(4) EW suite, with the others to get a variant of the UAT system now under development. Are to be capable of launching Sub-Harpoon antiship missiles, although that weapon is being withdrawn from RN service in 2008. The CESM communications intercept and D/F suite is based on U.S. Argon Engineering Associates technology. The type of towed passive array has not been decided; while a "fat line" system is in development, the U.S. TB-29A thin-line array may be selected instead.

♦ 7 Trafalgar class

Bldr: Marconi Electronic Systems Naval Systems–VSEL, Barrow-in-Furness

	Ordered	Laid down	L	In serv.
S 107 Trafalgar	7-4-77	25-4-79	1-7-81	27-5-83
S 87 Turbulent	28-7-78	8-5-80	1-12-82	28-4-84
S 88 Tireless	5-7-79	1981	13-7-84	5-10-85
S 90 Torbay	26-6-81	12-82	8-3-85	7-2-87
S 91 Trenchant	22-3-83	28-10-85	4-11-86	14-1-89
S 92 Talent	10-9-84	1986	15-4-88	28-5-90
S 93 Triumph	3-1-86	1987	16-2-91	12-10-91

NUCLEAR-POWERED ATTACK SUBMARINES [SSN] *(continued)*

Triumph (S 93) Maritime Photographic, 12-01

Trafalgar (S 107)—with five horizontal countermeasures tubes per side just abaft the sail Ben Sullivan, 9-00

Turbulent (S 87) Mike Welsford, 9-00

D: 4,740 tons surf./5,208 tons sub. **S:** 30 kts sub.
Dim: 85.38 × 9.83 × 8.25 (hull; 9.50 max. surf.)
A: 5 bow 533-mm TT (25 tot. weapons: UGM-84D-2 Harpoon missiles, Spearfish and Tigerfish Mk 24 Mod. 2 torpedoes, mines)—S 87, 93, and 107 also: UGM-109 Block III Tomahawk land-attack missiles in lieu of some torpedoes
Electronics:
Radar: 1 Kelvin-Hughes Type 1007 nav./surf. search
Sonar: Type 2020 MODEX bow MF active/passive array; Type 2072 (S 91: Type 2007) passive flank array; Type 2019 PARIS acoustic intercept array; Type 2046 (S 91: Type 2026) towed passive array; Type 2027 passive ranging; Type 2071 noise generator; Type 2077 active ice nav.; Type 2008 underwater telephone; Type 197 echo sounder; Type 728 and Type 780 upward-looking echo sounders—S 90: Type 2076 integrated suite (with Type 2074 active/passive bow array, Type 2077 HF under-ice nav. active, Type . . . towed passive array)
EW: Thales UAP(1) intercept suite (1–18 GHz); EADS CXA(1) Telegon-6 comms D/F; 4 (S 107: 10; S 93: 5) 102-mm SSE Mk 8 decoy tubes (Type 2066 Bandfish and Type 2071 decoys)
M: 1 Rolls-Royce pressurized-water PWR.1 reactor, 2 W. H. Allen turbogenerator sets, GEC-Alstom geared turbine drive; 1 pumpjet; 15,000 shp—diesel-electric emergency propulsion syst. with 2 Paxman 400-kw diesel generator sets; 1 retractable electric propulsor
Endurance: 85 days **Crew:** 18 officers, 112 enlisted

Remarks: An improved version of the *Swiftsure* class. The active units constitute the 2nd Submarine Squadron, based at Devonport. As of 1-01, were planned to be retired: S 107 in 2007, S 87 in 2008, S 88 in 2011, S 93 in 2017, S 92 in 2015, S 90 in 2020, and S 91 in 2022.

S 107 completed a 192-week refit at DML, Devonport, in 4-96. S 87 started a refit in 8-93 and was recommissioned at the end of 1997. S 88 was in refit from 6-96 to 26-6-99. S 90 began a major refit in 1-98 for completion during 2-01 (delayed to 9-01 by reactor control rod failure), receiving the Type 2076 integrated sonar suite.

S 91 suffered a minor steam leak in the reactor compartment at Lisbon in 10-98. In 1999, the submarine was used to test light blue camouflage paint schemes before entering refit at the end of the year.

S 88 experienced a reactor-plant piping leak in 5-00 and did not complete repairs at Gibraltar Dockyard until 7-5-01. Others found to have the same defect were S 107, S 87, and S 90, which was already at Devonport for refit with S 91. Thus, as of 1-01, only S 93 was available for operations.

Hull systems: Have more than 26,000 rubber anechoic coating tiles to reduce noise signature and are equipped with a degaussing system. S 107 has a standard seven-bladed propeller, while the others have pumpjet propulsors. Diving depths: 300 m normal operating, 590 m maximum. The pressure hull is built of NQ-1 (HY-80) steel. Have three internal decks and four watertight compartments. S 88 has had the sail and planes reinforced to permit under-ice operations.

Combat systems: S 91 has been backfitted with the Type DCB/DCG tactical data system; DCB employs two Ferranti F2420 computers and DCG one BAE Systems (ex-Dowty-Sema) SMCS computer. The others have the FM1600 computer, and all will standardize on the SMCS tactical data system. Under a 1997 contract, all are to be updated with the BAE Defence Systems Group Integrated Command Console to manage sensor employment and tactical information; the system integrates the Submarine Command System and Type 2076 sonar displays with ship-system data, periscope, and underwater television camera displays. Five of the class are to receive a new DML communications intercept system covering the HF through UHF bands, and the other two will be fitted to accept the equipment. All seven are to receive the DML–Argon Engineering Associates CESM communications intercept and D/F system in place of the current CXA(1) system by 2010. Marconi Electronic Systems (now part of BAE Systems) was given a contract late in 1998 to further update the system by employing COTS (Commercial Off-The-Shelf) Sun SPARC computers with the UNIX operating system, substituting NEC 20-in. color flat-screen displays, and replacing the magnetic tape decks with digital audio tape systems, while retaining current F2420 software. Are to be equipped with Link 11 tactical datalink by 2004 and with Link 16 satellite tactical datalink (using a towed transmit/receive buoy) by 2006. Plans call for later installation of Link 22.

Midlife refits are updating the sonar suite to the Thales (ex-Ferranti-Thomson) Type 2076 integrated array, retaining the 2020 transducer array and including Type 2074, 2077, and 2081 sonars; the first four backfit systems were ordered in 2-94. S 90 is equipped with prototype flank arrays for the Type 2076 passive sonar system. S 87 conducted trials with a reelable towed array (causing the hump to her casing abaft the sail); the others employ clip-on arrays.

The centerline torpedo tube cannot launch Harpoon missiles and is angled downward by 10°; the Harpoon missile is to be retired by 2008. S 88 (and possibly others) now carries only Spearfish torpedoes. It was announced in 7-98 that all seven were to be equipped to launch U.S. BGM-109 Block III Tomahawk land-attack cruise missiles; as of 12-01, three had the capability, and all are to be fitted by 2006. S 107 launched her first Tomahawk on 7-8-01. During the 2000–01 refit of S 90, provision was made for launch and recovery of the prototype Marlin LRMS (Long Range Mine Surveillance) unmanned underwater vehicle, which uses a Spearfish torpedo body with warhead replaced by active and passive mine detection and classification sonars.

They all have Pilkington Optronics CH 34 (1× to 5×) and CK 84 (6×) periscopes, the former also carrying the AZE92 antenna for the UAB/UAP EW intercept suite and the antennas for the UHF and VHF radio receivers and NAVSAT, while the latter is equipped with television and infrared intercept equipment. S 107 conducted sea trials with a prototype Pilkington Optronics CM010 nonpenetrating optronic sensor mast, beginning in 3-98.

♦ 5 Swiftsure class

Bldr: Marconi Electronic Systems Naval Systems–VSEL, Barrow-in-Furness

	Ordered	Laid down	L	In serv.
S 108 Sovereign	16-5-69	18-9-70	22-2-73	22-7-74
S 109 Superb	20-5-70	16-3-72	30-11-74	13-11-76
S 104 Sceptre	1-11-71	25-10-73	20-11-76	14-2-78
S 105 Spartan	7-2-73	26-3-76	7-4-78	22-9-79
S 106 Splendid (ex-*Severn*)	26-5-76	23-11-77	5-10-79	21-3-81

Splendid (S 106) Paul C. Clift, 3-00

NUCLEAR-POWERED ATTACK SUBMARINES [SSN] *(continued)*

Splendid (S 106) Mike Welsford, 7-00

Superb (S 109) Ben Sullivan, 8-99

D: 4,000 tons light; 4,200 tons surf./4,900 tons sub.
S: 20 kts surf./28 kts sub. **Dim:** 82.90 × 9.83 × 8.25
A: 5 bow 533-mm TT (20 Mk 24 Mod. 2 Tigerfish torpedoes and UGM-84D-2 Sub-Harpoon missiles)—S 105 and S 106 also: UGM-109 Block III Tomahawk land-attack missiles in lieu of some torpedoes
Electronics:
Radar: 1 Kelvin-Hughes 1006(1) nav./surf. search
Sonar: Type 2074 bow active/passive array; Type 2077 active classification; Type 2007 passive flank array; Type 2019 PARIS sonar intercept; Type 2046 clip-on towed passive array; Type 2035 or 2047 narrowband processor/wideband frequency analyzer; Type 183 underwater telephone; Type 197 echo sounder
EW: Thales UAP(1) intercept; EADS CXA(1) Telegon 6 comms D/F; 2 102-mm SSE Mk 8 decoy tubes (Type 2066 Bandfish and Type 2071 decoys)
M: 1 Rolls-Royce PWR.1 pressurized-water reactor; 2 sets GEC-Alstom turbines; 1 prop or pumpjet; 15,000 shp—1 Paxman 400-kw diesel alternator set; 1 drop-down electric emergency propulsor
Crew: accomm. for 12 officers, 85 enlisted—but up to 120 tot. normally aboard

Remarks: Are assigned to the 1st Submarine Squadron, Faslane. S 108 completed a 4-year refit at Rosyth 21-9-97. S 104 underwent a major refit by Babcock Defence at Rosyth during 1997–2000. S 105 began a 2-year overhaul at Rosyth 15-3-99. S 106 completed a 7-month refit 1-5-98 and is now equipped to launch Tomahawk Block III land-attack missiles. S 106 and 109 were declared nonoperational 7-9-00 because of concerns over the safety of the reactor system; at that time, both were at Faslane with S 108, which did not have the problem, while S 104 and 105, in overhaul at Rosyth, did not have the defect; thus, as of 1-01, none of the class were operational, although by 1-02, all had been repaired. As of 1-01, planned retirements were: S 106 in 2003, S 108 in 2005, S 105 and S 109 in 2006, and S 104 in 2010.
Disposals: Sister *Swiftsure* (S 126) began a "30 month" refit 5-10-88, but reactor problems were discovered, and she is stored, minus sail, pending disposal, having been formally retired in 5-92.
Hull systems: Have a 112-cell battery. The forward diving planes are below the surfaced waterline and retract within the outer hull. Have anechoic hull and sail coatings.
Combat systems: Have the DCB/DCG weapons-control system, with two Ferranti F2420 computers. Are equipped with Link 16 and are to receive Link 22 combat information datalink. Were to receive the Type 2076 integrated sonar suite and Dowty-Sema SMCS command/combat data system; Type 2074 has replaced Type 2020, Type 2082 will replace 2019, and the Type 2082 Parian ice-avoidance sonar was to be added. All carry HF, VHF, and UHF communications equipment, including U.S. WSC-3 UHF SATCOM terminals. All had the Pilkington Optronics CK 33 search periscopes updated by 1998 with a GPS navigational display using antennas added to the co-mounted Outfit AZE(2) antenna for the UAP(1) ESM system; a CH 83 attack periscope is fitted. S 105 carries a nonacoustic sensor mast alongside the sail to port.
S 106 launched two training Tomahawk missiles during 10-98 and a live shot on 18-11-98 off Southern California; she later launched up to a dozen at Serbian targets in 1999. S 105 began modification to handle Tomahawks during 4-99; the others will not be modified to carry the missile. Harpoon missiles are to be removed by 2008. The bow, centerline tube is angled downward and cannot be used to launch missiles.

Note: All earlier British SSNs are planned to be retained in storage (all defueled) through at least 2012 due to the lack of facilities for scrapping them safely. *Dreadnought, Swiftsure,* and *Churchill* are at Rosyth, while *Conqueror, Courageous, Valiant,* and *Warspite* are at Devonport. *Courageous* is to become a museum display at Devonport.
Submarine rescue duties are handled by the 1978-vintage chartered rescue submersible LR5, for which a replacement was being designed during 2000 in conjunction with other NATO navies. The new system is to be available by 2005, is planned to last to 2030, and is expected to cost £120 million to procure. LR5 is 9.2 m long and 3.5 m high.

GUIDED-MISSILE DESTROYERS [DDG]

♦ 0 (+ 6 + 6) D-class (Type 45) program

Bldrs: BAE Systems and Vosper Thornycroft; assembly: D 33 at BAE Systems, Scotstoun, others at BAE Systems, Barrow-in-Furness

	Laid down	L	In serv.
D 32 Daring	2002	2006	12-07
D 33 Dauntless	...	...	2009
D 34 Diamond	2003	...	2009
D 35 Dragon	...	...	2010
D 36 Defender	...	...	2010
D 37 Duncan	...	...	2011

Daring (D 33)—computer artist's concept BAE Systems, 3-01

Daring (D 33)—computer artist's concept BAE Systems, 3-01

Daring (D 33)—with Merlin HM.1 helicopter, which will not initially be carried; computer artist's rendering BAE Systems, 3-01

GUIDED-MISSILE DESTROYERS [DDG] *(continued)*

Daring (D 33)—computer artist's concept BAE Systems, 3-01

D: 7,350 tons (fl) **S:** 29 kts **Dim:** 152.4 × 21.2 (18.0 wl) × . . .
A: SAMP/N VLS SAM syst. (48 Sylver A50 cells; 16 Aster-30 and 32 Aster-15 missiles); 1 114-mm 55-cal.Vickers Mk 8 Mod. 1 DP; 2 single 30-mm 75-cal. DS-30B AA; 1 Lynx HMA.8 helicopter (Stingray torpedoes and Sea Skua missiles)—provision for: 2 20-mm Mk 15 Mod. 1A Phalanx CIWS; 2 twin 324-mm fixed ASW TT (Stingray torpedoes)
Electronics:
Radar: 1 Type 1008 nav.; 1 Siemens-Plessey SAMPSON 3-D target desig.; 1 BAE Systems–Thales S1850M Smartello early warning
Sonar: Type 2087 suite (with Ultra-EDO MFS 7000 hull-mounted LF; see remarks); provision for LF active towed linear array
EW: Thales . . . integrated intercept and jammer suite: Minerva data processor; 4 8-tube decoy RL; 4 DLJ(2) floating decoy launchers; SSTD/SLQ-25A(V) active and passive torpedo decoy syst.
E/O: GSA.8 optronic tracker
M: 2 Rolls-Royce–Northrop Grumman WR-21 intercooled recuperative gas turbines (33,530 shp each), Alstom Integrated Full-Electric Power (IFEP) drive: 2 Alstom 15-phase induction motors; 2 props; 53,648 shp—2 2,000-kw Wärtsilä 12V200 diesel-driven Hitzinger alternator sets for low-speed propulsion and/or electrical ship's service requirements
Range: 7,000/18 **Endurance:** 45 days
Crew: 20 officers, 170 enlisted (accomm. for 235 tot., including 60 marines or commandos)

Remarks: British participation in the 1991 Project Horizon Common New-Generation Frigate program with France and Italy was terminated 21-4-99, but the U.K. stated a commitment to continuing the program's PAAMS (Principal Anti-Air Missile System) development effort, with the French Aster-15 and Aster-30 missile family. To meet a still-standing requirement for a dozen new large AAW ships, a new design was prepared. BAE Systems (then BAe-Marconi Marine) won a preliminary design contract for the ships on 23-11-99, but Vosper Thornycroft has been brought into the program. The total program cost was estimated at $11.3 billion, with the unit cost hoped to be around $435 million and each ship to cost about $29 million per year to operate, but as of 7-01, the projected unit cost had risen to more than $1 billion each. The formal order for the first six was placed 18-2-02.

Were to be ordered in four batches of three, with the second trio to be ordered in 2004, but in 6-01 the M.O.D. decided to order the first six as one batch. The first three had been tentatively ordered 20-12-00 from BAE Systems, with one expected to be subcontracted to Vosper Thornycroft. Under the revised scheme, BAE Systems will assemble D 33 at Scotstoun, employing a 2,000-ton, pre-outfitted bow section, masts, and funnels built by Vosper Thornycroft at new facilities at the Portsmouth Naval Base; later ships will be assembled at Barrow-in-Furness and will incorporate pre-outfitted sections built at BAE Systems, Govan, with the same portions provided by Vosper Thornycroft, but with the bow section only 80% outfitted at delivery. No more ships are to be ordered until 2006, but doubts have been expressed that the full dozen will be built. Modern combat systems and weapons are being omitted to save costs. The 12-07 delivery date for D 33 remains unofficial, but as the start of construction continues to be delayed, the date becomes less and less realistic.

Hull systems: Limiting displacement is to be 8,000 tons. Changes in the design early in 2000 brought the hull flare up to the main deck, increasing overall beam and length, while the superstructure will be more sharply sloped than had originally been planned. The design will employ Lloyd's commercial rather than Admiralty construction standards for warships. Range will only be about half that originally planned, and maximum speed has been reduced. The Rolls-Royce–Northrop Grumman WR-21 ICR gas turbine employs the core of the Rolls-Royce RB-211-535 aircraft engine; the plant will be fuel-efficient over a wide speed range. An integrated electric drive propulsion plant and fixed-pitch propellers will be employed. Alstom Power Conversion received a contract on 31-7-00 to design and develop the electric motors for the class. Litton Marine Systems and Rockwell Automation will provide an integrated platform management system. Senior enlisted personnel will have two- and four-berth cabins and junior personnel six-berth cabins.

Combat systems: The combat system will be the BAE Defence Systems Group–Alenia Marconi Systems DNA91 (Eurocombat) and will be compatible with NATO Improved Link 11, Link 14, and Link 16; the system will incorporate mostly existing equipment. The U.S. CEC (Cooperative Engagement Capability) will not be fitted to at least the first three ships, further reducing their potential effectiveness. The ships will have a fully integrated communications system provided by Thales Communications (teamed with BAE Systems Avionics); it will include Thales SCOT-3 SHF and, possibly, EHF SATCOM systems. The Siemens-Plessey SAMPSON target tracking and illumination radar is a developed version of the Multifunction Electronically Scanned Adaptive Radar (MESAR). The long-range search radar will employ the antenna from the Thales SMART-L radar, integrated with a new transmitter based on that of the Marconi Martello radar. Raytheon Systems will provide the navigation and integrated bridge navigational systems.

Plans to omit a sonar fit to save costs in at least the first three ships were canceled 16-1-00, but the ASW torpedo tubes may not initially be installed. The hull-mounted sonar, a variant of the EDO Model 997 being refitted to the Brazilian *Niterói* class, was selected late during 2-01.

Also to be omitted are the planned two CIWS mountings and any antiship missile system. As completed, they will be unable to accommodate the new Merlin helicopter, due to the lack of a deck traversing system.

In place of the originally selected 127-mm weapon for the Horizon class, the first three ships will carry Vickers 114-mm Mk 8 mounts recycled from the Type 42 destroyers and updated to Mod. 2 status (losing the ready-service ring in favor of a direct hoist to the magazine). Substitution of the new U.S. 155-mm gun had been planned for units 4 and later, but it may be too large and heavy. Since the Aster-15 and Aster-30 SAMs have no antiship capability, the ships will have only the 114-mm gun and helicopter-launched Sea Skua missiles for surface warfare duties.

♦ 4 Manchester class (Type 42C)

	Bldr	Laid down	L	In serv.
D 95 Manchester	Vickers (SB) Ltd. Barrow-in-Furness	19-5-79	24-11-80	16-12-82
D 96 Gloucester	Vosper Thornycroft, Southampton	26-10-79	2-11-82	11-9-85
D 97 Edinburgh	Cammell Laird, Birkenhead	8-9-80	14-4-83	18-12-85
D 98 York	Swan Hunter, Wallsend-on-Tyne	18-1-80	21-6-82	9-8-85

York (D 98)—note heavy reinforcing strake down the sides at the main deck level
Mike Welsford, 6-01

D: 3,880 tons (4,775 fl) **S:** 29.5 kts (18 cruising)
Dim: 141.12 (132.3 wl) × 14.90 × 5.80 (4.20 hull)
A: 1 2-round Sea Dart GWS.30 SAM syst. (22 missiles); 1 114-mm 55-cal. Vickers Mk 8 DP; 2 20-mm Mk 15 Phalanx gatling CIWS; 2 single 20-mm 90-cal. Oerlikon GAM-B01 AA; 2 triple 324-mm STWS.3 ASW TT; 1 Lynx HAS.3/HMA.8 helicopter (with Sea Skua missiles and/or Stingray ASW torpedoes)

GUIDED-MISSILE DESTROYERS [DDG] *(continued)*

Edinburgh (D 97)—note bow bulwarks Maritime Photographic, 7-01

York (D 98)—with trials Sea RAM launcher installation to port abreast the stack replaced by the normal Phalanx CIWS Douglas A. Cromby, 10-01

Gloucester (D 96) Maritime Photographic, 9-00

Electronics:

Radar: 1 Kelvin-Hughes Type 1007 nav.; 1 Decca Type 1008 nav.; 1 BAE Systems Type 996(1) surf./air search; 1 BAE Systems–Thales Type 1022 early warning; 2 BAE Systems Type 909(1) f.c.; 2 General Dynamics Mk 90 Phalanx f.c.

Sonar: BAE Systems Type 2050 hull-mounted; Kelvin-Hughes Type 162M bottomed-target classification (50 kHz); Type 185 underwater telephone

EW: UAT(5) intercept; DLB decoy syst. (4 6-round Mk 137 RL); 2 DEC laser dazzler; 4 DLJ(2) floating decoy dispensers; Type 182 or Type 2070 (U.S. SLQ-25A Nixie) towed torpedo decoy syst.

E/O: 2 Rademac 2100 optronic surveillance and target desig.

M: COGOG: 2 Rolls-Royce Olympus TM-3B gas turbines (27,200 shp each) for high speeds, 2 Rolls-Royce Tyne RM-1C (5,340 shp each) for cruise; 2 5-bladed CP props; 54,400 shp max.

Electric: 4,000 kw (4 × 1,000-kw Paxman diesel sets) **Range:** 4,750/18
Fuel: 610 tons **Crew:** 27 officers, 74 senior petty officers, 184 other enlisted

Remarks: A lengthened version of the *Sheffield* class, intended to provide better seaworthiness, endurance, and habitability but having no major change in armament despite the additional 16 m overall length. D 95 was ordered 10-11-78, D 96 on 27-3-79, and D 97 and D 98 on 25-4-79. D 96 shot down an Iraqi-launched Silkworm antiship missile with a Sea Dart on 25-2-91 in the northern Persian Gulf. The last is to be retired in 2015. Based at Portsmouth.

Hull systems: Received hull strengthening strakes amidships due to weight growth and cracking. There are two pairs of fin stabilizers. D 97 retains the bow bulwarks added when she carried a single Mk 15 Phalanx CIWS forward.

Combat systems: The ADAWS 7 combat data system initially carried has been upgraded to ADAWS 8. The missile direction system is GWS.30 Mod. 2, with a GSA.1 backup system for the 114-mm gun. Have NATO Link 10, 11, 14, and 16 JTIDS (Joint Tactical Information Distribution System) datalinks. The UAT(5) EW system incorporates the UCB(1) Electronic Warfare Control Processor. The Type 675(2) active EW jammers have been deactivated or removed. All now have the CCA (Captain's Combat Aid) computerized decision-making system. D 96 and later have a larger command center. Several portable 7.62-mm mg are carried, including one to be fitted on each bridge wing. All carry two SCOT-1C antennas for the Skynet SATCOM system and one commercial SATCOM terminal.

In 1990, D 97 received a single 20-mm Mk 15 CIWS forward and had bulwarks added at the bow; a 54-week refit in 1995–96 at Rosyth brought the ship to class standard with two Phalanx mounts amidships in place of the twin 30-mm mounts. D 98 is planned to receive a 114-mm Mk 8 Mod. 1 gunmount by 9-03. The Raytheon lightweight Sea RAM point-defense missile system was installed in place of the portside Phalanx mount on D 98 from 2-01 to 10-01 for compatibility trials. Two single 20-mm GAM-B01 AA mounts flanking the helicopter hangar were removed from all during 2000–01.

♦ 7 Sheffield class (Type 42A and 42B*)

	Bldr	Laid down	L	In serv.
D 87 Newcastle	Swan Hunter, Wallsend-on-Tyne	21-2-73	24-4-75	23-3-78
D 88 Glasgow	Swan Hunter, Wallsend-on-Tyne	7-3-74	14-4-76	24-5-79
D 108 Cardiff	Vickers (SB), Ltd., Barrow-in-Furness	3-11-72	22-2-74	24-9-79
D 89 Exeter*	Swan Hunter, Wallsend-on-Tyne	22-7-76	25-4-78	19-9-80
D 90 Southampton*	Vosper Thornycroft, Southampton	21-10-76	29-1-79	23-7-81
D 91 Nottingham*	Vosper Thornycroft, Southampton	6-2-78	12-2-80	8-4-83
D 92 Liverpool*	Cammell Laird, Birkenhead	5-7-78	25-9-80	9-7-82

GUIDED-MISSILE DESTROYERS [DDG] *(continued)*

Nottingham (D 91) Derek Fox, 7-01

Cardiff (D 108)—still carrying 20-mm Mk 7A gunmounts abaft the pilothouse Maritime Photographic, 2-01

Glasgow (D 88) Mike Welsford, 7-00

Exeter (D 89) Mike Welsford, 6-01

Southampton (D 90) Derek Fox, 6-01

Newcastle (D 87) Mike Welsford, 3-00

D: 3,560 tons (4,250 fl) **S:** 28 kts (18 cruising)
Dim: 125.0 (119.5 pp) × 14.34 × 5.9 (4.3 hull)
A: 1 2-round Sea Dart GWS.30 Mod. 2 SAM syst. (22 missiles); 1 114-mm 55-cal. Vickers Mk 8 DP; 2 20-mm Mk 15 Phalanx CIWS; 2 single 20-mm 90-cal. Oerlikon GAM-B01 AA—D 88, 108: 2 single 20-mm 70-cal. Oerlikon Mk 7A AA—all: 1 Lynx HAS.3/HMA.8 helicopter (Sea Skua missiles and/or Stingray torpedoes)
Electronics:
Radar: 1 Kelvin-Hughes Type 1007 nav.; 1 Decca 1008 nav.; 1 BAE Systems Type 996(1) 3-D surf./air search; 1 BAE Systems–Thales Type 1022 early warning; 2 BAE Systems Type 909(1) f.c.; 2 General Dynamics Mk 90 Phalanx f.c.
Sonar: BAE Systems Type 2016 (D 89–92: Type 2050) hull-mounted; Kelvin-Hughes Type 162M bottomed-target classification (50 kHz); Type 185 underwater telephone
EW: D 89, 90: UAT(5) intercept—others: UAA(2) intercept—all: DLD decoy syst. (4 6-round Mk 137 RL); 2 DEC laser dazzlers; 4 DLF(2) or DLF(3) floating decoy launchers; Type 182 or Type 2070 towed torpedo decoy—D 89, 90 also: UCB(1) EW control syst.
M: COGOG: 2 Rolls-Royce Olympus TM-3B gas turbines (27,200 shp each) for high speed; 2 Rolls-Royce Tyne RM-1A (D 89–92: Tyne RM-1C) cruise gas turbines (4,100 [D 89–92: 5,340] shp each); 2 5-bladed CP props; 54,400 shp max.
Electric: 4,000 kw (4 × 1,000-kw Paxman diesel sets)
Range: 650/30; 4,500/18 **Crew:** 24 officers, 229 enlisted

Remarks: This class was found to be deficient in damage control during the Falklands War and also to be limited in sensor capability and self-defense, although the Sea Dart system functioned effectively. D 108, delayed by labor problems, was completed by Swan Hunter. D 91 completed an 18-month refit and recommissioned 9-2-01. All are based at Portsmouth.
Disposals and losses: Class prototype *Sheffield* (D 80) foundered 10-5-82, having been hit by an Argentine AM 39 Exocet missile on 4-5-82. *Coventry* (D 118) was lost to Argentine bombs on 25-5-82. *Birmingham* (D 86) was deactivated 12-11-99, cannibalized for spares, and towed away for scrap 20-10-00.
Hull systems: Are very cramped; can accommodate up to 312 personnel. Have the Agouti bubble ejector system for the propellers (which rotate inwardly) to reduce cavitation noise. Two pairs of fin stabilizers are fitted. Modernizations have increased the draft by 0.3 m and the displacement by perhaps 100 tons. Have stack water spray equipment to reduce their IR signature. The Type 42B ships have slightly less-rounded sterns.
Combat systems: Have the ADAWS 7 (D 89, 90: Mod. 1) data system with NATO Link 10, 11, 14, and 16 JTIDS (Joint Tactical Information Distribution System) datalinks and the CCA (Captain's Combat Aid) computerized decision-making system. All are equipped to carry SCOT-1C radomes for the Skynet SHF SATCOM system and also carry a commercial NAVSAT terminal. The helicopter is used for surveillance and attack (with Sea Skua missiles) as well as ASW. The Type 965M radar was replaced by Type 1022 in the Type 42A ships. During refits, Type 996 radar replaced Type 992Q, except in the stricken D 86. Type 42B ships are to receive the UAT(5) EW suite, with UCB(1) Electronic Warfare Control Processor (EWCP). The Type 275 jammers were deactivated or removed by end-2000. All have two MSI–Defence Systems stabilized director aiming sights. D 89–92 received Type 2050 hull-mounted sonars (4.5–7.5 kHz) during refits; the earlier units have Type 2016 in place of their original Type 184P sets. Triple STWS.2 ASW torpedo tubes have been removed to save weight and to provide space for stowing rigid inflatable boats, handled by the former torpedo reloading davits. D 88 and 108 retained two 20-mm Mk.7A Oerlikon mountings abaft the bridge into 2001, in addition to carrying a 20-mm GAM-B01 mount on either side of the hangar; in the others, the GAM-B01 mounts are on the bridge deck, abaft the pilothouse. D 89 in 1998 carried the Type 2070 torpedo decoy (U.S. SLQ-25A), but the system is cross-decked to deploying units.

GUIDED-MISSILE FRIGATES [FFG]

Note: A "Future Surface Combatant" (formerly "Future Escort") class, intended to replace the Type 22 frigates and later the Type 23s, is planned to begin entering service around 2013, with the prime contractor to be selected in 2007. Various design proposals are already under consideration, most including the use of a trimaran hullform, for which the trials ship *Triton* is being employed by the Defence Evaluation and Research Agency (see the entry at the end of the U.K. section). Weapons systems under consideration as of 1998 included the U.S. 127-mm 62-cal. Mk 45 Mod. 4 DP gun with EX-171 extended-range ammunition, the Land-Attack Standard Missile, and tactical variants of the Tomahawk missile. The ships are expected to employ the Type 2087 sonar suite and a point defense SAM system.

GUIDED-MISSILE FRIGATES [FFG] *(continued)*

Future Surface Combatant study—trimaran configuration with long outrigger hulls M. Hawken/DPA, 1999

Future Surface Combatant study—stealthy monohull configuration BAE Systems, 2000

FRIGATES [FF]

♦ 16 Duke-class (Type 23) general-purpose

Bldr: Marconi Marine–Yarrow (Shipbuilders), Scotstoun, Glasgow (F 233, F 237–239: Swan Hunter Shipbuilders, Wallsend-on-Tyne)

	Laid down	L	In serv.
F 230 Norfolk	14-12-85	10-7-87	1-6-90
F 231 Argyll	20-3-87	8-4-89	30-5-91
F 233 Marlborough	22-10-87	21-1-89	14-6-91
F 229 Lancaster	18-12-87	24-5-90	1-5-92
F 234 Iron Duke	12-12-88	28-3-91	20-5-93
F 235 Monmouth	1-6-89	13-11-91	24-9-93
F 236 Montrose	1-11-89	31-7-92	2-6-94
F 237 Westminster	18-1-91	4-2-92	13-5-94
F 238 Northumberland	4-4-91	4-4-92	29-11-94
F 239 Richmond	16-2-92	6-4-93	22-6-95
F 82 Somerset	12-10-92	25-6-94	20-9-96
F 80 Grafton	13-5-93	5-11-94	29-5-97
F 81 Sutherland	14-10-93	9-3-96	4-7-97
F 78 Kent	16-4-97	27-5-98	8-6-00
F 79 Portland	14-1-98	15-5-99	3-5-01
F 83 St. Albans	5-3-99	6-5-00	6-6-02 (del. 27-10-01)

St. Albans (F 83)—the final Type 23 Marian Wright, 11-01

Norfolk (F 230)—with 114-mm Mk 8 Mod. 1 gun and its faceted gunhouse Bernard Prézelin, 8-01

Argyll (F 231) Mike Welsford, 6-01

Lancaster (F 229)—with towed-array dispenser port at the stern centerline Douglas A. Cromby, 9-00

D: 3,600 tons (4,300 fl) **S:** 28 (F 237 and later: 30) kts (15 on electric drive)
Dim: 133.00 (123.00 pp) × 16.10 (15.00 wl) × 4.30 (5.50 max. nav.)
A: 8 RGM-84C Harpoon (GWS.60) SSM; Sea Wolf GWS.26 vertical-launch SAM syst. (32 missiles); 1 114-mm 55-cal. Vickers Mk 8 (F 230: Mod. 1) DP; 2 single 30-mm 75-cal. DES-30B AA; 4 fixed 324-mm Cray Marine DMTS 90 ASW TT (Stingray torpedoes); 1 Lynx HAS.3/HMA.8 (F 229, 233: Merlin HM.1) helicopter (Sea Skua missiles and/or Stingray ASW torpedoes)

FRIGATES [FF] *(continued)*

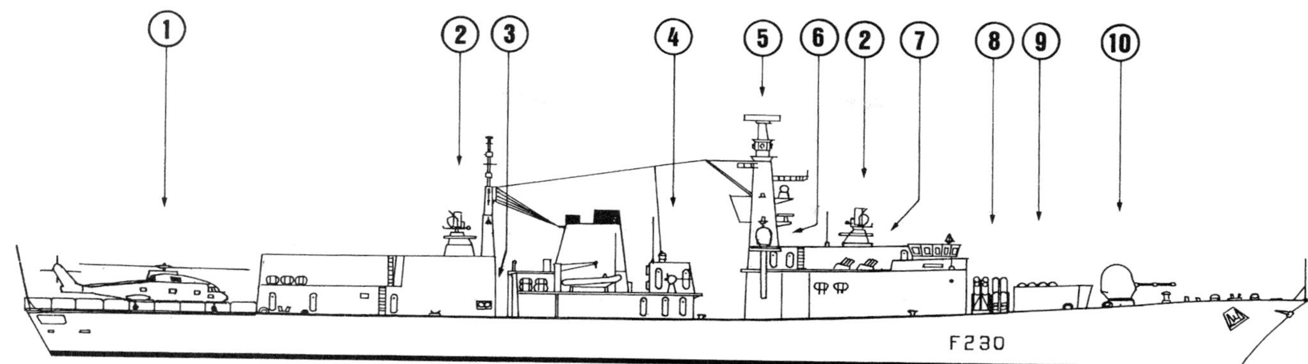

Norfolk (F 230) 1. Merlin HM.1 helicopter 2. Type 911(1) radar illuminator for Sea Wolf SAM system 3. fixed 324-mm ASW TT (two per side) 4. 30-mm AA 5. Type 996(2) 3-D surf./air-search radar 6. SCOT-1C SHF SATCOM antenna radome (port and starboard) 7. DLB decoy launchers 8. Harpoon SSM 9. Sea Wolf GWS.26 vertical missile launch group 10. 114-mm Mk 8 DP gun
Drawing by Jean Moulin, from *Flottes de Combat*

Portland (F 79)—note the absence of a towed-array port at the stern centerline, characteristic of later units of the class Maritime Photographic, 2-01

Richmond (F 239) Douglas A. Cromby, 9-01

Sutherland (F 81) Mike Welsford, 9-01

Westminster (F 237) Findler & Winter, 6-01

Northumberland (F 238)—three semicircular baffles atop the hangar improve the effectiveness of the after Type 911(1) radar tracker/illuminator; a single such baffle is placed atop the pilothouse for the forward Type 911(1) Mike Welsford, 6-01

FRIGATES [FF] *(continued)*

Electronics:

Radar: 1 Kelvin-Hughes Type 1007 nav.; 1 Decca Type 1008 nav.; 1 BAE Systems Type 996(2) 3-D surf./air search; 2 BAE Systems Type 911(1) missile/gun f.c.

Sonar: Thales Type 2050NE bow-mounted (4.5–7.5 kHz); Dowty Type 2031(Z) towed linear passive array (not in last six)

EW: F 238 and later: UAT(1) intercept—others: Racal UAF(1) Cutlass intercept—all: DLB decoy syst. (4 6-round RL); 2 DEC laser dazzler; 2 DLF(2) floating decoy dispensers; Type 182 or Type 2070 (SLQ-25A) towed torpedo decoy syst.

E/O: 1 GSA.8/GPEOD Sea Archer gun f.c. and surveillance

M: CODLAG (Combined Diesel-Electric and Gas Turbine): first seven: 2 Rolls-Royce SM-1A Spey gas turbines (18,770 shp each, 17,000 shp sust.); F 237 and later: 2 Rolls-Royce SM-1C Spey gas turbines (26,150 shp each)—all: 4 Paxman Valenta 12 RPA 200CZ diesel generator sets (5,200 kw total), 2 2,000-shp electric cruise motors; 2 props; F 229–236: 41,540 shp max. (F 237 and later: 52,300 shp max.)

Electric: 1,890 kw tot. (see remarks)

Range: 7,800/17 **Fuel:** 800 tons

Crew: 17 officers, 57 senior ratings, 111 junior ratings

Remarks: Intended as lineal replacements for the *Leander*-class frigates. Originally intended to serve for only 18 years, without midlife modernization, but are now to serve longer, with upgrades to begin around 2005. F 230 cost £135.5 million; the others cost between £60 and £96 million each. F 230 was ordered 29-10-84, F 231–233 on 15-7-86, F 234–236 on 11-7-88, F 237–239 on 19-12-89, F 80–82 on 23-1-92, and the final three on 28-2-96. The class originally was to have totaled 24. F 229's pennant was changed from the original F 232 because a "Form 232" is used to report a collision or grounding. With completion of the class, 12 are expected to be operational at any one time, with the other four in refit. F 78 began sea trials 27-5-99. F 229 had the hangar altered to accept the Merlin helicopter in a refit concluded in 8-99; also added were enlarged weapons sponsons amidships and improved communications systems. F 80 ran aground near Oslo, Norway, 11-9-00 but was soon pulled off with minor damage.

The initial group of six became the 6th Frigate Squadron on 23-3-93, based at Devonport and with F 231 as flagship. The 4th Frigate Squadron, based at Portsmouth, was formed later and now includes F 78, 80, 83, 229, 233, 234, 237, and 239, while the 6th Frigate Squadron includes F 79, 81, 82, 230, 231, 235, 236, and 238.

Hull systems: Have a flush-decked hull, a large helicopter hangar, a helicopter in-haul system, and one set of fin stabilizers. The design grew considerably as a result of Falklands War "lessons learned." The propulsion system permits running the shaft-concentric electric propulsion motors with the power from any combination of the four 1,300-kw ship's service generators; power from both the gas turbines and the electric motors can be obtained. Ship's service power is derived from two 945-kw converter sets, and there is also a 250-kw emergency alternator powered by a Perkins CV 250GTCA diesel. Have fixed-pitch props, with astern power available only by electric drive. The more-powerful engines in F 237 and later provide 1–2 kts additional speed, and F 79 made 30.8 kts during builder's trials. Superstructure external bulkheads are sloped about 7° to reduce radar signature, and radar-absorbent coatings are applied.

Combat systems: The planned Ferranti CACS 4 combat data/control system for these ships was canceled in 7-87; its replacement, the BAE Defence Systems Group (ex-Dowty-Sema-Racal) Outfit DNA(1) SSCS (Surface Ship Control System), with parallel processing, modular software, and Link 11 and 14 compatibility, was not ordered until 10-8-89. The first seagoing outfit DNA(1) was fitted in F 237, and the earlier ships were severely handicapped for combat until they could be backfitted; full system operability was implemented in a series of software updates that continued into 1999. F 233 ran trials during 1992 with the Data-Fusion Technology Demonstrator (TDS), employing five Microvax 3800 and five Sigmax 6264 computers. F 234 has the Marconi ICS 4 integrated communications system, with U.S. URC-109 components; the others have the Redifon ICS 6. All are equipped with two SCOT-1C antennas for the Skynet SATCOM system and also carry a commercial SATCOM terminal (with its antenna mounted on the forward edge of the stack). There have been problems with the accuracy of the Type 996(2) radar, which also produces excess numbers of false tracks, and there have been software problems with the vertical-launch missile system. All are to be equipped with the U.S. Navy's Cooperative Engagement Capability (CEC), with the necessary work to begin in 2004.

Have the first bow-mounted sonars in the Royal Navy. The sterns have had to be strengthened to permit towing the Type 2031(Z) array. Around 2006, Thales Type 2087 bistatic VLF towed arrays will begin to replace 2031(Z) in the ships that had it and will eventually be fitted to all; plans call for using one ship for trials with the LF active towed linear array. F 234 is equipped with a prototype TRAMP (Torpedo Recognition Acoustic Multibeam Processor) for trials in connection with the new SSTD torpedo countermeasures system.

Decca Type 1008 navigational radars have been added to all, with the antenna mounted to starboard atop the pilothouse; the antenna for the older Type 1007 radar is mounted off-center to port on the mainmast to allow an aft view for helicopter flight-control employment. F 238 and later have UAT vice UAF-1 EW equipment. The Racal 7.5- to 18.0-GHz Scorpion jammer may be added to the EW suite. UAT(7) is to replace UAF EW equipment in the first seven. The Type 275 jammers were deactivated or removed by end-2000.

The 114-mm guns are to be updated by VSEL to Mod. 1 status, saving about 6 tons in weight and considerable belowdecks volume; the first installation, in F 230, was to complete in 11-00, followed in sequence by F 234, 233, 235, and 236 by 9-03. The GSA.8/GPEOD Sea Archer optronic/IR director is mounted on the mast for the 114-mm gun. There is no provision for a CIWS, and until SSCS installation was completed, the ships were able to control only one Sea Wolf missile at a time.

When the class is completed, six of the 12 operational units will operate with Merlin HM.1 helicopters and the other six with Lynx HMA.8s. As of 4-00, F 229 was fitted to carry the Merlin HM.1 helicopter for trials, while F 233 became the first of the class with a fully operational Merlin HM.1. Merlin-equipped ships have the PRISM deck-handling system, a new glide-path indicator and gyro-stabilized horizon indicator, new deck lighting, modular servicing systems in the hangar, and a bridge Ship Helicopter Operating Limits Instrumentation System (SHOLIS) on the bridge.

♦ 4 Cornwall-class (Type 22 Batch 3) general-purpose

	Bldr	Laid down	L	In serv.
F 99 Cornwall	Yarrow (Shipbuilders), Scotstoun, Glasgow	12-9-83	14-10-85	23-4-88
F 85 Cumberland	Yarrow (Shipbuilders), Scotstoun, Glasgow	12-10-84	21-6-86	10-6-89
F 86 Campbeltown	Cammell Laird, Birkenhead	4-12-85	7-10-87	27-5-89
F 87 Chatham	Swan Hunter, Wallsend-on-Tyne	12-5-86	20-1-88	4-5-90

Chatham (F 87) Mike Welsford, 7-01

Cumberland (F 85) Brian Morrison, 2-01

Campbeltown (F 86) Derek Fox, 7-01

Cornwall (F 99)—note twin hangars Rob Cabo, 6-01

D: 4,280 tons (4,850 fl) **S:** 30 kts (18 on Tyne gas turbines)

Dim: 148.10 (135.65 pp) × 14.75 × 5.35 (hull; 6.40 max.)

A: 8 RGM-84C Harpoon SSM; 2 6-round Sea Wolf GWS.25 Mod. 3 SAM syst.; 1 114-mm 55-cal. Vickers Mk 8 (F 85: Mod. 1) DP; 1 30-mm Goalkeeper CIWS; 2 single 30-mm 75-cal. DES-30B AA; 2 triple 324-mm STWS.2 ASW TT (Stingray torpedoes); 1 or 2 Lynx HAS.3/HMA.8 helicopters (Sea Skua missiles and/or Stingray torpedoes) *or* 1 Sea King HAS.6 helicopter—F 87 also: 2 single 20-mm . . . AA

FRIGATES [FF] *(continued)*

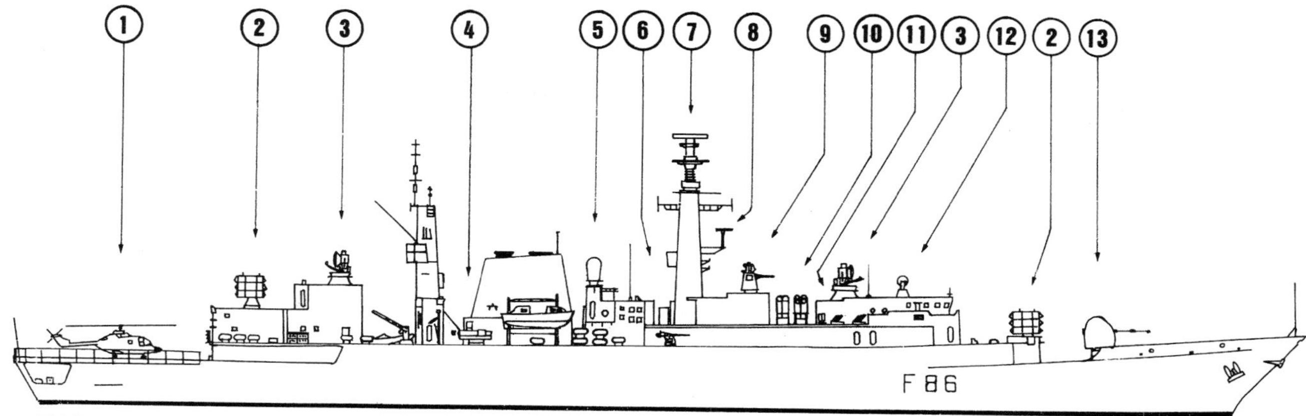

Campbeltown (F 86) 1. Lynx HAS.3 helicopter 2. Sea Wolf GWS.25 system sextuple SAM launchers 3. Type 911 radar illuminators for Sea Wolf missiles 4. triple 324-mm ASW TT 5. SCOT-1C SATCOM radomes (port and starboard) 6. 30-mm DES-30B gun 7. Type 967-968 dual surface- and air-search radars 8. Type 1006 navigational radar 9. 30-mm Goalkeeper CIWS 10. Harpoon SSM 11. DLB decoy launchers 12. Sea Archer E/O gun directors (port and starboard) 13. 114-mm Mk 8 DP gun

Drawing by Jean Moulin, from *Flottes de Combat*

Electronics:

Radar: 1 Kelvin-Hughes Type 1006 nav.; 1 BAE Systems Type 967M-968 surf./air search; 2 BAE Systems Type 911 f.c.; 1 Thales Goalkeeper f.c.

Sonar: Thales Type 2050 (F 99: Type 2016) hull-mounted (4.5–7.5 kHz)

EW: Racal UAT(5) or UAT(6) intercept; UAD/UAK COBLU comms intercept; DLB decoy RL syst. (4 6-round Mk 137 RL); 2 DEC laser dazzler; 4 DLF(2) floating decoy launchers; Type 182 towed torpedo decoy syst.

E/O: 2 GSA.8/GPEOD Sea Archer gun f.c. and surveillance

M: COGAG: 2 Rolls-Royce Spey SM-1A DR boost gas turbines (18,770 shp each), 2 Rolls-Royce Tyne RM-1C gas turbines (5,340 shp each); 2 5-bladed Stone Manganese CP props; 48,220 shp max.

Electric: 4,000 kw (4 × 1,000-kw Paxman Valenta 12PA 200CZ diesel sets)

Range: 7,000/18 (on Tyne gas turbines); 12,000/14 (one shaft)

Fuel: 700 tons + 80 tons aviation fuel

Crew: 13 officers, 62 petty officers, 157 other enlisted (as flagships: 21 officers, 65 petty officers, 159 other enlisted)

Remarks: Third series in the Type 22/*Broadsword*-class design, with same basic hull as the *Boxer* class but with a 114-mm gun on the forecastle and the antiship missile launchers moved to abaft the pilothouse and oriented athwartships. The first two were ordered 14-12-82 and the third and fourth on 28-1-85. F 86 ran aground off Tromsø, Norway, on 5-9-01, damaging the starboard propeller shaft. With *Sheffield* (F 96), they form the 2nd Frigate Squadron, based at Devonport.

Hull systems: Maximum generator output is 5,200 kw for short periods. The flight deck is sized for Merlin HM.1, but the hangar reportedly is too low to accommodate the helicopter.

Combat systems: All have the DFA-7 (CACS 5) Computer-Assisted Command System, with Link 11 and 14 compatibility. The CCA (Captain's Combat Aid) computerized decision-making system has been added. They are equipped with the ICS 3 communications suite and SCOT-1C SHF and Marisat SATCOM terminals. The GSA-8/GPEOD (Gun System Automation 8/General-Purpose Electro-Optical Director) t.v./IR/laser backup directors are for the 114-mm gun. The Goalkeeper gatling AA gunmount has its own integral I-band search/tracker and I/K-band tracking radars. The Decca Type 1008 navigational radar may be added to supplement Type 1007. All four received new communications suites at Devonport Dockyard, Plymouth, during 2001. The Type 2031(Z) passive linear towed hydrophone array systems and their towing winches were removed during 2000 and the winch compartments were converted for use as gymnasiums. F 85 was to have had the 114-mm mount replaced with a low-radar-reflective Mk 8 Mod. 1 mounting and the former towed sonar array winch room converted to a joint operations planning room during an overhaul completed late in 2001. The Type 275 jammers were deactivated or removed by end-2000. The COBLU (Cooperative Outboard Logistics Update) communications intercept system is an updated version of the UAD/UAK suite aboard *Sheffield* (F 96), itself a variant of the U.S. SSQ-108(V) OUTBOARD (Organizational Unit Tactical Baseline Operational Area Radio Detection Countermeasures Exploitation System); all but F 86 had had the upgrade by end-2001.

♦ 1 Boxer-class (Type 22 Batch 2) ASW

Bldr: Swan Hunter (Shipbuilders), Wallsend-on-Tyne

	Ordered	Laid down	L	In serv.
F 96 SHEFFIELD	14-12-82	29-3-84	26-3-86	26-7-88

Sheffield (F 96) Piet Sinke, 6-00

D: 4,250 tons (4,850 fl) **S:** 30 kts (18 on cruise engines)

Dim: 148.10 (140.00 pp) × 14.75 × 4.30 (hull; 6.00 max.)

Sheffield (F 96) Jaroslaw Cislak, 6-00

A: 2 6-round Sea Wolf GWS.25 Mod. 3 SAM syst.; 2 twin 30-mm 75-cal. Oerlikon GCM-A03-2 AA; 2 single 20-mm 90-cal. Oerlikon GAM-B01 AA; 2 triple 324-mm STWS.2 ASW TT; 1 or 2 Lynx HAS.3/HMA.8 helicopters (Sea Skua missiles and/or Stingray torpedoes)

Electronics:

Radar: 1 Kelvin-Hughes Type 1007 nav.; 1 BAE Systems Type 967M-968 surf./air search; 2 BAE Systems Type 911 missile f.c.

Sonar: BAE Systems Type 2016 hull-mounted (4.5–7.5 kHz)

EW: Racal UAA(2) intercept; UAD/UAK comms intercept (U.S. SSQ-108(V)2); SRD-19 LF–UHFD/F; SLR-16 countermeasures receiver; SLR-23 automated narrowband receiver; DLB decoy syst. (4 6-round Mk 137 RL); 2 DEC laser dazzler; 4 DLF(2) floating decoy launchers; Type 182 towed torpedo decoy syst.

M: COGAG: 2 Rolls-Royce Spey SM-1A boost gas turbines (18,770 shp each), 2 Rolls-Royce Tyne RM-1C cruise gas turbines (5,340 shp each); 2 CP props; 48,220 shp max.

Electric: 4,000 kw (4 × 1,000-kw Paxman Valenta 12PA 200CZ diesel-driven alternator sets)

Range: 7,000/18; 12,000/14 (one shaft) **Fuel:** 700 tons + 80 tons aviation fuel

Crew: 19 officers, 246 enlisted (accomm. for 320 tot.)

Remarks: Batch 2 employs a lengthened hull over the original *Broadsword* class to improve seaworthiness, endurance, and habitability and to provide space for handling the Type 2031 towed linear passive hydrophone array. Assigned to the 2nd Frigate Squadron, based at Devonport, F 96 is to be placed in reserve in 2003.

Disposals: Sister *Beaver* (F 93) was decommissioned 5-2-99 and began a tow to Turkey for scrapping 21-2-01. *London* (F 95) paid off at Devonport on 36 hours' sailing notice 22-1-99 but continued to operate until decommissioned 11-6-99. *Boxer* (F 92) paid off 22-3-99, was decommissioned and stricken 4-8-99, and was placed up for sale 29-10-99. *Brave* (F 94) was deactivated 1-4-99. *Coventry* (F 98) began a 5-month Caribbean deployment 13-7-01, paid off 26-11-01, and was decommissioned 28-2-02; she and *London* were to be transferred to Romania in the fall of 2002.

Hull systems: Two auxiliary boilers and two 50-ton/day flash evaporators are installed. Water-displacement fuel tanks are used, and the class is said to have twice the range of the Batch 1 *Broadsword* class. Has a fin stabilization system and the Agouti bubble sound-damping system.

Combat systems: Has the CACS 1 combat data system with 26 operators and 16 displays. Is NATO Link 11 and Link 14 compatible and has SCOT-1C SHF and Marisat commercial SATCOM terminals. Has been fitted with the U.S. SSQ-108(V)2 Outboard combat direction-finding and intercept system, with SRD-19 D/F, SLR-16 receiver, OK-324/SYQ system supervisor station, and J-band SLR-23 D/F array. All Exocet equipment, including the launch canisters and supports, had been removed by 4-00. The Type 275(2) jammers and the Type 2031Z towed linear passive hydrophone array have also been removed.

PATROL SHIPS [PS]

♦ 0 (+ 3) River-class chartered fisheries patrol ships

Bldr: Vosper Thornycroft, Woolston, Southampton

	Start	Laid down	L	In serv.
P 281 TYNE	8-5-01	19-9-01	27-4-02	7-11-02 (del.)
P 282 SEVERN	5-11-01	. . .	21-10-02	3-03 (del. 7-5-02)
P 283 MERSEY	6-5-02	. . .	19-4-03	9-03 (del. 7-11-03)

PATROL SHIPS [PS] *(continued)*

Tyne (P 281)—artist's rendering Vosper Thornycroft, 2001

D: 1,677 tons (fl) **S:** 20 kts **Dim:** 79.75 (73.60 pp) × 13.60 × 3.80
A: 1 20-mm 85-cal. Oerlikon GAM-B01 AA; 2 single 7.62-mm mg
Electronics: Radar: 2 Kelvin-Hughes Nucleus3 5000 ARPA nav./surf. search
M: M.A.N.–Burmeister & Wain–Ruston 12RK270 diesels; 2 Lips CP props; 11,280 bhp
Electric: 920 kw tot. (3 × 250-kw, 1 × 170-kw diesel alternator sets; 440 V)
Range: 5,500/15 **Fuel:** 325 tons **Crew:** 30 tot. + . . . marine commandos

Remarks: Ordered 8-5-01 as replacements for the remaining Island-class offshore patrol ships in the fisheries protection role. The ships are to be RN crewed but owned by the contractor and leased to the Royal Navy for 5 years, with options for a 10-year renewal, purchase, or return to the builder/owner. The ships are expected to operate for 320 days per year and are to be based at Portsmouth. Each unit will be assigned a rotating pool of 48 crew, 30 of whom will be aboard at any given time. Officers and senior enlisted will have single-berth cabins, junior ratings two-berth cabins. Two Halmatic inspection RIBs will be carried, and a 25-ton-capacity crane will be fitted to handle containerized disaster relief, antipollution, firefighting, rescue, and other modules. One radar is X-band, the other S-band.

♦ 2 Castle-class offshore patrol vessels

Bldr: Hall Russell, Aberdeen, Scotland

	Laid down	L	In serv.
P 258 Leeds Castle	18-10-79	22-10-80	27-10-81
P 265 Dumbarton Castle	25-6-80	3-6-81	12-3-82

Leeds Castle (P 258) Maritime Photographic, 1-01

Dumbarton Castle (P 265) Marian Wright, 12-01

D: 1,350 tons (1,550 fl) **S:** 20 kts **Dim:** 81.00 (75.00 pp) × 11.50 × 3.42
A: 1 30-mm 75-cal. Oerlikon DES-30B AA; 2 single 7.62-mm mg
Electronics:
Radar: 1 Kelvin-Hughes Type 1006 nav.; 1 BAE Systems Type 994 surf./air search
EW: RRDS UAN(1) radar warning intercept; DLE decoy RL syst. (4 6-tube Shield RL); DLF(2) floating decoy dispenser syst. (2 twin racks)
M: 2 Ruston 12 RK 320DM diesels; 2 CP props; 5,640 bhp (4,380 sust.)
Electric: 890 kw tot. (3 × 280-kw alternators, Paxman 6RPHCZ diesels driving; 1 × 50-kw emergency set, Perkins 6.354 diesel driving; 440 V a.c.)
Range: 10,000/12 **Fuel:** 186 tons **Endurance:** 28 days
Crew: 6 officers, 39 enlisted (52 tot. accomm.)

Remarks: Ordered 8-8-80, *after* both had been laid down. Based at Portsmouth. P 265 relieved P 258 as Falkland Islands Patrol Vessel in 1-98 and returned from South Atlantic waters 9-4-01, having been relieved by P 258 on 20-2-01. P 265 then underwent a 5-month overhaul and was equipped to serve as a "Mine Countermeasures Tasking Authority" ship as a replacement for the retired survey vessel *Herald* (H 138); the ship was to take over as flagship of the NATO Mine Countermeasures North Standing Naval Force during 4-02.

Hull systems: P 265 operated at more than 2,000 tons displacement during the Falklands War. Can carry 19.5 tons of helicopter fuel, 110 tons of fresh water, and 30 tons of oil-spill dispersant detergent. Have Decca CANE-2 (Computer-Assisted Navigation Equipment), NAVSAT, and Omega navigational systems. Two Avon Searaider rubber rescue/inspection dinghies are carried. Have one fire monitor and two oil-dispersing spray booms. Intended for 21-day patrols. The helicopter deck is large enough to accommodate either a Lynx or Sea King helicopter. Vosper Thornycroft D88 electronic machinery control systems were added during mid-1990s refits. Have additional accommodations for a 25-strong Royal Marine detachment, if required.
Combat systems: Can carry acoustic and mechanical mine-sweeping gear as well as being able to lay mines. Carry two 50-mm rocket flare launchers. P 258 conducted minelaying trials in mid-1983. In these ships, the Type 994 radar employs the antenna from the AWS-4 commercial radar. The UAN(1) Orange Crop intercept equipment was developed for helicopter use and covers 0.5–18.0 GHz. Are equipped with a Marisat commercial SATCOM terminal. Originally had a 40-mm 60-cal. Mk 9 AA mount. On P 265, the space beneath the gunmount has been converted into a mine countermeasures operations and planning room.

♦ 5 Island-class offshore patrol vessels

Bldr: Hall Russell, Aberdeen

	L	In serv.
P 277 Anglesey	18-10-78	1-6-79
P 278 Alderney	27-2-79	6-10-79
P 297 Guernsey	17-2-77	28-10-77
P 298 Shetland	22-11-76	14-7-77
P 300 Lindisfarne	1-6-77	26-1-78

Alderney (P 278) Rob Cabo, 6-01

Lindisfarne (P 300) Bernard Prézelin, 5-01

D: 998 tons (1,280 fl) **S:** 16.5 kts **Dim:** 61.10 (51.97 pp) × 11.00 × 4.27
A: 1 30-mm 75-cal. DES-30B AA; 2 single 7.62-mm mg
Electronics:
Radar: 1 Kelvin-Hughes Type 1006 nav.
Sonar: Simrad SU "Sidescan"
EW: Racal UAN(1) Orange Crop intercept
M: 2 Ruston 12 RK 3 CM diesels (750 rpm); 1 CP prop; 5,640 bhp (4,380 sust.)
Electric: 536 kw tot. (3 × 162-kw, 1 × 50-kw diesel alternator sets; 440 V a.c.)
Range: 11,000/12 **Fuel:** 310 tons **Crew:** 4 officers, 29 enlisted

Remarks: Near-duplicates of the former Scottish Fisheries Patrol Agency ships *Jura* and *Westra*. Five were ordered 11-2-75 and another pair on 21-10-77. Will be replaced by the new River class. All are based at Portsmouth.
Disposals: *Jersey* (P 295) paid off for disposal 16-12-93 and was sold to Bangladesh. *Orkney* (P 299) was decommissioned 27-5-99 and sold to Trinidad and Tobago, transferring 18-12-00. P 298 was to be retired 28-6-02.
Hull systems: P 277 and 278 had fin stabilizers on completion; they were backfitted in the others. Can maintain 12–15 kts in a Force 8 gale. Two Avon Searaider semirigid dinghies replaced the original Geminis for inspection purposes. Carry 28.6 tons of detergent (a 6-hour supply) for oil-spill cleanup. Have additional accommodations for a 25-strong Royal Marine detachment, if required.
Combat systems: The Racal CANE DEA-1 action data system is installed. During refits in the mid-1990s, 30-mm DES-30 guns replaced the hand-operated 40-mm guns, with P 277, 278, and 299 having had 20-mm GAM-B01 mounts as interim fits. Are fitted with Marisat commercial SATCOM terminals as needed.

PATROL BOATS [PB]

♦ 16 Archer (P.2000) class

Bldrs: first 14: Watercraft, Shoreham-by-Sea (last nine completed by Vosper Thornycroft); P 274, 275: BMT Marine Procurement—see remarks)

2 patrol and search-and-rescue craft at Gibraltar:

	In serv.		In serv.
P 293 Ranger	3-8-88	P 294 Trumpeter	8-11-88

PATROL BOATS [PB] *(continued)*

13 University Reserve Naval Unit training:

	In serv.	Unit Assigned
P 163 Express	26-5-88	Cardiff
P 164 Explorer	18-10-85	Northumbria
P 165 Example	16-1-86	Yorkshire
P 167 Exploit	17-8-88	Birmingham
P 264 Archer	1-3-86	Aberdeen
P 270 Biter	5-11-85	Manchester
P 272 Smiter	7-2-86	Glasgow
P 273 Pursuer	19-2-88	Sussex
P 279 Blazer	15-3-88	Southampton
P 280 Dasher	6-5-88	Bristol
P 291 Puncher	13-7-88	London
P 292 Charger	8-7-88	Liverpool
P 274 Tracker	8-5-98	Portsmouth

1 Britannia Royal Naval College training tender:

	In serv.
P 275 Raider	8-5-98

Pursuer (P 273) Maritime Photographic, 8-01

Explorer (P 164)—like P 163, P 165, and P 167, has a black hull and blue-gray superstructure Piet Sinke, 6-01

D: 44 tons (49 fl) **S:** 22.5 (P 274, 275: 25) kts
Dim: 20.80 (18.00 pp) × 5.80 × 1.80 **A:** provision for 1 7.62-mm mg
Electronics: Radar: 1 Decca AC 1216 nav.
M: first 14: 2 Perkins CV M800T diesels; 2 props; 1,590 bhp (1,380 sust.)—P 274, 275: 2 MTU 12V193 TB92 diesels; 2 props; 2,000 bhp
Electric: 62 kVA tot. **Range:** 330/20; 550/15
Crew: 1 officer, 4 enlisted, 13 trainees

Remarks: The first 14 were ordered in 7-84 and the other two in 2-97. Now assigned to the Inshore Training Squadron and affiliated as shown above. Nine were incomplete (with P 273 ready for trials) when Watercraft closed. BMT (British Marine Technology) was a project management firm located at Bath that subcontracted the actual construction of P 274 and 275, with the hulls molded by Kingfisher Boats, Falmouth, and outfitting performed by Ailsa-Troon, Scotland. P 293 and 294 have been based at Gibraltar as patrol craft since 1-91. P 163–165 and 167 originally bore A-series pennants as training craft for the Royal Naval Auxiliary Service; they paid off early in 1994 and recommissioned in 7-94. P 275 was reassigned as navigational training tender to the Britannia Royal Naval College, Dartmouth, during 2001.
Hull systems: Have GRP-construction, deep-vee, hard-chine hulls designed by Amgram, Ltd. The final pair have a modified, bulged transom stern.
Combat systems: P 293 and 294 at Gibraltar no longer carry an armament of one 20-mm 90-cal. GAM-B01 AA and two single 7.62-mm mg.

Note: Patrol boats operated by the Ministry of Defence Police are listed at the end of the U.K. section.

MINE COUNTERMEASURES SHIPS

Note: Under the $240 million RIMS (Replacement Influence Minesweeping System) project, the Royal Navy is exploring several unconventional concepts, including a remote-control drone system, with three 12.2-m, GRP-hulled drones controlled by a Hunt-class ship; a remotely controlled tug that would tow an influence-generating sweep; a new sweep array for the Hunt class; a clip-on sweep array; cast-concrete floating modules that could be combined to simulate specific pressure and other signatures; and helicopter-towed influence sweep arrays.
The new hydrographic survey ships *Echo* and *Enterprise* are designed to be used as mine countermeasures support ships if needed; see under [AGS].

♦ 11 Sandown-class Single-Role Mine Hunters (SRMH)
Bldr: Vosper Thornycroft, Woolston (Southampton) and Portsmouth

	Laid down	L	In serv.
M 101 Sandown	2-2-87	18-4-88	9-6-89
M 102 Inverness	11-5-89	27-2-90	5-3-91
M 104 Walney	5-90	25-11-91	20-2-93
M 105 Bridport	1-6-91	30-7-92	7-11-93
M 106 Penzance	25-9-95	11-3-97	14-5-98
M 107 Pembroke	. . .	15-12-97	6-7-00
M 108 Grimsby	. . .	10-8-98	25-9-99
M 109 Bangor	3-98	16-4-99	26-7-00
M 110 Ramsey	. . .	25-11-99	22-6-01
M 111 Blyth	30-5-99	4-7-00	14-8-01
M 112 Shoreham	2-00	9-4-01	20-7-02

Shoreham (M 112)—the final *Sandown*-class minehunter Derek Fox, 11-01

Bridport (M 105) Findler & Winter, 10-01

Inverness (M 102) Maritime Photographic, 8-01

MINE COUNTERMEASURES SHIPS *(continued)*

Ramsey (M 110) Douglas A. Cromby, 10-01

D: 378 tons light; 450 tons std. (484 fl) **S:** 15 kts (6.5 max. hunting)
Dim: 52.50 (50.00 pp) × 10.50 (9.00 wl) × 2.30
A: 1 30-mm 75-cal. DES-30B AA
Electronics:
Radar: 1 Kelvin-Hughes Type 1007 nav.
Sonar: Type 2093 variable-depth minehunting
EW: fitted for DLK decoy syst. (2 18-round Wallop Barricade 57-mm RL)
M: 2 Paxman Valenta 6RPA 200-EM 1500 diesels; 2 Voith-Schneider vertical cycloidal props; 2,024 bhp—2 200-hp electric motors (6.5 kts)—2 Schottel bow-thrusters
Electric: 750 kw tot. (3 diesel sets) **Range:** 2,600/11
Crew: 5 officers, 29 enlisted (40 accomm.)

Remarks: Pure minehunters, with no minesweeping capability. The original plan called for construction of as many as 20 for the Royal Navy. Are named for coastal resort towns. M 101 was ordered 28-8-85, M 102–105 on 23-7-87 (but not funded until 1988–89). Requests for bids for seven more were issued 22-10-90, but in 2-91 the process was suspended; the seven were finally ordered during 7-94. M 101 was not accepted for operational service until 12-92, despite her commissioning in 6-89, because of difficulties with the sonar suite. M 110 cost about $46 million. Plans call for them to be operational for 6,000 hours between overhauls. M 107 successfully underwent class shock trials during 5-99. Three sisters have been completed for Saudi Arabia, and Spain is building a modified version under license. They constitute the 3rd Mine Countermeasures Squadron, based at Faslane.
Disposals: *Cromer* (M 103) paid off 10-10-01 and decommissioned for disposal 26-11-01 after only 9 years' service; she will be used as a static training hulk at the Britannia Royal Naval College, Dartmouth.
Hull systems: GRP construction. Use electric drive for low-speed, quiet operation. M 101–106 have three Mawdsley generators, each powered by a 335-bhp Perkins V8-250G diesel. Navigational equipment includes Decca Hyperfix, QM-14, and Navigator Mk 21 (being replaced by Navigator Mk 53) radio navaids. M 106 and later have larger, more powerful, 1.8-m-diameter cycloidal propeller sets, and their GRP superstructures were molded via the SCRIMP (Seeman Composite Resin Infusion Molding Process) method, which reduces structural weight by about 15 tons; the air-conditioning was also improved in these units. M 108 and later are equipped to accommodate female crewmembers.
Combat systems: Have the NAUTIS-M minehunting operations system. The Type 2093 sonar uses a variable-depth vertical lozenge-shaped towed body lowered beneath the hull; it has search, depth-finder, classification, and route survey modes. The ships carry two Remote-Controlled Mine Disposal System Mk 2 (improved PAP 104 Mk 5) submersibles with up to 2,000 m of control cable and a depth capability of 300 m for mine identification and disposal. They also carry a mine-clearance diver team. M 106 and later have a new davit for the Remote-Controlled Mine Disposal System Mk 2 submersible and also carry two-man portable diver decompression chambers. Two Wallop Barricade decoy rocket launchers can be added for deployments to high-threat areas, but there is no electronic intercept equipment. M 104 received a portable decompression chamber early in 2001, doubling the depth that mine disposal divers can work to 80 m; a second mine countermeasures equipment crane was added aft, and the air-conditioning and ship's accommodations were improved.

♦ 11 Hunt-class minehunters

Bldr: Vosper Thornycroft, Woolston (M 32, 34: Yarrow [Shipbuilders], Scotstoun, Glasgow)

	Laid down	L	In serv.
M 29 Brecon	15-9-75	21-6-78	21-3-80
M 30 Ledbury	5-10-77	5-12-79	11-6-81
M 31 Cattistock	20-6-79	22-1-81	16-6-82
M 32 Cottesmore	27-9-79	9-2-82	24-6-83
M 33 Brocklesby	8-5-80	12-1-82	3-2-83
M 34 Middleton	1-7-80	27-4-83	15-8-84
M 35 Dulverton	1-6-81	3-11-82	4-11-83
M 37 Chiddingfold	. . .	6-10-83	26-10-84
M 38 Atherstone	9-1-84	1-3-86	30-1-87
M 39 Hurworth	1-83	25-9-84	19-7-85
M 41 Quorn	2-6-86	23-1-88	21-4-89

D: 625 tons (725 fl) **S:** 17 kts (15 sust.; 8 on hydraulic drive)
Dim: 60.00 (56.60 pp) × 9.85 × 2.20 (hull; 3.40 max.)
A: 1 30-mm 75-cal. DES-30B AA; 2 single 7.62-mm mg; provision for 2 single 20-mm 90-cal. Oerlikon GAM-B01 AA (see remarks)
Electronics:
Radar: 1 Kelvin-Hughes Type 1006(4) or Type 1007 nav.
Sonar: Thales Type 193M Mod. 1 variable-depth minehunting (100–300 kHz), with Mills Cross Type 2059 submersible tracking set incorporated
EW: provision for: MEL UAR Matilda threat warning (7.5–18 GHz); 2 2-round DLJ(2) floating radar decoy dispenser syst.; DLK decoy syst. (2 18-round Wallop Barricade 57-mm RL)

Atherstone (M 38) Derek Fox, 11-01

Quorn (M 41) Maritime Photographic, 8-01

Dulverton (M 35)—after conversion for Northern Ireland patrol duties; note the davits and boats that replaced the mine countermeasures gear on the fantail
R. J. L. Fry, 5-98

M: 2 Ruston-Paxman Deltic 9-59K diesels (1,600 rpm); 2 props; 1,900 bhp (1,770 sust.)—slow-speed hydraulic drive for hunting (8 kts)—bow-thruster
Electric: 1,140 kw (3 Foden FD 12 Mk 7 diesel alternators of 200 kw each for ship's service, plus one 525-kw Deltic 9-55B diesel alternator for magnetic minesweeping and one 60-kw emergency set)
Range: 1,500/12 **Crew:** 5 officers, 40 enlisted

Remarks: Equipped for both hunting and sweeping mines. M 33 was laid down *prior* to ordering on 19-6-80; M 41 was ordered 4-6-85. M 32, with her pennant number painted out and sweep gear removed, completed conversion 20-11-97 to perform patrol duties off Northern Ireland, followed by M 35 and M 29. The entire class has been based at Portsmouth since the closure of Rosyth. M 29, 34, 37, and 41 are in the 1st Mine Countermeasures Squadron; M 31, 32, 38, and 39 are in the 2nd Mine Countermeasures Squadron; M 30, 33, and 35 are in the 4th Mine Countermeasures Squadron.
Disposals: *Bicester* (M 36) was stricken 29-6-00 and *Berkeley* (M 40) on 20-2-01; they were transferred to Greece on 31-7-00 and 28-2-01, respectively.
Hull systems: Hulls are constructed of glass-reinforced plastic. One 645-bhp Deltic 9-59B diesel powers the 525-kw sweep current alternator *or* four Dowty hydraulic pumps used to power the props during minehunting; the engine also provides power for the bow-thruster and the sweep winch. All are receiving the Thales VIMOS (Vibration Monitoring System), which is expected to cut radiated noise by 3–10 dB.
Combat systems: Are equipped with CAAIS DBA-4 (64-contact tracking) data system (upgraded to permit integration of the Navpac positioning aid) and Decca HiFix Mk 21 navigation system. Most carry a Marisat SATCOM terminal. Carry six or seven divers and two French PAP 104 Mk 3 remote-controlled mine location submersibles. Have Sperry Osborn TA 6 acoustic, M.Mk 11 magnetic loop, and M.Mk 8 Orepesa wire sweeping gear as well.

When deployed in high-threat areas, can be equipped with single 20-mm AA mounts on platforms abreast the stack, decoy rocket launchers, DLF-2(2) Replica floating decoys, and Matilda-E radar intercept gear. The original 40-mm 60-cal. Mk 9 AA mounts have been replaced by stabilized DES-30B 30-mm AA mounts. For Northern Ireland patrol duties, M 29, 32, and 35 have had two Caley articulating cranes atop cylindrical bases added on the fantail to tend two Pacific and one Arctic rigid inflatable launches, and all their portable mine countermeasures equipment has been removed.
Modernization: After an 18-month feasibility study, plans were dropped in 1996 for a major life-extension program to keep the ships in service for 40 years; the planned equipment changes would have been too heavy. The replacement "Hunt Minimum Up-

MINE COUNTERMEASURES SHIPS *(continued)*

date" planned to commence around 2000 has been deferred to 2003 and is to be performed on only the eight units still in use as mine countermeasures assets; it is to include the Thales Type 2193 wideband minehunting sonar to detect bottomed mines to 80-m depths, updates to the MS 14 and MSSA Mk 1 influence sweep arrays, and substitution of a new Nautis-III mine warfare combat data system. The program would add about 5–10 years to the ships' service lives.

AMPHIBIOUS WARFARE SHIPS

Note: Landing ships and craft subordinated to the Royal Logistic Corps (formerly Royal Corps of Transport) are covered in the British Army entry at the conclusion of the U.K. section. *Invincible*-class aircraft carriers can also carry troops, as can the helicopter transport *Argus* (A 135), while nearly every seagoing combatant class can be adapted to carry small numbers of Royal Marines.

♦ 1 Assault Helicopter Carrier [LPH]

Bldrs: BAE Systems (formerly Kvaerner Govan), Govan, Scotland, and BAE Systems (formerly VSEL), Barrow-in-Furness, Scotland

	Laid down	L	In serv.
L 12 Ocean	30-3-95	11-10-95	19-3-99 (del. 30-9-98)

Ocean (L 12) Cem D. Yaylali, 11-00

Ocean (L 12) Maritime Photographic, 12-99

Ocean (L 12) Mike Welsford, 6-01

Ocean (L 12)—with small stern ramp deployed to a floating stage; note the British Army Chinook helicopter on the flight deck Rob Cabo, 6-01

D: 21,578 tons (fl) **S:** 19 kts (18 sust.)
Dim: 203.4 (193.0 pp) × 32.6 (28.5 wl; 36.1 extreme) × 6.65
Air group: 12 Sea King HC.4 troop helicopters and 6 Lynx AH.7 or WAH-64D Apache attack helicopters or up to 15 Harrier FA.2 fighter-bombers (for transport)
A: 3 twin 30-mm 75-cal. Oerlikon GCM-B03 DP; 3 20-mm Mk 15 Phalanx gatling CIWS

Electronics:
Radar: 2 Kelvin-Hughes Type 1007 nav.; 1 BAE Systems Type 996(2) surf./air search; 3 General Dynamics Mk 90 Phalanx f.c.
EW: Racal UAT(7) intercept; DLJ(2) Sea Gnat decoy RL syst. (8 6-tube Mk 137 launchers); 2 DLH SIREN offboard jammer launchers; provision for towed torpedo decoy

M: 2 Crossley-Pielstick 12 PC2.6 V400 diesels; 2 5-bladed props; 18,360 bhp—electric low-speed drive—Stone-Vickers bow-thruster
Electric: 8,000 kw tot. (4 × 2,000-kw Ruston 12RKC diesel sets, 1 . . .-kw Paxman Vega 12JZ emergency diesel set)
Range: 8,000/15 **Fuel:** 1,500 tons + 1,500 tons aviation fuel
Crew: 311 tot. (461 accomm.) + up to 186 aircrew + 500 Royal Marine troops and 26 Royal Marine boat crew

Remarks: Originally referred to as the ASS (Aviation Support Ship) and intended to replace the vertical assault capability lost with the disposal of the carriers *Hermes* and *Bulwark*. Now referred to as an LPH. Formally ordered 1-9-93. Cost was £150.6 million. The hull was built to merchant vessel standards by Kvaerner at Govan and christened by Queen Elizabeth II 20-2-98. During dock trials early in 4-98, the port propeller shaft and reduction gearing were damaged, delaying delivery and costing £0.5 million in repairs. Became fully operational during 3-99 after extensive trials. Does not have command and control facilities for a flag or Royal Marine brigade staff. Cannot transport heavy armored vehicles and is handicapped by low speed. During a 12-00 to 5-01 refit, received new landing craft davits, improvements to replenishment-at-sea equipment and accommodations facilities, and a new computer data network. No. 9 Assault Squadron Royal Marines is permanently assigned to the ship and operates the four landing craft as well as providing firefighting, security, and bridge watchstanding personnel. Based at Devonport.
Hull systems: The ship in general resembles an *Invincible* (and has a similar underwater hullform), but with a full-length flight deck and no ski jump. Four LCVP Mk 5 landing craft, each capable of carrying 35 troops and 2 tons of equipment, are carried in side embrasures. Brown Brothers folding-fin stabilizers are fitted. There is a small stern ramp for light vehicles; 40 half-ton trucks, 34 trailers, and six 105-mm towed guns can be carried. In an emergency, 303 additional troops can be carried, for a total of 803. There are 17 weapon and ammunition magazines, totaling 180 tons capacity. Four reverse-osmosis plants can produce a total of 320 tons of potable water per day. The main engines themselves must be stopped and reversed in rotation to provide astern power.
Aviation systems: The flight deck has six "spots" for Merlin-size helicopters and can also accommodate CH-47 Chinook helicopters. The WAH-64 Longbow Apache is due to enter service with the British Army in 2002. The principal employment with Sea Harriers would be as a transport; there are no support facilities for the aircraft. The hangar can accommodate up to 12 Merlin or 12 Sea King HC.4 and six Lynx helicopters and is divided into three sections by fire curtains. Flight deck freeboard is 15.3 m, and flight deck dimensions are 170 × 31.7 m. There are two aircraft elevators, and a vehicle ramp reaches the flight deck on the starboard side, aft.
Combat systems: The Ferranti ADAWS 2000 Mod. 1 command system is installed. Has a BAE DIMPS (Distributed Message Processing System), Marconi-Matra SCOT-1D SHF SATCOM system, and Marisat commercial SATCOM terminal. Links 11 and 14 are fitted, with provision for later installation of Link 16 (JTIDS).

♦ 0 (+ 2) Albion-class Assault Landing Ships [LPD]

Bldr: BAE Systems (formerly Marconi Marine–VSEL), Barrow-in-Furness

	Laid down	L	In serv.
L 14 Albion	22-5-98	9-3-01	4-03
L 15 Bulwark	2000	15-11-01	2004

Albion (L 14)—at launch RN, 3-01

Albion (L 14)—afloat, immediately after launch; note the stern door, whose upper portion folds upward and the lower folds down BAE Systems, 3-01

AMPHIBIOUS WARFARE SHIPS *(continued)*

Albion (L 14)—when operational; computer graphic M.O.D. U.K., 2001

D: 14,600 tons (16,981 fl; 18,500 flooded) **S:** 18 kts (17.5 sust.)
Dim: 178.00 (164.7 wl; 162.0 pp) × 28.9 × 6.1
A: 2 30-mm Goalkeeper CIWS; 2 twin 30-mm 90-cal. Oerlikon GCM-A03-2 AA; 2–3 Sea King HC.4 or Merlin HC.3 troop-carrying helicopters
Electronics:
Radar: 2 Kelvin-Hughes Type 1008 nav.; 1 BAE Systems Type 996(2) surf./air search; 2 Thales Goalkeeper f.c. suite
EW: Racal UAT(7) intercept; DLJ(2) decoy syst. with DLH launch capability (8 6-round RL); towed torpedo decoy syst.
M: Diesel-electric: 2 Wärtsilä Vasa 16V32E diesels (8,377 bhp each), 2 Wärtsilä Vasa 1432E diesels (2,091 bhp each) (15,620 kw tot. generator output), 2 electric motors; 2 4-m-dia. props; 16,000 shp—294-shp bow-thruster
Range: . . ./. . . **Crew:** 325 tot. + 305 troops (710 in emergency)

Remarks: Were originally to have been ordered in 1988 to replace the *Fearless* (L 10) and *Intrepid* (L 11). The design contract was awarded to the Y-ARD–VSEL–Dowty-SEMA consortium in 1992; the construction contract, worth more than £450 million, was awarded 18-7-96 after prolonged negotiations with the only bidder. As of 7-01, L 14 alone was estimated to cost £385 million. Much of the prefabrication work for L 15 was performed at the former Kvaerner yard at Govan. The ships are to be based at Devonport. L 14 was to be delivered 9-8-02.
Hull systems: Have two flight-deck spots for Merlin-size helicopters, four LCU Mk 10 landing craft (or two U.S. LCAC) in floodable well deck, and four LCVP Mk 5 landing craft in davits. When fully flooded, the docking well has 3 m of water above the deck. An 11.8-m side ramp is fitted to starboard forward, and there is a small door on either beam amidships for cargo pallet loading and offloading. The 17.2-m-wide stern door articulates to form a 7.5-m-wide by 10.5-m-long vehicle ramp. The vehicle cargo capacity (twice that of the *Fearless*) is 6 Challenger-2 main battle tanks or 16 2-ton trucks, 36 smaller vehicles, and 30 tons of stores. There are 550 linear meters of vehicle parking space, with MacGregor hoistable internal vehicle ramps from the lower vehicle deck to the upper deck aft and between the lower and mezzanine decks forward and amidships.
The hullform is adapted from that of modern commercial vehicle/passenger ferries and incorporates a bow bulb; its structure exceeds naval strength standards. A computerized ballasting system preserves trim while loading and unloading. CAE Electronics supplied an automated machinery and damage-control system.
Combat systems: Have the Marconi Electronic Systems ADAWS 2000 Mod. 1 combat data system and BAE MPS2000 message-handling system. A terminal for the drone aircraft–carried Airborne Stand-Off Radar (ASTOR) is to be fitted. A Marconi-Matra SCOT-2D SHF SATCOM terminal, with two antennas, is carried. The 72-station Command Support System (CSS) is intended to support the staffs of an embarked Commander, Amphibious Task Group, and Commander, Land Forces.

♦ 1 Fearless-class amphibious assault ship [LPD]

	Bldr	Laid down	L	In serv.
L 10 Fearless	Harland & Wolff, Belfast	25-7-62	19-12-63	25-11-65

Fearless (L 10) Derek Fox, 6-01

D: 11,582 tons (12,642 fl; 16,950 with well deck flooded) **S:** 21 kts
Dim: 158.5 (152.4 pp) × 24.38 × 6.20 (9.15 with well deck flooded)
Air group: up to 4 Sea King HC.4 helicopters
A: 2 twin 30-mm 75-cal. Oerlikon GCM-A03-2 AA; 2 single 20-mm Mk 15 CIWS; 2 single 20-mm 90-cal. Oerlikon GAM-B01 AA
Electronics:
Radar: 1 Kelvin-Hughes Type 1006 nav.; 1 BAE Systems Type 994 surf./air search; 2 General Dynamics Mk 90 Phalanx f.c.
EW: BAE Systems Mentor-A intercept; DLJ(2) decoy syst. (8 6-round Mk 137 RL); DLF(2) twin floating decoy dispenser syst.
M: 2 sets English Electric geared steam turbines; 2 props; 22,000 shp
Boilers: 2 Babcock & Wilcox, 38.66 kg/cm^2, 454° C superheat
Electric: 4,000 kw tot. **Range:** 5,000/20
Crew: 50 officers, 500 enlisted + air group: 3 officers, 19 enlisted + Royal Marine detachment: 3 officers, 85 enlisted + 380–700 troops

Remarks: Intended to act as a command ship for amphibious assaults as well as carrying troops and equipment. Had a serious engine room fire on 2-11-00 but was back in service as of 6-01. The ship's retirement, originally planned for 10-02, was moved forward to 18-3-02.
Disposals: Sister *Intrepid* (L 11), in reserve at Portsmouth since late 1990, was reduced to 9-month availability reserve status on 31-8-99 and had a caretaker crew of 15; she was retired in 7-01 and may replace *Rame Head* as training hulk.
Hull systems: During a 6-88 to 9-11-90 refit, additional aviation fuel capacity was added, the mainmast was heightened by 3.7 m, and her machinery and piping received a major rehabilitation. In emergencies, can carry up to 1,000 troops. Carried in davits are four LCVP Mk 4 landing craft, which can transport 35 personnel or a 5.5-ton vehicle. The well deck accommodates four LCM(9) landing craft carrying two Chieftain tanks or four vehicles or 100 tons of supplies each; four additional tanks can be carried on the tank deck. The vehicles are divided between the tank deck, a lower deck, and a half-deck reserved for jeeps. L 10 is the last steamship in Royal Navy service.
Combat systems: Has the Nautis-M combat data system. The Type 994 radar employs a "quarter-cheese"-type antenna. Is equipped with the two SCOT-1D antennas for the Skynet SHF SATCOM system and also has a Marisat commercial SATCOM terminal.

♦ 0 (+ 4) Largs Bay–class dock landing ships [LSD]

Bldr: first two: Swan Hunter (Tyneside), Wallsend-on-Tyne; others: BAE Systems, Govan, Scotland

	Laid down	L	In serv.
L 3006 Largs Bay	1-10-01	. . .	19-1-04 (del.)
L 3007 Lyme Bay	1-10-01	. . .	19-1-05 (del.)
L 3008 Mounts Bay	. . .	2003	2005
L 3009 Cardigan Bay	. . .	. . .	2005

Largs Bay class—computer graphic; most of the deck space aft is taken up with cargo containers and vehicles, and there is only to be one helicopter spot Swan Hunter, 2000

Largs Bay class—computer graphic; the large, dark object on the hull side is a Mexiflote sectional landing pontoon Swan Hunter, 2000

D: 16,160 tons (fl) **S:** 18 kts (sust.) **Dim:** 176.6 × 26.4 × 5.8 (max.)
A: . . .
Electronics: . . .
M: 2 Wärtsilä 12V26 and 2 Wärtsilä 8L26 diesels, 4 generator sets, electric drive; 2 ABB Azipod azimuthal props; . . . shp
Range: . . ./. . . **Crew:** 60 tot. RFA + 356 troops

AMPHIBIOUS WARFARE SHIPS *(continued)*

Largs Bay class—note that the engine exhausts are at the extreme stern, flanking the stern well, shown flooded in this computer graphic Swan Hunter, 2000

Remarks: Officially styled ALSL (Alternative Landing Ship Logistic). The design is based on that of Royal Schelde's *Rotterdam*-class LPD. Two new "Landing Ships Logistic" (i.e., LSTs) were to be procured as a result of the 1998 Defence White Paper decisions to replace the *Sir Geraint* (L 3027) and *Sir Percivale* (L 3036), but the program was expanded to four ships in 10-00, for a planned total cost of £300 million. Will be operated by the Royal Fleet Auxiliary. The first two were ordered for £140 million during 12-00, the second pair for £120 million on 19-11-01.
Hull systems: Will have 1,200 lane-meters of vehicle accommodation internally and on the flight deck and will be able to transport 200 tons of combat cargo such as fuel, ammunition, and stores. Two Mexiflote powered pontoons will be stowable on the hull sides. A large helicopter/vehicle/container deck is to be fitted but no helicopter hangar; there will be only one helicopter "spot." The ships will not be capable of beaching. A stern docking well will hold one Utility Landing Craft Mk 10, and no landing craft will be carried in davits. A typical vehicle load would be 36 Challenger-2 tanks or up to 150 light trucks. Will employ azimuthal propellers and have no rudders. Two vehicle and cargo-handling cranes will be fitted amidships.

♦ 1 Sir Galahad–class tank landing ship [LST]
Bldr: Swan Hunter Shipbuilders, Wallsend-on-Tyne

	Laid down	L	In serv.
L 3005 Sir Galahad	12-7-85	13-12-86	7-12-87

Sir Galahad (L 3005) H&L Van Ginderen, 6-00

D: 7,441 tons light (8,585 fl) **S:** 18 kts
Dim: 140.47 (126.02 pp) × 20.02 (19.50 hull) × 4.57 (3.97 light)
A: provision for: 2 single 20-mm GAM-B01 AA; 2 single 12.7-mm mg
Electronics:
Radar: 1 Kelvin-Hughes Type 1007 nav.; 1 Decca Type 1008 nav.; 1 . . . S-band nav.
EW: . . . intercept; DLE decoy syst. (4 6-round Shield RL); Type 182 towed torpedo decoy
M: 2 Mirrlees-Blackstone KMR9 Mk 3 Major diesels; 2 CP props; 13,310 bhp
Electric: 2,460 kw (4 × 540-kw, 1 × 300-kw diesel sets)
Range: 13,000/15 **Fuel:** 1,260 tons
Crew: 15 officers, 34 unlicensed + 340 troops (see remarks)

Remarks: 8,861 grt/3,077 dwt. Ordered 6-9-84 as the replacement for a ship of the same name lost in the Falklands War. Completed trials 10-7-87. Underwent a refit in 1997–98. Is operated by the Royal Fleet Auxiliary.
Hull systems: Has Decca-Racal CANE navigational system. One 25-ton crane is installed forward of the bridge, and there are two 8.6-ton cranes forward. The bow ramp has a visor-type one-piece door, and there is also a stern vehicle ramp. A 20-ton scissor lift is fitted amidships to the forward vehicle/helicopter deck; there is a 20-ton traveling crane on the upper of the two internal vehicle decks within the 8.57-m-molded-depth hull. Can accommodate an additional 133 troops in public spaces, plus another 64 without berths, for a maximum of 537. Four Mexiflote pontoons can be stowed on the hull sides.
Combat systems: The two 20-mm AA had been removed from the forecastle by mid-2000. Two commercial SATCOM system radomes are fitted.

♦ 4 Sir Bedivere–class tank landing ships [LST]
Bldr: Hawthorn Leslie, Hebburn-on-Tyne (L 3027: Alex Stephen, Linthouse, Glasgow, Scotland)

	Laid down	L	In serv.
L 3004 Sir Bedivere	10-65	20-7-66	18-5-67
L 3027 Sir Geraint	6-65	26-1-67	12-7-67
L 3036 Sir Percivale	4-66	4-10-67	23-3-68
L 3505 Sir Tristram	2-66	12-12-66	14-9-67

Sir Bedivere (L 3004)—with lower helicopter deck and two-legged mainmast Derek Fox, 2001

Sir Tristram (L 3505)—as refitted with two-legged mainmast and revised bridge superstructure Derek Fox, 9-00

Sir Percivale (L 3036)—note the stowed stern ramp, which rises nearly to the flight deck, and the Mexiflote sectional pontoon stowed on the hull side amidships Douglas A. Cromby, 8-01

D: L 3004: 6,700 tons (fl)—L 3505: 5,794 tons (fl)—others: 3,362 tons light (5,674–5,794 fl)
S: 17.25 kts
Dim: L 3004: 139.02 (124.64 pp) × 17.94 (17.70 wl) × . . .—L 3505: 134.72 (120.55 pp) × 17.94 (17.70 wl) × 3.98—others: 126.02 (111.64 pp) × 17.94 (17.70 wl) × 3.98
A: provision for 4 single 20-mm 90-cal. Oerlikon GAM-B01 AA
Electronics:
Radar: 1 Kelvin-Hughes Type 1007 nav.; 1 . . . X-band nav.; 1 . . . S-band nav.
EW: . . . intercept; DLE decoy syst. (4 6-round Shield RL)
M: L 3004: 2 Stork-Wärtsilä 12SW280 diesels; 2 props; 9,840 bhp—others: 2 Mirrlees 10-ALSSDM 10-cyl. diesels; 2 props; 9,400 bhp (8,460 sust.)—all: 495-shp (L 3004: 985-shp) bow-thruster
Electric: 1,600 (L 3505: 2,000) kw tot. **Range:** 8,000/15
Fuel: 811 (L 3505: 888) tons
Crew: 21 officers, 44 enlisted (L 3505: 18 officers, 32 enlisted) + 402 troops

Remarks: 4,473 (L 3505: 4,775) grt; 2,443 dwt. In 1963 the Ministry of Transportation ordered the first of six specially designed LST-type ships for the British Army, to be chartered in peacetime to various private maritime firms. In 1970 the ships came under the control of the Royal Fleet Auxiliary Service. They are to be replaced by the new *Largs Bay* class.

L 3505 was badly damaged 8-6-82 but was carried home in 6-82 and repaired by Tyne Ship Repair, South Shields, from 7-84 to 7-85; a new 120-ton, 8.915-m midsection was added, along with rehabilitated accommodations, increased generator capacity, a larger helicopter deck, a bow-thruster, and increased engineering automation. The rebuilding was not entirely successful, as the ship trims down by the stern and can no longer load tanks in the after portion of the main vehicle deck.

The other three were to receive a similar modernization and 13-m lengthening to extend their useful lives another 15 years, beginning with L 3004 in 1994. The conversion was authorized 11-11-92, with L 3004 contracted to Babcock Rosyth Defence 19-7-94; the work, which began 15-11-94 and was expected to take 70 weeks, was in fact delayed into early 1998. Plans to perform similar work on the remaining two were abandoned during 11-97, but both received further minor refits during 2000–01.

AMPHIBIOUS WARFARE SHIPS *(continued)*

Disposals: The original *Sir Galahad* (L 3005) was fatally damaged 8-6-82 and was scuttled 24-6-82. Half-sister *Sir Lancelot* (L 3029) was sold commercial 1-6-89 as *Lowland Lancer* and was purchased in 10-92 for the Singapore Navy.
Hull systems: Have bow and stern ramps for vehicles; interior ramps connect the two decks. There is a helicopter platform and three cranes (two of 8.5-ton capacity, one 20-ton), except on L 3004, whose 20-ton crane has been replaced by a 25-ton-capacity Clark Chapman crane. On L 3004, in addition, the amidships helicopter deck has been strengthened and the after one lowered one deck, most of the shade deck openings in the side were plated in, and the one-piece stern ramp was replaced by an articulating two-piece ramp; the ship is able to transport 440 troops and carries four LCVP Mk 4 landing craft and one 6.5-m rigid inflatable boat. All have Marisat commercial SATCOM terminals and can carry 2,077 tons of water ballast. The bow doors on L 3027 were welded shut during a 1994 minor refit, but they split open again in heavy seas on 3-4-98 in the Atlantic; the class is no longer considered suitable for beaching.

♦ 2 (+ 8) LCU Mk 10–class medium landing craft [LCM]
Bldr: BAE Systems, Govan, Clyde (LCU 01, 02: Ailsa Troon Shipbuilders, Clyde)

	L	In serv.		L	In serv.
LCU 01 A1	30-7-99	25-11-99	LCU 06 . . .	. . .	. . .
LCU 02 A2	9-99	25-11-99	LCU 07 . . .	. . .	. . .
LCU 03 A3	. . .	. . .	LCU 08 . . .	. . .	. . .
LCU 04 A4	. . .	. . .	LCU 09 . . .	. . .	. . .
LCU 05 A5	. . .	. . .	LCU 10 . . .	. . .	2-03

LCU Mk 10 class—artist's rendering BAE Systems, 1998

D: 170 tons light (240 fl) **S:** 10 kts (loaded) **Dim:** 29.80 × 7.40 × 1.50
Electronics: Radar: 1 . . . nav.
M: 2 M.A.N. . . . diesels; 2 Schottel waterjets; . . . bhp—bow-thruster
Electric: . . . kw tot. (2 Cummins . . . diesels driving)
Range: 600/10 **Endurance:** 14 days (stores) **Crew:** 7 tot.

Remarks: For use with the new *Albion* class. Ordered in 7-98 from BAE Systems for $57 million total, with construction subcontracted to Ailsa Troon. The first two were to be completed and to have successfully run trials by 9-00 before the other eight commenced construction, with delivery of the third to be in 12-01 and the last in 2003. Total program cost is to be $51.2 million. As of 8-00, the program was about a year behind schedule, and the second unit was still under construction when the Ailsa Troon yard was closed; in 11-00, the construction was reassigned to the Govan yard, where LCU 03 was laid down during 3-01. The original completion date for LCU 02 was to have been 25-11-99 and for LCU 10, 28-2-03. LCU 03 was laid down 11-6-01 and LCU 05 on 6-8-01.
Hull systems: Have a drive-through configuration, with ramps fore and aft and the pilothouse to starboard, aft. Carry one heavy tank or four heavy trucks or up to 120 troops plus two snow-capable vehicles. Steel construction.

♦ 12 LCM(9)-class medium landing craft [LCM]
Bldrs: L 702: Brooke Marine, Lowestoft; L 704–709: Richard Dunston, Thorne; L 710, 711: J. Bolson, Poole; L 713–715: McTay Marine, Liverpool (In serv.: first nine: 1963–66; L 713–715: 1986)

L 702	L 705	L 707	L 709	L 711	L 714
L 704	L 706	L 708	L 710	L 713	L 715

LCM(9)-class unit from the Fearless (L 10) Maritime Photographic, 6-98

D: 115 tons light (160 fl) **S:** 10 kts (9 loaded) **Dim:** 25.7 × 6.5 × 1.7
Electronics: Radar: 1 Raytheon . . . nav.
M: 2 Paxman YHXAM diesels; Kort-nozzle props; 624 bhp (474 sust.)
Range: 300/9 **Crew:** 7 tot.

Remarks: Can carry two tanks or 70 tons of cargo. Most are naval manned, but L 713 and one other are assigned to No. 539 Assault Squadron, Royal Marines. *Fearless* (L 10) can carry four of this class.

Disposals: L 703 (F4—*Fearless* No. 4) was lost to a bomb 8-6-82. Stricken have been class prototype L 3508 and L 700 and 701.
Hull systems: L 713–L 715 had Dorman 8 JTM diesels (270 bhp each) as built and have grill-reinforced bow ramps. The hull sides on all have been built up amidships, and shelter covers to the tank deck are carried. The original full-load displacement was 176 tons, but loading is now restricted. L 710 was employed as trials craft for the new LCU Mk 10 class; the craft was fitted early in 1993 with twin Schottel swiveling pumpjet propulsors by J. Bolson, Poole. Six of the survivors have been refitted by Marine and Port Services, Milford Haven Ship Repairers, under a 7-98 contract that was completed by 3-99; new engines and Schottel waterjets were fitted, and the six are typed LCM(9)S.

♦ 5 (+ 12) LCVP Mk 5–class vehicle landing craft [LCVP]
Bldr: first five: Vosper Thornycroft, Southampton; others: FBM Babcock Marine, Rosyth Royal DY (In serv.: first five: 1-96 to 12-97; others: 2003)

LCVP Mk 5 class Mike Welsford, 6-01

D: 16 tons light (23 fl) **S:** 25 kts (light; 16 loaded)
Dim: 15.25 (14.00 pp) × 4.20 × 0.55
Electronics: Radar: 1 Raytheon . . . nav.
M: 2 Volvo Penta TAMD-72WJ diesels; 2 PP170 waterjets; 860 bhp
Range: 210/16 **Crew:** 3 tot. + 15–35 troops

Remarks: Prototype ordered in 2-95. Four more were ordered 23-10-96 for delivery by 12-97 for use aboard *Ocean* (L 12). Another dozen were ordered 6-8-01 for use (four each) aboard *Albion* (L 14) and *Bulwark* (L 15) and as training and spares. Are expected to serve for 20 years each. Can be distinguished from the LCVP Mk 4 by the six-sided (vice rectangular) pilothouse.
Hull systems: Aluminum construction with planing hullform. The prototype reached 30 kts during initial trials. Cargo capacity includes 2 tons of equipment, in addition to 35 troops or two TUM light trucks, one 105-mm or 155-mm howitzer, or one Bv-206 Arctic tracked vehicle and trailer.

♦ 19 LCVP Mk 4–class vehicle landing craft [LCVP]
Bldr: W. A. Souter, Cowes (8301: Fairey Allday Marine, Hamble)

	In serv.		In serv.		In serv.
8301	1982	8408	12-8-85	8416	1986
8401	5-3-85	8410	11-10-85	8417	1986
8403	29-3-85	8411	3-12-85	8418	1987
8404	1-5-85	8412	15-1-86	8621	1987
8405	30-5-85	8413	1986	8622	1987
8406	10-7-85	8414	1986		
8407	18-7-85	8415	1986		

LCVP Mk 4—suspended from starboard forward davit on *Fearless* (L 10) Paul C. Clift, 5-99

D: 10.5 tons (16 fl) **S:** 20 kts (15 loaded) **Dim:** 13.00 (11.90 pp) × 3.20 × 0.80
A: 2 single 7.62-mm mg **Electronics:** Radar: 1 Raytheon . . . nav.
M: 2 Perkins 76-3544 diesels; 2 props; 440 bhp (8416–8418: 2 Dorman diesels; 2 CP props; . . . bhp)
Range: 150/14; 200/12 (8416–8418: 300/12) **Crew:** 3 tot. + 20–35 troops

Remarks: Prototype 8301, ordered 6-2-80, is 13.50 m long by 3.50 m in beam; the production units were ordered 21-8-84. Have a 8.80 × 2.13–m cargo well and a cargo capacity of 5.5 tons. Aluminum construction. The cargo well can be fitted with a windowed, segmented cover. 8416–8418 can reach 22 kts. Four others (LCVP 8402, 8409, 8419, and 8420) serve the British Army's Royal Logistic Corps. Most will probably be retired when the new Mk 5 variant completes delivery.

AMPHIBIOUS WARFARE SHIPS *(continued)*

♦ 4 Type 2000 TDX(M) assault hovercraft [LCPA]

Bldr: Griffon Hovercraft, Salisbury Green (In serv. 1993)

C 21 C 22 C 23 C 24

C 24 A. A. de Kruijf, 8-98

D: 6.75 tons (fl) **S:** 40 kts **Dim:** 11.04 × 4.60 (5.78 over skirt) × 0.52
A: 1 7.62-mm mg **Electronics:** Radar: 1 Raytheon . . . nav.
M: 1 Deutz BF8L-513 diesel driving; 0.91-m-dia. lift fan and 1.8-m-dia. CP airscrew; 355 bhp (320 sust.)
Range: 300/40 **Fuel:** 284 liters **Crew:** 2 tot. + 16 troops

Remarks: Ordered 26-4-93; first two were delivered 23-11-93. Aluminum hull structure. Payload is 16 troops or 2 tons of equipment. Maximum speed can be attained in Sea State 1; 25 kts is maintainable in Sea State 3. The craft are able to travel over land and ice as well as water. Have GPS receivers and HF and VHF radios. Are operated by No. 539 Assault Squadron, Royal Marines, as part of No. 3 Commando Brigade. Can operate from the well deck of utility landing craft *Fearless* (L 10). Can also be accommodated in a C-130 Hercules transport. The cab top can be removed to permit carrying two 1-ton NATO standard cargo pallets.

Note: As a result of the success of the Type 2000 TDX(M) craft, the Royal Marines are seeking funding for several larger, "LCAC"-type air-cushion landing craft capable of carrying both troops and vehicles.

Requests for bids were issued in 1-01 for a new class of "Fast Transit Craft" to replace current Royal Marine Special Boat Service craft beginning in 2004; the craft are to be capable of being carried in a C-130 Hercules or beneath a CH-47 Chinook helicopter and to carry a 2.6-ton payload (10 troops and equipment) at 45 kts for 600 n.m. in a State 4 sea; the low-observable craft must be able to remain operable in up to State 6 seas.

♦ 2 FIC 145–class covert operations boats [LCP]

Bldr: Vosper Thornycroft–Halmatic, Havant (In serv. 12-94)

FIC 145 class—painted medium green Maritime Photographic, 8-01

D: 9 tons light (12.5 fl) **S:** 45 kts **Dim:** 14.50 × 2.85 × 1.35 (at rest)
A: 2 single 12.7 or 7.62-mm mg **Electronics:** Radar: 1 Decca . . . nav.
M: 2 Seatek . . . diesels; 2 Rolla outdrive props, 1,160 bhp
Range: 225/45 **Crew:** 2 tot. + . . . special forces

Remarks: Ordered 3-9-93. GRP and Kevlar, balsa-cored hulls with two hydroplane steps. Designed by Italian race boat designer Fabio Buzzi. At least two covert operations boats of an earlier design were in service by 7-93. Are operated by the Royal Marine Special Boat Service.

Earlier-model FIC—high-speed craft with canoe-like hullform forward
H. M. Steele, 10-99

♦ 45 Rigid Raider assault boat Mk 3 [LCP]

Bldr: Vosper–RTK Marine, Poole, Dorset (In serv. 1996–99)

D: 2.2 tons light **S:** 40 kts (36 loaded) **Dim:** 7.58 × 2.75 × . . .
M: 1 Yamaha gasoline outboard; 220 bhp **Crew:** 2 tot. + 8 commandos

Remarks: A lengthened version of the Mk 2 to improve handling. Two were donated to Georgia 11-1-99.

Note: Procurement plans for 1999–2001 called for the acquisition of 5-m and 6.5-m Rigid Raiding Craft, and a diesel-powered 8.5-m RIB prototype.

Rigid Raider assault boat Mk 3 Maritime Photographic, 8-98

♦ 38 Rigid Raider assault boat Mk 2 [LCP]

Bldr: Vosper–RTK Marine, Poole, Dorset (In serv. 1993–96)

Rigid Raider assault boat Mk 2 H&L Van Ginderen, 8-98

D: 1.37 tons light **S:** 40 kts (30 loaded) **Dim:** 6.50 × . . . × . . .
M: 2 Suzuki gasoline outboards; 280 bhp **Crew:** 2 tot. + 8 commandos

Remarks: Ordered in late 1994. Have a GRP hull with stainless steel skegs and elastomer-coated foam-filled fender. Removable seats permit transporting up to 680 kg of cargo. Can reach 40 kts in light condition. Can also be operated with only one outboard motor.

♦ 24 Europower RIB assault craft [LCP]

Bldr: . . . (In serv. 1993–. . .)

Europower assault craft—aboard *Newton* (A 367) Ben Sullivan, 5-01

Remarks: No data available, other than that they are powered by two Mercury 200-bhp gasoline outboards, have seven seats in addition to that of the driver, have VHF communications and a GPS terminal, and are employed by No. 539 Assault Squadron.

♦ 8 Arctic 22 Rigid Raider Inflatables [LCP] Bldr: Osborne, U.K.

Arctic 22–class Rigid Raider Maritime Photographic, 8-98

AMPHIBIOUS WARFARE SHIPS *(continued)*

D: 1.4 tons light **S:** 40+ kts **Dim:** 7.2 × . . . × . . .
M: 2 OMC or Suzuki DT140 outboards; 280 shp
Range: 30/40 **Cargo:** 15 troops or 1.12 tons of stores

♦ 6 (+ 24) Pacific 22 Mk II Rigid Inflatables [LCP]
Bldr: Halmatic, Portchester (In serv. 1-00 to . . .)

Pacific 22–class Rigid Raider Maritime Photographic, 7-98

D: 1.75 tons light **S:** 32 kts **Dim:** 6.8 × . . . × . . .
M: 1 Ford Mermaid diesel; 1 waterjet; 140 bhp
Range: 85/26 **Crew:** 1 tot. + 5 passengers or 1.12 tons stores

Remarks: The prototype and four others were in service aboard landing ships as of 7-01, while two others were to be carried aboard frigates *Kent* (F 78) and *Coventry* (F 98) starting at the end of 6-01. Can carry 1.12 tons of stores in place of five people. Production of about 10 per year was expected to be announced in 11-01 after further trials, with deliveries starting in 2002.

Note: The Royal Navy also operates 70 Pacific 22 Mk I and Mk II RIBs as ship's boats; these have a maximum speed of 24 kts and do not have shock-resistant seating like the Royal Marine variant.

♦ 3 U.S. Mk 8 Mod. 1 swimmer delivery vehicles [LSDV]
Bldr: Maritime Special Operations Division, U.S. Naval Surface Warfare Center Coastal Systems Station, Panama City, Fla.

Remarks: Purchased in 1999 to replace Mk 8 Mod. 0 craft for use by the Royal Marine Special Boat Service. Have double the range and a 50% speed increase over the Mod. 0, of which they are rebuilt examples. During reconstruction, they received new motors, sonar, and navigational systems. The first unit was delivered in 3-99 and the other two in 6-99.

♦ 35 or more Mexiflote self-propelled pontoons

Mexiflote sectional pontoon—on starboard side of *Sir Tristram* (L 3505); British Army workboat *Perch* (WB 06) is visible on deck at left Douglas A. Cromby, 3-01

Remarks: Rectangular, modular pontoon float assemblies that can be stowed vertically on the sides of landing ships. Powered by large diesel outdrives.

AUXILIARIES

Note: Ships not listed below as Royal Fleet Auxiliaries (RFA) are crewed by the Royal Navy or civilian contractor personnel.

♦ 2 Fort Grange–class ammunition, food, and stores ships [AE]
Bldr: Scott-Lithgow, Greenock, Scotland

	Laid down	L	In serv.
A 385 Fort Rosalie (ex-*Fort Grange*)	9-11-73	9-12-76	6-4-78
A 386 Fort Austin	9-12-75	9-3-78	11-5-79

Fort Austin (A 386) Derek Fox, 6-01

Fort Rosalie (A 385)—note twin hangar Wolfgang Becker, 6-01

D: 22,749 tons (fl) **S:** 20 kts **Dim:** 183.78 (170.00 pp) × 24.06 × 9.03
A: 2 single 20-mm 90-cal. Oerlikon GAM-B01 AA; 4 single 7.62-mm mg
Electronics:
Radar: 1 Type 1006 nav.; 1 Kelvin-Hughes 21/16P nav.; 1 Kelvin-Hughes 14/12 nav.
EW: DLJ(2) decoy syst. (8 6-round RL); Type 182 towed torpedo decoy
M: 1 Sulzer 8RND90 diesel; 1 prop; 23,200 bhp—2 690-shp bow-thrusters
Electric: 4,120 kw tot. (8 × 515-kw diesel sets) **Range:** 10,000/20
Crew: 31 officers, 83 unlicensed RFA + 36 civilian supply staff + 45 RN flight personnel

Remarks: A 385: 16,046 grt/8,300 dwt; A 386: 16,054 grt/8,165 dwt. Ordered 11-71 and 7-72, respectively. RFA operated. The name for A 385 was changed in 6-00 at the end of a refit—the ship had been stationed at Split, Croatia, from 4-97 to 1-00 and the name change was made to avoid confusion with that of *Fort George* (A 388); the new name commemorates that of a World War II stores issue ship.
Hull systems: Four holds, totaling 6,234 m^3, carry guided weapons, ammunition, and general stores, including 2,300 m^3 of refrigerated provisions. Have three sliding-stay, constant-tension, alongside-replenishment stations on each side. There are two 10-ton and four 5-ton electric stores cranes. Have two auxiliary boilers. In addition to the flight deck at the stern, the hangar roof can be used to operate helicopters.
Combat systems: Two additional 20-mm AA can be installed aft. Are to be backfitted with Outfit DLH offboard seduction decoy launchers when available. One Sea King helicopter is normally carried, although up to four can be accommodated (A 386 acted as helicopter training ship while *Argus* [A 135] was operating in support of U.N. forces in the Middle East during 1991), and they can theoretically be operated as auxiliary ASW helicopter support ships. A Marisat commercial SATCOM terminal is fitted.

♦ 1 Throsk-class ammunition transport [AE]
Bldr: Cleland SB, Wallsend

	Laid down	L	In serv.
A 378 Kinterbury	1980	8-11-80	20-1-81

Kinterbury (A 378) H&L Van Ginderen, 7-98

D: 2,193 tons (fl) **S:** 14 kts **Dim:** 70.57 (64.31 pp) × 11.9 × 4.57
Electronics: Radar: 1 Type 1006 nav.
M: 2 Mirrlees-Blackstone diesels; 1 prop; 3,000 bhp
Range: 1,500/14; 5,000/10 **Crew:** 8 officers, 16 unlicensed

AUXILIARIES *(continued)*

Remarks: 1,150 dwt. Continues to be RMAS operated and is based at Portsmouth. Entered refit in 3-90 but was placed up for sale late in 1991; in 1993–94, the ship was reactivated. Collided with a jetty during 12-99 but was repaired at Rosyth by 2-00. Gearbox problems prevented operations during 7-01, but repairs were completed at Gibraltar by 20-8-01.
Disposals: *Throsk* (A 379) was put up for sale in 7-91 and sold to Ecuador in 1-92. *Arrochar* (A 382, ex-*St. George*) was stricken during 12-99.
Hull systems: Two holds total 750 m^3. Has two 5-ton cranes. Can transport 760 tons in the holds, plus 25 tons of cargo on deck.

♦ 1 Antarctic patrol ship [AG]
Bldr: B. H. Ulstein SY, Hatlo, Norway (In serv. 1990)

A 171 Endurance (ex-A 176, ex-*Polar Circle*)

Endurance (A 171)—red hull, white superstructure, buff stack Marian Wright, 7-01

Endurance (A 171) Douglas A. Cromby, 7-01

D: 6,500 tons (fl) **S:** 12 kts **Dim:** 91.00 (82.50 pp) × 17.90 × 6.50
A: none (see remarks)
Electronics:
Radar: 1 Kelvin-Hughes Type 1006 nav.; 1 Furuno R 84 nav.; 1 Furuno M 34 ARG surf. search (see remarks)
Sonar: Type 2053 echo sounder; Type 2090 echo sounder; Furuno 60-88 obstacle avoidance
M: 2 Ulstein-Bergen BRM-8 diesels; 1 4-bladed Kort-nozzle prop; 8,152 bhp—1,000-shp bow-thruster—775-shp stern side-thruster
Electric: 5,170 kw tot. (2 × 1,980-kw Leroy Somer shaft generators, 2 × 605-kw Mitsubishi diesel-driven sets)
Range: 4,000–5,000/12 **Fuel:** 600 tons **Endurance:** 120 days
Crew: 15 officers, 97 enlisted + 14 marines

Remarks: 5,129 grt/2,200 dwt. RN operated. Was chartered 14-10-91 for one year, with an option to purchase, from Rieber Shipping, Norway, and purchased outright on 24-1-92. The ship serves as Antarctic Territories patrol ship to guarantee the continuation of British sovereignty over the Falkland, South Georgia, and South Shetland Islands in the Antarctic Atlantic, where the ship also performs hydrographic survey duties. The original name was retained through her first deployment to the South Atlantic, ending in 5-92; the initial pennant number was changed during 10-92 to commemorate her predecessor. Became subordinated to the Hydrographic Surveying Squadron in summer 1995 and is expected to remain in service well into this century. Refitted by FSL, Portsmouth, from 6-99 to 10-99, with new radars and new computer.
Hull systems: Built as a combination commercial Arctic exploration and research vessel, icebreaker, and supply vessel. Able to break 3-ft. ice at 3 kts. The double-skinned hull is equipped with ice fins forward of the propeller to break up trash ice, and the rudder foundation has ice knives fitted for the same purpose. The elevator-equipped helicopter hangar is below the flight deck. During a major refit completed on 9-10-92, most of the scientific equipment (including the stern gantry) was removed and the helicopter hangar was greatly enlarged. There are 27- and 5-ton electrohydraulic cranes to handle cargo in a forward hold. Carries 78 m^3 of aviation fuel and 250 m^3 of potable water. Crew accommodations include a sauna, infirmary, and exercise room.
Combat systems: Has no armament and no countermeasures equipment. Navigation equipment provides fixes to 5-m accuracy and includes two gyrocompasses, an electromagnetic log, several echo sounders, a Furuno object-avoidance sonar, a Robertson autopilot, and a homing beacon for the Lynx HAS.3 helicopter. A commercial SATCOM terminal is fitted. The radar suite listed above is what was aboard prior to the 1999 refit.

♦ 1 special forces support ship and cable tender [AG]
Bldr: Scott-Lithgow, Greenock, Scotland

	Laid down	L	In serv.
A 367 Newton	19-12-73	26-6-75	17-6-76

Newton (A 367)—with assault boats stowed forward Ben Sullivan, 5-01

Newton (A 367)—black hull, buff superstructure Derek Fox, 7-01

D: 3,140 tons light (4,652 fl) **S:** 14 kts **Dim:** 98.6 (88.7 pp) × 16.15 × 5.7
Electronics:
Radar: 1 Kelvin-Hughes Type 1006 nav.
Sonar: Type 185 underwater telephone; Type 2010 and Type 2013 echo sounders
M: 3 Ruston 8RK-215 diesels (1,840 bhp each), electric drive; 1 Kort-nozzle prop; 2,680 shp—300-shp electric low-speed motor
Electric: 2,150 kw tot.
Range: 5,000/9 **Fuel:** 244 tons **Crew:** 61 tot. (incl. 12 technicians)

Remarks: Was originally intended for sonar-propagation trials and was also fitted to lay cable over the bows. Was modified to serve as a special forces support ship during a 2000–01 refit by Cammell Laird, Birkenhead. Continues to be operated by the RMAS, based at Devonport.
Hull systems: Equipped with a 350-hp retractable bow-thruster and passive tank stabilization system. The propulsion plant is extremely quiet. Has four laboratories and seven special winches. Can carry and lay 400 tons of undersea cable and 361 tons of cable repeaters. Navigation equipment includes SINS, communications and navigational satellite receivers, two optical range-finders, Decca Mk 21, and considerable other equipment. Was re-engined in 2000 by Ocean Fleets, Birkenhead. Has had davits added to support Special Boat Squadron RIB assault craft.

Note: The trials ship *Colonel Templer* and the new trimaran-hulled concept trials ship *Triton* are the property of the Defence Evaluation and Research Agency and are described under that section.

♦ 1 Aviation Training and Primary Casualty Reception Ship [AGH]
Bldr: CNR Breda, Venice, Italy

	L	In serv.
A 135 Argus (ex-*Contender Bezant*)	1981	1-6-88

Argus (A 135) Maritime Photographic, 8-01

D: 22,256 tons light (28,480 fl) **S:** 22 max. (19 sust.)
Dim: 173.01 (163.63 pp) × 30.64 × 8.20
Air Group: 6 Sea King helicopters or 12 Sea Harrier V/STOL fighters (8 operational)
A: 2 single 20-mm 90-cal. Oerlikon GAM-B01 AA; 4 single 7.62-mm mg
Electronics:
Radar: 1 Kelvin-Hughes Type 1006 nav.; 1 Kelvin-Hughes Type 1007 nav.; 1 BAE Systems Type 994 surf./air search
EW: UAN(1) (Racal Guardian) intercept; DLJ(2) decoy syst. (2 6-round Shield RL); Type 182 towed torpedo decoy

AUXILIARIES *(continued)*

M: Electric drive: 2 Lindholmen-Pielstick 18 PC2.5 V400 diesel generator sets, 2 Lindholmen propulsion motors; 2 props; 23,400 shp
Electric: 3,850 kw (3 × 1,200-kw, 1 × 250-kw diesel sets)
Range: 20,000/19 **Fuel:** 5,617 tons heavy oil + 3,251 tons aviation fuel
Crew: 22 officers, 58 unlicensed RFA + 3 officers, 25 enlisted RN + training detachment: 42 officers, 95 enlisted RN (or up to 750 troops in emergency)

Remarks: 26,421 grt/12,221 dwt. Former roll-on/roll-off vehicle and container cargo ship, purchased 2-3-84, having been on charter since 5-82, when she was used as an aircraft transport during the Falklands War; initially intended to act as a helicopter training ship or as a transport for Harrier/Sea Harrier aircraft. Harland & Wolff, Belfast, converted the vehicle cargo decks into a hangar and added elevators. Was initially accepted 28-10-87, officially accepted 3-3-88, and "dedicated" 1-6-88—but continued in a trials status until completing a 17-7-89 to 3-10-89 refit. Deployed twice to the Persian Gulf during the 1990–91 war: on 16-10-90 equipped with a 100-bed emergency hospital and carrying four Sea King helicopters; and during 4-91 with 11 Sea King HC.4 and several Lynx and Gazelle helicopters. Has developed hull cracking and is generally considered not to be a successful ship. She was found to be unsuitable for long-term troop deployments during operations in the Adriatic in 1993. During a refit from 1-01 to 5-01 at Cammell Laird, Hebburn-on-Tyne, as an "Aviation Training and Primary Casualty Reception Ship," was given a permanent medical facility with beds for 90 casualties, 20 berths for intensive care patients, and four operating theaters, all fitted into the space below the helicopter deck, which was modified to have multiple helicopter operating spots.
Hull systems: Passive tank stabilization was added and the watertight compartmentation improved during naval conversion. Can carry 5,405 tons of water ballast and can also transfer fuel to ships in company.
Aviation systems: Has space for eight Sea Harriers and three helicopters on the hangar deck and three helicopters on deck, aft. There are two aircraft elevators. The hangar segregates into four sections. The flight deck (created by upending the former hatch covers, filling these with 1.9-m-thick concrete, and then laying over with steel for ballast and stability purposes) measures 113.52 × 28 m but is encumbered by the stack and superstructure to starboard that create unpredictable airflow over the deck.
Combat systems: Racal supplied the sensors, CANE (DEB-1) data system, communications, and weapons-control package. The Type 994 radar uses a parabolic antenna from the AWS-4 radar. The listed gun armament is not normally carried. Two mounting positions abaft the stack for twin 30-mm 90-cal. Oerlikon AA have been empty for many years.

♦ 0 (+ 2) Echo-class hydrographic survey ships [AGS]
Bldr: Appledore Shipbuilders, Appledore, Devon

	Laid down	L	In serv.
H 87 Echo	10-4-01	4-3-02	2003
H 88 Enterprise	10-4-01	24-8-02	2003

Echo-class survey ship—artist's rendering Russell/Vosper Thornycroft, 2001

D: 3,500 tons **S:** 15 kts **Dim:** 90.0 × 16.00 × 5.50
A: provision for 4 single 20-mm 90-cal. Oerlikon GAM-B01 AA
Electronics:
Radar: 1 Decca BridgeMaster-E 180 nav.; 1 . . . nav.
Sonar: . . .
M: diesel-electric drive: 2 ABB Compact Azipod electric azimuthal thrusters; 4,600 shp
Range: 9,000/12 **Crew:** 46 tot. (accomm. for 81; see remarks)

Remarks: A request for bids was originally made in 1-97 for replacements for *Roebuck* (H 130), *Herald* (H 138), *Bulldog* (H 317), and *Beagle* (H 319). The contract, for only two, was let 21-6-00 for $197 million to Vosper Thornycroft, which will also manage the operations of the ships for 25 years; the actual construction was subcontracted to Appledore. Designed by Kvaerner–Masa Marine. Will use naval crews, rotating aboard as in the *Scott* (H 131) but with 23 personnel in each of the three watches, two being aboard and one ashore at any given time; this is intended to permit 334 days of operation per ship per year. They will also be usable as mine countermeasures support ships, when another 35 personnel would come aboard. Both were laid down on the same day.
Hull systems: The power system can deliver anywhere from 400 to 3,000 kw to the propulsion plant.
Mission systems: Multibeam echo sounders and side-looking mapping sonars will be fitted, and one survey launch will be carried. A helicopter deck with an elevator to the hangar below will be fitted forward of the bridge. Norway's Kongsberg Simrad will supply the integrated survey system for the two ships and their survey motor boats, including multibeam echo sounders, processing, and data storage.

Note: Hydrographic survey ships began to be painted standard gray in 1997 in place of the traditional white with buff stack and masts; in 7-98, the pennant numbers were changed from "A" to "H" flag superior and are now painted on the hull sides. The Antarctic patrol ship *Endurance* (A 171) is subordinated to the Hydrographic Survey Squadron and performs surveys in the southern Atlantic region in addition to her other duties.

♦ 1 Scott-class Ocean Survey Ship [AGS]
Bldr: Appledore Shipbuilders, Bideford

	Laid down	L	In serv.
H 131 Scott	20-1-95	13-10-96	19-9-97 (del. 30-6-97)

Scott (H 131) A. A. de Kruijf, 3-00

D: 13,500 tons (fl) **S:** 17.6 kts (sust.) **Dim:** 131.13 × 21.50 × 8.30
Electronics:
Radar: 1 Decca 1626C ARPA nav.; 1 . . . surf. search
Sonar: SASS Mk 4 multibeam mapping, Type 2090 echo sounder
M: 2 MaK 9M32 medium-speed diesels; 1 Lips CP prop; 10,800 bhp—1 7-ton-thrust retracting azimuthal bow-thruster
Electric: 2,400 kw tot. (4 × 600-kw, Cummins diesel-driven)
Range: . . ./. . . **Endurance:** 35+ days
Crew: 12 officers, 51 enlisted, incl. 35-person survey team (accomm. for 70; see remarks)

Remarks: Ordered 20-1-95 from BAE Defence Systems Group, which subcontracted the construction to Appledore. Her large size was dictated by the need for 8.4-m draft and a flat hull bottom for the mapping sonar transducer array. Is intended to operate 307 days out of the year, with 42 of the total assigned crew of 63 aboard at any one time; crewmembers rotate aboard, 70 days on and 30 days off. Initial employment was a delineation of the boundary of the U.K.'s continental shelf. Based at Devonport, from which she was deployed to the Indian Ocean from 9-98 to 30-9-99. Exercised as a mine countermeasures support ship in the Aegean during 10-00, equipped to support four mine countermeasures ships with enhanced communications systems, additional stores, and an at-sea refueling system for the mine countermeasures ships.
Hull systems: Has an ice-strengthened hull of 14 m molded depth, with the draft kept constant by a ballasting system during survey operations. Is also equipped with oceanographic research equipment. Has two large cranes aft. By 1998, the area on the upper deck forward of the boat stowage had been adapted as a helicopter pad. The Sonar Array Sounding System (SASS) Mk 4 wide-swath sonar and navigation systems are the same as those used in USN survey ships: the U.S. SQN-17 Bottom Topographic Survey System (BOTOSS) and two BQN-33 narrowbeam sonars. The keel-mounted mapping sonar covers a 5.6-km-wide, 120° swath at 4,000-m depth, permitting coverage of 150 km^2 of ocean floor per hour; it has a total of 144 transmitter hydrophones on the longitudinal array and 90 on the transverse array. Gravimetric sensors with automatic data recording are also fitted. Is able to maintain 13 kts in Sea State 5. The engine room is not manned during normal operations. Personnel are accommodated in individual cabins, and a large gymnasium is fitted. Ballast tanks can hold 8,900 tons of seawater. The foredeck is strengthened to accept standard cargo containers.

♦ 1 Roebuck-class coastal survey ship [AGS]
Bldr: Brooke Marine, Lowestoft

	L	In serv.
H 130 Roebuck	14-11-85	30-10-86

Roebuck (H 130) Bernard Prézelin, 5-01

D: 1,105 tons light (1,477 fl) **S:** 15 kts **Dim:** 63.89 (57.00 pp) × 13.00 × 4.00
Electronics:
Radar: 1 Decca 1626C ARPA nav.
Sonar: BAE Systems Type 2034BC Hydrosearch; Waverley Type 2033BB Sidescan
M: 4 Mirrlees ES-8 Mk 1 diesels; 2 CP props; 3,040 bhp
Range: 4,000/10 **Crew:** 6 officers, 40 enlisted

Remarks: Ordered 21-5-84 as the first of a planned quartet. Can theoretically be adapted to serve as a mine countermeasures support ship but has not yet been so assigned. Plana are to retire her in 4-03 after an unusually brief service for this type of ship.
Hull systems: Three generator sets are fitted. Has the Qubit SIPS (Survey Information Processing System). Other survey equipment includes Types 780AA and 778AG echo sounders and Racal Hyperfix radio navigation aid. Hydrosearch sonar provides high-definition imaging to 600-m depths. Has an A-frame at the stern to tow a magnetometer and the Waverley Sidescan sonar. Carries two survey launches, *Batchellor Delight* and *Jolly Prize,* described below under [YGS]. Equipped with Marisat commercial SATCOM terminal.

AUXILIARIES *(continued)*

Disposal note: The Improved *Hecla*–class ocean survey vessel *Herald* (H 138) was decommissioned 31-5-01 and is for sale. Of the four ships of the *Bulldog* class, *Fox* (A 320) was stricken 31-1-89, *Fawn* (A 335) was paid off 27-9-91, *Bulldog* (H 317, ex-A 317) was paid off 6-7-01, and *Beagle* (H 319, ex-A 319, ex-*Barracuda*) was retired 18-2-02.

♦ **1 chartered ocean survey vessel [AGS]**
Bldr: A.G. Weser Werk Seebeck, Bremen, Germany (In serv. 1965)

Marine Explorer (ex-*Trinity Explorer,* ex-*Sir Tristan,* ex-*Sir Walter Raleigh,* ex-*Swanella,* ex-*British Viking,* ex-*Vickers Viking,* ex-*Dortmund,* ex-*Danasbank,* ex-*Hamburg*)

Marine Explorer Maritime Photographic, 7-93

D: approx. 3,300 tons (fl) **S:** 13 kts **Dim:** 83.60 (72.40 pp) × 13.64 × 5.49
M: 1 Klockner-Humboldt-Deutz 12-cyl. diesel; 1 CP prop; 3,000 bhp—bow-thruster
Electric: 536 kw tot. (1 × 416-kw, 1 × 120-kw diesel sets)
Range: . . ./. . . **Crew:** . . .

Remarks: 1,963 grt/990 dwt. Former stern-trawler, chartered in 6-92 from Eidesvik Shipping, Ltd., as a survey vessel. Hull is painted red, superstructure and stack white. Built as a stern-haul trawler and converted in 1974 for Vickers as a submersible mother-ship. Carries RN survey team Naval Party 1008.

Note: Small motor vessel *Proud Seahorse* has been on charter since 1985 for coastal survey work, with the owner's crew plus a navy survey team. Other small inshore survey boats are described under [YGS] in the Service Craft section.

♦ **0 (+ 1 + 1) Primary Casualty Receiving Ships [AH]**
Bldr: . . . . . . (In serv. 2005)

Remarks: Program was included in the 1998 Strategic Defence Review, but as of 12-01 was still being studied. The first may be a new or converted vessel, a modular system capable of being deployed aboard a variety of commercial or naval hulls, or merely an extension of the existing standby PCRS, *Argus* (A 135), and is to be ordered in 2002 and available by 2005. A second, chartered hospital ship of around 20,000 tons (fl) displacement may also be placed on standby availability. Both would have a 200-bed casualty facility, intensive care units, operating theaters, a crew of about 350 (including the medical staff), and a helicopter deck with one landing and one parking spot. A side ramp will allow embarkation and debarkation of casualties while alongside a pier. The second PCRS would be expected to operate about 12 weeks per year each on exercises for the U.K. M.O.D. and the rest of the year on civilian healthcare duties.

♦ **0 (+ 6) Hartland Point (Ro-Ro-2700)–class vehicle cargo ships [AK]** Bldrs: first two: Harland & Wolff, Belfast, Northern Ireland; others: Flensburger Schiffsbau–Gesellschaft (FSG), Flensburg, Germany

	Laid down	L	In serv.
Hartland Point	10-01	. . .	10-02
Anvil Point	. . .	. . .	1-03
Hurst Point	4-9-01	19-4-02	26-9-03 (del.)
Eddystone	. . .	8-02	2004
Longstone	. . .	11-02	2004
Beachy Head	. . .	2-03	2004

Hartland Point–class vehicle cargo ship—computer graphic
M.O.D., U.K., 2001

D: 20,000 tons (fl) **S:** 21.5 kts (loaded) **Dim:** 193.00 (182.39 pp) × 26.00 × 7.40
M: 2 MaK 9M43 heavy-oil diesels; 2 CP props; 21,700 bhp—CP bow-thruster
Electric: 6,080 kw tot. (2 × 1,600-kw, 2 × 1,440-kw diesel sets)
Range: 9,200/21.5 **Fuel:** 1,104 tons heavy oil; 113 tons diesel **Crew:** 18 tot.

Remarks: 22,900 grt/14,200 dwt. It was announced in 7-98 that four additional roll-on/roll-off vehicle cargo ships would be acquired to support the Joint Rapid Deployment Force; the number was increased to six in 10-00, when AWSR Shipping (Andrew Weir Shipping, James Fisher, Houlder Offshore Engineering, and Bibby Line) was named as the winning bidder on the $1.8 billion contract to operate the ships on charter for 25 years. The ships may be available for commercial charter when not carrying military cargoes. The two Harland & Wolff–built ships were ordered 11-3-01 and the German-built quartet during 8-01. The design will be very similar to that of *Sea Centurion* (A 98), but with strengthened vehicle decks. The cost of each of the German-built ships will be about $105 million. They will not have pennant numbers.
Hull systems: The planned vehicle load is 130 armored vehicles, tracked reconnaissance vehicles, infantry fighting vehicles, armored personnel carriers, engineer vehicles, and 155-mm artillery pieces, plus 60 trucks, helicopters, and ammunition stores. There will be a centerline stern ramp, and vehicles will be carried on the upper deck as well as on cargo decks within the hull, for a total capacity of 2,640 lane-meters.

♦ **1 Stena 4-Runner–class vehicle cargo ship [AK]**
Bldr: Società Esercizo Cantieri (SEC), Viareggio, Italy

	L	In serv.
A 98 Sea Centurion (ex-*Stena Grecia,* ex-*UND Ausonia*)	12-5-98	18-10-98

Sea Centurion (A 98)—dark blue hull, white upperworks, blue-gray stacks
Derek Fox, 2-01

D: 22,000 tons (fl) **S:** 24 kts (22 sust.) **Dim:** 182.60 (165.40 pp) × 25.80 × 7.40
Electronics: Radar: . . .
M: 4 Sulzer 8ZA40S diesels; 2 Lips CP props; 30,880 bhp (at 510 rpm)—2 1,340-shp side-thrusters
Electric: 6,400 kw tot. (2 × 1,700-kw, 2 × 1,500-kw diesel-driven sets)
Range: 6,000/22 **Fuel:** 1,499 tons heavy oil + 152.7 tons diesel
Crew: 17 tot.

Remarks: 21,104-grt/12,350-dwt roll-on/roll-off vehicle carrier. Charter contract was signed in 10-97 for 18 months with Stena Ferries, Sweden. In 4-01, the charter was extended for 16 months. "Centurion" in the name commemorates a British Army heavy tank name. Originally, the second and third ships of this commercial class were to have been chartered, but the first ship (originally to have been for a Turkish owner) was substituted to meet operational requirements, and, after the builder's bankruptcy, the charter was canceled before delivery; the other ship was to have been named *Sea Chieftain.* Provides short-notice strategic sealift capacity for the Joint Rapid Deployment Force, formed in 4-99. Operates from the Marchwood Military Port, Southampton. Painted with blue hull, white superstructure, and gray funnels.
Hull systems: Is equipped with two flap rudders to aid in harbor maneuvering. The upper, weather deck has 1,145 lane-meters of vehicle parking space, the main deck 1,055, and the lower hold 515—the total equating to 211 40-ft. trailers or 800 standard 20-ft. cargo containers. The weather deck has a height clearance of 5 m (partially under the forward superstructure), the main deck 6.80 m, and the lower hold 5 m. There is a single stern vehicle cargo door with a 19-m-long by 17.2-m-wide ramp. Internal movement of vehicles is via several MacGregor ramps.

♦ **1 Celestine-class vehicle cargo ship [AK]**
Bldr: Kawasaki Heavy Industries, Sakaide, Japan (In serv. 4-10-96)

A 96 Sea Crusader (ex-*Celestine*)

Sea Crusader (A 96)—gray hull and stacks, white upperworks, no pennant number showing
Douglas A. Cromby, 4-01

D: 25,500 tons (fl) **S:** 19 kts (17.8 sust.) **Dim:** 162.49 (150.00 pp) × 25.64 × 6.52
Electronics:
Radar: 1 Raytheon . . . E/F-band nav.; 1 Raytheon . . . ARPA X-band nav.
M: 2 Kawasaki-M.A.N. 7L40/54, 7-cyl. diesels; 2 CP props; 13,383 bhp—2 1,000-shp bow-thrusters
Electric: 3,300 kw tot. (1 × 1,700-kw, 2 × 800-kw diesel-driven; 440 V, 60 Hz)
Range: 13,278/17.8 **Fuel:** 1,380 tons heavy oil + 35 tons diesel **Crew:** 17 tot.

Remarks: 23,986-grt/9,677-dwt roll-on/roll-off vehicle carrier. Chartered 10-10-96 for two years from Oceanarrow, Ltd., Panama City, Panama, for RFA service; the charter was renewed in 10-98, extended when the charter of the second *Stena 4-Runner*–class vehicle cargo ship was canceled in 4-99, and extended again from 1-2-01 to 1-3-03. Supports the Joint Rapid Deployment Force. Based at Marchwood Military Port, Southampton.

AUXILIARIES *(continued)*

Hull systems: Can carry up to 350 armored vehicles, trucks, and trailers on a total of 2,300 lane-meters on three internal decks, while additional vehicles can be parked on the upper deck. The stern ramp is 22.9 m long by 21.7 m wide and can support 150 tons. Hull molded depth is 15.45 m. The ship appears to be operating at an 18,031-ton displacement restriction in RFA service.

♦ 1 . . .-class vehicle cargo ship [AK]
Bldr: Kawasaki Heavy Industries, Sakaide, Japan (In serv. 12-80)

DART 10 (ex-*Mont Ventoux,* ex-*Dart 10,* ex-*Zhang Jia Kou*)

Dart 10 Maritime Photographic, 6-01

D: approx. 22,500 tons (fl) **S:** 21 kts **Dim:** 176.98 (160.00 pp) × 26.55 × 8.52
Electronics: Radar: 1 . . . X-band nav.; 1 . . . S-band nav.
M: 1 M.A.N. 7L52/55A diesel (7,382 bhp), 1 M.A.N. 8L52/55A diesel (8,429 bhp); 1 prop; 15,811 bhp—1 CP and 1 fixed-pitch bow-thruster—1 azimuthal stern-thruster
Electric: 3,296 kw tot. (1 × 1,120 kw, 2 × 1,088 kw; 390 V a.c.)
Range: 20,160/21 **Fuel:** 2,089 tons heavy oil + 244 tons diesel **Crew:** . . .

Remarks: 22,748 grt/13,996 dwt. Chartered from British Linen Shipping from 8-3-01 to 1-11-02 and is operated by her commercial crew. Does not carry a pennant number.
Hull systems: The engines, of differing power, are geared to the same shaft. The hull is ice-strengthened. Has 2,723 lane-meters of vehicle cargo capacity (assuming 8-ft. width), with a clear height of 6.75 m on the 139.3-m internal cargo deck, the equivalent of 213 standard cargo trailers. The open upper cargo deck is 83 m long. Container capacity is 729 20-ft. equivalent. Has a single, nonslewing stern vehicle ramp.

♦ 0 (+ 2) Wave-class replenishment oilers [AO]
Bldr: BAE Systems, Barrow-in-Furness (A 390: Govan), Scotland

	Laid down	L	In serv.
A 389 WAVE KNIGHT	22-5-98	29-9-00	2002
A 390 WAVE RULER	. . .	9-2-01	2003

Wave-class oiler—artist's rendering BAE Systems, 2001

Wave Ruler (A 390)—shortly after launch BAE Systems, 2-01

D: 12,500 tons light (31,500 fl) **S:** 18 kts **Dim:** 196.45 × 27.20 × 9.5
A: 2 single 30-mm 75-cal. DES-30B AA; 4 single 7.62-mm mg; provision for 2 20-mm Mk 15 Phalanx gatling CIWS
Electronics:
Radar: 2 Kelvin Hughes 6000 ARPA nav. (E/F- and I-band)
EW: . . .
M: diesel-electric drive: 4 Wärtsilä 12V32E diesels (6,290 bhp each), 4 GECLM generator sets; 1 prop; 18,776 shp—KaMeWa bow- and stern-thrusters (10-ton thrust each)
Range: 10,000/15; 8,000/18 **Crew:** 80 RFA + 22 RN aircrew

Remarks: Request for proposals was issued in 3-96. Are to replace the stricken *Olwen*-class replenishment oilers *Olwen* and *Olna* and will be RFA operated. The final design and construction order, placed 16-7-97 for about $160 million each, was for a slightly larger and slower design than originally planned. They were contracted for delivery during 9-00 and 10-01, respectively. The start of A 390 was delayed, and the work was reassigned to BAE Systems' Govan facility; Harland & Wolff, Belfast, built the cargo tankage for both ships, but A 390 was otherwise built entirely at Govan. A 389's stern section was built by Cammell Laird, Newcastle-on-Tyne, and was attached to the ship beginning 27-1-00. Two further units of the class may be ordered to replace the four Leaf-series oilers. Labor troubles have slowed delivery of A 389.
Hull systems: Have 16,500 m^3 total tankage for diesel (15,000 tons) and aviation fuel (3,000 m^3), lube oil, and cargo water; 500 m^3 dry cargo; and space for eight 20-ft. refrigerated provisions containers offloadable with a shipboard crane. There are three replenishment stations per side. Built to commercial standards, except for naval intact and damaged stability criteria. Double-hull construction. Have a helicopter hangar and flight deck capable of handling one Merlin HM.1 helicopter. Superstructure and replenishment-rig kingposts are sloped 6° from vertical to reduce radar return. Have totally enclosed bridges with integrated controls and have simplified replenishment rigs. One emergency diesel alternator set is provided.

Note: All Royal Fleet Auxiliary liquid replenishment vessels employ 6-inch (152-mm) hoses and pump at 100 p.s.i. and can transfer about 500 tons per hour per station. An *Invincible*-class carrier requires only about 2 hours to refuel and frigates about 40 minutes.

♦ 1 Oakleaf-class replenishment oiler [AO]
Bldr: Uddevallavarvet, Uddevalla, Sweden

	L	In serv
A 111 OAKLEAF (ex-*Oktania*)	1981	14-8-86 (in RFA)

Oakleaf (A 111) Martin Mokrus, 6-01

D: 49,377 tons (fl) **S:** 15.75 kts (14.5 sust.)
Dim: 173.69 (168.00 wl) × 32.26 × 11.20 (max.)
A: 2 single 20-mm 70-cal. Oerlikon Mk 7A AA; 2 single 7.62-mm mg
Electronics:
Radar: 2 Decca BridgeMaster Mk II ARPA (X- and S-band)
EW: provision for 2 DLB decoy syst. (2 6-round Barricade RL)
M: 2 Uddevalla–Burmeister & Wain 4L80GFCA 4-cyl., 2-stroke diesels; 1 CP prop; 12,250 bhp—bow and stern tunnel-thrusters
Electric: 2,472 kw (3 × 800-kw, 1 × 72-kw diesel set)
Range: . . ./. . . **Crew:** 14 officers, 21 unlicensed

Remarks: 24,608 grt/34,800 dwt. Former Norwegian commercial tanker, leased in 7-85 to replace *Plumleaf* (A 78). Converted for naval support service by Falmouth Ship Repairers from 17-2-86 to 14-8-86. Refitted in 1994–95. Charter was renewed in 6-97 for five years. Refitted 4-00 to 10-00 by A&P, Falmouth, and charter was to be renewed again in 6-02. The 20-mm AA are not always mounted.
Hull systems: Cargo: 43,020 m^3 in 16 tanks; no dry cargo. Can carry up to 15,430 tons of water ballast. During conversion, received two alongside fueling stations (one per side) with raised working deck, astern refueling capability, two additional generator sets, additional communications, NAVSAT equipment, and Marisat SATCOM terminal. Has three 13.7-kg/cm^2 auxiliary boilers. Retained the sauna. Engineering spaces are automated and are not occupied when the ship is under way. Hull is reinforced for ice navigation.

♦ 3 Leaf-class replenishment oilers [AO]
Bldr: Cammell Laird, Birkenhead

	L	In serv.
A 81 BRAMBLELEAF (ex-*Hudson Deep*)	22-1-76	3-80
A 109 BAYLEAF	27-10-81	26-3-82
A 110 ORANGELEAF (ex-*Balder London,* ex-*Hudson Progress*)	. . .	2-5-84 (in RFA)

Brambleleaf (A 81) Ben Sullivan, 4-01

D: 40,870 (A 109: 37,747) tons (fl) **S:** 16.5 kts (15.5 sust.)
Dim: 170.69 (163.51 pp) × 25.94 × 11.56
A: 2 single 20-mm 90-cal. Oerlikon GAM-B01 AA; 4 single 7.62-mm mg

AUXILIARIES *(continued)*

Bayleaf (A 109) Michael W. Young, 10-00

Electronics:
Radar: 1 Decca TM1226 nav.; 1 Decca 1229 nav.
EW: 2 DLB decoy syst. (2 6-round Barricade RL)
M: 2 Crossley-Pielstick 14 PC2 V400 diesels; 1 CP prop; 14,000 bhp
Electric: 6,660 kw tot. (2 × 2,704-kw, 2 × 626-kw diesel sets)
Range: . . ./. . . **Fuel:** 2,498 tons **Crew:** 19 officers, 37 unlicensed

Remarks: A 81: 20,440 grt/33,257 dwt; A 109: 20,086 grt/29,999 dwt; A 110: 20,284 grt/33,751 dwt. RFA operated. A 81 was acquired in 1979 and refitted for naval service by Cammell Laird during 1979–80; her stack was raised 3.5 m, a dry cargo hold added forward, a replenishment-at-sea working deck added amidships, and the superstructure enlarged aft. A 109, on which construction work had been suspended while still on the ways, was chartered 3-4-81 from Lombard Leasing Services and similarly altered. A 110, completed in 1979 and on charter since 4-82 from Lloyd's Industrial Leasing, was rechartered 26-3-84 and initially operated without replenishment equipment, receiving a similar conversion to that of her sisters from 1985 to 2-5-86. All are planned to be retired by 2010.
Disposals: *Appleleaf* (A 79) was leased to Australia for 5 years on 26-9-89 and purchased in 1994.
Hull systems: Liquid cargo capacity is 32,309 (A 110: 41,881) m^3 in 24 tanks, and they normally carry 22,000 m^3 of marine gas turbine fuel and 3,800 m^3 of aviation gas turbine fuel; there is a small dry cargo capacity. All now have one refueling station per side, over-the-stern fueling capability, and a Marisat SATCOM terminal. Have three auxiliary boilers. A 110 received new navigational radars (probably Decca BridgeMaster Mk II ARPA, X- and S-band) during a 2001 refit.

♦ 3 Rover-class replenishment oilers [AO]
Bldr: Swan Hunter, Hebburn-on-Tyne

	L	In serv.
A 269 Grey Rover	17-4-69	10-4-70
A 271 Gold Rover	7-3-73	22-3-74
A 273 Black Rover	30-10-73	23-8-74

Grey Rover (A 269) Derek Fox, 9-01

Gold Rover (A 271) Mike Welsford, 7-00

D: 4,700 tons light (11,522 fl) **S:** 19.25 kts (17 sust.)
Dim: 140.34 (131.07 pp) × 19.23 × 7.23
A: 2 single 20-mm 70-cal. Oerlikon Mk 7A AA; 2 single 7.62-mm mg
Electronics:
Radar: 1 Kelvin-Hughes Type 1006 nav.; 1 Decca S2690 ARPA nav.; 1 Decca 1690 nav.
M: 2 SEMT-Pielstick 16 PC2 2V400 (A 269: Crossley-Pielstick 16 PA4) diesels; 1 CP prop; 15,360 bhp—500-shp bow-thruster
Electric: 2,720 kw tot. (8 × 340-kw diesel sets)
Range: 14,000/15 **Fuel:** 965 tons heavy oil + 123 tons diesel
Crew: 18 officers, 37 unlicensed (A 269: 17 officers, 31 unlicensed)

Remarks: A 269: 7,513 grt/6,931 dwt; A 271: 7,574 grt/6,365 dwt; A 273: 7,574 grt/6,799 dwt. RFA operated. A 271 has been used to support the training squadron. A 269 was re-engined in 1973–74; she was to have been deactivated during 1993 for later sale to Pakistan (which bought a Netherlands oiler instead), but was instead designated to remain active until the end of 1997 and is now to be extended until at least 2007. A 273 departed U.K. waters during 2-01 for an 11-month South Atlantic tour in support of the Falkland Islands guard ship, relieving A 271.
Disposals: *Green Rover* (A 268) was placed in reserve on 30 days' notice 27-5-88 and was sold to Indonesia in 1-92. *Blue Rover* (A 270) was sold to Portugal and transferred 31-3-93.
Hull systems: Cargo capacity includes 7,460 m^3 of fuel, 325 m^3 of water, and 70 m^3 of lube oil; 600 m^3 of aviation fuel or gasoline can be carried in lieu of ship fuel. Have a 25.9-m-long by 15.55-m-wide helicopter deck served by a stores elevator, but there is no hangar. The stern shapes vary, early units having had two stern anchors and later units one. A 269 and A 273 have gun platforms on their forecastles.

Disposal note: *Olwen*-class replenishment oilers *Olwen* (A 122, ex-*Olynthus*) and *Olna* (A 123) were placed up for sale 25-8-00; both were laid up 27-9-00 at Portsmouth.

♦ 2 Fort Victoria–class replenishment ships [AOR]

	Bldr	Laid down	L	In serv.
A 387 Fort Victoria	Harland & Wolff, Belfast	15-9-88	12-6-90	24-6-94
A 388 Fort George	Swan Hunter, Wallsend	9-3-89	1-3-91	16-7-93

Fort Victoria (A 387) Jaroslaw Cislak, 6-01

Fort George (A 388) Bernard Prézelin, 4-00

D: 36,580 (fl) **S:** 20 kts **Dim:** 203.93 (185.00 pp) × 30.36 (28.50 wl) × 9.77
A: 2 single 30-mm 75-cal. MSI DS-30B AA; 2 20-mm Mk 15 Phalanx gatling CIWS; 3 Sea King helicopters
Electronics:
Radar: 1 Kelvin-Hughes Type 1007 nav.; 1 Decca Type 1008 ARPA nav.; 2 General Dynamics Mk 90 Phalanx f.c.
TACAN: Kelvin-Hughes NUCLEUS
EW: UAT intercept; DLB(1) Sea Gnat decoy syst. (4 6-round RL); Type 182 towed torpedo decoy
M: 2 Crossley-Pielstick 16 PC2.6 V400 medium-speed diesels; 2 props; 25,083 bhp (23,892 sust.)
Electric: 3,900 kw tot. (6 × 650-kw Cummins KTA 386I diesel sets)
Range: . . ./. . . **Fuel:** . . . tons
Crew: 24 officers, 71 unlicensed RFA + 1 officer, 27 enlisted RN stores personnel + 28 officers, 126 enlisted RN air group

Remarks: 28,821 grt/16,967 dwt. Were to have been a class of six, to be followed by six more of a simplified variant. A 387 was ordered 8-5-86 and A 388 on 18-12-87. Completion of A 387 was delayed by a terrorist explosion 6-9-90; the ship arrived at Cammell Laird, Birkenhead, 7-7-92 to complete fitting out after a serious propulsion system failure during sea trials and by 9-93 was £76 million over her planned cost.
Hull systems: Can carry about 70,000 barrels (12,505 m^3) of liquid cargo, consisting of about 12,000 tons of diesel fuel and 1,000 tons of aviation fuel, and 6,000 tons (6,234 m^3) of munitions, dry stores, and refrigerated cargo. They have two Clark Chapman dual-purpose liquid/solid replenishment stations per side, plus vertical replenishment and astern refueling capability; all replenishment stations are remotely controlled from a large station amidships. Have two pair of fin stabilizers. One 25-ton, two 10-ton, and two 5-ton electric cranes are fitted, with one 10-ton crane capable of supporting an additional underway-refueling rig. The large helicopter flight deck, with two landing spots, can land Sea Harrier attack fighters under emergency conditions. The twin hangar, which has extensive helicopter repair facilities, can accommodate up to five Sea King or Merlin helicopters, but the usual peacetime complement is three Sea Kings.
Combat systems: The planned installation of vertical launchers for 32 Sea Wolf SAMs (GWS.26 system), controlled by two Marconi Type 911 radar directors, was initially deferred and then canceled, although space and weight reservations remain available. Also omitted was the planned Type 996 air/surface-search radar. They were

AUXILIARIES *(continued)*

to have had the BAE Defence Systems Group DNA(2) Surface Ship Command System (SSCS). A 388 received two Phalanx CIWS and the UAT intercept system during a refit concluded 15-10-98; A 387 was similarly equipped during her 1-2-99 to 7-99 refit, during which the command support system was also updated. The Phalanx mounts are atop the pilothouse and atop the hangar. Can carry ASW ordnance for their helicopters. Have SCOT-1D antennas for the SHF Skynet IV SATCOM systems.

♦ 1 repair ship [AR]
Bldr: Øresundsvarvet, Landskrona, Sweden

	L	In serv.
A 132 Diligence (ex-*Bar Protector*, ex-*Stena Protector*)	1981	12-3-84 (RFA)

Diligence (A 132) Maritime Photographic, 8-01

Diligence (A 132) Derek Fox, 6-01

D: 10,765 tons (fl) **S:** 15.5 kts **Dim:** 111.47 (101.30 pp) × 20.97 × 6.70
A: 2 single 20-mm 90-cal. Oerlikon GAM-B01 AA; 4 single 7.62-mm mg
Electronics:
Radar: 3 . . . nav.
EW: UAR(1) Matilda radar warning; DLE decoy syst. (4 6-round Shield RL)
M: 5 Nohab Polar F216V-D 16-cyl. diesels (3,600 bhp each), electric drive; 1 CP prop; 6,000 shp—2 KaMeWa 1,500-shp side-thrusters forward—2 KaMeWa 1,500-shp rotatable thrusters aft
Electric: 4,400 kw from main engines + 2 208-kw emergency generators
Range: 5,000/12 **Fuel:** 837 tons
Crew: 15 officers, 26 unlicensed RFA + 100 tot. naval repair party (accomm. for 147 + 55 temporary)

Remarks: 6,544 grt/4,941 dwt. Built as a North Sea oilfield support ship and chartered during the Falklands War for emergency repair work in the open sea, where she proved extremely successful as a floating maintenance depot. Purchased outright 31-10-83 from Stena (U.K.) and accepted for Royal Fleet Auxiliary service 12-3-84 after conversion to install additional repair features. Capable of being used for fire fighting, towing, and salvage. Used as a submarine tender during 1997 and as a mine countermeasures support ship in the Persian Gulf during 1998 and was deployed in 3-99 to the Falklands as general support ship. The crew in 1999 included 38 civilians. Refitted by A&P Group, Wallsend, from 30-8-99 to 10-12-99.
Hull systems: Has an ice-strengthened hull with a centerline moonpool for use by divers. The flight deck atop the pilothouse can accept helicopters up to Chinook size. Has seven cranes: four 20- to 40-ton , one 20-ton, one 15-ton, and one 5-ton. Is very maneuverable and can make 6 kts sideways. A Köngsberg Albatross dynamic positioning system and four 5-ton anchors for a four-point moor are provided. Additions during conversion for naval use included a large hull and machinery repair workshop in the well deck aft, increased accommodations, a saturation diving facility, armament, magazines, increased communications equipment, additional cranes, and fuel, water, and electrical power overside transfer facilities. Can carry 2,313 tons of cargo fuel for ships moored alongside.
Combat systems: Two of the four 20-mm AA had been removed by early 2000.

♦ 1 Sal-class mooring, salvage, and net tender [ARS]
Bldr: Hall Russell, Aberdeen, Scotland

	Laid down	L	In serv.
A 185 Salmoor	19-4-84	8-5-85	12-11-85

D: 1,604 tons light (2,225 fl) **S:** 15 kts **Dim:** 77.10 (65.80 pp) × 14.80 × 3.80
Electronics: Radar: 1 Decca 1226 nav.
M: 2 Ruston-Paxman 8RKCM diesels; 1 CP prop; 4,000 bhp
Range: . . . **Crew:** 4 officers, 13 unlicensed + 27 spare berths

Remarks: 1,967 grt. Ordered 29-1-84 to replace the Kin class. Based on the River Clyde and operated by SERCO-Denholm.

Salmoor (A 185) A. A. de Kruijf, 4-01

Disposals: *Salmaid* (A 187) was laid up at Devonport, for sale, as of 8-00, and *Salmaster* (A 186) was placed up for sale during 2001.
Hull systems: Capable of mooring, buoy tending, salvage, diving support, and fire fighting. Has a 400-ton tidal lift/200-ton deadlift capacity. Can carry a 14-person salvage party.

Disposal note: The River-class navigational training ship and ex-minesweeper *Orwell* (M 2011) was stricken 13-7-00 and was sold to Guyana during 4-01.

SERVICE CRAFT

Note: Most service craft were operated by the Royal Maritime Auxiliary Service (RMAS) until 8-7-96, when their operation was contracted to SERCO-Denholm, which bareboat charters the craft from the government. A few units remain naval operated or are operated for the Ministry of Defence Marine Services Agency by other contractors, and several are still operated by the RMAS (primarily ships and craft engaged in hazardous activities). In most cases, craft that bore pennant numbers when in RMAS service continue to bear them. Most smaller powered craft have four-digit hull numbers, with the first two digits indicating the year of their authorization (many such craft at Portsmouth have local pennants, and a few have unofficial names). Most non-self-propelled craft have numbers ending with a letter or letters in parentheses indicating their functions.

♦ 2 towed hydrophone array tenders [YAG]
Bldr: McTay Marine, Bromborough (In serv. 1986)

TRV 8612 Ohm's Law TRV 8613 Cormorant

Ohm's Law (TRV 8612)—with towed array cable faked down on deck Maritime Photographic, 7-98

D: . . . **S:** 12.5 kts **Dim:** 20.10 (19.88 wl) × 6.00 × . . .
Electronics: Radar: 1 Decca 150 nav.
M: 2 Perkins 6/3544 diesels; 2 Kort-nozzle props; 400 bhp **Crew:** 8 tot.

Remarks: Catamaran aluminum hulls were built by Hall's Aluminium Shipbuilders, Portchester. Intended to service clip-on linear hydrophone arrays for submarines. The towed array is stowed faked down on the deck of the craft, which can operate connected to a smaller launch (*Chaser* serves *Ohm's Law*); the submarine passes between the pair and snags the line, which is connected to the end of the array. *Ohm's Law* is at Plymouth, and *Cormorant* is at Gibraltar. They are naval operated. Sister *Sapper* (ex-*Tarv,* TRV 8611) has been reconfigured as a diving training boat [YDT].

♦ 1 trials tender [YAGE]
Bldr: Richards SB, Lowestoft

	Laid down	L	In serv.
A 368 Warden	16-8-88	29-5-89	20-11-89

D: 621 tons light (approx. 900 fl) **S:** 15 kts
Dim: 48.63 (42.00 pp) × 10.50 × 3.50
Electronics:
Radar: 2 Decca RM 1250 nav.
Sonar: BAE Systems Type 2053 hull-mounted
M: 2 Ruston 8 RKCM diesels; 2 CP props; 3,800 bhp
Range: . . . **Crew:** 4 officers, 7 unlicensed

Remarks: Ordered 25-4-88. Formerly a range maintenance vessel, converted to a trials vessel beginning 6-10-98 at A&P Appledore, Falmouth. She is operated by the RMAS at the Kyle of Lochalsh, Scotland.
Hull systems: Has two Gardner diesel alternators and two shaft-driven alternators. The large traveling quadrantial A-frame gantry on the fantail has been removed and replaced with two electrohydraulic cranes to handle RIB workboats.

SERVICE CRAFT *(continued)*

Warden (A 368)—as modified Piet Sinke, 11-00

Note: The 12,000-ton, 108-m, M.O.D.-owned guided-missile trials support barge *Longbow* (ex-*Dynamic Servant*), laid up since the late 1980s, is to be reactivated starting in 2003 for use by a private contractor for trials with the SAM system for the new *Daring*-class (Type 45) guided-missile destroyers. Missile trials are to begin at Aberporth Range, Wales, in 2005.

Disposal note: Dog-class trials tender *Cairn* (A 126) was for sale as of 11-99, and sister *Collie* (A 328) was sold commercial during fall 2001.

♦ 4 200-ton Stores Lighters [YC]

1107(S) 1109(S) 1110(S)M 1111(S)

200-ton Stores Lighter 1109(S)—with tug *Georgina* to port providing motive power Mike Welsford, 7-00

Remarks: Operated by SERCO-Denholm at Devonport and Plymouth. Are 26.5 m long and non-self-propelled. Sister 1101(S) is laid up and for sale at Portsmouth.

♦ 5 Talisman 47–class diver support craft [YDT]
Bldr: Halmatic, Northam (In serv. 1997–98)

♦ 2 clearance diving tenders [YDT] (1 in *reserve*)
Bldr: Halmatic, Northam

9040 MINER III (In serv. 9-93) 9041 *DATCHET* (In serv. 7-94)

Miner III (9040) H&L Van Ginderen, 5-95

D: 21.5 tons (fl) **S:** 10.5 kts **Dim:** 14.20 × 4.45 × 1.60
Electronics: Radar: 1 Raytheon . . . nav.
M: 1 Ford Sabre 350C diesel; 1 prop; 350 bhp **Crew:** 3 tot.

Remarks: Ordered in 5-93. GRP construction. 9040 is operated by the Royal Navy Southern Diving Group at Devonport, where 9041 was laid up during 1998.

♦ 1 diver training tender [YDT]
Bldr: McTay Marine, Bromborough (In serv. 1986)

SAPPER (ex-*Tarv,* TRV 8611)

Sapper Douglas A. Cromby, 10-01

D: . . . **S:** 12.5 kts **Dim:** 20.10 (19.88 wl) × 6.00 × . . .
Electronics: Radar: 1 Raytheon . . . nav.
M: 2 Perkins 6/3544 diesels; 2 Kort-nozzle props; 400 bhp **Crew:** 8 tot.

Remarks: Former towed sonar array tender (sister to two others currently in service as YAGs), reconfigured as a diver training craft; reentered service 20-1-99 at Portsmouth. Has a catamaran hull built by Hall's Aluminium Shipbuilders, Portchester.

♦ 4 11-meter-class diver support craft [YDT]
Bldr: Tough, Teddington (In serv. 1981–82)

7646 7647 7648 DIVER 8000 RECLAIM

Reclaim (8000) Maritime Photographic, 6-98

D: 10 tons (fl) **S:** 8.5 kts **Dim:** 11.7 × 4.3 × 1.4
M: 1 Perkins 6-354.4 diesel; 1 prop; 120 bhp **Crew:** 2 tot. + 12 divers

Remarks: Naval operated: 7646 at Portsmouth, 7647 at Pembroke Dock, 7648 at Faslane, and 8000 at Portsmouth, attached to HMS *Vernon.* GRP construction. Eight very similar craft are operated by the British Army Royal Logistic Corps.

♦ 2 modified Cartmel-class diving tenders [YDT]
Bldr: Gregson Ltd., Blyth (In serv. 1974)

A 308 ILCHESTER A 309 INSTOW

D: 150 tons (fl) **S:** 10.5 kts **Dim:** 24.38 (22.86 fl) × 6.40 × 2.10
Electronics: Radar: 1 . . . nav.
M: 1 Lister-Blackstone ERS-4-MGR diesel; 1 prop; 330 bhp
Electric: 106 kw **Range:** 700/10 **Crew:** 6 tot. + . . . divers

Remarks: Are Marine Services Agency craft operated on the Clyde (A 308) and on the Kyle of Lochalsh (A 309) by SERCO-Denholm. Have a decompression chamber on deck forward, beneath a stowage platform for a Gemini dinghy. Can be used for harbor mine clearance.
Disposals: *Ironbridge* (A 311, ex-*Invergordon*) and *Ixworth* (A 318) were discarded during 1996.

SERVICE CRAFT *(continued)*

Ilchester (A 308) Piet Sinke, 11-00

♦ 25 200-ton Ammunition Lighters [YEN]

1201(A)	1207(A)	1214(A)	1224(A)	1229(A)	1236(A)
1202(A)	1209(A)	1215(A)	1225(A)	1230(A)	
1203(A)	1210(A)	1216(A)	1226(A)	1232(A)	
1205(A)	1211(A)	1217(A)	1227(A)	1234(A)	
1206(A)	1213(A)	1223(A)	1228(A)	1235(A)	

200-ton Ammunition Lighter 1236(A)—being moved by a tug; note the electrohydraulic crane added to this unit. A. A. de Kruijf, 9-00

Remarks: 1201(A), 1202(A), 1205(A)–1207(A), 1215(A), 1223(A), 1224(A), 1226(A), and 1236(A) are at Portsmouth; 1227(A) is at Gibraltar; and the others are at Devonport. Are 28 m long and non-self-propelled. 1236(A) has an electrohydraulic crane, but most have no cargo-handling gear of their own. Sister 1208(A) had been stricken by 8-00.

♦ 4 100-ton Ammunition Lighters [YEN]

329(A) 330(A) 344(A) 345(A)

Remarks: All are based at Portsmouth and operated by SERCO-Denholm. Are 21.3 m long and non-self-propelled.

♦ 3 Oban-class personnel and stores lighters [YF]
Bldr: McTay Marine, Bromborough

	L	In serv.
A 283 Oban (ex-*Padstow*)	25-10-99	4-2-00
A 284 Oronsay	26-5-00	12-6-00
A 285 Omagh	14-8-00	26-9-00

Oban Ralph Edwards, 6-01

D: approx. 320 tons (fl) **S:** 10 kts (sust.) **Dim:** 27.65 (25.80 pp) × 7.30 × 2.74
Electronics: Radar: 1 . . . nav.
M: 2 Cummins N14M 6-cyl. diesels; 2 Kort-nozzle props; 1,080 bhp
Electric: 218 kw tot. (2 × 109-kw diesel-driven sets)
Range: 2,000/10 **Fuel:** 26 tons **Crew:** 8 tot. + 60 passengers

Remarks: 199 grt. Ordered in late 1998 to replace *Melton* (A 83), *Menai* (A 84), and *Meon* (A 87) as personnel ferries and stores carriers in the Clyde region.

Disposal note: Of the eight units of the Insect class, *Cricket* (A 229) was placed in reserve 4-2-94 and sold commercial as *Sapphire* in 6-95, along with *Gnat* (A 239), renamed *North Star; Cicala* (A 263) was sold commercial in summer 1996; *Scarab* (A 272) was sold to a commercial operator 24-9-96; *Bee* (A 216) was for sale at Portsmouth as of 8-00; *Cockchafer* (A 230) was sold to TAE Marine during 2001; and *Ladybird* (A 253) was for sale at Devonport as of mid-2001.

♦ 5 Cartmel-class stores lighters [YF]
Bldr: C. D. Holmes, Beverley (A 274: J. Cook, Wivenhoe)

	In serv.	Based at
A 83 Melton	21-8-81	Kyle of Lochalsh
A 84 Menai	4-11-81	Devonport
A 87 Meon	9-11-82	Devonport
A 274 Ettrick	1970	Gibraltar
A 1776 Headcorn	1972	Falmouth

Cartmel-class stores lighter Lamlash (A 208)—since stricken
Douglas A. Cromby, 9-00

D: 143 tons (fl) **S:** 10.5 kts **Dim:** 24.38 (22.86 pp) × 6.40 × 1.98
Electronics: Radar: 1 Decca 360 nav.
M: 1 Lister-Blackstone ERS-4-MGR diesel; 1 prop; 330 bhp
Electric: 106 kw tot. (2 × 53-kw diesel sets)
Range: 1,000/10; 2,000/6 **Crew:** 6 tot.

Remarks: A 83 through A 87, ordered 25-2-80, are sometimes considered a separate class but are in all significant respects identical to the others. A 274 (not stricken in 1994 as previously reported) is operated by the navy at Gibraltar as a stores carrier and local patrol craft; A 83 is operated by the RMAS at the Kyle of Lochalsh; and the others are Marine Services Agency craft operated by SERCO-Denholm. A 1776 is based at Falmouth in support of rescue helicopters operating from Culdrose. All have a 2-ton stores derrick.
Disposals: Sister *Cawsand* (A 351) was placed up for sale in 10-85; *Cartmel* (A 350) was stricken in 1989 and sold for scrap 24-6-93; *Denmead* (A 363) was stricken in 1991; *Criccieth* (A 391) was sold in 7-92; *Dunster* (A 393) and *Fotherby* (A 341) were discarded in 1993; *Froxfield* (A 354), *Clovelly* (A 389), and *Cromarty* (A 488) were sold to a French operator for commercial service during 7-94; *Glencoe* (A 392) was for sale as of late 1994; *Elsing* (A 277) was for sale at Gibraltar in mid-1995; *Dornoch* (A 490), *Felsted* (A 348), *Fintry* (A 394), *Fulbeck* (A 365), *Landovery* (A 207), and *Cricklade* (A 381) were stricken in 1996 and placed up for sale for commercial use (*Fintry* was purchased in 1998 by SERCO-Denholm, was renamed *Eilidh-M,* and is on MoD charter at Devonport); *Elkstone* (A 353), *Epworth* (A 355), *Grasmere* (A 402), and *Holmwood* (A 1772) were laid up at Devonport as of spring 1999 and are not likely to see further service; *Harlech* (A 1768), *Hambledon* (A 1769), *Horning* (A 1773), and *Lamlash* (A 208) were deactivated and offered for sale during 2000–01; *Lechlade* (A 211) and *Hever* (A 1776) were laid up and for sale as of mid-2001; and *Milford* (A 91) was sold in fall 2001 for service on the Amazon at Iquitos, Peru, as the *Amazon Hope.*

Note: The Ministry of Defence expected to acquire 40 motorized canoes, 60 4.5- to 6.5-m inflatable boats, 75 RIB safety and raiding craft, 125 RIBs ranging from 5 to 9 m overall, 4 patrol launches, and an unspecified number of workboats ranging from 12 to 20 m in length during 2001–05; some would go to the navy and others to the army.

♦ 4 Newhaven-class catamaran personnel ferries [YFL]
Bldr: Aluminium Shipbuilders, Fishbourne, Isle of Wight

	L	In serv.	Based at
A 280 Newhaven	10-4-00	1-8-00	Portsmouth
A 281 Nutbourne	14-8-00	10-10-00	Portsmouth
A 282 Netley	14-10-00	10-1-01	Portsmouth
A 286 Padstow	7-4-00	8-6-00	Devonport

D: . . . tons **S:** . . . kts **Dim:** 18.0 × 7.0 × . . .
Electronics: Radar: 1 . . . nav. **M:** 2 . . . diesels; 2 props; . . . bhp
Crew: 3 tot. + 60 passengers

Remarks: Ordered 19-2-99. All are operated by SERCO-Denholm. Have steel hulls with a two-deck aluminum deckhouse.

SERVICE CRAFT *(continued)*

Padstow (A 286) Mike Welsford, 10-01

Netley (A 282) Maritime Photographic, 8-01

♦ 2 Bovisand-class SWATH personnel ferries [YFL]

Bldr: FBM Babcock Marine, Cowes

A 191 Bovisand (In serv. 7-97) A 192 Cawsand (In serv. 9-97)

Bovisand (A 191) Rob Cabo, 6-01

D: . . . tons **S:** 15.5 kts (11 sust.) **Dim:** 23.90 (21.00 wl) × 11.10 × 2.25
Electronics: Radar: 1 . . . nav.
M: 2 diesels; 2 props; 1,224 bhp **Crew:** 4 tot. + up to 75 passengers

Remarks: Ordered in 5-96 for use by Flag Officer, Sea Training, Devonport, to transfer crewmembers to ships undergoing training while at sea; operated by SERCO-Denholm. Are the only British units to use Small Waterplane Area, Twin Hull (SWATH) catamaran hullform, which provides great stability in a seaway. They use hydraulically adjusted telescopic gangways to transfer personnel in up to Sea State 3 conditions. Aluminum construction.

♦ 1 catamaran submarine support personnel ferry [YFL]

Bldr: FBM Babcock Marine, Cowes (In serv. 18-1-93)

A 232 Adamant

D: . . . tons **S:** 23 kts **Dim:** 30.80 (27.50 pp) × 7.80 × 1.10
Electronics: Radar: 1 Decca . . . nav.
M: 2 Cummins KTA 19MS diesels; 2 MJP J650 waterjets; 1,360 bhp
Electric: 60 kw tot. (2 × 30 kw) **Range:** 250/23; 350/. . . **Crew:** 5 tot.

Remarks: Ordered 30-11-91 and launched 8-10-92. Marine Services Agency craft, operated by SERCO-Denholm to serve ballistic-missile submarine crews based at Faslane on the Firth of Clyde. Aluminum hull construction. Carries 36 personnel plus 1 ton of stores. To supply submarines offshore, has an 8.1-m, constant tension gangway and hydraulically operated fenders. Navigational equipment includes a Shipmate GPS receiver and video position plotter, S. G. Brown 100B gyrocompass, and Furuno echo sounder.

Adamant (A 232) H&L Van Ginderen, 10-97

♦ 1 catamaran harbor launch [YFL]

Bldr: FBM Babcock Marine, Cowes (In serv. 1989)

HL 8837

HL 8837 Maritime Photographic, 3-01

D: 20.5 tons **S:** 13 kts (10 loaded) **Dim:** 15.80 (13.80 wl) × 5.50 × 1.50
Electronics: Radar: 1 Decca . . . nav.
M: Ford Mermaid Turbo-4 diesels; 2 props; 280 bhp
Range: 400/10 **Crew:** 2 tot. + 30–60 passengers

Remarks: HL 8837 (normally known as "D 37") was the prototype for a new series to replace the large number of outdated harbor personnel launches, but no more were built. Can also carry 2 tons of stores with 30 passengers. Operated by the Marine Services Agency.

Note: SERCO-Denholm also operated the 50-passenger ferry *SD-9* and the 75-passenger *SD-12* at Devonport as of 1-02. The RMAS had chartered the 32-m commercial vehicle landing craft *Sara Maatje VI* from Van Stee Survey & Supply, Harlingen, the Netherlands, from 1-01 through 1-03.

Disposal note: *Seal*-class Long-Range Recovery and Support Craft *Seal* (5000) and *Seagull* (5001) were retired during 2001, with at least one of the pair sold for use as a yacht in the U.S.A.

♦ 0 (+ 6) Aircrew Training Vessels [YFL]

Bldr: FBM Babcock Marine, Rosyth, Scotland, and Cebu, the Philippines (In serv. . . .)

D: . . . tons **S:** 22 kts **Dim:** 27.84 (24.00 wl) × 6.70 × 1.70
M: 2 . . . diesels; 2 props; . . . bhp—1 . . . diesel; 1 centerline cruise waterjet; . . . bhp
Range: 650/. . . **Crew:** 6 tot.

Remarks: Ordered 18-1-02 by Smit International (Scotland), Ltd. Three are to be built in Scotland and three in the Philippines to a modified version of a 27-m patrol boat design. There is to be a ramp aft for weapons retrieval or stowage of a RIB. Aluminum construction. Will replace the *Spitfire* class on charter to the MoD.

SERVICE CRAFT *(continued)*

♦ **6 Spitfire-class Rescue and Target-Towing Craft [YFL]**
Bldr: James & Stone, Brightlingsea

	In serv.		In serv.
4000 Spitfire	1972	4005 Hurricane	1980
4003 Halifax	1977	4006 Lancaster	1981
4004 Hampden	1980	4007 Wellington	25-5-81

Spitfire (4000)—the other units of the class do not have exhaust stacks
Mike Welsford, 11-00

D: 48 tons (59 fl) **S:** 22 kts **Dim:** 24.08 (22.53 wl) × 5.50 × 1.64 (max., aft)
Electronics: Radar: 1 Decca . . . nav.
M: 2 Paxman 8YJCM4 diesels; 2 props; 2,000 bhp
Electric: 30 kVA (2 × 15-kVA G&M diesel-driven sets; 440 V a.c.)
Range: 500/21; 1,000/15 **Fuel:** 10 tons **Crew:** 6 tot.

Remarks: Former RAF craft transferred to the RMAS 1-2-91. 4005 operates from Invergordon, 4000 and 4003 from Plymouth, and the others from Great Yarmouth, on contract with Smit Scotland. 4000 is 20.6 m o.a. and has two side-by-side stacks; the other units discharge exhaust through ports in the stern.
Disposals: Sisters *Sunderland* (4001) and *Stirling* (4002), transferred to the navy in 8-85 as *Hart* (P 257) and *Cormorant* (P 256), were stricken during 1-91 after serving as patrol boats at Gibraltar. Range Safety Craft sisters *Falconet* (YO 1, ex-*Michael Murphy, V.C.*) and *Petard* (YO 2, ex-*Alfred Herring, V.C.*), which had supported British Army artillery ranges, were discarded during 2001.

♦ **14 Talisman-49-class utility launches [YFL]**
Bldr: first four: Anderson, Rigden & Perkins; others: Halmatic, Havant

	In serv.	Based at
RSC 7713 Samuel Morley, V.C.	1980	Whitehaven
RSC 7820 Richard Masters, V.C.	1981	Weymouth
RSC 7821 Joseph Hughes, G.C.	1981	Weymouth
RSC 7822 James Dalton, V.C.	1981	Dover
RSC 8125 Sir Paul Travers	20-10-82	Pembroke
RSC 8126 Sir Cecil Smith	6-7-82	Dover
RSC 8128 Sir Reginald Kerr	17-3-83	Dover
RSC 8129 Sir Humphrey Gale	8-4-83	Dover
RSC 8487 Geoffrey Rackham, G.C.	19-12-85	Weymouth
RSC 8488 Walter Cleal, G.C.	1986	Dover
RSC 8489 Sir Evan Gibb	8-86	Pembroke
L.01	1-91	Portsmouth
L.02	1-91	Portsmouth
L.03	1-91	Portsmouth

L-series pilot launch St. Clement Marian Wright, 10-01

D: 20.24–20.6 tons light (23.6 fl) **S:** 20–22 kts
Dim: 14.71 (13.27 wl) × 4.42 × 1.625 (max.)
Electronics: Radar: 1 Furuno . . . or Raytheon . . . nav.
M: 2 Fiat 828SM diesels; 2 props; 880 bhp
Range: 300/20 **Crew:** 3 tot. (civilian)

Remarks: L.01–L.03 were ordered during 1991 for delivery 1-91 for use as pilot boats; one of the three is named *St. Clement.* The other units were transferred from the British Army to the RMAS on 1-10-88 and are now operated by Smit Scotland on contract. Sister *Sir William Roe* remains in army service, and others, including *Swift* and *Panther,* have been built for the customs service.
Hull systems: GRP Talisman-49 hulls. RSC 8125–8129 displace 20.59 tons light and are 14.90 m long, 4.66 m in beam, and 1.65 m max. draft. RSC 7820–7822 displace 19.684 tons light. The RSC-designated units have superstructures like those of the 15-m utility launches but slightly lower; L.01–L.03 have their pilothouses near the stern.

♦ **5 15-meter utility launches [YFL]**
Bldrs: Vosper Thornycroft (Halmatic), Havant (In serv. 1983–92)

8303 8304 Swift 8305 Opal 9295 9296

15-meter utility launch Swift (8304) Piet Sinke, 11-00

D: 20.6 tons (23.6 fl) **S:** 20 kts **Dim:** 14.94 (13.41 wl) × 4.65 × 1.30
Electronics: Radar: 1 Furuno . . . or Raytheon . . . nav.
M: 2 Rolls-Royce C8M410 diesels; 2 props; 820 bhp
Range: 300/20 **Crew:** 3 tot.

Remarks: 8303, based at Portsmouth, is used on occasion as a pilot launch. 9295 and 9296, based at Faslane, are general-purpose launches. The other two are pilot boats based at Devonport. All employ the Talisman-49 GRP hull used by the 14 boats of the Talisman-49 class. One of the class has been named *Rapid.* Six sisters (8551–8556) serve the Ministry of Defence Police (q.v.).

Disposal note: RAF 1300-series general-purpose launches 1374 and 1392 were for sale as of 1999.

♦ **15 16-meter harbor launches [YFL]** Bldr: . . . (In serv. 1965–70)

6421	6510 (D 15)	6517	7016 (D 10)	7020 Emu
6473	6512	6807	7017	7021
6506	6513 (D 19)	7015	7018	7024 Kiwi

16-meter harbor launch 7016 (D 10) Maritime Photographic, 6-94

Remarks: Local identifying pennants are listed in parentheses. 7017–7024 are "New Zealand type." Twenty others have been retired since 1995. 7018 is at Gibraltar; 6510, 6513, 6807, 7015, 7016, and 7024 are at Portsmouth; 7021 is at Rosyth; and the others are at Devonport.

♦ **4 14-meter Target Service Launches [YFL]**

7442 7443 8845 8846

Remarks: 7442 and 7443 are based at Rosyth, 8845 and 8846 on the Clyde.

♦ **5 13.90-meter harbor launches [YFL]**
Bldr: R. Dunston, Hessle (In serv. 1981)

HL 8090 Cyclone	HL 8092	HL 8095 Starling
HL 8091 Sparrow	HL 8093 Metro	

Starling (HL 8095) Rob Cabo, 6-01

SERVICE CRAFT *(continued)*

Remarks: HL 8090 is based at Gibraltar, HL 8091 at Devonport, and the others at Portsmouth. Sister HL 8094 was stricken by 11-93 and HL 8096 by 1-96. Have a small navigational radar.

♦ **8 new 11-meter harbor launches [YFL]**
Bldr: Holyhead Marine Services, Holyhead (In serv. 9-99 through . . .-00)

9894	9896	9898	. . .
9895	9897	. . .	. . .

D: . . . tons **S:** . . . **Dim:** 11.20 × . . . × 1.2
M: 1 Sabre M130C diesel; 1 prop; 130 bhp
Range: 130/8 **Fuel:** 450 liters **Crew:** . . .

Remarks: Ordered in 4-99. GRP construction.

♦ **up to 7 old 11-meter harbor launches [YFL]** (In serv. 1979–88)

HL 7992	HL 7998	HL 8812	HL 8847 Firecrest
HL 7996	HL 8001	HL 8813	

Old 11-meter harbor launch Paul C. Clift, 5-98

Remarks: HL 7998 and 8813 are based at Devonport on pollution-control duties, the others at Portsmouth for general stores and transportation duties. GRP construction. Are apparently being—or to be—replaced by the new 11-m harbor launches.

♦ **5 10-meter fast harbor launches [YFL]**
Bldr: Holyhead Marine Services, Holyhead (In serv. 4-00 through . . .-00)

9893 . . . .

D: . . . **S:** . . . **Dim:** 10.0 × . . . × . . .

Remarks: Ordered in 4-99. GRP construction.

Note: Other launches in service include 10.4-m Fast Motor Launch Mk 8 HL 7144 (based at Portsmouth); 10.4-m Fast Motor Launches HL 6750 and 6754 (both based at Gibraltar); 10-m Fast Motor Launches HL 9313 through 9316 (two based at Portsmouth, two at Devonport); 8.53-m General Service Launches HL 6994, 8474, 8475, 8829, 8832, and 8833 (HL 8474 and 8475 at Faslane, HL 6994 and 8832 at Portsmouth, HL 8829 and 8833 at Devonport); 7.6-m Motor Boats HL 7981 and 7989 (both at Portsmouth); 7.3-m Ferry Boats HL 7447 and 7448 (both assigned to RAF support); 6.7-m Pacific-22 rigid inflatables HL 9502 and 9503 (at Portsmouth); and up to 21 Searider rigid inflatables.

♦ **2 generator test barges [YFP]**
Bldr: Richard Dunston, Hessle

	Laid down	L	In serv.
MAC.1020	24-4-86	22-7-86	5-2-87
MAC.1021	2-5-86	17-11-86	1987

MAC.1021 H&L Van Ginderen, 8-83

Remarks: Ordered 19-12-85. Displace 260 tons (fl). RN operated.

♦ **4 or more miscellaneous generator barges [YFP]**

MAC.1001 MAC.1002 MAC.1009 MAC.1010

MAC.1001 Piet Sinke, 7-97

Remarks: RN operated. MAC.1001 was built on a 150-ton barge hull, and MAC.1002 is a converted commercial cargo barge hull. MAC.1009 and MAC.1010 are sisters. No other data available.

♦ **1 chartered survey boat [YGS]**
Bldr: Halter Marine, Moss Point, Miss. (In serv. . . .)

Confidante

D: . . . tons **S:** 10 kts **Dim:** 28.45 (pp) × 7.30 × 1.50
M: 2 G.M. Detroit Diesel . . . diesels; 2 props; 830 bhp **Crew:** 16 tot.

Remarks: Chartered early in 2001.

♦ **4 Cook-class survey boats [YGS]**
Bldr: Vosper Thornycroft (Halmatic), Northam (In serv. 1996)

3423 Nesbitt 9424 Pat Barton 9425 Cook 9426 Owen

Pat Barton (9424) Rob Cabo, 6-01

D: 8.75 tons (11 fl) **S:** 13 kts (12 sust.) **Dim:** 8.94 (8.10 wl) × 3.60 × 0.99
M: 2 Perkins Sabre 6.3544 diesels; 2 props; 230 bhp
Electronics:
Radar: 1 . . . nav.
Sonar: STN Atlas Elektronik Fansweep 20 mapping; Simrad EM3000 multibeam mapping
Range: 200/13; 300/8 **Crew:** 2 tot. + 10 survey party

Remarks: GRP construction. Ordered in 1995 and built on Halmatic's Nelson 35 standard GRP hull. Are attached to the Hydrographic School and naval operated. Maximum survey speed is 3 kts. Have a GPS receiver and are equipped with Ultra 3000 side-scan sonar and Qubit survey data recording system.

Note: Two 10-m survey launches were to be ordered during 2001–02.

♦ **3 survey boats [YGS]** Bldr: Halmatic, Northam (In serv. 1986)

Batchellor Delight Jolly Prize . . .

D: 8.75 tons (fl) **S:** 13 kts **Dim:** 8.94 (8.10 wl) × 3.60 × 0.99
Electronics:
Radar: 1 . . . nav.
Sonar: STN Atlas Elektronik Fansweep 20 mapping; Simrad EM3000 multibeam mapping
M: 2 Perkins 6.3544 diesels; 2 props; 230 bhp **Range:** 200/13 **Crew:** 4 tot.

Remarks: GRP construction; builder's Serviceman hull design. Ordered in 12-84. The first two are carried by *Roebuck* (H 130); the other (with a wood-sheathed hull for ice protection) was carried by the former ice-patrol ship *Endurance.*

♦ **1 inshore survey craft [YGS]** Bldr: Emsworth SY, Emsworth

	L	In serv.
H 86 Gleaner	18-10-83	5-12-84

Gleaner (H 86) Mike Welsford, 7-00

SERVICE CRAFT *(continued)*

D: 20 tons (22 fl) **S:** 14 kts **Dim:** 14.81 × 4.55 × 1.30
Electronics:
Radar: 1 Decca 360 nav.
Sonar: STN Atlas Elektronik Fansweep 20 mapping; Simrad EM3000 multibeam mapping
M: 2 Rolls-Royce CG M-310 diesels; 2 props; 524 bhp—1 Perkins 4.236 M cruise diesel on centerline; 1 prop; 72 bhp
Range: 450/10 **Crew:** 1 officer, 4 enlisted + 1 spare berth

Remarks: Referred to as HMSML (Her Majesty's Survey Motor Launch) *Gleaner* and is the smallest commissioned "ship" in the Royal Navy. Intended for survey work in the Solent, Portsmouth, and Channel Islands areas. GRP hull molded by Halmatic. Speed on cruise engine is 3–7 kts. The pennant number flag superior was changed from "A" to "H" in 7-98 but is still not painted on the hull sides.

♦ 1 Oil-class fuel lighter [YO]
Bldr: Appledore SB, Appledore (L: 18-2-69)

Y 21 Oilpress

Oil-class fuel lighter Oilman (Y 26)—since discarded; *Oilpress* (Y 21) is similar
Ben Sullivan, 10-95

D: 208 tons light; 250 tons std. (543.2 fl) **S:** 10 kts
Dim: 42.65 (39.62 pp) × 7.87 (7.47 wl) × 2.68 (max.)
Electronics: Radar: 1 . . . nav.
M: 1 Lister-Blackstone ES-6-MGR diesel; 1 prop; 405 bhp
Electric: 225 kw (3 × 75-kw, 220 V dc, Foden FD.6 Mk VI diesels driving)
Range: 1,500/10 **Fuel:** 12 tons **Crew:** 4 officers, 7 unlicensed

Remarks: 362 grt. Marine Services Agency craft operated on the Clyde by SERCO-Denholm. Cargo capacity: 250 tons. Has two 100-ton/hr-capacity cargo pumps, and the six cargo tanks are heated.
Disposals: *Oilfield* (Y 24), in reserve since 9-5-87, was stricken in 1991 and sold 7-12-92; *Oilstone* (Y 22) was sold 17-12-92; *Oilbird* (Y 25) and *Oilwell* (Y 23) were sold for commercial use 17-9-98; and *Oilman* (Y 26) was sold for scrap early in 1999.

♦ 1 1600-series fuel oil barge [YON]
Bldr: Appledore Shipbuilders, Appledore (In serv. 1969)

1603(F)

Fuel barge 1603(F)—alongside *Gloucester* (D 96) A. A. de Kruijf, 9-00

D: 44.8 × 10.2 × . . .

Remarks: 369.1 grt/500 tons cargo deadweight. Based at Portsmouth and operated by SERCO-Denholm. Non-self-propelled. Has two 100-ton/hr cargo pumps, both powered by an 88-bhp Perkins 6-334(M) diesel. There are two 6-kw, 220-V dc generators, each powered by an Enfield HO2 Mk.III diesel.

♦ 9 1500-series fuel oil barges [YON]
Bldr: Appledore Shipbuilders, Appledore (In serv. 1965–76)

	Based at		Based at
1501(F)	Portsmouth	1509(F)	Gibraltar
1502(F)	Faslane	1512(F)	Devonport
1503(F)	Clyde	1514(F)	Portsmouth
1506(F)	Devonport	1515(F)	Devonport
1507(F)	Portsmouth		

D: . . . **Dim:** 27.12 × 7.85 × . . . **Cargo:** 250 tons

Remarks: Can carry diesel, oil, or aviation fuel. Non-self-propelled. Have two 100-ton/hr cargo pumps, both powered by an 88-bhp Perkins 6-334(M) diesel. There are two 6-kw, 220-V dc generators, each powered by an Enfield HO2 Mk.III diesel. The deckhouse has bunks for four personnel. 1515(F) was formerly used as water barge 1515(W). 1509(F) is naval operated at Gibraltar; the others are operated by SERCO-Denholm.

1500-series fuel barge 1514(F)—alongside *Argus* (A 135) Jim Sanderson, 10-01

♦ 1 Type 82 accommodations and training ship [YPB]
Bldr: Swan Hunter, Wallsend-on-Tyne

	Laid down	L	In serv.
D 23 Bristol	15-11-67	30-6-69	31-3-73

Bristol (D 23) Douglas A. Cromby, 3-99

D: 5,791 tons (7,100 fl as destroyer) **S:** 28 kts (when operational)
Dim: 154.60 (149.90 wl) × 16.77 × 5.20 **A:** deleted
M: nonoperational: COSAG: 2 A.E.I. geared steam turbines (15,000 shp each), 2 Rolls-Royce Olympus TM-1A gas turbines (22,300 shp each); 2 props; 74,600 shp
Boilers: 2 Babcock & Wilcox; 49.2 kg/cm^2, 510° C
Electric: 7,000 kw tot. **Range:** 5,000/18 (when active) **Crew:** . . .

Remarks: Replaced the County-class guided-missile destroyer *Kent* (D 12) as Sea Cadet Harbor Training Ship, Portsmouth, recommissioning 22-3-93; the ship is also used to provide accommodations for school children undergoing sail training. The 114-mm Mk 8 gun forward and the antenna for the Type 1022 air early-warning radar were removed prior to her assuming her new role, with the latter replaced by antennas from the *Kent.* Earlier, the Sea Dart SAM launcher had been removed; an Ikara ASW missile launcher and the one Limbo ASW mortar had been deleted in 1986 and 1978, respectively. Accommodations for 100 naval cadets were added during 1987 for her role as Cadet Training Ship, in which capacity she served until inactivated 27-6-91. Has about 400 berths for trainees.

♦ 2 Tornado-class torpedo retrievers [YPT]
Bldr: Hall Russell, Aberdeen, Scotland

	Laid down	L	In serv.
A 140 Tornado	2-11-78	24-5-79	15-11-79
A 142 Tormentor	19-3-79	6-11-79	29-4-80

Tormentor (A 142) Bernard Prézelin, 9-99

D: 553 tons light; 660 tons std. (698 fl) **S:** 14 kts
Dim: 47.47 (40.00 pp) × 8.53 × 3.31
Electronics: Radar: 1 Kelvin-Hughes Type 1006 nav.
M: 2 Lister-Blackstone ESL-8-MGR diesels; 2 props; 2,200 bhp
Range: 3,000/14 **Fuel:** 110 tons **Crew:** 14 tot.

SERVICE CRAFT *(continued)*

Remarks: 559 grt/80 dwt. Since 8-7-96, have been Marine Services Agency craft, operated by SERCO-Denholm on the River Clyde.
Disposals: *Toreador* (A 143) was laid up in the Clyde for disposal in 1995 and sold in 1999. *Torch* (A 141), laid up at Devonport, was offered for sale in 1998 but withdrawn from sale in 9-98.
Hull systems: Have a stern ramp for weapon recovery. A 140 was used in trials during 1987 with the Qubit TRAC IV B track recording system and Bathymetrics Bathyscan 300 precision side-looking sonar/echo sounder. Are fitted to accept the Fleet Exercise Minelaying System, which employs two sets of rails mounted on the fantail and adds 30 tons to the displacement when aboard; they can lay and recover 20 exercise mines or 16 Versatile Exercise Mines.

Disposal note: *Torrent*-class torpedo retriever *Torrent* (A 127) was sold during 2000 to the Nigerian firm Suffolk Petroleum Ltd., for use in offshore petroleum drilling support work.

♦ 3 torpedo recovery launches [YPT]
Bldr: R. Dunston, Thorne (In serv. 1979)

7868 7869 7870

D: 15 tons **S:** 9 kts **Dim:** 13.8 × 2.98 × 0.76
M: 1 Perkins 6-354 diesel; 1 prop; 104 bhp **Crew:** 4 tot.

Remarks: All based at Greenock, Scotland. RN operated.

♦ 3 Tank Cleaning Lighters [YRG]

TCL 1901 (ex-1901(TC)) TCL 1907 (ex-1907(TC))
TCL 1905 (ex-1905(TC))

Tank Cleaning Lighter TCL 1905 A. A. de Kruijf, 9-00

Remarks: TCL 1907 is based at Devonport, the others at Portsmouth. Non-self-propelled barges, all of the same design, equipped with boilers to provide steam-cleaning of fuel and other shipboard tankage and tanks to hold sludge; no data available. All are operated for the Marine Services Agency by SERCO-Denholm.

♦ 3 self-propelled lifting lighters [YRS]
Bldr: McTay Marine, Bromborough Dock, Wirral (A 72: Richard Dunston, Hessle)

	L	In serv.
Y 32 Moorhen	10-2-89	26-4-89
Y 33 Moorfowl	21-4-89	30-6-89
A 72 Cameron	13-3-91	31-5-91

Moorhen (Y 32) Ben Sullivan, 4-01

D: 530 tons (fl) **S:** 8 kts **Dim:** 32.25 (30.00 pp) × 11.50 × 2.00
Electronics: Radar: 1 Decca . . . nav.
M: 2 Cummins NT19M diesels; 2 Aquamaster azimuth props; 730 bhp—bow-thruster
Electric: 528 kw (2 Cummins NTA 853 diesels)
Range: . . ./. . . **Crew:** 2 officers, 8 unlicensed + 5 divers

Remarks: 530 grt. Y 32 and 33 were ordered 25-4-88. Y 32 replaced dumb barge/lifting craft 484 at Portsmouth, and Y 33 is at Devonport; both remain RMAS operated. A 72 was ordered in 2-90 for use as an underwater trials and experimental vessel for the Defence Research Agency at Rosyth. Have pontoon barge hulls with powerful winches on the fantail, the open deck to the bow spanned by the pilothouse/accommodations superstructure.

♦ 7 250-ton Sullage Barges [YSRN]
Bldr: D. E. Scarr, Ltd. (In serv. 1969–. . .)

1704(U) 1710(U) 1712(U) 1715(U)
1706(U) 1711(U) 1714(U)

Sullage Barge 1714(U)—with tug *Saluki* (A 182) in foreground Maritime Photographic, 7-98

Dim: 27.5 × 7.3 × 0.5 (light; 1.0 loaded)

Remarks: 166.63 grt. 1710(U) is based on the Clyde; 1706(U), 1712(U), and 1715(U) are at Portsmouth (last two are "sullage/separator lighters"); 1711(U) and 1714(U) are at Devonport (as sullage/separator lighters); and 1704(U), of a different configuration, is RN operated at Gibraltar. Non-self-propelled. Sister 1707(U) had been discarded by 2001.

Note: Also in service is Sullage Barge 1901(U), tonnage rating not available; the craft is based at Portsmouth.

♦ 2 100-ton Sullage Barges [YSRN]
Bldr: Dunston, Hessle (In serv. 1964–69)

1406(U) 1409(U)

Dim: 23.24 × 6.41 × 0.61 (light; 1.09 loaded)

Remarks: 104.66 grt. Have two liquid waste cargo tanks. Based at Gibraltar. Sisters 1402(U) and 1412(U) had been discarded by 8-00.

♦ 2 Impulse-class large water tractors [YTB]
Bldr: Richard Dunston, Hessle

	L	In serv.
A 344 Impulse	10-12-92	2-4-93
A 345 Impetus	8-2-93	11-6-93

Impetus (A 345) Christopher F. Hockaday, 8-96

D: 492.5 tons light (530 fl) **S:** 12.5 kts (12.75 trials, 12.0 sust.)
Dim: 32.53 (27.75 pp) × 10.42 × 4.07 **Electronics:** Radar: 1 . . . nav.
M: 2 W. H. Allen 8512, 8-cyl. diesels; 2 Aquamaster 1401 azimuthal props; 3,400 bhp—Jastrum 2-ton bow-thruster
Electric: 740 kw tot (2 × 370-kw Stamford alternators, Cummins KTA-19G2(M) 525-bhp diesels driving)
Range: 3,000/10 **Fuel:** 55 tons **Crew:** 6 tot.

Remarks: 319 grt. Were originally to have been ordered in 1989, but the bid process was canceled. Ordered 28-2-92 for use at Faslane, Scotland, to move ballistic-missile submarines on and off the ship repair facility ship-lift. Are Marine Services Agency craft operated by SERCO-Denholm.
Hull systems: Have 38.5-ton bollard pull ahead, 36 astern. Both are equipped for fire fighting with a 2,530-liter/min Angus water monitor and 3.25 tons of foam. Also carry 5 tons of oil-spill dispersant and 13 tons of fresh water. Have extensive fendering surrounding their hulls.

SERVICE CRAFT *(continued)*

♦ 9 Adept-class large harbor tugs [YTB]
Bldr: Richard Dunston, Hessle

	Laid down	L	In serv.	Based at
A 221 Forceful	30-3-84	. . .	29-3-85	Devonport
A 222 Nimble	27-4-84	21-3-85	25-6-85	Faslane
A 223 Powerful	21-6-84	3-6-85	3-10-85	Portsmouth
A 224 Adept	22-7-79	27-8-80	28-10-80	Devonport
A 225 Bustler	28-11-79	20-2-80	15-4-81	Portsmouth
A 226 Capable	5-9-80	2-7-81	11-9-81	Gibraltar
A 227 Careful	15-1-81	12-1-82	12-3-82	Devonport
A 228 Faithful	30-11-84	. . .	13-12-85	Devonport
A 231 Dexterous	18-4-85	25-2-86	24-4-86	Faslane

Powerful (A 223) Marian Wright, 8-01

Faithful (A 228) Rob Cabo, 6-01

D: 450 tons (fl) **S:** 12.5 kts **Dim:** 38.82 (37.00 pp) × 9.10 × 4.20 (3.40 mean)
Electronics: Radar: 1 Decca . . .
M: 2 Ruston 6 RKCM diesels; 2 Voith-Schneider vertical-cycloidal props; 2,640 bhp
Electric: 294 kw tot. **Fuel:** 49 tons **Crew:** 10 tot.

Remarks: Operated since 8-7-96 as Marine Services Agency craft on contract by SERCO-Denholm, except for A 226, which is operated by the navy and based at Gibraltar. The first four were ordered 22-2-79. Referred to as Twin Unit Tractor Tugs (TUTT). Have 27.5-ton bollard pull. Also used for coastal towing. Pennant numbers had been painted out by mid-1999.

♦ 6 Dog-class large harbor tugs [YTB]
Bldrs: Various (In serv. 1962–72)

	Based at		Based at
A 129 Dalmatian	Portsmouth	A 189 Setter	Portsmouth
A 178 Husky	Clyde	A 201 Spaniel	Clyde
A 182 Saluki	Devonport	A 250 Sheepdog	Portsmouth

D: 241 tons light (305 fl) **S:** 12 kts **Dim:** 28.65 (25.91 pp) × 7.72 × 3.87 (aft)
Electronics: Radar: 1 Decca . . . nav.
M: 2 Lister-Blackstone ERS-8-MGR diesels; 1 prop; 1,320 bhp
Electric: 40 kw tot. (1 × 40 kw, 220 V dc; Lister JK4MA diesel driving)
Range: 2,236/10 **Crew:** 8 tot.

Remarks: Operated since 8-7-96 on contract by SERCO-Denholm. Appearances vary, some having streamlined upper pilothouse structures, others higher pilothouses. Have 18.7-ton bollard pull and two Hamworthy C4 centrifugal salvage pumps capable of moving 200 tons of water for salvage purposes or 100 tons per hour for fire fighting. Pennant numbers had been painted out by spring 1999 but had been restored by summer 2000.
Disposals: *Airedale* (A 102) was sold commercially at Gibraltar in 12-84. *Alsatian* (A 106), *Pointer* (A 188), and *Corgi* (A 330) were discarded in fall 1993, with the last for sale at Devonport as of mid-1995 and the other pair sold commercial. *Foxhound* (A 326, ex-*Boxer*) and *Labrador* (A 168) were sold to private operators in early 1996. *Basset* (A 327, ex-*Beagle*) was sold to the port of Portland in mid-1996. *Sealyham* (A 187), *Deerhound* (A 155), and *Elkhound* (A 162) were discarded during 1996.

Dalmatian (A 129) Maritime Photographic, 3-01

Setter (A 189)—note clerestory window pilothouse Douglas A. Cromby, 7-00

Mastiff (A 180) was for sale at Devonport as of 8-00. *Cairn* (A 126) and *Collie* (A 328), converted during 1987 as trials craft [YAG] for use at Kyle of Lochalsh, have also been retired.

♦ 4 Felicity-class water tractors [YTM]
Bldrs: Richard Dunston, Thorne

	In serv.		In serv.
A 147 Frances	5-80	A 150 Genevieve	29-10-80
A 149 Florence	8-8-80	A 198 Helen	1974

Florence (A 149)—with water barge 1518(W) alongside Mike Welsford, 10-00

D: 220 tons (fl) **S:** 10.2 kts **Dim:** 22.25 (20.73 pp) × 6.40 × 2.97 (2.10 hull)
M: 1 Lister-Blackstone ERS-8-MGR diesel; 1 cycloidal prop; 615 bhp
Range: 1,800/8 **Fuel:** 12 tons **Crew:** 4 tot.

Remarks: 138 grt. Marine Services Agency craft operated since 8-7-96 on contract by SERCO-Denholm. Bollard pull: 5.9–6.1 tons. Do not have radars. The pennant numbers had been painted out by early 1999, but A 150 was wearing hers again as of 7-00; she was painted with a black hull with white trim, red lower superstructure, and yellow pilothouse and stack. A 147 and A 149 operate at Devonport, the other two at Portsmouth.
Disposals: Sisters *Georgina* (A 152) and *Gwendoline* (A 196) were sold commercial in mid-1996, the first two to SERCO-Denholm, which operates them on charter to the Royal Navy at Devonport and Portsmouth, respectively. *Felicity* (A 112) was laid up in 1996 and sold commercial in 1998. *Fiona* (A 148) was for sale as of mid-2001.

♦ 5 Triton-class water tractors [YTL]
Bldr: Richard Dunston, Thorne (In serv. 1972–73)

A 170 Kitty	A 190 Joan	A 205 Norah
A 172 Lesley	A 199 Myrtle	

SERVICE CRAFT *(continued)*

Norah (A 205) Maritime Photographic, 3-01

D: 107.5 tons (fl) **S:** 7.75 kts **Dim:** 17.65 (16.76 pp) × 5.26 × 2.8
M: 1 Lister-Blackstone ERS-4-M diesel; 1 Voith-Schneider vertical cycloidal prop; 330 bhp
Crew: 4 tot.

Remarks: 50 grt. Marine Services Agency craft operated since 8-7-96 on contract by SERCO-Denholm, A 170, A 190, and A 205 at Devonport and the others at Portsmouth. Have 3-ton bollard pull. Do not have radars.
Disposals: Sisters *Irene* (A 181) and *Joyce* (A 193) were placed up for sale in summer 1996, *Nancy* (A 202) was sold commercial in mid-1996, *Isabel* (A 183) was for sale as of 9-96, *Kathleen* (A 166) was sold commercial 24-9-96, *Mary* (A 175) was for sale at Devonport at the end of 1997, and *Lilah* (A 174) was for sale in 1999.

♦ 1 Water-class water lighter [YW]
Bldr: Richard Dunston, Hessle (In serv. 6-78)

A 146 Waterman

D: 344 tons (fl) **S:** 11 kts **Dim:** 40.02 (37.50 pp) × 7.50 × 2.44
Electronics: Radar: 1 . . . nav.
M: 1 Lister Blackstone ERS-8-MGR diesel; 1 prop; 600 bhp
Electric: 155 kw tot. **Range:** 1,500/11 **Crew:** 11 tot.

Remarks: Not discarded in 1998 as reported in the last edition. Is still in service on the Clyde, operated by SERCO-Denholm. Carries up to 150 tons of water.
Disposals: *Waterfall* (Y 17) was stricken during 1988 and scrapped in 4-96, *Waterside* (Y 20) was sold to Ecuador in 11-91, *Watershed* (Y 18) was sold for commercial service to a Maltese owner in 7-92, *Waterspout* (Y 19) was sold for scrap in mid-1996, *Watercourse* (Y 30) was placed up for sale in 6-98, and *Waterfowl* (Y 31) was placed up for sale in 10-98 and sold commercial early in 2000.

♦ 4 27-meter Water Barges [YWN]
1517(W) 1518(W) 1519(W) 1520(W)

Water Barge 1518(W)—alongside chartered SERCO-Denholm *Felicity*-class tug *Georgina* Maritime Photographic, 7-98

Remarks: 1518(W) and 1520(W) are at Devonport, the other two at Portsmouth. Cargo capacity: 250 tons. Non-self-propelled. 1510(W) was discarded by mid-2000 at Devonport and sold commercial during 2001. 1515(W) has been reassigned as fuel barge [YON] 1515(F) at Devonport (q.v.).

Disposal note: Ham-class leased training craft *Margherita* (ex-inshore minesweeper *Tresham,* M 2736) was returned to her owner, Vosper Thornycroft, during 2001.

♦ 1 Head-class counterterrorist training hulk [YXTN]
Bldr: Burrard SY, Vancouver, Canada

	Laid down	L	In serv.
Rame Head (ex-A 134)	12-7-44	22-11-44	18-8-45

D: 9,000 tons (11,270 fl) **S:** 10 kts (when operational)
Dim: 134.60 (126.8 pp) × 17.5 × 6.9

Rame Head Maritime Photographic, 11-98

M: nonoperational: 1 set triple-expansion reciprocating steam; 1 prop; 2,500 ihp
Boilers: nonoperational: 2 Foster-Wheeler, 17 kg/cm^2, 330° C

Remarks: Former escort maintenance ship employed as an accommodations hulk at Rosyth until towed to Portsmouth and stricken 13-3-87. Since then, has been employed to train commandos in clandestine boarding of ships occupied by terrorists. One 12-ton and two 5-ton cranes have been removed, along with all armament. To be replaced soon.

Note: Three so-called Motor Fishing Vessels (MFV) are still navy owned but are assigned to the Sea Cadets: *Navigator* (MFV 1502, ex-*Yarmouth Navigator*) at Portsmouth since 1-4-90; MFV.96 at the Kyle of Lochalsh; and MFV.15 at Rosyth. MFV.15 and MFV.96 are wooden-hulled craft of 28 tons (fl) and 19.2-m length built in 1942.
Former Ham-class inshore minesweeper *Pagham* is assigned to the Sea Scouts at Stranraer, Scotland.

BRITISH ARMY ROYAL LOGISTIC CORPS

AMPHIBIOUS WARFARE CRAFT

♦ 6 Arromanches-class utility landing craft [WLCU]

	Bldr	L	In serv.
L 105 Arromanches	Brooke Marine, Lowestoft	6-1-81	31-7-81
L 107 Andalsnes	James & Stone, Brightlingsea	16-3-84	22-5-84
L 109 Akyab	James & Stone, Brightlingsea	20-11-84	21-12-84
L 110 Aachen	James & Stone, Brightlingsea	25-6-86	26-1-87
L 111 Arezzo	James & Stone, Brightlingsea	18-11-86	2-3-87
L 113 Audemer	James & Stone, Brightlingsea	24-6-87	21-8-87

Arezzo (L 111) Douglas A. Cromby, 8-01

Arromanches (L 105)—with modular Portakabin on vehicle deck Derek Fox, 6-01

D: 290 tons (fl) **S:** 9.25 kts **Dim:** 33.26 (30.00 pp) × 8.30 × 1.45 (loaded)
Electronics: Radar: 1 Decca BridgeMaster-E 180 nav.
M: 2 Doorman 8 JTCWM diesels; 2 props; 660 bhp
Range: 900/9 **Fuel:** 17 tons **Crew:** 6 tot.

ROYAL LOGISTIC CORPS AMPHIBIOUS WARFARE CRAFT
(continued)

Remarks: Known as Ramped Craft, Logistic (RPL). Two were ordered 18-3-80, three on 31-3-83, and four more in 3-85. Cargo: 96 tons. L 105 displaces 282 tons (fl) and can make 10 kts at light load. Sisters *Antwerp* (L 106, with characteristics as per L 105) and *Agheila* (L 112) were placed up for sale at Cyprus in 11-94, and *Abbeville* (L 108) was also discarded during 1994. Decca BridgeMaster-E 180 replacement navigational radars were ordered for the craft in 4-00.

♦ 4 LCVP 4–class landing craft [WLCVP]
Bldr: W. A. Souter & Sons, Cowes

LCVP 8402 (In serv. 15-3-85) LCVP 8619 (In serv. 1987)
LCVP 8409 (In serv. 18-9-85) LCVP 8620 (In serv. 1987)

D: 10 tons (fl) **S:** 20 kts (16 loaded) **Dim:** 13.00 (11.90 pp) × 3.20 × 0.80
A: provision for 2 single 7.62-mm mg
M: 2 Perkins 76-3544 diesels; 2 props; 440 bhp
Range: 200/12 **Crew:** 3 tot. + 35 troops

Remarks: The 8.80 × 2.13–m cargo well has a 5.5-ton capacity. Aluminum construction. Seventeen sisters are in RN service. Two serve in the Falklands, one in Belize, one in the U.K.

SERVICE CRAFT

♦ 1 Samuel Morley, V.C.–class range safety craft [WYFL]
Bldr: Halmatic, Havant (In serv. 1983)

Sir William Roe

D: 20.6 tons (23.6 fl) **S:** 22 kts **Dim:** 14.94 (13.41 wl) × 4.65 × 1.30
Electronics: Radar: 1 Decca BridgeMaster-E 180 nav.
M: 2 Fiat 828SM diesels; 2 props; 880 bhp **Range:** 320/17 **Crew:** 3 tot.

Remarks: Based at Cyprus. GRP hull design is based on the commercial Talisman-49 hull. Twelve sisters were transferred to the RMAS 1-10-88.

♦ 1 general-purpose workboat [WYFL]
Bldr: James & Stone, Brightlingsea

	Laid down	L	In serv.
WB 08 Mill Reef	17-3-86	17-11-86	16-2-87

Mill Reef (WB 08) H&L Van Ginderen, 6-87

D: 25 tons (fl) **S:** . . . **Dim:** 14.75 × . . . × . . .
Electronics: Radar: 1 Decca BridgeMaster-E 180 nav.
M: 2 diesels; 2 props; . . . bhp **Crew:** 4 tot.

Remarks: Prototype of a design to replace the Mk II class. Ordered 6-12-85. Three planned sisters were not ordered.

Note: Three 14-m workboats were to be ordered during 2000–01 to replace existing units.

♦ 3 general-purpose workboats, Mk II [WYFL] (In serv. 1966–71)

WB 03 Bream WB 05 Roach WB 06 Perch

Perch (WB 06) Maritime Photographic, 8-98

D: 19 tons (fl) **S:** 8 kts **Dim:** 14.3 × . . . × . . .
M: 2 diesels; 2 props; . . . bhp **Crew:** 4 tot.

Remarks: Sister *Barbel* (WB 04) was stricken in 1987 and *Pike* (WB 07) in 1990.

♦ 8 workboats [WYFL]
Bldr: Anderson, Rigden & Perkins, Whitstable (In serv. 2-3-81, except W 208: 2-6-81)

W 201 (ex-HL 1) through W 208 (ex-HL 8)

Mary Brown (W 205) Maritime Photographic, 6-98

D: 8 tons (fl) **S:** 11 kts **Dim:** 11.2 × 3.5 × . . .
M: 1 Perkins T6-354 M diesel; 1 prop; 129 bhp **Crew:** 2 tot.

Remarks: GRP construction, using Halmatic GRP hulls. W 205, unofficially named *Mary Brown,* is employed as a diving tender. Five sisters were built for the navy.

♦ 2 air-cushion vehicles [WYFLA] Bldr: Air Vehicles, Cowes

SH 01 (In serv. 11-5-82) SH 02 (In serv. 15-7-82)

D: 1 ton (fl) **S:** 34 kts **Dim:** 8.45 × 4.57 × 2.18 (high)
M: 1 diesel; 1 airscrew prop, 1 lift fan; 200 bhp
Crew: 1 + 11 passengers

BRITISH ARMY ROYAL ENGINEERS

COMBAT SUPPORT BOATS [LCP]

♦ 32 8.8-meter Combat Support Boats
Bldr: Vosper–RTK Marine, Poole (In serv. 11-99 to . . .)

8.8-meter Combat Support Boat Brian Morrison, 10-01

D: 4 tons (fl) **S:** 30+ kts **Dim:** 8.80 × 2.74 × 0.70
M: 2 Yanmar 6-cyl. diesels; 2 Hamilton 274 waterjets; 420 bhp
Range: . . ./. . . **Crew:** 2 tot.

Remarks: The prototype was built in response to a 9-98 contract tender. The contract for two production prototypes plus two trailers was let in 6-99. Thirty more (plus option for an additional eight) were ordered in 6-00 as a replacement design for the River Crossing Boats. Can be used as pull- or push-tugs.
Hull systems: Catamaran-form, GRP-construction hull. Have 1.66-ton bollard pull. Can operate in Sea State 5. The pilothouse top is removable, and 2 tons of cargo can be carried on deck. Have a reflector, but no radar. Can be road-transported.

♦ . . . Fairey/FBM River Crossing Boats

D: 2 tons light (4 fl) **S:** 24 kts (17 loaded) **Dim:** 8.38 (6.98 wl) × 2.49 × 0.66
M: 2 Ford Sabre diesels; 2 Dowty waterjets; 420 bhp
Range: . . ./. . . **Fuel:** 270 liters **Crew:** 2 tot.

Remarks: Aluminum construction craft with twin push-fenders at the bow for maneuvering bridging sections. Design is also widely used by other armies around the world. Can carry a standard 1-ton NATO cargo pallet.

MINISTRY OF DEFENCE
DEFENCE POLICE

PATROL BOATS [WPB]

Note: Four new police launches are to be ordered during 2002. As of mid-2001, a new paint scheme incorporating a high-visibility yellow and blue checker trim stripe to the sides of the pilothouses had been adopted.

Aran-60-class motor lifeboat *Alster* was acquired 6-4-02 and renamed *Condor* (9362) for Defence Police use; no data available.

♦ 4 13.90-meter class
Bldr: Holyhead Marine (In serv. 7-4-97 to 2-98)

Endeavour Excaliber . . . . . .

13.90-meter Defence Police launch—with new checkered stripe Maritime Photographic, 8-01

D: 16 tons (fl) **S:** 21 kts **Dim:** 13.90 × 4.26 × 1.14
A: small arms **Electronics:** Radar: 1 . . . nav.
M: 2 Volvo Penta TAMD-71B diesels; 2 props; 720 bhp
Range: 250/. . . **Fuel:** 1,750 liters **Crew:** 4 tot.

Remarks: Two were ordered in 4-96, with an option for two more exercised in 4-97. GRP construction. Are an updated version of the Watercraft-45 class.

♦ 5 10.14-meter class
Bldr: Victoria Marine, Warsash (In serv. 1994)

9313 Omaha 9314 Utah 9315 Gold 9316 Juno . . . Hawk

Omaha (9313)—with new checkered stripe Maritime Photographic, 8-01

D: 8 tons (fl) **S:** 28 kts **Dim:** 10.14 (8.36 pp) × 3.45 × 0.96
A: small arms **Electronics:** Radar: 1 Raytheon. . . nav.
M: 2 Ford Sabre diesels; 2 props; 430 bhp
Range: 300/18 **Fuel:** 800 liters **Crew:** 3 tot.

Remarks: The first three were ordered 21-6-93 for use at Portsmouth, the fourth on 1-10-93. GRP construction. Named after landing beaches of the Normandy invasion. Have been found lacking in seaworthiness but are to be retained in service until replaced in 2004. *Hawk* may be a name change for one of the earlier four, as no new order for this class has been reported.

♦ 6 Watercraft-45 class
Bldr: Devonport DY (In serv.: first two: 5-93; second pair: 6-93; others: . . .)

8551 Agility 8553 Watchful 8555 Tactful
8552 Pegasus 8554 Sword 8556 Dignity

D: 15.5 tons (fl) **S:** 21 kts **Dim:** 13.90 (12.65 pp) × 4.26 × 1.14
M: 2 Volvo Penta TAMD-41A diesels; 2 props; 700 bhp
Range: . . ./. . . **Fuel:** 1,600 liters **Crew:** 2–4 tot.

Remarks: GRP construction, using Keith Nelson–designed hulls. All are based on the Clyde, except 8553 and 8554 at Portsmouth.

Watchful (8553) Piet Sinke, 11-00

Note: Also in use are 10.4-m Fast Motor Launch Mk 10 8810, a Fairey Huntress-class GRP-hulled VIP launch based at Portsmouth; 10.4-m Fast Motor Launch Mk 3 6547, based at Faslane on the Clyde; Jet Skis AB 8110 and AB 8339 (based on the Clyde); and several Avon Searider 5.4-m RIBs powered by a single Mariner gasoline outboard.

MINISTRY OF DEFENCE
DEFENCE EVALUATION AND RESEARCH AGENCY (DERA)

Note: Although a decision was announced 2-7-01 that the Defence Evaluation and Research Agency would be privatized as of 2002 under the name QinetiQ, that decision was challenged and had not been implemented as of 31-12-01. Of the agency's 12,000 employees, about 9,000 were to have gone to QinetiQ and the others were to remain under the M.O.D., which would have been QinetiQ's sole customer.

♦ 1 Triton-class trimaran trials ship [WAGE]
Bldr: Vosper Thornycroft, Woolston

	Laid down	L	In serv.
Triton	11-1-99	6-5-00	15-9-00

Triton Maritime Photographic, 12-00

Triton Maritime Photographic, 7-00

D: 1,100 tons (fl) **S:** 20 kts **Dim:** 98.00 (90.00 wl) × 22.50 × 3.20
Electronics:
Radar: 2 Decca BridgeMaster-E 340 ARPA (X- and S-band); 1 . . . wave-height measuring
M: diesel-electric drive: 2 Paxman 12VP185 diesels (2,800 bhp each), 2 generator sets (2,000 kw each), 2 electric motors; 1 prop; 4,700 shp—2 electric low-speed motors in outer hulls; 2 props; 938 shp
Range: 3,000/12 **Endurance:** 20 days
Crew: 12 tot. + 12 scientist/technicians

Remarks: Built to test the trimaran hull concept with a view toward using the hullform in frigates following the Horizon program. The $21.6 million contract was placed late in 7-98 and sea trials commenced in 10-00 in cooperation with the U.S. Naval Sea Systems Command. Australia, Norway, Germany, Italy, and the Netherlands have also expressed interest in participating in the trials program. Civilian crewed. After a refit, to complete in 5-04, plans are to employ the ship as a general-purpose trials vessel available for naval and commercial purposes. Based at Portsmouth.

DEFENCE EVALUATION AND RESEARCH AGENCY *(continued)*

Hull systems: Built to commercial standards. The trimaran configuration provides a 40% greater deck area per displacement ton than a conventional design and was expected to reduce wave-making drag by 20%, but initial trials showed that the hull does not handle well in a quartering sea. The side hulls are 34 m long, with a beam of 1.4 m; the centerline hull has a maximum beam of 7 m. A helicopter deck is fitted for aircraft of up to 5 tons; four standard 20-ft. container modules can be accommodated on deck. A 47-m^2 laboratory is installed, and there is a 1.2-ton crane. Carries a Halmatic Pacific 22 Mk II 4-m rigid inflatable launch. Litton Marine Systems provided an integrated navigational suite, including the radars, adaptive autopilot, Sperry Voyage Management System with electronic charts, doppler speed log, main steering system, magnetic and gyro compasses, GPS/DGPS and Loran-C receivers, weather sensors and Weatherfax, and echo sounder.

The main propulsion plant, with a Vosper Thornycroft control system, drives the propeller on the centerline hull, while two auxiliary propellers are mounted on the outer hulls. During a refit planned to start in 5-02, an electric propulsion plant is to be installed, possibly with a Permasyn motor. The prime mover may be changed to gas turbines of 8 MW or 1.25 MW output after initial trials with the original diesel engines.

♦ **1 aviation trials support ship [WAGE]**
Bldr: Hall Russell, Aberdeen, Scotland (In serv. 11-66)

A 229 COLONEL TEMPLER (ex-*Criscilla*)

Colonel Templer (A 229) Ralph Edwards, 5-01

D: 1,300 tons (fl) **S:** 13.6 kts **Dim:** 56.55 × 11.0 × 4.29
Electronics: Radar: 1 Decca BT 502 nav.; 1 Decca 2690 ARPA nav.
M: 2 Cummins KTA 38G4M diesels (1,260 bhp each), 2 Newage HC M734E1 generators (850 kw each); 1 Aquamaster Azimuthal thruster; 1,800 shp
Electric: 930 kw (2 × 260 kw, 2 × 180 kw, 1 × 50 kw)
Range: 7,000/. . . **Crew:** 14 tot. + 12 scientists

Remarks: 892 grt/268 nrt. Former stern-haul trawler, purchased in 1980 by the Royal Aerospace Establishment, Farnborough, for use in sonobuoy trials and transferred to RMAS operational control 1-10-88. Capsized during a fire while under refit at Hull in 1-91; was righted and refloated 8-2-91 and transferred to Portsmouth 30-4-91 for refit for further service. Repairs were completed in 10-92, but she was not recommissioned until 10-9-93. During the repairs, the ship was altered so that it can be leased for commercial scientific work. Was re-engined during a 15-1-97 to 25-4-97 refit at Hull. Two moonpool openings for lowering scientific gear have been opened into the bottom. The ship is fitted with Flume passive stabilization tanks and an auxiliary propulsion system for silent running. The after deck was fitted to accept a containerized laboratory, and a 5-ton crane was installed. Has the Racal MIRANS 3000 integrated navigation and bridge control system with MNS 2000 GPS receiver and VHFD/F. Carries a 9-m tender named *Quest* (Q 26). Received a pennant number after outright purchase by M.O.D. during 9-00. Operated by the AV Seawork division of Vosper Thornycroft.

MARITIME AND COAST GUARD AGENCY

The present organization was established in 4-98, combining the Coast Guard Agency and the Marine Safety Agency. The organization has four operational regions. Two Sikorsky S-61N helicopters are chartered from Bristow Helicopters for search-and-rescue duties in the English Channel area. Each winter, three salvage-and-rescue tugs are chartered as standby anchor-handling and towing vessels. For the winter 2001–02 season, these included the *Anglian Monarch* and *Nikolay Chiker* (ex-Russian Navy), both chartered 1-4-01. Permanently operated are two 7-m, 150-bhp Orkadian 23–class workboats, one in the Solent and one in the Clyde area, and a number of rigid inflatable boats.

SCOTTISH FISHERIES PATROL AGENCY

(Department of Agriculture and Fisheries for Scotland)

Scottish Fisheries Patrol Agency (SFPA) ships were painted white in 1998 and gained diagonal blue and yellow hull stripes on either beam forward and the letters "SFPA" on their sides. Aviation assets include a Cessna Titan, three Dornier Do-228-200, and two Cessna Caravan II, all with surveillance radars. About 260 personnel work for the agency. Fisheries protection ships and craft in service include the following (in-service dates in parentheses):

- *Sulisker* (1980), *Vigilant* (1982), and *Norna* (1988): 1,177 grt, 18 kts, range 7,000/13, crew of 15
- *Westra* (1974): 885 grt, 16.5 kts, range 10,000/12, crew of 15
- *Morven* and *Moidart* (1983): 44 tons, 20 kts, endurance 7 days, crew of 5
- *Skua* (4-84): 7.5 tons, 24 kts, range 200 n.m., crew of 3

The agency also operates the fisheries research ship *Scotia.* A new 47-m diesel-electric fisheries patrol ship was ordered during 2-02 from Ferguson Shipbuilders, Port Glasgow, to replace the *Westra.*

Note: The Cornwall Sea Fisheries Committee took delivery of the 27-m, 32-kt *St. Piran* from Damen Marine, the Netherlands, during 5-00.

H.M. CUSTOMS AND EXCISE MARINE BRANCH

The U.K. Customs and Excise Marine Branch operates the following unarmed patrol units (in-service dates in parentheses):

- *Seeker* (9-01): 205 tons, 26 kts, range 2,000/12, crew of 17 (sisters operate in the Netherlands West Indies Coast Guard and Netherlands Coast Guard)
- *Sentinel* (30-11-94): 172 tons, 30+ kts, range 2,300/12, crew of 17
- *Valiant, Venturous, Vigilant,* and *Vincent* (1988–93): 70 tons, 25 kts, crew of 8
- *Searcher* (1979): 160 tons, 21 kts, range 2,600/12, crew of 10
- *Swift* and *Panther* (1993–94): 23.6 tons, 22 kts, range 300/18, crew of 3
- *Avocet, Bittern, Courser, Diver,* and *Egret* (1984–. . .): 3.75 tons, 15 kts, crew of 2
- 60 miscellaneous small launches, including a large number of 4-m Avon Surfrider semi-rigid inflatables

Customs Patrol Craft Seeker Jim Sanderson, 9-01

Sentinel Maritime Photographic, 3-98

Valiant Douglas A. Cromby, 1-01

Searcher Derek Fox, 7-01

U.S.A.

United States of America

Personnel (1-02): 384,260 total (53,918 officers, 321,862 enlisted, and 4,240 midshipmen). Naval reservists as of 30-9-01 totaled 153,882, including 73,341 selected (actively drilling) and 80,541 individual (nondrilling). As of 31-10-01, there were 182,900 Department of the Navy civilians. The Marine Corps was authorized 172,600 active-duty and 39,558 reserve personnel during FY 02.

As of 16-6-01, the Military Sealift Command, which manages nearly all auxiliary vessels, had 3,540 civil service mariners, 2,001 contract mariners, 1,137 navy selected reserves, 968 active navy, and 1,148 civil service shore personnel.

Force Levels: As of 12-01, the Navy operated about 315 battle force ships, with several hundred more support and special mission ships not counted in that total. Under "Program Review '03," issued in 10-01, the fleet is to be reduced to 286 ships by 2007, although even that lower number does not seem likely to be maintained. The number of carriers will remain at 12, but the cruiser/destroyer/frigate force will be reduced from 116 ships at the end of 2001 to 98 in 2007.

Bases: Bases in the United States with 300 or more personnel assigned include, by geographic area:

Norfolk, Va., area: Commander-in-Chief U.S. Atlantic Fleet; Commander U.S. 2nd Fleet; Little Creek Naval Amphibious Base; Navy Region Mid-Atlantic; Dam Neck Fleet Combat Training Center Atlantic, Virginia Beach; Northwest Naval Security Group Activity, Chesapeake; Norfolk Naval Shipyard, Portsmouth; Oceana Naval Air Station, Virginia Beach (with Oceana Detachment Norfolk at Chambers Field, formerly Norfolk Naval Air Station); Portsmouth Naval Medical Center; and Yorktown Naval Weapons Station

Washington, D.C., area: Naval Support Activity (formerly Anacostia Naval Station); Washington Navy Yard, D.C.; Bethesda National Naval Medical Center, Md.; Dahlgren Naval Surface Warfare Center, Va.; Annapolis Naval Station, Md.; U.S. Naval Academy, Annapolis, Md.; Naval Air Facility D.C., Andrews AFB, Md.; and Patuxent River Naval Air Station, Lexington Park, Md. (the Naval Security Station was disestablished 16-10-98)

New England and Northeast area: Navy Region Northeast, New London, Conn.; Naval Submarine Base, New London, Conn.; Brunswick Naval Air Station, Maine; Portsmouth Naval Shipyard, Maine; Newport Naval Station, R.I.; Newport Naval Educational Training Center, R.I.; New London Naval Submarine Base, Groton, Conn.; Ballston Spa, Scotia Naval Administrative Unit, Schenectady, N.Y.; Willow Grove Naval Air Station, Joint Reserve Base, Horsham, Pa.; Earle Naval Weapons Station, Colts Neck, N.J.; and Lakehurst Naval Air Engineering Station, Toms River, N.J.

Southeast area: Commander Navy Region Southeast, Jacksonville, Fla.; Jacksonville Naval Air Station, Fla.; Charleston Naval Hospital, S.C.; Beaufort Naval Hospital, S.C.; Atlanta Naval Air Station, Marietta, Ga.; Kings Bay Naval Submarine Base, St. Marys, Ga.; Cherry Point Naval Air Depot, N.C.; Naval Air Depot, Jacksonville, Fla.; and Key West Naval Air Station, Fla. (Naval Training Center, Orlando, Fla., was closed 18-12-98)

Midwest area: Great Lakes Naval Training Center, Ill.; and Memphis Naval Support Activity, Millington, Tenn.

Gulf Coast area: Panama City Coastal Systems Station, Fla.; Corry Station, Pensacola, Fla.; Pensacola Naval Air Station, Fla.; Pensacola Naval Hospital, Fla.; Whiting Field Naval Air Station, Milton, Fla.; Meridian Naval Air Station, Miss.; Pascagoula Naval Station, Miss.; Gulfport Naval Construction Battalion Center, Miss.; New Orleans Naval Air Station, La.; Joint Reserve Base, Belle Chasse, La.; New Orleans Naval Support Activity, La.; Fort Worth Naval Air Station and Joint Reserve Base, Texas; Ingleside Naval Station, Texas; Corpus Christi Naval Air Station, Texas; and Kingsville Naval Air Station, Texas

West Coast area: Navy Region Northwest, Seattle, Wash.; Whidbey Island Naval Air Station, Oak Harbor, Wash.; Everett Naval Station, Wash.; Bangor Naval Submarine Base, Silverdale, Wash.; Bremerton Naval Hospital, Wash., Puget Sound Naval Shipyard, Bremerton, Wash.; Bremerton Naval Station, Wash.; Fallon Naval Air Station, Nev.; Santa Clara Naval Air Reserve Station, Moffett Field, Calif.; Naval Postgraduate School, Monterey, Calif.; Lemoore Naval Air Station, Calif.; China Lake Naval Air Weapons Station, Ridgecrest, Calif.; Point Mugu Naval Air Station, Calif.; and Port Hueneme Naval Construction Battalion Center, Calif. (Concord Naval Weapons Station, Calif., was transferred to the U.S. Army 1-10-99)

San Diego, Calif., area: Naval Region Southwest; U.S. 3rd Fleet; San Diego Naval Base (incorporating San Diego Naval Station, San Diego Naval Medical Center, and the Navy Broadway complex); Coronado Naval Base (North and South Facilities, incorporating the former North Island Naval Air Station, which was redesignated a naval air depot on 20-4-01; Coronado Naval Amphibious Base; Imperial Beach Outlying Field; and San Clemente Island Naval Auxiliary Landing Field); Point Loma Naval Base (incorporating the former Antisubmarine Warfare Training Center Pacific, Space and Naval Warfare Command Headquarters Facility, Point Loma Space and Naval Warfare Command Support Center, and the Navy Consolidated Brig at Marine Corps Air Station, Miramar); and El Centro Naval Air Facility, Seeley, Calif.

Hawaiian Islands: Commander-in-Chief U.S. Pacific Fleet, Pearl Harbor; Navy Region Hawaii, Pearl Harbor; Pearl Harbor Naval Station (which subsumed the naval submarine base on 9-11-98); Naval Computer and Telecommunications Area Master Station Pacific, Honolulu; and Pearl Harbor Naval Shipyard and Intermediate Maintenance Facility

Overseas facilities include:

Caribbean area: Naval Station Guantanamo Bay, Cuba; and Roosevelt Roads Naval Station, Puerto Rico

North Atlantic area: Fleet Air Keflavik Naval Air Station, Iceland; U.S. Naval Activities United Kingdom; Commander U.S. Naval Forces Europe, London; Rota Naval Station, Spain

Mediterranean area: La Maddalena Naval Support Activity, Sardinia, Italy; U.S. 6th Fleet, Gaeta, Italy; Sigonella Naval Air Station, Sicily, Italy; Naples Naval Support Activity, Italy; Fleet Air Mediterranean, Naples, Italy; and Souda Bay Naval Support Activity, Crete, Greece

Indian Ocean area: U.S. Naval Forces Central Command (5th Fleet), Manama, Bahrain; and Diego Garcia Naval Support Facility

Western Pacific area: U.S. 7th Fleet, Yokosuka, Japan; U.S. Fleet Activities, Yokosuka; Atsugi Naval Air Facility and Naval Air Pacific Repair Activity, Japan; Misawa Naval Air Facility, Japan; U.S. Fleet Activities, Sasebo, Japan; U.S. Fleet Activities, Okinawa, Japan; U.S. Naval Forces, Korea Fleet Activities, Chinhae, South Korea; U.S. Naval Forces Marianas, Guam; and U.S. Naval Logistics Group, Western Pacific, Singapore

Note: To consolidate administrative functions, in 1999 the Norfolk Naval Base became the Navy Region Mid-Atlantic, the Pearl Harbor Naval Base became the Navy Region Hawaii, the San Diego Naval Base became the Navy Region Southwest, and the Seattle Naval Base became the Navy Region Northwest. There are a large number of smaller facilities both on U.S. territory and overseas.

Naval Aviation: Individual aircraft numbers and characteristics are presented after the aircraft carrier entries below. The navy operates 10 air wings, while the Naval Reserve Air Forces operate one tactical air wing, two patrol/ASW air wings, one helicopter wing, and one reserve logistics air wing; the Marine Corps has three active and one reserve air wing.

Shipbuilding Program, Fiscal Years 2001–2007

	FY 01	FY 02	FY 03	FY 04	FY 05	FY 06	FY 07
New Construction:							
CVN 77	1	—	—	—	—	—	—
CVN 78	*	*	*	*	*	*	1
SSN, *Virginia*	1	1	1	1	1	1	1
DDX	—	—	—	—	1	—	—
DDG, *Arleigh Burke*	3	3	2	2	2	2	2
LHD, *Wasp*	*	1	—	—	—	—	—
LPD, *San Antonio*	—	—	1	1	1	1	1
T-AKE, *Lewis and Clark*	1	1	1	1	2	2	3
AGF(X) (JCC)	—	—	—	—	—	1	2
T-AGS	—	—	—	—	—	1	—
M PF(F)	—	—	—	—	—	—	—
Total	6	6	5	5	6	7	10
New LCU	—	—	—	—	5	5	5
Conversions / upgrades:							
CVN refuel/overhaul	*	1	*	*	1	—	*
CG update	—	—	—	1	2	4	4
SSGN conversion	—	—	2	2	—	—	—
SSN/SSBN refuel	—	2	1	2	1	3	4
LCAC	1	2	3	4	4	6	6

* Advance procurement

Note: As is usually the case, the numbers go up in the "out years," which enables the DoD to show a higher average construction rate than will actually occur, since the out-year numbers are inevitably reduced later.

Marine Corps

The major operational unit is the Marine Expeditionary Force (MEF), which consists of one division, one air wing, and Fleet Marine Forces (FMF) augmentation, for a total of about 58,000 Marines. There are three MEF divisions (one stationed in Okinawa, two in the United States), each of 32,600 personnel, and three active and one reserve air wings, organized under two FMFs. These last also maintain heavy support elements for the divisions. A fourth division/wing team constitutes a reserve cadre.

The 1st Marine Expeditionary Brigade (MEB) was reestablished within the 1st MEF on 23-11-99. The MEB is intended to provide a highly mobile, quick-response force. Amphibious ships currently in service provide sufficient capacity to permit the rapid overseas deployment of only MEBs. A MEB consists of one regimental landing team, a strong unit with two or more battalion landing teams of about 822 men each; one mixed air group of 110 fighter/attack fixed-wing aircraft and 120 helicopters; 15 tanks; and 30 artillery batteries, along with some augmentation from the FMF, for a total of about 15,500 Marines.

The smallest assault unit is the Marine Expeditionary Unit (MEU), with a landing team, air squadrons, and support personnel, totaling 2,500 troops. Attached are 5 tanks, 6 aircraft, 30 helicopters, and 5 artillery batteries.

Bases: Principal facilities at Camp Pendleton, Calif.; Twentynine Palms, Calif.; Camp H. M. Smith, Hawaii; Camp Lejeune, N.C.; and Camp Smedley D. Butler, Okinawa. Marine Corps air stations (MCAS) are at Beaufort, S.C.; Cherry Point, N.C.; Quantico, Va.; New River (Jacksonville), Fla.; Miramar, San Diego, Calif.; Yuma, Ariz.; Kaneohe Bay, Oahu, Hawaii; and Iwakuni, Japan. A Marine Corps helicopter facility (MCHF) is located at Futenma, Okinawa. Numerous other training, research, communications, etc., facilities exist. Marine Corps Air Stations El Toro and Tustin, Calif., closed 2-7-99.

Special Forces

U.S. Special Forces consist of 2,200 men, all capable of aerial or seaborne insertion: 6 SEAL Teams (8 platoons each), 2 Swimmer Delivery Vehicle Teams, 3 Special Boat Squadrons, and 4 reserve platoons. SEALs operate under the joint-services Special Warfare Command. During 2002, the number of SEAL Teams was to be increased to 10 by reducing the number of platoons in each to six.

Naval Reserve Force

Naval Reserve Force ships have cadre crews of regular naval personnel, with reserve augmentation personnel constituting up to two-thirds of the total crew assigned. Also incorporated in the Naval Reserve program are about 3,000 other units supporting 35 or more programs to augment regular navy staffs in wartime.

As of 1-02, the Naval Reserve Force included 10 guided-missile frigates, 1 tank landing ship, 1 mine countermeasures support ship, 7 mine countermeasures ships, and 10 minehunters. It also operated around 260 aircraft, including C-130T, C-9, DC-9, and C-40A transports; C-20G VIP transports; C-12B light transports; E-2C AEW aircraft; F-5 combat-training fighters; F/A-18-series fighters; P-3C maritime patrol aircraft; MH-53E mine countermeasures helicopters; HH-60H combat rescue helicopters; and H-3-series helicopters.

Military Sealift Command

The Military Sealift Command (MSC), under the joint-services Transportation Command, operates or charters ships in support of the U.S. Navy and the other armed services. Headed by an active-duty U.S. Navy flag officer, its ships are manned primarily by civilians, either civil service or contractor mariners. During 2000, the MSC transported some 774,000 tons of dry cargo and 5,173,000 tons of petroleum products, and its Special Mission Ships provided 6,300 sea-days of operations.

WEAPONS AND SYSTEMS

A. MISSILES

♦ Fleet ballistic missiles

Trident-1 C-4 (UGM-96A) Bldr: Lockheed Martin

Operational in 1978. Designed for the *Ohio*-class SSBNs, which carry 24, and for 12 now-retired *Lafayette-* and *Benjamin Franklin*–class SSBNs, which carried 16 each. To be phased out by early 2005. The final three test launches were performed by the *Ohio* (SSBN 726) on 19-12-01.

Length: 10.4 m **Weight:** 31.75 tons at launch
Warhead: 8 Mk 4 MIRV with 100-kT W 76 warheads
Propulsion: solid propellant, three stages
Range: 4,350 n.m. **Guidance:** inertial

Trident-2 D-5 (UGM-133A) Bldr: Lockheed Martin

Officially entered operational service 29-3-90 on SSBN 734. The first 21 were authorized under FY 87, 66 under FY 88 and 89, 41 under FY 90, 52 under FY 91, 28 under FY 92, 21 under FY 93, and 24 under FY 94. Procurement through 1999 was planned at 24 per year, but only 18 were requested and approved under FY 95, 6 under FY 96, 7 under FY 97, 5 (at $48.71 million each) under FY 98, and 5 under FY 99. Twelve per year are being procured under the FY 00 through 05 budgets to permit rearming four Trident-1-armed SSBNs. The total planned inventory is 425. The 92nd through 94th consecutive successful trials launches were carried out on 25-6-01 by the *Louisiana* (SSBN 743); as of that date, 384 missiles had been ordered from Lockheed Martin. The missile is planned to remain in service until 2042.

The first stage weighs 39.15 metric tons, of which 36.9 metric tons is propellant; the second stage 11.84 metric tons, of which 11.05 metric tons is propellant; and the third stage 2.19 metric tons, of which 2.03 metric tons is propellant.

All were to get the new W 88 warhead, but a shortage of nuclear weapons production facilities forced retention of the W 76 warhead on some. A variant with a conventional warhead and employing GPS guidance was reportedly tested on 18-11-93 but did not enter production.

Length: 13.44 m **Diameter:** 2.11 m **Weight:** 53.18 metric tons at launch
Warhead: Mk 12A reentry vehicles with 100-kT W 76 or 300- to 475-kT W 88 warheads
Propulsion: solid propellant, three stages
Range: 6,000 n.m. with 122-m circular error probable (CEP)

♦ Surface-to-surface missiles

NATACMS (Navy Tactical Missile System) Bldr: Loral Vought Systems

A contract was let in 2-94 for development of a weapon to replace the shore bombardment capability lost with the retirement of the four battleships and the great reduction in the number of ships with 127-mm guns. NATACMS was to be launchable from Mk 41 vertical launch cells on surface ships and from vertical launchers on submarines running submerged. The first sea trials were held 12-2-95 aboard the *Mount Vernon* (LSD 39) using an Army M 270 launcher with Block IA missiles to a range of 75 n.m. The first vertical launch from a land-based Mk 41 cell took place 21-11-96. The rocket has a length of 14 ft., a diameter of 2 ft., and a range of 75 n.m. (to be extended to 150 n.m. and later to 250 n.m.); it has inertial guidance, but incorporation of GPS is foreseen. Cost per missile was about $750,000 as of 7-97.

The NATACMS was terminated in 5-98 in favor of the LASM (Land-Attack Standard Missile) because the bomblet payload in the Block IA version would have had to be reduced from 900 to 350 in order to achieve range goals and NATACMS was not meeting accuracy requirements. Political pressures have revived the program, but the weapon will probably be canceled again.

Note: The Sea Ferret small, multipurpose cruise missile program appears to have been abandoned, and there has been no recent public discussion of pursuing further the Polyphem short-range, wire-guided surface-attack missile. The Boeing Fasthawk and the ALAM (Advanced Land-Attack Missile) have been canceled as well.

LASM (Land-Attack Standard Missile)
Bldr: Raytheon Systems, Tucson, Ariz.

A shore-attack weapon using surplus Standard SM-2 Block II and III airframes with modified payload sections incorporating the standard Mk 125 blast/fragmentation warhead, an inertial guidance system, and a GPS receiver. Later versions may carry 748 M-80 submunitions. A longer-range, two-stage version is also feasible, and Raytheon has also proposed using a new 533-mm-diameter variant with three times the payload. The weapon will be carried in Mk 41 vertical launchers aboard DDG 81 and subsequent *Arleigh Burke* Flight IIA destroyers and also by 22 *Ticonderoga*-class cruisers. Only 800 are now planned, but another 1,200 surplus SM-2 Block II and III airframes are available for conversion. LASM was to enter service in 2004, and a design and testing contract went to Raytheon on 31-8-00, with the work to be completed by 12-03, but as of 12-01, there was no indication of any intent to pursue acquisition and the program was reported to be near termination; it will be replaced by the previously canceled ALAM (Advanced Land-Attack Missile) program, with renewed development to start in FY 04.

Length: 4.75 m **Diameter:** 0.343 m **Wingspan:** 0.58 m
Weight: 699 kg **Warhead:** Mk 125 blast/fragmentation **Range:** 240 km

Tomahawk (BGM-109)
Bldr: Raytheon Systems, Tucson, Ariz. (formerly Hughes)

Only the conventionally armed land-attack versions of Tomahawk remain in service, for launch by submarines (using torpedo tubes or special vertical launch tubes), surface ships (using Mk 41 vertical launch cells), and aircraft. During 1993, the first Block III missiles, with better fuzing, a 320-kg warhead, 50% more fuel, F-107-WR-402 turbojets with 19% more thrust, a Mk 111 booster, GPS, and faster missile mission planning entered service; the missiles also featured "time of arrival" control, permitting coordinated simultaneous attacks.

The remaining Block II missiles are being updated to Block IVA with the GPS receiver, a new computer, and a satellite datalink; a contract to convert the first 35 missiles was issued in 3-97. The Block IVA has 3-m accuracy at maximum range, improved targeting support, a communications link to the launch platform to permit revised targeting while in flight, improved terminal homing, and a warhead capable of hardened-target destruction.

The datalink-equipped, 1,600-n.m.-range Block V Tactical Tomahawk variant, able to loiter for upwards of 2 hours over a battlefield before being directed to attack a point target, is planned to enter production in mid-2004, with 1,353 missiles to have been delivered by the end of FY 07. The low-cost ($575,000) Block V missile is to carry either 16 BAT (Brilliant Anti-Tank), 32 SADARM, or 16 sensor-fuzed munitions; a television camera may later be added to some missiles to act as a battle-damage assessment aid. Tactical Tomahawk is currently to be launchable only from vertical tubes on submarines operating at periscope depth, but an encapsulated, torpedo tube–launchable version is being developed for Royal Navy and USN use, with the missile planned to become operational in horizontal launch mode in FY 06.

In 4-99, conversion of 200 AGM-109B and 424 Block II Tomahawk missiles to Block IIIC Tactical Land-Attack Missiles (TLAM) was ordered; the last were to be delivered by Raytheon during 4-02. The updated missiles have improved Digital Scene-Matching Area Correlation and either a 454-kg Bullpup-B or 166-bomblet BLU-97B warhead. The deep-penetration version of Tomahawk, using the British Lancer multiwarhead penetrator system, had its successful final test on 5-12-01 and is equipped with a high-temperature incendiary warhead equipped to penetrate some 6 m (20 ft.) of concrete prior to detonation. This missile will cruise at or above 25,000 ft., diving to the target; during trials, the 500-kg test warhead penetrated a 6-m reinforced concrete target, 10 m of sand, and then traveled another 800 m. Future Tomahawks are to be powered by a version of the Williams F-122 turbojet.

Procurement of 34 new Block V missiles was approved in the FY 02 budget. Planned procurement includes 106 in FY 03, 319 in FY 04, 351 in FY 05, 483 in FY 06, and 469 in FY 07.

Data for the current, $1.4 million Block III version include:

Length: 6.17 m **Diameter:** 0.52 m
Weight: 1,542 kg at launch (1,816 encapsulated for submarine launch)
Warhead: 454 kg
Propulsion: solid booster, F-107 turbojet sustainer **Range:** 1,400 n.m.

Harpoon (RGM-84A/D/F; UGM-84A/B/C/G; AGM-84A/B/C/F)
Bldr: Boeing

An all-weather cruise missile that can be launched by aircraft, surface ships, or submarines. For USN use, 2,006 were procured between FY 82 and FY 91. The submarine-launched, encapsulated UGM-84 version was retired in 1997 as a money-saving measure but is still used by some foreign navies. Many surface ships capable of carrying the RGM-84 missile carry fewer than the possible total or none at all. The AGM-84 can be carried by P-3C, S-3B, and USAF B-52 (up to 12 each) aircraft. The USAF acquired 85 undelivered Iranian AGM-84 missiles in 8-84.

Length: 4.628 m (RGM-84 ship-launched); 3.848 m (AGM-84 air-launched)
Diameter: 0.343 m **Wingspan:** 0.914 m
Weight: 681 kg (from canister); 680 kg (from SAM launcher with booster); 526 kg (air-launched)
Warhead: 227 kg
Propulsion: CAE-JA02 turbojet, with a rocket booster added to the ship- and submarine-launched versions
Speed: Mach 0.85 **Range:** "over 67" n.m.
Guidance: inertial, then active homing on J band in the final trajectory

Block I Harpoon missiles had improved seekers and operational software compared to the Block 0, while Block IB added a sea-skimming capability with a lower mid-course altitude. Beginning with FY 88 procurement, Block IC had the "Dash-4" seeker and improved guidance. Block ID missiles (first launch 4-9-91, but none yet ordered) were designated AGM-84F and were to have had a fuselage 0.9 m longer to provide sufficient additional fuel to double the range and also have a reattack feature if the missile missed on the first pass; its weight was 771 kg. Missiles exported since 1995 are of the RGM/UGM/AGM-84M Block ICR version with software revised to permit reattacks in case of misses, improved ECCM, and a lower flight altitude; none have been procured for the USN. The SLAM and SLAM-ER-series missiles derived from Harpoon are described separately under Air-to-Surface Missiles.

Boeing offers an RGM/UGM/AGM-84 Block II Harpoon 2000 "littoral region" conversion kit for existing Harpoon missiles that would upgrade the seeker, provide improved target discrimination, and add a GPS employment capability and a datalink to the launch platform. The missiles would also be able to make several waypoint turns prior to homing on the intended target. The development program was financed by Denmark, the first customer. The update cost is projected at $200,000 per missile. The navy designation for the update program is Harpoon Block II (earlier: Block IJ), but no procurement plans have been announced. Successful first sea trials with the Block II were conducted during 6-01.

Note: The Marine Corps plans to acquire 45 wheeled HIMAR rocket-launching vehicles to equip two battalions of the 14th Artillery Regiment. Using standard MLRS (Multiple Launch Rocket System) launchers, the vehicles are planned to enter service in 2008–09.

♦ Surface-to-air missiles

Standard SM-3 LEAP (RIM-161A) Bldr: Raytheon Systems, Tucson, Ariz.

LEAP (Lightweight Exoatmospheric Projectile) is a developmental system using a modified RIM-67E-2 Standard SM-2 Block III extended-range missile with an ASAS (Advanced Solid Axial Stage) rocket motor and Hughes kinetic kill vehicle to destroy tactical ballistic missiles. Proof-of-concept trials were conducted unsuccessfully during late winter 1995 with missiles fired from the *Richmond K. Turner* (CG 20). The first flight demonstration took place from the *Shiloh* (CG 67) on 24-9-99, but what was also described as the first launch was reported to have taken place from the *Lake Erie* (CG 70) on 25-1-01; a further test from CG 70 on 25-1-02 resulted in a direct hit. The program has not yet been affected by the cancellation of the simpler SM-2 Block IVA Lower Tier Theater Anti-Missile Defense System.

WEAPONS AND SYSTEMS *(continued)*

Standard SM-2 ER Block IIIB (RIM-67C) and IVA (RIM-156A "Aegis ER") Bldr: Raytheon Systems, Tucson, Ariz.

The Block IIIB is a considerably reworked version of the Block III for use in Mk 41 vertical launchers on CG 52 and later *Ticonderoga*-class cruisers and the DDG 51 class. It has a dual-mode radar/infrared seeker; improved radome, guidance, and autopilot; modified dorsal and control fins; and a new, shorter but larger-diameter EX-72 booster with thrust vector control. In 7-95 initial contracts were placed for the development of the Missile Homing Improvement Program, which would add an infrared seeker to the Block IIIB's radar homing system. Through FY 94, 2,075 new Block IIIB and 845 Block IIIA-to-IIIB kits had been procured. In 3-98, 68 new Standard SM-2 Block IIIA and 73 Block III-to-IIIA update kits were ordered. Approved for purchase were 202 Block III under FY 95, 64 under FY 96, 127 under FY 97, 114 under FY 98 (the total to include initial low-production-rate procurement of Block IV), and 103 under FY 99. Some 108 were requested under FY 01. Under FY 01, 86 Block IIIB missiles were authorized, with another 96 under FY 02. Under FY 03, 93 were requested, while 139 each are to be requested under FY 04 and FY 05, 209 under FY 06, and 239 under FY 07.

Block IVA was to be a heat-seeking BMD (Ballistic Missile Defense) version and was first tested successfully on 24-1-97; it was to be operational by late 2000 in the SAM role but the program was 57% over budget and several years behind schedule when it was canceled on 14-12-01; since the need for such a weapon has been validated, however, the program is planned to be reborn employing a more advanced missile, which, if nothing else, will further increase the program cost and delay its operational inception. Only 750 Block IVA missiles were planned.

Standard SM-1 MR (RIM-66B/RIM-67E)
Bldr: Raytheon Systems, Tucson, Ariz.

A single-stage missile that replaced Tartar. The system comprises a Mk 13 single launcher with a vertical ready-service magazine containing 40 missiles, a computer, an air-search radar, and SPG-51 illumination radars. Procurement ended with 650 under FY 83. Used by the FFG 7 class. RIM-66B production totals for the USN and export included 1,194 Block III, 1,665 Block IV with improved ECCM, and 2,141 Block V.

Length: 4.47 m **Diameter:** 0.34 m **Weight:** 625 kg
Range: 25 n.m. **Altitude:** 150–60,000 ft. **Guidance:** semiactive homing

Evolved Sea Sparrow (RIM-162) Bldr: Raytheon Systems, Tucson, Ariz.

An initial 54-month contract was let in 6-95 to Hughes (now Raytheon) and a consortium of United Defense, Alliant/Hercules, and Norwegian, German, Australian, Canadian, Spanish, Danish, Turkish, and Greek firms for a performance upgrade version of the RIM-7P missile, with 35- to 50-g. maneuverability, increased range, and doubled speed. The missile uses a 254-mm-diameter motor and has a WAU-17B fragmentation warhead. The initial variant will concentrate on modifying the control system, while a second generation is to replace RAM and a third is to provide further range and performance improvements. The Evolved Sea Sparrow Missile (ESSM) will be carried in Mk 25 Mod. 0 "Quad Pack" containers in Mk 41 vertical launch cells; at a later date, a new seeker and versions capable of launch from Mk 48 VLS cells (one each) and Mk 29 box launchers may also be developed. The first 28 production missiles were requested under FY 99; only 36 were requested under FY 01—a considerable reduction from earlier planning. Introduction into service has been delayed to FY 05 and planned acquisition for the USN for FY 02 through FY 05. Twenty-nine were authorized under FY 01 and 26 under FY 02; future requests are to be 146 under FY 03, 182 under FY 04, 384 under FY 05, 441 under FY 06, and 298 under FY 07.

Length: 3.657 m **Diameter:** 0.254 m
Wingspan: 1.016 m (open; 0.635 folded)
Weight: 281.2 kg **Warhead:** 38.6 kg **Range:** 8 n.m.

A prototype Ship Defense Launching System for the Evolved Sea Sparrow was tested early in 1998 and was to be installed on the *Nimitz* (CVN 75) in 2001; 38 of the launchers, which employ a fixed, inclined box-launch configuration carrying four quad pack launch cells, may be acquired to replace Mk 29 launchers on aircraft carriers and LHDs.

Sea Sparrow (RIM-7 series) Bldr: Raytheon Systems, Tucson, Ariz.

Known initially as the BPDMS (Basic Point Defense Missile System). A lightweight launcher, Mk 29, employing eight folding-fin missiles and the Mk 91 radar fire-control system, is now in use. In Europe, this later system, IPDMS (Independent Point Defense Missile System), is also known as NATO Sea Sparrow. The current RIM-7M version uses a blast-fragmentation warhead vice the earlier RIM-7H's expanding rod variety and has a monopulse radar. Latest variant in service is the RIM-7P, which uses the 203-mm-diameter Hercules Mk 58 Mod. 4 rocket motor.

Length: 3.657 m **Diameter:** 0.203 m
Wingspan: 1.016 m (open; 0.635 folded) **Weight:** 231.5 kg
Warhead: 38.6 kg **Speed:** Mach 3.5 **Range:** 8 n.m.

Sea RAM Bldr: Raytheon Systems, Tucson, Ariz.

Sea RAM is the commercial name for an 11-round launcher for RIM-116A Mod. 1 missiles that also uses the same mounting, Mk 90 Ku-Band search-and-track radar, surface-mode E/O sensors, and belowdecks components as the 20-mm Phalanx CIWS. Instead of operating in self-guided mode, the missile becomes a beam-rider, using the radars within the Phalanx system. Installed on the left side of the mounting are a Pilkington Optronics FLIR detector and a low-light-level t.v. camera. The system is offered for export in cooperation with Germany's RAM-System GmbH, the U.K.'s DML, and Hunting Engineering. The mounting was given a compatibility test aboard the British destroyer *York* (D 98) between 2-01 and 10-01 and may be procured for installation aboard 12 FFG 7–class frigates, the first 27 DDG 51–class destroyers, and the LPD 17–class landing ships.

RAM (Rolling Airframe Missile) (RIM-116A Mod. 0/1)
Bldr: Raytheon Systems, Tucson, Ariz.

Developed by General Dynamics (later Hughes Missile Systems and now Raytheon) under a 7-76 agreement by the U.S.A., Denmark, and West Germany. The first 30 were built under FY 85. RAM became operational 14-11-92 on the *Peleliu* (LHA 5), more than 10 years behind schedule. It uses slow spinning for flight stability (hence the name). The missile homes on active radiation from the target until it picks up an infrared target signature and employs the current Stinger seeker in conjunction with Sidewinder fuzes, warheads, and rocket motors. The 21-missile Mk 49 launcher installation weighs 4,977 kg above deck, 800 kg below; the Mk 49 launcher has been installed on all LHDs, LHAs, and LSDs and on six DD 963–class destroyers. The USN plans to acquire 4,600 total. Unit cost in 1997 was a very expensive $440,000 each, but by FY 01, the price had dropped to $144,000 each.

The Mod. 1 missile, which completed successful trials in mid-1998, has a laser fuze and an improved, broader-view infrared seeker. A dual-thrust motor to improve range has been proposed. Raytheon received a contract for one launcher and 45 Mod. 1 missiles during 6-00. The RAM system is to be altered to make it usable against small, high-speed surface targets. Procurement of about 100 missiles per year is expected.

Length: 2.819 m **Diameter:** 0.127 m **Weight:** 73.5 kg
Speed: Mach 2+ **Range:** 6 n.m.

Stinger (FIM-92) Bldr: General Dynamics and Raytheon Systems

The Marine Corps employs the shoulder-launched, infrared-homing Stinger with troops, and the navy procured 585 for shipboard defense. The FIM-92A entered service in 1981; more than 16,000 have been delivered. Some FIM-92B "Stinger POST" missiles were delivered to the USMC. FIM-92C RMP (Reprogrammed Microprocessor) is the current version.

Length: 1.52 m **Diameter:** 0.07 m **Weight:** 15.1 kg
Warhead: 3 kg (proximity fuze) **Speed:** Mach 2.0

Hawk (MIM-23B) Bldr: Raytheon Systems, Tucson, Ariz.

A deployable point-defense SAM used by the USMC in its latest Improved Hawk ("I-Hawk") version for airfield and strong-point defense. Under FY 88, 525 I-Hawks were authorized, with another 467 in FY 89 and none since. It will be retired without replacement.

♦ Antisubmarine warfare missiles

ASROC (RUR-5A)
Bldr: Hughes Electronics Div., General Motors (now Raytheon Systems)

Some 12,000 ASROC rounds were procured between 1960 and 1970, when production ceased. The original, eight-celled Mk 112 trainable launcher version was retired from the USN under FY 94, with the launchers removed from those few remaining active ships that had them; it is still widely deployed in foreign fleets, although not all navies that received ships with the launchers also received the missiles. All nuclear rounds (used only by the USN) were retired by the end of FY 89. ASROC was also launched from the Mk 26 launchers on five early units of the CG 47 class. The missile is a solid-fueled, unguided rocket with a parachute-retarded Mk 46 torpedo payload. Its range is regulated by the combustion time of the rocket motor. Rocket–torpedo separation is timed. Fire control is made up of a computer linked with the sonar.

Length: 4.42 m **Diameter:** 0.324 m **Weight:** 454 kg **Range:** 9,200 m

Vertical-Launch ASROC (RUM-139B) Bldr: Loral

Full-scale production began in 3-93 for use with Mk 41 launchers in CG 52 and later *Ticonderoga*-class cruisers and in DDG 51–class destroyers. With booster attached, the weapon is 5.08 m long and 0.358 m in diameter and weighs about 750 kg. The final 30 were ordered in 4-98 and delivered in 4-99, for a total of 443 produced for the USN; no more are planned. The relative handful built is cross-decked to deploying ships; none has been launched since the early 1990s, and the system is considered "not operationally effective." The missile has also been purchased by Japan, which has ordered more than 600.

♦ Air-to-surface missiles

Hystrike

The Naval Air Warfare Center Weapons Division, China Lake, Calif., is developing a Hypersonic Weapons Technology Program aimed at introducing the Hystrike land-attack missile around 2010. Some 1,200 missiles would be procured between FY 09 and FY 15 at around $350,000 apiece. Intended to attack hardened targets at ranges of up to 600 n.m., Hystrike would travel at Mach 3.5–7.0 and would be able to penetrate up to 11 m of concrete. The missile could be launched by aircraft, surface ships, and submarines and would replace the Tomahawk land-attack, Harpoon, SLAM, and SLAM-ER missiles.

Note: The Joint Air-to-Surface Standoff Missile (JASSM) program has been canceled.

JDAM (Joint Direct Attack Munition)
Bldr: Boeing (formerly McDonnell Douglas)

Not a missile per se but rather a conversion kit for 2,000-lb. BLU-109 and Mk 84 bombs, adding a GPS-aided inertial navigation system to produce a better-than-11-m CEP accuracy. A contract was let in 10-95 for the initial increment. Plans are to acquire 25,496 over 11 years, with the initial 937 conversion kits having begun delivery during 1998 for use on F/A-18-series aircraft. A version for use with Mk 82 500-lb. bombs is to be developed. On 25-2-00, 916 were ordered for Navy BLU-109 bombs. Procurement of 1,417 was approved in the FY 02 budget. Under FY 03, however, 9,880 were requested, and 7,626 are to be requested under FY 04, 5,964 under FY 05, 7,230 under FY 06, and 6,456 under FY 07.

JSOW (Joint Standoff Weapon) (AGM-154A/B/C)
Bldr: Raytheon Systems Co., Lewisville, Texas

Formerly called AIWS (Advanced Interdiction Weapon System) and originally developed by Texas Instruments; a joint Navy–Air Force program for an unpowered, 24-n.m., "fire-and-forget" ground-attack weapon to replace Skipper, Walleye, Paveway, and Laser Maverick. The Texas Instruments design was selected in 12-91 and the development contract placed in 7-92; it entered limited service late in 1997. JSOW weighs up to 1,000 kg, with either a 444- or an 888-kg explosive or cluster bomb payload. Television, infrared, and fiber-optic guidance are all being considered. As many

WEAPONS AND SYSTEMS *(continued)*

as 6,300 are planned for both services. The USAF version dispenses six sensor-fuzed antitank submunitions; the navy AGM-154A version dispenses BLU-97A or -97B bomblets. The AGM-154B version will use BLU-108B sensor-fuzed anti-armor submunitions, and AGM-154C is to use a unitary warhead.

JSOW unit cost in FY 98 was $519,469, which was expected to fall to $401,852 by 2003. An initial 100 AGM-154A production missiles were funded under FY 97, with 180 under FY 98, 328 under FY 99, 454 under FY 00, and 762 under FY 02. Planned procurement includes 363 in FY 03, 555 in FY 04, 522 in FY 05, 502 in FY 06, and 424 in FY 07. On 29-12-98, the first 328 AGM-154A and 3 AGM-154B missiles were ordered for the navy; 414 more were ordered during 1-00. The AGM-154B and C variants were to enter service in FY 02 and 03, respectively. AGM-154C uses the British BAE Systems Bomb Royal Ordnance Augmented Charge (BROACH) penetrating warhead. In combat usage, the missile initially experienced accuracy problems.

SLAM (AGM-84E) Bldr: Boeing

Only 290 total AGM-84E SLAM (Standoff Land-Attack Missiles) were originally planned, but another 200 were procured under FY 92, 90 under FY 93, 75 under FY 94, 58 under FY 95, and 75 under FY 96, the final year of procurement; under FY 97, Congress added 25 more—but these were not procured. SLAM incorporates GPS and uses the Harpoon's missile propulsion section and warhead, the AGM-65D Maverick's infrared seeker, and the Walleye missile's datalink. Four can be carried by F/A-18 aircraft.

Length: 4.49 m **Diameter:** 0.343 m **Weight:** 628 kg
Warhead: 227 kg **Propulsion:** CAE-JA02 turbojet **Speed:** Mach 0.85

SLAM-ER (AGM-84H) Bldr: Boeing

The SLAM-ER (Stand-off Land Attack Missile—Expanded Response), authorized by DoD in 2-95 as a replacement for the canceled AGM-137 TSSAM, is a conversion of the AGM-84E SLAM with long-span folding wings to extend its range beyond 150 n.m. The weapon has a cylindrical warhead with PBX-C-129 explosive and a tapered forward end for penetration. Initial low rate of production of SLAM-ER began in 1999 with the conversion of 60 existing SLAM missiles to SLAM-ER configuration; as of 2-01, 346 conversions from SLAM had been ordered. Thirty each were approved under FY 00 and FY 01. Beginning in 2000, an automatic target acquisition capability was added to the missile, making it the SLAM-ER+. SLAM-ER will be carried by P-3 Orion aircraft, as well as the F/A-18. Planned procurement of SLAM-ER conversions include 120 in FY 03, 84 in FY 04, and 90 in FY 05, with none thereafter.

Length: 4.34 m **Diameter:** 0.343 m **Weight:** 725 kg
Warhead: 227 kg **Propulsion:** CAE-JA02 turbojet **Speed:** Mach 0.85

Penguin Mk 2 Mod. 7 (AGM-119B) Bldr: Kongsberg/Northrop Grumman

Initially tested for the USN in 1982–83 as a surface ship–launched weapon, Penguin was procured for launch by SH-60B LAMPS-III helicopters. It has solid-fueled rocket propulsion, programmable inertial midcourse guidance, and infrared terminal homing. Only 193 operational weapons were planned for procurement, and total procurement was later reduced to just 106, vastly increasing the unit cost; only 28 helicopters were modified to carry the missile. The missile first became operational in 5-94 aboard the *Conolly* (DD 979). In 8-95, Congress expressed a desire for the navy to request additional missiles for FY 97; an order for six more for delivery by 4-99 was placed with Kongsberg in 7-97 at a very uneconomical total cost of $6.05 million.

Length: 3.00 m **Diameter:** 0.28 m **Wingspan:** 1.40 m (0.56 folded)
Weight: 385 kg **Warhead:** Bullpup Mk 19 (120 kg SAP with 50 kg explosive)
Range: 21+ n.m.

Maverick (AGM-65E/F)
Bldr: Raytheon Systems (formerly Hughes Missile Systems)

Developed from the Air Force's AGM-65D, the AGM-65E is a laser-designated, air-launched missile for the USMC, while the AGM-65F version for the navy on F/A-18 aircraft uses infrared homing. Both have the same 136-kg penetrator, with a 56.8-kg blast-fragment warhead. A rapid escalation in price initially forced scaling back of procurement: 90 were procured under FY 83 and 165 under FY 84. Subsequent authorizations were 600 total under FY 85, 1,500 AGM-65E and 195 AGM-65F under FY 86, 248 AGM-65F under FY 87, 1,300 AGM-65E and 425 AGM-65F under FY 88, 731 AGM-65F under FY 89, and 560 total under FY 90, the last year of procurement.

Length: 2.49 m **Diameter:** 0.305 m **Wingspan:** 0.72 m
Weight: AGM-65E: 293 kg; AGM-65F: 307 kg
Propulsion: solid-fuel rocket **Range:** 50 n.m.

HARPOON (AGM-84)

See description under Surface-to-Surface Missiles.

HARM (AGM-88A/B/C) Bldr: Texas Instruments and Ford Instrument

HARM (High-speed Antiradiation Missile) can be employed by the F/A-18 and S-3B to suppress or destroy ground defenses. From FY 83 through FY 92, 9,591 were procured. Ford Instrument developed the AGM-88B "low-cost seeker" variant, which began production in 1990. A total of 5,300 missiles are to be upgraded to AGM-88B (Block IIIA) and 2,700 to AGM-88C (Block V) with a home-on-jam capability. Block VI, being developed in cooperation with Germany and Italy, will add precision GPS to the guidance system.

Length: 4.17 m **Diameter:** 0.253 m **Wingspan:** 1.13 m
Weight: 360 kg **Propulsion:** solid-propellant, low-smoke rocket
Speed: Mach 2.0+ **Range:** . . .

A request for proposals for an improved HSARM (Higher-Speed Antiradiation Missile) upgrade program was issued 1-11-01; the missile would use tail-controlled steering and variable-flow ducted rocket engine to achieve a 100- to 120-n.m. range, better maneuverability, and higher speed. About 1,350 HARMs would be modified to HSARM status. Also in development under the Quick Bolt program is a multimode seeker for the HSARM.

♦ Anti-armored vehicle missiles

Common Missile

A notional replacement for the current Hellfire, Maverick, and TOW (but not Longbow TOW) anti-armor missiles. Initiated by the U.S. Army and joined by the USN and USMC in 8-00. Procurement would be 25,000–28,000 for aviation use and 8,000–9,000 for ground forces. Plans are for it to enter engineering and manufacturing development during FY 04, with production to begin in FY 08. The system will employ a 152-mm-diameter fire-and-forget missile with controllable-thrust rocket propulsion. The program will probably replace the less-expensive, in-house Spike.

SPIKE Bldr: Naval Air Warfare Center Weapons Division, China Lake, Calif.

A developmental fire-and-forget weapon for use against light vehicles, helicopters, personnel, and buildings. For use by the U.S. Special Operations Command and Marines and from unmanned aerial vehicles, Spike is intended as a squad weapon and will employ an imaging seeker that will also home on reflected laser illumination. Alternate penetration, fragmentation, and concussion warheads are planned. The cost goal is less than $10,000 per round.

Length: 0.51 m **Diameter:** 40 mm **Weight:** 2.0 kg (2.3 with launcher)
Propulsion: solid rocket (6- to 8-second burn)
Speed: 340 m/sec **Range:** 3,200 m

TOW-2 (MGM-71) Bldr: Raytheon Systems

A wire-guided, helicopter- or ground-launched antitank weapon that uses an optical sight and tube launcher. TOW = Tube-launched, Optically tracked, Wire-guided. More than 400,000 TOWs have been built since 1970 for all customers. TOW-2A detonates reactive armor, then penetrates; 16,000 were in service by 4-88. TOW-2 has not been procured since early 1990s.

Length: 1.174 m **Diameter:** 0.152 m **Wingspan:** 1.14 m
Weight: 18.9 kg; ITOW (Improved TOW): 19.1 kg; ITOW-2: 21.5 kg
Warhead: 3.6-kg hollow, shaped-charge
Propulsion: solid-propellant rocket **Range:** 2.3 n.m. at Mach 1.0

Hellfire (AGM-114A/B/K/M) Bldr: Lockheed Martin–Boeing

A USMC lightweight antitank missile. It has three major variants: Laser-designated (1.625 m, 45.7 kg), RF/IR (Radio-Frequency Infrared), and IRIS (Imaging Infrared). Can be carried by navy SH-60-series helicopters.

Length: 1.727 or 1.778 m (IRIS)
Diameter: 0.178 m **Wingspan:** 0.3262 m
Weight: 45.70–47.88 kg (71 in container)
Speed: Mach 1.0+ **Range:** 5+ km

Under development for the army and the Marines by Lockheed Martin and Boeing is the AGM-114K HOMS (Hellfire Optimized Missile System) with semiactive laser seeker, longer range, and 40% fewer parts; the first 100 rounds for the navy were to be delivered in 5-00. Also delivered in 2000 were 100 AGM-114M rounds with 12.5-kg blast-fragmentation warheads for antiship use from helicopters. That variant is being developed by Lockheed Martin as the Seagull system, using either fixed or rotating launchers for small combatant use. Its characteristics include:

Length: 1.626 m **Diameter:** 0.178 m **Weight:** 45 kg **Range:** 0.5–9.0 km

The first of 100 AGM-114M missiles were delivered during 9-00 for use with navy SH-60B Seahawk and Marine AH-1W SuperCobra helicopters. This 47.6-kg variant is equipped with a 12.5-kg blast-fragmentation warhead and a delayed proximity fuze. AGM-114M has a maximum speed of Mach 1.3 and a maximum flight duration of 39 seconds, and one round can disable a ship of up to 700 tons displacement. Turkey took delivery of 10 training rounds in 3-00 and 84 with blast-fragmentation warheads for antiship use starting in 2-01; the Japanese Maritime Self-Defense Force ordered six for trials. Unit cost is about $77,000.

Note: Also for air-launched use, some 4,000 ADM-141 TALD (Tactical Air-Launched Decoy) glide-missiles in three variants have been acquired: RF for defense saturation, chaff for force-masking, and IR for infrared missile training. ITALD (Improved TALD), with turbojet propulsion, is in development.

Javelin (. . .) Bldrs: Texas Instruments and Lockheed Martin

A developmental man-portable fire-and-forget antitank weapon that entered low-rate production in 1994, with full-rate production to have begun 5-97. Some 171 were procured under the FY 97 budget and 380 under FY 98; funds for 741 were approved under FY 99. Is ready to fire in less than 30 seconds and requires less than 20 seconds to reload. Missile shelf life is 10 years. Uses a passive integrated daylight and thermal sight with a 4-hour battery.

Length: 1.0812 m (launch tube: 1.198 m) **Diameter:** 126.9 mm
Weight: 11.8 kg (22.3 with launch tube and command unit) **Range:** 2,000 m

Dragon-II (AGM-. . .) Bldrs: McDonnell Douglas and Raytheon Systems

A small anti-armor weapon, of which 4,259 were ordered under FY 88 and 14,599 under FY 89 for the Marines; none were requested under FY 90 or subsequently. Delivered ready-to-fire in a GRP storage/launch container. Cannot defeat the latest tanks with add-on armor. Has interchangeable day and IR night sights; as of 12-95, only 1,055 day tracker and 923 night tracker sights were available.

Length: 0.86 m (launcher: 1.15 m)
Weight: 15.3 kg (with launcher; 22.0 with night tracker)
Time of flight: 11.2 seconds **Range:** 1,000 m

SMAW (Shoulder-launched Multipurpose Assault Weapon)

Weapon for the USMC, using the Mk 153 Mod. 1 launcher with a laser designation sight to fire either Mk 6 Mod. 0 HEAA (High Explosive Anti-Armor) or general-purpose HEDP (High-Explosive Dual Purpose) rockets. Derived from the Israeli B-300 system.

Length: 0.787 m (stowed; launcher: 1.378 m in firing condition)
Diameter: 83 mm (rocket)
Weight: rocket: 6.71 kg HEAA/5.89 kg HEDP; launcher: 5.89 kg
Range: 500 m (stationary target)

WEAPONS AND SYSTEMS *(continued)*

♦ Air-to-air missiles

Evolved Sidewinder (AIM-9X) Bldr: Raytheon Systems, Tucson, Ariz.

Contract awarded in 12-96. Uses the 127-mm-diameter Sidewinder body and solid rocket engine coupled with thrust vector control to improve maneuverability. Its first test air launch, on 18-3-99, was successful. To enter service during FY 02. Under the FY 01 budget, 63 missiles were requested, but for FY 02 through FY 05, the number to be procured was reduced in 6-00 from 1,629 to only 756, although an eventual production total of 5,000 for the navy over a period of 18 years is foreseen. On 21-2-00, 103 missiles and 39 captive training missiles were ordered for USN and USAF use. Employs operator helmet control.

Sparrow-III (AIM-7F/M) Bldr: Raytheon Systems

The AIM-7F entered service in 1976 with a continuous-rod warhead. The AIM-7M, the current version, entered service in 1983 with a blast/fragmentation warhead, active fuze, and improved seeker. In FY 85, 936 were authorized for procurement; 1,948 for both air and surface launch were authorized in FY 86, 1,716 in FY 87, 600 in FY 88, 450 in FY 89, but none thereafter.

Length: 3.65 m **Diameter:** 0.203 m **Weight:** 232 kg
Warhead: 27 kg (proximity fuze) **Propulsion:** solid-fuel rocket
Speed: Mach 2.5 **Range:** 26 km **Guidance:** semiactive homing

Sidewinder (AIM-9M/S) Bldrs: Raytheon Systems and Ford Aerospace/Loral

More than 110,000 Sidewinder missiles have been built. The AIM-9L version used an active optical fuze and had a guidance system permitting all-angle attacks. The AIM-9M version supplanted the AIM-9L in production in 1981 and has improved capabilities against countermeasures and against targets seen against warm backgrounds. Some 8,000 AIM-9M were inventory as of 1991. An AIM-9R with improvements to counter-countermeasures was canceled by Congress during 1992, but the AIM-9X (Evolved Sidewinder; see separate entry) is to deploy in FY 02. AIM-9P is an export version for aircraft without internal cooling systems. The AIM-9L is also manufactured by a German/Italian/Norwegian/British consortium:

Length: 2.90 m **Diameter:** 0.127 m **Wingspan:** 0.63 m **Weight:** 84.4 kg
Warhead: 9.45 kg (fragmentation) **Propulsion:** solid-fueled rocket
Speed: Mach 2.5 **Range:** 22 km **Guidance:** infrared homing

The AIM-9S version now in production weighs 86 kg and has a 10.15-kg warhead with proximity and contact fuzing. The AIM-9M has an 11.35-kg warhead.

Phoenix (AIM-54A/C) Bldr: Raytheon Systems

AIM-54A ceased production in 1980 after only 2,500 had been built for F-14 Tomcat-series interceptors for the USN and, unfortunately, Iran. The first 30 pilot-production AIM-54C were delivered 10-81, with 60 more to follow. By 10-88, 1,000 AIM-54C had been delivered. From FY 83 through FY 90 (the final year of procurement), 2,310 were authorized. It will be phased out with the retirement of the remaining F-14-series fighters.

Length: 3.96 m **Diameter:** 0.380 m **Wingspan:** 0.914 m
Weight: 453 kg **Warhead:** 60.3 kg (continuous rod)
Propulsion: solid-fueled rocket **Range:** about 120 km

AMRAAM (AIM-120A/B/C) Bldr: Raytheon Systems

AMRAAM (Advanced Medium-Range Air-to-Air Missile) was intended to replace the AIM-7F Sparrow. Its first firings were in 1985. The navy goal was 7,249 total, out of 24,320 planned for all users. However, from FY 89 through FY 00, Congress authorized purchase of only 1,553; another 75 were requested under FY 01, while 150 are to be requested under FY 02 and 125 under FY 03. The AIM-120B, with a reprogrammable seeker and infrared homing, entered service during 4-95. The AIM-120C version, with clipped wings for internal storage, increased warhead lethality, an improved engine, improved aerodynamic performance, and improved counter-countermeasures capabilities, entered service in 1996. An order to Raytheon on 7-5-01 for the year 2001 increment included only 63 for the navy and Marine Corps.

In 4-01, the Marine Corps selected a ground-launched version of the AMRAAM as the CLAWS (Complementary Low-Altitude Weapon System), using the HMMWV (High-Mobility Multipurpose Wheeled Vehicle) as the platform. The system may enter service during FY 05, and up to 95 CLAWS may be acquired.

Length: 3.65 m **Diameter:** 0.178 m **Weight:** 151.5 kg
Warhead: 22.7 kg **Range:** more than 74 km
Guidance: inertial midcourse, active terminal homing

B. GUNS

155-mm Advanced Gun System Bldr: United Defense LP

The replacement under development for the General Dynamics 155-mm VGAS (Vertical Gun for Advanced Ships), which never achieved prototype stage. It was to employ a fully trainable and elevatable mount and be capable of firing 12 rds/min, with 600 to 750 rounds in each magazine and two guns on each DD 21–class Land Attack Destroyer; the new gun will have an accuracy within 10 m at maximum range of 100 n.m., using GPS. The program began in 1999, with firing trials in 2002 and the first two mounts to be delivered in 1-07—an unusually brief development cycle by U.S. standards and possibly unachievable. The gun will have a trapezoidal-external-section, water-cooled barrel 62 calibers long and a low-radar-cross-section mounting. Muzzle impulse is to be 30–35 megajoules. Initially to fire army XM982 projectiles or a new, 260-lb., 88-in.-long Extended Range Guided Munition (ERGM). A projectile that is planned would carry 88 M42E1 DPICM bomblets, and would be followed by variants with 10.9-kg blast fragmentation warheads and with an anti-armor warhead (the army SADARM—Sense And Destroy Armor—submunition is a candidate for the latter role). Initial firing trials were successfully completed by 26-11-01. It will probably be employed on the DD 21 replacement, the DD(X).

155-mm XM777 ultra-lightweight howitzer

A Marine Corps towed or helicopter-deployed weapon, made by BAE Systems RO Defence. The first was delivered in 6-00, with a total of 426 planned to replace the 155-mm M 198. Uses a 39-caliber barrel manufactured by the U.S. Army's Watervliet Arsenal. Can be towed by a 5-ton 6×6 truck or lifted by helicopters or MV-22 Osprey aircraft; two can be accommodated in a C-130 aircraft.

Note: The USMC was to test several new 120-mm mortars during 2002, including its in-house automatic Dragonfire.

127-mm Mk 42
Bldr: Northern Ordnance/FMC (now United Defense LP, Armament Systems Division)

Single-barrel, dual-purpose gun. No longer in U.S. Navy active service, it remains aboard *Knox*-class frigates in foreign fleets and on several Japanese-built classes. Loading is entirely automatic from two ammunition drums in the handling room up to the loading tray by means of a rotating hoist. Each drum contains 20 rounds. The rate of fire can be maintained for only 1 minute, inasmuch as it is necessary to reload the drums. The firing rate was reduced from the original 40 rds/min for safety. Most mounts were converted to Mk 42 Mod. 10 configuration with greatly improved reliability.

Length: 54 calibers **Mount weight:** 65.8 tons; Mod. 10: 63.9 tons
Projectile weight: 32 kg **Muzzle velocity:** 810 m/sec
Rate of fire: 20 rds/min **Arc of elevation:** –5° to +80°
Training speed: 50°/sec **Elevation speed:** 80°/sec
Range: 23,700 m horizontal/14,840 m vertical
Fire control: Mk 68 system with SPG-53 radar in most ships
Personnel: 13 men, with 2 in mount

127-mm Mk 45 Bldr: United Defense LP, Armament Systems Division

Single-barrel mount fitted on CG 47–, DD 963–, and DDG 51–class vessels, as well as in foreign ships. The Mk 45 mount uses the Mk 48 gun with a one-piece Mk 19 Mod. 2 or two-piece Mk 19 Mod. 0 barrel. The manufacturer was formerly named Northern Ordnance/FMC. The Mod. 1 version permits rapid switching from one type of ammunition to another and has an electronic vice mechanical fuze-setter.

Length: 54 calibers **Mount weight:** 22.23 tons
Projectile weight: 31.75 kg **Muzzle velocity:** 807.72 m/sec
Rate of fire: 16–20 rds/min **Arc of elevation:** –5° to +65°
Range: 23,700 m horizontal/14,840 m vertical
Fire control: Mk 86 GFCS with SPQ-9 search radar; SPG-60 tracking radar
Personnel: none on mount; 6 in handling room to reload ammunition drums

A "Mk 45 Gun System Technical Improvement Program" is in production as the Mk 45 Mod. 4, with a low-observable, faceted gunmount and a rate of fire of 20 rds/min (10 rds with ERGM—see below). The muzzle velocity is 762 m/sec with a 45-kg projectile or 914 m/sec with a 32-kg projectile. A new 62-cal. barrel is fitted, along with a new breech and breech-operating mechanism, a modified slide, a new loader drum, and a system that "recognizes" and selects the proper rounds. The gun is aboard DDG 81 and later *Arleigh Burke*–class destroyers and is to be backfitted to CG 52–73.

Texas Instruments (now Raytheon Systems, Tucson, Ariz.) received a $44 million contract in 10-96 to develop the rocket-assisted EX-171 ERGM (Extended Range Guided Munition) for the Mk 45 gun; the projectiles will employ an onboard inertial guidance system and miniature GPS receivers. At a range of 63 n.m., the projectiles would have a CEP of 10–20 m. Some 8,000 rounds are planned for procurement. Initial deliveries were to have begun in 2001 under FY 98–99 funding, but service introduction has been delayed to 2006. The 50-kg, 1.55-m-long projectiles are to carry a payload of 72 M-80 bomblets, with dispersion selectable over an area from 30 to 100 m^2.

An industry team led by Alliant Techsystems successfully tested its competing GPS-guided ANSR (Autonomous Naval Support Round) early in 1-02, with the two test rounds traveling up to 51 n.m. A production version of ANSR would cost less than $20,000 per round and would have a range in excess of 70 n.m. at an initial muzzle velocity of more than 3,400 ft./sec. The round would also be produced in a 155-mm diameter for the larger Advanced Gun System.

76-mm Mk 75
Bldrs: United Defense LP, Armament Systems Division, and OTOBreda

Single-barrel, license-built version of the OTOBreda Compact, tested in the frigate *Talbot* and used in the FFG 7 class and Coast Guard cutters. Built in the U.S.A., except for an FY 85 order to OTO Melara (now OTOBreda). Northern Ordnance/FMC became United Defense LP, Armament Systems Division, in 1994.

Length: 62 calibers **Mount weight:** 6.2 tons
Projectile weight: 6.4 kg **Rate of fire:** 85 rds/min
Range: 19,200 m horizontal/11,900 m vertical
Fire control: Mk 92 radar system **Personnel:** 4, below decks

40-mm Mk 19 Mod. 3 grenade launcher Bldr: Socko Corp.

A lightweight rapid-fire grenade launcher in portable tripod-legged mountings, found aboard small combatants, auxiliaries, and Coast Guard ships. Range is 2,212 m (1,500 m effective); rate of fire is 300 rds/min, and muzzle velocity is 240 m/sec. The launcher is also employed on the Mk 96 Mod. 0 stabilized mount, collocated with a 25-mm M 242 Bushmaster cannon (see below). For use by the Special Forces Command, the navy ordered 305 Mk 47 40-mm Advanced Lightweight Grenade Launchers (ALGL) from General Dynamics late in 2001; the Mk 47 has a range of 2,000 m.

Note: The General Electric 20-mm and 25-mm Sea Vulcan gatling guns have been sold abroad but have not yet been acquired for the USN. Sea Vulcan 25 uses the GAU-12/U gun (900 or 2,000 rds/min) with 500 rounds on-mount.

30-mm Mk 46 Mod. 0 and Mod. 1 Bldr: General Dynamics

The Mod. 0 version is intended for the AAAV amphibious assault vehicle and the Mod. 1 version (without smoke rocket launchers) for fitting aboard the LPD 17 class for defense against smallcraft, helicopters, and light aircraft. Maximum range is 6,800 m (5,200 m effective). The Mod. 0 mount will have 220 rounds of ready-service ammunition, the Mod. 1 more than 550. Both mounts have two-axis stabilization.

WEAPONS AND SYSTEMS *(continued)*

25-mm Mk 38 Mod. 1 (M 242 Bushmaster)
Bldr: Boeing–McDonnell Douglas

A "chain gun," using the M 242 gun, Mk 88 Mod. 0 mounting, and linked Oerlikon M790 ammunition, for use on major surface combatants, *Cyclone*-class patrol craft, amphibious warfare ships, and Coast Guard ships and craft. From FY 86 through FY 92, Congress authorized procurement of 265 total. The gun also fires Alliant PGU-32/U semi-armor-piercing, high-explosive, incendiary-tracer rounds. The Mk 88 mounting holds 400 rounds of ready-service ammunition and can be reloaded in four minutes, but it is awkward to use, due to its low configuration.

Length: 2.74 m overall **Weight:** 109 kg (gun)
Muzzle velocity: 1,100 m/sec **Rate of fire:** single-shot or 100 or 200 rds/min
Range: 6,598 m (2,469 effective) **Fire control:** ringsight

Now installed in *Cyclone*-class patrol craft, the Mk 96 Mod. 0 stabilized mount carries both a 25-mm M 242 Bushmaster gun and a 40-mm Mk 19 grenade launcher; 96 grenades and 400 rounds of 25-mm ammunition are carried on the mount, which weighs 1,230 kg without ammunition and 1,430 kg loaded and requires a crew of three. Kollmorgen has built three lightweight Mk 98 stabilized Bushmaster gun mountings, of which two went to the Bahamas and one was used for trials by the U.S. Southern Command (SOCOM).

20-mm Phalanx Mk 15 Mod. 0 Block I, IA, and IB CIWS (Close-In Weapon System)
Bldr: General Dynamics (with G.E. gun) or Raytheon Systems (ex-General Electric)

The Vulcan/Phalanx "Close-in" system designed to destroy missiles, consisting of a multibarrel M61A1 20-mm gun co-mounted with two radars, one of which follows the target and the other the projectile stream, using the Mk 90 integrated fire-control system. A computer furnishes necessary corrections for train and elevation so that the two radar returns (target and projectiles) coincide, bringing heavy fire to bear on the target. Only 989 rounds were carried in the Block 0 magazine. The first production unit was completed 9-8-79. The improved Block I version, with 1,550 rounds on-mount and a higher rate of fire, entered service in late 1988—five years late—and all remaining U.S. Navy Phalanx mounts have since been converted to Block I. The system originally used Mk 149 projectiles with depleted uranium subcaliber penetrators; later, heavier nickel-iron rounds were introduced, and 105-g nickel-cobalt-tungsten rounds with 50% greater penetration are now being phased in. As of 7-98, 840 mounts had been produced.

Block IA Phalanx substituted an improved computer to improve capabilities against rapidly maneuvering targets. Block IB adds a Pilkington Optronics IR imaging and tracking system to the mount; 11 update kits have been ordered for use on FFG 7–class frigates, and more may be procured for amphibious warfare ships and Phalanx-equipped DDG 51–class destroyers. Other modifications to Block IB include low-sidelobe modification to the tracking radar, a tunable narrowband filter added to the search radar, substitution of longer (480-mm) gun barrels on the pneumatic-drive guns, electric controls, and improved, sturdier supports for the gun to reduce dispersion. Raytheon began delivering new mounts from a Louisville, Ky., facility in 1999, and the first production mount was placed on FFG 50 in 9-00:

Mount weight: 5.4 tons
Rate of fire: 3,000 rds/min (Block I: 3,000 or 4,500 rds/min)
Range: 1,486 m horizontal max.

12.7-mm GAU-19/A
Bldr: General Dynamics Armament Systems

A three-barreled gatling gun with a 1,000- or 2,000-rd/min firing rate, developed for use aboard patrol and special forces boats. The mount weighs 168.2 kg empty and 260 kg with 800-round ammunition feed. Effective range is more than 1,500 m. The gun uses a Mk 16 Mod. 7 pintle mount, but the manufacturer, with Israel's Rafael, is offering the stabilized, powered Typhoon mounting, which weighs 630 kg loaded; it has not yet been procured for the USN.

Note: Browning M 2–series 12.7-mm machineguns in single and twin mountings are widely available for installation on U.S. Navy ships and craft, and smaller 7.62-mm machineguns are used aboard special forces boats.

C. TORPEDOES

Note: As of 9-95, the USN was said by the General Accounting Office to have had approximately 4,000 heavy torpedoes (i.e., Mk 48 series) and 14,000 lightweight (Mk 46 series and Mk 50) torpedoes in inventory. With the delivery of the last Mk 48 and Mk 50 torpedoes in 1996, the navy is not expected to require any wholly new torpedoes until 2020.

Mk 54 Mod. 0 LHT (Lightweight Hybrid Torpedo)
Bldr: Raytheon NAMS, Keyport, Wash.

Not an entirely new weapon but rather the program name for remanufactured Mk 50 and Mk 46 Mod. 5A(S) torpedoes. Initial production of 31 prototypes began in 1997, and 100 per year are to be converted from FY 01 forward until about 1,000 Mk 46 Mod. 5 and Mk 50 torpedoes are reworked. Employs the Mk 103 warhead and the propulsion system of the Mk 46 torpedo, the sensor from the Mk 50, and the variable-speed control system from the Mk 48 ADCAP; to these are added new digital data distribution, a bottom sensor, a new data processor and software, and a new outer shell. Successful trails with four prototypes were held in summer 2001, and it is planned to reach fleet use in FY 03.

Mk 50 Barracuda ALWT
Bldr: Raytheon NAMS, Keyport, Wash.

The ALWT (Advanced Lightweight Torpedo) was conceived as a replacement for the Mk 46 series and was supplied in surface-launched and air-droppable configurations. It is of roughly the same weight as the Mk 46 and of the same dimensions, but is deeper diving (in excess of 600 m), faster (more than 40 kts), employs lithium fuel, has digital guidance and control systems, and has better homing and counter-countermeasures capabilities. Due to continuing program delays, it did not enter service until 1991. Weight: 362 kg; length: 2.93 m. The program was to be terminated under FY 94, with only 1,039 total operational weapons of the originally planned 7,851 procured, but Congress required that 24 more be procured under FY 96, the last year of procurement; the last was delivered in 1999. Upgrade 1, being incorporated as of 1998, improved shallow water performance.

Mk 48 Mod. 6
Bldr: Raytheon, Keyport, Wash.

Two sequential upgrades to existing Mk 48 Mod. 5 ADCAP torpedoes are being undertaken to provide a quieter-running torpedo with upgraded guidance and control. Upgrades to the existing inventory began in 1998 and are to be completed in 2005. Raytheon received an order for 115 modification kits on 22-3-01 for delivery by end-2004. In addition, new Ada-based Block IV software began being incorporated starting in FY 01, while conversion to employ CBASS (Common Broadband Advanced Sonar System) is planned to begin in FY 05. As of fall 2001, Raytheon and the Naval Undersea Warfare Center, Newport, R.I., were developing the Mk 48 Mod. 6AT variant for export, using the same digital beamforming sonar employed by the Mk 48 Mod. 5 ADCAP and a 295-kg PBXN-5 explosive warhead; the torpedo body also incorporates an internal noise muffler and a skewed-blade shrouded propeller.

Mk 48 Mod. 5 ADCAP
Bldr: Westinghouse

The Mk 48 Mod. 5 program began in 1978 to provide a weapon with significant performance improvements over the earlier Mk 48 Mod. 4. The ADCAP (Advanced Capability) entered service in 1989; 1,427 were authorized for procurement from FY 85 through FY 94.

Diameter: 0.533 m **Length:** 5.84 m **Weight:** 1,565 kg
Warhead: 295 kg PBXN-103
Speed: More than 28 kts **Range:** 10 n.m.

Mk 48 Mod. 1/3/4
Bldrs: Westinghouse and Hughes Helicopter

The Mk 48 Mod. 1 entered service in 1972. It can be launched from a submarine against a surface target or a submarine, using its own active-passive or acoustic homing system or with a wire-guidance system. The first "Near-Term Update" Mk 48 Mod. 4 torpedo was delivered in 12-80. A total of 3,884 Mk 48s was procured through FY 85, plus 56 for Australia and 92 for the Netherlands.

Diameter: 0.533 m **Length:** 5.84 m **Weight:** 633 kg
Propulsion: 500-hp Otto-cycle swashplate engine
Speed: 55 kts **Range:** 50 km max. **Depth:** to 760 m

Mk 46 Mod. 1/2/5/6 NEARTIP
Bldr: Raytheon Systems, Mukilteo, Wash. (formerly Hughes Electronics Div., General Motors Telesystems, and previously Honeywell)

Lightweight ASW torpedo, using liquid fuel (Otto fuel) and twin, counterrotating props. Entered service in 1963. Has active-passive guidance and is launched from Mk 32 ASW torpedo tubes or as the payload of the ASROC ASW missile system. Some 25,000 of all versions of Mk 46 have been procured for 26 countries. The torpedo is planned to remain in service through 2017.

The Mk 46 Mod. 1 (surface-launched) and Mod. 2 (air-dropped) have been upgraded to Mod. 6 NEARTIP (Near-Term Improvement Program) status, with an improved acoustic homing system and countermeasures resistance. Mod. 5 torpedoes are being upgraded to Mod. 5A, with improved sonar; some 2,700 torpedoes have been updated. The Mk 46 Mod. 4 is the payload for the CAPTOR mine. A Mod. 7 upgrade program is in development, and Mk 46 shallow-water performance and service-life extension upgrades are to replace further procurement of Mk 50 torpedoes. Under FY 94, $21 million was funded to begin upgrading Mk 46 torpedoes with Mk 50 components in order to improve shallow-water performance. The first of the upgraded torpedoes is finally to enter service in 2003. The planned remanufacture rate is 16 under FY 00, 39 under FY 01, 53 under FY 02, 73 in FY 03, and 97 each in FY 04 and FY 05. Data for the Mk 46 Mod. 5 include:

Diameter: 0.324 m **Length:** 2.60 m (4.50 with ASROC booster)
Weight: 232.4 kg **Warhead:** 45.4 kg HE

Seahuntor (NT-37E)
Bldr: Raytheon NAMS, Mukilteo, Wash. (formerly Hughes Electronics Div., General Motors Telesystems; formerly Alliant)

Remanufactured and greatly improved Mk 37 homing torpedoes, available for export but not used by the USN; the last U.S. Navy Mk 37–series torpedo was retired 30-9-86. The Seahuntor is propelled by a 90-hp Otto-fuel motor. A further improvement, the NT-37F, was ordered by Egypt in 7-91; employing further improvements in guidance and controls, it has a 148-kg HBX warhead. Data for NT-37E include:

Diameter: 0.483 m **Length:** 3.467 m **Weight:** . . .
Warhead: 148 kg HE **Speed:** 35 kts **Range:** 18 km

D. MINES

Mk 52 Mod. 1/2/3/5/6: Air-dropped bottom mines. All versions are 2.75 m long and 338 mm in diameter (830 mm over fins) and carry 270 kg of HBX explosive. Mod. 1, which entered service in 1955, is a 542.5-kg acoustic mine; Mod. 2 is a 568-kg magnetic influence version; Mod. 3 is a 572.5-kg dual pressure/magnetic influence version; Mod. 5 is a 570.7-kg acoustic/magnetic influence version; and Mod. 6 is a 546-kg pressure/acoustic/magnetic influence version. All can be laid in depths of up to 47 m, except Mod. 2 to 183 m, and can be carried by USAF B-52H bombers as well as navy aircraft.

Mk 55 Mod. 2/3/5/6/7/11/12/13: Air-dropped ASW bottom mines. All versions are 2.89 kg long and 592 mm in diameter (1.03 m over fins) and carry 577 kg of HBX-1 explosive. Versions are: Mod. 2: magnetic influence, weighing 989 kg; Mod. 3: pressure/magnetic, 994 kg; Mod. 5: acoustic/magnetic, 994 kg; Mod. 6: pressure/acoustic/magnetic, 997 kg; Mod. 7: dual-channel magnetic, 996 kg; Mod. 11: magnetic or magnetic/seismic; Mod. 12: magnetic; and Mod. 13: pressure/magnetic. All can be laid in water 46 m deep, except Mods. 2 and 7 to 183 m. They can also be laid by surface ships, using portable rails. The Mk 55 entered service in 1956.

Mk 56 Mod. 0: Air-dropped ASW moored mine. Weighs 968 kg and measures 2.89 m long by 558 mm in diameter (1.06 over fins). Uses a total-field magnetic influence exploder and carries 163 kg of HBX-3 explosive. Depth: 365 m. Entered service in 1966.

WEAPONS AND SYSTEMS *(continued)*

Mk 60 CAPTOR Mod. 1: Submarine-laid or aircraft-dropped. CAPTOR = enCAPsulated TORpedo. Uses a Mk 46 Mod. 4 acoustic-homing torpedo payload. Primarily ASW in function. Development began in 1961, but service readiness was not declared until 9-79. From FY 80 through FY 86, 1,510 were authorized. The air-dropped variant weighs 1,075 kg and is 3.68 m long, the submarine-launched version weighs 932 kg and measures 3.35 m; both are 533 mm in diameter. The torpedo warhead has 43.5 kg of PXBN-103 explosive. All Mod. 0 were converted to Mod. 1 to give improved target detection and a shallower minimum depth; they have 300-m mooring depth capability. Soon to be retired.

Mk 62 DST-36 Quickstrike series Mod. 0/1/2/3/4/5: Air-dropped bottom mines. Converted from the 500-lb (227-kg) Mk 82 standard aircraft bomb. Use a TDD Mk 57 magnetic/seismic, TDD Mk 58 magnetic/seismic/pressure, TDD Mk 70 magnetic/seismic, or TDD Mk 71 pressure/magnetic/seismic fuze. Weight: 261 kg with an 87-kg H-6 explosive charge. Length: 2.26 m; diameter: 384 mm.

Mk 63 DST-40 Quickstrike series Mod. 0/1/2/3/4/5: Air-dropped bottom mines. Converted from the 1,000-lb (454-kg) Mk 83 standard aircraft bomb. Uses a TDD Mk 57 magnetic/seismic, TDD Mk 58 magnetic/seismic/pressure, TDD Mk 70 magnetic/seismic, or TDD Mk 71 pressure/magnetic/seismic fuze. Weight: 459 kg, with a 204-kg H-6 explosive charge. Length: 2.80 m; diameter: 572 mm.

Mk 64 DST-41 Quickstrike series Mod. 0/1/2/3/4/5: Air-dropped bottom mines. Converted from the 2,000-lb (908-kg) Mk 84 bomb. Uses a TDD Mk 57 magnetic/seismic, TDD Mk 58 magnetic/seismic/pressure, TDD Mk 70 magnetic/seismic, or TDD Mk 71 pressure/magnetic/seismic fuze. Weight: 902 kg, with a 429-kg H-6 explosive charge. Length: 3.67 m; diameter: 457 mm.

Mk 65 Quickstrike Mod. 0/1: Air-launched bottom mines based on the 2,000-lb (908-kg) Mk 84 bomb. Approved for service in 1983. Mod. 0 uses the Mk 57 magnetic/seismic fuze, Mod. 1 the Mk 58 magnetic/seismic/pressure fuze. Weight: 1,084 kg, with . . . kg of PBX explosive. Length: 3.25 m; diameter: 531 mm (737 mm across fins). In 1985, 1,000 were on order.

Mk 66: A practice version of CAPTOR.

GATOR: Bldr: Aerojet. An air-dropped *land* mine using CBU-78/B mines. Weighs 227 kg.

T.MMD-2: A Polish-manufactured mine, of which 100 were on order as of 2-01. Weight: 640 kg, with a 240-kg warhead. Length: 1.815 m; diameter: 572 mm.

Note: Quickstrike-series mines are to be upgraded with the Mk 71 Target-Detecting Device, which has been ready for service since 1995 but was only to begin procurement during FY 01.

The Mk 67 SLMM (Submarine-Launched Mobile Mine) began to be phased out of service in 2000 and the joint U.S./U.K./Australian ISLMM (Improved Submarine-Launched Mobile Mine) program intended to replace it was terminated during 6-00.

No surface ships are permanently equipped for minelaying except LCU 1641; portable rails have been developed and tested on a number of ship types. Naval aircraft of the S-3 and P-3 types are capable of laying mines, as are some USAF B-52H bombers. All U.S. Navy attack submarines, except early units of the SSN 688 class, can lay mines from their torpedo tubes.

E. RADARS

♦ Surface-search and navigation radars

BPS-15/15A/15H: X band. Made by Litton/Sperry Marine. Submarine search, navigational, and fire-control radar. Mounted on telescoping masts. Being updated to BPS-15H with Litton ECDIS-N (Electronic Chart Display and Information System) and Voyage Management System (VMS).

BPS-16(V): X band. Successor to the BPS-15. The first of 35 was delivered in 1990. Being upgraded to BPS-16(V) with Litton ECDIS-N (Electronic Chart Display and Information System) and Voyage Management System (VMS). Used on most SSBNs, four late SSN 688s, and the SSN 21 and SSN 773 classes.

SPS-10: C band. Made by Raytheon. Mods. B through F are in service. Was the primary surface-search set before the introduction of the SPS-55. Most have been replaced by SPS-67 in USN service.

SPS-53: X band. Made by Litton/Sperry Marine. A navigational set, replaced by later radars but still in use abroad.

SPS-55: X-band, slotted waveguide antenna. Made by Cardion. On DD 963–class destroyers, FFG 7–class frigates, *Avenger*-class minehunters, and others.

SPS-59: X band. Official designation for the Canadian Marconi LN-66 navigational radar. Most have been replaced by SPS-69, SPS-73, and other later equipment.

SPS-64: X band, except (V)4 and (V)6 are S band. Made by Raytheon. **Range:** about 48 n.m. Can automatically track 20 targets. Used by the navy in the (V)9, 15, and 18 versions; by the Coast Guard in the (V)1–4, 6–8, 10, and 11 versions; and by the army in the (V)5, 12–14, 16, and 17 versions. Commercial trade names are RM 1010, RM 1020, RM 1220, RM 1250, RM 1620, or Raypath + a four-digit number, depending on features. Uses a 6-, 9-, or 12-ft. antenna, depending on version. Being replaced by the SPS-73 in Coast Guard service.

SPS-66: X band. Raytheon 1900 Pathfinder navigational set.

SPS-67: C band. Made by DRS Technologies, Gaithersburg, Md.; formerly made by AIL Systems, a division of the Eaton Corp. (formerly Norden). A solid-state replacement for the SPS-10, using a similar antenna. Also has an ultrashort pulse mode for navigation. SPS-67(V)1 uses the SPS-10 antenna; (V)2 has new antenna with vertical beamwidth increased from 17° to 31.5°, two scan rates (15 and 30 rpm), and integrated IFF; (V)3 adds automatic detect and track, a gunfire-control interface, motion-compensated digital moving target indicator, and a track correlator/processor. More than 125 systems have been built for the USN and foreign navies. The lightweight, sturdier (V)4 antenna, in trials on DDG 53 in 1996 and now aboard all DDG 51–class destroyers, uses a bar-type antenna.

SPS-69: X band. Raytheon 1900 Pathfinder raster-scan, solid-state replacement for SPS-66, with four different antennas: R20X and R40X in radomes and R21X and R41X slotted-waveguide. Max. power: 4 kw.

SPS-73: X band. Japanese Furuno-designed radar made by Hughes Aircraft as successor to the SPS-64. Has a color display. Widely used by the Coast Guard.

SPS-. . .: DRS/Thales Nederland Scout low-probability-of-intercept surface-search and navigational radar. Being added to the CG 47 class and currently aboard the cable layer *Zeus* (T-ARC 7).

Note: The UPS-3 TDAR (Tactical Defense Alert Radar), a land-based portable set, is available for use aboard amphibious warfare ships. Japanese Furuno 8050D and 904 X-band navigational radars are widely employed on USN service craft.

♦ Two-dimensional air-search radars

SPS-40-series: B band (400–450 MHz). Made by Lockheed (SPS-40), Sperry (SPS-40A), Norden (SPS-40B), and Westinghouse (SPS-40E). Peak power: 130 kw. Beamwidth: 11° in azimuth, 19° in elevation. Range against medium bombers: 150–200 n.m. Earlier SPS-40A models with mixed tube and transistor technology were modernized to SPS-40D; all-transistor SPS-40B sets were upgraded to SPS-40C with improved low-flyer detection, higher peak power, and ECCM improvements. SPS-40E is an update to B/C/D models using a solid-state transmitter with a very low failure rate.

SPS-49: L band (851–942 MHz). Made by Raytheon. (V)1 is aboard FFG 7–class frigates; (V)2 is for the New Threat Upgrade (NTU) cruisers; (V)3 is for Canadian *Halifax*-class frigates; (V)5 is the current version, with digital pulse-doppler processing; and (V)7 is for Aegis ships. Development of the MPRFU (Medium Pulse Repetition Frequency Upgrade) was begun by Raytheon in mid-1995 under the sponsorship of the Naval Research Laboratory, adding new signal processing capabilities; the modernized radars are typed SPS-49A(V)1 and are being installed on FFGs, LSD 41/49–class landing ships, the LHD 1 class, and CVNs 68, 69, and 76.

♦ Three-dimensional air-search radars

SEAPAR (Self-defense ESSM Active Phased-Array Radar): X band. A Raytheon–Thales Nederland developmental radar intended to optimize the use of the ESSM version of the Sea Sparrow SAM. An active, electronically scanned radar that may be available by 2006, it will use technology developed for the Thales APAR and Raytheon SPY-3 radars, but in a more compact form. To be capable of horizon search to 30-km ranges and limited volume search at greater ranges, able to support four missile engagements simultaneously.

SPS-48C/E: S band (2900–3100.5 MHz). Made by ITT-Gilfillan. SPS-48C had electronic frequency scanning in elevation; the E version has doubled power, an armored antenna, reduced side-lobe levels, adaptive energy beam management, a solid-state transmitter, and three transmitter power modes. SPS-48E radars added to CG 16– and CG 26–class cruisers during the early 1980s have been recycled to ships previously equipped with SPS-48C or SPS-52C sets.

SPQ-9B: X band. Made by Northrop Grumman. Successor to the TAS/Mk 23 system. A multimode, narrowbeam, pulse-doppler radar for detection of sea-skimming missiles at the horizon. Features narrow elevation and azimuth beamwidths; variable air channel pulsewidths; fixed surface channel pulsewidth; very high clutter discrimination improvement; a high scan rate with single-scan detection and track; simultaneous air search, surface search, and beacon tracking; and built-in testing. Its initial use will be as a stand-alone system on the LPD 17 class, but it is to replace the TAS/Mk 23 on aircraft carriers. Five (with an update kit for a new, lightweight antenna) were ordered 21-2-01 for LPD 17–20, CVN 69, and backfit to the prototype SPQ-9B on a *Spruance*-class DD.

TAS/Mk 23: L band. Made by Hughes Ground Systems Group. Technically a target acquisition system, employing a rapidly rotating, stabilized, linear-array antenna in conjunction with a UYK-20 computer to counter high- and low-angle aircraft and cruise-missile attacks. Range: 20 n.m. on small missiles to 90 n.m. on aircraft. Mod. 1 is on the DD 963 class, Mod. 2 (with UYA-4 console) on the AOE 1 class, and Mod. 3 on aircraft carriers and the LHD 1 and LHA 1 classes. Can track 54 targets simultaneously.

SPY-1 Aegis system: S band. Made by Lockheed Martin (formerly R.C.A.). Obtaining a directional effect by an electronic sweep, it has four fixed phased-array antennas that provide 360° coverage. There are 4,096 transmitting and 4,352 receiving elements to the antenna array. Provides long-range air search, target tracking, and missile guidance. SPY-1B, with reduced side lobes, entered service in 1988; SPY-1C was developed for possible use on carriers and the lighter-weight SPY-1D for the DDG 51 program. SPY-1D(V), formerly SPY-1E, with greater effectiveness against sea-skimming missiles and low-observable targets in cluttered coastal waters, will be introduced on DDG 87. SPY-1F, with 8-ft.-diameter antenna faces and a total of 1,856 transmitter elements, is to be used on Norwegian *Nansen*-class frigates, while SPY-1F(V), with enhanced littoral warfare and antiship missile combat capabilities, and SPY-1K, with a 5-ft.-diameter antenna and 912 elements for use on small combatants, are on offer.

SPY-2 VSR (Volume-Search Radar): L (D) band. A complement to the SPY-3 MFR, its development contract has not yet been let, with Raytheon and Lockheed Martin competing. It is intended to be aboard the DD(X)-class destroyers and CVN 77.

SPY-3 MFR (Multi-Function Radar): I/J (X) band. A development contract for $140.4 million was awarded to Raytheon on 2-6-99 for a single multipurpose search, low-altitude target-designation, target-tracking, and target-illumination radar for use on the DD(X) class and CVN 77; it may be backfitted into CVN 70–76. In effect, it replaces the SPY-1-series Aegis radar and/or the TAS/Mk 23 and SPQ-9B. The full, 34,952-lb., $30 million system will use three 14,000-lb., 8 × 6 × 2–ft. antenna arrays, each with several thousand receiver/transmitters. The land-based test version was to be operational in 2002.

♦ Fire-control radars

Mk 86: SPG-60 and SPQ-9A radars combined into a single system. Made by Lockheed. Versions currently in use include Mod. 3, with Mk 152 computer, in the DD 963 class; Mod. 8, with UYK-7 computer, in the German DDG 2 class; Mod. 9, without the SPG-60 radar, in Aegis cruisers; Mod. 10, an upgrade to Mod. 3 substituting the UYK-7 computer; Mod. 11 (now inactivated), an upgraded Mod. 3 for the LHA 1 class; and Mod. 12, an upgraded Mod. 5.

Mk 90: Technically, the fire-control *system* for the General Dynamics Mk 15 Phalanx CIWS. Uses two radar antennas, one to track the target and one to track the outgoing stream of projectiles.

Mk 92: X band. Made by Paramax. USN adaptation of the Dutch Hollandse Signaal Apparaaten (now Thales Nederland) WM-20 series track-while-scan gun/missile fire-control system, itself designated the Mk 94. Used in the FFG 7 class and on Coast Guard cutters. Search and fire-control antennas are dual mounted in an egg-shaped radome. Is combined with a STIR (Separate Target Illumination Radar—a modified SPG-60) antenna in the FFG 7 class. An improvement program in FFG 7 ended Phase I in 1984. Phase II CORT (Coherent Receive/Transmit) was intended to further update the system; six sets were authorized under FY 88 (one as a trainer)

WEAPONS AND SYSTEMS *(continued)*

and the first installed on FFG 61 and FFG 36. Further CORT upgrades were canceled. The radar antenna in all versions is the Mk 53 Mod. 0. The Mk 92 Mod. 1 is in Coast Guard ships; Mod. 2 is a version designed for use with the STIR second-channel director in the FFG 7 class; Mod. 5 was the version for use on the Saudi Arabian PCG and PCC classes; and Mod. 6 is the CORT upgrade program version for use with the SYS-2 integrated automatic detection and tracking system.

Mk 95: Used with the Mk 91 fire-control *system* for the Sea Sparrow SAM system, with either one (Mod. 0) or two (Mod. 1) radar directors per Mk 29 launcher. The radar has separate transmitter and receiver antennas mounted on the same pedestal.

SPG-51B/C/D: Standard SM-1 MR illuminator-tracker; used with the Mk 74 missile fire-control system.

SPG-55A/B: Standard SM-2 ER illuminator-tracker; used with the Mk 76 missile fire-control system.

SPG-60: X band. Made by Lockheed Martin. Standard SM-1 MR missile system, four-horn monopulse, pulse-doppler illuminator-tracker for guns in conjunction with Mk 86 GFCS. The STIR (Separate Target Illumination Radar) version, used on the FFG 7 class, is modified for use with Mk 92 Mod. 2 missile/gun-control system. Can track Mach 3.0 targets to 183 km. Has a co-mounted t.v. tracker.

SPG-62: X band. Made by Raytheon. Standard SM-2 illuminator; used with the Aegis system in the CG 47 class. Slaved to the SPY-1 Aegis system.

SPQ-9: X band. Made by Lockheed. Track-while-scan special surface search and weapons control for use with Mk 86 GFCS. Antenna is mounted in a spherical radome. Range: 36 km. Received moving target indicator and "low-noise front end" kits starting in 1989.

♦ Air-control radars

SPN-35A: X band. Made by ITT-Gilfillan. Blind-approach radar, with its antenna in a large spherical radome. The ship-based version of the TPN-8.

SPN-42: Ka-band ACLS (Automated Carrier Landing System) radar with X-band beacon receiver for aircraft marshaling on LHD 1 and LHA 1 classes.

SPN-43A/B: S band (3590–3700 MHz). Made by ITT-Gilfillan. The two-dimensional marshaling component of a landing system that also employs the SPN 42 or Textron SPN-46(V) controlling radar. Can also be used as a backup air-search radar. Range is about 50 n.m. Had replaced SPN-35 installations in carriers by 1996.

SPN-46(V): Ka (33.0–33.4 GHz) and X band. Made by Textron. Low-probability-of-intercept air traffic control replacement for SPN-42, using the same AS-1347 antenna. Installed in pairs.

F. ELECTRONIC WARFARE COUNTERMEASURES SYSTEMS

Note: This section lists alphabetically systems classified as "countermeasures" by the U.S. Navy, including active and passive electronic systems; mine countermeasures systems are listed separately at the end of this section.

ADC Mk 1–5, 7–10: Various expendable, submarine-launched decoys, most self-propelled.

APR-39: Litton Applied Technology Division helicopter radar-warning set, adapted for use on *Cyclone*-class patrol craft. The commercial version, Triton, has been sold to Egypt.

AR-900: Commercial foreign sales system by the ArgoSystems division of Boeing. Offers 360° intercept coverage from 2 to 18 GHz with 2–3° accuracy. Can track 500 emitters and has a library of up to 5,000 signals. The company also offers the CLOAC (Compact Lightweight Omnidirectional Active Countermeasures) system, APECS-II (Advanced Programmable Electronic Countermeasures System), and MAP (Maritime Patrol) system, as well as the earlier AR-700 system.

BLQ-10: Made by Lockheed Martin, Syracuse, N.Y. Integrated EW system for the SSN 774–class submarine program; it may be backfitted to the SSN 21 class and to some units of the SSN 688 class. The first at-sea tests were held early in FY 00.

Note: The BLQ-11 LMRS (Long-term Mine Reconnaissance System) is discussed in the Mine Countermeasures Devices section.

BLR-1 through -10, -13, -15: Radar warning systems for submarines.

BLR-14 BSAWS (Basic Submarine Acoustic Warfare System): Made by Sperry. Used to detect, evade, and counter torpedoes, employing the WLR-9A/12 detection systems and WLR-14 processor. Also directs the launching of countermeasures.

BZA (Beach Zone Array): A 45 × 45–m explosive net to clear beach landing zones of antipersonnel mines. Deployed via a GPS-navigated glider from a CH-53E helicopter. In development.

COBLU (Cooperative Outboard Logistics Update): An improved version of the SRS-1A system, to enter service in 2000 on new *Arleigh Burke* Flight IIA destroyers. See also the entry for the SSQ-108.

CSA Mk 2: Countermeasures launching system for submarines, employing the Mk 151 launcher. Employed in ballistic-missile and SSN 637– and SSN 688–class submarines.

Mk 30: A submarine target simulator, rather than an operational decoy. Made by Goodyear Aerospace. In service since 1978. The torpedo-like device, 6.223 m long and 533 mm in diameter, has an endurance of 30 minutes at 30 kts or up to 4 hours at 7 kts and is capable of operating at depths between 7.6 and 610 m. It can be preprogrammed to perform three-dimensional maneuvers or can be controlled by external acoustic signals. For training runs, it is tracked by acoustic or magnetic sensors. It can emit acoustic signals or provide a specific magnetic signature. Only 16 were made, and they are operated at the Barking Sands Underwater Test Range, Hawaii; Atlantic Undersea Test and Evaluation Center (AUTEC), Bahamas; and Atlantic Fleet Warfare Training Facility, St. Croix.

Mk 33/34 RBOC (Rapid-Blooming Offboard Chaff): Chaff launcher, now largely replaced by the Mk 36. Mk 33 employed four Mk 135 launchers and was used by frigate-size and larger ships; Mk 34 employed only two launchers.

Mk 36 SRBOC: "Super RBOC." The Mod. 1 version, with two 6-tube mortars, is for ships under 140 m in length, and the Mod. 2, with four 6-tube mortars, is for larger ships. Both types use 130-mm Mk 182 chaff-dispensing cartridges, which climb to 244 m; NATO Sea Gnat Mk 241 seduction and Mk 216 distraction rounds; and the Mk 245 Mod. 0 GIANT three-part infrared decoy. SRBOC employs the Mk 137 sextuple launcher, with tubes fixed at 45° or 60° elevation. Sippican purchased the Hycor firm that developed and initially manufactured the system, and Sippican was taken over by Raytheon Systems. Several different decoys are in development for launching from the SRBOC system, including the HIRAM-III (Hycor Infrared Anti-Missile) decoy, TORCH floating infrared decoy, CAD radar simulator, ALEX (Automatic Launch of Expendables), and the Sippican–Office of Naval Research Multicloud projectile. Super Chaffstar is the commercial name for the Mk 241 Sea Gnat round. The parachute-equipped Mk 251 Siren active decoy round entered Royal Navy use during 2001.

A Launchable-Expendable Acoustic Decoy (LEAD) torpedo decoy round entered service in 10-99; it employs Mk 12 rocket-powered and Mk 15 mortar rounds, both for use with Mk 137 launchers. The Naval Research Laboratory has developed the Multicloud multistage infrared decoy for the Mk 137 launcher to provide a more realistic decoy to incoming seeker systems.

Mk 53 SRBOC: Employs four twin, fixed, vertical launch containers to fire Mk 214 and Mk 215 Nulka hovering decoy rockets. The launchers were originally to have been added to the Mk 137 launchers of the Mk 36 SRBOC system but are being installed in a separate group. The first 11 launchers were ordered during 2-99 for use on refitting CG 47–class cruisers and DDG 51–class destroyers.

Mk 70 MOSS (Mobile Submarine Simulator): Small torpedo-like device for launch by *Ohio*-class SSBNs.

SALAD (Shipboard Automatic Liquid Agent Detection): Detects traces of chemical, biological, and radiological agents. Tests were completed in 6-98, with eight sets to be ordered initially and 255 ultimately for installation on all surface ships. A production contract has not yet been placed.

Sea Nymph: Modular submarine SIGINT package; numerical designation not available.

SLA-12: Passive D/F and EW receiver used in conjunction with ULQ-6 and SLQ-22/23/24. Fixed and trainable antenna arrays.

SLA-15: Trainable tracker array for ULQ-6. No longer in USN service.

SLQ-20B: Programmable shipboard signal processor system, made by BAE Systems; an adjunct to the SLQ-32-series intercept systems. Used aboard CVNs and CG 47–class guided-missile cruisers.

SLQ-25 Nixie: Towed noisemaker, made by Northrop Grumman (formerly Aerojet). Employs two winches, each with one towed body and one acting as a spare. It is being updated to SLQ-25A with an active component to defeat torpedo influence fuzes. SLQ-25B adds a towed torpedo detection array, an SLX-1 Multi-Sensor Torpedo Recognition and Alertment Processor (MSTRAP), and the Launched Expendable Acoustic Decoy (LEAD), the latter to be launched by the Raytheon (ex-Sippican, ex-Hycor) Mk 137 launchers of the Mk 36 and Mk 50 SRBOC decoy systems.

SLQ-29: The combined WLR-1H/WLR-8/WLR-11 package.

SLQ-32(V)1: Raytheon radar warning (H, I, and J bands) for auxiliaries and amphibious ships. Most have now been upgraded to (V)2.

SLQ-32(V)2: Radar warning (B–J bands) for newer destroyers and frigates. It replaced WLR-1 where it had been fitted.

SLQ-32A(V)3: Radar warning (B–J bands) *and* jamming/spoofing (H–J bands) for cruisers and major amphibious ships.

SLQ-32A(V)4: Replacement for SLQ-17 on carriers.

SLQ-32A(V)5: SLQ-32(V)2 with a Sidekick active jammer adjunct.

SLQ-33: Ship-towed acoustic deception device.

SLQ-34: The Classic Outboard (Organizational Unit Tactical Baseline Operational Area Radio Detection Countermeasures Exploitation) intelligence collection system, with SRD-19 D/F and SLR-16. Carried in 28 ships. Being superseded by the Combat D/F system, which will be carried by later units of the DDG 51 class.

Note: Mine countermeasures associated SLQ-series systems are described under Mine Countermeasures.

SLQ-39: Chaff-dispensing buoy, made by Raytheon.

SLQ-41 through -47: Active expendable EW buoys.

SLQ-49: Known as "Rubber Duck." Air- or surface-launched inflatable decoy, the U.S. version of the British DLF(2). Some 1,650 were procured from Irvin Aerospace. Decoys weigh 68 kg each in GRP containers and are deployed from overside launchers. In 1999, the USN was evaluating DLF(3), which can create the illusion of a 50,000-m^2 target. A normal complement is 70 buoys per ship in the Royal Navy.

SLQ-50: The Battle Group Passive Horizon-Extension System (BGPHES), made by E-Systems. Employs an airborne passive intercept detector and a shipboard processing system comprising three UYQ-23 terminals.

SLQ-650: Small-ship EW system using the SLR-640 intercept and SLQ-630 jammer.

SLR-16: HF SIGINT receiver set using SRD-19 antenna arrays; part of the SSQ-72 Classic Outboard system. Made by Lockheed Martin (formerly Southwestern Research).

SLR-23: Intercept D/F (J band). Works with WLR-1 and SLQ-32. Made by Lockheed Martin (formerly Southwestern Research).

SLR-24: Towed torpedo detection array. In service since 1995 on the *Nimitz* (CVN 68).

SLR-600: EW intercept system (2–20 GHz) for small ships.

SLR-610: Another small-ship EW intercept system (6.5–22 GHz).

SLR-640: Improved SLR-610.

SLT-5 and -8: Communications jammers.

SLX-1 MSTRAP (Multi-Sensor Torpedo Recognition and Alertment Processor): Westinghouse processor, using existing sonar suites to provide alerting data to countermeasures against antiship torpedoes. Trials were conducted during 1997 aboard the *Arleigh Burke* (DDG 51). In 5-99, 14 production sets were ordered from Northrop Grumman Oceanic and Naval Systems for delivery by 3-00.

SLY-2 AIEWS (Advanced Integrated Electronic Warfare System): Being developed as the successor to the SLQ-32 series under a 1998 contract by Lockheed Martin. To be installed in the CG 47–class cruisers, DDG 51– and DD 21–class destroyers, the LPD 17 and other amphibious ship classes, and aircraft carriers. Will employ COTS (Commercial-Off-The-Shelf) components and other existing hardware and software. To undergo sea trials in 2002. Formerly was designated SLQ-52.

WEAPONS AND SYSTEMS *(continued)*

SRD-19: The Classic Outboard system's LF/MF/VHF shipboard SIGINT exploitation component, using 24 small deck-edge antennas, whip antennas, and a masthead Adcock-type VHF D/F array. It is used in conjunction with SLR-16 as part of the SSQ-72 system. Made by Lockheed Martin (formerly by Southwestern Research).

SRS-1: Combat D/F Block 0. A less-elaborate version of SSQ-72/108 Classic Outboard to detect, process, and target threat signals. Made by Lockheed Martin (formerly Southwestern Research Inst.). SRS-1A adds the Automated Digital Acquisition Subsystem to exploit "unconventional and low-probability-of-intercept signals." SRS-1 is in the *Wasp* (LHD 1)-class amphibious ships and *Arleigh Burke* Flight II (DDG 72 and later) and Flight IIA destroyers. SRS-1A is to be backfitted or fitted in the same ships and three shore stations.

SSQ-72: Classic Outboard Combat D/F suite, with SRD-19 and SLR-16 antennas (the later SSQ-74 is on DD 974). SSQ-108 is a more elaborate version, of which more were acquired.

SSQ-95(V): Active Electronic Buoy (AEB) by Litton/Magnavox. Fits in an A-size sonobuoy housing and inflates in the water; has a seawater-activated battery. Weighs 17.2 kg and is 0.914 m long.

SSQ-108: Classic Outboard (Organizational Unit Tactical Baseline Operational Area Radio Detection Countermeasures Exploitation System) Combat D/F suite, made by Sanders Surveillance Systems; the current version of SSQ-72, used by the USN and the Royal Navy. Sanders received a contract to update 35 USN and British systems with a COBLU (Cooperative Outboard Logistics Update) in 6-00. Operates in the HF, UHF, and VHF bands. COBLU is to be installed on some CG 47–class and all *Arleigh Burke* Flight IIA ships by 2005.

SSTDS (Surface Ship Torpedo Decoy System): An umbrella program encompassing towed and hull-mounted sensors to detect torpedoes and, for highly valuable ships such as aircraft carriers, launchers for modified Mk 46 ASW torpedoes to counter Russian Type 65-80 wake-homing torpedoes; the first 172 production active countermeasures were procured under the FY 93 budget. Phase I, introduced in 1987, employed the SLQ-25A Nixie. Deliveries of Phase II, with the SLR-24 detector, were to begin in 1992. Raytheon received a contract in 1-92 to develop the DCLASP (Detection-Classification-Localization Acoustic Signal Processor) in connection with the SSTDS program. A parallel program with the U.K. was canceled in 7-94. The U.S. program, with the SLR-24 processor and modified Mk 46 torpedoes, did not pass operational evaluation during mid-1994, and a new joint U.K.-U.S. development program contract planned to be let in 1-95 was canceled in 9-96, leaving USN ships still vulnerable to modern antiship torpedoes.

T Mk 6 Fanfare: Mechanical towed antitorpedo noisemaker. No longer in USN service but still used by foreign fleets.

TRAFS (Torpedo Recognition and Alertment Functional Segment): An adjunct added to eight *Ticonderoga*-class CGs and nine *Spruance*-class DDs by 12-99 that integrates sensors of the SQQ-89 sonar suite to provide a torpedo detection and countermeasures capability. An outgrowth of the Northrop Grumman SLX-1 program.

ULQ-6: Deception repeater/jammer, in cruisers and destroyers. Has been largely replaced by SLQ-32(V)3 in high-value ships, but is still in use on a few ships transferred abroad.

ULQ-21: Function uncertain. As of 12-00, 371 sets were in use.

Ultrabarricade: A trainable, elevatable decoy launcher, made by Wallop in the U.K. The initial U.S. installation is on PC 14. Several dozen launchers are to be purchased during 2000 and more in the future as a replacement for the SRBOC system. The launcher carries 24 quick-reaction 102-mm rocket decoys in groups of three, plus two tube-launchers; it trains through 270° and elevates to 70°. The system fires 20- to 80-m-range seduction, 400- to 600-m-range dump, 800- to 1,000-m-range distraction, and 1,800- to 12,000-m-range confusion decoys and can also launch illumination rockets, torpedo decoys, and potentially small artillery rockets, point-defense missiles, active offboard decoys, and laser and optical obscurants.

URD-9(V): Radar D/F (225–400 MHz).

URD-27: Broadcast frequency D/F device for SIGINT (250 MHz–18 GHz).

WLQ-4E: Sea Nymph ESM system, developed by GTE-Sylvania. WLQ-4(V)1 is used by the SSN 21 class.

WLR-1H(V)7: Obsolescent intercept and analysis system still aboard CV 67 and CVN 65.

WLR-3: Radar warning and signal collection, installed in ships and also in some submarines.

WLR-4: ESM receiver.

WLR-5: Acoustic intercept receiver.

WLR-6: Reconnaissance signal collection system; called "Waterboy" in submarines. Made by Aitken Industries.

WLR-8: Radar warning system covering 0.5–18 GHz. The (V)2 version is in the SSN 688 class, (V)5 in *Ohio*-class SSBNs. A surface-ship version was canceled in 1983, although one (V)3 set was installed in the *Enterprise* (CVN 65). Made by GTE-Sylvania.

WLR-9: Sonar detection system.

WLR-10: Radar warning receiver for submarines. Shares the telescoping mast array with WLR-8(V)2/5.

WLR-11A: Radar warning/SIGINT system (7–18 GHz). Uses the WLR-1's antenna suite.

WLR-13: Infrared/electro-optical warning receiver.

WSQ-5: Portable ELINT collection system for SSN 688 class; known as Cluster Spectator. Made by Watkins-Johnson.

WSQ-11: An active torpedo countermeasure antitorpedo torpedo system known as Tripwire intended to intercept and destroy attacking torpedoes at ranges up to 5,000 yards. Will be mounted on carriers, large combatants, and major amphibious warfare ships and will use 160-mm launch tubes or modified CSA Mk 2 submarine countermeasures launch tubes. To enter service around 2011.

G. SONARS

♦ Bottom-array sonars

ADS (Advanced Deployable System): Under development by Lockheed Martin Federal Systems; to become operational around 2004. Would be deployed by small-craft operating from amphibious ships or laid by submarines or aircraft in littoral areas to provide protection from quiet submarines and minelaying activities. The demonstration contract was signed in 4-95, at which time production contracts were planned for FY 01 or FY 02.

FDS-C (Fixed Distributed Systems–COTS): Being developed from the canceled FDS program. Uses an Underwater Segment (UWS) in development by Lucent and an associated Shore Signal and Information Processing System (SSIPS) is under development by Lockheed Martin. Would employ fixed, bottom-deployed sensor arrays either in deep-ocean areas or across choke points and could also be deployed in strategic shallow-water areas. To use an all fiber-optic passive hydrophone array. Essentially a successor to the SOSUS system.

SOSUS (Sound Surveillance System): Currently supported by Lucent for the sensor arrays and Lockheed Martin for the shore-based signal processing. For detection and tracking of submarines, surface ships, fish, marine mammals, and seismic events. Originally developed in the 1950s and continuously modified and updated since.

♦ Surface ship sonars

Distant Thunder: BBN Technologies completed trials with four sets of its Distant Thunder developmental sonar for DARPA early in 1998. The system provides a low-frequency, multistatic active sonar for organic rapid area search and localization of quiet diesel-electric submarines in "acoustically adverse" waters. Trials with 10 upgraded versions in South Korean waters during 1999 were said to be extremely successful.

LBVDS (Lightweight Broadband Variable-Depth Sonar): Lockheed Martin developmental program for a 1- to 6-kHz, active, towed sonar array originally intended for use with the SQQ-89(V)15 sonar suite on the DD 21 class. It is intended to improve submarine detection to ranges of 12–15 n.m. in shallow waters.

MFTA (Multi-Function Towed Array): Towed array system for use on DDG 51–class units post-2005 and later on the DD(X) class in conjunction with the SQQ-89(V)15 sonar suite. The array would have high-, medium-, and low-frequency modules, a dual-density tow cable, and the existing tow winch from the SQR-19 system.

SLR-24: A towed linear passive torpedo detection sensor, in service since 1995 aboard the *Nimitz* (CVN 68) as part of the CST Mk 1 torpedo countermeasures system.

SQQ-14: High-frequency, minehunting, and classification set in a variable-depth, retractable transducer array for mine countermeasures ships. Essentially combines the 1950s-era UQS-1 for detection and the U.K.-developed Type 193 sonar for classification. Frequency: 80 kHz in search mode; 350 kHz for classification. A retractable strut version deployed to 46 m, the cable-deployed version currently in use to 120 m. Entered service in 1960. No longer in USN service, but is still found on ships transferred abroad, and it has been made under license in Italy.

SQQ-28: LAMPS-III helicopter datalink processing system; not a sonar, but employed in ASW.

SQQ-30: Minehunting sonar developed by General Electric for use on mine countermeasures ships. Essentially a digital, solid-state SQQ-14, using cable-tow transducer deployment to greater depths. Superseded by SQQ-32.

SQQ-32: Raytheon-Thales sonar for later units of the MCM 1 class and for the MSH 1 class. Separate detection and classification transducers are lowered through a well and towed deep below the hull. Uses two UYK-44 computers. Performed extremely well during operations in the Persian Gulf in 1991.

SQQ-89: Suite integrating the SQR-19 towed array, SQS-53B hull-mounted sonar, Mk 116 Underwater Fire Control System, LAMPS-III helicopter, SQQ-28 processor, and UYQ-28 SIMAS (Sonar In-Situ Mode Assessment System) for cruisers, destroyers, and frigates. Trialed in DD 980 in late 1985. An Acoustic Video Processor was added under FY 90. Its planned successor, SQQ-89I, has been redesignated SQY-1 (q.v.).

The SQQ-89(V)6 baseline system incorporated the USQ-132 Tactical Decision Support System, UYQ-25 SIMAS II, USH-XX System Level Recorder, and SQQ-89 Adjunct Processor, with one TAC-3 and one UYQ-65 workstations. Backfits to earlier installations of SQQ-89 include Block I, with a multisensor torpedo warning feature linked to decoy systems; Block II, for shallow-water operations, with an echo tracker classifier and reduced false-target generation; Block III, a multistatic upgrade and acoustic processor to provide below-the-layer processing of sonar signals from the active sonar on the helicopter and the SQS-53C sonar; and Block IV, which added a broadband variable-depth sonar capability. DDG 91 and later are to have the SQQ-89(V)15, which will incorporate controls and displays for the WLD-1(V)1 remote minehunting vehicle system. The 100th SQQ-89-series system was installed on DDG 87.

SQR-17: Passive classification device for processing data transmitted from sonobuoys via the now-retired SH-2G SeaSprite LAMPS-I helicopters in Naval Reserve FFG 7–class frigates. Uses the SKR-4 link receiver, AKT-22 link, ARR-75 sonobuoy receiver, and UYS-1 processor. For shipboard use, 97 sets were procured by 1989 (far more than ever would have been needed), plus 16 for Naval Reserve Mobile Inshore Undersea Warfare units.

SQR-18A TACTAS (Tactical Towed Acoustic Sensor): Built by EDO; 47 sets had been delivered by 1989. Twelve more SQR-18A were ordered in 6-88 for use on the now-deactivated FF 1052 class equipped with SQS-35 VDS; the array was attached to the VDS towed body. Normal cable length: 1,706 m; towed at depths up to 366 m. The array is 82.6 mm in diameter and 222.5 m long. SQR-18(V)1, with 730 m of cable, was aboard 35 FF 1052–class ships; it used eight modular hydrophone sections. SQR-18A(V)2 used an SQR-19 towing rig for the non-VDS-equipped units of the FF 1052 class and had a 1,524-m tow cable. SQR-18 is no longer in use by the USN.

SQR-19A/B: Improved TACTAS for use on the CG 47, DD 963, and FFG 7 classes. It is deployed through a port in the stern; cable length: 1,707 m. Has 16 acoustic reception modules in the array: eight VLF, four LF, two MF, and two HF. Uses a UYQ-21 display. SQR-19A has UYH-3 data storage. SQR-19B has four UYK-44 computers vice UYK-20 and began deliveries in 1-91. Most have been stored ashore due to the USN's de-emphasis on ASW, changes in operating areas, and fiscal constraints.

WEAPONS AND SYSTEMS *(continued)*

SQS-26: Bow-mounted, low-frequency set, in AXR, BX, and CX versions. Transmits at around 3.5 kHz and receives at between 1.5 and 4.0 kHz. No longer in USN use but is found on *Knox*-class frigates transferred abroad.

SQS-53: SQS-26 with a digital computer interface, for use with the Mk 116 UWFCS (Underwater Fire Control System) on the DD 963, DDG 993, and CG 47 classes. The digital SQS-53B, made by General Electric/Hughes Electronics, has multiple target tracking and classification aids, weapons checkout routines, UYK-44 imbedded computers, a UYQ-21 display, a UYS-1 signal processor, a 60% reduction in required manning, a 2,000-hour mean time between failures, and a 30-minute mean time to repair. The SQS-53C has improved active performance, simultaneous active/passive modes, more power, greater bandwidth, UYH-1 mass memory, faster reaction time, and so forth. The SQS-53C Kingfisher/SWAK (Shallow-Water Active Kit) provided a 120° forward-arc mine-avoidance capability at 2.5-, 5-, 10-, and 20-kiloyard range scales; EC-16 (Engineering Change 16) added the same capability to SQS-53A/B ships (DDG 993–996 and CG 47–55). EC-84 added the same capability to the DD 963 class. The first 10 of the latest variant, the SQS-53D, were ordered 30-12-96.

SQS-56: USN variant of the Raytheon 1160B commercial active-passive, hull-mounted, medium-frequency set; used in FFG 7 class. Operates at 5.6, 7.5, and 8.4 kHz. All active units have been or will be equipped with Kingfisher mine-avoidance system covering a 90° forward arc; EC-10 added the SWAK (Shallow-Water Active Kit) with additional display capabilities to the 12 FFGs with the CORT combat system upgrade.

SQS-58: Made by Raytheon. Special set for the private R&D trials ship *Sub Sig II;* solid-state MF set, offered for export sale as the DE 1167 system.

SQY-1: Successor system to SQQ-89, with first installations to be in later units of the DDG 51 class. Initially called SQQ-89I and later SQQ-89(V)X. Still in development, it will employ about 50% commercial-off-the-shelf (COTS) computers and software (and later 100% COTS equipment) for sonar signal processing, fire control, and training. Both versions will employ Link 16 to link with MH-60R helicopters and their sonar sensors.

UQQ-2 SURTASS (Surveillance Towed-Array Sonar System): For use in the *Stalwart* (T-AGOS 1) class. Tows a 1,830-m passive hydrophone array at about 3 kts. A Twin Line dual-array version has been employed by the *Bold* (T-AGOS 12) since 1994, and later by the *Assertive* (T-AGOS 9), to detect small diesel submarines in waters as shallow as 50 m. Funding for six more Twin Line arrays was acquired under the FY 00 budget; they are to be cross-decked to ships for operation in littoral waters. Original UQQ-2 arrays are being refurbished to A-180R status with COTS telemetry and 180 acoustic channels.

♦ Submarine sonars

AMDS (Advanced Mine Detector Sonar): A chin-mounted active sonar for the *Los Angeles* class; installed for trials in the *Asheville* (SSN 758). The configuration includes a large-diameter horizontal array with two protruding transducer domes.

BQG-5A Wide Aperture Array (WAA): The BQG-5 passive sonar receiving set was demonstrated aboard the *Augusta* (SSN 710) in 1985, is fitted in the *Seawolf* (SSN 21), and was backfitted in one SSN 688I–class unit in 1997. The more affordable BQG-5A was ordered 27-12-95 from Lockheed Martin Federal Systems, working in cooperation with Raytheon, Northrop Grumman, and Litton Industries, and is being fitted on other SSN 688I-series and SSN 774–class submarines. BQG-5A uses COTS equipment and a repackaged UYQ-70 display console. The first system was to be delivered early in 1999.

BQQ-5: Active-passive system on the SSN 21– and SSN 688–class attack submarines and on *Parche* (SSN 683). Incorporates a BQS-11, -12, or -13 spherical bow hydrophone array. BQQ-5C has expanded DIFAR reception. BQQ-5D, with the TB-23 long-aperture, thin-line array, was operational in 1988. BQQ-5E is integrated with the TB-29 thin-line towed passive array. BQQ-5E(V)4, with no active element, is the suite used by later units of the *Ohio*-class SSBNs.

BQQ-6: Passive-only version of the BQQ-5 system, for earlier units of the SSBN 726 class. Has 944 hydrophone transducers mounted on a spherical frame.

BQQ-9: Towed array signal-processing system for BQR-15; made by Rockwell. Also known as the TASPE (Towed Array Signal Processing Equipment) on the *Ohio*-class SSBN.

BQQ-10 ARCI (Acoustic Rapid COTS Insertion): Sonar suite to update and coordinate existing BSY-1 and BQQ-5 or BQQ-6 sonar equipment in the SSN 688/688I classes. Made by Lockheed Martin, Manassas, Va.

BQR-15: Towed array sonar system in the *Ohio*-class SSBNs. Uses a 45.7-m-long array of 42 hydrophones towed by a 670-m cable.

BQR-19: Active, short-range, navigational set for SSBNs. Made by Raytheon.

BQR-23: STASS (Submarine Towed Array Sonar System) processor. Current version: BQR-23A.

BQS-13: Active component of the BQQ-5 system; uses low-frequency transmission (around 3.5 kHz). Made by Raytheon.

BQS-15: Under-ice active set tailored to the requirements of the SSN 688 class.

BQS-20: HF under-ice and mine-avoidance set, used mostly on later SSNs. Part of the BQQ-2, -5, and -6 systems.

BQS-24 MIDAS (Mine Detection and Avoidance Sonar): Active set for the SSN 688 class and for *Ohio*-class SSBNs.

BSY-1 SUBACS: The "basic" BSY-1 is the suite for SSN 651–773. It uses a UYS-1 signal processor, USH-26 signal recorder, and UYK-20A data processor and has passive arrays, plus SADS (Submarine Active Detection Sonar, i.e., BQS-24) and a towed passive array. IBM is the prime contractor. The first suite was delivered in 7-87; SSN 756 and later have full capabilities.

BSY-2: For the *Seawolf* class, BSY-2 uses distributed processing and has six ship data displays and 11 consoles. Associated sensors include an external spherical bow array, an LF array inside the bow, an active hemispherical array in the lower part of the bow, an HF active array (BQS-24) in the sail, the BQG-5 Wide Aperture Array on the flank, the long TB-12X towed array, and a shorter TB-16D towed array. General Electric is the prime contractor.

WLY-1: Acoustic intercept system for the SSN 774 class, used to provide target identification, range, and bearing.

♦ Helicopter sonars

AQS-14: Mine countermeasures set used by MH-53E helicopters. It is to be updated to AQS-14A with a laser E/O scanner; an initial 1-year development contract was issued to Northrop Grumman during 5-99.

AQS-20: Towed mine detection set for the MH-53E to replace AQS-14 and for use by the MH-60S multipurpose helicopter. Made by Raytheon (formerly Westinghouse, with EDO and ARINC). It is also to be developed for use as a mine warning sensor for surface ships and will be integrated into the Boeing BLQ-11 Long-term Mine Reconnaissance System (LMRS), along with an airborne laser minehunting system, an airborne mine neutralization system, a shallow-water influence minesweep system, and the Rapid Airborne Mine Countermeasures System; this version is planned to enter service in 2005 for use in waters 30 to 600 ft. deep. An AQS-20X version with a laser mine identification feature is also planned, for tow by the MH-60S helicopter; the volume-search sonar is replaced by an Areté Associates E/O mine identification device.

AQS-22: Hughes Undersea Systems–Thales FLASH (Folding Light Acoustic Sonar for Helicopters) for up to 185 SH-60B and 158 SH-60F helicopters (where it replaces AQS-13). Also known as ALFS (Airborne Low-Frequency Sonar).

Note: Under development as a helicopter-borne antisubmarine sensor is the Kaman April Showers pod-mounted blue-green laser, which can be employed at altitudes of up to 10,000 ft. and at speeds to 200 kts.

♦ Sonobuoys

A wide variety of sonobuoys is in use, including the following, which are current production:

- SSQ-36 bathythermograph
- SSQ-53D DIFAR
- SSQ-57 special-purpose
- SSQ-62B DICASS (Directional Command-Activated Sonobuoy System)
- SSQ-75 ERAPS (Expendable Reliable Acoustic Path Sonobuoy), which descends to as much as 16,000-ft. depths
- SSQ-77A/B VLAD (Vertical Line-Array DIFAR)
- SSQ-86 DLC
- SSQ-102 ADAR TSS (Air-Deployed Active Receiver Tactical Surveillance Sonar), a bistatic/multistatic sonobuoy that can work with a shipboard sonar acting as its illuminator
- SSQ-110 EER (Extended Echo Ranging), which drops charges on demand to create echoes

In addition, SSQ-71 and SSQ-86 are two-way, aircraft/submarine communications buoys.

H. ELECTRO-OPTICAL SYSTEMS

IRST (Infrared Search and Track): System that provides automatic surveillance, detection, and tracking of a variety of potential targets, plus detection of low-altitude antiship missiles. Made by Lockheed Martin, Orlando, Fla., and Raytheon Systems, El Segundo, Calif. At-sea trials were held in 1999, with fleet introduction planned for FY 03. The USN is decades behind other countries in this field, having tried and discarded several unsuccessful systems since the 1980s. IRST Phase II employs a Raytheon-SAGEM on-mast sensor and Lockheed Martin belowdecks signal processor; trials were to start on the *Anzio* (CG 68) and *Cape St. George* (CG 71) in 3-99.

Mk 46 Mod. 0: Optronic gunfire-control and surveillance system, mounted on DDG 51–class destroyers. Made by Kollmorgen. An improved Mod. 1 variant is aboard DDG 85 and later.

TISS (Thermal Imaging Sensor System): Modular system ordered in 10-95 from Boeing, Huntington Beach, Calif. Some 24 were procured for deployment aboard frigates and destroyers attached to the 5th Fleet in the Middle East.

I. TACTICAL DATA PROCESSING

Project Akcita

Not an acronym, the name Akcita was taken from the Lakota Sioux Indian tribal self-defense force. Intended to provide an integrated air defense system for the CVN 76–class carriers, DD 21–class destroyers, and LPD 17–class landing ships, Akcita will incorporate elements of a multifunction radar, the Evolved Sea Sparrow missile, and the Advanced Integrated Electronic Warfare System (AIEWS), which will include advanced decoys such as the Australian Nulka. The first unit to have the system is expected to be LPD 22, completing after 2006. The new D-band radar will incorporate monolithic microwave integrated-circuit technology and will be able to track more than 1,000 targets to ranges of 400 km. Akcita will incorporate and supersede the technology of the earlier Ship Self-Defense System.

ULQ-20 BGPHES-ST

BGPHES = Battle Group Passive Horizon-Extension System. In development for over a decade by Navy SPAWAR and Raytheon, it is intended to extend battle-group passive threat detection range to 900 n.m. by controlling remote receivers on a deployed aircraft, with data transmitted to the flagship's surface terminal via the Common High Bandwidth Data Link (CHBDL). Will be interoperable with USAF U-2R reconnaissance aircraft and was to have been installed in ES-3A shipboard aircraft (now in storage). The data collected are to be received and analyzed at workstations aboard 23 carriers and LHA/LHD. Trials were conducted 1996 in the *John F. Kennedy* (CV 67).

USG-1 and USG-2 CEC (Cooperative Engagement Capability)

Intended to link all radar and ESM sensors and all target data within a distributed fleet so that any unit can be defended against enemy attack by any ship within range, regardless of whether the target or the firing ship holds the threat on its own sen-

WEAPONS AND SYSTEMS *(continued)*

sors. Uses data from sensors on Aegis-equipped ships, aircraft carriers, and major amphibious warfare ships (including the new LPD 17 class). The link is maintained via a circular Data Distribution System antenna mounted on the principal mast. Development began in 1990 at the Johns Hopkins University Applied Physics Lab in cooperation with Raytheon and other companies. The first ships equipped with developmental USG-1 systems for trials in 1993–94 were the carrier *Eisenhower* (CVN-69), cruisers *Anzio* (CG 68) and *Cape St. George* (CG 70), destroyer *Kidd* (DDG 993), and helicopter carrier *Wasp* (LHD 1); also used was a customs service P-3 Orion aircraft with APS-38 radar.

In FY 97, two more CGs, a CVN, and an LHA were to be equipped with the USG-2 Common Equipment Set, the production version of the CEC; 26 additional units were to have the system by the end of FY 01. In 6-98, however, the planned operational test for the production CEC system was delayed by two years because of the scope of the systems integration effort. With USG-2, total weight was reduced from original USG-1's 9,000 lb. to only 550 lb. As of 12-96, the CEC program envisioned some 122 ships having the system by the end of FY 07, but the number has since been greatly curtailed. Authorization to purchase sets for LPD 18, DDG 84–86, DDG 91 and 92, CVN 69, and two E-2C Hawkeye aircraft was given on 1-5-00, but plans to install it on the LSD 41, LHA 1, and DD 963 classes were dropped in 6-00.

Live-fire tests conducted between 9-5-00 and 24-5-00 with the CV 67 battle group off Puerto Rico were highly successful. A successful technical evaluation (TECHEVAL) from 9-2-01 to 3-3-01 led to an equally successful operational evaluation during 5-01 and 6-01; the system has demonstrated resistance to jamming.

NTDS (Naval Tactical Data System)

Uses USQ-20 digital computers to give an overall picture of a tactical situation—air, surface, and underwater—and enables a commander to employ the means necessary to oppose the enemy. Excellent automatic data transmission systems (Link 11 and Link 14) permit the exchange of tactical information with similarly equipped ships, P-3C Orion and S-3B Viking aircraft carrying the Air Tactical Data System (ATDS), and amphibious landing forces equipped with NTDS. Now used only on the FFG 7, DD 963, and LCC 19 classes.

Note: The Tactical Flag Command Center (TFCC) was superseded by the NTCS-A (Naval Tactical Command System–Afloat), which employs commercial-off-the-shelf DTC, TAC-3, and TAC-4 computers (q.v.).

All ships are equipped to receive commercial satellite communications (SATCOM) messages, while most can send ultra-high-frequency (UHF) messages via satellite and at least 31 can transmit and receive super-high-frequency (SHF) messages. T-AGOS sonar surveillance ships first used the WSC-6-series VHF SATCOM system, which is now widely installed in combatants in the Raytheon WSC-6(V)4, (V)5, and (V)6 and Harris WSC-6(V)8 (or WSC-9) models. Extremely high-frequency (EHF) SATCOM employs the USC-38 terminal, which was to be replaced starting in 2001 with a new system from Raytheon.

WSC-8 (Challenge Athena)

A program to employ C-band commercial satellite systems to transmit data at very high rates (1,544,000 bits/sec). It is used to transmit intelligence data such as imagery and also for shipboard personnel communications with family members at home. It employs a 2.7-m-diameter, radome-enclosed dish antenna. First trialed on the *George Washington* (CVN 73), it has been widely deployed since then; a datalink system is to be developed to allow CGs, DDGs, and FFGs to link with Challenge Athena equipment on the larger ships.

CHBDL (Common High-Bandwidth Data Link)

Permits data from various remote collection platforms to be received and distributed to various shipboard users; the system supports the Advanced Tactical Airborne Reconnaissance System (ATARS) and the Battle Group Passive Horizon-Extension System (BGPHES). Successful trials in the *John F. Kennedy* (CV 67) resulted in an initial contract in 1-98 for further systems.

IT-21 (Information Technology for the 21st Century)

A standard "architecture" for data and transmission capacity imposed on shipboard and land information (command, control, communications, and intelligence) facilities to ensure intercommunication. Initially deployed with CVN 65 in late 1998, CV 67 in 1999, and CVN 70 in 2000, it is to be in all carrier group and amphibious ready groups by 2003 and all shore facilities by 2008. IT-21 allows ships and facilities to optimize the use of their existing equipment with commercial computing and satellite communications services.

JMICS (Joint Maritime Information Communications System)

Used to pass Tomahawk targeting data worldwide. Uses the NTCS-A imagery workstation.

JMOCC (Joint Maritime Operations Command Center)

JOTS (Joint Operations Terminal System)—a display terminal

JSIPS (Joint Services Imagery Processing System)

System for receiving satellite and other imagery via communications satellites, installed on carriers, all LHA/LHD, and LCC 19 and 20.

NTCS-A (Naval Tactical Command System–Afloat)

An imagery exploitation workstation that employs commercial-off-the-shelf DTC, TAC-3, and TAC-4 computers.

SSDS (Ship Self-Defense System)

Hughes Naval and Maritime Systems program to provide 31 non-Aegis ships with an integrated air-defense system by linking existing sensors and weapons. Trials were conducted with the *Ashland* (LSD 48) commencing in 3-97, using the existing SPS-49 and SPS-67 radars, SLQ-32 intercept system, Mk 36 decoy launch system, and Phalanx and RAM weapons systems; ships equipped with NATO Sea Sparrow and Evolved Sea Sparrow will also have those weapons integrated. Lack of funding has seriously hurt the program, which was originally to have been extended to FFG 7–class frigates and DD 963–class destroyers; current plans call for a slowdown in fleet introduction and a reduction in the number of affected ships to the LHD 1–, LSD 41–, and LPD 17–class amphibious warfare ships and to aircraft carriers. The *Dwight D. Eisenhower* (CVN 69) and *Wasp* (LHD 1) received the first ACDS (Advanced Combat Defense System) Mk 1 variant of the system. No systems were bought with FY 98 funding, but 3–4 per year were to be acquired from FY 99 on. The *Nimitz* (CVN 68) received an SSDS Mk 2 Mod. 0 installation during 2001.

TAMPS (Tactical Aircraft Mission Planning System)

TERS (Tactical Event Reporting System)

TIBS (Tactical Information Broadcast System)

J. MINE COUNTERMEASURES DEVICES

♦ Surface-ship mine countermeasures systems

ALISS (Advanced Lightweight Influence Sweep System): In development. Uses spark-gap transducer arrays and superconducting magnetic technology in combination with lightweight, high-speed towed arrays. If successful, the system would be packaged in modular form for use on LCAC air-cushion landing craft as well as on other mine countermeasures platforms.

A Mk 4(V): Towed acoustic sweep hammer box, a World War II–era development still in use. It is streamed from a float and towed about 1,100 m abaft the minesweeper.

A Mk 6(B): Low-frequency acoustic sweep, also of World War II origin. Uses an electrically driven hammer in a streamlined housing towed about 1,100 m abaft the minesweeper, suspended from a float.

AMNS (Airborne Mine Neutralization System): Developmental U.S. version of the German Sea Fox, intended to destroy mines already detected. Employs a torpedo-shaped vehicle to be towed by an MH-60S helicopter; sonar and video sensors classify the mine, and the vehicle launches self-propelled weapons to destroy it.

DET (Distributed Explosive Technology): A rocket-launched explosive net for use in clearing amphibious assault lanes in the surf zone; launched from LCAC amphibious craft after SABRE mine-clearance rockets (q.v.) have been employed. Was to enter service in 2001, with an improved version to have longer range, a fire-control system, and an autopilot for the LCAC planned for 2004.

M Mk 3/4/5(A): Two-electrode magnetic sweep array of World War II origin. M Mk 3 is a static sweep used in confined areas, with the minesweeper stationary and the array being towed about by small boats. The two-ship version is M Mk 4. M Mk 5 can be deployed either diverted by floats to either side of the ship or in a closed-loop mode.

M Mk 6: Electromagnetic sweep in three versions: M Mk 6(A) ("J-sweep"), with long sections curving to meet a diverted cable also towed by the sweeper and connected to an Oropesa wire sweep and a kite depressor; M Mk 6(B), a single-ship closed-loop array that uses Oropesa floats to keep the loop sides apart; and M Mk 6(H), a closed-loop sweep with two legs meeting at a diverter line streamed from an Oropesa float.

Oropesa (O): Wire sweeps in various sizes for sweeping buoyant mines near the sea surface. Size 1 is the largest; a 548-m wire can be towed at up to 8 kts at depths of 9.1 to 73 m. The swept path for a double sweep array is 457 m wide.

SABRE (Shallow-Water Assault Breaching System): Rocket-launched, explosive line charge for launch from LCAC amphibious craft to clear assault lanes in the surf zone. Was to enter service in 2001, with an improved version to have longer range, a fire-control system, and an autopilot for the LCAC planned for 2004.

SLQ-37: A combined array for the MCM 1 class, using an M Mk 5(A) straight-tail magnetic sweep combined with an A Mk 4(V) or A Mk 6(B) acoustic sweep (qq.v.).

SLQ-38: Latest version of Oropesa sweep. Can be streamed between two ships. Used on the MCM 1 class.

SLQ-48(V) Mine Neutralization System (MNS): Unmanned, tethered, remotely operated submersible used to examine and dispose of mines located by the ship's sonar system. Made by Hughes Electronics Division, General Motors (formerly Honeywell, then Alliant). Travels at up to 6 kts and has a small, high-definition sonar, an acoustic transponder, and a low-light-level television camera. Uses MP-1 (Mk 26 Mod. 0) cable cutters and an MP-2 (Mk 57 Mod.) explosive mine-destruction charge. SLQ-48(V) is powered by two 15-shp electric motors to ranges of up to 1,000 m from the ship. The umbilical cable is 1,067 m long. The device (less cable) weighs 1,225 kg and is 3.67 m long and 0.91 m wide. Total system weight is 11.8 metric tons.

MNS II, also developed by Hughes Electronics, completed prototype trials early in 1996; it had a speed of 8 kts, a new autopilot, fiber-optic cable guidance, and a lower-cost operating console, but it was not procured in quantity.

SLQ-53 Single-Ship Deep Sweep (SSDS): Developed from the helicopter-towed A/N-37U-1 for the MHC 51 class and possibly later for the MCM 1 class.

SPU-1W MOP (Magnetic Orange Pipe): A magnetized, 9.14-m-long, 0.273-m-diameter hollow pipe filled with Styrofoam for buoyancy. Weight: 454 kg. One helicopter can tow three in tandem to increase mine sensor's ship-count rate.

WLD-1(V)1/3 Remote Minehunting System (RMS): Developed by Lockheed Martin Naval Electronics and Surveillance Systems, Syracuse, N.Y. The program was previously known as RMS(V)3. Rockwell Autonetics developed the (V)1 prototype, known as the RMOP (Remote Minehunting Operational Prototype) when trials began in 1994; the ROV then carried AQS-14 and SeaBat sonars. The WLD-1(V)1 is powered by a 370-bhp Cummins diesel. The body is 7 m long and 1.2 m in diameter and weighs 7,300 kg. Maximum speed is 16 kts, while 24-hour patrol speed is 12 kts. The *Cushing* (DD 985) undertook operational trials of the WLD-1(V)3 early in 1997, and the initial production variant, which interfaces with the shipboard SQQ-89 sonar system, was to have entered production in 1999 for deployment aboard DD 963–class destroyers; the first production order, however, for only two units, was placed with Lockheed Martin 15-1-02 for delivery in 2004 and operational evaluation during 2005. The modular (V)4 full-scale production version, planned to enter service in 2005 with DDG 91 and later *Arleigh Burke* Flight IIA

WEAPONS AND SYSTEMS *(continued)*

units, will employ a 7.5-m-long by 1.2-m-diameter ROV weighing 6,400 kg; eventually, all cruisers, destroyers, frigates, and major amphibious warfare ships are to be able to employ the (V)4 variant. The (V)3 and (V)4 have 24-hour endurance and a radius of about 50 n.m. and will tow an AQS-20/R mine countermeasures sonar body.

Note: Mine countermeasures divers use the Mk 16 nonferrous recycling underwater breathing apparatus, PQS-2 handheld mine-location sonars (50–90 kHz), 40-kHz marker beacons, and Mk 25 ferrous metals ordnance locators; the Mk 25 is usable in depths of up to 90 m and has a range of up to 18 m.

♦ Submarine-deployed mine countermeasures systems

BLQ-11 LMRS (Long-term Mine Reconnaissance System): Being developed by Boeing, with the prototype to be completed in 9-03. Uses preprogrammed, torpedo tube–deployed and –recovered, unmanned submersibles with an endurance of 40 hours. The 5-kt BLQ-11 is to have a 288-n.m. range on its nonrechargeable lithium battery and to be able to reconnoiter 650 km^2 during a typical mission. A full outfit would replace eight torpedoes and would include three unmanned underwater vehicles, the recovery arm machinery, spare batteries, and control and display modules; it would be operated by four personnel. A more capable reconnaissance and target-detection version is planned to enter service around 2009. One BLQ-11 is to be carried by *Virginia*-class SSNs and two by *Ohio*-class SSBNs.

♦ Helicopter-towed or -carried mine countermeasures systems

AES-1 ALMDS (Airborne Laser Mine Detection System): In development to replace the Magic Lantern system starting in 2005; will be used on MH-60 and other H-60 airframe helicopters starting around 2003. Employs a LIDAR (Light Detection and Ranging) laser sensor and is a follow-on to the early 1990s ATD-111 project.

A Mk 2(G) acoustic sweep ("rattle bars"): Towed broadside-on by helicopters at up to 10 kts. Can also be towed by surface ships. Water flow between parallel pipes creates MF to HF banging.

AMNS (Advanced Mine Neutralization System): German STN Atlas Elektronik mine disposal system, using a remotely operated, disposable, $45,000 submersible with four propulsors that carries a 1.2-kg shaped-charge warhead. Employed by MH-53E helicopters.

LTMRS (Long-Term Mine Reconnaissance System): In development for deployment from MH-53E and MH-60S helicopters, it will incorporate (as needed) the AQS-20X dipping sonar, an AES-1 Airborne Laser Mine Detection System (ALMDS), an Advanced Mine Neutralization System (AMNS), a Shallow-Water Influence Minesweep System (SWIMS), and the Rapid Airborne Mine Countermeasures System (RAMICS).

Magic Lantern: As of 1998, two Naval Reserve SH-2G helicopters were equipped with a Kaman-developed laser mine detector system known as Magic Lantern. It is to be replaced by the AES-1 ALMDS (q.v.). The retired SH-2G aircraft are to be replaced by MH-60S helicopters in 2003.

Mk 103: Moored minesweeping system with tow wire, sweep wires with explosive cutters, floats, depressor, and otter pendants. The A/N-37U-1 variant has controlled depth for use against deeper mines and has been adapted for surface ship use as the SLQ-53 SSDS.

Mk 104: Acoustic mine countermeasures system with a cavitating disk within a venturi tube. Minimum water depth: 9 m. Length: 1.24 m; height: 0.889 m; width: 0.660 m.

Mk 105: Hydrofoil minesweeping sled; made by EDO and in service since 1970. Towed at 20–25 kts about 140 m behind the helicopter. Has a gas turbine generator to provide an electric field for two 183-m-long open-electrode sweep wires streamed from the hydrofoil raft. Minimum usable water depth is only 3.6 m. Can be refueled from the helicopter while streamed and can also tow A Mk 2(G) or Mk 104 arrays in addition to the electrodes. Sled is deployed from a mother ship. The planned ALQ-166 replacement has been canceled. The Mk 105 Mod. 4, with improved ease of maintenance, was to enter service in 2001–02 and to weigh 4,081 kg fully fueled; it is 8.30 m long.

Mk 106: Helicopter-towed array incorporating the Mk 105 hydrofoil sled with a Mk 104 acoustic array attached to the end of one of the magnetic electrode tails.

OASIS (Organic Airborne and Surface Influence Sweep): A replacement for the SPU-1W (q.v.) and the Mk 105 sled, which is too heavy to be towed by the MH-60S helicopter; by 2005, it is hoped to have a system about half as effective as the Mk 105. Uses an 800-ft. tow cable and operates to 100-ft. depths.

RAMACS (Rapid Airborne Mine Clearance System): A helicopter-mounted 20-mm or 30-mm gun system, to fire supercavitating incendiary shells into the water to destroy mines at depths of up to 40 ft. May enter service in 2005.

Note: General Dynamics announced an agreement to purchase Newport News Shipbuilding on 25-4-01; the company already owns National Steel and Shipbuilding Co. (NASSCO) and Bath Iron Works, as well as its Electric Boat division. Also during 2001, Northrop Grumman acquired the Litton concern, along with its shipbuilding division comprising Avondale Shipyards and Ingalls Shipbuilding; the two shipyards now make up Northrop Grumman Ship Systems. Thus, the construction of naval vessels in the United States had been concentrated under only two large conglomerate firms.

NUCLEAR-POWERED AIRCRAFT CARRIERS [CVN]

Air Group Composition: Carrier wings by FY 07 are to be reduced to 30 F/A-18E/F, 15 F/A-18C (primarily for use in aerial refueling), 4 EA-6B ICAP III, and 4 E-2C fixed-wing aircraft. By 2011, manned fixed-wing assets in a carrier wing are to be 30 F/A-18E/F, 12 F-35C, 6 F/A-18G ICAP III+, and 6 E-2D, plus 6 unmanned reconnaissance drones, leaving an even greater unused aircraft capacity in each carrier. In terms of FY 00 dollars, it will cost $27 billion to operate a new CVN and its air group for 50 years (and $334 billion for a fleet of 12).

♦ 0 (+ 2) CVNX 1 class

Bldr: Northrop Grumman Newport News (formerly Newport News SB), Newport News, Va.

	Laid down	L	In serv.
CVN 78 (CVNX 1)	2008	. . .	2014
CVN 79 (CVNX 2)	2011	. . .	2018

D: . . . **S:** . . . kts **Dim:** . . . × . . . × . . .

Air group: 30 F/A-18E/F fighters, 12 F-35C attack aircraft, 6 F/A-18G electronic support aircraft, 6 E-2D aerial surveillance aircraft, and 6 H-60-series helicopters

Electronics:

Radar: 1 . . . nav.; 1 Lockheed Martin SPY-2 volume search; 1 Raytheon SPY-3 MFR (Multi-Function Radar) target detection, tracking, and illumination; . . .

M: probable: 2 G.E. A4W/A1G pressurized-water reactors (42.3 kg/cm^2), 4 sets geared steam turbines; 4 props; 280,000 shp (see remarks)

Electric: approx. 64,000 kw tot. hotel services + 8,000 kw emergency

Range: . . ./. . . **Crew:** . . .

Remarks: Congress provided $21.9 million in advance procurement and design funding for CVN 78 in the FY 01 budget. Some $3.6 billion is expected to be expended on research and development in connection with the design of CVN 78 and 79, which are to have a new nuclear propulsion system possibly incorporating a new-design reactor and probably electric drive. The reactors are expected to operate for 50 years without refueling. Both will employ all-electric auxiliary systems. Despite the huge development costs, the basic design is expected to be evolutionary rather than departing significantly from the configuration established by previous classes. As of 11-01, the planned request for authorization to build the first ship was slipped to FY 07, with half the building funding to be requested in FY 07 and half in FY 08.

CVN 79 may employ a larger hull than CVN 78, with a ship some 354.8 m long and 80.8 m wide and displacing 114,000 tons (fl) that would not fit in any current U.S. commercial or naval building dock or dry dock. Both are planned to employ 93-m linear electromagnetic motor catapults capable of launching a 45-ton aircraft to more than 130 kts; CVN 79 is also planned to employ an electromagnetic arrestor gear system and may have only three elevators, the island moved further forward, the deck landing area moved further to port so as to permit simultaneous takeoffs and landings, and the fitting of 18 flight deck fast fueling and arming stations. As of 4-00, however, there were plans to keep CVN 78 essentially identical to the CVN 77 in order to save design costs of more than $900 million.

♦ 0 (+ 1) CVN 77 class

Bldr: Northrop Grumman Newport News (formerly Newport News SB), Newport News, Va.

	Laid down	L	In serv.
CVN 77	1-5-03	2-06	5-08 (del.)

CVN 77—builder's model Gen. Dynamics Newport News, 7-99

D: approx. 98,000 tons (fl) **S:** 30.9 kts

Dim: 330 (317.00 wl) × 41.0 (78.0 flight deck) × 11.9 (mean)

Air group: 30 F/A-18E/F, 15 F/A-18C, 6 EA-6B, 6 E-2C, 6 H-60-series

A: . . .

Electronics:

Radar: 1 . . . nav.; 1 Lockheed Martin SPY-2 volume search; 1 Raytheon SPY-3 MFR (Multi-Function Radar) target detection, tracking, and illumination—see remarks

M: 2 G.E. A4W/A1G pressurized-water reactors (42.3 kg/cm^2), 4 sets geared steam turbines; 4 props; 280,000 shp (see remarks)

Electric: approx. 64,000 kw tot. hotel services + 8,000 kw emergency

Range: . . ./. . . **Crew:** 2,500 ship's company + air wing

Remarks: CVN 77 is to have integrated information systems, open-system architecture for computers and combat systems, fiber-optic cabling, zonal electrical distribution, multifunctional embedded antennas, and composite construction for the island. Concepts and systems are to be employed with a goal of reducing the lifetime operating cost of the ship by about 20% and the crew by 500 from that of its predecessors. The aircraft complement will be significantly reduced from that operating on USN carriers of the 1990s. The first incremental advance procurement contract for CVN 77 was let 3-9-98. Congress authorized construction of CVN 77 in the FY 01 budget and provided $4.0537 billion. The $3,829,260,045 construction contract was signed 26-1-01, and work on the ship started 15-3-01.

Combat systems: Lockheed Martin (in partnership with Northrop Grumman and Solipsys) was selected as systems integrator on 31-1-00. The ship will have the SSDS Mk 2 self-defense system and CEC (Cooperative Engagement Capability). If development of the preferred SPY-2/SPY-3 search and target-designation radar suite falls further behind schedule, the Lockheed Martin SPY-1D(V) or SPY-1F Aegis radar will be installed instead.

NUCLEAR-POWERED AIRCRAFT CARRIERS [CVN] *(continued)*

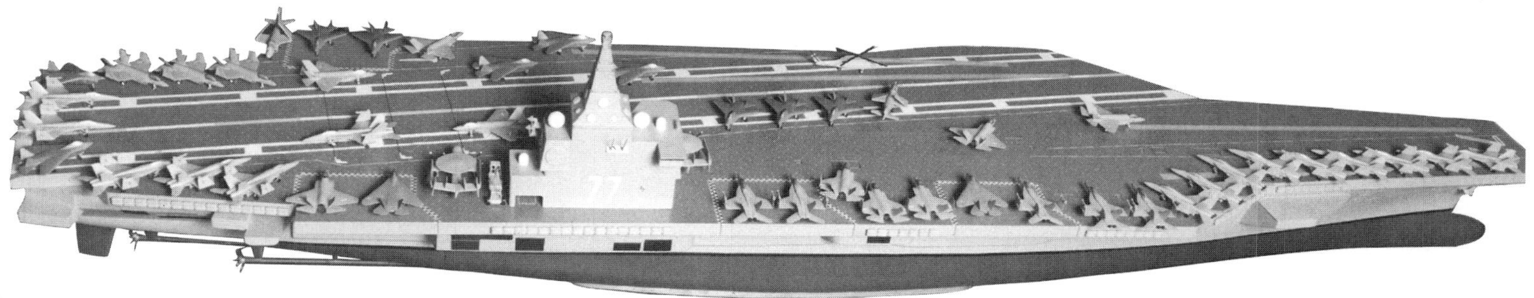

CVN 77—builder's model Gen. Dynamics Newport News, 7-99

♦ 5 (+ 1) Theodore Roosevelt class

Bldr: Northrop Grumman Newport News (formerly Newport News SB), Newport News, Va. (*Atlantic/†Pacific Fleet)

	Laid down	L	In serv.
CVN 71 THEODORE ROOSEVELT*	31-10-81	27-10-84	25-10-86
CVN 72 ABRAHAM LINCOLN†	3-11-84	13-2-88	11-11-89
CVN 73 GEORGE WASHINGTON*	25-8-86	21-7-90	4-7-92
CVN 74 JOHN C. STENNIS†	13-3-91	13-11-93	9-12-95
CVN 75 HARRY S. TRUMAN* (ex-*United States*)	29-11-93	7-9-96	25-7-98
CVN 76 RONALD REAGAN†	12-2-98	10-3-01	4-03 (del.)

D: CVN 71: 80,753 tons light (103,658 fl); CVN 72: 81,147 tons light (104,242 fl); CVN 73: 81,083 tons light (104,208 fl); CVN 74: 80,085 tons light (103,020 fl); CVN 75: 78,453 tons light (101,390 fl); CVN 76: 77,607 tons light (98,235 fl)
S: 30.9 kts
Dim: 332.85 (CVN 76: 334.67) (all except CVN 76: 317.00 wl) × 40.85 (78.33 flight deck) × 12.50 (mean hull)
Air group: 10 F-14A/B/D, 36 F/A-18A/C, 4 EA-6B, 4 E-2C, 8 S-3B, 7 SH-60F/HH-60H, 2 C-2A
A: 3 8-round Mk 29 launchers (RIM-7P Sea Sparrow SAM); 4 20-mm Mk 15 Phalanx CIWS gatling AA—CVN 76 also: 2 21-round RAM Mk 31 SAM syst. (RIM-116A missiles)
Electronics:
Radar: 1 Furuno 900 (CVN 72: Sperry Raster) nav.; 1 SPS-64(V)9 nav.; 1 SPS-67(V)1 surf. search; 1 SPS-48E 3-D air search; 1 SPS-49(V)5 (CVN 76: SPS-49A(V)1) 2-D air search; 1 TAS/Mk 23 (CVN 76: SPQ-9B) target detection; 2 SPN-46 CCA; 1 SPN-43B air control; 1 SPN-44 microwave landing aid; 6 Mk 95 Sea Sparrow missile f.c.; 4 Mk 90 Phalanx f.c.
TACAN: URN-25
EW: Raytheon SLQ-32(V)4 suite; BAE Systems SLQ-20B signal processor; Mk 36 SRBOC decoy syst. (8 6-round Mk 137 RL); SLQ-25A Nixie SSTDS
M: 2 G.E. A4W/A1G pressurized-water reactors (42.3 kg/cm^2), 4 sets geared steam turbines; 4 props; 280,000 shp
Electric: 64,000 kw tot. (turboalternators) + 8,000 kw emergency power (4 diesel sets)
Crew: 161–163 officers, 2,932–2,952 enlisted + air wing: 365 officers, 2,500 enlisted + flag staff: 25 officers, 45 enlisted + Marines: 2 officers, 70 enlisted (6,275 tot. accomm.)

Remarks: CVN 71 was authorized under FY 80, CVN 72 and 73 under FY 83, CVN 74 and 75 under FY 88, and CVN 76 under FY 95. CVN 74 and 75 were ordered 30-6-88 and CVN 76 on 8-12-94. Initial long-lead funding of $832 million for CVN 76 was provided under the FY 93 budget, with $1.2 billion more in the FY 94 budget; as of 9-99, however, the ship was $200 million over budget. The ships are expected to serve until 2036, 2039, 2042, 2045, 2047, and 2052, respectively.

Harry S. Truman (CVN 75) William H. Clarke, 11-00

Harry S. Truman (CVN 75)—island detail William H. Clarke, 11-00

John C. Stennis (CVN 74) Brian Morrison, 6-00

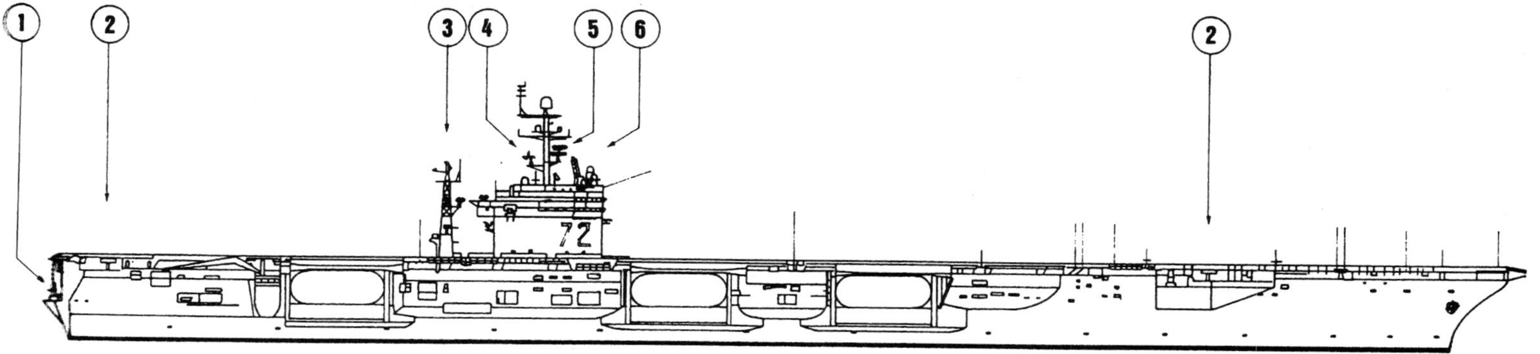

Abraham Lincoln (CVN 72) 1. Mk 15 Phalanx CIWS 2. Mk 29 Sea Sparrow SAM launcher 3. SPS-49 air-search radar 4. SPN-43 air-control radar 5. TAS/Mk 23 target-designation radar 6. SPS-48E 3-D early warning radar
Drawing by Jean Moulin, from *Flottes de Combat*

NUCLEAR-POWERED AIRCRAFT CARRIERS [CVN] *(continued)*

John C. Stennis (CVN 74) Jim Sanderson, 6-01

George Washington (CVN 73) William H. Clarke, 7-00

Abraham Lincoln (CVN 72) Kurt Greiner/SeaPhoto 10-99

Abraham Lincoln (CVN 72) A. A. de Kruijf, 6-00

Ronald Reagan (CVN 76)—official model; note the prominent bulbous bow
Chris Oxley, Gen. Dynamics Newport News, 7-99

Ronald Reagan (CVN 76)—computer-generated official view
Chris Oxley, Gen. Dynamics Newport News, 2000

Theodore Roosevelt (CVN 71)—island structure H&L Van Ginderen, 9-00

CVN 72 has been homeported at Everett, Wash., since 8-1-97. CVN 73 is homeported at Norfolk. CVN 74 moved to North Island, San Diego, on 26-8-98, and CVN 76 is also to be homeported there; CVN 74 is to move to Bremerton, Wash., in FY 05. CVN 75 completed a $110 million, six-month overhaul at Newport News 26-2-02.

Hull systems: Expected to operate for 15 years between refuelings (about 800,000 to 1,000,000 n.m. of steaming). Kevlar armor 63.5 mm thick is fitted over vital spaces, and hull-protection arrangements have been improved relative to earlier carriers. The two rudders weigh 50 tons each and are 8.84 m high. The distillation plants provide 400,000 gallons of potable water per day. CVN 76 has a prominent, 10.4-m-long bow bulb to the hull, while the island superstructure is one deck lower than in the earlier ships and supports two masts; the ship will have improved air-conditioning systems and berthing facilities and some 182,880 m of fiber-optic internal communications cabling. CVN 76 will use 50-person life rafts rather than the current 25-person rafts and will carry two rigid inflatable boats.

Aviation systems: The angled deck is 237.7 m long and is equipped with three arrestor wires (four on CVN 71) and a Mk 7 Mod. 3 barrier, as well as four 21.3 × 15.8–m, 47-ton-capacity elevators. The hangar has 7.6 m clear height. An aviation payload of some 14,909 tons is carried, including 9,000 tons of aviation fuel and 1,954 tons of aviation ordnance. CVN 71 has four 92.1-m-long C13 Mod. 1 catapults; the others have new, lower-pressure catapults. The arrestor gear system uses 35-mm-diameter cables set 0.14 m above the deck at 10.7-m intervals, with the tension on the cables automatically determined by the weight of the landing aircraft. Other data under the *Nimitz* class generally apply. CVN 76 has the three-wire Mk 7 Mod. 4 arrestor system, with stronger sheaves and more accessible arrestor engines. CVN 76 also has the amidships weapons elevator relocated within the island structure; a larger, two-level, 270°-view flight deck control position; improved-design, one-piece jet blast deflectors; and flight deck operations reoriented to the port side of the ship, with simultaneous landings and takeoffs possible from the longer angled-deck extension. CVN 76 can carry 3.4 million gallons of jet fuel.

Combat systems: The combat data systems include NTDS and ACDS, JDTS, POST, and CVIC. Datalinks include Links 4A, 11, and 14. SATCOM equipment includes SSQ-82, SRR-1, WSC-3 (UHF), WSC-6 (SHF), and USC-38 (EHF). Have SRN-9 and SRN-19 NAVSAT receivers, an SMQ-11 weather satellite receiver, and WRN-6 GPS receivers. The Sea Sparrow missile systems are supported by three Mk 91 Mod. 1 control systems, each with two Mk 95 radar directors. CVN 71 was fitted with the SLQ-32(V)4 EW system in 1997–98, and the others have been updated. The Joint Services Imagery Processing System–Navy (JSIPS-N) is now fitted to all. CVN 75 has a Sperry Marine Integrated Bridge System, which reduces the number of bridge personnel by more than 80%. CVN 76 will have the Integrated Combat Direction System (ICDS) to coordinate various self-defense systems. All are to receive two Mk 31 RAM missile launchers each. CVN 71 has received a Telephonics Corp. integrated air-traffic sensor coordination system. All ships of the class will eventually receive the SPQ-9B low-altitude target detection and designation radar in place of the current Mk 23 TAS.

NUCLEAR-POWERED AIRCRAFT CARRIERS [CVN] *(continued)*

♦ 3 Nimitz class (SCB 102 type)

Bldr: Northrop Grumman Newport News (formerly Newport News Sb), Newport News, Va. (*Atlantic/†Pacific Fleet)

	Laid down	L	In serv.
CVN 68 Nimitz†	22-6-68	13-5-72	3-5-75
CVN 69 Dwight D. Eisenhower*	15-8-70	11-10-75	18-10-77
CVN 70 Carl Vinson*	11-10-75	15-3-80	13-3-82

D: CVN 68: 78,280 tons light (101,196 fl); CVN 69: 78,793 tons light (101,713 fl); CVN 70: 78,172 tons light (101,089 fl)
S: 31.5 kts
Dim: 334.70 (317.00 wl) × 40.85 (77.11 flight deck; 89.4 max.) × 12.50
Air group: 11 F-14A/B/D, 36 F/A-18A/C, 4 EA-6B, 4 E-2C, 7 S-3B, 7 SH-60F/HH-60H, 2 C-2A
A: 3 (CVN 68: 2) 8-round Mk 29 SAM launchers (RIM-7P Sea Sparrow missiles)—CVN 68 only: 2 21-round RAM Mk 31 SAM syst. (RIM-116A missiles)—3 (CVN 68: none; CVN 70: 4) 20-mm Mk 15 Phalanx CIWS
Electronics:
Radar: 1 Furuno 900 nav.; 1 SPS-64(V)9 nav.; 1 SPS-67(V)1 surf. search; 1 Mk 23 TAS (CVN 69: SPQ-9B) target detection; 1 SPS-49(V)5 air search; 1 SPS-48E 3-D air search; 1 SPN-44 CCA; 1 SPN-43B air control; 6 Mk 95 missile f.c.; 3 or 4 Mk 90 Phalanx f.c.
TACAN: URN-25
EW: Raytheon SLQ-32(V)4 suite; BAE Systems SLQ-20B signal processor; Mk 36 SRBOC decoy syst. (8 6-round Mk 137 RL); SLQ-25A SSTDS

Nimitz (CVN 68) Takatoshi Okano, 9-01

Carl Vinson (CVN 70)—departing San Francisco Kurt Greiner/SeaPhoto, 11-00

Carl Vinson (CVN 70) Jim Sanderson, 6-01

M: 2 G.E. A4W/A1G pressurized-water reactors, 4 sets geared steam turbines; 4 props; 280,000 shp
Electric: 64,000 kw (turboalternators) + 8,000 kw emergency power (4 diesel sets)
Endurance: 90 days (limited by provisions)
Crew: 158–160 officers, 2,939–2,963 enlisted + air wing: 365 officers, 2,500 enlisted + flag staff: 25 officers, 45 enlisted + Marines: 2 officers, 70 enlisted (tot. accomm.: 558–568 officers, 5,046–5,244 enlisted)

Remarks: CVN 68 was authorized under FY 67, CVN 69 under FY 70, and CVN 70 under FY 74. Were originally expected to remain in service until 2025, 2027, and 2032, respectively, but CVN 69 may now be retired around 2017. CVN 68 began her first $1.2 billion RCOH (Refueling Complex Overhaul) at Newport News SB & DD on 29-5-98, completing 28-6-01; the ship arrived at her new home port, San Diego, 13-11-01. CVN 69 underwent a $404.3 million overhaul from 1995 to 1-97 at Newport News SB & DD that did not include nuclear reactor recoring; a 3-year recoring overhaul began 22-5-01 at Newport News. CVN 70 changed her home port to Bremerton, Wash., in 10-96 and underwent a six-month refit there from 7-3-02 to 30-9-02. CVN 70 is to be refueled and overhauled under FY 04 funding.
Hull systems: Decks and hull are of extra-strong, high-tensile steel to limit the impact of semi-armor-piercing bombs. Apart from the longitudinal bulkheads, there are 23 transverse watertight bulkheads (with more than 2,000 hull compartments) and 10 firewall bulkheads. Foam devices for fire fighting are very well developed, and pumping equipment is excellent, a 15° list being correctable in 20 minutes. Can withstand three times the severe pounding survived by the *Essex*-class aircraft carriers in 1944–45, and can take impacts and shock waves in the same proportion. Have been equipped with 65-mm Kevlar armor over vital spaces during refits. Were planned to require only one reactor recoring during their expected 50-year life spans. The evaporators can produce 1,520 tons of fresh water per day. During her 1998–2001 refueling overhaul, CVN 68 had the two upper levels of the island superstructure altered and a new integrated mast/antenna shelter installed.
Aviation systems: The angled part of the flight deck is 237.7 m long and has three Mk 14 arrestor wires and a barrier to halt aircraft. There are four side elevators: two forward, one aft of the island to starboard, and one on the stern to port. The four C13 Mod. 1 steam catapults are 94.5 m long. The 15,134 m^3 of aviation magazine spaces can hold 1,954 tons of aviation ordnance, and the total aviation-associated payload is on the order of 15,000 tons; sufficient aviation fuel for 16 days' operations is carried. The hangar has 7.8 m clear height. CVN 69 had the prototype of AVCARS (Augmented Visual Carrier Aircraft Recovery System), which is now fitted to the entire class. CVN 68 conducted trials in late 1997 aimed at increasing the number of F/A-18 strike sorties per day from the normal 125–140 to more than 200; 20 additional pilots and 100 additional maintenance personnel were embarked.
Combat systems: The ASCAC (Antisubmarine Classification and Analysis Center) permits instant sharing of target data among the carrier, its ASW aircraft, and escorting ships. CVN 70 was completed with three Mk 29 launchers for Sea Sparrow, six Mk 95 radar directors for the missiles, and four Mk 15 CIWS (Vulcan/Phalanx) gatling AA guns. The others have been similarly refitted but still have only three Phalanx CIWS. All Mk 15 CIWS are now protected by "maintenance enclosures." Have three Mk 95 Mod. 1 missile-control systems with two Mk 95 radar directors each to control Sea Sparrow missiles. The Mk 23 TAS was added to improve defense against low fliers and cruise missiles and will be replaced in all by the SPQ-9B, which provides target detection and designation against low-flying threats. SATCOM equipment includes SSQ-82, SRR-1, WSC-3 (UHF), WSC-6 (SHF), and USC-38 (EHF). Have SRN-9 and SRN-19 NAVSAT receivers, an SMQ-11 receiver for the TIROS-N ocean weather forecasting satellite, and WRN-6 GPS receivers. All now have JSIPS-N (Joint Services Imagery Processing System–Navy). CVN 69 became the first carrier with the ACDS (Aircraft Carrier Defense System) variant of the SSDS (Ship Self-Defense System) weapon and sensor integration package under FY 97 funding. CVN 68 and CVN 69 have had their SPS-49 radars upgraded to SPS-49A(V)1. CVN 68 had the Integrated Combat Direction System (ICDS) added during her 1998–2001 refit to coordinate the various self-defense systems. Are to receive two RAM missile launchers each. The USG-2 Cooperative Engagement Capability system was installed on CVN 69 during 2000–02; the ship has also received a Telephonics Corp. integrated air traffic sensor coordination system. From 1995 to 2000, CVN 68 carried the SLR-24 towed passive linear torpedo detection sensor as part of the prototype CST-1 torpedo countermeasures system; in its stead, the ship received the Raytheon SSDS (Ship Self-Defense System) Mk 2 Mod. 0 system during 2001. CVN 68 had the Phalanx mounts and one Mk 29 SAM launcher removed during her recent refit, while two RAM Mk 31 missile systems were added.

Nimitz (CVN 68)—departing for new home port, San Diego; note the new island structure and masts Takatoshi Okano, *Ships of the World,* 9-01

NUCLEAR-POWERED AIRCRAFT CARRIERS [CVN] *(continued)*

Dwight D. Eisenhower (CVN 69) U.S. Navy, 2000

♦ 1 Enterprise class (SCB 160 type)

Bldr: Northrop Grumman Newport News (formerly Newport News SB), Newport News, Va. (Atlantic Fleet)

	Laid down	L	In serv.
CVN 65 Enterprise	4-2-58	24-9-60	25-11-61

D: 75,704 tons light (93,284 fl) **S:** 33.6 kts
Dim: 331.63 (317.00 wl) × 40.54 (78.4 flight deck) × 11.88 (mean hull)
Air group: 10 F-14B/D, 36 F/A-18C, 4 EA-6B, 4 E-2C, 8 S-3B, 7 SH-60F/HH-60H, 2 C-2A
A: 3 8-round Mk 29 SAM launchers (RIM-7P Sea Sparrow SAM); 2 21-round RAM Mk 31 SAM syst. (RIM-116A missiles); 3 20-mm Mk 15 Phalanx CIWS gatling AA

Enterprise (CVN 65) Mike Welsford, 6-01

Enterprise (CVN 65) Jim Sanderson, 6-01

Enterprise (CVN 65)—detail of the "blockhouse" island structure
Jim Sanderson, 6-01

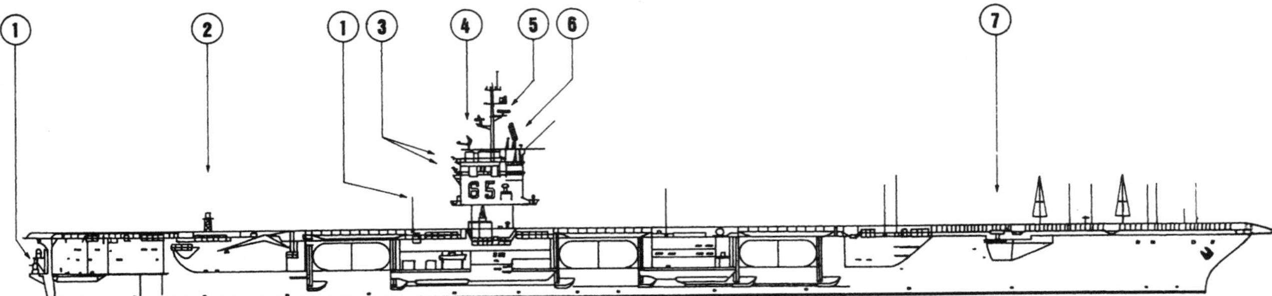

Enterprise (CVN 65) 1. Mk 15 Phalanx CIWS 2. SPN-43A air-control radar 3. SPN-46 landing-aid radars (now side-by-side) 4. SPS-49 air-search radar 5. SPS-67 surface-search radar 6. SPS-48E 3-D early-warning radar 7. Mk 29 Sea Sparrow SAM launcher
Drawing by Jean Moulin, from *Flottes de Combat*

NUCLEAR-POWERED AIRCRAFT CARRIERS [CVN] *(continued)*

Electronics:
Radar: 1 Furuno 900 nav.; 1 SPS-64(V)9 nav.; 1 SPS-67(V)1 surf. search; 1 Mk 23 TAS target acquisition; 1 SPS-48E 3-D air search; 1 SPS-49(V)5 air search; 1 SPN-44 microwave landing aid; 1 SPN-43A air control; 2 SPN-46 CCA; 6 Mk 95 missile f.c.; 3 Mk 90 Phalanx f.c.
TACAN: URN-25
EW: Raytheon SLQ-32(V)4 suite; WLR-1H(V)7 intercept; BAE Systems SLQ-20B signal processor; Mk 36 SRBOC decoy syst. (8 6-round Mk 137 RL); SLQ-25A SSTDS
M: 8 Westinghouse A2W reactors, supplying 32 Foster-Wheeler heat exchangers; 4 sets Westinghouse geared steam turbines; 4 props; 280,000+ shp
Electric: 40,000 kw (turboalternators) + 8,000 kw emergency (4 diesel sets)
Crew: 169 officers, 3,149 enlisted + air wing: 358 officers, 2,122 enlisted + flag staff: 25 officers, 45 enlisted + Marines: 2 officers, 70 enlisted (tot. accomm.: 571 officers, 5,244 enlisted)

Remarks: Authorized under FY 58. Modernized 15-1-79 to 3-82 at Puget Sound NSY, during which the radar and other electronics suites were extensively renovated. Refitted and refueled at the builder's 8-1-91 to 27-9-94; an extra six months of repair and upgrade work was required after sea trials, however, delaying availability until 7-7-95. The entire refueling and overhaul cost was over $3.1 billion. Given an $80 million refit by the builder from 8-99 to 18-12-99. A 1-year, $191 million "extended dry dock selected restricted availability" contract was given to the builder on 7-1-02 (to be performed at the Portsmouth NSY, Va.). Currently expected to remain in service until 2013 but may be retired much sooner. Homeported at Norfolk.
Hull systems: Has four rudders vice the two on other U.S. CV/CVNs. When new could make nearly 36 kts; maximum speed is now limited primarily by shaft torque. Two of the eight nuclear reactors are now kept nonoperational, limiting maximum speed to around 31 kts.
Aviation systems: There are four C13 Mod. 1 steam catapults and four elevators: one on the port side of the angled deck and three to starboard—two of which are forward of and one abaft the island. The elevators are steel and alloy, weigh 105 tons, are 26 m long and 16 m wide, and lift 45 tons. The hangar is 7.62 m high and the flight deck has an area of more than 20,000 m^2. Carries 8,500 tons of aviation fuel, which permits up to 12 days of intensive aerial operations without replenishment. Also carries fuel to replenish other ships. Retains both bow catapult bridle "horns," although the USN no longer operates aircraft that require bridles to launch them.
Combat systems: Has NTDS, an ASCAC (Antisubmarine Classification and Analysis Center), and a TFCC (Tactical Flag Communications Center). Links 4A, 11, 14, and 16 are fitted. There are three Mk 91 Mod. 1 fire-control systems for the Sea Sparrow missiles, each with two Mk 95 radar directors. SATCOM equipment includes SSQ-82, SRR-1, WSC-3 (UHF), WSC-6 (SHF), and USC-38 (EHF). Has SRN-9 and SRN-19 NAVSAT receivers, an SMQ-11 receiver for the TIROS-N ocean weather forecasting satellite, and WRN-6 GPS receivers.

CONVENTIONALLY POWERED AIRCRAFT CARRIERS [CV]

♦ 1 John F. Kennedy class (SCB 127C type)
Bldr: Northrop Grumman Newport News (formerly Newport News SB), Newport News, Va. (Atlantic Fleet)

	Laid down	L	In serv.
CV 67 John F. Kennedy	22-10-64	27-5-67	7-9-68

John F. Kennedy (CV 67) H&L Van Ginderen, 1-00

John F. Kennedy (CV 67) U.S. Navy, 7-00

John F. Kennedy (CV 67) H&L Van Ginderen, 7-00

D: 60,728 tons light (82,655 fl) **S:** 32 kts
Dim: 327.05 (304.54 wl) × 39.62 (81.38 flight deck; 85.95 max.) × 11.28
Air group: 10 F-14B/D, 36 F/A-18C, 4 EA-6B, 4 E-2C, 8 S-3B, 7 SH-60F/HH-60H, 2 C-2A
A: 3 8-round Mk 29 SAM syst. (RIM-7M Sea Sparrow missiles); 3 20-mm Mk 15 Block I Phalanx CIWS gatling AA
Electronics:
Radar: 1 Furuno 900 nav.; 1 Raytheon SPS-64(V)9 nav.; 1 SPS-67(V)1 surf. search; 1 Mk 23 TAS target acquisition; 1 SPS-49(V)5 air search; 1 SPS-48E 3-D air search; 1 SPN-41 microwave landing aid; 1 SPN-43C air control; SPN-44 microwave landing aid; 2 SPN-46 CCA; 6 Mk 95 missile f.c.; 3 Mk 90 Phalanx f.c.
TACAN: URN-25
EW: Raytheon SLQ-32(V)4 suite; WLR-1H(V)7 intercept; BAE Systems SLQ-20B signal processor; Mk 36 SRBOC decoy syst. (8 6-round Mk 137 RL); SLQ-25A Nixie SSTDS
M: 4 sets G.E. geared steam turbines; 4 props; 280,000 shp
Boilers: 8 Foster-Wheeler; 83.4 kg/cm^2, 520° C
Electric: 17,000 kw tot. (turboalternators and emergency diesel sets)
Crew: 135 officers, 2,443 enlisted + air wing: 329 officers, 1,950 enlisted + flag staff: 25 officers, 45 enlisted + Marines: 2 officers, 70 enlisted (tot. accomm.: 540 officers, 4,818 enlisted)

Remarks: Authorized under FY 63. Built with conventional steam propulsion as an economy measure. A distinguishing feature is the stack, which is angled outboard as on some World War II–era Japanese carriers. Was to have received a full SLEP modernization in 1993–95 but instead had only a 14-month "complex overhaul" funded under FY 93. Home port was changed from Norfolk to Mayport, Fla., during 1995. Was transferred to the Naval Reserve Force on 1-10-94 to become "operational reserve/training carrier" on completion of the overhaul on 13-9-95 but was subsequently deployed as if she were a regular Navy carrier; reverted to regular USN status as of 1-10-00. Is unrealistically expected to remain in service until 2018. Although due for deployment in 1-02, the ship badly failed a major material inspection early in 12-01, and the commanding officer was relieved; the carrier's material condition had been allowed to decline during the period of its assignment to the NRF.
Aviation systems: Has four side elevators: three to starboard (two forward of and one abaft the island) and one on the port quarter. Has a completely automatic landing system, permitting all-weather operation. There are four arrestor wires and a barrier on the 227-m angled flight deck, along with one 94.5-m C13-1 and three 90-m C13 catapults. The 11,808-m^3 aviation-ordnance magazine can accommodate 1,250 tons of ammunition. Carries 5,919 tons of aviation fuel.

John F. Kennedy (CV 67) 1. Mk 29 launcher for Sea Sparrow SAM 2. SPN-44 landing aid radar 3. SPS-48E 3-D early-warning radar 4. SPN-43A air-control radar 5. WSC-6 satellite communications antenna radome 6. SPS-49 air-search radar 7. Mk 15 Phalanx CIWS (alongside the island) Drawing by Jean Moulin, from *Flottes de Combat*

CONVENTIONALLY POWERED AIRCRAFT CARRIERS [CV] *(continued)*

Combat systems: The ship's Combat Direction System Block I failed repeated tests during 1999 and is considered only marginally effective. SATCOM equipment includes SSQ-82, SRR-1, WSC-3 (UHF), WSC-6(V)4 (SHF), and USC-38(V)4 (EHF). Has SRN-19 and SRN-25 NAVSAT receivers, a WRN-6 GPS receiver, and an SMQ-11 weather satellite receiver. Is planned to receive two RAM Mk 31 point-defense missile launchers.

♦ 2 Kitty Hawk class (*Atlantic/†Pacific Fleet)

	Bldr	Laid down	L	In serv.
CV 63 Kitty Hawk†	New York SB, Camden, N.J.	27-12-56	21-5-60	29-4-61
CV 64 Constellation*	Brooklyn NSY, N.Y.	14-9-57	8-10-60	27-10-61

D: CV 63: 60,933 tons light (81,780 fl); CV 64: 61,981 tons light (82,538 fl)
S: 33 kts
Dim: 325.83 (CV 64: 327.05; 301.76 wl) × 39.62 (76.81 flight deck; 85.95 max.) × 11.58 (mean hull)
Air group: 10 F-14B/D, 36 F/A-18C, 4 EA-6B, 4 E-2C, 8 S-3B, 7 SH-60F/HH-60H, 2 C-2A

Kitty Hawk (CV 63) Brian Morrison, 5-01

Kitty Hawk (CV 63)—note launcher for RIM-116 RAM missiles on forward starboard sponson below the flight deck U.S. Navy, 12-01

Kitty Hawk (CV 63) Brian Morrison, 5-01

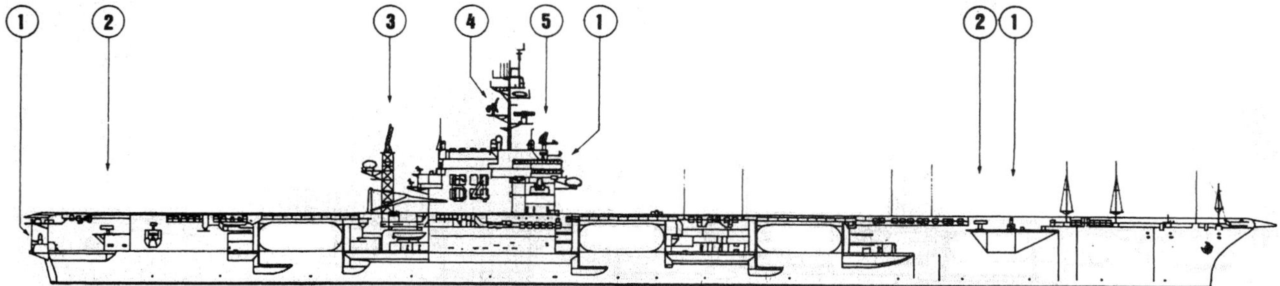

Constellation (CV 64) 1. Mk 15 Phalanx CIWS 2. Mk 29 Sea Sparrow launcher 3. SPS-48E 3-D early-warning radar 4. SPN-43A air-control radar 5. SPS-49 air-search radar
Drawing by Jean Moulin, from *Flottes de Combat*

Constellation (CV 64) Kurt Greiner/SeaPhoto, 10-00

CONVENTIONALLY POWERED AIRCRAFT CARRIERS [CV] *(continued)*

Kitty Hawk (CV 63) Brian Morrison, 5-01

Constellation (CV 64) W. Michael Young, 10-00

A: CV 64 only: 3 8-round Mk 29 SAM launchers (RIM-7M Sea Sparrow missiles)—CV 63 only: 2 21-round RAM Mk 31 SAM syst. (RIM-116A missiles)—both: 3 20-mm Mk 15 Phalanx CIWS gatling AA

Electronics:

Radar: 1 Furuno 900 nav.; 1 SPS-64(V)9 nav.; 1 SPS-67(V)1 surf. search; 1 Mk 23 TAS target acquisition; 1 SPS-49(V)5 air search; 1 SPS-48E 3-D air search; 1 SPN-41 microwave landing aid; 1 SPN-43A or -43C air control; 2 SPN-46 CCA; 6 Mk 95 missile f.c.; 3 Mk 90 Phalanx f.c.

TACAN: URN-25

EW: Raytheon SLQ-32(V)4 suite; BAE Systems SLQ-20B signal processor; Mk 36 SRBOC decoy syst. (8 6-round Mk 137 RL); SLQ-25A Nixie SSTDS

M: 4 sets Westinghouse geared steam turbines; 4 props; 280,000 shp

Boilers: 8 Foster-Wheeler, 83.4 kg/cm^2, 520° C

Electric: 15,000 kw tot. (6 turboalternators, 2 emergency diesel sets)

Range: 4,000/30; 8,000/20 **Fuel:** 7,800 tons

Crew: 147–148 officers, 2,743–2,766 enlisted + air group: 295 officers, 1,815 enlisted + flag staff: 25 officers, 45 enlisted + Marines: 2 officers, 70 enlisted (tot. accomm.: 575–578 officers, 5,046–5,049 enlisted)

Remarks: CV 63 was authorized under FY 56, CV 64 under FY 57. These ships were a great improvement over the *Forrestal* class, on which they were based, and have one significant difference: three elevators on the starboard side (two forward of and one abaft the island) and one to port, abaft the angled flight deck. CV 63 underwent a SLEP (Service Life Extension Program) overhaul 28-1-88 to 2-8-91; CV 64 received a similar SLEP overhaul 2-7-90 to 5-3-93 at Philadelphia and then returned to her San Diego home port. CV 63 moved her home port to Yokosuka, Japan, arriving 11-8-98 and replacing the *Independence* (CV 62) there. CV 64 is to be decommissioned late in 2002, going into mobilization reserve as replacement for the *Ranger* (CV 61); a broken gearbox may mean that the ship's final deployment is conducted with only three shafts operational. CV 63, as the oldest active commissioned ship in the USN, flies a special jack when in port; the ship carried a special assault helicopter air group during her 10-01 to 12-01 deployment to the Arabian Sea. CV 63 is to be retired in 2008.

Disposals: Sister *America* (CV 66), decommissioned 9-8-96, was placed in Mobilization Category B reserve on 30-9-96; on 20-10-98, her striking was *retroactively* backdated to 9-8-96, and she is to be scrapped.

Aviation systems: Have four C13 steam catapults. Carry 5,882 tons of aviation fuel. Received new catapult rotary engines, Mk 7 Mod. 3 arrestor gear (three wires), and SPN-46 landing-aid radar during their SLEP overhauls.

Combat systems: CV 64 retained two Mk 10 twin launchers for Terrier HT missiles and two SPQ-55B radar directors until her 12-82 to 2-84 refit. Have three Mk 91 Mod. 1 missile control systems, each with two radar directors, for the Sea Sparrow SAM system. Have SRN-9 and -19 NAVSAT receivers, an SMQ-6 or -11 receiver for weather forecasting satellite, and WRN-6 GPS receivers. SATCOM equipment includes SSQ-82, SRR-1, WSC-3 (UHF), WSC-6 (SHF), and USC-38 (EHF). CV 64 had JSIPS-N (Joint Services Imagery Processing System–Navy) in 1996, and the CV 63 received it later. During their SLEP overhauls, both received SPS-48E and SPS-49(V) upgrade air-search radars, the Mk 23 TAS low-altitude radar, the SYS-2(V)4 sensor data fusion system, updated NTDS (Naval Tactical Data System), a torpedo decoy system, the WQN-1 Channel-Finder sonar, and upgraded EW equipment. CV 63 received two RAM missile launchers in place of three Sea Sparrow launchers in a refit at Yokosuka that ended during 8-01. CV 64 is fitted with a trial version of the Harris–BAE Systems, Ku-band, wideband Tactical Common Data Link (TCDL) and carries two SH-60B helicopters equipped to datalink IRST video to the ship from ranges of up to 70 n.m.

♦ 2 Forrestal class (SCB 80M type) (in *reserve*)

Bldrs: CV 61: Newport News SB; CV 62: Brooklyn NSY, N.Y.

	Laid down	L	In serv.	Decomm.
CV 61 *Ranger*	2-8-54	29-9-56	10-8-57	10-7-93
CV 62 *Independence*	1-7-55	6-6-58	10-1-59	30-9-98

Independence (CV 62)—during final active deployment RAN, 3-97

D: CV 61: 60,787 tons light (81,003 fl); CV 62: 60,059 tons light (80,678 fl)

S: 33 kts

Dim: 326.4 (CV 62: 326.1; 319.13 flight deck; 301.8 wl) × 39.63 (82.3 max.) × 11.3

A: 3 (CV 61: 2) 8-round Mk 29 launchers (RIM-7P Sea Sparrow missiles); 3 20-mm Mk 15 Phalanx CIWS gatling AA

Electronics:

Radar: 1 Furuno 900 nav.; 1 SPS-64(V)9 nav.; 1 SPS-67(V)1 surf. search; 1 Mk 23 TAS target acquisition; 1 SPS-49(V)5 air search; 1 SPS-48C 3-D air search; 1 SPN-41 microwave landing aid; 1 SPN-43A air control, 1 SPN-44 microwave landing aid; 2 SPN-42 CCA; 6 Mk 95 missile f.c.; 3 Mk 90 Phalanx f.c.

TACAN: URN-25

EW: SLQ-29 suite (WLR-1H, WLR-8, WLR-11, SLQ-17A); Mk 36 SRBOC decoy syst. (8 6-round Mk 137 RL)—CV 62 also: SLQ-25A SSTDS

M: 4 sets G.E. or Westinghouse geared steam turbines; 4 props; 280,000 shp

Boilers: 8 Babcock & Wilcox: 83.4 kg/cm^2, 520° C **Electric:** 15,000 kw tot.

Range: 4,000/30; 8,000/20 **Fuel:** 7,800 tons

Crew: CV 62: 147 officers, 2,979 enlisted + air wing: 294 officers, 1,795 enlisted + flag staff: 25 officers, 45 enlisted + Marines: 2 officers, 70 enlisted

Remarks: CV 61 was authorized under FY 54, CV 62 under FY 55. CV 62 was in SLEP modernization from 18-4-85 to 2-88. CV 61 did not receive SLEP, but did get an extensive overhaul at Puget Sound NSY from 5-84 to 6-85. CV 61 was decommissioned to reserve 10-7-93 and is to be retained until 2003. CV 62 transferred to the Pacific Fleet 8-10-88; she was homeported at Yokosuka, Japan, from 11-9-91 and was decommissioned 30-9-98 for retention. She is in excellent condition and could have served actively for many more years; consideration was briefly given to recommissioning her at the beginning of the Afghan War.

Disposals: Sister *Forrestal* (CV 59) was redesignated training carrier AVT 59 on 4-2-91, decommissioned 9-9-93, and stricken 10-9-93; the hulk has been stored at Newport, R.I., since 18-9-98. *Saratoga* (CV 60) was decommissioned 20-8-94 and stricken 30-9-94; she is to be employed in pierside trials with concepts for the CV(X) program and has been stored at Newport, R.I., since 7-8-98.

Hull systems: Deck protection and internal compartmentation are extensive; there are 1,200 watertight compartments. Two longitudinal bulkheads are fitted from keel to waterline and from stem to stern; there are transverse bulkheads about every 10 m.

Aviation systems: The hangar is 7.6 m high and 234–240 m long. Have four 15.95 × 18.9–m side elevators. The flight deck is angled at 8° and armored. Have four-cable arresting gear and four C7 steam catapults. Carry 5,880 tons of aviation fuel.

Combat systems: Originally carried eight single 127-mm 54-cal. Mk 42 gunmounts; CV 61 relinquished her last two guns in 1977, later than her sisters did, and retains her forward gun sponsons. CV 62 has three Mk 91 Mod. 1 fire-control systems, each with two Mk 95 radar directors, for the Sea Sparrow missiles. CV 62 had SRN-9 and -19 NAVSAT receivers, an SMQ-11 receiver for the TIROS-N ocean weather forecasting satellite, and WRN-6 GPS receivers. SATCOM equipment includes SSQ-82, SRR-1, WSC-3 (UHF), WSC-6 (SHF), and USC-38 (EHF). During SLEP, CV 62 received the TFCC (Tactical Flag Command Center). Most electronics arrays and armament listed above has been dismounted for preservation.

♦ 0 Project Corsair light carriers [CVL]

Remarks: A notional 4,000-ton minicarrier intended to operate up to seven F-35B Joint Strike Fighters. Its tactical employment was tested at Naval War College war games during 8-00. A group of seven Corsairs, each with a crew of 100, would operate as a task force.

♦ 0 (+ 3) Joint Mobile Offshore Base project

Remarks: The Senate first requested the navy to study employing the Mobile Offshore Base (MOB) concept under the FY 90 budget. In 4-97, a Boeing-Kvaerner (Norway) team beat Brown & Root/McDermott for a $200 million, 18-month feasibility study for a 1,609-m-long Joint Mobile Offshore Base (JMOB) floating runway composed of five semisubmersible modules; the system could be used to transport up to 10,000 troops and to operate C-17 transport aircraft. Kvaerner later teamed with McDermott and the U.S. Bechtel construction company to carry out the study. Such a system would to some extent free U.S. forces of the political constraints of maintaining garrison forces ashore in politically sensitive areas. One operational concept would collocate MOBs with the Marine Corps–dedicated Maritime Prepositioning Force flotillas. Another foresees three JMOBs: one structured for ground warfare, another for air warfare to be deployed in Asian waters, and a third nonspecialized JMOB for Mediterranean or Western Hemisphere deployment. The cost for one JMOB has been estimated to be between $5 and $10 billion, making the project unlikely to proceed, although the Marine Corps planned to continue the studies with FY 02 money.

NAVAL AND MARINE CORPS AVIATION

U.S. Navy and Marine Corps Active Aircraft Totals (as of 30-9-01)

♦ **1,080 fighters** (1,008 combatant)

25 F-4 Phantom II		
1	F-4S	In storage for eventual conversion to QF-4S
3	QF-4N	Unmanned target drone conversion
20	QF-4S	Unmanned target drone conversion; replacing QF-4N
1	YF-4J	Ejection-seat testing
36 F-5 Tiger II		
32	F-5E	Single-seat adversary training aircraft
4	F-5F	Two-seat adversary training aircraft
183 F-14 Tomcat		
62	F-14A	Front-line fighter aircraft, underpowered with TF-30 engines
70	F-14B	Re-engined F-14A
46	F-14D	Super Tomcat; improved systems, new engines
5	NF-14A/B/D	Permanently modified for test duties
836 F/A-18 Hornet		
186	F/A-18A	Initial version, single-seat fighter/attack aircraft (includes one lost 16-1-02 in a landing accident)
31	F/A-18B	Two-seat combat trainer version
406	F/A-18C	Upgraded F/A-18A, AMRAAM-capable
142	F/A-18D	Two-seat attack version of F/A-18C, for USMC
31	F/A-18E	Super Hornet; single-seat upgrade, new production
34	F/A-18F	Super Hornet; two-seat upgrade, new production
0	EA-18G	Proposed Growler EW variant to supplement EA-6B Prowler
6	NF/A-18A/C/D	Permanently modified for test duties

♦ **156 attack aircraft** (133 combatant)

7 A-4 Skyhawk		
7	TA-4J	Training; last squadron (VC-8, at Roosevelt Roads, P.R.) to retire in 2005
149 AV-8 Harrier-II		
133	AV-8B	Major redesign, with improved capability; Harrier-II+ has APG-65 radar
1	NAV-8B	Modified AV-8B for testing
15	TAV-8B	Two-seat trainer; some used for systems evaluations

♦ **122 electronic attack aircraft** (122 combatant)

122 EA-6 Prowler		
122	EA-6B	EW mission; HARM missile capable (one of these was lost 15-11-01 in Olympic National Park and a Marine EA-6B was lost off the North Carolina coast 21-11-01; both crews were saved)

♦ **267 patrol aircraft** (234 combatant)

267 P-3 Orion		
2	P-3B	P-3A with T56-A-14 engines
223	P-3C	Improved avionics systems, for maritime patrol
11	EP-3E	Electronic reconnaissance ("Aries-II"); one more being converted
11	NP-3C	Configured for trials
11	NP-3D	One converted as Hawkeye 2000 trials aircraft, with rotating radome; others assigned to naval weapons test squadrons, operating from China Lake and Point Mugu, Calif.
4	UP-3A	Utility transport and equipment trials
5	VP-3A	Executive transport

♦ **112 antisubmarine warfare aircraft** (112 combatant)

112 S-3 Viking		
112	S-3B	S-3A with improved avionics

♦ **67 airborne early warning aircraft** (65 combatant)

67 E-2 Hawkeye		
65	E-2C	Improved system, several electronics configurations
2	TE-2C	Pilot trainer for E-2C

♦ **16 strategic communications relay aircraft**

16 E-6 Mercury		
3	E-6A	TACAMO (used by VQ-3 and VQ-4); formerly "Hermes"
13	E-6B	Modified E-6A capable of communicating with all U.S. strategic weapons systems

♦ **279 transports**

36 C-2 Greyhound		
36	C-2A	Aircraft carrier logistics support
28 C-9 Skytrain II		
17	C-9B	Militarized commercial DC-9, for casualty evacuation and transport; two operated by USMC, others by Naval Reserve
11	DC-9	Former commercial aircraft
87 C-12 Huron		
4	C-12C	On loan from U.S. Army; used at Naval Test Pilot School, NAS Patuxent River, Md.
2	RC-12F	Former range-control aircraft, now used as utility transports
2	RC-12M	Range surveillance and clearing
21	TC-12B	Former UC-12B converted for training to augment T-44
38	UC-12B	Passenger logistics; six more are in storage
10	UC-12F	Improved UC-12B, with newer engines and avionics
10	UC-12M	Utility transports, with improved engines and avionics
7 C-20 Gulfstream		
2	C-20D	Gulfstream-III executive transport
5	C-20G	Gulfstream-IV cargo/personnel transport
7 C-26 Metro		
7	C-26D	Ex-Air National Guard C-26B light transports refurbished in 1998–99 by Fairchild for liaison use
3 C-35 Citation		
2	UC-35C	Two Citation Ultra delivered to USMCR as transports in 2000
1	UC-35D	First Citation Encore delivered mid-2001 to USMC as VIP transport; 2 more to follow in 2002, with a total of five planned
4 C-40A Clipper		
4	C-40A	Boeing 737-700IGW transport, to replace C-9B/DC-9
107 C-130 Hercules		
20	C-130T	Logistics transport, improved over earlier C-130s
1	DC-130A	Drone target launcher and controller; contractor operated
35	KC-130F	Tactical tanker/cargo transport (used by VMGR-152, -252, and -352)
6	KC-130J	Latest variant, with increased cargo capacity and six-bladed props; first of 11 on order flew 9-6-00, with a total force of 51 desired (first three assigned to VMGR-252)
14	KC-130R	Tactical tanker/transport (used by VMGR-252 and -352) (one lost in Afghanistan 9-1-02)
28	KC-130T	Improved avionics, tanker capabilities (used by VMGR-234 and -432)
2	NC-130H	One is ex-USCG, with rotating radome; at NAS Patuxent River
1	TC-130G	Support aircraft for Blue Angels

♦ **629 trainer and research aircraft**

96 T-2 Buckeye		
96	T-2C	Basic two-seat jet trainer, with J85 engines; 31 in storage
0 T-6 Texan II		
0	T-6A	Joint Primary Aircraft Training System (JPATS) propeller trainer, based on Pilatus PC-9; to enter USN service in 2003, with a total procurement of 328 planned
305 T-34 Mentor		
304	T-34C	Two-seat basic trainer, with PT6A-25 turboprop engine
1	NT-34C	Modified for avionics testing
9 T-38 Talon		
9	T-38A	Naval Test Pilot School trainer
27 T-39 Sabreliner		
1	T-39D	Utility transport and research; at China Lake, Calif.
8	T-39G	Modified CT-39G used for naval flight officer training
17	T-39N	Trainer for naval flight officers
1	CT-39G	Used by USMC for training and as a transport
55 T-44 Pegasus		
55	T-44A	Advanced multiengine trainer
131 T-45 Goshawk		
74	T-45A	Advanced trainer
57	T-45C	Improved avionics
1 U-1 Otter		
1	NU-1B	Naval Test Pilot School trainer
2 U-6 Beaver		
2	U-6A	Naval Test Pilot School trainer
2 X-26		
2	X-26A	Naval Test Pilot School powered glider trainer
1 X-31		
1	X-31A	Angle-of-attack research

♦ **7 tilt-rotor assault aircraft**

7 V-22 Osprey		
0	HV-22B	Proposed navy combat rescue aircraft
7	MV-22B	Marine Corps transport; production version (grounded through 3-02 due to several crashes)

♦ **1,365 helicopters** (980 combat)

127 H-1 Iroquois/Huey (103 combatant)		
24	HH-1N	Search-and-rescue variant
100	UH-1N	Special armed transport, with twin T400-CP-400 engines
3	UH-1Y	Remanufactured, modernized UH-1N with four-bladed rotor
198 AH-1 SeaCobra (198 combatant)		
194	AH-1W	Two T-700-GE-401 engines
4	AH-1Z	Planned upgrade with four-bladed rotor, three stores stations, new avionics
67 H-3 Sea King		
2	SH-3H	Updated SH-3G with T58-GE-10 engines; utility duties
51	UH-3H	Utility and rescue
2	VH-3A/D	Executive transport conversions
11	VH-3D	Assigned to HMX-1, Quantico, Va., for presidential use
1	NVH-3A	VH-3A permanently modified for test duties
6 H-6 Cayuse		
6	TH-6B	Naval Test Pilot School helicopter trainer; on loan from U.S. Army
305 H-46 Sea Knight (153 combatant)		
25	CH-46D	Improved T58-GE-10 engines
228	CH-46E	Improved T58-GE-16 engines; all are USMC transports
41	HH-46D	Utility and rescue
11	UH-46D	Utility version for vertical replenishment, with T58-GE-10 engines (one of these was lost off the U.S. East Coast 7-2-02)
40 H-53 Sea Stallion (40 combatant)		
40	CH-53D	Marine Corps heavy-lift helicopter

NAVAL AND MARINE CORPS AVIATION *(continued)*

193 H-53E Super Stallion/Sea Dragon (193 combatant)		
153	CH-53E	Marine Corps medium-lift helicopter
40	MH-53E	Navy mine countermeasures version of CH-53E, with larger fuel tanks (one of these was lost 20-1-02 in Afghanistan in a hard landing)
118 H-57 Sea Ranger		
44	TH-57B	Basic trainer
74	TH-57C	Advanced instrument trainer
3 H-58 Kiowa		
3	OH-58C	Naval Test Pilot School helicopter trainers; on loan from U.S. Army
308 H-60 Seahawk (293 combatant)		
39	HH-60H	Combat support strike/rescue variant
4	MH-60R	Planned upgrade of SH-60B/F to common standard; termed the SH-60R until 25-5-01
18	MH-60S	Fleet combat/logistics support variant, termed the CH-60S until 6-2-01; 237 are planned; known as the "Knighthawk"
158	SH-60B	Sea-based LAMPS-III ASW
2	NSH-60B	SH-60Bs used as trainers at Naval Test Pilot School
74	SH-60F	Carrier-based, with dipping sonar
1	YSH-60F	Prototype MH-60F, modified under a 28-9-00 contract to test a vectored-thrust ducted propeller and composite lifting wing during 2003–04
1	UH-60A	Naval Test Pilot School trainer; on loan from U.S. Army
3	UH-60L	Naval Test Pilot School trainers; on loan from U.S. Army
8	VH-60N	USMC VIP transport; assigned to HMX-1, Quantico, Va., for presidential use

Total active inventory: 4,100 (2,654 first-line combatant)

Squadron Designations

Air squadrons are designated alphanumerically, the letter prefixes for the principal squadron types being:

Navy:

HC	Helicopter Combat Support (CH-46D, HH-46D, UH-46D, UH-3H)
HCS	Helicopter Combat Search-and-Rescue/Special Warfare Support (HH-60H)
HM	Helicopter Mine Countermeasures (MH-53E)
HS	Helicopter Antisubmarine (SH-60F)
HSL	Light Helicopter Antisubmarine (SH-60B)
HT	Helicopter Training (TH-57)
VAQ	Electronic Attack (EA-6B)
VAW	Carrier Airborne Early Warning (E-2C)
VC	Fleet Composite (utility aircraft)
VF	Fighter (F-14)
VFA	Strike Fighter (F/A-18)
VFC	Fighter Composite (F-5, F-14, F/A-18)
VP	Patrol (P-3)
VPU	Special Projects Patrol (P-3 series)
VQ	Fleet Air Reconnaissance (EP-3); Strategic Communications (E-6A/B)
VR	Fleet Logistics Support (C-9/DC-9, UC-12, C-130)
VRC	Fleet Logistics Support/COD (Carrier Onboard Delivery) (C-2A)
VS	Sea Control (S-3B)
VT	Training (T-2C, TC-12B, T-34C, T-39G/N, T-44A, T-45A)
VX	Air Test and Evaluation

Marine Corps:

HMH	Marine Heavy Helicopter (CH-53D/E)
HMLA	Marine Light Attack Helicopter (AH-1W, UH-1N)
HMM	Marine Medium Helicopter (CH-46E)
HMM(T)	Marine Medium Helicopter Training (CH-46E)
HMT	Marine Helicopter Training
HMX	Marine Helicopter (VH-3D, CH-46E, CH-53E, VH-60N)
VMA	Marine Attack (AV-8B)
VMAQ	Marine Electronic Warfare (EA-6B)
VMFA	Marine Fighter-Attack (F/A-18A/C)
VMFA(AW)	Marine Fighter-Attack (All-Weather) (F/A-18B/D/F)
VMGR	Marine Refueler-Transport (KC-130F/J/R/T)
VMGRT	Marine Refueler-Transport Training (KC-130F/J)
VMMT	Marine Tilt-rotor Training (MV-22)
VMR	Marine Transport Squadron (C-9B)

New Aircraft Procurement

	FY 00	FY 01	FY 02	FY 03	FY 04	FY 05	FY 06	FY 07
F-35B/C JSF	—	—	—	—	—	—	4	8
F/A-18E/F Hornet	36	39	48	44	42	43	50	55
E-2C Hawkeye	3	5	5	5	2	3	4	4
MV-22B Osprey	11	11	9	11	13	15	20	27
MH-60S Seahawk	16	15	13	15	13	22	26	27
MH-60R Seahawk	—	—	—	—	6	10	10	10
T-45C Goshawk	15	14	6	8	—	—	—	—
T-6A Texan-II JPATS	12	24	6	—	—	—	—	24
MMA	—	—	—	—	—	—	—	2
UC-35	2	1	1	—	—	1	2	2
C-37	—	1	—	—	—	—	2	—
C-40A Clipper	1	1	—	—	—	—	3	1
KC-130J Hercules	1	3	2	4	—	—	4	5
Total	97	114	90	87	76	94	125	165
Modernizations:								
UH-1Y and AH-1Z	—	—	—	—	9	11	22	28

Marine Corps Aviation

Marine Corps aircraft are procured and "owned" by the navy and are intended to operate principally from land bases and amphibious-warfare ships, but squadrons of helicopters and attack, reconnaissance, and electronic warfare fixed-wing aircraft can operate from carriers as well. Combat aviation is organized into three active Marine Air Wings (MAW)—the 1st MAW based at Futenma, Okinawa; 2nd MAW at Cherry Point, N.C.; and 3rd MAW at Miramar, Calif.—and one reserve wing. In addition, there are four training squadrons for fixed-wing aircraft, three for helicopters, and one Base and Command Support squadron. Unmanned aerial vehicle (UAV) squadrons VMU-1 and VMU-2 were established 15-1-96 at Cherry Point, N.C., and Yuma, Ariz., respectively, to operate RQ-2A/B Predator drone reconnaissance aircraft.

Naval Aircraft Designation System

In addition to the nickname given to each basic aircraft design (Hornet, Tomcat, Orion, etc.), each basic aircraft type is alphanumerically designated as follows:

1. The letter immediately preceding the hyphen indicates the basic type:

A—attack
B—bomber
C—cargo/transport
E—airborne early warning
F—fighter
H—helicopter
K—tanker, inflight refueling
O—observation
P—patrol
S—antisubmarine
T—training
U—utility
V—VTOL/STOL, vertical or short takeoff and landing
X—research

2. The figure that comes immediately after the hyphen is the design sequence number. When a letter follows this figure, its position in the alphabet indicates that the aircraft is the first, second, third, etc., modification to the original design. Example: F-14D = fighter aircraft, 14th fighter design, fourth major variant.

3. When a basic aircraft is configured for a function that is not its original mission, an amending letter indicating the new function precedes the letter for the original mission (see para. 1 above):

A—attack
C—cargo/transport
D—direction or control of drones, aircraft, or missiles
E—special electronic installation
H—search and rescue
K—tanker, inflight, refueling
L—cold weather; for arctic regions
M—multimission or mine countermeasures
Q—drone aircraft
R—reconnaissance
S—antisubmarine
T—trainer
U—utility, general service
V—staff
W—weather, meteorology*

4. The following letters, prefixed ahead of an aircraft's designation, mean:

G—permanently grounded*
J—temporary special test*
N—permanent special test
X—experimental
Y—prototype
Z—planning*

*Not currently used

Principal Combat Aircraft

♦ **F-35B/C Joint Strike Fighter (JSF)**
Mfr: Lockheed Martin Corp., Fort Worth, Texas

X-35 JSF prototype Lockheed Martin, 2001

X-35C JSF prototype in U.S. Navy configuration Lockheed Martin, 2001

NAVAL AND MARINE CORPS AVIATION *(continued)*

Remarks: The JSF will be a STOVL (Short Take-Off/Vertical Landing) attack fighter, the use of which will permit either the construction of smaller carriers or the carrying of additional strike fighters on existing carrier designs. The initial $18,981,928,201 contract was awarded to Lockheed Martin 26-10-01, at which time DoD planning called for 1,763 F-35A models for the USAF, 480 F-35C for the USN, and 609 F-35B for the USMC (with another 150 for the U.K.); the total to be procured for the USN and USMC may be cut to 680, however. The different variants are to have a 70–90% commonality. Target production price is $28 million each in FY 99 dollars (or $78 million each if R&D costs are included). The designation F-35 is completely out of sequence and is apparently the result of a slip of the tongue on the part of the secretary of the air force that will not be corrected. Five F-35B and four F-35C flying prototypes are to be built. The first four operational aircraft are to be ordered under FY 06; the F-35B is planned to enter operational service with the USMC in 2010 and the F-35C with the USN in 2012. The Pratt & Whitney F135 engine and the G.E.–Rolls Royce F120 are to be interchangeable in the aircraft. No characteristics or performance data have been released.

♦ F/A-18E/F Super Hornet fighter-bombers

Mfr: Boeing, St. Louis, Mo.

Wingspan: 13.62 m (9.94 folded) **Length:** 18.38 m **Height:** 4.88 m
Weight: 13,386 kg light/29,931 kg max. takeoff **Wing area:** 46.5 m^2
Speed: Mach 1.8 max.
Engines: 2 G.E. F414-GE-400 turbojets; 9,977 kg thrust each
Ceiling: 50,000+ ft.
Range: 2,303 n.m. ferry; 665 n.m. radius with 1,814-kg payload
Fuel: 6,558 kg internal; up to 7,429 kg external (3 × 480-gal. tanks)
Armament: 8,050 kg conventional or nuclear stores on 11 stores positions; 1 20-mm M61A1 internal cannon
Avionics: APG-73 radar; AAS-38 FLIR-pod capable; ALQ-165 ASPJ EW

Remarks: The E-model is single seat; the F is a two-seat variant originally intended to be for training. Have improved low-observable characteristics over earlier, smaller F/A-18 models.

The planning goal of 1,000 aircraft was cut to 732 in 5-97 and to 548 later that year; under a plan announced in 3-02, the total may be cut to 460. Unit cost for F/A-18E/F as of 1-01 was $80 million.

The prototype (the first of seven developmental aircraft) rolled out in 9-95. The contract for the first production increment was awarded 3-6-97 for four F/A-18E and four F/A-18F; the first production F/A-18E flew 6-11-98 and was accepted 18-12-98. The first squadron was VFA-122 at Lemoore, Calif., established 1-10-98. The first fleet deployment of the F/A-18E was expected for spring 2002.

Can carry a maximum of eight AIM-7 Sparrow (plus two AIM-9), 12 AIM-9 Sidewinder, or 12 AIM-120 AMRAAM AAM; five 330- or 480-gal. external tanks; 11 1,000-lb. Mk 83 bombs; six AGM-65 Maverick, AGM-154 JSOW, or AGM-88 HARM ASM; or AGM-84H SLAM-ER ASM. Can also carry a centerline aerial refueling store. The combat radius of 665 n.m. would be achieved in Hi-Hi-Hi flight profile with two AIM-9 AAM, four Mk 83 bombs, three 480-gal. external tanks, and two sensor pods. Can land aboard with 4,082 kg of armament stores. The deck "spot" area is 23% greater than for earlier F/A-18-series models.

To be added to later aircraft are the Boeing Advanced Targeting Forward-Looking Infrared (ATFLIR) pod; Raytheon Active Electronically Scanned Array (AESA) radar, in place of the APG-73; Lockheed Martin ALQ-214 Integrated Defensive Electronic Countermeasures System (IDECM); capability to employ the AIM-9X missile; and a helmet-mounted cueing system. AESA radar is to be fitted to the 237th and later aircraft.

The design may be further developed to produce an EA-18G Growler electronic support successor to the EA-6B, to enter service in 2010. The aircraft would be about 99% common with the F/A-18F and would carry three EW pods. A concept demonstrator was flown during 2001; system development may start early in 2003.

F/A-18F Super Hornet—from VFA-122 Boeing, 3-01

F/A-18F Super Hornet—with five ALQ-99 jamming pods and two HARM missiles to demonstrate the F/A-18G configuration Boeing, 2001

F/A-18E Super Hornet Boeing, 1996

♦ F/A-18A/B/C/D Hornet fighter-bombers

Mfr: Boeing–McDonnell Douglas, St. Louis, Mo.

Wingspan: 11.43 m (12.3 with missiles) **Length:** 17.07 m **Height:** 4.67 m
Weight: 10,620 kg empty/25,541 kg max. **Speed:** Mach 1.8 max.
Engines: 2 G.E. F404-GE-400 turbojets; 6,800 kg thrust each
Ceiling: 50,000+ ft.
Range: 2,303 n.m. ferry; 410 n.m. radius with 1,814 kg payload
Armament: 5,900 kg conventional or nuclear stores, including up to 4 Harpoon, 2 Sidewinder, and 4 Sparrow missiles; 1 20-mm M61A1 internal cannon
Avionics: APG-65 radar; AAS-38 FLIR-pod capable; ALQ-165 ASPJ EW

Remarks: Multirole strike fighter. The B and D models are two-seat versions. Carry 4,930 kg internal fuel and 7,711 kg max. external fuel. F/A-18C/D have APG-73 radar, and 135 earlier aircraft were to have APG-73 backfitted. Use a microprocessor to control the various weapons systems, depending on the combat mode. The first USMC squadron was operational 7-1-83, the first USN during 10-83. F/A-18C/D have AMRAAM and IR Maverick missile capability. F/A-18D for the USMC have the ATARS

F/A-18D Hornet—from VFA-125 David D. Broecker, 5-99

F/A-18B Hornet—from VFA-125 David D. Broecker, 5-99

F/A-18A Hornet—from VFA-97 David D. Broecker, 5-99

NAVAL AND MARINE CORPS AVIATION *(continued)*

F/A-18C Hornet—from VFA-37 Lt. Jeff Cooper, USN

tactical reconnaissance pod and are capable of all-weather attack. During 1990–96, 130 F/A-18A were retired. Single-seat USMC F/A-18C squadrons began to be integrated aboard carriers beginning 10-94; the shorter-range Marine F/A-18D two-seaters will not go aboard carriers. The SHARP reconnaissance pod is being developed to permit the F/A-18F to replace TARPS-equipped F-14As around 2003. The last in the series, an F/A-18D for the USMC, was delivered 25-8-00. As of 2001, structural problems were beginning to afflict the F/A-18C model.

♦ F-14A/B/D Tomcat interceptors
Mfr: Grumman Corp. Aircraft Systems Div., Calverton, N.Y.

An F-14 Tomcat catches the wire—note the wings in forward position, with slats and spoilers set RAN, 12-99

F-14 Tomcat from CVW-5 Mitsuhiro Kadota, 9-99

Wingspan: 19.53 m extended/11.63 m swept **Length:** 18.85 m
Height: 4.88 m **Weight:** 18,186 kg empty/28,236 (F-14D: 32,865) kg max.
Speed: Mach 2.34 max./Mach 1.88 operational
Engines: F-14A: 2 Pratt & Whitney TF30-P-414A turbojets; 9,480 kg thrust each, with afterburner—F-14B, D: 2 G.E. F110-GE-4400; 12,698 kg thrust each
Ceiling: 60,000 ft. **Range:** 2,000 n.m. ferry; 500 n.m. combat radius (2.5–3.0 hr)
Armament: 6 Phoenix, Sparrow, or Sidewinder AAM; 1 20-mm M61A1 cannon
Avionics: AWG-9 (F-14D: APG-71) radar; TARPS recce pod on three in each squadron

Remarks: The last of 712 was delivered 21-7-92. Thirty-eight F-14B were new-built; the remainder were re-engined F-14As. F-14D has new engines, plus APG-71 radar and ALR-67 and ALQ-165 EW equipment; they were also to get the ASPJ jammer. More than 140 of all variants have been lost to accidents, none in combat. Although the F-14 is a superior air-to-air interceptor to the F-18 series and can carry more air-to-ground ordnance, all F-14As are to be retired by the end of FY 03, leaving the B and D variants to serve until 2008.

The last F-14A-to-D conversion was delivered in 5-95. The first F-14B entered squadron service during FY 97. A total of 49 F-14Ds were wired for TARPS photo-reconnaissance pod and 54 F-14Bs were fitted to employ LANTIRN (Low Altitude Targeting and Infrared for Night) FLIR sensor pods. All three variants are now intended to be able to drop ordnance, carrying up to 8,000 lb. of bombs each. All now have GPS receivers.

Note: Some 90 modernized, rewinged A-6E Intruder all-weather attack aircraft are stored at Davis-Monthan AFB, Tucson, Ariz.

♦ AV-8B Harrier-II V/STOL attack fighters
Mfr: Boeing–McDonnell Douglas, St. Louis, Mo.

AV-8B Harrier Boeing–McDonnell Douglas

Wingspan: 9.24 m **Length:** 14.10 (Harrier-II+: 14.55) m **Height:** 3.53 m
Weight: AV-8B: 8,720 kg max. takeoff (in VTOL mode; 13,492 in STOL mode); Harrier-II+: 6,742 kg empty/14,059 kg max. (STOL)
Speed: 650 kts max. (585 at sea level)
Engines: 1 Rolls-Royce Pegasus F402-RR-408; 9,751 kg thrust
Ceiling: 50,000 ft. **Range:** 2,460 n.m. max. ferry; 100+ n.m. VTOL radius
Armament: 1 25-mm GAU-12/U gatling gun; 2–4 Sidewinder AAM; up to 14 227-kg or 6 454-kg bombs, Maverick, Walleye

Remarks: A total of 276 were procured for the USMC; 17 others were two-seat TAV-8B trainers. The first squadron became operational in 6-85. The first of 60 of the night-capable variant, with FLIR, flew in 6-87. Average cost: $21.6 million. The 167th built and later had the more powerful F402-RR-408 engine. The final 27 had the APG-65 radar added. Can deploy aboard LHA 1– and LHD 1–class amphibious warfare ships. Plans to update 114 of the surviving units to AV-8B Harrier-II+ with APG-65 radar and other improved avionics were canceled in 3-92, but were reinstated by 5-93 with a new goal of 72 upgraded aircraft; funds to convert the first two production versions were provided under FY 94, and by FY 97, a steady 12 per year were to be modernized, with the last delivered late in 2001.

♦ S-3B Viking shipboard multirole aircraft
Mfr: Lockheed California Co., Burbank, Calif.

S-3B Viking—from VS-29 David D. Broecker, 8-99

Wingspan: 20.93 m **Length:** 16.26 m **Height:** 6.94 m
Weight: 12,160 kg empty/23,853 kg max.
Speed: 450 kts max./350 kts cruise/210 kts patrol
Engines: 2 G.E. TF34-GE-400 turbofans; 4,210 kg thrust each
Ceiling: 40,000 ft.
Range: 3,000 n.m. ferry; 1,150 n.m. patrol radius **Endurance:** 9 hr
Armament: 4 Mk 46 or Mk 50 torpedoes, 4 d.c., 4 mines, or 4 Mk 82 or Mk 83 bombs; 2 Harpoon ASM on underwing stations—see remarks
Avionics: APS-137(V)1 radar; ASQ-81(V)1 MAD; ALE-40 ECM; 60 sonobuoys; 90 expendable decoys

Remarks: A total of 187 S-3As were built, primarily for use as carrier-deployed ASW aircraft. Beginning in 3-87, 132 were to be updated to S-3B configuration, with APS-137(V)1 inverse synthetic aperture radar, Harpoon ASM launch capability, a new auxiliary power unit, ALE-40 countermeasures dispenser, and other updated avionics; the last conversion was completed in 1994. ASW-dedicated aircrew and equipment were being removed from the aircraft as of 1998, and the surviving aircraft are now dedicated to surveillance, photoreconnaissance, and aerial refueling missions. Starting in FY 02, all remaining aircraft are to be retired, with the last leaving service during FY 07, although the S-3B upgrade was intended to keep the aircraft flying into 2015.

One S-3B was updated to S-3B SSU (Surveillance Systems Upgrade) configuration prior to 2000 and proved so valuable during operations over Afghanistan that conversion of four more was requested. The S-3B SSU carries the APS-137(V)5 radar, with improved range and resolution.

Sixteen S-3As (out of a requirement for 36) were converted to ES-3A Shadow BGPHES (Battle Group Passive Horizon-Extension System) ELINT aircraft to replace the retired EA-3B. Their weight was increased to 13,520 kg empty and 63 antennas were fitted, along with the ALR-76, ALR-81, ALR-82, ALR-92, and ALD-9 electronic support measures systems and APS-137 inverse synthetic aperture radar. The first operational aircraft was delivered to VQ-5 on 22-5-92, but all 16 were withdrawn from service starting 2-99, with most of the aircraft placed in storage with unconverted S-3As in Arizona.

US-3A COD (Carrier Onboard Delivery) conversions are all now in storage; the one KS-3A tanker prototype was converted to a US-3A in 1984 and subsequently lost. One S-3A is being used for structural life extension update prototype by Lockheed Martin, starting in 1999.

NAVAL AND MARINE CORPS AVIATION *(continued)*

♦ E-2C Hawkeye airborne early warning and air control aircraft
Mfr: Northrop Grumman, Grumman Aerospace Corp., Bethpage, N.Y., and St. Augustine, Fla.

E-2C Hawkeye—from VAW-117 David D. Broecker, 5-99

E-2C Hawkeye—from VAW-115 Mitsuhiro Kadota, 7-00

Wingspan: 24.58 m **Length:** 17.60 m **Height:** 5.59 m
Weight: 18,364 kg empty/24,689 kg max. **Wing area:** 65.03 m^2
Speed: 315 kts max./260 kts cruise
Engines: 2 Allison T56-A-427 turboprops; 5,100 shp each
Ceiling: 37,000 ft. **Range:** 1,540 n.m. ferry **Endurance:** 6 hr
Fuel: 5,625 kg internal **Crew:** 5 **Armament:** none
Avionics: APS-138, -139, or -145 radar; ESM suite

Remarks: The original APS-125 radar was replaced by the APS-138 TRAC-A (Total Radiation Aperture Control Antenna) to reduce side lobes; it can track upwards of 600 air and surface targets within a 250 n.m. radius while the aircraft controls up to 25 intercepts. The 122nd and 17 later aircraft got the APS-139 radar with improved ECCM. Aircraft delivered since 1992 have the APS-145 radar with overland capability, a new IFF, GPS, Link 16, and JTDS (Joint Tactical Information Distribution System); the APS-145 radar increases target detection capability 15-fold and covers an area of 6 million square miles. Current plans call for continuing low-rate E-2C production indefinitely and for the introduction of an updated E-2D variant after 2010; the latter will employ a Northrop Grumman solid-state, electronically steered UHF radar and will have ballistic-missile detection and tracking capabilities. The E-2D is also to have a tactical cockpit, allowing the pilot to function as a fourth mission system operator; a new communications suite; new generators; improved IFF; and an updated mission computer and software.

The first Hawkeye-2000 (H-2000) variant of the E-2C, equipped with CEC (Cooperative Engagement Capability) sensor fusion and data distribution equipment, first flew 11-4-98, but the first new-production Hawkeye-2000 was not delivered until 10-01, and the aircraft was not expected to be operationally ready until 2004. All aircraft currently on order or programmed will have the CEC feature. All aircraft are to be fitted with new, eight-bladed, narrow-chord props by 2006, and a new SIRST (Surveillance Infrared Search and Track) sensor is to be added.

♦ EA-6B Prowler combat EW aircraft
Mfr: Northrop Grumman, Grumman Aerospace Corp., Calverton, N.Y.

EA-6B Prowler Walter Angermeier, 9-99

EA-6B Prowler—from VAQ-137 David D. Broecker, 8-99

Wingspan: 16.15 m **Length:** 18.11 m **Height:** 4.95 m
Weight: 12,185 kg empty/27,392 kg max. **Speed:** 520 kts max./410 kts cruise
Engines: 2 Pratt & Whitney J52-P-409 turbojets; 5,442 kg thrust each
Ceiling: 34,400 ft. **Range:** 2,400 n.m. ferry; 710 n.m. combat radius
Crew: 4 **Armament:** recent aircraft: HARM missiles
Avionics: ALQ-149; ALQ-99F jammers; APS-130 radar; . . .

Remarks: A total of 170 were delivered between 1-71 and 11-91; the Marines have 22. The first EA-6B ADVCAP (Advanced Capability) was delivered in 10-89 with J52-P-409 engines, new slats, improved flaps, ALQ-149 communications intercept/jammer, and other improvements. HARM missile capability was added in 1985. The last nine new EA-6Bs were procured under FY 89. A program to update 102 earlier aircraft to ADVCAP configuration was canceled. VAQ-129 at Whidbey Island, Wash., was established 30-9-95 to provide land-based joint USN/USAF electronic support and crews; VAQ-133 and VAQ-137 were established in 1996, VAQ-142 was established in 4-97, and VAQ-143 is to form late in 2002. The aircraft are heavily used; as of 12-01, eight of the 122 in service had been grounded for wing stress cracks, 17 others showed signs of the problem, and 40% of the entire force had been restricted in flight maneuvers to reduce stress on their aging airframes.

Surviving aircraft are configured in one of two "blocks," Block 82 and Block 89A. Block 82 aircraft have improved structural, safety, and supportability features. Block 89A aircraft, of which the prototype conversion was delivered in 8-97, have enhanced computers, ARC-210 radios, and an integral GPS/inertial navigation system; production conversions were to begin delivery in 1999, and all remaining aircraft may ultimately be affected. Further "ICAP III" or Block 89A improvements were funded under FY 99 to retain the aircraft in service through 2015 (although they will probably be retired much sooner); ICAP III aircraft will receive GPS systems, an improved ALQ-99 noise jammer that will be able to direct higher energies at specific threat signals, new radios, and provision for later SATCOM transceiver installation and Link 16. The first of two prototype ICAP III aircraft flew 16-11-01, and production conversions will become operational in 2005. Plans to convert 18 EA-6B aircraft from Block 82 to Block 89A configuration were terminated in 6-00.

♦ C-2A Greyhound carrier onboard delivery aircraft
Mfr: Northrop Grumman, Grumman Aerospace Corp., Bethpage, N.Y.

C-2A Greyhound Northrop Grumman

Wingspan: 24.57 m **Length:** 17.27 m **Height:** 4.85 m
Weight: 14,175 kg empty/24,668 kg max. **Speed:** 343 kts max./257 kts cruise
Engines: 2 Allison T56-A-425 turboprops; 4,910 shp each
Ceiling: 33,800 ft. **Range:** 1,490 n.m. at 260 kts
Crew: 3 + up to 32 passengers or 20 litter patients

Remarks: A variant of the E-2 Hawkeye series with a larger-diameter fuselage. Of the original 17 ordered in 1964, 12 remained when a second batch of 39 with uprated engines was ordered in 1983; production ended in 1989. Have a rear loading ramp. Payload: 5,535 kg. Usage has been heavier than expected, and only 39 remained in service at the end of 2001, with no replacement or service-life extension program programmed.

♦ Multimission Maritime Aircraft (MMA)

Boeing's 737 concept for the Multimission Maritime Aircraft Boeing, 1999

Remarks: Formerly known as the Large Land-Based Aircraft (LLBA). Studies began late in 1996 for a follow-on airframe to replace the P-3C Orion, the EP-3E Aries-II EW aircraft, and the C-130 transport. As of 2001, two versions of the same airframe were planned: one for maritime patrol and attack, the other for surveillance and intelligence collection. Boeing has offered a maritime patrol version of its 737-700 transport; Raytheon and Lockheed Martin reworked P-3C airframe concepts; EADS an aircraft based on the Airbus A-320 or A-321 transport; and BAE Systems a variant of the dated Nimrod airframe. The Northrop Grumman offer of a family of designs based on its RQ-4A Global Hawk high-altitude reconnaissance drone was eliminated from contention early in 2002. The MMA, under current planning (which changes frequently), could enter service between 2010 and 2012, with as many as 200 to be procured.

NAVAL AND MARINE CORPS AVIATION *(continued)*

♦ P-3C Orion maritime surveillance aircraft and variants
Mfr: Lockheed Martin, Lockheed Aeronautical Systems Co., Burbank, Calif.

P-3C Orion Leo Dirkx, 10-99

EP-3E Aries-II U.S. Navy, 1999

NP-3D Orion—assigned to the Naval Research Laboratory Mike Wilson, USN

Wingspan: 31.13 m **Length:** 36.61 m **Height:** 10.28 m
Weight: 27,892 kg empty/62,994 kg max. **Speed:** 405 kts max./209 kts patrol
Engines: 4 Allison T65-A-14 turboprops; 4,910 shp each
Ceiling: 34,000 ft. **Range:** 4,500 n.m. ferry; 2,380 n.m. patrol radius
Endurance: 14.5 hr **Crew:** up to 15
Armament: 7,700 kg disposable ordnance, including 4 Mk 46 or Mk 50 torpedoes, 4 SLAM or Maverick ASM, 6 908-kg mines, etc.
Avionics: APS-115 or -137(V) radar; AQS-81(V)1 MAD; ASQ-114 digital computer; AAS-36 FLIR; 87 sonobuoys

Remarks: Current plans call for upgrading 68 of the 111 Update II and II.5 P-3Cs to Update III configuration by 2006, for a total of 208; they are to be equipped to track small patrol craft and vehicles ashore. The P-3C Update III is fitted with an A-NEW central operations module built around the ASQ-114 computer, APS-137 ISAR (Inverse Synthetic Aperture Radar), ALQ-16 and ALR-66(V)5 EW equipment, AAS-36 infrared detector, AAR-47 missile-warning system, ALE-47 countermeasures dispensing system, AQS-81 MAD, Boeing UYS-1 acoustic processor, GPS receivers, and the capability to carry AGM-65F Maverick and/or AGM-84E SLAM antiship missiles. In a further BMUP (Block Modification Update Program), the aircraft are to receive the ASQ-227 mission computer in place of the ASQ-212, the ALR-66B(V) EW system, the USQ-78B acoustic receiver system, and improved flat-panel display screens. For 221 aircraft, the airframe fatigue life of 38 years may be extended to 48 years in a Service Life Extension Program (SLEP).

A Sustained Readiness Program (SRP) rehabilitation for 32 aircraft contracted to E-Systems (now Raytheon) in 1994 was canceled in 2-00 with only six aircraft delivered; another seven are to be completed and the equipment purchased for the remainder delivered to the navy for use on 19 follow-on SRP Aircraft Recovery Program (SARP) aircraft. The navy requires 146 P-3C aircraft to be updated under the Antisurface Improvement Program (AIP) but was able to budget for only 58 over the 2001–09 decade. The AIP version—used extensively over Bosnia, Kosovo, and Afghanistan—employs the Advanced Imaging Multispectral Sensor (AIMS) for standoff optical surveillance and targeting and has the ability to launch AGM-84E SLAM and AGM-84H SLAM-ER missiles. About 40 current aircraft will have to be retired by 2005.

Other variants: The first of 13 P-3Cs converted to EP-3E Aries-II ELINT aircraft for squadrons VQ-1 and VQ-2 was delivered to VQ-1 on 7-8-90 to replace the earlier EP-3B/E Aries-I. The EP-3E aircraft have APS-134 Big Look radars; carry 60,000 lb. of fuel for a max. gross takeoff weight of 142,000 lb.; have crews of 7 officers and 17 enlisted, an endurance of 12 hours, a ceiling of 30,000 ft., and a maximum airspeed of 345 kts; and are 30.38 m long. The older EP-3Es will reach retirement age in 2007. A P-3C was converted to an EP-3E in 1999–2000 as a replacement for an EP-3E that crashed in 1997. One EP-3E was captured by China after it was severely damaged by a Chinese fighter during 4-01; although eventually returned to U.S. custody, it was to reenter service during 2002.

Utility conversions of the P-3 airframe in service include five VP-3A VIP transports and four UP-3A utility aircraft; one NP-3C and 13 NP-3D conversions are employed in various systems trials (one NP-3D carries an E-2C radar and the Hawkeye-2000 avionics upgrade suite for trials, while the sole NP-3C "Hairy Buffalo" carries the APY-6 synthetic aperture radar).

♦ E-6A/B Mercury strategic communications aircraft
Mfr: Boeing Aerospace Div., Boeing, Seattle

E-6B Mercury U.S. Navy, 1998

Wingspan: 45.60 m **Length:** 46.61 m **Height:** 12.93 m
Weight: 78,365 kg empty/155,102 kg max. **Speed:** 530 kts max./442 kts cruise
Engines: 4 CFM Intl. F108-CF-100 turbofans; 9,977 kg thrust each
Ceiling: 42,000 ft. (cruise) **Range:** 6,600 n.m. ferry
Endurance: 16.2 hr (72 with aerial refueling) **Crew:** 10 + 8 relief
Avionics: VLF comms suite; ALR-68(V)4 ESM; Bendix APS-133 weather radar; Litton LTN-90 inertial nav.; Omega nav.

Remarks: Ordered 29-4-83 to replace EC-130Q TACAMO ("Take Charge and Move Out") strategic communications aircraft. First flight took place 19-2-87 and all had been delivered by end-1991. Nickname was changed from "Hermes" in 1992. Operated by VQ-3 from Barbers Point, Oahu, Hawaii, and VQ-4 from Patuxent River, Md., until 29-5-92, when both squadrons moved to Tinker AFB, Okla., under Strategic Communications Wing 1. Have an 8,535-m trailing-wire main VLF antenna and a 1,524-m short trailing wire VHF dipole; an ECM pod is installed on the starboard wingtip. Uses the Boeing 707-320B transport airframe. The prototype upgraded E-6B aircraft was delivered 16-6-94 by Chrysler Technologies Airborne Systems, Waco, Texas, with enhanced message-handling capabilities, a Milstar SATCOM terminal, and a 1553B digital databus. Six series E-6B airborne command post conversions, with the capability to communicate with all U.S. strategic weapons systems command centers on land and sea, were ordered 31-1-95 for $95.5 million. All were to have been converted to E-6B by 12-00, with the first production conversion handed over 10-10-97; by 10-01, however, only 13 of the 16 had been converted. A single Boeing 737 was leased by L-3 Communications during 3-01 for use as a flight trainer for the E-6B.

♦ C-40A Clipper transports
Mfr: Boeing, Seattle

C-40A Clipper Boeing

Wingspan: 34.32 m **Length:** 33.63 m **Height:** 12.55 m
Weight: 77,551 kg max. takeoff **Speed:** Mach 0.78–0.82
Engines: 2 G.E. CFM56-7 turbofans; 24,000 lb. thrust each (at sea level)
Ceiling: 41,000 ft. **Range:** 3,800 n.m. max.

Remarks: Two Boeing 737-700C airframes were ordered 29-8-97 as C-40A Clippers; a third was ordered in 6-98, a fourth on 30-7-99 (for delivery 8-01), a fifth in 6-00, and the sixth on 3-1-01. Two more are programmed through FY 05, and an eventual total of as many as 30 is foreseen. The convertible aircraft can carry up to 121 passengers, up to eight cargo pallets (17.46 metric tons max.), or a combination of up to three pallets and 70 passengers. They are to replace aging C-9B/DC-9 transports in naval reserve service. The first four C-40As were assigned to VR-59, Ft. Worth, Texas, beginning in 1-01, and the next two will be with VR-58 at Jacksonville, Fla., starting 6-02.

♦ MV-22B Osprey tilt-rotor assault troop carriers
Mfrs: Boeing, Vertol Div., Morton, Pa., and Bell Helicopter Textron, Amarillo, Texas

Wingspan: 14.17 m (25.78 over rotors) **Length:** 17.48 m
Height: 6.73 m (5.28 folded) **Speed:** 340 kts max./275 kts cruise
Weight: 15,821 kg empty/24,948 kg max. (21,500 for vertical takeoff)
Engines: 2 Allison T406-AD-400 turboshafts; 6,150 shp each (sust.)
Ceiling: 32,000 ft.
Range: 2,100 n.m. max. unrefueled ferry; 1,200 n.m. at 275 kts with 1,814 kg of cargo

Remarks: A total of 360 (reduced in 1997 from 473) is planned. The last of 10 developmental aircraft was delivered 9-2-98 and the first production aircraft during 5-99. The navy plans to acquire 48 of the total as HV-22 combat rescue variants, and the U.S. Special Operations Command wants some 50 CV-22Bs for the USAF, the first of which was completed 25-7-00. The first five fully operational MV-22Bs were

NAVAL AND MARINE CORPS AVIATION *(continued)*

MV-22A Osprey—hovering Boeing, 1998

MV-22A Osprey—in forward flight mode Boeing, 1998

ordered 28-4-97 for $402 million; they went to Marine squadron VMMT-204 at New River, N.C. Due to two losses, however, all operational aircraft were grounded during 2001, with flight testing to resume in 4-02. Production orders have nonetheless continued, with 11 per year authorized during FY 00 and 01, 12 in FY 02, and 11 planned for FY 03; by FY 07, the number procured per year is to rise to 27.

Intended to carry 24 troops or 12 litters up to 200 n.m. at about 3,000 ft. altitude. Alternatively, can carry 30 passengers or 9,000 kg of cargo internally or a 4,535-kg external load. The rotor/propeller blade diameter is 11.58 m, giving an overall span of 25.78 m over the rotors. Maximum vertical rate of climb is 1,090 ft./min. in vertical mode, and the hover ceiling is 14,200 ft. Carry 7,600 liters of fuel internally and have the capacity for four auxiliary cabin tanks with another 9,200 liters for ferrying; can also be aerial refueled. General Dynamics received a contract in 4-01 to develop a turret-mounted 12.7-mm GAU-19/A gatling gun for the MV-22B to provide a suppression-fire capability. The USAF CV-22 special forces variant has additional fuel tanks to double the unrefueled range.

♦ SH-60B (LAMPS-III), SH-60F, HH-60H, and MH-60R Seahawk helicopters

Mfr: Sikorsky Aircraft Div., United Aircraft Corp., Stratford, Conn.

SH-60B Seahawk—LAMPS III ASW version LSPH Darren Yates, RAN, 1-01

Rotor diameter: 16.36 m **Length:** 19.76 m (15.26 fuselage, 12.47 folded)
Height: 5.23 m
Weight: SH-60B: 6,190 kg empty/9,927 kg max. takeoff; SH-60F: 10,658 kg max.
Speed: 150 kts (126 cruise)
Engines: 2 T700-GE-401C turboshafts; 1,940 shp max./1,662 shp continuous each

SH-60F Seahawk—carrier-borne ASW variant Mitsuhiro Kadota, 9-99

HH-60H Seahawk—combat rescue variant George R. Schneider, 10-00

Range: 678 n.m. ferry; 150 n.m. mission radius (4 hr) **Endurance:** 6 hr max.
Armament: 2 Mk 46 or Mk 50 torpedoes (or 1–2 AGM-119B Penguin ASM in some SH-60B or 2 Hellfire ASM)—HH-60H: Hellfire missiles and GAU-17, M-240, or M-60D guns
Avionics: SH-60B: APS-124 radar; ASQ-81(V)2 MAD; UYS-1 Proteus sonobuoy processor; 25 A-size sonobuoys; ALQ-142 ESM; Link 11—SH-60F: AQS-13F dipping sonar; no radar or sonobuoy facilities—HH-60: APR-39A(V)2 EW; ALE-47 EW; ALQ-144A EW; SATCOM; FLIR

Remarks: The SH-60B, flown by 12 HSL (Light Helicopter Antisubmarine) squadrons, was intended for use aboard frigates and destroyers as part of an ASW suite, with the helicopter linked to the ship by datalink for data processing, the sensors displaying on the ship. First flight took place 12-12-79. Have a crew of three. The Block I update, awarded in 12-89, added Mk 50 torpedo and Penguin missile capability, a 99-channel sonobuoy processor, GPS, and a third weapons station; a total of 171 were to be able to launch AGM-119B Penguin—far more helicopters than there were missiles—but the conversion program was curtailed after 28 had been completed. Block II, which entered service in 1996, substituted a multimode inverse synthetic aperture radar (ISAR) and added the AQS-22 FLASH dipping sonar, FLIR, helo-to-helo datalink capability, and a targeting capability for ship-launched SLAM missiles and improved countermeasures. Most SH-60Bs now have the more powerful T700-GE-401C engines. For antisurface warfare, 46 SH-60B and 42 HH-60H have been fitted to carry Hellfire missiles, a video datalink, a 7.62-mm machinegun, and AAS-44 FLIR.

The first production SH-60F first flew on 19-3-87 as a replacement for the carrier-based SH-3 Sea King and differed from the SH-60B in having most of the LAMPS-II equipment deleted and replaced by an AQS-13F dipping sonar. No radar or EW gear is fitted. The last aircraft was delivered 1-12-94.

Up to 170 SH-60B and 59 SH-60F are to be converted to MH-60R by 2012, with further conversions to be delivered later for a total of 243. The prototype conversion flew on 22-12-99, and the first of four test conversion aircraft ordered 16-7-99 flew on 19-7-01. The first five production conversions were ordered during 3-00, with four more approved under FY 01; during 2001, however, the concept was changed to buying all-new MH-60R airframes, starting with six in the FY 04 budget. The original designation SH-60R was changed to MH-60R on 25-5-01, but the unofficial nickname "Strikehawk" was not adopted. MH-60Rs are to have AQS-22 dipping sonars, AYK-14 integrated mission processors, a thermal imager, a laser mine detection system, APS-147 synthetic aperture radar, passive target classification features added to the ALQ-142 EW system, the UYS-2A acoustic processor, and a new sonobuoy launcher; the MAD gear and flotation bags are to be removed to save weight. The MH-60R will be able to launch AGM-119 Penguin and AGM-114 Hellfire missiles and Mk 46 and Mk 50 torpedoes and will have a door-mounted 7.62-mm mg. Initial planned production of the MH-60R is 6 under FY 04 and 10 per year under FY 05–07.

Of 42 new HH-60H procured (of which 39 were still in service as of 6-99), 24 are operated by the regular navy and the rest by the Naval Reserve Force. Plans to update 14 HH-60H to MH-60R have been canceled. Nine VH-60N VIP transports were delivered to the Marine Corps in 1988–89 as replacements for the VH-1N in the Presidential Flight; one was lost during 5-93. Plans to update 14 to MH-60R have been canceled.

♦ MH-60S Knighthawk support helicopters

Mfr: Sikorsky Aircraft Div., United Aircraft Corp., Stratford, Conn.

Rotor diameter: 16.36 m **Length:** 19.76 m (15.26 fuselage; 15.70 folded)
Height: 4.87 m **Weight:** 6,281 kg empty/10,658 kg max.
Speed: 150 kts max./130 kts cruise
Engines: 2 T700-GE-401C turboshafts; 1,940 shp max./1,662 shp continuous each
Range: 620 n.m. (with two 230-gal. external tanks) **Crew:** 4 + 13 passengers
Armament: Hellfire missiles; 1 7.62-mm mg
Avionics: up to 9,000 lb. external cargo; 1 AQS-20(X) towed minehunting sonar; AES-1 Airborne Laser Mine Detection System (ALMDS); Organic Airborne and Surface Influence Sweep (OASIS); SPU-1W Magnetic Orange Pipe (MOP); A Mk 2(G) towed acoustic mine countermeasure

Remarks: Designation changed from CH-60S to MH-60S on 6-2-01, with the "M" standing for "Multimission"; the aircraft was officially named Seahawk on the same

NAVAL AND MARINE CORPS AVIATION *(continued)*

MH-60S Knighthawk—testing mine countermeasures gear U.S. Navy, 2001

date, the name "Knighthawk" having previously been used unofficially but finally authorized during 3-02. Intended to replace all H-46D and UH-3 utility helicopters, the first of a planned 237 MH-60S entered service in 2001 with HC-3, which was to have 10 aircraft by 11-01 and 17 total by 2005. The YCH-60 demonstrator, converted from an army UH-60L, first flew on 6-10-97, and two production aircraft were added to the FY 98 budget by Congress. The first production conversion flight came on 27-1-00; 25 are to have been delivered by 1-03.

Lightweight mine countermeasures modules will be provided for the MH-60S, theoretically allowing it to replace the MH-53E; it is also to be able to launch Hellfire missiles and will be equipped with a FLIR. Maximum payload is 4,000 lb. internal and 9,000 lb. external (10,000 lb. max. total).

Missions for the aircraft include organic airborne mine countermeasures, fleet combat logistic support, search and rescue, medical evacuation, vertical onboard delivery, special warfare support, humanitarian assistance, and torpedo, UAV, and UUV recovery. They have a rescue hoist, automatic blade fold, and capacity to carry two standard cargo pallets internally.

Disposal note: The remaining SH-2G Super SeaSprite LAMPS-I ASW helicopters were retired during FY 01 with the disestablishment of reserve squadrons HSL-94 and HSL-84; the relatively new aircraft were to be transferred to foreign navies.

♦ CH-53E Super Stallion transport and MH-53E Sea Dragon mine countermeasures helicopters

Mfr: Sikorsky Aircraft Div., United Aircraft Corp., Stratford, Conn.

MH-53E Sea Dragon mine countermeasures helicopter
Maritime Photographic, 3-98

CH-53E Super Stallion heavy-lift helicopter—aboard *Boxer* (LHD 4)
Julio Montes, 10-00

Rotor diameter: 24.08 m **Length:** 30.18 m (22.35 fuselage; 18.44 folded)
Height: 8.64 m **Weight:** 15,071 (MH-53E: 16,482) kg empty/33,339 kg max.
Speed: 170 kts (150 cruise)
Engines: 3 G.E. T64-GE-416 turboshafts; 4,380 shp max./3,695 shp continuous each
Ceiling: 18,500 ft.
Range: 1,000 n.m. unrefueled ferry; 230 n.m. with 8,630 kg cargo; 50 n.m. with 14,512 kg cargo
Endurance: MH-53E: 4 hr **Crew:** 3

Remarks: The YCH-53E first flew on 1-3-74, the YMH-53E on 23-12-81. A CH-53E can carry 56 fully equipped troops or up to 14,512 kg of cargo. All now operate with the USMC. Have a seven-bladed main rotor. The CH-53E can also be used to tow Mk 105 mine countermeasures sleds. Both versions are aerial refuelable. The final two CH-53Es were ordered 21-6-95 for delivery by 7-97; one is configured to carry presidential vehicles.

The MH-53E can deploy the AQS-14 minehunting sonar, Mk 104 acoustic sled, Mk 105 magnetic sled, or one or more Mk 103 mechanical cutter sleds; a 12.7-mm mg is carried for mine disposal. The MH-53E has enlarged side sponsons holding 4,478 kg of fuel (enough for 4.5 hours) and has a cable winch exerting a 13.6-ton pull; it can also be used to carry 56 troops. Two MH-53Es can be accommodated in one C-5B transport. The MH-53E, although relatively new, is to be phased out and replaced by MH-60R/S helicopters with less-effective mine countermeasures modules. As an interim measure, however, four sets of air-towed AQS-14A(V)1 mine detection sonars are being acquired

The USMC is considering a life-extension program to improve capabilities, reduce maintenance costs, and extend service to 2025 for 111 CH-53Es; the cost would be about $22 million per aircraft, and production updates would start with 15 aircraft in FY 11. The "CH-53X" would be re-engined with the Rolls-Royce AE1107C turbofan, receive new composite rotor blades and elastomeric rotor head to increase lift capacity from 7,600 lb. to 28,000 lb. under "hot and high" conditions (and maximum takeoff weight to 35,607 kg), get a new cargo hook, and have new cockpit avionics and displays.

♦ CH-53D Sea Stallion transport helicopters

Mfr: Sikorsky Aircraft Div., United Aircraft Corp., Stratford, Conn.

CH-53D Sea Stallion Julio Montes, 10-95

Rotor diameter: 22.04 m **Length:** 26.92 m (20.48 fuselage)
Height: 7.59 m **Weight:** 10,718 kg empty/19,050 kg max.
Speed: 170 kts max./150 kts cruise
Engines: 2 G.E. T64-GE-413 turboshafts; 2,925 shp each **Ceiling:** 21,000 ft.
Range: 886 n.m. ferry; 540 n.m. mission **Endurance:** 3.5 hr

Remarks: First ordered in 8-62 for the Marine Corps. The last of 174 CH-53Ds was delivered in 1-72. Can carry 55 combat-equipped troops, 24 stretchers and 4 attendants, or 4 tons of cargo. The 40 remaining in service are now considered to be medium-lift helicopters.

♦ CH/UH/HH-46D and CH-46E Sea Knight transport helicopters

Mfr: Boeing, Vertol Div., Morton, Pa.

USMC CH-46E Sea Knight—from HMM-163 Jürg E. Kürsener, 6-01

Rotor diameter: 15.54 m **Length:** 25.70 m (13.92 fuselage)
Height: 5.17 m **Weight:** 7,048 kg empty/11,023 kg max.
Speed: 143 kts max./134 kts cruise
Engines: 2 G.E. T58-GE-16 turboshafts; 1,870 shp each (1,770 sust.)
Ceiling: 14,000 ft. **Range:** 744 n.m. ferry; 206 n.m. mission
Fuel: 2,498 liters max. **Crew:** 2

Remarks: First flight took place 16-10-62, and 624 were procured through 1970. Data above are for the CH-46E. Some 228 CH-46Es are operated by 13 USMC regular and reserve squadrons. The CH-46D vertical replenishment version with T58-GE-10 en-

NAVAL AND MARINE CORPS AVIATION *(continued)*

gines is operated by the navy on replenishment ships; these weigh 6,388 kg empty/9535 kg max. takeoff, and the remaining 40 are planned to be retired by 12-03. The CH-46E can accommodate 25 assault troops, or 15 stretchers and two attendants, while the UH-46D can carry 1,360 kg of internal cargo or 4,536 kg slung beneath. Pairs of HH-46D SAR versions deploy on LHA/LHDs for SAR and utility duties. Surviving aircraft have been updated with an automatic navigation system, armored seats, glass-reinforced plastic rotor blades, and infrared jamming devices.

♦ AH-1W SuperCobra/AH-1Z ground attack helicopters
Mfr: Bell Helicopter Textron, Ft. Worth, Texas

AH-1W SuperCobra—from HMLA-169 Jürg E. Kürsener, 6-01

AH-1Z—note the four-bladed rotor and the sensor radome above the gunmount Sikorsky, 2001

Rotor diameter: 13.42 m **Length:** 17.47 m (12.93 fuselage) **Height:** 4.17 m
Weight: 4,626 kg empty/6,689 kg max. **Speed:** 180 kts max.
Engines: 2 G.E. T700-GE-410 turboshafts; 1,690 shp each
Ceiling: 10,500 ft. **Range:** 360 n.m. (2 hr)
Armament: 1 20-mm XM-197 gatling gun; 76 2.75-in. rockets or 2 20-mm miniguns in pods; TOW and Hellfire ASM and/or Sidearm or Sidewinder AAM

Remarks: The improved AH-1T (with T400-CP-400 engines) first flew on 20-5-76, and 55 production versions were ordered, of which 37 survivors had been converted to AH-1W standard by 1990. Deliveries of the new up-engined AH-1W began 27-3-87. Five were transferred from USMC stocks to Turkey in 1991. One USMC unit was lost on 31-1-00 in Jordan during an exercise.

The AH-1W is to be given a Lockheed Martin infrared sight, color t.v., and laser rangefinder and tracker; an integrated weapons-system control; an additional weapons stores pylon to permit carrying up to 16 AGM-114 Hellfire missiles; and four-bladed rotors. The first 18 conversions were funded under FY 98, and the first of 180 production conversions rolled out 20-11-00. DoD selected the name "Viper" for the AH-1Z, but the USMC does not use it. Production conversion onset, however, has been delayed to FY 04, when only 12 UH-1Y/AH-1Z conversions are planned to be requested, with 16 to follow in FY 05, 33 in FY 06, and 41 in FY 07.

♦ HH/UH-1N Iroquois and UH-1Y transport/utility helicopters
Mfr: Bell Helicopter Textron, Ft. Worth, Texas

UH-1Y—artist's rendering Bill Dale/Sikorsky, 1997

Rotor diameter: 14.70 m **Length:** 17.47 m (12.93 fuselage)
Height: 4.39 m **Weight:** 2,517 kg empty/4,763 kg max. **Speed:** 110 kts
Engines: 2 Pratt & Whitney T400-CP-400 turboshafts; 1,250 shp each (max.)
Ceiling: 15,000 ft. **Range:** 250 n.m. (2 hr)
Armament: 2 7.62-mm mg; 2 rocket pods (7 2.75-in. rockets each)

Remarks: Normally known as the "Huey." The UH-1N is used by the USMC as an armed assault helicopter and the UH-1N and HH-1N by the navy as utility and rescue helicopters. The first UH-1N was delivered in 1971. The USMC plans to update UH-1Ns to the UH-1Y configuration with G.E. T700 engines, four-bladed rotors, and new avionics; the aircraft will be able to carry eight (vice four) troops and will have double the combat radius. Production conversion onset, however, has been delayed to FY 04, when only 12 UH-1Y/AH-1Z conversions are planned, with 16 to follow in FY 05, 33 in FY 06, and 41 in FY 07; 100 total are planned to be converted. The U.S. Army plans to retire all of its H-1-series helicopters during FY 02. Although the DoD selected the name "Venom" for the UH-1Y, but the USMC does not use it.

Note: The navy plans to acquire 328 T-6A Texan-II JPATS (Joint Primary Aircraft Training System) basic trainers to replace the T-34C Mentor, with deliveries spread out from 2002 to 2017. The T-6A will enter service in 2003 with Training Wing 5 (TW-5) at Whiting Field, Fla., and will also be used by TW-6 at Pensacola, Fla., and TW-4 at Corpus Christi, Texas. The first six were ordered in 2000, and 24 more were ordered on 3-4-01; on 2-1-02, Raytheon Aircraft was given a 1-year production contract with four 1-year options.

Eight elderly T-39G Sabreliners have replaced 10 USAF T-1A Jayhawk joint services navigational and naval flight officer training aircraft at Pensacola.

Nine ex-Air National Guard C-26B Metro light transports were refurbished by Fairchild Aerospace as C-26Ds; of the seven in service as of 12-01, four are assigned to Naples Naval Air Facility and Sigonella Naval Air Station in Italy and the others to the Pacific Missile Test Range, Barking Sands, Hawaii.

A $31.2 million contract with Geo-Seis Helicopters to provide two Aérospatiale AS.33J Puma helicopters for replenishment services from aboard T-AFS supply ships in the Mediterranean through 12-02 was signed during 11-99—the first such contract to a foreign organization.

Support aircraft squadron assignments are:
- C-9B and DC-9 Skytrain-II transports: VR-46, -52, -56, -57, -58, -59, and -61 (all Naval Reserve) and Marine Reserve squadron VMR-1
- TC-12B: VT-35
- UC-12B: VRC-30
- C-20D: VR-1 (Naval Reserve)
- C-20G: VR-48 and -51 (Naval Reserve)
- C-40A: VR-58 and -59 (Naval Reserve)
- C-130T Hercules transports: VR-53, -54, -55, and -62 (all Naval Reserve)
- TA-4J Skyhawk: VC-8
- F-5E/F: VFC-13 (Naval Reserve)
- T-2C Buckeye: VT-9 and -86
- T-34C Mentor trainers: VT-1, -3, -4, -6, -10, -27, and -28
- T-39G Sabreliner: VT-4 and -10
- T-39N Sabreliner: VT-86
- T-44A Pegasus trainers: VT-31
- T-45A Goshawk: VT-7, -21, and -22
- TH-57B/C Sea Ranger: HT-8 and -18
- UH-3H Sea King: fleet readiness squadron HC-2, HC-11, HC-85 (Naval Reserve), HSL-51 Det., and VC-8

Squadrons with miscellaneous aircraft assigned include VX-1; VX-9; Naval Weapons Test Squadron, Point Mugu; Naval Weapons Test Squadron, China Lake; Naval Strike Aircraft Test Squadron; Naval Force Aircraft Test Squadron; Naval Rotary-Wing Aircraft Test Squadron; and the Naval Test Pilot School.

C-9B Skytrain-II—from VR-57 David D. Broecker, 5-99

C-20G Gulfstream-IV Vernon Pugh/U.S. Navy, 5-94

USMC UC-35D Citation Encore U.S. Navy, 2000

NAVAL AND MARINE CORPS AVIATION *(continued)*

DC-130A Hercules drone controller David D. Broecker, 8-99

F-5E Tiger II—of VFC-13 David D. Broecker, 8-99

T-45A Goshawk trainer Chris A. Neill/U.S. Navy

T-2C Buckeye trainer Takatoshi Okano, 9-01

T-34C Mentor trainer David D. Broecker, 5-96

UC-12B Huron transports—USMC and USN Jürg Kürsener, 1-95

T-44A Pegasus trainer A. D. Baker III, 8-97

VH-3D Sea King executive transport—ComThirdFlt aircraft, aboard *Coronado* (AGF-11) Kurt Greiner/SeaPhoto, 10-00

NUCLEAR-POWERED BALLISTIC-MISSILE SUBMARINES [SSBN]

Note: Planning will commence around 2010 for a successor to the *Ohio* class, with the design possibly to be based on the smaller *Virginia*-class SSN.

♦ 18 Ohio class (SCB 304 design)

Bldr: General Dynamics, Electric Boat Div., Groton, Conn. (*Atlantic/†Pacific Fleet)

	Program	Laid down	L	In serv.
SSBN 726 Ohio†	FY 74	10-4-76	7-4-79	11-11-81
SSBN 727 Michigan†	FY 75	4-4-77	26-4-80	11-9-82
SSBN 728 Florida†	FY 75	9-6-77	14-11-81	8-6-83
SSBN 729 Georgia†	FY 76	7-4-79	6-11-82	11-2-84
SSBN 730 Henry M. Jackson† (ex-*Rhode Island*)	FY 77	19-1-81	15-10-83	6-10-84
SSBN 731 Alabama†	FY 78	27-8-81	19-5-84	20-5-85
SSBN 732 Alaska†	FY 78	9-3-83	12-1-85	25-1-86
SSBN 733 Nevada†	FY 80	8-8-83	14-9-85	16-8-86
SSBN 734 Tennessee*	FY 81	9-6-86	13-12-86	17-12-88
SSBN 735 Pennsylvania*	FY 83	2-3-87	23-4-88	9-9-89
SSBN 736 West Virginia*	FY 84	18-12-87	14-10-89	20-10-90
SSBN 737 Kentucky*	FY 85	. . .	11-8-90	13-7-91
SSBN 738 Maryland*	FY 86	. . .	10-8-91	13-6-92
SSBN 739 Nebraska*	FY 87	. . .	15-8-92	10-7-93
SSBN 740 Rhode Island*	FY 88	3-7-90	17-7-93	9-7-94
SSBN 741 Maine*	FY 89	. . .	16-7-94	29-7-95
SSBN 742 Wyoming*	FY 90	. . .	15-7-95	13-7-96
SSBN 743 Louisiana*	FY 91	. . .	27-7-96	6-9-97

Florida (SSBN 728) M. Piché, 7-01

Ohio (SSBN 726) Jürg E. Kürsener, 6-01

NUCLEAR-POWERED BALLISTIC-MISSILE SUBMARINES [SSBN] *(continued)*

Maryland (SSBN 738) H&L Van Ginderen, 6-99

D: 12,500 tons (light); 16,764 tons surf./18,750 tons sub. **S:** 25 kts sub.
Dim: 170.69 × 12.80 × 11.13 (surf.)
A: 24 Trident D-5 (SSBN 726–731: Trident C-4) strategic ballistic missiles; 4 bow 533-mm Mk 68 TT (Mk 48 or Mk 48 ADCAP torpedoes; Mk 30 decoys; etc.)
Electronics:
Radar: Litton-Sperry BPS-15H (SSBN 741–743: BPS-16(V)) nav./surf. search
Sonar: BQQ-5E(V)4 or BQQ-6 passive suite: BQS-13 active; BQS-15 ice avoidance; BQR-15 towed array with TB-23 thin-line array; BQR-19 active nav.; BQQ-9 TASPE; BQQ-22A (EC-15) sonar receiving set; UQN-4A secure echo sounder
EW: WLR-8(V)5 suite; WLR-10 radar intercept; 8 CSA Mk 1 (SSBN 738–743: 14 CSA Mk 2 Mod. 0/1) countermeasures launchers
M: 1 G.E. S8G natural-circulation pressurized-water reactor, turbo-reduction drive; 1 prop; 35,000 shp
Endurance: 70 days **Crew:** 15 officers, 148 enlisted (2 crews)

Remarks: As a class, the *Ohios* are currently achieving 92.2% operational availability: normally, five submarines are on station on patrol, five more are coming or going from patrol stations but still able to launch missiles, and the others are in port or in overhaul. Because of the provisions of the START-I treaty, *Ohio*-class SSBNs adapted for nonstrategic roles would still count as carrying 192 strategic warheads. SSBN 726–729 must be withdrawn from strategic missile duties in 2002–03 under current treaties; authorization was given during 12-00 to began stripping SSBN 726 and 728 for placement in "In commission, In Reserve" status during 10-02 for later striking and disposal, although SSBN 726 launched three C-4 missiles on 19-12-01. The Trident D-5–equipped submarines are now each planned to remain in service for 44 years. SSBN 726–729 are to be converted to SSGN (q.v.).

The first eight units, with Trident C-4 missiles, are based at Bangor, Wash., in Subron 17 and operate in the Pacific; the later, Trident D-5 missile–equipped units are based at Kings Bay, Ga., with the even-numbered units in Subron 20 and odd-numbered ones in Subron 16. Two or three Trident D-5 units are to be transferred from Kings Bay to the Bangor base, which is being reconfigured to handle the missile: SSBN 737 in 5-02, SSBN 735 in 7-02, and possibly one other later.

Hull systems: Have a hull life of 40 years. Able to submerge to 300 m. The reactor plant reportedly does not generate the full rated horsepower in service.

Combat systems: SSBN 734 and later had Trident D-5 missiles as built. SSBN 734–737 initially carried D-5 missiles with the newer Mk 5/W88, 300- to 450-kT, variable-yield reentry body/warhead; later units initially had the earlier, 100-kT Mk 4/W76 combination. All carry the CCS Mk 2 Mod. 3 combat data system and have two Mk 2 SINS (Ship's Inertial Navigational System) and NAVSAT receivers. The Mk 98 digital computer missile fire-control system and Mk 118 torpedo fire-control system are installed. All have one Kollmorgen Type 152 and one Type 82 periscopes. In SSBN 726–737, four 127-mm horizontal countermeasures launch tubes per side are located in the casing below the sail; in SSBN 738, the tubes are 152 mm in diameter and there are four forward of the missile bay and three aft on each side. Early units had BQQ-9 broadband sound processing equipment for their BQR-15 towed arrays; five later units did not receive the equipment and instead received Rockwell TABIDU (Towed Array Broadband Interim Display Units) during 1994, using commercial off-the-shelf components to save considerable cost and complexity. SSBN 734 and 735 tested prototype Lockheed Martin UGM (Universal Gravity Module) passive seabed profilers; the production UGM may be backfitted to all. During 9-94, DoD decided to backfit all but the first four Trident C-4 units with the D-5 missile, later reduced to all but the first six. SSBN 732 began the first modernization at Puget Sound Naval Shipyard in 2000 and was completed during 2-02; SSBN 733 began conversion in 2001, and SSBN 730 and 731 are to follow.

Note: U.S. Navy nuclear-powered ships, by law, must have crews aboard until the reactor is "safed." Thus, upon deactivation, they are placed in "In Commission, In Reserve" (ICIR) status until they have been stripped of useful materials and the reactor system has been defueled, at which time they are officially decommissioned and stricken. Once a ship has been placed in ICIR status, it effectively cannot be recalled to active service.

Ex-*Daniel Webster* (SSBN 626) and ex-*Sam Rayburn* (SSBN 635), classified as floating equipment, are moored at Charleston, S.C., as training facilities for nuclear power equipment. Their missile compartments have been removed and the remaining spaces altered to facilitate training, with the S5W reactor plants remaining fully operational. The ex-*Sam Rayburn* was refitted at Norfolk Navy Yard, Va., in 1998.

NUCLEAR-POWERED CRUISE MISSILE SUBMARINES [SSGN]

♦ 0 (+ 4) converted Ohio class

Bldr: General Dynamics, Electric Boat Div., Groton, Conn.

	Laid down	L	In serv.
SSGN 726 Ohio (ex-SSBN 726)	10-4-76	7-4-79	11-11-81
SSGN 727 Michigan (ex-SSBN 727)	4-4-77	26-4-80	11-9-82
SSGN 728 Florida (ex-SSBN 728)	9-6-77	14-11-81	8-6-83
SSGN 729 Georgia (ex-SSBN 729)	7-4-79	6-11-82	11-2-84

Ohio-class SSGN conversion—artist's rendering U.S. Navy, 2001

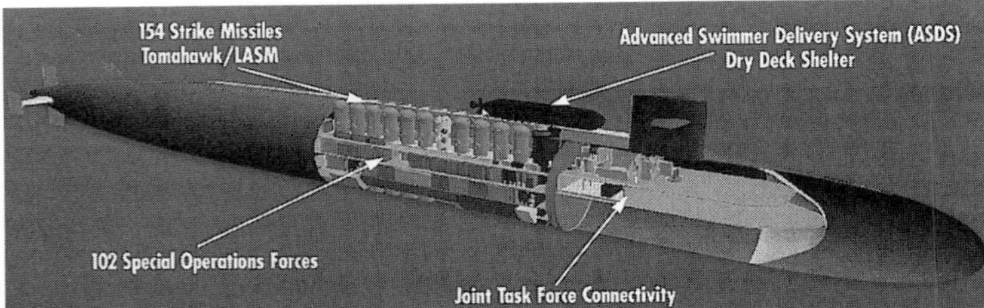

Ohio-class SSGN conversion General Dynamics, 1999

D: 12,500 tons (light); 16,764 tons surf./18,750 tons sub. **S:** 25 kts sub.
Dim: 170.69 × 12.80 × 11.13 (surf.)
A: 22 vertical-launch tubes (up to 154 Tomahawk and Tactical Tomahawk missiles); 4 bow 533-mm Mk 68 TT (Mk 48 or Mk 48 ADCAP torpedoes; Mk 30 decoys; etc.)
Electronics:
Radar: Litton-Sperry BPS-15H nav./surf. search
Sonar: BQQ-5E(V)4 passive suite; BQS-13 active; BQS-15 active ice avoidance; BQR-15 towed array with TB-23 thin-line array; BQR-19 active nav.; BQQ-9 TASPE; BQQ-22A (EC-15) sonar receiving set; UQN-4A secure echo sounder
EW: BLQ-10(V)2 intercept; 4 countermeasures launchers
M: 1 G.E. S8G natural-circulation pressurized-water reactor, turbo-reduction drive; 1 prop; 35,000 shp
Endurance: 70 days **Crew:** 140 tot. + 66 SEAL commandos

Remarks: SSBN 726 and 727 are to be converted to SSGN under FY 03 and are to be redelivered in 2007, becoming fully operational in 2008; SSBN 728 and 729 are to begin conversion during FY 04. Under the FY 02 budget, Congress provided $440 million to begin planning for four SSBN refuelings and conversions, which are expected to cost $834 million each; SSBN 726 and 727 are to be converted at Puget Sound Naval Shipyard, Bremerton, Wash., and the others at Norfolk, Va. Each will use 22 tubes, carrying seven Tomahawks each, with the missiles diverted from stocks intended for the *Los Angeles* class. The converted and refueled SSGN 726–729 are expected to serve to 2027–28. Will have COTS signal processors, the BLQ-10(V)2 EW suite, and Type 18 periscopes.

Hull systems: Have a hull life of 40 years. Able to submerge to 300 m. During conversion, the existing Trident missile control facilities will be replaced by a special operations forces planning compartment, the two forwardmost ballistic-missile tubes will be altered for use as nine-man diver lockout chambers. Two midget submarines or Dry Deck Shelters (or one of each), and a 66-man SEAL force (up to 102 in an emergency) and its equipment will be able to be accommodated. High data-rate SATCOM will be fitted, along with a special forces command center.

Combat systems: Carry the CCS Mk 2 Mod. 3 combat data system and two Mk 2 SINS (Ship's Inertial Navigational System) and have navigational satellite receivers. The Mk 98 digital computer missile fire-control system and Mk 118 torpedo fire-control system are installed. During conversion, Kollmorgen Type 18 periscopes will be fitted, as will the BLQ-10(V)2 EW system and COTS signal processors. The BLQ-11 Long-term Mine Reconnaissance System is also to be carried, and they may be equipped to launch and operate ADM-160A Miniature Air-launched Decoys.

NUCLEAR-POWERED ATTACK SUBMARINES [SSN]

♦ 0 (+ 4 + 26) Virginia class

Bldrs: General Dynamics, Electric Boat Div., Groton, Conn., and Northrop Grumman Newport News (formerly Newport News SB), Newport News, Va.

	Final assembly	Begun	L	In serv.
SSN 774 Virginia	Gen. Dyn.	3-10-97	. . .	6-04 (del.)
SSN 775 Texas	Northrop	8-9-98	. . .	6-05 (del.)

NUCLEAR-POWERED ATTACK SUBMARINES [SSN] *(continued)*

	Final assembly	Begun	L	In serv.
SSN 776 HAWAII	Gen. Dyn.	26-10-99	...	12-06 (del.)
SSN 777 NORTH CAROLINA	Northrop	2-3-01	...	12-07 (del.)
SSN 778	...	2005	...	FY 10
SSN 779	...	2006	...	FY 11
SSN 780	...	2006	...	FY 12
SSN 781	...	...	...	FY 12
SSN 782	...	...	...	FY 13
SSN 783	...	...	...	FY 13

Virginia (SSN 774) Nate Ostrow/McDermott, Inc., 1999

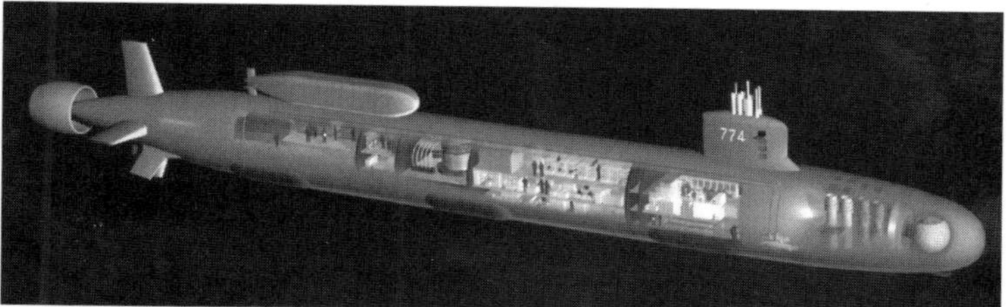

Virginia (SSN 774)—with SEAL ASDS on deck aft; note the pumpjet propulsor U.S. Navy, 2001

D: 7,800 tons sub. **S:** 35 kts sub. **Dim:** 114.91 × 10.36 × 9.30
A: 12 vertical launch tubes for Tomahawk missiles; 4 533-mm TT (38 tot. weapons, incl. 16 Tomahawk missiles, Mk 48 ADCAP torpedoes, mines, UUVs, etc.)
Electronics:
Radar: Sperry BPS-16(V) ARPA nav./surf. search
Sonar: Lockheed Martin BQQ-10 suite: spherical bow active/passive array; TB-29(A) thin-line towed passive array; TB-16 fat-line towed array; HF active bow and sail mine avoidance; BQG-5A WAA lightweight wide-aperture passive flank array; WLY-1 acoustic intercept; Advanced Deployable System offboard sensor on UAV; BQN-17 secure echo sounder; ACOMMS covert underwater comms
EW: Lockheed Martin BLQ-10(V) intercept; 1 76.2-mm reloadable decoy launcher; 14 152-mm external decoy launchers
E/O: 2 BVS-1 nonpenetrating photonic-imaging masts
M: 1 S9G pressurized-water reactor; 1 pumpjet; approx. 40,000 shp
Crew: 12 officers, 101 enlisted

Remarks: Referred to as the "Centurion" class until late 1993, then renamed the NAS (New Attack Submarine) and again renamed the New Nuclear-powered Attack Submarine (NSSN) by 1995. Hull numbers return to the traditional sequence, but a plan to return to traditional "fish" names was thwarted by political considerations; SSN 774 was formally named on 23-9-98 and SSN 775 on 13-11-98. Are being authorized at the rate of one per year; a plan to begin ordering two per year under FY 07 was deferred to FY 12 during 11-01. Electric Boat is building the bows and sterns and Newport News the midbodies for the first four boats—a distinct departure from previous U.S. submarine construction practice; the yards will alternate final assembly and outfitting. Later units may be competed, with one yard building the entire submarine. The assembly of the initial sections for SSN 774 began 2-9-99.

A full 30-unit program was optimistically estimated to cost $56 billion in FY 98 dollars. As of 12-96, costs were estimated as $3.272 billion for the first unit, $2.543 billion for the second, $2.093 billion for the third, and $2.112 billion for the fourth. A contract for $206.77 million was let 17-1-95 to General Dynamics to design and construct the propulsion plant for the first unit. In 1996, Congress mandated the ordering of one per year from FY 98 through FY 01. Under the FY 97 budget, Congress provided $296 million for advance procurement for the FY 98 first unit, $701 million for advance procurement and preparations for the FY 99 unit, $488 million for continuing design work on the class as a whole, and $98 million for R&D related to the class. The initial $4.2 billion construction contract for SSN 774 was given to Electric Boat as lead yard on 30-9-98. As of 3-01, SSN 774 was $341 million over budget and SSN 775 $78 million, due in large part to a 43% increase in the combat data system cost. Construction costs were expected to be $112 million (12%) over target for SSN 774 and $168 million (17%) for SSN 775, a trend expected to continue with later units of the class.

Hull systems: Test depth: 488 m. The single S9G pressurized-water reactor is to have a core expected to last for the 30-year life of the submarines. To be "as quiet at 25 kts as an SSN 688 is alongside the pier," making them clearly superior in noise reduction to all Russian designs. Will have the Litton Marine WSN-7B ring-laser gyro inertial navigation system. Cost-saving measures include the use of commercial fasteners, spliced cables, combined pumping systems, reverse-osmosis potable water generation, and reduced-volume sound-quieting measures.

The first eight units will not have an under-ice operational capability. Some later units of the class may have a 30-ft. section inserted amidships to accommodate SEAL equipment and up to 50 special forces personnel, as in the *Jimmy Carter* (SSN 23); this would add about 800 tons to the submerged displacement. SSN 777 and later are to have a new mold-in-place anechoic outer hull coating. SSN 782 and later units are planned to have enlarged sails, additional countermeasures and Tomahawk missile capacity, and the equipment necessary to permit under-ice operations. SSN 782 or later may also have a bow conformal sonar array instead of the current spherical array within a flooded bow dome. Submarines of the FY 10 program and later are hoped to employ all-electric drive systems, dispensing with main propulsion turbines; this may result in a complete redesign of the internal arrangements for the submarines and possibly even a new hullform with a fuller form aft.

Combat systems: The combat system design contract was let to a consortium of Lockheed Martin, Raytheon, and Northrop Grumman on 30-9-96, with Raytheon responsible for design of the system to coordinate targeting and torpedo/missile launching and for the sonar system transmitters; it is to have 26 times the signal-processing capability and 55 times the data-processing capability of the BSY-2 system in the SSN 21 class. The contract for the first ship-set was issued in 3-97 to Lockheed Martin Federal Systems, for $31.5 million. Two Kollmorgen Model 86 nonpressure-hull-penetrating Universal Modular Masts will be fitted; the masts will incorporate ESM arrays, a SATCOM antenna, a NAVSAT antenna, other communications antennas, and optronic sensors. All will have a new high-data-rate, 43-cm-diameter, multiband dish antenna for WSC-6 Milstar and Global Broadcast Service SATCOM connection. All will probably carry Lockheed Martin UGM (Universal Gravity Module) passive bottom profilers as a navigation aid. The navigational/surface-search radar will be supplemented by Litton's ECDIS-N (Electronic Chart Display and Information System) and Voyage Management System (VMS).

SSN 777 and later are to have the CAVES (Conformal Acoustic Velocity Sonar), replacing the current WAA (Wide Aperture Array) passive arrays. All will have high-frequency sail- and chin-mounted active sonar arrays for accurate bottom mapping, object location and tracking, and obstacle avoidance. Units ordered after 2006 are planned to have a conformal rather than spherical bow sonar array; they will also be able to employ offboard sensors.

A special, half-length variant of the Mk 48 ADCAP torpedo employing the seeker from the Mk 46 ASW torpedo may be developed to provide this class to provide a shallow-water antisubmarine capability; the weapon may be launched from *external* tubes in later units. A proposed intelligence-collection variant may house a large SHF intercept antenna within a "stealth" sail structure. Another variant may be used for mine countermeasures, employing the Submarine Offboard Mine Search System, a remotely piloted submersible launched from a standard 533-mm torpedo tube. The weapons payload in the initial units totals about 86 tons.

Initial units are to have 12 vertical launch weapons tubes for Tomahawk or NATACMS missiles, but the number of tubes may be increased in later units; 38 total weapons are to be carried initially, including four Tomahawk missiles for horizontal launch. A later variant of the design may be modified to incorporate between 75 and 100 vertical launch tubes for Tomahawk tactical strike missiles. SSN 777 and later may employ an elastomeric weapon ejection system, based on pressurizing a 7-ft.-diameter rubber disc, which, when pressure is released, will deliver about 2,400 hp in the form of a water slug to eject weapons from the tubes.

Will be equipped with a nine-man lockout chamber and stowage space for SEAL Team Combat Rubber Raiding Craft. The torpedo room will be reconfigurable to give 68 m^3 of stowage space for SEAL equipment and berthing for 40 SEALs. At least the first six of the submarines will be equipped to carry the new 19.8-m Advanced SEAL Delivery Vehicle (ASDS; see under [LSDV]); their sails will have provision for a modular special forces communications mast.

Note: During 2-99, Newport News received a $47 million contract to design and build a 33.83-m operating scale model of a *Virginia*-class submarine, the *Cutthroat* (LSV-2: Large-Scale Vehicle 2), as a test bed for related technologies and acoustic silencing techniques operated on Lake Pend Oreille, Idaho, at the Acoustic Research Detachment, Bayview. *Cutthroat* has some components manufactured by Electric Boat and was christened on 15-11-00. The craft is propelled by a battery-driven, 6,000-shp permanent magnet electric motor.

Cutthroat (LSV 2)—the large-scale operating model for the Virginia class NAVSEA, 2001

♦ 2 (+ 1) Seawolf class

Bldr: General Dynamics, Electric Boat Div., Groton, Conn. (*Atlantic/†Pacific Fleet)

	Begun	L	In serv.
SSN 21 SEAWOLF*	25-10-89	24-6-95	19-7-97
SSN 22 CONNECTICUT*	14-9-92	1-9-97	11-12-98
SSN 23 JIMMY CARTER†	12-12-95	3-02	6-04 (del.)

NUCLEAR-POWERED ATTACK SUBMARINES [SSN] *(continued)*

Seawolf (SSN 21) U.S. Navy, 1996

Seawolf (SSN 21) General Dynamics, 1998

Connecticut (SSN 22)—at commissioning ceremonies Paul C. Clift, 12-98

D: SSN 21, 22: 7,467 tons surf./9,137 tons sub.; SSN 23: . . . tons
S: 35+ kts sub. **Dim:** 107.60 (SSN 23: 115.83) × 12.80 × 10.95
A: 8 amidships 673-mm TT (50 Tomahawk missiles and Mk 48 ADCAP torpedoes, or up to 100 mines)
Electronics:
Radar: 1 Litton-Sperry BPS-16(V) ARPA nav./surf. search
Sonar: BQQ-5D suite: WAA (wide-aperture passive array); BQS-24 nav./ice avoidance; TB-23 towed array; TB-16D towed array—SSN 23 also: 3 BLQ-11 Mine Reconnaissance System UUV
EW: WLQ-4(V)1 suite; BLD-1 D/F; . . . decoy syst.
M: 1 G.E. S6W pressurized-water reactor (200 Mw), . . . drive; 1 pumpjet; 45,500 shp—1 (SSN 23: 2) drop-down azimuthal maneuvering thruster
Electric: 6,000 kw tot. (2 turbogenerators + auxiliary diesel set)
Crew: 12 officers, 121 enlisted

Remarks: SSN 21 was authorized under FY 89 and ordered 9-1-89. SSN 22 was authorized under FY 91 and ordered on 17-3-92. SSN 23 was authorized under FY 92, although final construction authority was not granted by Congress until FY 96 and funding was not provided until FY 97; the construction order was placed 29-6-96 (although much of the necessary equipment had already long since been purchased). As of 1999, the total cost of the three-submarine program was estimated at $16 billion, including R&D expenditures.

The hull numbering sequence is unusual and nontraditional, as USN hull numbers are by regulation to be sequential and not reused, yet the basic SS 21 number dates to 1912! The anomaly apparently came about when "SSN-21" was applied as the project title, indicating "Submarine for the 21st Century." The name *Connecticut* is also nontraditional for an attack submarine, as is the name announced 8-4-98 for the third unit.

Although commissioned in 7-97, SSN 21 did not commence her first operational patrol until 25-6-01, at which time the Tomahawk launch capability had still not been incorporated, the submarine was still experiencing problems with the pumpjet propulsor, and the BSY-2 combat system was still not operating satisfactorily—nearly 17 years after project inception and well over a decade since the submarine was ordered. SSN 21 and 22 are based at New London, Conn.; SSN 23 is to be based at Bangor, Wash.

The USN announced on 29-1-99 that SSN 23 was to be longer so as to incorporate advanced technologies and the capability to carry special warfare forces; under a 10-12-99 contract, the changes will add $887 million to the cost of the submarine and will delay her launch by 27 months. The submarine's capabilities in tactical surveillance and mine warfare are also being enhanced. The additional 8.2-m section is being added aft of the sail area to accommodate 50 SEALs (at $17.74 million apiece) and their equipment, plus displays for remote-controlled minehunting submersibles and other remotely operated vehicles, which will be stowed in a flush hangar-like section. The section is being added abaft the sail and forward of the reactor compartment; the pressure hull will neck down to a 3-m-diameter section, with the concentric space within the outer hull used for SEAL vehicles and remote-controlled underwater vehicles including the BLQ-11 mine reconnaissance vehicle, 8–12 of which will be maintained at Bangor. A 1.52-m-diameter air lock will be fitted to allow the deployment of personnel and submersibles from within the pressure hull, which will be reinforced with HY-100 high-strength steel in the region of the hull extension. The additional length and weight are expected to cost the boat about 1 kt in maximum speed. SSN 23 will, in effect, replace the capabilities now inherent in the *Parche* (SSN 683) and *Memphis* (SSN 691) and the already-retired *Kamehameha* (SSN 642).

SSN 21 was placed out of service during 8-00 due to the discovery of cracking in air flasks needed for the ballast system; the other two boats do not have the problem, due to the use of different materials.

Hull systems: Test depth: 395 m. The design provides significant improvements over the *Los Angeles* class in speed, quietness, weapons load, sonar processing, and so on. Are able to travel at up to 20 kts while silent. Designed for reliability and ease of maintenance, to operate for 15 years before first overhaul. The submarines have a smaller length-to-beam ratio than the SSN 688 class to improve maneuverability. Retractable bow planes and six fixed stern fins are fitted. A small wedge at the base of the forward edge of the sail improves hydrodynamic flow. The propeller is of shrouded pumpjet configuration. The pressure hull is constructed of HY-100 steel. Under FY 95 funding, a pre-swirl, fixed-vane water flow system and open propulsor was to be developed for installation in one unit of this class by 2000, presumably to replace the pumpjet system; it may be fitted in SSN 23. All three have a drop-down azimuthal maneuvering thruster aft, while SSN 23 will have a second one forward. First two have WSN-2 ring-laser gyros, while SSN 23 will have the WSN-7B, which will be backfitted later in the others.

Combat systems: Have the Lockheed Martin BSY-2(V) Combat Control System and the Submarine Active Detection System (SADS), with bow-mounted MF and HF active sonar capability. The BQQ-5D passive sonar suite includes three flank arrays per side. The TB-23 thin-line towed array has full-spectrum acoustic processing. The torpedo tubes were originally referred to as being 30 inches in diameter, but liners and other fittings restrict to 26.5 inches the diameter of weapons and remotely controlled reconnaissance vehicles launched from them; the launch system is virtually soundless, but the outer doors cannot be opened when the submarine is traveling at maximum speeds. Up to 12 Tomahawk missiles are planned to be carried in lieu of torpedoes; the U.S. and U.K. began a cooperative program to develop a horizontally launchable version of the new Tactical Tomahawk missile for use in this class and RN submarines.

♦ 50 Los Angeles class (SCB 303 type)

Bldrs: EB: General Dynamics, Electric Boat Div., Groton, Conn.; NN: Northrop Grumman Newport News, Newport News, Va. (*Atlantic/†Pacific Fleet)

	Bldr	Laid down	L	In serv.
SSN 688 Los Angeles†	NN	8-1-72	6-4-74	13-11-76
SSN 690 Philadelphia*	EB	12-8-72	19-10-74	25-6-77
SSN 691 Memphis*	NN	23-6-73	3-4-76	17-12-77
SSN 698 Bremerton†	EB	8-5-76	22-7-78	28-3-81
SSN 699 Jacksonville*	EB	21-2-76	18-11-78	16-5-81
SSN 700 Dallas*	EB	9-10-76	28-4-79	18-7-81
SSN 701 La Jolla†	EB	16-10-76	11-8-79	24-10-81
SSN 705 City of Corpus Christi*	EB	4-9-79	25-4-81	8-1-83
SSN 706 Albuquerque*	EB	27-12-79	13-3-82	21-5-83
SSN 707 Portsmouth*	EB	8-5-80	18-9-82	1-10-83
SSN 708 Minneapolis–Saint Paul*	EB	20-1-81	19-3-83	10-3-84
SSN 709 Hyman G. Rickover*	EB	23-7-81	27-8-83	21-7-84
SSN 710 Augusta*	EN	1-4-82	21-1-84	19-1-85
SSN 711 San Francisco†	NN	26-5-77	27-10-79	24-4-81
SSN 714 Norfolk*	NN	1-8-79	31-10-81	21-5-83
SSN 715 Buffalo†	NN	25-1-80	8-5-82	5-11-83
SSN 716 Salt Lake City*	NN	26-8-80	16-10-82	12-5-84
SSN 717 Olympia†	NN	31-3-81	30-4-83	17-11-84
SSN 718 Honolulu†	NN	10-11-81	24-9-83	6-7-85
SSN 719 Providence*	EB	30-9-82	4-8-84	27-7-85
SSN 720 Pittsburgh*	EB	15-4-83	8-12-84	23-11-85
SSN 721 Chicago†	NN	5-1-83	13-10-84	27-9-86
SSN 722 Key West*	NN	6-7-83	20-7-85	12-9-87
SSN 723 Oklahoma City*	NN	4-1-84	2-11-85	9-7-88
SSN 724 Louisville*	EB	16-9-84	14-12-85	8-11-86
SSN 725 Helena†	EB	28-3-85	28-6-86	11-7-87
SSN 750 Newport News*	NN	3-3-84	15-3-86	3-6-89
SSN 751 San Juan*	EB	16-8-85	6-12-86	6-8-88
SSN 752 Pasadena†	EB	20-5-86	12-9-87	11-2-89
SSN 753 Albany*	NN	22-4-85	13-6-87	7-4-90
SSN 754 Topeka*	EB	13-5-86	23-1-88	21-10-88
SSN 755 Miami*	EB	24-10-86	12-11-88	30-6-90
SSN 756 Scranton*	NN	29-8-86	3-7-89	26-1-91
SSN 757 Alexandria*	EB	19-6-87	23-6-90	29-6-91
SSN 758 Asheville*	NN	9-1-87	28-10-89	28-9-91
SSN 759 Jefferson City†	NN	21-9-87	17-8-90	28-2-92
SSN 760 Annapolis*	EB	15-6-88	19-5-91	11-4-92
SSN 761 Springfield†	EB	29-1-90	4-1-92	9-1-93
SSN 762 Columbus*	EB	7-1-91	1-8-92	24-7-93
SSN 763 Santa Fe*	EB	9-7-91	12-12-92	9-1-94
SSN 764 Boise* (ex-*Hartford*)	NN	25-8-88	23-3-91	7-11-92
SSN 765 Montpelier*	NN	19-5-89	23-8-91	13-3-93
SSN 766 Charlotte*	NN	17-8-90	3-10-92	16-9-94
SSN 767 Hampton*	NN	2-3-90	3-4-92	6-11-93
SSN 768 Hartford* (ex-*Boise*)	EB	27-4-92	4-12-93	10-12-94
SSN 769 Toledo*	NN	6-5-91	28-8-93	24-2-95
SSN 770 Tucson†	NN	15-8-91	20-3-94	9-9-95
SSN 771 Columbia†	EB	21-4-93	24-9-94	9-10-95
SSN 772 Greeneville†	NN	28-2-92	17-9-94	16-2-96
SSN 773 Cheyenne†	NN	6-7-92	16-4-95	13-9-96

NUCLEAR-POWERED ATTACK SUBMARINES [SSN] *(continued)*

Asheville (SSN 758) ABPH Tony Barclay-Jeffs, RAN, 7-01

Hampton (SSN 767) Jim Sanderson, 6-01

Cheyenne (SSN 773)—the final SSN 688I LSPH Darren Yates, RAN, 1-01

Philadelphia (SSN 690)—with Dry Deck Shelter aboard; note left-opening door Bernard Prézelin, 5-01

Chicago (SSN 721) LSPH Darren Yates, RAN, 8-01

NUCLEAR-POWERED ATTACK SUBMARINES [SSN] *(continued)*

Dallas (SSN 700)—with right-opening Dry Deck Shelter; note the fairing added to the hull to port to provide a working space on deck H&L Van Ginderen, 7-00

Key West (SSN 722)—note the bow dive planes on the sail Findler & Winter, 10-00

Memphis (SSN 691)—employed as an experimental unit Findler & Winter, 11-00

Oklahoma City (SSN 723) Douglas A. Cromby, 7-00

D: SSN 688–699: 6,080 tons surf./6,927 tons sub.; SSN 700–714: 6,130 tons surf./6,977 tons sub.; SSN 716–718: 6,165 tons surf./7,012 tons sub.; SSN 719–750: 6,255 tons surf./7,102 tons sub.; SSN 751–770: 6,300 tons surf./7,147 tons sub.; SSN 771–773: 6,330 tons surf./7,177 tons sub.
S: 30+ kts sub. **Dim:** 109.73 × 10.06 × 9.75
A: SSN 719 and later: 12 Mk 36 vertical tubes for Tomahawk missiles—all: 4 amidships 533-mm Mk 67 TT (26 Tomahawk missiles, Mk 48 and Mk 48 ADCAP torpedoes, etc.)—SSN 756 and later: mining capability
Electronics:
Radar: 1 BPS-15H or BPS-16(V) nav./surf. search
Sonar: SSN 688–709, 711–750: BQQ-5A(V)1 or BQQ-5C (SSN 716 and later: BQQ-5D; SSN 708, 724: BQQ-10 ARCI) suite; BQS-15 under-ice active; BQR-15 towed array with BQR-23 signal processor or TB-16D and TB-23 or TB-29 (10 units) towed arrays—SSN 710, 751 and later: BSY-1 suite: BQQ-5D; BQG-5D WAA flank arrays; BQS-15 under-ice active; TB-29 towed array—SSN 758 only: HF active array (see remarks)
EW: BRD-7; D/F WLR-8(V)2 intercept; WLR-10 intercept; WLR-9/12 acoustic emission receiver/processor; WLR-1H intercept; WSQ-5 portable ELINT collection; CSA Mk 1 Mod. 2 acoustic decoy launchers—SSN 760 only: BLQ-10 EW suite
E/O: SSN 760 only: 1 BVS-1 photonic-imaging nonpenetrating mast

M: G.E. S6G pressurized-water reactor, 2 sets geared steam turbines; 1 7-bladed prop (pumpjet in SSN 773 and several others); 35,000 shp
Crew: 14 officers, 127 enlisted (SSN 724: 15 officers, 149 enlisted)

Remarks: Authorizations: SSN 688–690 in FY 70, SSN 691–694 in FY 71, SSN 695–700 in FY 72, SSN 701–705 in FY 73, SSN 706–710 in FY 74, SSN 711–713 in FY 75, SSN 714 and 715 in FY 76, SSN 716–718 in FY 77, SSN 719 in FY 78, SSN 720 in FY 79, SSN 721 and 722 in FY 80, SSN 723 and 724 in FY 81, SSN 725 and 750 in FY 82, SSN 751 and 752 in FY 83, SSN 753–755 in FY 84, SSN 756–759 in FY 85, SSN 760–763 in FY 86, SSN 764–767 in FY 87, SSN 768–770 in FY 88, SSN 771 and 772 in FY 89, and SSN 773 in FY 90. Another four (one in FY 90, two in FY 91, one in FY 92) were canceled.

Normally operate on a 24-month cycle, out of which they undertake one 6-month deployment. SSN 773 operated for 203 continuous hours at maximum speed during one 36,034-n.m. deployment in 1999. SSN 701 was refueled with FY 99 funding, and SSN 705 and 711 were refueled under FY 00; SSN 705 was re-homeported to Guam under Subron 15 on completion of the recoring in 2002. Funds to refuel SSN 706 ($282.7 million) were approved under FY 01. SSN 713 is planned to refuel under FY 02; SSN 698, 699, and 714 under FY 03; SSN 707, 708, and 715 under FY 03; SSN 709 and 715 under FY 04; SSN 716 under FY 05; SSN 717 under FY 06; SSN 718 under FY 07; and SSN 710 under FY 08. Refuelings for subsequent units have not been planned, but SSN 719 and later are now planned to remain in service for 33 years each.

SSN 751 and later are described as "Arctic-capable" and are referred to as the SSN 688I (for "Improved") class.

SSN 772 collided with and sank the 499-grt Japanese fisheries training ship *Ehime Maru* off Honolulu 9-2-01 while surfacing, later that year grounded briefly at Saipan, and on 27-1-02 had a minor collision with the *Ogden* (LPD 5).

Disposals: U.S. Navy nuclear-powered ships are retired by placing them initially in "In Commission, In Reserve" (ICIR) status, with partial crews aboard for safety purposes until the nuclear power plants are deactivated and rendered safe. The ships are then formally decommissioned and usually (but not always) stricken from the Navy List on the same date.

Retirements to date include:

	ICIR	Decomm.	Stricken
SSN 689 *Baton Rouge*	1-11-93	13-1-94	13-2-95
SSN 692 *Omaha*	7-2-95	5-10-95	5-10-95
SSN 693 *Cincinnati*	5-1-95	31-7-95	29-7-96
SSN 694 *Groton*	19-9-96	7-11-97	7-11-97
SSN 695 *Birmingham*	17-4-97	12-97	12-97
SSN 696 *New York City*	19-3-96	30-4-97	30-4-97
SSN 697 *Indianapolis*	2-3-98	. . .	. . .
SSN 702 *Phoenix*	18-9-97	29-7-98	29-7-98
SSN 703 *Boston*	15-3-99	19-11-99	19-11-99
SSN 704 *Baltimore*	1-10-97	10-7-98	10-7-98
SSN 712 *Atlanta*	1-3-99	. . .	. . .
SSN 713 *Houston*	4-1-01	. . .	. . .

Planned future retirements through FY 20 include SSN 698, 699, and 714 (FY 16 if refueled) in FY 02; SSN 717 in FY 06 (FY 18 if refueled); SSN 718 in FY 07 (FY 18 if refueled); SSN 710 in FY 08 (FY 18 if refueled); SSN 688 and 690 in FY 10; SSN 691 in FY 11; SSN 700 and 711 in FY 12; SSN 715 in FY 13; SSN 698, 699, 707, and 708 in FY 14; SSN 701, 709, and 713 in FY 15; SSN 705 and 706 in FY 16; SSN 716, 721, 724, and 725 in FY 17; SSN 719 and 723 in FY 18; SSN 720 and 752 in FY 19; and SSN 722 and 754 in FY 20.

Hull systems: Maximum operating depth: 450 m. SSN 753 and 754 had partial HY-100 steel pressure-hull sections to test fabrication procedures for the SSN 21 class; the others have HY-80 steel hulls. The bow is built of glass-reinforced plastic as a streamlined fairing over the spherical BQQ-5A(V)1 sonar array. All have one Fairbanks-Morse 38D8Q diesel generator set and batteries for emergency propulsion. The reactor core was intended to last 10–13 years between refuelings. SSN 751 and later have bow-mounted vice sail-mounted diving planes and most are equipped with additional anhedral fins at the stern to support towed arrays; these fins are being fitted with seven-cell launchers for 127-mm countermeasures, and the fins have also been added to a few earlier units of the class. SSN 768 and later have improved sound quieting and propulsion systems. Several later units (including SSN 773) have shrouded pumpjet propellers, and a few have the propellers themselves connected at the tips by a circular ring to reduce cavitation. Have berths for only 124 personnel, so there is some "hot-bunking." There are two SINS (Ship's Inertial Navigational Systems), which are being replaced by the Litton Marine WSSN-7 ring-laser gyro inertial navigation system. SSN 719 and later trim level on the surface, while earlier boats without the vertical missile tubes forward trim up by the bow.

Combat systems: SSN 751 and later have the first-generation BSY-1 (formerly Submarine Advanced Combat System, or SUBACS) integrated sonar/weapons-control suite; its development problems slowed delivery of these units, and SSN 751–755 had to be backfitted with their UYK-43 computers after completion. SSN 755 was the first unit with a fully functional BSY-1 system. All carry a UYK-7 general-purpose computer and have WSC-3 UHF SATCOM gear. One Mk 2F optical attack and one Sperry Mk 18 (Mk 15D on early units) multifunction periscopes are fitted; later units also have the Sperry Naval Electronic System for Infrared Exploitation (NESSIE), with FLIR, low-light-level t.v., and an EHF SATCOM antenna. The BLD-1 electromagnetic interferometer was added beginning in 1985. The Mk 113 Mod. 10 torpedo fire-control system was originally installed in SSN 688–699; the Mk 117 was installed in later units through SSN 750 and subsequently backfitted into SSN 688–699. Under FY 83, the Mk 117 f.c.s. was modified in many to permit launching SUBROC missiles, which were then removed in 1989. SSN 719 and later have 12 vertical-launch tubes for Tomahawk cruise missiles, located between the forward end of the pressure hull and the spherical array for the BQQ-5 bow sonar; the arrangement of the tubes differs in SSN 719. SSN 688–718 can carry eight torpedo tube–launched Tomahawk cruise missiles; later units can carry 20 (including the 12 in the vertical launchers). In peacetime, bunks occupy four reload weapon spaces, and four other reload spaces remain empty so that torpedo tubes can be emptied when in port. UGM-84-series Sub-Harpoon missiles were removed during 1996–97.

Under development for employment with this class was the Northrop Grumman NMRS (Near-term Mine Reconnaissance System) unmanned underwater vehicle (UUV), a 533-mm-diameter, 5.23-m-long surveillance drone fitted with AMDS forward-looking and ADS-14-derived side-looking sonar systems and capable of being launched and recovered from the submarine's torpedo tubes; when carried, the sys-

NUCLEAR-POWERED ATTACK SUBMARINES [SSN] *(continued)*

tem and its associated equipment would reduce the torpedo loadout by six or seven weapons. The NMRS is controlled by 50 n.m. of fiber-optic cable and will travel at 4–7 kts for up to 5 hours; it was expected to enter service in 1998. The BLQ-11 LMRS (Long-term Mine Reconnaissance System) is being developed by Boeing as a successor to the NMRS and is planned to enter service around 2005; it uses preprogrammed, torpedo tube–deployed and –recovered UUVs with a range of about 70 n.m. and an endurance of 40 hours. The 5-kt BLQ-11 is to have a 288 n.m. range on its nonrechargeable lithium battery and to be able to reconnoiter 650 km^2 during a typical mission. A full outfit would replace eight torpedoes and would include three UUVs, the recovery arm machinery, spare batteries, and control and display modules; it would be operated by four personnel.

Up to 10 units of the class have the TB-29 thin-line towed array instead of TB-16D or TB-23, but further procurement was canceled due to excessive production costs; production of the cheaper TB-29A was authorized during 2000. Sonar-processing systems are being updated to a common software configuration between 1997 and 2005 under the ARCI (Acoustic Rapid COTS Insertion) program using commercial-off-the-shelf (COTS) computer equipment. One SSN 751–series (688I) boat was to receive the BQG-5D WAA wide-aperture passive side array in a refit that commenced in 1997, but all other 688I units were planned to receive the less-expensive BQG-5A WAA starting around 2000.

Trials units: SSN 691 was redesignated as experimental submarine during 1989 to test composite hull structures, UUVs, advanced sonars, hull friction reduction, and so forth for the SSN 688 and SSN 21 classes, but remains combat capable. During a mid-1990s refit, she received a GRP turtleback abaft the sail to accommodate remotely operated vehicles and a towing winch and drum for experimental towed sonar arrays, 4.27-m-high by 1.37-m-wide vertical surfaces at the ends of the stern stabilizers to accommodate sonar transducer arrays, a 54-mm-diameter towed array dispenser in the port fin (leading to the new winch abaft the sail), supports for the stern stabilizers, new hydraulic systems, a fiber-optic databus, and 58 standardized equipment racks to accommodate a wide variety of electronic test gear. The modifications added about 50 tons to the displacement, most of it aft. SSN 691 has also tested a composite material propeller shaft of about half-normal weight and, in 1998, the Lockheed Martin Undersea Systems Universal Gravity Module (UGM) passive bottom profiler navigational system.

SSN 710 has served as trials boat for the BQG-5D WAA passive sonar system since 7-87. SSN 710 and 724 carry prototype BQQ-10 ARCI sonars, which incorporate off-the-shelf computer components, allowing easy introduction of modular upgrades. SSN 773 has been used to develop new flat-screen, interoperative sonar displays based on commercially available equipment.

Early in 1996, SSN 721 operated the Predator Tier II aerial reconnaissance drone to ranges of 100 n.m. and altitudes of up to 20,000 ft. while operating at periscope depths. SSN 758 was used in trials with the Northrop Grumman Sea Ferret reconnaissance drone during 12-96; eventually, Sea Ferret may be launched from within a modified Sub-Harpoon missile canister and controlled by a submerged submarine. Submarine-launched aerial reconnaissance drones are foreseen as useful for covert surveillance, weapons targeting, choke point interdiction, and battle damage assessment.

SSN 758 is fitted with a developmental Advanced Mine Detection System (AMDS), HF active sonar array with transmitters and receivers in the sail and in a disc-shaped chin sonar dome beneath the hull at the bow. The system is used for target detection, mine avoidance, and bottom navigation.

In 1999, SSN 760 had the BLQ-21 EW suite and BVS-1 photonic mast systems installed for trials.

Special warfare capabilities: Six portable Dry Deck Shelters (DDS) are in use by the USN, all built by Electric Boat Co. DDS-01S ("S" for starboard-side use on twin DDS installations) was completed in 1982 and DDS-02P ("P" for port), -03P, -04S, -05-S, and -06P between 1987 and 1991; displacing some 30 tons when the submarine is submerged, they are 11.58 m long and 2.74 m high and wide and are expected to remain in use for about 40 years. Each DDS has three pressure sections within the outer GRP fairing: a spherical hyperbaric chamber at the forward end to treat injured divers, a smaller spherical transfer trunk, and a cylindrical hangar with elliptical ends to house a swimmer-delivery vehicle (SDV) or 20 SEALs with four Combat Rubber Raiding Craft (CRRC). The DDS can be transported by trucks or C-5A Galaxy aircraft and require about 1–3 days to install and test. They can be carried by SSN 688, 690, 700, 701, and 715.

SSN 772 completed conversion in 3-99 with internal access to the 19.8-m Advanced SEAL Delivery System (ASDS; see description under [LSDV]) while submerged. SSN 776 completed at similar modification during mid-2000, and four more of the class were to be similarly fitted.

♦ 1 Sturgeon-class special operations submarine

Bldr: Northrop Grumman Ingalls, Pascagoula, Miss. (Pacific Fleet)

	Laid down	L	In serv.
SSN 683 Parche	10-12-70	13-1-73	17-8-74

Parche (SSN 683) U.S. Navy

Parche (SSN 683) *Ships of the World,* 8-00

D: 6,140 tons surf./7,140 tons sub. **S:** 15 kts surf./30 kts sub.
Dim: 122.40 × 9.65 × 10.67
A: 4 amidships 533-mm Mk 63 TT (25 Mk 48 ADCAP torpedoes)
Electronics:
Radar: 1 BPS-15A nav./surf. search
Sonar: BQQ-5 with BQS-11-series spherical bow passive hydrophone array; BQS-14A active; BQR-15 towed array with BQR-23 signal processor
EW: WLQ-4E Sea Nymph suite; BRD-7 D/F; Mk 2 acoustic countermeasures launchers

M: 1 Westinghouse S5W2 pressurized-water reactor, 2 sets G.E. or de Laval geared steam turbines; 1 prop; 20,000 shp
Crew: 14 officers, 133 enlisted

Remarks: Authorized in FY 68; other units of the class were authorized: SSN 637–639 in FY 62, SSN 646–653 in FY 63, SSN 660–664 in FY 64, SSN 665–670 in FY 65, SSN 672–677 in FY 66, SSN 678–682 in FY 67, SSN 684 in FY 68, and SSN 686 and 687 in FY 69. Based at Bangor, Wash., since 11-94. Equipped to recover objects from the bottom of the sea, as well as to perform trials of specialized navigation and position-keeping equipment and to support research in shallow-water ASW; requires a shore staff of 166 Navy and civilian personnel. Planned to be retired during 10-03.

Disposals: SSN 677 has been transferred to the city of Vallejo, Calif., as a museum ship. The *Sturgeon* class has been retired as follows:

	ICIR	Decomm.	Stricken
SSN 637 *Sturgeon*	5-4-94	1-8-94	1-8-94
SSN 638 *Whale*	20-10-95	25-6-96	25-6-96
SSN 639 *Tautog*	1-11-96	31-3-97	31-3-97
SSN 646 *Grayling*	8-3-97	18-7-97	18-7-97
SSN 647 *Pogy*	4-1-99	11-6-99	11-6-99
SSN 648 *Aspro*	11-10-94	3-3-95	3-3-95
SSN 649 *Sunfish*	4-11-96	28-3-97	28-3-97
SSN 650 *Pargo*	31-8-94	14-4-95	14-4-95
SSN 651 *Queenfish*	27-9-90	8-11-91	14-4-92
SSN 652 *Puffer*	20-10-95	3-7-96	3-7-96
SSN 653 *Ray*	3-8-92	1993	1993
SSN 660 *Sandlance*	1-4-98	7-8-98	7-8-98
SSN 661 *Lapon*	1-10-91	. . .	8-8-92
SSN 662 *Gurnard*	12-8-94	28-4-95	28-4-95
SSN 663 *Hammerhead*	31-12-93	30-7-94	3-3-95
SSN 664 *Sea Devil*	25-2-91	16-10-91	16-10-91
SSN 665 *Guitarro*	1-10-91	. . .	29-5-92
SSN 666 *Hawkbill*	1-10-99	15-3-00	15-3-00
SSN 667 *Bergall*	4-8-95	30-5-96	6-6-97
SSN 668 *Spadefish*	18-10-96	11-4-97	11-4-97
SSN 669 *Seahorse*	1-3-95	. . .	. . .
SSN 670 *Finback*	4-11-96	28-3-97	28-3-97
SSN 672 *Pintado*	1-10-97	26-2-98	26-2-98
SSN 673 *Flying Fish*	10-7-95	19-5-96	19-5-96
SSN 674 *Trepang*	4-1-99	1-6-99	1-6-99
SSN 675 *Bluefish*	1-2-96	31-5-96	31-5-96
SSN 676 *Billfish*	4-1-99	1-7-99	1-7-99
SSN 677 *Drum*	6-6-95	30-10-95	30-10-95
SSN 678 *Archerfish*	1-10-97	31-3-98	31-3-98
SSN 679 *Silversides*	4-3-94	2-8-94	2-8-94
SSN 680 *William H. Bates*	1-9-99	11-2-00	11-2-00
SSN 681 *Batfish*	2-11-98	9-7-99	. . .
SSN 682 *Tunny*	2-9-97	13-3-98	13-3-98
SSN 683 *Parche*	. . .-02	. . .	. . .
SSN 684 *Cavalla*	1-10-97	30-3-98	30-3-98
SSN 686 *L. Mendel Rivers*	30-11-00	10-5-01	10-5-01
SSN 687 *Richard B. Russell*	1-7-93	30-7-94	30-7-94

Hull systems: SSN 683 was lengthened by 27.68 m during a 1-87 to 1991 refit at Mare Island Naval Shipyard; the submarine has a large, flat-topped casing atop the pressure hull and extending about 10 m forward of the sail to accommodate bottomed-object recovery equipment; a large sonar dome is mounted topside aft. Diving planes are each 3.5 m wide, and the sail is 6.25 m high. Maximum diving depth is about 400 m. The 70-Mw S5W reactor plant operates at 160 kg/cm^2 steam pressure and has two primary steam loops and two steam generators to supply the two steam turbines. Original core life was 5,000 hours. Has an anechoic hull coating.

Disposal note: *Benjamin Franklin*–class special forces transport submarine *Kamehameha* (SSN 642, ex-SSBN 642), after 36 years' service, was placed in In Commission, In Reserve status on 1-10-01 and stricken 2-4-02. Sister *James K. Polk* (SSN 645, ex-SSBN 645) was placed in ICIR status 16-2-99 and decommissioned and stricken 8-7-99.

NUCLEAR-POWERED AUXILIARY SUBMARINES [SSAN]

♦ 1 NR-1-class nuclear-powered, deep-diving research submarine

Bldr: General Dynamics, Electric Boat Div., Groton, Conn.

	Laid down	L	In serv.
NR-1	10-6-67	25-1-69	27-10-69

NR-1—with red-painted sail and rudder Mike Welsford, 6-00

NUCLEAR-POWERED AUXILIARY SUBMARINES [SSAN] *(continued)*

D: 366 tons surf./394 tons sub. **S:** 4.5 kts surf./3.5 kts sub.
Dim: 44.44 (41.45 wl) × 3.81 (4.83 over stern planes) × 4.60
Electronics:
Radar: portable nav.
Sonar: DSOAS 3-array active; Klein 4000 side-scan
M: 1 pressurized-water rector, turboelectric drive; 2 3-bladed props; 100 shp—4 7-shp electric thrusters
Endurance: 210 crew days (330 max.) **Crew:** 3 officers, 8 enlisted + 2 scientists

Remarks: Project approved 18-4-65 and funded under FY 1966. Fitted for military and civilian oceanographic missions and for bottom salvage. Now operated by the Naval Submarine Support Group, New London, Conn. The chartered *Carolyn Chouest* acts as tender and tows the submarine to and from operating locations. Planned for retirement in 2012; planning for a replacement has begun.
Hull systems: Has a thick HY-80 steel cylindrical pressure hull, 29.29 m long. Operating depth: 724 m. Has permanent berths for only four personnel, plus up to three auxiliary berths. Scientific payload: 908 kg. Can remain submerged for up to 30 days. Carries 9,980 kg of lead-shot expendable ballast. The electric main propulsion motors are external to the pressure hull. The four electric thrusters are paired fore and aft in an X-configuration and can maneuver the craft in pitch, roll, elevation, and sideways, delivering 136 kg of thrust each. Two alcohol-filled rubber tires can be lowered to permit the craft to travel on suitable bottoms, and there is a stern anchor to permit hovering or precise depth keeping above a bottom. Has a GPS receiver.

Mission systems: The DSOAS (Deep Submergence Obstacle Avoidance Sonar) system employs three separate HF and LF transducer arrays. The Klein 4000 side-scan sonar replaced an earlier array during 1998. Also fitted are bow- and stern-mounted echo sounders, a VLF sub-bottom profiler, and a 300-kHz doppler own-speed measurer for use within 600 ft. of the bottom. Has a BQN-13 rescue-pinger acoustic beacon. There are three optical viewing ports on the lower edge of the forward end of the pressure hull; 25 external lights, a low-level light t.v. camera (with zoom), and recording cameras are fitted, but no periscope. Manipulators can pick up objects weighing as much as 113 kg from the sea bottom, and a recovery claw can pick up larger objects. A waterjet device can be used to uncover or bury objects on the bottom.

AUXILIARY SUBMARINES [SSA]

♦ 1 Dolphin-class (SCB 207 type) research submarine
Bldr: Portsmouth NSY, N.H.

	Laid down	L	In serv.
AGSS 555 DOLPHIN	9-11-62	8-6-68	17-8-69

Dolphin (AGSS 555) Winter & Findler, 9-97

D: 805 tons light; 861 tons surf./950 tons sub.
S: 7.5 kts surf./10 or 15 kts sub. (see remarks) **Dim:** 50.29 × 5.92 × 4.9
Electronics:
Radar: SPS-53 (portable)
Sonar: BQS-15 active; BQR-2 bow passive array; towed array
M: diesel-electric: 2 G.M. Detroit 12V71 diesels; 1 prop; 1,650 shp
Endurance: 14 days (12 hr sub.) **Crew:** 7 officers, 20 enlisted

Remarks: Authorized under FY 61. Used for deep-diving tests as well as acoustic and oceanographic experiments. Most support is shore-based at her home port of San Diego.
Hull systems: The pressure hull is a perfect cylinder, 5.49 m in diameter, strongly braced and closed at the forward and after ends by two hemispheric bulkheads. The single torpedo tube was removed in 1970. Scientific payload: 12 tons. Using two 165-cell, 250-V, lead-acid batteries, can reach 10 kts when submerged; when silver-zinc batteries are substituted, the speed is 15 kts. The machinery is very quiet. Has four minicomputers for scientific data processing. Several scientific, passive multi-hydrophone arrays are fitted at the bow, and acoustic arrays can be towed at up to 4,000 ft. behind the craft.

♦ 1 Tang-class drone target submarine (In reserve)
Bldr: General Dynamics, Electric Boat Div., Groton, Conn.

	Laid down	L	In serv.
TROUT (ex-SS 566)	1-12-49	21-8-51	27-6-52

D: 2,050 tons surf./2,700 tons sub. **S:** 15.6 kts surf./18.3 kts sub.
Dim: 87.50 × 8.33 × 5.70 **A:** inoperative: 8 533-mm TT (6 fwd, 2 short aft)
Electronics:
Radar: 1 Fairchild BPS-12 search
Sonar: EDO BQS-4 passive; Raytheon BQG-4 (PUFFS) passive-ranging; EDO BQR-2B active
EW: WLR-1 intercept
M: 3 Fairbanks-Morse 38D8⅛ × 10 diesels, 2 Westinghouse motors; 2 props; 3,430 bhp surf./5,600 shp sub.
Range: 7,600/15 surf.; 17/9 sub. **Crew:** . . . tot.

Remarks: Decommissioned in 1978 and sold to Iran in 1979 but retained in the United States. Is stored at Key West, Fla., awaiting adaptation. Has been adapted as a drone underwater acoustic target for use by the Naval Air Warfare Center Aircraft Division Detachment, Key West, to which it was transferred in 8-97. Operating diving depth: greater than 215 m.

Note: The various research and rescue submersibles [YSS] are described later under miscellaneous craft. Swimmer delivery vehicles [LSDV] are described at the end of the Amphibious Warfare Ships and Craft section.

BATTLESHIPS [BB]

Note: While the *Iowa*-class battleships *Iowa* (BB 61) and *Wisconsin* (BB 64) remain officially on the Naval Vessel Register, neither of the ships is ever likely to operate again, as the necessary spare parts and operating skills are no longer available, the ships are vulnerable to modern weapons, and the reactivation, maintenance, and operating costs would far outweigh any remaining military value. BB 61 was required by Congress to be relocated under the FY 00 budget and began a tow on 8-3-01 from Newport, R.I., to Suisun Bay, Calif., arriving 21-4-01; she is to be stored through 2004 as a possible future exhibit at San Francisco. BB 61 was restored to the Navy List on 4-1-99. The *New Jersey* (BB 62) was stricken 8-1-99 to become a memorial at Camden, N.J., and the *Missouri* (BB 63) was transferred to a private organization on 4-5-98 to become a memorial at Pearl Harbor. BB 64 is on display at Norfolk, open above decks to the public, and is planned to be stricken during FY 03 or 04.

GUIDED-MISSILE CRUISERS [CG]

Note: In a return to the original concept behind the canceled DD 21 program, the navy began discussing a "CG(X)" program in guidance issued during 1-02; the design would be an outgrowth of the DD(X) design, as the *Ticonderoga* class was from the *Spruance*-class destroyer.

♦ 27 Ticonderoga class
Bldrs: A: Northrop Grumman Ship Systems, Ingalls Div., Pascagoula, Miss.;
B: General Dynamics Bath Iron Works, Bath, Maine (*Atlantic/†Pacific Fleet)

	Bldr	Laid down	L	In serv.
CG 47 TICONDEROGA*	A	21-1-80	25-4-81	22-1-83
CG 48 YORKTOWN*	A	19-10-81	17-1-83	4-7-84
CG 49 VINCENNES†	A	20-10-82	14-1-84	6-7-85
CG 50 VALLEY FORGE*	A	14-4-83	23-6-84	11-1-86
CG 51 THOMAS S. GATES*	B	31-8-84	14-12-85	22-8-87
CG 52 BUNKER HILL*	A	11-1-84	11-3-85	20-9-86
CG 53 MOBILE BAY†	A	6-6-84	22-8-85	21-2-87
CG 54 ANTIETAM†	A	15-11-84	14-2-86	6-6-87
CG 55 LEYTE GULF*	A	18-3-85	20-6-86	26-9-87
CG 56 SAN JACINTO*	A	22-7-85	14-11-86	23-1-88
CG 57 LAKE CHAMPLAIN†	A	3-3-86	3-4-87	12-8-88
CG 58 PHILIPPINE SEA*	B	8-5-86	25-4-87	18-3-89
CG 59 PRINCETON†	A	15-10-86	2-10-87	11-2-89
CG 60 NORMANDY*	B	7-4-87	19-3-88	9-12-89
CG 61 MONTEREY†	B	19-8-87	22-10-88	16-6-90
CG 62 CHANCELLORSVILLE†	A	24-6-87	15-7-88	4-11-89
CG 63 COWPENS†	B	23-12-87	11-3-89	9-3-91
CG 64 GETTYSBURG*	B	17-8-88	22-7-89	22-6-91
CG 65 CHOSIN (ex-*Shiloh*)†	A	22-7-88	1-9-89	12-1-91
CG 66 HUE CITY* (ex-*Chosin*)	A	20-2-89	1-6-90	14-9-91
CG 67 SHILOH†	B	1-8-89	14-7-90	18-7-92
CG 68 ANZIO*	A	21-8-89	2-11-90	2-5-92
CG 69 VICKSBURG* (ex-*Port Royal*)	A	30-5-90	2-8-91	14-11-92
CG 70 LAKE ERIE†	B	14-3-90	13-7-91	24-7-93
CG 71 CAPE ST. GEORGE*	A	19-11-90	10-1-92	12-6-93
CG 72 VELLA GULF*	A	22-4-91	13-6-92	18-9-93
CG 73 PORT ROYAL†	A	18-10-91	20-11-92	30-4-94

Lake Erie (CG 70)—trials ship for the Standard SM-3 ABM system; note the additional large SATCOM antenna mounted on the forward port corner of the forward stack: CG 53 and CG 67 have the same feature, and all three ships have a similar radome mounted to starboard atop the hangar Brian Morrison, 6-00

Thomas S. Gates (CG 51)—with Mk 26 missile launchers Bernard Prézelin, 8-00

GUIDED-MISSILE CRUISERS [CG] *(continued)*

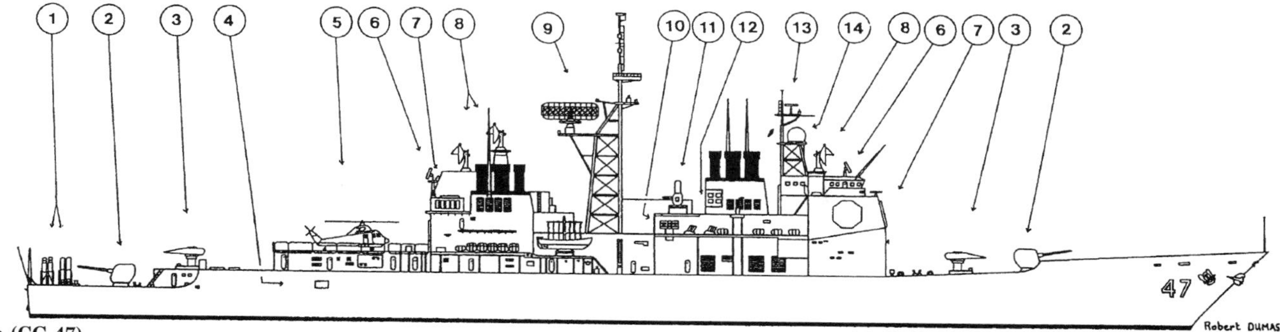

Ticonderoga (CG 47)

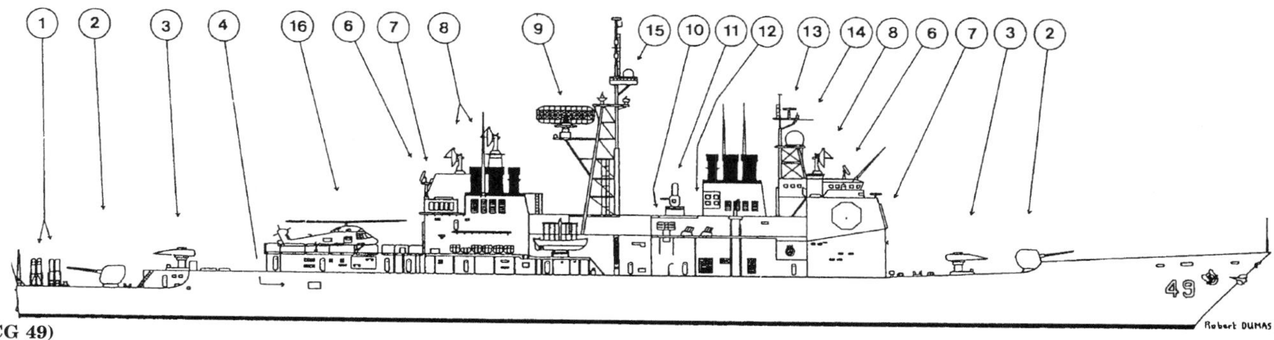

Vincennes (CG 49)

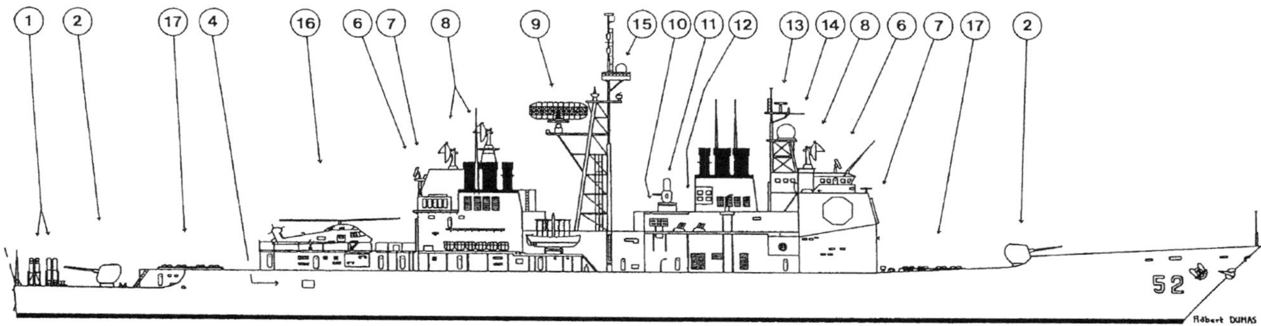

Bunker Hill (CG 52)

1. Harpoon SSM canister-launchers 2. 127-mm Mk 45 DP guns 3. Mk 26 Mod.1 twin-arm guided missile launchers 4. Mk 32 triple ASW TT (behind closed shutters) 5. SH-60B Seahawk LAMPS-III ASW helicopter 6. OE-82 antenna for WSC-3 UHF SATCOM 7. SPY-1A/B 3-D fixed radar antenna arrays 8. SPG-62 radar illuminators 9. SPS-49 2-D air-search radar 10. SLQ-32A(V)3 EW antenna group 11. 20-mm Mk 15 Phalanx CIWS 12. Mk 137 launchers for the Mk 36 SRBOC decoy system 13. SPS-55 surface-search radar 14. SPQ-9A surface gun f.c. radar 15. antenna for SQQ-28 helicopter datalink, atop IFF interrogator array 16. SH-60B Seahawk LAMPS-III ASW helicopter 17. Mk 41 vertical missile-launch system

Drawings by Robert Dumas from *Flottes de Combat*

Ticonderoga (CG 47)—note the twin-armed Mk 26 missile launch systems fore and aft

Maritime Photographic, 7-01

GUIDED-MISSILE CRUISERS [CG] *(continued)*

Anzio (CG 68) Martin Mokrus, 6-01

Bunker Hill (CG 52)—note that only four Harpoon missiles are being carried on a deployed ship Brian Morrison, 1-01

Cowpens (CG 63) Brian Morrison, 2-01

Port Royal (CG 73) W. Michael Young, 4-01

San Jacinto (CG 56) William H. Clarke, 8-01

GUIDED-MISSILE CRUISERS [CG] *(continued)*

Mobile Bay (CG 53) Kurt Greiner/SeaPhoto, 10-00

D: CG 47: 7,646 tons light (10,142 fl); CG 48: 7,592 tons light (10,090 fl); others: 6,997–7,242 tons light (9,763–10,010 fl)

S: 30+ kts **Dim:** 172.46 (162.36 wl) × 16.76 × 7.46 (10.51 over sonar)

A: CG 47–51: 2 twin-armed Mk 26 Mod. 1 launchers (88 Standard SM-2 MR missiles); up to 8 Harpoon SSM; 2 single 127-mm 54-cal. Mk 45 Mod. 0 DP; 2 20-mm Mk 15 Block I Phalanx gatling CIWS; 2 single 25-mm Mk 38 Bushmaster low-angle guns; 4 single 12.7-mm mg; 2 triple 324-mm Mk 32 Mod. 14 ASW TT; 1 or 2 SH-60 Seahawk LAMPS-III ASW helicopters—CG 52–73: 2 Mk 41 Mod. 0 VLS (122 Standard SM-2 MR, Tomahawk, or ASROC missiles); up to 8 Harpoon SSM; 2 single 127-mm 54-cal. Mk 45 Mod. 1 DP; 2 20-mm Mk 15 Mod. 12 Block I Phalanx gatling CIWS; 2 single 25-mm Mk 38 Bushmaster low-angle guns; 4 single 12.7-mm mg; 2 triple 324-mm Mk 32 Mod. 14 ASW TT; 1–2 SH-60B LAMPS-III ASW helicopters

Shiloh (CG 67)—with large SATCOM radomes atop forward stack and abaft the after funnel Brian Morrison, 1-01

Electronics:

Radar: 1 Raytheon SPS-64(V)9 (CG 72: DRS/Thales Scout) nav.; 1 Cardion SPS-55 surf. search; 1 Raytheon SPS-49(V)6, (V)7, or (V)8 air search; 1 Lockheed Martin SPY-1A (CG 59–73: SPY-1B) 3-D air search/f.c.; 4 Raytheon SPG-62 target illumination; 1 Lockheed Martin SPQ-9A surf. gun f.c.; 2 General Dynamics Mk 90 Phalanx f.c.

Sonar: CG 47–53: EDO-G.E. SQS-53A bow-mounted LF—CG 54, 55: SQQ-89(V)3 suite (SQS-53A and G.E.–Lockheed Martin SQR-19 towed array)—CG 56–67: SQQ-89(V)3 suite (SQS-53B and SQR-19)—CG 68–73: SQQ-89(V). . . suite (SQS-53C and SQR-19)

TACAN: URN-25

EW: Raytheon SLQ-32A(V)3 active/passive; BAE Systems SLQ-20B signal processor; Mk 50 SRBOC decoy RL syst. (8 6-round Mk 137 RL); SLQ-25A Nixie towed torpedo decoy syst.; SLQ-49 floating radar reflector buoys—CG 58, 59, 63 also: 4 twin Mk 53 Nulka decoy RL

M: 4 G.E. LM-2500 gas turbines; 2 5-bladed CP props; 100,000 shp (max.; 86,000 normal)

Electric: 7,500 kw (3 × 2,500-kw Allison 501K gas turbine sets)

Range: 6,000/20 **Fuel:** 2,000 tons

Crew: CG 47, 49–51: 27 officers, 350–353 enlisted; CG 48: 22 officers, 306 enlisted; CG 53: 22 officers, 287 enlisted; others: 28 officers, 342–359 enlisted

Remarks: A greatly revised version of the *Spruance*-class destroyer, using the same hull and propulsion but incorporating the Aegis Mk 7 weapon system (SPY-1-series phased-array radar, four missile illuminator radars, Mk 26 or Mk 41 missile-launch system, etc.). Designation was changed from DDG to CG on 1-1-80. Named for battles and campaigns (except for CG 51, named for a former secretary of defense and of the navy).

CG 47 was authorized in FY 78, CG 48 in FY 80, CG 49 and 50 in FY 81, CG 51–53 in FY 82, CG 54–56 in FY 83, CG 57–59 in FY 84, CG 60–62 in FY 85, CG 63–65 in FY 86, CG 66–68 in FY 87, and CG 69–73 in FY 88. CG 60–62 were ordered 26-11-84, CG 63 and 64 on 9-1-86, CG 65 on 8-1-86, CG 66–68 on 16-4-87, and CG 69–73 on 25-2-88.

The 22 VLS-equipped ships of the class are planned for extensive modernizations; 12 of the ships may also receive enhanced antiair control capabilities to enable them to act as joint air-defense command ships. Plans to equip CG 52–58 with a COTS (Commercial Off-The-Shelf) computer system architecture to enable them to perform anti–theater ballistic missile functions have probably been abandoned, due to the cancellation of the Standard SM-2 Block IVA anti–ballistic missile program in 11-01; originally, they were to get improved command-and-control systems, new computers, missile launcher improvements, new Mk 45 Mod. 4 extended-range guns, better machinery control systems, and updates to hull structure and support systems, but a 1-01 decision limited the gun upgrade to 14 of the ships. The updates were planned to extend service life from the original 35 years to 40 years.

CG 70 was designated a full-time trials ship for the Standard SM-2 Block IVA and SM-3 antiballistic missiles early in 2001 and conducted the first multistage Standard SM-3 launch on 25-1-01. CG 73 has also been used extensively as a trials ship for the program.

Problems in mid-1998 with Aegis software updates to CG 66 and 69 caused a two-year delay in an effort to integrate all combat systems in the class with the CEC update (see below). CG 61 was delayed 3 months in deploying in 1998 because of software problems with the Tomahawk land-attack missile system.

Hull systems: Have a sufficient stability margin to operate at up to 10,200 tons full load—a figure that some of them were approaching by 2001. Displacements have grown over time, with the first two having been completed before a rigorous weight-reduction program was instituted. Even so, CG 57 as of 2001 displaced 10,100 tons full load, while CG 73, originally listed at 9,613 tons fl, now displaces 9,966 tons. As completed, CG 47 and 48 carried a small amount of lead ballast, but later units did not. Bow bulwarks were required to keep the decks dry, as draft was increased about 1 m over that of the original *Spruance* design. CG 51's hull is misaligned by several degrees. Habitability in these ships is cramped. No fin stabilization is fitted. CG 49 and later have lighter tripod after masts. Kevlar armor is incorporated over vital spaces.

CG 48 was selected in 1996 as the Atlantic Fleet "Smart Ship" trials platform for labor and cost savings experiments; homeported at Pascagoula, Miss., on 1-9-96, the ship has tested some 800 different concepts, including the use of off-the-shelf computers, the Sperry Marine integrated bridge, and new paints. CG 51 received similar integrated ship controls system modifications during 1998 and CG 47 and 61 during 2000 and modifications to CG 53 began during 11-00 and to CG 54 during 2001, all at Pascagoula; the modifications cost about $8 million per ship but save $3 million per year each. CG 58 and 61 were selected during 8-01 to serve as trials ships for two years for further personnel reductions.

GUIDED-MISSILE CRUISERS [CG] *(continued)*

Combat systems: On CG 47–51, each Mk 26 Mod. 1 missile-launcher magazine holds 44 missiles. In the VLS ships, the at-sea reload cranes in the VLS complexes have been deleted to permit carrying six more missiles. The Mk 86 Mod. 9 fire-control system for the 127-mm guns provides no AA capability, as no SPG-60 radar is carried. In the earliest ships, the Aegis Mk 7 Mod. 2 system, which used 12 UYK-7 and 1 UYK-20 computers, employs the four fixed faces of the SPY-1A radar to detect and track up to several hundred targets simultaneously; the four radar illuminators are slaved to the system and can, through time-share switching, serve more than a dozen missiles in the air at once; the Mk 99 missile fire-control *system* uses four Mk 80 *illuminator-directors* with SPG-62 *radars.* The UPX-29 IFF circular antenna array is carried on the mainmast.

The Harpoon missiles, which are launched by the SWG-1 launch control system, are in an exposed position at the extreme stern, and most ships now carry only four missiles while deployed. All ships have Link 4A, 11, and 14 datalink capability, UQN-4 echo sounders, and WRN-5 and WSC-6 SATCOM terminals. All are having the Litton Marine WSN-7 ring-laser gyro inertial navigation system installed during refits, beginning in 2000.

Vertical-Launch ASROC antisubmarine missiles can be carried in the Mk 41 vertical launchers, but Mk 26 launcher-equipped units cannot employ the missile. All can carry up to 36 Mk 46 ASW torpedoes for their SH-60B helicopters. During 1990s overhauls, the ships had the 127-mm guns upgraded to Mk 45 Mod. 1 and the Phalanx CIWS systems upgraded to Block I. CG 48 has a Kollmorgen Mk 46 Mod. 1/2 optronic sensor with a t.v. camera and laser rangefinder for trials.

During 1999, CG 58, 59, and 63 became the first of the class to be fitted to launch Nulka hovering decoys from their Mk 137 decoy launchers; the number of Mk 137 launchers for the SRBOC system has been doubled to eight in all (with the system itself now designated Mk 50 vice Mk 36). By 12-99, eight ships of the class had been fitted with TRAFS (Torpedo Recognition and Alertment Functional Segment), a torpedo detection function added to the SQQ-89 system; seven more of the class are to have TRAFS by 2003.

Upgrades to the Aegis system software are improving the coordination of combat data. CG 65 has been the trials ship for the associated Link 16 TADIL-J (Tactical Distribution Link–Joint) datalink. For the VLS ships, the SWG-3 Tomahawk launch control system is fitted. CG 56 introduced the SQQ-89(V)3 integrated ASW suite, with SQQ-53B hull-mounted sonar, SQR-19 towed array, and the Mk 116 Mod. 6 ASW fire-control system, although the towed arrays have been removed from the class and stored ashore. CG 65–73 have UYK-43B and UYK-44 computers in place of the heavier UYK-7/UYK-20 combination used in earlier ships; they also have the improved UYS-20 data display system and various decision aids and were equipped with the SQS-53C bow sonar and SQR-17 sonar data processor. The computers have been similarly updated during refits of earlier units.

In 1996, CG 61 became the first VLS ship to receive the Baseline 5 Phase III computer program and equipment upgrade, with Joint Tactical Information Display System (JTIDS, Link 16 Mod. 5), the latest UYK-21 display system, and UYK-43 computers in place of UYK-7; CG 59–64 were to receive similar upgrades, except that CG 59 and 64 were to get UYQ-70 displays in place of UYK-21.

Modernization: A proposed Cruiser Conversion Program (CCP) master plan to update all 27 units of the *Ticonderoga* class was promulgated early in 1999, although it is probable that CG 47–51 will not receive the upgrades and will be retired starting around 2005 for funding reasons. The RIM-162 ESSM Evolved Sea Sparrow SAM is to be employed, rather than an earlier plan to substitute lightweight RIM-116 RAM missile launch system for the Phalanx CIWS; the RIM-162 missiles will be carried in quad packs in the already-overburdened Mk 41 VLS cells. The secondary search radars will be upgraded to SPS-49A(V)1 and the SPQ-9 gun fire-control radars will be replaced by SPQ-9B low-altitude search and target-designation radars. Additionally, the Lockheed Martin SNL-2(V) Advanced Integrated Electronic Warfare System (AIEWS) may replace the current, obsolescent SLQ-32. CG 52–73 were planned also to be equipped to carry the Northrop Grumman Fire Scout remotely operated, helicopter-type reconnaissance drones equipped with SIGINT, IR, and optical sensors, starting in FY 05. Three ships of the class may also be provided with an Area Air-Defense Command capability. As of 2-02, plans called for funding the modernization of one ship under the FY 04 budget, two under FY 05, and four each under FY 06 and FY 07.

GUIDED-MISSILE DESTROYERS [DDG]

♦ 0 (+ . . .) DD(X) program

The "Gold Team" concept for the DD 21/DD(X)—with flush deck, both 155-mm gunmounts forward, the vertical-launch missile tubes distributed down the sides, and conventional propeller shafts — DD 21 Gold Team, 2001

The "Blue Team" concept for the DD 21/DD(X)—with long forecastle deck, 155-mm guns fore and aft, vertical missile launch groups concentrated forward and abaft the superstructure, and podded propellers — Norman Friedman, 4-01

Remarks: The DD 21 or *Zumwalt*-class guided-missile destroyer program was reconstituted as the DD(X) on 1-11-01. Well over $1 billion in development and design contracts had already been expended when the program was halted. The original DD 21 design teams remained in existence and were to be requested to offer new bids in 3-02 for the DD(X), indicating that the new design is likely to be basically the same as the old, and a return to an earlier "family of ships" concept, with different variants for different missions, may be reinstituted. The DoD decided that the DD 21 was too specialized a ship and requested that the new DD(X) be capable of more general-purpose duties and also (although the request was vaguely worded) that it be a smaller ship than the 15,400-ton, 216-m designs offered for the DD 21. The first ship is now not to be requested until the FY 05 budget (DD 21 was originally to have been in the FY 02 budget. The Navy Area Missile Defense System, which was to have been used by the new DD(X), was canceled 14-12-01.

The original two competing design teams remain involved: the Blue Team with General Dynamics' Bath Iron Works, Lockheed Martin, and Northrop Grumman; and the Gold Team with Northrop Grumman's Ingalls Shipbuilding, Raytheon, and Boeing. Some $961 million was requested under the FY 03 budget for technology development for the DD(X).

♦ 6 (+ 29) Arleigh Burke Flight IIA class

Bldrs: General Dynamics Bath Iron Works, Bath, Maine, and Northrop Grumman Ship Systems, Ingalls Div., Pascagoula, Miss. (*Atlantic/†Pacific Fleet)

	Bldr	Laid down	L	In serv.
DDG 79 Oscar Austin*	Bath	9-10-97	7-11-98	19-8-00
DDG 80 Roosevelt*	Ingalls	15-12-97	10-1-99	14-10-00
DDG 81 Winston S. Churchill*	Bath	7-5-98	17-4-99	10-3-01
DDG 82 Lassen†	Ingalls	24-8-98	15-10-99	21-4-01
DDG 83 Howard†	Bath	9-12-98	20-11-99	20-10-01
DDG 84 Bulkeley*	Ingalls	10-5-99	21-6-00	8-12-01
DDG 85 McCampbell†	Bath	15-7-99	2-7-00	5-02 (del.)
DDG 86 Shoup†	Ingalls	13-12-99	22-11-00	1-6-02
DDG 87 Mason*	Bath	20-1-00	23-6-01	3-03 (del.)
DDG 88 Preble†	Ingalls	22-6-00	1-6-01	11-02 (del.)
DDG 89 Mustin†	Ingalls	15-1-01	12-12-01	5-03 (del.)
DDG 90 Chafee†	Bath	12-4-01	10-02	9-03 (del.)
DDG 91 Pinckney	Ingalls	16-7-01	6-02	12-03 (del.)
DDG 92 Momsen	Bath	25-11-01	5-03	5-04 (del.)
DDG 93 Chung-Hoon	Ingalls	14-1-02	12-02	6-04 (del.)
DDG 94 Nitze	Bath	11-02	3-04	1-05 (del.)
DDG 95 James E. Williams	Ingalls	7-02	6-03	11-04 (del.)
DDG 96	Bath	6-03	10-04	9-05 (del.)
DDG 97	Ingalls	1-03	12-03	4-05 (del.)
DDG 98	Ingalls	7-03	7-04	8-05 (del.)
DDG 99	Bath	7-03	11-04	2-06 (del.)
DDG 100	Ingalls	1-04	12-04	2-06 (del.)
DDG 101	Bath	3-04	7-05	4-06 (del.)
DDG 102	Ingalls	. . .	. . .	. . .
DDG 103	. . .	. . .	. . .	. . .
DDG 104	. . .	. . .	. . .	. . .
DDG 105	. . .	. . .	. . .	. . .
DDG 106	. . .	. . .	. . .	. . .
DDG 107	. . .	. . .	. . .	. . .
DDG 108	. . .	. . .	. . .	. . .
DDG 109	. . .	. . .	. . .	. . .
DDG 110	. . .	. . .	. . .	. . .
DDG 111	. . .	. . .	. . .	. . .
DDG 112	. . .	. . .	. . .	. . .

D: DDG 79–90: 9,238 tons (fl); DDG 91–108: 9,338 tons (fl) **S:** 30+ kts

Dim: 155.30 (143.56 wl) × 20.27 (18.0 wl) × 6.35 (9.39 over sonar)

A: DDG 79, 80: 2 Mk 41 Mod. 0 vertical-launch groups (1 64-cell, 1 32-cell; 96 Standard SM-2 MR Block IV SAM, VLA, and Tomahawk missiles); 1 127-mm 54-cal. Mk 45 Mod. 1 DP; 2 20-mm Mk 15 Mod. 0 Block I Phalanx gatling CIWS; 2 single 25-mm 75-cal. Mk 38 Mod. 1 Bushmaster guns; 4 single 12.7-mm mg; 2 triple 324-mm Mk 32 Mod. 14 ASW TT (Mk 46 and Mk 50 torpedoes); 2 SH-60R Seahawk helicopters (Penguin and Hellfire missiles, Mk 46 and Mk 50 torpedoes)

DDG 81 and later: 2 Mk 41 Mod. 0 vertical-launch groups (1 64-cell, 1 32-cell; 92 Standard SM-2 MR Block IV, LASM, VLA, and Tomahawk missiles; 24 RIM-162 ESSM Sea Sparrow SAM); 1 127-mm 62-cal. Mk 45 Mod. 4 DP—DDG 81–84 only: 2 20-mm Mk 15 Mod. 0 Block I Phalanx gatling CIWS—all: 2 single 25-mm 25-mm 75-cal. Mk 38 Mod. 1 Bushmaster guns; 4 single 12.7-mm mg; 2 triple 324-mm Mk 32 Mod. 14 ASW TT (Mk 46 and Mk 50 torpedoes; Mk 54 on DDG 91 and later); 2 SH-60R Seahawk helicopters (Penguin and Hellfire missiles, Mk 46 and Mk 50 torpedoes)—see remarks

Electronics:

Radar: 1 Raytheon SPS-64(V)9 (DDG 87 and later: Decca BridgeMaster-E ARPA) nav.; 1 AIL SPS-67(V)4 surf. search; 1 Lockheed Martin SPY-1D(V) 3-D search/weapons control; 3 Raytheon SPG-62 target illumination—DDG 79–84 only: 2 Mk 90 Phalanx f.c.

Sonar: DDG 79–90: SQQ-89(V)14 suite: SQS-53C(V)1 hull-mounted, with Kingfisher HF mine-avoidance set, Northrop Grumman SLX-1 Multi-Sensor Torpedo Recognition and Alertment Processor (MSTRAP)—DDG 91 and later: SQQ-89(V)15, with same systems, plus WLD-1(V)1/3 Remote Minehunting System

TACAN: URN-25

EW: Raytheon SLQ-32A(V)3 (DDG 85–90: SLQ(V)2 intercept only; DDG 91 and later: Lockheed Martin SLY-2) active/passive; Lockheed Martin SRS-1A combat D/F suite (COBLU Phase I on later ships); Mk 36 Mod. 12 SRBOC decoy syst. (4 6-round Mk 137 RL); SLQ-25A Nixie towed torpedo decoy syst. (with SSTD Phase I)—DDG 91 and later: Nulka decoy syst. (4 twin RL)—all: SLQ-39 decoy buoy launch syst.

E/O: 1 Kollmorgen Mk 46 Mod. 0 (DDG 85 and later: Mod. 1) optronic f.c./surveillance director

GUIDED-MISSILE DESTROYERS [DDG] *(continued)*

Bulkeley (DDG 84)

Northrop Grumman Ship Systems, 7-01

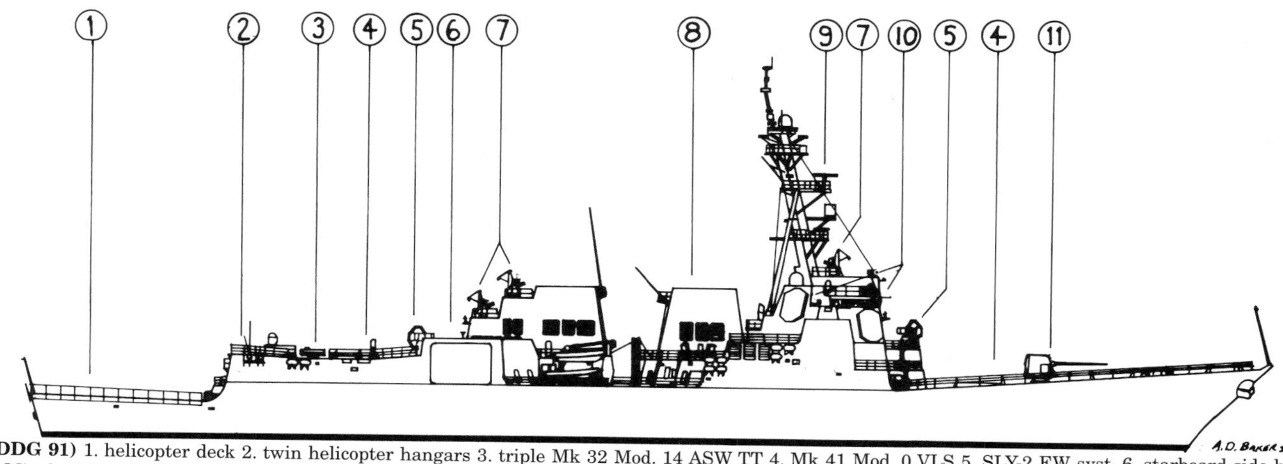

Pinckney (DDG 91) 1. helicopter deck 2. twin helicopter hangars 3. triple Mk 32 Mod. 14 ASW TT 4. Mk 41 Mod. 0 VLS 5. SLY-2 EW syst. 6. starboard-side hangar for WLD-1(V) Remote Minehunting System 7. SPG-62 target illuminators 8. decoy launchers 9. SPS-67(V)4 surface-search radar 10. SPY-1D(V) Aegis radar antenna arrays 11. 127-mm 62-cal. Mk 45 Mod. 4 DP gun

Drawing by A. D. Baker III

M: 4 G.E. LM-2500-30 gas turbines; 2 5-bladed CP props; 105,000 shp (90,000 sust.)
Electric: 7,500 kw tot. (3 Allison 501-K34 gas turbines driving)
Range: 4,400/20 **Fuel:** . . . tons
Crew: 32 officers, 348 enlisted (incl. helicopter detachment: 4 officers, 14 enlisted)

Remarks: A lengthened version of the basic *Arleigh Burke* design, with hangars added for two helicopters and later equipment. DDG 79 was authorized under FY 94, DDG 80–82 under FY 95, DDG 83 and 84 under FY 96, DDG 85–88 under FY 97, which also authorized advance procurement for three more. Under FY 98, DDG 89–101 were authorized in a multiyear procurement for FY 98–01 (with DDG 102 an option); Ingalls was to build seven ships and Bath Iron Works six. The contracts were signed on 6-3-98, with Ingalls receiving an option contract for two additional units (DDG 98, 100) on 14-12-98. The contracts for DDG 99–101 were given a $998 million increase on 8-12-00, and the option for DDG 102 was taken up on 21-11-01. DDG 102–107 long-lead contracts were placed on 5-6-01. Three per year were authorized during FY 01 and FY 02, with two requested for FY 03 and two planned for FY 04 through FY 07. The FY 03 pair were budgeted at $1.2 billion each. Discussions under way early in 2002 may result in all future ships of the class being built by Bath Iron Works.

GUIDED-MISSILE DESTROYERS [DDG] *(continued)*

Oscar Austin (DDG 79) William H. Clarke, 8-00

Lassen (DDG 82)—note the faceted gunhouse Victor Baca, Photomarine Archives, 8-01

Winston S. Churchill (DDG 81) Marion Wright, 8-01

Howard (DDG 83) Bath Iron Works, 6-01

GUIDED-MISSILE DESTROYERS [DDG] *(continued)*

Roosevelt (DDG 80)—with Seahawk helicopter hovering above the helicopter deck; note the deck traversing tracks leading to the two hangars, which flank the after vertical missile launcher group Northrop Grumman Ship System, 5-00

McCampbell (DDG 85)—note absence of provision for Phalanx mountings Bath Iron Works, 12-01

DDG 80 was named 22-10-96 in honor of both former President Franklin Delano Roosevelt and his wife Eleanor Roosevelt. DDG 81 is named in honor of Sir Winston Churchill; the name was officially changed to add the middle initial on 19-7-99.

Operational deployment of the first 11 ships may be delayed by as much as three years, due to the need to certify the major changes in the combat system software being incorporated. DDG 83 and 84 have Baseline 6.1 software and Phalanx CIWS rather than the planned Baseline 6.3, with no Phalanx but with the Evolved Sea Sparrow Missile, in order to get the ships to the fleet sooner.

Hull systems: The hull was lengthened 5 ft. over that of the DDG 51 class, while weight and metacentric height have been reduced through the use of lighter superstructure scantlings. Plating thickness to the lower hull has been increased over three-quarters of the hull length amidships; and the propellers have an improved section to reduce the onset of cavitation. In addition, the stern wedge (which improves fuel efficiency at cruising speeds) has been extended past the transom through the use of a fixed flap attached at the lower edge of the transom. They do not have fin stabilizers but are equipped with rudder roll-rate reduction. They also have a twisted-section rudder to improve maneuvering efficiency; Bath Iron Works received a contract during 9-01 to develop a composite-construction version of the rudder to reduce corrosion. All have the Prairie/Masker air bubbler system to reduce machinery noise radiation below the waterline.

Accommodations have been increased for the air group, and berthing has been provided for four female officers, six female CPOs, and 18 female enlisted. There is no high-pressure air system; auxiliary power units are used to start the generators. A commercial slewing-arm davit handles the 7.3-m rigid inflatable boats. The computerized Operational Readiness Test System uses one UYK-44 computer with five OJ-454(V)/UYK display consoles in the weapon system equipment rooms. Other changes include the addition of five blast-hardened bulkheads to lessen vulnerability, a solid waste management system, and air-conditioning system improvements.

DDG 81 was constructed via a new fabrication technique in which outfitting of hull subsections was undertaken before their integration into major hull sections.

DDG 83 and later have the "Smart Ship" operational cost-savings features and procedures developed with the cruiser *Yorktown* (CG 48). Systems to be incorporated include the Integrated Condition Assessment System (ICAS) to monitor ship operations; Damage Control System (DCS), with computers, high-speed processors, and touchscreens to monitor ship integrity status; Integrated Bridge System (IBS), which automates bridge and navigational functions, reducing required personnel to as few as two; Standard Monitoring and Control System (SMCS), a computerized propulsion control system; and installation of a fiber-optic local area network (LAN). Units under construction as of 1999 have the Litton Marine WSN-7 ring-laser gyro inertial navigation system, which will be backfitted in the earlier ships. All earlier ships of the class are planned to complete the Smart Ship update by the end of FY 04. DDG 91 and later are to have 50 tons of ballast added to port to counter the weight of the hangar, two WLD-1(V)1 minehunting drones, and their hoist gear mounted to starboard.

Aviation systems: Twin hangars aft are served by a RAST (Recovery Assist, Secure, and Traverse) system; the aft warping capstan and towing padeye are retractable to keep the helicopter deck clear. Are able to operate Seahawk helicopters in up to State 5 seas. DDG 86 and later may employ composite-structure helicopter hangars to reduce the ships' radar signatures; earlier units have composite hangar doors. All ships of this class are to be equipped to carry Northrop Grumman Fire Scout remotely operated, helicopter-type reconnaissance drones equipped with SIGINT, IR, and optical sensors, starting in FY 05.

Combat systems: Have Aegis Weapons System Mk 7 Mod. 11, with the aft pair of SPY-1D antenna panels raised 2.44 m to clear the helicopter hangars. Are to incorporate CEC (Cooperative Engagement Capability); USG-2 CEC systems were authorized on 1-5-00 for DDG 84–86, 91, and 92. The combat systems use UYQ-70 displays and a commercial fiber-optic distributed data interface network. Have color large-screen displays in the Combat Information Center. The Aegis radar system incorporates a TIP (Track Initiation Processor). DDG 88 is programmed to receive the first Engineering Development Model 4B variant SPY-1E radar, with signal-processing and transmitter changes to improve the radar's capability to detect low-observable targets under clutter conditions. The COBLU (Cooperative Outboard Logistics Update) Phase I variant of the SRS-1A Combat D/F system will be installed on DDG 91 and later ships. All ships of the class have the UPX-29 IFF interrogator/transponder system.

The at-sea reload systems for the VLS groups were eliminated to permit adding three VLS cells per group. RIM-9P Evolved Sea Sparrow Missiles (ESSM) will replace the Phalanx installations in DDG 86 and later ships; four missiles will be carried in each of six Mk 41 VLS cells. Harpoon missiles were eliminated to reduce costs, but there is provision to install them later between the stacks; without Harpoon, the ships have no dedicated onboard antiship missile system. DDG 83 and 84 have Phalanx Block IB CIWS.

DDG 81 and later are to be able to carry and employ the Tomahawk Land-Attack Standard Missile (LASM) against shore targets. DDG 81–95 will have stand-alone Tactical Tomahawk Weapons Control Systems, while in later units, missile launch control will be integrated into the overall combat control system.

DDG 81 and later are also receiving the updated 127-mm 62-cal. Mk 45 Mod. 4 gun, with the capability to fire ERGM (Extended-Range Guided Munition) projectiles to 63-n.m. ranges; they will carry 232 ERGM rounds and 232 regular rounds of ammunition when the ERGM rounds become available. All except DDG 79 have a faceted, low-radar-reflectivity housing for the 127-mm gun. The Mk 46 Mod. 1 optronic director for the 127-mm gun has a laser rangefinder, narrow-field-of-view t.v. camera, and (on DDG 82 and later) a thermal imager. Consideration was being given as of 4-01 to replacing the 25-mm Mk 88 portable mountings with two stabilized General Dynamics 30-mm Mk 46 gun systems to improve defenses against smallcraft attacks.

The class does not have a towed-array sonar capability. The SQQ-89(V)10 ASW system, which incorporates the Enhanced Modular Signal Processor (EMSP), uses UYQ-65 displays. The torpedo reload magazine, which can carry up to 40 ASW torpedoes for shipboard and helicopter use, can also accommodate Penguin and Hellfire air-to-ground missiles, Stinger infrared surface-to-air missiles, LAU 68 2.75-in. rockets, and 25-mm gun and 40-mm grenade ammunition.

DDG 91 and later will have the Baseline 7.1 combat system, with a new SPY-1D(V) radar incorporating advanced signal processors; the ships are also to have the SLY-2(V) Advanced Integrated Electronic Warfare System (AIEWS), with the antennas to be mounted where the CIWS are located in earlier ships. DDG 91 is also planned to introduce the WLD-1(V) long-range autonomous mine countermeasures unmanned underwater vehicle (UUV), with the stowage and handling gear mounted in a hangar on the starboard side. DDG 91 and later will also carry Tomahawk Block IV cruise missiles.

Note: Preliminary design work was completed on a 10,722-ton, lengthened version of the basic *Arleigh Burke* class, the "Flight III," but it was canceled in favor of the DD 21 program, itself now cancelled and reconstituted as the DD(X). The Flight III, however, could form the basis for continued production of the *Burke* series if the DD(X) is delayed or canceled.

♦ 28 Arleigh Burke class, Flights I and II

Bldrs: General Dynamics Bath Iron Works, Bath, Maine, and Northrop Grumman Ship Systems, Ingalls Div., Pascagoula, Miss. (*Atlantic/†Pacific Fleet)

	Bldr	Laid down	L	In serv.
21 Flight I:				
DDG 51 Arleigh Burke*	Bath	6-12-88	16-9-89	4-7-91
DDG 52 Barry* (ex-*John Barry*, ex-*Barry*, ex-*John Barry*)	Ingalls	29-2-90	10-5-91	12-12-92
DDG 53 John Paul Jones†	Bath	8-8-90	26-10-91	18-12-93
DDG 54 Curtis Wilbur†	Bath	12-3-91	16-5-92	19-3-94
DDG 55 Stout*	Ingalls	13-9-91	16-10-92	13-8-94
DDG 56 John S. McCain†	Bath	3-9-91	26-9-92	2-7-94
DDG 57 Mitscher*	Ingalls	12-2-92	7-5-93	10-12-94
DDG 58 Laboon*	Bath	23-3-92	20-2-93	18-3-95
DDG 59 Russell†	Ingalls	27-7-92	20-10-93	20-5-95
DDG 60 Paul Hamilton†	Bath	24-8-92	24-7-93	27-5-95
DDG 61 Ramage*	Ingalls	4-1-93	11-2-94	22-7-95

GUIDED-MISSILE DESTROYERS [DDG] *(continued)*

Arleigh Burke (DDG 51) Leo Van Ginderen, 12-00

Cole (DDG 67) Camil Busquets i Vilanova, 8-00

Laboon (DDG 58) Takatoshi Okano, 4-01

Paul Hamilton (DDG 60)—Flight I ship John Mortimer, 1-01

McFaul (DDG 74)—Flight II ship Mike Welsford, 6-01

GUIDED-MISSILE DESTROYERS [DDG] *(continued)*

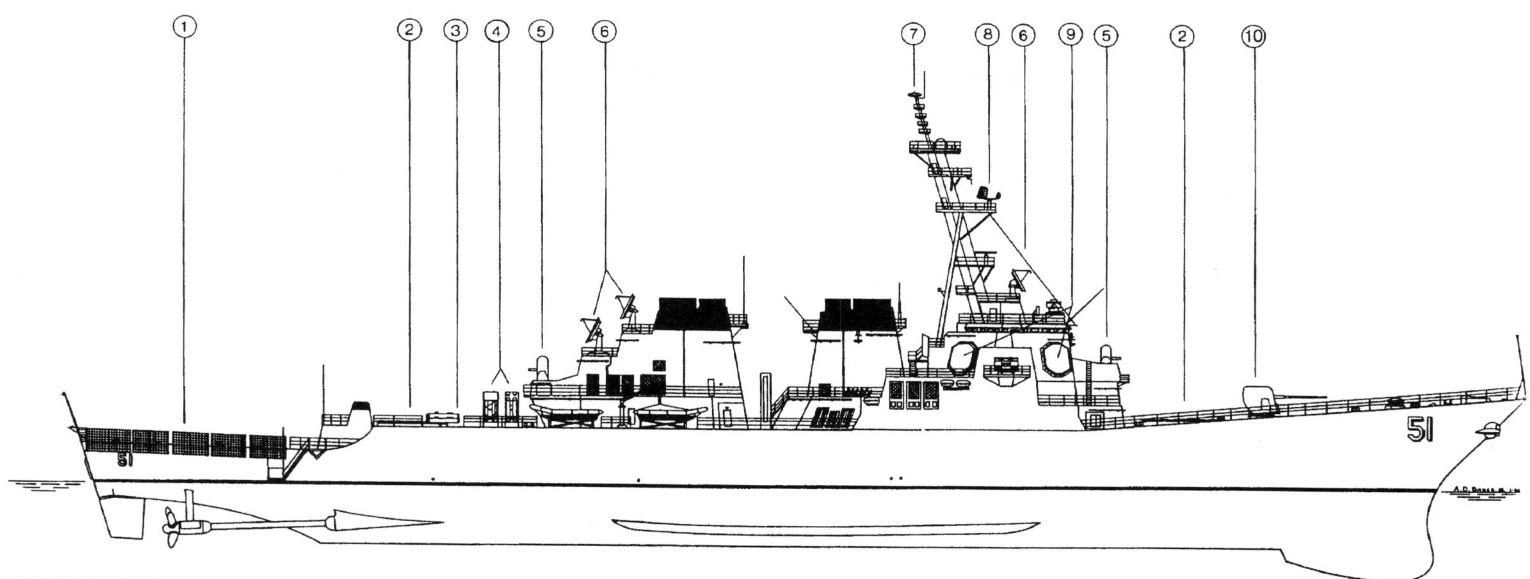

Arleigh Burke (DDG 51) 1. helicopter deck 2. Mk 41 vertical-launch system 3. Mk 32 triple ASW TT 4. Harpoon antiship missile launch canisters 5. 20-mm Mk 15 Phalanx CIWS 6. SPG-62 radar illuminators 7. URN-25 TACAN 8. SPS-67(V)4 surface-search radar (now a slotted waveguide antenna) 9. SPY-1D Aegis antenna arrays 10. 127-mm Mk 45 DP gun

Drawing by A. D. Baker III

Gonzalez (DDG 66)

Maritime Photographic, 4-00

	Bldr	Laid down	L	In serv.
DDG 62 FITZGERALD†	Bath	9-2-93	29-1-94	14-10-95
DDG 63 STETHEM†	Ingalls	10-5-93	17-6-94	21-10-95
DDG 64 CARNEY*	Bath	3-8-93	23-7-94	8-4-96
DDG 65 BENFOLD†	Ingalls	27-9-93	5-11-94	30-3-96
DDG 66 GONZALEZ*	Bath	3-2-94	18-2-95	12-10-96
DDG 67 COLE*	Ingalls	28-2-94	10-2-95	8-6-96
DDG 68 THE SULLIVANS*	Bath	27-7-94	12-8-95	19-4-97
DDG 69 MILIUS†	Ingalls	8-8-94	1-8-95	23-11-96
DDG 70 HOPPER†	Bath	26-2-95	3-2-96	6-9-97
DDG 71 ROSS*	Ingalls	10-4-95	23-3-96	28-6-97
7 Flight II:				
DDG 72 MAHAN*	Bath	18-6-95	29-6-96	14-2-98
DDG 73 DECATUR†	Bath	15-1-96	9-11-96	29-8-98
DDG 74 MCFAUL*	Ingalls	12-2-96	11-1-97	17-4-98
DDG 75 DONALD COOK*	Bath	7-7-96	3-5-97	4-12-98
DDG 76 HIGGINS*	Bath	17-11-96	4-10-97	24-4-99
DDG 77 O'KANE†	Bath	11-5-97	28-3-98	23-10-99
DDG 78 PORTER*	Ingalls	2-12-96	15-10-97	20-3-99

D: DDG 51–71: 6,731 tons light (8,850 fl); DDG 72–78: 6,914 tons light (9,033 fl)
S: 31+ kts

Dim: 153.77 (142.03 wl; 135.94 pp) × 20.27 (18.0 wl) × 6.31 (9.35 over sonar; DDG 72–78: 6.60 hull/9.90 over sonar)
A: 2 Mk 41 Mod. 0 vertical-launch groups (1 61-cell, 1 29-cell; 90 Standard SM-2 MR Block III SAM, VLA, and Tomahawk missiles); 4–8 Harpoon SSM; 1 127-mm 54-cal. Mk 45 Mod. 1 DP; 2 20-mm Mk 15 Mod. 1 Phalanx gatling CIWS; 2 single 25-mm 75-cal. Mk 38 Mod. 1 Bushmaster guns; 4 single 12.7-mm mg; 2 triple 324-mm Mk 32 Mod. 14 ASW TT (Mk 46 and Mk 50 torpedoes)
Electronics:
Radar: 1 Raytheon SPS-64(V)9 nav.; 1 AIL SPS-67(V)4 surf. search; 1 Lockheed Martin SPY-1D 3-D search/weapons control; 3 Raytheon SPG-62 target illumination; 2 Mk 90 Phalanx f.c.
Sonar: SQQ-89(V)4 suite: SQS-53C(V)1 bow-mounted; Kingfisher mine-avoidance; provision for SQR-19B(V)1 towed array
TACAN: URN-25
EW: Raytheon SLQ-32(V)5 (DDG 68 and later: SLQ-32(V)3) active/passive—DDG 72–78 only: Sanders SRS-1A Combat D/F—all: Mk 36 Mod. 12 SRBOC decoy syst. (4 6-round Mk 137 RL); SLQ-25A Nixie towed torpedo decoy syst. (with SSTD Phase I); SLQ-39 decoy buoy launch syst.—DDG 52 also: 4 twin Mk 53 Nulka decoy RL
E/O: Kollmorgen Mk 46 Mod. 0 optronic director
M: 4 G.E. LM-2500-30 gas turbines; 2 5-bladed CP props; 105,000 shp (90,000 sust.)
Electric: 7,500 kw tot. (3 Allison 501-K34 gas turbines driving)
Range: 4,400/20 **Fuel:** . . . tons
Crew: 21–22 officers, 315 enlisted (DDG 69: 28 officers, 231 enlisted)

GUIDED-MISSILE DESTROYERS [DDG] *(continued)*

Milius (DDG 69) Brian Morrison, 12-00

Porter (DDG 78) Camil Busquets i Vilanova, 12-00

Decatur (DDG 73) Brian Morrison, 5-00

Remarks: DDG 51 was authorized in FY 85, DDG 52–54 in FY 87 (DDG 54 funded in FY 89), DDG 55–58 in FY 89, DDG 59–63 in FY 90, DDG 64–67 in FY 91, DDG 68–72 in FY 92, DDG 73–76 in FY 93, and DDG 77 and 78 in FY 94. DDG 51 was ordered 2-4-85, DDG 52 on 26-5-87, and DDG 53 in 8-87. Congress required a third yard to participate in the FY 89 construction, but none was selected. Only three were requested for FY 89 in 2-88, but Congress authorized and appropriated funds for three ($2.062 billion) and authorized the use of unexpended prior-year funds for two more; all five were ordered 13-12-88. DDG 59–63 were ordered 22-2-90, DDG 64–67 on 16-1-91, DDG 68–72 on 8-4-92, and DDG 73–76 (authorized and appropriated for $3.25 billion under FY 93) on 21-1-93. DDG 77–79 were funded at $2.9 billion under FY 94, with DDG 79 being the prototype for the follow-on Flight IIA group.

The name for DDG 52 was changed three times—twice in 1989. DDG 70 is named for a woman, Rear Adm. Grace Hopper. DDG 54 became the first of the class to be based overseas, at Yokosuka, Japan, on 30-9-96, followed by DDG 56 on 30-6-97.

DDG 66 ran aground 12-11-96, less than a month after commissioning, on a charted rock near St. Martin in the Caribbean, damaging the sonar dome, propellers, and shaft struts. Repairs by Bath Iron Works were initially expected to cost $56 million but were instead completed during 9-97 for about $10 million.

DDG 67 was heavily damaged by a terrorist attack at Aden, Yemen, on 12-10-00, with 17 killed and 35 injured. The explosion tore a 40 × 40–ft. hole in the ship's side, flooding the forward generator room and destroying the enlisted mess decks. Repairs were expected to cost as much as $170 million. The repair contract was issued to Ingalls Shipbuilding, Pascagoula, during 1-01 and the ship was relaunched 15-9-01, with all work to be completed by 2-02.

Under a 7-5-01 decision, DDG 69 and 72 are to be operated experimentally for two years by only 150 personnel in a program to develop more efficient use of personnel resources; it seems unlikely that operational performance will not be impaired.

Hull systems: Have steel superstructures and the first comprehensive CBR protection system in a U.S. Navy ship. More than 130 tons of Kevlar or plastic armor are used for vital spaces, including 70 tons around the combat control spaces. In a weight-saving program, DDG 78 and later employed about 50 tons less structural steel than earlier ships. Fin stabilizers are not fitted, but the ships do have rudder roll-rate reduction. Prairie/Masker air bubbler systems are fitted to the hulls and propellers to reduce machinery noise radiation below the waterline.

The hullform is unusually broad in relation to length. The concept of the broad hull was borne out during sea trials for DDG 51, which was able to maintain 30 kts in 35-ft. seas and a 60-kt gale. The ships heel only slightly with full rudder at full speed. Although the hull was configured with a stern wedge to reduce "squatting" at higher speeds and improve fuel endurance, a fixed stern flap is being fitted to the transom below the waterline to further improve fuel efficiency; it had been fitted to DDG 59 and 61 and several others by 4-01.

Have an automated digital steering system, wherein course is entered and automatically maintained. DDG 64 and later have the Litton Marine WSN-5 ring-laser gyro inertial navigation system, and the Litton Marine WSN-7 ring-laser gyro inertial navigation system is to be backfitted in all during overhauls. Carry two 7.32-m rigid inflatable boats and 15 25-person encapsulated life rafts. The increase in full-load displacements over the originally announced 8,315 tons is primarily the result of adapting void tanks to carry fuel.

Combat systems: Have the Mk 8 weapons-control system. The Aegis SPY-1D radar has all four faces mounted on the forward superstructure; the system employs five UYK-43B computers. The Combat Information Center is below the main deck. DDG 69 was the first with Aegis Baseline 5 Phase III, which incorporates a SPY-1D Track Initiation Processor (permitting the screening of transient detections prior to transition-to-track), X-Windows-format Tactical Graphics Capability, and an embedded Command and Control Processor with joint Link 16 capability. WSC-3 UHF SATCOM terminals and Links 11 and 14 are fitted, and during the 1990s, the WSC-6 SHF SATCOM system was added. Commercial SATCOM terminals have also been added to all. The Rockwell USQ-82(V) databus is employed for internal data distribution. DDG 58 and later have improved fire control, extended-range Standard missile employment capability, NTDS Mod. 5, improved displays, and later communications systems.

Block II ships (DDG 72–78) have the Joint Tactical Information Distribution System (JTDS) command-and-control processor, Combat D/F, Tactical Information Exchange System (TADIX-B), SLQ-32(V)3 active electronics countermeasures, and the capability to launch and control the Aegis Standard ER missile added.

No helicopter hangar is fitted. The flight deck can accept SH-60B or SH-60F Seahawk helicopters, and the SQQ-28 LAMPS-III datalink/control system is installed. DDG 52 and later have helicopter refueling/rearming facilities, which added 58 tons to the full-load displacement; they can carry nine spare ASW torpedoes for helicopters in a small magazine near the helicopter deck.

GUIDED-MISSILE DESTROYERS [DDG] *(continued)*

The 127-mm gun is controlled by the Mk 34 Mod. 0 gun weapon system with Mk 160 Mod. 4 gun computing system (which uses radar input data from the SPS-67(V)4 surface-search radar or the SPY-1D Aegis system). The planned Mk 121 Mod. 0 Seafire t.v./laser/infrared director was canceled and replaced by a less costly system, the Kollmorgen Passive Optical Sight Mk 46 Mod. 0, which is mounted atop an extended deckhouse forward of the forward Mk 99 illuminator; all are being brought up to Mod. 1 standard, with the addition of a laser rangefinder, narrow-field-of-view t.v. camera, and new thermal imager. The gun has a secondary antiaircraft capability and is furnished with 600 rounds of ammunition. The Standard SM-2 MR Block II missiles are controlled by the Aegis system, with the Mk 99 missile fire-control system using the three Mk 80 illuminator systems' SPG-62 radars for terminal designation only. The normal deployed load of missiles includes 74 Standard SM-2 MR SAMs. Tomahawk launch control is by the SWG-3A system and Harpoon by the SWG-1A(V) system; the Block II ships do not normally carry the Harpoon missiles, although the racks for two sets of four canister launchers are present.

The SQQ-89(V)4 ASW suite includes the SQS-53C bow-mounted sonar, SQR-19 towed passive sonar array, SQQ-28 helicopter datalink, SIMAS, and the Mk 116 Mod. 7 weapon-control system. Most ships of the class have had their towed hydrophone arrays removed and put into storage. The Mk 116 Mod. 7 ASW f.c.s. is carried to handle the launch of shipboard torpedoes and vertical-launch ASROC missiles.

The SLQ-32(V)2 passive-only EW suite in early Flight I units of the class has been upgraded to (V)5 through the addition of "Sidekick" jammers; later Flight I ships were completed with Sidekick and Flight II ships have the integrated SLQ-32(V)3 intercept and jamming array.

May have one Phalanx mount updated to Block IB electro-optical configuration to deal with smallcraft, mines, and other small targets. Following the attack on the DDG 67 in 10-00, deployed ships are now receiving two 25-mm Boeing Mk 88 Bushmaster low-angle guns and four 12.7-mm machineguns, and consideration was being given as of 4-01 to adding two General Dynamics 30-mm Mk 46 gun systems to improve defenses against smallcraft attacks.

Disposal note: Of the four relatively new and powerful *Kidd*-class guided-missile destroyers, *Kidd* (DDG 993, ex-Iranian *Kouroush*) was decommissioned 12-3-98, *Callaghan* (DDG 994, ex-*Daryush*) on 31-3-98, *Scott* (DDG 995, ex-*Nader*) on 15-12-98, and *Chandler* (DDG 996, ex-*Andushirvan*) on 24-9-99. They were offered to Taiwan during 1-01 and formally requested 2-10-01 for activation and transfer between 2004 and 2006.

DESTROYERS [DD]

♦ **23 Spruance class** (3 in *reserve*)
Bldr: Ingalls SB, Pascagoula, Miss. (Litton Industries) (*Atlantic/†Pacific Fleet)

	Laid down	L	In serv.
DD 963 Spruance*	7-11-72	10-11-73	20-9-75
DD 964 Paul F. Foster†	6-2-73	23-2-74	21-2-76
DD 965 Kinkaid†	19-4-73	25-5-74	10-7-76
DD 967 Elliot†	15-10-73	19-12-74	22-1-77
DD 968 Arthur W. Radford*	14-1-74	1-3-75	16-4-77
DD 969 Peterson*	29-4-74	21-6-75	9-7-77
DD 970 *Caron*	1-7-74	24-6-75	1-10-77
DD 971 David R. Ray†	23-9-74	23-8-75	19-11-77
DD 972 Oldendorf†	27-12-74	21-10-75	4-3-78
DD 973 John Young†	17-2-75	7-2-76	20-5-78
DD 975 O'Brien†	9-5-75	8-7-76	3-12-77
DD 977 Briscoe*	21-7-75	15-12-76	3-6-78
DD 978 Stump*	25-8-75	29-1-77	19-8-78
DD 980 *Moosbrugger*	3-11-75	23-7-77	16-12-78
DD 981 *John Hancock*	16-1-76	29-10-77	10-3-79
DD 982 Nicholson*	20-2-76	11-11-77	12-5-79
DD 985 Cushing†	2-2-77	17-6-78	21-9-79
DD 987 O'Bannon*	24-6-77	25-9-78	15-12-79
DD 988 Thorn*	29-8-77	22-11-78	16-2-80
DD 989 Deyo*	14-10-77	27-1-79	22-3-80
DD 991 Fife†	6-3-78	1-5-79	31-5-80
DD 992 Fletcher†	24-4-78	16-6-79	12-7-80
DD 997 Hayler*	20-10-80	2-3-82	5-3-83

Arthur W. Radford (DD 968)—with prototype enclosed mast enveloping the SPS-40 and TAS/Mk 23 radar antennas and other electronics
William H. Clarke, 2-00

Oldendorf (DD 972)—note larger radome on foremast platform for the SPQ-9B low-altitude search radar being tested in this ship
Jim Sanderson, 6-01

Kinkaid (DD 965) Findler & Winter, 10-00

Hayler (DD 997)—with SPS-49 air-search radar Peruvian Navy, 11-00

Deyo (DD 989) William H. Clarke, 9-01

Peterson (DD 969) Mike Welsford, 5-00

DESTROYERS [DD] *(continued)*

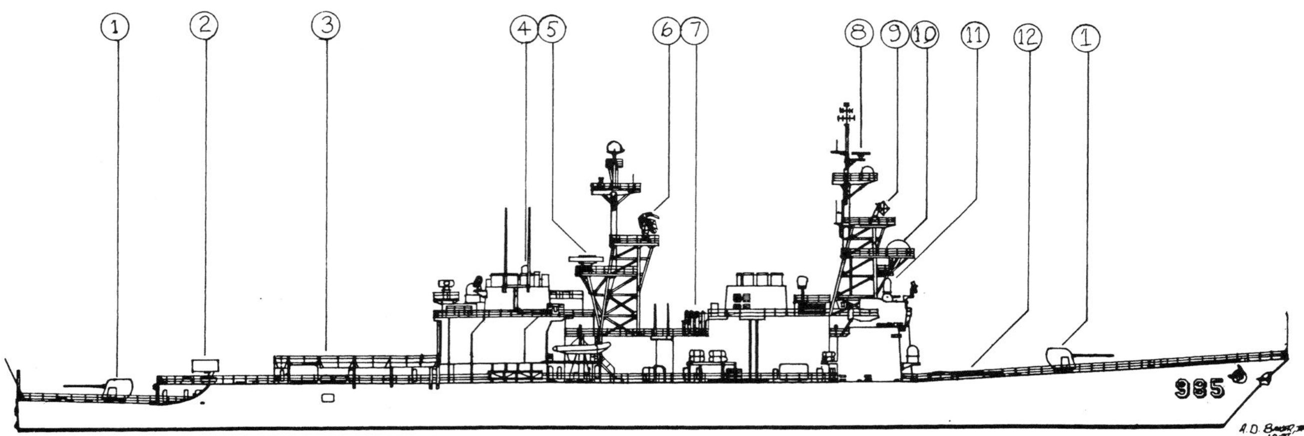

Cushing (DD 985) 1. 127-mm Mk 45 DP gun 2. Mk 29 octuple Sea Sparrow SAM launcher 3. triple Mk 32 ASW TT (behind shutters) 4. portside 20-mm Mk 15 Phalanx CIWS (behind exhaust stacks) 5. TAS/Mk 23 low-flying target-designation radar 6. SPS-40E air-search radar 7. Harpoon antiship missile launch canisters 8. SPS-55 surface-search radar 9. SPG-60 AA gun f.c. radar 10. SPQ-9A surface gun f.c. radar 11. starboard 20-mm Mk 15 Phalanx CIWS 12. Mk 41 vertical missile launch system

Drawing by A. D. Baker III

Thorn (DD 988)—with RAM point-defense missile launcher on starboard quarter — Maritime Photographic, 4-00

Elliot (DD 967) — Brian Morrison, 6-00

D: DD 963–992: 6,593–7,121 tons light (9,040–9,533 fl); DD 997: 7,467 tons light (9,884 fl)
S: 32.5 kts
Dim: 171.68 (161.25 pp) × 16.76 × 7.00 (10.05 over sonar)
A: 1 Mk 41 VLS group (61 Tomahawk SSM and VLA ASW missiles); 4–8 RGM-84 Harpoon SSM; 1 8-round Mk 29 launcher (24 RIM-7P Sea Sparrow SAM); 2 single 127-mm 54-cal. Mk 45 DP; 2 20-mm Mk 15 Phalanx gatling CIWS; 4 12.7-mm mg; 2 triple 324-mm Mk 32 Mod. 5 ASW TT (18 Mk 46 torpedoes); 1 or 2 SH-60B Seahawk LAMPS-III ASW helicopters (see remarks)—DD 972, 973, 977, 982, 987, 988, and 992 also: 1 21-round Mk 49 RAM SAM launcher (RIM-116A missiles)—deployed units also: 2 single 25-mm 75-cal. Mk 38 Mod. 1 Bushmaster low-angle guns
Electronics:
Radar: 1 Raytheon SPS-64(V)9; 1 Cardion SPS-55 surf. search; 1 Lockheed SPS-40B/C/D/E (DD 997: Raytheon SPS-49(V)2) air search; 1 Hughes TAS/Mk 23 Mod. 0 target desig.; 1 Lockheed SPQ-9A (DD 972: SPQ-9B) surf. gun f.c.; 1 Lockheed SPG-60 gun f.c.; 1 Mk 95 SAM f.c.; 2 Mk 90 Phalanx f.c. (on mounts)
Sonar: SSQ-89(V)5, (V)6, or (V)8 suite: EDO-G.E. SQS-53B/C hull-mounted LF; SQR-19(V)3, SQR-19A(V)3, or SQR-19B(V) TACTAS; WQC-2 and WQC-6 underwater telephones
TACAN: URN-25
EW: DD 968, 970, 971, 975, 981, 991: SLQ-32(V)2 intercept—others: SLQ-32(V)3 intercept/jamming—all: Mk 36 SRBOC decoy syst. (4 6-round Mk 137 RL)—DD 963–970, 972, 985, 988–992: SSQ-108 Outboard D/F—all: SLQ-25 or SLQ-25A (with SSTD) Nixie towed torpedo decoy syst.; SLQ-49 floating radar reflector buoys
E/O: 12 ships: 2 Boeing TISS Mk 8 Mod. 1 IR imaging
M: 4 G.E. LM-2500 gas turbines; 2 5-bladed CP props; 86,000 shp (80,000 sust.)
Electric: 6,000 kw tot. (3 × 2,000-kw Allison 501-K17 gas turbine–driven sets)
Range: 3,300/30; 6,000/20; 8,000/17 **Fuel:** 1,534 tons + 72 tons aviation fuel
Crew: 24–27 officers, 272–315 enlisted + air group: 8–10 officers, 30 enlisted

Remarks: Although these ships carry as many as five different kinds of guided missiles, they are not considered to be guided-missile destroyers. DD 963–965 were authorized in FY 70, DD 966–971 in FY 71, DD 972–978 in FY 72, DD 979–985 in FY 74, DD 986–992 in FY 75, and DD 997 in FY 78. DD 997 was intended by Congress to be of an "air-capable" design, with an enlarged hangar for four ASW helicopters, but costs rose to the point that the ship was ordered 29-9-79 as a nearly standard version of the class. The basic *Spruance* hull and propulsion plant have also served as the basis for the *Kidd* (DDG 993) and *Ticonderoga* (CG 47, ex-DDG 47) designs. DD 981 carries her name across the stern in script, duplicating the signature of the

DESTROYERS [DD] *(continued)*

first signer of the Declaration of Independence. DD 968 was rammed by merchant vessel *Saudi Riyadh* on 4-2-99 off Virginia Beach, Va., causing a severe gash in the hull forward and dismounting the forward 127-mm gun; the $32.7 million, 15-week repair was performed by Norfolk Naval Shipyard.

Disposals: The seven ships of the class without vertical missile launchers were retired during FY 98; all are to be scrapped except DD 979, which is being retained as a possible museum ship, and DD 974, being kept as a spare parts source. During 11-01, the navy announced that of the remaining 19 active ships at the end of FY 02, six would be retired each year from FY 03 through FY 05 and the final ship during FY 06, five years earlier than had been planned a year before, and well prior to their 45-year originally planned service lives. Units decommissioned through 2001 are listed below; DD 971 was scheduled for decommissioning on 28-2-02.

	Decomm.	Stricken	Remarks
DD 966 *Hewitt*	19-7-01	. . .	
DD 970 *Caron*	18-10-01	—	Retained for experimental use
DD 974 *Comte de Grasse*	5-6-98	5-6-98	
DD 976 *Merrill*	26-3-98	26-3-98	
DD 979 *Conolly*	18-9-98	18-9-98	
DD 980 *Moosbrugger*	15-12-00	. . .	
DD 981 *John Hancock*	16-10-00	. . .	
DD 983 *John Rodgers*	4-9-98	4-9-98	
DD 984 *Leftwich*	28-3-98	28-3-98	
DD 986 *Harry W. Hill*	29-5-98	29-5-98	
DD 990 *Ingersoll*	24-7-98	23-8-98	

Hull systems: Displacements have risen drastically as equipment has been added, and vary widely from ship to ship in this class; the ships were originally intended to displace under 7,000 tons full load. DD 997, with additional Kevlar armor, displaced 8,250 tons full load as completed (and has since gained 1,634 tons); Kevlar plastic armor was added to inside vital spaces of all units of the class by 1986. The superstructure is fabricated of aluminum, welded to the hull via bimetallic strips. Radar cross-section reduction measures have been instituted, including the addition of radar-absorbent materials to the superstructure and masts and alterations to the antenna installations. The hullform was designed to minimize rolling and pitching; there are no fin stabilizers.

Habitability received particular attention, living spaces being divided by partitions and intended for no more than six personnel each, with a recreational area and good sanitary facilities. Originally were operated with 232 enlisted but now have up to 360. DD 968 was given a new Ingalls-built Advanced Enclosed Mast/Sensor System (AEM/S) composite-construction replacement mainmast during an FY 97 refit. DD 992 in 1999 began testing an infrared-reflection reduction paint that lasts longer than regular paints and also serves to cool interior temperatures by about 15° F on a hot day.

The propulsion machinery is very quiet. Prairie/Masker hull and propeller bubbler systems are installed to enhance quietness. The controllable-pitch propellers are 5.1 m in diameter and rotate at 168 rpm at 30 kts. Full speed can be reached from 12 kts in only 53 seconds. All propulsion machinery is under the control of a single operator in a central control station (CCS). Endurance can be extended greatly by using one engine on one shaft for cruising. The mean time between overhauls for the LM-2500 gas turbines has been extended to more than 9,000 hours. DD 963 has electric heating; the others retain the waste-heat boilers that have caused continuing maintenance problems.

Aviation systems: Hangars on DD 969, 972, 974, 976–979, 982, 983, 985, 987, 989, 990, 992, and 997 were widened flush with the starboard side during overhauls to permit carrying two SH-60B LAMPS-III helicopters, and dual RAST haul-down and deck traversing equipment was installed. Torpedo magazines were altered to accommodate Penguin Mk 2 Mod. 7 missiles for the LAMPS-III helicopters; Penguin first became operational in 5-94 aboard DD 979.

Combat systems: The Mk 91 Mod. 0 fire-control system for Sea Sparrow uses a single Mk 95 radar director. The Mk 86 Mod. 3 gun fire-control system for the 127-mm guns uses the SPG-60 radar for AA and the SPQ-9A for surface fire; there are also two remote optical target-designation sights. DD 977 has had the gun f.c.s. modified to Mk 86 Mod. 10 (with a UYK-7 computer in place of the Mk 152 computer, Mk 113 display consoles, new fuze-setters, etc.) to conduct trials with semiactive laser-guided projectiles. DD 972 has been acting as trials ship for the SPQ-9B radar, which is intended as a low-altitude-threat detection and designation system rather than as a fire-control radar. Magazines hold 1,200 rounds of 127-mm ammunition. The Mk 16 ASROC ASW missile system, with its eight-round Mk 112 box launcher and belowdecks vertical loading system has been removed from all ships of the class.

Seven ships received two quadruple Tomahawk cruise missile elevatable Mk 44 armored box launchers; firing trials were carried out on DD 976 in 1-81, while first operational installation was in DD 974 in late 1984. DD 989 had the armored box Tomahawk launcher system replaced by the 61-cell VLS during a 1-9-95 to 11-96 refit at Newport News SB & DD. DD 986 never had a Tomahawk launch system of either kind. The other ships of the class were backfitted with a 61-cell Mk 41 Mod. 0 vertical-launch group in place of the ASROC launcher; the nominal loadout is 45 Tomahawk cruise missiles and 16 Vertical Launch ASROC ASW missiles, but ships normally deploy with only four ASROC missiles. Tomahawk launch is performed by the SWG-3B launch system.

Plans to add the Cooperative Engagement Capability (CEC) to 12 units were terminated in 6-00. A dozen ships of the class were planned to receive one RAM launcher, but only the seven listed above have it, mounted on the starboard quarter of the fantail. The Mk 15 CIWS mounts, upgraded to Block I configuration, have been installed in "maintenance enclosures" in most of the class, with the after mount raised atop a new deckhouse.

All ships have the NATO Link 11 data-sharing system. DD 971 carried the prototype USC-38(V) EHF SATCOM installation ("FLTSAT-7"), and most of the class have now had the WSC-6 SHF SATCOM system installed (with radome-mounted antennas at the forward edge of the superstructure and atop the hangar). The Hughes Mk 23 TAS (Target Acquisition System), which uses a high-rpm radar, was backfitted on all units except the stricken DD 986 on an aft-projecting platform on the mainmast to detect low-flying, high-speed missiles and aircraft. The SPS-55 surface-search radar antenna was moved to a new, higher platform on the foremast in order to accommodate the radome housing the antenna for the LAMPS-III helicopter datalink.

All units retained in service have the updated SQQ-89(V)8 ASW system, with Lockheed Martin SQS-53D sonar, SQR-19 towed array, SQQ-28 helicopter ASW datalink, Mk 116 Mod. 5 (or the updated Mod. 8) ASW f.c.s., and SIMAS processing installed. All carry the SLQ-17 sonar signal processor, SRQ-4 helicopter datalink receiver, SQQ-28 sonobuoy analyzer, UYQ-25 acoustic range predictor, and UYS-1 acoustic spectrum analyzer. The towed hydrophone arrays were removed and put into storage. By 12-99, nine ships of the class had been fitted with TRAFS (Torpedo Recognition and Alertment Functional Segment), a torpedo detection function added to the SQQ-89 system.

Early units were given the WLR-1 EW system as an interim EW installation until SLQ-32(V)2 was available. The original SLQ-32(V)2 intercept-only EW system has been augmented in all but six of the remaining ships by the Raytheon Short Stop active jammer, upgrading the EW system to SLQ-32(V)5. In ships that have had Mk 15 CIWS maintenance enclosures added, the portside SLQ-32(V)5 antenna array has been moved aft to beneath the CIWS mounting.

The SYQ-17 RAIDS (Rapid Antiship Integrated Defense System) was being installed in the entire class during mid-1990s overhauls; the electronic system serves as a rule-based planning aid to coordinate the use of the ships' defensive systems and uses target input from the Phalanx CIWS radars. During a 1994–95 modernization refit, DD 997 became the first USN ship to carry the Westinghouse MSTRAP (Multi-Sensor Torpedo Recognition and Alertment Processor).

DD 985 was used for trials with the Remote Minehunting Operational Prototype (V)2 (RMOP) during 8-96, using a winch and recovery system mounted on the portside boat deck. DD 969 in 8-98 conducted acceptance trials for the Australian Nulka hovering decoy system. DD 978 was used during 1998 for trials of the Automatic Radar Periscope Detection and Discrimination system, for which the antenna for an APS-137 aircraft radar was mounted on the foremast in place of the SPS-55 set.

GUIDED-MISSILE FRIGATES [FFG]

Note: One outcome of the cancellation of the DD 21–class destroyer on 1-11-01 was the initiation of a program to study the possible acquisition of a class of 4,000- to 5,000-ton "Littoral Combat Ships" (LCS)—that is, frigates—for use in coastal waters.

♦ 35 Oliver Hazard Perry class (SCN 207/2081 type)

Bldrs: A: General Dynamics Bath Iron Works, Bath, Maine; B: Todd, San Pedro, Calif.; C: Todd, Seattle (*Atlantic/†Pacific Fleet; 8 Naval Reserve Force ships: FFG 9, 12–15, 28, 29, 38)

	Bldr	Laid down	L	In serv.
FFG 8 McInerney*	A	16-1-78	4-11-78	15-12-79
FFG 9 Wadsworth†	B	13-7-77	29-7-78	28-2-80
FFG 12 George Philip†	B	14-12-77	16-12-78	15-11-80
FFG 13 Samuel Eliot Morison*	A	4-12-78	14-7-79	10-10-80
FFG 14 Sides†	B	7-8-78	19-5-79	30-5-81
FFG 15 Estocin*	A	2-4-79	3-11-79	10-1-81
FFG 28 Boone*	C	27-3-79	16-1-80	15-5-82
FFG 29 Stephen W. Groves*	A	16-9-80	4-4-81	17-4-82
FFG 32 John L. Hall*	A	5-1-81	24-7-81	26-6-82
FFG 33 Jarrett†	B	11-2-81	17-10-81	2-7-83
FFG 36 Underwood*	A	3-8-81	6-2-82	29-1-83
FFG 37 Crommelin†	C	30-5-80	1-7-81	18-6-83
FFG 38 Curts†	B	1-7-81	6-3-82	8-10-83
FFG 39 Doyle*	A	16-11-81	22-5-82	21-5-83
FFG 40 Halyburton*	C	26-9-80	13-10-81	7-1-84
FFG 41 McCluskey†	B	21-10-81	18-9-82	10-12-83
FFG 42 Klakring*	A	19-2-82	18-9-82	20-8-83
FFG 43 Thach†	B	6-2-82	18-12-82	17-3-84
FFG 45 De Wert*	A	14-6-82	18-12-82	19-11-83
FFG 46 Rentz†	B	18-9-82	16-7-83	30-6-84
FFG 47 Nicholas*	A	27-9-82	23-4-83	10-3-84
FFG 48 Vandegrift†	C	13-10-81	15-10-82	24-11-84
FFG 49 Robert G. Bradley*	A	28-12-82	13-8-83	11-8-84
FFG 50 Taylor*	A	5-5-83	5-11-83	1-12-84
FFG 51 Gary†	B	18-12-82	19-11-83	17-11-84
FFG 52 Carr*	C	26-3-82	26-2-83	27-7-85
FFG 53 Hawes*	A	22-8-83	17-2-84	9-2-85
FFG 54 Ford†	B	16-7-83	23-6-84	29-6-85
FFG 55 Elrod*	A	14-11-83	12-5-84	6-7-85
FFG 56 Simpson*	A	27-2-84	31-8-84	9-11-85
FFG 57 Reuben James†	B	10-9-83	8-2-85	22-3-86
FFG 58 Samuel B. Roberts*	A	21-5-84	8-12-84	12-4-86
FFG 59 Kauffman*	A	8-4-85	29-3-86	21-2-87
FFG 60 Rodney M. Davis*	B	8-2-85	11-1-86	9-5-87
FFG 61 Ingraham†	B	30-3-87	26-6-88	5-8-89

McInerney (FFG 8) William H. Clarke, 1-01

GUIDED-MISSILE FRIGATES [FFG] *(continued)*

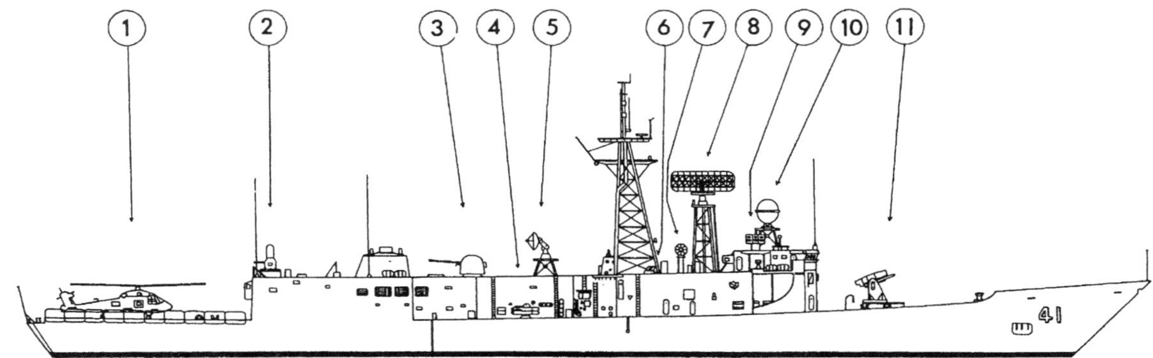

McCluskey (FFG 41) 1. SH-60B Seahawk LAMPS-III ASW helicopter 2. 20-mm Mk 15 Phalanx CIWS 3. 76-mm Mk 75 DP gun 4. triple Mk 32 ASW TT 5. STIR gun and missile f.c. 6. Mk 137 launchers for the Mk 36 SRBOC decoy system 7. OE-82 antennas (port and starboard) for the WSC-3 UHF SATCOM system. 8. SPS-49 air-search radar 9. SLQ-32(V)2 EW antenna group 10. Mk 92 radar f.c. director 11. Mk 13 Mod. 4 missile launcher Drawing by Robert Dumas from *Flottes de Combat*

Samuel Eliot Morison (FFG 13)—a short-hull Naval Reserve Force unit due for transfer to Turkey in 4-02 Maritime Photographic, 8-01

Rodney M. Davis (FFG 60)—a long-hulled regular navy unit; note the deck traversing system tracks on the helicopter deck leading to the twin hangars
Maritime Photographic, 7-01

GUIDED-MISSILE FRIGATES [FFG] *(continued)*

John L. Hall (FFG 32) Martin Mokrus, 6-01

Thach (FFG 43) Findler & Winter, 10-00

Kauffman (FFG 59) H&L Van Ginderen, 3-00

D: FFG 9–15: 3,087–3,197 tons light (3,973–4,082 fl)—others: 3,101–3,204 tons light (4,016–4,108 fl)
S: 29 kts (30.6 trials)
Dim: 138.80 (FFG 9–15: 135.64; all: 125.9 wl) × 13.72 × 5.8 (6.7 max.)
A: 1 single-rail Mk 13 Mod. 4 launcher (4 Harpoon and 36 Standard SM-1 Block VIB missiles); 1 76-mm 62-cal. Mk 75 DP; 1 20-mm Mk 15 Phalanx Block I or IA (FFG 50: Block IB) gatling CIWS; 2 single 25-mm 75-cal. Mk 38 Bushmaster low-angle guns; 2 or 4 single 12.7-mm mg; 2 triple 324-mm Mk 32 Mod. 7 ASW TT—FFG 8, 28 and later: 1 or 2 SH-60B Seahawk LAMPS-III ASW helicopters
Electronics:
Radar: 1 Cardion SPS-55 surf. search; 1 Raytheon SPS-49(V)4 or (V)5 air search; 1 Raytheon Mk 92 Mod. 4 or Mod. 6 missile/gun f.c.; 1 Lockheed STIR (SPG-60 Mod.) missile/gun f.c. (see remarks)
Sonar: SQQ-89(V)2 or (V)9 suite: Raytheon SQS-56 hull-mounted LF; Gould SQR-19(V)2 or SQR-19B(V)2 TACTASS towed array (see remarks)
TACAN: URN-25
EW: FFG 29, 32, 36, 40, 45–59, 61: Raytheon SLQ-32(V)5 with Sidekick jammer—others: Raytheon SLQ-32(V)2 intercept only—all: Mk 36 SRBOC decoy syst. (2 6-round Mk 137 RL); SLQ-25 (FFG 36, 47, 51–53, 55, 57–60: SLQ-25A) Nixie towed acoustic torpedo decoy syst.
M: 2 G.E. LM-2500 gas turbines; 1 5.5-m-diameter, CP, 5-bladed prop; 41,000 shp (40,000 sust.)—2 350-shp drop-down electric propulsors
Electric: 3,000 kw tot.
Range: 4,200/20; 5,000/18 **Fuel:** 587 tons + 64 tons helicopter fuel
Crew: 17–19 officers, 198 enlisted (FFG 53: 23 officers, 204 enlisted)

Gary (FFG 51) Brian Morrison, 5-01

Remarks: These ships were originally conceived as low-cost convoy escorts (hence the original PF 109–112 hull numbers for FFG 7–10). As older first-line destroyers and frigates were retired without replacement, however, the FFG 7 class has been integrated into the fleet, and numerous updates have been applied to permit it to cope with modern combat conditions. As a result, the fully equipped units displace nearly 700 tons more than the designed displacement, and crews have been greatly enlarged. The soundness of the design has permitted the expansion, and the ships have proven remarkably sturdy. FFG 17, 18, 35, and 44 of this class were built by Todd, Seattle, for Australia, which also built two more in-country. Spain has built six and Taiwan seven (with one more under construction). Others have been transferred abroad (see table below).

The original complement was planned at 17 officers, 167 enlisted, which was found to be too few enlisted to operate and maintain the ships. Therefore, FFG 19 and later were fitted with 30 additional enlisted bunks, and the others were backfitted. Naval Reserve Force ships have about 76 naval reservists in their complements.

As of the end of 2001, FFG 8, 13, 28, 36, 39, 42, 45, 49, 50, and 56 were based at Mayport, Fla.; FFG 15, 40, 47, 52, 53, 55, 58, and 59 at Norfolk; FFG 29 and 32 at Pascagoula, Miss.; FFG 9, 12, 14, 33, 38, 41, 43, and 46 at San Diego; FFG 37 and 57 at Pearl Harbor, Hawaii; FFG 48 and 51 at Yokosuka, Japan; and FFG 54, 60, and 61 at Everett, Wash.

Disposals: The fates of the class as of 2001 are shown in the following table (NRF = Naval Reserve Force, active units crewed in part by Naval Reservists).

	Decomm.	Action
FFG 7 *Oliver Hazard Perry*	20-2-97	Stricken 3-5-99
FFG 8 *McInerney*	FY 11	To reserve
FFG 9 *Wadsworth**	1-10-02	To Poland 1-10-02
FFG 10 *Duncan*	17-12-94	Stricken 5-1-98; sold to Turkey for spares in 10-99
FFG 11 *Clark*	15-11-99	Donated to Poland 15-3-00
FFG 12 *George Philip**	FY 03	For foreign sale
FFG 13 *Samuel Eliot Morison**	10-4-02	Sold to Turkey 10-4-02
FFG 14 *Sides**	FY 03	For foreign sale
FFG 15 *Estocin**	FY 05	Sale to Turkey 10-04
FFG 16 *Clifton Sprague*	2-6-95	To Turkey 12-1-98
FFG 19 *John A. Moore**	1-9-00	Sold to Turkey 1-9-00
FFG 20 *Antrim*	8-5-96	To Turkey 12-1-98
FFG 21 *Flatley*	11-5-96	To Turkey 12-1-98
FFG 22 *Fahrion*	31-3-98	To Egypt 31-3-98
FFG 23 *Lewis B. Puller*	18-9-98	To Egypt 18-9-98
FFG 24 *Jack Williams*	13-9-96	To Bahrain 15-9-96
FFG 25 *Copeland*	18-9-96	To Egypt 18-9-96
FFG 26 *Gallery*	25-9-96	Sold to Egypt 25-9-96
FFG 27 *Mahlon S. Tisdale*	27-9-96	Stricken 20-2-98; to Turkey in 10-99
FFG 28 *Boone**	FY 13	To NRF 30-9-98
FFG 29 *Stephen W. Groves**	FY 07	To NRF 1-4-97
FFG 30 *Reid*	25-9-98	Stricken 25-9-98; sold to Turkey in FY 99
FFG 31 *Stark*	7-5-99	Stricken for scrap 7-5-99
FFG 32 *John L. Hall*	FY 07	To reserve
FFG 33 *Jarrett*	FY 12	For scrap or sale
FFG 34 *Aubrey Fitch*	12-12-97	Stricken 3-5-99
FFG 36 *Underwood*	FY 13	For scrap or sale
FFG 37 *Crommelin*	FY 09	To reserve
FFG 38 *Curts**	FY 16	To NRF (for FFG 23) FY 98
FFG 39 *Doyle*	FY 13	To NRF FY 02
FFG 40 *Halyburton*	FY 12	To NRF FY 03
FFG 41 *McClusky*	FY 08	For scrap or sale
FFG 42 *Klakring*	FY 14	To NRF FY 02
FFG 43 *Thach*	FY 10	To reserve
FFG 45 *De Wert*	FY 15	For scrap or sale
FFG 46 *Rentz*	FY 09	For scrap or sale
FFG 47 *Nicholas*	FY 15	To NRF FY 12
FFG 48 *Vandegrift*	FY 14	For scrap or sale
FFG 49 *Robert G. Bradley*	FY 15	For scrap or sale
FFG 50 *Taylor*	FY 17	To NRF FY 12
FFG 51 *Gary*	FY 14	For scrap or sale
FFG 52 *Carr*	FY 17	To NRF FY 13
FFG 53 *Hawes*	FY 13	For scrap or sale
FFG 54 *Ford*	FY 16	For scrap or sale
FFG 55 *Elrod*	FY 16	For scrap or sale
FFG 56 *Simpson*	FY 18	To NRF FY 03
FFG 57 *Reuben James*	FY 18	To NRF FY 18
FFG 58 *Samuel B. Roberts*	FY 18	To NRF FY 05
FFG 59 *Kauffman*	FY 19	To NRF FY 14
FFG 60 *Rodney M. Davis*	FY 19	To NRF FY 15
FFG 61 *Ingraham*	FY 21	To NRF FY 15

* In Naval Reserve Force, partially crewed by Naval Reservists, as of 1-00.

GUIDED-MISSILE FRIGATES [FFG] *(continued)*

Hull systems: Displacements have steadily increased, to the detriment of stability. FFG 59 was delivered at 4,100 tons full load, although the class was designed for just 3,600 tons and with only 39 tons planned growth margin. The ships are particularly well protected against splinter and fragmentation damage, with 19-mm aluminum-alloy armor over magazine spaces, 16-mm steel over the main engine-control room, and 19-mm Kevlar plastic armor over vital electronics and command spaces. Because of a hull twisting problem, doubler plates have been added over the hull sides amidships just below the main deck.

Speed on one turbine alone is 25 kts. The auxiliary propulsion system uses two retractable, pivoting pods located well forward and can drive the ships at up to 6 kts and can also be used as a side-thruster. Fin stabilizers began to be backfitted in earlier units, beginning with FFG 26 in 1982. Each fin extends 2.36 m and has a mean chord of 2.36 m; they are located 57.9 m abaft the bow perpendicular. As of 1-99, 21 active units of the class had received the Passive Countermeasures System (PCMS) to reduce radar cross-section.

Aviation systems: Although the ships were intended to operate the LAMPS-III ASW helicopter, FFG 7–35 as completed lacked the equipment necessary to handle them. Beginning with the FY 79 ships (FFG 36 and later), helicopter support equipment was aboard on completion. The RAST (Recovery Assistance, Securing, and Traversing) system, fitted as completed beginning with FFG 50, permits helicopter launch and recovery with the ship rolling through 28° and pitching 5°. The equipment was first installed in *McInerney* (FFG 8), which was reconstructed, completing 12-2-81 at Bath Iron Works, to act as SH-60B Seahawk LAMPS-III helicopter trials ship; the stern was lengthened by 3.16 m by changing the rake of the stern (the extension is slightly lower than the flight deck, to provide clearance for mooring equipment). Of the earlier short-hull ships, FFG 28, 29, 32, and 33 were lengthened and given the RAST system. FFG 12 is unusual in having the electronics fit for the LAMPS-III system but not having had the hull extension to permit flying SH-60B LAMPS-III helicopters.

Combat systems: The ships have the Mk 13 weapons-direction system. The Mk 92 Mod. 4 fire-control system controls missile and 76-mm gun fire; it uses a STIR (Separate Target Illumination Radar, a modified SPG-60) antenna amidships and a U.S.-built version of the Thales Nederland WM-28 radar forward and can track four separate targets. The Phase II CORT (Coherent Receiver/Transmitter) upgraded the Mk 92 Mod. 4 weapons-control system to Mod. 6 to improve performance in jamming and clutter; the search radar was upgraded to SPS-49(V)5, and the SYS-2(V)2 integrated action data system was fitted. CORT had been added to FFG 36, 47, 48, 50–55, 57, 59, and 61 by end-1995 when the update program was terminated. Ten other units of the class received the CANDO (Commercial-off-the-shelf Affordable Near-term Deficiency-correcting Ordalts) upgrade to the Mk 92 Mod. 2 fire-control system, incorporating improved clutter rejection in the radars, automatic target track display, and further improvements to the SPS-49(V)4 radar to detect small radar cross-section targets over land and in severe clutter conditions. FFG 47, 48, 50–55, 57, 59, and 61 by 1-99 had the RAIDS (Rapid Antiship Integrated Defense System) modification, which uses a COTS computer to integrate the combat direction system with threat data from the SLQ-32 EW system and the fire-control radar of the CIWS. As of 1998, the SPS-49(V)5 radars were planned to be updated to SPS-49A(V)1 in all surviving ships.

A few ships have been given Furuno-made navigational radars. All have SRR-1 and WSC-3 SATCOM equipment. Harpoon missiles are launched via the SWG-1 launch control system, and the missiles (when carried) are stowed in the vertical magazine for the Mk 13 missile launcher along with the Standard SM-1 SAMs.

The Mk 75 gun is a license-built version of the OTOBreda Compact. Two Mk 24 optical missile and gun target designators (mounted in tubs atop the pilothouse) were not fitted to the ships as completed until FFG 27 but have been backfitted in the earlier ships. The only ship-launched ASW weapons are the Mk 46 or Mk 50 torpedoes in the two triple torpedo tubes; a total of 24 torpedoes can be carried for shipboard and helicopter use. FFG 40, 43, 46, 47, 50–56, 58, and 59 by 1-99 had the FUSS (Flexible Universal Storage System) magazine modification to permit carrying both Penguin missiles and Mk 46 Mod. 5 and Mk 50 ASW torpedoes for the helicopters.

The 20-mm Mk 15 CIWS Phalanx was backfitted into all by end-1988. The improved Mk 15 Block I was backfitted in 1990s, and the Block IB, with a surface engagement capability, is to be substituted on 24 surviving units (trials with the first mount were conducted on FFG 36 during 2-99; the mount was then transferred to FFG 50 in 9-00).

Two variants of the SQQ-89 sonar system are in service on this class: SQQ-89(V)10 on FFG 14, 34, 37, 50, 51, 52, and 54, with SQR-19B(V)2 towed array sonar; and SQQ-89(V)2 on FFG 12, 13, 28, 29, 32, 33, 36, 38–43, 45–49, 53, 55–59, and 61, with SQR-19(V)2 and the UYQ-25A(V)2 processor. Most ships of the class, however, have had the towed hydrophone arrays removed and put into storage. The antenna for the SRQ-4 helicopter-to-ship ASW datalink of the LAMPS-III system is carried within a radome atop the mainmast. The Kingfisher mine-avoidance modification to the SQS-56 sonar, first installed in FFG 47, is being backfitted as funds permit.

Modernization: As of mid-2001, consideration was being given to updating the 24 newest ships (12 of which would eventually serve in the Naval Reserve Force) and extending their service lives by 10–15 years. All would receive hull, engineering, and electrical upgrades and a renewal of their auxiliary equipment; Nulka decoy launchers and an IR surveillance system would be added. The dozen ships to remain in regular navy service may also receive the RAM missile system and a more capable IRST (Infrared Search and Track) system.

PATROL CRAFT [PC]

♦ 0 (+ 1 + up to 9) Littoral Warfare Fast Patrol Craft
Bldr: . . . . . . (In serv. 2006–. . .)

D: 200–400 tons light (up to 1,000 fl) **S:** 40+ kts **Dim:** . . . × . . . × . . .
A: . . .
M: . . .; 2 pumpjets; . . . shp
Range: 4,000/. . .

Remarks: A program initiated by the Naval War College (where it was referred to as "Streetfighter") and the Office of Naval Research and employing the hull design technology tested in the trials craft *Slice* [YAGE] (q.v.). Would provide logistical support of up to 225 tons/70,000 ft.^{3} of supplies and a helicopter deck large enough to accommodate an MV-22 Osprey tilt-rotor transport or two helicopters. Cost is estimated at less than $25 million per ship. The same basic design would be offered to the Coast Guard as a patrol craft. The navy has not yet developed an operational requirement for the ship but was employing the chartered wave-piercing passenger catamaran *Joint Venture* (IX 532) and the chartered Norwegian Navy air-cushion guided-missile patrol craft *Skjold* in trials with the concept during 2001–02.

♦ 13 Cyclone class
Bldr: Bollinger Machine Shop & SY, Lockport, La. (*Atlantic/†Pacific Fleet)

	Laid down	L	In serv.
PC 2 Tempest*	30-9-91	4-4-92	21-8-93
PC 3 Hurricane†	20-11-91	6-6-92	15-10-93
PC 4 Monsoon†	15-2-92	6-3-93	22-1-94
PC 5 Typhoon*	15-5-92	3-3-93	12-2-94
PC 6 Sirocco*	20-6-92	29-5-93	11-6-94
PC 7 Squall†	17-2-93	28-8-93	4-7-94
PC 8 Zephyr†	6-3-93	3-12-93	15-10-94
PC 9 Chinook*	16-6-93	6-2-94	26-1-95
PC 10 Firebolt*	17-9-93	10-6-94	10-6-95
PC 11 Whirlwind*	4-3-94	9-9-94	1-7-95
PC 12 Thunderbolt*	9-6-94	2-12-94	7-10-95
PC 13 Shamal*	22-9-94	3-3-95	27-1-96
PC 14 Tornado*	25-8-98	7-6-99	24-6-00

Zephyr (PC 8) Kurt Greiner/SeaPhoto, 10-00

Shamal (PC 13)—after hull lengthening and installation of stern ramp
A. D. Baker III, 6-00

Tornado (PC 14)—built with stern ramp, and the only unit of the class with bow bulwarks and signature-reduction measures to the superstructure
Wallop Defence Systems, 2000

PATROL CRAFT [PC] *(continued)*

Whirlwind (PC 11)—with original, short stern H&L Van Ginderen, 3-00

Firebolt (PC 10)—short-hulled variant, with boat-handling crane aft William H. Clarke, 3-01

D: PC 2, 8, 13, 14: 352 tons light (387 fl); others: 288 tons light (334 fl)
S: 35 kts (25 cruise)
Dim: 51.62 (48.00 wl; PC 2, 8, 13, 14: 54.36 o.a.) × 7.62 × 2.44
A: 1 Stinger point-defense SAM station (6 FIM-92 missiles); 1 25-mm Bushmaster gun/40-mm Mk 19 Mod. 3 grenade launcher in Mk 96 Mod. 0 stabilized mount—PC 14 also: 1 25-mm Mk 88 Bushmaster Mk 38 Mod. 0 low-angle mount—all: 2 twin and 1 single 12.7-mm M2-HB mg; 2 single 7.62-mm M-60D mg; 1 40-mm Mk 19 Mod. 3 grenade launcher
Electronics:
Radar: 1 Sperry Rascar 3400C X-band nav./surf. search; Sperry Rascar 3400C S-band nav./surf. search
EW: APR-39(V)1 Privateer radar warning—PC 2–13: 2 Mk 52 Mod. 0 decoy syst. (2 6-round Mk 137 RL)—PC 14 only: 2 Wallop Ultrabarricade decoy syst. (2 26-round RL)
Sonar: Wesmar side-scanning hull-mounted HF
E/O: Marconi Vistar FLIR—PC 14 also: Viper optronic gunsight
M: 4 Paxman Valenta 16V RP-200 CM diesels; 4 5-bladed (PC 14: 6-bladed) props; 13,400 bhp
Electric: 310 kw tot. (2 × 155-kw Caterpillar 3306B DIT Series C diesel sets)
Range: 595/35; 3,000+/12 **Fuel:** 40 tons (47,772 liters/12,620 gal.)
Endurance: 10 days
Crew: 5 officers, 23 enlisted + SEAL special forces team: 2 officers, 7 enlisted; or 6 Coast Guard law-enforcement detachment

Remarks: PC = Coastal Patrol Boat; typed PBC (Patrol Boat, Coastal) until 6-91. Was originally to have been a class of 16, intended to replace the 17 over-aged PB Mk-III for use by SEAL Special Boat Squadrons. The craft are able to transport nine-man SEAL teams and their specialized delivery craft or Coast Guard boarding teams for counterdrug inspections. Pacific Fleet units are based at San Diego, Atlantic Fleet units at Little Creek, Va., in Special Boat Squadron 2.

On 7-11-01, San Diego–based PC 3 and 4 and Little Creek–based PC 10–13 were assigned to homeland defense duties under Operation Noble Eagle for at least six months and transferred to Coast Guard operational control; the remaining craft were added to the force 27-12-01. The craft retain their navy crews and also carry a six-person USCG Tactical Law Enforcement Team for police duties. Under a 9-01 decision, all were to have been decommissioned and stricken by the third quarter of FY 03, with no funding provided after the end of FY 02 (30-9-02); the craft were to be offered to other U.S. government agencies or offered for foreign transfer. PC 5 and 6 had been scheduled for decommissioning during 2-02 but are now to remain operating until at least 30-9-02.

The first seven were authorized under FY 90 and were ordered for $91.3 million on 3-8-90, with an option for five more; the next five were authorized under FY 91, with the option picked up on 19-7-91 for $48.7 million. The remaining three were not requested, in part because it was belatedly discovered that they are too large for the close inshore work for which they were intended. PC 14 was added for $9.2 million by Congress under FY 96, but pressure for a 15th under FY 97 ($20 million) was successfully resisted; PC 14 was subsequently ordered 14-8-97 for $23.19 million, more than twice the unit cost of the original units. PC 12 was temporarily transferred to the Coast Guard 2-3-98 for a series of trials through 17-7-98.

Disposals: *Cyclone* (PC 1) was decommissioned 29-2-00 to provide a crew and operating funds for PC 14. She was transferred to the Coast Guard 1-3-00 but not reactivated (and was stricken during 2001 and was to be transferred to the Philippines during 2002).

Hull systems: Are about 10 times the size of their predecessors but carry about the same payload. Have a Vosper fin-stabilization system and a stern wedge to improve trim at high speeds. Kevlar armor is fitted to the command space. PC 5 and later employed heavier superstructure plating. Minimum speed is 3 kts. Were to carry two 16-ft. SEAL CRRC (Combat Rubber Raiding Craft) and one 6-m rigid inflatable swimmer delivery craft, but as completed carry only the RIB. There is a recessed platform at the stern for swimmer debarkation and embarkation on the unlengthened units.

Each unit deploying overseas is supported by a shore-based maintenance support team with three 20-ft. vans for spares and repair work. Can refuel at sea, using astern fueling rigs. An active radiated-noise cancellation system is to be added.

PC 14 has improved propellers, stern flaps to improve endurance, an increased fuel supply, and sound-reduction measures; the hull was also strengthened over that of the earlier units and lengthened to incorporate a ramp at the stern incorporating the Combatant Craft Retrieval System (CCRS) to enable the launch and recovery of special warfare boats up to 9.75 m long. PC 13, 8, and 2 (in that order) were lengthened and given CCRS stern ramps like that on the PC 14 under a 5-10-99 contract with the builder; the work was started during 12-99 and completed on all three by 30-6-00.

Combat systems: The Sperry Vision 2100M combat system employs the navigational radars and the Sperry Voyage Management System integrated navigation and control system as a combat data suite. The craft have a Sperry Marine automated Integrated Bridge System (IBS). Navigation systems include GPS and Loran receivers. Radio gear includes LST-5C SATCOM/line-of-sight UHF transceiver, A5 Spectra VHF radio, ICM120 Marine Band radio, and RF 5000 HF, VRC-92A VHF, and VRC-83(V)2 VHF/UHF transceivers. SAT-2A infrared signaling systems are fitted, and the Marconi Vistar stabilized FLIR sensor with integral low-light-level t.v. camera is mounted on the mast. Have an IFF transponder but no interrogation capability, although that may be added later. The sonar transducer is retracted within the hull at speeds above 14 kts.

The radar intercept equipment was originally developed for use on helicopters. Each Mk 52 decoy rocket launcher carries 12 ready-service rounds, and 15 more rockets per launcher are carried in adjacent lockers. PC 14 has two 12-round, 102-mm Wallop Ultrabarricade rocket launchers mounted on superstructure platforms for trials; the craft also has an Electronic Chart Display and Information System (ECDIS).

Carry 2,000 rounds of 25-mm, 2,000 rounds of 12.7-mm, 2,000 rounds of 7.62-mm ammunition, and 1,000 40-mm grenades. The original Mk 38 gun mounting aft has been replaced with a stabilized Mk 96 mount with combined Viper optronic sight, 25-mm gun, and 40-mm grenade launcher. Several of the Mk 38 mounts forward have been lost at sea due to wave action, and they are often not carried. Successful trials were conducted in 9-00 with a four-cell Raytheon Stinger Standard Vehicle-Mounted Launcher installed on a Mk 96 gunmount, and the system may be adapted for the active units of the class to improve their weak AAW capabilities.

PATROL BOATS [PB]

♦ 2 2680 Coastal Runner class

Bldr: Glacier Bay Cats, Monroe, Wash.

HVA Escort (In serv. 15-1-01) . . . (In serv. 2-1-02)

HVA Escort—on road-travel trailer Glacier Bay Cats, 1-01

D: 2.38 tons light **S:** 30+ kts **Dim:** 7.92 × 2.59 × 0.56
A: 2 single 7.62-mm M-60 mg
Electronics: Radar: 1 Furuno . . . nav.
M: 2 Yamaha 150HDPI gasoline outboards; 300 bhp
Range: 100/29 **Fuel:** 180 gallons **Crew:** 2–3 tot.

Remarks: *HVA Escort* is based at Norfolk and the second craft at Groton, Conn., both to escort submarines entering and leaving port. GRP-hulled sport-fishing catamaran design, modified with weapons mounts, ammunition stowage, minor structural strengthening, and a heavy-duty fender surrounding the hull. Have GPS and VHF radio.

♦ 3 32-foot Inshore Boat class

Bldr: Willard Marine, Anaheim, Calif. (In serv. 2001)

32IB0001 32IB0002 32IB0003

Remarks: Assigned to Naval Coastal Warfare Group 1, San Diego, and used for harbor counterterrorism patrol. Additional units are likely to be procured. Design is the builder's Kingston 32 and employs an aluminum hull and superstructure with a rigid inflatable collar. Can be transported in a C-130 aircraft.

PATROL BOATS [PB] *(continued)*

32-ft. Inshore Boat class unit W. Michael Young, 6-01

♦ **2 36-foot harbor patrol boats**
Bldrs: PCH3500: Voyager Marine, Bahrain (In serv. 6-97); 36NS9802: Dakota Yacht Industries, . . . (In serv. 1998)

PCH3500 (36NS9801) . . . . . . (36NS9802)

PCH3500 (36NS9801)—at Bahrain Maritime Photographic, 2-99

Remarks: Assigned to U.S. Naval Forces, Central Command, Bahrain. Are of different but similar designs. GRP construction, powered by two 250-bhp Mercury outboard motors and equipped with a 12.7-mm mg forward.

Note: Also assigned for service in Bahrain are 32HS0101 through 32HS0103, bought locally during 2001 and assigned to Naval Support Activity, Bahrain.

♦ **22 27-foot Inshore Boat class**
Bldr: . . . . (In serv. 1994)

8MIB9401 through 8MIB9422

27-ft. Inshore Boat–class patrol launch H&L Van Ginderen, 7-00

Remarks: Aluminum-construction craft 8.23 m long used as deployable harbor patrol boats; origin unknown. Are assigned to Naval Coastal Warfare Group 1, San Diego, and Naval Coastal Warfare Group 2, Little Creek, Va. Have a Furuno radar and mounts for two 7.62-mm mg. Powered by two diesel-driven waterjets. Can be carried aboard ships to provide harbor security support. No further data available.

♦ **58 24-foot Harbor Security Boats**
Bldr: Peterson Bldrs, Sturgeon Bay, Wis. (In serv. 29-2-88 to 1990)

From among:
24HS8701 through 24HS8750 24HS8901 through 24HS8910
24HS8801 through 24HS8825

24-ft. Harbor Security Boat 24HS8733 Takatoshi Okano, 8-00

D: 2.5 tons (3.8 fl) **S:** 22.5 kts (with 4 aboard)
Dim: 7.32 × 2.31 × 1.57 (molded depth)
A: 1 12.7-mm or 7.62-mm mg **Electronics:** Radar: none
M: 2 Volvo Penta AQAD 41A diesels with Type 290 outdrives; 165 bhp
Range: . . ./. . . **Crew:** 4 tot.

Remarks: Survivors of 85 built; the first 50 were ordered 29-7-87, 25 more on 9-11-87, and final 10 in 3-88. Aluminum construction. For counterterrorist patrol in sheltered waters. Have 12-V-dc, 50-Amp electrical power. Built to essentially the same design as the 24WB-series workboats (see under [YFU]).

♦ **4 Raider-class Harbor Security Boats**
Bldr: NAPCO International, North Miami, Fla. (In serv. 1986)

Raider-class Harbor Security Boat Paul C. Clift, 5-00

D: 2.0 tons (2.95 fl) **S:** 40 kts **Dim:** 6.81 (6.40 pp) × 2.26 × 0.86
A: 2 single 12.7-mm M2 mg **Electronics:** Radar: none
M: 2 Johnson or Evinrude gasoline outboards; 280 bhp
Range: 167/40; 222/30 **Crew:** 3 tot.

Remarks: GRP construction, using Boston Whaler hulls. Acquired for counterterrorist work. The class is also used by the Coast Guard and has been widely exported; a number of similar craft, outfitted by Boston Whaler itself, are in use for harbor police duties.

♦ **4 3010-V Protector-class Range Security Boats**
Bldr: SeaArk Marine, Monticello, Ark. (In serv. 1985–86)

30WB8501 30WB8502 30WB8601 30WB8602 2 others

D: . . . tons **S:** . . . kts **Dim:** 9.80 × 3.40 × 0.60
M: 2 Volvo Penta AQAD outdrive diesels; . . . bhp
Crew: 4 tot. + 7 passengers

Remarks: Acquired for range safety work at the Dahlgren Proving Range, Va. Two others were bought for use at Point Mugu, Calif., but are no longer listed. Aluminum construction.

Note: Also from SeaArk, two 30-ft. (9.14-m) patrol boats were delivered 28-1-87.

♦ **4 ex-Coast Guard Ports and Waterways boats [YFL]**
Bldr: Willard Marine, Anaheim, Calif. (In serv. 1977)

32NS7701 32NS9301 32NS9302 34FR7801

D: 7.5 tons light (8.6 fl) **S:** 20.4 kts **Dim:** 10.16 × 3.58 × 0.86
Electronics: Radar: 1 Raytheon SPS-69 nav.
M: 2 Caterpillar 3208 diesels; 2 props; 406 bhp
Range: 190/16.5 **Fuel:** 0.65 tons **Crew:** 2–3 tot.

Remarks: GRP-construction craft, used for local police duties at the Norfolk Naval Base, Va. For the Coast Guard, 52 sisters were built. One other may remain in USMC use.

PATROL BOATS [PB] *(continued)*

Pearlcraft-built GRP harbor patrol launch 101 (shown here) and 102 are stationed at Bahrain—armed with one 7.62-mm mg and equipped with a Raytheon radar, they are powered by two Yamaha gasoline outboards and crewed by three
Joe Straczek, 11-01

Boston Whaler Naval Security Boat 05, attached to the submarine base at Gravel Point, San Diego, is typical of the numerous Whalers used for harbor patrol duties
George R. Schneider, 6-01

MINE WARFARE SHIPS

Note: In addition to the ships and craft listed below, 43 MH-53E minesweeping helicopters are in service. Sixteen Marine Corps CH-53D helicopters can also be used to tow sweep gear. The entire MH-53E force is to be replaced by less-capable MH-60 helicopters during the first decade of the 21st century, primarily for reasons of operating cost.

The navy for many years has also had an extensive Marine Mammal Program using trained dolphins maintained by Explosive Ordnance Disposal Mobile Unit 3, San Diego.

In the face of what is said to be an increasing mine threat, navy proposals continue to be made to retire much of the present, relatively new mine countermeasures force and to add mine countermeasures capabilities to existing combatant ship classes—but in obviously inadequate quantities.

MINE COUNTERMEASURES SUPPORT SHIPS [MCS]

Disposal note: The *Iwo Jima*–class mine countermeasures ship *Inchon* (MCS 12, ex-LPH 12), laid up at Corpus Christi, Texas, after a 19-10-01 fire, was to be decommissioned and stricken during 7-02 due to the expected $10 million repair cost and the expense ($43 million per year) of operating the 32-year-old ship. No replacement was immediately available.

Note: Maritime Applied Physics Corp., Annapolis, Md., was awarded a concept design contract for a 2,200-ton HYSWAS (Hydrofoil Small Waterplane Area Ship) mine countermeasures ship to act as a carrier and deployment ship for autonomous and semiautonomous mine countermeasures drones. The design is to be based on the HYSWAS prototype craft *Quest* (see under [YAGE]).

♦ 12 Osprey-class coastal minehunters [MHS]

Bldrs: Intermarine U.S.A., Savannah, Ga.; B: Avondale Marine, Gulfport, Miss.
(Atlantic Fleet; all Naval Reserve Force except MHC 60 and 61)

	Bldr	Begun	L	In serv.
MHC 51 Osprey	Intermarine	16-5-88	23-3-91	20-11-93
MHC 52 Heron	Intermarine	7-4-89	21-3-92	6-8-94
MHC 53 Pelican	Avondale	6-5-91	27-2-93	18-11-95
MHC 54 Robin	Avondale	28-1-92	11-9-93	11-5-96
MHC 55 Oriole	Intermarine	8-5-91	22-5-93	13-9-95
MHC 56 Kingfisher	Avondale	24-3-92	18-6-94	9-8-96
MHC 57 Cormorant	Avondale	8-4-92	21-10-95	5-4-97
MHC 58 Black Hawk	Intermarine	12-5-92	27-8-94	11-5-96
MHC 59 Falcon	Intermarine	3-4-93	3-6-95	8-2-97
MHC 60 Cardinal	Intermarine	1-2-94	9-3-96	18-10-97
MHC 61 Raven	Intermarine	15-11-94	28-9-96	5-9-98
MHC 62 Shrike	Intermarine	1-8-95	24-5-97	31-5-99

Kingfisher (MHC 56)
Marc Piché, 7-00

Raven (MHC 61)—with *Cardinal* (MHC 60), aboard heavy-lift ship *Blue Marlin* for transport to Bahrain
U.S. Navy, 9-00

Black Hawk (MHC 58)
H&L Van Ginderen, 4-97

D: 796–886 tons light (882–973 fl) **S:** 12 kts
Dim: 57.25 (53.10 pp) × 10.95 × 3.35 (max.)
A: 2 single 12.7-mm M2 mg
Electronics:
Radar: 1 Raytheon SPS-64(V)9 nav.
Sonar: Raytheon SQQ-32 variable-depth minehunting
M: 2 Isotta-Fraschini ID 36 SS 8V-AM diesels; 2 Voith-Schneider vertical cycloidal props; 1,600 bhp—2 180-shp hydraulic motors for quiet running—1 180-shp bow-thruster
Electric: 900 kw (3 × 300 kw, Isotta-Fraschini ID SS 6V-AM diesels driving)
Range: 2,500/12 **Endurance:** 5 days **Crew:** 5 officers, 46 enlisted

Remarks: MHC 51 was authorized under FY 86, MHC 52 and 53 under FY 89, MHC 54 and 55 under FY 90, MHC 56 and 57 under FY 91, MC 58–60 under FY 92, and MHC 61 and 62 under FY 93. MHC 51 was ordered 20-2-87. Plans to construct a total of 17 were scaled back to 12 in spring 1992. MHC 57 transferred to the NRF 11-1-98, MHC 59 on 8-2-98, MHC 60 on 18-10-98, MHC 62 on 1-4-00, and MHC 51 on 1-10-00. MHC 60 and MHC 61 were returned to the active navy 1-9-00 and are "permanently" based at Bahrain. The others will continue to be based at Ingleside, Texas—far removed from any potential area of operations.
Hull systems: Displacement grew by 110 tons during the final design phase and has continued to rise since completions. Have monocoque foam-core GRP hull construction, with the design based on that of the Italian Navy *Lerici* class. Have the SSQ-109 Ship/Machinery Control System and two 400-Hz motor-generator sets. Later units have additional space for provisions and stores. There is berthing space for 15 women crewmembers.
Combat systems: Employ the Alliant SLQ-48(V)2 Mine Neutralization System remote-controlled submersible. Have Paramax SYQ-13 tactical navigation/command and control equipment, which integrates machinery and ship control, the minehunting sonar, the mine neutralization system, inputs from the surface search radar, the precision navigation systems, and various environmental sensors; the SYQ-13 system is to be replaced after 2004 by a new COTS open-architecture system under development by Lockheed Martin. Other navigation equipment includes a WRN-6 GPS terminal and Decca URN-30 Hyperfix radio navaid.

MINE COUNTERMEASURES SUPPORT SHIPS [MCS] *(continued)*

The Modular Influence Minesweeping System (MIMS), a towed influence sweep with its own gas-turbine sweep current generator, is under development to permit the MHC 51 class to act as sweepers as well as hunters; when it is in use, the SLQ-48 would have to be removed. Also under development for these ships is the SLQ-53 Single-Ship Deep Sweep (SSDS), a surface ship–towed version of the A/N-37U helicopter Controlled-Depth Moored Sweep, and the MP3 (Mission Package 3) variant of the SLQ-48 Mine Neutralization System, which is planned to be introduced to allow the MNS vehicle to destroy moored mines without having to cut the cables. The ships have an Indal three-drum winch capable of carrying 1,524 m of sweep cable on the main drum and 595 m each on the other drums to stream and tow the SLQ-53 array.

♦ 14 Avenger-class oceangoing minesweeper/minehunters [MHS]

Bldrs: Peterson Bldrs, Sturgeon Bay, Wis., and Marinette Marine, Marinette, Wis. (Atlantic Fleet; *Naval Reserve Force)

	Bldr	Laid down	L	In serv.
MCM 1 Avenger*	Peterson Bldrs	3-6-83	15-6-85	12-9-87
MCM 2 Defender*	Marinette Marine	1-12-83	4-4-87	30-9-89
MCM 3 Sentry*	Peterson Bldrs	8-10-84	20-9-86	2-9-89
MCM 4 Champion*	Marinette Marine	28-6-84	15-4-89	27-7-91
MCM 5 Guardian	Peterson Bldrs	8-5-85	20-6-87	16-12-89
MCM 6 Devastator	Peterson Bldrs	9-2-87	11-6-88	6-10-90
MCM 7 Patriot	Marinette Marine	31-3-87	15-5-90	18-10-91
MCM 8 Scout	Peterson Bldrs	8-6-87	20-5-89	15-12-90
MCM 9 Pioneer*	Peterson Bldrs	5-6-89	25-8-90	7-12-92
MCM 10 Warrior*	Peterson Bldrs	25-9-89	8-12-90	3-4-93
MCM 11 Gladiator*	Peterson Bldrs	7-5-90	29-6-91	18-9-93
MCM 12 Ardent	Peterson Bldrs	22-10-90	16-11-91	18-2-94
MCM 13 Dexterous	Peterson Bldrs	11-3-91	20-6-92	9-6-94
MCM 14 Chief	Peterson Bldrs	19-8-91	16-12-93	5-11-94

Patriot (MCM 7) Takatoshi Okano, 9-00

Scout (MCM 8) Jim Sanderson, 6-01

Chief (MCM 14) Kurt Greiner/SeaPhoto, 5-01

Devastator (MCM 6) Camil Busquets i Vilanova, 3-99

D: 1,249–1,336 tons light (1,362–1,447 fl) **S:** 13.5 kts
Dim: 68.37 (64.80 wl) × 11.86 × 3.71 (hull)
A: MCM 11: 1 25-mm Mk 88 Bushmaster low-angle gun; 1 7.62-mm gatling mg—others: 2 single 12.7-mm M2 mg
Electronics:
Radar: 1 Raytheon SPS-66(V)9 nav.; 1 Cardion SPS-55 surf. search
Sonar: Raytheon SQQ-32 (MCM 2, 8: SQQ-30) variable-depth minehunting; WQN-1 channel finder
M: MCM 1, 2: 4 Waukesha L-1616 diesels; 2 CP props; 2,600 bhp—others: 4 Isotta-Fraschini ID 36 SS 6V-AM diesels; 2 CP props; 2,280 bhp—all: 2 200-shp Hansome low-speed motors geared to props; 1 350-shp Omnithruster bow-thruster
Electric: 2,875 kw tot. (1 × 1,750-kw Siemens-Allis-Solar gas turbine sweep generator; 3 × 375-kw Isotta-Fraschini ID 36 SS 6V-AM [MCM 1, 2: Waukesha] diesels driving; 451 V, 60 Hz a.c.)
Range: . . ./. . . **Crew:** 6–8 officers, 75 enlisted

Remarks: MCM 1 was authorized in FY 82, MCM 2 in FY 83, MCM 3–5 in FY 84, MCM 6–9 in FY 85, MCM 10 and 11 in FY 86, and MCM 12–14 in FY 90. MCM 1 was ordered on 29-6-82. MCM 5 and 7 were deployed to Japan in 1994, and their crews are rotated to the United States every six months. MCM 12 and 13 were homeported at Bahrain on 1-3-00 and 1-6-00, respectively; the others are based at Ingleside, Texas. MCM 1 and 2 transferred to the Naval Reserve Force 30-9-95; MCM 4, 9, and 10 on 30-9-96; and MCM 11 on 1-10-00; the others are now to remain in regular USN service. No replacement class is planned to begin entering service until 2020.

Hull systems: The wooden hull employs four glued layers of 127-mm planking over 254 × 457–mm frames spaced at 1.07-m intervals. Displacements grew as the class progressed, with later units being about 80 tons heavier. All structural members are built up from thinner materials, using phenol/resorcinol glue. The hull for MCM 1 had to be lengthened by about 1.8 m after construction had begun, due to stability problems, and the ship was also delayed by other design problems and the discovery that the main engines rotated opposite to the gear boxes. The superstructures are constructed of GRP. The ID 36 SS 6V-AM engines are reported to be unreliable, with inadequate cooling, electrical problems, and frequent clutch and bearing failures. The sweep generator provides 5,000-amp, 350-V dc power.

Combat systems: Are able to sweep deep-moored mines to 180 m as well as to sweep magnetic and acoustic mines. The Mk 116 Mod. 0 Mine Neutralization System (MNS) includes two Alliant (formerly Honeywell) SLQ-48 MNS, a remote-controlled minehunting and destruction device 3.8 m long by 0.9 m high, weighing 1,136 kg, powered by two 15-hp hydraulic motors for 6-kt speeds, and having 1,524 m of control cable. Also aboard are the SLQ-37(V)3 magnetic/acoustic sweep array (incorporating the A Mk 2, A Mk 4(V), and A Mk 6(B) acoustic and M Mk 5, M Mk 6, and M Mk 7 magnetic arrays), SLQ-38 (Type 0 Size 1) mechanical sweep gear, and two RIBs for mine disposal divers. Carry the SSN-2(V) PINS (Precision-Integrated Navigation System) and the SYQ-13 navigational/command-and-control system, which employs the Decca URN-30 Hyperfix radio-navaid, WRN-6 GPS terminal, Loran, Motorola MX 610 doppler log, and a WQN-1 Channel-Finder doppler precision sonar; 12 ships of the class received the GEC-Marconi SYQ-15 (Nautis) system vice SYQ-13, beginning in 5-94. The SYQ-13 and SYQ-15 systems are to be replaced after 2004 by a new COTS open-architecture system under development by Lockheed Martin. Although the early ships that had SQQ-30 sonars (a digital version of the obsolescent SQQ-14) were to have had them replaced by the end of 1992, that goal will not be met until 9-00 in MCM 2 and 8. The original 2,500-amp magnetic pulse sweep generators had to be replaced because the Siemens-made sets broke down after 48 hours' use; MagneTek solid-state replacements were first fitted to MCM 9.

MHC 53 conducted a four-day trial with the German STN Atlas Elektronik Sea Fox C EMNS (Expendable Mine Neutralization System) autonomous mine destruction vehicle in a demonstration that ended 26-3-01; the system may be purchased via Lockheed Martin for surface ship and MH-53E helicopter employment.

MINESWEEPING BOATS [MSB]

♦ 1 SWATH explosive ordnance disposal boat

Bldr: Swath Ocean Systems, National City, Calif. (In serv. 5-98)

40MC9601 MHS-1 Swath 1

D: . . . tons **S:** . . . kts **Dim:** 12.19 × 5.49 × . . .
A: small arms
Electronics:
Radar: 1 . . . nav.
Sonar: Klein 5500 Multibeam towed side-scan HF; Simrad SM 2000 mine avoidance HF

MINESWEEPING BOATS [MSB] *(continued)*

MHS-1 Swath 1 (40MC9601) George R. Schneider, 5-01

MHS-1 Swath 1 (40MC9601) W. Michael Young, 5-99

M: 2 . . . diesels; 2 props; . . . bhp
Crew: 2 enlisted + 4 Area-Search Detachment enlisted sonar party

Remarks: The name and "MHS-1" hull number are unofficial; the "MC" in the serial number stands for "mine countermeasures." Can be land-transported and also carried within a C-5A Galaxy transport aircraft, one of which flew the craft to an exercise in Thailand during 4-00. Is assigned to Explosive Ordnance Disposal Mobile Unit 7 (EODMU 7) at San Diego.
Hull systems: Aluminum construction. Has been equipped with a quadrantial davit at the stern to handle a Deep Ocean Engineering Phantom HD 2+2 remotely operated, high-definition sonar submersible used for identifying bottomed objects. Roll is limited to 2° in 3- to 4-m seas by the automated stabilization system.

Note: The RMOP (Remote Minehunting Operational Prototype), RMS(V)2, and RMS(V)3 remotely operated mine countermeasures drone programs are discussed in the Mine Countermeasures Systems entry at the beginning of the U.S. Navy section.
At least 14 24-ft. RIB craft are used to support mine countermeasures helicopters, acting as tow craft and for connecting and disconnecting mine countermeasures sleds. By mid-2001, all 14 had completed being re-engined by Saunders Engine Co., Panama City, Fla. The 2.4-ton (loaded) craft are now powered by a single 260-bhp Cummins BT.59M1 diesel with Konrad 520 outdrive and can achieve 34 kts and a 2,170-lb. bollard pull.

AMPHIBIOUS WARFARE SHIPS AND CRAFT

AMPHIBIOUS WARFARE COMMAND SHIPS [LCC]

♦ 0 (+ 3) Joint Command Ship/JCC(X) class
Bldr: . . .

Remarks: Intended as replacements for the *Blue Ridge* class and the two auxiliary command ships. As of 11-01, one ship was to be ordered under FY 06 and two under FY 07. Initially they were to be modified versions of the LPD 17 design, but ever-growing personnel space requirements (over 2,000 staff would be accommodated) have forced a change to a larger and far more expensive alternative. To emphasize the "jointness" of the ships' purpose, they have been referred to as the JCC(X) (Joint Command Ship) class and for political purposes will probably receive nonstandard hull numbers in the JCC series, if built. Congress cut design funds from the FY 01 budget and may have different ideas as to how elaborate the ships should be. Pressure from Congress has also been brought to bear on the navy to acquire two incomplete cruise ships building at Northrop Grumman Ingalls for adaptation as joint command ships, although the ships in question are almost certainly unsuitable for the role.

♦ 2 Blue Ridge class (SCN 400-65 type)
Bldrs: LCC 19: Philadelphia NSY; LCC 20: Newport News SB & DD, Va.
(*Atlantic/†Pacific Fleet)

	Laid down	L	In serv.
LCC 19 Blue Ridge†	27-2-67	4-1-69	14-11-70
LCC 20 Mount Whitney*	8-1-69	8-1-70	16-1-71

Blue Ridge (LCC 19) U.S. Navy, 2000

Blue Ridge (LCC 19) Brian Morrison, 5-01

Mount Whitney (LCC 20) Martin Mokrus, 2-02

D: LCC 19: 13,038 tons light (19,609 fl); LCC 20: 12,815 tons light (19,729 fl)
S: 21.5 kts
Dim: 193.98 (176.8 wl) × 32.9 (25.0 wl; 54.6 max. extensions) × 8.84 (max.)
A: 2 single 25-mm 75-cal. Mk 38 Bushmaster low-angle guns; 2 20-mm Mk 15 Phalanx gatling CIWS; 4 single 12.7-mm mg
Electronics:
Radar: 1 Raytheon SPS-64(V)9 nav.; 1 Lockheed Martin SPS-67(V)1 surf. search; 1 Lockheed SPS-40E air search; 1 ITT-Gilfillan SPS-48E 3-D air search; 2 Mk 91 Phalanx f.c.
TACAN: URN-25
EW: Raytheon SLQ-32(V)3 active/passive; Mk 36 SRBOC decoy syst. (4 6-round Mk 137 RL); SLQ-25A SSTD Nixie towed acoustic torpedo decoy syst.
M: 1 set G.E. geared steam turbines; 1 prop; 22,000 shp
Boilers: 2 Foster-Wheeler; 42.3 kg/cm^2, 467° C
Range: 13,000/16 **Fuel:** 2,800 tons
Crew: LCC 19: 268 officers, 1,173 enlisted; LCC 20: 201 officers, 1,083 enlisted (incl. flag staff personnel)

Remarks: Authorized in FY 65 and 66. Both were originally intended to act as amphibious force flagships, but LCC 19 is now the flagship of the Seventh Fleet and is based at Yokosuka, while LCC 20 is the flagship of the Second Fleet and is based at Norfolk. Both have recently been *unofficially* referred to as JCC 19 and 20, with JCC standing for "Joint Command Ship."
Hull systems: Have the same machinery and basic hullform as the *Iwo Jima*–class LPH. Are air-conditioned and have fin stabilizers, and Kevlar plastic armor has been added. Carry three LCP, two LCVP landing craft, and one 10-m personnel launch in Welin davits. Have no helicopter hangar, but a landing pad is fitted at the stern and 123,510 gallons of aircraft fuel can be carried.
Combat systems: SATCOM equipment includes SSR-1, WSC-3 UHF, WSC-6 SHF, and USC-38 EHF SATCOM systems; antennas on the after masts differ. Combat data analysis systems include ACIS (Amphibious Command Information System), NIPS (Naval Intelligence Processing System), NTDS (with Links 4A, 11, and 14), and photographic laboratories and document-publication facilities. Command facilities include a Ship Signals Exploitation Space (SSES), Flag Plot, Landing Force Operations Center (LFOC), Joint Intelligence Center (JIC), Supporting Arms Coordination Center (SACC), Helicopter Logistics Support Group (HLSG), Tactical Air Control Center (TACC), Helicopter Direction Center (HDC), and Helicopter Coordination Section (HCS). Have the SMQ-6 weather satellite receiver and the Joint Services Imagery Processing System–Navy (JSIPS-N).

AMPHIBIOUS WARFARE COMMAND SHIPS [LCC] *(continued)*

Planned armament modifications include installing Mk 49 launchers for the RAM point-defense missile fore and aft. LCC 19 received a Mk 15 CIWS in 1985 and LCC 20 in 1987, with added stern sponson and bow bulwarks lengthening the ships some 5 m overall. Two twin 76.2-mm DP gunmounts and two octuple Mk 25 BPDMS Sea Sparrow SAM launchers were removed during 1992. During the mid-1990s, the SPS-48C 3-D early-warning radars were replaced by SPS-48E sets taken from retired cruisers.

AMPHIBIOUS WARFARE HELICOPTER CARRIERS [LH]

Note: The first unit of a replacement program for the *Tarawa* class, initially referred to as the L(X) class and now as the LHA(R) for LHA Replacement, is planned to be included in the FY 08 budget request; the ships are expected to carry an air group of up to 10 F-35C strike fighters, 12 MV-22 Osprey, eight UH-1Y Huey and AH-1Z SuperCobra helicopters, and four CH-53E heavy-lift helicopters. Three concepts are under study: a 50,000-ton incremental improvement on the *Wasp*-class design, with gas-turbine electric propulsion and an additional 17 m of length and 3.35 m of beam; a 285-m design displacing 58,000 tons; and a 285-m design displacing 53,000 tons. The larger designs would carry some 2,000 troops.

♦ 7 (+ 1) Wasp-class helicopter/dock landing ships

Bldr: Ingalls SB, Pascagoula, Miss. (*Atlantic/†Pacific Fleet)

	Laid down	L	In serv.
LHD 1 Wasp*	30-5-85	4-8-87	29-7-89
LHD 2 Essex†	20-3-89	4-1-91	17-10-92
LHD 3 Kearsarge*	6-2-90	26-3-92	25-9-93
LHD 4 Boxer†	8-4-91	13-8-93	11-2-95
LHD 5 Bataan*	22-6-94	15-3-96	20-9-97
LHD 6 Bonhomme Richard†	18-4-95	14-3-97	15-8-98
LHD 7 Iwo Jima*	12-12-97	25-3-00	14-6-01
LHD 8	. . .	. . .	. . .

Boxer (LHD 4) Julio Montes, 10-00

Iwo Jima (LHD 7) William H. Clarke, 7-01

Boxer (LHD 4)—note that the SPS-48E radar antenna is mounted lower on this and the three earlier ships of the class Findler & Winter, 10-00

D: 27,565–28,295 tons light (40,329–41,133 fl; approx. 55,000 ballasted)
S: 24 kts (22 sust.)
Dim: 257.30 (237.14 wl) × 42.67 (32.31 wl) × 8.53 (max. unballasted)
Air group: Assault mode: 30–32 CH-46 (or fewer CH-53) helicopters and 6–8 AV-8B+ Harriers—carrier mode: 20 AV-8B+ Harriers and 4–6 SH-60F ASW helicopters (see remarks)
A: 2 8-cell Mk 29 SAM launchers (no reloads; RIM-7P Sea Sparrow missiles); 2 21-round RAM Mk 31 SAM launchers (RIM-116A missiles); 2 20-mm Mk 15 Mod. 13 Phalanx CIWS; 3 single 25-mm 75-cal. Mk 38 Mod. 0 Bushmaster low-angle guns; 4 single 12.7-mm M2-HB mg
Electronics:
Radar: 1 Raytheon SPS-64(V)9 nav.; 1 Norden SPS-67(V)3 surf. search; 1 Raytheon SPS-49(V)5 air search; 1 ITT-Gilfillan SPS-48E 3-D early warning; 1 Hughes Mk 23 Mod. 3 TAS target desig.; 2 Mk 95 f.c. (for Mk 91 f.c.s.); 1 SPN-35A air control; 1 SPN-43B CCA; 1 SPN-47 precision CCA; 2 Mk 90 Phalanx f.c.
Sonar: WSC-1 Channel Finder mine avoidance (6 transducers)
TACAN: URN-25
EW: SRS-1 Combat D/F syst.; Raytheon SLQ-32(V)3 active/passive; Mk 36 Mod. 12 SRBOC decoy syst. (6 6-round Mk 137 launchers); SLQ-25A Nixie towed acoustic torpedo decoy syst.

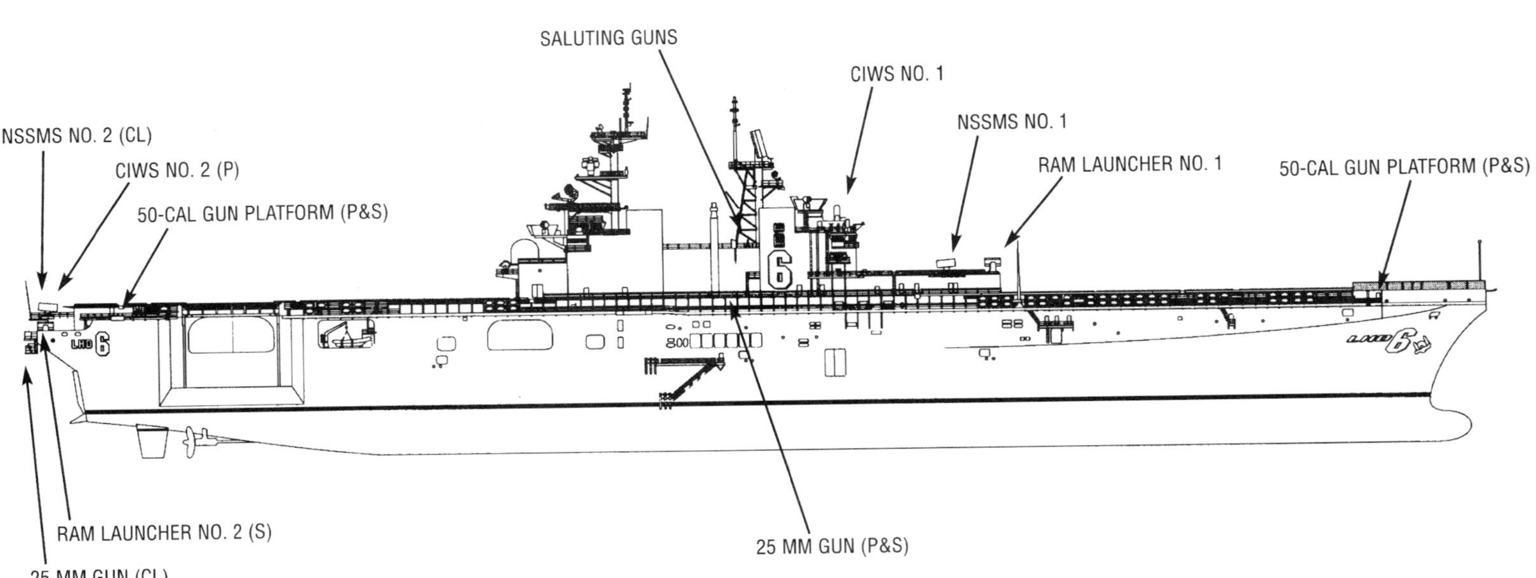

Bonhomme Richard (LHD 6) Northrop Grumman Ingalls

AMPHIBIOUS WARFARE HELICOPTER CARRIERS [LH] *(continued)*

Iwo Jima (LHD 7) Northrop Grumman Ingalls, 4-01

Bonhomme Richard (LHD 6) Jürg E. Kürsener, 6-01

Wasp (LHD 1) Bernard Prézelin, 6-00

Kearsarge (LHD 3)—showing the stern door
Guy Shaeffer, via Paolo Marsan, 8-01

AMPHIBIOUS WARFARE HELICOPTER CARRIERS [LH]
(continued)

M: LHD 1–7: 2 sets Westinghouse geared steam turbines; 2 props; 77,000 shp (70,000 sust.)—LHD 8: 2 G.E. LM-2500+ gas turbines; 2 props; 72,000 shp; 2 electric low-speed propulsion motors; 10,000 shp (12–13 kts)
Boilers: 2 Combustion Engineering; 49.3 kg/cm^2, 482° C (not in LHD 8)
Electric: LHD 1–7: 14,000 kw (5 × 2,000-kw turboalternators, 2 × 2,000-kw diesel alternator sets)
Range: 9,500/20 **Fuel:** 6,200 tons + 1,232 tons JP-5 for aircraft
Crew: 73 officers, 1,009 enlisted + troops: 173 officers, 1,720 enlisted + 200 additional emergency troop accomm.

Remarks: Design is based on that of the *Tarawa* (LHA 1) class, but the ships were intended to be convertible from assault ships to ASW ships with Harrier V/STOL fighters for ground support. LHD 1 was authorized in FY 84, LHD 2 in FY 86, LHD 3 in FY 88, LHD 4 in FY 89, LHD 5 in FY 91, LHD 6 in FY 93, and LHD 7 (the last steam-powered ship to be built for the U.S. Navy) in FY 96. LHD 8 will replace LHA 1 in service. LHD 1 was ordered 28-2-84, LHD 2 on 11-9-85, LHD 3 on 24-11-87, LHD 4 on 3-10-88, LHD 5 on 20-12-91, LHD 6 on 11-12-92, and LHD 7 on 28-12-96. LHD 8 was inserted in the FY 99 defense budget by Congress, additional funding for construction was provided under FY 00, another $460 million was added by Congress under the FY 01 budget, and final funding was approved under FY 02; the ship has not yet been ordered, however. Against USN wishes, a small sum for advance procurement for LHD 9 was added to the FY 02 budget, and Congress was reported to be planning to add about $400 million to the president's FY 03 budget request toward the unwanted ship. At one point, a total of 11 was planned. LHD 2 has been homeported at Sasebo, Japan, since 26-7-00, replacing the *Belleau Wood* (LHA 3).

Hull systems: The ships can take on up to 15,000 tons of water ballast to launch landing craft from the floodable stern docking well. Have more than 1,500 hull and superstructure compartments. Differences from the LHA 1 class include use of an LSD/LPD-type lowering stern gate vice the sectional, rising gate of the LHA; provision for three LCACs in a single-bay, longer, narrower (98.1 × 15.2 × 8.5 m high) docking well, which can alternatively hold up to six LCM(8) or two LCU landing craft; revised and strengthened aircraft elevators; internal stowage for ship's boats; a bulbous forefoot to the bow; larger-area bilge-keels; a squared-off flight deck forward (made possible by the omission of the 127-mm guns and making the entire deck capable of spotting nine CH-53E helicopters at once); use of HY-100 steel to construct the stronger flight deck; additional cargo elevators (six 5.4-ton capacity, totaling 7.6 × 3.6 m); a lower, narrower, and longer island; a narrower vehicle ramp to the flight deck; and better ballistic protection. In addition to embarked landing craft, the ships carry four LCPLs and two 12.2-m utility boats. They have 2,127 m^2 of vehicle parking space and 3,087 m^3 of dry cargo space. There are four 2,000-gallon/min turbopumps and eight 1,000-gallon/min motor-driven pumps fitted. Hospital facilities include six operating rooms and 578 beds.

A contract was let 28-7-00 to Ingalls to design a gas-turbine propulsion plant and all-electric auxiliary engineering systems for LHD 8 as a precursor to the follow-on L(X)—now LHA(R)—program. The design was to be completed by 30-7-02. The gas turbine plant will provide lower lifetime operating cost despite having slightly higher fuel consumption than the steam systems used in previous units of the class; electric auxiliary power will drive the ship at up to 13 kts.

Aviation systems: Because of the desire to maximize the number of deck spots, no ski-jump V/STOL ramp was fitted, reducing the potential effectiveness of the Harrier contingent. The hangar has 6.4-m vertical clearance and is 25.9 m wide; it can accommodate 28 CH-46 helicopter equivalents. Have two 34-ton-capacity, 15.2 × 13.7–m aircraft elevators, with the stern elevator relocated to starboard from the centerline aft position on the LHA 1 class. In addition to the listed aircraft fuel, about 50 tons of vehicle fuel can be carried.

A typical all-helicopter air group includes 20 CH-46E, 10 CH-53E, 6 AH-1W, and 3 UH-1N. With 6 AV-8B Harriers aboard, the number of helicopters falls to 14 CH-46E, 6 CH-53E, 6 AH-1W, and 4 UH-1N; in the absence of helicopters, up to 28 AV-8B can be carried. In a mine countermeasures role, the ships would carry 20 CH-46E and 6 MH-53E helicopters and 6 Mk 105 countermeasures sleds.

Combat systems: Command facilities include an Integrated Tactical Amphibious Warfare Data System, Ship Signals Exploitation Space, Flag Plot, Landing Force Operations Center, Joint Intelligence Center, Supporting Arms Coordination Center, Tactical-Logistical Group, Helicopter Logistics Group, Tactical Air Control Center, Helicopter Direction Center, and Helicopter Coordination Section. LHD 1 was originally fitted with the SPS-52 3-D early-warning radar (replaced by SPS-48E) and had the SYS-2(V)3 sensor fusion system for defensive weapons control; later units had SYS-2(V)5. The SPS-48E antennas were mounted higher, atop the foremast, in LHD 5 and later. The USQ-119(V)11 Naval Tactical Command System, Marconi ICS.3 (URC-109) integrated communications system, SMQ-11 weather satellite receiving system, and USQ-82(V) data multiplexing system are fitted. Are to receive the Joint Services Imagery Processing System–Navy (JSIPS-N). Beginning with LHD 1 in 1996–97, all ships of the class have received the SSDS (Ship Self-Defense System) Block I integration system for the sensors and weapons to improve response time against antiship missiles; Mk 31 RAM launchers have been mounted at the forward end of the island superstructure and on the starboard quarter, the latter replacing one Phalanx mounting. Two 25-mm guns are mounted to port and one on the starboard side. The SPS-49(V)5 radars are to be upgraded to SPS-49A(V)1. LHD 7 is to have the Sperry Integrated Bridge System and color electronic chart display. Have USC-1(V), USC-6 (Challenge Athena) UHF, Marisat MHF, and USC-38(V)1 EHF SATCOM terminals.

♦ 5 Tarawa-class amphibious assault ships (SCB 410 type)
Bldr: Ingalls SB, Pascagoula, Miss. (*Atlantic/†Pacific Fleet)

	Laid down	L	In serv.
LHA 1 TARAWA†	15-11-71	1-12-73	29-5-76
LHA 2 SAIPAN*	21-7-72	18-7-74	15-10-77
LHA 3 BELLEAU WOOD†	5-3-73	11-4-77	23-9-78
LHA 4 NASSAU*	13-8-73	21-1-78	28-7-79
LHA 5 PELELIU (ex-*Da Nang*)†	12-11-76	25-11-78	3-5-80

Tarawa (LHA 1) Kurt Greiner/SeaPhoto, 3-00

Belleau Wood (LHA 3) Jim Sanderson, 6-01

Nassau (LHA 4) Guy Schaeffer, via Paolo Marsan, 2-01

Peleliu (LHA 5) Jim Sanderson, 6-01

Saipan (LHA 2)—showing the stern gate, with centerline stern helicopter elevator recess above it Christopher P. Cavas, 9-99

AMPHIBIOUS WARFARE HELICOPTER CARRIERS [LH] *(continued)*

Peleliu (LHA 5)—with 4 AV-8B Harrier, 2 CH-53E Super Stallion, 9 CH-46E Sea Knight, 3 AH-1W SuperCobra, and 2 UH-1N Iroquois visible on deck Jürg Kürsener, 6-01

D: 25,884–27,165 tons light (39,438–40,891 fl) **S:** 24 kts (25.3 on trials)
Dim: 254.20 (237.14 pp) × 40.23 (32.31 wl) × 8.23 (max. unballasted)
Air group: typical: 16 CH-46E, 6 CH-53E, and 4 UH-1N helicopters; max.: 43 CH-46 equivalents (see remarks)
A: 2 21-round RAM Mk 31 SAM syst. (RIM-116 missiles); 2 20-mm Mk 15 Phalanx gatling CIWS; 2 single 25-mm 75-cal. Mk 38 Bushmaster low-angle guns; 8 single 12.7-mm M2 mg
Electronics:
Radar: 1 Raytheon SPS-64(V)9 nav.; 1 Norden SPS-67(V)3 surf. search; 1 Lockheed Martin SPS-40E air search; 1 ITT-Gilfillan SPS-48E 3-D early warning; 1 Hughes Mk 23 Mod. 3 TAS target desig.; 1 SPN-35A air control; 1 SPN-43B CCA; 2 Mk 90 Phalanx f.c.
TACAN: URN-25
EW: Raytheon SLQ-32(V)3 active/passive; Mk 36 SRBOC decoy syst. (4 6-round Mk 137 RL); SLQ-25A Nixie SSTD towed acoustic torpedo decoy syst.
M: 2 sets Westinghouse geared steam turbines; 2 props; 77,000 shp (70,000 sust.)—900-hp bow-thruster
Boilers: 2 Combustion Engineering Type V2M-VS; 49.3 kg/cm^2, 482° C
Electric: 14,600 kw (4 × 2,500-kw turboalternators, 2 × 2,000-kw diesel alternator sets; 4 × 150-kw emergency diesel alternator sets)
Range: 10,000/20 **Fuel:** 5,900 tons + 1,200 tons JP-5 for aircraft
Crew: 86–94 officers, 871–979 enlisted + troops: 172 officers, 1,731 enlisted

Remarks: LHA 1 was authorized in FY 69, LHA 2 and 3 in FY 70, and LHA 4 and 5 in FY 71. Were originally to have been a class of nine, with four already on order canceled in 1971. LHA 5 was renamed on 15-2-78. The ships are aging more quickly than expected and suffer from thin flight decks, cramped command and berthing spaces, electric power distribution problems, control deficiencies, and obsolete piping systems. They were to have been given a major SLEP (Service Life Extension Program) modernization, with advance procurement funding for the first ship to have been requested under the FY 03 budget, but instead they are to be retired in 2011–15 and replaced by LHD 8 and the planned new LHA(R) class. LHA 3, homeported in Japan for eight years, returned to the U.S. for a major overhaul in 7-00.
Hull systems: The boilers were the largest ever installed in USN ships. The propulsion plant is highly automated. Are receiving digital computer-controlled propulsion systems to help optimize boiler performance. Have a very complete 352-bed hospital, including four operating rooms and even mortuary facilities. Are completely air-conditioned. The planned addition of a bulbous bow has been canceled. Originally had a boat crane and stowage for landing craft on the flight deck abaft the island, now removed.
Aviation systems: The normal air group includes 18 CH-46E, 10 CH-53E, 6 AH-1W, and 3 UH-1N helicopters. With six AV-8B Harriers aboard, the helicopter complement is 12 CH-46E, 6 CH-53E, 6 AH-1W, and 4 UH-1N; up to 20 AV-8B Harriers can be carried if no helicopters are aboard. In a mine countermeasures role, 18 CH-46E and 6 MH-53E helicopters would be carried, along with six Mk 105 mine countermeasures sleds. Have nine deck landing spots and helicopter elevators to port (20-ton, folding) and aft (40-ton). There is a 76 × 23.2 × 8.1–m (high) well deck for up to four LCU 1610 class, one LCAC, or seven LCM(8) landing craft. The vehicle stowage garage forward of the docking well provides 3,134 m^2 of parking space, and the palletized cargo holds total 3,311 m^3.
Combat systems: Communications systems include SRR-1, WSC-3 UHF, WSC-6 SHF, and USC-38 EHF SATCOM receivers and an SMQ-11 weather satellite receiver. As completed, carried two Mk 25 Mod. 1 BPDMS launchers for Sea Sparrow SAMs, controlled by two Mk 71 directors with Mk 115 radars, and three 127-mm DP guns. The Sea Sparrow launchers and the port aft 127-mm gun were removed from all during the early 1990s, and the remaining two gunmounts were deleted during 1997; the associated SPQ-9A surface-fire control radar and SPG-60 AA f.c.s. were removed during 1998–99. Six single 20-mm AA guns have also been removed. All have received two Mk 49, 21-cell RAM point-defense missile launchers sited to port atop the pilothouse and to starboard at the aft end of the flight deck and controlled by the SWY-2 weapons-control system. LHA 1 completed an overhaul in 1-95, with RAM launchers, Mk 23 TAS radar, and SPS-48E 3-D radar in place of SPS-52B—a modification now accomplished in all by using radar sets taken from retired CG 16– and CG 26–class cruisers. The ships of this class are no longer scheduled to receive the SSDS (Ship Self-Defense System) Block I update and plans to add the CEC (Cooperative Engagement Capability) were terminated in 6-00. All have had their original WLR-1 EW suites replaced by SLQ-32(V)3 and URN-20 TACANs replaced by URN-25.

AMPHIBIOUS TRANSPORTS, DOCK [LPD]

♦ 0 (+ 12) San Antonio–class dock landing ships

Bldrs: Northrop Grumman Avondale, New Orleans; and General Dynamics Bath Iron Works, Bath, Maine

	Bldr	Laid down	L	In serv.
LPD 17 San Antonio	Avondale	9-12-00	4-03	1-05 (del.)
LPD 18 New Orleans	Avondale	9-02	12-03	9-05 (del.)
LPD 19 Mesa Verde	Bath Iron Works	8-02	5-04	12-05 (del.)
LPD 20 Green Bay	Avondale	5-03	8-04	5-06 (del.)
LPD 21	Avondale	. . .	. . .	. . .
LPD 22	Bath Iron Works	. . .	. . .	. . .
LPD 23	Avondale	. . .	. . .	. . .
LPD 24	Avondale	. . .	. . .	. . .
LPD 25	Bath Iron Works	. . .	. . .	. . .
LPD 26	Avondale	. . .	. . .	. . .
LPD 27	Avondale	. . .	. . .	. . .
LPD 28	Bath Iron Works	. . .	. . .	. . .

San Antonio (LPD 17)—the mainmast will envelop the antenna for the SPS-48E radar and the foremast various electronic warfare and IFF antennas Northrop Grumman Ship Systems

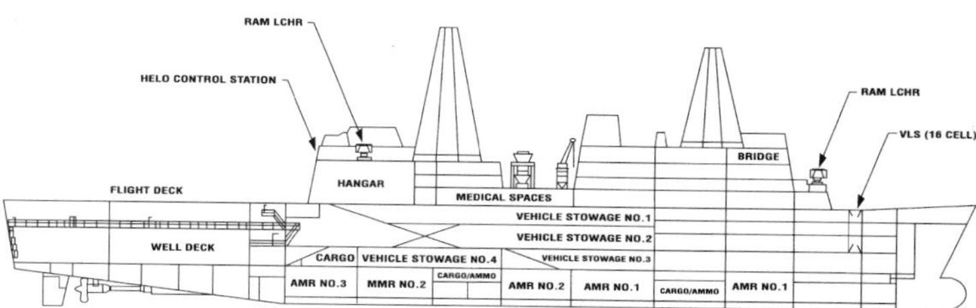

San Antonio (LPD 17) class Northrop Grumman Ship Systems

D: 25,296 tons (fl) **S:** 22+ kts **Dim:** 208.48 (200.00 wl) × 32.00 (29.5 wl) × 7.01
A: 2 21-round RAM Mk 31 Mod. 0 SAM launchers (RIM-116A missiles); 2 single 30-mm Mk 46 Mod. 1 (LPD 17: 3 single 25-mm 75-cal. Mk 38 Mod. 0 Bushmaster) low-angle guns; 2 single 12.7-mm Mk 26 Mod. 18 mg
Air group: 2 CH-53E or 4 AH/UH-1 or 4 CH-46E helicopters or 2 MV-22B Osprey
Electronics:
Radar: 2 Hughes-Furuno SPS-73 surf. search; 1 Raytheon SPS-48E 3-D air search; 1 Northrop Grumman SPQ-9B horizon search and target desig.
TACAN: . . .
EW: Raytheon SLQ-32A(V)2 intercept; SLA-10B; SLQ-49 floating decoy syst.; Mk 36 Mod. 12 SRBOC decoy syst. (4 6-round Mk 137 RL, 4 2-round Mk 53 Nulka hovering decoy RL); SLQ-25A Nixie SSTD towed torpedo decoy syst. (see remarks)
M: 4 Colt-Pielstick PC2.5 STC 16-cyl., medium-speed diesels; 2 5-bladed Bird-Johnson CP props; 41,600 bhp

AMPHIBIOUS TRANSPORTS, DOCK [LPD] *(continued)*

Electric: 12,500 kw tot. (5 × 2,500-kw Kato sets, Caterpillar 3608 diesel-driven)
Range: . . ./. . . **Fuel:** . . . tons + 1,196 m^3 aviation fuel, 38 m^3 vehicle fuel
Crew: 361 tot. (accomm. for 30 officers, 392 enlisted) + troops: 66 officers, 639 enlisted + 95 spare

Remarks: LPD 17 was authorized in FY 96, LPD 18 in FY 99, and LPD 19 and 20 in FY 00. Major delays and large cost increases have delayed further authorizations and none were approved under the FY 01 and FY 02 budgets; one was requested in the FY 03 budget, and one per year is to be requested under the FY 04 through FY 07 budgets. At one time, as many as 46 were planned. The 12 ships remaining in the LPD 17 program are to replace the existing LKAs, LPDs, *Newport*-class LSTs, and the LSD 36 class. Intended to be in service for 40 years. Are excessively elaborate and overly large for the missions foreseen.

The "winner-take-all" construction contract was awarded 17-12-96 to a consortium of Avondale Shipyards, Bath Iron Works, Hughes, Loral, Sperry Marine, CAE, AT&T, and Intergraph, with every third ship to be built at Bath's facility in Maine and the others in Louisiana. The initial contract provided $641,370,625 for LPD 17 and options to build the next two. LPD 18 was ordered on 18-12-98; the FY 99 Defense Authorization Act also directed that the next ship of the class be named the *Clifton B. Cates* after a former USMC commandant, but this has not been done and the intent is to continue naming the ships for cities (although LPD 19 is named for a national park in Colorado, departing from the traditional LPD city-name source). LPD 19 was ordered 22-12-99 (work began 16-7-01) and LPD 20 on 30-5-00 (for $477,675,955). As of 5-6-00, work had yet to begin on construction of LPD 17, whose estimated cost had risen to $1.16 billion, while LPD 18 was projected to have a final cost of $781 million, LPD 19 $856 million, and LPD 20 $702 million. Congress provided only $560.7 for construction of LPD 21 and LPD 22 ($949.3 million less than requested) under FY 01, and they have not been ordered. None were authorized under the FY 02 budget, and only one was requested under FY 03. All construction past LPD 21 may be transferred to Northrop Grumman Ingalls, Pascagoula, in return for all future destroyer construction being transferred to Bath Iron Works, under an agreement being negotiated early in 2002.

Hull systems: Will not have a significantly greater payload than the much smaller LPD 4 class. The docking well is about the size of that on the LPD 4 class and will accommodate two LCAC air-cushion landing craft and 14 AAAV amphibious vehicles. There will be two spots for helicopters of up to CH-53E size; three AH-1Z, two CH-46E, or one CH-53E or MV-22 Ospreys are to be accommodated in the hangar. Will also be able to support AV-8B Harrier-II aircraft. Cargo capacity is to include 2,323 m^2 of vehicle parking space on three decks and 708 m^3 of palletized ammunition cargo space. Two cargo ammunition magazines will total 1,007 m^3, and the ships will be able to carry 1,196 m^3 of JP-5 cargo fuel and 38 m^3 of cargo gasoline.

Medical facilities include 24 beds, two operating rooms, and space for 100 additional casualties. The hull was designed to reduce the cost of fabrication and is shaped to reduce radar cross-section; the radar cross-section is planned to be only 1% that of the LPD 4 class, and even the 10-ton, 19.8-m-reach Allied Systems boat crane incorporates signature-reduction features. The principal radars and communication antennas will be enveloped within two composite-material, octagonal "Advanced Enclosed Mast/Sensor" structures to reduce radar signature and required maintenance. Are to have a bow bulb, twin rudders, and no side-thrusters. Seven 700-kw air-conditioning plants, five 45,000-liter/day reverse osmosis water desalinators, 10 3,800-liter/min firepumps, and eight air compressors will be installed. As displacement has grown, expected speed has dropped by 1 kt. Will carry two 7-m RIB-type ship's boats and one of 11 m; stowage will also be provided for two additional special forces RIBs, if required. Are the first USN ships designed from the outset to accommodate women crewmembers. The original total crew size has been reduced due to increased automation and the deletion of a number of combat systems. The Sperry Marine Integrated Bridge System (IBS) and CAE's computerized engineering controls system will be installed.

Combat systems: All will have Advanced Combat Direction System (ACDS) Block I, USQ-119C(V)27 Joint Maritime Command Information System (JMCIS), KSQ-1 amphibious assault direction system, SPQ-12(V) radar display distribution system, Mk 2 Ship Self-Defense System (SSDS), and the Integrated Combat Direction System (ICDS) to coordinate various self-defense systems. In addition, LPD 18 and later are to receive the USG-2(V) Cooperative Engagement Capability (CEC) system and will have Links 11 and 16, JTIDS, SI communications, ADNS, and TADIX-A capabilities. The UPX-29 IFF system and SPQ-14(V) radar display distribution system will be fitted.

The navigation suite is to include a WSN-7(V)1 inertial system, digital flux gate magnetic compass, WRN-6(V)1 GPS receiver, WQN-1 Channel Finder mine-avoidance sonar, SSN-6 digital mapping system, UQN-4A echo sounder, and WQN-2 doppler speed log. Will have a 100% redundant Shipboard-Wide Area Network (SWAN) Asynchronous Transfer Mode-based shipwide fiber-optic data network to carry internal and external communications and data. Are to have HF, UHF, VHF, EHF, and SHF radio communications, including the Challenge Athena SATCOM system.

Originally, all were to have had 16 Mk 41 vertical missile launch cells forward of the superstructure to carry a total of 64 RIM-162 Evolved Sea Sparrow SAMs. The SAM system was initially deleted from the first three and has now been deleted from all, although weight and space provisions remain. Two planned Mk 15 Mod. 12 Phalanx 20-mm CIWS have also been omitted. The General Dynamics 30-mm Mk 46 Mod. 1 stabilized gun in the same armored turret that will be used on the new AAAV (amphibious armored assault vehicle) will be substituted for the 25-mm guns in order to deal with smallcraft, helicopters, and light aircraft.

The Lockheed Martin SLY-2(V) Advanced Integrated Electronic Warfare System (AIEWS) may replace the current, obsolescent SLQ-32(V)2 system in LPD 22 and later ships. LPD 22 will be the first to have the Project Akcita air-defense sensor and weapon integration system, which is planned to be backfitted later in earlier units; a new D-band radar may replace the SPS-48E.

♦ 11 Austin class (SCB 187B type) (*Atlantic/†Pacific Fleet)

	Bldr	Laid down	L	In serv.
LPD 4 Austin*	New York NSY	4-2-63	27-6-64	6-2-65
LPD 5 Ogden†	New York NSY	4-2-63	27-6-64	19-6-65
LPD 6 Duluth†	New York NSY	18-12-63	14-8-65	18-12-65
LPD 7 Cleveland†	Ingalls, Pascagoula	30-11-64	7-5-66	21-4-67
LPD 8 Dubuque†	Ingalls, Pascagoula	25-1-65	6-8-66	1-9-67
LPD 9 Denver†	Lockheed SB, Seattle	7-2-64	23-1-65	26-10-68
LPD 10 Juneau†	Lockheed SB, Seattle	23-1-65	12-2-66	12-7-69
LPD 12 Shreveport*	Lockheed SB, Seattle	27-12-65	25-10-66	12-2-70
LPD 13 Nashville*	Lockheed SB, Seattle	14-3-66	7-10-67	14-2-70
LPD 14 Trenton*	Lockheed SB, Seattle	8-8-66	3-8-68	6-3-71
LPD 15 Ponce*	Lockheed SB, Seattle	31-10-66	20-5-70	10-7-71

Nashville (LPD 13)—flagship variant — Bernard Prézelin, 7-01

Shreveport (LPD 12) — Takatoshi Okano, 4-01

Cleveland (LPD 7)—flagship variant — Findler & Winter, 10-00

Duluth (LPD 6) — Kurt Greiner/SeaPhoto, 3-00

AMPHIBIOUS TRANSPORTS, DOCK [LPD] *(continued)*

Dubuque (LPD 8) W. Michael Young, 5-00

Ponce (LPD 15) William H. Clarke, 11-00

D: 8,883–9,962 tons light (16,590–17,479 fl) **S:** 21 kts
Dim: 173.4 × 25.6 (hull) × 7.0–7.2
A: 2 20-mm Mk 15 Phalanx gatling CIWS; 2 single 25-mm 75-cal. Mk 38 Mod. 0 Bushmaster low-angle guns; 8 single 12.7-mm M2 mg
Electronics:
Radar: 1 Raytheon SPS-64(V)9 nav.; 1 Raytheon SPS-10F surf. search; 1 Lockheed Martin SPS-40E air search; 2 Mk 90 Phalanx f.c.
TACAN: URN-25
EW: Raytheon SLQ-32(V)1 intercept; Mk 36 SRBOC decoy RL syst. (4 6-round Mk 137 RL)—all except LPD 4: SLQ-25A Nixie towed torpedo decoy syst.
M: 2 sets de Laval geared steam turbines; 2 props; 24,000 shp
Boilers: 2 Foster-Wheeler (LPD 5, 12: Babcock & Wilcox), 42.3 kg/cm², 467° C
Range: 7,700/20
Crew: 28–29 officers, 361–375 enlisted + 60 staff in LPD 7–13 + troops: 69 officers, 812 enlisted (LPD 4–6, 14, 15: 79 officers, 756 enlisted)

Remarks: Three were authorized in FY 62, four in FY 63, three in FY 64, and two in FY 65; LPD 16, funded and authorized under FY 66, was deferred in favor of the LHA program and canceled entirely during 2-69. A lengthened version of the preceding *Raleigh* (LDP 1) class, combining the capabilities of LPA assault troop transports and LSD dock landing ships. LPD 10 is homeported at Sasebo, Japan, having replaced LPD 8 there on 28-7-99. LPD 12 grounded in the Suez Canal on 14-2-00, causing propeller and shaft damage that was repaired at Haifa, Israel. LPD 9 collided with the MSC oiler *Yukon* (T-AO 202) on 14-7-00 during refueling operations. All of these ships are in urgent need of replacement. LPD 4 was in a collision with the *Greeneville* (SSN 772) on 27-1-02.
Disposals: LPD 7 and 8 were scheduled to be decommissioned and stricken during FY 05 but may be delayed due to problems with the LPD 18–class program. *Coronado* (LPD 11) was redesignated as flagship AGF 11 on 1-10-80 and has operated as the flagship of Third Fleet since 26-11-86; see under [AGF].
Hull systems: As with many older USN classes, displacements vary widely as a result of modifications over the years. Can carry one LCAC, one LCU and four LCM(8), or 28 LVT in the 120.00 × 15.24–m (687-m²) well deck. Have one 30-ton and six 4-ton cranes, one 8.15-ton elevator, and two forklifts. Up to six CH-46E helicopters can be carried for brief periods on the 1,394-m² flight deck, but the small, telescoping hangar can accommodate only one utility helicopter; there is no hangar in LPD 4. LPD 7–13 were originally fitted for flagship duty and have one additional superstructure deck. All have 1,379 m² of vehicle parking space and 1,540 m³ of ammunition stowage, and they can carry 224,500 gallons of aviation fuel and 119,000 gallons of vehicle fuel.
Combat systems: Command facilities include a CIC, Troop Operations and Logistics Center, and Helicopter Coordination Center; LPD 7–13 also have a Flag Plot, Ship Signals Exploitation Space, and Supporting Arms Coordination Center (some of this equipment had been removed by 1998). All lost their one Mk 56 and two Mk 63 gun fire-control directors in the late 1980s, leaving the 76.2-mm guns locally controlled. Two twin 76.2-mm DP guns (port fwd, starboard aft) were removed in 1977–78, and the remaining mounts in 1992–93. In LPD 4–6, 14, and 15, the SPS-40 radar's antenna is set on a platform well below the apex of the tripod mast; on the others, it is on the masthead platform. LPD 4 has no torpedo decoy system.

LPD 12 in the Atlantic and LPD 9 in the Pacific were equipped during 11-92 and 1-93 to accommodate and control the Pioneer reconnaissance drone; each ship carried five to eight of the drones and was equipped fore and aft with radome-covered tracking and control radars for the Pioneers. Subsequently, the drone equipment was added to LPD 4 and by 1999 it was aboard LPD 7, 12, 13, and 15.

DOCK LANDING SHIPS [LSD]

♦ 4 Harpers Ferry class
Bldr: Northrop Grumman Avondale, New Orleans (*Atlantic/†Pacific Fleet)

	Laid down	L	In serv.
LSD 49 HARPERS FERRY†	15-4-91	16-1-93	7-1-95
LSD 50 CARTER HALL*	11-11-91	2-10-93	30-9-95
LSD 51 OAK HILL*	21-9-92	11-6-94	8-6-96
LSD 52 PEARL HARBOR†	27-1-95	24-2-96	30-5-98

Oak Hill (LSD 51) Bernard Prézelin, 6-00

Pearl Harbor (LSD 52) Jim Sanderson, 6-01

Harpers Ferry (LSD 49) Findler & Winter, 10-00

D: 11,251–11,604 tons light (16,088–16,601 fl) **S:** 22 kts
Dim: 185.80 (176.80 wl) × 25.60 × 6.04
A: 2 21-round RAM Mk 31 SAM syst. (RIM-116 missiles); 2 20-mm Mk 15 Phalanx gatling CIWS; 2 single 25-mm 75-cal. Mk 38 Mod. 0 Bushmaster low-angle guns; 8 single 12.7-mm M2 mg
Electronics:
Radar: 1 Raytheon SPS-64(V)9 nav.; 1 Norden SPS-67(V)1 surf. search; 1 Raytheon SPS-49(V)5 air search; 2 Mk 90 Phalanx f.c.
TACAN: URN-25
EW: Raytheon SLQ-32(V)1 intercept; Mk 36 SRBOC decoy syst. (6 6-round Mk 137 RL); SLQ-25 Nixie towed torpedo decoy syst.
M: 4 Colt-Pielstick 16 PC2.5 V400 diesels; 2 CP props; 41,600 bhp (33,600 sust.)
Electric: 5,200 kw (4 × 1,300-kw Fairbanks-Morse 12D38⅛ diesel alternator sets)
Range: 8,000/18 **Fuel:** 2,000 tons **Endurance:** 75 days
Crew: 21 officers, 312–313 enlisted + troops: 27 officers, 375 enlisted + emergency accomm. for 7 officers, 95 enlisted

DOCK LANDING SHIPS [LSD] *(continued)*

Harpers Ferry (LSD 49) W. Michael Young, 10-00

Remarks: Authorized in FY 88, 90, 91, and 92, respectively. Officially referred to as the "LSD 41 CV (Cargo Variant)" class. Were originally to have been a class of 12, but the program was terminated in 1992 in favor of development of the *San Antonio* class; funds to build LSD 52, approved under FY 92, were rescinded by the first Bush administration, but Congress again appropriated money to build the vessel under FY 93. LSD 49 was ordered 26-12-89, LSD 50 on 22-12-89, LSD 51 on 27-3-91, and LSD 52 during 10-93. LSD 49's home port was changed to Sasebo, Japan, on 1-9-01, replacing LSD 42 there.
Hull systems: A modification of the LSD 41 design, with increased cargo capacity at the expense of a shorter well deck able to accommodate only two LCACs, one LCU, or four LCM(8). Carry one 12.2-m utility boat and two LCPLs on deck, tended by a single starboard-side 30-ton crane. Cargo space: 1,208 m^2 vehicle parking, 1,133 m^3 cargo volume. Have greater air-conditioning capacity than the LSD 41 class. The flight deck is fixed, as on the LSD 41 class, has two landing spots, and is served by an 8-ton cargo elevator.
Combat systems: All ships of the class are to have received the SSDS Block I combat system by 2004, beginning with LSD 49 in 1997. The associated Mk 31 RAM SAM launchers were mounted atop the pilothouse and to port, amidships, in all by 1999. Plans to add the CEC (Cooperative Engagement Capability) were terminated in 6-00.

♦ 8 Whidbey Island class (*Atlantic/†Pacific Fleet)
Bldrs: Lockheed, Seattle, and Avondale SY

	Bldr	Laid down	L	In serv.
LSD 41 Whidbey Island*	Lockheed	4-8-81	10-6-83	9-2-85
LSD 42 Germantown†	Lockheed	5-8-82	29-6-84	8-2-86
LSD 43 Fort McHenry†	Lockheed	10-6-83	1-2-86	8-8-87
LSD 44 Gunston Hall*	Avondale	26-5-86	27-6-87	24-2-89
LSD 45 Comstock†	Avondale	27-10-86	16-1-88	3-2-90
LSD 46 Tortuga*	Avondale	23-3-87	15-9-88	17-11-90
LSD 47 Rushmore†	Avondale	9-11-87	6-5-89	1-6-91
LSD 48 Ashland*	Avondale	4-4-88	11-11-89	9-5-92

Comstock (LSD 45) Jim Sanderson, 6-01

Whidbey Island (LSD 41) Maurizio Brescia, 1-00

Tortuga (LSD 46) Martin Mokrus, 3-02

D: 11,099–11,590 tons light (15,883–16,568 fl) **S:** 22 kts
Dim: 185.80 (176.80 wl) × 25.60 × 6.25 (hull)
A: 2 21-round RAM Mk 31 SAM syst. (RIM-116 missiles); 2 20-mm Mk 15 Phalanx gatling CIWS; 2 single 25-mm 75-cal. Mk 38 Mod. 0 Bushmaster low-angle guns; 6 single 12.7-mm M2 mg
Electronics:
Radar: 1 . . . nav.; 1 Raytheon SPS-64(V)9 nav.; 1 Norden SPS-67(V) surf. search; 1 Raytheon SPS-49(V)1 (LSD 45–48: (V)5) air search; 2 Mk 90 Phalanx f.c.
TACAN: URN-25
EW: Raytheon SLQ-32(V)1 intercept; Mk 36 Mod. 6 SRBOC decoy RL syst. (4 6-round Mk 137 RL); SLQ-25 Nixie towed torpedo decoy syst.
M: 4 Colt-Pielstick 16 PC2.5 V400 diesels; 2 5-bladed CP props; 41,600 bhp (33,600 sust.)
Electric: 5,200 kw (4 × 1,300-kw Fairbanks-Morse 12D38⅛ diesel alternator sets)
Range: 8,000/18 **Fuel:** 2,000 tons **Endurance:** 75 days
Crew: 21 officers, 289–299 enlisted + troops: 27 officers, 375 enlisted (including 64 LCAC personnel) + emergency accomm. for 7 officers, 95 enlisted

Remarks: The design was originally to have been a near-repeat of the LSD 36 class, adapted for diesel propulsion and able to accommodate four LCAC air-cushion landing craft. LSD 41 was authorized in FY 81, LSD 42 in FY 82, LSD 43 in FY 83, LSD 44 in FY 84, LSD 45 and 46 in FY 85, and LSD 47 and 48 in FY 86. In 7-99, LSD 47 began testing systems and concepts intended for use in the LPD 17 class, including new damage control techniques, a local-area data network, integrated bridge systems, and automated maintenance systems; LSD 47 is also the "Smart Gator" amphibious warfare ship trials platform for "Smart Ship" labor-saving concepts, which were planned to be incorporated in the entire class by 2003; the cost-saving program, however, was canceled during 6-00—on cost grounds.
Hull systems: The docking well measures 134.0 × 15.24 m clear (1,220 m^2) and floods to 1.8 m forward/3.0 m aft; the ships can ballast down in 15 minutes and deballast in 30, with a total ballast water capacity of 12,860 tons (and full load displacement of more than 29,000 metric tons when in ballast). The helicopter deck is raised above the docking well (which can accommodate 4 LCAC, 3 LCU, 10 LCM(8), or 64 LVTP) in order to provide all-around ventilation for the gas turbine-engined LCACs. There are two landing spots on the 64.6 × 25.3–m flight deck for up to CH-53E-size helicopters, but no hangar facilities; 90 tons of JP-5 fuel is carried for helicopters. Forward of the docking well is 1,214 m^2 of vehicle parking space and space for 149 m^3 of palletized cargo. Medical facilities include an operating room and eight beds. Carry one 15.24-m utility boat, two LCPL Mk 11, and one LCVP on deck, handled by two (20-ton and 60-ton) cranes. LSD 44–48 have a collective biological/chemical warfare protection system. All have the Inogen Leading Mark optical guidance system for LCAC entry to the well deck. LSD 47 was fitted with the Raytheon fiber-optic, closed-loop steering system in 1998 under the "Smart Gator" ship systems improvement developmental program.
Combat systems: Two Mk 49, 21-cell launchers for the RAM missile have been added. In 1999, LSD 44 became the first ship fitted with RAM Mod. 1 (RIM-116A) missiles. LSD 48 received SSDS (Ship Self-Defense System) Block I during a 9-96 to 1-97 refit, LSD 44 received it during 1997 and LSD 45 by 1999, and all are to have received it by 2004. The SPS-49(V)1 radars are planned to be upgraded to SPS-49A(V)1. Plans to add the CEC (Cooperative Engagement Capability) were terminated in 6-00.

♦ 3 Anchorage class
Bldrs: LSD 36: Ingalls, Pascagoula, Miss.; LSD 37, 39: General Dynamics, Quincy, Mass. (*Atlantic/†Pacific Fleet)

	Laid down	L	In serv.
LSD 36 Anchorage†	13-3-67	5-5-68	15-3-69
LSD 37 Portland*	21-9-67	20-12-69	3-10-70
LSD 39 Mount Vernon†	29-1-70	17-4-71	13-5-72

D: 8,325–8,762 tons light (14,095–14,202 fl) **S:** 22 kts
Dim: 168.66 (162.8 wl) × 25.9 × 6.1 (max.)
A: 2 20-mm Mk 15 Phalanx gatling CIWS; 2 single 25-mm 75-cal. Mk 38 Mod. 0 Bushmaster low-angle guns; 6 single 12.7-mm M2 mg

DOCK LANDING SHIPS [LSD] *(continued)*

Mount Vernon (LSD 39) Jim Sanderson, 6-01

Portland (LSD 37) Guy Schaeffer, via Paolo Marsan, 2-01

Anchorage (LSD 36) Kurt Greiner/SeaPhoto, 3-00

Electronics:
Radar: 1 Raytheon SPS-64(V)9 (LSD 37: SPS-73(V)12) nav.; 1 Raytheon SPS-67(V)1 surf. search; 1 Lockheed SPS-40E air search; 2 Mk 90 Phalanx f.c.
EW: Raytheon SLQ-32(V)1 intercept; Mk 36 Mod. 6 SRBOC decoy RL syst.; SLQ-25 Nixie towed torpedo decoy syst.—LSD 36 also: Mk 50 Mod. 0 decoy syst. (for SLQ-49 Rubber Duck floating decoys)

M: 2 sets de Laval geared steam turbines; 2 props; 24,000 shp
Boilers: 2 Foster-Wheeler (LSD 36: Combustion Eng.); 42.3 kg/cm², 467° C
Range: 14,800/12 **Fuel:** 2,750 tons
Crew: 18 officers, 303–304 enlisted + troops: 25 officers, 311 enlisted

Remarks: First of class authorized in FY 65, three in FY 66, and the last in FY 67. LSD 37 is now planned for retention through 30-9-06.
Disposals: *Pensacola* (LSD 38) was decommissioned and transferred by sale to Taiwan 22-9-99. *Fort Fisher* (LSD 40) was decommissioned and stricken 27-2-98; offered for sale to Malaysia and to Taiwan during FY 00, the ship was not accepted and remains in MARAD custody awaiting disposal.
Hull systems: Can accommodate (with/without portable mezzanine deck installed) 2/3 LCAC, 1/3 LCU, 6/9 LCM(8), or 50 LVT in the 131.06 × 15.24–m well deck. Four LCPLs can be stowed on deck, handled by the two 50-ton cranes. Have 1,115 m² of vehicle parking space forward of the docking well. The helicopter deck is removable and has one landing spot; 90 tons of JP-5 fuel is carried for helicopters.
Combat systems: Mk 56 and Mk 63 directors were removed in 1977, two twin 76.2-mm gunmounts by 1990, and the remaining 76.2-mm mounts in 1993–94. LSD 39 was employed for the first at-sea firings of the army ATACMS artillery rocket system, achieving a 75-n.m. range on 12-2-95.

Disposal note: Of the eight *Thomaston*-class dock landing ships, *Thomaston* (LSD 28) was transferred to the Maritime Administration 28-10-91 and sold for scrap 7-9-95; *Plymouth Rock* (LSD 29) was transferred to MARAD 8-11-91 and sold for scrap 23-6-95; *Fort Snelling* (LSD 30) was transferred to MARAD 7-9-89 and sold for scrap 23-6-95; *Point Defiance* (LSD 31) was transferred to MARAD 12-8-91 and sold for scrap 7-9-95; *Spiegel Grove* (LSD 32) was placed in reserve 2-10-89 and stricken in 2-94; *Alamo* (LSD 33) was decommissioned and leased to Brazil 2-11-90; *Hermitage* (LSD 34) was decommissioned and leased to Brazil 2-10-89; and *Monticello* (LSD 35) was transferred to MARAD 2-8-91 and sold for scrap 7-9-95.
The former LSD 15 (ex-*Shadwell*) is employed at Mobile, Ala., by the Office of Naval Research as a damage control trials hulk for the DC-ARM (Damage Control Automation for Reduced Manning) program.

TANK LANDING SHIPS [LST]

♦ 5 Newport class (SCN 405-66 type) (4 in *reserve*)

Bldr: General Dynamics National Steel SB, San Diego (†Pacific Fleet, Naval Reserve Force)

	Laid down	L	In serv.	Decomm.
LST 1182 *Fresno*	16-12-67	28-9-68	22-11-69	8-4-93
LST 1184 Frederick†	13-4-68	8-3-69	11-4-70	2002
LST 1187 *Tuscaloosa*	23-11-68	6-9-69	24-10-70	18-2-94
LST 1190 *Boulder*	6-9-69	22-5-70	4-6-71	28-2-94
LST 1191 *Racine*	13-12-69	15-8-70	9-7-71	2-10-93

Frederick (LST 1184) M. Claude, 8-01

D: LST 1184: 5,170 tons light (8,770 fl) **S:** 23 kts (20 sust.)
Dim: 159.2 (171.3 over horns) × 21.18 × 5.79 (aft)
A: LST 1184 only: 1 20-mm Mk. 15 Phalanx CIWS; 4 single 12.7-mm mg
Electronics:
Radar: 1 Raytheon SPS-64(V)9 nav.; 1 Raytheon SPS-10F surf. search—LST 1184 only: 1 Mk 90 Phalanx f.c.
M: 6 Alco 16-251 diesels; 2 CP props; 16,500 bhp—bow-thruster
Electric: 2,250 kw tot. (3 × 750 kw, Alco 251-E diesels driving; 450 V, 60 Hz a.c.)
Range: 14,250/14 **Fuel:** 1,750 tons
Crew: LST 1184: 12 officers, 219 enlisted + troops: 20 officers, 294 enlisted + emergency accomm. for 72

Remarks: Class authorized: 1 in FY 65, 8 in FY 66, and 11 in FY 67; seven more planned under FY 71 were canceled. LST 1184 was transferred to the Naval Reserve Force 31-1-95 and is active, homeported at San Diego; the crew includes 11 officers and 180 enlisted of the regular navy, augmented by 4 officer and 67 enlisted naval reservists. The other four are retained in reserve on 180-day recall with selected reserve crews of 5 officers and 45 enlisted assigned full-time. LST 1184 is to be retired late in 2002.
Disposals: The decommissioned units listed below have been transferred abroad or as of 1-02 were in Category "C" reserve pending disposal:

	Decomm.	Remarks
LST 1179 *Newport*	30-9-92	Sold to Mexico 18-1-01
LST 1180 *Manitowoc*	30-6-93	Leased to Taiwan 1-7-95; sale FY 99
LST 1181 *Sumter*	30-9-93	Leased to Taiwan 1-7-95; sale FY 99
LST 1183 *Peoria*	28-1-94	For disposal 1999; offered Egypt but not accepted
LST 1185 *Schenectady*	15-12-93	Offered to Taiwan but not accepted; stricken for disposal 13-7-01
LST 1186 *Cayuga*	30-7-94	Leased to Brazil, transferred 26-8-94; sold outright FY 99
LST 1188 *Saginaw*	28-6-94	Sold to Australia, transferred 28-6-94
LST 1189 *San Bernardino*	30-9-95	Leased to Chile, transferred 30-9-95; sale FY 99

TANK LANDING SHIPS [LST] *(continued)*

	Decomm.	Remarks
LST 1192 *Spartanburg County*	16-12-94	Sold to Malaysia, transferred 16-12-94
LST 1193 *Fairfax County*	27-9-94	Sold to Australia, transferred 27-9-94
LST 1194 *La Moure County*	17-11-00	Ran aground in Chile 12-9-00; stricken 17-11-00 and sunk as a target 10-7-01
LST 1195 *Barbour County*	31-3-92	Stricken for disposal 13-7-01
LST 1196 *Harlan County*	14-4-95	Leased to Spain 14-4-95; sale FY 99
LST 1197 *Barnstable County*	29-6-94	Leased to Spain 26-8-94; sale FY 99
LST 1198 *Bristol County*	15-7-94	Leased to Morocco 16-8-94

LST 1183, leased to Venezuela 31-12-95 as the *Golfo de Venezuela* (T-81), never left U.S. waters and was repossessed on 31-5-96 when a lease payment was missed. Other than LST 1185, no more overseas transfers are expected.

Hull systems: Can transport 2,000 tons of cargo, or 500 tons for beaching, on 1,765 m^2 of deck space. The 34-m-long, 75-ton-capacity mobile aluminum ramp forward is linked to the tank deck by a second ramp from the upper deck. To aft are a 242-m^2 helicopter platform and a stern door for loading and unloading vehicles. Four pontoon causeway sections can be carried on the hull sides. The tank deck, which has a 75-ton-capacity turntable at both ends, can carry 23 AAV-7A1 armored personnel carriers or 29 M 48 tanks or 41 2.5-ton trucks, while the upper deck can accept 29 2.5-ton trucks. Normally carry three LCVPs and one LCP in Welin davits. Have two 10-ton cranes. Carry 141,600 gallons of vehicle fuel.

Combat systems: The Mk 63 radar gunfire-control systems were removed in 1977–78 and the two twin 76.2-mm DP gunmounts during the early 1990s, except from the stricken LST 1195. The SLQ-32(V)1 warning EW installation has been abandoned.

AMPHIBIOUS CARGO SHIPS [LKA]

♦ 5 Charleston class (SCB 403 type) (In reserve)

Bldr: Northrop Grumman Newport News, Newport News, Va.

	Laid down	L	In serv.	Decomm.
LKA 113 CHARLESTON	5-12-66	2-12-67	14-12-68	27-4-92
LKA 114 DURHAM	10-7-67	29-3-68	24-5-69	25-2-94
LKA 115 MOBILE	15-1-68	19-10-68	29-9-69	21-1-94
LKA 116 ST. LOUIS	3-4-68	4-1-69	22-11-69	30-9-93
LKA 117 EL PASO	22-10-68	17-5-69	17-1-70	21-4-94

Durham (LKA 114)—stored at Pearl Harbor Brian Morrison, 6-00

D: 9,937–10,455 tons light (18,322–19,323 fl) **S:** 20 kts
Dim: 175.26 (167.6 wl) × 24.99 × 7.62 (max.)
A: removed or inactivated (see remarks)
Electronics:
Radar: 1 SPS-59 (Canadian Marconi LN-66) nav.; 1 Raytheon SPS-10F surf. search
EW: Raytheon SLQ-32(V)1 intercept; Mk 36 SRBOC decoy syst. (4 6-round Mk 137 RL)—LKA 117 only: fitted for SLQ-25 Nixie towed torpedo decoy syst.
M: 1 set Westinghouse geared steam turbines; 1 prop; 22,000 shp (19,250 sust.)
Boilers: 2 Combustion Engineering; 42.2 kg/cm^2, 443° C
Range: 9,600/16 **Fuel:** 2,400 tons
Crew: 22 officers, 334 enlisted + troops: 15 officers, 211 enlisted

Remarks: LKA 114 and 115 were authorized in FY 65, LKA 117 in FY 66. All are being retained as mobilization reserve (Category B) assets at 180-day readiness; LKA 113, 115, and 117 are stored at Philadelphia and the other two at Pearl Harbor. LKA 115 and 117 were to be brought to 5-day readiness for deployment under Military Sealift Command control during refits at Bethlehem Shipyard, Sparrows Point, Md., that began on 12-2-96 for LKA 117 and 26-4-96 for LKA 115; funding was withdrawn, however, when the work was nearly completed and the ships were returned to storage at Philadelphia, with LKA 117 and an MSC crew sailing there from Baltimore in one day under her own power and again being placed out of service on 23-10-96 and LKA 115 following on 1-11-96.

Hull systems: Are air-conditioned. Machinery control is automatic. Have a 565-m^2 helicopter platform. Cargo capacity is 2,420 m^3, including 4,371 m^2 of vehicle parking space and 741 m^3 of ammunition stowage. There are one 6-ton and five 2-ton stores elevators. Fittings include two 70-ton heavy-lift derricks, two 40-ton derricks, and eight 15-ton derricks. When active, they normally carried four aluminum LCM(8) Mk 2 and two LCPL landing craft.

Combat systems: Two Mk 56 radar gunfire-control systems and one twin 76.2-mm gunmount were removed in 1977–78 and another gunmount later in preparation for installation of two 20-mm Mk 15 CIWS. LKA 117 is unique in retaining the two twin 76.2-mm mounts, which are cocooned.

UTILITY LANDING CRAFT, SURFACE-EFFECT [LCUA]

♦ 90 (+ 1) LCAC 1 class

Bldr: Textron, New Orleans (LCAC 15–23, 34–36, 49–51: Avondale, Gulfport)

	In serv.		In serv.		In serv.
LCAC 1	14-12-84	LCAC 32	1-5-91	LCAC 63	30-9-93
LCAC 2	22-2-86	LCAC 33	4-6-91	LCAC 64	27-10-93
LCAC 3	9-6-86	LCAC 34	31-5-92	LCAC 65	24-11-93
LCAC 4	13-8-86	LCAC 35	31-5-92	LCAC 66	28-12-93
LCAC 5	26-11-86	LCAC 36	1-5-92	LCAC 67	25-2-94
LCAC 6	1-12-86	LCAC 37	31-7-91	LCAC 68	25-3-94
LCAC 7	18-3-87	LCAC 38	6-9-91	LCAC 69	29-4-94
LCAC 8	3-6-87	LCAC 39	30-9-91	LCAC 70	5-6-94
LCAC 9	26-6-87	LCAC 40	6-11-91	LCAC 71	21-6-94
LCAC 10	4-9-87	LCAC 41	27-11-91	LCAC 72	31-7-94
LCAC 11	7-12-87	LCAC 42	12-12-91	LCAC 73	30-9-94
LCAC 12	23-12-87	LCAC 43	21-2-92	LCAC 74	10-11-94
LCAC 13	30-9-88	LCAC 44	28-2-92	LCAC 75	6-1-95
LCAC 14	3-11-88	LCAC 45	26-3-92	LCAC 76	14-2-95
LCAC 15	20-9-88	LCAC 46	8-5-92	LCAC 77	29-3-95
LCAC 16	4-11-88	LCAC 47	24-6-92	LCAC 78	23-5-95
LCAC 17	1989	LCAC 48	17-7-92	LCAC 79	20-7-95
LCAC 18	1989	LCAC 49	16-10-92	LCAC 80	23-8-95
LCAC 19	5-90	LCAC 50	2-93	LCAC 81	25-10-95
LCAC 20	1990	LCAC 51	6-93	LCAC 82	13-12-95
LCAC 21	1990	LCAC 52	2-9-92	LCAC 83	29-2-96
LCAC 22	11-90	LCAC 53	10-7-92	LCAC 84	25-4-96
LCAC 23	15-6-91	LCAC 54	30-10-92	LCAC 85	25-7-96
LCAC 24	1-3-90	LCAC 55	30-11-92	LCAC 86	26-9-96
LCAC 25	29-6-90	LCAC 56	8-1-93	LCAC 87	20-11-96
LCAC 26	7-90	LCAC 57	26-2-93	LCAC 88	19-2-97
LCAC 27	24-8-90	LCAC 58	31-3-93	LCAC 89	15-4-97
LCAC 28	12-10-90	LCAC 59	30-4-93	LCAC 90	24-10-97
LCAC 29	18-12-90	LCAC 60	4-6-93	LCAC 91	3-01
LCAC 30	19-12-90	LCAC 61	30-7-93		
LCAC 31	27-2-91	LCAC 62	31-8-93		

LCAC 88 Takatoshi Okano, 4-01

LCAC 16 George R. Schneider, 7-00

D: 87.9–93.4 tons light (166.6 fl; 181.6 overload) **S:** 54 kts (40 when loaded)
Dim: 26.80 (24.69 hull) × 14.33 (13.31 hull) × 0.78 (at rest, loaded)
A: none (see remarks)
Electronics: Radar: 1 Canadian Marconi CMR-91 Seemaster nav.
M: 4 Avco TF40B gas turbines (3,955 shp each; 2 for lift); 2 3.58-m-dia. shrouded airscrews, 4 1.60-m-dia. centrifugal lift fans; 7,910 shp (sust.) for propulsion
Electric: 120 kw tot. (2 × 60-kw Turbomach T-62 gas turbine APU)
Range: 223/48 light; 200/40 loaded **Fuel:** 6.2 tons (7,132 gallons)
Crew: 5 tot. + 24 troops + (in personnel module, when fitted) 180 troops or 54 medical litters

Remarks: Authorizations: 3 in FY 82, 3 in FY 83, 6 in FY 84, 9 in FY 85, 12 in FY 86, 15 in FY 89, 12 in FY 90, 24 in FY 91, and 12 in FY 92 (of which not all were ordered); the original program was for 108. First unit was launched 2-5-84. The first 12 were ordered from Bell-Halter, the next two from Lockheed during 10-85, with orders for seven other FY 85 units delayed; Avondale bought the Lockheed facility and contracts in 1-88. On 23-6-92, Avondale was given a contract to produce spare LCAC structures, including "several" complete hull modules, for delivery during 1993–94.

LCAC 91 was delivered more than three years late after her use as a prototype for the LCAC SLEP (Service Life Extension Program). Although the craft were originally intended to last 30 years, they have proven vulnerable to corrosion, and retirements would have been necessitated beginning no later than 2004; thus, a major life-extension program commenced with one unit under the FY 01 budget ($15.6 million provided by Congress); two are to follow under FY 02, three under FY 03, four

UTILITY LANDING CRAFT, SURFACE-EFFECT [LCUA] *(continued)*

LCAC 91—the final unit of the LCAC series Carl Gustafson/Textron, 2001

each year under FY 04 and 05, and six each year under FY 06 and 07—a rate that will ultimately not sustain retaining the entire inventory goal, which has been reduced to 74 active, with the others maintained in ready reserve. The first three units are to be modernized under a $35 million contract signed 27-4-01; see Modernization below for details of the planned updates.

Atlantic Fleet units are assigned to Amphibious Craft Unit 4 (ACU-4), Little Creek, Va. Pacific Fleet units are assigned to ACU-5, Coronado, Calif.

Hull systems: Cargo capacity: 60 tons normal, 75 tons overload. The bow ramp is 8.8 m wide, the stern ramp 4.6 m. The deck has 168 m^2 of parking area and is 204 m long and 8.3 m wide. They are difficult to tow if they break down and are vulnerable to defensive fire. The operator, engineer, navigator, and nine troops travel in the starboard side compartment, while the deck hand, assistant engineer, loadmaster, and 16 troops travel in port compartments. Navigational equipment includes a GPS receiver.

Can achieve about 50 kts when loaded and are able to maintain 30 kts loaded in a State 3 sea. The airscrew propellers provide 80% of the thrust and the two swiveling bow ducts the remainder. Can be stopped from full speed in about 460 m. The turning radius at speed is a very unhandy 1,830 m. Can be operated in temperatures from –30° to 100° F, making them unsuitable for hot desert climates. Can beach on slopes up to 5° and can clear a 1.2-m obstacle. LCAC 91 has Vericor ETF40B gas turbines of 4,745 shp each. Troops cannot be carried in the open on the cargo deck because of dangerously high noise levels.

The first four of nine modular Personnel Transport Modules (PTM) acquired in 1994–95 were deployed to the Mediterranean in early 1996 for use with LCACs temporarily redesignated MCAC (Multimission Craft, Air Cushion). The PTMs can accommodate 145 fully equipped troops (and 684 ft^3 of stores) or 54 hospital litters plus medical personnel; 180 persons can be accommodated for evacuation duties. The 6,087-kg PTM can be assembled from pieces weighing 75 kg or less by 12 persons in four hours and has integral ventilation, lighting, and communications systems. Disassembled, the PTM fits in a standard 20-ft. cargo container.

Combat systems: Sixteen M58 modular lane-sweeping mine countermeasures deployment packages (at $40 million each) have been acquired for these craft, permitting them to employ the same towed mine countermeasures sleds that are used by MH-53E helicopters; the first three were delivered in summer 1993. LCAC 66 was used in trials during 1996 with a 30-mm GAU-13 gatling gun in a GPU-5 pod to provide an organic shore fire suppression capability; if adopted, the LCACs could accommodate two modular installations with a total of four 30-mm gatling guns, 5-inch rocket pods, and Hellfire missiles, while another module could be installed facing aft to cover withdrawal. The radar on these craft is the current version of the Canadian Marconi LN-66.

By 2000, the USN had hoped to have portable surf and beach mine clearance systems for LCACs, using the DET (Distributed Explosive Technology) rocket-propelled explosive net array and the SABRE (Shallow-water Assault Breaching) linear demolition charge; each beachhead mine clearance LCAC would carry nine SABRE launchers and two DETs. The DET uses two rockets to launch a parachute-retarded explosive net that deploys to cover a 54.9-m-square area. The SABREs will be launched consecutively to clear a lane for the LCACs to approach the beach to launch their DET arrays.

Modernization: Textron Marine and Land Service is modernizing LCACs with more powerful Vericor ETF40B engines of 4,745 shp each; a new fuel system; new lightweight, longer-wearing skirts; replacement of the keel air bag with a "buoyancy box"; upgraded communication and navigation systems; improved data displays; and structural reinforcements. Completed units will be referred to as "LCAC Mk II." The program is planned to end in 2016 with a total of 74 updated. The modifications are intended to increase the service life of the craft to 30 years.

UTILITY LANDING CRAFT [LCU]

Note: All utility landing craft (and the remaining LCM(8) LCMs) are administratively assigned either to Assault Craft Unit 1 (ACU-1) and ACU-3 at Coronado, Calif., or ACU-2 at Little Creek, Va., for assignment to larger landing ships as needed.

♦ 0 (+ 35) LCU(X) class

Bldr: . . .

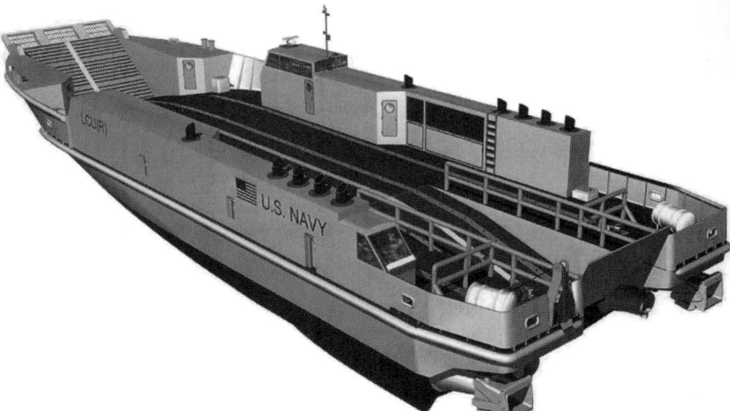

LCU(X) planing-hulled, waterjet-powered monohull concept Textron, 2001

Remarks: To have a payload of 160–200 tons, a sustained speed of 20+ kts, a range of 1,000 n.m., and a 10-day endurance. May have partial air-cushion hull support, a wave-piercing hull, or some other new hullform. Will have bow-thrusters to improve maneuverability. As of 4-01, six companies had $50,000 contracts to develop design concepts, with three to win $200,000 detailed design contracts and a lead-unit contract to be placed in mid-2004. A production rate of seven per year is desired, but with planned funding of only $12 million per year, that goal is highly unlikely to be met. Of the two Textron designs depicted, one is essentially an enlarged LCAC and the other a planing-hulled LCU. No design had been selected as of 4-02.

UTILITY LANDING CRAFT [LCU] *(continued)*

LCU(X) air-cushion vehicle concept Textron, 2001

♦ 37 LCU 1610 class (SCB 149, 149B, and 406 types)

Bldrs: See remarks (In serv. 6-59 to 12-71, except LCU 1680: 11-10-87, and LCU 1681: 12-11-87)

LCU 1616	LCU 1627	LCU 1648–LCU 1651
LCU 1617	LCU 1629–LCU 1635	LCU 1653–LCU 1666
LCU 1619	LCU 1641	LCU 1680 (135CU8501)
LCU 1624	LCU 1643–LCU 1646	LCU 1681 (135CU8502)

LCU 1661 George R. Schneider, 9-99

LCU 1655 Guy Schaeffer, via Paolo Marsan, 2-01

LCU 1648 Jim Sanderson, 6-01

D: 190 tons std.; 390 normal (437 fl; LCU 1680, 1681: 404 tons fl)
S: 11 kts **Dim:** 41.07 × 9.07 × 2.08 **A:** 2 12.7-mm M2 mg
Electronics: Radar: 1 Furuno . . . nav.
M: 4 G.M. 6-71 diesels; 2 Kort-nozzle props; 1,200 bhp (LCU 1680, 1681: 2 G.M. 12V71 TI diesels; 2 Kort-nozzle props; 1,700 bhp)
Range: 1,200/11 **Fuel:** 13 tons
Crew: 10 enlisted (LCU 1680, 1681: 2 officers, 12 enlisted)

Remarks: LCU 1616–1619, 1623, and 1624 were delivered by Gunderson Bros., Portland, Ore., between 6-59 and 9-60; LCU 1621, 1626, 1629, and 1630 by Southern Shipbuilding, Slidell, La., between 6-60 and 1968; LCU 1627, 1628, and 1631–1635 by General Ship & Eng. Works, East Boston, Mass.; LCU 1643–1645 by Marinette Marine, Marinette, Wis., between 8-67 and 1969; LCU 1646–1666 by Defoe SB, Bay City, Wis., in 1969–70; and LCU 1667–1670 by General Ship & Eng. Works. LCU 1680 and 1681 ordered during 10-85 from Moss Point Marine, Escatawpa, Miss., for delivery in 9-86 to Naval Reserve Force units; both were laid down 2-4-86 but not delivered until late 1987.

Atlantic Fleet units are assigned to Amphibious Craft Unit 2 (ACU-2), Little Creek, Va.; Pacific Fleet units to ACU-1 and ACU-3, Coronado, Calif., except LCU 1665, which is assigned to Fleet Activities, Sasebo, Japan, and LCU 1680 and LCU 1681, which are assigned to Naval Reserve Force training.

Twelve of these extremely useful craft were rehabilitated, beginning with two under FY 87; the others were to have been discarded by the mid-1990s but remain in service. LCU 1641 acts as an exercise minelayer with a single mine rail over the stern, an enlarged pilothouse, and a derrick to port. Three others (LCU 1621, 1623, and 1628) have been designated as ASDV (Auxiliary Swimmer Delivery Vehicle; see under [LSDV] carriers. LCU 1647 is a workboat assigned to the Naval Air Warfare Center, Aircraft Division, and operates from Fort Lauderdale, Fla.; see under [YAGE].

Disposals: LCU 1613, formerly used as a workboat at Port Hueneme, Calif., was stricken and sold in 1-93. LCU 1652 was scrapped at San Diego between 3-98 and mid-4-98 after grounding on San Clemente Island early in 2-98. LCU 1614 was stricken during 2001. Other missing numbers have either been redesignated as yard craft (see under [YFU]) or transferred to the U.S. Army (LCU 1667–1679).

Hull systems: Cargo capacity: 180 tons; cargo space: 36.9 × 7.62 m max. (4.5-m-wide bow ramp). Are usually unarmed. Up to 400 troops can be accommodated for short periods on deck. Drive-through feature permits marrying the bow and stern to other landing craft or causeways. Minor differences developed as construction progressed. Have a kedging anchor on the starboard side aft to assist in extraction from beaches.

♦ 1 ex-U.S. Army LCU 1466 class

Bldr: Kewaunee SB (In serv. 1954)

LCU 1590 (ex-*Spotsylvania*)

LCU 1590 H&L Van Ginderen, 10-00

D: 180 tons light (347 fl) **S:** 8 kts **Dim:** 35.08 × 10.36 × 1.60 (aft)
M: 3 G.M. Gray Marine 64 YTL diesels; 3 props; 675 bhp **Electric:** 40 kw tot.
Range: 1,200/6 (700/7 loaded) **Fuel:** 11 tons **Crew:** 11 tot.

Remarks: Transferred from the army in 1992 and now used by Mobile Diving and Salvage Unit 2 as a diving tender and support craft. Can carry 150 tons of cargo or 300 troops on the 15.8 × 9.0–m deck, with a 4.3-m-wide bow ramp. Sister LCU 1486, retained when built for the navy, became YFU 50 and was again redesignated in 1985 as a workboat, 119WB8501.

MINOR LANDING CRAFT

♦ 16 LCM(8) Mk 4– and Mk 6–class aluminum-hulled [LCM]

(In serv. 1967–79)

D: 107 tons (fl) **S:** 12 kts **Dim:** 22.70 × 6.43 × 1.17 (fwd; 1.30 aft)
M: 2 G.M. Detroit 12V-71 diesels; 2 props; 1,080 bhp
Range: 150/12 **Crew:** 4–5 enlisted

Remarks: Can carry up to 80 tons of cargo or 200 troops in its 12.8 × 5.2–m, 66.3-m^2 cargo well. Seventeen new aluminum-hulled Mk 6 versions were purchased with surplus FY 90/91 funds.

♦ 62 LCM(8) Mk 3– and Mk 5–class steel-hulled [LCM]

Bldr: Higgins Industries, New Orleans (In serv. 1953–55, 1985–88, 1991–92)

LCM(8) Mk 3 C200620 George R. Schneider, 8-98

D: 34 tons light (121 fl) **S:** 9 kts **Dim:** 22.43 × 6.43 × 1.35 (fwd; 1.47 aft)
M: 4 G.M. Detroit Diesel 6-71N or 2 12V-71 diesels; 2 props; 1,080 bhp
Range: 190/9 (loaded) **Crew:** 4–5 enlisted

MINOR LANDING CRAFT *(continued)*

Remarks: Can carry 60 tons of cargo or 150 troops for short distances in the 12.8 × 4.3–m, 54.6-m^2 open well. Some have two G.M. 12V71 diesels. Ten Mk 5, with two G.M. 8V92 diesels, were ordered 2-3-90 from Swiftships, and 10 more in 1991. Most Mk 3s are rebuilt Mk 1s. Some 34 of the steel-hulled Mk 3 class were rehabilitated under FY 92 and 93. In addition to the above units, 14 Mk 2 and Mk 4 and 19 Mk 1 and Mk 3 variants remain in service from among others modified for service craft duties. One was donated to Venezuela during 4-99. The U.S. Army operates 94 LCM(8) Mk 1.

Disposal note: All remaining LCM(6) Mk 2 and Mk 3 landing craft have either been discarded or adapted for workboat duties and are no longer attached to amphibious warfare units. All remaining LCM(3) Mk 3 landing craft remaining in service are configured as workboats and are described in the workboat section.

♦ 3 LCVP Mk 7 class [LCVP] (In serv. 1966–69)

D: 13 tons (fl) **S:** 9 kts **Dim:** 10.90 × 3.21 × 1.04 (aft)
M: 1 Gray Marine 64HN9 diesel; 1 prop; 225 bhp **Range:** 110/9

Remarks: GRP hulls. Can carry 36 troops or 3.5 tons of cargo. Cargo deck measures 5.24 × 2.29 m, with a 2.00-m-wide access through the bow ramp. Are being phased out. One other is on display.

♦ 7 LCPL FY 92 class [LCP]
Bldr: Peterson Bldrs, Sturgeon Bay, Wis. (In serv. 1993 to 5-94)

D: 9 tons light (9.5 fl) **S:** 21 kts **Dim:** 10.95 × 3.67 × 1.10
Electronics: Radar: 1 . . . nav.
M: 1 G.M. 6V92 TA diesel; 1 prop; 455 bhp **Range:** 150/19
Fuel: 630 liters **Crew:** 3 tot. + 17 passengers

Remarks: Ordered 26-10-92. Single-skin GRP and vinylester plastic construction. Have an open cockpit forward rather than the deck found on earlier LCPLs. Have 24-V dc electrical power.

♦ 84 LCPL Mk 11, Mk 12, and Mk 13 classes [LCP]

LCPL Mk 12–class 36PL8032 George R. Schneider, 10-00

D: 9.75 tons light (13 fl) **S:** 19 kts **Dim:** 10.98 (9.26 pp) × 3.97 × 1.13
Electronics: Radar: 1 SPS-59 (Canadian Marconi LN-66) nav.
M: 1 G.M. 8V71 TI diesel; 1 prop; 350–425 bhp **Range:** 150/19
Fuel: 630 liters **Crew:** 3 tot. + 17 passengers

Remarks: GRP construction. For use as control craft or to carry Explosive Ordnance Disposal swimmers, but can also carry 2 tons of cargo or be fitted with a 12.7-mm mg for patrol duties. Are carried aboard LHA, LPD, LSD, LST, and similar classes. The total includes 75 LCPL Mk 12 ordered from Watercraft America, Edgewater, Fla., 30-6-83, delivered from 8-84 to 9-85. Earlier Mk 12s were delivered from 9-81 to 4-84. Eight LCPL Mk 13 class (36PL9001 through 36PL9008) were ordered in 1989 from Bollinger Boat, Lockport, La., and delivered 17-10-90 through 20-3-91.

♦ 1 steel-hulled LCPL Mk 4 class [LCP]

Remarks: Data similar to the LCPL Mk 11–13 classes (q.v.). Assigned to a shore facility.

♦ 60 Joint Modular Lighter System cargo lighters [LCU]
Bldr: Baltimore Marine Industries, Baltimore (In serv. 1-00 to 4-00)

Joint Modular Lighter System cargo lighter Kurt Greiner/SeaPhoto, 6-00

D: . . . tons **S:** . . . kts **Dim:** 12.19 × 2.44 × . . .
M: 4 units only: 1 Cummins QSK19 6-cyl. diesel; 1 Omega waterjet; 760 bhp

Remarks: Four powered and 56 unpowered cargo modules were ordered at the behest of the Navy SeaBee Logistics Center in 1999, with each module sized to that of a standard 40 × 8 × 8–ft. international cargo container to permit stowage aboard strategic sealift ships; the power plants are contained in a 10.67 × 2.13 × 1.22–m module within each powered unit. The Omega waterjet system employs four exhaust ducts to provide both propulsion and steering. The lighters are operable in up to Sea State 3 and are used to move cargo ashore when a port is unavailable or damaged.

♦ 21 side-loading warping tugs
Bldr: Oregon Iron Works, Klackamas, Ore. (In serv. 1994 to 1-96)

Side-loading warping tug 5LWT04-064—of the 1994 series George R. Schneider, 5-99

D: 100 tons (light) **S:** 5 kts **Dim:** 24.38 × 6.71 × . . .
M: 2 G.M. Detroit Diesel 6V92 diesels; 2 azimuthal waterjets; 860 bhp
Fuel: 650 gallons

Remarks: Intended for use by Rapid Deployment Force vehicle cargo ships. Each unit consists of 36 sections that can be disassembled for ease of shipping. A small pilothouse module is fitted to starboard, with hydraulic, electric, and manual steering possible. Are in two versions: 16 self-powered causeways and five side-loadable warping tugs, with the latter having a hinged A-frame at the bow for anchor handling.

♦ 3 side-loading warping tugs
Bldr: PACECO, Gulfport, Miss. (In serv. 1989)

SLWT 4013 SLWT 4014 SLWT 4015

SLWT 4014 George R. Schneider, 9-94

Remarks: No data available, but probably similar to LWT 1. The original SLWT 1–5 were stricken in 1989. SLWT 4013 and 4014 are located at San Diego and SLWT 4015 at Port Hueneme, Calif. PACECO also built eight self-propelled causeway sections and eight non-self-propelled sections during 1989.

♦ 1 LWT 1–class amphibious warfare warping tug
Bldr: Campbell Machine Works, San Diego (In serv. 4-70)

85WT681 LWT 1

D: 61 tons light **S:** 9 kts **Dim:** 25.9 × 6.7 × 2.1
M: 2 G.M. 8V71 diesels; 2 steerable props; 420 bhp **Crew:** 6 tot.

Remarks: Aluminum construction, intended for handling causeway sections and ship-to-beach fuel lines. Series production was not pursued, and sister 85WT682 was discarded during the early 1990s.

SPECIAL WARFARE CRAFT

♦ 20 Mk V Pegasus-class Special Operations Craft [LCW]
Bldr: Trinity-Equitable SY, New Orleans (In serv.: first pair: 27-8-95; second pair: 1-96; third pair: 8-96; last: 1999)

MKVSOC9. . . series

Special Operations Craft MKVSOC964 Dieter Wolf, 6-01

SPECIAL WARFARE CRAFT *(continued)*

Special Operations Craft MKVSOC964—note stern ramp Peter Voss, 5-01

D: 57 tons (68 fl) **S:** 50+ kts (30 sust.) **Dim:** 24.99 × 5.33 × 1.32
A: 2–4 twin 12.7-mm M2-HB mg; 2 single 7.62-mm M60 mg; 2 single 40-mm Mk 19 Mod. 3 grenade launchers
Electronics: Radar: 1 Furuno . . . nav.
M: 2 MTU 16V396 TE94 diesels; 2 KaMeWa K50S waterjets; 4,570 bhp
Electric: 50 kw tot. (2 × 25-kw diesel sets) **Range:** 500/50; 550/35
Fuel: . . . tons (2,600 gallons) **Crew:** 5 tot. + 16 special forces personnel

Remarks: Two since-discarded prototypes, to two different designs, were ordered in 8-93 from Halter Marine for $4.7 million each, including land/air transportation skids. Initial production of two standard units, with an option for 38 additional, was ordered in 9-94; the $11 million contract included one transportation support suite for each craft. Six near-sisters were built for Sri Lanka in 1996–97. Six are assigned to Special Boat Unit 2 (SBU-2) at Little Creek, Va.; 12 to SBU-1 at Coronado, Calif.; and two (numbered 25MPB0001 and 25MPB9501) to the Naval Surface Warfare Center, Carderock Division Detachment, Norfolk.
Hull systems: Aluminum construction. The craft on its transport trailer (with M916A1Ea prime mover vehicle) fits within an Air Force C-5A Galaxy transport. Each boat can launch and retrieve four inflated rubber raiding craft and can also carry a 500-gallon fuel bladder. The open cockpit can be covered by removable hard canopies. All seating is shock mounted. The hull is designed for minimum radar and heat signature. Hull molded depth is 2.36 m. Can tow two 9.14-m rigid inflatable raider boats at 50 kts and can operate in Sea State 3 at 35 kts. A 220-gallon/day potable water generator is fitted.
Combat systems: Communications equipment includes two SATCOM receivers. Have an APX-100(V) IFF transponder. The navigation suite includes a Magnavox MX200 NAVSAT receiver, GPS receiver, Raytheon echo sounder, and chart plotter. Have five weapons-mounting positions, each suitable for 40-mm grenade launchers, twin 12.7-mm mg, or 7.62-mm mg. Can also carry Stinger SAMs.

♦ 32 Stinger-class riverine assault craft [LCW]
Bldrs: first 14: SeaArk Marine, Monticello, Ark. (In serv.: 7 in 31-7-90, 7 in 1991); others: Swiftships, Morgan City, La. (In serv. 1994)

Stinger class SeaArk Marine, 1990

D: 7.48 tons (fl) **S:** 38 kts (34.6 sust.) **Dim:** 10.64 × 2.82 × 0.66 (loaded)
A: 2 single 12.7-mm M2 mg; 2 single 7.62-mm M60 mg (see remarks)
Electronics: Radar: 1 Raytheon SPS-69 Pathfinder nav.
M: 2 Cummins BTA5.9M2 diesels; 1 Hamilton 271 waterjet; 600 bhp
Range: . . ./. . . **Fuel:** 567 liters **Crew:** 4 tot. + 10 troops

Remarks: First seven were ordered 5-5-90 as replacements for PBR-type riverine patrol craft for use by Special Boat Units; a second "company" of seven was in service by 6-92. A second contract was let under FY 92 to Swiftships for 10, followed by an order for another eight under FY 93. All are based at Camp Lejeune, N.C. Aluminum construction with $\frac{3}{16}$-in. plating. Have weapons positions fore and aft that are convertible for twin or single 12.7-mm mg or a single Mk 19 40-mm grenade launcher. Can be carried by a C-130 Hercules aircraft.

Note: Plans call for procuring 30–40 Special Operations Craft, Riverine (SOC-R) craft to replace the Mini-ATC, Sea Spectre Mk IV, 20 Light Counter Drug Patrol Boats (Boston Whalers), and the five PBRs assigned to SEAL Special Boat Squadrons. The craft were to have a range of 170 n.m. The four Mk 64 Mod. 4 multipurpose weapons mounts would accommodate Mk 19 40-mm grenade launchers, 12.7-mm mg, or 7.62-mm M60 mg, and an additional M60 would be mountable at the bow. Stinger surface-to-air missiles are to be carried. The craft are to accommodate four CRRC (Combat Rubber Raiding Craft), launched or retrieved via a stern ramp while under way. Procurement was to begin under FY 98, but no contracts have been announced.

♦ 72 Navy Special Warfare RIB raiding craft [LCW]
Bldr: United States Marine, New Orleans (In serv. 15-11-97 to 2001)

11MRIBAAOO-1 through 11MRIBAAOO-72

11MRIB-series 36-ft. SEAL raiding craft George R. Schneider, 7-00

D: 8.24 tons (fl) **S:** 45+ kts (33 sust.) **Dim:** 10.97 × 3.20 × 0.91 (max.)
A: 1 or 2 single 12.7-mm mg; 0 or 1 40-mm Mk 19 Mod. 3 grenade launcher; 1 or 2 single 7.62-mm mg
Electronics: 1 Furuno 841 nav.
M: 2 Puckett-Caterpillar 3126 turbocharged diesels; 2 KaMeWa FF280 waterjets; 940 bhp
Range: 200/33 **Fuel:** 180 gal. **Crew:** 3 tot. + 8 special forces personnel

Remarks: A development contract was placed in 6-96 for a prototype of a new generation of 35-ft. rigid inflatable landing craft for use by SEALs. The three prototypes began a 170-day competitive trials period on 25-11-96 at MacDill Air Force Base (Tampa Bay), Fla. A total of 72 production versions were procured under the FY 97–00 budgets. The first two production units were delivered to Special Boat Unit 20, Norfolk, 15-11-97.
Hull systems: Have Kevlar-reinforced vinylester deep-vee hull with rigid inflatable nylon-reinforced neoprene sponsons. As an alternative to personnel, the craft can carry 1.45 metric tons of cargo. Can carry two outboard motors for Combat Rigid Raiding Craft. Navigation equipment includes a Furuno 1600 echo sounder, PSN-11 GPS receiver, and Ritchie magnetic compass. Payload is 3,200 lb. (1,451 kg). Are not air droppable. One spare engine for every two boats was delivered as part of the production package.
Combat systems: Standard armament is a 12.7-mm mg forward and either a 40-mm grenade launcher or a second 12.7-mm mg aft; the 7.62-mm mg are usually also carried.

♦ 18 Interim Rigid Inflatable Boats (IRIB) [LCW]
Bldr: Novamarine and Bollinger Machine Shop & SY, Lockport, La. (In serv. 1992–93)

10MRB- series

Novamarine Interim Rigid Inflatable Boat George R. Schneider, 8-96

Bollinger Interim Rigid Inflatable Boat 10MRB9307 George R. Schneider, 6-98

D: . . . tons (fl) **S:** 30+ kts **Dim:** 9.14 × 2.74 × 0.61
A: 1 7.62-mm mg or 40-mm Mk 19 Mod. 3 grenade launcher
Electronics: 1 Furuno 1731 nav.
M: 2 Iveco diesels; 2 Parker waterjets; 600 bhp
Range: . . ./. . . **Crew:** 2 tot. + 8 special forces personnel

Remarks: The 1992 order for 18 9-m rigid inflatable raiding craft with Novamarine was canceled when the contractor went bankrupt; a replacement contract with Bollinger Machine Ship and Shipyard in 2-93 produced a prototype that had too lit-

SPECIAL WARFARE CRAFT *(continued)*

tle freeboard, and the program was canceled after 16 were built. Have fiberglass gel-coated hulls with Hypalon-coated nylon inflated sponsons and are air droppable. Can operate in Sea State 4 and survive in Sea State 5. Are equipped with a Ritchie magnetic compass and PSN-11 GPS receiver.

Note: At present, the SEALs employ some 50–54 24-ft. RIBs (in two different models, each capable of transporting four special forces personnel) and 18 10-m RIBs in addition to the classes described above. In 1-98, Zodiac North America, Stevensville, Md., won a contract to supply a large number of its F 470 rigid inflatable boats, in part for special forces work; the craft are 4.57 m long and are powered by two 35-bhp or one 55-bhp Johnson MARS ASML35D submersible gasoline outboard.

24RX-series rigid inflatable Special Operations Craft George R. Schneider, 8-98

A small SEAL Rubber Raiding Craft of the type carried aboard the Mk V Pegasus class George R. Schneider, 8-99

♦ 0 (+ 75) Small Unit Riverine Craft (SURC) Program [LCP]
Bldr: . . .

D: . . . tons **S:** 30–35 kts (loaded) **Dim:** . . . × . . . × 0.61
A: 1 or 2 12.7-mm and/or 7.62-mm mg **M:** . . .
Crew: 2 tot. + 18 Marines

Remarks: Program was begun in 1-01 as a replacement for the Marine Rigid Raider craft. To be capable of lift by a CH-53D helicopter and carriage on its trailer within a C-130 transport. Will be beachable and will have GPS and Combat Net SATCOM equipment. Developmental testing is to take place in FY 02, with operational testing and a production contract to follow in FY 03. The winning design is expected to be an adaptation of an existing commercial design.

♦ 122 Marine Rigid Raider craft [LCW]
Bldr: Boston Whaler, Rockland, Mass. (In serv. 1988)

Marine Rigid Raider class U.S. DoD, 1998

D: 1.2 tons (fl) **S:** 35 kts **Dim:** 6.81 × 2.26 × 0.46
A: 1 7.62-mm mg **M:** 2 outboard motors; 140 bhp
Range: 136/32 **Fuel:** 212 liters **Crew:** 1 coxswain, 9–10 assault troops

Remarks: For U.S. Marine Expeditionary Unit (MEU) use. GRP construction. Are road transportable on a special "combat trailer." Replace older Zodiac rigid inflatable craft. Each MEU has 15.

♦ . . . inflatable Combat Rubber Reconnaissance Craft (CRRC) [LCW]
Bldr: . . . (In serv. 1990s)

D: 120 kg empty **S:** . . . kts **Dim:** 4.70 × 1.90 × . . .
M: 2 I-MARS Kort-nozzle gasoline outboards; 70 bhp

Remarks: As of 1-95, 407 served the active Marine Corps and another 27 were used by reservists. Intended for riverine, raiding, and reconnaissance duties. "I-MARS" stands for "Improved Military Amphibious Reconnaissance System," and the engines are specially shielded to reduce noise and heat signatures. Cost $10,700 each.

Disposal note: The remaining three High Speed Boats (HSB) were stricken in 2001 and made available for sale.

♦ 5 PBR (Patrol Boat, Riverine) Mk II [LCW]
Bldr: Uniflite, Bellingham, Wash. (In serv. 12-81 to 8-83)

D: 8.9 tons (fl) **S:** 24 kts **Dim:** 9.73 × 3.53 × 0.81
A: 1 twin and 1 single 12.7-mm mg; 1 60-mm mortar
Electronics: Radar: 1 Raytheon 1900 Pathfinder (SPS-66) nav.
M: 2 G.M. 6V53N diesels; 2 Jacuzzi waterjets; 420 bhp
Range: 150/23 **Crew:** 4 tot.

Remarks: Have a GRP hull and plastic armor. Used for naval reserve training by Special Boat Unit 22. Three others are museum displays.

♦ 3 Auxiliary Swimmer Delivery Vehicle carriers [LCW]
Bldr: Southern SB, Slidell, La. (In serv. 1960–68)

ASDV 1 (ex-LCU 1621) ASDV 3 (ex-LCU 1628)
ASDV 2 (ex-LCU 1623)

ASDV 1 H&L Van Ginderen, 8-99

ASDV 3 H&L Van Ginderen, 7-96

D: approx. 210 tons (390 fl) **S:** 11 kts **Dim:** 41.07 × 9.07 × 2.08 (max.)
A: none **Electronics:** 1 Raytheon SPS-69 Pathfinder nav.
M: 4 G.M. 6-71 diesels; 2 Kort-nozzle (vertical cycloidal on ASDV 1) props; 1,200 bhp
Range: 1,200/11 **Fuel:** 13 tons **Crew:** 10–14 tot

Remarks: Two are assigned to Little Creek, Va., and one to Coronado, Calif. Converted to train combat swimmers and to handle and service their equipment. ASDV 1 and 2 have a large superstructure built on the former vehicle deck, carry a decompression chamber, and have a large crane on the port quarter; ASDV 3 retains the basic LCU configuration.

SWIMMER DELIVERY VEHICLES [LSDV]

♦ 1 (+ 3 + 2) Advanced SEAL Delivery System (ASDS) class
Bldr: Northrop Grumman Oceanic Systems, Annapolis, Md. (In serv. 24-8-01 to . . .)

ASDS 1

D: 55 tons surf./60 tons sub. **S:** 8 kts sub. **Dim:** 19.81 × 2.44 × . . .
Electronics: Sonar: . . . HF
M: 14 batteries, 1 electric motor; 1 prop—eight electric thrusters
Range: 125/8 sub. **Crew:** 2 tot. + 8 special forces swimmers

Remarks: The prototype new ASDS (Advanced SEAL Delivery System)—formerly the ASDV (Advanced SEAL Delivery Vehicle)—was ordered from Westinghouse Electric Oceanic Division (now Northrop Grumman Oceanic Systems) on 29-9-94 for $69.8 million. The craft was supposed to have been delivered in 8-97, but by 5-98, the program cost had risen to $169.6 million and the craft was not to be ready until mid-1999; the actual final delivery was four years late. Follow-on craft are expected to cost $58.8 million (up from $30 million in 1994). A second craft is planned to be ordered under the FY 03 budget, with further units to be ordered one each year under the FY 05, 07, 09, and 11 budgets. The craft are to mate via their underside hatch to SSN 688–class submarines, of which the first, the *Greeneville* (SSN 772), was under conversion in 1998; five other SSN 688s, including the *Charlotte* (SSN 766), will be able to carry an ASDV, while the *Jimmy Carter* (SSN 23) and the first six *Virginia*-

SWIMMER DELIVERY VEHICLES [LSDV] *(continued)*

ASDS 1—on travel trailer U.S. DoD, 2001

ASDS 1—running in surface trim U.S. DoD, 2001

class SSNs are also planned to have the capability. The first ASDS 1, delivered for trials in 5-00, is operated by SEAL Delivery Team 1 (SDCT-1), Pearl Harbor, Hawaii, with the chartered *C/Commando* as tender. The crew consists of a submarine officer as pilot and a SEAL as copilot.
Hull systems: The 14 batteries are carried in individual external titanium cylinders; the batteries are to be replaced with longer-lasting lithium ion batteries. Ballast tanks are fitted within each end of the pressure hull. Top and bottom access hatches are fitted for the swimmer egress trunk amidships. The retractable electric maneuvering thrusters are mounted in an X-configuration fore and aft. The steel pressure hull for the first ASDS was fabricated by Chicago Bridge and Iron, Kankakee, Ill., which has since closed its facility; the source for future hulls has not been identified. Bow and stern fairings are made of composites. Will have an automated life-support system and an integrated control and display system. Two folding masts support communications antennas and a non-hull-penetrating electro-optical periscope.

♦ 10 Mk VIII Mod. 1 Swimmer Delivery Vehicles

SDV Mk VIII *Ships of the World,* 1999

Remarks: Used by Navy SEAL special forces. The 6.70-m-long craft can be accommodated in the Dry Deck Shelters carried by SSNs and can carry four swimmers, as well as mines and other weapons. The swimmers are not carried within a dry pressure hull. Ten of the craft began a life-extension refit program at Panama City, Fla., in 1995 and are being equipped with increased range and speed, improved sonar, and improved instrumentation. Three were transferred to the U.K. during 1999, and another has been retired.

♦ 3 (+ 10 + 1,200) Advanced Amphibious Assault Vehicles (AAAV)
Bldr: General Dynamics Land Systems, Woodbridge, Va. (In serv. 6-99 to 2012)

Weight: 27,943 kg empty; 32,166 kg max. **S:** 25–29 kts afloat, 45 mph ashore
Dim: 11.84 (max. afloat; 8.97 on land) × 4.46 × 2.83 (high, in afloat mode; 3.65 high from tracks to turret top)
A: 1 30-mm Bushmaster Mk 44 cannon with coaxial 7.62-mm M240 mg
M: 1 MTU MT883 K-523 diesel; twin tracks in land mode (850 bhp max.) or two waterjets (2,700 bhp max.)
Range: 70/20–25 afloat; 400 stat. mi./45 mph ashore **Fuel:** 372 gal.
Crew: 3 tot. + 17 troops

Remarks: Due to reliability problems with the prototype, the first 15 are now scheduled to enter service late in 2007, a two-year delay over plans announced in 2000; some 1,013 (down from 1,123) total are planned to be procured (including 78 configured as command vehicles), but the total may be reduced to as few as 330, with

AAAV prototype General Dynamics

refurbished AAV-7s to fill the remainder of the requirement. The General Dynamics design won a contract during 6-96 for three prototypes (one in command configuration) for $200 million; the initial prototype was delivered in 6-99 and the other two by end-2001. Ten preproduction vehicles were ordered in 7-01. Series production is now to commence in 2006, with final deliveries in 2016–17.
Hull systems: Afloat, the tracks retract and are covered by plating, while a bow flap is extended and the waterjets are deployed. Can carry 2,326 kg of cargo in lieu of troops. Have armor protection against 14-mm mg projectiles and fragments from 155-mm artillery. Full climate control and NBC protection are provided. Hull has 27% reserve buoyancy and can recover from a 110° roll. The prototype achieved 37 kts on trials in light condition. Survivability improvements were to be developed starting during FY 02.
Combat systems: Will carry 200 ready-service and 400 stowed rounds of 30-mm and 800 ready-service and 1,600 stowed rounds of 7.62-mm ammunition.

Note: Marine Corps AAV-7A1-series armored tracked vehicles available for amphibious assault include 853 LVTP-7 and 294 LVTP-7A1 personnel carriers, 77 LVTC-7 and 29 LVTC-7A command vehicles, and 54 LVTR-7 and 10 LVTR-7A recovery vehicles. The "7A-" series vehicles were built during 1983–85, while the earlier units were extensively overhauled and modernized during the 1980s.

LVTP-7A1 armored amphibious personnel carrier AVTB, 1998

AUXILIARIES

Note: As of 1-02, the U.S. Navy had only 15 active auxiliaries crewed with uniformed personnel; all other auxiliaries are operated by the Military Sealift Command (MSC) with either civil service or contractor personnel. For this edition, the Auxiliaries section includes regular navy–subordinated (active and reserve) ships, navy-chartered ships, research ships operated by private and public research facilities that were built with navy funding, and ships operated by or long-term chartered by the MSC. MSC-subordinated units, both chartered and navy "owned," usually have hull numbers prefixed by "T-." The four-digit hull numbers given in parentheses for some ships have been assigned by the MSC for administrative purposes and are not true U.S. Navy hull numbers; some long-term chartered units do not have any number assigned at all.

As of 17-3-01, the MSC had 7,508 personnel assigned: 150 active duty U.S. Navy officers and 880 enlisted, 3,388 civil service mariners (847 licensed, 5,541 unlicensed), 1,848 contract commercial mariners, 1,242 civilian shore staff, and 1,075 selected reserves. MSC-subordinated military cargo and vehicle prepositioning ships are organized into three Maritime Prepositioning Squadrons (MPS): MPS-1, based in the Mediterranean; MPS-2, based at Diego Garcia; and MPS-3, based near Saipan.

Maritime Administration (MARAD) Ready Reserve Force (RRF) ships activated for service with prepositioning squadrons remain listed in the Ready Reserve Force section; when they are activated, however, they are administered by the MSC rather than MARAD. As of late 2001, the activated RRF ships were the crane ship *Gopher State* (T-ACS 4, serving with MPS-3); cargo ship *Cape Jacob* (T-AK 5029, with MPS-2); and tankers *Chesapeake* (T-AOT 5084, with MPS-2) and *Petersburg* (T-AOT 9101, with MPS-3). In addition, MSC *Henry J. Kaiser*–class oiler *Henry J. Kaiser* (T-AO 187) was assigned to MPS-2.

The MSC also charters ships for single-voyage deliveries, as well as managing the shipment of all military cargo by sea by means of contracts with established U.S.-flag shipping lines. MSC-chartered harbor tugs are listed in the Service Craft section.

AUXILIARIES *(continued)*

The MSC chartered two AS.330J Puma helicopters and their crews for Mediterranean service from Geo-Seis Helicopters, Ft. Collins, Colo., on 26-10-99 for three years, with a two-year extension option. The aircraft began operations 8-2-00 with the *Sirius* (T-AFS 8).

♦ 0 (+ 3 + 9) Lewis and Clark–class "Auxiliary Dry Cargo Carriers" [AE]

Bldr: General Dynamics National Steel & SB Co. (NASSCO), San Diego

	Laid down	L	In serv.
T-AKE 1 Lewis and Clark	2002	...	2006
T-AKE 2 Sacagawea	2003	...	2006
T-AKE 3	2003	...	2007
T-AKE 4	2004	...	2008
T-AKE 5	2004	...	2008
T-AKE 6	2004	...	2008
T-AKE 7	2005	...	2009
T-AKE 8	2005	...	2009
T-AKE 9	2005	...	2009
T-AKE 10	2006	...	2010
T-AKE 11	2006	...	2010
T-AKE 12	2006	...	2010

D: 23,852 tons light (40,298 fl) **S:** 20 kts (sust.)
Dim: 210.01 (200.47 pp) × 32.20 × 9.12
A: provision for 1 20-mm Mk 15 Block I Phalanx CIWS
Electronics:
Radar: . . .
EW: SLQ-25A(V) Nixie towed torpedo decoy syst.
M: diesel, diesel-electric, gas turbine, or gas turbine–electric; 1 prop; . . . hp
Range: 14,000/20 **Fuel:** 25,000 bbl
Crew: 123 MSC civil service mariners, 49 navy (accomm. for 209 tot.)

Remarks: The Auxiliary Dry Cargo Ship, or ADC(X)1, class, first programmed in 1992, was dropped from the FY 95 budget but reinstated in FY 96. Again deleted from the FY 98–03 shipbuilding program in favor of since-canceled life-extension overhauls to the MSC's *Kilauea* (T-AE 26)-class ammunition ships and *Mars* (AFS 1)-class stores ships, the program was once again revived in the FY 99 budget, and the first was funded under FY 00.

The $406.9 million contract for T-AKE 1 was let 18-10-01, and T-AKE 2 was simultaneously ordered for $301.6 million; options for 10 additional ships were let to NASSCO at the same time, providing a potential $3.7 billion in costs if the entire class of 12 is built. T-AKE 1 was funded under FY 01 and T-AKE 2 under FY 02; one each year is planned under FY 03 and 04, two under FY 05, three under FY 06 (likely to be reduced), and two under FY 07.

The names for the first two were announced 27-10-00, with the class name category stated to be "explorers" in order to convey a nonbelligerent impression—in lieu of providing adequate defensive measures. The cargo capacity is exceedingly small for the size of the ships, which are intended to obtain their cargo fuels from T-AOs in rear areas and then to convey them to ships in a combat zone.

Hull systems: Cargo: 6,675 metric tons (21,181 m^3) dry cargo, 1,716 tons (5,543 m^3) frozen and refrigerated provisions, 3,242 metric tons (23,450 bbl) cargo fuel, and 200 metric tons potable water. Will use current underway replenishment systems but will have improved pre-staging and inventory management, incorporating some 12,788 m^2 of cargo pre-staging space. Replenishment stations will include three stores transfer stations to port and two to starboard, with a sliding padeye receiving station to starboard; will be able to refuel other ships from one station on each beam and to receive fuel to starboard. Two cargo holds will carry dry stores and munitions and one will carry frozen, chilled, and dry stores; three specialty cargo and spares holds will be incorporated, as will specialty cargo spaces on the 01 level. There will be four 4-ton cargo elevators. Four 5-ton cranes will be fitted for cargo loading and unloading alongside a pier or at anchor. Five cargo fuel and two potable water tanks will be incorporated. Will employ computerized inventory, cargo tracking, and planning aids, fiber optics for lighting and interior communications systems, and automation to reduce crew requirement. Hangar space for two UH-46D or MH-60 helicopters will be provided.

♦ 7 Kilauea-class ammunition ships [AE] (3 in *reserve*)

Bldrs: T-AE 26, T-AE 27: Gen. Dynamics, Quincy, Mass.: others: Northrop Grumman Ship Systems, Ingalls Div., Pascagoula, Miss. (*Atlantic/†Pacific Fleet)

	Laid down	L	In serv.
T-AE 26 *Kilauea*	10-3-66	9-8-67	10-8-68
T-AE 27 *Butte*	21-7-66	9-8-67	14-12-68
T-AE 28 *Santa Barbara*	20-12-66	23-1-68	11-7-70
T-AE 32 Flint†	4-8-69	9-11-70	20-11-71
T-AE 33 Shasta†	10-11-69	3-4-71	26-2-72
T-AE 34 Mount Baker*	10-5-70	23-10-71	22-7-72
T-AE 35 Kiska†	4-8-71	11-3-72	16-12-72

Kiska (T-AE 35) Leo Dirkx, 2-00

Kilauea (T-AE 26) Winter & Findler, 9-00

D: 10,073–10,524 tons light (18,444–20,068 fl) (T-AE 26: 11,915 tons light/ 20,169 tons fl)
S: 20 kts **Dim:** 171.90 (164.59 pp) × 24.69 × 8.50 **A:** removed
Electronics:
Radar: 1 . . . nav.; 1 Raytheon SPS-10-series surf. search
TACAN: URN-25
M: 3 sets G.E. geared steam turbines; 1 prop; 36,661 shp
Boilers: 3 Foster-Wheeler; 42.3 kg/cm^2, 467° C **Electric:** 3,000 kw tot.
Fuel: 2,612 tons **Crew:** 125 MSC civil service mariners, 24 navy

Lewis and Clark (T-AKE 1) NASSCO, 2001

AUXILIARIES *(continued)*

Mount Baker (T-AE 34) Carlo Martinelli, 3-00

Remarks: 18,257 grt/8,593 dwt. T-AE 26 transferred to the MSC 1-10-80, T-AE 32 on 4-8-95, T-AE 27 on 3-6-96, T-AE 35 on 1-8-96, T-AE 34 on 18-12-96, and T-AE 33 on 1-8-97. T-AE 28 was transferred to the MSC 1-10-98 but was placed in reduced operating status on 90-day recall at Charleston, S.C., without modification. T-AE 26 was placed in 90-day recall reserve during 10-01 and is stored at Port Hueneme, Calif., with a small caretaker crew. T-AE 27 began a refit at Bethlehem Steel, Sparrows Point, Md., in 8-96 to alter her accommodations and equipment for MSC service but was placed in 90-day reduced operating status at New Orleans when the yard went insolvent. T-AE 34 completed modifications to MSC standards on 29-4-98 and T-AE 35 on 12-10-98. T-AE 33 was towed from San Diego 20-1-99 for conversion to MSC accommodations standard by Norfolk SB & DD Co. at Norfolk; she collided with the *Guadalupe* (T-AO 200) on 26-2-01, off Pt. Loma, Calif. The USN personnel aboard the active units perform ammunition handling and operate the communications systems and helicopters.
Disposals: *Mount Hood* (AE 29) was to transfer to the MSC 3-8-98 but was instead decommissioned and stricken 13-8-99 and transferred to MARAD 17-8-99; the ship was transferred to MARAD "ownership" on 29-11-01 for eventual scrapping.
Hull systems: Can carry about 6,000 tons of munitions and 2,500 tons of cargo fuel. Have a hangar and flight deck for two UH-46D replenishment helicopters. Seven underway replenishment stations are fitted: four to port and three to starboard. Can refuel ships alongside, using the forward starboard station. On T-AE 26, the superstructure is filled in on the starboard side to increase accommodations space; the other active units have had only minor alterations to improve accommodations for their civilian crews.

♦ **3 ex-U.K. Lyness-class combat stores ships [AF]**
Bldrs: Swan Hunter & Wigham Richardson, Wallsend-on-Tyne (Atlantic Fleet)

	Laid down	L	In serv.
T-AFS 8 Sirius (ex-*Lyness*)	4-65	7-4-66	22-12-66
T-AFS 9 Spica (ex-*Tarbatness*)	4-66	22-2-67	10-8-67
T-AFS 10 Saturn (ex-*Stromness*)	10-65	16-9-66	21-3-67

Spica (T-AFS 9) John Mortimer, 4-01

Spica (T-AFS 9)—note twin hangar Douglas A. Cromby, 7-99

Sirius (T-AFS 8) Winter & Findler, 9-98

D: 10,205 tons light (16,680 fl) **S:** 19 kts
Dim: 159.52 (149.35 pp) × 22.0 × 7.92 **A:** none
Electronics: Radar: 2 . . . nav.—TACAN: URN-25
M: 1 Sulzer 8RD76 diesel; 1 prop; 12,700 bhp
Electric: 3,575 kw tot. (5 × 715-kw diesel alternator sets)
Range: 11,000/19; 27,500/12 **Fuel:** 1,310 tons heavy oil, 264 tons diesel
Crew: 107 MSC civil service mariners, 44 navy + 27 navy helo detachment

Remarks: 12,358 grt/4,744 nrt. T-AFS 8 was leased from the U.K. 17-1-81 for one year for use in the Mediterranean and was purchased outright 1-3-82, T-AFS 9 was leased 30-9-81 and purchased 30-9-82, and T-AFS 10 was purchased 13-12-83. T-AFS 10 was modernized under FY 85 with improved helicopter facilities, improved communications, five STREAM transfer stations, an automated data facility, and conversion to use U.S. Navy fuel; T-AFS 8 completed a similar upgrading 1-10-83 and T-AFS 9 by 1986. Are very successful, comfortable ships. T-AFS 9 transferred to Atlantic operations 13-5-01.
Hull systems: Can support 15,000 personnel at sea for one month. Total cargo volume: 12,234 m^3 (8,313 m^3 dry stores, 3,921 m^3 refrigerated/frozen); this equates to some 3,665 metric tons of cargo, including 2,363 tons of provisions and upwards of 40,000 different fleet spare parts items, and an additional 490 tons can be carried on the flight deck and other topside spaces. Have four holds, with 15 levels, and eight stores elevators. Cranes: one 25-ton, two 12.5-ton, one 12-ton, and two 5-ton. The helicopter deck aft measures 33.5 × 18.3 m; they normally carry two UH-46E Sea Knight cargo helicopters. The diesel generators were replaced, the cargo-handling and stowage arrangements upgraded, and an underway refueling station added forward, to port, in all three during 1990s refits.

♦ **5 Mars-class combat stores ships [AF]** (2 in *reserve*)
Bldr: General Dynamics National Steel & SB Co. (NASSCO), San Diego (†Pacific Fleet)

	Laid down	L	In serv.	To MSC
T-AFS 1 *Mars*	5-5-62	15-6-63	21-12-63	1-2-93
T-AFS 3 Niagara Falls†	22-5-65	25-3-66	29-4-67	23-9-94
T-AFS 5 Concord†	26-3-66	17-12-66	27-11-68	15-10-92
T-AFS 6 *San Diego*	11-3-67	13-4-68	24-5-69	11-8-93
T-AFS 7 San Jose†	8-3-69	13-12-69	23-10-70	15-10-93

San Jose (T-AFS 7) Brian Morrison, 4-01

Concord (T-AFS 5) H&L Van Ginderen, 10-00

Concord (T-AFS 5) Takatoshi Okano, 8-00

D: 9,574–9,852 tons light (17,098–17,383 fl) **S:** 20 kts
Dim: 177.08 (161.54 pp) × 24.08 × 7.32 **A:** removed
Electronics:
Radar: 1 Raytheon . . . S-band nav.; 1 Raytheon . . . X-band nav.
TACAN: URN-25
M: 2 sets de Laval (T-AFS 6: Westinghouse) geared steam turbines; 1 prop; 22,000 shp
Boilers: 3 Babcock & Wilcox; 40.8 kg/cm^2, 440° C
Electric: 4,800 kw tot. **Range:** 10,000/20; 18,000/11
Crew: 124 MSC civil service mariners, 49 navy (5 officers, 44 enlisted)

Remarks: Class authorizations: one in FY 61, one in FY 62, one in FY 64, two in FY 65, one in FY 66, and one in FY 67. T-AFS 6 has been in Category B mobilization reserve since 14-12-97. T-AFS 1 was in 30-day recall layup at Oakland, Calif., at the beginning of 1997 but was placed in Category B mobilization reserve 19-2-97 and towed to Pearl Harbor for storage during 2-98. Are to be replaced by the new T-AKE class. T-AFS 5 transferred to Pacific operations 13-5-01.

AUXILIARIES *(continued)*

Disposals: *Sylvania* (AFS 2) was stricken 5-1-95, stored in the James River 12-9-00 for transfer to MARAD, and sold for scrap 28-7-01. The last *Mars*-class combat stores ship in regular navy service, the *White Plains* (AFS 4), was decommissioned 17-4-95 and stricken 24-8-95.
Hull systems: Cargo: 16,597 m^3 total stores volume. Have four M-shaped cargo king-posts with constant-tension equipment; the equipment can transfer cargo from the supply ship to the receiving ship in 90 seconds. The five holds (Nos. 1 and 5 for spare parts, 2 for aviation parts, and 3 and 4 for provisions) have only two hatches. Eleven 5.5-ton cargo elevators link the decks; several others feed into the helicopter area. There are four refrigerated cargo compartments and three for the storage of dried provisions. One boiler is always kept in reserve. Conversion for MSC service entailed adding five cargo elevators, adding permanent ballast to compensate for some 23 tons of removed topweight, greatly upgrading the accommodations (to place all civilian officers in one-person staterooms and all unlicensed personnel in two-person staterooms), rehabilitating the propulsion plants, and greatly revising the composition and number of different stores types carried for transfer.
Combat systems: Removed prior to transfer to the MSC were the SPS-40 air-search radar, Mk 56 fire-control directors, two twin 76.2-mm gunmounts, two 20-mm Mk 15 CIWS, SLQ-32(V)1 intercept equipment, Mk 36 SRBOC decoy launching system, and SLQ-25 Nixie towed torpedo decoy system. Have a helicopter platform and hangar for two UH-46D Sea Knights.

♦ 1 chartered special warfare submersible support ship [AG]
Bldr: North American SB, Larose, La. (In serv. 5-97)

C/COMMANDO

C/Commando—with red-orange hull, cream upperworks — Ralph Edwards, 9-01

D: 3,773 tons (fl) **S:** 12 kts **Dim:** 67.05 × 17.06 × 5.71
M: 2 Caterpillar 3516 DITA 16-cyl. diesels; 2 CP props; 3,420 bhp—bow-thruster
Electric: 900 kw (3 × 300-kw sets)

Remarks: 2,053 grt/2,206 dwt. Former offshore tug/supply vessel, chartered 19-1-00 from Edison Chouest Offshore, Galliano, La., for $55.7 million to serve as the support ship for the Naval Special Warfare Command Advanced SEAL Delivery System (ASDS) submersible (see under [LSDV]). Has been based at Pearl Harbor since 3-01.

♦ 1 Waters-class special mission ship [AG]
Bldr: Northrop Grumman Avondale (formerly Avondale SY), New Orleans

	Laid down	L	In serv.
T-AGS 45 WATERS	21-5-91	6-6-92	26-5-93

Waters (T-AGS 45) — French Navy, 11-00

D: 7,320 tons light (12,208 fl) **S:** 13.2 kts (12 sust.)
Dim: 138.7 (130.6 wl) × 21.0 × 6.40
Electronics:
Radar: 1 Raytheon X-band ARPA nav.; 1 Raytheon S-band ARPA nav.
Sonar: G.E. Sea Beam 853E mapping
M: electric drive: 5 G.M. EMD 16-cyl. diesels, 5 2,500-kw generators, 2 Westinghouse motors; 2 props; 7,400 shp (6,800 sust.)—4 1,200-shp electric tunnel-thrusters
Electric: ship's service from propulsion generators + 365-kw emergency diesel set
Range: 6,500/12 + 30 days on station **Fuel:** 2,000 tons **Endurance:** 60 days
Crew: 37 officer and 52 unlicensed MSC civil service mariners, 6 navy (enlisted)

Remarks: Authorized under FY 90; ordered 4-4-90. Sponsorship for the vessel was transferred to the Director of Strategic Systems Programs during 1-97, and the ship was refitted from 4-98 to 10-98 to conduct submarine navigation system testing and ballistic-missile flight test support services; the type-designation and hull number, however, were not changed. Was originally intended to conduct hydrographic and oceanographic surveys in support of the Integrated Undersea Surveillance System and was capable of general oceanographic, bathymetric, and hydrographic survey work. Has a centerline moonpool for the launch and recovery of a remotely operated vehicle (ROV). Named for Rear Adm. Odale Waters, Jr. (1910–1986), oceanographer of the navy from 1965 to 1970.

♦ 1 Hayes-class sound trials ship [AG]
Bldr: Todd SY, Seattle

	Laid down	L	In serv.
T-AG 195 HAYES (ex-T-AGOR 16)	12-11-69	2-7-70	21-7-71

Hayes (T-AG 195) — John Gourley, 3-01

D: 2,329 tons light (4,521 fl) **S:** 12 kts (11 sust.)
Dim: 75.10 (67.06 pp) × 22.86 × 6.68
Electronics:
Radar: 1 Raytheon TM 1650/6X nav.; 1 Raytheon TM 1660/12S nav.
Sonar: TUMS towed sound-measurement array
M: diesel-electric drive: 3 Caterpillar 3516 diesels (1,410 bhp each), 3 Kato 1,100-kw alternators, 2 Westinghouse motors; 2 props; 2,400 shp—2 165-shp low-speed motors
Electric: 640 kw tot. (2 × 320 kw, Caterpillar 3412 diesels driving)
Range: 6,000/12 **Endurance:** 30 days
Crew: 11 officer and 30 unlicensed MSC civil service mariners + 33 technicians

Remarks: Conducts sound-measuring acoustic surveys in support of the submarine noise-reduction program. Was not a success in her original configuration as an oceanographic research platform, suffering from excessive pitching. Was laid up in 1982 at Bayonne, N.J., until transferred from the oceanographer of the navy to the Naval Ships Research and Development Center (now Carderock Division, Naval Surface Warfare Center) in 1983 awaiting conversion. Was being converted as a sound trials vessel from 8-7-87 to 12-90 by Tacoma Boat, Tacoma, Wash., under FY 86 to replace *Monob One* (YAG 61); the bankruptcy of the conversion yard in 11-90, however, forced the ship to be towed to the Puget Sound Naval Shipyard, Bremerton, Wash., where a new conversion contract was placed 25-3-91 and the work was completed 19-6-92. Based at Port Canaveral, Fla.
Hull systems: Has a catamaran configuration hull, with each hull having a beam of 7.3 m. There is 371.6 m^2 of laboratory space. The original four high-speed diesels driving controllable-pitch props have been replaced by a diesel-electric plant with fixed-pitch props that are cavitation-free to 10 kts. The new propulsion plant is suspended in a vibration-damping compartment above decks, along with the two diesel generator sets.

♦ 1 Austin-class miscellaneous command ship [AGF]
Bldr: Lockheed SB, Seattle (Pacific Fleet)

	Laid down	L	In serv.
AGF 11 CORONADO (ex-LPD 11)	3-5-65	30-7-66	23-5-70

Coronado (AGF 11) — Jim Sanderson, 6-01

AUXILIARIES *(continued)*

Coronado (AGF 11) Findler & Winter, 10-00

D: 11,878 tons (16,405 fl) **S:** 21 kts **Dim:** 173.4 × 25.6 (hull) × 7.2
A: 2 single 20-mm Mk 15 Phalanx gatling CIWS; 2 single 12.7-mm mg
Electronics:
Radar: 1 Raytheon SPS-64(V)9 nav.; 1 Raytheon SPS-10F surf. search; 1 Lockheed Martin SPS-40E air search; 2 Mk 90 Phalanx f.c.
TACAN: URN-25
EW: Raytheon SLQ-32(V)1 intercept; WLR-1H intercept; Mk 36 SRBOC decoy syst. (2 6-round Mk 137 RL)
M: 2 sets de Laval geared steam turbines; 2 props; 24,000 shp
Boilers: 2 Foster-Wheeler; 42.3 kg/cm^2, 467° C
Range: 7,700/20 **Crew:** 24 officers, 433 enlisted + 387 staff

Remarks: Authorized under FY 63. Redesignated AGF on 1-10-80. Replaced the *Puget Sound* (AD 38) as flagship of the Sixth Fleet from 8-85 to 6-86, then transferred to the Pacific Fleet and became flagship of the Third Fleet 26-11-86, homeported at San Diego. Was designated the "Sea-Based Battle Lab" in 10-00 and will be used to test new information management equipment and procedures at sea.
Hull systems: During a 1996–97 refit, the forward portion of the docking well was modified with a three-deck, 3,251-m^2 structure with 220 additional crew berthing spaces, a command-and-control center, briefing rooms, computer facilities, a videoteleconferencing area, secure intelligence spaces, a galley, and a news media space. The stern gate to the docking well has been replaced by a permanent bulkhead, and the ship can no longer be flooded down to accept or launch smallcraft.

♦ 1 Raleigh-class auxiliary command ship [AGF]
Bldr: New York NSY, Brooklyn, N.Y. (Atlantic Fleet)

	Laid down	L	In serv.
AGF 3 La Salle (ex-LPD 3)	2-4-62	3-8-63	22-2-64

D: 9,559 tons light (13,634 fl) **S:** 21.6 kts **Dim:** 158.80 (155.4 wl) × 25.60 × 7.00
A: 2 single 25-mm 75-cal. Mk 38 Bushmaster low-angle guns; 2 20-mm Mk 15 Phalanx gatling CIWS; 2 single 12.7-mm mg
Electronics:
Radar: 1 Raytheon SPS-64(V)9 nav.; 1 Raytheon SPS-10F surf. search; 1 Lockheed Martin SPS-40E air search; 2 General Dynamics Mk 90 Phalanx f.c.
TACAN: URN-25
EW: Raytheon SLQ-32(V)1 intercept; Mk 36 SRBOC decoy syst. (4 6-round Mk 137 RL); SLQ-25 towed acoustic torpedo decoy syst.
M: 2 sets de Laval geared steam turbines; 2 props; 24,000 shp
Boilers: 2 Babcock & Wilcox; 42.2 kg/cm^2, 467° C
Electric: 3,600 kw tot. **Range:** 9,600/16; 16,500/10
Crew: 25 officers, 420 enlisted + flag staff: 48 officers, 90 enlisted

La Salle (AGF 3) H&L Van Ginderen, 12-00

Remarks: Authorized under FY 61 as an amphibious ship. Redesignated as a command ship 1-7-72 and employed until 1993 as flagship of the Commander, Middle East Force. Assigned as Sixth Fleet flagship in the Mediterranean in 11-94. Refitted from 5-99 to 10-99 by DCN, Toulon, and at Malta Drydocks from 4-01 to 6-01.
Hull systems: A 14.5 × 5.9–m helicopter hangar is located on the flight deck, to port, with a shelter for ceremonial activities to starboard. During an overhaul at Portsmouth, Va., from 14-5-93 to 5-94, the ship was reboilered, accommodations for women crewmembers were improved, and much of the former well deck was converted into a two-deck-high office complex for Sixth Fleet staff. During the 2001 refit at Malta, the well deck stern door was replaced by welded plating, the remaining large crane was removed, a crane-handled RIB was substituted for the ship's boat, and navigation systems were upgraded with a ring-laser gyro.

♦ 1 Impeccable-class SWATH ocean surveillance ship [AGI]
Bldr: Friede Goldman Halter, Moss Point, Miss.

	Laid down	L	Del	In serv.
T-AGOS 23 Impeccable	21-1-96*	25-4-98	13-10-00	23-3-01

*Original keel-laying 15-3-92

AUXILIARIES *(continued)*

Impeccable (T-AGOS 23) J. & K. Van Raemdonck, 3-01

Impeccable (T-AGOS 23) Leo Dirkx, 9-00

Impeccable (T-AGOS 23)—note torpedo-shaped hull underbodies Leo Dirkx, 10-00

D: 2,809 tons light (5,380 fl) **S:** 15 kts (12 sust.)
Dim: 85.80 (70.71 wl) × 29.20 × 7.92
Electronics:
Radar: . . . nav.
Sonar: SQQ-2 SURTASS LFA towed passive array
M: 3 G.E. Electromotive Division 12-645F8B diesel generator sets (2,000 kw each), 2 Westinghouse electric motors; 2 5-bladed props; 5,000 shp—2 900-shp Omnithruster JT 1110 omnidirectional jet-thrusters
Electric: main generators + 450-kw diesel emergency set
Range: 8,000/15 **Endurance:** 60 days
Crew: 22 civilian contract mariners, 20 navy + 8 contract technicians

Remarks: Authorized under FY 90. Sister *Integrity* (T-AGOS 24) was authorized under the FY 92 budget but was not ordered, and a T-AGOS 25 was to have been requested in FY 99 but was dropped from the FY 98 five-year program. Originally, at least six were planned. An enlarged version of the T-AGOS 19 SWATH (Small Waterplane Area, Twin-Hull) design. A report by the General Accounting Office released in 1-93 severely criticized this program on the grounds that the intended WQT-2 active LF array and its mating to a SWATH-type platform had not been sufficiently operationally tested; the WQT-2 suite has not been installed.

Was ordered 28-3-91 under FY 90 from Tampa Shipyard Div., American Shipbuilding Co., Tampa, Fla., with an option for two more; work did not begin until 23-3-92 and progressed extremely slowly, stopping entirely during 10-93; the navy then issued a "cure notice" during 11-93 and, after negotiations, a settlement was made and the construction contract canceled. The contract was reassigned during 6-95 to Halter Marine, which employed materials originally ordered and delivered to American Shipbuilding, which had completed about 50% of the lower hull structures; most of the structures already completed for the ship were barged to Mississippi. Was not formally christened until 1-11-00, two and a half years after launch. The initial operating contract went to Maersk Line, Norfolk, on 16-8-00 and extends through 8-05.

Hull systems: The design incorporates measures to improve seakeeping relative to the *Victorious* class. The skew-bladed, fixed-pitch propellers have a diameter of 4.57 m. Two waste-heat distillers provide 4,100 gallons of fresh water per day. Normal mission speed is 3 kts.
Mission systems: Has WSC-3(V)3 and WSC-6(V) SATCOM systems, the latter for datalinking information obtained from the surveillance sonar array. The canceled WQT-2 Active Towed Array Sonar (ATAS) was to have had 10 separate active LF sonar transducers; successful trials were conducted with the leased vessel *Cory Chouest* starting in 1992. The only existing SQQ-2 SURTASS LFA system was to be transferred to T-AGOS 23 from the *Cory Chouest* during FY 01.

♦ 4 Victorious-class SWATH ocean surveillance ships [AGI]
Bldr: McDermott, Morgan City, La. (*Atlantic/†Pacific Fleet)

	Laid down	L	In serv.
T-AGOS 19 VICTORIOUS†	12-4-88	3-5-90	13-8-91
T-AGOS 20 ABLE*	23-5-89	16-2-91	24-7-92
T-AGOS 21 EFFECTIVE†	15-2-91	26-9-91	15-1-93
T-AGOS 22 LOYAL*	7-10-91	19-9-92	11-7-93

Victorious (T-AGOS 19) Mitsuhiro Kadota, 7-01

Able (T-AGOS 20) Christopher C. Cavas, 7-00

Effective (T-AGOS 21) George R. Schneider, 1-00

AUXILIARIES *(continued)*

D: 3,100 tons light (3,384 fl) **S:** 16 kts (9.6 sust. with SURTASS deployed)
Dim: 70.71 (58.14 pp) × 28.96 × 7.62
Electronics:
Radar: 2 Raytheon . . . nav.
Sonar: UQQ-2 SURTASS towed passive array
M: 4 Caterpillar-Kato 3512-TA 835-kw diesel generator sets (2 for ship's service; 600 V, 60 Hz a.c.); 2 G.E. 750-V dc inductance motors (185 rpm max.); 2 props; 3,200 shp—2 600-hp Omnithruster omnidirectional jet-thrusters
Electric: 1,970 kw tot. (2 × 835-kw main generators, 1 × 300-kw emergency)
Range: 3,000/9.6 + . . ./3 **Fuel:** 778 tons **Endurance:** 90 days
Crew: 9 officer and 13 unlicensed contractor crew + 12 contract technicians

Remarks: T-AGOS 19 was authorized in FY 87, the others in FY 89; T-AGOS 19 was ordered 31-10-86, the other three 7-10-88. Operation was contracted to Maersk Line, Norfolk, on 16-8-00, through 8-05.
Hull systems: Has a SWATH (Small Waterplane Area, Twin-Hull) hullform, with two submerged pontoons for buoyancy. Horizontal fins between the hulls control pitching. Are stable ships, able to operate in higher latitudes in winter than the *Stalwart* class, although they are reported to be difficult to handle in high winds; they can maintain heading in Sea State 6, however, and have successfully sustained operations at Sea State 9.
Mission systems: The SURTASS (Surveillance Towed Array Sonar System) array is 2,614 m long and is towed at depths between 152 and 457 m. Carry the same sensor payload as the ASW-dedicated *Stalwart*-class units, including the WSC-6(V)1 SATCOM datalink. Are to be backfitted with a lightweight, low-power Low Frequency Active (LFA) sonar array.

♦ 6 Stalwart-class ocean surveillance ships [AGI]

Bldr: Tacoma Boat, Tacoma, Wash. (T-AGOS 16: Friede Goldman Halter, Moss Point, Miss.) (*Atlantic/†Pacific Fleet)

	Laid down	L	In serv.
T-AGOS 1 Stalwart*	3-11-82	11-7-83	9-4-84
T-AGOS 7 Indomitable*	26-1-85	16-7-85	1-12-85
T-AGOS 8 Prevail*	13-3-85	7-12-85	5-3-86
T-AGOS 9 Assertive†	30-7-85	20-6-86	12-9-86
T-AGOS 12 Bold* (ex-*Vigorous*)	13-6-88	22-5-89	20-10-89
T-AGOS 16 Capable*	17-10-87	28-10-88	9-6-89

Bold (T-AGOS 12)—ASW surveillance configuration A. A. de Kruijf, 6-01

Prevail (T-AGOS 8)—ASW surveillance configuration Takatoshi Okano, 4-01

Capable (T-AGOS 16)—drug patrol configuration Walter Angermeier, 9-99

D: 1,459 tons light (2,262–2,282 fl) **S:** 11 kts
Dim: 68.28 (59.13 pp) × 13.11 × 4.60
Electronics:
Radar: 2 . . . nav.—T-AGOS 1, 7: 1 Raytheon SPS-49(V)3 air search—T-AGOS 16: 1 Lockheed SPS-40E air search
Sonar: T-AGOS 8, 9, 12 only: UQQ-2 SURTASS (Twin-Line on T-AGOS 9, 12)
M: 4 Caterpillar-Kato D-398B 800-bhp diesels, G.E. electric drive; 2 4-bladed props; 2,200 shp (1,600 sust.)—550-hp bow-thruster
Electric: 1,500 kVA from main generators + 265-kw emergency set
Range: 11,200/11 + 2,088/3 **Fuel:** 657 tons **Endurance:** 98 days
Crew: 6–8 officer and 11–12 unlicensed MSC contract crew + 11 civilian technicians (T-AGOS 1, 7, 16: 2 USN officers, 17 enlisted instead of technicians)

Remarks: 1,472–1,486 grt/786 dwt. T-AGOS 1 was authorized in FY 79, T-AGOS 7 and 8 in FY 81, T-AGOS 9 and 12 in FY 82, and T-AGOS 16 in FY 867; T-AGOS 1 was ordered 26-9-80. Operation was contracted to Maersk Line, Norfolk, on 16-8-00, through 8-05. Sister *Invincible* (T-AGM 24, ex-T-AGOS 10) is operated for the USAF under MSC contract as a missile-range monitoring ship [AGM] (q.v.).
Status: Because the mission to provide surveillance of hostile submarines has largely disappeared, the ships of this class were mostly adapted for other roles, transferred to other agencies, or deactivated. T-AGOS 1 was transferred to the Naval Surface Warfare Center Detachment, Key West, Fla., on 1-10-92 and was to be deactivated 30-9-93; however, the ship was instead adapted as a prototype drug interdiction patrol vessel, and T-AGOS 16 was similarly modified. T-AGOS 7 was transferred to the Naval Ships Research Center 21-11-92 for use as a trials vessel and was laid up at Port Canaveral, Fla., into summer 1993, when she was activated and converted for drug interdiction work. T-AGOS 1, 7, and 16 are assigned to the Joint Interagency Task Force East for drug interdiction duties. The other three active units remain in use as antisubmarine warfare assets.
Fates of the other units of the class are:

	Deactivated	Remarks
Contender (T-AGOS 2)	1-10-92	To U.S. Merchant Marine Academy, Kings Point, N.Y., as *Kings Pointer*
Vindicator (T-AGOS 3)	5-01	To USCG 20-5-94; to MSC for charter operation for USCG in 1999; returned to USCG for deactivation 5-01; to NOAA 12-01
Triumph (T-AGOS 4)	20-6-94	Stricken 6-1-96 for possible foreign transfer; to MARAD for storage 9-2-96
Assurance (T-AGOS 5)	28-3-94	To MARAD; reacquired by USN 7-4-96 for possible transfer to USAF; returned to MARAD 14-2-96; sold to Portugal 28-10-99
Persistent (T-AGOS 6)	15-5-01	To USCG 11-10-94; laid up; reactivated 28-10-99 under MSC charter; returned to USCG for layup 1-5-01 as WMEC 6; to MARAD 11-01 for use as Great Lakes Maritime Academy school ship
Invincible (T-AGOS 10)	6-2-95	Stricken 9-5-96; reactivated in 1998; became T-AGM 24 (q.v.) 4-4-00
Audacious (T-AGOS 11)	30-11-95	Transferred to Portugal 9-12-96
Adventurous (T-AGOS 13)	1-6-92	Stricken 3-6-92; to National Oceanographic and Atmospheric Administration (NOAA) 5-6-92; reactivated in FY 02 as fisheries research ship R 331
Worthy (T-AGOS 14)	17-3-93	Stricken 20-5-93; to MARAD; to U.S. Geological Survey 30-9-93; to U.S. Army (contractor operated)
Titan (T-AGOS 15)	30-8-93	To NOAA in 11-93 as *Ka'Imimoana* (R 333)
Tenacious (T-AGOS 17)	6-2-95	Stricken 14-2-95; transferred to New Zealand 10-10-96
Relentless (T-AGOS 18)	17-3-93	To NOAA 17-3-93; reactivated in 8-98 as *Gordon Gunter* (R 336)

T-AGOS 4 was originally to have been transferred to State University of New York Maritime Academy and renamed *Empire State* but was instead laid up at San Diego.
Hull systems: Have a flat-chine hullform without bilge keels. Have passive tank roll stabilization. Originally intended to conduct 60- to 90-day patrols and to be at sea 292 days per year, they have outstanding endurance and recreational facilities for their crews but are considered to be rough-riding vessels during the winter months in the higher latitudes where they were intended to work. Up to 518 tons of water ballast can be carried.
Mission systems: The UQQ-2 SURTASS (Surveillance Towed Array Sonar System) on T-AGOS 8 is a 1,829-m linear hydrophone array deployed over the ship's stern in a flexible, neutrally buoyant cable. The output from the SURTASS is instantaneously relayed to shore monitoring stations via WSC-6 SATCOM; the onboard technicians are primarily for maintenance and backup. T-AGOS 12 was used for trials with the shallow water–capable "Twin Line" variant of the UQQ-2 system in 1994, and it has since been fitted to T-AGOS 9 as well. The main engine motor/generator sets also supply ship's service power.
T-AGOS 1, 7, and 16 have had the antenna for the WSC-6 SATCOM system replaced with an SPS-49(V)-series (SPS-40 on T-AGOS 16) air-search radar antenna, the SURTASS equipment deleted, VHFD/F antennas added to the foremast, and WSC-3 UHF SATCOM equipment added.

♦ 1 chartered undersea surveillance ship [AGI]

Bldr: Ulstein Hatlo A/S, Ulsteinvik, Norway (In serv. 1974)

Cory Chouest (ex-*Far Clipper,* ex-*Tender Clipper*)

D: approx. 3,900 tons (fl) **S:** 13.75 kts **Dim:** 81.08 (76.21 pp) × 18.04 × 4.32
Electronics:
Radar: . . .
Sonar: SQQ-2 SURTASS LFA (Low Frequency Active) array
M: 2 Atlas-MaK 6M453AK diesels; 2 CP props; 4,000 bhp
Electric: 2,350 kw tot. (2 × 800 kw, 3 × 250 kw)

AUXILIARIES *(continued)*

Cory Chouest George R. Schneider, 4-97

Range: 5,940/13.75 **Fuel:** 265 tons
Crew: 16 contract mariners + 41 technicians

Remarks: A 1,597-grt/1,800-dwt former oilfield deck cargo/pipe carrier, converted into a diving support, firefighting, and pollution-control vessel. Chartered 14-11-91 for 17 months (with two 12-month extension options) from Alpha Marine Services, Galliano, La., as the primary platform for the development of low-frequency active (LFA) acoustic technology in support of the Space and Naval Warfare Systems Command (SPAWAR); the charter was renewed in 10-98 for five years for operation by Edison Chouest Offshore, and she was to be replaced during FY 01 by the *Impeccable* (T-AGOS 23). Sister *Amy Chouest* was chartered 9-90 to 1993 for acoustic research trials.

♦ **1 Stalwart-class missile-range tracking ship [AGM]**
Bldr: Tacoma Boat, Tacoma, Wash.

	Laid down	L	In serv.
T-AGM 24 Invincible (ex-T-AGOS 10)	8-11-85	1-11-86	30-1-87

Invincible (T-AGM 24)—as T-AGOS 10, but in same configuration *Ships of the World,* 6-99

D: 1,459 tons light (2,282 fl) **S:** 11 kts **Dim:** 68.28 (59.13 pp) × 13.11 × 4.60
Electronics:
Radar: 2 . . . nav.; 1 Cluster Gemini dual-band tracking and air search
M: 4 Caterpillar-Kato D-398B 800-bhp diesels, G.E. electric drive; 2 4-bladed props; 2,200 shp (1,600 sust.)—550-hp bow-thruster
Electric: 1,500 kVA from main generators + 265-kw emergency set
Range: 11,200/11 + 2,088/3 **Fuel:** 657 tons **Endurance:** 98 days
Crew: 6–8 officer and 11–12 unlicensed contract crew + 11 technicians

Remarks: Authorized under FY 82 as an ocean submarine tracking ship; deactivated 6-2-95 and stricken 9-5-96. Began reactivation 13-3-98 in support of an Air Force program for monitoring missile tests by North Korea and China. Is painted white, without a hull number visible, and is equipped with a large radome-enclosed radar known as Cluster Gemini. Operation was contracted to Maersk Line, Norfolk, on 16-8-00, through 8-05. Redesignated T-AGM 24 on 4-4-00.
Hull systems: Has a flat-chine hullform without bilge keels. Has passive tank roll stabilization. Up to 518 tons of water ballast can be carried.
Mission systems: Has a new SATCOM antenna radome atop the mainmast and carries a large radome-enclosed air-search radar antenna on the deckhouse abaft the stacks.

♦ **1 Mariner-class missile-tracking ship [AGM]**
Bldr: New York SB, Camden, N.J.

	L	In serv.
T-AGM 23 Observation Island (ex-AG 154, ex-YAG 57, ex-*Empire State Mariner*)	15-8-53	5-12-53

D: 12,978 tons light (16,076 fl) **S:** 20 kts **Dim:** 171.81 (161.09 pp) × 23.16 × 9.14
Electronics:
Radar: 1 Raytheon 1650/9X nav.; 1 Raytheon 1660/12S nav.; 1 SPQ-11 tracking; 1 . . . tracking
TACAN: URN-25
M: 2 sets G.E. geared steam turbines; 1 prop; 19,251 shp—2 3,000-shp Omnithruster WP 1700 directional pumpjet thrusters

Observation Island (T-AGM 23) Takatoshi Okano, 6-00

Observation Island (T-AGM 23) Takatoshi Okano, 6-00

Boilers: 2 Combustion Engineering, 42.3 kg/cm^2, 467° C
Range: 17,000/13 **Fuel:** 2,652 tons
Crew: 66 MSC civil service mariners + 35 civilian technicians + . . . USAF personnel (accomm. for 93 officers, 465 enlisted)

Remarks: 14,029 grt/6,322 nrt. Begun as a seven-hold cargo ship. Acquired by the navy 10-9-56 and used for Polaris and Poseidon missile trials until placed in reserve 29-9-72. Reclassified T-AGM 23 on 1-5-79. Sponsored by the Ballistic Missile Defense Office in part for strategic arms limitation treaty verification duties; operates mainly in the Pacific.
Hull systems: Painted white. Refitted 10-84 to 3-85 by Northwest Marine, Portland, Ore., with a new foremast, heightened stacks, three new turbogenerator sets, new deckhouses, two new evaporators, and upgraded electronics (including an new X-band tracking radar abaft the stack). A 70-seat movie theater, racquetball and volleyball courts, two gymnasiums, and a sauna are fitted.
Mission systems: Converted between 7-79 and 4-81 to carry the Cobra Judy (SPQ-11) missile-tracking, trainable phased-array radar aft; the trainable antenna weighs 250 tons and has more than 12,000 radiating elements. Two parabolic collection antennas are mounted in 9.75-m-diameter geodesic radomes atop the bridge. The twin kingposts forward support four antennas for the WSC-3 UHF SATCOM system as well as the TACAN antenna and the two navigational radar antennas.

Note: *Pathfinder*-class survey ship *Pathfinder* (T-AGS 60) has been equipped with telemetry/tracking arrays to support ballistic-missile tests and is based at Port Canaveral, Fla.; see under [AGS] for details.

♦ **0 (+ 1) SWATH oceanographic research ship [AGOR]**
Bldr: Atlantic Marine, Inc. (AMI), Jacksonville, Fla.

	Laid down	L	In serv.
AGOR 26 Kilo Moana	9-2-01	17-11-01	10-02

Kilo Moana (AGOR 26)—official model J&D Enterprises, 11-01

D: 1,996 tons light (2,542 fl) **S:** 15 kts (12 sust.)
Dim: 56.57 (52.43 wl) × 26.82 × 7.62
Electronics:
Radar: 1 Raytheon 3-cm Pathfinder nav.; 1 Raytheon 10-cm Pathfinder nav.
Sonar: Simrad EM 120 deepwater multibeam sounder (12 kHz); Simrad EM 1002 shallow water multibeam echo sounder (95 kHz); Simrad EA 500 hydrographic echo sounder (12, 38, and 200 kHz); Simrad HPR 418 acoustic positioning syst.; Raytheon Model 795 digital depth finder

AUXILIARIES *(continued)*

M: 4 Caterpillar 3508B SCAC diesel generator sets (1,220 bhp each), 2 Westinghouse 1,500-kw electric motors; 2 fixed-pitch props; 4,024 shp—1 Elliot White Gill 40 azimuthal bow-thruster (starboard hull)
Range: 10,000/11 **Endurance:** 50 days
Crew: 17 tot. + 31 scientists and technicians

Remarks: Added to the FY 97 budget by Congress. Ordered 27-10-99 for $42.3 million under the UNOLS (University-National Oceanographic Laboratory System) program for bail to the University of Hawaii's School of Ocean and Earth Science and Technology. Lockheed Martin is managing the construction program, with Atlantic Marine constructing the ship and with input from Pacific Marine & Supply, Mitsui Eng. & SB, Syntek, and GTE/BBN. The name means "Oceanographer" in Hawaiian.
Hull systems: Employs a catamaran SWATH (Small Waterplane Area, Twin-Hull) hullform. The mapping sonar functions to 11,000-m depths. Intended primarily to study high sea states and will be fully operational in Sea State 6. There is 4,460 ft^2 of working space on deck, and a 100-ton mission payload can be accommodated. Is equipped with equipment for precise navigation, including station keeping and trackline maneuvering. Can launch and retrieve remotely operated underwater vehicles, scientific instruments, and deep-sea moorings. The lower hulls are 52.12 m long and have fixed stabilizer fins aft and adjustable canard stabilization fins forward. The bow-thruster is to be used to tow up to 9-ton (10,000-lb.) arrays at 3 kts in order to avoid fouling the main propellers. Has a dynamic positioning system, integrated bridge, TSS POS/MV 320 inertial reference unit, POS/MV 30 inertial reference unit, Raytheon STD-20 gyrocompass, Raytheon Raychart 420 Differential GPS, and Inmarsat SATCOM. A 20,000-lb. (at 30-ft. radius)/5,000-lb. (at 40-ft. radius) crane is located aft, to port, and the Uframe stern crane can handle a 20,000-lb. weight.

♦ 3 Thomas G. Thompson–class oceanographic research ships [AGOR] Bldr: Friede Goldman Halter, Moss Point, Miss.

	Laid down	L	In serv.
AGOR 23 THOMAS G. THOMPSON (ex-*Ewing*)	29-3-89	27-7-90	8-7-91
AGOR 24 ROGER REVELLE	9-12-93	20-4-95	8-6-96
AGOR 25 ATLANTIS	16-8-94	1-2-96	15-4-97

Atlantis (AGOR 25) H&L Van Ginderen, 10-00

Roger Revelle (AGOR 24) H&L Van Ginderen, 11-98

D: 2,155 tons light (3,200 fl; AGOR 23: 3,051 fl) **S:** 15 kts
Dim: 83.52 × 16.00 × 5.18 (hull)
Electronics:
Radar: 2 Raytheon Pathfinder (3 cm and 10 cm) nav.
Sonar: AGOR 23: STN Atlas Elektronik Hydrosweep DS mapping; 2 Raytheon RD-500 depth finders; 3.5-kHz sub-bottom profiler; 2 12-kHz bottom profilers—AGOR 24, 25: Sea Beam 2112A multibeam mapping system (12 kHz); ODEC deep- and shallow-water bottom profiler (12 and 33 kHz); ODEC sub-bottom profiler (12 TR-109 transducers); RD VM-150-18HP doppler current profiler (150 kHz); 2 Raytheon RD-500 echo sounders

M: 3 Caterpillar 3516 TA diesel generator sets (1,500 kw each), 2 G.E. CD6999 motors; 2 Lips FS-2500-450/1510BO azimuth-thruster props; 6,000 shp—1,117-shp Elliott Gill Model 50 T 35 azimuthal bow-thruster
Electric: 2,395 kw tot. (3 × 715-kw Caterpillar 3508TA diesel sets, 1 × 250-kw Caterpillar 3406TA emergency diesel set)
Range: 11,300/12 + 30 days on station **Endurance:** 60 days
Crew: 20–22 tot. + 37 scientists

Remarks: Authorized in FY 88, 92, and 94, respectively. AGOR 23 was ordered 10-6-88 to replace the earlier *Thomas G. Thompson* (AGOR 3), as part of the UNOLS (University-National Oceanographic Laboratory System); she was bailed to the University of Washington on completion and is entirely civilian operated. AGOR 24, ordered 13-1-93 (with an option to build two more), was loaned 11-6-96 to the Scripps Institution of Oceanography, La Jolla, Calif., to replace the *Thomas Washington* (AGOR 10); the ship has a dark blue–painted hull. AGOR 25, ordered 17-2-94, was bailed on completion to the Woods Hole Oceanographic Institution in Massachusetts to replace the *Atlantis II*. A fourth unit, the *Researcher* (later renamed *Ronald S. Brown*), also ordered 17-2-94, was built for the National Ocean and Atmospheric Administration (NOAA) and was not numbered in the U.S. Navy series (although the ship has been incorrectly referred to as "AGOR 26" in some official publications).

Are capable of all-purpose oceanographic research, including chemical and biological oceanography, multidiscipline environmental investigations, ocean engineering, marine acoustics, marine geology, and geophysics. Can also carry out bathymetric, seismic, and magnetometry surveys. AGOR 25 is equipped to support the navy's research submersible *Alvin* (DSV 2).
Hull systems: Any combination of diesel generators can be employed for 600-V propulsion or 480-V ship's service power. Have the Robertson RMP ROBPOS dynamic positioning system, accurate to 300 ft. in a 27-kt wind and 11-ft. seas. Other navaids include two Sperry Mk 37 gyros, a Mackay 4005 D/F, a Morris Tiger Shark Loran-C receiver, a Magnavox MX-1107 GPS, a Honeywell R/S 906 acoustic positioning system, and an ODEC DSN450 dual-axis doppler speed log. Have the Telesystems MCS 9120 SATCOM. Are equipped with a seismic survey system using two Price A-300 air compressors for the two towed air/water guns. The conductivity-, temperature-, and depth-measuring system operates to 11,000-m depths.

Laboratory space totals 372 m^2, including 700-ft.^{2} hydrographic, 235-ft.^{2} wet, 1,730-ft.^{2} main, 359-ft.^{2} bioanalytical, and 820-ft.^{2} electronics and computer labs and a 380-ft.^{2} staging bay. Four additional portable lab/accommodations vans can be accommodated on deck. Working space on deck totals 325 m^2. Have a Markey DESH-9-11 double-drum waterfall winch with 10,000 m of cable; the winch has a 9-ton bollard pull at 2.5 kts for scientific packages. Also have two Markey DESH-5 hydrographic winches. Carry two 19-ton telescoping boom cranes, two portable foldable 1-ton boom cranes, a hydrographic sampling equipment boom, and a stern-mounted equipment A-frame crane.

♦ 2 Melville-class (SCB 710 type) oceanographic research ships [AGOR] Bldr: Defoe SB, Bay City, Mich.

	Laid down	L	In serv.	Modified
AGOR 14 MELVILLE	12-7-67	10-7-68	27-8-69	7-89 to 6-90
AGOR 15 KNORR	9-8-67	21-8-68	14-1-70	11-88 to 1989

Melville (AGOR 14) *Ships of the World,* 8-01

D: 2,670 tons (fl) **S:** 14 kts **Dim:** 85.0 × 14.03 × 4.87
Electronics: Radar: 2 Raytheon ST-series ARPA nav.
M: 4 Caterpillar 3516 diesel generator sets, electric drive; 3 Z-drive props (1 retractable fwd); 3,000 shp
Electric: 800 kw tot. (2 × 300-kw, 1 × 200-kw diesel sets)
Range: 12,000/12 **Fuel:** 342 tons **Endurance:** 35–40 days
Crew: 24 tot. + 34 scientists

Remarks: 2,100 grt. Operated for the Office of Naval Research, AGOR 14 by Scripps Institution of Oceanography, La Jolla, Calif., and AGOR 15 by Woods Hole Oceanographic Institution, Mass. The contracts were renewed for five years on 28-7-96 and 4-8-96, respectively. The planned AGOR 19 and 20 of this class were canceled.
Hull systems: Originally had one vertical cycloidal propeller forward and a larger unit aft; these were intended for precise maneuvering but, because mechanical rather than electric drive was used, proved troublesome. A new 10.36-m midbody was added, and the ships were re-engined, with the original cycloidal props replaced; accommodations were enlarged and the scientific equipment updated. Have six general-purpose labs totaling 341.9 m^2 lab of space and 349.7 m^2 of deck working space; also have a 550-ft^3 storage hold. Two Magnavox 200 GPS receivers, a Sperry SRD-301 log, an RDI 150-kHz current profiler, and a Magnavox MX-2400 Inmarsat SATCOM are fitted. Winches include two Markey DESH-5 hydrographic (with 10 km cable each), one Northern Line trawl (9 km cable), and one portable Dynacon traction (9 km wire). AGOR 15 has a Sea Beam 2112A (12-kHz) mapping sonar.

Note: A new T-AGS has been programmed for the FY 06 budget; no data available.

AUXILIARIES *(continued)*

♦ 6 Pathfinder-class hydrographic survey ships [AGS]

Bldr: Friede Goldman Halter, Moss Point, Miss.

	Laid down	L	In serv.
T-AGS 60 Pathfinder	3-8-92	4-10-93	5-12-94
T-AGS 61 Sumner	18-11-92	19-5-94	30-5-95
T-AGS 62 Bowditch	18-8-93	15-10-94	19-7-96
T-AGS 63 Henson	13-10-95	21-10-96	20-2-98
T-AGS 64 Bruce C. Heezen	19-8-97	25-3-99	13-1-00
T-AGS 65 Mary Sears	28-7-99	19-10-00	17-12-01

Pathfinder (T-AGS 60)—with telemetry tracking antennas John Gourley, 11-01

Bruce C. Heezen (T-AGS 64) H&L Van Ginderen, 9-00

Bowditch (T-AGS 62) Piet Sinke, 9-98

D: 3,019 tons light (4,260 fl; T-AGS 64, 65: 4,772 fl) **S:** 16 kts
Dim: 100.13 (94.49 pp) × 17.68 × 5.79 (hull)
Electronics:
Radar: 2 . . . nav.—T-AGS . . . also: 1 . . . telemetry tracking
Sonar: Simrad EM121A multibeam echo sounder (12 kHz); ODEC Bathy 2000 echo sounder (12/33 kHz); ODEC Bathy 2000 bottom profiler (3 kHz); RD Instruments VM-0150 acoustic doppler current profiler (150 kHz); Sea Beam 2100-series mapping set; DWS towed seismic sub-bottom profiler
M: 2 G.E. Electromotive Div. EMD 16-645F7B diesels (3,505 bhp each) with Baylor 855 VUV-372 generators (2,435 kw each), 2 G.E. Electromotive Div. EMD 12-645F76B diesels (2,550 bhp each) with Baylor 855PUV-372 generators (1,822 kw each), 2 G.E. CDF 1944 Model EN14655 motors; 2 4-bladed azimuthal props; 8,000 shp—G.E. CD4773 Model 5CD473NA802C800 electric motor, Lips FS500-234MNR azimuthal, retractable bow-thruster; 1,500 shp
Electric: Main alternator plant + 250-kw emergency alternator (G.M. Detroit Diesel 6V92 TA diesel driving)
Range: 12,000/16; or 12,000/12 + 29 days on station at 3 kts
Fuel: 1,221 tons **Endurance:** 70 days
Crew: 25 tot. + 27 scientists, 3 spare berths

Remarks: Authorized: 2 in FY 90, 1 in FY 91, 1 in FY 94, 1 in FY 96, and 1 in FY 99. Essentially an enlarged AGOR 23, with increased space to meet MSC accommodations standards and for specialized survey equipment. T-AGS 60 and 61 were ordered 30-1-91, T-AGS 62 on 29-5-92, T-AGS 63 on 20-10-94, T-AGS 64 on 15-1-97 for $51.7 million, and T-AGS 65 on 22-12-98 for $53,618,360. A new AGS-designated ship is planned to be requested in the FY 07 budget, although it may not be another unit of the *Pathfinder* class. T-AGS 64 was named on 5-6-98, following a nationwide contest for schoolchildren, in honor of a deceased USN oceanographer known for work on plate tectonics and sea-floor mapping.

Operated on contract for the Naval Meteorology and Oceanography Command by Dyn Marine Services, Reston, Va., through 7-02, these ships are intended to conduct physical, chemical, and biological oceanography; multidisciplinary environmental investigations; ocean engineering and marine acoustics research; coastal hydrographic surveys; marine geology and geophysics research; and bathymetric, gravity, and magnetic surveys in deep ocean and coastal areas. One unit has been adapted as a missile-range instrumentation ship and is based at Port Canaveral, Fla.

Hull systems: Antirolling tanks, precision navigation equipment, and onboard data processing equipment are fitted. Are able to launch, operate, and recover remotely operated vehicles. Carry 962 tons of ballast water, 32 tons of potable water, and 24 tons of lube oil. The electric generator plant is integrated to provide power for the propulsion system, ship's service needs, and the laboratories. A portable generator module can be installed on deck to provide power for "silent" operations. Have three multipurpose cranes and five specialized scientific equipment winches. Flow fins have been added forward to reduce bubble interference with the sonar sets.

Mission systems: Laboratory spaces include the 232-m^2 main, 16.8-m^2 wet, 28.2-m^2 dry and biochemical, and 7.4-m^2 climate-controlled chamber/salinometer labs. Spaces also include a 32.5-m^2 staging bay contiguous to the 325-m^2 working deck and the wet lab, a 5.9-m^2 darkroom, a 7.4-m^2 survey freezer, an 18.6-m^2 electricians' shop, a 22.3-m^2 drafting room, and a 32.5-m^2 library/conference room, plus 217.2 m^2 of survey equipment storage. The 121-beam mapping sonars are able to cover a swath as wide as 12 n.m. at a time, and the navigation system can determine ship's position to within 50 ft. Navigational equipment includes a Megapulse Accufix 500N Loran-C receiver, Rockwell-Collins WRN-6(V)1 NAVSTAR GPS receiver, Sperry Mk 39 ring-laser gyro, and Simrad/Robertson DPS automatic positioning and course-maintaining propulsor control. The 5- to 50-kHz Benthos DS-7000-16 acoustic positioning system uses Datasonic BFP-312 bottom transponders. Have an EG&G G811/813 magnetometer for magnetic field mapping, General Oceanics water sampler, Falmouth ICTD conductivity and temperature depth system to measure water properties to 7,000-m depths, and Sippican expendable sensor launcher and monitor system.

T-AGS 63 carries two 10.36-m inshore survey boats, each equipped with a Simrad EM 1000 multibeam bathymetric system and multibeam survey sonar; the others will be similarly equipped later. All units of the class, and all of their inshore survey boats, have Datasonics SIS-1500 high-resolution side-scan sonar sets.

♦ 2 John McDonnell–class coastal survey ships [AGS]

Bldr: Friede Goldman Halter, Moss Point, Miss.

	Laid down	L	In serv.
T-AGS 51 John D. McDonnell	3-8-89	13-12-90	15-11-91
T-AGS 52 Littlehales	25-10-89	14-2-92	10-1-93

John D. McDonnell (T-AGS 51) W. Michael Young, 11-01

D: 1,394 tons light (2,238 fl) **S:** 14 kts (12 sust.) **Dim:** 63.40 × 13.72 × 4.27
Electronics:
Radar: 1 . . . 3-cm nav.; 1 . . . 10-cm nav.
Sonar: Simrad Multibeam hull-mounted (95 kHz); Datasonics SIS-1500 towed side-scan (105 kHz); 2 12-kHz deepwater echo sounders; 2 24-kHz shallow-water echo sounders; 2 200-kHz shallow-water echo sounders
M: 1 G.M. EMD12-645F7B turbocharged, 900-rpm diesel; 1 prop; 2,550 bhp—1 230-bhp Detroit Diesel 6V92N cruising diesel
Electric: 1,200 kw tot. (3 × 350-kw, G.M. 8V92TAB diesel-driven ship's service; 1 × 150-kw, G.M. 6V92N-driven emergency set)
Range: 12,000/12 **Crew:** 22 tot. + 11 survey party

Remarks: Added to the FY 87 budget by Congress with a nonbinding suggestion that they be converted from existing tuna clippers. A delay in ordering to 10-11-88 was occasioned by the need to define characteristics for the unexpected gifts. A second pair to replace T-AGS 33 and 34 was to have been included in the FY 94 budget but were dropped. Both are operated for the Naval Meteorology and Oceanography Command by Dyn Marine Services, Reston, Va., on contract through 7-02.

Hull systems: Intended to collect hydrographic data in waters from 10 to 4,000 m deep. The smaller "son" diesel propels the ships at speeds of 4–6 kts. Have a roll stabilization tank. Navigation equipment includes GPS and Loran-C receivers, a collision avoidance system, a dual-axis doppler speed log, and the HYSTAR II computerized data collection system. Have 700 $ft.^2$ of laboratory space, 1,500 $ft.^2$ of deck working space, and 2,300 $ft.^2$ of scientific storage space. Two telescopic, 7-ton-max. cranes are fitted. Carry two 10.36 × 2.82 × 0.91–m, 7.4-ton survey launches, equipped with a single 225-bhp diesel for 16 kts. The launches carry a towing winch for a 105-kHz side-scan sonar (range: 600 m; towing speed: 12.7 kts) and have two 24-kHz and two 200-kHz echo sounders fitted; the craft have GPS and a microfix radio navigation system and can interface with the mother ship's HYSTAR II computerized survey data storage system. There is also a 5.33-m semi-rigid inflatable workboat. Both units of the class, and their inshore survey boats, are to receive Datasonics SIS-1500 high-resolution side-scan sonar sets.

Disposal note: Of the *Silas Bent*–class survey ships, *Silas Bent* (T-AGS 26) was stricken and transferred to Turkey 28-10-99; *Kane* (T-AGS 27) was placed out of service, stricken, and transferred to Turkey 14-3-01; *Wilkes* (T-AGS 33) was deactivated and transferred by grant to Tunisia 29-9-95; and *Wyman* (T-AGS 34) was deactivated 10-3-97, stricken 3-5-99, and transferred to MARAD for disposal during 3-01.

AUXILIARIES *(continued)*

♦ 2 Mercy-class hospital ships [AH]

Bldr: General Dynamics National Steel & SB Co. (NASSCO), San Diego

	L	Conv. start	In serv.
T-AH 19 Mercy (ex-*Worth*)	1976	20-7-84	28-2-87
T-AH 20 Comfort (ex-*Rose City*)	1976	2-4-85	1-12-87

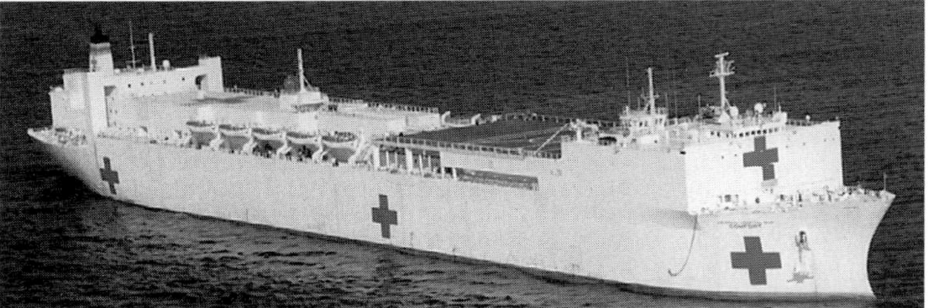

Comfort (T-AH 20) Stefan Marx, 6-98

Mercy (T-AH 19) Jürg E. Kürsener, 6-01

D: 24,752 tons light (69,360 fl) **S:** 17.5 kts (16.5 sust.)
Dim: 272.49 (260.61 pp) × 32.23 × 9.98
Electronics: Radar: 1 . . . nav.; 1 Norden SPS-67 surf. search—TACAN: URN-25
M: 2 sets G.E. geared steam turbines; 1 prop; 24,500 shp **Boilers:** 2 . . .
Electric: 9,250 kw tot. (3 × 2,000-kw diesel sets, 1 × 1,500-kw diesel set, 1 × 1,000-kw turboalternator, 1 × 750-kw emergency diesel set)
Range: 13,420/17.5 **Fuel:** 5,445 tons
Crew: active: 68 MSC civil service mariners, 1,508 navy staff + 1,000 patients—inactive: 12 MSC caretaker crew + Navy Medical Treatment Facility staff: 6 officers, 39 enlisted

Remarks: 54,367 grt/45,480 dwt. The builder was contracted 29-6-83 to convert Apex Marine's *San Clemente*–class commercial tanker *Worth* to a hospital ship with FY 83 funds; *Rose City*'s conversion was ordered from same yard 16-12-83 with FY 84 funds. Were originally 44,875 grt/91,849 dwt. T-AH 19 is maintained in layberth at San Diego and T-AH 20 at Baltimore. Both are normally maintained on 5-day steaming notice.
Hull systems: The entire amidships area was altered to provide a large helicopter deck, accommodations, and boat stowage. Have 12 operating rooms, four X-ray rooms, an 80-bed intensive-care unit, a burn-care facility, a 50-bed reception/triage area, and 1,000 ward beds. Of the 1,508 accommodations for naval personnel, there are 259 for officers, 31 for CPOs, and 530 for other enlisted, augmented in emergencies by 372 naval medical support personnel; also aboard would be 14 communications specialists. Freshwater tankage for 1,525 tons is carried, and there are two 278-ton/day distilling plants. Much of the displacement is seawater ballast, some of which can be discharged to allow the ships to enter shallow ports and harbors. There are two 7,000-ton/hr ballast pumps.

♦ . . . "Maritime Prepositioned Force-Future" program [AK]

Remarks: The MPF(F) is a study initiated in 1999 by the USN and USMC to design a single replacement class for the current force of prepositioning ships dedicated to Marine Corps vehicles and equipment. Intended to enter service around 2010, the new class would be compatible with LCAC 1–class air-cushion landing craft and would have a helicopter deck large enough to handle more than one heavy-lift helicopter or MV-22 tilt-rotor aircraft, sufficient deck space to allow for shifting cargo around while at sea to allow for changing mission requirements, and a means to allow Marines to board the ship while it is en route to its destination. Such a design would rule out easy adaptation of existing commercial vessels and would doubtless be very expensive to acquire and more expensive to operate than the current generation of prepositioning ships. The first ship in this series is to be requested under the FY 07 budget.

♦ 7 (+ 1) Watson-class Large Medium-Speed Roll-on Sealift Ships [AK]

Bldr: National Steel & SB (NASSCO), San Diego

	Laid down	L	In serv.
T-AKR 310 Watson	23-5-96	26-7-97	9-12-99
T-AKR 311 Sisler	15-4-97	28-2-98	1-12-98
T-AKR 312 Dahl	12-11-97	2-10-98	13-7-99
T-AKR 313 Red Cloud	29-6-98	7-8-99	23-5-00
T-AKR 314 Charlton	19-1-99	11-12-99	23-5-00
T-AKR 315 Watkins	30-8-99	28-7-00	2-3-01
T-AKR 316 Pomeroy	23-3-00	10-3-01	14-8-01
T-AKR 317 Soderman	31-10-00	26-4-02	9-02

Dahl (T-AKR 312) Douglas A. Cromby, 6-01

Sisler (T-AKR 311) John Mortimer, 8-00

Watson (T-AKR 310) Joe Straczek, 11-01

Charlton (T-AKR 314) Joe Straczek, 11-01

D: 36,114 tons (62,700 fl at 10.36-m draft) **S:** 24.9 kts (24 sust.)
Dim: 289.56 (271.28 wl; 275.85 pp) × 32.23 × 12.19 (max.; 10.36 mean)
Electronics: Radar: . . .
M: 2 G.E. LM-2500-30 gas turbines; 2 7.3-m-dia. CP props; 64,000 shp at 95 rpm (59,000 sust.)—3,000-shp bow-thruster
Electric: 14,500 kw tot. (5 × 2,500-kw diesel sets; 2,000 kw tot. emergency diesel)
Range: 13,800/24
Crew: 25 civilians (accomm. for 13 officers, 32 unlicensed + military: 2 officers, 48 enlisted + 300 troops)

Remarks: Officially referred to as Large Medium-Speed Roll-on Sealift Ships (LMSR). Operated under a 30-7-97 contract by Maersk Line, they are part of the Brigade Afloat Force, carrying U.S. Army heavy equipment for use in the Middle East and Far East, and are all in or will be assigned to MPS-2 at Diego Garcia. The initial operating contract expires in 9-02.

T-AKR 310 was ordered 15-9-93 for $269 million, with an option for a further five ships; the ship was delivered 23-6-98 but did not enter service for another six months. T-AKR 311 and 312 were ordered 20-10-94 for $436 million total, T-AKR 313 on 30-1-96, T-AKR 314 on 26-11-96 for $200.25 million, T-AKR 315 in 5-97, T-AKR 316 on 14-11-97, and T-AKR 317 on 28-2-00 for $230,626,488. T-AKR 317 was added to the FY 00 budget by Congress in lieu of a planned third Sealift Enhancement Ship for the Marine Corps.

Were originally planned to be 36-kt-capable ships, but costs would have been prohibitive and the strategic advantages minimal. The building yard was purchased by General Dynamics on 8-10-98 but retains its corporate identity.
Hull systems: Have two twin Hägglunds 55-ton-capacity (at 29 m; 35-ton at 40 m) pedestal cranes, two side vehicle cargo ports (with modular ramps extendable to 40 m), and a 40-m-long, 7.3-m-wide slewing stern ramp. Are able to carry 13,260 tons of military cargo on 35,300 m^2 of parking space, including 58 tanks, 48 other tracked vehicles, and 900 trucks and other wheeled vehicles. The gas-turbine main propulsion engines are uprated from the standard version through improved cooling and the use of advanced materials; they employ G.E. double-reduction gearboxes. These are the world's largest gas-turbine-powered ships.

AUXILIARIES *(continued)*

♦ 5 (+ 2) Bob Hope–class Large Medium-Speed Roll-on Sealift Ships [AK] Bldr: Northrop Grumman Avondale, New Orleans

	Laid down	L	In serv.
T-AKR 300 Bob Hope	29-5-95	27-3-97	18-11-98
T-AKR 301 Fisher	15-4-96	21-10-97	24-8-99
T-AKR 302 Seay	24-3-97	25-6-98	28-3-00
T-AKR 303 Mendonca	3-11-97	25-9-99	30-1-00
T-AKR 304 Pililaau	29-6-98	29-1-00	24-7-01
T-AKR 305 Brittin	3-5-99	11-11-00	18-7-02
T-AKR 306 Benevidez	15-12-99	11-8-01	. . .

Fisher (T-AKR 301) Northrop Grumman Avondale, 6-99

Mendonca (T-AKR 303) Northrop Grumman Avondale, 1-00

Bob Hope (T-AKR 300) H&L Van Ginderen, 6-99

D: 34,408 tons light (62,096 fl) **S:** 24.9 kts (sust.)
Dim: 289.56 (271.28 pp) × 32.30 × 11.25 (max.)
Electronics: Radar: . . .
M: 4 Colt-Pielstick 10 PC4.2 V400, 105-rpm diesels; 2 props; 65,160 bhp—2 1,500-shp bow-thrusters
Electric: 5,000 kw (2 × 2,500-kw diesel sets) **Range:** 13,800/24
Crew: 27 contract civilians (accomm. for 95) + 300 troops

Remarks: Officially referred to as Large Medium-Speed Roll-on Sealift Ships (LMSR). First unit was added by Congress to the FY 90 shipbuilding request due to concerns that the U.S. and its allies lack sufficient sealift assets, military or commercial. T-AKR 300 was ordered 2-9-93 for $265 million from Avondale, with an option to build five more. T-AKR 301 and 302 were ordered 27-9-94, T-AKR 303 on 27-12-95 for $206.43 million, T-AKR 304 on 26-11-96 for $211.1 million, T-AKR 305 on 14-11-97 for $240 million, and T-AKR 306, an FY 99 ship, on 18-12-98. Hull numbers AKR 308 and 309 were reserved for possible future additional orders for units of this class.

As of 9-01, T-AKR 300 was assigned to MPS-1 and was being operated by Maersk Line, while T-AKR 301–303 were being maintained by Patriot Contracting Services in 4-day ready-to-operate condition at U.S. ports.

Hull systems: Are able to carry 13,260 tons of military cargo. In military cargo configuration, have 39,920 m^2 of vehicle parking space, enough for more than 1,000 military vehicles, including tanks. Are fitted with a 41-m-long, 7.3-m-wide, 160-ton-capacity centerline stern slewing ramp, internal vehicle ramps, side-port vehicle ramps on each beam (with ramps 15.2 m long and 12.2 m wide), and two paired 58-ton-capacity (at 29-m radius) electric cranes; when the cranes are operating together, the pairs can lift 112 tons each. There is a modular, portable ramp that can be attached to any of the three sides of the side ramps in lengths of up to 50 m when all four sections are used; it has a vehicle weight capacity of 160 tons and can be used to join the ship to a pier or lighter in up to a State 3 sea.

♦ 3 Shughart-class Large Medium-Speed Roll-on Sealift Ships [AK] Bldr: Odense Staalskibsværft, Lindo, Denmark (In serv. 1980–81)

	Conv. start	In serv.
T-AKR 295 Shughart (ex-*Laura Maersk*)	24-6-94	7-5-96
T-AKR 297 Yano (ex-*Leise Maersk*)	17-5-95	8-2-97
(T-AK 3017) GySgt Fred W. Stockham (ex-*Soderman,* T-AKR 299; ex-*Lica Maersk*)	12-10-95	18-11-97

Yano (T-AKR 297) A. D. Baker III, 10-00

Shughart (T-AKR 295) William H. Clarke, 4-00

GySgt Fred W. Stockham (T-AK 3017)—with black hull, white upperworks Joe Straczek, 11-01

D: 33,971 tons light (55,123 fl) **S:** 24 kts (sust.)
Dim: 276.43 (269.79 hull; 259.32 pp) × 32.28 × 10.64 (design; 11.18 max.)
Electronics: Radar: . . ./Sperry RASCAR-ARPA nav.
M: 2 Burmeister & Wain 12L90-GFCA diesel; 1 6-bladed, 7.51-m-dia. prop; 47,300 bhp (at 97 rpm)—bow and stern CP side-thrusters
Electric: 12,560 kw tot. ship's service + 1,750 kw tot. emergency (3 × 2,500-kw, 3 × . . .-kw, 1 × 1,750-kw diesel sets)
Range: 12,200/24 **Fuel:** 22,600 barrels heavy oil, 659 tons diesel
Crew: 13 officer and 32 unlicensed contract mariners, 50 navy (2 officers, 48 enlisted; *Stockham:* up to 100 USN and USMC personnel)

Remarks: 43,325 grt/approx. 53,000 dwt (prior to conversion). Former 3,000-TEU containerships. A contract for $634.9 million was let 30-7-93 for long-term lease from Maersk Line and conversion as military vehicle carriers for army equipment and supplies by National Steel & Shipbuilding (NASSCO), San Diego. Named for U.S. Army Medal of Honor awardees. Referred to as LMSR (Large Medium-Speed Roll-on/roll-off) ships. Conversion of this class and the *Gordon* class cost $1.06 billion total. During 2000, T-AKR 295 and 297 were reassigned to surge force duties and placed in layup at Norfolk; they are operated by Patriot Contract Services.

Under a 6-1-99 contract, NASSCO converted the former T-AKR 299 into a Marine Corps prepositioning ship; a further contract added $18 million to the work package on 5-5-00, and the work was completed 1-3-01. She was reaccepted 6-7-01 after the conversion and is now part of MPS-2 at Diego Garcia, carrying a cargo of SeaBee (Construction Corps) equipment, USMC airfield matting, and a field hospital. For reasons obscure, the *Stockham* has lost her Naval Vessel Registry hull number but has been assigned the unofficial administrative number T-AK 3017; the name was changed on 16-1-01.

Hull systems: T-AKR 295 and 297 are intended to carry equipment for an army Armor Task Force, with 58 M1 Abrams tanks, 48 other tracked vehicles, and 900 trucks and other wheeled vehicles. Have six vehicle cargo decks; total cargo/parking area: 29,356 m^2. They are fitted with a 41-m-long, 7.3-m-wide, 160-ton-capacity centerline stern slewing ramp, internal vehicle ramps, side-port vehicle ramps on each beam

AUXILIARIES *(continued)*

(with ramps 15.2 m long and 12.2 m wide), and two paired 58-ton-capacity (at 29 m radius) electric cranes; when the cranes are operating together, the pairs can lift 112 tons each. Some container cell guides have been retained. There is a modular, portable ramp that can be attached to any of the three sides of the side ramps in lengths of up to 50 m when all four sections are used; it has a vehicle weight capacity of 160 tons and can be used to join the ship to a pier or lighter in up to a State 3 sea. A helicopter platform has been added forward of the pilothouse. As merchant ships, they were lengthened during 1987 by Hitachi from the original 212.48 m o.a. (202.01 pp). Fin stabilizers were added during the conversion, and the generator capacity was greatly increased. Were equipped with a Sperry SRD 331 doppler log, SRD 421/S two-axis speed logs, a Mk 37 Mod. E gyro, an ADG 6000 steering control, and GMDSS radio systems during conversions. The conversions came in 808 tons heavier than planned. They have a bulbous bow form.

During her 2000–01 modifications, *Stockham* had accommodations for 50 military personnel added, the helicopter facilities enhanced, and the stern ramp reconfigured so they can be lowered below the water's surface to allow launch and recovery of amphibious vehicles.

♦ 2 Gordon-class Large Medium-Speed Roll-on Sealift Ships [AK]

Bldr: Burmeister & Wain's Skibsbyggeri, Copenhagen, Denmark

	L	Conv. start	In serv.
T-AKR 296 Gordon (ex-*Jutlandia*)	1972	15-10-93	23-8-96
T-AKR 298 Gilliland (ex-*Selandia*)	1973	21-10-93	24-5-97

Gilliland (T-AKR 298)—the helicopter deck is forward of the bridge in this class; note the portable vehicle ramp stowed to starboard of the first pair of cranes
General Dynamics Newport News, 5-97

Gilliland (T-AKR 298) NAVPIC-Holland, 6-98

D: 33,163 tons light (57,000 fl) **S:** 24 kts (22 sust.)
Dim: 291.39 (272.65 pp) × 32.24 × 11.00
Electronics: Radar: . . . Sperry RASCAR-ARPA nav.
M: 1 Burmeister & Wain 12K84EF diesel (31,400 bhp), 2 Burmeister & Wain 9K84EF diesels (23,600 bhp each); 3 props; 78,600 bhp—CP bow-thruster
Electric: 12,560 kw tot. ship's service + 1,750 kw tot. emergency
Range: 27,000/22 **Fuel:** 8,486 tons heavy oil, 874 tons diesel
Crew: 13 officers, 32 unlicensed, 50 navy (2 officers, 48 enlisted)

Remarks: 54,035 grt (prior to conversion). Former 3,000-TEU container ships. A contract was let 30-7-93 for $425.6 million for long-term lease from Maersk/East Asia Co. and conversion as military vehicle carriers by Newport News SB & DD. Renamed for U.S. Army Medal of Honor recipients. Delivery dates slipped by about eight months. Conversion of this class and the *Shughart* class cost $1.06 billion total. Both were initially assigned to MPS-2 at Diego Garcia, but during 2001, both were reassigned to Surge Force duties and placed in 4-day reduced operating status layup at Norfolk, where they are managed by Patriot Contract Services.
Hull systems: Both were lengthened in 1984 by Hyundai Mipo Dockyard, Ulsan, South Korea. During conversion in the U.S.A., were fitted with a 41-m-long, 7.3-m-wide, 160-ton-capacity centerline stern slewing ramp, internal vehicle ramps, sideport vehicle ramps on each beam (with ramps 15.2 m long and 12.2 m wide), and two paired 57.5-ton-capacity (at 29-m radius) electric cranes; when the cranes are operating together, the pairs can lift 114 tons each at 29-m radius. Some container cell guides have been retained. There is a modular, portable ramp that can be attached to any of the three sides of the side ramps in lengths of up to 50 m when all four sections are used; it has a vehicle weight capacity of 160 tons and can be used to join the ship to a pier or lighter in up to a State 3 sea. Fin stabilizers were also added. Have six vehicle cargo decks totaling 30,843 m^2. The ships can be unloaded in 96 hours. The centerline propeller has controllable pitch, while the outboard pair has fixed-pitch propellers. Were equipped with a Sperry SRD 331 doppler log, SRD 421/S two-axis speed logs, a Mk 37 Mod. E gyro, an ADG 6000 steering control, and GMDSS radio systems during conversions.

Note: The *Algol* (SL-7)-class vehicle cargo ships (T-AKR 287 through T-AKR 294) are used for transportation rather than prepositioning; see under [AK].

♦ 0 (+ 1) Wheat-class chartered Maritime Prepositioning Ship [AK]

Bldr: Chernomorskiy Zavod, Mikolayiv, Ukraine (In serv. 1987)

(T-AK 3016) LCpl Roy M. Wheat (ex-*Bazaliya*, ex-*Vladimir Vaslayayev*)

LCpl Roy M. Wheat (T-AK 3016)—as *Bazaliya,* arriving in Alabama for her unusually protracted conversion MSC, 7-97

D: 50,570 tons (fl) **S:** 26.5 kts (22 sust.) **Dim:** 263.31 (239.97 pp) × 30.01 × 10.67
M: 2 Mashproekt-Zorya M-25 reversible gas turbines (18,000 shp each); 2 waste-heat steam turbines (5,300 shp each); 2 props; 46,000 shp—. . .-shp bow-thruster—872-shp KaMeWa stern-thruster
Electric: . . . kw tot. **Range:** 40,000/26.5 **Fuel:** 8,380 tons
Crew: 25 contract mariners, . . . navy

Remarks: 32,264 grt. The second conversion unit for the Maritime Prepositioning Force (Enhanced) was authorized in the FY 97 budget; the name was assigned on 1-11-96 in honor of a Marine Vietnam War Medal of Honor recipient. To be commercially operated and manned, with a small navy contingent aboard. A contract for $150 million was placed 9-4-97 with Ocean Marine Navigation Co., Annapolis, Md., to purchase, convert, operate, and maintain the ship for five years. The ship never having operated, a new contract for $27.1 million was placed 28-6-01 with Keystone Prepositioning Services, Bala Cynwyd, Pa., to operate the ship until 6-06. Built in Ukraine, the ship was registered in Jamaica at the time of charter. She is being converted for MSC service for $134 million by Bender Shipbuilding and Repair, Mobile, Ala., starting 18-7-97 and now not expected to be delivered until spring 2002, when she will be attached to MPS-3; the conversion has required an inordinate amount of time, and the cost of the conversion has more than doubled since the contract was placed. The unexpected need to remove asbestos (widely used in former Warsaw Pact nation merchant and naval ships) added to the already-high cost of the conversion. Due to its origins, the ship should prove expensive to operate and difficult to maintain.
Hull systems: The conversion entailed inserting a 35.97-m midbody section (built by Tampa SY and by Brown & Root, Houston, Texas) to increase vehicle capacity and installing a paired cargo crane and a helicopter platform; the section added about 0.7 m to the draft and 14,340 tons to the full-load displacement. New Ukrainian-made Zorya M-25 gas turbines were installed during conversion. The three original diesel generator sets had their Sulzer diesels overhauled and new Kato generators provided, while two new 1,815-kw sets (powered by Caterpillar 3516B diesels) and an 850-kw emergency diesel set (powered by a Caterpillar 3508B) were added.

♦ 1 Therese Delmas–class USAF–chartered Maritime Prepositioning Ship [AK]

Bldr: Ch. d'Atlantique, St.-Nazaire, France (In serv. 1983)

(T-AK 4638) A1C William H. Pitsenbarger (ex-*Therese Delmas*)

D: approx. 40,000 tons (fl) **S:** 18 kts **Dim:** 189.01 (175.42 pp) × 32.21 × 11.40
Electronics: Radar: . . .
M: 1 Sulzer 7RLB66 7-cyl. slow-speed diesel; 1 prop; 13,800 bhp—1,184-shp CP bow-thruster
Electric: 3,000 kw tot. (3 × 1,000-kw Wärtsilä diesel-driven sets; 440 V, 50 Hz a.c.)
Range: 21,600/18 **Fuel:** 2,197.5 tons heavy oil; 297.5 tons diesel
Crew: 20 tot.

Remarks: 30,750 grt/32,709 dwt. Chartered 15-6-01 from RR & VO LLC for $50,913,041 for use as a prepositioning ship for Air Force containerized equipment and munitions at Diego Garcia from 11-01 through 11-05. Previously under Bahamian registry, she has been reflagged in the U.S. and renamed for a Vietnam War Medal of Honor recipient. Was delivered 28-11-01 after a refit at Detyens SY, Charleston, S.C., and is now operated by Red River Shipping, Rockville, Md.
Hull systems: Single-deck container ship with fixed guides and 22 hatches. Although configured to carry 1,417 TEU when chartered, after conversion she carries only 885 TEU, of which 135 are in a new "cocoon" above decks. All cargo spaces are dehumidified and air-conditioned. Has five 40-ton Brissonneau & Lotz cranes.

♦ 2 chartered Maritime Prepositioning Ships [AK]

Bldr: Daewoo SB & Heavy Machinery, Koje (*Carter:* Kyung), South Korea

	L
(T-AKR 4496) Ltc John U. D. Page (ex-*Newark Bay*, ex-*Utah*, ex-*Irene D*, ex-*American Utah*)	9-85
(T-AKR 4544) SSgt Edward A. Carter, Jr. (ex-*Sea-Land Oregon*, ex-*OOCL Innovation*, ex-*Nedlloyd Hudson*, ex-*Nebraska*, ex-*Susan C*, ex-*American Nebraska*)	4-85

AUXILIARIES *(continued)*

SSgt Edward A. Carter, Jr. (T-AKR 4544) Takatoshi Okano, 9-01

D: 74,500 tons (fl) **S:** 18 kts **Dim:** 289.52 (279.00 pp) × 32.31 × 10.67
Electronics: Radar: . . .
M: 1 Sulzer-Hyundai 9RL890 low-speed diesel; 1 prop; 28,000 bhp
Electric: *Page:* 3,300 kw (1 diesel generator)—*Carter:* 3,300 kw tot. (3 × 1,000-kw, 1 × 300-kw diesel sets)
Range: 37,000/18 **Fuel:** 6,770.5 tons heavy oil, 950 tons diesel
Crew: 22 contract civilians

Remarks: *Page:* 57,075 grt/58,869 dwt; *Carter:* 57,075 grt/57,939 dwt. Chartered through 5-06 from the operator, Maersk Line, Norfolk, to act as containerized U.S. Army ammunition prepositioning ships at Diego Garcia. *Page* was delivered 2-3-01 and *Carter* on 15-6-01. *Carter* suffered a serious engine room fire 14-7-01 while loading ammunition at Southport, N.C., with four dead.
Hull systems: Carry 2,500 20-ft. containers (2,230 below decks and 270 in four new cocoon structures on the upper deck at the bases of the four new cargo cranes. As commercial container vessels, could carry 4,258 20-ft. containers in 11 holds. There are 36 wing tanks. The main engine is direct reversing. In merchant service, they displaced up to 81,281 tons full load and operated at up to 12.68 m draft.

♦ 3 Sea Wolf–class chartered Maritime Prepositioning Ships [AK]
Bldr: Odense Staalskibsværft, Lindo, Denmark

	In serv.	In MSC
(T-AK 4396) Maj Bernard Fisher (ex-*Sea Fox,* ex-*American Hawaii,* ex-*Sea Fox*)	1985	9-9-99
(T-AK 5089) Ltc Calvin P. Titus (ex-*American Michigan,* ex-*Sea Lion*)	1985	1-6-99
(T-AK 5091) Sp5 Eric G. Gibson (ex-*Lykes Adventurer,* ex-*Sea Wolf,* ex-*American North Carolina,* ex-*Sea Wolf*)	1984	7-7-99

D: approx. 44,000 tons (fl) **S:** 18.5 kts **Dim:** 198.86 (186.42 pp) × 32.24 × 10.99
Electronics: Radar: . . .
M: 1 Sulzer 7RTA76 7-cyl. diesel; 1 prop; 23,030 bhp—CP bow- and stern-thrusters
Electric: 5,550 kw tot. (3 × 1,500-kw, 1 × 1,050-kw diesel sets)
Crew: 25 contract mariners

Remarks: 34,318 grt/24,500 dwt. Ro-Ro and container ships. *Titus* and *Gibson* were chartered 23-11-98 from Crowley American Transport, Jacksonville, Fla., for 59 months. They are assigned to MPS-3 at Saipan, with army equipment in the *Titus* and Air Force equipment in the *Gibson. Fisher* was chartered 2-12-98 from Sealift Inc., Oyster Bay, N.Y., for 59 months and is based at Diego Garcia in MPS-2 with Air Force equipment aboard. Were renamed for Medal of Honor recipients, with two of the names being reused from ships that went off-charter earlier in 1999.
Hull systems: Have a quarter stern door and a 19.50-m-long, 6.25-m-wide ramp to the vehicle deck, which has a total lane length of 335 m (about 27 standard trailers). Container capacity: 1,914 TEU. Have 200 ft.^{2} of refrigerated cargo space, nine centerline and 20 wing hatches, and two 40-ton cranes.

♦ 1 chartered Maritime Prepositioning Ship [AK]
Bldr: Samsung, Koje, South Korea (In serv. 10-84)

(T-AK 4296) Capt Steven L. Bennett (ex-*Sea Pride,* ex-*Martha* II, ex-*TNT Express*)

Capt Steven L. Bennett (T-AK 4296)—note the white-painted sliding cover over the containerized cargo Ulrich Streich, 9-00

D: 59,207 tons (fl) **S:** 18.25 kts **Dim:** 209.40 (200.01 pp) × 30.41 × 11.60
Electronics: Radar: . . .
M: 1 Sulzer 6RLB76 diesel; 1 prop; 16,320 bhp
Electric: 4,080 kw tot. (4 × 1,020-kw diesel sets; 450 V a.c.)
Range: . . ./. . . **Fuel:** 2,857 tons heavy oil **Crew:** 24 tot.

Remarks: 29,223 grt/41,151 dwt. Former bulk cargo vessel, with nine holds. Chartered in 5-97 for $47.02 million from Ultra Maritime, a division of Sealift, Inc., for operation through 4-01 (later renewed) to preposition some 1,922 standard 20-ft. cargo containers of USAF munitions in the Mediterranean as part of MPS-1. Converted for MSC service at Bender Shipbuilding, Mobile, Ala., to replace the *American Merlin.* Renamed on 1-10-97 for an Air Force officer. Delivered 30-9-98.

♦ 1 1st Lt Harry L. Martin–class chartered Maritime Prepositioning Ship [AK]
Bldr: Bremer Vulkan, Bremen-Vegesack, Germany (In serv. 3-79)

(T-AK 3015) 1st Lt Harry L. Martin (ex-*Tarago,* ex-*Nosac Cedar,* ex-*CGM Rabelais,* ex-*Rabelais,* ex-*Liliooet*)

1st Lt Harry L. Martin (T-AK 3015) Paul Ginnane, 5-01

D: 51,531 tons (fl) **S:** 21.5 kts **Dim:** 229.85 (210.04 pp) × 32.31 × 10.94
M: 1 Bremer Vulkan–M.A.N. K7-SZ-90/160 diesel; 1 prop; 25,704 bhp
Electric: 5,880 kw tot. (2 × 2,140-kw, 1 × 1,600-kw diesel sets)
Range: . . ./. . . **Fuel:** 4,336 tons heavy oil, 668 tons diesel
Crew: 24 contract mariners

Remarks: 39,441 grt/34,100 dwt (prior to conversion). $110 million was included in the FY 95 budget to acquire and convert one Maritime Prepositioning Force (Enhanced)/MPF(E) ship for the Marine Corps; the money was not allocated during FY 95 but the funding authorization was extended into FY 96. The ship was chartered for five years from Tarago Shipholding, Bethesda, Md., on 14-2-97 for $145.7 million, $100 million of which was for conversion and refit at Atlantic Drydock, Jacksonville, Fla. Delivery was expected in 2-99, but the ship was not delivered until 21-4-00, entering MSC service 13-5-00. Cargo cranes were added, the cargo facilities altered, and a helicopter platform installed. Named 14-3-95 in honor of a World War II Marine Medal of Honor recipient. Is attached to MPS-1 in the Mediterranean and is operated on contract by Osprey-Accomarit Management.
Hull systems: The stern-quarter vehicle ramp is 48.74 m long and 12 m wide; it has been adapted to permit driving vehicles onto shuttle craft and pontoons. The vehicle cargo space, including the new two-level structure forward, is climate controlled. Fifteen hydraulically controlled watertight bulkhead doors have been added on the lower four vehicle decks. One 13.4 × 5.5–m and four 14.6 × 5.5–m cargo hatches were added, and the ship can now carry ammunition containers.

♦ 5 2nd Lt John P. Bobo–class chartered Maritime Prepositioning Ships [AK]
Bldr: General Dynamics, Quincy, Mass.

	Laid down	L	In serv.
(T-AK 3008) 2nd Lt John P. Bobo	1-7-83	19-1-85	14-2-85
(T-AK 3009) PFC Dewayne T. Williams	1-9-83	18-5-85	6-6-85
(T-AK 3010) 1st Lt Baldomero Lopez	23-3-84	26-10-85	21-11-85
(T-AK 3011) 1st Lt Jack Lummus	22-6-84	22-2-86	6-3-86
(T-AK 3012) Sgt William R. Button	22-8-84	17-5-86	22-5-86

2nd Lt John P. Bobo (T-AK 3008) William H. Clarke, 7-01

1st Lt Baldomero Lopez (T-AK 3010) Douglas A. Cromby, 7-99

D: 19,588 tons light (46,111 fl) **S:** 23 kts (18 sust.)
Dim: 205.18 (187.32 pp; 199.00 wl) × 32.16 × 4.50 (light; 9.78 max. loaded)
Electronics: Radar: 2 . . . nav.
M: 2 Stork Werkspoor 18TM410V diesels; 1 prop; 26,400 bhp—1,000-shp bow-thruster
Electric: 7,850 kw tot. **Range:** 15,000/18 **Fuel:** 3,080 tons
Crew: 30 contract mariners, 7 MSC crew, 7 navy + 25 vehicle maintenance personnel

AUXILIARIES *(continued)*

Remarks: 44,543 grt/26,523 dwt (22,454 cargo dwt)/14,461 nrt. MARAD C8-M-MA134j design. The first two were contracted for on 17-8-82, the others on 14-1-83. Are intended to transport the materiel needed for one Marine Expeditionary Brigade. Are owned by a variety of private holding corporations and are operated on an expected 25-year charter by American Overseas Marine Corp., a subsidiary of General Dynamics. *Bobo* is in MPS-1 in the Atlantic; the rest formed MPS-3 in 10-86, operating in the Guam-Saipan area and carrying equipment for the 1st Marine Expeditionary Brigade, Kaneohe Bay, Oahu, Hawaii. *Williams* was refitted at Newport News SB from 12-2-01 to 7-3-01 and *Button* from 26-4-01 to 8-5-01.
Hull systems: Cargo: 25,384 tons max., including up to 522 standard 20-ft. vans (350 for ammunition, 110 for general stores, 30 for fuel drums, and 32 refrigerated), plus 14,000 m^2 of roll-on/roll-off vehicle capacity to carry up to 1,400 vehicles. A 66-long-ton-capacity, 32-m-long, 4.9-m-wide Navire stern slewing ramp provides access to the six vehicle decks and can discharge either vehicles to a pier or amphibious vehicles of up to 23 tons directly into the water; the stern door measures 11 × 4.55 m. The upper deck can stow two LCM(8) landing craft, six unpowered causeway sections, four powered causeway sections, a warping tug, four pipe trailers, and 16 hose reels. Carry 5,764.6 m^3 (1,523,000 gallons) of transferable bulk fuel, plus 2,039 55-gallon fuel drums. Can also transport 307 m^3 of potable water. Five 39-ton pedestal cranes are fitted, with two sets being paired, and there is a large helicopter deck at the stern. Unloading rates: all vehicles and cargo at a pier in 12 hours; all cargo at a pier in 3 days; all cargo while moored out in 5 days. There is a four-point mooring system. In addition to those for the listed personnel, there are 102 temporary berths for vehicle crews.

♦ 5 Cpl Louis J. Hauge, Jr.–class chartered Maritime Prepositioning Ships [AK]
Bldr: Odense Staalskibsværft, Lindo, Denmark

	In serv.	Acq.	In serv.
(T-AK 3000) Cpl Louis J. Hauge, Jr. (ex-*Estelle Maersk*)	10-79	3-1-84	7-9-84
(T-AK 3001) PFC William B. Baugh (ex-*Eleo Maersk*)	4-79	17-1-83	30-10-84
(T-AK 3002) PFC James Anderson, Jr. (ex-*Emma Maersk*)	7-79	31-10-83	26-3-85
(T-AK 3003) 1st Lt Alex Bonnyman (ex-*Emelie Maersk*)	1-80	30-1-84	26-9-85
(T-AK 3004) Pvt F. J. Phillips (ex-*Pvt Franklin S. Phillips,* ex-*Pvt Harry Fisher,* ex-*Evelyn Maersk*)	4-80	2-4-83	12-9-85

1st Lt Alex Bonnyman (T-AK 3003) Joe Straczek, 11-01

D: 23,414 tons light (49,453 fl) **S:** 21 kts (18.5 sust.)
Dim: 230.25 (215.00 pp) × 27.48 × 5.41 (light; 10.02 max. loaded)
Electronics: Radar: 2 . . . nav.
M: 1 Sulzer 7RND 76M, 7-cyl. diesel; 1 prop; 16,800 bhp—bow-thruster
Electric: 4,250 kw tot. **Range:** 15,000/18.5 **Fuel:** 1,902 tons
Crew: 20 contract mariners, 7 MSC crew + 30 maintenance crew + 80 troops

Remarks: Operated by the former owner, Maersk Line, on long-term charter; now owned by several private investment corporations. The first three conversions were ordered 17-8-82, the others on 14-1-83. Three were converted by Bethlehem Steel at Sparrows Point, Md., *Baugh* and *Bonnyman* at Beaumont, Texas. All five are part of MPS-2 at Diego Garcia, with *Phillips,* as flagship, carrying an eight-man navy communications team and equipment for the 7th Marine Expeditionary Brigade, Twenty-Nine Palms, Calif.

Bonnyman was originally to be named *1st Lt Alexander Bonnyman, Jr.;* changed 4-3-86. The name of *Phillips* was belatedly changed from *Pvt Harry Fisher* during 1991 under a secretary of the navy directive signed 27-6-88; "Harry Fisher" was the pseudonym used by Pvt. Phillips at the time he won the Medal of Honor, having deserted from the Marine Corps earlier under his real name.
Hull systems: Cargo: 23,000 tons max. Each carries one fifth of the vehicles, equipment, and supplies to outfit a Marine Expeditionary Brigade. Transport up to 413 containers (280 ammunition, 86 general cargo, 23 drummed fuel, 24 refrigerated), plus providing 11,369 m^2 vehicle cargo space. There are four 30-ton and two 36-ton pedestal cranes, side-loading vehicle ports amidships (with portable 13.7- or 27.4-m ramps), and a 66-long-ton-capacity, 32-m-long, 4.9-m-wide Navire slewing ramp aft beneath a helicopter deck. There are eight cargo hatches and three vehicle parking decks. Liquid cargo includes 4,920 m^3 of transferable vehicle fuel, 504 m^3 of potable water, and 2,252 m^3 of lube oil.

♦ 3 Sgt Matej Kocak–class chartered Maritime Prepositioning Ships [AK]
Bldr: Sun SB, Chester, Pa. (Conv. by National Steel and SB, San Diego)

	In serv.	Conv. completed
(T-AK 3005) Sgt Matej Kocak (ex-*John B. Waterman*)	14-3-81	5-10-84
(T-AK 3006) PFC Eugene A. Obregon (ex-*Thomas Heyward*)	1-11-82	15-1-85
(T-AK 3007) Maj Stephen W. Pless (ex-*Charles Carroll*)	14-3-83	1-5-85

PFC Eugene A. Obregon (T-AK 3006) Jaroslaw Cislak, 6-01

Sgt Matej Kocak (T-AK 3005) Stefan Marx, 6-98

D: 19,588 tons light (51,612 fl) **S:** 20.9 kts (18 sust.)
Dim: 250.24 (234.85 pp) × 32.16 × 5.66 (light; 10.21 max. loaded)
Electronics: Radar: 2 . . . nav.
M: 2 sets G.E. geared steam turbines; 1 6-bladed prop; 32,000 shp
Boilers: 2 Combustion Engineering
Range: 13,000/20.9 **Fuel:** 3,450 tons + 300 tons diesel
Crew: 85 contract mariners, 7 MSC crew, 8 navy + 25 maintenance crew

Remarks: 25,426 grt/22,910 dwt. The first two conversions were contracted for 17-8-82 and the third on 14-1-83, all with Waterman Steamship Co. as operator. Now owned by separate private investment corporations, all are operated by Waterman in the Mediterranean as MPS-1, carrying equipment intended for the 6th Marine Expeditionary Brigade (MEB), Camp Lejeune, N.C.
Hull systems: Cargo: 25,000 tons max. Each is intended to transport one fourth of the vehicles, fuel, supplies, and provisions to support the MEB. In the forward three holds, can carry 213 ammunition, 150 "Lo/Lo," 10 general-cargo, 32 drummed-fuel, and 32 refrigerated containers. The remainder of the cargo consists of a large number of vehicles and cargo fuel and water. Were lengthened 39.8 m during conversion, and a helicopter deck and ramp were added. Have paired 50-ton and paired 35-ton portal cranes and retain a 30-ton-capacity traveling gantry forward to handle containerized cargo. The articulating stern ramp can support up to 200 tons and is 40.8 m long. There is a 65-ton-capacity, 13.6 × 4.4–m internal vehicle elevator.

♦ 1 chartered heavy-lift Maritime Prepositioning Ship [AK]
Bldr: Bremer Vulkan, Bremen-Vegesack, Germany (In serv. 1984)

T-AKR 9205 Strong Virginian (ex-*St. Magnus,* ex-*Jolly Indaco,* ex-*St. Magnus*)

Strong Virginian (T-AKR 9205)—with containerized cargo, beneath a heat-shield shed H&L Van Ginderen, 2-00

D: 31,390 tons (fl) **S:** 16.5 kts **Dim:** 156.06 (145.01 pp) × 32.03 × 9.02
M: 2 MaK 6M601AK diesels; 2 CP props; 16,320 bhp—bow-thruster
Electric: 4,080 kw tot. (2 × 1,480-kw, 2 × 560-kw diesel-driven sets)
Range: . . ./. . . **Crew:** 19 contract mariners, 6 army

Remarks: 16,169 grt/21,541 dwt. A combination roll-on/roll-off cargo ship, heavy-lift ship, and dock cargo ship. Chartered in 7-92 from Van Ommeren Shipping USA; was off charter in 1997 but again chartered in mid-1998. Prepositions four U.S. Army 2000 Design utility landing craft, 150 army vehicles, and some 420,000 gallons of marine diesel fuel at Diego Garcia as part of MPS-2.
Hull systems: Has 2,500 m of vehicle parking lanes with 6.9-m clear height (space for 188 standard-length trailers) and can also transport 1,413 standard 20-ft. freight containers. Has one cargo hold with 24,235 m^3 capacity, two 50-ton traveling cranes, and one 800-ton heavy-lift derrick. The stern loading ramp is 13.4 m long and 26.0 m wide; two 24.16-m-long by 5.0-m-wide angled side ramps port and starboard are also fitted. The hull is reinforced for operations in ice.

AUXILIARIES *(continued)*

Strong Virginian (T-AKR 9205)—with Army landing craft on deck
Douglas A. Cromby, 7-99

♦ **1 chartered heavy-lift Maritime Prepositioning Ship [AK]**
Bldr: Eriksbergs Mek. Verkstads, Gothenburg, Sweden (In serv. 17-9-75)

(T-AK 2062) American Cormorant (ex-*Ferncarrier,* ex-*Kollbris*)

American Cormorant (T-AK 2062)—in light condition, with no cargo
Douglas A. Cromby, 8-01

D: 70,692 tons (fl) **S:** 16 kts
Dim: 225.08 (211.82 pp) × 41.18 × 10.55 (19.81 flooded)
M: 1 Eriksberg–Burmeister & Wain 10K84EF 10-cyl., 114-rpm diesel; 1 prop; 25,000 bhp (19,900 under owner's restrictions)—1,500-hp thrusters fore and aft
Electric: 3,360 kw tot. **Range:** 27,000/16
Fuel: 5,635 tons heavy oil, 489 tons diesel **Endurance:** 70 days
Crew: 19 contract mariners

Remarks: 10,195-grt/52,092-dwt dock cargo ship. Former 135,900-dwt tanker, converted to a heavy-lift float-on/float-off cargo ship in 1982. Lease renewed in 5-92; now owned by Cormorant Shipholding and operated by Osprey-Accomarit Ship Management. Has been assigned to MPS-2 at Diego Garcia since 1985 with 7,000 tons of U.S. Army floating equipment: two BD-series floating cranes, four LCU 1466 and 10 LCM(8) landing craft, four 32.6-m tugs, and two LASH barges; stowed atop these are four cranes, nine fork-lifts, and various cargo-handling gear.
Hull systems: Capacity: 45,000 tons on the 120 × 42–m, 4,870-m² midbody cargo deck created by removing the upper portions of the cargo tanks and reducing the original length by 55 m. Can also be used to transport 10,000 bbl of liquid cargo and can also stow 25 40-ft. containers (15 refrigerated) on fantail. Takes four hours to ballast/deballast in order to load.

♦ **1 . . .-class chartered prepositioning support ship [AK]**
Bldr: Yardimçi Gemi Insa Anonim Sirketi, Istanbul, Turkey (In serv. 7-96)

Sagamore (ex-*Mint Arrow,* ex-*Fas Red Sea II*)

D: 7,101 tons (fl) **S:** 12 kts **Dim:** 100.74 (94.00 pp) × 16.00 × 6.17
Electronics: Radar: . . .
M: 1 Wärtsilä 8R32E diesel; 1 CP prop; 4,400 bhp
Electric: 1,500 kw tot. (1 × 700-kw, 2 × 400-kw diesel sets)
Range: . . ./. . . **Crew:** 15 contract mariners

Remarks: 3,838 grt/5,070 dwt. A breakbulk/container ship, chartered for $7,892,750 on 30-6-00 from Sealift, Inc., Oyster Bay, N.Y., through 12-04 to carry prepositioned ammunition, rations, and vehicles in support of prepositioning ships at Diego Garcia. Operates between Guam, Singapore, and Diego Garcia. Was previously registered in the Bahamas and owned by Moliva Denizcilik. No T-AK-series administrative hull number has been assigned.
Hull systems: Has one 61.92-m-long hold, served by two 39.4-ton-capacity container cranes mounted to port. Can accommodate 144 TEU below decks and 220 TEU topside. Hull has five watertight compartments.

Disposal note: Prepositioning ship *Green Ridge* (T-AK 9655, ex-*Woerman Mercur,* ex-*Sloman Mercur,* ex-*Carol Mercur,* ex-*Sloman Mercur*) was returned to her owners 30-9-01. Prepositioning roll-on/roll-off cargo ship *Buffalo Soldier* (T-AK 9881, ex-*CGM Monet,* ex-*Monet*) was returned to her owners in 7-01. LASH-type cargo barge carriers *Jeb Stuart* (T-AK 9204) and *Green Valley* (T-AK 2049) were discarded early in 2001 and scrapped at Alang, India, starting in 7-01; sister *Green Harbour* (T-AK 2064) was sold for scrap in Bangladesh during 4-01.

♦ **2 Wright-class aviation logistic support ships [AK]**
Bldr: Ingalls SB, Pascagoula, Miss.

	In serv.	Conv.
T-AVB 3 Wright (ex-*Young America,* ex-*Mormacsun*)	1970	14-12-84 to 14-5-86
T-AVB 4 Curtiss (ex-*Great Republic,* ex-*Mormacsky*)	1969	17-12-85 to 18-8-87

Curtiss (T-AVB 4)—in layup at San Diego George R. Schneider, 6-01

Wright (T-AVB 3)—in layup at Baltimore
Marty N. Goppert and Don S. Montgomery, USN, 8-94

D: 12,409 tons light (23,800 fl) **S:** 23.6 kts
Dim: 183.49 (170.69 pp) × 27.43 × 10.36
Electronics: Radar: 2 . . . nav.
M: 2 sets G.E. geared steam turbines; 1 prop; 30,000 shp
Boilers: 2 Combustion Engineering **Electric:** 3,000 kw tot. (2 × 1,500 kw)
Range: 9,000/23 **Fuel:** 2,781 tons fuel oil, 839 tons diesel
Crew: 11 officers, 22 unlicensed + 300 Marines

Remarks: 23,255 grt/13,651 dwt. MARAD C5-S-78a, Seabridge-type, roll-on/roll-off vehicle cargo and container carriers, converted by Todd SY, Galveston, Texas, to transport the men and equipment vans of a Marine Intermediate Maintenance Activity in support of aircraft deployed ashore. On 1-10-97, the ships were returned to Maritime Administration custody, which assigned them to the Ready Reserve Force on the same date. T-AVB 3 is in layberth at Baltimore and T-AVB 4 at San Diego, both on 5-day recall; they are maintained by (and would be operated by, if activated) American Overseas Marine.
Hull systems: Additional accommodations were built aft and a helicopter deck was added over the former forward holds. Cargo capacity: 34,903 m³ grain/31,824 m³ bale, including 170-m³ refrigerated cargo. In Intermediate Maintenance Activity mode, carry up to 300 Mobile Maintenance Facility modules and 52 "Access Modules," each the size of a standard 20-ft. cargo container. In Resupply mode (e.g., on subsequent voyages after delivering the aircraft support facility), can carry up to 332 40-ft. containers or 654 20-ft. containers, or 352 vehicles and 14,000 bbl of liquid cargo. Have a stern ramp and two side doors aft for vehicles, one 70-ton and 10 30-ton cargo derricks, and six holds; the forward two holds can be unloaded only by off-ship cranes.

Disposal note: Container-cargo vessel *Margaret B. Chouest* went off charter in 11-00 and was converted as a commercial offshore supply vessel.

AUXILIARIES *(continued)*

♦ 8 SL-7-class Fast Sealift ships [AK]

	Bldr	In serv.	To USN	Conv.
T-AKR 287 ALGOL (ex-*Sea-Land Exchange*)	Rotterdamse DDM, Rotterdam	7-5-73	13-10-81	22-6-84
T-AKR 288 BELLATRIX (ex-*Sea-Land Trade*)	Rheinstahl Nordseewerke, Emden	6-4-73	13-10-81	10-9-84
T-AKR 289 DENEBOLA (ex-*Sea-Land Resource*)	Rotterdamse DDM, Rotterdam	4-12-73	27-10-81	10-10-85
T-AKR 290 POLLUX (ex-*Sea-Land Market*)	A. G. Weser, Bremen	20-9-73	16-11-81	27-3-86
T-AKR 291 ALTAIR (ex-*Sea-Land Finance*)	Rheinstahl Nordseewerke, Emden	17-9-73	5-1-82	13-11-85
T-AKR 292 REGULUS (ex-*Sea-Land Commerce*)	A. G. Weser, Bremen	30-3-73	27-10-81	28-8-85
T-AKR 293 CAPELLA (ex-*Sea-Land McLean*)	Rotterdamse DDM, Rotterdam	4-10-72	16-4-82	30-6-84
T-AKR 294 ANTARES (ex-*Sea-Land Galloway*)	A. G. Weser, Bremen	27-9-72	16-4-82	12-7-84

Bellatrix (T-AKR 288) Leo Dirkx, 2-01

Altair (T-AKR 291) Leo Dirkx, 2-01

Altair (T-AKR 291) Leo Dirkx, 2-01

D: T-AKR 287, 288, 292: 29,993 tons light (55,588 fl); T-AKR 289, 293: 30,391 tons light (55,560 fl); T-AKR 290, 291: 31,017 tons light (55,425 fl); T-AKR 294: 29,692 tons light (55,350 fl)
S: 33 kts (30.1 loaded; 25 sust.)
Dim: 288.38 (268.37 pp) × 32.16 × 11.22 (max.; T-AKR 287, 288, 292, 294: 11.18)
Electronics: Radar: 2 . . . nav.
M: 2 sets G.E. MST-19 geared steam turbines; 2 props; 120,000 shp
Boilers: 2 Foster-Wheeler; 61.6 kg/cm^2, 507° C
Electric: 8,000 kw tot. (2 × 3,000-kw, 1 × 1,500-kw, 1 × 500-kw diesel sets)
Range: 14,000/33 light; 12,200/27 loaded **Fuel:** 5,384 tons
Crew: 43 contract mariners (12 tot. layup caretaker crew)

Remarks: Typical: 48,525 grt/24,270 dwt. Six were acquired under FY 81 and two under FY 82, with the original intent of extensively converting them to serve as T-AKR, roll-on/roll-off vehicle cargo ships for the Rapid Deployment Force. Instead, under FY 82 Congress mandated that four be given a "partial" Ro/Ro conversion and the other four only a "minimodification." This was later changed to give all essentially the same modification, T-AKR 287, 288, 293, and 294 under FY 82 and the others under FY 84. The conversions were performed by National Steel, San Diego (T-AKR 287, 288, and 292), Pennsylvania SB, Chester, Pa. (T-AKR 289 and 293), and Avondale SY, Westwego, La. (T-AKR 290, 291, and 294); the Avondale conversions have an additional hinged internal ramp. The ships were given T-AK-series hull numbers when purchased; these were changed to T-AKR without changing the numbers assigned, AKR 287 on 19-6-84, AKR 288 on 10-9-84, AKR 293 and 294 on 30-6-84, and the rest on 1-11-83.

Pollux (T-AKR 290)—with portable vehicle ramp deployed to starboard A. D. Baker III, 10-00

Have been operated by American Overseas Marine, a division of General Dynamics, since 5-00; the contract was for 3 years, with two 1-year options. Maintained in ready-to-steam status: T-AKR 287, 288, 290, and 292 at New Orleans; T-AKR 289 at Brooklyn, N.Y.; T-AKR 291 at Norfolk; and T-AKR 293 and 294 at Baltimore. During Operation Desert Shield/Desert Storm in 1990–91, steamed at an average of 27 kts and performed the work of an estimated 116 World War II–era break-bulk ships; seven of the ships carried 11% of all the cargo transported to the Middle East.
Hull systems: Cargo: 25,500 tons max. The side vehicle loading ramps are 22.3 m long and 6 m wide and can support 65 tons. The conversion entailed filling in the amidships portion to produce a five-deck vehicle cargo area and helicopter hangar totaling 12,170 m^2 (which can accommodate up to 120 UH-1 helicopters or 183 M1 tanks). This is topped by a 3,252-m^2 flight deck with a twin 35-ton crane plumbing two hatches interrupting the forward half. The stern provides 1,719 m^2 of vehicle parking, as well as cargo space for eight "Sea Shed" containerized vehicle stowage or 44 or 46 20-ft. containers; it is served by a twin 50-ton crane. There are vehicle access ramps amidships, port and starboard.
Were originally tailored to transport up to 1,086 nonstandard 35-ft. containers (standard cargo containers are either 20 or 40 ft. in length); 4,000 of these containers were purchased along with the first six ships. Proved too expensive to operate for the former merchant owner, and their sophisticated propulsion plants have not been overly reliable in navy service. Made 35 kts on trials in light condition, 33 kts at 32,600 tons. Fuel tankage originally included 5,384 tons of fuel oil and 3,116 tons of diesel. Also carry 569 tons of potable water and 4,893 tons of permanent ballast water. Up to 9,484 tons of saltwater ballast can be carried.

♦ 1 chartered general cargo ship [AK]
Bldr: Howaldtswerke, Kiel, Germany (In serv. 1-80)

(T-AK 2050) GREEN WAVE (ex-*Woerman Mira,* ex-*Sloman Mira*)

Green Wave (T-AK 2050) George R. Schneider, 12-00

D: 5,691 tons light (18,178 fl) **S:** 18 kts (17 sust.)
Dim: 154.57 (146.06 pp) × 21.26 × 3.68 (light; 7.46 max. loaded)
M: 1 Krupp-MaK 8M601AK diesel; 1 prop; 10,000 bhp
Electric: 410 kw tot. (1 × 380-kw, 1 × 30-kw diesel sets)
Range: 14,400/17 **Fuel:** 1,052 tons heavy oil; 168 tons diesel
Crew: 9 officer and 12 unlicensed contract mariners

Remarks: 9,521 grt/12,487 dwt. Chartered from Central Gulf Lines during 8-84 (renewed 30-11-88 for 17 months, plus two 17-month extension options) for Greenland and Antarctic supply; the charter has since been extended. Operates from Port Hueneme, Calif., and has made annual Antarctic supply voyages for the National Science Foundation since the late 1980s.
Hull systems: Has an ice-strengthened hull, four long hatches and four holds, 543-TEU container capacity, and six 25-ton cranes (four of which can be ganged to lift 80 tons from hold no. 4). Cargo capacity: 9,388 tons max. (21,210 m^3 grain, 19,142 m^3 bale).

AUXILIARIES *(continued)*

♦ 1 chartered combination cargo ship [AK]
Bldr: Odense Staalskibsværft, Lindo, Denmark (In serv. 1980)

(T-AK 9656) Maersk Constellation (ex-*Elizabeth Maersk,* ex-*C.R. Marseille,* ex-*Elizabeth Maersk*)

Maersk Constellation (T-AK 9656) Piet Sinke, 6-95

D: 11,717 tons light (32,242 fl) **S:** 18.5 kts (sust.)
Dim: 182.28 (168.21 pp) × 27.49 × 3.99 (light; 9.76 max. loaded)
M: 1 Sulzer 7-cyl. diesel; 1 prop; 15,960 bhp—bow-thruster
Electric: 2,550 kw tot. (3 × 850-kw diesel sets)
Range: . . ./. . . **Fuel:** 2,653 tons heavy oil, 160 tons diesel **Crew:** . . .

Remarks: 20,529 grt/21,050 dwt. Chartered 30-11-88 for 17 months (with two 17-month extension options) from Maersk Line, which operates her for Pacific area service.
Hull systems: Cargo: 17,369 tons max. (37,860 m^3 grain/32,446 m^3 bale). Can carry 566 standard 20-ft. cargo containers. Has four holds, eight hatches, five 30-ton cranes, and one 15-ton crane. The fixed quarter stern vehicle ramp has a length of 31.5 m and a width of 4.5 m; some 7,859 m^2 of deck space is available for vehicle parking.

♦ 1 Dock Express–class chartered heavy-lift cargo ship [AK]
Bldr: Arnhemsche Schipswerf Maats., Arnhem, the Netherlands (In serv. 1976)

Strong Texan (ex-*Dock Express Texas,* ex-*Happy Runner*)

Strong Texan George R. Schneider, 2-98

D: 5,454 tons (fl) **S:** 12 kts **Dim:** 81.82 (74.40 pp) × 15.70 × 4.98
M: 2 Stork-Kromhout 9F-CHD240 diesels; 2 props; 2,500 bhp—bow-thruster
Electric: 720 kw (3 × 240-kw diesel sets)
Fuel: 421 tons **Crew:** . . .

Remarks: 1,382 grt/2,776 dwt. Roll-on/roll-off and heavy-lift cargo ship, chartered from and operated by Van Ommeren Shipping USA for transportation between the U.S. West Coast and the Far East. Due to be returned to her owners 11-3-02. As commercial *Happy Runner,* had capsized and sunk in the Mississippi River in 1983. No administrative T-AK-series hull number is assigned.
Hull systems: Has two 160-ton-capacity derricks and a 1,000-ton-capacity stern door/ramp leading to the single cargo deck. Can accommodate 225 standard 20-ft. cargo containers. One hold/one hatch: 62.1 × 11.9 m. There are 30 ballast tanks to compensate for load distribution.

♦ 1 chartered Down-Range Support Ship [AK]
Bldr: Scully Bros. Bldrs, Morgan City, La. (In serv. 1-79)

Megan Beyel III (ex-*Treasure Gull,* ex-*Tarheel III*)

D: . . . **S:** 10 kts **Dim:** 35.35 × 7.92 × 2.55
M: 2 diesels; 2 props; 2,700 bhp **Electric:** 300 kw tot.
Range: . . ./. . . **Crew:** . . .

Remarks: Tug/supply vessel chartered during 2002 from Beyel Brothers Towing to support the Atlantic Missile Test Range at Andros Island, the Bahamas. Replaced the *Seacor Clipper* (ex-*Nicor Clipper*), which went off charter 19-12-01.

♦ 16 Henry J. Kaiser–class replenishment oilers [AO] (2 in *reserve*)
Bldr: Northrop Grumman Avondale, Westwego, La. (*Atlantic/†Pacific Fleet)

	Laid down	L	In serv.
T-AO 187 Henry J. Kaiser†	22-8-84	5-10-85	19-12-86
T-AO 188 *Joshua Humphreys*	17-12-84	22-2-86	3-4-87
T-AO 189 John Lenthall*	15-7-85	9-8-86	25-6-87
T-AO 190 *Andrew J. Higgins*	21-11-85	17-1-87	22-10-87
T-AO 193 Walter S. Diehl†	7-8-86	2-10-87	13-9-88
T-AO 194 John Ericsson†	15-3-89	21-4-90	19-3-91
T-AO 195 Leroy Grumman*	6-7-87	3-12-88	2-8-89
T-AO 196 Kanawha*	13-7-89	22-9-90	6-12-91
T-AO 197 Pecos†	17-2-88	23-9-89	6-7-90
T-AO 198 Big Horn*	9-10-89	2-2-91	21-5-92
T-AO 199 Tippecanoe†	19-11-90	16-5-92	26-3-93
T-AO 200 Guadalupe†	9-7-90	5-10-91	26-10-92
T-AO 201 Patuxent*	16-10-91	23-7-94	21-6-95
T-AO 202 Yukon†	13-5-91	6-2-93	27-4-94
T-AO 203 Laramie*	10-1-94	6-5-95	7-5-96
T-AO 204 Rappahannock†	29-6-92	14-1-95	7-11-95

Patuxent (T-AO 201) Camil Busquets i Vilanova, 12-00

Walter S. Diehl (T-AO 193) Douglas A. Cromby, 6-00

Guadalupe (T-AO 200) Findler & Winter, 10-00

Guadalupe (T-AO 200) Findler & Winter, 10-00

AUXILIARIES *(continued)*

Big Horn (T-AO 198) Takatoshi Okano, 9-01

D: 9,500 tons light (40,700–42,000 fl) **S:** 20 kts (sust.)
Dim: 206.51 (198.13 pp) × 29.75 × 10.97 (max.)
A: provision for 2 20-mm Mk 15 Phalanx gatling CIWS
Electronics:
Radar: 2 Raytheon . . . nav.
EW: SLQ-25 towed torpedo decoy syst.
M: 2 Colt-Pielstick 10 PC4.2 V570 diesels; 2 CP props; 32,540 bhp—diesel-electric low-speed drive
Electric: 12,000 kw tot. (2 × 3,500-kw, 2 × 2,500-kw diesel sets)
Range: 6,000/20 **Fuel:** 1,629 tons heavy oil, 165 tons diesel
Crew: 10 officer and 76 unlicensed MSC civil service mariners, 23 navy (1 officer, 22 enlisted) (T-AO 187: 8 officer and 16 unlicensed MSC civil service mariners; T-AO 194: 66 tot. MSC civil service mariners, 24 navy)

Remarks: 20,706 grt/28,407 dwt, except T-AO 202–204: 20,706 grt/24,825.5 dwt. T-AO 187 was authorized in FY 82, T-AO 188 in FY 83, T-AO 189 and 190 in FY 84, T-AO 191–193 in FY 85, T-AO 194 and 195 in FY 86, T-AO 196 and 197 in FY 87, T-AO 198 and 199 in FY 88, and T-AO 200–204 in FY 89. The navy had requested only one for FY 89 and planned two each year in FY 90 and 91; instead, Congress "bought out" remainder of the program. The design contract was let to George Sharp, Inc., 11-7-80. Deliveries were greatly delayed by the bankruptcy of the second-source builder, PennShip, Chester, Pa., but Avondale's work was also well behind schedule. T-AO 194 and 196 were originally ordered 7-86 from PennShip, but were canceled at the yard's request and reordered 16-6-88 from Avondale. T-AO 198, 200, 202, and 204 were ordered 6-10-88; T-AO 199, 201, and 203 were to have gone to an alternate yard, but instead, Avondale bid lowest and won the contract 28-3-89, accounting for the out-of-sequence construction schedule.

Have proven very successful in service. Plans to convert three of the class to ammunition ships were dropped. T-AO 202 collided with small civilian cargo ship *Inchcape-14* off Jebel Ali, Dubai, on 27-2-00. The same ship was also in a collision with the *Denver* (LPD 9) on 13-7-00 near Hawaii; repairs were completed early in 1-01. T-AO 200 was in a collision with the *Shasta* (T-AE 33) on 26-2-01 off Pt. Loma, Calif.

Disposals: The incomplete *Benjamin Isherwood* (T-AO 191) and *Henry Eckford* (T-AO 192) were transferred to MARAD on 15-8-93 for long-term layup in the James River, Va.; T-AO 191 was 95.3% complete and T-AO 192 84.0% complete. Both ships were stricken and transferred to the MARAD for disposal 29-12-97. On 16-7-01, CCC Marine was reported to have been allowed to purchase T-AO 191 with the intent of selling the ship to an unidentified NATO navy, but as of 1-02, the ownership of both was said to have been transferred to Joseph D'Alessio & Co. for the same purpose.

Status: T-AO 187 was to have been deactivated in 9-94 but was instead assigned to MPS-2 at Diego Garcia, carrying JP-4 jet fuel for the USAF; the crew was reduced to 24 civil service mariners, three of the five underway replenishment stations were deactivated, and three of the accommodations decks were closed, although the ship was reactivated as a replenishment oiler and her crew augmented by 11 personnel in 2-97 to 3-97 for an exercise. T-AO 188 was placed in reduced operating status in 10-93 with a crew of 25, was reactivated from 1-94 through 16-12-94, was placed out of service in reserve on 29-6-96, and is currently laid up at Philadelphia under USN control. T-AO 189 was placed in reserve on 11-11-96 but reactivated on 8-2-99. T-AO 190 was placed in reduced operating status in the second quarter of FY 95 and placed out of service in reserve on 1-4-96; on 6-5-96, ownership was transferred to MARAD. T-AO 194 was laid up at Portland, Ore., in 1-97 but reactivated during 12-98.

Hull systems: Cargo: T-AO 187–200: 32 tanks totaling 21,161 m^3, equating to 180,000 bbl of liquids (86,400 bbl fuel oil, 54,000 bbl JP-5, and 39,600 bbl convertible, plus 327 tons of feedwater and 390 tons of potable water), along with 534 pallets of dry cargo and eight 20-ft. provisions containers. Under a contract modification required by Congress and signed 16-9-92, the final three (T-AO 201, 203, and 204) have double-hull construction, increasing their cost and decreasing their capacity by 17%, with a possible small increase in survivability. The three have a liquid capacity of 29,820 m^3 in 27 tanks (159,500 barrels); some of the double-hull voids, however, have been fitted with valves and piping to permit them to be used for cargo fuel stowage in time of war and restoring most of the lost capacity. All have five alongside liquid transfer stations (three to port) and one solid transfer station per side; however, T-AO 194, 197, and 200 have only three replenishment stations in service, due to personnel restrictions. Have eight cargo pumps, with a combined capacity of 5,448 tons/hr. There is a helicopter deck aft but no hangar. The engines for the first two were made by Alstom in France. A CGEE-Alstom integrated auxiliary electric drive system is fitted for low speeds, driving either or both props.

♦ 4 Supply-class fast combat support ships [AOR]

Bldr: General Dynamics National Steel & SB Co. (NASSCO), San Diego (*Atlantic/†Pacific Fleet)

	Laid down	L	In serv.
T-AOE 6 Supply*	24-2-89	6-10-90	26-2-94
AOE 7 Rainier† (ex-*Paul Hamilton*)	31-5-90	28-9-91	21-1-95
AOE 8 Arctic*	2-12-91	30-10-93	16-9-95
AOE 10 Bridge†	2-8-94	24-8-96	5-8-98

D: T-AOE 6: 20,796 tons light (50,858 fl); others: 20,669–20,674 tons light (50,731–50,794 fl)
S: 26 kts **Dim:** 229.73 (222.56 wl) × 32.61 × 11.66 (11.53 mean)

Rainier (AOE 7) W. Michael Young, 1-01

Bridge (AOE 10)—note the folding boat stage across the stern
Brian Morrison, 6-00

Arctic (AOE 8) H&L Van Ginderen, 2-99

A: T-AOE 6: none—others: inactivated: 1 8-round Mk 29 SAM launcher (RIM-7P Sea Sparrow missiles); 2 single 25-mm 75-cal. Mk 38 Bushmaster low-angle guns; 2 20-mm Mk 15 Phalanx gatling CIWS; 4 single 12.7-mm M2 mg (see remarks)
Electronics:
Radar: 1 Raytheon SPS-64(V)9 nav.; 1 Norden SPS-67(V)1 surf. search—AOE 7–10 only: 1 Hughes Mk 23 TAS target desig.; 2 Raytheon Mk 95 SAM f.c.; 2 Mk 90 Phalanx f.c. (see remarks)
TACAN: URN-25
EW: AOE 7–10 only: Raytheon SLQ-32(V)3 active/passive; Mk 36 SRBOC decoy syst. (4- or 6-round Mk 137 RL); SLQ-25 Nixie towed passive torpedo decoy syst. (see remarks)
M: 4 G.E. LM-2500-30 gas turbines; 2 6-bladed fixed-pitch props; 105,000 shp
Electric: 12,500 kw (5 × 2,500-kw Caterpillar 3608, 3,100-bhp, diesel-driven sets)
Range: 6,000/22 **Fuel:** 2,654 tons
Crew: T-AOE 6: 176 MSC civil service, 59 navy; others: 27–28 officers, 534–551 enlisted (accomm. for 40 officers, 36 CPOs, and 591 other enlisted)

Remarks: Modified versions of the AOE 1 class with better protective systems and modern propulsion plants. Authorized in FY 87, 89, 90, and 92, respectively. AOE 6 was ordered 23-1-87, with option to build AOE 7–9; AOE 7 was ordered 3-11-88, AOE 8 on 6-12-89. AOE 9 (reportedly planned to have been named *Conecuh*) was authorized and funded under FY 91 but the funding was rescinded by the administration and the ship canceled. AOE 10, authorized and funded under FY 92, was ordered 15-1-93. There were originally to have been seven, but no additional units are now planned. The original name for AOE 7 was reassigned to DDG 60. Completions were delayed by engineering and labor problems, and there were considerable cost overruns with the program. On 3-3-00, 17 MSC civilian stewards replaced 24 enlisted food servicemen aboard AOE 6 for a year's trial; the ship was transferred to the MSC on 13-7-01 as T-AOE 6. T-AOE 8 was to follow on 14-6-02 and the other two by 7-04. The 58-strong navy contingent on the T-AOE ships includes 31 assigned to the helicopter detachment. AOE 6 and 8 are based at Earle, N.J., the other two at Bremerton, Wash.

AUXILIARIES *(continued)*

Hull systems: Cargo: 156,000 bbl liquids (30% fuel oil, 40% JP-5, 30% convertible), 500 55-gallon drums fuel oil, 20,000 gallons potable water, and 2,450 tons dry stores (including 1,800 tons ammunition, 400 tons refrigerated provisions, 250 tons other stores, and 800 gas bottles). Have five refueling at sea stations and six solids replenishment-at-sea stations. There are four 10-ton-capacity cargo derricks. The hangar can accommodate two UH-46D utility/vertical replenishment helicopters.
Combat systems: The weapon systems were to be inactivated in FY 99 to reduce crew requirements by one officer and 40 enlisted personnel. The weapons and all sensors other than the navigational radars are being removed as part of the transfer to MSC.

♦ **4 Sacramento-class (SCB 196 type) fast combat support ships [AOR]** Bldr: Puget Sound NSY, Bremerton, Wash. (AOE 2: New York SB, Camden, N.J.) (*Atlantic/†Pacific Fleet)

	Laid down	L	In serv.
AOE 1 Sacramento†	30-6-61	14-9-63	14-3-64
AOE 2 Camden†	17-2-64	29-5-65	1-4-67
AOE 3 Seattle*	1-10-65	2-3-68	5-4-69
AOE 4 Detroit*	29-11-66	21-6-69	28-3-70

Sacramento (AOE 1) Douglas A. Cromby, 2-98

Detroit (AOE 4) Maritime Photographic, 3-99

Camden (AOE 2) W. Michael Young, 9-01

D: AOE 1: 18,884 tons light (49,956 fl); others: 20,144–20,717 tons light (50,561–53,138 fl)
S: 26 kts **Dim:** 242.24 (234.75 pp) × 32.90 × 11.60
A: inactivated: 1 8-round Mk 29 SAM launcher (RIM-7P Sea Sparrow missiles); 2 20-mm Mk 15 Phalanx gatling CIWS; 4 single 12.7-mm mg
Electronics:
Radar: 1 Raytheon SPS-64(V)9 nav.; 1 Raytheon SPS-10F surf. search; 1 Hughes Mk 23 TAS target desig.; 2 Raytheon Mk 95 missile f.c.; 2 Mk 90 Phalanx f.c. (see remarks)
TACAN: URN-25
EW: Raytheon SLQ-32(V)3 active/passive; Mk 36 SRBOC decoy syst. (4 6-round Mk 137 RL); SLQ-25 towed acoustic torpedo decoy syst.
M: 2 sets G.E. geared steam turbines; 2 props; 106,000 shp
Boilers: 4 Combustion Engineering, 42.2 kg/cm^2, 480° C
Range: 6,000/26; 10,000/17
Crew: AOE 1: 34 officers, 602 enlisted; AOE 2: 52 officers, 627 enlisted; AOE 3: 43 officers, 712 enlisted; AOE 4: 48 officers, 678 enlisted

Remarks: Authorized in FY 61, 63, 65, and 66, respectively; an authorized fifth unit was canceled. The class was to have been given a service life extension program (SLEP) modernization and refit, beginning with one unit to be funded under FY 99, at which point the oldest ship would already have seen 35 years' service, and a second under FY 02; however, the program has been dropped, although the over-aged ships have continued in service. AOE 4 was officially reported to be in very bad condition as of 9-99; the ship began an 8-month refit at Metro Machine Corp., Philadelphia, in early 2000, and is expected to operate until 2006; on 27-8-00, AOE 4 was in a collision with the *Nicholson* (DD 982) and on 14-9-00 was hit by a harbor tug and leaked some 30,000 gallons of fuel at Earle, N.J. AOE 1 and AOE 2 are based at Bremerton, Wash., AOE 3 at Norfolk, and AOE 4 at Earle. A plan to transfer them to the MSC has been shelved, and there are no plans to replace them when they are all retired during 2007.
Hull systems: The steam turbines in AOE 1 and 2 were taken from the uncompleted battleship *Kentucky* (BB 66). Carry 177,000 barrels of fuel, 2,150 tons of ammunition, and 750 tons of provisions. Have a helicopter hangar and flight deck for 2–3 UH-46 Sea Knight vertical-replenishment helicopters. AOE 2 is testing the "Standard Navy UNREP" suite, with new winches, rams, ram-tensioners, and control booths.
Combat systems: The Sea Sparrow launcher and Mk 91 Mod. 1 control system, with two Mk 95 radar directors, replaced two twin 76.2-mm DP forward; two Mk 56 gunfire-control systems were removed. The two remaining 76.2-mm gunmounts aft were replaced by two 20-mm Mk 15 CIWS. The SLQ-32(V)3 ECM replaced WLR-1. AOE 3 was the first to get the Mk 23 TAS Mod. 2 (Target Acquisition System), which in these ships is a stand-alone system employing a UYA-4 computer; by 1999, it had been fitted in all four, and the SPS-40 air-search radars previously fitted only in AOE 1 and 2 had been removed. The weapons systems were to be inactivated during FY 99 to reduce crew requirements by one officer and 40 enlisted personnel.

♦ **1 T-1-type chartered coastal transport tanker [AOT]**
Bldr: Tuzla Gemi Endustrisi, Tuzla, Turkey (In serv. 1999)

Montauk (ex-*Bitten Theresa*)

Montauk—as *Bitten Theresa* Jan Van Den Klooster, 11-00

D: approx. 7,000 tons (fl) **S:** 13 kts **Dim:** 109.10 (99.60 pp) × 16.00 × 5.69
M: 1 M.A.N.–Burmeister & Wain Alpha 8L28/32 diesel; 1 CP prop; 2,665 bhp—bow-thruster
Range: . . ./. . . **Crew:** . . .

Remarks: 3,457 grt/4,780 dwt. Former Danish chemical tanker, chartered 27-11-00 through 8-02 from Sealift, Inc., for $10.751 million to transport fuels from Korea to Japan; the contract may later be extended. Cargo: 5,850 m^3 of liquids in 12 tanks. The ship replaced the *Valiant* (ex-*Seta,* ex-*Chimorazo*, ex-*Thomona*).

♦ **5 Paul Buck (T5-M-PVT022)–class chartered transport tankers [AOT]** Bldr: American SB, Tampa, Fla.

	Laid down	L	In serv.
Paul Buck (ex-*Ocean Champion*)	28-10-84	1-6-85	11-9-85
Gus W. Darnell (ex-*Ocean Freedom*)	25-11-84	10-8-85	11-9-85
Samuel L. Cobb (ex-*Ocean Triumph*)	17-4-85	2-11-85	15-11-85
Richard G. Matthiesen (ex-*Ocean Spirit*)	13-8-85	15-2-86	18-2-86
Lawrence H. Gianella (ex-*Ocean Star*)	2-12-85	19-4-86	22-4-86

Lawrence H. Gianella—with two portable underway refueling rigs positioned to port Douglas A. Cromby, 6-01

Lawrence H. Gianella—note the astern refueling hose reel on the platform above the stern Douglas A. Cromby, 6-01

AUXILIARIES *(continued)*

D: 9,000 tons light (39,624 fl) **S:** 16 kts **Dim:** 187.45 (179.07 pp) × 27.43 × 10.36
Electronics: Radar: 1 . . . nav.
M: 1 Mitsubishi- or Ishikawajima-Sulzer 5RTA-76 diesel; 1 prop; 15,300 bhp
Electric: 2,250 kw tot. (3 × 750-kw heavy oil sets)
Range: 12,000/16 **Fuel:** 1,422 tons heavy oil, 254 tons diesel
Crew: 9 officer and 15 unlicensed contract mariners

Remarks: 21,471 grt. *Buck* and *Darnell:* 29,500 dwt; *Matthiesen:* 29,526 dwt; *Cobb:* 32,572 dwt; and *Gianella:* 32,965 dwt. The first two were contracted for on 30-9-82 and the other three were ordered 24-4-83. Some sections of the ships built at Nashville, Tenn., for later joining to the main body, and the forebodies were subcontracted to Avondale SY. Were originally chartered for five years; charter has been renewed. Operated by Ocean Ship Holdings (*Cobb* by Sealift, Inc., of New York) for investor-owners. *Gianella* acted as a strategic prepositioning ship at Diego Garcia in 1994–95 but is now, like the others, used on worldwide freighting duties. *Matthieson* was refitted in Greece during 1999.
Hull systems: Have ice-strengthened hulls. The engines in the first two were built by Mitsubishi, the others by Ishikawajima-Harima Heavy Industries. Cargo: 238,400 bbl (*Matthieson* and *Gianella:* 239,500 bbl). All have three Caterpillar 3/50 diesel generator sets, plus a Nishishiba shaft generator and a G.M. emergency diesel generator. Can make 16 kts at 75% power. Can carry up to 14,675 bbl of liquid ballast. *Matthieson* and *Gianella* have two Modular Fuel Delivery System (MFDS) equipment installations, permitting their use in alongside, underway refueling; they also have an over-the-stern refueling capability.

♦ 0 (+ 14) Theater Support Vessel program [AP]

D: . . . **S:** 41 kts gas turbine/35.5 kts diesel **Dim:** 101.0 × . . . × . . .
A: . . .
M: 4 G.E. LM-500 gas turbines or 4 Caterpillar 3618 or MTU 20V Mega diesels
Range: 3,000/. . . empty; 1,200/40 loaded **Crew:** . . .

Remarks: 750 dwt. Discussion of a craft capable of carrying 400 short tons of cargo and 600–800 troops at a 40-kt average speed for up to 1,200 miles began during 2000. The craft would have to have a drive-on/drive-off vehicle cargo capability via bow and stern ramps; and the commercial design could accommodate 950 troops, 100 HMMWV light vehicles, 4 heavy trucks, and 12 helicopters (with a single helicopter operating position). Construction would be of aluminum, and a high degree of automation would be incorporated. Unit cost is estimated at $50 million, and the privately funded prototype was to be completed by mid-2001. A proposed 125-m version would accommodate 1,700 troops, plus 114 HMMWVs, 4 large trucks, and 14 helicopters. The chartered Australian wave-piercing catamaran vehicle/passenger ferry *Joint Venture* (IX 532; q.v.) was being employed in part to test this concept during 2001–03, as is the similar *Westpac Express.*

♦ 1 chartered Auto Express 101–class Theater Logistics Vessel troop and vehicle transport [AP]
Bldr: Austal Ltd., Fremantle, Australia (In serv. 2001)

Westpac Express

Westpac Express—at Yokosuka; the bow vehicle ramp is lowered
Mitsuhiro Kadota, 7-01

Westpac Express—at her builder's Austal Ltd., 2001

D: . . . tons **S:** 37 kts (33 loaded)
Dim: 101.00 (88.70 hulls immersed) × 26.65 × 4.20
A: none **Electronics:** Radar: . . .
M: 4 Caterpillar 3618 diesels; 4 KaMeWa 125S11 waterjets; 40,236 bhp
Fuel: 160,000 liters + 240,000 liters in long-range tanks
Crew: . . . + 970 troops

Remarks: 750 dwt. Chartered 3-7-01 for two months starting 11-7-01 (extendable by another six months) by the 3rd Marine Expeditionary Force, Okinawa, to transport Marine Corps personnel and vehicles between White Beach, Okinawa, and Japanese ports, including Yokosuka and Iwakuni; the charter is in effect a trial of the effectiveness of the Theater Support Vessel program concept. Retains the builder's blue-and-white paint scheme and carries "Austal.com" on the sides. The charter was transferred to the MSC and extended for three years on 30-1-02, the ship having proved extremely useful.
Hull systems: Wave-piercing, catamaran-hull design. Can carry up to 550 tons of vehicle cargo in addition to up to 951 Marines. Some 100 HMMWV four-wheel vehicles or 251 automobiles can be stowed on the mezzanine deck, with four trucks and up to 12 UH-1-size helicopters on the main deck. The mezzanine deck has 1,190 lane-meters of vehicle parking space, with 341 lane-meters down the center being high enough to accommodate ten 40-ton trucks, and the vehicle axle load is 15 tons. The entire deck is hoistable in four sections, and there is a bow door for unloading vehicles to a pier. The 7,500-kw diesel engines drive four Reintjes VLJ6831 gearboxes, which in turn drive the four waterjets. The ship would not be suitable for combat service, due to a lack of damaged stability and battle-damage control systems.

♦ 2 Samuel Gompers–class destroyer tenders [AR] (In reserve)
Bldrs: AD 38: Puget Sound NSY; AD 42: General Dynamics National Steel & SB Co. (NASSCO), San Diego

	Laid down	L	In serv.	To reserve
AD 38 Puget Sound	15-2-65	16-9-66	27-4-68	27-1-96
AD 42 Acadia	14-2-78	28-7-79	6-6-81	16-12-94

Acadia (AD 42)—in reserve at Pearl Harbor Brian Morrison, 6-00

D: AD 38: 14,156 tons light (20,830 fl); AD 42: 13,526 tons light (20,473 fl)
S: 20 kts **Dim:** 196.29 × 25.91 × 6.86 **A:** removed
Electronics:
Radar: 1 Raytheon SPS-64(V)9 nav.; 1 Raytheon SPS-10 surf. search
TACAN: AD 38 only: URN-25
M: 2 sets de Laval geared steam turbines; 1 prop; 20,000 shp
Boilers: 2 Combustion Engineering; 43.6 kg/cm^2, 462° C **Electric:** 12,000 kw tot.
Crew: 43 officers, 578–583 enlisted + repair party: 798 enlisted (accomm. for: AD 38: 106 officers, 1,314 enlisted; AD 42: 87 officers, 1,508 enlisted)

Remarks: Maintenance ships for cruisers, destroyers, and frigates. Similar in external appearance to *L. Y. Spear*–class submarine tenders. AD 42 (and later sisters) were considered a separate class (SCB 700 type) and had facilities to carry and overhaul LM-2500 gas turbines, having been tailored to support DD 963–, DDG 993–, and FFG 7–class ships. AD 38 is stored at Pearl Harbor and AD 42 at Philadelphia.
Disposals: *Samuel Gompers* (AD 37) was decommissioned 27-10-95, *Yellowstone* (AD 41) on 31-1-96, *Cape Cod* (AD 43) on 23-9-95, and *Shenandoah* (AD 44) on 13-9-96. All six of the class were to be retained indefinitely as mobilization assets, but under a 20-2-98 decision, all except AD 37 were to be stricken and scrapped, depriving the USN of a potential mobile repair and support capability for surface warships. Finally, however, AD 37 was stricken along with AD 41, 43, and 44 on 7-4-99. AD 41 had been planned to be reactivated under MSC control during FY 99, but the option was dropped from the FY 99 budget. AD 41, 43, and 44 were permanently transferred to MARAD 28-7-01, while AD 37 is kept by the navy at the Norfolk Naval Shipyard, Portsmouth, Va.
Hull systems: Have a helo deck aft, but only AD 38 has a hangar. There are two 30-ton cranes and two 3.5-ton traveling cranes. Have excellent workshops for electronic equipment and surface-to-air missiles. Can carry 60,000 different types of repair parts in 65 storerooms totaling 1,795 m^3.
Combat systems: AD 41 and later were originally planned to carry Sea Sparrow launchers. One 127-mm DP gun was removed from AD 38 in 1979; the others never carried the weapon. AD 38 served as Sixth Fleet flagship from 7-80 to 4-10-85, having received an extra mast to support a special SATCOM antenna (all had the standard WSC-3 SATCOM installation, with two OE-82 drum-shaped antennas).

♦ 1 Zeus-class cable ship [ARC]
Bldr: National Steel & SB Co. (NASSCO), San Diego

	Laid down	L	In serv.
T-ARC 7 Zeus	1-6-81	9-10-82	19-3-84

D: 9,110 tons light (14,225 fl) **S:** 15.6 kts **Dim:** 153.2 (138.4 pp) × 22.3 × 7.92
Electronics: Radar: 1 . . . nav.; 1 Thales-DRS Scout surf. search
M: 5 G.M. EMD 20-cyl., 3,600-bhp diesels, electric drive; 2 CP props; 12,500 shp—4 1,200-shp side thrusters (2 forward, 2 aft)
Electric: 3,500 kw tot. **Range:** 10,000/15 **Fuel:** 1,816 tons
Crew: 88 MSC civil service crew, 6 navy (enlisted) + 32 civilian technicians

Remarks: 3,750 dwt. Authorized under FY 79 and ordered 17-8-79. Plans to request a second were canceled. After 15 years of primarily Pacific Ocean operations, was transferred to the Atlantic 24-3-97 and refitted at Mobile, Ala. Operates at sea about 300 days per year. Painted white.

AUXILIARIES *(continued)*

Zeus (T-ARC 7) Mike Welsford, 10-01

Zeus (T-ARC 7) Takatoshi Okano, 4-01

Hull systems: Cable capacity: 1,170 m^3 coiled (about 590 n.m.), plus 1,004 m^3 spare capacity (506 n.m.); up to 3,117 tons of cable repeaters can be stowed. Can lay cable in water up to 9,000-ft. deep. Able to conduct acoustic, hydrographic, and bathymetric surveys. The five main engines also provide for the ship's service generators; there is also a 500-kw emergency generator. Has passive tank roll stabilization.

Note: Five commercial cable ships owned by the British Cable and Wireless Marine were under short-term charter to MSC during mid-2001: *Monarch, Nexus, Seaspread, Sovereign,* and *Sir Eric Sharpe.*

♦ 4 Safeguard-class salvage ships [ARS]

Bldr: Peterson Bldrs, Sturgeon Bay, Wis. (*Atlantic/†Pacific Fleet)

	Laid down	L	In serv.
ARS 50 Safeguard†	8-11-82	12-11-83	17-8-85
ARS 51 Grasp*	30-3-83	21-4-84	14-12-85
ARS 52 Salvor†	16-9-83	28-7-84	14-6-86
ARS 53 Grapple*	25-4-84	8-12-84	15-11-86

Grasp (ARS 51) Takatoshi Okano, 9-01

Grasp (ARS 51) Camil Busquets i Vilanova, 5-00

D: 2,482–2,633 tons light (3,181–3,317 fl) **S:** 13.5 kts
Dim: 77.72 (73.15 wl) × 15.54 × 5.49 **A:** 2 single 12.7-mm mg
Electronics: Radar: 1 Raytheon SPS-69 nav.; 1 Raytheon SPS-64(V)9 nav.
M: 4 Caterpillar D399, 16-cyl. diesels, geared drive; 2 CP Kort-nozzle props; 4,400 bhp—500-shp electric bow-thruster
Electric: 2,250 kw tot. (3 Caterpillar D399 diesel sets driving; 450 V, 60 Hz a.c.)
Range: 8,000/12 **Crew:** 7 officers, 92 enlisted

Remarks: ARS 50 was authorized in FY 81, ARS 51 and 52 in FY 82, and ARS 53 in FY 83. ARS 50 was ordered during 1981, with an option for four more. One additional unit of this class was planned for request under FY 91, then deferred to FY 94, and finally dropped; in FY 91, it was planned to request *two* under FY 96, but by FY 93, the ships had disappeared from the building program. Design was developed from the ARS 38. Up to 25% of the crew can be women. Although these are excellent ships, the USN in general lacks sufficient salvage assets and requires commercial assistance in most major salvage efforts. ARS 50 has been homeported at Sasebo, Japan, since 16-6-99; ARS 50 is based at Pearl Harbor, and the other two operate from Norfolk.

Hull systems: Have 54-ton open-ocean bollard pull and, using beach extraction gear, are able to exert 360-ton pull. Have a 40-ton boom aft and a 7.5-ton boom forward. Are able to dead-lift 150 tons over the bow or stern. Cargo hold measures 596 m^3. There are two 914-m-long, 57-mm towing hawsers, able to tow a CVN at 5 kts. Have the Mk 12 diving system and are able to support hard-hat divers to 58 m and SCUBA divers; a decompression chamber is fitted. Four foam firefighting monitors are carried. Can deploy several different types of remotely operated salvage submersibles.

♦ 1 chartered deep submergence rescue tender [ARS]

Bldr: North American SB, Larose, La. (In serv. 17-3-96)

Kellie Chouest

Kellie Chouest Jim Sanderson, 6-01

D: . . . (fl) **S:** . . . kts **Dim:** 94.48 (88.88 pp) × 15.80 × 4.58
M: 2 G.M. Electromotive Div. 16-cyl. diesels; 2 props; 3,900 bhp
Electric: 900 kw tot. (3 × 300-kw diesel sets)

Remarks: 2,786 grt/2,373 dwt. Edison Chouest Offshore, Galliano, La., received a $6.7 million contract from the MSC on 16-8-94 to build and operate on charter a deep submergence vehicle support ship for the Commander, Submarine Force Atlantic. On completion by 1-3-96, ship was to be on a 17-month charter, with options for renewal; in 10-98, Congress approved leasing the ship through 30-9-03. During 9-96, the *Kellie Chouest* operated the remote-controlled salvage submersible *Scorpio* and a submarine personnel rescue chamber. Has also been used to deploy a DSRV rescue submersible. There is a submersible lifting platform at the stern to launch and retrieve submersibles. Equipped with a four-point mooring system, Robertson dynamic positioning system, ORE Trackpoint II and Nautronix RS-916 tracking systems, and a Racal Pelagos Winfrom integrated navigation system. A 68-ton-capacity submersible elevator is used to launch and recover submersibles.

♦ 1 chartered deep submergence support tender [ARS]

Bldr: North American SB, Galliano, La. (In serv. 1978)

Dolores Chouest

Dolores Chouest Takatoshi Okano, 8-00

D: approx. 1,600 tons (fl) **S:** 13 kts **Dim:** . . . (54.87 pp) × 12.20 × 3.64
Electronics: Radar: . . .
M: 2 Caterpillar D399-SCAC diesels; 2 CP props; 2,250 bhp
Fuel: 148.5 tons **Crew:** . . .

Remarks: 199 grt. Former oilfield supply tug, on charter to support the rescue submersible *Mystic* (DSRV 1) and based at North Island Naval Air Station, San Diego. The hull is painted orange and the superstructure cream. Operated by her owner, Edison Chouest Offshore, in support of Commander, Submarine Force Pacific. Although the ship was to be returned to the owner during FY 98, in 10-98 Congress required leasing the ship through 30-9-03. There is a lift platform at the stern for launch and recovery of submersibles.

AUXILIARIES *(continued)*

♦ 1 chartered deep submergence support tender [ARS]
Bldr: North American SB, Larose, La. (In serv. 1994)

CAROLYN CHOUEST

Carolyn Chouest—with NR-1 and a diving tender alongside at the stern H&L Van Ginderen, 6-99

D: approx. 1,700 tons (fl) **S:** 12 kts **Dim:** 50.45 × 11.60 × 3.65
M: 2 Caterpillar D399TA diesels; 2 props; 2,440 bhp
Crew: 14 tot. + up to 32 navy support personnel

Remarks: 199 grt/450 dwt. Former oilfield tug/supply vessel. Acts as tender to the nuclear-powered submersible NR-1 and is based at Groton, Conn. The initial charter contract was let to Edison Chouest Offshore, Galliano, La., in 6-93. In 10-98, Congress approved leasing the ship through 30-9-03. Prior to conversion, had two 99-kw diesel generator sets. Two OE-82 antennas are fitted for the WSC-1(V) UHF SATCOM system. Is painted with red-orange hull and cream upperworks.

♦ 1 chartered submersible tender [ARS]
Bldr: American Marine, New Orleans (In serv. 1972)

DENNY TIDE (ex-*Research Tide*)

Denny Tide George R. Schneider, 1-00

D: approx. 2,600 tons (fl) **S:** 10.5 kts **Dim:** 66.15 (61.88 pp) × 17.07 × 4.04
Electronics: Radar: . . .
M: 2 G.M. Electromotive Div. 12-cyl. diesels; 2 CP props; 3,000 bhp—bow- and stern-thrusters
Electric: 1,050 kw tot. (3 × 450-kw diesel-driven sets)
Range: . . ./. . . **Fuel:** 460.5 tons **Crew:** . . . tot.

Remarks: 497 grt/1,571 dwt. Modified oilfield tug/supply vessel. Has been stationed at Port Hueneme, Calif., since completion and is for unspecified research purposes. Has a twin hangar aft for probable submersible equipment.

♦ 3 L. Y. Spear–class submarine tenders [AS] (1 in *reserve*)
Bldr: Lockheed SB, Seattle (*Atlantic/†Pacific Fleet)

	Laid down	L	In serv.
AS 39 EMORY S. LAND*	2-3-76	4-5-77	7-7-79
AS 40 FRANK CABLE†	2-3-76	14-1-78	5-2-80
AS 41 *MCKEE*	14-1-78	16-2-80	15-8-81

D: AS 39: 13,911 tons light (22,978 fl); AS 40: 13,758 tons light (22,826 fl); AS 41: 14,135 tons light (23,128 fl)
S: 20 kts (18 sust.) **Dim:** 196.29 × 25.91 × 8.83 (max.)
A: 4 single 12.7-mm mg
Electronics:
Radar: 1 Raytheon SPS-64(V)9 nav.; 1 Raytheon SPS-10-series surf. search

Frank Cable (AS 40)—with staging around foremast Mitsuhiro Kadota, 4-01

Emory S. Land (AS 39) Bernard Prézelin, 2-01

M: 1 set de Laval geared steam turbines; 1 prop; 20,000 shp
Boilers: 2 Combustion Engineering; 43.6 kg/cm², 462° C
Electric: 11,000 kw tot.
Crew: AS 39: 83 officers, 1,286 enlisted; AS 40: 81 officers, 1,270 enlisted

Remarks: Were intended to provide support to up to 12 submarines, with up to four alongside at once, and were specifically tailored to the needs of the SSN 688 class. AS 39 became Sixth Fleet/Mediterranean repair ship at La Maddalena, Sardinia, on 24-4-99. AS 40 was to have been decommissioned 1-7-95 but will be retained active at Guam. AS 41 was deactivated 16-7-99 and decommissioned 30-9-99 and is being held as a mobilization reserve asset, stored at Portsmouth, Va.
Disposals: The unnamed AS 38 (in the FY 69 budget) was canceled 27-3-69. *L. Y. Spear* (AS 36), decommissioned 6-9-96, was stricken 3-5-99 and transferred to MARAD for disposal. *Dixon* (AS 37) was decommissioned 30-9-95 and stricken 18-3-96 for scrapping.
Hull systems: Have one 30-ton crane and two 5-ton traveling cranes; a total of 53 specialized repair shops; medical facilities, including an operating room, a 23-bed ward, and a dental clinic; and a helicopter deck but no hangar.
Combat systems: It was originally planned to fit Mk 15 Phalanx CIWS or Sea Sparrow SAM in later ships. The Mk 67 20-mm guns have been replaced with 12.7-mm machineguns.

♦ 1 Simon Lake–class submarine tender [AS] (In reserve)
Bldr: Puget Sound NSY, Bremerton, Wash.

	Laid down	L	In serv.
AS 33 *SIMON LAKE*	7-1-63	8-2-64	7-11-64

Simon Lake (AS 33)—when active H&L Van Ginderen, 1996

D: 13,797 tons light (20.088 fl) **S:** 18 kts **Dim:** 196.2 × 25.9 × 9.1
A: 4 single 12.7-mm mg
Electronics:
Radar: 1 Canadian Marconi LN-66 nav.; 1 Raytheon SPS-10-series surf. search
M: 1 set de Laval geared steam turbines; 1 prop; 20,000 shp
Boilers: 2 Combustion Engineering; 43.6 kg/cm², 462° C
Electric: 11,000 kw tot. **Range:** 7,600/18
Crew: 62 officers, 550 enlisted (when active)

Remarks: Authorized in FY 63. Former Atlantic Fleet unit, decommissioned 10-9-99 but retained in reserve at Portsmouth, Va., for possible reactivation.

AUXILIARIES *(continued)*

Disposals: Sister AS 35 was canceled 3-12-64. *Canopus* (AS 34) was decommissioned 30-11-94, stricken 3-5-95, and transferred to MARAD for disposal 1-5-99.
Hull systems: Equipped to support SSBNs. Can stow 16 spare ballistic missiles vertically in an amidships magazine. Modified in 1978 to support the *Ohio*-class SSBNs. Has two 30-ton cranes to handle boats and missiles and four 5-ton traveling cranes mounted on upper-deck rails. Has a helicopter deck but no hangar.

◆ **6 Powhatan-class fleet tugs [ATA]** (1 in *reserve*)
Bldr: Marinette Marine, Marinette, Wis. (*Atlantic/†Pacific Fleet)

	Laid down	L	In serv.
Narragansett (ex-T-ATF 167)	5-5-77	28-11-78	9-1-79
T-ATF 168 Catawba†	14-12-77	12-5-79	28-5-80
T-ATF 169 Navajo†	14-12-77	20-12-79	13-6-80
T-ATF 170 Mohawk*	22-3-79	5-4-80	16-10-80
T-ATF 171 Sioux†	22-3-79	30-10-80	12-5-81
T-ATF 172 Apache*	22-3-79	20-12-80	30-7-81

Navajo (T-ATF 169) Brian Morrison, 1-01

Apache (T-ATF 172) H&L Van Ginderen, 9-00

D: 1,647 tons light (2,260 fl) **S:** 15 kts **Dim:** 73.20 (68.88 pp) × 12.80 × 4.74
Electronics: Radar: 1 Raytheon TM 1660/12S nav.; 1 Raytheon SPS-64(V)9 nav.
M: 2 G.M. EMD 20-645X7 20-cyl. diesels, electric drive; 2 Kort-nozzle CP props; 4,500 shp (3,600 sust.)
Electric: 1,200 kw (3 × 400-kw diesel sets)
Range: 10,000/13 **Fuel:** 600 tons
Crew: 6 officer and 14 unlicensed MSC civil service mariners + 4 navy enlisted communications team

Remarks: 902 grt/613 nrt. One was authorized in FY 75, three in FY 76, and three in FY 78. Modified oilfield tug/supply vessel design built to merchant marine specifications. *Narragansett* was deactivated 18-10-99, transferred to a commercial salvage company, and chartered the same day by the MSC, but has since been inactive, laid up at Port Hueneme, Calif.
Disposals: Sister *Powhatan* (T-ATF 166) was deactivated 1-2-99 and leased to Donjon Marine, Hillside, N.J., for five years starting in 3-99 as standby salvage and towing services tug at New York City.
Hull systems: Have a 300-hp bow-thruster and one 10-ton electrohydraulic crane. Can carry the Mk 1 Mod. 1, 90-ton deep-diving support module on the stern and can support a 20-man navy salvage team. Have a 60-ton bollard-pull capacity. Foam fire-fighting equipment is fitted. Hull has double hard-chine configuration.

Sioux (T-ATF 171) Jim Sanderson, 6-01

UNCLASSIFIED MISCELLANEOUS SHIPS (IX)

Note: The ships and craft in this section are listed in descending order of IX-series hull number rather than by age. The entries marked with an asterisk (*) are non-self-propelled. The IX category seems to be evolving into a catch-all, although most of the craft could have been categorized under one of the USN's existing type designations. Applicable type designations are provided at the ends of the entry header.

◆ **1 chartered fast passenger and vehicle ferry [AP]**
Bldr: Incat, Hobart, Tasmania, Australia

	Laid down	L	In serv.
IX 532 Joint Venture (ex-HSV-X1, ex-*Incat 050*, ex-*TopCat*, ex-*DevilCat*)	19-1-98	7-11-98	21-11-98

Joint Venture (IX 532)—at Kiel, Germany Martin Mokrus, 3-02

Joint Venture (IX 532) Bollinger/Incat U.S.A., 9-01

D: 940 tons light (1,668 fl) **S:** 50 kts light (37.5 fully loaded)
Dim: 96.00 (86.00 hulls) × 26.00 × 3.96 (max.)
A: none **Electronics:** Radar: . . .
M: 4 Caterpillar 3618 diesels; 4 Lips 50D waterjets; 30,000 bhp (at 1,030 rpm)
Electric: 920 kw tot. (4 × 230 kw, 4 Caterpillar 3406B diesels driving; 415 V a.c.)
Range: 1,100/35 (fully loaded; normal fuel)
Fuel: 120 m^3 normal; 490 m^3 max. ferry **Crew:** 5 officers, 25 enlisted

Remarks: Chartered 25-7-01 by the army Tank-Automotive and Armament Command (TACOM) on behalf of the army, navy, and Coast Guard for West Coast U.S.

UNCLASSIFIED MISCELLANEOUS SHIPS (IX) *(continued)*

"proof of concept" trials. Although assigned navy number IX 532 on 5-10-01, she continues to wear the owner's pennant number HSV-X1. Accepted for service 11-10-01. Is to be employed for 18–24 months to determine whether such craft can be of use in training and support roles. The contract is being managed by Incat's U.S. partner, Bollinger SY. Long-term army plans call for acquiring 14 fast ferries of this type. She was assigned to army control on 1-3-02 for trials. Was initially based at the Naval Amphibious Base, Little Creek, Va.

Hull systems: Wave-piercing catamaran design, with 4.50-m beam to each hull. During a refit prior to the trials, a launch and recovery system to handle RIB craft up to 11.9 m long was fitted, and a 472-m^2 helicopter platform was added to handle aircraft up to SH-60 and CH-46 size. Cargo deadweight is 800 tons, including the 600 passengers and crew. Has 330 lane-meters of vehicle capacity, 2.7-m clear width, and 4.3-m clear height. A slewing stern vehicle ramp that can handle military loads is fitted. Has four Reintges VIJ6031 gearboxes to transfer power from the engines to the waterjets, and the engineering plant is highly automated. Normal fuel is carried in four 30-m^3 tanks, while two 170-m^3 tanks in the lower hulls can be employed for fuel when cargo is not carried.

♦ 1 YP 676–class trials craft [YAGE]

Bldr: Peterson Bldrs, Sturgeon Bay, Wis.

	Laid down	L	In serv.
IX 531 (ex-YP 679)	18-4-84	11-12-84	6-6-85

D: 172 tons (176 fl) **S:** 13.25 kts (12 sust.)
Dim: 32.92 (30.99 pp) × 7.39 × 1.83
Electric Equipt: Radar: 1 SPS-64(V)9 nav.
M: 2 G.M. Detroit Diesel 12V-71N diesels; 2 props; 874 bhp—60-shp bow-thruster
Electric: 100 kw tot. (2 × 50 kw, G.M. Detroit Diesel 3-71 diesels driving)
Range: 1,400/12 **Fuel:** 6,550 gallons **Crew:** 2 officers, 4 enlisted

Remarks: Reclassified from YP 679 on 7-8-01 for use by the Office of Naval Research "in support of various HM&E [Hull, Machinery, and Engineering]-related research and development programs." Two dozen sisters serve as training craft (see under [YXT]).

Hull systems: Wooden hull, aluminum superstructure. Made up to 13.3 kts on trials. Has a NAVSAT receiver, two echo sounders, a Sperry Mk 27 gyrocompass with six repeaters, a speed log, an anemometer, the Sippican expendable bathythermograph system, and a GPS receiver.

♦ 1 YFND 5–class diving tender* [YDTN]

Bldr: Associated Shipbuilders, Seattle

	Laid down	L	In serv.
IX 530 (ex-YFND 5, ex-YFN 268, ex-YF 268)	10-11-40	1-12-40	1-2-41

D: 170 tons (590 fl) **Dim:** 33.53 × 10.66 × 2.13

Remarks: Former dry dock companion craft, stricken 25-6-99 but reinstated as IX 530 on 6-9-00 for use as a diving tender for the Consolidated Divers' Unit, Southwest Regional Maintenance Center, San Diego. Is a rectangular covered barge hull with deckhouse.

♦ 1 signature-reduction trials craft [YAGE]

Bldr: Lockheed SB, Redwood City, Calif. (In serv. 1983)

IX 529 Sea Shadow

Sea Shadow (IX 529) W. Michael Young, 8-99

Sea Shadow support barge HMB-1 W. Michael Young, 6-00

D: 499 tons light (563 fl) **S:** 15.1 kts (13 sust.)
Dim: 49.99 (36.00 wl) × 20.73 (17.68 wl) × 4.57 (max.)
Electronics: Radar: 1 . . . nav.
M: 2 G.M. Detroit Diesel 12V149 TI diesels, 2 Kato generators (750 kw each), 2 electric motors; 2 props; 1,600 shp
Electric: 150 kw tot. (1 × 100-kw, 2 × 25-kw motor generators—all driven by the main engines; principal voltage: 600 V a.c.)
Range: 2,250/9 **Crew:** 12 tot. + 12 scientists/technicians

Remarks: Funded jointly by the Defense Advanced Research Projects Agency and the navy for about $50 million as part of a 10-year, $195 million program to test "stealth" ship design concepts, ship control systems, and automation concepts. Took 27 months to build. Was assembled in the covered, semisubmersible "mining barge" HMB-1, built to accompany the special auxiliary *Hughes Glomar Explorer* (AG 193); HMB-1 was also used as tender and hangar to the craft. HMB-1 displaced 5,800 tons (fl) and measured 98.75 × 32.00 × 2.44 m (12.80 m depth ballasted down for launch and recovery). *Sea Shadow* was laid up in 1986 for lack of operating funds; she was reactivated under the FY 93 budget and trials resumed 9-4-93, but the ship was again laid up in 5-95. Once again reactivated in 3-99 for a six-year series of trials in support of the DD 21 destroyer program, the ship operates off the U.S. West Coast. Was placed on the Naval Vessel Registry and given hull number IX 529 on 15-3-00. Has been repainted during 2001 with a new, low-visibility camouflage scheme.

Hull systems: Has a SWATH (Small Waterplane Area, Twin-Hull) hull configuration, using towed-out buoyancy pontoons on the ends of 45°-inclined pylons. Trims down intentionally by the stern. Has a 51-ton payload with an instrumentation compartment aft. Fore and aft, independently computer-controlled fins provide steering, roll, and pitch control. Capable of operation in sea states up to 5. Computerized navigation equipment includes a ring-laser gyro inertial navigation unit, a Mk 27 gyrocompass, and several GPS receivers. Radios include WSC-3 UHF and ARC-182 transceivers and a commercial VHF set. Berthing for 12 is provided.

♦ 1 YRDH 1–class trials barge* [YAGE]

Bldr: Associated Shipbuilders, Seattle (In serv. 1943)

IX 528 (ex-YRDH 1, ex-YR 55)

D: 460 tons (750 fl) **Dim:** 46.02 (45.72 wl) × 10.7 × 1.8

Remarks: Reclassified from a floating dry dock workshop (non-self-propelled) on 7-4-99 for use in support of submarine tests for the Naval Surface Warfare Center, Carderock Division, Bremerton Detachment, Wash., and its Southeast Alaska Acoustic Measurement Facility at Ketchikan, Alaska. Three sisters remain typed YRDH. Was originally built as a general-purpose repair barge and has berthing for one officer and 46 enlisted.

♦ 1 YFN 1254–class trials barge* [YAGE]

Bldr: Steel Style, Inc. (In serv. 1-6-82)

IX 527 (ex-YFN 1259)

D: 174 tons (699 fl) **Dim:** 33.53 (28.65 wl) × 10.67 (9.75 wl) × 2.44

Remarks: Reclassified 7-4-99 for use in submarine tests by the Naval Surface Warfare Center, Carderock Division, Bremerton Detachment, Wash., and its Southeast Alaska Acoustic Measurement Facility at Ketchikan, Alaska. Construction was authorized under FY 81 as a covered lighter, non-self-propelled. Is a rectangular steel barge hull with a small deckhouse.

Note: IX 526 (ex-YRST 1, ex-YDT 11) was reclassified as YR 94 on 3-4-00.

♦ 4 AFDB 1–class aerial target service barges* [YGTN]

IX 521 (ex-AFDB 1, Section D; ex-ABSD 1, Section D; ex-ABD 7)
IX 522 (ex-AFDB 2, Section D; ex-ABSD 2, Section D; ex-ABD 14)
IX 524 MATSS-1 (ex-AFDB 2, Section F; ex-ABSD 2, Section F; ex-ABD 22)
IX 525 MATSS-2 (ex-AFDB 1, Section C; ex-ABSD 1, Section C; ex-ABD 3)

IX 524—with UH-3H Sea King helicopter aboard Nick Galante/ITT, 1997

D: 2,064 tons (fl) **Dim:** 78.03 × 24.38 × 1.52
Electric: 700 kw tot. (2 × 350-kw diesel sets)
Fuel: 6,400 gallons **Crew:** . . .

Remarks: Modules of large sectional floating dry docks that had been in storage at Pearl Harbor. IX 521 and 522 were reclassified 16-8-96 and remain stored at Pearl Harbor. IX 524 was reclassified 25-4-97 for use at the Pacific Missile Test Range Facility, Kekaha, Kauai, Hawaii, along with IX 525; both are used as support platforms for the Mobile Aerial Target Support System (MATSS). IX 524 and 525 are based at the Naval Inactive Ship Maintenance Facility, Pearl Harbor, and are towed and tended by a tug when in use; they have been converted as sensor and communications platforms and have crew accommodations.

AFDB 2, Section H (ex-ABSD 2, Section F; ex-ABD 10) was to have been reclassified as IX 525 during 1997; however, the requirement was canceled and, when it was reinstated 2-3-98, a different dock section was selected. The ABD numbers listed were assigned when the craft were built as sections of large floating dry docks during World War II.

UNCLASSIFIED MISCELLANEOUS SHIPS (IX) *(continued)*

Hull systems: Data above apply to IX 524, which has a deck area of 1,765 m^2, with the forward end used as a helicopter platform; 5,500 gallons of JP-5 helo fuel are carried. IX 524 also has launchers for four BQM-74 target drones, a Stabilized High-accuracy Optical Tracking System (SHOTS), a C-band tracking radar with coherent signal processor, Inmarsat and Vsat SATCOM links, and a 10-ton-capacity deck crane and can carry 23,200 gallons of drinking water and 40,000 gallons of washdown water. Personnel spaces are air-conditioned.

Fully assembled with all 10 of their sections, AFDB 1 and 2 were some 282.55 m long by 78 m wide (40.7 m clear width inside dock walls) by 2.74 m draft in light condition; maximum flooded draft was 23.77 m, providing up to 14 m inside draft over the keel blocks. They were intended to support battleships and large aircraft carriers. Each of the 10 sections could be towed separately, and the dock walls could be pivoted to fold flat against the dock floor. Maximum rated lift for all 10 sections together was 90,000 tons.

♦ 1 training craft [YXT]

	Bldr	Laid down	L	In serv.
IX 523 (ex-YOG 93)	RTC SB, Camden, N.J.	16-4-45	8-9-45	8-2-46

D: 440 tons light (1,390 fl) **Dim:** 53.04 × 9.75 × 3.96
M: nonoperational: 1 G.M. diesel; 1 prop; 640 bhp **Electric:** 80 kw tot.

Remarks: Former self-propelled aviation fuel lighter, reclassified 25-11-96 and assigned to the Fleet Training Group, Norfolk. Moored at Little Creek, Va., and used by the Expeditionary Warfare Training Group Atlantic for its Visit, Board, Search, and Seizure course.

Disposal note: Accommodations barge IX 520 (ex-APL 19) was stricken 13-3-01.

♦ 1 boat landing float* [YAGN]
Bldr: Orange SB, Orange, Texas (In serv. 1-3-91)

IX 519 (ex-YC 1643)

D: 115 tons light (659 fl) **Dim:** 33.53 × 9.75 × 1.98 (max.)

Remarks: Originally ordered in 1989 as a non-self-propelled open barge. Reclassified as an IX during 27-8-96 and assigned to support the *La Salle* (AGF 3) at Gaeta, Italy.

Disposal note: *Proteus*-class accommodations hulk *Proteus* (IX 518, ex-AS 19) was transferred to MARAD for disposal 24-9-99, later retrieved by the navy, and again stricken 13-3-01.

♦ 1 Robert D. Conrad–class former oceanographic research ship [YAGE]
Bldr: Marinette Marine, Marinette, Wis.

	Laid down	L	In serv.
IX 517 GOSPORT (ex-*Pacific Escort;* ex-*Thomas G. Thompson,* AGOR 9)	9-63	18-7-64	4-9-65

Gosport (IX 517) William H. Clarke, 4-00

D: 990 tons light (1,400 fl) **S:** 13.5 kts (12 cruising, 9 on one engine)
Dim: 63.65 (59.7 pp) × 12.2 (11.88 wl) × 4.26 (hull; 5.94 max.)
Electronics:
Radar: 1 Hughes Aircraft SPS-73 surf. search; 1 Furuno 2010 ARPA nav.; 1 Furuno FCR-1411 nav.
Sonar: SQS-4 Mod. 3 MF active hull-mounted with WLR-9 acoustic analyzer; UQC-1 underwater telephone; 2 WQC-2 underwater telephones; WQM-6 variable-depth acoustic target source; Furuno FCV-552 6,000-ft. echo sounder; Furuno FE-880 3,000-ft. echo sounder
M: 2 Cummins diesel generator sets (825 bhp each), 2 electric motors; 1 5-bladed prop; 1,125 shp—175-shp azimuthal bow-thruster
Electric: 850 kw tot. (2 × 300-kw, 1 × 200-kw diesel sets)
Range: 12,000/10 **Fuel:** 211 tons (277 m^3) **Endurance:** 45 days
Crew: 14 tot. + up to 27 scientific party

Remarks: 1,400 grt. Formerly assigned to the University of Washington, Seattle, as an oceanographic research ship; reclassified as IX 517 on 11-12-89 as replacement for the tug *Pacific Escort* (143WB8401, ex-LT 535) in support of sea trials for ships overhauled at Mare Island Naval Shipyard, Calif. Renamed in 4-97 and assigned to the Norfolk Naval Shipyard, Portsmouth, Va., for use on general research, trials, and test support duties by USN laboratories and USN contractors. Has also been used for target drone recovery.
Hull systems: The retractable electric bow-thruster/propulsor can provide up to 4.5 kts. There are a 6-ton articulating crane and a 3-ton A-frame gantry at the stern and 3-ton and 2-ton cranes on the upper deck for handling overside equipment.
Mission systems: Has 56 m^2 of laboratory space and 223 m^2 of free working-deck area. Has an integrated navigational system with Furuno LC-90 Mk II Loran and three GPS receivers (two Furuno GP-80 differential, one Furuno GP-1250 multiscale). The communications suite includes Inmarsat B and C terminals and radios covering the MF through UHF bands. Secure communications are available. The WQM-6 sonar set is employed in sonar systems certification work. Deck space is available for portable vans.

♦ 1 Trident missile–firing simulator barge* [YAGN]
Bldr: Seatrain SB, Brooklyn, N.Y. (In serv. 1976)

IX 516 (ex-barge *Matthew,* ex-*Christina F*)

D: 3,122 tons light (3,476 fl) **Dim:** 92.28 × 27.43 × 6.71

Remarks: Former 5,279-grt cargo barge, converted to a commercial tank barge in 1980. Acquired from Allied Barge Co. and converted by McDermott, Inc., Morgan City, La., as missile-launch simulation barge for service at the Trident SSBN facility, Kings Bay, Ga. Delivered 15-4-88.

♦ 1 BH 110–class Rigid Sidewall Surface Effect Trials craft [YAGEA]
Bldr: Bell-Halter, New Orleans

	L	In serv.
IX 515 (ex-SES-200; ex-USCG *Dorado,* WSES 1)	12-78	9-80

IX 515 Findler & Winter, 9-98

D: 128 tons light (205 fl) **S:** 40+ kts (in calm water)
Dim: 48.77 × 12.50 × 2.83 (at rest; 1.68 on cushion)
Electronics: Radar: 2 Decca nav.
M: 2 MTU 16V396 TB94 diesels for propulsion; 2 KaMeWa 71S62/6-SII waterjets; 6,960 bhp—2 MTU 6V396 TB83 diesels for lift; 4 1.07-m-dia. centrifugal fans; 1,980 hp
Electric: 140 kw **Range:** 3,700/23; 2,950/30 **Fuel:** 59.6 tons
Crew: 3 officers, 10 enlisted

Remarks: Designed by Bell Aerospace–Textron and built by Halter Marine in a jointly financed effort. Leased in 1-80 for one month by the Coast Guard and then again for a longer trials period in 1981. On 29-9-82 the ship came under U.S. Navy control and had accommodations for 14 additional personnel added. Assigned to Carderock Division, Naval Surface Warfare Center, Special Trials Unit, Patuxent River, Md. Unofficially named *Jaeger* for a European tour in 1985–86. Redesignated IX 515 on 11-5-87, although is still generally known as "SES-200."
Hull systems: Functions by trapping a fan-generated air bubble between the rigid sidewalls and rubber seals at bow and stern. Two more lift-fans were added in 1984, and the original G.M. 8V92 TI lift-fan engines were replaced in 1988. Was refitted with waterjet propulsion by the builder from 4-90 to 2-2-91; the original G.M. 16V149 TI diesels (1,600 bhp each) were replaced by MTU diesels, with those to be replaced during 2002 by two M.A.N. B&W Diesel 18PV185 diesels of 5,364 bhp each.
Combat systems: Conducted trials with the G.E. EX-25, 25-mm gatling gun in spring 1987 and with the Rockwell Crossbow multiuse stabilized weapons/sensor platform in 3-89. From 1997 on, was used as the trials ship for the Advanced Lightweight Influence Sweep System (ALISS), which was to use spark-gap transducer arrays and superconducting magnetic technology in combination with lightweight, high-speed towed arrays.

♦ 1 YFU 71–class helicopter training craft [YXT]
Bldr: Pacific Coast Eng. Co., Alameda, Calif.

	Laid down	L	In serv.
IX 514 BAY LANDER (ex-HTL-514, ex-YFU 79)	12-67	5-68	7-68

Bay Lander (IX 514) H&L Van Ginderen, 12-94

D: 220 tons (380 fl) **S:** 8 kts **Dim:** 38.1 × 10.97 × 2.30
Electronics: Radar: 1 Decca . . . nav.
M: 4 G.M. Detroit Diesel 6-71 diesels; 2 props; 1,000 bhp
Crew: 23 civilian contract mariners, 1 navy helo control officer

UNCLASSIFIED MISCELLANEOUS SHIPS (IX) *(continued)*

Remarks: Originally built for the U.S. Army. Redesignated an IX on 31-3-86 and completed conversion 28-4-86 to serve as helicopter landing platform training craft at Pensacola Naval Air Station, Fla. HTL = Helicopter Landing Trainer. Operation was contracted to Seward Services, Ft. Lauderdale, Fla., on 17-12-99; the ship remains navy property. From 1985 through 1999, the ship conducted 73,000 army, navy, and other government agency helicopter training landings.
Hull systems: The bow ramp has been welded closed and a new superstructure with a rudimentary flight-control station and a 25.6-m-long, 9.75-m-wide flight deck were added.

♦ 1 satellite navigation systems trials craft [YAGE]
Bldr: Gunderson Bros., Portland, Ore. (In serv. 6-59)

IX 508 Orca (ex-LCU 1618)

Orca (IX 508)—with two-level electronics van on former vehicle cargo deck
H&L Van Ginderen, 9-99

D: 196 tons light (390 fl) **S:** 11 kts **Dim:** 41.07 × 9.07 (hull) × 2.08
M: 4 G.M. 6-71 diesels; 2 Kort-nozzle props; 1,200 bhp
Range: 1,200/11 **Fuel:** 13 tons **Crew:** . . .

Remarks: Adapted in 1978 for what is now the Naval Space and Warfare Systems Center, San Diego, to conduct trials with the NAVSTAR GPS. Reclassified IX from LCU on 1-12-79. Transferred to the Naval Oceanographic Center, Bay St. Louis, Miss., late in 5-98, the ship is now operated for the navy by the University of Southern Mississippi in trials of autonomous underwater vehicles (AUV), in conjunction with the University of Texas research ship *Gyre.*

Note: *Benewah*-class barracks ships *Mercer* (IX 502, ex-APB 39, ex-APL 39) and *Nueces* (IX 503, ex-APB 40, ex-APL 40) were reclassified as APL 39 and APL 40, respectively, on 7-3-01; see under [YPL] in the Service Craft section.

♦ 1 sonar test barge* [YAGE]

IX 310

IX 310 U.S. Navy, 2000

Remarks: Built in 1917 as a barge and placed in service as an acoustic trials barge on 1-4-71. Is subordinated to the Naval Undersea Warfare Center Division, Seneca Lake, N.Y., where the craft is moored with YCF 16 and YFNX 22 (qq.v.). As of 2000, IX 310 consisted of two large barges with a bridge joining them. Each barge supports one kingpost for a heavy-lift derrick to handle underwater arrays.

Disposal note: *Elk River* (IX 501, ex-LSMR 501) was stricken 13-8-99 and sunk as a gunnery target 24-2-01.

SERVICE CRAFT

Note: Craft in this section are grouped in the traditional U.S. Navy order, with the universal ship-typing system designations not necessarily in alphabetical order. The entries marked with an asterisk are non-self-propelled.

♦ 1 former commercial floating dry dock* [YFDB]
Bldr: Sun Ship, Chester, Pa. (In serv. 1974)

AFDB 9

AFDB 9—in two sections George R. Schneider, 2-92

Dim: 213.36 × 67.06 × 5.18 (empty) **Capacity:** . . . tons

Remarks: Acquired in 7-90. Sections A and B were leased to a private contractor 14-6-93.

♦ 1 small auxiliary floating dock* [YFDL]
Bldr: Chicago Bridge & Iron (In serv. 3-44)

AFDL 6 Dynamic

Dynamic (AFDL 6)—at Little Creek, Va. George R. Schneider, 2-99

Dim: 61.0 × 19.5 **Capacity:** 1,000 tons **Crew:** 1 officer, 23 enlisted

Remarks: Sister *Adept* (AFDL 23), of 1,900-ton capacity, was towed from Subic Bay 22-2-92, arriving at Guam 6-3-92; she was leased 15-7-94 to Gulf-Cooper Manufacturing, Arkansas Pass, Texas, and supports the mine countermeasures ships at Ingleside, Texas. *Reliance* (AFDL 47) had been reacquired 18-1-81 from Maritime Administration reserve, but was returned 12-8-81; on 15-5-91, the craft was leased to Detyans Shipyard, Mount Pleasant, S.C.

♦ 1 AFDM 3–class medium auxiliary floating dry dock* [YFDM]
Bldr: Everett Pacific (In serv. 1945)

AFDM 10 Resolute (ex-YFD 67)

Resolute (AFDM 10)—at Norfolk Christopher P. Cavas, 7-00

D: 21,380 (max. load) **Dim:** 189.59 × 37.8 (29.26 clear width) × 1.9 (16.1 sub.)
Capacity: 18,000 tons **Crew:** 85 tot. (accomm. for 4 officers, 139 enlisted)

Remarks: Active. Built in three sections, with 26.5-m end sections bolted to the midsection. Refitted by Baltimore Marine Industries from 9-00 to 3-01.

SERVICE CRAFT *(continued)*

♦ 2 APL 65–class barracks craft* [YPL]

Bldr: Marinette Marine, Marinette, Wis.

	L	In serv.
APL 65	30-10-99	8-00
APL 66	. . .	12-00

APL 65—at San Diego — George R. Schneider, 6-01

APL 66—at Norfolk — Takatoshi Okano, 4-01

D: 3,162 tons (fl) **Dim:** 82.00 × 21.00 × 1.57

Remarks: Ordered 31-8-98 for $32.5 million. Provide accommodations for ships under repair or overhaul and are capable of being towed at sea. Have berthing for 250 personnel, can provide food services to up to 1,150 each, and have post office, banking, fitness center, barber shop, classroom, laundry, and medical facilities. APL 65 is based at San Diego, APL 66 at Norfolk. Hull numbers APL 63 and APL 64 were never assigned.

♦ 2 APL 61–class barracks craft* [YPL]

Bldr: Halter Marine–Gulf Coast Fabrication, Pearlington, Miss.

	Laid down	L	In serv.	Location
APL 61	9-2-96	22-8-96	20-10-97	San Diego
APL 62	. . .	18-4-97	2-98	. . .

D: 4,680 tons (fl) **Dim:** 109.72 × 28.65 × 1.89

Remarks: Ordered in 1995 for $50 million. Have accommodations for 600 personnel, plus dining and locker facilities for 3,020 additional personnel, and are fitted with office, training, medical, recreation, and other personnel support spaces.

♦ 2 Benewah-class barracks barges [YPL] Bldr: Boston NSY

	Laid down	L	In serv.
APL 39 Mercer (ex-IX 502, ex-APB 39, ex-APL 39)	25-8-44	17-11-44	19-9-45
APL 40 Nueces (ex-IX 503, ex-APB 40, ex-APL 40)	2-1-45	6-5-45	30-11-45

Mercer (APL 39)—as IX 502 — Takatoshi Okano, 9-00

D: 2,189 tons light (3,640 fl) **Dim:** 100.0 × 15.2 × 3.4
M: Nonoperational: 2 G.M. 12-267 ATL diesels; 2 props; 1,600 bhp
Electric: 500 kw tot. **Crew:** accomm. for 39 officers, 1,295 enlisted

Remarks: Were reclassified from IX on 7-3-01. Built on LST 1/LST 542–class landing ship hulls. Recommissioned in 1968 for service in Vietnam, they were placed back in reserve during 1969–71, then activated again 1-11-75 as barracks ships. The propulsion plants were inactivated and eight 40-mm AA removed. Names were restored in 1986. Sister *Echols* (IX 504, ex-APB 37) was stricken 22-12-95. APL 39 is at San Diego, and APL 40 is assigned to the Naval Ships Repair Facility, Yokosuka, Japan.

♦ 11 APL 2–class barracks craft* [YPL]

	Bldr	In serv.
APL 2	Puget Sound NSY	23-5-45
APL 4	Everett Pacific Co.	21-9-45
APL 5	Puget Sound NSY	5-11-45
APL 15	Nashville Bridge	1-8-44
APL 18	Tampa SY, Fla.	20-9-44
APL 29	Tampa SY, Fla.	14-5-45
APL 32	Boston NSY	11-1-45
APL 42	Willamette Iron & Steel, Ore.	30-4-45
APL 45	Willamette Iron & Steel, Ore.	28-7-45
APL 50	Puget Sound Bldg. & Dock, Wash.	2-1-46
APL 58	Nashville Bridge	16-7-45

APL 50—at Norfolk — Christopher P. Cavas, 7-00

APL 15—under tow, at San Diego — Winter & Findler, 9-00

D: 1,300 tons light (2,580 fl) **Dim:** 79.55 (79.25 wl) × 14.93 × 3.04

Remarks: APL 2–18 are in the Pacific Fleet, the others in the Atlantic. Most can accommodate six officers and 680–792 enlisted (APL 18: 5 officers, 358 enlisted) and have 300-kw generator capacity. APL 45 was officially stricken from the Naval Vessel Registry 1-11-72 but remains in use in the Atlantic Fleet under her original designation. APL 18 was originally to have been YF 631.
Recent disposals: APL 31 was stricken for disposal 1-8-00 and sunk as an artificial reef 23-7-01.

♦ 2 Shippingport-class submarine support docks* [YFDM]

	Bldr	In serv.
ARDM 4 Shippingport	Bethlehem Steel, Sparrows Pt., Md.	27-1-79
ARDM 5 Arco	Todd Pacific, Seattle	27-2-86

Arco (ARDM 5)—at Ballast Point, San Diego — W. Michael Young, 8-00

Dim: 150.0 × 29.3 (29.3 clear width) × 16.6 (max.)
Capacity: 7,800 tons (8,400 emergency) **Crew:** 5–6 officers, 125 enlisted

Remarks: ARDM = Medium Support Dock. Intended to support SSN 688–class submarines. Are the first floating dry docks built for the U.S. Navy since World War II. Length of blocks: 118 m. Require shore support. Have two 25-ton cranes. ARDM 5 was ordered 13-10-82, laid down 25-7-83, and launched 14-12-84. Have accommodations for 12. ARDM 4 is based at New London, Conn., ARDM 5 at San Diego.

♦ 1 ARD 12–class submarine support dock* [YFDM] (In reserve)

Bldr: Pacific Bridge, Alameda, Calif. (In serv. 3-44)

ARDM 1 *Oak Ridge* (ex-ARD 19)

Dim: 163.4 × 24.7 (13.0 clear width) × 2.2 (13.1 sub.)
Capacity: 8,000 tons **Crew:** 5 officers, 174 enlisted

SERVICE CRAFT *(continued)*

Remarks: Was lengthened and had her capacity increased from 3,500 tons to serve as a submarine repair dock. One end is closed to permit towing. Transferred from Kings Bay, Ga., to Groton, Conn., arriving 19-5-97. Was deactivated 10-8-01 and is being retained in reserve.
Disposals: Sister *Alamogordo* (ARDM 2, ex-ARD 26) was stricken 23-11-93 and transferred to the Maritime Administration 21-3-95 for disposal; the dock was transferred to Ecuador on 26-2-01. *Endurance* (ARDM 3, ex-ARD 18), stricken 31-7-95, was offered to Ecuador for sale under FY 00 but not accepted.

♦ 168 YC open lighters* [YC] (9 in *reserve*)
Bldrs: Various (see remarks) (In serv. 5-37 through 27-8-96)

YC 688	*YC 1375*	YC 1482	YC 1543	YC 1595	YC 1640
YC 728	YC 1378	YC 1484	YC 1548	YC 1596	*YC 1641*
YC 746	YC 1379	YC 1485	YC 1549	YC 1598	*YC 1642*
YC 757	YC 1380	YC 1486	YC 1568	YC 1599	YC 1644
YC 775	YC 1381	YC 1489	*YC 1569*	YC 1600	YC 1646
YC 783	YC 1382	YC 1490	YC 1570	YC 1601	YC 1647
YC 800	YC 1389	YC 1491	YC 1571	YC 1602	YC 1648
YC 804	YC 1391	YC 1492	YC 1572	YC 1605	YC 1649
YC 821	YC 1400	YC 1494	YC 1573	YC 1606	YC 1650
YC 980	YC 1406	YC 1495	YC 1574	YC 1615	YC 1651
YC 981	YC 1407	YC 1500	YC 1575	YC 1619	YC 1652
YC 984	YC 1409	YC 1501	YC 1576	YC 1620	YC 1653
YC 1027	YC 1410	YC 1502	YC 1577	YC 1622	YC 1654
YC 1029	YC 1417	YC 1510	YC 1578	YC 1623	YC 1655
YC 1068	YC 1419	YC 1511	YC 1579	YC 1624	YC 1656
YC 1069	YC 1431	YC 1513	YC 1580	YC 1625	YC 1657
YC 1070	YC 1432	YC 1523	YC 1583	YC 1626	YC 1658
YC 1073	YC 1433	YC 1524	YC 1584	YC 1627	YC 1659
YC 1080	YC 1445	YC 1526	YC 1585	YC 1628	YC 1660
YC 1081	YC 1464	YC 1527	YC 1586	YC 1631	YC 1661
YC 1090	YC 1469	YC 1528	YC 1587	YC 1632	YC 1662
YC 1091	YC 1470	YC 1531	YC 1588	YC 1633	YC 1663
YC 1121	YC 1473	YC 1534	YC 1589	*YC 1634*	YC 1664
YC 1321	YC 1474	YC 1535	YC 1590	*YC 1635*	YC 1665
YC 1329	YC 1475	YC 1536	YC 1591	YC 1636	YC 1666
YC 1351	YC 1476	YC 1537	YC 1592	*YC 1637*	YC 1667
YC 1368	YC 1477	YC 1538	YC 1593	*YC 1638*	YC 1668
YC 1371	YC 1478	*YC 1542*	YC 1594	YC 1639	

YC 1500 H&L Van Ginderen, 10-00

YC 1473 George R. Schneider, 5-00

Remarks: YC 1523–1527: delivered 5-81 to 7-81 by Marine Industries; 135 tons light (685 fl). YC 1572–1602: delivered 27-2-85 to 23-4-87 by Moss Point Marine, Escatawpa, Miss.; 250 tons light (660 fl); 33.53 × 9.75 × 1.98 (max.) m. YC 1615–1666: delivered 1-90 to 27-8-96 by Orange SB, Orange, Texas; 115 tons light (659 fl); 33.53 × 9.75 × 2.13 m.

YC 1583–1586 were converted in 4-86 as cable-reel support barges for the T-AGOS program. YC 1519 became YFNX 40 on 1-2-94. YC 1643 was reclassified as IX 519 late in 1996 and assigned to support the *La Salle* (AGF 3). YC 1631 and 1633, assigned to the Naval Undersea Warfare Center, Keyport, Wash., as range-support craft—along with YC 1329 and 1470, which have one or more sheds built on deck—are self-propelled, with two 450-bhp G.M. Detroit Diesel 12V-71 outdrive systems providing 7-kt speeds; both have a 125-kw diesel generator, while YC 1470 has 60- and 80-kw generators. YC 1594 is employed as a service barge for the nuclear-powered deep-submergence submersible NR-1 at New London, Conn. The previously-stricken YC 1073 was restored to service 1-7-98 for use at the Trident submarine facility at Bangor, Wash. YC 1525 was redesignated salvage lighter YLC 2 on 5-6-98. YC 813 and 1084 became YFNX 45 and 46, respectively, on 14-7-98.
Recent disposals: YC 1448, 1449, and 1607 were stricken for disposal 5-1-01. YC 709, 772, 1076, 1077, 1089, and 1630 were stricken 13-3-01 and YC 1493 on 19-3-01.

Note: In use at Sasebo, Japan, are locally procured barges YC 1 and YC 2, built in 1941, and the 1942-vintage YC 7 is used at Yokosuka; these craft are not on the official Naval Vessel Register, and no data are available.

♦ 1 YCF car float* [YAGE]
Bldr: J.K. Welding Co. (In serv. 25-1-42)

YCF 16

D: 170 tons light (420 fl) **Dim:** 45.72 × 10.21 × 1.22

Remarks: Rectangular barge, formerly used to transport railroad cars. Moored at Seneca Lake, N.Y., in support of sonar system trials, along with barge IX 310 and YFNX 22 (qq.v.).

♦ 8 YCV 7–class aircraft transportation lighters* [YC]
Bldrs: YCV 10, 11: Naval Base, Pearl Harbor; YCV 16: Bethlehem Steel, San Francisco; others: Alabama SY, Mobile, Ala.

	In serv.	Assigned to		In serv.	Assigned to
YCV 10	21-8-44	Sasebo, Japan	YCV 20	5-89	Yokosuka, Japan
YCV 11	6-10-44	Pearl Harbor	YCV 21	3-90	Pearl Harbor
YCV 16	29-8-45	Yokosuka, Japan	YCV 22	1-4-91	Sasebo, Japan
YCV 19	4-90	Yokosuka, Japan	YCV 23	2-2-91	Pearl Harbor

D: 480 tons light (2,480 fl) **Dim:** 60.96 (54.86 wl loaded) × 19.81 × 2.13 (loaded)

Remarks: All are active in the Pacific Fleet and are used to move aircraft and stores between shore facilities and aircraft carriers. YCV 19–21 were approved under FY 88 and YCV 22 and 23 under FY 90 to replace earlier units; they duplicated the basic characteristics of the World War II–built units.

♦ 1 nuclear reactor transport barge* [YC] (In reserve)
Bldr: American Marine, New Orleans (In serv. 1984)

BARGE 40 (ex-ATB 210, ex-*Cheramie Bros. 107*)

D: . . . tons **Dim:** 64.00 × 20.73 × 4.57

Remarks: 2,142 grt. Purchased in 1992 from Anderson Tug and Barge, Seward, Alaska, and refitted in 1993 by Puget Sound Naval Shipyard to transport 1,000-ton nuclear reactor compartments cut from retired submarines at Bremerton to Hanford, Wash., for burial. Not on the Navy List.

♦ 1 nuclear reactor transport barge* [YC]
Bldr: Zidell Dismantling, Tacoma, Wash. (In serv. 1981)

BARGE 60 (ex-ZB 1801)

D: . . . tons **Dim:** 70.10 × 18.28 × 4.57

Remarks: 1775 grt. Modified from a commercial salvage barge by Marine Industries Northwest, Tacoma, in 1996. A sister to the *Edgecumbe,* below.

Note: The navy owns three other former commercial barges that have no Navy List hull numbers; all are assigned to the Puget Sound Naval Shipyard, Bremerton, Wash.:
- *Beluga* (In serv. 12-91): 41.45 × 18.28 × 3.96 m; built by Alabama SY, Mobile, Ala.; 1774 grt
- *Edgecumbe* (In serv. 4-78): 70.1 × 18.28 × 4.57 m, built by Zidell Dismantling, Tacoma, Wash.; 1775 grt
- *Nestucca* (In serv. 1-69): 70.1 × 16.76 × 4.64 m, built by Wall SY/M&W Marine Ways, Harvey, La.; 1,612 grt

♦ 32 YD floating cranes* [YD] (2 in *reserve*)
Bldrs: Various (see remarks)

YD 117	YD 217	YD 232	YD 246	*YD 253*	YD 260
YD 189	YD 218	YD 233	YD 247	YD 254	YD 261
YD 196	YD 224	*YD 234*	YD 248	YD 255	
YD 200	YD 225	YD 237	YD 249	YD 256	
YD 204	YD 226	YD 243	YD 251	YD 257	
YD 214	YD 229	YD 245	YD 252	YD 259	

YD 247–class floating crane YD 256—at San Diego George R. Schneider, 6-01

Remarks: YD 117 was built by Dravo, Wilmington, Del. (in serv. 1945); YD 189 by Odenbach SB (in serv. 6-44); YD 196, 217, 232–234, 237, 243, and 245 by Dravo, Pittsburgh, Pa. (in serv. 1-54, 6-54, 6-52, 6-53, 6-53, 6-54, 6-52, and 9-44, respectively); YD 200 by Avondale SY, New Orleans (in serv. 4-55); YD 204 and 224 by Wiley Co. (in serv. 9-54 and 4-68, respectively); YD 218 by Gunter & Zimmerman (in serv. 6-53); YD 225, 226, and 229 by Star Iron & Steel (in serv. 1969–70); YD 246, 248, and 254–261 by Halter Marine, Lockport, Miss. (in serv. 2-91 to 6-94); and YD 247 and 249–253 by Westmont Industries, Los Angeles (in serv. 4-91 to 11-91). YD 254–261 were originally ordered 25-7-91 from Alabama SY, Mobile, but the order was transferred to Halter Marine.

SERVICE CRAFT *(continued)*

Army Design 264B–class floating crane YD 233—at Norfolk Naval Shipyard
Takatoshi Okano, 9-01

YD 117 was built on a 42.67 × 21.3–m barge hull and displaces 1,407 tons light (1,560 fl). YD 189, 200, 214, 217, 218, 232–234, 243, and 245 are ex-U.S. Army Design 264B–class floating cranes: 1,630 tons (fl), 42.67 × 21.34 × 1.91 m, 90–100 tons capacity. YD 204 is 43.9 × 19.5 × 1.8 m and displaces 1,064 tons light. YD 246, 248, and 254–261 are 53.34 × 22.86 × 3.96 m (molded depth). YD 247 and 249–253 are 2,134 tons (fl) and 53.49 × 22.41 × 1.53 m and have crew of 12, a 100-ton crane, and 150-bhp Caterpillar 3304 diesel maneuvering propulsion.
Recent disposals: YD 222 was stricken 31-8-00 and YD 120 and 150 on 13-3-01.

♦ 2 former Japanese self-propelled floating cranes [YD]
Bldr: Ishikawajima Heavy Industries (IHI), Tokyo (In serv. 1954)

IX 30-1 . . .

D: 600 tons **S:** . . . kts **Dim:** 28.30 × . . . × . . .
M: 2 diesel generator sets, electric drive; 2 props; . . .

Remarks: On loan from the government of Japan since 1954. IX 30-1 is at the Ship Repair Facility, Yokosuka, and the other at Sasebo. Crane capacity is 30 tons.

♦ 2 YDT 17–class diving tenders [YDT]
Bldr: Swiftships, Morgan City, La.

YDT 17 Neptune (In serv. 25-2-99) YDT 18 Poseidon (In serv. 19-5-99)

Neptune (YDT 17) Skeets Photo Service/Swiftships, 2-99

D: 275 tons (fl) **S:** 20 kts **Dim:** 41.15 (39.93 pp) × 8.23 × 1.83
Electronics: Radar: 1 Raytheon . . . nav.—Sonar: . . . hull-mounted HF
M: 2 Caterpillar 3508 DITA diesels; 2 Hamilton waterjets; 2,600 bhp—90-shp electric bow-thruster
Electric: 290 kw tot. (2 × 125 kw, Caterpillar 3306 DIT diesel-driven; 1 × 40 kw, Caterpillar 3304 DINA diesel-driven emergency)
Range: 540/20 **Fuel:** 2,000 gallons **Crew:** 8 tot. + 7 instructors, 25 trainees

Remarks: Diver training craft, ordered in 6-97 for $10.5 million to replace YDT 14 and 15 at the Naval Diving and Salvage Training Center, Panama City, Fla.
Hull systems: Aluminum construction. Capable of operating in Sea State 4 and up to 200 n.m. from land. Have six watertight compartments and tankage for 4,666 gallons of fresh water. The radar and sonar are interfaced with a GPS system. Carry a Zodiac Hurricane 472, 4.9-m RIB with a 25-bhp outboard. Two diver support cranes are fitted, and there is a large decompression chamber within the main deck superstructure.

Disposal note: Self-propelled covered lighter [YF] *Keyport* (YF 885), in reserve since 23-8-90, was for sale as of 5-01.

♦ 2 YFB 92–class ferry boats [YFB]
Bldr: Bender SB & Repair, Mobile, Ala. (In serv. 30-1-95)

YFB 92 R. W. Huntington (ex-*Windward*)
YFB 93 William H. Allen (ex-*Leeward*)

D: 200 tons (light) **S:** 10 kts **Dim:** 44.50 × 10.97 × 1.68
Electronics: Radar: 1 Furuno 1830 nav.
M: 2 G.M. Detroit Diesel 12V-71 diesels; 2 props; 720 bhp

R. W. Huntington (YFB 92) U.S. Navy, 1998

Electric: 200 kw tot. (2 × 75-kw Kato generators, powered by 2 Detroit Diesel 4-71 diesels; 1 × 50-kw emergency set, Detroit Diesel 4-71 diesel driving)
Range: 1,000/10 **Fuel:** 4,050 gallons **Crew:** 4 tot. + 80 passengers

Remarks: Ordered in 11-92 for use at Guantanamo Bay, Cuba; launched in 10-93 and 12-93. In addition to 100 passengers (40 seated), can carry 15 automobiles or two M1A1 tanks. The propellers are mounted at each end, and the craft are designed to mate with special shore ramps. Renamed in 10-95 in honor of Lt. Col. Robert W. Huntington, USMC, who led the first Marines ashore in Cuba on 10-6-1898, and Lt. Cdr. William H. Allen, the first commandant of the U.S. Naval Station at Guantanamo Bay, 10-12-1903 to 5-1904.

♦ 1 LCU 1466–class ferry boat [YFB]
Bldr: Avondale SY, Westwego, La. (In serv. 1954)

YFB 94 (ex-YFB 1504; ex-U.S. Army *Hampton Roads,* LCU 1504)

D: 180 tons (347 fl) **S:** 8 kts **Dim:** 35.08 × 10.36 × 1.60 (aft)
M: 3 G.M. Gray Marine 64YTL diesels; 3 props; 675 bhp **Electric:** 40 kw tot.
Range: 1,200/6 (700/7 loaded) **Fuel:** 11 tons **Crew:** . . . tot.

Remarks: Stricken from the U.S. Army Corps of Transportation fleet in 1990–92 and transferred to the USN for use at Guantanamo Bay, Cuba. Was stricken 3-3-98 but reactivated for service at Roosevelt Roads, P.R., 25-6-99. Cargo: 150 tons or 300 personnel on the 125.8 × 9.0–m open vehicle deck, with a 4.3-m-wide bow ramp. Sister YFB 95 (ex-U.S. Army *Shenandoah,* LCU 1516) was sold for scrap 5-1-97.

♦ 7 YFN 1277–class covered lighters* [YC] (3 in *reserve*)
Bldr: Basic Marine, Inc. (In serv. 10-93 to 3-94)

YFN 1277 *YFN 1279* YFN 1281 YFN 1284
YFN 1278 YFN 1280 YFN 1282

D: 685 tons (fl) **Dim:** . . . × . . . × . . .

Remarks: Under FY 90, 12 were to be ordered, with an option for 22 additional (YFN 1289–1310) that was authorized under FY 91, but only YFN 1277–1284 were ordered. Sister YFN 1283 has already been stricken. YFN 1277–1279 are assigned to the Naval Intermediate Ships Maintenance Facility, Philadelphia, and are inactive; the others are at the Naval Weapons Station, Seal Beach, Calif.

♦ 13 YFN 1254–class covered lighters* [YC] (1 in *reserve*)
Bldrs: YFN 1256–1262: Steel Style, Inc. (In serv. 6-82); others: Eastern Marine (In serv. 1-87 to 4-88)

YFN 1256 YFN 1262 YFN 1267 YFN 1270 YFN 1274
YFN 1258 YFN 1265 YFN 1268 *YFN 1272*
YFN 1261 YFN 1266 YFN 1269 YFN 1273

YFN 1254–class covered barge YFN 1267 H&L Van Ginderen, 7-97

D: 174 tons (699 fl) **Dim:** 33.53 (28.65 wl) × 10.67 (9.75 wl) × 2.44

Remarks: Rectangular steel barge hulls with a small deckhouse. Authorized under FY 81 (11 actually built), six under FY 85 (three ordered), and two under FY 86. Were initially said to be 260 tons light (660 fl). YFN 1265–1274 are rated at 144 tons light (694 fl). YFN 1265 was delivered in 1-87, YFN 1266–1270 in 8-87, and YFN 1272–1274 on 18-4-88.

SERVICE CRAFT *(continued)*

YFN 1254–class covered barge YFN 1262—converted as Norfolk Naval Shipyard Code 950 Electrical Test Barge, alongside *Peterson* (DD 969)
Christopher P. Cavas, 7-00

YFN 1256 and 1258 are assigned to ComSubRon 8; YFN 1261 and 1262 to the Norfolk NSY (YFN 1262 is equipped as an electrical test barge); YFN 1265, 1269, and 1270 to the Yorktown Naval Weapons Station, Va.; YFN 1266 to ComSubRon 11; YFN 1267 to North Island, San Diego; YFN 1268 to the Naval Ship Repair Facility, Yokosuka; YFN 1272 to Pearl Harbor NSY; and YFN 1273 and 1274 to the Naval Station, Everett, Wash. YFN 1255 was reclassified YFNX 42 on 17-7-95, and YFN 1271 became YFNX 43 on 16-8-96. YFN 1259 was reclassified as IX 527 on 7-4-99. YFN 1262 is named *Test Barge X-51.*
Disposals: YFN 1266 was stricken 5-1-01 but was reinstated the same day. YFN 1254, 1257, and 1275 were stricken 13-3-01.

♦ **1 YFN 1239–class covered lighter* [YC]**
Bldr: General Steel Tank (In serv. 1970)

YFN 1252

D: 137 tons (685 fl) **Dim:** 33.53 × 10.67 × 2.44

Remarks: Rectangular barge hull with a deckhouse having a peaked roof. Assigned to the Naval Weapons Station, Concord, Calif. YFN 1250 was placed in reserve 22-1-99 at Pearl Harbor and stricken 13-3-01.

♦ **1 YFN 1237–class covered lighter* [YC]**
Bldr: San Francisco NSY (In serv. 8-72)

YFN 1237

D: 677 tons (722 fl) **Dim:** 38.71 × 10.67 × 2.13

Remarks: Rectangular barge hull with a deckhouse. Assigned to the Puget Sound NSY, Bremerton, Wash.

♦ **4 YFN 1196–class covered lighters* [YC]**
Bldrs: YFN 1203, 1204: Gulfport SB Corp., Gulfport, Miss. (In serv. 6-5-54 and 12-10-64); others: Harbor Boat Bldg. (In serv. 2-65 and 6-65)

YFN 1203 YFN 1204 YFN 1217 YFN 1222

YFN 1196–class covered barge YFN 1221—since stricken
Winter & Findler, 9-99

D: 144 tons (694 fl) **Dim:** 33.53 × 9.75 × 2.44

Remarks: Rectangular barge hulls with a deckhouse having a peaked roof. YFN 1203, 1204, and 1222 are assigned to Pearl Harbor.
Recent disposals: YFN 1221 was stricken 5-1-01, YFN 1199 and 1200 on 13-3-01, and YFN 1213 on 24-9-01.

♦ **5 YFN 1173–class covered lighters* [YC]**
Bldr: Richmond Steel, Richmond, Va. (In serv. 1964)

YFN 1173 YFN 1175 YFN 1176 YFN 1194 YFN 1195

D: 144 tons (694 fl) **Dim:** 33.53 × 10.36 × 2.43

Remarks: Rectangular barge hull with a deckhouse having a peaked roof. YFN 1195 is assigned to the Yorktown Naval Weapons Station, Va.

♦ **1 YFN 1172–class covered lighter* [YC]**

YFN 1172 (In serv. 6-55)

D: 110 tons (360 fl) **Dim:** 33.53 × 9.14 × 1.22

Remarks: Rectangular barge hull with a deckhouse having a peaked roof.

♦ **3 YFN 1154–class covered lighters* [YC]**
Bldr: Burton Construction & SB (YFN 1163: Kyle & Co., Stockton, Calif.) (In serv. 1952)

YFN 1155 YFN 1156 YFN 1163

D: 160 tons (590 fl) **Dim:** 33.53 × 10.67 (10.36 wl) × 2.44

Remarks: Rectangular steel barge hulls with a deckhouse. YFN 1156, which was stricken 21-8-97 but restored to service 1-7-98, is assigned to Portsmouth NSY, Va.; the others are assigned to the Yorktown Weapons Station, Va.

♦ **19 YFN 161–class covered lighters [YC]** (1 in *reserve*)
Bldrs: YFN 284: J.K. Welding; YFN 306, 308: Dravo, Wilmington, Del.; YFN 645: Eureka SB; YFN 652, 797, 800, 801, 901: Bushnell-Lyons; YFN 656: American Pipe, La.; YFN 704, 934: Bellingham Iron Works, Wash.; YFN 793, 794: American Electric Welding, Md.; YFN 806, 917: Pointer-William; YFN 958: Mare Island NSY, Calif.; YFN 968, 973: Gunderson Bros., Portland, Ore. (In serv. 4-41 to 4-45)

YFN 284 YFN 652 YFN 794 YFN 806 YFN 968
YFN 306 YFN 656 YFN 797 YFN 917 *YFN 973*
YFN 308 YFN 704 YFN 800 YFN 934 YFN 978
YFN 645 YFN 793 YFN 801 YFN 958

YFN 161–class covered barge YFN 652—a typical U.S. Navy World War II–built U.S. Navy barge
Christopher P. Cavas, 7-00

D: 160 tons (590 fl) **Dim:** 33.53 × 10.67 (10.36 wl) × 2.43

Remarks: Rectangular barge hulls with a deckhouse having a peaked roof. Most are employed for temporary ammunition storage at naval weapons stations or naval shipyards. YFN 284 and 306 are at the Naval Inactive Ship Maintenance Facility, Portsmouth, Va.; YFN 308 at the Naval Inactive Ship Maintenance Facility, Philadelphia; YFN 645 and 806 at Pearl Harbor; YFN 652 at Norfolk NSY; YFN 656 at the Naval Weapons Station, Seal Beach, Calif.; YFN 704 at Sasebo, Japan; YFN 794, 800, and 801 at the Yorktown Weapons Station, Va.; and YFN 797 at the Naval Nuclear Power Training Unit, Charleston, S.C.
Recent disposals: YFN 276, 278, 691, 694, 803, 901, 956, 962, 964, 980, 981, 983, and 984 were stricken 13-3-01. YFN 941 was restored to the Navy List 11-12-98 for use in the Near-term Mine Reconnaissance System development program at the Naval Undersea Warfare Center Division, Keyport, Wash., but was for sale as of early 2002.

♦ **5 YFNB 1–class large covered lighters* [YFNB]** (1 in *reserve*)
Bldrs: Pollock-Stockton, Stockton, Calif. (YFNB 39: Missouri Valley Bridge & Iron Works) (In serv. 1944–45)

YFNB 19 YFNB 31 YFNB 32 *YFNB 39* YFNB 41

YFNB 1–class cargo barge YFNB 31 H&L Van Ginderen, 10-00

D: 831 tons light (2,780 fl) **Dim:** 79.24 × 14.63 × 1.07 (light; 2.90 loaded)

Remarks: YFNB 31 returned in 4-92 from Holy Loch, Scotland, to Norfolk Naval Base. YFNB 30 was reclassified YR 93 on 3-4-00. YFNB 37 was reclassified YRB 30 on 3-4-00. Sister YFNB 4 is on loan to the Maritime Administration.

♦ **1 YFNB 47–class large covered lighter* [YFNB]**
Bldr: Puget Sound Building and Dock (In serv. 6-45)

YFNB 47 (ex-YRR 9)

D: 770 tons (fl) **Dim:** 46.6 × 18.7 × 1.8

Remarks: Reclassified from YRR 9 during 11-83.

♦ **1 YFND 31–class dry dock companion craft* [YFND]**
Bldr: Gretna Machine & Iron Works (In serv. 7-65)

YFND 31 (ex-YFNX 34, ex-YFN 1209)

D: 144 tons (694 fl) **Dim:** 33.53 × 9.75 × 2.44

Remarks: Reclassified from postwar YFN on 1-11-92. Active at the Shore Intermediate Maintenance Facility Activity, Norfolk.

♦ **1 YFND 30–class dry dock companion craft* [YFND]**

YFND 30 (ex-YFN 1253)

D: 137 tons (685 fl) **Dim:** 33.53 × 9.75 × 2.44

Remarks: Reclassified from YFN on 1-11-92. Active at the Atlantic Fleet Weapons Training Facility, Roosevelt Roads, P.R.

SERVICE CRAFT *(continued)*

♦ 1 YFND 5–class dry dock companion craft* [YFND]

	Bldr	Laid down	L	In serv.
YFND 29 (ex-YFN 974)	Gunderson Bros.	7-45	8-45	28-8-45

D: 170 tons (590 fl) **Dim:** 33.53 × 10.66 × . . .

Remarks: Rectangular covered barge hull with a deckhouse. Active at Keyport, Wash. Sister YFND 5 (ex-YFN 268) was stricken 25-6-99 but was reinstated as IX 530 on 6-9-00.

♦ 12 YFNX-series miscellaneous special-purpose lighters* [YAG]

	Bldr	In serv.
YFNX 15 (ex-YNG 22)	Dravo, Pittsburgh	6-41
YFNX 20	Burton Const. & SB	6-52
YFNX 22	Island Dock Co., Inc.	6-52
YFNX 24 (ex-YFN 1215)	Harbor Boat & Bridge	6-52
YFNX 30 (ex-*Sea Turtle,* ex-YFN 1186, ex-USAF U-32-1501)	Kyled Co., Stockton, Calif.	3-52
YFNX 37 (ex-YFN 1198)	Richmond Steel, Va.	7-64
YFNX 39 (ex-YFN 1276)	Eastern Marine	4-88
YFNX 40 (ex-YC 1519)	Diamond Mfg. Co.	6-77
YFNX 42 Spruce Barge (ex-YFN 1255)	Steel Style, Inc.	6-82
YFNX 43 (ex-YFN 1271)	Eastern Marine	8-87
YFNX 45 (ex-YC 813, ex-YF 334)	Puget Sound NSY	31-5-42
YFNX 46 (ex-YC 1084)	Soule Steel, San Francisco	1-6-46

Spruce Barge (YFNX 42)—at Norfolk Christopher P. Cavas, 6-00

YFNX 30—configured as a submersible support craft H&L Van Ginderen, 7-97

Remarks: Rectangular barge hulls. All are 33.5 m long and 2.4 m in draft, with a beam of either 9.8 or 10.4 m. YFNX 15 is at Pearl Harbor; YFNX 20 at the Naval Nuclear Power Training Unit, Charleston, S.C.; YFNX 22 at Seneca Lake, N.Y., assigned to the Naval Undersea Warfare Center; YFNX 24, a berthing barge for divers, at the Portsmouth (N.H.) Naval Shipyard detachment, San Diego; YFNX 30 at San Diego (see below); YFNX 37, 39, 42, and 43 at Norfolk; and YFNX 40 at the Submarine Support Facility, New London, Conn.

YFNX 37 and 39 were reclassified from YFN on 1-11-92. YC 1519 became YFNX 40 on 1-2-94. YFN 1255 was reclassified YFNX 42 on 17-7-95 and assigned to Submarine Squadron 8 at Norfolk. YFNX 45 and 46 were redesignated 14-7-98 for use as storage and workshop barges at the Naval Inactive Ship Maintenance Facility, Bremerton, Wash.

YFNX 30 was converted to be the tender to the CURV III tethered, remotely operated submersible and was assigned to the Space and Naval Warfare Systems Center at San Diego until 1998, when she was transferred to the Portsmouth (N.H.) Naval Shipyard detachment at San Diego as a tender to the *Dolphin* (AGSS 555) along with YFNX 24. YFNX 30 displaces 420 tons (fl) on a draft of 1.52 m and is powered by fore-and-aft Voith Schneider vertical cycloidal propellers for speeds of 5.5 kts ahead or astern, 2 kts sideways, or 1.5 rpm for rotating the hull. Converted from a basic 33.3 × 10–m barge hull, YFNX 30 can berth 24 persons and has a 30-day endurance. Tankage totaling 51,700 gallons can be used either for ballast water or diesel fuel. Two 300-kw and one 60-kw diesel generators are installed.

Recent disposals: YFNX 35 and 36 were stricken 5-1-01 for disposal. YFNX 44 was sold 17-5-00.

♦ 1 YFP-series floating power barge* [YFP]

Bldr: Gretna Machine & Iron Works (In serv. 4-65)

YFP 11 (ex-YFN 1207)

D: 144 tons light (694 fl) **Dim:** 33.5 × 9.7 × 2.4

Remarks: Located at Naples, Italy, to support Commander, Service Force, Sixth Fleet Ship Repair Unit, Naples. Has a total generator capacity of 2,000 kw.

Disposal note: Range tender *Potential* (YFRT 520) was stricken 11-12-00, having been in reserve at Keyport, Wash., for many years.

♦ 1 LCU 1608–class harbor utility craft [YFU]

Bldr: Defoe SB, Bay City, Mich. (In serv. 1957)

YFU 91 (ex-LCU 1608)

YFU 91—at Roosevelt Roads, P.R. H&L Van Ginderen, 5-99

D: 196 tons (413 fl) **S:** 8 kts **Dim:** 35.11 × 10.36 × 1.52 (aft)
M: 3 G.M. Gray Marine 64HN12 diesels; 3 Kort-nozzle props; 675 bhp (495 sust.)
Electric: 120 kw tot. (2 × 60-kw diesel sets)
Range: 1,200/6 **Fuel:** 11.7 tons **Crew:** 8 enlisted

Remarks: Converted landing craft, now based at Roosevelt Roads, P.R. Can transport up to 183 tons of deck cargo or vehicles. Has a bow ramp.

♦ 1 YFU 71–class harbor utility craft [YFU]

Bldr: Pacific Coast Eng., Alameda, Calif. (In serv. 9-68)

YFU 81

YFU 81—at Roosevelt Roads, P.R. H&L Van Ginderen, 5-99

D: 220 tons light (380 tons fl) **S:** 8 kts **Dim:** 38.10 × 10.97 × 2.29
M: 4 G.M. 6-71 diesels; 2 Kort-nozzle props; 1,000 bhp **Electric:** 120 kw
Range: . . . **Crew:** 10 enlisted

Remarks: Built as a YFU, the last of 12 sisters intended for Vietnam service. The engines and superstructure are on centerline aft. Has a bow ramp. Currently assigned to Naval Station, Roosevelt Roads, P.R. Sister YFU 79 became IX 514.

♦ 3 YGN 80–class garbage lighters* [YGN]

Bldr: Zidell Explorations, Portland, Ore. (In serv. 1970–71)

YGN 80 YGN 81 YGN 83

D: 309 tons light (855 fl) **Dim:** 37.8 × 10.7 × 1.2

Remarks: 546 dwt. Rectangular barges. All are active, based at Pearl Harbor. Have hopper-type bottoms to permit dumping at sea. Ex-YGN 40, 70, and 73, redesignated as "floating equipment" in 1-84, remain available also.

♦ 2 YLC salvage lift craft* [YRS]

YLC 1 (ex-YFNX 33, ex-YFN 1192) YLC 2 (ex-YC 1525)

Remarks: YLC 1, completed in 6-52 as a covered lighter, became a YFNX in 12-74; she was redesignated a salvage lift craft in 6-86 and is attached to Mobile Diving and Salvage Unit 2, Norfolk. Standard navy 685-ton, 33.5 × 9.8–m barge hull. YLC 2 was redesignated 5-6-98 and serves Mobile Diving and Salvage Unit 1.

Disposal note: Dredge [YM] YMN 1, completed in 1992, was stricken 13-3-01.

♦ 1 YNG 1–class gate craft* [YAG]

Bldr: Moore Dry Dock (In serv. 6-41)

YNG 17

D: 110 tons (225 fl) **Dim:** 33.5 × 10.5 × 1.2 **Crew:** 15 tot.

Remarks: Built to tend harbor-defense nets. Based at Pearl Harbor.

♦ 1 YOGN 123–class aviation fuel barge* [YON]

Bldr: Albina Engineering & Machinery, Albina, Ore. (In serv. 6-54)

YOGN 123

SERVICE CRAFT *(continued)*

D: 434 tons light (2,784 fl) **Dim:** 70.1 × 12.8 × 2.4

Remarks: Based at the Fleet Supply Center, Bremerton, Wash. YOGN 126–131 were authorized under FY 91 budget but not ordered.

♦ 6 YOGN 106–class aviation fuel barges* [YON]

Bldr: YOGN 111, 113: Nashville Bridge Co.; others: Albina Engineering & Machinery, Albina, Ore.

	In serv.		In serv.		In serv.
YOGN 111	10-53	YOGN 114	6-54	YOGN 124	6-53
YOGN 113	12-53	YOGN 115	9-52	YOGN 125	6-54

D: 245 tons light (1,360 fl; see remarks) **Dim:** 50.3 × 12.8 × 2.4

Remarks: YOGN 114 is listed as displacing 297 tons light (1,776 fl). YOGN 111 is based at Norfolk; YOGN 113 at Naval Station, Roosevelt Roads, P.R.; YOGN 114 at Fleet Supply Center, Puget Sound, Wash.; YOGN 115 at Yokosuka, Japan; YOGN 124 at Puget Sound Naval Base, Bremerton, Wash.; and YOGN 125 at Pearl Harbor.

♦ 2 YOGN 8–class aviation fuel barges* [YON]

Bldrs: YOGN 8: Dravo, Pittsburgh, Pa. (In serv. 7-42); YOGN 26: American Electric Welding, Md. (In serv. 9-44)

YOGN 8 YOGN 26

YOGN 8–class aviation fuel barge YOGN 26—at Norfolk, with repair, berthing, and messing barge YRBM 9 in background Christopher P. Cavas, 7-97

D: 220 tons light (1,270 fl) **Dim:** 50.3 × 10.7 × 2.4

Remarks: Based at Philadelphia and at the Norfolk Naval Shipyard, respectively.

♦ 2 YON 305–class fuel-oil barges* [YON]

Bldr: . . . (In serv. 1-6-52)

YON 305 YON 306

D: 185 tons light (578 fl) **Dim:** 36.58 × 10.06 × 2.44

Remarks: YON 305 is based at Yokosuka, Japan, and YON 306 at Diego Garcia.

♦ 14 YON 301–class fuel-oil barges* [YON]

Bldrs: YON 301, 302: Southwest Marine; YON 308, 309: Alabama SY; YON 311–319: Orange SB, Orange, Texas

	In serv.	Assigned to		In serv.	Assigned to
YON 301	16-1-83	San Diego	YON 313	5-93	Norfolk
YON 302	16-1-83	San Diego	YON 314	12-93	Puget Sound NSY
YON 307	. . .	Diego Garcia	YON 315	12-93	Puget Sound NSY
YON 308	12-89	Norfolk	YON 316	1-94	San Diego
YON 309	1-90	Puget Sound NSY	YON 317	1-94	San Diego
YON 311	5-93	Norfolk	YON 318	12-95	Norfolk
YON 312	5-93	Norfolk	YON 319	1-96	Puget Sound NSY

YON 301–class fuel barge YON 313 A. D. Baker III, 10-00

D: 382 tons light (1,806 fl) **Dim:** 56.00 × 10.67 × 3.05

Remarks: A modernized version of the YON 245 class design, assigned to various naval stations, naval shipyards, and supply depots. YON 307 was stricken 4-9-98 after only eight years' service, but was reinstated on the Naval Vessel Registry on 3-8-00 for service at Diego Garcia. Unlike the others, YON 318 and 319 have no sheer to the hull at the bow end.

♦ 20 YON 245–class fuel-oil barges* [YON]

Bldrs: YON 258–275: Gretna Machine & Iron Works; YON 280–283: Marine Power & Equipment; others: Brown-Minneapolis

	In serv.	Assigned to		In serv.	Assigned to
YON 258	17-1-66	Guantanamo Bay	YON 283	8-73	Little Creek, Va.
YON 260	20-1-66	Little Creek, Va.	YON 284	12-74	Norfolk
YON 262	5-5-66	Norfolk NSY	YON 285	9-75	Yokosuka, Japan
YON 271	5-4-68	Roosevelt Roads	YON 287	1-75	Yokosuka, Japan
YON 272	5-4-68	Diego Garcia	YON 288	9-75	San Diego
YON 273	1-7-68	Pearl Harbor	YON 289	10-75	Pearl Harbor
YON 274	1-7-68	Pearl Harbor	YON 291	10-75	Guam
YON 280	3-72	San Diego	YON 292	11-75	San Diego
YON 281	3-73	Pearl Harbor	YON 293	10-75	Guam
YON 282	8-73	Little Creek, Va.	YON 295	3-76	Little Creek, Va.

YON 245–class fuel barge YON 292 George R. Schneider, 9-94

D: 250 tons light (1,445 fl) **Dim:** 50.29 × 12.19 × 2.44

Remarks: Hull numbers YON 296–300 were reserved for additional units of this class that were never built. Units built by Brown-Minneapolis were 1 ft. longer and displace 267 tons light (1,506 fl). Several are assigned permanent crews of four enlisted personnel. Sister YON 270 was reassigned as "floating equipment." YON 291 was stricken 13-12-95 but reinstated 7-8-01, having in the interim remained in service at Guam.

♦ 1 YON 245–class fuel-oil barge* [YON]

Bldr: Gunderson Brothers SB, Portland, Ore. (In serv. 6-54)

YON 290

D: 185 tons light (578 fl) **Dim:** 36.58 × 10.06 × 2.44

Remarks: Assigned to the Fleet and Industrial Supply Center Detachment, Sasebo, Japan.

♦ 4 YON 89–class fuel-oil barges* [YON]

Bldrs: YON 91: California Steel; YON 98, 102: American Electric Welding

	In serv.	Assigned to		In serv.	Assigned to
YON 90	6-43	Guam	YON 98	12-43	Norfolk
YON 91	7-43	San Diego	YON 102	6-44	Puget Sound NSY

D: 220 tons light (1,270 fl) **Dim:** 50.29 × 10.67 × 2.44

Remarks: Survivors from among a once much larger class, all built during World War II; the same hull was employed for other liquid transportation barge types such as YOSs and YWNs. YON 91 has four enlisted personnel assigned. YON 90 was driven ashore at Guam during Typhoon Paka on 16-12-97 and stricken the following month; repaired, she continued to serve as an oily waste reception and storage barge and was reinstated on the Naval Vessel Register on 7-8-01.

♦ 3 YOS-series oil-storage barges* [YON]

	Bldr	In serv.
YOS 24	Maxon Const. Co.	4-46
YOS 33 (ex-YSR 46)	Eureka SB	6-40
YOS 36	Alabama SY, Mobile, Ala.	6-90

Oil-storage barge YOS 36 A. D. Baker III, 10-00

Remarks: All are active. YOS 24 displaces 100 tons light and measures 24.4 × 10.4 m. YOS 36 (725 tons fl) was requested under FY 87, ordered 29-7-88, and delivered in 6-90. Two new YOSs were funded under the FY 94 budget but not built.
Recent disposals: YOS 17 was stricken 13-3-01.

Note: The former YOS 34 (ex-Army OB61-2), acquired 1-9-79, has been reclassified as floating property and serves as Former Hull 61-2 at Norfolk Naval Shipyard: 140 tons light; 33.5 × 10.4 m; the hull number YOS 34 is still painted on, however.

♦ 23 YP 676–class patrol craft/training tenders [YXT]

Bldr: Marinette SB, Marinette, Wis. (YP 676–682: Peterson Bldrs, Sturgeon Bay, Wis.)

	Laid down	L	In serv.
YP 676	7-4-83	9-4-84	14-11-84
YP 677	10-10-83	23-6-84	5-12-84
YP 680	2-7-84	23-3-85	8-8-85
YP 681	29-10-84	1-6-85	30-9-85
YP 682	7-1-85	3-8-85	18-11-85
YP 683	23-7-85	19-6-86	13-10-86
YP 684	29-8-85	14-8-86	10-12-86
YP 685	8-10-85	25-9-86	23-11-86
YP 686	23-1-86	25-10-86	12-86
YP 687	27-2-86	3-87	7-3-87
YP 688	7-4-86	4-87	15-3-87
YP 689	15-7-86	5-87	10-6-87
YP 690	18-8-86	4-87	10-6-87
YP 691	28-10-86	5-87	7-87
YP 692	10-12-86	18-6-87	27-7-87
YP 694	25-2-87	21-9-87	27-10-87
YP 695	24-3-87	26-10-87	1-12-87
YP 696	23-4-87	. . .	10-5-88
YP 697	26-5-87	1-2-88	26-5-88
YP 698	22-6-87	29-3-88	16-6-88
YP 700	22-9-87	12-5-88	21-7-88
YP 701	28-10-87	14-6-88	9-8-88
YP 702	10-12-87	19-7-88	2-9-88

SERVICE CRAFT *(continued)*

YP 697 Victor M. Baca, 1-01

YP 702 H&L Van Ginderen, 10-00

D: 173 tons (fl) **S:** 13.25 kts (12 sust.) **Dim:** 32.92 (30.99 pp) × 7.39 × 1.83
Electronics: Radar: 1 SPS-64(V)9 nav.
M: 2 G.M. Detroit Diesel 12V-71N diesels; 2 props; 874 bhp—60-shp bow-thruster
Electric: 100 kw tot. (2 × 50 kw, G.M. Detroit Diesel 3-71 diesels driving)
Range: 1,400/12 **Fuel:** 6,550 gallons
Crew: 4 enlisted + 2 officer instructors and 24 midshipmen (30 berths)

Remarks: Wooden-construction boats to replace the YP 655 class. YP 676 was ordered 15-10-82, YP 677–682 on 25-5-83, YP 683–695 on 12-6-84, and YP 696–702 on 13-9-85. Under FY 88, Congress directed that YP 702 be completed as a prototype inshore minehunter, a conversion neither required nor desired by the navy, which did not comply; Congress then demanded trials under FY 89, but they do not seem to have been carried out. All but four are assigned to Naval Academy, Annapolis, Md. The exceptions are YP 696, assigned to Pensacola Naval Air Station, Fla.; YP 697 and 701 at the Naval Undersea Warfare Center, Keyport, Wash., the latter for use as a sound target boat and personnel transport, with a crew of seven and facilities for up to 24 passengers; and YP 702, which was stricken 20-11-98, reinstated on the Naval Vessel Registry 3-4-00, and assigned to the Pensacola Naval Air Station.
Disposals: YP 678 and YP 679 were stricken 20-11-98; the former is used by a private agency as a training craft and the latter was restored to service 25-6-99 and assigned to the Office of Naval Research for a science and technology demonstration program, being redesignated IX 531 on 7-8-01. YP 693 and 699 were stricken on 13-3-01.
Hull systems: Aluminum superstructure. Made up to 13.3 kts on trials. Have a Magnavox MX 1105 NAVSAT receiver, an EPSCO plotter, Kenyon D5300 and Furuno FCV-261 echo sounders, a Sperry Mk 27 gyrocompass with six repeaters, a speed log, an anemometer, the Sippican expendable bathythermograph system, and a Magellan GPS receiver. YP 686 is equipped for oceanographic research and has three small towing and hydrographic winches, four portable davits, and a stern A-frame crane, as well as a dry lab with four IBM computers and a small wet lab. Marinette-built units can be distinguished by their single ladder forward to the bridge deck; the Peterson-built craft have two.

♦ 2 YP 655–class patrol craft/training tenders [YXT]

	Bldr	Laid down	L	In serv.
YP 663	Stephens Bros.	15-11-57	12-3-58	15-11-58
YP 665	Elizabeth City SY, N.C.	9-12-59	27-8-60	28-11-60

D: 55 tons (65 fl) **S:** 12.6 kts **Dim:** 24.51 × 5.72 × 1.60
Electronics: Radar: 1 Raytheon 1220 nav.
M: 2 G.M. Detroit Diesel 6-71 diesels; 2 props; 590 bhp
Range: 400/12 **Crew:** 2 officers, 8 enlisted

Remarks: Survivors of a class of 20. Both are employed as harbor utility craft at Bremerton, Wash. Wooden construction. Sisters YP 659 and 660 were transferred to the COOP naval reserve mine countermeasures program in 1985, as were YP 654, 661, 664, 666, and 668–675 in 1986–88; all of these have since been discarded. YP 655, 656, 657, 658 *(Perseverance),* and 667 were stricken 12-2-93; YP 657 and 667 were donated to the Pittsburgh Voyager Project in 11-93.

♦ 2 miscellaneous YPD-series floating pile drivers* [YAG]

Bldrs: YPD 37: Todd Pacific, Seattle (In serv. 1-7-56); YPD 45: San Diego Marine (In serv. 4-69)

YPD 37   YPD 45 Wharf Rat (ex-YC 1498)

Wharf Rat (YPD 45) George R. Schneider, 8-98

Remarks: YPD 37, built as a floating pile driver and based at Mare Island, Calif., was listed as due for disposal but was still active as of 12-99; she displaces 260 tons light and is 31.7 m o.a. by 9.4 m beam. YPD 45, based at San Diego Naval Station, is a 680-ton (fl), 33.52 × 10.36 × 2.44–m converted barge; she carries crane truck USN 82-05058.

♦ 1 floating workshop* [YR] Bldr: Everett Pacific Corp. (In serv. 13-2-45)

YR 94 (ex-IX 526, ex-YRST 1, ex-YDT 11, ex-YFNB 12, ex-YFN 723)

D: 700 tons light (2,700 fl) **Dim:** 79.6 × 14.6 × 2.7

Remarks: Rectangular barge hull with large deckhouse; former salvage-craft tender (and, before that, a diving tender). Reclassified as IX 526 on 26-3-98 for use as an office and work barge at Pearl Harbor, and reclassified again 3-4-00 as a repair barge. Has accommodations for 15 officers and 71 enlisted. YRB 30 is very similar in appearance.

♦ 1 YFNB 1–class floating workshop* [YR]

Bldr: Nashville Bridge Co., Nashville, Tenn.

	Laid down	L	In serv.
YR 93 (ex-YFNB 30, ex-YFN 899)	27-3-45	18-6-45	26-1-46

YR 93 George R. Schneider, 5-01

D: 831 tons light (2,780 fl) **Dim:** 79.24 × 14.63 × 1.07 (light; 2.90 loaded)

Remarks: Reclassified on 3-4-00 and employed in the Pacific Fleet. Has same general appearance as YRBM 20 and YRBM 47 (q.v.).

♦ 2 miscellaneous floating workshops* [YR]

	Bldr	In serv.
YR 83 (ex-YRL 5)	Northeast Boiler & Welding	16-1-43
YR 92 (ex-YRB 22, ex-YC 1079)	Soule Steel, San Francisco	23-4-45

D: YR 83: 140 tons light (250 fl); YR 92: 170 tons light (288 fl)
Dim: YR 83: 33.8 × 9.4 × 0.9; YR 92: 33.52 (29.87 wl) × 10.36 × 1.22

Remarks: YR 83 is stationed at Pearl Harbor. YR 92 was reclassified from YRB 22 on 25-6-99 and is employed at the Naval Intermediate Maintenance Facility Pacific, Northwest Facility, Everett, Wash. YR 89 (ex-YRR 4, ex-YFN 685), completed in 1937, was stricken 24-9-01. YR 91 was reclassified YRBM 53 on 3-4-00.

♦ 3 ex-U.S. Army Design 7011 floating machine shops* [YR]

	Bldr	In serv.
YR 84 (ex-Army FMS 6)	. . .	6-44
YR 85 Quality (ex-Army FMS 87)	Bethlehem Steel, Staten I., N.Y.	6-54
YR 86 (ex-Army FMS 811)	Les. F. Alexander	6-54

D: 1,160 tons light (1,525 fl) **Dim:** 64.14 (53.62 wl) × 12.19 × 2.36 (max.)
Electric: 400 kw (4 × 100-kw diesel sets) **Fuel:** 140 tons
Crew: YR 84, 86: 12 enlisted; YR 85: 4 officers, 40 enlisted

SERVICE CRAFT *(continued)*

Quality (YR 85)—at Sasebo Takatoshi Okano, 9-00

Remarks: Modified from Army Design 7016 refrigerated stores barges (which they outwardly resemble). Have an 8.9-ton crane amidships. Workshops include battery, blacksmith, carpentry, electrical, electronics, engine, fuel injector, machine, paint, pipe-fitting, refrigeration, sheet metal, shipfitting, and welding. YR 85 is located at Sasebo, Japan. YR 86 is assigned to Everett, Wash. Two sisters remain in U.S. Army service and one is in the Chinese People's Liberation Army Navy.

♦ 8 YR 1–class floating workshops* [YR]

	Bldr	In serv.
YR 29	Cramp SB, Philadelphia	24-11-41
YR 50	Mare Island NSY	22-9-44
YR 63	Mare Island NSY	5-2-46
YR 64	Panama Canal Co.	13-5-46
YR 68	Pollock-Stockton	10-11-44
YR 70	Puget Sound Building and Dock	10-2-45
YR 78	Puget Sound Building and Dock	19-6-45
YR 90 (ex-YRR 7)	Cramp SB, Philadelphia	1-42

YR 1–class floating workshop YR 78—standard configuration Findler & Winter, 9-97

YR 1–class floating workshop YR 29—with additional deckhouse amidships atop the original superstructure Christopher P. Cavas, 7-97

D: 530 tons light (760 fl) **Dim:** 46.6 (45.7 wl) × 10.7 × 1.8
Crew: 1–4 officers, 40–47 enlisted

Remarks: A once-uniform design, but several now have had additional superstructure added. Are all equipped with machine shops and berthing facilities. YR 70, stricken 4-4-95, was restored to the Naval Vessel Register 15-6-00 for use at the Naval Ship Repair Facility, Yokosuka, Japan; the craft is listed at 600 tons light (990 fl) and has a beam of 12.0 m, indicating that it was initially one of a small number equipped as torpedo repair barges and given a bulged hull midbody to improve stability.
Recent disposals: YR 76 was stricken 13-3-01.

♦ 3 YR 1–class repair and berthing barges* [YPB]

	Bldr	In serv.
YRB 31 (ex-YR 36)	Mare Isl. NSY	15-5-42
YRB 32 (ex-YR 67)	Pollock-Stockton	15-9-44
YRB 33 (ex-YR 73)	Puget Sound B&D	9-4-45

YR 1–class repair and berthing barge YRB 32—as YR 67 H&L Van Ginderen, 8-99

D: 530 tons light (760 fl) **Dim:** 46.6 (45.7 wl) × 10.7 × 1.8
Crew: 1–4 officers, 40–47 enlisted

Remarks: Reclassified on 3-4-00 and assigned to Commander in Chief, Pacific Fleet.

♦ 1 YFNB 1–class repair and berthing barge* [YR]
Bldr: Missouri Valley Bridge Co.

	Laid down	L	In serv.
YRB 30 (ex-YFNB 37, ex-YFN 64)	13-3-45	12-5-45	28-5-45

YFNB 1–class repair and berthing barge YRB 30 George R. Schneider, 5-01

D: 700 tons light (2,200 fl) **Dim:** 79.24 × 14.63 × 1.07 (light; 2.90 loaded)

Remarks: Reclassified YRB 30 on 3-4-00 and employed at San Diego. Has same general appearance as YRBM 20 and YRBM 47 (q.v.).

♦ 1 YR 91–class repair, berthing, and messing barge* [YPBN]
Bldr: Halter Marine, Moss Point, Miss. (In serv. 3-93)

YRBM 53 (ex-YR 91)

D: 825 tons (fl) **Dim:** . . . × . . . × . . .

Remarks: Ordered 8-11-91 for service at Pearl Harbor; reclassified on 3-4-00.

♦ 5 YR 1–class repair, berthing, and messing barges* [YPBN]

	Bldr	In serv.
YRBM 48 (ex-YR 44)	Cramp SB	22-9-43
YRBM 49 (ex-YR 46)	Cramp SB	26-11-43
YRBM 50 (ex-YR 50)	Mare Island NSY	22-9-44
YRBM 51 (ex-YR 60)	Dekon SB	30-9-44
YRBM 52 (ex-YR 77)	Puget Sound B&D	9-6-45

YR 1–class repair, berthing, and messing barge YRBM 51—still carrying previous hull number YR 60, 15 months after reclassification W. Michael Young, 9-01

D: 530 tons light (760 fl) **Dim:** 46.6 (45.7 wl) × 10.7 × 1.8
Crew: 1–4 officers, 40–47 enlisted

Remarks: All were reclassified on 3-4-00. A once-uniform design, several now have had additional superstructure added. YRBM 50, based at San Diego, is listed at 600 tons light (990 fl) and has a beam of 12.0 m. Are all equipped with machine shops, berthing facilities, and a galley.

♦ 16 YRBM 31–class repair, berthing, and messing barges* [YPBN]
Bldr: Marinette Marine, Marinette, Wis.

	In serv.		In serv.		In serv.
YRBM 31	2-81	YRBM 37	6-82	YRBM 43	5-83
YRBM 32	3-81	YRBM 38	6-82	YRBM 44	5-83
YRBM 33	6-81	YRBM 39	8-82	YRBM 45	6-83
YRBM 34	6-81	YRBM 40	7-82	YRBM 46	7-83
YRBM 35	11-81	YRBM 41	11-82		
YRBM 36	11-81	YRBM 42	11-82		

SERVICE CRAFT *(continued)*

YRBM 31–class repair, berthing, and messing barge YRBM 42 Christopher P. Cavas, 7-00

D: 603 tons (688 fl) **Dim:** 44.50 × 14.0 × 1.1

Remarks: All YRBMs support ships in overhaul. Have berthing for 26 officers and 231 enlisted. Are equipped with office, workshop, eating, and recreation spaces, a 96-seat training theater, a galley, and so forth. YRBM 33–36, 40–43, 45, and 46 are in the Atlantic area, the others in the Pacific.

♦ 8 YRBM 23–class repair, berthing, and messing barges* [YPBN]
Bldr: Marinette Marine, Marinette, Wis.

	In serv.		In serv.		In serv.
YRBM 23	8-70	YRBM 26	10-70	YRBM 29	6-71
YRBM 24	8-70	YRBM 27	4-71	YRBM 30	6-71
YRBM 25	10-70	YRBM 28	5-71		

YRBM 23–class repair, berthing, and messing barge YRBM 25—with an LCM(8) landing craft alongside; YRBMs based at San Diego have white superstructures George R. Schneider, 6-01

D: 498 tons (585 fl) **Dim:** 44.50 × 14.0 × 1.1

Remarks: Have berthing for 26 officers and 231 enlisted. YRBM 23, 24, 27, and 28 are in the Atlantic area, the others in the Pacific. YRBM 27 carries the designation YRBM(L) 27, the reason not known.

♦ 7 YRBM 5–class repair, berthing, and messing barges* [YPBN] (2 in *reserve*)
Bldrs: YRBM 5, 6: Marinette Marine, Marinette, Wis.; others: Gretna Machine & Iron Works

	In serv.		In serv.		In serv.
YRBM 5	25-6-60	YRBM 9	15-12-62	YRBM 15	1-4-64
YRBM 6	25-6-60	YRBM 13	28-12-63		
YRBM 8	17-9-62	YRBM 14	10-3-64		

YRBM 5–class repair, berthing, and messing barge YRBM 15 William H. Clarke, 10-00

D: 236 tons light (310 fl) **Dim:** 34.14 (33.53 wl) × 10.97 (10.36 wl) × 0.91

Remarks: Have berthing for 10 officers and 90 enlisted. YRBM 5 and 6 were placed in reserve on 7-2-96; they are assigned to the Atlantic Fleet. YRBM 9 and 15 are based at Norfolk.
Disposals: Sister YRBM 7 (ex-YFNX 32, reclassified as YRBM 7 on 1-5-92) was stricken 26-10-93, YRBM 10 on 11-12-92, YRBM 11 on 25-11-96, and YRBM 12 on 7-5-98.

Disposal note: YRBM 1–class repair, berthing, and messing barge YRBM 3 was stricken 31-8-00.

♦ 2 YFNB 1–class repair, berthing, and messing barges* [YPBN]
Bldrs: YRBM 20: Willamette Iron and Steel, Ore.; YRBM 47: American Bridge, Ambridge, Pa.

	L	In serv.
YRBM 20 (ex-YFNB 26, ex-YFN 751)	23-12-44	9-1-45
YRBM 47 (ex-YFNX 2, ex-YFNB 2, ex YFN 1070)	14-4-45	15-6-45

YRBM 20—at San Diego George R. Schneider, 2-93

D: 700 tons light (2,000 fl) **Dim:** 79.55 × 14.63 × 2.74

Remarks: YRBM 20 is based at San Diego and displaces 2,700 tons full load. YRBM 47 is assigned to Submarine Squadron 22 at La Maddalena, Sardinia, and can berth 287 personnel; she was reclassified from YFNX 2 in 9-78.

♦ 3 YRDH 1–class floating dry dock workshops, hull* [YFND] (2 in *reserve*) Bldr: Puget Sound NSY (YRDH 2: Associated SB)

	In serv.		In serv.
YRDH 2 (ex-YR 56)	31-12-43	YRDH 6	31-3-44
YRDH 7	15-5-44		

D: 460 tons (750–770 fl) **Dim:** 46.6 × 10.7 × 1.8

Remarks: YRDH 6 is active at Pearl Harbor. YRDH 2 was placed in reserve on 11-3-67 and YRDH 7 on 1-5-46. Have berthing for one officer and 46 enlisted. Externally, they are nearly identical to the YRDM 5 and 7. Sister YRDH 1 (ex-YR 55) became IX 528 on 7-4-99.

♦ 2 YRDM 1–class floating machinery dry dock workshops* [YFND] (1 in *reserve*)
Bldrs: YRDM 5: Norfolk NSY; YRDM 7: Puget Sound Boat & Dockyard

YRDM 5 (In serv. 22-4-44) *YRDM 7* (In serv. 15-5-44)

YRDM 5—the YRDH 1–class units are nearly identical H&L Van Ginderen, 5-99

D: 490 tons (750 fl) **Dim:** 46.6 × 10.7 × 1.8

Remarks: YRDM 5 is active, YRDM 7 in reserve at Pearl Harbor. Bow ends are pointed, to improve towing speed.

♦ 3 YRR radiological repair barges* [YRRN]

	Bldr	In serv.
YRR 10 (ex-YR 79)	Puget Sound Barge & Dock	11-45
YRR 11 (ex-YRDH 3)	Norfolk NSY	12-43
YRR 14 (ex-YRDM 4)	Norfolk NSY	4-44

D: YRR 10: 500 tons light (760 fl); YRR 11, 14: 460 tons light (750 fl)
Dim: YRR 10: 46.63 × 10.97 × 1.83; YRR 11, 14: 46.03 × 10.67 × 1.83

Remarks: All are active in support of submarines, YRR 10 at Pearl Harbor, YRR 11 at Puget Sound Naval SY, and YRR 14 at New London, Conn. Are essentially of two dissimilar designs, with YRR 10 having a low-freeboard hull and the others a high-freeboard hull with little superstructure. Have berthing for one officer and 46 enlisted. YRR 9 was reclassified YFNB 47 in 11-83. YRR 7 was converted at Portsmouth Naval Shipyard and redesignated YR 90 on 1-8-91.
Disposals: YRR 4 became YR 89 on 15-8-86 and was stricken 24-9-01. YRR 1 and 13 were stricken 19-9-94, YRR 6 (ex-YR 39) and YRR 12 (ex-YRDH 4) on 31-7-95, YRR 2 (ex-YR 74) on 3-3-98, and YRR 5 (ex-YRDM 8) on 7-2-99. YRR 3 (ex-YFN 333) was stricken 25-11-96 but was reclassified as floating equipment on 27-3-97 for further use at Pearl Harbor.

SERVICE CRAFT *(continued)*

YRR 11—note the two additional decks built onto the original YRDH 1–class hull
Winter & Findler, 9-97

♦ 1 YSD 11–class seaplane wrecking derrick [YD]

Bldr: Pearl Harbor NSY

	Laid down	L	In serv.
YSD 74	1-5-43	5-6-43	15-7-44

D: 240 tons (270 fl) **S:** 6 kts **Dim:** 31.70 (30.48 wl) × 9.50 × 1.20
M: 2 Superior diesels; 2 props; 320 bhp **Crew:** 1 officer, 15 enlisted

Remarks: Employed as a self-propelled crane at the Naval Intermediate Ships Maintenance Facility, Pearl Harbor. This class was designed to support seaplanes, and the craft were known as "Mary Anns." Has a 10-ton crane.

♦ 1 YSR 30–class sludge-removal barge* [YSR]

Bldr: Maxon Construction Co. (In serv. 17-4-46)

YSR 39

Sludge removal barge YSD 39 George R. Schneider, 2-99

D: 230 tons light (650 fl) **Dim:** 33.5 × 10.4 × 2.1

Remarks: Assigned to Naval Amphibious Base, Little Creek, Va. Has a sludge treatment plant atop a rectangular barge hull. Was for sale as of 3-02.

♦ 30 Natick-class large harbor tugs [YTB]

Bldrs: YTB 760: Jakobson SY, Oyster Bay, N.Y.; YTB 767, 771: Mobile Ship Repair, Mobile, Ala.; YTB 775, 782–798, 818–836: Marinette Marine Corp., Marinette, Wis.; YTB 807–812: Peterson Bldrs, Sturgeon Bay, Wis.

	Laid down	L	In serv.	Based at
YTB 760 Natick	1-9-60	28-2-61	30-6-61	La Maddalena, Sardinia
YTB 761 Ottumwa	27-12-60	30-5-61	9-10-61	Bangor, Wash.
YTB 764 Mishawaka	1-2-62	8-8-62	19-4-63	Bangor, Wash.
YTB 765 Okmulgee	3-7-62	18-4-63	25-7-63	Norfolk
YTB 767 Apalachicola	1-5-63	26-10-63	9-6-64	Bremerton, Wash.
YTB 771 Keokuk	5-12-63	. . .	23-8-64	Portsmouth, N.H.
YTB 775 Wauwatosa	21-8-64	19-5-65	21-6-65	Diego Garcia
YTB 779 Manhattan	1-10-64	15-7-65	1-12-65	Bangor, Wash.
YTB 782 Manistee	9-8-65	20-10-65	1-2-66	Yokosuka, Japan
YTB 783 Redwing	18-9-65	12-11-65	1-2-66	Adak, Alaska
YTB 784 Kalispel	14-9-65	13-12-65	4-5-66	Diego Garcia
YTB 787 Kittanning	22-12-65	29-3-66	19-5-66	Yokosuka, Japan
YTB 789 Tomahawk	31-1-66	1-5-66	7-6-66	Guantanamo Bay, Cuba
YTB 796 Saco	12-1-68	1-7-68	1-1-69	Diego Garcia
YTB 797 Tamaqua	16-1-68	1-8-68	1-1-69	Diego Garcia
YTB 798 Opelika	23-2-68	1-8-68	1-1-69	Yokosuka, Japan
YTB 807 Massapequa	1-10-69	1-5-70	1-11-70	Yokosuka, Japan
YTB 808 Wenatchee	12-69	7-70	12-70	Bremerton, Wash.
YTB 812 Accomac	1-71	6-71	11-71	Bremerton, Wash.
YTB 815 Neodesha	10-5-71	6-10-71	2-1-72	Pearl Harbor
YTB 818 Mecosta	8-72	3-73	6-73	Adak, Alaska
YTB 820 Wanamassa	10-72	5-73	7-73	Guantanamo Bay, Cuba
YTB 822 Pawhuska	1-73	6-73	9-73	Bremerton, Wash.
YTB 823 Canonchet	2-73	7-73	9-73	Bremerton, Wash.
YTB 824 Santaquin	3-73	8-73	9-73	Little Creek, Va.
YTB 828 Catahecassa	9-73	5-74	8-74	Bremerton, Wash.
YTB 831 Dekanawida	12-73	9-74	10-74	Norfolk
YTB 832 Petalesharo	12-73	10-74	11-74	La Maddalena, Sardinia
YTB 833 Shabonee	6-74	10-74	12-74	Little Creek, Va.
YTB 835 Skenandoa	9-9-74	3-4-75	10-6-75	Bremerton, Wash.
YTB 836 Pokagon	10-74	4-75	6-75	Bremerton, Wash.

Manhattan (YTB 779) Victor M. Baca, 8-01

Tamaqua (YTB 797) Joe Straczek, 11-01

Canonchet (YTB 823) Victor M. Baca, 8-01

D: 286 tons (356 fl) **S:** 12.5 kts **Dim:** 33.05 × 9.3 × 4.14
Electronics:
Radar: 1 SPS-59 (Canadian Marconi LN-66) or Raytheon SPS-69 nav.
M: 1 Fairbanks-Morse 38D8⅛ × 12 diesel; 1 prop; 2,000 bhp
Electric: 120 kw tot. **Range:** 2,000/12 **Crew:** 11 tot. (all enlisted)

Remarks: Named for Native American tribes. All are active. Three others were built for Saudi Arabia. YTB 836 was overhauled and modified in 1998 with new deck line-handling machinery (a split-drum bowline winch forward, new roller fairleads, new mooring bits, new chocks, etc.); after a 1-year evaluation, others were to have been similarly altered. YTB 808 and 823 are operated by civilian crews.
Disposals: *Edenshaw* (YTB 752) was stricken on 5-5-94 (and transferred to the U.S. Coast Guard and stricken during 2001), *Marin* (YTB 753) on 14-11-94, *Pontiac* (YTB 756) on 27-11-92, *Oshkosh* (YTB 757) on 25-4-96, *Paducah* (YTB 758) on 25-6-99, *Bogalusa* (YTB 759) on 7-8-96, *Tuscumbia* (YTB 762) on 11-9-95, *Wapakoneta* (YTB 766) on 16-4-01, *Arcata* (YTB 768) on 4-4-95, *Dahlonega* (YTB 770) on 13-3-01, *Nashua* (YTB 774) on 6-5-94, *Weehawken* (YTB 776) on 5-1-01, *Nogalesen* (YTB 777) on 13-3-01, *Apopka* (YTB 778) on 26-6-96, *Saugus* (YTB 780) on 28-10-97, *Winnemucca* (YTB 785) on 26-12-95, *Tonkawa* (YTB 786) on 7-12-92, *Wapato* (YTB 788) on 25-4-96, *Menomenee* (YTB 790) on 4-9-98, *Antigo* (YTB 792) on 25-6-99, *Piqua* (YTB 793) on 13-3-01, *Mandan* (YTB 794) and *Ketchikan* (YTB 795) on 5-1-01, *Natchitoches* (YTB 799) on 13-10-95, *Eufaula* (YTB 800) on 7-12-92, *Palatka* (YTB 801) on 4-4-95, *Cheraw* (YTB 802) on 29-2-96, *Nanticoke* (YTB 803) on 1-2-99, *Ahuskie* (YTB 804) on 7-3-96, *Ocala* (YTB 805) on 28-10-97, *Agawam* (YTB 809) on 1-2-99, *Anoka* (YTB 810) on 13-3-01, *Houma* (YTB 811) on 1-2-99, *Campti* (YTB 816; placed in reserve on 1-2-99) on 9-11-99, *Hyannis* (YTB 817) on 21-8-97, *Iuka* (YTB 819) on 19-10-95, *Tontocany* (YTB 821) on 13-3-01, *Wahtena* (YTB 825) on 28-10-97, *Washtuena* (YTB 826) on 21-8-97, *Chetek* (YTB 827) on 29-2-96, *Metacom*

SERVICE CRAFT *(continued)*

(YTB 829; inactivated 6-11-99) on 5-1-01, and *Pushmataha* (YTB 830) on 2-10-95. Most stricken units are to be scrapped, but YTB 817 and 826 were transferred to the U.S. Fish and Wildlife Service at Midway Island, YTB 802 and 827 to the Army Corps of Engineers on 29-2-96, and YTB 759 and 778 to the Maritime Administration for use at the James River, Va., Reserve Fleet anchorage. *Newagen* (YTB 834) was inactivated 6-11-99, preparatory to disposal. *Dahlonega* (YTB 702) was placed out of service 2-2-00, *Marinette* (YTB 791) on 30-6-00, and *Chesaning* (YTB 769) on 9-6-00; all three are to be sold.

Note: MSC-chartered large harbor tugs are listed and described in a separate section at the end of the numbered service craft.

♦ 1 YTL 422–class small harbor tug [YTL]

Bldr: Robert Jacob, City I., N.Y. (In serv. 10-45)

YTL 602

D: 70 tons light (80 fl) **S:** 8 kts **Dim:** 20.12 (18.90 wl) × 5.49 × 2.44
M: 1 diesel; 375 bhp **Crew:** 4 tot.

Remarks: Active at the Pearl Harbor Naval Shipyard, the only Navy Vessel Register survivor of several hundred YTL 422–class tugs; many still serve in foreign navies.

Note: A number of LCM(6) landing craft have been converted for use as push-tugs for local use, in place of YTLs; they are listed under workboats [YFU]. The commercial tug *Mitchell Herbert,* classified as an "uninspected towing vessel," is on contract to the Naval Submarine Base, Bangor, Wash., and is used for a variety of support duties in the Puget Sound and San Juan Islands areas.

♦ 2 YTT 9–class torpedo trials ships [YPT]

Bldr: McDermott, Morgan City, La.

	Laid down	L	In serv.
YTT 10 Battle Point	5-10-88	17-8-89	30-11-91
YTT 11 Discovery Bay	3-4-89	22-2-90	30-5-92

Battle Point (YTT 10) McDermott SY, 10-90

D: 1,000 tons light (1,168 fl) **S:** 11 kts (sust.)
Dim: 56.85 (53.83 pp) × 12.19 × 3.23
A: 2 fixed, underwater 533-mm Mk 59 TT; 1 triple 324-mm Mk 32 Mod. 5 ASW TT
Electronics: Radar: 2 Raytheon SPS-64(V)9 ARPA nav.
M: 1 Cummins KTA-50M diesel; 1 prop; 1,250 bhp—2 electric Z-drive thrusters (300 shp each)—400-shp bow-thruster
Electric: 1,310 kw tot. (3 × 395-kw Cummins VTA-28 GS/G.C. sets, 1 × 125-kw emergency set)
Range: 1,800/11 **Fuel:** 70 tons **Endurance:** 12 days
Crew: 31 tot. + 9 civilian technicians

Remarks: Assigned to the Naval Underwater Warfare Engineering Station, Keyport, Wash., which evidently did not need as many as were ordered on its behalf; only two were ever operational at one time. YTT 10 was ordered in 8-87 and YTT 11 on 31-3-88. Although delivered on date shown, YTT 11 was not activated until 14-4-94. Both are operated on contract by SSI Corporation. YTT 11 has been assigned to the joint NOAA/National Geographic Society Sustainable Sea Expedition five-year study of U.S. coastal waters and carries manned research submersibles; she does not display her hull number.
Disposals: *Agate Pass* (YTT 12) was stricken 13-8-99, never having been made operational; she was transferred to NOAA on 31-1-01. *Cape Flattery* (YTT 9), deactivated 2-20-96, was stricken 13-8-99 and transferred on 26-9-00 to another government agency, which makes the craft available for charter.
Hull systems: Have a 7.3-ton-capacity electrohydraulic crane to recover torpedoes and to handle sensor arrays and recovery equipment. Also carry smaller 4.5-ton (to handle recovery vehicles) and 3.5-ton cranes and have four 10-ton vertical traction winches. There is a working deck aft. Can operate on battery power for quiet operations and can maneuver precisely with Z-drive thrusters aft and the bow-thruster. Perform tests with Mk 48 ADCAP, Mk 46, and Mk 50 ASW torpedoes. Have extensive telemetry and communications systems, GPS, Loran-C, a Raytheon RD-500 echo sounder, and a WQC-2 underwater telephone.

Note: The Naval Underwater Warfare Engineering Station, Keyport, Wash., also operates a 72-ft., wooden-hulled torpedo retriever *(Torpedo Retriever Boat 31);* yard patrol craft *YP 697* (see above under YP for data); 44-ft. Mk 2 *Guard Boat 16* (C2579); 24-ft. aluminum-hulled *Maintenance Boat 40;* barges YC 1329, YC 1470, YC 1631 (self-propelled), and YC 1633; and 11 smaller, self-propelled workboats (including three Boston Whalers, the 23.75-ft. rigid inflatable launch 24WB841, two 30-ft. hawser-handling launches (30HH652 and 30HH679), four 22-ft. Boston Whaler launches, and a 19.6-ft. oil pollution–cleanup launch).

♦ 1 YWN 156–class water barge* [YWN]

Bldr: J. Russell Engineering Works (In serv. 6-52)

YWN 156

D: 175 tons light **Dim:** 36.6 × 10.1 × 2.44

Remarks: Based at La Maddalena, Sardinia, in support of Submarine Squadron 22.

♦ 3 YWN 71–class water barges* [YWN] (1 in *reserve*)

	Bldr	In serv.
YWN 78	Eureka SB	13-12-43
YWN 82	American Pipe, La.	8-1-44
YWN 79	Nelson Boiler & Tank	25-4-44

YWN 71–class water barge YWN 78—being moved by commercial tug *Taft Beach* at Norfolk George R. Schneider, 9-99

D: 220 tons light (1,270 fl) **Dim:** 50.3 × 10.7 × 2.4

Remarks: YWN 78 is assigned to the Norfolk Naval Station and YWN 82 to the Naval Activity, Guam. YWN 79 has been in reserve since 10-71.

Note: YWN 5 is a locally applied, unofficial number given to a 1930s-vintage, Japanese-built water barge in use at Sasebo; no data available.

Military Sealift Command–Chartered Harbor Tugs

As of 1995, the Military Sealift Command (MSC) took over management of the contracts for all privately owned harbor tugs on charter to support U.S. Navy operations as the current contracts expired. Commercial tugs had already been used since the late 1980s to supplement USN tugs or replace them entirely at such bases as Kings Bay, Ga. Although initially tugs of any and all descriptions were chartered, by 1996 specialized tugs of nearly standardized design were beginning to predominate.

In 12-97, the MSC announced that 40 U.S. Navy YTBs would be retired and replaced with commercial tugs, starting at Naval Station Pearl Harbor, Naval Activities Guam, and Submarine Base Bangor in 3-98. In addition to the units listed below, in 4-99 Puerto Rico Towing and Barge received a 5-year contract to provide two tugs to replace three Navy YTBs at Roosevelt Roads, P.R.; and McAllister Towing & Transportation Co., N.Y., received a contract to operate a single tug at the Yorktown, Va., Naval Weapons Station.

A chartered tractor tug named *Delta Linda* was in use at Pearl Harbor as of 1-00.

♦ 1 Paul A. Wronowksi–class large tractor harbor tug [YTB]

Bldr: . . . . (In serv. 1980)

Paul A. Wronowksi

D: . . . tons **S:** . . . kts **Dim:** 27.4 × . . . × . . .
M: 2 Cummins . . . diesels; 2 Niigata azimuthal drives; 3,200 bhp

Remarks: Leased in 2-00 for 17 months, with two 17-month options, from Thames Towing for use at the submarine base, New London, Conn.

♦ 2 KST 35–class tractor large harbor tugs [YTB]

Bldr: Keppel Shipyard, Singapore (In serv. 1998)

KST 35 KST 36

D: . . . **S:** 12 kts **Dim:** 28.96 (22.50 pp) × 8.50 × 3.50
M: 2 Niigata 6L25Hx diesels; 2 Niigata Z-peller ZP-21 Kaplan azimuthal drives; 3,000 bhp
Electric: 160 kVA tot. (2 × 80-kw sets, G.M. Detroit Diesel 4-71T diesels driving)
Range: . . ./. . . **Fuel:** 56 tons **Crew:** . . . tot.

Remarks: 233 grt. Leased in late summer 1999 by Seay Corp., Seattle, from Keppel Smit, Singapore, for 5–7 years to provide tug services at Diego Garcia. KST 35 began service 15-7-99 and KST 36 on 1-10-99. Both are British flagged and crewed by Singaporeans. Bollard pull: 42.2 tons. Have a 100-ton-capacity windlass/towing winch forward and one aft. Can carry 14 tons of fresh water. Equipped with an echo sounder, GPS, autopilot, SSB radio, and VHF radio.

♦ 6 Marci Moran–class tractor large harbor tugs [YTB]

Bldr: Washburn & Doughty, East Boothbay, Maine

Marci Moran (In serv. 9-99)	Susan Moran (In serv. 3-00)
Karen Moran (In serv. 2-00)	Tracey Moran (In serv. 4-00)
Surrie Moran (In serv. 5-10-00)	Wendy Moran (In serv. 6-00)

Wendy Moran A. D. Baker III, 10-00

SERVICE CRAFT *(continued)*

D: approx. 740 tons (fl) **S:** 13 kts **Dim:** 28.75 × 9.75 × 4.19
Electronics: Radar: 1 Furuno FR 7062/4 nav.
M: 2 G.M. EMD 16-645-E2 diesels; 2 Ulstein 1350H Z-drives with Kort-nozzles; 4,200 bhp—2 Ulstein bow-thrusters
Electric: 100 kw tot. (2 × 50-kw G.M. Detroit Diesel 4-71RC "N" diesel generator sets)
Range: . . ./. . . **Fuel:** 35,000 gallons **Crew:** 3 civilian mariners

Remarks: 200 grt. Chartered for 24 months (with 36-month renewal option) from Moran Towing Co., Baltimore, to replace 11 USN YTBs at Little Creek and Norfolk, Va. The first contract tug was originally to be in service 9-99, but full service was not inaugurated until 10-00. At the time of contract award, Moran owned only one tractor tug, the *Elizabeth Turecamo,* and was to acquire new tugs to meet the requirements of the contract. The class-name ship was built for another private firm. Two were ordered 21-12-98, with options for the others taken up later.
Hull systems: Have two firefighting monitors connected to an Aurora centrifugal pump driven by a Detroit Diesel 8V-71T diesel. Fenders will be fitted along the sides, bow, and stern and along the chine line to prevent damage to submarines. Bollard pull is 136 tons aft, 45 tons forward. Navigational equipment includes a Furuno GP 35 GPS terminal.

Note: Moran tugs *Kerry Moran* and *Patricia Moran* were modified during 2000 with the same tractor propulsion systems used in the *Marci Moran* class to fulfill the 1-12-98 contract to provide eight private tugs for service in the Hampton Roads area.

♦ 2 Punta Lima–class large harbor tugs [YTB]
Bldr: Great Lakes Towing Co., Cleveland, Ohio

	In serv.
Punta Lima (ex-*New Mexico,* ex-*W. L. Mercereau*)	1910
Punta Tuna (ex-*Michigan,* ex-*Polk,* ex-*Missouri*)	1915

D: . . . **S:** . . . kts **Dim:** 24.69 × 6.13 × . . .
M: 2 diesels; 1 prop; 1,600 bhp

Remarks: Operated by Puerto Rico Tug and Barge, a subsidiary of Great Lakes Towing Co., for service at Roosevelt Roads, P.R. Are traditional single-screw tugs, modified many times during their nine decades of service. Have riveted-construction steel hulls.

♦ 4 Z-One-class large harbor tugs [YTB]
Bldr: Marco SY, Seattle (L: 13-2-99; in serv.: 1-3-99)

Z-One Z-Three Z-Four Z-Five

Z-Four—at Pearl Harbor Brian Morrison, 6-00

D: approx. 260 tons (fl) **S:** 14 kts (12 cruise)
Dim: 28.65 × 9.75 × 3.60 (4.49 molded depth)
M: 2 Caterpillar 12-cyl. 3516B diesels; 2 Ulstein 1650H azimuthal drives, 2 4-bladed Kort-nozzle props; 4,000 bhp at 1,600 rpm
Electric: 204 kw (1 × 105-kw Caterpillar 3404BT and 1 × 99-kw Caterpillar 3306C DIT diesel sets)
Range: . . ./. . . **Fuel:** 30,000 gallons **Crew:** 8–10 tot. (accomm. for 10 tot.)

Remarks: On completion, *Z-Three, Z-Four,* and *Z-Five* were chartered from the Tugz International (formerly Admiral Towing and Barge) division of Great Lakes Towing, Cleveland, Ohio, and will be stationed at Pearl Harbor, to support submarines under a two-year contract; an option for three additional units was included in the construction contract. *Z-One* was chartered from the same owner by Moran Brothers Towing, Baltimore, to fulfill its contract to provide tugs at Norfolk Naval Base.
Hull systems: Have a 45-metric-ton bollard pull and two towing winches aft with 610 m of towing wire. The 3406C DIT diesel generator set also drives a 3,000-gallon/minute pump that supplies two 1,500-gallon/minute fire monitors. Carry 12,228 gallons of ballast water and 1,775 gallons of potable water. Have a 4-ton-capacity hydraulic crane to handle submarine personnel brows and are sheathed with rubber fendering below the waterline to protect submarine hulls.

♦ 14 C-Tractor-series large harbor tugs [YTB]
Bldr: North American SB, Galliano, La. (In serv. 1989–96)

C-Tractor 1 through C-Tractor 14

D: 265 tons (fl) **S:** 12 kts **Dim:** 32.00 (29.28 pp) × 11.30 (10.05 wl) × 3.96
M: 2 Caterpillar 12-cyl. diesels; 2 Ulstein Z-drive props; 3,960–4,000 bhp
Electric: 300 kw (2 × 150-kw diesel sets) **Crew:** 3 tot.

Remarks: 190 grt. Push-tugs chartered from and operated by Edison Chouest/Alpha Marine Services. *C-Tractor 1* and *2* are stationed at Kings Bay, Ga.; *C-Tractor 3–5, 12,* and *13* at Mayport, Fla.; *C-Tractor 6* at New London, Conn., reassigned there in 1-00; and *C-Tractor 7–11* and *14* at San Diego. *C-Tractor 12* and *13* were chartered in 1997, Data apply to *C-Tractor 1–5, 12,* and *13;* most of the others are 27.43 × 10.05 × 3.44 m and are powered by two 12-cyl. Caterpillar diesels producing a total of 2,400 bhp. *C-Tractor 14,* which arrived at Naval Station, San Diego, in 9-99, is larger and more powerful than the earlier units, displacing 365 tons, measuring 35.66 × 12.52 m, and having 8,000 bhp for a bollard pull of 25 tons.

C-Tractor 14 W. Michael Young, 6-01

Unnumbered Navy Service Craft

In addition to the above Navy Vessel Registry yard and service craft, there were some 2,055 craft assigned to various ships, commands, and shore stations as of 2001, including landing craft and small patrol boats. Most of the more significant units are identified by a numbering system that begins with digits signifying the craft's length to the nearest foot (or, in recent years, meter), followed by an alphabetical designator indicating the craft's type, two digits indicating the fiscal year in which the craft was authorized, and subsequent digits indicating *which* craft of that year—for example, "65PB778" is the eighth 65-ft. patrol boat built under FY 77. Numerous older units, however, are still carried under an earlier numbering system that begins with the letter "C," and some small craft assigned to public works organizations at navy facilities carry numbers in yet another series. *Unofficial* names and hull numbers are in widespread use. The craft appear below in the standard *Combat Fleets* ship-typing system order.

♦ 15 24-foot Boom Handling Boats [YAG]
Bldr: SeaArk Marine, Monticello, Ark. (In serv. 1980-89)

24BH- series

24-ft. Boom Handling Boat A. D. Baker III, 10-01

D: 4.6 tons (fl) **S:** 16.5 kts **Dim:** 23.86 × 2.41 × 0.52
M: 1 G.M. Detroit Diesel 6V-53T diesel; 1 prop; 260 bhp
Range: . . ./. . . **Fuel:** 130 gal. **Crew:** . . . tot.

Remarks: Welded aluminum-construction boats, intended to tow Open Seas Oil Containment Boom, Dunlop Dracone, and Marco Skimmer Boat oil-spill containment devices. Bow and appendages are removable for ease of transportation within a standard 20 × 8 × 8–ft. container. Normally operated in pairs and are stowed ashore when not in use.

♦ 1 Ecology Sampling Boat [YAG]
Bldr: Munson Mfg., Edmonds, Wash. (In serv. 1988)

40NS8901 Ecos

Ecology Sampling Boat Ecos (40NS8901) George R. Schneider, 2-93

D: 11.3 tons (fl) **S:** 15 kts **Dim:** 12.19 × 3.66 × 0.91
M: 2 Volvo AQAD 40 outdrive diesels; 2 props; . . . bhp
Electric: 12 kw tot. **Fuel:** 100 gallons **Crew:** . . .

Remarks: Built for the Naval Ocean Systems Center, San Diego. All-aluminum construction, unpainted. Has two 450-kg portable equipment davits and a hydraulic winch.

♦ 43 DIP-3001-series oil-skimmer launches [YAG]
Bldr: Kvichak Marine Industries, Seattle (In serv. 1994–98)

D: . . . tons **S:** . . . kts **Dim:** 8.53 × 2.44 × . . .
M: 1 Volvo Penta inboard/outboard diesel; 1 prop; . . . bhp

SERVICE CRAFT *(continued)*

DIP-3001-series oil-skimmer launch—on travel trailer
George R. Schneider, 12-97

Remarks: Sweeper boats with "jaws" at the bow to broaden the sweep of collection. Assigned to local Navy Public Works organizations at naval facilities. In 1998, Kvichak also delivered six 5.49 × 2.41–m, aluminum-construction "Boom Skiffs" for pollution control work.

Note: The navy operates numerous other oil-spill sweeping and boom containment craft with a variety of serial numbers in the 25DP-, 26NS-, 26WB-, 27WB-, and 28UB-series, built by Marco Marine, Willard, SeaArk, and JBF Scientific.

21-ft. SeaArk-built Boom Handling Boat—at San Diego; aluminum-construction boat powered by one 150-bhp Johnson outboard George R. Schneider, 11-98

18-ft. Boom-Handling Boat UB-1—assigned to the Norfolk Naval Shipyard
Takatoshi Okano, 8-00

♦ 1 former U.S. Air Force space booster recovery ship [YAG]
Bldr: Halter Marine, Moss Point, Miss. (L: 27-2-85)

INDEPENDENCE

D: 1,798 tons (fl) **S:** 13 kts **Dim:** 60.96 (55.47 wl) × 12.19 × 4.11
Electronics:
Radar: 1 STN Atlas Elektronik 8500 nav.; 1 STN Atlas Elektronik 5500 nav.
M: 2 Cummins KTA 3067-M 16-cyl. diesels; 2 props; 2,500 bhp—2 azimuth thrusters (1,000 shp)—Elliott-White-Gill bow- and stern-thrusters
Electric: 550 kw tot. (2 × 275-kw sets, Cummins KT 1150-GC diesels)
Range: 7,800/13; 8,500/11 **Fuel:** 99,419 gallons **Endurance:** 30 days
Crew: 13 tot. + 14 scientists/technicians

Independence George R. Schneider, 12-97

Remarks: Originally built to recover solid-fuel boosters launched from Vandenberg Air Force Base on the California coast. Transferred to the navy in 1988 and operated for the Naval Facilities Engineering Services Center, Port Hueneme, Calif., by Western Instrument Corporation. Employed to test underwater sensors and also available to other government agencies for charter.
Hull systems: Has elaborate navigational equipment, including a Magnavox MX 4400 GPS receiver, a Magnavox 11072 NAVSAT receiver, a Robertson dynamic positioning system, and two Simrad echo sounders. Has Flume passive-tank stabilization system. Can carry 388 tons of deck cargo, including modular laboratories. Has a small laboratory and a hyperbaric chamber capable of accommodating seven divers. Equipped with a 22-ton crane that telescopes to 19.8-m reach.

♦ 1 sail frigate relic [YAG]
Bldr: Hart's SY, Boston

	Laid down	L	In serv.
CONSTITUTION (ex-IX 21)	11-1-1794	21-10-1797	1-10-1798

Constitution U.S. Navy, 7-97

D: 2,200 tons (fl) **S:** 13 kts (sail) **Dim:** 62.18 (53.34 hull) × 13.26 × 6.86
A: 32 single 24 pdr.; 26 single 32-pdr. carronade; 2 single 24-pdr. bow-chasers
M: 3,968 m^2 sail area
Crew: 2 officers, 45 enlisted (originally 450 tot., incl. 55 Marines and 30 "boys")

Remarks: The world's oldest warship in full commission. Wooden construction. First went to sea 22-7-1798. Has three masts, 28.7, 31.7, and 24.7 m high. Bore the name *Old Constitution* from 1917 to 1925 and was designated IX 21 from 8-12-1941 to 1-9-1975. Was extensively refitted from 1994 to mid-1997, with restoration of the original diagonal internal hull bracing and new rigging, permitting her to be sailed under her own power for the first time since 1886 with an augmented crew of 133 on 21-7-1997 from Marblehead, Mass., to Boston. Is on display at the former Charlestown Naval Base, Boston.

♦ 1 Guardian 85-foot-class trials craft [YAGE]
Bldr: Guardian Marine, Tacoma, Wash. (In serv. 2000)

25WB. . .

D: 105 tons (fl) **S:** 40 kts **Dim:** 25.91 × 7.01 × 1.67
Electronics: 1 Furuno FR-8251 X-band nav.
M: 2 MTU DDC 12V4000 diesels; 2 props; 4,920 bhp
Electric: 64 kw tot. (2 × 32-kw Northern Lights Mod. M984K alternators)
Range: 1,700/. . . **Endurance:** 7 days **Crew:** . . .

Remarks: GRP-construction, planing-hull "Fast Patrol Craft." Assigned to the Naval Surface Warfare Center, Carderock Division, Norfolk Detachment, Va. A sister with a more powerful version of the same engines was ordered for the Coast Guard for delivery in 7-02. Eight others have been built for commercial use, six as tour boats and two as personnel ferries. The hull was molded by ModuTech Marine, Tacoma, Wash.

SERVICE CRAFT *(continued)*

Guardian 85-ft. class Guardian Marine

♦ **1 leased Norwegian Skjold-class surface-effect craft [YAGE]**
Bldr: Kværner Mandal, Mandal

	Laid down	L	In serv.
P 960 SKJOLD	8-97	22-9-98	17-4-99

Skjold (P 960)—stern view; for other views of the craft, see the Norway entry
Ben Sullivan, 9-99

D: 260 tons (fl) **S:** 55 kts (57.1 on trials)
Dim: 46.79 (41.50 pp) × 13.50 × 2.25 (0.83 on cushion)
A: none (see remarks)
Electronics:
Radar: 1 Ericsson Sea Giraffe surf./air search; 1 Saab CEROS 200 f.c.
EW: . . . intercept
E/O: SAGEM VIGY 20 optronic f.c.
M: CODOG: 2 Rolls-Royce–Allison 571-KF9 gas turbines (8,160 shp each), 2 MTU 6R183 TE92 auxiliary diesels (500 bhp each); 2 KaMeWa 80S2 waterjets; 16,320 shp—2 MTU 12V183 TE92 diesels (985 bhp each) driving lift-fans
Electric: 456 kw tot (2 MTU 6R183 TE52 diesels driving)
Range: . . ./. . . **Endurance:** 14 days **Crew:** 4 officers, 11 enlisted

Remarks: Leased for one year, with a Norwegian Navy crew. Arrived at Norfolk on 18-9-01 and was assigned to Special Boat Squadron 2, Little Creek, Va., for trials. A formal one-year lease was signed 1-2-02. *Skjold* is the prototype for a new class of guided-missile patrol craft for the Norwegian Navy; the name means "Shield." See entry in the Norway section for additional program details.
Hull systems: GRP-construction, rigid sidewall surface-effect ship, with infrared and radio energy shielding molded into the structure to reduce signature. Has an automatic ride-control system. Production versions may have a different propulsion system with Rolls-Royce–Allison 571KF11 gas turbines of up to 16,400 kw total output to sustain 55 kts. The craft is to be able to sustain 44 kts in a State 3 sea. Can operate in waters as shallow as 1 m.
Combat systems: Unarmed as delivered; was intended to mount four NSM antiship missiles, one 76-mm 62-cal. OTOBreda SuperRapid DP, and one 2-round Simbad point-defense SAM launcher (Mistral missiles). The intended SENIT 2000 combat system has also not yet been installed. The communications system includes HF through UHF radios, cryptographic systems, and Link 11.

♦ **1 Small Waterplane Area Ship test craft [YAGE]**
Bldr: Pacific Marine & Supply, Honolulu (L: 11-96)

SLICE

D: 183 tons (fl) **S:** 31.6 kts (on trials) **Dim:** 31.70 × 16.80 × 4.30
A: 1 30-mm Millennium CIWS; 1 Netfire missile launcher
Electronics: Radar: 2 Furuno . . . nav.
M: 2 MTU 16V396 TB 94 diesels; 2 2.2-m-dia. Lips CP props; 6,850 bhp
Electric: 720 kw tot. (2 × 360-kw Caterpillar 3306 DITA diesel sets)
Range: 400/30; 2,000/22 **Fuel:** . . . tons **Crew:** 2 operators, 4 trials technicians

Slice U.S. Navy, 3-99

Remarks: Jointly funded by the Office of Naval Research ($14.5 million) and the Pacific Marine and Supply Co. as a prototype commercial interisland personnel ferry. Intended to test high-speed SWATH (Small Waterplane Area, Twin-Hull) design concepts. No immediate military application is foreseen, but the craft is foreseen as a potential mine countermeasures or small missile combatant platform. Has a potential payload of 51 tons in up to Sea State 5. In 1999, $9.5 million was to be used to construct a cargo-barge version of the design to be towed by the *Slice;* the barge may also be evaluated as a missile-launch platform. After losing a fin off Kauai during 1999, the craft was placed in reserve. She was refitted and reactivated in 6-01 for a series of demonstration cruises along the Pacific Coast, with an Atlantic Coast cruise to follow in 2002 and a Great Lakes cruise in 2003; in addition to acting as a technology demonstrator for the Office of Naval Research, the craft is acting as a recruiting tool and has been painted in a bright silver, blue, red, and yellow paint scheme.
Hull systems: Aluminum-alloy structure. The Lockheed Martin hull design employs four torpedo-shaped underwater hulls, two per side, with the propellers mounted on the forward pair, which is closer together than the after pair to avoid propeller wake effects. Armed during spring 2002 for trials; see addenda.

♦ **1 Hydrofoil Small Waterplane-Area Ship test craft [YAGE]**
Bldr: Maritime Applied Physics Corp., Laurel, Md. (L: 7-7-95)

HYSWAS 1 QUEST

Quest (HYSWAS 1) Maritime Applied Physics, 7-95

D: 12 tons (fl) **S:** 37 kts **Dim:** 8.22 × . . . (3.1 over foil) × 2.0 (3.0 hullborne)
M: 2 Cummins . . . diesels; 1 prop; . . .

Remarks: HYSWAS = Hydrofoil Small Waterplane-Area Ship. Has a single centerline pylon below the trimaran hull, with two sets of variable-incidence foils mounted on the bulbous foot. Total height is 3.9 m. Trials were conducted from Annapolis, Md., commencing in 7-95. Intended to maintain 35 kts in Sea State 5. The builder received a design feasibility contract for a 1,000-ton mine countermeasures version of this design during 2001.

♦ **1 49-foot hydrological research boat [YAGE]**
Bldr: Munson Mfg., Edmonds, Wash. (In serv. 1992)

49NS9201

Hydrological research boat 49NS9201 George R. Schneider, 12-97

SERVICE CRAFT *(continued)*

D: 16.5 tons **S:** 22 kts **Dim:** 14.9 × 4.6 × 1.2
Electronics: Radar: 1 Furuno . . . nav.
M: 2 G.M. Detroit Diesel 6V92 diesels; 2 props; . . . bhp
Fuel: 2270 liters **Crew:** . . . tot.

Remarks: Built for the Naval Facilities Engineering Service Center, Port Hueneme, Calif., to conduct hydrological research. Builder's Hammerhead 48 design. All-aluminum construction.

♦ 1 acoustic trials support craft [YAGE]
Bldr: Gladding-Hearn SB, Somerset, Mass. (In serv. 7-91)

60NS9001

D: . . . tons **S:** 30 kts **Dim:** 18.28 × 5.79 × 1.82
M: 2 G.M. Detroit Diesel 12 V92TA diesels; 2 props; 1,800 bhp
Electric: 65 kw tot (1 × 45-kw, 1 × 20-kw Onan sets, Cummins diesel-driven)
Range: 1,200/30 **Fuel:** 2,271 liters **Crew:** . . . tot.

Remarks: Aluminum construction, unpainted. Built for use by the Naval Ships Research and Development Center's Acoustical Research Detachment, Lake Pend Oreille, Idaho, as a towboat. Is able to tow a 1.5-ton object at 15 kts.

♦ 1 Decatur-class Self-Defense Test Ship [YAGE]
Bldr: Bethlehem Steel, Quincy, Mass.

	Laid down	L	In serv.
E 31 Decatur (ex-DDG 31, ex-DD 936)	13-9-54	15-12-55	7-12-56

Decatur (E 31) George R. Schneider, 5-00

D: 2,967 tons light **S:** 10 kts **Dim:** 127.40 × 13.70 × . . .
A: 1 8-round Mk 29 missile launcher (AIM-9P NATO Sea Sparrow missiles); 1 20-mm Mk 15 Phalanx CIWS
Electronics:
Radar: 1 R70A nav.; 1 SPS-49(V) air search; 1 Mk 23 TAS target desig.; 1 HFSWR air search (see remarks); 2 Mk 95 Sea Sparrow f.c.; 1 Mk 90 Phalanx f.c.
EW: SLQ-32(V)3 intercept/jammer
M: 2 Harbormaster diesel azimuthal outdrives; 2,400 bhp—bow-thruster
Electric: 1,750 kw tot. (3 × 550-kw, 1 × 100-kw diesel sets)
Range: . . ./. . . **Endurance:** 30 days **Crew:** 50 tot. (civilian contractor)

Remarks: Built as a DD; converted to guided-missile destroyer, recommissioning 15-6-67 and decommissioning 30-6-83. The present conversion was ordered in 4-88, with work beginning 10-89 at Puget Sound Naval Shipyard and being completed at the Naval Surface Warfare Center, Port Hueneme Division, Calif., in 9-94. Is operated for the Sea Test Range Control Center, Point Mugu, Calif., by Matson Marine under contract to Litton/PRC as either a manned or a remotely controlled self-defense weapons test platform. The combat systems are operated by the Naval Surface Warfare Center, Port Hueneme. The ship is expected to average one month of operations at sea per quarter through 2010. Is referred to as "EDDG 31" or the "SDTS" (Self-Defense Test Ship) and has "E 31" painted on the hull; the name *Decatur* is still commonly used.
Hull systems: The azimuthal outdrives are mounted in recesses cut into the corners of the transom stern. A third 550-kw generator set was added during 1995, and there are three 100-kVA static frequency converters to provide 400-Hz power for the combat systems. A helicopter platform has been added at the stern, and permanent fittings to assist in towing the ship have been added forward. Berthing for the crew includes accommodations for up to four female personnel.
Combat systems: At a later date, it is planned to install an electrothermal gun, an SPQ-9B surface-search/target-designation radar (in place of the Mk 23 TAS), a thermal imaging system, Mk 36 SRBOC decoy launchers, and the complete Mk 1 integrated Ship Self-Defense System (SSDS). The Mk 29 launcher will be used for testing both the NATO Sea Sparrow and the Evolved Sea Sparrow missile systems. Foreign systems may also be tested.

Note: Of other former U.S. Navy ships recently employed as targets, the ex-*Somers* (DDG 32) was sunk as a SINKEX target on 17-7-00. The ex-*Buchanan* (DDG 14) was sunk as an artificial reef on 13-6-00, ex-*Ramsey* (FFG 2) and ex-*Gen. Hugh J. Gaffey* (IX 507, ex-T-AP 121) were sunk on 15-6-00, and ex-*Worden* (CG 18) was sunk on 17-6-00—all as targets during the annual RIMPAC exercise. Sunk as targets during 2001 were the ex-*Barbel* (SS 580) on 30-1-01, ex-*Reeves* (CG 24) by Royal Australian Air Force aircraft on 31-5-01, ex-*Lynde McCormick* (DDG 8) on 24-2-01, and ex-*John Paul Jones* (DDG 32, ex-DD 932) on 31-1-01.

Note: The signature-reduction trials craft *Sea Shadow* was designated IX 529 on 28-4-00 and is now described with the other IX-series ships and craft in this volume.

♦ 2 Sea Spectre PB Mk-III class [YAGE]
Bldr: Peterson Bldrs, Sturgeon Bay, Wis. (In serv. 1974–78)

65PB734 Navy Prince 65PB777 Plymouth

Plymouth (65PB777)—with stabilized gunmount for trials S.E.I., Inc., 8-96

D: 28 tons (36.7 fl) **S:** 30 kts (now less) **Dim:** 19.78 × 5.50 × 1.80 (props)
A: various **Electronics:** Radar: 1 or 2 . . . nav.
M: 3 G.M. 8V71 TI diesels; 3 props; 1,800 bhp
Range: 450/26; 2,000/. . . **Endurance:** 3 days **Crew:** 1 officer, 8 enlisted

Remarks: Survivors of 8 built under FY 73, 10 under FY 75, and 3 under FY 77. 65PB777 has been used in trials with stabilized automatic gun systems. Both are assigned to the Naval Surface Warfare Center, Dahlgren, Va.

♦ 3 Asheville-class engineering-trials ships [YAGE]
Bldr: Tacoma Boat, Tacoma, Wash.

	In serv.
165NS761 Athena (ex-*Chehalis,* PG 94)	11-8-69
165NS762 Athena II (ex-*Grand Rapids,* PG 98)	9-5-70
165NS763 Lauren (ex-*Douglas,* PG 100)	6-2-71

Athena (165NS8761) Dr. Giorgio Arra, 1992

D: 225 tons (250 fl) **S:** 35 kts (13 on diesels)
Dim: 50.14 × 7.28 × 2.9 (3.20 over props)
Electronics: Radar: 2 . . . nav.
M: CODOG: 1 G.E. 7LM-1500-PE 102 LM-1500 gas turbine (12,500 shp), 2 Cummins VT12-875-M diesels (1,450 bhp); 2 CP props
Electric: 260 kw tot. (2 × 100-kw, 1 × 60-kw diesel sets)
Range: 325/37; 2,300/13 **Fuel:** 50 tons **Crew:** 10 tot. + up to 18 scientific party

Remarks: The first two are operated from Port Lauderdale, Fla., by MAR, Inc., for the Naval Surface Warfare Center, Carderock Division. Have civilian crews and are disarmed. 165NS761 was reclassified as "floating equipment" 21-8-75 and 165NS762 on 1-10-77; both are now used in the development of high-speed towed sensors, airborne mine countermeasures, communications systems, and full-scale verifications of propeller designs. 165NS763 was activated in 1990 for trials with the Integrated Warship System Demonstration Program and appears to be involved in signature-reduction trials; she received the Northrop Grumman Low-Observable Multifunction Stack for trials from Panama City, Fla., during 7-01. Two additional units of the class, *Gallup* (PG 85) and *Canon* (PG 90) were transferred to the control of the Naval Ships Research Center, Carderock, Md., in 7-92 and, although still afloat, have been heavily cannibalized for parts for the three active units.
Hull systems: 165NS763 was given a 50-ton chilled water installation and a stack extension during a refit completed 2-95. 165NS761 and 165NS762 have 366 ft.^{2} of air-conditioned laboratory space and 850 ft.^{2} of working space on the fantail; they have a 10-ton instrumentation payload and both can carry a 14.9-m, portable, GRP laboratory on the stern, while 165NS761 has a permanent 18.6-m lab added forward. Fuel consumption at 35 kts is 1,000 gallons/hr. Navigational equipment included GPS, NAVSAT, and Loran receivers, an echo sounder, and a gyrocompass. 165NS763 is to be fitted in 2001 with a Boeing lightweight, phased-array SATCOM antenna.

♦ 2 trials support ships [YAGE]
Bldr: McDermott SY, New Iberia, La. (In serv. 1981)

192UB8701 Ranger (ex-*Seacor Ranger,* ex-*NUSC Ranger,* ex-*Sea Level 27*)
192UB8702 NAWC 38 (ex-NADC 38, *Sea Level No. 7*)

D: approx. 1,800 tons (fl) **S:** 12 kts **Dim:** 58.52 × 12.19 × 4.27
A: 192UB8701 only: 1 bow, submerged 533-mm TT; 1 triple 324-mm Mk 32 ASW TT
Electronics:
Radar: 192UB8702: 1 . . . ARPA X-band nav.; 1 . . . ARPA S-band nav.

SERVICE CRAFT *(continued)*

NAWC 38 (192UB8702) Winter & Findler, 9-01

M: 2 G.M. Electromotive Div. 12-645-E6 diesels; 2 props; 3,000 bhp—300-shp bow tunnel-thruster (G.M. 8V-71 diesel driving)
Electric: 300 kw tot. (2 × 150-kw sets, G.M. 8V-71 diesels driving)—192UB8702 also: 1,200 kw (2 × 600-kw sets, Solar gas turbines driving)
Range: 8,600/12 (192UB8702: 5,000/10)
Endurance: 192UB8702: 20–25 days
Crew: 192UB8702: 8 civilian crew + up to 22 scientific party (civilian)

Remarks: 300 grt/1,200 dwt. Converted oilfield tug/supply vessels, acquired in 1986 and employed as tenders for trials services. 192UB8701 is used in support of the AUTEC (Atlantic Undersea Test and Evaluation Center) range at Andros Island, the Bahamas; she is chartered from Seacor/MSO, Inc., which operates her. 192UB8702 is operated for the Naval Air Warfare Center, Aircraft Division, from Fort Lauderdale, Fla., as a trials craft for littoral warfare technology testing and is equipped with a 79-ton crane (limited to 36 tons at sea), an A-frame gantry at the stern, a 2.9 × 7.9–m centerline moonpool, four-point mooring capability in depths of up to 600 ft., and state-of-the-art navigational systems.

♦ 1 sonobuoy trials craft [YAGE]
Bldr: Halter Marine, Moss Point, Miss. (In serv. 1981)

180WB8701 Acoustic Pioneer (ex-*September Morn*)

Acoustic Pioneer (180WB8701) Dr. Giorgio Arra, 4-93

D: approx. 1,500 tons (fl) **S:** 12 kts **Dim:** 54.86 × 12.19 × 4.27 (3.66 hull)
Electronics: Radar: 1 . . . X-band nav.; 1 . . . S-band nav.
M: 2 G.M. Electromotive Div. 12-567BC diesels; 2 props; 2,500 bhp—300-shp bow tunnel-thruster (G.M. 8V-71 diesel driving)
Electric: 253 kw tot. (2 × 99-kw sets, G.M. 8V-71 diesels driving; 1 × 55-kw set, G.M. 4-71 diesel driving)
Range: 6,000/10 **Endurance:** 20–27 days **Crew:** 7 tot. + up to 11 scientific party

Remarks: Former 282-grt oilfield supply boat, acquired in 1986 and formerly employed with the *Acoustic Explorer* at the Naval Avionics Development Center, St. Croix, Virgin Islands, for sonobuoy testing. Now assigned to the Naval Air Warfare Center, Aircraft Division, from Fort Lauderdale, Fla. Has two 4 × 4.6–m laboratories below decks and can accommodate portable deck laboratory vans. Navigation suite includes GPS and Differential GPS receivers, a Loran-C receiver, a precision echo sounder, and a Sperry gyrocompass. Has an A-frame lift gantry at the stern.

♦ 1 sonobuoy trials craft [YAGE]
Bldr: Eastern Marine, Panama City, Fla. (In serv. 12-81)

111NS8801 Acoustic Explorer (ex-*Strong Brio*)

D: . . . tons (fl) **S:** . . . kts **Dim:** 38.1 × 9.14 × 1.42
M: 2 diesels; 2 props; . . . bhp

Remarks: Acquired in 1988. Assigned to the Space and Naval Warfare Systems Center (formerly Naval Command, Control, and Ocean Surveillance Center), San Diego. Has 23 m^2 of laboratory space.

Disposal note: SWATH (Small Waterplane Area, Twin-Hull) research craft *Kaimalino* (SSP 1, 90WB8701), out of service since 1997 and laid up midway through modifications, had been discarded by 2001.

Acoustic Explorer (111NS8801) George R. Schneider, 10-00

♦ 1 LCU 1610–class trials craft [YAGE]
Bldr: Defoe SB, Bay City, Wis. (In serv. 1969)

LCU 1647 MDSU 2

D: 190 tons (390 normal, 437 fl) **S:** 11 kts **Dim:** 41.07 × 9.07 × 2.08
Electronics: Radar: 1 Raytheon SPS-69 Pathfinder nav.
M: 2 G.M. 12V-71 diesels; 2 Kort-nozzle props; 800 bhp—White-Gill bow- and stern-thrusters (275-bhp G.M. 6-71 diesel driving forward, 230-bhp G.M. 6V-53 diesel driving aft)
Electric: 110 kw tot (2 × 40-kw, 1 × 30-kw diesel sets)
Range: 1,000/10 **Fuel:** 13 tons **Endurance:** 4–6 days
Crew: 6 tot. + 9 scientific party

Remarks: Assigned to the Naval Air Warfare Center, Aircraft Division, as a workboat and operates from Fort Lauderdale, Fla.
Hull systems: Cargo capacity: 180 tons; cargo space: 36.9 × 7.62 m max., with a 4.5-m-wide bow ramp. Has a 22.7-ton-capacity, 16.8-m-reach crane on the port quarter. Can be two-point moored in up to 300 ft. of water. Has an A-frame crane and various winches. Navigational suite includes Loran-C and Differential GPS receivers and an echo sounder.

♦ 1 former U.S. Coast Guard buoy boat trials craft [YAGE]
Bldr: . . . (In serv. . . .)

65NS733 NAWC 03 (ex-USCG 65402)

D: . . . tons **S:** 12 kts **Dim:** 19.81 × 7.92 × 1.83
Electronics: Radar: 1 . . . X-band nav.
M: 2 G.M. 12V-71 TI diesels; 2 props; 1,000 bhp
Electric: 30 kw tot. (1 × 30-kw diesel driving)
Range: 600/12 **Endurance:** 1–2 days **Crew:** 6 tot.

Remarks: Former USCG small buoy tender, stricken in 1998 and transferred to the navy for use as a workboat at the Naval Air Warfare Center, Aircraft Division, operating from Key West, Fla. Aluminum construction. Has a dive platform at the stern. Is equipped with Loran-C and portable Differential GPS receivers.

Note: Also in service is 65NS732, assigned to Stennis Space Center, Miss., built in 1973 and acquired in 2000; no data available.

♦ 1 LCM(8)-class trials craft [YAGE]
Bldr: . . . (In serv. . . .)

74CM6757 NAWC 57

D: . . . tons **S:** 12 kts **Dim:** 22.55 × 6.40 × 3.28
Electronics: Radar: none
M: 2 G.M. 12V-71 diesels; 2 props; 800 bhp
Electric: 32 kw tot. (1 × 32 kw, G.M. 3-71 diesel driving)
Range: 225/12 **Crew:** . . . (no accomm.)

Remarks: Assigned as a workboat to the Naval Air Warfare Center, Aircraft Division, operating from Fort Lauderdale, Fla. Aluminum-construction former landing craft with a functional bow ramp and a 12.80 × 5.18–m well deck. Equipped with Loran-C and portable Differential GPS receivers and an echo sounder. Used for coastal research operations (including object recovery) and as a diving tender. Can carry up to 54 tons of equipment or stores.

♦ 1 semisubmersible oceanographic research barge [YAGEN]
Bldr: Gunderson Bros., Portland, Ore. (In serv. 6-8-62)

Flip

Flip—in transit configuration George R. Schneider, 4-94

D: 700 tons (fl) **S:** 2–3 kts **Dim:** 109.73 × 8.53 × 3.81
M: 1 60-hp thruster **Crew:** . . .

SERVICE CRAFT *(continued)*

Remarks: *Flip* is also an acronym for "Floating Instrument Platform." Operated for and by the Scripps Institute of Oceanography, La Jolla, Calif., although navy-owned. Designed to be towed into position and then "flipped" (hence the name) upright to provide a vertical enclosed column for water-property research; essentially a long cylinder with a ship-type bow at one end for towing. Refitted at San Diego in 1998.

♦ 1 36-foot Hammerhead-class diving trials launch [YDT]
Bldr: Munson Mfg., Edmonds, Wash. (In serv. 1990)

36NS9101 Captain Bart

D: . . . tons **S:** 30 kts **Dim:** 10.97 × . . . × . . .
M: 2 G.M. Detroit Diesel 6V53 TI diesels; 2 Hamilton 291 waterjets; 800 bhp
Fuel: 300 gal.

Remarks: Aluminum construction. Assigned to the Naval Experimental Diving Unit, Port Hueneme, Calif. Named for a highly respected USN salvage expert.

♦ 8 Mk II Dive Boats [YDT]
Bldr: Peterson Bldrs, Sturgeon Bay, Wis. (In serv. 1989–90)

50DW8901 through 50DW8908

Mk II Dive Boat H&L Van Ginderen, 10-00

D: 25.2 tons light (37.6 fl) **S:** 9 kts **Dim:** 15.24 × 4.50 × 0.84
M: 2 . . . diesels; 2 props; 346 bhp
Range: 220/9 **Fuel:** 418 gallons **Crew:** 5 tot. + 5 divers

Remarks: Steel construction. Carry a 5.0 × 3.7 × 2.34–m, 11-ton diving module with compressors and a decompression chamber. Can support hard-hat divers to 58 m with Mk 12 diving gear.

♦ 5 65-foot Explosive Ordnance Disposal Support Craft [YDT]
Bldr: First two: Swiftships, Morgan City, La.; others: Oregon Iron Works (In serv. 1989–92)

65SC8701 65SC8801 65SC9101 65SC9102 65SC9201

65-ft. divers' support and training boat 65SC9102—at San Diego George R. Schneider, 6-96

D: 34.51 tons light (41.15 fl) **S:** . . . kts **Dim:** 19.66 × 5.74 × 1.17
Electronics: Radar: 1 . . . nav.
M: 2 G.M. Detroit Diesel 8V71N diesels; 2 props; 544 bhp
Range: 324/. . . **Fuel:** 886 gallons **Crew:** 4 tot.

Remarks: Originally chartered, then purchased outright. Aluminum construction. Have a diver's platform at the stern.

Note: For other craft employed as harbor diving tenders, see workboats [YFU].

♦ 6 70-foot Personnel Boats [YFL]
Bldr: Modutech Marine, Portland, Ore. (In serv.: four in 1970, two in 1990)

70PE8101 TB-13 70PE8103 TB-21 70PE9001
70PE8102 TB-19 70PE8104 TB-24 70PE9002

Remarks: Attached to the Pearl Harbor Naval Station and employed in support of transporting tourists to the USS *Arizona* (BB 39) Memorial. TB = Tourist Boat. GRP construction. No further data available.

♦ 1 Chief of Naval Operations Yacht [YFL]
Bldr: Burger Boats, Manitowoc, Wis. (In serv. 1965)

63CC791 (ex-*Concorde*, ex-*Encore III*, ex-*Still Rovin' V*)

D: approx. 60 tons (fl) **S:** . . . kts **Dim:** 19.28 × 4.88 × 1.37
M: 2 G.M. Detroit Diesel 8-cyl. diesels; 2 props; 360 bhp

Remarks: Seized by counterdrug forces at Miami in 1978 and turned over to the navy. Operates from Washington Navy Yard, D.C. Aluminum construction.

♦ 1 63-foot former Air-Sea Rescue Boat [YFL]

C3007

D: 17.7 tons light (29.3 fl) **S:** 28 kts **Dim:** 19.30 × 4.67 × 1.22 (max.)
Electronics: Radar: 1 . . . nav.
M: 2 G.M. Detroit Diesel . . . diesels; 2 props; 660 bhp
Range: 450/24 **Fuel:** 1,580 gallons **Crew:** 6 tot.

Remarks: Wooden-construction craft of World War II–era design and construction, employed as a yacht for CINCPACFLT at Pearl Harbor. Sister C3148, formerly used as yacht for Commander Naval Forces Marianas at Guam, was placed up for sale in 9-00.

Note: Other personal launches assigned to operational flag officers are usually from among the 40PE-series personnel launches.

♦ 4 13-meter Personnel Boats [YFL]
Bldr: Willard Marine, Anaheim, Calif. (In serv. 1-10-99 to . . .)

13MPE9901 13MPE9902 13MPE9903 13MPE9904

13-meter Personnel Boat 13MPE9904—on skids at San Diego George R. Schneider, 6-00

D: . . . tons **S:** 23 kts **Dim:** 11.2 × . . . × . . .
M: . . . **Crew:** 3 tot. + 40 passengers

Remarks: GRP construction. Intended to serve for 20 years.

♦ 40 40-foot Personnel Boats Mk 7 [YFL]

40PE- and 12MUB- series

40-ft. Personnel Boat Mk 7—assigned to Commander Submarines Pacific (COMSUBPAC) at Pearl Harbor Brian Morrison, 6-00

D: 10 tons light (12.7 fl) **S:** 22.5 kts **Dim:** 12.56 × 3.61 × 1.10
M: 1 Cummins 6BTA5.9-M2 diesel; 1 prop; 214 bhp
Range: . . ./. . . **Fuel:** 150 gallons **Crew:** 3 tot. + 40 passengers

Remarks: GRP construction with Airex foam core. Intended for VIP and other local transportation. Can be carried aboard ships. The 12MUB- series were built to metric standards and have greater rake to the bows.

♦ 29 33-foot Personnel Boats Mk 4 [YFL]

33PE- and 10MPE- series

D: 5 tons light (8.2 fl) **S:** 10 or 15 kts **Dim:** 10.17 × 3.25 × 0.91
M: 1 Detroit Diesel Allison 4-53N Model 5042-4000 diesel; 1 prop; 100 bhp—*or* 1 G.M. Detroit Diesel 6-71N diesel; 1 prop; 280 bhp
Range: 150/10 **Fuel:** 100 gallons **Crew:** 3 tot. + 42 passengers

Remarks: GRP-construction craft for shipboard or naval base use. Can be fitted with a portable fabric canopy over the passenger well. Hull has a round bilge forward, tapering to a flat bottom at the stern. 10MPE-series units were built to metric standards.

SERVICE CRAFT *(continued)*

33-ft. Personnel Boat 33PE8705—at San Diego George R. Schneider, 6-96

♦ 2 25-foot Workskiff launches

Bldr: Workskiff, Inc., Burlington, Wash. (In serv. 9-00)

D: . . . **S:** 38 kts **Dim:** 7.62 × 2.59 × . . .
M: 2 Honda gasoline outboards; 230 bhp

Remarks: Monocoque aluminum hull. Function not available. Were delivered with road trailers.

♦ 442 miscellaneous personnel launches [YFL]

Remarks: Other launch classes of 40-ft. (12.2 m) or less overall length as of 1-01 included (MRB = Metric Rigid Inflatable Boat):

- 44 26-ft. Personnel Boats (8MPE- series; being replaced by 24RB- and 7MRB- series)
- 20 26-ft. Motor Whaleboats (being retired and replaced by 24RB- and 7MRB- series)
- 22 26-ft. GRP Inshore Boats (8MIB- series)
- 313 24-ft. Rigid Inflatables (24RB- and 7MRB- series)
- 43 miscellaneous craft under 18 ft. long

♦ 1 95-foot utility boat [YFU]

Bldr: U.S. Coast Guard Yard, Curtis Bay, Md. (In serv. 15-12-53)

95NS8801 951 VENTURE (ex-*Cape Wash,* WPB 95310)

D: 87 tons (106 fl) **S:** 18 kts **Dim:** 28.96 × 6.1 × 1.55
Electronics: Radar: 1 SPS-64(V)1 nav.
M: 4 Cummins VT-12-M-700 diesels; 2 props; 2,324 bhp
Electric: 40 kw tot. **Range:** 570/20; 1,300/9 **Crew:** 6–8 tot.

Remarks: Unofficial hull number 951 appears on both sides of the bow. Former U.S. Coast Guard Cape-class cutter, stricken 1-6-87 and transferred to the navy for use at the Naval Submarine Base, Bangor, Wash., as a local security patrol craft. Sister *Vanguard* (ex-*Cape Hedge,* WPB 95311) was returned to the Coast Guard for transfer to Mexico during 1-90.

♦ 27 converted LCM(8)-class work and diving boats [YFU]

(In serv. 1953–56, 1969)

74CM6720—a converted LCM(8) landing craft modified as a diving training craft for the Deep Submergence Unit at San Diego W. Michael Young, 12-99

D: 59 tons (116 fl) **S:** 9 kts **Dim:** 22.40 × 6.42 × 1.40 (mean)
M: 2 G.M. Detroit Diesel 6-71 diesels; 2 props; 600 bhp

Remarks: Standard U.S. Navy LCM(8) landing craft of different marks adapted for a variety of utility tasks. Twelve are aluminum-hulled Mk 2, 4, and 6 and the other 15 are steel-hulled Mod. 1, 3, and 5. Most, if not all, retain their original 74CM- or C- series landing craft serial numbers. One, used as a liberty launch at La Maddalena, Sardinia, sank on 3-1-01 but was salvaged.

Disposal note: The 64-ft. Distribution Box Boat diving tender C12739 was transferred to the city of Long Beach, Calif., which later sold the craft commercial.

♦ 25 50-foot Workboats Mk 3 [YFU]

Bldr: Gulf Copper and Mfg., Port Arthur, Texas (In serv. 1994 to 4-95)

50WB- and 15MWB- series

50-ft. Workboat 50WB8708—variant with open cargo well George R. Schneider, 4-00

D: 25.6 tons light (42.05 fl) **S:** 9.5 kts (loaded) **Dim:** 15.34 × 4.38 × 0.89
M: 2 Cummins 6BTA5.9-M2 diesels; 2 props; 440 bhp
Range: 208/9.5 **Fuel:** 1,850 liters **Crew:** 5 tot.

Remarks: Steel construction. Cargo capacity is 17.5 tons, carried in an 11.6 × 4.6 × 1.6–m deep cargo well forward.

♦ 87 50-foot Workboats Mk 1 and 2 [YFU]

Bldrs: 52 were made by Marinette Marine, Marinette, Wis. (in serv. 1984 to 16-12-85); 67 by Oregon Iron Works, Clackamas, Ore. (in serv. 1987–89); and 25 by Gulf Copper (in serv. 1994–. . .)

50WB- and 15MWB- series

50-ft. Workboat—variant with cargo well decked over; note push knees at bow H&L Van Ginderen, 3-99

D: 25.6 tons light (43 fl) **S:** 10 kts **Dim:** 15.24 × 4.49 × 1.07
M: 2 G.M. Detroit Diesel 6V71 Mod. 4 diesels; 2 props; 400 bhp
Electric: 15 kw tot. **Range:** 130/. . . **Fuel:** 490 gallons **Crew:** 3 tot.

Remarks: Used as general-purpose workboats and push-tugs. Steel construction. The first 28 were ordered in 2-84 and another 24 in 11-84 from Marinette; 50 were ordered 12-9-86 from Oregon Iron Works, with 17 more ordered in 11-88 (an option for a further 64 was not taken up). The 25 ordered in 1994 from Gulf Copper were powered by two Cummins 69TA5.9M2 diesels for a total of 450 bhp. Have either an open or covered 11.6 × 4.6 × 1.6–m cargo compartment forward. At least 57 have been stricken.

♦ 92 converted LCM(6)-class work and diving boats [YFU]

50UB- and 15MUB- series

LCM(6) C201044—one of several identical converted LCM(6) landing craft converted for use as personnel ferries at La Maddalena, Sardinia, for Submarine Squadron 22; others carry numbers 85 and 87 on the sides of the pilothouse Maurizio Brescia, 6-99

D: 24 tons (64 fl) **S:** 10.2 kts **Dim:** 17.07 × 4.37 × 1.22 (fwd; 1.52 aft)
M: 2 Gray Marine 64HN9 (G.M. 6V71 on Mk 3) diesels; 2 props; 330 bhp
Range: 140/10 **Crew:** 4–5 tot.

Remarks: Designed as landing craft and built between 1952 and 1968. Used as push-tugs, waste recovery craft, diving tenders, and so forth. Five—locally numbered M-1, M-3, M-4, M-5, and M-6—are stationed at New London, Conn. Three others are on loan to the Defense Nuclear Agency and are used at Johnston Atoll.

SERVICE CRAFT *(continued)*

LCM(6) converted as a divers' workboat—at New London, Conn. Paul C. Clift, 12-98

56UB7843—an LCM(6) converted for use as a tug and hose tender aboard Ready Reserve Force Offshore Petroleum Discharge System (OPDS) tankers; the craft is aboard the *Petersburg* (T-AOT 5075) in this view George R. Schneider, 7-97

♦ 57 50-foot Utility Boats Mk 2 and 3 [YFU]

50UB- series

50-ft Utility Boat Mk 2 50UB795 George R. Schneider, 10-91

D: 11.3 tons light (22.2 fl) **S:** 10.5 tons (loaded) **Dim:** 15.36 × 4.43 × 1.32
M: 1 G.M. Gray Marine 64HN9 or 6-71N diesel; 1 prop; 165 bhp
Range: 100/10.5 (loaded) **Crew:** 4 tot. + up to 146 passengers

Remarks: Although typed as Utility Boats, these are actually personnel launches—although they are also employed to carry supplies. The Mk 2 has a GRP hull and is capable of reaching 11 kts, while the heavier Mk 3 was built of wood.

♦ 14 50-foot converted LCM(3) workboats and diving boats [YFU]

50CM- series

D: 23.6 tons light (50.8 fl) **S:** 9.5 kts **Dim:** 15.28 × 4.27 × 1.22
M: 2 G.M. Gray Marine 64HN9 diesels; 2 props; 450 bhp (330 sust.)
Range: 130/9.5 **Fuel:** 1,730 liters **Crew:** 2–3 tot.

Remarks: Converted from landing craft. The original cargo well has been decked over and the bow ramp welded shut or deleted entirely.

♦ 5 ex-U.S. Army Design 320 Workboat class [YFU]

45WB711 45WB831 Duke 45WB833 C5840 C5841

D: . . . tons **S:** 9 kts **Dim:** 13.72 × 3.96 × 2.13
M: 1 G.M. diesel; 1 prop; 170 bhp

Remarks: Steel construction. Resemble small tugboats. The first three are based at Norfolk and the other two at Portsmouth NSY, N.H. Sister *Sacajawea* (YWB 1, 45WB771) was placed up for sale in 1998. Two others, C8194 and 45WB710, remain in land storage at the Cheatham Annex supply depot, Williamsburg, Va. There were 118 built during World War II and 98 in the early 1950s, originally as tenders to army dredges. The Army Corps of Engineers still operates several others.

U.S. Army Design 320 Workboat–class Duke (45WB831)—at Norfolk Naval Base Christopher P. Cavas, 7-00

♦ 54 24-foot Workboat class [YFU]

Bldr: MonArk Marine, Monticello, Ark. (In serv. 1980–86)

From among:

24WB801–24WB808	24WB831–24WB8316	24WB851–24WB858
24WB821–24WB828	24WB841–24WB8426	24WB8601–24WB8608

24-ft. Workboat OP 2—at New London, Conn. Paul C. Clift, 12-98

D: 2.5 tons (3.8 fl) **S:** 22.5 kts (with 4 aboard)
Dim: 7.32 × 2.31 × 1.57 (molded depth)
M: 2 Volvo Penta AGAD 41A diesels with Type 290 outdrives; 165 bhp
Range: . . ./. . . **Crew:** 4 tot.

Remarks: Aluminum construction. Survivors of 74 built to essentially the same design as the 24-ft. 24HS-series Harbor Security launches (see under patrol boats [PB]). No radar is fitted.

♦ up to 628 miscellaneous utility boats [YFU]

- 2 41-ft. Sea Mule workboats (41WB- series)
- 14 40-ft. Utility Boats (40UB- and 12MUB- series)
- 12 33-ft. Utility Boats (33UB- and 10MUB- series)
- 39 27-ft. Utility Boats (27AP-, 27MC-, 27NS-, 27SC-, and 27UB- series)
- 55 25-ft. Utility Boats (25MM-, 25BW-, 25NS-, and 25UB- series)
- 216 22-ft. Utility Boats (22BH-, 22BW-, 22NS-, 22SC-, 22UB-, and 22DS- series)
- 19 21-ft. Utility Boats
- 20 20-ft. Utility Boats (20UB- series)
- 83 19-ft. Utility Boats (19UB- series)
- 125 18-ft. Utility Boats (18UB- series)
- 43 launches under 18-ft. overall

♦ 1 aerial target-launch craft [YGT]

Bldr: Halter Marine, Moss Point, Miss.

	L	In serv.
ATLS 9701	18-9-97	1-98

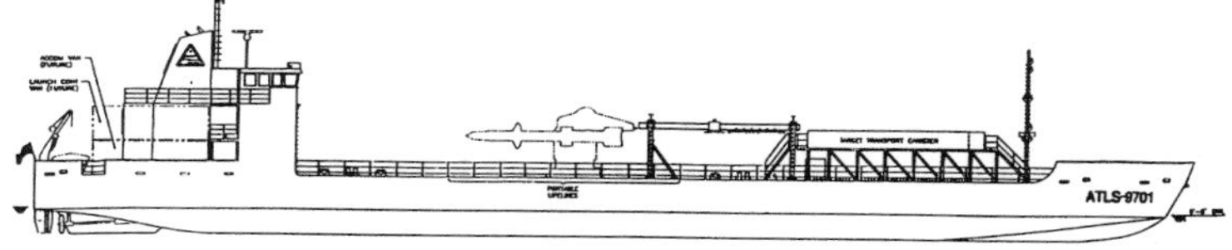

ATLS 9701 U.S. Navy, 1997

D: 857 tons (fl) **S:** 8 kts **Dim:** 80.77 × 7.92 × 1.98
M: 2 . . . diesels; 2 props; 1,342 bhp

SERVICE CRAFT *(continued)*

Remarks: Ordered in late 1995 for the Naval Air Warfare Center, Point Mugu, Calif., outside of the normal USN ship acquisition process. Is equipped with a Mk 10 twin launcher for Vandal (converted Talos) supersonic targets; reload missiles are carried in a horizontal magazine forward of the launcher. Is later to receive an accommodations module and a rigid inflatable boat. Most of the hull space is taken up by ballast tanks and voids. Operates from Port Hueneme, Calif.

♦ **1 large target craft [YGT]**
Bldr: Maritime Contractors, Bellingham, Wash. (In serv. 1994)

MST 9301

MST 9301 U.S. Navy, 1994

D: 850 tons (fl) **S:** 15 kts **Dim:** 79.25 (76.5 wl) × 7.92 × 2.13
M: 2 . . . diesels; 2 props; . . . bhp

Remarks: Referred to as the "SST." Radio-controlled target, operated by the Surface Targets Team, Naval Air Warfare Center, Weapons Division, Point Mugu, Calif., and based at Port Hueneme. Uses condemned 20-ft. cargo containers stacked to simulate various radar targets.

♦ **. . . QST 35A–class (SEPTAR) target drones [YGT]**
(In serv. 1970s–. . .)

QST 35A–class (SEPTAR) target boat 9301 A. D. Baker III, 6-00

D: 13.3 tons light (17.9 fl) **S:** 35 kts **Dim:** 16.68 × 4.15 × 0.70
M: early version: five Mercury 3-325-622 gasoline engines; 5 props; 1,625 bhp
Range: 160/35 **Fuel:** 2,000 liters **Crew:** 4 tot. (ferrying)

Remarks: Data are for the earlier 54-ft. Mk 35 model, now superseded by a 56-ft. version with four Mercruiser engines. Can tow target sleds, as well as launching aerial target drones. On some, a tall lattice mast supports various target enhancement devices and radio control antennas. The latest version, now being delivered, is built by Willard Marine under a 1995 contract and uses the hull mold from the previous builder, Hood Industries. Are currently numbered in the 17MTD- series. All are assigned to the Naval Air Warfare Center, Point Mugu, Calif., which distributes them as needed fleetwide for exercises; they are based at Port Hueneme, Calif.

Note: Horizon Shipbuilding, Bayou La Batre, Ala., delivered 39 GRP, 8.23 × 2.44–m "Improved Surface-Towed Target Vessel" tow-targets to the USN in 2000–01.

♦ **2 40-foot Plane Personnel Rescue Boats Mk 5 [YH]**
Bldr: Willard Marine, Anaheim, Calif. (In serv. 1991)

40PR9001 40PR9002

D: 11.34 tons light (13.15 fl) **S:** . . . kts **Dim:** 12.19 × 3.47 × 1.09
Electronics: Radar: 1 . . . nav.
M: 2 Cummins 6BTA5.9-M2 diesels; 2 props; 486 bhp
Range: . . ./. . . **Fuel:** 500 gallons **Crew:** 3 tot.

Remarks: GRP and vinylester construction. Can carry 4,000 lbs of personnel and cargo in addition to the crew and are equipped for fire fighting. Both are assigned to Jacksonville Naval Air Station, Fla.

♦ **3 42-foot Protector class air-sea rescue boats [YH]**
Bldr: SeaArk Marine, Monticello, Ark. (In serv. 14-10-86 to 6-87)

42PR852 42PR853 42PR855

Remarks: Aluminum construction. Stationed at Patuxent River Naval Air Station, Md.; Pearl Harbor; Iwakuni Marine Corps Air Station, Japan; and Bangor Naval Submarine Base, Wash. Sister 42PR851 is in land storage, 42PR854 was stricken in 1995 and placed up for sale 25-2-99, and 42PR856 was transferred to the Maritime Administration for use at Suisun Bay, Calif., as a tender and is now named *Syrah* (PF 69).

Disposal note: The 65-ft. air-sea rescue boat AVR 681 (65AR681) was on offer to other government agencies as of 2-00; sister 65AR682 was transferred to Jordan in 1996.

Note: The U.S. Navy also uses a variety of towed targets for gunnery and aerial-attack training purposes. A number of Boeing Canada Technology, 7.30 × 2.74–m, remote-controlled Barracuda target boats, each powered by a 300-hp diesel for 36-kt maximum speeds or 30 kts for 6 hours, were ordered during the early 1990s.

♦ **1 85-foot Personnel Boat [YH]**
Bldr: Sewart Seacraft, Berwick, La. (In serv. 1964)

C14252 TRB 3

TRB 3 (C14252) Chris Cavas, 3-02

D: 43 tons (53 fl) **S:** 22 kts **Dim:** 25.9 × 5.8 × 2.2 (props)
Electronics: Radar: Furuno . . . I-band nav.
M: 3 G.M. Detroit Diesel 8V92TA diesels; 3 props; 1,950 bhp
Electric: 70 kw tot. (2 × 35-kw Perkins diesel sets)
Range: 780/15 **Fuel:** 8 tons **Crew:** . . . tot.

Remarks: Although referred to as a personnel boat, is used as rescue craft in support of helicopter squadron HM-14. Sisters C14253 and C1907 were stricken 19-12-97 and donated in 3-98 to the Sea Scouts at San Francisco.

♦ **2 ex-U.S. Air Force 120-foot-class weapons retrievers [YPT]**
Bldr: Swiftships, Morgan City, La. (In serv. 1988–89)

120MR8804 SL-120 (ex-MR-120-8804)
120NS8801 Seadog (ex-MR-120-8805)

SL-120 (120MR8804)—at Port Hueneme, Calif. George R. Schneider, 7-95

D: 91 tons light (113 operational; 133 fl) **S:** 30 kts (27 sust.)
Dim: 35.78 × 7.51 × 2.06 (max. aft)
Electronics: Radar: 1 Furuno . . .
M: 4 G.M. Detroit Diesel 16V92 MTA diesels; 4 props; 5,600 bhp
Electric: 50 kw (2 × 25 kw)
Range: 600/27 **Fuel:** 4,920 gallons **Crew:** 10 tot.

Remarks: Intended for location and recovery of practice missiles. Can transport 20 tons of deck cargo and carry 1,100 gallons water for washing down recovered missiles. All were to have been transferred from Air Force control to the navy in 1996. Aluminum construction. 120MR8804 operates from Port Hueneme, Calif., as a range safety craft. 120NS8801, formerly at Wallace Air Base, the Philippines, has been relocated to Kadena Air Base, Okinawa.

SERVICE CRAFT *(continued)*

♦ **6 TWR 821–class torpedo retrievers [YPT]** (1 in *reserve*)
Bldr: Peterson Bldrs, Sturgeon Bay, Wis.

	Laid down	L	In serv.
120TR821 TWR 821 Swamp Fox	...	17-10-84	4-11-85
120TR823 TWR 823 Porpoise	22-8-84	4-5-85	6-12-85
120TR832 *TWR 832*	10-5-85	22-3-86	3-7-86
120TR833 TWR 833	28-5-85	4-4-86	3-7-86
120TR841 TWR 841	2-8-85	15-8-86	18-10-86
120TR842 TWR 842 Narwhal	23-8-85	22-9-86	24-12-86

Porpoise (TWR 823; 120TR823)—at Ballast Point, San Diego
W. Michael Young, 8-01

D: 174 tons (213 fl) **S:** 16 kts **Dim:** 36.58 × 7.62 × 3.65
Electronics: Radar: 1 Raytheon . . . nav.
M: 2 Caterpillar D 3512 diesels; 2 props; 2,350 bhp **Electric:** 128 kw tot.
Range: 1,700/16 **Fuel:** 28 tons **Endurance:** 7 days
Crew: 1 officer, 14 enlisted

Remarks: Five were ordered 8-7-83 for delivery between 15-12-84 and 15-3-85; three more were ordered in 10-83, all for delivery in 7-85, and another two in 2-85 for delivery in 6-86. Congress halted further procurement in 1985. Have a stern ramp and electrohydraulic crane aft. Can carry 14 Mk 48 torpedoes. Have 43.7 tons of permanent ballast. TWR 821 has been reassigned to New London, Conn., and may no longer carry the unofficial name *Swamp Fox.* TWR 833 and 841 have been modified to act as diver-support tenders.
Disposals: TWR 824 and 831 were irreparably damaged during Hurricane Hugo in 1990 at Roosevelt Roads, P.R. TWR 822 and 825 were stricken during 1997.

♦ **1 Hugo-class torpedo retriever conversion [YPT]**
Bldr: McDermott Shipyards, New Iberia, La. (In serv. 1982)

180NS8201 Hugo (ex-*Crystal Pelham*)

Hugo (180NS8201) H&L Van Ginderen, 2-99

D: approx. 1,300 tons (fl) **S:** 12 kts **Dim:** 50.32 × 12.19 × 3.35
M: 2 Caterpillar D399SCAC 16-cyl. diesels; 2 props; 2,250 bhp—bow-thruster
Electric: 270 kw tot. (2 × 135 kw) **Crew:** . . . tot.

Remarks: 298 grt. Former oilfield tug/supply vessel, converted by Leevac Shipyard as a replacement for TWR 824, lost to the hurricane for which the replacement craft is named. Delivered 3-7-91 after conversion. Based at Roosevelt Roads, P.R.

♦ **1 Hunter-class torpedo retriever conversion [YPT]**
Bldr: Quality Shipbuilders, Moss Point, Miss. (In serv. 1981)

180NS8202 Hunter (ex-*Nola Pelham*)

Hunter (180NS8202) Mike Louagie, 1995

D: approx. 1,300 tons (fl) **S:** 12 kts **Dim:** 54.86 × 11.58 × 3.96
M: 2 Caterpillar D399SCAC diesels; 2 props; 2,250 bhp
Electric: 270 kw tot. (2 × 135 kw) **Crew:** . . . tot.

Remarks: 258 grt. Former oilfield tug/supply vessel, converted by Leevac Shipyard as a replacement for TWR 825. Delivered 3-7-91 after conversion. Based at Roosevelt Roads, P.R.

♦ **1 Rangemaster-class exercise torpedo and decoy service craft [YPT]** Bldr: Steiner Fabricators, Bayou La Batre, Ala. (In serv. 1981)

110WB8501 Rangemaster (ex-*Hull 108*)

D: . . . tons **S:** . . . kts **Dim:** 33.53 × 7.92 × 3.51
M: 1 . . . diesel; 1 prop; . . . bhp

Remarks: 99 grt. Built as a crewboat for the RCA company to support a navy contract. Purchased in 1985 for use in launch and recovery of mobile targets and exercise torpedoes at the AUTEC Range in the Bahamas.

♦ **2 Transporter-class weapons retrievers [YPT]**
Bldr: Swiftships, Morgan City, La. (In serv. 1978)

100NS7801 Transporter (ex-*Seaco Transporter,* ex-*Alexandra Robin*)
100NS8702 DLR 3 Retriever (ex-*Seaco Traveller,* ex-*Lorraine Robin*)

Retriever (DLR 3; 100NS8702)—with Chukar target on deck aft
A. D. Baker III, 6-00

D: . . . tons **S:** 20 kts (18 sust.) **Dim:** 30.48 × 6.10 × 2.13 (max.)
Electronics: Radar: 2 Furuno . . . nav.
M: 3 G.M. Detroit Diesel 12V-71 TI diesels; 3 props; 1,650 bhp
Electric: 60 kw tot. (2 × 30-kw diesel sets; 208 V, 3 phase, 60 Hz a.c.)
Range: 800/18 **Fuel:** 4,000 gallons **Endurance:** 3–5 days **Crew:** 12 tot.

Remarks: 85 grt. 100NS7801 is operated by the Naval Air Warfare Center, Patuxent River Naval Air Station, and 100NS8702 by FleetCompRon 6, Atlantic Test Range, Norfolk (where the local hull number assigned is DLR 3). Both were acquired by the navy 2-11-89 from Seaco International. They are aluminum-construction former oilfield crewboats capable of transporting 60 passengers and up to 24 tons of cargo on the afterdeck. Are equipped with a Furuno GPS, a Micrologic Loran-C receiver, a Furuno echo sounder, and HF, VHF, and secure VHF radios. Used for high-speed towing, ordnance recovery, and towing of side-scan sonar arrays. A deck crane is fitted.

♦ **1 100-foot torpedo retriever [YPT]**
Bldr: Peterson Bldrs, Sturgeon Bay, Wis. (In serv. 1969–70)

100TR771 TWR 771 Phoenix

Phoenix (TWR 771; 100TR771) Kurt Greiner/SeaPhoto, 6-00

D: 110 tons light (162 fl) **S:** 17 kts **Dim:** 31.09 × 6.40 × 2.36
Electronics: Radar: 1 Raytheon SPS-69 nav.
M: 4 G.M. 12V149 diesels; 2 props; 2,000 bhp **Electric:** 60 kw tot. (2 × 30 kw)
Range: 1,920/10 **Fuel:** 27 tons **Crew:** 1 officer, 13 enlisted

Remarks: Design is based on the PGM 59–class patrol boat. Has a ramp at the stern and stowage for 17 tons of recovered ordnance. Maximum displacement without torpedoes is 149 tons. Based at Port Hueneme, Calif.
Disposals: *Crayfish* (TWR 682) was stricken in 1991. 100TR711 (TWR 711) was sold 27-5-94 for scrap. *Labrador* (TWR 681, 100TR681) was stricken early in 1995 and transferred to the New York City Fire Department but not used and was for sale as of 7-01. *Diamond* (TWR 1, C13728) had been stricken by 1994. *Ferret* (TWR 6, C14251) was for sale at Pearl Harbor as of 7-01. *Condor* (TWR 3, C13729) had been stricken by fall 8-00.

♦ **2 85-foot torpedo retrievers [YPT]**
Bldr: Tacoma Boat, Tacoma, Wash. (In serv. 1975)

85TR761 (TWR 8) Iliwai   85TR762 (TWR 7) Chaparral

SERVICE CRAFT *(continued)*

Chaparral (TWR 7; 85TR762) Brian Morrison, 6-00

D: . . . **S:** 18 kts **Dim:** 25.9 × . . . × . . .
Electronics: Radar: 1 LN-66 nav.
M: 4 G.M. diesels; 2 props; . . . bhp **Crew:** . . .

Remarks: Aluminum construction. 85TR762 was deactivated in 1992 but restored to service in 1997. Both are assigned to the Naval Station, Pearl Harbor.

♦ **1 ex-U.S. Air Force 85-foot Weapons Retriever class [YPT]**
Bldr: Swiftships, Morgan City, La. (In serv. 1967)

85NS681 HM 8

HM 8 (85NS681) George R. Schneider, 8-01

D: 43.5 tons light (54 fl) **S:** 21.7 kts **Dim:** 25.91 × 5.69 × 2.10
M: 2 G.M. Detroit Diesel 16V71N diesels; 2 props; 1,400 bhp
Electric: 40 kw tot. (2 × 20-kw G.M. E5252 ABS diesel sets)
Range: 800/21.7 **Fuel:** 10,787 liters **Crew:** 8 tot.

Remarks: Operates from Port Hueneme, Calif. Numerous sisters were built as patrol boats (the "85-ft. Commercial Cruiser class") under foreign aid programs. Aluminum construction.
Disposals: HM 9 (85NS691) went aground and was lost 21-1-99 at Point Conception, Calif. TWR 4 (85NS9001, ex-USAF MR-85-1608) was stricken during 1999, and ex-USAF MR-85-1603 had been stricken by 2001.

♦ **3 85-foot torpedo retrievers [YPT]**
Bldr: Sewart Seacraft, Berwick, La. (In serv. 1966)

85TR651 85TR653 85TR654

D: 61 tons (fl) **S:** 21 kts **Dim:** 25.91 × 5.69 × 1.73
M: 2 G.M. Detroit Diesel 16V71 diesels; 2 props; 1,160 bhp
Range: 1,000/. . . **Fuel:** 2,400 gallons **Crew:** 8 tot.

Remarks: Aluminum construction. Capable of retrieving and stowing up to eight 1,254-kg practice torpedoes. Sister 85TR652 has been stricken.

♦ **2 72-foot torpedo retrievers Mk 2 [YPT]**
Bldr: . . . (In serv. 1964–65)

72TR645 TRB 32 72TR652 TRB 33

D: 41.2 tons (53 fl) **S:** 18 kts **Dim:** 22.17 × 5.18 × 1.68
Electronics: Radar: 1 Raytheon SPS-69 Pathfinder nav.
M: 2 G.M. Detroit Diesel 12V71 diesels; 2 props; 1,000 bhp
Electric: 22.5 kw tot. (1 × 15-kw, 1 × 7.5-kw diesel sets)
Range: 440/16 **Fuel:** 1,800 gallons **Crew:** 5–6 tot.

Remarks: Wooden-hulled craft capable of retrieving and stowing up to 10,884 kg in practice torpedoes or other ordnance. Sister TRB 31 (C3211) was discarded during 1995, 72TR653 in 1996, TRB 37 (C9426) in 1999, and TRB 36 (C4560) during 2001.

♦ **3 65-foot torpedo retrievers [YPT]**
Bldr: . . . (In serv. 10-67)

65TR671 65TR675 Harrier 65TR676 Peregrine

Harrier (65TR675) Brian Morrison, 6-00

D: 34.8 tons (35.2 fl) **S:** 24 kts **Dim:** 19.80 × 5.25 × 1.14
Electronics: Radar: 1 . . . nav.
M: 2 G.M. Detroit Diesel 12V71 diesels; 2 props; 1,008 bhp (800 sust.)
Electric: 10 kw **Range:** 280/18 **Crew:** 6 tot.

Remarks: Aluminum construction. Can recover up to 5 tons of weapons (three torpedoes). 65TR671 is based at Roosevelt Roads, P.R.; 65TR675 at Hawaii; and 65TR676 at Keyport, Wash.

♦ **48 SWOB waste-disposal barges [YRGN]**
Bldrs: 42 were made by Marine Power Equipment, Seattle; 18 later units by Tacoma Boat, Tacoma, Wash. (In serv. 1970s)

SWOB WE01- and SWOB WE10- series

SWOB 21 (WE10-021) Jürg Kürsener, 6-01

D: 105.3 tons light (394.4 fl) **Dim:** 32.84 × 8.43 × 1.80 (0.58 light)

Remarks: SWOB = Ship Waste Oil Barge. Carry liquid wastes from shipboard holding tanks to shore treatment stations. SWOBs 1 through 42 and 56 through 60 were configured as oil waste barges, while SWOBs 43 through 55 carry sewage to shore processing facilities. Are considered to be "equipment" and are assigned to local Navy Facilities Engineering Command organizations. SWOB 5, 14, 20–22, 39, 40, 45, and 56–59 have been discarded. The "WE" in the serial number indicates SWOB, the next two numbers (01 or 10) the function (human waste or waste oil collection), and the last three numbers the sequential construction number for the craft (001 through 060). Waste-oil barges carry up to 77,000 gallons in four tanks.

Note: Also in use for waste collection are open-bottom oil/water separator waste oil rafts called "Donuts."

♦ **19 35-foot salvage workboats [YRS]** (5 in reserve)
Bldr: SeaArk Marine, Monticello, Ark. (In serv. 1984, except 35WB9001–35WB9003: 1991)

35WB831–35WB839 35WB841–35WB845 35WB9001–35WB9003

Salvage Workboat 35WB845 George R. Schneider, 9-99

D: 6 tons light (9.5 fl) **S:** 11 kts **Dim:** 10.92 × 3.39 × 0.91
M: 2 G.M. Detroit Diesel 4-53N diesels; 2 props; 280 bhp
Range: 85/11 **Fuel:** 379 liters **Crew:** 3 tot.

Remarks: Each *Grapple* (ARS 50)-class salvage ship carries one of these, while others are assigned to shore stations and five are in land storage, having been removed from AOE 1–class replenishment ships. All-aluminum construction. Have a two-ton winch. A bow ramp leads to a 5.2 × 2.3–m cargo well forward.

♦ **2 U.S. Coast Guard Balsam-class salvage training hulks [YRSN]**
Bldr: Zenith Dredge (180NS4401: Marine Iron and SB), Duluth, Minn.

	Laid down	L	In serv.
180NS4401 (ex-*Blackhaw*, WLB 390)	16-4-43	18-6-43	17-2-44
180NS. . . (ex-*Mariposa*, WLB 397)	25-10-43	14-1-44	1-7-44

SERVICE CRAFT *(continued)*

180NS4401 George R. Schneider, 9-99

D: 697 tons light (1,038 fl) **Dim:** 54.9 (51.8 pp) × 11.3 × 4.0

Remarks: 180NS4401 was stricken from the Coast Guard 26-2-93, transferred to the Maritime Administration 31-3-94, and reclaimed during 2000 for service with Mobile Diving and Salvage Unit 2 at Little Creek, Va., as a damage-control training hulk to replace the 143NS9201. The machinery and electronics systems have either been removed or are nonoperational, and the hulk is intended to be sunk and salvaged repeatedly. *Mariposa* was transferred to the USN 17-4-00 for use as a nonoperational platform for ship-boarding practice and damage-control training and is stationed at Everett, Wash.

Note: The hulk of the former landing ship dock [LSD] *Shadwell* (LSD 15) is also used for damage-control training and for trials with the DC-ARM (Damage Control–Automation for Reduced Manning) program for testing new damage-control techniques and equipment.

Disposal note: Salvage training hulk 143NS9201 (ex-*Keywadin,* ATA 213, ex-ATR 140) was sunk as a target during 6-01.

♦ 2 DSRV-class deep submergence rescue vehicles [YSS] (1 in *reserve*)
Bldr: Lockheed Missile & Space Co., Sunnyvale, Calif.

	In serv.	Accepted		In serv.	Accepted
DSRV 1 Mystic	6-8-71	4-11-77	DSRV 2 *Avalon*	28-7-72	1-1-78

Mystic (DSRV 1)—aboard tender *Dolores Chouest;* note how the shrouded main propulsion thruster at the stern of the craft swivels up and down to act as a diving plane George R. Schneider, 5-00

D: 30.5 tons surf./37 tons sub. **S:** 4.5 kts sub.
Dim: 15.0 × 2.5 × 3.28 (high)
Electronics: Sonar: 1 . . . obstacle avoidance
M: 1 electric motor; 1 shrouded-pivoting prop; 15 shp
Endurance: 16.4/4.1, 15/1.5 sub. **Crew:** 4 tot. + 24 rescued personnel

Remarks: A cost overrun of nearly 1,500% prevented the procurement of any more DSRVs. Twelve were originally planned, later reduced to six, and finally two. Their size and weight were determined by the possible need to airlift them in an Air Force Lockheed C-141 Starlifter cargo plane. In addition, SSNs have received the equipment necessary to fasten a DSRV to their decks and can transport the DSRV submerged at 15 kts; the SSN would then serve as a base for the DSRV. DSRV 1 was carried aboard the *Dallas* (SSN 700) during Exercise Sorbet Royal in Turkish waters during 9-00. The unofficial names were assigned in 1977. DSRV 1 is based at North Island, San Diego, assisted by the chartered tender *Dolores Chouest;* DSRV 1 completed a one-year overhaul in 4-00 and is to remain in service until 2005. DSRV 2 was inactivated 31-8-00 and placed in land storage at North Island. Employ support crews of 3 officers and 17 enlisted personnel in addition to the crew.
Hull systems: The DSRVs were intended to operate at a maximum depth of 1,500 m, to stand pressures equal to 2,750-m depth, to dive and rise at 30 m/min, to make a maximum speed of 5 kts while submerged, to remain submerged for 30 hours at 3 kts, to maintain station in a 1-kt current, and to operate all machinery even while submerged at a 45° angle. The motor, powered by two 700-amp-hr silver-zinc batteries, turns a regular propulsion propeller and two thrusters (one forward and one aft), which can be positioned to permit a close approach to a sunken object. The hull consists of two HY-140 steel spheres surrounded by a fiberglass outer hull. One received a potassium superoxide (KO) breathing system in 1982, providing a submerged endurance of 480 man-hours. Have one 1,000-lb. capacity manipulation arm and one color and five black-and-white underwater television cameras.

Note: Also available for submarine rescue duties are two McCann/Erickson Submarine Rescue Chambers, SRC 8 (ex-YRC 8) and SRC 21 (ex-YRC 17), completed in 1942 and 1944, respectively, at the New York Navy Yard. They are the survivors of 18 completed in 1931–44 and were recently outfitted with new lightweight mooring system. They can be transported in C-5A Galaxy transports. Each can rescue up to eight personnel per cycle from depths up to 260 m.

DSRV 1 and DSRV 2 are planned to be replaced with the SDRS (Submarine Rescue Diving Recompression System), a tethered submersible based on the Australian Remora and intended to be operated from surface ships. The SDRS will be able to mate with rescue hatches on submarines inclined as much as 60° from the vertical.

♦ 1 Alvin-class research submersible [YSS]
Bldr: General Mills, Minneapolis, Minn. (In serv. 6-64)

DSV 2 Alvin

D: 16 tons **S:** 2 kts **Dim:** 6.9 × 2.4 × . . .
M: electric motors; 1 prop, 2 thrusters **Crew:** 1 + 2 scientists

Remarks: Operated by the civilian Woods Hole Oceanographic Institution on contract to the navy since 6-71. Sank on 16-10-68, but was raised, repaired, and returned to service in 11-72. The single titanium pressure sphere permits descents to 4,000 m. The digital sonar from *Sea Cliff* (DSV 4) was transferred to DSV 2 in 1998.

♦ 3 Log Bronco dry dock support tugs [YTL]
Bldr: Modutech, Tacoma, Wash. (In serv. 2001)

D: 12.7 tons (fl) **S:** . . . kts **Dim:** 7.01 × 3.35 × 0.58
M: 1 Cummins 6-cyl. C-series diesel; 360° hydraulically steerable prop; 255 bhp

Remarks: Two were delivered in 8-01, one later. Employed at Puget Sound Naval Shipyard to position submarines and surface ships in floating dry docks. Have rectangular planform hulls and two push knees at the bow. Can turn in their own lengths.

♦ 1 specialized push-tug [YTL]
Bldr: Marine Inland Fabricators, Panama City, Fla. (L: 6-96)

36NS9501

D: . . . tons **S:** 7 kts **Dim:** 10.67 × 4.11 × . . .
M: 2 John Deere 6076 AFM diesels; 2 props; 250 bhp
Electric: 20 kw **Crew:** . . .

Remarks: Built for the Navy Facilities Engineering Service, Port Hueneme, Calif., for use by a research facility on Lake Pend Oreille, Idaho, to support an acoustic research platform. Has a bollard pull of 4.5 tons.

♦ 21 Navy-44-class sail-training cutters [YTS]
Bldr: Uniflite-Tillotson-Pearson, Warren, R.I. (In serv. 1987–89)

NA-1 Audacious	NA-8 Fearless	NA-15 Frolic
NA-2 Courageous	NA-9 Flirt	NA-16 Restless
NA-3 Invincible	NA-10 Lively	NA-17 Dandy
NA-4 Valiant	NA-11 Swift	NA-18 Dash
NA-5 Active	NA-12 Vigilant	NA-19 Bold
NA-6 Alert	NA-13 Resolute	NA-20 Challenger
NA-7 Dauntless	NA-14 Intrepid	NA-21 . . . . . .

Challenger (NA-20)—and a row of sisters, including *Dandy* (NA-17), at the U.S. Naval Academy George R. Schneider, 9-99

SERVICE CRAFT *(continued)*

D: 14.35 tons (fl) **S:** . . . **Dim:** 13.41 (10.91 wl) × 3.40 × 2.26
Electronics: Radar: 1 Raytheon SPS-66 (1900 Pathfinder) nav.
M: 1 auxiliary diesel; 1 prop; 33 bhp—sail area: 88 m^2 max.
Crew: 8–10 midshipmen

Remarks: All used at the U.S. Naval Academy, Annapolis, Md. The first eight were ordered in 3-87, with options for 20 more, only 13 of which were ordered. NA-1 was delivered 21-5-87 for extensive trials; NA-2 through NA-8 were delivered in spring 1988. GRP construction. Mast height: 19.66 m above water. Intended to replace the Naval Academy's 12 Luders yawls and 18 miscellaneous donated craft used for midshipman training; the older boats in good condition were sent to universities with Naval Reserve Officer Training Centers. Designed by McCurdy and Rhodes, Inc., NA-9 through NA-12 are used by the varsity sailing team. Are reputed to be excellent sailers. NA-1 through NA-8 are registered as 44ST8701–44ST8708; NA-9 through NA-20 are 44ST8901–44ST8912. Four others were built for the U.S. Coast Guard Academy.

Disposal note: Naval Academy Swan 48–class sloops *Constellation* (48SB721) and *Insurgente* (48SB801) were removed from the navy smallcraft listing in 1999 but may remain in use.

♦ 1 Sparkman & Stephens 49 sloop [YTS] Bldr: . . . (In serv. . . .)

49SB831 14786 Cinnabar

D: 12.61 metric tons (fl) **S:** . . . kts **Dim:** 14.97 (12.30 wl) × 2.44
Electronics: Radar: 1 Raytheon SPS-66 (1900 Pathfinder) nav.
M: 1 auxiliary diesel; 1 prop; . . . bhp **Crew:** 12 midshipmen

Remarks: Mast height: 21.49 m above water. GRP construction.

Note: Also in use at the naval academy are the sailing yacht *American Promise* (60SB8701), received by donation in 1987, and the following sail training craft: 12 J-24 sloops (numbers and names: 31 *Aegis,* 32 *Harpoon,* 33 *Tomahawk,* 34 *Terrier,* 35 *Phalanx,* 36 *Vampire,* 37 *Goblin,* 38 *Panther,* 39 *Bulldog,* 40 *Madman,* 41 *Tally Ho,* 42 *Bogie;* their official hull numbers are 24SL8702–24SL8711, 24SL8713, and 24SL8712, respectively), 20 FJ sloops, 1 J-22 sloop, 24 420 sloops, 100 Laser sloops, 6 Interclub dinghies, 3 Tech dinghies, and 60 sailboards (24 Imco, 24 Bermuda, and 12 Funboard). The naval academy also has a large number of oar-powered racing shells and several rigid inflatable speedboats for coaching and rescue duties. Naval Reserve Officer Training Center facilities at several universities and colleges also possess sail training craft.

♦ 1 Pidgeon-class ship-assault training hulk [YXTN]
Bldr: Alabama Dry Dock & SB, Mobile, Ala.

	Laid down	L	In serv.
. . . (ex-*Pidgeon,* ASR 21)	17-7-68	13-8-69	28-4-73

Training hulk ex-Pidgeon W. Michael Young, 5-01

D: 3,411 tons light **Dim:** 76.5 × 26.2 × . . .

Remarks: Former submarine rescue ship, decommissioned 31-8-92. Assigned as an "Immobile Shipboard Security and Engagement Tactics Training Device" for special forces at the San Diego Naval Station during 2001, replacing the stricken *Elk River* (IX 501); the hulk has not yet been assigned an official number. The catamaran hulls each have a beam of 7.92 m and are separated by 10.36 m. Shipboard equipment and the engineering plant remain aboard but are unmaintained.

U.S. MARITIME ADMINISTRATION READY RESERVE FORCE

The Ready Reserve Force (RRF), created in 1976, is intended to compensate for the decline of the U.S.-flag merchant marine as a wartime strategic sealift asset. The RRF is maintained within the National Defense Reserve Fleet (NDRF) by the Maritime Administration (MARAD) of the Department of Transportation in 4-, 5-, 10-, or 20-day readiness status. RRF ships are activated by a Military Sealift Command (MSC) request to MARAD and are under the operational control of MSC when active. Selected ships are exercised periodically, and a small number are active and operating at any given time in support of U.S. forces worldwide (as of 1-02, only the cargo ship *Cape Jacob* and tankers *Chesapeake* and *Petersburg* were activated, all assigned to Maritime Prepositioning Squadrons).

Through FY 89, acquisition and maintenance of the RRF ships was funded by the navy, which retains ownership of former naval units included in the fleet. On 1-10-90, MARAD became responsible for all funding for the RRF, except for some sealift-capability enhancements. Responsibility for acquisition of *additional* ships for the RRF, however, was returned to the navy in FY 91.

Administrative responsibility for the RRF ships is maintained at NDRF anchorages at Beaumont, Texas; in Suisun Bay, Calif.; and in the James River, Va., but most of the vessels are kept at layberth under management contracts in various ports around the United States in proximity to the shipyards that are under contract to maintain and activate them. In addition to these ships, there are a few older, militarily useful ex-naval or merchant marine ships in the NDRF that could be activated given longer notice.

Before inclusion in the RRF, ships have their navigation, safety, and communications systems updated (including provision of a Marisat SATCOM facility) and are repainted gray, with red, white, and blue stack striping. Certain sealift enhancement features specified by the MSC are added during the acquisition overhauls or during later maintenance overhauls; these include such items as provision to carry "Seashed" or "Flatrack" large-capacity containers, helicopter decks, refueling-at-sea gear, and extra tie-downs.

New five-year operating contracts for 74 of the RRF ships were announced 9-5-00 to American Overseas Marine Corp. (9 ships, $41.4 million); Crowley Liner Services (8 ships, $34.9 million), Interocean Ugland Management (11 ships, $35.4 million), Keystone Shipping (12 ships, $57.2 million), Marine Transport Lines (9 ships. $49.2 million), Mormac Marine (9 ships, $33.9 million), Ocean Duchess (3 ships, $2.6 million), Pacific Gulf Marine (8 ships, $31 million), and Patriot Contract Services (6 ships for $30.8 million). The contractors will have the ships maintained and will provide crews to activated units.

As of 1-02, there were 80 ships remaining in the RRF, including the navy-"owned" *Wright* (T-AVB 3) and *Curtiss* (T-AVB 4), which are listed in the Auxiliaries section. The four-digit T-series numbers listed in parentheses before the ships' names are administrative numbers assigned by MSC and MARAD and are not U.S. Navy hull numbers. Of the inactive units, 55 are maintained on four- or five-day readiness to sail and 23 others on 10- or 20-day readiness.

♦ 2 Taabo Italia–class roll-on/roll-off vehicle cargo ships [WAK]
Bldr: Fincantieri, Genoa, Italy (In serv. 1984)

	Acquired	To RRF
(T-AKR 9701) Cape Victory (ex-*Merzario Britannia*)	2-4-93	2-9-94
(T-AKR 9666) Cape Vincent (ex-*Taabo Italia,* ex-*Merzario Italia*)	13-5-93	19-8-94

Cape Vincent (T-AKR 9666) N. Brogar, 12-98

D: approx. 27,000 tons (fl) **S:** 16 kts (15.5 sust.)
Dim: 192.62 (172.80 pp) × 26.55 × 8.47
M: 1 GMT-Sulzer 6RNB 66/140 diesel; 1 CP prop; 11,850 bhp
Electric: 4,280 kw tot. (1 × 1,280-kw, 3 × 1,000-kw diesel sets)—bow-thruster
Range: 21,000/16 **Fuel:** 1,840 tons heavy oil, 375 tons diesel **Crew:** . . .

Remarks: 22,423 grt/21,439 dwt. Purchased 12-92 from CNM (Compagnia di Navigazione Merzario). Both are in layberth at Beaumont, Texas. When active, are operated by Keystone Shipping.
Hull systems: Hull molded depth is 16.10 m. Have a 100,299-ft.^{2} military cargo capacity (with 2,480 m of vehicle parking lanes). Stern slewing ramp is 28.0 m long and 7.2 m wide. Can carry 1,306 standard 20-ft. cargo containers. Had spar decks added by Bender Shipbuilding and Repair, Mobile, Ala., with *Cape Victory* completing modifications in 9-98 and *Cape Vincent* during 11-98; the decks provide additional vehicle parking space topside.

♦ 2 Hual Trader–class roll-on/roll-off vehicle cargo ships [WAK]
Bldr: Stocznia imeni Komuny Paryskiej, Gdynia, Poland

	In serv.	Acquired	To RRF
(T-AKR 9961) Cape Washington (ex-*Hual Trader,* ex-*Hoegh Trader*)	1981	. . .	5-4-94
(T-AKR 9962) Cape Wrath (ex-*Hual Transporter*)	1982	14-5-93	3-3-94

Cape Wrath (T-AKR 9962) Jürg Kürsener, 8-97

D: approx. 47,000 tons (fl) **S:** 17 kts (15.2 sust.)
Dim: 212.61 (195.76 pp) × 32.28 × 11.63
M: 1 Cegielski-Sulzer 6RND 90/155 diesel; 1 CP prop; 17,400 bhp—bow- and stern-thrusters

U.S. MARITIME ADMINISTRATION READY RESERVE FORCE
(continued)

Cape Washington (T-AKR 9961) Leo Van Ginderen, 4-94

Electric: 4,800 kw tot. (5 × 960-kw Sulzer diesel sets)
Range: . . ./. . . **Fuel:** 3,811 tons heavy oil **Crew:** . . .

Remarks: *Cape Washington:* 23,597 grt/32,695 dwt; *Cape Wrath:* 20,563 grt/32,722 dwt. Former automobile carriers, purchased in 12-92 from Leif Hoegh & Co./Grace Marine, Panama. Both were assigned to the army Interim Brigade Afloat Force and were based at Saipan carrying prepositioned equipment; they were returned to RRF layup on 27-6-97 and 20-1-97, respectively, with both berthed at Baltimore on four-day recall.
Hull systems: Hull molded depth is 21.60 m. Originally had 170,762 ft.^{2} of military cargo capacity; they could carry 6,000 automobiles or 1,203 20-ft. standard cargo containers—but the decks were too weak to support heavy military vehicles. They have now had their seven vehicle decks replaced by three stronger decks capable of supporting military vehicles and adding 156,000 ft.^{2} of useful capacity; work on *Cape Washington* began 10-99 and on *Cape Wrath* during 4-00. Have ice-strengthened hulls with side doors and 31-m-long by 8-m-wide stern-quarter door/ramps. Clear height in the vehicle decks is 6.1 m. Have two 5-ton cranes. Both can carry 789 tons of diesel fuel for the auxiliary engines.

♦ 1 Finneagle-class roll-on/roll-off vehicle cargo ship [WAK]
Bldr: Kockums AB, Malmö, Sweden (In serv. 20-2-81)

	Acquired	To RRF
(T-AKR 2044) Cape Orlando (ex-*American Eagle,* ex-*Zenit Eagle,* ex-*Finneagle*)	15-4-93	12-9-94

Cape Orlando (T-AKR 2044) Pradignac & Léo, 2-98

D: 12,500 tons light (32,799 fl) **S:** 22 kts (19.5 light)
Dim: 193.63 (180.83 pp) × 28.01 × 3.94 (light; 9.22 max. loaded)
M: 2 Cegielski-Sulzer 6RND68M diesels; 1 prop; 21,600 bhp
Electric: 4,200 kw (3 × 1,400 kw) **Range:** 7,748/19.5
Fuel: 2,833 tons **Crew:** 8 officers, 12 unlicensed

Remarks: 15,632 grt/20,404 dwt. Had been on charter since 22-8-83 from American Automar, being operated by Pacific Gulf Marine for U.S.-to-Europe service, until purchased in 12-92 from the owner, Connecticut National Bank, for the RRF. Renamed in 1993. Assigned to the West Coast division of the RRF and in layberth at Hunters Point, San Francisco, on four-day recall.
Hull systems: Cargo capacity: 18,219 tons max. A versatile design, capable of transporting up to 252 standard 20-ft. cargo vans or vehicles, with 10,500 m^2 of parking space for the latter. Has a 108,157-ft.^{2} military cargo capacity rating. Has two side-by-side, 26.8-m-long, 8-m-wide slewing stern ramps and two bow-thrusters. Can carry up to 8,500 tons of seawater ballast. There are five holds and six hatches, and an internal 65-ton-capacity cargo elevator is fitted. Cranes include one of 25-ton capacity and one of 5-ton.

♦ 2 Cape Kennedy–class roll-on/roll-off vehicle cargo ships [WAK]
Bldr: Nippon Kokan, Tsurumi, Japan

	L	Acquired	To RRF
(T-AKR 5083) Cape Kennedy (ex-*Nedlloyd Rosario,* ex-*Rosario,* ex-*Nedlloyd Rosario*)	1-79	9-95	11-6-96
(T-AKR 5082) Cape Knox (ex-*Nedlloyd Rouen,* ex-*Rouen,* ex-*Nedlloyd Rouen*)	10-78	9-95	15-7-96

Cape Kennedy (T-AKR 5083), left, and Cape Knox (T-AKR 5082) Leo Dirkx, 2-01

D: 36,450 tons (fl) **S:** 19 kts **Dim:** 212.10 (198.81 pp) × 32.29 × 10.72
Electronics: Radar: 2 . . . nav.
M: 1 Sumitomo-Sulzer 8RND90M diesel; 1 prop; 25,400 bhp—1 CP bow-thruster
Electric: 6,400 kw tot. (4 × 1,600-kw diesel sets) **Range:** 21,600/19
Fuel: 4,241 tons heavy oil, 330 tons diesel **Crew:** . . . tot.

Remarks: 21,144 grt/29,218 dwt. Acquired in 2-95 with FY 95 funding from Nedlloyd Lines, Rotterdam. Modified for RRF service at Bender Shipbuilding and Repair, Mobile, Ala., *Cape Kennedy* beginning in 12-95 and *Cape Knox* in 1-96. Both are administratively assigned to the Beaumont, Texas, Gulf Coast RRF division and are berthed at New Orleans on four-day recall. Have two vehicle decks with 3,970 lane-meters total vehicle area; can also be used to carry 1,550 standard 20-ft. containers. Bale cargo capacity is rated at 67,290 m^3. Have an angled stern door and two ramps.

♦ 3 Barber Tiaf–class roll-on/roll-off vehicle cargo ships [WAK]

	Bldr	To RRF
(T-AKR 5067) Cape Henry (ex-*Barber Priam*)	Mitsubishi Heavy Ind., Nagasaki	29-9-86
(T-AKR 5068) Cape Horn (ex-*Barber Tønsberg*)	Kaldnes Mek. Versted, Tønsberg	15-12-86
(T-AKR 5066) Cape Hudson (ex-*Barber Tiaf*)	Tangen Vaerft, Kragerø	25-11-86

Cape Henry (T-AKR 5067) Werner Globke, 8-01

Cape Horn (T-AKR 5068) Leo Van Ginderen, 1-94

D: 19,091 tons light (51,007 fl) **S:** 21 kts (17 sust.)
Dim: 228.50 (211.50 pp) × 32.26 × 4.70 (light; 10.80 loaded)
M: 1 Burmeister & Wain (*Cape Henry:* Mitsubishi-Sulzer) diesel; 1 prop; 30,700 (*Cape Henry:* 30,150) bhp
Range: 24,317/17 **Fuel:** 3,638 tons **Crew:** 9 officers, 18 unlicensed

Remarks: Vary slightly in design: *Cape Henry* is 21,747 grt, *Cape Horn* 22,090 grt, and *Cape Hudson* 21,976 grt. Were completed during 1989, purchased 1-6-86, and overhauled at Norfolk SB & DD before entering the RRF. All three were activated in mid-1994 for use with the Army Interim Prepositioning Force at Diego Garcia; they were to be returned to RRF layup by 30-9-96 but remained active into 1997, with *Cape Hudson* deactivating 17-7-97 and *Cape Horn* 3-12-98; *Cape Henry* was reassigned to Operation Joint Guard service on 21-3-97 to support forces in Bosnia. Are now assigned to the Suisun Bay Fleet, with *Cape Henry* in layberth at San Francisco and the other two at Oakland, Calif. *Cape Horn,* activated 3-02, had a fire en route to an exercise in Thailand, with two killed.
Hull systems: All have one 39-ton crane. The stern ramp is 49.4 m long and 12 m wide and has a capacity of 63.9 tons. Cargo: 26,742 tons maximum. Can also carry 1,607–1,629 20-ft. containers. There are four internal vehicle cargo decks and a total of 18,287 m^2 of cargo space.

♦ 3 Saudi Riyadh–class roll-on/roll-off vehicle cargo ships [WAK]
Bldr: Kawasaki Heavy Industries, Sakaide, Japan

	In serv.	Acquired	To RRF
(T-AKR 9960) Cape Race (ex-*G and C Admiral,* ex-*Seaspeed America*)	7-77	28-4-93	11-9-94
(T-AKR 9679) Cape Ray (ex-*Saudi Makkah,* ex-*Seaspeed Asia*)	4-77	29-4-93	17-12-94
(T-AKR 9678) Cape Rise (ex-*Saudi Riyadh,* ex-*Seaspeed Arabia*)	2-77	9-8-93	21-11-94

Cape Race (T-AKR 9960)—with sisters *Cape Rise* (T-AKR 9678) and *Cape Ray* (T-AKR 9679) at Portsmouth, Va. A. D. Baker III, 10-00

U.S. MARITIME ADMINISTRATION READY RESERVE FORCE *(continued)*

D: approx, 32,000 tons (fl) **S:** 19.75 kts
Dim: 197.52 (180.02 pp) × 32.26 × 8.50
M: 2 Kawasaki-M.A.N. 14V 52/55A diesels; 1 CP prop; 28,000 bhp (at 430 rpm)—bow- and stern-thrusters
Electric: 6,640 kw tot. (2 × 1,920 kw, 2 × 1,400 kw)
Range: 21,000/18 **Fuel:** 4,590 tons heavy oil, 278 tons diesel **Crew:** . . .

Remarks: 14,825 grt/22,735 dwt. Purchased in 12-92, *Cape Race* from Sunpride, Inc., and the others from the National Shipping Company of Saudi Arabia. They are operated by Keystone Shipping, Bala Cynwyd, Pa., and are maintained at Moon Engineering Co., Portsmouth, Va., on four-day (*Cape Ray:* five-day) recall.
Hull systems: Hull molded depth is 19.87 m. Have a 141,685-ft.^{2} military cargo capacity rating (*Cape Race:* 141,600 ft.^{2}). Have side doors and stern ramps for vehicle cargo and four internal vehicle elevators. Can carry 1,315 standard 20-ft. cargo containers. Spar decks were added during 1998 to provide additional vehicle stowage, with *Cape Race* completed during 1-99 and *Cape Ray* in 4-99, both by Bender SB & Repair, Mobile, Ala., and *Cape Rise* late in 1999 at North Florida Shipyards.

♦ 3 Reichenfels-class roll-on/roll-off vehicle cargo ships [WAK]
Bldr: Howaldtswerke, Kiel (*Cape Taylor:* Sasebo Heavy Industries, Sasebo, Japan) (In serv. 1977)

	Acquired	To RRF
(T-AKR 113) Cape Taylor (ex-*Thekwini*, ex-*ASL Cygnus*, ex-*Cygnus*, ex-*Rabenfels*)	7-4-93	24-7-94
(T-AKR 112) Cape Texas (ex-*Lyra*, ex-*Reichenfels*)	5-2-93	19-8-94
(T-AKR 9711) Cape Trinity (ex-*Santos*, ex-*Canadian Forest*, ex-*Santos*, ex-*Radbod*, ex-*Norefjord*, ex-*Rheinfels*)	24-3-93	15-11-94

Cape Texas (T-AKR 112) Dr. Giorgio Arra, 3-94

D: *Cape Texas:* 9,870 tons light (24,551 fl); others: 26,455 tons (fl)
S: 20.5 kts (18 sust.) **Dim:** 191.29 (178.01 pp) × 27.21 × 4.05 light (8.60 max.)
Electronics: Radar: 1 Decca RM 1229 nav.; 1 Decca TM-S 1230 nav.
M: 2 M.A.N. 9L 52/55A heavy-oil diesels; 1 CP prop; 18,980 bhp—2 bow-thrusters
Electric: 3,420 kw tot. (2 × 1,250-kw, 1 × 980-kw diesel sets)
Range: 22,600/16.5 **Fuel:** 2,570 tons heavy oil, 601.5 tons diesel **Crew:** 49 tot.

Remarks: 14,174 grt/15,075 dwt (*Cape Texas:* 12,159 grt/15,074 dwt). Purchased 12-92 from Lykes Brothers. Made about 21.4 kts on trials. *Cape Texas* had operated previously in MSC service as *Lyra*. All three are in layberth at Houston, Texas, on four-day recall. *Cape Trinity* was activated to transport a 500-bed modular field hospital (400 containers and 100 vehicles) to Norway during 3-99.
Hull systems: Hull has a 17.60-m molded depth and is ice-strengthened. *Cape Texas* is 193.33 m overall (177.98 pp). *Cape Taylor* and *Cape Trinity* have a 112,700-ft.^{2} military cargo capacity rating, while the *Cape Texas* is rated at 112,761 ft^2. Cargo deadweight is 11,386 tons. Have 4.65 × 4.20–m side vehicle-loading doors port and starboard and a 160-long-ton-capacity, 10.85-m-long, 22-m-wide stern slewing ramp. Cargo lane length is 3,216 m for vehicles with 2.5-m width, and there is a clear height of 4.2 m between each of the three internal cargo decks. An internal 80-ton cargo elevator is fitted. Bale capacity is 44,400 m^3. Can carry 340 standard 20-ft. cargo containers or 233 cargo trailers.

♦ 4 Maritime Administration C7-S-95a roll-on/roll-off vehicle cargo ships [WAK]
Bldr: Bath Iron Works, Bath, Maine

	L	In serv.	To RRF
(T-AKR 5076) Cape Inscription (ex-*Tyson Lykes*, ex-*Maine*)	24-5-75	27-5-76	8-9-87
(T-AKR 11) Cape Intrepid (ex-*Jupiter*, T-AKR 11; ex-*Lipscomb Lykes*; ex-*Arizona*)	1-11-75	14-5-76	26-4-86
(T-AKR 5062) Cape Isabel (ex-*Charles Lykes*, ex-*Nevada*)	15-5-76	1977	9-6-86
(T-AKR 10) Cape Island (ex-*Mercury*, T-AKR 10; ex-*Illinois*)	7-76	1977	22-11-93

Cape Inscription (T-AKR 5076) W. Michael Young, 2-00

D: 14,767 tons light (33,900 fl) **S:** 24 kts (23 sust.)
Dim: 208.71 (195.07 pp) × 31.09 × 5.16 (light; 9.78 max. loaded)

Cape Isabel (T-AKR 5062)—with nonslewing vehicle ramp lowered George R. Schneider, 7-00

Electronics:
Radar: 1 Raytheon TM 1650/6X nav.; 1 Raytheon TM 1660/12S nav.
M: 2 sets G.E. geared steam turbines; 2 props; 37,000 shp
Boilers: 2 Babcock & Wilcox; 77.5 kg/cm^2 **Electric:** 4,000 kw tot.
Range: 12,600/23 **Fuel:** 3,465 tons **Crew:** 12 officers, 24 unlicensed

Remarks: 13,156 grt/19,172 dwt. *Cape Island* was in long-term charter from Lykes Brothers from 14-4-80; she was later sold to Wilmington Trust Co. and operated in cargo service in the Far East with an MSC civil service crew until transferred to the RRF. *Cape Intrepid* and *Cape Island* were renamed from *Jupiter* and *Mercury* in 1993. *Cape Intrepid* and *Cape Island* are in layberth at Tacoma, Wash., and *Cape Inscription* and *Cape Isabel* are at Long Beach, Calif.; all are on four-day recall.
Hull systems: Can carry containers or vehicles and 728 tons of liquid. Cargo deadweight capacity is 14,876 tons (56,640 m^3 bale, with 16,258 m^2 of vehicle cargo space on the four internal vehicle decks). Rated at 153,860 ft.^{2} military cargo capacity. Have two side doors and a 7.3-m-wide, 24.4-m-long, 100-ton-capacity stern-quarter ramp. There is one 30-ton-capacity crane.

♦ 5 Tombarra-class roll-on/roll-off vehicle cargo ships [WAK]
Bldrs: A: Eriksberg M/V, Lindholmen, Sweden; B: Ch. de France, Dunkerque, France

	Bldr	In serv.	To RRF
(T-AKR 5054) Cape Decision (ex-*Tombarra*)	A	30-8-73	10-10-85
(T-AKR 5055) Cape Diamond (ex-*Tricolor*)	B	22-9-72	15-10-85
(T-AKR 5053) Cape Domingo (ex-*Tarago*)	B	11-1-73	28-10-85
(T-AKR 5052) Cape Douglas (ex-*Lalandia*)	A	22-2-73	18-11-85
(T-AKR 5051) Cape Ducato (ex-*Barranduna*)	A	11-9-72	10-12-85

Cape Decision (T-AKR 5054) H&L Van Ginderen, 11-94

Cape Ducato (T-AKR 5051)—showing the nonslewing stern ramp in stowed position H&L Van Ginderen, 7-96

D: 13,140 tons light (34,790 fl) **S:** 22 kts (18 sust.)
Dim: 207.40 (193.24 pp) × 29.57 × 4.11 (light; 10.06 max. loaded)
Electronics: 2 Raytheon . . . nav.

U.S. MARITIME ADMINISTRATION READY RESERVE FORCE *(continued)*

M: French-built: 3 Ch. d'Atlantique–Pielstick diesels; 1 CP prop; 28,890 bhp—Swedish-built: 3 Lindholmen-Pielstick 18 PC2 V diesels; 1 CP prop; 27,000 bhp (22,860 sust.)—all: 1,500-hp bow-thruster; 1,000-hp stern-thruster
Electric: 6,384 kw (2 × 2,200-kw, 2 × 992-kw diesel sets)
Range: 19,000/18 **Fuel:** 3,200 tons heavy oil, 240 tons diesel
Crew: 9 officers, 18 unlicensed

Remarks: Tonnages vary: 23,972–24,437 grt/21,299–21,398 dwt. Five-deck vehicle cargo ships, purchased 1-85 and "reflagged" (safety features brought into line with USCG standards) by Bethlehem SY, Sparrows Point, Md. *Cape Douglas* was at Diego Garcia with Afloat Prepositioning Squadron Three (APS-3) until deactivated 20-5-98, and *Cape Decision* was returned to layup at Charleston, S.C., 10-3-97; the other three are in layberth at Jacksonville, Fla., on four-day recall.
Hull systems: Cargo capacity: 21,650 tons max. The 65-ton-capacity stern ramp is 32 m long and 7 m wide. Can carry 554 20-ft. containers and have 52,863 m^3 internal bale capacity, including 1,784 m^3 refrigerated. Vehicle cargo parking area (including the vehicle decks but not the weather-deck container space): 17,395.4 m^2 for the French-built units, 16,802.6 m^2 for the Swedish-built.

♦ 2 Federal Lakes–class roll-on/roll-off vehicle cargo ships [WAK]
Bldr: Port Weller Dry Dock, St. Catharines, Ont.

	In serv.	To RRF
(T-AKR 5077) CAPE LAMBERT (ex-*Federal Lakes*, ex-*Avon Forest*)	1973	5-11-87
(T-AKR 5078) CAPE LOBOS (ex-*Federal Seaway*, ex-*Laurentian Forest*, ex-*Grand Encounter*, ex-*Laurentian Forest*)	1972	14-3-88

Cape Lobos (T-AKR 5078) William H. Clarke, 11-99

D: 30,375 tons (fl) **S:** 19 kts **Dim:** 207.88 (189.44 pp) × 22.92 × 9.30
M: 2 Crossley-Pielstick 18 PC2 V400 diesels; 2 props; 18,000 bhp—bow-thruster
Electric: 2,700 kw (3 × 900-kw diesel sets)
Range: 6,000/17.5 **Fuel:** 1,207 tons heavy oil, 217 tons diesel
Crew: 10 officers, 17 unlicensed

Remarks: 15,005 grt/20,545 dwt. Former Great Lakes newsprint and vehicle carriers with ice-strengthened hulls. Purchased 5-6-87 for $14.5 million each from Fed Nav (U.S.A.), but permission to retain *Cape Lobos* in commercial service into 1988 was later granted. *Cape Lambert* is in layberth at Wilmington, N.C., on four-day recall, while *Cape Lobos* was moved to the James River, Va., reserve fleet during 11-99.
Hull systems: Have side doors and two vehicle ramps. Have 35,428 m^3 bale capacity and 17,094 m^2 of vehicle parking. Are somewhat limited in utility by their small vehicle loading doors and inability to carry cargo on the weather deck.

♦ 1 Parralla-class roll-on/roll-off vehicle cargo ship [WAK]
Bldr: Eriksberg M/V, Lindholmen, Sweden

	In serv.	To RRF
(T-AKR 5069) CAPE EDMONT (ex-*Parralla*)	1972	16-4-87

Cape Edmont (T-AKR 5069)—at Charleston, S.C. Marc Ottini, 9-00

D: 12,256 tons light (32,543 fl) **S:** 20.7 kts (17 sust.)
Dim: 199.02 (183.70 pp) × 28.71 × 3.81 (light; 9.60 max. loaded)
M: 3 Eriksberg-Pielstick 18 PC2 V400 diesels; 1 CP prop; 25,920 bhp—bow-thruster
Electric: 5,652 kw tot. (2 × 2,200 kw, 2 × 584 kw, 1 × 84 kw)
Range: 17,000/19; 20,000/17 **Fuel:** 3,250 tons heavy oil, 489 tons diesel
Crew: 32 tot.

Remarks: 12,902 grt/20,303 dwt. Is in layberth at Charleston, S.C., on four-day recall.
Hull systems: Container capacity: 309 TEU above decks, 903 below. Has 13,972 m^2 of vehicle parking space. Can carry 317 m^3 of liquid cargo (vehicle fuel). Has two 18-ton cranes on one foundation forward. Bale cargo capacity: 50,299 m^3. Cargo deadweight: 17,902 tons. Single stern ramp unfolds to 32 m long, is 6.98-m wide, and can support 220 tons.

♦ 1 Admiral Wm. M. Callaghan–class vehicle cargo ship [WAK]
Bldr: Sun SB & DD, Chester, Pa.

	L	In serv.	To RRF
(T-AKR 1001) ADMIRAL WM. M. CALLAGHAN	17-10-67	12-67	25-6-87

Admiral Wm. M. Callaghan (T-AKR 1001) Don. S. Montgomery, USN, 4-93

D: 13,161 tons light (26,537 fl) **S:** 26 kts (20 sust.)
Dim: 211.61 (193.12 pp) × 28.00 × 5.18 (light; 8.86 max. loaded)
Electronics: Radar: 1 . . . nav.
M: 2 G.E. LM-2500 gas turbines; 2 props; 40,000 shp **Electric:** 1,500 kw tot.
Range: 6,000/25; 12,000/20 **Fuel:** 3,939 tons **Crew:** 10 officers, 18 unlicensed

Remarks: 24,471 grt/13,500 dwt. Built for U.S. Navy service, the earliest example of the current "build-and-charter" concept. Had been on MSC charter from MARAD for 20 years prior to transfer to the RRF. Is now in layberth at Hunters Point, San Francisco, on four-day recall.
Hull systems: The original Pratt & Whitney FT-4 gas turbines were replaced during 12-77 with LM-2500 engines; served as trials ship for LM-2500 engine life extension and fuel economy improvements. Cargo deadweight: 9,519 tons. Has a 12.8-m-long, 4.5-m-wide, 55.8-ton-capacity stern ramp and four side-loading ports with 18-m-long by 4.5-m-wide portable ramps. Can carry up to 750 vehicles, on 15,607 m^2 of parking area. Rated at 212 TEU for cargo container carrying. Is unusual for a "Ro/Ro" in having a full set of cargo derricks: two of 120 tons capacity, six of 25 tons, and 10 of 15 tons; flush hatches permit access to 38,515 m^3 of cargo space.

♦ 1 Meteor-class (C4-ST-67a type) vehicle cargo ship [WAK]
Bldr: Puget Sound Bridge & DD

	Laid down	L	In serv.	To RRF
T-AKR 9 METEOR (ex-*Sea Lift*, ex-LSV 9)	19-5-64	18-4-64	25-5-67	3-10-85

Meteor (T-AKR 9) Winter & Findler, 9-99

D: 9,154 tons light (21,480 fl) **S:** 21.25 kts (20 sust.)
Dim: 164.7 × 25.5 × 4.50 (light; 8.86 max. loaded)
Electronics:
Radar: 1 Raytheon TM 1650/6X nav.; 1 Raytheon TM 1660/12S nav.
M: 2 sets geared steam turbines; 2 props; 19,400 shp
Boilers: 2; 52.8 kg/cm^2, 471° C
Range: 10,000/20 **Fuel:** 2,120 tons **Crew:** . . .

Remarks: 16,467 grt/12,326 dwt. Authorized as T-AK 278, completed as T-LSV 9, and retyped T-AKR on 14-8-69. Was renamed 12-9-75. Since 29-2-00, has been in layberth at Suisun Bay, Calif., on four-day recall. Was transferred to MARAD ownership from the navy during 11-01.
Hull systems: Cargo: 9,030 tons max. Has 26,819 m^3 of vehicle parking volume (7,896 m^2 deck space). There are two 70-ton, 14 15-ton, and two 10-ton cranes. Has a 13.7-m-long, 5.5-m-wide, 56-ton-capacity straight stern ramp and 13.9-m-long, 4.6-m-wide, 54-ton-capacity portable side vehicle loading ramps. Can carry 12 passengers. The superstructure is set 4 m above the upper deck to permit vehicles to be stowed beneath it.

♦ 1 Maritime Administration C3-ST-14a vehicle cargo ship [WAK]
Bldr: Sun SB & DD, Chester, Pa.

	Laid down	L	In serv.	To RRF
T-AKR 7 COMET	15-5-56	31-7-57	27-1-58	15-3-85

D: 7,605 tons light (18,150 fl) **S:** 19 kts (18 sust.)
Dim: 152.1 (141.73 pp) × 23.77 × 4.29 (light; 8.23 max. loaded)
Electronics:
Radar: 1 Raytheon TM 1650/6X nav.; 1 Raytheon TM 1660/12S nav.
M: 2 sets G.E. geared steam turbines; 2 props; 13,200 shp
Boilers: 2 Babcock & Wilcox; 43.3 kg/cm^2, 454° C
Electric: 1,200 kw (2 × 600-kw turboalternators) **Range:** 13,000/18
Fuel: 2,370 tons **Crew:** 11 officers, 33 unlicensed

U.S. MARITIME ADMINISTRATION READY RESERVE FORCE
(continued)

Comet (T-AKR 7) Findler & Winter, 10-99

Remarks: 13,792 grt/10,111 dwt. Authorized as T-AK 269, then changed to T-LSV 7 on 1-6-63, and finally to T-AKR 7 on 1-1-69. Deactivated 22-4-84, she remains navy property. Transferred to MARAD ownership from the navy during 11-01 and is now in layberth at Alameda, Calif., on four-day recall.
Hull systems: Can carry 8,730 tons of cargo or more than 700 military vehicles in holds totaling 19,370 m^3 volume (7,525 m^2 deck space). Has two 60-ton, four 10-ton, and 16 15-ton derricks. The fixed stern ramp has a capacity of 60 tons and is 9 m long by 5.8 m wide; portable, 12.2-m-long, 4.6-m-wide, 60-ton-capacity side vehicle ramps can be fitted. Denny-Brown fin stabilizers are fitted.

♦ 2 Maritime Administration C6-S-MA60d auxiliary crane-ships [WAK]
Bldr: Ingalls SB, Pascagoula, Miss.

	Laid down	L	In serv.	To RRF
T-ACS 9 GREEN MOUNTAIN STATE (ex-*American Altair*, ex-*Mormacaltair*)	2-12-63	20-8-64	23-6-65	15-3-92
T-ACS 10 BEAVER STATE (ex-*American Draco*, ex-*Mormacdraco*)	19-4-64	14-1-65	28-5-65	6-1-97

Beaver State (T-ACS 10) Winter & Findler, 9-97

D: 11,720 tons light (27,900 fl) **S:** 21 kts
Dim: 202.98 (193.55 pp) × 22.96 × 10.06
M: 2 sets G.E. geared steam turbines; 1 prop; 19,000 shp
Boilers: 2 Combustion Engineering
Electric: 4,780 kw (2 × 1,640-kw turboalternators, 2 × 750-kw diesel sets)
Range: 17,000/20 **Fuel:** 4,083 tons **Crew:** 64 tot. + 35 spare berths

Remarks: 16,180 dwt. Conversion was authorized under FY 88, with the conversion contract let 27-1-89. Work on T-ACS 9 began 28-2-89 at Norshipco, Norfolk, but was slowed by lack of funding. Conversion of T-ACS 10 was begun 26-3-89, also by Norshipco, but was canceled 12-1-90; the work was reassigned to the Charleston Naval Shipyard, S.C., and the ship was laid up in the NDRF at Beaumont, Texas. T-ACS 9 is now in layberth at Portland, Ore., and T-ACS 10 at Bremerton, Wash., both on five-day recall. For this class, the assigned numbers are actual U.S. Navy hull numbers.
Hull systems: Have three pairs of 30-ton-capacity, 36.9-m-reach electrohydraulic cranes mounted to starboard.

♦ 2 Maritime Administration C6-S-MA1xb auxiliary crane-ships [WAK]
Bldr: Todd SY, San Pedro, Calif.

	Laid down	L	In serv.	To RRF
T-ACS 7 DIAMOND STATE (ex-*President Truman*, ex-*Japan Mail*)	22-11-60	8-8-61	14-4-62	22-2-89
T-ACS 8 EQUALITY STATE (ex-*American Builder*, ex-*Philippine Mail*, ex-*Santa Rosa*, ex-*President Roosevelt*, ex-*Washington Mail*)	12-5-61	6-1-62	25-7-62	24-5-89

Diamond State (T-ACS 7) H&L Van Ginderen, 6-99

D: 15,138 tons (25,660 fl) **S:** 20 kts **Dim:** 203.61 (192.95 pp) × 23.22 × 10.13
Electronics: Radar: 2 . . . nav.
M: 2 sets G.E. geared steam turbines; 1 prop; 22,000 shp
Boilers: 2 Combustion Engineering **Electric:** 2,275 kw
Range: 14,000/20 **Fuel:** 3,124 tons **Crew:** . . .

Remarks: Were 16,518-grt/19,871-dwt container ships prior to their conversion under FY 86, which was contracted with Tampa SB, Tampa, Fla., 14-9-87. Both are in layberth at Houston, Texas, on five-day recall. Sister *American Banker* is maintained in the NDRF in the James River as a potential conversion to T-ACS 11. For this class, the assigned numbers are actual U.S. Navy hull numbers.
Hull systems: Resemble the *Keystone State* (T-ACS 1), with three pairs of 30-ton-capacity, 36.9-m-reach electrohydraulic cranes mounted to starboard. Had 625 20-ft. container capacity prior to conversion.

♦ 3 Maritime Administration C5-S-73c auxiliary crane-ships [WAK]
Bldr: Bath Iron Works, Bath, Maine

	In serv.	Converted	To RRF
T-ACS 4 GOPHER STATE (ex-*Export Leader*)	1969	21-10-86 to 22-10-87	1-1-87
T-ACS 5 FLICKERTAIL STATE (ex-*Lightning*)	1970	18-12-86 to 8-2-88	9-2-88
T-ACS 6 CORNHUSKER STATE (ex-*Staghound*)	20-6-69	3-87 to 12-4-88	12-4-88

Flickertail State (T-ACS 5) William H. Clarke, 2-00

Cornhusker State (T-ACS 6) Paul C. Clift, 5-00

D: 15,060 tons light (25,000 fl) **S:** 20 kts (sust.)
Dim: 185.93 (177.35) × 23.83 × 9.63 **Electronics:** Radar: 2 . . . nav.
M: 2 sets G.E. geared steam turbines; 1 prop; 17,500 shp
Boilers: 2 Babcock & Wilcox
Range: 9,340/20 **Fuel:** 3,576 tons **Crew:** 11 officers, 41 unlicensed

Remarks: 17,904 grt/16,709 dwt. Acquired 11-8-86 from MARAD for conversion by Norshipco, Norfolk. All three were activated for Desert Shield/Desert Storm in 8-90; T-ACS 4 and 5 remained active through 5-92. Are assigned to the James River Fleet, with T-ACS 5 and 6 in layberth at Newport News, Va., on five-day recall. T-ACS 4 was transferred to the Army Interim Prepositioning fleet 30-9-94, operated for the army under MSC administration under contract by Inter Ocean Management; she is stationed at Guam and is attached to Maritime Prepositioning Squadron 3, carrying army port facility equipment and vehicles. For this class, the assigned numbers are actual U.S. Navy hull numbers.
Hull systems: Cargo capacity includes 1,070 standard 20-ft. containers (56 refrigerated). Two pairs of 30-ton-capacity, 36.9-m-reach electrohydraulic cranes are mounted on the starboard side. Are equipped to stow sea shed and standard cargo containers. Can carry three LCM(8) landing craft and two side-loading warping tugs (self-propelled pontoons) and pontoon sections on deck. A bow-thruster has been added. Two 1,200-kw diesel generators were added in the after hold during conversion. Have 5,800 tons of fixed and portable ballast. There are 32 lighter mooring fittings on the hull sides.

♦ 3 Maritime Administration C6-S-MA1qd auxiliary crane-ships [WAK]
Bldr: National Steel, San Diego

	L	In serv.	Converted	To RRF
T-ACS 1 KEYSTONE STATE (ex-*President Harrison*)	2-10-65	1-66	21-3-83 to 7-5-84	1-12-86
T-ACS 2 GEM STATE (ex-*President Monroe*)	22-5-65	1965	26-9-84 to 31-10-85	31-10-85
T-ACS 3 GRAND CANYON STATE (ex-*President Polk*)	23-1-65	1966	28-10-85 to 27-10-87	12-12-86

D: 16,599 tons light (31,500 fl) **S:** 20.25 kts (19.5 sust.)
Dim: 203.82 (192.95 pp) × 23.22 × 5.79 (light; 10.06 max. loaded)
Electronics: Radar: 2 . . . nav.
M: 2 sets G.E. geared steam turbines; 1 prop; 19,250 shp
Boilers: 2 Foster-Wheeler **Electric:** 4,780 kw tot.
Range: 13,000/19.5 **Fuel:** 3,126 tons **Crew:** 14 officers, 50 unlicensed

U.S. MARITIME ADMINISTRATION READY RESERVE FORCE
(continued)

Keystone State (T-ACS 1) Jürg Kürsener, 6-01

Grand Canyon State (T-ACS 3) Findler & Winter, 10-95

Remarks: 16,819 grt/17,729 dwt. Conversion of T-ACS 1 by Bay Shipbuilding, Sturgeon Bay, Wis., took place under FY 83 funding and was ordered 18-3-83. T-ACS 2 (FY 84) was converted by Continental Marine, San Francisco, and T-ACS 3 (FY 85) by Dillingham, San Francisco. All are in layberth at Alameda, Calif., all on five-day recall. For this class, the assigned numbers are actual U.S. Navy hull numbers.
Hull systems: Cargo: 10,370 tons max., including 190 20-ft. containers. The original cargo-handling gear was replaced by three sets of twin 30-ton cranes mounted on the starboard side; the four forwardmost cranes can be ganged together to lift 105 tons. A T-ACS is expected to unload its own container cargo and then unload containers from non-self-sustaining container carriers at the rate of about 300 containers per day. The cranes have a 33-m reach. An additional 3,280 kw of generator capacity was added.

♦ 3 Sea Bee–class, Maritime Administration C8-S-82a cargo-barge carriers [WAK]
Bldr: General Dynamics, Quincy, Mass.

	In serv.	To RRF
(T-AK 5063) Cape May (ex-*Almeria Lykes*)	1972	25-7-86
(T-AK 5064) Cape Mendocino (ex-*Doctor Lykes*)	1972	2-10-86
(T-AK 5065) Cape Mohican (ex-*Tillie Lykes*)	1973	13-9-86

Cape Mohican (T-AK 5065)—at San Diego W. Michael Young, 8-00

Cape May (T-AK 5063)—showing the cargo barge-lifting platform at the stern
Don S. Montgomery, USN, 6-96

D: 18,880 tons light (57,290 fl) **S:** 20.5 kts (19.25 sust.)
Dim: 266.39 (219.92 pp) × 32.31 × 5.44 (light; 11.93 max. loaded)
Electronics: Radar: 2 . . . nav.
M: 2 sets G.E. geared steam turbines; 1 prop; 36,000 shp
Boilers: 2 Babcock & Wilcox
Electric: 4,000 kw (2 × 2,000-kw turbogenerators)
Range: 14,300/19.5 **Fuel:** 6,260 tons **Crew:** 12 officers, 26 unlicensed

Remarks: 21,667 grt/38,410 dwt. Purchased in 1-86. *Cape May* is in layberth at Baltimore on five-day recall, *Cape Mendocino* in the James River, Va., on 10-day recall, and *Cape Mohican* at Alameda, Calif., on five-day recall. *Cape Mohican* went aground on the South Korean coast 22-5-01 but, despite severe damage to shafts and engine mountings, was repaired at Sasebo, Japan.
Hull systems: Cargo capacity: 29,780 tons max. The "Sea Bee" design was intended to carry 38 cargo barges (totaling 41,476 m^3 bale capacity) placed in the water via a 2,000-ton-capacity elevator at the stern. Can also accommodate 4,000 (*Cape Mohican:* 11,000) bbl of liquid cargo and 797 tons of water. Have 797-ton-capacity passive anti-rolling tanks. Each has 24 Sea Bee barges stored aboard.

♦ 2 Maritime Administration C9-S-81d cargo-barge carriers [WAK]
Bldr: Avondale SY, Westwego, La.

	In serv.	To RRF
(T-AK 5073) Cape Farewell (ex-*Delta Mar*)	1973	2-4-87
(T-AK 5070) Cape Flattery (ex-*Delta Norte*)	1973	14-5-87

Cape Farewell (T-AK 5073)—with a full load of LASH cargo containers
H&L Van Ginderen, 2-95

D: 16,490 tons light (57,082 fl) **S:** 22.75 kts (19.1 sust.)
Dim: 272.30 (243.03) × 30.56 × 4.42 (light; 12.44 max. loaded)
Electronics: Radar: 2 . . . nav.
M: 2 sets de Laval geared steam turbines; 1 prop; 32,000 shp
Boilers: 2 Combustion Engineering; 75.7 kg/cm^2
Electric: 4,000 kw (2 × 2,000-kw turbogenerators)
Range: 15,000/19.1 **Fuel:** 5,840 tons **Crew:** 12 officers, 20 unlicensed

Remarks: 29,508 grt/41,363 dwt. Purchased in 1-86, along with *Delta Sud,* which was to have become *Cape Fear* but suffered severe machinery damage during RRF overhaul and was returned to MARAD for disposal. Both are in layberth at Beaumont, Texas, on 10-day recall.
Hull systems: Cargo: 36,650 tons max. Have a 455-ton traveling crane to handle 89 LASH (Lighter Aboard Ship) cargo lighters. Neither is equipped to carry containers. Both had the 89 barges aboard in 1999.

♦ 2 Maritime Administration C8-S-81b cargo-barge carriers [WAK]
Bldr: Avondale SY, Westwego, La.

	In serv.	To RRF
(T-AK 5061) Cape Fear (ex-*Austral Lightning,* ex-*Lash España*)	4-71	13-5-85
(T-AK 5071) Cape Florida (ex-*Delta Caribe,* ex-*Lash Turkiye*)	1971	17-2-87

Cape Florida (T-AK 5071)—with LASH barges aboard H&L Van Ginderen, 1-95

D: 14,230 tons light (44,250 fl) **S:** 22.5 kts (20 sust.)
Dim: 249.94 (220.68 pp) × 30.48 × 4.65 (light; 10.70 max. loaded)
M: 1 set de Laval geared steam turbines; 1 prop; 32,000 shp
Boilers: 2 Babcock & Wilcox
Electric: 4,500 kw tot. (1 × 2,500 kw, 1 × 2,000 kw)
Range: 15,000/20 **Fuel:** 4,928 tons **Crew:** 12 officers, 20 unlicensed

Remarks: 26,406 grt/30,298 dwt. *Cape Fear* had been chartered for the Near-Term Prepositioning Force until 1-4-85. *Cape Florida* is in layberth at Beaumont, Texas, and *Cape Fear* (renamed in 1993) at Suisun Bay, Calif., both on 10-day recall.
Hull systems: Cargo capacity: 30,020 tons max. Originally were LASH (Lighter Aboard Ship) carriers only, but *Cape Fear* was later converted to a container or barge carrier. Can carry up to 77 LASH cargo barges (or 840 standard cargo containers on *Cape Fear*), handled by a 30-ton traveling crane. The traveling barge crane can lift 446 tons. Also have two 5-ton cranes. The barges each have 165.9 m^2 of cargo area. As of 11-99, *Cape Florida* had 77 LASH barges aboard and *Cape Fear* 73.

U.S. MARITIME ADMINISTRATION READY RESERVE FORCE
(continued)

♦ 1 Maritime Administration C5-78 combination cargo ship [WAK]
Bldr: Ingalls SY, Pascagoula, Miss.

	In serv.	To RRF
(T-AK 1014) Cape Nome (ex-*Rapid*, ex-*American Rapid*, ex-*Red Jacket*, ex-*Mormacstar*)	9-69	4-12-87

Cape Nome (T-AK 1014) Takatoshi Okano, 10-97

D: 27,980 tons (fl) **S:** 23.5 kts **Dim:** 183.34 (170.69 pp) × 27.49 × 10.39
Electronics: Radar: 2 . . . nav.
M: 2 sets G.E. geared steam turbines; 1 prop; 30,000 shp
Boilers: 2 Combustion Engineering; 74 kg/cm^2 **Electric:** 3,000 kw
Range: 24,000/23.5 **Fuel:** 5,007 tons **Crew:** 11 officers, 23 unlicensed

Remarks: 11,757 grt/15,946 dwt. Off charter to MSC from Central Gulf Lines in 12-85 and to MARAD in 6-87. Currently in layberth at the James River RRF facility on 10-day recall. Two sisters became USN Aviation Logistic Support Ships *Wright* (T-AVB 3) and *Curtiss* (T-AVB 4); another sister, *Rover,* was on commercial charter to MSC for several years as a cargo vessel.
Hull systems: Cargo: 37,095 m^3 grain/33,782 m^3 bale, including up to 758 standard 20-ft. containers. Has a stern door for vehicle cargo and six cargo holds. Cargo-handling gear includes two 5-ton cranes, 10 30-ton derricks, and one 70-ton heavy-lift derrick.

♦ 2 Maritime Administration C5-S-75a combination cargo ships [WAK]
Bldr: Newport News SB & DD (In serv. 1968)

	To RRF
(T-AK 5051) Cape Gibson (ex-*President Jackson*, ex-*Indian Mail*)	1-4-88
(T-AK 2039) Cape Girardeau (ex-*President Adams*, ex-*Alaskan Mail*)	12-4-88

Cape Girardeau (T-AK 2039)—in layup at Alameda, Calif.; note the ramp on the starboard side, aft, leading from the main deck to the helicopter platform Jürg Kürsener, 6-01

D: 9,790 tons light (31,995 fl) **S:** 20.75 kts (19.5 sust.)
Dim: 184.41 (177.55 pp) × 25.05 × 9.50 (10.68 max. loaded)
Electronics: Radar: 2 . . . nav.
M: 2 sets G.E. geared steam turbines; 1 prop; 24,000 shp—bow-thruster
Boilers: 2 Babcock & Wilcox **Electric:** 2,500 kw tot. (2 × 1,250 kw)
Range: 23,200/19.5 **Fuel:** 3,668 tons **Crew:** 47 tot.

Remarks: 11,559 grt/18,289 dwt at 9.50-m draft; 15,949 grt/22,564 dwt at 10.68-m draft. Purchased from American President Lines 5-6-87 for $5 million each. Are attached to the Suisun Bay RRF facility, both in layberth at Alameda, Calif., on five-day recall. Sister *President Taylor* (ex-*Korean Mail*) was acquired at the same time and was to have become *Cape Grieg,* but she remains in the NDRF.
Hull systems: Self-sustaining container/break-bulk ships with six holds and seven hatches. Cargo capacity: 17,832 tons max., with 409 20-ft. containers/28,830 m^3 bale dry cargo (623 m^3 refrigerated), 17,000 bbl liquid (2,757 m^3), and 22 passengers. Have one 70-ton, 20 20-ton, and four 15-ton-capacity cargo derricks. Are equipped to carry one Modular Cargo Delivery System (MCDS) solid-cargo station on the port side aft; when the gear is installed, 37 naval reservists augment the crew to operate it. Have a helicopter deck and a broad ramp leading to it from the upper deck on the starboard side.

♦ 4 Maritime Administration C4-S-1u combination cargo ships [WAK]
Bldrs: *Cape Jacob, Cape Juby:* Newport News SB & DD; *Cape John, Cape Johnson:* National Steel, San Diego

	L	In serv.	To RRF
(T-AK 5029) Cape Jacob (ex-*California*, ex-*Santa Rita*, ex-*California*)	28-7-61	1962	15-12-80
(T-AK 5022) Cape John (ex-*Santa Ana*, ex-*C. E. Dant*)	18-8-62	1962	27-5-80
(T-AK 5075) Cape Johnson (ex-*Mormacsaga*, ex-*M. M. Dant*)	5-5-62	26-11-62	17-6-88
(T-AK 5077) Cape Juby (ex-*Mormacsea*, ex-*Hawaii*)	9-2-62	16-8-62	20-7-88

Cape John (T-AK 5022)—in layup at Violet, La., on the Mississippi River; note the Modular Cargo Delivery System (MCDS) to port alongside cargo hold no. 3 to permit transferring ammunition and provisions to ships alongside Leo Dirkx, 10-99

Cape Jacob (T-AK 5029)—at Diego Garcia; note the helicopter platform at the stern, the ramp from the starboard side of the main deck, and the MCDS rig installed on the port side opposite the after hold Joe Straczek, 11-01

D: 9,892 tons light (22,629 fl) **S:** 20.75 kts (19.8 sust.)
Dim: 172.22 (161.09 pp) × 23.22 × 4.74 (light; 9.64 max. loaded)
M: 2 sets G.E. geared steam turbines; 1 prop; 19,250 shp
Boilers: 2 Foster-Wheeler **Electric:** 1,500 (*Cape Juby:* 1,200) kw tot.
Range: 12,600/19.8 **Fuel:** 3,255 tons
Crew: 14 officers, 30 unlicensed (see remarks)

Remarks: *Cape Jacob:* 9,301 grt normal (12,693 max.)/14,349 dwt. *Cape John:* 9,345 grt normal (12,724 max.)/14,607 dwt max. *Cape Johnson:* 9,345 grt normal (12,724 max.)/14,699 dwt max. *Cape Juby:* 9,298 grt normal (12,691 max.)/14,554 dwt max. Were selected in 1986 from ships turned in to MARAD and stored in the NDRF. Sister *Mormactide* (ex-*Oregon*) was to have become *Cape Junction* but has instead been converted as the New York State Maritime Academy training ship *Empire State* and is assigned to the RRF as a "transport" (see under [WAP]). *Cape Jacob* and *Cape John* received their current names in 1993. *Cape Johnson* has been in layberth on five-day recall at Wilmington, N.C., since 20-1-00, as has *Cape Juby* since 27-1-00; *Cape John* is at Violet, La., on 20-day recall. *Cape Jacob* was activated 30-9-98 and assigned to the Afloat Prepositioned Ship force at Diego Garcia 28-5-99.
Hull systems: Cargo: 9,875 tons max. in six holds. Can carry up to 200 20-ft. containers and 753 m^3 of liquid cargo. *Cape Jacob:* 22,002 m^3 bale capacity (1,103 m^3 insulated). *Cape Johnson:* 22,952 m^3 bale capacity/17,266 m^3 grain (1,103 m^3 insulated). *Cape Juby:* 17,266 m^3 bale (1,104 m^3 insulated). Have one 60-ton, 10 20-ton, two 10-ton, and 10 5-ton cargo derricks. *Cape Johnson* and *Cape Jacob* underwent modifications at Bender SB & Repair, Mobile, Ala., commencing in 9-92, to equip them with Modular Cargo Delivery System (MCDS) stations to allow their use as fleet underway ammunition and stores supply ships; the other two are now similarly equipped. When the MCDS is activated, 37 naval reserve Cargo Rig Team (CART) personnel are added to the crew to operate it. In 1999, *Cape Juby* and *Cape John* were fitted with articulating cranes for ammunition handling.

♦ 4 Maritime Administration C4-S-66a break-bulk cargo ships [WAK]
Bldr: Avondale SY, Westwego, La.

	L	In serv.	To RRF
(T-AK 5060) Cape Blanco (ex-*Mason Lykes*)	10-7-65	9-66	9-7-85
(T-AK 5058) Cape Borda (ex-*Howell Lykes*)	16-4-66	1-67	25-4-85
(T-AK 5057) Cape Bover (ex-*Frederick Lykes*)	12-2-66	1-67	1-4-85
(T-AK 5056) Cape Breton (ex-*Dolly Turman*)	4-6-66	5-67	1-5-85

Cape Breton (T-AK 5056)—at Alameda, Calif. Jürg Kürsener, 6-01

U.S. MARITIME ADMINISTRATION READY RESERVE FORCE
(continued)

Cape Bover (T-AK 5057)—activated for an exercise H&L Van Ginderen, 3-99

D: 7,178 tons light (20,986 fl) **S:** 21 kts (20 sust.)
Dim: 164.60 (156.95 pp) × 23.22 × 3.86 (light; 9.63 max. loaded)
Electronics: Radar: 1 . . . nav.
M: 2 sets de Laval or Westinghouse geared steam turbines; 1 prop; 15,500 shp
Boilers: 2 Foster-Wheeler; 49 kg/cm^2 **Electric:** 1,500 kw (2 × 750 kw)
Range: 13,660/20 **Fuel:** 2,503 tons **Crew:** 12 officers, 26 unlicensed

Remarks: Typical: 7,189 grt/10,996 dwt normal; 10,723 grt/14,897 dwt max. Break-bulk ships, purchased from Lykes Brothers Lines for $21,250,000 in 1-85. *Cape Blanco* and *Cape Borda* are in layberth at Alameda, Calif., on five-day recall; *Cape Bover* is in layberth at Hunter's Point, San Francisco, on five-day recall; and *Cape Breton* is laid up in Suisun Bay on 20-day recall. Sister *Cape Bon* (ex-*Velma Lykes*) began conversion in 11-99 at Mobile, Ala., to serve as Massachusetts Maritime Academy training ship *Enterprise* and is listed under transports [WAP].
Hull systems: Cargo: 9,160 tons max. (22,874 m^3 grain/21,240 m^3 bale plus 4,000 bbl liquid/884 m^3). Have four holds, six hatches, one 88-ton heavy-lift derrick, and 20 15-ton derricks.

♦ 4 Maritime Administration C4-S-58a break-bulk cargo ships [WAK] Bldr: Ingalls SY, Pascagoula, Miss.

	L	To RRF
(T-AK 5010) Cape Alexander (ex-*Meteor,* ex-*African Meteor*)	7-7-62	1-4-80
(T-AK 5009) Cape Ann (ex-*Mercury,* ex-*African Mercury*)	12-5-62	19-3-80
(T-AK 5011) Cape Archway (ex-*Neptune,* ex-*African Neptune*)	15-9-62	2-4-80
(T-AK 5013) Cape Avinoff (ex-*Sun,* ex-*African Sun*)	8-12-62	14-4-80

Cape Alexander (T-AK 5010)—with Modular Cargo Delivery System (MCDS) station to port abreast hold no. 3 Ross Gillett, 6-94

D: 7,380 tons light (20,310 fl) **S:** 21.5 kts (20 sust.)
Dim: 174.35 (164.90 pp) × 22.92 × 3.96 (light; 9.40 max. loaded)
M: 2 sets G.E. geared steam turbines; 1 prop; 18,150 shp
Boilers: 2 . . . **Electric:** 1,800 kw tot. (3 × 600 kw)
Range: 13,300/20 **Fuel:** 3,296 tons **Crew:** 11 officers, 28 unlicensed

Remarks: 11,309 grt/12,932 dwt. *Cape Alexander* and *Cape Avinoff* are in layberth at Baltimore on five-day recall; the other two are in the James River on 10-day recall. Sister *Cape Alava* (ex-*Comet,* ex-*African Comet*) was reassigned to the NDRF 1-10-00.
Hull systems: Cargo: 8,800 tons max. (19,385 m^3 grain/19,022 m^3 bale) in seven holds. Have one 60-ton, eight 10-ton, and 14 5-ton cargo derricks. *Cape Ann, Cape Archway,* and *Cape Avinoff* received helicopter decks and other sealift-enhancement features during overhauls in the late 1980s. *Cape Alexander* received the first of 11 planned sets of the Modular Cargo Delivery System (MCDS) in an overhaul ending 2-89, with two solid-transfer STREAM system positions added on the port side; when the system is in use, the crew is augmented by 37 naval reservists. *Cape Ann* and *Cape Archway* have underway replenishment and vertical replenishment capabilities. *Cape Avinoff* has MCDS equipment, plus a vertical replenishment station.

Cape Ann (T-AK 5009) Don S. Montgomery, USN, 4-96

Disposal note: Break-bulk cargo ships reassigned to the NDRF on 1-10-00 included the Maritime Administration C3-S-37d ships *Gulf Banker* and *Gulf Trader;* C3-S-46a ships *Banner* (ex-*Export Banner*) and *Courier* (ex-*Export Courier*); C3-S-37C ships *Cape Chalmers* (ex-*Adabelle Lykes*) and *Cape Cod* (ex-*Sheldon Lykes*); C4-S-57a ships *Pioneer Commander* (ex-*American Commander*) and *Pioneer Contractor* (ex-*American Contractor*); and C3-S-33a ships *Cape Catawba* (ex-*Cape,* ex-*Mormaccape*), *Lake* (ex-*Mormaclake*), and *Scan* (ex-*Mormacscan*). C3-S-33a unit *Northern Light* (T-AK 284, ex-*Cove,* ex-*Mormaccove*) was returned to the NDRF during 2001.

Note: Marine Corps aviation support ships *Wright* (T-AVB 3) and *Curtiss* (T-AVB 4) are considered part of the RRF while laid up at Baltimore and at Port Hueneme, Calif., respectively; the MSC, however, considers them to be part of its assets, and the pair is described in the Auxiliaries section.

Since 1999, the former RRF cargo ship *Del Monte* of the C3-S-76a class has been used at Norfolk for cargo-handling training by the USNR but is not part of the RRF; the ship had been returned to the NDRF on 1-4-94.

♦ 1 Falcon-class tanker [WAOT]
Bldr: Ingalls SY, Pascagoula, Miss.

	L	In serv.	To RRF
(T-AOT 5005) Mission Capistrano (ex-*Falcon Lady;* ex-*Columbia,* T-AOT 182; ex-*Falcon Lady*)	12-9-70	11-3-71	1-3-88

Mission Capistrano (T-AOT 5005)—as *Columbia* (T-AOT 182) Bernard Prézelin, 1982

D: 45,877 tons (fl) **S:** 16.5 kts **Dim:** 204.93 (194.47 pp) × 27.18 × 11.04
M: 2 Crossley-Pielstick 16 PC2 V400 diesels; 1 prop; 16,000 bhp
Electric: 1,000 kw (2 × 500-kw diesel sets) **Range:** 16,000/16.5
Fuel: 2,272 tons heavy oil **Crew:** 9 officers, 14 unlicensed

Remarks: 20,751 grt/37,874 dwt. Served on charter to the navy from 1974 to 1985. Purchased 5-6-87 from Falcon Carriers for $10.9 million. Assigned to the Beaumont, Texas, reserve fleet on 20-day recall.
Hull systems: Cargo: 303,000 bbl (49,213 m^3) in 18 tanks.

♦ 2 Chesapeake-class tankers [WAOT]
Bldr: Bethlehem SY, Sparrows Point, Md.

	In serv.	Acquired	To RRF
(T-AOT 5084) Chesapeake (ex-*Hess Voyager*)	1964	20-7-91	20-7-91
(T-AOT 5075) Petersburg (ex-*Sinclair Texas,* ex-*Charles Kurz,* ex-*Keystone*)	1963	1-8-91	1-8-94

Chesapeake (T-AOT 5084)—at Diego Garcia, with full fuel load; note the five LCM(6) landing craft modified as push-tugs stowed abreast on deck, forward of the OPDS barge Joe Straczek, 11-01

D: *Chesapeake:* approx. 65,000 tons (fl); *Petersburg:* 48,993 tons (fl)
S: 15.0–15.5 kts **Dim:** 224.44 (214.89 pp) × 31.22 × 12.13
M: 2 sets Bethlehem geared steam turbines; 1 prop; 15,000 shp

U.S. MARITIME ADMINISTRATION READY RESERVE FORCE
(continued)

Petersburg (T-AOT 5075)—in light condition; note the OPDS barge stowed on an inclined skid to permit its launch to port and the crane installed to handle the five LCM(6) push-tugs Brian Morrison, 8-00

Boilers: 2 . . . **Electric:** 1,200 (*Chesapeake:* 1,800) kw
Range: . . ./. . . **Fuel:** 1,420 tons fuel oil, 80 tons diesel **Crew:** . . .

Remarks: *Chesapeake:* 27,015 grt/50,826 dwt; *Petersburg:* 27,469 grt/50,072 dwt. *Petersburg* was acquired 11-1-88 but her upgrading to RRF was delayed by funding and engineering problems. *Chesapeake* was acquired in 1989 for conversion as the third ship with the Offshore Petroleum Distribution System (OPDS; see note below for description). *Petersburg* also received the OPDS. As of 1-02, *Chesapeake* was active with Maritime Prepositioning Squadron 2 (MPS-2) at Diego Garcia and *Petersburg* with MPS-3 at Saipan.
Hull systems: Cargo volume: *Petersburg:* 61,730 m^3 (25 tanks); *Chesapeake:* 56,146 m^3 (21 tanks). A 53-metric-ton-capacity crane, platforms for boats, and numerous large hose reels were added to both as part of the OPDS program. Both carry an OPDS utility boat to maneuver the OPDS barge.

Note: For transportation aboard RRF tankers, six Offshore Petroleum Discharge Systems (OPDS) were procured. The prototype, SALM I, was transferred to the U.S. Virgin Islands for use as a mooring pontoon in 3-01. *American Osprey* had the first production set, consisting of a skid launching system for a 45.7 × 16.5–m barge, a four-point mooring system, and hydraulic-powered reels for 6,400 m of 152-mm fuel hose to act as an offshore fuel transfer point to serve beachheads. A 53-metric-ton-capacity crane and boat stowage were also added on the main deck. *Petersburg* and *Chesapeake* were equipped next. The fifth and sixth sets, funded under FY 91 and 92, were delivered in 6-91 and 10-92 by Orange Shipbuilding, Orange, Texas. To act as towboats for the OPDS barges, 15 LCM(6) landing craft were converted and renumbered as utility boats: 56UB775, 779, 7710, 7717, 7719, 784, 785, 789, 7813, 7821, 7841–7843, 8601, and 8602.

♦ 1 Mount Washington–class tanker [WAOT]
Bldr: Bethlehem SY, Quincy, Mass.

	In serv.	Acquired	To RRF
(T-AOT 5076) Mount Washington	1963	30-9-89	30-10-89

D: approx. 65,800 tons (fl) **S:** 17.5 kts
Dim: 224.44 (215.50 pp) × 31.17 × 12.26
M: 2 sets Bethlehem geared steam turbines; 1 prop; 21,500 shp
Boilers: 2 Foster-Wheeler **Electric:** 1,500 kw (2 × 750 kw)
Range: . . ./. . . **Fuel:** 4,356 tons **Crew:** . . .

Remarks: 27,412 grt/47,751 dwt. Purchased 30-9-89. Is in layberth at Houston, Texas, on five-day recall. Converted to OPDS-5 (Offshore Petroleum Distribution Ship) with FY 93 funding.
Disposals: Sister *Mount Vernon* (ex-*Mount Vernon Victory*), which joined the RRF 31-3-90, was reassigned to the NDRF in early FY 95 and is berthed at Beaumont, Texas.
Hull systems: Has 31 cargo tanks, with 59,494 m^3 total cargo capacity.

♦ 1 Mission Buenaventura–class tanker [WAOT]
Bldr: Bethlehem SY, Sparrows Point, Md. (In serv. 1968)

	To RRF
(T-AOT 1012) Mission Buenaventura (ex-*Spirit of Liberty*)	22-10-87

D: 46,243 tons (fl) **S:** 16.5 kts **Dim:** 201.23 (192.03 pp) × 27.49 × 11.67
M: 2 sets G.E. geared steam turbines; 1 prop; 15,000 shp
Boilers: 2 Foster-Wheeler **Electric:** 2,000 kw tot.
Range: 12,000/16.5 **Fuel:** 2,869 tons **Crew:** 9 officers, 17 unlicensed

Remarks: 20,947 grt/38,851 dwt. Purchased 5-6-87 from Keystone Shipping for $9.0 million and delivered to the RRF 9-10-87. Assigned to the Beaumont, Texas, RRF facility, on 20-day recall.
Hull systems: Cargo: 326,000 bbl (53,186 m^3) in 16 tanks.

♦ 1 American Osprey–class tanker [WAOT]
Bldr: Bethlehem SY, Sparrows Point, Md.

	In serv.	To RRF
(T-AOT 5075) American Osprey (ex-*Gulf Prince*)	1958	26-6-87

American Osprey (T-AOT 5075)—with OPDS barge but without push-tugs *Ships of the World,* 1992

D: 44,840 tons (fl) **S:** 17 kts **Dim:** 201.5 × 27.4 × 11.0
Electronics: Radar: 2 . . . nav.
M: 2 sets Bethlehem geared steam turbines; 1 prop; 15,000 shp
Boilers: 2 Foster-Wheeler
Range: 14,000/17 **Fuel:** 2,871 tons **Crew:** 11 officers, 26 unlicensed

Remarks: 20,143 grt/34,723 dwt. Cargo: 268,000 bbl. Taken from the NDRF and contracted to Alabama Drydock 30-10-87 for conversion and installation of an OPDS (Offshore Petroleum Discharge System) barge skid launching system, four-point mooring equipment, and hydraulic-powered reels for 6,400 m of 152-mm fuel piping to act as an offshore fuel transfer point to serve beachheads. Conversion was completed in 7-88. The anchor barge is stowed on slip-skids launching to port. Was stored at Beaumont, Texas, until reactivated 1991 to become part of the Maritime Prepositioning Squadron 2 at Diego Garcia; was again deactivated to storage at Beaumont, Texas, 27-12-98.

Disposal note: The OPDS-equipped T5-2-12A *Potomac* (T-AOT 181; ex-*Shenandoah;* ex-*Potomac,* T-AO 150) was deactivated 30-9-92. Her ownership was transferred to MARAD during 11-01, and the ship was downrated from the RRF to the NDRF, where she is being retained as being "militarily useful."

♦ 2 Alatna-class (T1-MET-24a type) small transport tankers [WAOT]
Bldr: Bethlehem Steel SY, Staten Island, N.Y.

	L	In serv.	To RRF
T-AOG 81 Alatna	6-9-56	7-57	22-1-85
T-AOG 82 Chattahoochee	4-12-56	22-10-57	22-1-85

Alatna (T-AOG 81) Takatoshi Okano, 10-96

D: 5,720 tons (fl) **S:** 12 kts **Dim:** 92.00 (87.20 pp) × 18.57 × 6.87
Electronics: Radar: 2 . . . nav.
M: 4 Alco 16-cyl. diesels, 4 generator sets, Westinghouse motors; 2 props; 4,000 shp
Electric: 700 kw tot. (2 × 300-kw, 1 × 100-kw diesel-driven sets)
Range: 5,760/10 **Fuel:** 562 tons **Crew:** 9 officers, 15 unlicensed

Remarks: 3,459 grt/5,012 dwt. Have icebreaker-type hulls, as they were originally intended as Arctic/Antarctic aviation support ships. Both were placed in the NDRF 8-8-72. Reacquired by the MSC on 10-5-79 and 24-5-79, respectively, they were reactivated and re-engined to replace two *Nodaway*-class tankers on 3-2-82 and 11-1-82, respectively, and then again laid up in Japan on 22-1-85 and transferred to the RRF. Were scheduled to be downgraded to the NDRF in 1994 and again in 1997 but are now to be retained in RRF for several more years. Ownership was transferred from the navy to MARAD during 11-01. Are maintained in layberth at Tsuneishi, Japan, maintained by Crowley Marine Services. Cargo: 30,000 bbl (15,659 m^3) light petroleum products in 16 tanks.

♦ 1 Tonti-class (T1-M-BT2 type) small transport tanker [WAOT]
Bldr: Todd-Houston SY, Houston, Texas

	Laid down	L	In serv.	To RRF
T-AOG 78 Nodaway (ex-*Belridge,* ex-*Tarcoola*)	19-2-42	15-5-45	11-9-50	30-9-85

Nodaway (T-AOG 78)—at right, in board the *Chattahoochee* (T-AOG 82) Takatoshi Okano, 10-96

D: 2,060 tons light (5,984 fl) **S:** 10 kts **Dim:** 99.10 (94.18 pp) × 14.69 × 5.90
M: 2 Nordberg diesels; 1 prop; 1,400 bhp **Electric:** 515 kw tot.
Range: 5,500/10 **Fuel:** 154 tons **Crew:** 9 officers, 15 unlicensed

U.S. MARITIME ADMINISTRATION READY RESERVE FORCE
(continued)

Remarks: 3,160 grt/3,933 dwt. Deactivated by the MSC 22-7-84. Maintained in Japan. Cargo: 31,284 bbl of light fuels (diesel, JP-5, gasoline). Was to have been downgraded to NDRF in 1994 and again in 1997 but will now be retained in the RRF for several more years in layberth at Tsuneishi, Japan, maintained by Crowley Marine Services. Ownership was transferred from the navy to MARAD during 11-01.

♦ 2 ex-U.S. Navy Maury-class troopships [WAP]
Bldr: Bethlehem Shipyard, Sparrows Pt., Md.

	Laid down	L	In serv.	To RRF
Golden Bear (ex-*Maury,* T-AGS 39)	29-7-86	4-9-87	31-3-89	5-4-99
State of Maine (ex-*Tanner,* T-AGS 40)	22-10-86	28-2-89	31-9-90	. . .

Golden Bear George R. Schneider, 8-00

State of Maine H&L Van Ginderen, 6-99

D: 8,810 tons light (15,821 fl) **S:** 21 kts (20 sust.)
Dim: 152.35 (142.04 pp; 145.09 wl) × 21.95 × 9.33
Electronics: Radar: 2 . . . nav.
M: 2 diesels; 1 CP prop; 25,000 bhp
Electric: 2,700 kw tot. (3 × 900-kw diesel sets)
Range: 17,800/20 **Fuel:** 3,200 tons **Crew:** . . . tot. + 250 troop berths

Remarks: 12,517 grt/3,755 nrt. *Golden Bear* has 250 berths available for troop transportation and *State of Maine* 2,888. Can carry up to 7,339 tons of seawater ballast. The original diesel engines have been replaced due to the unavailability of spares. Have no cargo-handling equipment and would be of little use for sealift duties. Neither has been assigned an administrative number.

♦ 1 Maritime Administration C4-S-66a troopship [WAP]
Bldr: Avondale SY, Westwego, La.

	L	In serv.	To RRF
(T-AP 1003) Enterprise (ex-*Cape Bon,* ex-*Velma Lykes*)	16-7-65	1-67	26-6-85

Enterprise (T-AP 1003)—as *Cape Bon,* prior to conversion Peter Voss, 3-91

D: 7,178 tons light (20,986 fl) **S:** 21 kts (20 sust.)
Dim: 164.60 (156.95 pp) × 23.22 × 3.86 (light; 9.63 max. loaded)
Electronics: Radar: . . .
M: 2 sets de Laval or Westinghouse geared steam turbines; 1 prop; 15,500 shp
Boilers: 2 Foster-Wheeler; 49 kg/cm² **Electric:** 1,500 kw (2 × 750 kw)
Range: 13,660/20 **Fuel:** 2,503 tons
Crew: 12 officers, 26 unlicensed (accomm. for 600 tot.)

Remarks: Former break-bulk cargo ship, purchased from Lykes Brothers Lines in 1-85. Was selected to replace the former *Patriot State* as training ship for the Massachusetts Maritime Academy late in 1999 but was returned to the NDRF 1-10-00 and briefly used as a training platform by the 11th Marine Expeditionary Force in the James River Reserve Fleet, Va. Began conversion as a "troop ship" 14-1-01 at Bender Shipbuilding & Repair for $24.4 million to qualify for RRF subsidy; was expected to return to service early in 2002, based at Buzzards Bay, Mass. The ship is on 10-day recall to serve as a troop transport. The name duplicates that of navy carrier CVN 65.
Hull systems: Diesel generator capacity has been increased, the auxiliary machinery room has been rebuilt as a training facility, and galley and stores facilities have been expanded. A new auxiliary machinery compartment houses a Wärtsilä 8L20 diesel-powered generator set that is also employed to simulate a diesel prime mover for training purposes.

♦ 1 Maritime Administration S5-S-MA1ua troopship [WAP]
Bldr: Newport News SB & DD, Newport News, Va.

	Laid down	L	In serv.	To RRF
(T-AP 1001) Empire State (ex-*Cape Junction,* ex-*Mormactide,* ex-*Oregon*)	1-3-61	16-9-61	19-4-62	20-11-89

Empire State (T-AP 1001) Alexander George, 7-00

D: 22,629 tons (fl) **S:** 20 kts **Dim:** 172.22 (161.09) × 23.22 × 9.63
M: 2 sets G.E. geared steam turbines; 1 prop; 17,500 shp
Boilers: 2 Foster-Wheeler **Electric:** 1,500 kw tot.
Range: . . ./. . . **Fuel:** 3,538 tons
Crew: 107 tot. + 684 cadets or 791 troops

Remarks: 9,298 grt/12,691 dwt (prior to conversion). Built as a MARAD C4-S-1u cargo vessel. Acquired 14-10-88 from the NDRF and converted by Bay Shipbuilding, Wis., as the New York State Maritime Academy training ship in place of *Empire State V* (ex-*Barrett,* AP 196). Was used in 1994 to return U.S. troops from Somalia, using an OMI Corp. contract crew and 14 New York State Maritime Academy instructors. Is administratively assigned to the James River fleet but berthed at Fort Schuyler, N.Y., fully operational. Was on loan to Massachusetts Maritime Academy from late 2000 to mid-2001. Four sisters are in the RRF as cargo ships.
Hull systems: Originally had six holds and one 60-ton, 10 20-ton, two 10-ton, and 10 5-ton derricks, but some facilities have converted for berthing and classrooms. Has 791 berths available for passengers.

♦ 1 U.S. Navy Chauvenet-class troopship [WAP]
Bldr: Upper Clyde Shipbuilding, Glasgow, Scotland

	Laid down	L	In serv.
Texas Clipper II (ex-*Chauvenet,* T-AGS 29)	24-5-67	13-5-68	13-11-70

D: 3,540 tons (4,830 fl) **S:** 15 kts **Dim:** 119.8 (101.8 pp) × 16.5 × 5.1
M: 2 Alco diesels, 1 Westinghouse electric motor; 1 CP prop; 3,600 shp
Electric: 1,500 kw tot. **Range:** 9,300/14; 15,000/12 **Fuel:** 824 tons
Endurance: 90 days **Crew:** approx. 60 tot. + . . . cadets or 250 troops

Remarks: Has some 250 berths available for troops and no cargo-handling equipment or cargo holds. Is typed by MARAD as an S3-M-MA-153a merchant ship. Operated by Texas A&M University and berthed at Galveston, Texas. Sister *Harkness* (T-AGS 32) was briefly activated from the NDRF to act as an alongside training ship for the Massachusetts Maritime Academy but was returned to storage on 6-6-01.

Note: The five state maritime academy training ships are in the RRF fleet primarily as means of obtaining federal funding for their operation and maintenance. They would have almost no value as transports if mobilized, except possibly to transfer ambulatory patients to the U.S.A.

UNITED STATES COAST GUARD

The Revenue Marine, which was created in 1790, became the U.S. Coast Guard on 28-1-1915 by act of Congress. On 1-4-67, the Coast Guard was transferred from the Department of the Treasury to the Department of Transportation (DoT). The act that created the service calls for it to operate in time of crisis under the control of the navy. In a 1995 reorganization, the Coast Guard was given as its principal responsibilities maritime law enforcement, maritime safety, marine environmental protection, and national security. At the end of 2001, consideration was being given to combining the Coast Guard with the U.S. Customs Service and the U.S. Border Patrol to provide better coordination of U.S. internal security efforts.

Personnel (31-10-01): 36,310 active uniformed (5,567 officers, 875 USCG Academy cadets, and 40 Officer's Candidate School, 166 Public Health Service officers, 1,419 warrant officers, 21,569 petty officers, 5,833 nonrated, and 841 recruits), 5,998 selected reserves (683 officers, 115 chief warrant officers, 5,200 enlisted), 4,861 inactive Ready Reserve (142 officers, 29 chief warrant officers, 4,690 enlisted), and 5,715 civilians

Organization: The Coast Guard is divided into two main areas, one for the Pacific and one for the Atlantic. It is further divided into 10 Coast Guard Districts in order to fulfill its responsibilities along the U.S. coastline (more than 10,000 n.m., not including Hawaii).

A four-star admiral heads the Coast Guard. He is appointed for four years and is assisted by a general staff. The commandant reports to the secretary of transportation.

The names of commissioned Coast Guard ships are preceded by "USCGC" (United States Coast Guard Cutter). Cutters and patrol craft are painted white; icebreakers have red hulls, buoy tenders and tugs, black hulls. All ships and craft carry diagonal international orange (with thin white and blue) stripes and the USCG shield on the hull.

UNITED STATES COAST GUARD *(continued)*

Coast Guard Aviation: Some 900 officers and 3,000 enlisted are involved. Atlantic bases are at Cape Cod, Mass.; Cape May, N.J.; Elizabeth City, N.C.; Savannah, Ga.; Miami; and Borinquen, P.R. Gulf of Mexico bases are at Clearwater, Fla.; Mobile, Ala.; New Orleans; and Houston and Corpus Christi, Texas. Great Lakes bases are at Chicago and Detroit and Traverse City, Mich. Pacific bases are at Port Angeles, Wash.; Astoria and North Bend, Ore.; Humboldt Bay, Sacramento, San Francisco, Los Angeles, and San Diego, Calif.; and Barbers Point, Hawaii. Alaska bases are at Sitka and Kodiak. Two VIP transports are kept at Washington, D.C. Aircraft are primarily white in color, but the Dolphin and Mako helicopters are painted orange. Under the Deepwater Capability Replacement Project initiated in 2-98, most existing aircraft are to be upgraded or replaced.

Port Security Units (PSU): There are six deployable PSUs and one training detachment. PSUs are composed of five active duty personnel and 112 selected reservists and are each equipped with six transportable 25-ft. Boston Whaler patrol launches, powered by two 75-bhp outboards each. A PSU can be deployed within 96 hours to provide continual port security services worldwide. PSU 305 is based at Ft. Eustis, Va.; PSU 307 at St. Petersburg, Fla.; PSU 308 at Gulfport, Miss.; PSU 309 at Port Clinton, Ohio; PSU 311 at Long Beach, Calif.; and PSU 313 at Seattle. The Training Detachment (TRADET) is at Camp Lejeune, N.C.

PRINCIPAL U.S. COAST GUARD AIRCRAFT

♦ 23 HC-130H and 4 HC-130H-7 Hercules SAR/cargo/personnel transports
Mfr: Lockheed-Georgia, Marietta, Ga.

HC-130H Hercules Lockheed Martin

Wingspan: 40.42 m **Length:** 29.80 m **Height:** 11.66 m
Weight: 35,050 kg empty/49,780 kg loaded/70,300 kg max.
Speed: 302 kts max./287 kts cruise
Engines: 4 Allison T56-A-15 turboprops; 4,508 shp each (4,061 sust.)
Ceiling: 25,000 ft. **Endurance:** 17 hr max.
Range: 3,734 n.m. ferry; 2,517 n.m. with max. payload at 5,000 ft.
Fuel: 36,416 liters (10,599 in external tanks)

Remarks: Most HC-130Hs have APS-125 radars, but those based at Clearwater have APS-137 radars. The four HC-130H-7s, all at Sacramento, Calif., have FLIR turrets. Two HC-130Hs have side-looking radars for ice-patrol duties. There were 26 in regular service during 2001, including those based at Elizabeth City (4), Clearwater (5), Kodiak (6), Sacramento (4), and Barbers Point (3). Cabin volume is 128 m^3 (12.5-m length, 3.0-m width, 2.7-m height). Three older HC-130H aircraft based at Borinquen were retired at the end of FY 01.

Note: Six HC-130J SAR transports were ordered for the Coast Guard during 1-01.

♦ 7 HU-25A and 1 HU-25D SAR, 7 HU-25B oil-spill detection, 2 HU-25C+ drug intercept Guardian
Mfr: Dassault Aviation, Vaucresson, France

HU-25A Guardian SAR aircraft USCG

Wingspan: 16.30 m **Length:** 17.15 m **Height:** 5.32 m
Weight: 8,618 kg empty/9,476 kg loaded/14,515 kg max.
Speed: 461 kts max./150 kts search
Engines: 2 Garrett AiResearch ATF3-6-2C turbofans; 2,512 kg thrust each
Ceiling: 40,000 ft. **Range:** 2,250 n.m. in SAR mode **Crew:** 5 tot.

Remarks: Were initially unsuccessful, not meeting performance specifications. Eighteen of the 25 remaining HU-25A search-and-rescue variants of the design were placed in storage during 1996, with the HU-25Bs subsequently being used primarily for SAR duties; 13 more were to be deactivated at the end of FY 01, including some aircraft recently modernized.

The HU-25B has the APS-127 radar; APG-65 is carried by the drug-hunting HU-25C. Conversion of nine HU-25As to HU-25B began 1-4-87; they have SLAR (Side-Looking Airborne Radar), an IR/ultraviolet line-scanner, a KS-87B aerial camera, and an active-gated television camera and are used for detection of oil spills, mapping, and on the International Ice Patrol. Crew includes two pilots, a surveillance systems operator, and two search crew; can also carry four stretchers. Fifteen HU-25A and -25C aircraft are being upgraded with the Wescam 16D FLIR, Telephonics APS-143 synthetic aperture radar (nine aircraft only), and a new integrated workstation under an 18-4-00 contract with California Microwave Systems; the first aircraft was to redeliver in 3-01 and the others at 45- to 90-day intervals, with the upgraded HU-25As becoming HU-25Ds and the HU-25Cs becoming HU-25C+.

♦ 46 HH-60J Jayhawk search-and-rescue helicopters
Mfr: Sikorsky Aircraft Div., United Technologies, Stratford, Conn.

HH-60J Jayhawk Sikorsky

Rotor diameter: 16.36 m **Length:** 19.76 m (15.24 fuselage)
Height: 5.23 m **Weight:** 9,435 kg max.
Speed: 150 kts max./140 kts cruise
Engines: 2 G.E. T700-GE-401 turboshafts; 1,723 shp max./1,543 shp sust. each
Range: 700 n.m. radius with 3.5 hr on station; 300 n.m. radius with 45 min on station

Remarks: First flight 8-8-89. Based at Cape Cod, Traverse City, Elizabeth City, Mobile, San Francisco, and Sitka. One was lost at sea in an accident 8-7-97. All have the Bendix RDR-1300C search radar and can carry six rescuees in addition to the crew of four.

♦ 74 HH-65A Dolphin search-and-rescue helicopters
Mfr: Aérospatiale SNI, Helicopter Div., Marignane, France

HH-65A Dolphin—aboard *Healy* (WAGB 20) Jim Sanderson, 7-01

Rotor diameter: 11.94 m **Length:** 13.68 m (over rotor)
Height: 3.99 m **Weight:** 2,717 kg empty/4,049 kg max.
Speed: 150 kts max./139 kts cruise/128 kts search
Engines: 2 Avco-Lycoming LTS 101-750B2 turboshafts; 680 shp each (646 sust.)
Ceiling: 7,150 ft. **Range:** 400 n.m. max. **Endurance:** 3.8 hr mission

Remarks: Entered service 19-11-84, with a total of 93 procured, all assembled in Texas; the last unit was delivered 24-4-89. Are badly underpowered and cannot lift their full fuel load with a crew of four and all equipment aboard, but their engines are being increased by 23% in power (to 836 shp) under a $40 million effort begun in 2-00. Carry a crew of two pilots, an aircrew/hoist-operator, and up to six passengers. Are based at Cape May, Savannah, Borinquen, Miami, Mobile, Detroit, Chicago, New Orleans, Houston, Corpus Christi, Kodiak, Port Angeles, Astoria, North Bend, Humboldt Bay, Los Angeles, San Diego, and Barbers Point. Three were retired at the end of FY 01.

♦ 8 MH-68A Mako Shark armed helicopters
Mfr: Augusta Westland, Italy

Rotor diameter: 11.0 m **Length:** 13.03 m (max. over rotors)
Height: 3.5 m **Weight:** 1,570 kg empty/2,850 kg max. takeoff
Speed: 168 kts max./156 kts cruise
Engines: 2 Pratt & Whitney 206C turboshafts; 670.5 shp each
Ceiling: 20,000 ft. **Range:** 502 n.m. at 5,000 ft. **Endurance:** 5 hr max.

Remarks: Selected after trials during 4-00 with two leased A-109 Power light helicopters. The MH-68A is an A-109E Power modified for USCG requirements, including fitting a FLIR. All are operated by Helicopter Interdiction Squadron 10 (HITRON-10), Jacksonville, Fla. The first two were delivered in 9-00. Are armed with an M240 machinegun and a 12.7-mm Robar sniping rifle.

PRINCIPAL U.S. COAST GUARD AIRCRAFT *(continued)*

Three MH-68A Mako Shark Dana Ward/USCG

Note: Other aircraft in service include one Grumman Gulfstream-I turboprop VIP transport and one Grumman C-20B Gulfstream-IV jet VIP transport. The Gulfstream-I was acquired in 11-01 to replace the grounded USCG VC-4A Gulfstream, and a single C-37A Gulfstream-V turbofan VIP transport was ordered during 12-00 for delivery early in 2002 to replace the C-20B Gulfstream-IV. The RU-38A surveillance aircraft program was terminated during 2000.

The Coast Guard is considering the procurement of the Bell Helicopters HV-609, a commercial variant of the original XV-15 experimental tilt-rotor aircraft, for use in offshore operations; the XV-15 was found to be fully compatible with a standard WMEC flight deck during trials in 1999.

HIGH-ENDURANCE CUTTERS [WFF]

♦ 0 (+ . . .) Deepwater Project new-construction

Bldr: . . .

D: 3,000–4,000 tons (fl) **S:** . . . kts **Dim:** 107.0 × . . . × 5.2–5.5
A: 1 76-mm 62-cal. Mk 75 DP; 1 20-mm Mk 15 Mod. 3 Phalanx CIWS; 1 . . . helicopter
Electronics: . . .
M: . . .
Range: . . ./. . . **Crew:** up to 80 tot.

Remarks: The "Deepwater Capability Replacement Program" was initiated in 2-98 as a 10-year, $8 billion effort to replace the existing *Hamilton-*, Famous-, and *Reliance*-class cutters. The size listed above is considered optimum. Selection of a lead contractor has been delayed to summer 2002, but the first ship (perhaps overoptimistically) is planned to enter service in 2006. The three eligible industry teams are lead by Avondale Shipyards (a division of Northrop Grumman Ship Systems), Lockheed Martin Naval Electronics and Surveillance Systems, and Science Applications International Corp. (SAIC), and the winner was to be announced during 4-02. The design will also be marketed to foreign navies and coast guards. Some $320 million in developmental funding was approved under the FY 02 budget, and the yearly average acquisition cost during the program will be about $535 million. The ships will have weight and space allocation for an ASW capability and will be equipped with EW systems. All ships will have a Link 11 capability.

♦ 12 Hamilton class (378-foot class) Bldr: Avondale SY, Westwego, La.

	Laid down	L	In serv.	Based at
WHEC 715 Hamilton	23-11-65	18-12-65	20-2-67	San Diego
WHEC 716 Dallas	7-2-66	1-10-66	1-10-67	Charleston, S.C.
WHEC 717 Mellon	25-7-66	11-2-67	22-12-67	Seattle
WHEC 718 Chase	15-10-66	20-5-67	1-3-68	San Diego
WHEC 719 Boutwell	12-12-66	17-6-67	14-6-68	Alameda, Calif.
WHEC 720 Sherman	13-2-67	23-9-67	23-8-68	Alameda, Calif.
WHEC 721 Gallatin	17-4-67	18-11-67	20-12-68	Charleston, S.C.
WHEC 722 Morgenthau	17-7-67	10-2-68	14-2-69	Alameda, Calif.
WHEC 723 Rush	23-10-67	16-11-68	3-7-69	Honolulu
WHEC 724 Munro	18-2-70	5-12-70	10-9-71	Alameda, Calif.
WHEC 725 Jarvis	9-9-70	24-4-71	30-12-71	Honolulu
WHEC 726 Midgett	5-4-71	4-9-71	17-3-72	Seattle

D: 2,716 tons (3,050 fl) **S:** 29 kts (28.4 postmodernization)
Dim: 115.37 (106.68 pp) × 13.06 × 4.27 (6.2 over sonar)
A: provision for up to 8 RGM-84A Harpoon SSM—fitted with: 1 76-mm 62-cal. Mk 75 DP; 1 20-mm Mk 15 CIWS; 2 single 25-mm 87-cal. Mk 88 Bushmaster low-angle guns; 1 HH-65 Dolphin helicopter

Mellon (WHEC 717) H&L Van Ginderen, 2-00

Munro (WHEC 724) W. Michael Young, 3-00

Morgenthau (WHEC 722)—with telescoping hangar extended George R. Schneider, 10-00

Electronics:
Radar: 2 Raytheon SPS-64(V)6 nav.; 1 Lockheed SPS-40B air search; 1 Sperry Mk 92 Mod. 1 f.c.
Sonar: removed
TACAN: URN-25
EW: WLR-1C intercept; WLR-3 intercept; Mk 36 SRBOC decoy syst. (2 6-round Mk 137 RL)

M: CODOG: 2 Fairbanks-Morse 38TD8⅛, 12-cyl. diesels (3,500 bhp each); 2 Pratt & Whitney FT4-A6 gas turbines (18,000 shp each); 2 CP props; 36,000 shp—350-shp retractable bow-thruster
Electric: 1,500 kw tot.
Range: 2,400/29, 9,600/19 (gas turbines); 14,000/11 (diesel)
Fuel: 800 tons **Endurance:** 45 days **Crew:** 21 officers, 156 enlisted

Remarks: Named after early secretaries of the treasury and Coast Guard heroes. Thirty-six were planned, but only 12 were built. The entire class has received a midlife modernization—WHEC 715, 716, 718, and 721 by Bath Iron Works, Maine, and the others by Todd SY, Seattle—as follows:

WHEC 715	10-85 to 15-11-88	WHEC 721	3-90 to 26-1-92
WHEC 716	11-86 to 12-89	WHEC 722	11-11-89 to 12-91
WHEC 717	10-85 to 3-6-89	WHEC 723	7-89 to 9-91
WHEC 718	7-89 to 5-3-91	WHEC 724	12-86 to 11-11-89
WHEC 719	3-3-89 to 4-91	WHEC 725	3-91 to 11-12-92
WHEC 720	14-5-86 to 2-90	WHEC 726	9-90 to 31-3-92

They are planned to be retired between 2002 and 2008 but will probably serve longer, as replacements are as yet unavailable.

Hull systems: Welded-steel hull; aluminum superstructure. Living spaces are air-conditioned. Have laboratories for weather and oceanographic research. WHEC 716–723 have synchronizing clutches; the final three have synchro-self-shifting (SSS) clutches. WHEC 717, 722, and 725 have rudder roll-stabilization systems. During modernization, the hangars were reactivated and a telescoping section was added; all have Fairey Hydraulics Talon helicopter landing systems. The helicopter platform measures 26.82 × 12.20 m. Are equipped with a 6.86-m Zodiac Hurricane 630 rigid inflatable boat with a Volvo Penta outdrive diesel engine; the boats have a GPS receiver and an echo sounder and can carry 11 personnel. WHEC 725 was slightly damaged 22-12-01 when a commercial dry dock collapsed and sank beneath her at Honolulu.

Combat systems: Modernizations included replacing the 127-mm gun and Mk 56 gunfire-control system with a 76-mm Mk 75 (OTOBreda Compact) gun and Mk 92 Mod. 1 radar gunfire-control system, replacing the SPS-29D radar with SPS-40B, and adding one Mk 15 Phalanx CIWS, a URN-25 TACAN, and satellite and secure

COAST GUARD HIGH-ENDURANCE CUTTERS [WFF] *(continued)*

Chase (WHEC 718) Kurt Greiner/SeaPhoto, 10-00

communications gear. Navigational equipment was updated through the addition of RAYCAS (Raytheon Collision-Avoidance System) and an HP-9020 computer. All were given the capability to carry Harpoon missiles, but only five ships actually have carried the weapon and none had it as of 2001. Planned improvements *not* carried out included the replacement of the WLR-1 EW system with SLQ-32(V)1, addition of the SLQ-25 Nixie towed torpedo decoy system, and provision to carry the since-retired LAMPS-I ASW helicopter. The decision was made in 7-92 to remove the SQS-38 hull-mounted sonar, two sets Mk 32 Mod. 7 ASW torpedo tubes, Mk 109 underwater fire-control system, and SQR-17A(V)1 sonobuoy analyzers. All are now fitted with WSC-3 UHF SATCOM terminals.

MEDIUM-ENDURANCE CUTTERS [WPS]

♦ 13 Famous class (270-foot class)

Bldrs: WMEC 901–904: Tacoma Boatbuilding, Tacoma, Wash.; WMEC 905–913: Robert E. Derecktor, Middletown, R.I.

	Laid down	L	In serv.	Based at
WMEC 901 Bear	23-8-79	25-9-80	4-2-83	Portsmouth, Va.
WMEC 902 Tampa	2-4-80	19-3-81	16-3-84	Portsmouth, Va.
WMEC 903 Harriet Lane	15-10-80	6-2-82	20-9-84	Portsmouth, Va.
WMEC 904 Northland	9-4-81	7-5-82	17-12-84	Portsmouth, Va.
WMEC 905 Spencer (ex-*Seneca*)	26-6-82	16-6-84	28-6-86	Boston
WMEC 906 Seneca (ex-*Pickering*)	16-9-82	16-6-84	4-5-87	Boston
WMEC 907 Escanaba	1-4-83	24-8-85	27-8-87	Boston
WMEC 908 Tahoma (ex-*Legare*)	28-6-83	24-8-85	6-4-88	New Bedford, Mass.
WMEC 909 Campbell (ex-*Argus*)	10-8-84	30-8-86	19-8-88	New Bedford, Mass.
WMEC 910 Thetis (ex-*Tahoma*)	24-8-84	30-8-86	30-6-89	Key West, Fla.
WMEC 911 Forward (ex-*Erie*)	11-7-86	18-8-87	4-8-90	Portsmouth, Va.
WMEC 912 Legare (ex-*McCulloch*)	11-7-86	18-8-87	4-8-90	Portsmouth, Va.
WMEC 913 Mohawk (ex-*Ewing*)	18-6-87	18-5-88	20-3-90	Key West, Fla.

D: 1,200 tons light (1,780 fl) **S:** 19.5 kts **Dim:** 82.3 (77.7 wl) × 11.58 × 4.11
A: 1 76-mm 62-cal. Mk 75 DP; 2 single 12.7-mm mg; 1 HH-65 Dolphin helicopter
Electronics:
Radar: 1 Raytheon SPS-64(V)1 nav.; 1 Raytheon SPS-64(V)6 nav.; 1 Sperry Mk 92 Mod. 1 f.c.
TACAN: URN-25
EW: Raytheon SLQ-32(V)2 intercept; Mk 36 SRBOC decoy syst. (2 6-round Mk 137 RL)
M: 2 Alco Model 18V-251E, 18-cyl. diesels; 2 Escher-Wyss CP props; 7,200 bhp
Electric: 1,350 kw (3 × 475-kw Kato sets, Caterpillar D398 diesels driving)
Range: 3,850/19.5; 6,370/15; 10,250/12 **Endurance:** 14 days
Crew: 11 officers, 89 enlisted + 16 aircrew

Remarks: Two were authorized in FY 77, two in FY 78, two in FY 79, three in FY 80, one in FY 81, and three in FY 82. Officially styled the "Famous" class because all are named for well-known earlier cutters. The program suffered numerous delays; the first ship was to have completed 31-12-80, and WMEC 913 entered active service over three years late. WMEC 905–913 were originally ordered from Tacoma Boat in 8-80, but a lawsuit caused reassignment to Derecktor 17-1-81. Were originally intended to be able to act as ASW escorts in wartime—a mission no longer foreseen. Planned to be retired between 2011 and 2020. WMEC 913 was under conversion to carry two interceptor launches at the U.S. Coast Guard Yard, Curtis Bay, Md., during 2001, but the program was then canceled.

Bear (WMEC 901) Takatoshi Okano, 4-01

Harriet Lane (WMEC 903) A. D. Baker III, 6-00

Campbell (WMEC 909) Findler & Winter, 6-00

COAST GUARD MEDIUM-ENDURANCE CUTTERS [WPS]
(continued)

Legare (WMEC 912)—with telescoping hangar extended Leo Dirkx, 6-01

Hull systems: The COMDAC computerized control system on this class has given considerable difficulty. They are reportedly overloaded and very uncomfortable ships in a seaway. Have accommodations for up to 17 officers and 123 enlisted. Have a telescoping helicopter hangar and provision for later installation of fin stabilization. By 2004, all are to have received Sperry Mk 39 Mod. 3A ring-laser gyros in place of the original Mk 29 gyros.
Combat systems: Have no hull-mounted sonar or onboard ASW weapons. Space and weight are reserved for Mk 15 CIWS 20-mm gatling AA gun and two quadruple Harpoon missile-launch canisters, but they are very unlikely ever to have them installed. The WSC-3 UHF SATCOM system is carried. Have six light weapons mounting positions capable of accepting 12.7-mm mg or 40-mm Mk 19 grenade launchers.

♦ 1 U.S. Navy Edenton class
Bldr: Brooke Marine, Lowestoft, U.K.

	Laid down	L	In serv.	Based at
WMEC 39 ALEX HALEY (ex-*Edenton,* ATS 1)	1-4-67	15-5-68	23-1-71	Kodiak, Alaska

Alex Haley (WMEC 39) William M. Rau, 9-99

Alex Haley (WMEC 39) George R. Schneider, 9-99

D: 2,650 tons (2,929 fl) **S:** 16 kts **Dim:** 88.0 (80.5 pp) × 15.25 × 4.6
A: 2 single 25-mm 87-cal. Mk 38 Bushmaster low-angle guns; 2 single 12.7-mm M2 mg
Electronics: Radar: 1 Hughes-Furuno SPS-73 nav.; 1 . . . surf. search
M: 4 Caterpillar 3516 diesels; 2 Escher-Wyss 4-bladed CP props; 6,800 bhp—bow-thruster
Electric: 1,200 kw tot. **Range:** 10,000/13 **Crew:** 7 officers, 92 enlisted

Remarks: Former U.S. Navy salvage and rescue ship, decommissioned to reserve 29-3-96 and transferred to the Coast Guard 17-11-97. Converted for use as a cutter at the U.S. Coast Guard Yard, Curtis Bay, Md., recommissioning 10-7-99 and being formally commissioned 16-12-99 at her base in Kodiak, from where she is employed on fisheries patrol ("Living Marine Resources") and search-and-rescue duties. Sisters *Beaufort* (ATS 2) and *Brunswick* (ATS 3) were transferred to South Korea 12-12-96.
Hull systems: Received new main engines and Caterpillar diesel-driven Onan generator sets during an early 1990s refit and new generators during the conversion for USCG service. Most salvage equipment (including the towing winch, cranes, and divers' decompression chamber) was removed during conversion. A helicopter platform has been erected over the fantail (additional accommodations may later be added below the helicopter deck, which can accommodate HH-60 and HH-65 aircraft). Carries two RIB inspection craft. Navigational suite includes a Sperry Mk 27 gyro, a Trimble NT2000 GPS, and Raytheon CRP V850 and SQN-15 echo sounders.

♦ 14 Reliance class (210-foot class)
Bldrs: A: Todd Shipyards, Houston, Texas; B: Christy Corp., Sturgeon Bay, Wis.; C: Coast Guard SY, Curtis Bay, Md.; D: American SB, Lorain, Ohio

	Bldr	L	In serv.	Based at
WMEC 615 RELIANCE	A	25-5-63	20-6-64	New Castle, N.H.
WMEC 616 DILIGENCE	A	20-7-63	26-8-64	Wilmington, N.C.
WMEC 617 VIGILANT	A	24-12-63	3-10-64	Cape Canaveral, Fla.
WMEC 618 ACTIVE	B	31-7-65	17-9-66	Port Angeles, Wash.
WMEC 619 CONFIDENCE	C	8-5-65	19-2-66	Cape Canaveral, Fla.
WMEC 620 RESOLUTE	C	30-4-66	8-12-66	St. Petersburg, Fla.
WMEC 621 VALIANT	D	14-1-67	28-10-67	Miami
WMEC 623 STEADFAST	D	24-6-67	25-9-68	Astoria, Ore.
WMEC 624 DAUNTLESS	D	21-10-67	10-6-68	Galveston, Texas
WMEC 625 VENTUROUS	D	11-11-67	16-8-68	St. Petersburg, Fla.
WMEC 626 DEPENDABLE	D	16-3-68	27-11-68	Portsmouth, Va.
WMEC 627 VIGOROUS	D	4-5-68	2-5-69	Cape May, N.J.
WMEC 629 DECISIVE	C	14-12-67	23-8-68	Cape May, N.J.
WMEC 630 ALERT	C	19-10-68	4-8-69	Astoria, Ore.

Reliance (WMEC 615) Takatoshi Okano, 9-01

Steadfast (WMEC 623) Jürg Kürsener, 6-01

Valiant (WMEC 621) H&L Van Ginderen, 5-99

D: 879 tons (1,050 fl) **S:** 18 kts **Dim:** 64.16 (60.96 pp) × 10.36 × 3.25
A: 1 25-mm 87-cal. Mk 38 Bushmaster low-angle gun; 2 single 12.7-mm M2 mg; 1 HH-65 helicopter
Electronics: Radar: 2 Hughes-Furuno SPS-73 nav.
M: 2 Alco 16V-251B diesels; 2 CP props; 5,000 bhp
Electric: 500 kw tot. **Range:** 2,700/18; 6,100/14 **Endurance:** 30 days
Crew: 12 officers, 63 enlisted (accomm. for 12 officers, 72 enlisted)

Remarks: Designed to operate up to 500 miles off the coast. Were modernized by the U.S. Coast Guard Yard, Curtis Bay, Md., as follows:

WMEC 615	6-4-87 to 1-89	WMEC 623	6-92 to 14-2-94
WMEC 616	7-90 to 12-91	WMEC 624	7-8-93 to 24-2-95
WMEC 617	2-89 to 6-90	WMEC 625	11-2-94 to 27-10-95
WMEC 618	1-10-84 to 12-2-87	WMEC 626	24-2-95 to 15-8-97
WMEC 619	18-10-86 to 6-88	WMEC 627	6-91 to 11-92
WMEC 620	8-94 to 13-9-96	WMEC 629	13-9-96 to 10-10-98
WMEC 621	12-91 to 5-93	WMEC 630	12-92 to 2-9-94

COAST GUARD MEDIUM-ENDURANCE CUTTERS [WPS]
(continued)

Disposals: *Courageous* (WMEC 622) was decommissioned 27-9-10 and *Durable* (WMEC 628) on 20-9-01; both are in storage at Curtis Bay, awaiting a decision on their fates. The entire class is planned to be retired by 2011.
Hull systems: During modernization, the ships received a new stack, an enlarged superstructure, and greater firefighting capability; topweight was reduced, but the helo deck was reduced in area. The crews were enlarged to 86 total, provisions capacities were enlarged, and engine exhausts were rearranged; displacements rose from 930 to more than 1,050 tons. The high superstructure permits 360° visibility. Can tow a 10,000-ton ship. Are air-conditioned. WMEC 615–619 originally had CODAG propulsion, with two 1,500-bhp Cooper-Bessemer FVBM12-T diesels and two Solar Saturn T-100s gas turbines providing an additional 2,000 shp; the gas turbines were soon removed, and the ships were re-engined with Alco 251B engines during the class modernization program. All are now equipped with 6.86-m Zodiac Hurricane 630 rigid inflatable boats with Volvo Penta outdrive diesel engines; the boats have a GPS receiver and an echo sounder and can carry 11 personnel. One 25-ft. Mk V Motor Surf Boat is also carried.
Combat systems: The obsolete 76.2-mm 50-cal. gun formerly carried on the forecastle has been replaced by the 25-mm Bushmaster chain gun. The Raytheon SPS-64-series navigational radars have been replaced by two SPS-73 sets, for which there are three displays. By 6-01, the entire class had been fitted with an electronic Integrated Navigation System (INS) employing electronic charts.

♦ 1 U.S. Navy Diver class (213-foot class)
Bldr: Basalt Rock Co., Napa, Calif.

	Laid down	L	In serv.
WMEC 167 Acushnet (ex-WAGO 167; ex-WAT 167; ex-*Shackle,* ARS 9)	26-11-42	1-4-43	5-2-44

Acushnet (WMEC 167) Chris Sattler, 8-00

D: 1,246 tons (1,746 fl) **S:** 15.5 kts (13 sust.)
Dim: 65.08 (63.09 wl) × 12.50 × 4.57 **A:** 3 12.7-mm mg
Electronics: Radar: 2 Raytheon SPS-64(V)1 nav.
M: 4 Cooper-Bessemer GSB-8 diesels, electric drive; 2 props; 3,030 shp
Electric: 460 kw tot. **Range:** 10,000/14.5; 13,700/10.3 **Fuel:** 300 tons
Crew: 7 officers, 65 enlisted

Remarks: Taken over from the navy in 1946. Based at Ketchikan, Alaska, since 8-98, when it was originally planned that she would be retired. Will now serve at least through 2002.
Disposals: Sister *Escape* (WMEC 6) was stricken 29-6-95 and returned to the USN 12-7-95 for disposal. *Yocona* (WMEC 168; ex-WAT 168; ex-*Seize,* ARS 26) was stricken 6-6-96 and is currently employed at Pearl Harbor as Navy Afloat Training Group Mid-Pacific's "Visit, Board, Search, and Seizure" (VBSS) training hulk.

♦ 1 Storis class (230-foot class)
Bldr: Toledo SB, Toledo, Ohio

	Laid down	L	In serv.	Based at
WMEC 38 Storis (ex-*Eskimo*)	14-7-41	4-4-42	30-9-42	Kodiak, Alaska

Storis (WMEC 38) H&L Van Ginderen, 3-98

D: 1,296 tons light (1,916 fl) **S:** 14 kts **Dim:** 70.1 × 13.1 × 4.6
A: 1 25-mm 87-cal. Mk 38 Bushmaster low-angle gun; 4 single 12.7-mm M2 mg
Electronics: Radar: 2 Hughes-Furuno SPS-73 nav.
M: 3 Fairbanks-Morse 38D8⅛ diesels, electric drive; 1 prop; 1,800 shp
Range: 12,000/14; 22,000/8 **Fuel:** 330 tons **Crew:** 10 officers, 96 enlisted

Remarks: Rated as a WAG until 1966 and WAGB until 1-7-72, when she was retyped WMEC. Resembles a *Balsam*-class buoy tender, but is larger. Will be retained in service for the foreseeable future. Has an icebreaker hull, but is no longer considered capable of breaking ice. The obsolete 76.2-mm 50-cal. gun formerly carried on the forecastle was replaced by the 25-mm chain gun during 1994. Is equipped with 6.86-m Zodiac Hurricane 630 rigid inflatable boats with a 135-bhp Volvo Penta outdrive diesel engine; the boats have a GPS receiver and an echo sounder and can carry 11 personnel and one ton of cargo.

Disposal note: The *Stalwart*-class drug interdiction cutter *Vindicator* (T-AGOS 3, ex-WMEC 3, ex-T-AGOS 3) was transferred to USCG control 20-5-94 and temporarily commissioned for Haiti blockade duties, then decommissioned 19-8-94 and laid up at Curtis Bay, Md. She was reactivated in 2000 after conversion to carry two Fountain Powerboats "Deployable Pursuit Boats" and operated by an Military Sealift Command (MSC) contractor crew under Coast Guard control and with a 17-strong USCG detachment on counternarcotics duties. Due to budget problems, the ship was deactivated and returned to the USCG for layup at Curtis Bay 5-5-01 without having made an operational patrol. She was transferred to the National Oceanographic and Atmospheric Administration (NOAA) during 2001. Sister *Persistent* (WMEC 6, ex-T-AGOS 6) was deactivated from the MSC 30-6-94, transferred to the USCG 11-10-94, and laid up; she reentered service 28-10-99 (but was then briefly placed in reduced operating condition at Miami awaiting operating funds) but was again laid up at Curtis Bay 15-5-01 and transferred to Maritime Administration custody during 11-01 for possible use as the Great Lakes Maritime Academy school ship.

PATROL CRAFT [WPC]

Disposal note: Former U.S. Navy *Cyclone*-class patrol craft *Cyclone* (PC 1), transferred to the Coast Guard 1-3-00, was stored at Curtis Bay, Md., and never reactivated; the ship was offered to the Philippines by President Bush during 11-01, for transfer during 2002. The other 13 units of the class were transferred to Coast Guard operational control, six on 7-11-01 and the other seven on 27-12-01, for U.S. homeland defense duties under Operation Noble Eagle, with navy crews and operating funding and six USCG Tactical Law Enforcement Team personnel aboard for policing functions; see the entry under [PC] in the navy section for data.

♦ 0 (+ 1) Guardian 85-foot class
Bldr: Guardian Marine, Tacoma, Wash. (In serv. 30-8-02)

WPB 85 . . .

Guardian 85-ft. class Guardian Marine, 2001

D: 105 tons (fl) **S:** 42 kts **Dim:** 25.91 × 7.01 × 1.67
A: . . . **Electronics:** Radar: 1 Furuno FR-8251 X-band nav.
M: 2 MTU DDC 12V4000 diesels; 2 props; 5,470 bhp
Electric: 64 kw tot. (2 × 32-kw Northern Lights Mod. M984K alternators)
Range: 1,700/. . . **Endurance:** 7 days **Crew:** . . .

Remarks: GRP-construction, planing-hulled "Fast Patrol Craft" based on the builder's 1999 privately funded design, of which one is now operated by the U.S. Navy. Ordered 1-3-02 for $4.65 million. Eight others have been built for commercial use, six as tour boats and two as personnel ferries. Additional units may be procured.

♦ 49 Island class (110-foot class)
Bldr: Bollinger Machine Shop & SY, Lockport, La.

	Laid down	L	In serv.	Based at
WPB 1301 Farallon	. . .	27-8-85	21-2-86	Miami Beach, Fla.
WPB 1302 Manitou	. . .	9-10-85	28-2-86	Miami Beach, Fla.
WPB 1303 Matagorda	. . .	15-12-85	25-4-86	Miami Beach, Fla.
WPB 1304 Maui	. . .	13-1-86	9-5-86	Miami Beach, Fla.
WPB 1305 Monhegan	. . .	15-2-86	16-6-86	Key West, Fla.
WPB 1306 Nunivak	. . .	15-3-86	4-7-86	San Juan, P.R.
WPB 1307 Ocracoke	. . .	12-4-86	4-8-86	San Juan, P.R.
WPB 1308 Vashon	. . .	10-5-86	15-8-86	San Juan, P.R.
WPB 1309 Aquidneck	. . .	14-6-86	26-9-86	Portsmouth, Va.
WPB 1310 Mustang	. . .	11-7-86	29-8-86	Seward, Alaska
WPB 1311 Naushon	. . .	22-8-86	3-10-86	Ketchikan, Alaska
WPB 1312 Sanibel	. . .	3-10-86	14-11-86	Woods Hole, Mass.
WPB 1313 Edisto	. . .	21-11-86	7-1-87	San Diego
WPB 1314 Sapelo	. . .	8-1-87	24-2-87	Key West, Fla.
WPB 1315 Matinicus	. . .	26-2-87	16-4-87	San Juan, P.R.
WPB 1316 Nantucket	. . .	17-4-87	4-6-87	Key West, Fla.
WPB 1317 Attu	4-5-87	4-12-87	9-5-88	San Juan, P.R.
WPB 1318 Baranof	8-6-87	15-1-88	20-5-88	Miami Beach, Fla.
WPB 1319 Chandeleur	13-7-87	19-2-88	8-6-88	Miami Beach, Fla.
WPB 1320 Chincoteague	17-8-87	25-3-88	8-8-88	Mobile, Ala.
WPB 1321 Cushing	21-9-87	29-4-88	8-8-88	San Juan, P.R.
WPB 1322 Cuttyhunk	26-10-87	3-6-88	15-10-88	Port Angeles, Wash.

COAST GUARD PATROL CRAFT [WPC] *(continued)*

	Laid down	L	In serv.	Based at
WPB 1323 Drummond	23-11-87	8-7-88	19-10-88	Port Canaveral, Fla.
WPB 1324 Key Largo (ex-*Largo*)	1-1-88	12-8-88	24-12-88	Key West, Fla.
WPB 1325 Metomkin	1-2-88	16-9-88	12-1-89	Key West, Fla.
WPB 1326 Monomoy	21-3-88	21-10-88	16-12-88	Woods Hole, Mass.
WPB 1327 Orcas	25-4-88	25-11-88	14-4-89	Coos Bay, Ore.
WPB 1328 Padre	30-3-88	6-1-89	24-2-89	Key West, Fla.
WPB 1329 Sitkinak	4-7-88	10-2-89	31-3-89	Key West, Fla.
WPB 1330 Tybee	8-8-88	17-3-89	9-5-89	San Diego
WPB 1331 Washington	12-9-88	21-4-89	1989	Honolulu
WPB 1332 Wrangell	17-10-88	26-5-89	24-6-89	Portland, Maine
WPB 1333 Adak	25-11-88	30-6-89	17-11-89	Sandy Hook, N.J.
WPB 1334 Liberty	26-12-88	4-8-89	22-9-89	Auke Bay, Alaska
WPB 1335 Anacapa	30-1-89	8-9-89	13-1-90	Petersburg, Alaska
WPB 1336 Kiska	6-3-89	13-10-89	1-12-89*	Hilo, Hawaii
WPB 1337 Assateague	10-4-89	17-11-89	1-1-90*	Honolulu
WPB 1338 Grand Isle	18-6-90	. . .	14-12-90*	Gloucester, Mass.
WPB 1339 Key Biscayne	16-7-90	. . .	27-4-91	Corpus Christi, Texas
WPB 1340 Jefferson Island	20-8-90	. . .	17-4-91	Portland, Maine
WPB 1341 Kodiak Island	24-9-90	8-2-91	21-6-91	St. Petersburg, Fla.
WPB 1342 Long Island	29-10-90	19-3-91	27-8-91	San Diego
WPB 1343 Bainbridge Island	3-12-90	19-4-91	14-6-91*	Sandy Hook, N.J.
WPB 1344 Block Island	14-1-91	. . .	19-7-91*	Atlantic Beach, N.C.
WPB 1345 Staten Island	18-2-91	. . .	23-8-91*	Atlantic Beach, N.C.
WPB 1346 Roanoke Island	25-3-91	. . .	27-9-91*	Homer, Alaska
WPB 1347 Pea Island	29-4-91	. . .	1-11-91*	St. Petersburg, Fla.
WPB 1348 Knight Island	3-10-91	6-9-91	6-12-91*	St. Petersburg, Fla.
WPB 1349 Galveston Island	8-7-91	15-11-91	17-1-92*	Apra Harbor, Guam

*Delivery date vice commissioning date

Matagorda (WPB 1303) Winter & Findler, 9-01

Long Island (WPB 1342) W. Michael Young, 2-01

Kodiak Island (WPB 1341) Leo Dirkx, 3-01

D: WPB 1301–1317: 117 tons light (165 fl); WPB 1318–1337: 107 tons light (155 fl); WPB 1338–1349: 153 tons (fl)
S: 29.7 (WPB 1338–1349: 28) kts **Dim:** 33.53 × 6.40 × 2.23 (max.)
A: 1 25-mm 87-cal. Mk 38 Bushmaster low-angle gun; 2 single 12.7-mm M2 mg
Electronics: Radar: 1 Raytheon SPS-64(V)1 or Hughes-Furuno SPS-73 nav.
M: WPB 1301–1337: 2 Alco-Paxman Valenta 16 RP200-1 CM diesels; 2 props; 5,820 bhp (5,760 sust.)—WPB 1338–1349: 2 Caterpillar 3516 diesels; 2 props; 5,460 bhp
Electric: 198 kw tot. (2 × 99-kw Caterpillar 3304T diesel-driven sets)
Range: 1,853 n.m. at 26 kts for 24 hr + 13.1 kts for 96 hr; 3,380/8
Endurance: 5 days **Crew:** 2 officers, 2 CPOs, 12 enlisted

Remarks: Fifteen were ordered in 8-84 from Marine Power & Equipment, Seattle, but the award was contested by Bollinger and reassigned; the 16th was ordered 3-5-85. Another 16 were ordered 11-2-87 under the Congressional Coast Defense Augmentation, and five more 24-2-87 under the Drug Omnibus Act of 1987. WPB 1338–1349 were ordered 26-12-89 under FY 90 with navy funds. The 21 later units have minor improvements, including heavier bow plating, a better anchor, addition of a 300-gallon/day water generator, and relocation of the captain's cabin. Cost about $6.5 million each. Are planned to be retired between 2004 and 2012, an unusually short lifespan for this type of craft in USCG service.
Hull systems: Modified Vosper-Thornycroft design, with increased top-hamper. Have a steel hull and aluminum deck and superstructure. Fin stabilizers are fitted. Carry Loran-C and Omega receivers, an IFF transponder, and an SQN-18 echo sounder. The Paxman engines are governor-limited to 2,880 bhp each from a nominal max. 4,000 bhp. Minimum speed is about 8 kts, making them difficult to employ in SAR and small boat towing. Several ships of the class were used to evaluate a GEC-Alstom pulsed clutch that can produce continuous slow speeds down to 2.5 kts. Are now equipped with 5.59-m Zodiac 530 RIBs powered by a 60-bhp outboard engine; the RIBs are equipped with a GPS receiver and an echo sounder.
Combat systems: WPB 1301–1337 were initially armed with a 20-mm 70-cal. Mk 67 AA gun, a weapon no longer supported by the U.S. Navy. The 25-mm chain gun had replaced all 20-mm weapons by the end of 1994.

PATROL BOATS [WPB]

Disposal note: The eight Deployable Pursuit Boats (380100 series) were deactivated 1-5-01; six were placed in land storage and the other two loaned to the U.S. Army for special forces training duties at Ft. Bragg, N.C. With the demise of the short-lived drug interdiction program using two reactivated T-AGOS ships to carry two of the Deployable Pursuit Boats each, the boats are unlikely to be returned to service; they had proven unsuitable for their intended role and dangerous to their crews when operating on the open ocean.

♦ 39 (+ 11) Marine Protector–class (87-foot-class) Coastal Patrol Boats Bldr: Bollinger Shipyards, Lockport, La.

	L	Del.	Comm.	Based at
WPB 87301 Barracuda	1-9-97	7-4-98	24-4-98	Eureka, Calif.
WPB 87302 Hammerhead	11-5-98	29-7-98	16-10-98	Woods Hole, Mass.
WPB 87303 Mako	29-6-98	9-9-98	11-12-98	Cape May, N.J.
WPB 87304 Marlin	3-8-98	2-12-98	22-1-99	Ft. Myers, Fla.
WPB 87305 Stingray	2-9-98	12-1-99	. . .	Mobile, Ala.
WPB 87306 Dorado	7-12-98	23-2-99	23-4-99	Crescent City, Calif.
WPB 87307 Osprey	18-1-99	6-4-99	19-6-99	Port Townsend, Wash.
WPB 87308 Chinook	1-3-99	18-5-99	19-5-99	New London, Conn.
WPB 87309 Albacore	6-4-99	29-6-99	20-8-99	Little Creek, Va.
WPB 87310 Tarpon	18-5-99	10-8-99	22-10-99	Tybee Island, Ga.
WPB 87311 Cobia	15-6-99	7-9-99	29-10-99	Mobile, Ala.
WPB 87312 Hawksbill	27-7-99	5-10-99	7-1-00	Oceanside, Calif.
WPB 87313 Cormorant	24-8-99	2-11-99	10-12-99	Ft. Pierce, Fla.
WPB 87314 Finback	21-9-99	30-11-99	13-1-00	Cape May, N.J.
WPB 87315 Amberjack	19-10-99	28-12-99	25-1-00	Port Isabel, Texas
WPB 87316 Kittiwake	16-11-99	25-1-00	30-6-00	Niwiliwilli, Hawaii
WPB 87317 Blackfin	14-12-99	22-2-00	4-5-00	Santa Barbara, Calif.
WPB 87318 Bluefin	11-1-00	21-3-00	27-4-00	Ft. Pierce, Fla.
WPB 87319 Yellowfin	8-2-00	18-4-00	12-6-00	Charleston, S.C.
WPB 87320 Manta	8-3-00	17-6-00	31-7-00	Freeport, Texas
WPB 87321 Coho	4-4-00	13-6-00	13-6-00	Panama City, Fla.
WPB 87322 Kingfisher	5-6-00	11-7-00	11-7-00	Mayport, Fla.
WPB 87323 Seahawk	30-5-00	8-9-00	8-9-00	Clearwater, Fla.
WPB 87324 Steelhead	27-6-00	5-9-00	13-12-00	Port Aransas, Texas
WPB 87325 Beluga	25-7-00	3-10-00	21-11-00	Little Creek, Va.
WPB 87326 Blacktip	22-8-00	1-11-00	1-2-01	Oxnard, Calif.
WPB 87327 Pelican	18-9-00	29-11-00	8-1-01	Morgan City, La.
WPB 87328 Ridley	17-10-00	27-12-00	23-3-01	Moriches, N.Y.
WPB 87329 Cochito	14-11-00	24-1-01	24-3-01	Little Creek, Va.
WPB 87330 Man O' War	13-12-00	20-2-01	31-3-01	Galveston, Texas
WPB 87331 Moray	16-1-00	20-3-01	4-5-01	Jonesport, Maine
WPB 87332 Razorbill	6-2-00	17-4-01	30-5-01	Gulfport, Miss.
WPB 87333 Adelie	6-3-01	15-5-01	17-8-01	Port Angeles, Wash.
WPB 87334 Gannet	3-4-01	12-6-01	28-7-01	Miami, Fla.
WPB 87335 Narwhal	1-5-01	10-7-01	2-11-01	Newport Beach, Calif.
WPB 87336 Sturgeon	29-5-01	7-8-01	28-9-01	Grand Isle, La.
WPB 87337 Sockeye	26-6-01	4-9-01	14-1-02	Bodega Bay, Calif.
WPB 87338 Ibis	24-7-01	3-10-01	7-12-01	Cape May, N.J.
WPB 87339 Pompano	28-8-01	31-10-01	14-12-01	Gulfport, Miss.
WPB 87340 Halibut	18-9-01	27-11-01	. . .	Marina Del Ray, Calif.
WPB 87341 Bonito	16-10-01	2-1-02	1-02	Pensacola, Fla.
WPB 87342 Shrike	13-11-01	23-1-02	. . .	Cape Canaveral, Fla.
WPB 87343 Tern	11-12-01	20-2-02	. . .	San Francisco
WPB 87344 Heron	8-1-02	19-3-02	. . .	Sabine, Texas
WPB 87345 Wahoo	5-2-02	16-4-02	. . .	Port Angeles, Wash.
WPB 87346 Flyingfish	5-3-02	14-5-02	. . .	Gloucester, Mass.
WPB 87347 Haddock	2-4-02	11-6-02	. . .	San Diego
WPB 87348 Brant	30-4-02	9-7-02	. . .	Corpus Christi, Texas
WPB 87349 Shearwater	28-5-02	6-8-02	. . .	Portsmouth, Va.
WPB 87350 Petrel	28-5-02	6-9-02	. . .	San Diego

COAST GUARD PATROL BOATS [WPB] *(continued)*

Albacore (WPB 87309) A. D. Baker III, 6-00

Osprey (WPB 87307) Victor M. Baca, 8-01

Dorado (WPB 87306) Leo Dirkx, 2-00

Beluga (WPB 87325) Takatoshi Okano, 9-01

D: 91.1 tons (fl) **S:** 27 kts **Dim:** 26.52 (24.87 pp) × 5.92 × 1.74
A: 2 single 12.7-mm M2 mg
Electronics: Radar: 1 Hughes-Furuno SPS-73 nav.
M: 2 MTU 8V396 TE94 diesels; 2 5-bladed props; 2,950 bhp (2,680 sust.)
Electric: 120 kw tot. (2 × 60-kw Stamford sets, 2 M.A.N. D 0824 LF01 diesel-driven)
Range: 882/10 **Fuel:** 2,500 gallons **Endurance:** 10 days (5 days' provisions)
Crew: 10 tot. (accomm. for 11 tot.)

Remarks: Originally to have been known as the "Endangered Species" class (with the first to have been named *Condor*) and later the "Marine Species" class, the name source has been changed to sea creatures (fish and birds). The $8.9 million contract for design and construction of the prototype was let in 3-96; six more were ordered 15-8-97, two on 4-3-98, 13 on 1-11-98, and eight more early in 1999 (with an option for 19 additional).The eighth and later units have design improvements based on tests with WPB 87301. The unceremonial launches are performed by a crane. Average cost is about $3.5 million. Projected launch and delivery dates and intended bases listed above may change. A sister was ordered for Malta 30-7-01, for completion 15-11-02.
Hull systems: Hullform is based on the Netherlands builder Damen's STANPAT 2600 design, which was employed on a number of Hong Kong police patrol boats built since 1980. Have steel-hull construction with Russian-made extruded aluminum panel superstructure. Use a stern ramp to launch and recover a 4.6-m aluminum-construction rigid inflatable Ambar AM 550-CPB inspection/rescue boat in seas up to 2.5 m high; the launch is powered by a 100-bhp Yanmar diesel driving a North American Marine Jet waterjet for 30-kt top speeds. Have an integrated pilothouse with radar, echo sounder, GPS receiver, and other sensors linked to a central Sperry Electronic Chart Display and Information System. There is tankage for 1,500 liters of potable water, with a 750-liter/day distillation capacity. Are able to operate safely in water as shallow as 2 m and can maneuver at 4 kts. Are considered safe to operate in seas up to 9 m high. Crew have two-person staterooms.

♦ 44 25-foot Transportable Port Security Boats
Bldr: Boston Whaler, Edgewater, Fla. (In serv. 1996–99)

25300 series

25-ft. Guardian-class armed launch Tom Gillespie/USCG, 2001

D: 1.622 tons light (3 fl) **S:** 40 kts **Dim:** 7.50 × 2.45 × 0.41 (hull)
A: 1 12.7-mm mg; 2 single 7.62-mm M60 mg
Electronics: Radar: 1 Raytheon 2400 or RL70RC nav.
M: 2 Cummins diesel outboards; 380 bhp
Range: . . ./. . . **Fuel:** 655 liters **Crew:** 3 or 4 tot.

Remarks: Foam-core, unsinkable GRP hull construction; the builder's Guardian design. Eleven were in service as of 1998, and another 33 were ordered in 7-98 for use as Transportable Port Security Boats by six Port Security Units based at coastal cities in the U.S.A. Have a night vision device, differential GPS, and encrypted radios. Can carry up to 12 persons. The 33 units ordered in 1998 had the later-model RL70RC radar; the original 11 built had 150-bhp gasoline outboard engines.

Disposal note: The final 82-ft. Point-class cutter, *Point Baker* (WPB 82342), was to be retired at Sabine Pass, Texas, 12-2-02 and transferred to the Republic of Georgia Coast Guard. During 1969–70, 26 units of the class had been transferred to Vietnam. The following table indicates the fates of the units operated since 1990:

	Decomm.	Transferred	To
WPB 82302 *Point Hope*	3-5-91	3-5-91	Costa Rica
WPB 82311 *Point Verde*	12-6-91	12-6-91	Mexico
WPB 82312 *Point Swift*	30-3-95	. . .	scrapped
WPB 82314 *Point Thatcher*	13-3-92	. . .	firefighting training
WPB 82318 *Point Herron*	26-7-91	26-7-91	Mexico
WPB 82332 *Point Roberts*	2-92	. . .	scrapped
WPB 82333 *Point Highland*	24-7-01	24-7-01	Trinidad & Tobago
WPB 82334 *Point Ledge*	3-8-98	3-8-98	Venezuela
WPB 82335 *Point Countess*	24-5-00	6-00	Georgia
WPB 82336 *Point Glass*	16-4-01	16-4-01	NOAA
WPB 82337 *Point Divide*	30-3-95	30-3-95	Washington Maritime Academy, Seattle
WPB 82338 *Point Bridge*	28-9-01	28-9-01	Costa Rica
WPB 82339 *Point Chico*	22-6-01	22-6-01	Costa Rica
WPB 82340 *Point Batan*	17-9-99	1-10-99	Dominican Republic
WPB 82341 *Point Lookout*	24-3-94	. . .	scrapped
WPB 82342 *Point Baker*	5-2-02	5-2-02	Georgia
WPB 82343 *Point Wells*	18-10-00	18-10-00	Colombia
WPB 82344 *Point Estero*	8-2-01	8-2-01	Colombia
WPB 82345 *Point Judith*	15-1-92	15-1-92	Venezuela
WPB 82346 *Point Arena*	30-3-95	. . .	scrapped
WPB 82347 *Point Bonita*	14-11-00	14-11-00	Trinidad & Tobago

COAST GUARD PATROL BOATS [WPB] *(continued)*

	Decomm.	Transferred	To
WPB 82348 *Point Barrow*	7-6-91	7-6-91	Panama
WPB 82349 *Point Spencer*	12-12-00	12-12-00	Dominican Republic
WPB 82350 *Point Franklin*	23-6-98	3-8-98	Venezuela
WPB 82351 *Point Bennett*	26-1-99	12-2-99	Trinidad & Tobago
WPB 82352 *Point Sal*	24-5-01	24-5-01	Colombia
WPB 82353 *Point Monroe*	19-8-01	19-8-01	NOAA
WPB 82354 *Point Evans*	1-12-99	1-12-99	Philippines
WPB 82355 *Point Hannon*	11-1-01	11-1-01	Panama
WPB 82356 *Point Francis*	9-3-99	12-4-99	Panama
WPB 82357 *Point Huron*	12-4-99	12-4-99	Panama
WPB 82358 *Point Stuart*	26-4-01	26-4-01	El Salvador
WPB 82359 *Point Steele*	9-7-98	17-7-98	Antigua-Barbuda
WPB 82360 *Point Winslow*	19-9-00	20-9-00	Panama
WPB 82361 *Point Charles*	13-12-91	. . .	Texas A&M University
WPB 82362 *Point Brown*	30-9-91	30-9-91	Kingsborough Community College, Brooklyn, N.Y.
WPB 82363 *Point Nowell*	19-10-99	19-10-99	Jamaica
WPB 82364 *Point Whitehorn*	30-3-95	. . .	scrapped
WPB 82365 *Point Turner*	3-4-98	15-4-98	St. Lucia
WPB 82366 *Point Lobos*	13-10-01	13-10-01	NOAA
WPB 82367 *Point Knoll*	11-9-91	20-12-91	Venezuela
WPB 82368 *Point Warde*	29-6-00	30-6-00	Colombia
WPB 82369 *Point Heyer*	11-12-98	12-2-99	Trinidad & Tobago
WPB 82370 *Point Richmond*	30-6-97	22-8-97	Ecuador
WPB 82371 *Point Barnes*	14-1-00	14-1-00	Jamaica
WPB 82372 *Point Brower*	9-12-01	9-12-01	U.S. Navy
WPB 82373 *Point Camden*	10-12-99	10-12-99	Costa Rica
WPB 82374 *Point Carrew*	22-8-00	22-8-00	Argentina
WPB 82375 *Point Doran*	6-3-01	6-3-01	Philippines
WPB 82376 *Point Harris**	4-12-92	. . .	donated at Honolulu
WPB 82377 *Point Hobart*	8-7-99	8-7-99	Argentina
WPB 82378 *Point Jackson*	30-5-00	30-5-00	Turkmenistan
WPB 82379 *Point Martin*	24-8-99	1-10-99	Dominican Republic

*"Irreparably damaged" during Hurricane Iniki at Kauai, Hawaii, on 11-9-92—but had been refitted for further local government service by 2000.

AUXILIARIES

♦ 0 (+ 1) new-construction lake icebreaker [WAGB]
Bldr: Marinette Marine, Marinette, Wis. (In serv. 10-05)

	Laid down	L	In serv.
WAGB 30 Mackinaw	. . .	. . .	. . . (del. 10-05)

Mackinaw (WAGB 30)—official drawing U.S. Coast Guard, 2001

D: 3,500 tons (fl) **S:** . . . kts **Dim:** 73.15 × 18.28 × . . .
Electronics: Radar: . . .
M: diesel-electric; 2 azimuthal prop pods; 10,000 shp **Crew:** 50 tot.

Remarks: In the FY 99 budget, Congress provided $5.3 million toward the design of a replacement for the *Mackinaw* (WAGB 83); the contract was let 16-10-01 for $82,474,830. The ship, which will be much less powerful than its predecessor, will be able to operate for 185 days of the year and will be configured for use as a navigational aids tender during the nonwinter seasons. Intended to be able to break 32-in. layered ice at 3 kts and also to be used for law-enforcement, environmental protection, and national security missions. Assistance with the hull design is being provided by Kvaerner Masa Marine and Masa-Yards Technology Center in Finland and Sweden.

♦ 1 Healy-class polar icebreaker [WAGB]
Bldr: Avondale Industries, New Orleans

	Laid down	L	Del.	Comm.	Based at
WAGB 20 Healy	16-9-96	15-11-97	10-11-99	8-00	Seattle

D: 17,170 tons (fl) **S:** 17 kts (12.5 cruise)
Dim: 128.02 (121.23 pp) × 24.99 × 8.91
A: 2 single 12.7-mm M2 mg; 1 or 2 HH-65A helicopters
Electronics:
Radar: 1 . . . nav.; 1 . . . surf. search
Sonar: MultiBeam Type 2112 hydrographic mapping set
TACAN: URN-25
M: diesel-electric: 4 Sulzer-Westinghouse 12 ZA40S medium-speed diesels (10,600 bhp each); 4 8,000-kw, 6,600-V main alternators and 2 motors; 2 fixed-pitch, 4.88-m-dia. props; 30,000 shp—2,000-shp bow-thruster
Electric: 1,500-kw harbor set **Range:** 16,000/12.5; 37,000/9.25

Healy (WAGB 20) Kurt Greiner/SeaPhoto, 5-01

Healy (WAGB 20) Jim Sanderson, 7-01

Endurance: 180 days **Fuel:** 3,400 tons + 120 tons aviation fuel
Crew: 67 ship's company + 35 scientific party (accomm. for 75 USCG, 50 science party)

Remarks: Under the FY 90 navy budget, $274.8 million was authorized and appropriated to pay for a new Coast Guard icebreaker; another $62 million was added by Congress under FY 92. Bids were requested 13-3-91, but the bidding was canceled 16-3-92 after no yard bid within the available funds. A second round of bidding resulted in a contract signed 16-7-93 for $232 million. A planned second unit was omitted from the FY 92 budget. Named for Michael M. Healy, a pioneering 19th-century Revenue Service officer in Alaskan waters.
Hull systems: Capable of breaking 1.4-m ice at 3 kts continuously or 2.4-m ice by backing and ramming. Has a conventional icebreaker hull not incorporating modern icebreaking technologies. Framing is at 15-in. spacing. Has five laboratories totaling 377 m^2, four cranes, and an LCVP-type landing craft to port. Two 40-ft. equipment vans can be carried in lieu of two of the boats. The engines are mounted on the main deck. Alstom Drives and Controls (formerly Cegelec Projects, Rugby, U.K.) provided engineering and propulsion system integration. All accommodations are in the superstructure, and all cabins have outside ports. Heating is by conventional boilers. Has a liquid tank-type stabilization system and liquid bow-wash system to lubricate the hull during icebreaking. Is fitted with integrated navigation systems (electronic charts, autopilot, and GPS) and a dynamic positioning system.

♦ 2 Polar Star–class (399-foot-class) polar icebreakers [WAGB]
Bldr: Lockheed SB, Seattle

	Laid down	L	In serv.	Based at
WAGB 10 Polar Star	15-5-72	17-11-73	19-1-76	Seattle
WAGB 11 Polar Sea	27-11-73	24-6-75	23-2-78	Seattle

Polar Star (WAGB 10) Brian Morrison, 12-01

COAST GUARD AUXILIARIES *(continued)*

Polar Sea (WAGB 11) Brian Morrison, 12-00

D: 10,863 tons (13,623 fl) **S:** 15 kts **Dim:** 121.91 (102.78 pp) × 25.45 × 1.14
A: provision for: 2 single 12.7-mm mg; 2 helicopters
Electronics: Radar: 2 Raytheon SPS-64(V)-series nav.—TACAN: SRN-15
M: CODAG: 6 Alco 16V251 diesels (3,000 bhp each), 3 Pratt & Whitney FT-4A12 gas turbines (25,000 shp each, down-rated), electric drive; 3 CP props; 75,000 shp (66,000 sust.)
Range: 16,000/18; 28,275/13 **Fuel:** 3,555 tons
Endurance: 38 days at full power; 14 months' provisions
Crew: 14 officers, 128 enlisted + helicopter detachment: 4 officers, 8 enlisted + up to 30 scientists

Remarks: Scientific facilities were upgraded in WAGB 10 in 1990–91 and in WAGB 11 during 1992–93. WAGB 11 reached the North Pole in company with the Canadian Coast Guard's *Louis S. St. Laurent* on 26-7-94, breaking ice up to 12 ft. thick.
Hull systems: Can break 2-m ice at 3 kts and up to 6.4-m ice by ramming. The propulsion plant is completely cross-connected and automatic. Have two 15-ton cranes. Can carry 400 tons (600 m³) of general stores. Fuel capacity is 1,345,168 gallons of diesel and 45,981 gallons of aviation JP-5; in addition, 22,684 gallons of lube oil and 26,586 gallons of potable water can be accommodated. Carry two Packman-class 34-ft. aluminum landing craft as tenders.

♦ 1 Mackinaw-class (290-foot-class) lake icebreaker [WAGB]

Bldr: Toledo SB, Toledo, Ohio

	Laid down	L	In serv.	Based at
WAGB 83 Mackinaw (ex-*Manitowoc*)	20-3-43	4-3-44	20-12-44	Cheboygan, Wis.

Mackinaw (WAGB 83) U.S. Coast Guard, 1985

D: 3,049 tons (5,252 fl) **S:** 18.7 kts **Dim:** 88.39 × 22.66 × 5.79
A: none **Electronics:** Radar: 2 Raytheon SPS-64(V)-series nav.
M: 6 Fairbanks-Morse 38D8⅛ × 12 diesels, electric drive; 3 props (2 aft, 1 fwd); 10,000 shp
Electric: 1,260 kw tot. **Range:** 10,000/18.7; 41,000/9
Crew: 10 officers, 97 enlisted

Remarks: Built for use on the Great Lakes. Received an extensive refit during 1991, and was repainted with a red hull and white superstructure in 6-98. To be replaced in 2005 by the new Great Lakes icebreaker/navaids tender *Mackinaw* (WAGB 30) (q.v.).
Hull systems: Has a helicopter platform. Is fitted with two 12-ton cranes. Can break 0.76-m ice continuously or 3.3-m ice by backing and ramming.

♦ 8 (+ 8) Juniper-class seagoing buoy tenders [WAGL]

Bldr: Marinette Marine, Marinette, Wis.

	L	Del.	In serv.	Based at
WLB 201 Juniper	24-6-95	14-1-96	5-7-96	Newport, R.I.
WLB 202 Willow	15-6-96	29-11-96	10-4-97	Newport, R.I.
WLB 203 Kukui	3-5-97	9-10-97	1-1-98	Honolulu
WLB 204 Elm	24-1-98	29-6-98	20-11-98	Atlantic Beach, N.C.
WLB 205 Walnut	22-8-98	22-2-99	12-7-99	Honolulu
WLB 206 Spar	12-8-00	9-3-01	3-8-01	Kodiak, Alaska
WLB 207 Maple	16-12-00	21-6-01	19-10-01	Sitka, Alaska
WLB 208 Aspen	21-4-01	28-9-01	12-01	San Francisco
WLB 209 Sycamore	28-7-01	1-3-02	...	Cordova, Alaska
WLB 210 Cypress	29-10-01	24-6-02	...	Mobile, Ala.
WLB 211 Oak	26-1-02	17-10-02	...	Charleston, S.C.
WLB 212 Hickory	4-5-02	6-3-03	...	Homer, Alaska
WLB 213 Fir	20-7-02	5-6-03	...	Astoria, Ore.
WLB 214 Sequoia	5-10-02	4-9-03	...	Apra Harbor, Guam
WLB 215 Hollyhock	...	14-4-04	...	Port Huron, Mich.
WLB 216 Alder	...	2-9-04	...	Charlevoix, Mich.

Walnut (WLB 205) H&L Van Ginderen, 2-00

Elm (WLB 204) Val Ihde/Marinette Marine, 8-98

D: 2,000 tons (fl) **S:** 15 kts **Dim:** 68.58 (62.79 pp) × 14.02 × 3.96
A: provision for 1 25-mm 87-cal. Mk 38 Bushmaster low-angle gun
Electronics: Radar: 2 Decca BridgeMaster-E 340 ARPA nav.
M: 2 Caterpillar 3608 TA diesels; 1 4-bladed CP prop; 6,200 bhp—460-shp bow-thruster—550-shp stern-thruster
Electric: 1,950 kw tot. (2 × 450-kw Caterpillar 3508, 1 × 800-kw reduction gear-driven, 1 × 250-kw Caterpillar 3406 emergency diesel set)
Range: 6,000/12 **Endurance:** 45 days **Crew:** 6 officers, 34 enlisted

Remarks: Intended to perform navigational buoy tender, environmental cleanup, search-and-rescue, and law enforcement duties. The first unit (with an option for four more) was ordered 28-1-94, the second in 7-94. A second pair was authorized under FY 94, with the third unit ordered 1-95 and the fourth and fifth during 3-96. WLB 206 and 207 were ordered 4-9-98, and WLB 208 and 209 were funded in the FY 99 budget (for $72.6 million total) and ordered 12-2-99. WLB 215 and 216 were ordered 27-11-01. The first five ships are considered the "A" group and the remainder the "B" group, with minor modifications to piping runs, equipment locations, and so forth. All are named for previous buoy tenders named for trees, except for WLB 206, which commemorates the 10,000 World War II–era USCG women's volunteer group, the SPARs ("Semper Paratus Always Ready"). The builder became a subsidiary of the Manitowoc Marine Group on 20-11-00. The FY 03 budget contained a request for 25-mm guns for this class.
Hull systems: Capable of breaking 0.35-m ice continuously at 3 kts or 1.1-m ice by ramming. A Nautronix ASK 4000 dynamic positioning system and bridge-controlled engines are employed. Navigational aids include a Sperry SRD 500 dual-axis speed log and Sperry Mk 27 gyrocompass. Have a 20-ton-capacity, 18-m-reach buoy crane, a 2,875-ft.² working deck, and the ability to handle buoys in 8-ft. seas. Deck equipment includes four hydraulic winches and a continuous in-haul chain-handling winch, two anchor winches, and three mooring winches; there is a stern anchor. Are capable of towing. Are being equipped with 6.86-m Zodiac Hurricane 630 RIBs powered by a 135-bhp Volvo Penta outdrive engine and equipped with GPS receivers and an echo sounder; the craft can carry 1,122 kg of cargo and 11 personnel.

♦ 9 Balsam-class seagoing buoy tenders [WAGL]

Bldrs: WLB 302: Zenith Dredge Co., Duluth, Minn.; WLB 392, 393, 406: Duluth Iron & SB Co.; others: Marine Iron SB Co.

	Laid down	L	In serv.	Based at
WLB 277 Cowslip	16-9-41	11-4-42	17-10-42	Astoria, Ore.
WLB 302 Madrona	6-7-42	11-11-42	30-5-43	Charleston, S.C.
WLB 309 Sweetgum	21-2-43	15-4-43	20-11-43	Mobile, Ala.
WLB 392 Bramble	2-8-43	23-10-43	22-4-44	Port Huron, Mich.
WLB 393 Firebush	12-11-43	3-2-44	20-7-44	Kodiak, Alaska
WLB 401 Sassafras	16-8-43	5-10-43	23-5-44	Apra Harbor, Guam
WLB 402 Sedge	6-10-43	27-11-43	5-7-44	Homer, Alaska
WLB 404 Sundew	29-11-43	8-2-44	24-8-44	Duluth, Minn.
WLB 406 Acacia (ex-*Thistle*)	16-1-44	7-4-44	1-9-44	Charlevoix, Mich.

D: 697 tons light (1,038 fl) **S:** 12.8–13 kts **Dim:** 54.9 (51.8 pp) × 11.3 × 4.0
A: 2 single 12.7-mm M2 mg
Electronics: Radar: 1 Hughes-Furuno SPS-73 nav.
M: 2 G.E. EMD 645 diesels, electric drive; 1 prop; 1,200 (WLB 277: 1,070; WLB 404: 1,800) shp

COAST GUARD AUXILIARIES *(continued)*

Madrona (WLB 302) H&L Van Ginderen, 3-99

Electric: 400 kw tot.
Range: 4,600/12–18; 14,000/7.4 (WLB 392, 406: 10,500/13; 31,000/7.5—WLB 401: 8,000/12; 23,500/7.5)
Fuel: varies **Crew:** 6 officers, 47 enlisted

Remarks: Very robustly constructed vessels that still have a number of years' service remaining despite their advanced age. WLB 277 and 309 received major SLEP (Service Life Extension Program) overhauls between 1983 and 1991, and WLB 392, 402, 404, and 406 had earlier received major modernizations; WLB 401 received a minor modernization in the 1970s, and WLB 309 has never been extensively updated. *Gentian* (WLB 290) was redesignated WIX 290 during 9-99 (see under [WAXT]). WLB 277 (previously stricken 23-3-73, sold during 1976, repurchased 19-1-81, and recommissioned 9-11-81) was to have been decommissioned 26-10-01, but on 7-11-01 her active service was extended to 30-9-02, when she is to be transferred to Nigeria. WLB 309 was to be decommissioned 19-9-02 and transferred to Panama. WLB 302 was retired 12-4-02 and was to be transferred to El Salvador 30-5-02.
Disposals: *Laurel* (WLB 291) was stricken 10-12-99. *Evergreen* (WLB 295) was converted as an oceanographic research ship and later used as a patrol ship and then stricken. *Sorrel* (WLB 296) was declared "excess" 28-6-96 and is now operated by the Sea Scouts. *Ironwood* (WLB 297) was stricken 6-10-00. *Citrus* (ex-WLB 300) served as medium-endurance cutter WMEC 300 from 1979 until stricken in 1994 and was later transferred to the Dominican Republic. *Conifer* (WLB 301) was stricken 21-7-00. *Mesquite* (WLB 305) went aground 5-12-89 in the Great Lakes and was declared a total loss. *Buttonwood* (WLB 306) was stricken 28-6-01 (and donated to the Dominican Republic), *Planetree* (WLB 307) on 31-3-99, and *Pawpaw* (WLB 308) on 23-7-99. *Sweetgum* (WLB 309) was to be retired 15-2-02 and transferred to Panama. *Basswood* (WLB 388) was stricken 4-9-98. *Bittersweet* (WLB 389) was declared excess 18-8-97 and transferred to Estonia 5-9-97. *Blackhaw* (WLB 390) was declared excess 26-2-93 and cannibalized; the hulk is now used by the navy as a salvage training device. *Blackthorn* (WLB 391) was rammed and sunk 28-1-80. *Hornbeam* (WLB 394) was declared excess 30-10-98 and stricken 30-9-99. *Mallow* (WLB 395) was declared excess 24-5-97 and *Iris* (WLB 396) on 20-6-95. *Mariposa* (WLB 397) was stricken 31-3-00 and transferred to the navy 17-4-00 for use as a damage-control training platform. *Sagebrush* (WLB 399) and *Salvia* (WLB 400) were declared excess on 26-4-88 and 12-4-91, respectively. *Sweetbrier* (WLB 401) was stricken 27-8-01 and transferred to Ghana 26-10-01. *Spar* (WLB 403) was declared excess 28-2-97. *Woodrush* (WLB 407) was stricken 28-4-01 and transferred to Ghana 4-5-01. The others are to have been retired by the end of 2005.
Hull systems: WLB 392, 402, and 404 have strengthened hulls for icebreaking, but all have an icebreaker hullform. Have a 20-ton derrick. Ships that have gone through SLEP have rebuilt G.E. EMD 8-645E6A engines and propulsion motors, improved habitability, hydraulic cargo-handling gear, bow-thrusters, and new generator sets (including three G.M. 6-71 diesels and one 8V-71 diesel); their endurance has been increased to 5,500 n.m at 10 kts. WLB 404, without governors on her engines, has a maximum speed of 15 kts. WLB 402 and 407 have long-range communications suites. All have been equipped with 6.86-m Zodiac Hurricane 630 RIBs, powered by a 135-bhp Volvo Penta outdrive engine and equipped with GPS receivers and an echo sounder; the RIBs can carry 1,122 kg of cargo and 11 personnel.

♦ 14 Keeper-class coastal buoy tenders [WAGL]

Bldr: Marinette Marine, Marinette, Wis.

	L	Del.	In serv.	Based at
WLM 551 Ida Lewis	14-10-95	1-11-96	11-4-97	Newport, R.I.
WLM 552 Katherine Walker	14-9-96	27-6-97	1-11-97	Bayonne, N.J.
WLM 553 Abbie Burgess (ex-*Abigail Burgess*)	5-4-97	19-9-97	31-7-98	Rockland, Maine
WLM 554 Marcus Hanna	23-8-97	26-11-97	19-5-98	S. Portland, Maine
WLM 555 James Rankin	25-4-98	25-4-98	1-5-99	Baltimore
WLM 556 Joshua Appleby	8-8-98	25-11-98	7-5-99	St. Petersburg, Fla.
WLM 557 Frank Drew	5-12-98	17-6-99	. . .	Portsmouth, Va.
WLM 558 Anthony Petit	30-1-99	1-7-99	18-5-00	Ketchikan, Alaska
WLM 559 Barbara Mabrity	27-3-99	29-7-99	. . .	Mobile, Ala.
WLM 560 William Tate	8-5-99	16-9-99	3-6-00	Philadelphia
WLM 561 Harry Claiborne	12-6-99	28-10-99	31-3-00	Galveston, Texas
WLM 562 Maria Bray	28-8-99	6-4-00	. . .	Mayport, Fla.
WLM 563 Henry Blake	20-11-99	22-6-00	12-10-00	Seattle
WLM 564 George Cobb	18-12-99	. . .	27-10-00	San Pedro, Calif.

D: 845 tons (fl) **S:** 12 kts **Dim:** 53.34 (47.24 pp) × 10.97 × 2.42
Electronics: Radar: 1 Raytheon SPS-64(V)1 or Hughes-Furuno SPS-73 nav.
M: 2 Caterpillar 3508 TA diesels; 2 Ulstein Model 1350H Z-drive azimuth props; 1,998 bhp (1,710 sust.)—400-shp bow-thruster
Electric: 750 kw tot. (3 × 250-kw sets, Caterpillar 3406 DIT diesels driving)

Maria Bray (WLM 562) Douglas A. Cromby, 5-00

Katherine Walker (WLM 552) William M. Rau, 7-00

Frank Drew (WLM 557)—with navigational aids buoy on deck
Val Ihde/Marinette Marine, 1999

Range: 2,000/10 **Fuel:** 40 tons
Crew: 1 officer, 17 enlisted + 6 passengers

Remarks: Lead ship was ordered 22-6-93 for $22 million, with an option for 13 more. WLM 552–556 were ordered in 1-97 for $73 million total, and WLM 557–564 were ordered during 9-97. Are intended to perform aids-to-navigation maintenance, marine environmental protection, search-and-rescue, national defense and economic exclusion zone patrol, and icebreaking duties. The crew size listed is the maximum; most currently operate with one officer and 14 enlisted. The builder became a subsidiary of Manitowoc Marine Group 20-11-00.
Hull systems: Intended to be able to break 23 mm of freshwater ice at 3 kts and 46 mm by ramming. Have a 10-ton-capacity, 12.8-m-reach hydraulic crane forward, with a 3.75-ton auxiliary lift capacity. The ships are also able to operate an oil-skimming and recovery system. Have a hydraulic windlass with two capstans forward, one electric capstan aft, and hydraulic buoy-hauling winches on the working deck forward. The VOOS (Vessel Of Opportunity System) depot-maintained oil-spill recovery system is employed, with outriggers, floats, containment booms, and Weir skimmer pumps being prepositioned at 12 East Coast, six West Coast, and one Hawaiian port; the equipment can also be employed by available small commercial ships such as trawlers, and the recovered oil is stowed in collapsible barges. Are being equipped with 5.59-m Zodiac 530 rigid inflatable boats powered by a 60-bhp outboard engine; the boats will be equipped with a GPS receiver and an echo sounder.

♦ 1 White-class (133-foot-class) coastal buoy tender [WAGL]

Bldr: Niagara SB, Buffalo, N.Y.

	Laid down	L	In serv.
WLM 540 White Sumac (ex-YF 416)	31-8-42	14-6-43	6-11-43

D: 435 tons (600 fl) **S:** 9.8 kts **Dim:** 40.49 × 9.14 × 2.67
Electronics: Radar: 1 Raytheon SPS-64(V)9 nav.
M: 2 diesels; 2 props; 600 bhp **Electric:** 90 kw tot.
Range: 2,100/9.8; 4,500/5.1 **Fuel:** 40 tons **Crew:** 1 officer, 23 enlisted

Remarks: Transferred from the navy 19-9-47. Based at New Orleans. Has one 10-ton buoy derrick.
Disposals: *White Bush* (WLM 542, ex-YF 339) was declared excess 16-9-85, *White Holly* (WLM 543) on 30-9-98, *White Sage* (WLM 544) on 28-6-96, *White Heath* (WLM 545) on 31-3-98, *White Lupine* (WLM 546) on 12-2-98, and *White Pine* (WLM 547) on 29-6-99. WLM 545 and 546 were transferred to Tunisia 10-6-98 and WLM 547 to the Dominican Republic 29-6-99.

COAST GUARD AUXILIARIES *(continued)*

White Sumac (WLM 540) Leo Dirkx, 10-99

♦ 9 Katmai Bay–class (140-foot-class) icebreaking seagoing tugs [WATA]
Bldrs: Tacoma Boatbuilding (WTGB 107, 109: Bay City Marine), Tacoma, Wash.

	Laid down	L	In serv.	Based at
WTGB 101 Katmai Bay	7-11-77	8-4-78	8-1-79	Sault St. Marie, Mich.
WTGB 102 Bristol Bay	13-2-78	22-7-78	5-4-79	Detroit, Mich.
WTGB 103 Mobile Bay	13-2-78	11-11-78	6-5-79	Sturgeon Bay, Wis.
WTGB 104 Biscayne Bay	29-8-78	3-2-79	8-12-79	St. Ignace, Mich.
WTGB 105 Neah Bay	6-8-79	2-2-80	18-8-80	Cleveland, Ohio
WTGB 106 Morro Bay	6-8-79	11-7-80	25-1-81	Yorktown, Va.
WTGB 107 Penobscot Bay	1-7-83	27-7-84	2-1-85	Bayonne, N.J.
WTGB 108 Thunder Bay	20-7-84	15-8-85	4-11-85	Rockland, Maine
WTGB 109 Sturgeon Bay	9-7-86	12-9-87	20-8-88	Bayonne, N.J.

Sturgeon Bay (WTGB 109) H&L Van Ginderen, 7-98

D: 662 tons (fl) **S:** 14.7 kts **Dim:** 42.67 (39.62 pp) × 11.43 × 3.66
Electronics: Radar: 1 Raytheon SPS-64(V)1 or Hughes-Furuno SPS-73 nav.
M: 2 Fairbanks-Morse 38D8⅛ diesels, Westinghouse electric drive; 1 prop; 2,500 shp
Electric: 250 kw tot. (2 × 125 kw)
Range: 1,800/14.7; 4,000/12 **Fuel:** 71 tons **Crew:** 3 officers, 14 enlisted

Remarks: Initially intended to replace the older WYTMs in service. WTGB 109 was ordered 11-2-86, using navy funds; at least one more was planned, to be named *Curtis Bay,* but funds were not available. Were reclassified from WYTM on 5-2-79. WTGB 106, used at Yorktown for enlisted training and painted all white, was laid up 30-9-98 for lack of operating funds; the ship was refitted at Curtis Bay, Md., for reactivation, completing during 1-01, but then laid up until late in 2001 when she was again reactivated.
Hull systems: Displace 673 tons in fresh water. Can break 0.51-m ice continuously or 1.8-m ice by backing and ramming. Have a portable bubble-generator system housed in a removable deckhouse on the fantail. There are two firefighting monitors atop the pilothouse, which provides near-360° viewing. One 2-ton crane handles a 4.9-m plastic workboat. All are now equipped with a 5.59-m Zodiac Hurricane 530 RIB powered by a 60-bhp outboard and equipped with a GPS receiver and an echo sounder.
WTGB 102 and 103 operate with 45.72 × 18.29–m aids-to-navigation barges 12001 and 12002, respectively; crewed by seven personnel each, the barges were delivered in 7-91 and 4-92 by Marinette Marine, Marinette, Wis., and are equipped with a 20-ton crane, machine shop, paint locker, bridge/pilothouse, bow-thruster, and indented sterns to permit pushing by another vessel.

♦ 1 Balsam-class training ship [WAXT]
Bldrs: Duluth Iron & SB, Duluth, Minn.

	Laid down	L	In serv.
WIX 290 Gentian (ex-WLB 290)	3-10-41	23-5-42	3-11-43

D: 697 tons light (1,038 fl) **S:** 12.8–13 kts **Dim:** 54.9 (51.8 pp) × 11.3 × 4.0
A: 2 12.7-mm M2 mg **Electronics:** Radar: 1 Raytheon SPS-64(V)1 nav.
M: 2 diesels, electric drive; 1 prop; 1,070 shp **Electric:** 400 kw tot.
Range: 4,600/12–18; 14,000/7.4 **Crew:** 6 officers, 47 enlisted

Remarks: Former seagoing buoy tender, deactivated at Atlantic Beach, N.C., 15-5-98 and placed in "special commission" layup at Curtis Bay, Md., until reactivated 1-4-99. On 27-9-99, the ship was recommissioned at Miami as a "Caribbean Support Tender," with a U.S., Bahamian, Trinidadian, and Dominican Republic multinational crew. Has been repainted white.

Gentian (WIX 290) Dave Silva/USCG, 9-99

♦ 1 German Horst Wessel–class sail-training cutter [WAXT]
Bldr: Blohm + Voss, Hamburg

	L	Based at
WIX 327 Eagle (ex-*Horst Wessel*)	13-6-36	New London, Conn.

Eagle (WIX 327) A. D. Baker III, 6-00

D: 1,519 tons light (1,816 fl) **S:** 17 kts (10 under power)
Dim: 89.92 (70.41 wl) × 11.92 × 5.18
Electronics: Radar: 1 Raytheon SPS-64(V)1 nav.
M: 1 Caterpillar D-399, V-16 diesel; 1 prop; 1,000 bhp (10 kts)—sail area: 1,983 m^2
Electric: 450 kw **Range:** 5,450/7.5 (diesel) **Fuel:** 79 tons
Crew: 19 officers, 46 enlisted + 175 cadets and instructors

Remarks: Training ship at the U.S. Coast Guard Academy. Sisters operate in the Portuguese Navy and Russian merchant marine. Has 344 tons of fixed ballast. Mast heights: foremast and mainmast: 45.8 m, mizzen: 40.2 m.

SERVICE CRAFT

♦ 1 Buckthorn-class inland buoy tender [WYGL]
Bldr: Mobile Ship Repair, Mobile, Ala.

	Laid down	L	In serv.	Based at
WLI 642 Buckthorn	1962	. . .	17-7-64	Sault Ste. Marie, Mich.

Buckthorn (WLI 642) Victor M. Baca, 1991

COAST GUARD SERVICE CRAFT *(continued)*

D: 188 tons (196 fl) **S:** 11.9 kts **Dim:** 30.48 (29.26 pp) × 7.32 × 1.42
M: 2 Caterpillar diesels; 2 props; 600 bhp
Range: 1,300/11.9; 2,000/7.3 **Crew:** 1 warrant officer, 13 enlisted

Remarks: Bow is rectangular at the main deck. Has one 5-ton boom.

♦ 2 Bayberry-class (65-foot class) inland buoy tenders [WYGL]
Bldr: Reliable Welding Works, Olympia, Wash. (L: 2-6-54; In serv. 28-6-54)

	Based at
WLI 65400 Bayberry	Seattle
WLI 65401 Elderberry	Petersburg, Alaska

Bayberry (WLI 65400)—note blunt bow form Hartmut Ehlers, 5-99

D: 68 tons (71 fl) **S:** 11.3 kts **Dim:** 19.91 × 5.18 × 1.32
M: 2 G.M. 6-71 diesels; 2 props; 400 bhp
Range: 800/11.3; 1,700/6 **Crew:** 5 tot.

♦ 1 Blackberry-class (65300-class) inland buoy tender [WYGL]
Bldr: Dubuque Boat & Boiler, Dubuque, Iowa (In serv. 24-8-46)

WLI 65303 Blackberry

Chokeberry (WLI 65304)—stricken in 2000 Hartmut Ehlers, 6-95

D: 50 tons light (68 fl) **S:** 9 kts **Dim:** 19.81 (19.20 pp) × 5.18 × 1.07
M: 1 G.M. diesel; 1 prop; 220 bhp **Range:** 700/9; 1,500/5 **Crew:** 5 tot.

Remarks: Based at Long Beach, N.C. Sister *Chokeberry* (WLI 65304) was retired 31-7-00.

♦ 1 Cosmos-class (100-foot-class) inland buoy tender [WYGL]
Bldr: Birchfield Boiler Co., Tacoma, Wash.

	Laid down	L	In serv.	Based at
WLI 313 Bluebell	20-3-44	28-9-44	24-3-45	Portland, Ore.

Bluebell (WLI 313) George R. Schneider, 11-93

D: 153 tons light (178 fl) **S:** 10.5 kts **Dim:** 30.48 (29.26 pp) × 7.49 × 1.62
M: 2 Waukesha diesels; 2 props; 600 bhp **Range:** 1,400/10.5; 2,700/7
Crew: 1 warrant officer, 14 enlisted

Remarks: Four sisters were retyped WLIC on 1-10-79, of which *Smilax* (WLIC 315) is still active as an inland construction tender. Carries four 19-ft. (5.8-m) aids-to-navigation skiffs, delivered in 1993 by Workboats Northwest, Seattle.

♦ 2 Kankakee-class (75-foot/F class) river buoy tenders [WYGL]
Bldr: Avondale Industries, New Orleans

	L	In serv.	Based at
WLR 75500 Kankakee	8-7-89	1-90	Memphis, Tenn.
WLR 75501 Greenbrier	. . .	12-4-90	Natchez, Miss.

Kankakee (WLR 75500) Avondale, 7-89

D: 136 tons (175 fl) **S:** 12 kts **Dim:** 22.86 (22.25 wl) × 7.32 × 1.53
Electronics: Radar: 1 . . . nav.
M: 2 Caterpillar 3412-DIT diesels; 2 props; 1,024 bhp
Range: 600/11 **Fuel:** 11 tons **Crew:** 13 tot.

Remarks: Approved under the FY 86 budget, to act as push-tugs for aids-to-navigation barges 74 and 75, respectively. They were originally employed on the Arkansas River. Ordered in 3-88. Have six rudders.

♦ 9 Gasconade-class (75-foot class) river buoy tenders [WYGL]
Bldrs: WLR 75401: St. Louis SB & DD, St. Louis, Mo.; WLR 75402–75405: Maxon Construction Co., Tell City, Ind.; others: Halter Marine, New Orleans

	In serv.	Barge assigned	Based at
WLR 75401 Gasconade	15-1-64	90013	Omaha, Neb.
WLR 75402 Muskingum	25-3-65	68	Sallisaw, Okla.
WLR 75403 Wyaconda	30-5-65	69	Dubuque, Iowa
WLR 75404 Chippewa	5-10-65	76	Parris Landing, Tenn.
WLR 75405 Cheyenne	3-10-66	99004	St. Louis, Mo.
WLR 75406 Kickapoo	20-5-69	77	Vicksburg, Miss.
WLR 75407 Kanawha	22-9-69	73	Pine Bluff, Ark.
WLR 75408 Patoka	9-2-70	72	Greenville, Miss.
WLR 75409 Chena	27-5-70	71	Hickman, Ky.

Cheyenne (WLR 75405)—pushing 99-ft. construction barge CGB 9904
Victor M. Baca, 1993

D: 127 tons light (141 fl) **S:** 7.6–8.7 kts **Dim:** 22.86 (22.25 pp) × 6.73 × 1.37
M: 2 Caterpillar diesels; 2 props; 600 bhp
Range: 1,600/7.6; 3,100/6.5 **Crew:** 12 tot.

Remarks: Flat-ended, barge-like hulls. WLR 75405 has an associated buoy push-barge and a slightly larger crew. Have one 1-ton crane. All operate on the Mississippi River and its tributaries. Four new 39.62 × 9.14–m construction barges were ordered for this class in 1985 from Thrift SB & Repair, Sulpher, La.; when the yard went bankrupt, the two incomplete units were completed at the U.S. Coast Guard Yard, Curtis Bay, Md., which delivered barge CG 72 for use with WLR 75408 and CG 73 for use with WLR 75407 in 4-88.

COAST GUARD SERVICE CRAFT *(continued)*

♦ 6 Ouachita-class (65-foot-class) river buoy tenders [WYGL]

Bldrs: WLR 65501, 65502: Platzer SY, Houston, Texas; others: Gibbs Corp., Jacksonville, Fla.

	In serv.	Barge assigned	Based at
WLR 65501 OUACHITA	22-7-60	67	Chattanooga, Tenn.
WLR 65502 CIMARRON	30-9-60	70	Paris Landing, Tenn.
WLR 65503 OBION	5-1-62	99008	Owensboro, Ky.
WLR 65504 SCIOTO	27-3-62	99002	Keokuk, Iowa
WLR 65505 OSAGE	15-5-62	99003	Sewickley, Pa.
WLR 65506 SANGAMON	16-6-62	99005	Peoria, Ill.

D: 130 tons light (145 fl) **S:** 10 kts **Dim:** 20.02 × 6.40 × 1.52
M: 2 Caterpillar diesels; 2 props; 600 bhp
Range: 1,700/10.5; 3,500/6 **Crew:** 10 tot.

Remarks: WLR 65504 has a larger crew and an associated push-type buoy barge with a 3-ton crane. All have an onboard 3-ton crane. Operate on the Mississippi River and its tributaries.

♦ 4 Pamlico-class (160-foot-class) inland construction tenders [WYGL]

Bldr: U.S. Coast Guard Yard, Curtis Bay, Md.

	Laid down	L	In serv.	Based at
WLIC 800 PAMLICO	1-6-74	13-12-75	11-8-76	New Orleans
WLIC 801 HUDSON	6-6-75	29-5-76	14-10-76	Miami Beach, Fla.
WLIC 802 KENNEBEC	9-1-76	11-12-76	6-4-77	Portsmouth, Va.
WLIC 803 SAGINAW	5-7-76	11-6-77	22-9-77	Mobile, Ala.

Hudson (WLIC 801) Winter & Findler, 9-01

D: 413 tons light (459 fl) **S:** 11.5 kts **Dim:** 30.48 × 9.14 × 1.17
Electronics: Radar: 1 Raytheon SPS-69 (1900 Pathfinder) nav.
M: 2 Cummins D379, 8-cyl. diesels; 2 props; 1,000 bhp
Range: 1,400/11; 2,200/6.5 **Crew:** 1 officer, 13 enlisted

Remarks: Design combines the capabilities of the *Anvil* class and their associated equipment barges. Have one 9-ton crane. All operate on Atlantic Coast inland waterways.

♦ 8 Anvil-class (75-foot-class) inland construction tenders [WYGL]

Bldrs: WLIC 75301, 75302: Gibbs SY, Jacksonville, Fla.; WLIC 75303–75305: McDermott Fabricators, Morgan City, La.; WLIC 75306: Sturgeon Bay SB & DD, Sturgeon Bay, Wis.; WLIC 75309, 75310: Dorchester SB, Dorchester, N.J.

	In serv.	Barge assigned	Based at
WLIC 75301 ANVIL	14-5-62	68013	Charleston, S.C.
WLIC 75302 HAMMER	20-11-62	68014	Mayport, Fla.
WLIC 75303 SLEDGE	5-12-62	8400	Baltimore, Md.
WLIC 75304 MALLET	1-2-63	84002	Corpus Christi, Texas
WLIC 75305 VISE	14-3-63	68012	St. Petersburg, Fla.
WLIC 75306 CLAMP	24-11-64	68016	Galveston, Texas
WLIC 75309 HATCHET	23-6-66	68018	Galveston, Texas
WLIC 75310 AXE	17-10-66	68020	Mobile, Ala.

Vise (WLIC 75305)—pushing construction barge CGB 68012 Leo Dirkx, 3-01

D: 129 tons light (145 fl) **S:** 9.1 kts **Dim:** 23.19 (22.26 pp) × 6.83 × 1.37
M: 2 diesels; 2 props; 600 bhp **Range:** 1,000/10 (see remarks)
Crew: 0 or 1 officer, 9 enlisted

Remarks: All except WLIC 75301 and 75304 have an associated push-type barge with a 9-ton crane. WLIC 75306 and 75310 are 23.2 m overall and can make 9.4 kts. Ranges vary: WLIC 75301, 75302: 1,300/9, 2,400/5; WLIC 75303–75305: 1,000/9, 2,200/5; others: 1,050/9, 2,500/5.
Disposals: Sister *Spike* (WLIC 75308) and her associated barge were stricken 30-5-86, and *Wedge* (WLIC 75307) has also been stricken.

♦ 1 Cosmos-class (100-foot-class) inland construction tender [WYGL]

Bldr: Dubuque Bopat & Boiler, Dubuque, Iowa

	Laid down	L	In serv.
WLIC 315 SMILAX	26-11-43	18-8-44	1-11-44

D: 178 tons (fl) **S:** 10.5 kts **Dim:** 30.48 (29.26 pp) × 7.49 × 1.62
Electronics: Radar: 1 Raytheon SPS-69 (1500 Pathfinder) nav.
M: 2 Waukesha diesels; 2 props; 600 bhp
Range: 1,400/10.5; 2,700/7 **Crew:** 1 officer, 14 enlisted

Remarks: Based at Atlantic Beach, N.C., since 7-99. Has a 5-ton crane. Is assigned aids-to-navigation barge 70018. Sister *Bluebell* (WLI 313) is typed as an inland buoy tender.
Disposals: *Cosmos* (WLIC 293) was stricken in 1985, *Rambler* (WLIC 298) on 3-6-98, and *Primrose* (WLIC 316) on 22-8-99.

Note: In use on inland waterways are 99-ft. (30.2-m), 90-ft. (27.4-m), and 68-ft. (20.7-m) aids-to-navigation barges, which are pushed by the various WLR- and WLIC-series tenders and two of the WYTL tugs; for individual units, see the listings under WLR, WLIC, and WYTL.

Disposal note: Former U.S. Navy large harbor tug [WYTB] *Edenshaw* (50, ex-YTB 752) was stricken and sold commercial during 2001. Tug services at the U.S. Coast Guard Yard, Curtis Bay, Md., are now performed by contract tugs, as needed.

♦ 11 65-foot-class small harbor tugs [WYTM]

Bldrs: WYTL 65607–65612: Barbour Boat, New Bern, N.C.; WYTL 65614, 65615: Western Boatbldg, Tacoma, Wash.; others: Gibbs Corp., Jacksonville, Fla.

	In serv.	Based at
WYTL 65601 CAPSTAN	19-7-61	Philadelphia
WYTL 65602 CHOCK	12-9-62	Portsmouth, Va.
WYTL 65604 TACKLE	1962	Crisfield, Md.
WYTL 65607 BRIDLE	3-4-63	Southwest Harbor, Maine
WYTL 65608 PENDANT	8-63	Boston
WYTL 65609 SHACKLE	7-5-63	South Portland, Maine
WYTL 65610 HAWSER	17-1-63	Bayonne, N.J.
WYTL 65611 LINE	21-2-63	Bayonne, N.J.
WYTL 65612 WIRE	19-3-63	Saugerties, N.Y.
WYTL 65614 BOLLARD	10-4-67	New Haven, Conn.
WYTL 65615 CLEAT	10-5-67	Philadelphia

Chock (WYTL 65602) William H. Clarke, 1-00

D: 62 tons light (72 fl) **S:** 9.8 (first six: 10.5) kts
Dim: 19.79 (19.08 pp) × 5.82 × 2.74
Electronics: Radar: 1 Raytheon SPS-66A or SPS-69 nav.
M: 1 diesel; 1 prop; 400 bhp (see remarks)
Range: 850/9.8; 2,700/5.8 (WYTL 65601–65604: 3,600/6.8, 8,900/10.5)
Crew: 10 tot.

Remarks: Can break ice up to 152 mm thick. Six were re-engined during 1993–94 with Caterpillar 3412 diesels of 475 bhp each. USCG plans to retire all remaining units before 30-9-00 were thwarted by Congress, which required them to remain operational, although they are of very little utility except as harbor icebreakers. Aids-to-navigation barge 31016 is assigned to WYTL 65608.
Disposals: Sister *Bitt* (WYTL 65613) was stricken 10-4-82, and *Swivel* (WYTL 65603), *Towline* (WYTL 65605), and *Catenary* (WYTL 65606) on 1-5-95.

SMALLCRAFT

Note: The craft described below are listed in descending order of overall length, within type categories.

♦ 3 32-foot oil-spill control launches [WYAG]

Bldr: Munson Mfg., Edmonds, Wash.

327001 (In serv. 1986) 327032 (In serv. 1991) 327100 (In serv. 1987)

D: 7.5 tons light (8.6 fl) **S:** 20.4 kts **Dim:** 10.16 × 3.58 × 0.86
Electronics: Radar: 1 Raytheon SPS-69 (1900 Pathfinder) nav.
M: 2 Caterpillar 3208 diesels; 2 props; 406 bhp
Range: 190/16.5 **Fuel:** 0.65 tons **Crew:** 3 tot.

Remarks: Former Ports and Waterways boats, used for oil-spill control by Strike Team Gulf, Strike Team Atlantic, and Strike Team Pacific. GRP construction. Fifty-two of them were built in the late 1970s to replace the 30-ft. Mk-III class. Have a 90-bhp G.M. 3-53 diesel to drive a 500-gallon/min firepump. Four sisters are used by the navy at Norfolk, while 49 others in the Ports and Waterways Boat category had been retired by 1-01.

COAST GUARD SMALLCRAFT *(continued)*

♦ 1 50-foot Passenger Boat [WYFL]
Bldr: Munson Mfg., Edmonds, Wash. (In serv. 1992)

502001

D: . . . tons **S:** . . . kts **Dim:** 15.24 × 4.97 × . . .
M: 2 G.M. Detroit Diesel . . . diesels; 2 props; 1,300 bhp

Remarks: Operated since 1-95 at Fort Totten, N.Y.

♦ up to 168 41-foot Utility Boats [WYFL]
Bldr: USCG Yard, Curtis Bay, Md. (In serv. 1973–82)

41300–41507 series

41-ft. Utility Boat 41436—at Norfolk Takatoshi Okano, 4-01

D: 13–14 tons (fl) **S:** 22–26 kts **Dim:** 12.40 × 4.11 × 1.22
Electronics: Radar: 1 SPS-69 (Raytheon 1900) nav.
M: 2 Cummins V903M or VT903M diesels; 2 props; 560 or 636 bhp
Range: 300/18 **Fuel:** 1.54 tons **Crew:** 3 tot.

Remarks: Prototype was delivered in 1971, and between 1973 and 1982, some 206 more followed. Are being replaced by 27-ft. Whaler and Safe Boats Bayliner RIB rescue craft. Aluminum construction. 41400 has special vanes on the propeller shafts, adding 2.5 kts to her speed; these were to be backfitted to the others. Designed weight was 12.97 tons, but displacements have increased to almost 14 tons. Have a 250-gallon/min firepump. Of the total, three are assigned as Aviation Training Boats and one is in reserve. The class is now being replaced by Bayliner 27-ft. RIBs (q.v.), but a number of the units inactivated have been brought back into service for antiterrorism defense duties.

Disposal note: As of 1-01, the 38-ft. utility boats 38501 and 38502 were no longer listed as USCG assets.

Note: All but three 32-ft. Ports and Waterways Boat–class launches that had been reassigned as oil-spill control craft [WYAG] had been retired by 1-01.

♦ 7 or more 30-foot Hurricane RIB Utility Boats [WYFL]
Bldr: American Zodiac, Annapolis, Md. (In serv. 1998–2000)

304430 304431 304435 304437 304440 304444 304450

D: . . . tons **S:** 47 kts **Dim:** 9.14 × 3.04 × 1.00 (max.)
M: 2 gasoline outboards; 450 bhp **Range:** 85/. . . **Crew:** . . . tot.

Remarks: Aluminum hulls with rigid inflatable collars. More have probably been procured since 2000.

♦ 1 28-foot Protector-class Ports and Waterways Boat [WYFL]
Bldr: SeaArk, Monticello, Ark. (In serv. 1997)

286608

D: 4 tons (fl) **S:** . . . kts **Dim:** 8.53 × 3.91 × 0.61
M: 2 . . . diesels; 2 props; 600 bhp

Remarks: Aluminum-construction craft. Assigned to Valdez, Alaska.

Note: Also in service is 28-ft. Utility Boat 282000, delivered in 1989 by SeaArk and equipped with two OMC 200-bhp gasoline outboards for speeds to 35 kts.

♦ 4 miscellaneous 28-foot Utility Boats [WYFL]

	In serv.	Bldr	M	S
208500	1987	SeaArk	2 OMC 225-bhp gasoline outboards	40 kts
208501	1988	SeaArk	2 OMC 225-bhp gasoline outboards	40 kts
282000	1989	SeaArk	2 OMC 200-bhp gasoline outboards	35 kts
284397	1997	Safe Boats	2 Mercury 200-bhp outboards	48 kts

Remarks: 284397 is the builder's American Eagle class and is assigned to Duluth, Minn. 208500 is assigned to Baltimore.

♦ 38 (+ 18) Bayliner 27-foot RIB utility launches [WYFL]
Bldr: Safe Boats International, Bremerton, Wash. (In serv. 22-8-00 to 2001)

270500–270503 272501–272508 275589
272002–272007 275586 and others

Bayliner 27-ft. RIB 275586 Safe Boats Intl., 8-00

D: 3.63 tons (fl) **S:** 50+ kts **Dim:** 8.23 × 3.05 × 1.40 (max.)
Electronics: Radar: 1 Raytheon . . . nav.
M: 2 Mercury or Cummins gasoline outboards; 450 or 500 bhp
Range: 250/. . . **Crew:** 5 tot.

Remarks: Rigid aluminum structure with solid, closed-cell polyethylene-foam bumper skirt. Have an enclosed pilothouse. The prototype operates from Bellingham, Wash. As of 6-01, 12 had been delivered, and 25 more were on order as replacements for 41-ft. Utility Boats in the 5th, 7th, 8th, 11th, 13th, and 17th Coast Guard Districts at a cost of about $140,000 each. An additional 18 were ordered 11-3-02.

♦ 7 27-foot Vigilant-class launches [WYFL]
Bldr: Boston Whaler, Edgewater, Fla. (In serv. 1990–2000)

273501–273505 273508 273509

27-ft. Vigilant-class 273502 George R. Schneider, 9-99

D: 2.27 tons light (4.0 fl) **S:** 34 kts **Dim:** 8.10 × 3.05 × 0.48
Electronics: Radar: 1 Furuno or Raytheon . . . nav.
M: 2 Johnson gasoline outboards; 350 bhp
Range: . . ./. . . **Fuel:** 802 liters **Crew:** 4 tot.

Remarks: GRP foam-core construction. Are employed for harbor patrol duties and replaced 41-ft. Utility Boats in the 7th, 8th, 11th, and 17th Coast Guard Districts. Sisters have been transferred to Romania and Kazakhstan, with USCG training assistance. Can carry up to 12 people. Class prototype 273501 has a smaller pilothouse than the others.

Note: Also in use is SeaArk Commander-class Utility Boat 274426, completed in 1997 and assigned to Harbor Beach, Calif.; she has two 175-bhp Mercury outboards and can reach 42 kts.

♦ 2 26-foot Utility Boats [WYFL] Bldr: Ambar (In serv. 1999)

26501 26502

Remarks: Assigned to Gulfport, Miss., and Ft. Myers Beach, Fla., respectively. The aluminum hulls have a 2.9-m beam, and the craft are powered by two Mercury 150-bhp outboards for 46 kts and 150 n.m. range.

♦ 1 26-foot Honolulu personnel launch [WYFL]
Bldr: Munson Mfg., Edmonds, Wash. (In serv. early 1990s)

266200

26-ft. Honolulu personnel launch 266200 Victor M. Baca, 3-94

COAST GUARD SMALLCRAFT *(continued)*

D: 3.2 tons (fl) **S:** 25 kts **Dim:** 7.92 × 3.05 × 0.61
M: 1 Volvo AQAD 41 200 diesel; Volvo SP 290 inboard/outboard drive; 200 bhp
Crew: 1 tot.

Remarks: Aluminum-construction, 12-passenger launch used to shuttle Coast Guard personnel within the Honolulu harbor area.

♦ **6 miscellaneous 25-foot Whaler launches [WYFL]**
Bldr: Boston Whaler, Edgewater, Fla. (In serv. 1990s)

25-ft. Vigilant-class launch 253503 H&L Van Ginderen, 3-96

D: 1.86 tons light (3.2 fl) **S:** 30+ kts **Dim:** 7.50 × 2.45 × 0.41
Electronics: Radar: 1 Raytheon . . . nav.
M: 2 Johnson gasoline outboards; 300 bhp **Fuel:** 534 liters

Remarks: Data apply to Challenger-class units 254308 and 254333, completed in 1987 and 1990. Also included in this category are the Sentry-class 252510 (in serv. 1987), Frontier-class 252519 (1991), Vigilant-class 253503 (1989), and Outrage-class 256550 (1990). All are of GRP foam-core construction.

Note: Other 25-ft craft in service include up to five Zodiac Hurricane RIBs, four Mako aluminum-hulled launches (252503 and 252522–252524; in serv. 1987–95), four SeaArk launches (253504, 254396, 254400, and 254439; in serv. 1994–2000), and seven Safe Boats RIBs (252525, 252526, 254581, 256000, and 256609–256611; in serv. 1997–2000).

♦ **1 24-foot V-Commander-class Utility Launch [WYFL]**
Bldr: SeaArk, Monticello, Ark. (In serv. 1998)

245564

D: 1.589 tons (light) **S:** 32 kts **Dim:** 7.00 × 2.60 × 0.40
M: 1 Volvo Penta TAMD . . . diesel outdrive; 270 bhp

Remarks: Assigned to Portland, Ore. Aluminum construction.

Note: Other 24-ft. launches in service include five built by Munson (247055 for Strike Team Gulf, 247103 for Strike Team Pacific, and 244501–244503 for use on California inland waterways); Avon RIB 242503 (in serv. 1990), based at San Juan, P.R.; and up to 10 Zodiac Hurricane Model 733 RIBs.

♦ **. . . 22-foot Sentry-class launches [WYFL]**
Bldr: Boston Whaler, Edgewater, Fla. (In serv. 1990s)

22-ft. Sentry-class launch 220512 Boston Whaler

D: 1.29 tons light (2.5 fl) **S:** 30+ kts **Dim:** 6.80 × 2.30 × 0.36
Electronics: Radar: 1 Raytheon . . . nav.
M: 2 Johnson gasoline outboards; 160 bhp **Fuel:** 291 liters

Remarks: GRP foam-core construction. Can carry up to nine persons. Differ from Guardian class in having a covered foredeck and a full-width cockpit with windshield.

♦ **38 or more 22-foot Guardian-class launches [WYFL]**
Bldr: Boston Whaler, Edgewater, Fla. (In serv. 1990s)

22-ft. Guardian-class launch 223506—on trailer Leo Dirkx, 11-99

D: 1.2 tons light (2.3 fl) **S:** 30+ kts **Dim:** 6.80 × 2.30 × 0.36
Electronics: Radar: 1 Raytheon . . . nav.
M: 2 Johnson gasoline outboards; 160 bhp **Fuel:** 291 liters

Remarks: GRP foam-core construction. Can carry up to 11 persons. From 1987 to 6-89, NAPCO International, Hopkins, Minn., delivered 24 militarized variants of this design for use by Coast Guard harbor protection personnel; they have since been replaced by larger craft.

♦ **18 21-foot Commander-class patrol launches [WYFL]**
Bldr: SeaArk, Monticello, Ark. (In serv.: 2 in 8-91, 2 in 9-91, others from 12-92 to . . .-94)

21-ft. Commander-class launch 21544—at Savannah, Ga. Leo Dirkx, 5-98

D: 1.362 tons (1.9 fl) **S:** 32 kts **Dim:** 6.40 × 2.60 × 0.44
M: 2 Evinrude gasoline outboards; 200 bhp

Remarks: Aluminum-construction, trailer-transportable, deep-vee-hulled craft for use on central U.S. inland waters for patrol and search-and-rescue duties. Hulls plane at 18 kts on one engine.

♦ **134 Searider RIB launches [WYFL]**
Bldr: Avon, . . . (In serv. 1999–2000)

Remarks: Six-meter craft powered by one or two 90-bhp gasoline outboards and intended to be carried aboard larger ships and craft.

♦ **166 21-foot Hurricane rigid inflatable boats [WYFL]**
(In serv. 1992–. . .) Bldr: American Zodiac

21-ft. Hurricane-class RIB 214385—with two Honda outboard motors and Raytheon radar George R. Schneider, 7-01

COAST GUARD SMALLCRAFT *(continued)*

D: . . . **S:** 35–37 kts **Dim:** 6.40 × . . . × . . .
M: 1 outdrive diesel or one or two gasoline outboards

Remarks: Acquired to replace Boston Whalers, both as shipboard launches and as utility and rescue launches attached to shore stations. Are radar equipped and transportable by trailers. The initial units were deployed to the Hawaiian Islands in 10-92. Most have a small Raytheon navigational radar.

Note: Other launches [WYFL] in U.S. Coast Guard service as of 2001 included:
- 23-ft.: 30 Safe Boats aluminum launches for shore stations and 1 Huskey D-9 airboat (232448; in serv. 2000)
- 22-ft.: 61 Zodiac Hurricane RIBs with 130-bhp Volvo or Caterpillar inboard/outboard diesels; 18 Ambar-built RIBs for shore stations (in serv. 1998–2000); and up to 29 Boston Whalers of various models
- 21-ft: 5 Safe Boats RIBs delivered in 1997–99 and 4 Willard RIBs delivered in 1996
- 20-ft.: 31 miscellaneous work punts assigned to various ships
- 19-ft.: 6 miscellaneous aluminum utility boats; 20 Avon RIBs (in serv. 1982–97); and 10 Zodiac Hurricane RIBs (in serv. 1986–2000)
- 18-ft.: 59 miscellaneous RIBs and 47 miscellaneous work punts
- 17-ft.: 87 miscellaneous RIBs and 53 miscellaneous aluminum utility launches
- 15-ft.: 35 miscellaneous Zodiac Hurricane RIBs and aluminum work punts
- 14-ft.: 34 ice skiffs and 39 miscellaneous boats
- 13-ft.: 28 miscellaneous shipboard launches
- 12-ft.: 6 miscellaneous launches
- 10- to 11-ft.: 14 work punts

♦ 5 Packman-class landing craft [WYFU]
Bldr: William E. Munson Co., Mt. Vernon, Wash. (In serv. 9-01)

D: . . . tons **S:** 40 kts (23 sust.) **Dim:** 10.36 × 3.66 × . . .
Electronics: Radar: one only: 1 Furuno . . . nav.
M: 2 Volvo KAD43-DP outdrive diesels; 2 props; 460 bhp **Crew:** 2 tot.

Remarks: Employed as onboard workboats for icebreakers based at Seattle, with one of the five equipped as an Arctic survey craft with a crew of six and fitted with a radar, GPS, echo sounder, and 8-kw generator set. All have a 2.1-m-wide bow door/ramp leading to a 5.5-m vehicle and cargo deck. Aluminum construction.

♦ 3 64-foot-class Buoy-Tending Boats [WYGL]
Bldr: Owen-Short Marine, Bayou La Batre, Ala.

	L	In serv.		L	In serv.
643501	18-6-96	12-12-96	643503	14-2-97	10-4-97
643502	19-11-96	10-1-97			

D: approx. 130 tons (fl) **S:** 10 kts **Dim:** 19.50 × 7.32 × 1.19
Electronics: Radar: 1 . . . nav.
M: 2 Cummins 6CTA8.3M1 diesels; 2 5-bladed props; 500 bhp
Electric: 100 kw tot. (2 × 50 kw, 2 Cummins 6B5.9MG diesels driving)
Range: . . ./. . . **Crew:** 6 tot.

Remarks: Three were ordered in 1-96, with an option for two more that was taken up; two were left incomplete, however, when the builder went out of business and were placed up for sale for commercial use. Have a 2-ton crane and can accommodate up to 13.6 metric tons of cargo on deck.

♦ 1 63-foot Aids-to-Navigation Boat [WYGL]
Bldr: . . . (In serv. 1975)

63107

D: approx. 30 tons (fl) **S:** . . . kts **Dim:** 19.20 × 5.64 × . . .
M: 2 G.M. diesels; 2 props; 800 bhp

Remarks: Transferred from Detroit, Mich., to Chincoteague, Va., during 10-00.

♦ 20 55-foot-class Aids-to-Navigation Boats [WYGL]
Bldrs: 55103–55112: Robert E. Derecktor, Mamaroneck, N.Y. (In serv. 1977); others: U.S. Coast Guard Yard, Curtis Bay, Md. (In serv. 1980–88)

55103 through 55122

55-ft. Aids-to-Navigation Boat 55114 H&L Van Ginderen, 10-00

D: 28.8 tons (31.25 fl) **S:** 22 kts **Dim:** 17.68 × 5.18 × 1.52
Electronics: Radar: 1 Raytheon SPS-69 (1900 Pathfinder) nav.
M: 2 G.M. Detroit Diesel 12 V71 TI diesels; 2 props; 1,080 bhp
Range: 350/18 **Fuel:** 3,995 liters **Crew:** 4 tot.

Remarks: Aluminum construction. Can carry 4,000 lb. of cargo; have a 1,000-lb. crane. 55101 was retired in 2000 and 55102 was sold commercial in 1999.

♦ 26 49-foot BUSL (Boat, Utility, Stern-Load)-class Aids-to-Navigation Boats [WYGL]
Bldr: U.S. Coast Guard Yard, Curtis Bay, Md. (In serv. 9-97 to 11-00)

49401 through 49426

49-ft. BUSL 49402 Christopher P. Cavas, 2-01

D: . . . tons **S:** 11 kts (10 sust.) **Dim:** 14.9 × 4.82 × . . .
M: 2 Cummins diesels; 2 props; 1,220 bhp
Range: 200/10 **Crew:** 4 tot.

Remarks: Was to have been a class of 40, but the program was curtailed at 26; the initial builder had a contract for four but completed only two, which were not delivered. Thirteen more were funded for $18.5 million under FY 95 and were delivered at six-week intervals by the Coast Guard Yard; a second group was ordered later. Have a 2-ton-capacity A-frame crane over the stern and can carry 7.25 tons of stores; can also break 100-mm ice and perform search-and-rescue operations. Aluminum construction.

Disposal note: All remaining 45-ft. Aids-to-Navigation Boats were to have been retired by the end of 2001, as were all nine 46-foot Stern-Loading Buoy Boats [WYGL].

♦ 2 34-foot Aids-to-Navigation Boats [WYGL]
Bldr: Munson Mfg., Edmonds, Wash.

342500 (In serv. 1987) 344266 (In serv. 1984)

Remarks: Dissimilar craft, but both built of aluminum. 342500 has two 200-bhp Volvo outdrive engines for 28 kts and is based at St. Petersburg, Fla. 344266 has two 250-bhp Mercury outboards for 37 kts and is based at Portage, Mich.

♦ 28 23-foot Trailerable Aids-to-Navigation Boats [WYGL]
Bldr: SeaArk, Monticello, Ark. (In serv. 1991–. . .)

D: 1.27 tons (3.08 fl) **S:** . . . kts **Dim:** 7.10 × 2.40 × 0.36 (hull)
M: 1 gasoline outboard; 130 bhp

Remarks: Builder's Navigator design. Are used as utility boats aboard buoy tenders and, as the older WLBs are retired, as shore-based aids-to-navigation service boats.

♦ 90 21-foot Trailerable Aids-to-Navigation Boats [WYGL]
Bldr: MonArk, Monticello, Ark. (In serv. 1991–92)

21-ft. Trailerable Aids-to-Navigation Boat 21460 George R. Schneider, 7-01

D: 1.59 tons light (3.17 fl) **S:** 28 kts **Dim:** 6.56 × 2.24 × 0.36 (hull)
M: 1 gasoline engine; 1 prop; 228 bhp—or Mercruiser/OMC 165 bhp outboard
Range: 100/20 **Crew:** . . . tot.

Remarks: Aluminum construction. Design is based on the builder's 21-V, deep-vee hull design. Can be mounted on a trailer for land transport. Four were delivered in 11-92 and four more during 12-92. Some are painted black, while others have been left in unpainted aluminum except for the Coast Guard stripes.

Note: One 19-ft. (5.8-m) skiff was delivered in 9-94 by Munson Boats, La Conner, Wash.; no details available.

COAST GUARD SMALLCRAFT *(continued)*

♦ 2 18-foot-class Navigational Aid Skiffs [WYGL]
Bldr: Kvichak Marine Industries, Seattle (In serv. 1994)

D: . . . tons (fl) **S:** 35+ kts **Dim:** 5.49 × 2.13 × 0.28
M: 2 OMC gasoline outboard motors; 140 bhp **Crew:** 2 tot.

Remarks: Aluminum hulls with foam flotation. Based at Port Angeles and Kennewick, Wash.

♦ 36 18-foot Seasled-class Utility Boats [WYGL]
Bldr: Munson Mfg., Edmonds, Wash.

18-ft. Seasled-class buoy recovery boat Munson, 1993

D: 0.8 tons (fl) **S:** 30 kts **Dim:** 5.49 × 2.29 × 0.30
M: 2 Johnson gasoline outboards; 80 bhp

Remarks: Employed on the Mississippi, Ohio, and Missouri River systems as buoy recovery craft. Normally carried aboard river tenders. Aluminum construction. The second order, for 20, was completed in 4-93.

Note: Also in use are 11 other 18-ft. workboats, built by SeaArk, Workboats, Boston Whaler, Mako, Kann, and Lowe.

♦ 95 (+ 23) 47-foot Motor Life Boat class [WYH]
Bldr: Textron Marine and Land Systems, New Orleans (In serv. 17-4-98 to . . .)

MLB 47206 through MLB 47314

47-ft. Motor Life Boat MLB 47267 George R. Schneider, 10-00

47-ft. Motor Life Boat MLB 47246 A. D. Baker III, 6-00

D: 18.15 tons (fl) **S:** 25 kts (20 sust.)
Dim: 14.61 (13.11 wl) × 4.27 × 1.32 (0.80 hull)
Electronics: Radar: 1 Raytheon 41X nav.
M: 2 G.M. Detroit Diesel 6V92 TA diesels; 2 props; 840 bhp
Range: 220/25; 208/10 **Fuel:** 1,560 liters **Crew:** 4 tot. + 5 survivors

Remarks: Intended to replace the 44-ft. class and to provide significantly greater speed of reaction, with up to 123 to be built. The first unit, 47200, was laid down 1-8-89 and delivered 25-6-90, and five preproduction boats were ordered 9-12-91 and completed during 1993; all six were retired in 1998 and transferred to the customs service and local law enforcement agencies. Twenty production versions were ordered 11-9-95, 20 more the following year, 30 in 1-98, 23 early in 1999, and the final 24 late that year. During 2000–01, deliveries were being made every 18 days. The boats are taken by truck to final fitting-out facilities at Astoria, Ore.; Alameda, Calif.; Detroit, Mich.; and Portsmouth, Va. Eleven sisters were ordered 1-4-97 for the Canadian Coast Guard from MIL Systems Engineering, Ottawa, and MetalCraft Marine, Kingston, Ont., and another 20 were ordered during 10-01 from Victoria Shipyards, Victoria, B.C.
Hull systems: Aluminum construction, with a deep-vee, self-righting hullform. Trials in heavy seas were highly successful: they can maintain 20 kts in 2-ft. seas and tow craft displacing up to 150 tons; can survive an end-for-end pitch-pole; and are capable of operating in 80-kt gales with 9-m swells and 6-m breaking seas. Carry a Motorola MCX1000 VHF radio.

♦ 2 Hammerhead 24–class search-and-rescue launches [WYH]
Bldr: Munson Mfg., Edmonds, Wash. (In serv. early 1990s)

D: 2.8 tons (fl) **S:** 45 kts **Dim:** 7.31 × 2.59 × 0.61
M: 2 Evinrude V-6 gasoline outboards

Remarks: Employed at the Lake Tahoe, Calif., search-and-rescue station, operating 7,000 ft. above sea level. Aluminum construction.

♦ 1 Lake Champlain search-and-rescue launch [WYH]
Bldr: SeaArk Boat, Monticello, Ark. (In serv. 1987)

D: . . . **S:** 38 kts **Dim:** 8.69 × 3.56 × 0.56
Electronics: Radar: 1 Furuno . . . nav.
M: 2 Volvo AQAD 41/290 outdrive diesels; 2 props; 400 bhp **Crew:** 2–3 tot.

Remarks: Aluminum construction. Based at Burlington, Vt. Used for search and rescue.

Disposal note: All 44-ft. Motor Life Boats had been retired by the end of 2001. Five were donated to the Seychelles in 8-00, nine to Uruguay in 8-99, and four to El Salvador during 2001.

♦ 4 52-foot Motor Life Boat class [WYH]
Bldr: U.S. Coast Guard Yard, Curtis Bay, Md.

52312 VICTORY (In serv. 29-11-56)	52314 TRIUMPH II (In serv. 1-4-61)
52313 INVINCIBLE (In serv. 11-10-60)	52315 INTREPID (In serv. 11-10-61)

D: 31.7 tons (35 fl) **S:** 11 kts **Dim:** 15.85 × 4.43 × 1.91
M: 2 G.M. Detroit Diesel 6-71 diesels; 2 props; 340 bhp
Range: 495/11; 650/. . . **Crew:** 5 + up to 35 rescued personnel

Remarks: Designed for service under extremely heavy sea conditions. All are in service on the Pacific Northwest coast. Have a 250-gallon/min firefighting and salvage pump. Are to serve until 2012 or later.

Disposal note: All remaining 30-ft. Surf Rescue Boats were to have been retired by the end of 2001.

♦ 53 Mk V 26-foot Motor Surf Boats [WYH]
Bldr: Ocean Technical Services, Harvey, La. (In serv. 5-95 to 3-97)

D: . . . tons (fl) **S:** 18 kts **Dim:** 7.93 × 2.16 × . . .
M: 1 Cummins 4BT3.9M diesel; 1 prop; 130 bhp **Crew:** 3 tot.

Remarks: The first 45 were ordered in spring 1995 for $4.7 million, with an option for 10 more. GRP construction, with 1.37-m molded depth. Capable of carrying up to 13 rescuees. Two others, 26508 and 26539, have been stricken.

Disposal note: All remaining 25-ft. Motor Surf Boats have been retired.

♦ 1 LCM(8)-class cable repair craft [WYRC]
72015

D: 34 tons light (121 fl) **S:** 9 kts **Dim:** 22.43 × 6.43 × 1.35 (fwd; 1.47 aft)
M: 4 G.M. Detroit Diesel 6-71N or 2 12V-71 diesels; 2 props; 1,080 bhp
Range: 190/9 (loaded) **Crew:** 4–5 tot.

Remarks: Converted from a U.S. Navy LCM(8) landing craft in 1979 and now stationed at Detroit, Mich., as a telephone- and power-cable layer. A new pilothouse and several gooseneck davits have been added and the bow altered. Sister 748281 is assigned to “Detachment Fire and Safety Test”; no other information available.

♦ 1 LCM(6)-class cable repair craft [WYRC]
Bldr: Grafton Boat Co. (In serv. 1969)

560500 (ex-56CM6841)

LCM(6)-class cable repair craft 560500 H&L Van Ginderen, 9-94

D: 50 tons (fl) **S:** 10 kts **Dim:** 17.07 × 4.37 × 1.17
Electronics: Radar: 1 Raytheon SPS-69 (1900 Pathfinder) nav.
M: 2 G.M. Detroit Diesel 6-71 diesels; 2 props; 330 bhp **Range:** 130/10

COAST GUARD SMALLCRAFT *(continued)*

Remarks: On loan from the navy. Conversion to cable tender was completed in 6-86 at the USCG Yard, Curtis Bay, Md., for service at South Portland, Maine, as a telephone- and power-cable layer. A new pilothouse, cable reels, and several gooseneck davits were added, and the bow was altered. Sister 56025 is employed for "Detachment Fire and Safety Test"; no other information available.

♦ 4 Navy-44-class sail training craft [WYTS]

Bldr: Uniflite-Tillotson-Pearson, Warren, R.I. (In serv. 1987–89)

Arctic Tern   Blue Goose   Shearwater   Stormy Petrel

D: 14.35 tons (fl) **S:** . . . **Dim:** 13.41 (10.91 wl) × 3.40 × 2.26
Electronics: Radar: 1 Raytheon SPS-66 nav.
M: 1 auxiliary diesel; 1 prop; 33 bhp—sail area: 88 m^2 **Crew:** 8–10 cadets

Remarks: GRP construction "Luders Yawls." Mast height above the water: 19.66 m. Sisters to a series built for the U.S. Naval Academy. These are assigned to the U.S. Coast Guard Academy, New London, Conn. Also in service at the academy are the sloop *Rampage;* the sailing craft *Crew 18, Dyer, Eastern 18, Eddystone Light, Fly Junior,* and *Interclub;* 19 22-ft. (6.7-m) J-22-class, 28 16-ft. (4.9-m), 19 14-ft. (4.3-m), and 27 12-ft. (3.7-m) Laser 13-F sailboats; and smallcraft *Steamboat, Tigger,* SISU-30, and CT-64.

U.S. ARMY

The U.S. Army's fleet is divided into landing craft and logistics support craft operated by the Transportation Corps and units operated by the Corps of Engineers (primarily survey craft, dredges, and construction craft). Combat troops also operate large numbers of river-crossing craft.

U.S. ARMY TRANSPORTATION CORPS

Bases: Principal facilities at Ft. Eustis, Virginia; Southampton, England; and Military Ocean Terminal Concord, Calif. (with the latter having been handed over by the U.S. Navy on 22-10-99)

Note: U.S. Army Transportation Corps ships and craft are classed by design number. They carry alphanumeric serials in the following categories:

BC	Barge, dry cargo, non-self-propelled
BCDK	Barge, decked
BD	Crane, floating
BG	Barge, liquid cargo, non-self-propelled
BK	Barge, dry cargo, non-self-propelled, knock-down
BPL	Pier, barge-type, self-elevating
BR	Barge, refrigerated, non-self-propelled
FB	Ferry
FMS	Repair shop, floating, marine repair, non-self-propelled
HSPC	High-Speed Patrol Craft
J	Work and inspection boat, under 50 ft. (15.24 m) o.a.
LARC	Lighter, Amphibious, Resupply, Cargo
LCM	Landing Craft, Mechanized
LCU	Landing Craft, Utility
LSV	Logistic Support Vessel
LT	Tug, large, 100 ft. (30.48 m) and over
ST	Tug, Small, under 100 ft. (30.48 m)
T	Freight and supply vessel, small, under 100 ft. (3.48 m)

LOGISTICS SUPPORT SHIPS

Note: In 5-00, the army requested bids for concept designs for 14 units of a successor class to the *Gen. Frank S. Besson, Jr.* class. The TLV (Theater Logistics Vessel) would have 15,000 ft.^{2} of deck space and would carry up to 2,650 tons of vehicle cargo at 24 kts (with designs requested for ships capable of 40 kts while carrying 2,000 tons). Gas turbine-electric drive may be employed, and waterjets may replace propellers. The structure is to be of aluminum alloy. The initial units would be ordered under the FY 07 budget, with one per year planned to be ordered through FY 21.

♦ 6 (+ 1 + 2) Gen. Frank S. Besson, Jr. class [WLST]

Bldr: Friede Goldman Halter, Moss Point, Miss.

	L	In serv.	Based at
LSV-1 Gen. Frank S. Besson, Jr.	30-6-87	20-1-88	Ft. Eustis, Va.
LSV-2 CW3 Harold C. Clinger	16-9-87	20-4-88	Ford I., Oahu, Hawaii
LSV-3 Gen. Brehon B. Somervell	18-11-87	26-7-88	Tacoma, Wash.
LSV-4 Lt. Gen. William B. Bunker	11-1-88	1-9-88	Ft. Eustis, Va.
LSV-5 MGen. Charles P. Gross	11-7-90	30-4-91	Ford I., Oahu, Hawaii
LSV-6 Sp.4 James A. Loux	7-4-94	5-7-95	Ft. Eustis, Va.
LSV-7	. . .	5-03	. . .
LSV-8	. . .	. . .	. . .
LSV-9	. . .	. . .	. . .

Lt. Gen. William B. Bunker (LSV-4) Takatoshi Okano, 4-01

CW3 Harold C. Clinger (LSV-2) Brian Morrison, 6-00

Lt. Gen. William B. Bunker (LSV-4) A. D. Baker III, 6-00

D: first 6: 1,612 tons light (4,199 fl) **S:** 12 kts trials (11.6 sust.)
Dim: first 6: 83.14 (78.03 pp) × 18.28 (18.16 wl) × 1.75 (light; 3.66 max. loaded)
A: none
Electronics: Radar: 2 Decca BridgeMaster-E ARPA nav. (X- and S-band)
M: 2 G.M. EMD 16-645-E2 diesels; 2 props; 3,900 bhp—250-shp Schottel bow-thruster
Electric: 599 kw (2 × 250-kw Caterpillar 3406, 1 × 99-kw Caterpillar 3304 diesel sets)
Range: 5,500/12; 8,358/11 **Fuel:** 524 tons **Endurance:** 38 days
Crew: 6 officers, 24 enlisted

Remarks: The first four were ordered 19-9-86, the fifth in 3-90, and the sixth in 1993. The design is based on the Australian roll-on/roll-off, beachable cargo ship *Frances Bay.* Built to commercial specifications. LSV 1 was laid down 16-1-87. All use rebuilt diesel engines. Two near-sisters were ordered for the Philippines in 1992. LSV 3 was employed by the Washington State Army National Guard until 1995, when she was transferred to the U.S. Army Reserve program. Three longer variants (dubbed the ELSV [Enhanced Landing Ship, Vehicle] by the builder) are being requested under the FY 01–03 budgets, and the first of these, LSV-7, was ordered from Friede Goldman Halter for $26.9 million 28-5-01, with an option for two more; after a contract protest, work was allowed to begin after 29-9-01.
Hull systems: Are intended to transport 816–1,815 metric tons of vehicles or containers on the 975-m^2 cargo deck. Rated at 48 TEU container capacity. Carry up to 122 tons of potable water and 1,631 tons of seawater ballast. Have 8.23-m-wide bow and stern ramps, the bow ramp 15.2 m long and the stern 4.87 m. There is a 5.18-m-high vehicle cargo space beneath the stern superstructure. LSV-6 can carry a 20-person training classroom made up of four 40-ft. container modules. Starting with LSV-4 during 1999, their original Raytheon radars have been replaced with Litton Decca sets, while Litton-Sperry Voyage Management Systems, Litton-Sperry adaptive autopilot, Litton-Sperry Electronic Chart Display, a GPS receiver, and a weather satellite receiving system were added at a cost of about $5 million per ship. LSV-7 and later are to be 95.40 m o.a.; they will have visor-type rounded bow doors to improve seakeeping.

♦ 35 2000 Design utility landing craft [WLCU]

Bldrs: Friede Goldman Halter (formerly Trinity–Moss Point Marine), Escatawpa, Miss. (first three: Lockheed SB, Savannah Div., Savannah, Ga.)—see remarks

	Laid down	L	In serv.
LCU-2001 Runnymede	2-12-86	14-8-87	21-2-90
LCU-2002 Kennesaw Mountain	22-5-87	6-10-87	28-2-90
LCU-2003 Macon	1-10-87	1-2-88	23-3-90
LCU-2004 Aldie	11-4-88	4-89	23-2-90
LCU-2005 Brandy Station	11-9-88	5-89	7-3-90
LCU-2006 Bristoe Station	11-2-89	31-7-89	30-3-90
LCU-2007 Broad Run	11-3-89	28-8-89	4-5-90
LCU-2008 Buena Vista	11-4-89	10-9-89	18-4-90
LCU-2009 Calaboza	22-11-89	9-2-90	13-7-90
LCU-2010 Cedar Run	27-12-89	12-3-90	17-8-90
LCU-2011 Chickahominy	31-1-90	16-4-90	21-9-90
LCU-2012 Chickasaw Bayou	7-3-90	26-5-90	26-10-90
LCU-2013 Churubusco	11-4-90	25-6-90	10-90
LCU-2014 Coamo	16-5-90	28-7-90	4-1-91
LCU-2015 Contreras	20-6-90	3-9-90	8-2-91
LCU-2016 Corinth	25-7-90	10-90	15-3-91
LCU-2017 El Caney	29-8-90	11-90	19-4-91
LCU-2018 Five Forks	3-10-90	17-12-90	24-5-91
LCU-2019 Fort Donelson	7-11-90	1-91	28-6-91

ARMY LOGISTICS SUPPORT SHIPS *(continued)*

	Laid down	L	In serv.
LCU-2020 Fort McHenry	12-12-90	2-91	2-8-91
LCU-2021 Great Bridge	16-1-91	1-4-91	6-9-91
LCU-2022 Harpers Ferry	2-91	5-91	11-10-91
LCU-2023 Hobkirk	27-3-91	6-91	15-11-91
LCU-2024 Hormigueros	1-5-91	15-7-91	20-12-91
LCU-2025 Malvern Hill	5-6-91	8-91	24-1-92
LCU-2026 Matamoros	10-7-91	9-91	28-2-92
LCU-2027 Mechanicsville	8-91	10-91	3-4-92
LCU-2028 Missionary Ridge	18-9-91	11-91	8-5-92
LCU-2029 Molino Del Rey	22-4-91	7-11-91	11-5-92
LCU-2030 Monterrey	27-5-91	5-12-91	15-5-92
LCU-2031 New Orleans	20-6-91	10-1-92	1-6-92
LCU-2032 Palo Alto	15-7-91	6-2-92	9-7-92
LCU-2033 Paulus Hook	15-8-91	5-3-92	18-9-92
LCU-2034 Perryville	15-9-91	2-4-92	4-8-92
LCU-2035 Port Hudson	15-10-91	30-4-92	1-9-92

Port Hudson (LCU-2035) A. D. Baker III, 6-00

Port Hudson (LCU-2035) A. D. Baker III, 6-00

D: 672 tons light (1,102 fl) **S:** 11.5 kts
Dim: 53.03 (47.55 pp) × 12.80 × 1.43 (2.60 max. loaded) **A:** none
Electronics: Radar: 1 Raytheon SPS-64(V)2 nav.; 1 Raytheon SPS-64(V) . . . nav.
M: 2 Cummins KTA-50M diesels, 2 Kort-nozzle props; 2,500 bhp—300-shp bow-thruster
Electric: 540 kw (2 × 250 kw, 1 × 40 kw)
Range: 4,500/11.5 (light) **Fuel:** 282 tons **Endurance:** 18 days
Crew: 2 officers, 11 enlisted

Remarks: The first seven were ordered 11-6-86, followed by seven more on 31-3-87, three on 22-9-87, five on 26-2-88, one on 30-8-88, and the remainder on 11-1-89—all from Thunderbolt Marine, Savannah, Ga. Another two, to have been named *Sacketts Harbor* and *Sayler's Creek,* were not ordered. The program, including the uncompleted first three, were transferred to Moss Point when Trinity Marine purchased Thunderbolt Marine from Lockheed; some outfitting was also performed at Moss Point Marine's South Moss Point facility. LCU-2007, -2008, and two others have been based at Diego Garcia since 1998 aboard the Military Sealift Command–chartered lift-ship *Strong Virginian.*
Hull systems: Can carry up to 350 tons of beaching cargo, including up to five M1A1 tanks or 24 standard 20-ft. shipping containers. Vehicle/container deck covers 237.8 m^2. Beaching draft forward is 1.22 m. There is a 50-ton kedging winch. Have a 6.56-m-long, 4.48-m-wide MacGregor-Navire bow ramp. Were built to commercial, vice military, standards. Range can be extended to 10,000 n.m. using voids for fuel.

♦ 13 U.S. Navy LCU 1646–class utility landing craft [WLCU]
Bldr: General Ship & Eng. Works (In serv. 1976–78)

LCU-1667 Manassas	LCU-1674 St. Mihiel
LCU-1668 Belleau-Wood	LCU-1675 Commando
LCU-1669 Marseilles	LCU-1676 Birmingham
LCU-1670 San Isidro	LCU-1677 Brandywine
LCU-1671 Catawba Ford	LCU-1678 Naha
LCU-1672 Bush Master	LCU-1679 Chateau-Thierry
LCU-1673 Double Eagle	

Birmingham (LCU-1676) George R. Schneider, 9-99

Commando (LCU-1675) H&L Van Ginderen, 10-00

D: 170 tons light (390 fl) **S:** 11 kts **Dim:** 41.07 × 9.07 × 2.08 (max.)
M: 4 G.M. Detroit Diesel 6-71 diesels; 2 Kort-nozzle props; 1,200 bhp
Electric: 80 kw tot. (2 × 40-kw diesel sets)
Range: 1,200/11 (light) **Fuel:** 13 tons **Crew:** 6 tot.

Remarks: Retain the U.S. Navy hull numbers assigned when built. Cargo: 145 tons max. in a 30.48 × 5.49–m cargo deck with ramps at both ends. Have a small navigational radar. LCU-1667 through -1669 are assigned to Kwajalein; LCU-1670 to the 329th Transportation Company, Ft. Eustis, Va.; LCU-1671, -1672, -1676, and -1677 to the 824th Transportation Company, U.S. Army Reserve, Stockton, Calif.; LCU-1673 to the 506th Transportation Company, Washington Army National Guard, Tacoma, Wash.; and LCU-1675 to the 558th Transportation Company, Ft. Eustis. LCU-1678 and -1679 are prepositioned at Diego Garcia in the Indian Ocean. Are to be retained into 2008.

♦ 1 U.S. Navy LCU 1466–class utility landing craft [WLCU]
Bldr: . . . (In serv. 1954)

LCU-1509 Antietam

D: 180 tons (347 fl) **S:** 8 kts **Dim:** 35.08 × 10.36 × 1.60 (aft)
M: 3 G.M. Gray Marine 64YTL diesels; 3 props; 675 bhp **Electric:** 40 kw tot.
Range: 1,200/6 (700/7 loaded) **Fuel:** 11 tons **Crew:** 11 tot.

Remarks: Sole survivor in army service of an original group of 42. Cargo: 150 tons or 300 troops on a 15.8 × 9.0–m deck, with a 4.3-m-wide bow ramp.

♦ 29 Modular Causeway Systems [WLCU]
Bldr: Lake Shore, Inc., Iron Mountain, Mich. (In serv. 1995–96)

Army Modular Causeway power unit—at center of three 8-ft. modules George R. Schneider, 9-99

D: . . . tons (fl) **S:** 6+ kts **Dim:** 99.98 × 7.32 × 0.91 (loaded; 0.30 light)
M: 2 . . . diesels; 2 waterjets; . . . bhp

Remarks: Hull is made up of air-, rail-, and truck-transportable 20 × 8 × 4–ft. modules that can be joined together while afloat in up to State 3 seas. In the full-length, 328-ft. configuration, the joined units can support 350 tons of cargo. A small modular pilothouse is used for conning.

♦ 94 U.S. Navy LCM(8) Mod. 1–class landing craft [WLCM]
(In serv. 1954–72)

D: 58.8 tons light (116 fl) **S:** 9.2 kts (loaded) **Dim:** 22.40 × 6.42 × 1.40 (mean)
Electronics: Radar: LCM-8596 and possibly others: 1 Raytheon. . . nav.

ARMY LOGISTICS SUPPORT SHIPS *(continued)*

Army LCM(8) LCM-8604 Takatoshi Okano, 8-00

Army LCM(8) LCM-8596—converted into a push-tug and fireboat at Hythe, England Jim Sanderson, 7-99

M: 2 G.M. Detroit Diesel 6-71 diesels; 2 props; 600 bhp
Range: 150/9.2 (loaded) **Fuel:** 2.4 tons **Crew:** 2–4 tot.

Remarks: Assignments: 18 at Ft. Eustis, Va.; 15 at Ft. Clayton, Panama; 15 at Ft. Belvoir, Va. (army reserve); 5 at Kwajalein; 8 in Puerto Rico (4 national guard); 1 in Okinawa; 4 in the Azores; 2 in Japan; 1 in South Korea; 6 in Alaska (national guard); 13 in Florida (army reserve); 18 at Tacoma, Wash. (national guard); 10 at Diego Garcia; 4 prepositioned on LASH ships (LCM-8511, -8517, -8583, and -8585); and 3 in storage/repair at Charleston, S.C. A rehabilitation program is under way for all the survivors. LCM-8596 was modernized at Hythe, England, in 1999 to function as a push-tug, with bow fenders, a deckhouse in the after half of the tank deck, and an enlarged pilothouse; the bow ramp remains functional. LCM-8265 (ex-Navy C200779) and LCM-8268 (ex-Navy C200782) were donated to Tunisia during summer 2000.

♦ up to 22 LARC LX (Design 2303) amphibious transport vehicles [WLVP] Bldr: . . .

LARC LX-06, -08, -16, -17, -18, -20, -27, -37, -38, -40, -41, -43, -46, -47, -48, -49, -50, -52, -53, -54, -55, -56, -57

Army LARC LX-41 Paul C. Clift, 6-97

D: 88 tons light (about 190 fl) **S:** 6.5 kts max./15.2 mph on land
Dim: 19.07 × 8.10 × 5.92 **M:** 4 diesels; 2 props; 660 bhp
Range: 75/6 (60-ton load) **Crew:** . . .

Remarks: Four-wheeled vehicles with 100-ton maximum payloads (60 tons normal). Cargo well measures 12.9 × 4.1 m, with a full-width bow ramp. Were to have been retained until 2008, but at least one was for sale as of 1-02.

AUXILIARIES

Note: Although chartered 25-7-01 with U.S. Army Tank-Automotive and Armament Command (TACAN) funds and temporarily numbered "HSV-X1" after delivery, the wave-piercing catamaran troop and vehicle transport *Joint Venture* became the U.S. Navy's IX 532 (q.v.) on 5-10-01.

♦ 6 LT 130 Design Large Diesel Waterway Tugs [WATA]

Bldrs: First three: Robert E. Derecktor SY, Middletown, R.I.; others: Friede Goldman Halter, Moss Point, Miss.

	Laid down	L	In serv.
LT-801 MGen. Nathanael Greene	25-3-88	4-7-89	6-3-94
LT-802 MGen. Henry Knox	. . .	10-89	7-5-94
LT-803 MGen. Anthony Wayne	11-1-89	2-8-90	7-5-94
LT-804 BGen. Zebulon Pike	. . .	. . .	30-9-94
LT-805 MGen. Winfield Scott	. . .	. . .	30-9-94
LT-806 Col. Seth Warner	. . .	16-12-93	15-11-94

Col. Seth Warner (LT-806) A. D. Baker III, 6-00

Col. Seth Warner (LT-806) A. D. Baker III, 6-00

D: 924 tons (fl) **S:** 12 kts **Dim:** 39.01 (37.57 pp) × 10.97 × 4.73
A: provision for 4 single 12.7-mm mg **Electronics:** Radar: 2 . . . nav.
M: 2 G.M. EMD 12-645 FM8 diesels; 2 props; 5,100 bhp
Electric: 550 kw (2 × 275 kw) **Range:** 5,000/12 **Fuel:** 224 tons **Crew:** . . .

Remarks: The first two were ordered from Derecktor 5-1-88 under FY 87 funding, with an option for eight more. Two more were ordered in 1988, a fifth on 22-2-89, and another two in 9-89. The original planned total was 13. The builder defaulted early in 1992, and the contract to finish the ships for which construction was in various stages of completion was awarded to Trinity Industries. The first five had been launched by the Derecktor yard, while LT-806 was transported by barge to Mississippi for launch and outfitting. The names for LT-807 and LT-808, which were never begun, were to have been *SgM. John Champe* and *MGen. Jacob Brown,* respectively. Several have been assigned to the army reserve for operation.

SERVICE CRAFT

♦ 3 decked, enclosed conversion kit barges [WYC] (In serv. 1950s)

BCDK-6204 BCDK-6462 BCDK-6464

D: 175 tons (760 fl) **Dim:** 36.58 × 10.06 × 2.44

Remarks: Employed as spare parts storage barges. Are to be retained through 2008.

♦ 5 Deck Cargo Barges, Design 218D/E [WYC]

BK-8415 BK-8469 BK-8472 BK-8477 BK-8479

D: 185 tons (578 fl) **Dim:** 36.58 × 10.06 × 2.59 (loaded)

♦ 2 Nesting Deck Cargo Barges, Design 7001 [WYC]

BK-8327 BK-8336

D: 51 tons (181 fl) **Dim:** 24.69 × 6.70 × 1.45

♦ 8 Deck or Liquid Cargo Barges, Design 231B/C [WYC]

BG- series

D: 185 tons light (763 fl) **Dim:** 36.58 × 10.06 × 2.59

ARMY SERVICE CRAFT *(continued)*

Liquid Cargo Barge BG-6087 George R. Schneider, 9-99

♦ 42 miscellaneous BC-series Deck Cargo Barges, Harbor or Ocean Towing [WYC]

Deck Cargo Barge BC-6189 George R. Schneider, 12-92

D: 120 tons (690 fl) **Dim:** 33.53 × 9.75 × 2.34 **Cargo:** 570 tons

Remarks: Most are in storage at Hythe, England.

Note: In addition to the barges listed above, there are also 12 Design 455, 6 Design 456, and 3 Design 457 assembly barges and 30 portable barge propulsion devices in service. As many as 19 Modular Causeway Systems (consisting of 6 vehicle cargo discharge platforms, 5 causeway piers, and 8 causeway ferries) were to have been acquired by 1999. All Delong Type A mobile piers had been deleted by the end of 1995.

♦ 4 BD-105-class Barge Derricks [WYD]
Bldr: Bollinger Machine Shop & SY, Lockport, La.

	Laid down	L	In serv.
BD-6801 Keystone State (ex-*Sacketts Harbor*)	6-96	6-97	20-6-98
BD-6802 Saltillo	9-97	6-98	4-99
BD-6803 Springfield	3-98	1-99	3-00
BD-6804 Sausalito	3-99	11-99	11-00

Keystone State (BD-6801) Bollinger Shipyards, 5-98

D: 2,000 tons (fl) **Dim:** 60.96 × 24.38 × 4.37 (loaded)
Electric: 300 kw tot. (1 × 300-kw Kato generator, Cummins 855-G3 diesel driving)
Endurance: 20 days **Crew:** 1 officer or 2 warrant officers, 13 enlisted

Remarks: Are intended to work with Military Sealift Command Large Medium-Speed Roll-on/Roll-off ships. The first two (with an option for four more) were ordered for $29 million during 4-97; the options for two more were later exercised, but two others, to have been named *Casablanca* and *Bull Run,* were not ordered. BD-6801 was delivered to the 949th Transportation Company, Brandt U.S. Army Reserve Center, Baltimore, Md.; BD-6802 to the 73rd Transportation Company, Ft. Eustis, Va.; and BD-6803 to the 7th Transportation Group, Ft. Eustis. The name for BD-6801 was changed to commemorate 13 army reserve soldiers from Greensburg, Pa., killed in Saudi Arabia in 1991; the name duplicates that of navy crane ship T-ACS 1.
Hull systems: The crane, built by AmClyde Engineered Products, can lift 115 tons at 18.3-m radius and 50 tons at 53.3-m radius; it is powered by a 1,200-bhp Cummins KTA-38 G2 diesel. The barge hull can also accommodate 453 metric tons of deck cargo and has a galley, mess, recreation space, medical space, and machine shop. Carry GPS and a VHF radio communications station.

♦ 10 Design 264B floating cranes [WYD] Bldr: . . . (In serv. 1950s)

BD-6070 Qui Nhon	BD-6659 Wilderness
BD-6072 Algiers	BD-6660 Prairie Fire
BD-6073 Pine Ridge	BD-6661 Diamond Island
BD-6074 Naples	BD-6700 Big Switch
BD-6658 Mindanao	BD-6701 Big Bethel

Mindanao (BD-6658) George R. Schneider, 11-93

D: 1,630 tons (fl) **Dim:** 42.67 × 21.34 × 1.91
Electric: 250 kw **Fuel:** 40 tons

Remarks: Crane capacity is 89 tons at 24.4-m radius or 75 tons at 31.8-m radius; an auxiliary hook can lift 15 tons at 37.3 m. BD-6659 was refitted in 1989 as the prototype for a class-wide refurbishment program. BD-6073 is in storage at Hythe, England, and BD-6072 and -6074 are prepositioned at Diego Garcia; the others are all in active service. *Sicily* (BD-6071) was stricken in 1990, *Luzon* (BD-6069) in 6-93, and one other in 1996. The entire class was to have been retired by end-2002, and some of those listed above may no longer be in service.

♦ 2 T-boat Design 2001 inshore transports [WYF] (In serv. 1950s)

T-449 T-600

U.S. Army T-boat T-449 W. Michael Young, 10-00

D: 66 tons (95 fl) **S:** 10.5 kts **Dim:** 19.98 × 5.38 × 1.98 (max.)
M: 1 diesel; 1 prop; 300 bhp **Range:** 596/10.5 light; 397/7 loaded
Electric: 5 kw **Crew:** 4 tot. + 24 passengers

Remarks: Steel construction. Intended to transport passengers and cargo at harbors and on inland waters. Can carry 24 tons of cargo. Have one hatch and a 1-ton derrick. T-449 is located at Oakland, Calif., and T-600 at Kwajalein.

♦ 1 Double-ended Harbor Ferry [WYFB] (In serv. . . .)

FB-814

Remarks: No data available. Used at U.S. Military Academy, West Point.

♦ 2 41-foot catamaran patrol launches (WYFL)
Bldr: United States Marine, Trinity Marine Group, New Orleans (In serv. 3-92)

HSPC-1 HSPC-2

HSPC-1 and HSPC-2 Trinity Marine, 3-92

D: . . . tons **S:** 45 kts **Dim:** 12.50 × . . . × . . .
M: 2 Ford Merlin turbocharged diesels; 2 Arneson ASD 10 surface outdrives; 800 bhp
Crew: 3 tot. + 8 passengers

ARMY SERVICE CRAFT *(continued)*

Remarks: Employed at Kwajalein Atoll in the Marshall Islands. Have a forward-looking infrared sensor, navigational radar, and secure communications and can carry two Zodiac F470 rigid inflatable raiding craft. Hulls are constructed of Kevlar fabric over polyvinyl chloride foam cores. HSPC = High-Speed Patrol Craft.

♦ **2 catamaran personnel launches [WYFL]**
Bldr: Nichols Bros., Whidbey Island, Wash.

FB-816 Jera (In serv. 2-88) FB-817 Jelang K (In serv. 1988)

D: 63.7 tons (fl) **S:** 25 kts **Dim:** 23.00 × 8.68 × 1.80
Electronics: Radar: 1 Furuno FCR 1411/6 nav.; 1 Furuno 8030D nav.
M: 2 G.M. 16V92 TA diesels; 2 props; 1,920 bhp **Electric:** 100 kw

Remarks: Intended to carry 75 passengers at Kwajalein. Are of the Wavepiercer proprietary design from Australia. Are to be retired by 2002.

♦ **11 High Speed Patrol launches [WYFL]**
Bldr: Livesay Boats, San Diego (In serv. 1990s)

J-7850 J-7852 through J-7858 J-7861 Destorm J-7863 J-7864

Destorm (J-7861)—at Monterey, Calif. George R. Schneider, 5-94

Remarks: Are 8.23-m overall and are powered by one outdrive diesel engine. Used as range safety boats at Aberdeen Proving Ground on the Chesapeake Bay, Md., and at Fort Ord, Calif. Some, like J-7861, have locally applied names. No further data available.

♦ **1 J-boat Design 243B picket boat [WYFL]**
Bldr: Lock City Marine (In serv. 1954)

J-3761

J-3761 William Rau, 1-96

D: 6.7 tons (light) **S:** 15 kts **Dim:** 14.12 × 3.23 × 0.99
M: 2 diesels; 2 props; 400 bhp **Range:** 355/15

Remarks: Steel construction. Located at the U.S. Military Academy, West Point, N.Y. Is to be retained through 2002.

♦ **1 liquid cargo barge [WYON]**
Bldr: Conrad Industries Orange SB, Orange, Texas (In serv. 1996)

BK-9603

Remarks: 59.44-m overall; no other information available.

♦ **2 Design 7011 floating machine shops [WYR]** Bldr: . . .

FMS-786 Athena FMS-789 Vulcan

D: 1,160 tons light (1,525 fl) **Dim:** 64.14 × 12.19 × 2.36 (max.)
Electric: 400 kw (4 × 100 kw) **Fuel:** 140 tons **Crew:** 30 tot.

Remarks: Modified from Design 7016 refrigerated stores barges. Have an 8.9-ton crane amidships. Workshops include battery, blacksmith, carpentry, electrical, electronic, engine, fuel injector, machine, paint, pipefitting, refrigeration, sheet metal, shipfitting, and welding. FMS-786 is at Hythe, England, and FMS-789 with the national guard at Tacoma, Wash. Sister *Ares* (FMS-788) was stricken in 1997. Sisters are in U.S. Navy service and one is in the Chinese People's Liberation Army Navy.

♦ **10 (+ 4) ST-900-class push-tugs [WYTB]**
Bldr: Conrad Industries Orange SB, Orange, Texas

	In serv.		In serv.
ST-901 Dorchester Heights	2-9-98	ST-908 Sacketts Harbor	20-6-00
ST-902 Pelham Point	15-12-99	ST-909 Bunker Hill	15-6-01
ST-903 Fort Stanwix	21-12-99	ST-910 Santiago	13-12-01
ST-904 Green Springs	21-12-99	ST-911 Vincennes	1-02
ST-905 Scholarie	28-3-00	ST-912 Fort Moultrie	15-3-02
ST-906 Sag Harbor	28-3-00	ST-913	1-03
ST-907 Appomattox	24-3-00	ST-914	3-03

Dorchester Heights (ST-901)—note the twin push-knees at the bow
A. D. Baker III, 6-00

D: 109 long tons (light) **S:** 10.5 kts **Dim:** 18.19 × 6.90 (6.70 wl) × 2.03
A: 5 5.66-mm M-16 automatic rifles
Electronics: Radar: 1 Raytheon R40XX nav.
M: 2 Cummins KTA19-M3 diesels; 2 4-bladed Kaplan swiveling-nozzle props; 1,280 bhp
Electric: 110 kw tot. (2 × 55-kw Onan/Admiral MCGGA diesel-driven sets)
Range: 700/10.5 **Fuel:** 3,000 gallons **Crew:** 4 tot. (accomm. for 5)

Remarks: Nine were ordered in 6-96 for $30 million to be transported aboard army-support Military Sealift Command supply ships to move LASH and general cargo barges in harbors and on inland and coastal waterways; they were delivered at one-month intervals, with three more ordered later. ST-913 and -914 were ordered 12-11-01. Designed by Corning Townsend of C.T. Marine. Are intended to serve for at least 25 years.
Hull systems: Have 16.8-ton bollard pull ahead, 12.2-ton bollard pull astern, and 1.8-ton bollard pull athwartships. Hull molded depth is 2.44 m. Navigation equipment includes a Rockwell GPS receiver. Have four rudders and can turn 360° in their own length in 34 seconds.

♦ **2 former commercial large harbor tugs [WYTB]**
Bldr: Quality SY, Houma, La.

LT-101 Gulf Condor (In serv. 3-81)
LT-102 Mystic (ex-*Gulf Raven*) (In serv. 4-81)

D: . . . tons **S:** . . . kts **Dim:** 36.88 × 10.36 × 4.24
Electronics: Radar: . . .
M: 2 G.M. Electromotive Div. 12-cyl. diesels; 2 props; 4,200 bhp
Electric: 150 kw tot. (2 × 75-kw diesel sets) **Range:** . . ./. . . **Fuel:** 47.9 tons

Remarks: 193 grt. Are employed at Kwajalein and owned by the Army Transportation Corps.

♦ **14 Design 3006 large harbor tugs [WYTB]**
Bldr: . . . (In serv. mid-1950s)

LT-1937 Sgt. William W. Seay	LT-2076 New Guinea
LT-1956 Fredericksburg	LT-2081 San Sapor
LT-1960 Lundy's Lane	LT-2085 Anzio
LT-1970 Okinawa	LT-2088 Petersburg
LT-1972 Gettysburg	LT-2090 Sp.4 Larry G. Dahl
LT-1973 Shiloh	LT-2092 North Africa
LT-1974 Champagne-Marne	LT-2096 Valley Forge

ARMY SERVICE CRAFT *(continued)*

Champagne-Marne (LT-1974) A. D. Baker III, 6-00

D: 295 tons light (390 fl) **S:** 12.75 kts **Dim:** 32.61 × 8.08 × 3.71 (max.)
M: 1 Fairbanks-Morse diesel; 1 prop; 1,200 bhp (see remarks)
Electric: 80 kw **Range:** 3,323/12 light **Fuel:** 54 tons
Crew: 16 tot. (accomm. for 20)

Remarks: Bollard pull: 12 tons. Built in two series: LT-1936 through -1977 and LT-2202, and LT-2075 through -2096. LT-2081, -2085, -2090, and -2092 are prepositioned at Diego Garcia. All but two were to be retired by 2008, but seven have recently been rehabilitated: LT-1973, -1974, -2081, -2085, -2090, -2092, and -2096 were refitted at Hythe, England, and re-engined in 1995–2001 with one 2,350-bhp G.E. EMD 12V-645-E7 diesel; they now have a bollard pull of 31.5 tons and a 12.8-kt maximum speed, while the generator plant now totals 330 kw from two Caterpillar 3306-D1 diesel-driven generators, and they can pump 2,000 gallons of firefighting foam per minute.
Disposals: *Bataan* (LT-2086) and *Kwajalein* (LT-2087) were stricken in 2-94 and *Murfreesboro* (LT-1959) in 1995–96. In 8-97, Congress directed the transfer of *Normandy* (LT-1971) and *Salerno* (LT-1953) to the Brownsville (Texas) Navigational District. Congress also required the transfer of the *Attleboro* (LT-1977) to a private agency under the FY 99 Defense Authorization Act.

Disposal note: The 11 remaining units of the Design 3004–class 600-bhp medium harbor tug design were to have been retired by 1999 and several have since been offered for commercial sale.

U.S. ARMY CORPS OF ENGINEERS

The U.S. Army Corps of Engineers Dredging and Navigation Branch operates hundreds of tugs, utility craft, and barges in construction, local transportation, and survey service. The major vessels are the following 12 dredges [WYM]:

	Annual capacity (m^3)	Home port	Operating area
Hopper dredges:			
Essayons	5,390,430	Portland, Ore.	Pacific Coast
Hurley	6,116,800	Memphis, Tenn.	Inland rivers
Jadwin	1,433,625	Vicksburg, Miss.	Inland rivers
McFarland	3,173,090	Philadelphia	In reserve
Potter	5,398,993	St. Louis, Mo.	Inland rivers
Wheeler	11,469,000	New Orleans	In reserve
Yaquina	715,665	Portland, Ore.	Pacific Coast
Sidecaster dredges:			
Fry	188,856	Wilmington, N.C.	Atlantic Coast inlets
Merritt	304,310	Wilmington, N.C.	Atlantic Coast inlets
Schweizer	473,287	Wilmington, N.C.	Atlantic Coast inlets
Pipeline dredge:			
Thompson	755,316	Saint Paul, Minn.	Inland rivers
Special-purpose dredge:			
Currituck	584,537	Wilmington, N.C.	Atlantic Coast inlets

Wheeler was placed in ready reserve on 1-10-97. *McFarland* was to be overhauled from 2001 to 2003 and then placed in reserve.

U.S. ARMY SPACE AND STRATEGIC DEFENSE COMMAND

Note: Headquartered at Redstone Arsenal, Huntsville, Ala., the Space and Strategic Defense Command operates the missile test and instrumentation range at Kwajalein Atoll in the South Pacific.

♦ 1 Stalwart-class former ocean surveillance ship [WAGM]
Bldr: Friede Goldman Halter, Moss Point, Miss.

	Laid down	L	In serv.
WORTHY (ex-T-AGOS 14)	3-4-86	6-2-88	7-4-89

D: 1,467 tons light (2,258 fl) **S:** 11 kts **Dim:** 68.28 (59.13 pp) × 13.11 × 4.57
Electronics: Radar: 2 Raytheon . . . nav. (S- and X-band)
M: 4 Caterpillar-Kato D-398B 800-bhp diesels, G.E. electric drive; 2 4-bladed props; 2,200 shp (1,600 sust.)—550-hp bow-thruster
Electric: 1,500 kVA from main generators, plus 250-kw emergency diesel set
Range: 11,200/11 + 2,088/3 **Fuel:** 657 tons **Endurance:** 98 days **Crew:** . . .

Remarks: A former ocean surveillance ship transferred 30-9-93 from the Military Sealift Command to the U.S. Geological Survey and laid up at Redwood City, Calif., through 6-94. $23.1 million was included in the FY 94 budget to convert her as a research ship to be homeported at Redwood City; instead, in 1995 the ship was placed on indefinite loan to the U.S. Army Space and Strategic Defense Command for use as a missile range instrumentation ship at Kwajalein Atoll in the Marshall Islands. She is operated under contract by Raytheon Range Systems Engineering and is used to track and collect telemetry from missiles launched from Vandenberg Air Force Base, Calif., as the platform for the Kwajalein Mobile Range Safety System (KMRSS).

Worthy U.S. Army, 1999

Mission systems: Two 6.70-m-diameter radomes cover the two collocated HELIX command-and-control and telemetry system antennas, and the former SURTASS control room is used as the KMRSS operations center. Three Inmarsat SATCOM antennas are installed forward of the stacks, and there are four GPS receivers. A Mk 51 Optical Acquisition Aid was placed atop the pilothouse.

Note: The U.S. Army also operates several hundred Fairey Marine bridge erection boats.

U.S. DEPARTMENT OF COMMERCE
NATIONAL OCEANIC AND ATMOSPHERIC ADMINISTRATION

Personnel (1-02): 299 commissioned officers, approx. 400 civilians

Organization: The National Oceanic and Atmospheric Administration (NOAA) operates a fleet of research ships divided into two categories: Research and Survey. Headquartered in Rockville, Md., NOAA has its major maritime facilities at the Atlantic Marine Center in Norfolk, Va., and the Pacific Marine Center in Seattle; minor NOAA maritime facilities exist at Woods Hole, Mass.; Pascagoula, Miss.; Miami; La Jolla, Calif.; and Honolulu.
Subordinated to NOAA is the National Marine Fisheries Service, which operates an unspecified number of small patrol craft. These display the words "NOAA Enforcement" on the hull sides.

Aviation: NOAA, using about 25 NOAA Corps and 50 civilian personnel, operates two WP-3D Orion, one Gulfstream-IVSP, two DeHavilland DHC-6 Twin Otter, two Shrike Commander 500s, one Turbo Commander 690A, one Cessna Citation-II 550, and two Lake LA-250 Turbo Renegade research aircraft, as well as one McDonnell-Douglas MD-500D and two Bell 212 helicopters. Aviation activities are headquartered at MacDill Air Force Base, Tampa, Fla.

Note: Hulls and superstructures are painted white, masts and stacks buff. Hull numbers appear on either side (preceded by "R" for research or "S" for Survey) above the letters "NOAA." The first digit in the three-digit hull number is the NOAA class (i.e., size) number for the ship, determined from the gross tonnage and horsepower.
In addition to the ships described below, NOAA operates the former U.S. Navy YTT 9–class torpedo trials ship *Agate Pass* (YTT 12), transferred 31-1-01; for characteristics, see [YPT].

OCEANOGRAPHIC RESEARCH SHIPS [WAGOR]

♦ 0 (+ 4) FRV-40-class fisheries research ships
Bldr: Friede Goldman Halter, Moss Point, Miss.

	Laid down	L	In serv.
R . . . OSCAR DYSON	. . .	. . .	1-04
R	. . .	. . .	. . .
R	. . .	. . .	. . .
R	. . .	. . .	. . .

D: . . . tons **S:** 14 kts **Dim:** 63.60 × 14.94 × . . . (8.65-m molded depth)
Electronics: Radar: . . .
M: integrated diesel-electric plant: 2 Caterpillar 3512B DITA diesels (1,824 bhp each), 2 Caterpillar 3508B diesels (1,220 bhp each); 1 prop;—bow-thruster
Range: . . ./. . . **Endurance:** 40 days
Crew: 20 tot. + up to 19 scientific party

Remarks: The design process was begun in 6-93 and the first unit was ordered 18-1-01 for $38.3 million. Initial funding of $39.6 million was requested in the FY 99 budget, and three additional were to be requested, the last in FY 03; instead, the first was authorized under FY 00—but not funded sufficiently to permit construction—while the other three were to be requested under FY 02 through FY 04. Construction start has been delayed by design problems and the builder's financial condition. Are to be based at Kodiak, Alaska; Woods Hole, Mass.; Pascagoula, Miss.; and Newport, Ore.
Mission systems: Characteristics listed are provisional; the ships may grow somewhat, as it has proven difficult to fit all the desired features. Will be equipped for fisheries research, hydroacoustic surveys, bottom and pelagic trawling, marine mammal observation, general oceanographic research, and hydrographic survey. Will have a dynamic positioning system, support systems for remotely operated vehicles (ROVs), and several different sonar systems. There will be a fish laboratory, wet and dry laboratories, an autosalinometer room, and chemistry, hydrographic, acoustic, and computer laboratories. The integrated propulsion plant will allow any or all of the four 600-V-a.c. diesel generator sets to provide the necessary power for propulsion and ship systems operation.

NOAA OCEANOGRAPHIC RESEARCH SHIPS [WAGOR] *(continued)*

♦ 1 Thomas G. Thompson class
Bldr: Trinity Marine Halter SY, Moss Point, Miss.

	Laid down	L	In serv.
R 104 Ronald S. Brown (ex-*Researcher*)	21-2-95	30-5-96	19-7-97

Ronald S. Brown (R 104) Mitshuhiro Kadota, 4-01

Ronald S. Brown (R 104) Leo Dirkx, 2-00

D: 2,100 tons light (3,250 fl) **S:** 15 kts **Dim:** 83.52 × 16.00 × 5.18
Electronics:
Radar: 2 Sperry RASCAR nav.; Radtec-Enterprise WSR-74C Doppler weather-mapping
Sonar: Sea Beam 2112A mapping (12 kHz); Ocean Data sub-bottom profiler (3.5 kHz); Nautronix RS916 acoustic positioning syst.
M: 3 Caterpillar 3516TA diesels, 3 1,500-kw Kato generators, 2 G.E. electric motors; 2 LIPS azimuth props; 6,000 shp—1,117-shp Elliot White Gill bow-thruster
Electric: 2,500 kw tot. (3 × 750-kw Kato sets, Caterpillar 3508TA diesels driving; 1 × 250-kw Kato emergency set, Caterpillar 3406TA diesel driving)
Range: 11,300/12 + 30 days on station **Endurance:** 60 days
Crew: 20 tot. + 25 scientists (+ 10 in accommodations vans)

Remarks: 3,180 grt. Ordered 17-2-94 as the fourth unit of the U.S. Navy's *Thomas G. Thompson* (AGOR 23) class but not numbered in the navy series as an AGOR. Work began 15-9-94. Was accepted by the Military Sealift Command 25-4-97 and transferred on the same date to NOAA. Was renamed 30-5-96 in honor of the former secretary of commerce killed 3-4-96 in airplane crash in Bosnia. Ran aground in Swanson Bay, B.C., 23-4-00, holing a fuel tank. Is homeported at Charleston, S.C. During 4-01, conducted the Aerosol Characterization Experiment off the coasts of Japan and Korea, in conjunction with a National Science Foundation C-130 and a navy Twin Otter light transport.

Capable of all-purpose oceanographic research, specifically chemical and biological oceanography, multidisciplinary environmental investigations, ocean engineering, marine acoustics, marine geology, and geophysics. Is also capable of carrying out bathymetric and magnetometry surveys. The ship is initially involved in worldwide climate change research.

Hull systems: Has a dynamic positioning system accurate to 300 ft. in a 27-kt wind and 11-ft. seas. Has 372 m^2 of laboratory space and space for four lab/accommodations vans on deck, 325 m^2 of working space on deck, stern A-frame and starboard oceanographic gantries, and a Markey DESH-9-11 double-drum waterfall winch. Navigational equipment included a DSN-450 doppler speed log, a VN-150-HP acoustic doppler current profiler, Sperry Mk 37 and Mk 39 ring-laser gyrocompasses, Northstar 941X and Ashtech 3DF GPS receivers, and two Raytheon RD-500 echo sounders. Has a Leica MX-2400 Inmarsat-A SATCOM transceiver. The 18-ft.-diameter radome for the weather-mapping radar is mounted atop the foremast; the radar has a peak power of 250 kw and can track, detail, and record storms within 150 n.m. of the ship. A 951-MHz wind-profiling system is to be installed. A 10-m-tall bow-mounted tower supports equipment for the IMET (Improved Meteorological) World Ocean Circulation Experiment.

♦ 4 Stalwart-class former ocean surveillance ships
Bldr: Halter Marine, Moss Point, Miss.

	Laid down	L	In serv.
R 333 Ka'imimoana (ex-*Titan,* T-AGOS 15)	30-10-86	18-6-88	8-3-89
R 334 Vindicator (ex-T-AGOS 3, ex-WMEC 3, ex-T-AGOS 3)	14-4-83	1-6-84	21-11-84
R 335 Oscar Elton Sette (ex-*Adventurous,* T-AGOS 13)	19-12-85	23-9-87	19-8-88
R 336 Gordon Gunter (ex-*Relentless,* T-AGOS 18)	22-4-88	12-5-89	12-1-90

Ka'imimoana (R 333) NOAA, 1999

Gordon Gunter (R 336) NOAA, 1999

Oscar Elton Sette (R 335)—as *Adventurous,* prior to conversion
Takatoshi Okano, 4-01

Vindicator (T-AGOS 3)—prior to conversion for NOAA as R 334
George R. Schneider, 7-00

D: 1,652 tons light (2,301 fl) **S:** 11 kts **Dim:** 68.28 (62.1 wl) × 13.10 × 4.57
Electronics: Radar: 2 . . . nav.—Sonar: . . . . . . side-scan mapping
M: 4 Caterpillar-Kato D-398B 800-bhp diesels, G.E. electric drive; 2 4-bladed props; 2,200 shp (1,600 sust.)—550-hp bow-thruster
Electric: 1,500 kVA from main generators, plus 265-kw emergency set
Range: 8,000/10.5 (R 336: 5,500/11) **Fuel:** 904 tons **Endurance:** 30 days
Crew: 5 officers, 3 licensed engineers, 13 unlicensed + 10–15 scientific party

NOAA OCEANOGRAPHIC RESEARCH SHIPS [WAGOR] *(continued)*

Remarks: R 333: 2,014 grt; others 1,486 grt/786 dwt. Data above refer specifically to R 333.

R 333, deactivated 33-8-93 from the Military Sealift Command (MSC), was transferred in 11-93 and converted 5-95 to 3-96 by Maritime Contractors, Bellingham, Wash., to serve as a tender to the Tropic Atmosphere Ocean Buoy Array. The ship supports the Global Ocean Atmosphere Land System program and is homeported at Honolulu. R 333 has a 950-ft.^{2} laboratory and an oceanographic gallows crane at the stern. An Inmarsat-A SATCOM terminal was added during 1997 for transmittal of research data.

R 334 was transferred to NOAA 30-10-01 and was to depart the U.S. Coast Guard Yard, Curtis Bay, Md., for Seattle 1-2-02 to begin modification as a fisheries research ship for operations in Hawaiian waters to replace the *McArthur* (S 330). R 334 will be renamed when the conversion has been completed.

R 335 (initially to have been R 331) was transferred to NOAA 1-6-92 and delivered to Norfolk, with the intent to outfit her as a survey ship. The ship was used for basic training during 1993 and then laid up without modifications. Using FY 01 funding, she is undergoing conversion as a fisheries research vessel from 10-01 to 6-02 at Atlantic Dry Dock Corp., Jacksonville, Fla. and will operate from Hawaii as a replacement for the *Townsend Cromwell* (R 443). The afterdeck was cleared for use as a long-line fisheries deck, and the ship was equipped with a multibeam echo sounder and other echo sounders to permit her use in charting.

R 336, deactivated 17-3-93 from the MSC, was inactive at Norfolk until 1996, when she was towed to Pascagoula, Miss. Recommissioned as a fisheries research ship 28-8-98 to replace the *Chapman* (R 446), she is based at Pascagoula. R 336 has a 480-ft.^{2} wet lab, 480-ft.^{2} dry lab, 260-ft.^{2} chemistry/hydrology lab, 170-ft.^{2} computer lab, and 100-ft.^{2} electronics lab. During conversion, a stern trawl ramp and handling gear and nine deck and oceanographic winches were added.

♦ 1 Miller Freeman class   Bldr: American SB, Lorain, Ohio

	L	In serv.	Based at
R 223 MILLER FREEMAN	1967	1974	Seattle

Miller Freeman (R 223)   Victor M. Baca, 2-01

D: 1,920 tons (fl) **S:** 14 kts (sust.) **Dim:** 66.0 × 12.5 × 6.1
Electronics: Radar: 1 . . . X-band nav.; 1 . . . S-band nav.
M: 1 G.M. diesel; 1 CP prop; 2,200 bhp—400-shp Schottel retractable bow-thruster
Electric: 700 kw tot.
Range: 8,900/12 **Fuel:** 450 tons **Endurance:** 41 days
Crew: 7 NOAA officers, 4 licensed officers, 29 unlicensed + 11 scientists

Remarks: 1,515 grt/680 nrt. Conducts fisheries and living marine resources research. Was to be replaced during 1990s but remained in trawling survey work during 1996–97.
Hull systems: Has chemical, wet oceanographic, fish processing, and utility labs. Equipment includes fish-finder sonars and several echo sounders. Has a stern trawl ramp and net-handling gallows. A retractable stabilization centerboard provides mounting positions for oceanographic and acoustic research sensors; when deployed it increases draft to 9.3 m. An Inmarsat-B SATCOM terminal added in 1997 for automatic transmittal of research data.

♦ 1 Oregon II class   Bldr: Ingalls SB, Pascagoula, Miss.

	L	In serv.	Based at
R 332 OREGON II	2-67	8-67	Pascagoula, Miss.

Oregon II (R 332)   NOAA, 1987

D: 952 tons **S:** 12 kts (sust.) **Dim:** 51.8 × 10.4 × 4.3
M: 2 Fairbanks-Morse diesels; 1 CP prop; 1,600 bhp **Electric:** 400 kw tot.
Range: 9,500/12 **Fuel:** 255 tons **Endurance:** 30 days
Crew: 6 licensed officers, 10 unlicensed + 11 scientists

Remarks: 703 grt/228 nrt. Conducts fisheries and living marine resource research for the National Marine Fisheries Service in the Gulf of Mexico, Caribbean, and South Atlantic and along the southeast U.S. Atlantic Coast. Has two trawls, a hydrographic winch, a bathythermographic winch, and five laboratories.

♦ 1 Albatross IV class   Bldr: Southern SB, Slidell, La.

	L	In serv.	Based at
R 342 ALBATROSS IV	4-62	5-63	Woods Hole, Mass.

Albatross IV (R 342)   NOAA, 1987

D: 1,089 tons (fl) **S:** 12 kts (sust.) **Dim:** 57.0 × 10.0 × 4.9
M: 2 Caterpillar diesels; 1 Kort-nozzle CP prop; 1,130 bhp **Electric:** 450 kw tot.
Range: 3,933/10 **Fuel:** 150 tons **Endurance:** 16 days
Crew: 4 NOAA officers, 3 licensed engineers, 13 unlicensed + 14 scientists

Remarks: 1,115 grt/413 nrt. Has conducted fisheries and living marine resources research off the U.S. northeastern Atlantic Coast. Was inactive in 1988 but was reactivated under FY 92; was to be replaced during the 1990s, but underwent a repair period in mid-1993 and was refitted again in 1995–96.
Hull systems: Has wet and dry oceanographic, photographic, biological, plankton, and electronics laboratories. Equipment includes four scientific winches, a vertical fish-finding sonar, and deep- and shallow-water echo sounders. There is a 125-hp bow-thruster. An Inmarsat-B terminal was added in 1997 for transmittal of research data.

♦ 1 Townsend Cromwell class
Bldr: J. Ray McDermott Co., Morgan City, La.

	L	In serv.	Based at
R 443 TOWNSEND CROMWELL	7-62	7-63	Honolulu

Townsend Cromwell (R 443)   Victor M. Baca, 3-94

D: 652 tons (fl) **S:** 11.5 kts (sust.) **Dim:** 49.7 × 10.0 × 3.9
M: 2 White-Superior diesels; 2 CP props; 800 bhp **Electric:** 350 kw tot.
Range: 8,300/11.5 **Fuel:** 132 tons **Endurance:** 30 days
Crew: 4 NOAA officers, 3 licensed officers, 10 unlicensed + 9 scientists

Remarks: 564 grt/384 nrt. Conducts fisheries and living marine resources research off the Hawaiian Islands and in the central Pacific. Has a single oceanographic laboratory, an underwater bow observation chamber, and a decompression chamber for scuba divers. Taken over by NOAA in 6-75. Was refitted in 1994–95 at Maritime Contractors, Bellingham, Wash., receiving a bow-thruster, an extended deckhouse, habitability and laboratory facility improvements, and upgrades to the generator sets. Normally spends about 250 days at sea. To be retired in mid-2002.

♦ 1 David Starr Jordan class   Bldr: Christy Corp., Sturgeon Bay, Wis.

	L	In serv.	Based at
R 444 DAVID STARR JORDAN	12-64	1-66	San Diego

D: 993 tons (fl) **S:** 11.5 kts (sust.) **Dim:** 52.1 × 11.2 × 3.8 (4.8 over sonar)
M: 2 White-Superior diesels; 2 CP props; 1,086 bhp **Electric:** 400 kw tot.

NOAA OCEANOGRAPHIC RESEARCH SHIPS [WAGOR] *(continued)*

David Starr Jordan (R 444) H&L Van Ginderen, 9-99

Range: 8,560/11.5 **Fuel:** 180 tons **Endurance:** 30 days
Crew: 6 licensed officers, 10 unlicensed + 15 scientists

Remarks: 873 grt/262 nrt. Conducts fisheries and living marine resources research off the U.S., Central American, and South American Pacific coasts. Has physical and biological oceanography, chemical, and photographic labs and an underwater observation chamber at the bow. Equipment includes a retractable fish-finding sonar, a vertical fish-finder, and several echo sounders. Has a Schottel retractable bow-thruster of 200 hp.

♦ 1 Delaware II class
Bldr: South Portland Engineering Corp., South Portland, Maine

	L	In serv.	Based at
R 445 Delaware II	12-67	10-68	Woods Hole, Mass.

Delaware II (R 445) NOAA, 1992

D: 758 tons (fl) **S:** 11.5 kts (sust.) **Dim:** 47.2 × 9.2 × 4.5
M: 1 G.M. diesel; 1 prop; 1,230 bhp **Electric:** 300 kw tot.
Range: 6,600/11.5 **Fuel:** 132 tons **Endurance:** 24 days
Crew: 6 licensed officers, 9 unlicensed + 10 scientists

Remarks: 483 grt/231 nrt. Conducts fisheries and living marine resources research off the U.S. Atlantic coast. Has two oceanographic labs, fish-finding sonars, and a stern net ramp. Was modernized for an additional 10–12 years' service under FY 94 funding, receiving new oceanographic equipment, additional scientist berthing spaces, and fisheries hydroacoustic equipment; the modernization was completed in 5-96 at Detyens Shipyard, Mt. Pleasant, S.C.

♦ 1 Ferrel class
Bldr: Zigler SY, Jennings, La.

	L	In serv.	Based at
R 492 Ferrel (ex-S 492)	4-4-68	4-6-68	Charleston, S.C.

Ferrel (R 492) Paul C. Clift, 5-00

D: 360 tons (fl) **S:** 10 kts (sust.) **Dim:** 40.5 × 9.8 × 2.5
M: 2 Caterpillar diesels; 2 props; 750 bhp **Electric:** 300 kw tot.
Range: 2,200/10 **Fuel:** 46 tons **Endurance:** 9 days
Crew: 5 NOAA officers, 2 licensed officers, 12 unlicensed

Remarks: 349 grt/86 nrt. Maritime Administration S1-MT-MA83a design. Has a PDP 11/34 data-processing computer. Conducts coastal and estuarine seawater circulation studies off the U.S. East Coast and Gulf of Mexico. Has an electronics laboratory, a small oceanographic laboratory, and a computerized data-recording system. Carries an 8.5-m workboat. A 100-hp G.E. bow-thruster is fitted. Was redesignated from survey ship to research ship in 1996.

♦ 1 John N. Cobb class
Bldr: Western Boatbuilding, Tacoma, Wash.

	L	In serv.	Based at
R 552 John N. Cobb	1-50	2-50	Seattle

John N. Cobb (R 552) NOAA

D: 250 tons (fl) **S:** 9.3 kts (sust.) **Dim:** 28.3 × 7.9 × 3.3
M: 1 Fairbanks-Morse diesel; 1 prop; 325 bhp **Electric:** 60 kw tot.
Range: 2,900/9.3 **Fuel:** 25 tons **Endurance:** 13 days
Crew: 4 licensed officers, 4 unlicensed + 4 scientists

Remarks: 185 grt/78 nrt. Formerly conducted fisheries and living marine resources research off southeastern Alaska and the U.S. Pacific Northwest. Has a single laboratory. Was inactivated in 1989, but in 1994 was being employed in ocean salmon trawling studies, operating from Juneau, Alaska; was intended to be replaced during the 1990s.

HYDROGRAPHIC SURVEY SHIPS [WAGS]

♦ 1 Mt. Mitchell class
Bldr: Aerojet General SY, Jacksonville, Fla.

	L	In serv.	Based at
S 221 Rainier	15-3-67	2-10-68	Seattle

Rainier (S 221)—with survey launches aboard Victor M. Baca, 1-01

D: 1,800 tons (fl) **S:** 13 kts (sust.) **Dim:** 70.4 × 12.8 × 4.2
M: 2 G.M. diesels; 2 CP props; 2,400 bhp **Electric:** 600 kw tot.
Range: 7,000/13 **Fuel:** 353 tons **Endurance:** 22 days
Crew: 12 NOAA officers, 5 licensed officers, 52 unlicensed + 4 scientists

Remarks: 1,591 grt. Maritime Administration S1-MT-72a design. Sisters *Fairweather* (S 220) and *Mt. Mitchell* (S 222), inactivated in 1988 and 9-95, respectively, have been stricken from the NOAA fleet. S 221, inactivated at Seattle in 1995, was reactivated as of 1-99, performing research off the U.S. West Coast.

NOAA HYDROGRAPHIC SURVEY SHIPS [WAGS] *(continued)*

♦ 1 McArthur class
Bldr: Norfolk SB & DD, Norfolk, Va.

	L	In serv.	Based at
S 330 McArthur	15-11-65	15-12-66	Seattle

McArthur (S 330) W. Michael Young, 12-01

D: 995 tons (fl) **S:** 13 kts (sust.) **Dim:** 53.3 × 11.6 × 3.7
M: 2 G.M. diesels; 2 CP props; 1,600 bhp **Electric:** 440 kw tot.
Range: 4,500/13; 6,000/12 **Fuel:** 186 tons **Endurance:** 30 days
Crew: 8 NOAA officers, 3 licensed officers, 27 unlicensed + 12 scientists

Remarks: 854 grt/207 nrt. Maritime Administration S1-MT-70a design. Primarily performs seawater circulatory studies off the U.S. Pacific Coast and in Alaskan coastal waters. Is to be replaced by the former *Vindicator* (T-AGOS 3) during 2003. Sister *Davidson* (S 331) was deactivated in FY 89 and had been stricken by 1996.
Hull systems: Has the Hydroplot data-recording system with a PDP 11/34 computer to record current data. Carries three RIB launches.

♦ 1 Peirce class
Bldr: Marietta Mfg., Pt. Pleasant, W.Va.

	L	In serv.	Based at
S 329 Whiting	20-11-62	8-7-63	Norfolk

Whiting (S 329) Christopher P. Cavas, 9-99

D: 907 tons (fl) **S:** 12 kts (sust.) **Dim:** 49.7 × 10.1 × 3.4 (4.0 over sonar)
Electronics:
Radar: 1 . . . X-band; 1 . . . S-band nav.
Sonar: EG&G 720 side-scan mapping; Klein T-5000 precision side-scan; 12-kHz deepwater echo sounder; 100-kHz shallow-water echo sounder; 24- and 100-kHz survey sounder; 36-kHz Intermediate Depth Swath Survey System
M: 2 G.M. diesels; 2 CP props; 1,600 bhp **Electric:** 408 kw tot.
Range: 5,700/12 **Fuel:** 138 tons **Endurance:** 20 days
Crew: 7 NOAA officers, 3 licensed officers, 25 unlicensed

Remarks: 696 grt/151 nrt. Maritime Administration S1-MT-59a design. Works on the U.S. Atlantic Coast, in the Gulf of Mexico, and in U.S. Caribbean possessions. Sister *Peirce* (S 328) was laid up in 1987, reactivated in 1991 for training cruises, inactive again by 1993, and finally donated to New York City and renamed the *Elizabeth A. Fisher* as a training vessel.
Hull systems: Has the Hydrochart II data system to record hydrographic data; the system is also fitted to the two 8.8-m Jensen survey launches. Has deep, shallow, and hydrographic survey echo sounders and tows side-scan mapping sonars. Has Differential GPS and Loran-C receivers.

♦ 1 Rude class
Bldr: Jakobson SY, Oyster Bay, N.Y.

	L	In serv.	Based at
S 590 Rude	17-8-66	3-67	Norfolk

D: 220 tons (fl) **S:** 10 kts (sust.) **Dim:** 27.4 × 6.7 × 2.2
M: 2 Cummins diesels; 2 Kort-nozzle props; 800 bhp **Electric:** 120 kw tot.
Range: 1,000/10 **Fuel:** 12 tons **Endurance:** 3 days
Crew: 3 NOAA officers, 1 licensed officer, 7 unlicensed

Rude (S 590) 2001

Remarks: 150 grt/42 nrt. Was in refit at end-1995 and is now equipped with the Reson SeaBat 9001S multibeam mapping sonar system. Has side-scan and multibeam bathymetric sonars and a computerized data storage and is equipped with a differential GPS receiver. Has two 70-hp hydraulic auxiliary drives, and can support diving teams intended to inspect submerged objects. Was designed to work together with sister *Heck* (S 591) in making wire drag surveys off the U.S. Atlantic and Gulf coasts, but no longer does so; S 591 was deactivated 30-9-95 for disposal and was sold to Marex Oceanographic Services, Memphis, Tenn.

SERVICE CRAFT

♦ 1 chartered debris-removal ship [WYAG]
Bldr: Marco, Seattle (In serv. 1977)

Ocean Fury

D: . . . **S:** . . . kts **Dim:** 37.19 × 8.62 × . . .
M: 1 Caterpillar D-398 diesel; 1 prop; 850 bhp
Crew: 4 tot. + 7 scientists/technicians

Remarks: King crab fishing vessel, chartered in 10-01 for several years from Pacific Fishermen, Inc. (a subsidiary of Fury Group, Edmonds, Wash.), for use in clearing debris from along reefs and atolls in the Midway Island–Hawaiian Islands corridor. Was lengthened and widened in 1991.

♦ 3 ex-U.S. Coast Guard 82-foot Point-class support craft [WYAG]
Bldr: U.S. Coast Guard Yard, Curtis Bay, Md. (*Point Monroe:* J. Martinac SB, Tacoma, Wash.)

	In serv.
Point Glass (ex-WPB 82336)	29-8-62
Point Lobos (ex-WPB 82366)	29-5-67
Point Monroe (ex-WPB 82353)	27-12-66

D: 64 tons (66–69 fl) **S:** 23.7 kts (see remarks) **Dim:** 25.3 × 5.23 × 1.95
Electronics: Radar: 1 Hughes-Furuno SPS-73 nav.
M: 2 Caterpillar 3412 diesels; 2 props; 1,480 bhp
Range: 490/23.7; 1,500/8 **Fuel:** 5.7 tons **Crew:** 8 tot.

Remarks: *Point Glass* was transferred in 4-01, *Point Monroe* on 19-8-01, and *Point Lobos* on 13-10-01 on retirement from the Coast Guard, all for service at the Florida Keys National Marine Sanctuary, Key West, Fla. Hull is built of mild steel. High-speed diesels are controlled from the bridge. Are equipped with a 4.27-m Avon Searider rigid inflatable boat powered by a 40-bhp outboard engine; the RIB is equipped with a GPS receiver and an echo sounder.

♦ 2 ex-U.S. Army T-boat research craft [WYAG]
Bldr: Missouri Valley Steel, Leavenworth, Kans. (In serv. 1953)

R 693 Shenehon (ex-T-465)
R . . . Jane Yarn (ex-USN 65WB801, ex-Army T-460)

Shenehon (R 693) George R. Schneider, 7-01

NOAA SERVICE CRAFT *(continued)*

D: 69 tons light (98 fl) **S:** 10 kts **Dim:** 19.96 × 5.38 × 2.00
M: 1 Caterpillar D375 diesel; 1 prop; 270 bhp **Electric:** 42 kw tot.
Range: 700/10 **Fuel:** 3.7 tons **Crew:** 4–6 tot.

Remarks: R 693 was acquired 25-6-65 from the U.S. Army and operates on the Great Lakes from Muskegon, Mich., for the Great Lakes Environmental Research Laboratory and the National Weather Service. Appearance is similar to craft depicted in the army section. Sister *Virginia Key* (ex-Army T-433), formerly used for training at the NOAA Training Center, Ft. Eustis, Va., has been discarded.

♦ 1 small research craft [WYAG] Bldr: Equitable SY, New Orleans

Laidly (ex-. . .)

D: . . . tons **S:** 18–20 kts **Dim:** 17.98 × . . . × 1.06
M: 2 G.M. 12V71 diesels; 2 props; . . . bhp

Remarks: Former oilfield crewboat. Operates from Solomon's Island, Md. Also in use are the former shrimp boat *Gloria Michelle,* on Narragansett Bay, R.I.; several 30-ft. hydrographic launches; and three 7.92 × 2.74–m aluminum research boats (one powered by a Mercruiser 7.4 inboard/outboard engine and the others by Volvo Penta outdrive diesels) delivered in 8-91 by SeaArk, Monticello, Ark.

♦ 1 Frigatebird-class inshore survey craft [WYGS]
Bldr: Princess Yachts, Tacoma, Wash.

	In serv.	Based at
Bay Hydrographer (ex-*Frigatebird,* CT 21)	15-10-88	Norfolk

Bay Hydrographer—as *Frigatebird* (CT 21) George R. Schneider, 5-94

D: 20.4 tons light **S:** 12 kts **Dim:** 17.07 × 5.18 × 1.22
Electronics:
Radar: 1 Raytheon 1220 nav.
Sonar: Dowty Type 3010 towed side-scan array
M: 2 G.M. Detroit Diesel 6-71 diesels; 2 props; 330 bhp **Electric:** 15 kw tot.
Range: 750/12 **Crew:** 9 tot.

Remarks: Prototype for the now-canceled program to build COOP (Craft of Opportunity) mine countermeasures craft for the Naval Reserve Force. GRP construction. Resembles a small, flush-decked fishing boat. On loan to NOAA as a research craft since 1994. Sister *Ballena* (ex-*Albatross,* CT 22, renamed to avoid conflict with NOAA's *Albatross IV*) was swamped, ran aground, and was lost 4-11-00 while serving the Channel Islands National Marine Sanctuary, Santa Barbara, Calif.

Note: U.S. Navy sludge-removal barge YSR 29 was transferred to NOAA in 8-85 for use as an underwater habitat support barge. Completed in 12-45, the craft displaces 160 tons light (360 fl) and measures 24.4 × 9.8 m. It was re-equipped with a centerline moonpool.

Also operated by NOAA are a 10.97 × 3.66–m research craft delivered in 10-94 by Munson Boats, La Conner, Wash., and a 7.92 × 3.04–m tender completed in 8-94 by the same builder.

Almar fisheries protection craft for NOAA Almar, 2000

The NOAA-subordinated National Marine Fisheries Service operates small patrol boats on fisheries protection service. Among the boats in service are four rigid inflatable craft delivered by Almar (Aluminum Marine Construction), Tacoma, Wash., from late 1999 to mid-2000. The first two are 8.2-m-long, 49.7-kt craft powered by twin 225-bhp Evinrude outboards and are based at Homer and Dutch Harbor, Alaska. The third is 9.75 × 3.58 m and is based at Sitka. The fourth is 10.97 × 3.96 m and is based at Kodiak.

Under a 7-00 contract, Science Applications International Corp. (SAIC) received a three-year, $9 million contract to operate the 18.3-m research craft *Ocean Explorer* (on long-term charter from NorthEast Marine Services, Portland, Ore.) on coastal surveys for NOAA between Norfolk, Va., and Eastport, Maine.

U.S. CUSTOMS SERVICE

The U.S. Customs Service operates approximately 150 small patrol boats at various U.S. ports. A complete list of the craft in use is not available. A Fountain interdiction boat ordered in 1997 is typical of the faster units: the 47-ft. craft is capable of 70 kts and is equipped with a Furuno M841 LCD radar, GP1600F GPS receiver, FM2610 VHF radio, and DC 2000 digital compass.

Also in service in Puerto Rican waters is the 40-ft. Dauntless-class aluminum patrol boat *Patrol Inspector Lon Parker,* delivered in 1-94 by SeaArk Marine, Monticello, Ark., and powered by three Cummins diesels driving Hamilton waterjets for a 32-kt maximum speed. The craft draws only 0.66 m.

URUGUAY

Eastern Republic of Uruguay

Personnel (2001): 5,000 total (500 officers), including 500 Fusileros Navales, 300 Air Arm, and 1,800 Prefectura Marítima

Bases: Headquarters and principal base at Punta Lobos, Montevideo; minor facility at Ernesto Motto Naval Station at La Paloma; and air base at Capitán Carlos A. Curbelo Naval Air Station at Laguna la Sauce, Maldonado

Naval Aviation: Fixed-wing aircraft include two Jetstream T.2 and two S-2G Tracker patrol aircraft, two Beech T-34B and two T-34C-1 trainers, two Piper PA-34-200 light transports, and three Cessna 182 light liaison aircraft. The *Escuadrón de Helicópteros* operates five Westland Wessex HC.2 transports and one Bell 47G-5 trainer; three Westland Wessex Mk 60 helicopters are in storage. The ex-Royal Navy Jetstream T.2 aircraft were acquired in 1999 to replace S-2 Tracker aircraft.

Note: Ship names are formally preceded by ROU *(República Oriental del Uruguay).*

FRIGATES [FF]

Note: Published reports of the purchase during summer 2000 of the U.K. Type 22 Batch 2 frigate *Brave* (F 94) proved erroneous.

♦ 3 French Commandant Riviere class Bldr: DCAN, Lorient

	Laid down	L	In serv.
1 Uruguay (ex-*Commandant Bourdais*)	4-59	15-4-61	10-3-63
2 Artigas (ex-*Victor Schoelcher*)	10-57	11-10-58	15-10-62
3 Montevideo (ex-*Amiral Charner*)	11-58	12-3-60	14-12-62

Uruguay (1), Montevideo (3), and Artigas (2)—at Montevideo
Ralph Edwards, 5-00

D: 1,750 tons (2,070 normal; 2,230 fl) **S:** 26 kts
Dim: 102.70 (98.00 pp) × 11.80 × 4.35 (max.)
A: 2 single 100-mm 55-cal. Model 1963 DP; 2 single 40-mm 70-cal. Bofors L70 AA; 2 triple 550-mm ASW TT (L 3 torpedoes)
Electronics:
Radar: 1 Decca 1226 nav.; 1 Thales DRBV 22A air search; 1 Thales DRBC 32C f.c.
Sonar: EDO SQS-17 hull-mounted MF search; Thales DUBA 3 HF attack
EW: ARBR-16 intercept
M: 4 SEMT-Pielstick 12 PC1 V400 diesels; 2 props; 16,000 bhp
Electric: 1,280 kw tot. **Range:** 2,300/26; 7,500/16.5 **Fuel:** 210 tons
Endurance: 45 days **Crew:** 9 officers, 150 enlisted

Remarks: *General Artigas* transferred 19-12-88 and was refitted through 9-1-89. *Uruguay* transferred 20-8-90 after striking from the French Navy 27-4-90, and *Montevideo* transferred 28-1-91. All three can carry a flag officer and staff; can also carry up to 80 troops. *Uruguay* was placed out of commission in 5-00 for a major overhaul.

FRIGATES [FF] *(continued)*

Artigas (2)—note that the Exocet missile canisters are missing within the sheet-metal heat shields Hartmut Ehlers, 5-00

Montevideo (3) Ignacio Amendolara, 2000

Combat systems: *Uruguay* was transferred without MM 38 Exocet antiship missiles but received them in 1991–92; the other pair were delivered with missiles aboard. By 2001, however, the missile had been removed due to shelf-life expiration. The four-barrel 305-mm mortar is no longer operational and is to be removed from all three. There is a Sagem DMAA optical secondary gun director atop the bridge; the stabilized, radar-equipped main battery director is aft. All three had two Dagaie decoy rocket launchers removed prior to transfer. The 40-mm AA mounts have been given GRP enclosures.

PATROL CRAFT [PC]

♦ 3 Vigilante class Bldr: CMN, Cherbourg, France

	Laid down	L	In serv.
5 25 de Agosto	6-12-79	16-10-80	25-3-81
6 15 de Noviembre	6-2-80	11-12-80	25-3-81
7 Comodoro Coe	16-5-80	27-1-81	25-3-81

15 de Noviembre (6) Ignacio Amendolara, 3-01

D: 166 tons (191 fl) **S:** 28 kts **Dim:** 41.15 (38.00 pp) × 6.80 × 2.50 (1.50 hull)
A: 1 40-mm 70-cal. Bofors AA
Electronics: Radar: 1 Decca TM 1226C nav.; 1 Decca 1229 nav.
M: 2 MTU 12V538 TB91 diesels; 2 props; 5,400 bhp
Range: 2,400/15 **Crew:** 5 officers, 23 enlisted

Remarks: Ordered in 1978. All were commissioned on their date of departure under their own power from Cherbourg to Montevideo. Are considered poor seaboats in the conditions off the Uruguayan coast and were placed up for sale in mid-1992; no purchasers appeared, however, and the boats remain in service, with the *15 de Noviembre* in major overhaul during 2000. All are based at La Paloma.
Combat systems: Have a Matra Défense Panda optronic director for the 40-mm gun, which has a GRP weather shield. The twin 20-mm 70-cal. Oerlikon AA planned for installation aft was never mounted. Have HFD/F, with an antenna atop the mast.

♦ 2 ex-U.S. Coast Guard 95-foot Cape class
Bldr: U.S. Coast Guard Yard, Curtis Bay, Md.

	In serv.
10 Colonia (ex-*Cape Higgon,* WPB 95302)	14-10-53
11 Río Negro (ex-*Cape Horn,* WPB 95322)	3-9-58

Río Negro (11) Guillermo C. Berger, 4-00

Colonia (10)—outboard the *Paysandú* (12) Ralph Edwards, 5-00

D: 90 tons (106 fl) **S:** 20 kts **Dim:** 28.96 × 6.10 × 1.55
A: 1 12.7-mm M2 mg
Electronics: Radar: 1 Raytheon SPS-64(V)1 nav.
M: 2 G.M. Detroit Diesel 16V149 TI diesels; 2 props; 2,470 bhp
Electric: 60 kw tot. **Range:** 556/20; 1,900/11.5 **Endurance:** 5 days
Crew: 1 officer, 13 enlisted

Remarks: Both were transferred 25-1-90, left for Uruguay under their own power, and are based at Paysandú. Were re-engined while in USCG service, completing 13-2-81 and 21-1-83, respectively. Have an SQN-18 echo sounder and Loran-C and SATNAV receivers. Unarmed at transfer, they had previously carried two single 12.7-mm mg and two single 40-mm Mk 64 grenade launchers. Despite their considerable age, they are rugged craft and are being employed on search-and-rescue duties, based at Montevideo.

Disposal note: *Paysandú*-class patrol craft *Salto* (14, ex-GS 24) was stricken in 1999 for display at a museum at Montevideo.

PATROL BOATS [PB]

♦ 1 U.S. 85-foot Commercial Cruiser
Bldr: Sewart Seacraft, Morgan City, La. (L: 11-68)

12 Paysandú (ex-U.S. 85NS684)

Paysandú (12) Paolo Marsan, 8-99

PATROL BOATS [PB] *(continued)*

D: 43.5 tons (54 fl) **S:** 22 kts **Dim:** 25.91 × 5.69 × 2.1
A: 3 single 12.7-mm M2 mg
Electronics: Radar: 1 Raytheon 1500B Pathfinder nav.
M: 2 G.M. 16V71N diesels; 2 props; 1,400 shp **Electric:** 40 kw tot.
Range: 800/21 **Crew:** 8 tot.

Remarks: Built under the U.S. Military Assistance Program. Aluminum construction. Based at Montevideo and used for patrolling the Río de la Plata estuary.

MINE COUNTERMEASURES SHIPS

♦ 3 ex-East German Kondor II–class patrol minesweepers [MSC]
Bldr: VEB Peenewerft, Wolgast

	Laid down	L	In serv.
31 TEMERARIO (ex-*Riesa,* 322)	15-5-72	2-10-72	3-2-73
33 FORTUNA (ex-*Bernau,* M 2673, ex-343)	28-3-72	3-8-72	1-12-72
34 AUDAZ (ex-*Eisleben,* M 2671, ex-312)	9-8-72	2-1-73	24-5-73

Fortuna (33) Guillermo C. Berger, 8-00

Temerario (31)—outboard the *Fortuna* (33) Ralph Edwards, 5-00

D: 414 tons (479 fl) **S:** 18 kts **Dim:** 56.52 × 7.78 × 2.46
A: 1 40-mm 70-cal. Bofors AA
Electronics: Radar: 1 Raytheon 1900 Pathfinder nav.
M: 2 Russkiy Dizel Type 40-DM diesels; 2 CP Kort-nozzle props; 4,400 bhp
Electric: 625 kw (5 × 125-kw diesel sets)
Range: 2,000/15 **Endurance:** 10 days **Crew:** 6 officers, 25 enlisted

Remarks: Former Volksmarine units; 32–34 had served in the Bundesmarine briefly after German unification. Transferred 8-11-91 with a five-year supply of spare parts. Left Germany for Montevideo 13-11-91 under their own power, arriving 23-12-91. Sister *Valiente* (32; ex-*Eilenburg,* M 2674, ex-334) was hit by the Panamanian merchant ship *Skyros* 3-8-00 and sank, with eight killed and three personnel missing.
Combat systems: A quadruple SA-5 Grail point-defense SAM launcher and three twin 25-mm Soviet 2M-8 AA were removed prior to transfer; a single 40-mm AA has replaced the forward 25-mm mount. Two mine rails remain, but no mines were transferred. The HF hull-mounted sonar has probably been removed. Although most of the sweep gear was transferred with the ships, they are employed primarily as patrol boats; the MSG-3 magnetic influence sweep array is still carried.

AMPHIBIOUS WARFARE CRAFT

♦ 1 ex-German self-propelled pontoon [LCU]

LD 44 (ex-*Hochtief 208*)

Remarks: Former German construction company self-propelled barge; no data available.

LD 44, at left—with LD 41 Ralph Edwards, 5-00

♦ 1 LD 42–class landing craft [LCM]
Bldr: Dieque Nacional, Montevideo (In serv. 26-7-78)

LD 42

LD 42 Hartmut Ehlers, 4-92

D: 15 tons (31.4 fl) **S:** 9 kts **Dim:** 14.1 × 3.50 × 0.80
M: 2 G.M. Detroit Diesel 6-71 diesels; 2 props; 272 bhp
Range: 580/9 **Crew:** 5 tot.

Remarks: Can carry 10 tons of cargo. Was refitted in 2000–01 by Servicio de Construcciones y Reparaciones de la Armada (S.C.R.A.), Punta Lobos, Montevideo

♦ 1 U.S. LCM(6)-class landing craft [LCM]
Bldr: Servicio de Construcciones y Reparaciones de la Armada (S.C.R.A.), Punta Lobos, Montevideo (L: 29-12-89)

LD 41

LD 41 Ralph Edwards, 5-00

D: 24 tons (57 fl) **S:** 10 kts **Dim:** 17.07 × 4.37 × 1.17
M: 2 G.M. Detroit Diesel 4-71 diesels; 2 props; 450 bhp
Range: 130/9 **Crew:** 5 tot.

Remarks: Sister LD 40 was reported stricken in 1997. Cargo: 30 tons.

♦ 3 LD 43–class vehicle and personnel landing craft [LCVP]
Bldr: Servicio de Construcciones y Reparaciones de la Armada (S.C.R.A.), Punta Lobos, Montevideo

LD 43 (L: 12-5-78) LD 45 (L: 14-11-79) LD 46 (L: 9-8-82)

LD 45—with an unidentified small boat alongside Hartmut Ehlers, 12-97

AMPHIBIOUS WARFARE CRAFT *(continued)*

D: 12 tons light (15 fl) **S:** 6 kts **Dim:** 14.1 × 3.5 × 0.80
M: 1 G.M. Detroit Diesel 4-71 diesel; 1 prop; 115 bhp
Range: 580/9 **Crew:** 5 tot.

Remarks: LD 43, subordinated to the Naval Flying School at Laguna la Sauce, has two Bedford diesels totaling 192 bhp and is only 12.0 m o.a. All have a bow ramp and can accommodate light vehicles or cargo totaling about 3 tons.

AUXILIARIES

♦ 1 navigational buoy tender [AGL]
Bldr: Servicio de Construcciones y Reparaciones de la Armada (S.C.R.A.), Punta Lobos, Montevideo (L: 5-2-88)

21 Sirius

Sirius (21) Paolo Marsan, 8-99

D: 290 tons (fl) **S:** 11 kts **Dim:** 35.0 × 10.0 × 2.8
M: 2 G.M. Detroit Diesel 12V71 TA diesels; 2 props; 860 bhp
Endurance: 5 days **Crew:** 15 tot.

Remarks: Built with assistance from Damen SY, Hardinxveld, the Netherlands. Has an electrohydraulic articulated crane forward.

♦ 1 U.S. Auk-class research ship [AGOR]
Bldr: Defoe Boiler & Machine Works, Bay City, Mich.

	Laid down	L	In serv.
24 Comandante Pedro Campbell (ex-4; ex-MS 31; ex-*Chickadee,* MSF 59)	21-8-41	20-7-42	9-11-42

Comandante Pedro Campbell (24)—outboard the *Vanguardia* (26) Ralph Edwards, 5-00

D: 90 tons (1,250 fl) **S:** 18 kts **Dim:** 67.41 (65.53 wl) × 9.78 × 3.28
A: 1 76.2-mm 50-cal. U.S. Mk 22 DP; 2 single 20-mm 70-cal. Oerlikon Mk 10 AA
Electronics: Radar: 1 . . . nav.; 1 . . . surf. search
M: 4 Alco 539 diesels, electric drive; 2 props; 3,118 shp
Electric: 300 kw tot. **Range:** 4,300/10 **Crew:** 105 tot.

Remarks: Former fleet minesweeper, transferred 18-8-66 on loan and purchased outright 18-8-76. All minesweeping and ASW gear was removed, except for the sweep winch, which was used for towing. Typed as a corvette until late 1980s. Converted for service as a supply ship for the General Artigas Base in Antarctica in 1990 and left on her first Antarctic mission 15-1-91. By 1997, however, she had been rearmed, and the former red-and-white paint scheme returned to naval gray.

♦ 1 ex-German Helgoland-class (Type 720) survey ship [AGS]
Bldr: Schichau, Bremerhaven

	Laid down	L	In serv.
22 Oyarvide (ex-*Helgoland,* A 1457)	24-7-64	9-4-65	8-3-66

D: 1,304 tons (1,558 fl) **S:** 16.6 kts **Dim:** 67.91 × 12.74 × 4.60
A: removed **Electronics:** Radar: 1 Kelvin-Hughes 14/9 nav.
M: 4 MWM 12 RS 18/22-21 AE 1 diesel generator sets (700 kw each), electric drive; 2 props; 3,300 shp

Oyarvide (22) Guillermo C. Berger, 8-00

Electric: 1,065 kVA tot. (4 × 250-kVA, 1 × 65-kVA diesel sets)
Range: 6,400/16 **Crew:** 34 tot.

Remarks: 1,186 grt. Stricken from the German Navy 19-12-97 and transferred 1-9-98 after a refit at Neuen Jadewerft, Wilhelmshaven, departing for Uruguay 7-11-98. Is assigned to the Hydrographic Institute for use as a coastal survey ship, but was built as a salvage tug. May be employed as tender to the General Artigas Base in Antarctica. Has HF sonar equipment for salvage work, is equipped for fire fighting, and remains equipped with a submersible diver's decompression chamber and hoist system, as well as a full suite of salvage equipment. Her ice-strengthened hull permitted use as a harbor icebreaker in German service. Bollard pull: 40 tons. Has a GPS receiver.

♦ 1 Polish Piast-class salvage ship [ARS]
Bldr: Stocznia Polnocna, Gdansk (In serv. 29-12-76)

26 Vanguardia (ex-*Otto von Guericke,* A 441)

Vanguardia (26) Guillermo C. Berger, 10-00

D: 1,560 tons (1,732 fl) **S:** 16.5 kts **Dim:** 72.6 (67.2 pp) × 12.0 × 4.0
A: none **Electronics:** Radar: 2 TSR-333 nav.
M: 2 Cegielski-Sulzer 6TD48 diesels; 2 CP props; 3,600 bhp
Range: 3,000/12 **Crew:** 16 officers, 44 enlisted

Remarks: Acquired from the former East German Volksmarine by the newly unified Germany in 10-90. Was purchased by Uruguay in 10-91, refitted at Neptun-Warnow Werft in Rostock, and sailed for Montevideo in 1-92. Design is a variation of the *Moma* class navigational-aids and survey ship design, adapted for salvage and rescue duties. Has two sisters in the Polish Navy. Carries a submersible diver's decompression chamber to port. Can tow and has extensive pump and firefighting facilities.
Combat systems: Two twin 30-mm AK-230 AA mounts and two 25-mm 2M-8 AA mounts were removed, as was the MR-104 Rys' (Drum Tilt) radar director for the 30-mm AA.

♦ 1 sail-training ship [AXT]
Bldr: Soc. Española de Construcción Naval, Matagorda, Cádiz, Spain (In serv. 1930)

20 Capitán Miranda (ex-GS 20)

D: 587 tons (715 fl) **S:** 11 kts (14 under sail)
Dim: 54.60 (61.21 over bowsprit; 45.00 pp) × 8.40 × 3.60
Electronics: Radar: 1 Decca TM 1226C nav.
M: 1 G.M. diesel; 1 prop; 600 hp—sail area: 722 m^2
Fuel: 45 tons **Crew:** 49 tot.

Remarks: Originally built as a hydrographic survey ship. Was refitted, re-engined, and rigged as a three-masted schooner for cadet training, recommissioning in 1978. Received a further refit during 1993–94 in Spain.

AUXILIARIES *(continued)*

Capitán Miranda (20) A. D. Baker III, 6-00

SERVICE CRAFT

♦ **1 former East German coastal tug [YTB]**
Bldr: VEB Peenewerft, Wolgast

	Laid down	L	In serv.
27 Banco Ortiz (ex-*Zingst,* Y 1695; ex-*Elbe,* A 443)	9-1-58	4-4-59	10-9-59

Banco Ortiz (27) Guillermo C. Berger, 12-99

D: 261 tons (fl) **S:** 10 kts **Dim:** 30.50 × 8.00 (7.50 wl) × 2.50
Electronics: Radar: 1 . . . nav.
M: 1 Buckau-Wolff R6DV 148 diesel; 1 prop; 550 bhp
Range: 1,400/10 **Crew:** 12 tot.

Remarks: Acquired by Germany at unification in 10-90 and used by the Bundesmarine until transferred to Uruguay in 10-91; sailed for Montevideo under her own power 13-11-91. Has 9-ton bollard pull at 10 kts. Was given new auxiliary machinery during a refit in 1983.

♦ **1 training craft [YXT]**
Bldr: . . . . . ., Glasgow, Scotland (In serv. 1908)

26 Zapican (ex-*Vanguardia,* ex-*Balizador*)

D: 95 tons **S:** 12 kts **Dim:** approx. 32.0 × . . . × . . .
M: 1 set triple-expansion reciprocating steam; 1 prop; 200 ihp

Remarks: Originally a gunboat, then a hydrographic survey vessel and general-purpose tender. Was stricken in 1991 but then refitted in 1994 for further service as an immobile naval reserve training craft. The engine and boiler are no longer functional.

COAST GUARD

(Prefectura Marítima)

The Uruguayan Coast Guard has 100 officers and about 1,900 enlisted personnel. Primarily intended for a shore-based coast watch and port police function, it was integrated into the Uruguayan Navy by the end of 1992. In addition to the four units listed, it has four 4.9-m outboard-motor-powered semi-rigid inflatable rubber boats.

SERVICE CRAFT

♦ **9 ex-U.S. Coast Guard 44-foot rescue launches [WYH]**
Bldr: U.S. Coast Guard Yard, Curtis Bay, Md. (In serv. 31-3-61 to 8-5-73)

ROU 441 through ROU 449

ROU 446 Hartmut Ehlers, 5-00

D: 14.9 tons light (17.7 fl) **S:** 13 kts (11.8 sust.) **Dim:** 13.44 × 3.87 × 1.19
Electronics: Radar: 1 SPS-57 nav.
M: 2 G.M. Detroit Diesel 6V53 diesels; 2 props; 372 bhp
Range: 185/11.8; 200/11 **Fuel:** 1.2 tons **Crew:** 4 tot.

Remarks: Donated and transferred in 8-99. "Unsinkable" design. Can carry up to 21 rescued personnel. ROU 444 is the former USCG 44368.

♦ **3 23-meter tug/tenders [WYTL]**
Bldr: Regusci Voulminot, Montevideo (In serv. 1956–57)

ROU 70 (ex-PS 1) ROU 71 (ex-PS 2) ROU 72 (ex-PS 3)

ROU 70 Hartmut Ehlers, 5-00

D: 90 tons (fl) **S:** 12 kts **Dim:** 22.0 × 5.0 × 1.8
Electronics: Radar: 1 Raytheon . . . nav.
M: 2 G.M. Detroit Diesel diesels; 2 props; 400 bhp **Crew:** 8 tot.

♦ **1 tug/diving tender [WYTL]**
Bldr: J. Pollock, Faversham, U.K. (In serv. 1930)

ROU 73 (ex-*Grito de Asencio*)

ROU 73—inboard 44-ft. lifeboat ROU 448 Ralph Edwards, 5-00

Remarks: Transferred from the Harbor Board ANP in 1996. No data available, but of about the same size as the 23-m tug/tenders.

VANUATU

Republic of Vanuatu

MARINE POLICE

Base: Vita, Efate Island

Note: Ship names are preceded by RVS (Republic of Vanuatu Ship).

PATROL CRAFT [WPC]

♦ **1 Australian ASI 315 class**
Bldr: Transfield-ASI, South Coogie, Western Australia

	L	In serv.
Tukoro	20-5-87	13-6-87

Tukoro CC P. Valin, 9-98

D: 165 tons (fl) **S:** 20 kts **Dim:** 31.50 (28.60 wl) × 8.10 × 2.12 (1.80 hull)
A: 1 12.7-mm mg; 1 7.62-mm mg **Electronics:** Radar: 1 Furuno 1011 nav.
M: 2 Caterpillar 3516 diesels; 2 props; 2,820 bhp (2,400 sust.)
Electric: 116 kw tot. **Range:** 2,500/12 **Fuel:** 27.9 tons
Endurance: 8–10 days **Crew:** 3 officers, 15 constables

Remarks: Provided by the Australian Defense Cooperation Program and used for customs, fisheries patrol, and general police duties. Ordered 13-9-85. Carries a 5-m aluminum boarding boat. Has an extensive navigational suite, including a Furuno FSN-70 NAVSAT receiver, 525 HFD/F, 120 MF–HFD/F, FE-881 echo sounder, and DS-70 doppler log. The listed armament is not normally carried.

VENEZUELA

Bolivarian Republic of Venezuela

Personnel (2001): 18,300 total (including 400 in naval aviation and 7,800 marines)

Bases: Fleet headquarters and La Carlota Naval Air Station at Caracas, Federal District. Marine corps headquarters and the naval academy at Mamo. Naval Education Center at Catia la Mar. Simón Bolívar International Airport Naval Aviation Facility and Naval Police Training Center at Maiquetía. Fleet Command headquarters and 1st Marine Amphibious Brigade at Contralmirante Agustin Armario Main Naval Base, Puerto Cabello. Patrol craft squadron and Simón Bolívar Marine Tactical Unit at Mariscal Juan C. Falcón Naval Base at Punto Fijo, Falcón State. Eastern Naval Zone headquarters, Marine Amphibious Command No. 2, and Marine Training Center at Carúpano, Sucre State; a new naval station is under construction on the Macanao Peninsula on Margarita Island. River Command headquarters at Capitán de Fragata Tomás Machado Naval Base at Ciudad Bolívar, Bolívar State, with several subordinate naval posts on the Río Oronoco. Generalísimo Francisco de Marianada Marine Special Operations Command at Teniente de Navío Tomás Vega Naval Station, Turiamo Bay, Aragua State. General de Brigada Franz Rizquez Iribarren Marine Corps River Frontier Command headquarters at Puerto Ayacucho, Amazonas State, with several naval posts on the Río Oronoco and Río Meta. Marine River Brigade headquarters and Marine Axis Orinoco-Apuire Command headquarters at San Fernando, and Teniente de Navío Jacinto Muñoz Marine Corps River Frontier Command headquarters at El Amparo, Apure State, with several naval posts on the Río Arauca, Río Apure, and Río Barinas. Capitán de Navío Antonio Diaz Naval Station at Isla La Orchila and Teniente de Fragata Fernando Gómez Naval Station, Puerto Hierro, Sucre State. The Coast Guard Command headquarters is at La Guaira, Vargas State, with principal stations at La Guaira, Maracaibo, Punto Fijo, Puerto Cabello, Guanta, Pampatar, and Guiria, and secondary stations at Ilals Los Monjes, Las Aves de Sotavento, Los Roques, Los Testogos, and La Blanquilla.

Naval Program: The 1998–2007 strategic naval program foresaw acquisition of 2–3 new submarines, 4 stealth guided missile corvettes, 2–4 patrol ships, the 12 patrol boats already being delivered, mine countermeasures ships, 2 utility landing craft, the fleet replenishment ship ordered in 1999, 15 fast inshore patrol launches, 2 fleet tugs, and an unspecified number of riverine patrol and troop-carrying craft. Seven additional CASA-212-series maritime patrol aircraft and eight additional Bell 412P search-and-rescue/transport helicopters are also to be procured. During a 4-01 conference, Mexico and Venezuela agreed to coordinate their naval shipbuilding efforts.

Organization: The chain of command runs from the commander general of the navy to the inspector general of the navy to the chief of naval staff. Under the naval commander of operations are the commander of the fleet, commander of the marine division, commander of naval aviation, commander of the river command, and commander of the coast guard. All bases and stations are subordinated to the Naval Logistics Command. The Naval Personnel Command is responsible for the Naval War School, Naval Postgraduate School, Naval Academy, all enlisted basic and technical training schools, and the naval police and the Naval Police Training Center.

As of 2001, there were two naval zones: the Eastern Naval Zone (including the Atlantic Zone), headquartered at Carúpano, and the Western Naval Zone, headquartered at Falcón Naval Base, Punto Fijo. There are plans to establish a Central Naval Zone, headquartered at Puerto Cabello Naval Base, and a Southern Naval Zone, headquartered at Puerto Ayacucho on the Río Orinoco.

Under the Fleet Command at Puerto Cabello are the frigate, submarine, and amphibian and service ships squadrons and the sail training ship, one oceanographic research ship, and a fleet tug. The patrol squadron, with the six gun and missile craft, is at Falcón Naval Base.

Naval Aviation: For shipboard use, the helicopter squadron at Puerto Cabello has eight AQS-13 dipping sonar–equipped Agusta-Bell AB-212 and a single Bell 212 Twin Huey. The tactical support squadron at Puerto Cabello has four Bell 412EP SAR helicopters. The maritime patrol and ASW squadron at Puerto Cabello operates three CASA-212-S43 Aviocar maritime surveillance aircraft. The transport squadron at Maiquetía operates three CASA-210-400 and two CASA-212-200 Aviocar transports, one de Havilland DHC-7 Dash-7 transport, one Beech B-200 Super King Air, one Beech C-90 King Air, and one Aerocommando Turbo 980 light transports (the last three based at Caracas). The training squadron, at Puerto Cabello, has two Cessna Turbo 402, two Cessna Turbo 310Q/T, and one Cessna 210 light aircraft and one Bell 206B JetRanger helicopter. Two Bell TH-57A Sea Ranger helicopters are in storage.

The Bell AB-212 helicopters can be equipped to carry two Mk 46 or A-244AA torpedoes or two SS-12M Marte wire-guided air-to-ground missiles. The CASA-212-200MP, AB-212ASW, Bell 212, and Bell 412EP aircraft can be armed with 7.62-mm or 12.7-mm mg and 70-mm rocket pods. During 2001–02, AgustaWestland was overhauling four of the AB-212ASW helicopters with new avionics and EW equipment from Elisra, Israel. The remaining AB-212ASW, Bell 212, and TH-57A helicopters are to be overhauled and modernized. The CASA-212-200MP patrol aircraft completed an overhaul and upgrading to 212-400 status during 2000 at Construcciones Aeronáuticas, Seville, Spain. Planned for acquisition are three CASA-212-400MP patrol aircraft and four additional Bell 412EP helicopters, while the U.S. was requested in 2001 to provide ex-U.S. Navy S-3B Viking antisubmarine aircraft when they become available.

Venezuelan Air Force Mirage-50EV jet fighters of Grupo Aéreo de Caza No. 11 are equipped to launch the AM-39 Exocet antiship missile.

Marine Corps: In 2001, the Marine Corps was being reorganized (yet again) as a division, headquartered at Meseta de Mamo, Vargas State, with one support services battalion, a mixed artillery group, one amphibious armored vehicle battalion, one signal battalion, one replacement regiment, one training center, one special operations

Venezuelan CASA-212-S43 maritime patrol aircraft
Omar Quintero/FAV Club, 11-00

Venezuelan Agusta-Bell AB-212 José Lugo/FAV Club, 10-00

command (with combat swimmers and paracommando companies and support and special boat units); a headquarters battalion; two amphibious brigades, each with three marine battalions; one engineer brigade, with one combat and three construction battalions; and one river frontier brigade with three river commands and one river training center. Each river command, in turn, has one marine assault battalion, one service support unit, one maintenance unit, and four Naval Police posts and several river combat boat and service craft units.

Vehicles include 37 ENGESA 6×6 amphibious armored personnel carriers. Eleven U.S.-supplied LVT-7-series tracked amphibious armored personnel carriers (one LVTC-7 command vehicle, one LVTR-7 recovery vehicle, and nine LVTP-7 personnel carriers), in storage awaiting upgrading, were to be refurbished beginning in 1997 but are now in storage awaiting funding. Artillery includes 12 OTOBreda M-56 105-mm towed howitzers and 12 Thomson-Brandt 120-mm mortars. Antiaircraft defense is provided by 12 or more Bofors RBS-70 SAM systems. Riverine craft assigned to the marines include about 50 launches of the Guardian 25-ft., Guardian 22-ft., Cobia, Caroni, Manapiare, Frontera, and Apure/Apure II classes.

Naval police and security units are assigned to bases, stations, and other naval installations; the Marine Training Center at Carúpano, Sucre State; and the Naval Police Training Center, Maiquetía, Vargas State.

Coast Guard: The coast guard is one of the five navy operational commands and is headquartered at La Guaira. The ship squadron operates the two *Almirante Clemente*–class frigates, 12 Gavión-class and four ex-U.S. Coast Guard Point-class patrol boats, one harbor tug, and two salvage craft. Assigned to various coast guard stations and posts are two U.S. 36-ft. Protector 3612V-class patrol boats, seven UFPB-1/1000 Polaris-class and six Courage-class fast patrol launches, one Attack-class raider patrol launch, eight Punta Macoya-class aids-to-navigation launches, and several service craft. There is also an underwater salvage company and several boarding and inspection teams.

Note: All ship names are prefaced by A.R.B.V. *(Armada de la República Bolivariana de Venezuela).* Pennant numbers are now painted in low visibility U.S. Navy style.

ATTACK SUBMARINES [SS]

Note: Plans to acquire up to three additional submarines are retained in the 1998–2007 acquisition plan, although funding these may prove impossible.

♦ 2 German Type 209/1300 class Bldr: Howaldtswerke, Kiel

	Laid down	L	In serv.
S-31 Sábalo (ex-S-21)	2-5-73	1-7-75	6-8-76
S-32 Caribe (ex-S-22)	1-8-73	6-11-75	11-3-77

D: 1,100 tons light; 1,265 tons surf./1,295 tons sub.
S: 11 kts surf./22 kts sub. **Dim:** 61.20 × 6.30 × 5.50
A: 8 bow 533-mm TT (14 tot. U.S. Mk 37 Mod. 2 and STN Atlas Elektronik SST-4 Mod. 0 wire-guided torpedoes)

Sábalo (S-31) Carlos E. Hernández, 3-00

Caribe (S-32) Carlos E. Hernández, 3-00

Electronics:
Radar: Terma Scanter Mil 009 nav./surf. search
Sonar: STN Atlas Ekektronik CSU-3-32 suite; Thales DUUX-2 passive ranging
EW: Thales DR-2000 intercept
M: diesel-electric: 4 MTU 12V493 AZ80 GA31L diesels (600 bhp each), 4 405-kw alternators, Siemens electric motor; 1 prop; 5,000 shp (4,600 sust.)
Range: 7,500/10 surf.; 11,200/4 snorkel; 25/20, 445/4 sub.
Fuel: 108 tons **Endurance:** 50 days **Crew:** 5 officers, 28 enlisted

Remarks: Ordered in 1971; a planned second pair was not ordered. S-31 was damaged by fire in 1979 and overhauled at Kiel through 1981. S-32 was refitted by the builder in 1984. S-31 began refit to West German Navy Type 206A standard by builder in 4-90 and left Germany for Venezuela on 16-11-92 with some of the work incomplete, due to financial problems; S-32 began a similar refit in 10-92 and was completed and recommissioned in 1-95. Both are to be refitted again during 2002–04, with one to be overhauled at HDW in Germany or Brazil and the other done locally.
Hull systems: Operating depth: 250 m. Have four 120-cell batteries producing 11,500 amp-hr and weighing 257 tons total. During the latest refit, received a higher casing and sail and were re-engined.
Combat systems: Originally had an H.S.A. (now Thales) Mk 8 Mod. 24 fire-control system. The latest refit included the installation of the STN Atlas Elektronik ISUS integrated command, control, and sonar suite and substitution of a Carl Zeiss AS-40 attack periscope for the original AS C1B (the BS 19 search periscope was retained as part of the SERO 40 periscope system).

FRIGATES [FF]

♦ 6 Lupo class Bldr: CNR, Riva Trigoso (F-23, F-25: Ancona), Italy

	Laid down	L	In serv.
F-21 Mariscal Sucre	4-10-77	28-9-78	14-7-80
F-22 Almirante Brion	26-1-78	22-2-79	7-3-81
F-23 General Urdaneta	23-1-78	23-3-79	8-8-81
F-24 General Soublette	26-8-78	4-1-80	4-12-81
F-25 General Salom	7-11-78	13-1-80	3-4-82
F-26 Almirante José M. Garcia (ex-*General José Félix Ribas*)	21-8-79	4-10-80	30-7-82

Almirante José M. Garcia (F-26) Ralph Edwards, 4-00

General Salom (F-25) José Lugo/FAV Club, 10-00

D: 2,213 tons (2,525 fl) **S:** 35 kts (20.5 on diesels)
Dim: 112.8 (106.0 pp) × 11.98 × 3.84 (hull)
A: 8 Otomat Mk 2 SSM; 1 8-round Albatros SAM system (8 Aspide missiles); 1 127-mm 54-cal. OTOBreda DP; 2 twin 40-mm 70-cal. OTOBreda Dardo AA; 2 single 12.7-mm mg; 2 triple 324-mm Mk 32 ASW TT (A-244S torpedoes); 1 AB-212ASW helicopter
Electronics:
Radar: 1 SMA 3RM-20 nav.; 1 AESN RAN-11/X air/surf. search; 1 AESN RAN-10S (F-21, F-22: Elta EL/M-2238 STAR 3-D) air search; 2 AESN Orion RTN-10X f.c.; 2 AESN Orion RTN-20X (F-21, F-22: 3 Elta . . .) f.c.
Sonar: EDO 610E hull-mounted MF (F-21, F-22: Northrop Grumman 21HS-7 hull-mounted, 7 kHz)
TACAN: SRN-15A
EW: F-21, F-22: Elisra NS-9003/9005 intercept/jamming syst.; . . . decoy RL—others: Elettronica Lambda-F D/F-intercept; 2 Breda SCLAR decoy syst. (2 20-round RL)

FRIGATES [FF] *(continued)*

Mariscal Sucre (F-21)—on postmodernization trials Northrop Grumman Ship Systems

M: CODOG: 2 Fiat-G.E. LM-2500 gas turbines (25,000 shp each), 2 GMT A230-2M (F-21, F-22: MTU 20V1193-series) diesels (3,900 bhp each; F-21, F-22: 9,900 bhp each); 2 CP props; 50,000 shp max.
Electric: 3,120 kw tot. (F-21, F-22: 4 MTU 8V396-series diesel-driven sets)
Range: 900/35; 1,050/31.7; 5,500/16 **Crew:** 185 tot.

Remarks: Ordered 24-10-75. Near-sisters are in the Italian and Peruvian navies. Under a provisional contract signed in 7-92, F-21 and F-22 were to be updated and refitted by Ingalls Shipbuilding, Pascagoula, Miss.; the contract was finally signed 18-12-97 for $315 million. F-21 and F-22 arrived in the U.S.A. 10-1-98 and were to complete their refits in 2-00, although F-21 did not begin postmodernization trials until 25-6-01; Israel's Elbit performed the integration of the combat system and supplied a new command system for the ships. The other four are to be modernized in Venezuela to a lesser degree, with technical assistance from Ingalls; hull repairs will be performed by Diques y Astilleros Nacionales, C.A. (DIANCA) at Puerto Cabello, and new systems will be installed at the Contralmirante Armario Naval Base. Work was to start late in 1999 with F-24. The sextet constitutes the frigate squadron and is based at Puerto Cabello.
Hull systems: Fin stabilizers are fitted. F-21 and F-22 have received upgraded LM-2500 gas turbines, new MTU diesel engines (of nearly triple the original horsepower), new generator plants, new machinery control systems, and hull repairs. The engines on the others are to be overhauled under a 12-98 contract with Fiat Avio, Italy, and the ships are to have improved air-conditioning and reverse-osmosis freshwater generation systems added.
Combat systems: The 127-mm gun and missile fire control is provided by two Elsag NA-10 Mod. 0 systems. The Albatros system uses Aspide missiles, a re-engineered version of NATO Sea Sparrow. Each twin 40-mm Dardo system antiaircraft mount has an associated RTN-20X radar director. All weapons are controlled by an AESN IPN-10 computerized data system in the four unimproved units; in F-21 and F-22, the Israeli Elbit ENTCS 2000 combat information system has been substituted for IPN-10, and all weapons systems have been overhauled under the 1-98 contract, but the obsolescent Otomat missiles are to be retained. Have a fixed, nontelescopic helicopter hangar. The helicopter performs over-the-horizon targeting for the Otomat missiles, as well as ASW duties. The antenna for the TACAN system is mounted on a pole mast atop the forward superstructure.

The Northrop Grumman 21HS-7 sonar is an export version of the U.S. Navy's SQS-53C; a mine-avoidance capability is incorporated. The DRS Technologies, Canada, SHINCOM (Shipboard Integrated Communications) 2100 system was ordered for the two modernized ships in 1-99. The other four will receive the new sonar, but not the new radar and combat data systems, under a 3-1-01 contract with DRS Technologies, U.S.A., with the work to be completed by 3-03.

♦ 2 Almirante Clemente class Bldr: Ansaldo, Livorno

	Laid down	L	In serv.
GC-11 Almirante Clemente (ex-F-11, ex-D-12)	5-5-54	12-12-54	1956
GC-12 General José Trinidad Moran (ex-F-12, ex-D-22)	5-5-54	12-12-54	1956

D: 1,300 tons (1,500 fl) **S:** 22 kts **Dim:** 97.6 × 10.84 × 2.6
A: 2 single 76-mm 62-cal. OTOBreda Compact DP; 1 twin 40-mm 70-cal. OTOBreda AA; 2 triple 324-mm Whitehead Alenia ILAS-3 ASW TT (6 A-244S torpedoes)

Almirante Clemente (GC-11) H&L Van Ginderen, 8-99

General José Trinidad Moran (GC-12) French Navy, 1994

FRIGATES [FF] *(continued)*

Electronics:
Radar: 1 Decca 1226 nav.; 1 Plessey AWS-2 air/surf. search; 1 AESN Orion RTN-10X f.c.
Sonar: Plessey (now Thales) MS-26 hull-mounted (10 kHz)
M: 2 G.M.T. 16-645E7CA diesels; 2 props; 6,000 bhp
Range: 3,500/15 **Fuel:** 350 tons **Crew:** 12 officers, 150 enlisted

Remarks: Survivors of a class of six. Both were extensively refitted by Cammell Laird, Birkenhead, between 1968 and 1975–76 (much delayed by financial and labor problems). Have operated under the Coast Guard Command since 3-86. Are planned to be replaced with new patrol ships around 2003.
Disposals: *General José de Austria* was stricken in 1976, *Almirante José Garcia* in 1977, and *General Juan José Flores* and *Almirante Brion* in 1978.
Hull systems: When new, could make 32 kts. Very lightly built, with much use of aluminum alloy. Have Denny-Brown fin stabilizers. Were re-engined by CNR, Genoa, Italy, with diesels from 10-84 to 24-7-85.
Combat systems: OTOBreda Compact mounts replaced the original four 102-mm dual-purpose guns. Have the Elsag NA-10 gun f.c.s. for the 76-mm guns and a lead-computing sight for the 40-mm AA mount.

GUIDED-MISSILE PATROL CRAFT [PTG]

Note: A project to procure six stealth-technology guided-missile patrol combatants from Izar, Spain, announced in 9-99, was later canceled.

♦ 3 Federación class
Bldr: Vosper Thornycroft, Portsmouth, U.K.

	Laid down	L	In serv.
PC-12 Federación (ex-P-12)	8-73	26-2-74	25-3-75
PC-14 Libertad (ex-P-14)	9-73	5-3-74	12-6-75
PC-16 Victoria (ex-P-16)	3-73	3-9-74	22-9-75

Victoria (PC-16) Carlos E. Hernández, 7-88

D: 150 tons (170 fl) **S:** 31 kts **Dim:** 36.88 (33.53 wl) × 7.16 × 1.80 (hull)
A: 2 Otomat Mk 2 SSM; 1 30-mm 70-cal. OTOBreda Compact AA; 2 single 12.7-mm M2 mg
Electronics: Radar: 1 Decca . . . nav.; 1 SMA SPQ-2D surf. search
M: 2 MTU MD 16V538 TB90 diesels; 1 prop; 7,080 max. bhp (5,900 sust.)
Electric: 250 kw tot.
Range: 1,350/16 **Fuel:** 23.5 tons **Crew:** 3 officers, 17 enlisted

Remarks: Were refitted and modernized during 1992–95 by Unidad de Carenado de la Armada, Puerto Cabello, and were being re-engined during 2000–02. The 30-mm mount replaced the original Bofors 40-mm mount, and the missile launchers were modified to handle the Otomat Mk 2 SSM. With the *Constitución* class, they constitute the Fleet Command patrol squadron and are based at Falcón Naval Base, Punto Fijo.

PATROL CRAFT [PC]

♦ 3 Constitución class
Bldr: Vosper Thornycroft, Portsmouth, U.K.

	Laid down	L	In serv.
PC-11 Constitución	1-73	1-6-73	16-8-74
PC-13 Independencia	2-73	24-7-73	20-9-74
PC-15 Patria	3-73	27-9-73	9-1-75

D: 150 tons (170 fl) **S:** 31 kts **Dim:** 36.88 (33.53 wl) × 7.16 × 1.80 (hull)
A: 1 76-mm 62-cal. OTOBreda Compact DP; 2 single 12.7-mm M2 mg
Electronics:
Radar: 1 Decca . . . nav.; 1 SMA SPQ-2D surf. search; 1 AESN Orion RTN-10X f.c.
M: 2 MTU MD 16V538 TB90 diesels; 2 props; 7,080 max. bhp (5,900 sust.)
Electric: 250 kw tot.
Range: 1,350/16 **Fuel:** 23.5 tons **Crew:** 3 officers, 17 enlisted

Remarks: Ordered in 4-72. New hull numbers were assigned in 1978. All were modernized and refitted at the Navy Yard, Puerto Cabello, in 1992–95. Were being re-engined during 2000–02. With the *Federacíon* class, they constitute the Fleet Command patrol squadron and are based at Falcón Naval Base, Punto Fijo. Although they carried the word *"Guardacosta"* on their sides for a period during the 1980s, they were never subordinated to the coast guard proper.
Hull systems: Are equipped with Vosper fin stabilizers. Maximum sustained speed has been reduced to 12 kts.
Combat systems: Have the Elsag NA-10 Mod. 1 gun f.c.s., with a radar director for the 40-mm gun.

Constitución (PC-11) Venezuelan Navy, 7-98

PATROL BOATS [PB]

Note: Funding for 15 new U.S. 25-ft. inshore patrol boats and 60 new "river raider" patrol launches has been approved, but contracts have not yet been let.

♦ 12 Gavión-class coastal patrol boats
Bldr: Halter Marine Group, Equitable Shipyards, New Orleans

	In serv.		In serv.
PG-401 Gavión	26-8-99	PG-407 Fardela	2-00
PG-402 Alca	26-8-99	PG-408 Sumarela	2-00
PG-403 Bernacla	26-8-99	PG-409 Negrón	6-00
PG-404 Chamán	26-8-99	PG-410 Pigargo	6-00
PG-405 Cormorán	2-00	PG-411 Pagaza	6-00
PG-406 Colimbo	2-00	PG-412 Serreta	6-00

Alca (PG-402) Halter Marine, 1999

D: 48 tons (fl) **S:** 25 kts **Dim:** 24.30 × 5.44 × 1.75
A: 1 twin 12.7-mm Mk 95 mg; 1 12.7-mm M2 mg
Electronics: Radar: 1 Raytheon R1210 nav.
M: 2 G.M. Detroit Diesel 12V92 TA diesels; 2 props; 2,160 bhp
Electric: 250 kw tot. **Range:** 1,000/15 **Crew:** 2 officers, 8 enlisted

Remarks: Were originally to have been ordered in 12-96, but the contract was delayed to 24-4-98. Aluminum construction, with components fabricated by other Halter Marine yards. Carry an inspection and rescue dinghy on the fantail. The first four arrived at La Guaira 6-10-99.

Note: Acquired during 1997 were an unknown number of Rigid Raider rigid inflatable assault boats armed with two 7.62-mm mg and powered by two gasoline outboards; a crew of one and eight troops are carried. The six *Integredad*-class patrol launches have been redesignated as aids-to-navigation craft and are now listed under Service Craft.

♦ 2 U.S. 36-foot Protector 3612-V class coastal patrol boats
Bldr: SeaArk Marine, Monticello, Ark.

LG-31 Chichiriviche (In serv. 15-3-94) LG-32 Caruanta (In serv. 7-3-94)

D: 11.1 tons (fl) **S:** . . . kts **Dim:** 11.1 × 4.0 × 0.53 (hull)
A: 1 7.62-mm mg **Electronics:** Radar: 1 Raytheon . . . nav.
M: 2 . . . . . diesels; 2 props; . . . bhp **Crew:** 4 tot.

Remarks: Donated by the U.S.A. Aluminum construction. Assigned to the Coast Guard Command and based at La Guaira.

PATROL BOATS [PB] *(continued)*

♦ **4 U.S. Coast Guard Point-class coastal patrol boats**
Bldr: U.S. Coast Guard Yard, Curtis Bay, Md. (PG-32: J. Martinac SB, Tacoma, Wash.)

	In serv.	Transferred
PG-31 Petrel (ex-*Point Knoll,* WPB 82367)	26-6-67	18-10-91
PG-32 Alcatraz (ex-*Point Judith,* WPB 82345)	26-7-66	15-1-92
PG-33 Albatros (ex-*Point Ledge,* WPB 82334)	18-7-62	3-8-98
PG-34 Pelicano (ex-*Point Franklin,* WPB 82350)	14-11-66	3-8-98

Pelicano (PG-34) Carlos E. Hernández, 12-98

D: 64 tons (69 fl) **S:** 23 kts **Dim:** 25.30 × 5.23 × 1.95
A: 1 twin 12.7-mm mg **Electronics:** Radar: 1 Raytheon SPS-64(V)1 nav.
M: 2 Caterpillar 3412 diesels; 2 props; 1,480 bhp
Range: 490/23.7; 1,500/8 **Fuel:** 5.7 tons **Crew:** 1 officer, 9 enlisted

Remarks: Donated for use by the Coast Guard Command in antidrug work. Capable of towing and fire fighting. Were re-engined during the early 1990s.

♦ **4 or more 24-foot Misión-class riverine patrol launches**

Remarks: No data available, other than that they are armed with two single 7.62-mm mg and are assigned to the marine corps river frontier brigade. Additional units of this locally built class are planned.

♦ **1 (+ . . .) Attack-class raider riverine patrol launches**
Bldr: Intermarine C.A., Guatire, Miranda State (In serv. 1-99)

LRG-. . .

D: 1.2 tons (fl) **S:** 45 kts **Dim:** 7.32 × 2.40 × . . .
A: 3 single 7.62-mm mg **Electronics:** Radar: 1 Raytheon . . . nav.
M: 2 gasoline outboards; . . . bhp **Range:** 240/40 **Crew:** 4 tot.

Remarks: GRP construction. Has a GPS receiver. First unit assigned to Pampatar Coast Guard Station, Margarita Island. Additional units may be procured.

♦ **6 Courage-class fast patrol launches** Bldr: various local and foreign

	In serv.		In serv.
LRGC-001 Constancia	12-91	LRGC-004 Tenacidad	4-93
LRGC-002 Perseverancia	12-91	LRGC-005	. . .
LRGC-003 Honestidad	12-91	LRGC-006 Lealtad	. . .

Constancia (LRGC-001) Venezuelan Navy, 2-92

Remarks: First two were prototypes of a planned group of 20 delivered in 12-91 for use by the Coast Guard Command, but only six were ever delivered. Are about 7.3–10.0 m overall, of "cigarette boat" configuration, with GRP-construction hulls.

♦ **7 UFPB-1/1000-class coastal patrol launches**
Bldr: Cougar Marine, U.K. (In serv. 1987)

LG-21 Polaris, LG-22 Sirius, LG-23 Rigel, LG-24 Aldebaran, LG-25 Antares, LG-26 Canopus, LG-27 Altair

Aldebaran (LG-24) Venezuelan Navy, 1998

D: 5 tons (fl) **S:** 50 kts **Dim:** 10.05 (7.92 wl) × 2.60 × 0.78
A: 1 12.7-mm mg **Electronics:** Radar: 1 . . . nav.
M: 2 diesel outdrives; 400 bhp **Range:** 150/50 **Crew:** 4 tot.

Remarks: GRP construction. All were refitted in 1998–99 by Unidad de Carenado de la Armada, Puerto Cabello. Assigned to the coast guard for coastal service.

♦ **. . . 24-foot RIB raiding launches**
Bldr: Artigiana Batteli, . . . , Italy (In serv. 1997–98)

D: . . . tons **S:** . . . **Dim:** . . . × . . . × . . .
A: 2 7.62-mm mg **Electronics:** Radar: 1 . . . nav.
M: 2 Mercury gasoline outboards; . . . **Crew:** . . . tot.

Remarks: A large number of these launches are being procured under 1997 funding for the navy River Commands, the two marine corps River Frontier Commands, and the Coast Guard Command.

♦ **5 or more Caribe/Frontera-class riverine patrol launches**
Bldr: Intermarine C.A., Guatire, Miranda State (In serv. . . .)

D: . . . tons **S:** 39.7 kts **Dim:** 5.00 × 2.10 × 0.20
A: 1 7.62-mm mg **M:** 2 gasoline outboards; 130 bhp **Crew:** 6 tot.

Remarks: GRP construction. Assigned to the marine corps river frontier brigade. Additional units are planned.

♦ **2 or more 7.3-meter RIB assault launches**
Bldr: Artigana Battelli, . . ., Italy (In serv. 1997)

Remarks: Armed with two 7.62-mm mg and powered by two Mercury outboards. Assigned to the Coast Guard Command.

♦ **22 or more U.S. 22-foot Guardian-class raider patrol launches**
Bldr: Boston Whaler, Edgewater, Fla. (In serv. 10-97 to . . .)

COFFMU-323 and others

Three Venezuelan 22-ft. Guardian-class launches—on the Río Orinoco
Javier Nieves/FAV Club, 5-00

D: 1.2 tons (1.5 fl) **S:** 35 kts **Dim:** 6.81 × 2.30 × 0.36
A: 1 12.7-mm mg; 2 single 7.62-mm mg
Electronics: Radar: 1 Raytheon SPS-66 nav.
M: 2 gasoline outboard motors; 250 bhp **Range:** 167/40 **Crew:** 6 tot.

PATROL BOATS [PB] *(continued)*

22-ft. Guardian-class—with armament aboard Javier Nieves/FAV Club, 5-00

Remarks: Donated by the U.S. government for use by the two marine corps River Frontier Commands. GRP foam-core hull construction. Additional units are planned.

♦ **8 or more Manapiare-class riverine assault boats**
Bldr: Puerto la Cruz, Venezuela (In serv. 1996–. . .)

Remarks: Aluminum construction. Carry one 7.62-mm mg. Powered by two gasoline outboard motors. Are assigned to the marine corps river frontier brigade.

♦ **9 U.S. 22-foot Piranha-class river patrol launches**
Bldr: Boston Whaler, Rockland, Mass., and Edgewater, Fla. (In serv.: first two: 28-2-94; others: 1994 to 10-97)

LCF-101 through LCF-109

D: 1.6 tons light (2 fl) **S:** 39.1 kts **Dim:** 6.81 × 2.26 × 0.36
A: 2 single 12.7-mm mg; 2 single 7.62-mm mg
Electronics: Radar: 1 Raytheon SPS-66 nav.
M: 2 outboard motors; 300 bhp **Range:** 167/39 **Crew:** 4 tot.

Remarks: Donated by the U.S. government for use by the navy River Command and two marine corps River Frontier Commands. Additional units are planned. Foam-core, unsinkable GRP construction. Are painted olive drab.

♦ **5 or more Caroní-class riverine patrol launches**
Bldr: . . ., Venezuela (In serv. 1991–. . .)

D: . . . tons **S:** 39.1 kts **Dim:** 4.90 × 1.65 × 0.20
A: 1 7.62-mm mg **M:** 2 gasoline outboards; 130 bhp **Crew:** 6 tot.

Remarks: Aluminum construction. Assigned to the marine corps river frontier brigade.

♦ **2 Manaure-class river patrol launches** (In serv. 24-4-73)

PF-21 MANAURE PF-22 MARA

Mara (PF-22)—on the Río Orinoco Venezuelan Navy, 7-98

D: 15 tons (fl) **S:** 10 kts **Dim:** 16.5 × 4.3 × 1.3
A: 1 20-mm 70-cal. Oerlikon Mk 10 AA; 1 12.7-mm mg
Electronics: Radar: 1 Raytheon . . . nav.
M: 2 . . . diesels; 2 props; . . . bhp **Range:** 200/10 **Crew:** 8 tot.

Remarks: Resemble a U.S. Navy "Swiftboat" but have narrower beam. Are assigned to the River Command.

♦ **2 13.6-ton river patrol launches** (In serv. 24-4-73)

PF-23 GUAICAIPURO (ex-PF-11) PF-24 TAMANACO (ex-PF-12)

Remarks: Armed with one 12.7-mm mg. Assigned to the River Command.

♦ **5 Terepaima class** Bldr: Mercruiser, Miami (In serv. 1987)

LA-01 EL AMPARO PF-32 TIUNA PF-34 SOROCAIMA
PF-31 TEREPAIMA PF-33 YARACUY

D: 5 tons (fl) **S:** 35–50 kts **Dim:** 10.60 × 2.90 × 0.75
A: 1 7.62-mm mg **M:** 2 gasoline engines; 2 props; . . . bhp
Range: 200/. . . **Crew:** 4 tot.

Remarks: LA-01 is used as an ambulance boat. GRP construction. Are assigned to the River Command.

Terepaima (PF-31) Venezuelan Navy, 7-88

♦ **3 21-foot Cobia class** Bldr: SeaArk Marine, Monticello, Ark.

COFFMU-. . . (ex-ANMU-81) COFFRI-. . . (ex-PFPJQ-81)
COFFMU-. . . (ex-ANMU-82)

D: 0.5 tons light (1.25 fl) **S:** 30 kts **Dim:** 6.02 × 2.36 × 0.33
A: 1 12.7-mm mg **Electronics:** Radar: 1 Furuno FR 10 nav.
M: 2 Evinrude gasoline outboard motors; 230 bhp **Crew:** 4 tot.

Remarks: Aluminum construction. For river and lake patrol. Equipped with push-knees to act as push-tugs. Completed in 1984 but not delivered until 5-87. The last two are used as yachts. Ten sisters serve the national guard.

AMPHIBIOUS WARFARE SHIPS AND CRAFT

♦ **4 Capana-class tank landing ships [LST]**
Bldr: Korea-Tacoma SY, Masan, South Korea

	L	In serv.		L	In serv.
T-61 CAPANA	25-3-83	21-6-84	T-63 GOAJIRA	. . .	11-84
T-62 ESEQUIBO	25-3-83	21-6-84	T-64 LOS LLANOS	. . .	11-84

Esequibo (T-62) Ralph Edwards, 4-00

Goajira (T-63) Leo Dirkx, 5-99

D: 1,800 tons light (4,070 fl) **S:** 15 kts **Dim:** 104.0 × 15.4 × 3.0 (4.2 max.)
A: 1 twin 40-mm 70-cal. Breda Dardo AA; 2 single 20-mm 90-cal. Oerlikon GAM-B01 AA
Electronics: Radar: 1 . . . nav.
M: 2 SEMT-Pielstick 16 PA6 V diesels; 2 props; 6,400 bhp (5,600 sust.)
Electric: 750 kw tot. **Range:** 7,500/13
Crew: 13 officers, 104 enlisted + troops: 10 officers, 192 enlisted

Remarks: Ordered in 8-82. An improved version of U.S. World War II–era LST design. T-61 and T-62 arrived in Venezuela in 10-84, T-63 in 12-84, and T-64 early in 1985; all were delivered without armament. T-63 was heavily damaged by fire in 6-87 and not restored to service until 5-93. Have sisters in the Indonesian Navy. T-62 is employed in commercial cargo transport service between Caracas, Antigua, Grenada, and St. Lucia.
Hull systems: Cargo: 1,800 tons max., 690 tons beaching load. Have an elevator to the upper deck, a 50-ton tank turntable on the tank deck, and a helicopter deck aft.
Combat systems: There is an Alenia NA-18 optronic director for the 40-mm mount.

Note: Some $15.9 million was funded during 1997 for the purchase of two new utility landing craft of about 45-m length; negotiations began in 1998 with Halter Marine (now Friede Goldman Halter) in the U.S.A, but the program was canceled.

AMPHIBIOUS WARFARE SHIPS AND CRAFT *(continued)*

♦ 2 Margarita-class utility landing craft [LCU]
Bldr: Swiftships, Morgan City, La.

T-71 MARGARITA (In serv. 20-1-84) T-72 LA ORCHILA (In serv. 11-5-84)

Margarita (T-71) Carlos E. Hernández, 11-93

D: 428 tons (fl) **S:** 13 kts **Dim:** 39.62 × 10.97 × 1.30
A: 2 single 12.7-mm M2 mg **Electronics:** Radar: 1 Raytheon 6410 nav.
M: 2 G.M. Detroit Diesel 16V149N diesels; 2 props; 1,800 bhp
Electric: 150 kw tot. (2 × 75-kw Delco sets, G.M. 6-71 diesels driving)
Range: 2,500/10 **Fuel:** 64 tons **Crew:** 4 officers, 17 enlisted

Remarks: Aluminum construction. Cargo: vehicles, supplies, up to 108 tons fuel, and 149 tons water. Have a bow ramp and a 15-ton crane on bow. Carry 156 tons of ballast. Are intended for coastal and riverine use. Both were transferred to the River Command in 1984.

♦ 1 ex-U.S. LCM(8)-series landing craft [LCM] (In serv. 1967–79)
LC-21 CURIAPO

Curiapo (LC-21) Venezuelan Navy, 4-99

D: 58.8 tons light (116 fl) **S:** 9 kts **Dim:** 22.43 × 6.43 × 1.35 (fwd; 1.47 aft)
A: 1 12.7-mm mg **Electronics:** Radar: 1 . . . nav.
M: 2 G.M. Detroit Diesel 12V-71 diesels; 2 props; 590 bhp
Range: 150/9.2 (loaded) **Crew:** 1 officer, 5 enlisted

Remarks: Steel-hulled former U.S. Army unit donated in 4-99 for riverine transport and logistics support service. Carries up to 50 passengers. Cargo: 60 tons or 150 troops for short distances in a 12.8 × 4.3–m (54.6-m^2) open well. Assigned to the River Command.

♦ 1 riverine landing craft [LCVP]
Bldr: . . . (In serv. 1988)

LC-01 YOPITO

Yopito (LC-01)—on the Río Orinoco Venezuelan Navy, 7-99

D: 60 tons (fl) **S:** 8 kts **Dim:** 18.00 × 4.60 × 1.50
A: 1 12.7-mm mg **M:** 1 diesel; 1 prop; . . . bhp
Range: 200/8 **Crew:** 1 officer, 3 enlisted

♦ up to 32 Apure-class riverine assault boats [LCP]
Bldr: San Cristóbal, Venezuela (In serv. mid-1980s to 8-92)

ARV-001 series

Two Apure/Apure-II-class launches Venezuelan Navy, 2-92

D: 500 kg light **S:** 35 kts **Dim:** 5.55 × 2.15 × 0.15 **A:** 1 7.62-mm mg
M: 2 gasoline outboards; 130 bhp **Crew:** 2 tot. + 6 troops

Remarks: Aluminum construction. The Apure-II series was delivered in 8-92. ANFRI-52 was lost through fire on 2-12-88.

Note: Also reported in service are a single jet-ski craft delivered in 1999 and several other small launches assigned to the marine corps Special Operations Command and several other special forces launches. The marines also use a considerable number of inflatable rubber assault boats.

♦ 11 U.S. AAVP-7 amphibious armored personnel carriers

Remarks: Acquired new from FMC in the U.S.A. in 1973. Tracked vehicles for use by the Venezuelan Marines were an LVTC-7 command vehicle, an LVTR-7 recovery vehicle, and nine LVTP-7 personnel carriers. As of 2001, they were being refurbished by the Venezuelan Army Armored Maintenance Center.

AUXILIARIES

♦ 1 multipurpose hydrographic survey ship [AGS]
Bldr: Izar (formerly E.N. Bazán), San Fernando, Spain

	Laid down	L	In serv.
BO-11 PUNTA BRAVA	12-88	9-3-90	24-3-91

Punta Brava (BO-11) Carlos E. Hernández, 5-91

D: 1,170 tons (1,250 fl) **S:** 14.6 kts **Dim:** 61.70 (55.60 pp) × 11.90 × 3.46
A: none **Electronics:** Radar: 2 . . . . nav.
M: 2 Bazán-M.A.N. 7L 20/27 diesels; 2 props; 2,500 bhp—bow-thruster
Range: 8,000/12.8 **Fuel:** 210 tons
Crew: 6 officers, 8 non-commissioned officers, 20 enlisted + 12 scientists, 4 technicians

Remarks: Ordered in 9-88. Was initially assigned to the coast guard, but was transferred during 3-94 to the amphibian and service ships squadron of the Fleet Command, which operates her for the Navy Hydrographic and Navigation Bureau *(Dirección de Hydrografía y Navegación del la Armada)*. Was refitted in the U.S.A. during 2000, with navigational and scientific equipment updated.
Hull systems: Has biological, meteorological, geological, electronic, and oceanographic laboratories, in addition to cartographic facilities. Two 8.5-m hydrographic survey launches are carried. Has two Raytheon 6000-m echo sounders.

Disposal note: Refrigerated cargo transport [AK] *Puerto Cabello* (T-44) was stricken in mid-2001 and placed up for sale.

♦ 1 Ciudad Bolívar–class replenishment oiler [AOR]
Bldr: Hyundai Heavy Industries SY, Ulsan, South Korea

	Laid down	L	In serv.
T-81 CIUDAD BOLÍVAR	8-99	2000	23-9-01

D: 9,750 tons (fl) **S:** 18.6 kts **Dim:** 137.70 (122.5 pp) × 18.00 × 6.5
A: provision for: 1 twin 40-mm 70-cal. OTOBreda Fast Forty AA; 2 single 12.7-mm M2 mg
Electronics: Radar: 2 . . . nav.
M: 2 Caterpillar 3616V diesels; 2 CP props; 12,500 bhp **Electric:** 725 kw tot.
Range: 4,500/15 **Crew:** 22 officers, 56 enlisted (accomm. for 100 tot.)

AUXILIARIES *(continued)*

Ciudad Bolívar (T-81) Chris Cavas, 3-02

Remarks: Ordered in early 1999 for $59.8 million. As of 12-01, was about six months late in being delivered. Assigned to the amphibian and service ships squadron of the Fleet Command.

Hull systems: Cargo: 4,400 tons ship fuel, 100 tons JP-5 aviation fuel, 500 tons potable water, 150 tons munitions, 385 tons dry stores, 8.9 tons frozen provisions, and 8.9 tons refrigerated provisions. Has two replenishment stations on each beam, one for liquids and one for solid cargo transfer, the latter using the sliding-stay transfer system; can also refuel over the stern. Has a helicopter platform and hangar aft.
Combat systems: The listed armament was not aboard as of 3-02. The 40-mm mount will have a remote director.

♦ 1 ex-U.S. Achomawi-class fleet tug [ATA]
Bldr: Charleston SB & DD, Charleston, S.C.

	Laid down	L	In serv.
RA-33 Contralmirante Miguel Rodriguez (ex-R-23; ex-*Salinin,* ATF 161)	13-4-45	20-7-45	11-9-45

Contralmirante Miguel Rodriguez (RA-33) Hartmut Ehlers, 8-92

D: 1,235 tons (1,675 fl) **S:** 16.5 kts **Dim:** 62.48 (59.44 wl) × 11.74 × 4.67
A: 2 single 12.7-mm M2 mg **Electronics:** Radar: 1 . . . nav.
M: 4 G.M. 16-278A diesels, electric drive; 1 prop; 3,000 shp
Electric: 400 kw tot. **Range:** 7,000/15 **Fuel:** 300 tons **Crew:** 85 tot.

Remarks: Purchased 1-9-78. Sister *Antonio Picardi* (R-22; ex-*Nipmuc,* ATF 157) ran aground and was lost 12-4-82. Transferred to the coast guard in 1983 along with sister *Felipe Larrazabel* (ex-R-21; ex-*Utina,* ATF 163), which was stricken in 9-90. Was reassigned to the amphibian and service ships squadron of the Fleet Command in 3-94. Remains fully operational.

Note: Plans announced in 1997 called for the construction of two new fleet tugs (one to replace RA-33) between 1999 and 2001. As of late 2001, it was hoped to build the tugs at Astinave, Punto Fijo, Venezuela, with technical assistance and components provided by Damen Shipyards, Gorinchem, the Netherlands.

♦ 1 sail-training ship [AXT]
Bldr: Ast. Celeya, Bilbao, Spain

	Laid down	L	In serv.
BE-11 Simón Bolívar	5-6-79	21-9-79	14-8-80

D: 1,260 tons (fl) **S:** 10.5 kts **Dim:** 82.42 (58.5 pp) × 10.6 × 4.2
M: 1 G.M. Detroit Diesel 12V149T diesel; 1 prop; 875 bhp (750 sust.)—sail area: 1,650 m^2 (23 sails)
Crew: 17 officers, 76 enlisted + 18 instructors, 84 cadets

Remarks: 934 grt. Ordered in 7-78; sister to the Ecuadorian *Guayas.* Three-masted bark. Does not have pennant number painted on. Assigned to the amphibian and service ships squadron of the Fleet Command. To be refitted during 2002.

Note: The naval academy, at Meseta de Mamo, also employs several small sail craft, outboard-motor launches, and rigid inflatables for cadet training.

Simón Bolívar (BE-11) A. D. Baker III, 6-00

SERVICE CRAFT

Note: In addition to the craft listed below, plans call for the construction of a single vehicle and personnel ferry to support the naval facilities on the Los Monjes Islands in the Gulf of Venezuela.

♦ 2 miscellaneous riverine service barges [YC]

Manati Uribante (ex-ABX-669)

Remarks: *Manati* transferred to the navy from the National Dredging Institute *(Instituto Nacional de Canalizaciones)* 27-1-87 and the *Uribante*—a name also assigned to two other service craft—from the Amazonas State government on 14-11-96. Both are assigned to the River Command.

♦ 2 small VIP yachts [YFL]

La Almiralantaza . . .

Remarks: *La Almiralantaza* is assigned to the Venezuelan chief of naval operations and based at Puerto Cabello. Another VIP craft is based at Capitán de Navío Antonio Díaz Naval Station, La Orchila Island.

♦ 5 BANAR-01-class service launches [YFL]

BANAR-01 BANAR-02 BANAR-03 BANAR-04 BANAR-05

D: 12 tons (fl) **S:** 9 kts **Dim:** 10.9 × 3.2 × 1.0
M: 1 G.M. Detroit Diesel 6-71 diesel; 1 prop; 225 bhp
Range: 110/9 **Crew:** 3 tot.

Remarks: Former U.S.-built LCVP landing craft rebuilt by Diques y Astilleros Nacionales, C.A. (DIANCA), Puerto Cabello, in 1976–77. Are assigned to the Contralmirante Agustin Armario Naval Base, Puerto Cabello. BANAR = *Base Naval Armario.*

♦ 8 or more miscellaneous personnel launches [YFL]

ANGU-01	ESGLR-114 . . . . . .
ANGU-07	LG-0001 Pampatar
EPGMA-07 Bellatrix	LG-. . . (ex-EPGMA-01)
ESGLR-01 Zenit	LT-01 Turiamo (ex-ANTV-01)

Turiamo (LT-01) Venezuelan Navy, 7-99

Pampatar (LG-0001) Carlos E. Hernández, 12-98

Remarks: ANGU-01, completed in 5-80 by Astilleros del Lago, Maracaibo, and ANGU-07 are assigned to the Capitán de Navío Francisco Javier Gutiérres Naval Station, Puerto Hierro (ANGU = *Apostadero Naval Gutiérrez*). Ex-EPGMA-01 and EPGMA-07 are assigned to the Teniente de Navío Pedro Lucas Uribarri Coast Guard Station, Maracaibo. ESGLR-01 and ESGLR-114 are GRP-construction boats with a single outboard motor each and are assigned to Los Roques Secondary Coast Guard Station for search-and-rescue duties. LG-0001 is a 5.5-m GRP-construction "cigarette boat" assigned to the Pampatar Coast Guard Station, Margarita Island. LT-01 was completed by Navitech Industries, Miami, in 1983 and is assigned to Teniente de Navío Tomás Vega Naval Station, Turiamo Bay.

SERVICE CRAFT *(continued)*

♦ 6 miscellaneous riverine service launches [YFL]

COFFRI-. . . Río Atabapo (ex-PFCM-11)
COFFRI-. . . Río Orinoco (ex-ANFRI-12)
COFFRI-. . . Río Temi (ex-ANFRI-11)
COFFRI-. . . Río Ventuari (ex-PFCM-21)
COFFRI-. . . . . . (ex-ANFRI-13)
COFFRI-. . . . . . (ex-PFCM-12)

Remarks: All are assigned to the General Rizquez Iribarren Marine Corps River Frontier Command. *Río Temi* displaces 10 tons, *Río Orinoco* and *Río Atabapo* 4 tons, ex-PFCM-12 and ex-ANFRI-13 1.5 tons, and *Río Ventuari* 1.2 tons.

♦ 1 navigational aids tender [YGL]

Bldr: Unidad de Carenado de la Armada, Puerto Cabello (In serv. 7-98)

BB-11 Macuro

D: 10 tons (fl) **S:** 12 kts **Dim:** 13.00 × 6.85 × . . .
A: 1 20-mm 70-cal. Oerlikon AA—4 single 12.7-mm mg
Electronics: Radar: 1 . . . nav.
M: 2 diesels; 2 props; . . . bhp
Range: . . ./. . . **Fuel:** 12 m^3 **Crew:** . . . tot.

Remarks: Steel-construction catamaran laid down in 1996. Can carry a standard 20-ft. cargo container with 15 tons cargo, a navigational aids buoy, or a 23-ton fuel tank. Can also be used to tow targets. Additional units may be built.

Macuro (BB-11) Carlos E. Hernández, 3-00

♦ 8 Integridad-class aids-to-navigation launches [YGL]

Bldr: Intermarine, Guatire, Venezuela (In serv. 6-96 to 2-3-00)

LSM-001 Punta Macoya (ex-*Integridad,* LGI-101)
LSM-002 Farallón Centinela
LSM-003 Charagato
LSM-004 Bajo Brito
LSM-005 Bajo Araya
LSM-006 Carecare
LSM-007 Vela de Coro
LSM-008 Cayo Macereo

Bajo Araya (LSM-005) Carlos E. Hernández, 8-97

D: 5 tons (fl) **S:** 30 kts **Dim:** 12.70 × 2.74 × . . .
A: 2 single 7.62-mm M60A1 mg **Electronics:** Radar: 1 . . . nav.
M: 2 diesels; 2 props; 640 bhp **Range:** 520/20 **Crew:** 1 officer, 4 enlisted

Remarks: GRP construction. Subordinated to the coast guard. Originally typed *Lancha Interceptora Guardacosta* (Coast Guard Interceptor Launch) but were reclassified as *Lancha de Señalización Maritima* (Aids-to-Navigation Launch) in 1997. The first six were completed by 1997, with LSM-007 and LSM-008 delivered 2-3-00. The radar has a range of 24 n.m., and a GPS receiver and HF radios are fitted.

♦ 1 U.S. Coast Guard 21-foot aids-to-navigation boats [YGL]

Bldr: MonArk, Monticello, Ark. (In serv. late 1980s)

D: 1.59 tons (3.17 fl) **S:** 28 kts **Dim:** 6.56 × 2.24 × 0.36 (hull)
M: 1 gasoline outboard; 228 bhp **Range:** 100/20 **Crew:** . . . tot.

Remarks: One unit is assigned to the Puerto Cabello Coast Guard Station. Aluminum construction.

♦ 1 hydrographic survey launch [YGS]

Bldr: Diques y Astilleros Nacionales, C.A. (DIANCA), Puerto Cabello (In serv. 8-89)

Maquiritare (ex-F-001, ex-ANFRI-13)

Remarks: 1.5 tons. Built for the Dirección de Geografía y Cartografía de las Fuerzas Armadas, but was transferred to the navy and assigned to the River Command for use in riverine charting.

♦ 2 Gabriela-class hydrographic survey craft [YGS]

Bldr: Abeking & Rasmussen, Lemwerder, Germany

	Laid down	L	In serv.
LH-11 Gabriela (ex-*Península de Araya;* ex-*Gabriela,* LH-01)	10-3-73	29-11-73	5-2-74
LH-12 Lely (ex-*Península de Paraguana;* ex-*Lely,* LH-02)	28-5-73	12-12-73	7-2-74

Gabriela (LH-11) Maritime Photographic, 1-94

D: 90 tons (fl) **S:** 20 kts **Dim:** 27.0 × 5.6 × 1.5
M: 2 MTU diesels; 2 props; 2,300 bhp **Crew:** 1 officer, 9 enlisted

Remarks: Transferred to the navy in 9-86 from the Instituto Nacional de Canalizaciones and initially assigned to the River Command and Coast Guard Command, respectively. Now both serve the River Command. Have GPS terminals.

♦ 1 riverine accommodations craft [YPB]

Río Uribante

Remarks: Transferred from the Instituto Nacional de Canalizaciones in 12-93 for use as a mobile floating command post by the River Command on the Río Orinoco. Can accommodate 33 personnel.

♦ 2 salvage, search-and-rescue craft [YRS] Bldr: . . . (In serv. . . .)

LG-11 Los Taques (ex-LA-11, ex-LA-01, ex- . . .)
LG-12 Los Cayos (ex-LA-12, ex-LA-02, ex-*Puerto Sucre*)

Los Cayos (LG-12) Carlos E. Hernández, 7-88

D: 350 tons (fl) **S:** 8 kts **Dim:** 26.6 × 7.1 × 1.5
A: 2 single 12.7-mm mg **Electronics:** Radar: 1 Raytheon . . . nav.
M: 1 diesel; 1 prop; 850 bhp **Range:** 8,500/8 **Crew:** 10 tot.

Remarks: Small former fishing trawlers seized and transferred to the navy on 15-5-81 and in 9-84, respectively. Are assigned to the Coast Guard Command for search-and-rescue and light salvage duties.

♦ 2 miscellaneous river tugs [YTM]

R-. . . Cardones R-. . . Uribante

Remarks: *Cardones* was transferred to the navy in 1-86 by Maraven petroleum company and the *Uribante* in 2-95 by the Amazonas State Government; both have retained their original names. No further data available.

SERVICE CRAFT *(continued)*

♦ **1 ex-U.S. Cholocco-class medium harbor tug [YTM]**
Bldr: Commercial Iron Works, Portland, Ore.

	Laid down	L	In serv.
RP-21 Teniente de Navío Fernando Gómez (ex-R-11; ex-*General José Félix Ribas,* R-13; ex-*Oswegatchie,* YTM 778, ex-YTB 515)	13-8-45	24-10-45	14-12-45

Teniente de Navío Fernando Gómez (RP-21) Carlos E. Hernández, 7-88

D: 250 tons light (345 fl) **S:** 12 kts **Dim:** 30.48 × 7.92 × 2.92
A: 2 single 12.7-mm mg **Electronics:** Radar: 1 . . . nav.
M: 2 Enterprise diesels; 1 prop; 1,270 bhp **Crew:** 14 tot.

Remarks: Transferred from the U.S.A. 4-6-65; had been in reserve from 3-46 to 3-63. Transferred to the Coast Guard Command in 1989. Is equipped with oil skimming equipment, including a chemical dispenser on the bow.

NATIONAL GUARD
(Guardia Nacional)

The National Guard, Venezuela's fourth armed service organization, has about 30,000 personnel, all volunteers. It has nine regional commands, an Air Support Command with about 55 fixed-wing transports and helicopters, an Anti-Drug Command, and a Coastal Vigilance Command with more than 100 patrol boats for customs and internal security duties on the coast and on inland lakes and rivers. Four Enstrom 200FX light helicopters were acquired in 2-02 for training.

Note: National Guard craft display the words "Guardia Nacional" on either side of the hull or superstructure and carry blue-red-blue painted flag on either side of the bow, with the yellow letters "GN" superimposed.

PATROL BOATS [WPB]

Note: A 16-8-99 order for eight patrol boats from Israeli Aircraft Industries/RAMTA was later canceled.

♦ **0 (+ 6) lake patrol launches**
Bldr: Diancalum, C.A., Puerto Cabello (In serv. 2002)

Remarks: Aluminum-construction launches ordered in mid-2001 for use on Lake Maracaibo. No other data available.

♦ **10 54-foot-class search-and-rescue patrol boats**
Bldr: Halter Marine Equitable Shipyards, New Orleans (In serv. 2-99 to 12-99)

B-9801 Río Orinoco II	B-9805 Río	B-9809 Río . . . . . .
B-9802 Río Caroní	B-9806 Río	B-9810 Río . . . . . .
B-9803 Río	B-9807 Río	
B-9804 Río	B-9808 Río	

Río Orinoco II (B-9801) Halter Marine, 1999

D: 30 tons (fl) **S:** 36 kts **Dim:** 16.46 × . . . × . . .
A: 2 single 12.7-mm mg **Electronics:** Radar: 1 Raytheon R1210 nav.
M: 2 MTU 12V183 TE93 diesels; 2 props; 2,268 bhp
Range: 750/28 **Crew:** 5 tot.

Remarks: Were to have been ordered in 9-95 for delivery in 1996–97, but the contract not placed until 24-4-98. Additional units may be ordered. Aluminum construction. Funded by the Export-Import Bank. The first two were to complete in 12-98, then two each in 3-99, 5-99, 7-99, and 9-99, but the program fell behind by about four months. On the existing mountings, 40-mm Mk 19 grenade launchers can be substituted for the 12.7-mm machineguns.

♦ **5 U.S. 22-foot Guardian-class raider patrol launches**
Bldr: Boston Whaler, Edgewater, Fla. (In serv. 1998)

V-. . . series

D: 1.5 tons **S:** 35 kts **Dim:** 6.81 × 2.26 × . . .
A: 2 single 12.7-mm mg **Electronics:** Radar: 1 Raytheon SPS-66 nav.
M: 2 gasoline outboards; 250 bhp **Range:** 167/35 **Crew:** 4 tot.

Remarks: Donated by the U.S. government for river vigilance detachments. Foam-core GRP construction.

♦ **8 35-foot Raider patrol launches**
Bldr: C&W Industrial Fabrication and Marine Equipment, Canada (In serv. 6-99)

V-983501 (ex-GN-3501) through V-983508 (ex-GN-3508)

35-ft. Raider patrol launch Guardia Nacional, 9-00

D: . . . tons **S:** . . . kts **Dim:** 10.67 × . . . × . . .
A: 4 single 7.62-mm mg **Electronics:** Radar: 1 . . . nav.
M: 2 gasoline outboards; 350 bhp **Crew:** 6 tot.

Remarks: Ordered in 12-96. GRP construction. Are intended for riverine service to combat drug trade and insurgencies and are assigned to river detachments and painted olive drab. Have a GPS receiver and an HF radio.

♦ **25 30-foot Raider patrol launches**
Bldr: C&W Industrial Fabrications and Marine Equipment, Canada (In serv. 6-99)

V-983001 (ex-GN-3001) through V-983025 (ex-GN-3025)

D: . . . tons **S:** . . . kts **Dim:** 9.35 × . . . × . . .
A: 4 single 7.62-mm mg **Electronics:** Radar: 1 . . . nav.
M: 2 gasoline outboards; 350 bhp **Crew:** 6 tot.

Remarks: Ordered in 12-96. GRP construction. Assigned to coastal, river, and lakes vigilance detachments.

♦ **25 26-foot Raider patrol launches**
Bldr: C&W Industrial Fabrications and Marine Equipment, Canada (In serv. 6-99)

V-982601 (ex-GN-2601) through V-982625 (ex-GN-2625)

D: . . . tons **S:** 35–40 kts **Dim:** 7.92 × . . . × . . .
A: 4 single 7.62-mm mg **Electronics:** Radar: 1 . . . nav.
M: 2 gasoline outboards; 350 bhp **Crew:** 6 tot.

Remarks: Ordered in 1997. GRP construction. Assigned to coastal, river, and lakes vigilance detachments. Have an HF radio and a GPS receiver.

♦ **20 Precursor-class launches**
Bldr: Centro de Mantenimiento Naval, Guanta (In serv. 1996–. . .)

D: . . . tons **S:** 35 kts **Dim:** 4.8 × 1.6 × 0.9
A: 1 7.62-mm mg **M:** 1 gasoline outboard; 140 bhp
Endurance: 3 hr **Crew:** 1 coxswain + 4 troops

♦ **12 Protector class** Bldr: SeaArk Workboats, Monticello, Ark.

	In serv.		In serv.
B-8421 Río Arauca II	2-7-84	B-8427 Río Sarare	4-9-84
B-8422 Río Catatumbo II	2-7-84	B-8428 Río Uribante	4-9-84
B-8423 Río Apure II	1-8-84	B-8429 Río Cinaruco	1-11-84
B-8424 Río Nearo II	1-8-84	B-8430 Río Icabara	1-11-84
B-8425 Río Meta II	30-8-84	B-8431 Río Guarico II	1984
B-8426 Río Portuguesa II	1984	B-8432 Río Yaracuy	1984

D: 15 tons (fl) **S:** 28 kts **Dim:** 13.03 (12.55 pp) × 4.47 × 1.17
A: 2 single 12.7-mm mg; 2 single 7.62-mm mg
Electronics: Radar: 1 Furuno FR10 nav.
M: 2 G.M. Detroit Diesel 8V92 T diesels; 2 props; 1,100 bhp
Electric: 10.5 kw tot. **Range:** 600/25 **Crew:** 4 tot.

Remarks: Aluminum construction. Not delivered until 5-87. For river and lake patrol. Four of the craft were transferred to the navy's River Command but later returned.

NATIONAL GUARD PATROL BOATS [WPB] *(continued)*

Río Sarare (B-8427) H&L Van Ginderen, 2-96

♦ **10 21-foot Cobia design**
Bldr: SeaArk Workboats, Monticello, Ark. (In serv. 5-87)

A-6901 Lago 1
A-6902 Lago 2
A-6903 Lago 3
A-6904 Lago 4
A-7918 Río Cabriales
A-7919 Río Chama
A-7920 Río Caribe
A-7921 Río Tuy
A-7929 Manati
A-8223 Goaigoaza

SeaArk 21-ft. Cobia design SeaArk, 1984

D: 0.5 tons light (1.25 fl) **S:** 30 kts **Dim:** 6.02 × 2.36 × 0.33
A: 1 12.7-mm mg **Electronics:** Radar: 1 Furuno FR 10 nav.
M: 2 Evinrude gasoline outboard motors; 230 bhp **Crew:** 4 tot.

Remarks: Aluminum construction. For river and lake patrol. Equipped with push-knees to act as push-tugs. May have been renumbered with V-series pennants. A-7929 and A-8223 are used as yachts. Three sisters serve the navy.

♦ **15 18-foot chase-boat design**
Bldr: SeaArk Workboats, Monticello, Ark. (In serv. 5-87)

SeaArk 18-ft. chase boat SeaArk, 1984

D: 0.5 tons (fl) **S:** 30 kts **Dim:** 5.48 × 2.08 × 0.15 **A:** 1 12.7-mm mg
M: 1 Evinrude gasoline outboard motor; 140 bhp **Crew:** 4 tot.

Remarks: Completed 11-1-85, but delivery delayed. Aluminum construction.

♦ **12 Punta class** Bldr: Robert E. Derecktor SY, Mamaroneck, N.Y.

A-8201 Punta Barima
A-8202 Punta Mosquito
A-8203 Punta Barima
A-8204 Punta Perret
A-8205 Punta Cardon
A-8206 Punta Playa
A-8207 Punta Macoya
A-8208 Punta Moron
A-8209 Punta Unare
A-8210 Punta Ballena
A-8211 Punta Macuro
A-8212 Punta Mariusa

Punta-class—ramped stern version F. Nakajima/Derecktor SY, 1984

D: approx. 50 tons (fl) **S:** 35 kts **Dim:** 23.44 × 4.88 × 1.70
A: 1 12.7-mm mg **Electronics:** Radar: 1 Furuno . . . nav.
M: 2 MTU 12V183 TE93 diesels; 2 props; 2,268 bhp **Electric:** 60 kw tot.
Range: 1,100/24 **Fuel:** 16,000 liters **Crew:** 11 tot. + 40 troops

Remarks: The first six were ordered in 1980 and delivered in 8-82; the second six were ordered in 1982 for delivery by 10-84, but financing problems delayed arrival until 5-87. A-8201 through A-8203 and A-8207 through A-8209 have a vehicle ramp aft; the others have a small helicopter platform capable of accepting a Bell 206A JetRanger. Aluminum construction. Modernization and re-engining of this class were accomplished at the National Guard Naval Maintenance Center, Guanta, from 1996 to 1998 after most had become nonoperational; the armament was reduced to one 12.7-mm mg forward, the original General Motors diesels were replaced with a more powerful plant adding about 7 kts to the maximum speed, and a GPS receiver was added. A-8210 was the first to complete the modernization, in 8-96.

♦ **21 Italian A-type (Río Orinoco class)**
Bldrs: A-7414, A-7416 through A-7424: INMA, La Spezia, Italy; others: Diques y Astilleros Nacionales, C.A. (DIANCA), Puerto Cabello (In serv. 1974–76)

A-7414 Río Orinoco
A-7415 Río Cuyuni
A-7416 Río Ventuari
A-7417 Río Caparo
A-7418 Río Tucuyo
A-7419 Río Venamo
A-7420 Río Limon
A-7421 Río San Juan
A-7422 Río Turbio
A-7423 Río Torbes
A-7424 Río Escalante
A-7425 Río Canaparo
A-7426 Río Yurary
A-7427 Río Caura
A-7628 Río Motatan
A-7629 Río Grita
A-7630 Río Yuruan
A-7631 Río Bocono
A-7632 Río Neveri
A-7633 Río Goigoaza
A-7634 Río Guanare

D: 43 (INMA-made units: 48) tons (fl) **S:** 35 kts **Dim:** 23.8 × 4.8 × 1.5
A: 1 12.7-mm mg **Electronics:** Radar: 1 Furuno FR 711 or FR 24 nav.
M: 2 MTU 12V183 TE93 diesels; 2 props; 2,268 bhp
Range: 500–1,000/. . . **Crew:** 8–12 tot.

Remarks: Steel construction. Six sisters have been discarded, and the survivors were in poor condition until a refit program was completed in 1996 at the National Guard Naval Maintenance Center, Guanta. All have been re-engined, increasing their original speed by about 5 kts.

♦ **12 French B-type**
Bldr: . . . (In serv. 1979)

B-7918 Río Cabralles
B-7919 Río Chama
B-7920 Río Caribe
B-7921 Río Tuy
B-7929 . . . . . .
B-7930 Río Manatí
B-79. . . Río Guainia
B-79. . . Río Portuguesa
B-79. . . Río Uribante
B-79. . . . .
B-79. . . . .
B-79. . . . .

D: 45 tons (fl) **S:** 30 kts **Dim:** 21.7 × 4.9 × 1.5
A: 1 12.7-mm mg **Electronics:** Radar: 1 . . . nav.
M: 2 . . . diesels; 2 props; 3,000 bhp **Crew:** 12

Remarks: Some were no longer operational as of 1999. Were to be replaced by the now-canceled Israeli-built patrol boats.

♦ **10 Yamaha Mod. R.23 Enforcer launches**
Bldr: Yamaha Fibra, Venezuela (In serv. 1979)

Remarks: Assigned to coastal and lake patrol duties. Not all were operational as of 2001. Were built in two series, the 11.6-m *Batalla del Lago* and 8.5-m *General José Antonio Piez* classes, both with GRP hulls.

♦ **7 U.S. Enforcer series** Bldr: Bertram Yacht, Miami (In serv. 1978–80)

C-7918 and others

11.6-m Enforcer variant Guardia Nacional, 1-93

NATIONAL GUARD PATROL BOATS [WPB] *(continued)*

Remarks: Four of the 11.6-m version were delivered in 1978 and 10 more in 1980. One of the 14.0-m version and two of the 13.4-m version were delivered in 1980. All have outdrive motors and GRP hulls. Only seven, of various versions, were left in service as of 2001.

Note: Also in use are several rigid inflatable boats, including V-50, V-52, and V-69; these are armed with one 7.62-mm mg and were reportedly built by Boston Whaler, entering service in 1997. Locally built, aluminum-hulled launch V-81 is also in use, as well as several imported and locally fabricated RIB launches.

SERVICE CRAFT

♦ 5 (+ 2) miscellaneous river service barges [YPB]

Remarks: Two were acquired in 1983. Three were ordered in 1998 and entered service in 10-99 for assignment to river vigilance detachments as stores barges. Another two new aluminum-hulled barges were ordered from Diancalum, C.A., Puerto Cabello, in mid-2001.

♦ 4 afloat command post/accommodations lighters [WYFB]

Bldr: Caribbean Motors, Venezuela (In serv. late 1999)

Remarks: The first two were ordered in 12-98 for use as mobile floating command posts with river vigilance detachments.

ARMY OF VENEZUELA

(Ejército de Venezuela)

The Venezuelan Army has a significant number of aluminum and GRP-hulled boats and rubber inflatable boats for use by engineers, special forces, and other combat units. A series of assault boats with 75-bhp outboard motors was ordered in 1999, and several assault boats that can carry 15 troops each were procured in 1996. Amphibious vehicles in use by the army include 101 U.S.-built Dragoon 300–series wheeled vehicles (42 LFV-2 configured as armored cars with one Cockerill Mk III gun, 25 ASV troop carriers, 21 AMV configured to carry an 81-mm mortar, 11 ACV command and communications variants, and 2 ALV recovery vehicles) and 10 Thyssen-Henschel six-wheel Fuchs-I armored personnel carriers.

VENEZUELAN AIR FORCE

(Fuerza Aérea Venezolana)

The Venezuelan Air Force has several aluminum and GRP-construction launches and RIB launches based at Mariscal Sucre Air Base, Lago de Valencia, for local patrol, search-and-rescue, and utility duties. No data or total numbers available.

VIETNAM

Socialist Republic of Vietnam

Personnel (2001): Approx. 12,000 total, plus 25,000 Border Defense Corps (subordinate to the Ministry of Defense)

Bases: Headquarters at Hanoi, with units based at Cam Ranh Bay, Cân Tho, Da Nang, Hue, and Haiphong

Note: Most ship names are not known. The pennant number system works as follows: HQ- plus two digits: major combatant; HQ-100 series: seagoing patrol boat; HQ-200 series: harbor patrol craft; HQ-300 series: Soviet- and Russian-supplied seagoing patrol craft classes; HQ-400 series: landing craft; HQ-500 series: amphibious landing ships; HQ-600 series: cargo ships; HQ-700 series: fisheries protection craft; HQ-800 series: mine warfare units; and HQ-900: auxiliaries and service craft. Ships redesignated with BD- (*Bién-Dong* = East Sea) series pennants are assigned to Spratly Islands service.

Naval Aviation: Three Soviet Beriev Be-12 Mail antisubmarine patrol amphibians and eight Kamov Ka-28PL Helix-A land-based ASW helicopters

COASTAL SUBMARINES [SSC]

♦ 2 North Korean Sang-o class

Bldr: Bong Dao Bo SY, Singpo (In serv. 1991–. . .)

D: 295 tons surf./325 tons sub. **S:** 7 kts surf./8 kts sub. **Dim:** 34.0 × 3.8 × 3.2
A: 4 bow 533-mm TT (no reloads); 16 mines in external racks
Electronics:
Radar: 1 Furuno . . . nav.
Sonar: probably passive hull array only
M: 1 diesel generator set (probably 300 bhp); 1 shrouded prop; 200 shp
Range: 2,700/8 snorkel **Crew:** 19 tot.

Remarks: Reportedly transferred around mid-1997 in poor condition; as of 12-98 were being refurbished at Cam Ranh Bay naval base. Are probably configured as above, rather than being of the swimmer infiltration version captured by South Korea. Equipment is primitive, and the units are primarily useful for coast-defense purposes.

FRIGATES [FF]

♦ 0 (+ 1 + . . .) Russian KBO 2000 class

Bldr: Ho Chi Minh SY, Ho Chi Minh City (In serv. . . .)

D: 2,000 tons **S:** . . . kts **Dim:** . . . × . . . × . . .
A: 8 Kh-35 Uran (SS-N-25 Switchblade) SSM; 1 8-round Klinok SAM syst. (9M-330 missiles); 1 100-mm 59-cal. AK-190 DP; 2 single 30-mm 54-cal. AK-630 gatling AA; 2 twin 533-mm TT; 1 . . . helicopter
Electronics:
Radar: . . .
Sonar: . . .
EW: . . .
M: . . .
Range: . . ./. . . **Crew:** . . . tot.

Remarks: Negotiations were said to have begun with Russia's Northern Project Design Bureau in 1996 for the local construction of a 2,000-ton frigate design called the "KBO 2000"; no further details are available, but the size and armament reported suggest that it is a variant of the Gepard (Project 1166.1) class (see Russia section). "Design work" was reported complete in 3-99, at which time the ship was said already to have been ordered. There have been no further reports on any progress on its construction, however.

CORVETTES [FFL]

♦ 3 ex-Soviet Petya-II class (Project 159A)

Bldr: Khabarovsk Zavod, Russia

	Laid down	L	In serv.
HQ-13 (ex-SKR-141)	14-4-70	7-8-71	30-9-71
HQ-15 (ex-SKR-130)	11-2-70	5-9-70	20-10-70
HQ-17 (ex-SKR-135)	4-4-72	12-8-72	31-3-73

HQ-17 NAVPIC-Holland, 8-95

D: 938 tons light (1,077 fl) **S:** 29 kts
Dim: 81.80 (78.00 pp) × 9.20 × 2.85 (hull; 5.85 over sonar)
A: 2 twin 76.2-mm 59-cal. AK-276 DP; 2 quintuple 402-mm ASW TT; 2 12-round RBU-6000 ASW RL; 2 d.c. racks; mines

Vietnam's naval base at Da Nang—visible from left are Tarantul-I-class guided-missile patrol craft HQ-372 and HQ-371, two Turya-class torpedo boats, Sonya-class minesweeper HQ-864 and a sister, both Yurka-class minesweepers, and the *Dobrynya Nikitich*–class icebreaker H&L Van Ginderen, 6-96

CORVETTES [FFL] *(continued)*

HQ-13 Markus Berger, 11-97

Electronics:
Radar: 1 Don-2 nav.; 1 Fut-N (Strut Curve) air search; 1 Fut-B (Hawk Screech) gun f.c.
Sonar: Titan hull-mounted MF search; Vychegda HF attack
EW: 2 Bizan'-4B (Watch Dog) intercept (2–18 GHz)
M: CODAG: 2 M-2 gas turbines (15,000 shp each), 1 Type 61-B3 diesel (6,000 bhp); 3 props (CP on centerline)—2 low-speed maneuvering props (3 kts)
Range: 4,800/10 (diesel); 450/29 (CODAG) **Fuel:** 130 tons
Endurance: 10 days **Crew:** 8 officers, 84 enlisted

Remarks: HQ-13 was transferred during 1983, HQ-15 on 10-5-84, and HQ-17 during 12-84. As of 2-96, HQ-13 (ex-SKR-141) was disarmed and derelict at Ho Chi Minh City, but the ship had been refitted and repainted by late 1997.

♦ 2 ex-Soviet Petya-III class (Project 159AE)
Bldr: Khabarovsk Zavod, Russia

	Laid down	L	In serv.
HQ-09 (ex-SKR-82)	25-9-75	28-4-76	13-7-77
HQ-11 (ex-SKR-96)	27-6-75	25-4-76	29-6-78

HQ-11—rearmed with additional AA weapons in place of ASW ordnance NAVPIC-Holland, 8-95

HQ-09 NAVPIC-Holland, 8-95

D: 960 tons (1,040 fl) **S:** 29 kts
Dim: 81.80 (78.00 pp) × 9.20 × 2.72 (hull; 5.72 over sonar)
A: HQ-09: 2 twin 76.2-mm 59-cal. AK-276 DP; 1 triple 533-mm TT; 4 16-round RBU-2500 ASW RL; 2 d.c. racks; mines—HQ-11: 2 twin 76.2-mm 59-cal. AK-276 DP; 2 twin 37-mm 63-cal. AA; 2 twin 23-mm ZSU-23 AA; 4 16-round RBU-2500 ASW RL; 2 d.c. racks; mines
Electronics:
Radar: 1 Don-2 nav.; 1 Fut-N (Strut Curve) air search; 1 Fut-B (Hawk Screech) f.c.
Sonar: Titan hull-mounted MF search; Vychegda HF attack
EW: 2 Bizan'-4B (Watch Dog) intercept (2–18 GHz)
M: CODAG: 2 M-2 gas turbines (15,000 shp each), 1 Type 61-B3 diesel (6,000 bhp); 3 props—2 low-speed maneuvering props (3 kts)
Range: 4,800/10 (diesel); 450/29 (CODAG) **Fuel:** 130 tons
Crew: 8 officers, 84 enlisted

Remarks: Petya-III export models, transferred 21-12-78. By 1995, HQ-11 had had the torpedo tube mount replaced with two 37-mm twin AA mounts and the pair of RBU-2500 ASW rocket launchers forward replaced with two twin 23-mm AA. The ASW rocket launching systems may no longer be functional.

PATROL SHIPS [PS]

♦ 1 ex-U.S. Barnegat-class former seaplane tender
Bldr: Lake Washington SY, Houghton, Wash.

	Laid down	L	In serv.
HQ-01 Pham Ngu Lao (ex-*Tham Ngu Lao;* ex-USCG *Absecon,* WHEC 374, ex-AVP 23)	23-7-41	8-3-42	28-1-43

D: 1,766 tons (2,800 fl) **S:** 18 kts **Dim:** 94.7 (91.4 wl) × 12.5 × 4.1
A: 1 127-mm 38-cal. Mk 30 DP; 3 single 37-mm 63-cal. AA; 2 twin 25-mm 60-cal. 2M-3M AA; 2 4-round Fasta-4M point-defense SAM syst.
Electronics: Radar: . . .
M: 4 Fairbanks-Morse 38D8⅛ × 10 diesels; 2 props; 6,080 bhp
Electric: 600 kw **Range:** 20,000/10 **Fuel:** 26 tons **Crew:** approx. 200 tot.

Remarks: Transferred to South Vietnam in 1971, having served in the U.S. Coast Guard since 1948. Was equipped on the fantail with two SS-N-2A Styx missiles that had been removed from a stricken Komar-class missile boat during the late 1970s, but these have probably long since been removed. The close-in defensive suite was augmented, but the 127-mm gun is unlikely to be functional. Has no weapons-control system. Current status is uncertain, and the ship may have been discarded.

Disposal note: The U.S. *Savage*-class patrol ship *Dai Ky* (HQ-03, ex-*Tran Khan Du;* ex-*Forster,* DER 334) and U.S. *Admirable*-class patrol ship HQ-07 (ex-*Ha Hoi;* ex-*Prowess,* IX 305, ex-MSF 280) had been reduced to hulk status by 1998 but remain afloat as training and accommodations craft.

GUIDED-MISSILE PATROL COMBATANTS [PGG]

♦ 1 (+ 1) BPS 500 class (Russian Project 12418)
Bldr: Ho Chi Minh SY, Ho Chi Minh City (In serv. 1999–. . .)

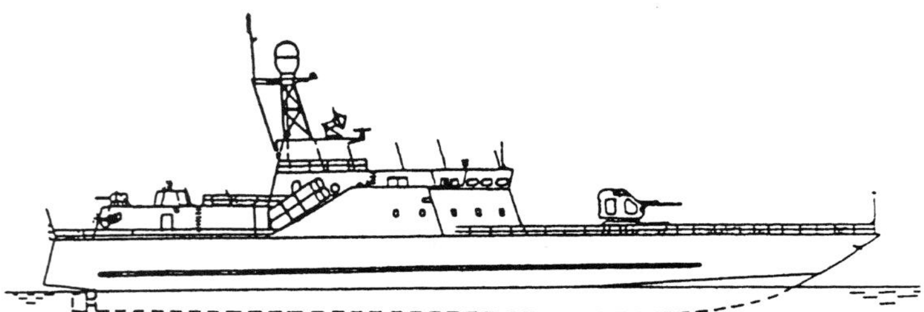

BPS 500 class *Sudostroeniye,* 1997

D: 517 tons (600 fl) **S:** 32 kts (15 cruise) **Dim:** 62.0 × 11.0 × 2.2 (hull)
A: 8 Kh-35 Uran (SS-N-25 Switchblade) SSM; 1 76.2-mm 59-cal. AK-176 DP; 1 30-mm AK-630 gatling CIWS; 2 single 12.7-mm mg
Electronics:
Radar: 1 . . . nav.; 1 MR-352 Pozitiv-E (Cross Dome) surf./air search; 1 MR-123E Vympel-E (Bass Tilt) gun f.c.
EW: . . . intercept; 2 16-round PK-16 decoy RL
M: 2 MTU . . . diesels; 2 KaMeWa waterjets; 19,600 bhp (14,400 sust.)
Range: 2,200/14 **Crew:** 28 tot.

Remarks: Designed by Severnoye Bureau, St. Petersburg, Russia, which is said to be providing construction assistance. Virtually all components have had to be imported. The design is of about the same size as the Tarantul class, but the hullform is wedge-shaped in plan view. The first unit was planned to be completed during 1997, but was still on the ways as of 11-97 and did not begin to run trials until 3-99. No further information about the status of this program has become available, and it may be that neither unit has entered service.
Hull systems: The waterjets have thrust-reversers to permit harbor maneuvering.
Combat systems: Sixteen Kh-35 missiles for the two craft were to be delivered in 1999, with another 30–48 to be ordered later. May also be fitted with the Vikhr'-K point-defense SAM system (with 24 missiles) and four ASW torpedo tubes. They were to have had a laser-rangefinder gun director.

♦ 2 Tarantul-I class (Project 1241RE)
Bldr: Volodarskiy SY, Rybinsk (In serv. 10-94)

HQ-371 HQ-372

D: 385 tons light (455 fl) **S:** 43 kts
Dim: 56.10 (49.50 pp) × 10.20 (9.40 wl) × 2.14 (hull; 3.59 props)
A: 4 P-20/21 Rubezh (SS-N-2C Styx) SSM; 1 76.2-mm 59-cal. AK-176 DP; 1 4-round MTU-40S SAM syst. (12 Strela missiles); 2 single 30-mm 65-cal. AK-630 gatling AA
Electronics:
Radar: 1 Kivach-3 nav.; 1 Garpun-E (Plank Shave) targeting; 1 MR-123 Vympel (Bass Tilt) f.c.
EW: 2 16-round PK-16 decoy RL
M: M-15E COGAG plant: 2 DMR-76 cruise gas turbines (4,000 shp each), 2 PR-77 boost gas turbines (12,000 shp each); 2 props; 32,000 shp
Electric: 500 kw tot. (2 × 200-kw, 1 × 100-kw diesel sets)
Range: 760/43; 1,400/13 **Fuel:** 122,634 liters **Endurance:** 10 days
Crew: 7 officers, 32 enlisted

Remarks: Standard export versions, delivered together in 10-94. Negotiations for another pair, ongoing for several years, reportedly resulted in a contract signing during 1-99 for delivery in 2000, indicating that they came from among units completed some years ago but not previously sold, but the contract was in the end *not* signed, due to Vietnamese funding shortages. Shore-based training simulators for this class were ordered in Russia during 3-01.
Hull systems: Stainless-steel-alloy, seven-watertight-compartment hull with aluminum alloy superstructure, decks, and internal bulkheads. Very strongly constructed and rugged. Have difficulty maneuvering below 10 kts due to the small size of their rudders.
Combat systems: Carry 252 ready-service rounds for the 76.2-mm gun and another 150 in reserve. The weapons system employs digital computers and has many backup features. Normally carry two infrared-homing and two radar-homing antiship missiles. The Garpun-E radar also serves as a passive intercept and targeting system.

GUIDED-MISSILE PATROL CRAFT [PTG]

♦ up to 8 Soviet Osa-II class (Project 205ME)

HQ-359	HQ-384	HQ- 386
HQ-360	HQ-385	up to 3 others

D: 184 tons (226 normal fl; 245 overload) **S:** 40 kts (35 sust.)
Dim: 38.6 (37.5 wl) × 7.6 (6.3 wl) × 2.0 (hull; 3.1 props)

GUIDED-MISSILE PATROL CRAFT [PTG] *(continued)*

A: 4 P-15M/20 Rubezh (SS-N-2B/C Styx) SSM; 2 twin 30-mm 65-cal. AK-230 AA
Electronics:
Radar: 1 Rangout (Square Tie) surf. search/target detection; 1 MR-104 Rys' (Drum Tilt) gun f.c.
M: 3 M-504 or M-504B diesels; 3 props; 15,000 bhp **Electric:** 400 kw tot.
Range: 500/34; 750/25 **Endurance:** 5 days **Crew:** 4 officers, 24 enlisted

Remarks: Two each were transferred in 10-79, 9-80, 11-80, and 2-81. Are probably in only marginal operating condition. The Rangout radar can be used in the passive mode to detect targets.

HYDROFOIL TORPEDO BOATS [PTH]

♦ 3 Turya (Shtorm)-class (Project 206M) semi-hydrofoils
Bldrs: Vladivostokskiy Sudostroitel'niy Zavod (Ulis), Vladivostok (In serv. 1984)

HQ-331 HQ-332 HQ-333

D: 215 tons (220 normal; 250 fl) **S:** 48 kts (37 sust.)
Dim: 39.6 (37.5 wl) × 7.6 (9.6 over foils; 6.3 wl) × 2.0 (4.0 over foils)
A: 1 twin 57-mm 70-cal. AK-725 AA; 1 twin 25-mm 80-cal. 2M-3M AA; 4 fixed 533-mm OTA-53-206M TT (2 Type 53-56B or 53-56BA and 2 Type 53-65K torpedoes)
Electronics:
Radar: 1 Baklan (Pot Drum) surf. search; 1 MR-103 Bars (Muff Cob) gun f.c.
Sonar: 1 Rat Tail Hormone helicopter-type, dipping
EW: 2 16-round PK-16 decoy RL
M: 3 M-504 diesels; 3 props; 15,000 bhp
Range: 600/37; 1,450/14 **Crew:** 5 officers, 21 enlisted

Remarks: Two were delivered in mid-1984 and one late in 1984; two of Project 206ME (without torpedo tubes) were delivered in 1-86 (see under [PCH]).
Hull systems: Have fixed hydrofoils forward only; the stern planes on the water's surface. Have Osa-II-class hull and propulsion. Are intended to be able to maintain 40 kts in a State 4 sea and 35 kts in Sea State 5; the 48-kt calm-water maximum speed listed is probably no longer attainable.
Combat systems: The dipping sonar is housed in a sponson over the starboard quarter. The torpedo tubes can launch both antiship and antisubmarine torpedoes.

TORPEDO BOATS [PT]

♦ 4 Soviet Shershen class (Project 206)

HQ-301 HQ-354 HQ-359 HQ-360

Shershen-class torpedo boat—under refit at Haiphong
G. Kuvel, via Paolo Marsan, 8-00

D: 129 tons light (161 fl) **S:** 41.9 kts
Dim: 34.60 (33.60 wl) × 6.74 (5.60 wl) × 1.72
A: 2 twin 30-mm 65-cal. AK-230 AA; 4 fixed 533-mm TT; mines
Electronics:
Radar: 1 Baklan (Pot Drum) surf. search; 1 MR-104 Rys' (Drum Tilt) gun f.c.
M: 3 M-503A diesels; 3 props; 12,000 bhp **Electric:** 84 kw tot. (3 × 28 kw)
Range: 460/42; 600/30; 2,000/14 **Fuel:** 30 tons **Crew:** 2 officers, 20 enlisted

Remarks: A total of 16 were transferred: two in 1973, two (without torpedo tubes) on 16-4-79, two on 12-9-79, two in 8-80, two in 10-80, two in 1981, and four in 6-83. At least 12 have been retired, and one of the above has had the torpedo tubes removed and is assigned to the national police force.

HYDROFOIL PATROL CRAFT [PCH]

♦ 2 Turya (Shtorm)-class (Project 206ME) semi-hydrofoils
Bldr: Vladivostokskiy Sudostroitel'niy Zavod (Ulis), Vladivostok (In serv. 1-86)

HQ-334 HQ-335

D: 215 tons (220 normal; 250 fl) **S:** 48 kts (37 sust.)
Dim: 39.6 (37.5 wl) × 7.6 (9.6 over foils; 6.3 wl) × 2.0 (4.0 over foils)
A: 1 twin 57-mm 70-cal. AK-725 AA; 1 twin 25-mm 80-cal. 2M-3M AA
Electronics:
Radar: 1 Baklan (Pot Drum) surf. search; 1 MR-103 Bars (Muff Cob) gun f.c.
EW: 2 16-round PK-16 decoy RL
M: 3 M-504 diesels; 3 props; 15,000 bhp
Range: 600/37; 1,450/14 **Endurance:** 5 days **Crew:** 5 officers, 21 enlisted

Remarks: Delivered in 1-86. May have originally been intended for another customer. Differ from the standard torpedo boat version in their lack of torpedo tubes and a dipping sonar. Three others, equipped with torpedo tubes (Project 206M), are listed above under [PTH].
Hull systems: Have fixed hydrofoils forward only; the stern planes on the water's surface. Have Osa-II-class hull and propulsion. Are intended to be able to maintain 40 kts in a State 4 sea and 35 kts in Sea State 5; the 48-kt calm-water maximum speed listed is probably no longer attainable.

PATROL CRAFT [PC]

♦ 0 (+ 2) Russian Svetlyak class (Project 1041.2)
Bldr: Sudostroitel'noye Obyedineniye "Almaz," Petrovskiy SY, St. Petersburg (In serv. 2002)

D: 328 tons light (365–375 normal fl; 382 max.) **S:** 32 kts (31 sust.)
Dim: 49.50 (45.00 wl) × 9.20 × 2.14 (hull; 2.50 props)
A: 1 76.2-mm 59-cal. AK-176M DP; 1 30-mm 54-cal. AK-630M gatling AA; 16 SA-14/16 Igla-series shoulder-launched SAMs (see remarks); 1 or 2 AGS-17 grenade launchers; 1 DP-64 antiswimmer grenade launcher
Electronics:
Radar: 1 Reyd (Peel Cone) and/or Mius nav./surf. search; 1 MR-123 Vympel-AM (Bass Tilt) f.c.
EW: Slyabing intercept; MFD/F; 2 16-round PK-16 decoy RL
M: 3 M-520B diesels; 3 props; 15,000 bhp
Electric: 400 kw tot. (1 × 200-kw, 2 × 100-kw diesel sets; 380 V, 50 Hz a.c.)
Range: 1,500/31–32; 2,200/12–13 **Endurance:** 10 days
Crew: 4 officers, 4 warrant officers, 20 enlisted (accomm. for 41 tot.)

Remarks: Said to have been ordered by 9-99 and to be under construction as of 5-00; both were fitting out as of 1-02. The Project 1041.2 version does not have ASW equipment.
Hull systems: Semi-planing, round-bilge hull with a low spray chine forward. Propellers do not project below keel. Steel hull with magnesium/aluminum alloy superstructure. Can survive with two compartments flooded. Have NBC warfare protection. Engine room is coated with vibration-damping material. The pilothouse is equipped with a centerline periscope.
Combat systems: There is an SP-521 Rakurs (Kolonka-2) ringsight backup director for the 30-mm gun; the 76.2-mm mount can be operated in local control and has an integral electro-optical sighting system. Carry 152 rounds of 76-mm ammunition (all on-mount) and up to 3,000 rounds of 30-mm. Navigational equipment includes a NAVSAT receiver, radio navaid receiver, automatic plot, and echo sounder.

Disposal note: The four ex-Soviet S.O.-I-class (Project 201M) patrol craft/submarine chasers listed in the previous edition are believed to have been retired by 2001.

PATROL BOATS [PB]

♦ 4 (+ 12) Stolkraft 22.4-meter design
Bldrs: first four: Brisbane Ship Construction, Australia; others: Pacific Asia Industries, Vung Tao, Vietnam (In serv. 3-98 to . . .)

HQ-56 HQ-57 HQ-58 HQ-59

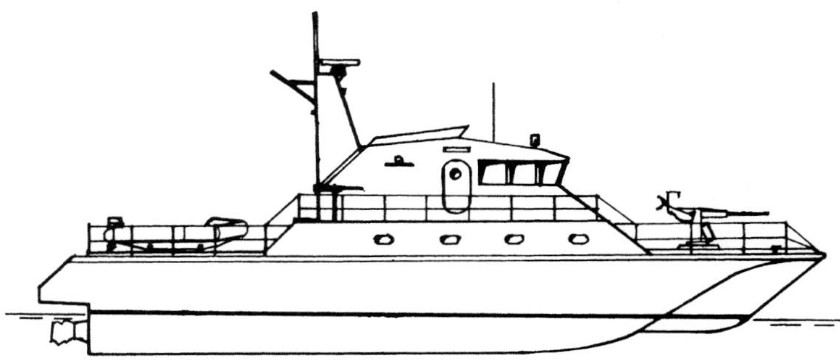

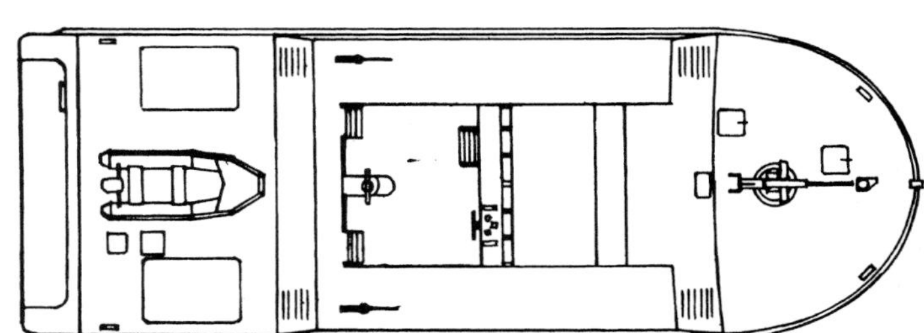

Stolkraft 22.4-m design A. D. Baker III

D: 36 tons (43.3 fl) **S:** 20+ kts **Dim:** 22.40 × 7.50 × 1.20
A: 1 20-mm 90-cal. Oerlikon AA **Electronics:** Radar: 1 . . . nav.
M: 2 Iveco-FIAT 8061-SRM-25 diesels; 2 Vosper Thornycroft PP waterjets; 1,000 bhp
Range: . . ./. . . **Fuel:** 8,000 liters **Endurance:** 5 days
Crew: 3 tot. + 38 passengers

Remarks: Ordered in early 1996 in a cooperative effort between John Lund Marine and Oceanfast of Australia and Pacific Asia Industries of Vietnam. Are intended for high-speed patrol, interception, rescue, and coordination duties, ostensibly for the customs service; the hull numbers, however, suggest that they have been incorporated into the navy instead. These first four were to be completed in 3-97 by Oceanfast Marine Group, Henderson, Western Australia, but the craft were instead built by Brisbane Ship Construction; further units were to be built in Vietnam. Use aluminum-construction trimaran hull that employs the Leo Stolk trapped-air-bubble concept to

PATROL BOATS [PB] *(continued)*

achieve very high speeds (90 kts in the more powerfully engined Australian prototype) and a stable ride in heavy seas. Can be beached. Were originally to have been equipped with much-more-powerful diesels.

♦ 4 HQ-37 class
Bldr: VINASHIN, Vietnam (In serv. 1998–. . .)

HQ-37 HQ-55 BP-29-01-01 . . .

HQ-55—a Shershen-class torpedo boat in refit is visible at the left
G. Kuvel, via Paolo Marsan, 8-00

BP-29-01-01—with machineguns fore and aft French Navy, 11-98

D: 38 tons light **S:** 30 kts **Dim:** 29.0 × . . . × . . .
A: 2 twin 14.5-mm mg **Electronics:** Radar: 1 Lotsiya nav.
M: 2 Saab Scania DI-14 diesels; 2 props; 2,500 bhp **Crew:** 11–14 tot.

Remarks: Design patterned after that of the Zhuk class, but with a simplified hullform and superstructure shape. BP-29-01-01 is probably assigned to the national police force.

♦ 11 Soviet Zhuk class (Project 1400M)

T-864 T-874 T-880 T-881 7 others

Zhuk-class T-880 and two sisters French Navy, 11-98

D: 35.9 tons (39.7 fl) **S:** 30 kts
Dim: 23.80 (21.70 wl) × 5.00 (3.80 wl) × 1.00 (hull; 1.90 max.)
A: 2 twin 12.7-mm 60-cal. Utës-Ma mg **Electronics:** Radar: 1 Lotsiya nav.
M: 2 M-401 diesels; 2 props; 2,200 bhp
Electric: 48 kw tot. (2 × 21-kw, 1 × 6-kw diesel sets)
Range: 500/13.5 **Endurance:** 5 days **Crew:** 1 officer, 9 enlisted

Remarks: Three were transferred in 1978, three in 11-80, one in 11-81, one in 5-85, three in 1986, two in 12-89, and two in 1990. Two more were delivered around 1996 from Ukraine. Six have been stricken, and the older survivors are probably in poor condition.
Hull systems: Aluminum alloy hull. Capable of operating in up to Sea State 4 or 5. Range is also reported as 700 n.m. at 28 kts and 1,100 n.m. at 15 kts. The earlier units were of Project 1400A, with M-50F-4 diesels.
Combat systems: Some carry only one twin machinegun mounting, forward.

Customs Patrol boat Do Dac Hien 01 G. Kuvel, via Paolo Marsan, 8-00

BP-29-12-01—a locally built patrol boat for which no information is available; the craft is **moored outboard** a locally built version of the Zhuk class
French Navy, 11-98

River Police (Canh Sat) patrol boat CA-75-51-09—at Hue
G. Kuvel, via Paolo Marsan, 8-00

♦ . . . ex-U.S. PBR (Patrol Boat, Riverine) Mk-II class
Bldr: Uniflite, Bellingham, Wash. (In serv. 1968–70)

D: 6.7 tons light (8 fl) **S:** 24 kts **Dim:** 9.73 × 3.53 × 0.6
A: 1 twin and 1 single 12.7-mm mg; 1 60-mm mortar
M: 2 G.M. 6V53N diesels; 2 Jacuzzi waterjets; 430 bhp
Range: 150/23 **Crew:** 4 tot.

Remarks: A few survivors of the more than 290 captured in 1975 probably remain in use on inland waterways.

MINE WARFARE SHIPS AND CRAFT

♦ 2 ex-Soviet Yurka-class (Project 266) fleet minesweepers [MSF]
Bldr: Vladivostokskiy Sudostroitel'niy Zavod (Ulis SY),Vladivostok (In serv. 1961–70)

HQ-851 HQ-885

D: 520 tons normal (560 fl; 619 max.) **S:** 16 kts
Dim: 52.10 (46.00 pp) × 9.60 (9.40 wl) × 2.65 (hull)
A: 2 twin 30-mm 65-cal. AK-230 AA; 2 mine rails (10 mines)
Electronics:
Radar: 1 or 2 Don-2 nav.; 1 MR-104 Rys' (Drum Tilt) gun f.c.
Sonar: MG-69 Lan' hull-mounted HF
M: 2 M-503B-3E diesels; 2 CP props; 5,000 bhp
Electric: 500 kw tot. (2 × 200-kw, 1 × 100-kw diesel sets)
Range: 600/16; 1,500/12 **Endurance:** 7 days **Crew:** 5 officers, 41 enlisted

Remarks: Both were transferred in 12-79 from the Soviet Pacific Fleet. Probably have little remaining service life.
Hull systems: Have a low-magnetic-signature, aluminum-steel alloy hull, with low-magnetic-signature machinery. The degaussing equipment is automatic controlled, with local coils around massive equipment. Also have special measures to reduce their acoustic signature. Maximum sweep speed with arrays deployed is 14 kts.
Combat systems: The sonar transducer is mounted in a large dome that can be hoisted within the hull. Are intended to sweep mines in 25- to 150-m depths. A towed television minehunting device is sometimes carried.

♦ 4 Sonya-class (Project 1265E) coastal minesweepers [MSC]
Bldr: Vladivostokskiy Sudostroitel'niy Zavod (Ulis SY),Vladivostok

HQ-864 and 3 others

D: 401 tons (430 fl) **S:** 14 kts **Dim:** 48.80 (46.00 wl) × 10.20 (9.20 wl) × 2.75
A: 1 twin 30-mm 65-cal. AK-230 AA; 1 twin 25-mm 80-cal. 2M-3M AA; 5 mines
Electronics:
Radar: 1 Mius (Spin Trough) nav.
Sonar: MG-89 Serna HF hull-mounted
M: 2 DRA-210-A diesels; 2 3-bladed CP props; 2,000 bhp—2 low-speed thrusters
Electric: 350 kw tot. (3 × 100-kw, 1 × 50-kw diesel sets; 380 V, 50 Hz a.c.)
Range: 1,500/10 **Fuel:** 27.1 tons **Endurance:** 10 days
Crew: 5–6 officers, 26 enlisted (accomm. for 45)

Remarks: Were delivered on 16-2-87, in 2-88, in 7-89, and in 3-90; all were probably new-construction.
Hull systems: Wooden construction with GRP plastic hull sheathing. The sweep winch can tow 10 tons at 9 kts.
Combat systems: Carry a GKT-2 contact sweep; ST-2, AT-2, and PEMT-2 influence sweeps; and an IT-3 mine detector/exploder. The sonar dome pivots at the after end to retract within the hull.

♦ 2 Soviet Yevgenya-class (Project 1258) inshore minesweepers [MSI]
Bldr: Sudostroitel'noye Obyedineniye "Almaz" (Sredniy Neva), Kolpino

D: 88.5 tons light; 94.5 normal (97.9 fl) **S:** 11 kts
Dim: 26.13 (24.20 wl) × 5.90 (5.10 wl) × 1.38

MINE WARFARE SHIPS AND CRAFT *(continued)*

A: 1 twin 14.5-mm 93-cal. 2M-7 AA; 1 7-round MRG-1 grenade launcher; 4 d.c. (+ 8 emergency stowage)
Electronics: Radar: 1 Mius (Spin Trough) nav.—Sonar: MG-7 HF dipping
M: 2 Type 3D12 diesels; 2 props; 600 bhp—hydraulic slow-speed drive
Electric: 100 kw tot. (2 × 50-kw diesel sets)
Range: 400/10 **Fuel:** 2.7 tons **Endurance:** 3 days
Crew: 1 officer, 9 enlisted (+ 2–3 mine clearance divers)

Remarks: Delivered to Cam Ranh Bay in 11-84. At least one other, delivered in 10-79, has been stricken.
Hull systems: GRP hull. Navigational equipment includes a Girya-MA gyrocompass and a NEL-7 echo sounder.
Combat systems: Can employ a Neva-1 television minehunting system, useful to 30-m depths, that dispenses marker buoys to permit later disposal of mines by divers or explosive charges. The sonar is lowered via one of the stern davits. Carry VKT-1 mechanical, AT-2 acoustic, and SEMT-1 solenoid coil sweep gear.

Disposal note: The ex-Soviet K-8-class (Project 361T) minesweeping boats [MSB] listed in the previous edition are believed to have been discarded by 2001.

AMPHIBIOUS WARFARE SHIPS

♦ 3 ex-U.S. LST 1– and LST 542–class tank landing ships [LST]
Bldrs: HQ-501: Bethlehem SY, Hingham, Mass.; HQ-502: Jeffersonville Boiler and Mach., Ind.; HQ-503: Chicago Bridge & Iron, Seneca, Ill.

	Laid down	L	In serv.
HQ-501 Tran Khanh Du (ex-*Da Nang;* ex-*Maricopa County,* LST 938)	12-7-44	15-8-44	9-9-94
HQ-502 Qui Nhon (ex-*Bullock County,* LST 509)	7-10-43	23-11-43	8-1-44
HQ-503 Vung Tau (ex-*Coconino County,* LST 603)	10-12-43	15-4-44	15-5-44

Tran Khanh Du (HQ-501) NAVPIC-Holland, 9-95

D: 1,623 tons light (4,080 fl) **S:** 11.6 kts **Dim:** 99.98 × 15.24 × 4.29
A: HQ-501: 2 twin 40-mm 60-cal. Bofors Mk 1 Mod. 2 AA; 4 single 40-mm 60-cal. Bofors Mk 3 AA; 4 single 20-mm 70-cal. Oerlikon Mk 10 AA—others: 2 twin 37-mm 63-cal. Type 74 AA
Electronics: Radar: 1 . . . nav.
M: 2 G.M. 12-567A diesels; 2 props; 1,700 bhp **Electric:** 300 kw
Range: 6,000/9 (loaded) **Fuel:** 590 tons **Crew:** approx. 100 tot.

Remarks: Transferred to South Vietnam 12-7-62, 8-4-70, and 4-4-69, respectively. All are believed to be operational, although in marginal condition. Have been rearmed in part with Soviet-supplied weapons.

♦ 3 ex-Soviet Polnocny-B-class (Project 771) medium landing ships [LSM]
Bldr: Stocznia Polnocna, Gdansk, Poland (In serv. 1968–70)

HQ-511 HQ-512 HQ-513

Polnocny-class HQ-511—outboard HQ-513 *Ships of the World,* 1996

D: 558 tons light; 640 tons std. (884 fl) **S:** 18 kts
Dim: 75.00 (70.00 wl) × 9.00 (8.60 wl) × 1.20 (fwd; 2.40 aft; 2.07 mean)
A: 2 twin 30-mm 65-cal. AK-230 AA; 2 18-round 140-mm WM-18 barrage RL (180 rockets)
Electronics: Radar: 1 Mius (Spin Trough); 1 MR-104 Rys' (Drum Tilt) f.c.
M: 2 Type 40DM diesels; 2 props; 4,400 bhp
Range: 700/18; 2,000/16 **Crew:** 5 officers, 32 enlisted + 60–180 troops

Remarks: Transferred in 5-79, 11-79, and 2-80. Were approaching derelict condition when sighted during 1995–96 but had been refitted by 2000 and remain in commission.
Hull systems: Have a bow door only. Hull has a pronounced "beak" at the bow to aid in beaching. Hatches to the upper deck are for loading and ventilation only. Cargo: 237 tons max., including six tanks, or 180 troops and their equipment; 30 vehicle crew are carried with tank loadout. The vehicle deck is 44.3 m long, 5.3 m wide, and 3.6 m high.

♦ up to 5 ex-U.S. LCU 1466–class utility landing craft [LCU]

D: 367 tons (fl) **S:** 8 kts **Dim:** 35.14 × 10.36 × 1.5
A: 2 twin 20-mm 70-cal. Oerlikon Mk 24 AA
M: 3 G.M. Gray Marine 64YTL diesels; 3 props; 675 bhp
Range: 1,200/6 **Fuel:** 11 tons **Crew:** 14 tot.

Remarks: Survivors of units transferred to South Vietnam between 1954 and 1971; captured in 1975 were LCU 1475, 1479, 1480, 1481, 1484, 1485, 1493, 1494, 1498, 1501, 1502, 1594, 1595, and YFU 90 (ex-LCU 1582). About 10 others have been stricken. Cargo: 150 tons or 300 troops on a 15.8 × 9.0–m deck, with a 4.3-m-wide bow ramp.

Note: Eighty-four U.S. LCM(6), 38 LCM(8), 40 LCVP, and several LCP-type landing craft were also abandoned to North Vietnam in 1975; some were probably returned to service.

♦ up to 12 ex-Soviet T4-class (Project 1785) landing craft [LCM]

D: 35 tons light (93 fl) **S:** 10 kts (light) **Dim:** 20.4 × 5.4 × 1.2 (max. aft)
M: 2 Type 3D-6 diesels; 2 props; 300 bhp
Range: 300/8 **Endurance:** 2 days **Crew:** 2–3 tot.

Remarks: Transferred in 1979 and later. Can accommodate up to 50 tons of cargo on the 9.5 × 3.9–m vehicle deck.

AUXILIARIES

♦ 1 ex-Russian Dobrynya Nikitich–class icebreaker [AGB]
Bldr: Admiralty SY, St. Petersburg (In serv. 1965)

. . . . . . (ex-*Semen Chelyushkin*)

D: 2,675–2,940 tons (fl) **S:** 14.5 kts (12.0 service)
Dim: 67.70 (62.01 pp) × 18.29 × 6.06
Electronics: Radar: 1 or 2 Don-2 nav.
M: 3 Type 13D100 diesel generator sets; 3 3-bladed props (1 fwd); 5,400 shp
Range: 5,500/12 **Fuel:** 600 tons **Crew:** 39 tot.

Remarks: 2,305 grt/1,092 dwt. Sighted in Vietnamese colors at Da Nang in 6-96 and probably used primarily as a seagoing tug and/or salvage vessel, as ice in Vietnam is normally only found in the form of cubes. The former name is tentative; *Semen Chelyushkin,* a Far Eastern unit, is the only unit of the class in that area known to have been stricken.

Note: The former Russian Navy Kamenka-class (Project 870) navigational aids tender, the former Russian Neptun-class (Project 706) moorings tender, and the former U.S. Army FS 381–class navigational aids tender listed in the previous edition are now believed to be civilian subordinated.

♦ 1 offshore supply vessel [AK]
Bldr: Halong SY, Vietnam (In serv. 1994)

HQ-966 Truong Sa-01

Truong Sa-01 (HQ-966) NAVPIC-Holland, 10-95

D: 1,200 tons **S:** . . . kts **Dim:** 70.6 × 11.8 × . . .
A: 2 twin 25-mm 80-cal. 2M-3M AA **M:** . . . diesels; 1 prop; . . . bhp

Remarks: 1,000 dwt. Intended to support garrisons in the disputed Spratly Islands. "Truong Sa" is the Vietnamese name for the Spratly Islands.

♦ 3 offshore supply vessels [AK]
Bldr: . . . (In serv. 1990s)

BD-621 BD-622 BD-632

BD-632 NAVPIC-Holland, 4-99

AUXILIARIES *(continued)*

D: approx. 1,200 tons (fl) **S:** . . . kts **Dim:** . . . × . . . × . . .
A: 2 single 12.7-mm 79-cal. mg **M:** 1 . . . diesel; 1 prop; . . . bhp

Remarks: Identical sisters intended for Spratly Islands support missions. Have two cargo holds and a single 1.5-ton-capacity crane. The first two originally bore pennants HQ-608 and HQ-624. BD = *Biến Dong.*

Note: Various fishing boats have been adapted for offshore supply missions as well; two of these are illustrated.

Note: Russian Iva-class salvage and firefighting tug *Vikhr-2* was transferred to Vietnam in 5-92 and operates as the civilian *Ben Dinh 01.*

♦ 1 ex-Soviet Sorum-class (Project 745.0) oceangoing tug [ATA]
Bldr: Yaroslavl SY, USSR (In serv. 1973–. . .)

BD-105 (ex-. . .)

BD-105 NAVPIC-Holland, 8-95

D: 1,210 tons (1,656 fl) **S:** 13.8 kts **Dim:** 55.50 × 12.60 × 4.60
Electronics: Radar: 2 Don-2 nav.
M: 2 Type 2D42 (6ChN 30/38) diesels, electric drive; 1 prop; 3,000 shp
Range: 6,200/11 **Fuel:** 322 tons **Endurance:** 40 days
Crew: 35 tot. (civilian) + 40 passengers/rescuees

Remarks: Transferred from Russia by 1995. Operates in support of Spratly Islands activities.

♦ 1 Voda (MVT-6)-class (Project 561) water tanker [AWT]
Bldr: Yantar Zavod, Kaliningrad (In serv. 1953–60)

BO-82 (ex-MVT-135?)

BO-82 Kramer, 5-96

D: 982 tons light (2,115 fl) **S:** 12 kts **Dim:** 81.50 × 11.50 × 3.25
Electronics: Radar: 1 Don-2 or Mius (Spin Trough) nav.
M: 2 Type 8DR30/50 diesels; 2 props; 1,600 bhp
Range: 2,000/9 **Endurance:** 15 days **Crew:** 38 tot.

Remarks: 1,000 grt. May be the former Russian Pacific Fleet unit MVT-135, which was retired 31-7-96, although BO-82 was in Vietnam by 5-96. Seventeen were completed, of which several, including BO-82, were equipped with working decks to permit their use as underway water replenishment ships for deployed steam-powered warships.
Hull systems: Cargo: 700 tons water. Has one 3-ton derrick for hose handling.

SERVICE CRAFT

♦ 2 Nyryat'-2-class (Project 376U) diving tenders [YDT]
Bldr: Yaroslavl Zavod (In serv. 1950s)

D: 50 tons (fl) **S:** 9 kts **Dim:** 21.0 × 3.9 × 1.5
M: 1 Type 3D-6 diesel; 1 prop; 150 bhp
Range: 1,600/8 **Endurance:** 5 days **Crew:** 10 tot.

Remarks: Built during the 1950s and transferred post-1975. Essentially similar to the PO-2-class patrol craft, except that the hull has bulwarks and there is a small derrick to handle divers.

♦ up to 2 ex-U.S. floating dry docks [YFDL] (In serv. 1944)

ex-HQ-9600 (ex-AFDL 13) ex-HQ-9604 (ex-AFDL 22)

Remarks: Ex-HQ-9600 has a capacity of 1,000 tons and measures 61.0 × 19.5 m. Ex-HQ-9604 has a capacity of 1,900 tons and is 87.8 × 19.5 m. Both were left behind in 1975.

Note: Also available are two Russian floating dry docks transferred during the 1980s for commercial employment, one with a capacity of 4,500 tons and the other of 8,500 tons.

♦ 2 Soviet PO-2-class (Project 376) launches [YFL]
Bldr: Yaroslavl Zavod (In serv. 1950s)

D: 47 tons (fl) **S:** 9 kts **Dim:** 21.0 × 3.9 × 1.4
A: when used as patrol craft: 2 single 12.7-mm 79-cal. mg
Electronics: Radar: 1 Mius (Spin Trough) nav. or none
M: 1 Type 3D-6 diesel; 1 prop; 150 bhp
Range: 1,600/8 **Endurance:** 5 days **Crew:** 6 tot.

Remarks: Transferred in 2-80. Utility craft, also usable as tugs or, with appropriate equipment, as diving tenders. Two near-sister Nyryat'-2-class diving tenders were also transferred.

♦ 2 ex-U.S. 174-foot-class gasoline tankers [YO]
Bldrs: ex-HQ-472: George Lawley & Sons, Neponset, Mass.; ex-HQ-475: R.T.C. SB, Camden, N.J.

	Laid down	L	In serv.
ex-HQ-472 (ex-YOG 67)	26-1-45	17-3-45	4-5-45
ex-HQ-475 (ex-YOG 56)	17-5-44	30-9-44	19-2-45

D: 440 tons light (1,390 fl) **S:** 11 kts **Dim:** 53.04 (51.2 pp) × 9.75 × 3.94
A: 2 single 20-mm 70-cal. Oerlikon Mk 10 AA
M: 1 G.M. diesel (ex-YOG 56: Union diesel); 1 prop; 640 bhp (ex-YOG 56: 540 bhp)
Electric: 80 kw **Fuel:** 25 tons **Cargo:** 860 tons **Crew:** 23 tot.

Remarks: Transferred to South Vietnam in 7-67 and 6-72, respectively. Remain in service as coastal tankers, employed in transporting diesel fuel. Sister ex-HQ 473 (ex-YOG 71) is believed to have been cannibalized to maintain these two.

♦ 2 ex-Soviet Poluchat-I-class (Project 368) torpedo retrievers [YPT]

D: 84.7 tons (92.8 fl) **S:** 21.6 kts
Dim: 29.60 × 6.10 (5.80 wl) × 1.56 (1.90 props)
A: 2 twin 14.5-mm 93-cal. 2M-7 AA
Electronics: Radar: 1 Mius (Spin Trough) nav.
M: 2 M-50F-4 diesels; 2 props; 2,400 bhp **Electric:** 14 kw tot.
Range: 250/21.6; 550/14 **Crew:** 3 officers, 12 enlisted

Remarks: Transferred in 1-90. Can also be employed as patrol boats. Have a ramp at the stern and a crane for recovering exercise torpedoes.

♦ up to 2 ex-U.S. Cholocco-class medium harbor tugs [YTM]
Bldr: Commercial Iron Works, Portland, Ore.

	In serv.
ex-HQ-9550 (ex-*Poknoket,* YTM 762, ex-YTB 517)	25-1-46
ex-HQ-9551 (ex-*Hombro,* YTM 769, ex-YTB 508)	7-7-45

Cholocco-class medium harbor tug NAVPIC-Holland, 9-95

D: 260 tons (350 fl) **S:** 11 kts **Dim:** 30.8 × 8.5 × 3.7
A: 2 single 12.7-mm mg **Electronics:** Radar: 2 . . . nav.
M: 2 Enterprise diesels; 1 prop; 1,270 bhp **Crew:** 8 tot.

Remarks: Reclassified YTM from YTB in 1966; transferred to South Vietnam in 1971. Sister HQ-9552 (ex-*Nootka,* YTM 771, ex-YTB 506) was lost during 1973 in a collision with a barge. One serves at Da Nang.

♦ up to 9 ex-U.S. YTL-type small harbor tugs [YTL]

ex-YTL 152	ex-YTL 245	ex-YTL 456
ex-YTL 200	ex-YTL 423	ex-YTL 457
ex-YTL 206	ex-YTL 452	ex-YTL 586

D: 70 tons (80 fl) **S:** 10 kts **Dim:** 20.16 × 5.18 × 2.44
M: 1 Hoover-Owens-Rentschler diesel; 1 prop; 300 bhp
Electric: 40 kw **Fuel:** 7 tons **Crew:** 4 tot.

Remarks: Built in 1941–45. Four were transferred to South Vietnam in 1955–56, two in 1969, and two in 1971. Quite possibly, any survivors have been turned over to civilian agencies; craft of this description are reported to be operating with CENAC-series alphanumeric pennants.

Note: Former U.S. Navy non-self-propelled harbor craft transferred to South Vietnam that may survive include large covered barges YFNB 18 and 28; open barges YC 791, 797, 806, 807, 1108, 1320, 1414, and 1415; floating cranes HQ-9650 (ex-YD 230) and HQ-9651 (ex-YD 195); repair, berthing, and messing barges HQ-9610 (ex-YRBM 17),

SERVICE CRAFT *(continued)*

HQ-9612 (ex-YRBM 16), HQ-9613 (ex-YRBM 21), and HQ-. . . (ex-YRBM 18); barracks barges HQ-9050 (ex-APL 26) and HQ-9051 (ex-APL 27); repair barges HQ-9601 (ex-YR 24) and HQ-9611 (ex-YR 71); and water barge HQ-9113 (ex-YWN 153). In addition to the ships and craft listed above, the Vietnamese Navy undoubtedly employs many smaller craft ("junks") in patrol and logistics duties.

COAST GUARD

Note: Formed in 1998, the coast guard as yet has no craft of its own. To meet a requirement for four to six seagoing patrol craft, as of late 1999 Russia's Almaz Central Design Bureau was offering a variant of its Mirazh class (Project 14310; see Russia section for data) and the United Kingdom's Vosper Thornycroft a 34-m version of the *Sentinel,* built for the U.K. Customs and Excise Service in 1994; the winning design would be built locally in Vietnam.

VIRGIN ISLANDS

British Virgin Islands

ROYAL VIRGIN ISLANDS POLICE FORCE

Base: Road Town, Tortola

PATROL BOATS [WPB]

♦ **1 U.S. 40-foot Dauntless class**
Bldr: SeaArk Marine, Monticello, Ark. (In serv. 1-94)

PB 1

D: 15 tons (fl) **S:** 28 kts **Dim:** 12.19 (11.13 wl) × 3.86 × 0.69 (hull)
A: 2 single 12.7-mm mg; 2 single 7.62-mm mg
Electronics: Radar: 1 Raytheon R40X nav.
M: 2 Caterpillar 3208TA diesels; 2 props; 850 bhp (720 sust.)
Range: 200/30; 400/22 **Fuel:** 250 gallons **Crew:** 5 tot.

Remarks: U.S. Grant-Aid. Aluminum construction. C. Raymond Hunt, "Deep-Vee" hull design. This unit is not the same boat as the U.S. Customs Service's PB 1, which is similar but has a different propulsion plant.

♦ **1 M 160 class** Bldr: Halmatic, Hamble, U.K. (In serv. 4-7-88)

St. Ursula

St. Ursula P. H. Nargeolet, 1998

D: 17.3 tons (fl) **S:** 27+ knots **Dim:** 15.40 (12.20 pp) × 3.86 × 1.15
A: 1 7.62-mm mg **Electronics:** Radar: 1 Decca 370BT nav.
M: 2 G.M. Detroit Diesel 6V92 TA diesels; 2 props; 1,100 bhp (770 sust.)
Range: 300/20 **Fuel:** 2,700 liters **Crew:** 6 tot.

Remarks: Provided by the U.K. government; has sisters in several other Caribbean island countries. GRP construction. Refitted in 1995. Has davits aft for inflatable inspection boat.

♦ **2 Model SR5M Searider dinghies** Bldr: Avon, U.K. (In serv. 1986)

Remarks: Semi-rigid inflatables with 70-bhp Evinrude outboards. Replaced two Sea Eagle RIBs delivered in 1980.

YEMEN

Yemen Arab Republic

Personnel (2001): Approx. 1,700 total, plus 250 naval port police and 500 naval infantry

Bases: Principal bases at Aden and Hodeida, with minor facilities at Al Katib, Mukalla, Perim, and Socotra

Coastal Defense: Two truck-mounted batteries for SSC-3 Styx-series antiship missiles were supplied by the USSR during the 1980s and may still be operational; each truck carries two missiles. Several fixed 100-mm guns in tank turrets are emplaced on Perim Island.

GUIDED-MISSILE PATROL CRAFT [PTG]

♦ **1 Tarantul-I class (Project 1241RE)**
Bldr: Volodarskiy SY, Rybinsk (Del. 7-12-90)

124 (ex-971)

124 U.S. Navy, 11-90

D: 385 tons light (455 fl) **S:** 43 kts
Dim: 56.10 (49.50 pp) × 10.20 (9.40 wl) × 2.14 (hull; 3.59 props)
A: 4 P-20/21 Termit (SS-N-2C Styx) SSM; 1 76.2-mm 59-cal. AK-176 DP; 1 4-round MTU-40S (SA-N-8) SAM syst. (12 Gremlin missiles); 2 single 30-mm 54-cal. AK-630 gatling AA—see remarks
Electronics:
Radar: 1 Kivach-3 nav.; 1 Garpun-E (Plank Shave) targeting; 1 MR-123 Vympel (Bass Tilt) gun f.c.
EW: 2 16-round PK-16 decoy RL
M: M-15E COGAG plant: 2 DMR-76 cruise gas turbines (4,000 shp each), 2 PR-77 boost gas turbines (12,000 shp each); 2 props; 32,000 shp
Electric: 500 kw tot. (2 × 200-kw, 1 × 100-kw diesel sets)
Range: 760/43; 1,400/13 **Fuel:** 122,634 liters **Endurance:** 10 days
Crew: 7 officers, 32 enlisted

Remarks: Survivor of a pair, one of which defected to Oman in mid-7-94 but was later returned. Standard export version. Sister 125 (ex-976), inoperable as of 1998, had been discarded by 2001, and 124 is in only marginal condition and probably without antiship missiles.
Hull systems: Stainless-steel-alloy, seven-watertight-compartment hull with aluminum alloy superstructure, decks, and internal bulkheads. Very strongly constructed and rugged. Has difficulty maneuvering below 10 kts due to the small size of her rudders. This version of the Tarantul-I is also stated to have a range of 2,350 n.m. at 12–13 kts (at 34° C) and a maximum speed of 43 kts at 15° C (35 kts at 34° C).
Combat systems: Carries 252 ready-service rounds for the 76.2-mm gun with another 150 in reserve. The weapons system employs digital computers and has many backup features. Normally carried two infrared-homing and two radar-homing antiship missiles, but the Yemeni Navy's missile storage and maintenance facility burned out in 1994, and there are probably no missiles available for the craft. The Garpun-E radar also serves as a passive intercept and targeting system.

♦ **3 Chinese Hounan class (Chinese Project 021)**
Bldr: Jiangnan SY, Shanghai (In serv. 1995)

126 127 128

GUIDED-MISSILE PATROL CRAFT [PTG] *(continued)*

Hounan class 127 and 128—during delivery voyage 92 Wing Det., RAAF, 5-95

D: 175 tons light; 186.5 tons normal (205 fl) **S:** 35 kts
Dim: 38.75 × 7.60 × 1.7 (mean)
A: 4 C-801 SSM; 1 2-round QW-1 Vanguard point-defense SAM syst.; 2 twin 30-mm 65-cal. Type 69 (AK-230) AA
Electronics:
Radar: 1 Type 352C (Square Tie) surf. search/target desig.; 1 Type 347G gun f.c.
M: 3 Type 42-160 (M503A) diesels; 3 props; 12,000 bhp **Electric:** 65 kw tot.
Range: 800/30 **Crew:** 28 tot.

Remarks: Although one was completed by 9-93, the three units transferred to Yemen were not delivered until 5-95. Design is a variation of the Chinese Huangfeng class, itself a variant of the Russian Osa-I, but with two paired launch containers for C-801 rocket-powered antiship missiles located aft and a Type 347G gun fire-control radar added; the superstructure is also somewhat wider than in the Huangfeng version. 128 ran aground in 9-97 but has been repaired; all three, however, are said to be in poor condition. Based at Al Katib.
Hull systems: Soviet-made M-503A multirow radial diesels are difficult to maintain and offer only about 600 hours between overhauls; it is likely that the Chinese-made 42-160 version is even less reliable.
Combat systems: The two-round, manned, infrared-homing SAM launcher is mounted amidships atop the superstructure; the missile is said to be a copy of the Russian SA-18. The antiship missiles may no longer be operational.

Disposal note: Of eight Osa-II-class guided-missile patrol craft transferred to Yemen between 2-79 and 9-83, five were lost or irreparably damaged during the Yemeni Civil War of 1994 and the three survivors—118, 121, and 122—were no longer in service as of 2001.

PATROL BOATS [PB]

♦ 6 CMN 15-60 class

Bldr: CMN, Cherbourg, France (In serv.: 1201–1205: 1-8-96; 1206: 1997)

1201 Baklan	1203 Zuhrab	1205 Hunaish
1202 Siyan	1204 Akissan	1206 Zakr

Yemeni CMN 15-60-class unit on trials CMN, 1996

D: 12 tons (fl) **S:** 60 kts (55 sust.) **Dim:** 15.50 (12.00 pp) × 3.00 × 0.80
A: 1 12.7-mm mg **Electronics:** Radar: 1 Furuno . . . nav.
M: 2 . . . diesels; 2 Arneson outdrive props; 1,680 bhp
Range: 500/35 **Crew:** 6 tot.

Remarks: Ordered in 3-96 at onset of Hanish Islands crisis with Eritrea. Operational deployment of the craft was held up through 4-97 by a lack of spares and maintenance support. The design is referred to by builder as an "ultra-fast interceptor" for police, antismuggling, surveillance, special forces, strike, and liaison duties.
Hull systems: GRP hull and superstructure. Equipped with a GPS receiver, a computer-aided navigation system, and HF/VHF/UHF transceivers.

♦ 1 U.S. Broadsword class

Bldr: Halter Marine, New Orleans (In serv. 1978)

141 25 September

D: 90 tons (fl) **S:** 28 kts **Dim:** 32.0 × 6.3 × 1.9
A: 1 twin 23-mm AA; 1 twin 14.5-mm 93-cal. mg; 2 single 12.7 mm mg
Electronics: Radar: 1 Decca 914 nav.
M: 3 G.M. Detroit Diesel 16V71 TI diesels; 3 props; 1,400 bhp
Electric: 120 kw tot. **Fuel:** 16.3 tons **Crew:** 14 tot.

Remarks: Ordered in 1977. Former North Yemeni asset, based at Hodeida. The armament, added after delivery, is of Soviet origin. Is in poor condition, but is still marginally operational. Sisters *Ramadan* (142, ex-*13 June*) and *Sana'a* (143) were discarded around 1997.

♦ 2 Soviet Zhuk class (Project 1400M)

202 203

Yemeni Zhuk 1981

D: 35.9 tons (39.7 fl) **S:** 30 kts
Dim: 23.80 (21.70 wl) × 5.00 (3.80 wl) × 1.00 (hull; 1.90 max.)
A: 2 twin 12.7-mm 60-cal. Utës-Ma mg **Electronics:** Radar: 1 Lotsiya nav.
M: 2 M-401 diesels; 2 props; 2,200 bhp
Electric: 48 kw total (2 × 21-kw, 1 × 6-kw diesel sets)
Range: 500/13.5 **Endurance:** 5 days **Crew:** 1 officer, 9 enlisted

Remarks: Two of this class were transferred to the former Yemen Arab Republic (North Yemen) in 12-84 and three in 1-87; two others were transferred to the People's Democratic Republic of Yemen (South Yemen) in 2-75. The two survivors are believed to be former North Yemeni boats; sisters 303 and 404 were discarded around 1997. The twin machineguns are mounted in enclosed gunhouses with hemispherical covers. The pair is used for a myriad of duties, including target towing.

MINE COUNTERMEASURES SHIPS AND CRAFT

♦ 1 Natya-I-class (Project 266ME) minesweeper [MSF]

Bldr: Sudostroitel'noye Obyedineniye "Almaz" (Sredniy Neva), Kolpino (In serv. 3-91)

201 (ex-641)

Yemeni Natya-class 201 Clark E. Castle, 3-99

D: 750 tons std.; 804 tons normal (873 fl) **S:** 17.6 kts (16 sust.)
Dim: 61.00 (57.6 wl) × 10.20 × 2.98 (hull)
A: 2 single 30-mm 54-cal. AK-630M gatling AA; 2 4-round Fasta-4M (SA-N-8) SAM syst. (16 Gremlin missiles); 2 5-round RBU-1200 ASW RL
Electronics:
Radar: 1 Don-2 nav.
Sonar: MG-89 HF hull-mounted (49 kHz)
M: 2 M-503B-3E diesels: 2 shrouded CP props; 5,000 bhp
Electric: 600 kw tot. (3 × 200-kw DGR-200/1500 diesel sets)
Range: 1,800/16; 3,000/12; 5,200/10 **Endurance:** 10–15 days
Crew: 8 officers, 59 enlisted

Remarks: A sister, bearing pennant 634, was delivered to Ethiopia in 1991 and defected to Yemen shortly thereafter; the ship was eventually interned at Djibouti in 1993 and sold for disposal in 1996. Both were of a new variant with single 30-mm AK-630 gatling guns substituted for the twin 30-mm AK-230 mounts, but without 25-mm guns, fire-control radar, or net trawl facilities. Are equipped also to serve as ASW escorts, with the RBU-1200 rocket launchers used for detonating mines.
Hull systems: Stem is cut back sharply below the waterline. Has a low-magnetic-signature, aluminum-steel-alloy hull and a DGR-450/1500P diesel-driven degaussing system.
Combat systems: The two SAM launchers are located just abaft the lattice mast. Sweep gear carried includes SEMP-3 magnetic and MPT-3 mechanical minesweeping arrays. The sonar incorporates a downward-looking, HF, bottomed-mine detection component. Can deploy television minehunting equipment. Has two short mine rails, but no mines are known to have been transferred to Yemen.

♦ 5 Soviet Yevgenya-class (Project 1258) inshore minehunter/sweepers [MSI]

Bldr: Sudostroitel'noye Obyedineniye "Almaz" (Sredniy Neva), Kolpino

11 12 15 20 . . .

D: 88.5 tons light; 94.5 tons normal (97.9 fl) **S:** 11 kts
Dim: 26.13 (24.20 wl) × 5.90 (5.10 wl) × 1.38
A: 1 twin 25-mm 80-cal. 2M-3M AA

MINE COUNTERMEASURES SHIPS AND CRAFT *(continued)*

Electronics:
Radar: 1 Mius (Spin Trough) nav.
Sonar: MG-7 HF dipping
M: 2 Type 3D12 diesels; 2 props; 600 bhp—hydraulic slow-speed drive
Electric: 100 kw tot. (2 × 50-kw diesel sets)
Range: 400/10 **Fuel:** 2.7 tons **Endurance:** 3 days
Crew: 1 officer, 9 enlisted + 2–3 mine clearance divers

Remarks: The first two were delivered to North Yemen in 5-82 and a third in 11-87; South Yemen received two in 12-89. Three are based at Aden and two at Al Katib, but as many as three may be nonoperational.
Hull systems: GRP hull. Navigational equipment includes a Girya-MA gyrocompass and a NEL-7 echo sounder.
Combat systems: Can employ a Neva-1 television minehunting system, useful to 30-m depths, that dispenses marker buoys to permit later disposal of mines by divers or explosive charges. The sonar is lowered via one of the stern davits. Carry VKT-1 mechanical, AT-2 acoustic, and SEMT-1 solenoid coil sweep gear.

AMPHIBIOUS WARFARE SHIPS AND CRAFT

Disposal note: Ropucha-class (Project 775) tank landing ship 139, laid up nonoperational in the mid-1990s, had been discarded by 2001, although the hulk is still afloat at Aden.

♦ 0 (+ 1) Polish Project NS-722 medium landing ship [LSM]
Bldr: Stocznia Polnocna, Gdansk (In serv. 2002)

BILQIS

Bilqis Jaroslaw Cislak, 10-01

D: 1,363 tons (1,410 fl) **S:** 16 kts **Dim:** 88.60 (79.00 pp) × 10.00 × 2.40
A: 1 30-mm 54-cal. AK-630M gatling AA; 1 twin 23-mm 87-cal. ZU-23-2 Wrobel-I AA; 2 4-round Fasta-4M (WM-4) launchers for Igla SAMs; 2 40-round 122-mm WM 122/20 artillery RL
Electronics: Radar: 1 . . . nav. (X-band); 1 . . . nav. (S-band)
M: 2 Caterpillar . . . diesels; 2 CP props; 5,200 bhp
Electric: 1,000 kw tot. (4 × 250-kw diesel-driven sets)
Range: 2,300/15; 3,600/11.5 **Endurance:** 30 days **Crew:** 49 tot. + 111 troops

Remarks: Ordered in 10-99 but canceled by Poland in 2-00 when the Polish ambassador to Yemen was kidnapped; the order was later reinstated after his release. Will be of the export version developed for India in the late 1980s but not purchased. Intended for use as a cadet training ship and for disaster relief in addition to the amphibious warfare role. Will be able to transport five 42-ton tanks, as well as the troops. Has a flight platform aft for an Agusta-Bell AB-205 or another 4-ton-class helicopter. The weapons-control system is named the Sarmat. The listed 30-mm gunmount may not initially be installed. Up to 169 troops can be carried for short periods, and the maximum cargo weight is 290 tons.

♦ 3 Deba-class (Project NS-717) utility landing craft [LCU]
Bldr: Stocznia Marynarki Wojennej, Gdynia (In serv. 30-6-01)

ABDULKORI (ex-*Thamoud*) HIMYER (ex-*Dhaffar*) SAB'A

Two Yemeni Deba-class landing craft Piet Sinke, 5-01

D: 238 tons (fl) **S:** 15 kts **Dim:** 41.10 (37.00 pp) × 7.20 (6.60 wl) × 1.65
A: 1 twin 23-mm 87-cal. ZU-23-2 Wrobel-I AA; 2 single 12.7-mm ZM Tarnow mg

Deba-class landing craft—aboard heavy-lift ship *Jumbo Vision* for delivery Jaroslaw Cislak, 5-01

Electronics: Radar: 1 SRN-207A nav.
M: 3 Caterpillar . . . diesels; 3 props; 3,150 bhp
Electric: 300 kw tot. (4 × 75-kw diesel alternator sets; 400 V, 50 Hz)
Range: 750/14.5; 1,150/9 **Endurance:** 6 days **Crew:** 10 tot. + 50 troops

Remarks: Ordered during 10-99. A tropicalized version of a design delivered to the Polish Navy during 1989–90. Work began 9-2-00, after a delay caused by the kidnapping of the Polish ambassador to Yemen. Can carry a 37-ton payload.

Note: A new utility landing craft capable of transporting tanks was said to be under construction for Yemen at a U.A.E. shipyard as of 4-97; no further information is available, nor does the craft appear to have been delivered.

♦ 2 ex-Soviet Ondatra-class (Project 1176) landing craft [LCM]
(In serv. 1971–79)

13 14

D: 90 tons normal (107.3 fl) **S:** 11.5 kts **Dim:** 24.50 × 6.00 × 1.55
A: none **Electronics:** Radar: 1 Mius (Spin Trough) nav. (portable)
M: 2 Type 3D-12 diesels; 2 props; 600 bhp
Range: 330/10; 500/5 **Endurance:** 2 days **Crew:** 6 tot. (enlisted)

Remarks: In all, 29 of this type were built for use aboard Soviet *Ivan Rogov*–class landing ships; these were transferred to Yemen in 1983. The 13.7 × 3.9–m cargo well can accommodate one 40-ton tank or up to 50 tons of general cargo; some 20 troops/vehicle crew can be carried.

♦ 1 ex-Soviet T4-class (Project 1785) landing craft [LCM]

134

D: 35 tons light (93 fl) **S:** 10 kts (light) **Dim:** 20.4 × 5.4 × 1.2 (max. aft)
M: 2 Type 3D-6 diesels; 2 props; 300 bhp
Range: 300/8 **Endurance:** 2 days **Crew:** 2–3 tot.

Remarks: Can accommodate up to 50 tons cargo on the 9.5 × 3.9–m vehicle deck.

SERVICE CRAFT

Disposal note: Two Russian Toplivo-2-class (Project 1844/1844D) coastal tankers (135 for water and 140 for fuels) had been discarded by 2001.

Note: A 4,500-ton, Soviet-supplied commercial floating dry dock is available at Aden. The Yemen Department of Maritime Affairs at Aden operates the *Zuqar,* an 18.13 × 5.38 × 1.70–m oil pollution–control boat delivered late in 1999 by Halmatic, U.K.; the craft is powered by two MTU 12V183 TE 72 diesels (810 bhp each) for a 20.5-kt maximum speed and is fitted with onboard tanks for 6,200 liters of spillage, a spray system, and a 400-m floating containment boom. Navigation equipment includes a Raytheon SL70 radar and 620 GPS.

YUGOSLAVIA

Federal Republic of Yugoslavia

Note: With the breakup of Yugoslavia in 1991, three separate navies were established in the formerly constituent republics; those of Croatia and Slovenia are described separately. While the so-called Federal Republic of Yugoslavia retained most of the fleet's afloat assets and all of its aircraft, the shipbuilding industry was concentrated almost entirely in Croatia and Slovenia. The Yugoslav Federation consists of the republics of Serbia and Montenegro, with only the latter having a seacoast.

Personnel (2002): Approx. 3,500 total, including 2,000 conscripts

Bases: Facilities on the shores of Kotor Bay include a headquarters at Kumbor, facilities for surface ships at Zelenika and Meljina, tunnels for smaller ships near Rakite and Spilice, and the naval academy at Bijela on Lustica Island. The principal munitions and fuel depot is at Pristan, and repairs are undertaken at the Sava Kovacevic Shipyard, Tivat. A new base is said to be under construction at Ulcinj in Montenegro on the Bay of Valdamos near the Albanian border. All aircraft are based at Podgorica, Montenegro. Repair facilities are inadequate, and there are no new construction yards, except on the Danube.

Organization: The fleet was reorganized during 1-01 into the rocket ships flotilla (frigates and missile craft), coastal flotilla, and submarine flotilla. The commander-in-chief of the navy is a rear admiral, with another rear admiral as the chief of the naval staff, while the commander of the fleet and the commander of the rocket ships flotilla are captains.

Naval Aviation: One squadron of two Ka-28PL Helix-A ASW and up to 20 Mi-8 Hip utility helicopters; there are also two DHC-2 Beaver utility and four CL-215 fire-fighting/SAR fixed-wing aircraft. The helicopters are assigned to the 748th ASW Squadron, based at Podgorica, Montenegro; the remaining Ka-25 Hormone helicopters were reported discarded as of 5-00, and the remaining Mi-14PL Haze ASW helicopters were destroyed by NATO bombing at Podgorica in 1999. The Yugoslav Air Force has a Naval Cooperation Regiment with 15–20 RJ-1 Jastreb reconnaissance aircraft, 18–24 MiG-21 fighters, 18 Jastreb and Orao B light attack aircraft, and several AS.341 Alouette-III helicopters.

Coastal Defense: Several mobile SSC-3 batteries are believed still to be operational. Mobile 88-mm and fixed 130-mm artillery is also employed for coastal defense.

Weapons and Sensors: Ships and craft are primarily equipped with imported weapon and sensor systems, but the M-71 single and M-75 quadruple 20-mm AA mountings were license-produced in the former Yugoslavia as copies of Hispano-Suiza weapons. Yugoslavia also has made some of its own mines.

ATTACK SUBMARINES [SS]

♦ 1 Sava class Bldr: Brodosplit, Split, Croatia

	Laid down	L	In serv.
P 831 Sava	1975	1977	1978

Sava (P 831) *Ships of the World,* 1998

D: 770 tons surf./964 tons sub. **S:** 10 kts surf./16 kts sub.
Dim: 55.8 × 7.2 × 5.5
A: 6 bow 533-mm TT (10 tot. Soviet Type 53 or Swedish Tp 61 wire-guided torpedoes or 20 mines)
Electronics:
Radar: 1 Flag (Snoop Plate) search
Sonar: STN Atlas Elektronik PRS-3 active/passive suite (see remarks)
EW: Stop Light intercept (2–18 GHz)
M: 2 Sulzer diesels (1,600 bhp each), 2 generators (1,000 kw each), 1 electric motor; 1 5-bladed prop; 1,560 shp
Endurance: 28 days **Crew:** 35 tot.

Remarks: P = *Podmornica* (submarine). Carries a mixture of Soviet and Western European equipment. Attached to the 88th Brigade. Sister *Drava* was laid up for lack of batteries and spare parts around 1993 and has since been stricken.
Hull systems: Pressure hull steel is of 56 kg/cm^2 strength. Maximum diving depth: 300 m. Outer hull is said to have been fabricated of glass-reinforced plastic.
Combat systems: Sonar suite is also reported to be a Soviet-supplied MG-15 Herkules active and MG-10 Feniks-M passive array.

MIDGET SUBMARINES [SSM]

♦ 3 Una (M-100D) class (2 *nonoperational*)
Bldr: Brodosplit, Split, Croatia

913 Zeta (In serv. 1985) 916 *Vrbas* (ex-*Vardar*) (In serv. 1989)
915 *Kupa* (In serv. 1988)

D: 76 tons surf./88 tons sub. **S:** 8.0 kts surf./11.0 kts sub.
Dim: 18.8 (16.5 wl) × 3.0 × 2.5
A: 6 mines or 4 R1 swimmer-delivery vehicles, externally carried
M: electric only: two 18-kw motors; 1 5-bladed prop
Electronics:
Radar: none
Sonar: STN Atlas Elektronik PP-10 active; PSU 1-2 passive
Range: 250/3 sub. **Crew:** 4 tot. + 6 swimmers

Remarks: Typed *Diverzantska Podmornica.* Sister *Soca* (914) was captured by Croatia in 1991 and put into service in 9-93; she was later lengthened and relaunched in 1996. *Tisa* (911) and *Una* (912) have been discarded, and 915 and 916 were nonoperational as of 2001.
Hull systems: Have no onboard generators; power is supplied by two shore-charged 128-cell, 1,450-amp-hr (5-hr rate) batteries. Working depth is 105 m, test depth 120 m, and estimated collapse depth 182 m. Theoretically is capable of remaining submerged for 96 hours. The R1 swimmer-delivery vehicles each weigh 145 kg, are 3.7 m long by 0.52 m in diameter, and have a range of 12 n.m. at 3 kts.

FRIGATES [FF]

♦ 2 Kotor class Bldr: Tito SY, Kraljevica, Croatia

	L	In serv.
VPB 33 Kotor	21-5-85	1-87
VPB 34 Novi Sad (ex-*Pula*)	18-12-86	11-88

Kotor (VPB 33)—with *Rade Končar*–class missile craft *Ante Banina* (RT 406) alongside *Ships of the World,* 2000

Novi Sad (VPB 34) ANBw/FAFIO, 3-99

Novi Sad (VPB 34) Frane Moric, via Dr. Zvonimir Freivogel, 5-92

D: 1,492 tons (1,850 fl) **S:** 27 kts
Dim: 96.70 (91.80 wl) × 11.70 × 3.55 (5.80 over sonar)
A: 4 P-20/21 Rubezh (SS-N-2C Styx) SSM; 1 2-round Osa-M (SA-N-4) SAM syst. (20 Gecko missiles); 1 twin 76.2-mm 59-cal. AK-726 DP; 2 4-round Fasta-4M SAM syst. (Grail missiles); 2 twin 30-mm 65-cal. AK-230 AA; 2 single 20-mm 90-cal. M-71 AA; 2 12-round RBU-6000 ASW RL
Electronics:
Radar: 1 Vaygach (Palm Frond) nav.; 1 MR-302 Rubka (Strut Curve) surf./air search; 1 MPZ-301 (Pop Group) SAM f.c.; 1 CelsiusTech 9LV 200 Mk 1 76.2-mm gun f.c.; 1 MR-104 Rys' (Drum Tilt) 30-mm gun f.c.
Sonar: MG-322T hull-mounted MF search; HF attack
EW: 2 intercept arrays; VHFD/F; 2 18-round Wallop Barricade decoy RL
M: CODAG: 2 SEMT-Pielstick 12 PA6 V280 diesels (4,800 bhp each), 1 Soviet gas turbine (19,000 shp); 3 props (CP outboard); 28,600 shp
Electric: 1,350 kw tot. **Crew:** approx. 90 tot.

Remarks: VPB = *Veliki Patrolni Brod* (Large Patrol Ship). VPB 33 was damaged by Croatian shore batteries in fall 1991 but appeared to be intact and in service as of 5-99. Design is Yugoslavian and is definitely *not* a modification of the somewhat similar Koni class, which has an entirely different hullform and layout. The name *Novi Sad* has also been attributed to a Yugoslav minesweeper and may not be correct.
Hull systems: The main-propulsion diesels were ordered in 6-80 (two to be built under license in Yugoslavia), and the first was delivered 31-3-81; the propulsion concept (but not layout) duplicates the arrangement in the Koni class. Two sets of Italian-made ILAS-3 ASW torpedo tubes, to have been mounted on the fantail, were not installed.

♦ 1 Soviet Koni class (Project 1159)
Bldr: Krasniy Metallist Zavod, Zelenodol'sk

	Laid down	L	In serv.
VPB 31 Beograd (ex-*Split,* ex-*Sokol*)	1978	21-4-79	10-3-80

D: 1,593 tons normal (1,593 fl) **S:** 27 kts (29.67 trials; 22 on diesels alone)
Dim: 96.51 × 12.55 × 4.12 (mean hull; 5.72 over sonar)
A: 4 P-20/21 Rubezh (SS-N-2C Styx) SSM; 1 4-round Osa-M (SA-N-4) SAM syst. (20 Gecko missiles); 2 twin 76.2-mm 59-cal. AK-726 DP; 2 twin 30-mm 65-cal. AK-230 AA; 2 12-round RBU-6000 ASW RL (120 RGB-60 rockets); 2 d.c. racks (6 BB-1 d.c. each); up to 14 mines in lieu of d.c.

FRIGATES [FF] *(continued)*

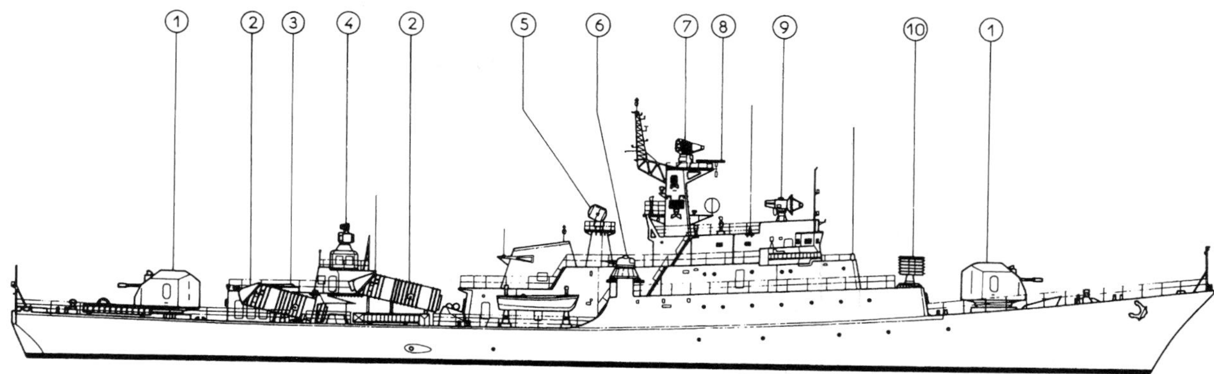

Beograd (VPB 31) 1. twin 76.2-mm AK-726 DP gunmounts 2. P-20 and P-21 antiship missile launchers (SS-N-2C Styx) 3. ZIF-122 twin launcher for the Osa-M (SA-N-4) SAM system 4. MPZ-301 radar director for SAM system 5. MR-104 Rys' radar director for AK-230 AA guns 6. twin 30-mm AK-230 AA mounts 7. MR-302 Rubka surface/air-search radar 8. Don-2 navigational radar 9. Fut-B fire-control radar for the 76.2-mm guns 10. 12-round RBU-6000 ASW rocket launchers

Drawing by Lucien Gassier, from *Flottes de Combat*

Podgorica (VPB 32)—since stricken
Livio Černjul, via Dr. Zvonimir Freivogel, 1992

Electronics:
Radar: 1 Don-2 nav.; 1 MR-302 Rubka (Strut Curve) air/surf. search; 1 MPZ-301 (Pop Group) missile f.c.; 1 Fut-B (Hawk Screech) 76.2-mm gun f.c.; 1 MR-104 Rys' (Drum Tilt) 30-mm gun f.c.
Sonar: 1 MG-322T hull-mounted MF; 1 hull-mounted HF f.c.
EW: 2 Bizan'-4B (Watch Dog) intercept (2–18 GHz); 1 MFD/F; 2 16-round PK-16 decoy RL

M: CODAG: 1 M-813 gas turbine (18,000 shp), 2 Type 68B diesels (9,000 bhp each); 3 props; 36,000 hp
Range: 4,456/14.98 **Crew:** 96 tot.

Remarks: VPB = *Veliki Patrolni Brod* (Large Patrol Ship). Was active by 6-00; sister *Podgorica* (VPB 32; ex-*Koper*, ex-SKR-481), which arrived in Yugoslavia 5-12-83, has been out of service since 1997. Has fin stabilizers. The mine rails can only be used to carry mines when the depth-charge racks are unbolted and removed. Sisters serve in the Algerian, Bulgarian, and Libyan navies.

GUIDED-MISSILE PATROL CRAFT [PTG]

♦ 5 Rade Končar class (Type 240) Bldr: Tito SY, Kraljevica, Croatia

	L	In serv.
RT 401 Rade Končar	15-10-76	4-77
RT 403 Ramiz Sadiku	24-4-78	10-9-78
RT 404 Hasan Zahirovič Lasa	9-11-78	11-79
RT 405 Jordan Nikolov-Orce	26-4-79	8-79
RT 406 Ante Banina	23-11-79	11-80

Jordan Nikolov-Orce (RT 405) Livio Černjul, via Dr. Zvonimir Freivogel, 1992

D: 242 tons (fl) **S:** 39 kts (37 sust.) **Dim:** 45.00 × 8.00 × 1.80 (2.50 props)
A: 2 P-20/21 Rubezh (SS-N-2B Styx) SSM; 2 (RT 401: 1) single 57-mm 70-cal. Bofors SAK 57 Mk 1 DP—RT 401 only: 1 30-mm AK-630 gatling AA
Electronics:
Radar: 1 Decca 1226 nav.; 1 CelsiusTech 9LV 200 Mk 2 target detection/f.c.
EW: 2 18-round Wallop Barricade decoy RL
M: CODAG: 2 Rolls-Royce Proteus gas turbines (4,500 shp each), 2 MTU 20V538 TB92 diesels (3,600 bhp each); 4 CP props; 16,200 hp max.
Electric: 300 kVA tot. **Range:** 880/23; 1,650/15 **Endurance:** 7 days
Crew: 5 officers, 10 petty officers, 15 other enlisted

Jordan Nikolov-Orce (RT 405) *Revista Marittima,* 1992

Remarks: RT = *Raketna Topovnjaca.* A Yugoslav design, using Swedish fire-control systems and guns and Soviet missiles. The names may have been changed, as they commemorate naval figures of Croatian, Bosnian, and Albanian ethnic origin.
Hull systems: Steel hull, aluminum superstructure. Have NBC warfare protection.
Combat systems: In RT 401 and RT 402 (ex-*Vlado Četovič,* now RTOP 21 *Šibenik* under Croatian control), the after 57-mm mount was removed and replaced with a Soviet-supplied 30-mm gatling gun to improve antimissile defenses; the gatling gun, however, is controlled only by a Kolonka-2 ringsight director mounted in a cupola just abaft the mast.

♦ 4 ex-Soviet Osa-I class (Project 205)

RČ 304 Steven Filipovič-Seljo
RČ 305 Zikica Jovanovic Spanac (ex-*Velimir Skorpik*)
RČ 306 Nikola Martinovič
RČ 307 Josip Mazar Sosa

D: 171 tons (209.5 fl) **S:** 38.5 kts
Dim: 38.6 (37.5 wl) × 7.6 (6.3 wl) × 1.8 (hull; 2.9 props)
A: 4 P-15 (SS-N-2C Styx) SSM; 2 twin 30-mm 65-cal. AK-230 AA
Electronics:
Radar: 1 Rangout (Square Tie) surf. search/target desig.; 1 MR-104 Rys' (Drum Tilt) gun f.c.
M: 3 M-503A2 diesels; 3 props; 12,000 bhp **Electric:** 200 kw tot.
Range: 500/34; 750/25 **Endurance:** 5 days **Crew:** 4 officers, 24 enlisted

Remarks: RČ = *Raketni Čamac.* Transferred in 1965–69. Names may have been changed. Sisters *Mitar Acev* (RČ 301) and *Zihaca Jovanovic-Spanac* (RČ 310) came under Croatian control; the former is still active as PBM 41 *Dubrovnik. Karlo Rojc* (RČ 308) was heavily damaged and has not been repaired. *Vlado Begat* (RČ 302), *Petar Drapsin* (RČ 303), and *Franc Rozman-Stane* (RČ 309) were cannibalized in 1992–93 for spares and discarded, and some or all of the above may also no longer be operational. Can be operated at 220 tons full load, with 11 tons extra fuel. The Rangout radar can also be operated in the passive mode for target detection and designation.

PATROL CRAFT [PC]

♦ 4 Mirna class (Type 140) (1 in *reserve*)
Bldr: Tito SY, Kraljevica, Croatia (In serv. 1981–82)

	L		L
RČ 175 *Grmec*	23-7-82	PČ 178 Kosmaju	9-9-83
PČ 177 Fruska-Gora	25-3-83	PČ 179 Zelengora	15-12-83

D: 125.3 tons (142.3 fl) **S:** 30 kts **Dim:** 32.00 (29.25 pp) × 6.68 × 1.76 (2.41 max.)
A: 1 40-mm 70-cal. Bofors L70 AA; 1 4-round Fasta-4M (SA-N-5) SAM syst. (12 missiles); 1 20-mm 90-cal. M-71 AA; 8 Type MDB-MT3 d.c.
Electronics:
Radar: 1 Decca 1216C nav.
Sonar: Simrad 5Q3D/SF hull-mounted HF
M: 2 SEMT-Pielstick 12 PA4 200GDS diesels; 2 props; 6,000 bhp—electric motors for low speeds (6 kts)
Range: 400/20 **Fuel:** 16.2 tons
Crew: 3 officers, 4 petty officers, 12 other enlisted

PATROL CRAFT [PC] *(continued)*

Kosmaju (PČ 178)—with quadruple 20-mm AA mount aft
Feda Klaric, via Dr. Zvonimir Freivogel, 10-91

Remarks: PČ = *Patrolni Čamac.* Sisters *Koprivnik* (PČ 171), *Mukos* (PČ 176), *Cer* (PČ 180), and *Kozolo* or *Durmitor* (PČ 181) are active in Croatian hands, while PČ 173 (name uncertain) has been cannibalized and discarded; ex-*Pohorje* (PČ 172) and ex-*Učka* (PČ 174) were reported inoperable in 1995 and have probably been discarded.
Hull systems: The first 10 propulsion diesels were ordered in 1979, for license production in Yugoslavia. Endurance at 20 kts can be increased to 530 n.m. in emergencies using void tankage. Peacetime endurance is four days; wartime, eight days.
Combat systems: Have two four-rail, S-2M, 128-mm M66 illumination rocket launchers amidships. There are also four chaff or illumination rocket rails on the sides of the 40-mm AA. The aftermost gunmount in some was originally a quadruple 20-mm M-75 mounting, and some may still have it vice the single mount listed.

PATROL BOATS [PB]

♦ 6 Type 20 riverine
Bldr: . . . ., Beograd (In serv. 1980–84)

PČ 211 PČ 212 PČ 213 PČ 214 PČ 215 PČ 216

PČ 216 *Front,* via Dr. Zvonimir Freivogel

D: 52 tons (56 fl) **S:** 16 kts **Dim:** 21.27 (20.06 wl) × 7.50 × 1.20
A: 2 single 20-mm 90-cal. M-71 AA; mines
Electronics: Radar: 1 Decca 110 nav.
M: 2 diesels; 2 props; 1,156 bhp **Range:** 200/15 **Crew:** 11 tot.

Remarks: Steel hull, GRP superstructure. All employed by the river flotilla on the Danube and tributaries. Can carry four R-1 or 6 KMD-2-500 mines.

♦ 1 Botica-class (Type 16) riverine
Bldr: . . ., Tivat (In serv. 1970)

PČ 303

D: 22.96 tons (24.07 fl) **S:** 15.1 kts
Dim: 17.04 × 3.60 × 0.85 (mean hull; 1.60 max.)
A: 1 20-mm 90-cal. M-71 AA; 7 single 7.62-mm mg
Electronics: Radar: 1 Decca 101 nav. **M:** 2 diesels; 2 props; 464 bhp
Range: 1,460/11.6 **Crew:** 7 tot. + 30 troops or combat swimmers

Remarks: "Botica" is the NATO class nickname. Are intended for patrol, troop transport, and logistic support duties, with up to 3 tons of cargo. All had been employed on lakes and rivers in Macedonia. PČ 305 was transferred to Tanzania. PČ 301 was stricken in 1992–93 and PČ 302, 304, and 305 during 1995.

♦ up to 11 Type 15 riverine and lake
From among: PČ 15-1 through PČ 15-12

D: 19.5 tons (fl) **S:** 16 kts **Dim:** 16.87 × 3.90 × 0.65 (0.70 props)
A: 1 20-mm 90-cal. M-71 AA; 2 single 7.62-mm mg
Electronics: Radar: 1 Decca 110 nav.
M: 2 diesels; 2 props; 330 bhp **Range:** 160/12 **Crew:** 6 tot.

Remarks: Steel hulls, GRP superstructures. Four near-sisters, referred to commercially as being of the Galeb class, were delivered to the Sudan in 5-89. Two sisters came under Croatian control, and one or more Yugoslav units have been stricken.

Type 15 patrol boat PČ 15-5 and two sisters 1984

♦ 1 ex-U.S. Rhine River patrol boat
Bldr: Theodor Hitzler Werft, Regensburg, Germany (In serv. 1956)

RPČ 111

D: 27.5 tons (29 fl) **S:** 17.8 kts **Dim:** 26.00 (24.10 pp) × 4.13 (3.90 wl) × 0.93
A: 2 single 20-mm 90-cal. M-71 AA
M: 2 MWM diesels; 2 props; 440 bhp **Range:** 870/14.6 **Crew:** 6 tot.

Remarks: Built for U.S. Navy's Rhine River Patrol and transferred to Yugoslavia during the late 1950s. One sister remains in service in the Belgian Navy. Probably does not have a radar.

♦ 3 CMP 25–class riverine patrol launches
Bldr: Vela Luka SY, Korčula Island, Croatia (In serv. 1986–87)

CMP 25 CMP 26 CMP 27

D: 2.7 tons (3.85 fl) **S:** 33.5 kts **Dim:** 9.00 × 2.90 × 0.51
A: 1 12.7-mm M2 mg **Electronics:** Radar: 1 Decca 170 nav.
M: 2 diesels; 2 props; 394 bhp **Range:** 240/30 **Crew:** 4 tot.

♦ 4 CMP 21–class riverine patrol launches

CMP 21 CMP 22 CMP 23 CMP 24

D: 2.64 tons (fl) **S:** 30.8 kts **Dim:** 8.00 × 2.95 × 0.85
A: 1 12.7-mm M2 mg **M:** 2 diesels; 2 props; 512 bhp **Crew:** 4 tot.

♦ 2 CM 81–class riverine patrol launches

CM 81 CM 82

D: 1.3 tons (1.7 fl) **S:** 35 kts **Dim:** 6.00 × 2.40 × 0.60 **A:** small arms
M: 1 Mercedes-Benz diesel; 1 prop; 235 bhp **Crew:** 1 tot.

MINE WARFARE SHIPS

♦ 2 French Sirius-class coastal minesweepers/hunters [MHC]
Bldrs: A. Normand, Le Havre, France

	In serv.
M 152 . . . (ex-*Podgora;* ex-*Smeli,* ex-MSC 230)	9-57
M 153 . . . (ex-*Blitvenica;* ex-*Slobodni,* ex-MSC 231)	9-57

D: 400 tons (440 fl) **S:** 15 kts (11.5 sweeping) **Dim:** 46.4 (42.7 pp) × 8.55 × 2.5
A: 1 twin 20-mm 70-cal. Oerlikon Mk 24 AA
Electronics:
Radar: 1 DRBN-30 nav.
Sonar: Thales TSM 2022 minehunting
M: 2 SEMT-Pielstick 16 PA1 175 diesels; 2 props; 2,000 bhp
Electric: 375 kw tot. **Range:** 3,000/10 **Fuel:** 48 tons **Crew:** 40 tot.

M 153 H&L Van Ginderen, 10-99

Remarks: M = *Minolovac.* Built with U.S. Offshore Procurement funds. Sister *Vukov Klanac* (M 151, ex-*Hrabri,* ex-U.S. MSC 229) was extensively damaged in 9-91, captured by Croatia, and later stricken. *Gradac* (M 161, ex-*Snazhi*) was stricken and scrapped during 1993, and M 153 may be in reserve or stricken. Have wooden-planked hulls with metal framing.
Combat systems: Have French PAP-104 remote-controlled minehunting/disposal submersibles and Decca HiFix precision navigation systems. New minehunting sonars replaced the Plessey Type 193M in both after 1988.

♦ 1 British Ham-class inshore minesweeper [MSI]
Bldr: Yugoslavia (In serv. 1964–65)

M 141 Milj (ex-MSI 98)

D: 123 tons (164 fl) **S:** 14 kts **Dim:** 32.43 × 6.45 × 1.7
A: 1 40-mm 60-cal. Bofors AA **Electronics:** Radar: 1 Decca 45 nav.
M: 2 Paxman YHAXM diesels; 2 props; 1,100 bhp
Range: 1,500/12; 2,000/9 **Fuel:** 15 tons **Crew:** 22 tot.

MINE WARFARE SHIPS *(continued)*

Remarks: Built under the U.S. Offshore Procurement Program. Sisters *Iz* (M 143, ex-MSI 100) and *Olib* (M 144, ex-MSI 101) have been discarded. *Brsec* (M 142, ex-MSI 99) had become derelict by 1996. Composite construction, with wooden planking over a metal-framed hull.

♦ **7 (+ 1) Nestin-class (Type 50) river minesweepers [MSB]**
Bldr: Brodotehnika, Belgrade

	L		L
RML 331 Nestin	20-12-75	RML 335 Vucedol	1979
RML 332 Motajica	18-12-76	RML 336 Djerdap	1980
RML 333 Belegis	1-77	RML 338 Novi Sad	6-6-96
RML 334 Bosut	1978	RML 339	. . .

D: 57.31 tons light; 68 tons std. (79.6 fl) **S:** 14 kts (11.9 sust.)
Dim: 27.00 × 6.50 × 1.08 (1.18 max.)
A: 1 quadruple 20-mm 90-cal. M-75 AA; 2 single 20-mm 90-cal. M-71 AA; 1 4-round MTU-4 SAM syst. (Strela-2M missiles); 24 R-1 moored or 18 AIM-M-82 acoustic bottom mines or 30 mine-destruction charges
Electronics:
Radar: 1 Decca RM 1216R (RML 338: RR 205 DMT) nav.
Sonar: PP-10M hull-mounted HF
M: 2 Torpedo B.539RM/22 diesels; 2 props; 512 bhp
Range: 1,720/11.9 **Fuel:** 10.7 tons **Endurance:** 15 days **Crew:** 17 tot.

Remarks: RML = *Recni Minolovac.* Used on the Danube River. RML 338 (Project S-25N) is the first warship built for the Federal Yugoslav Navy, and a sister was reported to be under construction as of 2000; the name *Novi Sad* duplicates that of one of the Kotor-class frigates. Three sisters were built for Iraq and six for Hungary. Sister *Panonsko More* (RML 337) was stricken in 1997.
Hull systems: Aluminum alloy construction. Navigation equipment includes an Anschutz-12 gyrocompass and an STN Atlas Elektronik 240 (RML 338: Ultrasound D-15) echo sounder. Can make 9.7 kts against the average Danube current or 14 kts downstream. Turning radius is 60 m. RML 338 has a reduced magnetic signature, increased hull strength, improved accommodations, air-conditioning, and a smokescreen generator. Can carry 100 troops for short distances.
Combat systems: Sweep gear includes Type PEAM-1A towed magnetic solenoid and acoustic sweep pontoon, Type AEL-1 explosive sweep (using 15-charge line charges), and Types MDL-1 or MDL-2R mechanical sweeps. Two illumination chaff rocket launchers are fitted. The armament listed is that mounted on RML 338, but the others probably have been brought up to the same standard. Alternate mine loads include 24 P-1 contact, 18 AIM-M.82 acoustic, 24 Rokan GM-100 magnetic, or 36-48 PLRM-1A free-floating contact/timed. The PEAM-1A towed mine countermeasures pontoon is 18.1 m long by 1.22 m beam and displaces 16.47 metric tons; it incorporates an acoustic generator in the bow and magnetic coils amidships, the latter energized by a 16-kw diesel generator, and the device is towed some 220 m abaft the minecraft.

AMPHIBIOUS WARFARE SHIPS

♦ **1 Silba-class tank landing craft/minelayer [LSM]** (In reserve)
Bldr: Brodosplit, Split, Croatia (In serv. 1990)

DBM 241 *Silba*

Silba (DBM 241)—when active ANBw/FAFIO, via Siegfried Breyer, 1998

D: 700 tons (880 fl) **S:** 12 kts **Dim:** 49.70 (43.90 pp) × 10.20 × 2.60 (max.)
A: 2 twin 30-mm 65-cal. AK-230 AA; 1 quadruple 20-mm 90-cal. M-75 AA; up to 94 Type SAG-1 mines
Electronics: Radar: 1 Decca 1290A nav.
M: 2 Burmeister & Wain Alpha 10V23L-VO diesels; 2 CP props; 3,100 bhp
Range: 1,200/12 **Crew:** 3 officers, 30 enlisted + up to 300 troops

Remarks: Was laid up at Tivat as of 10-98. Two sisters serve in the Croatian Navy.
Hull systems: Has bow and stern ramps, with a continuous covered vehicle deck also used for portable mine rails. Cargo capacity: 460 tons, four medium tanks, or up to seven armored personnel carriers.
Combat systems: Has two 128-mm rocket flare launchers. The 30-mm gunmounts are mounted port and starboard, just abaft the bridge, while the 20-mm mount is located near the stern.

♦ **6 DJČ 621-class (Type 22) landing craft [LCM]**
Bldr: Gleben SY, Vela Luka, Korčula (In serv. 1983–85)

DJČ 621 DJČ 625 DJČ 628 DJČ 630 DJČ 631 DJČ 632

DJČ 621-class DJČ 627—since lost Yugoslav Navy, 1989

D: 48 tons (fl) **S:** 30 kts **Dim:** 22.30 × 4.84 × 1.07 (1.58 props)
A: 2 single 20-mm 90-cal. M-71 AA; 1 30-mm PB-30 grenade launcher
Electronics: Radar: 1 Decca 101 nav.
M: 2 MTU diesels; 2 waterjets; 1,740 bhp
Range: 320/22 **Crew:** 8 tot. + 40 troops

Remarks: DJČ = *Desantni Jurisni Čamac.* All are assigned to the riverine flotilla. One sister is in the Croatian Navy and one in Croatian police service, and three others are used by Croatia as civilian fireboats. Additional power permits the hull to plane, greatly increasing the speed over the Type 21 design. GRP construction. Have a bow ramp. Can carry vehicles totaling 15 tons in a 32-m^2 cargo area. The waterjet propulsion system is said to be less than successful, and it is likely that some or all of these craft have been laid up or discarded.

♦ **up to 4 DJČ 613-class (Type 21) vehicle/personnel landing craft [LCM]** Bldr: Gleben SY, Vela Luka, Korčula (In serv. 1978)

DJČ 614 DJČ 616 DJČ 617 DJČ 618

D: 32 tons (38 fl) **S:** 25 kts **Dim:** 21.30 × 4.84 × 1.07 (1.58 props)
A: 1 20-mm 90-cal. M-71 AA; 1 30-mm PB-30 grenade launcher
Electronics: Radar: 1 Decca 101 nav.
M: 2 MTU 12V331 TC81 diesels; 2 props; 2,500 bhp
Range: 320/22 **Crew:** 7 tot. + 40 troops

Remarks: DJČ = *Desantni Jurisni Čamac.* Seven others were damaged or sunk during combat in 1991–92. GRP construction. The design is very similar to the earlier Type 11, but the propulsion plant is more powerful. Have a bow ramp. Can carry vehicles totaling 6 tons in a 32-m^2 cargo area.

♦ **up to 6 DJČ 601-class (Type 11) landing craft [LCM]**
Bldr: Gleben SY, Vela Luka, Korčula (In serv. 1976–77)

DJČ 604 DJČ 605 DJČ 606 DJČ 608 DJČ 609 DJČ 610

D: 32 tons (38 fl) **S:** 23.5 kts (21 sust.) **Dim:** 21.30 × 4.84 × 1.07 (1.58 props)
A: 1 20-mm 90-cal. M-71 AA; 1 30-mm PB-30 grenade launcher
Electronics: Radar: 1 Decca 101 nav.
M: 1 MTU 12V331 TC81 diesel; 1 prop; 1,450 bhp
Range: 320/22 **Crew:** 7 tot. + 40 troops

Remarks: DJČ = *Desantni Jurisni Čamac.* GRP construction. Sister DJČ 603 and two others were captured by Croatia, and a number of others were sunk.

♦ **2 DČ 101-class personnel landing craft [LCP]**
Bldr: Vela Luca, Korčula Island (In serv. 1982)

DČ 101 DČ 102

D: 5.5 tons light (11 fl) **S:** 25 kts (20 sust.) **Dim:** 11.30 × 3.10 × 0.32
A: 1 7.62-mm mg **Electronics:** Radar: 1 Decca 101 nav.
M: 2 diesels; 2 waterjets *or* 2 outdrives; 260 bhp **Range:** 100/15 **Crew:** 2 tot.

Remarks: DČ = *Desantni Čamac.* For riverine use. Can carry up to 30 troops.

♦ **2 BDČ 91-class personnel landing craft [LCP]**
Bldr: . . ., U.K. (In serv. 1976)

BDČ 91 BDČ 92

D: 2.5 tons (2.8 fl) **S:** 37.8 kts **Dim:** 7.37 × 3.00 × 0.75
M: 3 Mercedes-Benz gasoline engines; 3 props; 221 bhp
Range: 108/27 kts **Crew:** 3 tot.

Remarks: For transporting special forces personnel on the river system. GRP construction.

♦ **2 or more Type R2, Mala-class swimmer-delivery vehicles [LSDV]** Bldr: Brodosplit, Split, Croatia

D: 1.4 tons **S:** 4.4 kts **Dim:** 4.90 × 1.22 × 1.32 (1.70 fins) **A:** 2 50-kg mines
M: 1 electric motor; 1 prop; 6 hp **Range:** 18/4.4; 23/3.7 **Crew:** 2 tot.

Remarks: Diving depth: 60 m. Have a free-flooding personnel space enclosed within a clear-plastic dome. Sweden has acquired one, and six were sold to Libya; the USSR may also have received examples. Croatia is said to have captured two units of this class.

Note: Also available are a number of R1 "chariot"-type swimmer-delivery vehicles with a length of 3.72 m, a beam of 1.05 m, and a surfaced draft of 0.80 m; the craft have a range of 6 n.m. at 3 kts and can dive to 60 m. Three personnel can be carried astride the craft.

AMPHIBIOUS WARFARE SHIPS *(continued)*

Mala-class swimmer-delivery vehicle 1984

AUXILIARIES

♦ 1 City-class command ship and smallcraft tender [AGF]
Bldr: Uljanic SY, Pula, Croatia (In serv. 1956)

PB 25 Vɪs (ex-PB 35)

Vis (PB 25) Livio Černjul, via Dr. Zvonimir Freivogel, 1992

D: 510 tons (680 fl) **S:** 17 kts **Dim:** 57.0 × 8.5 × 3.5
A: 1 40-mm 60-cal. Bofors Mk 3 AA; 2 single 20-mm 90-cal. M-71 AA
M: 2 diesels; 2 props; 1,900 bhp

Remarks: PB = *Pomocni Brod* (Auxiliary Ship). Built to the same design as the now-discarded coastal passenger-cargo vessels *Sarajevo, Novi Sad,* and *Mostar.* Had served primarily as administrative flagship for the Adriatic Fleet.

Disposal note: Riverine command ship *Kozara* (RPB 30, ex-PB 30, ex-U.S. *Oregon,* ex-German *Kriemhild*) was reportedly stricken during 2000.

♦ 1 Lubin-class multipurpose cargo transport [AK]
Bldr: Brodosplit, Split, Croatia (In serv. mid-1980s)

PO 93 Kɪᴛ

D: 600 tons (882 fl; 1,000 max.) **S:** 16.2 kts (14.3 sust.)
Dim: 58.20 × 11.00 × 2.75 (mean)

Lubin (PO 91)—since stricken; *Kit* (PO 93) is identical Brodosplit, 1988

A: 1 40-mm 60-cal. Bofors Mk 3 AA; 1 quadruple 20-mm 90-cal. M-75 AA; 2 shoulder-fired Strela-2M SAM launch positions
Electronics: Radar: 1 . . . nav.
M: 2 diesels; 2 CP props; 3,480 bhp
Range: 1,500/14.3 **Endurance:** 10 days
Crew: 34 crew + 150 fully equipped troops, 6 vehicle drivers

Remarks: PO = *Pomocni Oruzar* (Ammunition Auxiliary). Is intended to supply combatants with missiles, torpedoes, mines, and other ordnance, using two slewing cranes on the upper deck. Sisters *Lubin* (PO 91) and *Ugor* (PO 92), laid up since 1991, were transferred to the Montenegrin government for commercial use or scrapping.
Hull systems: The continuous cargo deck can accommodate up to 6 tanks. Have a visor-type bow and extendable bow ramp and two electrohydraulic cranes. As ammunition transports, can carry up to 20 torpedoes or 40 sea mines. Have two S-2M, 128-mm M66 illumination rocket launchers.

SERVICE CRAFT

♦ 1 riverine degaussing craft [YDG]
Bldr: Brodotehnika, Belgrade (In serv. 1984)

RSRB 36 Sᴀʙᴀᴄ

D: 107.2 tons (115.8 fl) **S:** 11.9 kts **Dim:** 32.20 × 7.05 × 1.27
A: 2 single 20-mm M-71 AA; 1 4-round MTU-4 SAM syst. (Strela-2M missiles)
Electronics: Radar: 1 Decca 1216A nav.
M: 2 diesels; 2 props; 790 bhp **Range:** 716/10.8 **Crew:** 16 tot.

Remarks: Patrol boat-type hull, with the superstructure set well aft. Acts as deperming tender for Danube River Flotilla craft.

♦ up to 5 BRM 81–class diving tenders [YDT]
Bldr: Punat SY, Punat (In serv. 1978–84)

BRM 81 BRM 85 BRM 86 BRM 87 BRM 88

BRM 81 class Punat SY, via Dr. Zvonimir Freivogel, ca. 1978

D: 46 tons light (65 fl) **S:** 10.5 kts **Dim:** 22.10 (20.50 pp) × 5.66 × 1.90
A: 2 single 20-mm 90-cal. M-71 AA
Electronics: Radar: 1 Decca 101 nav.
M: 2 diesels; 2 props; 320 bhp **Range:** 400/12 **Crew:** 8 tot.

Remarks: Resemble the survey craft BH 11 and BH 12 and training craft BS 21 and BS 22, except that there is a low deckhouse forward of the pilothouse. Sister BRM 84 was lost to a mine 25-9-91. The armament may have been reduced or removed.

♦ 1 hydrofoil riverine yacht [YFL] Bldr: . . ., USSR (In serv. 1972)

Sᴀᴠᴀ

D: 47 tons (54.3 fl) **S:** 35 kts **Dim:** 34.60 × 9.50 × 2.35
Electronics: Radar: 1 Decca RM 1216R nav.
M: 2 M-50 diesels; 2 props; 2,170 bhp **Range:** 320/32 **Crew:** 9 tot.

Remarks: Can also be used to transport up to 40 troops. Former commercial craft. Dimensions above are over foils, at rest. Has a Kelvin-Hughes echo sounder.

♦ 1 riverine yacht [YFL]
Bldr: Tito SY, Belgrade (In serv. 1961)

Sᴜᴍᴀᴅɪɴᴋᴀ

D: 43 tons (47 fl) **S:** 15 kts **Dim:** 23.10 × 5.67 × 1.10
Electronics: Radar: 1 Decca 110 nav.
M: 2 diesels; 2 props; 986 bhp **Range:** 162/13 **Crew:** 8 tot.

♦ 2 inshore survey craft [YGS]
Bldr: . . . . . . SY, Yugoslavia (In serv. mid-1980s)

BH 11 (ex-BH 1) BH 12 (ex-BH 2)

D: 46 tons light (65 fl) **S:** 10.5 kts **Dim:** 22.10 (20.50 pp) × 5.66 × 1.90
Electronics: Radar: 1 Decca 101 nav.
M: 2 diesels; 2 props; 320 bhp **Range:** 400/12
Crew: 4 tot. + 6 survey personnel

Remarks: Same basic design as the PT 82–series transports.

Note: Also reported in use is the 4.5-ton survey launch CH 1.

SERVICE CRAFT *(continued)*

♦ **2 Drina-class fuel lighters [YO]** (1 in *reserve*)
Bldr: Tito SY, Kraljevica, Croatia

PN 26 *Liganj* (L: 18-5-88) PN 27 Sipa (L: 16-9-88)

Sipa (PN 27) ANBw/FAFIO, via Siegfried Breyer, 1998

D: approx. 600 tons (fl) **S:** . . . kts **Dim:** . . . × . . . × . . .
A: 1 quadruple 20-mm M-75 AA; 2 single 20-mm M-71 AA
Electronics: Radar: 1 . . . nav.
M: 1 . . . diesel; 1 prop; . . . bhp

Remarks: PN = *Pomocni Nafta* (Oil Fuel Auxiliary). Drina is the NATO nickname. Names mean "Squid" and "Cuttlefish," respectively. Based at Tivat. PN 26 may be sold for commercial employment and has been laid up for several years.

♦ **3 PR 37–class coastal tugs [YTM]** (1 in reserve)
Bldr: Split SY, Croatia (In serv. 1950s)

PR 37 Zubatac PR 38 . . . PR 48 . . .

D: 550 tons (fl) **S:** 11 kts **Dim:** 32.0 × 8.0 × 5.0
M: 2 diesels; 2 props; . . . bhp **Crew:** 18 tot.

Remarks: PR = *Pomorski Remorker* (Auxiliary Tug). Were originally reciprocating steam propelled but have been re-engined with diesels. Sister *Dupin* (PR 36) was captured by Croatia but not placed in service.

♦ **2 LR 67–class harbor tugs [YTM]**
Bldr: Split SY, Croatia (In serv. 1960s)

LR 72 LR 77

D: 550 tons (fl) **S:** 11 kts **Dim:** 32.0 × 8.0 × . . .
M: 2 diesels; 1 prop; . . . bhp

Remarks: LR = *Lucki Remorker* (Harbor Tug). Two others are in Croatian hands.

♦ **1 Alga-class water tanker [YW]**

PV 17 Alga

D: 200 tons (600 fl) **S:** 7.5 kts **Dim:** 44.00 × 7.90 × 3.20
A: 1 20-mm M-71 AA **Electronics:** Radar: 1 . . . nav.
M: 1 diesel; 1 prop; 300 bhp **Range:** 1,500/7.5 **Crew:** . . . tot.

Remarks: Used for supplying offshore islands with drinking water. Sister *Koral* (PV 16) was stricken during the 1980s.

Alga (PV 17) Dr. Eric Grove, 10-90

♦ **2 training craft [YXT]** (In serv. mid-1980s)

BS 21 BS 22

D: 46 tons light (65 fl) **S:** 10.5 kts **Dim:** 22.10 (20.50 pp) × 5.66 × 1.90
Electronics: Radar: 1 Decca 101 nav.
M: 2 diesels; 2 props; 320 bhp **Range:** 400/12 **Crew:** 2 officers, 18 cadets

Remarks: Same basic design as BRM 81–series diving tenders and the survey craft BH 11 and BH 12.

ZIMBABWE

DISTRICT DEVELOPMENT FUND FOR THE ADMINISTRATION AND DEVELOPMENT OF THE SOUTH BANK OF LAKE KARIBA

Bases: Binga and Harare

PATROL BOATS [WPB]

♦ **8 Type B 79 lake patrol boats**
Bldr: S.K.B. Yard, Antwerp, Belgium (In serv. 1986)

KF 590 Chipo Chebelgium
KF 591 Mudzimundiringe
KF 592 Chirovamura
KF 593 Vamashayamombe
KF 594 Chayamura Varwere
KF 595 Chifambisa Nyore
KF 596 Chiorora Mvura
KF 597 Chibatanidza Matunhu

Chibatanidza Matunhu (KF 597) H&L Van Ginderen, 6-86

D: approx. 14 tons (fl) **S:** 22–25 kts **Dim:** 11.50 × 3.85 × 0.65
M: 2 Caterpillar 3208 diesels; 2 props; 400 bhp **Crew:** . . .

Remarks: GRP police craft, shipped to Africa in 6-86. The first five are based at Kariba on Lake Kariba, about 300 km west of Harare, the others at Binga. Are used on patrol, medical assistance, and supply duties. Some may have been discarded.

ADDENDA

ALGERIA

Delivery of the first of six U.S. Beech 1900D Multimission Surveillance Aircraft for the Algerian Air Force was made during 7-01. The aircraft are equipped with inverse synthetic aperture surveillance radars.

ARGENTINA

♦ **1 dry cargo ship [AK]**
Bldr: . . . (In serv. 1973)

B . . . Capitán Tulio Panigadi

D: . . . tons **S:** 14 kts **Dim:** 150.00 × 17.20 × 6.60
M: 1 diesel; 1 prop; . . . bhp

Remarks: 6,794-dwt dry cargo ship, acquired in 2001 for revenue service. Has a naval crew.

AUSTRALIA

Two Australian Acoustic Generator (AAG) towed acoustic mine countermeasures sets (with another 16 planned) were ordered 5-6-01 for use with the *Huon* class and other RAN mine countermeasures craft. Powered by a water turbine, the AAG is intended to complement the DYAD magnetic system, with both being components of the Australian Minesweeping and Surveillance System (AMASS). The AAG is programmable to simulate different sizes and types of ships.

About 100 MU-90 Impact lightweight ASW torpedoes were ordered from Eurotorp on 18-2-02 for shipboard, helicopter, and RAAF AP-3 Orion aircraft use.

The three SH-2G Super SeaSprite helicopters thus far delivered were in storage as of 2-02, and the operational date for the helicopter has been delayed to 2004 due to late delivery of the Litton mission control system.

AZERBAIJAN

Two patrol and SAR launches were acquired during 2001 for the Border Guard:

♦ **2 AGC.1 class**
Bldr: Siver Ships, Theodore, U.K. (In serv. 4-01 and 8-01)

AGC.1 AGC.2

D: . . . tons **S:** 40 kts **Dim:** 14.50 (12.50 pp) × 3.70 × . . .
A: . . . **Electronics:** . . .
M: 2 Caterpillar 3196D geared diesels; Seafury surface-piercing props; 1,140 bhp
Electric: 8 kw tot. **Range:** 500/30 **Fuel:** 1,890 **Crew:** 6 tot.

Remarks: Aluminum construction.

BANGLADESH

The new frigate *Bangabandhu* (F 25) was decommissioned 14-2-02 and returned to her builder, Daewoo Shipbuilding and Marine Engineering Co., Okpo, South Korea, for repairs; the ship was said to be suffering from numerous defects to the engineering and combat systems. The maximum speed for the ship was said to be 25.3 kts. A new naval base at Mongla was opened in 4-02.

BELGIUM

Under the same 10-12-01 contract with STN Atlas Elektronik and Thales Underwater Systems that will see ten Royal Netherlands Navy Tripartite minehunters upgraded between 2004 and 2008, six Belgian Tripartites are to receive the same modification; see the Netherlands addenda for further details.

BRUNEI

The new British-built frigates have been assigned pennant numbers as follows: 28 *Nakhoda Ragam;* 29 *Bedahara Sakam;* and 30 *Jerambak*. The ships are officially styled as "Offshore Patrol Vessels" (OPV) by the builder but in fact have the capabilities and performance of frigates.

CANADA

Plans were announced in 8-01 to buy 100 new torpedoes and an air-defense/anti-smallcraft missile system for the *Upholder*-class submarines, with both systems to be installed during refits starting in 2009 and ending in 2014.

Seventeen Westcam 14 IR/laser/t.v. stand-alone electro-optical imaging systems were ordered 9-01 for use on the active units of the *Iroquois* and *Halifax* classes.

For the Canadian Coast Guard, two 10-m Zodiac aluminum-hulled RIBs were ordered from Zodiac Hurricane Technologies, Delta, on 1-2-02, for conservation and game protection duties at Prince Rupert and Queen Charlotte Islands. A 10-m RIB was ordered from Canadian Custom RIB on 11-2-02 for delivery by end 3-02; the craft was to be based at Victoria, B.C., for search-and-rescue duties.

Upholder-class submarine *Windsor* (SS 877) began refit 3-4-02 for installation of Canadian equipment; the transfer from the U.K. of sister *Corner Brook* (SS 878) was delayed to 10-02 and *Chicoutimi* (SS 879) to early 2003.

CHILE

Former Israeli Sa'ar II–class guided-missile patrol craft *Iquique* (LM 32; ex-*Hanit*) and *Covadonga* (LM 33; ex-*Hetz*) were retired during 2-00.

ASMAR 1160–class SAR RIB *Kimitahi* (LSR 1701) was stricken 29-12-00.

The six-ship Tridente (MEKO A-200) frigate program was canceled on 30-1-02 for lack of funds; a new agreement for a smaller number of frigates may be reached with Blohm + Voss, or the Chilean Navy may acquire several used frigates, possibly from the United States or the Netherlands.

Six ex-U.S. Coast Guard 44-ft. rescue launches were donated to the Chilean Coast Guard during 3-02 and were named *Pelluhue* (LSR 1703), *Arauco* (LSR 1704), *Chacao* (LSR 1705), *Queitao* (LSR 1706), *Guaiteca* (LSR 1707), and *Curaumilla* (LSR 1708). The 17.7-ton craft were completed between 1961 and 1973.

CHINA

Two Russian Tarantul-I-class (Project 12421) guided-missile patrol boats were reportedly ordered from Russia during 2001, with the first having been laid down during 2000 at Rybinsk on speculation. Some 200 Meteor-class surface-effect craft are said to have been purchased from a yard at Nizhniy Novgorod, Russia; these may be the small personnel landing craft seen during amphibious landing demonstrations in recent years.

A new cruise missile designated C-803 and with a range of 160 km was said to be in development as of 2001; no other data are yet available.

COLOMBIA

The first of a programmed total of 12 Nodriza-class riverine warfare support craft, the *Cl° Wilson Londoño* (146) was launched by the Cartagena Naval Shipyard during 6-98 and completed during 3-00; the second, *Araujo* (147) was launched during 9-98 and commissioned 19-4-00. A third was delivered in 2001, and the fourth was to be delivered during 1-02. Data include:

D: 260 tons **S:** 9 kts **Dim:** 38.4 × 9.5 × 2.8
A: 8 single 12.7-mm mg **Electronics:** Radar: 1 . . . nav.
M: 2 diesels; 2 props; 880 bhp **Crew:** 18 tot. + 82 troops

Remarks: Has 80-mm armor to the hull sides below the waterline. Medical facilities are fitted. The "2.8-m" figure in the dimensions may have referred to moulded depth rather than draft. A helicopter deck is fitted.

Colombian Navy Nodriza-class riverine warfare support craft Wilson Londoño (146)—at launch

CROATIA

Naval yacht *Učka* (ex-*Podgorka*) was damaged beyond repair in a fire during 2001.

Croatian Rade Končar–class guided-missile patrol boat Kralj Dmitar Zvonimir (RTOP 12)—shortly after launch 3-01

CYPRUS

The correct pennant numbers and names for the five ex-East German SAB 12–class patrol launches operated by the Cyprus Maritime Police are:

PL 11 Dionysos (ex-GS 12, ex-G 55)
PL 12 Kourion (ex-GS 27, ex-G 55)
PL 13 Ilarion (ex-GS 25, ex-G 52)
PL 14 Karpasia (ex-GS 10, ex-G 50)
PL 15 Akamas (ex-GS 28, ex-G 57)

DENMARK

Fifty 12.7-mm mg have been ordered to provide defense against terrorists for larger ships and craft. The Hvide Sande yard received an order for two 100-ton, 16-m tugs for the Danish Navy during 3-02; the craft will be powered by a 738-bhp MTU diesel and will be able to carry a single Standard Flex container and 12 passengers.

EAST TIMOR

Two former Portuguese Navy *Albatroz*-class patrol boats were transferred on 12-1-02 to form the initial fleet of the East Timor Navy; the pair have been renamed the *Oécusse* and *Ataúro* and are based at Dili. This new country was to become independent 20-5-02.

EGYPT

U.S. government approval for the construction of guided-missile boats for Egypt by Friede Goldman Halter was finally granted early in 2-02. Egypt has agreed to acquire German Navy Type 148 guided-missile patrol craft *Fuchs* (P 6146), *Löwe* (P 6148), *Panther* (P 6150), *Alk* (P 6155), *Dommel* (P 6156), *Weihe* (P 6157), *Pinguin* (P 6158), and *Reiher* (P 6159), along with the replenishment ship *Freiburg* (A 1413); the transfers will apparently begin early in 2003.

The first of a planned series of small vehicle landing craft was to be ordered in mid-2002 from Alexandria SY, with technical support to come from Germany's MPC Münchmeyer Petersen Marine.

EL SALVADOR

The pennant number prefixes were changed during 5-01, with PM indicating *Patrulla Marítima*, PC for *Patrullera Costera*, PF for *Patrullera Fluvial*, PFR for *Patrulla Fluvial Rápida*, and BD for *Buque de Desembarco;* all previous pennant numbers have been modified with the new prefixes. All 20-mm Mk 68 mountings have been changed to twin 12.7-mm mg mounts. Ten locally-built airboat shallow-draft personnel landing craft (PFR-01 through PFR-10) have been acquired; powered by a single gasoline engine driving a 5-bladed airscrew propeller, they can seat 8 troops in addition to the operator.

ESTONIA

During the third quarter of 2001, Baltic Ship Repair, Tallinn, delivered the 118-ton patrol craft *Vapper* (PVL 11) to the Border Guard. Armed with a twin 23-mm AA mount, the craft has dimensions of 31.40 (27.80 pp) × 6.00 × 1.66 m and can achieve 27 kts on the 4,080 bhp from two Deutz TBD620-V12 diesels. Tallinn Port Authority icebreaker *Karu* (ex-*Kapten Tchubakov*, ex-*Kapitan Chubakov*, ex-*Karhu*) was placed up for sale on 12-3-02.

FRANCE

The carrier *Charles de Gaulle* (R 91) deployed to the Indian Ocean 20-12-01 with 16 Super Étendard, 5 Rafale-M, 1 E-2C Hawkeye, and 4 helicopters. Eight additional Rafale-M fighters were ordered 26-12-01, bringing to 25 the number delivered or on order for the French Navy. Ballistic-missile submarine *Le Triomphant* (S 616) was to begin an overhaul and recoring during 4-02 for completion during 9-04.

A new intelligence collection ship [AGI] to replace the *Bougainville* (L 9077) was ordered 14-1-02, with Thales Naval France as prime contractor, Thales Communications responsible for electronics installations, Thales Systèmes Aéroportés responsible for the ELINT system, and Compagnie Nationale de Navigation's Compagnie Maritime Nantaise providing the ship platform, whose hull is to be built in the Netherlands by Royal Niester Sanders, Groningen. Intended to serve for 30 years and to be able to proceed at 16 kts in Sea State 3 and 10 kts in Sea State 6, the ship will be 100-m overall and carry a crew of 30, plus 78 technicians, for cruises of two months or longer. The new ship will be named the *Dupuy de Lôme* (A . . .) and will be laid down in 2003, launched in 2004, and delivered in 2005; an armament of two Simbad point-defense SAM launchers and two single 20-mm AA is to be fitted, and the ship will have a helicopter deck.

All destroyers of the *Georges Leygues* class were to have their hulls reinforced during 2002 due to hull cracking, which was particularly severe on *Georges Leygues* (D 640) and *Jean de Vienne* (D 643).

The weapons trials tender [YAGE] *Denti* (A 743), to have been retired during 2001, has been extended in service until 2006. The weapons trials ship *Île d'Oléron* (A 610) was not retired until 30-3-02.

The 22 new patrol boats for the Gendarmerie Maritime are to be delivered between 2003 and 2009 and are to be named for rivers: the *Aberwrach, Adour, Argens, Charente, Dumbea, Elorn, Escaut, Esteron, Gravona, Herault, Huvaune, Maury, Odet, Penfeld, Scarpe, Sevre, Tech, Trieux, Verdon, Vertonne, Vesubie,* and *Yser;* pennant numbers have not yet been announced. The craft are to displace 40 tons, will be capable of 25 kts, and are to be powered by two 750-bhp V12 diesels; crews of 8 will be carried.

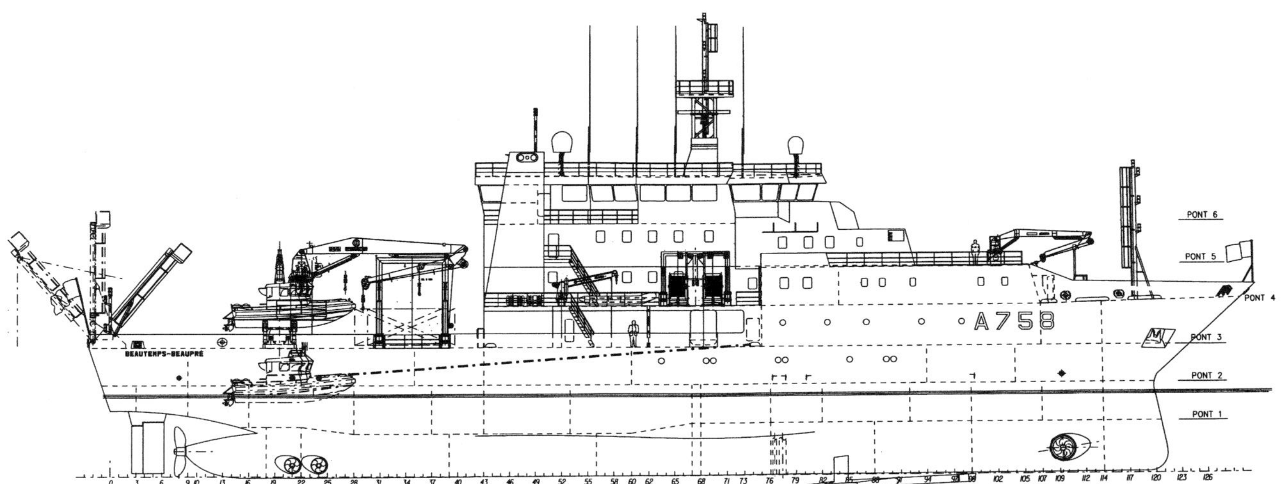

French Navy hydrographic survey ship Beautemps-Beaupré (A 758)—starboard view DCN, 2002

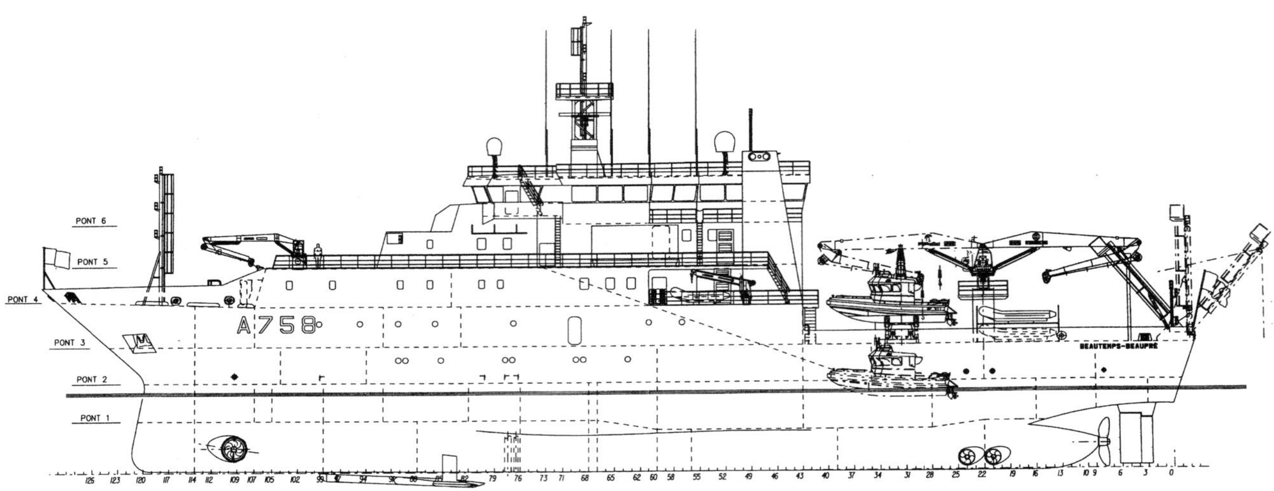

French Navy hydrographic survey ship Beautemps-Beaupré (A 758)—port view DCN, 2002

The new French Navy intelligence collection ship—computer rendering Thales, 2002

GERMANY

In the aftermath of the 11-9-01 terrorist attacks in the U.S.A., consideration is again being given to the construction of a large landing ship dock–type amphibious warfare transport for intervention forces. STN Atlas Elektronik received a contract early in 2002 to develop a low-frequency active towed-array sonar for the four Type 123 frigates, with the system to enter service in 2006.

Type 212A submarine U 31 was christened on 20-3-02 for launch early in 5-02.

Type 148 guided missile boat *Alk* (P 6155) was to be stricken on 25-4-02. The remaining Type 394A inshore minesweepers, *Frauenlob* (M 2658) and *Gefion* (M 2660), were decommissioned together on 27-3-02 and *Loreley* (M 2665) was decommissioned on 27-6-02. Type 520 utility landing craft *Zander* (L 769) was stricken 28-2-02. *Baltrum*-class (Type 722) seagoing tug *Norderney* (A 1455) was to be stricken on 27-9-02. Torpedo retriever TF 6 (Y 856) was to be stricken on 31-5-02. Sea Border Patrol ship *Bad Bramstedt* (BG 24) was delivered from Russia for fitting out during 11-01; the ship is to be delivered during 10-02; BG 25 will be named *Bayreuth* and BG 26 *Eschwege,* with the pair to be delivered in 5-03 and 12-03, respectively, and the current patrol craft with those names to be retired by 12-02.

GREECE

Retired Netherlands Navy *Kortenaer*-class frigate *Jan Van Brakel* (F 825) was purchased on 27-3-02 and was to be transferred during 12-02 as the *Kanaris* (F 464). The second and third Type 214 submarines are to be named *Papanikolis* (S 121) and *Pipinos* (S 122), respectively; the first, *Katonis,* is to be numbered S 120. *Charles F. Adams*–class guided-missile destroyer *Themistokles* (D 221; ex-*Berkeley,* DDG 15) was stricken on 18-2-02. An attempt to transfer two French-built Combattante II guided-missile patrol boats to Cyprus during 4-02 was stymied by French objections. *Etna*-class replenishment ship *Promithefs* will carry pennant number A 374.

INDIA

The expected agreement to acquire the aircraft carrier *Admiral Gorshkov* during a visit to Moscow by the Indian Prime Minister early in 11-01 did not take place, nor did it during the high-level meeting in New Delhi early in 2-02; the Indian government balked due to increases in the cost of the modernization program, and negotiations were reported under way for the possible lease of the Royal Thai Navy V/STOL aircraft carrier *Chakri Naruebet.* The size of the planned indigenous-construction Indian Navy carrier may be significantly increased, further delaying the program.

On 7-2-02, India turned down the $5 billion Russian offer to complete two Akula-series nuclear-powered attack submarines and deliver them to India in 2004 for five years; the units to have been transferred were the Akula-I-class *Nerpa* (K-152), building at Komsomol'sk, and the Akula-II-class *Kuguar* (K-337), building at Severodvinsk.

A renewed series of tests of the Dhanush shipboard land-attack ballistic missile was to be carried out during 3-02 and 4-02, with the intent to carry the weapon aboard *Delhi*-class guided-missile destroyers and some classes of frigates. The first successful tests of the Trishul surface-to-air missile against sea-skimming targets took place on 28 and 29 January 2002.

As many as twelve *Nilgiri*-class (Project 17) frigates may eventually be constructed. Tarantul-IV-class (Project 12418) guided-missile craft *Prabal* (K . . .) was commissioned on 11-4-02. Indian-built Griffon 8000TDX hovercraft H 184 was delivered to the coast guard 18-12-01.

Indian Navy Project 11356 frigate Talwar—on trials in the Baltic with the temporary Russian name and number *Dozorniy* (704) Flottenkommando, 1-02

INDONESIA

Three Indonesian Aerospace CN 235-220 maritime patrol aircraft with Thales Airborne Maritime Situation Control Systems (AMASCOS) were ordered during 6-01, with another six planned. Four new Mil Mi-171 helicopters were ordered during 2000, but plans to acquire additional Mi-171 and Mi-2 helicopters were canceled early in 2002 due to funding shortages. Three Eurocopter EC 120B Colibi helicopters were delivered during 7-01.

Negotiations with Russia to purchase 17 BTR-80A armored personnel carriers for the Marines were deadlocked as of 9-01, but 32 BMP-2 infantry fighting vehicles were delivered during 2001, with another 32 planned.

Singapore Navy diving tender *Jupiter* (A 102), retired during 9-01, was transferred to Indonesia on 21-3-02; renamed the *Cucut,* the craft is being used on patrol duties.

As of 11-01, the Australian government was considering the donation of five new Australian-built patrol boats to the Indonesian Marine Police to help combat the illegal immigrant trade.

An eighth 14,800-grt *Dobensolo*-class passenger vessel, the *Nggapulu,* was delivered by Meyewerft, Germany, on 26-2-02 to the Sea Communications Agency; sister *Doro Londo* was delivered during 6-01.

IRAN

Delivery of the *Mouj,* the first of a class of "destroyers," was officially said to be imminent as of 3-12-01—and again on 17-4-02. Also being built in Iran is a unit of the new Chinacat catamaran guided-missile boat design offered for export by China; as many as 10 of the craft, which carry up to four small antiship missiles and a light gun, may be acquired. Powered by two diesels, the 23-m prototype craft is claimed to have a speed of up to 50 kts and is fitted with a small search radar and an E/O gun/missile director.

ISRAEL

Six Super Dvora Mk II-I-class aluminum-construction patrol boats (with an option for five more) were ordered from RAMTA–Israeli Aircraft Industries (IAI), Be'er Sheva, on 13-1-02; the first is to deliver during 10-03. The craft will be 25 m long and capable of 45 kts on three diesel engines. The Super Dvora Mk II-I class will carry the Rafael Armament Development Authority Typhoon stabilized gun mounting, fitted with one 25-mm U.S. M242 chain gun; the same mounting is also to be substituted for the forward 20-mm mounts on Super Dvora and other existing patrol boat classes. Also on 13-1-02, two Shaldag-class patrol boats were ordered from Israeli Shipyards, Haifa; these will have essentially identical characteristics to the four delivered to Sri Lanka.

ITALY

An AgustaWestland A.109 Hirundo helicopter was acquired during 2001 for use as a VIP transport. The first Type 212A submarine has been named the *Salvatore Todaro.* Four more EH.191 helicopters, configured for amphibious warfare support duties, were ordered early in 2002, for delivery starting in 2005.

JAPAN

Ships requested under the FY 03 budget include a 7,700-ton Aegis DDG, 1 2,700-ton submarine, 1 510-ton minehunter, and 1 260-ton large harbor tug; aircraft include 7 SH-60K helicopters, 2 US-1A SAR amphibians, 1 TC-90 twin-engine trainer, and one OH-6DA training helicopter.

As of 2001, an indigenous version of the U.S. Vertical-Launch ASROC, the Improved Vertical-Launch Antisubmarine Rocket, was being developed by Mitsubishi Heavy Industries and the Defense Agency Technical Research and Development Institute.

Isoshio (SS 594) was commissioned 14-3-02, *Akebono* (DD 108) on 19-3-02, *Ariake* (DD 109) on 6-3-02, *Hayabusa* (PG 824) on 25-3-02, *Wakataka* (PG 825) on 11-3-02, *Toyoshima* (MSC 685) on 4-3-02, *Shimokita* (LST 4002) on 12-3-02, and *Hiuchi* (AMS 4301) on 27-3-02. *Hatsushima*-class mine countermeasures drone control ship *Niijima* (MCL 722) was stricken 4-3-02. Minesweeper *Hahajima* (MSC 660) was renumbered MCL 724 on 4-3-02 when reassigned to replace the *Niijima.* *Yamagumo*-class destroyer *Yugumo* (DD 121, ex-DDK 121) was redesignated as a training ship and renumbered TV 3515 during 4-02; the ship replaced the *Aokumo* (TV 3512, ex-DDK 119).

Two Gulfstream-V long-range search and rescue aircraft are to be delivered to the Japan Coast Guard in 2004 after outfitting by Thales and Marubeni with a surveillance radar and mission-system equipment. Two "High-Speed Special Patrol Ships" were under construction as of 3-02 for the coast guard, one each by Mitsubishi and Hitachi Zosen; the craft are to be powered by two Niigata Engineering V20FX 16-cyl. high-speed diesels of 5,365 bhp each.

Japan Maritime Self-Defense Force Osumi-class amphibious warfare ship Kunisaki (LST 4003)—at launch

Japan Maritime Self-Defense Force multipurpose auxiliary Hiuchi (AMS 4301)—at launch

KAZAKHSTAN

♦ **1 ex-Turkish AB 25–class patrol craft [PC]**
Bldr: Haliç SY (In serv. . . .)

. . . . . . (ex-AB 32)

D: 150 tons (170 fl) **S:** 22 kts **Dim:** 40.24 × 6.40 × 1.65
A: 1 40-mm 60-cal. Mk 3 Bofors AA; 1 20-mm 70-cal. Oerlikon AA; 2 single 12.7-mm mg
Electronics: Radar: 1 Decca TM 1226 nav.
M: 2 SACM-AGO V16CSHR diesels; 2 props; 4,800 bhp—2 cruise diesels; 300 bhp
Crew: 3 officers, 28 enlisted

Remarks: Transferred on 3-7-99 from the Turkish Navy. The cruise diesels are geared to the main shafts.

LIBYA

Amphibious landing ship *Ibn Harissa* (134) was under refit at Kraljevica Shipyard, Croatia, during 2001; although the ship still wore her naval pennant number, all armament had been removed.

Although reported to have been out of service since the 1980s, at least three of the French-built Combattante-II guided missile patrol boats were operational as of the fall of 2001 (although their Otomat 1 missile systems were probably not functional). Data for the class, with corrected spellings and pennant number/name attributions, are:

♦ **7 Combattante II–class guided-missile patrol boats [PTG]**
Bldr: CMN, Cherbourg, France

	Laid down	L	In serv.
518 Sharara (ex-*Beir Grassa*)	13-3-78	28-6-79	9-2-82
522 Shehab (ex-*Beir Gzir*)	10-6-78	22-1-80	3-4-82
524 Wahg (ex-*Beir Gtifa*)	30-1-79	20-5-80	29-5-82
525 Shouaiai (ex-*Beir Algandula*)	12-2-79	14-1-81	5-9-82
532 Shoula (ex-*Beir Alkitan*)	17-12-79	22-4-81	29-10-82
534 Shafak (ex-*Beir Alkirim*)	11-3-80	23-6-81	17-12-82
542 Laheeb (ex-*Beir Alkuesat*)	20-1-81	9-1-82	29-7-83

D: 258 tons (311 fl) **S:** 39 kts **Dim:** 49.00 (46.20 pp) × 7.10 × 2.00
A: 4 Otomat Mk 1 SSM; 1 76-mm 62-cal. OTOBreda Compact DP; 1 twin 40-mm 70-cal. Breda-Bofors AA
Electronics:
Radar: 1 Decca 1226 nav.; 1 Thales Triton surf./air search; 1 Thales Castor IIB gun f.c.
M: 4 MTU MD 20V538 TB 91 diesels; 4 props; 18,000 bhp
Range: 1,600/15 **Crew:** 8 officers, 19 enlisted

Remarks: Delivery was embargoed from 27-2-81 to 12-81 by the French government. Had been laid up for many years for lack of spares, but 522, 534, and 542 visited Malta in fall 2001, indicating that the relaxation on embargoes against Libya has resulted in the reactivation of at least three.

Disposals: *Waheed* (526) was sunk by U.S. forces on 24-3-86. *Bark* (536, ex-*Beir Alkardmen*) and *Rad* (538, ex-*Beir Alkur*) are reportedly beyond repair, although they may still be afloat and used as cannibalizations spares sources.

Combat systems: The gun fire-control system is the Thales Vega II. The Otomat missiles for these ships have long ago passed their shelf lives, but the missile launch canisters remain aboard; the missiles are probably no longer usable.

MALAYSIA

A new naval air base is to be built at Sungai Wangi, Sitiawan. A naval sail training ship is to begin construction at PSC-Naval Dockyard, Lumut, late in 2002 for delivery 18 months later; the ship will displace around 2,500 tons and be around 100 m overall. Contrary to French reports in 9-01, no final decision had been made on the acquisition of submarines as of 4-02.

Two Fast Troop Vessels were delivered during 2001:

♦ **2 Sri Gaya–class Fast Troop Vessels (FTV) [LCP]**
Bldr: PSC-Naval Dockyard, Lumut

331 Sri Gaya (In serv. 5-01) 332 Sri Tiga (In serv. 2001)

Sri Tiga (332) Ralph Edwards, 10-01

D: 116.5 tons (fl) **S:** 25 kts (loaded) **Dim:** 37.50 (30.30 wl) × 7.00 × 2.50
A: 2 single 7.62-mm mg **Electronics:** Radar: 1 . . . nav.
M: 4 MAN D2842 LE408 diesels; 4 Hamilton Type 521 waterjets; 3,940 bhp tot.
Electric: 160 kw tot. (2 × 80 kw, Cummins diesels driving)
Range: . . ./. . . **Crew:** . . . tot. + 32 troops

Remarks: Fully air-conditioned craft of aluminum construction, with the design based on that of the Australian WaveMaster commercial fast ferry. Can carry 4 tons of cargo (some of it refrigerated) in addition to the troops.

Malaysian Navy frigate Rahmat (24) Maritime Photographic, 11-01

A Malaysian Coast Guard is planned to be established to take over the coastal patrol functions of the Navy, Marine Police, and other government maritime agencies; the proposed force would be built around the assets of the current Marine Police.

MOROCCO

Floréal-class patrol ship Mohammed V (611) was delivered on 12-3-02.

NETHERLANDS

Under a 10-12-01 contract with STN Atlas Elektronik, the 10 Tripartite-class minehunters in the best condition are now to be upgraded to serve until 2020, while the other two are to be used for training and hydrographic survey duties. The upgrades will be performed at Den Helder between 2004 and 2009, with new sonars and command and control systems supplied by STN Atlas Elektronik, with Thales Underwater Systems, as subcontractor, providing the hull-mounted sonar and the sonar for the SAAB Bofors remotely operated underwater vehicles (only five ROVs are to be procured). Also to be carried will be a "One-Shot Mine Disposal System," using disposable wire-guided, self-powered submersibles. A minesweeping capability will be added, but a plan to procure up to a dozen mine countermeasures drones to be operated by the Tripartite ships has been canceled.

De Zeven Provinciën–class guided-missile frigate *De Ruyter* (F 804) was launched on 13-4-02. The hull for dock landing ship *Johan de Witt* (L 801) is to be built at Damen Shipyard Galatz, Galati, Romania.

NIGERIA

The planned transfer of the U.S. Coast Guard buoy tender *Cowslip* (WLB 277) to Nigeria was delayed to 30-9-02 when the ship was extended in U.S. service; also planned for transfer at an as-yet unspecified date is sister ship *Sedge* (WLB 409).

NORWAY

Under the new defense reductions to begin implementation in 2002 and be completed by 1-1-03, one *Alta*-class minesweeper is to be given to the new Clearance Diver Command as a support vessel; two of the three utility landing craft are to be mothballed; Olavsvern, Hysnes, Ulsnes, Marvika, and Karljohansvern Naval Bases will be closed; the Officer Candidate School will be established at Horten and the existing naval and coast artillery officer candidate schools closed; the Clearance Diver Command is being established at Haakonsvern; and the number of enlisted personnel to be trained at the KNM *Harald Hårfagre* Naval Training Center is to be reduced. Also, three Coastal Artillery controlled minefields, three land-based torpedo batteries, and all nine coastal artillery forts are to be mothballed, while the Coastal Artillery's separate training fort and training units will be disestablished. A new Coastal Ranger Command is being established at Trondenes to train and support the new Coastal Ranger squads. Under plans recommended during 4-02, Norway will withdraw from the Viking submarine project, and the navy will retire all three remaining large landing craft; a planned maritime surveillance center will not be built, and upgrades to the coastal radar system in the south will not be carried out. The first production *Skjold*-class missile boat will enter service in 2005.

Modernized Type 207 submarines *Skolpen* (S 306), *Stord* (S 308), *Svenner* (S 309), and *Kunna* (S 319) were withdrawn from service in Norway at the end of 2001 for Poland, two during 2002, one in 2003, and one in 2004.

Alta-class minesweeper *Karmøy* (M 341) conducted successful trials of the Kongsberg-Simrad Hugin-I autonomous underwater vehicle in a minehunting configuration during 12-01; a production version is to enter service around 2005.

Coast Guard patrol ship *Svalbard* (W 303) was delivered during 3-02; the ship is capable of breaking 1-m ice.

PALESTINE

A 5-strong fleet consisting of a yacht for Yasser Arafat and several small launches was established at Gaza City in 1994, but was all but destroyed during Israeli retaliatory raids in 12-01 and 1-02; only two of the craft had been radar-equipped, and, as of mid-1-01, only one out-of-service boat remained. The navy operated nine coastwatch stations along the Gaza Strip coast, but as of 1-02, only small facilities at Deir El Balah and the other two at Gaza City. As many as 1,000 personnel had been assigned to the navy, whose headquarters has been leveled.

PARAGUAY

A single unit of the Colombian Nodriza-class of riverine support lighters was to be delivered early in 2002; see the Colombia entry above for characteristics and appearance.

PHILIPPINES

During 11-01, U.S. President George W. Bush offered to donate the deactivated former U.S. Navy *Cyclone*-class patrol craft *Cyclone* (PC 1); transferred to the U.S. Coast Guard 1-3-00 but never operated by that agency, the craft was to be transferred to the Philippines during 2002.

POLAND

Modernized Type 207 submarines *Skolpen* (S 306), *Stord* (S 308), *Svenner* (S 309), and *Kunna* (S 319) were withdrawn from service in Norway at the end of 2001 and are to be transferred to Poland, the *Stord* during 5-02, *Skolpen* later in the year, *Svenner* in 2003, and *Kunna* during 2004; also to be transferred for spares is the *Kobben* (S 318).

Former Russian Modified Kashin-class (Project 61MP) guided-missile destroyer *Warszawa* (271, ex-*Smel'yy*) was offered for sale at the end of 2001. The 30 Eurotorp MU-90 Impact ASW torpedoes mentioned in the main text were ordered 18-2-02.

PORTUGAL

A contract for the first two of a planned dozen lightly armed seagoing patrol ships was to be signed during 6-02 with Estaleiros Navais de Viana do Castelo (ENVC), with construction to start early in 2003; one of the ships will be configured for pollution-control duties. The number of submarines to be ordered has been cut to two, with a third boat possibly to be leased.

ROMANIA

The purchase of Type 22 frigates *London* (F 95) and *Coventry* (F 98) from the U.K. was agreed to on 1-3-02; the ships were to be transferred in the fall of 2002 and modernized and refitted in a Romanian shipyard.

RUSSIA

The Russian naval base at Cam Ranh Bay, Vietnam, was definitely to be closed by the end of 2002; U.S. Navy attempts to gain use of the facility have thus far not been successful, although occasional visits may be permitted. Delta-IV SSBN *Yekaterinburg* (K-84), out of service since 1996, completed a non-refueling refit on 16-4-02. Sierra-II-class nuclear-powered attack submarine *Nizhniy Novgorod* (K-534, ex-*Zubatka*) is to be refitted, refueled, and returned to service, according to a 3-02 official statement. Kara-class guided-missile destroyer *Ochakov* was being scrapped at Sevastopol' during 4-02. Northern Fleet Grisha-V-class (Project 1244) corvette MPK-59 was named *Snezhnogorsk* on 2-6-91.

SAUDI ARABIA

The following six patrol boats are on order for the Saudi Navy:

♦ **0 (+ 6) Stan Patrol 2606 class**
Bldr: Damen Shipyards, Gorinchem, the Netherlands (In serv. 2002)

Assir	Al Dhahran	. . . . .
. . . . .	. . . . .	. . . . .

Al Dhahran—with *Assir* visible astern C. F. Boogert, via A. A. de Kruijf, 2-01

D: . . . tons **S:** 30 kts **Dim:** 26.0 × 6.0 × 1.80
A: . . . **Electronics:** Radar: 1 . . . nav.
M: 2 Caterpillar diesels; 2 props; . . . bhp

Remarks: The first two were running trials as of 25-1-02. Aluminum construction.

SINGAPORE

Route survey and diving tender *Jupiter* (A 102), retired during 9-01, was transferred to Indonesia on 21-3-02 for use as a patrol craft..

SRI LANKA

The Sri Lanka Coast Guard Service was established 10-1-01 under the Ministry of Fisheries and Aquatic Resources to protect maritime resources. Under the command of a former Sri Lanka Navy lieutenant commander, the 175 personnel operate direction-finding and communications facilities on land, as well as the 18.29-m patrol boat *Mahiraja*, 10.36-m launches *Maya* and *Ruhunu*, and 4.88-m launches *Girwaya, Kadira,* and *Magam*. All six craft are wooden hulled and painted white, with a blue upper strake to the hull and the words "Sri Lanka Coast Guard" on the hull sides near the bow.

SWEDEN

Coast Guard Kbv 201–class patrol craft Kbv 202 was delivered on 25-1-02, replacing the Kbv 103 in service. The Danish-built mine countermeasures drone delivered in 12-01 has been named the *Sökaren.*

UKRAINE

Grisha-V-class corvette *Ternopil* (U 202) was launched on 20-3-02. Grisha-II (Project 1124A) corvette *Chernigiv* (U 205, ex-Russian *Izmail*) was not striken as reported and remained in service as of 4-02; the ship was laid down on 12-9-78, launched on 22-6-80, and completed on 28-12-80.

UNITED ARAB EMIRATES

♦ **0 (+ 12) Trossbåt-class landing craft [LCVP]**
Bldr: Abu Dhabi Ship Building (In serv. . . .)

D: 30 tons (45 fl) **S:** 33 kts (23 loaded) **Dim:** 24.00 × 5.40 × 1.20
A: 1 12.7-mm mg **Electronics:** Radar: 1 . . . nav.
M: 2 MTU 12V 2000 diesels; 2 KaMeWa FF550 waterjets; . . . bhp
Range: 150/15 (loaded) **Fuel:** 15,000 liters **Crew:** 4 tot. + 17 troops

Remarks: Ordered 22-1-02 for $27 million for construction under license from SwedeShip. *Trossbåt* means "Support Boat" in Swedish, and the design is also used by the Swedish Coastal Artillery Service. Aluminum construction. Cargo: 15 tons on 14.0 × 4.5-m deck area or 2 m^3 water and 9 tons cargo or 8 m^3 diesel fuel or 7 m^3 of water and no deck cargo. Will have a folding bow ramp and a small crane.

UNITED KINGDOM

Retirements for *Trafalgar*-class nuclear-powered attack submarines are planned to be: *Trafalgar* (S 107) in 2007, *Turbulent* (S 87) in 2008, *Tireless* (S 88) in 2011, *Talent* (S 92) in 2017, *Triumph* (S 93) in 2019, *Torbay* (S 90) in 2021, and *Trenchant* (S 91) in 2023, the latter after 34 years' service. Retirements for the Type 42, *Sheffield*-class guided-missile destroyers are scheduled as follows: *Newcastle* (D 87) in 2007, *Cardiff* (D 108) in 2008, *Glasgow* (D 88) in 2009, *Exeter* (D 89) and *Liverpool* (D 92) in 2010, *Southampton* (D 90) in 2011, *Nottingham* (D 91) and *Manchester* (D 95) in 2012, *Gloucester* (D 96) and *Edinburgh* (D 97) in 2013, and *York* (D 98) in 2014. The deactivation to reserve of Type 22 Batch II frigate *Sheffield* (F 96) has been advanced to 11-02. LCU Mk 10 landing craft LCU 04 and LCU 05 were launched on 4-2-02 and 3-3-02, respectively. Piping defects and other engineering problems delayed sea trials for replenishment oiler *Wave Knight* (A 389) from 10-01 to 3-02. The launch of patrol ship *Tyne* (P 281) was delayed from 27-4-02 to late 6-02. Chartered vehicle cargo ship *Hurst Point* was launched 19-4-02.

On returning from the Mideast on 27-5-02, aircraft carrier *Illustrious* (R 06) was to be placed in reduced operational readiness until starting a refit during 11-02. Due to funding shortages, the start of a refit to frigate *Montrose* (F 236), which has been inactive since 2-02, will not begin until 11-02, for completion in 12-04.

U.S.A.

Aircraft carrier *Constellation* (CV 64) may be repaired and extended in service rather than retired during 2003 after her final operational deployment. Guided-missile destroyer *Cole* (DDG 67) returned to service on 19-4-02.

The $1.36 billion design contract for the DD(X) program was awarded to the Northrop Grumman-led "Gold Team" on 29-4-02, with a separate construction contract for the first ship planned to be competed in 2005 and the ship to be delivered in 2010. When the *Spruance*-class destroyer *Arthur W. Radford* (DD 968) is stricken during 2003, the ship will be bailed to Northrop Grumman for conversion as trials ship for the propulsion plant and weapon/sensor systems to be used on the DD(X); the ship will begin conducting systems trials in 2005, operated by a civilian crew. The winning DD(X) design will employ vertical-launch missile tubes in groups of four down the sides of the ship and will have a flush deck, with two helicopter spots aft and both 155-mm guns forward. The propulsion plant will employ large and small gas turbine engines driving alternator sets, with electric motors powering two fixed-pitch conventional propellers.

Former U.S. Navy submarine support dock *Oak Ridge* (ARDM 1, ex-ARD 19) was transferred to the U.S. Coast Guard in the spring of 2002 for use at U.S. Coast Guard Yard, Curtis Bay, Md.

Leased commercial wave-piercing catamaran *Joint Venture* was transferred to army control on 20-3-02; the craft has continued to wear hull number HSV-X1 and never did carry navy hull number IX 532, although it was officially designated as such. During its European tour in the spring of 2002, the craft was armed with four single 12.7-mm mg.

INDEX BY SHIPS

All ships are indexed by their full names, e.g., Almirante José Toribo Merino. Abbreviated ranks and titles are indexed as if spelled out.

About the Author

A. D. Baker III has compiled *Combat Fleets* since 1978. He also is a regular columnist for the U.S. Naval Institute magazines *Proceedings* and *Naval History* and has written or illustrated some sixty books on naval history and technology.

A magna cum laude graduate of Harvard University, Mr. Baker served as an officer in the U.S. Navy from 1963 through 1967 and as a civilian in the Department of the Navy from 1967 until his retirement in 1997. A special assistant to the secretary of the navy for intelligence and historical matters from 1982 to 1987, he served on the staff of the president's Commission on Merchant Marine and Defense from 1987 to 1989. He is a recipient of the navy's Distinguished Civilian Service Award.

The Naval Institute Press is the book-publishing arm of the U.S. Naval Institute, a private, nonprofit, membership society for sea service professionals and others who share an interest in naval and maritime affairs. Established in 1873 at the U.S. Naval Academy in Annapolis, Maryland, where its offices remain today, the Naval Institute has members worldwide.

Members of the Naval Institute support the education programs of the society and receive the influential monthly magazine *Proceedings* and discounts on fine nautical prints and on ship and aircraft photos. They also have access to the transcripts of the Institute's Oral History Program and get discounted admission to any of the Institute-sponsored seminars offered around the country. Discounts are also available to the colorful bimonthly magazine *Naval History*.

The Naval Institute's book-publishing program, begun in 1898 with basic guides to naval practices, has broadened its scope in recent years to include books of more general interest. Now the Naval Institute Press publishes about one hundred titles each year, ranging from how-to books on boating and navigation to battle histories, biographies, ship and aircraft guides, and novels. Institute members receive discounts of 20 to 50 percent on the Press's more than eight hundred books in print.

Full-time students are eligible for special half-price membership rates. Life memberships are also available.

For a free catalog describing Naval Institute Press books currently available, and for further information about joining the U.S. Naval Institute, please write to:

Membership Department
U.S. Naval Institute
291 Wood Road
Annapolis, MD 21402-5034
Telephone: (800) 233-8764
Fax: (410) 269-7940
Web address: www.navalinstitute.org